Definition of the Six Trigonometric Functions

Right triangle definitions, where $0 < \theta < \pi/2$

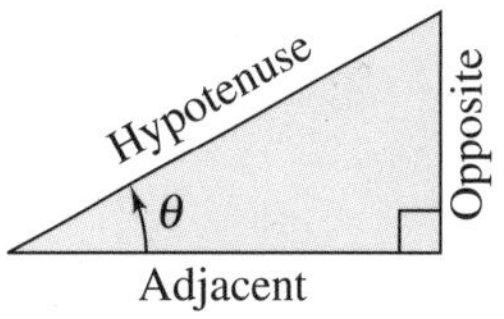

$\sin\theta = \dfrac{\text{opp.}}{\text{hyp.}}$ $\csc\theta = \dfrac{\text{hyp.}}{\text{opp.}}$

$\cos\theta = \dfrac{\text{adj.}}{\text{hyp.}}$ $\sec\theta = \dfrac{\text{hyp.}}{\text{adj.}}$

$\tan\theta = \dfrac{\text{opp.}}{\text{adj.}}$ $\cot\theta = \dfrac{\text{adj.}}{\text{opp.}}$

Circular function definitions, where θ *is any angle*

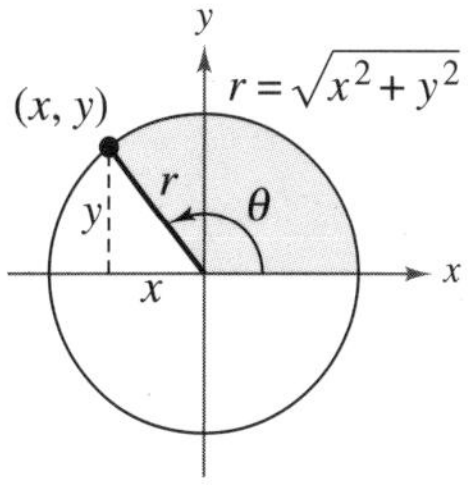

$\sin\theta = \dfrac{y}{r}$ $\csc\theta = \dfrac{r}{y}$

$\cos\theta = \dfrac{x}{r}$ $\sec\theta = \dfrac{r}{x}$

$\tan\theta = \dfrac{y}{x}$ $\cot\theta = \dfrac{x}{y}$

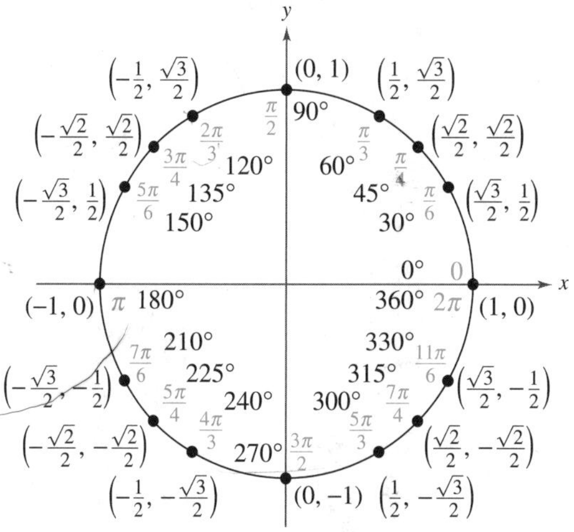

Reciprocal Identities

$\sin u = \dfrac{1}{\csc u}$ $\cos u = \dfrac{1}{\sec u}$ $\tan u = \dfrac{1}{\cot u}$

$\csc u = \dfrac{1}{\sin u}$ $\sec u = \dfrac{1}{\cos u}$ $\cot u = \dfrac{1}{\tan u}$

Quotient Identities

$\tan u = \dfrac{\sin u}{\cos u}$ $\cot u = \dfrac{\cos u}{\sin u}$

Pythagorean Identities

$\sin^2 u + \cos^2 u = 1$

$1 + \tan^2 u = \sec^2 u$ $1 + \cot^2 u = \csc^2 u$

Cofunction Identities

$\sin\left(\dfrac{\pi}{2} - u\right) = \cos u$ $\cot\left(\dfrac{\pi}{2} - u\right) = \tan u$

$\cos\left(\dfrac{\pi}{2} - u\right) = \sin u$ $\sec\left(\dfrac{\pi}{2} - u\right) = \csc u$

$\tan\left(\dfrac{\pi}{2} - u\right) = \cot u$ $\csc\left(\dfrac{\pi}{2} - u\right) = \sec u$

Even/Odd Identities

$\sin(-u) = -\sin u$ $\cot(-u) = -\cot u$

$\cos(-u) = \cos u$ $\sec(-u) = \sec u$

$\tan(-u) = -\tan u$ $\csc(-u) = -\csc u$

Sum and Difference Formulas

$\sin(u \pm v) = \sin u \cos v \pm \cos u \sin v$

$\cos(u \pm v) = \cos u \cos v \mp \sin u \sin v$

$\tan(u \pm v) = \dfrac{\tan u \pm \tan v}{1 \mp \tan u \tan v}$

Double-Angle Formulas

$\sin 2u = 2 \sin u \cos u$

$\cos 2u = \cos^2 u - \sin^2 u = 2\cos^2 u - 1 = 1 - 2\sin^2 u$

$\tan 2u = \dfrac{2 \tan u}{1 - \tan^2 u}$

Power-Reducing Formulas

$\sin^2 u = \dfrac{1 - \cos 2u}{2}$

$\cos^2 u = \dfrac{1 + \cos 2u}{2}$

$\tan^2 u = \dfrac{1 - \cos 2u}{1 + \cos 2u}$

Sum-to-Product Formulas

$\sin u + \sin v = 2\sin\left(\dfrac{u+v}{2}\right)\cos\left(\dfrac{u-v}{2}\right)$

$\sin u - \sin v = 2\cos\left(\dfrac{u+v}{2}\right)\sin\left(\dfrac{u-v}{2}\right)$

$\cos u + \cos v = 2\cos\left(\dfrac{u+v}{2}\right)\cos\left(\dfrac{u-v}{2}\right)$

$\cos u - \cos v = -2\sin\left(\dfrac{u+v}{2}\right)\sin\left(\dfrac{u-v}{2}\right)$

Product-to-Sum Formulas

$\sin u \sin v = \dfrac{1}{2}[\cos(u - v) - \cos(u + v)]$

$\cos u \cos v = \dfrac{1}{2}[\cos(u - v) + \cos(u + v)]$

$\sin u \cos v = \dfrac{1}{2}[\sin(u + v) + \sin(u - v)]$

$\cos u \sin v = \dfrac{1}{2}[\sin(u + v) - \sin(u - v)]$

FORMULAS FROM GEOMETRY

Triangle:

$h = a \sin\theta$

$\text{Area} = \frac{1}{2}bh$

$c^2 = a^2 + b^2 - 2ab\cos\theta$ (Law of Cosines)

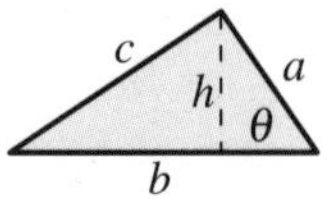

Right Triangle:

Pythagorean Theorem
$c^2 = a^2 + b^2$

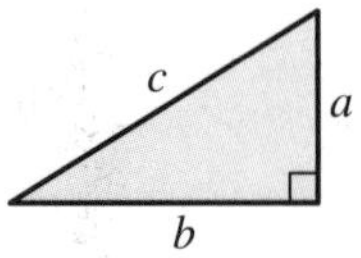

Equilateral Triangle:

$h = \frac{\sqrt{3}s}{2}$

$\text{Area} = \frac{\sqrt{3}s^2}{4}$

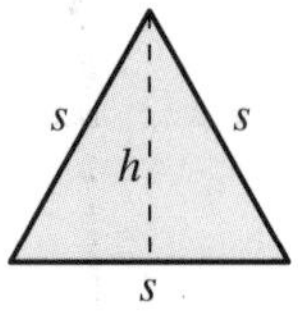

Parallelogram:

$\text{Area} = bh$

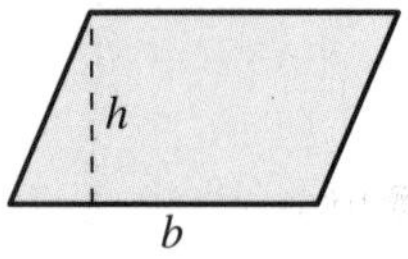

Trapezoid:

$\text{Area} = \frac{h}{2}(a + b)$

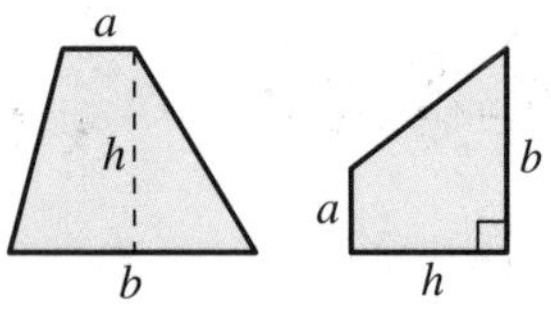

Circle:

$\text{Area} = \pi r^2$
$\text{Circumference} = 2\pi r$

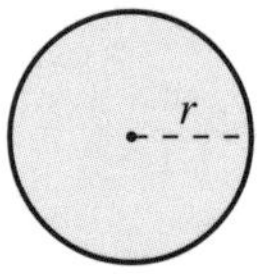

Sector of Circle:

$\text{Area} = \frac{\theta r^2}{2}$

$s = r\theta$

θ in radians

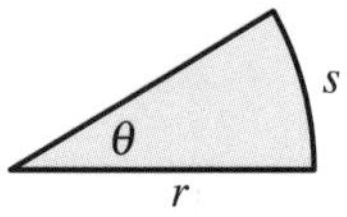

Circular Ring:

$\text{Area} = \pi(R^2 - r^2)$
$= 2\pi pw$
p = average radius,
w = width of ring

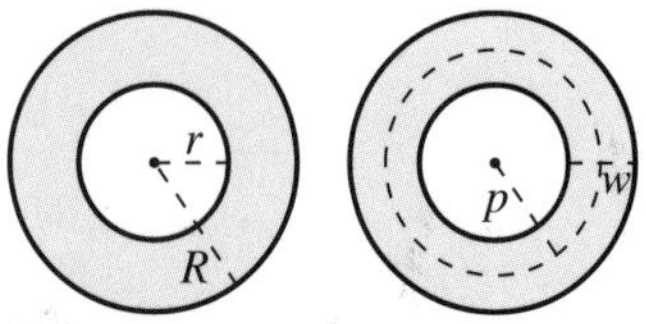

Sector of Circular Ring:

$\text{Area} = \theta pw$
p = average radius,
w = width of ring,
θ in radians

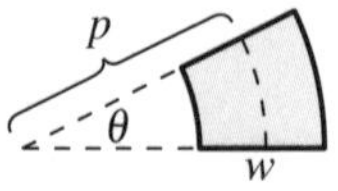

Ellipse:

$\text{Area} = \pi ab$

$\text{Circumference} \approx 2\pi\sqrt{\frac{a^2 + b^2}{2}}$

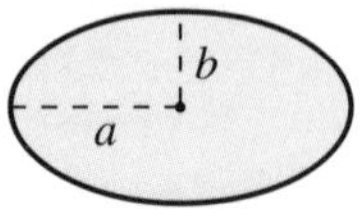

Cone:

$\text{Volume} = \frac{Ah}{3}$

A = area of base

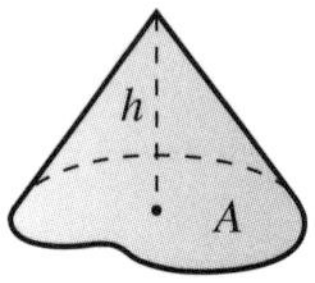

Right Circular Cone:

$\text{Volume} = \frac{\pi r^2 h}{3}$

$\text{Lateral Surface Area} = \pi r\sqrt{r^2 + h^2}$

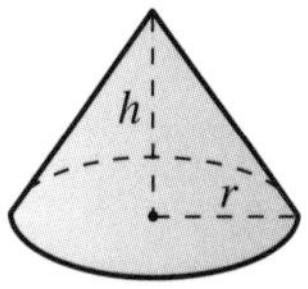

Frustum of Right Circular Cone:

$\text{Volume} = \frac{\pi(r^2 + rR + R^2)h}{3}$

$\text{Lateral Surface Area} = \pi s(R + r)$

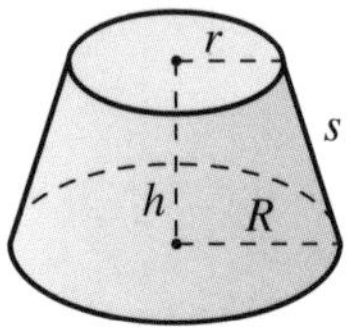

Right Circular Cylinder:

$\text{Volume} = \pi r^2 h$
$\text{Lateral Surface Area} = 2\pi rh$

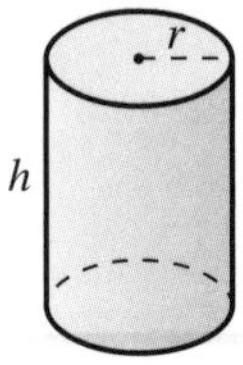

Sphere:

$\text{Volume} = \frac{4}{3}\pi r^3$

$\text{Surface Area} = 4\pi r^2$

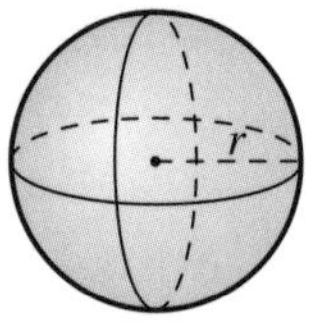

Wedge:

$A = B\sec\theta$
A = area of upper face,
B = area of base

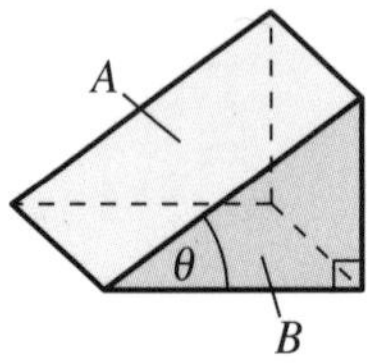

Precalculus with Limits

Second Edition

Teacher's Edition

Ron Larson

The Pennsylvania State University
The Behrend College

With the assistance of David C. Falvo

The Pennsylvania State University
The Behrend College

BROOKS/COLE
CENGAGE Learning™

Australia • Brazil • Japan • Korea • Mexico • Singapore • Spain • United Kingdom • United States

BROOKS/COLE
CENGAGE Learning™

Precalculus with Limits, Second Edition, Teacher's Edition
Ron Larson

Publisher: Charlie VanWagner
Acquiring Sponsoring Editor: Gary Whalen
Development Editor: Stacy Green
Assistant Editor: Cynthia Ashton
Editorial Assistant: Guanglei Zhang
Associate Media Editor: Lynh Pham
Marketing Manager: Myriah FitzGibbon
Marketing Coordinator: Angela Kim
Marketing Communications Manager: Katy Malatesta
Content Project Manager: Susan Miscio
Senior Art Director: Jill Ort
Senior Print Buyer: Diane Gibbons
Production Editor: Carol Merrigan
Text Designer: Walter Kopek
Rights Acquiring Account Manager, Photos: Don Schlotman
Photo Researcher: Prepress PMG
Cover Designer: Harold Burch
Cover Image: Richard Edelman/Woodstock Graphics Studio
Compositor: Larson Texts, Inc.

Library of Congress Control Number: 2009936914
ISBN-13: 978-0-538-73660-2
ISBN-10: 0-538-73660-7

Brooks/Cole
10 Davis Drive
Belmont, CA 94002-3098
USA

Printed in the United States of America
1 2 3 4 5 6 7 13 12 11 10 09

Contents

A Word from the Author

Welcome to the Second Edition of *Precalculus with Limits*! We are proud to offer you a new and revised version of our textbook. With the Second Edition, we have listened to you, our users, and have incorporated many of your suggestions for improvement.

2nd Edition

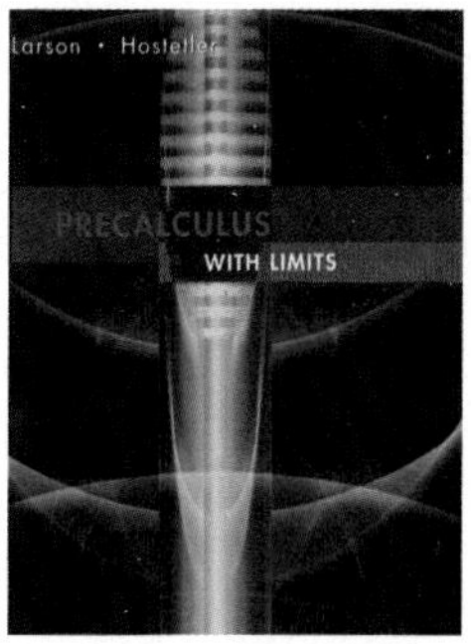

1st Edition

In this edition, we continue to offer teachers and students a text that is pedagogically sound, mathematically precise, and still comprehensible. There are many changes in the mathematics, art, and design; the more significant changes are noted here.

- ***New Chapter Openers*** Each *Chapter Opener* has three parts, *In Mathematics, In Real Life*, and *In Careers*. *In Mathematics* describes an important mathematical topic taught in the chapter. *In Real Life* tells students where they will encounter this topic in real-life situations. *In Careers* relates application exercises to a variety of careers.
- ***New Study Tips and Warning/Cautions*** Insightful information is given to students in two new features. The *Study Tip* provides students with useful information or suggestions for learning the topic. The *Warning/Caution* points out common mathematical errors made by students.
- ***New Algebra Helps*** *Algebra Help* directs students to sections of the textbook where they can review algebra skills needed to master the current topic.
- ***New Side-by-Side Examples*** Throughout the text, we present solutions to many examples from multiple perspectives—algebraically, graphically, and numerically. The side-by-side format of this pedagogical feature helps students to see that a problem can be solved in more than one way and to see that different methods yield the same result. The side-by-side format also addresses many different learning styles.

- ***New Capstone Exercises*** *Capstones* are conceptual problems that synthesize key topics and provide students with a better understanding of each section's concepts. Capstone exercises are excellent for classroom discussion or test prep, and teachers may find value in integrating these problems into their reviews of the section.
- ***New Chapter Summaries*** The *Chapter Summary* now includes an explanation and/or example of each objective taught in the chapter.
- ***Revised Exercise Sets*** The exercise sets have been carefully and extensively examined to ensure they are rigorous and cover all topics suggested by our users. Many new skill-building and challenging exercises have been added.

For the past several years, we've maintained an independent website—**CalcChat.com**—that provides free solutions to all odd-numbered exercises in the text. Thousands of students using our textbooks have visited the site for practice and help with their homework. For the Second Edition, we were able to use information from CalcChat.com, including which solutions students accessed most often, to help guide the revision of the exercises.

I hope you enjoy the Second Edition of *Precalculus with Limits*. As always, I welcome comments and suggestions for continued improvements.

Ron Larson

Acknowledgments

I would like to thank the many people who have helped me prepare the text and the supplements package. Their encouragement, criticisms, and suggestions have been invaluable.

Thank you to all of the college instructors and high school teachers who took the time to review the changes in this edition and to provide suggestions for improving it. Without your help, this book would not be possible.

Reviewers

Chad Pierson, *University of Minnesota-Duluth*; Sally Shao, *Cleveland State University*; Ed Stumpf, *Central Carolina Community College*; Fuzhen Zhang, *Nova Southeastern University*; Dennis Shepherd, *University of Colorado, Denver*; Rhonda Kilgo, *Jacksonville State University*; C. Altay Özgener, *Manatee Community College Bradenton*; William Forrest, *Baton Rouge Community College*; Tracy Cook, *University of Tennessee Knoxville*; Charles Hale, *California State Poly University Pomona*; Samuel Evers, *University of Alabama*; Seongchun Kwon, *University of Toledo*; Dr. Arun K. Agarwal, *Grambling State University*; Hyounkyun Oh, *Savannah State University*; Michael J. McConnell, *Clarion University*; Martha Chalhoub, *Collin County Community College*; Angela Lee Everett, *Chattanooga State Tech Community College*; Heather Van Dyke, *Walla Walla Community College*; Gregory Buthusiem, *Burlington County Community College*; Cathy Falk, *Greenhill School*; Jeff Lucia, *Providence Day School*; Stephanie Vanderford, *Providence Day School*; Gary Crossman, *Oregon Episcopal School*; Ward Shaffer, *College of Coastal Georgia*; Carmen Thomas, *Chatham University*

My thanks to David Falvo, The Behrend College, The Pennsylvania State University, for his contributions to this project. My thanks also to Robert Hostetler, The Behrend College, The Pennsylvania State University, and Bruce Edwards, University of Florida, for their significant contributions to previous editions of this text.

I would also like to thank the staff at Larson Texts, Inc. who assisted with proofreading the manuscript, preparing and proofreading the art package, and checking and typesetting the supplements.

On a personal level, I am grateful to my spouse, Deanna Gilbert Larson, for her love, patience, and support. Also, a special thanks goes to R. Scott O'Neil. If you have suggestions for improving this text, please feel free to write to me. Over the past two decades I have received many useful comments from both instructors and students, and I value these comments very highly.

Ron Larson

Supplements

Supplements for the Teacher

Teacher's Edition This TE is the complete student text plus point-of-use annotations for the teacher, including extra projects, classroom activities, teaching strategies, and additional examples. Answers to even-numbered text exercises, Vocabulary Checks, and Explorations are also provided.

Complete Solutions Manual This manual contains solutions to all exercises from the text, including Chapter Review Exercises and Chapter Tests.

Instructor's Companion Website This free companion website contains an abundance of teacher resources.

PowerLecture™ for High School with ExamView® The CD-ROM provides the teacher with dynamic media tools for teaching Precalculus while using an interactive white board. PowerPoint® lecture slides and art slides of the figures from the text, together with electronic files for the test bank, solutions manual, and a teacher's version of the Note Taking Guide, are available. The algorithmic ExamView allows you to create, deliver, and customize tests (both print and online) in minutes with this easy-to-use assessment system. JoinIn™ content for electronic response systems is tailored to Precalculus. Transform your classroom and assess your students' progress with instant in-class quizzes and polls.

Solutions Builder This is an electronic version of the complete solutions manual available via the PowerLecture and Instructor's Companion Website. It provides teachers with an efficient method for creating solution sets to homework or exams that can then be printed or posted.

Online TE to the Note Taking Guide This TE includes the answers to all problems in the innovative Note Taking Guide.

Supplements for the Student

Student Companion Website This free companion website contains an abundance of student resources.

Instructional DVDs Keyed to the text by section, these DVDs provide comprehensive coverage of the course—along with additional explanations of concepts, sample problems, and applications—to help students review essential topics.

Student Study and Solutions Manual This guide offers step-by-step solutions for all odd-numbered text exercises, Chapter and Cumulative Tests, and Practice Tests with solutions.

Premium eBook The Premium eBook offers an interactive version of the textbook with search features, highlighting and note-making tools, and direct links to videos or tutorials that elaborate on the text discussions.

Enhanced WebAssign Enhanced WebAssign is designed for students to do their homework online. This proven and reliable system uses pedagogy and content found in Larson's text, and then enhances it to help students learn Precalculus more effectively. Automatically graded homework allows students to focus on their learning and get interactive study assistance outside of class.

Note Taking Guide This is an innovative study aid, in the form of a notebook organizer, that helps students develop a section-by-section summary of key concepts.

Precalculus Course Overview

Introduction

The Precalculus course is designed for students who want to be better prepared for college Calculus or Advanced Placement courses while still in high school so that they may start in higher level courses upon entering college. The standard Precalculus course has been enhanced with additional materials and teaching tips that promote a deeper mathematical understanding of the topics, extend the topics past what is given in the standard course, and present new topics that are not typically included in a high school curriculum. The new and extended topics are specifically chosen to prepare the student for college Calculus or AP courses in terms of both their algebra and geometry skills and their understanding of the underlying concepts.

Grades are not the only indicator of who is likely to excel in the Precalculus program. Motivation and a willingness to work hard are two important factors for success that are very difficult to measure. Certain learning preferences and styles may also be more compatible with the Precalculus course than others. So, be prepared to consider a variety of factors as your school develops its Precalculus screening process.

Precalculus Students

Personality traits will differ from student to student. Some students will be extremely independent and prefer working alone, while others will be more social and prefer to work in a group where they can exchange ideas with others. Some students may tend to take a leadership role in the classroom, while others prefer to participate in a more discreet manner. Some students will want to figure everything out in a way that makes sense to them, while others are more willing to accept the teacher's explanations. Some students will be more intimidated by peer pressure than others, being concerned about giving a wrong answer when participating in class. Some students may not know when to stop struggling with a challenging problem and ask for help, while others may give up too soon and look for someone else to show them the solution. The Precalculus classroom should be an environment that meets the needs of all students, giving each student the opportunity to be himself or herself while providing an atmosphere for learning.

Remember that treating your students fairly may not mean treating them all the same. Treat each student in the manner that will most effectively encourage that student to work hard and succeed in the course.

Pre-AP Students

Students pursuing an Advanced Placement course of study may be motivated by a variety of reasons.

- Their tentative career choices
- Their love or aptitude for the subject matter
- Their parents' desire to have them excel
- The academic prestige brought to them by enrolling in the course

Some students may be pursuing this course of study for the wrong reasons; schools should carefully screen students to determine which students should enroll in the Pre-AP course. Students enrolling in the course and their parents should be fully informed of the expectations and demands of the Pre-AP course. It is also highly recommended that a system be in place whereby students enrolled in the Pre-AP course may be re-enrolled into a section of the standard course in the event that the teacher, the student, or the parents feel that the student is not well suited for the Pre-AP course once the course has begun.

Students who have earned high grades in previous mathematics courses are certainly candidates for admittance into the Pre-AP course. To determine whether these students should be admitted into the course, first determine whether there is any desire on the part of the student to follow the Pre-AP course of study. This may involve questioning the student about tentative career plans, enjoyment of mathematics, and general academic goals. Students who are motivated more by attaining high grades than by learning the material may not be the best fit for the Pre-AP course. Such students, as well as their parents, may become dissatisfied with the class, the teacher, or the school if they perceive that the student could be earning a higher grade in a standard course.

Consider as well that a student may have been able to maintain high grades in previous mathematics courses without developing a conceptual understanding of the mathematics. This could happen in situations where the concepts were presented but were never assessed as such. The student may have earned high grades by successfully learning how to work the exercises with limited understanding of the reasons for the processes. A student who does not pay attention while the teacher is developing the conceptual understanding, but pays attention when the teacher starts demonstrating how to work the exercises, may not be a good candidate for the Pre-AP course because of the level of conceptual understanding expected in the course. This level of conceptual understanding is necessary in order to pass the Advanced Placement exams. Watch out for the student whose attitude is along the lines of "just show me how to do the problem." Even though that student may maintain high grades, he or she may become defensive when challenged to justify the mathematical processes used to solve a problem and overall be uncomfortable in the Pre-AP classroom.

Be warned that students who have high expectations of themselves because of a history of high grades in mathematics courses may become frustrated when placed in a new environment where they do not perform as well as they did in the old environment. These problems can potentially be disruptive to the entire class if not handled properly by the teacher. These students may not accept their own responsibility, and may blame the teacher, the school, or the curriculum. Such students would be much happier in the standard course which would be more compatible with their learning preferences.

While there are definite benefits to screening students who have maintained high grades, do not overlook students with average grades who may benefit from the Pre-AP course. In some situations, a student's learning style may not have been compatible with the teaching style in previous courses causing the student's learning and, consequently, grades to suffer.

Among average grade earners, look for students who are highly motivated to learn and have a desire to understand the mathematical concepts and not just work problems. These students may not have learned as much as they could have in previous courses because the conceptual justifications for the mathematical methods were missing from the classroom. For these students, the Pre-AP classroom may be the perfect environment in which to thrive academically. Even if the student maintains the same grade level in the Pre-AP level as in previous courses, the student could be learning mathematics with a deeper understanding. Remember that it will take some time to make up for the learning missed in the past. If such students display a continued desire to learn and maintain a good attitude in the Pre-AP course, they should remain in the program and be encouraged to do their best.

However, some minimal level of past academic achievement must be set as a cut off point for admission to the Pre-AP course. Students should not be encouraged to get in over their heads where they are likely to fail. The goal is to have every student in the mathematics course that is the best fit for that student. The screening process will certainly need to be fine-tuned from time to time as you learn what works for your classroom and what does not.

In the Pre-AP classroom, students will need to be highly motivated to learn the subject matter. Try to learn what motivates each of the students in the Pre-AP course and build on that motivation whenever possible.

- If a student is motivated by a particular career possibility, point out in class how the material may be used in that career or in other courses that lead up to that career.
- For students who enjoy learning mathematics, be sure to include challenging problems, some of which may be games or puzzles, and present them as being fun.
- For students who have an aptitude in mathematics, be sure that they clearly see their successes in the course and their potential for continued success; this group may need the most encouragement during challenging topics because they are accustomed to mathematics being easy for them. Encourage such students to participate in mathematics competitions.
- Students who are in the class because of parental expectations may be seeking the approval of authority in general; praise these students as much as possible and find ways to acknowledge their accomplishments.

While most students in the Pre-AP classroom will want to be there, there may be the occasional student who really doesn't want to learn mathematics at the Pre-AP level. They may have appeared to meet all the criteria for the course and may have answered the screening questions correctly. These students may know how to play the academic game; rather than put their efforts into learning the subject matter, they put their efforts into working the system. These students may not be comfortable with open-ended assignments because they are looking for a formulaic method for success. Rather than doing their best, they want to do the minimal amount of work to earn the desired grade. In fact, they may actually ask the teacher *What do I need to do to get an A in this class?* They do not accept general answers such as *Participate in class discussions and do your best on the assignments*. As long as these students do not adversely affect other students, let them stay in the Pre-AP classroom and try to work with them, as best you can, to see that learning and understanding are the goals.

Parents of Pre-AP Students

Whenever possible, you should inform parents, at least in writing if not in person, of the increased expectations and demands on the student in the Pre-AP course. Parents should be aware that the Pre-AP course may have more homework than the standard course and that some of the material in the course may seem quite different than the material they may have seen in high school courses before. Though it is not always possible, encourage parents to take an active role in the students' learning. Parents who understand the goals of the course are more likely to be supportive of the course and encourage their student to excel.

The Classroom

The Pre-AP classroom should be an environment that inspires learning. Since learning styles differ even among Pre-AP students, it is important that the environment allows for a variety of learning styles. The in-class experience should set the example for the students' out-of-class work. Use a mixture of techniques such as class discussion, small group work, and individual work. In class, be involved in guiding students on how to use each of these techniques effectively. Then outside the classroom, when you are not present, the students will know your expectations of them as they complete assignments. Always set the example in class and encourage students to develop study habits that they can apply throughout their academic careers.

The class should be structured to allow students to express their ideas and talk through their thought processes as they make conjectures about new topics. All students need to be respectful of others' ideas, even when those ideas may seem farfetched. As the teacher, you must quickly deal with students who ridicule others for making mistakes or bad suggestions. Emphasize that many great mathematicians have gone down the wrong road many times before taking the right one.

The classroom also needs to be free from distractions that would keep students from being able to think deeply. Remember that you want the students to understand the mathematics behind the methods, which means they need to pay attention to logical arguments and follow the steps. This is hard to do in an environment where there may be other things attracting the students' attention. Set guidelines for appropriate classroom behavior. Do not allow students to do work for other classes or write notes or text messages during the vital classroom discussions of the Pre-AP class.

Encourage students to come to class prepared to learn. If you never express your expectations of the students, they may assume that your expectations are low. Thus, tell them that you expect them to be ready for class to begin when the bell rings, which might include having all necessary materials on the desktop and materials put away. (Since classroom time is usually limited, don't let students waste time doing what they should have done before class starts.) Tell them that they are expected to participate in all classroom activities whether those activities involve class discussion, small group work, or individual work. If you expect them to take notes or work along on their own calculators as you work an example on yours, you will need to tell them to do so. You are teaching more than mathematics in your classroom; you are teaching the work ethic that is necessary to succeed. The example you set of how you structure your classroom and use your time will reach far beyond your students' high school years.

Pre-AP Content

The Pre-AP course includes the content of the standard Precalculus course as well as additional content that brings the course to the Pre-AP level. The additional materials include more proofs and justifications for selected methods, further examples of applications for some of the topics, extensions of some methods to cover more cases, explanations of the connections between various topics, alternative methods of solving some problems, and some new topics with an emphasis on building the reasoning skills for calculus.

Some of the additional content may make more sense once students have started taking a calculus course. The goal is to introduce additional content in order to give students exposure but not necessarily to expect full comprehension and mastery of the additional topics.

Time for the additional content is carved out of the schedule by combining similar lessons into one lesson, especially where topics from previous mathematics courses are reviewed. Although review topics are included, you should be able to review material more quickly with Pre-AP level students.

Some themes are developed through the text and additional materials. Look for opportunities to reinforce these themes, which include logic and logical reasoning, geometric interpretations of algebra, graphing calculator solutions, undefined expressions, special cases, and exceptions to rules.

Pre-AP Pacing Guide

The Pacing and Assignment Guide provides a day-by-day plan for a 160-class course. The day-by-day plan includes days for review and assessment as well as classroom instruction. Suggested daily assignments are also included.

Where two consecutive lessons are to be covered in one class, the Pacing Guide gives an explanation of how to do this. In most cases, the topics are very similar and may be viewed as one cohesive topic rather than two separate topics so that the classroom experience need not feel like two lessons crammed into one day.

Pre-AP Assessment

The existing end-of-chapter assessment materials should be modified for the Pre-AP course to reflect both the additional topics that are covered as well as the depth at which the material is to be learned. Since it is difficult to assess understanding on a written test, some assessment should include the student presenting a solution to the teacher and explaining the methods used and why they work.

Ongoing assessment may be the best way to assess understanding and motivate students to work diligently on a daily basis. Students should know that all work may be assessed, so that no assignment is seen as unimportant or optional (unless it truly is optional). Assessment must go further than just determining whether the student can work the problems; it must include a component for mathematical understanding.

Conclusion

Once you begin your class, remember to be flexible. You may need to adjust the Pacing Guide or classroom procedures along the way. You may also find that the students are not responding as well as you had expected. Do not be discouraged. Modify the materials and suggestions to fit your needs. Even if you are not able to cover all the additional material in the Pre-AP course, if you emphasize mathematical understanding of the covered material, the students will still benefit greatly.

Remember that the students' goal is to be better prepared for college or AP Calculus courses, not to be perfect.

With its trademark clear examples and cohesive study aids, this text helps teachers **teach**, and learners **learn.**

Precalculus with Limits,* Second Edition,** provides the **sound, consistently structured explanations** of mathematical concepts that have helped thousands of high school students "get it." Designed for a two-term course, Ron Larson's text contains an effective combination of features that make it a **complete solution** for both students and instructors: an inviting design, interesting applications, step-by-step examples, carefully written exercises, and innovative supplemental resources. In addition to a brief algebra review and the core precalculus topics, ***Precalculus with Limits covers analytic geometry in three dimensions and introduces concepts covered in calculus.

The result? Students receive help that allows them to succeed and be prepared for their next mathematics courses, and teachers receive support that helps them do what they do best—*teach*.

Highlights of the Second Edition:

- Improved examples, featuring side-by-side graphical and algebraic solutions *(see page P-3)*
- New ***Algebra Help*** and ***Warnings/Caution*** features to keep students on track *(see page P-4)*
- Diverse exercise sets *(see pages P-5)*
- New ***Chapter Summaries*** linked to learning objectives and review problems *(see page P-6)*
- A complete teaching and learning package, including a comprehensive Teacher's Edition created specifically for high school teachers, and Cengage Learning's **Enhanced WebAssign®**, the most widely used online home work management system *(see pages P-7 and P-8)*. Ask your sales representative about discounts that may be available to your school.

Turn the page for a brief walkthrough of chapter features.

Chapter openers set the stage for learning

Exponential and Logarithmic Functions

3

In Mathematics

Exponential functions involve a constant base and a variable exponent. The inverse of an exponential function is a logarithmic function.

In Real Life

Exponential and logarithmic functions are widely used in describing economic and physical phenomena such as compound interest, population growth, memory retention, and decay of radioactive material. For instance, a logarithmic function can be used to relate an animal's weight and its lowest galloping speed. (See Exercise 95, page 242.)

IN CAREERS

There are many careers that use exponential and logarithmic functions. Several are listed below.

- Astronomer
  Example 7, page 240
- Archeologist
  Example 3, page 258
- Psychologist
  Exercise 136, page 253
- Forensic Scientist
  Exercise 75, page 266

215

New! New three-part chapter openers introduce topics to be covered in an engaging and practical context.

In Mathematics describes an important topic to be covered in the chapter. ***In Real Life*** tells students where they will encounter the topic.

In Careers relates some of the chapter's applications exercises to careers in which the mathematics is used, highlighting the relevance of the material.

Learning objectives help students focus

Each section begins with learning objectives that list ***what*** students should learn in the section. Larson then adds the element of motivation by also describing ***why*** students should learn it.

216 Chapter 3 Exponential and Logarithmic Functions

3.1 EXPONENTIAL FUNCTIONS AND THEIR GRAPHS

What you should learn

- Recognize and evaluate exponential functions with base *a*.
- Graph exponential functions and use the One-to-One Property.
- Recognize, evaluate, and graph exponential functions with base *e*.
- Use exponential functions to model and solve real-life problems.

Why you should learn it

Exponential functions can be used to model and solve real-life problems. For instance, in Exercise 76 on page 226, an exponential function is used to model the concentration of a drug in the bloodstream.

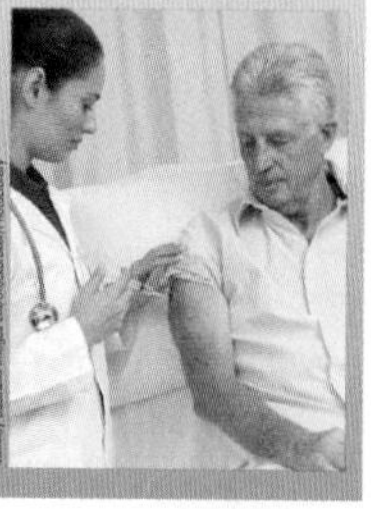

Exponential Functions

So far, this text has dealt mainly with **algebraic functions,** which include polynomial functions and rational functions. In this chapter, you will study two types of nonalgebraic functions—*exponential functions* and *logarithmic functions*. These functions are examples of **transcendental functions.**

Definition of Exponential Function

The **exponential function f with base a** is denoted by

$$f(x) = a^x$$

where $a > 0$, $a \neq 1$, and x is any real number.

The base $a = 1$ is excluded because it yields $f(x) = 1^x = 1$. This is a constant function, not an exponential function.

You have evaluated a^x for integer and rational values of x. For example, you know that $4^3 = 64$ and $4^{1/2} = 2$. However, to evaluate 4^x for any real number x, you need to interpret forms with *irrational* exponents. For the purposes of this text, it is sufficient to think of

$$a^{\sqrt{2}} \quad (\text{where } \sqrt{2} \approx 1.41421356)$$

as the number that has the successively closer approximations

$$a^{1.4}, a^{1.41}, a^{1.414}, a^{1.4142}, a^{1.41421}, \ldots .$$

Example 1 Evaluating Exponential Functions

Use a calculator to evaluate each function at the indicated value of x.

Function	*Value*
a. $f(x) = 2^x$	$x = -3.1$
b. $f(x) = 2^{-x}$	$x = \pi$
c. $f(x) = 0.6^x$	$x = \frac{3}{2}$

Clear, step-by-step examples demonstrate problem-solving

Example 2 Graphing a Parabola in Standard Form

Sketch the graph of $f(x) = 2x^2 + 8x + 7$ and identify the vertex and the axis of the parabola.

Solution

Begin by writing the quadratic function in standard form. Notice that the first step in completing the square is to factor out any coefficient of x^2 that is not 1.

$f(x) = 2x^2 + 8x + 7$ Write original function.

$= 2(x^2 + 4x) + 7$ Factor 2 out of x-terms.

$= 2(x^2 + 4x + 4 - 4) + 7$ Add and subtract 4 within parentheses.

$(4/2)^2$

After adding and subtracting 4 within the parentheses, you must now regroup the terms to form a perfect square trinomial. The -4 can be removed from inside the parentheses; however, because of the 2 outside of the parentheses, you must multiply -4 by 2, as shown below.

$f(x) = 2(x^2 + 4x + 4) - 2(4) + 7$ Regroup terms.

$= 2(x^2 + 4x + 4) - 8 + 7$ Simplify.

$= 2(x + 2)^2 - 1$ Write in standard form.

From this form, you can see that the graph of f is a parabola that opens upward and has its vertex at $(-2, -1)$. This corresponds to a left shift of two units and a downward shift of one unit relative to the graph of $y = 2x^2$, as shown in Figure 2.6. In the figure, you can see that the axis of the parabola is the vertical line through the vertex, $x = -2$.

CHECK *Point* Now try Exercise 19.

Examples are worked out step-by-step. Larson uses graphics, color, and precise annotations to clarify sound procedures and techniques.

Example 9 Finding a Minimum Area

A rectangular page is designed to contain 48 square inches of print. The margins at the top and bottom of the page are each 1 inch deep. The margins on each side are $1\frac{1}{2}$ inches wide. What should the dimensions of the page be so that the least amount of paper is used?

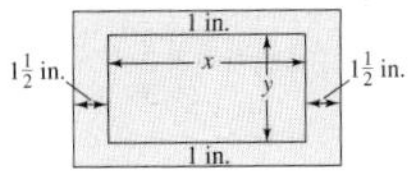

FIGURE 2.48

Graphical Solution

Let A be the area to be minimized. From Figure 2.48, you can write

$$A = (x + 3)(y + 2).$$

The printed area inside the margins is modeled by $48 = xy$ or $y = 48/x$. To find the minimum area, rewrite the equation for A in terms of just one variable by substituting $48/x$ for y.

$$A = (x + 3)\left(\frac{48}{x} + 2\right)$$

$$= \frac{(x + 3)(48 + 2x)}{x}, \quad x > 0$$

The graph of this rational function is shown in Figure 2.49. Because x represents the width of the printed area, you need consider only the portion of the graph for which x is positive. Using a graphing utility, you can approximate the minimum value of A to occur when $x \approx 8.5$ inches. The corresponding value of y is $48/8.5 \approx 5.6$ inches. So, the dimensions should be

$$x + 3 \approx 11.5 \text{ inches} \quad \text{by} \quad y + 2 \approx 7.6 \text{ inches}.$$

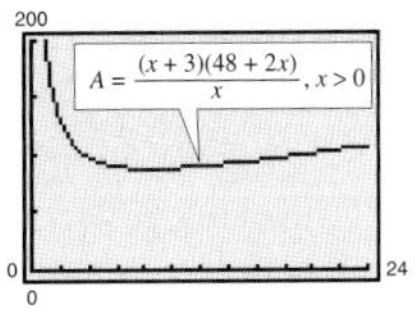

FIGURE 2.49

CHECK *Point* Now try Exercise 81.

Numerical Solution

Let A be the area to be minimized. From Figure 2.48, you can write

$$A = (x + 3)(y + 2).$$

The printed area inside the margins is modeled by $48 = xy$ or $y = 48/x$. To find the minimum area, rewrite the equation for A in terms of just one variable by substituting $48/x$ for y.

$$A = (x + 3)\left(\frac{48}{x} + 2\right)$$

$$= \frac{(x + 3)(48 + 2x)}{x}, \quad x > 0$$

Use the *table* feature of a graphing utility to create a table of values for the function

$$y_1 = \frac{(x + 3)(48 + 2x)}{x}$$

beginning at $x = 1$. From the table, you can see that the minimum value of y_1 occurs when x is somewhere between 8 and 9, as shown in Figure 2.50. To approximate the minimum value of y_1 to one decimal place, change the table so that it starts at $x = 8$ and increases by 0.1. The minimum value of y_1 occurs when $x \approx 8.5$, as shown in Figure 2.51. The corresponding value of y is $48/8.5 \approx 5.6$ inches. So, the dimensions should be $x + 3 \approx 11.5$ inches by $y + 2 \approx 7.6$ inches.

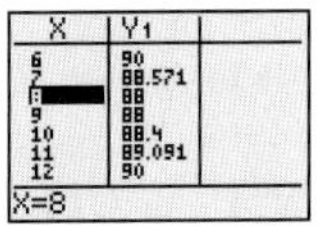

FIGURE 2.50

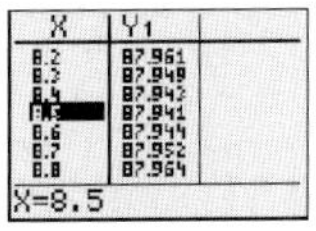

FIGURE 2.51

If you go on to take a course in calculus, you will learn an analytic technique for finding the exact value of x that produces a minimum area. In this case, that value is $x = 6\sqrt{2} \approx 8.485$.

Side-by-side example solutions for select examples include multiple problem solving approaches—such as algebraic, graphical, and numerical—to appeal to a variety of teaching and learning styles.

New! A greater number of side-by-side examples present graphical solutions to improve students' graphical understanding of algebra.

Example 5 Solving an Exponential Equation of Quadratic Type

Solve $e^{2x} - 3e^x + 2 = 0$.

Algebraic Solution

$e^{2x} - 3e^x + 2 = 0$ Write original equation.

$(e^x)^2 - 3e^x + 2 = 0$ Write in quadratic form.

$(e^x - 2)(e^x - 1) = 0$ Factor.

$e^x - 2 = 0$ Set 1st factor equal to 0.

$x = \ln 2$ Solution

$e^x - 1 = 0$ Set 2nd factor equal to 0.

$x = 0$ Solution

The solutions are $x = \ln 2 \approx 0.693$ and $x = 0$. Check these in the original equation.

Graphical Solution

Use a graphing utility to graph $y = e^{2x} - 3e^x + 2$. Use the *zero* or *root* feature or the *zoom* and *trace* features of the graphing utility to approximate the values of x for which $y = 0$. In Figure 3.28, you can see that the zeros occur at $x = 0$ and at $x \approx 0.693$. So, the solutions are $x = 0$ and $x \approx 0.693$.

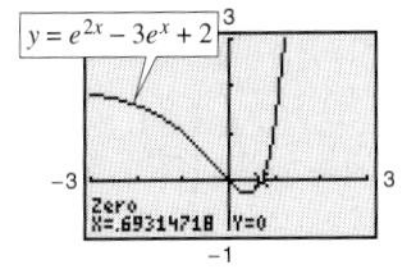

FIGURE 3.28

CHECK *Point* Now try Exercise 59.

A ***Checkpoint*** after each worked example refers students to similar drills in the section exercises, allowing them to practice and reinforce the concepts they just learned. Answers to ***Checkpoints*** are included at the back of the book.

CHECK *Point* Now try Exercise 59.

Insightful study tips and reminders

Larson guides and encourages students as they work through each section.

New! ***Algebra Help*** notes direct students to specific sections where they can review the algebra needed to master the current topic.

Graphs of Exponential Functions

The graphs of all exponential functions have similar characteristics, as shown in Examples 2, 3, and 5.

Algebra Help

You can review the techniques for sketching the graph of an equation in Section 1.2.

Example 2 Graphs of $y = a^x$

In the same coordinate plane, sketch the graph of each function.

a. $f(x) = 2^x$ **b.** $g(x) = 4^x$

Solution

The table below lists some values for each function, and Figure 3.1 shows the graphs of the two functions. Note that both graphs are increasing. Moreover, the graph of $g(x) = 4^x$ is increasing more rapidly than the graph of $f(x) = 2^x$.

x	-3	-2	-1	0	1	2
2^x	$\frac{1}{8}$	$\frac{1}{4}$	$\frac{1}{2}$	1	2	4
4^x	$\frac{1}{64}$	$\frac{1}{16}$	$\frac{1}{4}$	1	4	16

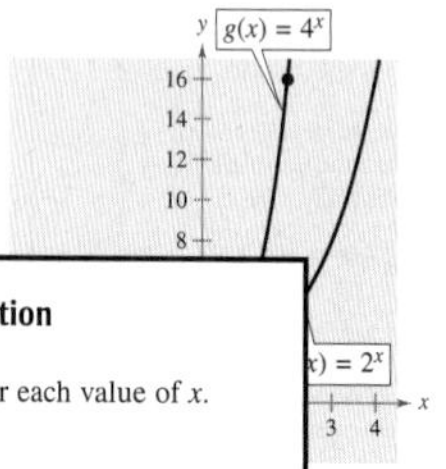

CHECKPoint Now try Exercise 17.

The table in Example 2 was evaluated by hand. You could, of course, use a graphing utility to construct tables with even more values.

Example 3 Graphs of $y = a^{-x}$

Example 8 Evaluating the Natural Logarithmic Function

Use a calculator to evaluate the function given by $f(x) = \ln x$ for each value of x.

a. $x = 2$

b. $x = 0.3$

c. $x = -1$

d. $x = 1 + \sqrt{2}$

Solution

	Function Value	*Graphing Calculator Keystrokes*	*Display*
a.	$f(2) = \ln 2$	LN 2 ENTER	0.6931472
b.	$f(0.3) = \ln 0.3$	LN .3 ENTER	–1.2039728
c.	$f(-1) = \ln(-1)$	LN (–) 1 ENTER	ERROR
d.	$f(1 + \sqrt{2}) = \ln(1 + \sqrt{2})$	LN (1 + √ 2) ENTER	0.8813736

CHECKPoint Now try Exercise 67.

WARNING/CAUTION

Notice that as with every other logarithmic function, the domain of the natural logarithmic function is the set of *positive real numbers*—be sure you see that ln x is not defined for zero or for negative numbers.

In Example 8, be sure you see that $\ln(-1)$ gives a calculators. (Some calculators may display a complex num the domain of ln x is the set of positive real numbers (see F undefined.

The four properties of logarithms listed on page 228 logarithms.

New! ***Caution/Warning*** boxes highlight common mathematical errors and pitfalls.

Improved! ***Study Tips*** provide useful information for learning the topic.

Example 10 Using Vectors to Find Speed and Direction

Study Tip

Recall from Section 4.8 that in air navigation, bearings can be measured in degrees clockwise from north.

An airplane is traveling at a speed of 500 miles per hour with a bearing of 330° at a fixed altitude with a negligible wind velocity as shown in Figure 6.32(a). When the airplane reaches a certain point, it encounters a wind with a velocity of 70 miles per hour in the direction N 45° E, as shown in Figure 6.32(b). What are the resultant speed and direction of the airplane?

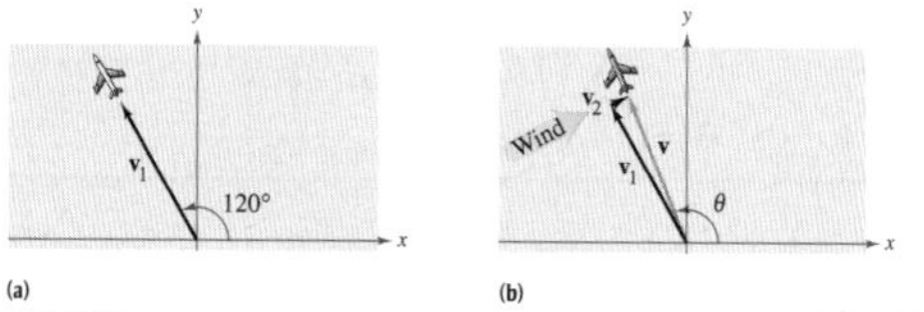

FIGURE 6.32

Solution

Using Figure 6.32, the velocity of the airplane (alone) is

$$\mathbf{v}_1 = 500\langle\cos 120°, \sin 120°\rangle$$
$$= \langle -250, 250\sqrt{3}\rangle$$

and the velocity of the wind is

$$\mathbf{v}_2 = 70\langle\cos 45°, \sin 45°\rangle$$
$$= \langle 35\sqrt{2}, 35\sqrt{2}\rangle.$$

So, the velocity of the airplane (in the wind) is

TECHNOLOGY

You can use the *table* feature of a graphing utility to approximate the zeros of a polynomial function. For instance, for the function given by

$$f(x) = -2x^3 - 3x^2 + 3$$

create a table that shows the function values for $-20 \le x \le 20$, as shown in the first table at the right. Scroll through the table looking for consecutive function values that differ in sign. From the table, you can see that $f(0)$ and $f(1)$ differ in sign. So, you can conclude from the Intermediate Value Theorem that the function has a zero between 0 and 1. You can adjust your table to show function values for $0 \le x \le 1$ using increments of 0.1, as shown in the second table at the right. By scrolling through the table you can see that $f(0.8)$ and $f(0.9)$ differ in sign. So, the function has a zero between 0.8 and 0.9. If you repeat this process several times, you should obtain $x \approx 0.806$ as the zero of the function. Use the *zero* or *root* feature of a graphing utility to confirm this result.

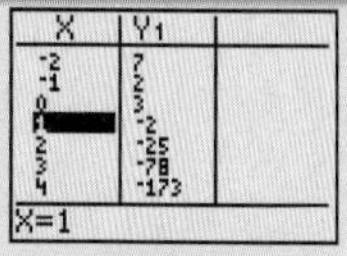

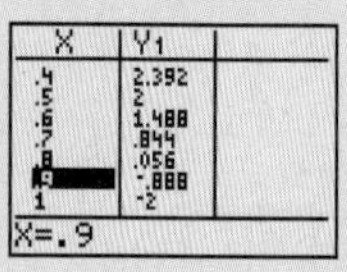

Technology **boxes** offer practical guidance in the use of graphing calculators to solve problems, helpful if you use technology in your course.

Diverse, categorized exercises—

including new capstone conceptual exercises

Revised and Improved! Multiple learning styles are addressed with a variety of exercise types and levels in every exercise set, including exercises involving vocabulary, skills and applications, graphing, and critical thinking ***(Exploration)***. Exercises appear at the end of every section and ***Review Exercises*** appear at the end of each chapter (see the facing page).

3.5 EXERCISES

See www.CalcChat.com for worked-out solutions to odd-numbered exercises.

VOCABULARY: Fill in the blanks.

1. An exponential growth model has the form ________ and an exponential decay model has the form ________.
2. A logarithmic model has the form ________ or ________.
3. Gaussian models are commonly used in probability and statistics to represent populations that are ________ ________.
4. The graph of a Gaussian model is ________ shaped, where the ________ ________ is the maximum y-value of the graph.
5. A logistic growth model has the form ________.
6. A logistic curve is also called a ________ curve.

SKILLS AND APPLICATIONS

In Exercises 7–12, match the function with its graph. [The graphs are labeled (a), (b), (c), (d), (e), and (f).]

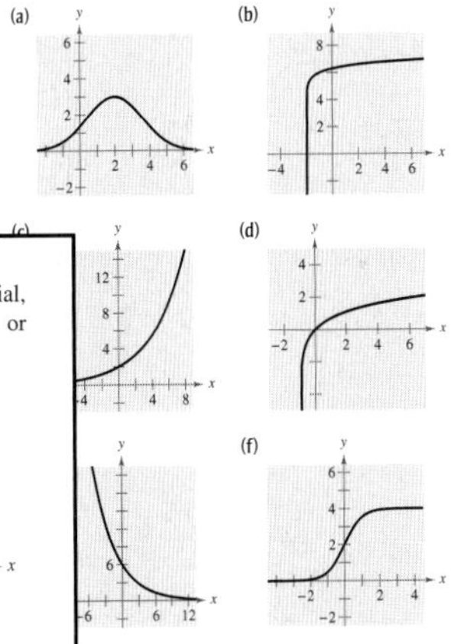

$2e^{x/4}$ 8. $y = 6e^{-x/4}$

$6 + \log(x + 2)$ 10. $y = 3e^{-(x-2)^2/5}$

$\ln(x + 1)$ 12. $y = \dfrac{4}{1 + e^{-2x}}$

ses 13 and 14, (a) solve for P and (b) solve for t.

Pe^{rt} 14. $A = P\left(1 + \dfrac{r}{n}\right)^{nt}$

COMPOUND INTEREST In Exercises 15–22, complete the table for a savings account in which interest is compounded continuously.

	Initial Investment	Annual % Rate	Time to Double	Amount After 10 Years
15.	\$1000	3.5%		
16.	\$750	$10\frac{1}{2}$%		
17.	\$750		$7\frac{3}{4}$ yr	
18.	\$10,000		12 yr	
19.	\$500			\$1505.00
20.	\$600			\$19,205.00
21.		4.5%		\$10,000.00
22.		2%		\$2000.00

COMPOUND INTEREST In Exercises 23 and 24, determine the principal P that must be invested at rate r, compounded monthly, so that \$500,000 will be available for retirement in t years.

23. $r = 5\%, t = 10$ 24. $r = 3\frac{1}{2}\%, t = 15$

COMPOUND INTEREST In Exercises 25 and 26, determine the time necessary for \$1000 to double if it is invested at interest rate r compounded (a) annually, (b) monthly, (c) daily, and (d) continuously.

25. $r = 10\%$ 26. $r = 6.5\%$

27. **COMPOUND INTEREST** Complete the table for the time t (in years) necessary for P dollars to triple if interest is compounded continuously at rate r.

r	2%	4%	6%	8%	10%	12%
t						

28. **MODELING DATA** Draw a scatter plot of the data in Exercise 27. Use the *regression* feature of a graphing utility to find a model for the data.

New! A ***Capstone*** exercise appears in each section's exercise set. These conceptual exercises synthesize the main concepts of the section, showing students how the various topics relate. They're excellent for both classroom discussion and test preparation.

84. **CAPSTONE** Identify each model as exponential, Gaussian, linear, logarithmic, logistic, quadratic, or none of the above. Explain your reasoning.

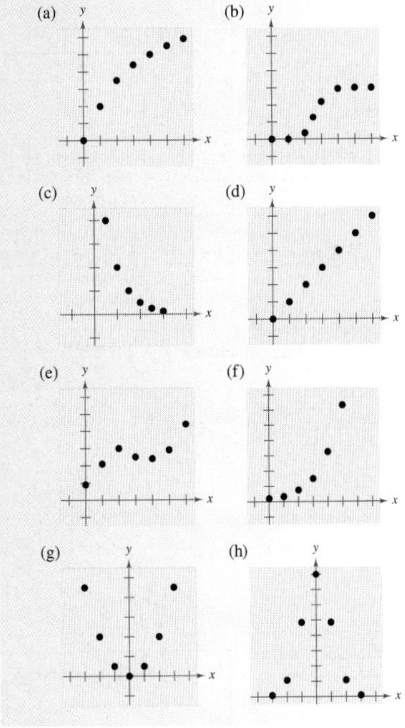

PROJECT: SALES PER SHARE To work an extended application analyzing the sales per share for Kohl's Corporation from 1992 through 2007, visit this text's website at *academic.cengage.com*. (Data Source: Kohl's Corporation)

PROBLEM SOLVING

This collection of thought-provoking and challenging exercises further explores and expands upon concepts learned in this chapter.

1. Graph the exponential function given by $y = a^x$ for $a = 0.5$, 1.2, and 2.0. Which of these curves intersects the line $y = x$? Determine all positive numbers a for which the curve $y = a^x$ intersects the line $y = x$.
2. Use a graphing utility to graph $y_1 = e^x$ and each of the functions $y_2 = x^2$, $y_3 = x^3$, $y_4 = \sqrt{x}$, and $y_5 = |x|$. Which function increases at the greatest rate as x approaches $+\infty$?
3. Use the result of Exercise 2 to make a conjecture about the rate of growth of $y_1 = e^x$ and $y = x^n$, where n is a natural number and x approaches $+\infty$.
4. Use the results of Exercises 2 and 3 to describe what is implied when it is stated that a quantity is growing exponentially.
5. Given the exponential function

$f(x) = a^x$

show that

(a) $f(u + v) = f(u) \cdot f(v)$.   (b) $f(2x) = [f(x)]^2$.

10. Find a pattern for $f^{-1}(x)$ if

$$f(x) = \frac{a^x + 1}{a^x - 1}$$

where $a > 0$, $a \neq 1$.

11. By observation, identify the equation that corresponds to the graph. Explain your reasoning.

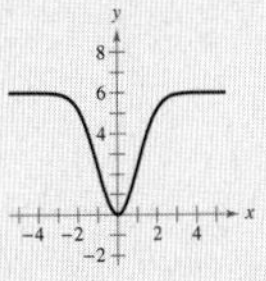

(a) $y = 6e^{-x^2/2}$

(b) $y = \dfrac{6}{1 + e^{-x/2}}$

New! This edition includes even more skill-building and challenging ***(Problem Solving)*** exercises, many reflecting topics requested by users.

Comprehensive chapter reviews organized by learning objectives

New! ***Chapter Summaries*** now include explanations and/or examples for all learning objectives, further promoting students' understanding of the material. Each objective/explanation is accompanied by problem numbers from the chapter ***Review Exercises*** that test students' understanding of the concept or technique involved.

3 Chapter Summary

	What Did You Learn?	Explanation/Examples	Review Exercises
Section 3.1	Recognize and evaluate exponential functions with base a *(p. 216)*.	The exponential function f with base a is denoted by $f(x) = a^x$ where $a > 0$, $a \neq 1$, and x is any real number.	1–6
	Graph exponential functions and use the One-to-One Property *(p. 217)*.	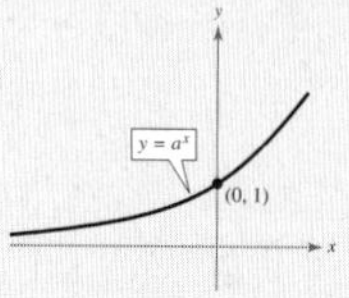 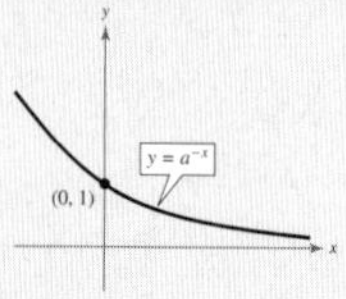 **One-to-One Property:** For $a > 0$ and $a \neq 1$, $a^x = a^y$ if and only if $x = y$.	7–24
	Recognize, evaluate, and graph exponential functions with base e *(p. 220)*.	The function $f(x) = e^x$ is called the natural exponential function. 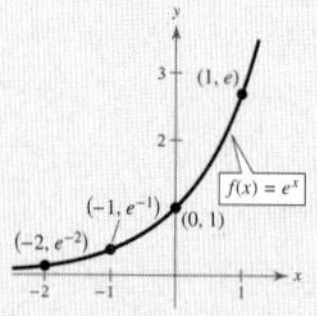	25–32
	Use exponential functions to model and solve real-life problems *(p. 221)*.	Exponential functions are used in compound interest formulas (See Example 8.) and in radioactive decay models. (See Example 9.)	33–36
Section 3.2	Recognize and evaluate logarithmic functions with base a *(p. 227)*.	For $x > 0$, $a > 0$, and $a \neq 1$, $y = \log_a x$ if and only if $x = a^y$. The function $f(x) = \log_a x$ is called the logarithmic function with base a. The logarithmic function with base 10 is the common logarithmic function. It is denoted by $\log_{10}$ or log.	37–48
	Graph logarithmic functions *(p. 229)* and recognize, evaluate, and graph natural logarithmic functions *(p. 231)*.	The graph of $y = \log_a x$ is a reflection of the graph of $y = a^x$ about the line $y = x$. The function defined by $f(x) = \ln x$, $x > 0$, is called the natural logarithmic function. Its graph is a reflection of the graph of $f(x) = e^x$ about the line $y = x$. 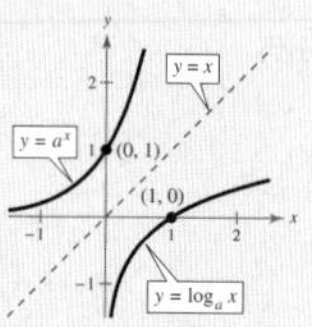 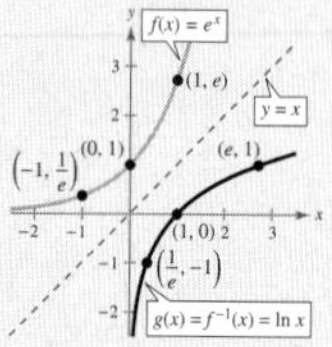	49–52 53–58
	Use logarithmic functions to model ... *(p. 233)*.	A logarithmic function is used in the human memory model. (See Example 11.)	59, 60

3 Chapter Test

See www.CalcChat.com for worked-out solutions to odd-numbered exercises.

Take this test as you would take a test in class. When you are finished, check your work against the answers given in the back of the book.

In Exercises 1–4, evaluate the expression. Approximate your result to three decimal places.

1. $4.2^{0.6}$ **2.** $4^{3\pi/2}$ **3.** $e^{-7/10}$ **4.** $e^{3.1}$

In Exercises 5–7, construct a table of values. Then sketch the graph of the function.

5. $f(x) = 10^{-x}$ **6.** $f(x) = -6^{x-2}$ **7.** $f(x) = 1 - e^{2x}$

8. Evaluate (a) $\log_7 7^{-0.89}$ and (b) $4.6 \ln e^2$.

In Exercises 9–11, construct a table of values. Then sketch the graph of the function. Identify any asymptotes.

9. $f(x) = -\log x - 6$ **10.** $f(x) = \ln(x - 4)$ **11.** $f(x) = 1 + \ln(x + 6)$

In Exercises 12–14, evaluate the logarithm using the change-of-base formula. Round your result to three decimal places.

12. $\log_7 44$ **13.** $\log_{16} 0.63$ **14.** $\log_{3/4} 24$

In Exercises 15–17, use the properties of logarithms to expand the expression as a sum, difference, and/or constant multiple of logarithms.

15. $\log_2 3a^4$ **16.** $\ln \frac{5\sqrt{x}}{6}$ **17.** $\log \frac{(x-1)^3}{y^2 z}$

Review Exercises (organized by section) are followed by a ***Chapter Test***, which students can take to evaluate their readiness for class tests. Answers to odd-numbered ***Review Exercises*** are available online; ***Chapter Test*** answers are at the back of the text.

A ***Cumulative Test*** appears after Chapters 3, 6, 9, and 12.

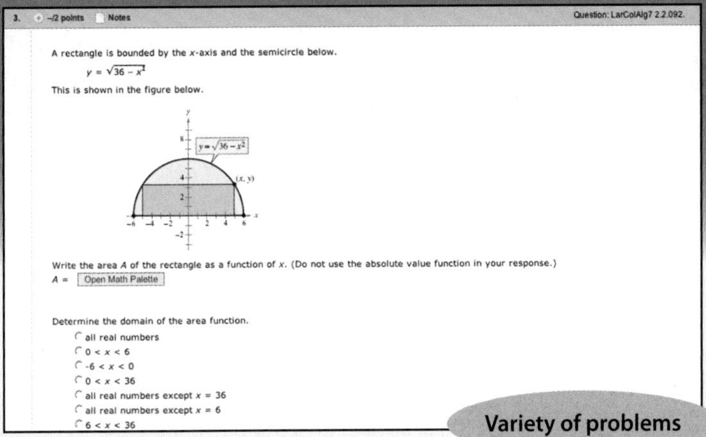

Variety of problems

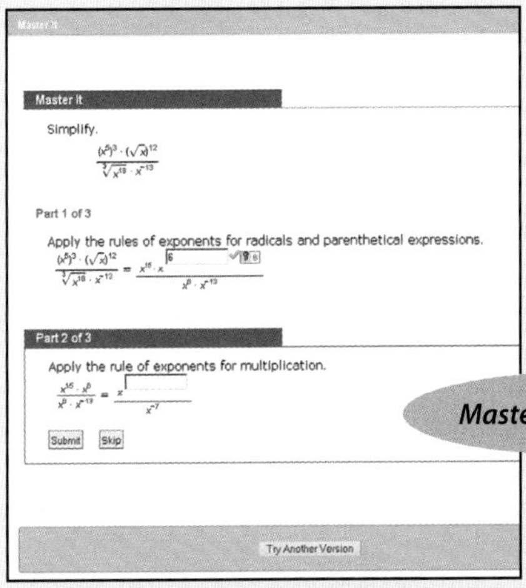

Master It tutorials

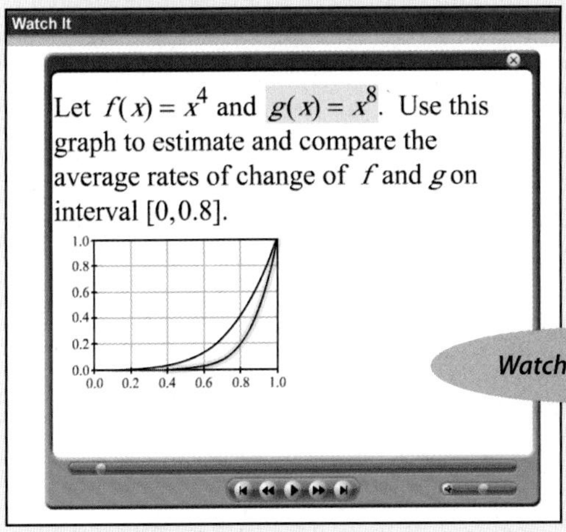

Watch It videos

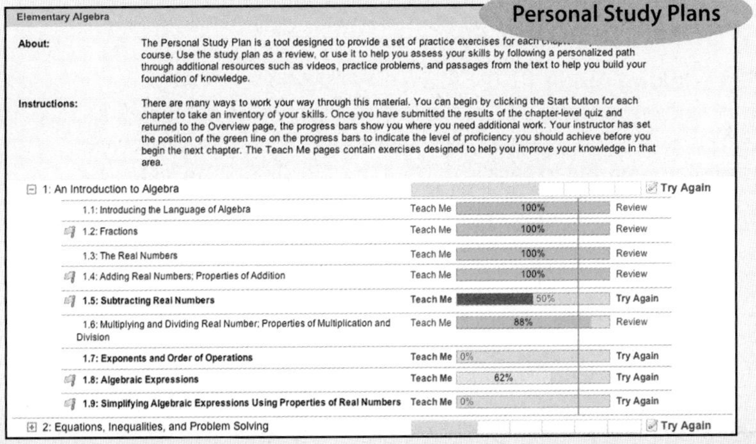

Personal Study Plans

ENHANCED WebAssign

Easy to assign.
Easy to use.
Easy to manage.

The most widely used online homework management system for mathematics—and available exclusively from Cengage Learning—**Enhanced WebAssign**® allows you to easily assign, collect, grade, and record homework assignments via the web. The pedagogy and exercises in Larson's text become even more effective in **Enhanced WebAssign**, supplemented by multimedia tutorial support and immediate feedback as students complete their assignments. And with its easy-to-use interface and automatic grading, **Enhanced WebAssign**® saves you time on homework management.

Highlights of Enhanced WebAssign

- ***Algorithmically generated homework problems*** based on over 4,000 end-of-section exercises
- ***Algorithmic solutions for key problems,*** showing students (at the instructor's discretion) how a problem is solved, step-by-step
- ***Concept reinforcement*** with "Watch It" links to videos of worked exercises and "Master It" step-by-step tutorials for specific problems and examples
- ***Personal Study Plans*** that identify concepts students still need to master, and direct them to the appropriate review resources
- ***Instructor gradebook*** with weighted categories and scores
- Compatible with Windows®, Apple® Macintosh, and Linux®
- Works with most web browsers: Mozilla Firefox®, Internet Explorer®, and Safari™

Contact your sales representative for details about discounts on ***Enhanced WebAssign*** *for you and your students.*

Screenshots shown here are for illustrative purposes, and may reflect content from courses other than precalculus.

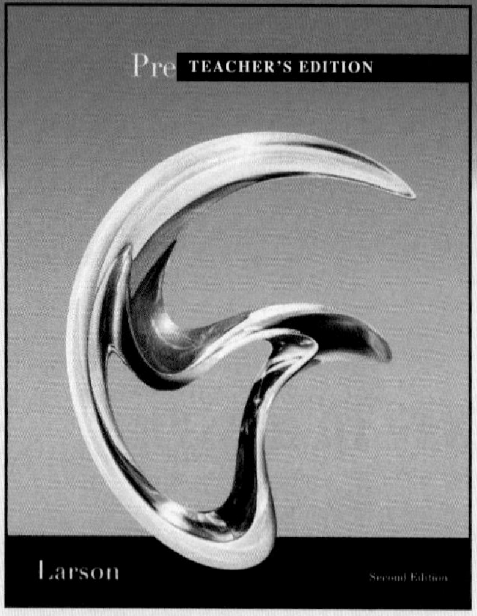

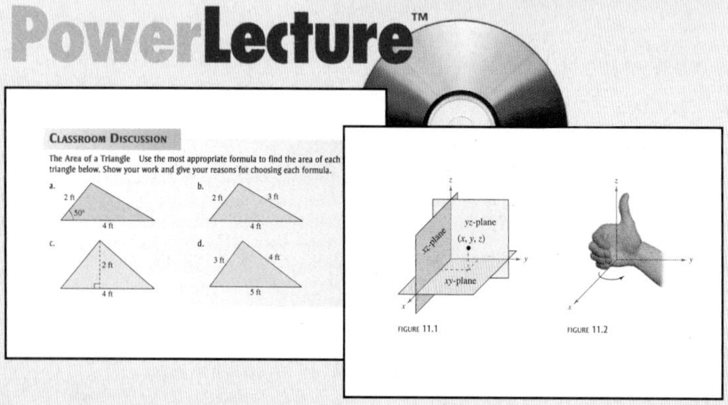

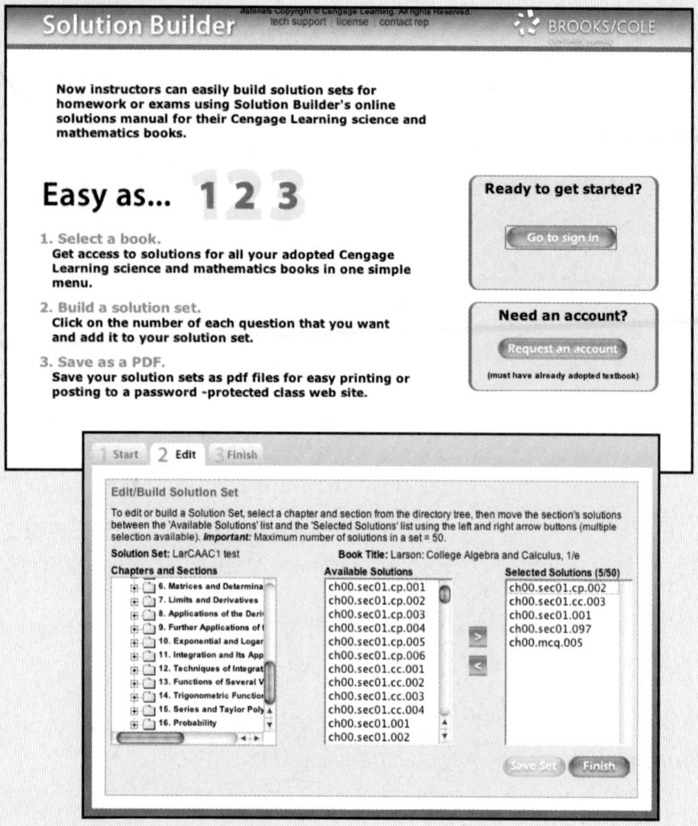

Other resources

INSTRUCTOR RESOURCES

Teacher's Edition This Teacher's Edition includes the complete student text plus a wealth of annotations on each page in a wraparound format. Each lesson provides a stepped-out process for the teacher to follow: 1) Plan and Prepare, 2) Focus and Motivate, 3) Teach, 4) Practice and Apply, and 5) Assess and Reteach. The teacher annotations include extra examples and projects, classroom activities, teaching strategies, and references to technology components and other program resources at point-of-use. Answers to even-numbered text exercises, *Vocabulary Checks*, and *Explorations* are also provided.

Lesson Plans ISBN: 978-0-538-73910-8
This complete set of section-by-section lesson plans serves as a guide for classroom instruction and facilitates instructional preparation.

Complete Solutions Manual ISBN: 978-0-538-73690-9
This manual contains solutions to all exercises from the text, including chapter *Review Exercises* and *Chapter Tests*.

PowerLecture™ for High Schools with ExamView®
ISBN: 978-0-538-73813-2
This CD-ROM provides teachers with dynamic media tools for teaching precalculus. Microsoft® PowerPoint® lecture slides, art slides of the figures from the text, electronic files for the test bank, and a link to the **Solution Builder** are all included, plus a guide to help you use these materials with interactive white board technology. An easy-to-use assessment system, the algorithmic **ExamView®** allows you to create, deliver, and customize tests (both print and online) in minutes.

Online Solutions Builder This flexible, personalized online tool lets you easily build and save your own personal solution sets either for printing or posting on password-protected class websites. It's an electronic version of the **Complete Solutions Manual** available via the **PowerLecture** and **Instructor's Companion Website**.

Test Bank ISBN: 978-0-538-73814-9

Text-Specific DVD ISBN: 978-0-538-73828-6
Keyed to the text by section, these DVDs provide comprehensive course coverage—along with additional explanations of concepts, sample problems, and applications—to help students review essential topics.

STUDENT RESOURCES

Note-Taking Guide ISBN: 978-0-538-73864-4
This innovative study aid helps students take full advantage of their textbook through pre- and post-reading activities and vocabulary reinforcement tied to each chapter. The guide features a lesson-by-lesson framework that promotes active learning by allowing students to take notes on and review the key concepts throughout the text. Upon completion, each chapter of the guide can serve as a study aid to help students prepare for chapter tests.

Student Solutions Manual ISBN: 978-0-538-73863-7
This guide offers step-by-step solutions for all odd-numbered text exercises, chapter and cumulative tests, and practice tests with solutions.

Pacing and Assignment Guide 1

REGULAR SCHEDULE

Lesson	Day	AVERAGE	ADVANCED
1.1	Day 1	pp. 8–12 Exs. 5–13 odd, 15–25, 39–59 odd, 63–68, 71, 72, 79–83, 85	pp. 8–12 Exs. 11–25, 39–42 even, 43–46, 47–56 even, 57, 58, 60, 63–69, 71, 74, 79, 80, 83–85
1.2	Day 1	pp. 21–23 Exs. 1–14, 15–87 odd, 88, 90	pp. 21–23 Exs. 7–14, 16–82 even, 83, 85, 87–90
1.3	Day 1	pp. 33–38 Exs. 1–105 odd, 107–110, 111–117 odd, 118, 119–135 odd, 137–144, 146	pp. 33–38 Exs. 10–106 even, 107–110, 112–116 even, 117, 118–136 even, 139–146, Project
1.4	Day 1	pp. 48–53 Exs. 1–6, 11–101 odd, 102, 103–109 odd, 111–124	pp. 48–53 Exs. 1–6, 12–110 even, 111–114, 119–124
1.5	Day 1	pp. 61–65 Exs. 1–12, 13–81 odd, 83–106, 110, 111–117 odd, 121–126, 131, 136	pp. 61–65 Exs. 1–8, 10–20 even, 33–38, 40–118 even, 121–136
1.6	Day 1	pp. 71–72 Exs. 11–18, 27–71 odd, 73–76	pp. 71–72 Exs. 11–18, 28–72 even, 73–76
1.7	Day 1	pp. 78–82 Exs. 1–6, 7–13 odd, 15–18, 19–79 odd, 81–85	pp. 78–82 Exs. 8–14 even, 15–18, 20–78 even, 79, 80, 86, 88–90
1.8	Day 1	pp. 88–91 Exs. 5–8, 9–31 odd, 33–40, 41–59 odd, 61–63, 65–74, 77–79, 81	pp. 88–91 Exs. 5–8, 10–32 even, 33–40, 42–60 even, 61–63, 65–74, 76–84
1.9	Day 1	pp. 98–101 Exs. 7–13 odd, 15–18, 23–33 odd, 35–42, 43–75 odd, 87–97, 99, 101, 103–108	pp. 98–101 Exs. 8–14 even, 15–18, 24–38 even, 39–42, 44–76 even, 87–101, 103–116
1.10	Day 1	pp. 108–113 Exs. 11–21 odd, 22, 23–85 odd, 87–89	pp. 108–113 Exs. 12–86 even, 87, 94
Review	Day 1	pp. 116–120 Exs. 1–162 odd	pp. 116–120 Exs. 1–162 odd
Assess	Day 1	Chapter 1 Test	Chapter 1 Test

Yearly Pacing Chapter 1 Total – 12 days Remaining – 148 days

BLOCK SCHEDULE

DAY 1	DAY 2	DAY 3	DAY 4	DAY 5	DAY 6
1.1	**1.3**	**1.5**	**1.7**	**1.9**	**REVIEW**
pp. 8–12 Exs. 5–13 odd, 15–25, 39–59 odd, 63–68, 71, 72, 79–83, 85	pp. 33–38 Exs. 1–105 odd, 107–110, 111–117 odd, 118, 119–135 odd, 137–144, 146	pp. 61–65 Exs. 1–12, 13–81 odd, 83–106, 110, 111–117 odd, 121–126, 131, 136	pp. 78–82 Exs. 1–6, 7–13 odd, 15–18, 19–79 odd, 81–85	pp. 98–101 Exs. 7–13 odd, 15–18, 23–33 odd, 35–42, 43–75 odd, 87–97, 99, 101, 103–108	pp. 116–120 Exs. 1–162 odd
1.2	**1.4**	**1.6**	**1.8**	**1.10**	**ASSESS**
pp. 21–23 Exs. 1–14, 15–87 odd, 88, 90	pp. 48–53 Exs. 1–6, 11–101 odd, 102, 103–109 odd, 111–124	pp. 71–72 Exs. 11–18, 27–71 odd, 73–76	pp. 88–91 Exs. 5–8, 9–31 odd, 33–40, 41–59 odd, 61–63, 65–74, 77–79, 81	pp. 108–113 Exs. 11–21 odd, 22, 23–85 odd, 87–89	Chapter 1 Test

Yearly Pacing Chapter 1 Total – 6 days Remaining – 74 days

Functions and Their Graphs

1

In Mathematics

Functions show how one variable is related to another variable.

In Real Life

Functions are used to estimate values, simulate processes, and discover relationships. For instance, you can model the enrollment rate of children in preschool and estimate the year in which the rate will reach a certain number. Such an estimate can be used to plan measures for meeting future needs, such as hiring additional teachers and buying more books. (See Exercise 113, page 64.)

Jose Luis Pelaez/Getty Images

IN CAREERS

There are many careers that use functions. Several are listed below.

- Financial analyst
  Exercise 95, page 51
- Biologist
  Exercise 73, page 91
- Tax preparer
  Example 3, page 104
- Oceanographer
  Exercise 83, page 112

PLAN AND PREPARE

Main Ideas

Chapter 1 addresses functions and their representation on the Cartesian plane. Students begin the chapter by applying the distance and midpoint formulas and by identifying intercepts, symmetry, and slope of graphs. These concepts are then used to identify, categorize, and describe functions. Students then learn how to identify the eight most commonly used functions in algebra and represent simple transformations of these functions. The chapter concludes by investigating the composition of more than one function, the inverse of a function, and the use of functions in modeling real-world data.

Chapter Planning Guide

Chapter Resources

- Complete Solutions Guide

Interactive Technology

- Instructor Success Organizer
- Notetaking Guide IAE
- Instructional DVDs
- Animated Precalculus
- PowerLecture with ExamView

1 PLAN AND PREPARE

Warm-up Exercises

Transparency Available
Available at the Instructor's companion site.

Notetaking Guide

Transparency Available
Promotes interactive learning and notetaking skills. Available at the Instructor's companion site.

Animated Precalculus

An **Animated Precalculus** tutorial is available at the Student companion site for **Section 1.1.**

Pacing

Average: 1 day
Advanced: 1 day
Block: 0.5 block with 1.2

2 FOCUS AND MOTIVATE

Essential Question

How do you locate points and find the distance and midpoint between two points in the Cartesian plane? **Tell students that they will learn how to answer this question by writing the locations of points as ordered pairs of coordinates and by using the Pythagorean Theorem and related formulas to find distances.**

1.1 Rectangular Coordinates

What you should learn

- Plot points in the Cartesian plane.
- Use the Distance Formula to find the distance between two points.
- Use the Midpoint Formula to find the midpoint of a line segment.
- Use a coordinate plane to model and solve real-life problems.

Why you should learn it

The Cartesian plane can be used to represent relationships between two variables. For instance, in Exercise 70 on page 11, a graph represents the minimum wage in the United States from 1950 to 2009.

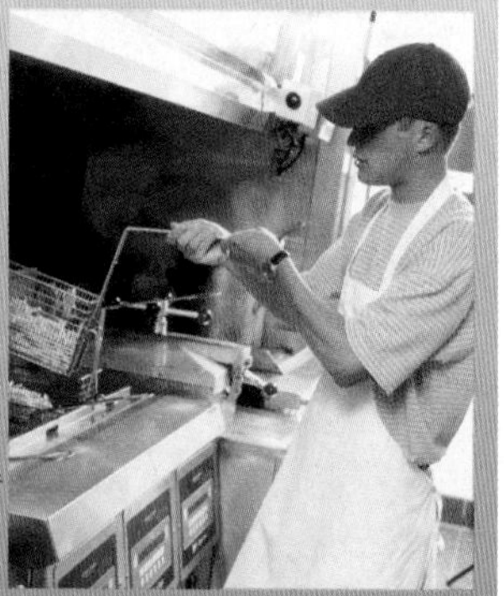

The Cartesian Plane

Just as you can represent real numbers by points on a real number line, you can represent ordered pairs of real numbers by points in a plane called the **rectangular coordinate system,** or the **Cartesian plane,** named after the French mathematician René Descartes (1596–1650).

The Cartesian plane is formed by using two real number lines intersecting at right angles, as shown in Figure 1.1. The horizontal real number line is usually called the ***x*-axis,** and the vertical real number line is usually called the ***y*-axis.** The point of intersection of these two axes is the **origin,** and the two axes divide the plane into four parts called **quadrants.**

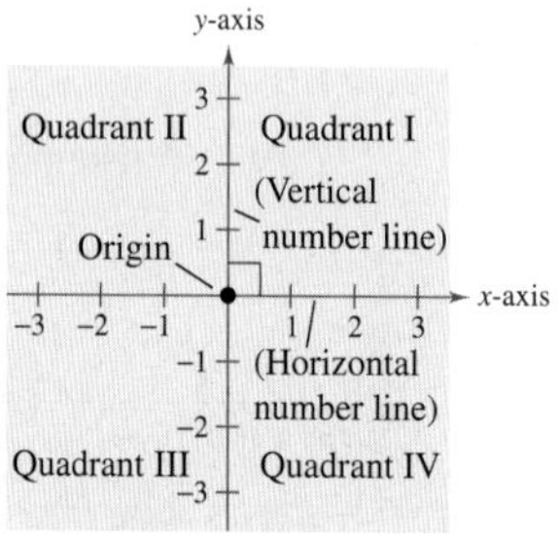

FIGURE 1.1

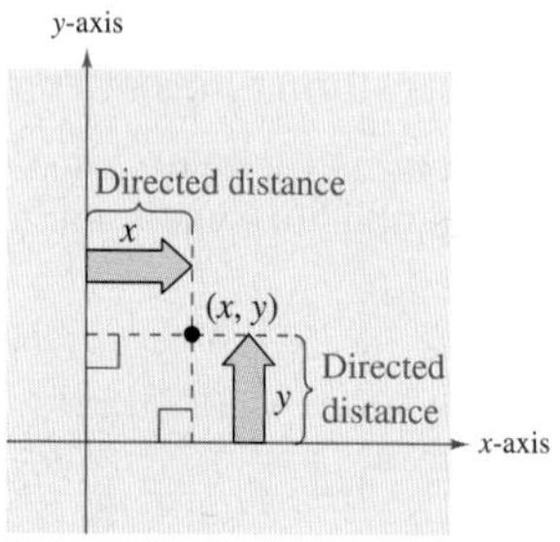

FIGURE 1.2

Each point in the plane corresponds to an **ordered pair** (x, y) of real numbers x and y, called **coordinates** of the point. The ***x*-coordinate** represents the directed distance from the y-axis to the point, and the ***y*-coordinate** represents the directed distance from the x-axis to the point, as shown in Figure 1.2.

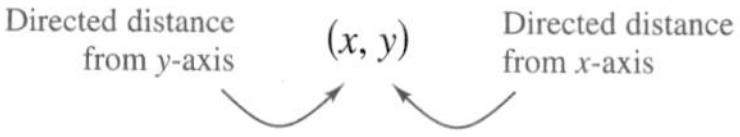

The notation (x, y) denotes both a point in the plane and an open interval on the real number line. The context will tell you which meaning is intended.

Example 1 Plotting Points in the Cartesian Plane

Plot the points $(-1, 2)$, $(3, 4)$, $(0, 0)$, $(3, 0)$, and $(-2, -3)$.

Solution

To plot the point $(-1, 2)$, imagine a vertical line through -1 on the x-axis and a horizontal line through 2 on the y-axis. The intersection of these two lines is the point $(-1, 2)$. The other four points can be plotted in a similar way, as shown in Figure 1.3.

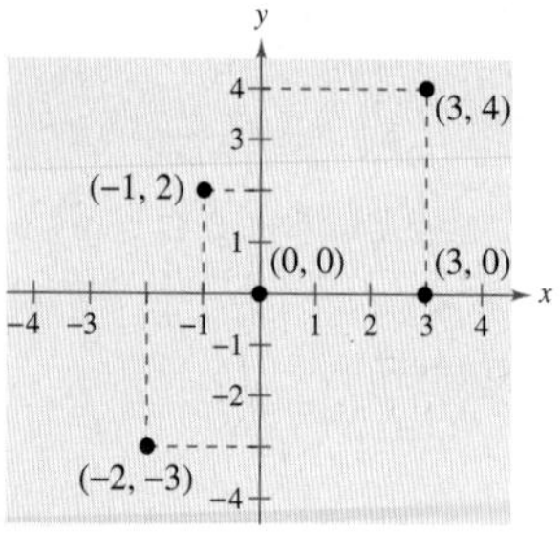

FIGURE 1.3

CHECK*Point* Now try Exercise 7.

Resource Planning Guide

Chapter Resources
- Complete Solutions Guide

Workbooks
- Notetaking Guide
- Student Solutions Guide

Interactive Technology
- Instructor Success Organizer
- Notetaking Guide IAE
- Instructional DVDs
- Animated Precalculus
- PowerLecture with ExamView

The beauty of a rectangular coordinate system is that it allows you to *see* relationships between two variables. It would be difficult to overestimate the importance of Descartes's introduction of coordinates in the plane. Today, his ideas are in common use in virtually every scientific and business-related field.

Example 2 Sketching a Scatter Plot

Year, t	Subscribers, N
1994	24.1
1995	33.8
1996	44.0
1997	55.3
1998	69.2
1999	86.0
2000	109.5
2001	128.4
2002	140.8
2003	158.7
2004	182.1
2005	207.9
2006	233.0
2007	255.4

From 1994 through 2007, the numbers N (in millions) of subscribers to a cellular telecommunication service in the United States are shown in the table, where t represents the year. Sketch a scatter plot of the data. (Source: CTIA-The Wireless Association)

Solution

To sketch a *scatter plot* of the data shown in the table, you simply represent each pair of values by an ordered pair (t, N) and plot the resulting points, as shown in Figure 1.4. For instance, the first pair of values is represented by the ordered pair (1994, 24.1). Note that the break in the t-axis indicates that the numbers between 0 and 1994 have been omitted.

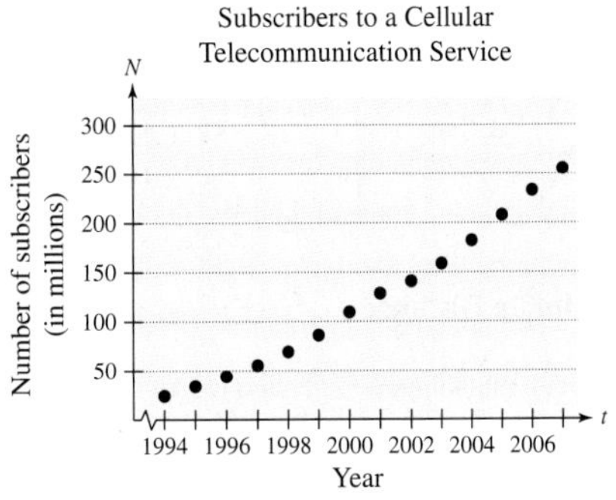

FIGURE 1.4

CHECKPoint Now try Exercise 25.

In Example 2, you could have let $t = 1$ represent the year 1994. In that case, the horizontal axis would not have been broken, and the tick marks would have been labeled 1 through 14 (instead of 1994 through 2007).

TECHNOLOGY

The scatter plot in Example 2 is only one way to represent the data graphically. You could also represent the data using a bar graph or a line graph. If you have access to a graphing utility, try using it to represent graphically the data given in Example 2.

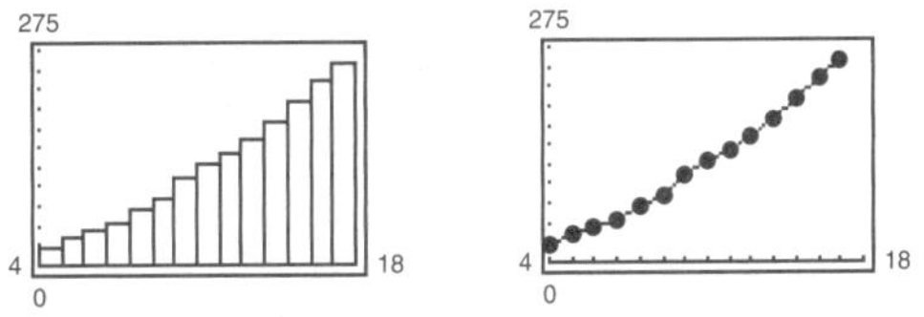

3 TEACH

Extra Example 1

Plot the points $(1, -2)$, $(4, -3)$, $(0, 0)$, $(5, 0)$, and $(-3, -1)$.

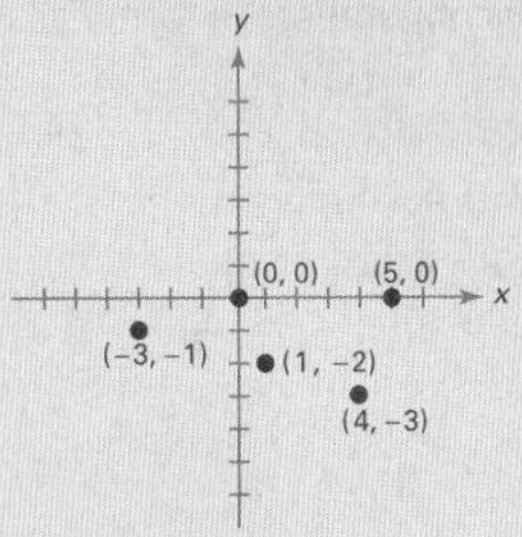

Extra Example 2

Sketch a scatter plot of the following data points:

x	y
0	1
1	3
2	6
3	8
4	4
5	5
6	7
7	8
8	10

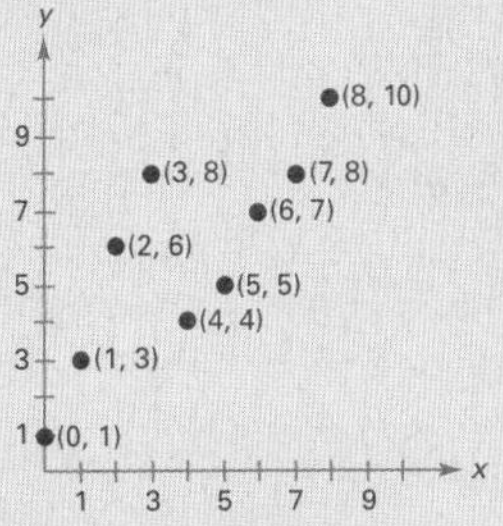

Avoiding Common Errors

Examples 3–7 Students sometimes make errors because they use the wrong formula or invert the x- and y-coordinates in the wrong part. Have students check their placements of numbers in formulas.

Extra Example 3

Find the distance between the points $(-5, 7)$ and $(3, -4)$.
$\sqrt{185} \approx 13.6$ **units**

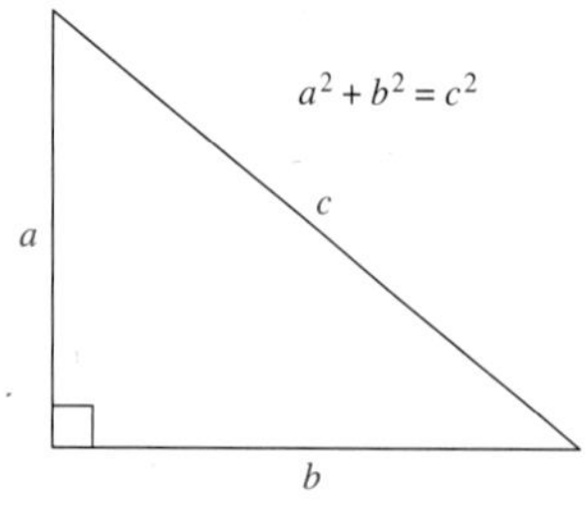

FIGURE 1.5

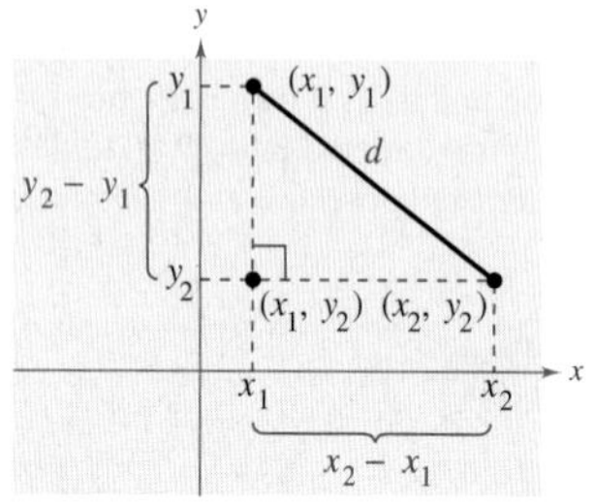

FIGURE 1.6

The Pythagorean Theorem and the Distance Formula

The following famous theorem is used extensively throughout this course.

> **Pythagorean Theorem**
>
> For a right triangle with hypotenuse of length c and sides of lengths a and b, you have $a^2 + b^2 = c^2$, as shown in Figure 1.5. (The converse is also true. That is, if $a^2 + b^2 = c^2$, then the triangle is a right triangle.)

Suppose you want to determine the distance d between two points (x_1, y_1) and (x_2, y_2) in the plane. With these two points, a right triangle can be formed, as shown in Figure 1.6. The length of the vertical side of the triangle is $|y_2 - y_1|$, and the length of the horizontal side is $|x_2 - x_1|$. By the Pythagorean Theorem, you can write

$$d^2 = |x_2 - x_1|^2 + |y_2 - y_1|^2$$

$$d = \sqrt{|x_2 - x_1|^2 + |y_2 - y_1|^2} = \sqrt{(x_2 - x_1)^2 + (y_2 - y_1)^2}.$$

This result is the **Distance Formula.**

> **The Distance Formula**
>
> The distance d between the points (x_1, y_1) and (x_2, y_2) in the plane is
>
> $$d = \sqrt{(x_2 - x_1)^2 + (y_2 - y_1)^2}.$$

Example 3 Finding a Distance

Find the distance between the points $(-2, 1)$ and $(3, 4)$.

Algebraic Solution

Let $(x_1, y_1) = (-2, 1)$ and $(x_2, y_2) = (3, 4)$. Then apply the Distance Formula.

$$d = \sqrt{(x_2 - x_1)^2 + (y_2 - y_1)^2} \quad \text{Distance Formula}$$

$$= \sqrt{[3 - (-2)]^2 + (4 - 1)^2} \quad \text{Substitute for } x_1, y_1, x_2, \text{ and } y_2.$$

$$= \sqrt{(5)^2 + (3)^2} \quad \text{Simplify.}$$

$$= \sqrt{34} \quad \text{Simplify.}$$

$$\approx 5.83 \quad \text{Use a calculator.}$$

So, the distance between the points is about 5.83 units. You can use the Pythagorean Theorem to check that the distance is correct.

$$d^2 \stackrel{?}{=} 3^2 + 5^2 \quad \text{Pythagorean Theorem}$$

$$\left(\sqrt{34}\right)^2 \stackrel{?}{=} 3^2 + 5^2 \quad \text{Substitute for } d.$$

$$34 = 34 \quad \text{Distance checks. ✓}$$

Graphical Solution

Use centimeter graph paper to plot the points $A(-2, 1)$ and $B(3, 4)$. Carefully sketch the line segment from A to B. Then use a centimeter ruler to measure the length of the segment.

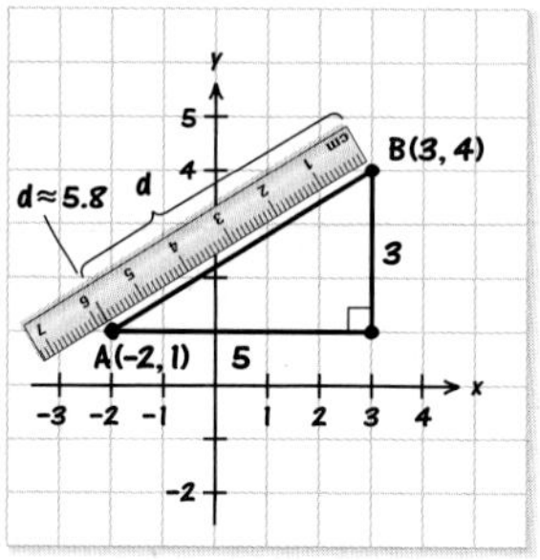

FIGURE 1.7

The line segment measures about 5.8 centimeters, as shown in Figure 1.7. So, the distance between the points is about 5.8 units.

CHECKPoint Now try Exercise 31.

Example 4 Verifying a Right Triangle

Show that the points (2, 1), (4, 0), and (5, 7) are vertices of a right triangle.

Solution

The three points are plotted in Figure 1.8. Using the Distance Formula, you can find the lengths of the three sides as follows.

$$d_1 = \sqrt{(5-2)^2 + (7-1)^2} = \sqrt{9+36} = \sqrt{45}$$

$$d_2 = \sqrt{(4-2)^2 + (0-1)^2} = \sqrt{4+1} = \sqrt{5}$$

$$d_3 = \sqrt{(5-4)^2 + (7-0)^2} = \sqrt{1+49} = \sqrt{50}$$

Because

$$(d_1)^2 + (d_2)^2 = 45 + 5 = 50 = (d_3)^2$$

you can conclude by the Pythagorean Theorem that the triangle must be a right triangle.

CHECKPoint Now try Exercise 43.

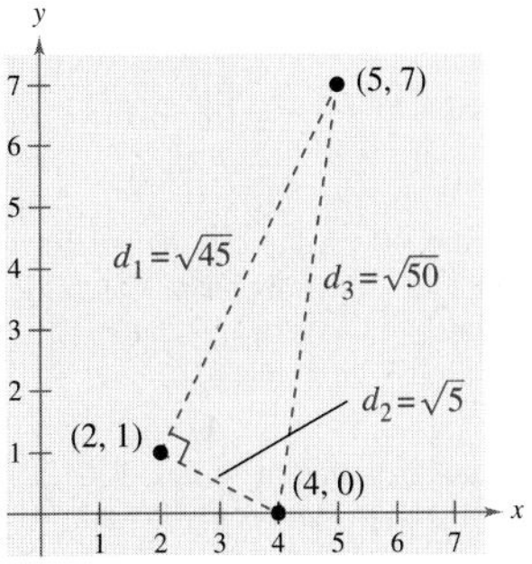

FIGURE 1.8

Algebra Help

You can review the techniques for evaluating a radical in Appendix A.2.

The Midpoint Formula

To find the **midpoint** of the line segment that joins two points in a coordinate plane, you can simply find the average values of the respective coordinates of the two endpoints using the **Midpoint Formula.**

> **The Midpoint Formula**
>
> The midpoint of the line segment joining the points (x_1, y_1) and (x_2, y_2) is given by the Midpoint Formula
>
> $$\text{Midpoint} = \left(\frac{x_1 + x_2}{2}, \frac{y_1 + y_2}{2}\right).$$

For a proof of the Midpoint Formula, see Proofs in Mathematics on page 122.

Example 5 Finding a Line Segment's Midpoint

Find the midpoint of the line segment joining the points $(-5, -3)$ and $(9, 3)$.

Solution

Let $(x_1, y_1) = (-5, -3)$ and $(x_2, y_2) = (9, 3)$.

$$\text{Midpoint} = \left(\frac{x_1 + x_2}{2}, \frac{y_1 + y_2}{2}\right) \quad \text{Midpoint Formula}$$

$$= \left(\frac{-5 + 9}{2}, \frac{-3 + 3}{2}\right) \quad \text{Substitute for } x_1, y_1, x_2, \text{ and } y_2.$$

$$= (2, 0) \quad \text{Simplify.}$$

The midpoint of the line segment is (2, 0), as shown in Figure 1.9.

CHECKPoint Now try Exercise 47(c).

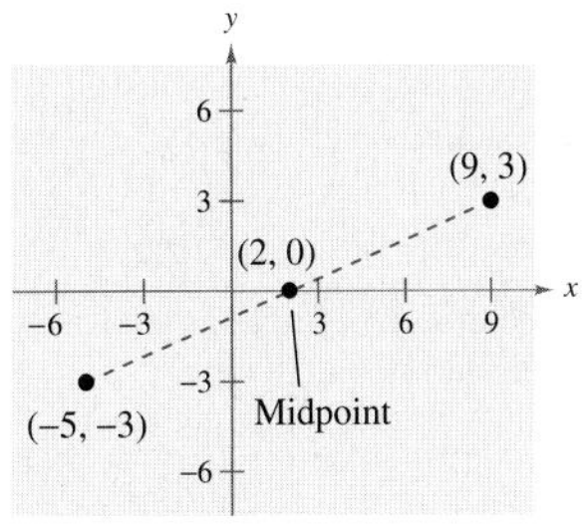

FIGURE 1.9

Extra Example 4

Show that the points (4, 0), (2, 1), and (−1, −5) are vertices of a right triangle. **$d_1 = \sqrt{5}$, $d_2 = \sqrt{45}$, $d_3 = \sqrt{50}$; Because $(d_1)^2 + (d_2)^2 = (\sqrt{5})^2 + (\sqrt{45})^2 = (d_3)^2 = (\sqrt{50})^2$, the triangle is a right triangle.**

Extra Example 5

Find the midpoint of the line segment joining the points (−6, 1) and (7, 4). **$\left(\frac{1}{2}, \frac{5}{2}\right)$**

Applications

Example 6 Finding the Length of a Pass

A football quarterback throws a pass from the 28-yard line, 40 yards from the sideline. The pass is caught by a wide receiver on the 5-yard line, 20 yards from the same sideline, as shown in Figure 1.10. How long is the pass?

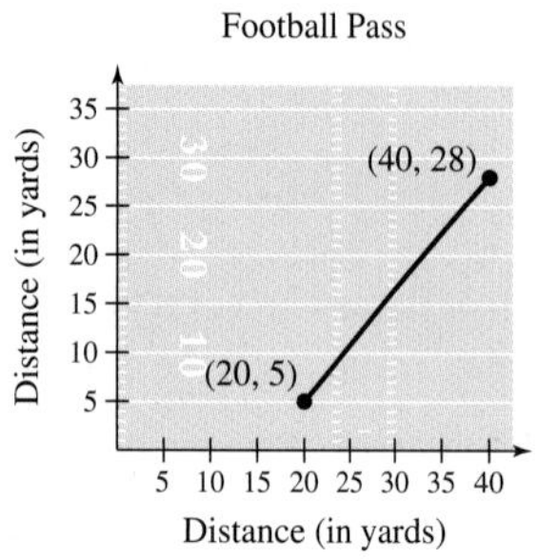

FIGURE 1.10

Solution

You can find the length of the pass by finding the distance between the points (40, 28) and (20, 5).

$$\begin{aligned} d &= \sqrt{(x_2 - x_1)^2 + (y_2 - y_1)^2} && \text{Distance Formula} \\ &= \sqrt{(40 - 20)^2 + (28 - 5)^2} && \text{Substitute for } x_1, y_1, x_2, \text{ and } y_2. \\ &= \sqrt{400 + 529} && \text{Simplify.} \\ &= \sqrt{929} && \text{Simplify.} \\ &\approx 30 && \text{Use a calculator.} \end{aligned}$$

So, the pass is about 30 yards long.

CHECK Point Now try Exercise 57.

In Example 6, the scale along the goal line does not normally appear on a football field. However, when you use coordinate geometry to solve real-life problems, you are free to place the coordinate system in any way that is convenient for the solution of the problem.

Example 7 Estimating Annual Revenue

Barnes & Noble had annual sales of approximately \$5.1 billion in 2005, and \$5.4 billion in 2007. Without knowing any additional information, what would you estimate the 2006 sales to have been? (Source: Barnes & Noble, Inc.)

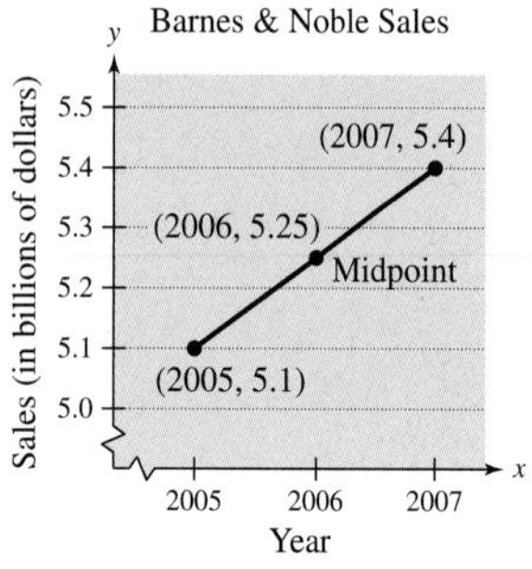

FIGURE 1.11

Solution

One solution to the problem is to assume that sales followed a linear pattern. With this assumption, you can estimate the 2006 sales by finding the midpoint of the line segment connecting the points (2005, 5.1) and (2007, 5.4).

$$\begin{aligned} \text{Midpoint} &= \left(\frac{x_1 + x_2}{2}, \frac{y_1 + y_2}{2}\right) && \text{Midpoint Formula} \\ &= \left(\frac{2005 + 2007}{2}, \frac{5.1 + 5.4}{2}\right) && \text{Substitute for } x_1, x_2, y_1 \text{ and } y_2. \\ &= (2006, 5.25) && \text{Simplify.} \end{aligned}$$

So, you would estimate the 2006 sales to have been about \$5.25 billion, as shown in Figure 1.11. (The actual 2006 sales were about \$5.26 billion.)

CHECK Point Now try Exercise 59.

Extra Example 6

During the third quarter of a recent game, the university's quarterback threw a pass from the 32-yard line, 40 yards from the sideline. The pass was caught by the wide receiver on the 3-yard line, 15 yards from the same sideline. How long was the pass? **$\sqrt{1466} \approx 38$ yards**

Extra Example 7

A local contracting company had annual revenues of \$15 million in 2007 and \$17.2 million in 2009. Without knowing any additional information, what figure would you estimate the 2008 revenue to have been? **\$16.1 million**

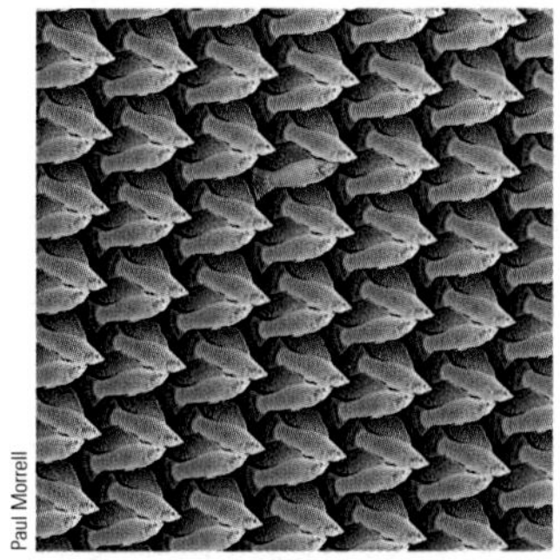

Much of computer graphics, including this computer-generated goldfish tessellation, consists of transformations of points in a coordinate plane. One type of transformation, a translation, is illustrated in Example 8. Other types include reflections, rotations, and stretches.

Example 8 Translating Points in the Plane

The triangle in Figure 1.12 has vertices at the points $(-1, 2)$, $(1, -4)$, and $(2, 3)$. Shift the triangle three units to the right and two units upward and find the vertices of the shifted triangle, as shown in Figure 1.13.

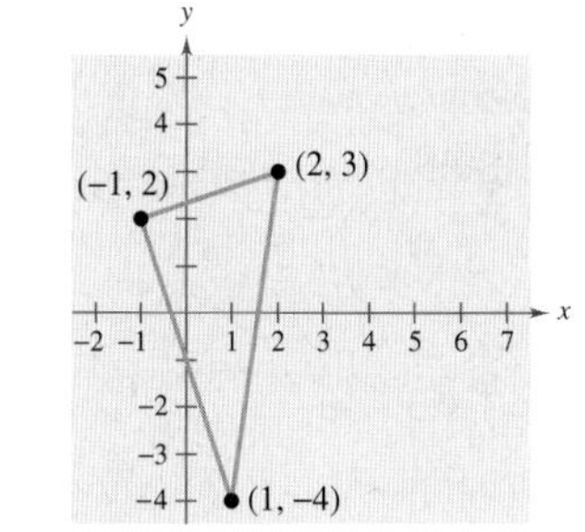

FIGURE 1.12

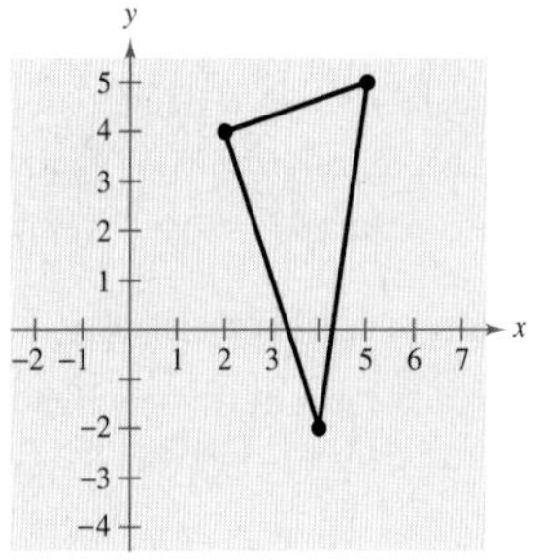

FIGURE 1.13

Solution

To shift the vertices three units to the right, add 3 to each of the x-coordinates. To shift the vertices two units upward, add 2 to each of the y-coordinates.

Original Point	*Translated Point*
$(-1, 2)$	$(-1 + 3, 2 + 2) = (2, 4)$
$(1, -4)$	$(1 + 3, -4 + 2) = (4, -2)$
$(2, 3)$	$(2 + 3, 3 + 2) = (5, 5)$

CHECK*Point* Now try Exercise 61.

The figures provided with Example 8 were not really essential to the solution. Nevertheless, it is strongly recommended that you develop the habit of including sketches with your solutions—even if they are not required.

Classroom Discussion

Extending the Example Example 8 shows how to translate points in a coordinate plane. Write a short paragraph describing how each of the following transformed points is related to the original point.

Original Point	*Transformed Point*
(x, y)	$(-x, y)$
(x, y)	$(x, -y)$
(x, y)	$(-x, -y)$

$(-x, y)$ reflects the point in the y-axis.
$(x, -y)$ reflects the point in the x-axis.
$(-x, -y)$ reflects the point through the origin.

Extra Example 8

A triangle has vertices at $(-1, -3)$, $(5, 1)$, and $(2, 4)$. Shift the triangle two units to the left and three units downward, and find the vertices of the shifted triangle.
$(-1, -3) \rightarrow (-3, -6)$,
$(5, 1) \rightarrow (3, -2)$,
$(2, 4) \rightarrow (0, 1)$

Closing the Lesson

Have students summarize the major points of the lesson and answer the Essential Question: How do you locate points and find the distance and midpoint between two points in the Cartesian plane?

- **Each point in the plane corresponds to an ordered pair (x, y) of real numbers x and y, called coordinates of the point.**
- **The distance and midpoint between two points in a plane can be found by using the distance and midpoint formulas.**

4 PRACTICE AND APPLY

Assignment Guide

Transparencies Available
Available at the Instructor's companion site.

Average:
Day 1: pp. 8–12
Exs. 5–13 odd, 15–25, 39–59 odd, 63–68, 71, 72, 79–83, 85

Advanced:
Day 1: pp. 8–12
Exs. 11–25, 39–42 even, 43–46, 47–56 even, 57, 58, 60, 63–69, 71, 74, 79, 80, 83–85

Block:
pp. 8–12
Exs. 5–13 odd, 15–25, 39–59 odd, 63–68, 71, 72, 79–83, 85 (with 1.2)

5. A: $(2, 6)$, B: $(-6, -2)$, C: $(4, -4)$, D: $(-3, 2)$

6. A: $\left(\frac{3}{2}, -4\right)$, B: $(0, -2)$, C: $\left(-3, \frac{5}{2}\right)$, D: $(-6, 0)$

7.

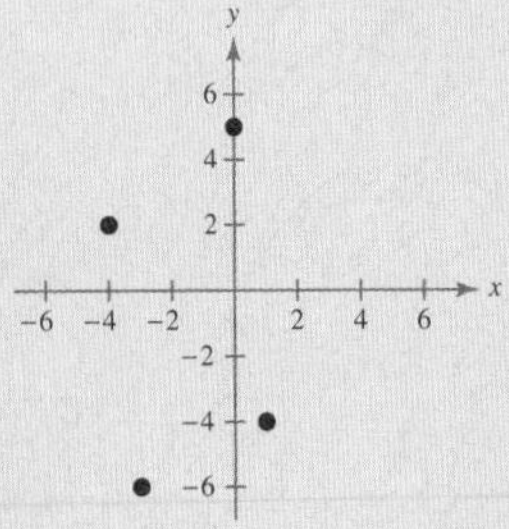

8.

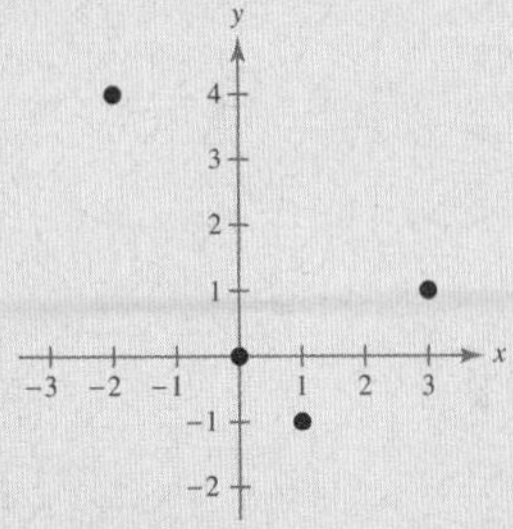

9.

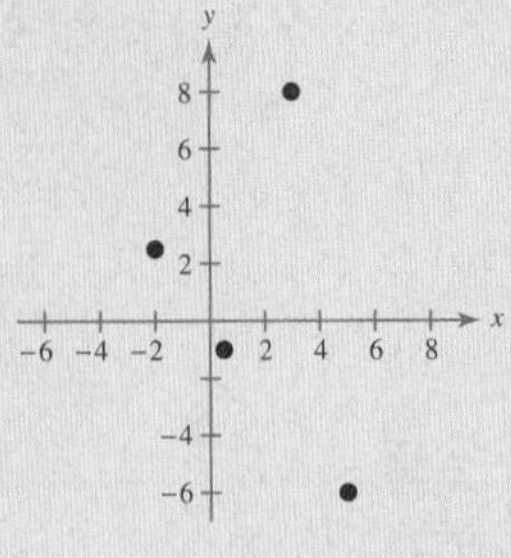

1.1 EXERCISES

See www.CalcChat.com for worked-out solutions to odd-numbered exercises.

VOCABULARY

1. Match each term with its definition.

(a) x-axis — (i) point of intersection of vertical axis and horizontal axis
(b) y-axis — (ii) directed distance from the x-axis
(c) origin — (iii) directed distance from the y-axis
(d) quadrants — (iv) four regions of the coordinate plane
(e) x-coordinate — (v) horizontal real number line
(f) y-coordinate — (vi) vertical real number line

In Exercises 2–4, fill in the blanks.

2. An ordered pair of real numbers can be represented in a plane called the rectangular coordinate system or the ________ plane. Cartesian

3. The ________ ________ is a result derived from the Pythagorean Theorem. Distance Formula

4. Finding the average values of the representative coordinates of the two endpoints of a line segment in a coordinate plane is also known as using the ________ ________. Midpoint Formula

SKILLS AND APPLICATIONS

In Exercises 5 and 6, approximate the coordinates of the points. 5–6. See margin.

5.

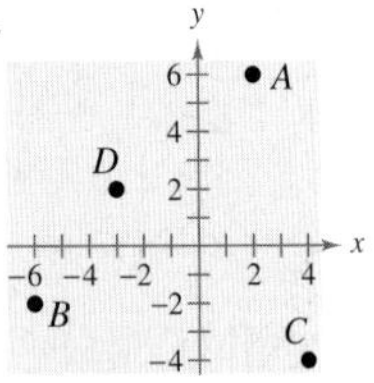

6.

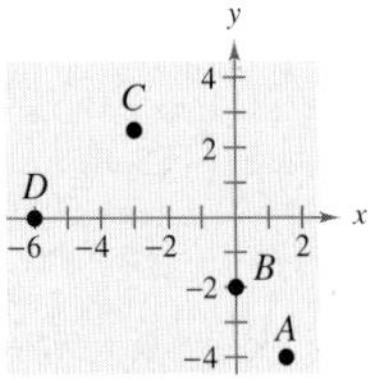

In Exercises 7–10, plot the points in the Cartesian plane.

7. $(-4, 2), (-3, -6), (0, 5), (1, -4)$ 7–10. See margin.

8. $(0, 0), (3, 1), (-2, 4), (1, -1)$

9. $(3, 8), (0.5, -1), (5, -6), (-2, 2.5)$

10. $\left(1, -\frac{1}{3}\right), \left(\frac{3}{4}, 3\right), (-3, 4), \left(-\frac{4}{3}, -\frac{3}{2}\right)$

In Exercises 11–14, find the coordinates of the point.

11. The point is located three units to the left of the y-axis and four units above the x-axis. $(-3, 4)$

12. The point is located eight units below the x-axis and four units to the right of the y-axis. $(4, -8)$

13. The point is located five units below the x-axis and the coordinates of the point are equal. $(-5, -5)$

14. The point is on the x-axis and 12 units to the left of the y-axis. $(-12, 0)$

In Exercises 15–24, determine the quadrant(s) in which (x, y) is located so that the condition(s) is (are) satisfied.

15. $x > 0$ and $y < 0$ IV
16. $x < 0$ and $y < 0$ III
17. $x = -4$ and $y > 0$ II
18. $x > 2$ and $y = 3$ I
19. $y < -5$ III or IV
20. $x > 4$ I or IV
21. $x < 0$ and $-y > 0$ III
22. $-x > 0$ and $y < 0$ III
23. $xy > 0$ I or III
24. $xy < 0$ II or IV

In Exercises 25 and 26, sketch a scatter plot of the data shown in the table.

25. NUMBER OF STORES The table shows the number y of Wal-Mart stores for each year x from 2000 through 2007. (Source: Wal-Mart Stores, Inc.) See margin.

Year, x	Number of stores, y
2000	4189
2001	4414
2002	4688
2003	4906
2004	5289
2005	6141
2006	6779
2007	7262

10.

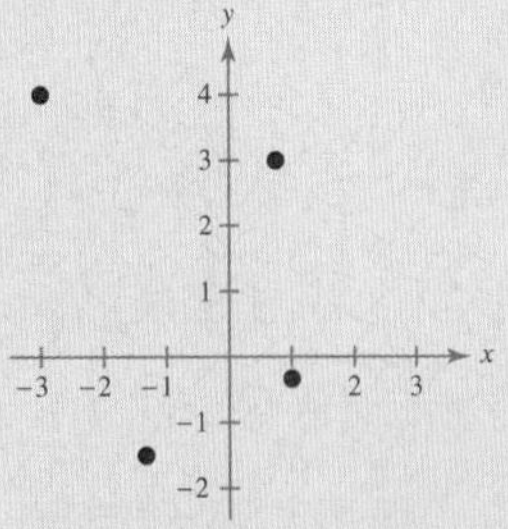

25.

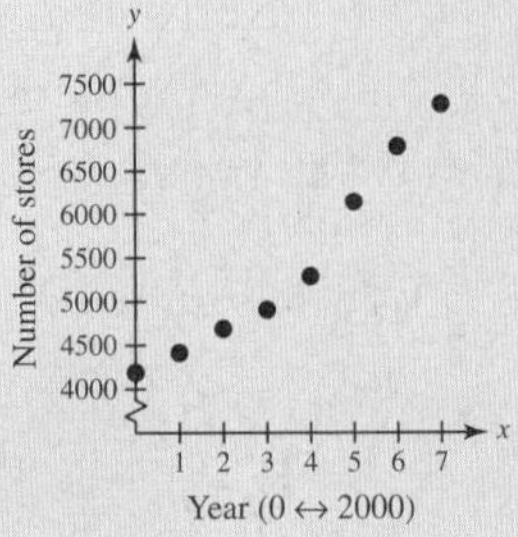

26. METEOROLOGY The table shows the lowest temperature on record y (in degrees Fahrenheit) in Duluth, Minnesota for each month x, where $x = 1$ represents January. (Source: NOAA) See margin.

Month, x	Temperature, y
1	-39
2	-39
3	-29
4	-5
5	17
6	27
7	35
8	32
9	22
10	8
11	-23
12	-34

In Exercises 27–38, find the distance between the points.

27. $(6, -3), (6, 5)$ 8
28. $(1, 4), (8, 4)$ 7
29. $(-3, -1), (2, -1)$ 5
30. $(-3, -4), (-3, 6)$ 10
31. $(-2, 6), (3, -6)$ 13
32. $(8, 5), (0, 20)$ 17
33. $(1, 4), (-5, -1)$ $\sqrt{61}$
34. $(1, 3), (3, -2)$ $\sqrt{29}$
35. $\left(\frac{1}{2}, \frac{4}{3}\right), (2, -1)$
36. $\left(-\frac{2}{3}, 3\right), \left(-1, \frac{5}{4}\right)$
37. $(-4.2, 3.1), (-12.5, 4.8)$ 8.47
38. $(9.5, -2.6), (-3.9, 8.2)$ 17.21

35–36. See margin.

In Exercises 39–42, (a) find the length of each side of the right triangle, and (b) show that these lengths satisfy the Pythagorean Theorem.

39. See margin.

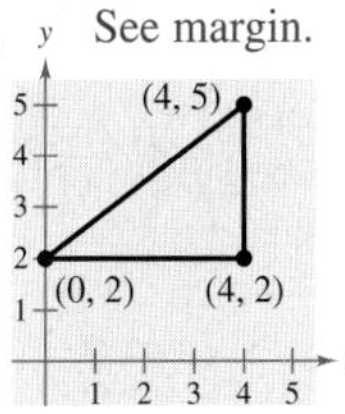

40. (a) 5, 12, 13 (b) $5^2 + 12^2 = 13^2$

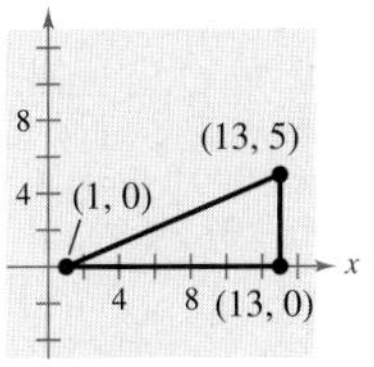

41.

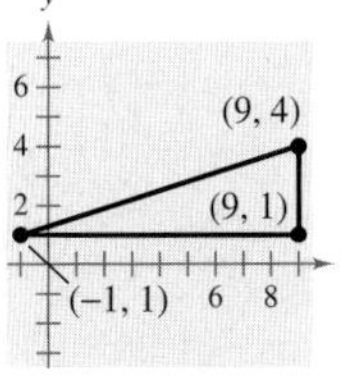

(a) 10, 3, $\sqrt{109}$
(b) $10^2 + 3^2 = \left(\sqrt{109}\right)^2$

42.

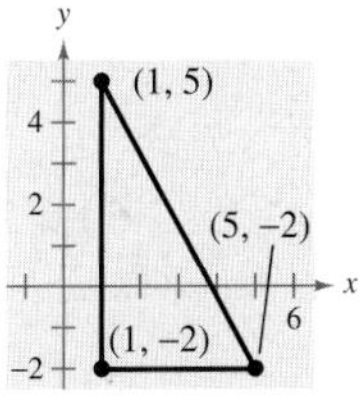

(a) 4, 7, $\sqrt{65}$
(b) $4^2 + 7^2 = \left(\sqrt{65}\right)^2$

In Exercises 43–46, show that the points form the vertices of the indicated polygon. 43–46. See margin.

43. Right triangle: $(4, 0), (2, 1), (-1, -5)$
44. Right triangle: $(-1, 3), (3, 5), (5, 1)$
45. Isosceles triangle: $(1, -3), (3, 2), (-2, 4)$
46. Isosceles triangle: $(2, 3), (4, 9), (-2, 7)$

In Exercises 47–56, (a) plot the points, (b) find the distance between the points, and (c) find the midpoint of the line segment joining the points. 47–56. See margin.

47. $(1, 1), (9, 7)$
48. $(1, 12), (6, 0)$
49. $(-4, 10), (4, -5)$
50. $(-7, -4), (2, 8)$
51. $(-1, 2), (5, 4)$
52. $(2, 10), (10, 2)$
53. $\left(\frac{1}{2}, 1\right), \left(-\frac{5}{2}, \frac{4}{3}\right)$
54. $\left(-\frac{1}{3}, -\frac{1}{3}\right), \left(-\frac{1}{6}, -\frac{1}{2}\right)$
55. $(6.2, 5.4), (-3.7, 1.8)$
56. $(-16.8, 12.3), (5.6, 4.9)$

57. FLYING DISTANCE An airplane flies from Naples, Italy in a straight line to Rome, Italy, which is 120 kilometers north and 150 kilometers west of Naples. How far does the plane fly? $30\sqrt{41} \approx 192$ km

58. SPORTS A soccer player passes the ball from a point that is 18 yards from the endline and 12 yards from the sideline. The pass is received by a teammate who is 42 yards from the same endline and 50 yards from the same sideline, as shown in the figure. How long is the pass? $2\sqrt{505} \approx 45$ yd

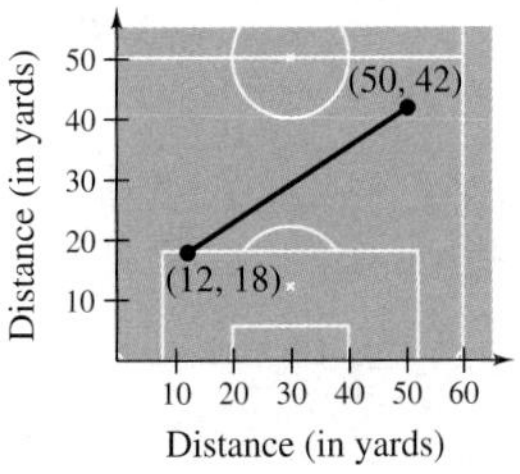

SALES **In Exercises 59 and 60, use the Midpoint Formula to estimate the sales of Big Lots, Inc. and Dollar Tree Stores, Inc. in 2005, given the sales in 2003 and 2007. Assume that the sales followed a linear pattern.** (Source: Big Lots, Inc.; Dollar Tree Stores, Inc.)

59. Big Lots $4415 million

Year	Sales (in millions)
2003	$4174
2007	$4656

26.

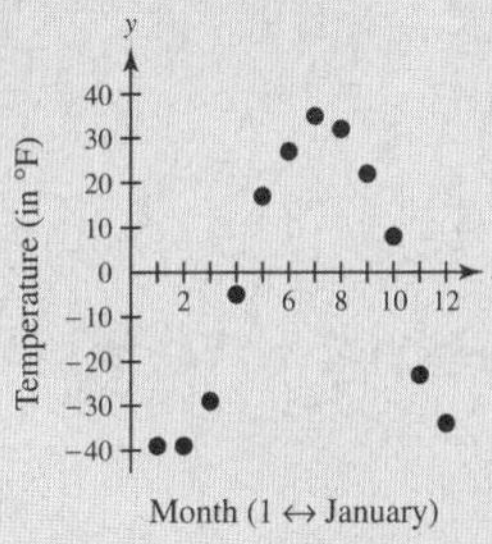

35. $\frac{\sqrt{277}}{6}$
36. $\frac{\sqrt{457}}{12}$
39. (a) 4, 3, 5 (b) $4^2 + 3^2 = 5^2$
43. $\left(\sqrt{5}\right)^2 + \left(\sqrt{45}\right)^2 = \left(\sqrt{50}\right)^2$
44. $\left(\sqrt{20}\right)^2 + \left(\sqrt{20}\right)^2 = \left(\sqrt{40}\right)^2$
45. Distances between the points: $\sqrt{29}, \sqrt{58}, \sqrt{29}$
46. Distances between the points: $\sqrt{40}, \sqrt{40}, \sqrt{32}$
47. (a)

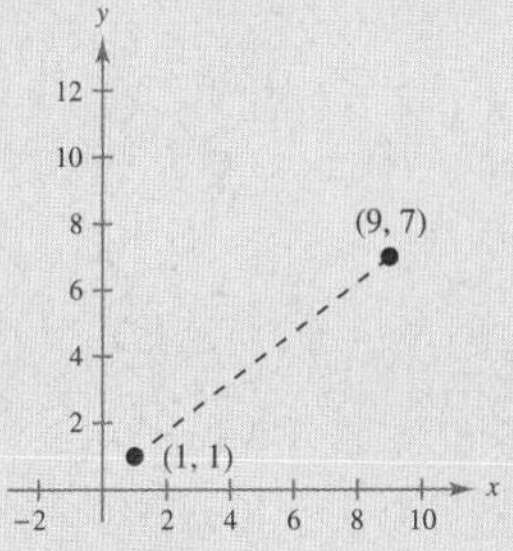

(b) 10 (c) $(5, 4)$

48. (a)

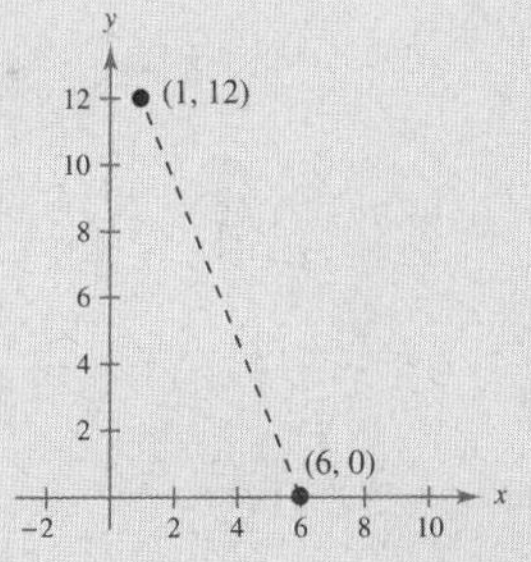

(b) 13 (c) $\left(\frac{7}{2}, 6\right)$

49. (a)

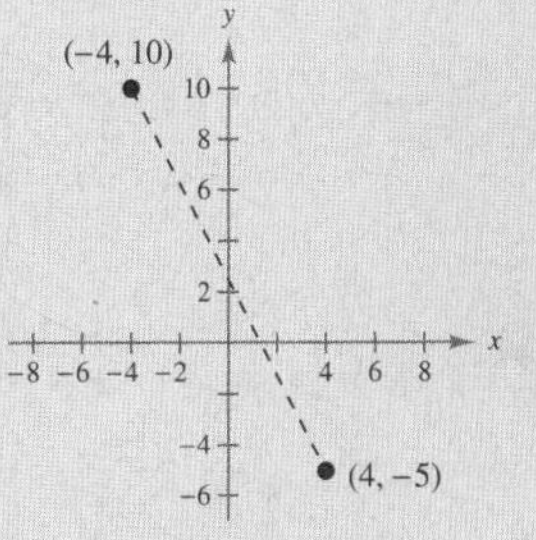

(b) 17 (c) $\left(0, \frac{5}{2}\right)$

50. (a)

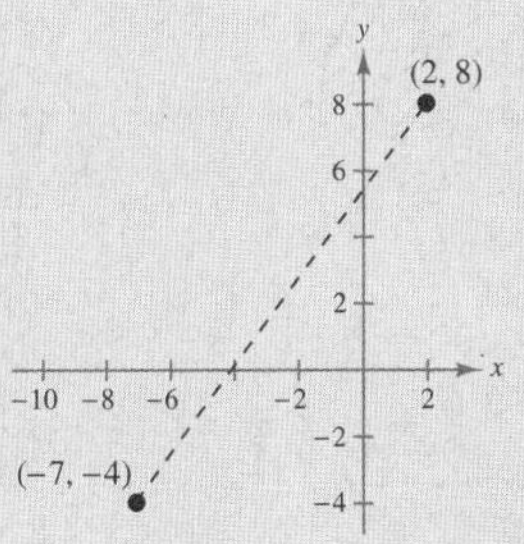

(b) 15
(c) $\left(-\frac{5}{2}, 2\right)$

51. (a)

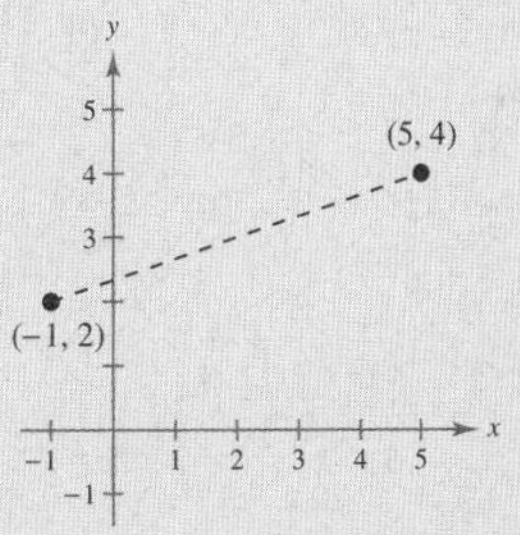

(b) $2\sqrt{10}$
(c) $(2, 3)$

52–56. See Additional Answers beginning on page AA1.

61. (0, 1), (4, 2), (1, 4)
62. (3, 3), (1, 0), (3, −3), (5, 0)
68. (a) About 62.3%
(b) About 113.8%
69. The number of performers elected each year seems to be nearly steady except for the middle years. Five performers will be elected in 2010.

60. Dollar Tree $3521.5 million

Year	Sales (in millions)
2003	\$2800
2007	\$4243

In Exercises 61–64, the polygon is shifted to a new position in the plane. Find the coordinates of the vertices of the polygon in its new position. 61–62. See margin.

61.

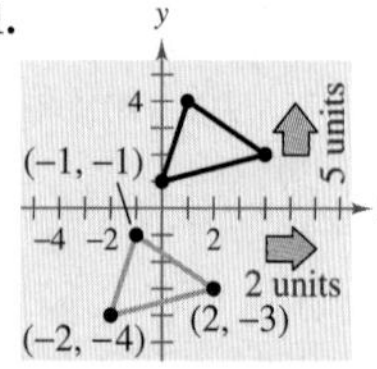

62.

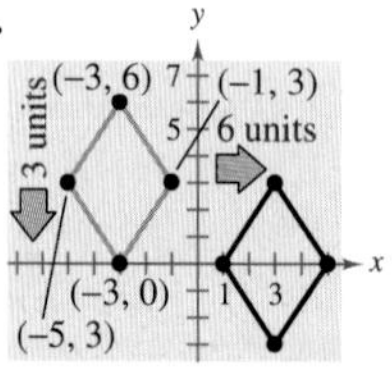

63. Original coordinates of vertices: (−7, −2),(−2, 2), (−2, −4), (−7, −4) (−3, 6), (2, 10), (2, 4), (−3, 4)
Shift: eight units upward, four units to the right

64. Original coordinates of vertices: (5, 8), (3, 6), (7, 6), (5, 2)
Shift: 6 units downward, 10 units to the left
(−5, 2), (−7, 0), (−3, 0), (−5, −4)

RETAIL PRICE In Exercises 65 and 66, use the graph, which shows the average retail prices of 1 gallon of whole milk from 1996 to 2007. (Source: U.S. Bureau of Labor Statistics)

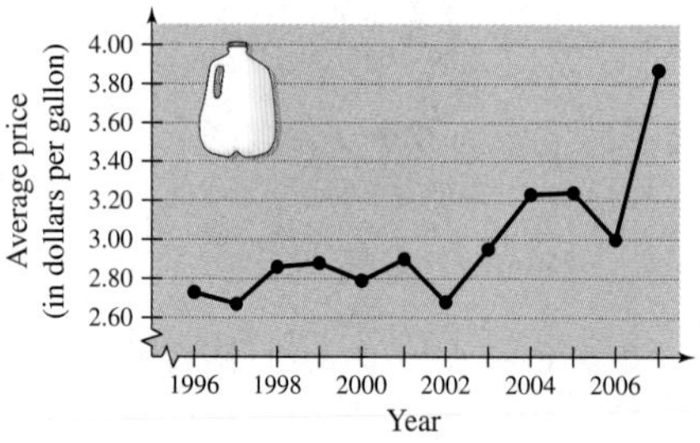

65. Approximate the highest price of a gallon of whole milk shown in the graph. When did this occur? $3.87/gal; 2007

66. Approximate the percent change in the price of milk from the price in 1996 to the highest price shown in the graph. About 42%

67. ADVERTISING The graph shows the average costs of a 30-second television spot (in thousands of dollars) during the Super Bowl from 2000 to 2008. (Source: Nielson Media and TNS Media Intelligence)

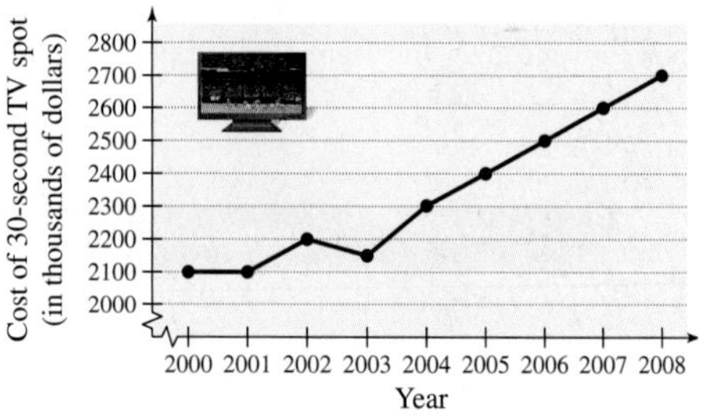

FIGURE FOR 67

(a) Estimate the percent increase in the average cost of a 30-second spot from Super Bowl XXXIV in 2000 to Super Bowl XXXVIII in 2004. About 9.6%

(b) Estimate the percent increase in the average cost of a 30-second spot from Super Bowl XXXIV in 2000 to Super Bowl XLII in 2008. About 28.6%

68. ADVERTISING The graph shows the average costs of a 30-second television spot (in thousands of dollars) during the Academy Awards from 1995 to 2007. (Source: Nielson Monitor-Plus) See margin.

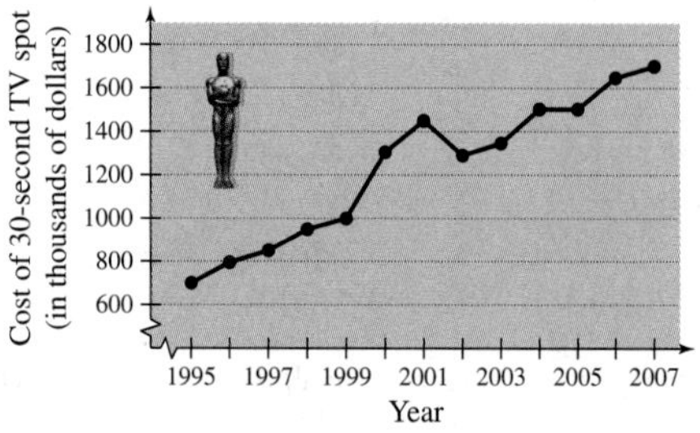

(a) Estimate the percent increase in the average cost of a 30-second spot in 1996 to the cost in 2002.

(b) Estimate the percent increase in the average cost of a 30-second spot in 1996 to the cost in 2007.

69. MUSIC The graph shows the numbers of performers who were elected to the Rock and Roll Hall of Fame from 1991 through 2008. Describe any trends in the data. From these trends, predict the number of performers elected in 2010. (Source: rockhall.com)

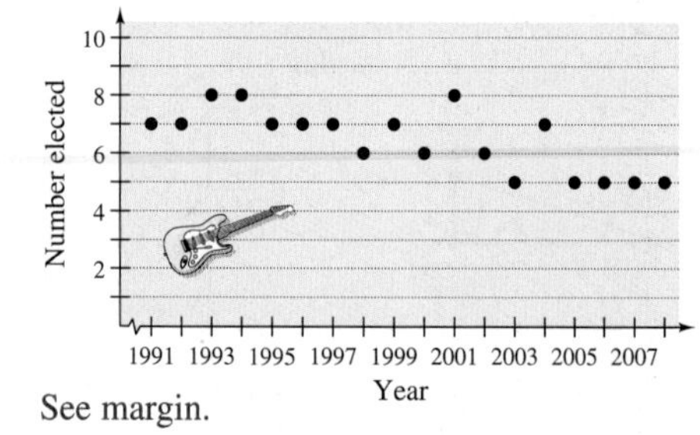

See margin.

70. LABOR FORCE Use the graph below, which shows the minimum wage in the United States (in dollars) from 1950 to 2009. (Source: U.S. Department of Labor)

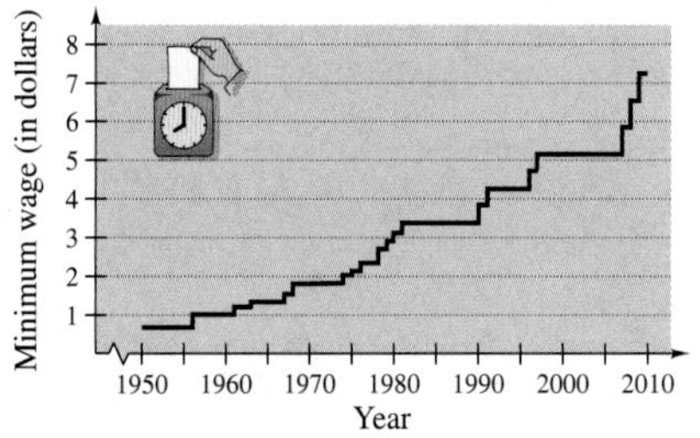

(a) Which decade shows the greatest increase in minimum wage? 2000s

(b) Approximate the percent increases in the minimum wage from 1990 to 1995 and from 1995 to 2009. 11.8%; 70.6%

(c) Use the percent increase from 1995 to 2009 to predict the minimum wage in 2013. $12.37

(d) Do you believe that your prediction in part (c) is reasonable? Explain. See margin.

71. SALES The Coca-Cola Company had sales of $19,805 million in 1999 and $28,857 million in 2007. Use the Midpoint Formula to estimate the sales in 2003. Assume that the sales followed a linear pattern. (Source: The Coca-Cola Company) $24,331 million

72. DATA ANALYSIS: EXAM SCORES The table shows the mathematics entrance test scores x and the final examination scores y in an algebra course for a sample of 10 students. See margin.

x	22	29	35	40	44	48	53	58	65	76
y	53	74	57	66	79	90	76	93	83	99

(a) Sketch a scatter plot of the data.

(b) Find the entrance test score of any student with a final exam score in the 80s.

(c) Does a higher entrance test score imply a higher final exam score? Explain.

73. DATA ANALYSIS: MAIL The table shows the number y of pieces of mail handled (in billions) by the U.S. Postal Service for each year x from 1996 through 2008. (Source: U.S. Postal Service)

See margin.

Year, x	Pieces of mail, y
1996	183
1997	191
1998	197
1999	202
2000	208
2001	207
2002	203
2003	202
2004	206
2005	212
2006	213
2007	212
2008	203

TABLE FOR 73

(a) Sketch a scatter plot of the data.

(b) Approximate the year in which there was the greatest decrease in the number of pieces of mail handled.

(c) Why do you think the number of pieces of mail handled decreased?

74. DATA ANALYSIS: ATHLETICS The table shows the numbers of men's M and women's W college basketball teams for each year x from 1994 through 2007. (Source: National Collegiate Athletic Association)

Year, x	Men's teams, M	Women's teams, W
1994	858	859
1995	868	864
1996	866	874
1997	865	879
1998	895	911
1999	926	940
2000	932	956
2001	937	958
2002	936	975
2003	967	1009
2004	981	1008
2005	983	1036
2006	984	1018
2007	982	1003

(a) Sketch scatter plots of these two sets of data on the same set of coordinate axes.

See margin.

70. (d) Answers will vary. Sample answer: No, the prediction is too high because it is likely that the percent increase over a 4-year period (2009–2013) will be less than the percent increase over a 14-year period (1995–2009).

72. (a)

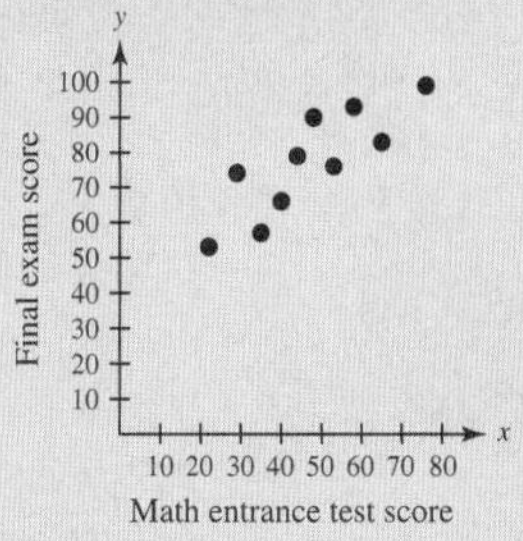

(b) 65

(c) No. There are many variables that will affect the final exam score.

73. (a)

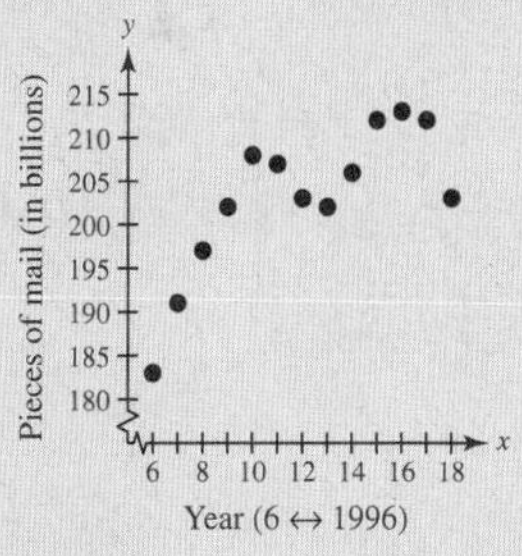

(b) 2008

(c) Answers will vary. Sample answer: Technology now enables us to transport information in many ways other than by mail. The Internet is one example.

74. (a)

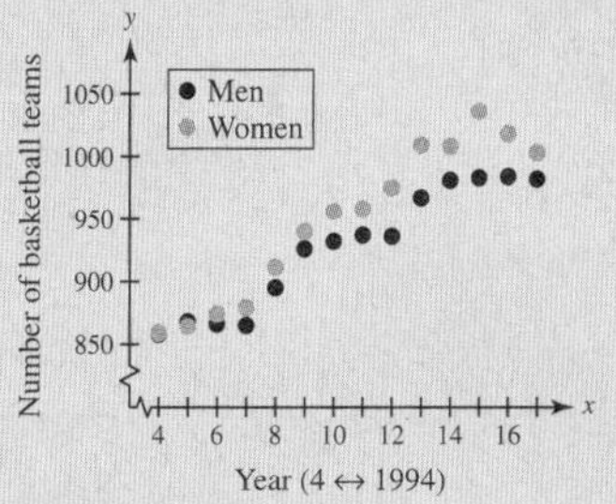

5 ASSESS AND RETEACH

Daily Homework Quiz

Transparency Available

Available at the Instructor's companion site.

75. $(2x_m - x_1, 2y_m - y_1)$

76. (a) $(7, 0)$ (b) $(9, -3)$

77. $\left(\frac{3x_1 + x_2}{4}, \frac{3y_1 + y_2}{4}\right)$, $\left(\frac{x_1 + x_2}{2}, \frac{y_1 + y_2}{2}\right)$, $\left(\frac{x_1 + 3x_2}{4}, \frac{y_1 + 3y_2}{4}\right)$

78. (a) $\left(\frac{7}{4}, -\frac{7}{4}\right), \left(\frac{5}{2}, -\frac{3}{2}\right), \left(\frac{13}{4}, -\frac{5}{4}\right)$
(b) $\left(-\frac{3}{2}, -\frac{9}{4}\right), \left(-1, -\frac{3}{2}\right), \left(-\frac{1}{2}, -\frac{3}{4}\right)$

79.

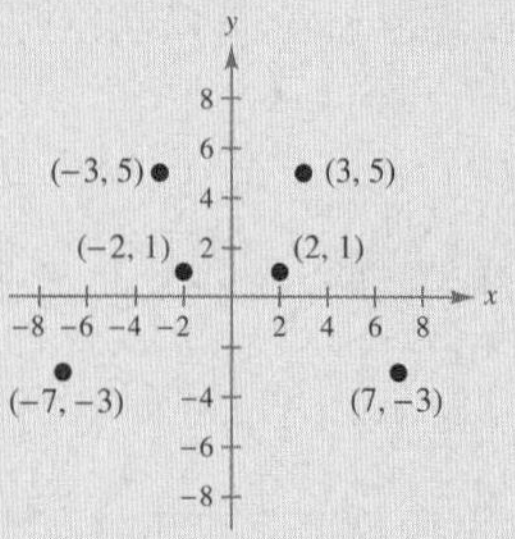

(a) The point is reflected through the y-axis.
(b) The point is reflected through the x-axis.
(c) The point is reflected through the origin.

80. (a)

Distance	First Set	Second Set
A to B	3	$\sqrt{10}$
B to C	5	$\sqrt{10}$
A to C	4	$\sqrt{40}$
	Right triangle	Isosceles triangle

(b)

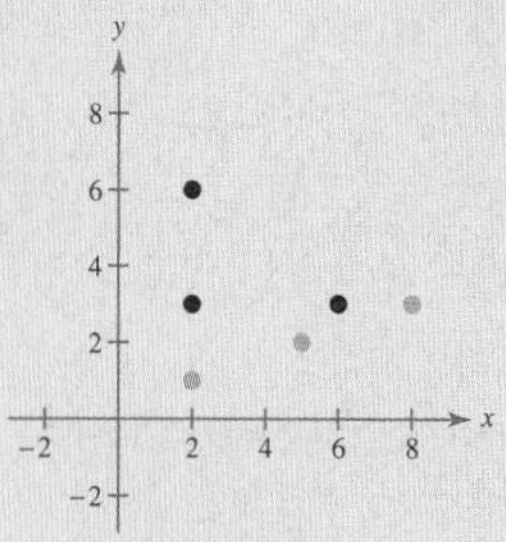

The first set of points is not collinear. The second set of points is collinear.

(c) A set of three points is collinear if the sum of two distances among the points is exactly equal to the third distance.

(b) Find the year in which the numbers of men's and women's teams were nearly equal. 1994

(c) Find the year in which the difference between the numbers of men's and women's teams was the greatest. What was this difference? 2005; 53 teams

EXPLORATION

75–80. See margin.

75. A line segment has (x_1, y_1) as one endpoint and (x_m, y_m) as its midpoint. Find the other endpoint (x_2, y_2) of the line segment in terms of x_1, y_1, x_m, and y_m.

76. Use the result of Exercise 75 to find the coordinates of the endpoint of a line segment if the coordinates of the other endpoint and midpoint are, respectively,

(a) $(1, -2), (4, -1)$ and (b) $(-5, 11), (2, 4)$.

77. Use the Midpoint Formula three times to find the three points that divide the line segment joining (x_1, y_1) and (x_2, y_2) into four parts.

78. Use the result of Exercise 77 to find the points that divide the line segment joining the given points into four equal parts.

(a) $(1, -2), (4, -1)$ (b) $(-2, -3), (0, 0)$

79. MAKE A CONJECTURE Plot the points $(2, 1)$, $(-3, 5)$, and $(7, -3)$ on a rectangular coordinate system. Then change the sign of the x-coordinate of each point and plot the three new points on the same rectangular coordinate system. Make a conjecture about the location of a point when each of the following occurs.

(a) The sign of the x-coordinate is changed.
(b) The sign of the y-coordinate is changed.
(c) The signs of both the x- and y-coordinates are changed.

80. COLLINEAR POINTS Three or more points are *collinear* if they all lie on the same line. Use the steps below to determine if the set of points $\{A(2, 3), B(2, 6), C(6, 3)\}$ and the set of points $\{A(8, 3), B(5, 2), C(2, 1)\}$ are collinear.

(a) For each set of points, use the Distance Formula to find the distances from A to B, from B to C, and from A to C. What relationship exists among these distances for each set of points?
(b) Plot each set of points in the Cartesian plane. Do all the points of either set appear to lie on the same line?
(c) Compare your conclusions from part (a) with the conclusions you made from the graphs in part (b). Make a general statement about how to use the Distance Formula to determine collinearity.

81–82. See margin.

TRUE OR FALSE? In Exercises 81 and 82, determine whether the statement is true or false. Justify your answer.

81. In order to divide a line segment into 16 equal parts, you would have to use the Midpoint Formula 16 times.

82. The points $(-8, 4)$, $(2, 11)$, and $(-5, 1)$ represent the vertices of an isosceles triangle.

83. THINK ABOUT IT When plotting points on the rectangular coordinate system, is it true that the scales on the x- and y-axes must be the same? Explain. See margin.

84. CAPSTONE Use the plot of the point (x_0, y_0) in the figure. Match the transformation of the point with the correct plot. Explain your reasoning. [The plots are labeled (i), (ii), (iii), and (iv).]

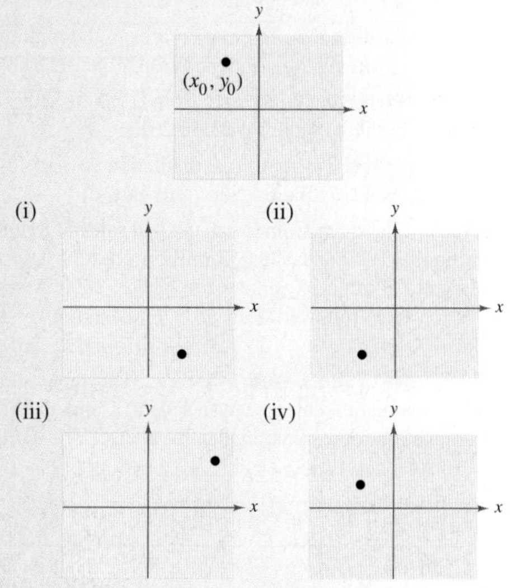

(a) $(x_0, -y_0)$ ii (b) $(-2x_0, y_0)$ iii
(c) $\left(x_0, \frac{1}{2}y_0\right)$ iv (d) $(-x_0, -y_0)$ i

85. PROOF Prove that the diagonals of the parallelogram in the figure intersect at their midpoints. See margin.

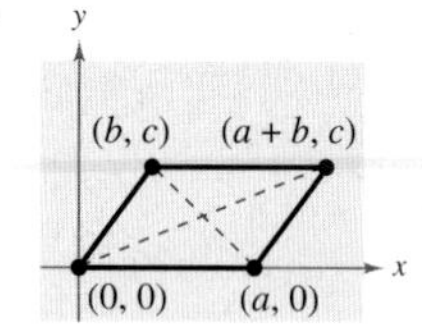

81. False. The Midpoint Formula would be used 15 times.

82. True. Two sides of the triangle have lengths of $\sqrt{149}$, and the third side has a length of $\sqrt{18}$.

83. No. It depends on the magnitudes of the quantities measured.

85. Use the Midpoint Formula to prove that the diagonals of the parallelogram bisect each other.

$$\left(\frac{b + a}{2}, \frac{c + 0}{2}\right) = \left(\frac{a + b}{2}, \frac{c}{2}\right)$$

$$\left(\frac{a + b + 0}{2}, \frac{c + 0}{2}\right) = \left(\frac{a + b}{2}, \frac{c}{2}\right)$$

1.2 Graphs of Equations

What you should learn

- Sketch graphs of equations.
- Find x- and y-intercepts of graphs of equations.
- Use symmetry to sketch graphs of equations.
- Find equations of and sketch graphs of circles.
- Use graphs of equations in solving real-life problems.

Why you should learn it

The graph of an equation can help you see relationships between real-life quantities. For example, in Exercise 87 on page 23, a graph can be used to estimate the life expectancies of children who are born in 2015.

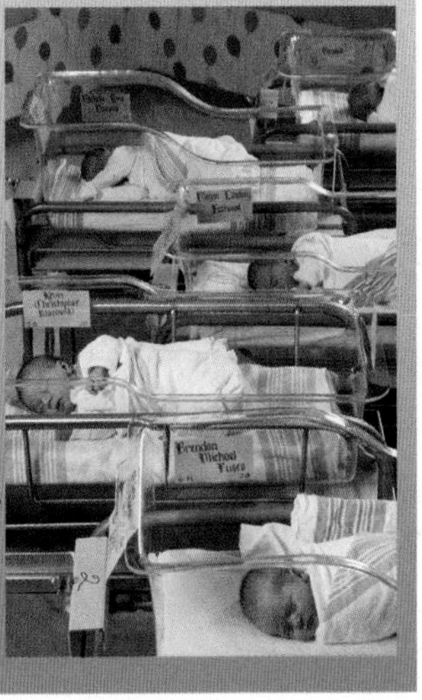

© John Griffin/The Image Works

The Graph of an Equation

In Section 1.1, you used a coordinate system to represent graphically the relationship between two quantities. There, the graphical picture consisted of a collection of points in a coordinate plane.

Frequently, a relationship between two quantities is expressed as an **equation in two variables.** For instance, $y = 7 - 3x$ is an equation in x and y. An ordered pair (a, b) is a **solution** or **solution point** of an equation in x and y if the equation is true when a is substituted for x and b is substituted for y. For instance, $(1, 4)$ is a solution of $y = 7 - 3x$ because $4 = 7 - 3(1)$ is a true statement.

In this section you will review some basic procedures for sketching the graph of an equation in two variables. The **graph of an equation** is the set of all points that are solutions of the equation.

Example 1 Determining Solution Points

Determine whether (a) $(2, 13)$ and (b) $(-1, -3)$ lie on the graph of $y = 10x - 7$.

Solution

a. $y = 10x - 7$ Write original equation.

$13 \stackrel{?}{=} 10(2) - 7$ Substitute 2 for x and 13 for y.

$13 = 13$ $(2, 13)$ is a solution. ✓

The point $(2, 13)$ *does* lie on the graph of $y = 10x - 7$ because it is a solution point of the equation.

b. $y = 10x - 7$ Write original equation.

$-3 \stackrel{?}{=} 10(-1) - 7$ Substitute -1 for x and -3 for y.

$-3 \neq -17$ $(-1, -3)$ is not a solution.

The point $(-1, -3)$ *does not* lie on the graph of $y = 10x - 7$ because it is *not* a solution point of the equation.

CHECKPoint Now try Exercise 7.

The basic technique used for sketching the graph of an equation is the **point-plotting method.**

Sketching the Graph of an Equation by Point Plotting

1. If possible, rewrite the equation so that one of the variables is isolated on one side of the equation.
2. Make a table of values showing several solution points.
3. Plot these points on a rectangular coordinate system.
4. Connect the points with a smooth curve or line.

Algebra Help

When evaluating an expression or an equation, remember to follow the Basic Rules of Algebra. To review these rules, see Appendix A.1.

1 PLAN AND PREPARE

Warm-up Exercises

Transparency Available
Available at the Instructor's companion site.

Notetaking Guide

Transparency Available
Promotes interactive learning and notetaking skills. Available at the Instructor's companion site.

Animated Precalculus

An **Animated Precalculus** tutorial is available at the Student companion site for **Section 1.2.**

Pacing

Average: 1 day
Advanced: 1 day
Block: 0.5 block with 1.1

2 FOCUS AND MOTIVATE

Essential Question

How do you identify intercepts and symmetry in order to sketch graphs of equations, including graphs of circles? **Tell students that they will learn how to answer this question by constructing and using tables, drawing and using graphs, and using the rules of algebra.**

Resource Planning Guide

Chapter Resources
- Complete Solutions Guide

Workbooks
- Notetaking Guide
- Student Solutions Guide

Interactive Technology
- Instructor Success Organizer
- Notetaking Guide IAE
- Instructional DVDs
- Animated Precalculus
- PowerLecture with ExamView

3 TEACH

Extra Example 1

Determine whether (a) (1, 3) and (b) (−2, 4) lie on the graph of $y = 8x - 5$.

(a) Does lie on the graph

(b) Does *not* lie on the graph

Extra Example 2

Sketch the graph of $y = -3x + 2$.

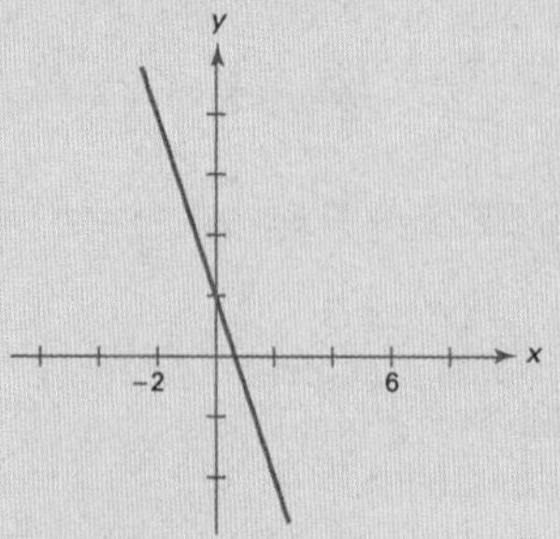

Example 2 Sketching the Graph of an Equation

Sketch the graph of

$$y = 7 - 3x.$$

Solution

Because the equation is already solved for y, construct a table of values that consists of several solution points of the equation. For instance, when $x = -1$,

$$y = 7 - 3(-1)$$
$$= 10$$

which implies that $(-1, 10)$ is a solution point of the graph.

x	$y = 7 - 3x$	(x, y)
-1	10	$(-1, 10)$
0	7	$(0, 7)$
1	4	$(1, 4)$
2	1	$(2, 1)$
3	-2	$(3, -2)$
4	-5	$(4, -5)$

From the table, it follows that

$$(-1, 10), (0, 7), (1, 4), (2, 1), (3, -2), \text{ and } (4, -5)$$

are solution points of the equation. After plotting these points, you can see that they appear to lie on a line, as shown in Figure 1.14. The graph of the equation is the line that passes through the six plotted points.

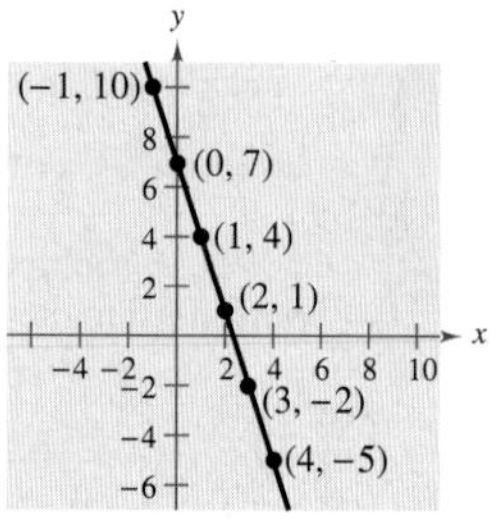

FIGURE 1.14

CHECKPoint Now try Exercise 15.

Example 3 Sketching the Graph of an Equation

Sketch the graph of

$$y = x^2 - 2.$$

Solution

Because the equation is already solved for y, begin by constructing a table of values.

x	-2	-1	0	1	2	3
$y = x^2 - 2$	2	-1	-2	-1	2	7
(x, y)	$(-2, 2)$	$(-1, -1)$	$(0, -2)$	$(1, -1)$	$(2, 2)$	$(3, 7)$

Study Tip

One of your goals in this course is to learn to classify the basic shape of a graph from its equation. For instance, you will learn that the *linear equation* in Example 2 has the form

$$y = mx + b$$

and its graph is a line. Similarly, the *quadratic equation* in Example 3 has the form

$$y = ax^2 + bx + c$$

and its graph is a parabola.

Next, plot the points given in the table, as shown in Figure 1.15. Finally, connect the points with a smooth curve, as shown in Figure 1.16.

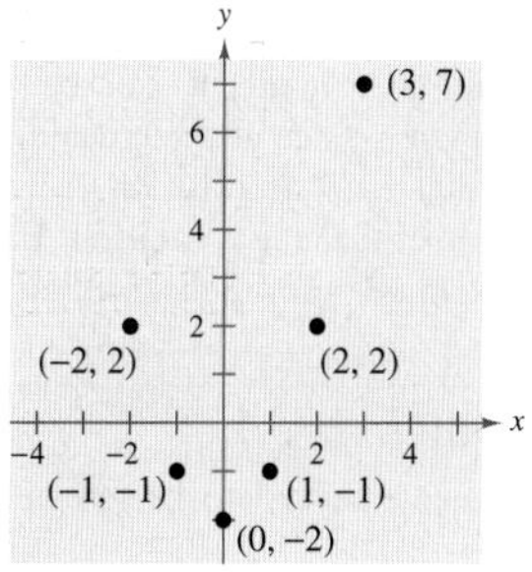

FIGURE 1.15

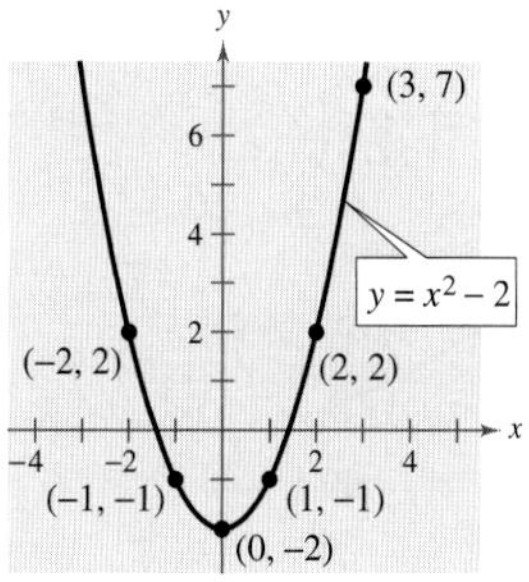

FIGURE 1.16

CHECKPoint Now try Exercise 17.

The point-plotting method demonstrated in Examples 2 and 3 is easy to use, but it has some shortcomings. With too few solution points, you can misrepresent the graph of an equation. For instance, if only the four points

$$(-2, 2), (-1, -1), (1, -1), \text{ and } (2, 2)$$

in Figure 1.15 were plotted, any one of the three graphs in Figure 1.17 would be reasonable.

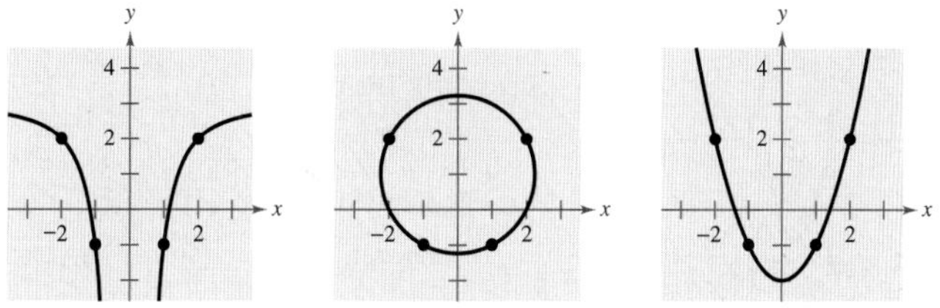

FIGURE 1.17

Extra Example 3

Sketch the graph of $y = 1 - x^2$.

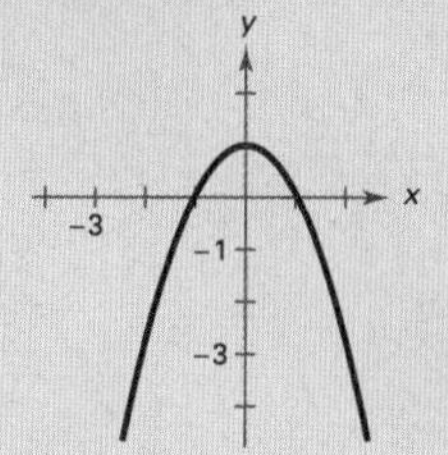

Extra Example 4

Find the x- and y-intercepts of the graph of $y = -x^2 - 5x$.

x-intercepts: (0, 0), (−5, 0);
y-intercept: (0, 0)

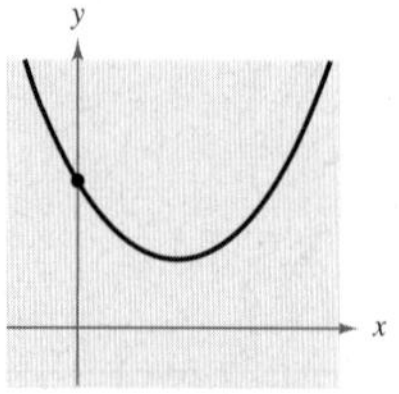

No x-intercepts; one y-intercept

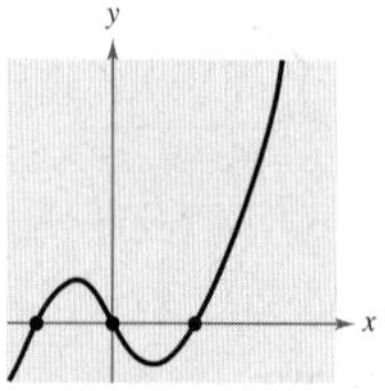

Three x-intercepts; one y-intercept

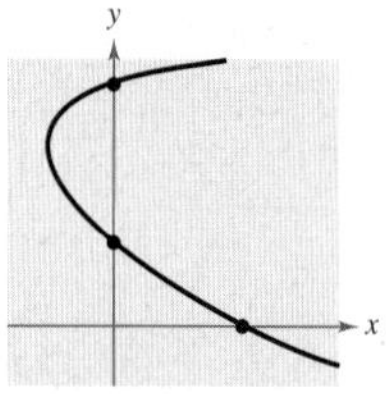

One x-intercept; two y-intercepts

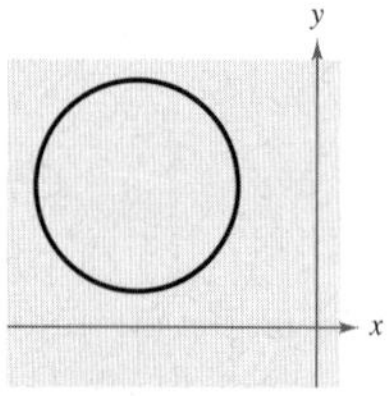

No intercepts

FIGURE 1.18

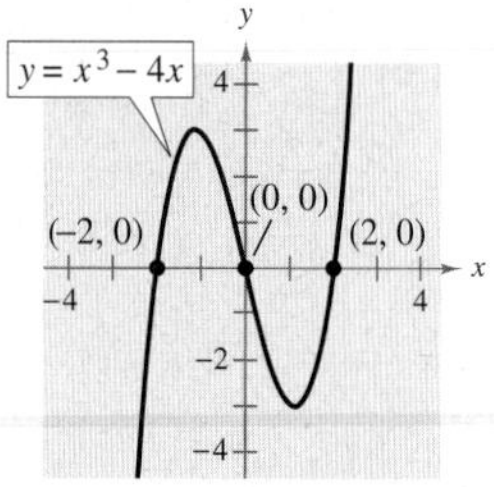

FIGURE 1.19

TECHNOLOGY

To graph an equation involving x and y on a graphing utility, use the following procedure.

1. Rewrite the equation so that y is isolated on the left side.
2. Enter the equation into the graphing utility.
3. Determine a *viewing window* that shows all important features of the graph.
4. Graph the equation.

Intercepts of a Graph

It is often easy to determine the solution points that have zero as either the x-coordinate or the y-coordinate. These points are called **intercepts** because they are the points at which the graph intersects or touches the x- or y-axis. It is possible for a graph to have no intercepts, one intercept, or several intercepts, as shown in Figure 1.18.

Note that an x-intercept can be written as the ordered pair $(x, 0)$ and a y-intercept can be written as the ordered pair $(0, y)$. Some texts denote the x-intercept as the x-coordinate of the point $(a, 0)$ [and the y-intercept as the y-coordinate of the point $(0, b)$] rather than the point itself. Unless it is necessary to make a distinction, we will use the term *intercept* to mean either the point or the coordinate.

Finding Intercepts

1. To find x-intercepts, let y be zero and solve the equation for x.
2. To find y-intercepts, let x be zero and solve the equation for y.

Example 4 Finding x- and y-Intercepts

Find the x- and y-intercepts of the graph of $y = x^3 - 4x$.

Solution

Let $y = 0$. Then

$$0 = x^3 - 4x = x(x^2 - 4)$$

has solutions $x = 0$ and $x = \pm 2$.

x-intercepts: $(0, 0), (2, 0), (-2, 0)$

Let $x = 0$. Then

$$y = (0)^3 - 4(0)$$

has one solution, $y = 0$.

y-intercept: $(0, 0)$ See Figure 1.19.

CHECKPoint Now try Exercise 23.

Symmetry

Graphs of equations can have **symmetry** with respect to one of the coordinate axes or with respect to the origin. Symmetry with respect to the x-axis means that if the Cartesian plane were folded along the x-axis, the portion of the graph above the x-axis would coincide with the portion below the x-axis. Symmetry with respect to the y-axis or the origin can be described in a similar manner, as shown in Figure 1.20.

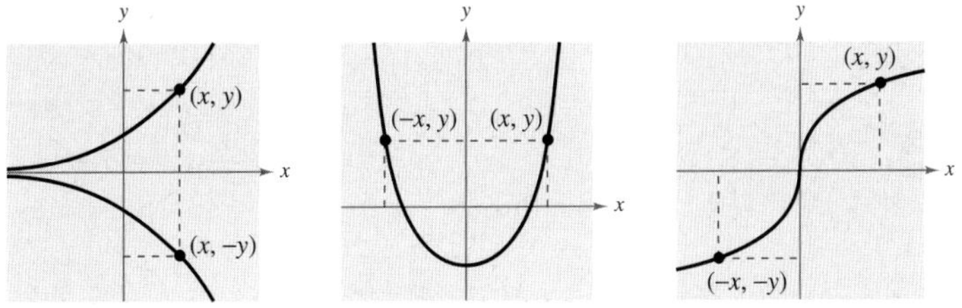

x-axis symmetry y-axis symmetry Origin symmetry

FIGURE 1.20

Knowing the symmetry of a graph *before* attempting to sketch it is helpful, because then you need only half as many solution points to sketch the graph. There are three basic types of symmetry, described as follows.

Graphical Tests for Symmetry

1. A graph is **symmetric with respect to the x-axis** if, whenever (x, y) is on the graph, $(x, -y)$ is also on the graph.
2. A graph is **symmetric with respect to the y-axis** if, whenever (x, y) is on the graph, $(-x, y)$ is also on the graph.
3. A graph is **symmetric with respect to the origin** if, whenever (x, y) is on the graph, $(-x, -y)$ is also on the graph.

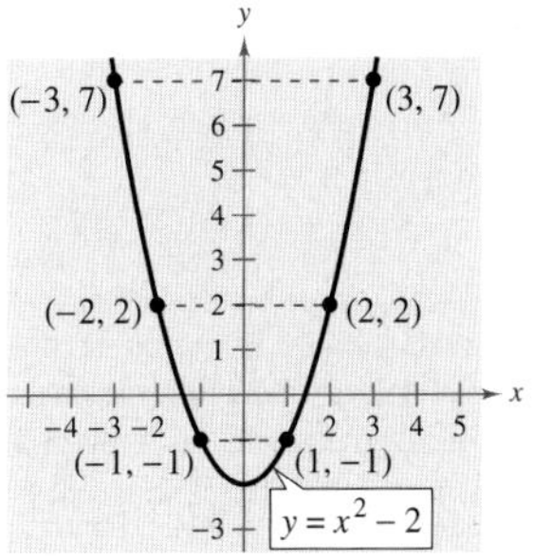

FIGURE 1.21 y-axis symmetry

You can conclude that the graph of $y = x^2 - 2$ is symmetric with respect to the y-axis because the point $(-x, y)$ is also on the graph of $y = x^2 - 2$. (See the table below and Figure 1.21.)

x	-3	-2	-1	1	2	3
y	7	2	-1	-1	2	7
(x, y)	$(-3, 7)$	$(-2, 2)$	$(-1, -1)$	$(1, -1)$	$(2, 2)$	$(3, 7)$

Algebraic Tests for Symmetry

1. The graph of an equation is symmetric with respect to the x-axis if replacing y with $-y$ yields an equivalent equation.
2. The graph of an equation is symmetric with respect to the y-axis if replacing x with $-x$ yields an equivalent equation.
3. The graph of an equation is symmetric with respect to the origin if replacing x with $-x$ and y with $-y$ yields an equivalent equation.

Differentiated Instruction

Kinesthetic Learners To help kinesthetic learners recognize symmetry more easily, have these students sketch the first two graphs shown on page 17 on two separate sheets of paper. Tell students to fold each sheet of paper in half on the line of symmetry. Discuss how knowing that the graph of an equation is symmetric can make the graph easier to sketch.

Extra Example 5

Determine the symmetry of the graph of $y^2 = 6 - x$.

Symmetric with respect to the x-axis

Extra Example 6

Use intercepts and symmetry to sketch the graph of $y = x^2 - 4$.

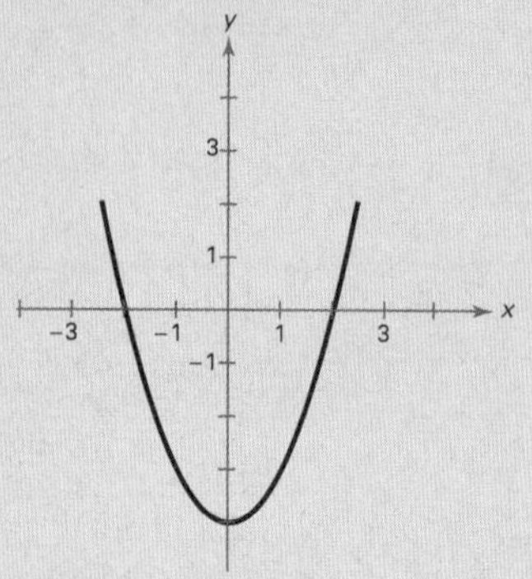

Extra Example 7

Sketch the graph of $y = |x - 2|$.

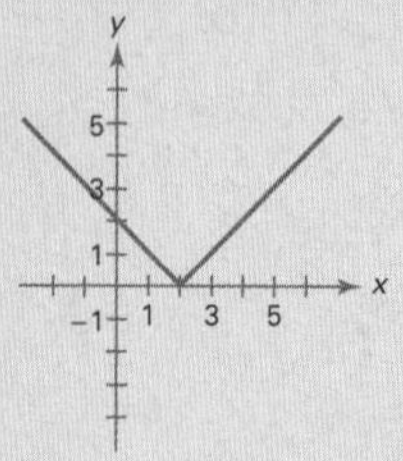

Example 5 Testing for Symmetry

Test $y = 2x^3$ for symmetry with respect to both axes and the origin.

Solution

x-axis:	$y = 2x^3$	Write original equation.
	$-y = 2x^3$	Replace y with $-y$. Result is *not* an equivalent equation.
y-axis:	$y = 2x^3$	Write original equation.
	$y = 2(-x)^3$	Replace x with $-x$.
	$y = -2x^3$	Simplify. Result is *not* an equivalent equation.
Origin:	$y = 2x^3$	Write original equation.
	$-y = 2(-x)^3$	Replace y with $-y$ and x with $-x$.
	$-y = -2x^3$	Simplify.
	$y = 2x^3$	Equivalent equation

Of the three tests for symmetry, the only one that is satisfied is the test for origin symmetry (see Figure 1.22).

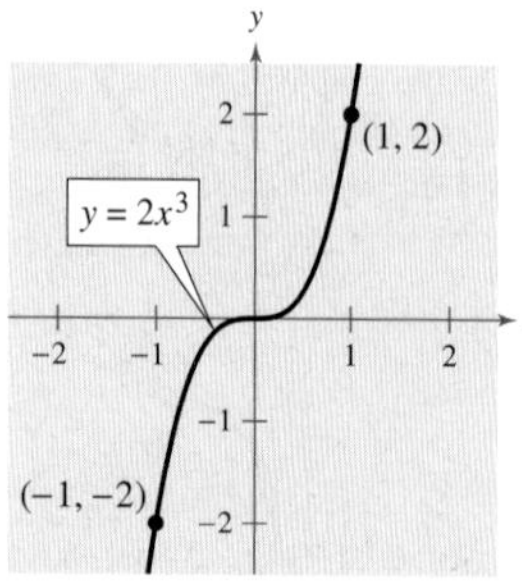

FIGURE 1.22

CHECK*Point* Now try Exercise 33.

Example 6 Using Symmetry as a Sketching Aid

Use symmetry to sketch the graph of $x - y^2 = 1$.

Solution

Of the three tests for symmetry, the only one that is satisfied is the test for x-axis symmetry because $x - (-y)^2 = 1$ is equivalent to $x - y^2 = 1$. So, the graph is symmetric with respect to the x-axis. Using symmetry, you only need to find the solution points above the x-axis and then reflect them to obtain the graph, as shown in Figure 1.23.

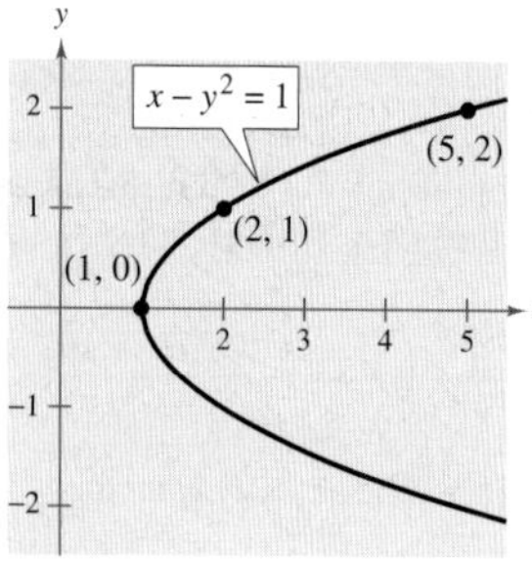

FIGURE 1.23

CHECK*Point* Now try Exercise 49.

Algebra Help

In Example 7, $|x - 1|$ is an absolute value expression. You can review the techniques for evaluating an absolute value expression in Appendix A.1.

Example 7 Sketching the Graph of an Equation

Sketch the graph of $y = |x - 1|$.

Solution

This equation fails all three tests for symmetry and consequently its graph is not symmetric with respect to either axis or to the origin. The absolute value sign indicates that y is always nonnegative. Create a table of values and plot the points, as shown in Figure 1.24. From the table, you can see that $x = 0$ when $y = 1$. So, the y-intercept is $(0, 1)$. Similarly, $y = 0$ when $x = 1$. So, the x-intercept is $(1, 0)$.

x	-2	-1	0	1	2	3	4
$y = \lvert x - 1\rvert$	3	2	1	0	1	2	3
(x, y)	$(-2, 3)$	$(-1, 2)$	$(0, 1)$	$(1, 0)$	$(2, 1)$	$(3, 2)$	$(4, 3)$

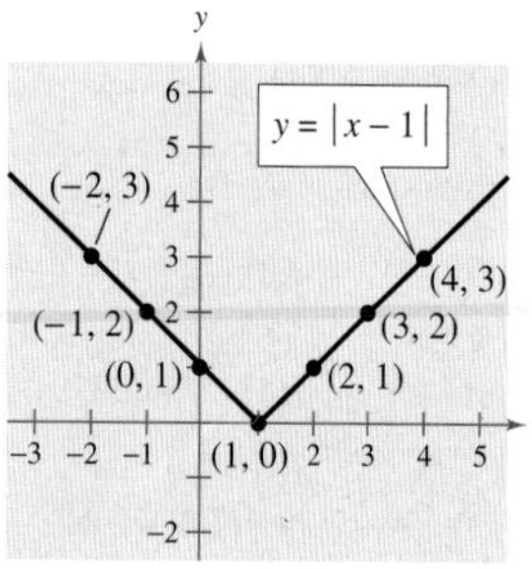

FIGURE 1.24

CHECK*Point* Now try Exercise 53.

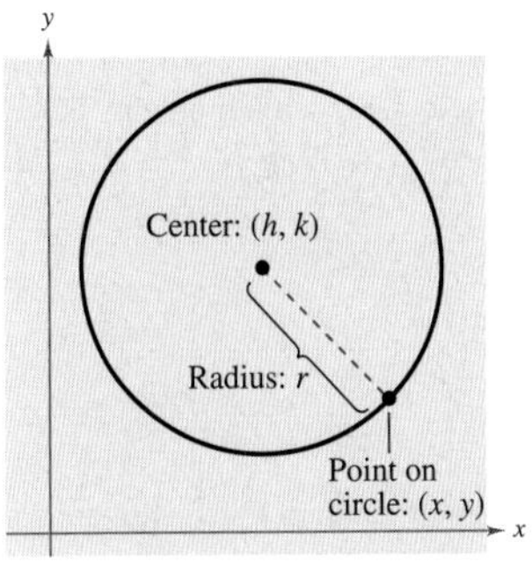

FIGURE 1.25

Throughout this course, you will learn to recognize several types of graphs from their equations. For instance, you will learn to recognize that the graph of a second-degree equation of the form

$$y = ax^2 + bx + c$$

is a parabola (see Example 3). The graph of a **circle** is also easy to recognize.

Circles

Consider the circle shown in Figure 1.25. A point (x, y) is on the circle if and only if its distance from the center (h, k) is r. By the Distance Formula,

$$\sqrt{(x - h)^2 + (y - k)^2} = r.$$

By squaring each side of this equation, you obtain the **standard form of the equation of a circle.**

Standard Form of the Equation of a Circle

The point (x, y) lies on the circle of **radius** r and **center** (h, k) if and only if

$$(x - h)^2 + (y - k)^2 = r^2.$$

WARNING/CAUTION

Be careful when you are finding h and k from the standard equation of a circle. For instance, to find the correct h and k from the equation of the circle in Example 8, rewrite the quantities $(x + 1)^2$ and $(y - 2)^2$ using subtraction.

$$(x + 1)^2 = [x - (-1)]^2,$$
$$(y - 2)^2 = [y - (2)]^2$$

So, $h = -1$ and $k = 2$.

From this result, you can see that the standard form of the equation of a circle *with its center at the origin,* $(h, k) = (0, 0)$, is simply

$$x^2 + y^2 = r^2. \qquad \text{Circle with center at origin}$$

Example 8 Finding the Equation of a Circle

The point $(3, 4)$ lies on a circle whose center is at $(-1, 2)$, as shown in Figure 1.26. Write the standard form of the equation of this circle.

Solution

The radius of the circle is the distance between $(-1, 2)$ and $(3, 4)$.

$$\begin{aligned} r &= \sqrt{(x - h)^2 + (y - k)^2} && \text{Distance Formula} \\ &= \sqrt{[3 - (-1)]^2 + (4 - 2)^2} && \text{Substitute for } x, y, h, \text{ and } k. \\ &= \sqrt{4^2 + 2^2} && \text{Simplify.} \\ &= \sqrt{16 + 4} && \text{Simplify.} \\ &= \sqrt{20} && \text{Radius} \end{aligned}$$

Using $(h, k) = (-1, 2)$ and $r = \sqrt{20}$, the equation of the circle is

$$\begin{aligned} (x - h)^2 + (y - k)^2 &= r^2 && \text{Equation of circle} \\ [x - (-1)]^2 + (y - 2)^2 &= (\sqrt{20})^2 && \text{Substitute for } h, k, \text{ and } r. \\ (x + 1)^2 + (y - 2)^2 &= 20. && \text{Standard form} \end{aligned}$$

CHECKPoint Now try Exercise 73.

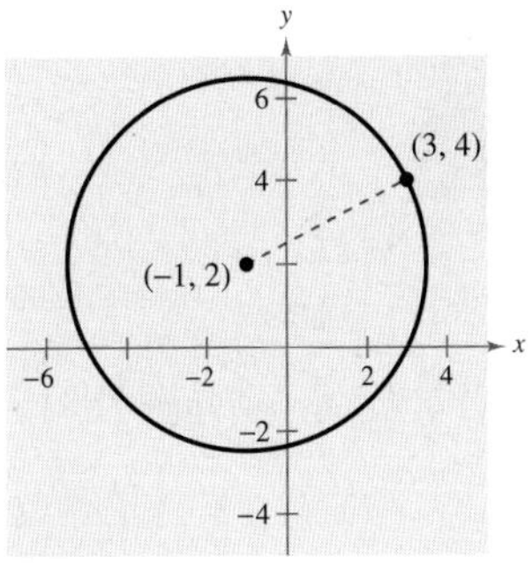

FIGURE 1.26

Extra Example 8

The point $(1, -2)$ lies on the circle whose center is at $(-3, -5)$. Write the standard form of the equation of the circle.

$(x + 3)^2 + (y + 5)^2 = 25$

Application

In this course, you will learn that there are many ways to approach a problem. Three common approaches are illustrated in Example 9.

A *Numerical Approach:* Construct and use a table.
A *Graphical Approach:* Draw and use a graph.
An *Algebraic Approach:* Use the rules of algebra.

Study Tip

You should develop the habit of using at least two approaches to solve every problem. This helps build your intuition and helps you check that your answers are reasonable.

Example 9 Recommended Weight

The median recommended weight y (in pounds) for men of medium frame who are 25 to 59 years old can be approximated by the mathematical model

$$y = 0.073x^2 - 6.99x + 289.0, \quad 62 \le x \le 76$$

where x is the man's height (in inches). (Source: Metropolitan Life Insurance Company)

a. Construct a table of values that shows the median recommended weights for men with heights of 62, 64, 66, 68, 70, 72, 74, and 76 inches.

b. Use the table of values to sketch a graph of the model. Then use the graph to estimate *graphically* the median recommended weight for a man whose height is 71 inches.

c. Use the model to confirm *algebraically* the estimate you found in part (b).

Solution

a. You can use a calculator to complete the table, as shown at the left.

Height, x	Weight, y
62	136.2
64	140.6
66	145.6
68	151.2
70	157.4
72	164.2
74	171.5
76	179.4

b. The table of values can be used to sketch the graph of the equation, as shown in Figure 1.27. From the graph, you can estimate that a height of 71 inches corresponds to a weight of about 161 pounds.

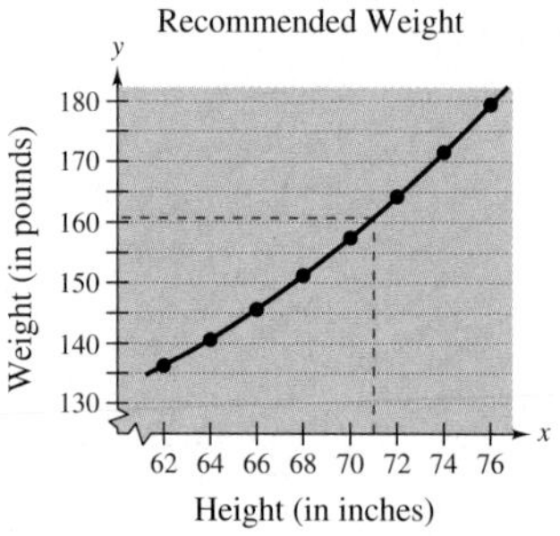

FIGURE 1.27

c. To confirm algebraically the estimate found in part (b), you can substitute 71 for x in the model.

$$y = 0.073(71)^2 - 6.99(71) + 289.0 \approx 160.70$$

So, the graphical estimate of 161 pounds is fairly good.

CHECKPoint Now try Exercise 87.

Extra Example 9

The net profits P (in millions of dollars) for a company from 2000 through 2006 can be approximated by the mathematical model $P = 48.3t + 100.04$, where t is the calendar year, with $t = 0$ corresponding to 2000.

a. Construct a table of values that shows the net profits for each year.

t	P
0	100.04
1	148.34
2	196.64
3	244.94
4	293.24
5	341.54
6	389.84

b. Use the table of values to sketch a graph of the model. Then use the graph to estimate graphically the net profit for the year 2015.

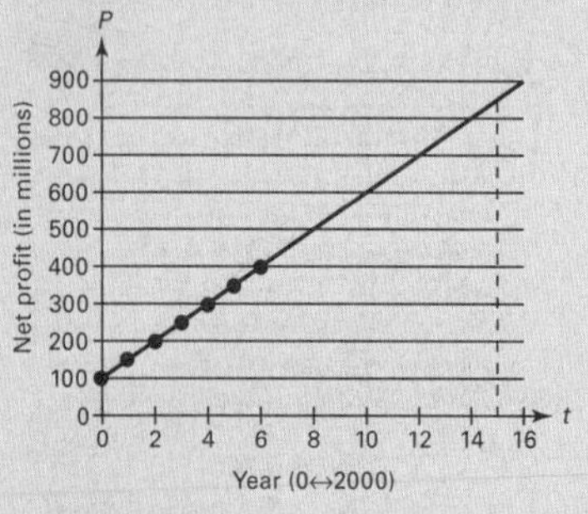

$825 million

c. Use the model to confirm *algebraically* the estimate you found in part (b).

Substitute 15 for t in the model.

$$P = 48.3t + 100.04$$
$$= 48.3(15) + 100.04 = 824.54$$

Closing the Lesson

Have students summarize the major points of the lesson and answer the Essential Question: How do you identify intercepts and symmetry in order to sketch graphs of equations, including graphs of circles?

- **Find intercepts by letting one variable be zero and solving for the other variable.**
- **Identify symmetry by choosing a point (x, y) on the graph and checking to see whether the points $(x, -y)$, $(-x, y)$, or $(-x, -y)$ are also on the graph.**
- **Use the standard form of the equation of a circle.**

1.2 EXERCISES

See www.CalcChat.com for worked-out solutions to odd-numbered exercises.

VOCABULARY: Fill in the blanks.

1. An ordered pair (a, b) is a ________ of an equation in x and y if the equation is true when a is substituted for x, and b is substituted for y. solution or solution point
2. The set of all solution points of an equation is the ________ of the equation. graph
3. The points at which a graph intersects or touches an axis are called the ________ of the graph. intercepts
4. A graph is symmetric with respect to the ________ if, whenever (x, y) is on the graph, $(-x, y)$ is also on the graph. y-axis
5. The equation $(x - h)^2 + (y - k)^2 = r^2$ is the standard form of the equation of a ________ with center ________ and radius ________. circle; (h, k); r
6. When you construct and use a table to solve a problem, you are using a ________ approach. numerical

SKILLS AND APPLICATIONS

In Exercises 7–14, determine whether each point lies on the graph of the equation.

Equation	Points	
7. $y = \sqrt{x + 4}$	(a) $(0, 2)$ Yes	(b) $(5, 3)$ Yes
8. $y = \sqrt{5 - x}$	(a) $(1, 2)$ Yes	(b) $(5, 0)$ Yes
9. $y = x^2 - 3x + 2$	(a) $(2, 0)$ Yes	(b) $(-2, 8)$ No
10. $y = 4 - \lvert x - 2 \rvert$	(a) $(1, 5)$ No	(b) $(6, 0)$ Yes
11. $y = \lvert x - 1 \rvert + 2$	(a) $(2, 3)$ Yes	(b) $(-1, 0)$ No
12. $2x - y - 3 = 0$	(a) $(1, 2)$ No	(b) $(1, -1)$ Yes
13. $x^2 + y^2 = 20$	(a) $(3, -2)$ No	(b) $(-4, 2)$ Yes
14. $y = \frac{1}{3}x^3 - 2x^2$	(a) $\left(2, -\frac{16}{3}\right)$ Yes	(b) $(-3, 9)$ No

In Exercises 15–18, complete the table. Use the resulting solution points to sketch the graph of the equation.

15. $y = -2x + 5$ 15–18. See margin.

x	-1	0	1	2	$\frac{5}{2}$
y					
(x, y)					

16. $y = \frac{3}{4}x - 1$

x	-2	0	1	$\frac{4}{3}$	2
y					
(x, y)					

17. $y = x^2 - 3x$

x	-1	0	1	2	3
y					
(x, y)					

18. $y = 5 - x^2$

x	-2	-1	0	1	2
y					
(x, y)					

19–22. See margin.

In Exercises 19–22, graphically estimate the x- and y-intercepts of the graph. Verify your results algebraically.

19. $y = (x - 3)^2$

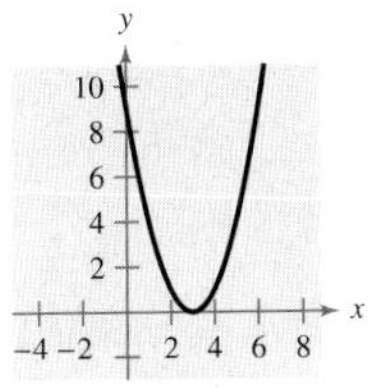

20. $y = 16 - 4x^2$

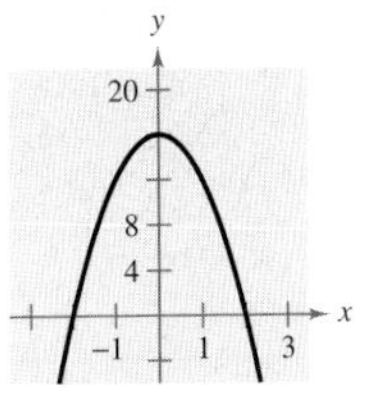

21. $y = \lvert x + 2 \rvert$

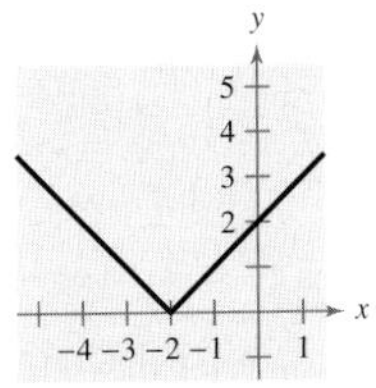

22. $y^2 = 4 - x$

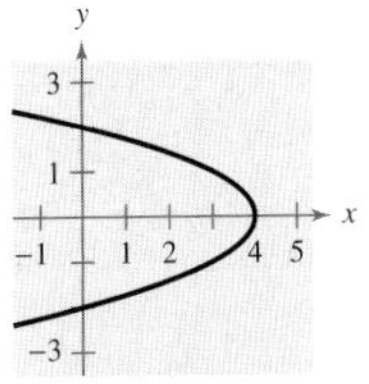

In Exercises 23–32, find the x- and y-intercepts of the graph of the equation. 23–32. See margin.

23. $y = 5x - 6$
24. $y = 8 - 3x$
25. $y = \sqrt{x + 4}$
26. $y = \sqrt{2x - 1}$
27. $y = \lvert 3x - 7 \rvert$
28. $y = -\lvert x + 10 \rvert$
29. $y = 2x^3 - 4x^2$
30. $y = x^4 - 25$
31. $y^2 = 6 - x$
32. $y^2 = x + 1$

15–18. See Additional Answers beginning on page AA1.

4 PRACTICE AND APPLY

Assignment Guide

Transparencies Available
Available at the Instructor's companion site.

Average:
Day 1: pp. 21–23
Exs. 1–14, 15–87 odd, 88, 90

Advanced:
Day 1: pp. 21–23
Exs. 7–14, 16–82 even, 83, 85, 87–90

Block:
pp. 21–23
Exs. 1–14, 15–87 odd, 88, 90
(with 1.1)

19. x-intercept: $(3, 0)$
y-intercept: $(0, 9)$
20. x-intercepts: $(\pm 2, 0)$
y-intercept: $(0, 16)$
21. x-intercept: $(-2, 0)$
y-intercept: $(0, 2)$
22. x-intercept: $(4, 0)$
y-intercepts: $(0, \pm 2)$
23. x-intercept: $\left(\frac{6}{5}, 0\right)$
y-intercept: $(0, -6)$
24. x-intercept: $\left(\frac{8}{3}, 0\right)$
y-intercept: $(0, 8)$
25. x-intercept: $(-4, 0)$
y-intercept: $(0, 2)$
26. x-intercept: $\left(\frac{1}{2}, 0\right)$
y-intercept: None
27. x-intercept: $\left(\frac{7}{3}, 0\right)$
y-intercept: $(0, 7)$
28. x-intercept: $(-10, 0)$
y-intercept: $(0, -10)$
29. x-intercepts: $(0, 0)$, $(2, 0)$
y-intercept: $(0, 0)$
30. x-intercepts: $(\pm\sqrt{5}, 0)$
y-intercept: $(0, -25)$
31. x-intercept: $(6, 0)$
y-intercepts: $(0, \pm\sqrt{6})$
32. x-intercept: $(-1, 0)$
y-intercepts: $(0, \pm 1)$

33–40. See margin.

In Exercises 33–40, use the algebraic tests to check for symmetry with respect to both axes and the origin.

33. $x^2 - y = 0$ **34.** $x - y^2 = 0$

35. $y = x^3$ **36.** $y = x^4 - x^2 + 3$

37. $y = \dfrac{x}{x^2 + 1}$ **38.** $y = \dfrac{1}{x^2 + 1}$

39. $xy^2 + 10 = 0$ **40.** $xy = 4$

In Exercises 41–44, assume that the graph has the indicated type of symmetry. Sketch the complete graph of the equation. To print an enlarged copy of the graph, go to the website *www.mathgraphs.com*. 41–44. See margin.

41.

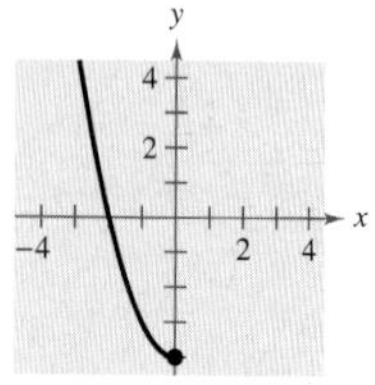

y-axis symmetry

42.

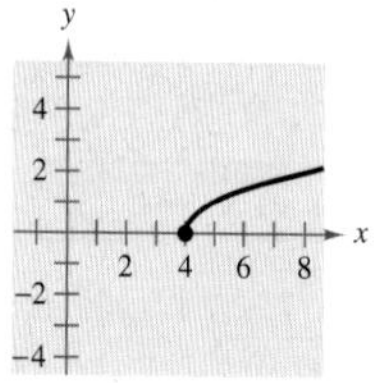

x-axis symmetry

43.

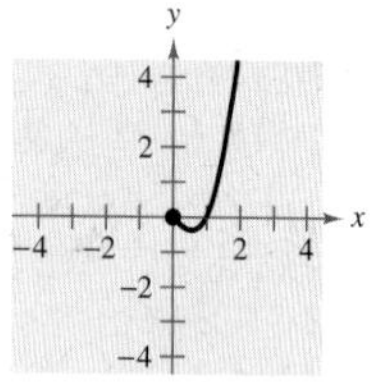

Origin symmetry

44.

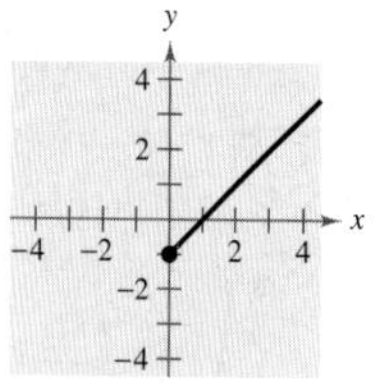

y-axis symmetry

In Exercises 45–56, identify any intercepts and test for symmetry. Then sketch the graph of the equation. 45–56. See margin.

45. $y = -3x + 1$ **46.** $y = 2x - 3$

47. $y = x^2 - 2x$ **48.** $y = -x^2 - 2x$

49. $y = x^3 + 3$ **50.** $y = x^3 - 1$

51. $y = \sqrt{x - 3}$ **52.** $y = \sqrt{1 - x}$

53. $y = |x - 6|$ **54.** $y = 1 - |x|$

55. $x = y^2 - 1$ **56.** $x = y^2 - 5$

In Exercises 57–68, use a graphing utility to graph the equation. Use a standard setting. Approximate any intercepts. 57–68. See margin.

57. $y = 3 - \frac{1}{2}x$ **58.** $y = \frac{2}{3}x - 1$

59. $y = x^2 - 4x + 3$ **60.** $y = x^2 + x - 2$

61. $y = \dfrac{2x}{x - 1}$ **62.** $y = \dfrac{4}{x^2 + 1}$

63. $y = \sqrt[3]{x} + 2$ **64.** $y = \sqrt[3]{x + 1}$

65. $y = x\sqrt{x + 6}$ **66.** $y = (6 - x)\sqrt{x}$

67. $y = |x + 3|$ **68.** $y = 2 - |x|$

In Exercises 69–76, write the standard form of the equation of the circle with the given characteristics.

69. Center: $(0, 0)$; Radius: 4 $x^2 + y^2 = 16$

70. Center: $(0, 0)$; Radius: 5 $x^2 + y^2 = 25$

71. Center: $(2, -1)$; Radius: 4 71–76. See margin.

72. Center: $(-7, -4)$; Radius: 7

73. Center: $(-1, 2)$; Solution point: $(0, 0)$

74. Center: $(3, -2)$; Solution point: $(-1, 1)$

75. Endpoints of a diameter: $(0, 0)$, $(6, 8)$

76. Endpoints of a diameter: $(-4, -1)$, $(4, 1)$

In Exercises 77–82, find the center and radius of the circle, and sketch its graph. 77–82. See margin.

77. $x^2 + y^2 = 25$ **78.** $x^2 + y^2 = 16$

79. $(x - 1)^2 + (y + 3)^2 = 9$ **80.** $x^2 + (y - 1)^2 = 1$

81. $\left(x - \frac{1}{2}\right)^2 + \left(y - \frac{1}{2}\right)^2 = \frac{9}{4}$

82. $(x - 2)^2 + (y + 3)^2 = \frac{16}{9}$

83. DEPRECIATION A hospital purchases a new magnetic resonance imaging (MRI) machine for \$500,000. The depreciated value y (reduced value) after t years is given by $y = 500{,}000 - 40{,}000t$, $0 \le t \le 8$. Sketch the graph of the equation. See margin.

84. CONSUMERISM You purchase an all-terrain vehicle (ATV) for \$8000. The depreciated value y after t years is given by $y = 8000 - 900t$, $0 \le t \le 6$. Sketch the graph of the equation. See margin.

85. GEOMETRY A regulation NFL playing field (including the end zones) of length x and width y has a perimeter of $346\frac{2}{3}$ or $\frac{1040}{3}$ yards. See margin.

(a) Draw a rectangle that gives a visual representation of the problem. Use the specified variables to label the sides of the rectangle.

(b) Show that the width of the rectangle is $y = \dfrac{520}{3} - x$ and its area is $A = x\left(\dfrac{520}{3} - x\right)$.

(c) Use a graphing utility to graph the area equation. Be sure to adjust your window settings.

(d) From the graph in part (c), estimate the dimensions of the rectangle that yield a maximum area.

(e) Use your school's library, the Internet, or some other reference source to find the actual dimensions and area of a regulation NFL playing field and compare your findings with the results of part (d).

The symbol indicates an exercise or a part of an exercise in which you are instructed to use a graphing utility.

33. y-axis symmetry
34. x-axis symmetry
35. Origin symmetry
36. y-axis symmetry
37. Origin symmetry
38. y-axis symmetry
39. x-axis symmetry
40. Origin symmetry

41.

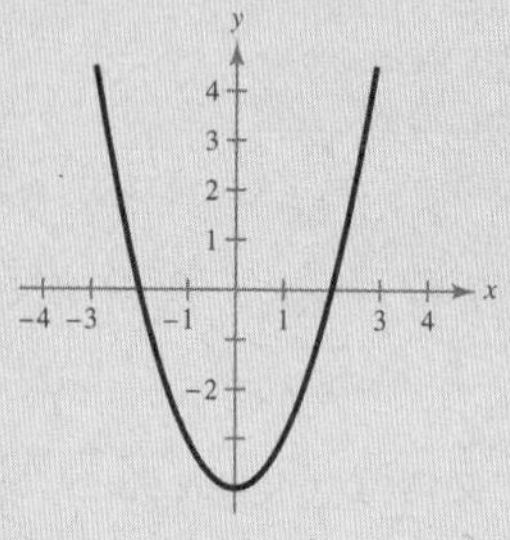

42.

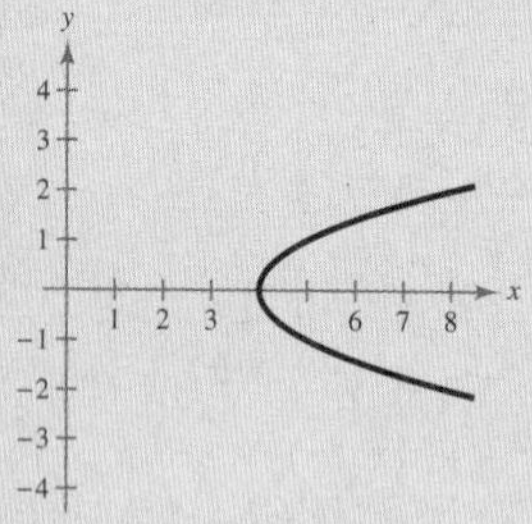

43.

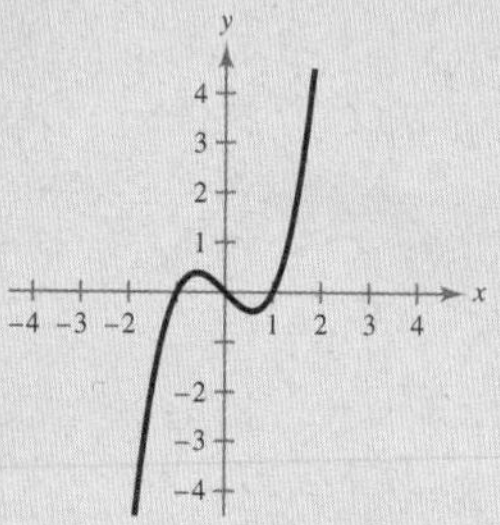

44.

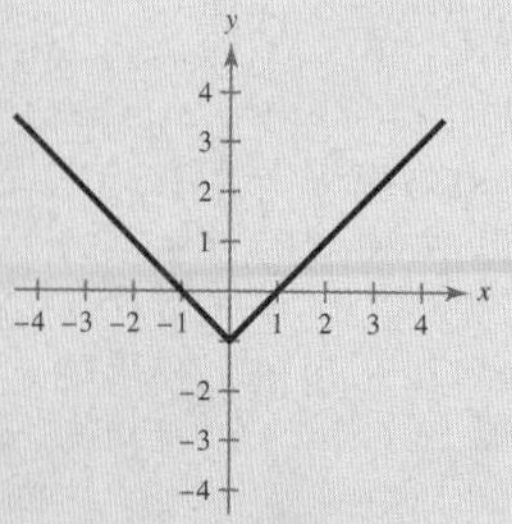

45. x-intercept: $\left(\frac{1}{3}, 0\right)$
y-intercept: $(0, 1)$
No symmetry

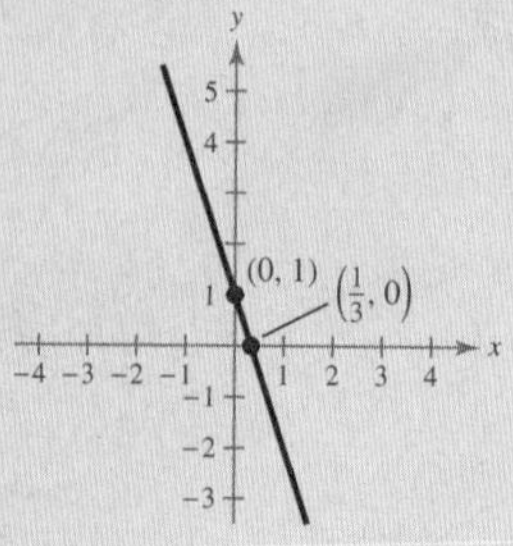

46. x-intercept: $\left(\frac{3}{2}, 0\right)$
y-intercept: $(0, -3)$
No symmetry

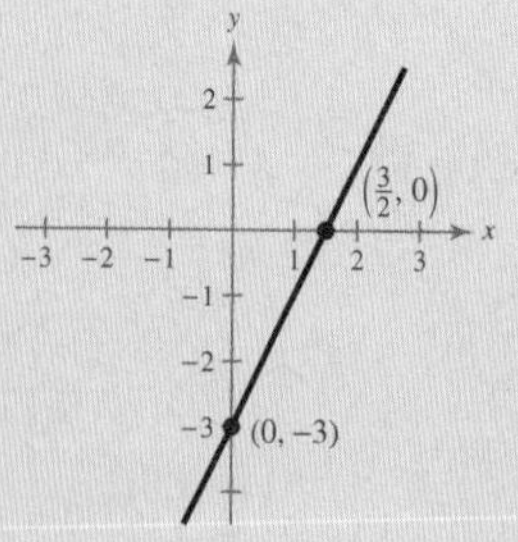

47. x-intercepts: $(0, 0)$, $(2, 0)$
y-intercept: $(0, 0)$
No symmetry

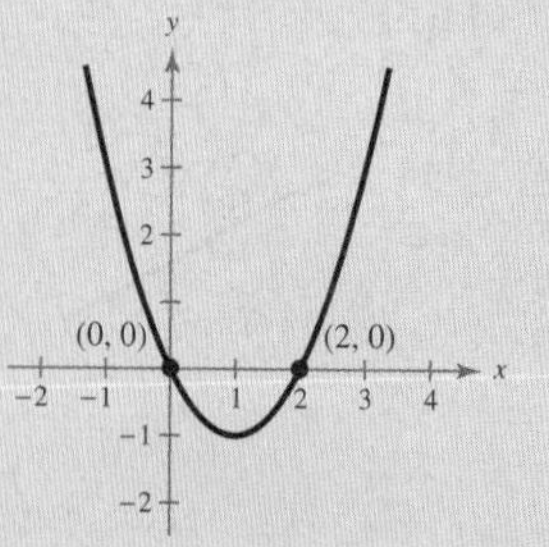

48–68, 71–85. See Additional Answers beginning on page AA1.

86. GEOMETRY A soccer playing field of length x and width y has a perimeter of 360 meters. See margin.

(a) Draw a rectangle that gives a visual representation of the problem. Use the specified variables to label the sides of the rectangle.

(b) Show that the width of the rectangle is $y = 180 - x$ and its area is $A = x(180 - x)$.

(c) Use a graphing utility to graph the area equation. Be sure to adjust your window settings.

(d) From the graph in part (c), estimate the dimensions of the rectangle that yield a maximum area.

(e) Use your school's library, the Internet, or some other reference source to find the actual dimensions and area of a regulation Major League Soccer field and compare your findings with the results of part (d).

87. POPULATION STATISTICS The table shows the life expectancies of a child (at birth) in the United States for selected years from 1920 to 2000. (Source: U.S. National Center for Health Statistics) See margin.

Year	Life Expectancy, y
1920	54.1
1930	59.7
1940	62.9
1950	68.2
1960	69.7
1970	70.8
1980	73.7
1990	75.4
2000	77.0

A model for the life expectancy during this period is

$$y = -0.0025t^2 + 0.574t + 44.25, \quad 20 \le t \le 100$$

where y represents the life expectancy and t is the time in years, with $t = 20$ corresponding to 1920.

(a) Use a graphing utility to graph the data from the table and the model in the same viewing window. How well does the model fit the data? Explain.

(b) Determine the life expectancy in 1990 both graphically and algebraically.

(c) Use the graph to determine the year when life expectancy was approximately 76.0. Verify your answer algebraically.

(d) One projection for the life expectancy of a child born in 2015 is 78.9. How does this compare with the projection given by the model?

(e) Do you think this model can be used to predict the life expectancy of a child 50 years from now? Explain.

88. ELECTRONICS The resistance y (in ohms) of 1000 feet of solid copper wire at 68 degrees Fahrenheit can be approximated by the model See margin.

$$y = \frac{10,770}{x^2} - 0.37, \quad 5 \le x \le 100$$

where x is the diameter of the wire in mils (0.001 inch). (Source: American Wire Gage)

(a) Complete the table.

x	5	10	20	30	40	50
y						

x	60	70	80	90	100
y					

(b) Use the table of values in part (a) to sketch a graph of the model. Then use your graph to estimate the resistance when $x = 85.5$.

(c) Use the model to confirm algebraically the estimate you found in part (b).

(d) What can you conclude in general about the relationship between the diameter of the copper wire and the resistance?

EXPLORATION

89. THINK ABOUT IT Find a and b if the graph of $y = ax^2 + bx^3$ is symmetric with respect to (a) the y-axis and (b) the origin. (There are many correct answers.) See margin.

90. CAPSTONE Match the equation or equations with the given characteristic. See margin.

(i) $y = 3x^3 - 3x$ (ii) $y = (x + 3)^2$

(iii) $y = 3x - 3$ (iv) $y = \sqrt[3]{x}$

(v) $y = 3x^2 + 3$ (vi) $y = \sqrt{x + 3}$

(a) Symmetric with respect to the y-axis

(b) Three x-intercepts

(c) Symmetric with respect to the x-axis

(d) $(-2, 1)$ is a point on the graph

(e) Symmetric with respect to the origin

(f) Graph passes through the origin

5 ASSESS AND RETEACH

Daily Homework Quiz

Transparency Available

Available at the Instructor's companion site.

86. (a)

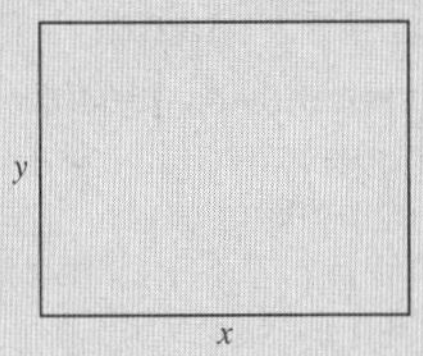

(b) Answers will vary.

(c)

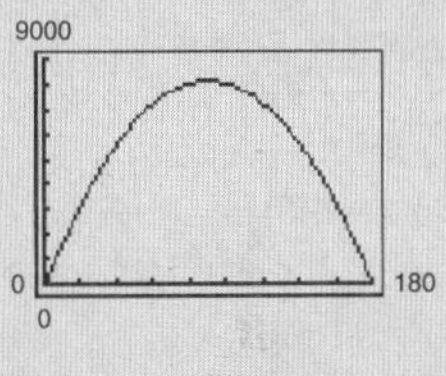

(d) $x = 90$, $y = 90$

(e) Answers will vary. Sample answer: There are no fixed dimensions for a regulation Major League Soccer field, but they are generally 110 to 115 yards (100.6 to 105.2 meters) long and 75 yards (68.6 meters) wide. This makes the area about 8250 square yards (6901.2 square meters).

87. (a)

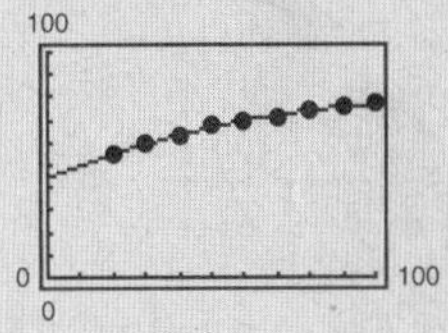

The model fits the data very well.

(b) 75.66 yr

(c) 1993

(d) The projection given by the model, 77.2 years, is less.

(e) Answers will vary.

89. (a) $a = 1, b = 0$

(b) $a = 0, b = 1$

90. (a) v (b) i (c) None

(d) ii, vi (e) i, iv (f) i, iv

88. See Additional Answers beginning on page AA1.

1 PLAN AND PREPARE

Warm-up Exercises

Transparency Available
Available at the Instructor's companion site.

Notetaking Guide

Transparency Available
Promotes interactive learning and notetaking skills. Available at the Instructor's companion site.

Animated Precalculus

An **Animated Precalculus** tutorial is available at the Student companion site for **Section 1.3.**

Pacing

Average: 1 day
Advanced: 1 day
Block: 0.5 block with 1.4

2 FOCUS AND MOTIVATE

Essential Question

How do you find the slope of a line and use it to write an equation for the line? **Tell students that they will learn how to answer this question by reviewing the formula for slope and summarizing the forms of linear equations.**

Resource Planning Guide

Chapter Resources
- Complete Solutions Guide

Workbooks
- Notetaking Guide
- Student Solutions Guide

Interactive Technology
- Instructor Success Organizer
- Notetaking Guide IAE
- Instructional DVDs
- Animated Precalculus
- PowerLecture with ExamView

1.3 LINEAR EQUATIONS IN TWO VARIABLES

What you should learn

- Use slope to graph linear equations in two variables.
- Find the slope of a line given two points on the line.
- Write linear equations in two variables.
- Use slope to identify parallel and perpendicular lines.
- Use slope and linear equations in two variables to model and solve real-life problems.

Why you should learn it

Linear equations in two variables can be used to model and solve real-life problems. For instance, in Exercise 129 on page 36, you will use a linear equation to model student enrollment at the Pennsylvania State University.

Courtesy of Pennsylvania State University

Using Slope

The simplest mathematical model for relating two variables is the **linear equation in two variables** $y = mx + b$. The equation is called *linear* because its graph is a line. (In mathematics, the term *line* means *straight line*.) By letting $x = 0$, you obtain

$$y = m(0) + b \qquad \text{Substitute 0 for } x.$$
$$= b.$$

So, the line crosses the y-axis at $y = b$, as shown in Figure 1.28. In other words, the y-intercept is $(0, b)$. The steepness or slope of the line is m.

$$y = mx + b$$

Slope ↑ ↑ y-Intercept

The **slope** of a nonvertical line is the number of units the line rises (or falls) vertically for each unit of horizontal change from left to right, as shown in Figure 1.28 and Figure 1.29.

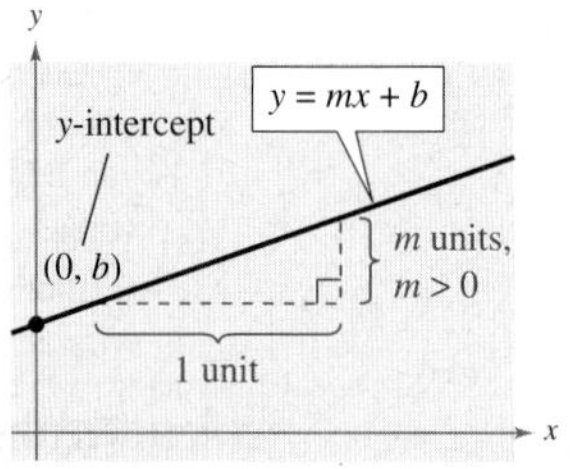

Positive slope, line rises.
FIGURE 1.28

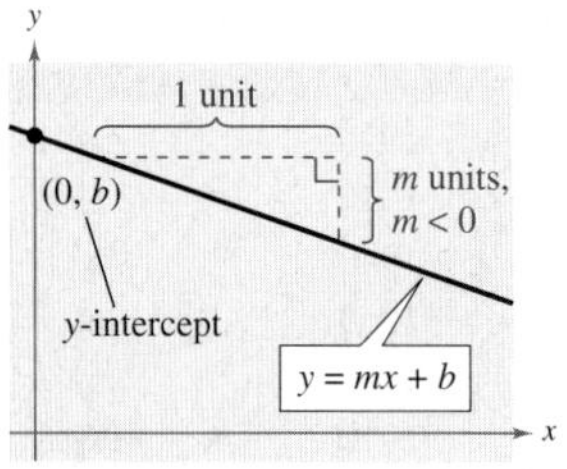

Negative slope, line falls.
FIGURE 1.29

A linear equation that is written in the form $y = mx + b$ is said to be written in **slope-intercept form.**

> **The Slope-Intercept Form of the Equation of a Line**
> The graph of the equation
> $$y = mx + b$$
> is a line whose slope is m and whose y-intercept is $(0, b)$.

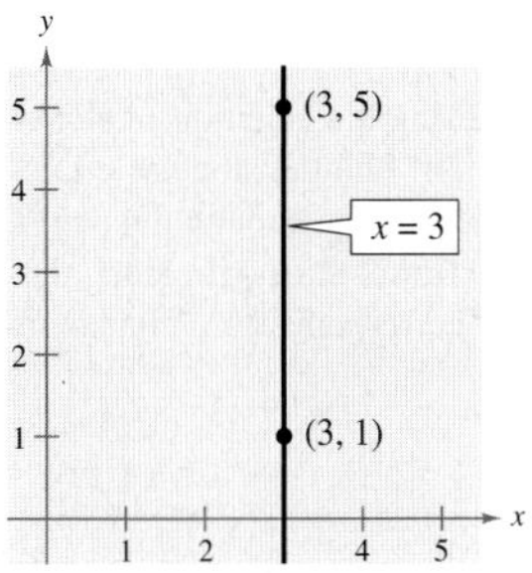

FIGURE 1.30 Slope is undefined.

Once you have determined the slope and the y-intercept of a line, it is a relatively simple matter to sketch its graph. In the next example, note that none of the lines is vertical. A vertical line has an equation of the form

$x = a.$ Vertical line

The equation of a vertical line cannot be written in the form $y = mx + b$ because the slope of a vertical line is undefined, as indicated in Figure 1.30.

Example 1 Graphing a Linear Equation

Sketch the graph of each linear equation.

a. $y = 2x + 1$

b. $y = 2$

c. $x + y = 2$

Solution

a. Because $b = 1$, the y-intercept is $(0, 1)$. Moreover, because the slope is $m = 2$, the line *rises* two units for each unit the line moves to the right, as shown in Figure 1.31.

b. By writing this equation in the form $y = (0)x + 2$, you can see that the y-intercept is $(0, 2)$ and the slope is zero. A zero slope implies that the line is horizontal—that is, it doesn't rise *or* fall, as shown in Figure 1.32.

c. By writing this equation in slope-intercept form

$x + y = 2$ Write original equation.

$y = -x + 2$ Subtract x from each side.

$y = (-1)x + 2$ Write in slope-intercept form.

you can see that the y-intercept is $(0, 2)$. Moreover, because the slope is $m = -1$, the line *falls* one unit for each unit the line moves to the right, as shown in Figure 1.33.

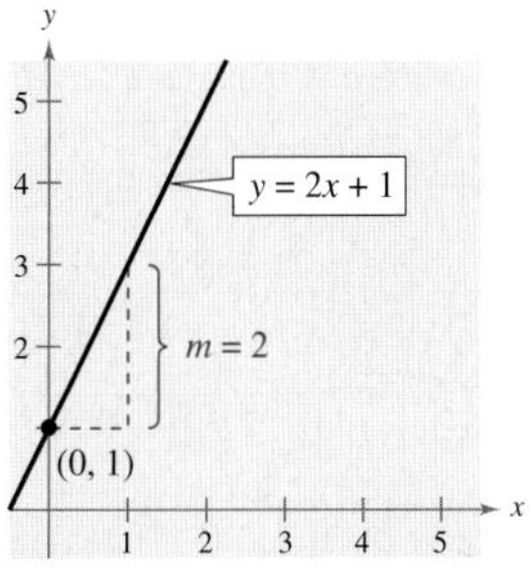

When m is positive, the line rises.
FIGURE 1.31

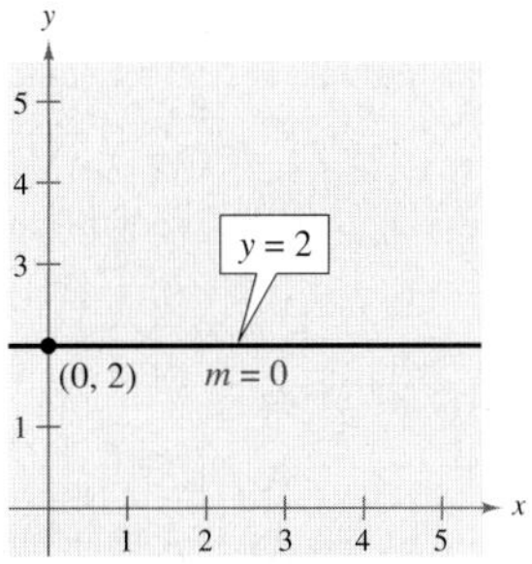

When m is 0, the line is horizontal.
FIGURE 1.32

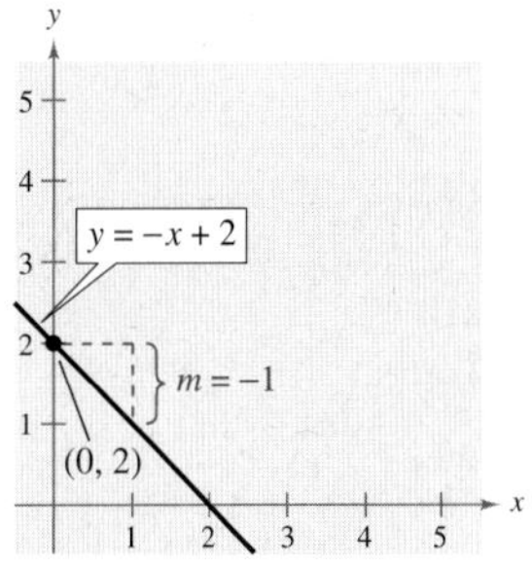

When m is negative, the line falls.
FIGURE 1.33

CHECKPoint Now try Exercise 17.

3 TEACH

Extra Example 1

Sketch the graph of $-4x - y + 5 = 0$.

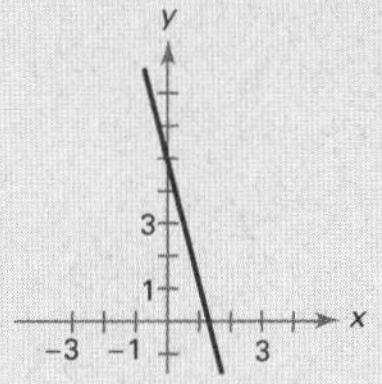

Finding the Slope of a Line

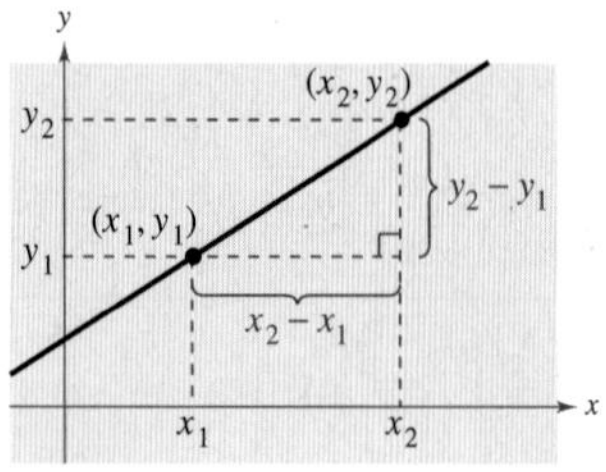

FIGURE 1.34

Given an equation of a line, you can find its slope by writing the equation in slope-intercept form. If you are not given an equation, you can still find the slope of a line. For instance, suppose you want to find the slope of the line passing through the points (x_1, y_1) and (x_2, y_2), as shown in Figure 1.34. As you move from left to right along this line, a change of $(y_2 - y_1)$ units in the vertical direction corresponds to a change of $(x_2 - x_1)$ units in the horizontal direction.

$$y_2 - y_1 = \text{the change in } y = \text{rise}$$

and

$$x_2 - x_1 = \text{the change in } x = \text{run}$$

The ratio of $(y_2 - y_1)$ to $(x_2 - x_1)$ represents the slope of the line that passes through the points (x_1, y_1) and (x_2, y_2).

$$\text{Slope} = \frac{\text{change in } y}{\text{change in } x}$$

$$= \frac{\text{rise}}{\text{run}}$$

$$= \frac{y_2 - y_1}{x_2 - x_1}$$

The Slope of a Line Passing Through Two Points

The **slope** m of the nonvertical line through (x_1, y_1) and (x_2, y_2) is

$$m = \frac{y_2 - y_1}{x_2 - x_1}$$

where $x_1 \neq x_2$.

When this formula is used for slope, the *order of subtraction* is important. Given two points on a line, you are free to label either one of them as (x_1, y_1) and the other as (x_2, y_2). However, once you have done this, you must form the numerator and denominator using the same order of subtraction.

$$\underbrace{m = \frac{y_2 - y_1}{x_2 - x_1}}_{\text{Correct}} \qquad \underbrace{m = \frac{y_1 - y_2}{x_1 - x_2}}_{\text{Correct}} \qquad \underbrace{\cancel{m = \frac{y_2 - y_1}{x_1 - x_2}}}_{\text{Incorrect}}$$

For instance, the slope of the line passing through the points (3, 4) and (5, 7) can be calculated as

$$m = \frac{7 - 4}{5 - 3} = \frac{3}{2}$$

or, reversing the subtraction order in both the numerator and denominator, as

$$m = \frac{4 - 7}{3 - 5} = \frac{-3}{-2} = \frac{3}{2}.$$

Example 2 Finding the Slope of a Line Through Two Points

Find the slope of the line passing through each pair of points.

a. $(-2,\ 0)$ and $(3,\ 1)$ **b.** $(-1,\ 2)$ and $(2,\ 2)$

c. $(0,\ 4)$ and $(1,\ -1)$ **d.** $(3,\ 4)$ and $(3,\ 1)$

Solution

a. Letting $(x_1, y_1) = (-2,\ 0)$ and $(x_2, y_2) = (3,\ 1)$, you obtain a slope of

$$m = \frac{y_2 - y_1}{x_2 - x_1} = \frac{1 - 0}{3 - (-2)} = \frac{1}{5}.$$ See Figure 1.35.

b. The slope of the line passing through $(-1,\ 2)$ and $(2,\ 2)$ is

$$m = \frac{2 - 2}{2 - (-1)} = \frac{0}{3} = 0.$$ See Figure 1.36.

c. The slope of the line passing through $(0,\ 4)$ and $(1,\ -1)$ is

$$m = \frac{-1 - 4}{1 - 0} = \frac{-5}{1} = -5.$$ See Figure 1.37.

d. The slope of the line passing through $(3,\ 4)$ and $(3,\ 1)$ is

$$m = \frac{1 - 4}{3 - 3} = \frac{-3}{0}.$$ See Figure 1.38.

Because division by 0 is undefined, the slope is undefined and the line is vertical.

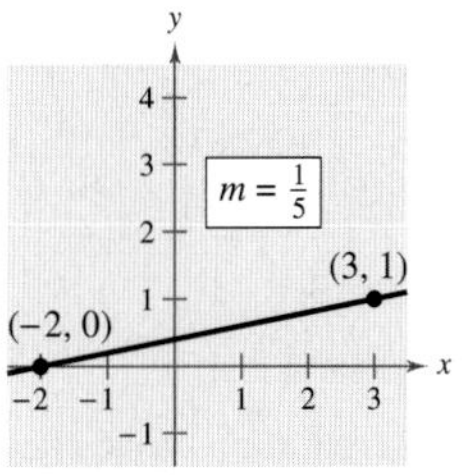

FIGURE 1.35

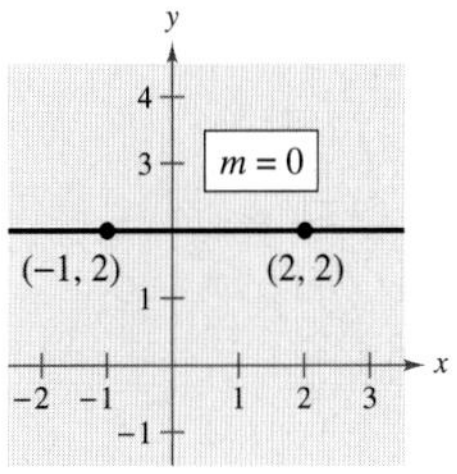

FIGURE 1.36

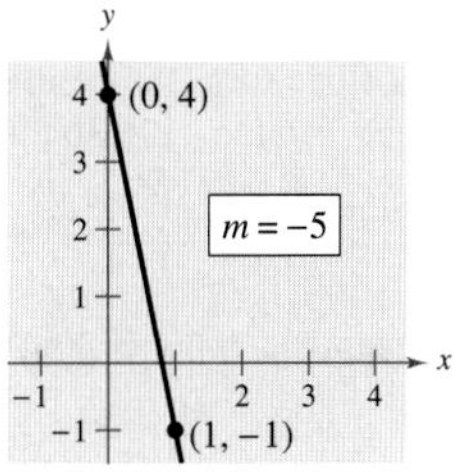

FIGURE 1.37

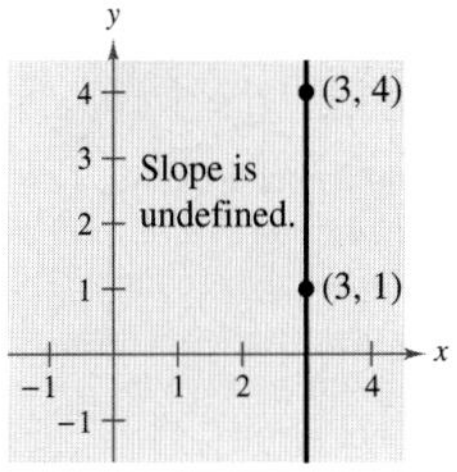

FIGURE 1.38

CHECKPoint Now try Exercise 31.

Algebra Help

To find the slopes in Example 2, you must be able to evaluate rational expressions. You can review the techniques for evaluating rational expressions in Appendix A.4.

Study Tip

In Figures 1.35 to 1.38, note the relationships between slope and the orientation of the line.

a. Positive slope: line rises from left to right

b. Zero slope: line is horizontal

c. Negative slope: line falls from left to right

d. Undefined slope: line is vertical

Extra Example 2

Find the slope of the line passing through (–5, –6) and (2, 8). 2

Avoiding Common Errors

Example 2 Students should be reminded to place the difference in the *y*-values in the numerator and the difference in the *x*-values in the denominator when finding slope.

Extra Example 3

Find the slope-intercept form of the equation of the line that has a slope of 2 and passes through the point (3, −7). Use this information to find three additional points on the line.

$y = 2x - 13$. ***Sample answer:*** (4, −5), (5, −3), (6, −1)

Writing Linear Equations in Two Variables

If (x_1, y_1) is a point on a line of slope m and (x, y) is *any other* point on the line, then

$$\frac{y - y_1}{x - x_1} = m.$$

This equation, involving the variables x and y, can be rewritten in the form

$$y - y_1 = m(x - x_1)$$

which is the **point-slope form** of the equation of a line.

> **Point-Slope Form of the Equation of a Line**
>
> The equation of the line with slope m passing through the point (x_1, y_1) is
>
> $$y - y_1 = m(x - x_1).$$

The point-slope form is most useful for *finding* the equation of a line. You should remember this form.

Example 3 Using the Point-Slope Form

Find the slope-intercept form of the equation of the line that has a slope of 3 and passes through the point $(1, -2)$.

Solution

Use the point-slope form with $m = 3$ and $(x_1, y_1) = (1, -2)$.

$$y - y_1 = m(x - x_1) \quad \text{Point-slope form}$$

$$y - (-2) = 3(x - 1) \quad \text{Substitute for } m, x_1, \text{ and } y_1.$$

$$y + 2 = 3x - 3 \quad \text{Simplify.}$$

$$y = 3x - 5 \quad \text{Write in slope-intercept form.}$$

The slope-intercept form of the equation of the line is $y = 3x - 5$. The graph of this line is shown in Figure 1.39.

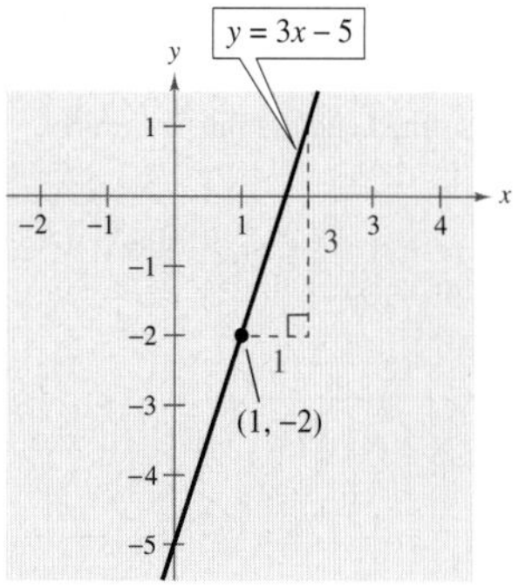

FIGURE 1.39

CHECKPoint Now try Exercise 51.

Study Tip

When you find an equation of the line that passes through two given points, you only need to substitute the coordinates of one of the points in the point-slope form. It does not matter which point you choose because both points will yield the same result.

The point-slope form can be used to find an equation of the line passing through two points (x_1, y_1) and (x_2, y_2). To do this, first find the slope of the line

$$m = \frac{y_2 - y_1}{x_2 - x_1}, \quad x_1 \neq x_2$$

and then use the point-slope form to obtain the equation

$$y - y_1 = \frac{y_2 - y_1}{x_2 - x_1}(x - x_1). \quad \text{Two-point form}$$

This is sometimes called the **two-point form** of the equation of a line.

Parallel and Perpendicular Lines

Slope can be used to decide whether two nonvertical lines in a plane are parallel, perpendicular, or neither.

> **Parallel and Perpendicular Lines**
>
> 1. Two distinct nonvertical lines are **parallel** if and only if their slopes are equal. That is, $m_1 = m_2$.
> 2. Two nonvertical lines are **perpendicular** if and only if their slopes are negative reciprocals of each other. That is, $m_1 = -1/m_2$.

Example 4 Finding Parallel and Perpendicular Lines

Find the slope-intercept forms of the equations of the lines that pass through the point $(2, -1)$ and are (a) parallel to and (b) perpendicular to the line $2x - 3y = 5$.

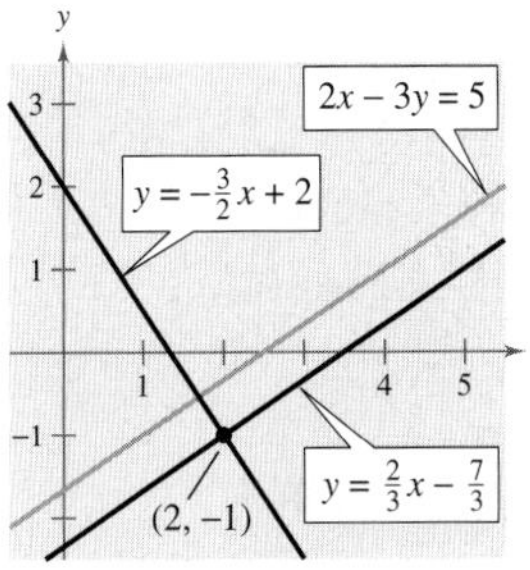

FIGURE 1.40

Solution

By writing the equation of the given line in slope-intercept form

$$2x - 3y = 5 \quad \text{Write original equation.}$$

$$-3y = -2x + 5 \quad \text{Subtract } 2x \text{ from each side.}$$

$$y = \tfrac{2}{3}x - \tfrac{5}{3} \quad \text{Write in slope-intercept form.}$$

you can see that it has a slope of $m = \frac{2}{3}$, as shown in Figure 1.40.

a. Any line parallel to the given line must also have a slope of $\frac{2}{3}$. So, the line through $(2, -1)$ that is parallel to the given line has the following equation.

$$y - (-1) = \tfrac{2}{3}(x - 2) \quad \text{Write in point-slope form.}$$

$$3(y + 1) = 2(x - 2) \quad \text{Multiply each side by 3.}$$

$$3y + 3 = 2x - 4 \quad \text{Distributive Property}$$

$$y = \tfrac{2}{3}x - \tfrac{7}{3} \quad \text{Write in slope-intercept form.}$$

b. Any line perpendicular to the given line must have a slope of $-\frac{3}{2}$ (because $-\frac{3}{2}$ is the negative reciprocal of $\frac{2}{3}$). So, the line through $(2, -1)$ that is perpendicular to the given line has the following equation.

$$y - (-1) = -\tfrac{3}{2}(x - 2) \quad \text{Write in point-slope form.}$$

$$2(y + 1) = -3(x - 2) \quad \text{Multiply each side by 2.}$$

$$2y + 2 = -3x + 6 \quad \text{Distributive Property}$$

$$y = -\tfrac{3}{2}x + 2 \quad \text{Write in slope-intercept form.}$$

CHECK*Point* Now try Exercise 87.

Notice in Example 4 how the slope-intercept form is used to obtain information about the graph of a line, whereas the point-slope form is used to write the equation of a line.

> **TECHNOLOGY**
>
> On a graphing utility, lines will not appear to have the correct slope unless you use a viewing window that has a square setting. For instance, try graphing the lines in Example 4 using the standard setting $-10 \le x \le 10$ and $-10 \le y \le 10$. Then reset the viewing window with the square setting $-9 \le x \le 9$ and $-6 \le y \le 6$. On which setting do the lines $y = \frac{2}{3}x - \frac{5}{3}$ and $y = -\frac{3}{2}x + 2$ appear to be perpendicular?

The lines appear perpendicular on the square setting.

Extra Example 4

Find the slope-intercept forms of the equations of the lines that pass through the point $(-4, 1)$ and are (a) parallel to and (b) perpendicular to the line $5x - 3y = 8$.

$y = \frac{5}{3}x + \frac{23}{3}$; $y = -\frac{3}{5}x - \frac{7}{5}$

Extra Example 5

When driving down a mountainside, you notice warning signs indicating that the road has a grade of twelve percent. This means that the slope of the road is $-\frac{12}{100}$. Approximate the amount of horizontal change in your position if you note from elevation markers that you have descended 2000 feet vertically.

16,666.67 feet

Extra Example 6

The following are the slopes of lines representing annual sales y in terms of time x in years. Use the slopes to interpret any change in annual sales for a 1-year increase in time.

a. The line has a slope of $m = 120$.
Sales are increasing by 120 units per year.

b. The line has a slope of $m = 0$.
There is no change in sales.

c. The line has a slope of $m = -35$.
Sales are decreasing by 35 units per year.

Applications

In real-life problems, the slope of a line can be interpreted as either a *ratio* or a *rate*. If the x-axis and y-axis have the same unit of measure, then the slope has no units and is a **ratio.** If the x-axis and y-axis have different units of measure, then the slope is a **rate** or **rate of change.**

Example 5 Using Slope as a Ratio

The maximum recommended slope of a wheelchair ramp is $\frac{1}{12}$. A business is installing a wheelchair ramp that rises 22 inches over a horizontal length of 24 feet. Is the ramp steeper than recommended? (Source: *Americans with Disabilities Act Handbook*)

Solution

The horizontal length of the ramp is 24 feet or $12(24) = 288$ inches, as shown in Figure 1.41. So, the slope of the ramp is

$$\text{Slope} = \frac{\text{vertical change}}{\text{horizontal change}} = \frac{22 \text{ in.}}{288 \text{ in.}} \approx 0.076.$$

Because $\frac{1}{12} \approx 0.083$, the slope of the ramp is not steeper than recommended.

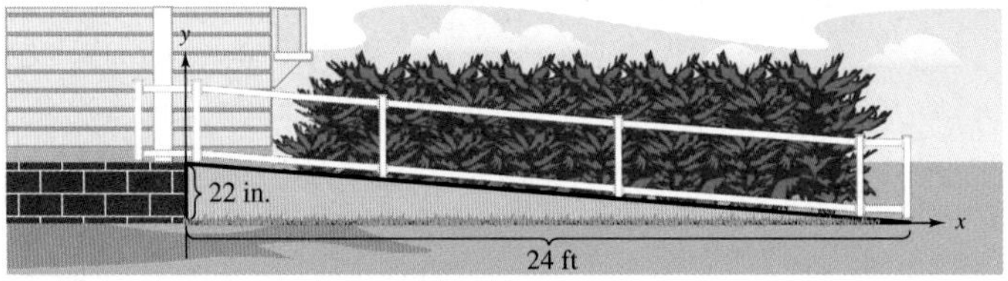

FIGURE 1.41

CHECKPoint Now try Exercise 115.

Example 6 Using Slope as a Rate of Change

A kitchen appliance manufacturing company determines that the total cost in dollars of producing x units of a blender is

$$C = 25x + 3500. \qquad \text{Cost equation}$$

Describe the practical significance of the y-intercept and slope of this line.

Solution

The y-intercept $(0, 3500)$ tells you that the cost of producing zero units is \$3500. This is the *fixed cost* of production—it includes costs that must be paid regardless of the number of units produced. The slope of $m = 25$ tells you that the cost of producing each unit is \$25, as shown in Figure 1.42. Economists call the cost per unit the *marginal cost*. If the production increases by one unit, then the "margin," or extra amount of cost, is \$25. So, the cost increases at a rate of \$25 per unit.

CHECKPoint Now try Exercise 119.

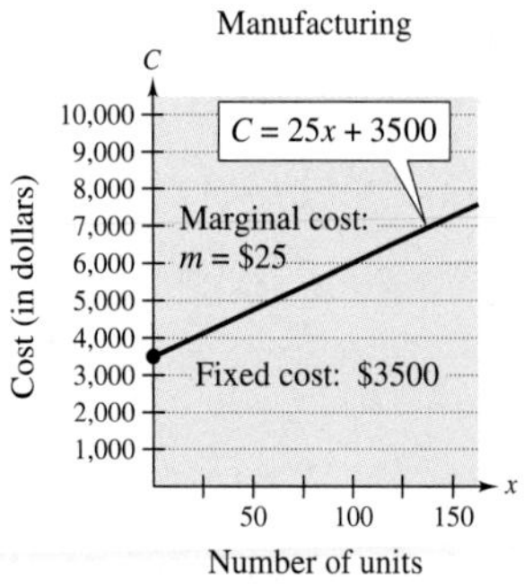

FIGURE 1.42 Production cost

Most business expenses can be deducted in the same year they occur. One exception is the cost of property that has a useful life of more than 1 year. Such costs must be *depreciated* (decreased in value) over the useful life of the property. If the *same amount* is depreciated each year, the procedure is called *linear* or *straight-line depreciation*. The *book value* is the difference between the original value and the total amount of depreciation accumulated to date.

Example 7 Straight-Line Depreciation

A college purchased exercise equipment worth $12,000 for the new campus fitness center. The equipment has a useful life of 8 years. The salvage value at the end of 8 years is $2000. Write a linear equation that describes the book value of the equipment each year.

Solution

Let V represent the value of the equipment at the end of year t. You can represent the initial value of the equipment by the data point (0, 12,000) and the salvage value of the equipment by the data point (8, 2000). The slope of the line is

$$m = \frac{2000 - 12{,}000}{8 - 0} = -\$1250$$

which represents the annual depreciation in *dollars per year*. Using the point-slope form, you can write the equation of the line as follows.

$$V - 12{,}000 = -1250(t - 0) \quad \text{Write in point-slope form.}$$

$$V = -1250t + 12{,}000 \quad \text{Write in slope-intercept form.}$$

The table shows the book value at the end of each year, and the graph of the equation is shown in Figure 1.43.

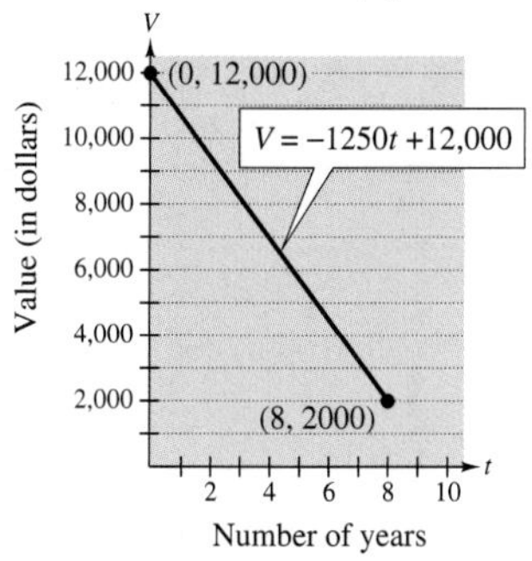

FIGURE 1.43 Straight-line depreciation

Year, t	Value, V
0	12,000
1	10,750
2	9500
3	8250
4	7000
5	5750
6	4500
7	3250
8	2000

CHECKPoint Now try Exercise 121.

In many real-life applications, the two data points that determine the line are often given in a disguised form. Note how the data points are described in Example 7.

Extra Example 7

A person purchases a car for $25,290. After 11 years, the car will have to be replaced. Its value at that time is expected to be $1200. Write a linear equation giving the value V of the car during the 11 years in which it will be used.

$V = -2190t + 25{,}290,\ 0 \le t \le 11$

Extra Example 8

A business purchases a piece of equipment for $34,200. After 15 years, the equipment will have to be replaced. Its value at that time is expected to be $1500.

a. Write a linear equation giving the value V of the equipment during the 15 years in which it will be used. **$V = -2180t + 34{,}200,\ 0 \le t \le 15$**

b. Use the equation to estimate the value of the equipment after 7 years. **$18,940**

Closing the Lesson

Have students summarize the major points of the lesson and answer the Essential Question: How do you find the slope of a line and use it to write an equation for the line?

- **Use the slope and the coordinates of a point to write equations for nonvertical lines and to determine whether two lines are perpendicular, parallel, or neither.**
- **Use the general form for writing an equation for any line.**
- **Use linear equations to model economic quantities.**

Example 8 Predicting Sales

The sales for Best Buy were approximately $35.9 billion in 2006 and $40.0 billion in 2007. Using only this information, write a linear equation that gives the sales (in billions of dollars) in terms of the year. Then predict the sales for 2010. (Source: Best Buy Company, Inc.)

Solution

Let $t = 6$ represent 2006. Then the two given values are represented by the data points (6, 35.9) and (7, 40.0). The slope of the line through these points is

$$m = \frac{40.0 - 35.9}{7 - 6}$$

$$= 4.1.$$

Using the point-slope form, you can find the equation that relates the sales y and the year t to be

$$y - 35.9 = 4.1(t - 6) \qquad \text{Write in point-slope form.}$$

$$y = 4.1t + 11.3. \qquad \text{Write in slope-intercept form.}$$

According to this equation, the sales for 2010 will be

$$y = 4.1(10) + 11.3 = 41 + 11.3 = \$52.3 \text{ billion. (See Figure 1.44.)}$$

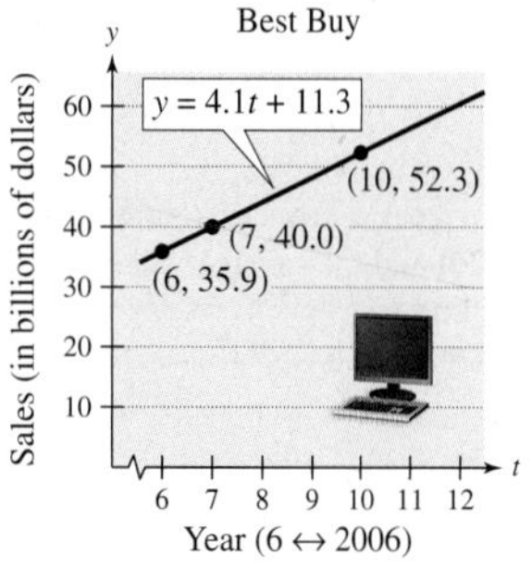

FIGURE 1.44

CHECKPoint Now try Exercise 129.

The prediction method illustrated in Example 8 is called **linear extrapolation.** Note in Figure 1.45 that an extrapolated point does not lie between the given points. When the estimated point lies between two given points, as shown in Figure 1.46, the procedure is called **linear interpolation.**

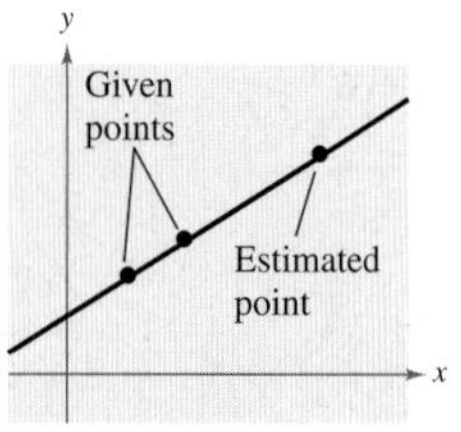

Linear extrapolation
FIGURE 1.45

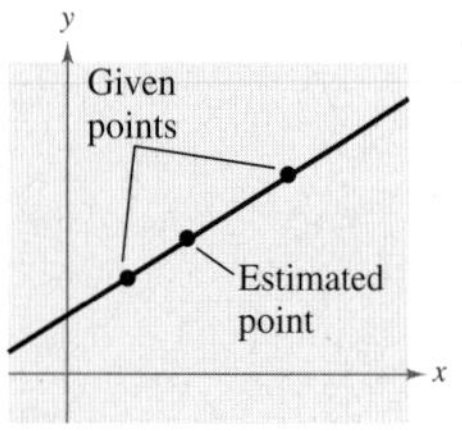

Linear interpolation
FIGURE 1.46

Because the slope of a vertical line is not defined, its equation cannot be written in slope-intercept form. However, every line has an equation that can be written in the **general form**

$$Ax + By + C = 0 \qquad \text{General form}$$

where A and B are not both zero. For instance, the vertical line given by $x = a$ can be represented by the general form $x - a = 0$.

Summary of Equations of Lines

1. General form: $Ax + By + C = 0$
2. Vertical line: $x = a$
3. Horizontal line: $y = b$
4. Slope-intercept form: $y = mx + b$
5. Point-slope form: $y - y_1 = m(x - x_1)$
6. Two-point form: $y - y_1 = \dfrac{y_2 - y_1}{x_2 - x_1}(x - x_1)$

1.3 EXERCISES

See www.CalcChat.com for worked-out solutions to odd-numbered exercises.

VOCABULARY

In Exercises 1–7, fill in the blanks.

1. The simplest mathematical model for relating two variables is the _linear_ equation in two variables $y = mx + b$.
2. For a line, the ratio of the change in y to the change in x is called the _slope_ of the line.
3. Two lines are _parallel_ if and only if their slopes are equal.
4. Two lines are ________ if and only if their slopes are negative reciprocals of each other. perpendicular
5. When the x-axis and y-axis have different units of measure, the slope can be interpreted as a _rate or rate of change_
6. The prediction method ________ ________ is the method used to estimate a point on a line when the point does not lie between the given points. linear extrapolation
7. Every line has an equation that can be written in ________ form. general
8. Match each equation of a line with its form.

(a) $Ax + By + C = 0$ (i) Vertical line
(b) $x = a$ (ii) Slope-intercept form
(c) $y = b$ (iii) General form
(d) $y = mx + b$ (iv) Point-slope form
(e) $y - y_1 = m(x - x_1)$ (v) Horizontal line

SKILLS AND APPLICATIONS

In Exercises 9 and 10, identify the line that has each slope.

9. (a) $m = \frac{2}{3}$ L_2
(b) m is undefined. L_3
(c) $m = -2$ L_1

10. (a) $m = 0$ L_2
(b) $m = -\frac{3}{4}$ L_1
(c) $m = 1$ L_3

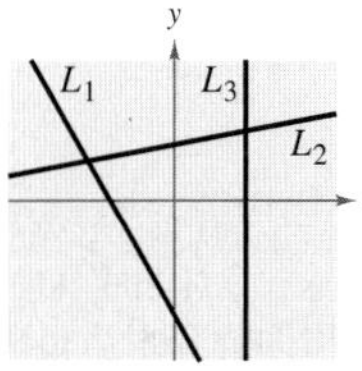

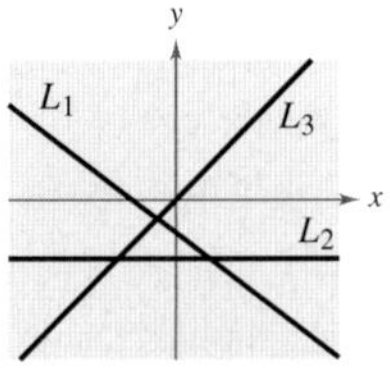

In Exercises 11 and 12, sketch the lines through the point with the indicated slopes on the same set of coordinate axes.

Point	*Slopes*
11. (2, 3)	(a) 0 (b) 1 (c) 2 (d) −3
12. (−4, 1)	(a) 3 (b) −3 (c) $\frac{1}{2}$ (d) Undefined

11–12. See margin.

In Exercises 13–16, estimate the slope of the line.

13. $\frac{3}{2}$

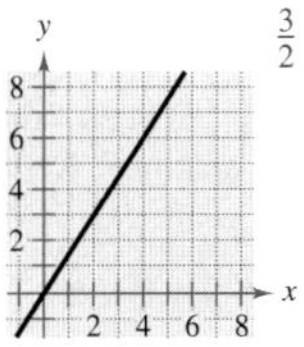

14. $\frac{5}{2}$

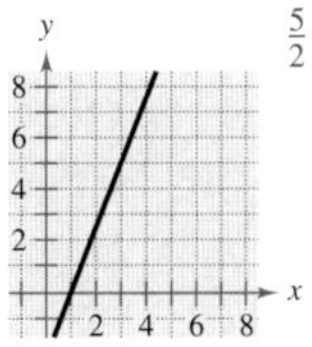

15. −4

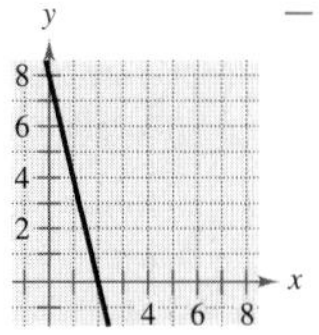

16. −1

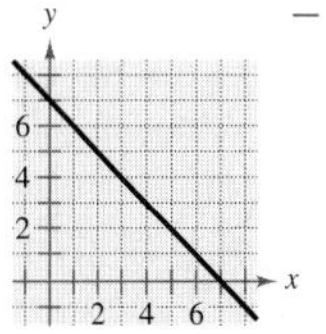

In Exercises 17–28, find the slope and y-intercept (if possible) of the equation of the line. Sketch the line. 17–28. See margin.

17. $y = 5x + 3$
18. $y = x - 10$
19. $y = -\frac{1}{2}x + 4$
20. $y = -\frac{3}{2}x + 6$
21. $5x - 2 = 0$
22. $3y + 5 = 0$
23. $7x + 6y = 30$
24. $2x + 3y = 9$
25. $y - 3 = 0$
26. $y + 4 = 0$
27. $x + 5 = 0$
28. $x - 2 = 0$

In Exercises 29–40, plot the points and find the slope of the line passing through the pair of points. 29–40. See margin.

29. (0, 9), (6, 0)
30. (12, 0), (0, −8)
31. (−3, −2), (1, 6)
32. (2, 4), (4, −4)
33. (5, −7), (8, −7)
34. (−2, 1), (−4, −5)
35. (−6, −1), (−6, 4)
36. (0, −10), (−4, 0)
37. $\left(\frac{11}{2}, -\frac{4}{3}\right), \left(-\frac{3}{2}, -\frac{1}{3}\right)$
38. $\left(\frac{7}{8}, \frac{3}{4}\right), \left(\frac{5}{4}, -\frac{1}{4}\right)$
39. (4.8, 3.1), (−5.2, 1.6)
40. (−1.75, −8.3), (2.25, −2.6)

4 PRACTICE AND APPLY

Assignment Guide

Transparencies Available
Available at the Instructor's companion site.

Average:
Day 1: pp. 33–38
Exs. 1–105 odd, 107–110, 111–117 odd, 118, 119–135 odd, 137–144, 146

Advanced:
Day 1: pp. 33–38
Exs. 10–106 even, 107–110, 112–116 even, 117, 118–136 even, 139–146, Project

Block:
pp. 33–38
Exs. 1–105 odd, 107–110, 111–117 odd, 118, 119–135 odd, 137–144, 146 (with 1.4)

11.

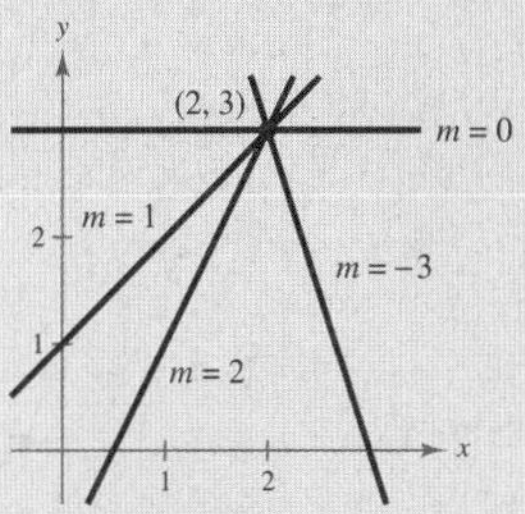

12.

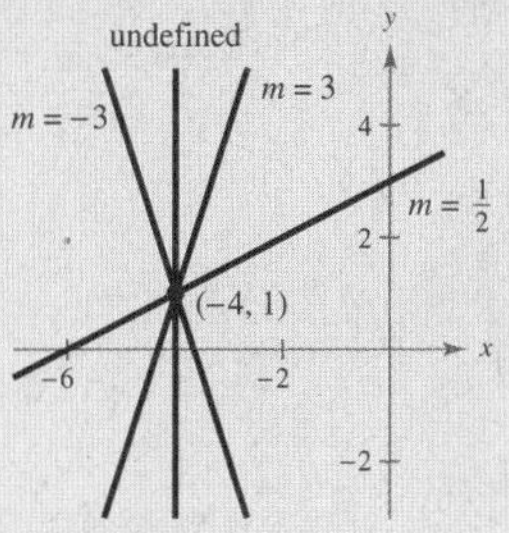

17. $m = 5$
y-intercept: (0, 3)

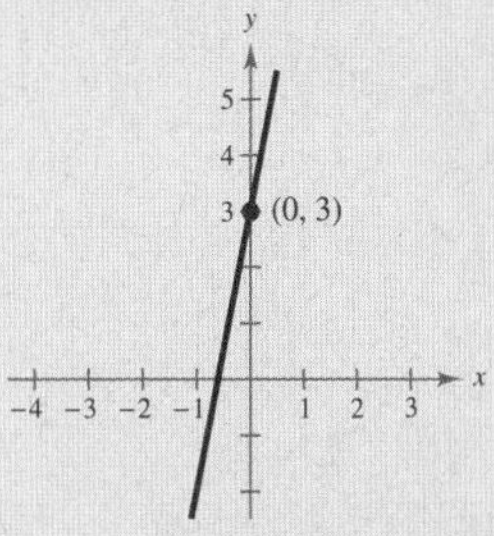

18. $m = 1$
y-intercept: (0, −10)

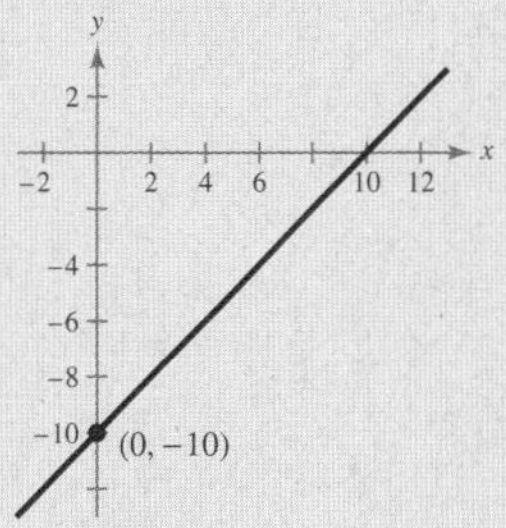

19. $m = -\frac{1}{2}$
y-intercept: (0, 4)

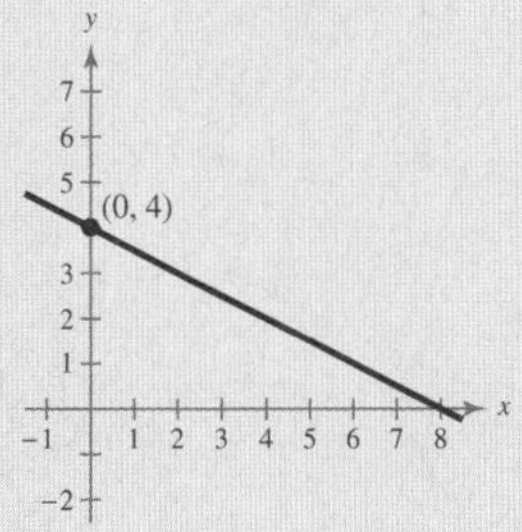

20–40. See Additional Answers beginning on page AA1.

In Exercises 41–50, use the point on the line and the slope m of the line to find three additional points through which the line passes. (There are many correct answers.) 41–44. See margin.

41. $(2, 1),\quad m = 0$ **42.** $(3, -2),\quad m = 0$

43. $(5, -6),\quad m = 1$ **44.** $(10, -6),\quad m = -1$

45. $(-8, 1),\quad m$ is undefined. $(-8, 0), (-8, 2), (-8, 3)$

46. $(1, 5),\quad m$ is undefined. $(1, 0), (1, -4), (1, 2)$

47. $(-5, 4),\quad m = 2$ **48.** $(0, -9),\quad m = -2$

49. $(7, -2),\quad m = \frac{1}{2}$ **50.** $(-1, -6),\quad m = -\frac{1}{2}$

47–50. See margin.

In Exercises 51–64, find the slope-intercept form of the equation of the line that passes through the given point and has the indicated slope m. Sketch the line. 51–64. See margin.

51. $(0, -2),\quad m = 3$ **52.** $(0, 10),\quad m = -1$

53. $(-3, 6),\quad m = -2$ **54.** $(0, 0),\quad m = 4$

55. $(4, 0),\quad m = -\frac{1}{3}$ **56.** $(8, 2),\quad m = \frac{1}{4}$

57. $(2, -3),\quad m = -\frac{1}{2}$ **58.** $(-2, -5),\quad m = \frac{3}{4}$

59. $(6, -1),\quad m$ is undefined.

60. $(-10, 4),\quad m$ is undefined.

61. $\left(4, \frac{5}{2}\right),\quad m = 0$ **62.** $\left(-\frac{1}{2}, \frac{3}{2}\right),\quad m = 0$

63. $(-5.1, 1.8),\quad m = 5$ **64.** $(2.3, -8.5),\quad m = -2.5$

In Exercises 65–78, find the slope-intercept form of the equation of the line passing through the points. Sketch the line. 65–78. See margin.

65. $(5, -1), (-5, 5)$ **66.** $(4, 3), (-4, -4)$

67. $(-8, 1), (-8, 7)$ **68.** $(-1, 4), (6, 4)$

69. $\left(2, \frac{1}{2}\right), \left(\frac{1}{2}, \frac{5}{4}\right)$ **70.** $(1, 1), \left(6, -\frac{2}{3}\right)$

71. $\left(-\frac{1}{10}, -\frac{3}{5}\right), \left(\frac{9}{10}, -\frac{9}{5}\right)$ **72.** $\left(\frac{3}{4}, \frac{3}{2}\right), \left(-\frac{4}{3}, \frac{7}{4}\right)$

73. $(1, 0.6), (-2, -0.6)$ **74.** $(-8, 0.6), (2, -2.4)$

75. $(2, -1), \left(\frac{1}{3}, -1\right)$ **76.** $\left(\frac{1}{5}, -2\right), (-6, -2)$

77. $\left(\frac{7}{3}, -8\right), \left(\frac{7}{3}, 1\right)$ **78.** $(1.5, -2), (1.5, 0.2)$

In Exercises 79–82, determine whether the lines are parallel, perpendicular, or neither.

79. L_1: $y = \frac{1}{3}x - 2$; L_2: $y = \frac{1}{3}x + 3$ Parallel

80. L_1: $y = 4x - 1$; L_2: $y = 4x + 7$ Parallel

81. L_1: $y = \frac{1}{2}x - 3$; L_2: $y = -\frac{1}{2}x + 1$ Neither

82. L_1: $y = -\frac{4}{5}x - 5$; L_2: $y = \frac{5}{4}x + 1$ Perpendicular

In Exercises 83–86, determine whether the lines L_1 and L_2 passing through the pairs of points are parallel, perpendicular, or neither.

83. L_1: $(0, -1), (5, 9)$; L_2: $(0, 3), (4, 1)$ Perpendicular

84. L_1: $(-2, -1), (1, 5)$; L_2: $(1, 3), (5, -5)$ Neither

85. L_1: $(3, 6), (-6, 0)$; L_2: $(0, -1), \left(5, \frac{7}{3}\right)$ Parallel

86. L_1: $(4, 8), (-4, 2)$; L_2: $(3, -5), \left(-1, \frac{1}{3}\right)$ Perpendicular

In Exercises 87–96, write the slope-intercept forms of the equations of the lines through the given point (a) parallel to the given line and (b) perpendicular to the given line. 87–94. See margin.

87. $4x - 2y = 3,\quad (2, 1)$ **88.** $x + y = 7,\quad (-3, 2)$

89. $3x + 4y = 7,\quad \left(-\frac{2}{3}, \frac{7}{8}\right)$ **90.** $5x + 3y = 0,\quad \left(\frac{7}{8}, \frac{3}{4}\right)$

91. $y + 3 = 0,\quad (-1, 0)$ **92.** $y - 2 = 0,\quad (-4, 1)$

93. $x - 4 = 0,\quad (3, -2)$ **94.** $x + 2 = 0,\quad (-5, 1)$

95. $x - y = 4,\quad (2.5, 6.8)$ (a) $y = x + 4.3$ (b) $y = -x + 9.3$

96. $6x + 2y = 9,\quad (-3.9, -1.4)$ (a) $y = -3x - 13.1$ (b) $y = \frac{1}{3}x - 0.1$

In Exercises 97–102, use the *intercept form* to find the equation of the line with the given intercepts. The intercept form of the equation of a line with intercepts $(a, 0)$ and $(0, b)$ is

$$\frac{x}{a} + \frac{y}{b} = 1,\ a \neq 0,\ b \neq 0.$$

97. x-intercept: $(2, 0)$; y-intercept: $(0, 3)$ $3x + 2y - 6 = 0$

98. x-intercept: $(-3, 0)$; y-intercept: $(0, 4)$ $4x - 3y + 12 = 0$

99. x-intercept: $\left(-\frac{1}{6}, 0\right)$; y-intercept: $\left(0, -\frac{2}{3}\right)$

100. x-intercept: $\left(\frac{2}{3}, 0\right)$; y-intercept: $(0, -2)$

99–100. See margin.

101. Point on line: $(1, 2)$; x-intercept: $(c, 0)$; y-intercept: $(0, c),\quad c \neq 0$ $x + y - 3 = 0$

102. Point on line: $(-3, 4)$; x-intercept: $(d, 0)$; y-intercept: $(0, d),\quad d \neq 0$ $x + y - 1 = 0$

GRAPHICAL ANALYSIS In Exercises 103–106, identify any relationships that exist among the lines, and then use a graphing utility to graph the three equations in the same viewing window. Adjust the viewing window so that the slope appears visually correct—that is, so that parallel lines appear parallel and perpendicular lines appear to intersect at right angles. 103–106. See margin.

103. (a) $y = 2x$ (b) $y = -2x$ (c) $y = \frac{1}{2}x$

104. (a) $y = \frac{2}{3}x$ (b) $y = -\frac{3}{2}x$ (c) $y = \frac{2}{3}x + 2$

105. (a) $y = -\frac{1}{2}x$ (b) $y = -\frac{1}{2}x + 3$ (c) $y = 2x - 4$

106. (a) $y = x - 8$ (b) $y = x + 1$ (c) $y = -x + 3$

In Exercises 107–110, find a relationship between x and y such that (x, y) is equidistant (the same distance) from the two points.

107. $(4, -1), (-2, 3)$ $3x - 2y - 1 = 0$

108. $(6, 5), (1, -8)$ $5x + 13y + 2 = 0$

109. $\left(3, \frac{5}{2}\right), (-7, 1)$ $80x + 12y + 139 = 0$

110. $\left(-\frac{1}{2}, -4\right), \left(\frac{7}{2}, \frac{5}{4}\right)$ $128x + 168y + 39 = 0$

41. $(0, 1), (3, 1), (-1, 1)$

42. $(1, -2), (10, -2), (-6, -2)$

43. $(6, -5), (7, -4), (8, -3)$

44. $(0, 4), (9, -5), (11, -7)$

47. $(-4, 6), (-3, 8), (-2, 10)$

48. $(-2, -5), (1, -11), (3, -15)$

49. $(9, -1), (11, 0), (13, 1)$

50. $(-3, -5), (1, -7), (5, -9)$

51. $y = 3x - 2$

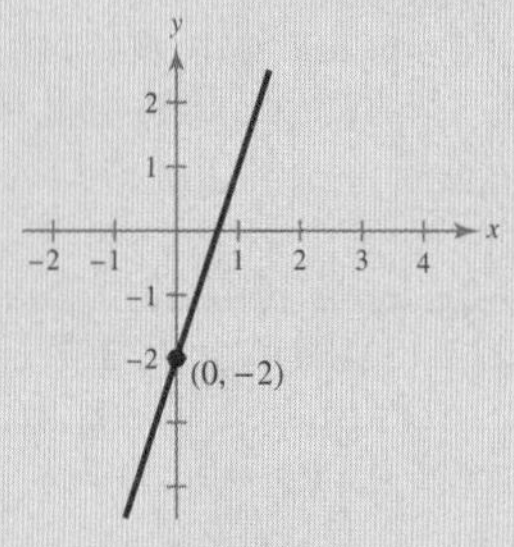

52. $y = -x + 10$

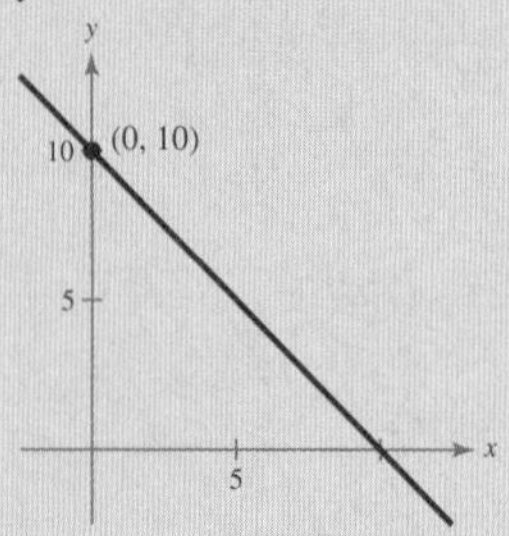

53. $y = -2x$

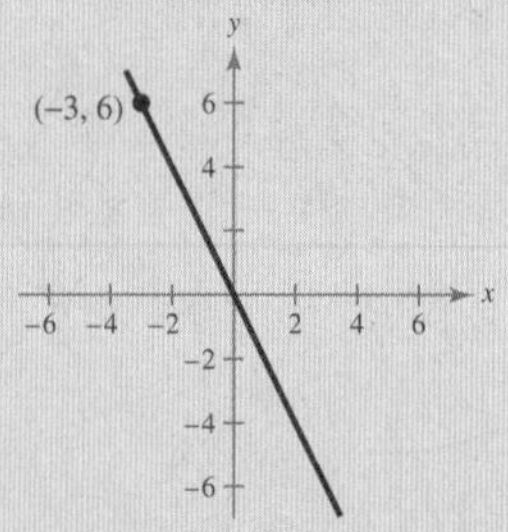

54. $y = 4x$

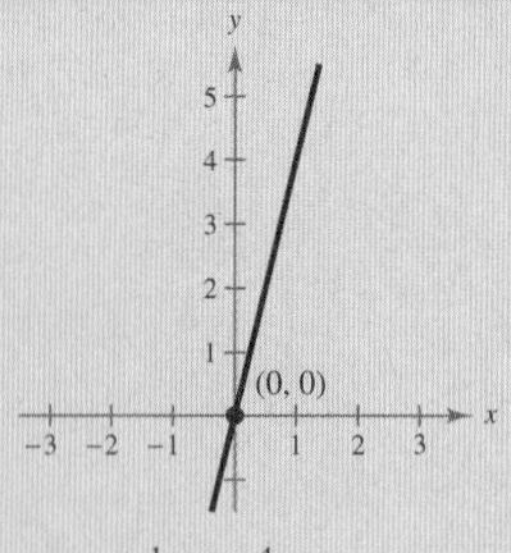

55. $y = -\frac{1}{3}x + \frac{4}{3}$

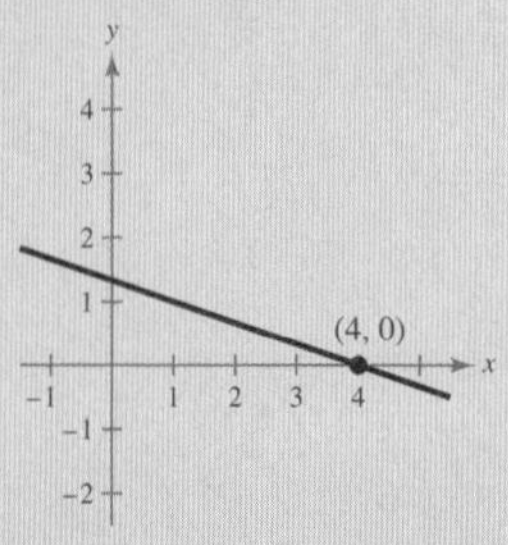

56. $y = \frac{1}{4}x$

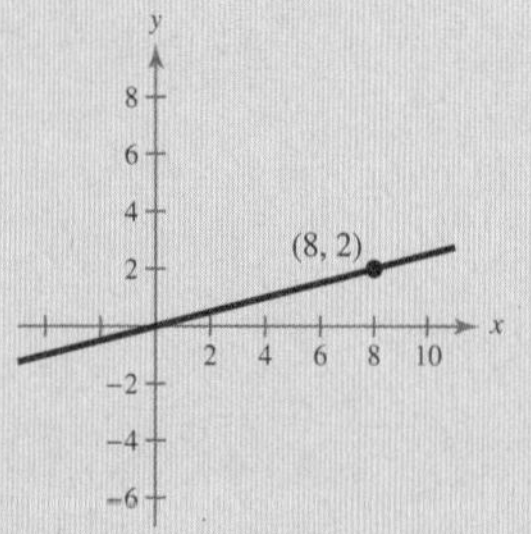

57. $y = -\frac{1}{2}x - 2$

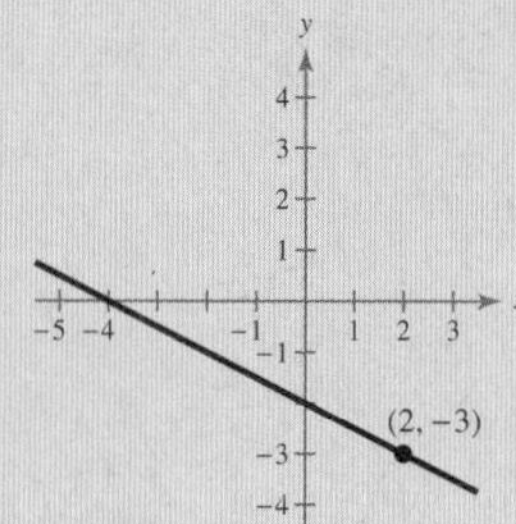

58–78, 87–94, 99–100, 103–106. See Additional Answers beginning on page AA1.

111. SALES The following are the slopes of lines representing annual sales y in terms of time x in years. Use the slopes to interpret any change in annual sales for a one-year increase in time. See margin.

(a) The line has a slope of $m = 135$.

(b) The line has a slope of $m = 0$.

(c) The line has a slope of $m = -40$.

112. REVENUE The following are the slopes of lines representing daily revenues y in terms of time x in days. Use the slopes to interpret any change in daily revenues for a one-day increase in time. See margin.

(a) The line has a slope of $m = 400$.

(b) The line has a slope of $m = 100$.

(c) The line has a slope of $m = 0$.

113. AVERAGE SALARY The graph shows the average salaries for senior high school principals from 1996 through 2008. (Source: Educational Research Service) See margin.

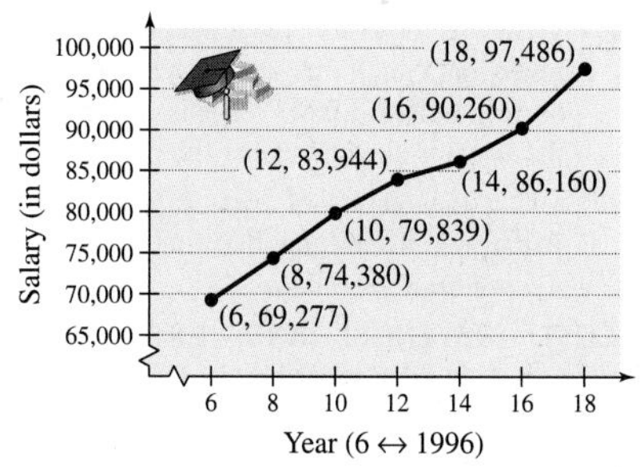

(a) Use the slopes of the line segments to determine the time periods in which the average salary increased the greatest and the least.

(b) Find the slope of the line segment connecting the points for the years 1996 and 2008.

(c) Interpret the meaning of the slope in part (b) in the context of the problem.

114. SALES The graph shows the sales (in billions of dollars) for Apple Inc. for the years 2001 through 2007. (Source: Apple Inc.) See margin.

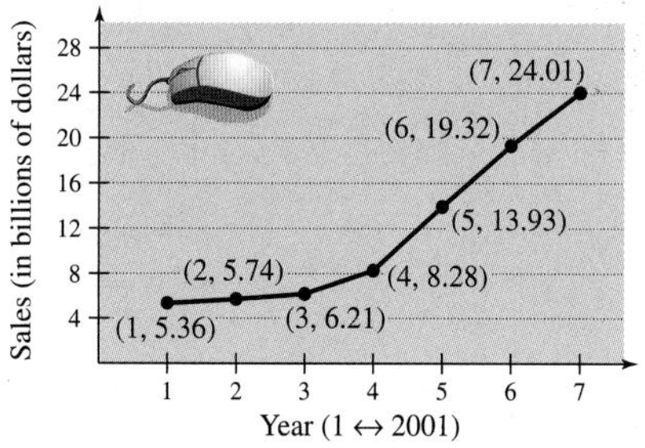

(a) Use the slopes of the line segments to determine the years in which the sales showed the greatest increase and the least increase.

(b) Find the slope of the line segment connecting the points for the years 2001 and 2007.

(c) Interpret the meaning of the slope in part (b) in the context of the problem.

115. ROAD GRADE You are driving on a road that has a 6% uphill grade (see figure). This means that the slope of the road is $\frac{6}{100}$. Approximate the amount of vertical change in your position if you drive 200 feet.
12 ft

116. ROAD GRADE From the top of a mountain road, a surveyor takes several horizontal measurements x and several vertical measurements y, as shown in the table (x and y are measured in feet). See margin.

x	300	600	900	1200	1500	1800	2100
y	-25	-50	-75	-100	-125	-150	-175

(a) Sketch a scatter plot of the data.

(b) Use a straightedge to sketch the line that you think best fits the data.

(c) Find an equation for the line you sketched in part (b).

(d) Interpret the meaning of the slope of the line in part (c) in the context of the problem.

(e) The surveyor needs to put up a road sign that indicates the steepness of the road. For instance, a surveyor would put up a sign that states "8% grade" on a road with a downhill grade that has a slope of $-\frac{8}{100}$. What should the sign state for the road in this problem?

RATE OF CHANGE In Exercises 117 and 118, you are given the dollar value of a product in 2010 and the rate at which the value of the product is expected to change during the next 5 years. Use this information to write a linear equation that gives the dollar value V of the product in terms of the year t. (Let $t = 10$ represent 2010.)

	2010 Value	*Rate*
117.	$2540	$125 decrease per year
118.	$156	$4.50 increase per year

117. $V(t) = 3790 - 125t$

118. $V(t) = 4.5t + 111$

111. (a) Sales increasing 135 units/yr
(b) No change in sales
(c) Sales decreasing 40 units/yr

112. (a) Revenues increasing $400 per day
(b) Revenues increasing $100 per day
(c) No change in revenues

113. (a) The average salary increased the greatest from 2006 to 2008 and increased the least from 2002 to 2004.
(b) $m = 2350.75$
(c) The average salary increased $2350.75 per year over the 12 years between 1996 and 2008.

114. (a) Sales showed the greatest increase in years 2004–2005 and the least increase in years 2001–2002.
(b) $m \approx 3.11$
(c) Sales increased an average of about 3.11 billion dollars per year over the 6 years between 2001 and 2007.

116. (a) and (b)

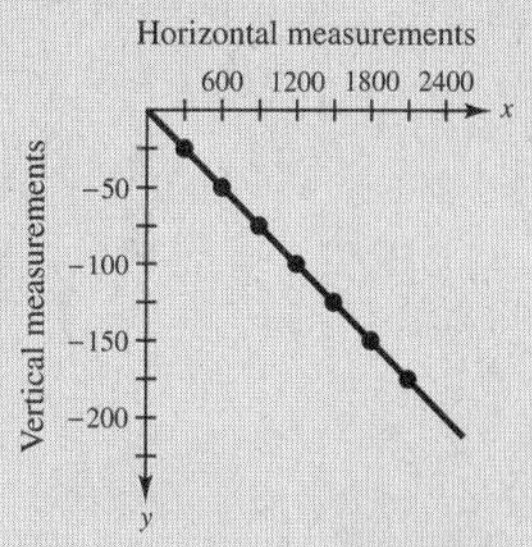

(c) $y = -\frac{1}{12}x$
(d) For every change in the horizontal measurement of 12 feet, the vertical measurement decreases by 1 foot.
(e) "8.3% grade"

120. C-intercept: fixed initial cost; Slope: cost of producing an additional laptop bag
121. $V = -175t + 875$
124. $W = 0.75x + 12.25$
125. $W = 0.07S + 2500$
126. $C = 0.55x + 120$
127. $y = 0.03125t + 0.92875$; $y(22) \approx \$1.62$; $y(24) \approx \$1.68$
129. (a) $y(t) = 442.625t + 40{,}571$
(b) $y(10) = 44{,}997$; $y(15) = 47{,}210$
(c) $m = 442.625$; Each year, enrollment increases by about 443 students.
130. (a) Average annual change from 2000 to 2008 was 663.25.
(b) 2002: 47,434; 2004: 48,760; 2006: 50,087
(c) $y(t) = 663.25t + 46{,}107$; $m = 663.25$; Each year, enrollment increases by about 663 students.
(d) Answers will vary.
131. (a) $C = 18t + 42{,}000$

119. DEPRECIATION The value V of a molding machine t years after it is purchased is V-intercept: initial cost

$$V = -4000t + 58{,}500, \quad 0 \le t \le 5.$$ Slope: annual depreciation

Explain what the V-intercept and the slope measure.

120. COST The cost C of producing n computer laptop bags is given by See margin.

$$C = 1.25n + 15{,}750, \quad 0 < n.$$

Explain what the C-intercept and the slope measure.

121. DEPRECIATION A sub shop purchases a used pizza oven for \$875. After 5 years, the oven will have to be replaced. Write a linear equation giving the value V of the equipment during the 5 years it will be in use. See margin.

122. DEPRECIATION A school district purchases a high-volume printer, copier, and scanner for \$25,000. After 10 years, the equipment will have to be replaced. Its value at that time is expected to be \$2000. Write a linear equation giving the value V of the equipment during the 10 years it will be in use. $V = 25{,}000 - 2300t$

123. SALES A discount outlet is offering a 20% discount on all items. Write a linear equation giving the sale price S for an item with a list price L. $S = 0.8L$

124. HOURLY WAGE A microchip manufacturer pays its assembly line workers \$12.25 per hour. In addition, workers receive a piecework rate of \$0.75 per unit produced. Write a linear equation for the hourly wage W in terms of the number of units x produced per hour. See margin.

125. MONTHLY SALARY A pharmaceutical salesperson receives a monthly salary of \$2500 plus a commission of 7% of sales. Write a linear equation for the salesperson's monthly wage W in terms of monthly sales S. See margin.

126. BUSINESS COSTS A sales representative of a company using a personal car receives \$120 per day for lodging and meals plus \$0.55 per mile driven. Write a linear equation giving the daily cost C to the company in terms of x, the number of miles driven. See margin.

127. CASH FLOW PER SHARE The cash flow per share for the Timberland Co. was \$1.21 in 1999 and \$1.46 in 2007. Write a linear equation that gives the cash flow per share in terms of the year. Let $t = 9$ represent 1999. Then predict the cash flows for the years 2012 and 2014. (Source: The Timberland Co.) See margin.

128. NUMBER OF STORES In 2003 there were 1078 J.C. Penney stores and in 2007 there were 1067 stores. Write a linear equation that gives the number of stores in terms of the year. Let $t = 3$ represent 2003. Then predict the numbers of stores for the years 2012 and 2014. Are your answers reasonable? Explain. (Source: J.C. Penney Co.)

$y = -2.75t + 1086.25$; $y(12) = 1053.25$; $y(14) = 1047.75$; Answers will vary.

129. COLLEGE ENROLLMENT The Pennsylvania State University had enrollments of 40,571 students in 2000 and 44,112 students in 2008 at its main campus in University Park, Pennsylvania. (Source: *Penn State Fact Book*) See margin.

(a) Assuming the enrollment growth is linear, find a linear model that gives the enrollment in terms of the year t, where $t = 0$ corresponds to 2000.

(b) Use your model from part (a) to predict the enrollments in 2010 and 2015.

(c) What is the slope of your model? Explain its meaning in the context of the situation.

130. COLLEGE ENROLLMENT The University of Florida had enrollments of 46,107 students in 2000 and 51,413 students in 2008. (Source: University of Florida)

(a) What was the average annual change in enrollment from 2000 to 2008? See margin.

(b) Use the average annual change in enrollment to estimate the enrollments in 2002, 2004, and 2006.

(c) Write the equation of a line that represents the given data in terms of the year t, where $t = 0$ corresponds to 2000. What is its slope? Interpret the slope in the context of the problem.

(d) Using the results of parts (a)–(c), write a short paragraph discussing the concepts of *slope* and *average rate of change*.

131. COST, REVENUE, AND PROFIT A roofing contractor purchases a shingle delivery truck with a shingle elevator for \$42,000. The vehicle requires an average expenditure of \$6.50 per hour for fuel and maintenance, and the operator is paid \$11.50 per hour.

(a) Write a linear equation giving the total cost C of operating this equipment for t hours. (Include the purchase cost of the equipment.) See margin.

(b) Assuming that customers are charged \$30 per hour of machine use, write an equation for the revenue R derived from t hours of use. $R = 30t$

(c) Use the formula for profit

$$P = R - C$$

to write an equation for the profit derived from t hours of use. $P = 12t - 42{,}000$

(d) Use the result of part (c) to find the break-even point—that is, the number of hours this equipment must be used to yield a profit of 0 dollars.
$t = 3500$ h

132. RENTAL DEMAND A real estate office handles an apartment complex with 50 units. When the rent per unit is \$580 per month, all 50 units are occupied. However, when the rent is \$625 per month, the average number of occupied units drops to 47. Assume that the relationship between the monthly rent p and the demand x is linear.

(a) Write the equation of the line giving the demand x in terms of the rent p. $x = -\frac{1}{15}p + \frac{266}{3}$

(b) Use this equation to predict the number of units occupied when the rent is \$655. 45

(c) Predict the number of units occupied when the rent is \$595. 49

133. GEOMETRY The length and width of a rectangular garden are 15 meters and 10 meters, respectively. A walkway of width x surrounds the garden. See margin.

(a) Draw a diagram that gives a visual representation of the problem.

(b) Write the equation for the perimeter y of the walkway in terms of x.

(c) Use a graphing utility to graph the equation for the perimeter.

(d) Determine the slope of the graph in part (c). For each additional one-meter increase in the width of the walkway, determine the increase in its perimeter.

134. AVERAGE ANNUAL SALARY The average salaries (in millions of dollars) of Major League Baseball players from 2000 through 2007 are shown in the scatter plot. Find the equation of the line that you think best fits these data. (Let y represent the average salary and let t represent the year, with $t = 0$ corresponding to 2000.) (Source: Major League Baseball Players Association) Answers will vary. Sample answer: $y = 0.12t + 2.0$

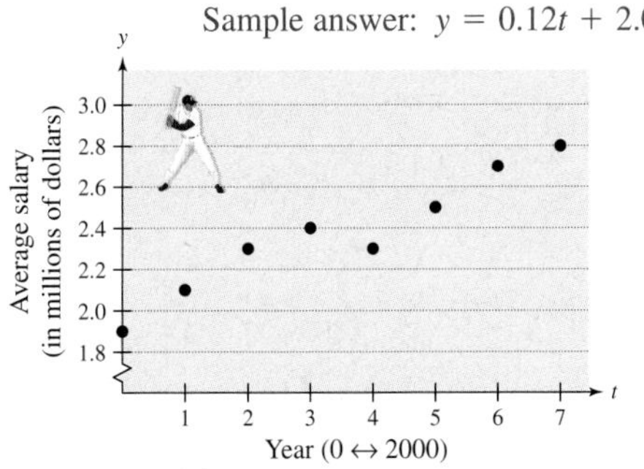

135. DATA ANALYSIS: NUMBER OF DOCTORS The numbers of doctors of osteopathic medicine y (in thousands) in the United States from 2000 through 2008, where x is the year, are shown as data points (x, y). (Source: American Osteopathic Association)

(2000, 44.9), (2001, 47.0), (2002, 49.2), (2003, 51.7), (2004, 54.1), (2005, 56.5), (2006, 58.9), (2007, 61.4), (2008, 64.0) See margin.

(a) Sketch a scatter plot of the data. Let $x = 0$ correspond to 2000.

(b) Use a straightedge to sketch the line that you think best fits the data.

(c) Find the equation of the line from part (b). Explain the procedure you used.

(d) Write a short paragraph explaining the meanings of the slope and y-intercept of the line in terms of the data.

(e) Compare the values obtained using your model with the actual values.

(f) Use your model to estimate the number of doctors of osteopathic medicine in 2012.

136. DATA ANALYSIS: AVERAGE SCORES An instructor gives regular 20-point quizzes and 100-point exams in an algebra course. Average scores for six students, given as data points (x, y), where x is the average quiz score and y is the average test score, are (18, 87), (10, 55), (19, 96), (16, 79), (13, 76), and (15, 82). [*Note:* There are many correct answers for parts (b)–(d).] (a)–(b). See margin.

(a) Sketch a scatter plot of the data.

(b) Use a straightedge to sketch the line that you think best fits the data.

(c) Find an equation for the line you sketched in part (b). $y = 4x + 19$

(d) Use the equation in part (c) to estimate the average test score for a person with an average quiz score of 17. 87

(e) The instructor adds 4 points to the average test score of each student in the class. Describe the changes in the positions of the plotted points and the change in the equation of the line.

Vertical shift four units upward

133. (a)

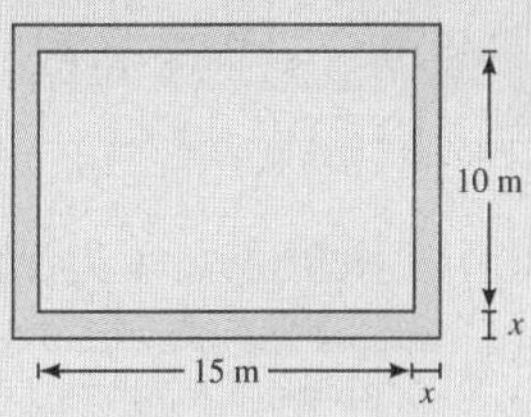

(b) $y = 8x + 50$

(c)

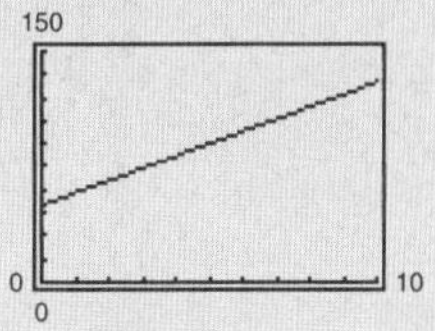

(d) $m = 8$, 8 m

135. (a) and (b)

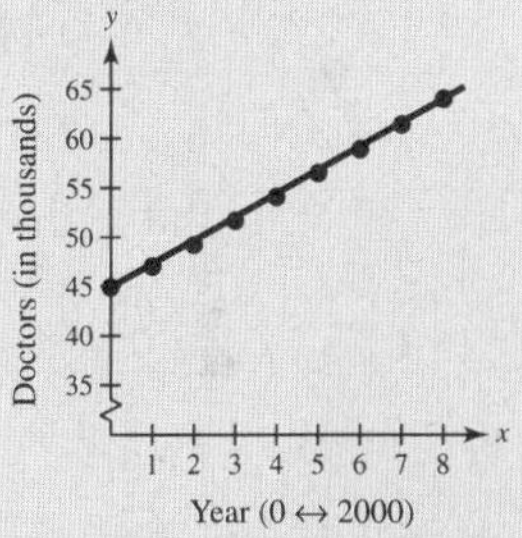

(c) Answers will vary. Sample answer: $y = 2.39x + 44.9$

(d) Answers will vary. Sample answer: The y-intercept indicates that in 2000 there were 44.9 thousand doctors of osteopathic medicine. The slope means that the number of doctors increases by 2.39 thousand each year.

(e) The model is accurate.

(f) Answers will vary. Sample answer: 73.6 thousand

136. (a) and (b)

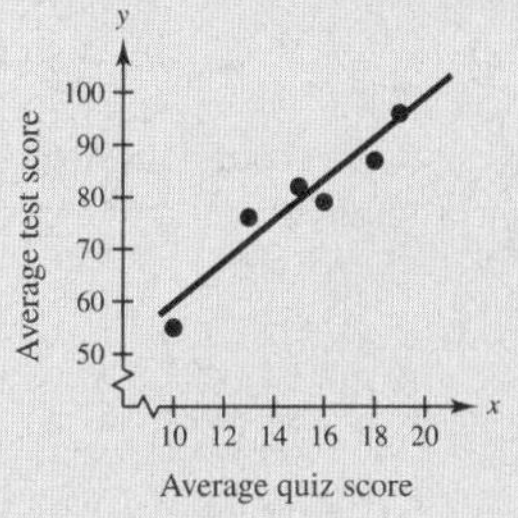

EXPLORATION

TRUE OR FALSE? In Exercises 137 and 138, determine whether the statement is true or false. Justify your answer.

137. A line with a slope of $-\frac{5}{7}$ is steeper than a line with a slope of $-\frac{6}{7}$. See margin.

138. The line through $(-8, 2)$ and $(-1, 4)$ and the line through $(0, -4)$ and $(-7, 7)$ are parallel. See margin.

See margin. **139.** Explain how you could show that the points $A(2, 3)$, $B(2, 9)$, and $C(4, 3)$ are the vertices of a right triangle.

140. Explain why the slope of a vertical line is said to be undefined. See margin.

141. With the information shown in the graphs, is it possible to determine the slope of each line? Is it possible that the lines could have the same slope? Explain.

(a) (b) See margin.

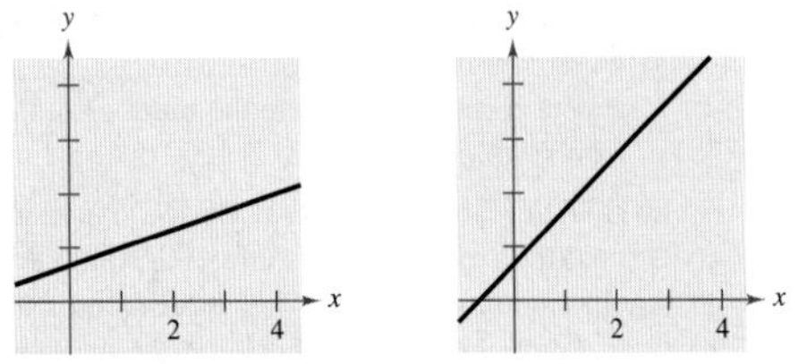

142. The slopes of two lines are -4 and $\frac{5}{2}$. Which is steeper? Explain. See margin.

143. Use a graphing utility to compare the slopes of the lines $y = mx$, where $m = 0.5, 1, 2$, and 4. Which line rises most quickly? Now, let $m = -0.5, -1, -2$, and -4. Which line falls most quickly? Use a square setting to obtain a true geometric perspective. What can you conclude about the slope and the "rate" at which the line rises or falls? See margin.

144. Find d_1 and d_2 in terms of m_1 and m_2, respectively (see figure). Then use the Pythagorean Theorem to find a relationship between m_1 and m_2.

$d_1 = \sqrt{1 + m_1^2}$; $d_2 = \sqrt{1 + m_2^2}$; $m_1 = \dfrac{-1}{m_2}$

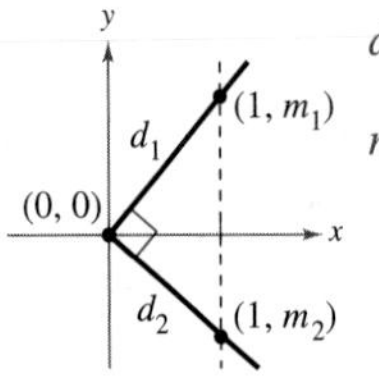

145. THINK ABOUT IT Is it possible for two lines with positive slopes to be perpendicular? Explain.

No. The slopes of two perpendicular lines have opposite signs (assume that neither line is vertical or horizontal).

146. CAPSTONE Match the description of the situation with its graph. Also determine the slope and y-intercept of each graph and interpret the slope and y-intercept in the context of the situation. [The graphs are labeled (i), (ii), (iii), and (iv).] See margin.

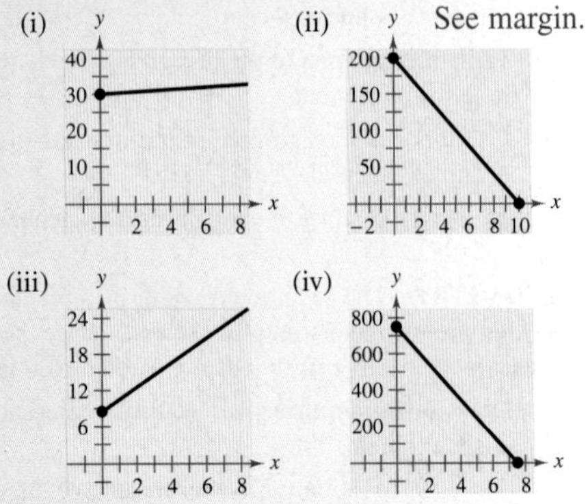

(a) A person is paying \$20 per week to a friend to repay a \$200 loan.

(b) An employee is paid \$8.50 per hour plus \$2 for each unit produced per hour.

(c) A sales representative receives \$30 per day for food plus \$0.32 for each mile traveled.

(d) A computer that was purchased for \$750 depreciates \$100 per year.

PROJECT: BACHELOR'S DEGREES To work an extended application analyzing the numbers of bachelor's degrees earned by women in the United States from 1996 through 2007, visit this text's website at *academic.cengage.com*. (Data Source: U.S. National Center for Education Statistics)

5 ASSESS AND RETEACH

Daily Homework Quiz

Transparency Available

Available at the Instructor's companion site.

137. False. The slope with the greatest magnitude corresponds to the steepest line.

138. False. The slope of the first line is $\frac{2}{7}$ and the slope of the second line is $-\frac{11}{7}$.

139. Find the distance between each two points and use the Pythagorean Theorem.

140. The slope of a vertical line is undefined because division by zero is undefined.

141. No. The slope cannot be determined without knowing the scale on the y-axis. The slopes could be the same.

142. The line with a slope of -4 is steeper. The slope with the greatest magnitude corresponds to the steepest line.

143. The line $y = 4x$ rises most quickly, and the line $y = -4x$ falls most quickly. The greater the magnitude of the slope (the absolute value of the slope), the faster the line rises or falls.

146. (a) ii; The slope is -20, which represents the decrease in the balance of the loan each week. The y-intercept is $(0, 200)$, which represents the original amount of the loan.

(b) iii; The slope is 2, which represents the increase in hourly wage per unit produced. The y-intercept is $(0, 8.50)$, which represents the initial hourly wage.

(c) i; The slope is 0.32, which represents the increase in travel cost for each mile driven. The y-intercept is $(0, 30)$, which represents the amount per day for food.

(d) iv; The slope is -100, which represents the decrease in the value of the word processor each year. The y-intercept is $(0, 750)$, which represents the initial purchase price of the computer.

1.4 FUNCTIONS

What you should learn

- Determine whether relations between two variables are functions.
- Use function notation and evaluate functions.
- Find the domains of functions.
- Use functions to model and solve real-life problems.
- Evaluate difference quotients.

Why you should learn it

Functions can be used to model and solve real-life problems. For instance, in Exercise 100 on page 52, you will use a function to model the force of water against the face of a dam.

© Lester Lefkowitz/Corbis

Introduction to Functions

Many everyday phenomena involve two quantities that are related to each other by some rule of correspondence. The mathematical term for such a rule of correspondence is a **relation.** In mathematics, relations are often represented by mathematical equations and formulas. For instance, the simple interest I earned on \$1000 for 1 year is related to the annual interest rate r by the formula $I = 1000r$.

The formula $I = 1000r$ represents a special kind of relation that matches each item from one set with *exactly one* item from a different set. Such a relation is called a **function.**

> **Definition of Function**
>
> A **function** f from a set A to a set B is a relation that assigns to each element x in the set A exactly one element y in the set B. The set A is the **domain** (or set of inputs) of the function f, and the set B contains the **range** (or set of outputs).

To help understand this definition, look at the function that relates the time of day to the temperature in Figure 1.47.

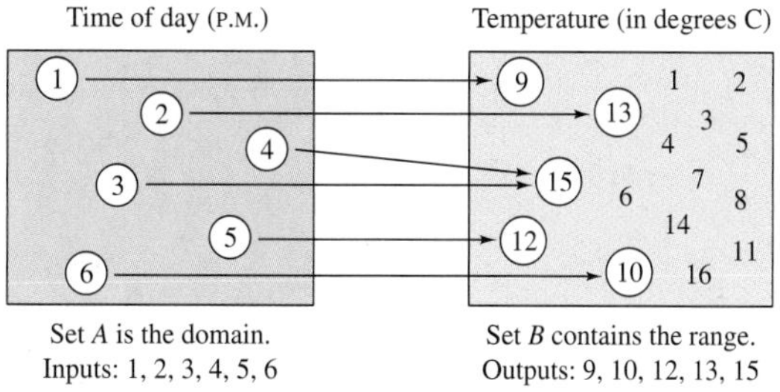

FIGURE 1.47

This function can be represented by the following ordered pairs, in which the first coordinate (x-value) is the input and the second coordinate (y-value) is the output.

$$\{(1, 9°), (2, 13°), (3, 15°), (4, 15°), (5, 12°), (6, 10°)\}$$

> **Characteristics of a Function from Set A to Set B**
>
> **1.** Each element in A must be matched with an element in B.
>
> **2.** Some elements in B may not be matched with any element in A.
>
> **3.** Two or more elements in A may be matched with the same element in B.
>
> **4.** An element in A (the domain) cannot be matched with two different elements in B.

1 PLAN AND PREPARE

Warm-up Exercises

Transparency Available
Available at the Instructor's companion site.

Notetaking Guide

Transparency Available
Promotes interactive learning and notetaking skills.
Available at the Instructor's companion site.

Animated Precalculus

An **Animated Precalculus** tutorial is available at the Student companion site for **Section 1.4.**

Pacing

Average: 1 day
Advanced: 1 day
Block: 0.5 block with 1.3

2 FOCUS AND MOTIVATE

Essential Question

What are the important defining characteristics and representations of a function? **Tell students that they will answer this question by studying relations between two variables represented in verbal, numeric, graphical, and algebraic form.**

Resource Planning Guide

Chapter Resources
- Complete Solutions Guide

Workbooks
- Notetaking Guide
- Student Solutions Guide

Interactive Technology
- Instructor Success Organizer
- Notetaking Guide IAE
- Instructional DVDs
- Animated Precalculus
- PowerLecture with ExamView

3 TEACH

Extra Example 1

Let $A = \{2, 3, 4, 5\}$ and $B = \{-3, -2, -1, 0, 1\}$. Which of the following sets of ordered pairs represents functions from set A to set B?

a. $\{(2, -2), (3, 0), (4, 1), (5, -1)\}$

Each element of A is matched with exactly one element of B, so this set represents a function.

b. $\{(4, -3), (2, 0), (5, -2), (3, 1), (2, -1)\}$

The element 2 in A is matched with two elements, 0 and −1, in B, so this set *does not* represent a function.

c. $\{(2, -1), (3, -1), (4, -1), (5, -1)\}$

Each element of A is matched with exactly one element of B, so this set represents a function.

d. $\{(3, -2), (5, 0), (2, -3)\}$

The element 4 in A is not matched with an element of B, so this set *does not* represent a function.

Functions are commonly represented in four ways.

Four Ways to Represent a Function

1. *Verbally* by a sentence that describes how the input variable is related to the output variable
2. *Numerically* by a table or a list of ordered pairs that matches input values with output values
3. *Graphically* by points on a graph in a coordinate plane in which the input values are represented by the horizontal axis and the output values are represented by the vertical axis
4. *Algebraically* by an equation in two variables

To determine whether or not a relation is a function, you must decide whether each input value is matched with exactly one output value. If any input value is matched with two or more output values, the relation is not a function.

Example 1 Testing for Functions

Determine whether the relation represents y as a function of x.

a. The input value x is the number of representatives from a state, and the output value y is the number of senators.

b.

Input, x	Output, y
2	11
2	10
3	8
4	5
5	1

c.

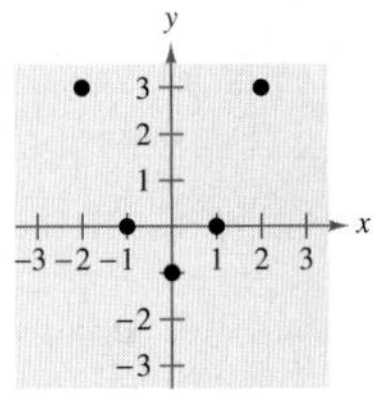

FIGURE 1.48

Solution

a. This verbal description *does* describe y as a function of x. Regardless of the value of x, the value of y is always 2. Such functions are called *constant functions.*

b. This table *does not* describe y as a function of x. The input value 2 is matched with two different y-values.

c. The graph in Figure 1.48 *does* describe y as a function of x. Each input value is matched with exactly one output value.

CHECK*Point* Now try Exercise 11.

Representing functions by sets of ordered pairs is common in *discrete mathematics.* In algebra, however, it is more common to represent functions by equations or formulas involving two variables. For instance, the equation

$$y = x^2 \qquad y \text{ is a function of } x.$$

represents the variable y as a function of the variable x. In this equation, x is

HISTORICAL NOTE

© Bettmann/Corbis

Leonhard Euler (1707–1783), a Swiss mathematician, is considered to have been the most prolific and productive mathematician in history. One of his greatest influences on mathematics was his use of symbols, or notation. The function notation $y = f(x)$ was introduced by Euler.

the **independent variable** and y is the **dependent variable.** The domain of the function is the set of all values taken on by the independent variable x, and the range of the function is the set of all values taken on by the dependent variable y.

Example 2 Testing for Functions Represented Algebraically

Which of the equations represent(s) y as a function of x?

a. $x^2 + y = 1$ **b.** $-x + y^2 = 1$

Solution

To determine whether y is a function of x, try to solve for y in terms of x.

a. Solving for y yields

$$x^2 + y = 1 \qquad \text{Write original equation.}$$
$$y = 1 - x^2. \qquad \text{Solve for } y.$$

To each value of x there corresponds exactly one value of y. So, y is a function of x.

b. Solving for y yields

$$-x + y^2 = 1 \qquad \text{Write original equation.}$$
$$y^2 = 1 + x \qquad \text{Add } x \text{ to each side.}$$
$$y = \pm\sqrt{1 + x}. \qquad \text{Solve for } y.$$

The $\pm$ indicates that to a given value of x there correspond two values of y. So, y is not a function of x.

CHECKPoint Now try Exercise 21.

Extra Example 2

Determine whether the equation $x^2 + y^2 = 8$ represents y as a function of x.

***y* is *not* a function of *x*.**

Function Notation

When an equation is used to represent a function, it is convenient to name the function so that it can be referenced easily. For example, you know that the equation $y = 1 - x^2$ describes y as a function of x. Suppose you give this function the name "f." Then you can use the following **function notation.**

Input	*Output*	*Equation*
x	$f(x)$	$f(x) = 1 - x^2$

The symbol $f(x)$ is read as *the value of f at x* or simply *f of x*. The symbol $f(x)$ corresponds to the y-value for a given x. So, you can write $y = f(x)$. Keep in mind that f is the *name* of the function, whereas $f(x)$ is the *value* of the function at x. For instance, the function given by

$$f(x) = 3 - 2x$$

has *function values* denoted by $f(-1)$, $f(0)$, $f(2)$, and so on. To find these values, substitute the specified input values into the given equation.

For $x = -1$, $\quad f(-1) = 3 - 2(-1) = 3 + 2 = 5.$

For $x = 0$, $\quad f(0) = 3 - 2(0) = 3 - 0 = 3.$

For $x = 2$, $\quad f(2) = 3 - 2(2) = 3 - 4 = -1.$

Extra Example 3

Let $f(x) = 10 - 3x^2$ and find the following.

a. $f(2)$ **−2**

b. $f(-4)$ **−38**

c. $f(x-1)$ $\mathbf{-3x^2 + 6x + 7}$

Extra Example 4

Evaluate the function

$$f(x) = \begin{cases} 3x - 4, & x < 0 \\ 3x + 1, & x \geq 0 \end{cases}$$

when $x = -2$, 0, and 2.

$\mathbf{f(-2) = -10,\ f(0) = 1,\ f(2) = 7}$

Although f is often used as a convenient function name and x is often used as the independent variable, you can use other letters. For instance,

$$f(x) = x^2 - 4x + 7, \quad f(t) = t^2 - 4t + 7, \quad \text{and} \quad g(s) = s^2 - 4s + 7$$

all define the same function. In fact, the role of the independent variable is that of a "placeholder." Consequently, the function could be described by

$$f(\quad) = (\quad)^2 - 4(\quad) + 7.$$

WARNING/CAUTION

In Example 3, note that $g(x + 2)$ is not equal to $g(x) + g(2)$. In general, $g(u + v) \neq g(u) + g(v)$.

Example 3 Evaluating a Function

Let $g(x) = -x^2 + 4x + 1$. Find each function value.

a. $g(2)$ **b.** $g(t)$ **c.** $g(x + 2)$

Solution

a. Replacing x with 2 in $g(x) = -x^2 + 4x + 1$ yields the following.

$$g(2) = -(2)^2 + 4(2) + 1 = -4 + 8 + 1 = 5$$

b. Replacing x with t yields the following.

$$g(t) = -(t)^2 + 4(t) + 1 = -t^2 + 4t + 1$$

c. Replacing x with $x + 2$ yields the following.

$$\begin{aligned} g(x + 2) &= -(x + 2)^2 + 4(x + 2) + 1 \\ &= -(x^2 + 4x + 4) + 4x + 8 + 1 \\ &= -x^2 - 4x - 4 + 4x + 8 + 1 \\ &= -x^2 + 5 \end{aligned}$$

CHECK*Point* Now try Exercise 41.

A function defined by two or more equations over a specified domain is called a **piecewise-defined function.**

Example 4 A Piecewise-Defined Function

Evaluate the function when $x = -1$, 0, and 1.

$$f(x) = \begin{cases} x^2 + 1, & x < 0 \\ x - 1, & x \geq 0 \end{cases}$$

Solution

Because $x = -1$ is less than 0, use $f(x) = x^2 + 1$ to obtain

$$f(-1) = (-1)^2 + 1 = 2.$$

For $x = 0$, use $f(x) = x - 1$ to obtain

$$f(0) = (0) - 1 = -1.$$

For $x = 1$, use $f(x) = x - 1$ to obtain

$$f(1) = (1) - 1 = 0.$$

CHECK*Point* Now try Exercise 49.

Example 5 Finding Values for Which $f(x) = 0$

Find all real values of x such that $f(x) = 0$.

a. $f(x) = -2x + 10$

b. $f(x) = x^2 - 5x + 6$

Solution

For each function, set $f(x) = 0$ and solve for x.

a. $-2x + 10 = 0$ — Set $f(x)$ equal to 0.

$-2x = -10$ — Subtract 10 from each side.

$x = 5$ — Divide each side by -2.

So, $f(x) = 0$ when $x = 5$.

b. $x^2 - 5x + 6 = 0$ — Set $f(x)$ equal to 0.

$(x - 2)(x - 3) = 0$ — Factor.

$x - 2 = 0 \Rightarrow x = 2$ — Set 1st factor equal to 0.

$x - 3 = 0 \Rightarrow x = 3$ — Set 2nd factor equal to 0.

So, $f(x) = 0$ when $x = 2$ or $x = 3$.

CHECKPoint Now try Exercise 59.

Example 6 Finding Values for Which $f(x) = g(x)$

Find the values of x for which $f(x) = g(x)$.

a. $f(x) = x^2 + 1$ and $g(x) = 3x - x^2$

b. $f(x) = x^2 - 1$ and $g(x) = -x^2 + x + 2$

Solution

a. $x^2 + 1 = 3x - x^2$ — Set $f(x)$ equal to $g(x)$.

$2x^2 - 3x + 1 = 0$ — Write in general form.

$(2x - 1)(x - 1) = 0$ — Factor.

$2x - 1 = 0 \Rightarrow x = \frac{1}{2}$ — Set 1st factor equal to 0.

$x - 1 = 0 \Rightarrow x = 1$ — Set 2nd factor equal to 0.

So, $f(x) = g(x)$ when $x = \dfrac{1}{2}$ or $x = 1$.

b. $x^2 - 1 = -x^2 + x + 2$ — Set $f(x)$ equal to $g(x)$.

$2x^2 - x - 3 = 0$ — Write in general form.

$(2x - 3)(x + 1) = 0$ — Factor.

$2x - 3 = 0 \Rightarrow x = \frac{3}{2}$ — Set 1st factor equal to 0.

$x + 1 = 0 \Rightarrow x = -1$ — Set 2nd factor equal to 0.

So, $f(x) = g(x)$ when $x = \dfrac{3}{2}$ or $x = -1$.

CHECKPoint Now try Exercise 67.

Algebra Help

To do Examples 5 and 6, you need to be able to solve equations. You can review the techniques for solving equations in Appendix A.5.

Extra Example 5

Find all real values of x such that $f(x) = 0$.

a. $f(x) = 21 - 7x$

$x = 3$

b. $f(x) = x^2 + 7x - 8$

$x = -8$ or $x = 1$

Extra Example 6

Find the values of x for which $f(x) = g(x)$.

a. $f(x) = 6x^2$ and $g(x) = x^2 - 14x + 3$

$x = \dfrac{1}{5}$ or $x = -3$

b. $f(x) = 3x^2 + 6$ and $g(x) = 8x + 2$

$x = \dfrac{2}{3}$ or $x = 2$

Extra Example 7

Find the domain of $g(x) = \sqrt{x - 16}$.

$x \geq 16$

TECHNOLOGY

Use a graphing utility to graph the functions given by $y = \sqrt{4 - x^2}$ and $y = \sqrt{x^2 - 4}$. What is the domain of each function? Do the domains of these two functions overlap? If so, for what values do the domains overlap?

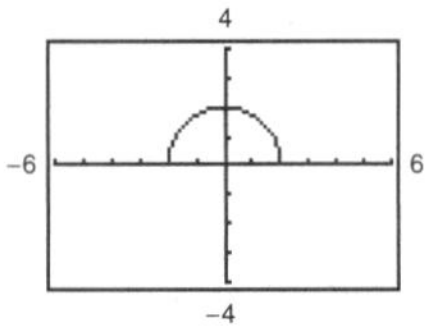

Domain: $[-2, 2]$

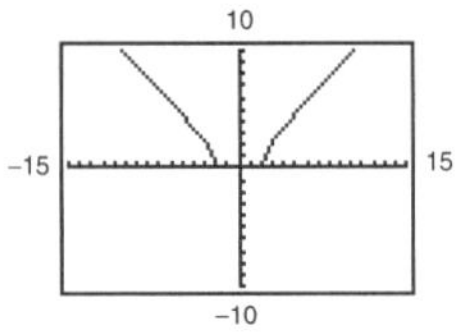

Domain: $(-\infty, -2] \cup [2, \infty)$
Yes, for -2 and 2.

Algebra Help

In Example 7(d), $4 - 3x \geq 0$ is a linear inequality. You can review the techniques for solving a linear inequality in Appendix A.6.

The Domain of a Function

The domain of a function can be described explicitly or it can be *implied* by the expression used to define the function. The **implied domain** is the set of all real numbers for which the expression is defined. For instance, the function given by

$$f(x) = \frac{1}{x^2 - 4}$$ Domain excludes x-values that result in division by zero.

has an implied domain that consists of all real x other than $x = \pm 2$. These two values are excluded from the domain because division by zero is undefined. Another common type of implied domain is that used to avoid even roots of negative numbers. For example, the function given by

$$f(x) = \sqrt{x}$$ Domain excludes x-values that result in even roots of negative numbers.

is defined only for $x \geq 0$. So, its implied domain is the interval $[0, \infty)$. In general, the domain of a function *excludes* values that would cause division by zero *or* that would result in the even root of a negative number.

Example 7 Finding the Domain of a Function

Find the domain of each function.

a. f: $\{(-3, 0), (-1, 4), (0, 2), (2, 2), (4, -1)\}$

b. $g(x) = \dfrac{1}{x + 5}$

c. Volume of a sphere: $V = \frac{4}{3}\pi r^3$

d. $h(x) = \sqrt{4 - 3x}$

Solution

a. The domain of f consists of all first coordinates in the set of ordered pairs.

Domain $= \{-3, -1, 0, 2, 4\}$

b. Excluding x-values that yield zero in the denominator, the domain of g is the set of all real numbers x except $x = -5$.

c. Because this function represents the volume of a sphere, the values of the radius r must be positive. So, the domain is the set of all real numbers r such that $r > 0$.

d. This function is defined only for x-values for which

$4 - 3x \geq 0.$

By solving this inequality, you can conclude that $x \leq \frac{4}{3}$. So, the domain is the interval $\left(-\infty, \frac{4}{3}\right]$.

CHECK*Point* Now try Exercise 73.

In Example 7(c), note that the domain of a function may be implied by the physical context. For instance, from the equation

$$V = \tfrac{4}{3}\pi r^3$$

you would have no reason to restrict r to positive values, but the physical context implies that a sphere cannot have a negative or zero radius.

Applications

FIGURE 1.49

Example 8 The Dimensions of a Container

You work in the marketing department of a soft-drink company and are experimenting with a new can for iced tea that is slightly narrower and taller than a standard can. For your experimental can, the ratio of the height to the radius is 4, as shown in Figure 1.49.

a. Write the volume of the can as a function of the radius r.

b. Write the volume of the can as a function of the height h.

Solution

a. $V(r) = \pi r^2 h = \pi r^2(4r) = 4\pi r^3$ — Write V as a function of r.

b. $V(h) = \pi\left(\frac{h}{4}\right)^2 h = \frac{\pi h^3}{16}$ — Write V as a function of h.

CHECKPoint Now try Exercise 87.

Example 9 The Path of a Baseball

A baseball is hit at a point 3 feet above ground at a velocity of 100 feet per second and an angle of 45°. The path of the baseball is given by the function

$$f(x) = -0.0032x^2 + x + 3$$

where x and $f(x)$ are measured in feet. Will the baseball clear a 10-foot fence located 300 feet from home plate?

Algebraic Solution

When $x = 300$, you can find the height of the baseball as follows.

$f(x) = -0.0032x^2 + x + 3$ — Write original function.

$f(300) = -0.0032(300)^2 + 300 + 3$ — Substitute 300 for x.

$= 15$ — Simplify.

When $x = 300$, the height of the baseball is 15 feet, so the baseball will clear a 10-foot fence.

CHECKPoint Now try Exercise 93.

Graphical Solution

Use a graphing utility to graph the function $y = -0.0032x^2 + x + 3$. Use the *value* feature or the *zoom* and *trace* features of the graphing utility to estimate that $y = 15$ when $x = 300$, as shown in Figure 1.50. So, the ball will clear a 10-foot fence.

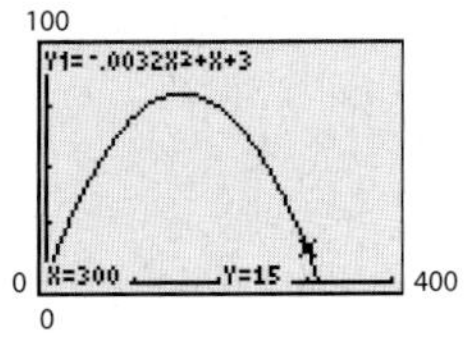

FIGURE 1.50

In the equation in Example 9, the height of the baseball is a function of the distance from home plate.

Extra Example 8

For a cone, the ratio of its height to its radius is 3. Express the volume of the cone, $V = \frac{1}{3}\pi r^2 h$, as a function of the radius r. $\boldsymbol{V(r) = \pi r^3}$

Extra Example 9

A baseball is hit at a point 3 feet above ground at a velocity of 100 feet per second and an angle of 45°. The path of the baseball is given by $y = -0.0032x^2 + x + 3$, where x and y are measured in feet. Will the baseball clear a 20-foot fence located 280 feet from home plate? **Yes. The ball will be 32 feet off the ground when it passes over the fence.**

Extra Example 10

The number of votes cast (in millions) for president in the United States from 1956 through 2008 can be approximated by the model

$$V(t) = \begin{cases} 1.06t + 2.3, & 56 \le t \le 92 \\ 3.01t - 193.5, & 96 \le t \le 108 \end{cases}$$

where $t = 56$ represents 1956. Use this model to approximate the number of votes cast for president in 1992, 1996, and 2008. (Source: U.S. House of Representatives and the National Archives and Records Administration)

1992: 99.82 million;
1996: 95.46 million;
2008: 131.58 million

Extra Example 11

For $f(x) = x^2 - 2x + 9$, find $\dfrac{f(4 + h) - f(4)}{h}$, $h \neq 0$.

$\boldsymbol{h + 6, h \neq 0}$

Example 10 Alternative-Fueled Vehicles

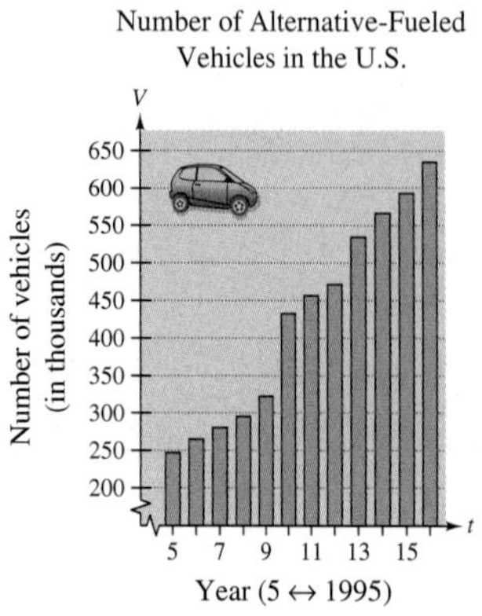

FIGURE 1.51

The number V (in thousands) of alternative-fueled vehicles in the United States increased in a linear pattern from 1995 to 1999, as shown in Figure 1.51. Then, in 2000, the number of vehicles took a jump and, until 2006, increased in a different linear pattern. These two patterns can be approximated by the function

$$V(t) = \begin{cases} 18.08t + 155.3, & 5 \le t \le 9 \\ 34.75t + 74.9, & 10 \le t \le 16 \end{cases}$$

where t represents the year, with $t = 5$ corresponding to 1995. Use this function to approximate the number of alternative-fueled vehicles for each year from 1995 to 2006. (Source: Science Applications International Corporation; Energy Information Administration)

Solution

From 1995 to 1999, use $V(t) = 18.08t + 155.3$.

245.7	263.8	281.9	299.9	318.0
1995	1996	1997	1998	1999

From 2000 to 2006, use $V(t) = 34.75t + 74.9$.

422.4	457.2	491.9	526.7	561.4	596.2	630.9
2000	2001	2002	2003	2004	2005	2006

CHECKPoint Now try Exercise 95.

Difference Quotients

One of the basic definitions in calculus employs the ratio

$$\frac{f(x + h) - f(x)}{h}, \quad h \neq 0.$$

This ratio is called a **difference quotient,** as illustrated in Example 11.

Example 11 Evaluating a Difference Quotient

For $f(x) = x^2 - 4x + 7$, find $\dfrac{f(x + h) - f(x)}{h}$.

Solution

$$\frac{f(x + h) - f(x)}{h} = \frac{[(x + h)^2 - 4(x + h) + 7] - (x^2 - 4x + 7)}{h}$$

$$= \frac{x^2 + 2xh + h^2 - 4x - 4h + 7 - x^2 + 4x - 7}{h}$$

$$= \frac{2xh + h^2 - 4h}{h} = \frac{h(2x + h - 4)}{h} = 2x + h - 4, \quad h \neq 0$$

CHECKPoint Now try Exercise 103.

The symbol $\int$ indicates an example or exercise that highlights algebraic techniques specifically used in calculus.

You may find it easier to calculate the difference quotient in Example 11 by first finding $f(x + h)$, and then substituting the resulting expression into the difference quotient, as follows.

$$f(x + h) = (x + h)^2 - 4(x + h) + 7 = x^2 + 2xh + h^2 - 4x - 4h + 7$$

$$\frac{f(x + h) - f(x)}{h} = \frac{(x^2 + 2xh + h^2 - 4x - 4h + 7) - (x^2 - 4x + 7)}{h}$$

$$= \frac{2xh + h^2 - 4h}{h} = \frac{h(2x + h - 4)}{h} = 2x + h - 4, \quad h \neq 0$$

Summary of Function Terminology

Function: A **function** is a relationship between two variables such that to each value of the independent variable there corresponds exactly one value of the dependent variable.

Function Notation: $y = f(x)$

f is the *name* of the function.

y is the **dependent variable.**

x is the **independent variable.**

$f(x)$ is the *value of the function at x.*

Domain: The **domain** of a function is the set of all values (inputs) of the independent variable for which the function is defined. If x is in the domain of f, f is said to be *defined* at x. If x is not in the domain of f, f is said to be *undefined* at x.

Range: The **range** of a function is the set of all values (outputs) assumed by the dependent variable (that is, the set of all function values).

Implied Domain: If f is defined by an algebraic expression and the domain is not specified, the **implied domain** consists of all real numbers for which the expression is defined.

Classroom Discussion

Everyday Functions In groups of two or three, identify common real-life functions. Consider everyday activities, events, and expenses, such as long distance telephone calls and car insurance. Here are two examples.

a. The statement, "Your happiness is a function of the grade you receive in this course" is *not* a correct mathematical use of the word "function." The word "happiness" is ambiguous.

b. The statement, "Your federal income tax is a function of your adjusted gross income" *is* a correct mathematical use of the word "function." Once you have determined your adjusted gross income, your income tax can be determined.

Describe your functions in words. Avoid using ambiguous words. Can you find an example of a piecewise-defined function? Answers will vary.

Closing the Lesson

Have students summarize the major points of the lesson and answer the Essential Question: What are the important defining characteristics and representations of a function?

- **A relation is a function if every element in a set *A* corresponds to exactly one element in a set *B*. More than one element of set *A* may correspond to a single element in set *B*, but an element in set *A* cannot be matched with two different elements in set *B*. Also, not all elements in set *B* must correspond to an element in set *A*.**
- **Functions can be represented verbally, numerically, graphically, and algebraically.**
- **Evaluate functions and piecewise-defined functions when given a specific value.**
- **Find the domain of a function.**
- **Evaluate the difference quotient of a function over a given interval.**

4 PRACTICE AND APPLY

Assignment Guide

Transparencies Available
Available at the Instructor's companion site.

Average:
Day 1: pp. 48–53
Exs. 1–6, 11–101 odd, 102, 103–109 odd, 111–124

Advanced:
Day 1: pp. 48–53
Exs. 1–6, 12–110 even, 111–114, 119–124

Block:
pp. 48–53
Exs. 1–6, 11–101 odd, 102, 103–109 odd, 111–124 (with 1.3)

2. verbally; numerically; graphically; algebraically
12. No, the input values 0 and 1 each have two different output values.
13. No, the input values 7 and 10 each have two different output values.
14. Yes, it does not matter that each input value has the same output value.
15. (a) Function
(b) Not a function, because the element 1 in A corresponds to two elements, -2 and 1, in B.
(c) Function
(d) Not a function, because not every element in A is matched with an element in B.
16. (a) Not a function, because the element c in A corresponds to two elements, 2 and 3, in B.
(b) Function
(c) Not a function from A to B. (It is instead a function from B to A.)
(d) Function

1.4 EXERCISES

See www.CalcChat.com for worked-out solutions to odd-numbered exercises.

VOCABULARY: Fill in the blanks.

1. A relation that assigns to each element x from a set of inputs, or ________, exactly one element y in a set of outputs, or ________, is called a ________. domain; range; function

2. Functions are commonly represented in four different ways, ________, See margin., and ________.

3. For an equation that represents y as a function of x, the set of all values taken on by the ________ variable x is the domain, and the set of all values taken on by the ________ variable y is the range. independent; dependent

4. The function given by

$$f(x) = \begin{cases} 2x - 1, & x < 0 \\ x^2 + 4, & x \geq 0 \end{cases}$$

is an example of a ________ function. piecewise-defined

5. If the domain of the function f is not given, then the set of values of the independent variable for which the expression is defined is called the ________ ________. implied domain

6. In calculus, one of the basic definitions is that of a ________ ________, given by $\dfrac{f(x+h) - f(x)}{h}$, $h \neq 0$. difference quotient

SKILLS AND APPLICATIONS

In Exercises 7–10, is the relationship a function?

7.
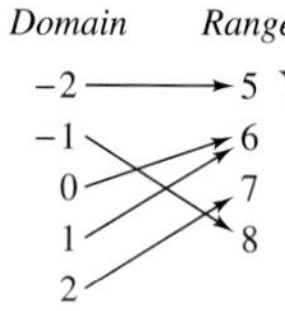

Yes

8.
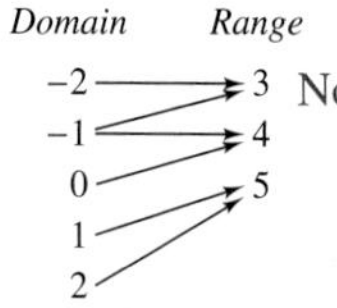

No

9.
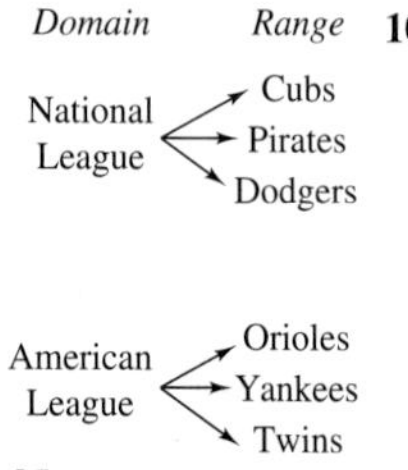

No

10.
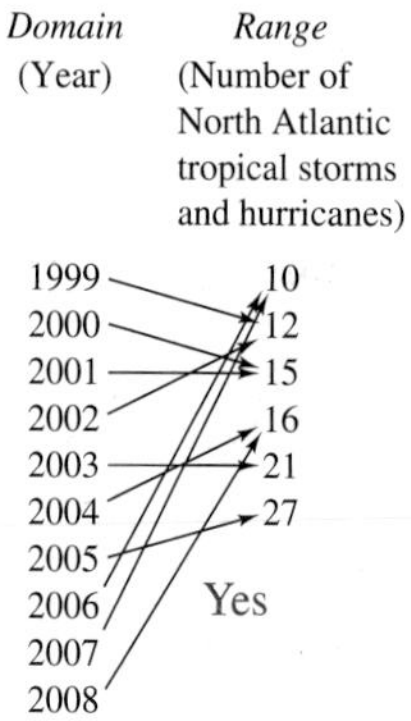

Yes

In Exercises 11–14, determine whether the relation represents y as a function of x.

11.

Input, x	-2	-1	0	1	2
Output, y	-8	-1	0	1	8

Yes, each input value has exactly one output value.

12–14. See margin.

12.

Input, x	0	1	2	1	0
Output, y	-4	-2	0	2	4

13.

Input, x	10	7	4	7	10
Output, y	3	6	9	12	15

14.

Input, x	0	3	9	12	15
Output, y	3	3	3	3	3

In Exercises 15 and 16, which sets of ordered pairs represent functions from A to B? Explain. 15–16. See margin.

15. $A = \{0, 1, 2, 3\}$ and $B = \{-2, -1, 0, 1, 2\}$
(a) $\{(0, 1), (1, -2), (2, 0), (3, 2)\}$
(b) $\{(0, -1), (2, 2), (1, -2), (3, 0), (1, 1)\}$
(c) $\{(0, 0), (1, 0), (2, 0), (3, 0)\}$
(d) $\{(0, 2), (3, 0), (1, 1)\}$

16. $A = \{a, b, c\}$ and $B = \{0, 1, 2, 3\}$
(a) $\{(a, 1), (c, 2), (c, 3), (b, 3)\}$
(b) $\{(a, 1), (b, 2), (c, 3)\}$
(c) $\{(1, a), (0, a), (2, c), (3, b)\}$
(d) $\{(c, 0), (b, 0), (a, 3)\}$

CIRCULATION OF NEWSPAPERS In Exercises 17 and 18, use the graph, which shows the circulation (in millions) of daily newspapers in the United States. (Source: Editor & Publisher Company)

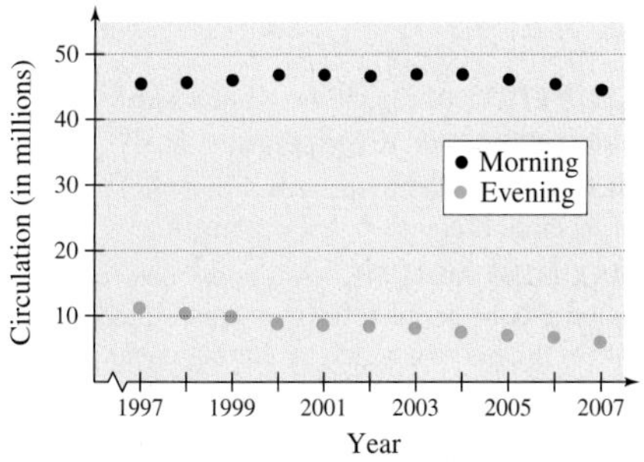

17. Is the circulation of morning newspapers a function of the year? Is the circulation of evening newspapers a function of the year? Explain. See margin.

18. Let $f(x)$ represent the circulation of evening newspapers in year x. Find $f(2002)$. 9 million

In Exercises 19–36, determine whether the equation represents y as a function of x.

19. $x^2 + y^2 = 4$ Not a function
20. $x^2 - y^2 = 16$ Not a function
21. $x^2 + y = 4$ Function
22. $y - 4x^2 = 36$ Function
23. $2x + 3y = 4$ Function
24. $2x + 5y = 10$ Function
25. $(x + 2)^2 + (y - 1)^2 = 25$ Not a function
26. $(x - 2)^2 + y^2 = 4$ Not a function
27. $y^2 = x^2 - 1$ Not a function
28. $x + y^2 = 4$ Not a function
29. $y = \sqrt{16 - x^2}$ Function
30. $y = \sqrt{x + 5}$ Function
31. $y = |4 - x|$ Function
32. $|y| = 4 - x$ Not a function
33. $x = 14$ Not a function
34. $y = -75$ Function
35. $y + 5 = 0$ Function
36. $x - 1 = 0$ Not a function

In Exercises 37–52, evaluate the function at each specified value of the independent variable and simplify.

37. $f(x) = 2x - 3$
(a) $f(1)$ -1 (b) $f(-3)$ -9 (c) $f(x - 1)$ $2x - 5$

38. $g(y) = 7 - 3y$
(a) $g(0)$ 7 (b) $g(\frac{7}{3})$ 0 (c) $g(s + 2)$ $1 - 3s$

39. $V(r) = \frac{4}{3}\pi r^3$
(a) $V(3)$ 36π (b) $V(\frac{3}{2})$ $\frac{9}{2}\pi$ (c) $V(2r)$ $\frac{32}{3}\pi r^3$

40. $S(r) = 4\pi r^2$
(a) $S(2)$ 16π (b) $S(\frac{1}{2})$ π (c) $S(3r)$ $36\pi r^2$

41. $g(t) = 4t^2 - 3t + 5$
(a) $g(2)$ 15 (b) $g(t - 2)$ $4t^2 - 19t + 27$ (c) $g(t) - g(2)$ $4t^2 - 3t - 10$

42. $h(t) = t^2 - 2t$
(a) $h(2)$ 0 (b) $h(1.5)$ -0.75 (c) $h(x + 2)$ $x^2 + 2x$

43. $f(y) = 3 - \sqrt{y}$
(a) $f(4)$ 1 (b) $f(0.25)$ 2.5 (c) $f(4x^2)$ $3 - 2|x|$

44. $f(x) = \sqrt{x + 8} + 2$
(a) $f(-8)$ 2 (b) $f(1)$ 5 (c) $f(x - 8)$ $\sqrt{x} + 2$

45. $q(x) = 1/(x^2 - 9)$ See margin.
(a) $q(0)$ (b) $q(3)$ (c) $q(y + 3)$

46. $q(t) = (2t^2 + 3)/t^2$ See margin.
(a) $q(2)$ (b) $q(0)$ (c) $q(-x)$

47. $f(x) = |x|/x$ See margin.
(a) $f(2)$ (b) $f(-2)$ (c) $f(x - 1)$

48. $f(x) = |x| + 4$
(a) $f(2)$ 6 (b) $f(-2)$ 6 (c) $f(x^2)$ $x^2 + 4$

49. $f(x) = \begin{cases} 2x + 1, & x < 0 \\ 2x + 2, & x \ge 0 \end{cases}$
(a) $f(-1)$ -1 (b) $f(0)$ 2 (c) $f(2)$ 6

50. $f(x) = \begin{cases} x^2 + 2, & x \le 1 \\ 2x^2 + 2, & x > 1 \end{cases}$
(a) $f(-2)$ 6 (b) $f(1)$ 3 (c) $f(2)$ 10

51. $f(x) = \begin{cases} 3x - 1, & x < -1 \\ 4, & -1 \le x \le 1 \\ x^2, & x > 1 \end{cases}$
(a) $f(-2)$ -7 (b) $f(-\frac{1}{2})$ 4 (c) $f(3)$ 9

52. $f(x) = \begin{cases} 4 - 5x, & x \le -2 \\ 0, & -2 < x < 2 \\ x^2 + 1, & x \ge 2 \end{cases}$
(a) $f(-3)$ 19 (b) $f(4)$ 17 (c) $f(-1)$ 0

In Exercises 53–58, complete the table.

53. $f(x) = x^2 - 3$

x	-2	-1	0	1	2
$f(x)$	1	-2	-3		1

-2

54. $g(x) = \sqrt{x - 3}$

x	3	4	5	6	7
$g(x)$	0	1			2

$\sqrt{2}$ $\sqrt{3}$

55. $h(t) = \frac{1}{2}|t + 3|$

t	-5	-4	-3	-2	-1
$h(t)$	1	$\frac{1}{2}$	0	$\frac{1}{2}$	1

17. Each is a function. For each year there corresponds one and only one circulation.

45. (a) $-\frac{1}{9}$
(b) Undefined
(c) $\frac{1}{y^2 + 6y}$

46. (a) $\frac{11}{4}$
(b) Undefined
(c) $\frac{2x^2 + 3}{x^2}$

47. (a) 1 (b) -1 (c) $\frac{|x - 1|}{x - 1}$

56. $f(s) = \dfrac{|s-2|}{s-2}$

s	0	1	$\frac{3}{2}$	$\frac{5}{2}$	4
$f(s)$	-1	-1	-1	1	1

57. $f(x) = \begin{cases} -\frac{1}{2}x + 4, & x \le 0 \\ (x-2)^2, & x > 0 \end{cases}$

x	-2	-1	0	1	2
$f(x)$	5	$\frac{9}{2}$	4	1	0

58. $f(x) = \begin{cases} 9 - x^2, & x < 3 \\ x - 3, & x \ge 3 \end{cases}$

x	1	2	3	4	5
$f(x)$	8	5	0	1	2

In Exercises 59–66, find all real values of x such that $f(x) = 0$.

59. $f(x) = 15 - 3x$ 5

60. $f(x) = 5x + 1$ $-\frac{1}{5}$

61. $f(x) = \dfrac{3x-4}{5}$ $\frac{4}{3}$

62. $f(x) = \dfrac{12 - x^2}{5}$ $\pm 2\sqrt{3}$

63. $f(x) = x^2 - 9$ ± 3

64. $f(x) = x^2 - 8x + 15$ 3, 5

65. $f(x) = x^3 - x$ $0, \pm 1$

66. $f(x) = x^3 - x^2 - 4x + 4$ $1, \pm 2$

In Exercises 67–70, find the value(s) of x for which $f(x) = g(x)$.

67. $f(x) = x^2, \quad g(x) = x + 2$ $-1, 2$

68. $f(x) = x^2 + 2x + 1, \quad g(x) = 7x - 5$ 2, 3

69. $f(x) = x^4 - 2x^2, \quad g(x) = 2x^2$ $0, \pm 2$

70. $f(x) = \sqrt{x} - 4, \quad g(x) = 2 - x$ 4

In Exercises 71–82, find the domain of the function.

71. $f(x) = 5x^2 + 2x - 1$

72. $g(x) = 1 - 2x^2$

73. $h(t) = \dfrac{4}{t}$

74. $s(y) = \dfrac{3y}{y+5}$

75. $g(y) = \sqrt{y - 10}$

76. $f(t) = \sqrt[3]{t+4}$

77. $g(x) = \dfrac{1}{x} - \dfrac{3}{x+2}$

78. $h(x) = \dfrac{10}{x^2 - 2x}$

79. $f(s) = \dfrac{\sqrt{s-1}}{s-4}$

80. $f(x) = \dfrac{\sqrt{x+6}}{6+x}$

81. $f(x) = \dfrac{x-4}{\sqrt{x}}$

82. $f(x) = \dfrac{x+2}{\sqrt{x-10}}$

71–82. See margin.

In Exercises 83–86, assume that the domain of f is the set $A = \{-2, -1, 0, 1, 2\}$. Determine the set of ordered pairs that represents the function f. 83–86. See margin.

83. $f(x) = x^2$

84. $f(x) = (x-3)^2$

85. $f(x) = |x| + 2$

86. $f(x) = |x + 1|$

87. GEOMETRY Write the area A of a square as a function of its perimeter P. See margin.

88. GEOMETRY Write the area A of a circle as a function of its circumference C. See margin.

89. MAXIMUM VOLUME An open box of maximum volume is to be made from a square piece of material 24 centimeters on a side by cutting equal squares from the corners and turning up the sides (see figure). See margin.

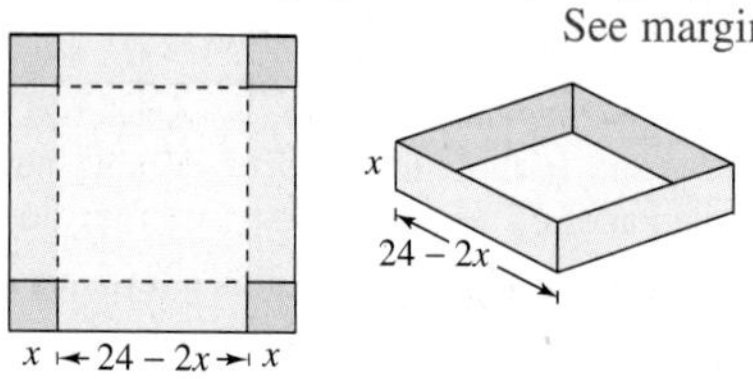

(a) The table shows the volumes V (in cubic centimeters) of the box for various heights x (in centimeters). Use the table to estimate the maximum volume.

Height, x	1	2	3	4	5	6
Volume, V	484	800	972	1024	980	864

(b) Plot the points (x, V) from the table in part (a). Does the relation defined by the ordered pairs represent V as a function of x?

(c) If V is a function of x, write the function and determine its domain.

90. MAXIMUM PROFIT The cost per unit in the production of an MP3 player is \$60. The manufacturer charges \$90 per unit for orders of 100 or less. To encourage large orders, the manufacturer reduces the charge by \$0.15 per MP3 player for each unit ordered in excess of 100 (for example, there would be a charge of \$87 per MP3 player for an order size of 120).

(a) The table shows the profits P (in dollars) for various numbers of units ordered, x. Use the table to estimate the maximum profit. See margin.

Units, x	110	120	130	140
Profit, P	3135	3240	3315	3360

Units, x	150	160	170
Profit, P	3375	3360	3315

71. All real numbers x

72. All real numbers x

73. All real numbers t except $t = 0$

74. All real numbers y except $y = -5$

75. All real numbers y such that $y \ge 10$

76. All real numbers t

77. All real numbers x except $x = 0, -2$

78. All real numbers x except $x = 0, 2$

79. All real numbers s such that $s \ge 1$ except $s = 4$

80. All real numbers x such that $x > -6$

81. All real numbers x such that $x > 0$

82. All real numbers x such that $x > 10$

87. $A = \dfrac{P^2}{16}$ **88.** $A = \dfrac{C^2}{4\pi}$

89. (a) The maximum volume is 1024 cubic centimeters.

(b)

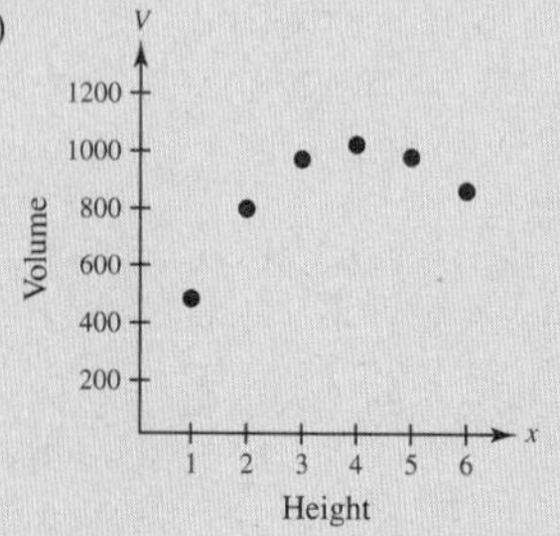

Yes, V is a function of x.

(c) $V = x(24 - 2x)^2$, $0 < x < 12$

90. (a) The maximum profit is \$3375.

83–86. See Additional Answers beginning on page AA1.

(b)–(c). See margin.

(b) Plot the points (x, P) from the table in part (a). Does the relation defined by the ordered pairs represent P as a function of x?

(c) If P is a function of x, write the function and determine its domain.

91. GEOMETRY A right triangle is formed in the first quadrant by the x- and y-axes and a line through the point $(2, 1)$ (see figure). Write the area A of the triangle as a function of x, and determine the domain of the function. $A = \dfrac{x^2}{2(x-2)},\ x > 2$

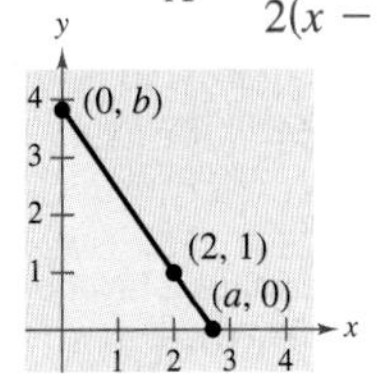

FIGURE FOR 91

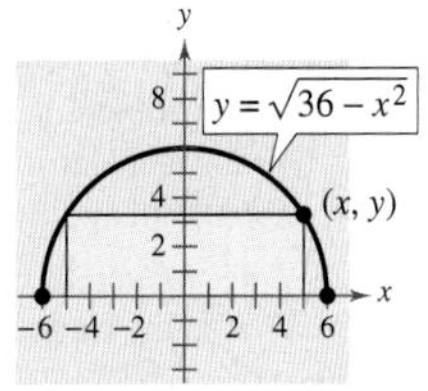

FIGURE FOR 92

92. See margin.

92. GEOMETRY A rectangle is bounded by the x-axis and the semicircle $y = \sqrt{36 - x^2}$ (see figure). Write the area A of the rectangle as a function of x, and graphically determine the domain of the function.

93. PATH OF A BALL The height y (in feet) of a baseball thrown by a child is

$$y = -\frac{1}{10}x^2 + 3x + 6$$

Yes, the ball will be at a height of 6 feet.

where x is the horizontal distance (in feet) from where the ball was thrown. Will the ball fly over the head of another child 30 feet away trying to catch the ball? (Assume that the child who is trying to catch the ball holds a baseball glove at a height of 5 feet.)

94. PRESCRIPTION DRUGS The numbers d (in millions) of drug prescriptions filled by independent outlets in the United States from 2000 through 2007 (see figure) can be approximated by the model

$$d(t) = \begin{cases} 10.6t + 699, & 0 \le t \le 4 \\ 15.5t + 637, & 5 \le t \le 7 \end{cases}$$

where t represents the year, with $t = 0$ corresponding to 2000. Use this model to find the number of drug prescriptions filled by independent outlets in each year from 2000 through 2007. (Source: National Association of Chain Drug Stores)

2000: 699 million	2004: 741.4 million
2001: 709.6 million	2005: 714.5 million
2002: 720.2 million	2006: 730 million
2003: 730.8 million	2007: 745.5 million

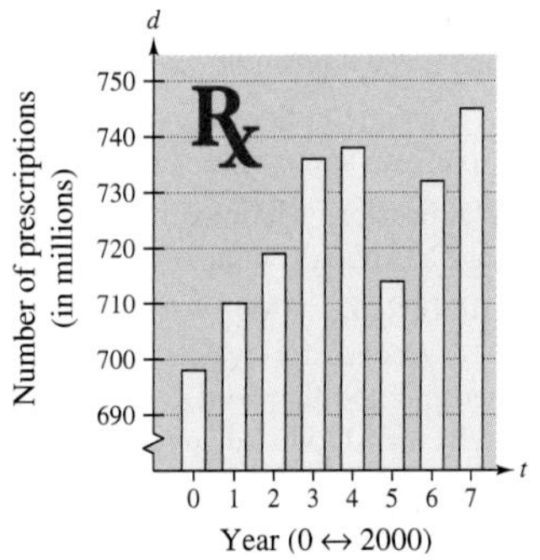

FIGURE FOR 94

95. MEDIAN SALES PRICE The median sale prices p (in thousands of dollars) of an existing one-family home in the United States from 1998 through 2007 (see figure) can be approximated by the model

$$p(t) = \begin{cases} 1.011t^2 - 12.38t + 170.5, & 8 \le t \le 13 \\ -6.950t^2 + 222.55t - 1557.6, & 14 \le t \le 17 \end{cases}$$

where t represents the year, with $t = 8$ corresponding to 1998. Use this model to find the median sale price of an existing one-family home in each year from 1998 through 2007. (Source: National Association of Realtors) See margin.

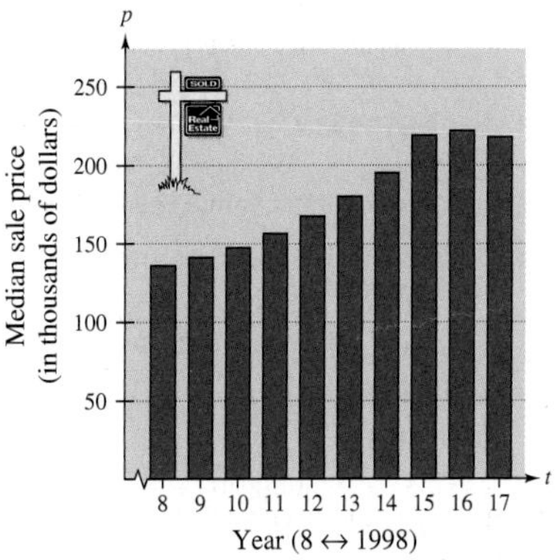

96. POSTAL REGULATIONS A rectangular package to be sent by the U.S. Postal Service can have a maximum combined length and girth (perimeter of a cross section) of 108 inches (see figure).

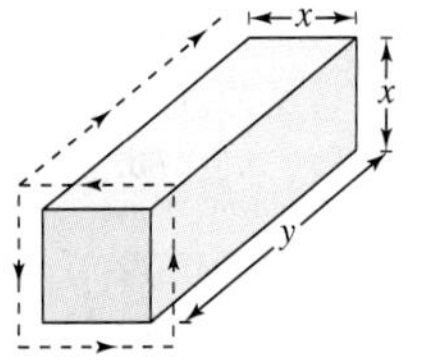

90. (b)

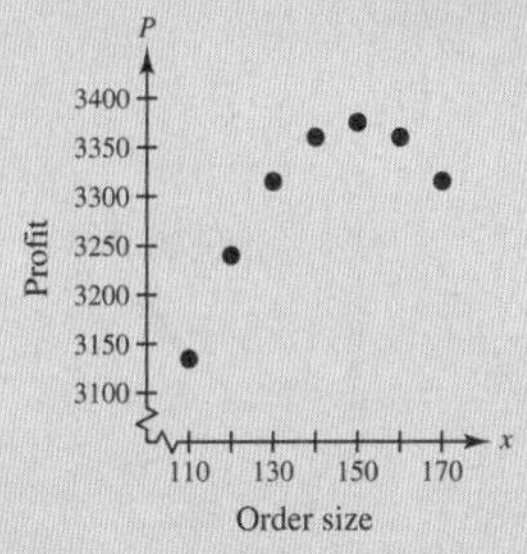

Yes, P is a function of x.

(c) $P = 45x - 0.15x^2,\ x > 100$

92. $A = 2xy = 2x\sqrt{36 - x^2},\ 0 < x < 6$

95. 1998: \$136,164
1999: \$140,971
2000: \$147,800
2001: \$156,651
2002: \$167,524
2003: \$180,419
2004: \$195,900
2005: \$216,900
2006: \$224,000
2007: \$217,200

(a)–(c). See margin.

(a) Write the volume V of the package as a function of x. What is the domain of the function?

(b) Use a graphing utility to graph your function. Be sure to use an appropriate window setting.

(c) What dimensions will maximize the volume of the package? Explain your answer.

97. COST, REVENUE, AND PROFIT A company produces a product for which the variable cost is \$12.30 per unit and the fixed costs are \$98,000. The product sells for \$17.98. Let x be the number of units produced and sold. $C = 12.30x + 98{,}000$

(a) The total cost for a business is the sum of the variable cost and the fixed costs. Write the total cost C as a function of the number of units produced.

(b) Write the revenue R as a function of the number of units sold. $R = 17.98x$

(c) Write the profit P as a function of the number of units sold. (*Note:* $P = R - C$) $P = 5.68x - 98{,}000$

98. AVERAGE COST The inventor of a new game believes that the variable cost for producing the game is \$0.95 per unit and the fixed costs are \$6000. The inventor sells each game for \$1.69. Let x be the number of games sold. See margin.

(a) The total cost for a business is the sum of the variable cost and the fixed costs. Write the total cost C as a function of the number of games sold.

(b) Write the average cost per unit $\overline{C} = C/x$ as a function of x.

99. TRANSPORTATION For groups of 80 or more people, a charter bus company determines the rate per person according to the formula

Rate $= 8 - 0.05(n - 80), \quad n \geq 80$

where the rate is given in dollars and n is the number of people. See margin.

(a) Write the revenue R for the bus company as a function of n.

(b) Use the function in part (a) to complete the table. What can you conclude?

n	90	100	110	120	130	140	150
$R(n)$							

100. PHYSICS The force F (in tons) of water against the face of a dam is estimated by the function $F(y) = 149.76\sqrt{10}y^{5/2}$, where y is the depth of the water (in feet).

(a) Complete the table. What can you conclude from the table? See margin.

y	5	10	20	30	40
$F(y)$					

(b) Use the table to approximate the depth at which the force against the dam is 1,000,000 tons. 21 ft

(c) Find the depth at which the force against the dam is 1,000,000 tons algebraically. 21.37 ft

101. HEIGHT OF A BALLOON A balloon carrying a transmitter ascends vertically from a point 3000 feet from the receiving station. See margin.

(a) Draw a diagram that gives a visual representation of the problem. Let h represent the height of the balloon and let d represent the distance between the balloon and the receiving station.

(b) Write the height of the balloon as a function of d. What is the domain of the function?

102. E-FILING The table shows the numbers of tax returns (in millions) made through e-file from 2000 through 2007. Let $f(t)$ represent the number of tax returns made through e-file in the year t. (Source: Internal Revenue Service) (a)–(d). See margin.

Year	Number of tax returns made through e-file
2000	35.4
2001	40.2
2002	46.9
2003	52.9
2004	61.5
2005	68.5
2006	73.3
2007	80.0

(a) Find $\dfrac{f(2007) - f(2000)}{2007 - 2000}$ and interpret the result in the context of the problem.

(b) Make a scatter plot of the data.

(c) Find a linear model for the data algebraically. Let N represent the number of tax returns made through e-file and let $t = 0$ correspond to 2000.

(d) Use the model found in part (c) to complete the table.

t	0	1	2	3	4	5	6	7
N								

96. (a) $V = x^2y$
$= x^2(108 - 4x)$
$= 108x^2 - 4x^3, \quad 0 < x < 27$

(b)

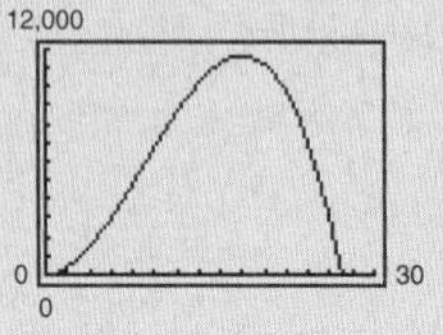

(c) 18 in. × 18 in. × 36 in.

98. (a) $C = 6000 + 0.95x$

(b) $\overline{C} = \dfrac{C}{x} = \dfrac{6000}{x} + 0.95$

99. (a) $R = \dfrac{240n - n^2}{20}, \quad n \geq 80$

(b)

n	90	100	110	120
$R(n)$	\$675	\$700	\$715	\$720

n	130	140	150
$R(n)$	\$715	\$700	\$675

The revenue is maximum when 120 people take the trip.

101. (a)

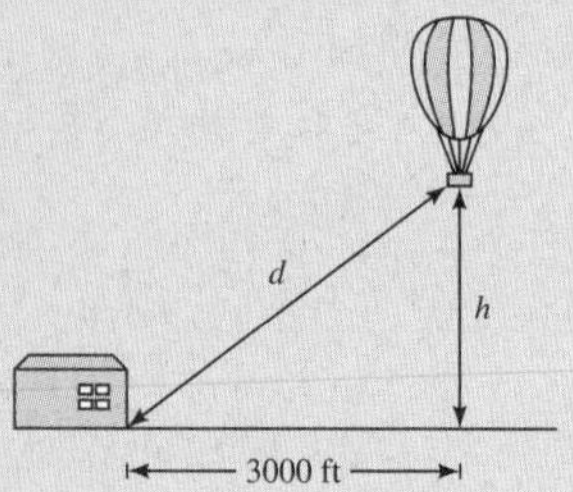

(b) $h = \sqrt{d^2 - 3000^2}, \quad d \geq 3000$

102. (a) About 6.37; Approximately 6.37 million more tax returns were made through e-file each year from 2000 to 2007.

(b)

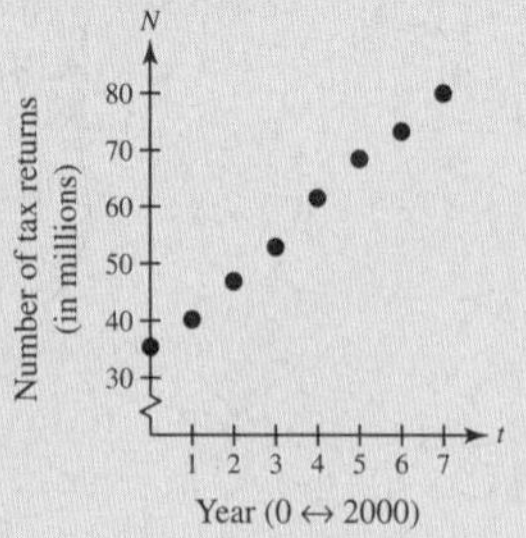

(c) $N = 6.37t + 35.4$

(d)

t	0	1	2	3
N	35.4	41.8	48.1	54.5

t	4	5	6	7
N	60.9	67.3	73.6	80.0

100 (a). See Additional Answers beginning on page AA1.

(e)–(f). See margin.

(e) Compare your results from part (d) with the actual data.

(f) Use a graphing utility to find a linear model for the data. Let $x = 0$ correspond to 2000. How does the model you found in part (c) compare with the model given by the graphing utility?

In Exercises 103–110, find the difference quotient and simplify your answer.

103. $f(x) = x^2 - x + 1, \quad \dfrac{f(2+h) - f(2)}{h}, \quad h \neq 0$ $\quad 3 + h,\ h \neq 0$

104. $f(x) = 5x - x^2, \quad \dfrac{f(5+h) - f(5)}{h}, \quad h \neq 0$ $\quad -(5 + h),\ h \neq 0$

105. $f(x) = x^3 + 3x, \quad \dfrac{f(x+h) - f(x)}{h}, \quad h \neq 0$ See margin.

106. $f(x) = 4x^2 - 2x, \quad \dfrac{f(x+h) - f(x)}{h}, \quad h \neq 0$ See margin.

107. $g(x) = \dfrac{1}{x^2}, \quad \dfrac{g(x) - g(3)}{x - 3}, \quad x \neq 3$ $\quad -\dfrac{x+3}{9x^2},\ x \neq 3$

108. $f(t) = \dfrac{1}{t - 2}, \quad \dfrac{f(t) - f(1)}{t - 1}, \quad t \neq 1$ $\quad -\dfrac{1}{t-2},\ t \neq 1$

109. $f(x) = \sqrt{5x}, \quad \dfrac{f(x) - f(5)}{x - 5}, \quad x \neq 5$ $\quad \dfrac{\sqrt{5x} - 5}{x - 5}$

110. $f(x) = x^{2/3} + 1, \quad \dfrac{f(x) - f(8)}{x - 8}, \quad x \neq 8$ $\quad \dfrac{x^{2/3} - 4}{x - 8}$

In Exercises 111–114, match the data with one of the following functions

$f(x) = cx,\ g(x) = cx^2,\ h(x) = c\sqrt{|x|},$ and $r(x) = \dfrac{c}{x}$

and determine the value of the constant c that will make the function fit the data in the table. $g(x) = cx^2;\ c = -2$

111.

x	-4	-1	0	1	4
y	-32	-2	0	-2	-32

112.

x	-4	-1	0	1	4
y	-1	$-\frac{1}{4}$	0	$\frac{1}{4}$	1

$f(x) = cx;\ c = \frac{1}{4}$

113.

x	-4	-1	0	1	4
y	-8	-32	Undefined	32	8

$r(x) = \dfrac{c}{x};\ c = 32$

114.

x	-4	-1	0	1	4
y	6	3	0	3	6

$h(x) = c\sqrt{|x|};\ c = 3$

EXPLORATION

TRUE OR FALSE? In Exercises 115–118, determine whether the statement is true or false. Justify your answer.

115. Every relation is a function. 115–118. See margin.

116. Every function is a relation.

117. The domain of the function given by $f(x) = x^4 - 1$ is $(-\infty, \infty)$, and the range of $f(x)$ is $(0, \infty)$.

118. The set of ordered pairs $\{(-8, -2), (-6, 0), (-4, 0), (-2, 2), (0, 4), (2, -2)\}$ represents a function.

119. THINK ABOUT IT Consider

$f(x) = \sqrt{x - 1}$ and $g(x) = \dfrac{1}{\sqrt{x - 1}}$. See margin.

Why are the domains of f and g different?

120. THINK ABOUT IT Consider $f(x) = \sqrt{x - 2}$ and $g(x) = \sqrt[3]{x - 2}$. Why are the domains of f and g different? See margin.

121. THINK ABOUT IT Given $f(x) = x^2$, is f the independent variable? Why or why not? See margin.

122. CAPSTONE See margin.

(a) Describe any differences between a *relation* and a *function*.

(b) In your own words, explain the meanings of *domain* and *range*.

In Exercises 123 and 124, determine whether the statements use the word *function* in ways that are mathematically correct. Explain your reasoning. 123–124. See margin.

123. (a) The sales tax on a purchased item is a function of the selling price.

(b) Your score on the next algebra exam is a function of the number of hours you study the night before the exam.

124. (a) The amount in your savings account is a function of your salary.

(b) The speed at which a free-falling baseball strikes the ground is a function of the height from which it was dropped.

The symbol indicates an example or exercise that highlights algebraic techniques specifically used in calculus.

124. (a) No, not necessarily. It depends on how you manage your money.

(b) Yes. The speed of the baseball will increase as the height from which it was dropped increases.

5 ASSESS AND RETEACH

Daily Homework Quiz

Transparency Available

Available at the Instructor's companion site.

102. (e) The algebraic model is a good fit to the actual data.

(f) $N = 6.56t + 34.4$; Both models are similar, but the model found in part (c) is a slightly better model.

105. $3x^2 + 3xh + h^2 + 3,\ h \neq 0$

106. $8x + 4h - 2,\ h \neq 0$

115. False. A function is a special type of relation.

116. True. A function is a special type of relation.

117. False. The range is $[-1, \infty)$.

118. True. Each x-value corresponds to one y-value.

119. Domain of $f(x)$: all real numbers $x \geq 1$

Domain of $g(x)$: all real numbers $x > 1$

Notice that the domain of $f(x)$ includes $x = 1$ and the domain of $g(x)$ does not because you cannot divide by 0.

120. Domain of $f(x)$: all real numbers x such that $x \geq 2$

Domain of $g(x)$: all real numbers x

121. No; x is the independent variable, f is the name of the function.

122. (a) Answers will vary. Sample answer: A relation is a rule of correspondence between two variables. A function is a particular relation that assigns exactly one output (y) to each input (x).

(b) The domain of a function is the set of all inputs of the independent variable for which the function is defined. The range of a function is the set of all possible outputs.

123. (a) Yes. The amount you pay in sales tax will increase as the price of the item purchased increases.

(b) No. The length of time that you study will not necessarily determine how well you do on an exam.

1 PLAN AND PREPARE

Warm-up Exercises

Transparency Available
Available at the Instructor's companion site.

Notetaking Guide

Transparency Available
Promotes interactive learning and notetaking skills. Available at the Instructor's companion site.

Animated Precalculus

An **Animated Precalculus** tutorial is available at the Student companion site for **Section 1.5.**

Pacing

Average: 1 day
Advanced: 1 day
Block: 0.5 block with 1.6

2 FOCUS AND MOTIVATE

Essential Question

How is the graph of a function used to determine the key elements of that function? **Tell students that they will learn how to answer this question by locating key points, studying rates of change, and identifying symmetry for a given function.**

1.5 ANALYZING GRAPHS OF FUNCTIONS

What you should learn

- Use the Vertical Line Test for functions.
- Find the zeros of functions.
- Determine intervals on which functions are increasing or decreasing and determine relative maximum and relative minimum values of functions.
- Determine the average rate of change of a function.
- Identify even and odd functions.

Why you should learn it

Graphs of functions can help you visualize relationships between variables in real life. For instance, in Exercise 110 on page 64, you will use the graph of a function to represent visually the temperature of a city over a 24-hour period.

The Graph of a Function

In Section 1.4, you studied functions from an algebraic point of view. In this section, you will study functions from a graphical perspective.

The **graph of a function** f is the collection of ordered pairs $(x, f(x))$ such that x is in the domain of f. As you study this section, remember that

$x =$ the directed distance from the y-axis

$y = f(x) =$ the directed distance from the x-axis

as shown in Figure 1.52.

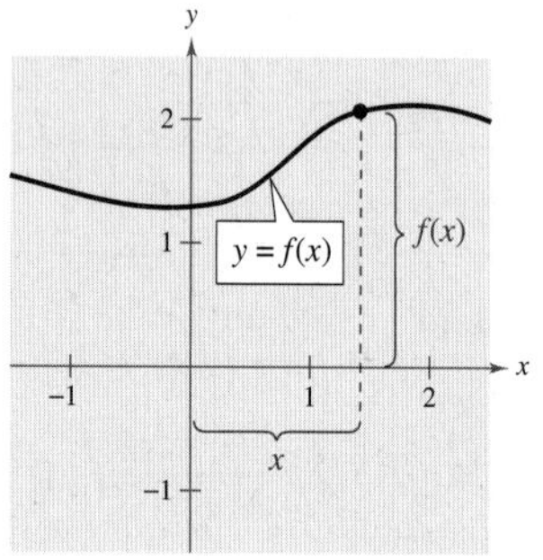

FIGURE 1.52

Example 1 Finding the Domain and Range of a Function

Use the graph of the function f, shown in Figure 1.53, to find (a) the domain of f, (b) the function values $f(-1)$ and $f(2)$, and (c) the range of f.

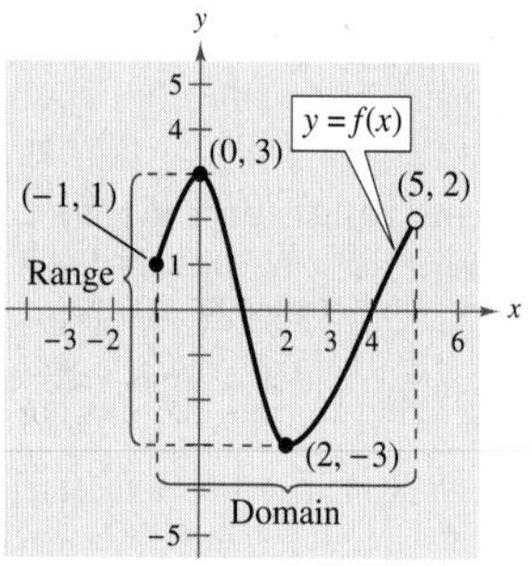

FIGURE 1.53

Solution

a. The closed dot at $(-1, 1)$ indicates that $x = -1$ is in the domain of f, whereas the open dot at $(5, 2)$ indicates that $x = 5$ is not in the domain. So, the domain of f is all x in the interval $[-1, 5)$.

b. Because $(-1, 1)$ is a point on the graph of f, it follows that $f(-1) = 1$. Similarly, because $(2, -3)$ is a point on the graph of f, it follows that $f(2) = -3$.

c. Because the graph does not extend below $f(2) = -3$ or above $f(0) = 3$, the range of f is the interval $[-3, 3]$.

CHECK Point Now try Exercise 9.

The use of dots (open or closed) at the extreme left and right points of a graph indicates that the graph does not extend beyond these points. If no such dots are shown, assume that the graph extends beyond these points.

Resource Planning Guide

Chapter Resources
- Complete Solutions Guide

Workbooks
- Notetaking Guide
- Student Solutions Guide

Interactive Technology
- Instructor Success Organizer
- Notetaking Guide IAE
- Instructional DVDs
- Animated Precalculus
- PowerLecture with ExamView

By the definition of a function, at most one y-value corresponds to a given x-value. This means that the graph of a function cannot have two or more different points with the same x-coordinate, and no two points on the graph of a function can be vertically above or below each other. It follows, then, that a vertical line can intersect the graph of a function at most once. This observation provides a convenient visual test called the **Vertical Line Test** for functions.

Vertical Line Test for Functions

A set of points in a coordinate plane is the graph of y as a function of x if and only if no *vertical* line intersects the graph at more than one point.

Example 2 Vertical Line Test for Functions

Use the Vertical Line Test to decide whether the graphs in Figure 1.54 represent y as a function of x.

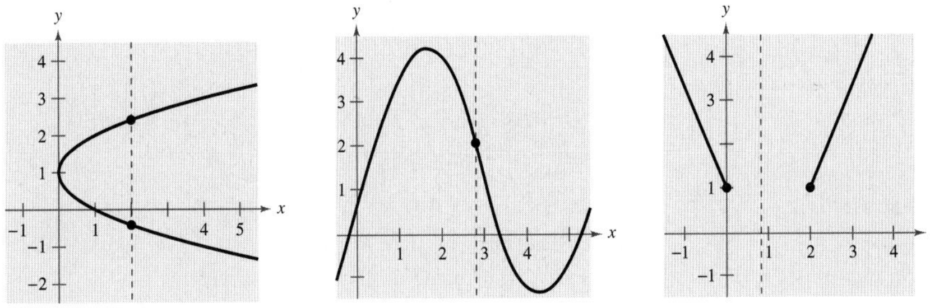

(a) (b) (c)

FIGURE 1.54

Solution

a. This *is not* a graph of y as a function of x, because you can find a vertical line that intersects the graph twice. That is, for a particular input x, there is more than one output y.

b. This *is* a graph of y as a function of x, because every vertical line intersects the graph at most once. That is, for a particular input x, there is at most one output y.

c. This *is* a graph of y as a function of x. (Note that if a vertical line does not intersect the graph, it simply means that the function is undefined for that particular value of x.) That is, for a particular input x, there is at most one output y.

CHECKPoint Now try Exercise 17.

TECHNOLOGY

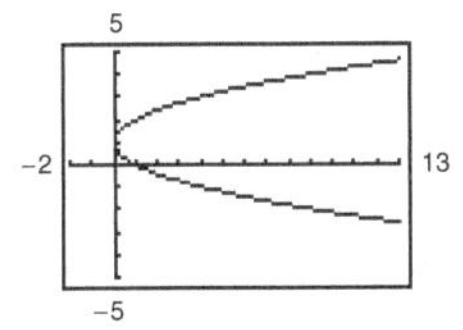

Most graphing utilities are designed to graph functions of x more easily than other types of equations. For instance, the graph shown in Figure 1.54(a) represents the equation $x - (y - 1)^2 = 0$. To use a graphing utility to duplicate this graph, you must first solve the equation for y to obtain $y = 1 \pm \sqrt{x}$, and then graph the two equations $y_1 = 1 + \sqrt{x}$ and $y_2 = 1 - \sqrt{x}$ in the same viewing window.

3 TEACH

Extra Example 1

Use the graph of $f(x) = 3 - x^2$ to find (a) the domain of f, and (b) the range of f.

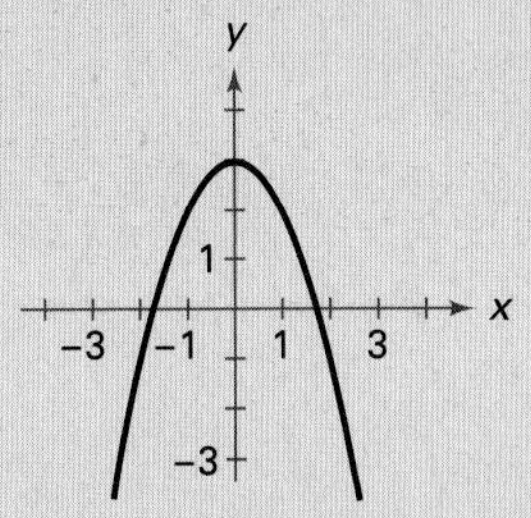

Domain: all real numbers x; range: $(-\infty, 3]$

Extra Example 2

Use the Vertical Line Test to decide whether the graph of $y = -\frac{1}{4}x^2$ represents y as a function of x.

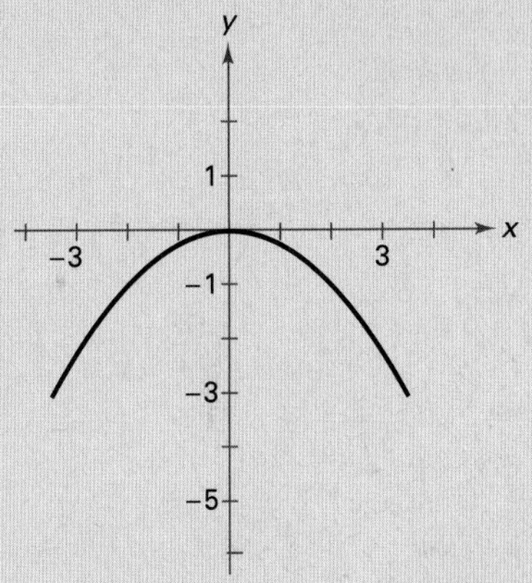

y is a function of x.

Extra Example 3

Find the zeros of the function $f(x) = 2x^2 + 13x - 24$.

$x = \frac{3}{2}, -8$

Algebra Help

To do Example 3, you need to be able to solve equations. You can review the techniques for solving equations in Appendix A.5.

Zeros of a Function

If the graph of a function of x has an x-intercept at $(a, 0)$, then a is a **zero** of the function.

> **Zeros of a Function**
>
> The **zeros of a function** f of x are the x-values for which $f(x) = 0$.

Example 3 Finding the Zeros of a Function

Find the zeros of each function.

a. $f(x) = 3x^2 + x - 10$ **b.** $g(x) = \sqrt{10 - x^2}$ **c.** $h(t) = \dfrac{2t - 3}{t + 5}$

Solution

To find the zeros of a function, set the function equal to zero and solve for the independent variable.

a.
$$3x^2 + x - 10 = 0 \qquad \text{Set } f(x) \text{ equal to 0.}$$
$$(3x - 5)(x + 2) = 0 \qquad \text{Factor.}$$
$$3x - 5 = 0 \Rightarrow x = \tfrac{5}{3} \qquad \text{Set 1st factor equal to 0.}$$
$$x + 2 = 0 \Rightarrow x = -2 \qquad \text{Set 2nd factor equal to 0.}$$

The zeros of f are $x = \frac{5}{3}$ and $x = -2$. In Figure 1.55, note that the graph of f has $\left(\frac{5}{3}, 0\right)$ and $(-2, 0)$ as its x-intercepts.

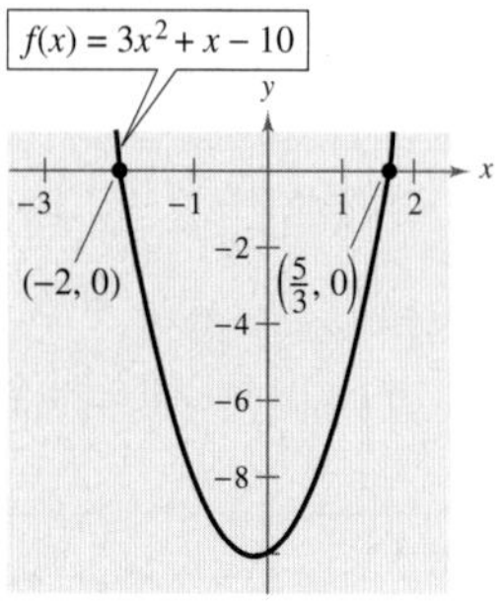

Zeros of f: $x = -2, x = \frac{5}{3}$

FIGURE 1.55

b.
$$\sqrt{10 - x^2} = 0 \qquad \text{Set } g(x) \text{ equal to 0.}$$
$$10 - x^2 = 0 \qquad \text{Square each side.}$$
$$10 = x^2 \qquad \text{Add } x^2 \text{ to each side.}$$
$$\pm\sqrt{10} = x \qquad \text{Extract square roots.}$$

The zeros of g are $x = -\sqrt{10}$ and $x = \sqrt{10}$. In Figure 1.56, note that the graph of g has $\left(-\sqrt{10}, 0\right)$ and $\left(\sqrt{10}, 0\right)$ as its x-intercepts.

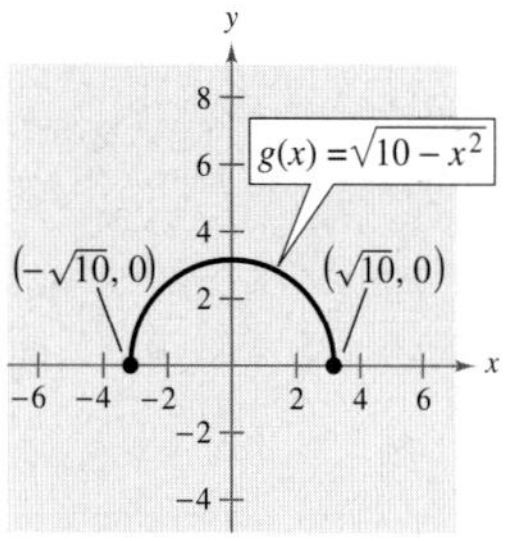

Zeros of g: $x = \pm\sqrt{10}$

FIGURE 1.56

c.
$$\frac{2t - 3}{t + 5} = 0 \qquad \text{Set } h(t) \text{ equal to 0.}$$
$$2t - 3 = 0 \qquad \text{Multiply each side by } t + 5.$$
$$2t = 3 \qquad \text{Add 3 to each side.}$$
$$t = \frac{3}{2} \qquad \text{Divide each side by 2.}$$

The zero of h is $t = \frac{3}{2}$. In Figure 1.57, note that the graph of h has $\left(\frac{3}{2}, 0\right)$ as its t-intercept.

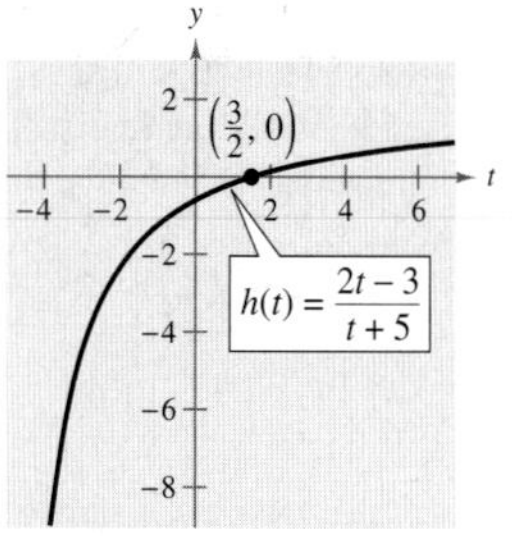

Zero of h: $t = \frac{3}{2}$

FIGURE 1.57

CHECKPoint Now try Exercise 23.

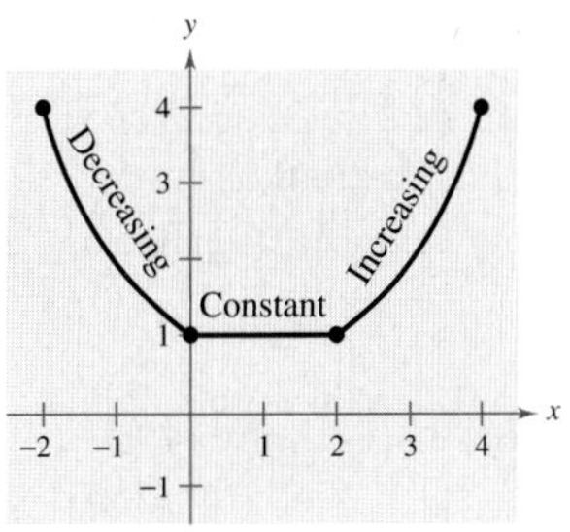

FIGURE 1.58

Increasing and Decreasing Functions

The more you know about the graph of a function, the more you know about the function itself. Consider the graph shown in Figure 1.58. As you move from *left to right*, this graph falls from $x = -2$ to $x = 0$, is constant from $x = 0$ to $x = 2$, and rises from $x = 2$ to $x = 4$.

Increasing, Decreasing, and Constant Functions

A function f is **increasing** on an interval if, for any x_1 and x_2 in the interval, $x_1 < x_2$ implies $f(x_1) < f(x_2)$.

A function f is **decreasing** on an interval if, for any x_1 and x_2 in the interval, $x_1 < x_2$ implies $f(x_1) > f(x_2)$.

A function f is **constant** on an interval if, for any x_1 and x_2 in the interval, $f(x_1) = f(x_2)$.

Example 4 Increasing and Decreasing Functions

Use the graphs in Figure 1.59 to describe the increasing or decreasing behavior of each function.

Solution

a. This function is increasing over the entire real line.

b. This function is increasing on the interval $(-\infty, -1)$, decreasing on the interval $(-1, 1)$, and increasing on the interval $(1, \infty)$.

c. This function is increasing on the interval $(-\infty, 0)$, constant on the interval $(0, 2)$, and decreasing on the interval $(2, \infty)$.

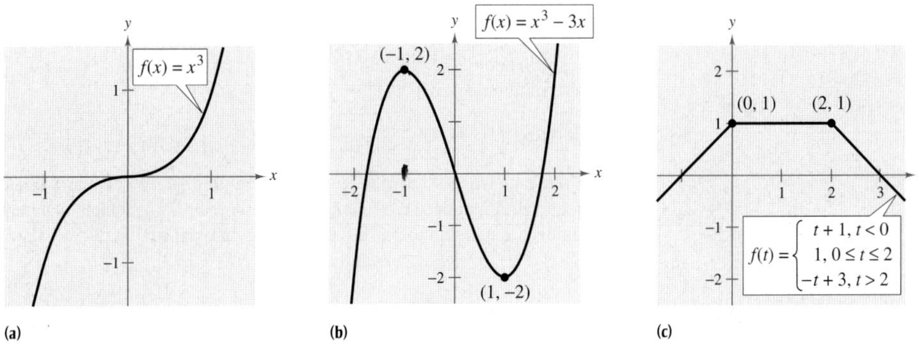

FIGURE 1.59

CHECKPoint Now try Exercise 41.

To help you decide whether a function is increasing, decreasing, or constant on an interval, you can evaluate the function for several values of x. However, calculus is needed to determine, for certain, all intervals on which a function is increasing, decreasing, or constant.

Extra Example 4

Use the graph shown to describe the increasing or decreasing behavior of the function $f(x) = x^3 + 3x^2 - 1$.

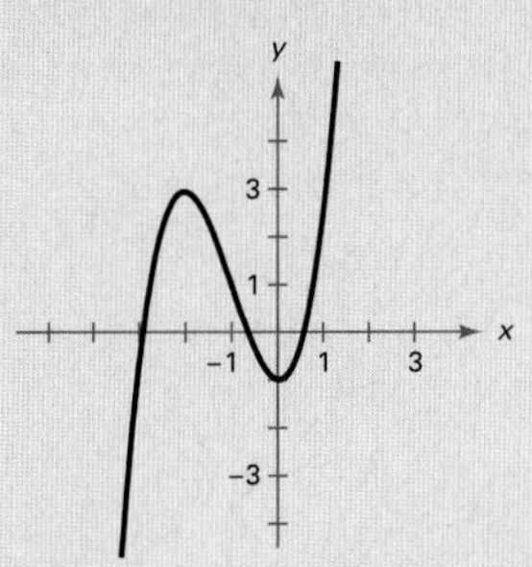

The function is increasing on the interval $(-\infty, -2)$, decreasing on the interval $(-2, 0)$, and increasing on the interval $(0, \infty)$.

Extra Example 5

Use a graphing utility to approximate the relative maximum of the function $f(x) = -4x^2 - 7x + 3$.

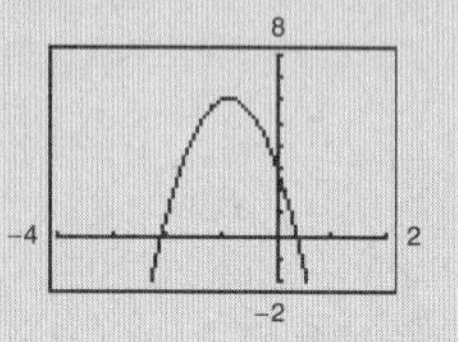

Max: (−0.875, 6.063)

Study Tip

A relative minimum or relative maximum is also referred to as a *local* minimum or *local* maximum.

The points at which a function changes its increasing, decreasing, or constant behavior are helpful in determining the **relative minimum** or **relative maximum** values of the function.

Definitions of Relative Minimum and Relative Maximum

A function value $f(a)$ is called a **relative minimum** of f if there exists an interval (x_1, x_2) that contains a such that

$$x_1 < x < x_2 \quad \text{implies} \quad f(a) \le f(x).$$

A function value $f(a)$ is called a **relative maximum** of f if there exists an interval (x_1, x_2) that contains a such that

$$x_1 < x < x_2 \quad \text{implies} \quad f(a) \ge f(x).$$

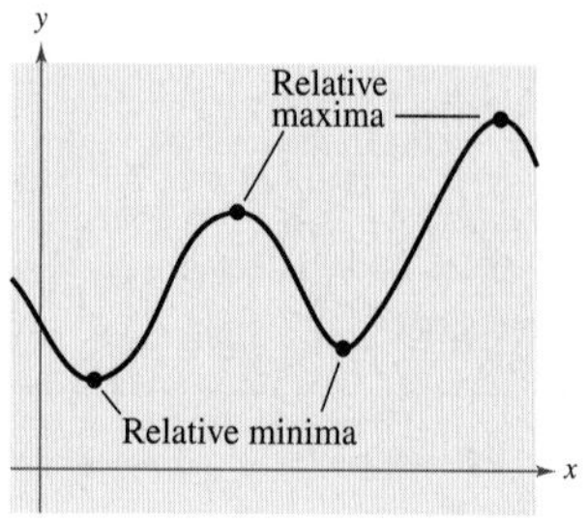

FIGURE 1.60

Figure 1.60 shows several different examples of relative minima and relative maxima. In Section 2.1, you will study a technique for finding the *exact point* at which a second-degree polynomial function has a relative minimum or relative maximum. For the time being, however, you can use a graphing utility to find reasonable approximations of these points.

Example 5 Approximating a Relative Minimum

Use a graphing utility to approximate the relative minimum of the function given by $f(x) = 3x^2 - 4x - 2$.

Solution

The graph of f is shown in Figure 1.61. By using the *zoom* and *trace* features or the *minimum* feature of a graphing utility, you can estimate that the function has a relative minimum at the point

$(0.67, -3.33)$. Relative minimum

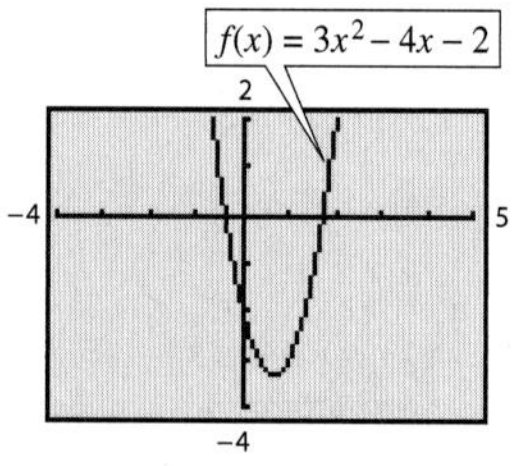

FIGURE 1.61

Later, in Section 2.1, you will be able to determine that the exact point at which the relative minimum occurs is $\left(\frac{2}{3}, -\frac{10}{3}\right)$.

CHECK*Point* Now try Exercise 57.

You can also use the *table* feature of a graphing utility to approximate numerically the relative minimum of the function in Example 5. Using a table that begins at 0.6 and increments the value of x by 0.01, you can approximate that the minimum of $f(x) = 3x^2 - 4x - 2$ occurs at the point $(0.67, -3.33)$.

TECHNOLOGY

If you use a graphing utility to estimate the x- and y-values of a relative minimum or relative maximum, the *zoom* feature will often produce graphs that are nearly flat. To overcome this problem, you can manually change the vertical setting of the viewing window. The graph will stretch vertically if the values of Ymin and Ymax are closer together.

Average Rate of Change

In Section 1.3, you learned that the slope of a line can be interpreted as a *rate of change*. For a nonlinear graph whose slope changes at each point, the **average rate of change** between any two points $(x_1, f(x_1))$ and $(x_2, f(x_2))$ is the slope of the line through the two points (see Figure 1.62). The line through the two points is called the **secant line,** and the slope of this line is denoted as m_{sec}.

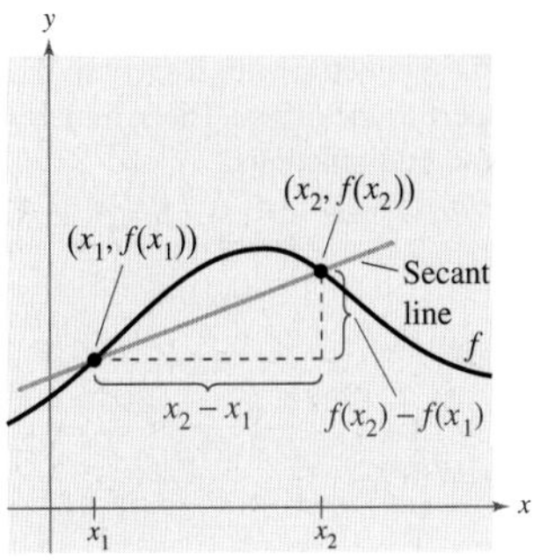

FIGURE 1.62

$$\text{Average rate of change of } f \text{ from } x_1 \text{ to } x_2 = \frac{f(x_2) - f(x_1)}{x_2 - x_1}$$
$$= \frac{\text{change in } y}{\text{change in } x}$$
$$= m_{sec}$$

Example 6 Average Rate of Change of a Function

Find the average rates of change of $f(x) = x^3 - 3x$ (a) from $x_1 = -2$ to $x_2 = 0$ and (b) from $x_1 = 0$ to $x_2 = 1$ (see Figure 1.63).

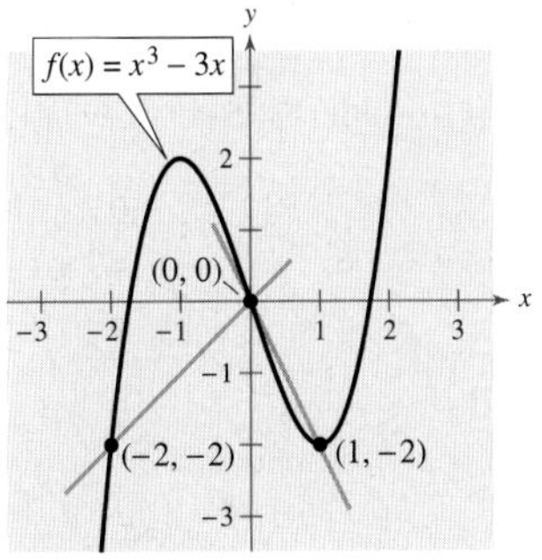

FIGURE 1.63

Solution

a. The average rate of change of f from $x_1 = -2$ to $x_2 = 0$ is

$$\frac{f(x_2) - f(x_1)}{x_2 - x_1} = \frac{f(0) - f(-2)}{0 - (-2)} = \frac{0 - (-2)}{2} = 1.$$ Secant line has positive slope.

b. The average rate of change of f from $x_1 = 0$ to $x_2 = 1$ is

$$\frac{f(x_2) - f(x_1)}{x_2 - x_1} = \frac{f(1) - f(0)}{1 - 0} = \frac{-2 - 0}{1} = -2.$$ Secant line has negative slope.

CHECKPoint Now try Exercise 75.

Example 7 Finding Average Speed

The distance s (in feet) a moving car is from a stoplight is given by the function $s(t) = 20t^{3/2}$, where t is the time (in seconds). Find the average speed of the car (a) from $t_1 = 0$ to $t_2 = 4$ seconds and (b) from $t_1 = 4$ to $t_2 = 9$ seconds.

Solution

a. The average speed of the car from $t_1 = 0$ to $t_2 = 4$ seconds is

$$\frac{s(t_2) - s(t_1)}{t_2 - t_1} = \frac{s(4) - s(0)}{4 - (0)} = \frac{160 - 0}{4} = 40 \text{ feet per second.}$$

b. The average speed of the car from $t_1 = 4$ to $t_2 = 9$ seconds is

$$\frac{s(t_2) - s(t_1)}{t_2 - t_1} = \frac{s(9) - s(4)}{9 - 4} = \frac{540 - 160}{5} = 76 \text{ feet per second.}$$

CHECKPoint Now try Exercise 113.

Extra Example 6

Find the average rates of change of $f(x) = x^2 - 2x$ (a) from $x_1 = -1$ to $x_2 = 3$ and (b) from $x_1 = 0$ to $x_2 = 1$.

0; −1

Extra Example 7

The distance s (in feet) of a moving car from a stoplight is given by the function $s(t) = 30t^{3/4}$. Find the average speed of the car from $t_1 = 0$ to $t_2 = 5$ seconds.

20.06 feet per second

Extra Example 8

Determine whether $f(x) = 5 - 3x$ is even, odd, or neither.

Neither even nor odd

Closing the Lesson

Have students summarize the major points of the lesson and answer the Essential Question: How is the graph of a function used to determine the key elements of that function?

- **Identify zeros of a given function.**
- **Identify relative minima and maxima for a given function.**
- **Identify functions as increasing, decreasing, or constant over a given interval.**
- **Find the average rate of change for a function between two points by finding the slope of the secant line.**
- **Identify a function as odd or even by studying the symmetry of its graph.**

Even and Odd Functions

In Section 1.2, you studied different types of symmetry of a graph. In the terminology of functions, a function is said to be **even** if its graph is symmetric with respect to the y-axis and to be **odd** if its graph is symmetric with respect to the origin. The symmetry tests in Section 1.2 yield the following tests for even and odd functions.

Tests for Even and Odd Functions

A function $y = f(x)$ is **even** if, for each x in the domain of f,

$$f(-x) = f(x).$$

A function $y = f(x)$ is **odd** if, for each x in the domain of f,

$$f(-x) = -f(x).$$

Example 8 Even and Odd Functions

a. The function $g(x) = x^3 - x$ is odd because $g(-x) = -g(x)$, as follows.

$g(-x) = (-x)^3 - (-x)$	Substitute $-x$ for x.
$= -x^3 + x$	Simplify.
$= -(x^3 - x)$	Distributive Property
$= -g(x)$	Test for odd function

b. The function $h(x) = x^2 + 1$ is even because $h(-x) = h(x)$, as follows.

$h(-x) = (-x)^2 + 1$	Substitute $-x$ for x.
$= x^2 + 1$	Simplify.
$= h(x)$	Test for even function

The graphs and symmetry of these two functions are shown in Figure 1.64.

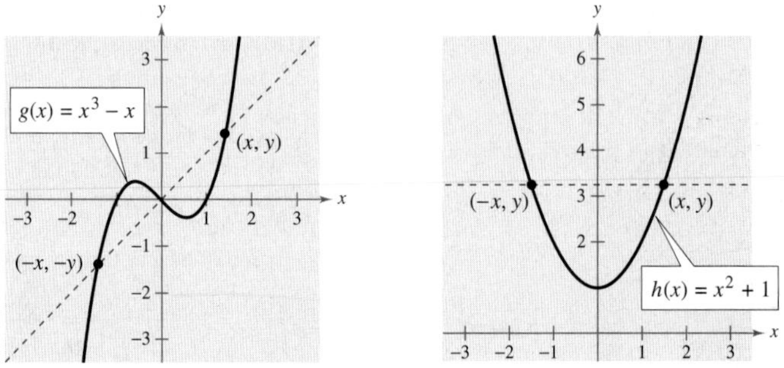

(a) Symmetric to origin: Odd Function

(b) Symmetric to y-axis: Even Function

FIGURE 1.64

CHECKPoint Now try Exercise 83.

1.5 EXERCISES

See www.CalcChat.com for worked-out solutions to odd-numbered exercises.

VOCABULARY: Fill in the blanks.

1. The graph of a function f is the collection of ordered pairs $(x, f(x))$ such that x is in the domain of f.
2. The Vertical Line Test is used to determine whether the graph of an equation is a function of y in terms of x.
3. The zeros of a function f are the values of x for which $f(x) = 0$.
4. A function f is ________ on an interval if, for any x_1 and x_2 in the interval, $x_1 < x_2$ implies $f(x_1) > f(x_2)$. decreasing
5. A function value $f(a)$ is a relative ________ of f if there exists an interval (x_1, x_2) containing a such that $x_1 < x < x_2$ implies $f(a) \geq f(x)$. maximum
6. The ________ ________ ________ ________ between any two points $(x_1, f(x_1))$ and $(x_2, f(x_2))$ is the slope of the line through the two points, and this line is called the ________ line. average rate of change; secant
7. A function f is odd if, for each x in the domain of f, $f(-x) = -f(x)$.
8. A function f is even if its graph is symmetric with respect to the y-axis.

SKILLS AND APPLICATIONS

In Exercises 9–12, use the graph of the function to find the domain and range of f. 9–12. See margin.

9.
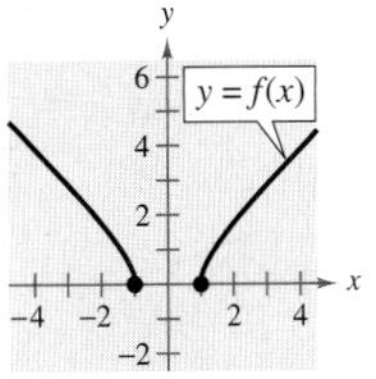

10.
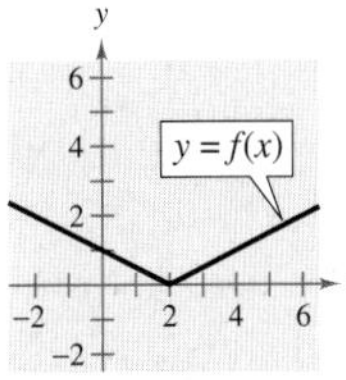

11.
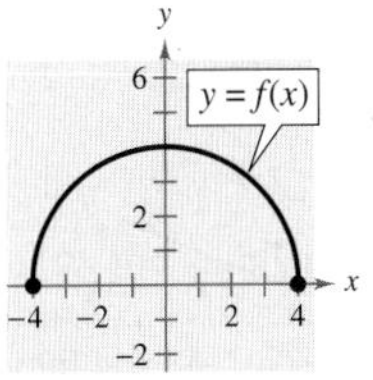

12.
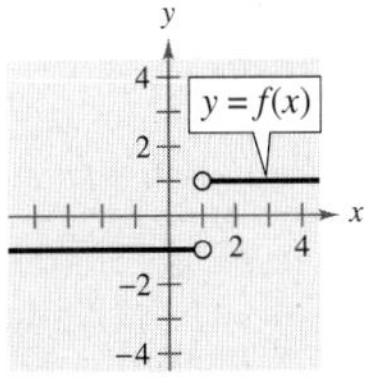

In Exercises 13–16, use the graph of the function to find the domain and range of f and the indicated function values.

13. (a) $f(-2)$ (b) $f(-1)$ (c) $f(\frac{1}{2})$ (d) $f(1)$

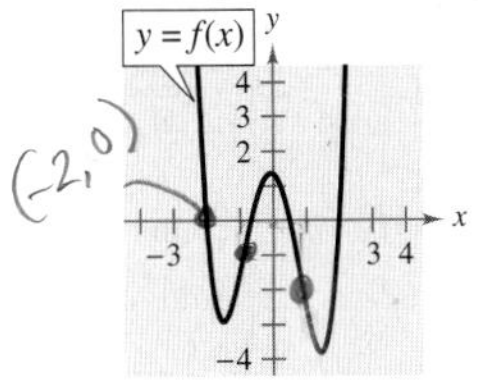

14. (a) $f(-1)$ (b) $f(2)$ (c) $f(0)$ (d) $f(1)$

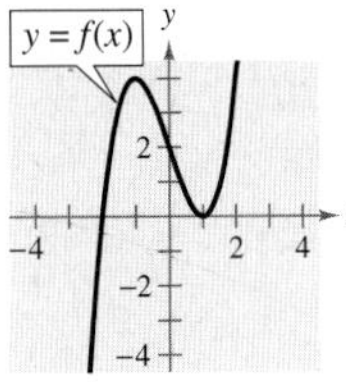

13–16. See margin.

15. (a) $f(2)$ (b) $f(1)$ (c) $f(3)$ (d) $f(-1)$

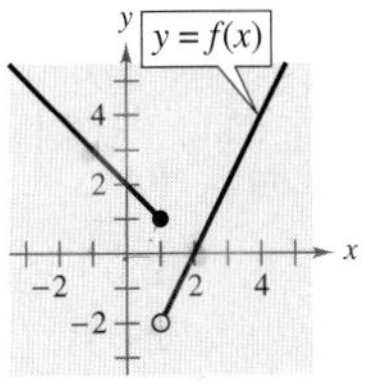

16. (a) $f(-2)$ (b) $f(1)$ (c) $f(0)$ (d) $f(2)$

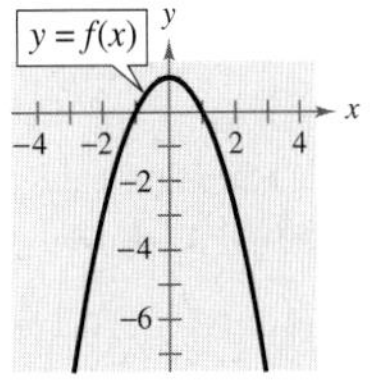

In Exercises 17–22, use the Vertical Line Test to determine whether y is a function of x. To print an enlarged copy of the graph, go to the website *www.mathgraphs.com*.

17. $y = \frac{1}{2}x^2$ Function

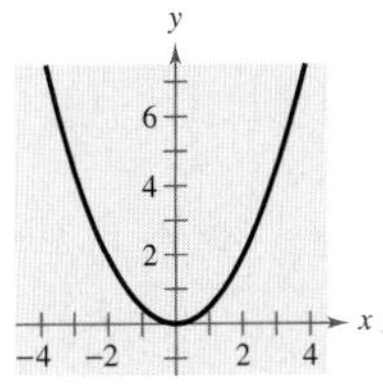

18. $y = \frac{1}{4}x^3$ Function

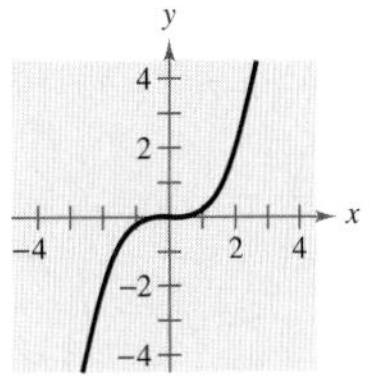

19. $x - y^2 = 1$ Not a function

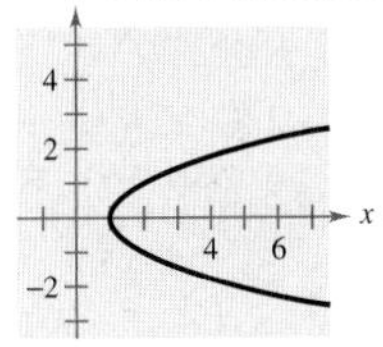

20. $x^2 + y^2 = 25$ Not a function

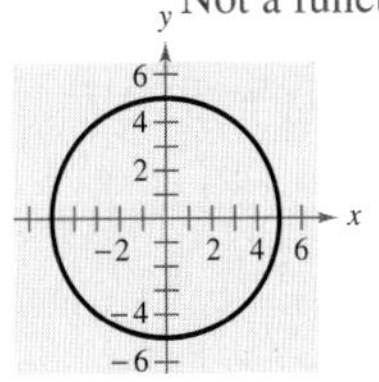

4 PRACTICE AND APPLY

Assignment Guide

Transparencies Available
Available at the Instructor's companion site.

Average:
Day 1: pp. 61–65
Exs. 1–12, 13–81 odd, 83–106, 110, 111–117 odd, 121–126, 131, 136

Advanced:
Day 1: pp. 61–65
Exs. 1–8, 10–20 even, 33–38, 40–118 even, 121–136

Block:
pp. 61–65
Exs. 1–12, 13–81 odd, 83–106, 110, 111–117 odd, 121–126, 131, 136 (with 1.6)

9. Domain: $(-\infty, -1] \cup [1, \infty)$
Range: $[0, \infty)$
10. Domain: $(-\infty, \infty)$
Range: $[0, \infty)$
11. Domain: $[-4, 4]$
Range: $[0, 4]$
12. Domain: $(-\infty, 1) \cup (1, \infty)$
Range: $-1, 1$
13. Domain: $(-\infty, \infty)$;
Range: $[-4, \infty)$
(a) 0 (b) -1
(c) 0 (d) -2
14. Domain: $(-\infty, \infty)$;
Range: $(-\infty, \infty)$
(a) 4 (b) 4 (c) 2 (d) 0
15. Domain: $(-\infty, \infty)$;
Range: $(-2, \infty)$
(a) 0 (b) 1 (c) 2 (d) 3
16. Domain: $(-\infty, \infty)$;
Range: $(-\infty, 1]$
(a) -3 (b) 0
(c) 1 (d) -3

21. $x^2 = 2xy - 1$ Function

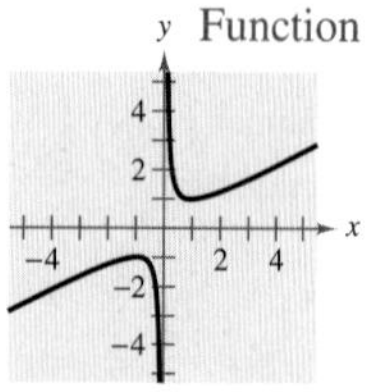

22. $x = |y + 2|$ Not a function

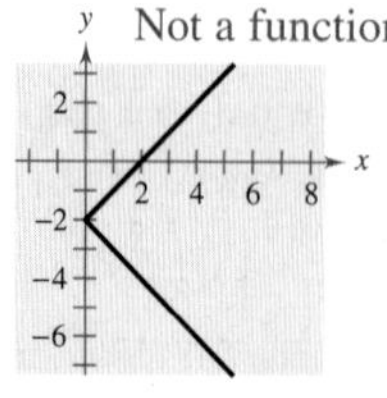

43. $f(x) = |x + 1| + |x - 1|$

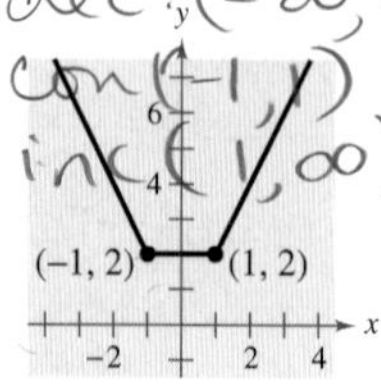

44. $f(x) = \dfrac{x^2 + x + 1}{x + 1}$

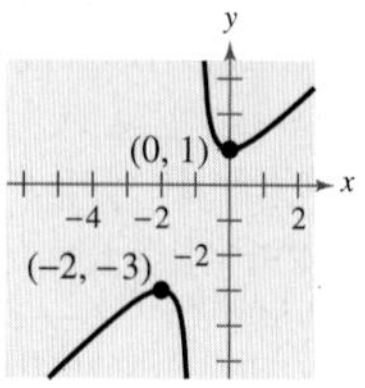

In Exercises 23–32, find the zeros of the function algebraically.

23. $f(x) = 2x^2 - 7x - 30$ $-\frac{5}{2}, 6$

24. $f(x) = 3x^2 + 22x - 16$ $-8, \frac{2}{3}$

25. $f(x) = \dfrac{x}{9x^2 - 4}$ 0

26. $f(x) = \dfrac{x^2 - 9x + 14}{4x}$ 2, 7

27. $f(x) = \frac{1}{2}x^3 - x$ $0, \pm\sqrt{2}$

28. $f(x) = x^3 - 4x^2 - 9x + 36$ $\pm 3, 4$

29. $f(x) = 4x^3 - 24x^2 - x + 6$ $\pm\frac{1}{2}, 6$

30. $f(x) = 9x^4 - 25x^2$ $0, \pm\frac{5}{3}$

31. $f(x) = \sqrt{2x} - 1$ $\frac{1}{2}$

32. $f(x) = \sqrt{3x + 2}$ $-\frac{2}{3}$

45. $f(x) = \begin{cases} x + 3, & x \le 0 \\ 3, & 0 < x \le 2 \\ 2x + 1, & x > 2 \end{cases}$

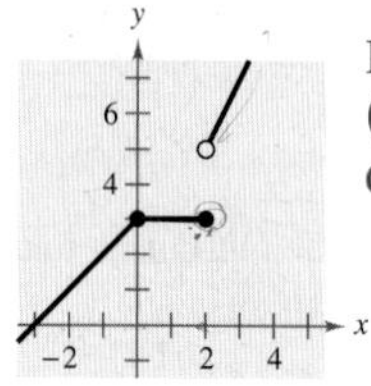

Increasing on $(-\infty, 0)$, $(2, \infty)$; Constant on $(0, 2)$

In Exercises 33–38, (a) use a graphing utility to graph the function and find the zeros of the function and (b) verify your results from part (a) algebraically. 33–38. See margin.

33. $f(x) = 3 + \dfrac{5}{x}$

34. $f(x) = x(x - 7)$

35. $f(x) = \sqrt{2x + 11}$

36. $f(x) = \sqrt{3x - 14} - 8$

37. $f(x) = \dfrac{3x - 1}{x - 6}$

38. $f(x) = \dfrac{2x^2 - 9}{3 - x}$

46. $f(x) = \begin{cases} 2x + 1, & x \le -1 \\ x^2 - 2, & x > -1 \end{cases}$

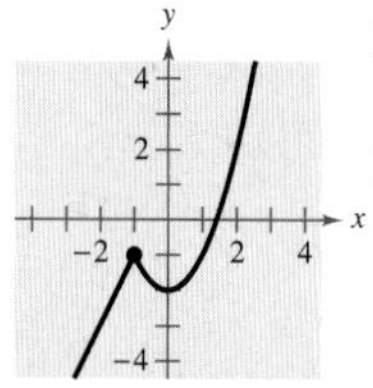

Increasing on $(-\infty, -1)$, $(0, \infty)$; Decreasing on $(-1, 0)$

In Exercises 39–46, determine the intervals over which the function is increasing, decreasing, or constant.

39. $f(x) = \frac{3}{2}x$ 39–44. See margin.

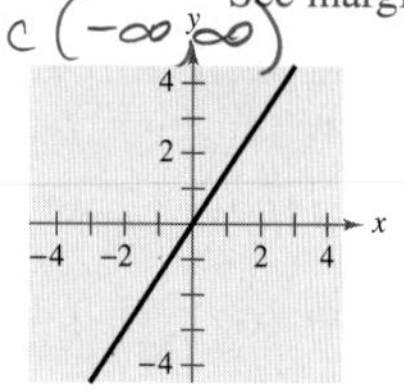

40. $f(x) = x^2 - 4x$

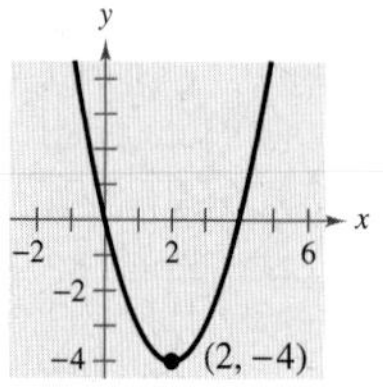

41. $f(x) = x^3 - 3x^2 + 2$

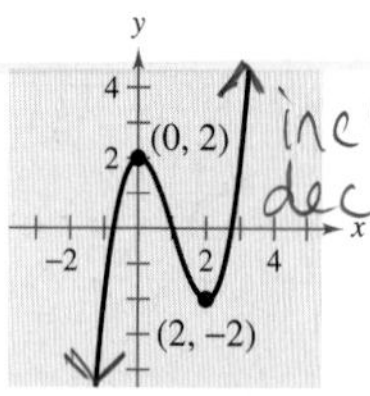

42. $f(x) = \sqrt{x^2 - 1}$

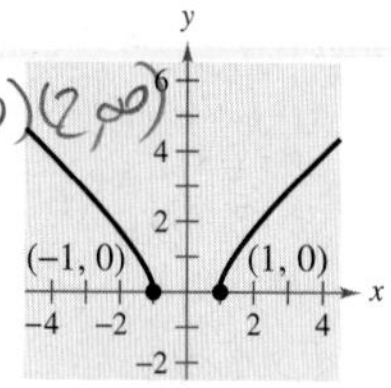

In Exercises 47–56, (a) use a graphing utility to graph the function and visually determine the intervals over which the function is increasing, decreasing, or constant, and (b) make a table of values to verify whether the function is increasing, decreasing, or constant over the intervals you identified in part (a). 47–56. See margin.

47. $f(x) = 3$

48. $g(x) = x$

49. $g(s) = \dfrac{s^2}{4}$

50. $h(x) = x^2 - 4$

51. $f(t) = -t^4$

52. $f(x) = 3x^4 - 6x^2$

53. $f(x) = \sqrt{1 - x}$

54. $f(x) = x\sqrt{x + 3}$

55. $f(x) = x^{3/2}$

56. $f(x) = x^{2/3}$

33.

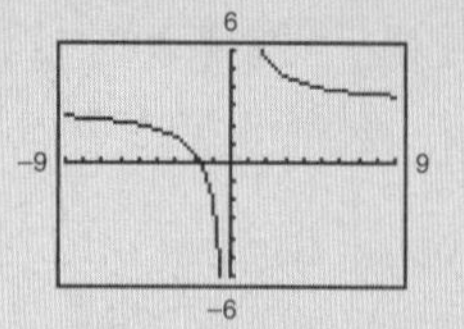

$-\frac{5}{3}$

34.

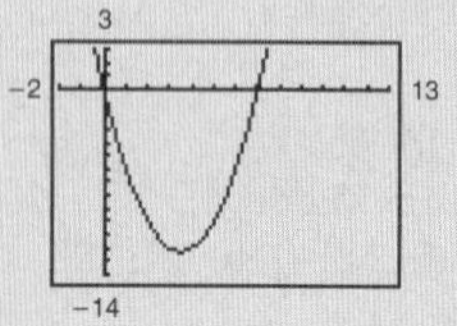

0, 7

35.

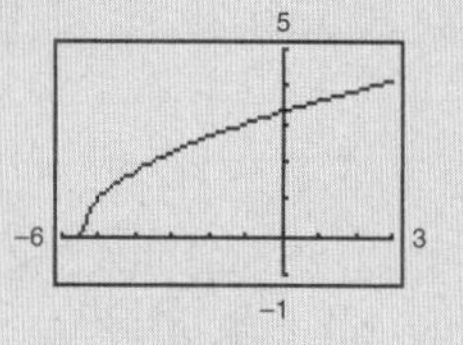

$-\frac{11}{2}$

36.

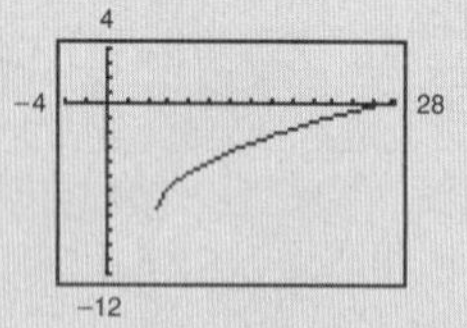

26

37.

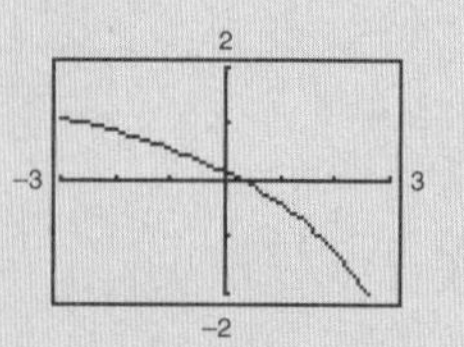

$\frac{1}{3}$

38.

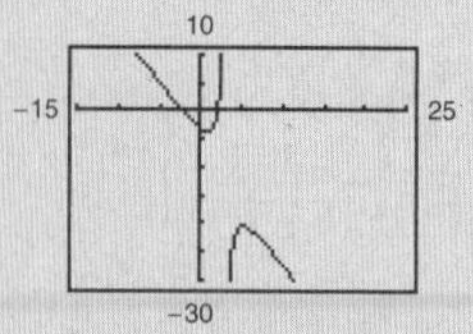

$\pm\frac{3\sqrt{2}}{2}$

39. Increasing on $(-\infty, \infty)$

40. Increasing on $(2, \infty)$; Decreasing on $(-\infty, 2)$

41. Increasing on $(-\infty, 0)$, $(2, \infty)$ Decreasing on $(0, 2)$

42. Increasing on $(1, \infty)$; Decreasing on $(-\infty, -1)$

43. Increasing on $(1, \infty)$; Decreasing on $(-\infty, -1)$ Constant on $(-1, 1)$

44. Increasing on $(-\infty, -2)$, $(0, \infty)$ Decreasing on $(-2, -1)$, $(-1, 0)$

47.

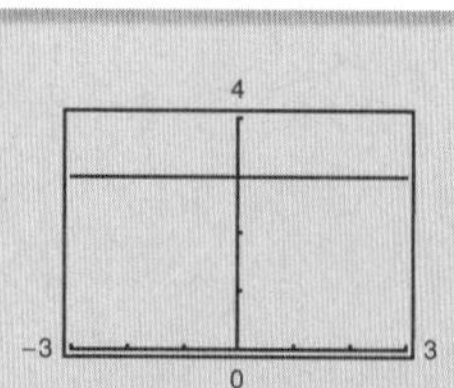

Constant on $(-\infty, \infty)$

48.

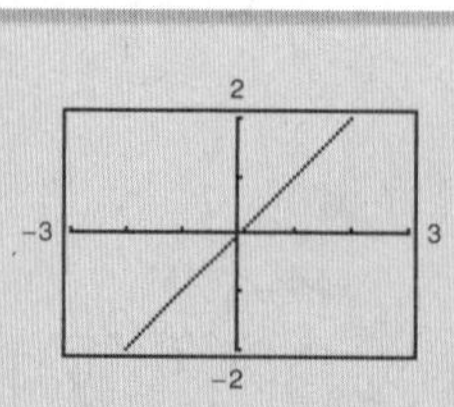

Increasing on $(-\infty, \infty)$

49.

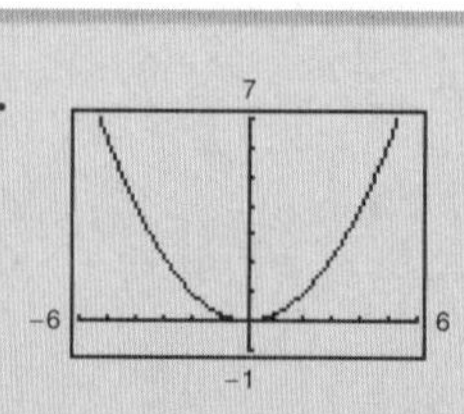

Decreasing on $(-\infty, 0)$ Increasing on $(0, \infty)$

50–56. See page 63.

In Exercises 57–66, use a graphing utility to graph the function and approximate (to two decimal places) any relative minimum or relative maximum values.

57. $f(x) = (x - 4)(x + 2)$
58. $f(x) = 3x^2 - 2x - 5$
59. $f(x) = -x^2 + 3x - 2$
60. $f(x) = -2x^2 + 9x$
61. $f(x) = x(x - 2)(x + 3)$
62. $f(x) = x^3 - 3x^2 - x + 1$
63. $g(x) = 2x^3 + 3x^2 - 12x$
64. $h(x) = x^3 - 6x^2 + 15$
65. $h(x) = (x - 1)\sqrt{x}$
66. $g(x) = x\sqrt{4 - x}$

57–66. See margin.

In Exercises 67–74, graph the function and determine the interval(s) for which $f(x) \geq 0$. 67–74. See margin.

67. $f(x) = 4 - x$
68. $f(x) = 4x + 2$
69. $f(x) = 9 - x^2$
70. $f(x) = x^2 - 4x$
71. $f(x) = \sqrt{x - 1}$
72. $f(x) = \sqrt{x + 2}$
73. $f(x) = -(1 + |x|)$
74. $f(x) = \frac{1}{2}(2 + |x|)$

In Exercises 75–82, find the average rate of change of the function from x_1 to x_2. 75–82. See margin.

Function	*x-Values*
75. $f(x) = -2x + 15$	$x_1 = 0, x_2 = 3$
76. $f(x) = 3x + 8$	$x_1 = 0, x_2 = 3$
77. $f(x) = x^2 + 12x - 4$	$x_1 = 1, x_2 = 5$
78. $f(x) = x^2 - 2x + 8$	$x_1 = 1, x_2 = 5$
79. $f(x) = x^3 - 3x^2 - x$	$x_1 = 1, x_2 = 3$
80. $f(x) = -x^3 + 6x^2 + x$	$x_1 = 1, x_2 = 6$
81. $f(x) = -\sqrt{x - 2} + 5$	$x_1 = 3, x_2 = 11$
82. $f(x) = -\sqrt{x + 1} + 3$	$x_1 = 3, x_2 = 8$

In Exercises 83–90, determine whether the function is even, odd, or neither. Then describe the symmetry. 83–90. See margin.

83. $f(x) = x^6 - 2x^2 + 3$
84. $h(x) = x^3 - 5$
85. $g(x) = x^3 - 5x$
86. $f(t) = t^2 + 2t - 3$
87. $h(x) = x\sqrt{x + 5}$
88. $f(x) = x\sqrt{1 - x^2}$
89. $f(s) = 4s^{3/2}$
90. $g(s) = 4s^{2/3}$

In Exercises 91–100, sketch a graph of the function and determine whether it is even, odd, or neither. Verify your answers algebraically. 91–100. See margin.

91. $f(x) = 5$
92. $f(x) = -9$
93. $f(x) = 3x - 2$
94. $f(x) = 5 - 3x$
95. $h(x) = x^2 - 4$
96. $f(x) = -x^2 - 8$
97. $f(x) = \sqrt{1 - x}$
98. $g(t) = \sqrt[3]{t - 1}$
99. $f(x) = |x + 2|$
100. $f(x) = -|x - 5|$

In Exercises 101–104, write the height h of the rectangle as a function of x.

101. $h = -x^2 + 4x - 3$

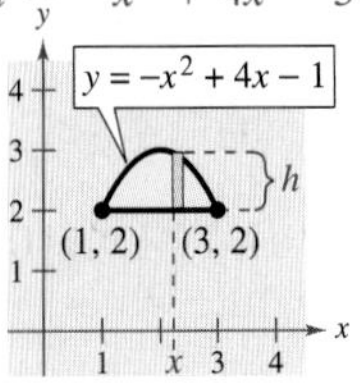

102. $h = 3 - 4x + x^2$

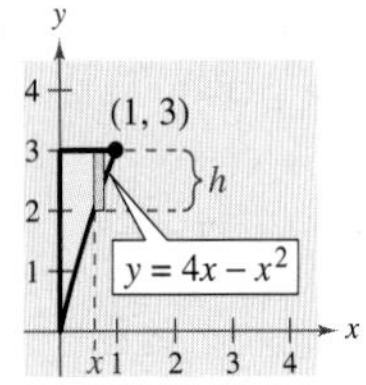

103.

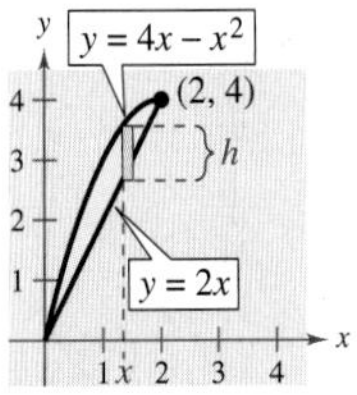

$h = 2x - x^2$

104.

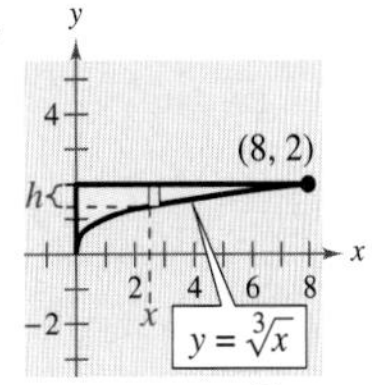

$h = 2 - \sqrt[3]{x}$

In Exercises 105–108, write the length L of the rectangle as a function of y.

105. $L = \frac{1}{2}y^2$

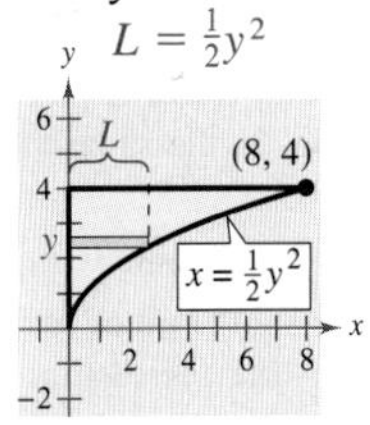

106. $L = 2 - \sqrt[3]{2y}$

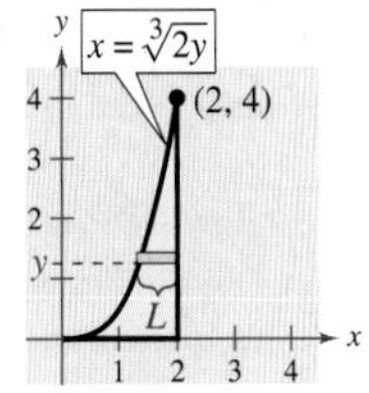

107. $L = 4 - y^2$

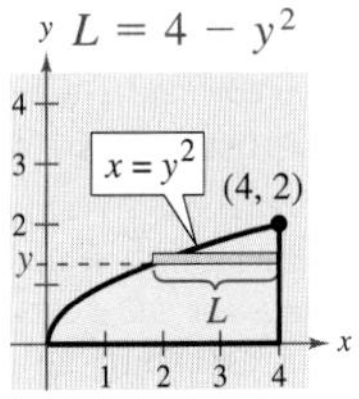

108. $L = \frac{2}{y}$

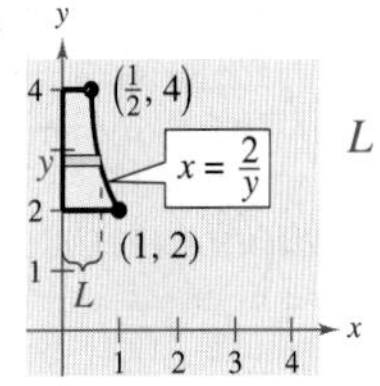

109. **ELECTRONICS** The number of lumens (time rate of flow of light) L from a fluorescent lamp can be approximated by the model See margin.

$$L = -0.294x^2 + 97.744x - 664.875, \quad 20 \leq x \leq 90$$

where x is the wattage of the lamp.

(a) Use a graphing utility to graph the function.

(b) Use the graph from part (a) to estimate the wattage necessary to obtain 2000 lumens.

50.

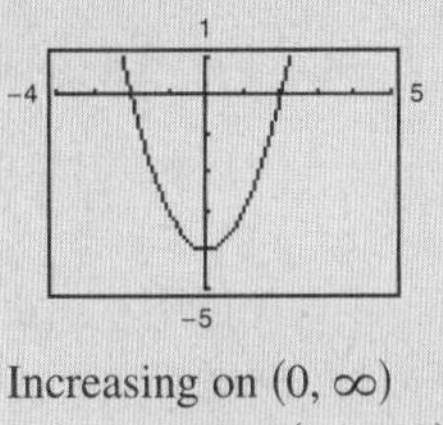

Increasing on $(0, \infty)$
Decreasing on $(-\infty, 0)$

51.

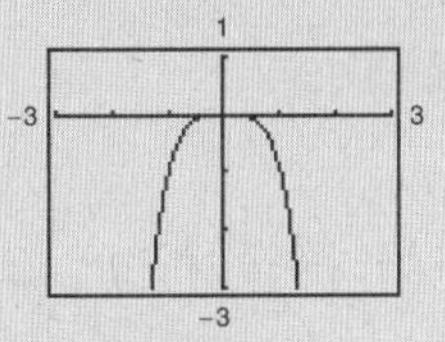

Increasing on $(-\infty, 0)$
Decreasing on $(0, \infty)$

52.

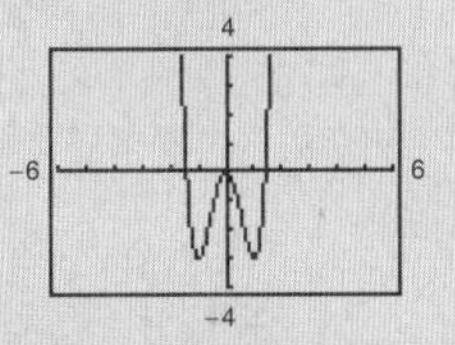

Increasing on $(-1, 0), (1, \infty)$
Decreasing on $(-\infty, -1), (0, 1)$

53.

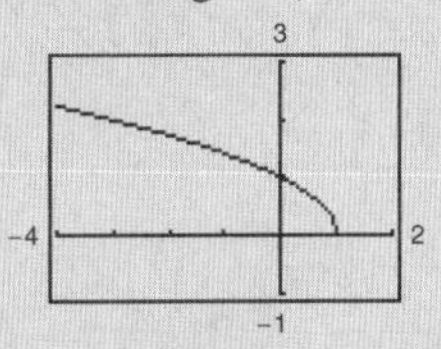

Decreasing on $(-\infty, 1)$

54.

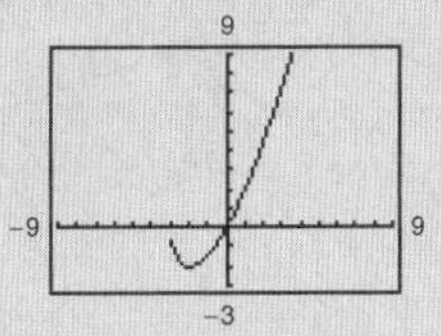

Increasing on $(-2, \infty)$
Decreasing on $(-3, -2)$

55.

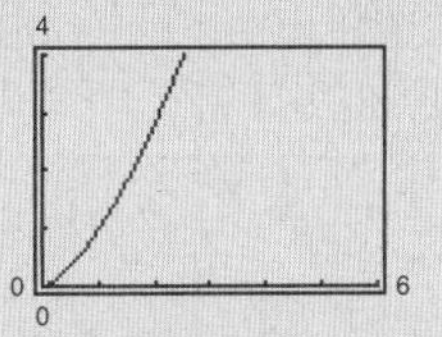

Increasing on $(0, \infty)$

56.

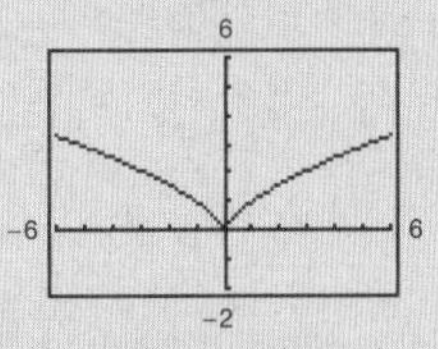

Increasing on $(0, \infty)$
Decreasing on $(-\infty, 0)$

57.

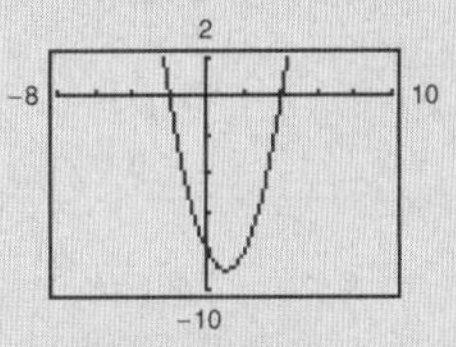

Relative minimum: $(1, -9)$

58.

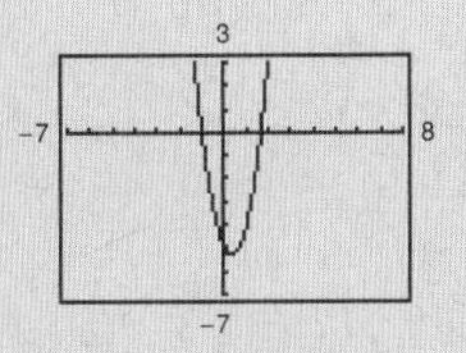

Relative minimum: $\left(\frac{1}{3}, -\frac{16}{3}\right)$

59.

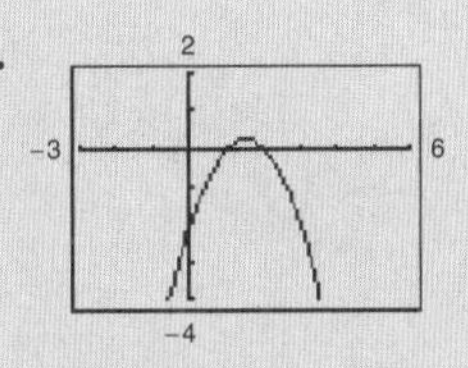

Relative maximum: $(1.5, 0.25)$

60.

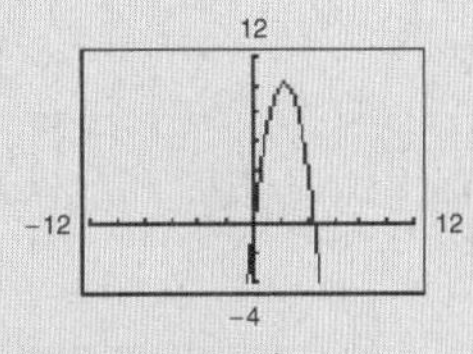

Relative maximum: $(2.25, 10.125)$

61–100, 109. See Additional Answers beginning on page AA1.

110. DATA ANALYSIS: TEMPERATURE The table shows the temperatures y (in degrees Fahrenheit) in a certain city over a 24-hour period. Let x represent the time of day, where $x = 0$ corresponds to 6 A.M. See margin.

Time, x	Temperature, y
0	34
2	50
4	60
6	64
8	63
10	59
12	53
14	46
16	40
18	36
20	34
22	37
24	45

A model that represents these data is given by

$$y = 0.026x^3 - 1.03x^2 + 10.2x + 34, \quad 0 \le x \le 24.$$

(a) Use a graphing utility to create a scatter plot of the data. Then graph the model in the same viewing window.

(b) How well does the model fit the data?

(c) Use the graph to approximate the times when the temperature was increasing and decreasing.

(d) Use the graph to approximate the maximum and minimum temperatures during this 24-hour period.

(e) Could this model be used to predict the temperatures in the city during the next 24-hour period? Why or why not?

111. COORDINATE AXIS SCALE Each function described below models the specified data for the years 1998 through 2008, with $t = 8$ corresponding to 1998. Estimate a reasonable scale for the vertical axis (e.g., hundreds, thousands, millions, etc.) of the graph and justify your answer. (There are many correct answers.)

(a) $f(t)$ represents the average salary of college professors. Ten thousands

(b) $f(t)$ represents the U.S. population. Ten millions

(c) $f(t)$ represents the percent of the civilian work force that is unemployed. Percents

112. GEOMETRY Corners of equal size are cut from a square with sides of length 8 meters (see figure). See margin.

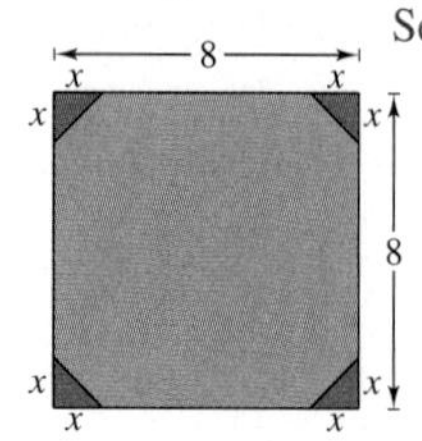

(a) Write the area A of the resulting figure as a function of x. Determine the domain of the function.

(b) Use a graphing utility to graph the area function over its domain. Use the graph to find the range of the function.

(c) Identify the figure that would result if x were chosen to be the maximum value in the domain of the function. What would be the length of each side of the figure?

113. ENROLLMENT RATE The enrollment rates r of children in preschool in the United States from 1970 through 2005 can be approximated by the model

$$r = -0.021t^2 + 1.44t + 39.3, \quad 0 \le t \le 35$$

where t represents the year, with $t = 0$ corresponding to 1970. (Source: U.S. Census Bureau) See margin.

(a) Use a graphing utility to graph the model.

(b) Find the average rate of change of the model from 1970 through 2005. Interpret your answer in the context of the problem.

114. VEHICLE TECHNOLOGY SALES The estimated revenues r (in millions of dollars) from sales of in-vehicle technologies in the United States from 2003 through 2008 can be approximated by the model

$$r = 157.30t^2 - 397.4t + 6114, \quad 3 \le t \le 8$$

See margin.

where t represents the year, with $t = 3$ corresponding to 2003. (Source: Consumer Electronics Association)

(a) Use a graphing utility to graph the model.

(b) Find the average rate of change of the model from 2003 through 2008. Interpret your answer in the context of the problem.

PHYSICS In Exercises 115–120, (a) use the position equation $s = -16t^2 + v_0t + s_0$ to write a function that represents the situation, (b) use a graphing utility to graph the function, (c) find the average rate of change of the function from t_1 to t_2, (d) describe the slope of the secant line through t_1 and t_2, (e) find the equation of the secant line through t_1 and t_2, and (f) graph the secant line in the same viewing window as your position function.

110. (a)

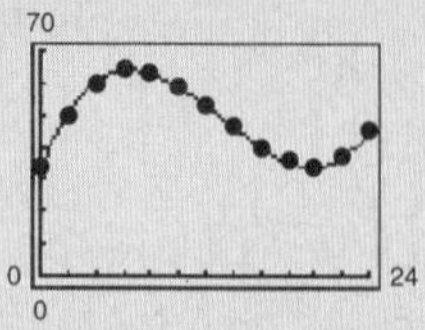

(b) The model fits the data very well.

(c) The temperature was increasing from 6 A.M. ($x = 0$) to noon ($x = 6$), and again from 2 A.M. ($x = 20$) to 6 A.M. ($x = 24$). The temperature was decreasing from noon to 2 A.M.

(d) The maximum temperature was 63.93°F and the minimum temperature was 33.98°F.

(e) Answers will vary.

112. (a) $A = 64 - 2x^2, \ 0 \le x \le 4$

(b)

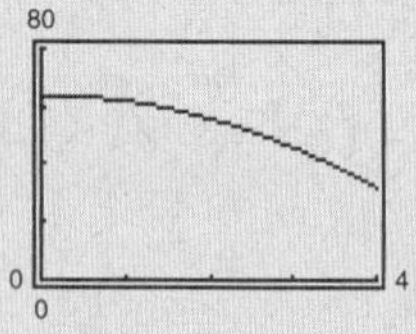

$32 \le A \le 64$

(c) Square with sides of $4\sqrt{2}$ m

113. (a)

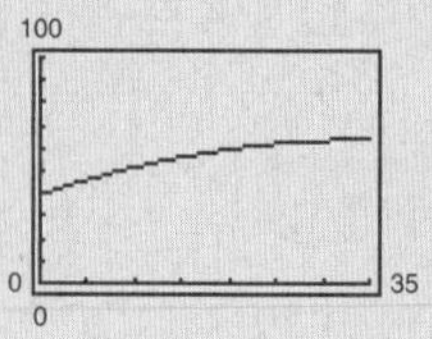

(b) The average rate of change from 1970 to 2005 is 0.705. The enrollment rate of children in preschool has slowly been increasing each year.

114. (a)

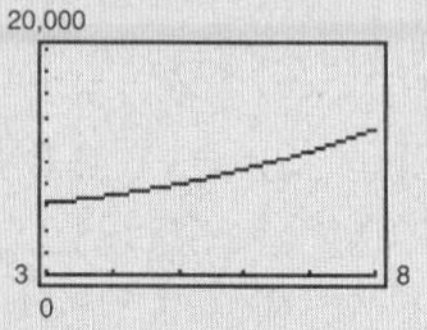

(b) The average rate of change from 2003 to 2008 is 1332.9 million. The revenues from sales of in-vehicle technologies has increased $1332.9 million each year.

115. (a) $s = -16t^2 + 64t + 6$

(b)

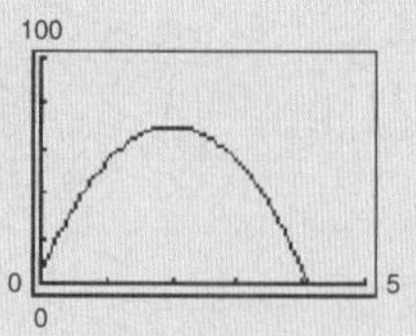

(c) Average rate of change = 16

(d) The slope of the secant line is positive.

(e) Secant line: $16t + 6$

(f)

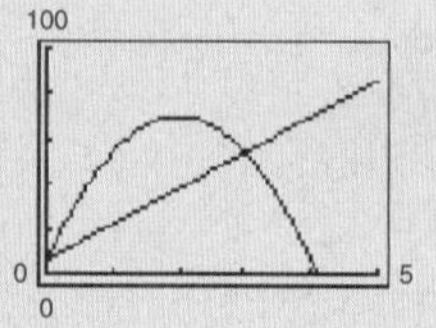

115. An object is thrown upward from a height of 6 feet at a velocity of 64 feet per second.

$t_1 = 0, t_2 = 3$ 115–120. See margin.

116. An object is thrown upward from a height of 6.5 feet at a velocity of 72 feet per second.

$t_1 = 0, t_2 = 4$

117. An object is thrown upward from ground level at a velocity of 120 feet per second.

$t_1 = 3, t_2 = 5$

118. An object is thrown upward from ground level at a velocity of 96 feet per second.

$t_1 = 2, t_2 = 5$

119. An object is dropped from a height of 120 feet.

$t_1 = 0, t_2 = 2$

120. An object is dropped from a height of 80 feet.

$t_1 = 1, t_2 = 2$

EXPLORATION

121–122. See margin.

TRUE OR FALSE? In Exercises 121 and 122, determine whether the statement is true or false. Justify your answer.

121. A function with a square root cannot have a domain that is the set of real numbers.

122. It is possible for an odd function to have the interval $[0, \infty)$ as its domain.

123. If f is an even function, determine whether g is even, odd, or neither. Explain. See margin.

(a) $g(x) = -f(x)$ (b) $g(x) = f(-x)$

(c) $g(x) = f(x) - 2$ (d) $g(x) = f(x - 2)$

124. THINK ABOUT IT Does the graph in Exercise 19 represent x as a function of y? Explain. See margin.

THINK ABOUT IT In Exercises 125–130, find the coordinates of a second point on the graph of a function f if the given point is on the graph and the function is (a) even and (b) odd. 125–130. See margin.

125. $\left(-\frac{3}{2}, 4\right)$ **126.** $\left(-\frac{5}{3}, -7\right)$

127. $(4, 9)$ **128.** $(5, -1)$

129. $(x, -y)$ **130.** $(2a, 2c)$

131. WRITING Use a graphing utility to graph each function. Write a paragraph describing any similarities and differences you observe among the graphs.

(a) $y = x$ (b) $y = x^2$ (c) $y = x^3$ See margin.

(d) $y = x^4$ (e) $y = x^5$ (f) $y = x^6$

132. CONJECTURE Use the results of Exercise 131 to make a conjecture about the graphs of $y = x^7$ and $y = x^8$. Use a graphing utility to graph the functions and compare the results with your conjecture. See margin.

133. Use the information in Example 7 to find the average speed of the car from $t_1 = 0$ to $t_2 = 9$ seconds. Explain why the result is less than the value obtained in part (b) of Example 7. See margin.

134. Graph each of the functions with a graphing utility. Determine whether the function is *even, odd,* or *neither.* See margin.

$f(x) = x^2 - x^4$

$g(x) = 2x^3 + 1$

$h(x) = x^5 - 2x^3 + x$

$j(x) = 2 - x^6 - x^8$

$k(x) = x^5 - 2x^4 + x - 2$

$p(x) = x^9 + 3x^5 - x^3 + x$

What do you notice about the equations of functions that are odd? What do you notice about the equations of functions that are even? Can you describe a way to identify a function as odd or even by inspecting the equation? Can you describe a way to identify a function as neither odd nor even by inspecting the equation?

135. WRITING Write a short paragraph describing three different functions that represent the behaviors of quantities between 1998 and 2009. Describe one quantity that decreased during this time, one that increased, and one that was constant. Present your results graphically. Answers will vary.

136. CAPSTONE Use the graph of the function to answer (a)–(e). See margin.

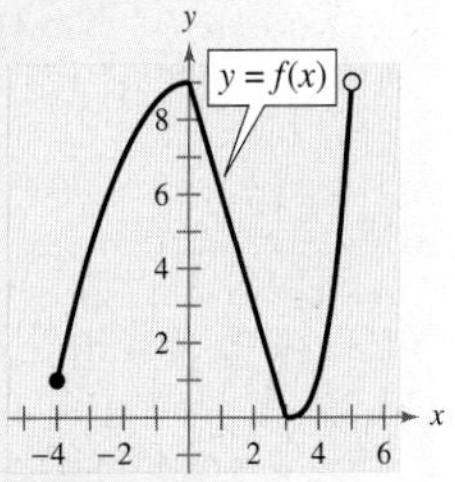

(a) Find the domain and range of f.

(b) Find the zero(s) of f.

(c) Determine the intervals over which f is increasing, decreasing, or constant.

(d) Approximate any relative minimum or relative maximum values of f.

(e) Is f even, odd, or neither?

5 ASSESS AND RETEACH

Daily Homework Quiz

Transparency Available
Available at the Instructor's companion site.

115. See margin on page 64.

116. (a) $s = -16t^2 + 72t + 6.5$

(b)

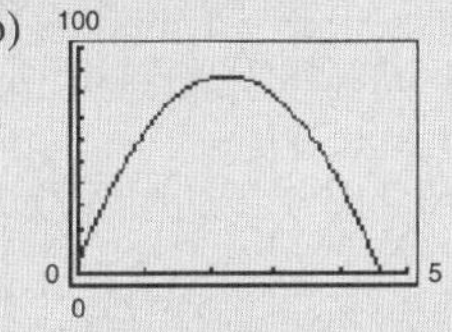

(c) Average rate of change $= 8$

(d) The slope of the secant line is positive.

(e) Secant line: $8t + 6.5$

(f)

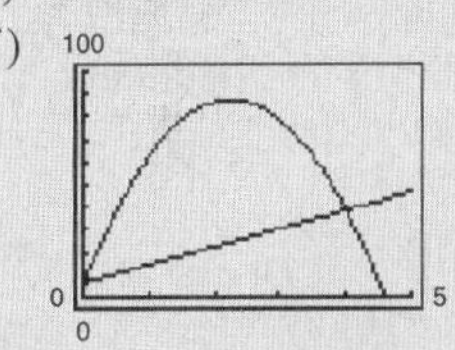

117. (a) $s = -16t^2 + 120t$

(b)

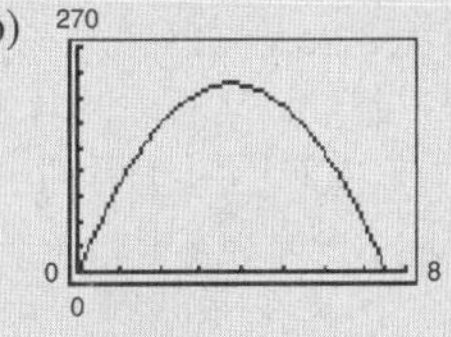

(c) Average rate of change $= -8$

(d) The slope of the secant line is negative.

(e) Secant line: $-8t + 240$

(f)

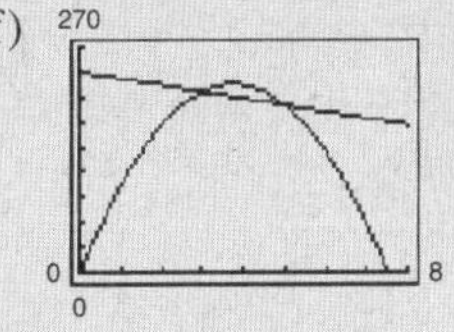

118. (a) $s = -16t^2 + 96t$

(b)

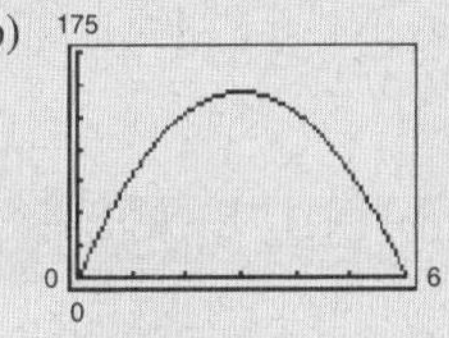

(c) Average rate of change $= -16$

(d) The slope of the secant line is negative.

(e) Secant line: $-16t + 160$

(f)

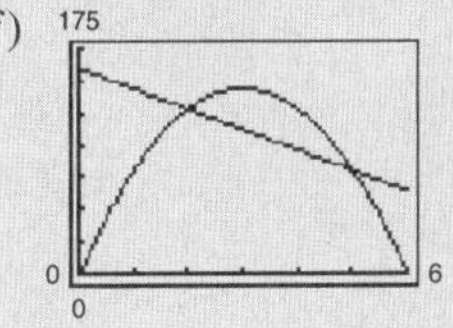

119. (a) $s = -16t^2 + 120$

(b)

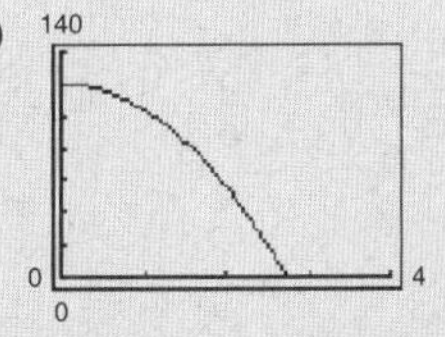

(c) Average rate of change $= -32$

(d) The slope of the secant line is negative.

(e) Secant line: $-32t + 120$

(f)

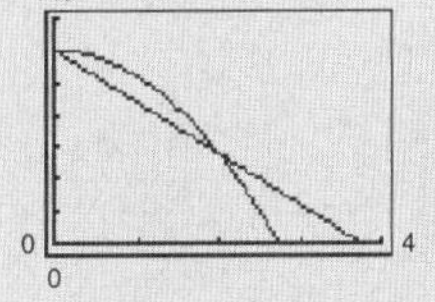

120–134, 136. See Additional Answers beginning on page AA1.

1 PLAN AND PREPARE

Warm-up Exercises

Transparency Available
Available at the Instructor's companion site.

Notetaking Guide

Transparency Available
Promotes interactive learning and notetaking skills. Available at the Instructor's companion site.

Animated Precalculus

An **Animated Precalculus** tutorial is available at the Student companion site for **Section 1.6.**

Pacing

Average: 1 day
Advanced: 1 day
Block: 0.5 block with 1.5

2 FOCUS AND MOTIVATE

Essential Question

What are the characteristics of the most commonly used functions in algebra? **Tell students that they will learn how to answer this question by identifying the domain, range, and important points for commonly used functions.**

What you should learn

- Identify and graph linear and squaring functions.
- Identify and graph cubic, square root, and reciprocal functions.
- Identify and graph step and other piecewise-defined functions.
- Recognize graphs of parent functions.

Why you should learn it

Step functions can be used to model real-life situations. For instance, in Exercise 69 on page 72, you will use a step function to model the cost of sending an overnight package from Los Angeles to Miami.

1.6 A Library of Parent Functions

Linear and Squaring Functions

One of the goals of this text is to enable you to recognize the basic shapes of the graphs of different types of functions. For instance, you know that the graph of the **linear function** $f(x) = ax + b$ is a line with slope $m = a$ and y-intercept at $(0, b)$. The graph of the linear function has the following characteristics.

- The domain of the function is the set of all real numbers.
- The range of the function is the set of all real numbers.
- The graph has an x-intercept of $(-b/m, 0)$ and a y-intercept of $(0, b)$.
- The graph is increasing if $m > 0$, decreasing if $m < 0$, and constant if $m = 0$.

Example 1 Writing a Linear Function

Write the linear function f for which $f(1) = 3$ and $f(4) = 0$.

Solution

To find the equation of the line that passes through $(x_1, y_1) = (1, 3)$ and $(x_2, y_2) = (4, 0)$, first find the slope of the line.

$$m = \frac{y_2 - y_1}{x_2 - x_1} = \frac{0 - 3}{4 - 1} = \frac{-3}{3} = -1$$

Next, use the point-slope form of the equation of a line.

$y - y_1 = m(x - x_1)$ Point-slope form

$y - 3 = -1(x - 1)$ Substitute for x_1, y_1, and m.

$y = -x + 4$ Simplify.

$f(x) = -x + 4$ Function notation

The graph of this function is shown in Figure 1.65.

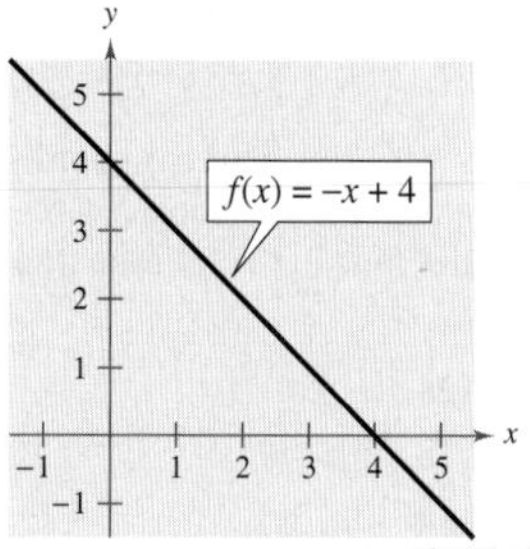

FIGURE 1.65

CHECKPoint Now try Exercise 11.

Resource Planning Guide

Chapter Resources
- Complete Solutions Guide

Workbooks
- Notetaking Guide
- Student Solutions Guide

Interactive Technology
- Instructor Success Organizer
- Notetaking Guide IAE
- Instructional DVDs
- Animated Precalculus
- PowerLecture with ExamView

There are two special types of linear functions, the **constant function** and the **identity function.** A constant function has the form

$$f(x) = c$$

and has the domain of all real numbers with a range consisting of a single real number c. The graph of a constant function is a horizontal line, as shown in Figure 1.66. The identity function has the form

$$f(x) = x.$$

Its domain and range are the set of all real numbers. The identity function has a slope of $m = 1$ and a y-intercept at $(0, 0)$. The graph of the identity function is a line for which each x-coordinate equals the corresponding y-coordinate. The graph is always increasing, as shown in Figure 1.67.

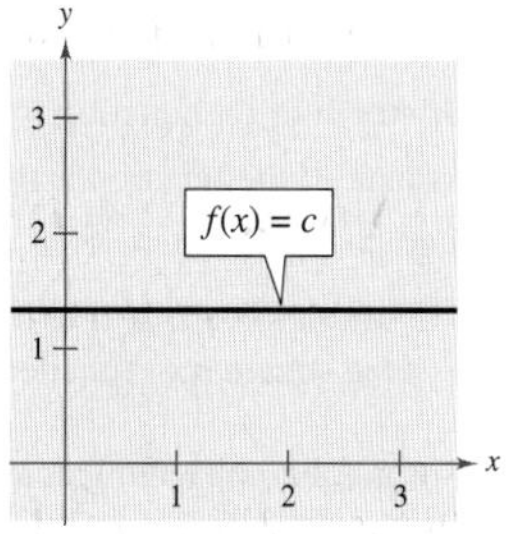

FIGURE 1.66

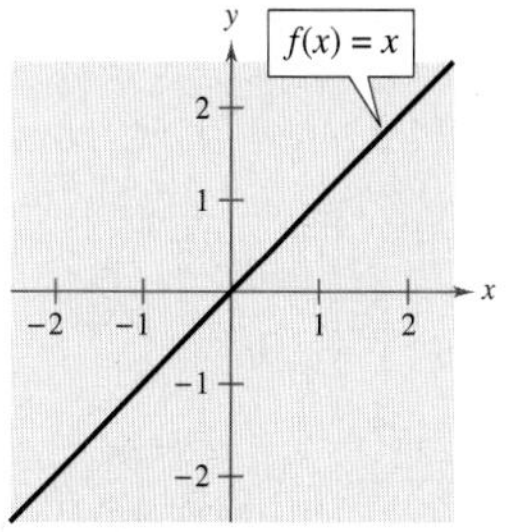

FIGURE 1.67

The graph of the **squaring function**

$$f(x) = x^2$$

is a U-shaped curve with the following characteristics.

- The domain of the function is the set of all real numbers.
- The range of the function is the set of all nonnegative real numbers.
- The function is even.
- The graph has an intercept at $(0, 0)$.
- The graph is decreasing on the interval $(-\infty, 0)$ and increasing on the interval $(0, \infty)$.
- The graph is symmetric with respect to the y-axis.
- The graph has a relative minimum at $(0, 0)$.

The graph of the squaring function is shown in Figure 1.68.

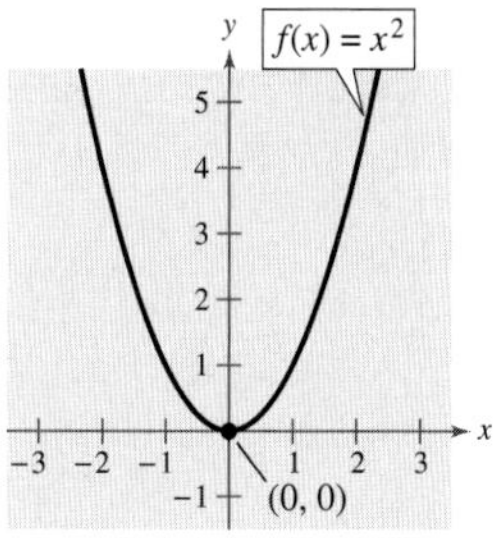

FIGURE 1.68

3 TEACH

Extra Example 1

Write the linear function $f(x)$ for which $f(-2) = 6$ and $f(4) = -9$.

$f(x) = -\frac{5}{2}x + 1$

Cubic, Square Root, and Reciprocal Functions

The basic characteristics of the graphs of the **cubic, square root,** and **reciprocal functions** are summarized below.

1. The graph of the *cubic* function $f(x) = x^3$ has the following characteristics.
- The domain of the function is the set of all real numbers.
- The range of the function is the set of all real numbers.
- The function is odd.
- The graph has an intercept at $(0, 0)$.
- The graph is increasing on the interval $(-\infty, \infty)$.
- The graph is symmetric with respect to the origin.

The graph of the cubic function is shown in Figure 1.69.

2. The graph of the *square root* function $f(x) = \sqrt{x}$ has the following characteristics.
- The domain of the function is the set of all nonnegative real numbers.
- The range of the function is the set of all nonnegative real numbers.
- The graph has an intercept at $(0, 0)$.
- The graph is increasing on the interval $(0, \infty)$.

The graph of the square root function is shown in Figure 1.70.

3. The graph of the *reciprocal* function $f(x) = \dfrac{1}{x}$ has the following characteristics.
- The domain of the function is $(-\infty, 0) \cup (0, \infty)$.
- The range of the function is $(-\infty, 0) \cup (0, \infty)$.
- The function is odd.
- The graph does not have any intercepts.
- The graph is decreasing on the intervals $(-\infty, 0)$ and $(0, \infty)$.
- The graph is symmetric with respect to the origin.

The graph of the reciprocal function is shown in Figure 1.71.

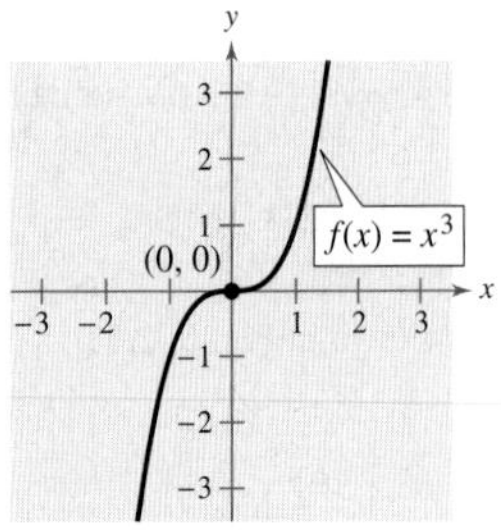

Cubic function
FIGURE 1.69

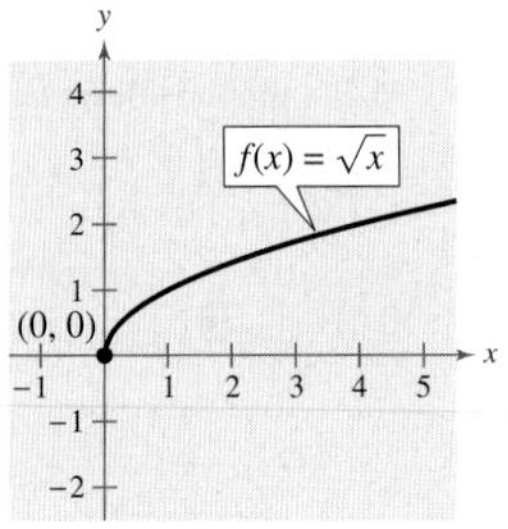

Square root function
FIGURE 1.70

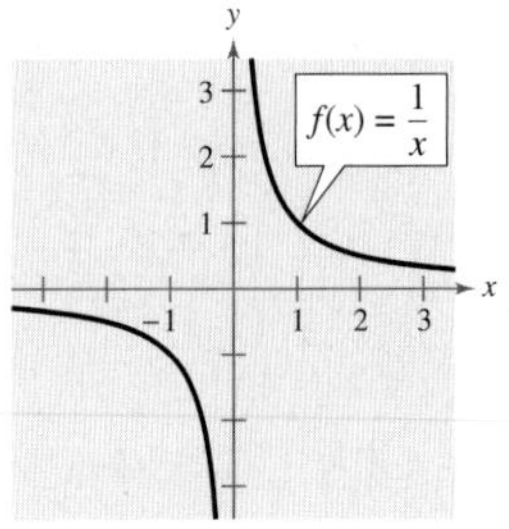

Reciprocal function
FIGURE 1.71

Step and Piecewise-Defined Functions

Functions whose graphs resemble sets of stairsteps are known as **step functions.** The most famous of the step functions is the **greatest integer function,** which is denoted by $[\![x]\!]$ and defined as

$$f(x) = [\![x]\!] = \textit{the greatest integer less than or equal to } x.$$

Some values of the greatest integer function are as follows.

$$[\![-1]\!] = (\text{greatest integer} \le -1) = -1$$

$$[\![-\tfrac{1}{2}]\!] = (\text{greatest integer} \le -\tfrac{1}{2}) = -1$$

$$[\![\tfrac{1}{10}]\!] = (\text{greatest integer} \le \tfrac{1}{10}) = 0$$

$$[\![1.5]\!] = (\text{greatest integer} \le 1.5) = 1$$

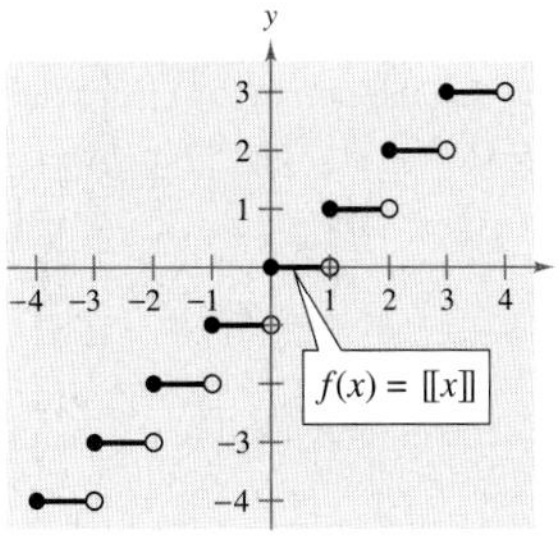

FIGURE 1.72

The graph of the greatest integer function

$$f(x) = [\![x]\!]$$

has the following characteristics, as shown in Figure 1.72.

- The domain of the function is the set of all real numbers.
- The range of the function is the set of all integers.
- The graph has a y-intercept at $(0, 0)$ and x-intercepts in the interval $[0, 1)$.
- The graph is constant between each pair of consecutive integers.
- The graph jumps vertically one unit at each integer value.

TECHNOLOGY

When graphing a step function, you should set your graphing utility to *dot* mode.

Example 2 Evaluating a Step Function

Evaluate the function when $x = -1, 2,$ and $\frac{3}{2}$.

$$f(x) = [\![x]\!] + 1$$

Solution

For $x = -1$, the greatest integer ≤ -1 is -1, so

$$f(-1) = [\![-1]\!] + 1 = -1 + 1 = 0.$$

For $x = 2$, the greatest integer ≤ 2 is 2, so

$$f(2) = [\![2]\!] + 1 = 2 + 1 = 3.$$

For $x = \frac{3}{2}$, the greatest integer $\le \frac{3}{2}$ is 1, so

$$f\left(\tfrac{3}{2}\right) = [\![\tfrac{3}{2}]\!] + 1 = 1 + 1 = 2.$$

You can verify your answers by examining the graph of $f(x) = [\![x]\!] + 1$ shown in Figure 1.73.

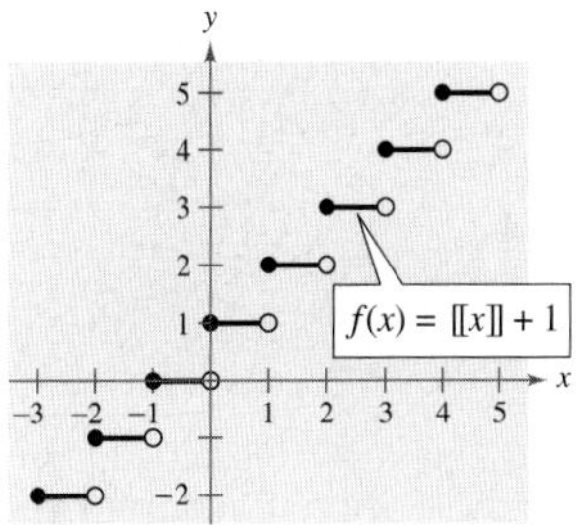

FIGURE 1.73

CHECK Point Now try Exercise 43.

Recall from Section 1.4 that a piecewise-defined function is defined by two or more equations over a specified domain. To graph a piecewise-defined function, graph each equation separately over the specified domain, as shown in Example 3.

Extra Example 2

Evaluate the function $f(x) = [\![x + 2]\!]$ when $x = -\frac{3}{2}$, 1, and $-\frac{5}{2}$.

$f\left(-\frac{3}{2}\right) = 0, f(1) = 3, f\left(-\frac{5}{2}\right) = -1$

Avoiding Common Errors

Examples 2 and 3 Remind students to place closed or open circles at the appropriate endpoints on each function to show the limits of the domain.

Extra Example 3

Sketch the graph of

$$f(x) = \begin{cases} -\frac{1}{2}x - 6, & x \le -4 \\ x + 5, & x > -4 \end{cases}.$$

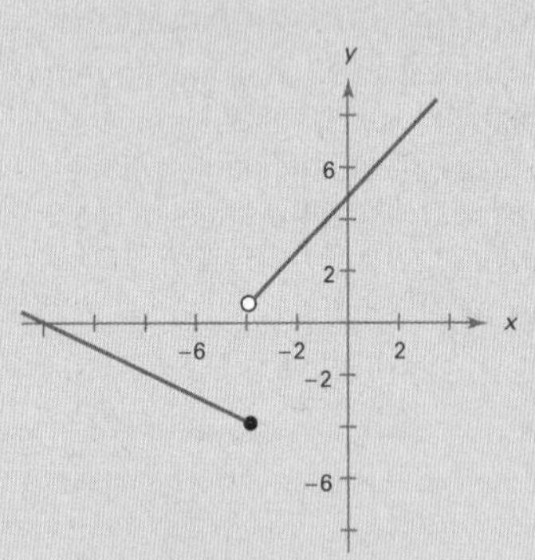

Closing the Lesson

Have students summarize the major points of the lesson and answer the Essential Question: What are the characteristics of the most commonly used functions in algebra?

- **The eight most commonly used parent functions in algebra are constant, identity, absolute value, square root, quadratic, cubic, reciprocal, and greatest integer. Each parent function has unique characteristics.**

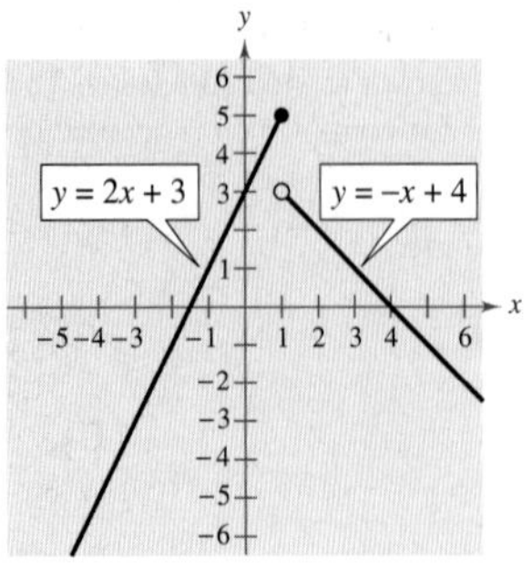

FIGURE 1.74

Example 3 Graphing a Piecewise-Defined Function

Sketch the graph of

$$f(x) = \begin{cases} 2x + 3, & x \le 1 \\ -x + 4, & x > 1 \end{cases}.$$

Solution

This piecewise-defined function is composed of two linear functions. At $x = 1$ and to the left of $x = 1$ the graph is the line $y = 2x + 3$, and to the right of $x = 1$ the graph is the line $y = -x + 4$, as shown in Figure 1.74. Notice that the point $(1, 5)$ is a solid dot and the point $(1, 3)$ is an open dot. This is because $f(1) = 2(1) + 3 = 5$.

CHECKPoint Now try Exercise 57.

Parent Functions

The eight graphs shown in Figure 1.75 represent the most commonly used functions in algebra. Familiarity with the basic characteristics of these simple graphs will help you analyze the shapes of more complicated graphs—in particular, graphs obtained from these graphs by the rigid and nonrigid transformations studied in the next section.

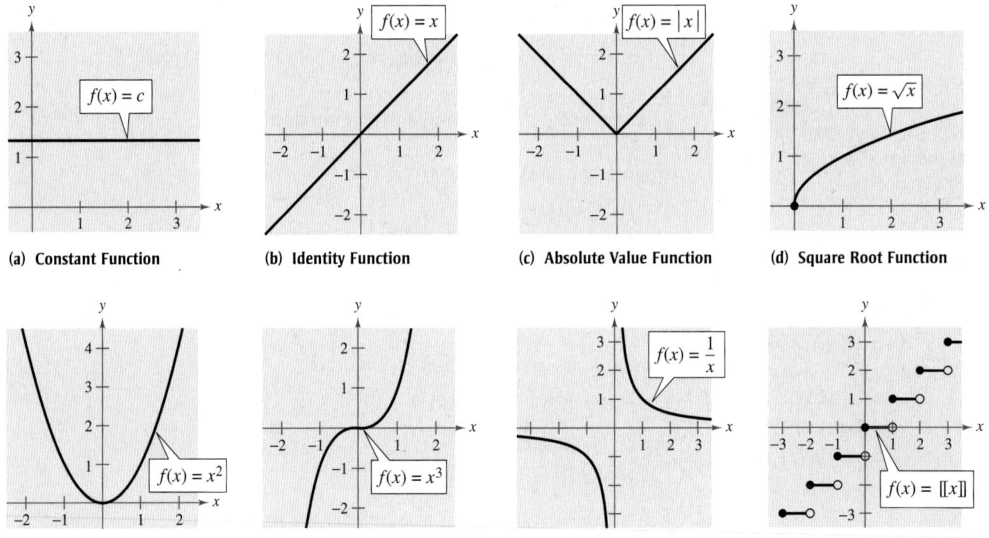

(a) Constant Function (b) Identity Function (c) Absolute Value Function (d) Square Root Function

(e) Quadratic Function (f) Cubic Function (g) Reciprocal Function (h) Greatest Integer Function

FIGURE 1.75

1.6 EXERCISES

See www.CalcChat.com for worked-out solutions to odd-numbered exercises.

VOCABULARY

In Exercises 1–9, match each function with its name.

1. $f(x) = [\![x]\!]$ g **2.** $f(x) = x$ i **3.** $f(x) = 1/x$ h

4. $f(x) = x^2$ a **5.** $f(x) = \sqrt{x}$ b **6.** $f(x) = c$ e

7. $f(x) = |x|$ f **8.** $f(x) = x^3$ c **9.** $f(x) = ax + b$ d

(a) squaring function (b) square root function (c) cubic function

(d) linear function (e) constant function (f) absolute value function

(g) greatest integer function (h) reciprocal function (i) identity function

10. Fill in the blank: The constant function and the identity function are two special types of linear functions.

SKILLS AND APPLICATIONS

In Exercises 11–18, (a) write the linear function f such that it has the indicated function values and (b) sketch the graph of the function. 11–18. See margin.

11. $f(1) = 4, f(0) = 6$ **12.** $f(-3) = -8, f(1) = 2$

13. $f(5) = -4, f(-2) = 17$ **14.** $f(3) = 9, f(-1) = -11$

15. $f(-5) = -1, f(5) = -1$

16. $f(-10) = 12, f(16) = -1$

17. $f(\frac{1}{2}) = -6, f(4) = -3$

18. $f(\frac{2}{3}) = -\frac{15}{2}, f(-4) = -11$

19–42. See margin.

In Exercises 19–42, use a graphing utility to graph the function. Be sure to choose an appropriate viewing window.

19. $f(x) = 0.8 - x$ **20.** $f(x) = 2.5x - 4.25$

21. $f(x) = -\frac{1}{6}x - \frac{5}{2}$ **22.** $f(x) = \frac{5}{6} - \frac{2}{3}x$

23. $g(x) = -2x^2$ **24.** $h(x) = 1.5 - x^2$

25. $f(x) = 3x^2 - 1.75$ **26.** $f(x) = 0.5x^2 + 2$

27. $f(x) = x^3 - 1$ **28.** $f(x) = 8 - x^3$

29. $f(x) = (x - 1)^3 + 2$ **30.** $g(x) = 2(x + 3)^3 + 1$

31. $f(x) = 4\sqrt{x}$ **32.** $f(x) = 4 - 2\sqrt{x}$

33. $g(x) = 2 - \sqrt{x + 4}$ **34.** $h(x) = \sqrt{x + 2} + 3$

35. $f(x) = -1/x$ **36.** $f(x) = 4 + (1/x)$

37. $h(x) = 1/(x + 2)$ **38.** $k(x) = 1/(x - 3)$

39. $g(x) = |x| - 5$ **40.** $h(x) = 3 - |x|$

41. $f(x) = |x + 4|$ **42.** $f(x) = |x - 1|$

In Exercises 43–50, evaluate the function for the indicated values.

43. $f(x) = [\![x]\!]$ (a) 2 (b) 2 (c) −4 (d) 3
(a) $f(2.1)$ (b) $f(2.9)$ (c) $f(-3.1)$ (d) $f(\frac{7}{2})$

44. $g(x) = 2[\![x]\!]$ (a) −6 (b) 0 (c) 18 (d) 6
(a) $g(-3)$ (b) $g(0.25)$ (c) $g(9.5)$ (d) $g(\frac{11}{3})$

45. $h(x) = [\![x + 3]\!]$ (a) 1 (b) 3 (c) 7 (d) −19
(a) $h(-2)$ (b) $h(\frac{1}{2})$ (c) $h(4.2)$ (d) $h(-21.6)$

46. $f(x) = 4[\![x]\!] + 7$ (a) 7 (b) −1 (c) 31 (d) 11
(a) $f(0)$ (b) $f(-1.5)$ (c) $f(6)$ (d) $f(\frac{5}{3})$

47. $h(x) = [\![3x - 1]\!]$ (a) 6 (b) −11 (c) 6 (d) −22
(a) $h(2.5)$ (b) $h(-3.2)$ (c) $h(\frac{7}{3})$ (d) $h(-\frac{21}{3})$

48. $k(x) = [\![\frac{1}{2}x + 6]\!]$ (a) 8 (b) 2 (c) 6 (d) 13
(a) $k(5)$ (b) $k(-6.1)$ (c) $k(0.1)$ (d) $k(15)$

49. $g(x) = 3[\![x - 2]\!] + 5$ (a) −10 (b) −4 (c) −1 (d) 41
(a) $g(-2.7)$ (b) $g(-1)$ (c) $g(0.8)$ (d) $g(14.5)$

50. $g(x) = -7[\![x + 4]\!] + 6$ (a) −22 (b) −85 (c) 6 (d) −29
(a) $g(\frac{1}{8})$ (b) $g(9)$ (c) $g(-4)$ (d) $g(\frac{3}{2})$

In Exercises 51–56, sketch the graph of the function.

51. $g(x) = -[\![x]\!]$ **52.** $g(x) = 4[\![x]\!]$

53. $g(x) = [\![x]\!] - 2$ 51–56. See margin.

54. $g(x) = [\![x]\!] - 1$

55. $g(x) = [\![x + 1]\!]$

56. $g(x) = [\![x - 3]\!]$

In Exercises 57–64, graph the function. 57–61. See margin.

57. $f(x) = \begin{cases} 2x + 3, & x < 0 \\ 3 - x, & x \ge 0 \end{cases}$

58. $g(x) = \begin{cases} x + 6, & x \le -4 \\ \frac{1}{2}x - 4, & x > -4 \end{cases}$

59. $f(x) = \begin{cases} \sqrt{4 + x}, & x < 0 \\ \sqrt{4 - x}, & x \ge 0 \end{cases}$

60. $f(x) = \begin{cases} 1 - (x - 1)^2, & x \le 2 \\ \sqrt{x - 2}, & x > 2 \end{cases}$

61. $f(x) = \begin{cases} x^2 + 5, & x \le 1 \\ -x^2 + 4x + 3, & x > 1 \end{cases}$

4 PRACTICE AND APPLY

Assignment Guide

Transparencies Available
Available at the Instructor's companion site.

Average:
Day 1: pp. 71–72
Exs. 11–18, 27–71 odd, 73–76

Advanced:
Day 1: pp. 71–72
Exs. 11–18, 28–72 even, 73–76

Block:
pp. 71–72
Exs. 11–18, 27–71 odd, 73–76 (with 1.5)

11. (a) $f(x) = -2x + 6$
(b)

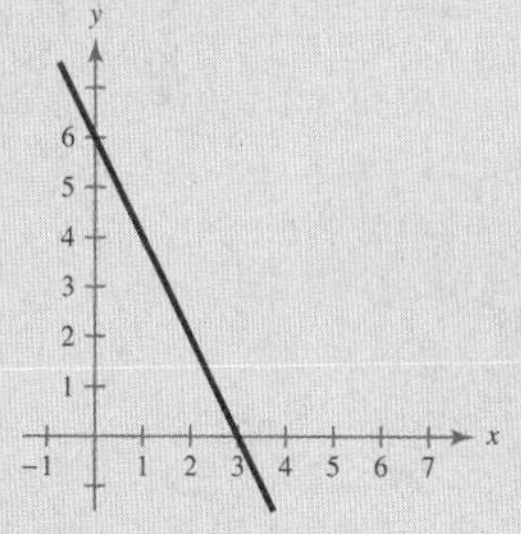

12. (a) $f(x) = \frac{5}{2}x - \frac{1}{2}$
(b)

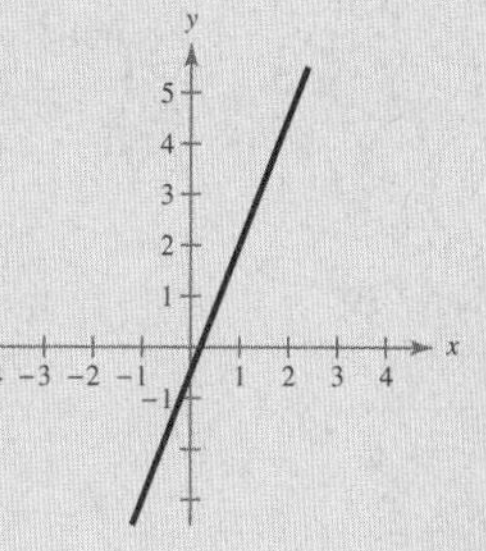

13. (a) $f(x) = -3x + 11$
(b)

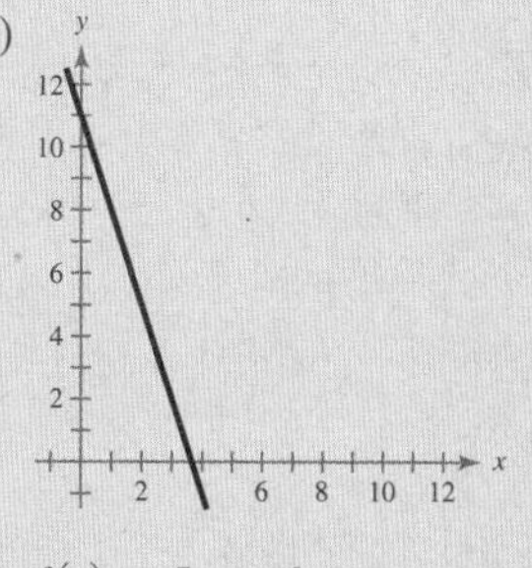

14. (a) $f(x) = 5x - 6$
(b)

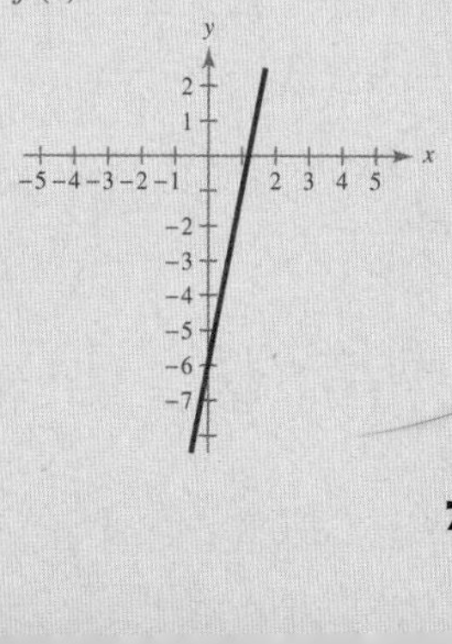

15. (a) $f(x) = -1$
(b)

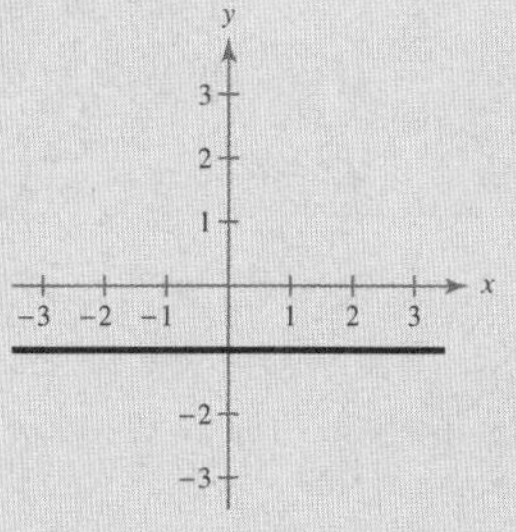

16. (a) $f(x) = -\frac{1}{2}x + 7$
(b)

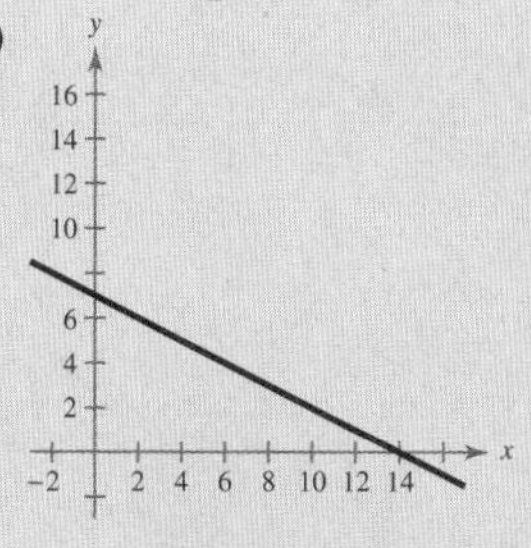

17. (a) $f(x) = \frac{6}{7}x - \frac{45}{7}$
(b)

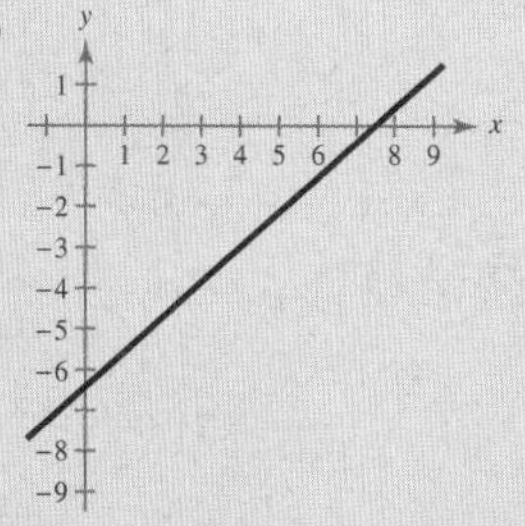

18–42, 51–61. See Additional Answers beginning on page AA1.

62. $h(x) = \begin{cases} 3 - x^2, & x < 0 \\ x^2 + 2, & x \ge 0 \end{cases}$ 62–64. See margin.

63. $h(x) = \begin{cases} 4 - x^2, & x < -2 \\ 3 + x, & -2 \le x < 0 \\ x^2 + 1, & x \ge 0 \end{cases}$

64. $k(x) = \begin{cases} 2x + 1, & x \le -1 \\ 2x^2 - 1, & -1 < x \le 1 \\ 1 - x^2, & x > 1 \end{cases}$

In Exercises 65–68, (a) use a graphing utility to graph the function, (b) state the domain and range of the function, and (c) describe the pattern of the graph. 65–68. See margin.

65. $s(x) = 2\left(\frac{1}{4}x - [\![\frac{1}{4}x]\!]\right)$ **66.** $g(x) = 2\left(\frac{1}{4}x - [\![\frac{1}{4}x]\!]\right)^2$

67. $h(x) = 4\left(\frac{1}{2}x - [\![\frac{1}{2}x]\!]\right)$ **68.** $k(x) = 4\left(\frac{1}{2}x - [\![\frac{1}{2}x]\!]\right)^2$

69. DELIVERY CHARGES The cost of sending an overnight package from Los Angeles to Miami is \$23.40 for a package weighing up to but not including 1 pound and \$3.75 for each additional pound or portion of a pound. A model for the total cost C (in dollars) of sending the package is $C = 23.40 + 3.75[\![x]\!]$, $x > 0$, where x is the weight in pounds.

(a) Sketch a graph of the model. See margin.

(b) Determine the cost of sending a package that weighs 9.25 pounds. \$57.15

70. DELIVERY CHARGES The cost of sending an overnight package from New York to Atlanta is \$22.65 for a package weighing up to but not including 1 pound and \$3.70 for each additional pound or portion of a pound.

(a) Use the greatest integer function to create a model for the cost C of overnight delivery of a package weighing x pounds, $x > 0$. $C = 22.65 + 3.7[\![x]\!]$

(b) Sketch the graph of the function. See margin.

71. WAGES A mechanic is paid \$14.00 per hour for regular time and time-and-a-half for overtime. The weekly wage function is given by See margin.

$$W(h) = \begin{cases} 14h, & 0 < h \le 40 \\ 21(h - 40) + 560, & h > 40 \end{cases}$$

where h is the number of hours worked in a week.

(a) Evaluate $W(30)$, $W(40)$, $W(45)$, and $W(50)$.

(b) The company increased the regular work week to 45 hours. What is the new weekly wage function?

72. SNOWSTORM During a nine-hour snowstorm, it snows at a rate of 1 inch per hour for the first 2 hours, at a rate of 2 inches per hour for the next 6 hours, and at a rate of 0.5 inch per hour for the final hour. Write and graph a piecewise-defined function that gives the depth of the snow during the snowstorm. How many inches of snow accumulated from the storm? See margin.

73. REVENUE The table shows the monthly revenue y (in thousands of dollars) of a landscaping business for each month of the year 2008, with $x = 1$ representing January. See margin.

Month, x	Revenue, y
1	5.2
2	5.6
3	6.6
4	8.3
5	11.5
6	15.8
7	12.8
8	10.1
9	8.6
10	6.9
11	4.5
12	2.7

A mathematical model that represents these data is

$$f(x) = \begin{cases} -1.97x + 26.3 \\ 0.505x^2 - 1.47x + 6.3 \end{cases}.$$

(a) Use a graphing utility to graph the model. What is the domain of each part of the piecewise-defined function? How can you tell? Explain your reasoning.

(b) Find $f(5)$ and $f(11)$, and interpret your results in the context of the problem.

(c) How do the values obtained from the model in part (a) compare with the actual data values?

EXPLORATION

74–75. See margin.

TRUE OR FALSE? In Exercises 74 and 75, determine whether the statement is true or false. Justify your answer.

74. A piecewise-defined function will always have at least one x-intercept or at least one y-intercept.

75. A linear equation will always have an x-intercept and a y-intercept.

76. CAPSTONE For each graph of f shown in Figure 1.75, do the following. See margin.

(a) Find the domain and range of f.

(b) Find the x- and y-intercepts of the graph of f.

(c) Determine the intervals over which f is increasing, decreasing, or constant.

(d) Determine whether f is even, odd, or neither. Then describe the symmetry.

5 ASSESS AND RETEACH

Daily Homework Quiz

Transparency Available

Available at the Instructor's companion site.

62.

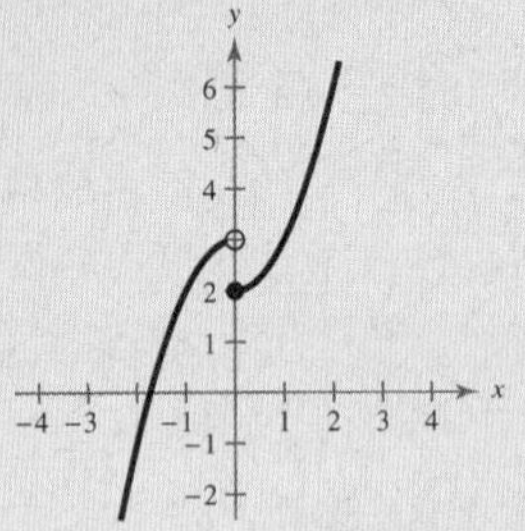

63.

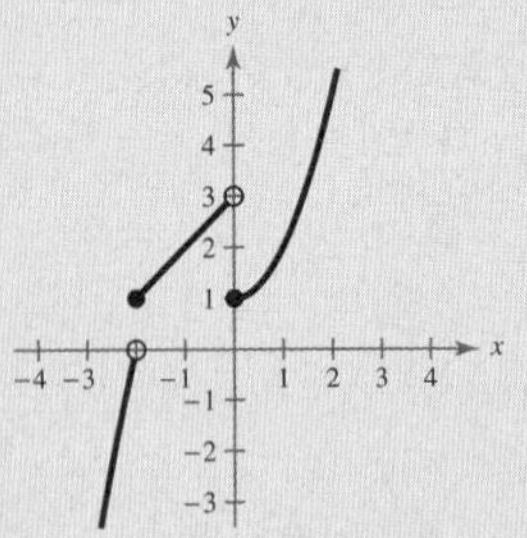

64.

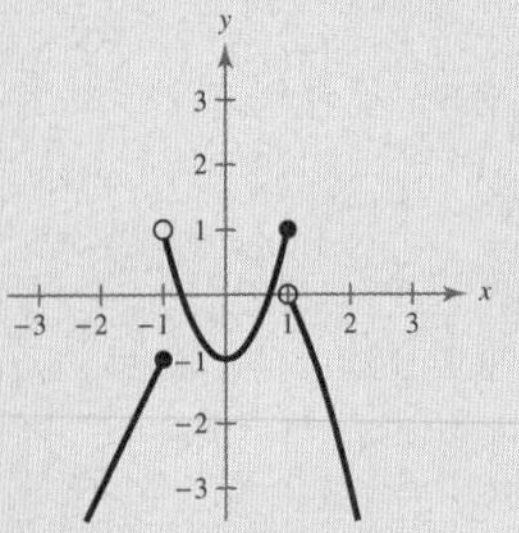

65. (a)

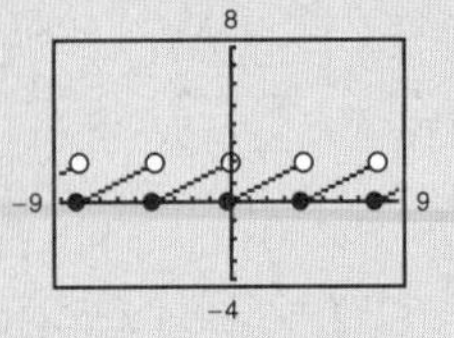

(b) Domain: $(-\infty, \infty)$
Range: $[0, 2)$

(c) Sawtooth pattern

66. (a)

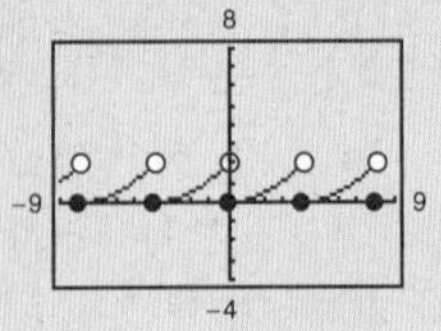

(b) Domain: $(-\infty, \infty)$
Range: $[0, 2)$

(c) Sawtooth pattern

67. (a)

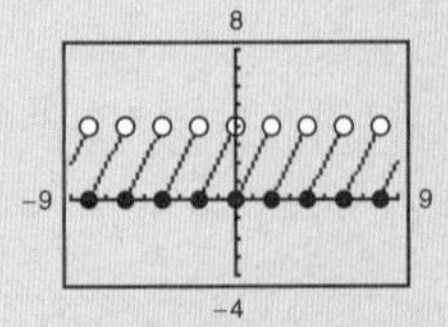

(b) Domain: $(-\infty, \infty)$
Range: $[0, 4)$

(c) Sawtooth pattern

68. (a)

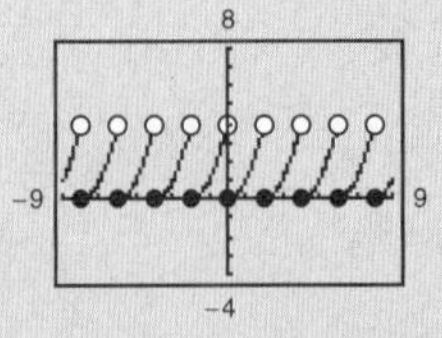

(b) Domain: $(-\infty, \infty)$
Range: $[0, 4)$

(c) Sawtooth pattern

69(a), 70(b), 71–76. See Additional Answers beginning on page AA1.

1.7 Transformations of Functions

What you should learn

- Use vertical and horizontal shifts to sketch graphs of functions.
- Use reflections to sketch graphs of functions.
- Use nonrigid transformations to sketch graphs of functions.

Why you should learn it

Transformations of functions can be used to model real-life applications. For instance, Exercise 79 on page 81 shows how a transformation of a function can be used to model the total numbers of miles driven by vans, pickups, and sport utility vehicles in the United States.

Shifting Graphs

Many functions have graphs that are simple transformations of the parent graphs summarized in Section 1.6. For example, you can obtain the graph of

$$h(x) = x^2 + 2$$

by shifting the graph of $f(x) = x^2$ *upward* two units, as shown in Figure 1.76. In function notation, h and f are related as follows.

$$h(x) = x^2 + 2 = f(x) + 2 \qquad \text{Upward shift of two units}$$

Similarly, you can obtain the graph of

$$g(x) = (x - 2)^2$$

by shifting the graph of $f(x) = x^2$ to the *right* two units, as shown in Figure 1.77. In this case, the functions g and f have the following relationship.

$$g(x) = (x - 2)^2 = f(x - 2) \qquad \text{Right shift of two units}$$

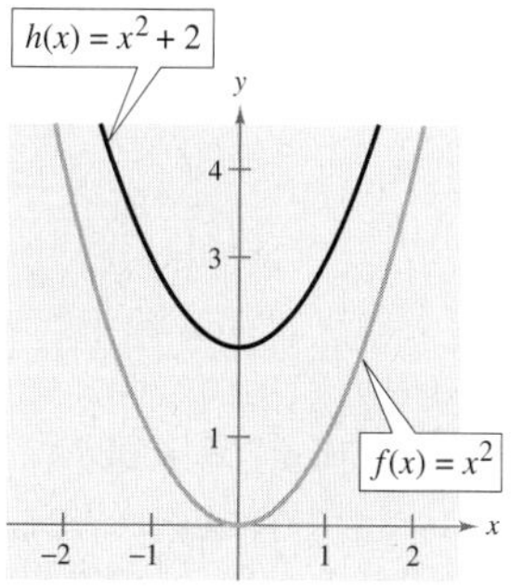

FIGURE 1.76

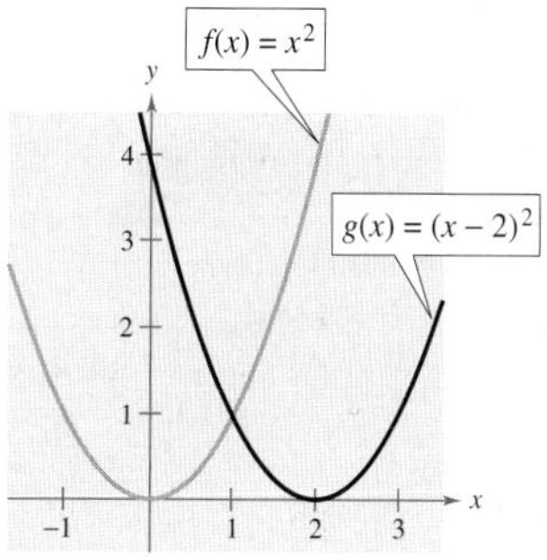

FIGURE 1.77

The following list summarizes this discussion about horizontal and vertical shifts.

Vertical and Horizontal Shifts

Let c be a positive real number. **Vertical and horizontal shifts** in the graph of $y = f(x)$ are represented as follows.

1. Vertical shift c units *upward*: $h(x) = f(x) + c$
2. Vertical shift c units *downward*: $h(x) = f(x) - c$
3. Horizontal shift c units to the *right*: $h(x) = f(x - c)$
4. Horizontal shift c units to the *left*: $h(x) = f(x + c)$

WARNING / CAUTION

In items 3 and 4, be sure you see that $h(x) = f(x - c)$ corresponds to a *right* shift and $h(x) = f(x + c)$ corresponds to a *left* shift for $c > 0$.

1 PLAN AND PREPARE

Warm-up Exercises

Transparency Available
Available at the Instructor's companion site.

Notetaking Guide

Transparency Available
Promotes interactive learning and notetaking skills. Available at the Instructor's companion site.

Animated Precalculus

An **Animated Precalculus** tutorial is available at the Student companion site for **Section 1.7.**

Pacing

Average: 1 day
Advanced: 1 day
Block: 0.5 block with 1.8

2 FOCUS AND MOTIVATE

Essential Question

How do you write equations and draw graphs for the simple transformations of a parent function? **Tell students that they will answer this question by studying the effects of translations, reflections, and stretches on the equations and graphs of functions.**

Resource Planning Guide

Chapter Resources

- Complete Solutions Guide

Workbooks

- Notetaking Guide
- Student Solutions Guide

Interactive Technology

- Instructor Success Organizer
- Notetaking Guide IAE
- Instructional DVDs
- Animated Precalculus
- PowerLecture with ExamView

3 TEACH

Avoiding Common Errors

Example 1 Remind students to be aware of the signs on both numbers and variables when describing and drawing transformations of graphs.

Extra Example 1

Use the graph of $f(x) = x^3$ to sketch the graph of each function.

a. $h(x) = x^3 + 5$

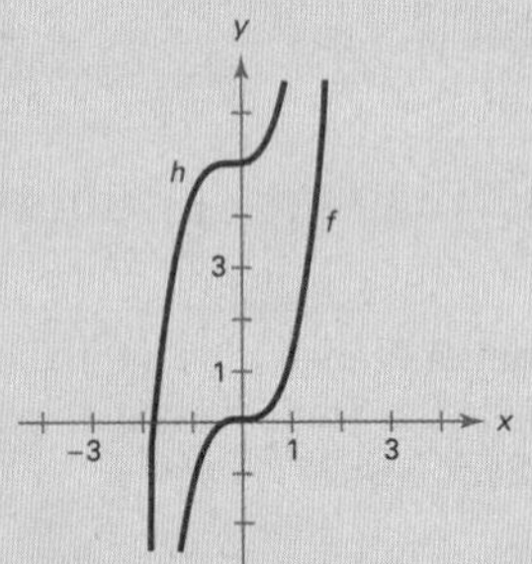

b. $g(x) = (x - 3)^3 + 2$

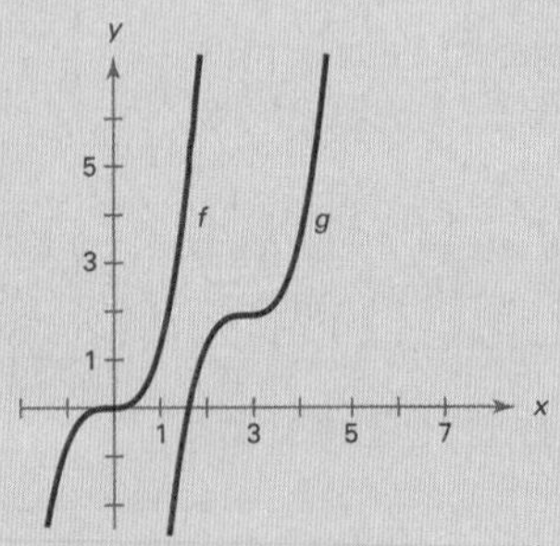

Some graphs can be obtained from combinations of vertical and horizontal shifts, as demonstrated in Example 1(b). Vertical and horizontal shifts generate a *family of functions*, each with the same shape but at different locations in the plane.

Example 1 Shifts in the Graphs of a Function

Use the graph of $f(x) = x^3$ to sketch the graph of each function.

a. $g(x) = x^3 - 1$ **b.** $h(x) = (x + 2)^3 + 1$

Solution

a. Relative to the graph of $f(x) = x^3$, the graph of

$$g(x) = x^3 - 1$$

is a downward shift of one unit, as shown in Figure 1.78.

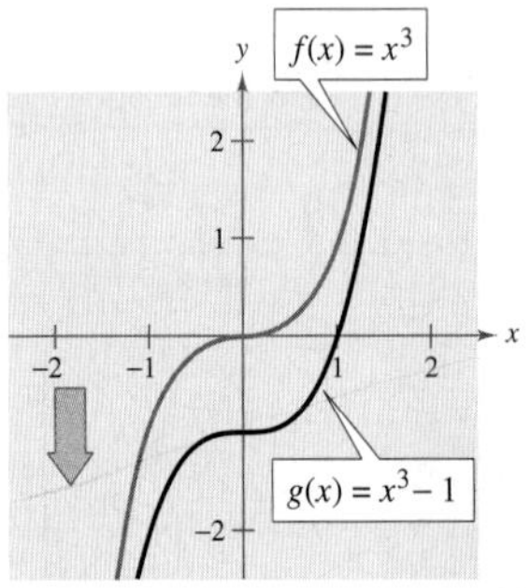

FIGURE 1.78

Study Tip

In Example 1(a), note that $g(x) = f(x) - 1$ and that in Example 1(b), $h(x) = f(x + 2) + 1$.

b. Relative to the graph of $f(x) = x^3$, the graph of

$$h(x) = (x + 2)^3 + 1$$

involves a left shift of two units and an upward shift of one unit, as shown in Figure 1.79.

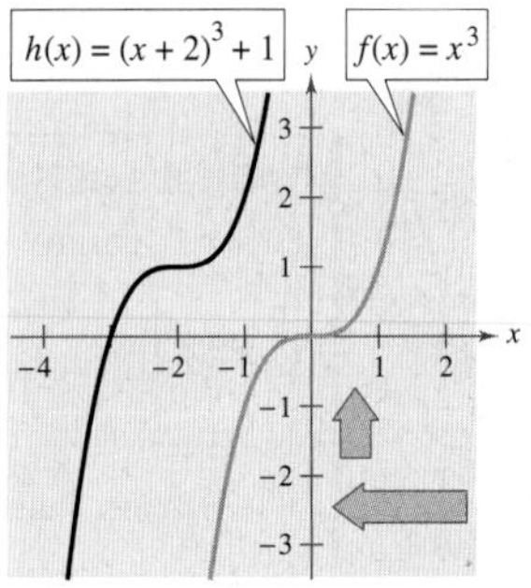

FIGURE 1.79

CHECKPoint Now try Exercise 7.

In Figure 1.79, notice that the same result is obtained if the vertical shift precedes the horizontal shift *or* if the horizontal shift precedes the vertical shift.

Differentiated Instruction

Visual and Auditory Learners Students should work Example 1 with a partner. After they have completed it, have them sketch the graph $f(x) = x^2$. Then have one student from each pair write and graph a function that transforms the parent graph. Ask them to explain the steps to graph the original function to their partners, write a function to transform the graph, and graph the new function.

Reflecting Graphs

The second common type of transformation is a **reflection.** For instance, if you consider the x-axis to be a mirror, the graph of

$$h(x) = -x^2$$

is the mirror image (or reflection) of the graph of

$$f(x) = x^2,$$

as shown in Figure 1.80.

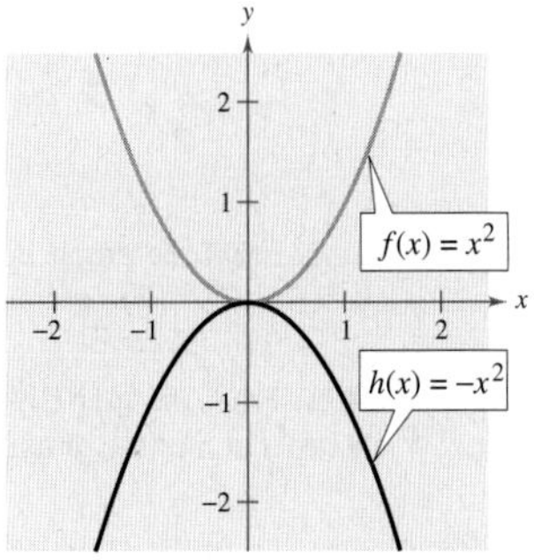

FIGURE 1.80

> ### Reflections in the Coordinate Axes
> **Reflections** in the coordinate axes of the graph of $y = f(x)$ are represented as follows.
>
> **1.** Reflection in the x-axis: $h(x) = -f(x)$
>
> **2.** Reflection in the y-axis: $h(x) = f(-x)$

Example 2 Finding Equations from Graphs

The graph of the function given by

$$f(x) = x^4$$

is shown in Figure 1.81. Each of the graphs in Figure 1.82 is a transformation of the graph of f. Find an equation for each of these functions.

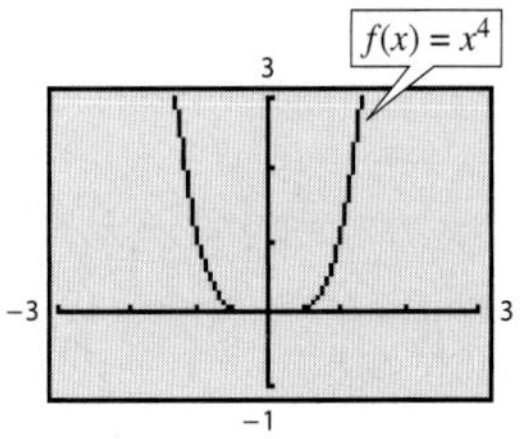

FIGURE 1.81

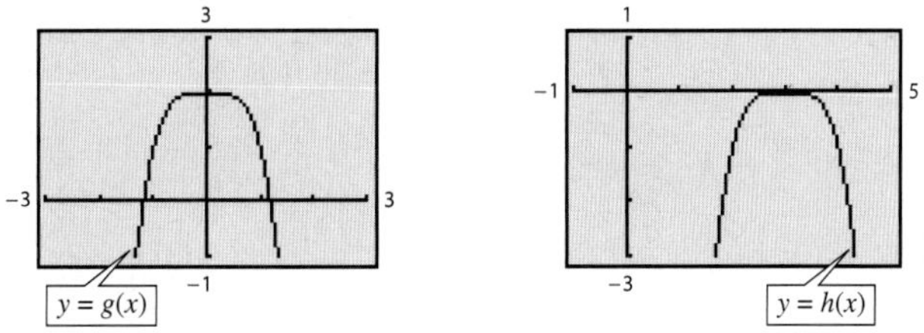

(a) (b)

FIGURE 1.82

Solution

a. The graph of g is a reflection in the x-axis *followed by* an upward shift of two units of the graph of $f(x) = x^4$. So, the equation for g is

$$g(x) = -x^4 + 2.$$

b. The graph of h is a horizontal shift of three units to the right *followed by* a reflection in the x-axis of the graph of $f(x) = x^4$. So, the equation for h is

$$h(x) = -(x - 3)^4.$$

CHECK Point Now try Exercise 15.

Extra Example 2

The function $g(x)$ shown in the figure is a transformation of the graph of $f(x) = x^4$. Find an equation for the function $g(x)$.

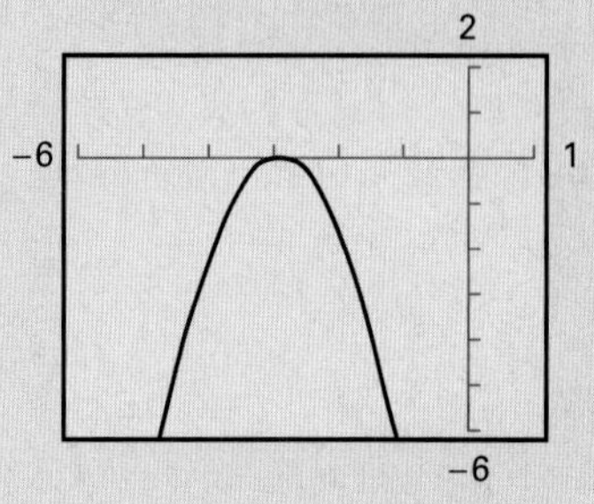

$g(x) = -(x + 3)^4$

Extra Example 3

Compare the graphs of each function with the graph of $f(x) = \sqrt{x - 1}$.

a. $g(x) = -\sqrt{x - 1}$

The graph of

$g(x) = -\left(\sqrt{x - 1}\right) = -f(x)$

is a reflection of the graph of *f* in the *x*-axis.

b. $h(x) = \sqrt{-x - 1}$

The graph of

$h(x) = \sqrt{(-x) - 1} = f(-x)$

is a reflection of the graph of *f* in the *y*-axis.

Example 3 Reflections and Shifts

Compare the graph of each function with the graph of $f(x) = \sqrt{x}$.

a. $g(x) = -\sqrt{x}$ **b.** $h(x) = \sqrt{-x}$ **c.** $k(x) = -\sqrt{x + 2}$

Algebraic Solution

a. The graph of g is a reflection of the graph of f in the x-axis because

$$g(x) = -\sqrt{x}$$
$$= -f(x).$$

b. The graph of h is a reflection of the graph of f in the y-axis because

$$h(x) = \sqrt{-x}$$
$$= f(-x).$$

c. The graph of k is a left shift of two units followed by a reflection in the x-axis because

$$k(x) = -\sqrt{x + 2}$$
$$= -f(x + 2).$$

Graphical Solution

a. Graph f and g on the same set of coordinate axes. From the graph in Figure 1.83, you can see that the graph of g is a reflection of the graph of f in the x-axis.

b. Graph f and h on the same set of coordinate axes. From the graph in Figure 1.84, you can see that the graph of h is a reflection of the graph of f in the y-axis.

c. Graph f and k on the same set of coordinate axes. From the graph in Figure 1.85, you can see that the graph of k is a left shift of two units of the graph of f, followed by a reflection in the x-axis.

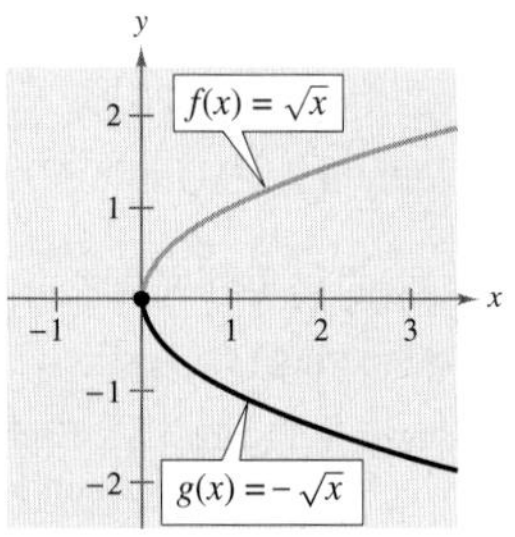

FIGURE 1.83

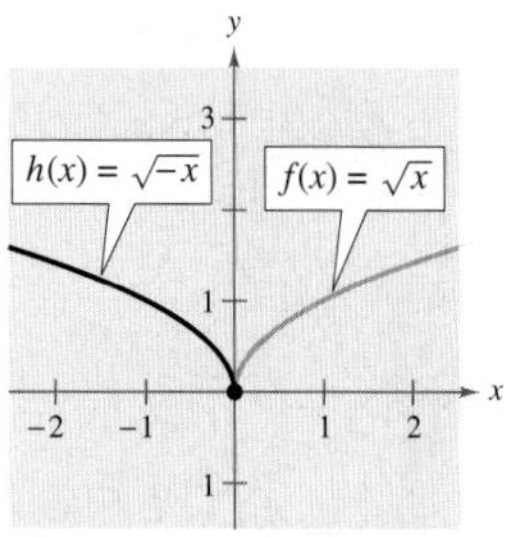

FIGURE 1.84

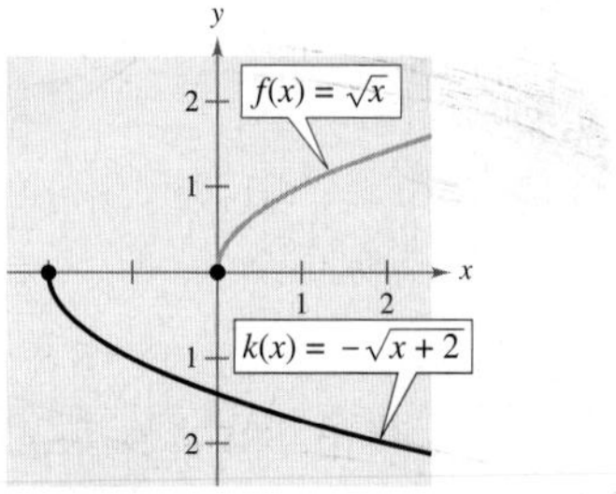

FIGURE 1.85

CHECKPoint Now try Exercise 25.

When sketching the graphs of functions involving square roots, remember that the domain must be restricted to exclude negative numbers inside the radical. For instance, here are the domains of the functions in Example 3.

Domain of $g(x) = -\sqrt{x}$: $x \geq 0$

Domain of $h(x) = \sqrt{-x}$: $x \leq 0$

Domain of $k(x) = -\sqrt{x + 2}$: $x \geq -2$

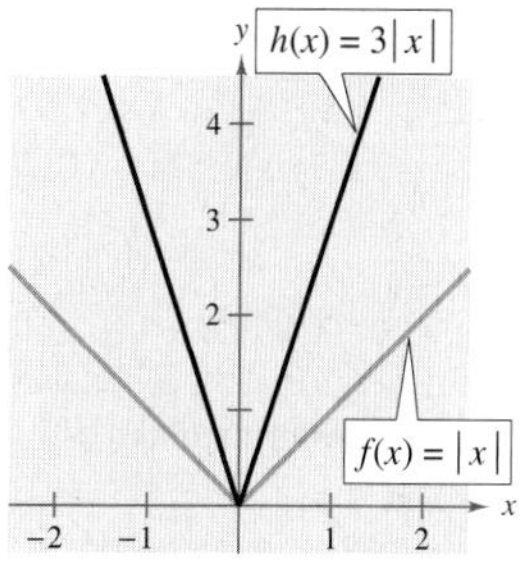

FIGURE 1.86

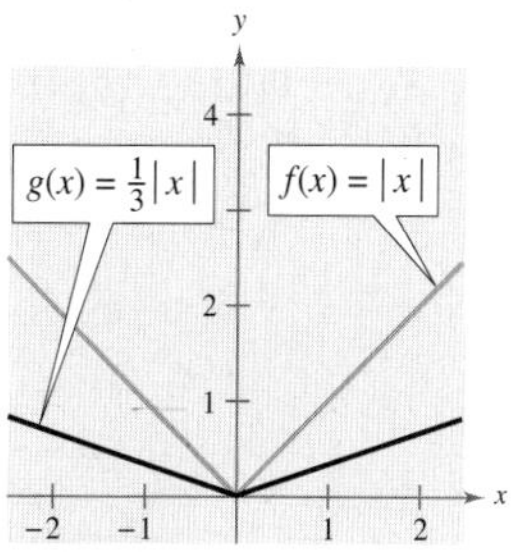

FIGURE 1.87

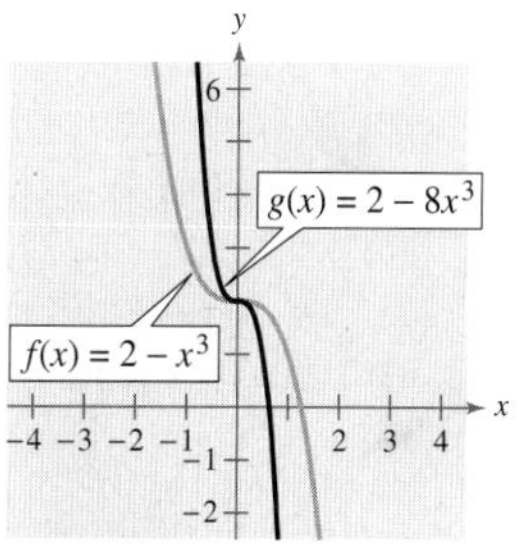

FIGURE 1.88

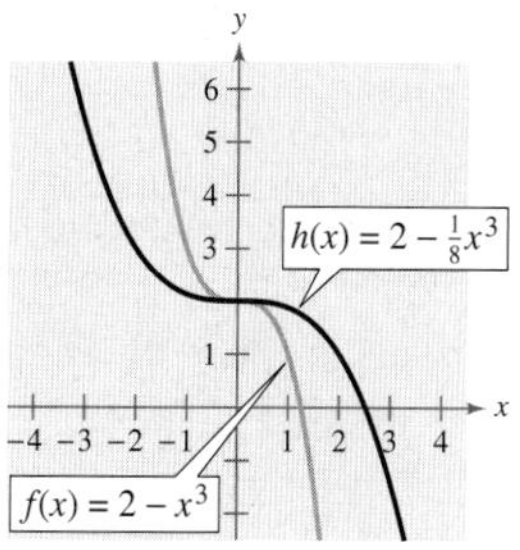

FIGURE 1.89

Nonrigid Transformations

Horizontal shifts, vertical shifts, and reflections are **rigid transformations** because the basic shape of the graph is unchanged. These transformations change only the *position* of the graph in the coordinate plane. **Nonrigid transformations** are those that cause a *distortion*—a change in the shape of the original graph. For instance, a nonrigid transformation of the graph of $y = f(x)$ is represented by $g(x) = cf(x)$, where the transformation is a **vertical stretch** if $c > 1$ and a **vertical shrink** if $0 < c < 1$. Another nonrigid transformation of the graph of $y = f(x)$ is represented by $h(x) = f(cx)$, where the transformation is a **horizontal shrink** if $c > 1$ and a **horizontal stretch** if $0 < c < 1$.

Example 4 Nonrigid Transformations

Compare the graph of each function with the graph of $f(x) = |x|$.

a. $h(x) = 3|x|$ **b.** $g(x) = \frac{1}{3}|x|$

Solution

a. Relative to the graph of $f(x) = |x|$, the graph of

$$h(x) = 3|x| = 3f(x)$$

is a vertical stretch (each y-value is multiplied by 3) of the graph of f. (See Figure 1.86.)

b. Similarly, the graph of

$$g(x) = \tfrac{1}{3}|x| = \tfrac{1}{3}f(x)$$

is a vertical shrink $\left(\text{each } y\text{-value is multiplied by } \frac{1}{3}\right)$ of the graph of f. (See Figure 1.87.)

CHECK*Point* Now try Exercise 29.

Example 5 Nonrigid Transformations

Compare the graph of each function with the graph of $f(x) = 2 - x^3$.

a. $g(x) = f(2x)$ **b.** $h(x) = f\left(\frac{1}{2}x\right)$

Solution

a. Relative to the graph of $f(x) = 2 - x^3$, the graph of

$$g(x) = f(2x) = 2 - (2x)^3 = 2 - 8x^3$$

is a horizontal shrink ($c > 1$) of the graph of f. (See Figure 1.88.)

b. Similarly, the graph of

$$h(x) = f\left(\tfrac{1}{2}x\right) = 2 - \left(\tfrac{1}{2}x\right)^3 = 2 - \tfrac{1}{8}x^3$$

is a horizontal stretch ($0 < c < 1$) of the graph of f. (See Figure 1.89.)

CHECK*Point* Now try Exercise 35.

Extra Example 4

Compare the graph of each function with the graph of $f(x) = x^2$.

a. $g(x) = 4x^2$

The graph of $g(x) = 4x^2 = 4f(x)$ is a vertical stretch of the graph of f.

b. $h(x) = \frac{1}{4}x^2$

The graph of $h(x) = \frac{1}{4}x^2 = \frac{1}{4}f(x)$ is a vertical shrink of the graph of f.

Extra Example 5

Compare the graph of each function with the graph of $f(x) = x^2 + 3$.

a. $g(x) = f(2x)$

The graph of

$$g(x) = f(2x)$$
$$= (2x)^2 + 3 = 4x^2 + 3$$

is a horizontal shrink of the graph of f.

b. $h(x) = f\left(\frac{1}{2}x\right)$

The graph of

$$h(x) = f\left(\tfrac{1}{2}x\right)$$
$$= \left(\tfrac{1}{2}x\right)^2 + 3 = \tfrac{1}{4}x^2 + 3$$

is a horizontal stretch of the graph of f.

Closing the Lesson

Have students summarize the major points of the lesson and answer the Essential Question: How do you write equations and draw graphs for the simple transformations of a parent function?

- **The function $h(x)$ is a horizontal translation of $f(x)$ if $h(x) = f(x - c)$ or a vertical translation of $f(x)$ if $h(x) = f(x) + c$.**
- **The function $h(x)$ is a reflection of $f(x)$ in the x-axis if $h(x) = -f(x)$ and in the y-axis if $h(x) = f(-x)$.**
- **The function $h(x)$ is a vertical stretch or shrink of $f(x)$ if $h(x) = cf(x)$ and a horizontal stretch or shrink of $f(x)$ if $h(x) = f(cx)$.**

4 PRACTICE AND APPLY

Assignment Guide

Transparencies Available
Available at the Instructor's companion site.

Average:
Day 1: pp. 78–82
Exs. 1–6, 7–13 odd, 15–18, 19–79 odd, 81–85

Advanced:
Day 1: pp. 78–82
Exs. 8–14 even, 15–18, 20–78 even, 79, 80, 86, 88–90

Block:
pp. 78–82
Exs. 1–6, 7–13 odd, 15–18, 19–79 odd, 81–85 (with 1.8)

7. (a)

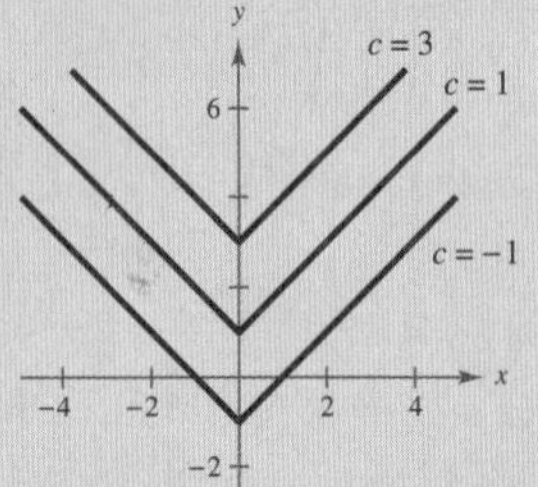

(b)

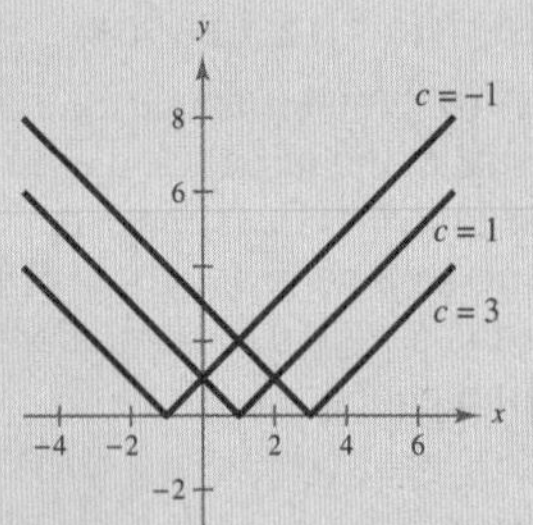

(c)

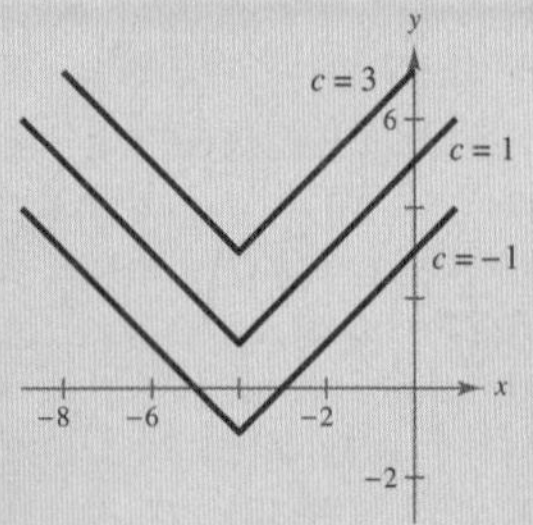

8. (a)

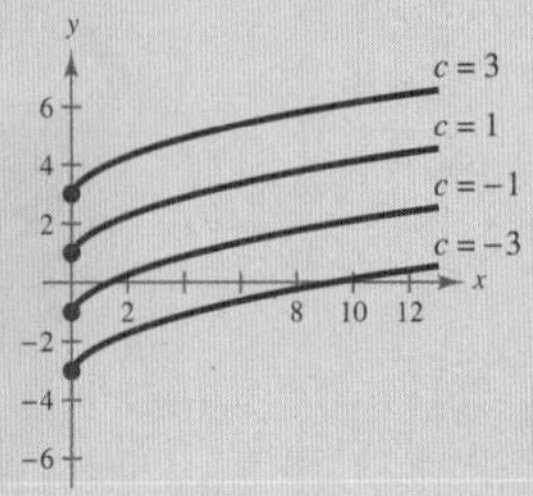

(b)

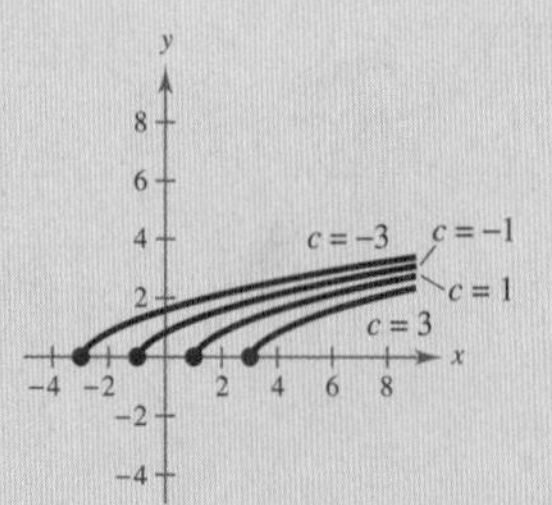

(c)

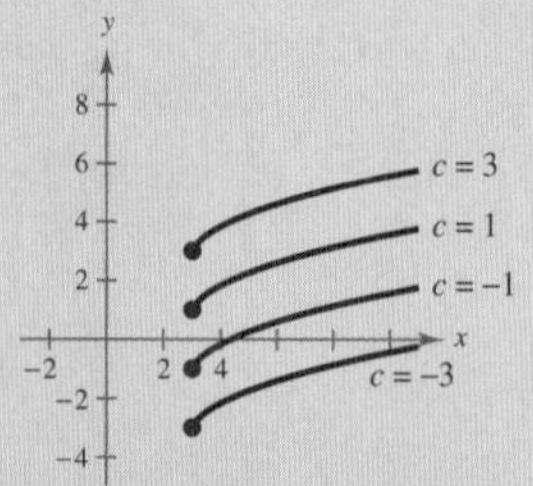

1.7 EXERCISES

See www.CalcChat.com for worked-out solutions to odd-numbered exercises.

VOCABULARY

In Exercises 1–5, fill in the blanks.

1. Horizontal shifts, vertical shifts, and reflections are called rigid transformations.

2. A reflection in the x-axis of $y = f(x)$ is represented by $h(x) = -f(x)$, while a reflection in the y-axis of $y = f(x)$ is represented by $h(x) = f(-x)$.

3. Transformations that cause a distortion in the shape of the graph of $y = f(x)$ are called nonrigid transformations.

4. A nonrigid transformation of $y = f(x)$ represented by $h(x) = f(cx)$ is a horizontal shrink if $c > 1$ and a horizontal stretch if $0 < c < 1$.

5. A nonrigid transformation of $y = f(x)$ represented by $g(x) = cf(x)$ is a vertical stretch if $c > 1$ and a vertical shrink if $0 < c < 1$.

6. Match the rigid transformation of $y = f(x)$ with the correct representation of the graph of h, where $c > 0$.

(a) $h(x) = f(x) + c$ (i) A horizontal shift of f, c units to the right
(b) $h(x) = f(x) - c$ (ii) A vertical shift of f, c units downward
(c) $h(x) = f(x + c)$ (iii) A horizontal shift of f, c units to the left
(d) $h(x) = f(x - c)$ (iv) A vertical shift of f, c units upward

SKILLS AND APPLICATIONS

7. For each function, sketch (on the same set of coordinate axes) a graph of each function for $c = -1, 1$, and 3.
(a) $f(x) = |x| + c$ See margin.
(b) $f(x) = |x - c|$
(c) $f(x) = |x + 4| + c$

8. For each function, sketch (on the same set of coordinate axes) a graph of each function for $c = -3, -1, 1$, and 3.
(a) $f(x) = \sqrt{x} + c$ See margin.
(b) $f(x) = \sqrt{x - c}$
(c) $f(x) = \sqrt{x - 3} + c$

9. For each function, sketch (on the same set of coordinate axes) a graph of each function for $c = -2, 0$, and 2.
(a) $f(x) = [\![x]\!] + c$ See margin.
(b) $f(x) = [\![x + c]\!]$
(c) $f(x) = [\![x - 1]\!] + c$

10. For each function, sketch (on the same set of coordinate axes) a graph of each function for $c = -3, -1, 1$, and 3.
(a) $f(x) = \begin{cases} x^2 + c, & x < 0 \\ -x^2 + c, & x \ge 0 \end{cases}$ See margin.
(b) $f(x) = \begin{cases} (x + c)^2, & x < 0 \\ -(x + c)^2, & x \ge 0 \end{cases}$

In Exercises 11–14, use the graph of f to sketch each graph. To print an enlarged copy of the graph, go to the website *www.mathgraphs.com*. 11–14. See margin.

11. (a) $y = f(x) + 2$
(b) $y = f(x - 2)$
(c) $y = 2f(x)$
(d) $y = -f(x)$
(e) $y = f(x + 3)$
(f) $y = f(-x)$
(g) $y = f(\frac{1}{2}x)$

12. (a) $y = f(-x)$
(b) $y = f(x) + 4$
(c) $y = 2f(x)$
(d) $y = -f(x - 4)$
(e) $y = f(x) - 3$
(f) $y = -f(x) - 1$
(g) $y = f(2x)$

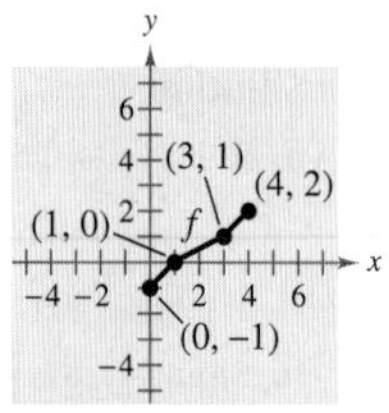

FIGURE FOR 11

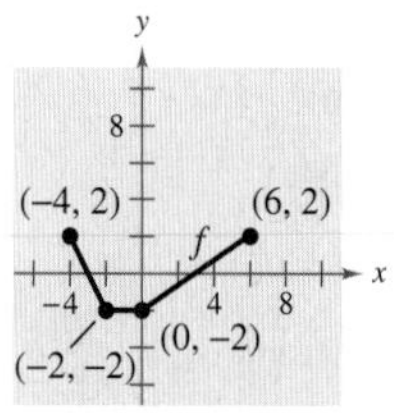

FIGURE FOR 12

13. (a) $y = f(x) - 1$
(b) $y = f(x - 1)$
(c) $y = f(-x)$
(d) $y = f(x + 1)$
(e) $y = -f(x - 2)$
(f) $y = \frac{1}{2}f(x)$
(g) $y = f(2x)$

14. (a) $y = f(x - 5)$
(b) $y = -f(x) + 3$
(c) $y = \frac{1}{3}f(x)$
(d) $y = -f(x + 1)$
(e) $y = f(-x)$
(f) $y = f(x) - 10$
(g) $y = f(\frac{1}{3}x)$

9–14. See Additional Answers beginning on page AA1.

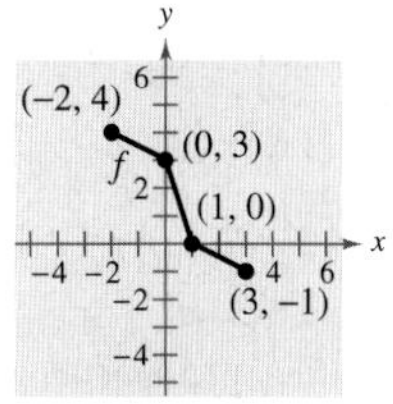

FIGURE FOR 13

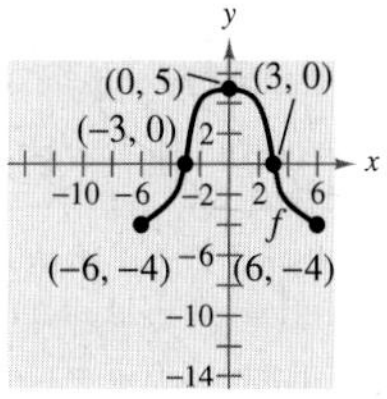

FIGURE FOR 14

15. Use the graph of $f(x) = x^2$ to write an equation for each function whose graph is shown. See margin.

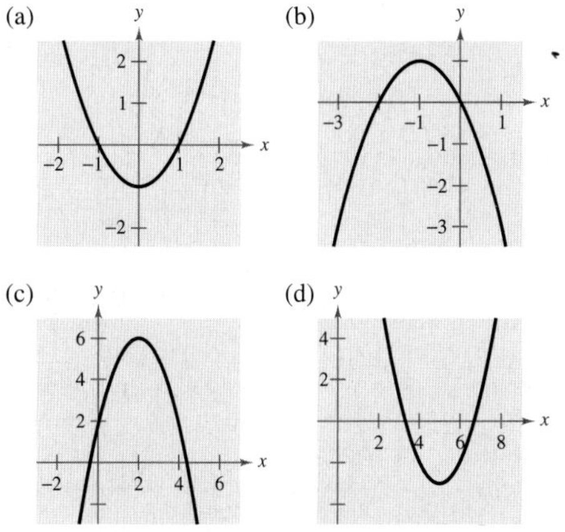

16. Use the graph of $f(x) = x^3$ to write an equation for each function whose graph is shown. See margin.

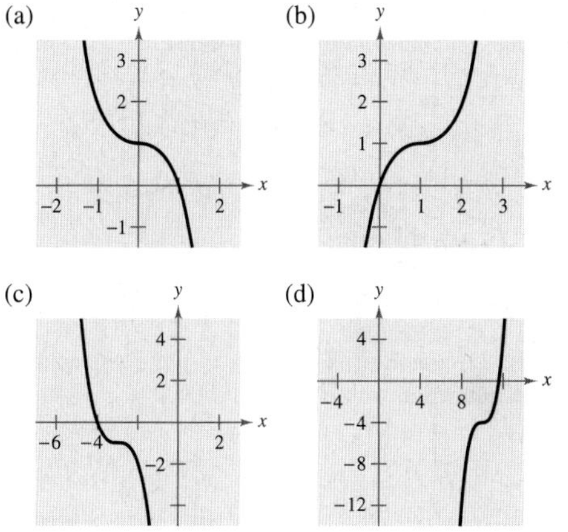

17. Use the graph of $f(x) = |x|$ to write an equation for each function whose graph is shown. See margin.

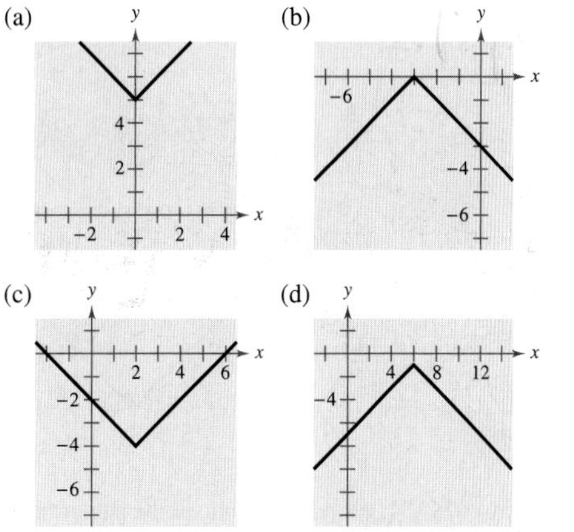

18. Use the graph of $f(x) = \sqrt{x}$ to write an equation for each function whose graph is shown. See margin.

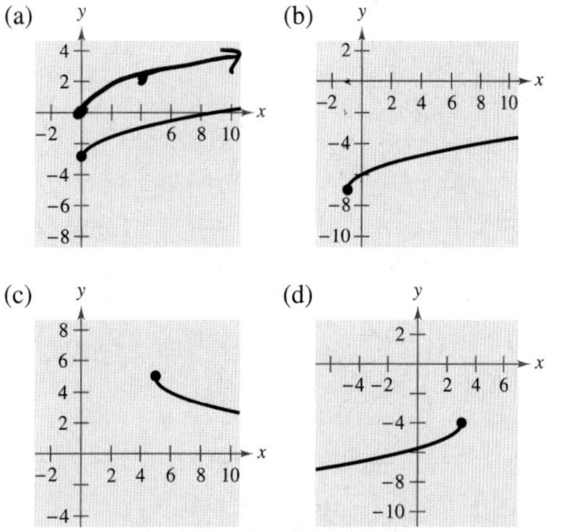

In Exercises 19–24, identify the parent function and the transformation shown in the graph. Write an equation for the function shown in the graph. 19–20. See margin.

19.

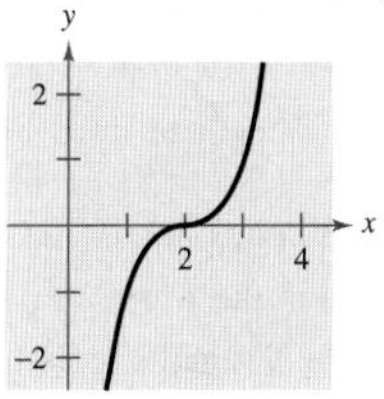

20.

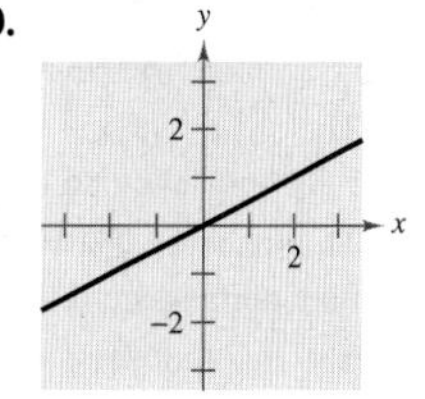

15. (a) $y = x^2 - 1$
(b) $y = 1 - (x + 1)^2$ $-(x+1)^2+1$
(c) $y = -(x - 2)^2 + 6$
(d) $y = (x - 5)^2 - 3$

16. (a) $y = 1 - x^3 = -x^3 + 1$
(b) $y = (x - 1)^3 + 1$
(c) $y = -(x + 3)^3 - 1$
(d) $y = (x - 10)^3 - 4$

17. (a) $y = |x| + 5$
(b) $y = -|x + 3|$
(c) $y = |x - 2| - 4$
(d) $y = -|x - 6| - 1$

18. (a) $y = \sqrt{x} - 3$
(b) $y = \sqrt{x + 1} - 7$
(c) $y = -\sqrt{x - 5} + 5$
(d) $y = -\sqrt{-x + 3} - 4$

19. Horizontal shift of $y = x^3$; $y = (x - 2)^3$

20. Vertical shrink of $y = x$; $y = \frac{1}{2}x$

21–24. See margin.

21.

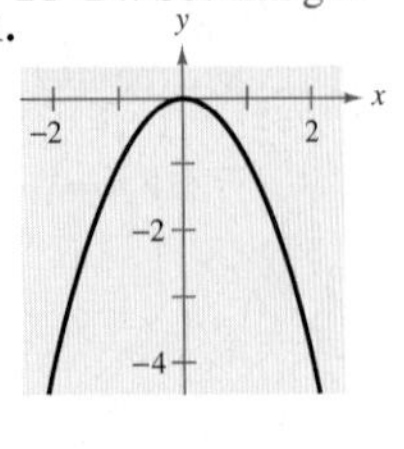

22.

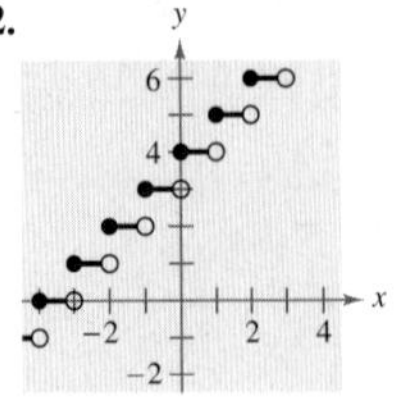

23.

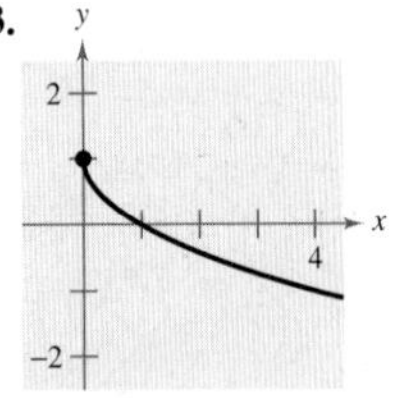

24.

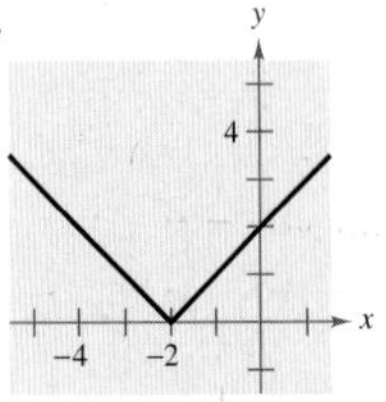

In Exercises 25–54, g is related to one of the parent functions described in Section 1.6. (a) Identify the parent function f. (b) Describe the sequence of transformations from f to g. (c) Sketch the graph of g. (d) Use function notation to write g in terms of f. 25–54. See margin.

25. $g(x) = 12 - x^2$
26. $g(x) = (x - 8)^2$
27. $g(x) = x^3 + 7$
28. $g(x) = -x^3 - 1$
29. $g(x) = \frac{2}{3}x^2 + 4$
30. $g(x) = 2(x - 7)^2$
31. $g(x) = 2 - (x + 5)^2$
32. $g(x) = -(x + 10)^2 + 5$
33. $g(x) = 3 + 2(x - 4)^2$
34. $g(x) = -\frac{1}{4}(x + 2)^2 - 2$
35. $g(x) = \sqrt{3x}$
36. $g(x) = \sqrt{\frac{1}{4}x}$
37. $g(x) = (x - 1)^3 + 2$
38. $g(x) = (x + 3)^3 - 10$
39. $g(x) = 3(x - 2)^3$
40. $g(x) = -\frac{1}{2}(x + 1)^3$
41. $g(x) = -|x| - 2$
42. $g(x) = 6 - |x + 5|$
43. $g(x) = -|x + 4| + 8$
44. $g(x) = |-x + 3| + 9$
45. $g(x) = -2|x - 1| - 4$
46. $g(x) = \frac{1}{2}|x - 2| - 3$
47. $g(x) = 3 - [\![x]\!]$
48. $g(x) = 2[\![x + 5]\!]$
49. $g(x) = \sqrt{x - 9}$
50. $g(x) = \sqrt{x + 4} + 8$
51. $g(x) = \sqrt{7 - x} - 2$
52. $g(x) = -\frac{1}{2}\sqrt{x + 3} - 1$
53. $g(x) = \sqrt{\frac{1}{2}x} - 4$
54. $g(x) = \sqrt{3x} + 1$

In Exercises 55–62, write an equation for the function that is described by the given characteristics.

55. The shape of $f(x) = x^2$, but shifted three units to the right and seven units downward $g(x) = (x - 3)^2 - 7$

56. The shape of $f(x) = x^2$, but shifted two units to the left, nine units upward, and reflected in the x-axis See margin.

57. The shape of $f(x) = x^3$, but shifted 13 units to the right See margin.

58. The shape of $f(x) = x^3$, but shifted six units to the left, six units downward, and reflected in the y-axis
$g(x) = (-x + 6)^3 - 6$

59. The shape of $f(x) = |x|$, but shifted 12 units upward and reflected in the x-axis $g(x) = -|x| + 12$

60. The shape of $f(x) = |x|$, but shifted four units to the left and eight units downward $g(x) = |x + 4| - 8$

61. The shape of $f(x) = \sqrt{x}$, but shifted six units to the left and reflected in both the x-axis and the y-axis See margin.

62. The shape of $f(x) = \sqrt{x}$, but shifted nine units downward and reflected in both the x-axis and the y-axis
$g(x) = -\sqrt{-x} + 9$

63. Use the graph of $f(x) = x^2$ to write an equation for each function whose graph is shown.

(a) $y = -3x^2$

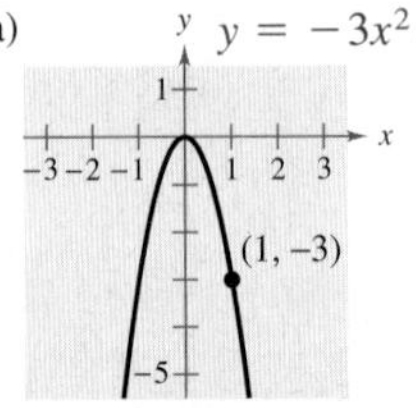

(b) $y = 4x^2 + 3$

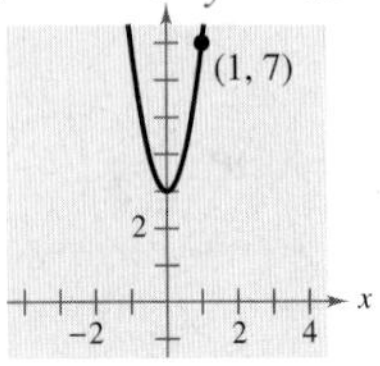

64. Use the graph of $f(x) = x^3$ to write an equation for each function whose graph is shown.

(a) $y = \frac{1}{4}x^3$

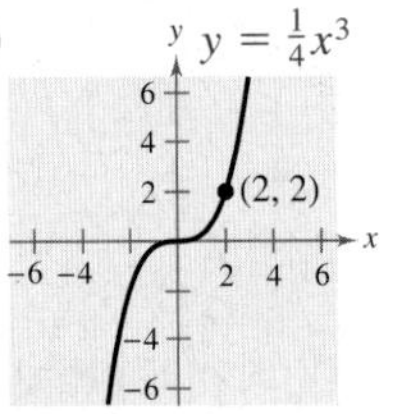

(b) $y = -2x^3$

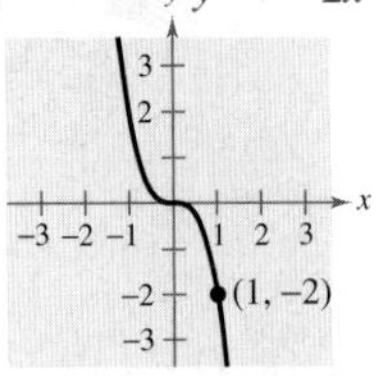

65. Use the graph of $f(x) = |x|$ to write an equation for each function whose graph is shown.

(a) $y = -\frac{1}{2}|x|$

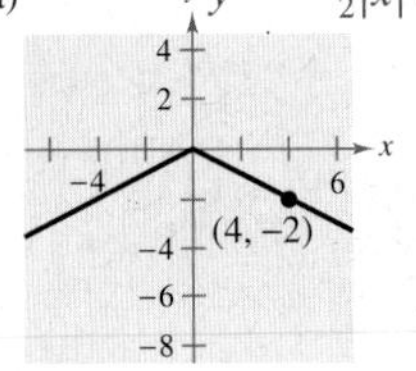

(b) $y = 3|x| - 3$

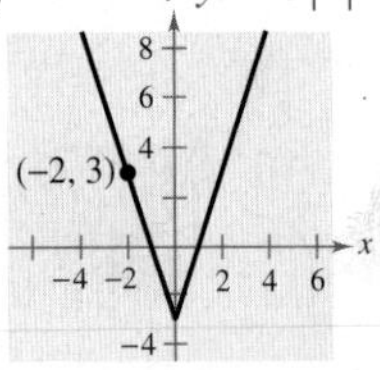

66. Use the graph of $f(x) = \sqrt{x}$ to write an equation for each function whose graph is shown.

(a) $y = 8\sqrt{x}$

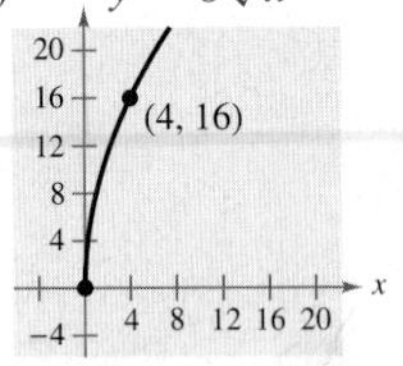

(b) $y = -\frac{1}{4}\sqrt{x}$

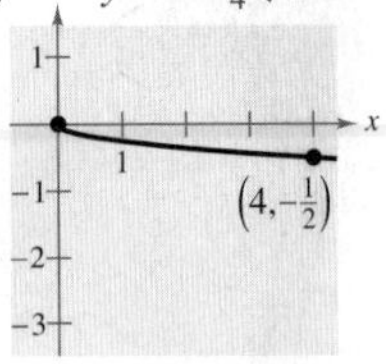

21. Reflection in the x-axis of $y = x^2$; $y = -x^2$

22. Vertical shift of $y = [\![x]\!]$; $y = [\![x]\!] + 4$

23. Reflection in the x-axis and vertical shift of $y = \sqrt{x}$; $y = 1 - \sqrt{x}$

24. Horizontal shift of $y = |x|$; $y = |x + 2|$

25. (a) $f(x) = x^2$
(b) Reflection in the x-axis and vertical shift 12 units upward
(c)

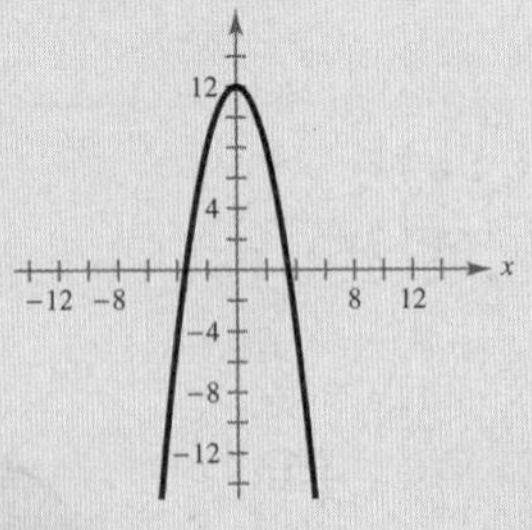

(d) $g(x) = 12 - f(x)$

26. (a) $f(x) = x^2$
(b) Horizontal shift eight units to the right
(c)

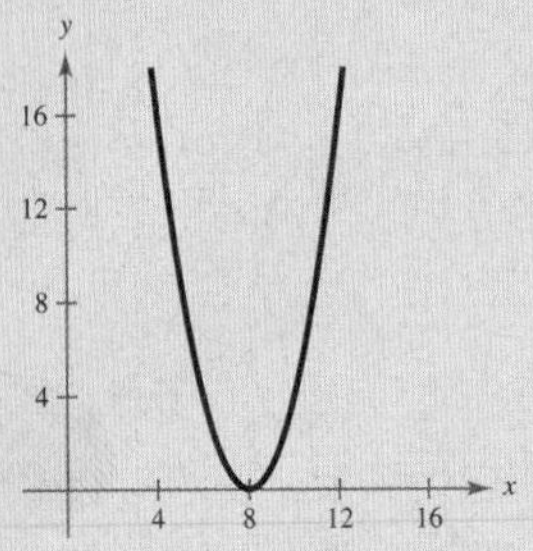

(d) $g(x) = f(x - 8)$

27. (a) $f(x) = x^3$
(b) Vertical shift seven units upward
(c)

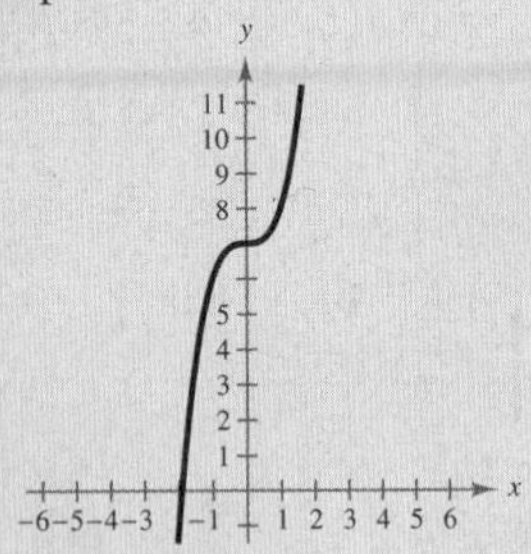

(d) $g(x) = f(x) + 7$

28. (a) $f(x) = x^3$
(b) Reflection in the x-axis and a vertical shift one unit downward
(c)

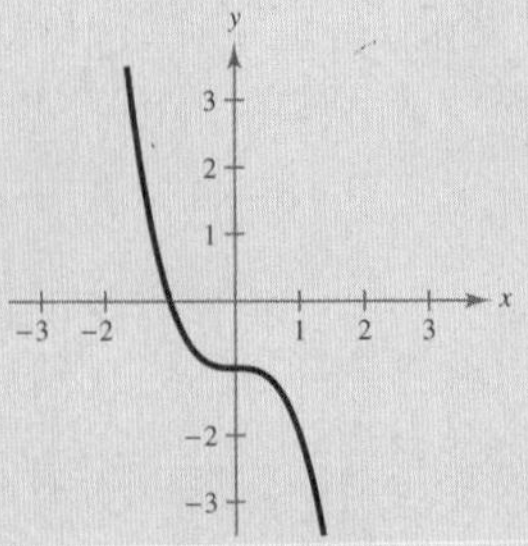

(d) $g(x) = -f(x) - 1$

29–54, 56–57, 61. See Additional Answers beginning on page AA1.

In Exercises 67–72, identify the parent function and the transformation shown in the graph. Write an equation for the function shown in the graph. Then use a graphing utility to verify your answer. 67–72. See margin.

67.

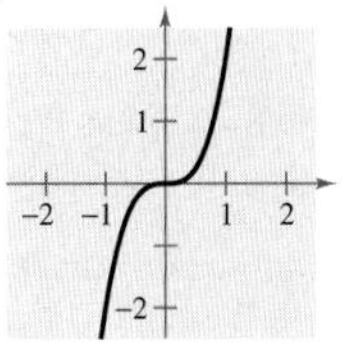

68.

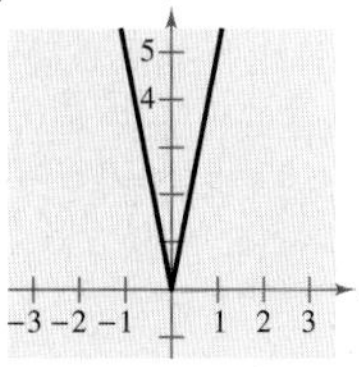

69.

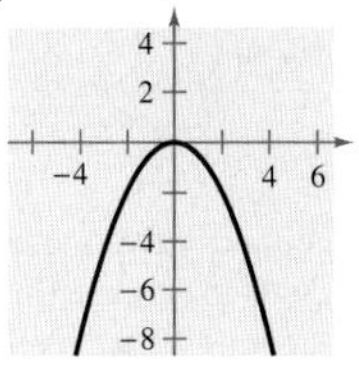

70.

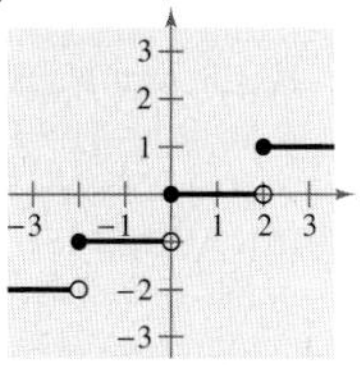

71.

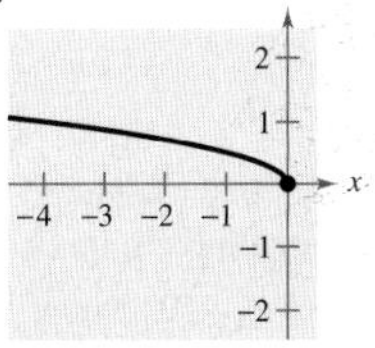

72.

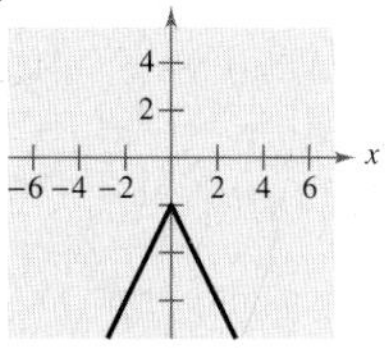

GRAPHICAL ANALYSIS In Exercises 73–76, use the viewing window shown to write a possible equation for the transformation of the parent function.

73. $y = -(x-2)^3 + 2$

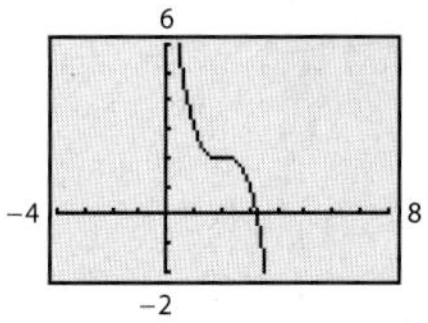

74. $y = |x+4| - 2$

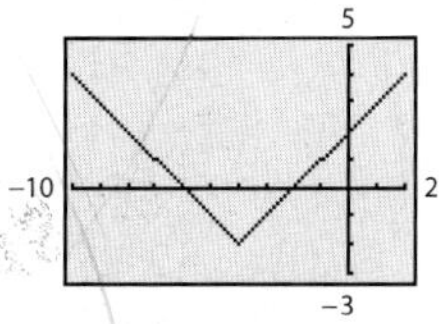

75. $y = -\sqrt{x} - 3$

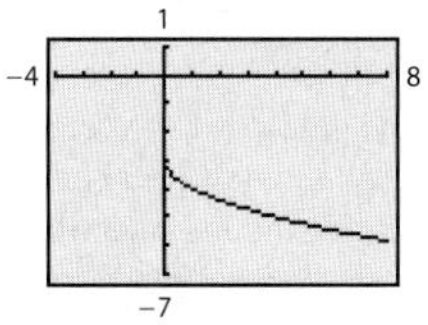

76. $y = (x-2)^2 + 4$

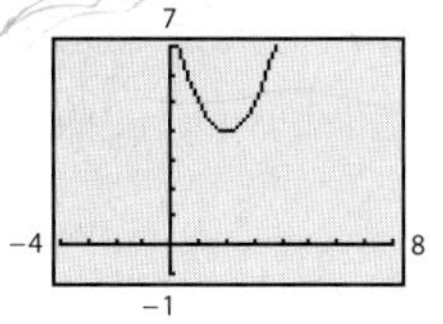

GRAPHICAL REASONING In Exercises 77 and 78, use the graph of f to sketch the graph of g. To print an enlarged copy of the graph, go to the website *www.mathgraphs.com*. 77–78. See margin.

77.

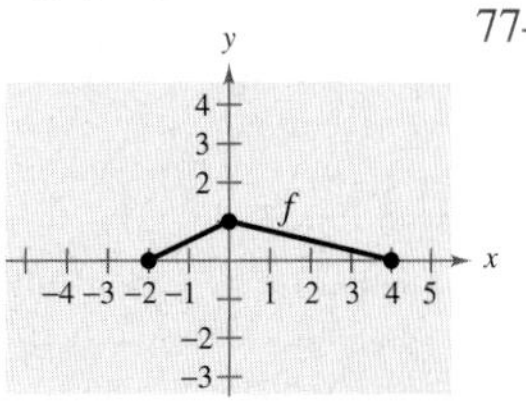

(a) $g(x) = f(x) + 2$ (b) $g(x) = f(x) - 1$

(c) $g(x) = f(-x)$ (d) $g(x) = -2f(x)$

(e) $g(x) = f(4x)$ (f) $g(x) = f\left(\frac{1}{2}x\right)$

78.

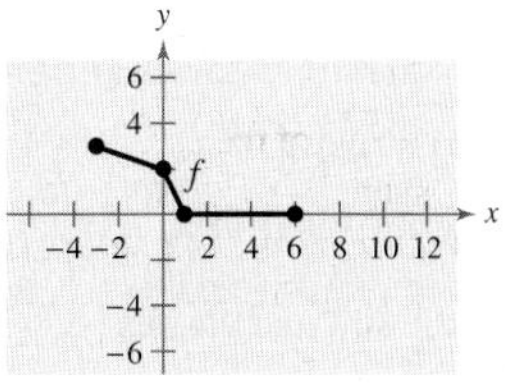

(a) $g(x) = f(x) - 5$ (b) $g(x) = f(x) + \frac{1}{2}$

(c) $g(x) = f(-x)$ (d) $g(x) = -4f(x)$

(e) $g(x) = f(2x) + 1$ (f) $g(x) = f\left(\frac{1}{4}x\right) - 2$

79. MILES DRIVEN The total numbers of miles M (in billions) driven by vans, pickups, and SUVs (sport utility vehicles) in the United States from 1990 through 2006 can be approximated by the function

$$M = 527 + 128.0\sqrt{t}, \quad 0 \le t \le 16$$ See margin.

where t represents the year, with $t = 0$ corresponding to 1990. (Source: U.S. Federal Highway Administration)

(a) Describe the transformation of the parent function $f(x) = \sqrt{x}$. Then use a graphing utility to graph the function over the specified domain.

(b) Find the average rate of change of the function from 1990 to 2006. Interpret your answer in the context of the problem.

(c) Rewrite the function so that $t = 0$ represents 2000. Explain how you got your answer.

(d) Use the model from part (c) to predict the number of miles driven by vans, pickups, and SUVs in 2012. Does your answer seem reasonable? Explain.

67. Vertical stretch of $y = x^3$; $y = 2x^3$

68. Vertical stretch of $y = |x|$; $y = 6|x|$

69. Reflection in the x-axis and vertical shrink of $y = x^2$; $y = -\frac{1}{2}x^2$

70. Horizontal stretch of $y = [\![x]\!]$; $y = [\![\frac{1}{2}x]\!]$

71. Reflection in the y-axis and vertical shrink of $y = \sqrt{x}$; $y = \frac{1}{2}\sqrt{-x}$

72. Reflection in the x-axis, vertical stretch, and vertical shift two units downward of $y = |x|$; $y = -2|x| - 2$

77. (a)

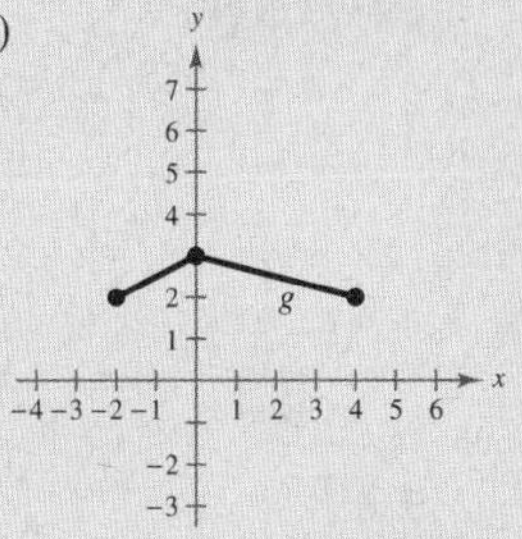

(b)

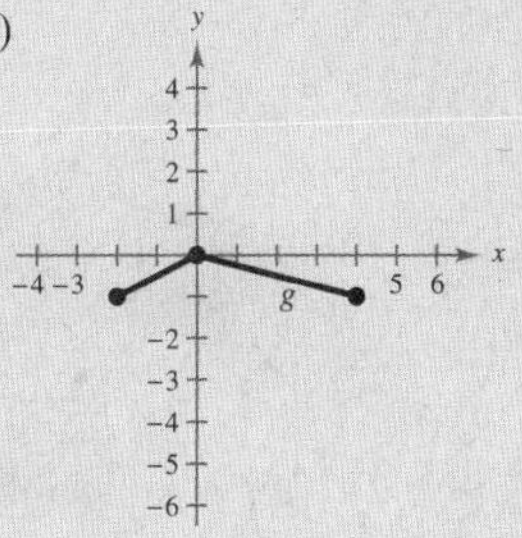

(c)

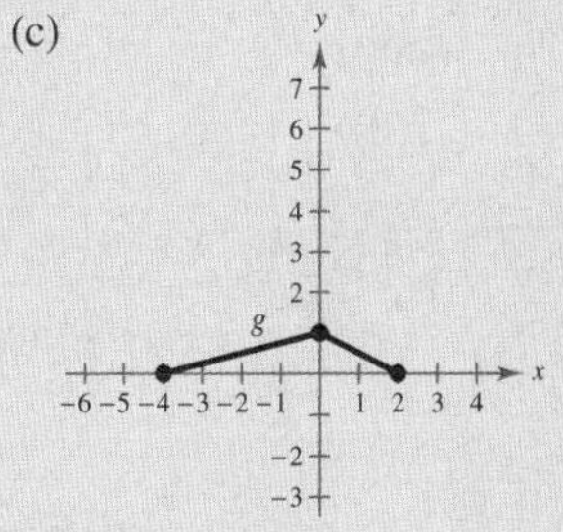

(d)

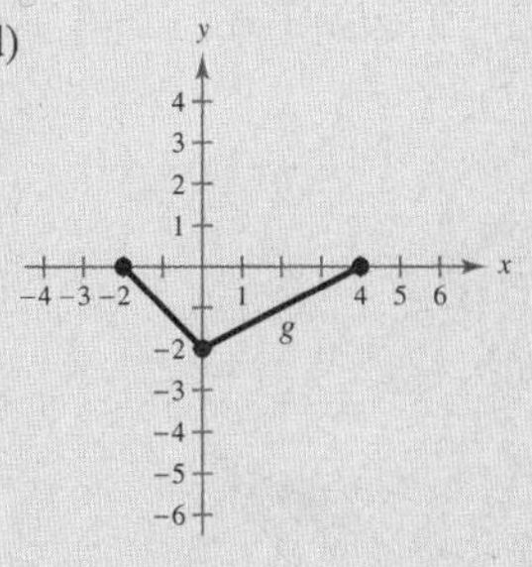

(e)

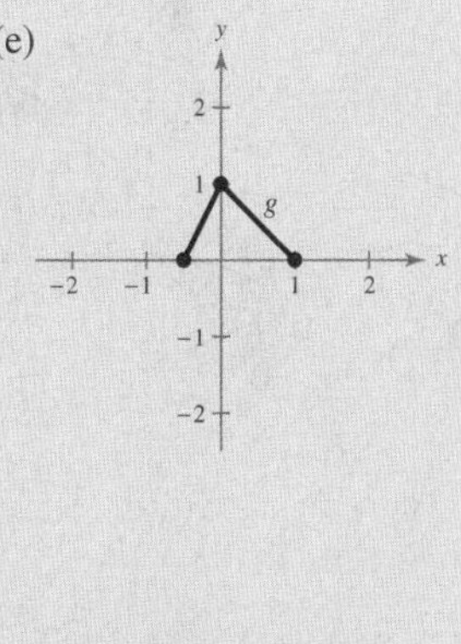

(f)

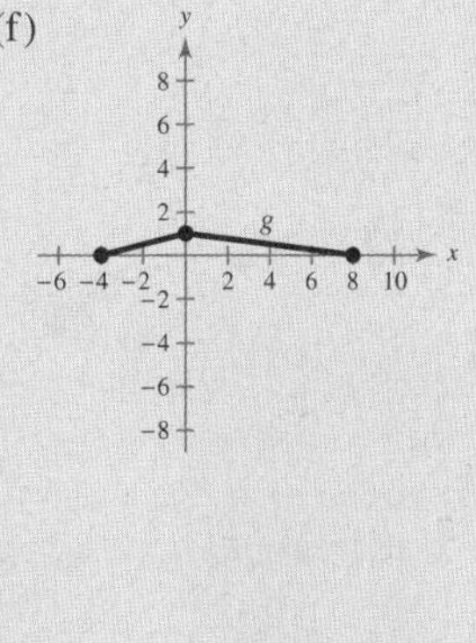

78–79. See Additional Answers beginning on page AA1.

80. MARRIED COUPLES The numbers N (in thousands) of married couples with stay-at-home mothers from 2000 through 2007 can be approximated by the function See margin.

$$N = -24.70(t - 5.99)^2 + 5617, \quad 0 \le t \le 7$$

where t represents the year, with $t = 0$ corresponding to 2000. (Source: U.S. Census Bureau)

(a) Describe the transformation of the parent function $f(x) = x^2$. Then use a graphing utility to graph the function over the specified domain.

(b) Find the average rate of the change of the function from 2000 to 2007. Interpret your answer in the context of the problem.

(c) Use the model to predict the number of married couples with stay-at-home mothers in 2015. Does your answer seem reasonable? Explain.

EXPLORATION

81–82. See margin.

TRUE OR FALSE? In Exercises 81–84, determine whether the statement is true or false. Justify your answer.

81. The graph of $y = f(-x)$ is a reflection of the graph of $y = f(x)$ in the x-axis.

82. The graph of $y = -f(x)$ is a reflection of the graph of $y = f(x)$ in the y-axis.

83. The graphs of

$f(x) = |x| + 6$

and True. $|-x| = |x|$

$f(x) = |-x| + 6$

are identical.

84. If the graph of the parent function $f(x) = x^2$ is shifted six units to the right, three units upward, and reflected in the x-axis, then the point $(-2, 19)$ will lie on the graph of the transformation. False. The point $(-2, -61)$ will lie on the transformation.

85. DESCRIBING PROFITS Management originally predicted that the profits from the sales of a new product would be approximated by the graph of the function f shown. The actual profits are shown by the function g along with a verbal description. Use the concepts of transformations of graphs to write g in terms of f.

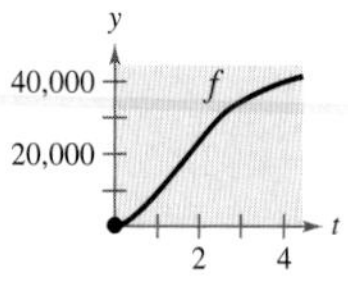

(a) The profits were only three-fourths as large as expected. $g(t) = \frac{3}{4}f(t)$

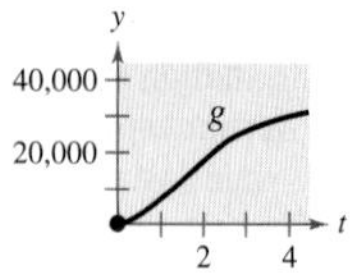

(b) The profits were consistently \$10,000 greater than predicted. $g(t) = f(t) + 10{,}000$

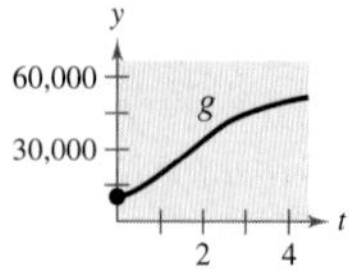

(c) There was a two-year delay in the introduction of the product. After sales began, profits grew as expected. $g(t) = f(t - 2)$

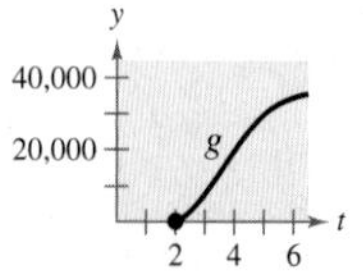

86. THINK ABOUT IT You can use either of two methods to graph a function: plotting points or translating a parent function as shown in this section. Which method of graphing do you prefer to use for each function? Explain. Answers will vary.

(a) $f(x) = 3x^2 - 4x + 1$

(b) $f(x) = 2(x - 1)^2 - 6$

87. The graph of $y = f(x)$ passes through the points $(0, 1)$, $(1, 2)$, and $(2, 3)$. Find the corresponding points on the graph of $y = f(x + 2) - 1$. $(-2, 0), (-1, 1), (0, 2)$

88. Use a graphing utility to graph f, g, and h in the same viewing window. Before looking at the graphs, try to predict how the graphs of g and h relate to the graph of f. See margin.

(a) $f(x) = x^2$, $g(x) = (x - 4)^2$, $h(x) = (x - 4)^2 + 3$

(b) $f(x) = x^2$, $g(x) = (x + 1)^2$, $h(x) = (x + 1)^2 - 2$

(c) $f(x) = x^2$, $g(x) = (x + 4)^2$, $h(x) = (x + 4)^2 + 2$

89. Reverse the order of transformations in Example 2(a). Do you obtain the same graph? Do the same for Example 2(b). Do you obtain the same graph? Explain. See margin.

90. CAPSTONE Use the fact that the graph of $y = f(x)$ is increasing on the intervals $(-\infty, -1)$ and $(2, \infty)$ and decreasing on the interval $(-1, 2)$ to find the intervals on which the graph is increasing and decreasing. If not possible, state the reason. See margin.

(a) $y = f(-x)$ (b) $y = -f(x)$ (c) $y = \frac{1}{2}f(x)$

(d) $y = -f(x - 1)$ (e) $y = f(x - 2) + 1$

5 ASSESS AND RETEACH

Daily Homework Quiz

Transparency Available

Available at the Instructor's companion site.

80. (a) Reflection in the x-axis, vertical stretch of 24.70, horizontal shift of 5.99 units to the right, and a vertical shift of 5617 units upward

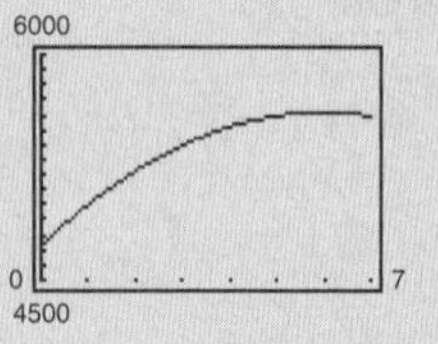

(b) 123; Each year, the number of married couples with stay-at-home mothers increases by an average of 123,000.

(c) 3,612,000; Answers will vary. Sample answer: No, because the number of stay-at-home mothers has been increasing on average.

81. False. The graph of $y = f(-x)$ is a reflection of the graph of $f(x)$ in the y-axis.

82. False. The graph of $y = -f(x)$ is a reflection of the graph of $f(x)$ in the x-axis.

88. (a)

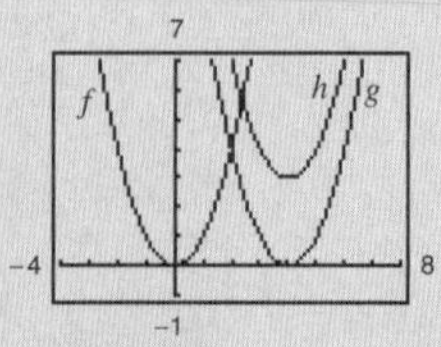

g is a right shift of four units. h is a right shift of four units and an upward shift of three units.

(b)

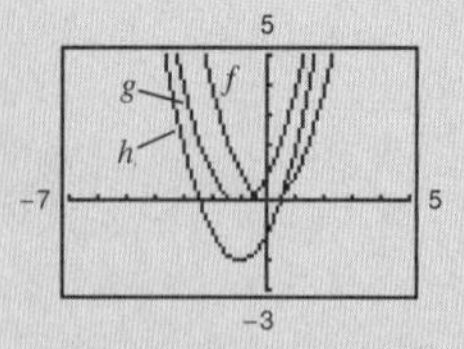

g is a left shift of one unit. h is a left shift of one unit and a downward shift of two units.

(c)

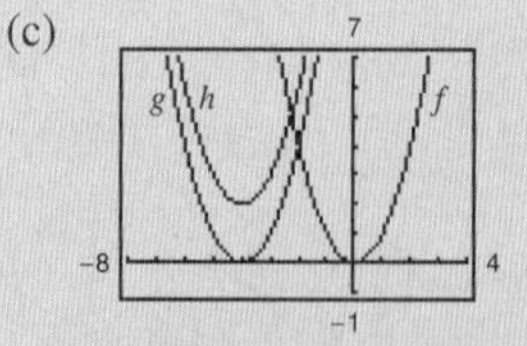

g is a left shift of four units. h is a left shift of four units and an upward shift of two units.

89. No. $g(x) = -x^4 - 2$. Yes. $h(x) = -(x - 3)^4$.

90. (a) Increasing on the interval $(-2, 1)$ and decreasing on the intervals $(-\infty, -2)$ and $(1, \infty)$

(b) Increasing on the interval $(-1, 2)$ and decreasing on the intervals $(-\infty, -1)$ and $(2, \infty)$

(c) Increasing on the intervals $(-\infty, -1)$ and $(2, \infty)$ and decreasing on the interval $(-1, 2)$

(d) Increasing on the interval $(0, 3)$ and decreasing on the intervals $(-\infty, 0)$ and $(3, \infty)$

(e) Increasing on the intervals $(-\infty, 1)$ and $(4, \infty)$ and decreasing on the interval $(1, 4)$

1.8 Combinations of Functions: Composite Functions

What you should learn

- Add, subtract, multiply, and divide functions.
- Find the composition of one function with another function.
- Use combinations and compositions of functions to model and solve real-life problems.

Why you should learn it

Compositions of functions can be used to model and solve real-life problems. For instance, in Exercise 76 on page 91, compositions of functions are used to determine the price of a new hybrid car.

© Jim West/The Image Works

Arithmetic Combinations of Functions

Just as two real numbers can be combined by the operations of addition, subtraction, multiplication, and division to form other real numbers, two *functions* can be combined to create new functions. For example, the functions given by $f(x) = 2x - 3$ and $g(x) = x^2 - 1$ can be combined to form the sum, difference, product, and quotient of f and g.

$$f(x) + g(x) = (2x - 3) + (x^2 - 1)$$
$$= x^2 + 2x - 4 \qquad \text{Sum}$$
$$f(x) - g(x) = (2x - 3) - (x^2 - 1)$$
$$= -x^2 + 2x - 2 \qquad \text{Difference}$$
$$f(x)g(x) = (2x - 3)(x^2 - 1)$$
$$= 2x^3 - 3x^2 - 2x + 3 \qquad \text{Product}$$
$$\frac{f(x)}{g(x)} = \frac{2x - 3}{x^2 - 1}, \quad x \neq \pm 1 \qquad \text{Quotient}$$

The domain of an **arithmetic combination** of functions f and g consists of all real numbers that are common to the domains of f and g. In the case of the quotient $f(x)/g(x)$, there is the further restriction that $g(x) \neq 0$.

Sum, Difference, Product, and Quotient of Functions

Let f and g be two functions with overlapping domains. Then, for all x common to both domains, the *sum*, *difference*, *product*, and *quotient* of f and g are defined as follows.

1. *Sum:* $(f + g)(x) = f(x) + g(x)$
2. *Difference:* $(f - g)(x) = f(x) - g(x)$
3. *Product:* $(fg)(x) = f(x) \cdot g(x)$
4. *Quotient:* $\left(\frac{f}{g}\right)(x) = \frac{f(x)}{g(x)}, \quad g(x) \neq 0$

Example 1 Finding the Sum of Two Functions

Given $f(x) = 2x + 1$ and $g(x) = x^2 + 2x - 1$, find $(f + g)(x)$. Then evaluate the sum when $x = 3$.

Solution

$$(f + g)(x) = f(x) + g(x) = (2x + 1) + (x^2 + 2x - 1) = x^2 + 4x$$

When $x = 3$, the value of this sum is

$$(f + g)(3) = 3^2 + 4(3) = 21.$$

CHECKPoint Now try Exercise 9(a).

1 PLAN AND PREPARE

Warm-up Exercises

Transparency Available
Available at the Instructor's companion site.

Notetaking Guide

Transparency Available
Promotes interactive learning and notetaking skills.
Available at the Instructor's companion site.

Animated Precalculus

An **Animated Precalculus** tutorial is available at the Student companion site for **Section 1.8.**

Pacing

Average: 1 day
Advanced: 1 day
Block: 0.5 block with 1.7

2 FOCUS AND MOTIVATE

Essential Question

How do you combine two parent functions to form a new function?
Tell students that they will learn how to answer this question by finding the sum, difference, product, quotient, and composition of two functions.

Resource Planning Guide

Chapter Resources

- Complete Solutions Guide

Workbooks

- Notetaking Guide
- Student Solutions Guide

Interactive Technology

- Instructor Success Organizer
- Notetaking Guide IAE
- Instructional DVDs
- Animated Precalculus
- PowerLecture with ExamView

3 TEACH

Extra Example 1

Given $f(x) = x^2$ and $g(x) = 1 - x$, find $(f + g)(x)$. Then evaluate the sum when $x = 2$.

$x^2 - x + 1$; 3

Extra Example 2

Given $f(x) = x^2$ and $g(x) = 1 - x$, find $(f - g)(x)$. Then evaluate the difference when $x = 3$.

$x^2 + x - 1$; 11

Extra Example 3

Given $f(x) = 5x + 2$ and $g(x) = 3x - 4$, find $(fg)(x)$. Then evaluate the product when $x = 2$.

$15x^2 - 14x - 8$; 24

Extra Example 4

Given $f(x) = x^2$ and $g(x) = 1 - x$, find $\left(\frac{f}{g}\right)(x)$ for the functions. Then find the domain of $\left(\frac{f}{g}\right)(x)$.

$\frac{x^2}{1 - x}$; All real numbers x except $x = 1$

Example 2 Finding the Difference of Two Functions

Given $f(x) = 2x + 1$ and $g(x) = x^2 + 2x - 1$, find $(f - g)(x)$. Then evaluate the difference when $x = 2$.

Solution

The difference of f and g is

$$(f - g)(x) = f(x) - g(x) = (2x + 1) - (x^2 + 2x - 1) = -x^2 + 2.$$

When $x = 2$, the value of this difference is

$$(f - g)(2) = -(2)^2 + 2 = -2.$$

CHECKPoint Now try Exercise 9(b).

Example 3 Finding the Product of Two Functions

Given $f(x) = x^2$ and $g(x) = x - 3$, find $(fg)(x)$. Then evaluate the product when $x = 4$.

Solution

$$(fg)(x) = f(x)g(x) = (x^2)(x - 3) = x^3 - 3x^2$$

When $x = 4$, the value of this product is

$$(fg)(4) = 4^3 - 3(4)^2 = 16.$$

CHECKPoint Now try Exercise 9(c).

In Examples 1–3, both f and g have domains that consist of all real numbers. So, the domains of $f + g$, $f - g$, and fg are also the set of all real numbers. Remember that any restrictions on the domains of f and g must be considered when forming the sum, difference, product, or quotient of f and g.

Example 4 Finding the Quotients of Two Functions

Find $(f/g)(x)$ and $(g/f)(x)$ for the functions given by $f(x) = \sqrt{x}$ and $g(x) = \sqrt{4 - x^2}$. Then find the domains of f/g and g/f.

Solution

The quotient of f and g is

$$\left(\frac{f}{g}\right)(x) = \frac{f(x)}{g(x)} = \frac{\sqrt{x}}{\sqrt{4 - x^2}}$$

and the quotient of g and f is

$$\left(\frac{g}{f}\right)(x) = \frac{g(x)}{f(x)} = \frac{\sqrt{4 - x^2}}{\sqrt{x}}.$$

The domain of f is $[0, \infty)$ and the domain of g is $[-2, 2]$. The intersection of these domains is $[0, 2]$. So, the domains of f/g and g/f are as follows.

Domain of f/g: $[0, 2)$ Domain of g/f: $(0, 2]$

CHECKPoint Now try Exercise 9(d).

Study Tip

Note that the domain of f/g includes $x = 0$, but not $x = 2$, because $x = 2$ yields a zero in the denominator, whereas the domain of g/f includes $x = 2$, but not $x = 0$, because $x = 0$ yields a zero in the denominator.

Composition of Functions

Another way of combining two functions is to form the **composition** of one with the other. For instance, if $f(x) = x^2$ and $g(x) = x + 1$, the composition of f with g is

$$f(g(x)) = f(x + 1)$$
$$= (x + 1)^2.$$

This composition is denoted as $f \circ g$ and reads as "f composed with g."

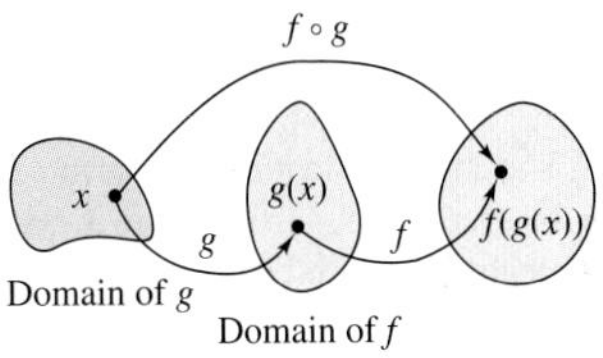

FIGURE 1.90

> **Definition of Composition of Two Functions**
>
> The **composition** of the function f with the function g is
>
> $$(f \circ g)(x) = f(g(x)).$$
>
> The domain of $f \circ g$ is the set of all x in the domain of g such that $g(x)$ is in the domain of f. (See Figure 1.90.)

Example 5 Composition of Functions

Given $f(x) = x + 2$ and $g(x) = 4 - x^2$, find the following.

a. $(f \circ g)(x)$ **b.** $(g \circ f)(x)$ **c.** $(g \circ f)(-2)$

Solution

a. The composition of f with g is as follows.

$(f \circ g)(x) = f(g(x))$ Definition of $f \circ g$

$= f(4 - x^2)$ Definition of $g(x)$

$= (4 - x^2) + 2$ Definition of $f(x)$

$= -x^2 + 6$ Simplify.

b. The composition of g with f is as follows.

$(g \circ f)(x) = g(f(x))$ Definition of $g \circ f$

$= g(x + 2)$ Definition of $f(x)$

$= 4 - (x + 2)^2$ Definition of $g(x)$

$= 4 - (x^2 + 4x + 4)$ Expand.

$= -x^2 - 4x$ Simplify.

Note that, in this case, $(f \circ g)(x) \neq (g \circ f)(x)$.

c. Using the result of part (b), you can write the following.

$(g \circ f)(-2) = -(-2)^2 - 4(-2)$ Substitute.

$= -4 + 8$ Simplify.

$= 4$ Simplify.

CHECKPoint Now try Exercise 37.

Study Tip

The following tables of values help illustrate the composition $(f \circ g)(x)$ given in Example 5.

x	0	1	2	3
$g(x)$	4	3	0	-5

$g(x)$	4	3	0	-5
$f(g(x))$	6	5	2	-3

x	0	1	2	3
$f(g(x))$	6	5	2	-3

Note that the first two tables can be combined (or "composed") to produce the values given in the third table.

Avoiding Common Errors

Example 5 Remind students to copy functions carefully when composing functions. They should also be sure to place parentheses around each function to make sure that they make any necessary sign changes.

Extra Example 5

Given $f(x) = 2x + 5$ and $g(x) = 4x^2 + 1$, find the following.

a. $(f \circ g)(x)$ $\mathbf{8x^2 + 7}$

b. $(g \circ f)(x)$ $\mathbf{16x^2 + 80x + 101}$

c. $(f \circ g)\left(-\frac{1}{2}\right)$ **9**

Extra Example 6

Find the composition $(f \circ g)(x)$ for the functions $f(x) = \sqrt{x}$ and $g(x) = x^2 + 4$. Then find the domain of $(f \circ g)(x)$.

$\sqrt{x^2 + 4}$; **All real numbers x**

Extra Example 7

Find two functions f and g such that $(f \circ g)(x) = h(x)$, where $h(x) = \dfrac{\sqrt[3]{8 - x}}{5}$.

Sample answer: $g(x) = 8 - x$, $f(x) = \dfrac{\sqrt[3]{x}}{5}$: $f(g(x)) = f(8 - x) = \dfrac{\sqrt[3]{8 - x}}{5} = h(x)$

Example 6 Finding the Domain of a Composite Function

Find the domain of $(f \circ g)(x)$ for the functions given by

$$f(x) = x^2 - 9 \quad \text{and} \quad g(x) = \sqrt{9 - x^2}.$$

Algebraic Solution

The composition of the functions is as follows.

$$\begin{aligned}(f \circ g)(x) &= f(g(x))\\ &= f\left(\sqrt{9 - x^2}\right)\\ &= \left(\sqrt{9 - x^2}\right)^2 - 9\\ &= 9 - x^2 - 9\\ &= -x^2\end{aligned}$$

From this, it might appear that the domain of the composition is the set of all real numbers. This, however, is not true. Because the domain of f is the set of all real numbers and the domain of g is $[-3, 3]$, the domain of $f \circ g$ is $[-3, 3]$.

Graphical Solution

You can use a graphing utility to graph the composition of the functions $(f \circ g)(x)$ as $y = \left(\sqrt{9 - x^2}\right)^2 - 9$. Enter the functions as follows.

$$y_1 = \sqrt{9 - x^2} \qquad y_2 = y_1^2 - 9$$

Graph y_2, as shown in Figure 1.91. Use the *trace* feature to determine that the x-coordinates of points on the graph extend from -3 to 3. So, you can graphically estimate the domain of $f \circ g$ to be $[-3, 3]$.

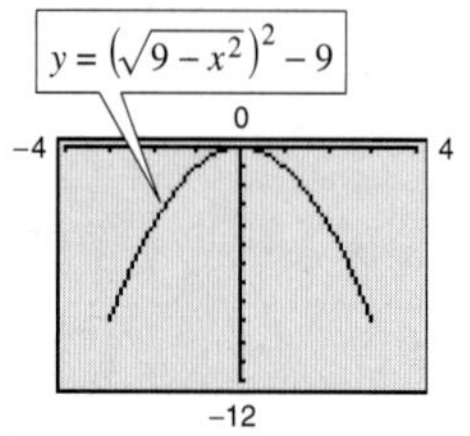

FIGURE 1.91

CHECK*Point* Now try Exercise 41.

In Examples 5 and 6, you formed the composition of two given functions. In calculus, it is also important to be able to identify two functions that make up a given composite function. For instance, the function h given by $h(x) = (3x - 5)^3$ is the composition of f with g, where $f(x) = x^3$ and $g(x) = 3x - 5$. That is,

$$h(x) = (3x - 5)^3 = [g(x)]^3 = f(g(x)).$$

Basically, to "decompose" a composite function, look for an "inner" function and an "outer" function. In the function h above, $g(x) = 3x - 5$ is the inner function and $f(x) = x^3$ is the outer function.

Example 7 Decomposing a Composite Function

Write the function given by $h(x) = \dfrac{1}{(x - 2)^2}$ as a composition of two functions.

Solution

One way to write h as a composition of two functions is to take the inner function to be $g(x) = x - 2$ and the outer function to be

$$f(x) = \frac{1}{x^2} = x^{-2}.$$

Then you can write

$$h(x) = \frac{1}{(x - 2)^2} = (x - 2)^{-2} = f(x - 2) = f(g(x)).$$

CHECK*Point* Now try Exercise 53.

Application

Example 8 Bacteria Count

The number N of bacteria in a refrigerated food is given by

$$N(T) = 20T^2 - 80T + 500, \quad 2 \le T \le 14$$

where T is the temperature of the food in degrees Celsius. When the food is removed from refrigeration, the temperature of the food is given by

$$T(t) = 4t + 2, \quad 0 \le t \le 3$$

where t is the time in hours. (a) Find the composition $N(T(t))$ and interpret its meaning in context. (b) Find the time when the bacteria count reaches 2000.

Solution

a.
$$\begin{aligned} N(T(t)) &= 20(4t + 2)^2 - 80(4t + 2) + 500 \\ &= 20(16t^2 + 16t + 4) - 320t - 160 + 500 \\ &= 320t^2 + 320t + 80 - 320t - 160 + 500 \\ &= 320t^2 + 420 \end{aligned}$$

The composite function $N(T(t))$ represents the number of bacteria in the food as a function of the amount of time the food has been out of refrigeration.

b. The bacteria count will reach 2000 when $320t^2 + 420 = 2000$. Solve this equation to find that the count will reach 2000 when $t \approx 2.2$ hours. When you solve this equation, note that the negative value is rejected because it is not in the domain of the composite function.

CHECKPoint Now try Exercise 73.

Classroom Discussion

Analyzing Arithmetic Combinations of Functions

a. Use the graphs of f and $(f + g)$ in Figure 1.92 to make a table showing the values of $g(x)$ when $x = 1, 2, 3, 4, 5$, and 6. Explain your reasoning.

b. Use the graphs of f and $(f - h)$ in Figure 1.92 to make a table showing the values of $h(x)$ when $x = 1, 2, 3, 4, 5$, and 6. Explain your reasoning.

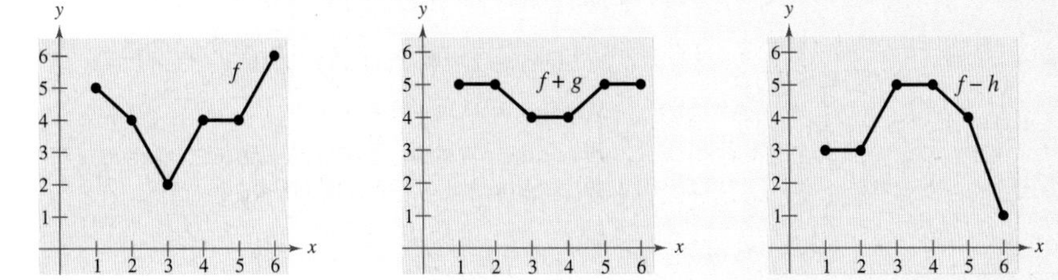

FIGURE 1.92

a.

x	1	2	3	4	5	6
$g(x)$	0	1	2	0	1	−1

b.

x	1	2	3	4	5	6
$h(x)$	2	1	−3	−1	0	5

Extra Example 8

The weekly cost of producing x units in a manufacturing process is given by the function $C(x) = 48x + 1150$. The number of units produced in t hours is given by $x(t) = 40t$. Find and interpret $(C \circ x)(t)$.

$1920t + 1150$; $(C \circ x)(t)$ represents the cost after t production hours.

Closing the Lesson

Have students summarize the major points of the lesson and answer the Essential Question: How do you combine two parent functions to form a new function?

- **Find an arithmetic combination of functions by adding, subtracting, multiplying, or dividing two parent functions.**
- **Find a composition of two functions or the decomposition of a composite function into two functions.**

1.8 EXERCISES

See www.CalcChat.com for worked-out solutions to odd-numbered exercises.

VOCABULARY: Fill in the blanks.

1. Two functions f and g can be combined by the arithmetic operations of ________, ________, ________, and ________ to create new functions. addition; subtraction; multiplication; division
2. The ________ of the function f with g is $(f \circ g)(x) = f(g(x))$. composition
3. The domain of $(f \circ g)$ is all x in the domain of g such that $\underline{g(x)}$ is in the domain of f.
4. To decompose a composite function, look for an $\underline{\text{inner}}$ function and an $\underline{\text{outer}}$ function.

SKILLS AND APPLICATIONS

In Exercises 5–8, use the graphs of f and g to graph $h(x) = (f + g)(x)$. To print an enlarged copy of the graph, go to the website *www.mathgraphs.com*. 5–8. See margin.

5.
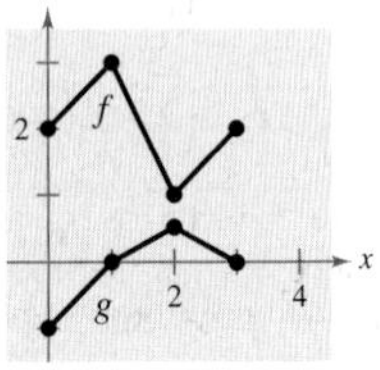

6.
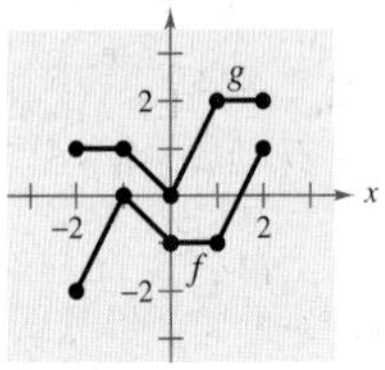

7.
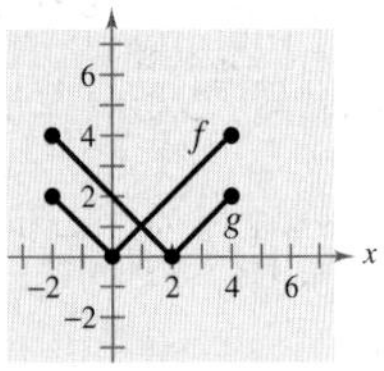

8.
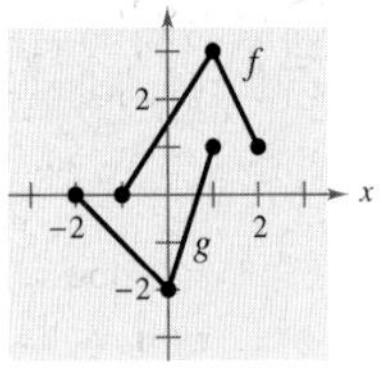

In Exercises 9–16, find (a) $(f + g)(x)$, (b) $(f - g)(x)$, (c) $(fg)(x)$, and (d) $(f/g)(x)$. What is the domain of f/g?

9. $f(x) = x + 2$, $g(x) = x - 2$ 9–16. See margin.
10. $f(x) = 2x - 5$, $g(x) = 2 - x$
11. $f(x) = x^2$, $g(x) = 4x - 5$
12. $f(x) = 3x + 1$, $g(x) = 5x - 4$
13. $f(x) = x^2 + 6$, $g(x) = \sqrt{1 - x}$
14. $f(x) = \sqrt{x^2 - 4}$, $g(x) = \dfrac{x^2}{x^2 + 1}$
15. $f(x) = \dfrac{1}{x}$, $g(x) = \dfrac{1}{x^2}$
16. $f(x) = \dfrac{x}{x + 1}$, $g(x) = x^3$

In Exercises 17–28, evaluate the indicated function for $f(x) = x^2 + 1$ and $g(x) = x - 4$.

17. $(f + g)(2)$ 3
18. $(f - g)(-1)$ 7
19. $(f - g)(0)$ 5
20. $(f + g)(1)$ -1
21. $(f - g)(3t)$ $9t^2 - 3t + 5$
22. $(f + g)(t - 2)$ $t^2 - 3t - 1$
23. $(fg)(6)$ 74
24. $(fg)(-6)$ -370
25. $(f/g)(5)$ 26
26. $(f/g)(0)$ $-\frac{1}{4}$
27. $(f/g)(-1) - g(3)$ $\frac{3}{5}$
28. $(fg)(5) + f(4)$ 43

In Exercises 29–32, graph the functions f, g, and $f + g$ on the same set of coordinate axes. 29–32. See margin.

29. $f(x) = \frac{1}{2}x$, $g(x) = x - 1$
30. $f(x) = \frac{1}{3}x$, $g(x) = -x + 4$
31. $f(x) = x^2$, $g(x) = -2x$
32. $f(x) = 4 - x^2$, $g(x) = x$

GRAPHICAL REASONING In Exercises 33–36, use a graphing utility to graph f, g, and $f + g$ in the same viewing window. Which function contributes most to the magnitude of the sum when $0 \le x \le 2$? Which function contributes most to the magnitude of the sum when $x > 6$? 33–36. See margin.

33. $f(x) = 3x$, $g(x) = -\dfrac{x^3}{10}$
34. $f(x) = \dfrac{x}{2}$, $g(x) = \sqrt{x}$
35. $f(x) = 3x + 2$, $g(x) = -\sqrt{x + 5}$
36. $f(x) = x^2 - \frac{1}{2}$, $g(x) = -3x^2 - 1$

In Exercises 37–40, find (a) $f \circ g$, (b) $g \circ f$, and (c) $g \circ g$.

37. $f(x) = x^2$, $g(x) = x - 1$ 37–40. See margin.
38. $f(x) = 3x + 5$, $g(x) = 5 - x$
39. $f(x) = \sqrt[3]{x - 1}$, $g(x) = x^3 + 1$
40. $f(x) = x^3$, $g(x) = \dfrac{1}{x}$

In Exercises 41–48, find (a) $f \circ g$ and (b) $g \circ f$. Find the domain of each function and each composite function.

41. $f(x) = \sqrt{x + 4}$, $g(x) = x^2$ 41–42. See margin.
42. $f(x) = \sqrt[3]{x - 5}$, $g(x) = x^3 + 1$

4 PRACTICE AND APPLY

Assignment Guide

Transparencies Available
Available at the Instructor's companion site.

Average:
Day 1: pp. 88–91
Exs. 5–8, 9–31 odd, 33–40, 41–59 odd, 61–63, 65–74, 77–79, 81

Advanced:
Day 1: pp. 88–91
Exs. 5–8, 10–32 even, 33–40, 42–60 even, 61–63, 65–74, 76–84

Block:
pp. 88–91
Exs. 5–8, 9–31 odd, 33–40, 41–59 odd, 61–63, 65–74, 77–79, 81 (with 1.7)

5.
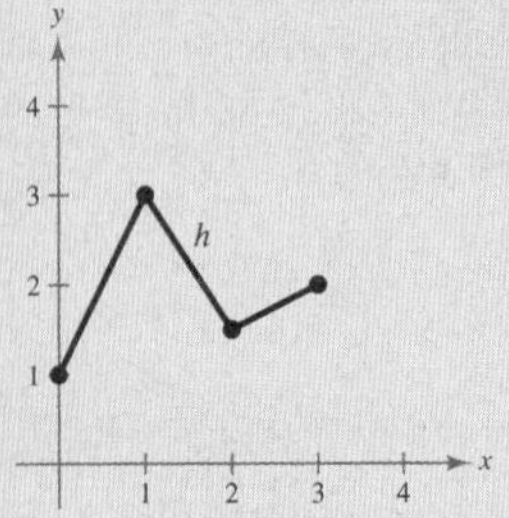

6.
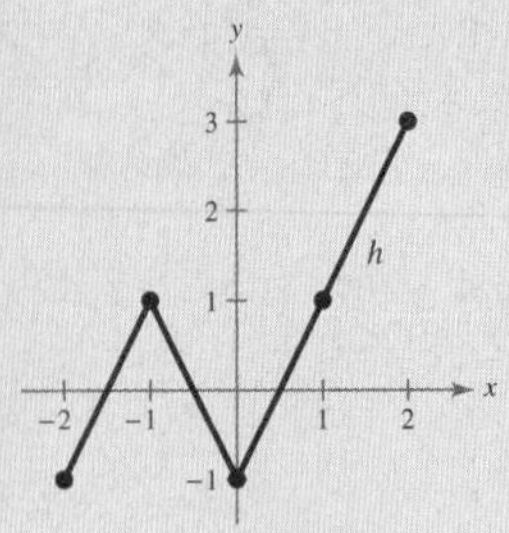

7.
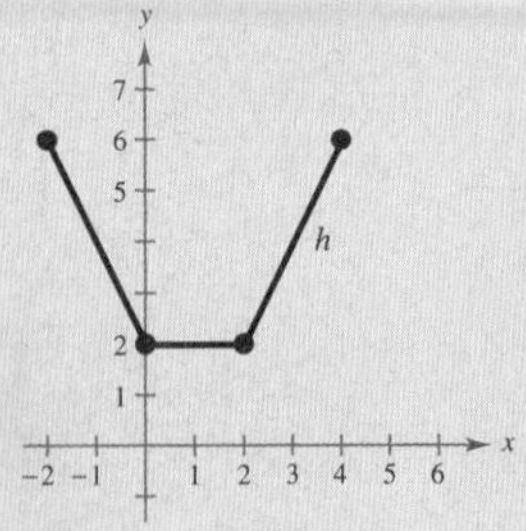

8.
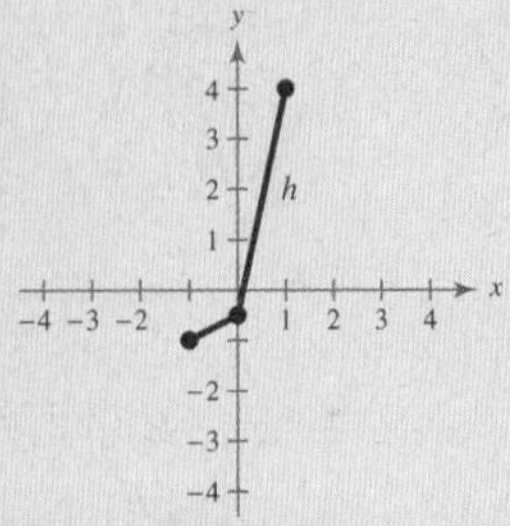

9. (a) $2x$ (b) 4 (c) $x^2 - 4$
(d) $\dfrac{x + 2}{x - 2}$; all real numbers x except $x = 2$

10. (a) $x - 3$ (b) $3x - 7$
(c) $-2x^2 + 9x - 10$
(d) $\dfrac{2x - 5}{2 - x}$; all real numbers x except $x = 2$

11. (a) $x^2 + 4x - 5$ (b) $x^2 - 4x + 5$
(c) $4x^3 - 5x^2$
(d) $\dfrac{x^2}{4x - 5}$; all real numbers x except $x = \dfrac{5}{4}$

12. (a) $8x - 3$ (b) $-2x + 5$
(c) $15x^2 - 7x - 4$
(d) $\dfrac{3x + 1}{5x - 4}$; all real numbers x except $x = \dfrac{4}{5}$

13. (a) $x^2 + 6 + \sqrt{1 - x}$ (b) $x^2 + 6 - \sqrt{1 - x}$
(c) $(x^2 + 6)\sqrt{1 - x}$
(d) $\dfrac{(x^2 + 6)\sqrt{1 - x}}{1 - x}$; all real numbers x such that $x < 1$

14–16, 29–42. See Additional Answers beginning on page AA1.

43. $f(x) = x^2 + 1,\quad g(x) = \sqrt{x}$ 43–48. See margin.

44. $f(x) = x^{2/3},\quad g(x) = x^6$

45. $f(x) = |x|,\quad g(x) = x + 6$

46. $f(x) = |x - 4|,\quad g(x) = 3 - x$

47. $f(x) = \dfrac{1}{x},\quad g(x) = x + 3$

48. $f(x) = \dfrac{3}{x^2 - 1},\quad g(x) = x + 1$

In Exercises 49–52, use the graphs of f and g to evaluate the functions.

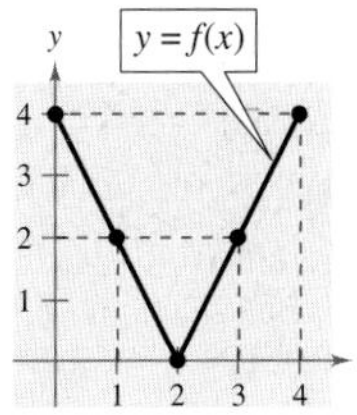

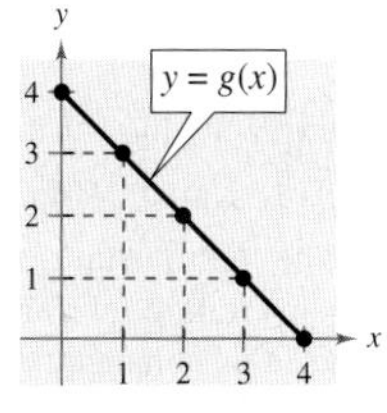

49. (a) $(f + g)(3)$ 3 (b) $(f/g)(2)$ 0

50. (a) $(f - g)(1)$ -1 (b) $(fg)(4)$ 0

51. (a) $(f \circ g)(2)$ 0 (b) $(g \circ f)(2)$ 4

52. (a) $(f \circ g)(1)$ 2 (b) $(g \circ f)(3)$ 2

In Exercises 53–60, find two functions f and g such that $(f \circ g)(x) = h(x)$. (There are many correct answers.)

53–60. See margin.

53. $h(x) = (2x + 1)^2$ **54.** $h(x) = (1 - x)^3$

55. $h(x) = \sqrt[3]{x^2 - 4}$ **56.** $h(x) = \sqrt{9 - x}$

57. $h(x) = \dfrac{1}{x + 2}$ **58.** $h(x) = \dfrac{4}{(5x + 2)^2}$

59. $h(x) = \dfrac{-x^2 + 3}{4 - x^2}$ **60.** $h(x) = \dfrac{27x^3 + 6x}{10 - 27x^3}$

61. STOPPING DISTANCE The research and development department of an automobile manufacturer has determined that when a driver is required to stop quickly to avoid an accident, the distance (in feet) the car travels during the driver's reaction time is given by $R(x) = \frac{3}{4}x$, where x is the speed of the car in miles per hour. The distance (in feet) traveled while the driver is braking is given by $B(x) = \frac{1}{15}x^2$.

(a) Find the function that represents the total stopping distance T. $T = \frac{3}{4}x + \frac{1}{15}x^2$

(b) Graph the functions R, B, and T on the same set of coordinate axes for $0 \le x \le 60$. See margin.

(c) Which function contributes most to the magnitude of the sum at higher speeds? Explain.

The braking function $B(x)$. As x increases, $B(x)$ increases at a faster rate than $R(x)$.

62. SALES From 2003 through 2008, the sales R_1 (in thousands of dollars) for one of two restaurants owned by the same parent company can be modeled by

$$R_1 = 480 - 8t - 0.8t^2,\quad t = 3, 4, 5, 6, 7, 8$$

where $t = 3$ represents 2003. During the same six-year period, the sales R_2 (in thousands of dollars) for the second restaurant can be modeled by

$$R_2 = 254 + 0.78t,\quad t = 3, 4, 5, 6, 7, 8.$$

(a) Write a function R_3 that represents the total sales of the two restaurants owned by the same parent company. $R_3 = 734 - 7.22t - 0.8t^2$

(b) Use a graphing utility to graph R_1, R_2, and R_3 in the same viewing window. See margin.

63. VITAL STATISTICS Let $b(t)$ be the number of births in the United States in year t, and let $d(t)$ represent the number of deaths in the United States in year t, where $t = 0$ corresponds to 2000. See margin.

(a) If $p(t)$ is the population of the United States in year t, find the function $c(t)$ that represents the percent change in the population of the United States.

(b) Interpret the value of $c(5)$.

64. PETS Let $d(t)$ be the number of dogs in the United States in year t, and let $c(t)$ be the number of cats in the United States in year t, where $t = 0$ corresponds to 2000. See margin.

(a) Find the function $p(t)$ that represents the total number of dogs and cats in the United States.

(b) Interpret the value of $p(5)$.

(c) Let $n(t)$ represent the population of the United States in year t, where $t = 0$ corresponds to 2000. Find and interpret

$$h(t) = \frac{p(t)}{n(t)}.$$

65. MILITARY PERSONNEL The total numbers of Navy personnel N (in thousands) and Marines personnel M (in thousands) from 2000 through 2007 can be approximated by the models See margin.

$$N(t) = 0.192t^3 - 3.88t^2 + 12.9t + 372$$

and

$$M(t) = 0.035t^3 - 0.23t^2 + 1.7t + 172$$

where t represents the year, with $t = 0$ corresponding to 2000. (Source: Department of Defense)

(a) Find and interpret $(N + M)(t)$. Evaluate this function for $t = 0$, 6, and 12.

(b) Find and interpret $(N - M)(t)$ Evaluate this function for $t = 0$, 6, and 12.

43. (a) $x + 1$ (b) $\sqrt{x^2 + 1}$
Domains of f and $g \circ f$: all real numbers x
Domains of g and $f \circ g$: all real numbers x such that $x \ge 0$

44. (a) x^4 (b) x^4
Domains of f, g, $f \circ g$, and $g \circ f$: all real numbers x

45. (a) $|x + 6|$ (b) $|x| + 6$
Domains of f, g, $f \circ g$, and $g \circ f$: all real numbers x

46. (a) $|-1 - x|$
(b) $3 - |x - 4|$
Domains of f, g, $f \circ g$, and $g \circ f$: all real numbers x

47. (a) $\dfrac{1}{x + 3}$ (b) $\dfrac{1}{x} + 3$
Domains of f and $g \circ f$: all real numbers x except $x = 0$
Domain of g: all real numbers x
Domain of $f \circ g$: all real numbers x except $x = -3$

48. (a) $\dfrac{3}{x^2 + 2x}$ (b) $\dfrac{x^2 + 2}{x^2 - 1}$
Domains of f and $g \circ f$: all real numbers x except $x = \pm 1$
Domain of g: all real numbers x
Domain of $f \circ g$: all real numbers x except $x = 0, -2$

53. $f(x) = x^2,\ g(x) = 2x + 1$

54. $f(x) = x^3,\ g(x) = 1 - x$

55. $f(x) = \sqrt[3]{x},\quad g(x) = x^2 - 4$

56. $f(x) = \sqrt{x},\ g(x) = 9 - x$

57. $f(x) = \dfrac{1}{x},\quad g(x) = x + 2$

58. $f(x) = \dfrac{4}{x^2},\quad g(x) = 5x + 2$

59. $f(x) = \dfrac{x + 3}{4 + x},\quad g(x) = -x^2$

60. $f(x) = \dfrac{27x + 6\sqrt[3]{x}}{10 - 27x},\quad g(x) = x^3$

61. (b)

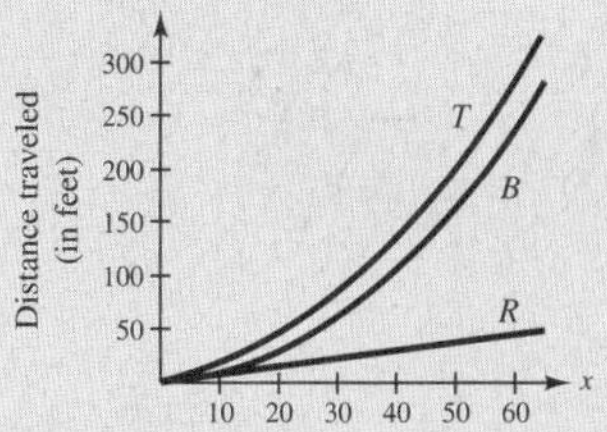

62. (b)

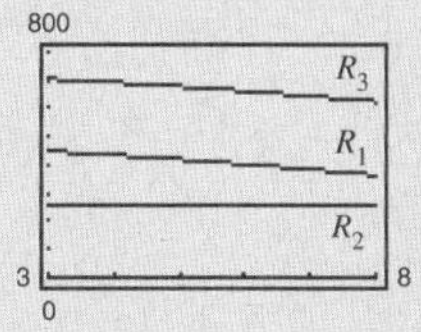

63. (a) $c(t) = \dfrac{b(t) - d(t)}{p(t)} \times 100$
(b) $c(5)$ is the percent change in the population due to births and deaths in the year 2005.

64. (a) $p(t) = d(t) + c(t)$
(b) $p(5) =$ Number of dogs and cats in the year 2005
(c) $h(t) = \dfrac{d(t) + c(t)}{n(t)}$;
The function $h(t)$ represents the number of dogs and cats per capita.

65. (a) $(N + M)(t) = 0.227t^3 - 4.11t^2 + 14.6t + 544$, which represents the total number of Navy and Marines personnel combined.
$(N + M)(0) = 544$
$(N + M)(6) \approx 533$
$(N + M)(12) \approx 520$
(b) $(N - M)(t) = 0.157t^3 - 3.65t^2 + 11.2t + 200$, which represents the difference between the number of Navy personnel and the number of Marines personnel.
$(N - M)(0) = 200$
$(N - M)(6) \approx 170$
$(N - M)(12) \approx 80$

68. $B(20) = 4388$; Births in 2010
$D(20) = 2413$; Deaths in 2010
$(B - D)(20) = 1975$; Population increase in 2010
$B(22) \approx 4439$; Births in 2012
$D(22) \approx 2387$; Deaths in 2012
$(B - D)(22) \approx 2052$; Population increase in 2012

69. (a) For each time t there corresponds one and only one temperature T.
(b) 60°, 72°
(c) All the temperature changes occur 1 hour later.
(d) The temperature is decreased by 1 degree.
(e)
$$T(t) = \begin{cases} 60, & 0 \le t \le 6 \\ 12t - 12, & 6 < t < 7 \\ 72, & 7 \le t \le 20 \\ -12t + 312, & 20 < t < 21 \\ 60, & 21 \le t \le 24 \end{cases}$$

70. (a) $r(x) = \dfrac{x}{2}$ (b) $A(r) = \pi r^2$
(c) $(A \circ r)(x) = \pi\left(\dfrac{x}{2}\right)^2$; $(A \circ r)(x)$ represents the area of the circular base of the tank on the square foundation with side length x.

71. $(A \circ r)(t) = 0.36\pi t^2$; $(A \circ r)(t)$ represents the area of the circle at time t.

66. SPORTS The numbers of people playing tennis T (in millions) in the United States from 2000 through 2007 can be approximated by the function See margin.

$$T(t) = 0.0233t^4 - 0.3408t^3 + 1.556t^2 - 1.86t + 22.8$$

and the U.S. population P (in millions) from 2000 through 2007 can be approximated by the function $P(t) = 2.78t + 282.5$, where t represents the year, with $t = 0$ corresponding to 2000. (Source: Tennis Industry Association, U.S. Census Bureau)

(a) Find and interpret $h(t) = \dfrac{T(t)}{P(t)}$.

(b) Evaluate the function in part (a) for $t = 0$, 3, and 6.

BIRTHS AND DEATHS In Exercises 67 and 68, use the table, which shows the total numbers of births B (in thousands) and deaths D (in thousands) in the United States from 1990 through 2006. (Source: U.S. Census Bureau) 67–68. See margin.

Year, t	Births, B	Deaths, D
1990	4158	2148
1991	4111	2170
1992	4065	2176
1993	4000	2269
1994	3953	2279
1995	3900	2312
1996	3891	2315
1997	3881	2314
1998	3942	2337
1999	3959	2391
2000	4059	2403
2001	4026	2416
2002	4022	2443
2003	4090	2448
2004	4112	2398
2005	4138	2448
2006	4266	2426

The models for these data are

$$B(t) = -0.197t^3 + 8.96t^2 - 90.0t + 4180$$

and

$$D(t) = -1.21t^2 + 38.0t + 2137$$

where t represents the year, with $t = 0$ corresponding to 1990.

67. Find and interpret $(B - D)(t)$.

68. Evaluate $B(t)$, $D(t)$, and $(B - D)(t)$ for the years 2010 and 2012. What does each function value represent?

69. GRAPHICAL REASONING An electronically controlled thermostat in a home is programmed to lower the temperature automatically during the night. The temperature in the house T (in degrees Fahrenheit) is given in terms of t, the time in hours on a 24-hour clock (see figure). See margin.

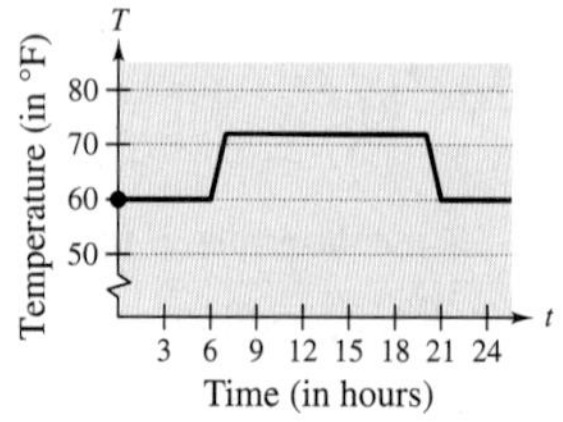

(a) Explain why T is a function of t.

(b) Approximate $T(4)$ and $T(15)$.

(c) The thermostat is reprogrammed to produce a temperature H for which $H(t) = T(t - 1)$. How does this change the temperature?

(d) The thermostat is reprogrammed to produce a temperature H for which $H(t) = T(t) - 1$. How does this change the temperature?

(e) Write a piecewise-defined function that represents the graph.

70. GEOMETRY A square concrete foundation is prepared as a base for a cylindrical tank (see figure). See margin.

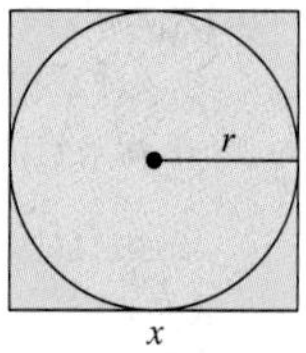

(a) Write the radius r of the tank as a function of the length x of the sides of the square.

(b) Write the area A of the circular base of the tank as a function of the radius r.

(c) Find and interpret $(A \circ r)(x)$.

71. RIPPLES A pebble is dropped into a calm pond, causing ripples in the form of concentric circles. The radius r (in feet) of the outer ripple is $r(t) = 0.6t$, where t is the time in seconds after the pebble strikes the water. The area A of the circle is given by the function $A(r) = \pi r^2$. Find and interpret $(A \circ r)(t)$. See margin.

72. POLLUTION The spread of a contaminant is increasing in a circular pattern on the surface of a lake. The radius of the contaminant can be modeled by $r(t) = 5.25\sqrt{t}$, where r is the radius in meters and t is the time in hours since contamination.

66–67. See Additional Answers beginning on page AA1.

$A(t) = 27.5625\pi t$

(a) Find a function that gives the area A of the circular leak in terms of the time t since the spread began.

(b) Find the size of the contaminated area after 36 hours. About 3117.2 m^2

(c) Find when the size of the contaminated area is 6250 square meters. About 72.2 h

73. BACTERIA COUNT The number N of bacteria in a refrigerated food is given by See margin.

$$N(T) = 10T^2 - 20T + 600, \quad 1 \le T \le 20$$

where T is the temperature of the food in degrees Celsius. When the food is removed from refrigeration, the temperature of the food is given by

$$T(t) = 3t + 2, \quad 0 \le t \le 6$$

where t is the time in hours.

(a) Find the composition $N(T(t))$ and interpret its meaning in context.

(b) Find the bacteria count after 0.5 hour.

(c) Find the time when the bacteria count reaches 1500.

74. COST The weekly cost C of producing x units in a manufacturing process is given by $C(x) = 60x + 750$. The number of units x produced in t hours is given by $x(t) = 50t$. See margin.

(a) Find and interpret $(C \circ x)(t)$.

(b) Find the cost of the units produced in 4 hours.

(c) Find the time that must elapse in order for the cost to increase to \$15,000.

75. SALARY You are a sales representative for a clothing manufacturer. You are paid an annual salary, plus a bonus of 3% of your sales over \$500,000. Consider the two functions given by $f(x) = x - 500{,}000$ and $g(x) = 0.03x$. If x is greater than \$500,000, which of the following represents your bonus? Explain your reasoning.

(a) $f(g(x))$ (b) $g(f(x))$ See margin.

76. CONSUMER AWARENESS The suggested retail price of a new hybrid car is p dollars. The dealership advertises a factory rebate of \$2000 and a 10% discount.

(a) Write a function R in terms of p giving the cost of the hybrid car after receiving the rebate from the factory. $R(p) = p - 2000$

(b) Write a function S in terms of p giving the cost of the hybrid car after receiving the dealership discount. $S(p) = 0.9p$

(c) Form the composite functions $(R \circ S)(p)$ and $(S \circ R)(p)$ and interpret each. See margin.

(d) Find $(R \circ S)(20{,}500)$ and $(S \circ R)(20{,}500)$. Which yields the lower cost for the hybrid car? Explain. See margin.

EXPLORATION

TRUE OR FALSE? In Exercises 77 and 78, determine whether the statement is true or false. Justify your answer.

77. If $f(x) = x + 1$ and $g(x) = 6x$, then

$(f \circ g)(x) = (g \circ f)(x)$. False. $(f \circ g)(x) = 6x + 1$ and $(g \circ f)(x) = 6x + 6$

78. If you are given two functions $f(x)$ and $g(x)$, you can calculate $(f \circ g)(x)$ if and only if the range of g is a subset of the domain of f. See margin.

In Exercises 79 and 80, three siblings are of three different ages. The oldest is twice the age of the middle sibling, and the middle sibling is six years older than one-half the age of the youngest.

79. (a) Write a composite function that gives the oldest sibling's age in terms of the youngest. Explain how you arrived at your answer. See margin.

(b) If the oldest sibling is 16 years old, find the ages of the other two siblings. See margin.

80. (a) Write a composite function that gives the youngest sibling's age in terms of the oldest. Explain how you arrived at your answer. $Y = O - 12$

(b) If the youngest sibling is two years old, find the ages of the other two siblings. See margin.

81. PROOF Prove that the product of two odd functions is an even function, and that the product of two even functions is an even function. Proof

82. CONJECTURE Use examples to hypothesize whether the product of an odd function and an even function is even or odd. Then prove your hypothesis. Proof

83. PROOF See margin.

(a) Given a function f, prove that $g(x)$ is even and $h(x)$ is odd, where $g(x) = \frac{1}{2}[f(x) + f(-x)]$ and $h(x) = \frac{1}{2}[f(x) - f(-x)]$.

(b) Use the result of part (a) to prove that any function can be written as a sum of even and odd functions. [*Hint:* Add the two equations in part (a).]

(c) Use the result of part (b) to write each function as a sum of even and odd functions.

$$f(x) = x^2 - 2x + 1, \quad k(x) = \frac{1}{x + 1}$$

84. CAPSTONE Consider the functions $f(x) = x^2$ and $g(x) = \sqrt{x}$. See margin.

(a) Find f/g and its domain.

(b) Find $f \circ g$ and $g \circ f$. Find the domain of each composite function. Are they the same? Explain.

5 ASSESS AND RETEACH

Daily Homework Quiz

Transparency Available

Available at the Instructor's companion site.

73. (a) $N(T(t)) = 30(3t^2 + 2t + 20)$; This represents the number of bacteria in the food as a function of time.

(b) About 653 bacteria

(c) 2.846 h

74. (a) $(C \circ x)(t) = 3000t + 750$; This represents the cost of t hours of production.

(b) \$12,750 (c) 4.75 h

75. $g(f(x))$ represents 3 percent of an amount over \$500,000.

76. (c) $(R \circ S)(p) = 0.9p - 2000$; $(R \circ S)(p)$ represents the dealership discount before the factory rebate.

$(S \circ R)(p) = 0.9(p - 2000)$; $(S \circ R)(p)$ represents the dealership discount after the factory rebate.

(d) $(R \circ S)(20{,}500) = \$16{,}450$

$(S \circ R)(20{,}500) = \$16{,}650$

$(R \circ S)(20{,}500)$ yields the lower cost because 10% of the price of the car is more than \$2000.

78. False. See Exercise 47.

79. (a) $O(M(Y)) = 2\left(6 + \frac{1}{2}Y\right) = 12 + Y$

(b) Middle child is 8 years old; youngest child is 4 years old.

80. (b) Middle child is 7 years old; oldest child is 14 years old.

83. (a) Proof

(b) $\frac{1}{2}[f(x) + f(-x)] + \frac{1}{2}[f(x) - f(-x)]$

$= \frac{1}{2}[f(x) + f(-x) + f(x) - f(-x)]$

$= \frac{1}{2}[2f(x)]$

$= f(x)$

(c) $f(x) = (x^2 + 1) + (-2x)$

$$k(x) = \frac{-1}{(x + 1)(x - 1)} + \frac{x}{(x + 1)(x - 1)}$$

84. (a) $\frac{f}{g} = x^{3/2}, \quad x > 0$

(b) $f \circ g = x, \quad x \ge 0$; $g \circ f = x$, all real numbers x; No, they are not the same because negative numbers are in the domain of $g \circ f$ but not in the domain of $f \circ g$.

1 PLAN AND PREPARE

Warm-up Exercises

Transparency Available
Available at the Instructor's companion site.

Notetaking Guide

Transparency Available
Promotes interactive learning and notetaking skills. Available at the Instructor's companion site.

Animated Precalculus

An **Animated Precalculus** tutorial is available at the Student companion site for **Section 1.9.**

Pacing

Average: 1 day
Advanced: 1 day
Block: 0.5 block with 1.10

2 FOCUS AND MOTIVATE

Essential Question

What is the inverse of a function, and how do you represent it graphically and algebraically? **Tell students that they will learn how to answer this question by comparing the solution set of a function and the solution set of its inverse numerically, graphically, and algebraically.**

1.9 INVERSE FUNCTIONS

What you should learn

- Find inverse functions informally and verify that two functions are inverse functions of each other.
- Use graphs of functions to determine whether functions have inverse functions.
- Use the Horizontal Line Test to determine if functions are one-to-one.
- Find inverse functions algebraically.

Why you should learn it

Inverse functions can be used to model and solve real-life problems. For instance, in Exercise 99 on page 100, an inverse function can be used to determine the year in which there was a given dollar amount of sales of LCD televisions in the United States.

Sean Gallup/Getty Images

Inverse Functions

Recall from Section 1.4 that a function can be represented by a set of ordered pairs. For instance, the function $f(x) = x + 4$ from the set $A = \{1, 2, 3, 4\}$ to the set $B = \{5, 6, 7, 8\}$ can be written as follows.

$$f(x) = x + 4: \ \{(1, 5), (2, 6), (3, 7), (4, 8)\}$$

In this case, by interchanging the first and second coordinates of each of these ordered pairs, you can form the **inverse function** of f, which is denoted by f^{-1}. It is a function from the set B to the set A, and can be written as follows.

$$f^{-1}(x) = x - 4: \ \{(5, 1), (6, 2), (7, 3), (8, 4)\}$$

Note that the domain of f is equal to the range of f^{-1}, and vice versa, as shown in Figure 1.93. Also note that the functions f and f^{-1} have the effect of "undoing" each other. In other words, when you form the composition of f with f^{-1} or the composition of f^{-1} with f, you obtain the identity function.

$$f(f^{-1}(x)) = f(x - 4) = (x - 4) + 4 = x$$

$$f^{-1}(f(x)) = f^{-1}(x + 4) = (x + 4) - 4 = x$$

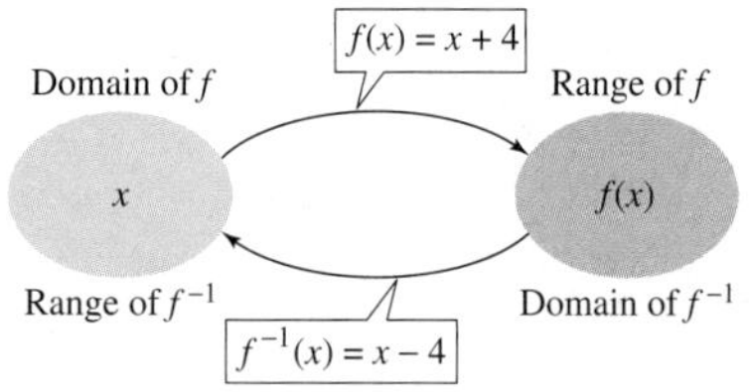

FIGURE 1.93

Example 1 Finding Inverse Functions Informally

Find the inverse function of $f(x) = 4x$. Then verify that both $f(f^{-1}(x))$ and $f^{-1}(f(x))$ are equal to the identity function.

Solution

The function f *multiplies* each input by 4. To "undo" this function, you need to *divide* each input by 4. So, the inverse function of $f(x) = 4x$ is

$$f^{-1}(x) = \frac{x}{4}.$$

You can verify that both $f(f^{-1}(x)) = x$ and $f^{-1}(f(x)) = x$ as follows.

$$f(f^{-1}(x)) = f\left(\frac{x}{4}\right) = 4\left(\frac{x}{4}\right) = x \qquad f^{-1}(f(x)) = f^{-1}(4x) = \frac{4x}{4} = x$$

CHECKPoint Now try Exercise 7.

Resource Planning Guide

Chapter Resources
- Complete Solutions Guide

Workbooks
- Notetaking Guide
- Student Solutions Guide

Interactive Technology
- Instructor Success Organizer
- Notetaking Guide IAE
- Instructional DVDs
- Animated Precalculus
- PowerLecture with ExamView

Definition of Inverse Function

Let f and g be two functions such that

$$f(g(x)) = x \quad \text{for every } x \text{ in the domain of } g$$

and

$$g(f(x)) = x \quad \text{for every } x \text{ in the domain of } f.$$

Under these conditions, the function g is the **inverse function** of the function f. The function g is denoted by f^{-1} (read "f-inverse"). So,

$$f(f^{-1}(x)) = x \quad \text{and} \quad f^{-1}(f(x)) = x.$$

The domain of f must be equal to the range of f^{-1}, and the range of f must be equal to the domain of f^{-1}.

Do not be confused by the use of -1 to denote the inverse function f^{-1}. In this text, whenever f^{-1} is written, it *always* refers to the inverse function of the function f and *not* to the reciprocal of $f(x)$.

If the function g is the inverse function of the function f, it must also be true that the function f is the inverse function of the function g. For this reason, you can say that the functions f and g are *inverse functions of each other*.

Example 2 Verifying Inverse Functions

Which of the functions is the inverse function of $f(x) = \dfrac{5}{x-2}$?

$$g(x) = \frac{x-2}{5} \qquad h(x) = \frac{5}{x} + 2$$

Solution

By forming the composition of f with g, you have

$$f(g(x)) = f\left(\frac{x-2}{5}\right) = \frac{5}{\left(\dfrac{x-2}{5}\right) - 2} = \frac{25}{x-12} \neq x.$$

Because this composition is not equal to the identity function x, it follows that g *is not* the inverse function of f. By forming the composition of f with h, you have

$$f(h(x)) = f\left(\frac{5}{x} + 2\right) = \frac{5}{\left(\dfrac{5}{x} + 2\right) - 2} = \frac{5}{\left(\dfrac{5}{x}\right)} = x.$$

So, it appears that h *is* the inverse function of f. You can confirm this by showing that the composition of h with f is also equal to the identity function, as shown below.

$$h(f(x)) = h\left(\frac{5}{x-2}\right) = \frac{5}{\left(\dfrac{5}{x-2}\right)} + 2 = x - 2 + 2 = x$$

CHECKPoint Now try Exercise 19.

3 TEACH

Extra Example 1

Find the inverse of $f(x) = 8x$. Then verify that both $f(f^{-1}(x))$ and $f^{-1}(f(x))$ are equal to the identity function.

$f^{-1}(x) = \dfrac{x}{8} = \dfrac{1}{8}x;$

$f(f^{-1}(x)) = f\left(\dfrac{x}{8}\right) = 8\left(\dfrac{x}{8}\right) = x;$

$f^{-1}(f(x)) = f^{-1}(8x) = \dfrac{8x}{8} = x$

Extra Example 2

Which of these functions is the inverse of $f(x) = 7x + 4$?

$g(x) = \dfrac{x-4}{7}$ or $h(x) = \dfrac{x-7}{4}$

$g(x)$

The Graph of an Inverse Function

The graphs of a function f and its inverse function f^{-1} are related to each other in the following way. If the point (a, b) lies on the graph of f, then the point (b, a) must lie on the graph of f^{-1}, and vice versa. This means that the graph of f^{-1} is a *reflection* of the graph of f in the line $y = x$, as shown in Figure 1.94.

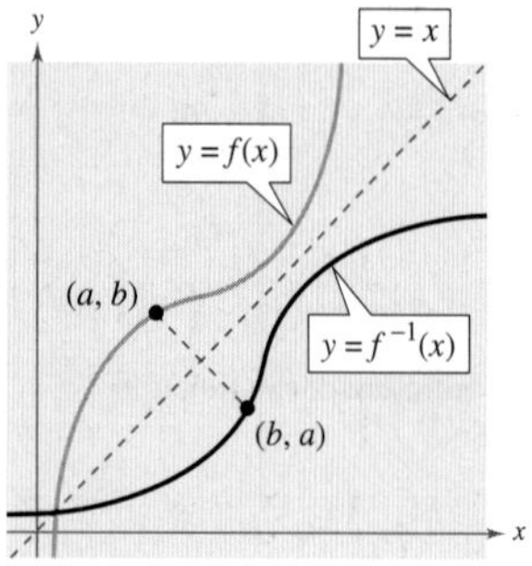

FIGURE 1.94

Example 3 Finding Inverse Functions Graphically

Sketch the graphs of the inverse functions $f(x) = 2x - 3$ and $f^{-1}(x) = \frac{1}{2}(x + 3)$ on the same rectangular coordinate system and show that the graphs are reflections of each other in the line $y = x$.

Solution

The graphs of f and f^{-1} are shown in Figure 1.95. It appears that the graphs are reflections of each other in the line $y = x$. You can further verify this reflective property by testing a few points on each graph. Note in the following list that if the point (a, b) is on the graph of f, the point (b, a) is on the graph of f^{-1}.

Graph of $f(x) = 2x - 3$	*Graph of* $f^{-1}(x) = \frac{1}{2}(x + 3)$
$(-1, -5)$	$(-5, -1)$
$(0, -3)$	$(-3, 0)$
$(1, -1)$	$(-1, 1)$
$(2, 1)$	$(1, 2)$
$(3, 3)$	$(3, 3)$

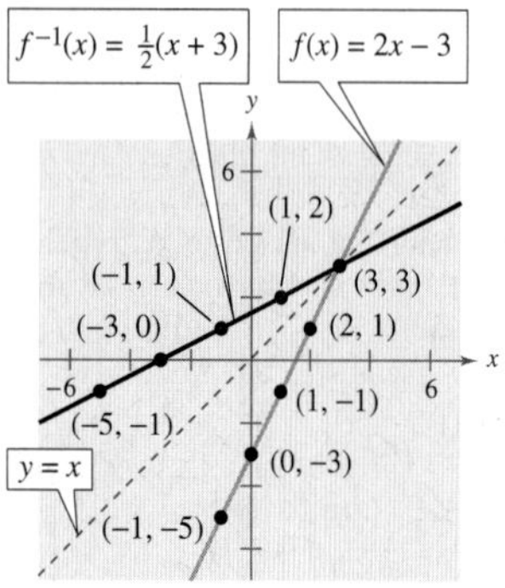

FIGURE 1.95

CHECK *Point* Now try Exercise 25.

Example 4 Finding Inverse Functions Graphically

Sketch the graphs of the inverse functions $f(x) = x^2$ $(x \geq 0)$ and $f^{-1}(x) = \sqrt{x}$ on the same rectangular coordinate system and show that the graphs are reflections of each other in the line $y = x$.

Solution

The graphs of f and f^{-1} are shown in Figure 1.96. It appears that the graphs are reflections of each other in the line $y = x$. You can further verify this reflective property by testing a few points on each graph. Note in the following list that if the point (a, b) is on the graph of f, the point (b, a) is on the graph of f^{-1}.

Graph of $f(x) = x^2, \quad x \geq 0$	*Graph of* $f^{-1}(x) = \sqrt{x}$
$(0, 0)$	$(0, 0)$
$(1, 1)$	$(1, 1)$
$(2, 4)$	$(4, 2)$
$(3, 9)$	$(9, 3)$

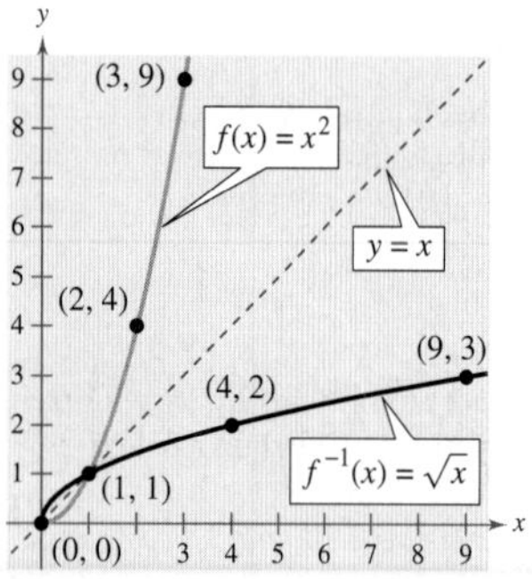

FIGURE 1.96

Try showing that $f(f^{-1}(x)) = x$ and $f^{-1}(f(x)) = x$.

CHECK *Point* Now try Exercise 27.

Extra Example 3

Sketch the graphs of the inverse functions $f(x) = 4x - 1$ and $f^{-1}(x) = \dfrac{x + 1}{4}$ on the same rectangular coordinate system, and show that the graphs are reflections of each other in the line $y = x$.

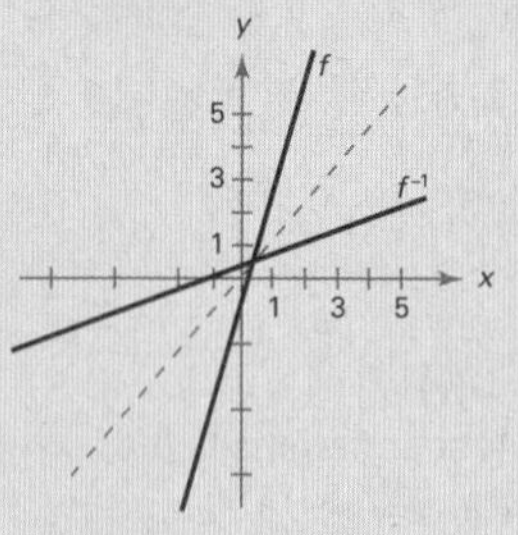

Sample answer:

Graph of $f(x) = 4x - 1$	Graph of $f^{-1}(x) = \dfrac{x + 1}{4}$
$(-2, -9)$	$(-9, -2)$
$(-1, -5)$	$(-5, -1)$
$(0, -1)$	$(-1, 0)$
$(1, 3)$	$(3, 1)$
$(2, 7)$	$(7, 2)$

From the table, note that if the point (a, b) is on the graph of f, the point (b, a) is on the graph of $f^{-1}(x)$.

Extra Example 4

Sketch the graphs of the inverse functions $f(x) = x^2 + 1, x \geq 0$ and $f^{-1}(x) = \sqrt{x - 1}$ on the same rectangular coordinate system, and show that the graphs are reflections of each other in the line $y = x$.

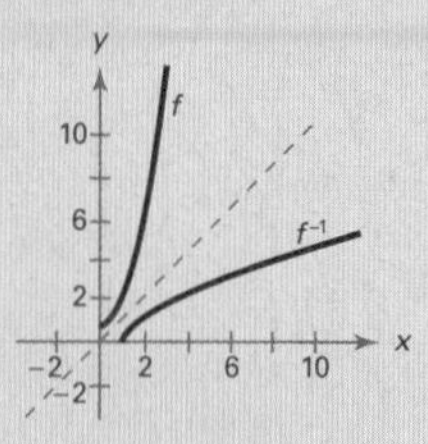

Sample answer:

Graph of $f(x) = x^2 + 1, x \geq 0$	Graph of $f^{-1}(x) = \sqrt{x - 1}$
$(0, 1)$	$(1, 0)$
$(1, 2)$	$(2, 1)$
$(2, 5)$	$(5, 2)$
$(3, 10)$	$(10, 3)$

From the table, note that if the point (a, b) is on the graph of f, the point (b, a) is on the graph of $f^{-1}(x)$.

One-to-One Functions

The reflective property of the graphs of inverse functions gives you a nice *geometric* test for determining whether a function has an inverse function. This test is called the **Horizontal Line Test** for inverse functions.

> **Horizontal Line Test for Inverse Functions**
>
> A function f has an inverse function if and only if no *horizontal* line intersects the graph of f at more than one point.

If no horizontal line intersects the graph of f at more than one point, then no y-value is matched with more than one x-value. This is the essential characteristic of what are called **one-to-one functions.**

> **One-to-One Functions**
>
> A function f is **one-to-one** if each value of the dependent variable corresponds to exactly one value of the independent variable. A function f has an inverse function if and only if f is one-to-one.

Consider the function given by $f(x) = x^2$. The table on the left is a table of values for $f(x) = x^2$. The table of values on the right is made up by interchanging the columns of the first table. The table on the right does not represent a function because the input $x = 4$ is matched with two different outputs: $y = -2$ and $y = 2$. So, $f(x) = x^2$ is not one-to-one and does not have an inverse function.

x	$f(x) = x^2$
-2	4
-1	1
0	0
1	1
2	4
3	9

x	y
4	-2
1	-1
0	0
1	1
4	2
9	3

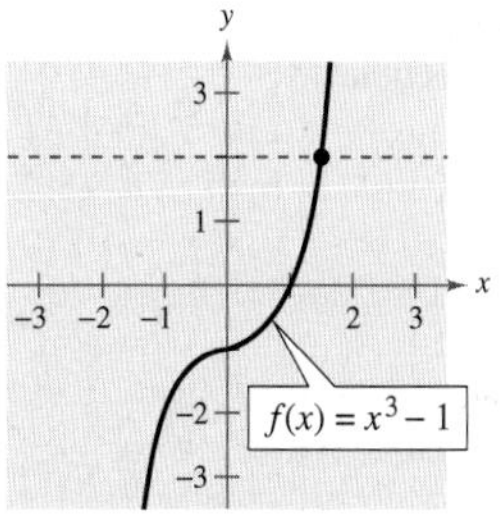

FIGURE 1.97

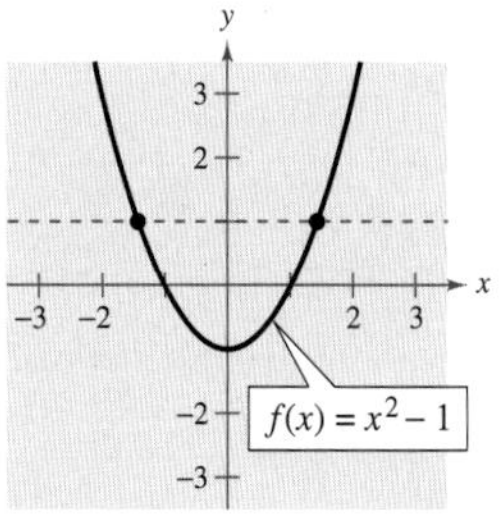

FIGURE 1.98

Example 5 Applying the Horizontal Line Test

a. The graph of the function given by $f(x) = x^3 - 1$ is shown in Figure 1.97. Because no horizontal line intersects the graph of f at more than one point, you can conclude that f *is* a one-to-one function and *does* have an inverse function.

b. The graph of the function given by $f(x) = x^2 - 1$ is shown in Figure 1.98. Because it is possible to find a horizontal line that intersects the graph of f at more than one point, you can conclude that f *is not* a one-to-one function and *does not* have an inverse function.

CHECK*Point* Now try Exercise 39.

Extra Example 5

Use the graph of the function $f(x) = \dfrac{3 - x}{2}$ and the Horizontal Line Test to determine whether the function has an inverse.

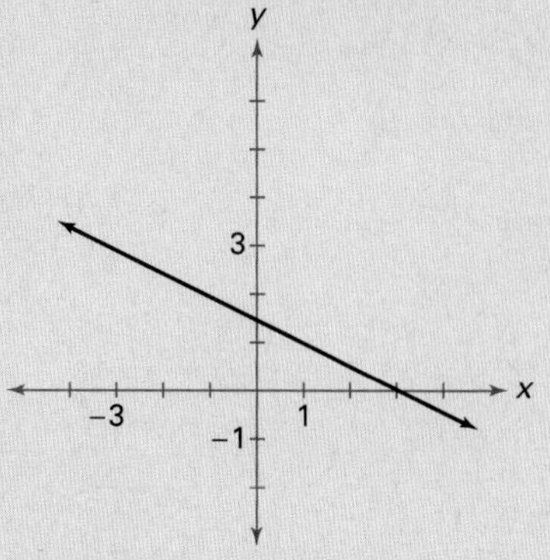

***f* passes the Horizontal Line Test, so *f* has an inverse.**

Extra Example 6

Find the inverse of $f(x) = -4x - 9$.

$f^{-1}(x) = -\dfrac{x+9}{4}$

WARNING/CAUTION

Note what happens when you try to find the inverse function of a function that is not one-to-one.

$f(x) = x^2 + 1$	Original function
$y = x^2 + 1$	Replace $f(x)$ by y.
$x = y^2 + 1$	Interchange x and y.
$x - 1 = y^2$	Isolate y-term.
$y = \pm\sqrt{x-1}$	Solve for y.

You obtain two y-values for each x.

Finding Inverse Functions Algebraically

For simple functions (such as the one in Example 1), you can find inverse functions by inspection. For more complicated functions, however, it is best to use the following guidelines. The key step in these guidelines is Step 3—interchanging the roles of x and y. This step corresponds to the fact that inverse functions have ordered pairs with the coordinates reversed.

Finding an Inverse Function

1. Use the Horizontal Line Test to decide whether f has an inverse function.
2. In the equation for $f(x)$, replace $f(x)$ by y.
3. Interchange the roles of x and y, and solve for y.
4. Replace y by $f^{-1}(x)$ in the new equation.
5. Verify that f and f^{-1} are inverse functions of each other by showing that the domain of f is equal to the range of f^{-1}, the range of f is equal to the domain of f^{-1}, and $f(f^{-1}(x)) = x$ and $f^{-1}(f(x)) = x$.

Example 6 Finding an Inverse Function Algebraically

Find the inverse function of

$$f(x) = \frac{5-3x}{2}.$$

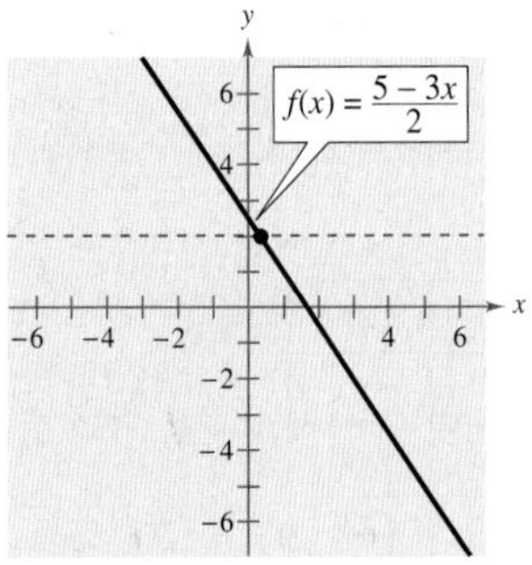

FIGURE 1.99

Solution

The graph of f is a line, as shown in Figure 1.99. This graph passes the Horizontal Line Test. So, you know that f is one-to-one and has an inverse function.

$f(x) = \dfrac{5-3x}{2}$	Write original function.
$y = \dfrac{5-3x}{2}$	Replace $f(x)$ by y.
$x = \dfrac{5-3y}{2}$	Interchange x and y.
$2x = 5 - 3y$	Multiply each side by 2.
$3y = 5 - 2x$	Isolate the y-term.
$y = \dfrac{5-2x}{3}$	Solve for y.
$f^{-1}(x) = \dfrac{5-2x}{3}$	Replace y by $f^{-1}(x)$.

Note that both f and f^{-1} have domains and ranges that consist of the entire set of real numbers. Check that $f(f^{-1}(x)) = x$ and $f^{-1}(f(x)) = x$.

CHECKPoint Now try Exercise 63.

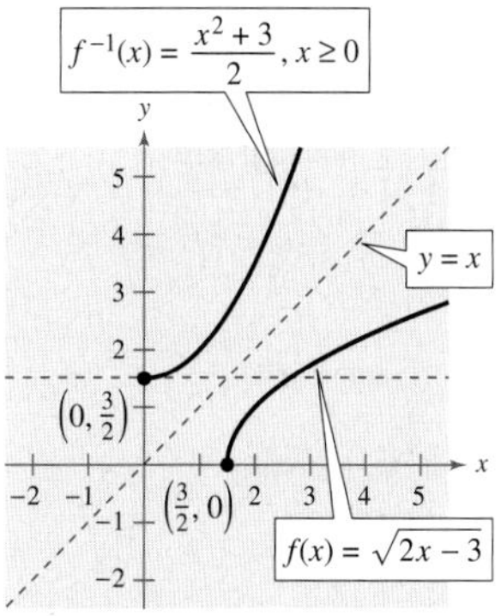

FIGURE 1.100

Example 7 Finding an Inverse Function

Find the inverse function of

$$f(x) = \sqrt{2x - 3}.$$

Solution

The graph of f is a curve, as shown in Figure 1.100. Because this graph passes the Horizontal Line Test, you know that f is one-to-one and has an inverse function.

$f(x) = \sqrt{2x - 3}$ Write original function.

$y = \sqrt{2x - 3}$ Replace $f(x)$ by y.

$x = \sqrt{2y - 3}$ Interchange x and y.

$x^2 = 2y - 3$ Square each side.

$2y = x^2 + 3$ Isolate y.

$y = \dfrac{x^2 + 3}{2}$ Solve for y.

$f^{-1}(x) = \dfrac{x^2 + 3}{2}, \quad x \geq 0$ Replace y by $f^{-1}(x)$.

The graph of f^{-1} in Figure 1.100 is the reflection of the graph of f in the line $y = x$. Note that the range of f is the interval $[0, \infty)$, which implies that the domain of f^{-1} is the interval $[0, \infty)$. Moreover, the domain of f is the interval $\left[\frac{3}{2}, \infty\right)$, which implies that the range of f^{-1} is the interval $\left[\frac{3}{2}, \infty\right)$. Verify that $f(f^{-1}(x)) = x$ and $f^{-1}(f(x)) = x$.

CHECK*Point* Now try Exercise 69.

Classroom Discussion

The Existence of an Inverse Function Write a short paragraph describing why the following functions do or do not have inverse functions.

a. Let x represent the retail price of an item (in dollars), and let $f(x)$ represent the sales tax on the item. Assume that the sales tax is 6% of the retail price *and* that the sales tax is rounded to the nearest cent. Does this function have an inverse function? (*Hint:* Can you undo this function? For instance, if you know that the sales tax is \$0.12, can you determine exactly what the retail price is?)

b. Let x represent the temperature in degrees Celsius, and let $f(x)$ represent the temperature in degrees Fahrenheit. Does this function have an inverse function? (*Hint:* The formula for converting from degrees Celsius to degrees Fahrenheit is $F = \frac{9}{5}C + 32$.)

a. The function does not have an inverse because the retail price cannot be determined exactly because the sales tax is rounded.

b. The function does have an inverse because $f(f^{-1}(x)) = x$ and $f^{-1}(f(x)) = x$.

Extra Example 7

Find the inverse of $f(x) = \sqrt[3]{10 + x}$.

$f^{-1}(x) = x^3 - 10$

Closing the Lesson

Have students summarize the major points of the lesson and answer the Essential Question: What is the inverse of a function, and how do you represent it graphically and algebraically?

- **A function's inverse "undoes" the operations of the original function, such that $f^{-1}(f(x)) = x$.**
- **The graph of a function's inverse $f^{-1}(x)$ is a reflection of $f(x)$ in the line $y = x$.**
- **A function f has an inverse function if and only if f is one-to-one.**
- **In order to find algebraically the inverse of a function $y = f(x)$, switch the variables x and y and solve for y.**

4 PRACTICE AND APPLY

Assignment Guide

Transparencies Available
Available at the Instructor's companion site.

Average:
Day 1: pp. 98–101
Exs. 7–13 odd, 15–18, 23–33 odd, 35–42, 43–75 odd, 87–97, 99, 101, 103–108

Advanced:
Day 1: pp. 98–101
Exs. 8–14 even, 15–18, 24–38 even, 39–42, 44–76 even, 87–101, 103–116

Block:
pp. 98–101
Exs. 7–13 odd, 15–18, 23–33 odd, 35–42, 43–75 odd, 87–97, 99, 101, 103–108 (with 1.10)

1.9 EXERCISES

See www.CalcChat.com for worked-out solutions to odd-numbered exercises.

VOCABULARY: Fill in the blanks.

1. If the composite functions $f(g(x))$ and $g(f(x))$ both equal x, then the function g is the _inverse_ function of f.
2. The inverse function of f is denoted by _f^{-1}_.
3. The domain of f is the _range_ of f^{-1}, and the _domain_ of f^{-1} is the range of f.
4. The graphs of f and f^{-1} are reflections of each other in the line _$y = x$_.
5. A function f is ________ if each value of the dependent variable corresponds to exactly one value of the independent variable. one-to-one
6. A graphical test for the existence of an inverse function of f is called the _______ Line Test. Horizontal

SKILLS AND APPLICATIONS

In Exercises 7–14, find the inverse function of f informally. Verify that $f(f^{-1}(x)) = x$ and $f^{-1}(f(x)) = x$.

7. $f(x) = 6x$ $f^{-1}(x) = \frac{1}{6}x$
8. $f(x) = \frac{1}{3}x$ $f^{-1}(x) = 3x$
9. $f(x) = x + 9$ 9, 11. See margin.
10. $f(x) = x - 4$ $f^{-1}(x) = x + 4$
11. $f(x) = 3x + 1$
12. $f(x) = \dfrac{x-1}{5}$ $f^{-1}(x) = 5x + 1$
13. $f(x) = \sqrt[3]{x}$ $f^{-1}(x) = x^3$
14. $f(x) = x^5$ $f^{-1}(x) = \sqrt[5]{x}$

In Exercises 15–18, match the graph of the function with the graph of its inverse function. [The graphs of the inverse functions are labeled (a), (b), (c), and (d).]

(a)

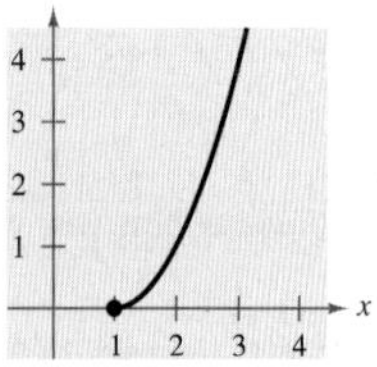

(b)

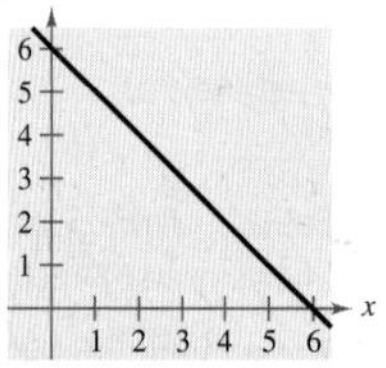

(c)

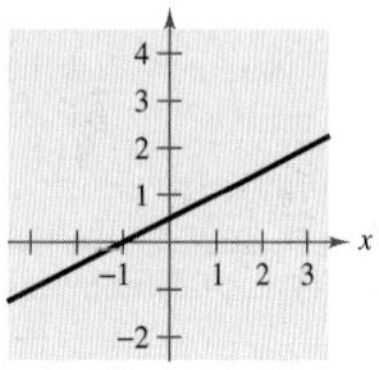

(d)

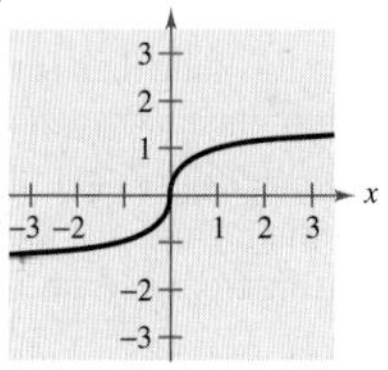

15. c

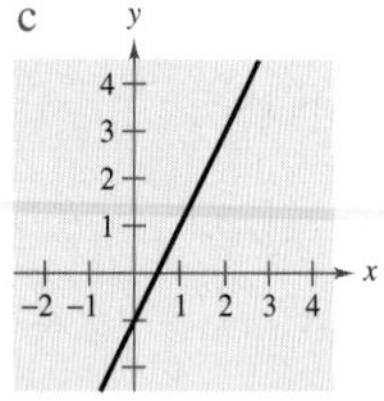

16. b

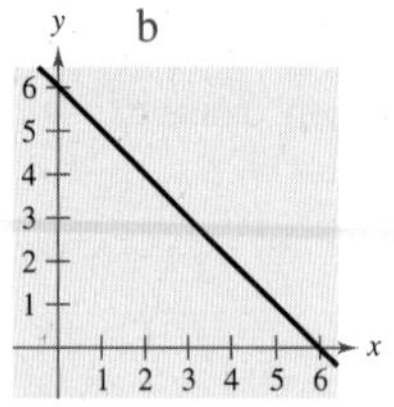

17. a

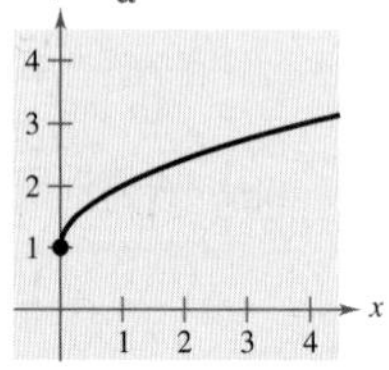

18. d

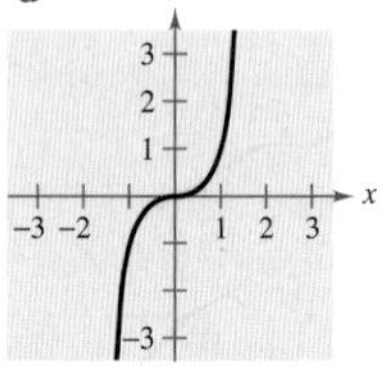

In Exercises 19–22, verify that f and g are inverse functions. 19–22. See margin.

19. $f(x) = -\frac{7}{2}x - 3,\quad g(x) = -\dfrac{2x+6}{7}$
20. $f(x) = \dfrac{x-9}{4},\quad g(x) = 4x + 9$
21. $f(x) = x^3 + 5,\quad g(x) = \sqrt[3]{x-5}$
22. $f(x) = \dfrac{x^3}{2},\quad g(x) = \sqrt[3]{2x}$

In Exercises 23–34, show that f and g are inverse functions (a) algebraically and (b) graphically. 23–31. See margin.

23. $f(x) = 2x,\quad g(x) = \dfrac{x}{2}$
24. $f(x) = x - 5,\quad g(x) = x + 5$
25. $f(x) = 7x + 1,\quad g(x) = \dfrac{x-1}{7}$
26. $f(x) = 3 - 4x,\quad g(x) = \dfrac{3-x}{4}$
27. $f(x) = \dfrac{x^3}{8},\quad g(x) = \sqrt[3]{8x}$
28. $f(x) = \dfrac{1}{x},\quad g(x) = \dfrac{1}{x}$
29. $f(x) = \sqrt{x-4},\quad g(x) = x^2 + 4,\quad x \ge 0$
30. $f(x) = 1 - x^3,\quad g(x) = \sqrt[3]{1-x}$
31. $f(x) = 9 - x^2,\quad x \ge 0,\quad g(x) = \sqrt{9-x},\quad x \le 9$

9. $f^{-1}(x) = x - 9$

11. $f^{-1}(x) = \dfrac{x-1}{3}$

23. (a) $f(g(x)) = f\left(\dfrac{x}{2}\right) = 2\left(\dfrac{x}{2}\right) = x$

$g(f(x)) = g(2x) = \dfrac{(2x)}{2} = x$

(b)

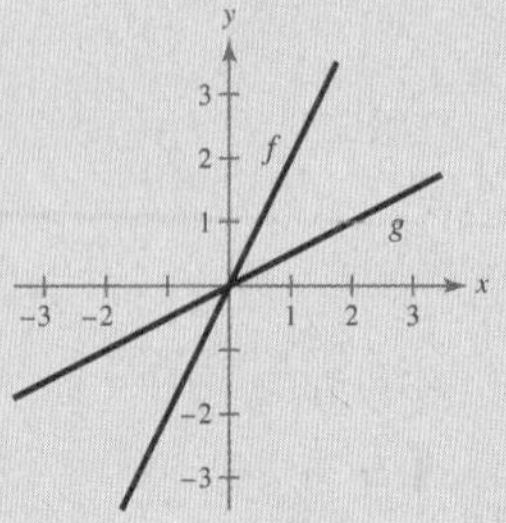

28. (a) $f(g(x)) = f\left(\dfrac{1}{x}\right) = \dfrac{1}{1/x} = x$

$g(f(x)) = g\left(\dfrac{1}{x}\right) = \dfrac{1}{1/x} = x$

(b)

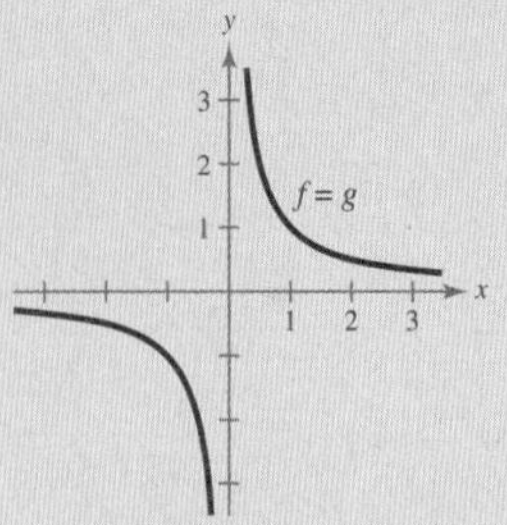

29. (a) $f(g(x)) = f(x^2 + 4),\ x \ge 0$
$= \sqrt{(x^2 + 4) - 4} = x$
$g(f(x)) = g\left(\sqrt{x-4}\right)$
$= \left(\sqrt{x-4}\right)^2 + 4 = x$

(b)

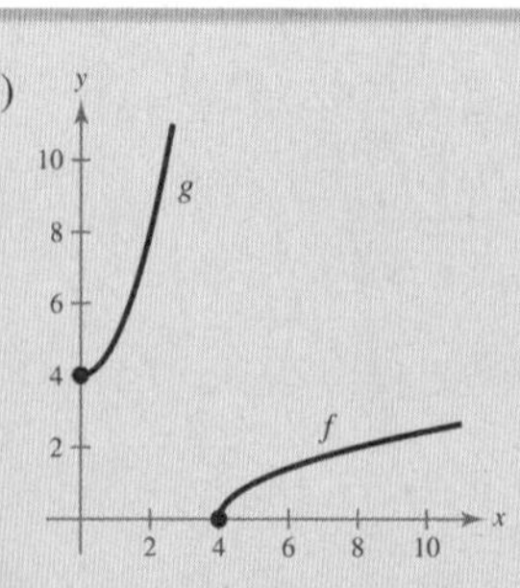

19–22, 24–27, 30–31. See Additional Answers beginning on page AA1.

32. $f(x) = \dfrac{1}{1+x},\ x \ge 0,\quad g(x) = \dfrac{1-x}{x},\ 0 < x \le 1$

33. $f(x) = \dfrac{x-1}{x+5},\quad g(x) = -\dfrac{5x+1}{x-1}$

34. $f(x) = \dfrac{x+3}{x-2},\quad g(x) = \dfrac{2x+3}{x-1}$ 32–34. See margin.

In Exercises 35 and 36, does the function have an inverse function?

35. No

x	-1	0	1	2	3	4
$f(x)$	-2	1	2	1	-2	-6

36. Yes

x	-3	-2	-1	0	2	3
$f(x)$	10	6	4	1	-3	-10

In Exercises 37 and 38, use the table of values for $y = f(x)$ to complete a table for $y = f^{-1}(x)$. 37–38. See margin.

37.

x	-2	-1	0	1	2	3
$f(x)$	-2	0	2	4	6	8

38.

x	-3	-2	-1	0	1	2
$f(x)$	-10	-7	-4	-1	2	5

In Exercises 39–42, does the function have an inverse function?

39. Yes

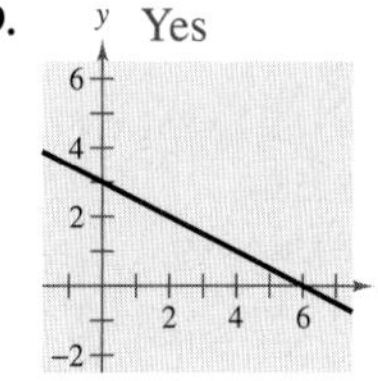

40. No

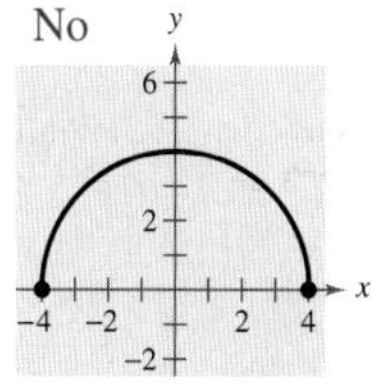

41. No

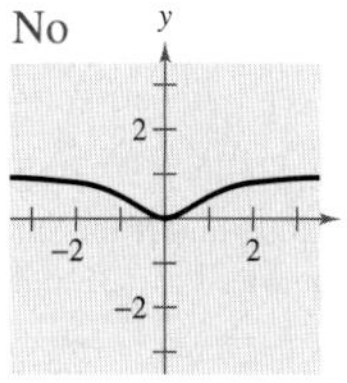

42. Yes

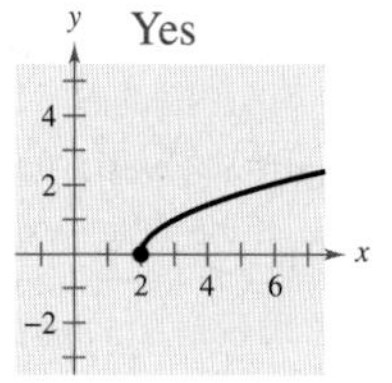

In Exercises 43–48, use a graphing utility to graph the function, and use the Horizontal Line Test to determine whether the function is one-to-one and so has an inverse function.

43–48. See margin.

43. $g(x) = \dfrac{4-x}{6}$

44. $f(x) = 10$

45. $h(x) = |x+4| - |x-4|$

46. $g(x) = (x+5)^3$

47. $f(x) = -2x\sqrt{16-x^2}$

48. $f(x) = \frac{1}{8}(x+2)^2 - 1$

In Exercises 49–62, (a) find the inverse function of f, (b) graph both f and f^{-1} on the same set of coordinate axes, (c) describe the relationship between the graphs of f and f^{-1}, and (d) state the domain and range of f and f^{-1}.

49. $f(x) = 2x - 3$

50. $f(x) = 3x + 1$

51. $f(x) = x^5 - 2$

52. $f(x) = x^3 + 1$

53. $f(x) = \sqrt{4-x^2},\quad 0 \le x \le 2$ 49–62. See margin.

54. $f(x) = x^2 - 2,\quad x \le 0$

55. $f(x) = \dfrac{4}{x}$

56. $f(x) = -\dfrac{2}{x}$

57. $f(x) = \dfrac{x+1}{x-2}$

58. $f(x) = \dfrac{x-3}{x+2}$

59. $f(x) = \sqrt[3]{x-1}$

60. $f(x) = x^{3/5}$

61. $f(x) = \dfrac{6x+4}{4x+5}$

62. $f(x) = \dfrac{8x-4}{2x+6}$

In Exercises 63–76, determine whether the function has an inverse function. If it does, find the inverse function.

63. $f(x) = x^4$ No inverse

64. $f(x) = \dfrac{1}{x^2}$ No inverse

65. $g(x) = \dfrac{x}{8}$ $g^{-1}(x) = 8x$

66. $f(x) = 3x + 5$ See margin.

67. $p(x) = -4$ No inverse

68. $f(x) = \dfrac{3x+4}{5}$ See margin.

69. $f(x) = (x+3)^2,\quad x \ge -3$ $f^{-1}(x) = \sqrt{x} - 3$

70. $q(x) = (x-5)^2$ No inverse

71. $f(x) = \begin{cases} x+3, & x < 0 \\ 6-x, & x \ge 0 \end{cases}$ No inverse

72. $f(x) = \begin{cases} -x, & x \le 0 \\ x^2 - 3x, & x > 0 \end{cases}$ No inverse

73. $h(x) = -\dfrac{4}{x^2}$ No inverse

74. $f(x) = |x-2|,\quad x \le 2$ See margin.

75. $f(x) = \sqrt{2x+3}$ $f^{-1}(x) = \dfrac{x^2-3}{2},\ x \ge 0$

76. $f(x) = \sqrt{x-2}$ $f^{-1}(x) = x^2 + 2,\ x \ge 0$

43.

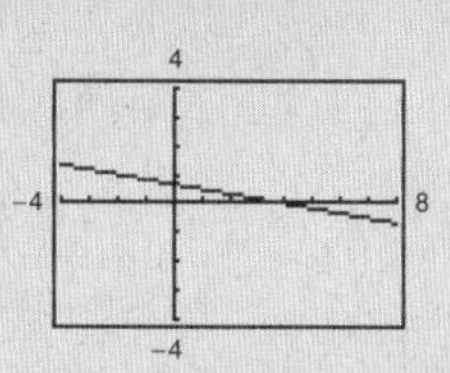

The function has an inverse.

44.

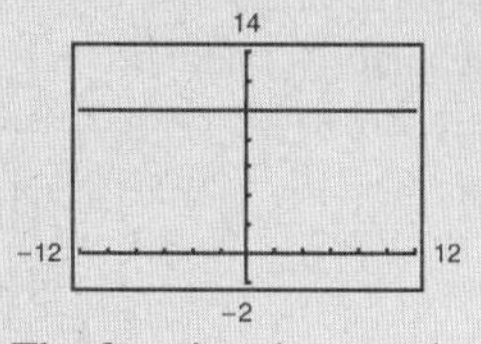

The function does not have an inverse.

45.

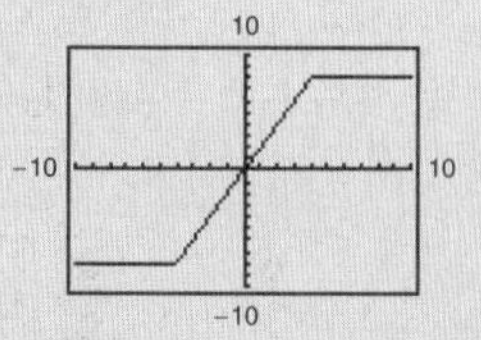

The function does not have an inverse.

46.

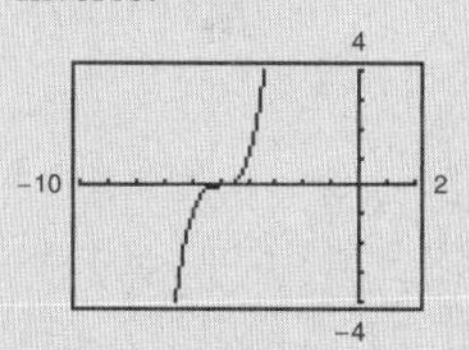

The function has an inverse.

47.

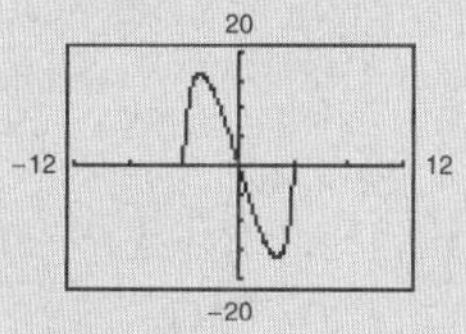

The function does not have an inverse.

48.

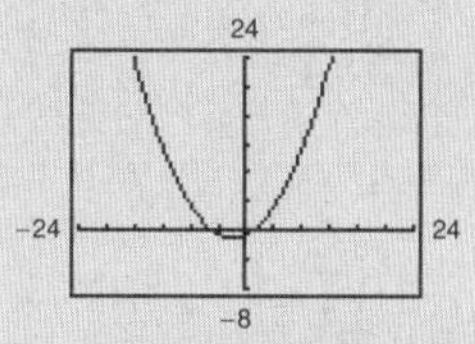

The function does not have an inverse.

49. (a) $f^{-1}(x) = \dfrac{x+3}{2}$

(b)

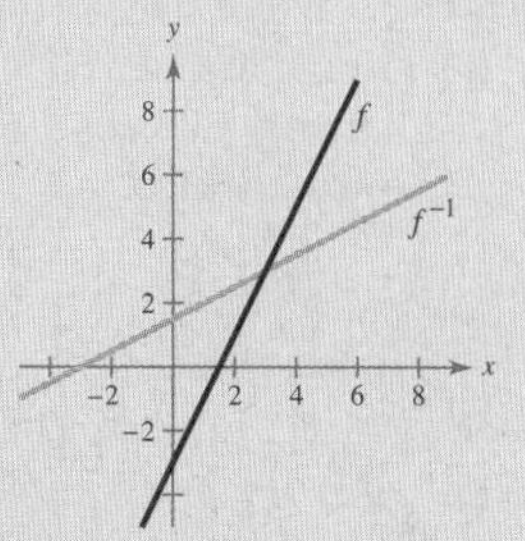

(c) The graph of f^{-1} is the reflection of the graph of f in the line $y = x$.

(d) The domains and ranges of f and f^{-1} are all real numbers.

50. (a) $f^{-1}(x) = \dfrac{x-1}{3}$

(b)

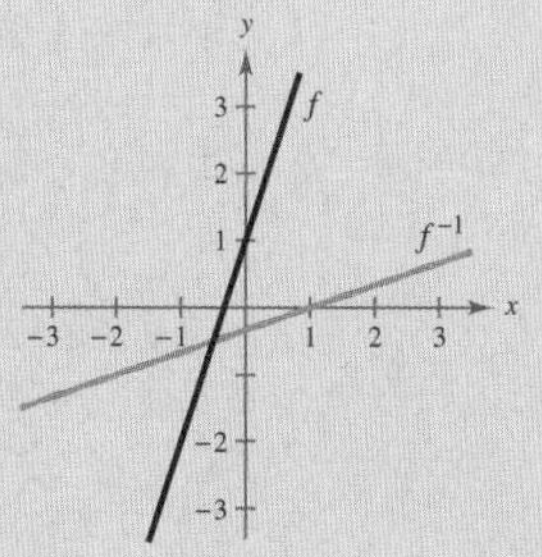

(c) The graph of f^{-1} is the reflection of the graph of f in the line $y = x$.

(d) The domains and ranges of f and f^{-1} are all real numbers.

66. $f^{-1}(x) = \dfrac{x-5}{3}$

68. $f^{-1}(x) = \dfrac{5x-4}{3}$

74. $f^{-1}(x) = 2 - x,\quad x \ge 0$

32–34, 37–38, 51–62. See Additional Answers beginning on page AA1.

THINK ABOUT IT In Exercises 77–86, restrict the domain of the function f so that the function is one-to-one and has an inverse function. Then find the inverse function f^{-1}. State the domains and ranges of f and f^{-1}. Explain your results. (There are many correct answers.) 77–86. See margin.

77. $f(x) = (x - 2)^2$ **78.** $f(x) = 1 - x^4$

79. $f(x) = |x + 2|$ **80.** $f(x) = |x - 5|$

81. $f(x) = (x + 6)^2$ **82.** $f(x) = (x - 4)^2$

83. $f(x) = -2x^2 + 5$ **84.** $f(x) = \frac{1}{2}x^2 - 1$

85. $f(x) = |x - 4| + 1$ **86.** $f(x) = -|x - 1| - 2$

In Exercises 87–92, use the functions given by $f(x) = \frac{1}{8}x - 3$ and $g(x) = x^3$ to find the indicated value or function.

87. $(f^{-1} \circ g^{-1})(1)$ 32 **88.** $(g^{-1} \circ f^{-1})(-3)$ 0

89. $(f^{-1} \circ f^{-1})(6)$ 600 **90.** $(g^{-1} \circ g^{-1})(-4)$ $\sqrt[9]{-4}$

91. $(f \circ g)^{-1}$ $2\sqrt[3]{x + 3}$ **92.** $g^{-1} \circ f^{-1}$ $2\sqrt[3]{x + 3}$

In Exercises 93–96, use the functions given by $f(x) = x + 4$ and $g(x) = 2x - 5$ to find the specified function. 93–96. See margin.

93. $g^{-1} \circ f^{-1}$ **94.** $f^{-1} \circ g^{-1}$

95. $(f \circ g)^{-1}$ **96.** $(g \circ f)^{-1}$

97. SHOE SIZES The table shows men's shoe sizes in the United States and the corresponding European shoe sizes. Let $y = f(x)$ represent the function that gives the men's European shoe size in terms of x, the men's U.S. size.

Men's U.S. shoe size	Men's European shoe size
8	41
9	42
10	43
11	45
12	46
13	47

(a) Is f one-to-one? Explain. Yes; each European shoe size corresponds to exactly one U.S. shoe size.
(b) Find $f(11)$. 45
(c) Find $f^{-1}(43)$, if possible. 10
(d) Find $f(f^{-1}(41))$. 41
(e) Find $f^{-1}(f(13))$. 13

98. SHOE SIZES The table shows women's shoe sizes in the United States and the corresponding European shoe sizes. Let $y = g(x)$ represent the function that gives the women's European shoe size in terms of x, the women's U.S. size.

Women's U.S. shoe size	Women's European shoe size
4	35
5	37
6	38
7	39
8	40
9	42

(a) Is g one-to-one? Explain. Yes; each European shoe size corresponds to exactly one U.S. shoe size.
(b) Find $g(6)$. 38
(c) Find $g^{-1}(42)$. 9
(d) Find $g(g^{-1}(39))$. 39
(e) Find $g^{-1}(g(5))$. 5

99. LCD TVS The sales S (in millions of dollars) of LCD televisions in the United States from 2001 through 2007 are shown in the table. The time (in years) is given by t, with $t = 1$ corresponding to 2001. (Source: Consumer Electronics Association)

Year, t	Sales, $S(t)$
1	62
2	246
3	664
4	1579
5	3258
6	8430
7	14,532

(a) Does S^{-1} exist? Yes
(b) If S^{-1} exists, what does it represent in the context of the problem? See margin.
(c) If S^{-1} exists, find $S^{-1}(8430)$. $S^{-1}(8430) = 6$
(d) If the table was extended to 2009 and if the sales of LCD televisions for that year was $14,532 million, would S^{-1} exist? Explain.

No, because then the sales for 2007 and 2009 would be the same, so the function would no longer be one-to-one.

77. $f^{-1}(x) = \sqrt{x} + 2$
The domain of f and the range of f^{-1} are all real numbers x such that $x \geq 2$. The domain of f^{-1} and the range of f are all real numbers x such that $x \geq 0$.

78. $f^{-1}(x) = \sqrt[4]{1 - x}$
The domain of f and the range of f^{-1} are all real numbers x such that $x \geq 0$. The domain of f^{-1} and the range of f are all real numbers x such that $x \leq 1$.

79. $f^{-1}(x) = x - 2$
The domain of f and the range of f^{-1} are all real numbers x such that $x \geq -2$. The domain of f^{-1} and the range of f are all real numbers x such that $x \geq 0$.

80. $f^{-1}(x) = x + 5$
The domain of f and the range of f^{-1} are all real numbers x such that $x \geq 5$. The domain of f^{-1} and the range of f are all real numbers x such that $x \geq 0$.

81. $f^{-1}(x) = \sqrt{x} - 6$
The domain of f and the range of f^{-1} are all real numbers x such that $x \geq -6$. The domain of f^{-1} and the range of f are all real numbers x such that $x \geq 0$.

82. $f^{-1}(x) = \sqrt{x} + 4$
The domain of f and the range of f^{-1} are all real numbers x such that $x \geq 4$. The domain of f^{-1} and the range of f are all real numbers x such that $x \geq 0$.

83. $f^{-1}(x) = \dfrac{\sqrt{-2(x - 5)}}{2}$
The domain of f and the range of f^{-1} are all real numbers x such that $x \geq 0$. The domain of f^{-1} and the range of f are all real numbers x such that $x \leq 5$.

84. $f^{-1}(x) = \sqrt{2x + 2}$
The domain of f and the range of f^{-1} are all real numbers x such that $x \geq 0$. The domain of f^{-1} and the range of f are all real numbers x such that $x \geq -1$.

85. $f^{-1}(x) = x + 3$
The domain of f and the range of f^{-1} are all real numbers x such that $x \geq 4$. The domain of f^{-1} and the range of f are all real numbers x such that $x \geq 1$.

86. $f^{-1}(x) = -x - 1$
The domain of f and the range of f^{-1} are all real numbers x such that $x \geq 1$. The domain of f^{-1} and the range of f are all real numbers x such that $x \leq -2$.

93. $\dfrac{x + 1}{2}$

94. $\dfrac{x - 3}{2}$

95. $\dfrac{x + 1}{2}$

96. $\dfrac{x - 3}{2}$

99. (b) S^{-1} represents the time in years for a given sales level.

100. POPULATION The projected populations P (in millions of people) in the United States for 2015 through 2040 are shown in the table. The time (in years) is given by t, with $t = 15$ corresponding to 2015. (Source: U.S. Census Bureau)

Year, t	Population, $P(t)$
15	325.5
20	341.4
25	357.5
30	373.5
35	389.5
40	405.7

(a) Does P^{-1} exist? Yes

(b) If P^{-1} exists, what does it represent in the context of the problem? See margin.

(c) If P^{-1} exists, find $P^{-1}(357.5)$. $P^{-1}(357.5) = 25$

(d) If the table was extended to 2050 and if the projected population of the U.S. for that year was 373.5 million, would P^{-1} exist? Explain. See margin.

101. HOURLY WAGE Your wage is \$10.00 per hour plus \$0.75 for each unit produced per hour. So, your hourly wage y in terms of the number of units produced x is $y = 10 + 0.75x$.

(a) Find the inverse function. What does each variable represent in the inverse function? See margin.

(b) Determine the number of units produced when your hourly wage is \$24.25. 19 units

102. DIESEL MECHANICS The function given by

$$y = 0.03x^2 + 245.50, \quad 0 < x < 100$$

approximates the exhaust temperature y in degrees Fahrenheit, where x is the percent load for a diesel engine.

(a) Find the inverse function. What does each variable represent in the inverse function? See margin.

(b) Use a graphing utility to graph the inverse function. See margin.

(c) The exhaust temperature of the engine must not exceed 500 degrees Fahrenheit. What is the percent load interval? $0 < x \le 92.11$

EXPLORATION

TRUE OR FALSE? In Exercises 103 and 104, determine whether the statement is true or false. Justify your answer.

103. If f is an even function, then f^{-1} exists. See margin.

104. If the inverse function of f exists and the graph of f has a y-intercept, then the y-intercept of f is an x-intercept of f^{-1}. True. If $f(x) = x - 6$ and $f^{-1}(x) = x + 6$, then the y-intercept of f is $(0, -6)$ and the x-intercept of f^{-1} is $(-6, 0)$.

105. PROOF Prove that if f and g are one-to-one functions, then $(f \circ g)^{-1}(x) = (g^{-1} \circ f^{-1})(x)$. Proof

106. PROOF Prove that if f is a one-to-one odd function, then f^{-1} is an odd function. Proof

In Exercises 107 and 108, use the graph of the function f to create a table of values for the given points. Then create a second table that can be used to find f^{-1}, and sketch the graph of f^{-1} if possible. 107–108. See margin.

107.

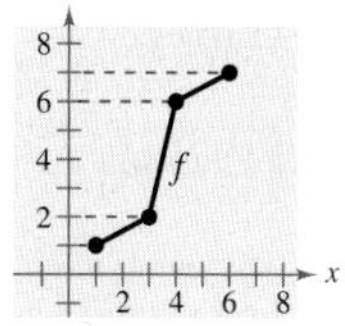

108.

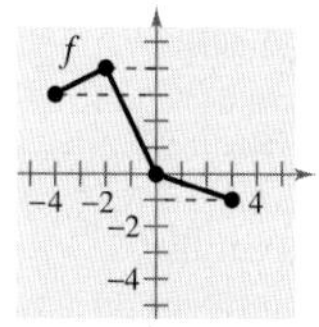

In Exercises 109–112, determine if the situation could be represented by a one-to-one function. If so, write a statement that describes the inverse function. 109–112. See margin.

109. The number of miles n a marathon runner has completed in terms of the time t in hours

110. The population p of South Carolina in terms of the year t from 1960 through 2008

111. The depth of the tide d at a beach in terms of the time t over a 24-hour period

112. The height h in inches of a human born in the year 2000 in terms of his or her age n in years.

113. THINK ABOUT IT The function given by $f(x) = k(2 - x - x^3)$ has an inverse function, and $f^{-1}(3) = -2$. Find k. $k = \frac{1}{4}$

114. THINK ABOUT IT Consider the functions given by $f(x) = x + 2$ and $f^{-1}(x) = x - 2$. Evaluate $f(f^{-1}(x))$ and $f^{-1}(f(x))$ for the indicated values of x. What can you conclude about the functions? See margin.

x	-10	0	7	45
$f(f^{-1}(x))$				
$f^{-1}(f(x))$				

115. THINK ABOUT IT Restrict the domain of $f(x) = x^2 + 1$ to $x \ge 0$. Use a graphing utility to graph the function. Does the restricted function have an inverse function? Explain. See margin.

116. CAPSTONE Describe and correct the error.

~~Given $f(x) = \sqrt{x - 6}$, then $f^{-1}(x) = \dfrac{1}{\sqrt{x - 6}}$.~~

The reciprocal, not the inverse, of $f(x)$ was found. Given $f(x) = \sqrt{x - 6}$, then $f^{-1}(x) = x^2 + 6, x \ge 0$.

5 ASSESS AND RETEACH

Daily Homework Quiz

Transparency Available

Available at the Instructor's companion site.

100. (b) P^{-1} represents the time in years for a given projected population.

(d) No, because then the projected populations for 2030 and 2050 would be the same, so the function would no longer be one-to-one.

101. (a) $y = \dfrac{x - 10}{0.75}$

x = hourly wage;

y = number of units produced

102. (a) $y = \sqrt{\dfrac{x - 245.50}{0.03}}$,

$245.5 < x < 545.5$

x = degrees Fahrenheit;

y = % load

(b)

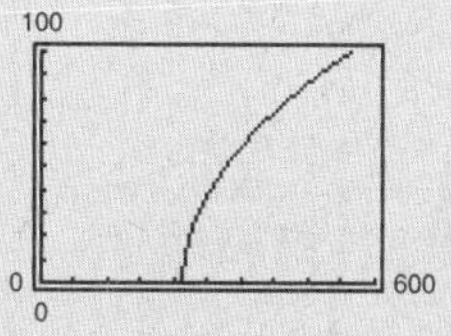

103. False. $f(x) = x^2$ has no inverse.

107.

x	1	3	4	6
y	1	2	6	7

x	1	2	6	7
$f^{-1}(x)$	1	3	4	6

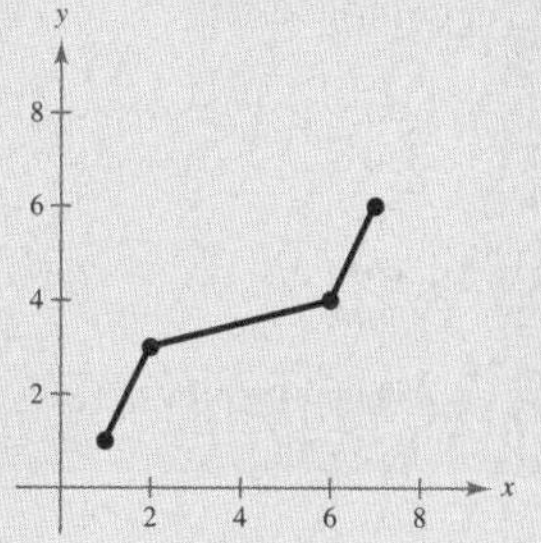

108.

x	-4	-2	0	3
y	3	4	0	-1

The graph of f does not pass the Horizontal Line Test, so $f^{-1}(x)$ does not exist.

109. This situation could be represented by a one-to-one function if the runner does not stop to rest. The inverse function would represent the time in hours for a given number of miles completed.

110. This situation could be represented by a one-to-one function if the population continues to increase. The inverse function would represent the year for a given population.

111. This function could not be represented by a one-to-one function because it oscillates.

112. This situation could not be represented by a one-to-one function because height remains constant after a certain age.

114.

x	-10	0	7	45
$f(f^{-1}(x))$	-10	0	7	45
$f^{-1}(f(x))$	-10	0	7	45

The functions are inverses of each other.

115. See Additional Answers beginning on page AA1.

1 PLAN AND PREPARE

Warm-up Exercises

Transparency Available
Available at the Instructor's companion site.

Notetaking Guide

Transparency Available
Promotes interactive learning and notetaking skills. Available at the Instructor's companion site.

Animated Precalculus

An **Animated Precalculus** tutorial is available at the Student companion site for **Section 1.10.**

Pacing

Average: 1 day
Advanced: 1 day
Block: 0.5 block with 1.9

2 FOCUS AND MOTIVATE

Essential Question

How do you write equations to model real-world data and identify different models of variation?
Tell students that they will learn how to answer this question by using graphing utilities to analyze data and study direct, inverse, and joint variation.

1.10 MATHEMATICAL MODELING AND VARIATION

What you should learn

- Use mathematical models to approximate sets of data points.
- Use the *regression* feature of a graphing utility to find the equation of a least squares regression line.
- Write mathematical models for direct variation.
- Write mathematical models for direct variation as an *n*th power.
- Write mathematical models for inverse variation.
- Write mathematical models for joint variation.

Why you should learn it

You can use functions as models to represent a wide variety of real-life data sets. For instance, in Exercise 83 on page 112, a variation model can be used to model the water temperatures of the ocean at various depths.

Introduction

You have already studied some techniques for fitting models to data. For instance, in Section 1.3, you learned how to find the equation of a line that passes through two points. In this section, you will study other techniques for fitting models to data: *least squares regression* and *direct and inverse variation.* The resulting models are either polynomial functions or rational functions. (Rational functions will be studied in Chapter 2.)

Example 1 A Mathematical Model

The populations y (in millions) of the United States from 2000 through 2007 are shown in the table. (Source: U.S. Census Bureau)

Year	Population, y
2000	282.4
2001	285.3
2002	288.2
2003	290.9
2004	293.6
2005	296.3
2006	299.2
2007	302.0

A linear model that approximates the data is $y = 2.78t + 282.5$ for $0 \le t \le 7$, where t is the year, with $t = 0$ corresponding to 2000. Plot the actual data *and* the model on the same graph. How closely does the model represent the data?

Solution

The actual data are plotted in Figure 1.101, along with the graph of the linear model. From the graph, it appears that the model is a "good fit" for the actual data. You can see how well the model fits by comparing the actual values of y with the values of y given by the model. The values given by the model are labeled $y*$ in the table below.

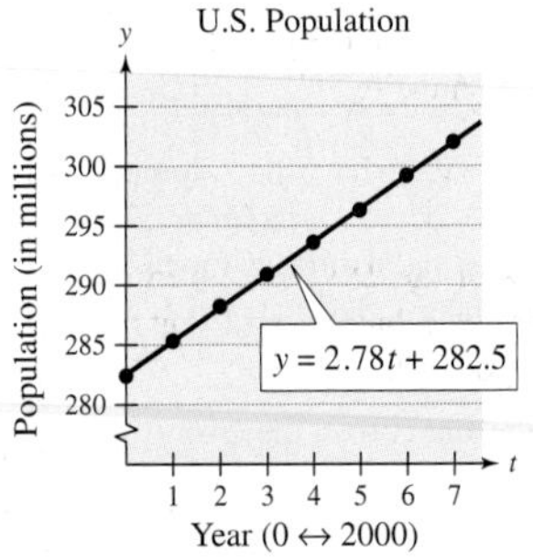

FIGURE 1.101

t	0	1	2	3	4	5	6	7
y	282.4	285.3	288.2	290.9	293.6	296.3	299.2	302.0
$y*$	282.5	285.3	288.1	290.8	293.6	296.4	299.2	302.0

CHECK*Point* Now try Exercise 11.

Note in Example 1 that you could have chosen any two points to find a line that fits the data. However, the given linear model was found using the *regression* feature of a graphing utility and is the line that *best* fits the data. This concept of a "best-fitting" line is discussed on the next page.

Resource Planning Guide

Chapter Resources
- Complete Solutions Guide

Workbooks
- Notetaking Guide
- Student Solutions Guide

Interactive Technology
- Instructor Success Organizer
- Notetaking Guide IAE
- Instructional DVDs
- Animated Precalculus
- PowerLecture with ExamView

Least Squares Regression and Graphing Utilities

So far in this text, you have worked with many different types of mathematical models that approximate real-life data. In some instances the model was given (as in Example 1), whereas in other instances you were asked to find the model using simple algebraic techniques or a graphing utility.

To find a model that approximates the data most accurately, statisticians use a measure called the **sum of square differences,** which is the sum of the squares of the differences between actual data values and model values. The "best-fitting" linear model, called the **least squares regression line,** is the one with the least sum of square differences. Recall that you can approximate this line visually by plotting the data points and drawing the line that appears to fit best—or you can enter the data points into a calculator or computer and use the *linear regression* feature of the calculator or computer. When you use the *regression* feature of a graphing calculator or computer program, you will notice that the program may also output an "r-value." This r-value is the **correlation coefficient** of the data and gives a measure of how well the model fits the data. The closer the value of $|r|$ is to 1, the better the fit.

Example 2 Finding a Least Squares Regression Line

The data in the table show the outstanding household credit market debt D (in trillions of dollars) from 2000 through 2007. Construct a scatter plot that represents the data and find the least squares regression line for the data. (Source: Board of Governors of the Federal Reserve System)

Year	Household credit market debt, D
2000	7.0
2001	7.7
2002	8.5
2003	9.5
2004	10.6
2005	11.8
2006	12.9
2007	13.8

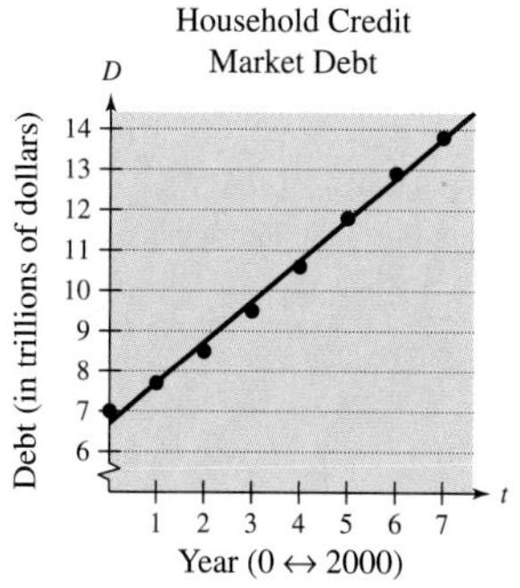

FIGURE 1.102

t	D	$D*$
0	7.0	6.7
1	7.7	7.7
2	8.5	8.7
3	9.5	9.7
4	10.6	10.7
5	11.8	11.8
6	12.9	12.8
7	13.8	13.8

Solution

Let $t = 0$ represent 2000. The scatter plot for the points is shown in Figure 1.102. Using the *regression* feature of a graphing utility, you can determine that the equation of the least squares regression line is

$$D = 1.01t + 6.7.$$

To check this model, compare the actual D-values with the D-values given by the model, which are labeled $D*$ in the table at the left. The correlation coefficient for this model is $r \approx 0.997$, which implies that the model is a good fit.

CHECKPoint Now try Exercise 17.

3 TEACH

Extra Example 1

The average prices (in dollars) of prescription drugs in the United States from 2000 to 2007 are shown in the table.

Year	Price, y
2000	45.79
2001	50.06
2002	55.37
2003	59.52
2004	62.64
2005	63.87
2006	66.97
2007	69.91

A linear model that approximates these data is $y = 3.357t + 47.52$, where y represents the average price (in dollars) of a prescription drug and $t = 0$ represents 2000. Plot the actual data and the model on the same graph. How closely does the model represent the data? (Source: National Association of Chain Drug Stores)

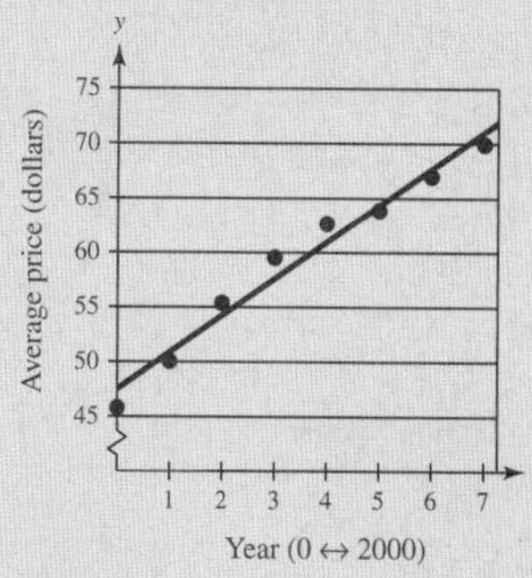

The model is a good fit for the data.

Avoiding Common Errors

Example 2 Students should always check to see that their model matches the data by graphing the data. Specifically, they should check to make sure that the y-intercept and the slope have not been transposed.

Extra Example 2

The numbers of women W (in millions) in the civilian labor force in the United States from 2000 to 2007 are shown in the table. (Source: U.S. Bureau of Labor Statistics)

Year	W
2000	66.3
2001	66.8
2002	67.4
2003	68.3

Year	W
2004	68.4
2005	69.3
2006	70.2
2007	71.0

a. Find the least squares regression line that fits these data, where $t = 0$ represents 2000.
$W = 0.66t + 66.1$

b. Sketch a scatter plot of the data, and graph the linear model on the same set of axes.

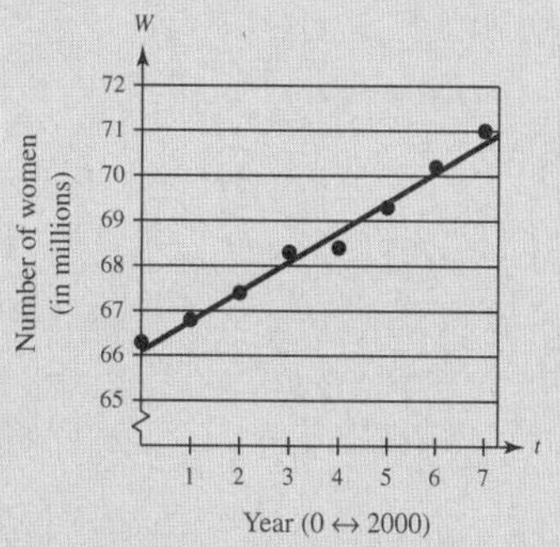

Extra Example 3

The simple interest on an investment is directly proportional to the amount of the investment. By investing \$2500 in a certain bond issue, you obtained an interest payment of \$187.50 at the end of 1 year. Find a mathematical model that gives the interest I for this bond issue at the end of 1 year in terms of the amount invested P.

$I = 0.075P$

Direct Variation

There are two basic types of linear models. The more general model has a y-intercept that is nonzero.

$$y = mx + b, \quad b \neq 0$$

The simpler model

$$y = kx$$

has a y-intercept that is zero. In the simpler model, y is said to **vary directly** as x, or to be **directly proportional** to x.

> **Direct Variation**
>
> The following statements are equivalent.
>
> **1.** y **varies directly** as x.
>
> **2.** y is **directly proportional** to x.
>
> **3.** $y = kx$ for some nonzero constant k.
>
> k is the **constant of variation** or the **constant of proportionality.**

Example 3 Direct Variation

In Pennsylvania, the state income tax is directly proportional to *gross income*. You are working in Pennsylvania and your state income tax deduction is \$46.05 for a gross monthly income of \$1500. Find a mathematical model that gives the Pennsylvania state income tax in terms of gross income.

Solution

Verbal Model: State income tax = k · Gross income

Labels:
State income tax = y (dollars)
Gross income = x (dollars)
Income tax rate = k (percent in decimal form)

Equation: $y = kx$

To solve for k, substitute the given information into the equation $y = kx$, and then solve for k.

$y = kx$ Write direct variation model.

$46.05 = k(1500)$ Substitute $y = 46.05$ and $x = 1500$.

$0.0307 = k$ Simplify.

So, the equation (or model) for state income tax in Pennsylvania is

$$y = 0.0307x.$$

In other words, Pennsylvania has a state income tax rate of 3.07% of gross income. The graph of this equation is shown in Figure 1.103.

CHECKPoint Now try Exercise 43.

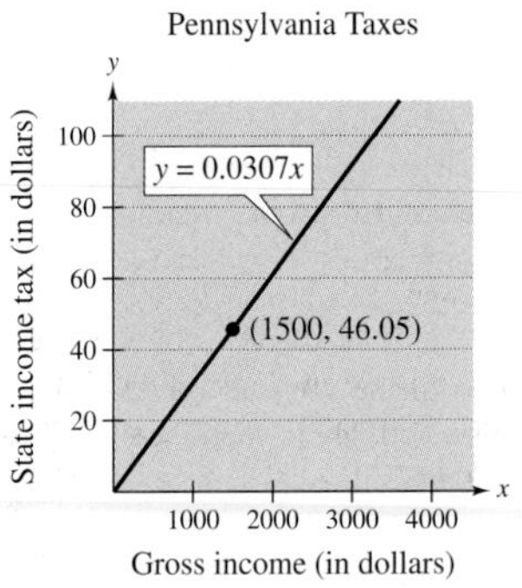

FIGURE 1.103

Direct Variation as an *n*th Power

Another type of direct variation relates one variable to a *power* of another variable. For example, in the formula for the area of a circle

$$A = \pi r^2$$

the area A is directly proportional to the square of the radius r. Note that for this formula, π is the constant of proportionality.

Study Tip

Note that the direct variation model $y = kx$ is a special case of $y = kx^n$ with $n = 1$.

Direct Variation as an *n*th Power

The following statements are equivalent.

1. y **varies directly as the *n*th power** of x.
2. y is **directly proportional to the *n*th power** of x.
3. $y = kx^n$ for some constant k.

Example 4 Direct Variation as *n*th Power

The distance a ball rolls down an inclined plane is directly proportional to the square of the time it rolls. During the first second, the ball rolls 8 feet. (See Figure 1.104.)

a. Write an equation relating the distance traveled to the time.
b. How far will the ball roll during the first 3 seconds?

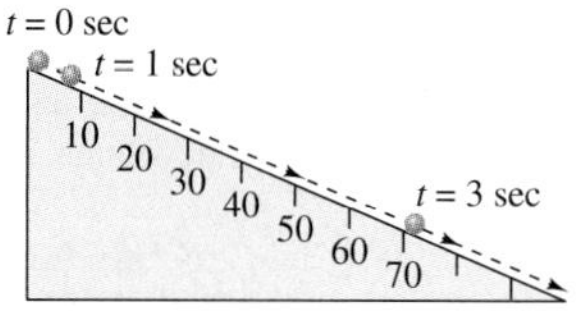

FIGURE 1.104

Solution

a. Letting d be the distance (in feet) the ball rolls and letting t be the time (in seconds), you have

$$d = kt^2.$$

Now, because $d = 8$ when $t = 1$, you can see that $k = 8$, as follows.

$$d = kt^2$$
$$8 = k(1)^2$$
$$8 = k$$

So, the equation relating distance to time is

$$d = 8t^2.$$

b. When $t = 3$, the distance traveled is $d = 8(3)^2 = 8(9) = 72$ feet.

CHECK**Point** Now try Exercise 75.

In Examples 3 and 4, the direct variations are such that an *increase* in one variable corresponds to an *increase* in the other variable. This is also true in the model $d = \frac{1}{5}F$, $F > 0$, where an increase in F results in an increase in d. You should not, however, assume that this always occurs with direct variation. For example, in the model $y = -3x$, an increase in x results in a *decrease* in y, and yet y is said to vary directly as x.

Extra Example 4

Neglecting air resistance, the distance s an object falls varies directly as the square of the duration t of the fall. An object falls a distance of 144 feet in 3 seconds.

a. Write an equation relating distance s and duration t.
   $s = 16t^2$
b. How far will an object fall in 6 seconds?
   576 feet

Extra Example 5

A company has found that the demand for its product varies inversely as the price of the product. When the price is \$2.75, the demand is 600 units.

a. Write an equation relating demand d and price p.

$$d = \frac{1650}{p}$$

b. Approximate the demand when the price is \$3.25.

508 units

Inverse Variation

Inverse Variation

The following statements are equivalent.

1. y **varies inversely** as x.
2. y is **inversely proportional** to x.
3. $y = \dfrac{k}{x}$ for some constant k.

If x and y are related by an equation of the form $y = k/x^n$, then y varies inversely as the nth power of x (or y is inversely proportional to the nth power of x).

Some applications of variation involve problems with *both* direct and inverse variation in the same model. These types of models are said to have **combined variation.**

Example 5 Direct and Inverse Variation

A gas law states that the volume of an enclosed gas varies directly as the temperature *and* inversely as the pressure, as shown in Figure 1.105. The pressure of a gas is 0.75 kilogram per square centimeter when the temperature is 294 K and the volume is 8000 cubic centimeters. (a) Write an equation relating pressure, temperature, and volume. (b) Find the pressure when the temperature is 300 K and the volume is 7000 cubic centimeters.

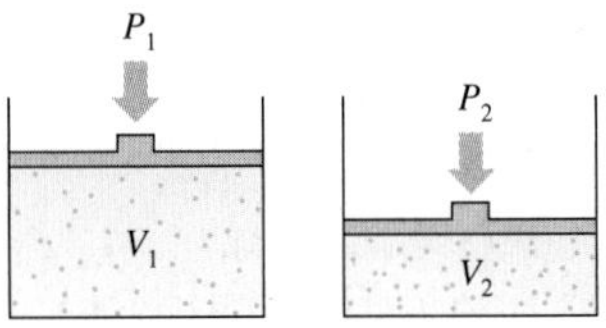

FIGURE 1.105 If the temperature is held constant and pressure increases, volume decreases.

Solution

a. Let V be volume (in cubic centimeters), let P be pressure (in kilograms per square centimeter), and let T be temperature (in Kelvin). Because V varies directly as T and inversely as P, you have

$$V = \frac{kT}{P}.$$

Now, because $P = 0.75$ when $T = 294$ and $V = 8000$, you have

$$8000 = \frac{k(294)}{0.75}$$

$$k = \frac{6000}{294} = \frac{1000}{49}.$$

So, the equation relating pressure, temperature, and volume is

$$V = \frac{1000}{49}\left(\frac{T}{P}\right).$$

b. When $T = 300$ and $V = 7000$, the pressure is

$$P = \frac{1000}{49}\left(\frac{300}{7000}\right) = \frac{300}{343} \approx 0.87 \text{ kilogram per square centimeter.}$$

CHECKPoint Now try Exercise 77.

Joint Variation

In Example 5, note that when a direct variation and an inverse variation occur in the same statement, they are coupled with the word "and." To describe two different *direct* variations in the same statement, the word **jointly** is used.

> **Joint Variation**
>
> The following statements are equivalent.
>
> 1. z **varies jointly** as x and y.
> 2. z is **jointly proportional** to x and y.
> 3. $z = kxy$ for some constant k.

If x, y, and z are related by an equation of the form

$$z = kx^n y^m$$

then z varies jointly as the nth power of x and the mth power of y.

Example 6 Joint Variation

The *simple* interest for a certain savings account is jointly proportional to the time and the principal. After one quarter (3 months), the interest on a principal of \$5000 is \$43.75.

a. Write an equation relating the interest, principal, and time.

b. Find the interest after three quarters.

Solution

a. Let I = interest (in dollars), P = principal (in dollars), and t = time (in years). Because I is jointly proportional to P and t, you have

$$I = kPt.$$

For $I = 43.75$, $P = 5000$, and $t = \frac{1}{4}$, you have

$$43.75 = k(5000)\left(\frac{1}{4}\right)$$

which implies that $k = 4(43.75)/5000 = 0.035$. So, the equation relating interest, principal, and time is

$$I = 0.035Pt$$

which is the familiar equation for simple interest where the constant of proportionality, 0.035, represents an annual interest rate of 3.5%.

b. When $P = \$5000$ and $t = \frac{3}{4}$, the interest is

$$I = (0.035)(5000)\left(\frac{3}{4}\right)$$

$$= \$131.25.$$

CHECKPoint Now try Exercise 79.

Extra Example 6

The maximum load that can be safely supported by a horizontal beam is jointly proportional to the width of the beam and the square of its depth, and inversely proportional to the length of the beam. Determine the change in the maximum safe load under the following conditions:

a. The width of the beam is doubled.
The safe load is doubled.

b. The depth of the beam is doubled.
The safe load is 4 times as great.

Closing the Lesson

Have students summarize the major points of the lesson and answer the Essential Question: How do you write equations to model real-world data and identify different models of variation?

- **A least-squares regression line represents the best-fitting linear model of a mathematical model that approximates data.**
- **The equation for direct variation as the nth power is $y = kx^n$.**
- **The equation for inverse variation as the nth power is $y = \frac{k}{x^n}$.**
- **The equation for joint variation as the nth power of x and the mth power of y is $z = kx^n y^m$.**

1.10 EXERCISES

See www.CalcChat.com for worked-out solutions to odd-numbered exercises.

VOCABULARY: Fill in the blanks.

1. Two techniques for fitting models to data are called direct variation and least squares regression
2. Statisticians use a measure called sum of square differences to find a model that approximates a set of data most accurately.
3. The linear model with the least sum of square differences is called the least squares regression line.
4. An r-value of a set of data, also called a correlation coefficient, gives a measure of how well a model fits a set of data.
5. Direct variation models can be described as "y varies directly as x," or "y is directly proportional to x."
6. In direct variation models of the form $y = kx$, k is called the constant of variation.
7. The direct variation model $y = kx^n$ can be described as "y varies directly as the nth power of x," or "y is directly proportional to the nth power of x."
8. The mathematical model $y = \frac{k}{x}$ is an example of inverse variation.
9. Mathematical models that involve both direct and inverse variation are said to have combined variation.
10. The joint variation model $z = kxy$ can be described as "z varies jointly as x and y," or "z is _______ _______ to x and y." jointly proportional

SKILLS AND APPLICATIONS

11. **EMPLOYMENT** The total numbers of people (in thousands) in the U.S. civilian labor force from 1992 through 2007 are given by the following ordered pairs. See margin.

(1992, 128,105)	(2000, 142,583)
(1993, 129,200)	(2001, 143,734)
(1994, 131,056)	(2002, 144,863)
(1995, 132,304)	(2003, 146,510)
(1996, 133,943)	(2004, 147,401)
(1997, 136,297)	(2005, 149,320)
(1998, 137,673)	(2006, 151,428)
(1999, 139,368)	(2007, 153,124)

A linear model that approximates the data is $y = 1695.9t + 124{,}320$, where y represents the number of employees (in thousands) and $t = 2$ represents 1992. Plot the actual data and the model on the same set of coordinate axes. How closely does the model represent the data? (Source: U.S. Bureau of Labor Statistics)

12. **SPORTS** The winning times (in minutes) in the women's 400-meter freestyle swimming event in the Olympics from 1948 through 2008 are given by the following ordered pairs. See margin.

(1948, 5.30)	(1972, 4.32)	(1996, 4.12)
(1952, 5.20)	(1976, 4.16)	(2000, 4.10)
(1956, 4.91)	(1980, 4.15)	(2004, 4.09)
(1960, 4.84)	(1984, 4.12)	(2008, 4.05)
(1964, 4.72)	(1988, 4.06)	
(1968, 4.53)	(1992, 4.12)	

A linear model that approximates the data is $y = -0.020t + 5.00$, where y represents the winning time (in minutes) and $t = 0$ represents 1950. Plot the actual data and the model on the same set of coordinate axes. How closely does the model represent the data? Does it appear that another type of model may be a better fit? Explain. (Source: International Olympic Committee)

In Exercises 13–16, sketch the line that you think best approximates the data in the scatter plot. Then find an equation of the line. To print an enlarged copy of the graph, go to the website *www.mathgraphs.com*.

13–16. See margin.

13.
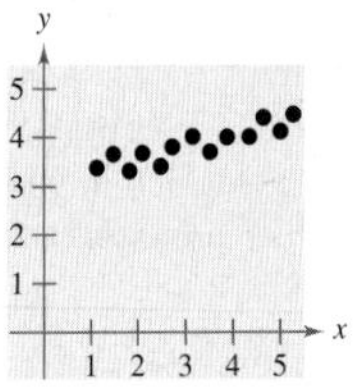

14.
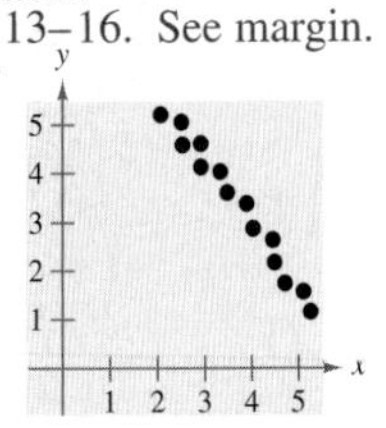

15.
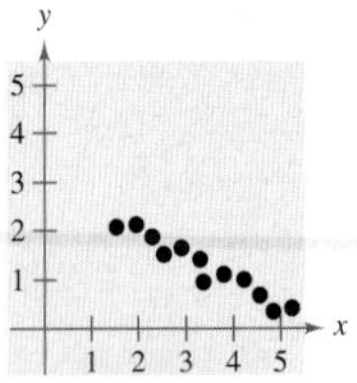

16.
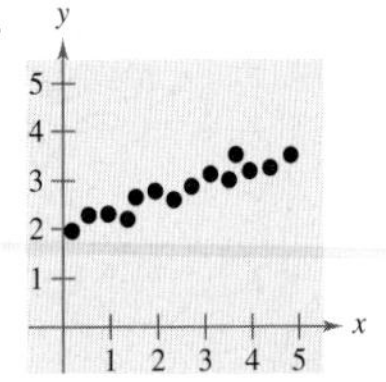

4 PRACTICE AND APPLY

Assignment Guide

Transparencies Available
Available at the Instructor's companion site.

Average:
Day 1: pp. 108–113
Exs. 11–21 odd, 22, 23–85 odd, 87–89

Advanced:
Day 1: pp. 108–113
Exs. 12–86 even, 87, 94

Block:
pp. 108–113
Exs. 11–21 odd, 22, 23–85 odd, 87–89 (with 1.9)

11.
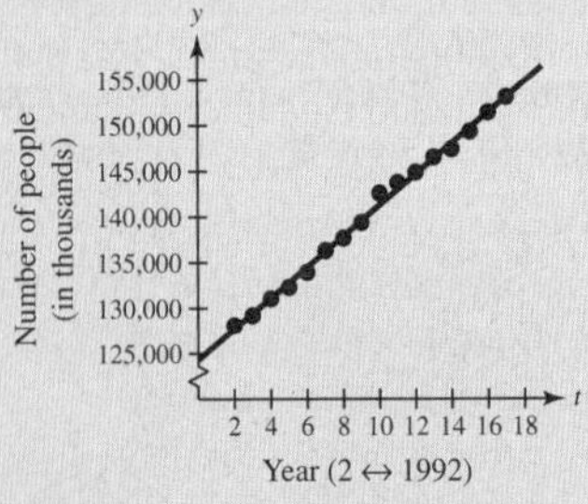

The model is a good fit for the actual data.

12.
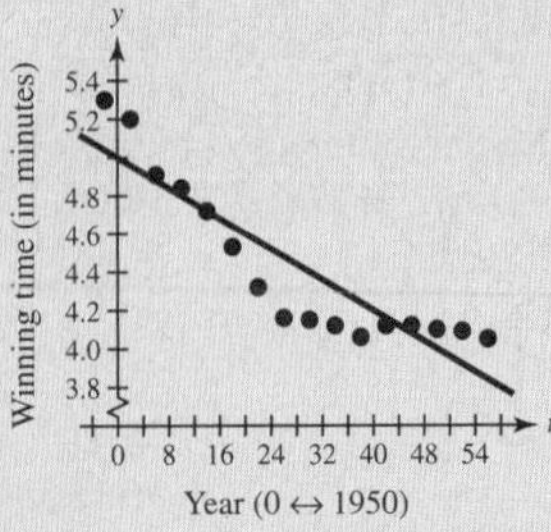

The model is not a good fit. Answers will vary.

13.
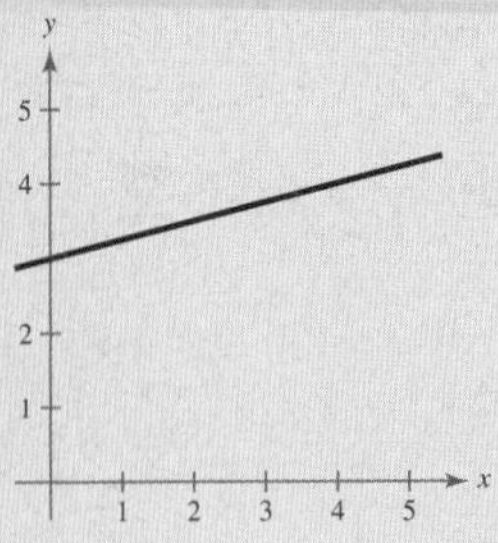

$y = \frac{1}{4}x + 3$

14.
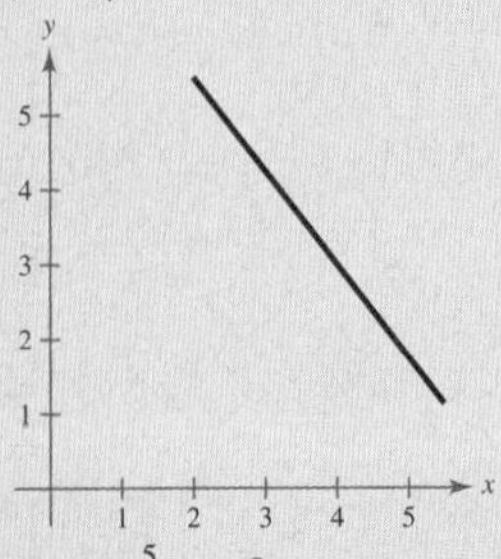

$y = -\frac{5}{4}x + 8$

15.
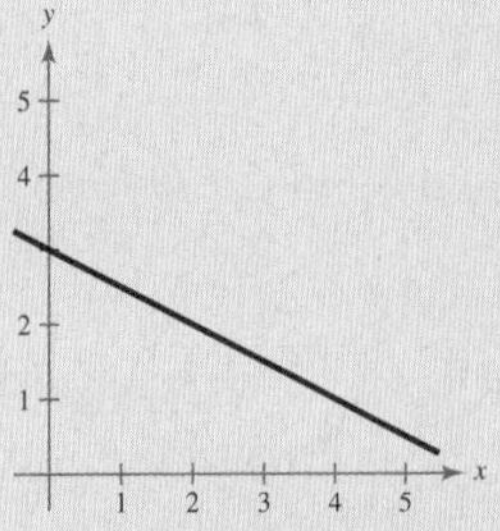

$y = -\frac{1}{2}x + 3$

16.
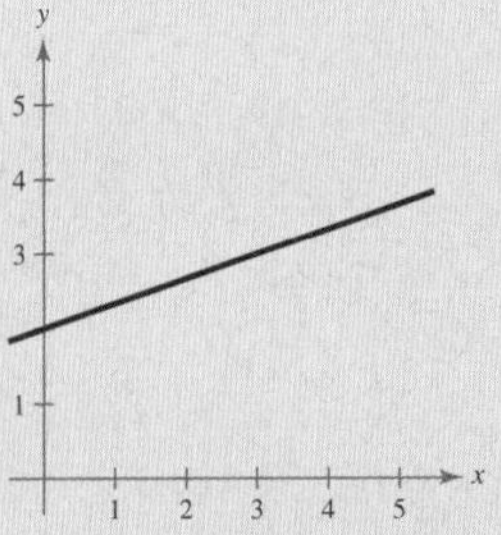

$y = \frac{1}{3}x + 2$

17. SPORTS The lengths (in feet) of the winning men's discus throws in the Olympics from 1920 through 2008 are listed below. (Source: International Olympic Committee) See margin.

1920	146.6	1956	184.9	1984	218.5
1924	151.3	1960	194.2	1988	225.8
1928	155.3	1964	200.1	1992	213.7
1932	162.3	1968	212.5	1996	227.7
1936	165.6	1972	211.3	2000	227.3
1948	173.2	1976	221.5	2004	229.3
1952	180.5	1980	218.7	2008	225.8

(a) Sketch a scatter plot of the data. Let y represent the length of the winning discus throw (in feet) and let $t = 20$ represent 1920.

(b) Use a straightedge to sketch the best-fitting line through the points and find an equation of the line.

(c) Use the *regression* feature of a graphing utility to find the least squares regression line that fits the data.

(d) Compare the linear model you found in part (b) with the linear model given by the graphing utility in part (c).

(e) Use the models from parts (b) and (c) to estimate the winning men's discus throw in the year 2012.

18. SALES The total sales (in billions of dollars) for Coca-Cola Enterprises from 2000 through 2007 are listed below. (Source: Coca-Cola Enterprises, Inc.) (a)–(c), (e). See margin.

2000	14.750	2004	18.185
2001	15.700	2005	18.706
2002	16.899	2006	19.804
2003	17.330	2007	20.936

(a) Sketch a scatter plot of the data. Let y represent the total revenue (in billions of dollars) and let $t = 0$ represent 2000.

(b) Use a straightedge to sketch the best-fitting line through the points and find an equation of the line.

(c) Use the *regression* feature of a graphing utility to find the least squares regression line that fits the data.

(d) Compare the linear model you found in part (b) with the linear model given by the graphing utility in part (c). The models are similar.

(e) Use the models from parts (b) and (c) to estimate the sales of Coca-Cola Enterprises in 2008.

(f) Use your school's library, the Internet, or some other reference source to analyze the accuracy of the estimate in part (e). Answers will vary.

19. DATA ANALYSIS: BROADWAY SHOWS The table shows the annual gross ticket sales S (in millions of dollars) for Broadway shows in New York City from 1995 through 2006. (Source: The League of American Theatres and Producers, Inc.) (a), (c)–(e). See margin.

Year	Sales, S
1995	406
1996	436
1997	499
1998	558
1999	588
2000	603
2001	666
2002	643
2003	721
2004	771
2005	769
2006	862

(a) Use a graphing utility to create a scatter plot of the data. Let $t = 5$ represent 1995.

(b) Use the *regression* feature of a graphing utility to find the equation of the least squares regression line that fits the data. $S = 38.3t + 224$

(c) Use the graphing utility to graph the scatter plot you created in part (a) and the model you found in part (b) in the same viewing window. How closely does the model represent the data?

(d) Use the model to estimate the annual gross ticket sales in 2007 and 2009.

(e) Interpret the meaning of the slope of the linear model in the context of the problem.

20. DATA ANALYSIS: TELEVISION SETS The table shows the numbers N (in millions) of television sets in U.S. households from 2000 through 2006. (Source: Television Bureau of Advertising, Inc.)

Year	Television sets, N
2000	245
2001	248
2002	254
2003	260
2004	268
2005	287
2006	301

18. (a) and (b)

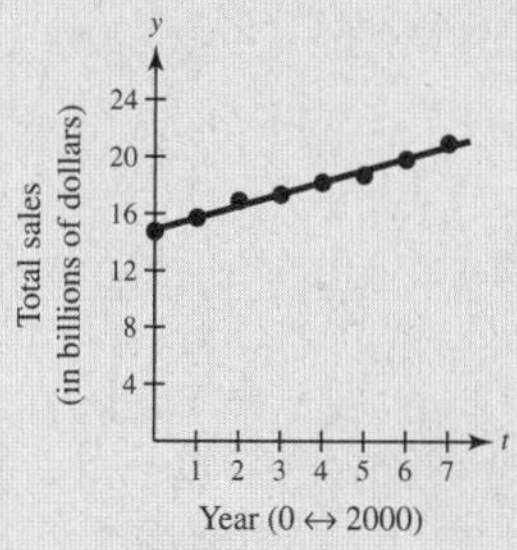

$y \approx 0.85t + 15$

(c) $y = 0.835t + 14.868$

(e) Part (b): \$21.8 billion;
Part (c): \$21.548 billion

19. (a)

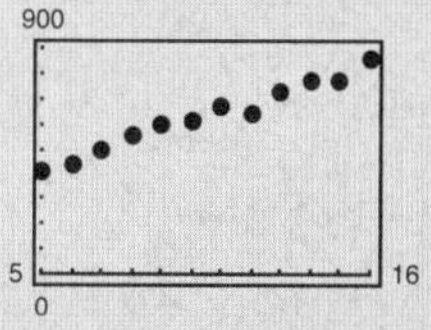

(c)

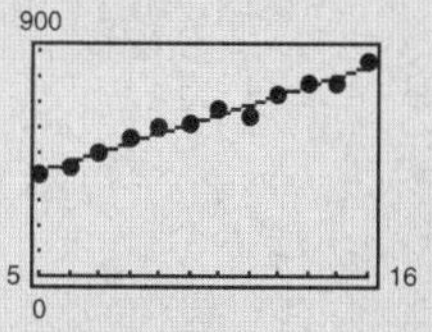

The model is a good fit.

(d) 2007: \$875.1 million;
2009: \$951.7 million

(e) Each year the annual gross ticket sales for Broadway shows in New York City increase by \$38.3 million.

17. See Additional Answers beginning on page AA1.

20. (a) $N = 9.29t + 238.29$

(b)

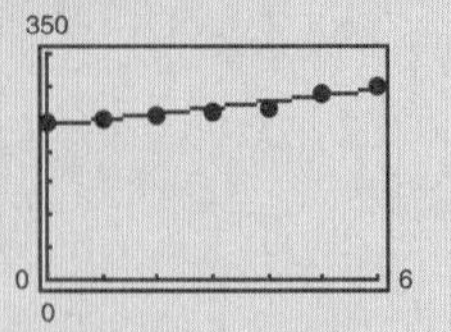

The model is a good fit.

(c) 312.6 million

(d) Answers will vary.

23.

x	2	4	6	8	10
$y = kx^2$	4	16	36	64	100

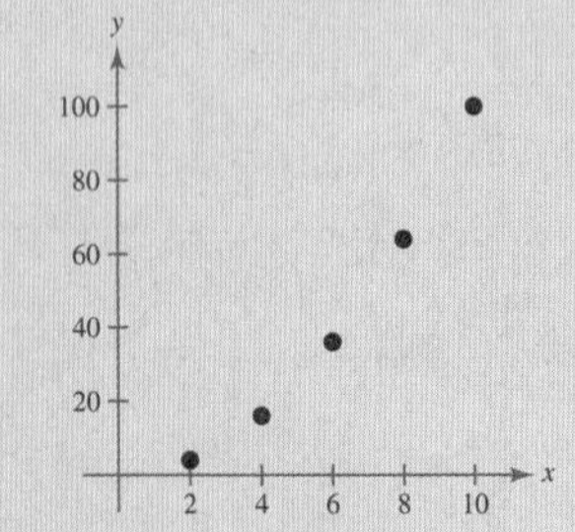

24.

x	2	4	6	8	10
$y = kx^2$	8	32	72	128	200

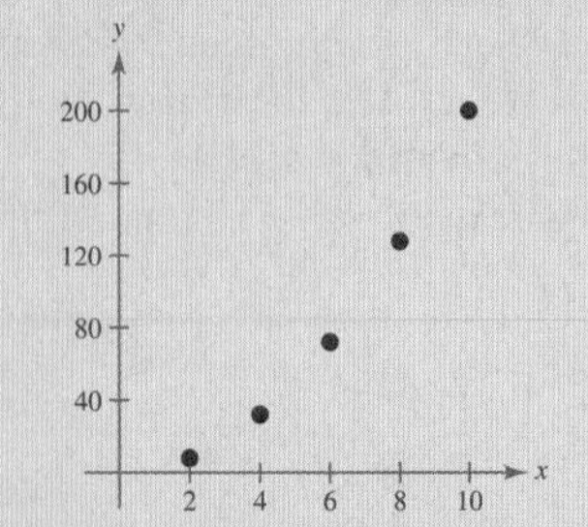

25.

x	2	4	6	8	10
$y = kx^2$	2	8	18	32	50

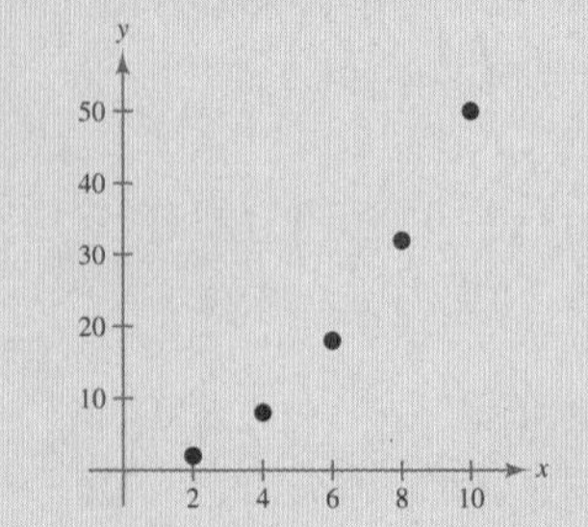

(a)–(d). See margin.

(a) Use the *regression* feature of a graphing utility to find the equation of the least squares regression line that fits the data. Let $t = 0$ represent 2000.

(b) Use the graphing utility to create a scatter plot of the data. Then graph the model you found in part (a) and the scatter plot in the same viewing window. How closely does the model represent the data?

(c) Use the model to estimate the number of television sets in U.S. households in 2008.

(d) Use your school's library, the Internet, or some other reference source to analyze the accuracy of the estimate in part (c).

THINK ABOUT IT In Exercises 21 and 22, use the graph to determine whether y varies directly as some power of x or inversely as some power of x. Explain.

21. Inversely

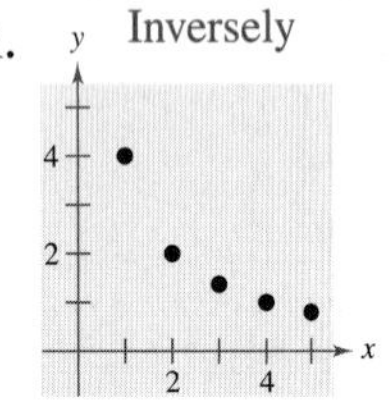

22. Directly

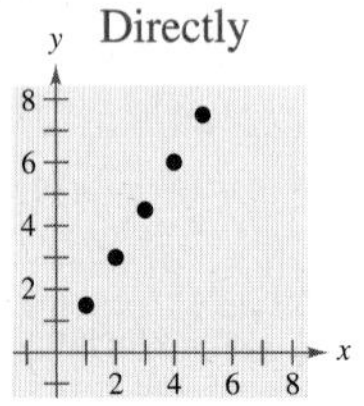

In Exercises 23–26, use the given value of k to complete the table for the direct variation model

$y = kx^2$. 23–26. See margin.

Plot the points on a rectangular coordinate system.

x	2	4	6	8	10
$y = kx^2$					

23. $k = 1$ **24.** $k = 2$

25. $k = \frac{1}{2}$ **26.** $k = \frac{1}{4}$

In Exercises 27–30, use the given value of k to complete the table for the inverse variation model

$$y = \frac{k}{x^2}.$$

Plot the points on a rectangular coordinate system.

x	2	4	6	8	10
$y = \frac{k}{x^2}$					

27–30. See margin.

27. $k = 2$ **28.** $k = 5$

29. $k = 10$ **30.** $k = 20$

In Exercises 31–34, determine whether the variation model is of the form $y = kx$ or $y = k/x$, and find k. Then write a model that relates y and x.

31. $y = \frac{5}{x}$

x	5	10	15	20	25
y	1	$\frac{1}{2}$	$\frac{1}{3}$	$\frac{1}{4}$	$\frac{1}{5}$

32. $y = \frac{2}{5}x$

x	5	10	15	20	25
y	2	4	6	8	10

33. $y = -\frac{7}{10}x$

x	5	10	15	20	25
y	−3.5	−7	−10.5	−14	−17.5

34. $y = \frac{120}{x}$

x	5	10	15	20	25
y	24	12	8	6	$\frac{24}{5}$

DIRECT VARIATION In Exercises 35–38, assume that y is directly proportional to x. Use the given x-value and y-value to find a linear model that relates y and x.

35. $x = 5, y = 12$ $y = \frac{12}{5}x$ **36.** $x = 2, y = 14$ $y = 7x$

37. $x = 10, y = 2050$ $y = 205x$ **38.** $x = 6, y = 580$ $y = \frac{290}{3}x$

39. SIMPLE INTEREST The simple interest on an investment is directly proportional to the amount of the investment. By investing \$3250 in a certain bond issue, you obtained an interest payment of \$113.75 after 1 year. Find a mathematical model that gives the interest I for this bond issue after 1 year in terms of the amount invested P. $I = 0.035P$

40. SIMPLE INTEREST The simple interest on an investment is directly proportional to the amount of the investment. By investing \$6500 in a municipal bond, you obtained an interest payment of \$211.25 after 1 year. Find a mathematical model that gives the interest I for this municipal bond after 1 year in terms of the amount invested P. $I = 0.0325P$

See margin. **41. MEASUREMENT** On a yardstick with scales in inches and centimeters, you notice that 13 inches is approximately the same length as 33 centimeters. Use this information to find a mathematical model that relates centimeters y to inches x. Then use the model to find the numbers of centimeters in 10 inches and 20 inches.

42. MEASUREMENT When buying gasoline, you notice that 14 gallons of gasoline is approximately the same amount of gasoline as 53 liters. Use this information to find a linear model that relates liters y to gallons x. Then use the model to find the numbers of liters in 5 gallons and 25 gallons.

Model: $y = \frac{53}{14}x$; 18.9 L, 94.6 L

26.

x	2	4	6	8	10
$y = kx^2$	1	4	9	16	25

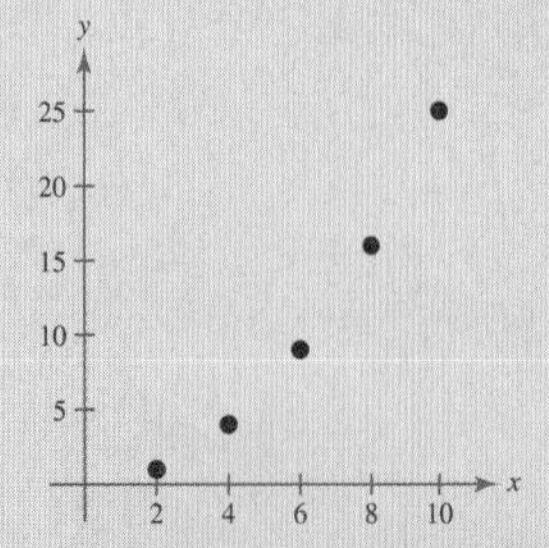

41. Model: $y = \frac{33}{13}x$; 25.4 cm, 50.8 cm

27–30. See Additional Answers beginning on page AA1.

$y = 0.0368x$; $8280

43. TAXES Property tax is based on the assessed value of a property. A house that has an assessed value of $150,000 has a property tax of $5520. Find a mathematical model that gives the amount of property tax y in terms of the assessed value x of the property. Use the model to find the property tax on a house that has an assessed value of $225,000.

44. TAXES State sales tax is based on retail price. An item that sells for $189.99 has a sales tax of $11.40. Find a mathematical model that gives the amount of sales tax y in terms of the retail price x. Use the model to find the sales tax on a $639.99 purchase. $y = 0.06x$; $38.40

HOOKE'S LAW In Exercises 45–48, use Hooke's Law for springs, which states that the distance a spring is stretched (or compressed) varies directly as the force on the spring.

45. A force of 265 newtons stretches a spring 0.15 meter (see figure).

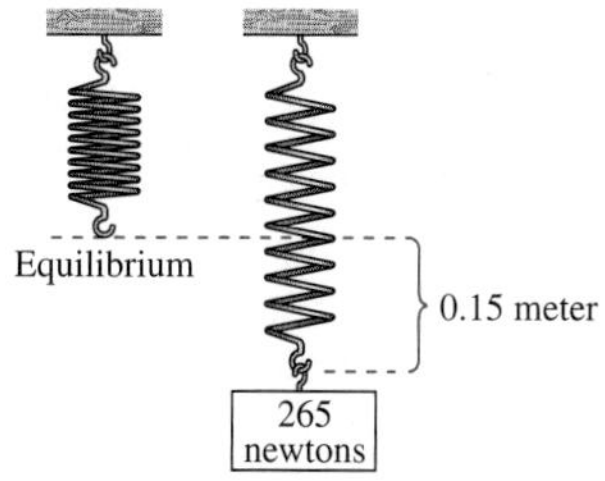

(a) How far will a force of 90 newtons stretch the spring? 0.05 m

(b) What force is required to stretch the spring 0.1 meter? $176\frac{2}{3}$ N

46. $293\frac{1}{3}$ N

46. A force of 220 newtons stretches a spring 0.12 meter. What force is required to stretch the spring 0.16 meter?

47. The coiled spring of a toy supports the weight of a child. The spring is compressed a distance of 1.9 inches by the weight of a 25-pound child. The toy will not work properly if its spring is compressed more than 3 inches. What is the weight of the heaviest child who should be allowed to use the toy? 39.47 lb

48. An overhead garage door has two springs, one on each side of the door (see figure). A force of 15 pounds is required to stretch each spring 1 foot. Because of a pulley system, the springs stretch only one-half the distance the door travels. The door moves a total of 8 feet, and the springs are at their natural length when the door is open. Find the combined lifting force applied to the door by the springs when the door is closed.
Combined lifting force $= 2F = 120$ lb

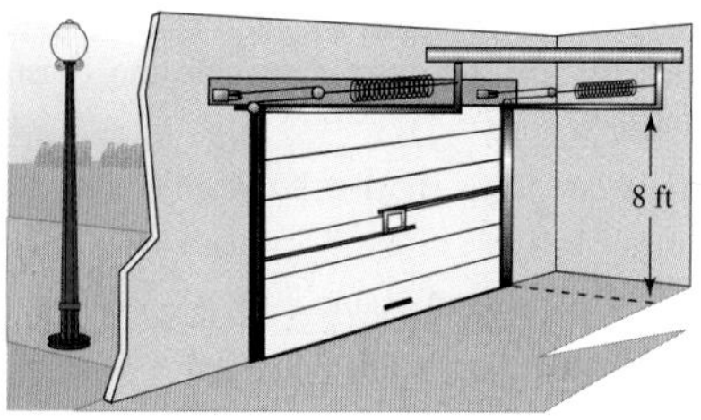

FIGURE FOR 48

In Exercises 49–58, find a mathematical model for the verbal statement.

49. A varies directly as the square of r. $A = kr^2$

50. V varies directly as the cube of e. $V = ke^3$

51. y varies inversely as the square of x. See margin.

52. h varies inversely as the square root of s. See margin.

53. F varies directly as g and inversely as r^2. See margin.

54. z is jointly proportional to the square of x and the cube of y. $z = kx^2y^3$

55. BOYLE'S LAW: For a constant temperature, the pressure P of a gas is inversely proportional to the volume V of the gas. $P = k/V$

56. NEWTON'S LAW OF COOLING: The rate of change R of the temperature of an object is proportional to the difference between the temperature T of the object and the temperature T_e of the environment in which the object is placed. $R = k(T - T_e)$

57. NEWTON'S LAW OF UNIVERSAL GRAVITATION: The gravitational attraction F between two objects of masses m_1 and m_2 is proportional to the product of the masses and inversely proportional to the square of the distance r between the objects. See margin.

58. LOGISTIC GROWTH: The rate of growth R of a population is jointly proportional to the size S of the population and the difference between S and the maximum population size L that the environment can support. $R = kS(L - S)$

In Exercises 59–66, write a sentence using the variation terminology of this section to describe the formula.

59–66. See margin.

59. ***Area of a triangle:*** $A = \frac{1}{2}bh$

60. ***Area of a rectangle:*** $A = lw$

61. ***Area of an equilateral triangle:*** $A = (\sqrt{3}s^2)/4$

62. ***Surface area of a sphere:*** $S = 4\pi r^2$

63. ***Volume of a sphere:*** $V = \frac{4}{3}\pi r^3$

64. ***Volume of a right circular cylinder:*** $V = \pi r^2 h$

65. ***Average speed:*** $r = d/t$

66. ***Free vibrations:*** $\omega = \sqrt{(kg)/W}$

51. $y = \dfrac{k}{x^2}$

52. $h = \dfrac{k}{\sqrt{s}}$

53. $F = \dfrac{kg}{r^2}$

57. $F = \dfrac{km_1m_2}{r^2}$

59. The area of a triangle is jointly proportional to its base and height.

60. The area of a rectangle is jointly proportional to its length and width.

61. The area of an equilateral triangle varies directly as the square of one of its sides.

62. The surface area of a sphere varies directly as the square of its radius.

63. The volume of a sphere varies directly as the cube of its radius.

64. The volume of a right circular cylinder is jointly proportional to its height and the square of its radius.

65. Average speed is directly proportional to the distance and inversely proportional to the time.

66. ω varies directly as the square root of g and inversely as the square root of W.

In Exercises 67–74, find a mathematical model representing the statement. (In each case, determine the constant of proportionality.)

67. A varies directly as r^2. ($A = 9\pi$ when $r = 3$.) $A = \pi r^2$

68. y varies inversely as x. ($y = 3$ when $x = 25$.) See margin.

69. y is inversely proportional to x. ($y = 7$ when $x = 4$.) See margin.

70. z varies jointly as x and y. ($z = 64$ when $x = 4$ and $y = 8$.) $z = 2xy$

71. F is jointly proportional to r and the third power of s. ($F = 4158$ when $r = 11$ and $s = 3$.) $F = 14rs^3$

72. P varies directly as x and inversely as the square of y. ($P = \frac{28}{3}$ when $x = 42$ and $y = 9$.) See margin.

73. z varies directly as the square of x and inversely as y. ($z = 6$ when $x = 6$ and $y = 4$.) See margin.

74. v varies jointly as p and q and inversely as the square of s. ($v = 1.5$ when $p = 4.1$, $q = 6.3$, and $s = 1.2$.) See margin.

ECOLOGY **In Exercises 75 and 76, use the fact that the diameter of the largest particle that can be moved by a stream varies approximately directly as the square of the velocity of the stream.**

75. A stream with a velocity of $\frac{1}{4}$ mile per hour can move coarse sand particles about 0.02 inch in diameter. Approximate the velocity required to carry particles 0.12 inch in diameter. About 0.61 mi/h

76. A stream of velocity v can move particles of diameter d or less. By what factor does d increase when the velocity is doubled? $\dfrac{k(2v)^2}{kv^2} = 4$

RESISTANCE **In Exercises 77 and 78, use the fact that the resistance of a wire carrying an electrical current is directly proportional to its length and inversely proportional to its cross-sectional area.**

77. If #28 copper wire (which has a diameter of 0.0126 inch) has a resistance of 66.17 ohms per thousand feet, what length of #28 copper wire will produce a resistance of 33.5 ohms? 506 ft

78. A 14-foot piece of copper wire produces a resistance of 0.05 ohm. Use the constant of proportionality from Exercise 77 to find the diameter of the wire. 0.054 in.

79. WORK The work W (in joules) done when lifting an object varies jointly with the mass m (in kilograms) of the object and the height h (in meters) that the object is lifted. The work done when a 120-kilogram object is lifted 1.8 meters is 2116.8 joules. How much work is done when lifting a 100-kilogram object 1.5 meters? 1470 J

80. MUSIC The frequency of vibrations of a piano string varies directly as the square root of the tension on the string and inversely as the length of the string. The middle A string has a frequency of 440 vibrations per second. Find the frequency of a string that has 1.25 times as much tension and is 1.2 times as long. 409.95 vibrations/sec

81. FLUID FLOW The velocity v of a fluid flowing in a conduit is inversely proportional to the cross-sectional area of the conduit. (Assume that the volume of the flow per unit of time is held constant.) Determine the change in the velocity of water flowing from a hose when a person places a finger over the end of the hose to decrease its cross-sectional area by 25%. See margin.

82. BEAM LOAD The maximum load that can be safely supported by a horizontal beam varies jointly as the width of the beam and the square of its depth, and inversely as the length of the beam. Determine the changes in the maximum safe load under the following conditions. See margin.

(a) The width and length of the beam are doubled.

(b) The width and depth of the beam are doubled.

(c) All three of the dimensions are doubled.

(d) The depth of the beam is halved.

83. DATA ANALYSIS: OCEAN TEMPERATURES An oceanographer took readings of the water temperatures C (in degrees Celsius) at several depths d (in meters). The data collected are shown in the table. See margin.

Depth, d	Temperature, C
1000	4.2°
2000	1.9°
3000	1.4°
4000	1.2°
5000	0.9°

(a) Sketch a scatter plot of the data.

(b) Does it appear that the data can be modeled by the inverse variation model $C = k/d$? If so, find k for each pair of coordinates.

(c) Determine the mean value of k from part (b) to find the inverse variation model $C = k/d$.

(d) Use a graphing utility to plot the data points and the inverse model from part (c).

(e) Use the model to approximate the depth at which the water temperature is 3°C.

68. $y = \dfrac{75}{x}$

69. $y = \dfrac{28}{x}$

72. $P = \dfrac{18x}{y^2}$

73. $z = \dfrac{2x^2}{3y}$

74. $v = \dfrac{24pq}{287s^2}$

81. The velocity is increased by one-third.

82. (a) The safe load is unchanged.

(b) The safe load is eight times as great.

(c) The safe load is four times as great.

(d) The safe load is one-fourth as great.

83. (a)

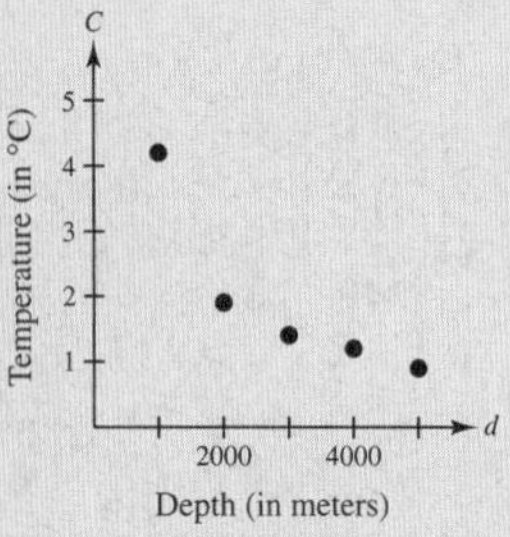

(b) Yes. $k_1 = 4200$, $k_2 = 3800$, $k_3 = 4200$, $k_4 = 4800$, $k_5 = 4500$

(c) $C = \dfrac{4300}{d}$

(d)

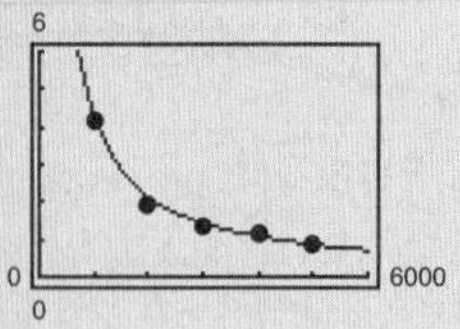

(e) About 1433 m

84. DATA ANALYSIS: PHYSICS EXPERIMENT An experiment in a physics lab requires a student to measure the compressed lengths y (in centimeters) of a spring when various forces of F pounds are applied. The data are shown in the table. See margin.

Force, F	Length, y
0	0
2	1.15
4	2.3
6	3.45
8	4.6
10	5.75
12	6.9

(a) Sketch a scatter plot of the data.

(b) Does it appear that the data can be modeled by Hooke's Law? If so, estimate k. (See Exercises 45–48.)

(c) Use the model in part (b) to approximate the force required to compress the spring 9 centimeters.

85. DATA ANALYSIS: LIGHT INTENSITY A light probe is located x centimeters from a light source, and the intensity y (in microwatts per square centimeter) of the light is measured. The results are shown as ordered pairs (x, y). See margin.

(30, 0.1881) (34, 0.1543) (38, 0.1172)

(42, 0.0998) (46, 0.0775) (50, 0.0645)

A model for the data is $y = 262.76/x^{2.12}$.

(a) Use a graphing utility to plot the data points and the model in the same viewing window.

(b) Use the model to approximate the light intensity 25 centimeters from the light source.

86. ILLUMINATION The illumination from a light source varies inversely as the square of the distance from the light source. When the distance from a light source is doubled, how does the illumination change? Discuss this model in terms of the data given in Exercise 85. Give a possible explanation of the difference. See margin.

EXPLORATION

TRUE OR FALSE? In Exercises 87 and 88, decide whether the statement is true or false. Justify your answer. 87–88. See margin.

87. In the equation for kinetic energy, $E = \frac{1}{2}mv^2$, the amount of kinetic energy E is directly proportional to the mass m of an object and the square of its velocity v.

88. If the correlation coefficient for a least squares regression line is close to -1, the regression line cannot be used to describe the data.

89. Discuss how well the data shown in each scatter plot can be approximated by a linear model. See margin.

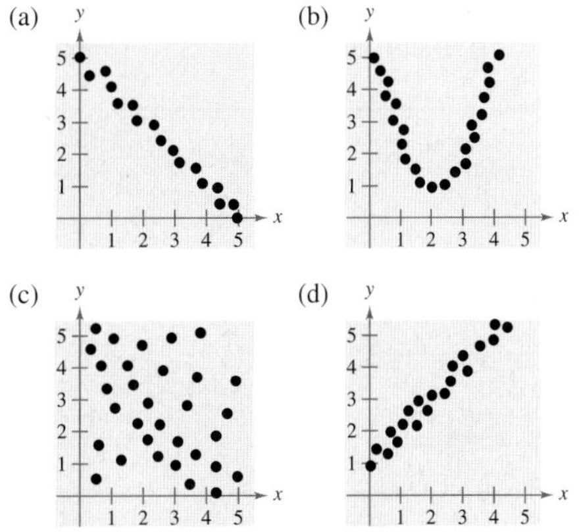

90. WRITING A linear model for predicting prize winnings at a race is based on data for 3 years. Write a paragraph discussing the potential accuracy or inaccuracy of such a model. See margin.

91. WRITING Suppose the constant of proportionality is positive and y varies directly as x. When one of the variables increases, how will the other change? Explain your reasoning. See margin.

92. WRITING Suppose the constant of proportionality is positive and y varies inversely as x. When one of the variables increases, how will the other change? Explain your reasoning. See margin.

93. WRITING See margin.

(a) Given that y varies inversely as the square of x and x is doubled, how will y change? Explain.

(b) Given that y varies directly as the square of x and x is doubled, how will y change? Explain.

94. CAPSTONE The prices of three sizes of pizza at a pizza shop are as follows. See margin.

9-inch: \$8.78, 12-inch: \$11.78, 15-inch: \$14.18

You would expect that the price of a certain size of pizza would be directly proportional to its surface area. Is that the case for this pizza shop? If not, which size of pizza is the best buy?

PROJECT: FRAUD AND IDENTITY THEFT To work an extended application analyzing the numbers of fraud complaints and identity theft victims in the United States in 2007, visit this text's website at *academic.cengage.com*. (Data Source: U.S. Census Bureau)

5 ASSESS AND RETEACH

Daily Homework Quiz

Transparency Available

Available at the Instructor's companion site.

84. (a)

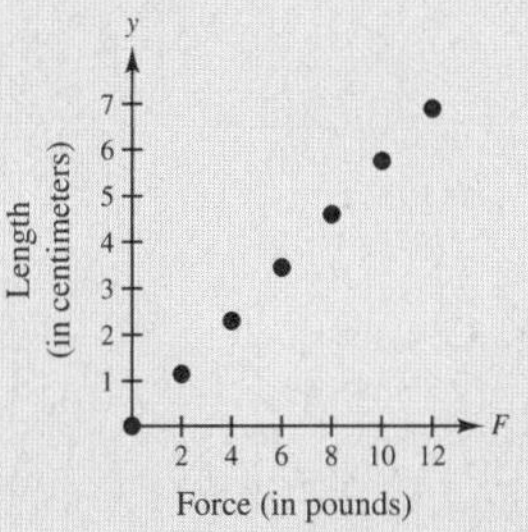

(b) Yes. $k = 0.575$

(c) 15.7 lb

85. (a)

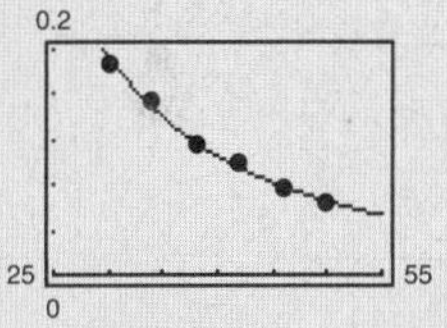

(b) $0.2857\ \mu W/cm^2$

86. The illumination is reduced to one-fourth of its original value. Explanations will vary.

87. False. E is jointly proportional to the mass of an object and the square of its velocity.

88. False. The closer the value of $|r|$ is to 1, the better the fit.

89. (a) Good approximation

(b) Poor approximation

(c) Poor approximation

(d) Good approximation

90. The accuracy is questionable when based on such limited data.

91. As one variable increases, the other variable will also increase.

92. As one variable increases, the other variable will decrease.

93. (a) y will change by a factor of one-fourth.

(b) y will change by a factor of four.

94. No. The 15-inch pizza is the best buy.

1 Chapter Summary

Section	What Did You Learn?	Explanation/Examples	Review Exercises
Section 1.1	Plot points in the Cartesian plane *(p. 2)*.	For an ordered pair (x, y), the x-coordinate is the directed distance from the y-axis to the point, and the y-coordinate is the directed distance from the x-axis to the point.	1–4
	Use the Distance Formula *(p. 4)* and the Midpoint Formula *(p. 5)*.	**Distance Formula:** $d = \sqrt{(x_2 - x_1)^2 + (y_2 - y_1)^2}$ **Midpoint Formula:** Midpoint $= \left(\frac{x_1 + x_2}{2}, \frac{y_1 + y_2}{2}\right)$	5–8
	Use a coordinate plane to model and solve real-life problems *(p. 6)*.	The coordinate plane can be used to find the length of a football pass (See Example 6).	9–12
Section 1.2	Sketch graphs of equations *(p. 13)*, find x- and y-intercepts of graphs *(p. 16)*, and use symmetry to sketch graphs of equations *(p. 17)*.	To graph an equation, make a table of values, plot the points, and connect the points with a smooth curve or line. To find x-intercepts, let y be zero and solve for x. To find y-intercepts, let x be zero and solve for y. Graphs can have symmetry with respect to one of the coordinate axes or with respect to the origin.	13–34
	Find equations of and sketch graphs of circles *(p. 19)*.	The point (x, y) lies on the circle of radius r and center (h, k) if and only if $(x - h)^2 + (y - k)^2 = r^2$.	35–42
	Use graphs of equations in solving real-life problems *(p. 20)*.	The graph of an equation can be used to estimate the recommended weight for a man. (See Example 9.)	43, 44
Section 1.3	Use slope to graph linear equations in two variables *(p. 24)*.	The graph of the equation $y = mx + b$ is a line whose slope is m and whose y-intercept is $(0, b)$.	45–48
	Find the slope of a line given two points on the line *(p. 26)*.	The slope m of the nonvertical line through (x_1, y_1) and (x_2, y_2) is $m = (y_2 - y_1)/(x_2 - x_1)$, where $x_1 \neq x_2$.	49–52
	Write linear equations in two variables *(p. 28)*.	The equation of the line with slope m passing through the point (x_1, y_1) is $y - y_1 = m(x - x_1)$.	53–60
	Use slope to identify parallel and perpendicular lines *(p. 29)*.	**Parallel lines:** Slopes are equal. **Perpendicular lines:** Slopes are negative reciprocals of each other.	61, 62
	Use slope and linear equations in two variables to model and solve real-life problems *(p. 30)*.	A linear equation in two variables can be used to describe the book value of exercise equipment in a given year. (See Example 7.)	63, 64
Section 1.4	Determine whether relations between two variables are functions *(p. 39)*.	A function f from a set A (domain) to a set B (range) is a relation that assigns to each element x in the set A exactly one element y in the set B.	65–68
	Use function notation, evaluate functions, and find domains *(p. 41)*.	**Equation:** $f(x) = 5 - x^2$ **$f(2)$:** $f(2) = 5 - 2^2 = 1$ **Domain of $f(x) = 5 - x^2$:** All real numbers	69–74
	Use functions to model and solve real-life problems *(p. 45)*.	A function can be used to model the number of alternative-fueled vehicles in the United States (See Example 10.)	75, 76
	Evaluate difference quotients *(p. 46)*.	**Difference quotient:** $[f(x + h) - f(x)]/h, h \neq 0$	77, 78
Section 1.5	Use the Vertical Line Test for functions *(p. 55)*.	A graph represents a function if and only if no *vertical* line intersects the graph at more than one point.	79–82
	Find the zeros of functions *(p. 56)*.	**Zeros of $f(x)$:** x-values for which $f(x) = 0$	83–86

Section	What Did You Learn?	Explanation/Examples	Review Exercises
Section 1.5	Determine intervals on which functions are increasing or decreasing *(p. 57)*, find relative minimum and maximum values *(p. 58)*, and find the average rate of change of a function *(p. 59)*.	To determine whether a function is increasing, decreasing, or constant on an interval, evaluate the function for several values of x. The points at which the behavior of a function changes can help determine the relative minimum or relative maximum. The average rate of change between any two points is the slope of the line (secant line) through the two points.	87–96
	Identify even and odd functions *(p. 60)*.	**Even:** For each x in the domain of f, $f(-x) = f(x)$. **Odd:** For each x in the domain of f, $f(-x) = -f(x)$.	97–100
Section 1.6	Identify and graph different types of functions *(p. 66)*, and recognize graphs of parent function *(p. 70)*.	**Linear:** $f(x) = ax + b$; **Squaring:** $f(x) = x^2$; **Cubic:** $f(x) = x^3$; **Square Root:** $f(x) = \sqrt{x}$; **Reciprocal:** $f(x) = 1/x$ Eight of the most commonly used functions in algebra are shown in Figure 1.75.	101–114
Section 1.7	Use vertical and horizontal shifts *(p. 73)*, reflections *(p. 75)*, and nonrigid transformations *(p. 77)* to sketch graphs of functions.	**Vertical shifts:** $h(x) = f(x) + c$ or $h(x) = f(x) - c$ **Horizontal shifts:** $h(x) = f(x - c)$ or $h(x) = f(x + c)$ **Reflection in *x*-axis:** $h(x) = -f(x)$ **Reflection in *y*-axis:** $h(x) = f(-x)$ **Nonrigid transformations:** $h(x) = cf(x)$ or $h(x) = f(cx)$	115–128
Section 1.8	Add, subtract, multiply, and divide functions *(p. 83)*, and find the compositions of functions *(p. 85)*.	$(f + g)(x) = f(x) + g(x)$ $(f - g)(x) = f(x) - g(x)$ $(fg)(x) = f(x) \cdot g(x)$ $(f/g)(x) = f(x)/g(x), g(x) \neq 0$ **Composition of Functions:** $(f \circ g)(x) = f(g(x))$	129–134
	Use combinations and compositions of functions to model and solve real-life problems *(p. 87)*.	A composite function can be used to represent the number of bacteria in food as a function of the amount of time the food has been out of refrigeration. (See Example 8.)	135, 136
Section 1.9	Find inverse functions informally and verify that two functions are inverse functions of each other *(p. 92)*.	Let f and g be two functions such that $f(g(x)) = x$ for every x in the domain of g and $g(f(x)) = x$ for every x in the domain of f. Under these conditions, the function g is the inverse function of the function f.	137, 138
	Use graphs of functions to determine whether functions have inverse functions *(p. 94)*.	If the point (a, b) lies on the graph of f, then the point (b, a) must lie on the graph of f^{-1}, and vice versa. In short, f^{-1} is a reflection of f in the line $y = x$.	139, 140
	Use the Horizontal Line Test to determine if functions are one-to-one *(p. 95)*.	**Horizontal Line Test for Inverse Functions** A function f has an inverse function if and only if no *horizontal* line intersects f at more than one point.	141–144
	Find inverse functions algebraically *(p.96)*.	To find inverse functions, replace $f(x)$ by y, interchange the roles of x and y, and solve for y. Replace y by $f^{-1}(x)$.	145–150
Section 1.10	Use mathematical models to approximate sets of data points *(p. 102)*, and use the *regression* feature of a graphing utility to find the equation of a least squares regression line *(p. 103)*.	To see how well a model fits a set of data, compare the actual values and model values of y. The sum of square differences is the sum of the squares of the differences between actual data values and model values. The least squares regression line is the linear model with the least sum of square differences.	151, 152
	Write mathematical models for direct variation, direct variation as an *n*th power, inverse variation, and joint variation *(pp. 104–107)*.	**Direct variation:** $y = kx$ for some nonzero constant k **Direct variation as an *n*th power:** $y = kx^n$ for some constant k **Inverse variation:** $y = k/x$ for some constant k **Joint variation:** $z = kxy$ for some constant k	153–158

1 Review Exercises

See www.CalcChat.com for worked-out solutions to odd-numbered exercises.

1.1 In Exercises 1 and 2, plot the points in the Cartesian plane. 1–2. See margin.

1. $(5, 5), (-2, 0), (-3, 6), (-1, -7)$

2. $(0, 6), (8, 1), (4, -2), (-3, -3)$

In Exercises 3 and 4, determine the quadrant(s) in which (x, y) is located so that the condition(s) is (are) satisfied.

3. $x > 0$ and $y = -2$ IV **4.** $xy = 4$ I or III

In Exercises 5–8, (a) plot the points, (b) find the distance between the points, and (c) find the midpoint of the line segment joining the points. 5–8. See margin.

5. $(-3, 8), (1, 5)$

6. $(-2, 6), (4, -3)$

7. $(5.6, 0), (0, 8.2)$

8. $(1.8, 7.4), (-0.6, -14.5)$

In Exercises 9 and 10, the polygon is shifted to a new position in the plane. Find the coordinates of the vertices of the polygon in its new position.

9. Original coordinates of vertices:

$(4, 8), (6, 8), (4, 3), (6, 3)$ $(0, 0), (2, 0), (0, -5), (2, -5)$

Shift: eight units downward, four units to the left

10. Original coordinates of vertices: $(-2, 4), (1, 6),$

$(0, 1), (3, 3), (0, 5), (-3, 3)$ $(-2, 8), (-5, 6)$

Shift: three units upward, two units to the left

11. SALES Starbucks had annual sales of \$2.17 billion in 2000 and \$10.38 billion in 2008. Use the Midpoint Formula to estimate the sales in 2004. (Source: Starbucks Corp.) \$6.275 billion

12. METEOROLOGY The apparent temperature is a measure of relative discomfort to a person from heat and high humidity. The table shows the actual temperatures x (in degrees Fahrenheit) versus the apparent temperatures y (in degrees Fahrenheit) for a relative humidity of 75%.

x	70	75	80	85	90	95	100
y	70	77	85	95	109	130	150

See margin.

(a) Sketch a scatter plot of the data shown in the table.

(b) Find the change in the apparent temperature when the actual temperature changes from 70°F to 100°F. 80°F

1.2 In Exercises 13–16, complete a table of values. Use the solution points to sketch the graph of the equation.

13. $y = 3x - 5$ **14.** $y = -\frac{1}{2}x + 2$

15. $y = x^2 - 3x$ **16.** $y = 2x^2 - x - 9$

13–16. See margin.

In Exercises 17–22, sketch the graph *by hand*.

17. $y - 2x - 3 = 0$ **18.** $3x + 2y + 6 = 0$

19. $y = \sqrt{5 - x}$ **20.** $y = \sqrt{x + 2}$

21. $y + 2x^2 = 0$ **22.** $y = x^2 - 4x$

17–22. See margin.

In Exercises 23–26, find the x- and y-intercepts of the graph of the equation. 23–26. See margin.

23. $y = 2x + 7$ **24.** $y = |x + 1| - 3$

25. $y = (x - 3)^2 - 4$ **26.** $y = x\sqrt{4 - x^2}$

In Exercises 27–34, identify any intercepts and test for symmetry. Then sketch the graph of the equation.

27. $y = -4x + 1$ **28.** $y = 5x - 6$

29. $y = 5 - x^2$ **30.** $y = x^2 - 10$

31. $y = x^3 + 3$ **32.** $y = -6 - x^3$

33. $y = \sqrt{x + 5}$ **34.** $y = |x| + 9$

27–34. See margin.

In Exercises 35–40, find the center and radius of the circle and sketch its graph. 35–40. See margin.

35. $x^2 + y^2 = 9$ **36.** $x^2 + y^2 = 4$

37. $(x + 2)^2 + y^2 = 16$

38. $x^2 + (y - 8)^2 = 81$

39. $\left(x - \frac{1}{2}\right)^2 + (y + 1)^2 = 36$

40. $(x + 4)^2 + \left(y - \frac{3}{2}\right)^2 = 100$

41. Find the standard form of the equation of the circle for which the endpoints of a diameter are $(0, 0)$ and $(4, -6)$. $(x - 2)^2 + (y + 3)^2 = 13$

42. Find the standard form of the equation of the circle for which the endpoints of a diameter are $(-2, -3)$ and $(4, -10)$. $(x - 1)^2 + \left(y + \frac{13}{2}\right)^2 = \frac{85}{4}$

43. NUMBER OF STORES The numbers N of Walgreen stores for the years 2000 through 2008 can be approximated by the model

$$N = 439.9t + 2987, \quad 0 \le t \le 8$$

where t represents the year, with $t = 0$ corresponding to 2000. (Source: Walgreen Co.)

(a) Sketch a graph of the model. See margin.

(b) Use the graph to estimate the year in which the number of stores was 6500. 2008

1.

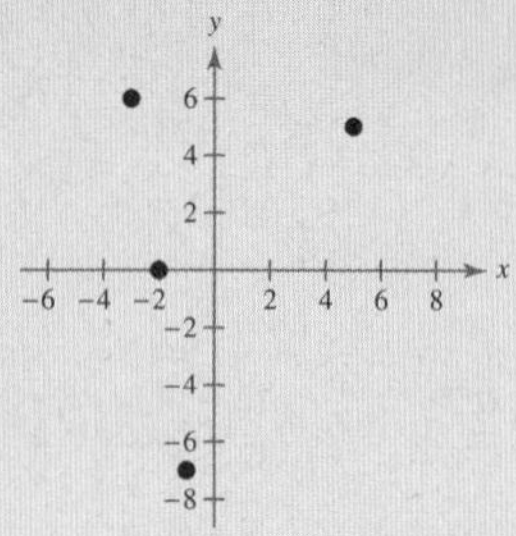

2.

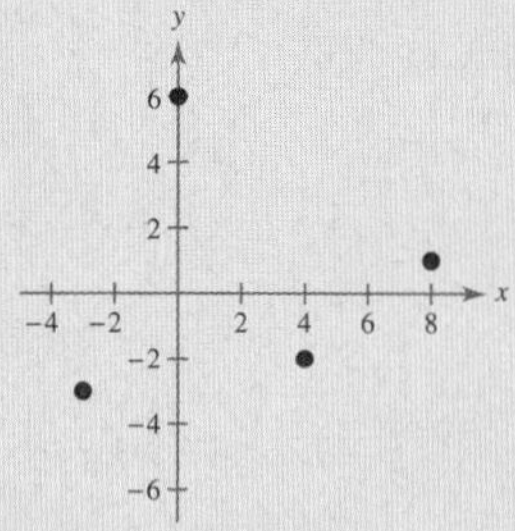

5. (a)

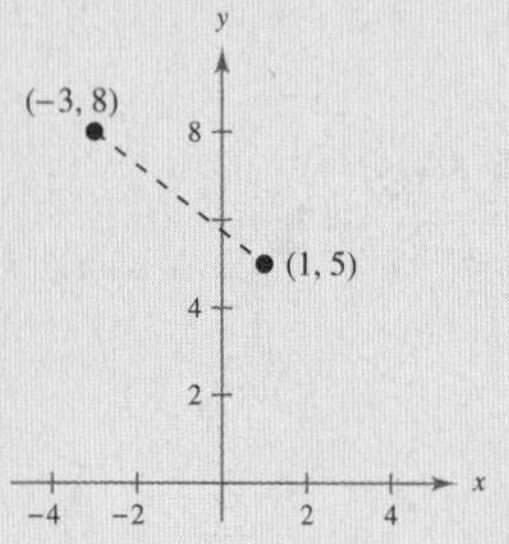

(b) 5 (c) $\left(-1, \frac{13}{2}\right)$

6. (a)

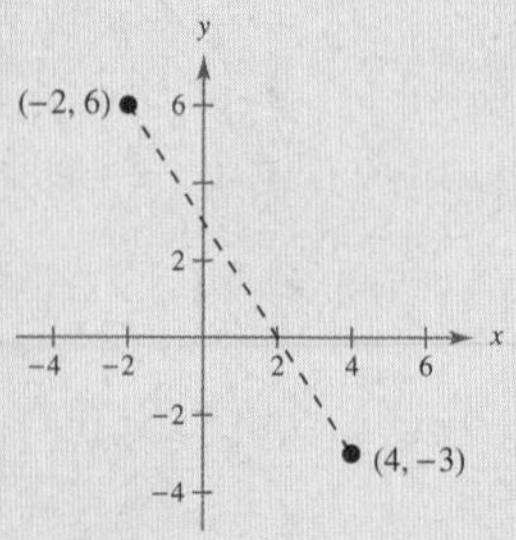

(b) $3\sqrt{13}$ (c) $\left(1, \frac{3}{2}\right)$

7. (a)

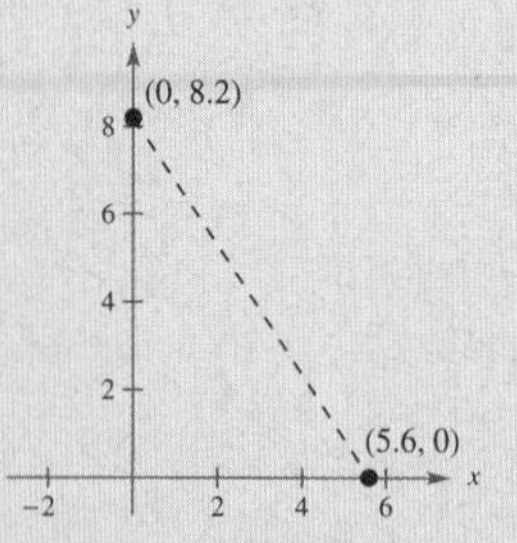

(b) $\sqrt{98.6}$ (c) $(2.8, 4.1)$

8. (a)

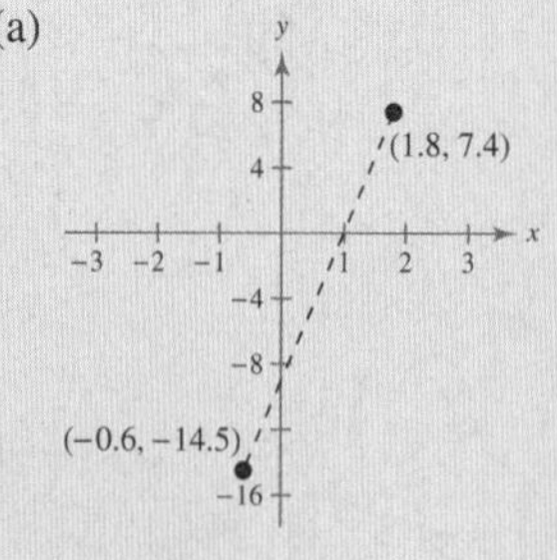

(b) $\sqrt{485.37}$

(c) $(0.6, -3.55)$

12. (a)

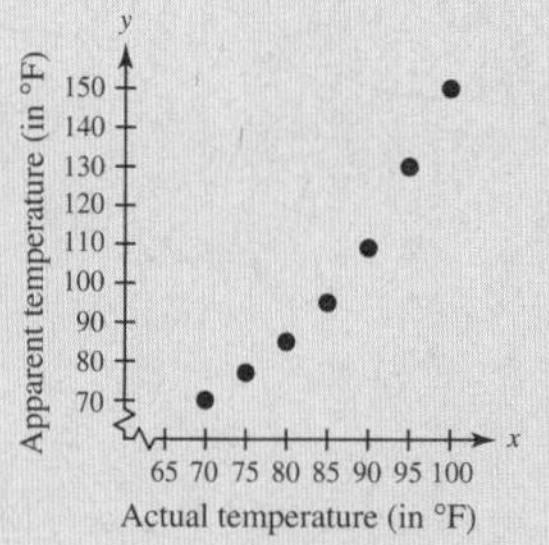

13–40, 43(a). See Additional Answers beginning on page AA1.

44. PHYSICS The force F (in pounds) required to stretch a spring x inches from its natural length (see figure) is

$F = \frac{5}{4}x,\ 0 \le x \le 20.$

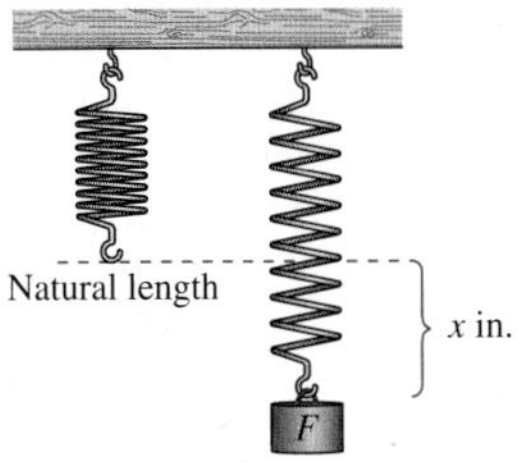

(a) Use the model to complete the table.

x	0	4	8	12	16	20
Force, F	0	5	10	15	20	25

(b) Sketch a graph of the model. See margin.

(c) Use the graph to estimate the force necessary to stretch the spring 10 inches. 12.5 lb

1.3 In Exercises 45–48, find the slope and y-intercept (if possible) of the equation of the line. Sketch the line. 45–48. See margin.

45. $y = 6$ **46.** $x = -3$

47. $y = 3x + 13$ **48.** $y = -10x + 9$

In Exercises 49–52, plot the points and find the slope of the line passing through the pair of points. 49–52. See margin.

49. $(6, 4), (-3, -4)$ **50.** $(\frac{3}{2}, 1), (5, \frac{5}{2})$

51. $(-4.5, 6), (2.1, 3)$ **52.** $(-3, 2), (8, 2)$

In Exercises 53–56, find the slope-intercept form of the equation of the line that passes through the given point and has the indicated slope. Sketch the line. 53–56. See margin.

Point	*Slope*
53. $(3, 0)$	$m = \frac{2}{3}$
54. $(-8, 5)$	$m = 0$
55. $(10, -3)$	$m = -\frac{1}{2}$
56. $(12, -6)$	m is undefined.

In Exercises 57–60, find the slope-intercept form of the equation of the line passing through the points.

57. $(0, 0), (0, 10)$ $x = 0$ **58.** $(2, -1), (4, -1)$ $y = -1$

59. $(-1, 0), (6, 2)$ **60.** $(11, -2), (6, -1)$

$y = \frac{2}{7}x + \frac{2}{7}$ $y = -\frac{1}{5}x + \frac{1}{5}$

In Exercises 61 and 62, write the slope-intercept forms of the equations of the lines through the given point (a) parallel to the given line and (b) perpendicular to the given line.

Point	*Line*
61. $(3, -2)$	$5x - 4y = 8$
62. $(-8, 3)$	$2x + 3y = 5$

61. (a) $y = \frac{5}{4}x - \frac{23}{4}$ (b) $y = -\frac{4}{5}x + \frac{2}{5}$

62. (a) $y = -\frac{2}{3}x - \frac{7}{3}$ (b) $y = \frac{3}{2}x + 15$

RATE OF CHANGE In Exercises 63 and 64, you are given the dollar value of a product in 2010 and the rate at which the value of the product is expected to change during the next 5 years. Use this information to write a linear equation that gives the dollar value V of the product in terms of the year t. (Let $t = 10$ represent 2010.) 63–64. See margin.

	2010 Value	*Rate*
63.	$12,500	$850 decrease per year
64.	$72.95	$5.15 increase per year

1.4 In Exercises 65–68, determine whether the equation represents y as a function of x.

65. $16x - y^4 = 0$ No **66.** $2x - y - 3 = 0$ Yes

67. $y = \sqrt{1 - x}$ Yes **68.** $|y| = x + 2$ No

In Exercises 69 and 70, evaluate the function at each specified value of the independent variable and simplify.

69. $f(x) = x^2 + 1$

(a) $f(2)$ 5 (b) $f(-4)$ 17 (c) $f(t^2)$ $t^4 + 1$ (d) $f(t + 1)$ $t^2 + 2t + 2$

70. $h(x) = \begin{cases} 2x + 1, & x \le -1 \\ x^2 + 2, & x > -1 \end{cases}$

(a) $h(-2)$ -3 (b) $h(-1)$ -1 (c) $h(0)$ 2 (d) $h(2)$ 6

In Exercises 71–74, find the domain of the function. Verify your result with a graph. 71–74. See margin.

71. $f(x) = \sqrt{25 - x^2}$

72. $g(s) = \dfrac{5s + 5}{3s - 9}$

73. $h(x) = \dfrac{x}{x^2 - x - 6}$

74. $h(t) = |t + 1|$

75. PHYSICS The velocity of a ball projected upward from ground level is given by $v(t) = -32t + 48$, where t is the time in seconds and v is the velocity in feet per second.

(a) Find the velocity when $t = 1$. 16 ft/sec

(b) Find the time when the ball reaches its maximum height. [*Hint:* Find the time when $v(t) = 0$.] 1.5 sec

(c) Find the velocity when $t = 2$. -16 ft/sec

44. (b)

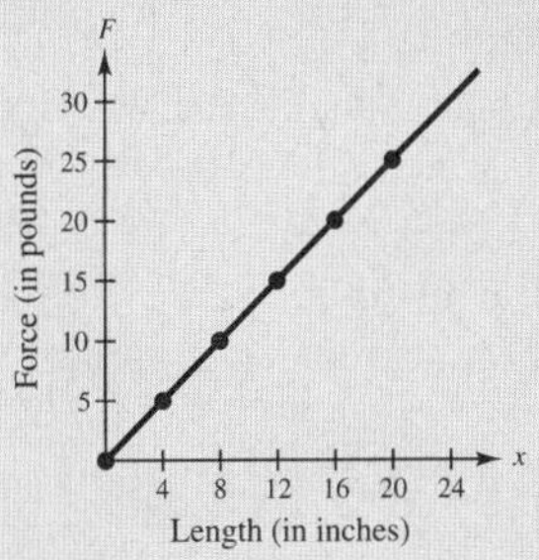

45. Slope: 0
y-intercept: 6

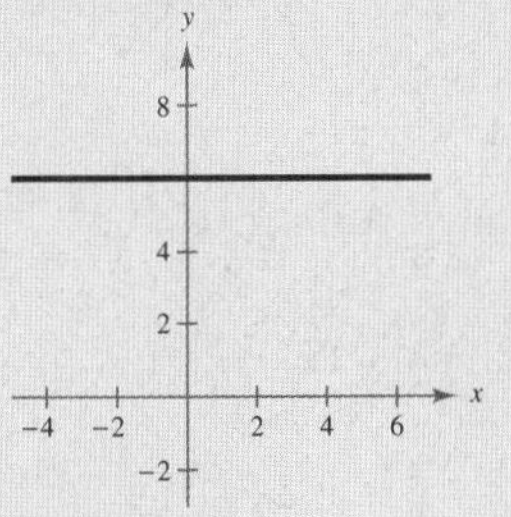

46. Slope: undefined
y-intercept: none

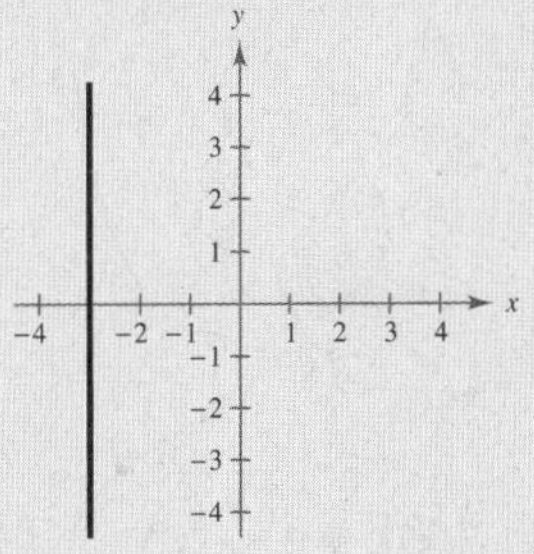

47. Slope: 3
y-intercept: 13

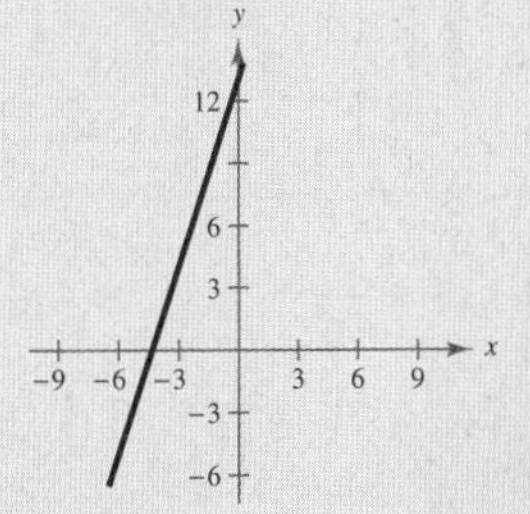

48. Slope: -10
y-intercept: 9

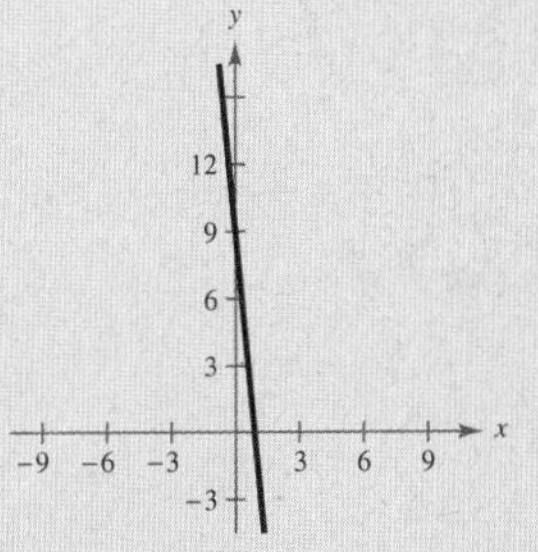

49.

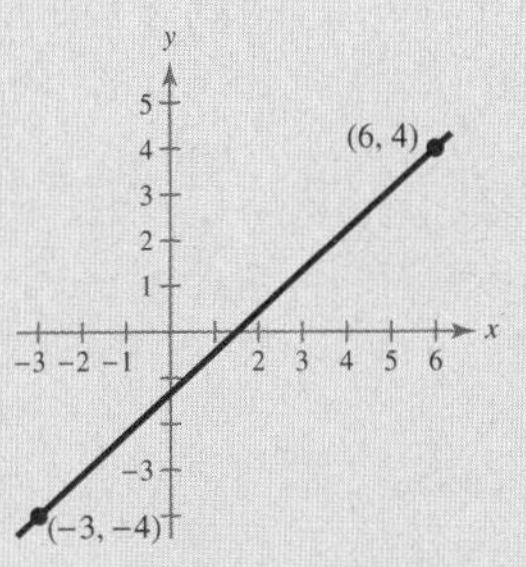

$m = \frac{8}{9}$

50.

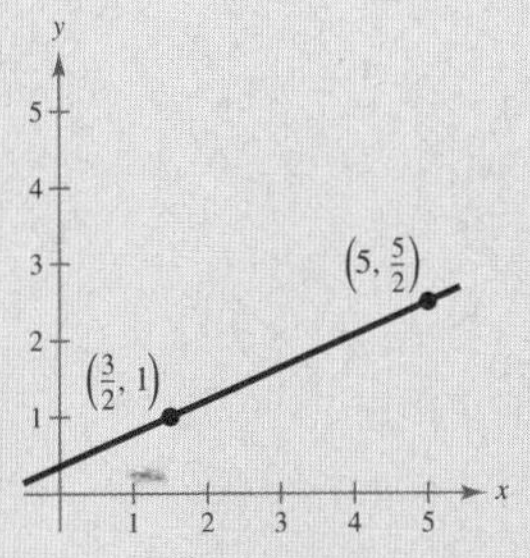

$m = \frac{3}{7}$

63. $V = -850t + 21{,}000,\quad 10 \le t \le 15$

64. $V = 5.15t + 21.45,\quad 10 \le t \le 15$

51–56, 71–74. See Additional Answers beginning on page AA1.

76. (a) $f(x) = 0.4(50 - x) + x$
$= 20 + 0.6x$
(b) Domain: $0 \le x \le 50$;
Range: $20 \le y \le 50$
(c) $8\frac{1}{3}$ L

77. $4x + 2h + 3, \quad h \ne 0$

78. $3x^2 + 3xh + h^2 - 10x - 5h + 1, \quad h \ne 0$

87.

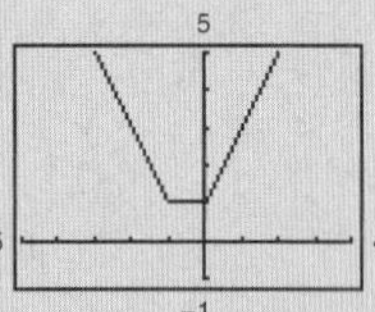

Increasing on $(0, \infty)$
Decreasing on $(-\infty, -1)$
Constant on $(-1, 0)$

88.

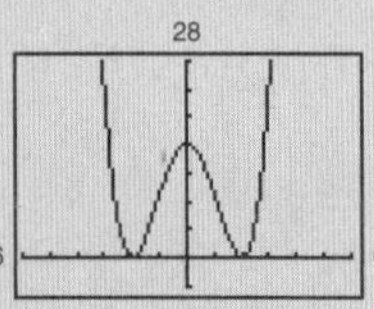

Increasing on $(-2, 0)$ and $(2, \infty)$
Decreasing on $(-\infty, -2)$ and $(0, 2)$

89.

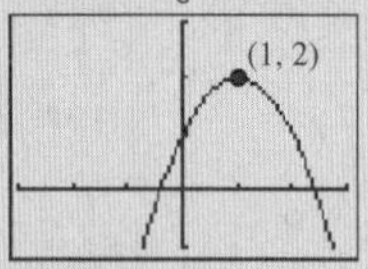

90.

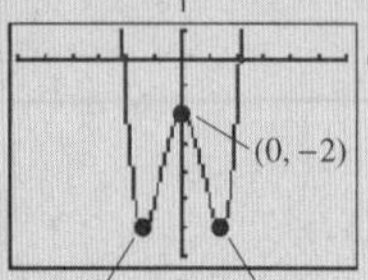

91.

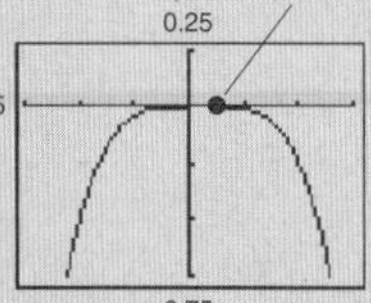

92.

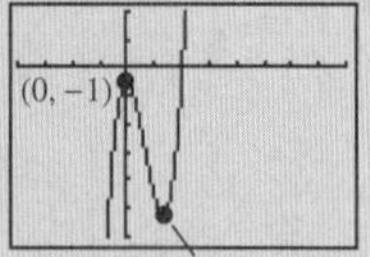

76. MIXTURE PROBLEM From a full 50-liter container of a 40% concentration of acid, x liters is removed and replaced with 100% acid. See margin.

(a) Write the amount of acid in the final mixture as a function of x.

(b) Determine the domain and range of the function.

(c) Determine x if the final mixture is 50% acid.

In Exercises 77 and 78, find the difference quotient and simplify your answer. 77–78. See margin.

77. $f(x) = 2x^2 + 3x - 1, \quad \dfrac{f(x+h) - f(x)}{h}, \quad h \ne 0$

78. $f(x) = x^3 - 5x^2 + x, \quad \dfrac{f(x+h) - f(x)}{h}, \quad h \ne 0$

1.5 In Exercises 79–82, use the Vertical Line Test to determine whether y is a function of x. To print an enlarged copy of the graph, go to the website *www.mathgraphs.com*.

79. $y = (x - 3)^2$ Function

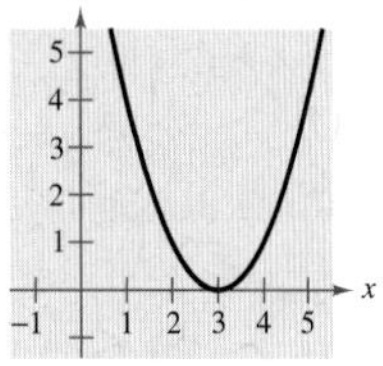

80. $y = -\frac{3}{5}x^3 - 2x + 1$ Function

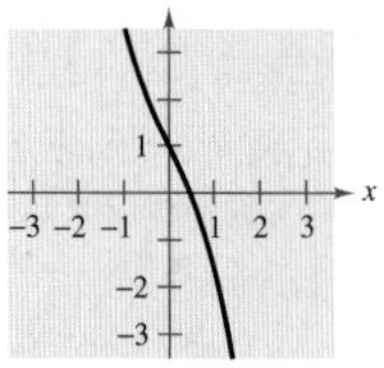

81. $x - 4 = y^2$ Not a function

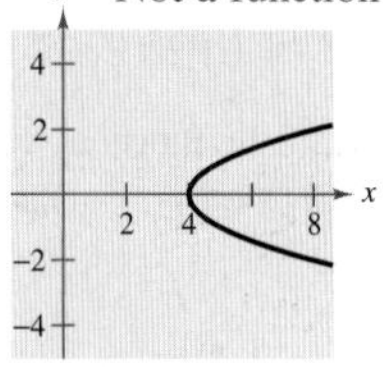

82. $x = -|4 - y|$ Not a function

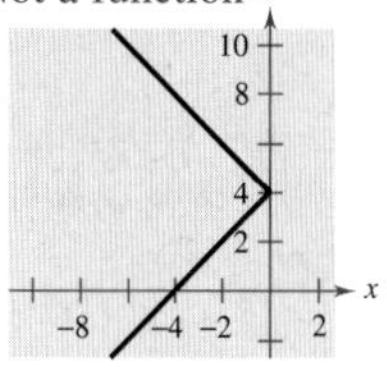

In Exercises 83–86, find the zeros of the function algebraically.

83. $f(x) = 3x^2 - 16x + 21$ $\frac{7}{3}, 3$

84. $f(x) = 5x^2 + 4x - 1$ $-1, \frac{1}{5}$

85. $f(x) = \dfrac{8x + 3}{11 - x}$ $-\frac{3}{8}$

86. $f(x) = x^3 - x^2 - 25x + 25$ $1, \pm 5$

In Exercises 87 and 88, use a graphing utility to graph the function and visually determine the intervals over which the function is increasing, decreasing, or constant.

87. $f(x) = |x| + |x + 1|$

88. $f(x) = (x^2 - 4)^2$

87–88. See margin.

In Exercises 89–92, use a graphing utility to graph the function and approximate any relative minimum or relative maximum values. 89–92. See margin.

89. $f(x) = -x^2 + 2x + 1$

90. $f(x) = x^4 - 4x^2 - 2$

91. $f(x) = x^3 - 6x^4$

92. $f(x) = x^3 - 4x^2 - 1$

In Exercises 93–96, find the average rate of change of the function from x_1 to x_2.

Function	*x-Values*	
93. $f(x) = -x^2 + 8x - 4$	$x_1 = 0, x_2 = 4$	4
94. $f(x) = x^3 + 12x - 2$	$x_1 = 0, x_2 = 4$	28
95. $f(x) = 2 - \sqrt{x + 1}$	$x_1 = 3, x_2 = 7$	$\frac{1 - \sqrt{2}}{2}$
96. $f(x) = 1 - \sqrt{x + 3}$	$x_1 = 1, x_2 = 6$	-0.2

In Exercises 97–100, determine whether the function is even, odd, or neither.

97. $f(x) = x^5 + 4x - 7$ Neither

98. $f(x) = x^4 - 20x^2$ Even

99. $f(x) = 2x\sqrt{x^2 + 3}$ Odd

100. $f(x) = \sqrt[5]{6x^2}$ Even

1.6 In Exercises 101 and 102, write the linear function f such that it has the indicated function values. Then sketch the graph of the function. 101–102. See margin.

101. $f(2) = -6, \; f(-1) = 3$

102. $f(0) = -5, \; f(4) = -8$

In Exercises 103–112, graph the function.

103. $f(x) = 3 - x^2$

104. $h(x) = x^3 - 2$

105. $f(x) = -\sqrt{x}$

106. $f(x) = \sqrt{x + 1}$

107. $g(x) = \dfrac{3}{x}$

108. $g(x) = \dfrac{1}{x + 5}$

109. $f(x) = [\![x]\!] + 2$ 103–112. See margin.

110. $g(x) = [\![x + 4]\!]$

111. $f(x) = \begin{cases} 5x - 3, & x \ge -1 \\ -4x + 5, & x < -1 \end{cases}$

112. $f(x) = \begin{cases} x^2 - 2, & x < -2 \\ 5, & -2 \le x \le 0 \\ 8x - 5, & x > 0 \end{cases}$

101. $f(x) = -3x$

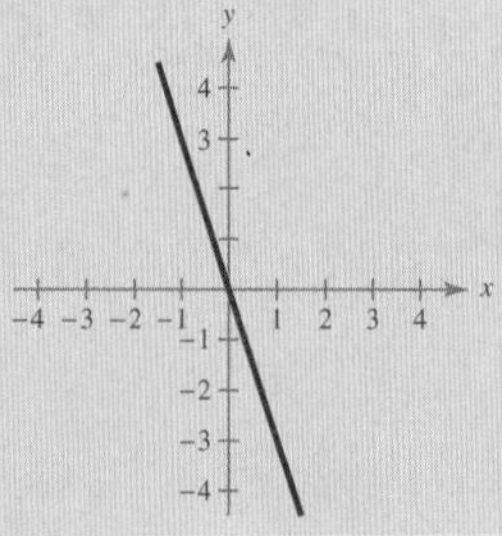

102. $f(x) = -\frac{3}{4}x - 5$

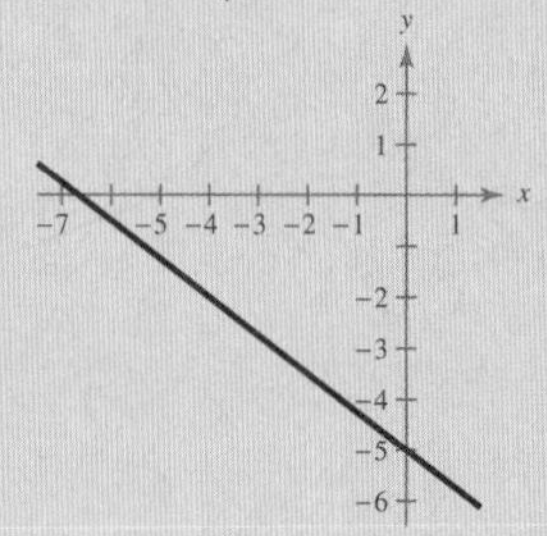

103–112. See Additional Answers beginning on page AA1.

In Exercises 113 and 114, the figure shows the graph of a transformed parent function. Identify the parent function.

113. $y = x^3$

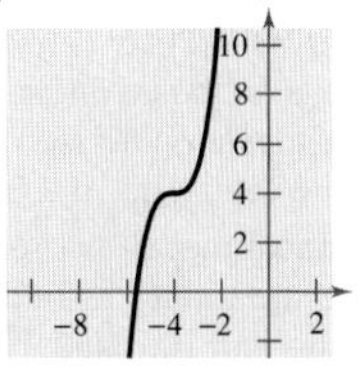

114. $y = \sqrt{x}$

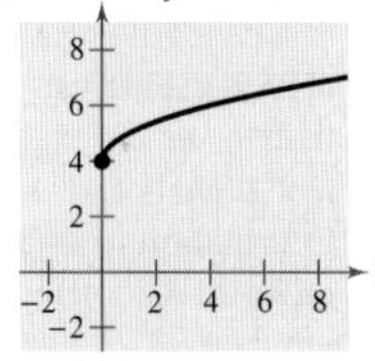

1.7 In Exercises 115–128, h is related to one of the parent functions described in this chapter. (a) Identify the parent function f. (b) Describe the sequence of transformations from f to h. (c) Sketch the graph of h. (d) Use function notation to write h in terms of f. 115–128. See margin.

115. $h(x) = x^2 - 9$ **116.** $h(x) = (x - 2)^3 + 2$

117. $h(x) = -\sqrt{x} + 4$ **118.** $h(x) = |x + 3| - 5$

119. $h(x) = -(x + 2)^2 + 3$ **120.** $h(x) = \frac{1}{2}(x - 1)^2 - 2$

121. $h(x) = -[\![x]\!] + 6$ **122.** $h(x) = -\sqrt{x + 1} + 9$

123. $h(x) = -|-x + 4| + 6$

124. $h(x) = -(x + 1)^2 - 3$

125. $h(x) = 5[\![x - 9]\!]$ **126.** $h(x) = -\frac{1}{3}x^3$

127. $h(x) = -2\sqrt{x - 4}$ **128.** $h(x) = \frac{1}{2}|x| - 1$

1.8 In Exercises 129 and 130, find (a) $(f + g)(x)$, (b) $(f - g)(x)$, (c) $(fg)(x)$, and (d) $(f/g)(x)$. What is the domain of f/g? 129–130. See margin.

129. $f(x) = x^2 + 3,\quad g(x) = 2x - 1$

130. $f(x) = x^2 - 4,\quad g(x) = \sqrt{3 - x}$

In Exercises 131 and 132, find (a) $f \circ g$ and (b) $g \circ f$. Find the domain of each function and each composite function. 131–132. See margin.

131. $f(x) = \frac{1}{3}x - 3,\quad g(x) = 3x + 1$

132. $f(x) = x^3 - 4,\quad g(x) = \sqrt[3]{x + 7}$

In Exercises 133 and 134, find two functions f and g such that $(f \circ g)(x) = h(x)$. (There are many correct answers.)

133. $h(x) = (1 - 2x)^3$ **134.** $h(x) = \sqrt[3]{x + 2}$

133–134. See margin.

135. PHONE EXPENDITURES The average annual expenditures (in dollars) for residential $r(t)$ and cellular $c(t)$ phone services from 2001 through 2006 can be approximated by the functions $r(t) = 27.5t + 705$ and $c(t) = 151.3t + 151$, where t represents the year, with $t = 1$ corresponding to 2001. (Source: Bureau of Labor Statistics)

(a) Find and interpret $(r + c)(t)$.
$(r + c)(t) = 178.8t + 856$; This represents the average annual expenditures for both residential and cellular phone services.

(b) Use a graphing utility to graph $r(t)$, $c(t)$, and $(r + c)(t)$ in the same viewing window. See margin.

(c) Find $(r + c)(13)$. Use the graph in part (b) to verify your result. $(r + c)(13) = \$3180.40$

136. BACTERIA COUNT The number N of bacteria in a refrigerated food is given by See margin.

$$N(T) = 25T^2 - 50T + 300,\quad 2 \le T \le 20$$

where T is the temperature of the food in degrees Celsius. When the food is removed from refrigeration, the temperature of the food is given by

$$T(t) = 2t + 1,\quad 0 \le t \le 9$$

where t is the time in hours. (a) Find the composition $N(T(t))$, and interpret its meaning in context, and (b) find the time when the bacteria count reaches 750.

1.9 In Exercises 137 and 138, find the inverse function of f informally. Verify that $f(f^{-1}(x)) = x$ and $f^{-1}(f(x)) = x$.

137. $f(x) = 3x + 8$ **138.** $f(x) = \dfrac{x - 4}{5}$

$f^{-1}(x) = \frac{1}{3}(x - 8)$ $f^{-1}(x) = 5x + 4$

In Exercises 139 and 140, determine whether the function has an inverse function.

139.

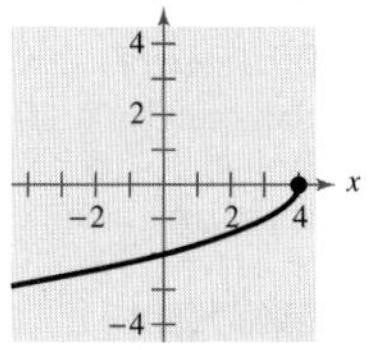

The function has an inverse.

140. The function does not have an inverse.

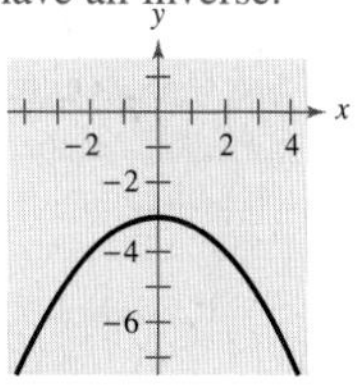

In Exercises 141–144, use a graphing utility to graph the function, and use the Horizontal Line Test to determine whether the function is one-to-one and so has an inverse function.

141. $f(x) = 4 - \frac{1}{3}x$ **142.** $f(x) = (x - 1)^2$

143. $h(t) = \dfrac{2}{t - 3}$ **144.** $g(x) = \sqrt{x + 6}$

141–144. See margin.

In Exercises 145–148, (a) find the inverse function of f, (b) graph both f and f^{-1} on the same set of coordinate axes, (c) describe the relationship between the graphs of f and f^{-1}, and (d) state the domains and ranges of f and f^{-1}.

145. $f(x) = \frac{1}{2}x - 3$ **146.** $f(x) = 5x - 7$

147. $f(x) = \sqrt{x + 1}$ **148.** $f(x) = x^3 + 2$

145–148. See margin.

In Exercises 149 and 150, restrict the domain of the function f to an interval over which the function is increasing and determine f^{-1} over that interval.

149. $f(x) = 2(x - 4)^2$ **150.** $f(x) = |x - 2|$

See margin. $x > 2;\ f^{-1}(x) = x + 2,\ x > 0$

115. (a) $f(x) = x^2$
(b) Vertical shift nine units downward
(c)

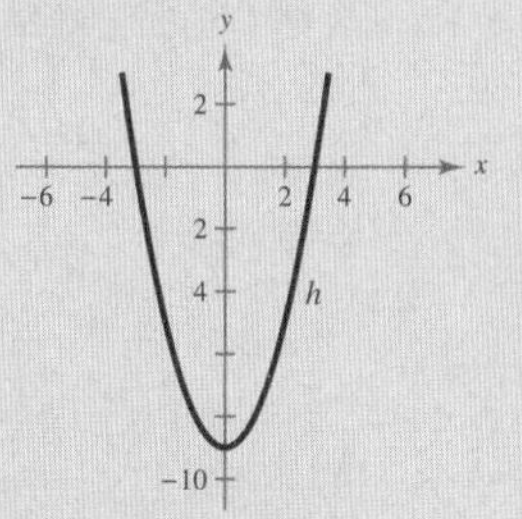

(d) $h(x) = f(x) - 9$

116. (a) $f(x) = x^3$
(b) Horizontal shift two units to the right and vertical shift two units upward
(c)

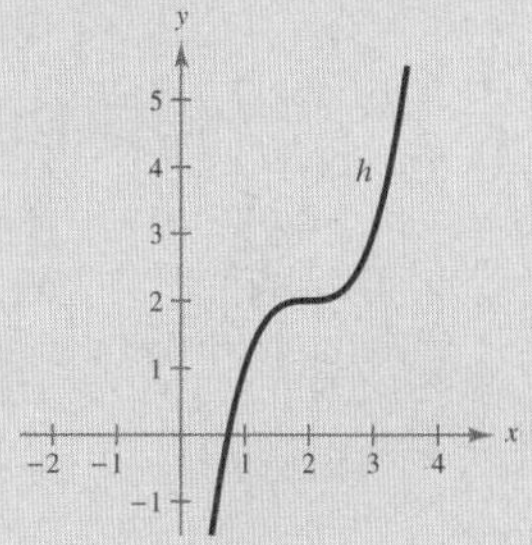

(d) $h(x) = f(x - 2) + 2$

117. (a) $f(x) = \sqrt{x}$
(b) Reflection in the x-axis and vertical shift four units upward
(c)

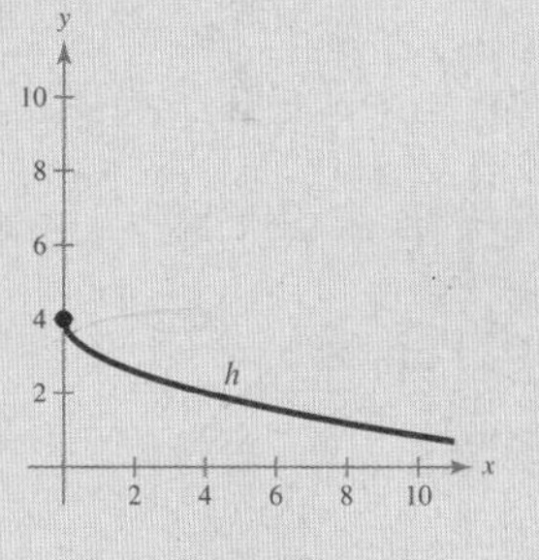

(d) $h(x) = -f(x) + 4$

118. (a) $f(x) = |x|$
(b) Horizontal shift three units to the left and vertical shift five units downward
(c)

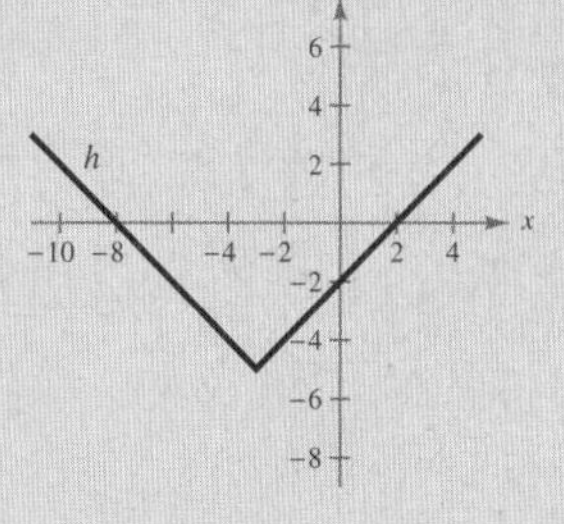

(d) $h(x) = f(x + 3) - 5$

119. (a) $f(x) = x^2$
(b) Reflection in the x-axis, horizontal shift two units to the left, and vertical shift three units upward
(c)

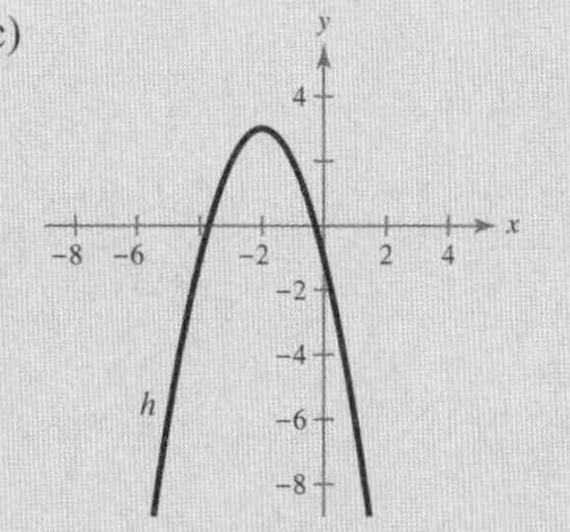

(d) $h(x) = -f(x + 2) + 3$

120–134, 135(b), 136, 141–149. See Additional Answers beginning on page AA1.

151. COMPACT DISCS The values V (in billions of dollars) of shipments of compact discs in the United States from 2000 through 2007 are shown in the table. A linear model that approximates these data is

$$V = -0.742t + 13.62$$ See margin.

where t represents the year, with $t = 0$ corresponding to 2000. (Source: Recording Industry Association of America)

Year	Value, V
2000	13.21
2001	12.91
2002	12.04
2003	11.23
2004	11.45
2005	10.52
2006	9.37
2007	7.45

(a) Plot the actual data and the model on the same set of coordinate axes.

(b) How closely does the model represent the data?

152. DATA ANALYSIS: TV USAGE The table shows the projected numbers of hours H of television usage in the United States from 2003 through 2011. (Source: Communications Industry Forecast and Report) See margin.

Year	Hours, H
2003	1615
2004	1620
2005	1659
2006	1673
2007	1686
2008	1704
2009	1714
2010	1728
2011	1742

(a) Use a graphing utility to create a scatter plot of the data. Let t represent the year, with $t = 3$ corresponding to 2003.

(b) Use the *regression* feature of the graphing utility to find the equation of the least squares regression line that fits the data. Then graph the model and the scatter plot you found in part (a) in the same viewing window. How closely does the model represent the data?

(c) Use the model to estimate the projected number of hours of television usage in 2020.

(d) Interpret the meaning of the slope of the linear model in the context of the problem.

153. MEASUREMENT You notice a billboard indicating that it is 2.5 miles or 4 kilometers to the next restaurant of a national fast-food chain. Use this information to find a mathematical model that relates miles to kilometers. Then use the model to find the numbers of kilometers in 2 miles and 10 miles. See margin.

154. ENERGY The power P produced by a wind turbine is proportional to the cube of the wind speed S. A wind speed of 27 miles per hour produces a power output of 750 kilowatts. Find the output for a wind speed of 40 miles per hour. 2438.7 kW

155. FRICTIONAL FORCE The frictional force F between the tires and the road required to keep a car on a curved section of a highway is directly proportional to the square of the speed s of the car. If the speed of the car is doubled, the force will change by what factor? A factor of 4

156. DEMAND A company has found that the daily demand x for its boxes of chocolates is inversely proportional to the price p. When the price is \$5, the demand is 800 boxes. Approximate the demand when the price is increased to \$6. 667 boxes

157. TRAVEL TIME The travel time between two cities is inversely proportional to the average speed. A train travels between the cities in 3 hours at an average speed of 65 miles per hour. How long would it take to travel between the cities at an average speed of 80 miles per hour? About 2 h, 26 min

158. COST The cost of constructing a wooden box with a square base varies jointly as the height of the box and the square of the width of the box. A box of height 16 inches and width 6 inches costs \$28.80. How much would a box of height 14 inches and width 8 inches cost? \$44.80

EXPLORATION

TRUE OR FALSE? In Exercises 159 and 160, determine whether the statement is true or false. Justify your answer.

159. Relative to the graph of $f(x) = \sqrt{x}$, the function given by $h(x) = -\sqrt{x+9} - 13$ is shifted 9 units to the left and 13 units downward, then reflected in the x-axis.

160. If f and g are two inverse functions, then the domain of g is equal to the range of f. 159–160. See margin.

161. WRITING Explain the difference between the Vertical Line Test and the Horizontal Line Test.

162. WRITING Explain how to tell whether a relation between two variables is a function.

161–162. See margin.

151. (a)

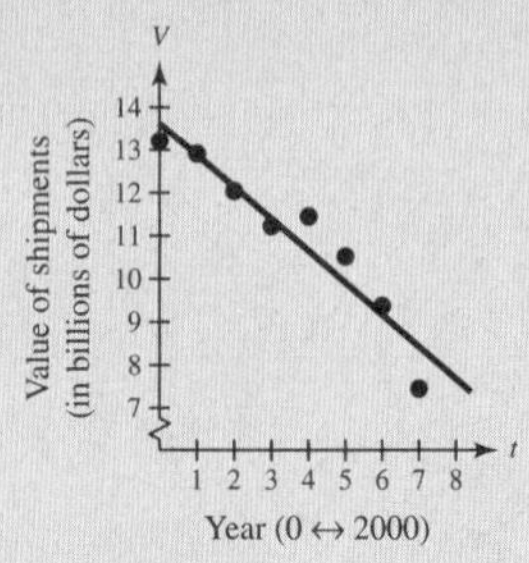

(b) The model is a good fit for the actual data.

152. (a) and (b)

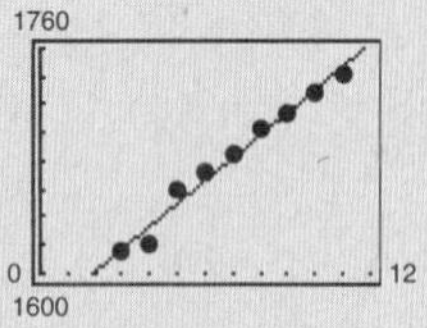

$H = 16.22t + 1568.8$

The model is a good fit for the actual data.

(c) $H(20) = 1893.2$ h

(d) The projected number of hours of television usage in the U.S. increases by 16.22 hours each year.

153. Model: $D = \frac{8}{5}m$; 3.2 km, 16 km

159. False. The graph is reflected in the x-axis, shifted 9 units to the left, and then shifted 13 units downward.

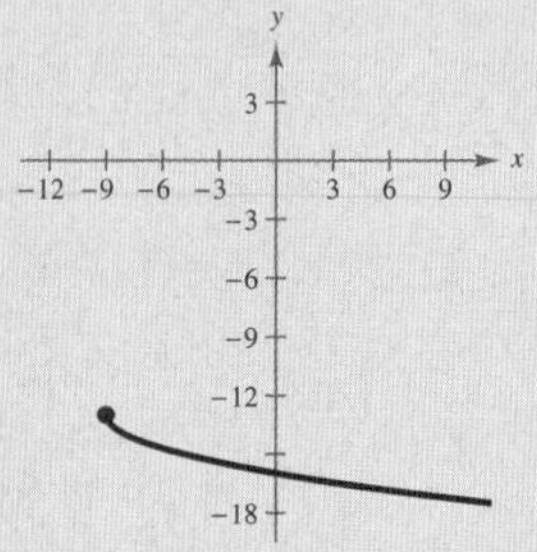

160. True. If $f(x) = x^3$ and $g(x) = \sqrt[3]{x}$, then the domain of g is all real numbers, which is equal to the range of f, and vice versa.

161. The Vertical Line Test is used to determine if the graph of y is a function of x. The Horizontal Line Test is used to determine if a function has an inverse function.

162. A function from a set A to a set B is a relation that assigns to each element x in the set A exactly one element y in the set B.

1 CHAPTER TEST

See www.CalcChat.com for worked-out solutions to odd-numbered exercises.

Take this test as you would take a test in class. When you are finished, check your work against the answers given in the back of the book.

1. Plot the points $(-2, 5)$ and $(6, 0)$. Find the coordinates of the midpoint of the line segment joining the points and the distance between the points. See margin.

2. A cylindrical can has a volume of 600 cubic centimeters and a radius of 4 centimeters. Find the height of the can. About 11.937 cm

3–5. See margin.

In Exercises 3–5, use intercepts and symmetry to sketch the graph of the equation.

3. $y = 3 - 5x$ 4. $y = 4 - |x|$ 5. $y = x^2 - 1$

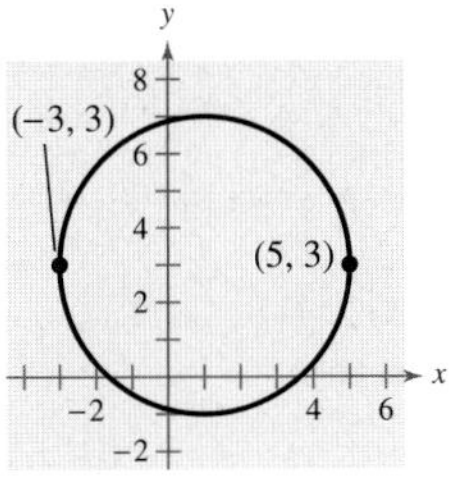

FIGURE FOR 6

6. Write the standard form of the equation of the circle shown at the left. $(x - 1)^2 + (y - 3)^2 = 16$

In Exercises 7 and 8, find the slope-intercept form of the equation of the line passing through the points.

7. $(2, -3), (-4, 9)$ $y = -2x + 1$ 8. $(3, 0.8), (7, -6)$ $y = -1.7x + 5.9$

9. Find equations of the lines that pass through the point $(0, 4)$ and are (a) parallel to and (b) perpendicular to the line $5x + 2y = 3$. (a) $5x + 2y - 8 = 0$ (b) $-2x + 5y - 20 = 0$

10. Evaluate $f(x) = \dfrac{\sqrt{x+9}}{x^2 - 81}$ at each value: (a) $f(7)$ (b) $f(-5)$ (c) $f(x - 9)$. See margin.

11. Find the domain of $f(x) = 10 - \sqrt{3 - x}$. $x \le 3$

In Exercises 12–14, (a) find the zeros of the function, (b) use a graphing utility to graph the function, (c) approximate the intervals over which the function is increasing, decreasing, or constant, and (d) determine whether the function is even, odd, or neither.

12. $f(x) = 2x^6 + 5x^4 - x^2$ 13. $f(x) = 4x\sqrt{3 - x}$ 14. $f(x) = |x + 5|$

15. Sketch the graph of $f(x) = \begin{cases} 3x + 7, & x \le -3 \\ 4x^2 - 1, & x > -3 \end{cases}$. 12–15. See margin.

In Exercises 16–18, identify the parent function in the transformation. Then sketch a graph of the function. 16–18. See margin.

16. $h(x) = -[\![x]\!]$ 17. $h(x) = -\sqrt{x + 5} + 8$ 18. $h(x) = -2(x - 5)^3 + 3$

In Exercises 19 and 20, find (a) $(f + g)(x)$, (b) $(f - g)(x)$, (c) $(fg)(x)$, (d) $(f/g)(x)$, (e) $(f \circ g)(x)$, and (f) $(g \circ f)(x)$. 19–20. See margin.

19. $f(x) = 3x^2 - 7$, $g(x) = -x^2 - 4x + 5$ 20. $f(x) = 1/x$, $g(x) = 2\sqrt{x}$

In Exercises 21–23, determine whether or not the function has an inverse function, and if so, find the inverse function.

21. $f(x) = x^3 + 8$ $f^{-1}(x) = \sqrt[3]{x - 8}$ 22. $f(x) = |x^2 - 3| + 6$ No inverse 23. $f(x) = 3x\sqrt{x}$ $f^{-1}(x) = \left(\frac{1}{3}x\right)^{2/3}$, $x \ge 0$

In Exercises 24–26, find a mathematical model representing the statement. (In each case, determine the constant of proportionality.)

24. v varies directly as the square root of s. ($v = 24$ when $s = 16$.) $v = 6\sqrt{s}$

25. A varies jointly as x and y. ($A = 500$ when $x = 15$ and $y = 8$.) $A = \dfrac{25}{6}xy$

26. b varies inversely as a. ($b = 32$ when $a = 1.5$.) $b = \dfrac{48}{a}$

1.

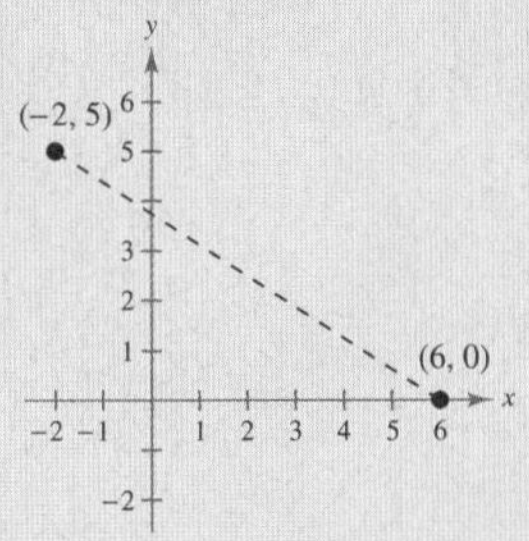

Midpoint: $\left(2, \frac{5}{2}\right)$; Distance: $\sqrt{89}$

3. No symmetry

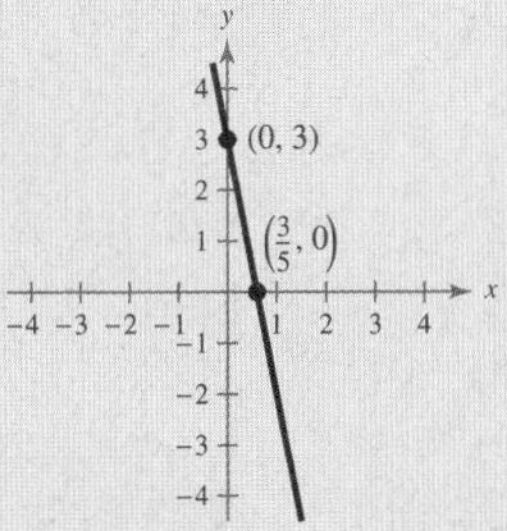

4. y-axis symmetry

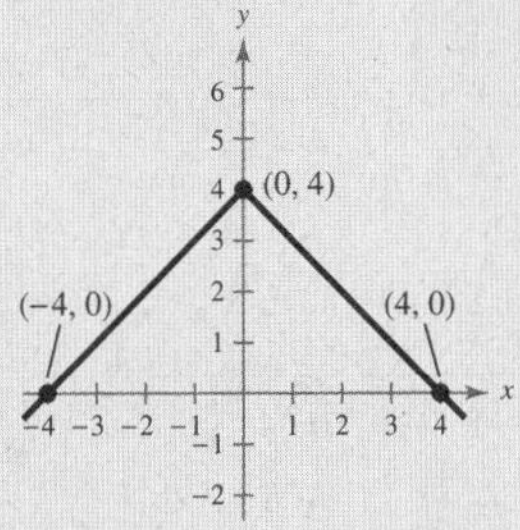

5. y-axis symmetry

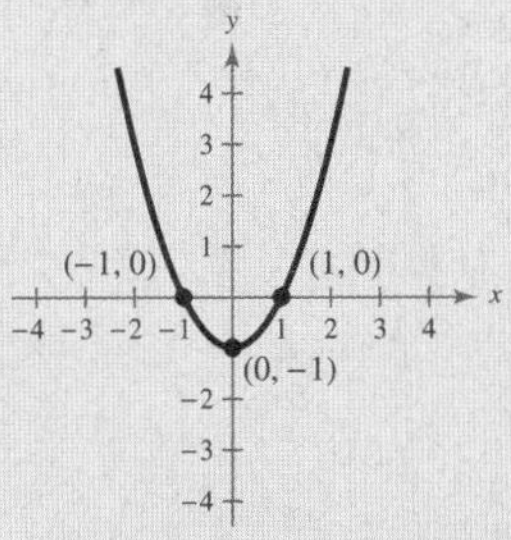

10. (a) $-\dfrac{1}{8}$ (b) $-\dfrac{1}{28}$ (c) $\dfrac{\sqrt{x}}{x^2 - 18x}$

12. (a) $0, \pm 0.4314$

(b)

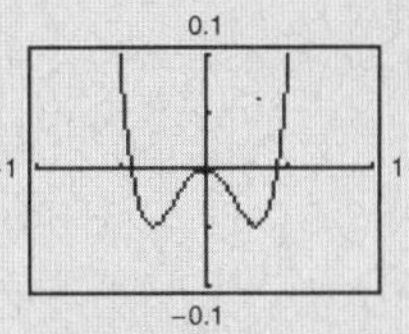

(c) Increasing on $(-0.31, 0), (0.31, \infty)$
Decreasing on $(-\infty, -0.31), (0, 0.31)$

(d) Even

13. (a) 0, 3

(b)

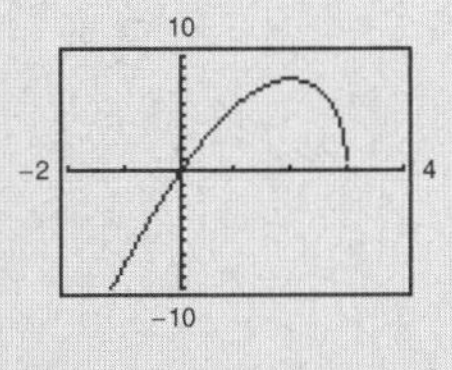

(c) Increasing on $(-\infty, 2)$
Decreasing on $(2, 3)$

(d) Neither

14. (a) -5

(b)

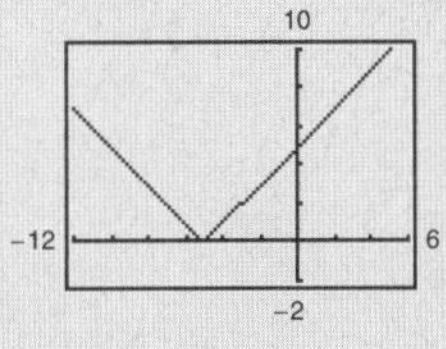

(c) Increasing on $(-5, \infty)$
Decreasing on $(-\infty, -5)$

(d) Neither

15–20. See Additional Answers beginning on page AA1.

PROOFS IN MATHEMATICS

What does the word *proof* mean to you? In mathematics, the word *proof* is used to mean simply a valid argument. When you are proving a statement or theorem, you must use facts, definitions, and accepted properties in a logical order. You can also use previously proved theorems in your proof. For instance, the Distance Formula is used in the proof of the Midpoint Formula below. There are several different proof methods, which you will see in later chapters.

The Midpoint Formula (p. 5)

The midpoint of the line segment joining the points (x_1, y_1) and (x_2, y_2) is given by the Midpoint Formula

$$\text{Midpoint} = \left(\frac{x_1 + x_2}{2}, \frac{y_1 + y_2}{2}\right).$$

The Cartesian Plane

The Cartesian plane was named after the French mathematician René Descartes (1596–1650). While Descartes was lying in bed, he noticed a fly buzzing around on the square ceiling tiles. He discovered that the position of the fly could be described by which ceiling tile the fly landed on. This led to the development of the Cartesian plane. Descartes felt that a coordinate plane could be used to facilitate description of the positions of objects.

Proof

Using the figure, you must show that $d_1 = d_2$ and $d_1 + d_2 = d_3$.

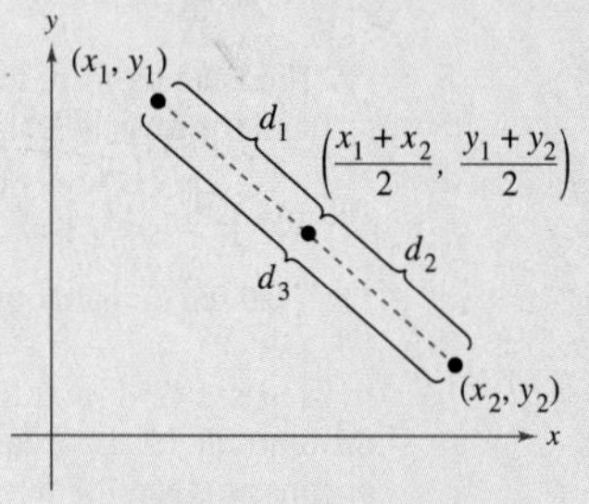

By the Distance Formula, you obtain

$$d_1 = \sqrt{\left(\frac{x_1 + x_2}{2} - x_1\right)^2 + \left(\frac{y_1 + y_2}{2} - y_1\right)^2}$$

$$= \frac{1}{2}\sqrt{(x_2 - x_1)^2 + (y_2 - y_1)^2}$$

$$d_2 = \sqrt{\left(x_2 - \frac{x_1 + x_2}{2}\right)^2 + \left(y_2 - \frac{y_1 + y_2}{2}\right)^2}$$

$$= \frac{1}{2}\sqrt{(x_2 - x_1)^2 + (y_2 - y_1)^2}$$

$$d_3 = \sqrt{(x_2 - x_1)^2 + (y_2 - y_1)^2}$$

So, it follows that $d_1 = d_2$ and $d_1 + d_2 = d_3$.

122

PROBLEM SOLVING

This collection of thought-provoking and challenging exercises further explores and expands upon concepts learned in this chapter.

1. As a salesperson, you receive a monthly salary of \$2000, plus a commission of 7% of sales. You are offered a new job at \$2300 per month, plus a commission of 5% of sales. See margin.

(a) Write a linear equation for your current monthly wage W_1 in terms of your monthly sales S.

(b) Write a linear equation for the monthly wage W_2 of your new job offer in terms of the monthly sales S.

(c) Use a graphing utility to graph both equations in the same viewing window. Find the point of intersection. What does it signify?

(d) You think you can sell \$20,000 per month. Should you change jobs? Explain.

2. For the numbers 2 through 9 on a telephone keypad (see figure), create two relations: one mapping numbers onto letters, and the other mapping letters onto numbers. Are both relations functions? Explain. See margin.

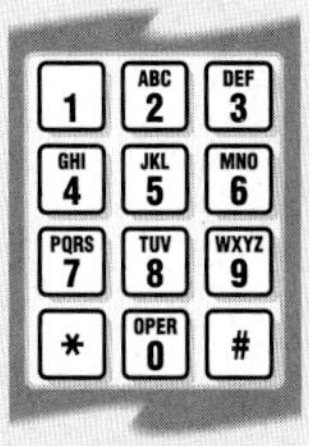

3. What can be said about the sum and difference of each of the following? See margin.

(a) Two even functions (b) Two odd functions

(c) An odd function and an even function

4. The two functions given by See margin.

$f(x) = x$ and $g(x) = -x$

are their own inverse functions. Graph each function and explain why this is true. Graph other linear functions that are their own inverse functions. Find a general formula for a family of linear functions that are their own inverse functions.

5. Prove that a function of the following form is even.

$y = a_{2n}x^{2n} + a_{2n-2}x^{2n-2} + \cdots + a_2x^2 + a_0$ See margin.

6. A miniature golf professional is trying to make a hole-in-one on the miniature golf green shown. A coordinate plane is placed over the golf green. The golf ball is at the point (2.5, 2) and the hole is at the point (9.5, 2). The professional wants to bank the ball off the side wall of the green at the point (x, y). Find the coordinates of the point (x, y). Then write an equation for the path of the ball. See margin.

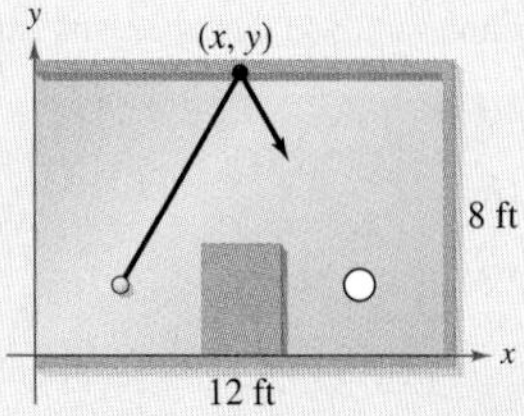

FIGURE FOR 6

7. At 2:00 P.M. on April 11, 1912, the *Titanic* left Cobh, Ireland, on her voyage to New York City. At 11:40 P.M. on April 14, the *Titanic* struck an iceberg and sank, having covered only about 2100 miles of the approximately 3400-mile trip. See margin.

(a) What was the total duration of the voyage in hours?

(b) What was the average speed in miles per hour?

(c) Write a function relating the distance of the *Titanic* from New York City and the number of hours traveled. Find the domain and range of the function.

(d) Graph the function from part (c).

8. Consider the function given by $f(x) = -x^2 + 4x - 3$. Find the average rate of change of the function from x_1 to x_2. See margin.

(a) $x_1 = 1, x_2 = 2$ (b) $x_1 = 1, x_2 = 1.5$

(c) $x_1 = 1, x_2 = 1.25$ (d) $x_1 = 1, x_2 = 1.125$

(e) $x_1 = 1, x_2 = 1.0625$

(f) Does the average rate of change seem to be approaching one value? If so, what value?

(g) Find the equations of the secant lines through the points $(x_1, f(x_1))$ and $(x_2, f(x_2))$ for parts (a)–(e).

(h) Find the equation of the line through the point $(1, f(1))$ using your answer from part (f) as the slope of the line.

9. Consider the functions given by $f(x) = 4x$ and $g(x) = x + 6$. See margin.

(a) Find $(f \circ g)(x)$. (b) Find $(f \circ g)^{-1}(x)$.

(c) Find $f^{-1}(x)$ and $g^{-1}(x)$.

(d) Find $(g^{-1} \circ f^{-1})(x)$ and compare the result with that of part (b).

(e) Repeat parts (a) through (d) for $f(x) = x^3 + 1$ and $g(x) = 2x$.

(f) Write two one-to-one functions f and g, and repeat parts (a) through (d) for these functions.

(g) Make a conjecture about $(f \circ g)^{-1}(x)$ and $(g^{-1} \circ f^{-1})(x)$.

1. (a) $W_1 = 2000 + 0.07S$

(b) $W_2 = 2300 + 0.05S$

(c)

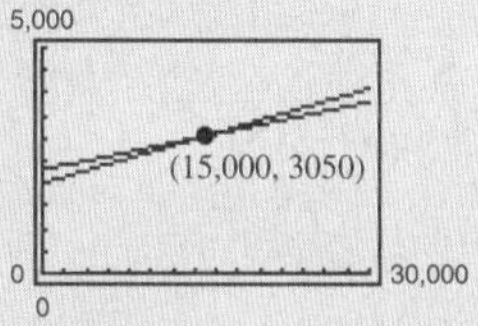

Both jobs pay the same monthly salary if sales equal \$15,000.

(d) No. Job 1 would pay \$3400 and job 2 would pay \$3300.

2. Mapping numbers onto letters is not a function because each number corresponds to three letters.

Mapping letters onto numbers is a function because every letter is assigned exactly one number.

3. (a) The function will be even.

(b) The function will be odd.

(c) The function will be neither even nor odd.

4. $f(x) = x$

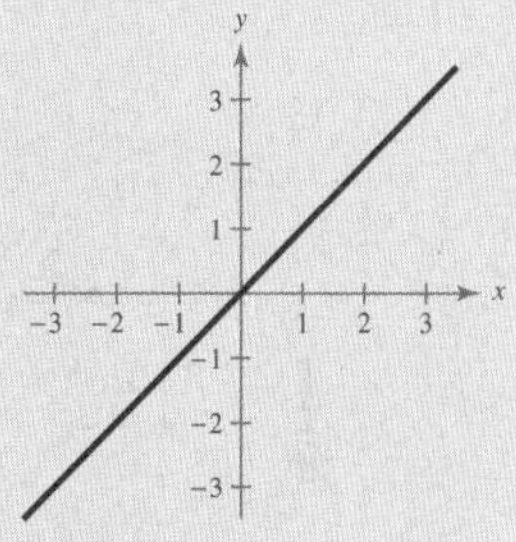

$g(x) = -x$

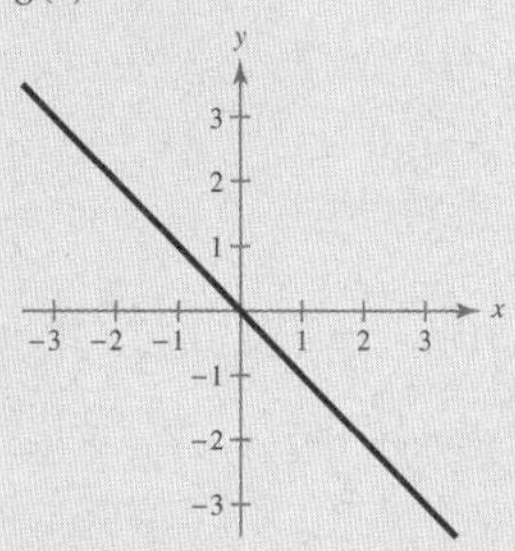

Both graphs are already symmetric with respect to the line $y = x$.

General formula: $y = -x + c$

5.

$$f(x) = a_{2n}x^{2n} + a_{2n-2}x^{2n-2} + \cdots + a_2x^2 + a_0$$

$$f(-x) = a_{2n}(-x)^{2n} + a_{2n-2}(-x)^{2n-2} + \cdots + a_2(-x)^2 + a_0$$

$$= f(x)$$

6. (6, 8)

$$f(x) = \begin{cases} \frac{12}{7}x - \frac{16}{7}, & 2.5 \le x \le 6 \\ -\frac{12}{7}x + \frac{128}{7}, & 6 < x \le 9.5 \end{cases}$$

7. (a) $81\frac{2}{3}$ h (b) $25\frac{5}{7}$ mi/h

(c) $y = -\frac{180}{7}x + 3400$

Domain: $0 \le x \le \frac{1190}{9}$

Range: $0 \le y \le 3400$

(d)

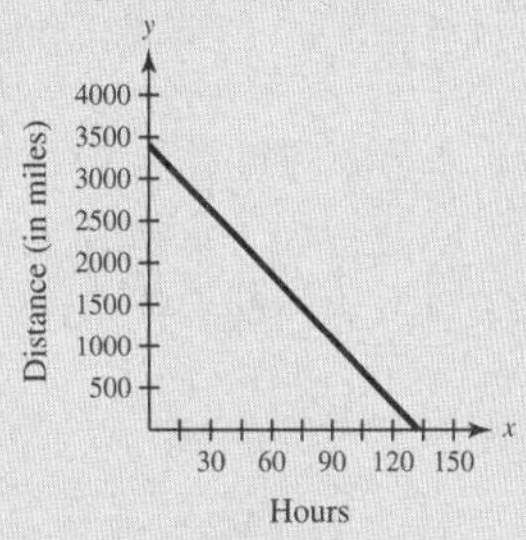

8–9. See Additional Answers beginning on page AA1.

10. You are in a boat 2 miles from the nearest point on the coast. You are to travel to a point Q, 3 miles down the coast and 1 mile inland (see figure). You can row at 2 miles per hour and you can walk at 4 miles per hour.

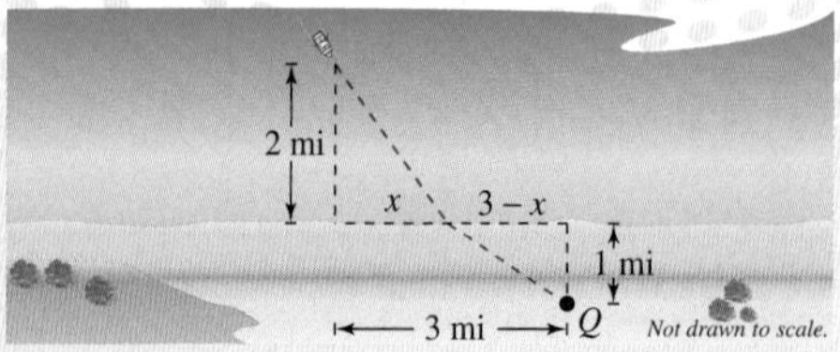

See margin.

(a) Write the total time T of the trip as a function of x.

(b) Determine the domain of the function.

(c) Use a graphing utility to graph the function. Be sure to choose an appropriate viewing window.

(d) Use the *zoom* and *trace* features to find the value of x that minimizes T.

(e) Write a brief paragraph interpreting these values.

11. The **Heaviside function** $H(x)$ is widely used in engineering applications. (See figure.) To print an enlarged copy of the graph, go to the website *www.mathgraphs.com.* See margin.

$$H(x) = \begin{cases} 1, & x \ge 0 \\ 0, & x < 0 \end{cases}$$

Sketch the graph of each function by hand.

(a) $H(x) - 2$ (b) $H(x - 2)$ (c) $-H(x)$

(d) $H(-x)$ (e) $\frac{1}{2}H(x)$ (f) $-H(x - 2) + 2$

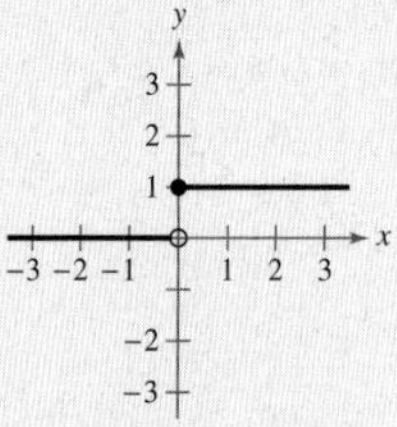

12. Let $f(x) = \dfrac{1}{1 - x}$. See margin.

(a) What are the domain and range of f?

(b) Find $f(f(x))$. What is the domain of this function?

(c) Find $f(f(f(x)))$. Is the graph a line? Why or why not?

13. Show that the Associative Property holds for compositions of functions—that is,

$$(f \circ (g \circ h))(x) = ((f \circ g) \circ h)(x).$$ Proof

14. Consider the graph of the function f shown in the figure. Use this graph to sketch the graph of each function. To print an enlarged copy of the graph, go to the website *www.mathgraphs.com.* See margin.

(a) $f(x + 1)$ (b) $f(x) + 1$ (c) $2f(x)$ (d) $f(-x)$

(e) $-f(x)$ (f) $|f(x)|$ (g) $f(|x|)$

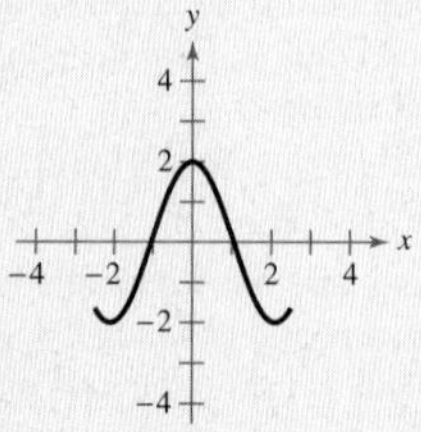

15. Use the graphs of f and f^{-1} to complete each table of function values.

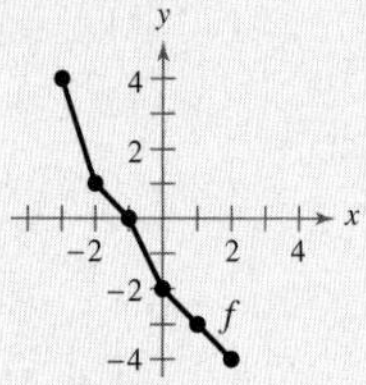

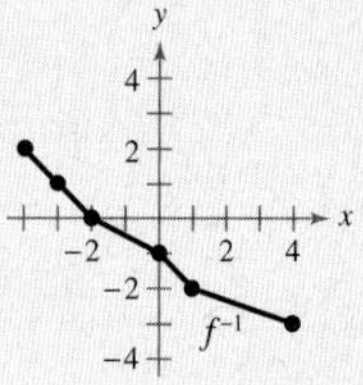

(a)

x	-4	-2	0	4
$(f(f^{-1}(x))$	-4	-2	0	4

(b)

x	-3	-2	0	1
$(f + f^{-1})(x)$	5	1	-3	-5

(c)

x	-3	-2	0	1
$(f \cdot f^{-1})(x)$	4	0	2	6

(d)

x	-4	-3	0	4
$\lvert f^{-1}(x)\rvert$	2	1	1	3

10. (a) $T = \frac{1}{2}\sqrt{4 + x^2} + \frac{1}{4}\sqrt{x^2 - 6x + 10}$

(b) $0 \le x \le 3$

(c)

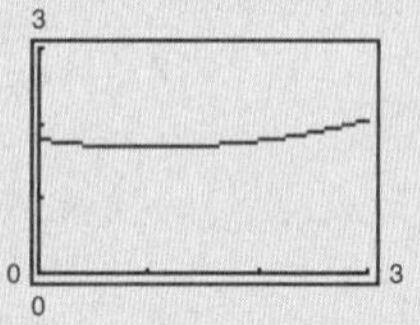

(d) $x = 1$

(e) The distance $x = 1$ yields a time of 1.68 hours.

11. (a)

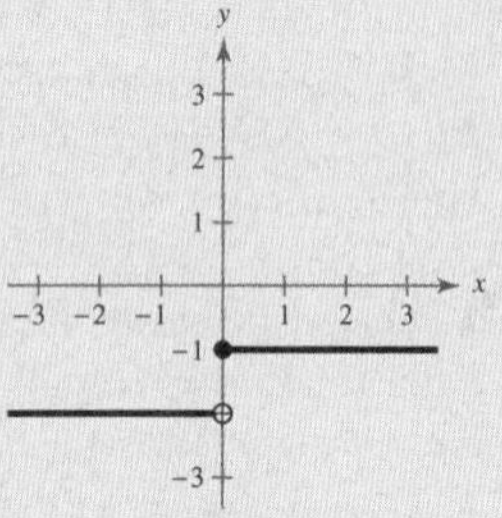

(b)

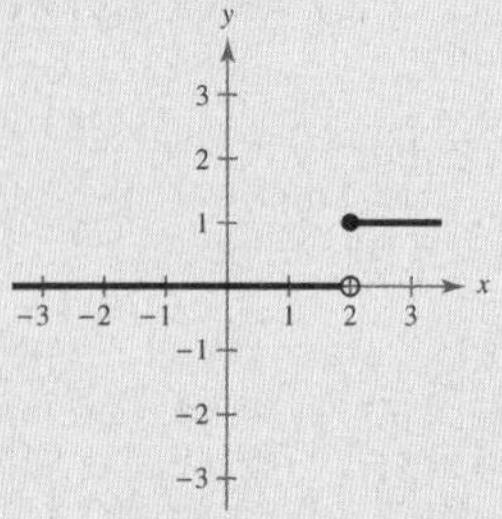

(c)

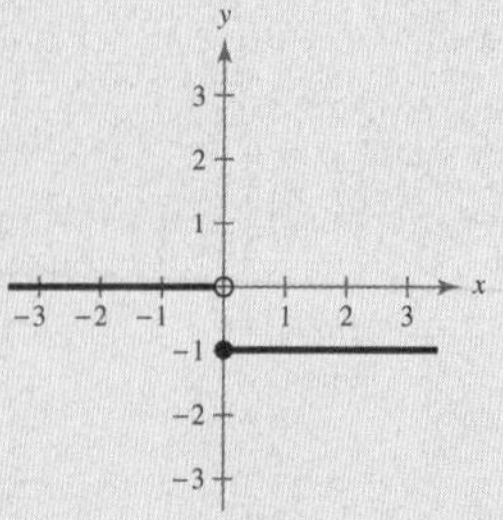

(d)

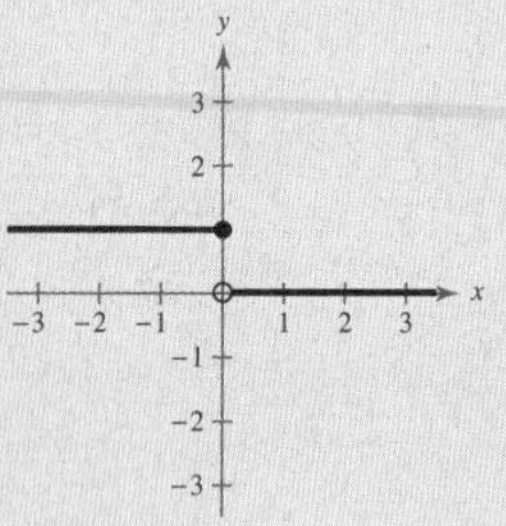

(e)

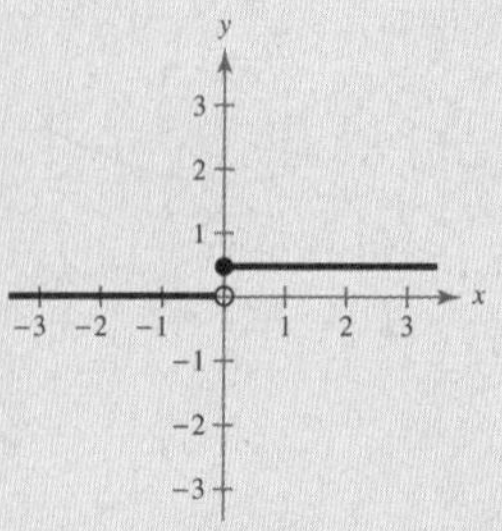

(f)

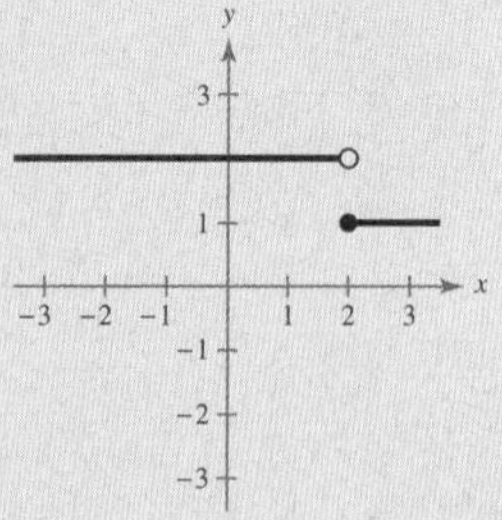

12. (a) Domain: all real numbers x except $x = 1$

Range: all real numbers y except $y = 0$

(b) $f(f(x)) = \dfrac{x - 1}{x}$

Domain: all real numbers x except $x = 0, 1$

(c) $f(f(f(x))) = x, x \ne 0, 1$

The graph is not a line because there are holes at $x = 0$ and $x = 1$.

14. See Additional Answers beginning on page AA1.

Pacing and Assignment Guide 2

REGULAR SCHEDULE

Lesson	Day	AVERAGE	ADVANCED
2.1	Day 1	pp. 132–135 Exs. 7–12, 15, 21–25 odd, 29, 31, 43–53 odd, 57, 58, 67, 69, 75–83 odd, 86–90, 95	pp. 132–135 Exs. 7–12, 16, 22, 28–34 even, 44, 46, 50–54 even, 67, 69, 74–76, 78, 80–83, 86–90, 92–96 even, 100
2.2	Day 1	pp. 145–149 Exs. 9, 17, 19, 27, 29, 41–49 odd, 59, 61, 65, 69, 71, 77–83 odd, 93, 97–99, 103, 105–108	pp. 145–149 Exs. 9–16, 18, 20, 28, 29, 42–50 even, 60–64 even, 69, 71, 74, 82–88 even, 96, 97–100, 103, 104, 107–111
2.3	Day 1	pp. 156–158 Exs. 7, 15–23 odd, 29–41 odd, 47–51 odd, 57, 61–71 odd, 83, 85, 87–89, 93, 95	pp. 156–158 Exs. 8, 16–26 even, 32–44 even, 50–56 even, 62–66 even, 69, 72, 84, 85, 90–100 even
2.4	Day 1	pp. 164–165 Exs. 1–4, 5–13 odd, 17, 23, 33–39 odd, 43, 49–53 odd, 59, 65, 67, 71, 79, 93–96	pp. 164–165 Exs. 6–12 even, 18–24 even, 32–38 even, 46–52 even, 58–62 even, 68, 70, 89, 90–96, 98–101
2.5	Day 1	pp. 176–177 Exs. 1–6, 11–17 odd, 21, 27, 29, 33, 37, 47–53 odd, 56, 59, 63–69 odd, 73, 75, 82	pp. 176–177 Exs. 12–18 even, 22, 28–34 even, 50–58 even, 62–70 even, 74, 78
	Day 2	pp. 176, 178–180 Exs. 7, 8, 89, 91, 96, 99, 103, 107–111, 116, 118, 121–123, 127, 129, 137	pp. 178–180 Exs. 92–96 even, 102–106 even, 107–111, 113, 116, 118, 122–128 even, 130–132, 135–139
2.6	Day 1	pp. 190–191 Exs. 1–3, 6, 9, 11, 15, 17–22, 25, 27, 33, 37, 41, 43, 45, 51	pp. 190–191 Exs. 6–16 even, 17–20, 22–26 even, 30, 32, 40–50 even, 52
	Day 2	pp. 190–193 Exs. 4, 57–61 odd, 67, 73, 75, 79, 81, 85–87, 90	pp. 191–193 Exs. 56–68 even, 74, 76, 79, 80, 83, 85–87, 90
2.7	Day 1	pp. 201–203 Exs. 1–4, 5–15 odd, 23, 27, 33, 41, 47–53 odd, 60, 67–73 odd, 76, 78, 81, 82	pp. 201–203 Exs. 8, 12, 26–30 even, 34, 36, 46, 50, 54, 62–66 even, 71–74, 76, 78, 79, 83–86, 88
Review	Day 1	pp. 206–209 Exs. 1, 5, 7, 15, 21, 25–31 odd, 37–43 odd, 49, 57–61 odd, 67–83 odd, 87, 94, 95, 103, 109–115 odd, 123, 131, 135, 140, 143, 147, 151	pp. 206–209 Exs. 2, 12, 16, 22, 24, 28, 34, 38–42 even, 48, 50, 54, 58–64 even, 68–84 even, 89, 90–96 even, 102, 104, 110–116 even, 120, 128, 136, 139, 140, 145, 151, 152
Assess	Day 1	Chapter 2 Test	Chapter 2 Test
Yearly Pacing		Chapter 2 Total – 11 days	Remaining – 137 days

BLOCK SCHEDULE

DAY 1	DAY 2	DAY 3	DAY 4	DAY 5	DAY 6
2.1	**2.3**	**2.5**	**2.6**	**2.7**	**ASSESS**
pp. 132–135 Exs. 7–12, 15, 21–25 odd, 29, 31, 43–53 odd, 57, 58, 67, 69, 75–83 odd, 86–90, 95	pp. 156–158 Exs. 7, 15–23 odd, 29–41 odd, 47–51 odd, 57, 61–71 odd, 83, 85, 87–89, 93, 95	pp. 176–180 Exs. 1–8, 11–17 odd, 21, 27, 29, 33, 37, 47–53 odd, 56, 59, 63–69 odd, 73, 75, 82, 89, 91, 96, 99, 103, 107–111, 116, 118, 121–123, 127, 129, 137	pp. 190–193 Exs. 1–4, 6, 9, 11, 15, 17–22, 25, 27, 33, 37, 41, 43, 45, 51, 57–61 odd, 67, 73, 75, 79, 81, 85–87, 90	pp. 201–203 Exs. 1–4, 5–15 odd, 23, 27, 33, 41, 47–53 odd, 60, 67–73 odd, 76, 78, 81, 82	Chapter 2 Test
2.2	**2.4**			**REVIEW**	
pp. 145–149 Exs. 9–17, 19, 27, 29, 41–49 odd, 59, 61, 65, 69, 71, 77–83 odd, 93, 97–99, 103, 105–108	pp. 164–165 Exs. 1–4, 5–13 odd, 17, 23, 33–39 odd, 43, 49–53 odd, 59, 65, 67, 71, 79, 93–96			pp. 206–209 Exs. 1, 5, 7, 15, 21, 25–31 odd, 37–43 odd, 49, 57–61 odd, 67–83 odd, 87, 94, 95, 103, 109–115 odd, 123, 131, 135, 140, 143, 147, 151	Begin Chapter 3
Yearly Pacing	Chapter 2 Total – 5.5 days		Remaining – 68.5 days		

Polynomial and Rational Functions

2

In Mathematics

Functions defined by polynomial expressions are called polynomial functions, and functions defined by rational expressions are called rational functions.

In Real Life

Polynomial and rational functions are often used to model real-life phenomena. For instance, you can model the per capita cigarette consumption in the United States with a polynomial function. You can use the model to determine whether the addition of cigarette warnings affected consumption. (See Exercise 85, page 134.)

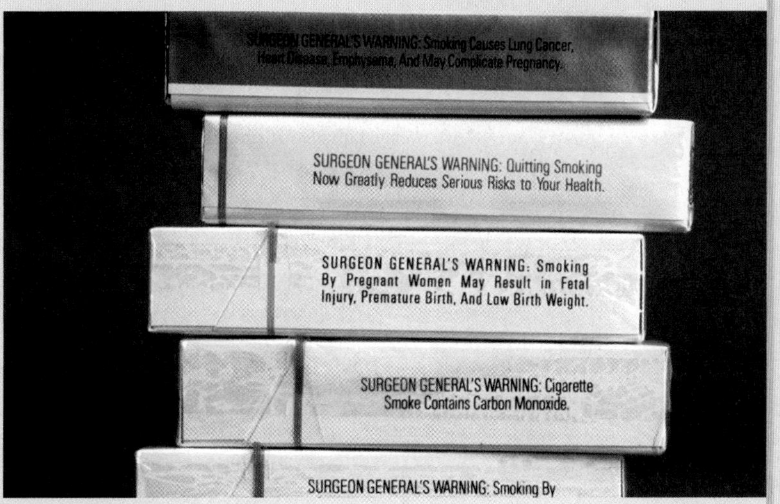

Michael Newman/PhotoEdit

IN CAREERS

There are many careers that use polynomial and rational functions. Several are listed below.

- Architect
  Exercise 82, page 134
- Chemist
  Example 80, page 192
- Forester
  Exercise 103, page 148
- Safety Engineer
  Exercise 78, page 203

PLAN AND PREPARE

Main Ideas

In Chapter 2, students learn to analyze and graph polynomial and rational functions. The chapter begins with identifying key characteristics and creating graphs of quadratic and other polynomial functions. Students then learn to use polynomial division to find both real and complex roots. Next they learn how to find asymptotes, intercepts, and holes as they graph rational functions. Finally, students learn how to solve problems by using nonlinear inequalities.

Chapter Planning Guide

Chapter Resources

- Complete Solutions Guide

Interactive Technology

- Instructor Success Organizer
- Notetaking Guide IAE
- Instructional DVDs
- Animated Precalculus
- PowerLecture with ExamView

1 PLAN AND PREPARE

Warm-up Exercises

Transparency Available
Available at the Instructor's companion site.

Notetaking Guide

Transparency Available
Promotes interactive learning and notetaking skills.
Available at the Instructor's companion site.

Animated Precalculus

An **Animated Precalculus** tutorial is available at the Student companion site for **Section 2.1.**

Pacing

Average: 1 day
Advanced: 1 day
Block: 0.5 block with 2.2

2 FOCUS AND MOTIVATE

Essential Question

How do you sketch graphs and write equations for parabolas? **Tell students that they will learn how to answer this question by studying transformations of $y = x^2$.**

2.1 Quadratic Functions and Models

What you should learn

- Analyze graphs of quadratic functions.
- Write quadratic functions in standard form and use the results to sketch graphs of functions.
- Find minimum and maximum values of quadratic functions in real-life applications.

Why you should learn it

Quadratic functions can be used to model data to analyze consumer behavior. For instance, in Exercise 79 on page 134, you will use a quadratic function to model the revenue earned from manufacturing handheld video games.

© John Henley/Corbis

The Graph of a Quadratic Function

In this and the next section, you will study the graphs of polynomial functions. In Section 1.6, you were introduced to the following basic functions.

$f(x) = ax + b$ Linear function

$f(x) = c$ Constant function

$f(x) = x^2$ Squaring function

These functions are examples of **polynomial functions.**

> **Definition of Polynomial Function**
>
> Let n be a nonnegative integer and let $a_n, a_{n-1}, \ldots, a_2, a_1, a_0$ be real numbers with $a_n \neq 0$. The function given by
>
> $$f(x) = a_nx^n + a_{n-1}x^{n-1} + \cdots + a_2x^2 + a_1x + a_0$$
>
> is called a **polynomial function of x with degree n.**

Polynomial functions are classified by degree. For instance, a constant function $f(x) = c$ with $c \neq 0$ has degree 0, and a linear function $f(x) = ax + b$ with $a \neq 0$ has degree 1. In this section, you will study second-degree polynomial functions, which are called **quadratic functions.**

For instance, each of the following functions is a quadratic function.

$$f(x) = x^2 + 6x + 2$$
$$g(x) = 2(x + 1)^2 - 3$$
$$h(x) = 9 + \tfrac{1}{4}x^2$$
$$k(x) = -3x^2 + 4$$
$$m(x) = (x - 2)(x + 1)$$

Note that the squaring function is a simple quadratic function that has degree 2.

> **Definition of Quadratic Function**
>
> Let a, b, and c be real numbers with $a \neq 0$. The function given by
>
> $f(x) = ax^2 + bx + c$ Quadratic function
>
> is called a **quadratic function.**

The graph of a quadratic function is a special type of "U"-shaped curve called a **parabola.** Parabolas occur in many real-life applications—especially those involving reflective properties of satellite dishes and flashlight reflectors. You will study these properties in Section 10.2.

Resource Planning Guide

Chapter Resources
- Complete Solutions Guide

Workbooks
- Notetaking Guide
- Student Solutions Guide

Interactive Technology
- Instructor Success Organizer
- Notetaking Guide IAE
- Instructional DVDs
- Animated Precalculus
- PowerLecture with ExamView

All parabolas are symmetric with respect to a line called the **axis of symmetry,** or simply the **axis** of the parabola. The point where the axis intersects the parabola is the **vertex** of the parabola, as shown in Figure 2.1. If the leading coefficient is positive, the graph of

$$f(x) = ax^2 + bx + c$$

is a parabola that opens upward. If the leading coefficient is negative, the graph of

$$f(x) = ax^2 + bx + c$$

is a parabola that opens downward.

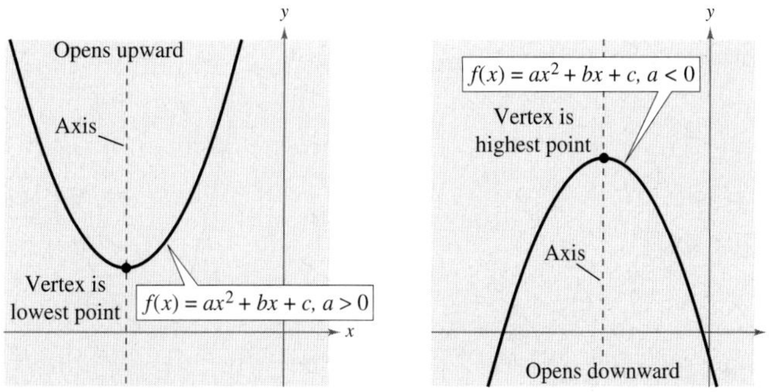

Leading coefficient is positive. Leading coefficient is negative.

FIGURE 2.1

The simplest type of quadratic function is

$$f(x) = ax^2.$$

Its graph is a parabola whose vertex is (0, 0). If $a > 0$, the vertex is the point with the *minimum* y-value on the graph, and if $a < 0$, the vertex is the point with the *maximum* y-value on the graph, as shown in Figure 2.2.

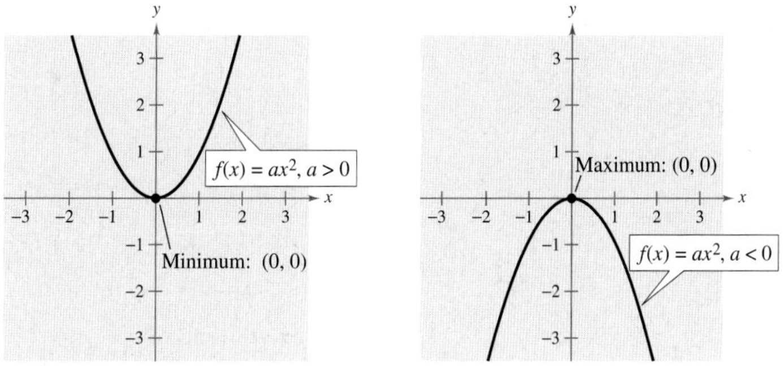

Leading coefficient is positive. Leading coefficient is negative.

FIGURE 2.2

When sketching the graph of $f(x) = ax^2$, it is helpful to use the graph of $y = x^2$ as a reference, as discussed in Section 1.7.

3 TEACH

Extra Example 1

a. Sketch and compare the graphs of $y = x^2$ and $h(x) = \frac{5}{2}x^2$.
Compared with $y = x^2$, each output of $h(x) = \frac{5}{2}x^2$ "stretches" by a factor of $\frac{5}{2}$, creating a narrower parabola.

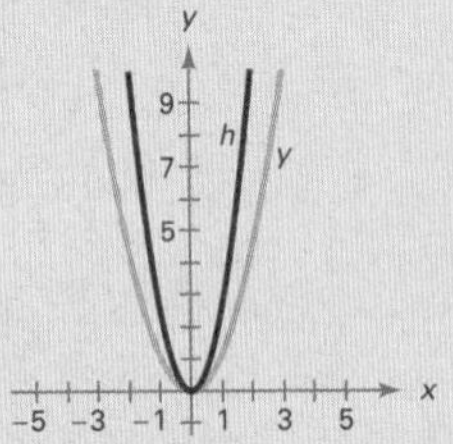

b. Sketch and compare the graphs of $y = x^2$ and $g(x) = -\frac{1}{6}x^2$.
Compared with $y = x^2$, each output of $g(x) = -\frac{1}{6}x^2$ "shrinks" by a factor of $\frac{1}{6}$, creating the broader parabola shown. Also, $g(x) = -\frac{1}{6}x^2$ is reflected over the x-axis.

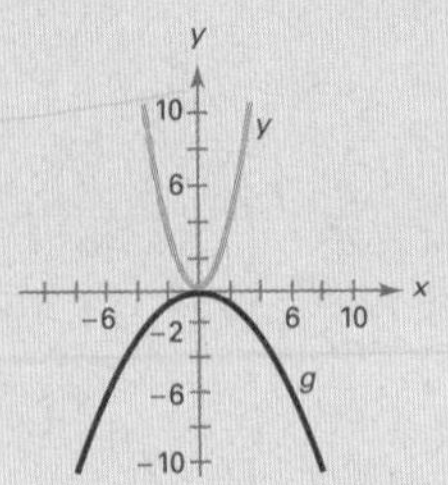

Example 1 Sketching Graphs of Quadratic Functions

a. Compare the graphs of $y = x^2$ and $f(x) = \frac{1}{3}x^2$.

b. Compare the graphs of $y = x^2$ and $g(x) = 2x^2$.

Algebra Help

You can review the techniques for shifting, reflecting, and stretching graphs in Section 1.7.

Solution

a. Compared with $y = x^2$, each output of $f(x) = \frac{1}{3}x^2$ "shrinks" by a factor of $\frac{1}{3}$, creating the broader parabola shown in Figure 2.3.

b. Compared with $y = x^2$, each output of $g(x) = 2x^2$ "stretches" by a factor of 2, creating the narrower parabola shown in Figure 2.4.

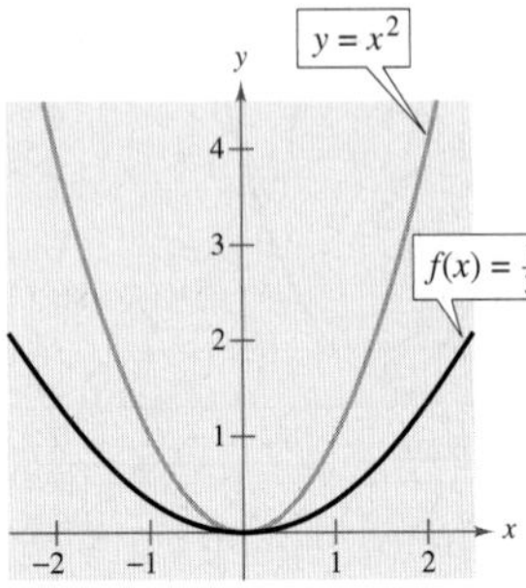

FIGURE 2.3

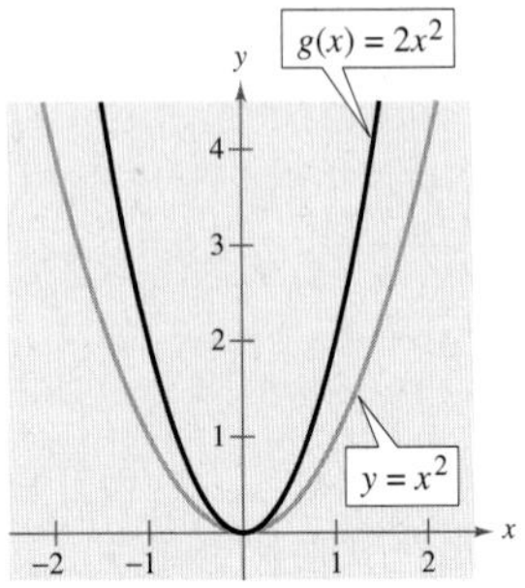

FIGURE 2.4

CHECKPoint Now try Exercise 13.

In Example 1, note that the coefficient a determines how widely the parabola given by $f(x) = ax^2$ opens. If $|a|$ is small, the parabola opens more widely than if $|a|$ is large.

Recall from Section 1.7 that the graphs of $y = f(x \pm c)$, $y = f(x) \pm c$, $y = f(-x)$, and $y = -f(x)$ are rigid transformations of the graph of $y = f(x)$. For instance, in Figure 2.5, notice how the graph of $y = x^2$ can be transformed to produce the graphs of $f(x) = -x^2 + 1$ and $g(x) = (x + 2)^2 - 3$.

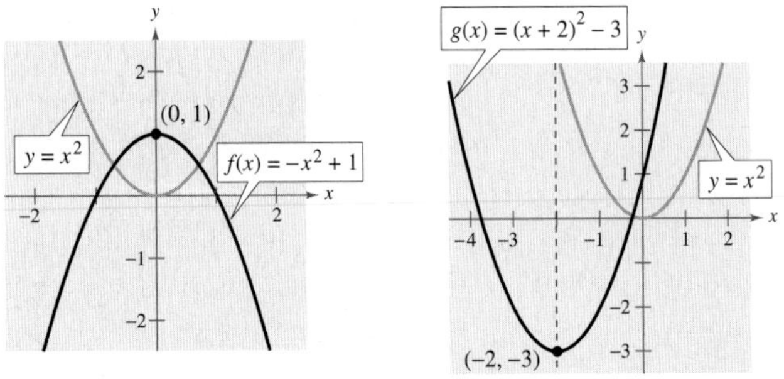

Reflection in x-axis followed by an upward shift of one unit

Left shift of two units followed by a downward shift of three units

FIGURE 2.5

The Standard Form of a Quadratic Function

The **standard form** of a quadratic function is $f(x) = a(x - h)^2 + k$. This form is especially convenient for sketching a parabola because it identifies the vertex of the parabola as (h, k).

> ### Study Tip
> The standard form of a quadratic function identifies four basic transformations of the graph of $y = x^2$.
>
> **a.** The factor $|a|$ produces a vertical stretch or shrink.
>
> **b.** If $a < 0$, the graph is reflected in the x-axis.
>
> **c.** The factor $(x - h)^2$ represents a horizontal shift of h units.
>
> **d.** The term k represents a vertical shift of k units.

> **Standard Form of a Quadratic Function**
>
> The quadratic function given by
>
> $$f(x) = a(x - h)^2 + k, \quad a \neq 0$$
>
> is in **standard form.** The graph of f is a parabola whose axis is the vertical line $x = h$ and whose vertex is the point (h, k). If $a > 0$, the parabola opens upward, and if $a < 0$, the parabola opens downward.

To graph a parabola, it is helpful to begin by writing the quadratic function in standard form using the process of completing the square, as illustrated in Example 2. In this example, notice that when completing the square, you *add and subtract* the square of half the coefficient of x within the parentheses instead of adding the value to each side of the equation as is done in Appendix A.5.

Example 2 Graphing a Parabola in Standard Form

Sketch the graph of $f(x) = 2x^2 + 8x + 7$ and identify the vertex and the axis of the parabola.

Solution

Begin by writing the quadratic function in standard form. Notice that the first step in completing the square is to factor out any coefficient of x^2 that is not 1.

> ### Algebra Help
> You can review the techniques for completing the square in Appendix A.5.

$f(x) = 2x^2 + 8x + 7$ — Write original function.

$= 2(x^2 + 4x) + 7$ — Factor 2 out of x-terms.

$= 2(x^2 + 4x + \underbrace{4}_{(4/2)^2} - 4) + 7$ — Add and subtract 4 within parentheses.

After adding and subtracting 4 within the parentheses, you must now regroup the terms to form a perfect square trinomial. The -4 can be removed from inside the parentheses; however, because of the 2 outside of the parentheses, you must multiply -4 by 2, as shown below.

$f(x) = 2(x^2 + 4x + 4) - 2(4) + 7$ — Regroup terms.

$= 2(x^2 + 4x + 4) - 8 + 7$ — Simplify.

$= 2(x + 2)^2 - 1$ — Write in standard form.

From this form, you can see that the graph of f is a parabola that opens upward and has its vertex at $(-2, -1)$. This corresponds to a left shift of two units and a downward shift of one unit relative to the graph of $y = 2x^2$, as shown in Figure 2.6. In the figure, you can see that the axis of the parabola is the vertical line through the vertex, $x = -2$.

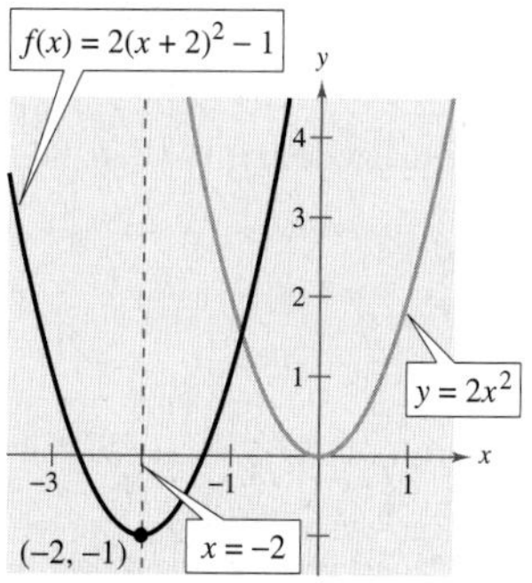

FIGURE 2.6

CHECKPoint Now try Exercise 19.

Extra Example 2

Sketch the graph of $f(x) = x^2 - 10x + 25$, and identify the vertex and the axis of the parabola.

Vertex: (5, 0); axis of the parabola: $x = 5$

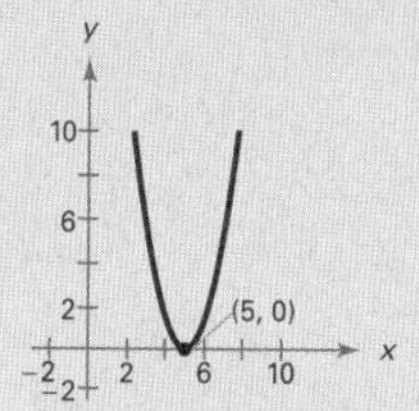

Avoiding Common Errors

When completing the square, students must be careful when introducing the necessary square. When regrouping, students often forget to multiply the subtracted square by the value factored out of the x-terms.

Extra Example 3

Sketch the graph of
$f(x) = -x^2 - 4x + 21$,
and identify the vertex and x-intercepts.

Vertex: $(-2, 25)$;
x-intercepts: $(-7, 0)$, $(3, 0)$

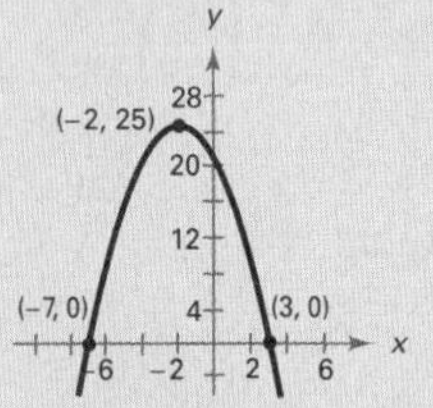

Extra Example 4

Write the standard form of the equation of the parabola whose vertex is $(-4, 11)$ and that passes through the point $(-6, 15)$.

$f(x) = (x + 4)^2 + 11$

Algebra Help

You can review the techniques for using the Quadratic Formula in Appendix A.5.

To find the x-intercepts of the graph of $f(x) = ax^2 + bx + c$, you must solve the equation $ax^2 + bx + c = 0$. If $ax^2 + bx + c$ does not factor, you can use the Quadratic Formula to find the x-intercepts. Remember, however, that a parabola may not have x-intercepts.

Example 3 Finding the Vertex and x-Intercepts of a Parabola

Sketch the graph of $f(x) = -x^2 + 6x - 8$ and identify the vertex and x-intercepts.

Solution

$f(x) = -x^2 + 6x - 8$	Write original function.
$= -(x^2 - 6x) - 8$	Factor -1 out of x-terms.
$= -(x^2 - 6x + 9 - 9) - 8$ (where $9 = (-6/2)^2$)	Add and subtract 9 within parentheses.
$= -(x^2 - 6x + 9) - (-9) - 8$	Regroup terms.
$= -(x - 3)^2 + 1$	Write in standard form.

From this form, you can see that f is a parabola that opens downward with vertex $(3, 1)$. The x-intercepts of the graph are determined as follows.

$-(x^2 - 6x + 8) = 0$	Factor out -1.
$-(x - 2)(x - 4) = 0$	Factor.
$x - 2 = 0 \Rightarrow x = 2$	Set 1st factor equal to 0.
$x - 4 = 0 \Rightarrow x = 4$	Set 2nd factor equal to 0.

So, the x-intercepts are $(2, 0)$ and $(4, 0)$, as shown in Figure 2.7.

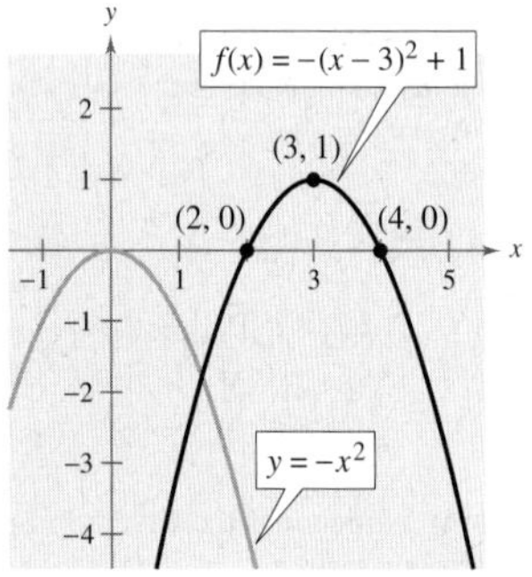

FIGURE 2.7

CHECKPoint Now try Exercise 25.

Example 4 Writing the Equation of a Parabola

Write the standard form of the equation of the parabola whose vertex is $(1, 2)$ and that passes through the point $(3, -6)$.

Solution

Because the vertex of the parabola is at $(h, k) = (1, 2)$, the equation has the form

$f(x) = a(x - 1)^2 + 2.$ Substitute for h and k in standard form.

Because the parabola passes through the point $(3, -6)$, it follows that $f(3) = -6$. So,

$f(x) = a(x - 1)^2 + 2$	Write in standard form.
$-6 = a(3 - 1)^2 + 2$	Substitute 3 for x and -6 for $f(x)$.
$-6 = 4a + 2$	Simplify.
$-8 = 4a$	Subtract 2 from each side.
$-2 = a.$	Divide each side by 4.

The equation in standard form is $f(x) = -2(x - 1)^2 + 2$. The graph of f is shown in Figure 2.8.

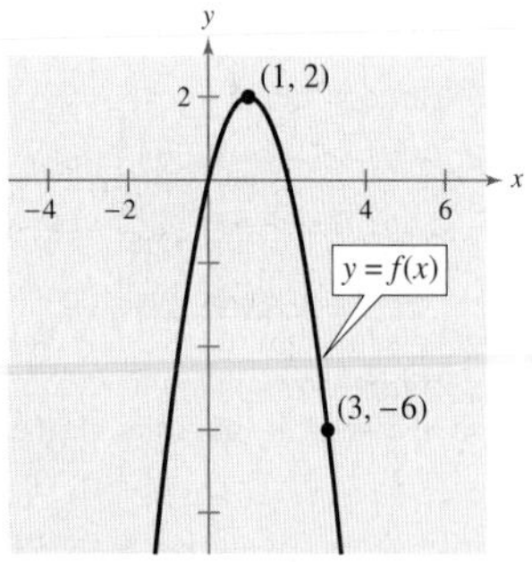

FIGURE 2.8

CHECKPoint Now try Exercise 47.

Differentiated Instruction

Visual Learners Display several graphs of various vertical and horizontal translations of a parabola. Have students practice identifying the vertex and x-intercepts of each parabola. Then have students use the vertex and x-intercepts to write the equation of each parabola.

Finding Minimum and Maximum Values

Many applications involve finding the maximum or minimum value of a quadratic function. By completing the square of the quadratic function $f(x) = ax^2 + bx + c$, you can rewrite the function in standard form (see Exercise 95).

$$f(x) = a\left(x + \frac{b}{2a}\right)^2 + \left(c - \frac{b^2}{4a}\right) \qquad \text{Standard form}$$

So, the vertex of the graph of f is $\left(-\frac{b}{2a}, f\left(-\frac{b}{2a}\right)\right)$, which implies the following.

Minimum and Maximum Values of Quadratic Functions

Consider the function $f(x) = ax^2 + bx + c$ with vertex $\left(-\frac{b}{2a}, f\left(-\frac{b}{2a}\right)\right)$.

1. If $a > 0$, f has a *minimum* at $x = -\frac{b}{2a}$. The minimum value is $f\left(-\frac{b}{2a}\right)$.

2. If $a < 0$, f has a *maximum* at $x = -\frac{b}{2a}$. The maximum value is $f\left(-\frac{b}{2a}\right)$.

Example 5 The Maximum Height of a Baseball

A baseball is hit at a point 3 feet above the ground at a velocity of 100 feet per second and at an angle of 45° with respect to the ground. The path of the baseball is given by the function $f(x) = -0.0032x^2 + x + 3$, where $f(x)$ is the height of the baseball (in feet) and x is the horizontal distance from home plate (in feet). What is the maximum height reached by the baseball?

Algebraic Solution

For this quadratic function, you have

$$f(x) = ax^2 + bx + c$$
$$= -0.0032x^2 + x + 3$$

which implies that $a = -0.0032$ and $b = 1$. Because $a < 0$, the function has a maximum when $x = -b/(2a)$. So, you can conclude that the baseball reaches its maximum height when it is x feet from home plate, where x is

$$x = -\frac{b}{2a}$$
$$= -\frac{1}{2(-0.0032)}$$
$$= 156.25 \text{ feet.}$$

At this distance, the maximum height is

$$f(156.25) = -0.0032(156.25)^2 + 156.25 + 3$$
$$= 81.125 \text{ feet.}$$

CHECKPoint Now try Exercise 75.

Graphical Solution

Use a graphing utility to graph

$$y = -0.0032x^2 + x + 3$$

so that you can see the important features of the parabola. Use the *maximum* feature (see Figure 2.9) or the *zoom* and *trace* features (see Figure 2.10) of the graphing utility to approximate the maximum height on the graph to be $y \approx 81.125$ feet at $x \approx 156.25$.

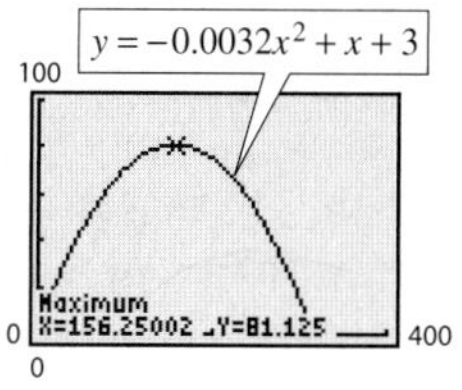

FIGURE 2.9

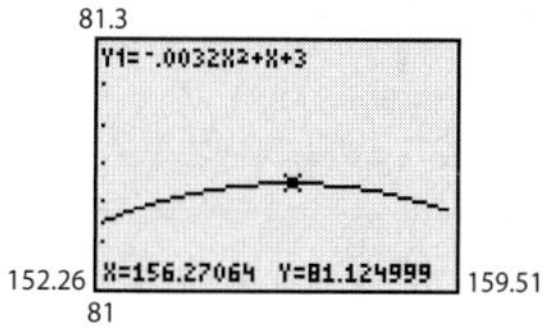

FIGURE 2.10

Extra Example 5

The height y (in feet) of a ball thrown by a child is given by $y = -\frac{1}{8}x^2 + x + 4$, where x is the horizontal distance (in feet) from where the ball is thrown (see figure). How high is the ball when it is at its maximum height?

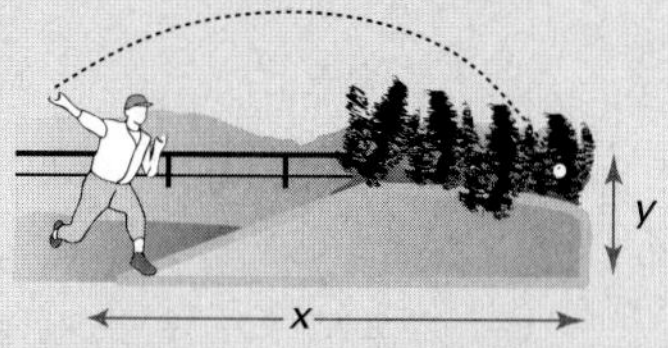

6 feet

Closing the Lesson

Have students summarize the major points of the lesson and answer the Essential Question: How do you sketch graphs and write equations for parabolas?

- **The standard form of a quadratic function $f(x) = a(x - h)^2 + k$ helps you identify the vertex point (h, k), the vertical stretch factor $|a|$, and reflection in the x-axis if $a < 0$.**
- **Use completing the square, factoring, and substitution to write equations in different forms to identify intercepts, vertex, stretch, and reflection.**
- **Find the vertex of a quadratic function $f(x) = ax^2 + bx + c$ by calculating the ordered pair $\left(-\frac{b}{2a}, f\left(-\frac{b}{2a}\right)\right)$.**

4 PRACTICE AND APPLY

Assignment Guide

Transparencies Available
Available at the Instructor's companion site.

Average:
Day 1: pp. 132–135
Exs. 7–12, 15, 21–25 odd, 29, 31, 43–53 odd, 57, 58, 67, 69, 75–83 odd, 86–90, 95

Advanced:
Day 1: pp. 132–135
Exs. 7–12, 16, 22, 28–34 even, 44, 46, 50–54 even, 67, 69, 74–76, 78, 80–83, 86–90, 92–96 even, 100

Block:
pp. 132–135
Exs. 7–12, 15, 21–25 odd, 29, 31, 43–53 odd, 57, 58, 67, 69, 75–83 odd, 86–90, 95 (with 2.2)

13. (a)

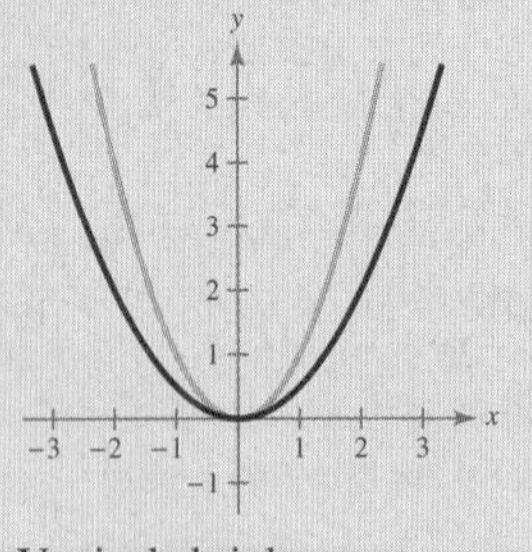

Vertical shrink

(b)

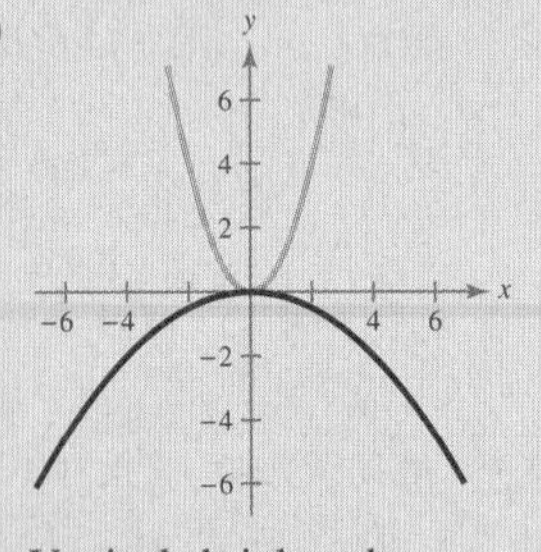

Vertical shrink and reflection in the x-axis

(c)

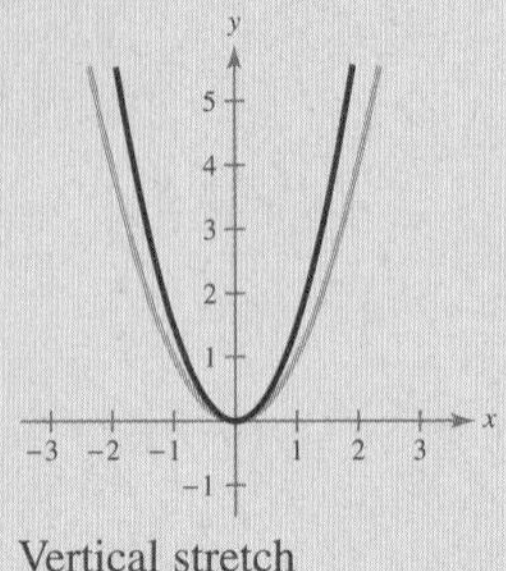

Vertical stretch

(d)

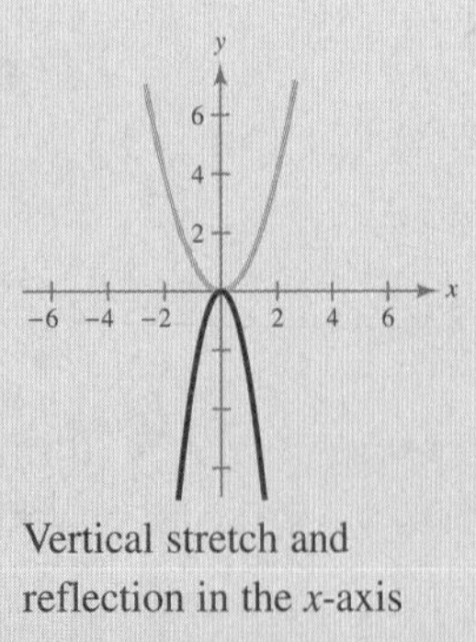

Vertical stretch and reflection in the x-axis

2.1 EXERCISES

See www.CalcChat.com for worked-out solutions to odd-numbered exercises.

VOCABULARY: Fill in the blanks.

1. Linear, constant, and squaring functions are examples of polynomial functions.
2. A polynomial function of degree n and leading coefficient a_n is a function of the form $f(x) = a_nx^n + a_{n-1}x^{n-1} + \cdots + a_1x + a_0$ $(a_n \neq 0)$ where n is a nonnegative integer and $a_n, a_{n-1}, \ldots, a_1, a_0$ are real numbers.
3. A quadratic function is a second-degree polynomial function, and its graph is called a parabola.
4. The graph of a quadratic function is symmetric about its axis.
5. If the graph of a quadratic function opens upward, then its leading coefficient is positive and the vertex of the graph is a minimum.
6. If the graph of a quadratic function opens downward, then its leading coefficient is negative and the vertex of the graph is a maximum.

SKILLS AND APPLICATIONS

In Exercises 7–12, match the quadratic function with its graph. [The graphs are labeled (a), (b), (c), (d), (e), and (f).]

(a)

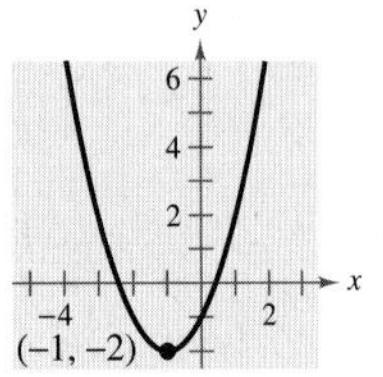

(b)

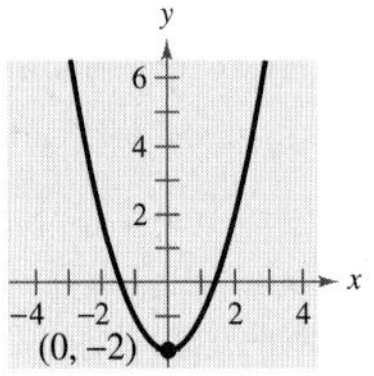

(c)

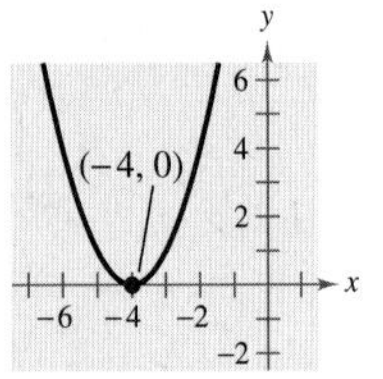

(d)

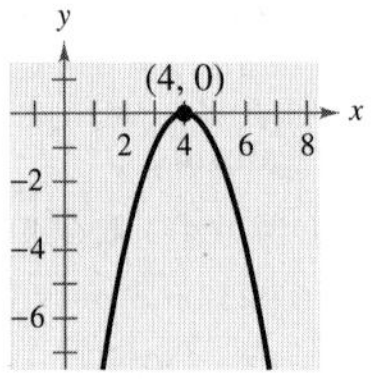

(e)

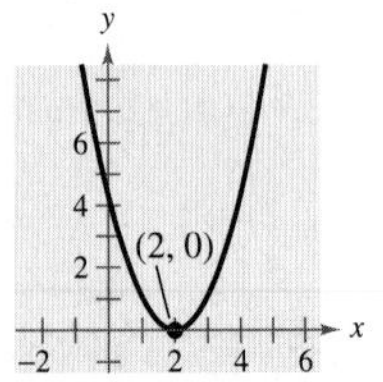

(f)

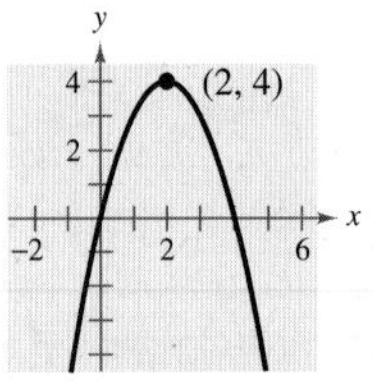

7. $f(x) = (x - 2)^2$ e
8. $f(x) = (x + 4)^2$ c
9. $f(x) = x^2 - 2$ b
10. $f(x) = (x + 1)^2 - 2$ a
11. $f(x) = 4 - (x - 2)^2$ f
12. $f(x) = -(x - 4)^2$ d

In Exercises 13–16, graph each function. Compare the graph of each function with the graph of $y = x^2$. 13–16. See margin.

13. (a) $f(x) = \frac{1}{2}x^2$ (b) $g(x) = -\frac{1}{8}x^2$
(c) $h(x) = \frac{3}{2}x^2$ (d) $k(x) = -3x^2$
14. (a) $f(x) = x^2 + 1$ (b) $g(x) = x^2 - 1$
(c) $h(x) = x^2 + 3$ (d) $k(x) = x^2 - 3$
15. (a) $f(x) = (x - 1)^2$ (b) $g(x) = (3x)^2 + 1$
(c) $h(x) = \left(\frac{1}{3}x\right)^2 - 3$ (d) $k(x) = (x + 3)^2$
16. (a) $f(x) = -\frac{1}{2}(x - 2)^2 + 1$
(b) $g(x) = \left[\frac{1}{2}(x - 1)\right]^2 - 3$
(c) $h(x) = -\frac{1}{2}(x + 2)^2 - 1$
(d) $k(x) = [2(x + 1)]^2 + 4$

In Exercises 17–34, sketch the graph of the quadratic function without using a graphing utility. Identify the vertex, axis of symmetry, and x-intercept(s). 17–34. See margin.

17. $f(x) = 1 - x^2$
18. $g(x) = x^2 - 8$
19. $f(x) = x^2 + 7$
20. $h(x) = 12 - x^2$
21. $f(x) = \frac{1}{2}x^2 - 4$
22. $f(x) = 16 - \frac{1}{4}x^2$
23. $f(x) = (x + 4)^2 - 3$
24. $f(x) = (x - 6)^2 + 8$
25. $h(x) = x^2 - 8x + 16$
26. $g(x) = x^2 + 2x + 1$
27. $f(x) = x^2 - x + \frac{5}{4}$
28. $f(x) = x^2 + 3x + \frac{1}{4}$
29. $f(x) = -x^2 + 2x + 5$
30. $f(x) = -x^2 - 4x + 1$
31. $h(x) = 4x^2 - 4x + 21$
32. $f(x) = 2x^2 - x + 1$
33. $f(x) = \frac{1}{4}x^2 - 2x - 12$
34. $f(x) = -\frac{1}{3}x^2 + 3x - 6$

In Exercises 35–42, use a graphing utility to graph the quadratic function. Identify the vertex, axis of symmetry, and x-intercepts. Then check your results algebraically by writing the quadratic function in standard form. 35–42. See margin.

35. $f(x) = -(x^2 + 2x - 3)$
36. $f(x) = -(x^2 + x - 30)$
37. $g(x) = x^2 + 8x + 11$
38. $f(x) = x^2 + 10x + 14$
39. $f(x) = 2x^2 - 16x + 31$
40. $f(x) = -4x^2 + 24x - 41$
41. $g(x) = \frac{1}{2}(x^2 + 4x - 2)$
42. $f(x) = \frac{3}{5}(x^2 + 6x - 5)$

14–42. See Additional Answers beginning on page AA1.

In Exercises 43–46, write an equation for the parabola in standard form.

43.

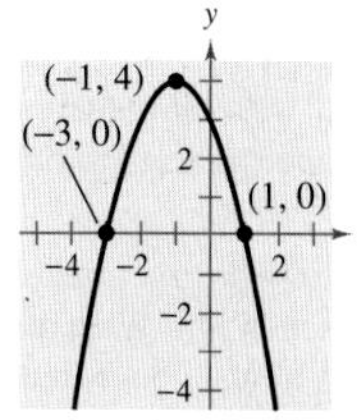

$y = -(x + 1)^2 + 4$

44.

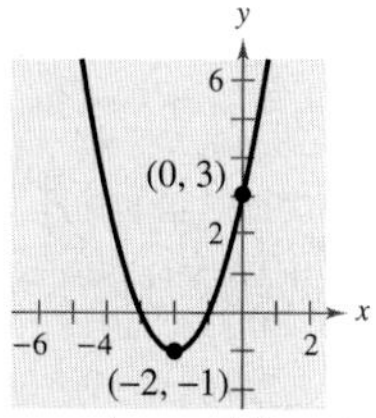

$y = (x + 2)^2 - 1$

45.

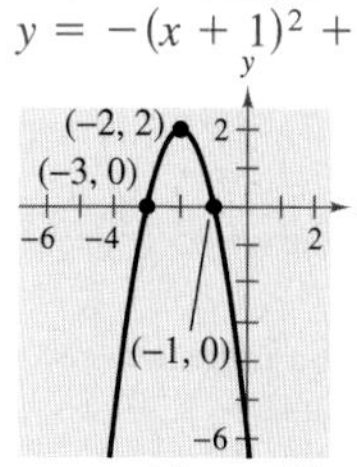

$y = -2(x + 2)^2 + 2$

46.

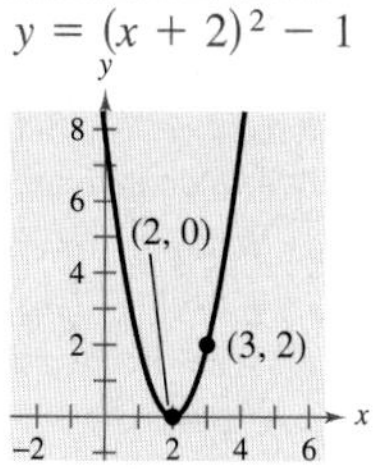

$y = 2(x - 2)^2$

In Exercises 47–56, write the standard form of the equation of the parabola that has the indicated vertex and whose graph passes through the given point.

47. Vertex: $(-2, 5)$; point: $(0, 9)$ $f(x) = (x + 2)^2 + 5$

48. Vertex: $(4, -1)$; point: $(2, 3)$ $f(x) = (x - 4)^2 - 1$

49. Vertex: $(1, -2)$; point: $(-1, 14)$ $f(x) = 4(x - 1)^2 - 2$

50. Vertex: $(2, 3)$; point: $(0, 2)$ $f(x) = -\frac{1}{4}(x - 2)^2 + 3$

51. Vertex: $(5, 12)$; point: $(7, 15)$ $f(x) = \frac{3}{4}(x - 5)^2 + 12$

52. Vertex: $(-2, -2)$; point: $(-1, 0)$ $f(x) = 2(x + 2)^2 - 2$

53. Vertex: $\left(-\frac{1}{4}, \frac{3}{2}\right)$; point: $(-2, 0)$ $f(x) = -\frac{24}{49}\left(x + \frac{1}{4}\right)^2 + \frac{3}{2}$

54. Vertex: $\left(\frac{5}{2}, -\frac{3}{4}\right)$; point: $(-2, 4)$ $f(x) = \frac{19}{81}\left(x - \frac{5}{2}\right)^2 - \frac{3}{4}$

55. Vertex: $\left(-\frac{5}{2}, 0\right)$; point: $\left(-\frac{7}{2}, -\frac{16}{3}\right)$ $f(x) = -\frac{16}{3}\left(x + \frac{5}{2}\right)^2$

56. Vertex: $(6, 6)$; point: $\left(\frac{61}{10}, \frac{3}{2}\right)$ $f(x) = -450(x - 6)^2 + 6$

GRAPHICAL REASONING In Exercises 57 and 58, determine the x-intercept(s) of the graph visually. Then find the x-intercept(s) algebraically to confirm your results.

57. $y = x^2 - 4x - 5$

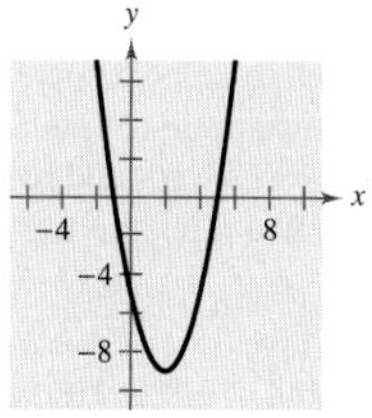

$(5, 0), (-1, 0)$

58. $y = 2x^2 + 5x - 3$

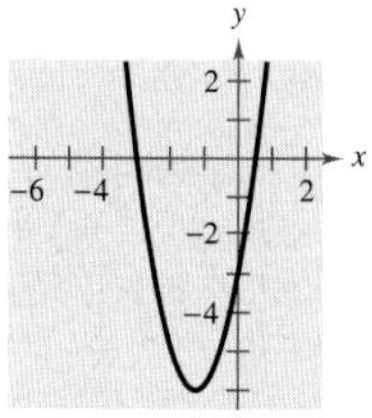

$(-3, 0), \left(\frac{1}{2}, 0\right)$

In Exercises 59–64, use a graphing utility to graph the quadratic function. Find the x-intercepts of the graph and compare them with the solutions of the corresponding quadratic equation when $f(x) = 0$. 59–64. See margin.

59. $f(x) = x^2 - 4x$

60. $f(x) = -2x^2 + 10x$

61. $f(x) = x^2 - 9x + 18$

62. $f(x) = x^2 - 8x - 20$

63. $f(x) = 2x^2 - 7x - 30$

64. $f(x) = \frac{7}{10}(x^2 + 12x - 45)$

In Exercises 65–70, find two quadratic functions, one that opens upward and one that opens downward, whose graphs have the given x-intercepts. (There are many correct answers.) 65–70. See margin.

65. $(-1, 0), (3, 0)$

66. $(-5, 0), (5, 0)$

67. $(0, 0), (10, 0)$

68. $(4, 0), (8, 0)$

69. $(-3, 0), \left(-\frac{1}{2}, 0\right)$

70. $\left(-\frac{5}{2}, 0\right), (2, 0)$

In Exercises 71–74, find two positive real numbers whose product is a maximum.

71. The sum is 110. 55, 55

72. The sum is S. $\frac{S}{2}, \frac{S}{2}$

73. The sum of the first and twice the second is 24. 12, 6

74. The sum of the first and three times the second is 42. 21, 7

75. PATH OF A DIVER The path of a diver is given by

$$y = -\frac{4}{9}x^2 + \frac{24}{9}x + 12$$

where y is the height (in feet) and x is the horizontal distance from the end of the diving board (in feet). What is the maximum height of the diver? 16 ft

76. HEIGHT OF A BALL The height y (in feet) of a punted football is given by

$$y = -\frac{16}{2025}x^2 + \frac{9}{5}x + 1.5$$

where x is the horizontal distance (in feet) from the point at which the ball is punted.

(a) How high is the ball when it is punted? 1.5 ft

(b) What is the maximum height of the punt? See margin.

(c) How long is the punt? About 228.64 ft

77. MINIMUM COST A manufacturer of lighting fixtures has daily production costs of $C = 800 - 10x + 0.25x^2$, where C is the total cost (in dollars) and x is the number of units produced. How many fixtures should be produced each day to yield a minimum cost? See margin.

78. MAXIMUM PROFIT The profit P (in hundreds of dollars) that a company makes depends on the amount x (in hundreds of dollars) the company spends on advertising according to the model $P = 230 + 20x - 0.5x^2$. What expenditure for advertising will yield a maximum profit? $2000

59.

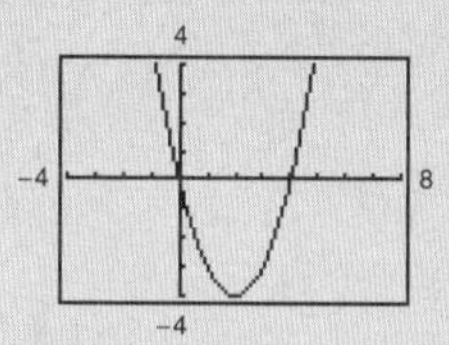

$(0, 0), (4, 0)$

60.

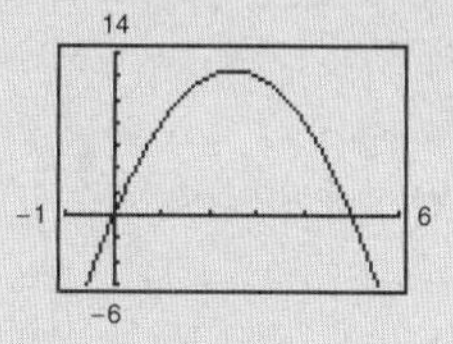

$(0, 0), (5, 0)$

61.

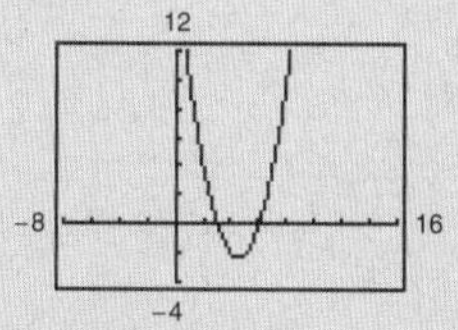

$(3, 0), (6, 0)$

62.

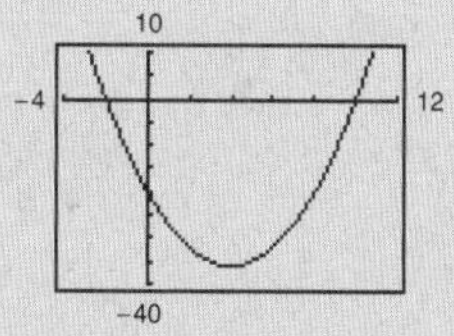

$(-2, 0), (10, 0)$

63.

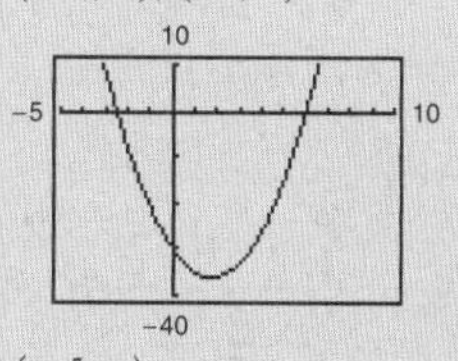

$\left(-\frac{5}{2}, 0\right), (6, 0)$

64.

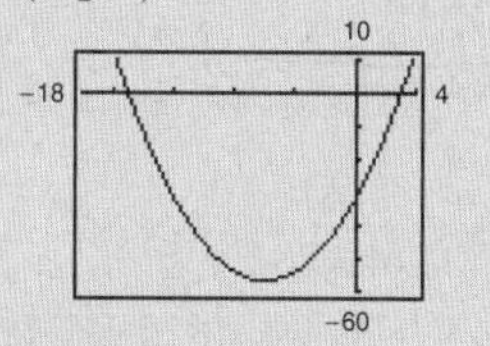

$(-15, 0), (3, 0)$

65. $f(x) = x^2 - 2x - 3$
$g(x) = -x^2 + 2x + 3$

66. $f(x) = x^2 - 25$
$g(x) = -x^2 + 25$

67. $f(x) = x^2 - 10x$
$g(x) = -x^2 + 10x$

68. $f(x) = x^2 - 12x + 32$
$g(x) = -x^2 + 12x - 32$

69. $f(x) = 2x^2 + 7x + 3$
$g(x) = -2x^2 - 7x - 3$

70. $f(x) = 2x^2 + x - 10$
$g(x) = -2x^2 - x + 10$

76. (b) $\frac{6657}{64}$ ft $\approx$ 104.02 ft

77. 20 fixtures

80. (a) \$408; \$468; \$432

(b) \$6.25 per pet; \$468.75

Answers will vary.

81. (a) $A = \dfrac{8x(50 - x)}{3}$

(c)

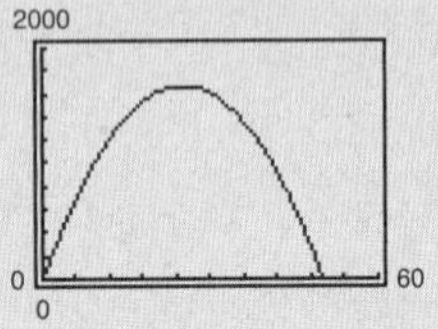

$x = 25$ ft, $y = 33\frac{1}{3}$ ft

(d) $A = -\frac{8}{3}(x - 25)^2 + \frac{5000}{3}$

(e) They are identical.

82. (a)

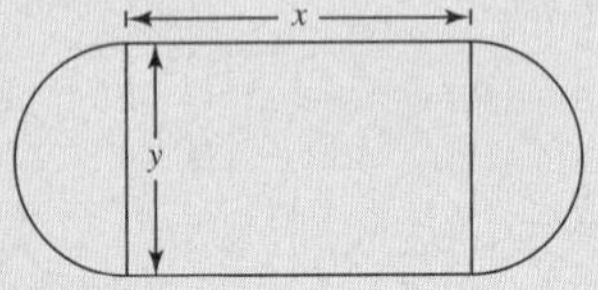

(b) $r = \dfrac{1}{2}y$; $d = y\pi$

(c) $y = \dfrac{200 - 2x}{\pi}$

(d) $A = x\left(\dfrac{200 - 2x}{\pi}\right)$;

$x = 50$ m, $y = \dfrac{100}{\pi}$ m

83. $R = -100x^2 + 3500x$, $15 \le x \le 20$

85. (a)

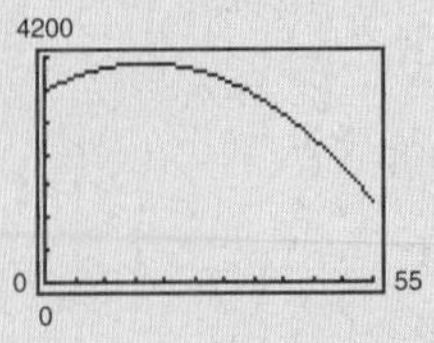

(b) 4075 cigarettes; Yes, the warning had an effect because the maximum consumption occurred in 1966.

(c) 7366 cigarettes per year; 20 cigarettes per day

79. MAXIMUM REVENUE The total revenue R earned (in thousands of dollars) from manufacturing handheld video games is given by

$$R(p) = -25p^2 + 1200p$$

where p is the price per unit (in dollars).

(a) Find the revenues when the price per unit is \$20, \$25, and \$30. \$14,000,000; \$14,375,000; \$13,500,000

(b) Find the unit price that will yield a maximum revenue. What is the maximum revenue? Explain your results. \$24; \$14,400,000; Answers will vary.

80. MAXIMUM REVENUE The total revenue R earned per day (in dollars) from a pet-sitting service is given by $R(p) = -12p^2 + 150p$, where p is the price charged per pet (in dollars). See margin.

(a) Find the revenues when the price per pet is \$4, \$6, and \$8.

(b) Find the price that will yield a maximum revenue. What is the maximum revenue? Explain your results.

81. NUMERICAL, GRAPHICAL, AND ANALYTICAL ANALYSIS A rancher has 200 feet of fencing to enclose two adjacent rectangular corrals (see figure). See margin.

(a) Write the area A of the corrals as a function of x.

(b) Create a table showing possible values of x and the corresponding areas of the corral. Use the table to estimate the dimensions that will produce the maximum enclosed area.

(c) Use a graphing utility to graph the area function. Use the graph to approximate the dimensions that will produce the maximum enclosed area.

(d) Write the area function in standard form to find analytically the dimensions that will produce the maximum area.

(e) Compare your results from parts (b), (c), and (d).

82. GEOMETRY An indoor physical fitness room consists of a rectangular region with a semicircle on each end. The perimeter of the room is to be a 200-meter single-lane running track. See margin.

(a) Draw a diagram that illustrates the problem. Let x and y represent the length and width of the rectangular region, respectively.

(b) Determine the radius of each semicircular end of the room. Determine the distance, in terms of y, around the inside edge of each semicircular part of the track.

(c) Use the result of part (b) to write an equation, in terms of x and y, for the distance traveled in one lap around the track. Solve for y.

(d) Use the result of part (c) to write the area A of the rectangular region as a function of x. What dimensions will produce a rectangle of maximum area?

83. MAXIMUM REVENUE A small theater has a seating capacity of 2000. When the ticket price is \$20, attendance is 1500. For each \$1 decrease in price, attendance increases by 100.

(a) Write the revenue R of the theater as a function of ticket price x. See margin.

(b) What ticket price will yield a maximum revenue? What is the maximum revenue? \$17.50; \$30,625

84. MAXIMUM AREA A Norman window is constructed by adjoining a semicircle to the top of an ordinary rectangular window (see figure). The perimeter of the window is 16 feet. (a) $A = \frac{1}{8}(64x - 4x^2 - \pi x^2)$

(a) Write the area A of the window as a function of x.

(b) What dimensions will produce a window of maximum area? $x \approx 4.48$ ft, $y \approx 2.24$ ft

85. GRAPHICAL ANALYSIS From 1950 through 2005, the per capita consumption C of cigarettes by Americans (age 18 and older) can be modeled by $C = 3565.0 + 60.30t - 1.783t^2$, $0 \le t \le 55$, where t is the year, with $t = 0$ corresponding to 1950. (Source: *Tobacco Outlook Report*) See margin.

(a) Use a graphing utility to graph the model.

(b) Use the graph of the model to approximate the maximum average annual consumption. Beginning in 1966, all cigarette packages were required by law to carry a health warning. Do you think the warning had any effect? Explain.

(c) In 2005, the U.S. population (age 18 and over) was 296,329,000. Of those, about 59,858,458 were smokers. What was the average annual cigarette consumption *per smoker* in 2005? What was the average daily cigarette consumption *per smoker*?

81(b). See Additional Answers beginning on page AA1.

86. DATA ANALYSIS: SALES The sales y (in billions of dollars) for Harley-Davidson from 2000 through 2007 are shown in the table. (Source: U.S. Harley-Davidson, Inc.) See margin.

Year	Sales, y
2000	2.91
2001	3.36
2002	4.09
2003	4.62
2004	5.02
2005	5.34
2006	5.80
2007	5.73

(a) Use a graphing utility to create a scatter plot of the data. Let x represent the year, with $x = 0$ corresponding to 2000.

(b) Use the *regression* feature of the graphing utility to find a quadratic model for the data.

(c) Use the graphing utility to graph the model in the same viewing window as the scatter plot. How well does the model fit the data?

(d) Use the *trace* feature of the graphing utility to approximate the year in which the sales for Harley-Davidson were the greatest.

(e) Verify your answer to part (d) algebraically.

(f) Use the model to predict the sales for Harley-Davidson in 2010.

EXPLORATION

87–90. See margin.

TRUE OR FALSE? **In Exercises 87–90, determine whether the statement is true or false. Justify your answer.**

87. The function given by $f(x) = -12x^2 - 1$ has no x-intercepts.

88. The graphs of $f(x) = -4x^2 - 10x + 7$ and $g(x) = 12x^2 + 30x + 1$ have the same axis of symmetry.

89. The graph of a quadratic function with a negative leading coefficient will have a maximum value at its vertex.

90. The graph of a quadratic function with a positive leading coefficient will have a minimum value at its vertex.

THINK ABOUT IT **In Exercises 91–94, find the values of b such that the function has the given maximum or minimum value.**

91. $f(x) = -x^2 + bx - 75$; Maximum value: 25 $b = \pm 20$

92. $f(x) = -x^2 + bx - 16$; Maximum value: 48 $b = \pm 16$

93. $f(x) = x^2 + bx + 26$; Minimum value: 10 $b = \pm 8$

94. $f(x) = x^2 + bx - 25$; Minimum value: -50 $b = \pm 10$

95. Write the quadratic function

$$f(x) = ax^2 + bx + c$$

in standard form to verify that the vertex occurs at

$$\left(-\frac{b}{2a}, f\left(-\frac{b}{2a}\right)\right). \quad f(x) = a\left(x + \frac{b}{2a}\right)^2 + \frac{4ac - b^2}{4a}$$

96. CAPSTONE The profit P (in millions of dollars) for a recreational vehicle retailer is modeled by a quadratic function of the form

$$P = at^2 + bt + c$$

where t represents the year. If you were president of the company, which of the models below would you prefer? Explain your reasoning. Conditions (a) and (d) are preferable because profits would be increasing.

(a) a is positive and $-b/(2a) \le t$.

(b) a is positive and $t \le -b/(2a)$.

(c) a is negative and $-b/(2a) \le t$.

(d) a is negative and $t \le -b/(2a)$.

97. GRAPHICAL ANALYSIS See margin.

(a) Graph $y = ax^2$ for $a = -2, -1, -0.5, 0.5, 1$ and 2. How does changing the value of a affect the graph?

(b) Graph $y = (x - h)^2$ for $h = -4, -2, 2$, and 4. How does changing the value of h affect the graph?

(c) Graph $y = x^2 + k$ for $k = -4, -2, 2$, and 4. How does changing the value of k affect the graph?

98. Describe the sequence of transformation from f to g given that $f(x) = x^2$ and $g(x) = a(x - h)^2 + k$. (Assume a, h, and k are positive.) See margin.

99. Is it possible for a quadratic equation to have only one x-intercept? Explain. See margin.

100. Assume that the function given by

$$f(x) = ax^2 + bx + c, \quad a \neq 0$$

has two real zeros. Show that the x-coordinate of the vertex of the graph is the average of the zeros of f. (*Hint:* Use the Quadratic Formula.) Answers will vary.

PROJECT: HEIGHT OF A BASKETBALL To work an extended application analyzing the height of a basketball after it has been dropped, visit this text's website at *academic.cengage.com*.

5 ASSESS AND RETEACH

Daily Homework Quiz

Transparency Available
Available at the Instructor's companion site.

86. (a) and (c)

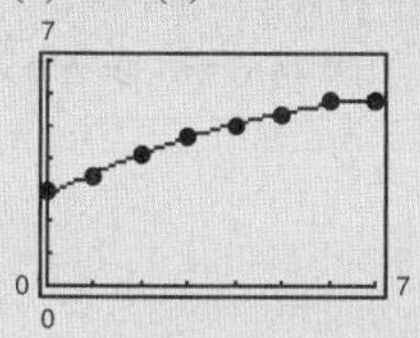

The model fits the data very well.

(b) $y = -0.0408x^2 + 0.715x + 2.82$

(d) 2007

(e) Answers will vary.

(f) \$5.89 billion

87. True. The equation has no real solutions, so the graph has no x-intercepts.

88. True. The vertex of $f(x)$ is $\left(-\frac{5}{4}, \frac{53}{4}\right)$ and the vertex of $g(x)$ is $\left(-\frac{5}{4}, -\frac{71}{4}\right)$.

89. True. The graph of a quadratic function with a negative leading coefficient will be a downward-opening parabola.

90. True. The graph of a quadratic function with a positive leading coefficient will be an upward-opening parabola.

97. (a)

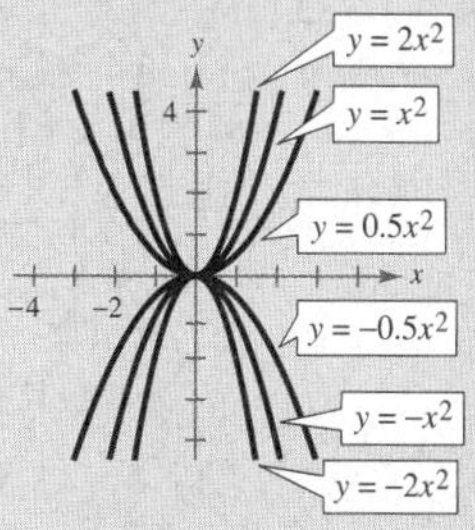

As $|a|$ increases, the parabola becomes narrower. For $a > 0$, the parabola opens upward. For $a < 0$, the parabola opens downward.

97. (b)

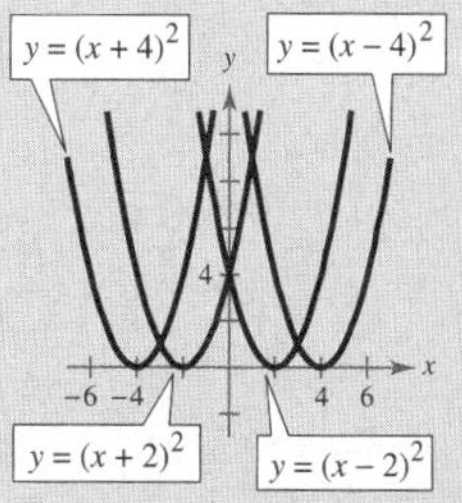

For $h < 0$, the vertex will be on the negative x-axis. For $h > 0$, the vertex will be on the positive x-axis. As $|h|$ increases, the parabola moves away from the origin.

(c)

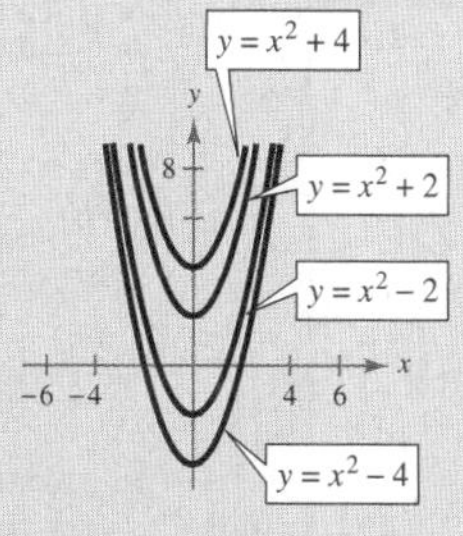

As $|k|$ increases, the vertex moves upward (for $k > 0$) or downward (for $k < 0$), away from the origin.

98. The vertex shifts horizontally to the right h units. The parabola will then become narrower ($a > 1$) or wider ($0 < a < 1$). The vertex will shift vertically k units upward.

99. Yes. A graph of a quadratic equation whose vertex is on the x-axis has only one x-intercept.

1 PLAN AND PREPARE

Warm-up Exercises

Transparency Available
Available at the Instructor's companion site.

Notetaking Guide

Transparency Available
Promotes interactive learning and notetaking skills. Available at the Instructor's companion site.

Animated Precalculus

An **Animated Precalculus** tutorial is available at the Student companion site for **Section 2.2.**

Pacing

Average: 1 day
Advanced: 1 day
Block: 0.5 block with 2.1

2 FOCUS AND MOTIVATE

Essential Question

How do you sketch the graphs of polynomial functions? **Tell students that they will learn how to answer this question by identifying end behavior, finding zeros, and plotting additional points.**

2.2 Polynomial Functions of Higher Degree

What you should learn

- Use transformations to sketch graphs of polynomial functions.
- Use the Leading Coefficient Test to determine the end behavior of graphs of polynomial functions.
- Find and use zeros of polynomial functions as sketching aids.
- Use the Intermediate Value Theorem to help locate zeros of polynomial functions.

Why you should learn it

You can use polynomial functions to analyze business situations such as how revenue is related to advertising expenses, as discussed in Exercise 104 on page 148.

Bill Aron/PhotoEdit, Inc.

Graphs of Polynomial Functions

In this section, you will study basic features of the graphs of polynomial functions. The first feature is that the graph of a polynomial function is **continuous.** Essentially, this means that the graph of a polynomial function has no breaks, holes, or gaps, as shown in Figure 2.11(a). The graph shown in Figure 2.11(b) is an example of a piecewise-defined function that is not continuous.

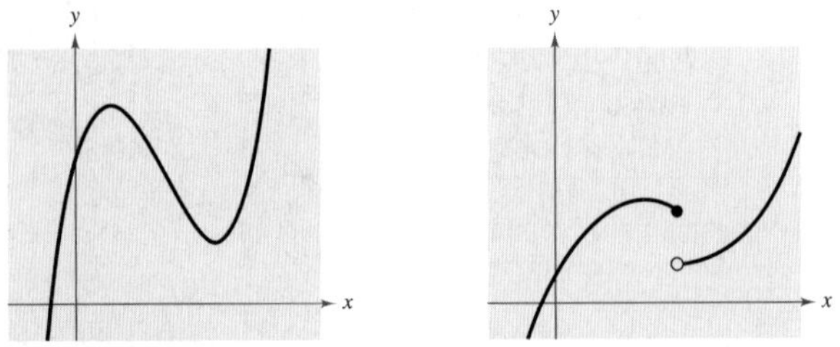

(a) Polynomial functions have continuous graphs.

(b) Functions with graphs that are not continuous are not polynomial functions.

FIGURE 2.11

The second feature is that the graph of a polynomial function has only smooth, rounded turns, as shown in Figure 2.12. A polynomial function cannot have a sharp turn. For instance, the function given by $f(x) = |x|$, which has a sharp turn at the point $(0, 0)$, as shown in Figure 2.13, is not a polynomial function.

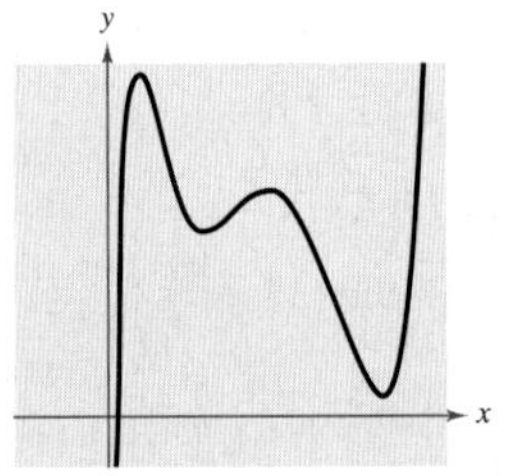

Polynomial functions have graphs with smooth, rounded turns.
FIGURE 2.12

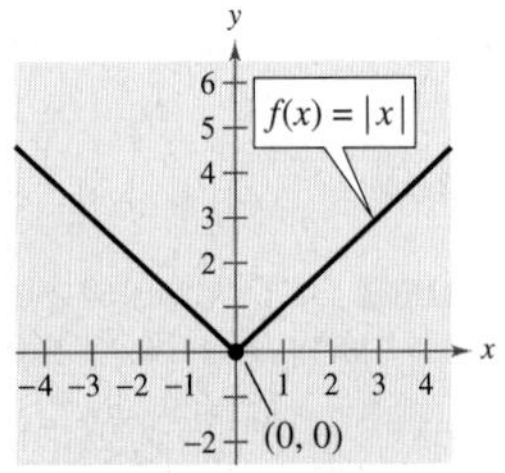

Graphs of polynomial functions cannot have sharp turns.
FIGURE 2.13

The graphs of polynomial functions of degree greater than 2 are more difficult to analyze than the graphs of polynomials of degree 0, 1, or 2. However, using the features presented in this section, coupled with your knowledge of point plotting, intercepts, and symmetry, you should be able to make reasonably accurate sketches *by hand.*

Resource Planning Guide

Chapter Resources
- Complete Solutions Guide

Workbooks
- Notetaking Guide
- Student Solutions Guide

Interactive Technology
- Instructor Success Organizer
- Notetaking Guide IAE
- Instructional DVDs
- Animated Precalculus
- PowerLecture with ExamView

Study Tip

For power functions given by $f(x) = x^n$, if n is even, then the graph of the function is symmetric with respect to the y-axis, and if n is odd, then the graph of the function is symmetric with respect to the origin.

The polynomial functions that have the simplest graphs are monomials of the form $f(x) = x^n$, where n is an integer greater than zero. From Figure 2.14, you can see that when n is *even*, the graph is similar to the graph of $f(x) = x^2$, and when n is *odd*, the graph is similar to the graph of $f(x) = x^3$. Moreover, the greater the value of n, the flatter the graph near the origin. Polynomial functions of the form $f(x) = x^n$ are often referred to as **power functions.**

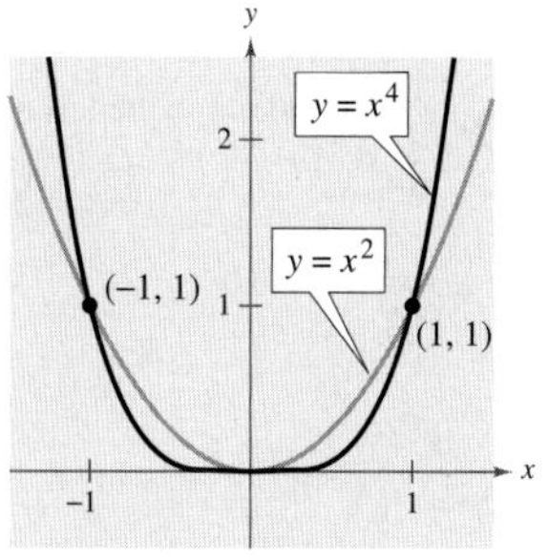

(a) If n is even, the graph of $y = x^n$ touches the axis at the x-intercept.

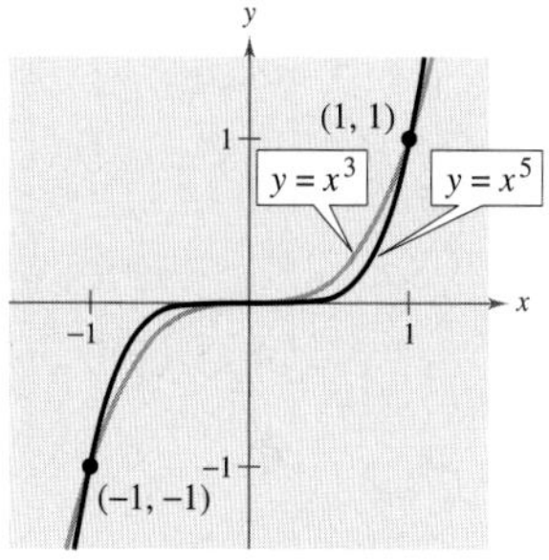

(b) If n is odd, the graph of $y = x^n$ crosses the axis at the x-intercept.

FIGURE 2.14

Example 1 Sketching Transformations of Polynomial Functions

Sketch the graph of each function.

a. $f(x) = -x^5$ **b.** $h(x) = (x + 1)^4$

Solution

a. Because the degree of $f(x) = -x^5$ is odd, its graph is similar to the graph of $y = x^3$. In Figure 2.15, note that the negative coefficient has the effect of reflecting the graph in the x-axis.

b. The graph of $h(x) = (x + 1)^4$, as shown in Figure 2.16, is a left shift by one unit of the graph of $y = x^4$.

Algebra Help

You can review the techniques for shifting, reflecting, and stretching graphs in Section 1.7.

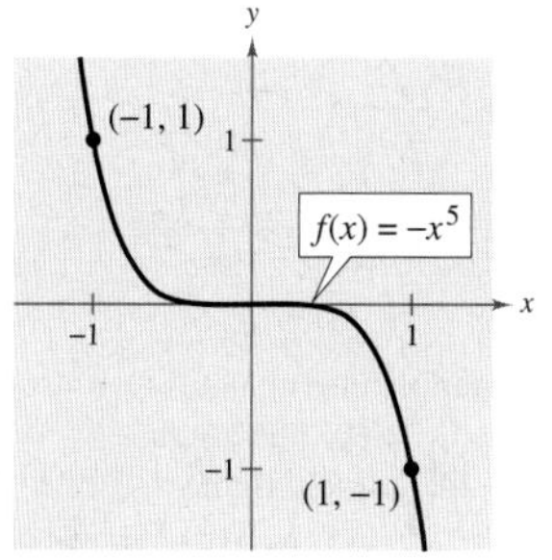

FIGURE 2.15

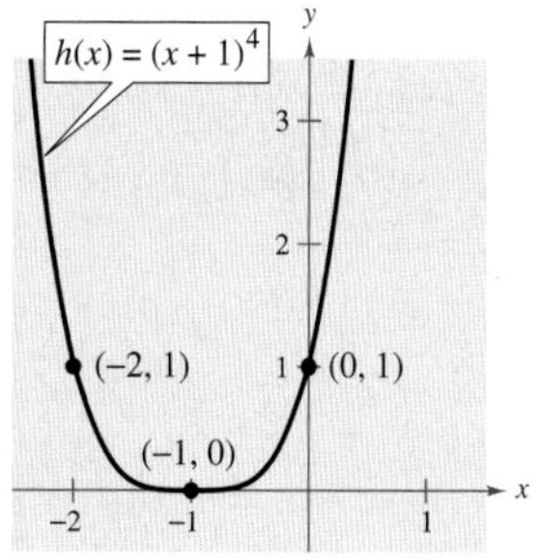

FIGURE 2.16

CHECKPoint Now try Exercise 17.

3 TEACH

Extra Example 1

Sketch the graph of each function.

a. $f(x) = (x + 5)^4$

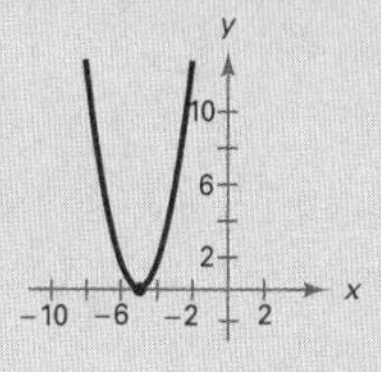

b. $k(x) = \frac{1}{4}(x - 3)^4$

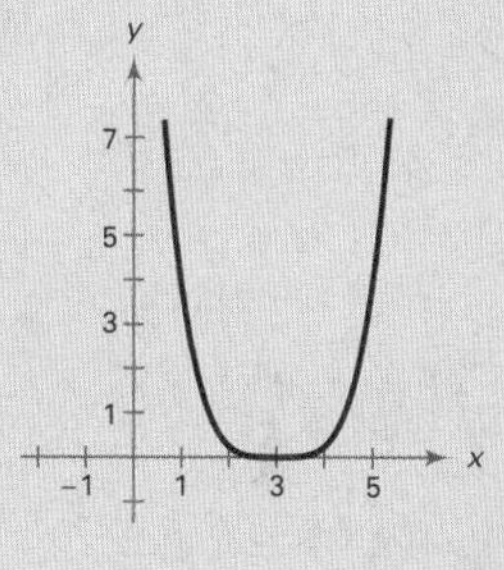

The Leading Coefficient Test

In Example 1, note that both graphs eventually rise or fall without bound as x moves to the right. Whether the graph of a polynomial function eventually rises or falls can be determined by the function's degree (even or odd) and by its leading coefficient, as indicated in the **Leading Coefficient Test.**

Leading Coefficient Test

As x moves without bound to the left or to the right, the graph of the polynomial function $f(x) = a_n x^n + \cdot \cdot \cdot + a_1 x + a_0$ eventually rises or falls in the following manner.

1. When n is *odd:*

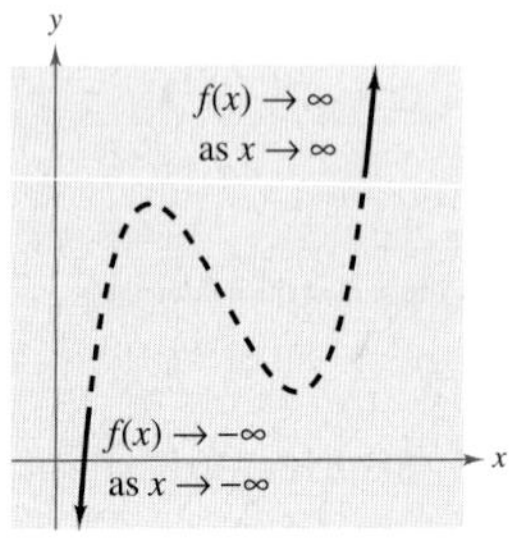

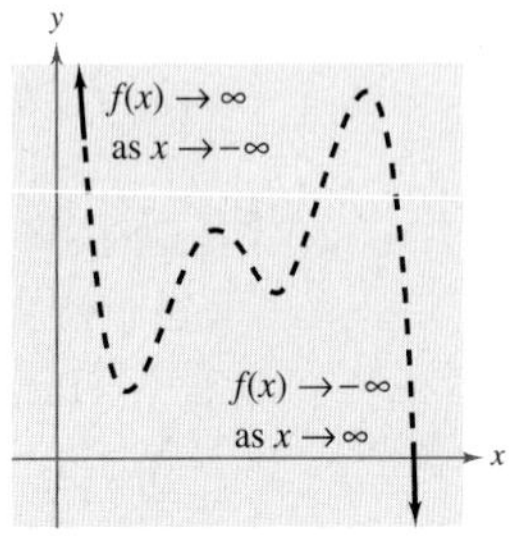

If the leading coefficient is positive ($a_n > 0$), the graph falls to the left and rises to the right.

If the leading coefficient is negative ($a_n < 0$), the graph rises to the left and falls to the right.

2. When n is *even:*

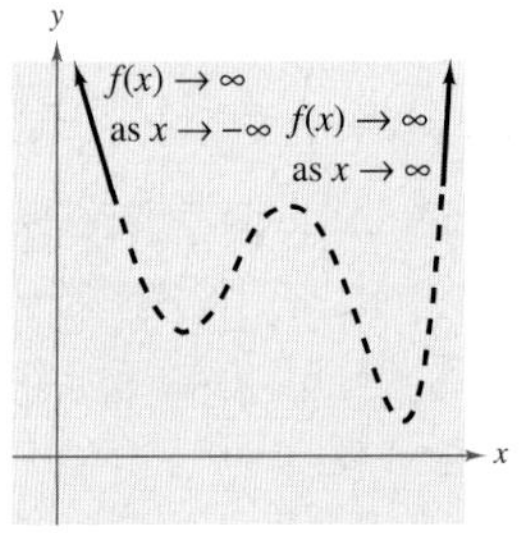

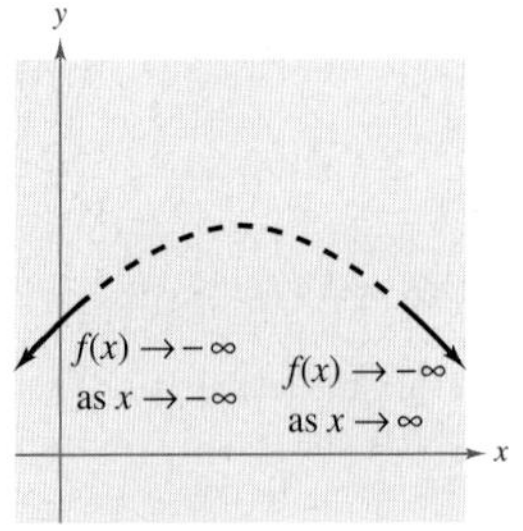

If the leading coefficient is positive ($a_n > 0$), the graph rises to the left and right.

If the leading coefficient is negative ($a_n < 0$), the graph falls to the left and right.

The dashed portions of the graphs indicate that the test determines *only* the right-hand and left-hand behavior of the graph.

Study Tip

The notation "$f(x) \to -\infty$ as $x \to -\infty$" indicates that the graph falls to the left. The notation "$f(x) \to \infty$ as $x \to \infty$" indicates that the graph rises to the right.

WARNING/CAUTION

A polynomial function is written in **standard form** if its terms are written in descending order of exponents from left to right. Before applying the Leading Coefficient Test to a polynomial function, it is a good idea to make sure that the polynomial function is written in standard form.

Example 2 Applying the Leading Coefficient Test

Describe the right-hand and left-hand behavior of the graph of each function.

a. $f(x) = -x^3 + 4x$ **b.** $f(x) = x^4 - 5x^2 + 4$ **c.** $f(x) = x^5 - x$

Solution

a. Because the degree is odd and the leading coefficient is negative, the graph rises to the left and falls to the right, as shown in Figure 2.17.

b. Because the degree is even and the leading coefficient is positive, the graph rises to the left and right, as shown in Figure 2.18.

c. Because the degree is odd and the leading coefficient is positive, the graph falls to the left and rises to the right, as shown in Figure 2.19.

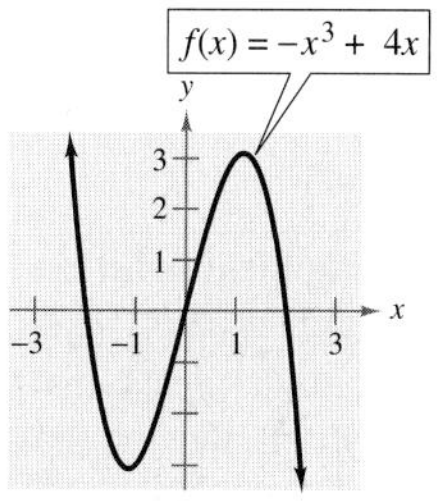

FIGURE 2.17

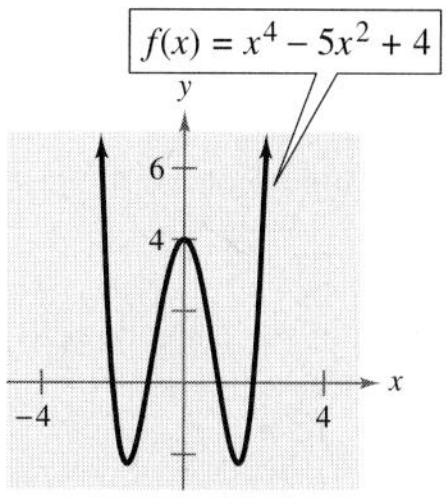

FIGURE 2.18

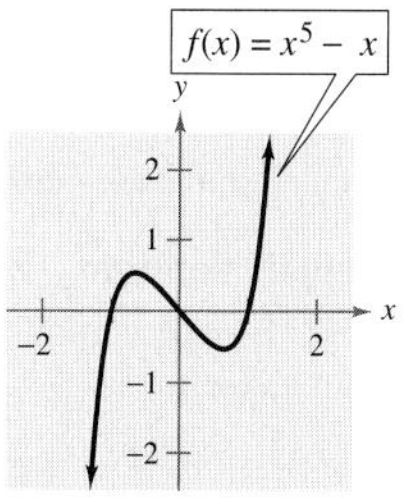

FIGURE 2.19

CHECKPoint Now try Exercise 23.

In Example 2, note that the Leading Coefficient Test tells you only whether the graph *eventually* rises or falls to the right or left. Other characteristics of the graph, such as intercepts and minimum and maximum points, must be determined by other tests.

Zeros of Polynomial Functions

It can be shown that for a polynomial function f of degree n, the following statements are true.

1. The function f has, at most, n real zeros. (You will study this result in detail in the discussion of the Fundamental Theorem of Algebra in Section 2.5.)
2. The graph of f has, at most, $n - 1$ turning points. (Turning points, also called relative minima or relative maxima, are points at which the graph changes from increasing to decreasing or vice versa.)

Study Tip

Remember that the *zeros* of a function of x are the x-values for which the function is zero.

Finding the zeros of polynomial functions is one of the most important problems in algebra. There is a strong interplay between graphical and algebraic approaches to this problem. Sometimes you can use information about the graph of a function to help find its zeros, and in other cases you can use information about the zeros of a function to help sketch its graph. Finding zeros of polynomial functions is closely related to factoring and finding x-intercepts.

Extra Example 2

Describe the left-hand and right-hand behavior of the graph of each function.

a. $f(x) = \frac{1}{4}x^3 - 2x$

The degree is odd and the leading coefficient is positive. The graph falls to the left and rises to the right.

b. $f(x) = -3.6x^5 + 5x^3 - 1$

The degree is odd and the leading coefficient is negative. The graph rises to the left and falls to the right.

Extra Example 3

Find all the real zeros of $f(x) = x^3 - 12x^2 + 36x$. Then determine the number of turning points of the graph of the function.

0, 6; Because the function is a third-degree polynomial, the graph can have at most 2 turning points.

Avoiding Common Errors

Students sometimes multiply the function by -1 in order to simplify factoring. This can be done after the function is set equal to zero, but creates a reflection if applied to the function alone. It is safer to factor out any constant, including -1, and then discard this as a possible zero factor later.

Algebra Help

To do Example 3 algebraically, you need to be able to completely factor polynomials. You can review the techniques for factoring in Appendix A.3.

Real Zeros of Polynomial Functions

If f is a polynomial function and a is a real number, the following statements are equivalent.

1. $x = a$ is a *zero* of the function f.
2. $x = a$ is a *solution* of the polynomial equation $f(x) = 0$.
3. $(x - a)$ is a *factor* of the polynomial $f(x)$.
4. $(a, 0)$ is an *x-intercept* of the graph of f.

Example 3 Finding the Zeros of a Polynomial Function

Find all real zeros of

$$f(x) = -2x^4 + 2x^2.$$

Then determine the number of turning points of the graph of the function.

Algebraic Solution

To find the real zeros of the function, set $f(x)$ equal to zero and solve for x.

$$-2x^4 + 2x^2 = 0$$ Set $f(x)$ equal to 0.

$$-2x^2(x^2 - 1) = 0$$ Remove common monomial factor.

$$-2x^2(x - 1)(x + 1) = 0$$ Factor completely.

So, the real zeros are $x = 0$, $x = 1$, and $x = -1$. Because the function is a fourth-degree polynomial, the graph of f can have at most $4 - 1 = 3$ turning points.

Graphical Solution

Use a graphing utility to graph $y = -2x^4 + 2x^2$. In Figure 2.20, the graph appears to have zeros at $(0, 0)$, $(1, 0)$, and $(-1, 0)$. Use the *zero* or *root* feature, or the *zoom* and *trace* features, of the graphing utility to verify these zeros. So, the real zeros are $x = 0$, $x = 1$, and $x = -1$. From the figure, you can see that the graph has three turning points. This is consistent with the fact that a fourth-degree polynomial can have at most three turning points.

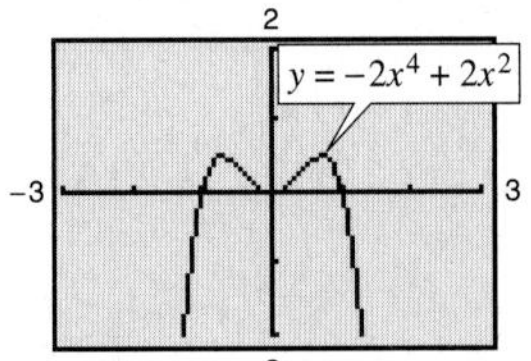

FIGURE 2.20

CHECKPoint Now try Exercise 35.

In Example 3, note that because the exponent is greater than 1, the factor $-2x^2$ yields the *repeated* zero $x = 0$. Because the exponent is even, the graph touches the x-axis at $x = 0$, as shown in Figure 2.20.

Repeated Zeros

A factor $(x - a)^k$, $k > 1$, yields a **repeated zero** $x = a$ of **multiplicity** k.

1. If k is odd, the graph *crosses* the x-axis at $x = a$.
2. If k is even, the graph *touches* the x-axis (but does not cross the x-axis) at $x = a$.

To graph polynomial functions, you can use the fact that a polynomial function can change signs only at its zeros. Between two consecutive zeros, a polynomial must be entirely positive or entirely negative. (This follows from the Intermediate Value Theorem, which you will study later in this section.) This means that when the real zeros of a polynomial function are put in order, they divide the real number line into intervals in which the function has no sign changes. These resulting intervals are **test intervals** in which a representative x-value in the interval is chosen to determine if the value of the polynomial function is positive (the graph lies above the x-axis) or negative (the graph lies below the x-axis).

Example 4 Sketching the Graph of a Polynomial Function

Sketch the graph of $f(x) = 3x^4 - 4x^3$.

Solution

1. *Apply the Leading Coefficient Test.* Because the leading coefficient is positive and the degree is even, you know that the graph eventually rises to the left and to the right (see Figure 2.21).
2. *Find the Zeros of the Polynomial.* By factoring $f(x) = 3x^4 - 4x^3$ as $f(x) = x^3(3x - 4)$, you can see that the zeros of f are $x = 0$ and $x = \frac{4}{3}$ (both of odd multiplicity). So, the x-intercepts occur at $(0, 0)$ and $\left(\frac{4}{3}, 0\right)$. Add these points to your graph, as shown in Figure 2.21.
3. *Plot a Few Additional Points.* Use the zeros of the polynomial to find the test intervals. In each test interval, choose a representative x-value and evaluate the polynomial function, as shown in the table.

Test interval	Representative x-value	Value of f	Sign	Point on graph
$(-\infty, 0)$	-1	$f(-1) = 7$	Positive	$(-1, 7)$
$\left(0, \frac{4}{3}\right)$	1	$f(1) = -1$	Negative	$(1, -1)$
$\left(\frac{4}{3}, \infty\right)$	1.5	$f(1.5) = 1.6875$	Positive	$(1.5, 1.6875)$

4. *Draw the Graph.* Draw a continuous curve through the points, as shown in Figure 2.22. Because both zeros are of odd multiplicity, you know that the graph should cross the x-axis at $x = 0$ and $x = \frac{4}{3}$.

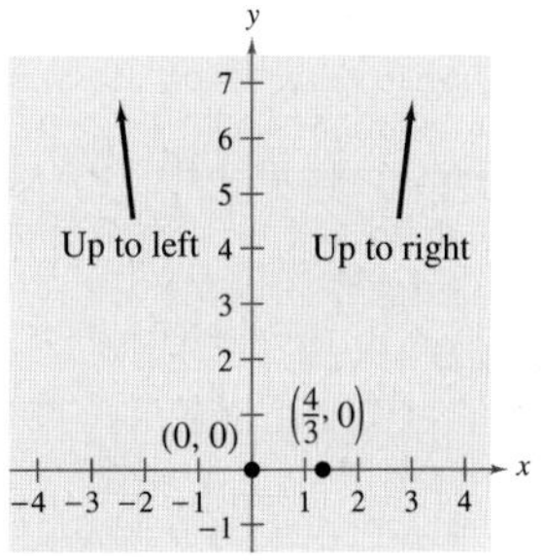

FIGURE 2.21

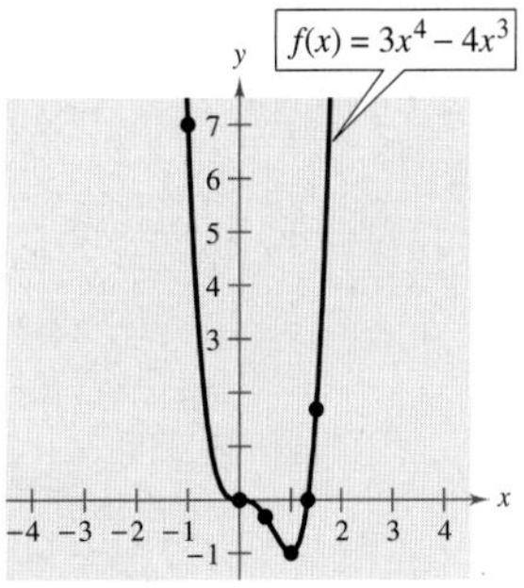

FIGURE 2.22

CHECKPoint Now try Exercise 75.

TECHNOLOGY

Example 4 uses an *algebraic approach* to describe the graph of the function. A graphing utility is a complement to this approach. Remember that an important aspect of using a graphing utility is to find a viewing window that shows all significant features of the graph. For instance, the viewing window in part (a) illustrates all of the significant features of the function in Example 4 while the viewing window in part (b) does not.

a.

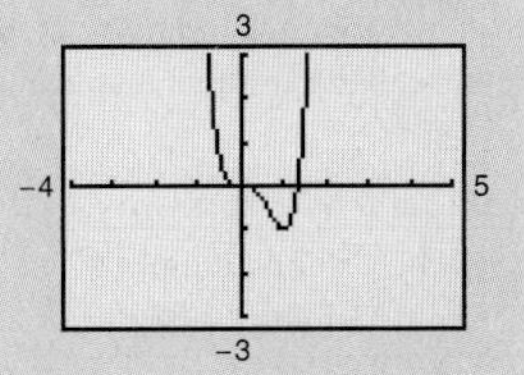

b.

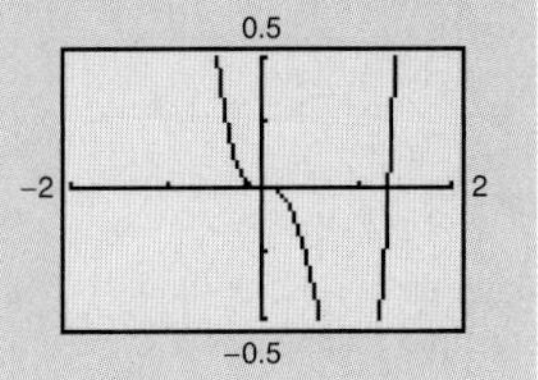

WARNING/CAUTION

If you are unsure of the shape of a portion of the graph of a polynomial function, plot some additional points, such as the point $(0.5, -0.3125)$, as shown in Figure 2.22.

Extra Example 4

Sketch the graph of $f(x) = 2x^3 - 6x^2$.

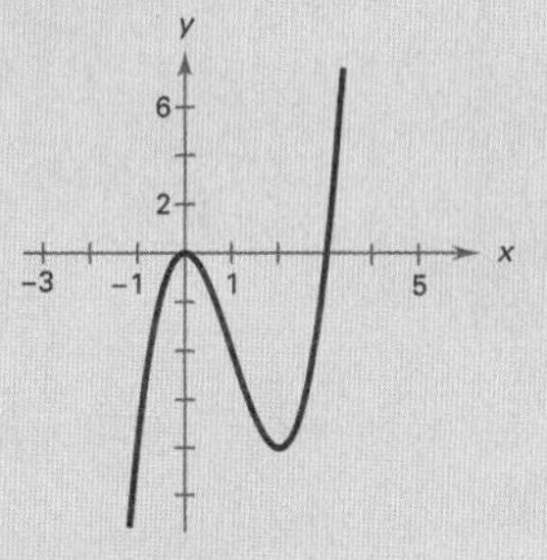

Differentiated Instruction

Auditory Learners To practice and reinforce the steps for sketching the graph of a polynomial function given in Example 4, have students choose a polynomial function to graph. Instruct them to graph the polynomial function while explaining the steps to a partner.

Extra Example 5

Sketch the graph of
$f(x) = -\frac{1}{4}x^4 + \frac{3}{2}x^3 - \frac{9}{4}x^2.$

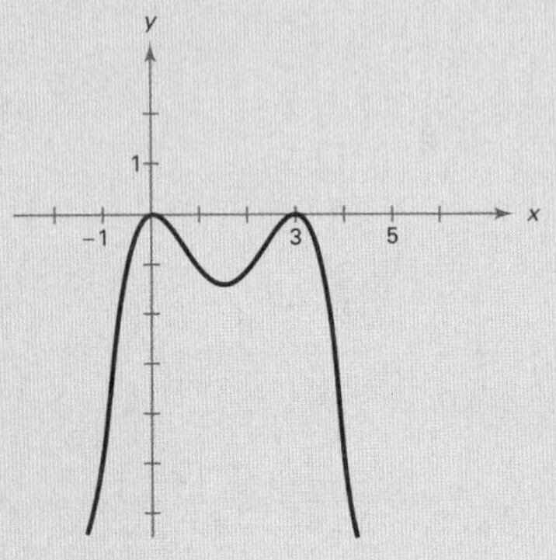

Example 5 Sketching the Graph of a Polynomial Function

Sketch the graph of $f(x) = -2x^3 + 6x^2 - \frac{9}{2}x$.

Solution

1. *Apply the Leading Coefficient Test.* Because the leading coefficient is negative and the degree is odd, you know that the graph eventually rises to the left and falls to the right (see Figure 2.23).

2. *Find the Zeros of the Polynomial.* By factoring

$$f(x) = -2x^3 + 6x^2 - \frac{9}{2}x$$
$$= -\frac{1}{2}x(4x^2 - 12x + 9)$$
$$= -\frac{1}{2}x(2x - 3)^2$$

you can see that the zeros of f are $x = 0$ (odd multiplicity) and $x = \frac{3}{2}$ (even multiplicity). So, the x-intercepts occur at $(0, 0)$ and $\left(\frac{3}{2}, 0\right)$. Add these points to your graph, as shown in Figure 2.23.

3. *Plot a Few Additional Points.* Use the zeros of the polynomial to find the test intervals. In each test interval, choose a representative x-value and evaluate the polynomial function, as shown in the table.

Test interval	Representative x-value	Value of f	Sign	Point on graph
$(-\infty, 0)$	-0.5	$f(-0.5) = 4$	Positive	$(-0.5, 4)$
$\left(0, \frac{3}{2}\right)$	0.5	$f(0.5) = -1$	Negative	$(0.5, -1)$
$\left(\frac{3}{2}, \infty\right)$	2	$f(2) = -1$	Negative	$(2, -1)$

4. *Draw the Graph.* Draw a continuous curve through the points, as shown in Figure 2.24. As indicated by the multiplicities of the zeros, the graph crosses the x-axis at $(0, 0)$ but does not cross the x-axis at $\left(\frac{3}{2}, 0\right)$.

Study Tip

Observe in Example 5 that the sign of $f(x)$ is positive to the left of and negative to the right of the zero $x = 0$. Similarly, the sign of $f(x)$ is negative to the left and to the right of the zero $x = \frac{3}{2}$. This suggests that if the zero of a polynomial function is of *odd* multiplicity, then the sign of $f(x)$ changes from one side of the zero to the other side. If the zero is of *even* multiplicity, then the sign of $f(x)$ does not change from one side of the zero to the other side.

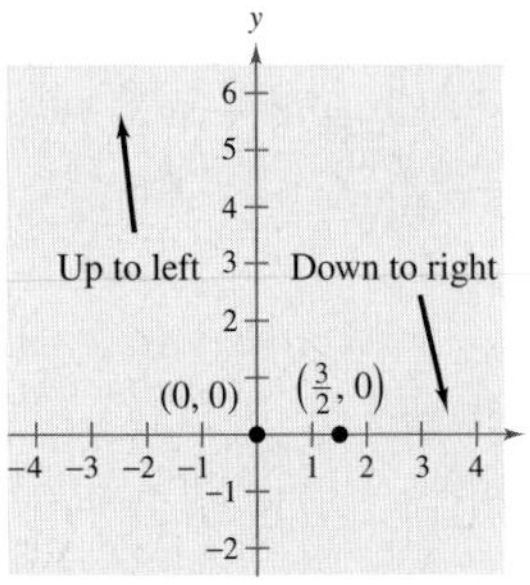

FIGURE 2.23

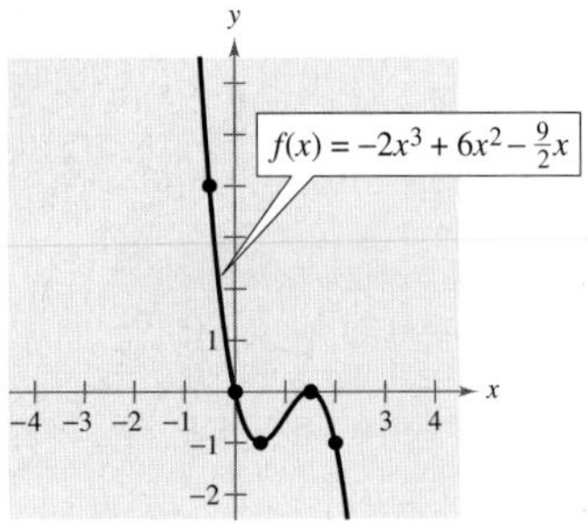

FIGURE 2.24

CHECKPoint Now try Exercise 77.

The Intermediate Value Theorem

The next theorem, called the **Intermediate Value Theorem,** illustrates the existence of real zeros of polynomial functions. This theorem implies that if $(a, f(a))$ and $(b, f(b))$ are two points on the graph of a polynomial function such that $f(a) \neq f(b)$, then for any number d between $f(a)$ and $f(b)$ there must be a number c between a and b such that $f(c) = d$. (See Figure 2.25.)

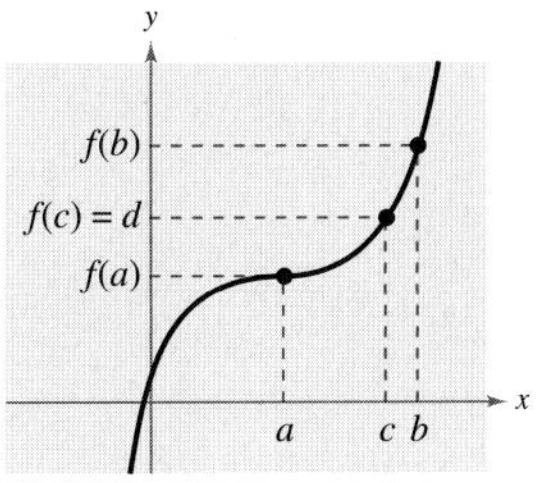

FIGURE 2.25

> **Intermediate Value Theorem**
>
> Let a and b be real numbers such that $a < b$. If f is a polynomial function such that $f(a) \neq f(b)$, then, in the interval $[a, b]$, f takes on every value between $f(a)$ and $f(b)$.

The Intermediate Value Theorem helps you locate the real zeros of a polynomial function in the following way. If you can find a value $x = a$ at which a polynomial function is positive, and another value $x = b$ at which it is negative, you can conclude that the function has at least one real zero between these two values. For example, the function given by $f(x) = x^3 + x^2 + 1$ is negative when $x = -2$ and positive when $x = -1$. Therefore, it follows from the Intermediate Value Theorem that f must have a real zero somewhere between -2 and -1, as shown in Figure 2.26.

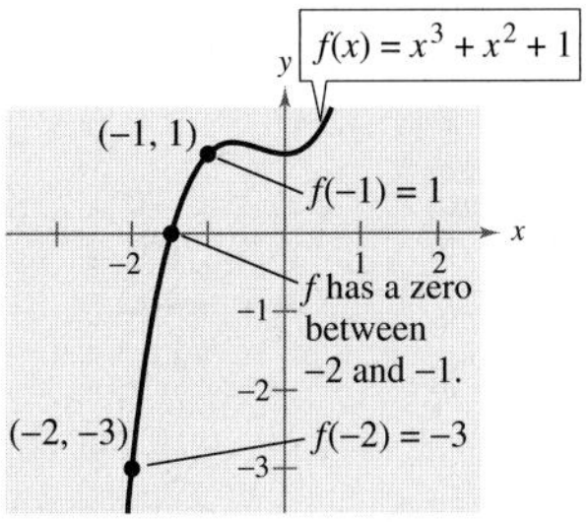

FIGURE 2.26

By continuing this line of reasoning, you can approximate any real zeros of a polynomial function to any desired accuracy. This concept is further demonstrated in Example 6.

Extra Example 6

Use the Intermediate Value Theorem to approximate the real zeros of $f(x) = -x^5 + 3x^3 - 2x + 2$ to the nearest hundredth.

The function has one zero; it is located between 1.64 and 1.65.

Closing the Lesson

Have students summarize the major points of the lesson and answer the Essential Question: How do you sketch the graphs of polynomial functions?

- **Identify end behavior of a polynomial by looking at its degree and the sign of its leading coefficient.**
- **Find zeros of a polynomial by factoring or by approximating, using the Intermediate Value Theorem.**
- **Locate additional points by evaluating the polynomial for one *x*-value in each test interval between and beyond the zeros.**

Example 6 Approximating a Zero of a Polynomial Function

Use the Intermediate Value Theorem to approximate the real zero of

$$f(x) = x^3 - x^2 + 1.$$

Solution

Begin by computing a few function values, as follows.

x	$f(x)$
-2	-11
-1	-1
0	1
1	1

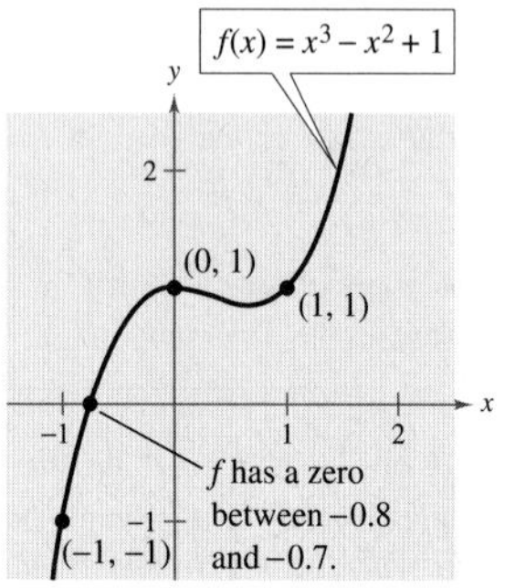

FIGURE 2.27

Because $f(-1)$ is negative and $f(0)$ is positive, you can apply the Intermediate Value Theorem to conclude that the function has a zero between -1 and 0. To pinpoint this zero more closely, divide the interval $[-1, 0]$ into tenths and evaluate the function at each point. When you do this, you will find that

$$f(-0.8) = -0.152 \quad \text{and} \quad f(-0.7) = 0.167.$$

So, f must have a zero between -0.8 and -0.7, as shown in Figure 2.27. For a more accurate approximation, compute function values between $f(-0.8)$ and $f(-0.7)$ and apply the Intermediate Value Theorem again. By continuing this process, you can approximate this zero to any desired accuracy.

CHECK*Point* Now try Exercise 93.

TECHNOLOGY

You can use the *table* feature of a graphing utility to approximate the zeros of a polynomial function. For instance, for the function given by

$$f(x) = -2x^3 - 3x^2 + 3$$

create a table that shows the function values for $-20 \le x \le 20$, as shown in the first table at the right. Scroll through the table looking for consecutive function values that differ in sign. From the table, you can see that $f(0)$ and $f(1)$ differ in sign. So, you can conclude from the Intermediate Value Theorem that the function has a zero between 0 and 1. You can adjust your table to show function values for $0 \le x \le 1$ using increments of 0.1, as shown in the second table at the right. By scrolling through the table you can see that $f(0.8)$ and $f(0.9)$ differ in sign. So, the function has a zero between 0.8 and 0.9. If you repeat this process several times, you should obtain $x \approx 0.806$ as the zero of the function. Use the *zero* or *root* feature of a graphing utility to confirm this result.

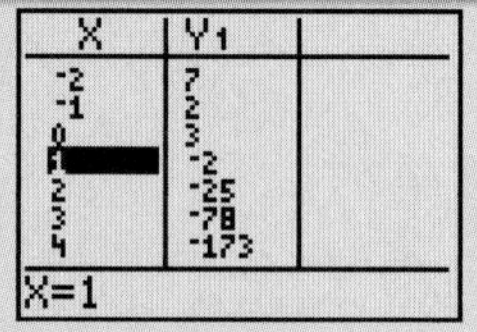

X	Y1
-2	7
-1	2
0	3
1	-2
2	-25
3	-78
4	-173

X=1

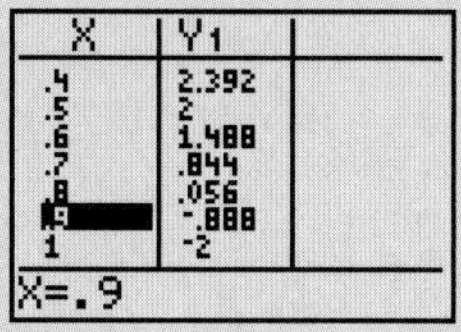

X	Y1
.4	2.392
.5	2
.6	1.488
.7	.844
.8	.056
.9	-.888
1	-2

X=.9

2.2 EXERCISES

See www.CalcChat.com for worked-out solutions to odd-numbered exercises.

VOCABULARY: Fill in the blanks.

1. The graphs of all polynomial functions are continuous, which means that the graphs have no breaks, holes, or gaps.
2. The Leading Coefficient Test is used to determine the left-hand and right-hand behavior of the graph of a polynomial function.
3. Polynomial functions of the form $f(x) =$ x^n are often referred to as power functions.
4. A polynomial function of degree n has at most n real zeros and at most $n - 1$ turning points.
5. If $x = a$ is a zero of a polynomial function f, then the following three statements are true.
   (a) $x = a$ is a solution of the polynomial equation $f(x) = 0$.
   (b) $(x - a)$ is a factor of the polynomial $f(x)$.
   (c) $(a, 0)$ is an ________ of the graph of f. x-intercept
6. If a real zero of a polynomial function is of even multiplicity, then the graph of f touches the x-axis at $x = a$, and if it is of odd multiplicity, then the graph of f crosses the x-axis at $x = a$.
7. A polynomial function is written in standard form if its terms are written in descending order of exponents from left to right.
8. The Intermediate Value Theorem states that if f is a polynomial function such that $f(a) \neq f(b)$, then, in the interval $[a, b]$, f takes on every value between $f(a)$ and $f(b)$.

SKILLS AND APPLICATIONS

In Exercises 9–16, match the polynomial function with its graph. [The graphs are labeled (a), (b), (c), (d), (e), (f), (g), and (h).]

(a)
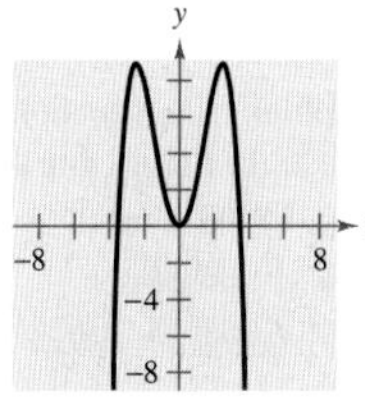

(b)
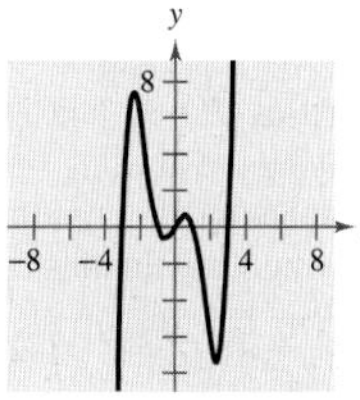

(c)
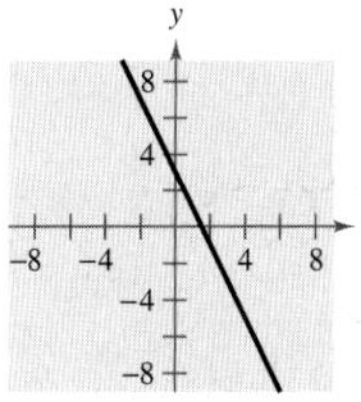

(d)
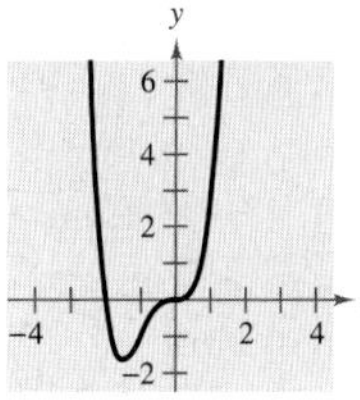

(e)
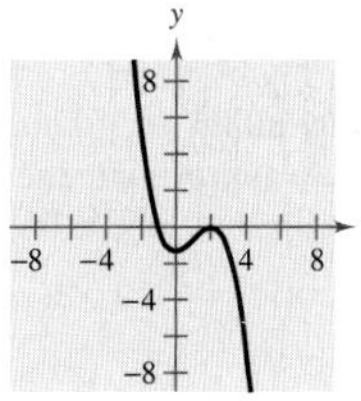

(f)
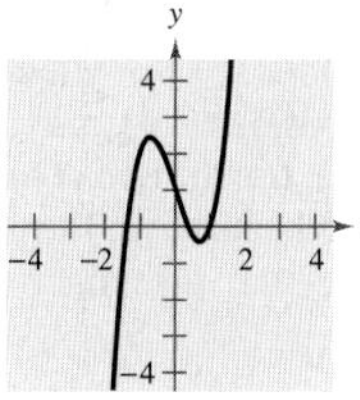

(g)
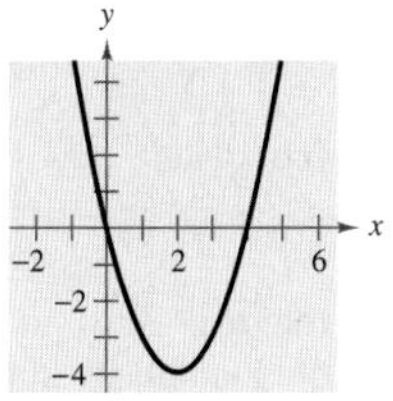

(h)
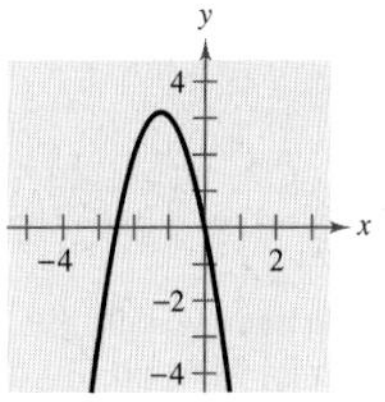

9. $f(x) = -2x + 3$ c
10. $f(x) = x^2 - 4x$ g
11. $f(x) = -2x^2 - 5x$ h
12. $f(x) = 2x^3 - 3x + 1$ f
13. $f(x) = -\frac{1}{4}x^4 + 3x^2$ a
14. $f(x) = -\frac{1}{3}x^3 + x^2 - \frac{4}{3}$ e
15. $f(x) = x^4 + 2x^3$ d
16. $f(x) = \frac{1}{5}x^5 - 2x^3 + \frac{9}{5}x$ b

In Exercises 17–20, sketch the graph of $y = x^n$ and each transformation. 17–19. See margin.

17. $y = x^3$
   (a) $f(x) = (x - 4)^3$ (b) $f(x) = x^3 - 4$
   (c) $f(x) = -\frac{1}{4}x^3$ (d) $f(x) = (x - 4)^3 - 4$
18. $y = x^5$
   (a) $f(x) = (x + 1)^5$ (b) $f(x) = x^5 + 1$
   (c) $f(x) = 1 - \frac{1}{2}x^5$ (d) $f(x) = -\frac{1}{2}(x + 1)^5$
19. $y = x^4$
   (a) $f(x) = (x + 3)^4$ (b) $f(x) = x^4 - 3$
   (c) $f(x) = 4 - x^4$ (d) $f(x) = \frac{1}{2}(x - 1)^4$
   (e) $f(x) = (2x)^4 + 1$ (f) $f(x) = \left(\frac{1}{2}x\right)^4 - 2$

4 PRACTICE AND APPLY

Assignment Guide

Transparencies Available
Available at the Instructor's companion site.

Average:
Day 1: pp. 145–149
Exs. 9–17, 19, 27, 29, 41–49 odd, 59, 61, 65, 69, 71, 77–83 odd, 93, 97–99, 103, 105–108

Advanced:
Day 1: pp. 145–149
Exs. 9–16, 18, 20, 28, 29, 42–50 even, 60–64 even, 69, 71, 74, 82–88 even, 96, 97–100, 103, 104, 107–111

Block:
pp. 145–149
Exs. 9–17, 19, 27, 29, 41–49 odd, 59, 61, 65, 69, 71, 77–83 odd, 93, 97–99, 103, 105–108 (with 2.1)

17. (a)
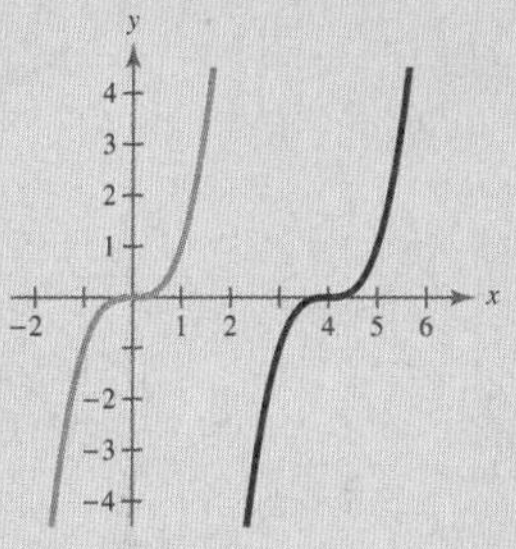

(b)
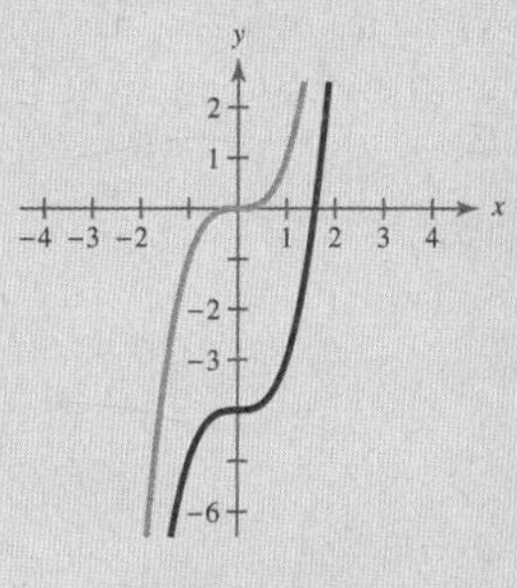

(c)
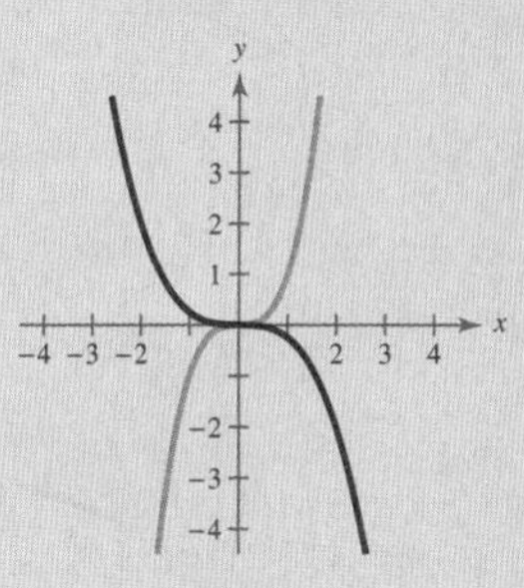

17. (d)
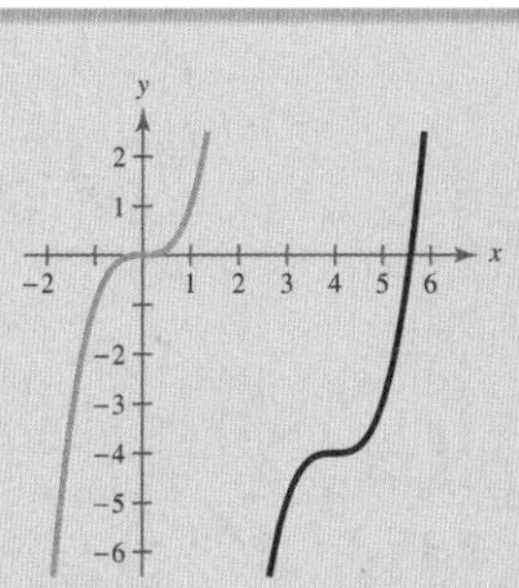

18–19. See Additional Answers beginning on page AA1.

20. $y = x^6$ See margin.

(a) $f(x) = -\frac{1}{8}x^6$ (b) $f(x) = (x + 2)^6 - 4$

(c) $f(x) = x^6 - 5$ (d) $f(x) = -\frac{1}{4}x^6 + 1$

(e) $f(x) = \left(\frac{1}{4}x\right)^6 - 2$ (f) $f(x) = (2x)^6 - 1$

21–30. See margin.

In Exercises 21–30, describe the right-hand and left-hand behavior of the graph of the polynomial function.

21. $f(x) = \frac{1}{5}x^3 + 4x$
22. $f(x) = 2x^2 - 3x + 1$
23. $g(x) = 5 - \frac{7}{2}x - 3x^2$
24. $h(x) = 1 - x^6$
25. $f(x) = -2.1x^5 + 4x^3 - 2$
26. $f(x) = 4x^5 - 7x + 6.5$
27. $f(x) = 6 - 2x + 4x^2 - 5x^3$
28. $f(x) = (3x^4 - 2x + 5)/4$
29. $h(t) = -\frac{3}{4}(t^2 - 3t + 6)$
30. $f(s) = -\frac{7}{8}(s^3 + 5s^2 - 7s + 1)$

31–34. See margin.

GRAPHICAL ANALYSIS In Exercises 31–34, use a graphing utility to graph the functions f and g in the same viewing window. Zoom out sufficiently far to show that the right-hand and left-hand behaviors of f and g appear identical.

31. $f(x) = 3x^3 - 9x + 1, \quad g(x) = 3x^3$
32. $f(x) = -\frac{1}{3}(x^3 - 3x + 2), \quad g(x) = -\frac{1}{3}x^3$
33. $f(x) = -(x^4 - 4x^3 + 16x), \quad g(x) = -x^4$
34. $f(x) = 3x^4 - 6x^2, \quad g(x) = 3x^4$

In Exercises 35–50, (a) find all the real zeros of the polynomial function, (b) determine the multiplicity of each zero and the number of turning points of the graph of the function, and (c) use a graphing utility to graph the function and verify your answers. 35–50. See margin.

35. $f(x) = x^2 - 36$
36. $f(x) = 81 - x^2$
37. $h(t) = t^2 - 6t + 9$
38. $f(x) = x^2 + 10x + 25$
39. $f(x) = \frac{1}{3}x^2 + \frac{1}{3}x - \frac{2}{3}$
40. $f(x) = \frac{1}{2}x^2 + \frac{5}{2}x - \frac{3}{2}$
41. $f(x) = 3x^3 - 12x^2 + 3x$
42. $g(x) = 5x(x^2 - 2x - 1)$
43. $f(t) = t^3 - 8t^2 + 16t$
44. $f(x) = x^4 - x^3 - 30x^2$
45. $g(t) = t^5 - 6t^3 + 9t$
46. $f(x) = x^5 + x^3 - 6x$
47. $f(x) = 3x^4 + 9x^2 + 6$
48. $f(x) = 2x^4 - 2x^2 - 40$
49. $g(x) = x^3 + 3x^2 - 4x - 12$
50. $f(x) = x^3 - 4x^2 - 25x + 100$

GRAPHICAL ANALYSIS In Exercises 51–54, (a) use a graphing utility to graph the function, (b) use the graph to approximate any x-intercepts of the graph, (c) set $y = 0$ and solve the resulting equation, and (d) compare the results of part (c) with any x-intercepts of the graph. 51–54. See margin.

51. $y = 4x^3 - 20x^2 + 25x$
52. $y = 4x^3 + 4x^2 - 8x - 8$
53. $y = x^5 - 5x^3 + 4x$
54. $y = \frac{1}{4}x^3(x^2 - 9)$

55–64. See margin.

In Exercises 55–64, find a polynomial function that has the given zeros. (There are many correct answers.)

55. 0, 8
56. 0, −7
57. 2, −6
58. −4, 5
59. 0, −4, −5
60. 0, 1, 10
61. 4, −3, 3, 0
62. −2, −1, 0, 1, 2
63. $1 + \sqrt{3}, 1 - \sqrt{3}$
64. $2, 4 + \sqrt{5}, 4 - \sqrt{5}$

65–74. See margin.

In Exercises 65–74, find a polynomial of degree n that has the given zero(s). (There are many correct answers.)

	Zero(s)	*Degree*
65.	$x = -3$	$n = 2$
66.	$x = -12, -6$	$n = 2$
67.	$x = -5, 0, 1$	$n = 3$
68.	$x = -2, 4, 7$	$n = 3$
69.	$x = 0, \sqrt{3}, -\sqrt{3}$	$n = 3$
70.	$x = 9$	$n = 3$
71.	$x = -5, 1, 2$	$n = 4$
72.	$x = -4, -1, 3, 6$	$n = 4$
73.	$x = 0, -4$	$n = 5$
74.	$x = -1, 4, 7, 8$	$n = 5$

75–88. See margin.

In Exercises 75–88, sketch the graph of the function by (a) applying the Leading Coefficient Test, (b) finding the zeros of the polynomial, (c) plotting sufficient solution points, and (d) drawing a continuous curve through the points.

75. $f(x) = x^3 - 25x$
76. $g(x) = x^4 - 9x^2$
77. $f(t) = \frac{1}{4}(t^2 - 2t + 15)$
78. $g(x) = -x^2 + 10x - 16$
79. $f(x) = x^3 - 2x^2$
80. $f(x) = 8 - x^3$
81. $f(x) = 3x^3 - 15x^2 + 18x$
82. $f(x) = -4x^3 + 4x^2 + 15x$
83. $f(x) = -5x^2 - x^3$
84. $f(x) = -48x^2 + 3x^4$
85. $f(x) = x^2(x - 4)$
86. $h(x) = \frac{1}{3}x^3(x - 4)^2$
87. $g(t) = -\frac{1}{4}(t - 2)^2(t + 2)^2$
88. $g(x) = \frac{1}{10}(x + 1)^2(x - 3)^3$

In Exercises 89–92, use a graphing utility to graph the function. Use the *zero* or *root* feature to approximate the real zeros of the function. Then determine the multiplicity of each zero. 89–92. See margin.

89. $f(x) = x^3 - 16x$
90. $f(x) = \frac{1}{4}x^4 - 2x^2$
91. $g(x) = \frac{1}{5}(x + 1)^2(x - 3)(2x - 9)$
92. $h(x) = \frac{1}{5}(x + 2)^2(3x - 5)^2$

20. (a)

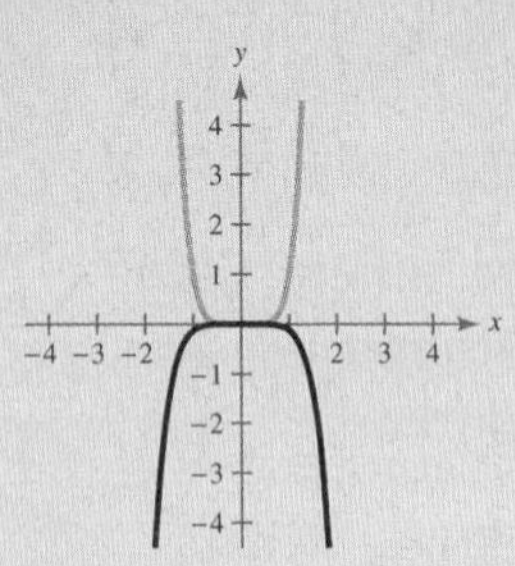

(b)

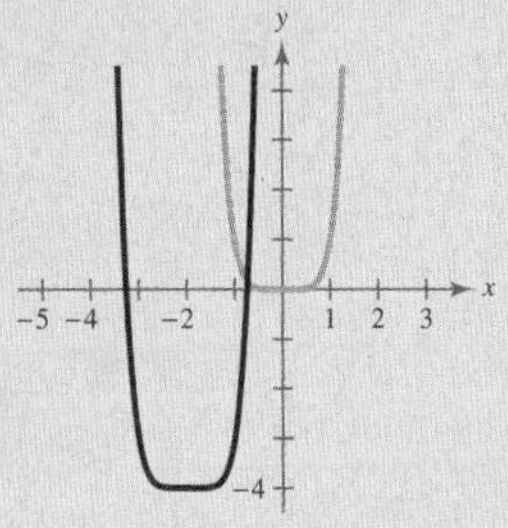

(c)

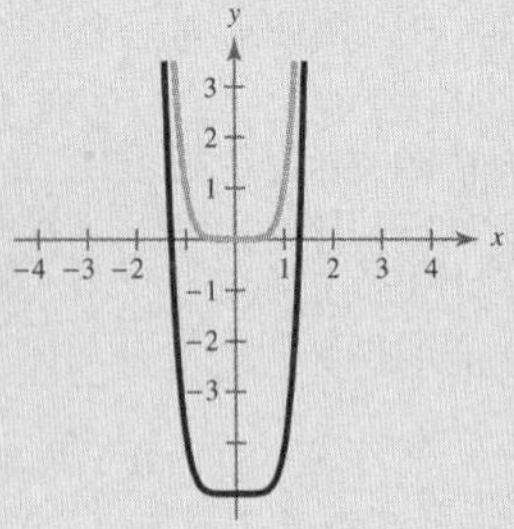

(d)

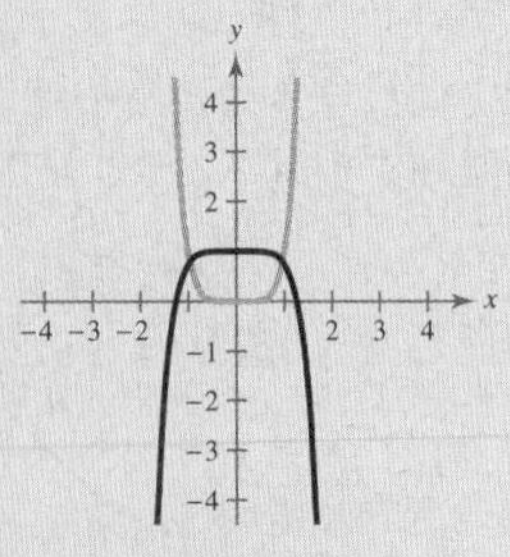

(e)

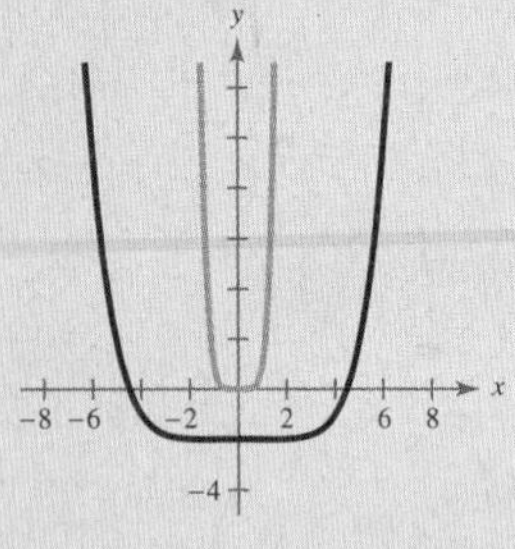

(f)

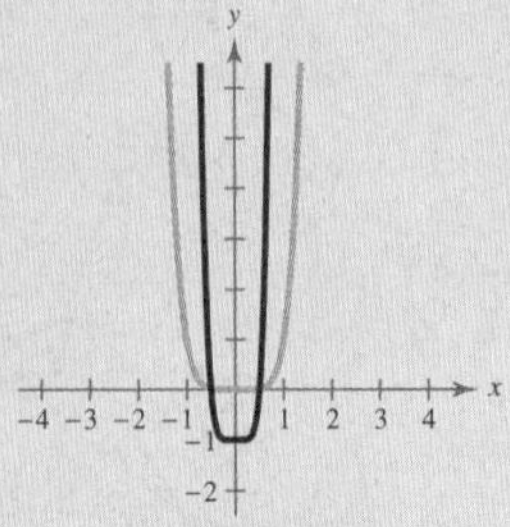

21. Falls to the left, rises to the right
22. Rises to the left, rises to the right
23. Falls to the left, falls to the right
24. Falls to the left, falls to the right
25. Rises to the left, falls to the right
26. Falls to the left, rises to the right
27. Rises to the left, falls to the right
28. Rises to the left, rises to the right
29. Falls to the left, falls to the right
30. Rises to the left, falls to the right

31.

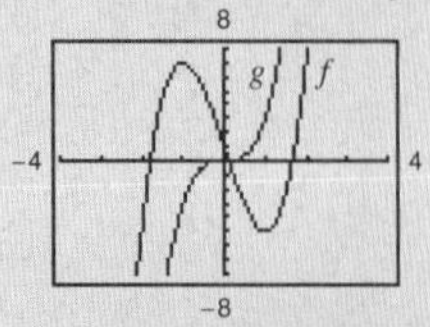

32.

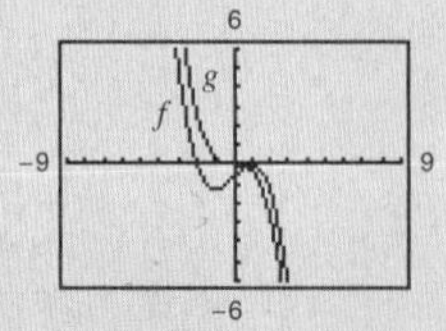

33.

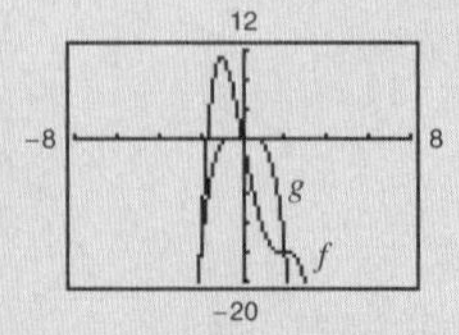

34.

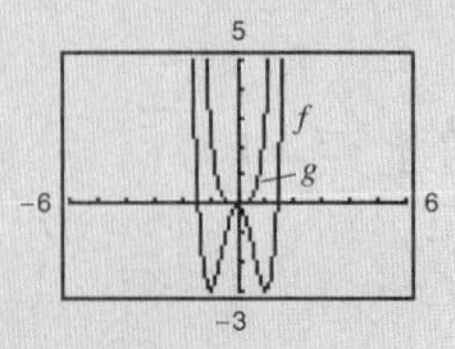

35–37. See page 147. 38–92. See Additional Answers beginning on page AA1.

In Exercises 93–96, use the Intermediate Value Theorem and the *table* feature of a graphing utility to find intervals one unit in length in which the polynomial function is guaranteed to have a zero. Adjust the table to approximate the zeros of the function. Use the *zero* or *root* feature of the graphing utility to verify your results. 93–96. See margin.

93. $f(x) = x^3 - 3x^2 + 3$

94. $f(x) = 0.11x^3 - 2.07x^2 + 9.81x - 6.88$

95. $g(x) = 3x^4 + 4x^3 - 3$

96. $h(x) = x^4 - 10x^2 + 3$

97. NUMERICAL AND GRAPHICAL ANALYSIS An open box is to be made from a square piece of material, 36 inches on a side, by cutting equal squares with sides of length x from the corners and turning up the sides (see figure).

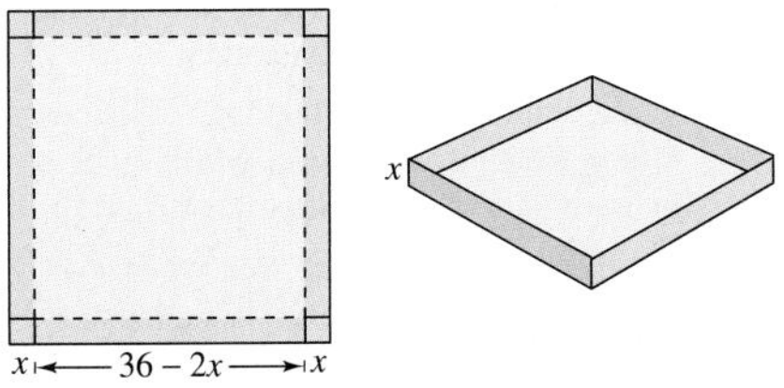

(a) Write a function $V(x)$ that represents the volume of the box. $V(x) = x(36 - 2x)^2$

(b) Determine the domain of the function. Domain: $0 < x < 18$

(c) Use a graphing utility to create a table that shows box heights x and the corresponding volumes V. Use the table to estimate the dimensions that will produce a maximum volume. (c)–(d). See margin.

(d) Use a graphing utility to graph V and use the graph to estimate the value of x for which $V(x)$ is maximum. Compare your result with that of part (c).

98. MAXIMUM VOLUME An open box with locking tabs is to be made from a square piece of material 24 inches on a side. This is to be done by cutting equal squares from the corners and folding along the dashed lines shown in the figure.

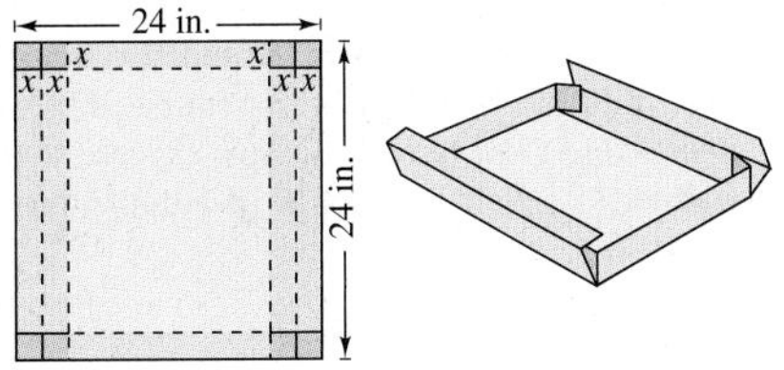

(a) Write a function $V(x)$ that represents the volume of the box. $V(x) = 8x(6 - x)(12 - x)$

(b) Determine the domain of the function V. Domain: $0 < x < 6$

(c) Sketch a graph of the function and estimate the value of x for which $V(x)$ is maximum. See margin.

99. CONSTRUCTION A roofing contractor is fabricating gutters from 12-inch aluminum sheeting. The contractor plans to use an aluminum siding folding press to create the gutter by creasing equal lengths for the sidewalls (see figure). See margin.

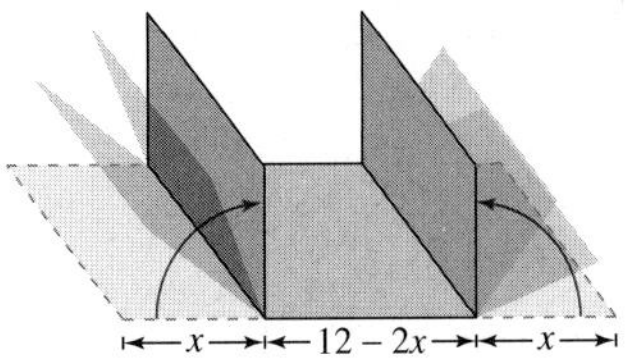

(a) Let x represent the height of the sidewall of the gutter. Write a function A that represents the cross-sectional area of the gutter.

(b) The length of the aluminum sheeting is 16 feet. Write a function V that represents the volume of one run of gutter in terms of x.

(c) Determine the domain of the function in part (b).

(d) Use a graphing utility to create a table that shows sidewall heights x and the corresponding volumes V. Use the table to estimate the dimensions that will produce a maximum volume.

(e) Use a graphing utility to graph V. Use the graph to estimate the value of x for which $V(x)$ is a maximum. Compare your result with that of part (d).

(f) Would the value of x change if the aluminum sheeting were of different lengths? Explain.

100. CONSTRUCTION An industrial propane tank is formed by adjoining two hemispheres to the ends of a right circular cylinder. The length of the cylindrical portion of the tank is four times the radius of the hemispherical components (see figure).

(a) Write a function that represents the total volume V of the tank in terms of r. $V = \frac{16}{3}\pi r^3$

(b) Find the domain of the function. $r \geq 0$

(c) Use a graphing utility to graph the function. See margin.

(d) The total volume of the tank is to be 120 cubic feet. Use the graph from part (c) to estimate the radius and length of the cylindrical portion of the tank. Radius $\approx$ 1.93 ft; Length $\approx$ 7.72 ft

35. (a) ± 6
(b) Odd multiplicity; number of turning points: 1
(c)

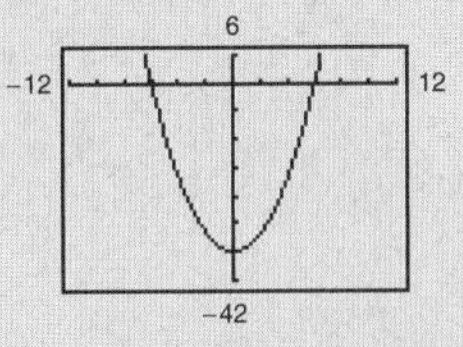

36. (a) ± 9
(b) Odd multiplicity; number of turning points: 1
(c)

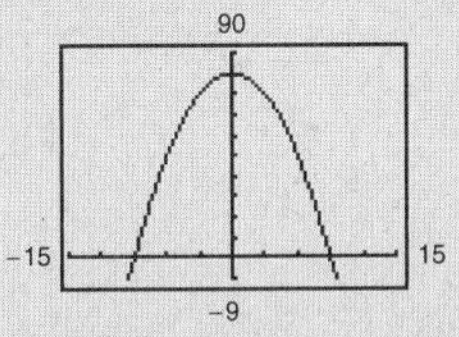

37. (a) 3
(b) Even multiplicity; number of turning points: 1
(c)

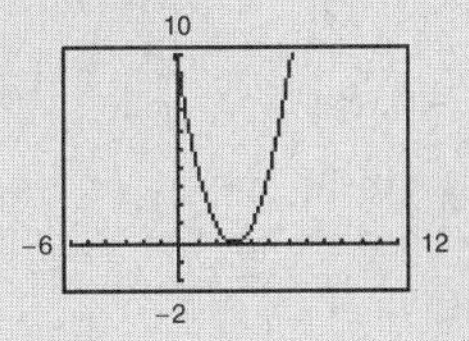

93. $[-1, 0], [1, 2], [2, 3]$; about $-0.879, 1.347, 2.532$

94. $[0, 1], [6, 7], [11, 12]$; about $0.845, 6.385, 11.588$

95. $[-2, -1], [0, 1]$; about $-1.585, 0.779$

96. $[-4, -3], [-1, 0], [0, 1], [3, 4]$; about $\pm 3.113, \pm 0.556$

97. (c)

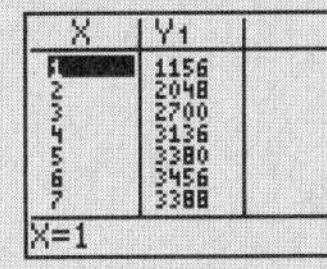

6 in. × 24 in. × 24 in.

(d)

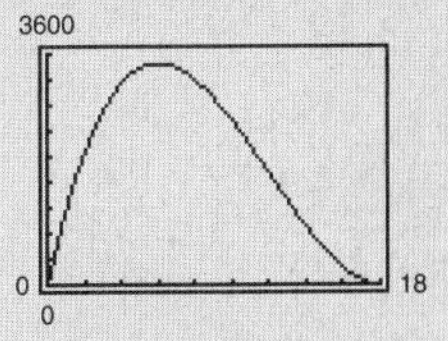

$x = 6$; The results are the same.

98. (c)

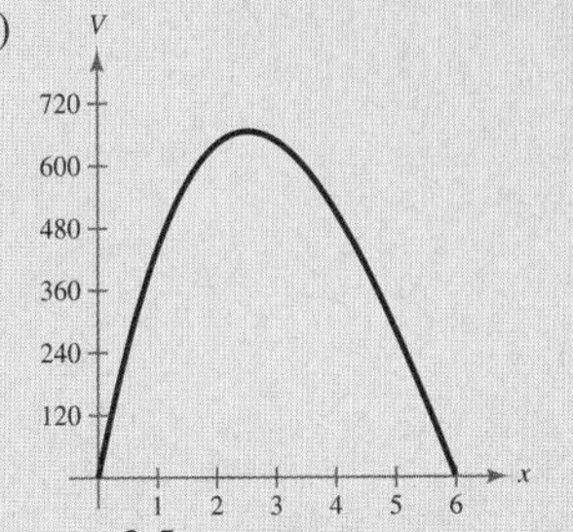

$x \approx 2.5$

99. (a) $A = -2x^2 + 12x$
(b) $V = -384x^2 + 2304x$
(c) 0 in. $< x <$ 6 in.
(d)

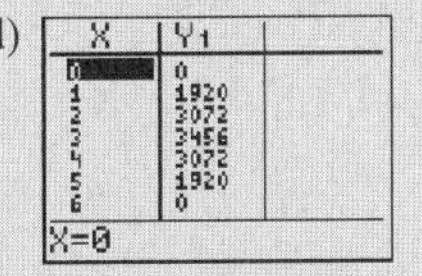

When $x = 3$, the volume is maximum at $V = 3456$; dimensions of gutter are 3 in. × 6 in. × 3 in.

(e)

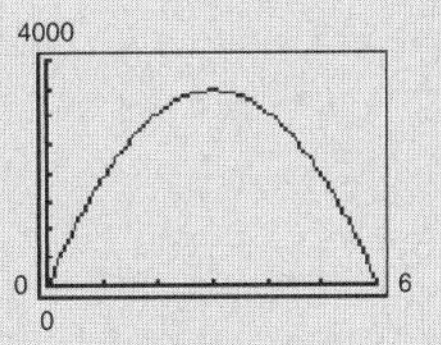

The maximum value is the same.

(f) No. Answers will vary.

100. (c)

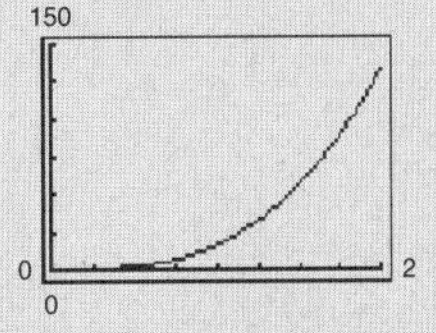

101. REVENUE The total revenues R (in millions of dollars) for Krispy Kreme from 2000 through 2007 are shown in the table.

Year	Revenue, R
2000	300.7
2001	394.4
2002	491.5
2003	665.6
2004	707.8
2005	543.4
2006	461.2
2007	429.3

A model that represents these data is given by $R = 3.0711t^4 - 42.803t^3 + 160.59t^2 - 62.6t + 307$, $0 \le t \le 7$, where t represents the year, with $t = 0$ corresponding to 2000. (Source: Krispy Kreme)

(a) Use a graphing utility to create a scatter plot of the data. Then graph the model in the same viewing window. See margin.

(b) How well does the model fit the data? The model fits the data well.

(c) Use a graphing utility to approximate any relative extrema of the model over its domain. (c)–(d). See margin.

(d) Use a graphing utility to approximate the intervals over which the revenue for Krispy Kreme was increasing and decreasing over its domain.

(e) Use the results of parts (c) and (d) to write a short paragraph about Krispy Kreme's revenue during this time period. Answers will vary.

102. REVENUE The total revenues R (in millions of dollars) for Papa John's International from 2000 through 2007 are shown in the table.

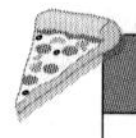

Year	Revenue, R
2000	944.7
2001	971.2
2002	946.2
2003	917.4
2004	942.4
2005	968.8
2006	1001.6
2007	1063.6

A model that represents these data is given by $R = -0.5635t^4 + 9.019t^3 - 40.20t^2 + 49.0t + 947$, $0 \le t \le 7$, where t represents the year, with $t = 0$ corresponding to 2000. (Source: Papa John's International)

(a) Use a graphing utility to create a scatter plot of the data. Then graph the model in the same viewing window. See margin. (b) The model fits the data well.

(b) How well does the model fit the data?

(c)–(d). See margin. (c) Use a graphing utility to approximate any relative extrema of the model over its domain.

(d) Use a graphing utility to approximate the intervals over which the revenue for Papa John's International was increasing and decreasing over its domain.

(e) Use the results of parts (c) and (d) to write a short paragraph about the revenue for Papa John's International during this time period. Answers will vary.

103. TREE GROWTH The growth of a red oak tree is approximated by the function

$$G = -0.003t^3 + 0.137t^2 + 0.458t - 0.839$$

where G is the height of the tree (in feet) and t $(2 \le t \le 34)$ is its age (in years).

(a) Use a graphing utility to graph the function. (*Hint:* Use a viewing window in which $-10 \le x \le 45$ and $-5 \le y \le 60$.) See margin.

(b) Estimate the age of the tree when it is growing most rapidly. This point is called the *point of diminishing returns* because the increase in size will be less with each additional year. $t \approx 15$

(c) Using calculus, the point of diminishing returns can also be found by finding the vertex of the parabola given by

$$y = -0.009t^2 + 0.274t + 0.458.$$

Vertex: (15.22, 2.54)

Find the vertex of this parabola.

(d) Compare your results from parts (b) and (c). See margin.

104. REVENUE The total revenue R (in millions of dollars) for a company is related to its advertising expense by the function

$$R = \frac{1}{100{,}000}(-x^3 + 600x^2), \quad 0 \le x \le 400$$

where x is the amount spent on advertising (in tens of thousands of dollars). Use the graph of this function, shown in the figure on the next page, to estimate the point on the graph at which the function is increasing most rapidly. This point is called the *point of diminishing returns* because any expense above this amount will yield less return per dollar invested in advertising. $x \approx 200$

101. (a)

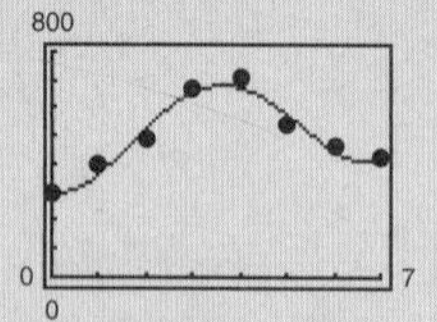

(c) Relative minima: (0.21, 300.54), (6.62, 410.74)
Relative maximum: (3.62, 681.72)

(d) Increasing: (0.21, 3.62), (6.62, 7)
Decreasing: (0, 0.21), (3.62, 6.62)

102. (a)

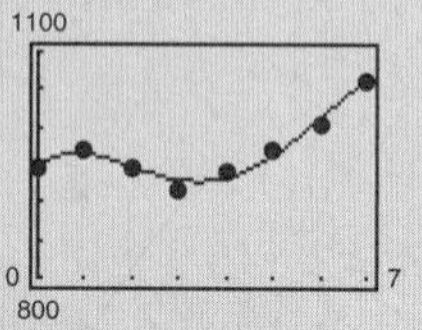

(c) Relative minimum: (3.41, 928.07)
Relative maxima: (0.82, 964.87), (7, 1060.75)

(d) Increasing: (0, 0.82), (3.41, 7)
Decreasing: (0.82, 3.41)

103. (a)

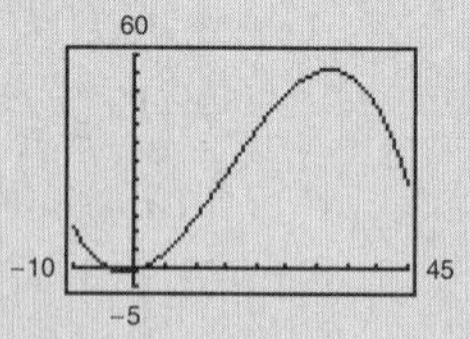

(d) The results are approximately equal.

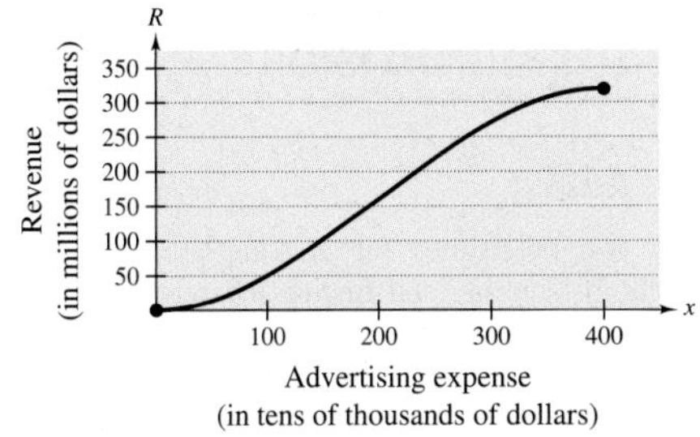

FIGURE FOR 104

EXPLORATION

105–107. See margin.

TRUE OR FALSE? In Exercises 105–107, determine whether the statement is true or false. Justify your answer.

105. A fifth-degree polynomial can have five turning points in its graph.

106. It is possible for a sixth-degree polynomial to have only one solution.

107. The graph of the function given by

$$f(x) = 2 + x - x^2 + x^3 - x^4 + x^5 + x^6 - x^7$$

rises to the left and falls to the right.

108. CAPSTONE For each graph, describe a polynomial function that could represent the graph. (Indicate the degree of the function and the sign of its leading coefficient.) See margin.

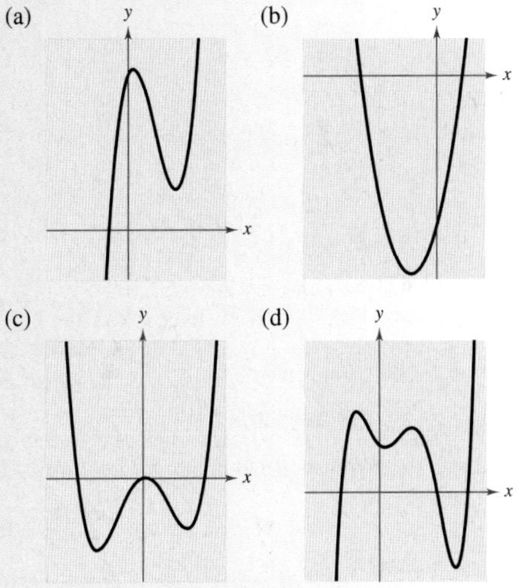

109. GRAPHICAL REASONING Sketch a graph of the function given by $f(x) = x^4$. Explain how the graph of each function g differs (if it does) from the graph of each function f. Determine whether g is odd, even, or neither. See margin.

(a) $g(x) = f(x) + 2$ (b) $g(x) = f(x + 2)$

(c) $g(x) = f(-x)$ (d) $g(x) = -f(x)$

(e) $g(x) = f\left(\frac{1}{2}x\right)$ (f) $g(x) = \frac{1}{2}f(x)$

(g) $g(x) = f\left(x^{3/4}\right)$ (h) $g(x) = (f \circ f)(x)$

110. THINK ABOUT IT For each function, identify the degree of the function and whether the degree of the function is even or odd. Identify the leading coefficient and whether the leading coefficient is positive or negative. Use a graphing utility to graph each function. Describe the relationship between the degree of the function and the sign of the leading coefficient of the function and the right-hand and left-hand behavior of the graph of the function. See margin.

(a) $f(x) = x^3 - 2x^2 - x + 1$

(b) $f(x) = 2x^5 + 2x^2 - 5x + 1$

(c) $f(x) = -2x^5 - x^2 + 5x + 3$

(d) $f(x) = -x^3 + 5x - 2$

(e) $f(x) = 2x^2 + 3x - 4$

(f) $f(x) = x^4 - 3x^2 + 2x - 1$

(g) $f(x) = x^2 + 3x + 2$

111. THINK ABOUT IT Sketch the graph of each polynomial function. Then count the number of zeros of the function and the numbers of relative minima and relative maxima. Compare these numbers with the degree of the polynomial. What do you observe?

(a) $f(x) = -x^3 + 9x$ (b) $f(x) = x^4 - 10x^2 + 9$

(c) $f(x) = x^5 - 16x$ (a)–(c). See margin.

112. Explore the transformations of the form

$$g(x) = a(x - h)^5 + k.$$ See margin.

(a) Use a graphing utility to graph the functions $y_1 = -\frac{1}{3}(x - 2)^5 + 1$ and $y_2 = \frac{3}{5}(x + 2)^5 - 3$. Determine whether the graphs are increasing or decreasing. Explain.

(b) Will the graph of g always be increasing or decreasing? If so, is this behavior determined by a, h, or k? Explain.

(c) Use a graphing utility to graph the function given by $H(x) = x^5 - 3x^3 + 2x + 1$. Use the graph and the result of part (b) to determine whether H can be written in the form $H(x) = a(x - h)^5 + k$. Explain.

5 ASSESS AND RETEACH

Daily Homework Quiz

Transparency Available

Available at the Instructor's companion site.

105. False. A fifth-degree polynomial can have at most four turning points.

106. True. $f(x) = (x - 1)^6$ has one repeated solution.

107. True. The degree of the function is odd and its leading coefficient is negative, so the graph rises to the left and falls to the right.

108. (a) Degree: 3; Leading coefficient: positive

(b) Degree: 2; Leading coefficient: positive

(c) Degree: 4; Leading coefficient: positive

(d) Degree: 5; Leading coefficient: positive

109.

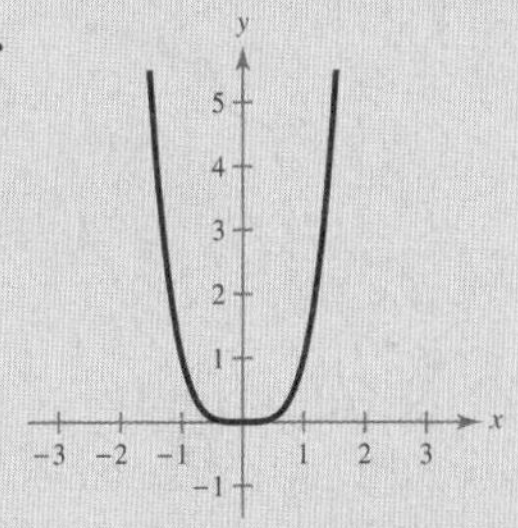

(a) Vertical shift two units upward; Even

(b) Horizontal shift two units to the left; Neither

(c) Reflection in the y-axis; Even

(d) Reflection in the x-axis; Even

(e) Horizontal stretch; Even

(f) Vertical shrink; Even

(g) $g(x) = x^3, x \geq 0$; Neither

(h) $g(x) = x^{16}$; Even

112. (a)

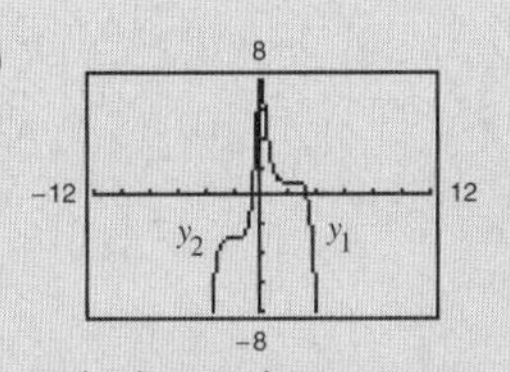

y_1 is decreasing.

y_2 is increasing.

(b) Either always increasing or always decreasing. The behavior is determined by a. If $a > 0$, $g(x)$ will always be increasing. If $a < 0$, $g(x)$ will always be decreasing.

(c)

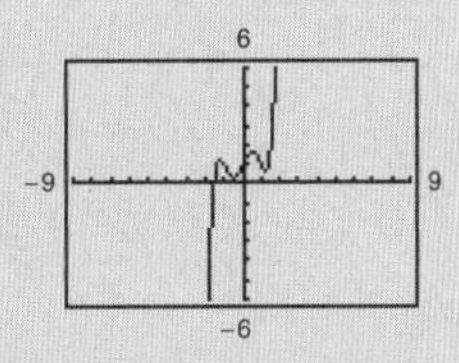

Because $H(x)$ is not always increasing or always decreasing, H cannot be written in the form $H(x) = a(x - h)^5 + k$.

110–111. See Additional Answers beginning on page AA1.

1 PLAN AND PREPARE

Warm-up Exercises

Transparency Available
Available at the Instructor's companion site.

Notetaking Guide

Transparency Available
Promotes interactive learning and notetaking skills.
Available at the Instructor's companion site.

Animated Precalculus

An **Animated Precalculus** tutorial is available at the Student companion site for **Section 2.3.**

Pacing

Average: 1 day
Advanced: 1 day
Block: 0.5 block with 2.4

2 FOCUS AND MOTIVATE

Essential Question

How do you divide a polynomial by another polynomial and interpret the result? **Tell students that they will learn how to answer this question by studying long division; synthetic division; and the meanings of dividend, divisor, quotient, and remainder in polynomial division.**

2.3 Polynomial and Synthetic Division

What you should learn

- Use long division to divide polynomials by other polynomials.
- Use synthetic division to divide polynomials by binomials of the form $(x - k)$.
- Use the Remainder Theorem and the Factor Theorem.

Why you should learn it

Synthetic division can help you evaluate polynomial functions. For instance, in Exercise 85 on page 157, you will use synthetic division to determine the amount donated to support higher education in the United States in 2010.

MBI/Alamy

Long Division of Polynomials

In this section, you will study two procedures for *dividing* polynomials. These procedures are especially valuable in factoring and finding the zeros of polynomial functions. To begin, suppose you are given the graph of

$$f(x) = 6x^3 - 19x^2 + 16x - 4.$$

Notice that a zero of f occurs at $x = 2$, as shown in Figure 2.28. Because $x = 2$ is a zero of f, you know that $(x - 2)$ is a factor of $f(x)$. This means that there exists a second-degree polynomial $q(x)$ such that

$$f(x) = (x - 2) \cdot q(x).$$

To find $q(x)$, you can use **long division,** as illustrated in Example 1.

Example 1 Long Division of Polynomials

Divide $6x^3 - 19x^2 + 16x - 4$ by $x - 2$, and use the result to factor the polynomial completely.

Solution

Think $\frac{6x^3}{x} = 6x^2$.

Think $\frac{-7x^2}{x} = -7x$.

Think $\frac{2x}{x} = 2$.

$$\begin{array}{r l}
 6x^2 - 7x + 2 & \\
x - 2 \,\big)\, 6x^3 - 19x^2 + 16x - 4 & \\
6x^3 - 12x^2 & \text{Multiply: } 6x^2(x - 2). \\
-7x^2 + 16x & \text{Subtract.} \\
-7x^2 + 14x & \text{Multiply: } -7x(x - 2). \\
2x - 4 & \text{Subtract.} \\
2x - 4 & \text{Multiply: } 2(x - 2). \\
0 & \text{Subtract.}
\end{array}$$

From this division, you can conclude that

$$6x^3 - 19x^2 + 16x - 4 = (x - 2)(6x^2 - 7x + 2)$$

and by factoring the quadratic $6x^2 - 7x + 2$, you have

$$6x^3 - 19x^2 + 16x - 4 = (x - 2)(2x - 1)(3x - 2).$$

Note that this factorization agrees with the graph shown in Figure 2.28 in that the three x-intercepts occur at $x = 2$, $x = \frac{1}{2}$, and $x = \frac{2}{3}$.

CHECKPoint Now try Exercise 11.

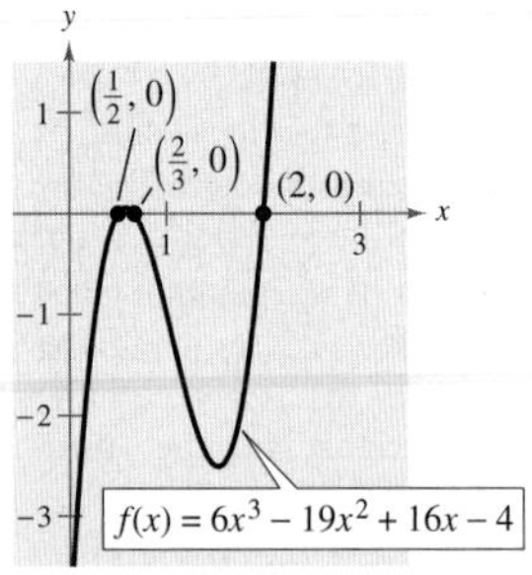

FIGURE 2.28

Resource Planning Guide

Chapter Resources
- Complete Solutions Guide

Workbooks
- Notetaking Guide
- Student Solutions Guide

Interactive Technology
- Instructor Success Organizer
- Notetaking Guide IAE
- Instructional DVDs
- Animated Precalculus
- PowerLecture with ExamView

In Example 1, $x - 2$ is a factor of the polynomial $6x^3 - 19x^2 + 16x - 4$, and the long division process produces a remainder of zero. Often, long division will produce a nonzero remainder. For instance, if you divide $x^2 + 3x + 5$ by $x + 1$, you obtain the following.

$$\begin{array}{rrl} & x + 2 & \leftarrow \text{Quotient} \\ \text{Divisor} \rightarrow \; x + 1 \,\big) & x^2 + 3x + 5 & \leftarrow \text{Dividend} \\ & \underline{x^2 + x} & \\ & 2x + 5 & \\ & \underline{2x + 2} & \\ & 3 & \leftarrow \text{Remainder} \end{array}$$

In fractional form, you can write this result as follows.

$$\underbrace{\overbrace{\frac{x^2 + 3x + 5}{x + 1}}^{\text{Dividend}}}_{\text{Divisor}} = \overbrace{x + 2}^{\text{Quotient}} + \underbrace{\overbrace{\frac{3}{x + 1}}^{\text{Remainder}}}_{\text{Divisor}}$$

This implies that

$$x^2 + 3x + 5 = (x + 1)(x + 2) + 3 \qquad \text{Multiply each side by } (x + 1).$$

which illustrates the following theorem, called the **Division Algorithm.**

The Division Algorithm

If $f(x)$ and $d(x)$ are polynomials such that $d(x) \neq 0$, and the degree of $d(x)$ is less than or equal to the degree of $f(x)$, there exist unique polynomials $q(x)$ and $r(x)$ such that

$$\underset{\text{Dividend}}{f(x)} = \underset{\text{Divisor}}{d(x)}\,\underset{\text{Quotient}}{q(x)} + \underset{\text{Remainder}}{r(x)}$$

where $r(x) = 0$ *or* the degree of $r(x)$ is less than the degree of $d(x)$. If the remainder $r(x)$ is zero, $d(x)$ *divides evenly* into $f(x)$.

The Division Algorithm can also be written as

$$\frac{f(x)}{d(x)} = q(x) + \frac{r(x)}{d(x)}.$$

In the Division Algorithm, the rational expression $f(x)/d(x)$ is **improper** because the degree of $f(x)$ is greater than or equal to the degree of $d(x)$. On the other hand, the rational expression $r(x)/d(x)$ is **proper** because the degree of $r(x)$ is less than the degree of $d(x)$.

3 TEACH

Extra Example 1

Divide $x^3 - 2x^2 - 9$ by $x - 3$, and use the result to factor the polynomial completely.

$x^3 - 2x^2 - 9 = (x - 3)(x^2 + x + 3)$

Extra Example 2

Divide $x^4 - 1$ by $x + 1$.

$$\frac{x^4 - 1}{x + 1} = x^3 - x^2 + x - 1$$

Extra Example 3

Divide $6x^4 - x^3 - x^2 + 9x - 3$ by $x^2 + x - 1$.

$$6x^2 - 7x + 12 + \frac{-10x + 9}{x^2 + x - 1}$$

Before you apply the Division Algorithm, follow these steps.

1. Write the dividend and divisor in descending powers of the variable.
2. Insert placeholders with zero coefficients for missing powers of the variable.

Example 2 Long Division of Polynomials

Divide $x^3 - 1$ by $x - 1$.

Solution

Because there is no x^2-term or x-term in the dividend, you need to line up the subtraction by using zero coefficients (or leaving spaces) for the missing terms.

$$\begin{array}{r@{}l}
 & x^2 + x + 1 \\
x - 1 \,\big)\! & \overline{x^3 + 0x^2 + 0x - 1} \\
 & \underline{x^3 - x^2} \\
 & \quad x^2 + 0x \\
 & \quad \underline{x^2 - x} \\
 & \qquad\quad x - 1 \\
 & \qquad\quad \underline{x - 1} \\
 & \qquad\qquad 0
\end{array}$$

So, $x - 1$ divides evenly into $x^3 - 1$, and you can write

$$\frac{x^3 - 1}{x - 1} = x^2 + x + 1, \quad x \neq 1.$$

CHECK Point Now try Exercise 17.

You can check the result of Example 2 by multiplying.

$$(x - 1)(x^2 + x + 1) = x^3 + x^2 + x - x^2 - x - 1 = x^3 - 1$$

Algebra Help

You can check a long division problem by multiplying. You can review the techniques for multiplying polynomials in Appendix A.3.

Example 3 Long Division of Polynomials

Divide $-5x^2 - 2 + 3x + 2x^4 + 4x^3$ by $2x - 3 + x^2$.

Solution

Begin by writing the dividend and divisor in descending powers of x.

$$\begin{array}{r@{}l}
 & 2x^2 \qquad\qquad + 1 \\
x^2 + 2x - 3 \,\big)\! & \overline{2x^4 + 4x^3 - 5x^2 + 3x - 2} \\
 & \underline{2x^4 + 4x^3 - 6x^2} \\
 & \qquad\qquad\quad x^2 + 3x - 2 \\
 & \qquad\qquad\quad \underline{x^2 + 2x - 3} \\
 & \qquad\qquad\qquad\quad x + 1
\end{array}$$

Note that the first subtraction eliminated two terms from the dividend. When this happens, the quotient skips a term. You can write the result as

$$\frac{2x^4 + 4x^3 - 5x^2 + 3x - 2}{x^2 + 2x - 3} = 2x^2 + 1 + \frac{x + 1}{x^2 + 2x - 3}.$$

CHECK Point Now try Exercise 23.

Synthetic Division

There is a nice shortcut for long division of polynomials by divisors of the form $x - k$. This shortcut is called **synthetic division.** The pattern for synthetic division of a cubic polynomial is summarized as follows. (The pattern for higher-degree polynomials is similar.)

Synthetic Division (for a Cubic Polynomial)

To divide $ax^3 + bx^2 + cx + d$ by $x - k$, use the following pattern.

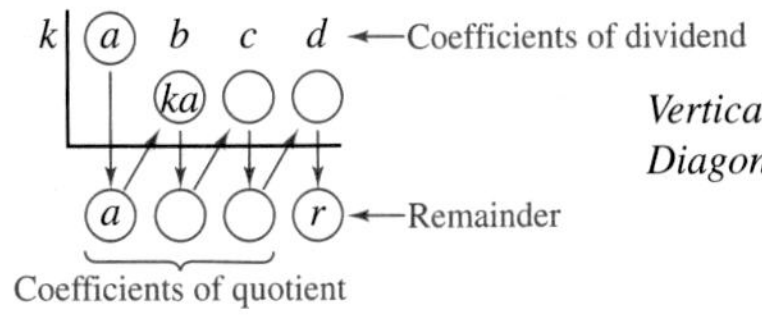

Vertical pattern: Add terms.
Diagonal pattern: Multiply by k.

This algorithm for synthetic division works only for divisors of the form $x - k$. Remember that $x + k = x - (-k)$.

Example 4 Using Synthetic Division

Use synthetic division to divide $x^4 - 10x^2 - 2x + 4$ by $x + 3$.

Solution

You should set up the array as follows. Note that a zero is included for the missing x^3-term in the dividend.

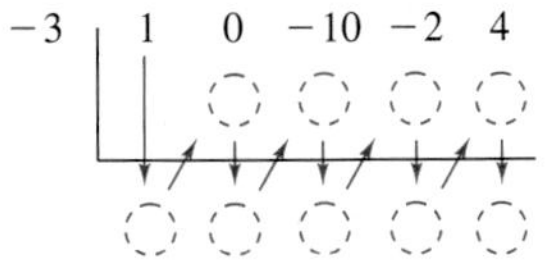

Then, use the synthetic division pattern by adding terms in columns and multiplying the results by -3.

Divisor: $x + 3$ Dividend: $x^4 - 10x^2 - 2x + 4$

−3	1	0	−10	−2	4
		−3	9	3	−3
	1	−3	−1	1	(1) ← Remainder: 1

Quotient: $x^3 - 3x^2 - x + 1$

So, you have

$$\frac{x^4 - 10x^2 - 2x + 4}{x + 3} = x^3 - 3x^2 - x + 1 + \frac{1}{x + 3}.$$

CHECKPoint Now try Exercise 27.

Extra Example 4

Use synthetic division to divide $5x^3 + 8x^2 - x + 6$ by $x + 2$.

$5x^2 - 2x + 3$

Avoiding Common Errors

If powers of x are missing from the dividend, there must be a placeholder in the synthetic division for each missing term. For example, $x^5 - 32$ would be represented by
1 0 0 0 0 −32.

Extra Example 5

Use the Remainder Theorem to evaluate $f(x) = 4x^3 + 10x^2 - 3x - 8$ at the value $f(-1)$.

Because the remainder is $r = 1$, $f(-1) = 1$.

The Remainder and Factor Theorems

The remainder obtained in the synthetic division process has an important interpretation, as described in the **Remainder Theorem.**

The Remainder Theorem

If a polynomial $f(x)$ is divided by $x - k$, the remainder is

$$r = f(k).$$

For a proof of the Remainder Theorem, see Proofs in Mathematics on page 211.

The Remainder Theorem tells you that synthetic division can be used to evaluate a polynomial function. That is, to evaluate a polynomial function $f(x)$ when $x = k$, divide $f(x)$ by $x - k$. The remainder will be $f(k)$, as illustrated in Example 5.

Example 5 Using the Remainder Theorem

Use the Remainder Theorem to evaluate the following function at $x = -2$.

$$f(x) = 3x^3 + 8x^2 + 5x - 7$$

Solution

Using synthetic division, you obtain the following.

-2	3	8	5	-7
		-6	-4	-2
	3	2	1	-9

Because the remainder is $r = -9$, you can conclude that

$$f(-2) = -9. \qquad r = f(k)$$

This means that $(-2, -9)$ is a point on the graph of f. You can check this by substituting $x = -2$ in the original function.

Check

$$f(-2) = 3(-2)^3 + 8(-2)^2 + 5(-2) - 7$$

$$= 3(-8) + 8(4) - 10 - 7 = -9$$

CHECK *Point* Now try Exercise 55.

Another important theorem is the **Factor Theorem,** stated below. This theorem states that you can test to see whether a polynomial has $(x - k)$ as a factor by evaluating the polynomial at $x = k$. If the result is 0, $(x - k)$ is a factor.

The Factor Theorem

A polynomial $f(x)$ has a factor $(x - k)$ if and only if $f(k) = 0$.

For a proof of the Factor Theorem, see Proofs in Mathematics on page 211.

Example 6 Factoring a Polynomial: Repeated Division

Show that $(x - 2)$ and $(x + 3)$ are factors of $f(x) = 2x^4 + 7x^3 - 4x^2 - 27x - 18$. Then find the remaining factors of $f(x)$.

Algebraic Solution

Using synthetic division with the factor $(x - 2)$, you obtain the following.

2	2	7	−4	−27	−18
		4	22	36	18
	2	11	18	9	0

0 remainder, so $f(2) = 0$ and $(x - 2)$ is a factor.

Take the result of this division and perform synthetic division again using the factor $(x + 3)$.

−3	2	11	18	9
		−6	−15	−9
	2	5	3	0

0 remainder, so $f(-3) = 0$ and $(x + 3)$ is a factor.

$2x^2 + 5x + 3$

Because the resulting quadratic expression factors as

$$2x^2 + 5x + 3 = (2x + 3)(x + 1)$$

the complete factorization of $f(x)$ is

$$f(x) = (x - 2)(x + 3)(2x + 3)(x + 1).$$

Graphical Solution

From the graph of $f(x) = 2x^4 + 7x^3 - 4x^2 - 27x - 18$, you can see that there are four x-intercepts (see Figure 2.29). These occur at $x = -3$, $x = -\frac{3}{2}$, $x = -1$, and $x = 2$. (Check this algebraically.) This implies that $(x + 3)$, $\left(x + \frac{3}{2}\right)$, $(x + 1)$, and $(x - 2)$ are factors of $f(x)$. $\left[\text{Note that } \left(x + \frac{3}{2}\right) \text{ and } (2x + 3) \text{ are equivalent factors because they both yield the same zero, } x = -\frac{3}{2}.\right]$

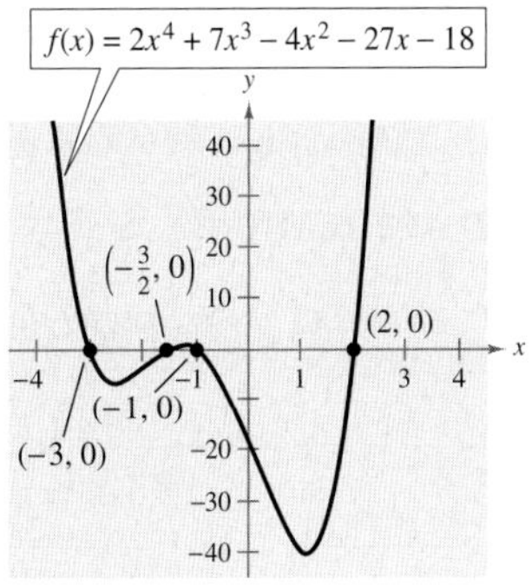

FIGURE 2.29

CHECK*Point* Now try Exercise 67.

Study Tip

Note in Example 6 that the complete factorization of $f(x)$ implies that f has four real zeros: $x = 2$, $x = -3$, $x = -\frac{3}{2}$, and $x = -1$. This is confirmed by the graph of f, which is shown in the Figure 2.29.

Uses of the Remainder in Synthetic Division

The remainder r, obtained in the synthetic division of $f(x)$ by $x - k$, provides the following information.

1. The remainder r gives the value of f at $x = k$. That is, $r = f(k)$.
2. If $r = 0$, $(x - k)$ is a factor of $f(x)$.
3. If $r = 0$, $(k, 0)$ is an x-intercept of the graph of f.

Throughout this text, the importance of developing several problem-solving strategies is emphasized. In the exercises for this section, try using more than one strategy to solve several of the exercises. For instance, if you find that $x - k$ divides evenly into $f(x)$ (with no remainder), try sketching the graph of f. You should find that $(k, 0)$ is an x-intercept of the graph.

Extra Example 6

Show that $(x + 3)$ is a factor of $f(x) = x^3 - 19x - 30 = 0$. Then find the remaining factors of $f(x)$.

$\mathbf{f(x) = (x + 3)(x - 5)(x + 2)}$

Closing the Lesson

Have students summarize the major points of the lesson and answer the Essential Question: How do you divide a polynomial by another polynomial and interpret the result?

- **Use long division to divide one polynomial by another, and use synthetic division to divide a polynomial by a binomial.**
- **Use division of a polynomial to confirm the location of its x-intercepts.**
- **Recognize that the remainder $r = f(k)$ results from dividing $f(x)$ by $x - k$.**

4 PRACTICE AND APPLY

Assignment Guide

Transparencies Available
Available at the Instructor's companion site.

Average:
Day 1: pp. 156–158
Exs. 7, 15–23 odd, 29–41 odd, 47–51 odd, 57, 61–71 odd, 83, 85, 87–89, 93, 95

Advanced:
Day 1: pp. 156–158
Exs. 8, 16–26 even, 32–44 even, 50–56 even, 62–66 even, 69, 72, 84, 85, 90–100 even

Block:
pp. 156–158
Exs. 7, 15–23 odd, 29–41 odd, 47–51 odd, 57, 61–71 odd, 83, 85, 87–89, 93, 95 (with 2.4)

2.3 EXERCISES

See www.CalcChat.com for worked-out solutions to odd-numbered exercises.

VOCABULARY

1. Two forms of the Division Algorithm are shown below. Identify and label each term or function.

$$f(x) = d(x)q(x) + r(x) \qquad \frac{f(x)}{d(x)} = q(x) + \frac{r(x)}{d(x)}$$

$f(x)$: dividend; $d(x)$: divisor; $q(x)$: quotient; $r(x)$: remainder

In Exercises 2–6, fill in the blanks.

2. The rational expression $p(x)/q(x)$ is called improper if the degree of the numerator is greater than or equal to that of the denominator, and is called proper if the degree of the numerator is less than that of the denominator.
3. In the Division Algorithm, the rational expression $f(x)/d(x)$ is improper because the degree of $f(x)$ is greater than or equal to the degree of $d(x)$.
4. An alternative method to long division of polynomials is called synthetic division, in which the divisor must be of the form $x - k$.
5. The Factor Theorem states that a polynomial $f(x)$ has a factor $(x - k)$ if and only if $f(k) = 0$.
6. The _______ Theorem states that if a polynomial $f(x)$ is divided by $x - k$, the remainder is $r = f(k)$. Remainder

SKILLS AND APPLICATIONS

ANALYTICAL ANALYSIS In Exercises 7 and 8, use long division to verify that $y_1 = y_2$. 7–8. Answers will vary.

7. $y_1 = \dfrac{x^2}{x+2}, \quad y_2 = x - 2 + \dfrac{4}{x+2}$

8. $y_1 = \dfrac{x^4 - 3x^2 - 1}{x^2 + 5}, \quad y_2 = x^2 - 8 + \dfrac{39}{x^2+5}$

GRAPHICAL ANALYSIS In Exercises 9 and 10, (a) use a graphing utility to graph the two equations in the same viewing window, (b) use the graphs to verify that the expressions are equivalent, and (c) use long division to verify the results algebraically. 9–10. See margin.

9. $y_1 = \dfrac{x^2 + 2x - 1}{x+3}, \quad y_2 = x - 1 + \dfrac{2}{x+3}$

10. $y_1 = \dfrac{x^4 + x^2 - 1}{x^2+1}, \quad y_2 = x^2 - \dfrac{1}{x^2+1}$

In Exercises 11–26, use long division to divide.

11. $(2x^2 + 10x + 12) \div (x + 3)$ $2x + 4, \; x \neq -3$
12. $(5x^2 - 17x - 12) \div (x - 4)$ $5x + 3, \; x \neq 4$
13. $(4x^3 - 7x^2 - 11x + 5) \div (4x + 5)$ 13–26. See margin.
14. $(6x^3 - 16x^2 + 17x - 6) \div (3x - 2)$
15. $(x^4 + 5x^3 + 6x^2 - x - 2) \div (x + 2)$
16. $(x^3 + 4x^2 - 3x - 12) \div (x - 3)$
17. $(x^3 - 27) \div (x - 3)$
18. $(x^3 + 125) \div (x + 5)$
19. $(7x + 3) \div (x + 2)$
20. $(8x - 5) \div (2x + 1)$
21. $(x^3 - 9) \div (x^2 + 1)$
22. $(x^5 + 7) \div (x^3 - 1)$
23. $(3x + 2x^3 - 9 - 8x^2) \div (x^2 + 1)$
24. $(5x^3 - 16 - 20x + x^4) \div (x^2 - x - 3)$
25. $\dfrac{x^4}{(x-1)^3}$
26. $\dfrac{2x^3 - 4x^2 - 15x + 5}{(x-1)^2}$

27–46. See margin.

In Exercises 27–46, use synthetic division to divide.

27. $(3x^3 - 17x^2 + 15x - 25) \div (x - 5)$
28. $(5x^3 + 18x^2 + 7x - 6) \div (x + 3)$
29. $(6x^3 + 7x^2 - x + 26) \div (x - 3)$
30. $(2x^3 + 14x^2 - 20x + 7) \div (x + 6)$
31. $(4x^3 - 9x + 8x^2 - 18) \div (x + 2)$
32. $(9x^3 - 16x - 18x^2 + 32) \div (x - 2)$
33. $(-x^3 + 75x - 250) \div (x + 10)$
34. $(3x^3 - 16x^2 - 72) \div (x - 6)$
35. $(5x^3 - 6x^2 + 8) \div (x - 4)$
36. $(5x^3 + 6x + 8) \div (x + 2)$
37. $\dfrac{10x^4 - 50x^3 - 800}{x - 6}$
38. $\dfrac{x^5 - 13x^4 - 120x + 80}{x + 3}$
39. $\dfrac{x^3 + 512}{x + 8}$
40. $\dfrac{x^3 - 729}{x - 9}$
41. $\dfrac{-3x^4}{x - 2}$
42. $\dfrac{-3x^4}{x + 2}$
43. $\dfrac{180x - x^4}{x - 6}$
44. $\dfrac{5 - 3x + 2x^2 - x^3}{x + 1}$
45. $\dfrac{4x^3 + 16x^2 - 23x - 15}{x + \frac{1}{2}}$
46. $\dfrac{3x^3 - 4x^2 + 5}{x - \frac{3}{2}}$

9. (a) and (b)

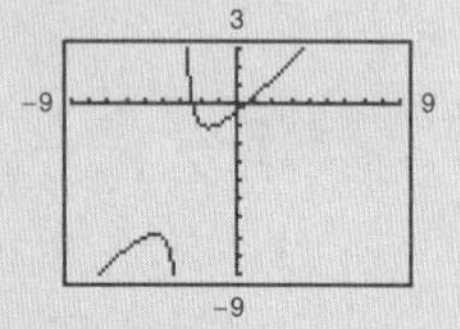

(c) Answers will vary.

10. (a) and (b)

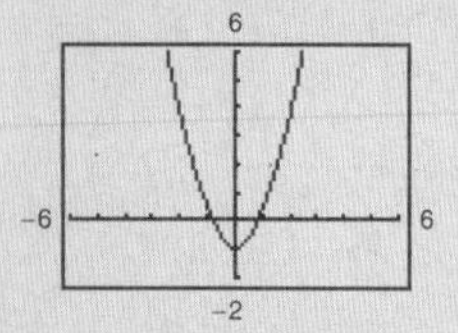

(c) Answers will vary.

13. $x^2 - 3x + 1, \quad x \neq -\frac{5}{4}$
14. $2x^2 - 4x + 3, \quad x \neq \frac{2}{3}$
15. $x^3 + 3x^2 - 1, \quad x \neq -2$
16. $x^2 + 7x + 18 + \dfrac{42}{x-3}$
17. $x^2 + 3x + 9, \quad x \neq 3$
18. $x^2 - 5x + 25, \quad x \neq -5$
19. $7 - \dfrac{11}{x+2}$
20. $4 - \dfrac{9}{2x+1}$
21. $x - \dfrac{x+9}{x^2+1}$
22. $x^2 + \dfrac{x^2+7}{x^3-1}$
23. $2x - 8 + \dfrac{x-1}{x^2+1}$
24. $x^2 + 6x + 9 + \dfrac{7x+11}{x^2-x-3}$
25. $x + 3 + \dfrac{6x^2 - 8x + 3}{(x-1)^3}$
26. $2x - \dfrac{17x - 5}{x^2 - 2x + 1}$
27. $3x^2 - 2x + 5, \quad x \neq 5$
28. $5x^2 + 3x - 2, \quad x \neq -3$
29. $6x^2 + 25x + 74 + \dfrac{248}{x-3}$
30. $2x^2 + 2x - 32 + \dfrac{199}{x+6}$
31. $4x^2 - 9, \quad x \neq -2$
32. $9x^2 - 16, \quad x \neq 2$
33. $-x^2 + 10x - 25, \quad x \neq -10$
34. $3x^2 + 2x + 12, \quad x \neq 6$
35. $5x^2 + 14x + 56 + \dfrac{232}{x-4}$
36. $5x^2 - 10x + 26 - \dfrac{44}{x+2}$
37. $10x^3 + 10x^2 + 60x + 360 + \dfrac{1360}{x-6}$
38. $x^4 - 16x^3 + 48x^2 - 144x + 312 - \dfrac{856}{x+3}$
39. $x^2 - 8x + 64, \quad x \neq -8$
40. $x^2 + 9x + 81, \quad x \neq 9$
41. $-3x^3 - 6x^2 - 12x - 24 - \dfrac{48}{x-2}$

42–46. See Additional Answers beginning on page AA1.

In Exercises 47–54, write the function in the form $f(x) = (x - k)q(x) + r$ for the given value of k, and demonstrate that $f(k) = r$. 47–54. See margin.

47. $f(x) = x^3 - x^2 - 14x + 11, \quad k = 4$

48. $f(x) = x^3 - 5x^2 - 11x + 8, \quad k = -2$

49. $f(x) = 15x^4 + 10x^3 - 6x^2 + 14, \quad k = -\frac{2}{3}$

50. $f(x) = 10x^3 - 22x^2 - 3x + 4, \quad k = \frac{1}{5}$

51. $f(x) = x^3 + 3x^2 - 2x - 14, \quad k = \sqrt{2}$

52. $f(x) = x^3 + 2x^2 - 5x - 4, \quad k = -\sqrt{5}$

53. $f(x) = -4x^3 + 6x^2 + 12x + 4, \quad k = 1 - \sqrt{3}$

54. $f(x) = -3x^3 + 8x^2 + 10x - 8, \quad k = 2 + \sqrt{2}$

In Exercises 55–58, use the Remainder Theorem and synthetic division to find each function value. Verify your answers using another method.

55. $f(x) = 2x^3 - 7x + 3$

(a) $f(1)$ -2 (b) $f(-2)$ 1 (c) $f(\frac{1}{2})$ $-\frac{1}{4}$ (d) $f(2)$ 5

56. $g(x) = 2x^6 + 3x^4 - x^2 + 3$ See margin.

(a) $g(2)$ (b) $g(1)$ (c) $g(3)$ (d) $g(-1)$

57. $h(x) = x^3 - 5x^2 - 7x + 4$ See margin.

(a) $h(3)$ (b) $h(2)$ (c) $h(-2)$ (d) $h(-5)$

58. $f(x) = 4x^4 - 16x^3 + 7x^2 + 20$

(a) $f(1)$ 15 (b) $f(-2)$ 240 (c) $f(5)$ 695 (d) $f(-10)$ 56,720

In Exercises 59–66, use synthetic division to show that x is a solution of the third-degree polynomial equation, and use the result to factor the polynomial completely. List all real solutions of the equation. 59–66. See margin.

59. $x^3 - 7x + 6 = 0, \quad x = 2$

60. $x^3 - 28x - 48 = 0, \quad x = -4$

61. $2x^3 - 15x^2 + 27x - 10 = 0, \quad x = \frac{1}{2}$

62. $48x^3 - 80x^2 + 41x - 6 = 0, \quad x = \frac{2}{3}$

63. $x^3 + 2x^2 - 3x - 6 = 0, \quad x = \sqrt{3}$

64. $x^3 + 2x^2 - 2x - 4 = 0, \quad x = \sqrt{2}$

65. $x^3 - 3x^2 + 2 = 0, \quad x = 1 + \sqrt{3}$

66. $x^3 - x^2 - 13x - 3 = 0, \quad x = 2 - \sqrt{5}$

In Exercises 67–74, (a) verify the given factors of the function f, (b) find the remaining factor(s) of f, (c) use your results to write the complete factorization of f, (d) list all real zeros of f, and (e) confirm your results by using a graphing utility to graph the function. 67–74. See margin.

	Function	*Factors*
67.	$f(x) = 2x^3 + x^2 - 5x + 2$	$(x + 2), (x - 1)$
68.	$f(x) = 3x^3 + 2x^2 - 19x + 6$	$(x + 3), (x - 2)$
69.	$f(x) = x^4 - 4x^3 - 15x^2 + 58x - 40$	$(x - 5), (x + 4)$
70.	$f(x) = 8x^4 - 14x^3 - 71x^2 - 10x + 24$	$(x + 2), (x - 4)$
71.	$f(x) = 6x^3 + 41x^2 - 9x - 14$	$(2x + 1), (3x - 2)$
72.	$f(x) = 10x^3 - 11x^2 - 72x + 45$	$(2x + 5), (5x - 3)$
73.	$f(x) = 2x^3 - x^2 - 10x + 5$	$(2x - 1), (x + \sqrt{5})$
74.	$f(x) = x^3 + 3x^2 - 48x - 144$	$(x + 4\sqrt{3}), (x + 3)$

GRAPHICAL ANALYSIS In Exercises 75–80, (a) use the *zero* or *root* feature of a graphing utility to approximate the zeros of the function accurate to three decimal places, (b) determine one of the exact zeros, and (c) use synthetic division to verify your result from part (b), and then factor the polynomial completely. 75–80. See margin.

75. $f(x) = x^3 - 2x^2 - 5x + 10$

76. $g(x) = x^3 - 4x^2 - 2x + 8$

77. $h(t) = t^3 - 2t^2 - 7t + 2$

78. $f(s) = s^3 - 12s^2 + 40s - 24$

79. $h(x) = x^5 - 7x^4 + 10x^3 + 14x^2 - 24x$

80. $g(x) = 6x^4 - 11x^3 - 51x^2 + 99x - 27$

In Exercises 81–84, simplify the rational expression by using long division or synthetic division. 81–84. See margin.

81. $\dfrac{4x^3 - 8x^2 + x + 3}{2x - 3}$

82. $\dfrac{x^3 + x^2 - 64x - 64}{x + 8}$

83. $\dfrac{x^4 + 6x^3 + 11x^2 + 6x}{x^2 + 3x + 2}$

84. $\dfrac{x^4 + 9x^3 - 5x^2 - 36x + 4}{x^2 - 4}$

85. DATA ANALYSIS: HIGHER EDUCATION The amounts A (in billions of dollars) donated to support higher education in the United States from 2000 through 2007 are shown in the table, where t represents the year, with $t = 0$ corresponding to 2000.

Year, t	Amount, A
0	23.2
1	24.2
2	23.9
3	23.9
4	24.4
5	25.6
6	28.0
7	29.8

56. (a) 175 (b) 7 (c) 1695 (d) 7

57. (a) -35 (b) -22 (c) -10 (d) -211

59. $(x - 2)(x + 3)(x - 1)$; Solutions: $2, -3, 1$

60. $(x + 4)(x + 2)(x - 6)$; Solutions: $-4, -2, 6$

61. $(2x - 1)(x - 5)(x - 2)$; Solutions: $\frac{1}{2}, 5, 2$

62. $(3x - 2)(4x - 3)(4x - 1)$; Solutions: $\frac{2}{3}, \frac{3}{4}, \frac{1}{4}$

63. $(x + \sqrt{3})(x - \sqrt{3})(x + 2)$; Solutions: $-\sqrt{3}, \sqrt{3}, -2$

64. $(x - \sqrt{2})(x + \sqrt{2})(x + 2)$; Solutions: $\sqrt{2}, -\sqrt{2}, -2$

65. $(x - 1)(x - 1 - \sqrt{3})(x - 1 + \sqrt{3})$; Solutions: $1, 1 + \sqrt{3}, 1 - \sqrt{3}$

66. $(x - 2 + \sqrt{5})(x - 2 - \sqrt{5})(x + 3)$; Solutions: $2 - \sqrt{5}, 2 + \sqrt{5}, -3$

67. (a) Answers will vary.
(b) $2x - 1$
(c) $f(x) = (2x - 1)(x + 2)(x - 1)$
(d) $\frac{1}{2}, -2, 1$
(e)

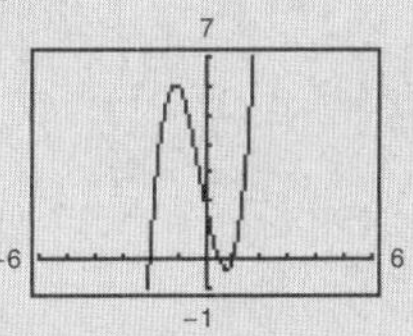

68. (a) Answers will vary.
(b) $3x - 1$
(c) $f(x) = (3x - 1)(x + 3)(x - 2)$
(d) $\frac{1}{3}, -3, 2$
(e)

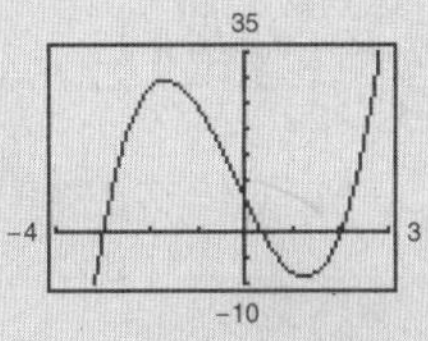

69. (a) Answers will vary.
(b) $(x - 1), (x - 2)$
(c) $f(x) = (x - 1)(x - 2)(x - 5)(x + 4)$
(d) $1, 2, 5, -4$
(e)

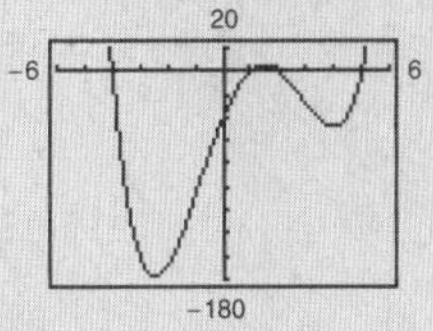

70. (a) Answers will vary.
(b) $(4x + 3), (2x - 1)$
(c) $f(x) = (4x + 3)(2x - 1)(x + 2)(x - 4)$
(d) $-\frac{3}{4}, \frac{1}{2}, -2, 4$
(e)

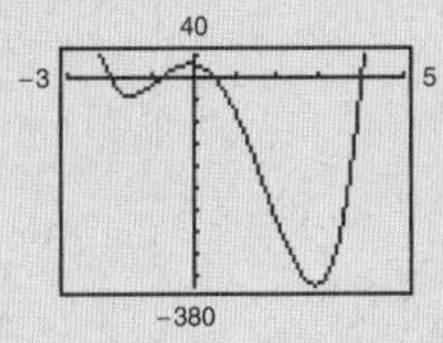

71. (a) Answers will vary.
(b) $x + 7$
(c) $f(x) = (x + 7)(2x + 1)(3x - 2)$
(d) $-7, -\frac{1}{2}, \frac{2}{3}$
(e)

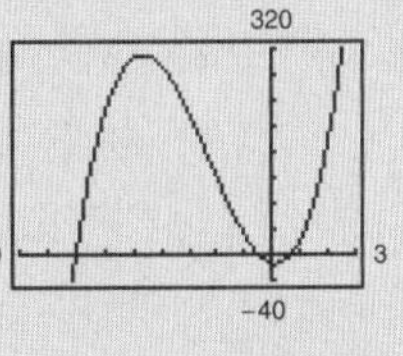

47–54, 72–84. See Additional Answers beginning on page AA1.

5 ASSESS AND RETEACH

Daily Homework Quiz

Transparency Available

Available at the Instructor's companion site.

85. (a) and (b)

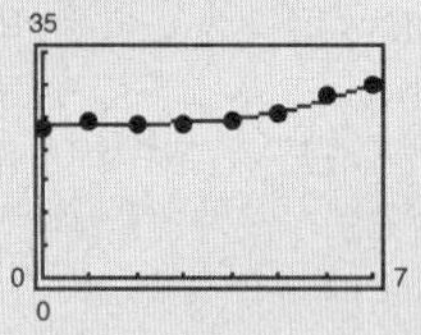

$A = 0.0349t^3 - 0.168t^2 + 0.42t + 23.4$

(c)

t	0	1	2	3
$A(t)$	23.4	23.7	23.8	24.1

t	4	5	6	7
$A(t)$	24.6	25.7	27.4	30.1

(d) $45.7 billion; No, because the model will approach infinity quickly.

86. (a) and (b)

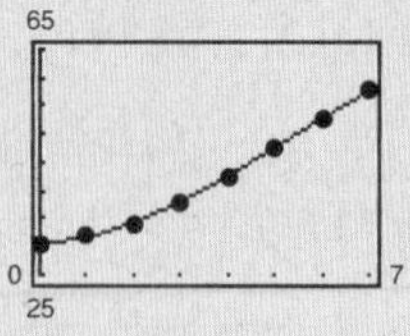

$A = -0.0576t^3 + 0.913t^2 + 0.28t + 30.7$

(c)

t	0	1	2	3
$A(t)$	30.7	31.8	34.5	38.2

t	4	5	6	7
$A(t)$	42.7	47.7	52.8	57.6

(d) $67.2 billion

90. (a) $f(x) = (x - 2)x^2 + 5$
$= x^3 - 2x^2 + 5$

(b) $f(x) = -(x + 3)x^2 + 1$
$= -x^3 - 3x^2 + 1$

94. Multiply the divisor and the quotient and add the remainder to obtain the dividend. Examples will vary.

(a)–(d). See margin.

(a) Use a graphing utility to create a scatter plot of the data.

(b) Use the *regression* feature of the graphing utility to find a cubic model for the data. Graph the model in the same viewing window as the scatter plot.

(c) Use the model to create a table of estimated values of A. Compare the model with the original data.

(d) Use synthetic division to evaluate the model for the year 2010. Even though the model is relatively accurate for estimating the given data, would you use this model to predict the amount donated to higher education in the future? Explain.

86. DATA ANALYSIS: HEALTH CARE The amounts A (in billions of dollars) of national health care expenditures in the United States from 2000 through 2007 are shown in the table, where t represents the year, with $t = 0$ corresponding to 2000. See margin.

Year, t	Amount, A
0	30.5
1	32.2
2	34.2
3	38.0
4	42.7
5	47.9
6	52.7
7	57.6

(a) Use a graphing utility to create a scatter plot of the data.

(b) Use the *regression* feature of the graphing utility to find a cubic model for the data. Graph the model in the same viewing window as the scatter plot.

(c) Use the model to create a table of estimated values of A. Compare the model with the original data.

(d) Use synthetic division to evaluate the model for the year 2010.

EXPLORATION

TRUE OR FALSE? In Exercises 87–89, determine whether the statement is true or false. Justify your answer.

87. If $(7x + 4)$ is a factor of some polynomial function f, then $\frac{4}{7}$ is a zero of f. False. $-\frac{4}{7}$ is a zero of f.

88. $(2x - 1)$ is a factor of the polynomial

$$6x^6 + x^5 - 92x^4 + 45x^3 + 184x^2 + 4x - 48.$$

True.
$f(x) = (2x - 1)(x + 1)(x - 2)(x - 3)(3x + 2)(x + 4)$

89. The rational expression

$$\frac{x^3 + 2x^2 - 13x + 10}{x^2 - 4x - 12}$$

is improper. True. The degree of the numerator is greater than the degree of the denominator.

90. Use the form $f(x) = (x - k)q(x) + r$ to create a cubic function that (a) passes through the point $(2, 5)$ and rises to the right, and (b) passes through the point $(-3, 1)$ and falls to the right. (There are many correct answers.) See margin.

THINK ABOUT IT In Exercises 91 and 92, perform the division by assuming that n is a positive integer.

91. $\dfrac{x^{3n} + 9x^{2n} + 27x^n + 27}{x^n + 3}$ $\quad x^{2n} + 6x^n + 9,\ x^n \neq -3$

92. $\dfrac{x^{3n} - 3x^{2n} + 5x^n - 6}{x^n - 2}$ $\quad x^{2n} - x^n + 3,\ x^n \neq 2$

93. WRITING Briefly explain what it means for a divisor to divide evenly into a dividend. The remainder is 0.

94. WRITING Briefly explain how to check polynomial division, and justify your reasoning. Give an example. See margin.

EXPLORATION In Exercises 95 and 96, find the constant c such that the denominator will divide evenly into the numerator.

95. $\dfrac{x^3 + 4x^2 - 3x + c}{x - 5}$ $\quad c = -210$

96. $\dfrac{x^5 - 2x^2 + x + c}{x + 2}$ $\quad c = 42$

97. THINK ABOUT IT Find the value of k such that $x - 4$ is a factor of $x^3 - kx^2 + 2kx - 8$. $k = 7$

98. THINK ABOUT IT Find the value of k such that $x - 3$ is a factor of $x^3 - kx^2 + 2kx - 12$. $k = 5$

99. WRITING Complete each polynomial division. Write a brief description of the pattern that you obtain, and use your result to find a formula for the polynomial division $(x^n - 1)/(x - 1)$. Create a numerical example to test your formula. See margin.

(a) $\dfrac{x^2 - 1}{x - 1} = \square$ (b) $\dfrac{x^3 - 1}{x - 1} = \square$

(c) $\dfrac{x^4 - 1}{x - 1} = \square$

100. CAPSTONE Consider the division

$f(x) \div (x - k)$

where

$f(x) = (x + 3)^2(x - 3)(x + 1)^3.$

(a) What is the remainder when $k = -3$? Explain. 0; $x + 3$ is a factor of f.

(b) If it is necessary to find $f(2)$, it is easier to evaluate the function directly or to use synthetic division? Explain. Because $f(x)$ is in factored form, it is easier to evaluate directly.

99. (a) $x + 1,\ x \neq 1$
(b) $x^2 + x + 1,\ x \neq 1$
(c) $x^3 + x^2 + x + 1,\ x \neq 1$
In general,
$\dfrac{x^n - 1}{x - 1} = x^{n-1} + x^{n-2} + \cdots + x + 1,\ x \neq 1.$

2.4 Complex Numbers

What you should learn

- Use the imaginary unit *i* to write complex numbers.
- Add, subtract, and multiply complex numbers.
- Use complex conjugates to write the quotient of two complex numbers in standard form.
- Find complex solutions of quadratic equations.

Why you should learn it

You can use complex numbers to model and solve real-life problems in electronics. For instance, in Exercise 89 on page 165, you will learn how to use complex numbers to find the impedance of an electrical circuit.

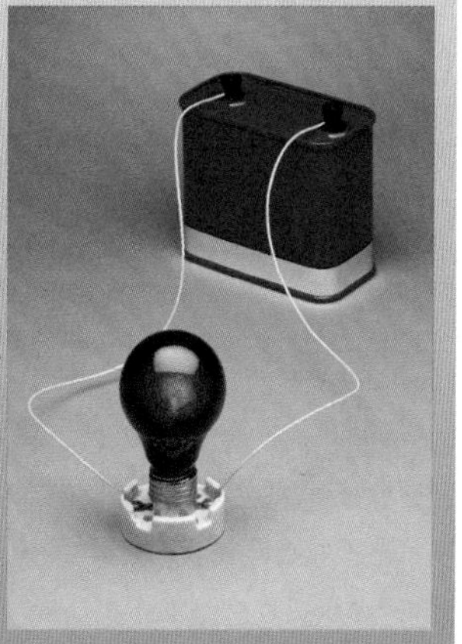

The Imaginary Unit *i*

You have learned that some quadratic equations have no real solutions. For instance, the quadratic equation $x^2 + 1 = 0$ has no real solution because there is no real number x that can be squared to produce -1. To overcome this deficiency, mathematicians created an expanded system of numbers using the **imaginary unit *i*,** defined as

$$i = \sqrt{-1} \qquad \text{Imaginary unit}$$

where $i^2 = -1$. By adding real numbers to real multiples of this imaginary unit, the set of **complex numbers** is obtained. Each complex number can be written in the **standard form *a* + *bi*.** For instance, the standard form of the complex number $-5 + \sqrt{-9}$ is $-5 + 3i$ because

$$-5 + \sqrt{-9} = -5 + \sqrt{3^2(-1)} = -5 + 3\sqrt{-1} = -5 + 3i.$$

In the standard form $a + bi$, the real number a is called the **real part** of the **complex number *a* + *bi*,** and the number bi (where b is a real number) is called the **imaginary part** of the complex number.

Definition of a Complex Number

If a and b are real numbers, the number $a + bi$ is a **complex number,** and it is said to be written in **standard form.** If $b = 0$, the number $a + bi = a$ is a real number. If $b \neq 0$, the number $a + bi$ is called an **imaginary number.** A number of the form bi, where $b \neq 0$, is called a **pure imaginary number.**

The set of real numbers is a subset of the set of complex numbers, as shown in Figure 2.30. This is true because every real number a can be written as a complex number using $b = 0$. That is, for every real number a, you can write $a = a + 0i$.

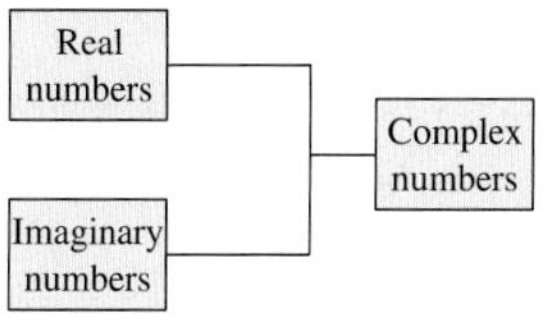

FIGURE 2.30

Equality of Complex Numbers

Two complex numbers $a + bi$ and $c + di$, written in standard form, are equal to each other

$$a + bi = c + di \qquad \text{Equality of two complex numbers}$$

if and only if $a = c$ and $b = d$.

1 PLAN AND PREPARE

Warm-up Exercises

Transparency Available
Available at the Instructor's companion site.

Notetaking Guide

Transparency Available
Promotes interactive learning and notetaking skills.
Available at the Instructor's companion site.

Animated Precalculus

An **Animated Precalculus** tutorial is available at the Student companion site for **Section 2.4.**

Pacing

Average: 1 day
Advanced: 1 day
Block: 0.5 block with 2.3

2 FOCUS AND MOTIVATE

Essential Question

How do you perform operations with complex numbers? **Tell students that they will learn how to answer this question by comparing operations with complex numbers and operations with binomials.**

Resource Planning Guide

Chapter Resources
- Complete Solutions Guide

Workbooks
- Notetaking Guide
- Student Solutions Guide

Interactive Technology
- Instructor Success Organizer
- Notetaking Guide IAE
- Instructional DVDs
- Animated Precalculus
- PowerLecture with ExamView

3 TEACH

Extra Example 1

Perform the addition or the subtraction and write the result in standard form.

a. $(7 + 3i) + (5 - 4i)$
$12 - i$

b. $(3 + 4i) - (5 - 2i)$
$-2 + 6i$

c. $4i - (-3 + 5i) + (2 - 6i)$
$5 - 7i$

d. $(5 - i) + (3 + 4i) - (8 + 3i)$
0

Operations with Complex Numbers

To add (or subtract) two complex numbers, you add (or subtract) the real and imaginary parts of the numbers separately.

Addition and Subtraction of Complex Numbers

If $a + bi$ and $c + di$ are two complex numbers written in standard form, their sum and difference are defined as follows.

Sum: $(a + bi) + (c + di) = (a + c) + (b + d)i$

Difference: $(a + bi) - (c + di) = (a - c) + (b - d)i$

The **additive identity** in the complex number system is zero (the same as in the real number system). Furthermore, the **additive inverse** of the complex number $a + bi$ is

$$-(a + bi) = -a - bi. \qquad \text{Additive inverse}$$

So, you have

$$(a + bi) + (-a - bi) = 0 + 0i = 0.$$

Example 1 Adding and Subtracting Complex Numbers

a. $(4 + 7i) + (1 - 6i) = 4 + 7i + 1 - 6i$ Remove parentheses.
$= (4 + 1) + (7i - 6i)$ Group like terms.
$= 5 + i$ Write in standard form.

b. $(1 + 2i) - (4 + 2i) = 1 + 2i - 4 - 2i$ Remove parentheses.
$= (1 - 4) + (2i - 2i)$ Group like terms.
$= -3 + 0$ Simplify.
$= -3$ Write in standard form.

c. $3i - (-2 + 3i) - (2 + 5i) = 3i + 2 - 3i - 2 - 5i$
$= (2 - 2) + (3i - 3i - 5i)$
$= 0 - 5i$
$= -5i$

d. $(3 + 2i) + (4 - i) - (7 + i) = 3 + 2i + 4 - i - 7 - i$
$= (3 + 4 - 7) + (2i - i - i)$
$= 0 + 0i$
$= 0$

CHECK Point Now try Exercise 21.

Note in Examples 1(b) and 1(d) that the sum of two complex numbers can be a real number.

Many of the properties of real numbers are valid for complex numbers as well. Here are some examples.

Associative Properties of Addition and Multiplication

Commutative Properties of Addition and Multiplication

Distributive Property of Multiplication Over Addition

Notice below how these properties are used when two complex numbers are multiplied.

$$\begin{aligned}(a + bi)(c + di) &= a(c + di) + bi(c + di) && \text{Distributive Property}\\ &= ac + (ad)i + (bc)i + (bd)i^2 && \text{Distributive Property}\\ &= ac + (ad)i + (bc)i + (bd)(-1) && i^2 = -1\\ &= ac - bd + (ad)i + (bc)i && \text{Commutative Property}\\ &= (ac - bd) + (ad + bc)i && \text{Associative Property}\end{aligned}$$

Rather than trying to memorize this multiplication rule, you should simply remember how the Distributive Property is used to multiply two complex numbers.

Example 2 Multiplying Complex Numbers

a. $$\begin{aligned}4(-2 + 3i) &= 4(-2) + 4(3i) && \text{Distributive Property}\\ &= -8 + 12i && \text{Simplify.}\end{aligned}$$

b. $$\begin{aligned}(2 - i)(4 + 3i) &= 2(4 + 3i) - i(4 + 3i) && \text{Distributive Property}\\ &= 8 + 6i - 4i - 3i^2 && \text{Distributive Property}\\ &= 8 + 6i - 4i - 3(-1) && i^2 = -1\\ &= (8 + 3) + (6i - 4i) && \text{Group like terms.}\\ &= 11 + 2i && \text{Write in standard form.}\end{aligned}$$

c. $$\begin{aligned}(3 + 2i)(3 - 2i) &= 3(3 - 2i) + 2i(3 - 2i) && \text{Distributive Property}\\ &= 9 - 6i + 6i - 4i^2 && \text{Distributive Property}\\ &= 9 - 6i + 6i - 4(-1) && i^2 = -1\\ &= 9 + 4 && \text{Simplify.}\\ &= 13 && \text{Write in standard form.}\end{aligned}$$

d. $$\begin{aligned}(3 + 2i)^2 &= (3 + 2i)(3 + 2i) && \text{Square of a binomial}\\ &= 3(3 + 2i) + 2i(3 + 2i) && \text{Distributive Property}\\ &= 9 + 6i + 6i + 4i^2 && \text{Distributive Property}\\ &= 9 + 6i + 6i + 4(-1) && i^2 = -1\\ &= 9 + 12i - 4 && \text{Simplify.}\\ &= 5 + 12i && \text{Write in standard form.}\end{aligned}$$

CHECKPoint Now try Exercise 31.

Study Tip

The procedure described above is similar to multiplying two polynomials and combining like terms, as in the FOIL Method shown in Appendix A.3. For instance, you can use the FOIL Method to multiply the two complex numbers from Example 2(b).

$$\overset{}{(2 - i)(4 + 3i)} = \overset{F}{8} + \overset{O}{6i} - \overset{I}{4i} - \overset{L}{3i^2}$$

Extra Example 2

Perform the multiplication and write the result in standard form.

a. $8i(4 - 3i)$

$24 + 32i$

b. $(3 - i)(5 + 4i)$

$19 + 7i$

c. $(2 + 4i)(2 - 4i)$

20

d. $(5 - 3i)^2$

$16 - 30i$

Avoiding Common Errors

Students should become very familiar with the powers of i. When the exponent is divided by four, the remainder will give an equal power in the first four powers of i.

Extra Example 3

Multiply each complex number by its complex conjugate.

a. $3 + i$

10

b. $5 - 4i$

41

Extra Example 4

Write the quotient $\frac{2 + i}{2 - i}$ in standard form.

$\frac{3}{5} + \frac{4}{5}i$

Complex Conjugates

Notice in Example 2(c) that the product of two complex numbers can be a real number. This occurs with pairs of complex numbers of the form $a + bi$ and $a - bi$, called **complex conjugates.**

$$\begin{aligned}(a + bi)(a - bi) &= a^2 - abi + abi - b^2i^2\\ &= a^2 - b^2(-1)\\ &= a^2 + b^2\end{aligned}$$

Algebra Help

You can compare complex conjugates with the method for rationalizing denominators in Appendix A.2.

Example 3 Multiplying Conjugates

Multiply each complex number by its complex conjugate.

a. $1 + i$ **b.** $4 - 3i$

Solution

a. The complex conjugate of $1 + i$ is $1 - i$.

$$(1 + i)(1 - i) = 1^2 - i^2 = 1 - (-1) = 2$$

b. The complex conjugate of $4 - 3i$ is $4 + 3i$.

$$(4 - 3i)(4 + 3i) = 4^2 - (3i)^2 = 16 - 9i^2 = 16 - 9(-1) = 25$$

CHECKPoint Now try Exercise 41.

To write the quotient of $a + bi$ and $c + di$ in standard form, where c and d are not both zero, multiply the numerator and denominator by the complex conjugate of the *denominator* to obtain

$$\begin{aligned}\frac{a + bi}{c + di} &= \frac{a + bi}{c + di}\left(\frac{c - di}{c - di}\right)\\ &= \frac{(ac + bd) + (bc - ad)i}{c^2 + d^2}. \qquad \text{Standard form}\end{aligned}$$

Study Tip

Note that when you multiply the numerator and denominator of a quotient of complex numbers by

$$\frac{c - di}{c - di}$$

you are actually multiplying the quotient by a form of 1. You are not changing the original expression, you are only creating an expression that is equivalent to the original expression.

Example 4 Writing a Quotient of Complex Numbers in Standard Form

$$\begin{aligned}\frac{2 + 3i}{4 - 2i} &= \frac{2 + 3i}{4 - 2i}\left(\frac{4 + 2i}{4 + 2i}\right) && \text{Multiply numerator and denominator by complex conjugate of denominator.}\\ &= \frac{8 + 4i + 12i + 6i^2}{16 - 4i^2} && \text{Expand.}\\ &= \frac{8 - 6 + 16i}{16 + 4} && i^2 = -1\\ &= \frac{2 + 16i}{20} && \text{Simplify.}\\ &= \frac{1}{10} + \frac{4}{5}i && \text{Write in standard form.}\end{aligned}$$

CHECKPoint Now try Exercise 53.

Complex Solutions of Quadratic Equations

When using the Quadratic Formula to solve a quadratic equation, you often obtain a result such as $\sqrt{-3}$, which you know is not a real number. By factoring out $i = \sqrt{-1}$, you can write this number in standard form.

$$\sqrt{-3} = \sqrt{3(-1)} = \sqrt{3}\sqrt{-1} = \sqrt{3}i$$

The number $\sqrt{3}i$ is called the *principal square root* of -3.

Algebra Help

You can review the techniques for using the Quadratic Formula in Appendix A.5.

WARNING / CAUTION

The definition of principal square root uses the rule

$$\sqrt{ab} = \sqrt{a}\sqrt{b}$$

for $a > 0$ and $b < 0$. This rule is not valid if *both* a and b are negative. For example,

$$\begin{aligned}\sqrt{-5}\sqrt{-5} &= \sqrt{5(-1)}\sqrt{5(-1)}\\ &= \sqrt{5}i\sqrt{5}i\\ &= \sqrt{25}i^2\\ &= 5i^2 = -5\end{aligned}$$

whereas

$$\sqrt{(-5)(-5)} = \sqrt{25} = 5.$$

To avoid problems with square roots of negative numbers, be sure to convert complex numbers to standard form *before* multiplying.

Principal Square Root of a Negative Number

If a is a positive number, the **principal square root** of the negative number $-a$ is defined as

$$\sqrt{-a} = \sqrt{a}i.$$

Example 5 Writing Complex Numbers in Standard Form

a. $\sqrt{-3}\sqrt{-12} = \sqrt{3}i\sqrt{12}i = \sqrt{36}i^2 = 6(-1) = -6$

b. $\sqrt{-48} - \sqrt{-27} = \sqrt{48}i - \sqrt{27}i = 4\sqrt{3}i - 3\sqrt{3}i = \sqrt{3}i$

c. $$\begin{aligned}(-1 + \sqrt{-3})^2 &= (-1 + \sqrt{3}i)^2\\ &= (-1)^2 - 2\sqrt{3}i + (\sqrt{3})^2(i^2)\\ &= 1 - 2\sqrt{3}i + 3(-1)\\ &= -2 - 2\sqrt{3}i\end{aligned}$$

CHECKPoint Now try Exercise 63.

Example 6 Complex Solutions of a Quadratic Equation

Solve (a) $x^2 + 4 = 0$ and (b) $3x^2 - 2x + 5 = 0$.

Solution

a. $x^2 + 4 = 0$ Write original equation.

$x^2 = -4$ Subtract 4 from each side.

$x = \pm 2i$ Extract square roots.

b. $3x^2 - 2x + 5 = 0$ Write original equation.

$x = \dfrac{-(-2) \pm \sqrt{(-2)^2 - 4(3)(5)}}{2(3)}$ Quadratic Formula

$= \dfrac{2 \pm \sqrt{-56}}{6}$ Simplify.

$= \dfrac{2 \pm 2\sqrt{14}i}{6}$ Write $\sqrt{-56}$ in standard form.

$= \dfrac{1}{3} \pm \dfrac{\sqrt{14}}{3}i$ Write in standard form.

CHECKPoint Now try Exercise 69.

Extra Example 5

Write the complex number in standard form.

a. $\sqrt{-14}\sqrt{-2}$
$-2\sqrt{7}$

b. $\sqrt{-27} - \sqrt{-12}$
$\sqrt{3}i$

c. $(-2 + \sqrt{-5})^2$
$-1 - 4\sqrt{5}i$

Extra Example 6

Use the Quadratic Formula to solve the quadratic equations.

a. $8x^2 + 14x + 9 = 0$
$-\dfrac{7}{8} \pm \dfrac{\sqrt{23}}{8}i$

b. $7x^2 + 5x + 2 = 0$
$-\dfrac{5}{14} \pm \dfrac{\sqrt{31}}{14}i$

Closing the Lesson

Have students summarize the major points of the lesson and answer the Essential Question: How do you perform operations with complex numbers?

- **To add (or subtract) two complex numbers, add (or subtract) the real and imaginary parts of the numbers separately.**
- **To multiply two complex numbers, use the Distributive Property and combine like terms, as is done when multiplying two binomials.**
- **To write the quotient of two complex numbers in standard form, multiply the numerator and the denominator by the complex conjugate of the denominator and simplify.**

4 PRACTICE AND APPLY

Assignment Guide

Transparencies Available
Available at the Instructor's companion site.

Average:
Day 1: pp. 164–165
Exs. 1–4, 5–13 odd, 17, 23, 33–39 odd, 43, 49–53 odd, 59, 65, 67, 71, 79, 93–96

Advanced:
Day 1: pp. 164–165
Exs. 6–12 even, 18–24 even, 32–38 even, 46–52 even, 58–62 even, 68, 70, 89, 90–96, 98–101

Block:
pp. 164–165
Exs. 1–4, 5–13 odd, 17, 23, 33–39 odd, 43, 49–53 odd, 59, 65, 67, 71, 79, 93–96 (with 2.3)

5. $a = -12,\ b = 7$
6. $a = 13,\ b = 4$
21. $10 - 3i$
22. $8 + 4i$
24. $-3 - 11i$
43. $-1 + \sqrt{5}i,\ 6$
44. $-3 - \sqrt{2}i,\ 11$
48. $1 + \sqrt{8},\ 9 + 4\sqrt{2}$

2.4 EXERCISES

See www.CalcChat.com for worked-out solutions to odd-numbered exercises.

VOCABULARY

1. Match the type of complex number with its definition.

(a) Real number (i) $a + bi,\ a \neq 0,\ b \neq 0$
(b) Imaginary number (ii) $a + bi,\ a = 0,\ b \neq 0$
(c) Pure imaginary number (iii) $a + bi,\ b = 0$

In Exercises 2–4, fill in the blanks.

2. The imaginary unit i is defined as $i =$ $\sqrt{-1}$, where $i^2 =$ -1.

3. If a is a positive number, the principal square root of the negative number $-a$ is defined as $\sqrt{-a} = \sqrt{a}i$.

4. The numbers $a + bi$ and $a - bi$ are called complex conjugates, and their product is a real number $a^2 + b^2$.

SKILLS AND APPLICATIONS

In Exercises 5–8, find real numbers a and b such that the equation is true. 5–6. See margin.

5. $a + bi = -12 + 7i$
6. $a + bi = 13 + 4i$
7. $(a - 1) + (b + 3)i = 5 + 8i$ $a = 6,\ b = 5$
8. $(a + 6) + 2bi = 6 - 5i$ $a = 0,\ b = -\frac{5}{2}$

In Exercises 9–20, write the complex number in standard form.

9. $8 + \sqrt{-25}$ $8 + 5i$
10. $5 + \sqrt{-36}$ $5 + 6i$
11. $2 - \sqrt{-27}$ $2 - 3\sqrt{3}i$
12. $1 + \sqrt{-8}$ $1 + 2\sqrt{2}i$
13. $\sqrt{-80}$ $4\sqrt{5}i$
14. $\sqrt{-4}$ $2i$
15. 14 14
16. 75 75
17. $-10i + i^2$ $-1 - 10i$
18. $-4i^2 + 2i$ $4 + 2i$
19. $\sqrt{-0.09}$ $0.3i$
20. $\sqrt{-0.0049}$ $0.07i$

In Exercises 21–30, perform the addition or subtraction and write the result in standard form. 21–22, 24. See margin.

21. $(7 + i) + (3 - 4i)$
22. $(13 - 2i) + (-5 + 6i)$
23. $(9 - i) - (8 - i)$ 1
24. $(3 + 2i) - (6 + 13i)$
25. $\left(-2 + \sqrt{-8}\right) + \left(5 - \sqrt{-50}\right)$ $3 - 3\sqrt{2}i$
26. $\left(8 + \sqrt{-18}\right) - \left(4 + 3\sqrt{2}i\right)$ 4
27. $13i - (14 - 7i)$ $-14 + 20i$
28. $25 + (-10 + 11i) + 15i$ $15 + 26i$
29. $-\left(\frac{3}{2} + \frac{5}{2}i\right) + \left(\frac{5}{3} + \frac{11}{3}i\right)$ $\frac{1}{6} + \frac{7}{6}i$
30. $(1.6 + 3.2i) + (-5.8 + 4.3i)$ $-4.2 + 7.5i$

In Exercises 31–40, perform the operation and write the result in standard form.

31. $(1 + i)(3 - 2i)$ $5 + i$
32. $(7 - 2i)(3 - 5i)$ $11 - 41i$
33. $12i(1 - 9i)$ $108 + 12i$
34. $-8i(9 + 4i)$ $32 - 72i$
35. $\left(\sqrt{14} + \sqrt{10}i\right)\left(\sqrt{14} - \sqrt{10}i\right)$ 24
36. $\left(\sqrt{3} + \sqrt{15}i\right)\left(\sqrt{3} - \sqrt{15}i\right)$ 18
37. $(6 + 7i)^2$ $-13 + 84i$
38. $(5 - 4i)^2$ $9 - 40i$
39. $(2 + 3i)^2 + (2 - 3i)^2$ -10
40. $(1 - 2i)^2 - (1 + 2i)^2$ $-8i$

In Exercises 41–48, write the complex conjugate of the complex number. Then multiply the number by its complex conjugate. 43–44, 48. See margin.

41. $9 + 2i$ $9 - 2i,\ 85$
42. $8 - 10i$ $8 + 10i,\ 164$
43. $-1 - \sqrt{5}i$
44. $-3 + \sqrt{2}i$
45. $\sqrt{-20}$ $-2\sqrt{5}i,\ 20$
46. $\sqrt{-15}$ $-\sqrt{15}i,\ 15$
47. $\sqrt{6}$ $\sqrt{6},\ 6$
48. $1 + \sqrt{8}$

In Exercises 49–58, write the quotient in standard form.

49. $\dfrac{3}{i}$ $-3i$
50. $-\dfrac{14}{2i}$ $7i$
51. $\dfrac{2}{4 - 5i}$ $\frac{8}{41} + \frac{10}{41}i$
52. $\dfrac{13}{1 - i}$ $\frac{13}{2} + \frac{13}{2}i$
53. $\dfrac{5 + i}{5 - i}$ $\frac{12}{13} + \frac{5}{13}i$
54. $\dfrac{6 - 7i}{1 - 2i}$ $4 + i$
55. $\dfrac{9 - 4i}{i}$ $-4 - 9i$
56. $\dfrac{8 + 16i}{2i}$ $8 - 4i$
57. $\dfrac{3i}{(4 - 5i)^2}$ $-\frac{120}{1681} - \frac{27}{1681}i$
58. $\dfrac{5i}{(2 + 3i)^2}$ $\frac{60}{169} - \frac{25}{169}i$

In Exercises 59–62, perform the operation and write the result in standard form.

59. $\dfrac{2}{1 + i} - \dfrac{3}{1 - i}$ $-\frac{1}{2} - \frac{5}{2}i$
60. $\dfrac{2i}{2 + i} + \dfrac{5}{2 - i}$ $\frac{12}{5} + \frac{9}{5}i$
61. $\dfrac{i}{3 - 2i} + \dfrac{2i}{3 + 8i}$ $\frac{62}{949} + \frac{297}{949}i$
62. $\dfrac{1 + i}{i} - \dfrac{3}{4 - i}$ $\frac{5}{17} - \frac{20}{17}i$

In Exercises 63–68, write the complex number in standard form.

63. $\sqrt{-6} \cdot \sqrt{-2}$ $-2\sqrt{3}$ **64.** $\sqrt{-5} \cdot \sqrt{-10}$ $-5\sqrt{2}$

65. $(\sqrt{-15})^2$ -15 **66.** $(\sqrt{-75})^2$ -75

67. $(3 + \sqrt{-5})(7 - \sqrt{-10})$ **68.** $(2 - \sqrt{-6})^2$

67–68. See margin.

In Exercises 69–78, use the Quadratic Formula to solve the quadratic equation. 69–78. See margin.

69. $x^2 - 2x + 2 = 0$ **70.** $x^2 + 6x + 10 = 0$

71. $4x^2 + 16x + 17 = 0$ **72.** $9x^2 - 6x + 37 = 0$

73. $4x^2 + 16x + 15 = 0$ **74.** $16t^2 - 4t + 3 = 0$

75. $\frac{3}{2}x^2 - 6x + 9 = 0$ **76.** $\frac{7}{8}x^2 - \frac{3}{4}x + \frac{5}{16} = 0$

77. $1.4x^2 - 2x - 10 = 0$ **78.** $4.5x^2 - 3x + 12 = 0$

In Exercises 79–88, simplify the complex number and write it in standard form.

79. $-6i^3 + i^2$ $-1 + 6i$ **80.** $4i^2 - 2i^3$ $-4 + 2i$

81. $-14i^5$ $-14i$ **82.** $(-i)^3$ i

83. $(\sqrt{-72})^3$ $-432\sqrt{2}i$ **84.** $(\sqrt{-2})^6$ -8

85. $\dfrac{1}{i^3}$ i **86.** $\dfrac{1}{(2i)^3}$ $\dfrac{1}{8}i$

87. $(3i)^4$ 81 **88.** $(-i)^6$ -1

89. IMPEDANCE The opposition to current in an electrical circuit is called its impedance. The impedance z in a parallel circuit with two pathways satisfies the equation

$$\frac{1}{z} = \frac{1}{z_1} + \frac{1}{z_2}$$

where z_1 is the impedance (in ohms) of pathway 1 and z_2 is the impedance of pathway 2. See margin.

(a) The impedance of each pathway in a parallel circuit is found by adding the impedances of all components in the pathway. Use the table to find z_1 and z_2.

(b) Find the impedance z.

	Resistor	Inductor	Capacitor
Symbol	$a\Omega$	$b\Omega$	$c\Omega$
Impedance	a	bi	$-ci$

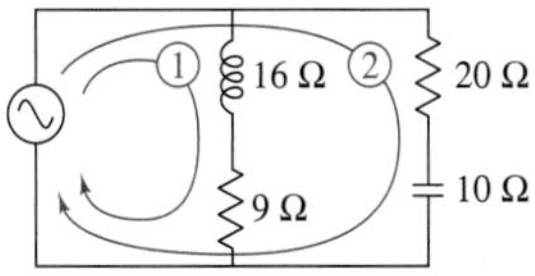

90. Cube each complex number.
(a) 2 8 (b) $-1 + \sqrt{3}i$ 8 (c) $-1 - \sqrt{3}i$ 8

91. Raise each complex number to the fourth power.
(a) 2 16 (b) -2 16 (c) $2i$ 16 (d) $-2i$ 16

92. Write each of the powers of i as i, $-i$, 1, or -1.
(a) i^{40} 1 (b) i^{25} i (c) i^{50} -1 (d) i^{67} $-i$

EXPLORATION

93–96. See margin.

TRUE OR FALSE? In Exercises 93–96, determine whether the statement is true or false. Justify your answer.

93. There is no complex number that is equal to its complex conjugate.

94. $-i\sqrt{6}$ is a solution of $x^4 - x^2 + 14 = 56$.

95. $i^{44} + i^{150} - i^{74} - i^{109} + i^{61} = -1$

96. The sum of two complex numbers is always a real number.

97. PATTERN RECOGNITION Complete the following.

$i^1 = i$	$i^2 = -1$	$i^3 = -i$	$i^4 = 1$
$i^5 =$	$i^6 =$	$i^7 =$	$i^8 =$
$i^9 =$	$i^{10} =$	$i^{11} =$	$i^{12} =$

What pattern do you see? Write a brief description of how you would find i raised to any positive integer power. See margin.

98. CAPSTONE Consider the functions See margin.

$f(x) = 2(x - 3)^2 - 4$ and $g(x) = -2(x - 3)^2 - 4$.

(a) Without graphing either function, determine whether the graph of f and the graph of g have x-intercepts. Explain your reasoning.

(b) Solve $f(x) = 0$ and $g(x) = 0$.

(c) Explain how the zeros of f and g are related to whether their graphs have x-intercepts.

(d) For the function $f(x) = a(x - h)^2 + k$, make a general statement about how a, h, and k affect whether the graph of f has x-intercepts, and whether the zeros of f are real or complex.

99. ERROR ANALYSIS Describe the error. See margin.

$$\sqrt{-6}\sqrt{-6} = \sqrt{(-6)(-6)} = \sqrt{36} = 6$$

100. PROOF Prove that the complex conjugate of the product of two complex numbers $a_1 + b_1i$ and $a_2 + b_2i$ is the product of their complex conjugates. Proof

101. PROOF Prove that the complex conjugate of the sum of two complex numbers $a_1 + b_1i$ and $a_2 + b_2i$ is the sum of their complex conjugates. Proof

98. (a) f has an x-intercept and g does not because when $g(x) = 0$, x is a complex number.
(b) $f(x) = 0$ when $x = 3 \pm \sqrt{2}$; $g(x) = 0$ when $x = 3 \pm \sqrt{2}i$
(c) If all of the zeros contain i, then the graph has no x-intercepts.
(d) If a and k have the same sign (both positive or both negative), then the graph of f has no x-intercepts and the zeros are complex. Otherwise, the graph of f has x-intercepts and the zeros are real.

99. $\sqrt{-6}\sqrt{-6} = \sqrt{6}i\sqrt{6}i = 6i^2 = -6$

5 ASSESS AND RETEACH

Daily Homework Quiz

Transparency Available
Available at the Instructor's companion site.

67. $(21 + 5\sqrt{2}) + (7\sqrt{5} - 3\sqrt{10})i$

68. $-2 - 4\sqrt{6}i$

69. $1 \pm i$ **70.** $-3 \pm i$

71. $-2 \pm \frac{1}{2}i$ **72.** $\frac{1}{3} \pm 2i$

73. $-\frac{5}{2}, -\frac{3}{2}$ **74.** $\frac{1}{8} \pm \frac{\sqrt{11}}{8}i$

75. $2 \pm \sqrt{2}i$ **76.** $\frac{3}{7} \pm \frac{\sqrt{34}}{14}i$

77. $\frac{5}{7} \pm \frac{5\sqrt{15}}{7}$ **78.** $\frac{1}{3} \pm \frac{\sqrt{23}}{3}i$

89. (a) $z_1 = 9 + 16i$, $z_2 = 20 - 10i$
(b) $z = \dfrac{11{,}240}{877} + \dfrac{4630}{877}i$

93. False. If the complex number is real, the number equals its conjugate.

94. True. $x^4 - x^2 + 14 = 56$
$(-i\sqrt{6})^4 - (-i\sqrt{6})^2 + 14 \stackrel{?}{=} 56$
$36 + 6 + 14 \stackrel{?}{=} 56$
$56 = 56$

95. False.
$i^{44} + i^{150} - i^{74} - i^{109} + i^{61}$
$= 1 - 1 + 1 - i + i = 1$

96. False. Sample answer:
$(1 + i) + (3 + i) = 4 + 2i$

97. $i, -1, -i, 1, i, -1, -i, 1$; The pattern repeats the first four results. Divide the exponent by 4.
If the remainder is 1, the result is i.
If the remainder is 2, the result is -1.
If the remainder is 3, the result is $-i$.
If the remainder is 0, the result is 1.

1 PLAN AND PREPARE

Warm-up Exercises

Transparency Available
Available at the Instructor's companion site.

Notetaking Guide

Transparency Available
Promotes interactive learning and notetaking skills.
Available at the Instructor's companion site.

Animated Precalculus

An **Animated Precalculus** tutorial is available at the Student companion site for **Section 2.5.**

Pacing

Average: 2 days
Advanced: 2 days
Block: 1 block

2 FOCUS AND MOTIVATE

Essential Question

How do you find all the zeros of a polynomial function? **Tell students that they will learn how to answer this question by studying strategies for identifying rational, irrational, and complex zeros.**

2.5 Zeros of Polynomial Functions

What you should learn

- Use the Fundamental Theorem of Algebra to determine the number of zeros of polynomial functions.
- Find rational zeros of polynomial functions.
- Find conjugate pairs of complex zeros.
- Find zeros of polynomials by factoring.
- Use Descartes's Rule of Signs and the Upper and Lower Bound Rules to find zeros of polynomials.

Why you should learn it

Finding zeros of polynomial functions is an important part of solving real-life problems. For instance, in Exercise 120 on page 179, the zeros of a polynomial function can help you analyze the attendance at women's college basketball games.

The Fundamental Theorem of Algebra

You know that an nth-degree polynomial can have at most n real zeros. In the complex number system, this statement can be improved. That is, in the complex number system, every nth-degree polynomial function has *precisely* n zeros. This important result is derived from the **Fundamental Theorem of Algebra,** first proved by the German mathematician Carl Friedrich Gauss (1777–1855).

> **The Fundamental Theorem of Algebra**
>
> If $f(x)$ is a polynomial of degree n, where $n > 0$, then f has at least one zero in the complex number system.

Using the Fundamental Theorem of Algebra and the equivalence of zeros and factors, you obtain the **Linear Factorization Theorem.**

> **Linear Factorization Theorem**
>
> If $f(x)$ is a polynomial of degree n, where $n > 0$, then f has precisely n linear factors
>
> $$f(x) = a_n(x - c_1)(x - c_2) \cdot \cdot \cdot (x - c_n)$$
>
> where $c_1, c_2, . . . , c_n$ are complex numbers.

For a proof of the Linear Factorization Theorem, see Proofs in Mathematics on page 212.

Note that the Fundamental Theorem of Algebra and the Linear Factorization Theorem tell you only that the zeros or factors of a polynomial exist, not how to find them. Such theorems are called *existence theorems*. Remember that the n zeros of a polynomial function can be real or complex, and they may be repeated.

Study Tip

Recall that in order to find the zeros of a function $f(x)$, set $f(x)$ equal to 0 and solve the resulting equation for x. For instance, the function in Example 1(a) has a zero at $x = 2$ because

$$x - 2 = 0$$
$$x = 2.$$

Algebra Help

Examples 1(b), 1(c), and 1(d) involve factoring polynomials. You can review the techniques for factoring polynomials in Appendix A.3.

Example 1 Zeros of Polynomial Functions

a. The first-degree polynomial $f(x) = x - 2$ has exactly *one* zero: $x = 2$.

b. Counting multiplicity, the second-degree polynomial function

$$f(x) = x^2 - 6x + 9 = (x - 3)(x - 3)$$

has exactly *two* zeros: $x = 3$ and $x = 3$. (This is called a *repeated zero.*)

c. The third-degree polynomial function

$$f(x) = x^3 + 4x = x(x^2 + 4) = x(x - 2i)(x + 2i)$$

has exactly *three* zeros: $x = 0, x = 2i$, and $x = -2i$.

d. The fourth-degree polynomial function

$$f(x) = x^4 - 1 = (x - 1)(x + 1)(x - i)(x + i)$$

has exactly *four* zeros: $x = 1, x = -1, x = i$, and $x = -i$.

CHECKPoint Now try Exercise 9.

Resource Planning Guide

Chapter Resources
- Complete Solutions Guide

Workbooks
- Notetaking Guide
- Student Solutions Guide

Interactive Technology
- Instructor Success Organizer
- Notetaking Guide IAE
- Instructional DVDs
- Animated Precalculus
- PowerLecture with ExamView

The Rational Zero Test

The **Rational Zero Test** relates the possible rational zeros of a polynomial (having integer coefficients) to the leading coefficient and to the constant term of the polynomial.

HISTORICAL NOTE

Although they were not contemporaries, Jean Le Rond d'Alembert (1717–1783) worked independently of Carl Gauss in trying to prove the Fundamental Theorem of Algebra. His efforts were such that, in France, the Fundamental Theorem of Algebra is frequently known as the Theorem of d'Alembert.

The Rational Zero Test

If the polynomial $f(x) = a_nx^n + a_{n-1}x^{n-1} + \cdot\cdot\cdot + a_2x^2 + a_1x + a_0$ has *integer* coefficients, every rational zero of f has the form

$$\text{Rational zero} = \frac{p}{q}$$

where p and q have no common factors other than 1, and

$p =$ a factor of the constant term a_0

$q =$ a factor of the leading coefficient a_n.

To use the Rational Zero Test, you should first list all rational numbers whose numerators are factors of the constant term and whose denominators are factors of the leading coefficient.

$$\text{Possible rational zeros} = \frac{\text{factors of constant term}}{\text{factors of leading coefficient}}$$

Having formed this list of *possible rational zeros*, use a trial-and-error method to determine which, if any, are actual zeros of the polynomial. Note that when the leading coefficient is 1, the possible rational zeros are simply the factors of the constant term.

Example 2 **Rational Zero Test with Leading Coefficient of 1**

Find the rational zeros of

$f(x) = x^3 + x + 1.$

Solution

Because the leading coefficient is 1, the possible rational zeros are ± 1, the factors of the constant term. By testing these possible zeros, you can see that neither works.

$$f(1) = (1)^3 + 1 + 1$$
$$= 3$$
$$f(-1) = (-1)^3 + (-1) + 1$$
$$= -1$$

So, you can conclude that the given polynomial has *no* rational zeros. Note from the graph of f in Figure 2.31 that f does have one real zero between -1 and 0. However, by the Rational Zero Test, you know that this real zero is *not* a rational number.

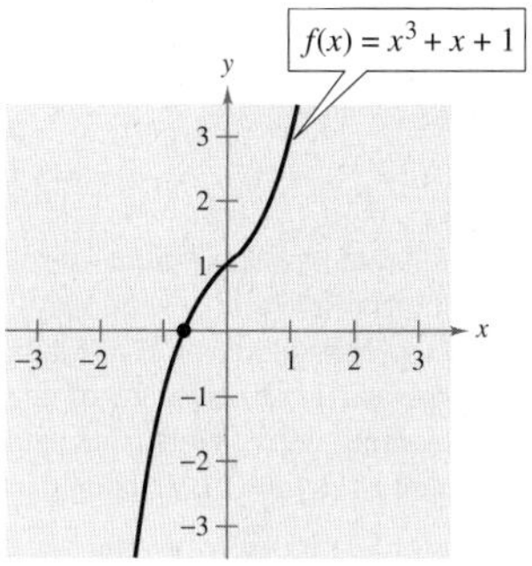

FIGURE 2.31

CHECKPoint Now try Exercise 15.

3 TEACH

Extra Example 1

Find all the zeros of each function.

a. $f(x) = x - 4$
4

b. $f(x) = x^2 - 4x + 4$
$= (x - 2)(x - 2)$
2

c. $f(x) = x^3 + 9x$
0, $\pm 3i$

d. $f(x) = x^4 - 16$
$\pm 2, \pm 2i$

Extra Example 2

Find the rational zeros of $f(x) = x^3 - 5x^2 + 2x + 8$.
$-1, 2, 4$

Avoiding Common Errors

When developing a list of possible real zeros by using the rational zero test, emphasize that both positive and negative values should be listed and tested. Remind students that finding a zero at $x = k$ means that $(x - k)$ is a factor.

Extra Example 3

Find the rational zeros of $f(x) = x^3 - 15x^2 + 75x - 125$.

5

Study Tip

When the list of possible rational zeros is small, as in Example 2, it may be quicker to test the zeros by evaluating the function. When the list of possible rational zeros is large, as in Example 3, it may be quicker to use a different approach to test the zeros, such as using synthetic division or sketching a graph.

Algebra Help

You can review the techniques for synthetic division in Section 2.3.

Example 3 Rational Zero Test with Leading Coefficient of 1

Find the rational zeros of $f(x) = x^4 - x^3 + x^2 - 3x - 6$.

Solution

Because the leading coefficient is 1, the possible rational zeros are the factors of the constant term.

Possible rational zeros: $\pm 1, \pm 2, \pm 3, \pm 6$

By applying synthetic division successively, you can determine that $x = -1$ and $x = 2$ are the only two rational zeros.

$$\begin{array}{r|rrrrr} -1 & 1 & -1 & 1 & -3 & -6 \\ & & -1 & 2 & -3 & 6 \\ \hline & 1 & -2 & 3 & -6 & 0 \end{array}$$

0 remainder, so $x = -1$ is a zero.

$$\begin{array}{r|rrrr} 2 & 1 & -2 & 3 & -6 \\ & & 2 & 0 & 6 \\ \hline & 1 & 0 & 3 & 0 \end{array}$$

0 remainder, so $x = 2$ is a zero.

So, $f(x)$ factors as

$$f(x) = (x + 1)(x - 2)(x^2 + 3).$$

Because the factor $(x^2 + 3)$ produces no real zeros, you can conclude that $x = -1$ and $x = 2$ are the only *real* zeros of f, which is verified in Figure 2.32.

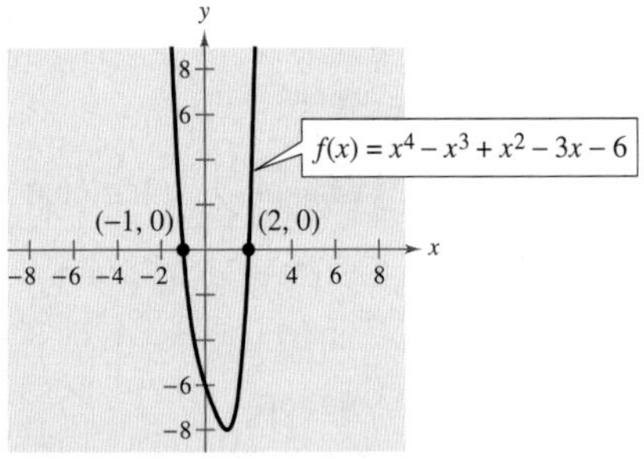

FIGURE 2.32

CHECK *Point* Now try Exercise 19.

If the leading coefficient of a polynomial is not 1, the list of possible rational zeros can increase dramatically. In such cases, the search can be shortened in several ways: (1) a programmable calculator can be used to speed up the calculations; (2) a graph, drawn either by hand or with a graphing utility, can give a good estimate of the locations of the zeros; (3) the Intermediate Value Theorem along with a table generated by a graphing utility can give approximations of zeros; and (4) synthetic division can be used to test the possible rational zeros.

Finding the first zero is often the most difficult part. After that, the search is simplified by working with the lower-degree polynomial obtained in synthetic division, as shown in Example 3.

Example 4 Using the Rational Zero Test

Find the rational zeros of $f(x) = 2x^3 + 3x^2 - 8x + 3$.

Solution

The leading coefficient is 2 and the constant term is 3.

$$\textit{Possible rational zeros: } \frac{\text{Factors of } 3}{\text{Factors of } 2} = \frac{\pm 1, \pm 3}{\pm 1, \pm 2} = \pm 1, \pm 3, \pm\frac{1}{2}, \pm\frac{3}{2}$$

By synthetic division, you can determine that $x = 1$ is a rational zero.

$$\begin{array}{r|rrrr} 1 & 2 & 3 & -8 & 3 \\ & & 2 & 5 & -3 \\ \hline & 2 & 5 & -3 & 0 \end{array}$$

So, $f(x)$ factors as

$$\begin{aligned} f(x) &= (x - 1)(2x^2 + 5x - 3) \\ &= (x - 1)(2x - 1)(x + 3) \end{aligned}$$

and you can conclude that the rational zeros of f are $x = 1$, $x = \frac{1}{2}$, and $x = -3$.

CHECKPoint Now try Exercise 25.

Study Tip

Remember that when you try to find the rational zeros of a polynomial function with many possible rational zeros, as in Example 4, you must use trial and error. There is no quick algebraic method to determine which of the possibilities is an actual zero; however, sketching a graph may be helpful.

Recall from Section 2.2 that if $x = a$ is a zero of the polynomial function f, then $x = a$ is a solution of the polynomial equation $f(x) = 0$.

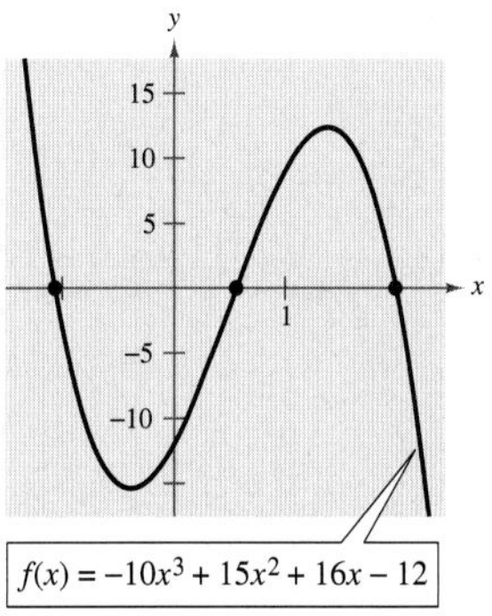

FIGURE 2.33

Example 5 Solving a Polynomial Equation

Find all the real solutions of $-10x^3 + 15x^2 + 16x - 12 = 0$.

Solution

The leading coefficient is -10 and the constant term is -12.

$$\textit{Possible rational solutions: } \frac{\text{Factors of } -12}{\text{Factors of } -10} = \frac{\pm 1, \pm 2, \pm 3, \pm 4, \pm 6, \pm 12}{\pm 1, \pm 2, \pm 5, \pm 10}$$

With so many possibilities (32, in fact), it is worth your time to stop and sketch a graph. From Figure 2.33, it looks like three reasonable solutions would be $x = -\frac{6}{5}$, $x = \frac{1}{2}$, and $x = 2$. Testing these by synthetic division shows that $x = 2$ is the only rational solution. So, you have

$$(x - 2)(-10x^2 - 5x + 6) = 0.$$

Using the Quadratic Formula for the second factor, you find that the two additional solutions are irrational numbers.

$$x = \frac{-5 - \sqrt{265}}{20} \approx -1.0639$$

and

$$x = \frac{-5 + \sqrt{265}}{20} \approx 0.5639$$

CHECKPoint Now try Exercise 31.

Algebra Help

You can review the techniques for using the Quadratic Formula in Appendix A.5.

Extra Example 4

Find the rational zeros of $f(x) = 2x^4 - 9x^3 - 18x^2 + 71x - 30$.

$-3, \frac{1}{2}, 2, 5$

Extra Example 5

Find all the real solutions of $x^3 - 7x^2 - 11x + 14 = 0$.

$-2, \dfrac{9 + \sqrt{53}}{2} \approx 8.1401, \dfrac{9 - \sqrt{53}}{2} \approx 0.8599$

Extra Example 6

Find a third-degree polynomial function with integer coefficients that has 2, $7i$, and $-7i$ as zeros.

$f(x) = x^3 - 2x^2 + 49x - 98$

Note:

$f(x) = a(x^3 - 2x^2 + 49x - 98)$ has the zeros 2, $7i$, and $-7i$ for all nonzero real numbers a.

Conjugate Pairs

In Examples 1(c) and 1(d), note that the pairs of complex zeros are **conjugates.** That is, they are of the form $a + bi$ and $a - bi$.

Complex Zeros Occur in Conjugate Pairs

Let $f(x)$ be a polynomial function that has *real coefficients*. If $a + bi$, where $b \neq 0$, is a zero of the function, the conjugate $a - bi$ is also a zero of the function.

Be sure you see that this result is true only if the polynomial function has *real coefficients*. For instance, the result applies to the function given by $f(x) = x^2 + 1$ but not to the function given by $g(x) = x - i$.

Example 6 Finding a Polynomial with Given Zeros

Find a fourth-degree polynomial function with real coefficients that has -1, -1, and $3i$ as zeros.

Solution

Because $3i$ is a zero *and* the polynomial is stated to have real coefficients, you know that the conjugate $-3i$ must also be a zero. So, from the Linear Factorization Theorem, $f(x)$ can be written as

$$f(x) = a(x + 1)(x + 1)(x - 3i)(x + 3i).$$

For simplicity, let $a = 1$ to obtain

$$f(x) = (x^2 + 2x + 1)(x^2 + 9)$$
$$= x^4 + 2x^3 + 10x^2 + 18x + 9.$$

CHECK*Point* Now try Exercise 45.

Factoring a Polynomial

The Linear Factorization Theorem shows that you can write any nth-degree polynomial as the product of n linear factors.

$$f(x) = a_n(x - c_1)(x - c_2)(x - c_3) \cdot \cdot \cdot (x - c_n)$$

However, this result includes the possibility that some of the values of c_i are complex. The following theorem says that even if you do not want to get involved with "complex factors," you can still write $f(x)$ as the product of linear and/or quadratic factors. For a proof of this theorem, see Proofs in Mathematics on page 212.

Factors of a Polynomial

Every polynomial of degree $n > 0$ with real coefficients can be written as the product of linear and quadratic factors with real coefficients, where the quadratic factors have no real zeros.

A quadratic factor with no real zeros is said to be *prime* or **irreducible over the reals.** Be sure you see that this is not the same as being *irreducible over the rationals*. For example, the quadratic $x^2 + 1 = (x - i)(x + i)$ is irreducible over the reals (and therefore over the rationals). On the other hand, the quadratic $x^2 - 2 = (x - \sqrt{2})(x + \sqrt{2})$ is irreducible over the rationals but *reducible* over the reals.

Extra Example 7

Find all the zeros of $f(x) = x^3 - 4x^2 + 21x - 34$, given that $1 + 4i$ is a zero of f.

$2, 1 + 4i, 1 - 4i$

Example 7 Finding the Zeros of a Polynomial Function

Find all the zeros of $f(x) = x^4 - 3x^3 + 6x^2 + 2x - 60$ given that $1 + 3i$ is a zero of f.

Algebraic Solution

Because complex zeros occur in conjugate pairs, you know that $1 - 3i$ is also a zero of f. This means that both

$$[x - (1 + 3i)] \quad \text{and} \quad [x - (1 - 3i)]$$

are factors of f. Multiplying these two factors produces

$$\begin{aligned}[x - (1 + 3i)][x - (1 - 3i)] &= [(x - 1) - 3i][(x - 1) + 3i] \\ &= (x - 1)^2 - 9i^2 \\ &= x^2 - 2x + 10.\end{aligned}$$

Using long division, you can divide $x^2 - 2x + 10$ into f to obtain the following.

$$\begin{array}{r} x^2 - x - 6 \\ x^2 - 2x + 10 \overline{\smash{)}\, x^4 - 3x^3 + 6x^2 + 2x - 60} \\ \underline{x^4 - 2x^3 + 10x^2} \qquad\qquad \\ -x^3 - 4x^2 + 2x \qquad \\ \underline{-x^3 + 2x^2 - 10x} \qquad \\ -6x^2 + 12x - 60 \\ \underline{-6x^2 + 12x - 60} \\ 0 \end{array}$$

So, you have

$$\begin{aligned}f(x) &= (x^2 - 2x + 10)(x^2 - x - 6) \\ &= (x^2 - 2x + 10)(x - 3)(x + 2)\end{aligned}$$

and you can conclude that the zeros of f are $x = 1 + 3i$, $x = 1 - 3i$, $x = 3$, and $x = -2$.

Graphical Solution

Because complex zeros always occur in conjugate pairs, you know that $1 - 3i$ is also a zero of f. Because the polynomial is a fourth-degree polynomial, you know that there are at most two other zeros of the function. Use a graphing utility to graph

$$y = x^4 - 3x^3 + 6x^2 + 2x - 60$$

as shown in Figure 2.34.

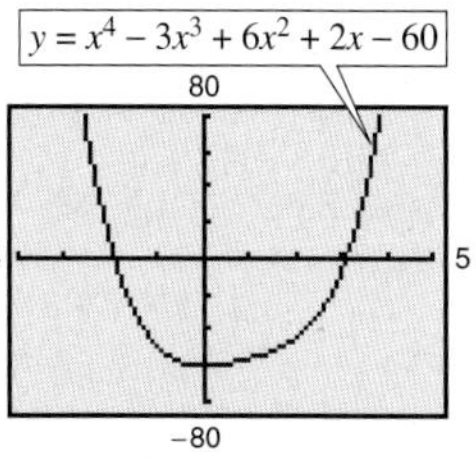

FIGURE 2.34

You can see that -2 and 3 appear to be zeros of the graph of the function. Use the *zero* or *root* feature or the *zoom* and *trace* features of the graphing utility to confirm that $x = -2$ and $x = 3$ are zeros of the graph. So, you can conclude that the zeros of f are $x = 1 + 3i$, $x = 1 - 3i$, $x = 3$, and $x = -2$.

CHECKPoint Now try Exercise 55.

Algebra Help

You can review the techniques for polynomial long division in Section 2.3.

In Example 7, if you were not told that $1 + 3i$ is a zero of f, you could still find all zeros of the function by using synthetic division to find the real zeros -2 and 3. Then you could factor the polynomial as $(x + 2)(x - 3)(x^2 - 2x + 10)$. Finally, by using the Quadratic Formula, you could determine that the zeros are $x = -2$, $x = 3$, $x = 1 + 3i$, and $x = 1 - 3i$.

Extra Example 8

Write $h(x) = x^3 - 11x^2 + 41x - 51$ as the product of linear factors, and list all of its zeros.

$h(x) =$
$(x - 3)(x - 4 - i)(x - 4 + i)$;
$3, 4 \pm i$

Study Tip

In Example 8, the fifth-degree polynomial function has three real zeros. In such cases, you can use the *zoom* and *trace* features or the *zero* or *root* feature of a graphing utility to approximate the real zeros. You can then use these real zeros to determine the complex zeros algebraically.

Example 8 shows how to find all the zeros of a polynomial function, including complex zeros.

Example 8 Finding the Zeros of a Polynomial Function

Write $f(x) = x^5 + x^3 + 2x^2 - 12x + 8$ as the product of linear factors, and list all of its zeros.

Solution

The possible rational zeros are $\pm 1, \pm 2, \pm 4$, and ± 8. Synthetic division produces the following.

$$\begin{array}{r|rrrrrr} 1 & 1 & 0 & 1 & 2 & -12 & 8 \\ & & 1 & 1 & 2 & 4 & -8 \\ \hline & 1 & 1 & 2 & 4 & -8 & 0 \end{array} \longrightarrow \text{1 is a zero.}$$

$$\begin{array}{r|rrrrr} -2 & 1 & 1 & 2 & 4 & -8 \\ & & -2 & 2 & -8 & 8 \\ \hline & 1 & -1 & 4 & -4 & 0 \end{array} \longrightarrow \text{-2 is a zero.}$$

So, you have

$$f(x) = x^5 + x^3 + 2x^2 - 12x + 8$$
$$= (x - 1)(x + 2)(x^3 - x^2 + 4x - 4).$$

You can factor $x^3 - x^2 + 4x - 4$ as $(x - 1)(x^2 + 4)$, and by factoring $x^2 + 4$ as

$$x^2 - (-4) = \left(x - \sqrt{-4}\right)\left(x + \sqrt{-4}\right)$$
$$= (x - 2i)(x + 2i)$$

you obtain

$$f(x) = (x - 1)(x - 1)(x + 2)(x - 2i)(x + 2i)$$

which gives the following five zeros of f.

$$x = 1, x = 1, x = -2, x = 2i, \quad \text{and} \quad x = -2i$$

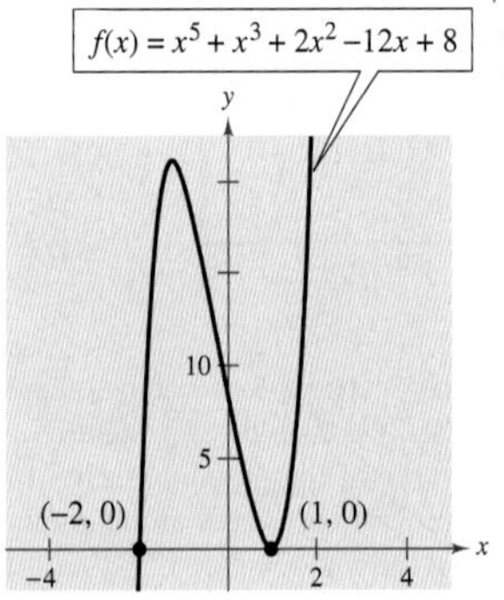

FIGURE 2.35

From the graph of f shown in Figure 2.35, you can see that the *real* zeros are the only ones that appear as x-intercepts. Note that $x = 1$ is a repeated zero.

CHECKPoint Now try Exercise 77.

TECHNOLOGY

You can use the *table* feature of a graphing utility to help you determine which of the possible rational zeros are zeros of the polynomial in Example 8. The table should be set to *ask* mode. Then enter each of the possible rational zeros in the table. When you do this, you will see that there are two rational zeros, −2 and 1, as shown at the right.

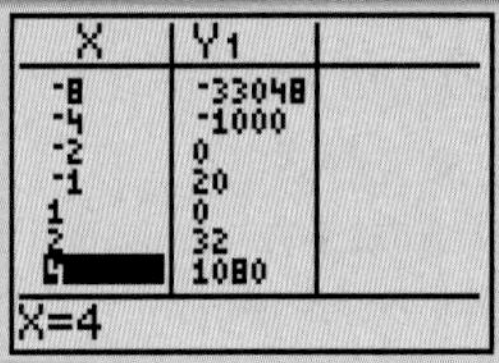

Other Tests for Zeros of Polynomials

You know that an nth-degree polynomial function can have *at most n* real zeros. Of course, many nth-degree polynomials do not have that many real zeros. For instance, $f(x) = x^2 + 1$ has no real zeros, and $f(x) = x^3 + 1$ has only one real zero. The following theorem, called **Descartes's Rule of Signs,** sheds more light on the number of real zeros of a polynomial.

Descartes's Rule of Signs

Let $f(x) = a_n x^n + a_{n-1}x^{n-1} + \cdot \cdot \cdot + a_2x^2 + a_1x + a_0$ be a polynomial with real coefficients and $a_0 \neq 0$.

1. The number of *positive real zeros* of f is either equal to the number of variations in sign of $f(x)$ or less than that number by an even integer.
2. The number of *negative real zeros* of f is either equal to the number of variations in sign of $f(-x)$ or less than that number by an even integer.

A **variation in sign** means that two consecutive coefficients have opposite signs.

When using Descartes's Rule of Signs, a zero of multiplicity k should be counted as k zeros. For instance, the polynomial $x^3 - 3x + 2$ has two variations in sign, and so has either two positive or no positive real zeros. Because

$$x^3 - 3x + 2 = (x - 1)(x - 1)(x + 2)$$

you can see that the two positive real zeros are $x = 1$ of multiplicity 2.

Example 9 Using Descartes's Rule of Signs

Describe the possible real zeros of

$$f(x) = 3x^3 - 5x^2 + 6x - 4.$$

Solution

The original polynomial has *three* variations in sign.

$$\begin{array}{c} + \text{ to } - \qquad + \text{ to } - \\ \downarrow \quad \downarrow \qquad \downarrow \quad \downarrow \\ f(x) = 3x^3 - 5x^2 + 6x - 4 \\ \uparrow \quad \uparrow \\ - \text{ to } + \end{array}$$

The polynomial

$$f(-x) = 3(-x)^3 - 5(-x)^2 + 6(-x) - 4$$
$$= -3x^3 - 5x^2 - 6x - 4$$

has no variations in sign. So, from Descartes's Rule of Signs, the polynomial $f(x) = 3x^3 - 5x^2 + 6x - 4$ has either three positive real zeros or one positive real zero, and has no negative real zeros. From the graph in Figure 2.36, you can see that the function has only one real zero, at $x = 1$.

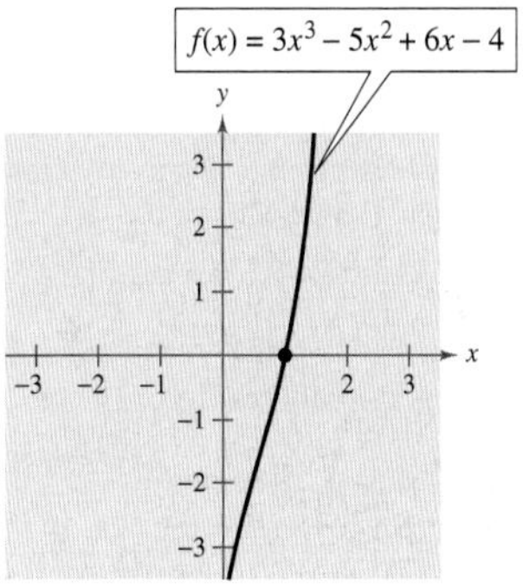

FIGURE 2.36

CHECKPoint Now try Exercise 87.

Extra Example 9

Describe the possible real zeros of $f(x) = -2x^3 + 5x^2 - x + 8$.

The polynomial $f(x)$ has three variations in sign. The polynomial $f(-x)$ has no variations in sign. So the polynomial $f(x)$ has either three positive real zeros or one positive real zero, and has no negative real zeros. The function $f(x)$ has only one real zero (it is between 2 and 3).

Extra Example 10

Find the real zeros of $f(x) = 8x^3 - 4x^2 + 6x - 3$.

$\frac{1}{2}$

Another test for zeros of a polynomial function is related to the sign pattern in the last row of the synthetic division array. This test can give you an upper or lower bound of the real zeros of f. A real number b is an **upper bound** for the real zeros of f if no zeros are greater than b. Similarly, b is a **lower bound** if no real zeros of f are less than b.

Upper and Lower Bound Rules

Let $f(x)$ be a polynomial with real coefficients and a positive leading coefficient. Suppose $f(x)$ is divided by $x - c$, using synthetic division.

1. If $c > 0$ and each number in the last row is either positive or zero, c is an **upper bound** for the real zeros of f.
2. If $c < 0$ and the numbers in the last row are alternately positive and negative (zero entries count as positive or negative), c is a **lower bound** for the real zeros of f.

Example 10 Finding the Zeros of a Polynomial Function

Find the real zeros of $f(x) = 6x^3 - 4x^2 + 3x - 2$.

Solution

The possible real zeros are as follows.

$$\frac{\text{Factors of } 2}{\text{Factors of } 6} = \frac{\pm 1, \pm 2}{\pm 1, \pm 2, \pm 3, \pm 6} = \pm 1, \pm\frac{1}{2}, \pm\frac{1}{3}, \pm\frac{1}{6}, \pm\frac{2}{3}, \pm 2$$

The original polynomial $f(x)$ has three variations in sign. The polynomial

$$f(-x) = 6(-x)^3 - 4(-x)^2 + 3(-x) - 2$$
$$= -6x^3 - 4x^2 - 3x - 2$$

has no variations in sign. As a result of these two findings, you can apply Descartes's Rule of Signs to conclude that there are three positive real zeros or one positive real zero, and no negative zeros. Trying $x = 1$ produces the following.

$$\begin{array}{r|rrrr} 1 & 6 & -4 & 3 & -2 \\ & & 6 & 2 & 5 \\ \hline & 6 & 2 & 5 & 3 \end{array}$$

So, $x = 1$ is not a zero, but because the last row has all positive entries, you know that $x = 1$ is an upper bound for the real zeros. So, you can restrict the search to zeros between 0 and 1. By trial and error, you can determine that $x = \frac{2}{3}$ is a zero. So,

$$f(x) = \left(x - \frac{2}{3}\right)(6x^2 + 3).$$

Because $6x^2 + 3$ has no real zeros, it follows that $x = \frac{2}{3}$ is the only real zero.

CHECK*Point* Now try Exercise 95.

Before concluding this section, here are two additional hints that can help you find the real zeros of a polynomial.

1. If the terms of $f(x)$ have a common monomial factor, it should be factored out before applying the tests in this section. For instance, by writing

$$f(x) = x^4 - 5x^3 + 3x^2 + x$$
$$= x(x^3 - 5x^2 + 3x + 1)$$

you can see that $x = 0$ is a zero of f and that the remaining zeros can be obtained by analyzing the cubic factor.

2. If you are able to find all but two zeros of $f(x)$, you can always use the Quadratic Formula on the remaining quadratic factor. For instance, if you succeeded in writing

$$f(x) = x^4 - 5x^3 + 3x^2 + x$$
$$= x(x - 1)(x^2 - 4x - 1)$$

you can apply the Quadratic Formula to $x^2 - 4x - 1$ to conclude that the two remaining zeros are $x = 2 + \sqrt{5}$ and $x = 2 - \sqrt{5}$.

Example 11 Using a Polynomial Model

You are designing candle-making kits. Each kit contains 25 cubic inches of candle wax and a mold for making a pyramid-shaped candle. You want the height of the candle to be 2 inches less than the length of each side of the candle's square base. What should the dimensions of your candle mold be?

Solution

The volume of a pyramid is $V = \frac{1}{3}Bh$, where B is the area of the base and h is the height. The area of the base is x^2 and the height is $(x - 2)$. So, the volume of the pyramid is $V = \frac{1}{3}x^2(x - 2)$. Substituting 25 for the volume yields the following.

$$25 = \frac{1}{3}x^2(x - 2) \quad \text{Substitute 25 for } V.$$

$$75 = x^3 - 2x^2 \quad \text{Multiply each side by 3.}$$

$$0 = x^3 - 2x^2 - 75 \quad \text{Write in general form.}$$

The possible rational solutions are $x = \pm1, \pm3, \pm5, \pm15, \pm25, \pm75$. Use synthetic division to test some of the possible solutions. Note that in this case, it makes sense to test only positive x-values. Using synthetic division, you can determine that $x = 5$ is a solution.

$$\begin{array}{r|rrrr} 5 & 1 & -2 & 0 & -75 \\ & & 5 & 15 & 75 \\ \hline & 1 & 3 & 15 & 0 \end{array}$$

The other two solutions, which satisfy $x^2 + 3x + 15 = 0$, are imaginary and can be discarded. You can conclude that the base of the candle mold should be 5 inches by 5 inches and the height of the mold should be $5 - 2 = 3$ inches.

CHECKPoint Now try Exercise 115.

Extra Example 11

You are creating a mold to make a pyramid-shaped resin trophy with a square base. You have 24 cubic inches of resin to pour into the mold, and you want the height of the trophy to be 5 inches more than the length of each side of the base.

a. Write a function that represents the volume V of the mold.

$V = \frac{1}{3}x^2(x + 5)$

b. What should be the dimensions of your trophy mold?

3 inches by 3 inches by 8 inches

Closing the Lesson

Have students summarize the major points of the lesson and answer the Essential Question: How do you find all the zeros of a polynomial function?

- **Use the Rational Zero Test to list all possible rational zeros of a polynomial.**
- **Sketch a graph to determine approximate locations of zeros.**
- **Use synthetic division to determine whether a possible rational zero is a zero.**
- **Use the quadratic formula to find irrational and complex roots.**
- **Use Descartes' Rule of Signs or Upper and Lower Bound Rules to determine the number and location of real zeros.**

4 PRACTICE AND APPLY

Assignment Guide

Transparencies Available
Available at the Instructor's companion site.

Average:
Day 1: pp. 176–177
Exs. 1–6, 11–17 odd, 21, 27, 29, 33, 37, 47–53 odd, 56, 59, 63–69 odd, 73, 75, 82
Day 2: pp. 176, 178–180
Exs. 7, 8, 89, 91, 96, 99, 103, 107–111, 116, 118, 121–123, 127, 129, 137

Advanced:
Day 1: pp. 176–177
Exs. 12–18 even, 22, 28–34 even, 50–58 even, 62–70 even, 74, 78
Day 2: pp. 178–180
Exs. 92–96 even, 102–106 even, 107–111, 113, 116, 118, 122–128 even, 130–132, 135–139

Block:
pp. 176–180
Exs. 1–8, 11–17 odd, 21, 27, 29, 33, 37, 47–53 odd, 56, 59, 63–69 odd, 73, 75, 82, 89, 91, 96, 99, 103, 107–111, 116, 118, 121–123, 127, 129, 137

2. Linear Factorization Theorem

2.5 EXERCISES

See www.CalcChat.com for worked-out solutions to odd-numbered exercises.

VOCABULARY: Fill in the blanks.

1. The ________ ________ of ________ states that if $f(x)$ is a polynomial of degree n $(n > 0)$, then f has at least one zero in the complex number system. Fundamental Theorem of Algebra
2. The ________ ________ ________ states that if $f(x)$ is a polynomial of degree n $(n > 0)$, then f has precisely n linear factors, $f(x) = a_n(x - c_1)(x - c_2) \cdot \cdot \cdot (x - c_n)$, where $c_1, c_2, \ldots, c_n$ are complex numbers. See margin.
3. The test that gives a list of the possible rational zeros of a polynomial function is called the Rational Zero Test.
4. If $a + bi$ is a complex zero of a polynomial with real coefficients, then so is its conjugate, $a - bi$.
5. Every polynomial of degree $n > 0$ with real coefficients can be written as the product of linear and quadratic factors with real coefficients, where the quadratic factors have no real zeros.
6. A quadratic factor that cannot be factored further as a product of linear factors containing real numbers is said to be ________ over the ________. irreducible; reals
7. The theorem that can be used to determine the possible numbers of positive real zeros and negative real zeros of a function is called Descartes's Rule of Signs.
8. A real number b is a(n) lower bound for the real zeros of f if no real zeros are less than b, and is a(n) upper bound if no real zeros are greater than b.

SKILLS AND APPLICATIONS

In Exercises 9–14, find all the zeros of the function.

9. $f(x) = x(x - 6)^2$ 0, 6
10. $f(x) = x^2(x + 3)(x^2 - 1)$ 0, −3, ±1
11. $g(x) = (x - 2)(x + 4)^3$ 2, −4
12. $f(x) = (x + 5)(x - 8)^2$ −5, 8
13. $f(x) = (x + 6)(x + i)(x - i)$ $-6, \pm i$
14. $h(t) = (t - 3)(t - 2)(t - 3i)(t + 3i)$ $3, 2, \pm 3i$

In Exercises 15–18, use the Rational Zero Test to list all possible rational zeros of f. Verify that the zeros of f shown on the graph are contained in the list.

15. $f(x) = x^3 + 2x^2 - x - 2$

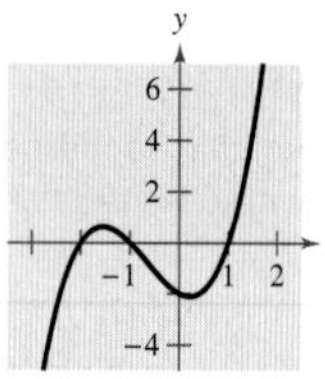

$\pm 1, \pm 2$

16. $f(x) = x^3 - 4x^2 - 4x + 16$

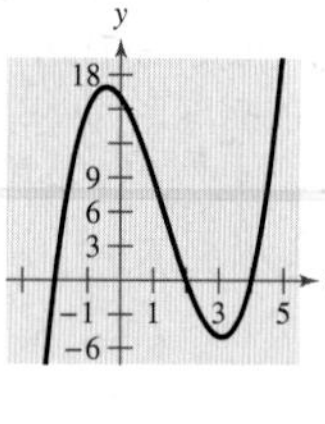

$\pm 1, \pm 2, \pm 4, \pm 8, \pm 16$

17. $f(x) = 2x^4 - 17x^3 + 35x^2 + 9x - 45$

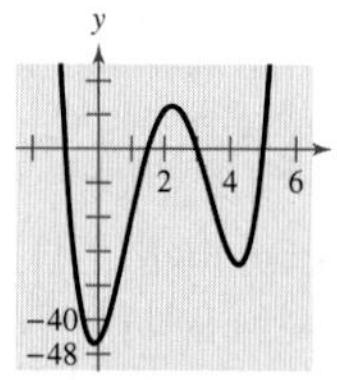

$\pm 1, \pm 3, \pm 5, \pm 9, \pm 15, \pm 45, \pm \frac{1}{2}, \pm \frac{3}{2}, \pm \frac{5}{2}, \pm \frac{9}{2}, \pm \frac{15}{2}, \pm \frac{45}{2}$

18. $f(x) = 4x^5 - 8x^4 - 5x^3 + 10x^2 + x - 2$

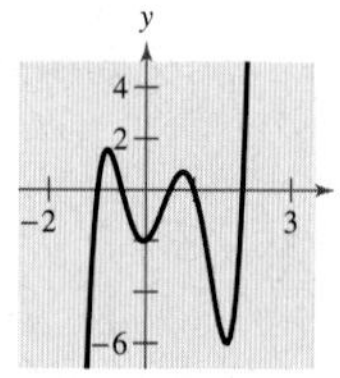

$\pm 1, \pm 2, \pm \frac{1}{2}, \pm \frac{1}{4}$

In Exercises 19–28, find all the rational zeros of the function.

19. $f(x) = x^3 - 6x^2 + 11x - 6$ 1, 2, 3
20. $f(x) = x^3 - 7x - 6$ −2, −1, 3
21. $g(x) = x^3 - 4x^2 - x + 4$ 1, −1, 4
22. $h(x) = x^3 - 9x^2 + 20x - 12$ 1, 2, 6
23. $h(t) = t^3 + 8t^2 + 13t + 6$ −6, −1
24. $p(x) = x^3 - 9x^2 + 27x - 27$ 3
25. $C(x) = 2x^3 + 3x^2 - 1$ $\frac{1}{2}, -1$
26. $f(x) = 3x^3 - 19x^2 + 33x - 9$ $\frac{1}{3}, 3$
27. $f(x) = 9x^4 - 9x^3 - 58x^2 + 4x + 24$ $-2, 3, \pm \frac{2}{3}$
28. $f(x) = 2x^4 - 15x^3 + 23x^2 + 15x - 25$ $\pm 1, 5, \frac{5}{2}$

In Exercises 29–32, find all real solutions of the polynomial equation.

29. $z^4 + z^3 + z^2 + 3z - 6 = 0$ $-2, 1$
30. $x^4 - 13x^2 - 12x = 0$ $0, -1, -3, 4$
31. $2y^4 + 3y^3 - 16y^2 + 15y - 4 = 0$ $-4, \frac{1}{2}, 1, 1$
32. $x^5 - x^4 - 3x^3 + 5x^2 - 2x = 0$ $-2, 0, 1$

In Exercises 33–36, (a) list the possible rational zeros of f, (b) sketch the graph of f so that some of the possible zeros in part (a) can be disregarded, and then (c) determine all real zeros of f. 33–36. See margin.

33. $f(x) = x^3 + x^2 - 4x - 4$
34. $f(x) = -3x^3 + 20x^2 - 36x + 16$
35. $f(x) = -4x^3 + 15x^2 - 8x - 3$
36. $f(x) = 4x^3 - 12x^2 - x + 15$

In Exercises 37–40, (a) list the possible rational zeros of f, (b) use a graphing utility to graph f so that some of the possible zeros in part (a) can be disregarded, and then (c) determine all real zeros of f. 37–40. See margin.

37. $f(x) = -2x^4 + 13x^3 - 21x^2 + 2x + 8$
38. $f(x) = 4x^4 - 17x^2 + 4$
39. $f(x) = 32x^3 - 52x^2 + 17x + 3$
40. $f(x) = 4x^3 + 7x^2 - 11x - 18$

41–44. See margin.

GRAPHICAL ANALYSIS In Exercises 41–44, (a) use the *zero* or *root* feature of a graphing utility to approximate the zeros of the function accurate to three decimal places, (b) determine one of the exact zeros (use synthetic division to verify your result), and (c) factor the polynomial completely.

41. $f(x) = x^4 - 3x^2 + 2$
42. $P(t) = t^4 - 7t^2 + 12$
43. $h(x) = x^5 - 7x^4 + 10x^3 + 14x^2 - 24x$
44. $g(x) = 6x^4 - 11x^3 - 51x^2 + 99x - 27$

In Exercises 45–50, find a polynomial function with real coefficients that has the given zeros. (There are many correct answers.) 45–50. See margin.

45. $1, 5i$
46. $4, -3i$
47. $2, 5 + i$
48. $5, 3 - 2i$
49. $\frac{2}{3}, -1, 3 + \sqrt{2}i$
50. $-5, -5, 1 + \sqrt{3}i$

In Exercises 51–54, write the polynomial (a) as the product of factors that are irreducible over the *rationals*, (b) as the product of linear and quadratic factors that are irreducible over the *reals*, and (c) in completely factored form.

51. $f(x) = x^4 + 6x^2 - 27$ 51–54. See margin.
52. $f(x) = x^4 - 2x^3 - 3x^2 + 12x - 18$
(*Hint:* One factor is $x^2 - 6$.)
53. $f(x) = x^4 - 4x^3 + 5x^2 - 2x - 6$
(*Hint:* One factor is $x^2 - 2x - 2$.)
54. $f(x) = x^4 - 3x^3 - x^2 - 12x - 20$
(*Hint:* One factor is $x^2 + 4$.)

In Exercises 55–62, use the given zero to find all the zeros of the function. 57, 59–61. See margin.

Function	Zero
55. $f(x) = x^3 - x^2 + 4x - 4$ $\pm 2i, 1$	$2i$
56. $f(x) = 2x^3 + 3x^2 + 18x + 27$ $\pm 3i, -\frac{3}{2}$	$3i$
57. $f(x) = 2x^4 - x^3 + 49x^2 - 25x - 25$	$5i$
58. $g(x) = x^3 - 7x^2 - x + 87$ $-3, 5 \pm 2i$	$5 + 2i$
59. $g(x) = 4x^3 + 23x^2 + 34x - 10$	$-3 + i$
60. $h(x) = 3x^3 - 4x^2 + 8x + 8$	$1 - \sqrt{3}i$
61. $f(x) = x^4 + 3x^3 - 5x^2 - 21x + 22$	$-3 + \sqrt{2}i$
62. $f(x) = x^3 + 4x^2 + 14x + 20$ $-2, -1 \pm 3i$	$-1 - 3i$

In Exercises 63–80, find all the zeros of the function and write the polynomial as a product of linear factors.

63. $f(x) = x^2 + 36$
64. $f(x) = x^2 - x + 56$
65. $h(x) = x^2 - 2x + 17$
66. $g(x) = x^2 + 10x + 17$
67. $f(x) = x^4 - 16$
68. $f(y) = y^4 - 256$
69. $f(z) = z^2 - 2z + 2$

63–80. See margin.

70. $h(x) = x^3 - 3x^2 + 4x - 2$
71. $g(x) = x^3 - 3x^2 + x + 5$
72. $f(x) = x^3 - x^2 + x + 39$
73. $h(x) = x^3 - x + 6$
74. $h(x) = x^3 + 9x^2 + 27x + 35$
75. $f(x) = 5x^3 - 9x^2 + 28x + 6$
76. $g(x) = 2x^3 - x^2 + 8x + 21$
77. $g(x) = x^4 - 4x^3 + 8x^2 - 16x + 16$
78. $h(x) = x^4 + 6x^3 + 10x^2 + 6x + 9$
79. $f(x) = x^4 + 10x^2 + 9$
80. $f(x) = x^4 + 29x^2 + 100$

In Exercises 81–86, find all the zeros of the function. When there is an extended list of possible rational zeros, use a graphing utility to graph the function in order to discard any rational zeros that are obviously not zeros of the function.

81. $f(x) = x^3 + 24x^2 + 214x + 740$ $-10, -7 \pm 5i$
82. $f(s) = 2s^3 - 5s^2 + 12s - 5$ $1 \pm 2i, \frac{1}{2}$
83. $f(x) = 16x^3 - 20x^2 - 4x + 15$ $-\frac{3}{4}, 1 \pm \frac{1}{2}i$
84. $f(x) = 9x^3 - 15x^2 + 11x - 5$ $\frac{1}{3} \pm \frac{2}{3}i, 1$
85. $f(x) = 2x^4 + 5x^3 + 4x^2 + 5x + 2$ $-2, -\frac{1}{2}, \pm i$
86. $g(x) = x^5 - 8x^4 + 28x^3 - 56x^2 + 64x - 32$
$1 \pm \sqrt{3}i, 2$

33. (a) $\pm 1, \pm 2, \pm 4$
(b)

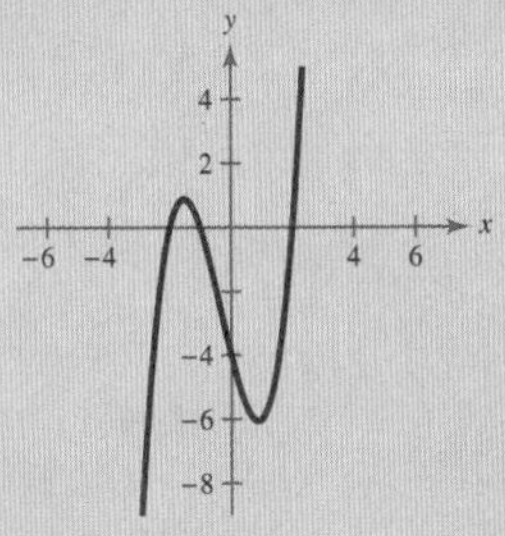

(c) $-2, -1, 2$

34. (a) $\pm 1, \pm 2, \pm 4, \pm 8, \pm 16, \pm\frac{1}{3}, \pm\frac{2}{3}, \pm\frac{4}{3}, \pm\frac{8}{3}, \pm\frac{16}{3}$
(b)

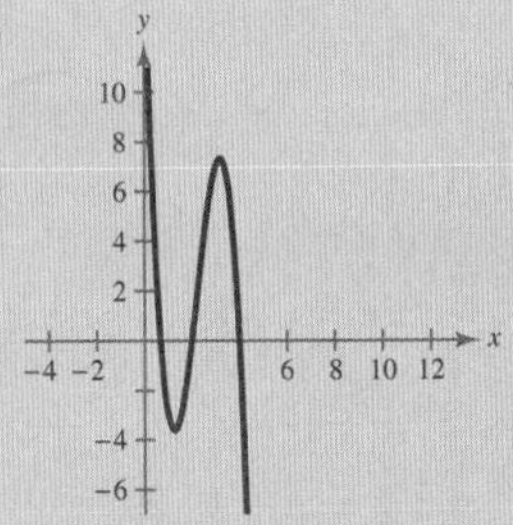

(c) $\frac{2}{3}, 2, 4$

35. (a) $\pm 1, \pm 3, \pm\frac{1}{2}, \pm\frac{3}{2}, \pm\frac{1}{4}, \pm\frac{3}{4}$
(b)

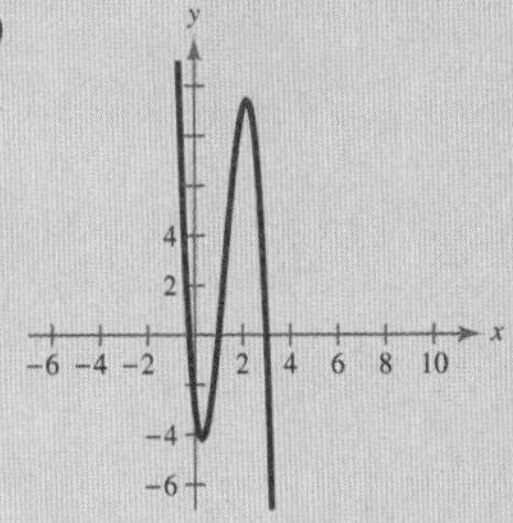

(c) $-\frac{1}{4}, 1, 3$

36. (a) $\pm 1, \pm 3, \pm 5, \pm 15, \pm\frac{1}{2}, \pm\frac{3}{2}, \pm\frac{5}{2}, \pm\frac{15}{2}, \pm\frac{1}{4}, \pm\frac{3}{4}, \pm\frac{5}{4}, \pm\frac{15}{4}$
(b)

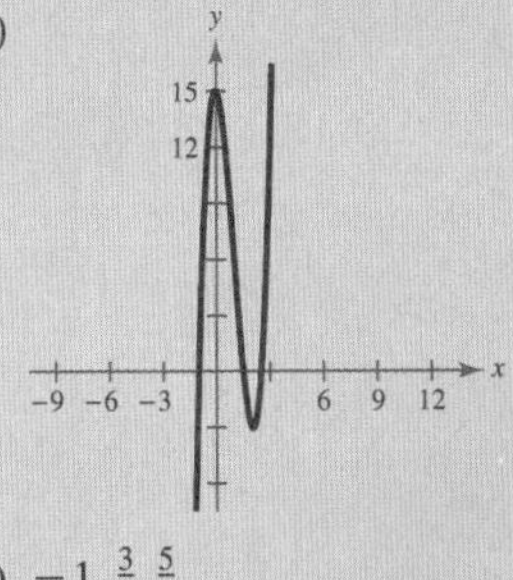

(c) $-1, \frac{3}{2}, \frac{5}{2}$

45. $x^3 - x^2 + 25x - 25$
46. $x^3 - 4x^2 + 9x - 36$
47. $x^3 - 12x^2 + 46x - 52$
48. $x^3 - 11x^2 + 43x - 65$
49. $3x^4 - 17x^3 + 25x^2 + 23x - 22$
50. $x^4 + 8x^3 + 9x^2 - 10x + 100$
51. (a) $(x^2 + 9)(x^2 - 3)$
(b) $(x^2 + 9)(x + \sqrt{3})(x - \sqrt{3})$
(c) $(x + 3i)(x - 3i)(x + \sqrt{3})(x - \sqrt{3})$

52. (a) $(x^2 - 6)(x^2 - 2x + 3)$
(b) $(x + \sqrt{6})(x - \sqrt{6})(x^2 - 2x + 3)$
(c) $(x + \sqrt{6})(x - \sqrt{6})(x - 1 - \sqrt{2}i)(x - 1 + \sqrt{2}i)$

53. (a) $(x^2 - 2x - 2)(x^2 - 2x + 3)$
(b) $(x - 1 + \sqrt{3})(x - 1 - \sqrt{3})(x^2 - 2x + 3)$
(c) $(x - 1 + \sqrt{3})(x - 1 - \sqrt{3})(x - 1 + \sqrt{2}i)(x - 1 - \sqrt{2}i)$

54. (a) $(x^2 + 4)(x^2 - 3x - 5)$
(b) $(x^2 + 4)\left(x - \dfrac{3 + \sqrt{29}}{2}\right)\left(x - \dfrac{3 - \sqrt{29}}{2}\right)$
(c) $(x + 2i)(x - 2i)\left(x - \dfrac{3 + \sqrt{29}}{2}\right)\left(x - \dfrac{3 - \sqrt{29}}{2}\right)$

57. $\pm 5i, -\frac{1}{2}, 1$
59. $-3 \pm i, \frac{1}{4}$
60. $-\frac{2}{3}, 1 \pm \sqrt{3}i$
61. $2, -3 \pm \sqrt{2}i, 1$

37–44, 63–80. See Additional Answers beginning on page AA1.

87. One positive zero
88. Two or no positive zeros
89. One negative zero
90. Two or no positive zeros
91. One positive zero, one negative zero
92. One or three positive zeros
93. One or three positive zeros
94. One or three negative zeros
111. (a)

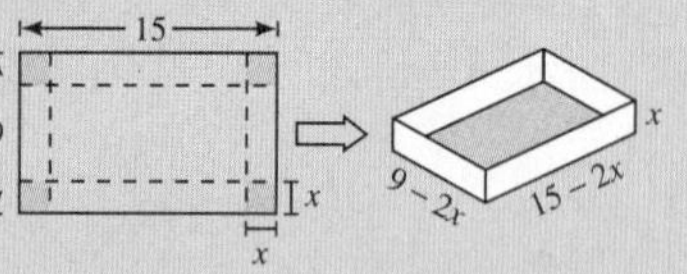

(b) $V(x) = x(9 - 2x)(15 - 2x)$
Domain: $0 < x < \frac{9}{2}$

(c)

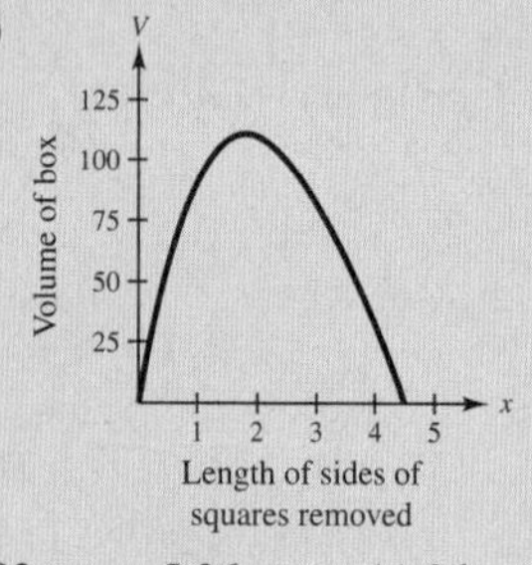

1.82 cm × 5.36 cm × 11.36 cm
(d) $\frac{1}{2}, \frac{7}{2}$, 8; 8 is not in the domain of V.

112. (b)

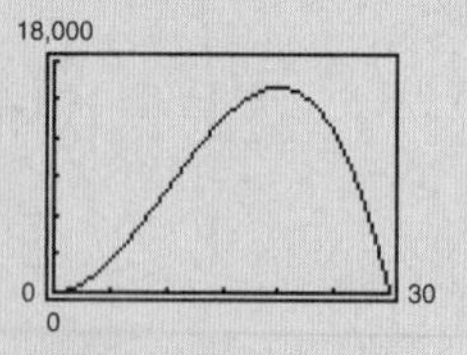

20 in. × 20 in. × 40 in.
(c) $15, \frac{15}{2} \pm \frac{15\sqrt{5}}{2}$; The value $\frac{15}{2} - \frac{15\sqrt{5}}{2}$ is physically impossible because x is negative.

In Exercises 87–94, use Descartes's Rule of Signs to determine the possible numbers of positive and negative zeros of the function. 87–94. See margin.

87. $g(x) = 2x^3 - 3x^2 - 3$
88. $h(x) = 4x^2 - 8x + 3$
89. $h(x) = 2x^3 + 3x^2 + 1$
90. $h(x) = 2x^4 - 3x + 2$
91. $g(x) = 5x^5 - 10x$
92. $f(x) = 4x^3 - 3x^2 + 2x - 1$
93. $f(x) = -5x^3 + x^2 - x + 5$
94. $f(x) = 3x^3 + 2x^2 + x + 3$

In Exercises 95–98, use synthetic division to verify the upper and lower bounds of the real zeros of *f*.

95. $f(x) = x^3 + 3x^2 - 2x + 1$ 95–98. Answers will vary.
(a) Upper: $x = 1$ (b) Lower: $x = -4$
96. $f(x) = x^3 - 4x^2 + 1$
(a) Upper: $x = 4$ (b) Lower: $x = -1$
97. $f(x) = x^4 - 4x^3 + 16x - 16$
(a) Upper: $x = 5$ (b) Lower: $x = -3$
98. $f(x) = 2x^4 - 8x + 3$
(a) Upper: $x = 3$ (b) Lower: $x = -4$

In Exercises 99–102, find all the real zeros of the function.

99. $f(x) = 4x^3 - 3x - 1$ $1, -\frac{1}{2}$
100. $f(z) = 12z^3 - 4z^2 - 27z + 9$ $\pm\frac{3}{2}, \frac{1}{3}$
101. $f(y) = 4y^3 + 3y^2 + 8y + 6$ $-\frac{3}{4}$
102. $g(x) = 3x^3 - 2x^2 + 15x - 10$ $\frac{2}{3}$

In Exercises 103–106, find all the rational zeros of the polynomial function.

103. $P(x) = x^4 - \frac{25}{4}x^2 + 9 = \frac{1}{4}(4x^4 - 25x^2 + 36)$ $\pm 2, \pm\frac{3}{2}$
104. $f(x) = x^3 - \frac{3}{2}x^2 - \frac{23}{2}x + 6 = \frac{1}{2}(2x^3 - 3x^2 - 23x + 12)$ $-3, \frac{1}{2}, 4$
105. $f(x) = x^3 - \frac{1}{4}x^2 - x + \frac{1}{4} = \frac{1}{4}(4x^3 - x^2 - 4x + 1)$ $\pm 1, \frac{1}{4}$
106. $f(z) = z^3 + \frac{11}{6}z^2 - \frac{1}{2}z - \frac{1}{3} = \frac{1}{6}(6z^3 + 11z^2 - 3z - 2)$ $-2, -\frac{1}{3}, \frac{1}{2}$

In Exercises 107–110, match the cubic function with the numbers of rational and irrational zeros.

(a) Rational zeros: 0; irrational zeros: 1
(b) Rational zeros: 3; irrational zeros: 0
(c) Rational zeros: 1; irrational zeros: 2
(d) Rational zeros: 1; irrational zeros: 0

107. $f(x) = x^3 - 1$ d
108. $f(x) = x^3 - 2$ a
109. $f(x) = x^3 - x$ b
110. $f(x) = x^3 - 2x$ c

111. GEOMETRY An open box is to be made from a rectangular piece of material, 15 centimeters by 9 centimeters, by cutting equal squares from the corners and turning up the sides. See margin.

(a) Let x represent the length of the sides of the squares removed. Draw a diagram showing the squares removed from the original piece of material and the resulting dimensions of the open box.
(b) Use the diagram to write the volume V of the box as a function of x. Determine the domain of the function.
(c) Sketch the graph of the function and approximate the dimensions of the box that will yield a maximum volume.
(d) Find values of x such that $V = 56$. Which of these values is a physical impossibility in the construction of the box? Explain.

112. GEOMETRY A rectangular package to be sent by a delivery service (see figure) can have a maximum combined length and girth (perimeter of a cross section) of 120 inches.

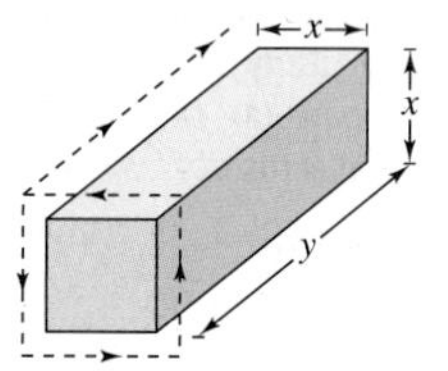

(a) Write a function $V(x)$ that represents the volume of the package. $V(x) = 4x^2(30 - x)$
(b) Use a graphing utility to graph the function and approximate the dimensions of the package that will yield a maximum volume. (b)–(c). See margin.
(c) Find values of x such that $V = 13{,}500$. Which of these values is a physical impossibility in the construction of the package? Explain.

113. ADVERTISING COST A company that produces MP3 players estimates that the profit P (in dollars) for selling a particular model is given by

$$P = -76x^3 + 4830x^2 - 320{,}000, \quad 0 \le x \le 60$$

where x is the advertising expense (in tens of thousands of dollars). Using this model, find the smaller of two advertising amounts that will yield a profit of \$2,500,000. $x \approx 38.4$, or \$384,000

114. ADVERTISING COST A company that manufactures bicycles estimates that the profit P (in dollars) for selling a particular model is given by

$$P = -45x^3 + 2500x^2 - 275{,}000, \quad 0 \le x \le 50$$

where x is the advertising expense (in tens of thousands of dollars). Using this model, find the smaller of two advertising amounts that will yield a profit of \$800,000. $x \approx 31.5$, or \$315,000

115. GEOMETRY A bulk food storage bin with dimensions 2 feet by 3 feet by 4 feet needs to be increased in size to hold five times as much food as the current bin. (Assume each dimension is increased by the same amount.)

(a) Write a function that represents the volume V of the new bin. $V(x) = x^3 + 9x^2 + 26x + 24 = 120$

(b) Find the dimensions of the new bin. 4 ft × 5 ft × 6 ft

116. GEOMETRY A manufacturer wants to enlarge an existing manufacturing facility such that the total floor area is 1.5 times that of the current facility. The floor area of the current facility is rectangular and measures 250 feet by 160 feet. The manufacturer wants to increase each dimension by the same amount.

(a) Write a function that represents the new floor area A. $A(x) = (250 + x)(160 + x) = 60{,}000 \text{ ft}^2$

(b) Find the dimensions of the new floor. 294.05 ft × 204.05 ft

(c) Another alternative is to increase the current floor's length by an amount that is twice an increase in the floor's width. The total floor area is 1.5 times that of the current facility. Repeat parts (a) and (b) using these criteria. See margin.

117. COST The ordering and transportation cost C (in thousands of dollars) for the components used in manufacturing a product is given by

$$C = 100\left(\frac{200}{x^2} + \frac{x}{x + 30}\right), \quad x \geq 1$$

where x is the order size (in hundreds). In calculus, it can be shown that the cost is a minimum when

$$3x^3 - 40x^2 - 2400x - 36{,}000 = 0.$$

Use a calculator to approximate the optimal order size to the nearest hundred units. $x \approx 40$, or 4000 units

118. HEIGHT OF A BASEBALL A baseball is thrown upward from a height of 6 feet with an initial velocity of 48 feet per second, and its height h (in feet) is

$$h(t) = -16t^2 + 48t + 6, \quad 0 \leq t \leq 3$$ See margin.

where t is the time (in seconds). You are told the ball reaches a height of 64 feet. Is this possible?

119. PROFIT The demand equation for a certain product is $p = 140 - 0.0001x$, where p is the unit price (in dollars) of the product and x is the number of units produced and sold. The cost equation for the product is $C = 80x + 150{,}000$, where C is the total cost (in dollars) and x is the number of units produced. The total profit obtained by producing and selling x units is $P = R - C = xp - C$. You are working in the marketing department of the company that produces this product, and you are asked to determine a price p that will yield a profit of 9 million dollars. Is this possible? Explain. See margin.

120. ATHLETICS The attendance A (in millions) at NCAA women's college basketball games for the years 2000 through 2007 is shown in the table. (Source: National Collegiate Athletic Association, Indianapolis, IN) See margin.

Year	Attendance, A
2000	8.7
2001	8.8
2002	9.5
2003	10.2
2004	10.0
2005	9.9
2006	9.9
2007	10.9

(a) Use a graphing utility to create a scatter plot of the data. Let t represent the year, with $t = 0$ corresponding to 2000.

(b) Use the *regression* feature of the graphing utility to find a quartic model for the data.

(c) Graph the model and the scatter plot in the same viewing window. How well does the model fit the data?

(d) According to the model in part (b), in what year(s) was the attendance at least 10 million?

(e) According to the model, will the attendance continue to increase? Explain.

EXPLORATION

TRUE OR FALSE? In Exercises 121 and 122, decide whether the statement is true or false. Justify your answer.

121. It is possible for a third-degree polynomial function with integer coefficients to have no real zeros. See margin.

122. If $x = -i$ is a zero of the function given by

$$f(x) = x^3 + ix^2 + ix - 1$$

then $x = i$ must also be a zero of f. False. f does not have real coefficients.

THINK ABOUT IT In Exercises 123–128, determine (if possible) the zeros of the function g if the function f has zeros at $x = r_1$, $x = r_2$, and $x = r_3$. 125–126. See margin.

123. $g(x) = -f(x)$ r_1, r_2, r_3

124. $g(x) = 3f(x)$ r_1, r_2, r_3

125. $g(x) = f(x - 5)$

126. $g(x) = f(2x)$

127. $g(x) = 3 + f(x)$ The zeros cannot be determined.

128. $g(x) = f(-x)$ $-r_1, -r_2, -r_3$

116. (c) $A(x) = (250 + 2x)(160 + x) = 60{,}000$; 313.2 ft × 191.6 ft

118. No. Setting $h = 64$ and solving the resulting equation yields imaginary roots.

119. No. Setting $p = 9{,}000{,}000$ and solving the resulting equation yields imaginary roots.

120. (a) and (c)

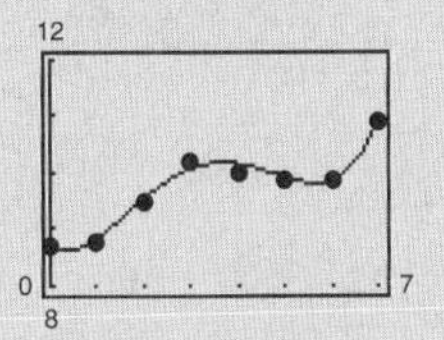

The model fits the data well.

(b) $A(t) = 0.01676t^4 - 0.2152t^3 + 0.794t^2 - 0.44t + 8.7$

(d) 2003, 2004, 2007

(e) Yes, the graph shows an upward trend after 2007.

121. False. The most complex zeros it can have is two, and the Linear Factorization Theorem guarantees that there are three linear factors, so one zero must be real.

125. $5 + r_1, 5 + r_2, 5 + r_3$

126. $\frac{r_1}{2}, \frac{r_2}{2}, \frac{r_3}{2}$

129. THINK ABOUT IT A third-degree polynomial function f has real zeros $-2, \frac{1}{2}$, and 3, and its leading coefficient is negative. Write an equation for f. Sketch the graph of f. How many different polynomial functions are possible for f? See margin.

130. CAPSTONE Use a graphing utility to graph the function given by $f(x) = x^4 - 4x^2 + k$ for different values of k. Find values of k such that the zeros of f satisfy the specified characteristics. (Some parts do not have unique answers.)

(a) Four real zeros $0 < k < 4$

(b) Two real zeros, each of multiplicity 2 $k = 4$

(c) Two real zeros and two complex zeros $k < 0$

(d) Four complex zeros $k > 4$

(e) Will the answers to parts (a) through (d) change for the function g, where $g(x) = f(x - 2)$? No

(f) Will the answers to parts (a) through (d) change for the function g, where $g(x) = f(2x)$? No

See margin.

131. THINK ABOUT IT Sketch the graph of a fifth-degree polynomial function whose leading coefficient is positive and that has a zero at $x = 3$ of multiplicity 2.

132. WRITING Compile a list of all the various techniques for factoring a polynomial that have been covered so far in the text. Give an example illustrating each technique, and write a paragraph discussing when the use of each technique is appropriate. Answers will vary.

133. THINK ABOUT IT Let $y = f(x)$ be a quartic polynomial with leading coefficient $a = 1$ and $f(i) = f(2i) = 0$. Write an equation for f. See margin.

134. THINK ABOUT IT Let $y = f(x)$ be a cubic polynomial with leading coefficient $a = -1$ and $f(2) = f(i) = 0$. Write an equation for f.
$f(x) = -x^3 + 2x^2 - x + 2$

In Exercises 135 and 136, the graph of a cubic polynomial function $y = f(x)$ is shown. It is known that one of the zeros is $1 + i$. Write an equation for f.

135.

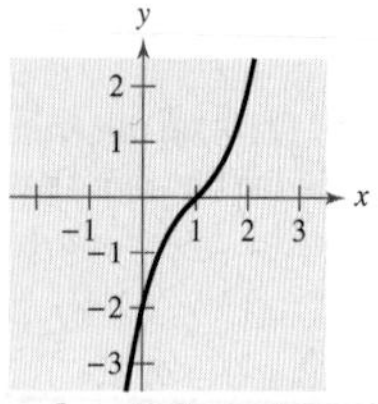

$f(x) = x^3 - 3x^2 + 4x - 2$

136.

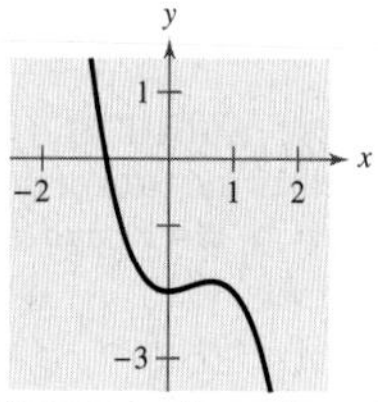

$f(x) = -x^3 + x^2 - 2$

137. Use the information in the table to answer each question.

Interval	Value of $f(x)$
$(-\infty, -2)$	Positive
$(-2, 1)$	Negative
$(1, 4)$	Negative
$(4, \infty)$	Positive

(a) What are the three real zeros of the polynomial function f? $-2, 1, 4$

(b) What can be said about the behavior of the graph of f at $x = 1$? (b)–(c). See margin.

(c) What is the least possible degree of f? Explain. Can the degree of f ever be odd? Explain.

(d) Is the leading coefficient of f positive or negative? Explain. See margin.

(e) Write an equation for f. (There are many correct answers.) $f(x) = x^4 - 4x^3 - 3x^2 + 14x - 8$

(f) Sketch a graph of the equation you wrote in part (e). See margin.

138. (a) Find a quadratic function f (with integer coefficients) that has $\pm\sqrt{b}i$ as zeros. Assume that b is a positive integer. $x^2 + b$

(b) Find a quadratic function f (with integer coefficients) that has $a \pm bi$ as zeros. Assume that b is a positive integer. $x^2 - 2ax + a^2 + b^2$

139. GRAPHICAL REASONING The graph of one of the following functions is shown below. Identify the function shown in the graph. Explain why each of the others is not the correct function. Use a graphing utility to verify your result. See margin.

(a) $f(x) = x^2(x + 2)(x - 3.5)$

(b) $g(x) = (x + 2)(x - 3.5)$

(c) $h(x) = (x + 2)(x - 3.5)(x^2 + 1)$

(d) $k(x) = (x + 1)(x + 2)(x - 3.5)$

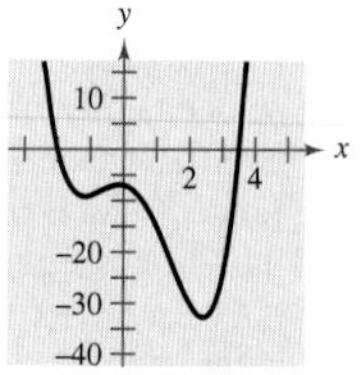

5 ASSESS AND RETEACH

Daily Homework Quiz

Transparency Available
Available at the Instructor's companion site.

129. Answers will vary. There are infinitely many possible functions for f. Sample equation and graph:
$f(x) = -2x^3 + 3x^2 + 11x - 6$

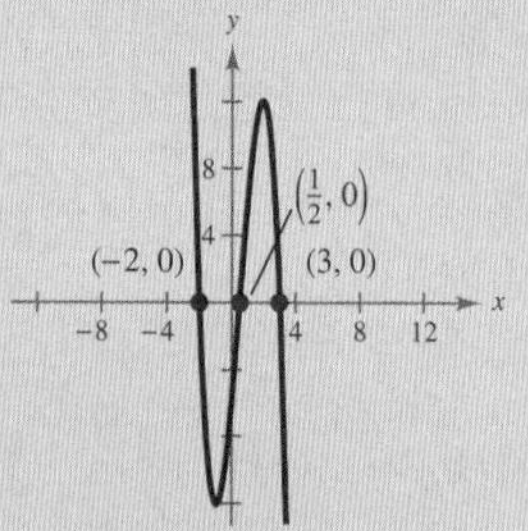

131. Answers will vary.
Sample graph:

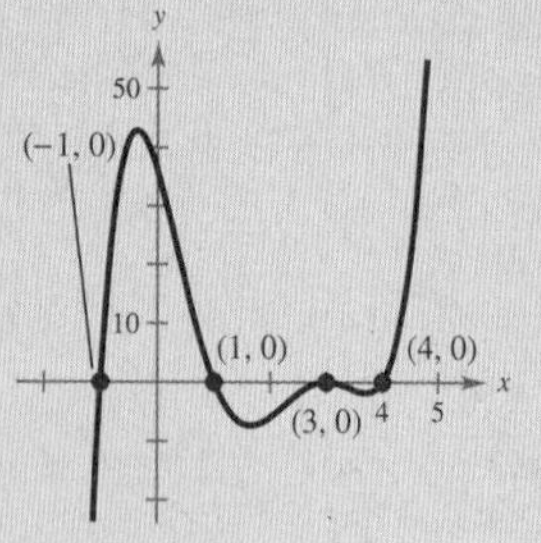

133. $f(x) = x^4 + 5x^2 + 4$

137. (b) The graph touches the x-axis at $x = 1$.

(c) The least possible degree of the function is 4, because there are at least four real zeros (1 is repeated) and a function can have at most the number of real zeros equal to the degree of the function. The degree cannot be odd by the definition of multiplicity.

(d) Positive. From the information in the table, it can be concluded that the graph will eventually rise to the left and rise to the right.

(f)

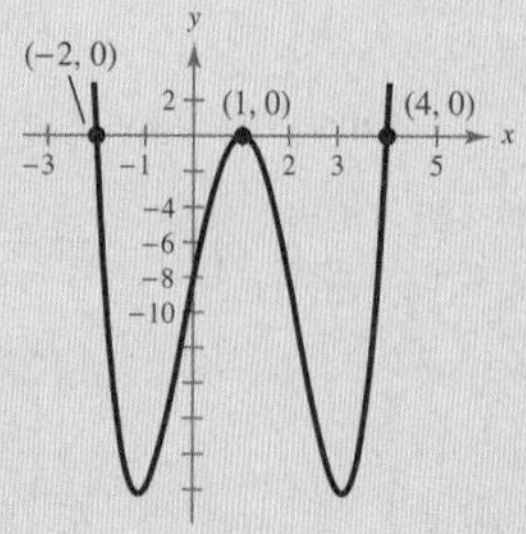

139. (a) Not correct because f has (0, 0) as an intercept.

(b) Not correct because the function must be at least a fourth-degree polynomial.

(c) Correct function

(d) Not correct because k has $(-1, 0)$ as an intercept.

2.6 RATIONAL FUNCTIONS

What you should learn

- Find the domains of rational functions.
- Find the vertical and horizontal asymptotes of graphs of rational functions.
- Analyze and sketch graphs of rational functions.
- Sketch graphs of rational functions that have slant asymptotes.
- Use rational functions to model and solve real-life problems.

Why you should learn it

Rational functions can be used to model and solve real-life problems relating to business. For instance, in Exercise 83 on page 193, a rational function is used to model average speed over a distance.

Mike Powell/Getty Images

Introduction

A **rational function** is a quotient of polynomial functions. It can be written in the form

$$f(x) = \frac{N(x)}{D(x)}$$

where $N(x)$ and $D(x)$ are polynomials and $D(x)$ is not the zero polynomial.

In general, the *domain* of a rational function of x includes all real numbers except x-values that make the denominator zero. Much of the discussion of rational functions will focus on their graphical behavior near the x-values excluded from the domain.

Example 1 Finding the Domain of a Rational Function

Find the domain of the reciprocal function $f(x) = \dfrac{1}{x}$ and discuss the behavior of f near any excluded x-values.

Solution

Because the denominator is zero when $x = 0$, the domain of f is all real numbers except $x = 0$. To determine the behavior of f near this excluded value, evaluate $f(x)$ to the left and right of $x = 0$, as indicated in the following tables.

x	-1	-0.5	-0.1	-0.01	-0.001	$\rightarrow 0$
$f(x)$	-1	-2	-10	-100	-1000	$\rightarrow -\infty$

x	$0 \leftarrow$	0.001	0.01	0.1	0.5	1
$f(x)$	$\infty \leftarrow$	1000	100	10	2	1

Note that as x approaches 0 *from the left*, $f(x)$ decreases without bound. In contrast, as x approaches 0 *from the right*, $f(x)$ increases without bound. The graph of f is shown in Figure 2.37.

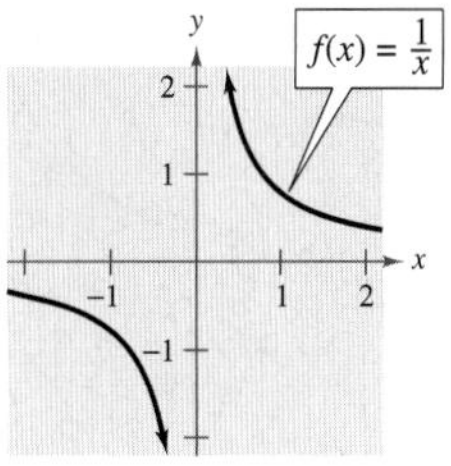

FIGURE 2.37

CHECKPoint Now try Exercise 5.

1 PLAN AND PREPARE

Warm-up Exercises

Transparency Available
Available at the Instructor's companion site.

Notetaking Guide

Transparency Available
Promotes interactive learning and notetaking skills. Available at the Instructor's companion site.

Animated Precalculus

An **Animated Precalculus** tutorial is available at the Student companion site for **Section 2.6.**

Pacing

Average: 2 days
Advanced: 2 days
Block: 1 block

2 FOCUS AND MOTIVATE

Essential Question

How do you sketch the graph of the rational function $f(x) = \dfrac{N(x)}{D(x)}$?

Tell students that they will learn how to answer this question by finding intercepts, locating asymptotes, and plotting select points.

Resource Planning Guide

Chapter Resources

- Complete Solutions Guide

Workbooks

- Notetaking Guide
- Student Solutions Guide

Interactive Technology

- Instructor Success Organizer
- Notetaking Guide IAE
- Instructional DVDs
- Animated Precalculus
- PowerLecture with ExamView

3 TEACH

Extra Example 1

Find the domain of $f(x) = \dfrac{3x}{x - 1}$ and discuss the behavior of f near any excluded x-values.

The domain of f is all real numbers x except $x = 1$. As x approaches 1 from the left, f decreases without bound. As x approaches 1 from the right, f increases without bound.

Vertical and Horizontal Asymptotes

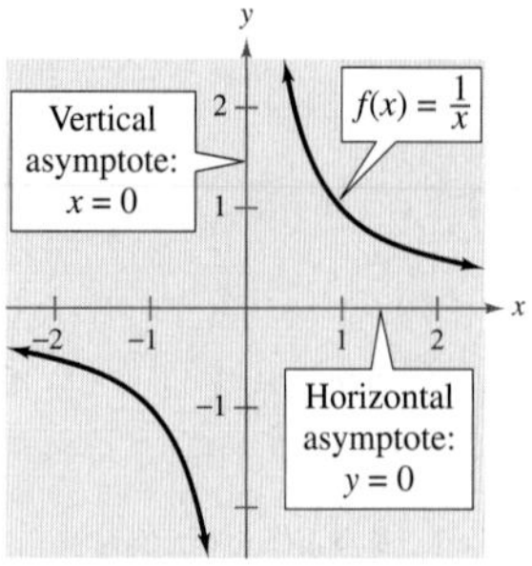

FIGURE 2.38

In Example 1, the behavior of f near $x = 0$ is denoted as follows.

$f(x) \longrightarrow -\infty$ as $x \longrightarrow 0^-$: $f(x)$ decreases without bound as x approaches 0 from the left.

$f(x) \longrightarrow \infty$ as $x \longrightarrow 0^+$: $f(x)$ increases without bound as x approaches 0 from the right.

The line $x = 0$ is a **vertical asymptote** of the graph of f, as shown in Figure 2.38. From this figure, you can see that the graph of f also has a **horizontal asymptote**—the line $y = 0$. This means that the values of $f(x) = \dfrac{1}{x}$ approach zero as x increases or decreases without bound.

$f(x) \longrightarrow 0$ as $x \longrightarrow -\infty$: $f(x)$ approaches 0 as x decreases without bound.

$f(x) \longrightarrow 0$ as $x \longrightarrow \infty$: $f(x)$ approaches 0 as x increases without bound.

> **Definitions of Vertical and Horizontal Asymptotes**
>
> 1. The line $x = a$ is a **vertical asymptote** of the graph of f if
>
> $$f(x) \longrightarrow \infty \quad \text{or} \quad f(x) \longrightarrow -\infty$$
>
> as $x \longrightarrow a$, either from the right or from the left.
>
> 2. The line $y = b$ is a **horizontal asymptote** of the graph of f if
>
> $$f(x) \longrightarrow b$$
>
> as $x \longrightarrow \infty$ or $x \longrightarrow -\infty$.

Eventually (as $x \longrightarrow \infty$ or $x \longrightarrow -\infty$), the distance between the horizontal asymptote and the points on the graph must approach zero. Figure 2.39 shows the vertical and horizontal asymptotes of the graphs of three rational functions.

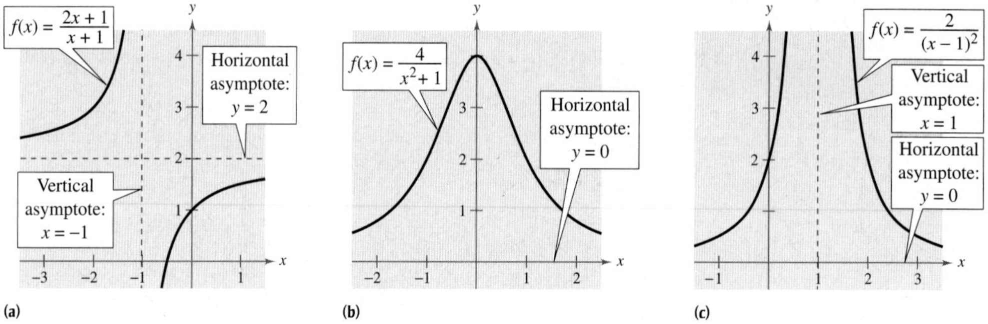

FIGURE 2.39

The graphs of $f(x) = \dfrac{1}{x}$ in Figure 2.38 and $f(x) = \dfrac{2x + 1}{x + 1}$ in Figure 2.39(a) are **hyperbolas.** You will study hyperbolas in Section 10.4.

Vertical and Horizontal Asymptotes of a Rational Function

Let f be the rational function given by

$$f(x) = \frac{N(x)}{D(x)} = \frac{a_n x^n + a_{n-1}x^{n-1} + \cdots + a_1 x + a_0}{b_m x^m + b_{m-1}x^{m-1} + \cdots + b_1 x + b_0}$$

where $N(x)$ and $D(x)$ have no common factors.

1. The graph of f has *vertical* asymptotes at the zeros of $D(x)$.
2. The graph of f has one or no *horizontal* asymptote determined by comparing the degrees of $N(x)$ and $D(x)$.
   a. If $n < m$, the graph of f has the line $y = 0$ (the x-axis) as a horizontal asymptote.
   b. If $n = m$, the graph of f has the line $y = \frac{a_n}{b_m}$ (ratio of the leading coefficients) as a horizontal asymptote.
   c. If $n > m$, the graph of f has no horizontal asymptote.

Example 2 Finding Vertical and Horizontal Asymptotes

Find all vertical and horizontal asymptotes of the graph of each rational function.

a. $f(x) = \dfrac{2x^2}{x^2 - 1}$ **b.** $f(x) = \dfrac{x^2 + x - 2}{x^2 - x - 6}$

Solution

a. For this rational function, the degree of the numerator is *equal to* the degree of the denominator. The leading coefficient of the numerator is 2 and the leading coefficient of the denominator is 1, so the graph has the line $y = 2$ as a horizontal asymptote. To find any vertical asymptotes, set the denominator equal to zero and solve the resulting equation for x.

$x^2 - 1 = 0$ Set denominator equal to zero.

$(x + 1)(x - 1) = 0$ Factor.

$x + 1 = 0 \Rightarrow x = -1$ Set 1st factor equal to 0.

$x - 1 = 0 \Rightarrow x = 1$ Set 2nd factor equal to 0.

This equation has two real solutions, $x = -1$ and $x = 1$, so the graph has the lines $x = -1$ and $x = 1$ as vertical asymptotes. The graph of the function is shown in Figure 2.40.

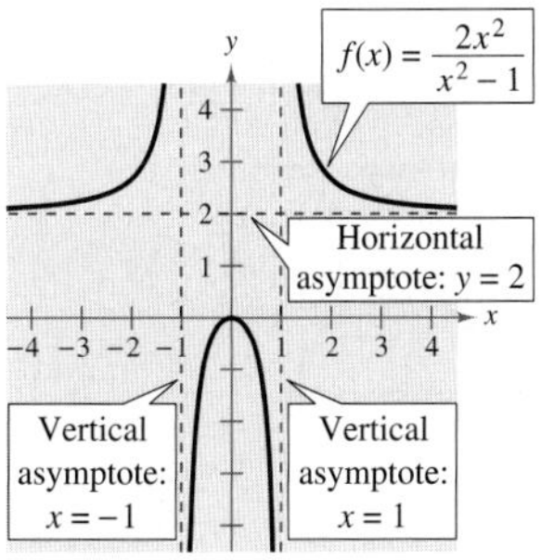

FIGURE 2.40

b. For this rational function, the degree of the numerator is *equal to* the degree of the denominator. The leading coefficient of both the numerator and denominator is 1, so the graph has the line $y = 1$ as a horizontal asymptote. To find any vertical asymptotes, first factor the numerator and denominator as follows.

$$f(x) = \frac{x^2 + x - 2}{x^2 - x - 6} = \frac{(x - 1)\cancel{(x + 2)}}{\cancel{(x + 2)}(x - 3)} = \frac{x - 1}{x - 3}, \quad x \neq -2$$

By setting the denominator $x - 3$ (of the simplified function) equal to zero, you can determine that the graph has the line $x = 3$ as a vertical asymptote.

CHECKPoint Now try Exercise 13.

Algebra Help

You can review the techniques for factoring in Appendix A.3.

Extra Example 2

Find the horizontal and vertical asymptotes of $f(x) = \dfrac{5x^2}{x^2 - 1}$.

Horizontal asymptote: $y = 5$; vertical asymptotes: $x = 1$, $x = -1$

Avoiding Common Errors

Remind students that the curves on opposite sides of vertical asymptotes do not necessarily head in opposite directions. The graph in Figure 2.39(c) on the previous page illustrates this. It is useful to use several test values on each side of the asymptote to verify the graph.

Analyzing Graphs of Rational Functions

To sketch the graph of a rational function, use the following guidelines.

Study Tip

You may also want to test for symmetry when graphing rational functions, especially for simple rational functions. Recall from Section 1.6 that the graph of the reciprocal function

$$f(x) = \frac{1}{x}$$

is symmetric with respect to the origin.

Guidelines for Analyzing Graphs of Rational Functions

Let $f(x) = \dfrac{N(x)}{D(x)}$, where $N(x)$ and $D(x)$ are polynomials.

1. Simplify f, if possible.
2. Find and plot the y-intercept (if any) by evaluating $f(0)$.
3. Find the zeros of the numerator (if any) by solving the equation $N(x) = 0$. Then plot the corresponding x-intercepts.
4. Find the zeros of the denominator (if any) by solving the equation $D(x) = 0$. Then sketch the corresponding vertical asymptotes.
5. Find and sketch the horizontal asymptote (if any) by using the rule for finding the horizontal asymptote of a rational function.
6. Plot at least one point *between* and one point *beyond* each x-intercept and vertical asymptote.
7. Use smooth curves to complete the graph between and beyond the vertical asymptotes.

TECHNOLOGY

Some graphing utilities have difficulty graphing rational functions that have vertical asymptotes. Often, the utility will connect parts of the graph that are not supposed to be connected. For instance, the top screen on the right shows the graph of

$$f(x) = \frac{1}{x-2}.$$

Notice that the graph should consist of two unconnected portions—one to the left of $x = 2$ and the other to the right of $x = 2$. To eliminate this problem, you can try changing the mode of the graphing utility to *dot mode*. The problem with this is that the graph is then represented as a collection of dots (as shown in the bottom screen on the right) rather than as a smooth curve.

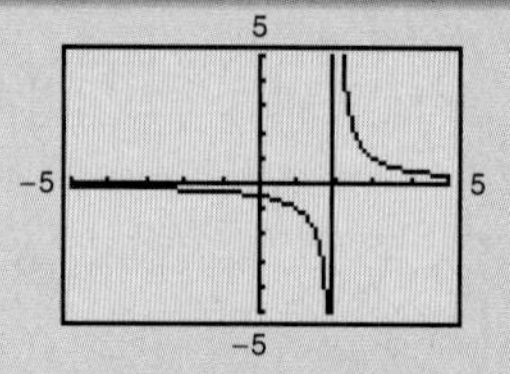

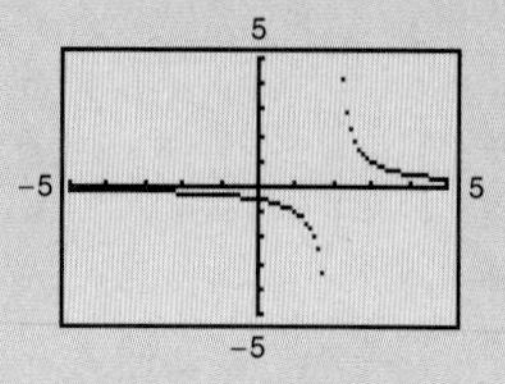

The concept of *test intervals* from Section 2.2 can be extended to graphing of rational functions. To do this, use the fact that a rational function can change signs only at its zeros and its undefined values (the x-values for which its denominator is zero). Between two consecutive zeros of the numerator and the denominator, a rational function must be entirely positive or entirely negative. This means that when the zeros of the numerator and the denominator of a rational function are put in order, they divide the real number line into test intervals in which the function has no sign changes. A representative x-value is chosen to determine if the value of the rational function is positive (the graph lies above the x-axis) or negative (the graph lies below the x-axis).

Study Tip

You can use transformations to help you sketch graphs of rational functions. For instance, the graph of g in Example 3 is a vertical stretch and a right shift of the graph of $f(x) = 1/x$ because

$$g(x) = \frac{3}{x-2} = 3\left(\frac{1}{x-2}\right) = 3f(x-2).$$

Example 3 Sketching the Graph of a Rational Function

Sketch the graph of $g(x) = \dfrac{3}{x-2}$ and state its domain.

Solution

y-intercept: $\left(0, -\frac{3}{2}\right)$, because $g(0) = -\frac{3}{2}$

x-intercept: None, because $3 \neq 0$

Vertical asymptote: $x = 2$, zero of denominator

Horizontal asymptote: $y = 0$, because degree of $N(x) <$ degree of $D(x)$

Additional points:

Test interval	Representative x-value	Value of g	Sign	Point on graph
$(-\infty, 2)$	-4	$g(-4) = -0.5$	Negative	$(-4, -0.5)$
$(2, \infty)$	3	$g(3) = 3$	Positive	$(3, 3)$

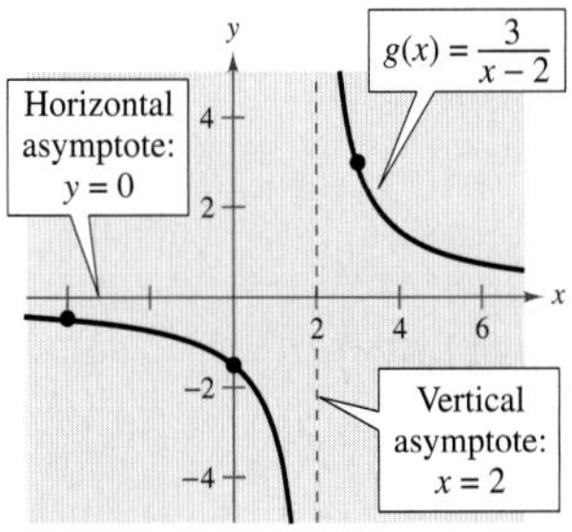

FIGURE 2.41

By plotting the intercepts, asymptotes, and a few additional points, you can obtain the graph shown in Figure 2.41. The domain of g is all real numbers x except $x = 2$.

CHECKPoint Now try Exercise 31.

Example 4 Sketching the Graph of a Rational Function

Sketch the graph of

$$f(x) = \frac{2x-1}{x}$$

and state its domain.

Solution

y-intercept: None, because $x = 0$ is not in the domain

x-intercept: $\left(\frac{1}{2}, 0\right)$, because $2x - 1 = 0$

Vertical asymptote: $x = 0$, zero of denominator

Horizontal asymptote: $y = 2$, because degree of $N(x) =$ degree of $D(x)$

Additional points:

Test interval	Representative x-value	Value of f	Sign	Point on graph
$(-\infty, 0)$	-1	$f(-1) = 3$	Positive	$(-1, 3)$
$\left(0, \frac{1}{2}\right)$	$\frac{1}{4}$	$f\left(\frac{1}{4}\right) = -2$	Negative	$\left(\frac{1}{4}, -2\right)$
$\left(\frac{1}{2}, \infty\right)$	4	$f(4) = 1.75$	Positive	$(4, 1.75)$

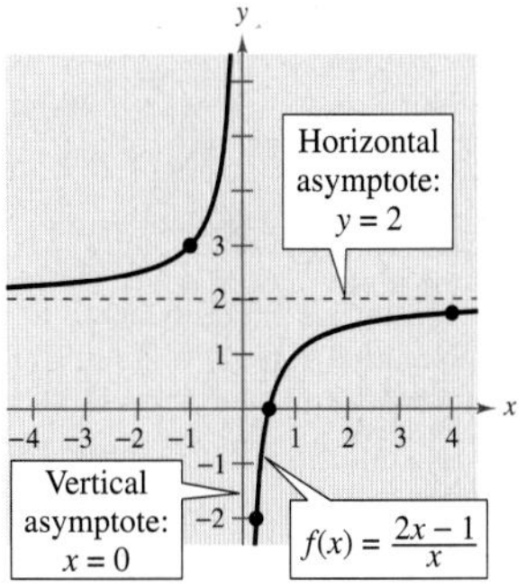

FIGURE 2.42

By plotting the intercepts, asymptotes, and a few additional points, you can obtain the graph shown in Figure 2.42. The domain of f is all real numbers x except $x = 0$.

CHECKPoint Now try Exercise 35.

Extra Example 3

Sketch the graph of $f(x) = \dfrac{1}{x+3}$ and state its domain.

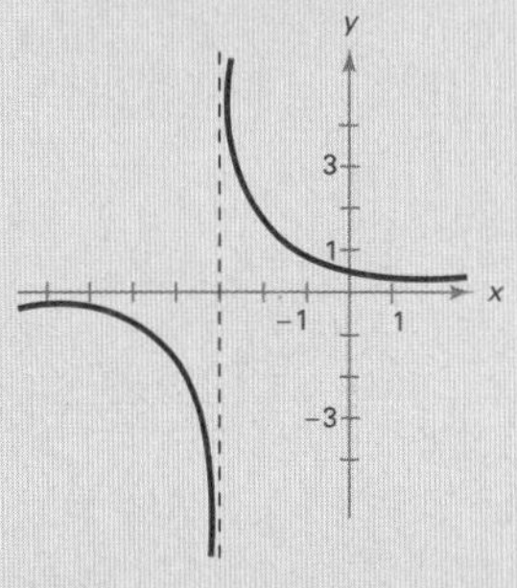

All real numbers x except $x = -3$

Extra Example 4

Sketch the graph of $C(x) = \dfrac{3+2x}{1+x}$ and state its domain.

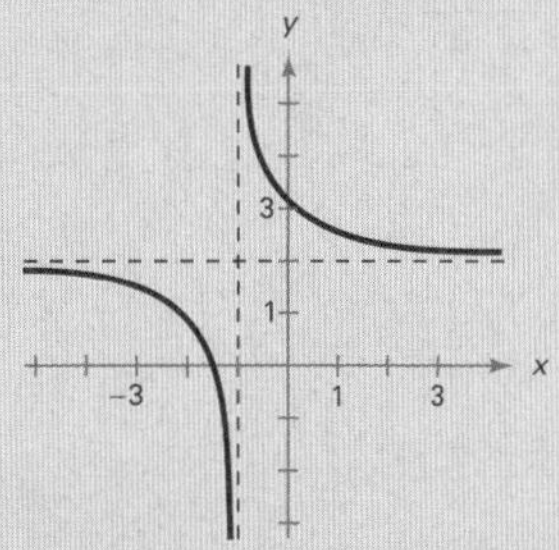

All real numbers x except $x = -1$

Extra Example 5

Sketch the graph of

$$f(x) = \frac{3x}{x^2 + x - 2}.$$

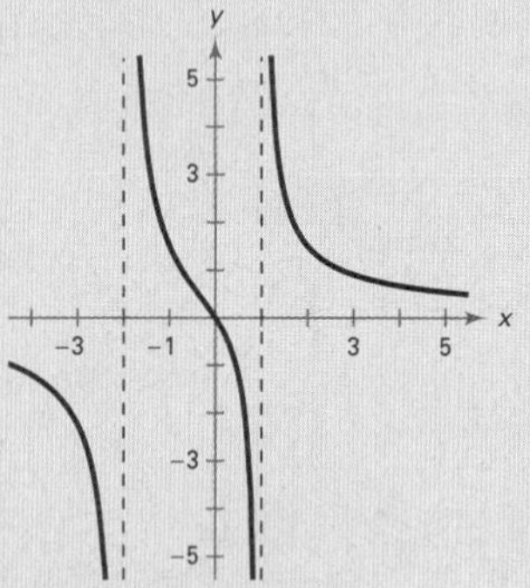

Extra Example 6

Sketch the graph of

$$f(x) = \frac{x^2 - 4}{x^2 + 4x + 4}.$$

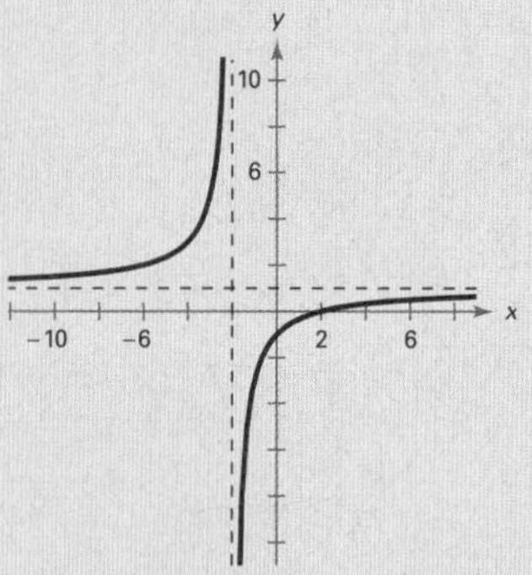

Example 5 Sketching the Graph of a Rational Function

Sketch the graph of $f(x) = x/(x^2 - x - 2)$.

Solution

Factoring the denominator, you have $f(x) = \dfrac{x}{(x + 1)(x - 2)}$.

y-intercept: (0, 0), because $f(0) = 0$

x-intercept: (0, 0)

Vertical asymptotes: $x = -1$, $x = 2$, zeros of denominator

Horizontal asymptote: $y = 0$, because degree of $N(x) <$ degree of $D(x)$

Additional points:

Test interval	Representative x-value	Value of f	Sign	Point on graph
$(-\infty, -1)$	-3	$f(-3) = -0.3$	Negative	$(-3, -0.3)$
$(-1, 0)$	-0.5	$f(-0.5) = 0.4$	Positive	$(-0.5, 0.4)$
$(0, 2)$	1	$f(1) = -0.5$	Negative	$(1, -0.5)$
$(2, \infty)$	3	$f(3) = 0.75$	Positive	$(3, 0.75)$

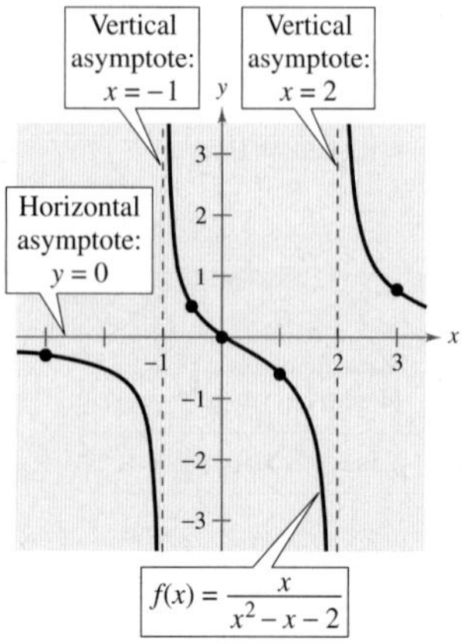

FIGURE 2.43

The graph is shown in Figure 2.43.

CHECKPoint Now try Exercise 39.

WARNING / CAUTION

If you are unsure of the shape of a portion of the graph of a rational function, plot some additional points. Also note that when the numerator and the denominator of a rational function have a common factor, the graph of the function has a *hole* at the zero of the common factor (see Example 6).

Example 6 A Rational Function with Common Factors

Sketch the graph of $f(x) = (x^2 - 9)/(x^2 - 2x - 3)$.

Solution

By factoring the numerator and denominator, you have

$$f(x) = \frac{x^2 - 9}{x^2 - 2x - 3} = \frac{\cancel{(x - 3)}(x + 3)}{\cancel{(x - 3)}(x + 1)} = \frac{x + 3}{x + 1}, \quad x \neq 3.$$

y-intercept: (0, 3), because $f(0) = 3$

x-intercept: $(-3, 0)$, because $f(-3) = 0$

Vertical asymptote: $x = -1$, zero of (simplified) denominator

Horizontal asymptote: $y = 1$, because degree of $N(x) =$ degree of $D(x)$

Additional points:

Test interval	Representative x-value	Value of f	Sign	Point on graph
$(-\infty, -3)$	-4	$f(-4) = 0.33$	Positive	$(-4, 0.33)$
$(-3, -1)$	-2	$f(-2) = -1$	Negative	$(-2, -1)$
$(-1, \infty)$	2	$f(2) = 1.67$	Positive	$(2, 1.67)$

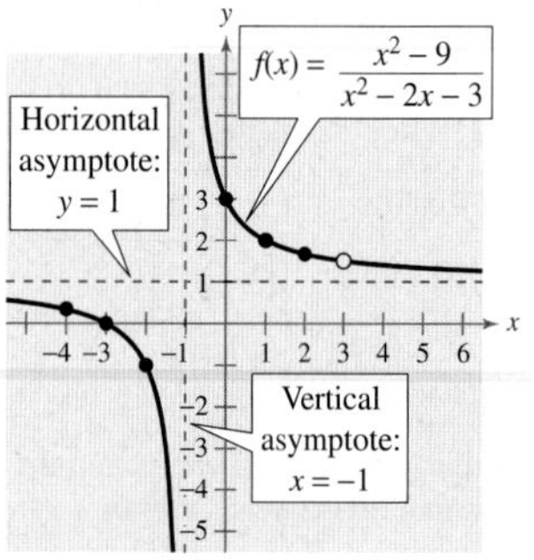

FIGURE 2.44 Hole at $x = 3$

The graph is shown in Figure 2.44. Notice that there is a hole in the graph at $x = 3$, because the function is not defined when $x = 3$.

CHECKPoint Now try Exercise 45.

Slant Asymptotes

Consider a rational function whose denominator is of degree 1 or greater. If the degree of the numerator is exactly *one more* than the degree of the denominator, the graph of the function has a **slant** (or **oblique**) **asymptote.** For example, the graph of

$$f(x) = \frac{x^2 - x}{x + 1}$$

has a slant asymptote, as shown in Figure 2.45. To find the equation of a slant asymptote, use long division. For instance, by dividing $x + 1$ into $x^2 - x$, you obtain

$$f(x) = \frac{x^2 - x}{x + 1} = \underbrace{x - 2}_{\substack{\text{Slant asymptote} \\ (y = x - 2)}} + \frac{2}{x + 1}.$$

As x increases or decreases without bound, the remainder term $2/(x + 1)$ approaches 0, so the graph of f approaches the line $y = x - 2$, as shown in Figure 2.45.

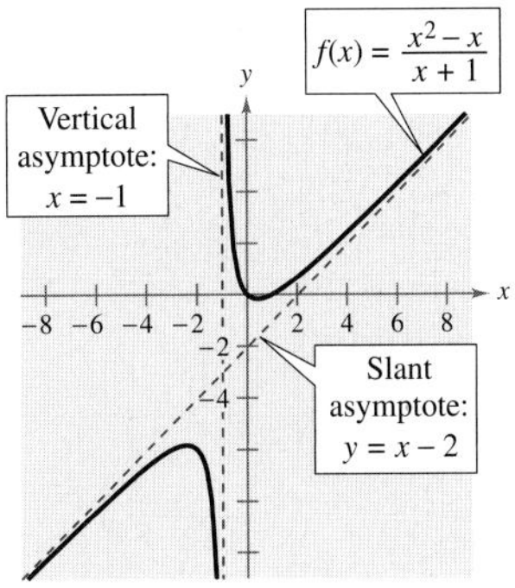

FIGURE 2.45

Example 7 A Rational Function with a Slant Asymptote

Sketch the graph of $f(x) = \dfrac{x^2 - x - 2}{x - 1}$.

Solution

Factoring the numerator as $(x - 2)(x + 1)$ allows you to recognize the x-intercepts. Using long division

$$f(x) = \frac{x^2 - x - 2}{x - 1} = x - \frac{2}{x - 1}$$

allows you to recognize that the line $y = x$ is a slant asymptote of the graph.

y-intercept: $(0, 2)$, because $f(0) = 2$

x-intercepts: $(-1, 0)$ and $(2, 0)$

Vertical asymptote: $x = 1$, zero of denominator

Slant asymptote: $y = x$

Additional points:

Test interval	Representative x-value	Value of f	Sign	Point on graph
$(-\infty, -1)$	-2	$f(-2) = -1.33$	Negative	$(-2, -1.33)$
$(-1, 1)$	0.5	$f(0.5) = 4.5$	Positive	$(0.5, 4.5)$
$(1, 2)$	1.5	$f(1.5) = -2.5$	Negative	$(1.5, -2.5)$
$(2, \infty)$	3	$f(3) = 2$	Positive	$(3, 2)$

The graph is shown in Figure 2.46.

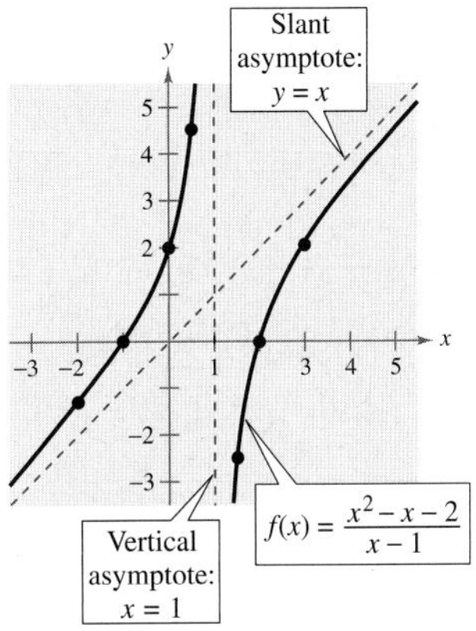

FIGURE 2.46

CHECKPoint Now try Exercise 65.

Extra Example 7

Sketch the graph of

$$f(x) = \frac{3x^2 + 1}{x}.$$

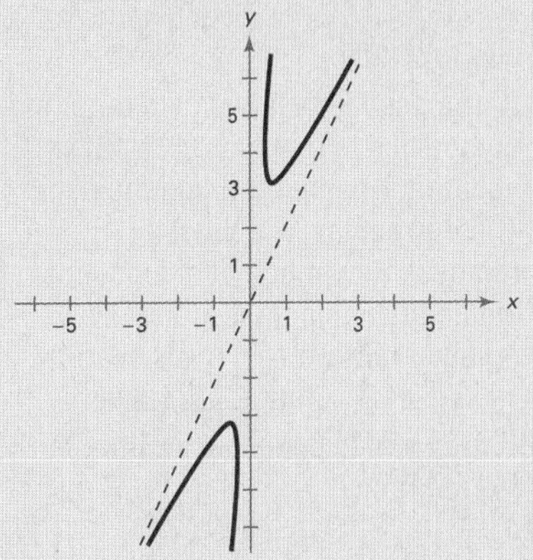

Extra Example 8

The cost C (in millions of dollars) for removing $p\%$ of the industrial pollutants discharged into a river is given by $C = \dfrac{255p}{100 - p}$ for $0 \le p < 100$.

A proposed new law would require companies to remove 80% of their pollutants discharged into the river. The current law requires 45% removal. How much additional cost would the companies incur as a result of this law?

The new law would require companies to spend an additional \$811 million.

Applications

There are many examples of asymptotic behavior in real life. For instance, Example 8 shows how a vertical asymptote can be used to analyze the cost of removing pollutants from smokestack emissions.

Example 8 Cost-Benefit Model

A utility company burns coal to generate electricity. The cost C (in dollars) of removing $p\%$ of the smokestack pollutants is given by

$$C = \frac{80{,}000p}{100 - p}$$

for $0 \le p < 100$. You are a member of a state legislature considering a law that would require utility companies to remove 90% of the pollutants from their smokestack emissions. The current law requires 85% removal. How much additional cost would the utility company incur as a result of the new law?

Algebraic Solution

Because the current law requires 85% removal, the current cost to the utility company is

$$C = \frac{80{,}000(85)}{100 - 85} \approx \$453{,}333. \quad \text{Evaluate } C \text{ when } p = 85.$$

If the new law increases the percent removal to 90%, the cost will be

$$C = \frac{80{,}000(90)}{100 - 90} = \$720{,}000. \quad \text{Evaluate } C \text{ when } p = 90.$$

So, the new law would require the utility company to spend an additional

$$720{,}000 - 453{,}333 = \$266{,}667. \quad \text{Subtract 85\% removal cost from 90\% removal cost.}$$

Graphical Solution

Use a graphing utility to graph the function

$$y_1 = \frac{80{,}000}{100 - x}$$

using a viewing window similar to that shown in Figure 2.47. Note that the graph has a vertical asymptote at $x = 100$. Then use the *trace* or *value* feature to approximate the values of y_1 when $x = 85$ and $x = 90$. You should obtain the following values.

When $x = 85$, $y_1 \approx 453{,}333$.

When $x = 90$, $y_1 = 720{,}000$.

So, the new law would require the utility company to spend an additional

$$720{,}000 - 453{,}333 = \$266{,}667.$$

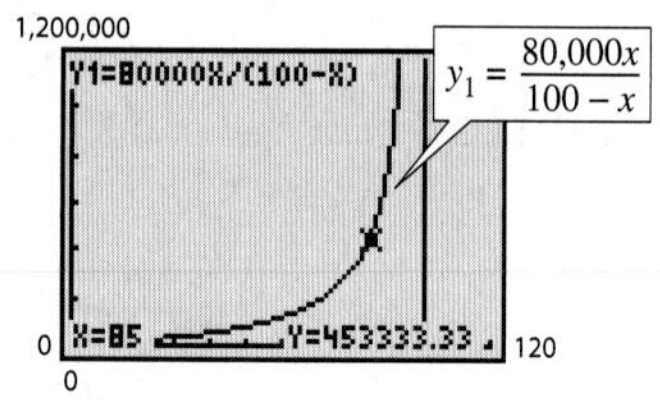

FIGURE 2.47

CHECK Point Now try Exercise 77.

Example 9 Finding a Minimum Area

A rectangular page is designed to contain 48 square inches of print. The margins at the top and bottom of the page are each 1 inch deep. The margins on each side are $1\frac{1}{2}$ inches wide. What should the dimensions of the page be so that the least amount of paper is used?

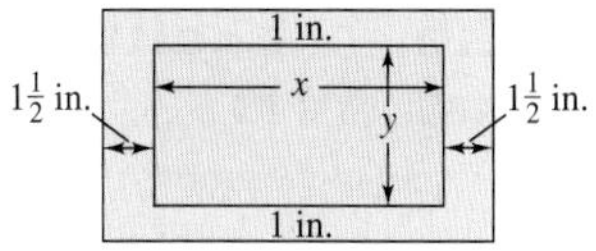

FIGURE 2.48

Graphical Solution

Let A be the area to be minimized. From Figure 2.48, you can write

$$A = (x + 3)(y + 2).$$

The printed area inside the margins is modeled by $48 = xy$ or $y = 48/x$. To find the minimum area, rewrite the equation for A in terms of just one variable by substituting $48/x$ for y.

$$A = (x + 3)\left(\frac{48}{x} + 2\right)$$

$$= \frac{(x + 3)(48 + 2x)}{x}, \quad x > 0$$

The graph of this rational function is shown in Figure 2.49. Because x represents the width of the printed area, you need consider only the portion of the graph for which x is positive. Using a graphing utility, you can approximate the minimum value of A to occur when $x \approx 8.5$ inches. The corresponding value of y is $48/8.5 \approx 5.6$ inches. So, the dimensions should be

$$x + 3 \approx 11.5 \text{ inches} \quad \text{by} \quad y + 2 \approx 7.6 \text{ inches}.$$

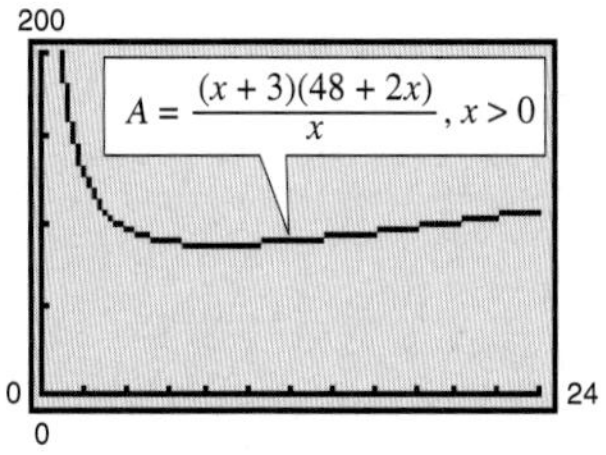

FIGURE 2.49

CHECKPoint Now try Exercise 81.

Numerical Solution

Let A be the area to be minimized. From Figure 2.48, you can write

$$A = (x + 3)(y + 2).$$

The printed area inside the margins is modeled by $48 = xy$ or $y = 48/x$. To find the minimum area, rewrite the equation for A in terms of just one variable by substituting $48/x$ for y.

$$A = (x + 3)\left(\frac{48}{x} + 2\right)$$

$$= \frac{(x + 3)(48 + 2x)}{x}, \quad x > 0$$

Use the *table* feature of a graphing utility to create a table of values for the function

$$y_1 = \frac{(x + 3)(48 + 2x)}{x}$$

beginning at $x = 1$. From the table, you can see that the minimum value of y_1 occurs when x is somewhere between 8 and 9, as shown in Figure 2.50. To approximate the minimum value of y_1 to one decimal place, change the table so that it starts at $x = 8$ and increases by 0.1. The minimum value of y_1 occurs when $x \approx 8.5$, as shown in Figure 2.51. The corresponding value of y is $48/8.5 \approx 5.6$ inches. So, the dimensions should be $x + 3 \approx 11.5$ inches by $y + 2 \approx 7.6$ inches.

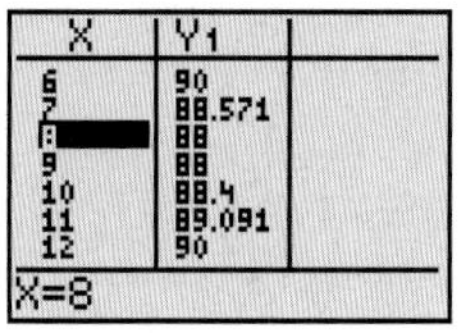

FIGURE 2.50

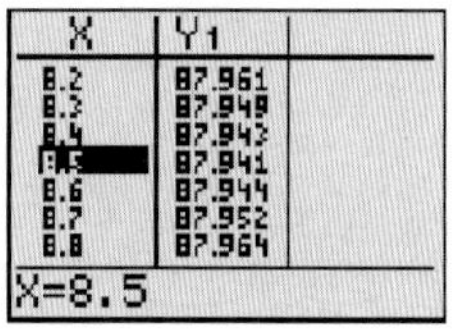

FIGURE 2.51

If you go on to take a course in calculus, you will learn an analytic technique for finding the exact value of x that produces a minimum area. In this case, that value is $x = 6\sqrt{2} \approx 8.485$.

Extra Example 9

A rectangular page is designed to contain 57 square inches of print. The margins on each side, as well as the top and bottom, are all 1 inch deep. What should the dimensions of the page be so that the least amount of paper is used?

9.55 inches high by 9.55 inches wide

Closing the Lesson

Have students summarize the major points of the lesson and answer the Essential Question: How do you sketch the graph of a rational function $f(x) = \frac{N(x)}{D(x)}$?

- **Identify x-intercepts by setting the numerator equal to zero.**
- **Identify vertical asymptotes by setting the denominator equal to zero.**
- **Identify horizontal asymptotes by looking at the degrees and leading coefficients of the numerator and denominator.**
- **If the degree of the numerator is greater than the degree of the denominator, use long division to identify slant asymptotes.**
- **Plot additional points between and beyond x-intercepts and vertical asymptotes.**

4 PRACTICE AND APPLY

Assignment Guide

Transparencies Available
Available at the Instructor's companion site.

Average:
Day 1: pp. 190–191
Exs. 1–3, 6, 9, 11, 15, 17–22, 25, 27, 33, 37, 41, 43, 45, 51
Day 2: pp. 190–193
Exs. 4, 57–61 odd, 67, 73, 75, 79, 81, 85–87, 90

Advanced:
Day 1: pp. 190–191
Exs. 6–16 even, 17–20, 22–26 even, 30, 32, 40–50 even, 52
Day 2: pp. 191–193
Exs. 56–68 even, 74, 76, 79, 80, 83, 85–87, 90

Block:
pp. 190–193
Exs. 1–4, 6, 9, 11, 15, 17–22, 25, 27, 33, 37, 41, 43, 45, 51, 57–61 odd, 67, 73, 75, 79, 81, 85–87, 90

9. Domain: all real numbers x except $x = 0$
Vertical asymptote: $x = 0$
Horizontal asymptote: $y = 0$
10. Domain: all real numbers x except $x = 2$
Vertical asymptote: $x = 2$
Horizontal asymptote: $y = 0$
11. Domain: all real numbers x except $x = 5$
Vertical asymptote: $x = 5$
Horizontal asymptote: $y = -1$
12. Domain: all real numbers x except $x = -\frac{3}{2}$
Vertical asymptote: $x = -\frac{3}{2}$
Horizontal asymptote: $y = -\frac{7}{2}$
13. Domain: all real numbers x except $x = \pm 1$
Vertical asymptotes: $x = \pm 1$
14. Domain: all real numbers x except $x = -2$
Vertical asymptote: $x = -2$
15. Domain: all real numbers x
Horizontal asymptote: $y = 3$
16. Domain: all real numbers x
Horizontal asymptote: $y = 3$

2.6 EXERCISES

See www.CalcChat.com for worked-out solutions to odd-numbered exercises.

VOCABULARY: Fill in the blanks.

1. Functions of the form $f(x) = N(x)/D(x)$, where $N(x)$ and $D(x)$ are polynomials and $D(x)$ is not the zero polynomial, are called rational functions.
2. If $f(x) \to \pm\infty$ as $x \to a$ from the left or the right, then $x = a$ is a vertical asymptote of the graph of f.
3. If $f(x) \to b$ as $x \to \pm\infty$, then $y = b$ is a ________ ________ of the graph of f. horizontal asymptote
4. For the rational function given by $f(x) = N(x)/D(x)$, if the degree of $N(x)$ is exactly one more than the degree of $D(x)$, then the graph of f has a slant (or oblique) asymptote

SKILLS AND APPLICATIONS

In Exercises 5–8, (a) complete each table for the function, (b) determine the vertical and horizontal asymptotes of the graph of the function, and (c) find the domain of the function. 5–8. See margin.

x	$f(x)$
0.5	
0.9	
0.99	
0.999	

x	$f(x)$
1.5	
1.1	
1.01	
1.001	

x	$f(x)$
5	
10	
100	
1000	

5. $f(x) = \dfrac{1}{x-1}$

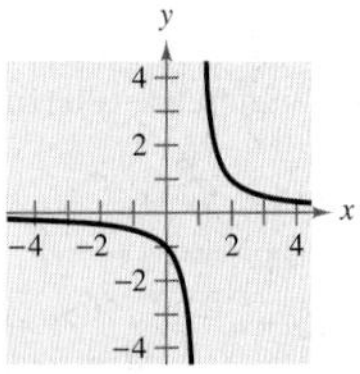

6. $f(x) = \dfrac{5x}{x-1}$

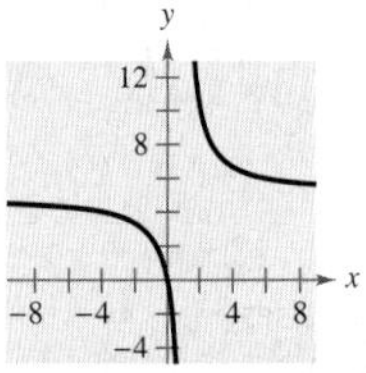

7. $f(x) = \dfrac{3x^2}{x^2-1}$

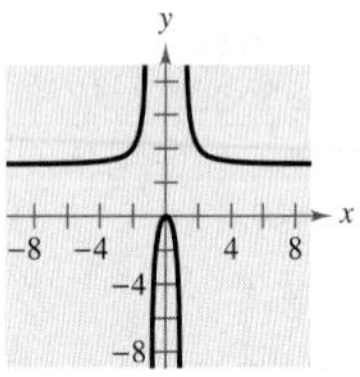

8. $f(x) = \dfrac{4x}{x^2-1}$

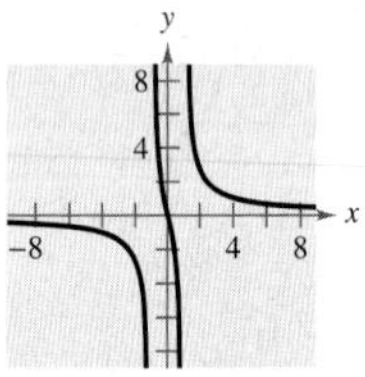

In Exercises 9–16, find the domain of the function and identify any vertical and horizontal asymptotes.

9. $f(x) = \dfrac{4}{x^2}$
10. $f(x) = \dfrac{4}{(x-2)^3}$

9–16. See margin.

11. $f(x) = \dfrac{5+x}{5-x}$
12. $f(x) = \dfrac{3-7x}{3+2x}$
13. $f(x) = \dfrac{x^3}{x^2-1}$
14. $f(x) = \dfrac{4x^2}{x+2}$
15. $f(x) = \dfrac{3x^2+1}{x^2+x+9}$
16. $f(x) = \dfrac{3x^2+x-5}{x^2+1}$

In Exercises 17–20, match the rational function with its graph. [The graphs are labeled (a), (b), (c), and (d).]

(a)

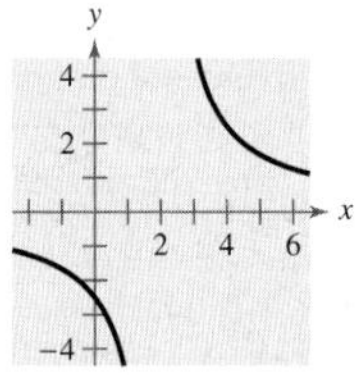

(b)

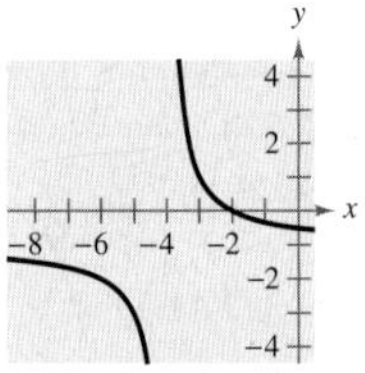

(c)

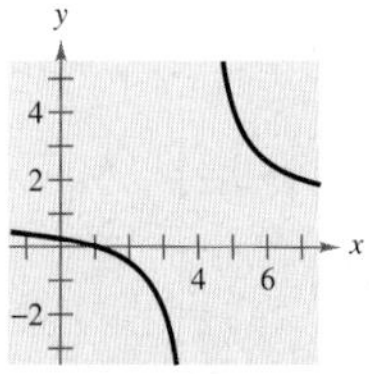

(d)

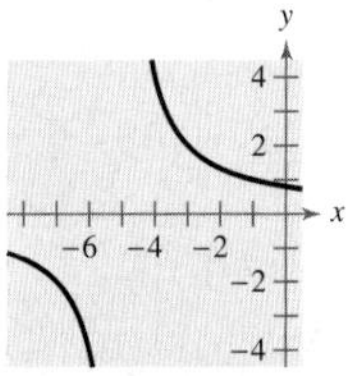

17. $f(x) = \dfrac{4}{x+5}$ d
18. $f(x) = \dfrac{5}{x-2}$ a
19. $f(x) = \dfrac{x-1}{x-4}$ c
20. $f(x) = -\dfrac{x+2}{x+4}$ b

In Exercises 21–24, find the zeros (if any) of the rational function.

21. $g(x) = \dfrac{x^2-9}{x+3}$ 3
22. $h(x) = 4 + \dfrac{10}{x^2+5}$ None
23. $f(x) = 1 - \dfrac{2}{x-7}$ 9
24. $g(x) = \dfrac{x^3-8}{x^2+1}$ 2

5–8. See Additional Answers beginning on page AA1.

In Exercises 25–30, find the domain of the function and identify any vertical and horizontal asymptotes.
25–30. See margin.

25. $f(x) = \dfrac{x-4}{x^2-16}$ 26. $f(x) = \dfrac{x+1}{x^2-1}$

27. $f(x) = \dfrac{x^2-25}{x^2-4x-5}$ 28. $f(x) = \dfrac{x^2-4}{x^2-3x+2}$

29. $f(x) = \dfrac{x^2-3x-4}{2x^2+x-1}$ 30. $f(x) = \dfrac{6x^2-11x+3}{6x^2-7x-3}$

In Exercises 31–50, (a) state the domain of the function, (b) identify all intercepts, (c) find any vertical and horizontal asymptotes, and (d) plot additional solution points as needed to sketch the graph of the rational function.
31–50. See margin.

31. $f(x) = \dfrac{1}{x+2}$ 32. $f(x) = \dfrac{1}{x-3}$

33. $h(x) = \dfrac{-1}{x+4}$ 34. $g(x) = \dfrac{1}{6-x}$

35. $C(x) = \dfrac{7+2x}{2+x}$ 36. $P(x) = \dfrac{1-3x}{1-x}$

37. $f(x) = \dfrac{x^2}{x^2+9}$ 38. $f(t) = \dfrac{1-2t}{t}$

39. $g(s) = \dfrac{4s}{s^2+4}$ 40. $f(x) = -\dfrac{1}{(x-2)^2}$

41. $h(x) = \dfrac{x^2-5x+4}{x^2-4}$ 42. $g(x) = \dfrac{x^2-2x-8}{x^2-9}$

43. $f(x) = \dfrac{2x^2-5x-3}{x^3-2x^2-x+2}$

44. $f(x) = \dfrac{x^2-x-2}{x^3-2x^2-5x+6}$

45. $f(x) = \dfrac{x^2+3x}{x^2+x-6}$ 46. $f(x) = \dfrac{5(x+4)}{x^2+x-12}$

47. $f(x) = \dfrac{2x^2-5x+2}{2x^2-x-6}$ 48. $f(x) = \dfrac{3x^2-8x+4}{2x^2-3x-2}$

49. $f(t) = \dfrac{t^2-1}{t-1}$ 50. $f(x) = \dfrac{x^2-36}{x+6}$

ANALYTICAL, NUMERICAL, AND GRAPHICAL ANALYSIS

In Exercises 51–54, do the following. 51–54. See margin.

(a) Determine the domains of f and g.

(b) Simplify f and find any vertical asymptotes of the graph of f.

(c) Compare the functions by completing the table.

(d) Use a graphing utility to graph f and g in the same viewing window.

(e) Explain why the graphing utility may not show the difference in the domains of f and g.

51. $f(x) = \dfrac{x^2-1}{x+1}$, $g(x) = x - 1$

x	-3	-2	-1.5	-1	-0.5	0	1
$f(x)$							
$g(x)$							

52. $f(x) = \dfrac{x^2(x-2)}{x^2-2x}$, $g(x) = x$

x	-1	0	1	1.5	2	2.5	3
$f(x)$							
$g(x)$							

53. $f(x) = \dfrac{x-2}{x^2-2x}$, $g(x) = \dfrac{1}{x}$

x	-0.5	0	0.5	1	1.5	2	3
$f(x)$							
$g(x)$							

54. $f(x) = \dfrac{2x-6}{x^2-7x+12}$, $g(x) = \dfrac{2}{x-4}$

x	0	1	2	3	4	5	6
$f(x)$							
$g(x)$							

In Exercises 55–68, (a) state the domain of the function, (b) identify all intercepts, (c) identify any vertical and slant asymptotes, and (d) plot additional solution points as needed to sketch the graph of the rational function.
55–66. See margin.

55. $h(x) = \dfrac{x^2-9}{x}$ 56. $g(x) = \dfrac{x^2+5}{x}$

57. $f(x) = \dfrac{2x^2+1}{x}$ 58. $f(x) = \dfrac{1-x^2}{x}$

59. $g(x) = \dfrac{x^2+1}{x}$ 60. $h(x) = \dfrac{x^2}{x-1}$

61. $f(t) = -\dfrac{t^2+1}{t+5}$ 62. $f(x) = \dfrac{x^2}{3x+1}$

63. $f(x) = \dfrac{x^3}{x^2-4}$ 64. $g(x) = \dfrac{x^3}{2x^2-8}$

65. $f(x) = \dfrac{x^2-x+1}{x-1}$ 66. $f(x) = \dfrac{2x^2-5x+5}{x-2}$

25. Domain: all real numbers x except $x = \pm 4$;
Vertical asymptote: $x = -4$;
Horizontal asymptote: $y = 0$

26. Domain: all real numbers x except $x = \pm 1$;
Vertical asymptote: $x = 1$;
Horizontal asymptote: $y = 0$

27. Domain: all real numbers x except $x = -1, 5$;
Vertical asymptote: $x = -1$;
Horizontal asymptote: $y = 1$

28. Domain: all real numbers x except $x = 1, 2$;
Vertical asymptote: $x = 1$;
Horizontal asymptote: $y = 1$

29. Domain: all real numbers x except $x = -1, \frac{1}{2}$;
Vertical asymptote: $x = \frac{1}{2}$;
Horizontal asymptote: $y = \frac{1}{2}$

30. Domain: all real numbers x except $x = -\frac{1}{3}, \frac{3}{2}$;
Vertical asymptote: $x = -\frac{1}{3}$;
Horizontal asymptote: $y = 1$

31. (a) Domain: all real numbers x except $x = -2$
(b) y-intercept: $\left(0, \frac{1}{2}\right)$
(c) Vertical asymptote: $x = -2$
Horizontal asymptote: $y = 0$
(d)

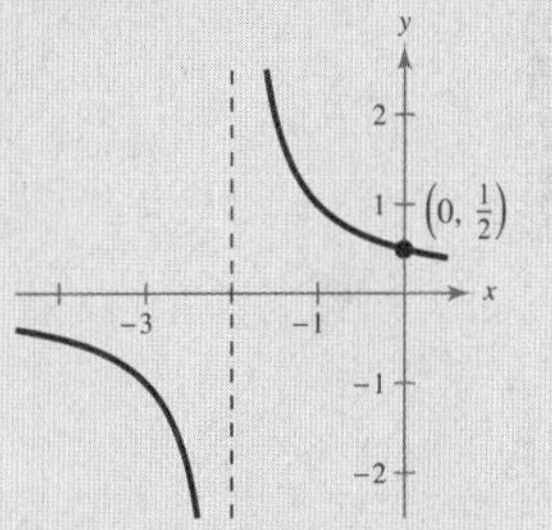

32. (a) Domain: all real numbers x except $x = 3$
(b) y-intercept: $\left(0, -\frac{1}{3}\right)$
(c) Vertical asymptote: $x = 3$
Horizontal asymptote: $y = 0$
(d)

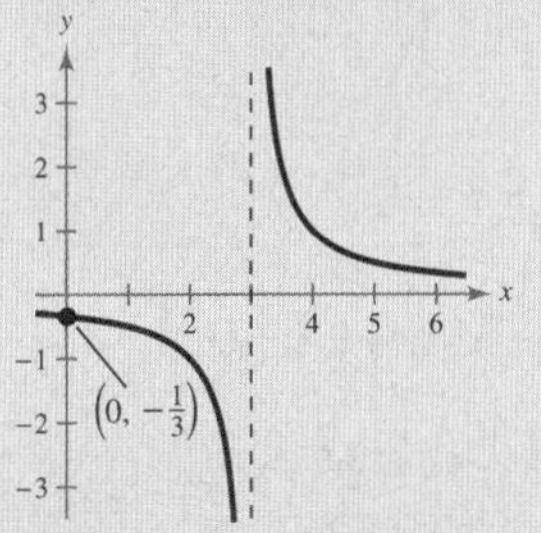

33. (a) Domain: all real numbers x except $x = -4$
(b) y-intercept: $\left(0, -\frac{1}{4}\right)$
(c) Vertical asymptote: $x = -4$
Horizontal asymptote: $y = 0$

33. (d)

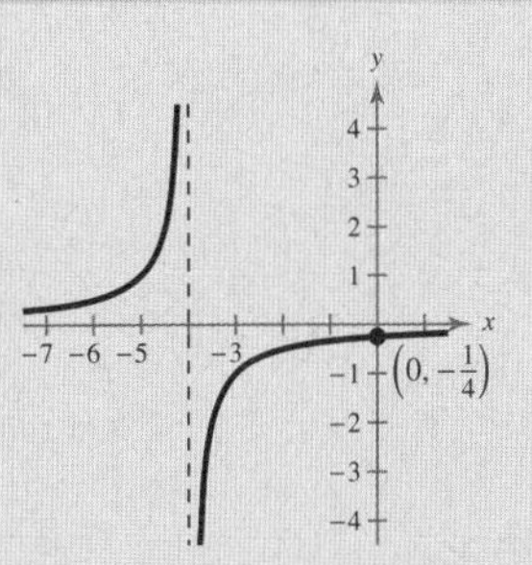

34. (a) Domain: all real numbers x except $x = 6$
(b) y-intercept: $\left(0, \frac{1}{6}\right)$
(c) Vertical asymptote: $x = 6$
Horizontal asymptote: $y = 0$
(d)

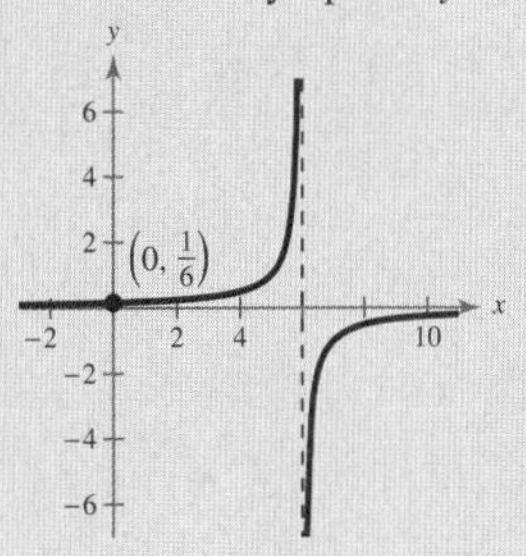

35–66. See Additional Answers beginning on page AA1.

67. $f(x) = \dfrac{2x^3 - x^2 - 2x + 1}{x^2 + 3x + 2}$ 67–68. See margin.

68. $f(x) = \dfrac{2x^3 + x^2 - 8x - 4}{x^2 - 3x + 2}$

69–72. See margin.

In Exercises 69–72, use a graphing utility to graph the rational function. Give the domain of the function and identify any asymptotes. Then zoom out sufficiently far so that the graph appears as a line. Identify the line.

69. $f(x) = \dfrac{x^2 + 5x + 8}{x + 3}$ **70.** $f(x) = \dfrac{2x^2 + x}{x + 1}$

71. $g(x) = \dfrac{1 + 3x^2 - x^3}{x^2}$ **72.** $h(x) = \dfrac{12 - 2x - x^2}{2(4 + x)}$

GRAPHICAL REASONING In Exercises 73–76, (a) use the graph to determine any x-intercepts of the graph of the rational function and (b) set $y = 0$ and solve the resulting equation to confirm your result in part (a).

73. $y = \dfrac{x + 1}{x - 3}$ (a) $(-1, 0)$ (b) -1

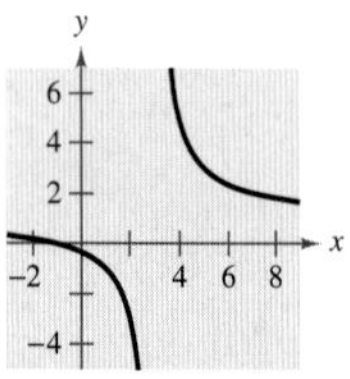

74. $y = \dfrac{2x}{x - 3}$ (a) $(0, 0)$ (b) 0

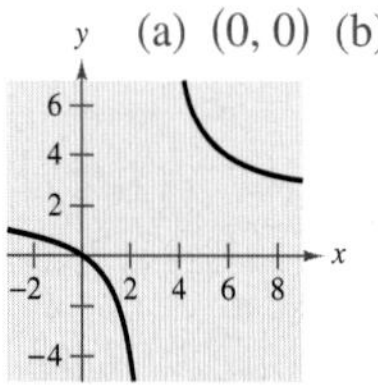

75. $y = \dfrac{1}{x} - x$ (a) $(1, 0), (-1, 0)$ (b) ± 1

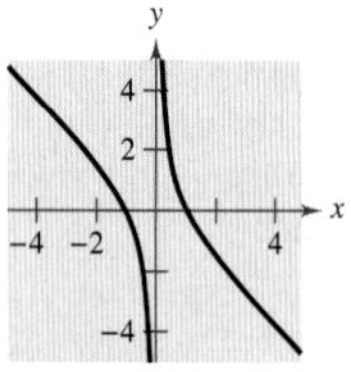

76. $y = x - 3 + \dfrac{2}{x}$ (a) $(1, 0), (2, 0)$ (b) $1, 2$

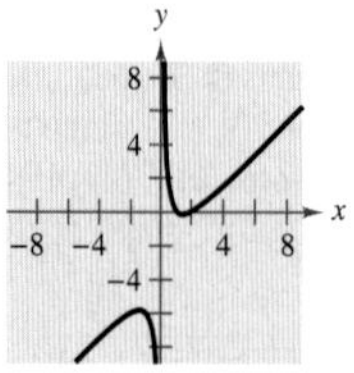

77. POLLUTION The cost C (in millions of dollars) of removing $p\%$ of the industrial and municipal pollutants discharged into a river is given by

$$C = \frac{255p}{100 - p}, \quad 0 \le p < 100.$$

See margin.

(a) Use a graphing utility to graph the cost function.

(b) Find the costs of removing 10%, 40%, and 75% of the pollutants. See margin.

(c) According to this model, would it be possible to remove 100% of the pollutants? Explain.
No. The function is undefined at $p = 100$.

78. RECYCLING In a pilot project, a rural township is given recycling bins for separating and storing recyclable products. The cost C (in dollars) of supplying bins to $p\%$ of the population is given by

$$C = \frac{25{,}000p}{100 - p}, \quad 0 \le p < 100.$$ See margin.

(a) Use a graphing utility to graph the cost function.

(b) Find the costs of supplying bins to 15%, 50%, and 90% of the population.

(c) According to this model, would it be possible to supply bins to 100% of the residents? Explain.

79. POPULATION GROWTH The game commission introduces 100 deer into newly acquired state game lands. The population N of the herd is modeled by

$$N = \frac{20(5 + 3t)}{1 + 0.04t}, \quad t \ge 0$$

where t is the time in years (see figure).

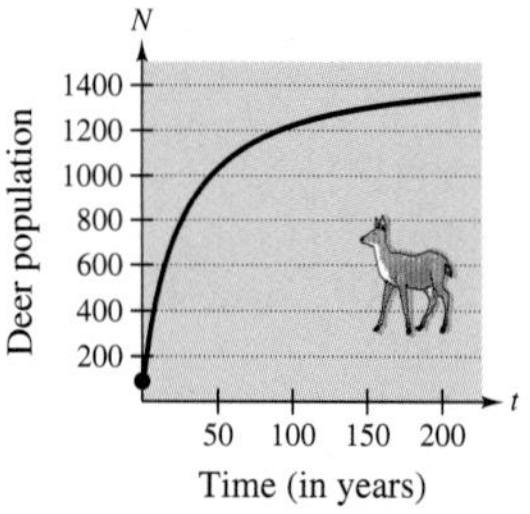

(a) Find the populations when $t = 5$, $t = 10$, and $t = 25$. 333 deer, 500 deer, 800 deer

(b) What is the limiting size of the herd as time increases? 1500 deer

80. CONCENTRATION OF A MIXTURE A 1000-liter tank contains 50 liters of a 25% brine solution. You add x liters of a 75% brine solution to the tank.

(a) Show that the concentration C, the proportion of brine to total solution, in the final mixture is

$$C = \frac{3x + 50}{4(x + 50)}.$$ Answers will vary.

(b) Determine the domain of the function based on the physical constraints of the problem. $[0, 950]$

(c) Sketch a graph of the concentration function. See margin.

(d) As the tank is filled, what happens to the rate at which the concentration of brine is increasing? What percent does the concentration of brine appear to approach?
Increases more and more slowly; 75%

67. (a) Domain: all real numbers x except $x = -1, -2$
(b) y-intercept: $(0, \frac{1}{2})$
x-intercepts: $(\frac{1}{2}, 0), (1, 0)$
(c) Vertical asymptote: $x = -2$
Slant asymptote: $y = 2x - 7$
(d)

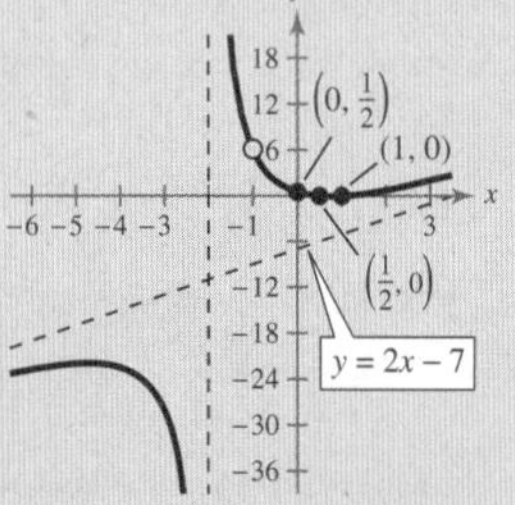

68. (a) Domain: all real numbers x except $x = 1, 2$
(b) y-intercept: $(0, -2)$
x-intercepts: $(-2, 0), (-\frac{1}{2}, 0)$
(c) Vertical asymptote: $x = 1$
Slant asymptote: $y = 2x + 7$
(d)

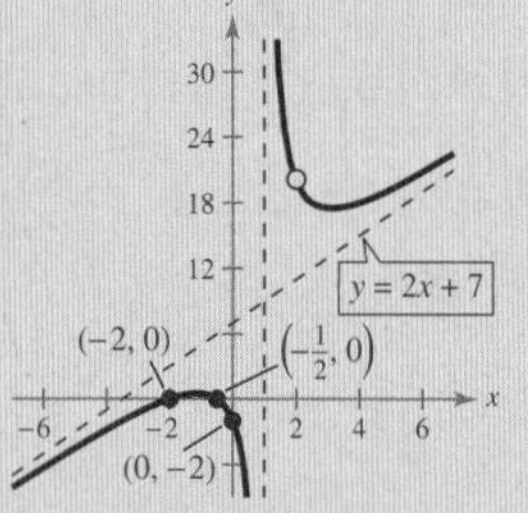

69.

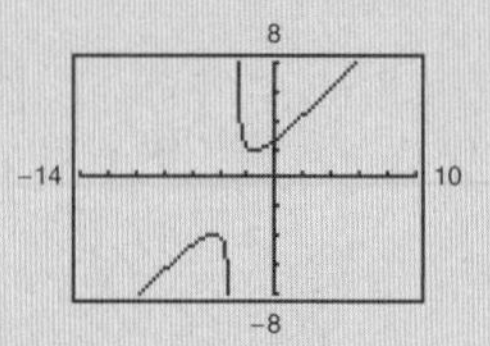

Domain: all real numbers x except $x = -3$
Vertical asymptote: $x = -3$
Slant asymptote: $y = x + 2$
$y = x + 2$

70.

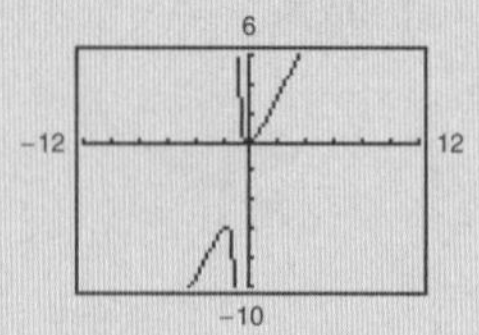

Domain: all real numbers x except $x = -1$
Vertical asymptote: $x = -1$
Slant asymptote: $y = 2x - 1$
$y = 2x - 1$

71.

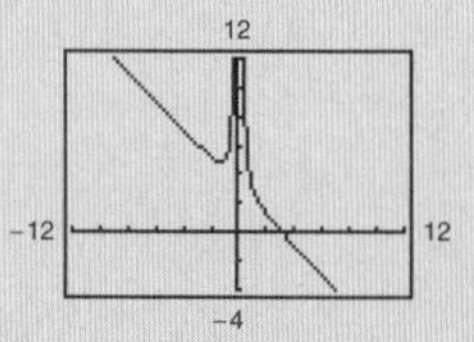

Domain: all real numbers x except $x = 0$
Vertical asymptote: $x = 0$
Slant asymptote: $y = -x + 3$
$y = -x + 3$

72.

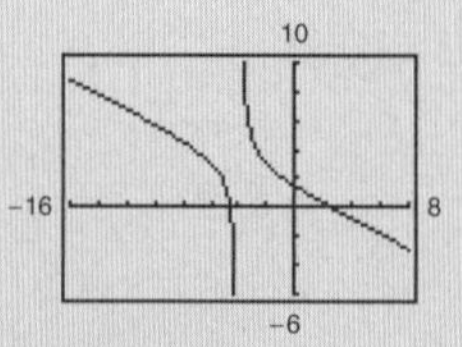

Domain: all real numbers x except $x = -4$
Vertical asymptote: $x = -4$
Slant asymptotes: $y = -\frac{1}{2}x + 1$
$y = -\frac{1}{2}x + 1$

77. (a)

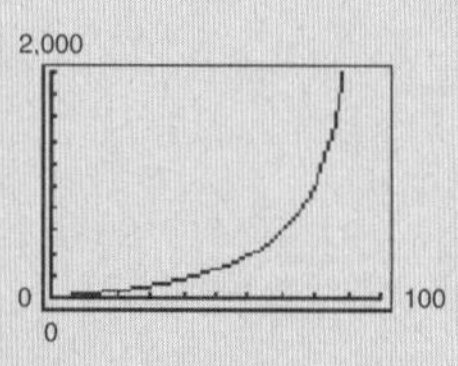

(b) \$28.33 million; \$170 million; \$765 million

78, 80(c). See Additional Answers beginning on page AA1.

81. PAGE DESIGN A page that is x inches wide and y inches high contains 30 square inches of print. The top and bottom margins are 1 inch deep, and the margins on each side are 2 inches wide (see figure).

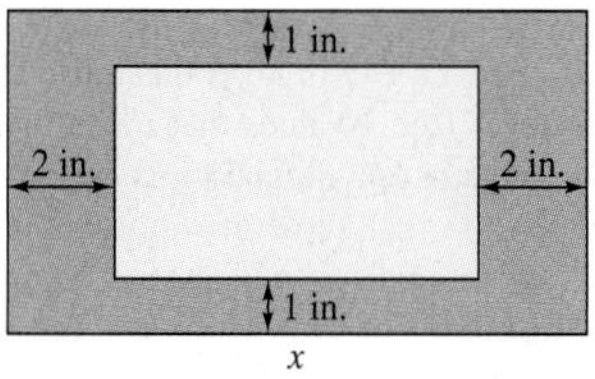

(a) Write a function for the total area A of the page in terms of x. See margin.

(b) Determine the domain of the function based on the physical constraints of the problem. $(4, \infty)$

(c) Use a graphing utility to graph the area function and approximate the page size for which the least amount of paper will be used. Verify your answer numerically using the *table* feature of the graphing utility. See margin.

82. PAGE DESIGN A rectangular page is designed to contain 64 square inches of print. The margins at the top and bottom of the page are each 1 inch deep. The margins on each side are $1\frac{1}{2}$ inches wide. What should the dimensions of the page be so that the least amount of paper is used? 12.8 in. × 8.5 in.

83. AVERAGE SPEED A driver averaged 50 miles per hour on the round trip between Akron, Ohio, and Columbus, Ohio, 100 miles away. The average speeds for going and returning were x and y miles per hour, respectively.

(a) Show that $y = \dfrac{25x}{x - 25}$. Answers will vary.

(b) Determine the vertical and horizontal asymptotes of the graph of the function. (b)–(c). See margin.

(c) Use a graphing utility to graph the function.

(d) Complete the table.

x	30	35	40	45	50	55	60
y	150	87.5	66.7	56.3	50	45.8	42.9

(e) Are the results in the table what you expected? Explain. (e)–(f). See margin.

(f) Is it possible to average 20 miles per hour in one direction and still average 50 miles per hour on the round trip? Explain.

EXPLORATION

84. WRITING Is every rational function a polynomial function? Is every polynomial function a rational function? Explain. See margin.

TRUE OR FALSE? In Exercises 85–87, determine whether the statement is true or false. Justify your answer.

85. A polynomial can have infinitely many vertical asymptotes.

86. The graph of a rational function can never cross one of its asymptotes. 85–87. See margin.

87. The graph of a function can have a vertical asymptote, a horizontal asymptote, and a slant asymptote.

LIBRARY OF PARENT FUNCTIONS In Exercises 88 and 89, identify the rational function represented by the graph.

88. b

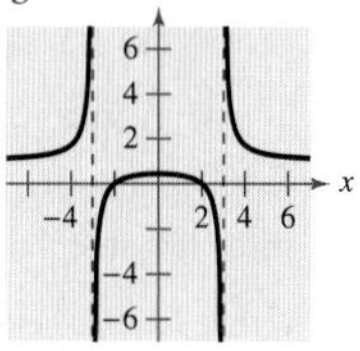

89. c

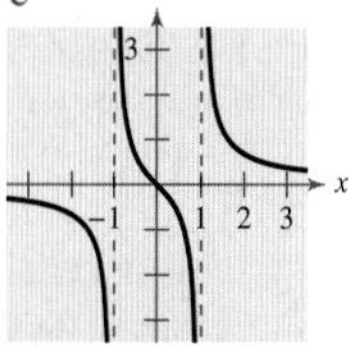

88.
(a) $f(x) = \dfrac{x^2 - 9}{x^2 - 4}$
(b) $f(x) = \dfrac{x^2 - 4}{x^2 - 9}$
(c) $f(x) = \dfrac{x - 4}{x^2 - 9}$
(d) $f(x) = \dfrac{x - 9}{x^2 - 4}$

89.
(a) $f(x) = \dfrac{x^2 - 1}{x^2 + 1}$
(b) $f(x) = \dfrac{x^2 + 1}{x^2 - 1}$
(c) $f(x) = \dfrac{x}{x^2 - 1}$
(d) $f(x) = \dfrac{x}{x^2 + 1}$

90. CAPSTONE Write a rational function f that has the specified characteristics. (There are many correct answers.)

(a) Vertical asymptote: $x = 2$
Horizontal asymptote: $y = 0$
Zero: $x = 1$
$f(x) = \dfrac{x - 1}{x^3 - 8}$

(b) Vertical asymptote: $x = -1$
Horizontal asymptote: $y = 0$
Zero: $x = 2$
$f(x) = \dfrac{x - 2}{x^3 + 1}$

(c) Vertical asymptotes: $x = -2, x = 1$
Horizontal asymptote: $y = 2$
Zeros: $x = 3, x = -3,$
$f(x) = \dfrac{2x^2 - 18}{x^2 + x - 2}$

(d) Vertical asymptotes: $x = -1, x = 2$
Horizontal asymptote: $y = -2$
Zeros: $x = -2, x = 3$
$f(x) = \dfrac{-2x^2 + 2x + 12}{x^2 - x - 2}$

PROJECT: DEPARTMENT OF DEFENSE To work an extended application analyzing the total numbers of the Department of Defense personnel from 1980 through 2007, visit this text's website at *academic.cengage.com.* (Data Source: U.S. Department of Defense)

5 ASSESS AND RETEACH

Daily Homework Quiz
Transparency Available
Available at the Instructor's companion site.

81. (a) $A = \dfrac{2x(x + 11)}{x - 4}$

(c)

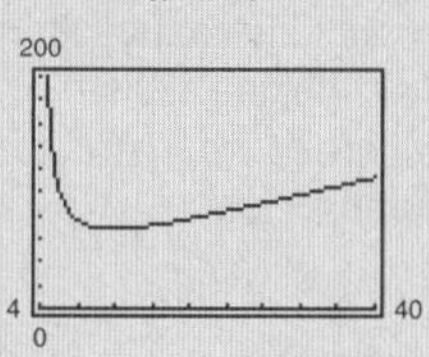

11.75 in. × 5.87 in.

83. (b) Vertical asymptote: $x = 25$
Horizontal asymptote: $y = 25$

(c)

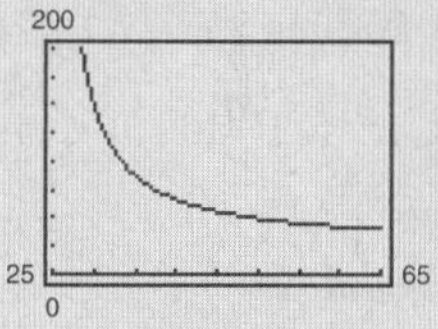

(e) Sample answer: No. You might expect the average speed for the round trip to be the average of the average speeds for the two parts of the trip.

(f) No. At 20 miles per hour you would use more time in one direction than is required for the round trip at an average speed of 50 miles per hour.

84. Yes; No; Every rational function is the ratio of two polynomial functions of the form $f(x) = \dfrac{N(x)}{D(x)}$.

85. False. Polynomials do not have vertical asymptotes.

86. False. The graph of $f(x) = \dfrac{x}{x^2 + 1}$ crosses $y = 0$, which is a horizontal asymptote.

87. False. If the degree of the numerator is greater than the degree of the denominator, no horizontal asymptote exists. However, a slant asymptote exists only if the degree of the numerator is one greater than the degree of the denominator.

1 PLAN AND PREPARE

Warm-up Exercises

Transparency Available
Available at the Instructor's companion site.

Notetaking Guide

Transparency Available
Promotes interactive learning and notetaking skills.
Available at the Instructor's companion site.

Animated Precalculus

An **Animated Precalculus** tutorial is available at the Student companion site for **Section 2.7.**

Pacing

Average: 1 day
Advanced: 1 day
Block: 0.5 block with review

2 FOCUS AND MOTIVATE

Essential Question

How do you find solutions of polynomial and rational inequalities? **Tell students that they will learn how to answer this question by finding zeros and asymptotes and testing values between these key points.**

Resource Planning Guide

Chapter Resources
- Complete Solutions Guide

Workbooks
- Notetaking Guide
- Student Solutions Guide

Interactive Technology
- Instructor Success Organizer
- Notetaking Guide IAE
- Instructional DVDs
- Animated Precalculus
- PowerLecture with ExamView

2.7 Nonlinear Inequalities

What you should learn
- Solve polynomial inequalities.
- Solve rational inequalities.
- Use inequalities to model and solve real-life problems.

Why you should learn it

Inequalities can be used to model and solve real-life problems. For instance, in Exercise 77 on page 202, a polynomial inequality is used to model school enrollment in the United States.

Ellen Senisi/The Image Works

Polynomial Inequalities

To solve a polynomial inequality such as $x^2 - 2x - 3 < 0$, you can use the fact that a polynomial can change signs only at its zeros (the x-values that make the polynomial equal to zero). Between two consecutive zeros, a polynomial must be entirely positive or entirely negative. This means that when the real zeros of a polynomial are put in order, they divide the real number line into intervals in which the polynomial has no sign changes. These zeros are the **key numbers** of the inequality, and the resulting intervals are the **test intervals** for the inequality. For instance, the polynomial above factors as

$$x^2 - 2x - 3 = (x + 1)(x - 3)$$

and has two zeros, $x = -1$ and $x = 3$. These zeros divide the real number line into three test intervals:

$$(-\infty, -1), \quad (-1, 3), \quad \text{and} \quad (3, \infty). \qquad \text{(See Figure 2.52.)}$$

So, to solve the inequality $x^2 - 2x - 3 < 0$, you need only test one value from each of these test intervals to determine whether the value satisfies the original inequality. If so, you can conclude that the interval is a solution of the inequality.

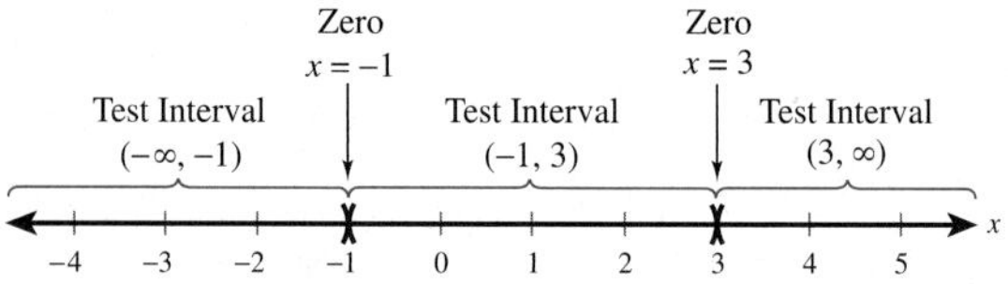

FIGURE 2.52 Three test intervals for $x^2 - 2x - 3$

You can use the same basic approach to determine the test intervals for any polynomial.

Finding Test Intervals for a Polynomial

To determine the intervals on which the values of a polynomial are entirely negative or entirely positive, use the following steps.

1. Find all real zeros of the polynomial, and arrange the zeros in increasing order (from smallest to largest). These zeros are the key numbers of the polynomial.
2. Use the key numbers of the polynomial to determine its test intervals.
3. Choose one representative x-value in each test interval and evaluate the polynomial at that value. If the value of the polynomial is negative, the polynomial will have negative values for every x-value in the interval. If the value of the polynomial is positive, the polynomial will have positive values for every x-value in the interval.

Algebra Help

You can review the techniques for factoring polynomials in Appendix A.3.

Example 1 Solving a Polynomial Inequality

Solve $x^2 - x - 6 < 0$.

Solution

By factoring the polynomial as

$$x^2 - x - 6 = (x + 2)(x - 3)$$

you can see that the key numbers are $x = -2$ and $x = 3$. So, the polynomial's test intervals are

$$(-\infty, -2),\quad (-2, 3),\quad \text{and}\quad (3, \infty). \qquad \text{Test intervals}$$

In each test interval, choose a representative x-value and evaluate the polynomial.

Test Interval	*x-Value*	*Polynomial Value*	*Conclusion*
$(-\infty, -2)$	$x = -3$	$(-3)^2 - (-3) - 6 = 6$	Positive
$(-2, 3)$	$x = 0$	$(0)^2 - (0) - 6 = -6$	Negative
$(3, \infty)$	$x = 4$	$(4)^2 - (4) - 6 = 6$	Positive

From this you can conclude that the inequality is satisfied for all x-values in $(-2, 3)$. This implies that the solution of the inequality $x^2 - x - 6 < 0$ is the interval $(-2, 3)$, as shown in Figure 2.53. Note that the original inequality contains a "less than" symbol. This means that the solution set does not contain the endpoints of the test interval $(-2, 3)$.

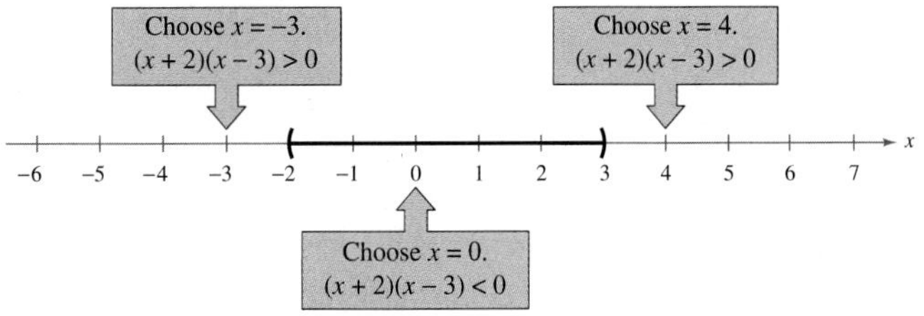

FIGURE 2.53

CHECKPoint Now try Exercise 21.

As with linear inequalities, you can check the reasonableness of a solution by substituting x-values into the original inequality. For instance, to check the solution found in Example 1, try substituting several x-values from the interval $(-2, 3)$ into the inequality

$$x^2 - x - 6 < 0.$$

Regardless of which x-values you choose, the inequality should be satisfied.

You can also use a graph to check the result of Example 1. Sketch the graph of $y = x^2 - x - 6$, as shown in Figure 2.54. Notice that the graph is below the x-axis on the interval $(-2, 3)$.

In Example 1, the polynomial inequality was given in general form (with the polynomial on one side and zero on the other). Whenever this is not the case, you should begin the solution process by writing the inequality in general form.

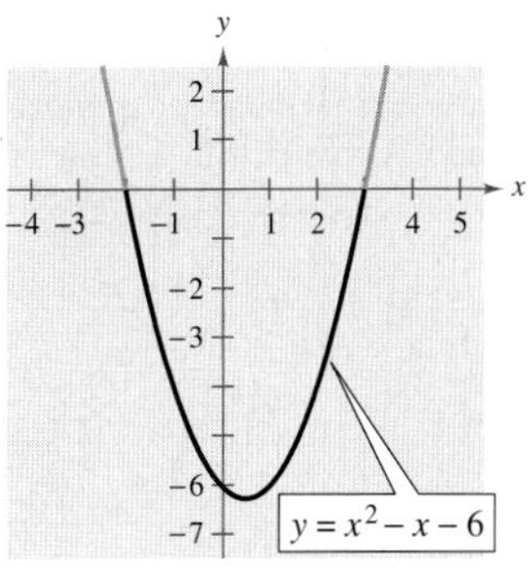

FIGURE 2.54

3 TEACH

Extra Example 1

Solve $x^2 - 5x - 6 < 0$.

$(-1, 6)$

Extra Example 2
Solve $3x^3 - 4x^2 - 12x > -16$.
$\left(-2, \frac{4}{3}\right) \cup (2, \infty)$

Extra Example 3
Solve $3x^2 - 11x > 4$.
$\left(-\infty, -\frac{1}{3}\right) \cup (4, \infty)$

Example 2 Solving a Polynomial Inequality

Solve $2x^3 - 3x^2 - 32x > -48$.

Solution

$$2x^3 - 3x^2 - 32x + 48 > 0 \qquad \text{Write in general form.}$$
$$(x - 4)(x + 4)(2x - 3) > 0 \qquad \text{Factor.}$$

The key numbers are $x = -4$, $x = \frac{3}{2}$, and $x = 4$, and the test intervals are $(-\infty, -4)$, $\left(-4, \frac{3}{2}\right)$, $\left(\frac{3}{2}, 4\right)$, and $(4, \infty)$.

Test Interval	*x-Value*	*Polynomial Value*	*Conclusion*
$(-\infty, -4)$	$x = -5$	$2(-5)^3 - 3(-5)^2 - 32(-5) + 48$	Negative
$\left(-4, \frac{3}{2}\right)$	$x = 0$	$2(0)^3 - 3(0)^2 - 32(0) + 48$	Positive
$\left(\frac{3}{2}, 4\right)$	$x = 2$	$2(2)^3 - 3(2)^2 - 32(2) + 48$	Negative
$(4, \infty)$	$x = 5$	$2(5)^3 - 3(5)^2 - 32(5) + 48$	Positive

From this you can conclude that the inequality is satisfied on the open intervals $\left(-4, \frac{3}{2}\right)$ and $(4, \infty)$. So, the solution set is $\left(-4, \frac{3}{2}\right) \cup (4, \infty)$, as shown in Figure 2.55.

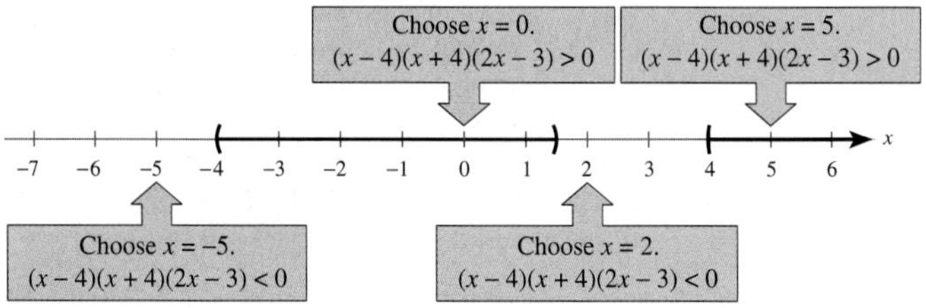

FIGURE 2.55

CHECKPoint Now try Exercise 27.

Example 3 Solving a Polynomial Inequality

Solve $4x^2 - 5x > 6$.

Algebraic Solution

$$4x^2 - 5x - 6 > 0 \qquad \text{Write in general form.}$$
$$(x - 2)(4x + 3) > 0 \qquad \text{Factor.}$$

Key Numbers: $x = -\frac{3}{4}$, $x = 2$

Test Intervals: $\left(-\infty, -\frac{3}{4}\right)$, $\left(-\frac{3}{4}, 2\right)$, $(2, \infty)$

Test: Is $(x - 2)(4x + 3) > 0$?

After testing these intervals, you can see that the polynomial $4x^2 - 5x - 6$ is positive on the open intervals $\left(-\infty, -\frac{3}{4}\right)$ and $(2, \infty)$. So, the solution set of the inequality is $\left(-\infty, -\frac{3}{4}\right) \cup (2, \infty)$.

CHECKPoint Now try Exercise 23.

Graphical Solution

First write the polynomial inequality $4x^2 - 5x > 6$ as $4x^2 - 5x - 6 > 0$. Then use a graphing utility to graph $y = 4x^2 - 5x - 6$. In Figure 2.56, you can see that the graph is *above* the x-axis when x is less than $-\frac{3}{4}$ *or* when x is greater than 2. So, you can graphically approximate the solution set to be $\left(-\infty, -\frac{3}{4}\right) \cup (2, \infty)$.

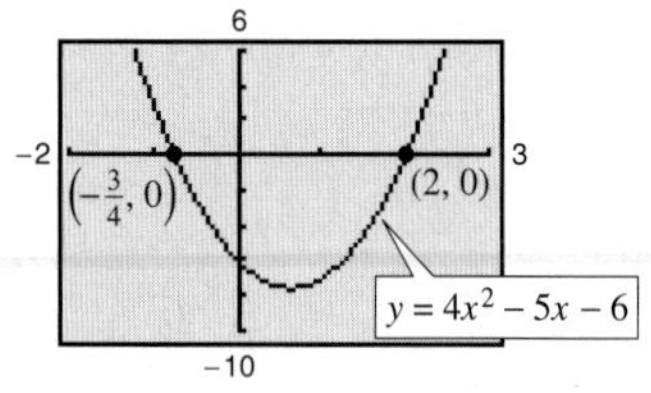

FIGURE 2.56

Study Tip

You may find it easier to determine the sign of a polynomial from its *factored* form. For instance, in Example 3, if the test value $x = 1$ is substituted into the factored form

$$(x - 2)(4x + 3)$$

you can see that the sign pattern of the factors is

$$(-)(+)$$

which yields a negative result. Try using the factored forms of the polynomials to determine the signs of the polynomials in the test intervals of the other examples in this section.

When solving a polynomial inequality, be sure you have accounted for the particular type of inequality symbol given in the inequality. For instance, in Example 3, note that the original inequality contained a "greater than" symbol and the solution consisted of two open intervals. If the original inequality had been

$$4x^2 - 5x \geq 6$$

the solution would have consisted of the intervals $\left(-\infty, -\frac{3}{4}\right]$ and $[2, \infty)$.

Each of the polynomial inequalities in Examples 1, 2, and 3 has a solution set that consists of a single interval or the union of two intervals. When solving the exercises for this section, watch for unusual solution sets, as illustrated in Example 4.

Example 4 Unusual Solution Sets

a. The solution set of the following inequality consists of the entire set of real numbers, $(-\infty, \infty)$. In other words, the value of the quadratic $x^2 + 2x + 4$ is positive for every real value of x.

$$x^2 + 2x + 4 > 0$$

b. The solution set of the following inequality consists of the single real number $\{-1\}$, because the quadratic $x^2 + 2x + 1$ has only one key number, $x = -1$, and it is the only value that satisfies the inequality.

$$x^2 + 2x + 1 \leq 0$$

c. The solution set of the following inequality is empty. In other words, the quadratic $x^2 + 3x + 5$ is not less than zero for any value of x.

$$x^2 + 3x + 5 < 0$$

d. The solution set of the following inequality consists of all real numbers except $x = 2$. In interval notation, this solution set can be written as $(-\infty, 2) \cup (2, \infty)$.

$$x^2 - 4x + 4 > 0$$

CHECK*Point* Now try Exercise 29.

Extra Example 4

Solve the polynomial inequalities.

a. $x^2 + 6x + 12 > 0$

The solution set of the inequality consists of the entire set of real numbers, $(-\infty, \infty)$. In other words, the value of the quadratic $x^2 + 6x + 12$ is positive for every value of x.

b. $x^2 + 4x + 4 \leq 0$

The solution set of the inequality consists of a single real number $\{-2\}$ because the quadratic $x^2 + 4x + 4$ has only one key number, $x = -2$, and it is the only value that satisfies the inequality.

c. $x^2 + 5x + 7 < 0$

The solution set is empty. In other words, the quadratic $x^2 + 5x + 7$ is not less than zero for any value of x.

d. $x^2 - 6x + 9 > 0$

The solution set of the inequality consists of all real numbers except $x = 3$. In interval notation, this solution set can be written as $(-\infty, 3) \cup (3, \infty)$.

Extra Example 5

Solve $\frac{3x - 5}{x - 3} \le 1$.

[1, 3)

Avoiding Common Errors

When testing rational inequalities by using their key numbers, exclude from the solution set any values that yield a zero denominator. Students must be careful to note these as open intervals.

Rational Inequalities

The concepts of key numbers and test intervals can be extended to rational inequalities. To do this, use the fact that the value of a rational expression can change sign only at its *zeros* (the x-values for which its numerator is zero) and its *undefined values* (the x-values for which its denominator is zero). These two types of numbers make up the *key numbers* of a rational inequality. When solving a rational inequality, begin by writing the inequality in general form with the rational expression on the left and zero on the right.

Study Tip

In Example 5, if you write 3 as $\frac{3}{1}$, you should be able to see that the LCD (least common denominator) is $(x - 5)(1) = x - 5$. So, you can rewrite the general form as

$$\frac{2x - 7}{x - 5} - \frac{3(x - 5)}{x - 5} \le 0,$$

which simplifies as shown.

Example 5 Solving a Rational Inequality

Solve $\frac{2x - 7}{x - 5} \le 3$.

Solution

$$\frac{2x - 7}{x - 5} \le 3 \qquad \text{Write original inequality.}$$

$$\frac{2x - 7}{x - 5} - 3 \le 0 \qquad \text{Write in general form.}$$

$$\frac{2x - 7 - 3x + 15}{x - 5} \le 0 \qquad \text{Find the LCD and subtract fractions.}$$

$$\frac{-x + 8}{x - 5} \le 0 \qquad \text{Simplify.}$$

Key numbers: $x = 5, x = 8$ — Zeros and undefined values of rational expression

Test intervals: $(-\infty, 5), (5, 8), (8, \infty)$

Test: Is $\frac{-x + 8}{x - 5} \le 0$?

After testing these intervals, as shown in Figure 2.57, you can see that the inequality is satisfied on the open intervals $(-\infty, 5)$ and $(8, \infty)$. Moreover, because $\frac{-x + 8}{x - 5} = 0$ when $x = 8$, you can conclude that the solution set consists of all real numbers in the intervals $(-\infty, 5) \cup [8, \infty)$. (Be sure to use a closed interval to indicate that x can equal 8.)

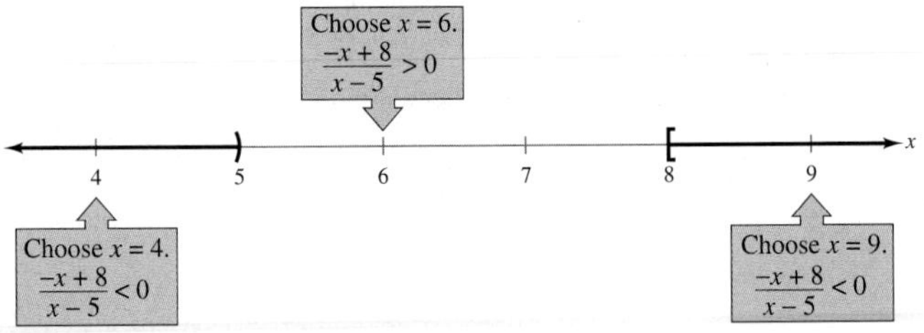

FIGURE 2.57

CHECKPoint Now try Exercise 45.

Applications

One common application of inequalities comes from business and involves profit, revenue, and cost. The formula that relates these three quantities is

Profit = Revenue − Cost

$$P = R - C.$$

Example 6 Increasing the Profit for a Product

The marketing department of a calculator manufacturer has determined that the demand for a new model of calculator is

$$p = 100 - 0.00001x, \quad 0 \le x \le 10{,}000{,}000 \qquad \text{Demand equation}$$

where p is the price per calculator (in dollars) and x represents the number of calculators sold. (If this model is accurate, no one would be willing to pay \$100 for the calculator. At the other extreme, the company couldn't sell more than 10 million calculators.) The revenue for selling x calculators is

$$R = xp = x(100 - 0.00001x) \qquad \text{Revenue equation}$$

as shown in Figure 2.58. The total cost of producing x calculators is \$10 per calculator plus a development cost of \$2,500,000. So, the total cost is

$$C = 10x + 2{,}500{,}000. \qquad \text{Cost equation}$$

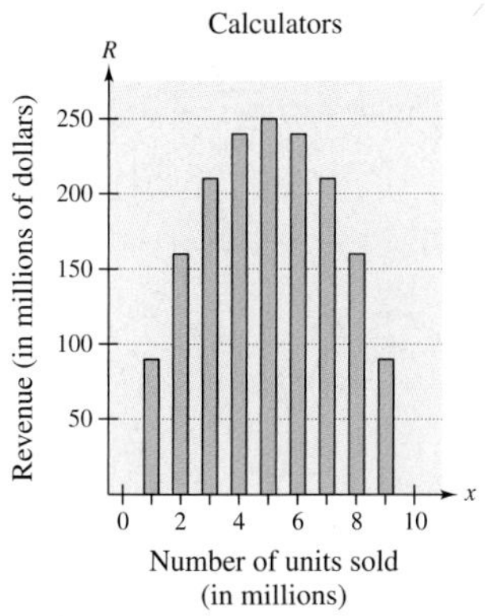

FIGURE 2.58

What price should the company charge per calculator to obtain a profit of at least \$190,000,000?

Solution

Verbal Model: Profit = Revenue − Cost

Equation: $P = R - C$

$$P = 100x - 0.00001x^2 - (10x + 2{,}500{,}000)$$

$$P = -0.00001x^2 + 90x - 2{,}500{,}000$$

To answer the question, solve the inequality

$$P \ge 190{,}000{,}000$$

$$-0.00001x^2 + 90x - 2{,}500{,}000 \ge 190{,}000{,}000.$$

When you write the inequality in general form, find the key numbers and the test intervals, and then test a value in each test interval, you can find the solution to be

$$3{,}500{,}000 \le x \le 5{,}500{,}000$$

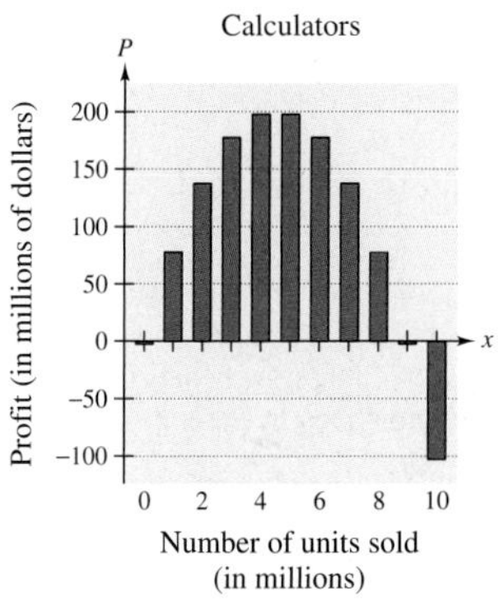

FIGURE 2.59

as shown in Figure 2.59. Substituting the x-values in the original price equation shows that prices of

$$\$45.00 \le p \le \$65.00$$

will yield a profit of at least \$190,000,000.

CHECKPoint Now try Exercise 75.

Extra Example 6

The marketing department of a manufacturer of personal electronic organizers has determined that the demand for a new model of organizer is $p = 500 - 0.00005x$, $0 \le x \le 10{,}000{,}000$, where p is the price per organizer (in dollars) and x represents the number of organizers sold. (If this model is accurate, no one would be willing to pay \$500 for the organizer. At the other extreme, the company couldn't sell more than 10 million organizers.) The revenue for selling x organizers is $R = xp = x(500 - 0.00005x)$. The total cost of producing x organizers is \$50 per organizer plus a development cost of \$2,500,000, so the total cost is $C = 50x + 2{,}500{,}000$.

What price should the company charge per organizer to obtain a profit of at least \$960,000,000?

The manufacturer will yield a profit of at least \$960,000,000 if \$225 $\le p \le$ \$325.

Extra Example 7

Find the domain of $\sqrt{216 - 6x^2}$.

$[-6, 6]$

Closing the Lesson

Have students summarize the major points of the lesson and answer the Essential Question: How do you find solutions of polynomial and rational inequalities?

- **Write the inequality in general form or as a ratio.**
- **Locate test intervals over which a function will not change sign by locating all of its zeros and vertical asymptotes.**
- **Identify the intervals over which the inequality is true by evaluating the function for a value within each test interval.**

Another common application of inequalities is finding the domain of an expression that involves a square root, as shown in Example 7.

Example 7 Finding the Domain of an Expression

Find the domain of $\sqrt{64 - 4x^2}$.

Algebraic Solution

Remember that the domain of an expression is the set of all x-values for which the expression is defined. Because $\sqrt{64 - 4x^2}$ is defined (has real values) only if $64 - 4x^2$ is nonnegative, the domain is given by $64 - 4x^2 \geq 0$.

$$64 - 4x^2 \geq 0 \quad \text{Write in general form.}$$

$$16 - x^2 \geq 0 \quad \text{Divide each side by 4.}$$

$$(4 - x)(4 + x) \geq 0 \quad \text{Write in factored form.}$$

So, the inequality has two key numbers: $x = -4$ and $x = 4$. You can use these two numbers to test the inequality as follows.

Key numbers: $x = -4, x = 4$

Test intervals: $(-\infty, -4), (-4, 4), (4, \infty)$

Test: For what values of x is $\sqrt{64 - 4x^2} \geq 0$?

A test shows that the inequality is satisfied in the *closed interval* $[-4, 4]$. So, the domain of the expression $\sqrt{64 - 4x^2}$ is the interval $[-4, 4]$.

CHECK**Point** Now try Exercise 59.

Graphical Solution

Begin by sketching the graph of the equation $y = \sqrt{64 - 4x^2}$, as shown in Figure 2.60. From the graph, you can determine that the x-values extend from -4 to 4 (including -4 and 4). So, the domain of the expression $\sqrt{64 - 4x^2}$ is the interval $[-4, 4]$.

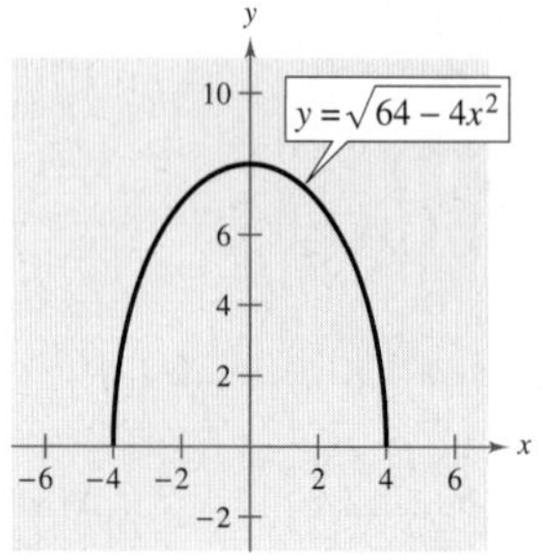

FIGURE 2.60

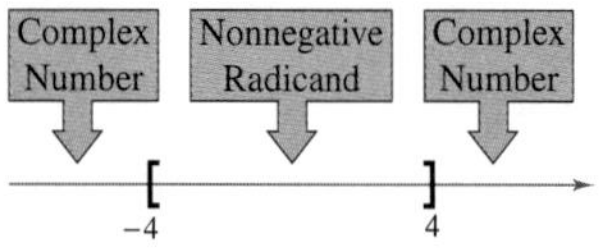

FIGURE 2.61

To analyze a test interval, choose a representative x-value in the interval and evaluate the expression at that value. For instance, in Example 7, if you substitute any number from the interval $[-4, 4]$ into the expression $\sqrt{64 - 4x^2}$, you will obtain a nonnegative number under the radical symbol that simplifies to a real number. If you substitute any number from the intervals $(-\infty, -4)$ and $(4, \infty)$, you will obtain a complex number. It might be helpful to draw a visual representation of the intervals, as shown in Figure 2.61.

Classroom Discussion

Profit Analysis Consider the relationship

$$P = R - C$$

described on page 199. Write a paragraph discussing why it might be beneficial to solve $P < 0$ if you owned a business. Use the situation described in Example 6 to illustrate your reasoning.

For planning purposes, it would be beneficial for a business owner to solve $P < 0$ to find the levels of production that *would not* lead to a profit.

Differentiated Instruction

English Language Learners It may be helpful for students learning English to think of the more common definition of the word *domain* to help them remember the mathematical definition. A domain is a region or an area defined by a specific feature, and the domain of an expression is specifically the set of all x-values.

2.7 EXERCISES

See www.CalcChat.com for worked-out solutions to odd-numbered exercises.

VOCABULARY: Fill in the blanks.

1. Between two consecutive zeros, a polynomial must be entirely ___positive___ or entirely ___negative___.
2. To solve a polynomial inequality, find the ___key___ numbers of the polynomial, and use these numbers to create ___test intervals___ for the inequality.
3. The key numbers of a rational expression are its ___zeros___ and its ___undefined values___.
4. The formula that relates cost, revenue, and profit is ___$P = R - C$___

SKILLS AND APPLICATIONS

In Exercises 5–8, determine whether each value of x is a solution of the inequality.

Inequality	Values	
5. $x^2 - 3 < 0$	No (a) $x = 3$	(b) $x = 0$ Yes
	Yes (c) $x = \frac{3}{2}$	(d) $x = -5$ No
6. $x^2 - x - 12 \geq 0$	Yes (a) $x = 5$	No (b) $x = 0$
	Yes (c) $x = -4$	(d) $x = -3$ Yes
7. $\dfrac{x+2}{x-4} \geq 3$	Yes (a) $x = 5$	(b) $x = 4$ No
	No (c) $x = -\frac{9}{2}$	(d) $x = \frac{9}{2}$ Yes
8. $\dfrac{3x^2}{x^2+4} < 1$	No (a) $x = -2$	(b) $x = -1$ Yes
	Yes (c) $x = 0$	(d) $x = 3$ No

In Exercises 9–12, find the key numbers of the expression.

9. $3x^2 - x - 2$ $\quad -\frac{2}{3}, 1$

10. $9x^3 - 25x^2$ $\quad 0, \frac{25}{9}$

11. $\dfrac{1}{x-5} + 1$ $\quad 4, 5$

12. $\dfrac{x}{x+2} - \dfrac{2}{x-1}$ $\quad -2, -1, 1, 4$

In Exercises 13–30, solve the inequality and graph the solution on the real number line. 13–30. See margin.

13. $x^2 < 9$
14. $x^2 \leq 16$
15. $(x+2)^2 \leq 25$
16. $(x-3)^2 \geq 1$
17. $x^2 + 4x + 4 \geq 9$
18. $x^2 - 6x + 9 < 16$
19. $x^2 + x < 6$
20. $x^2 + 2x > 3$
21. $x^2 + 2x - 3 < 0$
22. $x^2 > 2x + 8$
23. $3x^2 - 11x > 20$
24. $-2x^2 + 6x + 15 \leq 0$
25. $x^2 - 3x - 18 > 0$
26. $x^3 + 2x^2 - 4x - 8 \leq 0$
27. $x^3 - 3x^2 - x > -3$
28. $2x^3 + 13x^2 - 8x - 46 \geq 6$
29. $4x^2 - 4x + 1 \leq 0$
30. $x^2 + 3x + 8 > 0$

In Exercises 31–36, solve the inequality and write the solution set in interval notation.

31. $4x^3 - 6x^2 < 0$ See margin.
32. $4x^3 - 12x^2 > 0$ $\quad (3, \infty)$
33. $x^3 - 4x \geq 0$ See margin.
34. $2x^3 - x^4 \leq 0$ See margin.
35. $(x-1)^2(x+2)^3 \geq 0$ $\quad [-2, \infty)$
36. $x^4(x-3) \leq 0$ $\quad (-\infty, 3]$

GRAPHICAL ANALYSIS In Exercises 37–40, use a graphing utility to graph the equation. Use the graph to approximate the values of x that satisfy each inequality. 37–40. See margin.

Equation	Inequalities	
37. $y = -x^2 + 2x + 3$	(a) $y \leq 0$	(b) $y \geq 3$
38. $y = \frac{1}{2}x^2 - 2x + 1$	(a) $y \leq 0$	(b) $y \geq 7$
39. $y = \frac{1}{8}x^3 - \frac{1}{2}x$	(a) $y \geq 0$	(b) $y \leq 6$
40. $y = x^3 - x^2 - 16x + 16$	(a) $y \leq 0$	(b) $y \geq 36$

In Exercises 41–54, solve the inequality and graph the solution on the real number line. 41–54. See margin.

41. $\dfrac{4x-1}{x} > 0$
42. $\dfrac{x^2-1}{x} < 0$
43. $\dfrac{3x-5}{x-5} \geq 0$
44. $\dfrac{5+7x}{1+2x} \leq 4$
45. $\dfrac{x+6}{x+1} - 2 < 0$
46. $\dfrac{x+12}{x+2} - 3 \geq 0$
47. $\dfrac{2}{x+5} > \dfrac{1}{x-3}$
48. $\dfrac{5}{x-6} > \dfrac{3}{x+2}$
49. $\dfrac{1}{x-3} \leq \dfrac{9}{4x+3}$
50. $\dfrac{1}{x} \geq \dfrac{1}{x+3}$
51. $\dfrac{x^2+2x}{x^2-9} \leq 0$
52. $\dfrac{x^2+x-6}{x} \geq 0$
53. $\dfrac{3}{x-1} + \dfrac{2x}{x+1} > -1$
54. $\dfrac{3x}{x-1} \leq \dfrac{x}{x+4} + 3$

24. $\left(-\infty, \dfrac{3}{2} - \dfrac{\sqrt{39}}{2}\right] \cup \left[\dfrac{3}{2} + \dfrac{\sqrt{39}}{2}, \infty\right)$

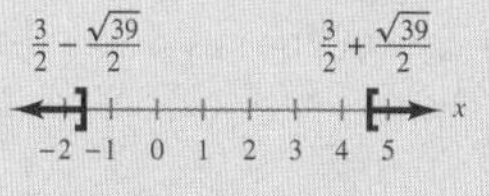

25. $(-\infty, -3) \cup (6, \infty)$

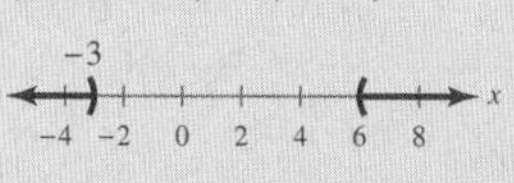

26. $(-\infty, 2]$

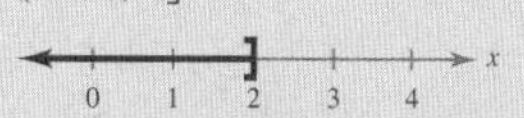

27. $(-1, 1) \cup (3, \infty)$

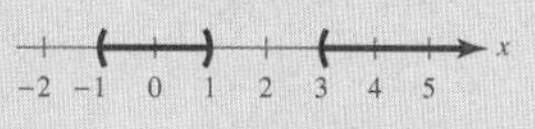

28. $\left[-\frac{13}{2}, -2\right] \cup [2, \infty)$

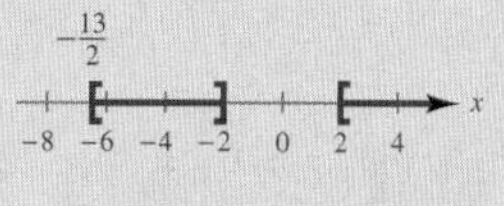

29–31, 33, 34, 37–54. See Additional Answers beginning on page AA1.

4 PRACTICE AND APPLY

Assignment Guide

Transparencies Available
Available at the Instructor's companion site.

Average:
Day 1: pp. 201–203
Exs. 1–4, 5–15 odd, 23, 27, 33, 41, 47–53 odd, 60, 67–73 odd, 76, 78, 81, 82

Advanced:
Day 1: pp. 201–203
Exs. 8, 12, 26–30 even, 34, 36, 46, 50, 54, 62–66 even, 71–74, 76, 78, 79, 83–86, 88

Block:
pp. 201–203
Exs. 1–4, 5–15 odd, 23, 27, 33, 41, 47–53 odd, 60, 67–73 odd, 76, 78, 81, 82 (with review)

13. $(-3, 3)$

14. $[-4, 4]$

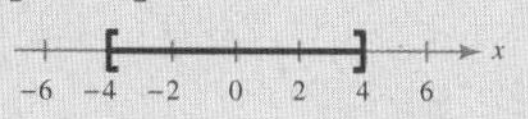

15. $[-7, 3]$

16. $(-\infty, 2] \cup [4, \infty)$

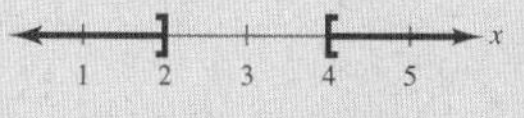

17. $(-\infty, -5] \cup [1, \infty)$

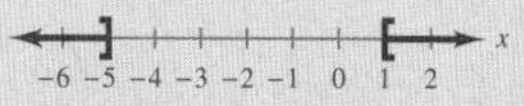

18. $(-1, 7)$

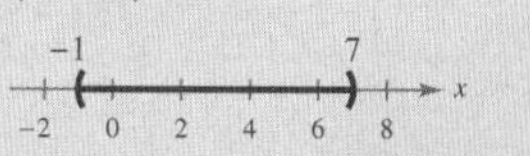

19. $(-3, 2)$

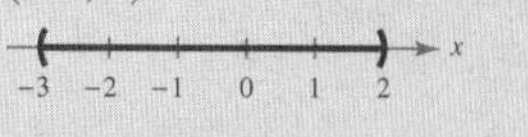

20. $(-\infty, -3) \cup (1, \infty)$

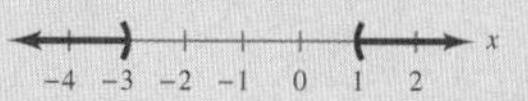

21. $(-3, 1)$

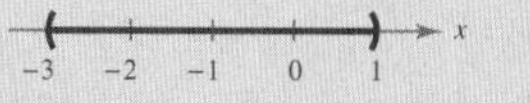

22. $(-\infty, -2) \cup (4, \infty)$

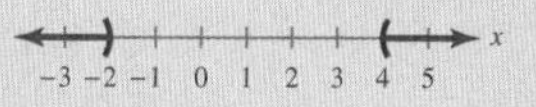

23. $\left(-\infty, -\frac{4}{3}\right) \cup (5, \infty)$

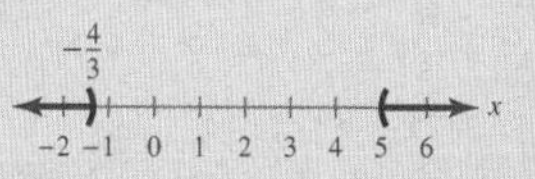

GRAPHICAL ANALYSIS In Exercises 55–58, use a graphing utility to graph the equation. Use the graph to approximate the values of x that satisfy each inequality. 55–58. See margin.

Equation	*Inequalities*	
55. $y = \dfrac{3x}{x - 2}$	(a) $y \le 0$	(b) $y \ge 6$
56. $y = \dfrac{2(x - 2)}{x + 1}$	(a) $y \le 0$	(b) $y \ge 8$
57. $y = \dfrac{2x^2}{x^2 + 4}$	(a) $y \ge 1$	(b) $y \le 2$
58. $y = \dfrac{5x}{x^2 + 4}$	(a) $y \ge 1$	(b) $y \le 0$

In Exercises 59–64, find the domain of x in the expression. Use a graphing utility to verify your result. 60–61. See margin.

59. $\sqrt{4 - x^2}$ $[-2, 2]$

60. $\sqrt{x^2 - 4}$

61. $\sqrt{x^2 - 9x + 20}$

62. $\sqrt{81 - 4x^2}$ $\left[-\frac{9}{2}, \frac{9}{2}\right]$

63. $\sqrt{\dfrac{x}{x^2 - 2x - 35}}$ $(-5, 0] \cup (7, \infty)$

64. $\sqrt{\dfrac{x}{x^2 - 9}}$ $(-3, 0] \cup (3, \infty)$

In Exercises 65–70, solve the inequality. (Round your answers to two decimal places.)

65. $0.4x^2 + 5.26 < 10.2$ $(-3.51, 3.51)$

66. $-1.3x^2 + 3.78 > 2.12$ $(-1.13, 1.13)$

67. $-0.5x^2 + 12.5x + 1.6 > 0$ $(-0.13, 25.13)$

68. $1.2x^2 + 4.8x + 3.1 < 5.3$ $(-4.42, 0.42)$

69. $\dfrac{1}{2.3x - 5.2} > 3.4$ $(2.26, 2.39)$

70. $\dfrac{2}{3.1x - 3.7} > 5.8$ $(1.19, 1.30)$

HEIGHT OF A PROJECTILE In Exercises 71 and 72, use the position equation $s = -16t^2 + v_0t + s_0$, where s represents the height of an object (in feet), v_0 represents the initial velocity of the object (in feet per second), s_0 represents the initial height of the object (in feet), and t represents the time (in seconds).

71. A projectile is fired straight upward from ground level ($s_0 = 0$) with an initial velocity of 160 feet per second.

(a) At what instant will it be back at ground level? $t = 10$ sec

(b) When will the height exceed 384 feet? See margin.

72. A projectile is fired straight upward from ground level ($s_0 = 0$) with an initial velocity of 128 feet per second.

(a) At what instant will it be back at ground level? $t = 8$ sec

(b) When will the height be less than 128 feet? See margin.

73. GEOMETRY A rectangular playing field with a perimeter of 100 meters is to have an area of at least 500 square meters. Within what bounds must the length of the rectangle lie? $13.8 \text{ m} \le L \le 36.2 \text{ m}$

74. GEOMETRY A rectangular parking lot with a perimeter of 440 feet is to have an area of at least 8000 square feet. Within what bounds must the length of the rectangle lie? $45.97 \text{ ft} \le L \le 174.03 \text{ ft}$

75. COST, REVENUE, AND PROFIT The revenue and cost equations for a product are $R = x(75 - 0.0005x)$ and $C = 30x + 250{,}000$, where R and C are measured in dollars and x represents the number of units sold. How many units must be sold to obtain a profit of at least \$750,000? What is the price per unit? See margin.

76. COST, REVENUE, AND PROFIT The revenue and cost equations for a product are

$$R = x(50 - 0.0002x) \quad \text{and} \quad C = 12x + 150{,}000$$

where R and C are measured in dollars and x represents the number of units sold. How many units must be sold to obtain a profit of at least \$1,650,000? What is the price per unit? See margin.

77. SCHOOL ENROLLMENT The numbers N (in millions) of students enrolled in schools in the United States from 1995 through 2006 are shown in the table. (Source: U.S. Census Bureau) See margin.

Year	Number, N
1995	69.8
1996	70.3
1997	72.0
1998	72.1
1999	72.4
2000	72.2
2001	73.1
2002	74.0
2003	74.9
2004	75.5
2005	75.8
2006	75.2

(a) Use a graphing utility to create a scatter plot of the data. Let t represent the year, with $t = 5$ corresponding to 1995.

(b) Use the *regression* feature of a graphing utility to find a quartic model for the data.

(c) Graph the model and the scatter plot in the same viewing window. How well does the model fit the data?

(d) According to the model, during what range of years will the number of students enrolled in schools exceed 74 million?

(e) Is the model valid for long-term predictions of student enrollment in schools? Explain.

55.

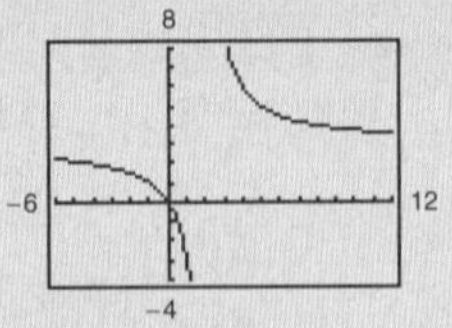

(a) $0 \le x < 2$

(b) $2 < x \le 4$

56.

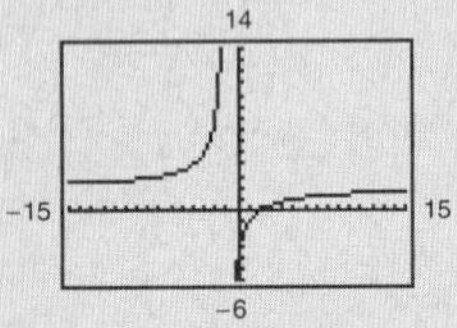

(a) $-1 < x \le 2$

(b) $-2 \le x < -1$

57.

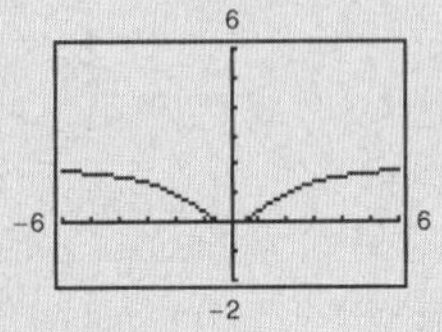

(a) $|x| \ge 2$

(b) $-\infty < x < \infty$

58.

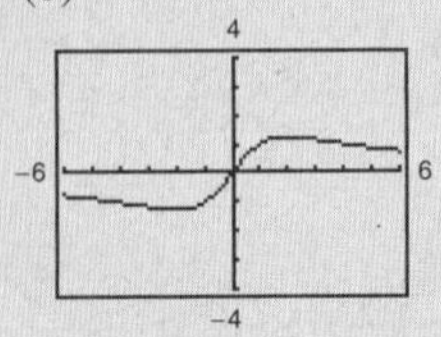

(a) $1 \le x \le 4$

(b) $-\infty < x \le 0$

60. $(-\infty, -2] \cup [2, \infty)$

61. $(-\infty, 4] \cup [5, \infty)$

71. (b) $4 \text{ sec} < t < 6 \text{ sec}$

72. (b) $0 \text{ sec} \le t < 4 - 2\sqrt{2} \text{ sec}$ and $4 + 2\sqrt{2} \text{ sec} < t \le 8 \text{ sec}$

75. $40{,}000 \le x \le 50{,}000$; $\$50.00 \le p \le \$55.00$

76. $90{,}000 \le x \le 100{,}000$; $\$30.00 \le p \le \$32.00$

77. (a) and (c)

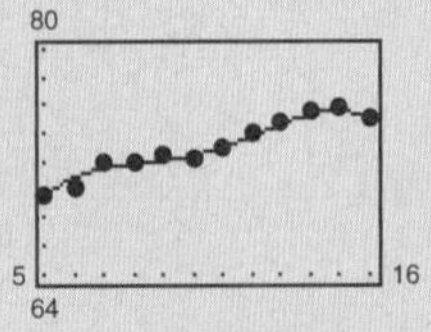

The model fits the data well.

(b) $N = -0.00412t^4 + 0.1705t^3 - 2.538t^2 + 16.55t + 31.5$

(d) 2003 to 2006

(e) No; The model decreases sharply after 2006.

78. SAFE LOAD The maximum safe load uniformly distributed over a one-foot section of a two-inch-wide wooden beam is approximated by the model Load $= 168.5d^2 - 472.1$, where d is the depth of the beam.

(a) Evaluate the model for $d = 4$, $d = 6$, $d = 8$, $d = 10$, and $d = 12$. Use the results to create a bar graph. See margin.

(b) Determine the minimum depth of the beam that will safely support a load of 2000 pounds. 3.83 in.

79. RESISTORS When two resistors of resistances R_1 and R_2 are connected in parallel (see figure), the total resistance R satisfies the equation

$$\frac{1}{R} = \frac{1}{R_1} + \frac{1}{R_2}.$$

Find R_1 for a parallel circuit in which $R_2 = 2$ ohms and R must be at least 1 ohm. $R_1 \geq 2$ ohms

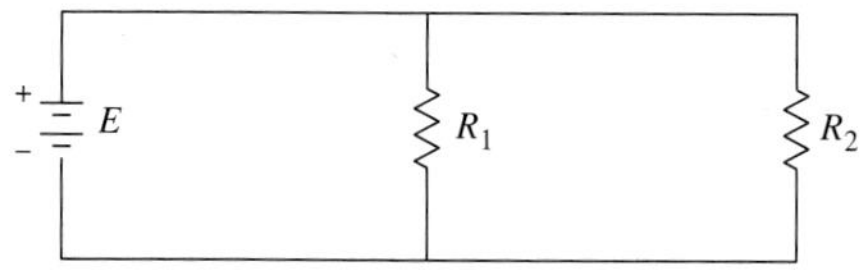

80. TEACHER SALARIES The mean salaries S (in thousands of dollars) of classroom teachers in the United States from 2000 through 2007 are shown in the table.

Year	Salary, S
2000	42.2
2001	43.7
2002	43.8
2003	45.0
2004	45.6
2005	45.9
2006	48.2
2007	49.3

A model that approximates these data is given by

$$S = \frac{42.6 - 1.95t}{1 - 0.06t}$$

where t represents the year, with $t = 0$ corresponding to 2000. (Source: Educational Research Service, Arlington, VA)

(a) Use a graphing utility to create a scatter plot of the data. Then graph the model in the same viewing window. See margin.

(b) How well does the model fit the data? Explain. The model fits the data well.

(c) According to the model, in what year will the salary for classroom teachers exceed \$60,000? 2011

(d) Is the model valid for long-term predictions of classroom teacher salaries? Explain. No; The model increases sharply after 2007.

EXPLORATION

81–82. See margin.

TRUE OR FALSE? In Exercises 81 and 82, determine whether the statement is true or false. Justify your answer.

81. The zeros of the polynomial $x^3 - 2x^2 - 11x + 12 \geq 0$ divide the real number line into four test intervals.

82. The solution set of the inequality $\frac{3}{2}x^2 + 3x + 6 \geq 0$ is the entire set of real numbers.

In Exercises 83–86, (a) find the interval(s) for b such that the equation has at least one real solution and (b) write a conjecture about the interval(s) based on the values of the coefficients. 83–86. See margin.

83. $x^2 + bx + 4 = 0$

84. $x^2 + bx - 4 = 0$

85. $3x^2 + bx + 10 = 0$

86. $2x^2 + bx + 5 = 0$

87. GRAPHICAL ANALYSIS You can use a graphing utility to verify the results in Example 4. For instance, the graph of $y = x^2 + 2x + 4$ is shown below. Notice that the y-values are greater than 0 for all values of x, as stated in Example 4(a). Use the graphing utility to graph $y = x^2 + 2x + 1$, $y = x^2 + 3x + 5$, and $y = x^2 - 4x + 4$. Explain how you can use the graphs to verify the results of parts (b), (c), and (d) of Example 4. See margin.

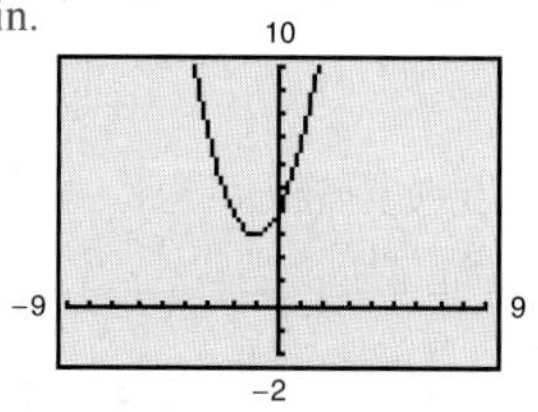

88. CAPSTONE Consider the polynomial

$(x - a)(x - b)$

and the real number line shown below.

(a) Identify the points on the line at which the polynomial is zero. $x = a$, $x = b$

(b) In each of the three subintervals of the line, write the sign of each factor and the sign of the product. See margin.

(c) At what x-values does the polynomial change signs? The real zeros of the polynomial

88. (b)

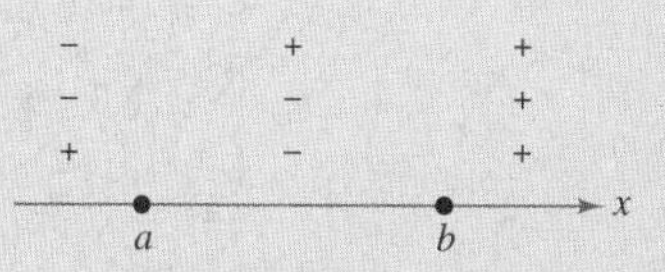

5 ASSESS AND RETEACH

Daily Homework Quiz

Transparency Available

Available at the Instructor's companion site.

80. (a)

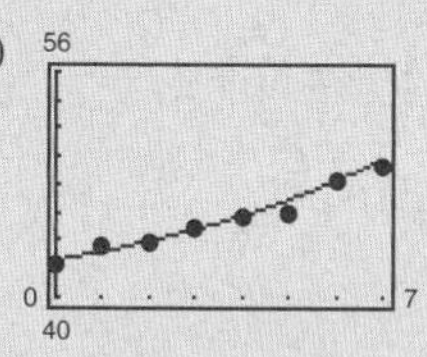

81. True. The test intervals are $(-\infty, -3)$, $(-3, 1)$, $(1, 4)$, and $(4, \infty)$.

82. True. The y-values are greater than zero for all values of x.

83. (a) $(-\infty, -4] \cup [4, \infty)$

(b) If $a > 0$ and $c > 0$, $b \leq -2\sqrt{ac}$ or $b \geq 2\sqrt{ac}$.

84. (a) $(-\infty, \infty)$

(b) If $a > 0$ and $c \leq 0$, b can be any real number.

85. (a) $\left(-\infty, -2\sqrt{30}\right] \cup \left[2\sqrt{30}, \infty\right)$

(b) If $a > 0$ and $c > 0$, $b \leq -2\sqrt{ac}$ or $b \geq 2\sqrt{ac}$.

86. (a) $\left(-\infty, -2\sqrt{10}\right] \cup \left[2\sqrt{10}, \infty\right)$

(b) If $a > 0$ and $c > 0$, $b \leq -2\sqrt{ac}$ or $b \geq 2\sqrt{ac}$.

87.

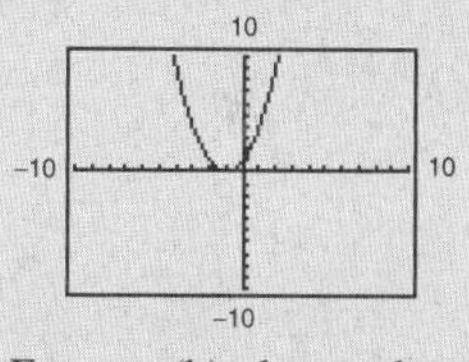

For part (b), the y-values that are less than or equal to 0 occur only at $x = -1$.

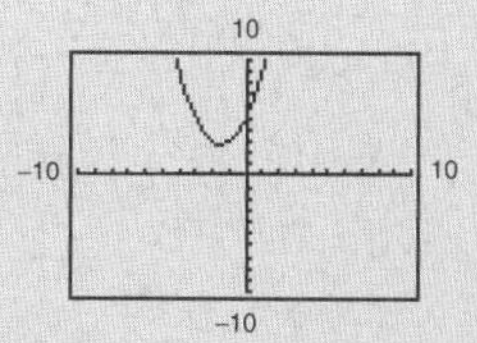

For part (c), there are no y-values that are less than 0.

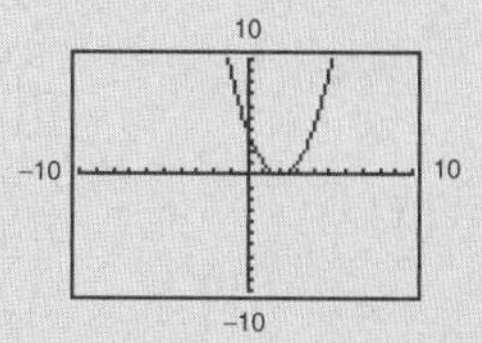

For part (d), the y-values that are greater than 0 occur for all values of x except 2.

78(a). See Additional Answers beginning on page AA1.

2 Chapter Summary

	What Did You Learn?	Explanation/Examples	Review Exercises
Section 2.1	Analyze graphs of quadratic functions *(p. 126)*.	Let a, b, and c be real numbers with $a \neq 0$. The function given by $f(x) = ax^2 + bx + c$ is called a quadratic function. Its graph is a "U-shaped" curve called a parabola.	1, 2
	Write quadratic functions in standard form and use the results to sketch graphs of functions *(p. 129)*.	The quadratic function $f(x) = a(x - h)^2 + k$, $a \neq 0$, is in standard form. The graph of f is a parabola whose axis is the vertical line $x = h$ and whose vertex is (h, k). If $a > 0$, the parabola opens upward. If $a < 0$, the parabola opens downward.	3–20
	Find minimum and maximum values of quadratic functions in real-life applications *(p. 131)*.	Consider $f(x) = ax^2 + bx + c$ with vertex $\left(-\frac{b}{2a}, f\left(\frac{b}{2a}\right)\right)$. If $a > 0$, f has a *minimum* at $x = -b/(2a)$. If $a < 0$, f has a *maximum* at $x = -b/(2a)$.	21–24
Section 2.2	Use transformations to sketch graphs of polynomial functions *(p. 136)*.	The graph of a polynomial function is continuous (no breaks, holes, or gaps) and has only smooth, rounded turns.	25–30
	Use the Leading Coefficient Test to determine the end behavior of graphs of polynomial functions *(p. 138)*.	Consider the graph of $f(x) = a_nx^n + \cdot \cdot \cdot + a_1x + a_0$. **When n is odd:** If $a_n > 0$, the graph falls to the left and rises to the right. If $a_n < 0$, the graph rises to the left and falls to the right. **When n is even:** If $a_n > 0$, the graph rises to the left and right. If $a_n < 0$, the graph falls to the left and right.	31–34
	Find and use zeros of polynomial functions as sketching aids *(p. 139)*.	If f is a polynomial function and a is a real number, the following are equivalent: (1) $x = a$ is a *zero* of f, (2) $x = a$ is a *solution* of the equation $f(x) = 0$, (3) $(x - a)$ is a *factor* of $f(x)$, and (4) $(a, 0)$ is an *x-intercept* of the graph of f.	35–44
	Use the Intermediate Value Theorem to help locate zeros of polynomial functions *(p. 143)*.	Let a and b be real numbers such that $a < b$. If f is a polynomial function such that $f(a) \neq f(b)$, then, in $[a, b]$, f takes on every value between $f(a)$ and $f(b)$.	45–48
Section 2.3	Use long division to divide polynomials by other polynomials *(p. 150)*.	Dividend → $x^2 + 3x + 5$; Divisor → $x + 1$; Quotient → $x + 2$; Remainder → 3; Divisor → $x + 1$ $\frac{x^2 + 3x + 5}{x + 1} = x + 2 + \frac{3}{x + 1}$	49–54
	Use synthetic division to divide polynomials by binomials of the form $(x - k)$ *(p. 153)*.	Divisor: $x + 3$ Dividend: $x^4 - 10x^2 - 2x + 4$ -3 | 1 0 −10 −2 4 −3 9 3 −3 1 −3 −1 1 (1) ← Remainder: 1 Quotient: $x^3 - 3x^2 - x + 1$	55–60
	Use the Remainder Theorem and the Factor Theorem *(p. 154)*.	**The Remainder Theorem:** If a polynomial $f(x)$ is divided by $x - k$, the remainder is $r = f(k)$. **The Factor Theorem:** A polynomial $f(x)$ has a factor $(x - k)$ if and only if $f(k) = 0$.	61–66
Section 2.4	Use the imaginary unit i to write complex numbers *(p. 159)*.	If a and b are real numbers, $a + bi$ is a complex number. Two complex numbers $a + bi$ and $c + di$, written in standard form, are equal to each other if and only if $a = c$ and $b = d$.	67–70

Section	What Did You Learn?	Explanation/Examples	Review Exercises
Section 2.4	Add, subtract, and multiply complex numbers *(p. 160)*.	**Sum:** $(a + bi) + (c + di) = (a + c) + (b + d)i$ **Difference:** $(a + bi) - (c + di) = (a - c) + (b - d)i$	71–78
	Use complex conjugates to write the quotient of two complex numbers in standard form *(p. 162)*.	The numbers $a + bi$ and $a - bi$ are complex conjugates. To write $(a + bi)/(c + di)$ in standard form, multiply the numerator and denominator by $c - di$.	79–82
	Find complex solutions of quadratic equations *(p. 163)*.	If a is a positive number, the principal square root of the negative number $-a$ is defined as $\sqrt{-a} = \sqrt{a}i$.	83–86
Section 2.5	Use the Fundamental Theorem of Algebra to find the number of zeros of polynomial functions *(p. 166)*.	**The Fundamental Theorem of Algebra** If $f(x)$ is a polynomial of degree n, where $n > 0$, then f has at least one zero in the complex number system.	87–92
	Find rational zeros of polynomial functions *(p. 167)*, and conjugate pairs of complex zeros *(p. 170)*.	The Rational Zero Test relates the possible rational zeros of a polynomial to the leading coefficient and to the constant term of the polynomial. Let $f(x)$ be a polynomial function that has real coefficients. If $a + bi$ $(b \neq 0)$ is a zero of the function, the conjugate $a - bi$ is also a zero of the function.	93–102
	Find zeros of polynomials by factoring *(p. 170)*.	Every polynomial of degree $n > 0$ with real coefficients can be written as the product of linear and quadratic factors with real coefficients, where the quadratic factors have no real zeros.	103–110
	Use Descartes's Rule of Signs *(p. 173)* and the Upper and Lower Bound Rules *(p. 174)* to find zeros of polynomials.	**Descartes's Rule of Signs** Let $f(x) = a_nx^n + a_{n-1}x^{n-1} + \cdot \cdot \cdot + a_2x^2 + a_1x + a_0$ be a polynomial with real coefficients and $a_0 \neq 0$. **1.** The number of *positive real zeros* of f is either equal to the number of variations in sign of $f(x)$ or less than that number by an even integer. **2.** The number of *negative real zeros* of f is either equal to the number of variations in sign of $f(-x)$ or less than that number by an even integer.	111–114
Section 2.6	Find the domains *(p. 181)*, and vertical and horizontal asymptotes *(p. 182)* of rational functions.	The domain of a rational function of x includes all real numbers except x-values that make the denominator zero. The line $x = a$ is a vertical asymptote of the graph of f if $f(x) \rightarrow \infty$ or $f(x) \rightarrow -\infty$ as $x \rightarrow a$, either from the right or from the left. The line $y = b$ is a horizontal asymptote of the graph of f if $f(x) \rightarrow b$ as $x \rightarrow \infty$. or $x \rightarrow -\infty$.	115–122
	Analyze and sketch graphs of rational functions *(p. 184)* including functions with slant asymptotes *(p. 187)*.	Consider a rational function whose denominator is of degree 1 or greater. If the degree of the numerator is exactly *one more* than the degree of the denominator, the graph of the function has a slant asymptote.	123–138
	Use rational functions to model and solve real-life problems *(p. 188)*.	A rational function can be used to model the cost of removing a given percent of smokestack pollutants at a utility company that burns coal. (See Example 8.)	139–142
Section 2.7	Solve polynomial *(p. 194)* and rational inequalities *(p. 198)*.	Use the concepts of key numbers and test intervals to solve both polynomial and rational inequalities.	143–150
	Use inequalities to model and solve real-life problems *(p. 199)*.	A common application of inequalities involves profit P, revenue R, and cost C. (See Example 6.)	151, 152

2 REVIEW EXERCISES

See www.CalcChat.com for worked-out solutions to odd-numbered exercises.

2.1 In Exercises 1 and 2, graph each function. Compare the graph of each function with the graph of $y = x^2$.

1. (a) $f(x) = 2x^2$ 1–2. See margin.
 (b) $g(x) = -2x^2$
 (c) $h(x) = x^2 + 2$
 (d) $k(x) = (x + 2)^2$
2. (a) $f(x) = x^2 - 4$
 (b) $g(x) = 4 - x^2$
 (c) $h(x) = (x - 3)^2$
 (d) $k(x) = \frac{1}{2}x^2 - 1$

In Exercises 3–14, write the quadratic function in standard form and sketch its graph. Identify the vertex, axis of symmetry, and x-intercept(s). 3–14. See margin.

3. $g(x) = x^2 - 2x$
4. $f(x) = 6x - x^2$
5. $f(x) = x^2 + 8x + 10$
6. $h(x) = 3 + 4x - x^2$
7. $f(t) = -2t^2 + 4t + 1$
8. $f(x) = x^2 - 8x + 12$
9. $h(x) = 4x^2 + 4x + 13$
10. $f(x) = x^2 - 6x + 1$
11. $h(x) = x^2 + 5x - 4$
12. $f(x) = 4x^2 + 4x + 5$
13. $f(x) = \frac{1}{3}(x^2 + 5x - 4)$
14. $f(x) = \frac{1}{2}(6x^2 - 24x + 22)$

In Exercises 15–20, write the standard form of the equation of the parabola that has the indicated vertex and whose graph passes through the given point.

15. See margin.

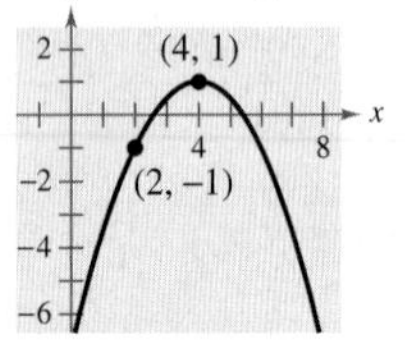

16. $f(x) = \frac{1}{4}(x - 2)^2 + 2$

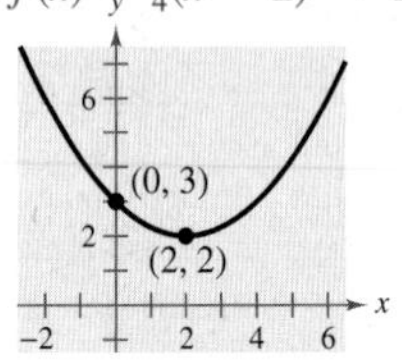

17. Vertex: $(1, -4)$; point: $(2, -3)$ $f(x) = (x - 1)^2 - 4$
18. Vertex: $(2, 3)$; point: $(-1, 6)$ $f(x) = \frac{1}{3}(x - 2)^2 + 3$
19. Vertex: $\left(-\frac{3}{2}, 0\right)$; point: $\left(-\frac{9}{2}, -\frac{11}{4}\right)$ $y = -\frac{11}{36}\left(x + \frac{3}{2}\right)^2$
20. Vertex: $(3, 3)$; point: $\left(\frac{1}{4}, \frac{4}{5}\right)$ $y = -\frac{16}{55}(x - 3)^2 + 3$

21. **GEOMETRY** The perimeter of a rectangle is 1000 meters.
 (a) Draw a diagram that gives a visual representation of the problem. Label the length and width as x and y, respectively. See margin.
 (b) Write y as a function of x. Use the result to write the area as a function of x. See margin.
 (c) Of all possible rectangles with perimeters of 1000 meters, find the dimensions of the one with the maximum area. $x = 250$, $y = 250$
22. **MAXIMUM REVENUE** The total revenue R earned (in dollars) from producing a gift box of candles is given by

 $$R(p) = -10p^2 + 800p$$

 where p is the price per unit (in dollars).
 (a) Find the revenues when the prices per box are \$20, \$25, and \$30. \$12,000; \$13,750; \$15,000
 (b) Find the unit price that will yield a maximum revenue. What is the maximum revenue? Explain your results. See margin.
23. **MINIMUM COST** A soft-drink manufacturer has daily production costs of

 $$C = 70{,}000 - 120x + 0.055x^2$$

 where C is the total cost (in dollars) and x is the number of units produced. How many units should be produced each day to yield a minimum cost? 1091 units
24. **SOCIOLOGY** The average age of the groom at a first marriage for a given age of the bride can be approximated by the model

 $$y = -0.107x^2 + 5.68x - 48.5, \quad 20 \le x \le 25$$

 where y is the age of the groom and x is the age of the bride. Sketch a graph of the model. For what age of the bride is the average age of the groom 26? (Source: U.S. Census Bureau) See margin.

2.2 In Exercises 25–30, sketch the graphs of $y = x^n$ and the transformation. 25–30. See margin.

25. $y = x^3$, $f(x) = -(x - 2)^3$
26. $y = x^3$, $f(x) = -4x^3$
27. $y = x^4$, $f(x) = 6 - x^4$
28. $y = x^4$, $f(x) = 2(x - 8)^4$
29. $y = x^5$, $f(x) = (x - 5)^5$
30. $y = x^5$, $f(x) = \frac{1}{2}x^5 + 3$

1. (a)

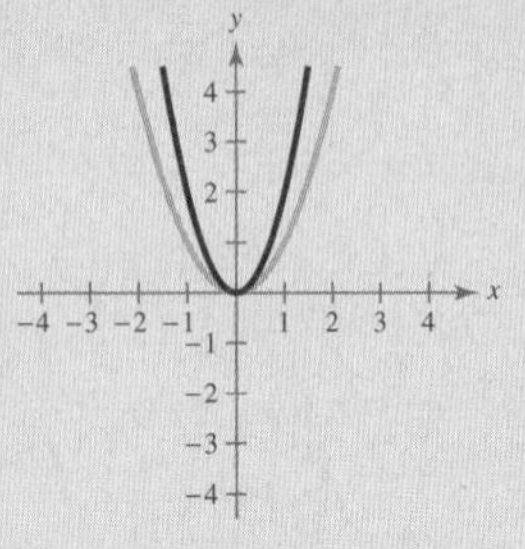

Vertical stretch

(b)

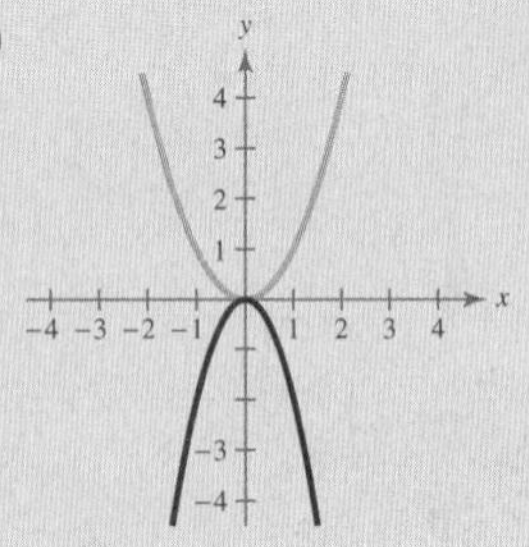

Vertical stretch and reflection in the x-axis

(c)

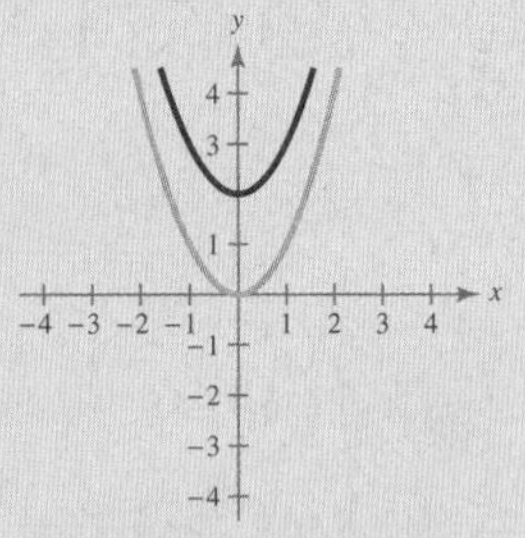

Vertical shift two units upward

(d)

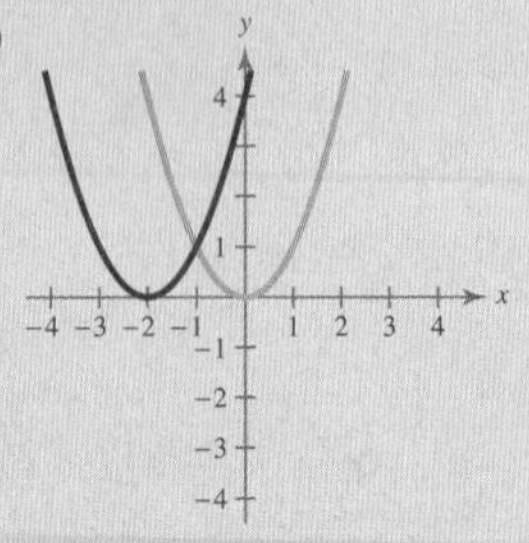

Horizontal shift two units to the left

2. (a)

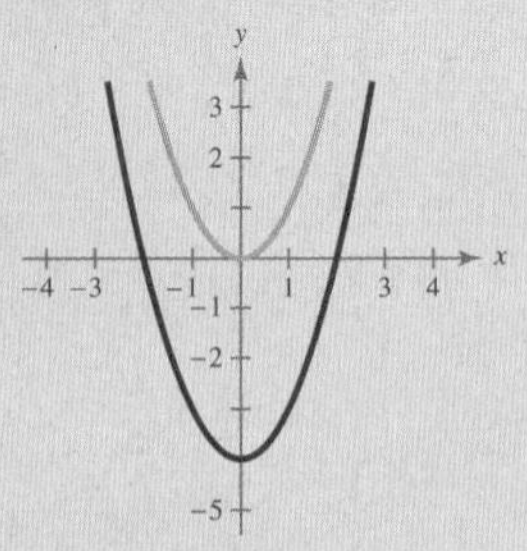

Vertical shift four units downward

(b)

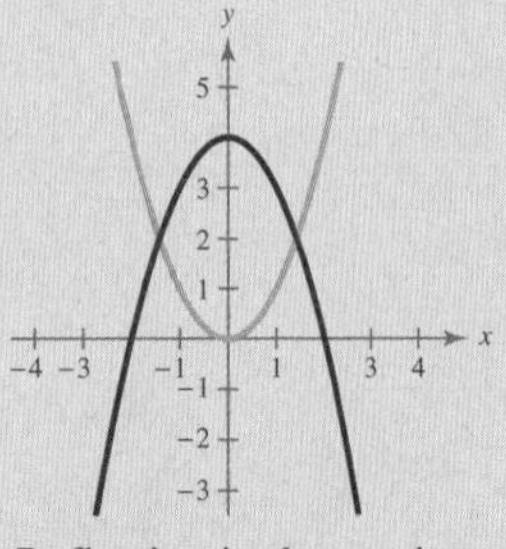

Reflection in the x-axis and vertical shift four units upward

(c)

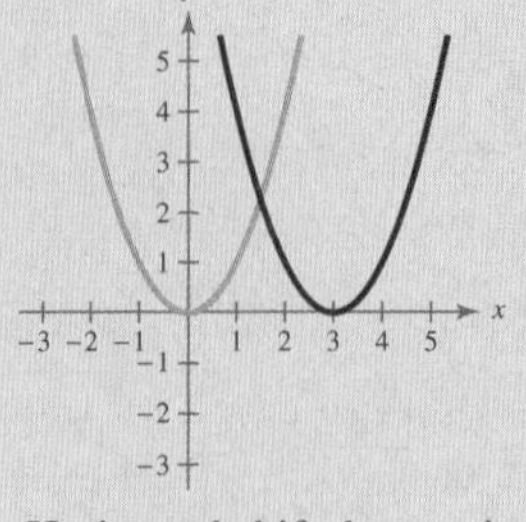

Horizontal shift three units to the right

(d)

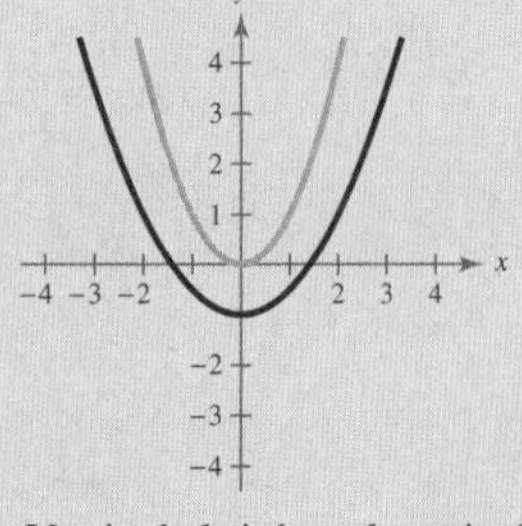

Vertical shrink and vertical shift one unit downward

3–15, 21(a)–(b), 22(b), 24–30. See Additional Answers beginning on page AA1.

In Exercises 31–34, describe the right-hand and left-hand behavior of the graph of the polynomial function.

31. $f(x) = -2x^2 - 5x + 12$ Falls to the left, falls to the right

32. $f(x) = \frac{1}{2}x^3 + 2x$ Falls to the left, rises to the right

33. $g(x) = \frac{3}{4}(x^4 + 3x^2 + 2)$ Rises to the left, rises to the right

34. $h(x) = -x^7 + 8x^2 - 8x$ Rises to the left, falls to the right

In Exercises 35–40, find all the real zeros of the polynomial function. Determine the multiplicity of each zero and the number of turning points of the graph of the function. Use a graphing utility to verify your answers. 35–40. See margin.

35. $f(x) = 3x^2 + 20x - 32$ **36.** $f(x) = x(x + 3)^2$

37. $f(t) = t^3 - 3t$ **38.** $f(x) = x^3 - 8x^2$

39. $f(x) = -18x^3 + 12x^2$ **40.** $g(x) = x^4 + x^3 - 12x^2$

In Exercises 41–44, sketch the graph of the function by (a) applying the Leading Coefficient Test, (b) finding the zeros of the polynomial, (c) plotting sufficient solution points, and (d) drawing a continuous curve through the points. 41–44. See margin.

41. $f(x) = -x^3 + x^2 - 2$

42. $g(x) = 2x^3 + 4x^2$

43. $f(x) = x(x^3 + x^2 - 5x + 3)$

44. $h(x) = 3x^2 - x^4$

In Exercises 45–48, (a) use the Intermediate Value Theorem and the *table* feature of a graphing utility to find intervals one unit in length in which the polynomial function is guaranteed to have a zero. (b) Adjust the table to approximate the zeros of the function. Use the *zero* or *root* feature of the graphing utility to verify your results. 45–48. See margin.

45. $f(x) = 3x^3 - x^2 + 3$

46. $f(x) = 0.25x^3 - 3.65x + 6.12$

47. $f(x) = x^4 - 5x - 1$

48. $f(x) = 7x^4 + 3x^3 - 8x^2 + 2$

2.3 In Exercises 49–54, use long division to divide. 49–50. See margin.

49. $\dfrac{30x^2 - 3x + 8}{5x - 3}$ **50.** $\dfrac{4x + 7}{3x - 2}$

51. $\dfrac{5x^3 - 21x^2 - 25x - 4}{x^2 - 5x - 1}$ $5x + 4,\ x \neq \dfrac{5}{2} \pm \dfrac{\sqrt{29}}{2}$

52. $\dfrac{3x^4}{x^2 - 1}$ $3x^2 + 3 + \dfrac{3}{x^2 - 1}$

53. $\dfrac{x^4 - 3x^3 + 4x^2 - 6x + 3}{x^2 + 2}$ $x^2 - 3x + 2 - \dfrac{1}{x^2 + 2}$

54. $\dfrac{6x^4 + 10x^3 + 13x^2 - 5x + 2}{2x^2 - 1}$ $3x^2 + 5x + 8 + \dfrac{10}{2x^2 - 1}$

In Exercises 55–58, use synthetic division to divide. 55–56. See margin.

55. $\dfrac{6x^4 - 4x^3 - 27x^2 + 18x}{x - 2}$ **56.** $\dfrac{0.1x^3 + 0.3x^2 - 0.5}{x - 5}$

57. $\dfrac{2x^3 - 25x^2 + 66x + 48}{x - 8}$ $2x^2 - 9x - 6,\ x \neq 8$

58. $\dfrac{5x^3 + 33x^2 + 50x - 8}{x + 4}$ $5x^2 + 13x - 2,\ x \neq -4$

In Exercises 59 and 60, use synthetic division to determine whether the given values of x are zeros of the function.

59. $f(x) = 20x^4 + 9x^3 - 14x^2 - 3x$

(a) $x = -1$ (b) $x = \frac{3}{4}$ (c) $x = 0$ (d) $x = 1$

(a) Yes (b) Yes (c) Yes (d) No

60. $f(x) = 3x^3 - 8x^2 - 20x + 16$

(a) $x = 4$ (b) $x = -4$ (c) $x = \frac{2}{3}$ (d) $x = -1$

(a) Yes (b) No (c) Yes (d) No

In Exercises 61 and 62, use the Remainder Theorem and synthetic division to find each function value.

61. $f(x) = x^4 + 10x^3 - 24x^2 + 20x + 44$

(a) $f(-3)$ (b) $f(-1)$ (a) -421 (b) -9

62. $g(t) = 2t^5 - 5t^4 - 8t + 20$

(a) $g(-4)$ (b) $g(\sqrt{2})$ (a) -3276 (b) 0

In Exercises 63–66, (a) verify the given factor(s) of the function f, (b) find the remaining factors of f, (c) use your results to write the complete factorization of f, (d) list all real zeros of f, and (e) confirm your results by using a graphing utility to graph the function. 63–66. See margin.

	Function	*Factor(s)*
63.	$f(x) = x^3 + 4x^2 - 25x - 28$	$(x - 4)$
64.	$f(x) = 2x^3 + 11x^2 - 21x - 90$	$(x + 6)$
65.	$f(x) = x^4 - 4x^3 - 7x^2 + 22x + 24$	$(x + 2)(x - 3)$
66.	$f(x) = x^4 - 11x^3 + 41x^2 - 61x + 30$	$(x - 2)(x - 5)$

2.4 In Exercises 67–70, write the complex number in standard form.

67. $8 + \sqrt{-100}$ $8 + 10i$ **68.** $5 - \sqrt{-49}$ $5 - 7i$

69. $i^2 + 3i$ $-1 + 3i$ **70.** $-5i + i^2$ $-1 - 5i$

In Exercises 71–78, perform the operation and write the result in standard form.

71. $(7 + 5i) + (-4 + 2i)$ $3 + 7i$

72. $\left(\dfrac{\sqrt{2}}{2} - \dfrac{\sqrt{2}}{2}i\right) - \left(\dfrac{\sqrt{2}}{2} + \dfrac{\sqrt{2}}{2}i\right)$ $-\sqrt{2}i$

73. $7i(11 - 9i)$ $63 + 77i$ **74.** $(1 + 6i)(5 - 2i)$ $17 + 28i$

75. $(10 - 8i)(2 - 3i)$ $-4 - 46i$ **76.** $i(6 + i)(3 - 2i)$ $9 + 20i$

77. $(8 - 5i)^2$ $39 - 80i$

78. $(4 + 7i)^2 + (4 - 7i)^2$ -66

35. $-8, \frac{4}{3}$, odd multiplicity; turning points: 1

36. 0, odd multiplicity; -3, even multiplicity; turning points: 2

37. $0, \pm\sqrt{3}$, odd multiplicity; turning points: 2

38. 8, odd multiplicity; 0, even multiplicity; turning points: 2

39. 0, even multiplicity; $\frac{2}{3}$, odd multiplicity; turning points: 2

40. $-4, 3$, odd multiplicity; 0, even multiplicity; turning points: 3

41. (a) Rises to the left, falls to the right
(b) -1
(c) Answers will vary.
(d)

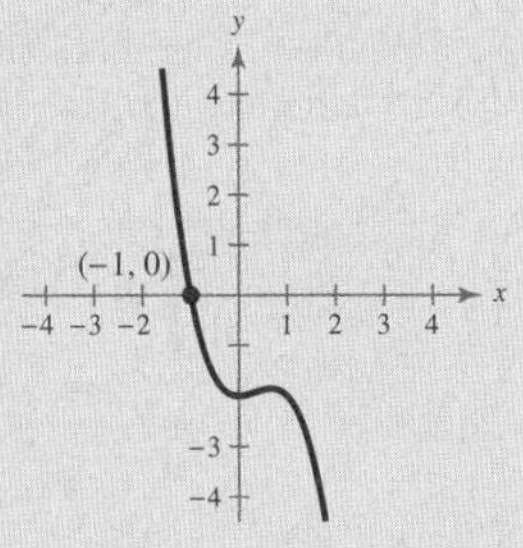

42. (a) Falls to the left, rises to the right
(b) $-2, 0$
(c) Answers will vary.
(d)

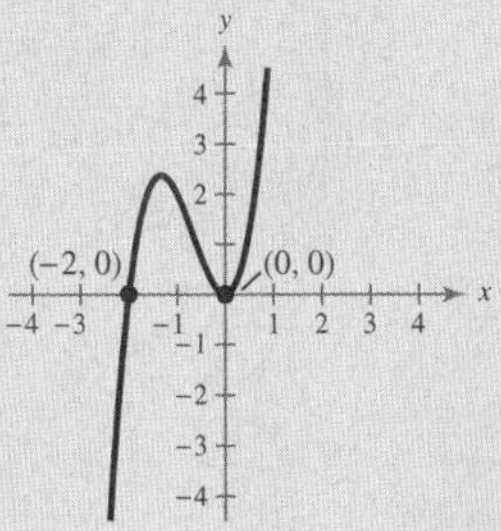

43. (a) Rises to the left, rises to the right
(b) $-3, 0, 1$
(c) Answers will vary.
(d)

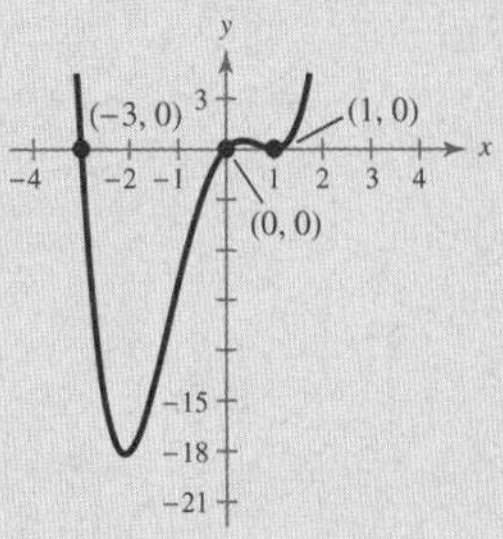

44. (a) Falls to the left, falls to the right
(b) $0, \pm\sqrt{3}$
(c) Answers will vary.

44. (d)

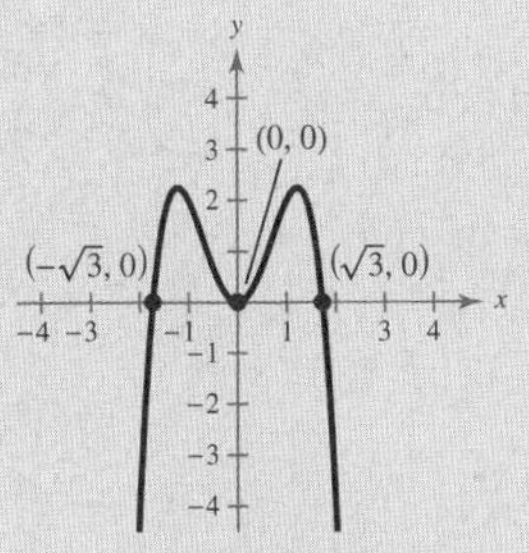

45. (a) $[-1, 0]$ (b) About -0.900

46. (a) $[-5, -4]$ (b) About -4.479

47. (a) $[-1, 0], [1, 2]$
(b) About -0.200, about 1.772

48. (a) $[-2, -1], [-1, 0]$
(b) About -0.509, about -1.211

49. $6x + 3 + \dfrac{17}{5x - 3}$

50. $\dfrac{4}{3} + \dfrac{29}{3(3x - 2)}$

55. $6x^3 + 8x^2 - 11x - 4 - \dfrac{8}{x - 2}$

56, 63–66. See Additional Answers beginning on page AA1.

In Exercises 79 and 80, write the quotient in standard form.

79. $\dfrac{6+i}{4-i}$ $\frac{23}{17}+\frac{10}{17}i$ **80.** $\dfrac{8-5i}{i}$ $-5-8i$

In Exercises 81 and 82, perform the operation and write the result in standard form.

81. $\dfrac{4}{2-3i}+\dfrac{2}{1+i}$ $\frac{21}{13}-\frac{1}{13}i$ **82.** $\dfrac{1}{2+i}-\dfrac{5}{1+4i}$ $\frac{9}{85}+\frac{83}{85}i$

In Exercises 83–86, find all solutions of the equation.

83. $5x^2+2=0$ See margin. **84.** $2+8x^2=0$ $\pm\frac{1}{2}i$

85. $x^2-2x+10=0$ $1\pm 3i$ **86.** $6x^2+3x+27=0$ See margin.

2.5 In Exercises 87–92, find all the zeros of the function.

87. $f(x)=4x(x-3)^2$ $0, 3$

88. $f(x)=(x-4)(x+9)^2$ $-9, 4$

89. $f(x)=x^2-11x+18$ $2, 9$

90. $f(x)=x^3+10x$ $0, \pm\sqrt{10}i$

91. $f(x)=(x+4)(x-6)(x-2i)(x+2i)$ $-4, 6, \pm 2i$

92. $f(x)=(x-8)(x-5)^2(x-3+i)(x-3-i)$ $5, 8, 3\pm i$

In Exercises 93 and 94, use the Rational Zero Test to list all possible rational zeros of f.

93. $f(x)=-4x^3+8x^2-3x+15$ $\pm1, \pm3, \pm5, \pm15, \pm\frac{1}{2}, \pm\frac{3}{2}, \pm\frac{5}{2}, \pm\frac{15}{2}, \pm\frac{1}{4}, \pm\frac{3}{4}, \pm\frac{5}{4}, \pm\frac{15}{4}$

94. $f(x)=3x^4+4x^3-5x^2-8$ $\pm1, \pm2, \pm4, \pm8, \pm\frac{1}{3}, \pm\frac{2}{3}, \pm\frac{4}{3}, \pm\frac{8}{3}$

In Exercises 95–100, find all the rational zeros of the function.

95. $f(x)=x^3+3x^2-28x-60$ $-6, -2, 5$

96. $f(x)=4x^3-27x^2+11x+42$ $-1, \frac{7}{4}, 6$

97. $f(x)=x^3-10x^2+17x-8$ $1, 8$

98. $f(x)=x^3+9x^2+24x+20$ $-5, -2$

99. $f(x)=x^4+x^3-11x^2+x-12$ $-4, 3$

100. $f(x)=25x^4+25x^3-154x^2-4x+24$ $-3, 2, \pm\frac{2}{5}$

In Exercises 101 and 102, find a polynomial function with real coefficients that has the given zeros. (There are many correct answers.)

101. $\frac{2}{3}, 4, \sqrt{3}i$ $f(x)=3x^4-14x^3+17x^2-42x+24$ **102.** $2, -3, 1-2i$ $f(x)=x^4-x^3-3x^2+17x-30$

In Exercises 103–106, use the given zero to find all the zeros of the function.

Function		Zero
103. $f(x)=x^3-4x^2+x-4$	$4, \pm i$	i
104. $h(x)=-x^3+2x^2-16x+32$	$2, \pm 4i$	$-4i$
105. $g(x)=2x^4-3x^3-13x^2+37x-15$		$2+i$
106. $f(x)=4x^4-11x^3+14x^2-6x$		$1-i$

105. $-3, \frac{1}{2}, 2\pm i$ 106. $0, \frac{3}{4}, 1\pm i$

In Exercises 107–110, find all the zeros of the function and write the polynomial as a product of linear factors.

107. $f(x)=x^3+4x^2-5x$ 107–110. See margin.

108. $g(x)=x^3-7x^2+36$

109. $g(x)=x^4+4x^3-3x^2+40x+208$

110. $f(x)=x^4+8x^3+8x^2-72x-153$

In Exercises 111 and 112, use Descartes's Rule of Signs to determine the possible numbers of positive and negative zeros of the function. 111–112. See margin.

111. $g(x)=5x^3+3x^2-6x+9$

112. $h(x)=-2x^5+4x^3-2x^2+5$

In Exercises 113 and 114, use synthetic division to verify the upper and lower bounds of the real zeros of f.

113. $f(x)=4x^3-3x^2+4x-3$ Answers will vary.

(a) Upper: $x=1$ (b) Lower: $x=-\frac{1}{4}$

114. $f(x)=2x^3-5x^2-14x+8$ Answers will vary.

(a) Upper: $x=8$ (b) Lower: $x=-4$

2.6 In Exercises 115–118, find the domain of the rational function. 115–118. See margin.

115. $f(x)=\dfrac{3x}{x+10}$ **116.** $f(x)=\dfrac{4x^3}{2+5x}$

117. $f(x)=\dfrac{8}{x^2-10x+24}$ **118.** $f(x)=\dfrac{x^2+x-2}{x^2+4}$

In Exercises 119–122, identify any vertical or horizontal asymptotes. 119–122. See margin.

119. $f(x)=\dfrac{4}{x+3}$ **120.** $f(x)=\dfrac{2x^2+5x-3}{x^2+2}$

121. $h(x)=\dfrac{5x+20}{x^2-2x-24}$ **122.** $h(x)=\dfrac{x^3-4x^2}{x^2+3x+2}$

In Exercises 123–134, (a) state the domain of the function, (b) identify all intercepts, (c) find any vertical and horizontal asymptotes, and (d) plot additional solution points as needed to sketch the graph of the rational function.

123. $f(x)=\dfrac{-3}{2x^2}$ **124.** $f(x)=\dfrac{4}{x}$

125. $g(x)=\dfrac{2+x}{1-x}$ **126.** $h(x)=\dfrac{x-4}{x-7}$

127. $p(x)=\dfrac{5x^2}{4x^2+1}$ **128.** $f(x)=\dfrac{2x}{x^2+4}$

129. $f(x)=\dfrac{x}{x^2+1}$ **130.** $h(x)=\dfrac{9}{(x-3)^2}$

123–130. See margin.

83. $\pm\dfrac{\sqrt{10}}{5}i$

86. $-\dfrac{1}{4}\pm\dfrac{\sqrt{71}}{4}i$

107. $0, 1, -5$; $f(x)=x(x-1)(x+5)$

111. Two or no positive zeros, one negative zero

112. One or three positive zeros, two or no negative zeros

115. Domain: all real numbers x except $x=-10$

116. Domain: all real numbers x except $x=-\frac{2}{5}$

117. Domain: all real numbers x except $x=6, 4$

118. Domain: all real numbers x

119. Vertical asymptote: $x=-3$ Horizontal asymptote: $y=0$

120. Horizontal asymptote: $y=2$

121. Vertical asymptote: $x=6$ Horizontal asymptote: $y=0$

122. Vertical asymptotes: $x=-2, -1$

123. (a) Domain: all real numbers x except $x=0$

(b) No intercepts

(c) Vertical asymptote: $x=0$ Horizontal asymptote: $y=0$

(d)

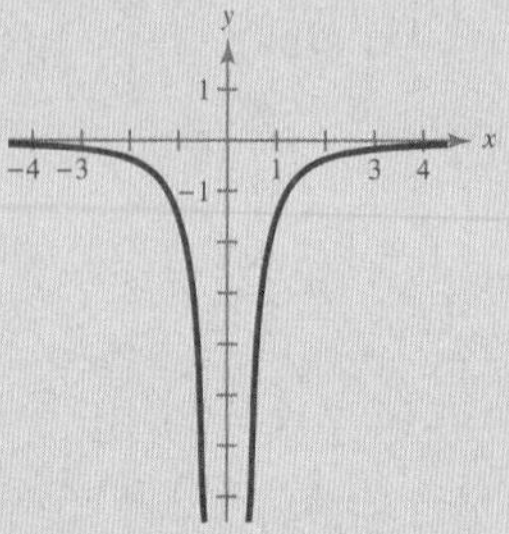

124. (a) Domain: all real numbers x except $x=0$

(b) No intercepts

(c) Vertical asymptote: $x=0$ Horizontal asymptote: $y=0$

(d)

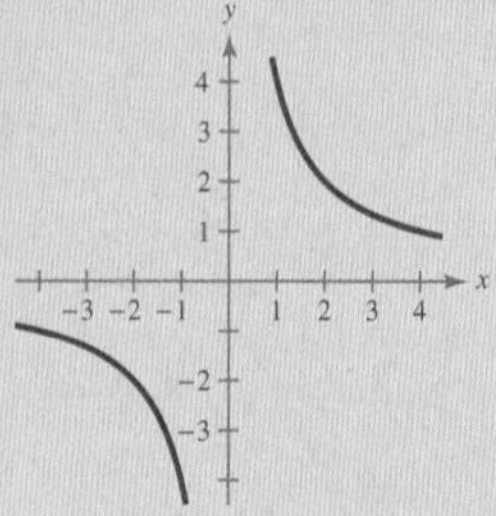

125. (a) Domain: all real numbers x except $x=1$

(b) x-intercept: $(-2, 0)$ y-intercept: $(0, 2)$

(c) Vertical asymptote: $x=1$ Horizontal asymptote: $y=-1$

(d)

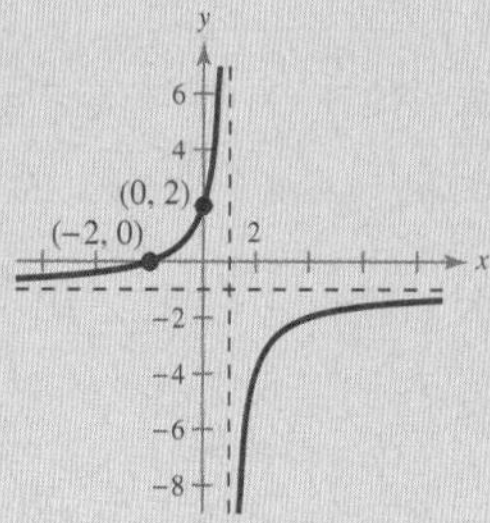

126. (a) Domain: all real numbers x except $x=7$

(b) x-intercept: $(4, 0)$ y-intercept: $\left(0, \frac{4}{7}\right)$

(c) Vertical asymptote: $x=7$ Horizontal asymptote: $y=1$

108–110, 126(d), 127–130. See Additional Answers beginning on page AA1.

131–134. See margin.

131. $f(x) = \dfrac{-6x^2}{x^2+1}$ **132.** $f(x) = \dfrac{2x^2}{x^2-4}$

133. $f(x) = \dfrac{6x^2-11x+3}{3x^2-x}$ **134.** $f(x) = \dfrac{6x^2-7x+2}{4x^2-1}$

In Exercises 135–138, (a) state the domain of the function, (b) identify all intercepts, (c) identify any vertical and slant asymptotes, and (d) plot additional solution points as needed to sketch the graph of the rational function.

135–138. See margin.

135. $f(x) = \dfrac{2x^3}{x^2+1}$ **136.** $f(x) = \dfrac{x^2+1}{x+1}$

137. $f(x) = \dfrac{3x^3-2x^2-3x+2}{3x^2-x-4}$

138. $f(x) = \dfrac{3x^3-4x^2-12x+16}{3x^2+5x-2}$

139. AVERAGE COST A business has a production cost of $C = 0.5x + 500$ for producing x units of a product. The average cost per unit, $\overline{C}$, is given by

$$\overline{C} = \frac{C}{x} = \frac{0.5x+500}{x}, \quad x > 0.$$

$\overline{C} = 0.5 = \$0.50$

Determine the average cost per unit as x increases without bound. (Find the horizontal asymptote.)

140. SEIZURE OF ILLEGAL DRUGS The cost C (in millions of dollars) for the federal government to seize $p\%$ of an illegal drug as it enters the country is given by

$$C = \frac{528p}{100-p}, \quad 0 \le p < 100.$$ See margin.

(a) Use a graphing utility to graph the cost function.

(b) Find the costs of seizing 25%, 50%, and 75% of the drug.

(c) According to this model, would it be possible to seize 100% of the drug?

141. PAGE DESIGN A page that is x inches wide and y inches high contains 30 square inches of print. The top and bottom margins are 2 inches deep and the margins on each side are 2 inches wide. See margin.

(a) Draw a diagram that gives a visual representation of the problem.

(b) Write a function for the total area A of the page in terms of x.

(c) Determine the domain of the function based on the physical constraints of the problem.

(d) Use a graphing utility to graph the area function and approximate the page size for which the least amount of paper will be used. Verify your answer numerically using the *table* feature of the graphing utility.

142. PHOTOSYNTHESIS The amount y of CO_2 uptake (in milligrams per square decimeter per hour) at optimal temperatures and with the natural supply of CO_2 is approximated by the model

$$y = \frac{18.47x - 2.96}{0.23x + 1}, \quad x > 0$$ See margin.

where x is the light intensity (in watts per square meter). Use a graphing utility to graph the function and determine the limiting amount of CO_2 uptake.

2.7 In Exercises 143–150, solve the inequality.

143. $12x^2 + 5x < 2$ $\left(-\frac{2}{3}, \frac{1}{4}\right)$ **144.** $3x^2 + x \ge 24$

145. $x^3 - 16x \ge 0$ **146.** $12x^3 - 20x^2 < 0$

144–148. See margin.

147. $\dfrac{2}{x+1} \le \dfrac{3}{x-1}$ **148.** $\dfrac{x-5}{3-x} < 0$

149. $\dfrac{x^2-9x+20}{x} \le 0$ $(-\infty, 0) \cup [4, 5]$ **150.** $\dfrac{1}{x-2} > \dfrac{1}{x}$ $(-\infty, 0) \cup (2, \infty)$

151. INVESTMENT P dollars invested at interest rate r compounded annually increases to an amount

$$A = P(1+r)^2$$

in 2 years. An investment of \$5000 is to increase to an amount greater than \$5500 in 2 years. The interest rate must be greater than what percent? 4.9%

152. POPULATION OF A SPECIES A biologist introduces 200 ladybugs into a crop field. The population P of the ladybugs is approximated by the model

$$P = \frac{1000(1+3t)}{5+t}$$ 9 days

where t is the time in days. Find the time required for the population to increase to at least 2000 ladybugs.

EXPLORATION

153–154. See margin.

TRUE OR FALSE? In Exercises 153 and 154, determine whether the statement is true or false. Justify your answer.

153. A fourth-degree polynomial with real coefficients can have -5, $-8i$, $4i$, and 5 as its zeros.

154. The domain of a rational function can never be the set of all real numbers.

155. WRITING Explain how to determine the maximum or minimum value of a quadratic function. See margin.

156. WRITING Explain the connections among factors of a polynomial, zeros of a polynomial function, and solutions of a polynomial equation. See margin.

157. WRITING Describe what is meant by an asymptote of a graph. See margin.

131. (a) Domain: all real numbers x
(b) Intercept: $(0, 0)$
(c) Horizontal asymptote: $y = -6$
(d)

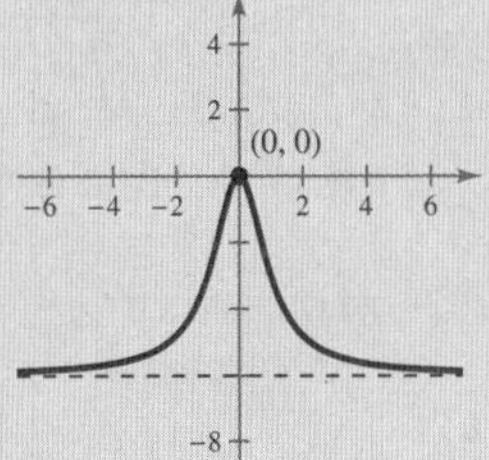

132. (a) Domain: all real numbers x except $x = \pm 2$
(b) Intercept: $(0, 0)$
(c) Vertical asymptotes: $x = \pm 2$
Horizontal asymptote: $y = 2$
(d)

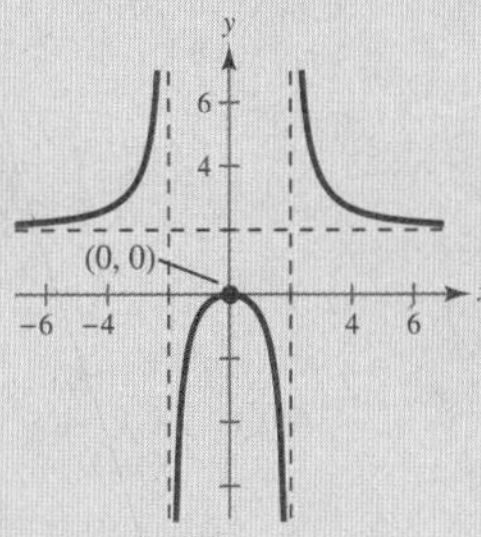

133. (a) Domain: all real numbers x except $x = 0, \frac{1}{3}$
(b) x-intercept: $\left(\frac{3}{2}, 0\right)$
(c) Vertical asymptote: $x = 0$
Horizontal asymptote: $y = 2$
(d)

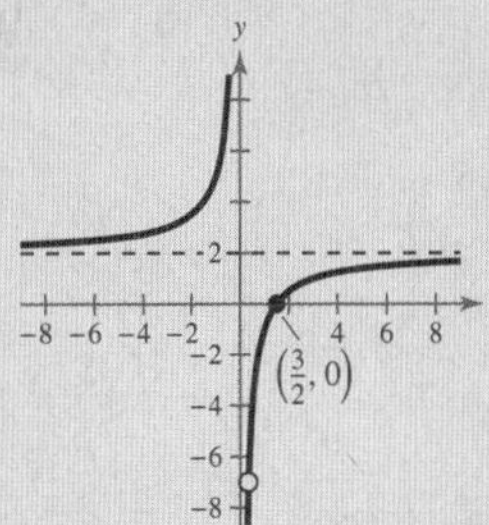

134. (a) Domain: all real numbers x except $x = \pm\frac{1}{2}$
(b) x-intercept: $\left(\frac{2}{3}, 0\right)$
y-intercept: $(0, -2)$
(c) Vertical asymptote: $x = -\frac{1}{2}$
Horizontal asymptote: $y = \frac{3}{2}$
(d)

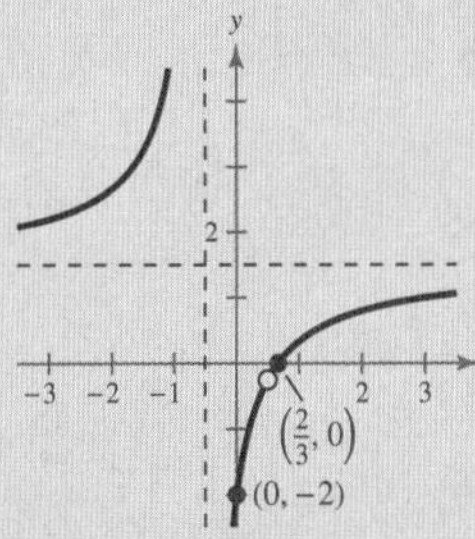

135. (a) Domain: all real numbers x
(b) Intercept: $(0, 0)$
(c) Slant asymptote: $y = 2x$
(d)

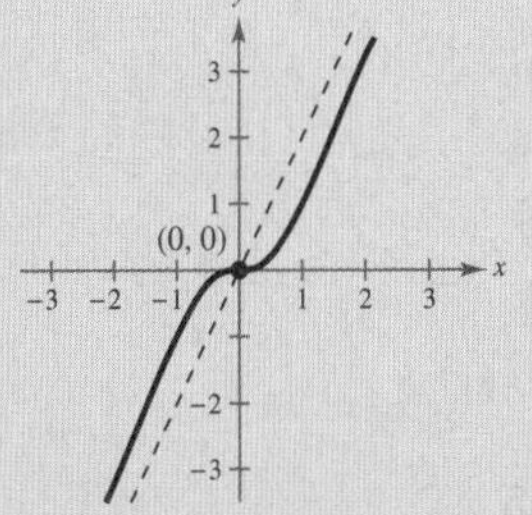

136. (a) Domain: all real numbers x except $x = -1$
(b) y-intercept: $(0, 1)$
(c) Vertical asymptote: $x = -1$
Slant asymptote: $y = x - 1$
(d)

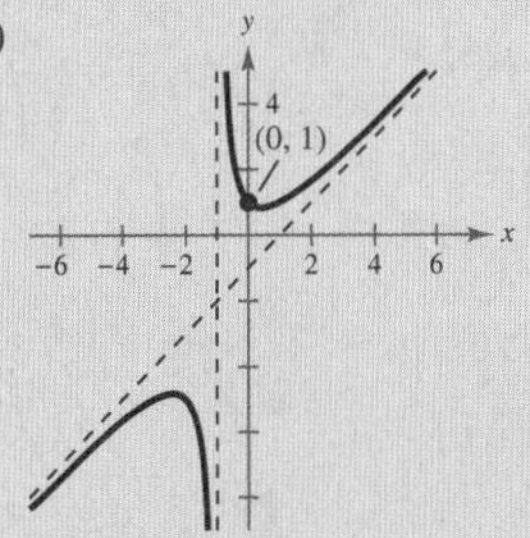

137–138, 140–142, 144–148, 153–157. See Additional Answers beginning on page AA1.

2 Chapter Test

See www.CalcChat.com for worked-out solutions to odd-numbered exercises.

Take this test as you would take a test in class. When you are finished, check your work against the answers given in the back of the book.

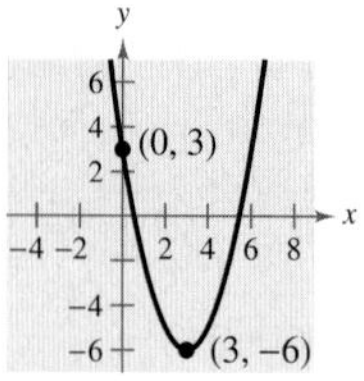

FIGURE FOR 2

1. Describe how the graph of g differs from the graph of $f(x) = x^2$. See margin.
   (a) $g(x) = 2 - x^2$ (b) $g(x) = \left(x - \frac{3}{2}\right)^2$
2. Find an equation of the parabola shown in the figure at the left. $y = (x - 3)^2 - 6$
3. The path of a ball is given by $y = -\frac{1}{20}x^2 + 3x + 5$, where y is the height (in feet) of the ball and x is the horizontal distance (in feet) from where the ball was thrown.
   (a) Find the maximum height of the ball. 50 ft
   (b) Which number determines the height at which the ball was thrown? Does changing this value change the coordinates of the maximum height of the ball? Explain. See margin.
4. Determine the right-hand and left-hand behavior of the graph of the function $h(t) = -\frac{3}{4}t^5 + 2t^2$. Then sketch its graph. See margin.
5. Divide using long division.
   $$\frac{3x^3 + 4x - 1}{x^2 + 1} \qquad 3x + \frac{x - 1}{x^2 + 1}$$
6. Divide using synthetic division.
   $$\frac{2x^4 - 5x^2 - 3}{x - 2}$$ See margin.
7. Use synthetic division to show that $x = \frac{5}{2}$ is a zero of the function given by
   $$f(x) = 2x^3 - 5x^2 - 6x + 15.$$
   Use the result to factor the polynomial function completely and list all the real zeros of the function. $(2x - 5)(x + \sqrt{3})(x - \sqrt{3})$; Zeros: $\frac{5}{2}, \pm\sqrt{3}$
8. Perform each operation and write the result in standard form.
   (a) $10i - (3 + \sqrt{-25})$ (b) $(2 + \sqrt{3}i)(2 - \sqrt{3}i)$ 7
   $-3 + 5i$
9. Write the quotient in standard form: $\frac{5}{2 + i}$. $2 - i$

In Exercises 10 and 11, find a polynomial function with real coefficients that has the given zeros. (There are many correct answers.)

10. $0, 3, 2 + i$
    $f(x) = x^4 - 7x^3 + 17x^2 - 15x$
11. $1 - \sqrt{3}i, 2, 2$
    $f(x) = x^4 - 6x^3 + 16x^2 - 24x + 16$

In Exercises 12 and 13, find all the zeros of the function.

12. $f(x) = 3x^3 + 14x^2 - 7x - 10$
    $-5, -\frac{2}{3}, 1$
13. $f(x) = x^4 - 9x^2 - 22x - 24$
    $-2, 4, -1 \pm \sqrt{2}i$

In Exercises 14–16, identify any intercepts and asymptotes of the graph of the function. Then sketch a graph of the function. 14–16. See margin.

14. $h(x) = \dfrac{4}{x^2} - 1$
15. $f(x) = \dfrac{2x^2 - 5x - 12}{x^2 - 16}$
16. $g(x) = \dfrac{x^2 + 2}{x - 1}$

In Exercises 17 and 18, solve the inequality. Sketch the solution set on the real number line.

17. $2x^2 + 5x > 12$
    $x < -4$ or $x > \frac{3}{2}$

18. $\dfrac{2}{x} \le \dfrac{1}{x + 6}$
    $x \le -12$ or $-6 < x < 0$

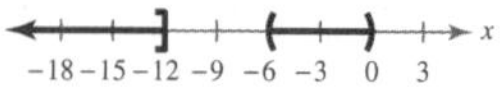

1. (a) Reflection in the x-axis followed by a vertical shift two units upward
   (b) Horizontal shift $\frac{3}{2}$ units to the right
3. (b) 5. Yes, changing the constant term results in a vertical translation of the graph and therefore changes the maximum height.
4. Rises to the left, falls to the right

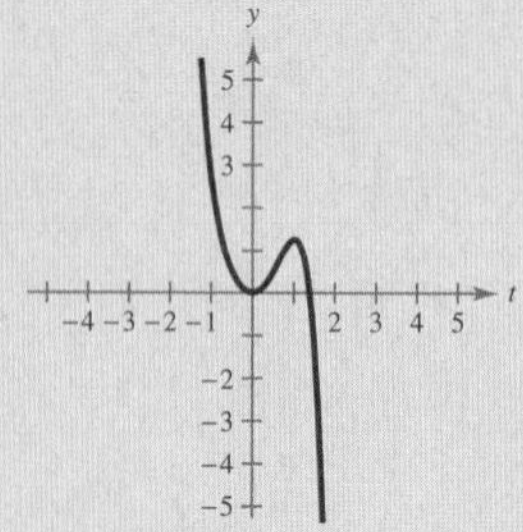

6. $2x^3 + 4x^2 + 3x + 6 + \dfrac{9}{x - 2}$
14. x-intercepts: $(-2, 0), (2, 0)$
    Vertical asymptote: $x = 0$
    Horizontal asymptote: $y = -1$

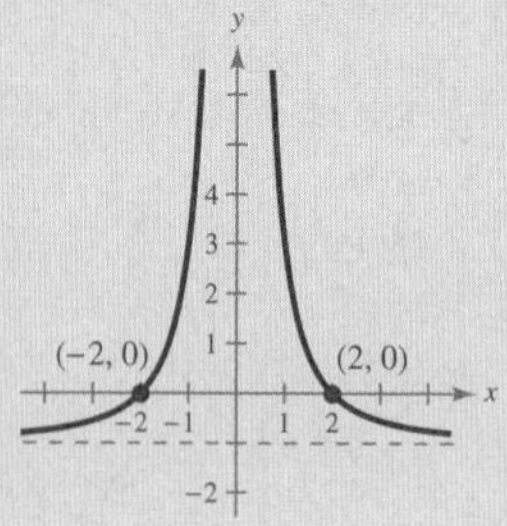

15. x-intercept: $\left(-\frac{3}{2}, 0\right)$
    y-intercept: $\left(0, \frac{3}{4}\right)$
    Vertical asymptote: $x = -4$
    Horizontal asymptote: $y = 2$

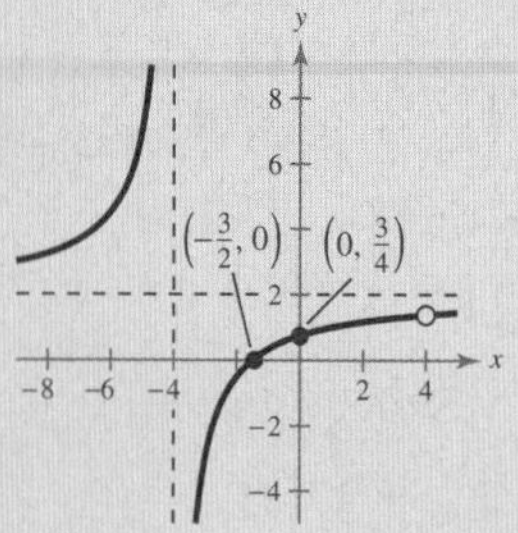

16. y-intercept: $(0, -2)$
    Vertical asymptote: $x = 1$
    Slant asymptote: $y = x + 1$

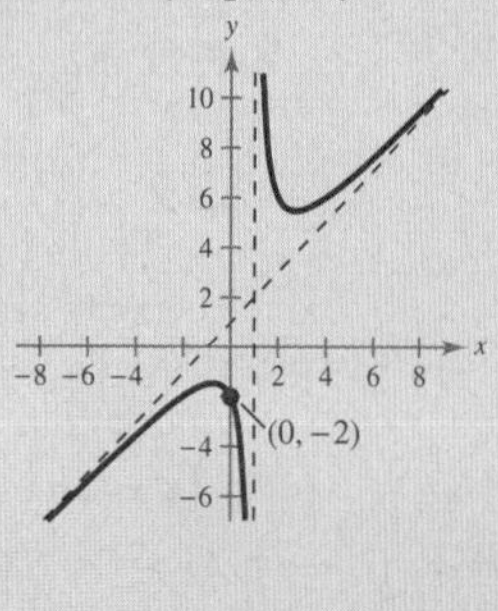

PROOFS IN MATHEMATICS

These two pages contain proofs of four important theorems about polynomial functions. The first two theorems are from Section 2.3, and the second two theorems are from Section 2.5.

The Remainder Theorem *(p. 154)*

If a polynomial $f(x)$ is divided by $x - k$, the remainder is

$$r = f(k).$$

Proof

From the Division Algorithm, you have

$$f(x) = (x - k)q(x) + r(x)$$

and because either $r(x) = 0$ or the degree of $r(x)$ is less than the degree of $x - k$, you know that $r(x)$ must be a constant. That is, $r(x) = r$. Now, by evaluating $f(x)$ at $x = k$, you have

$$\begin{aligned} f(k) &= (k - k)q(k) + r \\ &= (0)q(k) + r = r. \end{aligned}$$

To be successful in algebra, it is important that you understand the connection among *factors* of a polynomial, *zeros* of a polynomial function, and *solutions* or *roots* of a polynomial equation. The Factor Theorem is the basis for this connection.

The Factor Theorem *(p. 154)*

A polynomial $f(x)$ has a factor $(x - k)$ if and only if $f(k) = 0$.

Proof

Using the Division Algorithm with the factor $(x - k)$, you have

$$f(x) = (x - k)q(x) + r(x).$$

By the Remainder Theorem, $r(x) = r = f(k)$, and you have

$$f(x) = (x - k)q(x) + f(k)$$

where $q(x)$ is a polynomial of lesser degree than $f(x)$. If $f(k) = 0$, then

$$f(x) = (x - k)q(x)$$

and you see that $(x - k)$ is a factor of $f(x)$. Conversely, if $(x - k)$ is a factor of $f(x)$, division of $f(x)$ by $(x - k)$ yields a remainder of 0. So, by the Remainder Theorem, you have $f(k) = 0$.

211

Linear Factorization Theorem (p. 166)

If $f(x)$ is a polynomial of degree n, where $n > 0$, then f has precisely n linear factors

$$f(x) = a_n(x - c_1)(x - c_2) \cdot \cdot \cdot (x - c_n)$$

where $c_1, c_2, \ldots, c_n$ are complex numbers.

Proof

Using the Fundamental Theorem of Algebra, you know that f must have at least one zero, c_1. Consequently, $(x - c_1)$ is a factor of $f(x)$, and you have

$$f(x) = (x - c_1)f_1(x).$$

If the degree of $f_1(x)$ is greater than zero, you again apply the Fundamental Theorem to conclude that f_1 must have a zero c_2, which implies that

$$f(x) = (x - c_1)(x - c_2)f_2(x).$$

It is clear that the degree of $f_1(x)$ is $n - 1$, that the degree of $f_2(x)$ is $n - 2$, and that you can repeatedly apply the Fundamental Theorem n times until you obtain

$$f(x) = a_n(x - c_1)(x - c_2) \cdot \cdot \cdot (x - c_n)$$

where a_n is the leading coefficient of the polynomial $f(x)$.

The Fundamental Theorem of Algebra

The Linear Factorization Theorem is closely related to the Fundamental Theorem of Algebra. The Fundamental Theorem of Algebra has a long and interesting history. In the early work with polynomial equations, The Fundamental Theorem of Algebra was thought to have been not true, because imaginary solutions were not considered. In fact, in the very early work by mathematicians such as Abu al-Khwarizmi (c. 800 A.D.), negative solutions were also not considered.

Once imaginary numbers were accepted, several mathematicians attempted to give a general proof of the Fundamental Theorem of Algebra. These included Gottfried von Leibniz (1702), Jean d'Alembert (1746), Leonhard Euler (1749), Joseph-Louis Lagrange (1772), and Pierre Simon Laplace (1795). The mathematician usually credited with the first correct proof of the Fundamental Theorem of Algebra is Carl Friedrich Gauss, who published the proof in his doctoral thesis in 1799.

Factors of a Polynomial (p. 170)

Every polynomial of degree $n > 0$ with real coefficients can be written as the product of linear and quadratic factors with real coefficients, where the quadratic factors have no real zeros.

Proof

To begin, you use the Linear Factorization Theorem to conclude that $f(x)$ can be *completely* factored in the form

$$f(x) = d(x - c_1)(x - c_2)(x - c_3) \cdot \cdot \cdot (x - c_n).$$

If each c_i is real, there is nothing more to prove. If any c_i is complex ($c_i = a + bi$, $b \neq 0$), then, because the coefficients of $f(x)$ are real, you know that the conjugate $c_j = a - bi$ is also a zero. By multiplying the corresponding factors, you obtain

$$\begin{aligned}(x - c_i)(x - c_j) &= [x - (a + bi)][x - (a - bi)] \\ &= x^2 - 2ax + (a^2 + b^2)\end{aligned}$$

where each coefficient is real.

212

PROBLEM SOLVING

This collection of thought-provoking and challenging exercises further explores and expands upon concepts learned in this chapter.

1. Show that if $f(x) = ax^3 + bx^2 + cx + d$, then $f(k) = r$, where $r = ak^3 + bk^2 + ck + d$, using long division. In other words, verify the Remainder Theorem for a third-degree polynomial function. Answers will vary.

2. In 2000 B.C., the Babylonians solved polynomial equations by referring to tables of values. One such table gave the values of $y^3 + y^2$. To be able to use this table, the Babylonians sometimes had to manipulate the equation, as shown below.

$$ax^3 + bx^2 = c \qquad \text{Original equation}$$

$$\frac{a^3x^3}{b^3} + \frac{a^2x^2}{b^2} = \frac{a^2c}{b^3} \qquad \text{Multiply each side by } \frac{a^2}{b^3}.$$

$$\left(\frac{ax}{b}\right)^3 + \left(\frac{ax}{b}\right)^2 = \frac{a^2c}{b^3} \qquad \text{Rewrite.}$$

Then they would find $(a^2c)/b^3$ in the $y^3 + y^2$ column of the table. Because they knew that the corresponding y-value was equal to $(ax)/b$, they could conclude that $x = (by)/a$.

(a) Calculate $y^3 + y^2$ for $y = 1, 2, 3, \ldots, 10$. Record the values in a table. See margin.

Use the table from part (a) and the method above to solve each equation.

(b) $x^3 + x^2 = 252$ $\quad x = 6$

(c) $x^3 + 2x^2 = 288$ $\quad x = 6$

(d) $3x^3 + x^2 = 90$ $\quad x = 3$

(e) $2x^3 + 5x^2 = 2500$ $\quad x = 10$

(f) $7x^3 + 6x^2 = 1728$ $\quad x = 6$

(g) $10x^3 + 3x^2 = 297$ $\quad x = 3$

Using the methods from this chapter, verify your solution to each equation.

3. At a glassware factory, molten cobalt glass is poured into molds to make paperweights. Each mold is a rectangular prism whose height is 3 inches greater than the length of each side of the square base. A machine pours 20 cubic inches of liquid glass into each mold. What are the dimensions of the mold? 2 in. × 2 in. × 5 in.

4. Determine whether the statement is true or false. If false, provide one or more reasons why the statement is false and correct the statement. Let $f(x) = ax^3 + bx^2 + cx + d$, $a \neq 0$, and let $f(2) = -1$. Then

$$\frac{f(x)}{x+1} = q(x) + \frac{2}{x+1}$$

where $q(x)$ is a second-degree polynomial.

False. The statement would be true if $f(-1) = 2$.

5. The parabola shown in the figure has an equation of the form $y = ax^2 + bx + c$. Find the equation of this parabola by the following methods. (a) Find the equation analytically. (b) Use the *regression* feature of a graphing utility to find the equation. (a)–(b). $y = -x^2 + 5x - 4$

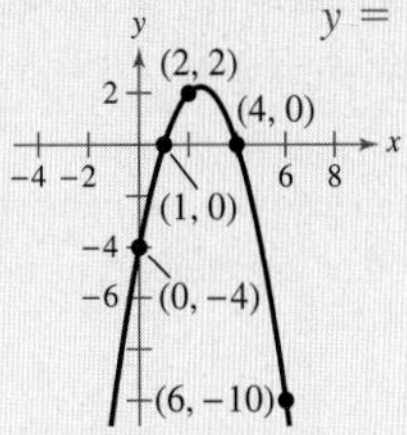

6. One of the fundamental themes of calculus is to find the slope of the tangent line to a curve at a point. To see how this can be done, consider the point (2, 4) on the graph of the quadratic function $f(x) = x^2$, which is shown in the figure.

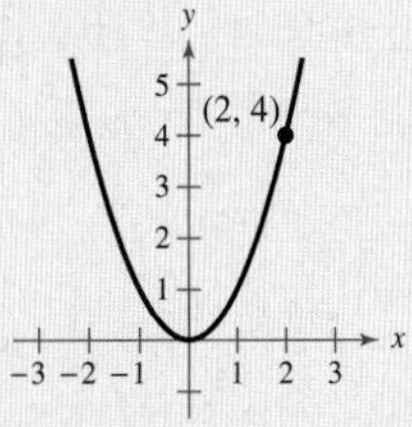

(a) Find the slope m_1 of the line joining (2, 4) and (3, 9). Is the slope of the tangent line at (2, 4) greater than or less than the slope of the line through (2, 4) and (3, 9)? $m_1 = 5$; less than

(b) Find the slope m_2 of the line joining (2, 4) and (1, 1). Is the slope of the tangent line at (2, 4) greater than or less than the slope of the line through (2, 4) and (1, 1)? $m_2 = 3$; greater than

(c) Find the slope m_3 of the line joining (2, 4) and (2.1, 4.41). Is the slope of the tangent line at (2, 4) greater than or less than the slope of the line through (2, 4) and (2.1, 4.41)? $m_3 = 4.1$; less than

(d) Find the slope m_h of the line joining (2, 4) and $(2 + h, f(2 + h))$ in terms of the nonzero number h. $m_h = h + 4$

(e) Evaluate the slope formula from part (d) for $h = -1$, 1, and 0.1. Compare these values with those in parts (a)–(c). $m_h = 3, 5, 4.1$; The values are the same.

(f) What can you conclude the slope m_{tan} of the tangent line at (2, 4) to be? Explain your answer.

$m_{tan} = 4$ because $h = 0$.

2. (a)

y	1	2	3	4	5
$y^3 + y^2$	2	12	36	80	150

y	6	7	8	9	10
$y^3 + y^2$	252	392	576	810	1100

213

7. (a) $f(x) = (x - 2)x^2 + 5$
$= x^3 - 2x^2 + 5$
(b) $f(x) = -(x + 3)x^2 + 1$
$= -x^3 - 3x^2 + 1$

11. (a) As $|a|$ increases, the graph stretches vertically. For $a < 0$, the graph is reflected in the x-axis.
(b) As $|b|$ increases, the vertical asymptote is translated. For $b > 0$, the graph is translated to the right. For $b < 0$, the graph is reflected in the x-axis and is translated to the left.

12. (a) $y_1 = 0.031x^2 - 1.59x + 21.0$

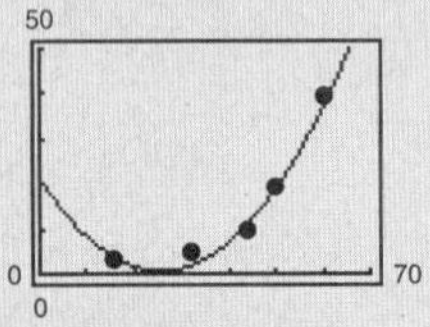

(b) $y_2 \approx \dfrac{1}{-0.007x + 0.44}$

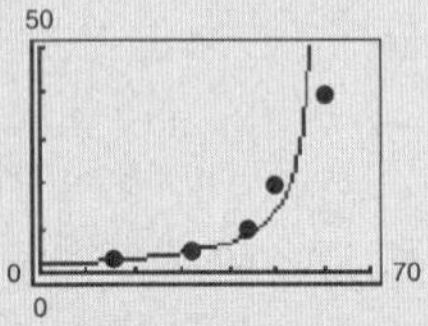

(c) The models are a good fit for the original data.
(d) $y_1(25) = 0.625$; $y_2(25) = 3.774$
The rational model is a better fit for the original data.
(e) The reciprocal model should not be used to predict the near point for a person who is 70 years old, because a negative value is obtained. The quadratic model is a better fit.

7. Use the form $f(x) = (x - k)q(x) + r$ to create a cubic function that (a) passes through the point $(2, 5)$ and rises to the right and (b) passes through the point $(-3, 1)$ and falls to the right. (There are many correct answers.) See margin.

8. The multiplicative inverse of z is a complex number z_m such that $z \cdot z_m = 1$. Find the multiplicative inverse of each complex number. (a) $\frac{1}{2} - \frac{1}{2}i$ (b) $\frac{3}{10} + \frac{1}{10}i$

(a) $z = 1 + i$ (b) $z = 3 - i$ (c) $z = -2 + 8i$ (c) $-\frac{1}{34} - \frac{2}{17}i$

9. Prove that the product of a complex number $a + bi$ and its complex conjugate is a real number. See margin.

10. Match the graph of the rational function given by

$$f(x) = \frac{ax + b}{cx + d}$$

with the given conditions.

(a)

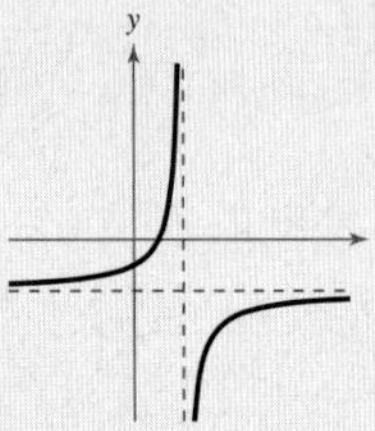

(b)

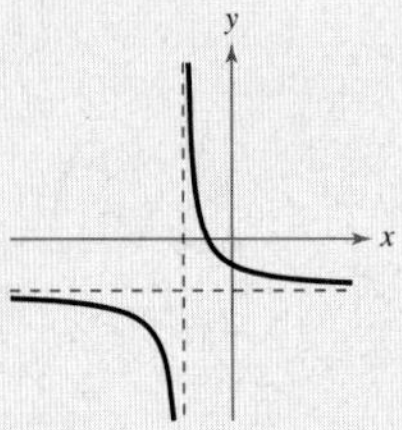

(c)

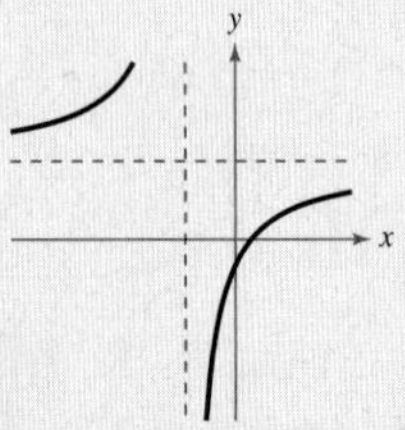

(d)

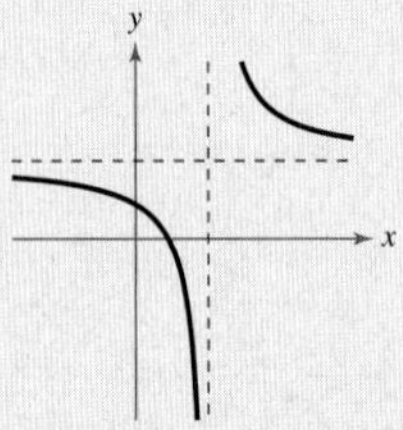

(i) $a > 0$ d (ii) $a > 0$ b (iii) $a < 0$ a (iv) $a > 0$ c
$b < 0$ | $b > 0$ | $b > 0$ | $b < 0$
$c > 0$ | $c < 0$ | $c > 0$ | $c > 0$
$d < 0$ | $d < 0$ | $d < 0$ | $d > 0$

11. Consider the function given by

$$f(x) = \frac{ax}{(x - b)^2}.$$ See margin.

(a) Determine the effect on the graph of f if $b \neq 0$ and a is varied. Consider cases in which a is positive and a is negative.

(b) Determine the effect on the graph of f if $a \neq 0$ and b is varied.

12. The endpoints of the interval over which distinct vision is possible are called the *near point* and *far point* of the eye (see figure). With increasing age, these points normally change. The table shows the approximate near points y (in inches) for various ages x (in years). See margin.

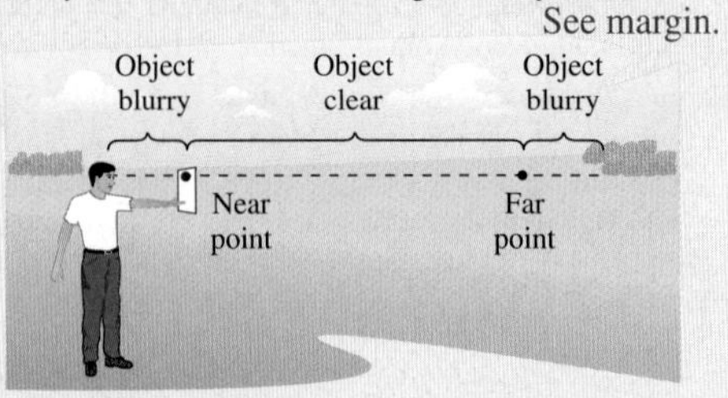

FIGURE FOR 12

Age, x	Near point, y
16	3.0
32	4.7
44	9.8
50	19.7
60	39.4

(a) Use the *regression* feature of a graphing utility to find a quadratic model y_1 for the data. Use a graphing utility to plot the data and graph the model in the same viewing window.

(b) Find a rational model y_2 for the data. Take the reciprocals of the near points to generate the points $(x, 1/y)$. Use the *regression* feature of a graphing utility to find a linear model for the data. The resulting line has the form

$$\frac{1}{y} = ax + b.$$

Solve for y. Use a graphing utility to plot the data and graph the model in the same viewing window.

(c) Use the *table* feature of a graphing utility to create a table showing the predicted near point based on each model for each of the ages in the original table. How well do the models fit the original data?

(d) Use both models to estimate the near point for a person who is 25 years old. Which model is a better fit?

(e) Do you think either model can be used to predict the near point for a person who is 70 years old? Explain.

9. See Additional Answers beginning on page AA1.

Pacing and Assignment Guide 3

REGULAR SCHEDULE

Lesson	Day	AVERAGE	ADVANCED
3.1	Day 1	pp. 224–226 Exs. 9, 11, 13–16, 21, 25, 26, 35–39 odd, 45, 53, 57, 60, 65, 67, 69, 70, 74, 77–83 odd, 88, 90	pp. 224–226 Exs. 12–16, 18, 24–28 even, 36–40 even, 52, 56, 58, 62, 64, 68, 71, 72, 74, 75, 80–88, 90, Project
3.2	Day 1	pp. 234–235 Exs. 1–6, 7–17 odd, 24–28, 31, 35, 39, 41, 45–50	pp. 234–235 Exs. 1–6, 12–18 even, 24–30 even, 34–44 even, 45–50
	Day 2	pp. 235–236 Exs. 51, 57–63 odd, 69–73 odd, 76, 77, 85, 91, 93, 98–100, 103, 108	pp. 235–236 Exs. 54–62 even, 68, 72–78 even, 90, 92–94, 98–101, 104, 107–109
3.3	Day 1	p. 241 Exs. 1–6, 9–17 odd, 25, 27, 31–43 odd, 49, 51, 55, 61, 65	p. 241 Exs. 1–6, 10–18 even, 24, 28, 30–44 even, 52–60 even, 66
	Day 2	pp. 242–243 Exs. 67–73 odd, 77–79, 83, 85, 87, 88, 96, 101–105 odd, 113	pp. 242–243 Exs. 68–78 even, 82, 84, 86, 87–90, 95, 97, 100–106 even, 115
3.4	Day 1	pp. 251–252 Exs. 1–4, 5–15 odd, 19–27 odd, 31–39 odd, 47, 51, 55, 61, 63, 67, 71, 73, 75	pp. 251–252 Exs. 1–4, 6–12 even, 16–24 even, 26, 28, 32–40 even, 50, 54–64 even, 68, 76–80 even
	Day 2	pp. 252–254 Exs. 87–91 odd, 98, 101–107 odd, 111, 113, 118, 121, 127, 129, 131, 135, 138–142	pp. 252–254 Exs. 88–100 even, 104, 108–112 even, 116, 118, 122, 126, 130, 132, 133, 136–138, 143–146, 148
3.5	Day 1	pp. 262–264 Exs. 1–3, 7–12, 15–21 odd, 25, 27, 33, 35, 39, 44, 47, 53, 55	pp. 262–265 Exs. 7–12, 16–26 even, 27, 32, 36–56 even
	Day 2	pp. 262–267 Exs. 4–6, 57, 62, 63–71 odd, 75, 76, 79–82, 84	pp. 265–267 Exs. 58–64, 66–76 even, 77, 79–82, 84
Review	Day 1	pp. 270–272 Exs. 1, 7, 21–25 odd, 33, 35, 39–45 odd, 49, 53–55, 61, 65, 69, 71–79 odd, 81, 83, 86, 89, 92, 95, 100, 109, 110, 117, 119, 121, 123	pp. 270–272 Exs. 6–14 even, 24–28 even, 36, 42–46 even, 52, 54, 56, 57, 59, 64, 68, 72–78 even, 81, 86–90 even, 92, 96, 106–116, 118–126 even
Assess	Day 1	Chapter 3 Test	Chapter 3 Test
Yearly Pacing		Chapter 3 Total – 11 days	Remaining – 125 days

BLOCK SCHEDULE

DAY 1	DAY 2	DAY 3	DAY 4	DAY 5	DAY 6
ASSESS	**3.2**	**3.3**	**3.4**	**3.5**	**REVIEW**
Chapter 2 Test	pp. 234–236 Exs. 1–6, 7–17 odd, 24–28, 31, 35, 39, 41, 45–51, 57–63 odd, 69–73 odd, 76, 77, 85, 91, 93, 98–100, 103, 108	pp. 241–243 Exs. 1–6, 9–17 odd, 25, 27, 31–43 odd, 49, 51, 55, 61, 65, 67–73 odd, 77–79, 83, 85, 87, 88, 96, 101–105 odd, 113	pp. 251–254 Exs. 1–4, 5–15 odd, 19–27 odd, 31–39 odd, 47, 51, 55, 61, 63, 67, 71, 73, 75, 87–91 odd, 98, 101–107 odd, 111, 113, 118, 121, 127, 129, 131, 135, 138–142	pp. 262–267 Exs. 1–12, 15–21 odd, 25, 27, 33, 35, 39, 44, 47, 53, 55, 57, 62, 63–71 odd, 75, 76, 79–82, 84	pp. 270–272 Exs. 1, 7, 21–25 odd, 33, 35, 39–45 odd, 49, 53–55, 61, 65, 69, 71–79 odd, 81, 83, 86, 89, 92, 95, 100, 109, 110, 117, 119, 121, 123
3.1					**ASSESS**
pp. 224–226 Exs. 9, 11, 13–16, 21, 25, 26, 35–39 odd, 45, 53, 57, 60, 65, 67, 69, 70, 74, 77–83 odd, 88, 90					Chapter 3 Test
Yearly Pacing	Chapter 3 Total – 5.5 days	Remaining – 63 days			

Exponential and Logarithmic Functions

3

In Mathematics

Exponential functions involve a constant base and a variable exponent. The inverse of an exponential function is a logarithmic function.

In Real Life

Exponential and logarithmic functions are widely used in describing economic and physical phenomena such as compound interest, population growth, memory retention, and decay of radioactive material. For instance, a logarithmic function can be used to relate an animal's weight and its lowest galloping speed. (See Exercise 95, page 242.)

Juniors Bildarchiv / Alamy

IN CAREERS

There are many careers that use exponential and logarithmic functions. Several are listed below.

- Astronomer
  Example 7, page 240
- Psychologist
  Exercise 136, page 253
- Archeologist
  Example 3, page 258
- Forensic Scientist
  Exercise 75, page 266

PLAN AND PREPARE

Main Ideas

In Chapter 3, students work with exponential and logarithmic functions. They begin by writing, graphing, and recognizing the basic characteristics of exponential and logarithmic functions. Students learn how to use these functions to model real-world problems including compound interest, radioactive decay, and human memory. They then expand their skills by using the properties of logarithms and exponents to manipulate expressions and solve equations. Finally, students learn five exponential and logarithmic models, which they then use to solve real-world problems from a variety of contexts.

Chapter Planning Guide

Chapter Resources

- Complete Solutions Guide

Interactive Technology

- Instructor Success Organizer
- Notetaking Guide IAE
- Instructional DVDs
- Animated Precalculus
- PowerLecture with ExamView

1 PLAN AND PREPARE

Warm-up Exercises

Transparency Available
Available at the Instructor's companion site.

Notetaking Guide

Transparency Available
Promotes interactive learning and notetaking skills.
Available at the Instructor's companion site.

Animated Precalculus

An **Animated Precalculus** tutorial is available at the Student companion site for **Section 3.1.**

Pacing

Average: 1 day
Advanced: 1 day
Block: 0.5 block with Chapter 2 Test

2 FOCUS AND MOTIVATE

Essential Question

How do you write and graph exponential functions? **Tell students that they will learn how to answer this question by studying the characteristics of the function $f(x) = a^x$.**

3.1 EXPONENTIAL FUNCTIONS AND THEIR GRAPHS

What you should learn

- Recognize and evaluate exponential functions with base *a*.
- Graph exponential functions and use the One-to-One Property.
- Recognize, evaluate, and graph exponential functions with base *e*.
- Use exponential functions to model and solve real-life problems.

Why you should learn it

Exponential functions can be used to model and solve real-life problems. For instance, in Exercise 76 on page 226, an exponential function is used to model the concentration of a drug in the bloodstream.

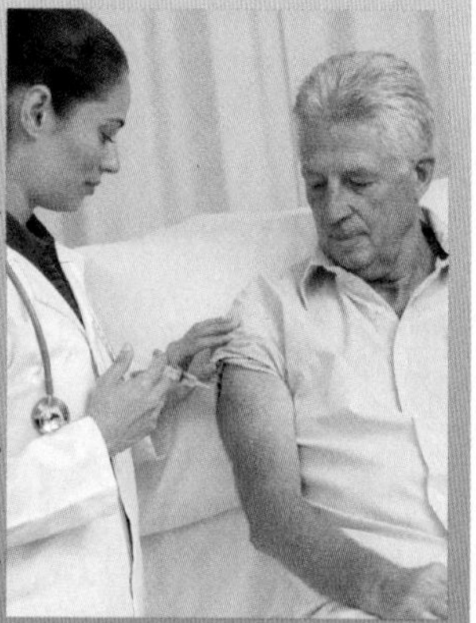

Monkey Business Images Ltd/Stockbroker/PhotoLibrary

Exponential Functions

So far, this text has dealt mainly with **algebraic functions,** which include polynomial functions and rational functions. In this chapter, you will study two types of nonalgebraic functions—*exponential functions* and *logarithmic functions*. These functions are examples of **transcendental functions.**

> **Definition of Exponential Function**
>
> The **exponential function f with base a** is denoted by
>
> $$f(x) = a^x$$
>
> where $a > 0$, $a \neq 1$, and x is any real number.

The base $a = 1$ is excluded because it yields $f(x) = 1^x = 1$. This is a constant function, not an exponential function.

You have evaluated a^x for integer and rational values of x. For example, you know that $4^3 = 64$ and $4^{1/2} = 2$. However, to evaluate 4^x for any real number x, you need to interpret forms with *irrational* exponents. For the purposes of this text, it is sufficient to think of

$$a^{\sqrt{2}} \quad (\text{where } \sqrt{2} \approx 1.41421356)$$

as the number that has the successively closer approximations

$$a^{1.4}, a^{1.41}, a^{1.414}, a^{1.4142}, a^{1.41421}, \ldots .$$

Example 1 Evaluating Exponential Functions

Use a calculator to evaluate each function at the indicated value of x.

	Function	*Value*
a.	$f(x) = 2^x$	$x = -3.1$
b.	$f(x) = 2^{-x}$	$x = \pi$
c.	$f(x) = 0.6^x$	$x = \frac{3}{2}$

Solution

	Function Value	*Graphing Calculator Keystrokes*	*Display*
a.	$f(-3.1) = 2^{-3.1}$	2 [^] [(−)] 3.1 [ENTER]	0.1166291
b.	$f(\pi) = 2^{-\pi}$	2 [^] [(−)] π [ENTER]	0.1133147
c.	$f(\frac{3}{2}) = (0.6)^{3/2}$	.6 [^] [(] 3 [÷] 2 [)] [ENTER]	0.4647580

CHECKPoint Now try Exercise 7.

When evaluating exponential functions with a calculator, remember to enclose fractional exponents in parentheses. Because the calculator follows the order of operations, parentheses are crucial in order to obtain the correct result.

Resource Planning Guide

Chapter Resources

- Complete Solutions Guide

Workbooks

- Notetaking Guide
- Student Solutions Guide

Interactive Technology

- Instructor Success Organizer
- Notetaking Guide IAE
- Instructional DVDs
- Animated Precalculus
- PowerLecture with ExamView

Graphs of Exponential Functions

The graphs of all exponential functions have similar characteristics, as shown in Examples 2, 3, and 5.

Example 2 Graphs of $y = a^x$

In the same coordinate plane, sketch the graph of each function.

a. $f(x) = 2^x$ **b.** $g(x) = 4^x$

Solution

The table below lists some values for each function, and Figure 3.1 shows the graphs of the two functions. Note that both graphs are increasing. Moreover, the graph of $g(x) = 4^x$ is increasing more rapidly than the graph of $f(x) = 2^x$.

x	-3	-2	-1	0	1	2
2^x	$\frac{1}{8}$	$\frac{1}{4}$	$\frac{1}{2}$	1	2	4
4^x	$\frac{1}{64}$	$\frac{1}{16}$	$\frac{1}{4}$	1	4	16

CHECKPoint Now try Exercise 17.

Algebra Help

You can review the techniques for sketching the graph of an equation in Section 1.2.

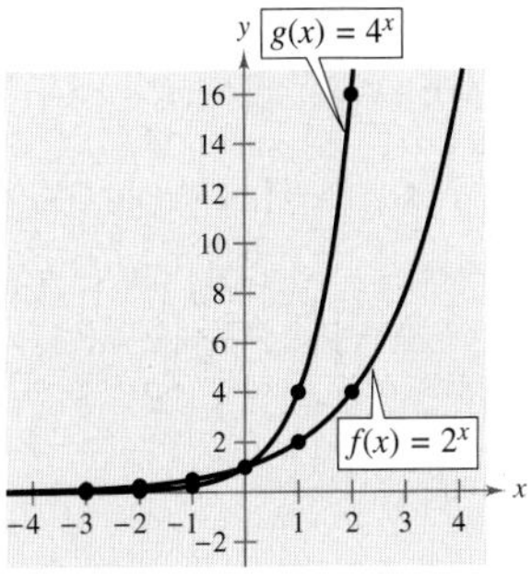

FIGURE 3.1

The table in Example 2 was evaluated by hand. You could, of course, use a graphing utility to construct tables with even more values.

Example 3 Graphs of $y = a^{-x}$

In the same coordinate plane, sketch the graph of each function.

a. $F(x) = 2^{-x}$ **b.** $G(x) = 4^{-x}$

Solution

The table below lists some values for each function, and Figure 3.2 shows the graphs of the two functions. Note that both graphs are decreasing. Moreover, the graph of $G(x) = 4^{-x}$ is decreasing more rapidly than the graph of $F(x) = 2^{-x}$.

x	-2	-1	0	1	2	3
2^{-x}	4	2	1	$\frac{1}{2}$	$\frac{1}{4}$	$\frac{1}{8}$
4^{-x}	16	4	1	$\frac{1}{4}$	$\frac{1}{16}$	$\frac{1}{64}$

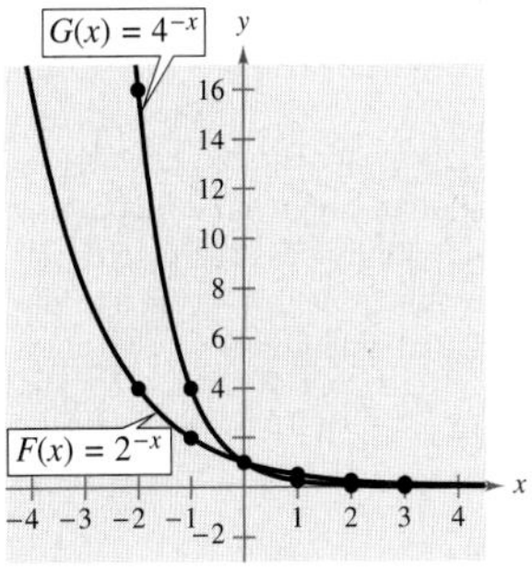

FIGURE 3.2

CHECKPoint Now try Exercise 19.

In Example 3, note that by using one of the properties of exponents, the functions $F(x) = 2^{-x}$ and $G(x) = 4^{-x}$ can be rewritten with positive exponents.

$$F(x) = 2^{-x} = \frac{1}{2^x} = \left(\frac{1}{2}\right)^x \quad \text{and} \quad G(x) = 4^{-x} = \frac{1}{4^x} = \left(\frac{1}{4}\right)^x$$

3 TEACH

Extra Example 1

Use a calculator to evaluate each function at the indicated value of x.

Function	Value
a. $f(x) = 8^x$	$x = \pi$
687.2913	
b. $f(x) = 8^{-x}$	$x = \frac{1}{2}$
0.3536	
c. $f(x) = 0.8^x$	$x = -2.5$
1.7469	

Extra Example 2

In the same coordinate plane, sketch the graph of each function.

a. $f(x) = 3^x$

b. $g(x) = 5^x$

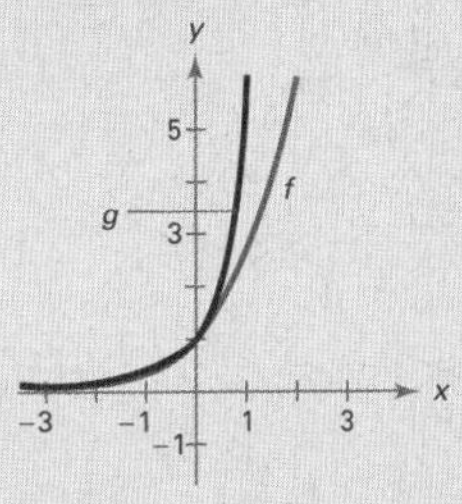

Extra Example 3

In the same coordinate plane, sketch the graph of each function.

a. $f(x) = 3^{-x}$

b. $g(x) = 5^{-x}$

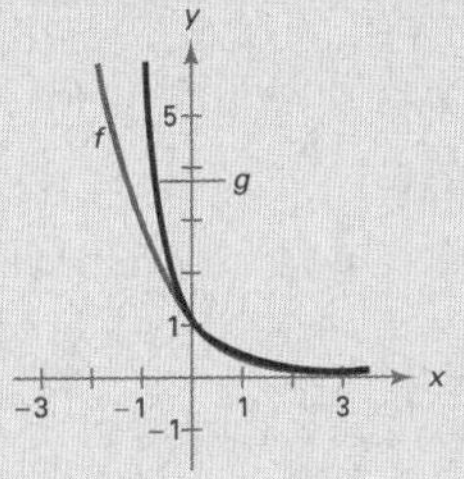

Extra Example 4

Solve.

a. $16 = 2^{x+2}$

$x = 2$

b. $\left(\frac{1}{3}\right)^x = 81$

$x = -4$

Comparing the functions in Examples 2 and 3, observe that

$$F(x) = 2^{-x} = f(-x) \qquad \text{and} \qquad G(x) = 4^{-x} = g(-x).$$

Consequently, the graph of F is a reflection (in the y-axis) of the graph of f. The graphs of G and g have the same relationship. The graphs in Figures 3.1 and 3.2 are typical of the exponential functions $y = a^x$ and $y = a^{-x}$. They have one y-intercept and one horizontal asymptote (the x-axis), and they are continuous. The basic characteristics of these exponential functions are summarized in Figures 3.3 and 3.4.

Study Tip

Notice that the range of an exponential function is $(0, \infty)$, which means that $a^x > 0$ for all values of x.

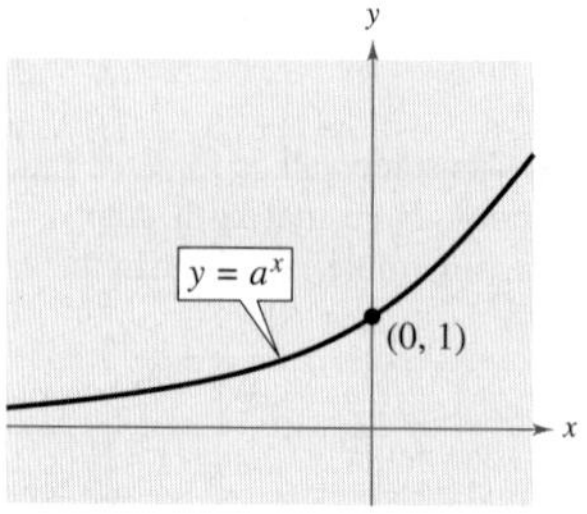

FIGURE 3.3

Graph of $y = a^x, a > 1$
- Domain: $(-\infty, \infty)$
- Range: $(0, \infty)$
- y-intercept: $(0, 1)$
- Increasing
- x-axis is a horizontal asymptote ($a^x \to 0$ as $x \to -\infty$).
- Continuous

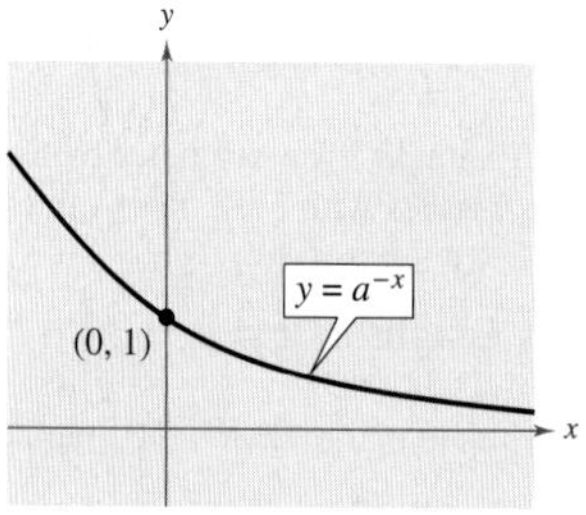

FIGURE 3.4

Graph of $y = a^{-x}, a > 1$
- Domain: $(-\infty, \infty)$
- Range: $(0, \infty)$
- y-intercept: $(0, 1)$
- Decreasing
- x-axis is a horizontal asymptote ($a^{-x} \to 0$ as $x \to \infty$).
- Continuous

From Figures 3.3 and 3.4, you can see that the graph of an exponential function is always increasing or always decreasing. As a result, the graphs pass the Horizontal Line Test, and therefore the functions are one-to-one functions. You can use the following **One-to-One Property** to solve simple exponential equations.

For $a > 0$ and $a \neq 1$, $a^x = a^y$ if and only if $x = y$. One-to-One Property

Example 4 Using the One-to-One Property

a. $9 = 3^{x+1}$ Original equation

$3^2 = 3^{x+1}$ $9 = 3^2$

$2 = x + 1$ One-to-One Property

$1 = x$ Solve for x.

b. $\left(\frac{1}{2}\right)^x = 8 \Rightarrow 2^{-x} = 2^3 \Rightarrow x = -3$

CHECKPoint Now try Exercise 51.

Differentiated Instruction

Inclusion To assist students in grasping the One-to-One Property, write two or three equations in one variable, such as $4x = 3x + 12$, on the board. Have students solve the equation for x. Then rewrite each side of the original equation as an exponent of a common base, such as $2^{4x} = 2^{3x+12}$. Have students substitute the value they found for each variable into the rewritten equations to observe the validity of the One-to-One Property.

In the following example, notice how the graph of $y = a^x$ can be used to sketch the graphs of functions of the form $f(x) = b \pm a^{x+c}$.

Algebra Help

You can review the techniques for transforming the graph of a function in Section 1.7.

Example 5 Transformations of Graphs of Exponential Functions

Each of the following graphs is a transformation of the graph of $f(x) = 3^x$.

a. Because $g(x) = 3^{x+1} = f(x + 1)$, the graph of g can be obtained by shifting the graph of f one unit to the *left*, as shown in Figure 3.5.

b. Because $h(x) = 3^x - 2 = f(x) - 2$, the graph of h can be obtained by shifting the graph of f *downward* two units, as shown in Figure 3.6.

c. Because $k(x) = -3^x = -f(x)$, the graph of k can be obtained by *reflecting* the graph of f in the x-axis, as shown in Figure 3.7.

d. Because $j(x) = 3^{-x} = f(-x)$, the graph of j can be obtained by *reflecting* the graph of f in the y-axis, as shown in Figure 3.8.

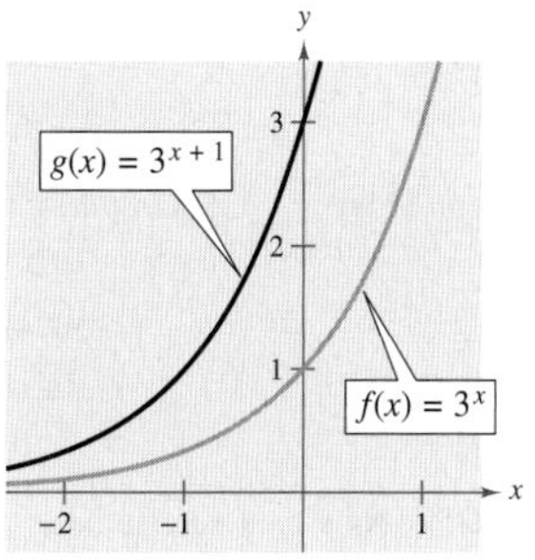

FIGURE 3.5 Horizontal shift

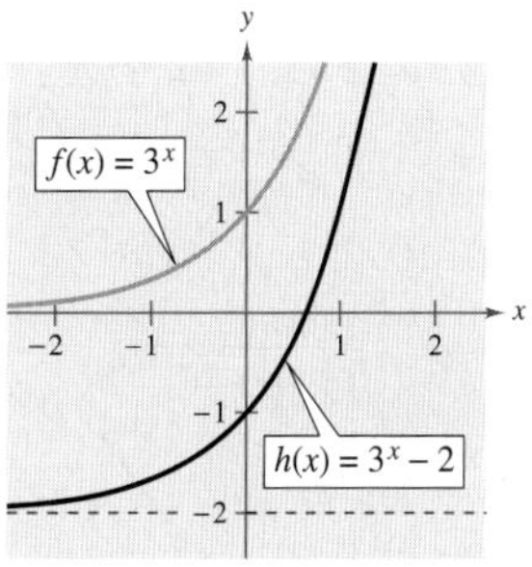

FIGURE 3.6 Vertical shift

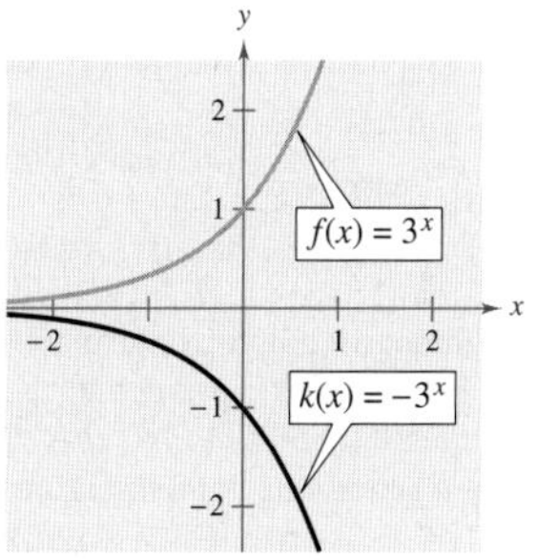

FIGURE 3.7 Reflection in x-axis

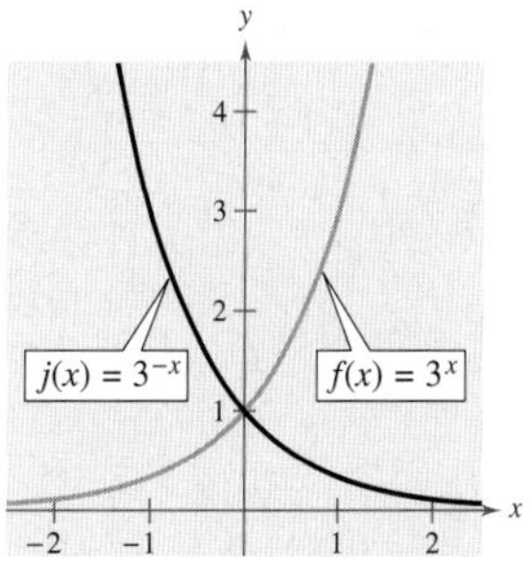

FIGURE 3.8 Reflection in y-axis

CHECKPoint Now try Exercise 23.

Notice that the transformations in Figures 3.5, 3.7, and 3.8 keep the x-axis as a horizontal asymptote, but the transformation in Figure 3.6 yields a new horizontal asymptote of $y = -2$. Also, be sure to note how the y-intercept is affected by each transformation.

Extra Example 5

Describe the graph as a transformation of the graph of $f(x) = 4^x$.

a. $g(x) = 4^{x-2}$

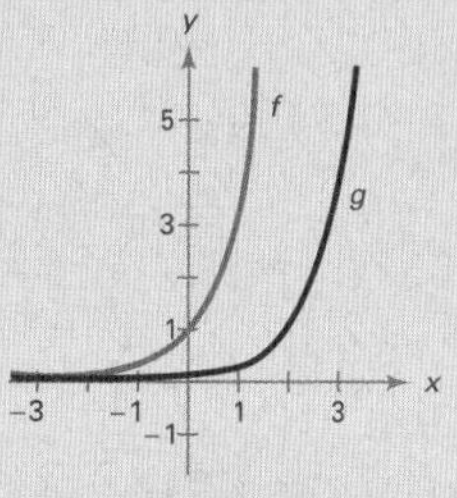

Because $g(x) = 4^{x-2} = f(x - 2)$, the graph of g can be obtained by shifting the graph of f two units to the right.

b. $h(x) = -\frac{1}{2}(4^x)$

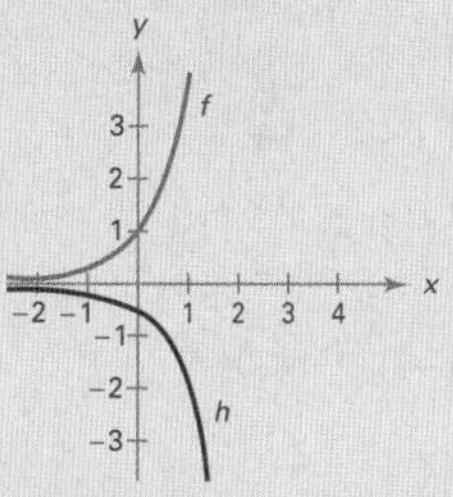

Because $h(x) = -\frac{1}{2}(4^x) = -\frac{1}{2}f(x)$, the graph of h can be obtained by a vertical shrink and reflecting the graph of f in the x-axis.

c. $q(x) = 4^{-x} + 3$

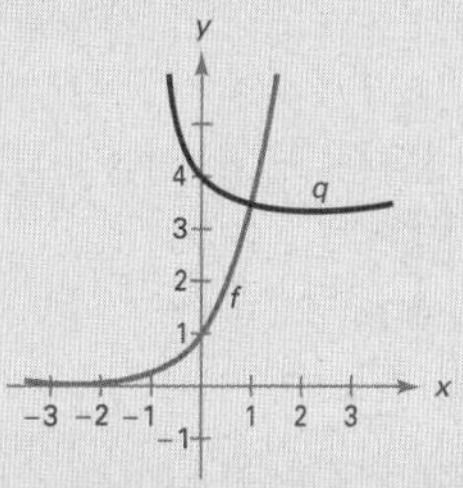

Because $q(x) = 4^{-x} + 3 = f(-x) + 3$, the graph of q can be obtained by reflecting the graph of f in the y-axis followed by a shift three units upward.

Avoiding Common Errors

Students need to be careful with negative values in exponential functions. Negative exponents create reciprocal values, reflecting the function in the y-axis. A negative appearing before the base, as in Example 5c, does not indicate a negative base, but the opposite of the function. This graph reflects the function in the x-axis.

Extra Example 6

Use a calculator to evaluate the function given by $f(x) = e^x$ at each individual value of x to four decimal places.

a. $x = 6.2$

492.7490

b. $x = -0.4$

0.6703

c. $x = -7.1$

0.0008

d. $x = 0.72$

2.0544

Extra Example 7

Sketch the graph of the natural exponential function $s(t) = 5e^{0.17t}$.

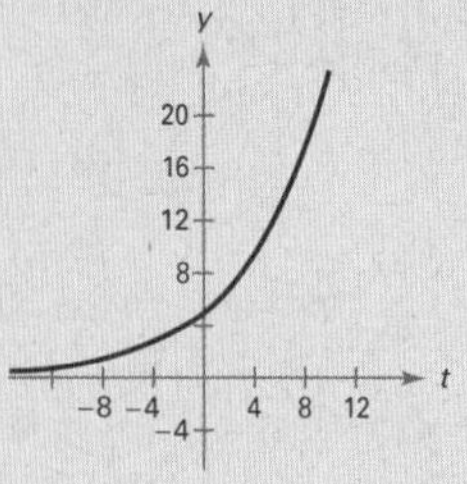

The Natural Base e

In many applications, the most convenient choice for a base is the irrational number

$$e \approx 2.718281828 \; . \; . \; . \; .$$

This number is called the **natural base.** The function given by $f(x) = e^x$ is called the **natural exponential function.** Its graph is shown in Figure 3.9. Be sure you see that for the exponential function $f(x) = e^x$, e is the constant $2.718281828 \ldots$, whereas x is the variable.

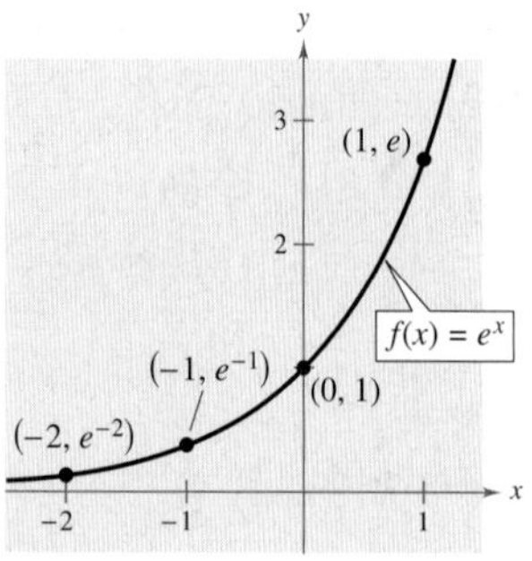

FIGURE 3.9

Example 6 Evaluating the Natural Exponential Function

Use a calculator to evaluate the function given by $f(x) = e^x$ at each indicated value of x.

a. $x = -2$

b. $x = -1$

c. $x = 0.25$

d. $x = -0.3$

Solution

Function Value	*Graphing Calculator Keystrokes*	*Display*
a. $f(-2) = e^{-2}$	(eˣ) ((−)) 2 (ENTER)	0.1353353
b. $f(-1) = e^{-1}$	(eˣ) ((−)) 1 (ENTER)	0.3678794
c. $f(0.25) = e^{0.25}$	(eˣ) 0.25 (ENTER)	1.2840254
d. $f(-0.3) = e^{-0.3}$	(eˣ) ((−)) 0.3 (ENTER)	0.7408182

CHECK*Point* Now try Exercise 33.

Example 7 Graphing Natural Exponential Functions

Sketch the graph of each natural exponential function.

a. $f(x) = 2e^{0.24x}$

b. $g(x) = \frac{1}{2}e^{-0.58x}$

Solution

To sketch these two graphs, you can use a graphing utility to construct a table of values, as shown below. After constructing the table, plot the points and connect them with smooth curves, as shown in Figures 3.10 and 3.11. Note that the graph in Figure 3.10 is increasing, whereas the graph in Figure 3.11 is decreasing.

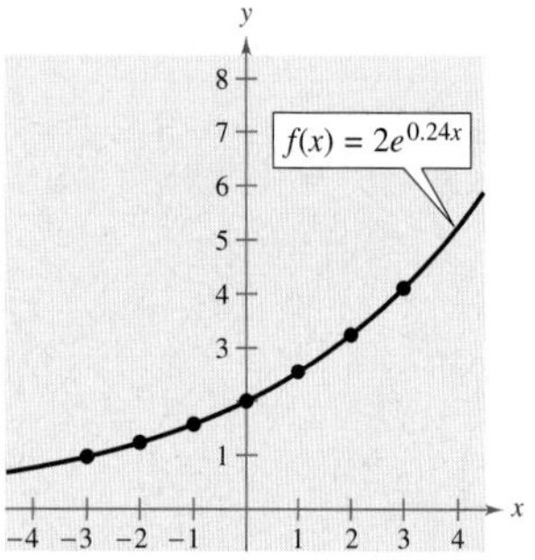

FIGURE 3.10

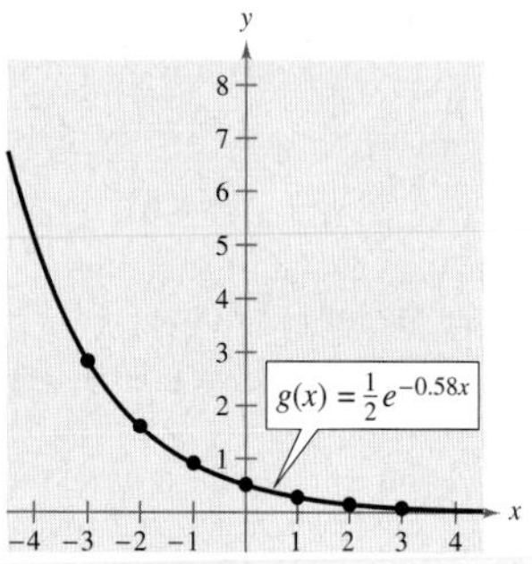

FIGURE 3.11

x	-3	-2	-1	0	1	2	3
$f(x)$	0.974	1.238	1.573	2.000	2.542	3.232	4.109
$g(x)$	2.849	1.595	0.893	0.500	0.280	0.157	0.088

CHECK*Point* Now try Exercise 41.

Applications

One of the most familiar examples of exponential growth is an investment earning *continuously compounded interest.* Using exponential functions, you can *develop* a formula for interest compounded n times per year and show how it leads to continuous compounding.

Suppose a principal P is invested at an annual interest rate r, compounded once per year. If the interest is added to the principal at the end of the year, the new balance P_1 is

$$P_1 = P + Pr$$
$$= P(1 + r).$$

This pattern of multiplying the previous principal by $1 + r$ is then repeated each successive year, as shown below.

Year	*Balance After Each Compounding*
0	$P = P$
1	$P_1 = P(1 + r)$
2	$P_2 = P_1(1 + r) = P(1 + r)(1 + r) = P(1 + r)^2$
3	$P_3 = P_2(1 + r) = P(1 + r)^2(1 + r) = P(1 + r)^3$
⋮	⋮
t	$P_t = P(1 + r)^t$

To accommodate more frequent (quarterly, monthly, or daily) compounding of interest, let n be the number of compoundings per year and let t be the number of years. Then the rate per compounding is r/n and the account balance after t years is

$$A = P\left(1 + \frac{r}{n}\right)^{nt}. \qquad \text{Amount (balance) with } n \text{ compoundings per year}$$

If you let the number of compoundings n increase without bound, the process approaches what is called **continuous compounding.** In the formula for n compoundings per year, let $m = n/r$. This produces

$$A = P\left(1 + \frac{r}{n}\right)^{nt} \qquad \text{Amount with } n \text{ compoundings per year}$$

$$= P\left(1 + \frac{r}{mr}\right)^{mrt} \qquad \text{Substitute } mr \text{ for } n.$$

$$= P\left(1 + \frac{1}{m}\right)^{mrt} \qquad \text{Simplify.}$$

$$= P\left[\left(1 + \frac{1}{m}\right)^{m}\right]^{rt}. \qquad \text{Property of exponents}$$

m	$\left(1 + \frac{1}{m}\right)^m$
1	2
10	2.59374246
100	2.704813829
1,000	2.716923932
10,000	2.718145927
100,000	2.718268237
1,000,000	2.718280469
10,000,000	2.718281693
↓	↓
∞	e

As m increases without bound, the table at the left shows that $[1 + (1/m)]^m \rightarrow e$ as $m \rightarrow \infty$. From this, you can conclude that the formula for continuous compounding is

$$A = Pe^{rt}. \qquad \text{Substitute } e \text{ for } (1 + 1/m)^m.$$

Extra Example 8

On the day of a child's birth, a deposit of $25,000 is made in a trust fund that pays 8.25% interest. Determine the balance in this account on the child's 26th birthday if the interest is compounded

a. quarterly.
$208,941.65

b. monthly.
$211,989.34

c. continuously.
$213,551.03

WARNING/CAUTION

Be sure you see that the annual interest rate must be written in decimal form. For instance, 6% should be written as 0.06.

Formulas for Compound Interest

After t years, the balance A in an account with principal P and annual interest rate r (in decimal form) is given by the following formulas.

1. For n compoundings per year: $A = P\left(1 + \frac{r}{n}\right)^{nt}$

2. For continuous compounding: $A = Pe^{rt}$

Example 8 Compound Interest

A total of $12,000 is invested at an annual interest rate of 9%. Find the balance after 5 years if it is compounded

a. quarterly.

b. monthly.

c. continuously.

Solution

a. For quarterly compounding, you have $n = 4$. So, in 5 years at 9%, the balance is

$$A = P\left(1 + \frac{r}{n}\right)^{nt} \qquad \text{Formula for compound interest}$$

$$= 12{,}000\left(1 + \frac{0.09}{4}\right)^{4(5)} \qquad \text{Substitute for } P, r, n, \text{ and } t.$$

$$\approx \$18{,}726.11. \qquad \text{Use a calculator.}$$

b. For monthly compounding, you have $n = 12$. So, in 5 years at 9%, the balance is

$$A = P\left(1 + \frac{r}{n}\right)^{nt} \qquad \text{Formula for compound interest}$$

$$= 12{,}000\left(1 + \frac{0.09}{12}\right)^{12(5)} \qquad \text{Substitute for } P, r, n, \text{ and } t.$$

$$\approx \$18{,}788.17. \qquad \text{Use a calculator.}$$

c. For continuous compounding, the balance is

$$A = Pe^{rt} \qquad \text{Formula for continuous compounding}$$

$$= 12{,}000e^{0.09(5)} \qquad \text{Substitute for } P, r, \text{ and } t.$$

$$\approx \$18{,}819.75. \qquad \text{Use a calculator.}$$

CHECK*Point* Now try Exercise 59.

In Example 8, note that continuous compounding yields more than quarterly or monthly compounding. This is typical of the two types of compounding. That is, for a given principal, interest rate, and time, continuous compounding will always yield a larger balance than compounding n times per year.

Example 9 Radioactive Decay

The *half-life* of radioactive radium (^{226}Ra) is about 1599 years. That is, for a given amount of radium, *half* of the original amount will remain after 1599 years. After another 1599 years, one-quarter of the original amount will remain, and so on. Let y represent the mass, in grams, of a quantity of radium. The quantity present after t years, then, is $y = 25\left(\frac{1}{2}\right)^{t/1599}$.

a. What is the initial mass (when $t = 0$)?

b. How much of the initial mass is present after 2500 years?

Algebraic Solution

a. $y = 25\left(\dfrac{1}{2}\right)^{t/1599}$ Write original equation.

$= 25\left(\dfrac{1}{2}\right)^{0/1599}$ Substitute 0 for t.

$= 25$ Simplify.

So, the initial mass is 25 grams.

b. $y = 25\left(\dfrac{1}{2}\right)^{t/1599}$ Write original equation.

$= 25\left(\dfrac{1}{2}\right)^{2500/1599}$ Substitute 2500 for t.

$\approx 25\left(\dfrac{1}{2}\right)^{1.563}$ Simplify.

≈ 8.46 Use a calculator.

So, about 8.46 grams is present after 2500 years.

CHECKPoint Now try Exercise 73.

Graphical Solution

Use a graphing utility to graph $y = 25\left(\frac{1}{2}\right)^{t/1599}$.

a. Use the *value* feature or the *zoom* and *trace* features of the graphing utility to determine that when $x = 0$, the value of y is 25, as shown in Figure 3.12. So, the initial mass is 25 grams.

b. Use the *value* feature or the *zoom* and *trace* features of the graphing utility to determine that when $x = 2500$, the value of y is about 8.46, as shown in Figure 3.13. So, about 8.46 grams is present after 2500 years.

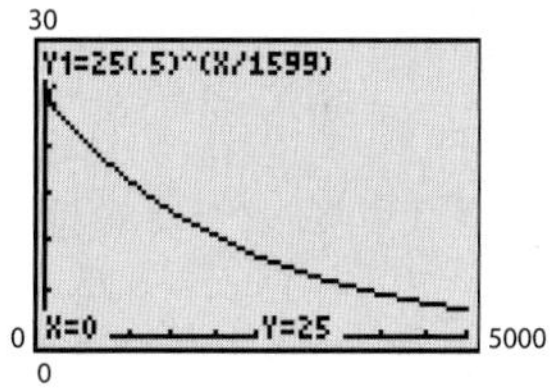

FIGURE 3.12

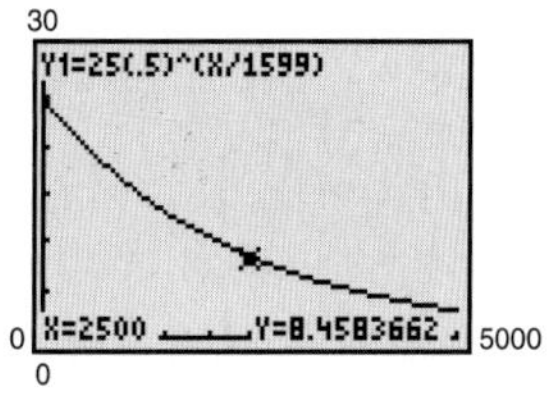

FIGURE 3.13

Classroom Discussion

Identifying Exponential Functions Which of the following functions generated the two tables below? Discuss how you were able to decide. What do these functions have in common? Are any of them the same? If so, explain why.

a. $f_1(x) = 2^{(x+3)}$ b. $f_2(x) = 8\left(\frac{1}{2}\right)^x$ c. $f_3(x) = \left(\frac{1}{2}\right)^{(x-3)}$

d. $f_4(x) = \left(\frac{1}{2}\right)^x + 7$ e. $f_5(x) = 7 + 2^x$ f. $f_6(x) = 8(2^x)$

x	-1	0	1	2	3
$g(x)$	7.5	8	9	11	15

x	-2	-1	0	1	2
$h(x)$	32	16	8	4	2

Create two different exponential functions of the forms $y = a(b)^x$ and $y = c^x + d$ with y-intercepts of $(0, -3)$.

See margin.

Extra Example 9

Let Q represent the mass of radium (^{226}Ra) whose half-life is 1620 years. The quantity of radium present after t years is given by $Q = 16\left(\frac{1}{2}\right)^{t/1620}$.

a. Sketch the graph of the function over the interval from $t = 0$ to $t = 5000$.

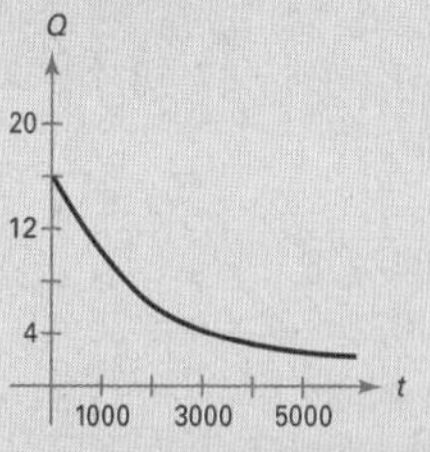

b. Determine the initial quantity (when $t = 0$).

16 grams

c. Determine the quantity present after 1000 years.

10.43 grams

Closing the Lesson

Have students summarize the major points of the lesson and answer the Essential Question: How do you write and graph exponential functions?

- **Evaluate and describe the basic characteristics of translations and reflections of the function $f(x) = a^x$.**
- **Use formulas for compound interest, and recognize that the irrational number e is used in situations where interest is compounded continuously.**
- **Use formulas where $0 < a < 1$ to model exponential decay.**

Classroom Discussion

$g(x)$ can be generated by f_5.

$h(x)$ can be generated by f_2 or f_3.

All six functions have (0, 8) as their y-intercept.

The functions f_2 and f_3 are the same because

$f_2(x) = 8\left(\frac{1}{2}\right)^x = 2^3(2)^{-x} = 2^{(3-x)} = \left(\frac{1}{2}\right)^{-(3-x)}$

$= \left(\frac{1}{2}\right)^{(x-3)} = f_3(x)$.

The functions f_1 and f_6 are the same because

$f_1(x) = 2^{(x+3)} = 2^x2^3 = (8)2^x = f_6(x)$.

Examples of exponential functions with y-intercepts of $(0, -3)$ will vary. Possibilities include $f(x) = -3(2^x)$ and $f(x) = \left(\frac{1}{3}\right)^x - 4$.

4 PRACTICE AND APPLY

Assignment Guide

Transparencies Available
Available at the Instructor's companion site.

Average:
Day 1: pp. 224–226
Exs. 9, 11, 13–16, 21, 25, 26, 35–39 odd, 45, 53, 57, 60, 65, 67, 69, 70, 74, 77–83 odd, 88, 90

Advanced:
Day 1: pp. 224–226
Exs. 12–16, 18, 24–28 even, 36–40 even, 52, 56, 58, 62, 64, 68, 71, 72, 74, 75, 80–88, 90, Project

Block:
pp. 224–226
Exs. 9, 11, 13–16, 21, 25, 26, 35–39 odd, 45, 53, 57, 60, 65, 67, 69, 70, 74, 77–83 odd, 88, 90 (with Chapter 2 Test)

23. Shift the graph of f one unit upward.
24. Shift the graph of f three units to the right.
25. Reflect the graph of f in the x-axis and shift three units upward.
26. Reflect the graph of f in the y-axis and shift three units to the right.
27. Reflect the graph of f in the origin.
28. Reflect the graph of f in the x-axis and shift five units upward.

29.

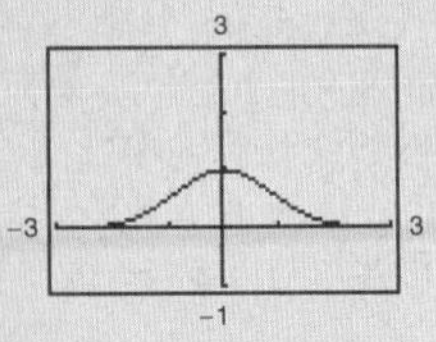

30.

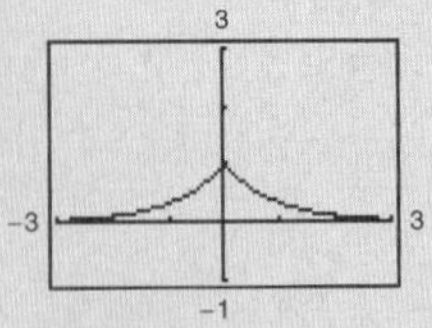

31.

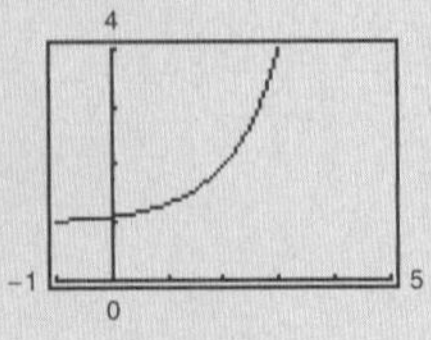

32.

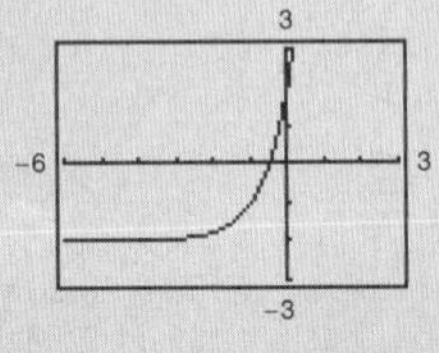

3.1 EXERCISES

See www.CalcChat.com for worked-out solutions to odd-numbered exercises.

VOCABULARY: Fill in the blanks.

1. Polynomial and rational functions are examples of algebraic functions.
2. Exponential and logarithmic functions are examples of nonalgebraic functions, also called transcendental functions.
3. You can use the One-to-One Property to solve simple exponential equations.
4. The exponential function given by $f(x) = e^x$ is called the natural exponential function, and the base e is called the natural base.
5. To find the amount A in an account after t years with principal P and an annual interest rate r compounded n times per year, you can use the formula $A = P\left(1 + \frac{r}{n}\right)^{nt}$.
6. To find the amount A in an account after t years with principal P and an annual interest rate r compounded continuously, you can use the formula $A = Pe^{rt}$.

SKILLS AND APPLICATIONS

In Exercises 7–12, evaluate the function at the indicated value of x. Round your result to three decimal places.

Function	Value	
7. $f(x) = 0.9^x$	$x = 1.4$	0.863
8. $f(x) = 2.3^x$	$x = \frac{3}{2}$	3.488
9. $f(x) = 5^x$	$x = -\pi$	0.006
10. $f(x) = \left(\frac{2}{3}\right)^{5x}$	$x = \frac{3}{10}$	0.544
11. $g(x) = 5000(2^x)$	$x = -1.5$	1767.767
12. $f(x) = 200(1.2)^{12x}$	$x = 24$	1.274×10^{25}

In Exercises 13–16, match the exponential function with its graph. [The graphs are labeled (a), (b), (c), and (d).]

(a)

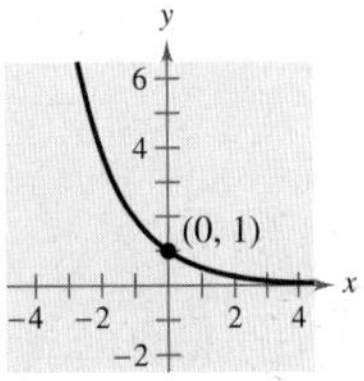

(b)

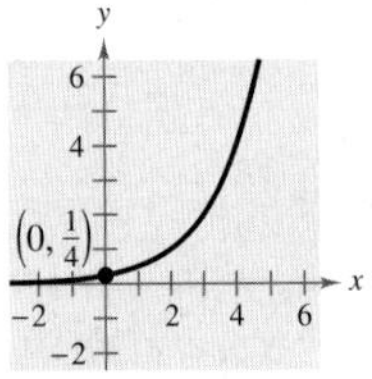

(c)

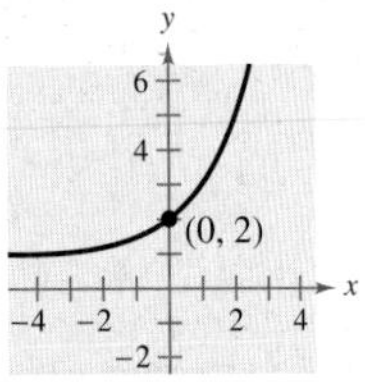

(d)

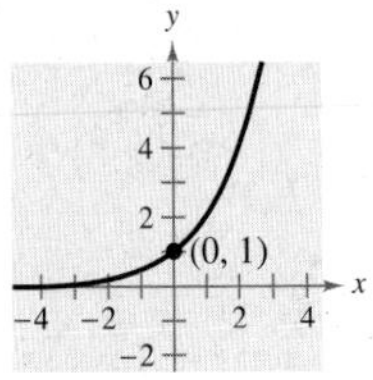

13. $f(x) = 2^x$ d
14. $f(x) = 2^x + 1$ c
15. $f(x) = 2^{-x}$ a
16. $f(x) = 2^{x-2}$ b

In Exercises 17–22, use a graphing utility to construct a table of values for the function. Then sketch the graph of the function. 17–22. See margin.

17. $f(x) = \left(\frac{1}{2}\right)^x$
18. $f(x) = \left(\frac{1}{2}\right)^{-x}$
19. $f(x) = 6^{-x}$
20. $f(x) = 6^x$
21. $f(x) = 2^{x-1}$
22. $f(x) = 4^{x-3} + 3$

In Exercises 23–28, use the graph of f to describe the transformation that yields the graph of g. 23–28. See margin.

23. $f(x) = 3^x$, $g(x) = 3^x + 1$
24. $f(x) = 4^x$, $g(x) = 4^{x-3}$
25. $f(x) = 2^x$, $g(x) = 3 - 2^x$
26. $f(x) = 10^x$, $g(x) = 10^{-x+3}$
27. $f(x) = \left(\frac{7}{2}\right)^x$, $g(x) = -\left(\frac{7}{2}\right)^{-x}$
28. $f(x) = 0.3^x$, $g(x) = -0.3^x + 5$

In Exercises 29–32, use a graphing utility to graph the exponential function. 29–32. See margin.

29. $y = 2^{-x^2}$
30. $y = 3^{-|x|}$
31. $y = 3^{x-2} + 1$
32. $y = 4^{x+1} - 2$

In Exercises 33–38, evaluate the function at the indicated value of x. Round your result to three decimal places.

Function	Value	
33. $h(x) = e^{-x}$	$x = \frac{3}{4}$	0.472
34. $f(x) = e^x$	$x = 3.2$	24.533
35. $f(x) = 2e^{-5x}$	$x = 10$	3.857×10^{-22}
36. $f(x) = 1.5e^{x/2}$	$x = 240$	1.956×10^{52}
37. $f(x) = 5000e^{0.06x}$	$x = 6$	7166.647
38. $f(x) = 250e^{0.05x}$	$x = 20$	679.570

17–22. See Additional Answers beginning on page AA1.

In Exercises 39–44, use a graphing utility to construct a table of values for the function. Then sketch the graph of the function. 39–44. See margin.

39. $f(x) = e^x$ **40.** $f(x) = e^{-x}$

41. $f(x) = 3e^{x+4}$ **42.** $f(x) = 2e^{-0.5x}$

43. $f(x) = 2e^{x-2} + 4$ **44.** $f(x) = 2 + e^{x-5}$

In Exercises 45–50, use a graphing utility to graph the exponential function. 45–50. See margin.

45. $y = 1.08^{-5x}$ **46.** $y = 1.08^{5x}$

47. $s(t) = 2e^{0.12t}$ **48.** $s(t) = 3e^{-0.2t}$

49. $g(x) = 1 + e^{-x}$ **50.** $h(x) = e^{x-2}$

In Exercises 51–58, use the One-to-One Property to solve the equation for *x*.

51. $3^{x+1} = 27$ $x = 2$ **52.** $2^{x-3} = 16$ $x = 7$

53. $\left(\frac{1}{2}\right)^x = 32$ $x = -5$ **54.** $5^{x-2} = \frac{1}{125}$ $x = -1$

55. $e^{3x+2} = e^3$ $x = \frac{1}{3}$ **56.** $e^{2x-1} = e^4$ $x = \frac{5}{2}$

57. $e^{x^2-3} = e^{2x}$ $x = 3, -1$ **58.** $e^{x^2+6} = e^{5x}$ $x = 2, 3$

COMPOUND INTEREST In Exercises 59–62, complete the table to determine the balance *A* for *P* dollars invested at rate *r* for *t* years and compounded *n* times per year.

n	1	2	4	12	365	Continuous
A						

59–62. See margin.

59. $P = \$1500$, $r = 2\%$, $t = 10$ years

60. $P = \$2500$, $r = 3.5\%$, $t = 10$ years

61. $P = \$2500$, $r = 4\%$, $t = 20$ years

62. $P = \$1000$, $r = 6\%$, $t = 40$ years

COMPOUND INTEREST In Exercises 63–66, complete the table to determine the balance *A* for \$12,000 invested at rate *r* for *t* years, compounded continuously.

t	10	20	30	40	50
A					

63–66. See margin.

63. $r = 4\%$ **64.** $r = 6\%$

65. $r = 6.5\%$ **66.** $r = 3.5\%$

67. TRUST FUND On the day of a child's birth, a deposit of \$30,000 is made in a trust fund that pays 5% interest, compounded continuously. Determine the balance in this account on the child's 25th birthday. \$104,710.29

68. TRUST FUND A deposit of \$5000 is made in a trust fund that pays 7.5% interest, compounded continuously. It is specified that the balance will be given to the college from which the donor graduated after the money has earned interest for 50 years. How much will the college receive? \$212,605.41

69. INFLATION If the annual rate of inflation averages 4% over the next 10 years, the approximate costs *C* of goods or services during any year in that decade will be modeled by $C(t) = P(1.04)^t$, where *t* is the time in years and *P* is the present cost. The price of an oil change for your car is presently \$23.95. Estimate the price 10 years from now. \$35.45

70. COMPUTER VIRUS The number *V* of computers infected by a computer virus increases according to the model $V(t) = 100e^{4.6052t}$, where *t* is the time in hours. Find the number of computers infected after (a) 1 hour, (b) 1.5 hours, and (c) 2 hours. See margin.

71. POPULATION GROWTH The projected populations of California for the years 2015 through 2030 can be modeled by $P = 34.696e^{0.0098t}$, where *P* is the population (in millions) and *t* is the time (in years), with $t = 15$ corresponding to 2015. (Source: U.S. Census Bureau)

(a) Use a graphing utility to graph the function for the years 2015 through 2030. See margin.

(b) Use the *table* feature of a graphing utility to create a table of values for the same time period as in part (a). See margin.

(c) According to the model, when will the population of California exceed 50 million? 2038

72. POPULATION The populations *P* (in millions) of Italy from 1990 through 2008 can be approximated by the model $P = 56.8e^{0.0015t}$, where *t* represents the year, with $t = 0$ corresponding to 1990. (Source: U.S. Census Bureau, International Data Base) See margin.

(a) According to the model, is the population of Italy increasing or decreasing? Explain.

(b) Find the populations of Italy in 2000 and 2008.

(c) Use the model to predict the populations of Italy in 2015 and 2020.

73. RADIOACTIVE DECAY Let *Q* represent a mass of radioactive plutonium (^{239}Pu) (in grams), whose half-life is 24,100 years. The quantity of plutonium present after *t* years is $Q = 16\left(\frac{1}{2}\right)^{t/24,100}$.

(a) Determine the initial quantity (when $t = 0$). 16 g

(b) Determine the quantity present after 75,000 years. 1.85 g

(c) Use a graphing utility to graph the function over the interval $t = 0$ to $t = 150,000$. See margin.

45.

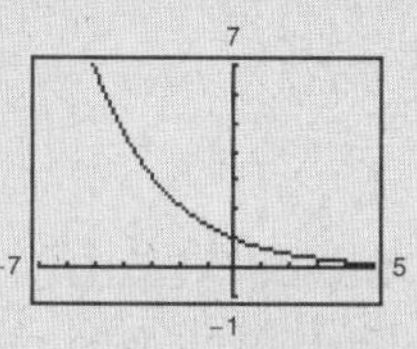

46.

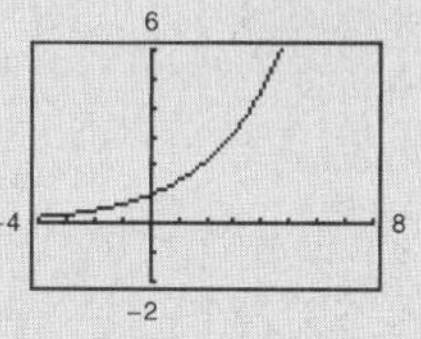

47.

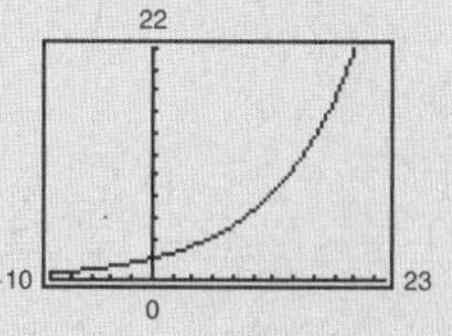

48.

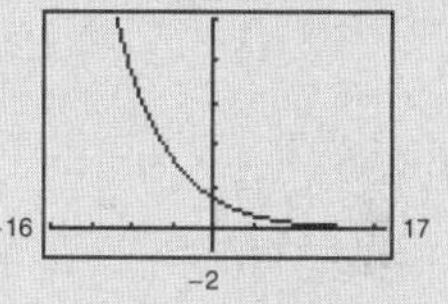

49.

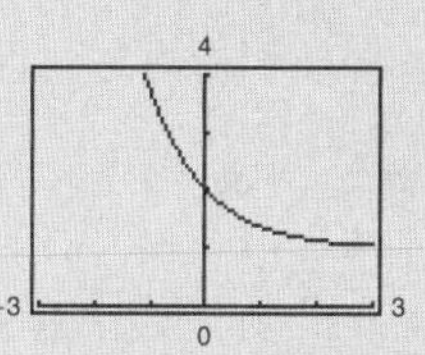

50.

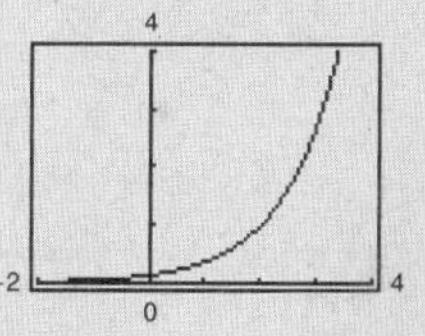

70. (a) $V(1) \approx 10,000$
(b) $V(1.5) \approx 100,004$
(c) $V(2) \approx 1,000,060$

71. (a)

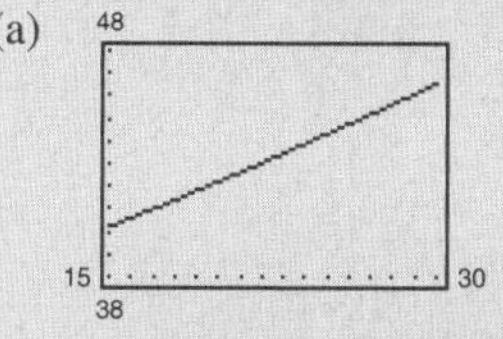

72. (a) Increasing because the exponent is positive.
(b) $P(10) \approx 57.66$ million; $P(18) \approx 58.35$ million
(c) $P(25) \approx 58.97$ million; $P(30) \approx 59.41$ million

73. (c)

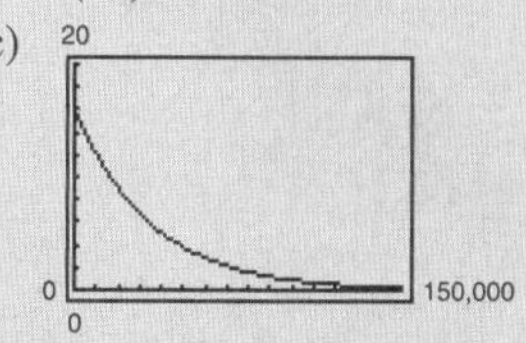

39–44, 59–66, 71(b). See Additional Answers beginning on page AA1.

74. RADIOACTIVE DECAY Let Q represent a mass of carbon 14 (^{14}C) (in grams), whose half-life is 5715 years. The quantity of carbon 14 present after t years is $Q = 10\left(\frac{1}{2}\right)^{t/5715}$.

(a) Determine the initial quantity (when $t = 0$). 10 g

(b) Determine the quantity present after 2000 years. 7.85 g

(c) Sketch the graph of this function over the interval $t = 0$ to $t = 10{,}000$. See margin.

75. DEPRECIATION After t years, the value of a wheelchair conversion van that originally cost \$30,500 depreciates so that each year it is worth $\frac{7}{8}$ of its value for the previous year.

(a) Find a model for $V(t)$, the value of the van after t years. $V(t) = 30{,}500\left(\frac{7}{8}\right)^t$

(b) Determine the value of the van 4 years after it was purchased. \$17,878.54

76. DRUG CONCENTRATION Immediately following an injection, the concentration of a drug in the bloodstream is 300 milligrams per milliliter. After t hours, the concentration is 75% of the level of the previous hour.

(a) Find a model for $C(t)$, the concentration of the drug after t hours. $300(0.75)^t$

(b) Determine the concentration of the drug after 8 hours. 30 mg/mL

EXPLORATION

TRUE OR FALSE? In Exercises 77 and 78, determine whether the statement is true or false. Justify your answer.

77. The line $y = -2$ is an asymptote for the graph of $f(x) = 10^x - 2$. See margin.

78. $e = \dfrac{271{,}801}{99{,}990}$ False. e is an irrational number.

THINK ABOUT IT In Exercises 79–82, use properties of exponents to determine which functions (if any) are the same.

79. $f(x) = 3^{x-2}$ $f(x) = h(x)$
$g(x) = 3^x - 9$
$h(x) = \frac{1}{9}(3^x)$

80. $f(x) = 4^x + 12$ $g(x) = h(x)$
$g(x) = 2^{2x+6}$
$h(x) = 64(4^x)$

81. $f(x) = 16(4^{-x})$
$g(x) = \left(\frac{1}{4}\right)^{x-2}$
$h(x) = 16(2^{-2x})$
$f(x) = g(x) = h(x)$

82. $f(x) = e^{-x} + 3$
$g(x) = e^{3-x}$ None are equal.
$h(x) = -e^{x-3}$

83. Graph the functions given by $y = 3^x$ and $y = 4^x$ and use the graphs to solve each inequality. See margin for graph.

(a) $4^x < 3^x$ $x < 0$ (b) $4^x > 3^x$ $x > 0$

84. Use a graphing utility to graph each function. Use the graph to find where the function is increasing and decreasing, and approximate any relative maximum or minimum values. See margin.

(a) $f(x) = x^2e^{-x}$ (b) $g(x) = x2^{3-x}$

85. GRAPHICAL ANALYSIS Use a graphing utility to graph $y_1 = (1 + 1/x)^x$ and $y_2 = e$ in the same viewing window. Using the *trace* feature, explain what happens to the graph of y_1 as x increases. See margin.

86. GRAPHICAL ANALYSIS Use a graphing utility to graph

$$f(x) = \left(1 + \frac{0.5}{x}\right)^x \quad \text{and} \quad g(x) = e^{0.5}$$

in the same viewing window. What is the relationship between f and g as x increases and decreases without bound? See margin.

87. GRAPHICAL ANALYSIS Use a graphing utility to graph each pair of functions in the same viewing window. Describe any similarities and differences in the graphs.

(a) $y_1 = 2^x, y_2 = x^2$ (b) $y_1 = 3^x, y_2 = x^3$ See margin.

88. THINK ABOUT IT Which functions are exponential?

(a) $3x$ (b) $3x^2$ (c) 3^x (d) 2^{-x} c, d

89. COMPOUND INTEREST Use the formula

$$A = P\left(1 + \frac{r}{n}\right)^{nt}$$

to calculate the balance of an account when $P = \$3000$, $r = 6\%$, and $t = 10$ years, and compounding is done (a) by the day, (b) by the hour, (c) by the minute, and (d) by the second. Does increasing the number of compoundings per year result in unlimited growth of the balance of the account? Explain. See margin.

90. CAPSTONE The figure shows the graphs of $y = 2^x$, $y = e^x$, $y = 10^x$, $y = 2^{-x}$, $y = e^{-x}$, and $y = 10^{-x}$. Match each function with its graph. [The graphs are labeled (a) through (f).] Explain your reasoning.

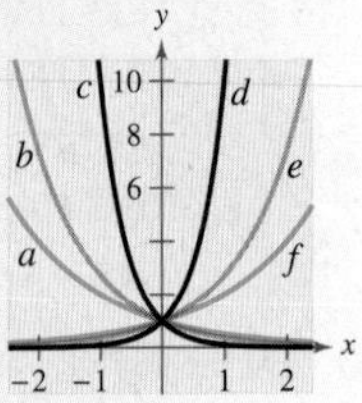

(a) $y = 2^{-x}$
(b) $y = e^{-x}$
(c) $y = 10^{-x}$
(d) $y = 10^x$
(e) $y = e^x$
(f) $y = 2^x$

PROJECT: POPULATION PER SQUARE MILE To work an extended application analyzing the population per square mile of the United States, visit this text's website at *academic.cengage.com*. (Data Source: U.S. Census Bureau)

5 ASSESS AND RETEACH

Daily Homework Quiz

Transparency Available
Available at the Instructor's companion site.

74. (c)

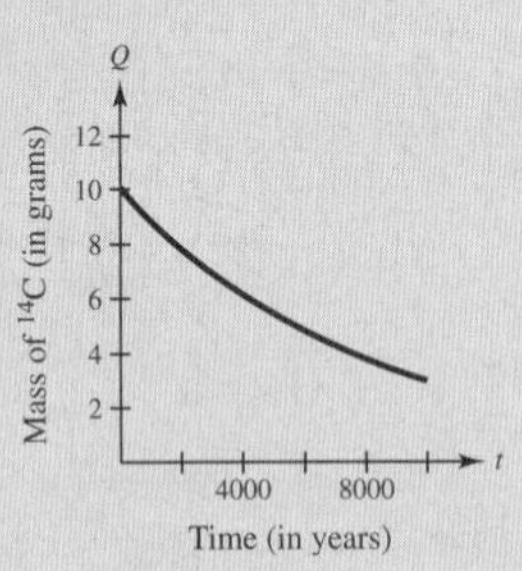

77. True. As $x \to -\infty, f(x) \to -2$ but never reaches -2.

83.

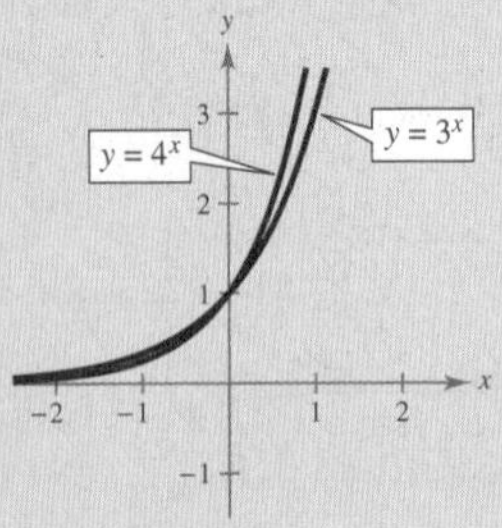

84. (a)

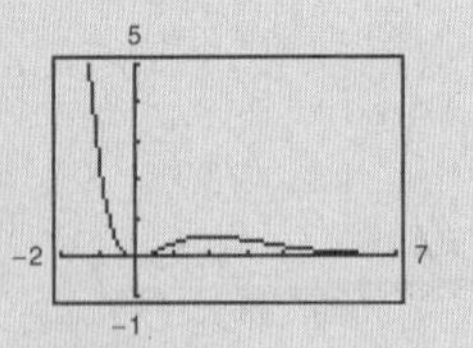

Decreasing: $(-\infty, 0), (2, \infty)$
Increasing: $(0, 2)$
Relative maximum: $(2, 4e^{-2})$
Relative minimum: $(0, 0)$

(b)

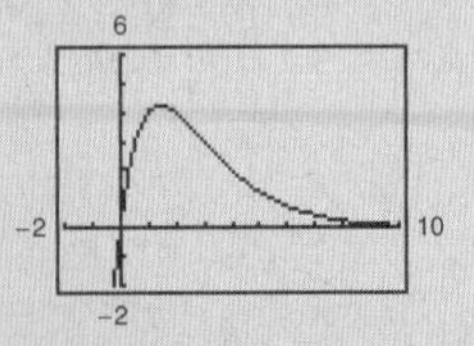

Decreasing: $(1.44, \infty)$
Increasing: $(-\infty, 1.44)$
Relative maximum: $(1.44, 4.25)$

85.

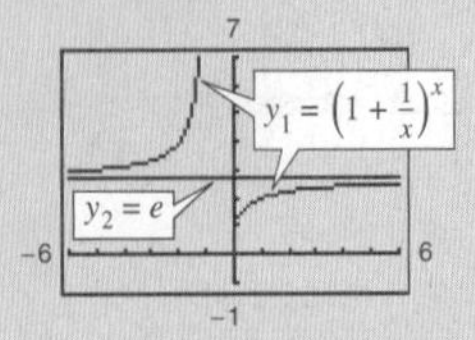

As the x-value increases, y_1 approaches the value of e.

86.

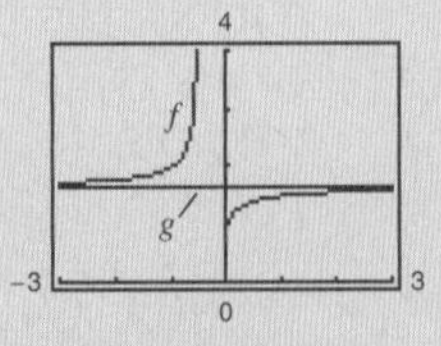

As $x \to \infty, f(x) \to g(x)$.
As $x \to -\infty, f(x) \to g(x)$.

87. (a)

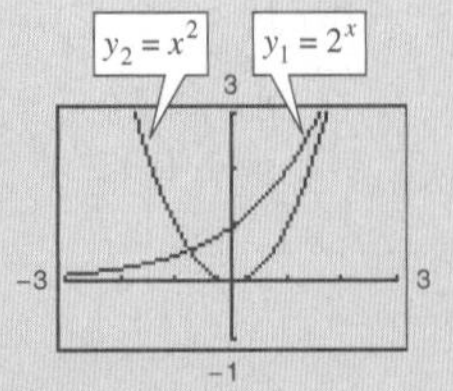

(b)

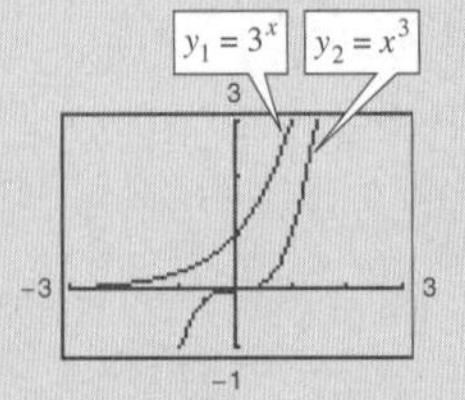

In both viewing windows, the constant raised to a variable power increases more rapidly than the variable raised to a constant power.

89. (a) $A = \$5466.09$ (b) $A = \$5466.35$
(c) $A = \$5466.36$ (d) $A = \$5466.38$
No. Answers will vary.

3.2 Logarithmic Functions and Their Graphs

What you should learn

- Recognize and evaluate logarithmic functions with base *a*.
- Graph logarithmic functions.
- Recognize, evaluate, and graph natural logarithmic functions.
- Use logarithmic functions to model and solve real-life problems.

Why you should learn it

Logarithmic functions are often used to model scientific observations. For instance, in Exercise 97 on page 236, a logarithmic function is used to model human memory.

Logarithmic Functions

In Section 1.9, you studied the concept of an inverse function. There, you learned that if a function is one-to-one—that is, if the function has the property that no horizontal line intersects the graph of the function more than once—the function must have an inverse function. By looking back at the graphs of the exponential functions introduced in Section 3.1, you will see that every function of the form $f(x) = a^x$ passes the Horizontal Line Test and therefore must have an inverse function. This inverse function is called the **logarithmic function with base *a*.**

> **Definition of Logarithmic Function with Base *a***
>
> For $x > 0$, $a > 0$, and $a \neq 1$,
>
> $y = \log_a x$ if and only if $x = a^y$.
>
> The function given by
>
> $f(x) = \log_a x$ Read as "log base *a* of *x*."
>
> is called the **logarithmic function with base *a*.**

The equations

$$y = \log_a x \quad \text{and} \quad x = a^y$$

are equivalent. The first equation is in logarithmic form and the second is in exponential form. For example, the logarithmic equation $2 = \log_3 9$ can be rewritten in exponential form as $9 = 3^2$. The exponential equation $5^3 = 125$ can be rewritten in logarithmic form as $\log_5 125 = 3$.

When evaluating logarithms, remember that *a logarithm is an exponent.* This means that $\log_a x$ is the exponent to which *a* must be raised to obtain *x*. For instance, $\log_2 8 = 3$ because 2 must be raised to the third power to get 8.

Example 1 Evaluating Logarithms

Use the definition of logarithmic function to evaluate each logarithm at the indicated value of *x*.

a. $f(x) = \log_2 x, \quad x = 32$ **b.** $f(x) = \log_3 x, \quad x = 1$

c. $f(x) = \log_4 x, \quad x = 2$ **d.** $f(x) = \log_{10} x, \quad x = \frac{1}{100}$

Solution

a. $f(32) = \log_2 32 = 5$ because $2^5 = 32$.

b. $f(1) = \log_3 1 = 0$ because $3^0 = 1$.

c. $f(2) = \log_4 2 = \frac{1}{2}$ because $4^{1/2} = \sqrt{4} = 2$.

d. $f\left(\frac{1}{100}\right) = \log_{10} \frac{1}{100} = -2$ because $10^{-2} = \frac{1}{10^2} = \frac{1}{100}$.

CHECKPoint Now try Exercise 23.

1 PLAN AND PREPARE

Warm-up Exercises

Transparency Available
Available at the Instructor's companion site.

Notetaking Guide

Transparency Available
Promotes interactive learning and notetaking skills.
Available at the Instructor's companion site.

Animated Precalculus

An **Animated Precalculus** tutorial is available at the Student companion site for **Section 3.2.**

Pacing

Average: 2 days
Advanced: 2 days
Block: 1 block

2 FOCUS AND MOTIVATE

Essential Question

How do you recognize, evaluate, and graph logarithmic functions?
Tell students that they will learn how to answer this question by studying properties of logarithms and the relationship between logarithmic and exponential form.

Resource Planning Guide

Chapter Resources

- Complete Solutions Guide

Workbooks

- Notetaking Guide
- Student Solutions Guide

Interactive Technology

- Instructor Success Organizer
- Notetaking Guide IAE
- Instructional DVDs
- Animated Precalculus
- PowerLecture with ExamView

3 TEACH

Extra Example 1

Use the definition of a logarithmic function to evaluate each logarithm at the indicated value of x.

a. $f(x) = \log_4 x$, $x = 16$
2

b. $f(x) = \log_2 x$, $x = 64$
6

c. $f(x) = \log_5 x$, $x = 1$
0

d. $f(x) = \log_3 x$, $x = \frac{1}{81}$
−4

Extra Example 2

Use a calculator to evaluate the function given by $f(x) = \log x$ at each value of x to four decimal places.

a. $x = 100$
2

b. $x = \frac{1}{5}$
−0.6990

c. $x = 3.25$
0.5119

d. $x = -4$
ERROR *Note:* Part (d) may also give a complex number as the answer.

Avoiding Common Errors

Students often encounter confusion with the meaning of the logarithmic function. Remind students that a logarithm is an exponent. Converting back and forth from logarithmic form to exponential form supports this concept.

Extra Example 3

Simplify.

a. $\log_5 1$
0

b. $\log_{\sqrt{11}} \sqrt{11}$
1

c. $8^{\log_8 30}$
30

The logarithmic function with base 10 is called the **common logarithmic function.** It is denoted by $\log_{10}$ or simply by log. On most calculators, this function is denoted by LOG. Example 2 shows how to use a calculator to evaluate common logarithmic functions. You will learn how to use a calculator to calculate logarithms to any base in the next section.

Example 2 Evaluating Common Logarithms on a Calculator

Use a calculator to evaluate the function given by $f(x) = \log x$ at each value of x.

a. $x = 10$ **b.** $x = \frac{1}{3}$ **c.** $x = 2.5$ **d.** $x = -2$

Solution

Function Value	*Graphing Calculator Keystrokes*	*Display*
a. $f(10) = \log 10$	LOG 10 ENTER	1
b. $f(\frac{1}{3}) = \log \frac{1}{3}$	LOG (1 ÷ 3) ENTER	−0.4771213
c. $f(2.5) = \log 2.5$	LOG 2.5 ENTER	0.3979400
d. $f(-2) = \log(-2)$	LOG (−) 2 ENTER	ERROR

Note that the calculator displays an error message (or a complex number) when you try to evaluate $\log(-2)$. The reason for this is that there is no real number power to which 10 can be raised to obtain -2.

CHECK*Point* Now try Exercise 29.

The following properties follow directly from the definition of the logarithmic function with base a.

Properties of Logarithms

1. $\log_a 1 = 0$ because $a^0 = 1$.
2. $\log_a a = 1$ because $a^1 = a$.
3. $\log_a a^x = x$ and $a^{\log_a x} = x$ — Inverse Properties
4. If $\log_a x = \log_a y$, then $x = y$. — One-to-One Property

Example 3 Using Properties of Logarithms

a. Simplify: $\log_4 1$ **b.** Simplify: $\log_{\sqrt{7}} \sqrt{7}$ **c.** Simplify: $6^{\log_6 20}$

Solution

a. Using Property 1, it follows that $\log_4 1 = 0$.

b. Using Property 2, you can conclude that $\log_{\sqrt{7}} \sqrt{7} = 1$.

c. Using the Inverse Property (Property 3), it follows that $6^{\log_6 20} = 20$.

CHECK*Point* Now try Exercise 33.

You can use the One-to-One Property (Property 4) to solve simple logarithmic equations, as shown in Example 4.

Example 4 Using the One-to-One Property

a. $\log_3 x = \log_3 12$ Original equation

$x = 12$ One-to-One Property

b. $\log(2x + 1) = \log 3x \Rightarrow 2x + 1 = 3x \Rightarrow 1 = x$

c. $\log_4(x^2 - 6) = \log_4 10 \Rightarrow x^2 - 6 = 10 \Rightarrow x^2 = 16 \Rightarrow x = \pm 4$

CHECKPoint Now try Exercise 85.

Graphs of Logarithmic Functions

To sketch the graph of $y = \log_a x$, you can use the fact that the graphs of inverse functions are reflections of each other in the line $y = x$.

Example 5 Graphs of Exponential and Logarithmic Functions

In the same coordinate plane, sketch the graph of each function.

a. $f(x) = 2^x$ **b.** $g(x) = \log_2 x$

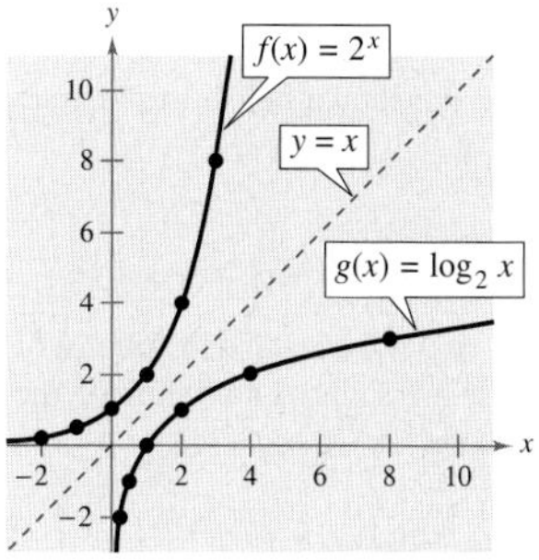

FIGURE 3.14

Solution

a. For $f(x) = 2^x$, construct a table of values. By plotting these points and connecting them with a smooth curve, you obtain the graph shown in Figure 3.14.

x	-2	-1	0	1	2	3
$f(x) = 2^x$	$\frac{1}{4}$	$\frac{1}{2}$	1	2	4	8

b. Because $g(x) = \log_2 x$ is the inverse function of $f(x) = 2^x$, the graph of g is obtained by plotting the points $(f(x), x)$ and connecting them with a smooth curve. The graph of g is a reflection of the graph of f in the line $y = x$, as shown in Figure 3.14.

CHECKPoint Now try Exercise 37.

Example 6 Sketching the Graph of a Logarithmic Function

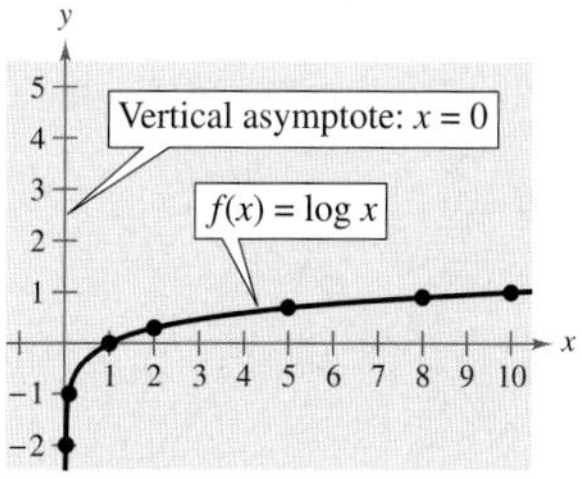

FIGURE 3.15

Sketch the graph of the common logarithmic function $f(x) = \log x$. Identify the vertical asymptote.

Solution

Begin by constructing a table of values. Note that some of the values can be obtained without a calculator by using the Inverse Property of Logarithms. Others require a calculator. Next, plot the points and connect them with a smooth curve, as shown in Figure 3.15. The vertical asymptote is $x = 0$ (y-axis).

	Without calculator				With calculator		
x	$\frac{1}{100}$	$\frac{1}{10}$	1	10	2	5	8
$f(x) = \log x$	-2	-1	0	1	0.301	0.699	0.903

CHECKPoint Now try Exercise 43.

Extra Example 4

Solve.

a. $\log_5 y = \log_5 16$

$y = 16$

b. $\log(4 - 3x) = \log(x + 2)$

$x = \frac{1}{2}$

c. $\log_3(x^2 + 4) = \log_3 29$

$x = \pm 5$

Extra Example 5

In the same coordinate plane, sketch the graph of each function.

a. $f(x) = 4^x$

b. $g(x) = \log_4 x$

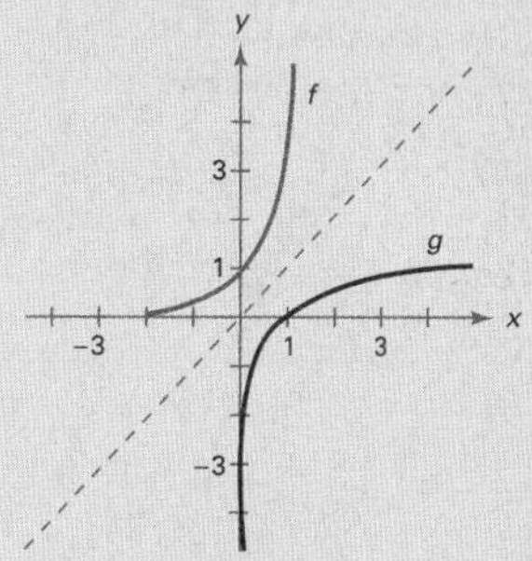

Extra Example 6

Sketch the graph of $f(x) = \log\left(\frac{x}{4}\right)$.

Identify the vertical asymptote.

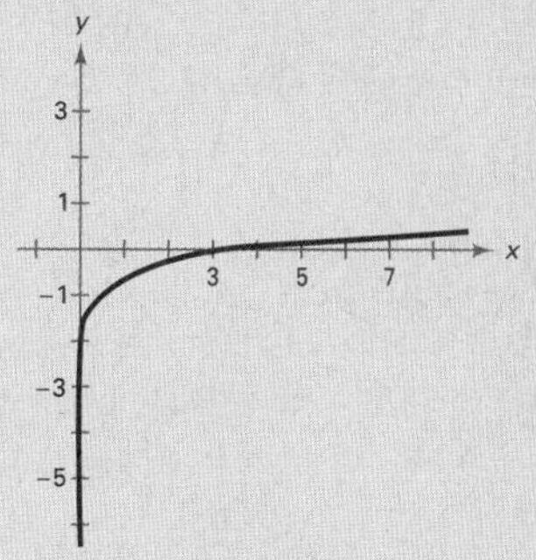

Vertical asymptote: $x = 0$

Extra Example 7

Describe the graph as a transformation of the graph of $f(x) = \log_3 x$.

a. $g(x) = \log_3 x - 1$

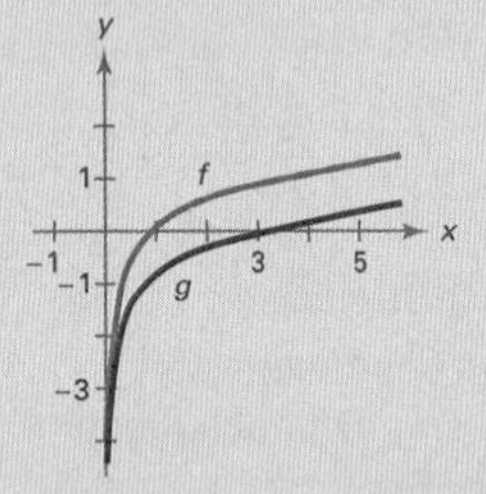

Because $g(x) = \log_3 x - 1 = f(x) - 1$, the graph of g can be obtained by shifting the graph of f one unit downward.

b. $h(x) = \log_3(x + 2)$

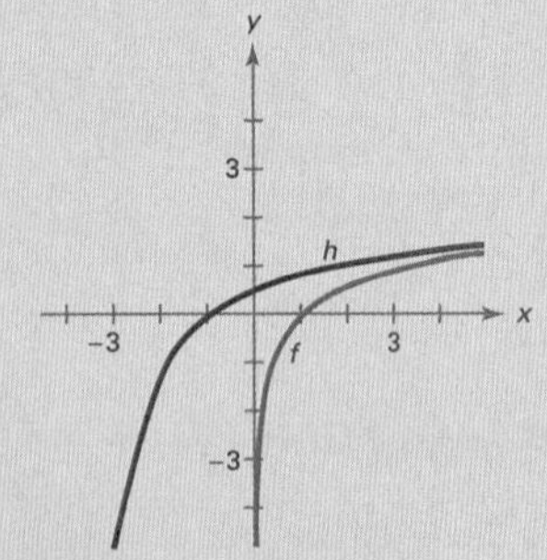

Because $h(x) = \log_3(x + 2) = f(x + 2)$, the graph of h can be obtained by shifting the graph of f two units to the left.

The nature of the graph in Figure 3.15 is typical of functions of the form $f(x) = \log_a x$, $a > 1$. They have one x-intercept and one vertical asymptote. Notice how slowly the graph rises for $x > 1$. The basic characteristics of logarithmic graphs are summarized in Figure 3.16.

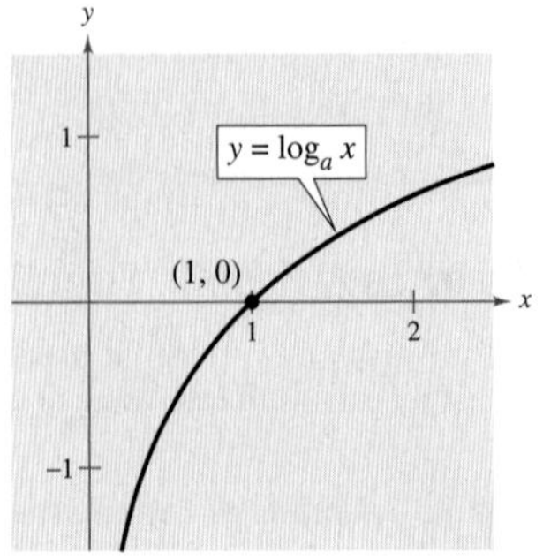

FIGURE 3.16

Graph of $y = \log_a x$, $a > 1$

- Domain: $(0, \infty)$
- Range: $(-\infty, \infty)$
- x-intercept: $(1, 0)$
- Increasing
- One-to-one, therefore has an inverse function
- y-axis is a vertical asymptote ($\log_a x \to -\infty$ as $x \to 0^+$).
- Continuous
- Reflection of graph of $y = a^x$ about the line $y = x$

The basic characteristics of the graph of $f(x) = a^x$ are shown below to illustrate the inverse relation between $f(x) = a^x$ and $g(x) = \log_a x$.

- Domain: $(-\infty, \infty)$
- Range: $(0, \infty)$
- y-intercept: $(0,1)$
- x-axis is a horizontal asymptote ($a^x \to 0$ as $x \to -\infty$).

In the next example, the graph of $y = \log_a x$ is used to sketch the graphs of functions of the form $f(x) = b \pm \log_a(x + c)$. Notice how a horizontal shift of the graph results in a horizontal shift of the vertical asymptote.

Study Tip

You can use your understanding of transformations to identify vertical asymptotes of logarithmic functions. For instance, in Example 7(a), the graph of $g(x) = f(x - 1)$ shifts the graph of $f(x)$ one unit to the right. So, the vertical asymptote of $g(x)$ is $x = 1$, one unit to the right of the vertical asymptote of the graph of $f(x)$.

Algebra Help

You can review the techniques for shifting, reflecting, and stretching graphs in Section 1.7.

Example 7 Shifting Graphs of Logarithmic Functions

The graph of each of the functions is similar to the graph of $f(x) = \log x$.

a. Because $g(x) = \log(x - 1) = f(x - 1)$, the graph of g can be obtained by shifting the graph of f one unit to the right, as shown in Figure 3.17.

b. Because $h(x) = 2 + \log x = 2 + f(x)$, the graph of h can be obtained by shifting the graph of f two units upward, as shown in Figure 3.18.

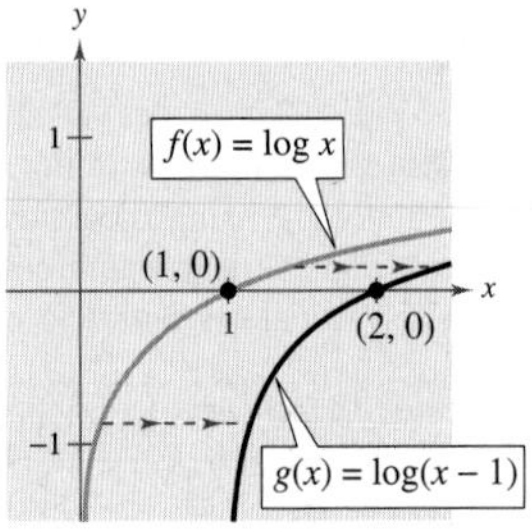

FIGURE 3.17

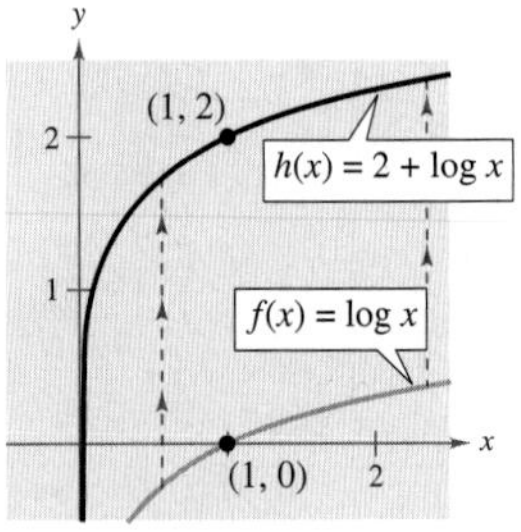

FIGURE 3.18

CHECKPoint Now try Exercise 45.

The Natural Logarithmic Function

By looking back at the graph of the natural exponential function introduced on page 220 in Section 3.1, you will see that $f(x) = e^x$ is one-to-one and so has an inverse function. This inverse function is called the **natural logarithmic function** and is denoted by the special symbol ln x, read as "the natural log of x" or "el en of x." Note that the natural logarithm is written without a base. The base is understood to be e.

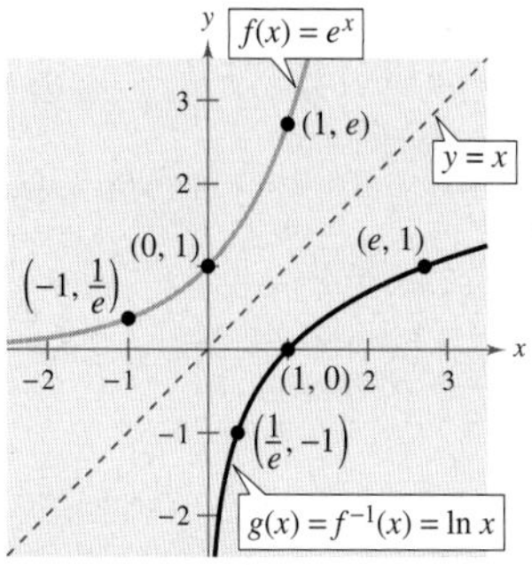

Reflection of graph of $f(x) = e^x$ about the line $y = x$
FIGURE 3.19

The Natural Logarithmic Function

The function defined by

$$f(x) = \log_e x = \ln x, \quad x > 0$$

is called the **natural logarithmic function.**

The definition above implies that the natural logarithmic function and the natural exponential function are inverse functions of each other. So, every logarithmic equation can be written in an equivalent exponential form, and every exponential equation can be written in logarithmic form. That is, $y = \ln x$ and $x = e^y$ are equivalent equations.

Because the functions given by $f(x) = e^x$ and $g(x) = \ln x$ are inverse functions of each other, their graphs are reflections of each other in the line $y = x$. This reflective property is illustrated in Figure 3.19.

On most calculators, the natural logarithm is denoted by LN, as illustrated in Example 8.

Example 8 Evaluating the Natural Logarithmic Function

Use a calculator to evaluate the function given by $f(x) = \ln x$ for each value of x.

a. $x = 2$
b. $x = 0.3$
c. $x = -1$
d. $x = 1 + \sqrt{2}$

Solution

	Function Value	Graphing Calculator Keystrokes	Display
a.	$f(2) = \ln 2$	LN 2 ENTER	0.6931472
b.	$f(0.3) = \ln 0.3$	LN .3 ENTER	−1.2039728
c.	$f(-1) = \ln(-1)$	LN (−) 1 ENTER	ERROR
d.	$f(1 + \sqrt{2}) = \ln(1 + \sqrt{2})$	LN (1 + √ 2) ENTER	0.8813736

CHECKPoint Now try Exercise 67.

WARNING / CAUTION

Notice that as with every other logarithmic function, the domain of the natural logarithmic function is the set of *positive real numbers*—be sure you see that ln x is not defined for zero or for negative numbers.

In Example 8, be sure you see that $\ln(-1)$ gives an error message on most calculators. (Some calculators may display a complex number.) This occurs because the domain of ln x is the set of positive real numbers (see Figure 3.19). So, $\ln(-1)$ is undefined.

The four properties of logarithms listed on page 228 are also valid for natural logarithms.

Extra Example 8

Use a calculator to evaluate the function given by $f(x) = \ln x + 1$ for each value of x to four decimal places.

a. $x = 73.25$
5.2939

b. $x = 0.4$
0.0837

c. $x = -2$
ERROR ***Note:*** **Part (c) may also give a complex number as an answer.**

d. $x = 2 + \sqrt{3}$
2.3170

Extra Example 9

Use the properties of natural logarithms to simplify each expression.

a. $\ln e^{1/3}$

$\frac{1}{3}$

b. $e^{\ln 8}$

8

c. $15 \ln 1$

0

d. $\frac{\ln e}{6}$

$\frac{1}{6}$

Extra Example 10

Find the domain of each function.

a. $f(x) = \ln(x + 3)$

$(-3, \infty)$

b. $f(x) = \ln(3 - x)$

$(-\infty, 3)$

c. $f(x) = \ln x^3$

$x > 0$

Properties of Natural Logarithms

1. $\ln 1 = 0$ because $e^0 = 1$.
2. $\ln e = 1$ because $e^1 = e$.
3. $\ln e^x = x$ and $e^{\ln x} = x$ — Inverse Properties
4. If $\ln x = \ln y$, then $x = y$. — One-to-One Property

Example 9 Using Properties of Natural Logarithms

Use the properties of natural logarithms to simplify each expression.

a. $\ln \frac{1}{e}$ **b.** $e^{\ln 5}$ **c.** $\frac{\ln 1}{3}$ **d.** $2 \ln e$

Solution

a. $\ln \frac{1}{e} = \ln e^{-1} = -1$ Inverse Property

b. $e^{\ln 5} = 5$ Inverse Property

c. $\frac{\ln 1}{3} = \frac{0}{3} = 0$ Property 1

d. $2 \ln e = 2(1) = 2$ Property 2

CHECKPoint Now try Exercise 71.

Example 10 Finding the Domains of Logarithmic Functions

Find the domain of each function.

a. $f(x) = \ln(x - 2)$ **b.** $g(x) = \ln(2 - x)$ **c.** $h(x) = \ln x^2$

Solution

a. Because $\ln(x - 2)$ is defined only if $x - 2 > 0$, it follows that the domain of f is $(2, \infty)$. The graph of f is shown in Figure 3.20.

b. Because $\ln(2 - x)$ is defined only if $2 - x > 0$, it follows that the domain of g is $(-\infty, 2)$. The graph of g is shown in Figure 3.21.

c. Because $\ln x^2$ is defined only if $x^2 > 0$, it follows that the domain of h is all real numbers except $x = 0$. The graph of h is shown in Figure 3.22.

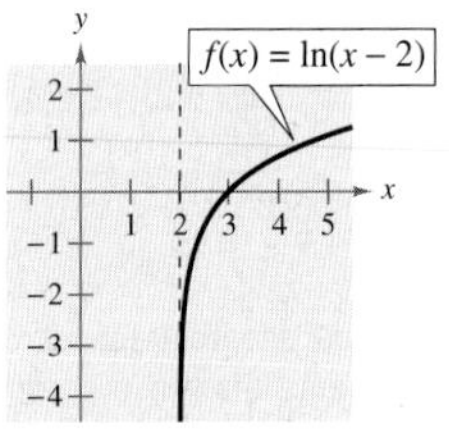

FIGURE 3.20

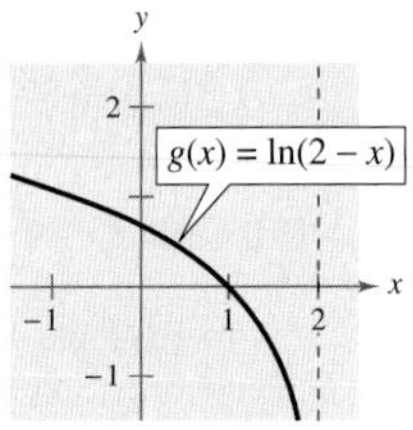

FIGURE 3.21

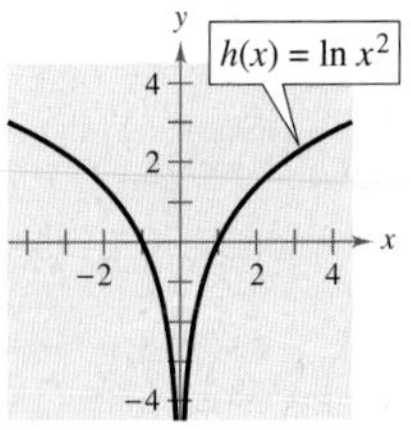

FIGURE 3.22

CHECKPoint Now try Exercise 75.

Application

Example 11 Human Memory Model

Students participating in a psychology experiment attended several lectures on a subject and were given an exam. Every month for a year after the exam, the students were retested to see how much of the material they remembered. The average scores for the group are given by the *human memory model* $f(t) = 75 - 6\ln(t + 1)$, $0 \le t \le 12$, where t is the time in months.

a. What was the average score on the original ($t = 0$) exam?

b. What was the average score at the end of $t = 2$ months?

c. What was the average score at the end of $t = 6$ months?

Algebraic Solution

a. The original average score was

$f(0) = 75 - 6\ln(0 + 1)$	Substitute 0 for t.
$= 75 - 6\ln 1$	Simplify.
$= 75 - 6(0)$	Property of natural logarithms
$= 75.$	Solution

b. After 2 months, the average score was

$f(2) = 75 - 6\ln(2 + 1)$	Substitute 2 for t.
$= 75 - 6\ln 3$	Simplify.
$\approx 75 - 6(1.0986)$	Use a calculator.
$\approx 68.4.$	Solution

c. After 6 months, the average score was

$f(6) = 75 - 6\ln(6 + 1)$	Substitute 6 for t.
$= 75 - 6\ln 7$	Simplify.
$\approx 75 - 6(1.9459)$	Use a calculator.
$\approx 63.3.$	Solution

Graphical Solution

Use a graphing utility to graph the model $y = 75 - 6\ln(x + 1)$. Then use the *value* or *trace* feature to approximate the following.

a. When $x = 0$, $y = 75$ (see Figure 3.23). So, the original average score was 75.

b. When $x = 2$, $y \approx 68.4$ (see Figure 3.24). So, the average score after 2 months was about 68.4.

c. When $x = 6$, $y \approx 63.3$ (see Figure 3.25). So, the average score after 6 months was about 63.3.

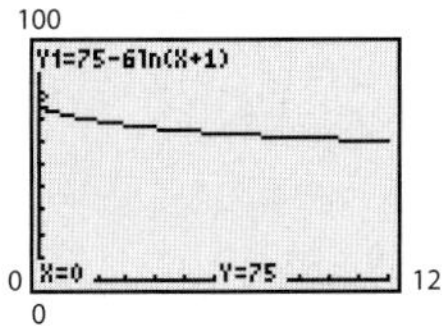

FIGURE 3.23

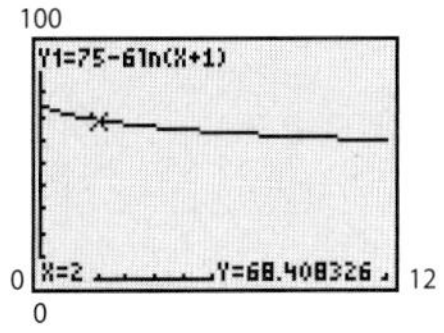

FIGURE 3.24

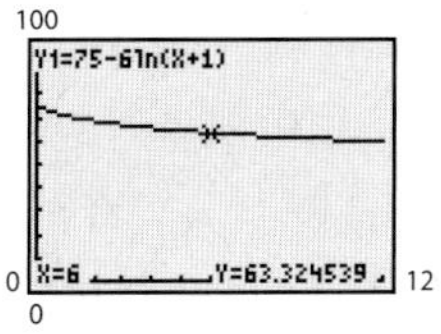

FIGURE 3.25

CHECKPoint Now try Exercise 97.

Classroom Discussion

Analyzing a Human Memory Model Use a graphing utility to determine the time in months when the average score in Example 11 was 60. Explain your method of solving the problem. Describe another way that you can use a graphing utility to determine the answer. Approximately 11 months. Explanations will vary.

Extra Example 11

Students in a mathematics class were given an exam and then retested monthly with an equivalent exam. The average scores for the class are given by the human memory model $f(t) = 78 - 17\log(t + 1)$, $0 \le t \le 12$, where t is time in months.

a. What was the average score on the original exam ($t = 0$)?
78.0

b. What was the average score after 3 months?
67.8

c. What was the average score after 11 months?
59.7

Closing the Lesson

Have students summarize the major points of the lesson and answer the Essential Question: How do you recognize, evaluate, and graph logarithmic functions?

- **Use the definition of a logarithm, the inverse properties, and the One-to-One Property to simplify logarithmic expressions.**
- **Identify the basic characteristics of a logarithmic graph by plotting points and by referring to the exponential graph of which it is an inverse.**
- **Solve problems using the natural logarithm.**

4 PRACTICE AND APPLY

Assignment Guide

Transparencies Available
Available at the Instructor's companion site.

Average:
Day 1: pp. 234–235
Exs. 1–6, 7–17 odd, 24–28, 31, 35, 39, 41, 45–50
Day 2: pp. 235–236
Exs. 51, 57–63 odd, 69–73 odd, 76, 77, 85, 91, 93, 98–100, 103, 108

Advanced:
Day 1: pp. 234–235
Exs. 1–6, 12–18 even, 24–30 even, 34–44 even, 45–50
Day 2: pp. 235–236
Exs. 54–62 even, 68, 72–78 even, 90, 92–94, 98–101, 104, 107–109

Block:
pp. 234–236
Exs. 1–6, 7–17 odd, 24–28, 31, 35, 39, 41, 45–51, 57–63 odd, 69–73 odd, 76, 77, 85, 91, 93, 98–100, 103, 108

37.

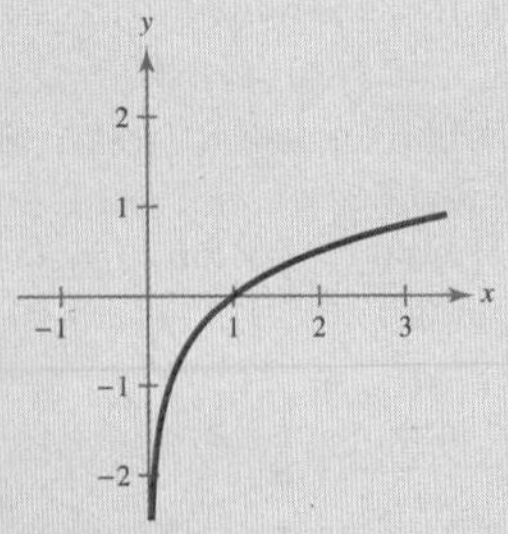

Domain: $(0, \infty)$
x-intercept: $(1, 0)$
Vertical asymptote: $x = 0$

38.

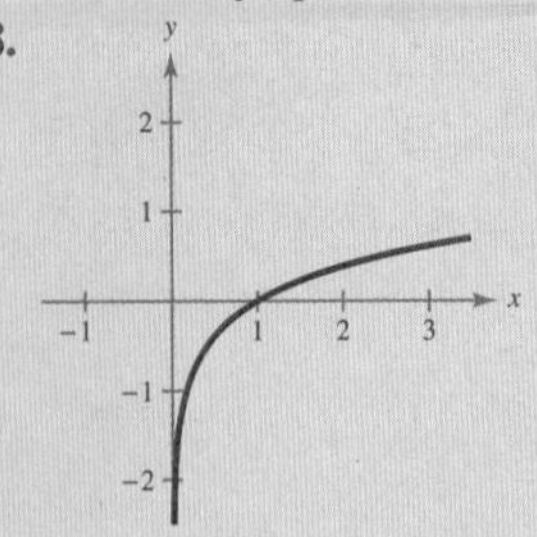

Domain: $(0, \infty)$
x-intercept: $(1, 0)$
Vertical asymptote: $x = 0$

3.2 EXERCISES

See www.CalcChat.com for worked-out solutions to odd-numbered exercises.

VOCABULARY: Fill in the blanks.

1. The inverse function of the exponential function given by $f(x) = a^x$ is called the __logarithmic__ function with base a.
2. The common logarithmic function has base __10__.
3. The logarithmic function given by $f(x) = \ln x$ is called the __natural__ logarithmic function and has base __e__.
4. The Inverse Properties of logarithms and exponentials state that $\log_a a^x = x$ and __$a^{\log_a x} = x$__.
5. The One-to-One Property of natural logarithms states that if $\ln x = \ln y$, then __$x = y$__.
6. The domain of the natural logarithmic function is the set of __positive real numbers__.

SKILLS AND APPLICATIONS

In Exercises 7–14, write the logarithmic equation in exponential form. For example, the exponential form of $\log_5 25 = 2$ is $5^2 = 25$.

7. $\log_4 16 = 2$ $4^2 = 16$
8. $\log_7 343 = 3$ $7^3 = 343$
9. $\log_9 \frac{1}{81} = -2$ $9^{-2} = \frac{1}{81}$
10. $\log \frac{1}{1000} = -3$ $10^{-3} = \frac{1}{1000}$
11. $\log_{32} 4 = \frac{2}{5}$ $32^{2/5} = 4$
12. $\log_{16} 8 = \frac{3}{4}$ $16^{3/4} = 8$
13. $\log_{64} 8 = \frac{1}{2}$ $64^{1/2} = 8$
14. $\log_8 4 = \frac{2}{3}$ $8^{2/3} = 4$

In Exercises 15–22, write the exponential equation in logarithmic form. For example, the logarithmic form of $2^3 = 8$ is $\log_2 8 = 3$.

15. $5^3 = 125$ $\log_5 125 = 3$
16. $13^2 = 169$ $\log_{13} 169 = 2$
17. $81^{1/4} = 3$ $\log_{81} 3 = \frac{1}{4}$
18. $9^{3/2} = 27$ $\log_9 27 = \frac{3}{2}$
19. $6^{-2} = \frac{1}{36}$ $\log_6 \frac{1}{36} = -2$
20. $4^{-3} = \frac{1}{64}$ $\log_4 \frac{1}{64} = -3$
21. $24^0 = 1$ $\log_{24} 1 = 0$
22. $10^{-3} = 0.001$ $\log 0.001 = -3$

In Exercises 23–28, evaluate the function at the indicated value of x without using a calculator.

	Function	*Value*	
23.	$f(x) = \log_2 x$	$x = 64$	6
24.	$f(x) = \log_{25} x$	$x = 5$	$\frac{1}{2}$
25.	$f(x) = \log_8 x$	$x = 1$	0
26.	$f(x) = \log x$	$x = 10$	1
27.	$g(x) = \log_a x$	$x = a^2$	2
28.	$g(x) = \log_b x$	$x = b^{-3}$	-3

In Exercises 29–32, use a calculator to evaluate $f(x) = \log x$ at the indicated value of x. Round your result to three decimal places.

29. $x = \frac{7}{8}$ -0.058
30. $x = \frac{1}{500}$ -2.699
31. $x = 12.5$ 1.097
32. $x = 96.75$ 1.986

In Exercises 33–36, use the properties of logarithms to simplify the expression.

33. $\log_{11} 11^7$ 7
34. $\log_{3.2} 1$ 0
35. $\log_\pi \pi$ 1
36. $9^{\log_9 15}$ 15

In Exercises 37–44, find the domain, x-intercept, and vertical asymptote of the logarithmic function and sketch its graph. 37–44. See margin.

37. $f(x) = \log_4 x$
38. $g(x) = \log_6 x$
39. $y = -\log_3 x + 2$
40. $h(x) = \log_4(x - 3)$
41. $f(x) = -\log_6(x + 2)$
42. $y = \log_5(x - 1) + 4$
43. $y = \log\left(\frac{x}{7}\right)$
44. $y = \log(-x)$

In Exercises 45–50, use the graph of $g(x) = \log_3 x$ to match the given function with its graph. Then describe the relationship between the graphs of f and g. [The graphs are labeled (a), (b), (c), (d), (e), and (f).] See page 235.

(a)

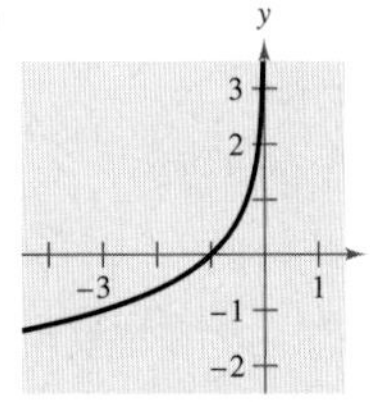

(b)

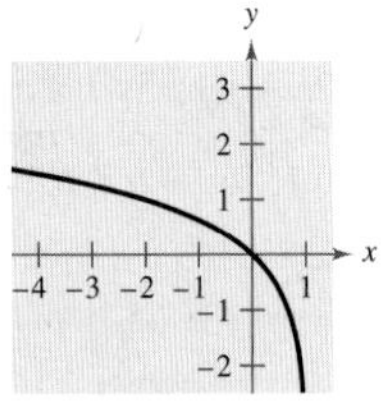

(c)

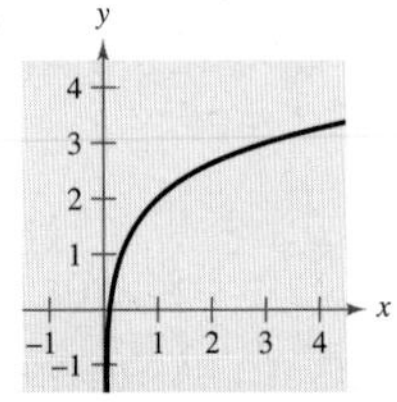

(d)

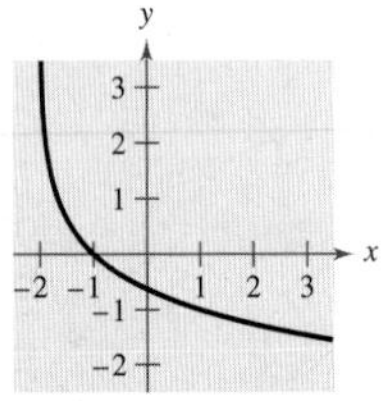

(e)

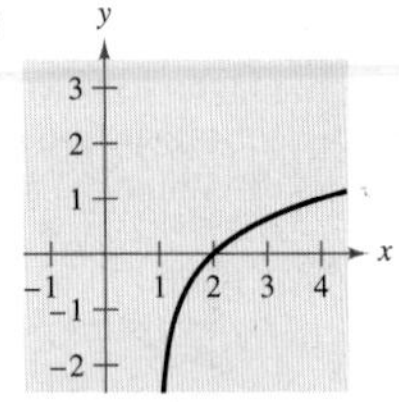

(f)

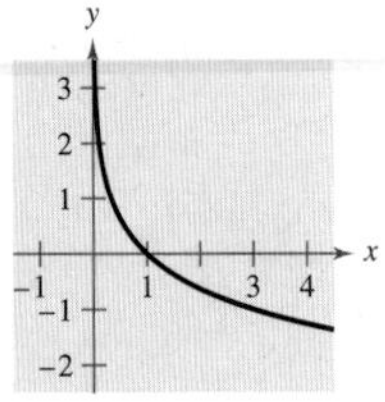

39.

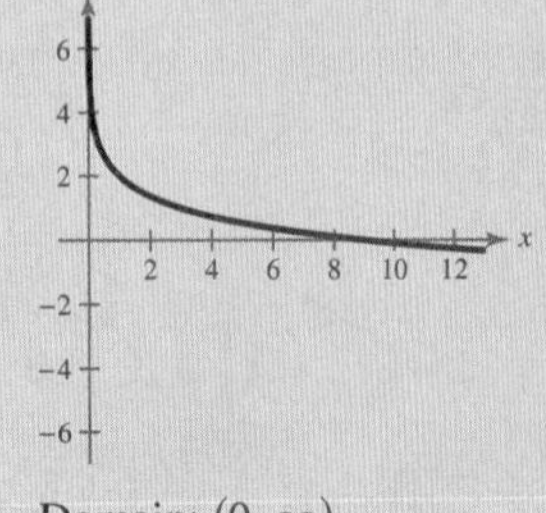

Domain: $(0, \infty)$
x-intercept: $(9, 0)$
Vertical asymptote: $x = 0$

40.

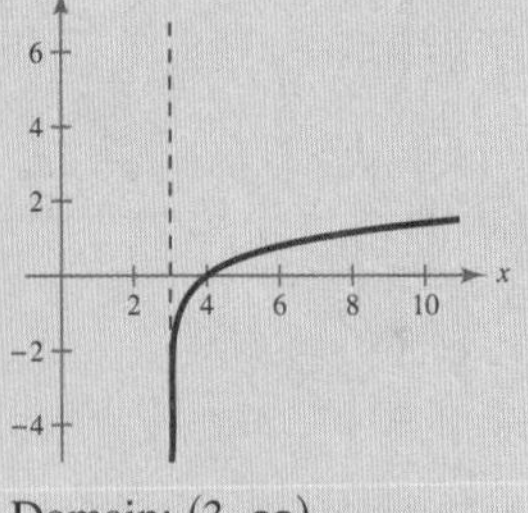

Domain: $(3, \infty)$
x-intercept: $(4, 0)$
Vertical asymptote: $x = 3$

41–44. See Additional Answers beginning on page AA1.

45. $f(x) = \log_3 x + 2$ c **46.** $f(x) = -\log_3 x$ f

47. $f(x) = -\log_3(x + 2)$ d **48.** $f(x) = \log_3(x - 1)$ e

49. $f(x) = \log_3(1 - x)$ b **50.** $f(x) = -\log_3(-x)$ a

In Exercises 51–58, write the logarithmic equation in exponential form. 51–56. See margin.

51. $\ln \frac{1}{2} = -0.693\ldots$ **52.** $\ln \frac{2}{5} = -0.916\ldots$

53. $\ln 7 = 1.945\ldots$ **54.** $\ln 10 = 2.302\ldots$

55. $\ln 250 = 5.521\ldots$ **56.** $\ln 1084 = 6.988\ldots$

57. $\ln 1 = 0$ $e^0 = 1$ **58.** $\ln e = 1$ $e^1 = e$

In Exercises 59–66, write the exponential equation in logarithmic form. 59–64. See margin.

59. $e^4 = 54.598\ldots$ **60.** $e^2 = 7.3890\ldots$

61. $e^{1/2} = 1.6487\ldots$ **62.** $e^{1/3} = 1.3956\ldots$

63. $e^{-0.9} = 0.406\ldots$ **64.** $e^{-4.1} = 0.0165\ldots$

65. $e^x = 4$ $\ln 4 = x$ **66.** $e^{2x} = 3$ $\ln 3 = 2x$

In Exercises 67–70, use a calculator to evaluate the function at the indicated value of x. Round your result to three decimal places.

	Function	*Value*	
67.	$f(x) = \ln x$	$x = 18.42$	2.913
68.	$f(x) = 3 \ln x$	$x = 0.74$	-0.903
69.	$g(x) = 8 \ln x$	$x = 0.05$	-23.966
70.	$g(x) = -\ln x$	$x = \frac{1}{2}$	0.693

In Exercises 71–74, evaluate $g(x) = \ln x$ at the indicated value of x without using a calculator.

71. $x = e^5$ 5 **72.** $x = e^{-4}$ -4

73. $x = e^{-5/6}$ $-\frac{5}{6}$ **74.** $x = e^{-5/2}$ $-\frac{5}{2}$

In Exercises 75–78, find the domain, x-intercept, and vertical asymptote of the logarithmic function and sketch its graph. 75–78. See margin.

75. $f(x) = \ln(x - 4)$ **76.** $h(x) = \ln(x + 5)$

77. $g(x) = \ln(-x)$ **78.** $f(x) = \ln(3 - x)$

In Exercises 79–84, use a graphing utility to graph the function. Be sure to use an appropriate viewing window. 79–84. See margin.

79. $f(x) = \log(x + 9)$ **80.** $f(x) = \log(x - 6)$

81. $f(x) = \ln(x - 1)$ **82.** $f(x) = \ln(x + 2)$

83. $f(x) = \ln x + 8$ **84.** $f(x) = 3 \ln x - 1$

In Exercises 85–92, use the One-to-One Property to solve the equation for x.

85. $\log_5(x + 1) = \log_5 6$ $x = 5$ **86.** $\log_2(x - 3) = \log_2 9$ $x = 12$

87. $\log(2x + 1) = \log 15$ $x = 7$ **88.** $\log(5x + 3) = \log 12$ $x = \frac{9}{5}$

89. $\ln(x + 4) = \ln 12$ $x = 8$ **90.** $\ln(x - 7) = \ln 7$ $x = 14$

91. $\ln(x^2 - 2) = \ln 23$ $x = -5, 5$ **92.** $\ln(x^2 - x) = \ln 6$ $x = -2, 3$

93. MONTHLY PAYMENT The model

$$t = 16.625 \ln\left(\frac{x}{x - 750}\right), \quad x > 750$$

approximates the length of a home mortgage of \$150,000 at 6% in terms of the monthly payment. In the model, t is the length of the mortgage in years and x is the monthly payment in dollars. See margin.

(a) Use the model to approximate the lengths of a \$150,000 mortgage at 6% when the monthly payment is \$897.72 and when the monthly payment is \$1659.24.

(b) Approximate the total amounts paid over the term of the mortgage with a monthly payment of \$897.72 and with a monthly payment of \$1659.24.

(c) Approximate the total interest charges for a monthly payment of \$897.72 and for a monthly payment of \$1659.24.

(d) What is the vertical asymptote for the model? Interpret its meaning in the context of the problem.

94. COMPOUND INTEREST A principal P, invested at $5\frac{1}{2}\%$ and compounded continuously, increases to an amount K times the original principal after t years, where t is given by $t = (\ln K)/0.055$. See margin.

(a) Complete the table and interpret your results.

K	1	2	4	6	8	10	12
t							

(b) Sketch a graph of the function.

95. CABLE TELEVISION The numbers of cable television systems C (in thousands) in the United States from 2001 through 2006 can be approximated by the model

$$C = 10.355 - 0.298t \ln t, \quad 1 \le t \le 6$$ See margin.

where t represents the year, with $t = 1$ corresponding to 2001. (Source: Warren Communication News)

(a) Complete the table.

t	1	2	3	4	5	6
C						

(b) Use a graphing utility to graph the function.

(c) Can the model be used to predict the numbers of cable television systems beyond 2006? Explain.

51. $e^{-0.693\ldots} = \frac{1}{2}$

52. $e^{-0.916\ldots} = \frac{2}{5}$

53. $e^{1.945\ldots} = 7$

54. $e^{2.302\ldots} = 10$

55. $e^{5.521\ldots} = 250$

56. $e^{6.988\ldots} = 1084$

59. $\ln 54.598\ldots = 4$

60. $\ln 7.3890\ldots = 2$

61. $\ln 1.6487\ldots = \frac{1}{2}$

62. $\ln 1.3956\ldots = \frac{1}{3}$

63. $\ln 0.406\ldots = -0.9$

64. $\ln 0.0165\ldots = -4.1$

79.

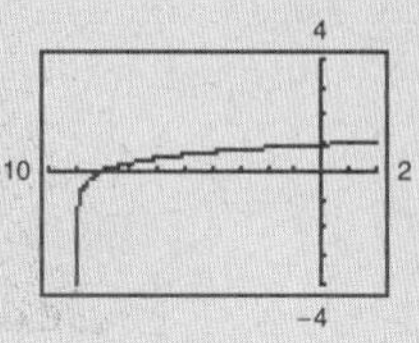

80.

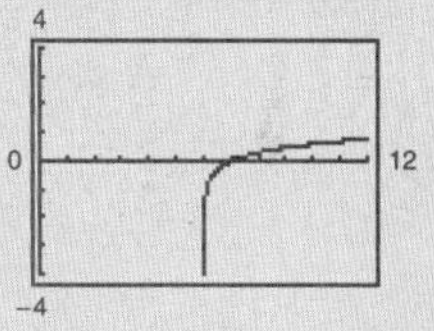

81.

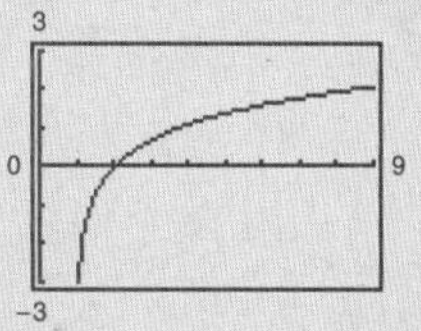

82.

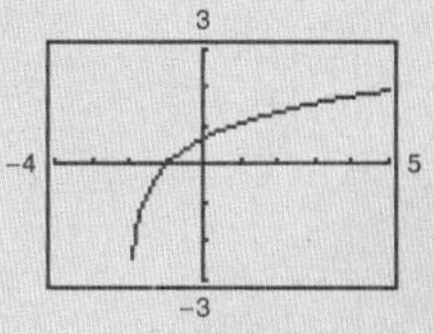

83.

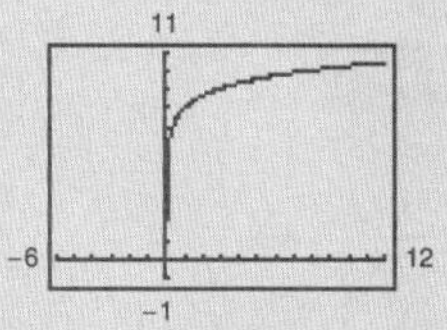

84.

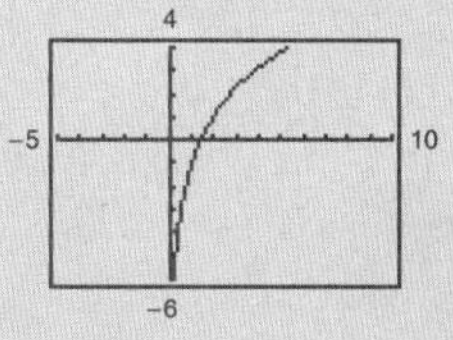

93. (a) 30 yr; 10 yr

(b) \$323,179; \$199,109

(c) \$173,179; \$49,109

(d) $x = 750$; The monthly payment must be greater than \$750.

94. (a)

K	1	2	4	6
t	0	12.60	25.21	32.57

K	8	10	12
t	37.81	41.87	45.18

The number of years required to multiply the original investment by K increases with K. However, the larger the value of K, the fewer the years required to increase the value of the investment by an additional multiple of the original investment.

(b)

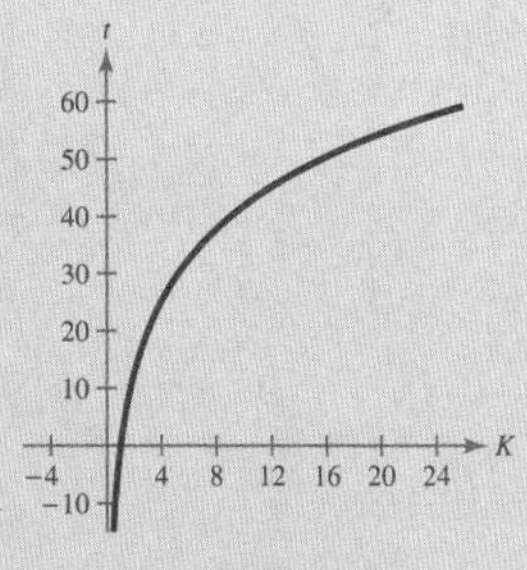

75–78, 95. See Additional Answers beginning on page AA1.

5 ASSESS AND RETEACH

Daily Homework Quiz

Transparency Available

Available at the Instructor's companion site.

96. (b)

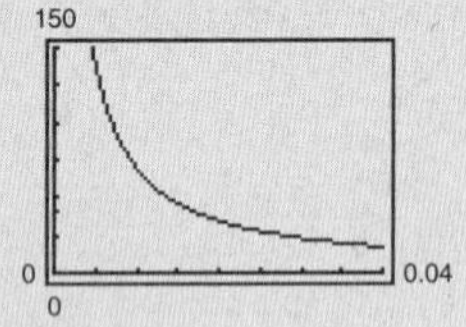

97. (a)

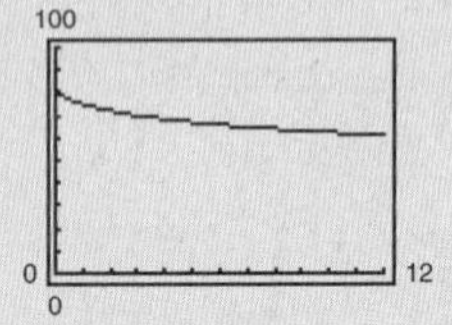

98. (c) No, the difference results from the logarithmic relationship between intensity and number of decibels.

99. False. Reflecting $g(x)$ about the line $y = x$ will determine the graph of $f(x)$.

100. True. $\log_3 27 = 3 \Longrightarrow 3^3 = 27$

101.

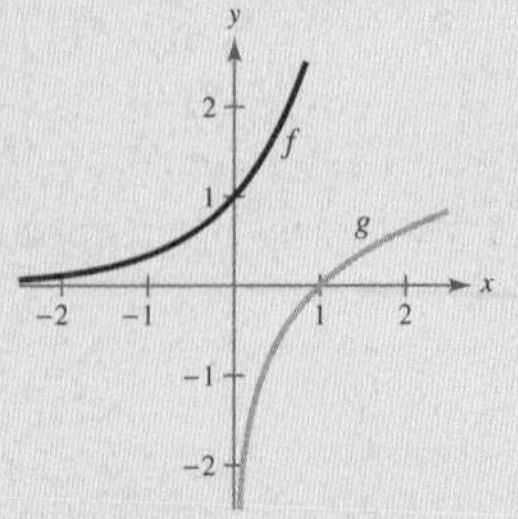

The functions f and g are inverses.

102.

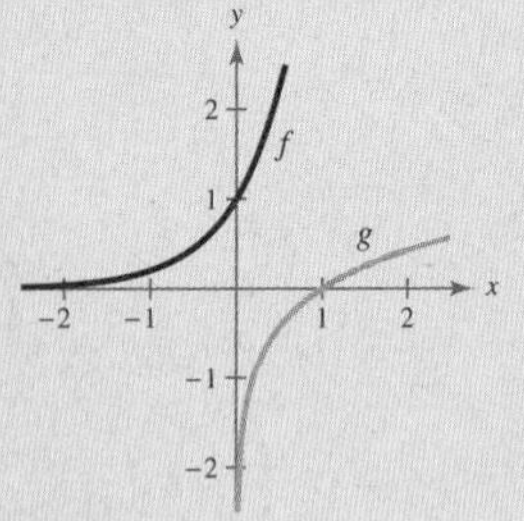

The functions f and g are inverses.

96. POPULATION The time t in years for the world population to double if it is increasing at a continuous rate of r is given by $t = (\ln 2)/r$. See margin.

(a) Complete the table and interpret your results.

r	0.005	0.010	0.015	0.020	0.025	0.030
t						

(b) Use a graphing utility to graph the function.

97. HUMAN MEMORY MODEL Students in a mathematics class were given an exam and then retested monthly with an equivalent exam. The average scores for the class are given by the human memory model $f(t) = 80 - 17\log(t + 1)$, $0 \le t \le 12$, where t is the time in months.

(a) Use a graphing utility to graph the model over the specified domain. See margin.

(b) What was the average score on the original exam $(t = 0)$? 80

(c) What was the average score after 4 months? 68.1

(d) What was the average score after 10 months? 62.3

98. SOUND INTENSITY The relationship between the number of decibels β and the intensity of a sound I in watts per square meter is

$$\beta = 10\log\left(\frac{I}{10^{-12}}\right).$$

(a) Determine the number of decibels of a sound with an intensity of 1 watt per square meter. 120 dB

(b) Determine the number of decibels of a sound with an intensity of 10^{-2} watt per square meter. 100 dB

(c) The intensity of the sound in part (a) is 100 times as great as that in part (b). Is the number of decibels 100 times as great? Explain. See margin.

EXPLORATION

99–100. See margin.

TRUE OR FALSE? In Exercises 99 and 100, determine whether the statement is true or false. Justify your answer.

99. You can determine the graph of $f(x) = \log_6 x$ by graphing $g(x) = 6^x$ and reflecting it about the x-axis.

100. The graph of $f(x) = \log_3 x$ contains the point $(27, 3)$.

In Exercises 101–104, sketch the graphs of f and g and describe the relationship between the graphs of f and g. What is the relationship between the functions f and g? 101–104. See margin.

101. $f(x) = 3^x$, $g(x) = \log_3 x$

102. $f(x) = 5^x$, $g(x) = \log_5 x$

103. $f(x) = e^x$, $g(x) = \ln x$

104. $f(x) = 8^x$, $g(x) = \log_8 x$

105. THINK ABOUT IT Complete the table for $f(x) = 10^x$.

x	-2	-1	0	1	2
$f(x)$					

Complete the table for $f(x) = \log x$.

x	$\frac{1}{100}$	$\frac{1}{10}$	1	10	100
$f(x)$					

Compare the two tables. What is the relationship between $f(x) = 10^x$ and $f(x) = \log x$? See margin.

106. GRAPHICAL ANALYSIS Use a graphing utility to graph f and g in the same viewing window and determine which is increasing at the greater rate as x approaches $+\infty$. What can you conclude about the rate of growth of the natural logarithmic function?

(a) $f(x) = \ln x$, $g(x) = \sqrt{x}$

(b) $f(x) = \ln x$, $g(x) = \sqrt[4]{x}$

(a)–(b). See margin.

107. (a) Complete the table for the function given by $f(x) = (\ln x)/x$. (a)–(c). See margin.

x	1	5	10	10^2	10^4	10^6
$f(x)$						

(b) Use the table in part (a) to determine what value $f(x)$ approaches as x increases without bound.

(c) Use a graphing utility to confirm the result of part (b).

108. CAPSTONE The table of values was obtained by evaluating a function. Determine which of the statements may be true and which must be false.

x	y
1	0
2	1
8	3

(a) y is an exponential function of x.

(b) y is a logarithmic function of x.

(c) x is an exponential function of y.

(d) y is a linear function of x.

See margin.

109. WRITING Explain why $\log_a x$ is defined only for $0 < a < 1$ and $a > 1$. Answers will vary.

In Exercises 110 and 111, (a) use a graphing utility to graph the function, (b) use the graph to determine the intervals in which the function is increasing and decreasing, and (c) approximate any relative maximum or minimum values of the function. 110–111. See margin.

110. $f(x) = |\ln x|$

111. $h(x) = \ln(x^2 + 1)$

103.

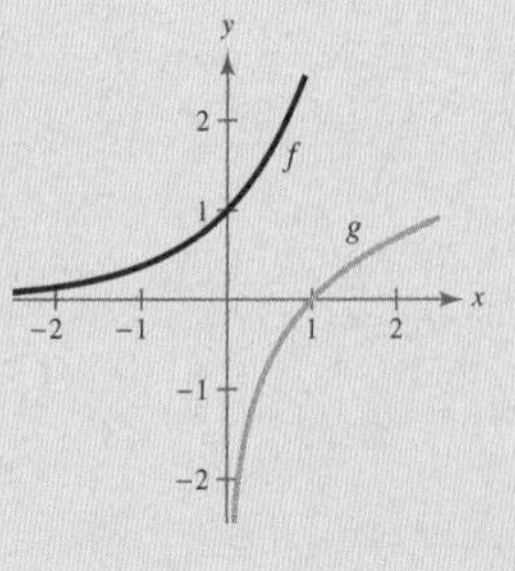

The functions f and g are inverses.

104.

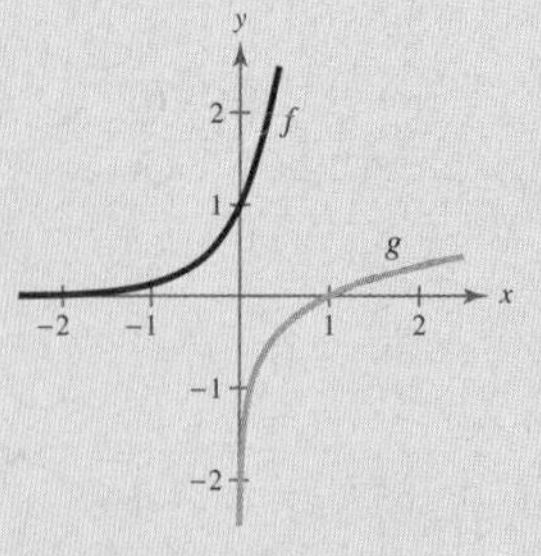

The functions f and g are inverses.

96(a), 105–108, 110–111. See Additional Answers beginning on page AA1.

3.3 Properties of Logarithms

What you should learn

- Use the change-of-base formula to rewrite and evaluate logarithmic expressions.
- Use properties of logarithms to evaluate or rewrite logarithmic expressions.
- Use properties of logarithms to expand or condense logarithmic expressions.
- Use logarithmic functions to model and solve real-life problems.

Why you should learn it

Logarithmic functions can be used to model and solve real-life problems. For instance, in Exercises 87–90 on page 242, a logarithmic function is used to model the relationship between the number of decibels and the intensity of a sound.

Dynamic Graphics/ Jupiter Images

Change of Base

Most calculators have only two types of log keys, one for common logarithms (base 10) and one for natural logarithms (base e). Although common logarithms and natural logarithms are the most frequently used, you may occasionally need to evaluate logarithms with other bases. To do this, you can use the following **change-of-base formula.**

> **Change-of-Base Formula**
>
> Let a, b, and x be positive real numbers such that $a \neq 1$ and $b \neq 1$. Then $\log_a x$ can be converted to a different base as follows.
>
> | *Base b* | *Base 10* | *Base e* |
> |---|---|---|
> | $\log_a x = \dfrac{\log_b x}{\log_b a}$ | $\log_a x = \dfrac{\log x}{\log a}$ | $\log_a x = \dfrac{\ln x}{\ln a}$ |

One way to look at the change-of-base formula is that logarithms with base a are simply *constant multiples* of logarithms with base b. The constant multiplier is $1/(\log_b a)$.

Example 1 Changing Bases Using Common Logarithms

a. $\log_4 25 = \dfrac{\log 25}{\log 4}$ $\quad \log_a x = \dfrac{\log x}{\log a}$

$\approx \dfrac{1.39794}{0.60206}$ $\quad$ Use a calculator.

≈ 2.3219 $\quad$ Simplify.

b. $\log_2 12 = \dfrac{\log 12}{\log 2} \approx \dfrac{1.07918}{0.30103} \approx 3.5850$

CHECK*Point* Now try Exercise 7(a).

Example 2 Changing Bases Using Natural Logarithms

a. $\log_4 25 = \dfrac{\ln 25}{\ln 4}$ $\quad \log_a x = \dfrac{\ln x}{\ln a}$

$\approx \dfrac{3.21888}{1.38629}$ $\quad$ Use a calculator.

≈ 2.3219 $\quad$ Simplify.

b. $\log_2 12 = \dfrac{\ln 12}{\ln 2} \approx \dfrac{2.48491}{0.69315} \approx 3.5850$

CHECK*Point* Now try Exercise 7(b).

1 PLAN AND PREPARE

Warm-up Exercises

Transparency Available
Available at the Instructor's companion site.

Notetaking Guide

Transparency Available
Promotes interactive learning and notetaking skills. Available at the Instructor's companion site.

Animated Precalculus

An **Animated Precalculus** tutorial is available at the Student companion site for **Section 3.3.**

Pacing

Average: 2 days
Advanced: 2 days
Block: 1 block

2 FOCUS AND MOTIVATE

Essential Question

How do you rewrite logarithmic expressions to simplify or evaluate them? **Tell students that they will learn how to answer this question by studying formulas and properties that expand or condense logarithmic expressions.**

Resource Planning Guide

Chapter Resources
- Complete Solutions Guide

Workbooks
- Notetaking Guide
- Student Solutions Guide

Interactive Technology
- Instructor Success Organizer
- Notetaking Guide IAE
- Instructional DVDs
- Animated Precalculus
- PowerLecture with ExamView

Properties of Logarithms

You know from the preceding section that the logarithmic function with base a is the *inverse function* of the exponential function with base a. So, it makes sense that the properties of exponents should have corresponding properties involving logarithms. For instance, the exponential property $a^0 = 1$ has the corresponding logarithmic property $\log_a 1 = 0$.

Properties of Logarithms

Let a be a positive number such that $a \neq 1$, and let n be a real number. If u and v are positive real numbers, the following properties are true.

	Logarithm with Base a	*Natural Logarithm*
1. Product Property:	$\log_a(uv) = \log_a u + \log_a v$	$\ln(uv) = \ln u + \ln v$
2. Quotient Property:	$\log_a \frac{u}{v} = \log_a u - \log_a v$	$\ln \frac{u}{v} = \ln u - \ln v$
3. Power Property:	$\log_a u^n = n \log_a u$	$\ln u^n = n \ln u$

For proofs of the properties listed above, see Proofs in Mathematics on page 276.

Example 3 **Using Properties of Logarithms**

Write each logarithm in terms of ln 2 and ln 3.

a. $\ln 6$ **b.** $\ln \frac{2}{27}$

Solution

a. $\ln 6 = \ln(2 \cdot 3)$ — Rewrite 6 as $2 \cdot 3$.

$= \ln 2 + \ln 3$ — Product Property

b. $\ln \frac{2}{27} = \ln 2 - \ln 27$ — Quotient Property

$= \ln 2 - \ln 3^3$ — Rewrite 27 as 3^3.

$= \ln 2 - 3 \ln 3$ — Power Property

CHECKPoint Now try Exercise 27.

Example 4 **Using Properties of Logarithms**

Find the exact value of each expression without using a calculator.

a. $\log_5 \sqrt[3]{5}$ **b.** $\ln e^6 - \ln e^2$

Solution

a. $\log_5 \sqrt[3]{5} = \log_5 5^{1/3} = \frac{1}{3} \log_5 5 = \frac{1}{3}(1) = \frac{1}{3}$

b. $\ln e^6 - \ln e^2 = \ln \frac{e^6}{e^2} = \ln e^4 = 4 \ln e = 4(1) = 4$

CHECKPoint Now try Exercise 29.

WARNING/CAUTION

There is no general property that can be used to rewrite $\log_a(u \pm v)$. Specifically, $\log_a(u + v)$ is *not* equal to $\log_a u + \log_a v$.

HISTORICAL NOTE

The Granger Collection

John Napier, a Scottish mathematician, developed logarithms as a way to simplify some of the tedious calculations of his day. Beginning in 1594, Napier worked about 20 years on the invention of logarithms. Napier was only partially successful in his quest to simplify tedious calculations. Nonetheless, the development of logarithms was a step forward and received immediate recognition.

3 TEACH

Extra Example 1

Evaluate each of the following, using the change-of-base formula with common logs. Approximate to four decimal places.

a. $\log_3 16$

2.5237

b. $\log_5 22$

1.9206

Extra Example 2

Evaluate each of the following, using the change-of-base formula with natural logarithms. Approximate to four decimal places.

a. $\log_3 16$

2.5237

b. $\log_5 22$

1.9206

Extra Example 3

Write each logarithm in terms of ln 2 and ln 5.

a. $\ln 10$

$\mathbf{\ln 2 + \ln 5}$

b. $\ln \frac{5}{3}$

$\mathbf{\ln 5 - 5 \ln 2}$

Extra Example 4

Find the exact value of each expression without using a calculator.

a. $\log_7 \sqrt[5]{7}$

$\frac{1}{5}$

b. $\ln e^{12} + \ln e^5$

17

Rewriting Logarithmic Expressions

The properties of logarithms are useful for rewriting logarithmic expressions in forms that simplify the operations of algebra. This is true because these properties convert complicated products, quotients, and exponential forms into simpler sums, differences, and products, respectively.

Example 5 Expanding Logarithmic Expressions

Expand each logarithmic expression.

a. $\log_4 5x^3y$ **b.** $\ln \frac{\sqrt{3x-5}}{7}$

Solution

a. $\log_4 5x^3y = \log_4 5 + \log_4 x^3 + \log_4 y$ Product Property

$= \log_4 5 + 3\log_4 x + \log_4 y$ Power Property

b. $\ln \frac{\sqrt{3x-5}}{7} = \ln \frac{(3x-5)^{1/2}}{7}$ Rewrite using rational exponent.

$= \ln(3x-5)^{1/2} - \ln 7$ Quotient Property

$= \frac{1}{2}\ln(3x-5) - \ln 7$ Power Property

CHECK*Point* Now try Exercise 53.

In Example 5, the properties of logarithms were used to *expand* logarithmic expressions. In Example 6, this procedure is reversed and the properties of logarithms are used to *condense* logarithmic expressions.

Example 6 Condensing Logarithmic Expressions

Condense each logarithmic expression.

a. $\frac{1}{2}\log x + 3\log(x+1)$ **b.** $2\ln(x+2) - \ln x$

c. $\frac{1}{3}[\log_2 x + \log_2(x+1)]$

Solution

a. $\frac{1}{2}\log x + 3\log(x+1) = \log x^{1/2} + \log(x+1)^3$ Power Property

$= \log\left[\sqrt{x}(x+1)^3\right]$ Product Property

b. $2\ln(x+2) - \ln x = \ln(x+2)^2 - \ln x$ Power Property

$= \ln \frac{(x+2)^2}{x}$ Quotient Property

c. $\frac{1}{3}[\log_2 x + \log_2(x+1)] = \frac{1}{3}\{\log_2[x(x+1)]\}$ Product Property

$= \log_2[x(x+1)]^{1/3}$ Power Property

$= \log_2 \sqrt[3]{x(x+1)}$ Rewrite with a radical.

CHECK*Point* Now try Exercise 75.

Algebra Help

You can review rewriting radicals and rational exponents in Appendix A.2.

Extra Example 5

Expand each logarithmic expression.

a. $\log 3x^2y$

$\log 3 + 2\log x + \log y$

b. $\ln \frac{\sqrt{4x+1}}{8}$

$\frac{1}{2}\ln(4x+1) - \ln 8$

Avoiding Common Errors

When expanding logarithmic expressions, students may incorrectly rewrite $\log ax^n$ as $n \log ax$ instead of $\log a + n\log x$.

Extra Example 6

Condense each logarithmic expression.

a. $\frac{1}{3}\log x + 5\log(x-3)$

$\log\left[\sqrt[3]{x}(x-3)^5\right]$

b. $4\ln(x-4) - 2\ln x$

$\ln \frac{(x-4)^4}{x^2}$

c. $\frac{1}{5}[\log_3 x + \log_3(x-2)]$

$\log_3 \sqrt[5]{x(x-2)}$

Avoiding Common Errors

When condensing logarithmic expressions, students may incorrectly rewrite $\log x - \log y$ as $\frac{\log x}{\log y}$ instead of $\log \frac{x}{y}$.

Extra Example 7

A pebble is dropped into a calm pond, causing ripples in the form of concentric circles. The table below gives the radius r and the area A of the outer ripple in feet. Find an equation that expresses A as a function of r.

Radius, r	Area, A
0.600	1.131
1.200	4.524
1.800	10.179
2.400	18.096
3.000	28.274
3.600	40.715

$\ln A = 2 \ln r + 1.145$

Closing the Lesson

Have students summarize the major points of the lesson and answer the Essential Question: How do you rewrite logarithmic expressions to simplify or evaluate them?

- **Use the change-of-base formula to rewrite logarithms that are in bases other than base 10 or base *e*.**
- **Use the product, quotient, and power properties to rewrite logarithmic expressions.**
- **Model nonlinear data by finding a linear equation that fits points whose coordinates are the natural logarithm of the original data.**

Application

One method of determining how the x- and y-values for a set of nonlinear data are related is to take the natural logarithm of each of the x- and y-values. If the points are graphed and fall on a line, then you can determine that the x- and y-values are related by the equation

$$\ln y = m \ln x$$

where m is the slope of the line.

Example 7 Finding a Mathematical Model

The table shows the mean distance from the sun x and the period y (the time it takes a planet to orbit the sun) for each of the six planets that are closest to the sun. In the table, the mean distance is given in terms of astronomical units (where Earth's mean distance is defined as 1.0), and the period is given in years. Find an equation that relates y and x.

Planet	Mean distance, x	Period, y
Mercury	0.387	0.241
Venus	0.723	0.615
Earth	1.000	1.000
Mars	1.524	1.881
Jupiter	5.203	11.860
Saturn	9.537	29.460

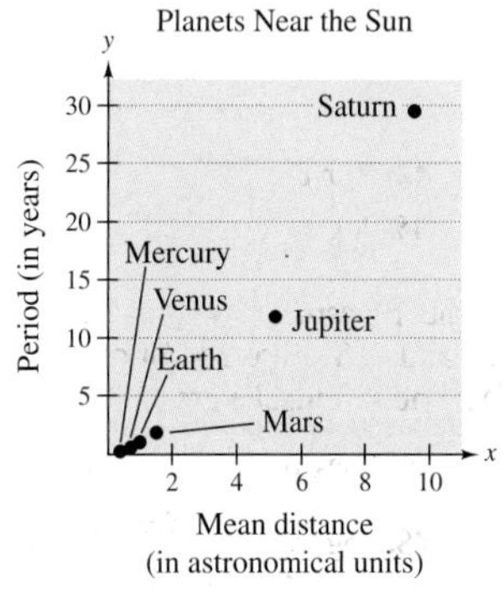

FIGURE 3.26

Solution

The points in the table above are plotted in Figure 3.26. From this figure it is not clear how to find an equation that relates y and x. To solve this problem, take the natural logarithm of each of the x- and y-values in the table. This produces the following results.

Planet	Mercury	Venus	Earth	Mars	Jupiter	Saturn
$\ln x$	-0.949	-0.324	0.000	0.421	1.649	2.255
$\ln y$	-1.423	-0.486	0.000	0.632	2.473	3.383

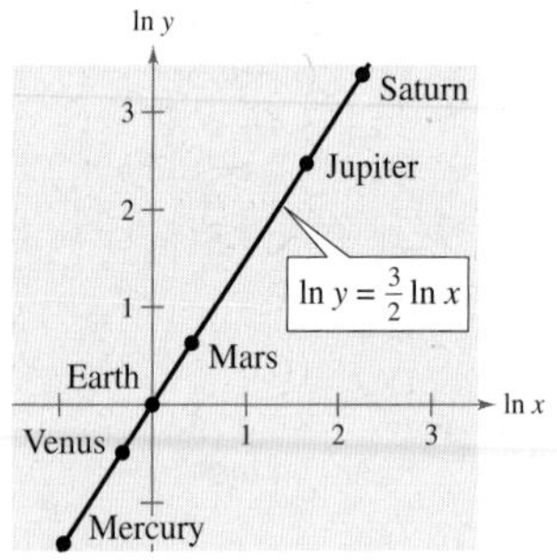

FIGURE 3.27

Now, by plotting the points in the second table, you can see that all six of the points appear to lie in a line (see Figure 3.27). Choose any two points to determine the slope of the line. Using the two points (0.421, 0.632) and (0, 0), you can determine that the slope of the line is

$$m = \frac{0.632 - 0}{0.421 - 0} \approx 1.5 = \frac{3}{2}.$$

By the point-slope form, the equation of the line is $Y = \frac{3}{2}X$, where $Y = \ln y$ and $X = \ln x$. You can therefore conclude that $\ln y = \frac{3}{2} \ln x$.

CHECKPoint Now try Exercise 91.

3.3 EXERCISES

See www.CalcChat.com for worked-out solutions to odd-numbered exercises.

VOCABULARY

In Exercises 1–3, fill in the blanks.

1. To evaluate a logarithm to any base, you can use the ________ formula. change-of-base
2. The change-of-base formula for base e is given by $\log_a x =$ ________. 2. $\dfrac{\log x}{\log a} = \dfrac{\ln x}{\ln a}$
3. You can consider $\log_a x$ to be a constant multiple of $\log_b x$; the constant multiplier is ________. $\dfrac{1}{\log_b a}$

In Exercises 4–6, match the property of logarithms with its name.

4. $\log_a(uv) = \log_a u + \log_a v$ — (a) Power Property
5. $\ln u^n = n \ln u$ — (b) Quotient Property
6. $\log_a \dfrac{u}{v} = \log_a u - \log_a v$ — (c) Product Property

(Answers: 4. (c) 5. (a) 6. (b))

SKILLS AND APPLICATIONS

In Exercises 7–14, rewrite the logarithm as a ratio of (a) common logarithms and (b) natural logarithms. 7–14. See margin.

7. $\log_5 16$
8. $\log_3 47$
9. $\log_{1/5} x$
10. $\log_{1/3} x$
11. $\log_x \frac{3}{10}$
12. $\log_x \frac{3}{4}$
13. $\log_{2.6} x$
14. $\log_{7.1} x$

In Exercises 15–22, evaluate the logarithm using the change-of-base formula. Round your result to three decimal places.

15. $\log_3 7$ 1.771
16. $\log_7 4$ 0.712
17. $\log_{1/2} 4$ −2.000
18. $\log_{1/4} 5$ −1.161
19. $\log_9 0.1$ −1.048
20. $\log_{20} 0.25$ −0.463
21. $\log_{15} 1250$ 2.633
22. $\log_3 0.015$ −3.823

In Exercises 23–28, use the properties of logarithms to rewrite and simplify the logarithmic expression.

23. $\log_4 8$ $\frac{3}{2}$
24. $\log_2(4^2 \cdot 3^4)$ $4 + 4\log_2 3$
25. $\log_5 \frac{1}{250}$ $-3 - \log_5 2$
26. $\log \frac{9}{300}$ $\log 3 - 2$
27. $\ln(5e^6)$ $6 + \ln 5$
28. $\ln \dfrac{6}{e^2}$ $\ln 6 - 2$

In Exercises 29–44, find the exact value of the logarithmic expression without using a calculator. (If this is not possible, state the reason.)

29. $\log_3 9$ 2
30. $\log_5 \frac{1}{125}$ −3
31. $\log_2 \sqrt[4]{8}$ $\frac{3}{4}$
32. $\log_6 \sqrt[3]{6}$ $\frac{1}{3}$
33. $\log_4 16^2$ 4
34. $\log_3 81^{-3}$ −12
35. $\log_2(-2)$ −2 is not in the domain of $\log_2 x$.
36. $\log_3(-27)$ −27 is not in the domain of $\log_3 x$.
37. $\ln e^{4.5}$ 4.5
38. $3 \ln e^4$ 12
39. $\ln \dfrac{1}{\sqrt{e}}$ $-\frac{1}{2}$
40. $\ln \sqrt[4]{e^3}$ $\frac{3}{4}$
41. $\ln e^2 + \ln e^5$ 7
42. $2 \ln e^6 - \ln e^5$ 7
43. $\log_5 75 - \log_5 3$ 2
44. $\log_4 2 + \log_4 32$ 3

In Exercises 45–66, use the properties of logarithms to expand the expression as a sum, difference, and/or constant multiple of logarithms. (Assume all variables are positive.)

45. $\ln 4x$ $\ln 4 + \ln x$
46. $\log_3 10z$ $\log_3 10 + \log_3 z$
47. $\log_8 x^4$ $4 \log_8 x$
48. $\log_{10} \dfrac{y}{2}$ $\log y - \log 2$
49. $\log_5 \dfrac{5}{x}$ $1 - \log_5 x$
50. $\log_6 \dfrac{1}{z^3}$ $-3 \log_6 z$
51. $\ln \sqrt{z}$ $\frac{1}{2} \ln z$
52. $\ln \sqrt[3]{t}$ $\frac{1}{3} \ln t$
53. $\ln xyz^2$
54. $\log 4x^2 y$
55. $\ln z(z-1)^2,\ z > 1$
56. $\ln\left(\dfrac{x^2-1}{x^3}\right),\ x > 1$
57. $\log_2 \dfrac{\sqrt{a-1}}{9},\ a > 1$
58. $\ln \dfrac{6}{\sqrt{x^2+1}}$

53–64. See margin.

59. $\ln \sqrt[3]{\dfrac{x}{y}}$
60. $\ln \sqrt{\dfrac{x^2}{y^3}}$
61. $\ln x^2 \sqrt{\dfrac{y}{z}}$
62. $\log_2 x^4 \sqrt{\dfrac{y}{z^3}}$
63. $\log_5 \dfrac{x^2}{y^2 z^3}$
64. $\log_{10} \dfrac{xy^4}{z^5}$
65. $\ln \sqrt[4]{x^3(x^2+3)}$ $\frac{3}{4}\ln x + \frac{1}{4}\ln(x^2+3)$
66. $\ln \sqrt{x^2(x+2)}$ $\ln x + \frac{1}{2}\ln(x+2)$

4 PRACTICE AND APPLY

Assignment Guide

Transparencies Available
Available at the Instructor's companion site.

Average:
Day 1: p. 241
Exs. 1–6, 9–17 odd, 25, 27, 31–43 odd, 49, 51, 55, 61, 65
Day 2: pp. 242–243
Exs. 67–73 odd, 77–79, 83, 85, 87, 88, 96, 101–105 odd, 113

Advanced:
Day 1: p. 241
Exs. 1–6, 10–18 even, 24, 28, 30–44 even, 52–60 even, 66
Day 2: pp. 242–243
Exs. 68–78 even, 82, 84, 86, 87–90, 95, 97, 100–106 even, 115

Block:
pp. 241–243
Exs. 1–6, 9–17 odd, 25, 27, 31–43 odd, 49, 51, 55, 61, 65, 67–73 odd, 77–79, 83, 85, 87, 88, 96, 101–105 odd, 113

7. (a) $\dfrac{\log 16}{\log 5}$ (b) $\dfrac{\ln 16}{\ln 5}$
8. (a) $\dfrac{\log 47}{\log 3}$ (b) $\dfrac{\ln 47}{\ln 3}$
9. (a) $\dfrac{\log x}{\log \frac{1}{5}}$ (b) $\dfrac{\ln x}{\ln \frac{1}{5}}$
10. (a) $\dfrac{\log x}{\log \frac{1}{3}}$ (b) $\dfrac{\ln x}{\ln \frac{1}{3}}$
11. (a) $\dfrac{\log \frac{3}{10}}{\log x}$ (b) $\dfrac{\ln \frac{3}{10}}{\ln x}$
12. (a) $\dfrac{\log \frac{3}{4}}{\log x}$ (b) $\dfrac{\ln \frac{3}{4}}{\ln x}$
13. (a) $\dfrac{\log x}{\log 2.6}$ (b) $\dfrac{\ln x}{\ln 2.6}$
14. (a) $\dfrac{\log x}{\log 7.1}$ (b) $\dfrac{\ln x}{\ln 7.1}$
53. $\ln x + \ln y + 2 \ln z$
54. $\log 4 + 2 \log x + \log y$
55. $\ln z + 2 \ln(z-1)$
56. $\ln(x+1) + \ln(x-1) - 3 \ln x$
57. $\frac{1}{2}\log_2(a-1) - 2\log_2 3$
58. $\ln 6 - \frac{1}{2}\ln(x^2+1)$
59. $\frac{1}{3}\ln x - \frac{1}{3}\ln y$
60. $\ln x - \frac{3}{2}\ln y$
61. $2 \ln x + \frac{1}{2}\ln y - \frac{1}{2}\ln z$
62. $4 \log_2 x + \frac{1}{2}\log_2 y - \frac{3}{2}\log_2 z$
63. $2 \log_5 x - 2 \log_5 y - 3 \log_5 z$
64. $\log x + 4 \log y - 5 \log z$

In Exercises 67–84, condense the expression to the logarithm of a single quantity.

67. $\ln 2 + \ln x$ $\ln 2x$

68. $\ln y + \ln t$ $\ln yt$

69. $\log_4 z - \log_4 y$

70. $\log_5 8 - \log_5 t$ 69–70. See margin.

71. $2 \log_2 x + 4 \log_2 y$ $\log_2 x^2y^4$

72. $\frac{2}{3} \log_7(z - 2)$ $\log_7(z - 2)^{2/3}$

73. $\frac{1}{4} \log_3 5x$ $\log_3 \sqrt[4]{5x}$

74. $-4 \log_6 2x$

75. $\log x - 2 \log(x + 1)$ 74–75. See margin.

76. $2 \ln 8 + 5 \ln(z - 4)$ $\ln 64(z - 4)^5$

77. $\log x - 2 \log y + 3 \log z$

78. $3 \log_3 x + 4 \log_3 y - 4 \log_3 z$

79. $\ln x - [\ln(x + 1) + \ln(x - 1)]$ 77–84. See margin.

80. $4[\ln z + \ln(z + 5)] - 2 \ln(z - 5)$

81. $\frac{1}{3}[2 \ln(x + 3) + \ln x - \ln(x^2 - 1)]$

82. $2[3 \ln x - \ln(x + 1) - \ln(x - 1)]$

83. $\frac{1}{3}[\log_8 y + 2 \log_8(y + 4)] - \log_8(y - 1)$

84. $\frac{1}{2}[\log_4(x + 1) + 2 \log_4(x - 1)] + 6 \log_4 x$

In Exercises 85 and 86, compare the logarithmic quantities. If two are equal, explain why. 85–86. See margin.

85. $\dfrac{\log_2 32}{\log_2 4}$, $\log_2 \dfrac{32}{4}$, $\log_2 32 - \log_2 4$

86. $\log_7 \sqrt{70}$, $\log_7 35$, $\frac{1}{2} + \log_7 \sqrt{10}$

SOUND INTENSITY In Exercises 87–90, use the following information. The relationship between the number of decibels β and the intensity of a sound I in watts per square meter is given by

$$\beta = 10 \log\left(\frac{I}{10^{-12}}\right).$$

$\beta = 10(\log I + 12)$; 60 dB

87. Use the properties of logarithms to write the formula in simpler form, and determine the number of decibels of a sound with an intensity of 10^{-6} watt per square meter.

88. Find the difference in loudness between an average office with an intensity of 1.26×10^{-7} watt per square meter and a broadcast studio with an intensity of 3.16×10^{-10} watt per square meter. About 26 dB

89. Find the difference in loudness between a vacuum cleaner with an intensity of 10^{-4} watt per square meter and rustling leaves with an intensity of 10^{-11} watt per square meter. 70 dB

90. You and your roommate are playing your stereos at the same time and at the same intensity. How much louder is the music when both stereos are playing compared with just one stereo playing? About 3 dB

CURVE FITTING In Exercises 91–94, find a logarithmic equation that relates y and x. Explain the steps used to find the equation. 91–94. See margin.

91.

x	1	2	3	4	5	6
y	1	1.189	1.316	1.414	1.495	1.565

92.

x	1	2	3	4	5	6
y	1	1.587	2.080	2.520	2.924	3.302

93.

x	1	2	3	4	5	6
y	2.5	2.102	1.9	1.768	1.672	1.597

94.

x	1	2	3	4	5	6
y	0.5	2.828	7.794	16	27.951	44.091

95. **GALLOPING SPEEDS OF ANIMALS** Four-legged animals run with two different types of motion: trotting and galloping. An animal that is trotting has at least one foot on the ground at all times, whereas an animal that is galloping has all four feet off the ground at some point in its stride. The number of strides per minute at which an animal breaks from a trot to a gallop depends on the weight of the animal. Use the table to find a logarithmic equation that relates an animal's weight x (in pounds) and its lowest galloping speed y (in strides per minute).

$y = 256.24 - 20.8 \ln x$

Weight, x	Galloping speed, y
25	191.5
35	182.7
50	173.8
75	164.2
500	125.9
1000	114.2

96. **NAIL LENGTH** The approximate lengths and diameters (in inches) of common nails are shown in the table. Find a logarithmic equation that relates the diameter y of a common nail to its length x.

Length, x	Diameter, y	Length, x	Diameter, y
1	0.072	4	0.203
2	0.120	5	0.238
3	0.148	6	0.284

$y = 0.1145 \ln x + 0.052$

69. $\log_4 \dfrac{z}{y}$

70. $\log_5 \dfrac{8}{t}$

74. $\log_6 \dfrac{1}{16x^4}$

75. $\log \dfrac{x}{(x + 1)^2}$

77. $\log \dfrac{xz^3}{y^2}$

78. $\log_3 \dfrac{x^3y^4}{z^4}$

79. $\ln \dfrac{x}{(x + 1)(x - 1)}$

80. $\ln \dfrac{z^4(z + 5)^4}{(z - 5)^2}$

81. $\ln \sqrt[3]{\dfrac{x(x + 3)^2}{x^2 - 1}}$

82. $\ln\left(\dfrac{x^3}{x^2 - 1}\right)^2$

83. $\log_8 \dfrac{\sqrt[3]{y(y + 4)^2}}{y - 1}$

84. $\log_4\left[x^6(x - 1)\sqrt{x + 1}\right]$

85. $\log_2 \frac{32}{4} = \log_2 32 - \log_2 4$; Property 2

86. $\log_7 \sqrt{70} = \frac{1}{2}(\log_7 7 + \log_7 10) = \frac{1}{2} + \log_7 \sqrt{10}$; Properties 1 and 3

91. $\ln y = \frac{1}{4} \ln x$

92. $\ln y = \frac{2}{3} \ln x$

93. $\ln y = -\frac{1}{4} \ln x + \ln \frac{5}{2}$

94. $\ln y = \frac{5}{2} \ln x - \ln 2$

97. COMPARING MODELS A cup of water at an initial temperature of 78°C is placed in a room at a constant temperature of 21°C. The temperature of the water is measured every 5 minutes during a half-hour period. The results are recorded as ordered pairs of the form (t, T), where t is the time (in minutes) and T is the temperature (in degrees Celsius).

(0, 78.0°), (5, 66.0°), (10, 57.5°), (15, 51.2°), (20, 46.3°), (25, 42.4°), (30, 39.6°) See margin.

(a) The graph of the model for the data should be asymptotic with the graph of the temperature of the room. Subtract the room temperature from each of the temperatures in the ordered pairs. Use a graphing utility to plot the data points (t, T) and $(t, T - 21)$.

(b) An exponential model for the data $(t, T - 21)$ is given by $T - 21 = 54.4(0.964)^t$. Solve for T and graph the model. Compare the result with the plot of the original data.

(c) Take the natural logarithms of the revised temperatures. Use a graphing utility to plot the points $(t, \ln(T - 21))$ and observe that the points appear to be linear. Use the *regression* feature of the graphing utility to fit a line to these data. This resulting line has the form $\ln(T - 21) = at + b$. Solve for T, and verify that the result is equivalent to the model in part (b).

(d) Fit a rational model to the data. Take the reciprocals of the y-coordinates of the revised data points to generate the points

$$\left(t, \frac{1}{T - 21}\right).$$

Use a graphing utility to graph these points and observe that they appear to be linear. Use the *regression* feature of a graphing utility to fit a line to these data. The resulting line has the form

$$\frac{1}{T - 21} = at + b.$$

Solve for T, and use a graphing utility to graph the rational function and the original data points.

(e) Why did taking the logarithms of the temperatures lead to a linear scatter plot? Why did taking the reciprocals of the temperatures lead to a linear scatter plot?

EXPLORATION

98. PROOF Prove that $\log_b \frac{u}{v} = \log_b u - \log_b v$. Proof

99. PROOF Prove that $\log_b u^n = n \log_b u$. Proof

100. CAPSTONE A classmate claims that the following are true. See margin.

(a) $\ln(u + v) = \ln u + \ln v = \ln(uv)$

(b) $\ln(u - v) = \ln u - \ln v = \ln \frac{u}{v}$

(c) $(\ln u)^n = n(\ln u) = \ln u^n$

Discuss how you would demonstrate that these claims are not true.

TRUE OR FALSE? In Exercises 101–106, determine whether the statement is true or false given that $f(x) = \ln x$. Justify your answer.

101. $f(0) = 0$ False; $\ln 1 = 0$

102. $f(ax) = f(a) + f(x)$, $a > 0, x > 0$ True; Property 1

103. $f(x - 2) = f(x) - f(2)$, $x > 2$ See margin.

104. $\sqrt{f(x)} = \frac{1}{2}f(x)$ False; $f(\sqrt{x}) = \frac{1}{2}f(x)$

105. If $f(u) = 2f(v)$, then $v = u^2$. False; $u = v^2$

106. If $f(x) < 0$, then $0 < x < 1$. True

In Exercises 107–112, use the change-of-base formula to rewrite the logarithm as a ratio of logarithms. Then use a graphing utility to graph the ratio. 107–112. See margin.

107. $f(x) = \log_2 x$

108. $f(x) = \log_4 x$

109. $f(x) = \log_{1/2} x$

110. $f(x) = \log_{1/4} x$

111. $f(x) = \log_{11.8} x$

112. $f(x) = \log_{12.4} x$

113. THINK ABOUT IT Consider the functions below. See margin.

$$f(x) = \ln\frac{x}{2}, \quad g(x) = \frac{\ln x}{\ln 2}, \quad h(x) = \ln x - \ln 2$$

Which two functions should have identical graphs? Verify your answer by sketching the graphs of all three functions on the same set of coordinate axes.

114. GRAPHICAL ANALYSIS Use a graphing utility to graph the functions given by $y_1 = \ln x - \ln(x - 3)$ and $y_2 = \ln\frac{x}{x - 3}$ in the same viewing window. Does the graphing utility show the functions with the same domain? If so, should it? Explain your reasoning. See margin.

115. THINK ABOUT IT For how many integers between 1 and 20 can the natural logarithms be approximated given the values $\ln 2 \approx 0.6931$, $\ln 3 \approx 1.0986$, and $\ln 5 \approx 1.6094$? Approximate these logarithms (do not use a calculator). See margin.

5 ASSESS AND RETEACH

Daily Homework Quiz

Transparency Available
Available at the Instructor's companion site.

97. (a) and (b)

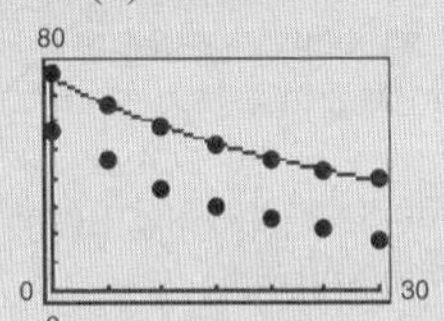

(c)

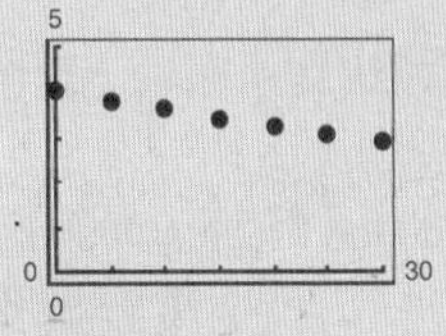

$T = 21 + e^{-0.037t + 3.997}$

The results are similar.

(d)

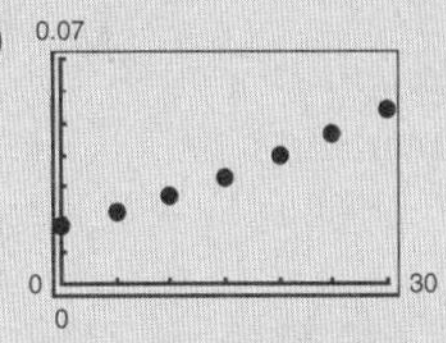

$$T = 21 + \frac{1}{0.001t + 0.016}$$

(e) Answers will vary.

103. False; $\ln(x - 2) \neq \ln x - \ln 2$

107. $f(x) = \frac{\log x}{\log 2} = \frac{\ln x}{\ln 2}$

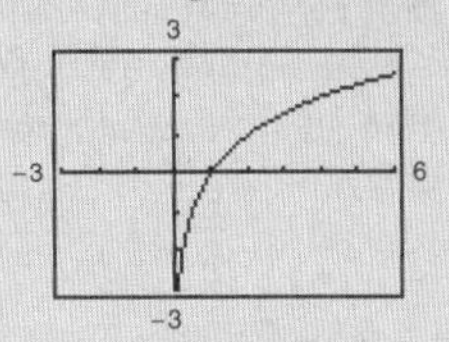

108. $f(x) = \frac{\log x}{\log 4} = \frac{\ln x}{\ln 4}$

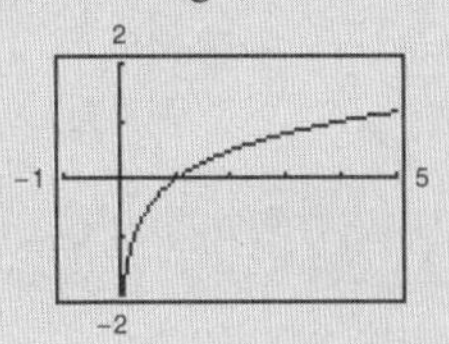

109. $f(x) = \frac{\log x}{\log \frac{1}{2}} = \frac{\ln x}{\ln \frac{1}{2}}$

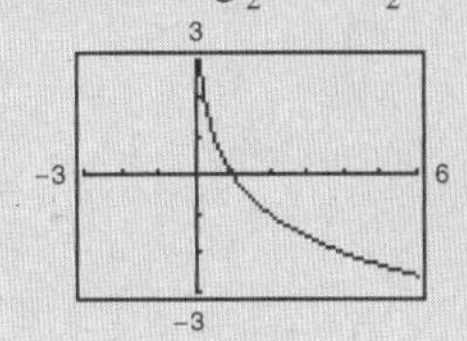

110. $f(x) = \frac{\log x}{\log \frac{1}{4}} = \frac{\ln x}{\ln \frac{1}{4}}$

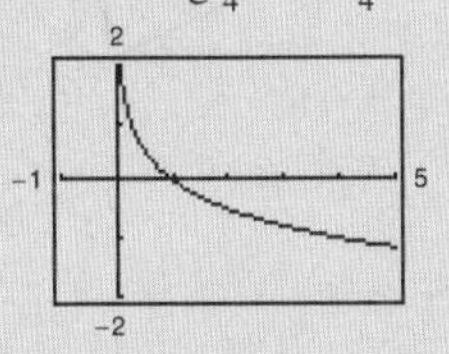

111. $f(x) = \frac{\log x}{\log 11.8} = \frac{\ln x}{\ln 11.8}$

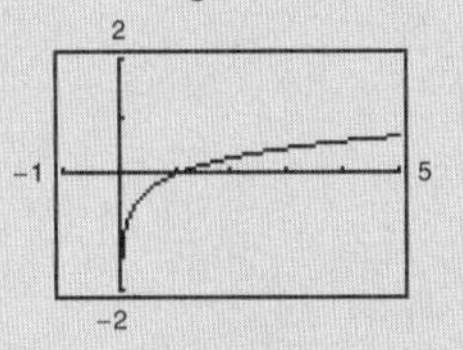

112. $f(x) = \frac{\log x}{\log 12.4} = \frac{\ln x}{\ln 12.4}$

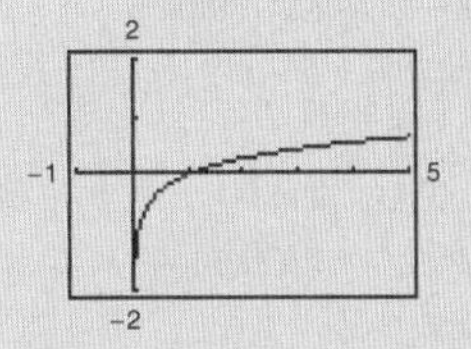

100, 113–115. See Additional Answers beginning on page AA1.

1 PLAN AND PREPARE

Warm-up Exercises

Transparency Available
Available at the Instructor's companion site.

Notetaking Guide

Transparency Available
Promotes interactive learning and notetaking skills.
Available at the Instructor's companion site.

Animated Precalculus

An **Animated Precalculus** tutorial is available at the Student companion site for **Section 3.4.**

Pacing

Average: 2 days
Advanced: 2 days
Block: 1 block

2 FOCUS AND MOTIVATE

Essential Question

How do you solve exponential and logarithmic equations? **Tell students that they will learn how to answer this question by studying strategies based on the definitions and properties of exponents and logarithms.**

3.4 EXPONENTIAL AND LOGARITHMIC EQUATIONS

What you should learn

- Solve simple exponential and logarithmic equations.
- Solve more complicated exponential equations.
- Solve more complicated logarithmic equations.
- Use exponential and logarithmic equations to model and solve real-life problems.

Why you should learn it

Exponential and logarithmic equations are used to model and solve life science applications. For instance, in Exercise 132 on page 253, an exponential function is used to model the number of trees per acre given the average diameter of the trees.

© James Marshall/Corbis

Introduction

So far in this chapter, you have studied the definitions, graphs, and properties of exponential and logarithmic functions. In this section, you will study procedures for *solving equations* involving these exponential and logarithmic functions.

There are two basic strategies for solving exponential or logarithmic equations. The first is based on the One-to-One Properties and was used to solve simple exponential and logarithmic equations in Sections 3.1 and 3.2. The second is based on the Inverse Properties. For $a > 0$ and $a \neq 1$, the following properties are true for all x and y for which $\log_a x$ and $\log_a y$ are defined.

One-to-One Properties

$a^x = a^y$ if and only if $x = y$.

$\log_a x = \log_a y$ if and only if $x = y$.

Inverse Properties

$a^{\log_a x} = x$

$\log_a a^x = x$

Example 1 Solving Simple Equations

	Original Equation	*Rewritten Equation*	*Solution*	*Property*
a.	$2^x = 32$	$2^x = 2^5$	$x = 5$	One-to-One
b.	$\ln x - \ln 3 = 0$	$\ln x = \ln 3$	$x = 3$	One-to-One
c.	$\left(\frac{1}{3}\right)^x = 9$	$3^{-x} = 3^2$	$x = -2$	One-to-One
d.	$e^x = 7$	$\ln e^x = \ln 7$	$x = \ln 7$	Inverse
e.	$\ln x = -3$	$e^{\ln x} = e^{-3}$	$x = e^{-3}$	Inverse
f.	$\log x = -1$	$10^{\log x} = 10^{-1}$	$x = 10^{-1} = \frac{1}{10}$	Inverse
g.	$\log_3 x = 4$	$3^{\log_3 x} = 3^4$	$x = 81$	Inverse

CHECKPoint Now try Exercise 17.

The strategies used in Example 1 are summarized as follows.

Strategies for Solving Exponential and Logarithmic Equations

1. Rewrite the original equation in a form that allows the use of the One-to-One Properties of exponential or logarithmic functions.
2. Rewrite an *exponential* equation in logarithmic form and apply the Inverse Property of logarithmic functions.
3. Rewrite a *logarithmic* equation in exponential form and apply the Inverse Property of exponential functions.

Resource Planning Guide

Chapter Resources
- Complete Solutions Guide

Workbooks
- Notetaking Guide
- Student Solutions Guide

Interactive Technology
- Instructor Success Organizer
- Notetaking Guide IAE
- Instructional DVDs
- Animated Precalculus
- PowerLecture with ExamView

Solving Exponential Equations

Example 2 Solving Exponential Equations

Solve each equation and approximate the result to three decimal places, if necessary.

a. $e^{-x^2} = e^{-3x-4}$

b. $3(2^x) = 42$

Solution

a.

$e^{-x^2} = e^{-3x-4}$	Write original equation.
$-x^2 = -3x - 4$	One-to-One Property
$x^2 - 3x - 4 = 0$	Write in general form.
$(x + 1)(x - 4) = 0$	Factor.
$(x + 1) = 0 \Rightarrow x = -1$	Set 1st factor equal to 0.
$(x - 4) = 0 \Rightarrow x = 4$	Set 2nd factor equal to 0.

The solutions are $x = -1$ and $x = 4$. Check these in the original equation.

b.

$3(2^x) = 42$	Write original equation.
$2^x = 14$	Divide each side by 3.
$\log_2 2^x = \log_2 14$	Take log (base 2) of each side.
$x = \log_2 14$	Inverse Property
$x = \frac{\ln 14}{\ln 2} \approx 3.807$	Change-of-base formula

The solution is $x = \log_2 14 \approx 3.807$. Check this in the original equation.

CHECKPoint Now try Exercise 29.

In Example 2(b), the exact solution is $x = \log_2 14$ and the approximate solution is $x \approx 3.807$. An exact answer is preferred when the solution is an intermediate step in a larger problem. For a final answer, an approximate solution is easier to comprehend.

Study Tip

Another way to solve Example 2(b) is by taking the natural log of each side and then applying the Power Property, as follows.

$$3(2^x) = 42$$
$$2^x = 14$$
$$\ln 2^x = \ln 14$$
$$x \ln 2 = \ln 14$$
$$x = \frac{\ln 14}{\ln 2} \approx 3.807$$

As you can see, you obtain the same result as in Example 2(b).

Example 3 Solving an Exponential Equation

Solve $e^x + 5 = 60$ and approximate the result to three decimal places.

Solution

$e^x + 5 = 60$	Write original equation.
$e^x = 55$	Subtract 5 from each side.
$\ln e^x = \ln 55$	Take natural log of each side.
$x = \ln 55 \approx 4.007$	Inverse Property

The solution is $x = \ln 55 \approx 4.007$. Check this in the original equation.

CHECKPoint Now try Exercise 55.

Study Tip

Remember that the natural logarithmic function has a base of *e*.

3 TEACH

Extra Example 1

Solve.

a. $2^x = 512$
  $x = 9$

b. $\ln 5 - \ln x = 0$
  $x = 5$

c. $\left(\frac{1}{5}\right)^x = 125$
  $x = -3$

d. $e^x = 13$
  $x = \ln 13$

e. $\ln x = -8$
  $x = e^{-8}$

f. $\log x = -2$
  $x = \frac{1}{100}$

Extra Example 2

Solve each equation and approximate the result to three decimal places if necessary.

a. $e^{-x^2} = e^{5x+6}$
  $x = -3, x = -2$

b. $4(3^x) = 64$
  $x \approx 2.524$

Extra Example 3

Solve $5 - 3e^x = 2$.
  $x = 0$

Differentiated Instruction

Kinesthetic Learners Kinesthetic learners may benefit from writing the equations in Examples 2 and 3 on a separate sheet of paper. Have students work out the solutions to the equations by following the directions shown in the right column of the solution. As they progress through the examples on the following pages, challenge students to cover the left column of the solution and use only the instructions in the right column to help them find the solutions.

Extra Example 4

Solve $6(2^{t+5}) + 4 = 11$ and approximate the solution to three decimal places.

$t = -4.778$

Avoiding Common Errors

Students may produce incorrect answers if they convert logarithms to approximate decimals in the process of solving equations.
To ensure that students avoid this error, require them to provide the exact algebraic solution as well as the numerical approximation.

Extra Example 5

Solve $e^{2x} - 7e^x + 12 = 0$.

$x = \ln 3 \approx 1.099,\ x = \ln 4 \approx 1.386$

Example 4 Solving an Exponential Equation

Solve $2(3^{2t-5}) - 4 = 11$ and approximate the result to three decimal places.

Solution

$2(3^{2t-5}) - 4 = 11$	Write original equation.
$2(3^{2t-5}) = 15$	Add 4 to each side.
$3^{2t-5} = \frac{15}{2}$	Divide each side by 2.
$\log_3 3^{2t-5} = \log_3 \frac{15}{2}$	Take log (base 3) of each side.
$2t - 5 = \log_3 \frac{15}{2}$	Inverse Property
$2t = 5 + \log_3 7.5$	Add 5 to each side.
$t = \frac{5}{2} + \frac{1}{2}\log_3 7.5$	Divide each side by 2.
$t \approx 3.417$	Use a calculator.

The solution is $t = \frac{5}{2} + \frac{1}{2}\log_3 7.5 \approx 3.417$. Check this in the original equation.

CHECKPoint Now try Exercise 57.

Study Tip

Remember that to evaluate a logarithm such as $\log_3 7.5$, you need to use the change-of-base formula.

$$\log_3 7.5 = \frac{\ln 7.5}{\ln 3} \approx 1.834$$

When an equation involves two or more exponential expressions, you can still use a procedure similar to that demonstrated in Examples 2, 3, and 4. However, the algebra is a bit more complicated.

Example 5 Solving an Exponential Equation of Quadratic Type

Solve $e^{2x} - 3e^x + 2 = 0$.

Algebraic Solution

$e^{2x} - 3e^x + 2 = 0$	Write original equation.
$(e^x)^2 - 3e^x + 2 = 0$	Write in quadratic form.
$(e^x - 2)(e^x - 1) = 0$	Factor.
$e^x - 2 = 0$	Set 1st factor equal to 0.
$x = \ln 2$	Solution
$e^x - 1 = 0$	Set 2nd factor equal to 0.
$x = 0$	Solution

The solutions are $x = \ln 2 \approx 0.693$ and $x = 0$. Check these in the original equation.

Graphical Solution

Use a graphing utility to graph $y = e^{2x} - 3e^x + 2$. Use the *zero* or *root* feature or the *zoom* and *trace* features of the graphing utility to approximate the values of x for which $y = 0$. In Figure 3.28, you can see that the zeros occur at $x = 0$ and at $x \approx 0.693$. So, the solutions are $x = 0$ and $x \approx 0.693$.

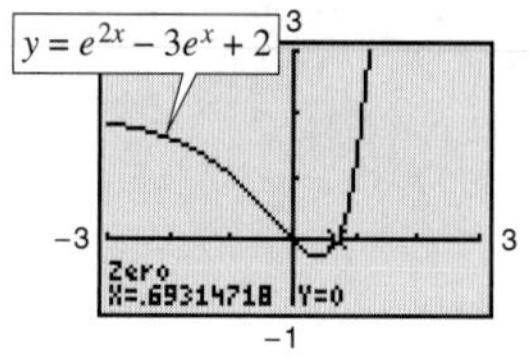

FIGURE 3.28

CHECKPoint Now try Exercise 59.

Solving Logarithmic Equations

To solve a logarithmic equation, you can write it in exponential form.

$\ln x = 3$	Logarithmic form
$e^{\ln x} = e^3$	Exponentiate each side.
$x = e^3$	Exponential form

This procedure is called *exponentiating* each side of an equation.

Example 6 Solving Logarithmic Equations

a. $\ln x = 2$	Original equation
$e^{\ln x} = e^2$	Exponentiate each side.
$x = e^2$	Inverse Property
b. $\log_3(5x - 1) = \log_3(x + 7)$	Original equation
$5x - 1 = x + 7$	One-to-One Property
$4x = 8$	Add $-x$ and 1 to each side.
$x = 2$	Divide each side by 4.
c. $\log_6(3x + 14) - \log_6 5 = \log_6 2x$	Original equation
$\log_6\left(\dfrac{3x + 14}{5}\right) = \log_6 2x$	Quotient Property of Logarithms
$\dfrac{3x + 14}{5} = 2x$	One-to-One Property
$3x + 14 = 10x$	Cross multiply.
$-7x = -14$	Isolate x.
$x = 2$	Divide each side by -7.

CHECKPoint Now try Exercise 83.

WARNING/CAUTION

Remember to check your solutions in the original equation when solving equations to verify that the answer is correct and to make sure that the answer lies in the domain of the original equation.

Example 7 Solving a Logarithmic Equation

Solve $5 + 2 \ln x = 4$ and approximate the result to three decimal places.

Algebraic Solution

$5 + 2 \ln x = 4$	Write original equation.
$2 \ln x = -1$	Subtract 5 from each side.
$\ln x = -\dfrac{1}{2}$	Divide each side by 2.
$e^{\ln x} = e^{-1/2}$	Exponentiate each side.
$x = e^{-1/2}$	Inverse Property
$x \approx 0.607$	Use a calculator.

CHECKPoint Now try Exercise 93.

Graphical Solution

Use a graphing utility to graph $y_1 = 5 + 2 \ln x$ and $y_2 = 4$ in the same viewing window. Use the *intersect* feature or the *zoom* and *trace* features to approximate the intersection point, as shown in Figure 3.29. So, the solution is $x \approx 0.607$.

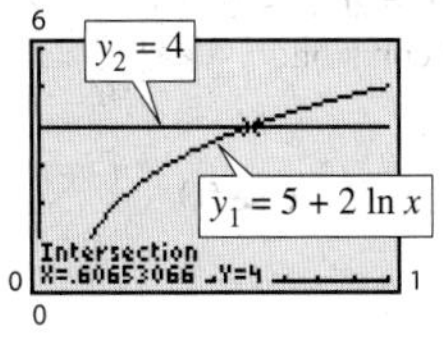

FIGURE 3.29

Extra Example 6

Solve.

a. $\ln x = \frac{2}{3}$

$x = e^{2/3} \approx 1.948$

b. $\log_4(3x + 2) = \log_4(6 - x)$

$x = 1$

c. $\log_3(5x + 13) - \log_3 6 = \log_3 3x$

$x = 1$

Extra Example 7

Solve $6 + 3 \ln x = 4$ and approximate the solution to three decimal places.

$x = e^{-2/3} \approx 0.513$

Extra Example 8
Solve $3 \log_4 6x = 9$.
$x = \frac{32}{3}$

Extra Example 9
Solve $\log_{10} x + \log_{10}(x - 9) = 1$.
$x = 10$

Example 8 Solving a Logarithmic Equation

Solve $2 \log_5 3x = 4$.

Solution

$2 \log_5 3x = 4$	Write original equation.
$\log_5 3x = 2$	Divide each side by 2.
$5^{\log_5 3x} = 5^2$	Exponentiate each side (base 5).
$3x = 25$	Inverse Property
$x = \frac{25}{3}$	Divide each side by 3.

The solution is $x = \frac{25}{3}$. Check this in the original equation.

CHECKPoint Now try Exercise 97.

Study Tip

Notice in Example 9 that the logarithmic part of the equation is condensed into a single logarithm before exponentiating each side of the equation.

Because the domain of a logarithmic function generally does not include all real numbers, you should be sure to check for extraneous solutions of logarithmic equations.

Example 9 Checking for Extraneous Solutions

Solve $\log 5x + \log(x - 1) = 2$.

Algebraic Solution

$\log 5x + \log(x - 1) = 2$	Write original equation.
$\log[5x(x - 1)] = 2$	Product Property of Logarithms
$10^{\log(5x^2 - 5x)} = 10^2$	Exponentiate each side (base 10).
$5x^2 - 5x = 100$	Inverse Property
$x^2 - x - 20 = 0$	Write in general form.
$(x - 5)(x + 4) = 0$	Factor.
$x - 5 = 0$	Set 1st factor equal to 0.
$x = 5$	Solution
$x + 4 = 0$	Set 2nd factor equal to 0.
$x = -4$	Solution

The solutions appear to be $x = 5$ and $x = -4$. However, when you check these in the original equation, you can see that $x = 5$ is the only solution.

CHECKPoint Now try Exercise 109.

Graphical Solution

Use a graphing utility to graph $y_1 = \log 5x + \log(x - 1)$ and $y_2 = 2$ in the same viewing window. From the graph shown in Figure 3.30, it appears that the graphs intersect at one point. Use the *intersect* feature or the *zoom* and *trace* features to determine that the graphs intersect at approximately (5, 2). So, the solution is $x = 5$. Verify that 5 is an exact solution algebraically.

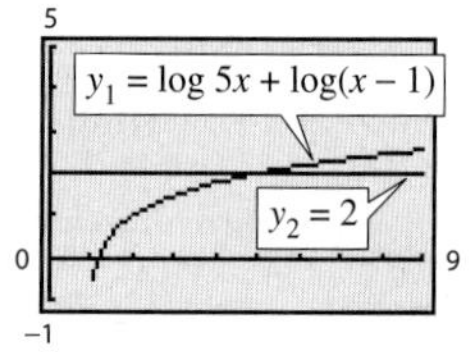

FIGURE 3.30

In Example 9, the domain of $\log 5x$ is $x > 0$ and the domain of $\log(x - 1)$ is $x > 1$, so the domain of the original equation is $x > 1$. Because the domain is all real numbers greater than 1, the solution $x = -4$ is extraneous. The graph in Figure 3.30 verifies this conclusion.

Applications

Example 10 Doubling an Investment

You have deposited \$500 in an account that pays 6.75% interest, compounded continuously. How long will it take your money to double?

Solution

Using the formula for continuous compounding, you can find that the balance in the account is

$$A = Pe^{rt}$$

$$A = 500e^{0.0675t}.$$

To find the time required for the balance to double, let $A = 1000$ and solve the resulting equation for t.

$$500e^{0.0675t} = 1000 \quad \text{Let } A = 1000.$$

$$e^{0.0675t} = 2 \quad \text{Divide each side by 500.}$$

$$\ln e^{0.0675t} = \ln 2 \quad \text{Take natural log of each side.}$$

$$0.0675t = \ln 2 \quad \text{Inverse Property}$$

$$t = \frac{\ln 2}{0.0675} \quad \text{Divide each side by 0.0675.}$$

$$t \approx 10.27 \quad \text{Use a calculator.}$$

The balance in the account will double after approximately 10.27 years. This result is demonstrated graphically in Figure 3.31.

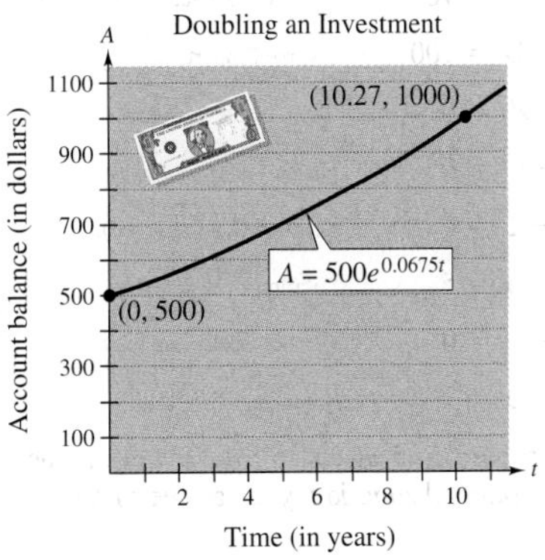

FIGURE 3.31

CHECKPoint Now try Exercise 117.

In Example 10, an approximate answer of 10.27 years is given. Within the context of the problem, the exact solution, $(\ln 2)/0.0675$ years, does not make sense as an answer.

Extra Example 10
You have deposited \$1000 in an account that pays 6.25% interest, compounded continuously. How long will it take your money to double? **11.1 years**

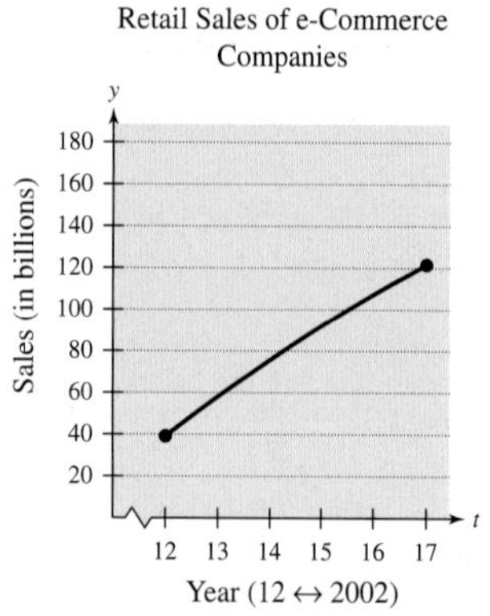

FIGURE 3.32

Example 11 Retail Sales

The retail sales y (in billions) of e-commerce companies in the United States from 2002 through 2007 can be modeled by

$$y = -549 + 236.7 \ln t, \quad 12 \le t \le 17$$

where t represents the year, with $t = 12$ corresponding to 2002 (see Figure 3.32). During which year did the sales reach \$108 billion? (Source: U.S. Census Bureau)

Solution

$$-549 + 236.7 \ln t = y \qquad \text{Write original equation.}$$

$$-549 + 236.7 \ln t = 108 \qquad \text{Substitute 108 for } y.$$

$$236.7 \ln t = 657 \qquad \text{Add 549 to each side.}$$

$$\ln t = \frac{657}{236.7} \qquad \text{Divide each side by 236.7.}$$

$$e^{\ln t} = e^{657/236.7} \qquad \text{Exponentiate each side.}$$

$$t = e^{657/236.7} \qquad \text{Inverse Property}$$

$$t \approx 16 \qquad \text{Use a calculator.}$$

The solution is $t \approx 16$. Because $t = 12$ represents 2002, it follows that the sales reached \$108 billion in 2006.

CHECKPoint Now try Exercise 133.

Classroom Discussion

Analyzing Relationships Numerically Use a calculator to fill in the table row-by-row. Discuss the resulting pattern. What can you conclude? Find two equations that summarize the relationships you discovered. See margin.

x	$\frac{1}{2}$	1	2	10	25	50
e^x						
$\ln(e^x)$						
$\ln x$						
$e^{\ln x}$						

Extra Example 11

The number y of endangered animal species on a protected wildlife preserve from 1990 to 2004 can be modeled by $y = -117 + 159 \ln t$, $10 \le t \le 24$, where t represents the year, with $t = 10$ corresponding to 1990. During which year did the number of endangered animal species reach 342?

$t \approx 18$ years; The number of endangered species reached 342 in 1998.

Closing the Lesson

Have students summarize the major points of the lesson and answer the Essential Question: How do you solve exponential and logarithmic equations?

- **Rewrite equations in order to apply One-to-One Properties.**
- **Rewrite an exponential equation as a logarithmic equation or a logarithmic equation as an exponential equation and apply an Inverse Property.**
- **Use a graphing utility to approximate solutions.**

Classroom Discussion

x	$\frac{1}{2}$	1	2	10	25	50
e^x	1.65	2.72	7.39	22,026	7.2×10^{10}	5.18×10^{21}
$\ln(e^x)$	$\frac{1}{2}$	1	2	10	25	50
$\ln x$	−0.69	0	0.69	2.30	3.22	3.91
$e^{\ln x}$	$\frac{1}{2}$	1	2	10	25	50

$e^{\ln x}$ and $\ln(e^x)$ simplify to x. e^x is greater than $\ln x$. e^x grows very quickly.

$e^{\ln x} = \ln(e^x) = x$

$e^x > \ln x$

3.4 EXERCISES

See www.CalcChat.com for worked-out solutions to odd-numbered exercises.

VOCABULARY: Fill in the blanks.

1. To ___solve___ an equation in x means to find all values of x for which the equation is true.
2. To solve exponential and logarithmic equations, you can use the following One-to-One and Inverse Properties.
   (a) $a^x = a^y$ if and only if ___$x = y$___. (b) $\log_a x = \log_a y$ if and only if ___$x = y$___.
   (c) $a^{\log_a x} =$ ___x___ (d) $\log_a a^x =$ ___x___
3. To solve exponential and logarithmic equations, you can use the following strategies.
   (a) Rewrite the original equation in a form that allows the use of the ________ Properties of exponential or logarithmic functions. One-to-One
   (b) Rewrite an exponential equation in ________ form and apply the Inverse Property of ________ functions. logarithmic; logarithmic
   (c) Rewrite a logarithmic equation in ________ form and apply the Inverse Property of ________ functions. exponential; exponential
4. An ________ solution does not satisfy the original equation. extraneous

SKILLS AND APPLICATIONS

In Exercises 5–12, determine whether each x-value is a solution (or an approximate solution) of the equation.

5. $4^{2x-7} = 64$
   (a) $x = 5$ Yes
   (b) $x = 2$ No
6. $2^{3x+1} = 32$
   (a) $x = -1$ No
   (b) $x = 2$ No
7. $3e^{x+2} = 75$
   (a) $x = -2 + e^{25}$ No
   (b) $x = -2 + \ln 25$ Yes
   (c) $x \approx 1.219$ Yes, approx.
8. $4e^{x-1} = 60$
   (a) $x = 1 + \ln 15$ Yes
   (b) $x \approx 3.7081$ Yes, approx.
   (c) $x = \ln 16$ No
9. $\log_4(3x) = 3$
   (a) $x \approx 21.333$ Yes, approx.
   (b) $x = -4$ No
   (c) $x = \frac{64}{3}$ Yes
10. $\log_2(x + 3) = 10$
    (a) $x = 1021$ Yes
    (b) $x = 17$ No
    (c) $x = 10^2 - 3$ No
11. $\ln(2x + 3) = 5.8$
    (a) $x = \frac{1}{2}(-3 + \ln 5.8)$ No
    (b) $x = \frac{1}{2}(-3 + e^{5.8})$ Yes
    (c) $x \approx 163.650$ Yes, approx.
12. $\ln(x - 1) = 3.8$
    (a) $x = 1 + e^{3.8}$ Yes
    (b) $x \approx 45.701$ Yes, approx.
    (c) $x = 1 + \ln 3.8$ No

In Exercises 13–24, solve for x.

13. $4^x = 16$ 2
14. $3^x = 243$ 5
15. $\left(\frac{1}{2}\right)^x = 32$ -5
16. $\left(\frac{1}{4}\right)^x = 64$ -3
17. $\ln x - \ln 2 = 0$ 2
18. $\ln x - \ln 5 = 0$ 5
19. $e^x = 2$ $\ln 2 \approx 0.693$
20. $e^x = 4$ $\ln 4 \approx 1.386$
21. $\ln x = -1$ See margin.
22. $\log x = -2$ 0.01
23. $\log_4 x = 3$ 64
24. $\log_5 x = \frac{1}{2}$ $\sqrt{5} \approx 2.236$

In Exercises 25–28, approximate the point of intersection of the graphs of f and g. Then solve the equation $f(x) = g(x)$ algebraically to verify your approximation.

25. $f(x) = 2^x$ $(3, 8)$
    $g(x) = 8$

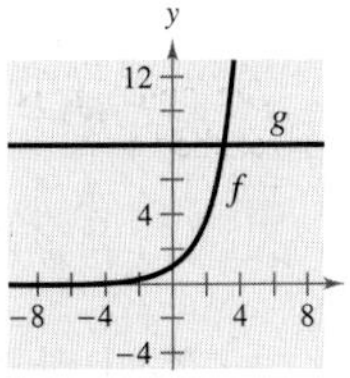

26. $f(x) = 27^x$ $\left(\frac{2}{3}, 9\right)$
    $g(x) = 9$

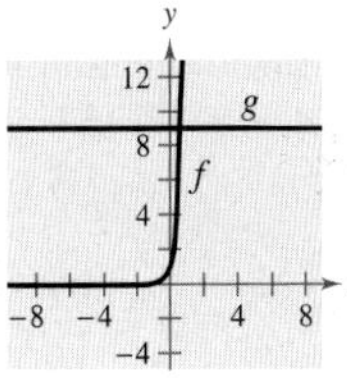

27. $f(x) = \log_3 x$ $(9, 2)$
    $g(x) = 2$

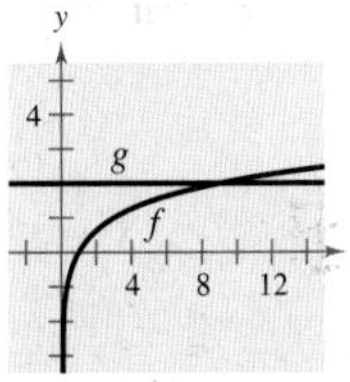

28. $f(x) = \ln(x - 4)$ $(5, 0)$
    $g(x) = 0$

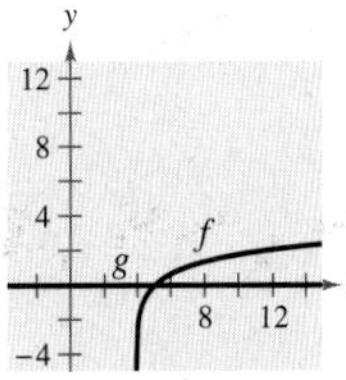

In Exercises 29–70, solve the exponential equation algebraically. Approximate the result to three decimal places.

29. $e^x = e^{x^2-2}$ $2, -1$
30. $e^{2x} = e^{x^2-8}$ $-2, 4$
31. $e^{x^2-3} = e^{x-2}$ 31, 33. See margin.
32. $e^{-x^2} = e^{x^2-2x}$ $0, 1$
33. $4(3^x) = 20$
34. $2(5^x) = 32$ See margin.
35. $2e^x = 10$ $\ln 5 \approx 1.609$
36. $4e^x = 91$ 36–40. See margin.
37. $e^x - 9 = 19$
38. $6^x + 10 = 47$
39. $3^{2x} = 80$
40. $6^{5x} = 3000$
41. $5^{-t/2} = 0.20$ 2
42. $4^{-3t} = 0.10$ See margin.
43. $3^{x-1} = 27$ 4
44. $2^{x-3} = 32$ 8
45. $2^{3-x} = 565$ $3 - \dfrac{\ln 565}{\ln 2} \approx -6.142$
46. $8^{-2-x} = 431$ $\dfrac{-\ln 64 - \ln 431}{\ln 8} \approx -4.917$

4 PRACTICE AND APPLY

Assignment Guide

Transparencies Available
Available at the Instructor's companion site.

Average:
Day 1: pp. 251–252
Exs. 1–4, 5–15 odd, 19–27 odd, 31–39 odd, 47, 51, 55, 61, 63, 67, 71, 73, 75
Day 2: pp. 252–254
Exs. 87–91 odd, 98, 101–107 odd, 111, 113, 118, 121, 127, 129, 131, 135, 138–142

Advanced:
Day 1: pp. 251–252
Exs. 1–4, 6–12 even, 16–24 even, 26, 28, 32–40 even, 50, 54–64 even, 68, 76–80 even
Day 2: pp. 252–254
Exs. 88–100 even, 104, 108–112 even, 116, 118, 122, 126, 130, 132, 133, 136–138, 143–146, 148

Block:
pp. 251–254
Exs. 1–4, 5–15 odd, 19–27 odd, 31–39 odd, 47, 51, 55, 61, 63, 67, 71, 73, 75, 87–91 odd, 98, 101–107 odd, 111, 113, 118, 121, 127, 129, 131, 135, 138–142

21. $e^{-1} \approx 0.368$
31. About 1.618, about -0.618
33. $\dfrac{\ln 5}{\ln 3} \approx 1.465$
34. $\dfrac{\ln 16}{\ln 5} \approx 1.723$
36. $\ln \frac{91}{4} \approx 3.125$
37. $\ln 28 \approx 3.332$
38. $\dfrac{\ln 37}{\ln 6} \approx 2.015$
39. $\dfrac{\ln 80}{2 \ln 3} \approx 1.994$
40. $\dfrac{\ln 3000}{5 \ln 6} \approx 0.894$
42. $-\dfrac{\ln(0.10)}{3 \ln 4} \approx 0.554$

47. $\frac{1}{3}\log\left(\frac{3}{2}\right) \approx 0.059$

48. $6 + \log\frac{7}{5} \approx 6.146$

49. $1 + \dfrac{\ln 7}{\ln 5} \approx 2.209$

50. $6 - \dfrac{\ln 5}{\ln 3} \approx 4.535$

51. $\dfrac{\ln 12}{3} \approx 0.828$

52. $\dfrac{\ln 50}{2} \approx 1.956$

53. $-\ln\frac{3}{5} \approx 0.511$

54. $-\frac{1}{4}\ln\frac{3}{40} \approx 0.648$

55. 0

56. $\ln\frac{25}{3} \approx 2.120$

57. $\dfrac{\ln\frac{8}{3}}{3\ln 2} + \dfrac{1}{3} \approx 0.805$

58. $3 - \dfrac{\ln\frac{7}{2}}{2\ln 4} \approx 2.548$

59. $\ln 5 \approx 1.609$

60. $\ln 2 \approx 0.693$; $\ln 3 \approx 1.099$

61. $\ln 4 \approx 1.386$

62. No solution

63. $2\ln 75 \approx 8.635$

64. $\ln 7 \approx 1.946$

65. $\frac{1}{2}\ln 1498 \approx 3.656$

66. $\dfrac{\ln 31}{6} \approx 0.572$

67. $\dfrac{\ln 4}{365\ln\left(1 + \frac{0.065}{365}\right)} \approx 21.330$

68. $\dfrac{\ln 21}{9\ln 3.938225} \approx 0.247$

69. $\dfrac{\ln 2}{12\ln\left(1 + \frac{0.10}{12}\right)} \approx 6.960$

70. $\dfrac{\ln 30}{3\ln\left(16 - \frac{0.878}{26}\right)} \approx 0.409$

71.

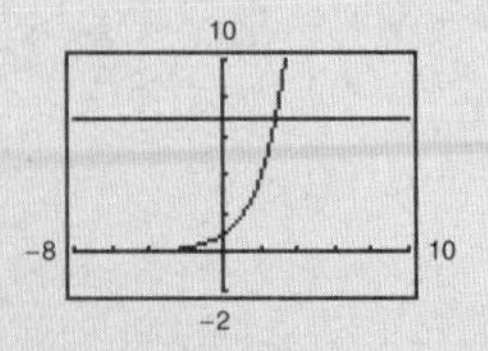

2.807

72.

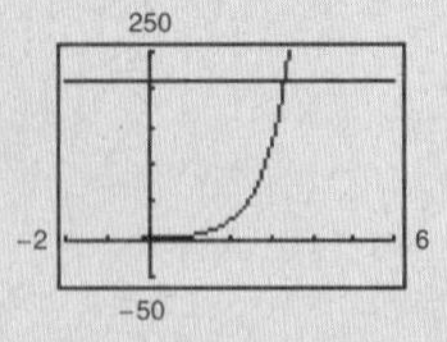

3.328

73.

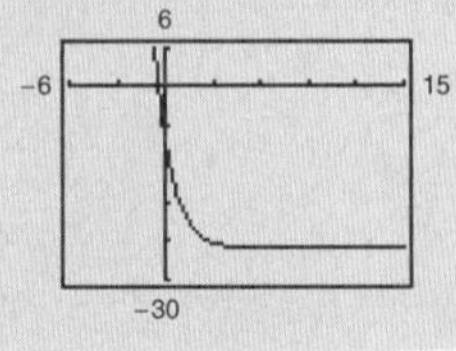

-0.427

47. $8(10^{3x}) = 12$

48. $5(10^{x-6}) = 7$

49. $3(5^{x-1}) = 21$

50. $8(3^{6-x}) = 40$ 47–70. See margin.

51. $e^{3x} = 12$

52. $e^{2x} = 50$

53. $500e^{-x} = 300$

54. $1000e^{-4x} = 75$

55. $7 - 2e^{x} = 5$

56. $-14 + 3e^{x} = 11$

57. $6(2^{3x-1}) - 7 = 9$

58. $8(4^{6-2x}) + 13 = 41$

59. $e^{2x} - 4e^{x} - 5 = 0$

60. $e^{2x} - 5e^{x} + 6 = 0$

61. $e^{2x} - 3e^{x} - 4 = 0$

62. $e^{2x} + 9e^{x} + 36 = 0$

63. $\dfrac{500}{100 - e^{x/2}} = 20$

64. $\dfrac{400}{1 + e^{-x}} = 350$

65. $\dfrac{3000}{2 + e^{2x}} = 2$

66. $\dfrac{119}{e^{6x} - 14} = 7$

67. $\left(1 + \dfrac{0.065}{365}\right)^{365t} = 4$

68. $\left(4 - \dfrac{2.471}{40}\right)^{9t} = 21$

69. $\left(1 + \dfrac{0.10}{12}\right)^{12t} = 2$

70. $\left(16 - \dfrac{0.878}{26}\right)^{3t} = 30$

In Exercises 71–80, use a graphing utility to graph and solve the equation. Approximate the result to three decimal places. Verify your result algebraically. 71–80. See margin.

71. $7 = 2^{x}$

72. $5^{x} = 212$

73. $6e^{1-x} = 25$

74. $-4e^{-x-1} + 15 = 0$

75. $3e^{3x/2} = 962$

76. $8e^{-2x/3} = 11$

77. $e^{0.09t} = 3$

78. $-e^{1.8x} + 7 = 0$

79. $e^{0.125t} - 8 = 0$

80. $e^{2.724x} = 29$

In Exercises 81–112, solve the logarithmic equation algebraically. Approximate the result to three decimal places.

81. $\ln x = -3$

82. $\ln x = 1.6$ 81–92. See margin.

83. $\ln x - 7 = 0$

84. $\ln x + 1 = 0$

85. $\ln 2x = 2.4$

86. $2.1 = \ln 6x$

87. $\log x = 6$

88. $\log 3z = 2$

89. $3\ln 5x = 10$

90. $2\ln x = 7$

91. $\ln\sqrt{x + 2} = 1$

92. $\ln\sqrt{x - 8} = 5$

93. $7 + 3\ln x = 5$ $e^{-2/3} \approx 0.513$

94. $2 - 6\ln x = 10$ $e^{-4/3} \approx 0.264$

95. $-2 + 2\ln 3x = 17$ See margin.

96. $2 + 3\ln x = 12$ $e^{10/3} \approx 28.032$

97. $6\log_3(0.5x) = 11$ $2(3^{11/6}) \approx 14.988$

98. $4\log(x - 6) = 11$ $10^{11/4} + 6 \approx 568.341$

99. $\ln x - \ln(x + 1) = 2$ No solution

100. $\ln x + \ln(x + 1) = 1$ See margin.

101. $\ln x + \ln(x - 2) = 1$ $1 + \sqrt{1 + e} \approx 2.928$

102. $\ln x + \ln(x + 3) = 1$ See margin.

103. $\ln(x + 5) = \ln(x - 1) - \ln(x + 1)$ No solution

104. $\ln(x + 1) - \ln(x - 2) = \ln x$ See margin.

105. $\log_2(2x - 3) = \log_2(x + 4)$ 7

106. $\log(3x + 4) = \log(x - 10)$ No solution

107. $\log(x + 4) - \log x = \log(x + 2)$ See margin.

108. $\log_2 x + \log_2(x + 2) = \log_2(x + 6)$ 2

109. $\log_4 x - \log_4(x - 1) = \frac{1}{2}$ 2

110. $\log_3 x + \log_3(x - 8) = 2$ 9

111. $\log 8x - \log\left(1 + \sqrt{x}\right) = 2$ See margin.

112. $\log 4x - \log\left(12 + \sqrt{x}\right) = 2$ See margin.

In Exercises 113–116, use a graphing utility to graph and solve the equation. Approximate the result to three decimal places. Verify your result algebraically. 113–116. See margin.

113. $3 - \ln x = 0$

114. $10 - 4\ln(x - 2) = 0$

115. $2\ln(x + 3) = 3$

116. $\ln(x + 1) = 2 - \ln x$

COMPOUND INTEREST In Exercises 117–120, \$2500 is invested in an account at interest rate r, compounded continuously. Find the time required for the amount to (a) double and (b) triple. 117–118. See margin.

117. $r = 0.05$

118. $r = 0.045$

119. $r = 0.025$ (a) 27.73 yr (b) 43.94 yr

120. $r = 0.0375$ (a) 18.48 yr (b) 29.30 yr

In Exercises 121–128, solve the equation algebraically. Round the result to three decimal places. Verify your answer using a graphing utility.

121. $2x^2e^{2x} + 2xe^{2x} = 0$ $-1, 0$

122. $-x^2e^{-x} + 2xe^{-x} = 0$ $2, 0$

123. $-xe^{-x} + e^{-x} = 0$ 1

124. $e^{-2x} - 2xe^{-2x} = 0$ $\frac{1}{2}$

125. $2x\ln x + x = 0$ $e^{-1/2} \approx 0.607$

126. $\dfrac{1 - \ln x}{x^2} = 0$ $e \approx 2.718$

127. $\dfrac{1 + \ln x}{2} = 0$ $e^{-1} \approx 0.368$

128. $2x\ln\left(\dfrac{1}{x}\right) - x = 0$ $e^{-1/2} \approx 0.607$

129. DEMAND The demand equation for a limited edition coin set is

$$p = 1000\left(1 - \frac{5}{5 + e^{-0.001x}}\right).$$

(a) 210 coins (b) 588 coins

Find the demand x for a price of (a) $p = \$139.50$ and (b) $p = \$99.99$.

130. DEMAND The demand equation for a hand-held electronic organizer is

Find the demand x for a price of (a) $p = \$600$ and (b) $p = \$400$.

74.

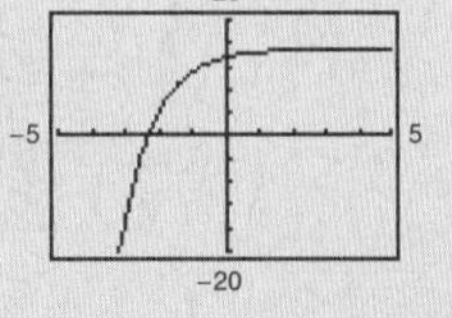

-2.322

75.

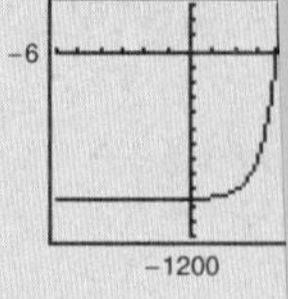

3.847

#101. NO

#103. OK

#105. OK

#107. No

#109. OK

#111. No

77–92, 95, 100, 102, 104, 107, 111–118. See Additional Answers beginning on page AA1.

131. FOREST YIELD The yield V (in millions of cubic feet per acre) for a forest at age t years is given by $V = 6.7e^{-48.1/t}$.

(a) Use a graphing utility to graph the function.

(b) Determine the horizontal asymptote of the function. Interpret its meaning in the context of the problem. (a)–(b). See margin.

(c) Find the time necessary to obtain a yield of 1.3 million cubic feet. 29.3 yr

132. TREES PER ACRE The number N of trees of a given species per acre is approximated by the model $N = 68(10^{-0.04x})$, $5 \le x \le 40$, where x is the average diameter of the trees (in inches) 3 feet above the ground. Use the model to approximate the average diameter of the trees in a test plot when $N = 21$. 12.76 in.

133. U.S. CURRENCY The values y (in billions of dollars) of U.S. currency in circulation in the years 2000 through 2007 can be modeled by $y = -451 + 444 \ln t$, $10 \le t \le 17$, where t represents the year, with $t = 10$ corresponding to 2000. During which year did the value of U.S. currency in circulation exceed \$690 billion? (Source: Board of Governors of the Federal Reserve System) 2003

134. MEDICINE The numbers y of freestanding ambulatory care surgery centers in the United States from 2000 through 2007 can be modeled by

$$y = 2875 + \frac{2635.11}{1 + 14.215e^{-0.8038t}}, \quad 0 \le t \le 7$$

where t represents the year, with $t = 0$ corresponding to 2000. (Source: Verispan)

(a) Use a graphing utility to graph the model. See margin.

(b) Use the *trace* feature of the graphing utility to estimate the year in which the number of surgery centers exceeded 3600. 2002

135. AVERAGE HEIGHTS The percent m of American males between the ages of 18 and 24 who are no more than x inches tall is modeled by

$$m(x) = \frac{100}{1 + e^{-0.6114(x-69.71)}}$$

and the percent f of American females between the ages of 18 and 24 who are no more than x inches tall is modeled by

$$f(x) = \frac{100}{1 + e^{-0.66607(x-64.51)}}.$$

(Source: U.S. National Center for Health Statistics)

(a) Use the graph to determine any horizontal asymptotes of the graphs of the functions. Interpret the meaning in the context of the problem.

$y = 100$ and $y = 0$; The range falls between 0% and 100%.

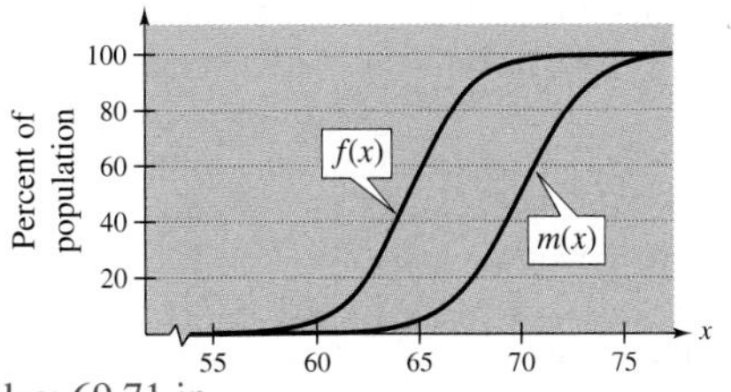

Males: 69.71 in.
Females: 64.51 in.

(b) What is the average height of each sex?

136. LEARNING CURVE In a group project in learning theory, a mathematical model for the proportion P of correct responses after n trials was found to be $P = 0.83/(1 + e^{-0.2n})$. See margin.

(a) Use a graphing utility to graph the function.

(b) Use the graph to determine any horizontal asymptotes of the graph of the function. Interpret the meaning of the upper asymptote in the context of this problem. See margin.

(c) After how many trials will 60% of the responses be correct? About 5 trials

137. AUTOMOBILES Automobiles are designed with crumple zones that help protect their occupants in crashes. The crumple zones allow the occupants to move short distances when the automobiles come to abrupt stops. The greater the distance moved, the fewer g's the crash victims experience. (One g is equal to the acceleration due to gravity. For very short periods of time, humans have withstood as much as 40 g's.) In crash tests with vehicles moving at 90 kilometers per hour, analysts measured the numbers of g's experienced during deceleration by crash dummies that were permitted to move x meters during impact. The data are shown in the table. A model for the data is given by $y = -3.00 + 11.88 \ln x + (36.94/x)$, where y is the number of g's.

x	g's
0.2	158
0.4	80
0.6	53
0.8	40
1.0	32

(a) Complete the table using the model.

x	0.2	0.4	0.6	0.8	1.0
y					

162.6 78.5 52.5 40.5 33.9

131. (a)

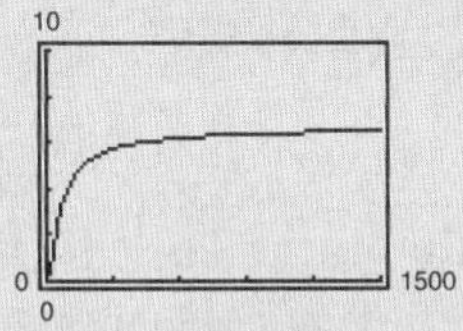

(b) $V = 6.7$; The yield will approach 6.7 million cubic feet per acre.

134. (a)

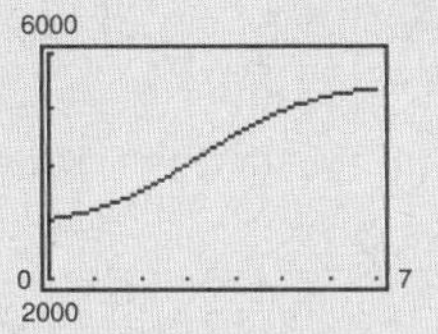

136. (a)

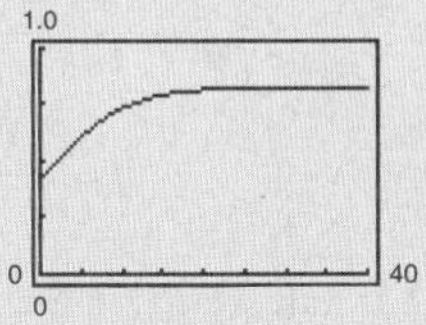

(b) Horizontal asymptotes: $P = 0$, $P = 0.83$
The proportion of correct responses will approach 0.83 as the number of trials increases.

5 ASSESS AND RETEACH

Daily Homework Quiz

Transparency Available
Available at the Instructor's companion site.

137. (b)

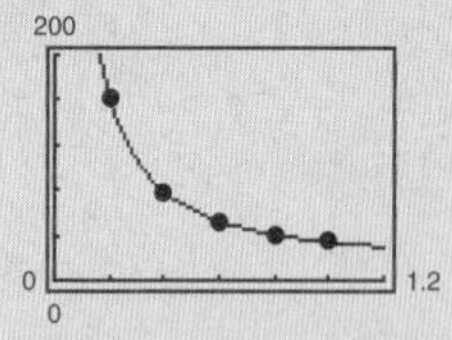

The model appears to fit the data well.

(d) No. According to the model, when the number of g's is less than 23, x is between 2.276 meters and 4.404 meters, which isn't realistic in most vehicles.

139. $\log_b uv = \log_b u + \log_b v$
True by Property 1 in Section 3.3.

140. $\log_b(u + v) = (\log_b u)(\log_b v)$
False
$2.04 \approx \log(10 + 100)$
$\neq (\log 10)(\log 100) = 2$

141. $\log_b(u - v) = \log_b u - \log_b v$
False
$1.95 \approx \log(100 - 10)$
$\neq \log 100 - \log 10 = 1$

142. $\log_b \dfrac{u}{v} = \log_b u - \log_b v$
True by Property 2 in Section 3.3.

144. For $rt < \ln 2$ years, double the amount you invest. For $rt > \ln 2$ years, double your interest rate or double the number of years, because either of these will double the exponent in the exponential function.

145. Yes. Time to double: $t = \dfrac{\ln 2}{r}$;
Time to quadruple:
$t = \dfrac{\ln 4}{r} = 2\left(\dfrac{\ln 2}{r}\right)$

146. (a) 7%
(b) 7.25%
(c) 7.19%
(d) 7.45%
The savings plan with the greatest effective yield and the highest balance after 5 years is plan (d).

(b) Use a graphing utility to graph the data points and the model in the same viewing window. How do they compare? See margin.

(c) Use the model to estimate the distance traveled during impact if the passenger deceleration must not exceed 30 g's. 1.2 m

(d) Do you think it is practical to lower the number of g's experienced during impact to fewer than 23? Explain your reasoning. See margin.

138. DATA ANALYSIS An object at a temperature of 160°C was removed from a furnace and placed in a room at 20°C. The temperature T of the object was measured each hour h and recorded in the table. A model for the data is given by $T = 20[1 + 7(2^{-h})]$. The graph of this model is shown in the figure.

Hour, h	Temperature, T
0	160°
1	90°
2	56°
3	38°
4	29°
5	24°

(a) Use the graph to identify the horizontal asymptote of the model and interpret the asymptote in the context of the problem. $T = 20$; Room temperature

(b) Use the model to approximate the time when the temperature of the object was 100°C.
About 0.81 h

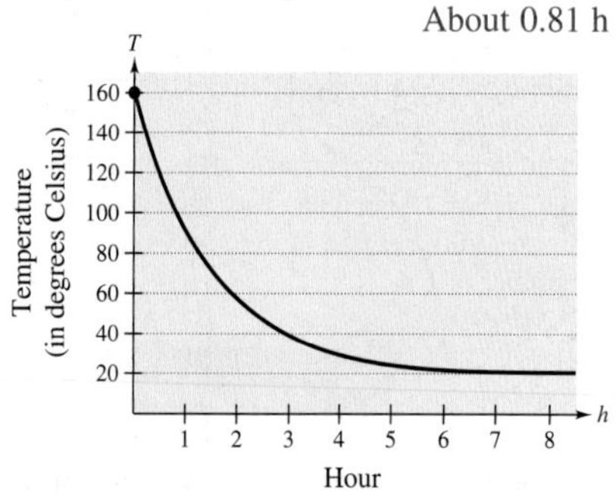

EXPLORATION

139–142. See margin.

TRUE OR FALSE? In Exercises 139–142, rewrite each verbal statement as an equation. Then decide whether the statement is true or false. Justify your answer.

139. The logarithm of the product of two numbers is equal to the sum of the logarithms of the numbers.

140. The logarithm of the sum of two numbers is equal to the product of the logarithms of the numbers.

141. The logarithm of the difference of two numbers is equal to the difference of the logarithms of the numbers.

142. The logarithm of the quotient of two numbers is equal to the difference of the logarithms of the numbers.

143. THINK ABOUT IT Is it possible for a logarithmic equation to have more than one extraneous solution? Explain. Yes. See Exercise 103.

144. FINANCE You are investing P dollars at an annual interest rate of r, compounded continuously, for t years. Which of the following would result in the highest value of the investment? Explain your reasoning. See margin.

(a) Double the amount you invest.

(b) Double your interest rate.

(c) Double the number of years.

145. See margin.

145. THINK ABOUT IT Are the times required for the investments in Exercises 117–120 to quadruple twice as long as the times for them to double? Give a reason for your answer and verify your answer algebraically.

146. The *effective yield* of a savings plan is the percent increase in the balance after 1 year. Find the effective yield for each savings plan when \$1000 is deposited in a savings account. Which savings plan has the greatest effective yield? Which savings plan will have the highest balance after 5 years? See margin.

(a) 7% annual interest rate, compounded annually

(b) 7% annual interest rate, compounded continuously

(c) 7% annual interest rate, compounded quarterly

(d) 7.25% annual interest rate, compounded quarterly

147. GRAPHICAL ANALYSIS Let $f(x) = \log_a x$ and $g(x) = a^x$, where $a > 1$.

(a) Let $a = 1.2$ and use a graphing utility to graph the two functions in the same viewing window. What do you observe? Approximate any points of intersection of the two graphs. See margin.

(b) Determine the value(s) of a for which the two graphs have one point of intersection. $a = e^{1/e}$

(c) Determine the value(s) of a for which the two graphs have two points of intersection. $1 < a < e^{1/e}$

148. CAPSTONE Write two or three sentences stating the general guidelines that you follow when solving (a) exponential equations and (b) logarithmic equations. Answers will vary.

147. (a)

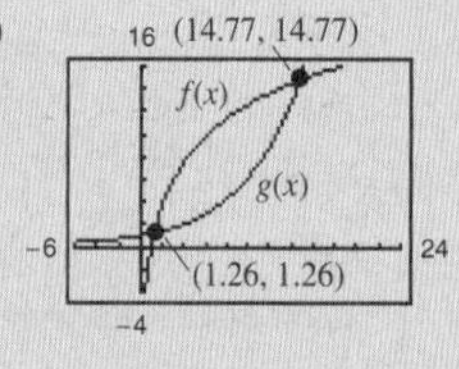

3.5 Exponential and Logarithmic Models

What you should learn

- Recognize the five most common types of models involving exponential and logarithmic functions.
- Use exponential growth and decay functions to model and solve real-life problems.
- Use Gaussian functions to model and solve real-life problems.
- Use logistic growth functions to model and solve real-life problems.
- Use logarithmic functions to model and solve real-life problems.

Why you should learn it

Exponential growth and decay models are often used to model the populations of countries. For instance, in Exercise 44 on page 263, you will use exponential growth and decay models to compare the populations of several countries.

Alan Becker/Stone/Getty Images

Introduction

The five most common types of mathematical models involving exponential functions and logarithmic functions are as follows.

1. **Exponential growth model:** $y = ae^{bx}, \quad b > 0$
2. **Exponential decay model:** $y = ae^{-bx}, \quad b > 0$
3. **Gaussian model:** $y = ae^{-(x-b)^2/c}$
4. **Logistic growth model:** $y = \dfrac{a}{1 + be^{-rx}}$
5. **Logarithmic models:** $y = a + b \ln x, \quad y = a + b \log x$

The basic shapes of the graphs of these functions are shown in Figure 3.33.

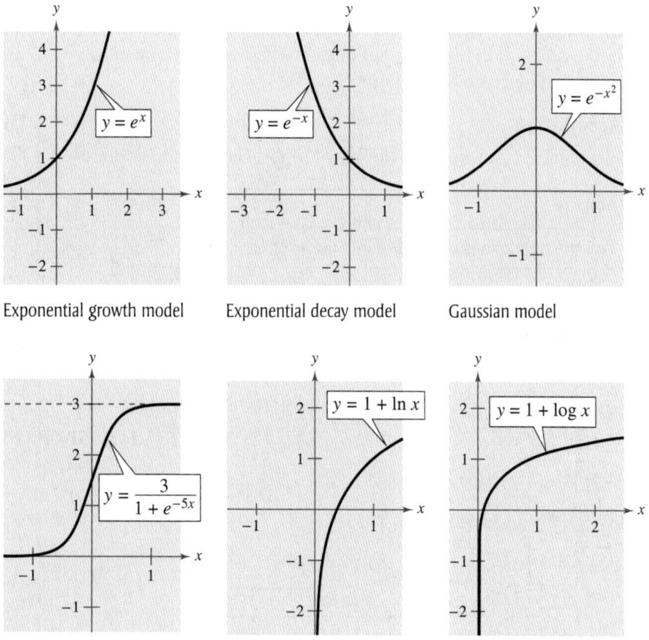

Exponential growth model — Exponential decay model — Gaussian model

Logistic growth model — Natural logarithmic model — Common logarithmic model

FIGURE 3.33

You can often gain quite a bit of insight into a situation modeled by an exponential or logarithmic function by identifying and interpreting the function's asymptotes. Use the graphs in Figure 3.33 to identify the asymptotes of the graph of each function.

1 PLAN AND PREPARE

Warm-up Exercises

Transparency Available
Available at the Instructor's companion site.

Notetaking Guide

Transparency Available
Promotes interactive learning and notetaking skills. Available at the Instructor's companion site.

Animated Precalculus

An **Animated Precalculus** tutorial is available at the Student companion site for **Section 3.5.**

Pacing

Average: 2 days
Advanced: 2 days
Block: 1 block

2 FOCUS AND MOTIVATE

Essential Question

How do you use exponents and logarithms to model a variety of situations? **Tell students that they will learn how to answer this question by studying five common mathematical models involving exponents and logarithms.**

Resource Planning Guide

Chapter Resources
- Complete Solutions Guide

Workbooks
- Notetaking Guide
- Student Solutions Guide

Interactive Technology
- Instructor Success Organizer
- Notetaking Guide IAE
- Instructional DVDs
- Animated Precalculus
- PowerLecture with ExamView

3 TEACH

Extra Example 1

The population P of a city is given by $P = 95{,}300e^{0.055t}$, where $t = 0$ represents 2001. According to this model, when did the population reach 150,000?

2009

Exponential Growth and Decay

Example 1 Online Advertising

Estimates of the amounts (in billions of dollars) of U.S. online advertising spending from 2007 through 2011 are shown in the table. A scatter plot of the data is shown in Figure 3.34. (Source: eMarketer)

Year	Advertising spending
2007	21.1
2008	23.6
2009	25.7
2010	28.5
2011	32.0

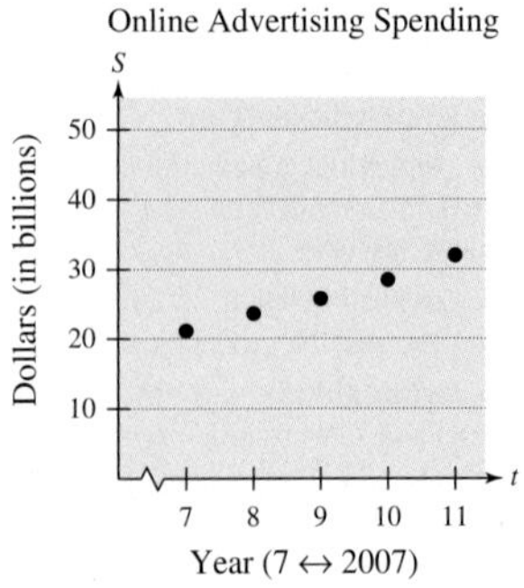

FIGURE 3.34

An exponential growth model that approximates these data is given by $S = 10.33e^{0.1022t}$, $7 \le t \le 11$, where S is the amount of spending (in billions) and $t = 7$ represents 2007. Compare the values given by the model with the estimates shown in the table. According to this model, when will the amount of U.S. online advertising spending reach \$40 billion?

Algebraic Solution

The following table compares the two sets of advertising spending figures.

Year	2007	2008	2009	2010	2011
Advertising spending	21.1	23.6	25.7	28.5	32.0
Model	21.1	23.4	25.9	28.7	31.8

To find when the amount of U.S. online advertising spending will reach \$40 billion, let $S = 40$ in the model and solve for t.

$10.33e^{0.1022t} = S$ Write original model.

$10.33e^{0.1022t} = 40$ Substitute 40 for S.

$e^{0.1022t} \approx 3.8722$ Divide each side by 10.33.

$\ln e^{0.1022t} \approx \ln 3.8722$ Take natural log of each side.

$0.1022t \approx 1.3538$ Inverse Property

$t \approx 13.2$ Divide each side by 0.1022.

According to the model, the amount of U.S. online advertising spending will reach \$40 billion in 2013.

CHECKPoint Now try Exercise 43.

Graphical Solution

Use a graphing utility to graph the model $y = 10.33e^{0.1022x}$ and the data in the same viewing window. You can see in Figure 3.35 that the model appears to fit the data closely.

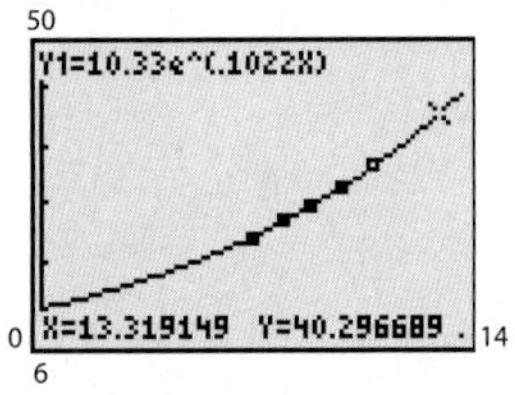

FIGURE 3.35

Use the *zoom* and *trace* features of the graphing utility to find that the approximate value of x for $y = 40$ is $x \approx 13.2$. So, according to the model, the amount of U.S. online advertising spending will reach \$40 billion in 2013.

TECHNOLOGY

Some graphing utilities have an *exponential regression* feature that can be used to find exponential models that represent data. If you have such a graphing utility, try using it to find an exponential model for the data given in Example 1. How does your model compare with the model given in Example 1? $S = 10.3305(1.1076)^t$

In Example 1, you were given the exponential growth model. But suppose this model were not given; how could you find such a model? One technique for doing this is demonstrated in Example 2.

Example 2 Modeling Population Growth

In a research experiment, a population of fruit flies is increasing according to the law of exponential growth. After 2 days there are 100 flies, and after 4 days there are 300 flies. How many flies will there be after 5 days?

Solution

Let y be the number of flies at time t. From the given information, you know that $y = 100$ when $t = 2$ and $y = 300$ when $t = 4$. Substituting this information into the model $y = ae^{bt}$ produces

$$100 = ae^{2b} \quad \text{and} \quad 300 = ae^{4b}.$$

To solve for b, solve for a in the first equation.

$$100 = ae^{2b} \quad \Longrightarrow \quad a = \frac{100}{e^{2b}}$$ Solve for a in the first equation.

Then substitute the result into the second equation.

$$300 = ae^{4b}$$ Write second equation.

$$300 = \left(\frac{100}{e^{2b}}\right)e^{4b}$$ Substitute $\frac{100}{e^{2b}}$ for a.

$$\frac{300}{100} = e^{2b}$$ Divide each side by 100.

$$\ln 3 = 2b$$ Take natural log of each side.

$$\frac{1}{2}\ln 3 = b$$ Solve for b.

Using $b = \frac{1}{2}\ln 3$ and the equation you found for a, you can determine that

$$a = \frac{100}{e^{2[(1/2)\ln 3]}}$$ Substitute $\frac{1}{2}\ln 3$ for b.

$$= \frac{100}{e^{\ln 3}}$$ Simplify.

$$= \frac{100}{3}$$ Inverse Property

$$\approx 33.33.$$ Simplify.

So, with $a \approx 33.33$ and $b = \frac{1}{2}\ln 3 \approx 0.5493$, the exponential growth model is

$$y = 33.33e^{0.5493t}$$

as shown in Figure 3.36. This implies that, after 5 days, the population will be

$$y = 33.33e^{0.5493(5)} \approx 520 \text{ flies.}$$

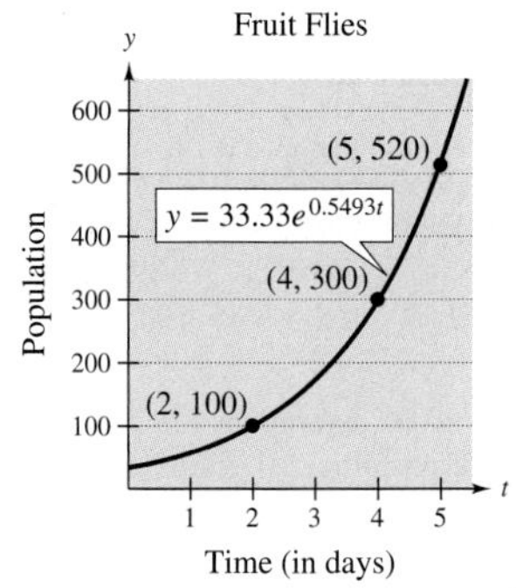

FIGURE 3.36

CHECKPoint Now try Exercise 49.

Extra Example 2

In a research experiment, a population of fruit flies is increasing according to the law of exponential growth. After 2 days there are 125 flies, and after 4 days there are 350 flies. How many flies will there be after 6 days?

980 fruit flies

Extra Example 3

Estimate the age of a newly discovered fossil in which the ratio of carbon 14 to carbon 12 is

$R = \frac{1}{10^{14}}$.

38,000 years

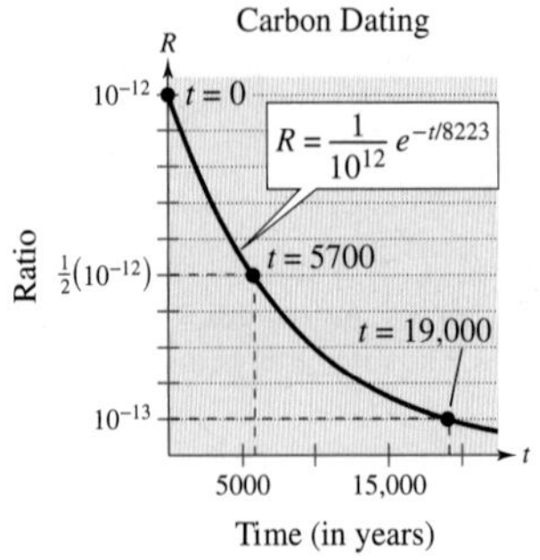

FIGURE 3.37

In living organic material, the ratio of the number of radioactive carbon isotopes (carbon 14) to the number of nonradioactive carbon isotopes (carbon 12) is about 1 to 10^{12}. When organic material dies, its carbon 12 content remains fixed, whereas its radioactive carbon 14 begins to decay with a half-life of about 5700 years. To estimate the age of dead organic material, scientists use the following formula, which denotes the ratio of carbon 14 to carbon 12 present at any time t (in years).

$$R = \frac{1}{10^{12}}e^{-t/8223} \qquad \text{Carbon dating model}$$

The graph of R is shown in Figure 3.37. Note that R decreases as t increases.

Example 3 Carbon Dating

Estimate the age of a newly discovered fossil in which the ratio of carbon 14 to carbon 12 is

$R = 1/10^{13}$.

Algebraic Solution

In the carbon dating model, substitute the given value of R to obtain the following.

$$\frac{1}{10^{12}}e^{-t/8223} = R \qquad \text{Write original model.}$$

$$\frac{e^{-t/8223}}{10^{12}} = \frac{1}{10^{13}} \qquad \text{Let } R = \frac{1}{10^{13}}.$$

$$e^{-t/8223} = \frac{1}{10} \qquad \text{Multiply each side by } 10^{12}.$$

$$\ln e^{-t/8223} = \ln\frac{1}{10} \qquad \text{Take natural log of each side.}$$

$$-\frac{t}{8223} \approx -2.3026 \qquad \text{Inverse Property}$$

$$t \approx 18{,}934 \qquad \text{Multiply each side by } -8223.$$

So, to the nearest thousand years, the age of the fossil is about 19,000 years.

Graphical Solution

Use a graphing utility to graph the formula for the ratio of carbon 14 to carbon 12 at any time t as

$$y_1 = \frac{1}{10^{12}}e^{-x/8223}.$$

In the same viewing window, graph $y_2 = 1/(10^{13})$. Use the *intersect* feature or the *zoom* and *trace* features of the graphing utility to estimate that $x \approx 18{,}934$ when $y = 1/(10^{13})$, as shown in Figure 3.38.

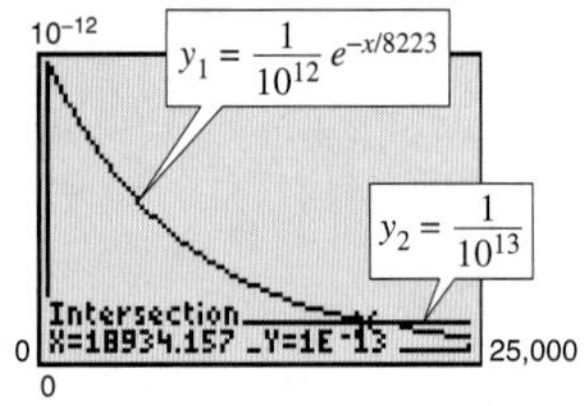

FIGURE 3.38

So, to the nearest thousand years, the age of the fossil is about 19,000 years.

CHECK *Point* Now try Exercise 51.

The value of b in the exponential decay model $y = ae^{-bt}$ determines the *decay* of radioactive isotopes. For instance, to find how much of an initial 10 grams of ^{226}Ra isotope with a half-life of 1599 years is left after 500 years, substitute this information into the model $y = ae^{-bt}$.

$$\frac{1}{2}(10) = 10e^{-b(1599)} \quad \Rightarrow \quad \ln\frac{1}{2} = -1599b \quad \Rightarrow \quad b = -\frac{\ln\frac{1}{2}}{1599}$$

Using the value of b found above and $a = 10$, the amount left is

$$y = 10e^{-[-\ln(1/2)/1599](500)} \approx 8.05 \text{ grams.}$$

Gaussian Models

As mentioned at the beginning of this section, Gaussian models are of the form

$$y = ae^{-(x-b)^2/c}.$$

This type of model is commonly used in probability and statistics to represent populations that are **normally distributed.** The graph of a Gaussian model is called a **bell-shaped curve.** Try graphing the normal distribution with a graphing utility. Can you see why it is called a bell-shaped curve?

For *standard* normal distributions, the model takes the form

$$y = \frac{1}{\sqrt{2\pi}}e^{-x^2/2}.$$

The **average value** of a population can be found from the bell-shaped curve by observing where the maximum y-value of the function occurs. The x-value corresponding to the maximum y-value of the function represents the average value of the independent variable—in this case, x.

Example 4 SAT Scores

In 2008, the Scholastic Aptitude Test (SAT) math scores for college-bound seniors roughly followed the normal distribution given by

$$y = 0.0034e^{-(x-515)^2/26,912}, \quad 200 \le x \le 800$$

where x is the SAT score for mathematics. Sketch the graph of this function. From the graph, estimate the average SAT score. (Source: College Board)

Solution

The graph of the function is shown in Figure 3.39. On this bell-shaped curve, the maximum value of the curve represents the average score. From the graph, you can estimate that the average mathematics score for college-bound seniors in 2008 was 515.

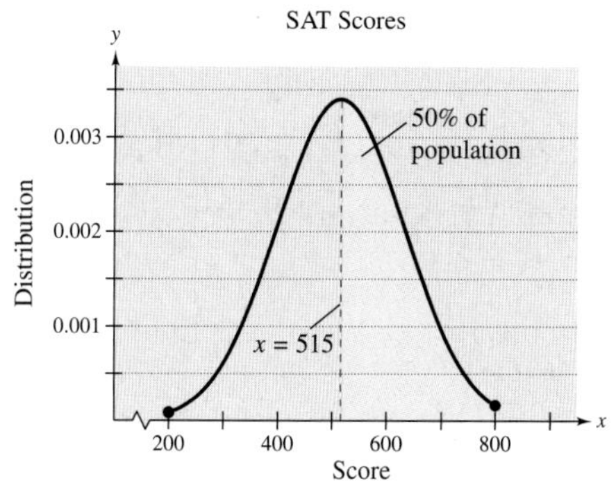

FIGURE 3.39

CHECKPoint Now try Exercise 57.

Extra Example 4

Last year, the math scores for students in a particular math class roughly followed the normal distribution given by

$y = 0.0399e^{-(x-74)^2/114}$,

$30 \le x \le 110$, where x is the math score. Sketch the graph of this function, and use it to estimate the average math score.

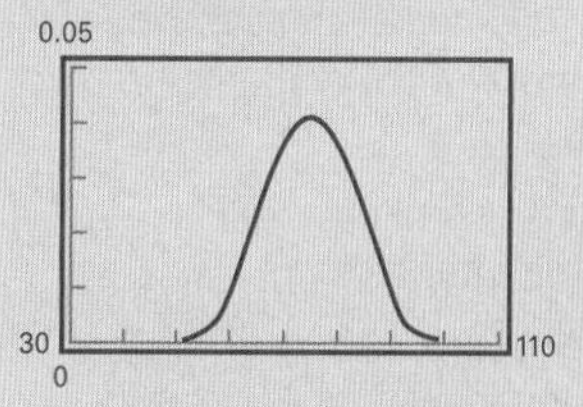

The average score for students in the math class was 74.

Extra Example 5

On a college campus of 7500 students, one student returns from vacation with a contagious and long-lasting virus. The spread of the virus is modeled by

$$y = \frac{7500}{1 + 7499^{-0.9t}}, \quad t \geq 0$$

where y is the total number of students affected after t days. The college will cancel classes when 30% or more of the students are infected.

a. How many students will be infected after 4 days?

36 students

b. After how many days will the college cancel classes?

9 days

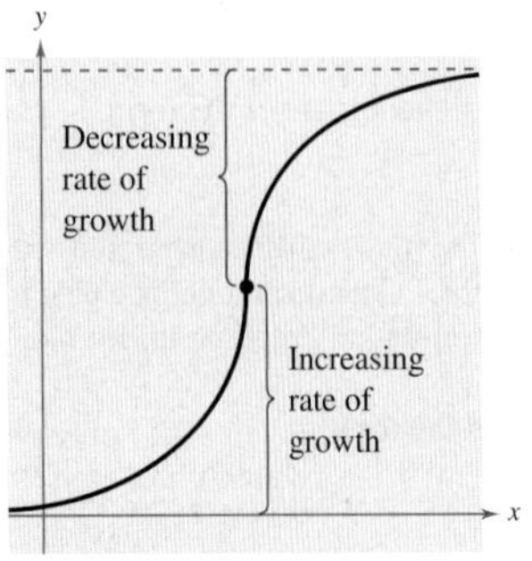

FIGURE 3.40

Logistic Growth Models

Some populations initially have rapid growth, followed by a declining rate of growth, as indicated by the graph in Figure 3.40. One model for describing this type of growth pattern is the **logistic curve** given by the function

$$y = \frac{a}{1 + be^{-rx}}$$

where y is the population size and x is the time. An example is a bacteria culture that is initially allowed to grow under ideal conditions, and then under less favorable conditions that inhibit growth. A logistic growth curve is also called a **sigmoidal curve.**

Example 5 Spread of a Virus

On a college campus of 5000 students, one student returns from vacation with a contagious and long-lasting flu virus. The spread of the virus is modeled by

$$y = \frac{5000}{1 + 4999e^{-0.8t}}, \quad t \geq 0$$

where y is the total number of students infected after t days. The college will cancel classes when 40% or more of the students are infected.

a. How many students are infected after 5 days?

b. After how many days will the college cancel classes?

Algebraic Solution

a. After 5 days, the number of students infected is

$$y = \frac{5000}{1 + 4999e^{-0.8(5)}} = \frac{5000}{1 + 4999e^{-4}} \approx 54.$$

b. Classes are canceled when the number infected is $(0.40)(5000) = 2000$.

$$2000 = \frac{5000}{1 + 4999e^{-0.8t}}$$

$$1 + 4999e^{-0.8t} = 2.5$$

$$e^{-0.8t} = \frac{1.5}{4999}$$

$$\ln e^{-0.8t} = \ln \frac{1.5}{4999}$$

$$-0.8t = \ln \frac{1.5}{4999}$$

$$t = -\frac{1}{0.8} \ln \frac{1.5}{4999}$$

$$t \approx 10.1$$

So, after about 10 days, at least 40% of the students will be infected, and the college will cancel classes.

CHECKPoint Now try Exercise 59.

Graphical Solution

a. Use a graphing utility to graph $y = \frac{5000}{1 + 4999e^{-0.8x}}$. Use the *value* feature or the *zoom* and *trace* features of the graphing utility to estimate that $y \approx 54$ when $x = 5$. So, after 5 days, about 54 students will be infected.

b. Classes are canceled when the number of infected students is $(0.40)(5000) = 2000$. Use a graphing utility to graph

$$y_1 = \frac{5000}{1 + 4999e^{-0.8x}} \quad \text{and} \quad y_2 = 2000$$

in the same viewing window. Use the *intersect* feature or the *zoom* and *trace* features of the graphing utility to find the point of intersection of the graphs. In Figure 3.41, you can see that the point of intersection occurs near $x \approx 10.1$. So, after about 10 days, at least 40% of the students will be infected, and the college will cancel classes.

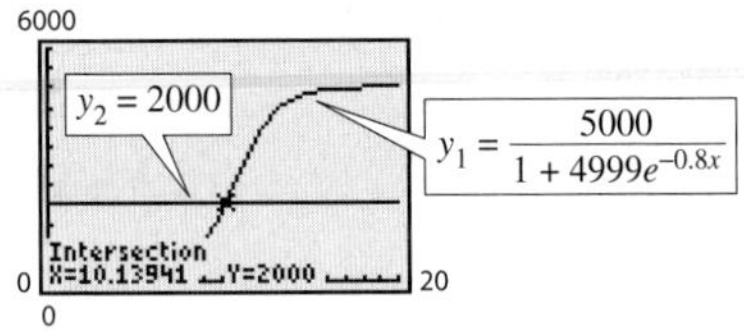

FIGURE 3.41

Logarithmic Models

Claro Cortes IV/Reuters /Landov

On May 12, 2008, an earthquake of magnitude 7.9 struck Eastern Sichuan Province, China. The total economic loss was estimated at 86 billion U.S. dollars.

Example 6 Magnitudes of Earthquakes

On the Richter scale, the magnitude R of an earthquake of intensity I is given by

$$R = \log \frac{I}{I_0}$$

where $I_0 = 1$ is the minimum intensity used for comparison. Find the intensity of each earthquake. (Intensity is a measure of the wave energy of an earthquake.)

a. Nevada in 2008: $R = 6.0$

b. Eastern Sichuan, China in 2008: $R = 7.9$

Solution

a. Because $I_0 = 1$ and $R = 6.0$, you have

$$6.0 = \log \frac{I}{1}$$ Substitute 1 for I_0 and 6.0 for R.

$$10^{6.0} = 10^{\log I}$$ Exponentiate each side.

$$I = 10^{6.0} = 1{,}000{,}000.$$ Inverse Property

b. For $R = 7.9$, you have

$$7.9 = \log \frac{I}{1}$$ Substitute 1 for I_0 and 7.9 for R.

$$10^{7.9} = 10^{\log I}$$ Exponentiate each side.

$$I = 10^{7.9} \approx 79{,}400{,}000.$$ Inverse Property

Note that an increase of 1.9 units on the Richter scale (from 6.0 to 7.9) represents an increase in intensity by a factor of

$$\frac{79{,}400{,}000}{1{,}000{,}000} = 79.4.$$

In other words, the intensity of the earthquake in Eastern Sichuan was about 79 times as great as that of the earthquake in Nevada.

CHECKPoint Now try Exercise 63.

Classroom Discussion

Comparing Population Models The populations P (in millions) of the United States for the census years from 1910 to 2000 are shown in the table at the left. Least squares regression analysis gives the best quadratic model for these data as $P = 1.0328t^2 + 9.607t + 81.82$, and the best exponential model for these data as $P = 82.677e^{0.124t}$. Which model better fits the data? Describe how you reached your conclusion. (Source: U.S. Census Bureau) The quadratic model is better.

t	Year	Population, P
1	1910	92.23
2	1920	106.02
3	1930	123.20
4	1940	132.16
5	1950	151.33
6	1960	179.32
7	1970	203.30
8	1980	226.54
9	1990	248.72
10	2000	281.42

Extra Example 6

On the Richter scale, the magnitude R of an earthquake of intensity I is given by

$$R = \log \frac{I}{I_0}$$

where $I_0 = 1$ is the minimum intensity used for comparison. Find the magnitude R of an earthquake of intensity I.

a. $I = 68{,}400{,}000$
$R = 7.84$

b. $I = 42{,}275{,}000$
$R = 7.63$

Closing the Lesson

Have students summarize the major points of the lesson and answer the Essential Question: How do you use exponents and logarithms to model a variety of situations?

- **Recognize the characteristics of the exponential growth and decay, Gaussian, logistic growth, and logarithmic models.**
- **Use definitions and properties to rewrite equations and solve problems, using models that include exponents and logarithms.**

4 PRACTICE AND APPLY

Assignment Guide

Transparencies Available
Available at the Instructor's companion site.

Average:
Day 1: pp. 262–264
Exs. 1–3, 7–12, 15–21 odd, 25, 27, 33, 35, 39, 44, 47, 53, 55
Day 2: pp. 262–267
Exs. 4–6, 57, 62, 63–71 odd, 75, 76, 79–82, 84

Advanced:
Day 1: pp. 262–265
Exs. 7–12, 16–26 even, 27, 32, 36–56 even
Day 2: pp. 265–267
Exs. 58–64, 66–76 even, 77, 79–82, 84

Block:
pp. 262–267
Exs. 1–12, 15–21 odd, 25, 27, 33, 35, 39, 44, 47, 53, 55, 57, 62, 63–71 odd, 75, 76, 79–82, 84

13. (a) $P = \dfrac{A}{e^{rt}}$ (b) $t = \dfrac{\ln\left(\frac{A}{P}\right)}{r}$

14. (a) $P = A\left(\dfrac{n}{r+n}\right)^{nt}$

(b) $t = \dfrac{\ln\left(\frac{A}{P}\right)}{n \cdot \ln\left(\frac{r+n}{n}\right)}$

25. (a) 7.27 yr (b) 6.96 yr
(c) 6.93 yr (d) 6.93 yr

26. (a) 11.01 yr (b) 10.69 yr
(c) 10.66 yr (d) 10.66 yr

3.5 EXERCISES

See www.CalcChat.com for worked-out solutions to odd-numbered exercises.

VOCABULARY: Fill in the blanks.

1. An exponential growth model has the form $y = ae^{bx}$ and an exponential decay model has the form $y = ae^{-bx}$.
2. A logarithmic model has the form ________ or ________. $y = a + b \ln x$; $y = a + b \log x$
3. Gaussian models are commonly used in probability and statistics to represent populations that are normally distributed.
4. The graph of a Gaussian model is bell shaped, where the average value is the maximum y-value of the graph.
5. A logistic growth model has the form ________. $y = \dfrac{a}{1 + be^{-rx}}$
6. A logistic curve is also called a ________ curve. sigmoidal

SKILLS AND APPLICATIONS

In Exercises 7–12, match the function with its graph. [The graphs are labeled (a), (b), (c), (d), (e), and (f).]

(a)

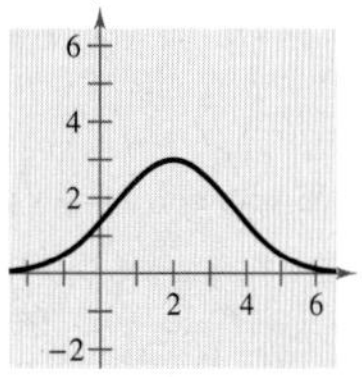

(b)

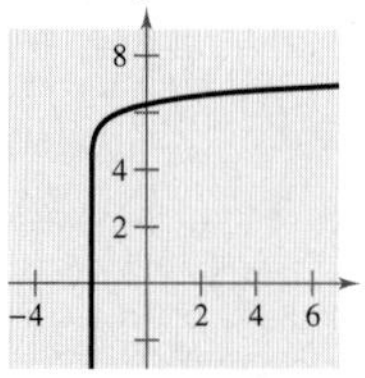

(c)

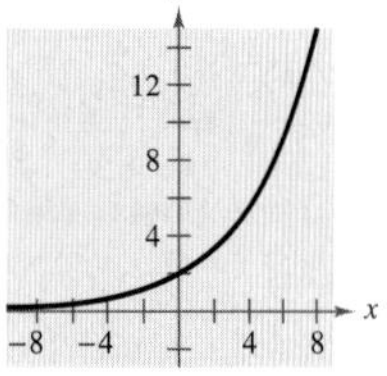

(d)

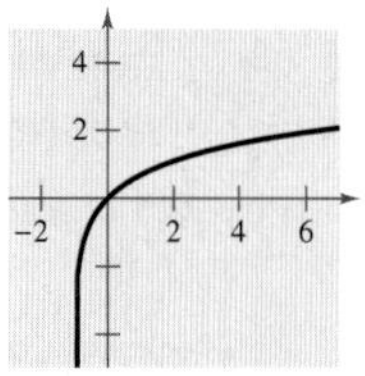

(e)

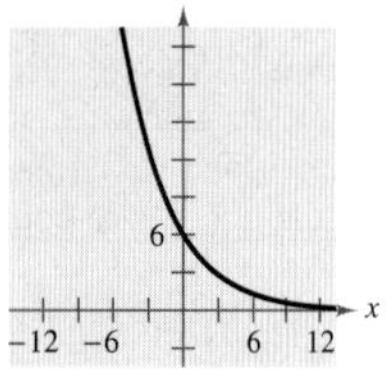

(f)

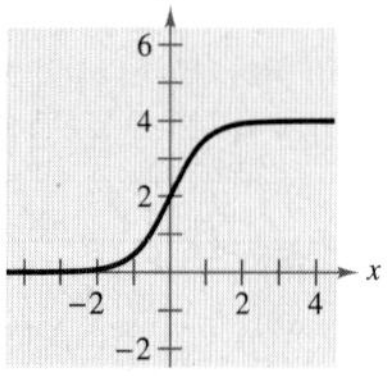

7. $y = 2e^{x/4}$ c
8. $y = 6e^{-x/4}$ e
9. $y = 6 + \log(x + 2)$ b
10. $y = 3e^{-(x-2)^2/5}$ a
11. $y = \ln(x + 1)$ d
12. $y = \dfrac{4}{1 + e^{-2x}}$ f

In Exercises 13 and 14, (a) solve for P and (b) solve for t. 13–14. See margin.

13. $A = Pe^{rt}$
14. $A = P\left(1 + \dfrac{r}{n}\right)^{nt}$

COMPOUND INTEREST In Exercises 15–22, complete the table for a savings account in which interest is compounded continuously.

	Initial Investment	*Annual % Rate*	*Time to Double*	*Amount After 10 Years*
15.	\$1000	3.5%	19.8 yr	\$1419.07
16.	\$750	$10\frac{1}{2}$%	6.60 yr	\$2143.24
17.	\$750	8.9438%	$7\frac{3}{4}$ yr	\$1834.37
18.	\$10,000	5.7762%	12 yr	\$17,817.97
19.	\$500	11.0%	6.3 yr	\$1505.00
20.	\$600	34.66%	2 yr	\$19,205.00
21.	\$6376.28	4.5%	15.4 yr	\$10,000.00
22.	\$1637.46	2%	34.7 yr	\$2000.00

COMPOUND INTEREST In Exercises 23 and 24, determine the principal P that must be invested at rate r, compounded monthly, so that \$500,000 will be available for retirement in t years.

23. $r = 5\%, t = 10$ \$303,580.52
24. $r = 3\frac{1}{2}\%, t = 15$ \$296,003.78

COMPOUND INTEREST In Exercises 25 and 26, determine the time necessary for \$1000 to double if it is invested at interest rate r compounded (a) annually, (b) monthly, (c) daily, and (d) continuously. 25–26. See margin.

25. $r = 10\%$
26. $r = 6.5\%$

27. **COMPOUND INTEREST** Complete the table for the time t (in years) necessary for P dollars to triple if interest is compounded continuously at rate r. See margin.

r	2%	4%	6%	8%	10%	12%
t						

28. **MODELING DATA** Draw a scatter plot of the data in Exercise 27. Use the *regression* feature of a graphing utility to find a model for the data. See margin.

27.

r	2%	4%	6%	8%	10%	12%
t	54.93	27.47	18.31	13.73	10.99	9.16

28.

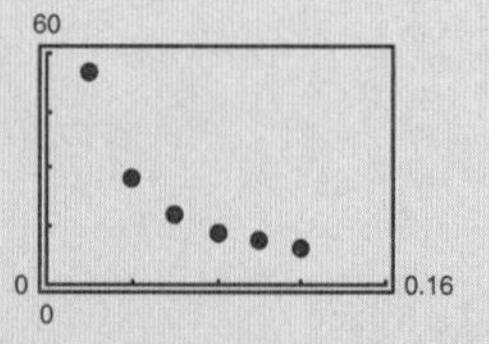

Use PwrReg: $t = 1.099r^{-1}$

29. COMPOUND INTEREST Complete the table for the time t (in years) necessary for P dollars to triple if interest is compounded annually at rate r. See margin.

r	2%	4%	6%	8%	10%	12%
t						

30. MODELING DATA Draw a scatter plot of the data in Exercise 29. Use the *regression* feature of a graphing utility to find a model for the data. See margin.

31. COMPARING MODELS If \$1 is invested in an account over a 10-year period, the amount in the account, where t represents the time in years, is given by $A = 1 + 0.075[\![t]\!]$ or $A = e^{0.07t}$ depending on whether the account pays simple interest at $7\frac{1}{2}\%$ or continuous compound interest at 7%. Graph each function on the same set of axes. Which grows at a higher rate? (Remember that $[\![t]\!]$ is the greatest integer function discussed in Section 1.6.) See margin.

32. COMPARING MODELS If \$1 is invested in an account over a 10-year period, the amount in the account, where t represents the time in years, is given by $A = 1 + 0.06[\![t]\!]$ or $A = [1 + (0.055/365)]^{[\![365t]\!]}$ depending on whether the account pays simple interest at 6% or compound interest at $5\frac{1}{2}\%$ compounded daily. Use a graphing utility to graph each function in the same viewing window. Which grows at a higher rate? See margin.

RADIOACTIVE DECAY In Exercises 33–38, complete the table for the radioactive isotope.

	Isotope	Half-life (years)	Initial Quantity	Amount After 1000 Years
33.	^{226}Ra	1599	10 g	6.48 g
34.	^{14}C	5715	6.5 g	5.76 g
35.	^{239}Pu	24,100	2.1g	2.04 g
36.	^{226}Ra	1599	3.09 g	2 g
37.	^{14}C	5715	2.26 g	2 g
38.	^{239}Pu	24,100	0.41 g	0.4 g

In Exercises 39–42, find the exponential model $y = ae^{bx}$ that fits the points shown in the graph or table.

39. $y = e^{0.7675x}$

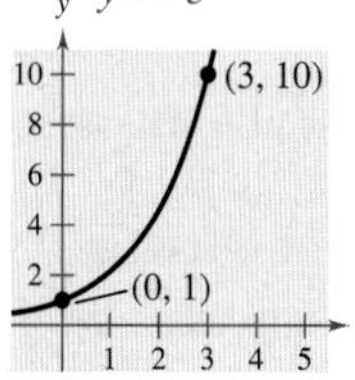

40. $y = \frac{1}{2}e^{0.5756x}$

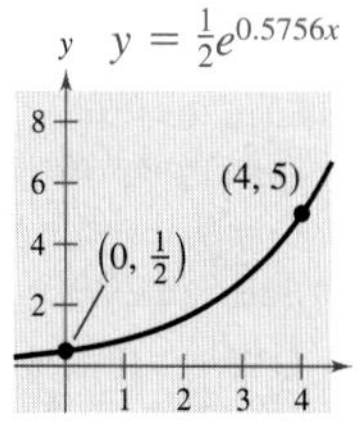

41.

x	0	4
y	5	1

$y = 5e^{-0.4024x}$

42.

x	0	3
y	1	$\frac{1}{4}$

$y = e^{-0.4621x}$

43. POPULATION The populations P (in thousands) of Horry County, South Carolina from 1970 through 2007 can be modeled by

$$P = -18.5 + 92.2e^{0.0282t}$$

where t represents the year, with $t = 0$ corresponding to 1970. (Source: U.S. Census Bureau)

(a) Use the model to complete the table. See margin.

Year	1970	1980	1990	2000	2007
Population					

(b) According to the model, when will the population of Horry County reach 300,000? 2014

(c) Do you think the model is valid for long-term predictions of the population? Explain. See margin.

44. POPULATION The table shows the populations (in millions) of five countries in 2000 and the projected populations (in millions) for the year 2015. (Source: U.S. Census Bureau) See margin.

Country	2000	2015
Bulgaria	7.8	6.9
Canada	31.1	35.1
China	1268.9	1393.4
United Kingdom	59.5	62.2
United States	282.2	325.5

(a) Find the exponential growth or decay model $y = ae^{bt}$ or $y = ae^{-bt}$ for the population of each country by letting $t = 0$ correspond to 2000. Use the model to predict the population of each country in 2030.

(b) You can see that the populations of the United States and the United Kingdom are growing at different rates. What constant in the equation $y = ae^{bt}$ is determined by these different growth rates? Discuss the relationship between the different growth rates and the magnitude of the constant.

(c) You can see that the population of China is increasing while the population of Bulgaria is decreasing. What constant in the equation $y = ae^{bt}$ reflects this difference? Explain.

29. See below.

30.

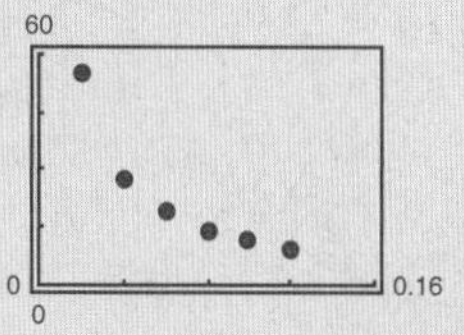

Use PwrReg: $t = 1.222r^{-1}$

31.

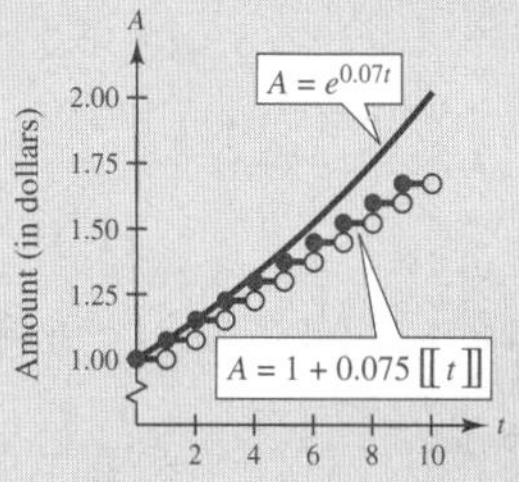

Continuous compounding

32.

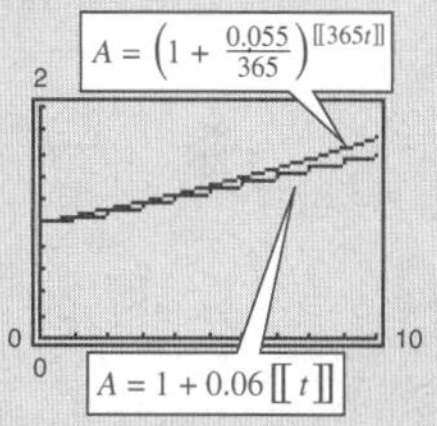

Daily compounding

43. See below.

44. (a) Bulgaria: $y = 7.8e^{-0.00817t}$; 6.10 million
Canada: $y = 31.1e^{0.00807t}$; 39.62 million
China: $y = 1268.9e^{0.00624t}$; 1530.13 million
United Kingdom: $y = 59.5e^{0.00296t}$; 65.03 million
United States: $y = 282.2e^{0.00952t}$; 375.48 million

(b) b; The greater the rate of growth, the greater the value of b.

(c) b determines whether the population is increasing ($b > 0$) or decreasing ($b < 0$).

29.

r	2%	4%	6%	8%	10%	12%
t	55.48	28.01	18.85	14.27	11.53	9.69

43. (a)

Year	1970	1980	1990	2000	2007
Population	73.7	103.74	143.56	196.35	243.24

(c) No; The population will not continue to grow at such a quick rate.

45. WEBSITE GROWTH The number y of hits a new search-engine website receives each month can be modeled by $y = 4080e^{kt}$, where t represents the number of months the website has been operating. In the website's third month, there were 10,000 hits. Find the value of k, and use this value to predict the number of hits the website will receive after 24 months. See margin.

46. VALUE OF A PAINTING The value V (in millions of dollars) of a famous painting can be modeled by $V = 10e^{kt}$, where t represents the year, with $t = 0$ corresponding to 2000. In 2008, the same painting was sold for \$65 million. Find the value of k, and use this value to predict the value of the painting in 2014. See margin.

47. POPULATION The populations P (in thousands) of Reno, Nevada from 2000 through 2007 can be modeled by $P = 346.8e^{kt}$, where t represents the year, with $t = 0$ corresponding to 2000. In 2005, the population of Reno was about 395,000. (Source: U.S. Census Bureau)

(a) Find the value of k. Is the population increasing or decreasing? Explain. See margin.

(b) Use the model to find the populations of Reno in 2010 and 2015. Are the results reasonable? Explain. 449,910; 512,447

(c) According to the model, during what year will the population reach 500,000? 2014

48. POPULATION The populations P (in thousands) of Orlando, Florida from 2000 through 2007 can be modeled by $P = 1656.2e^{kt}$, where t represents the year, with $t = 0$ corresponding to 2000. In 2005, the population of Orlando was about 1,940,000. (Source: U.S. Census Bureau)

(a) Find the value of k. Is the population increasing or decreasing? Explain. See margin.

(b) Use the model to find the populations of Orlando in 2010 and 2015. Are the results reasonable? Explain. 2,272,376; 2,661,729

(c) According to the model, during what year will the population reach 2.2 million? 2009

49. BACTERIA GROWTH The number of bacteria in a culture is increasing according to the law of exponential growth. After 3 hours, there are 100 bacteria, and after 5 hours, there are 400 bacteria. How many bacteria will there be after 6 hours? About 800 bacteria

50. BACTERIA GROWTH The number of bacteria in a culture is increasing according to the law of exponential growth. The initial population is 250 bacteria, and the population after 10 hours is double the population after 1 hour. How many bacteria will there be after 6 hours? About 397 bacteria

51. CARBON DATING

(a) The ratio of carbon 14 to carbon 12 in a piece of wood discovered in a cave is $R = 1/8^{14}$. Estimate the age of the piece of wood. About 12,180 yr old

(b) The ratio of carbon 14 to carbon 12 in a piece of paper buried in a tomb is $R = 1/13^{11}$. Estimate the age of the piece of paper. About 4797 yr old

52. RADIOACTIVE DECAY Carbon 14 dating assumes that the carbon dioxide on Earth today has the same radioactive content as it did centuries ago. If this is true, the amount of ^{14}C absorbed by a tree that grew several centuries ago should be the same as the amount of ^{14}C absorbed by a tree growing today. A piece of ancient charcoal contains only 15% as much radioactive carbon as a piece of modern charcoal. How long ago was the tree burned to make the ancient charcoal if the half-life of ^{14}C is 5715 years? 15,642 yr

53. DEPRECIATION A sport utility vehicle that costs \$23,300 new has a book value of \$12,500 after 2 years. See margin.

(a) Find the linear model $V = mt + b$.

(b) Find the exponential model $V = ae^{kt}$.

(c) Use a graphing utility to graph the two models in the same viewing window. Which model depreciates faster in the first 2 years?

(d) Find the book values of the vehicle after 1 year and after 3 years using each model.

(e) Explain the advantages and disadvantages of using each model to a buyer and a seller.

54. DEPRECIATION A laptop computer that costs \$1150 new has a book value of \$550 after 2 years. See margin.

(a) Find the linear model $V = mt + b$.

(b) Find the exponential model $V = ae^{kt}$.

(c) Use a graphing utility to graph the two models in the same viewing window. Which model depreciates faster in the first 2 years?

(d) Find the book values of the computer after 1 year and after 3 years using each model.

(e) Explain the advantages and disadvantages of using each model to a buyer and a seller.

55. SALES The sales S (in thousands of units) of a new CD burner after it has been on the market for t years are modeled by $S(t) = 100(1 - e^{kt})$. Fifteen thousand units of the new product were sold the first year.

(a) Complete the model by solving for k. See margin.

(b) Sketch the graph of the model. See margin.

(c) Use the model to estimate the number of units sold after 5 years. 55,625

---

45. $k = 0.2988$; About 5,309,734 hits

46. $k = 0.23398$; 264.62 million

47. (a) $k = 0.02603$; The population is increasing because $k > 0$.

48. (a) $k = 0.03163$; The population is increasing because $k > 0$.

53. (a) $V = -5400t + 23,300$

(b) $V = 23,300e^{-0.311t}$

(c)

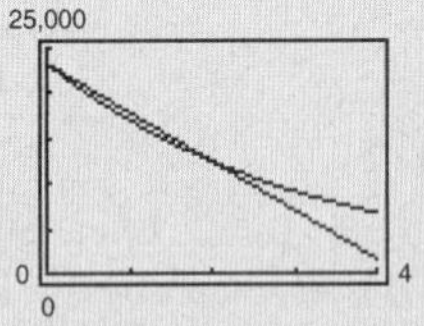

The exponential model depreciates faster.

(d)

t	1 yr	3 yr
$V = -5400t + 23,300$	17,900	7100
$V = 23,300e^{-0.311t}$	17,072	9166

(e) Answers will vary.

54. (a) $V = -300t + 1150$

(b) $V = 1150e^{-0.368799t}$

(c)

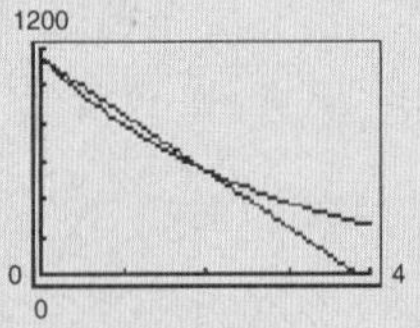

The exponential model depreciates faster.

(d)

t	1 yr	3 yr
$V = -300t + 1150$	850	250
$V = 1150e^{-0.368799t}$	795	380

(e) Answers will vary.

55. (a) $S(t) = 100(1 - e^{-0.1625t})$

(b)

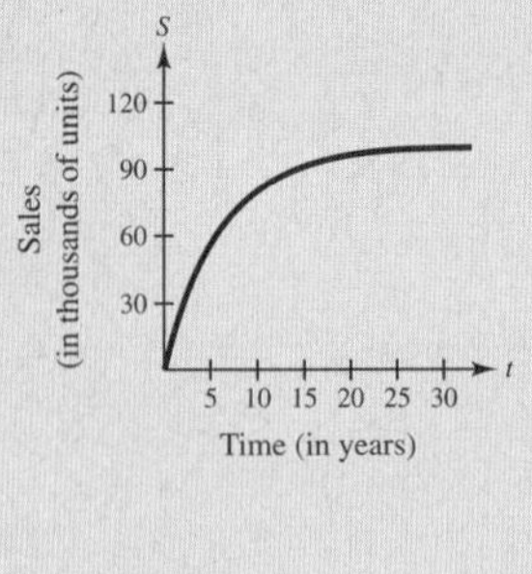

56. LEARNING CURVE The management at a plastics factory has found that the maximum number of units a worker can produce in a day is 30. The learning curve for the number N of units produced per day after a new employee has worked t days is modeled by $N = 30(1 - e^{kt})$. After 20 days on the job, a new employee produces 19 units.

(a) Find the learning curve for this employee (first, find the value of k). $N = 30(1 - e^{-0.050t})$

(b) How many days should pass before this employee is producing 25 units per day? 36 days

57. IQ SCORES The IQ scores for a sample of a class of returning adult students at a small northeastern college roughly follow the normal distribution $y = 0.0266e^{-(x-100)^2/450}$, $70 \le x \le 115$, where x is the IQ score. See margin.

(a) Use a graphing utility to graph the function.

(b) From the graph in part (a), estimate the average IQ score of an adult student. 100

58. EDUCATION The amount of time (in hours per week) a student utilizes a math-tutoring center roughly follows the normal distribution $y = 0.7979e^{-(x-5.4)^2/0.5}$, $4 \le x \le 7$, where x is the number of hours.

(a) Use a graphing utility to graph the function. See margin.

(b) From the graph in part (a), estimate the average number of hours per week a student uses the tutoring center. 5.4 h/wk

59. CELL SITES A cell site is a site where electronic communications equipment is placed in a cellular network for the use of mobile phones. The numbers y of cell sites from 1985 through 2008 can be modeled by

$$y = \frac{237{,}101}{1 + 1950e^{-0.355t}}$$ (a)–(b), (d). See margin.

where t represents the year, with $t = 5$ corresponding to 1985. (Source: CTIA-The Wireless Association)

(a) Use the model to find the numbers of cell sites in the years 1985, 2000, and 2006.

(b) Use a graphing utility to graph the function.

(c) Use the graph to determine the year in which the number of cell sites will reach 235,000. 2014

(d) Confirm your answer to part (c) algebraically.

60. POPULATION The populations P (in thousands) of Pittsburgh, Pennsylvania from 2000 through 2007 can be modeled by

$$P = \frac{2632}{1 + 0.083e^{0.0500t}}$$

where t represents the year, with $t = 0$ corresponding to 2000. (Source: U.S. Census Bureau) (a)–(b), (d). See margin.

(a) Use the model to find the populations of Pittsburgh in the years 2000, 2005, and 2007.

(b) Use a graphing utility to graph the function.

(c) Use the graph to determine the year in which the population will reach 2.2 million. 2017

(d) Confirm your answer to part (c) algebraically.

61. POPULATION GROWTH A conservation organization releases 100 animals of an endangered species into a game preserve. The organization believes that the preserve has a carrying capacity of 1000 animals and that the growth of the pack will be modeled by the logistic curve

$$p(t) = \frac{1000}{1 + 9e^{-0.1656t}}$$

where t is measured in months (see figure). See margin.

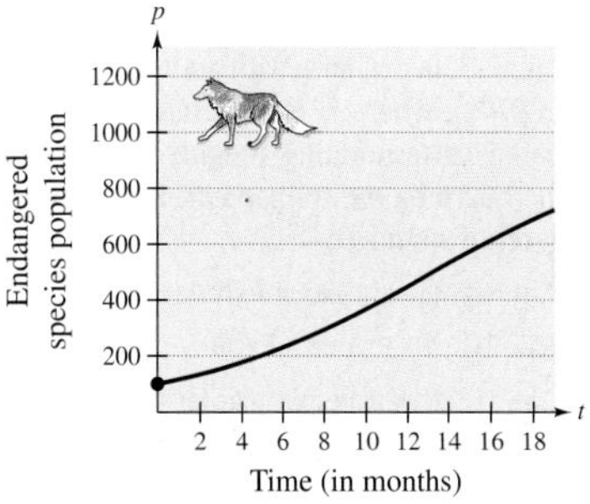

(a) Estimate the population after 5 months.

(b) After how many months will the population be 500?

(c) Use a graphing utility to graph the function. Use the graph to determine the horizontal asymptotes, and interpret the meaning of the asymptotes in the context of the problem.

62. SALES After discontinuing all advertising for a tool kit in 2004, the manufacturer noted that sales began to drop according to the model

$$S = \frac{500{,}000}{1 + 0.4e^{kt}}$$

where S represents the number of units sold and $t = 4$ represents 2004. In 2008, the company sold 300,000 units.

(a) Complete the model by solving for k. See margin.

(b) Estimate sales in 2012. 268,502 units sold

57. (a)

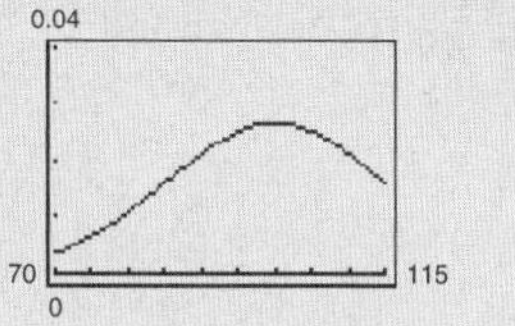

58. (a)

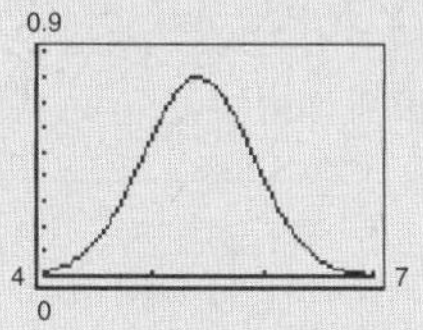

59. (a) 715; 90,880; 199,043

(b)

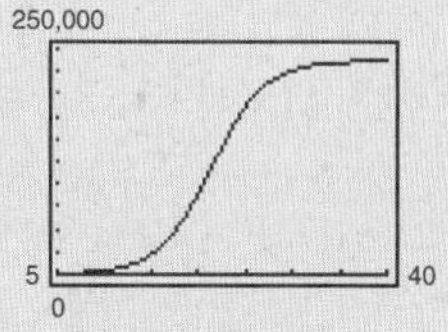

(d) $235{,}000 = \dfrac{237{,}101}{1 + 1950e^{-0.355t}}$

$t \approx 34.63$

60. (a) 2,430,286; 2,378,512; 2,354,662

(b)

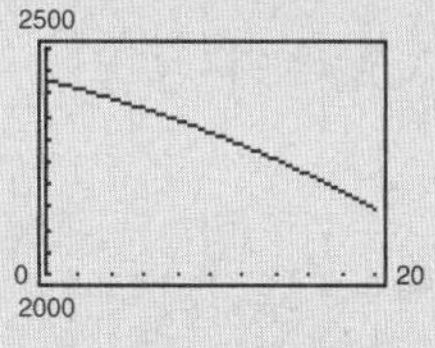

(d) $2200 = \dfrac{2632}{1 + 0.083e^{0.05t}}$

$t \approx 17.22$

61. (a) 203 animals

(b) 13 mo

(c)

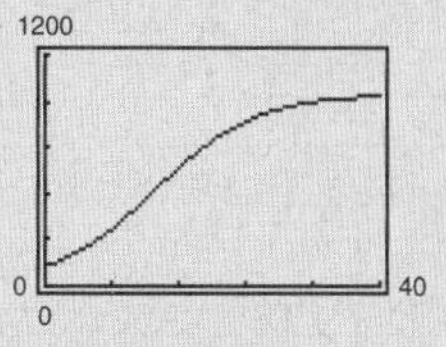

Horizontal asymptotes: $p = 0$, $p = 1000$

The population size will approach 1000 as time increases.

62. (a) $S = \dfrac{500{,}000}{1 + 0.4e^{0.064t}}$

63. (a) $10^{8.5} \approx 316,227,766$

76. (a)

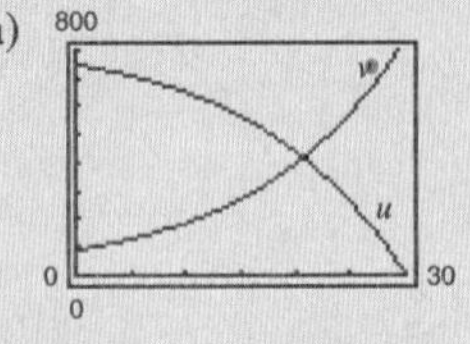

(b) Interest; $t \approx 21$ yr

(c)

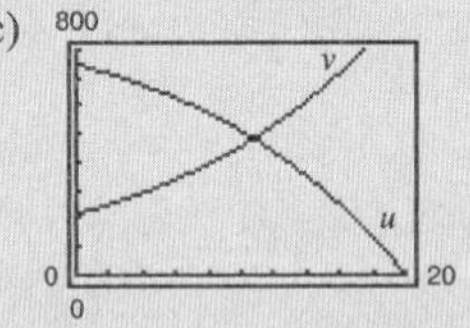

Interest; $t \approx 11$ yr
The interest is still the majority of the monthly payment in the early years, but now the principal and interest are nearly equal when $t \approx 11$ years.

GEOLOGY In Exercises 63 and 64, use the Richter scale

$$R = \log \frac{I}{I_0}$$

for measuring the magnitudes of earthquakes.

63. Find the intensity I of an earthquake measuring R on the Richter scale (let $I_0 = 1$). See margin.

(a) Southern Sumatra, Indonesia in 2007, $R = 8.5$

(b) Illinois in 2008, $R = 5.4$ $10^{5.4} \approx 251,189$

(c) Costa Rica in 2009, $R = 6.1$ $10^{6.1} \approx 1,258,925$

64. Find the magnitude R of each earthquake of intensity I (let $I_0 = 1$). 8.30

(a) $I = 199,500,000$ (b) $I = 48,275,000$ 7.68

(c) $I = 17,000$ 4.23

INTENSITY OF SOUND In Exercises 65–68, use the following information for determining sound intensity. The level of sound β, in decibels, with an intensity of I, is given by $\beta = 10 \log(I/I_0)$, where I_0 is an intensity of 10^{-12} watt per square meter, corresponding roughly to the faintest sound that can be heard by the human ear. In Exercises 65 and 66, find the level of sound β.

65. (a) $I = 10^{-10}$ watt per m^2 (quiet room) 20 dB

(b) $I = 10^{-5}$ watt per m^2 (busy street corner) 70 dB

(c) $I = 10^{-8}$ watt per m^2 (quiet radio) 40 dB

(d) $I = 10^{0}$ watt per m^2 (threshold of pain) 120 dB

66. (a) $I = 10^{-11}$ watt per m^2 (rustle of leaves) 10 dB

(b) $I = 10^{2}$ watt per m^2 (jet at 30 meters) 140 dB

(c) $I = 10^{-4}$ watt per m^2 (door slamming) 80 dB

(d) $I = 10^{-2}$ watt per m^2 (siren at 30 meters) 100 dB

67. Due to the installation of noise suppression materials, the noise level in an auditorium was reduced from 93 to 80 decibels. Find the percent decrease in the intensity level of the noise as a result of the installation of these materials. 95%

68. Due to the installation of a muffler, the noise level of an engine was reduced from 88 to 72 decibels. Find the percent decrease in the intensity level of the noise as a result of the installation of the muffler. 97%

pH LEVELS In Exercises 69–74, use the acidity model given by $\text{pH} = -\log[H^+]$, where acidity (pH) is a measure of the hydrogen ion concentration $[H^+]$ (measured in moles of hydrogen per liter) of a solution.

69. Find the pH if $[H^+] = 2.3 \times 10^{-5}$. 4.64

70. Find the pH if $[H^+] = 1.13 \times 10^{-5}$. 4.95

71. Compute $[H^+]$ for a solution in which $\text{pH} = 5.8$.

72. Compute $[H^+]$ for a solution in which $\text{pH} = 3.2$.

71. 1.58×10^{-6} moles/L

72. $10^{-3.2} \approx 6.3 \times 10^{-4}$ moles/L

$10^{5.1}$

73. Apple juice has a pH of 2.9 and drinking water has a pH of 8.0. The hydrogen ion concentration of the apple juice is how many times the concentration of drinking water?

74. The pH of a solution is decreased by one unit. The hydrogen ion concentration is increased by what factor? 10

75. FORENSICS At 8:30 A.M., a coroner was called to the home of a person who had died during the night. In order to estimate the time of death, the coroner took the person's temperature twice. At 9:00 A.M. the temperature was 85.7°F, and at 11:00 A.M. the temperature was 82.8°F. From these two temperatures, the coroner was able to determine that the time elapsed since death and the body temperature were related by the formula

$$t = -10 \ln \frac{T - 70}{98.6 - 70}$$

3:00 A.M.

where t is the time in hours elapsed since the person died and T is the temperature (in degrees Fahrenheit) of the person's body. (This formula is derived from a general cooling principle called *Newton's Law of Cooling*. It uses the assumptions that the person had a normal body temperature of 98.6°F at death, and that the room temperature was a constant 70°F.) Use the formula to estimate the time of death of the person.

76. HOME MORTGAGE A \$120,000 home mortgage for 30 years at $7\frac{1}{2}\%$ has a monthly payment of \$839.06. Part of the monthly payment is paid toward the interest charge on the unpaid balance, and the remainder of the payment is used to reduce the principal. The amount that is paid toward the interest is

$$u = M - \left(M - \frac{Pr}{12}\right)\left(1 + \frac{r}{12}\right)^{12t}$$

and the amount that is paid toward the reduction of the principal is

$$v = \left(M - \frac{Pr}{12}\right)\left(1 + \frac{r}{12}\right)^{12t}.$$

In these formulas, P is the size of the mortgage, r is the interest rate, M is the monthly payment, and t is the time (in years). See margin.

(a) Use a graphing utility to graph each function in the same viewing window. (The viewing window should show all 30 years of mortgage payments.)

(b) In the early years of the mortgage, is the larger part of the monthly payment paid toward the interest or the principal? Approximate the time when the monthly payment is evenly divided between interest and principal reduction.

(c) Repeat parts (a) and (b) for a repayment period of 20 years ($M = \$966.71$). What can you conclude?

77. HOME MORTGAGE The total interest u paid on a home mortgage of P dollars at interest rate r for t years is

$$u = P\left[\frac{rt}{1 - \left(\dfrac{1}{1 + r/12}\right)^{12t}} - 1\right].$$

Consider a \$120,000 home mortgage at $7\frac{1}{2}\%$. See margin.

(a) Use a graphing utility to graph the total interest function.

(b) Approximate the length of the mortgage for which the total interest paid is the same as the size of the mortgage. Is it possible that some people are paying twice as much in interest charges as the size of the mortgage? $t \approx 21$ yr; Yes

78. DATA ANALYSIS The table shows the time t (in seconds) required for a car to attain a speed of s miles per hour from a standing start.

Speed, s	Time, t
30	3.4
40	5.0
50	7.0
60	9.3
70	12.0
80	15.8
90	20.0

Two models for these data are as follows.

$t_1 = 40.757 + 0.556s - 15.817 \ln s$

$t_2 = 1.2259 + 0.0023s^2$ See margin.

(a) Use the *regression* feature of a graphing utility to find a linear model t_3 and an exponential model t_4 for the data.

(b) Use a graphing utility to graph the data and each model in the same viewing window.

(c) Create a table comparing the data with estimates obtained from each model.

(d) Use the results of part (c) to find the sum of the absolute values of the differences between the data and the estimated values given by each model. Based on the four sums, which model do you think best fits the data? Explain.

EXPLORATION

TRUE OR FALSE? In Exercises 79–82, determine whether the statement is true or false. Justify your answer.

79. The domain of a logistic growth function cannot be the set of real numbers. See margin.

80. A logistic growth function will always have an x-intercept. False. A logistic growth function never has an x-intercept.

81. The graph of $f(x) = \dfrac{4}{1 + 6e^{-2x}} + 5$ is the graph of $g(x) = \dfrac{4}{1 + 6e^{-2x}}$ shifted to the right five units. See margin.

82. The graph of a Gaussian model will never have an x-intercept. See margin.

83. WRITING Use your school's library, the Internet, or some other reference source to write a paper describing John Napier's work with logarithms. Answers will vary.

84. CAPSTONE Identify each model as exponential, Gaussian, linear, logarithmic, logistic, quadratic, or none of the above. Explain your reasoning.

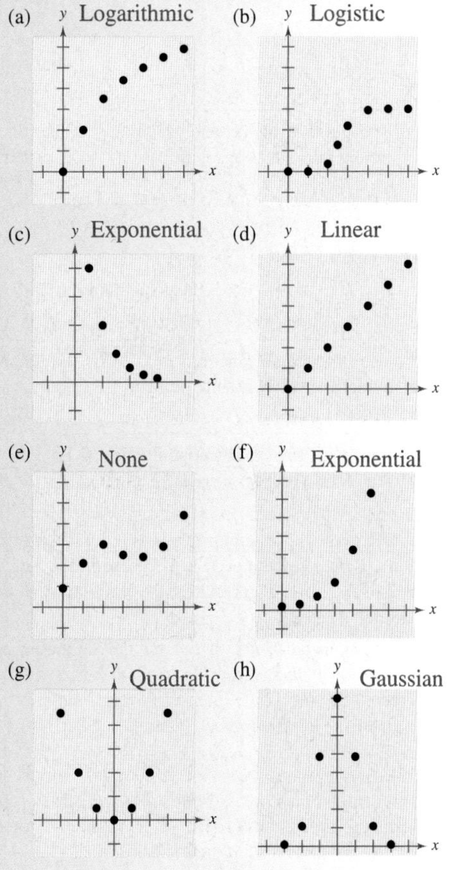

PROJECT: SALES PER SHARE To work an extended application analyzing the sales per share for Kohl's Corporation from 1992 through 2007, visit this text's website at *academic.cengage.com*. (Data Source: Kohl's Corporation)

5 ASSESS AND RETEACH

Daily Homework Quiz

Transparency Available

Available at the Instructor's companion site.

77. (a)

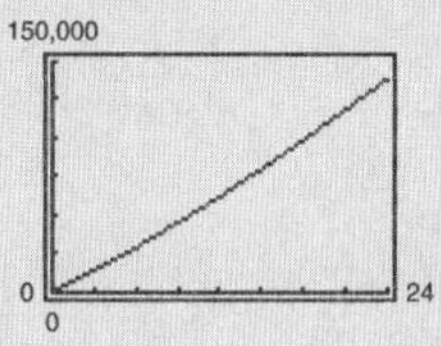

78. See below.

79. False. The domain can be the set of real numbers for a logistic growth function.

81. False. The graph of $f(x)$ is the graph of $g(x)$ shifted upward five units.

82. True. The graph of a Gaussian model will never have an x-intercept.

78. (a) $t_3 = 0.2729s - 6.0143$

$t_4 = 1.5385e^{0.02913s}$ or

$t_4 = 1.5385(1.0296)^s$

(b)

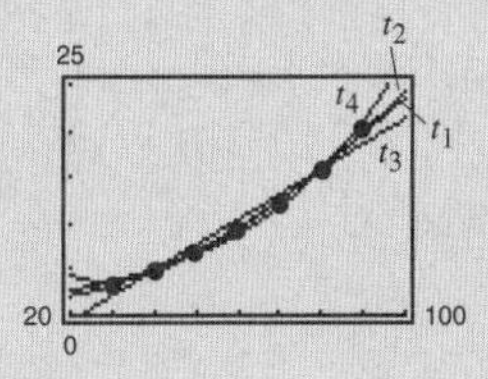

(c)

s	30	40	50	60	70	80	90
t_1	3.6	4.6	6.7	9.4	12.5	15.9	19.6
t_2	3.3	4.9	7.0	9.5	12.5	15.9	19.9
t_3	2.2	4.9	7.6	10.4	13.1	15.8	18.5
t_4	3.7	4.9	6.6	8.8	11.8	15.8	21.2

(d) Model t_1: Sum = 2.0

Model t_2: Sum = 1.1

Model t_3: Sum = 5.6

Model t_4: Sum = 2.7

The quadratic model (t_2) fits best.

3 Chapter Summary

<table>
<tr><th></th><th>What Did You Learn?</th><th>Explanation/Examples</th><th>Review Exercises</th></tr>
<tr><td rowspan="4">Section 3.1</td><td>Recognize and evaluate exponential functions with base a (p. 216).</td><td>The exponential function f with base a is denoted by $f(x) = a^x$ where $a > 0$, $a \neq 1$, and x is any real number.</td><td>1–6</td></tr>
<tr><td>Graph exponential functions and use the One-to-One Property (p. 217).</td><td>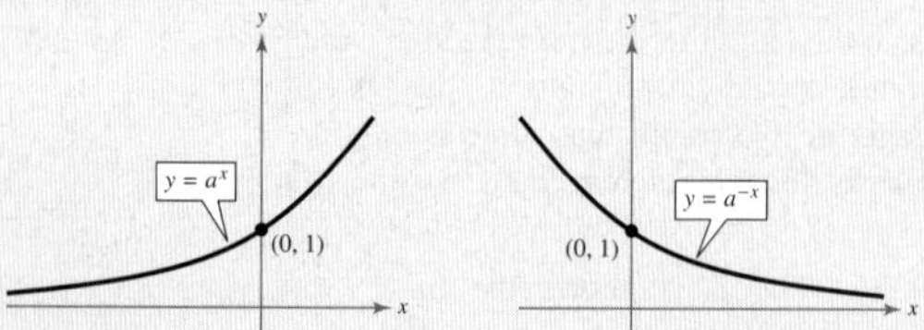

One-to-One Property: For $a > 0$ and $a \neq 1$, $a^x = a^y$ if and only if $x = y$.</td><td>7–24</td></tr>
<tr><td>Recognize, evaluate, and graph exponential functions with base e (p. 220).</td><td>The function $f(x) = e^x$ is called the natural exponential function.
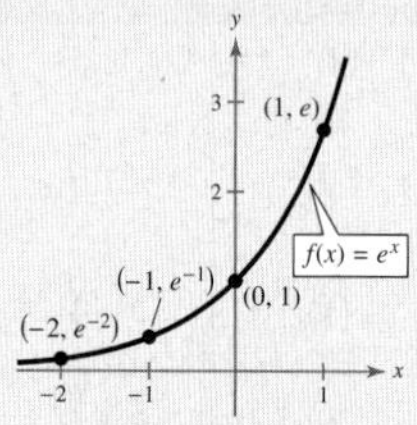
</td><td>25–32</td></tr>
<tr><td>Use exponential functions to model and solve real-life problems (p. 221).</td><td>Exponential functions are used in compound interest formulas (See Example 8.) and in radioactive decay models. (See Example 9.)</td><td>33–36</td></tr>
<tr><td rowspan="3">Section 3.2</td><td>Recognize and evaluate logarithmic functions with base a (p. 227).</td><td>For $x > 0$, $a > 0$, and $a \neq 1$, $y = \log_a x$ if and only if $x = a^y$. The function $f(x) = \log_a x$ is called the logarithmic function with base a. The logarithmic function with base 10 is the common logarithmic function. It is denoted by $\log_{10}$ or log.</td><td>37–48</td></tr>
<tr><td>Graph logarithmic functions (p. 229) and recognize, evaluate, and graph natural logarithmic functions (p. 231).</td><td>The graph of $y = \log_a x$ is a reflection of the graph of $y = a^x$ about the line $y = x$.

The function defined by $f(x) = \ln x$, $x > 0$, is called the natural logarithmic function. Its graph is a reflection of the graph of $f(x) = e^x$ about the line $y = x$.

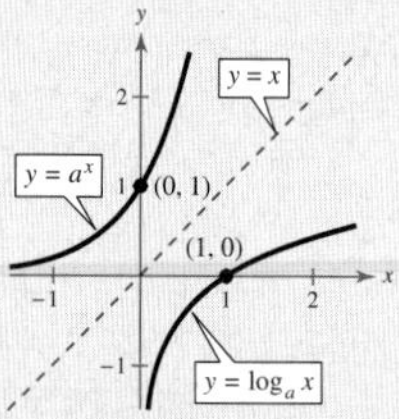

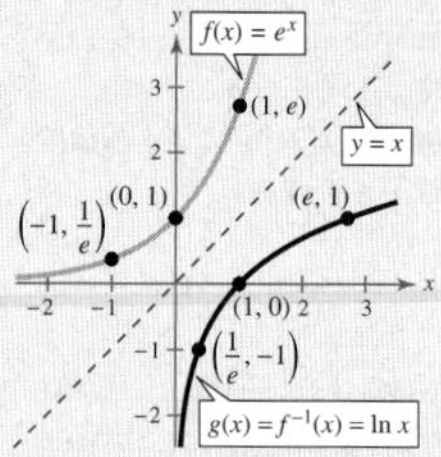
</td><td>49–52

53–58</td></tr>
<tr><td>Use logarithmic functions to model and solve real-life problems (p. 233).</td><td>A logarithmic function is used in the human memory model. (See Example 11.)</td><td>59, 60</td></tr>
</table>

	What Did You Learn?	Explanation/Examples	Review Exercises
Section 3.3	Use the change-of-base formula to rewrite and evaluate logarithmic expressions *(p. 237).*	Let a, b, and x be positive real numbers such that $a \neq 1$ and $b \neq 1$. Then $\log_a x$ can be converted to a different base as follows. *Base b*: $\log_a x = \dfrac{\log_b x}{\log_b a}$ *Base* 10: $\log_a x = \dfrac{\log x}{\log a}$ *Base e*: $\log_a x = \dfrac{\ln x}{\ln a}$	61–64
	Use properties of logarithms to evaluate, rewrite, expand, or condense logarithmic expressions *(p. 238).*	Let a be a positive number ($a \neq 1$), n be a real number, and u and v be positive real numbers. **1. Product Property:** $\log_a(uv) = \log_a u + \log_a v$ $\ln(uv) = \ln u + \ln v$ **2. Quotient Property:** $\log_a(u/v) = \log_a u - \log_a v$ $\ln(u/v) = \ln u - \ln v$ **3. Power Property:** $\log_a u^n = n \log_a u$, $\ln u^n = n \ln u$	65–80
	Use logarithmic functions to model and solve real-life problems *(p. 240).*	Logarithmic functions can be used to find an equation that relates the periods of several planets and their distances from the sun. (See Example 7.)	81, 82
Section 3.4	Solve simple exponential and logarithmic equations *(p. 244).*	One-to-One Properties and Inverse Properties of exponential or logarithmic functions can be used to help solve exponential or logarithmic equations.	83–88
	Solve more complicated exponential equations *(p. 245)* and logarithmic equations *(p. 247).*	To solve more complicated equations, rewrite the equations so that the One-to-One Properties and Inverse Properties of exponential or logarithmic functions can be used. (See Examples 2–8.)	89–108
	Use exponential and logarithmic equations to model and solve real-life problems *(p. 249).*	Exponential and logarithmic equations can be used to find how long it will take to double an investment (see Example 10) and to find the year in which companies reached a given amount of sales. (See Example 11.)	109, 110
Section 3.5	Recognize the five most common types of models involving exponential and logarithmic functions *(p. 255).*	**1. Exponential growth model:** $y = ae^{bx}$, $b > 0$ **2. Exponential decay model:** $y = ae^{-bx}$, $b > 0$ **3. Gaussian model:** $y = ae^{-(x-b)^2/c}$ **4. Logistic growth model:** $y = \dfrac{a}{1 + be^{-rx}}$ **5. Logarithmic models:** $y = a + b \ln x$, $y = a + b \log x$	111–116
	Use exponential growth and decay functions to model and solve real-life problems *(p. 256).*	An exponential growth function can be used to model a population of fruit flies (see Example 2) and an exponential decay function can be used to find the age of a fossil (see Example 3).	117–120
	Use Gaussian functions *(p. 259),* logistic growth functions *(p. 260),* and logarithmic functions *(p. 261)* to model and solve real-life problems.	A Gaussian function can be used to model SAT math scores for college-bound seniors. (See Example 4.) A logistic growth function can be used to model the spread of a flu virus. (See Example 5.) A logarithmic function can be used to find the intensity of an earthquake using its magnitude. (See Example 6.)	121–123

7. Shift the graph of f two units downward.
8. Shift the graph of f one unit upward.
9. Reflect f in the y-axis and shift two units to the right.
10. Shift the graph of f one unit to the left.
11. Reflect f in the x-axis and shift one unit upward.
12. Reflect f in the x-axis.
13. Reflect f in the x-axis and shift two units to the left.
14. Reflect f in the x-axis and shift eight units upward.

36. (a)

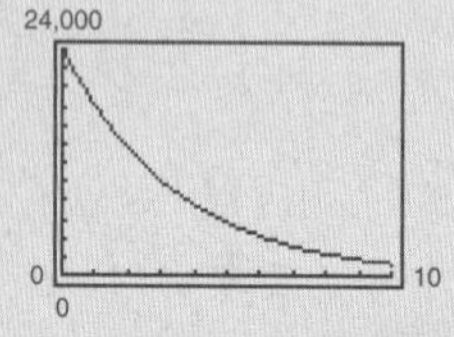

(c) At the beginning; Yes; Explanations will vary.

49. Domain: $(0, \infty)$
x-intercept: $(1, 0)$
Vertical asymptote: $x = 0$

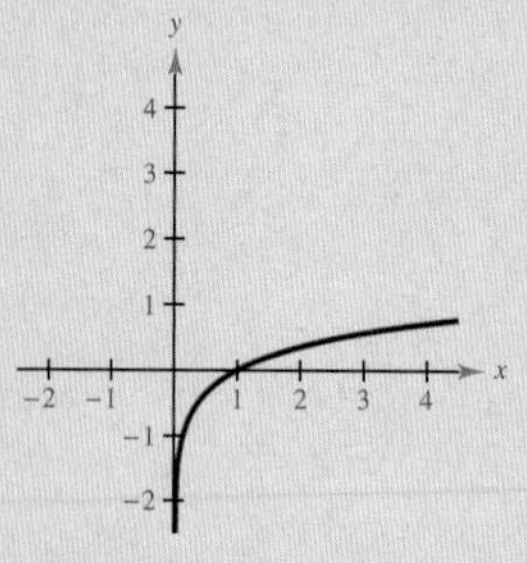

50. Domain: $(0, \infty)$
x-intercept: $(3, 0)$
Vertical asymptote: $x = 0$

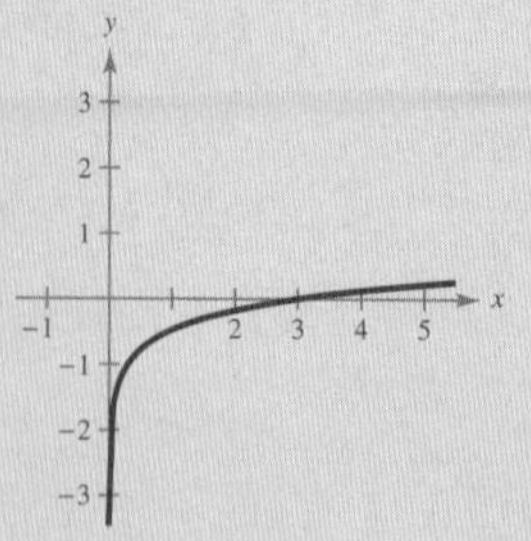

3 REVIEW EXERCISES

See www.CalcChat.com for worked-out solutions to odd-numbered exercises.

3.1 **In Exercises 1–6, evaluate the function at the indicated value of x. Round your result to three decimal places.**

0.164 **1.** $f(x) = 0.3^x, \quad x = 1.5$ **2.** $f(x) = 30^x, \quad x = \sqrt{3}$ 361.784

0.337 **3.** $f(x) = 2^{-0.5x}, \quad x = \pi$ **4.** $f(x) = 1278^{x/5}, \quad x = 1$ 4.181

5. $f(x) = 7(0.2^x), \quad x = -\sqrt{11}$ 1456.529

6. $f(x) = -14(5^x), \quad x = -0.8$ −3.863

In Exercises 7–14, use the graph of f to describe the transformation that yields the graph of g. 7–14. See margin.

7. $f(x) = 2^x, \quad g(x) = 2^x - 2$

8. $f(x) = 5^x, \quad g(x) = 5^x + 1$

9. $f(x) = 4^x, \quad g(x) = 4^{-x+2}$

10. $f(x) = 6^x, \quad g(x) = 6^{x+1}$

11. $f(x) = 3^x, \quad g(x) = 1 - 3^x$

12. $f(x) = 0.1^x, \quad g(x) = -0.1^x$

13. $f(x) = \left(\frac{1}{2}\right)^x, \quad g(x) = -\left(\frac{1}{2}\right)^{x+2}$

14. $f(x) = \left(\frac{2}{3}\right)^x, \quad g(x) = 8 - \left(\frac{2}{3}\right)^x$

In Exercises 15–20, use a graphing utility to construct a table of values for the function. Then sketch the graph of the function. 15–20. See margin.

15. $f(x) = 4^{-x} + 4$ **16.** $f(x) = 2.65^{x-1}$

17. $f(x) = 5^{x-2} + 4$ **18.** $f(x) = 2^{x-6} - 5$

19. $f(x) = \left(\frac{1}{2}\right)^{-x} + 3$ **20.** $f(x) = \left(\frac{1}{8}\right)^{x+2} - 5$

In Exercises 21–24, use the One-to-One Property to solve the equation for x.

21. $\left(\frac{1}{3}\right)^{x-3} = 9$ $x = 1$ **22.** $3^{x+3} = \frac{1}{81}$ $x = -7$

23. $e^{3x-5} = e^7$ $x = 4$ **24.** $e^{8-2x} = e^{-3}$ $x = \frac{11}{2}$

In Exercises 25–28, evaluate $f(x) = e^x$ at the indicated value of x. Round your result to three decimal places.

25. $x = 8$ 2980.958 **26.** $x = \frac{5}{8}$ 1.868

27. $x = -1.7$ 0.183 **28.** $x = 0.278$ 1.320

In Exercises 29–32, use a graphing utility to construct a table of values for the function. Then sketch the graph of the function. 29–32. See margin.

29. $h(x) = e^{-x/2}$ **30.** $h(x) = 2 - e^{-x/2}$

31. $f(x) = e^{x+2}$ **32.** $s(t) = 4e^{-2/t}, \quad t > 0$

COMPOUND INTEREST **In Exercises 33 and 34, complete the table to determine the balance A for P dollars invested at rate r for t years and compounded n times per year.**

n	1	2	4	12	365	Continuous
A						

TABLE FOR 33 AND 34 33–34. See margin.

33. $P = \$5000, \ r = 3\%, \ t = 10$ years

34. $P = \$4500, \ r = 2.5\%, \ t = 30$ years

35. WAITING TIMES The average time between incoming calls at a switchboard is 3 minutes. The probability F of waiting less than t minutes until the next incoming call is approximated by the model $F(t) = 1 - e^{-t/3}$. A call has just come in. Find the probability that the next call will be within (a) 0.154 (b) 0.487 (c) 0.811

(a) $\frac{1}{2}$ minute. (b) 2 minutes. (c) 5 minutes.

36. DEPRECIATION After t years, the value V of a car that originally cost \$23,970 is given by $V(t) = 23{,}970\left(\frac{3}{4}\right)^t$.

(a) Use a graphing utility to graph the function. See margin.

(b) Find the value of the car 2 years after it was purchased. \$13,483.13

See margin. (c) According to the model, when does the car depreciate most rapidly? Is this realistic? Explain.

(d) According to the model, when will the car have no value? Never

3.2 **In Exercises 37–40, write the exponential equation in logarithmic form. For example, the logarithmic form of $2^3 = 8$ is $\log_2 8 = 3$.**

37. $3^3 = 27$ $\log_3 27 = 3$ **38.** $25^{3/2} = 125$ $\log_{25} 125 = \frac{3}{2}$

39. $e^{0.8} = 2.2255 \ldots$ $\ln 2.2255 \ldots = 0.8$ **40.** $e^0 = 1$ $\ln 1 = 0$

In Exercises 41–44, evaluate the function at the indicated value of x without using a calculator.

41. $f(x) = \log x, x = 1000$ 3 **42.** $g(x) = \log_9 x, x = 3$ $\frac{1}{2}$

43. $g(x) = \log_2 x, x = \frac{1}{4}$ −2 **44.** $f(x) = \log_3 x, x = \frac{1}{81}$ −4

In Exercises 45–48, use the One-to-One Property to solve the equation for x.

45. $\log_4(x + 7) = \log_4 14$ $x = 7$ **46.** $\log_8(3x - 10) = \log_8 5$ $x = 5$

47. $\ln(x + 9) = \ln 4$ $x = -5$ **48.** $\ln(2x - 1) = \ln 11$ $x = 6$

In Exercises 49–52, find the domain, x-intercept, and vertical asymptote of the logarithmic function and sketch its graph. 49–52. See margin.

49. $g(x) = \log_7 x$ **50.** $f(x) = \log\left(\frac{x}{3}\right)$

51. $f(x) = 4 - \log(x + 5)$ **52.** $f(x) = \log(x - 3) + 1$

51. Domain: $(-5, \infty)$
x-intercept: $(9995, 0)$
Vertical asymptote: $x = -5$

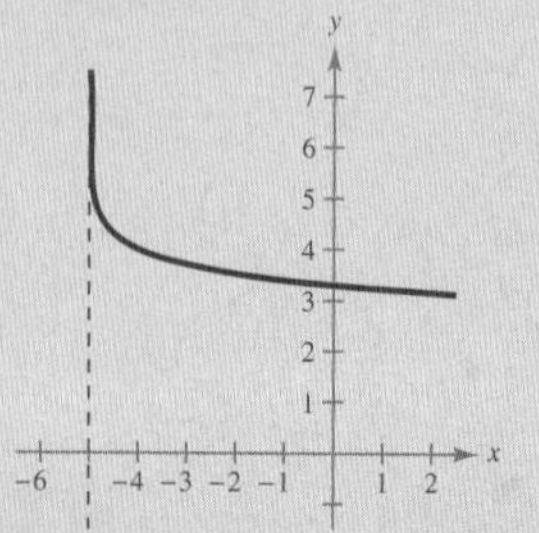

52. Domain: $(3, \infty)$
x-intercept: $(3.1, 0)$
Vertical asymptote: $x = 3$

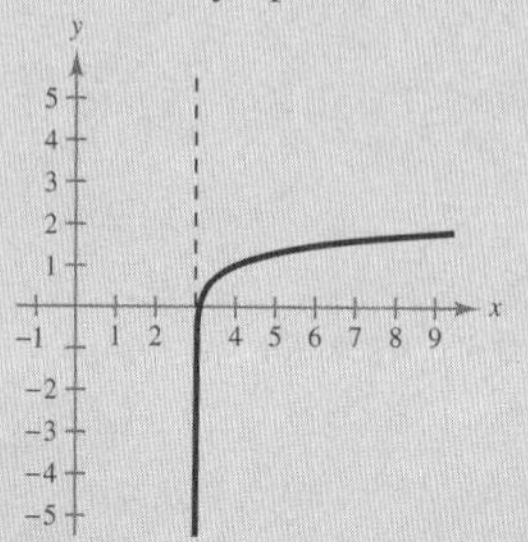

15–20, 29–34. See Additional Answers beginning on page AA1.

53. Use a calculator to evaluate $f(x) = \ln x$ at (a) $x = 22.6$ and (b) $x = 0.98$. Round your results to three decimal places if necessary. (a) 3.118 (b) -0.020

54. Use a calculator to evaluate $f(x) = 5 \ln x$ at (a) $x = e^{-12}$ and (b) $x = \sqrt{3}$. Round your results to three decimal places if necessary. (a) -60 (b) 2.747

In Exercises 55–58, find the domain, *x*-intercept, and vertical asymptote of the logarithmic function and sketch its graph. 55–58. See margin.

55. $f(x) = \ln x + 3$
56. $f(x) = \ln(x - 3)$
57. $h(x) = \ln(x^2)$
58. $f(x) = \frac{1}{4} \ln x$

59. **ANTLER SPREAD** The antler spread a (in inches) and shoulder height h (in inches) of an adult male American elk are related by the model $h = 116 \log(a + 40) - 176$. Approximate the shoulder height of a male American elk with an antler spread of 55 inches. 53.4 in.

60. **SNOW REMOVAL** The number of miles s of roads cleared of snow is approximated by the model

$$s = 25 - \frac{13 \ln(h/12)}{\ln 3}, \quad 2 \le h \le 15$$

where h is the depth of the snow in inches. Use this model to find s when $h = 10$ inches. 27.16 mi

3.3 **In Exercises 61–64, evaluate the logarithm using the change-of-base formula. Do each exercise twice, once with common logarithms and once with natural logarithms. Round the results to three decimal places.**

61. $\log_2 6$ 2.585
62. $\log_{12} 200$ 2.132
63. $\log_{1/2} 5$ -2.322
64. $\log_3 0.28$ -1.159

In Exercises 65–68, use the properties of logarithms to rewrite and simplify the logarithmic expression. 65–68. See margin.

65. $\log 18$
66. $\log_2(\frac{1}{12})$
67. $\ln 20$
68. $\ln(3e^{-4})$

In Exercises 69–74, use the properties of logarithms to expand the expression as a sum, difference, and/or constant multiple of logarithms. (Assume all variables are positive.)

69. $\log_5 5x^2$ $1 + 2 \log_5 x$
70. $\log 7x^4$ $\log 7 + 4 \log x$
71. $\log_3 \frac{9}{\sqrt{x}}$ $2 - \frac{1}{2} \log_3 x$
72. $\log_7 \frac{\sqrt[3]{x}}{14}$ 72–74. See margin.
73. $\ln x^2y^2z$
74. $\ln\left(\frac{y-1}{4}\right)^2, \quad y > 1$

In Exercises 75–80, condense the expression to the logarithm of a single quantity.

75. $\log_2 5 + \log_2 x$ $\log_2 5x$
76. $\log_6 y - 2 \log_6 z$ $\log_6 \frac{y}{z^2}$
77. $\ln x - \frac{1}{4} \ln y$ $\ln \frac{x}{\sqrt[4]{y}}$
78. $3 \ln x + 2 \ln(x + 1)$ $\ln x^3(x+1)^2$
79. $\frac{1}{2} \log_3 x - 2 \log_3(y + 8)$ 79–80. See margin.
80. $5 \ln(x - 2) - \ln(x + 2) - 3 \ln x$

81. **CLIMB RATE** The time t (in minutes) for a small plane to climb to an altitude of h feet is modeled by $t = 50 \log[18{,}000/(18{,}000 - h)]$, where 18,000 feet is the plane's absolute ceiling.

(a) Determine the domain of the function in the context of the problem. $0 \le h < 18{,}000$

(b) Use a graphing utility to graph the function and identify any asymptotes. See margin.

(c) As the plane approaches its absolute ceiling, what can be said about the time required to increase its altitude? See margin.

(d) Find the time for the plane to climb to an altitude of 4000 feet. 5.46 min

82. **HUMAN MEMORY MODEL** Students in a learning theory study were given an exam and then retested monthly for 6 months with an equivalent exam. The data obtained in the study are given as the ordered pairs (t, s), where t is the time in months after the initial exam and s is the average score for the class. Use these data to find a logarithmic equation that relates t and s.

(1, 84.2), (2, 78.4), (3, 72.1), (4, 68.5), (5, 67.1), (6, 65.3) $s = 84.66 - 11 \ln t$

3.4 **In Exercises 83–88, solve for *x*.**

83. $5^x = 125$ 3
84. $6^x = \frac{1}{216}$ -3
85. $e^x = 3$ $\ln 3 \approx 1.099$
86. $\log_6 x = -1$ $\frac{1}{6}$
87. $\ln x = 4$ $e^4 \approx 54.598$
88. $\ln x = -1.6$ $e^{-1.6} \approx 0.202$

In Exercises 89–92, solve the exponential equation algebraically. Approximate your result to three decimal places.

89. $e^{4x} = e^{x^2+3}$ $x = 1, 3$
90. $e^{3x} = 25$ 90–92. See margin.
91. $2^x - 3 = 29$
92. $e^{2x} - 6e^x + 8 = 0$

In Exercises 93 and 94, use a graphing utility to graph and solve the equation. Approximate the result to three decimal places. 93–94. See margin.

93. $25e^{-0.3x} = 12$
94. $2^x = 3 + x - e^x$

In Exercises 95–104, solve the logarithmic equation algebraically. Approximate the result to three decimal places.

95. $\ln 3x = 8.2$
96. $4 \ln 3x = 15$
97. $\ln x - \ln 3 = 2$
98. $\ln x - \ln 5 = 4$
99. $\ln \sqrt{x} = 4$
100. $\ln \sqrt{x + 8} = 3$

95–100. See margin.

79. $\log_3 \frac{\sqrt{x}}{(y+8)^2}$

80. $\ln \frac{(x-2)^5}{x^3(x+2)}$

81. (b)

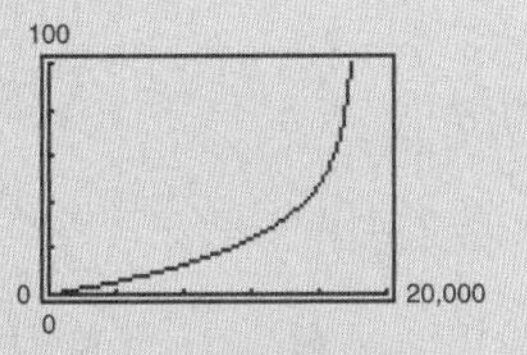

Vertical asymptote: $h = 18{,}000$

(c) The plane is climbing at a slower rate, so the time required increases.

90. $\frac{\ln 25}{3} \approx 1.073$

91. $\frac{\ln 32}{\ln 2} = 5$

92. $\ln 2 \approx 0.693, \ln 4 \approx 1.386$

93–100. See Additional Answers beginning on page AA1.

55. Domain: $(0, \infty)$
x-intercept: $(e^{-3}, 0)$
Vertical asymptote: $x = 0$

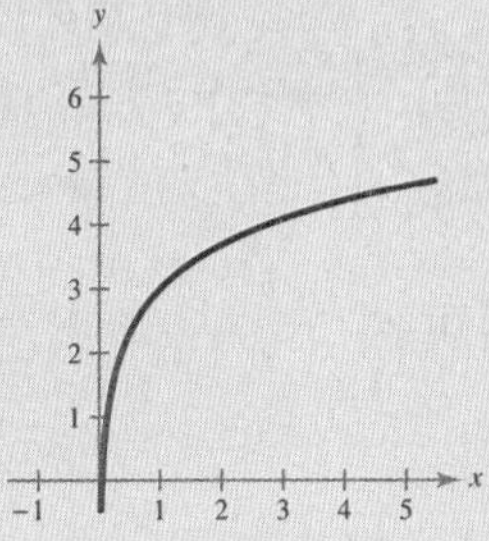

56. Domain: $(3, \infty)$
x-intercept: $(4, 0)$
Vertical asymptote: $x = 3$

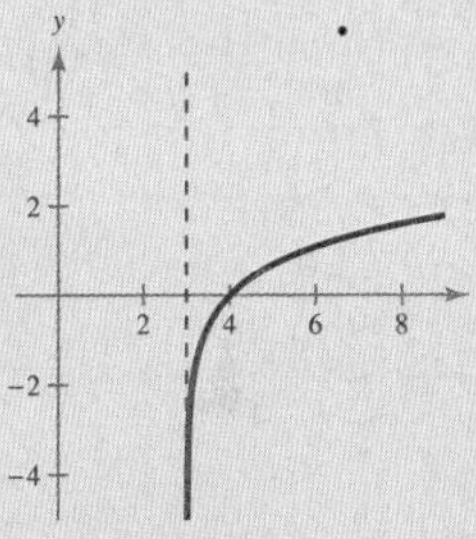

57. Domain: $(-\infty, 0), (0, \infty)$
x-intercept: $(\pm 1, 0)$
Vertical asymptote: $x = 0$

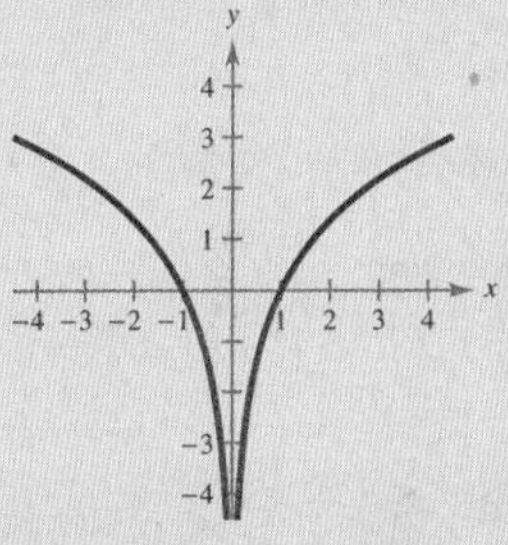

58. Domain: $(0, \infty)$
x-intercept: $(1, 0)$
Vertical asymptote: $x = 0$

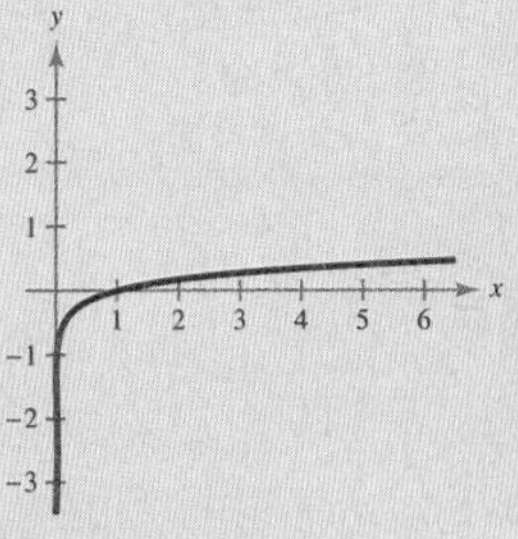

65. $\log 2 + 2 \log 3 \approx 1.255$

66. $\frac{\log 1 - \log 3 - 2 \log 2}{\log 2} \approx -3.585$

67. $2 \ln 2 + \ln 5 \approx 2.996$

68. $\ln(3) - 4 \approx -2.901$

72. $\frac{1}{3} \log_7 x - 1 - \log_7 2$

73. $2 \ln x + 2 \ln y + \ln z$

74. $2 \ln(y - 1) - \ln 16$

101. $\log_8(x-1) = \log_8(x-2) - \log_8(x+2)$ No solution

102. $\log_6(x+2) - \log_6 x = \log_6(x+5)$ $-2+\sqrt{6} \approx 0.449$

103. $\log(1-x) = -1$ 0.900 **104.** $\log(-x-4) = 2$ -104

In Exercises 105–108, use a graphing utility to graph and solve the equation. Approximate the result to three decimal places. 105–108. See margin.

105. $2\ln(x+3) - 3 = 0$ **106.** $x - 2\log(x+4) = 0$

107. $6\log(x^2+1) - x = 0$

108. $3\ln x + 2\log x = e^x - 25$

109. COMPOUND INTEREST You deposit \$8500 in an account that pays 3.5% interest, compounded continuously. How long will it take for the money to triple? 31.4 yr

110. METEOROLOGY The speed of the wind S (in miles per hour) near the center of a tornado and the distance d (in miles) the tornado travels are related by the model $S = 93\log d + 65$. On March 18, 1925, a large tornado struck portions of Missouri, Illinois, and Indiana with a wind speed at the center of about 283 miles per hour. Approximate the distance traveled by this tornado. $d \approx 221$ mi

3.5 In Exercises 111–116, match the function with its graph. [The graphs are labeled (a), (b), (c), (d), (e), and (f).]

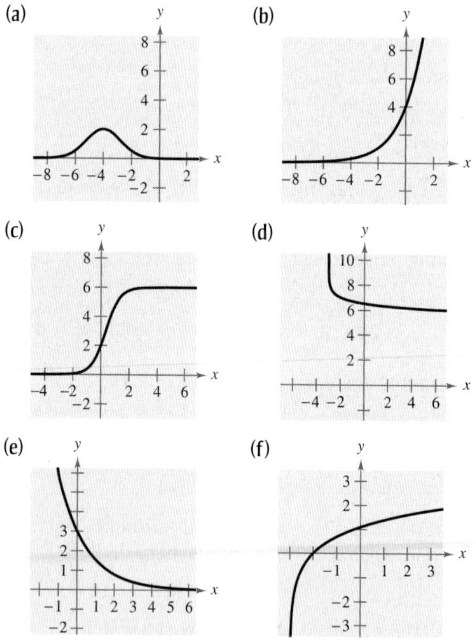

111. $y = 3e^{-2x/3}$ e **112.** $y = 4e^{2x/3}$ b

113. $y = \ln(x+3)$ f **114.** $y = 7 - \log(x+3)$ d

115. $y = 2e^{-(x+4)^2/3}$ a **116.** $y = \dfrac{6}{1+2e^{-2x}}$ c

In Exercises 117 and 118, find the exponential model $y = ae^{bx}$ that passes through the points. 117–118. See margin.

117. $(0, 2), (4, 3)$ **118.** $\left(0, \frac{1}{2}\right), (5, 5)$

119. POPULATION In 2007, the population of Florida residents aged 65 and over was about 3.10 million. In 2015 and 2020, the populations of Florida residents aged 65 and over are projected to be about 4.13 million and 5.11 million, respectively. An exponential growth model that approximates these data is given by $P = 2.36e^{0.0382t}$, $7 \le t \le 20$, where P is the population (in millions) and $t = 7$ represents 2007. (Source: U.S. Census Bureau) See margin.

(a) Use a graphing utility to graph the model and the data in the same viewing window. Is the model a good fit for the data? Explain.

(b) According to the model, when will the population of Florida residents aged 65 and over reach 5.5 million? Does your answer seem reasonable? Explain.

120. WILDLIFE POPULATION A species of bat is in danger of becoming extinct. Five years ago, the total population of the species was 2000. Two years ago, the total population of the species was 1400. What was the total population of the species one year ago? 1243

121. TEST SCORES The test scores for a biology test follow a normal distribution modeled by $y = 0.0499e^{-(x-71)^2/128}$, $40 \le x \le 100$, where x is the test score. Use a graphing utility to graph the equation and estimate the average test score. See margin.

122. TYPING SPEED In a typing class, the average number N of words per minute typed after t weeks of lessons was found to be $N = 157/(1 + 5.4e^{-0.12t})$. Find the time necessary to type (a) 50 words per minute and (b) 75 words per minute. See margin.

123. SOUND INTENSITY The relationship between the number of decibels β and the intensity of a sound I in watts per square meter is $\beta = 10\log(I/10^{-12})$. Find I for each decibel level β. See margin.

(a) $\beta = 60$ (b) $\beta = 135$ (c) $\beta = 1$

EXPLORATION

124. Consider the graph of $y = e^{kt}$. Describe the characteristics of the graph when k is positive and when k is negative. See margin.

TRUE OR FALSE? In Exercises 125 and 126, determine whether the equation is true or false. Justify your answer.

125. $\log_b b^{2x} = 2x$ **126.** $\ln(x+y) = \ln x + \ln y$

125–126. See margin.

105.

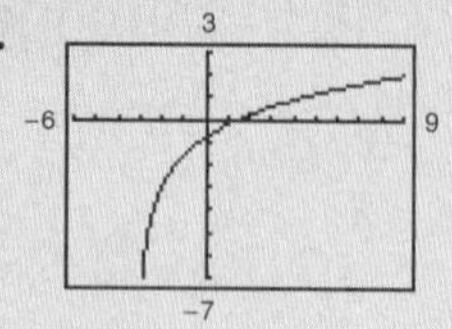

1.482

106.

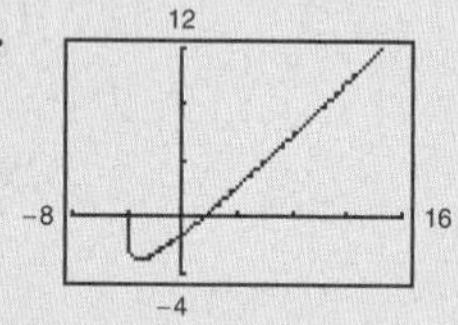

$-3.990, 1.477$

107.

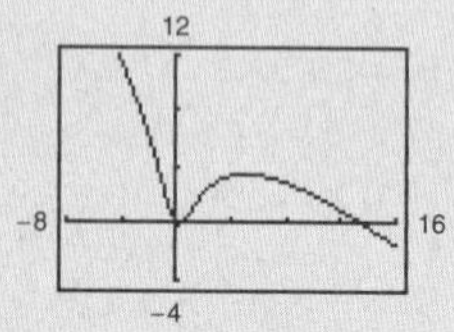

0, 0.416, 13.627

108.

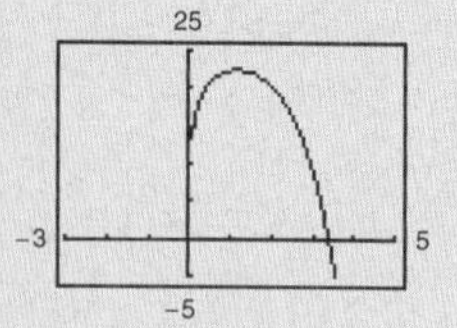

0.002, 3.392

117. $y = 2e^{0.1014x}$

118. $y = \frac{1}{2}e^{0.4605x}$

119. (a)

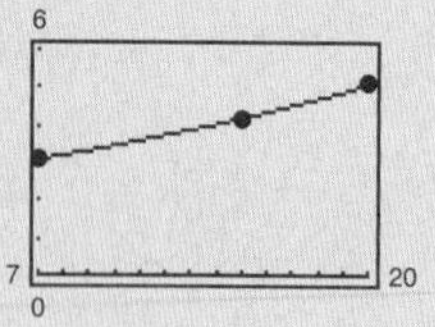

The model fits the data well.

(b) 2022; Answers will vary.

121. (a)

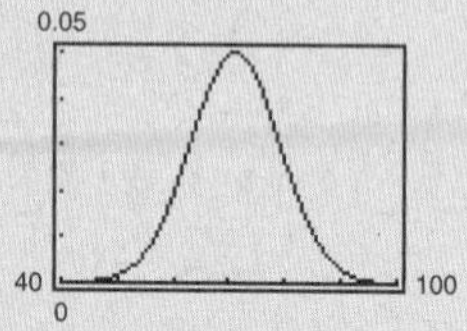

(b) 71

122. (a) 7.7 wk (b) 13.3 wk

123. (a) 10^{-6} W/m^2

(b) $10\sqrt{10}$ W/m^2

(c) 1.259×10^{-12} W/m^2

124. When k is positive, the graph is increasing because $e^{kt} \to 0$ as $x \to -\infty$. When k is negative, the graph is decreasing because $e^{kt} \to 0$ as $x \to \infty$.

125. True by the inverse properties

126. False.

$\ln x + \ln y = \ln(xy)$

$\neq \ln(x+y)$

3 CHAPTER TEST

See www.CalcChat.com for worked-out solutions to odd-numbered exercises.

5. See below.
6. See below.
15. $\log_2 3 + 4\log_2|a|$
16. $\ln 5 + \frac{1}{2}\ln x - \ln 6$
17. $3\log(x-1) - 2\log y - \log z$
27. $y = 2745e^{0.1570t}$

Take this test as you would take a test in class. When you are finished, check your work against the answers given in the back of the book.

In Exercises 1–4, evaluate the expression. Approximate your result to three decimal places.

1. $4.2^{0.6}$ 2.366 **2.** $4^{3\pi/2}$ 687.291 **3.** $e^{-7/10}$ 0.497 **4.** $e^{3.1}$ 22.198

In Exercises 5–7, construct a table of values. Then sketch the graph of the function. 5–7. See margin.

5. $f(x) = 10^{-x}$ **6.** $f(x) = -6^{x-2}$ **7.** $f(x) = 1 - e^{2x}$

8. Evaluate (a) $\log_7 7^{-0.89}$ and (b) $4.6 \ln e^2$. (a) -0.89 (b) 9.2

In Exercises 9–11, construct a table of values. Then sketch the graph of the function. Identify any asymptotes. 9–11. See margin.

9. $f(x) = -\log x - 6$ **10.** $f(x) = \ln(x-4)$ **11.** $f(x) = 1 + \ln(x+6)$

In Exercises 12–14, evaluate the logarithm using the change-of-base formula. Round your result to three decimal places.

12. $\log_7 44$ 1.945 **13.** $\log_{16} 0.63$ -0.167 **14.** $\log_{3/4} 24$ -11.047

In Exercises 15–17, use the properties of logarithms to expand the expression as a sum, difference, and/or constant multiple of logarithms. 15–17. See margin.

15. $\log_2 3a^4$ **16.** $\ln \frac{5\sqrt{x}}{6}$ **17.** $\log \frac{(x-1)^3}{y^2 z}$

In Exercises 18–20, condense the expression to the logarithm of a single quantity.

18. $\log_3 13 + \log_3 y$ $\log_3 13y$ **19.** $4\ln x - 4\ln y$ $\ln \frac{x^4}{y^4}$

20. $3\ln x - \ln(x+3) + 2\ln y$ $\ln\left(\frac{x^3y^2}{x+3}\right)$

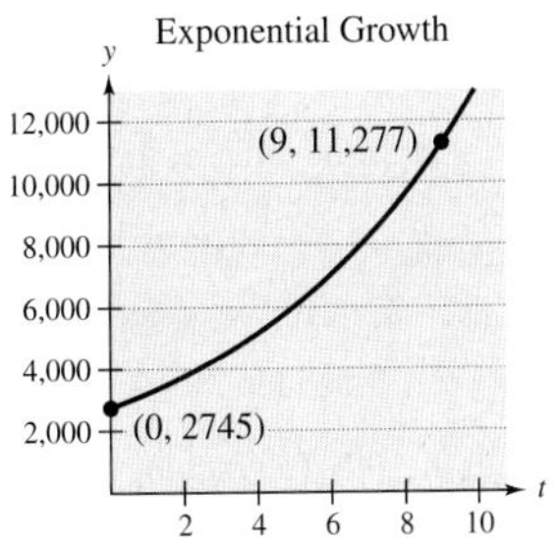

FIGURE FOR 27

In Exercises 21–26, solve the equation algebraically. Approximate your result to three decimal places.

21. $5^x = \frac{1}{25}$ $x = -2$ **22.** $3e^{-5x} = 132$ $x = \frac{\ln 44}{-5} \approx -0.757$

23. $\frac{1025}{8 + e^{4x}} = 5$ $\frac{\ln 197}{4} \approx 1.321$ **24.** $\ln x = \frac{1}{2}$ $e^{1/2} \approx 1.649$

25. $18 + 4\ln x = 7$ $e^{-11/4} \approx 0.0639$ **26.** $\log x + \log(x - 15) = 2$ 20

27. Find an exponential growth model for the graph shown in the figure. See margin.

28. The half-life of radioactive actinium (^{227}Ac) is 21.77 years. What percent of a present amount of radioactive actinium will remain after 19 years? 55%

29. A model that can be used for predicting the height H (in centimeters) of a child based on his or her age is $H = 70.228 + 5.104x + 9.222 \ln x$, $\frac{1}{4} \le x \le 6$, where x is the age of the child in years. (Source: Snapshots of Applications in Mathematics)

(a) Construct a table of values. Then sketch the graph of the model. See margin.

(b) Use the graph from part (a) to estimate the height of a four-year-old child. Then calculate the actual height using the model. 103 cm; 103.43 cm

5.

x	-1	$-\frac{1}{2}$	0	$\frac{1}{2}$	1
$f(x)$	10	3.162	1	0.316	0.1

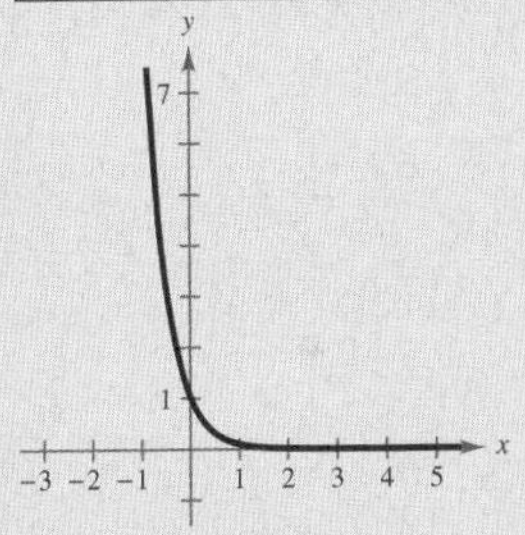

6.

x	-1	0	1	2	3
$f(x)$	-0.005	-0.028	-0.167	-1	-6

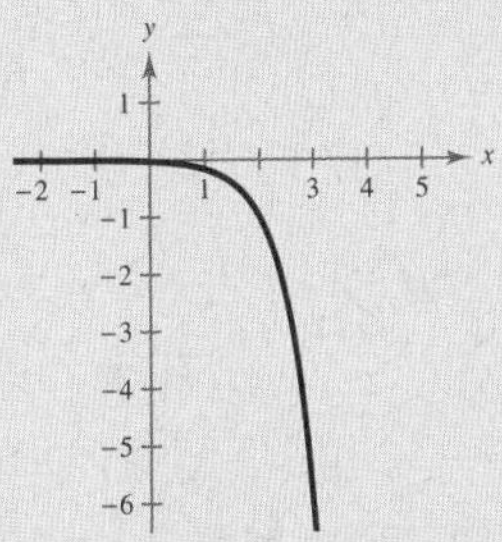

7, 9–11, 29(a). See Additional Answers beginning on page AA1.

3 CUMULATIVE TEST FOR CHAPTERS 1–3

See www.CalcChat.com for worked-out solutions to odd-numbered exercises.

Take this test as you would take a test in class. When you are finished, check your work against the answers given in the back of the book.

1. Plot the points $(-2, 5)$ and $(3, -1)$. Find the coordinates of the midpoint of the line segment joining the points and the distance between the points. See margin.

In Exercises 2–4, graph the equation without using a graphing utility. 2–4. See margin.

2. $x - 3y + 12 = 0$ **3.** $y = x^2 - 9$ **4.** $y = \sqrt{4 - x}$

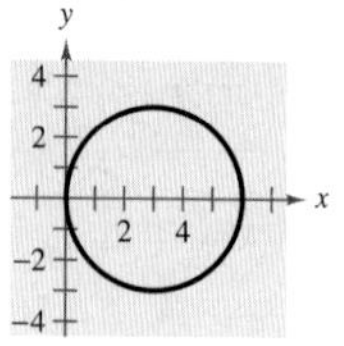

FIGURE FOR 6

5. Find an equation of the line passing through $\left(-\frac{1}{2}, 1\right)$ and $(3, 8)$. $y = 2x + 2$

6. Explain why the graph at the left does not represent y as a function of x. See margin.

7. Evaluate (if possible) the function given by $f(x) = \dfrac{x}{x - 2}$ for each value.

(a) $f(6)$ $\dfrac{3}{2}$ (b) $f(2)$ Division by 0 is undefined. (c) $f(s + 2)$ $\dfrac{s + 2}{s}$

8. Compare the graph of each function with the graph of $y = \sqrt[3]{x}$. (*Note:* It is not necessary to sketch the graphs.) See margin.

(a) $r(x) = \frac{1}{2}\sqrt[3]{x}$ (b) $h(x) = \sqrt[3]{x} + 2$ (c) $g(x) = \sqrt[3]{x + 2}$

In Exercises 9 and 10, find (a) $(f + g)(x)$, (b) $(f - g)(x)$, (c) $(fg)(x)$, and (d) $(f/g)(x)$. What is the domain of f/g? 9–10. See margin.

9. $f(x) = x - 3,\quad g(x) = 4x + 1$ **10.** $f(x) = \sqrt{x - 1},\quad g(x) = x^2 + 1$

In Exercises 11 and 12, find (a) $f \circ g$ and (b) $g \circ f$. Find the domain of each composite function. 11–12. See margin.

11. $f(x) = 2x^2,\quad g(x) = \sqrt{x + 6}$

12. $f(x) = x - 2,\quad g(x) = |x|$

13. Determine whether $h(x) = -5x + 3$ has an inverse function. If so, find the inverse function. Yes; $h^{-1}(x) = -\frac{1}{5}(x - 3)$

14. The power P produced by a wind turbine is proportional to the cube of the wind speed S. A wind speed of 27 miles per hour produces a power output of 750 kilowatts. Find the output for a wind speed of 40 miles per hour. 2438.65 kW

15. Find the quadratic function whose graph has a vertex at $(-8, 5)$ and passes through the point $(-4, -7)$. $y = -\frac{3}{4}(x + 8)^2 + 5$

In Exercises 16–18, sketch the graph of the function without the aid of a graphing utility.

16. $h(x) = -(x^2 + 4x)$ **17.** $f(t) = \frac{1}{4}t(t - 2)^2$

18. $g(s) = s^2 + 4s + 10$ 16–18. See margin.

In Exercises 19–21, find all the zeros of the function and write the function as a product of linear factors.

19. $f(x) = x^3 + 2x^2 + 4x + 8$ $-2, \pm 2i;\ (x + 2)(x + 2i)(x - 2i)$

20. $f(x) = x^4 + 4x^3 - 21x^2$ $-7, 0, 3;\ x(x)(x - 3)(x + 7)$

21. $f(x) = 2x^4 - 11x^3 + 30x^2 - 62x - 40$

$4, -\frac{1}{2}, 1 \pm 3i;\ (x - 4)(2x + 1)(x - 1 + 3i)(x - 1 - 3i)$

1.

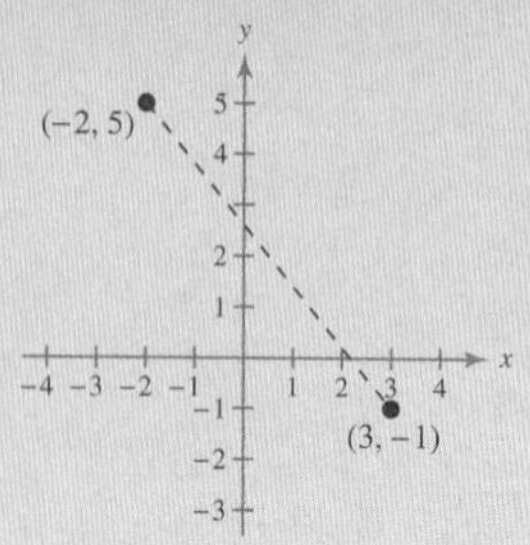

Midpoint: $\left(\frac{1}{2}, 2\right)$; Distance: $\sqrt{61}$

2.

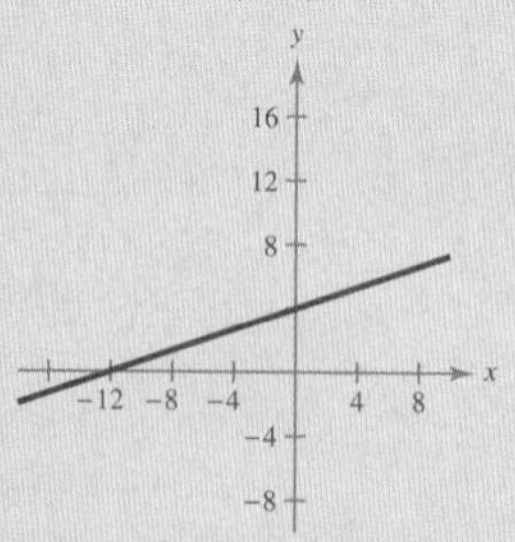

3.

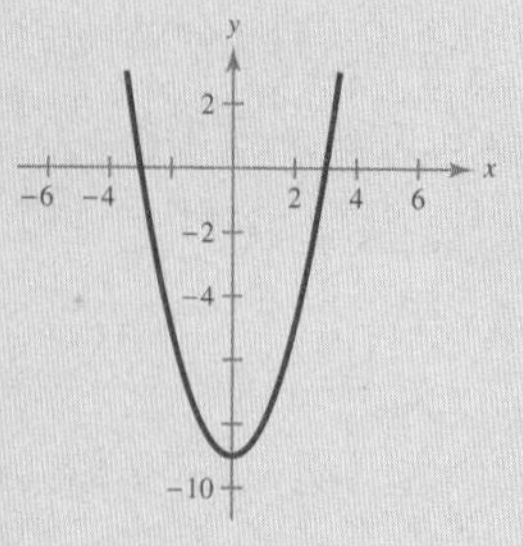

4.

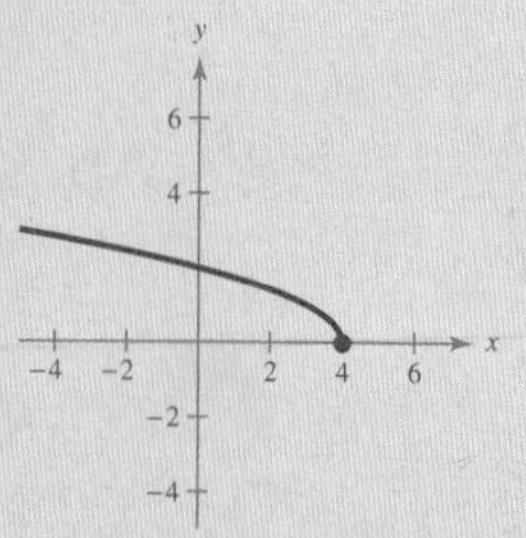

6. For some values of x there correspond two values of y.

8. (a) Vertical shrink by $\frac{1}{2}$
   (b) Vertical shift two units upward
   (c) Horizontal shift two units to the left

9. (a) $5x - 2$
   (b) $-3x - 4$
   (c) $4x^2 - 11x - 3$
   (d) $\dfrac{x - 3}{4x + 1}$; Domain: all real numbers x except $x = -\frac{1}{4}$

10. (a) $\sqrt{x - 1} + x^2 + 1$
    (b) $\sqrt{x - 1} - x^2 - 1$
    (c) $x^2\sqrt{x - 1} + \sqrt{x - 1}$
    (d) $\dfrac{\sqrt{x - 1}}{x^2 + 1}$; Domain: all real numbers x such that $x \geq 1$

11. (a) $2x + 12$
    (b) $\sqrt{2x^2 + 6}$
    Domain of $f \circ g$: all real numbers x such that $x \geq -6$
    Domain of $g \circ f$: all real numbers

12. (a) $|x| - 2$
    (b) $|x - 2|$
    Domain of $f \circ g$ and $g \circ f$: all real numbers

16.

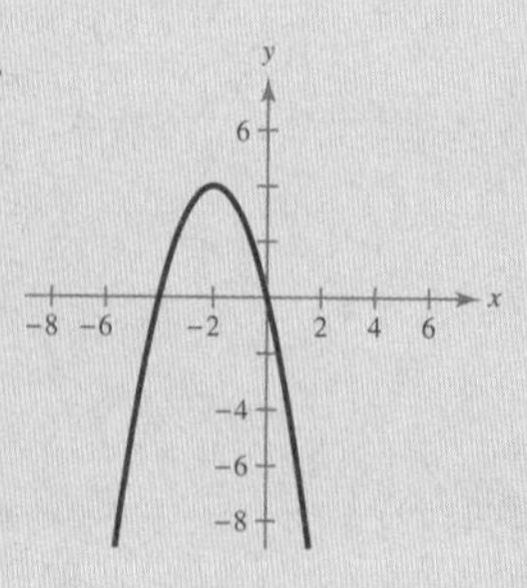

17–18. See Additional Answers beginning on page AA1.

22. Use long division to divide $6x^3 - 4x^2$ by $2x^2 + 1$. $3x - 2 - \dfrac{3x - 2}{2x^2 + 1}$

23. Use synthetic division to divide $3x^4 + 2x^2 - 5x + 3$ by $x - 2$. See margin.

24. Use the Intermediate Value Theorem and a graphing utility to find intervals one unit in length in which the function $g(x) = x^3 + 3x^2 - 6$ is guaranteed to have a zero. Approximate the real zeros of the function. See margin.

In Exercises 25–27, sketch the graph of the rational function by hand. Be sure to identify all intercepts and asymptotes. 25–27. See margin.

25. $f(x) = \dfrac{2x}{x^2 + 2x - 3}$

26. $f(x) = \dfrac{x^2 - 4}{x^2 + x - 2}$

27. $f(x) = \dfrac{x^3 - 2x^2 - 9x + 18}{x^2 + 4x + 3}$

In Exercises 28 and 29, solve the inequality. Sketch the solution set on the real number line. 28–29. See margin.

28. $2x^3 - 18x \leq 0$

29. $\dfrac{1}{x + 1} \geq \dfrac{1}{x + 5}$

In Exercises 30 and 31, use the graph of f to describe the transformation that yields the graph of g. 30–31. See margin.

30. $f(x) = \left(\frac{2}{5}\right)^x$, $g(x) = -\left(\frac{2}{5}\right)^{-x+3}$

31. $f(x) = 2.2^x$, $g(x) = -2.2^x + 4$

In Exercises 32–35, use a calculator to evaluate the expression. Round your result to three decimal places.

32. $\log 98$ 1.991

33. $\log\left(\frac{6}{7}\right)$ −0.067

34. $\ln\sqrt{31}$ 1.717

35. $\ln\left(\sqrt{40} - 5\right)$ 0.281

36. Use the properties of logarithms to expand $\ln\left(\dfrac{x^2 - 16}{x^4}\right)$, where $x > 4$. See margin.

37. Write $2 \ln x - \frac{1}{2} \ln(x + 5)$ as a logarithm of a single quantity. See margin.

In Exercises 38–40, solve the equation algebraically. Approximate the result to three decimal places. 38–40. See margin.

38. $6e^{2x} = 72$

39. $e^{2x} - 13e^x + 42 = 0$

40. $\ln\sqrt{x + 2} = 3$

41. The sales S (in billions of dollars) of lottery tickets in the United States from 1997 through 2007 are shown in the table. (Source: TLF Publications, Inc.)

(a) Use a graphing utility to create a scatter plot of the data. Let t represent the year, with $t = 7$ corresponding to 1997. See margin.

(b) Use the *regression* feature of the graphing utility to find a cubic model for the data. $S = -0.0297t^3 + 1.175t^2 - 12.96t + 79.0$

(c) Use the graphing utility to graph the model in the same viewing window used for the scatter plot. How well does the model fit the data? See margin.

(d) Use the model to predict the sales of lottery tickets in 2015. Does your answer seem reasonable? Explain. See margin.

Year	Sales, S
1997	35.5
1998	35.6
1999	36.0
2000	37.2
2001	38.4
2002	42.0
2003	43.5
2004	47.7
2005	47.4
2006	51.6
2007	52.4

TABLE FOR 41

42. The number N of bacteria in a culture is given by the model $N = 175e^{kt}$, where t is the time in hours. If $N = 420$ when $t = 8$, estimate the time required for the population to double in size. 6.3 h

30. Reflect f in the x-axis and y-axis, and shift three units to the right.

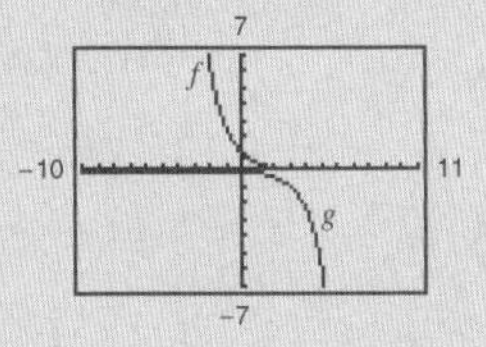

31. Reflect f in the x-axis, and shift four units upward.

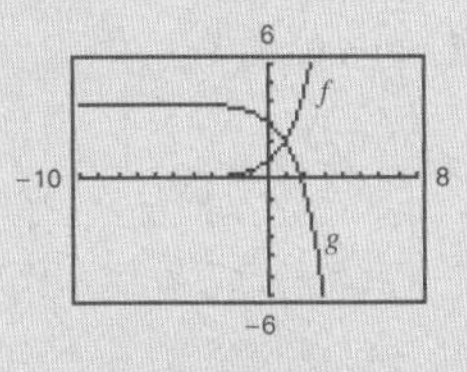

36. $\ln(x + 4) + \ln(x - 4) - 4 \ln x$, $x > 4$

37. $\ln \dfrac{x^2}{\sqrt{x + 5}}$, $x > 0$

38. $x = \dfrac{\ln 12}{2} \approx 1.242$

39. $\ln 6 \approx 1.792$ or $\ln 7 \approx 1.946$

40. $e^6 - 2 \approx 401.429$

23. $3x^3 + 6x^2 + 14x + 23 + \dfrac{49}{x - 2}$

24.

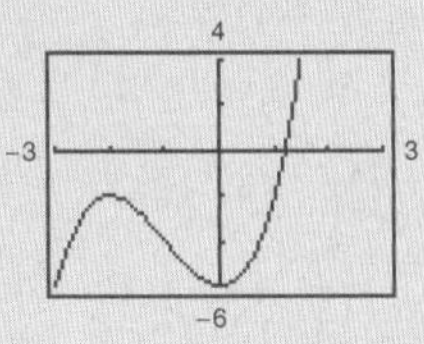

Interval: $[1, 2]$; 1.20

25. Intercept: $(0, 0)$
Vertical asymptotes: $x = -3, x = 1$
Horizontal asymptote: $y = 0$

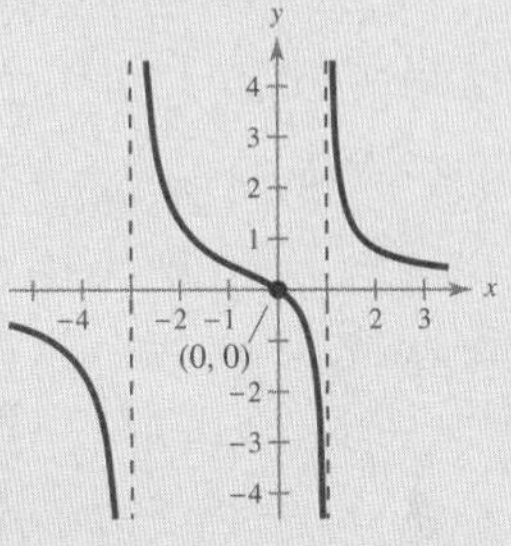

26. y-intercept: $(0, 2)$
x-intercept: $(2, 0)$
Vertical asymptote: $x = 1$
Horizontal asymptote: $y = 1$

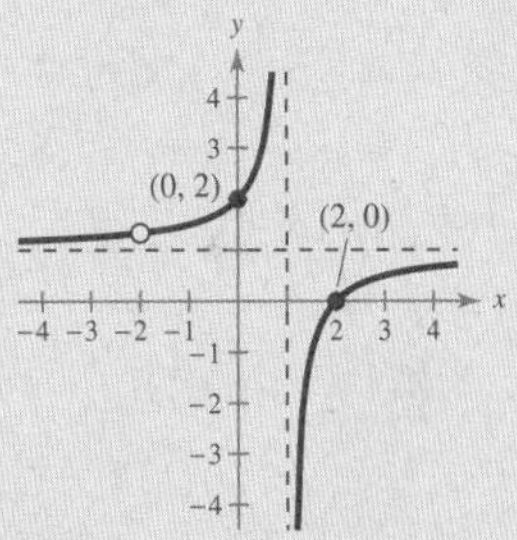

27. y-intercept: $(0, 6)$
x-intercepts: $(2, 0), (3, 0)$
Vertical asymptote: $x = -1$
Slant asymptote: $y = x - 6$

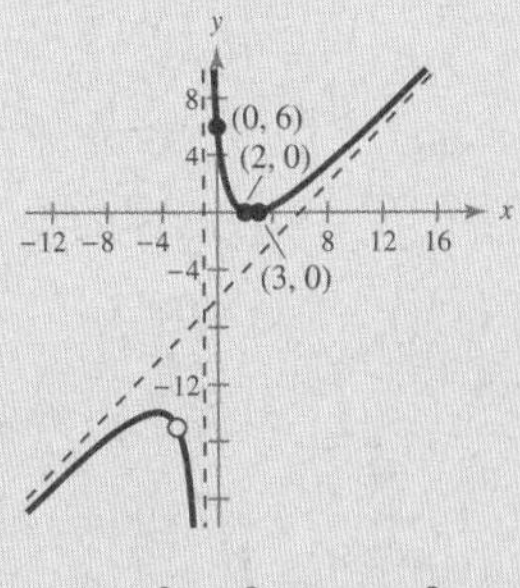

28. $x \leq -3$ or $0 \leq x \leq 3$

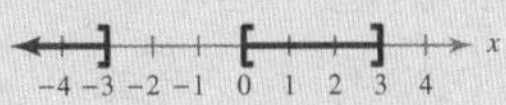

29. All real numbers x such that $x < -5$ or $x > -1$

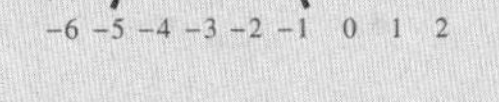

41(a), (c), (d). See Additional Answers beginning on page AA1.

PROOFS IN MATHEMATICS

Each of the following three properties of logarithms can be proved by using properties of exponential functions.

Slide Rules

The slide rule was invented by William Oughtred (1574–1660) in 1625. The slide rule is a computational device with a sliding portion and a fixed portion. A slide rule enables you to perform multiplication by using the Product Property of Logarithms. There are other slide rules that allow for the calculation of roots and trigonometric functions. Slide rules were used by mathematicians and engineers until the invention of the hand-held calculator in 1972.

Properties of Logarithms *(p. 238)*

Let a be a positive number such that $a \neq 1$, and let n be a real number. If u and v are positive real numbers, the following properties are true.

	Logarithm with Base a	*Natural Logarithm*
1. Product Property:	$\log_a(uv) = \log_a u + \log_a v$	$\ln(uv) = \ln u + \ln v$
2. Quotient Property:	$\log_a \frac{u}{v} = \log_a u - \log_a v$	$\ln \frac{u}{v} = \ln u - \ln v$
3. Power Property:	$\log_a u^n = n \log_a u$	$\ln u^n = n \ln u$

Proof

Let

$$x = \log_a u \quad \text{and} \quad y = \log_a v.$$

The corresponding exponential forms of these two equations are

$$a^x = u \quad \text{and} \quad a^y = v.$$

To prove the Product Property, multiply u and v to obtain

$$uv = a^x a^y = a^{x+y}.$$

The corresponding logarithmic form of $uv = a^{x+y}$ is $\log_a(uv) = x + y$. So,

$$\log_a(uv) = \log_a u + \log_a v.$$

To prove the Quotient Property, divide u by v to obtain

$$\frac{u}{v} = \frac{a^x}{a^y} = a^{x-y}.$$

The corresponding logarithmic form of $\frac{u}{v} = a^{x-y}$ is $\log_a \frac{u}{v} = x - y$. So,

$$\log_a \frac{u}{v} = \log_a u - \log_a v.$$

To prove the Power Property, substitute a^x for u in the expression $\log_a u^n$, as follows.

$$\begin{aligned} \log_a u^n &= \log_a(a^x)^n && \text{Substitute } a^x \text{ for } u. \\ &= \log_a a^{nx} && \text{Property of Exponents} \\ &= nx && \text{Inverse Property of Logarithms} \\ &= n \log_a u && \text{Substitute } \log_a u \text{ for } x. \end{aligned}$$

So, $\log_a u^n = n \log_a u$.

276

PROBLEM SOLVING

This collection of thought-provoking and challenging exercises further explores and expands upon concepts learned in this chapter.

1. Graph the exponential function given by $y = a^x$ for $a = 0.5$, 1.2, and 2.0. Which of these curves intersects the line $y = x$? Determine all positive numbers a for which the curve $y = a^x$ intersects the line $y = x$. See margin.

2. Use a graphing utility to graph $y_1 = e^x$ and each of the functions $y_2 = x^2$, $y_3 = x^3$, $y_4 = \sqrt{x}$, and $y_5 = |x|$. Which function increases at the greatest rate as x approaches $+\infty$? See margin.

3. Use the result of Exercise 2 to make a conjecture about the rate of growth of $y_1 = e^x$ and $y = x^n$, where n is a natural number and x approaches $+\infty$. See margin.

4. Use the results of Exercises 2 and 3 to describe what is implied when it is stated that a quantity is growing exponentially. Answers will vary.

5. Given the exponential function

$$f(x) = a^x$$

show that Answers will vary.

(a) $f(u + v) = f(u) \cdot f(v)$. (b) $f(2x) = [f(x)]^2$.

6. Given that

$$f(x) = \frac{e^x + e^{-x}}{2} \text{ and } g(x) = \frac{e^x - e^{-x}}{2}$$

show that

$[f(x)]^2 - [g(x)]^2 = 1$. Answers will vary.

7. Use a graphing utility to compare the graph of the function given by $y = e^x$ with the graph of each given function. [$n!$ (read "n factorial") is defined as $n! = 1 \cdot 2 \cdot 3 \cdots (n - 1) \cdot n$.] See margin.

(a) $y_1 = 1 + \dfrac{x}{1!}$

(b) $y_2 = 1 + \dfrac{x}{1!} + \dfrac{x^2}{2!}$

(c) $y_3 = 1 + \dfrac{x}{1!} + \dfrac{x^2}{2!} + \dfrac{x^3}{3!}$

8. Identify the pattern of successive polynomials given in Exercise 7. Extend the pattern one more term and compare the graph of the resulting polynomial function with the graph of $y = e^x$. What do you think this pattern implies? See margin.

9. Graph the function given by

$$f(x) = e^x - e^{-x}.$$

From the graph, the function appears to be one-to-one. Assuming that the function has an inverse function, find $f^{-1}(x)$. See margin.

10. Find a pattern for $f^{-1}(x)$ if

$$f(x) = \frac{a^x + 1}{a^x - 1} \qquad f^{-1}(x) = \frac{\ln\left(\dfrac{x+1}{x-1}\right)}{\ln a}$$

where $a > 0$, $a \neq 1$.

11. By observation, identify the equation that corresponds to the graph. Explain your reasoning. c

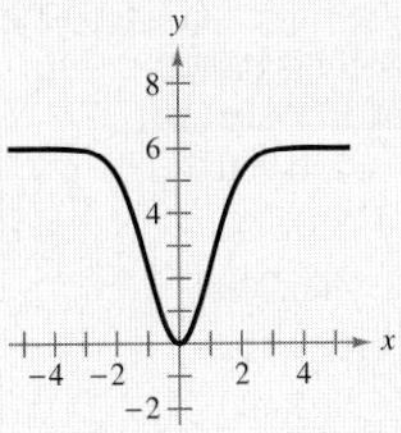

(a) $y = 6e^{-x^2/2}$

(b) $y = \dfrac{6}{1 + e^{-x/2}}$

(c) $y = 6(1 - e^{-x^2/2})$

12. You have two options for investing \$500. The first earns 7% compounded annually and the second earns 7% simple interest. The figure shows the growth of each investment over a 30-year period. See margin.

(a) Identify which graph represents each type of investment. Explain your reasoning.

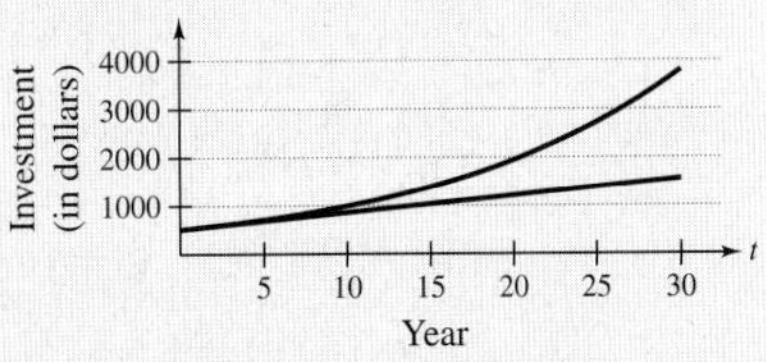

(b) Verify your answer in part (a) by finding the equations that model the investment growth and graphing the models.

(c) Which option would you choose? Explain your reasoning.

13. Two different samples of radioactive isotopes are decaying. The isotopes have initial amounts of c_1 and c_2, as well as half-lives of k_1 and k_2, respectively. Find the time t required for the samples to decay to equal amounts. $t = \dfrac{\ln c_1 - \ln c_2}{\left(\dfrac{1}{k_2} - \dfrac{1}{k_1}\right)\ln\dfrac{1}{2}}$

9.

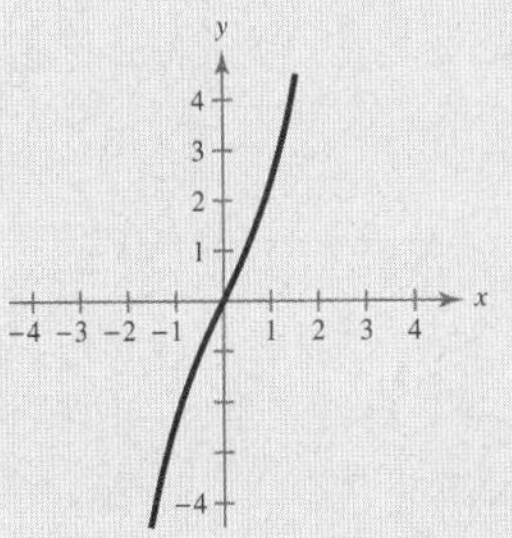

$$f^{-1}(x) = \ln\left(\frac{x + \sqrt{x^2 + 4}}{2}\right)$$

12. See Additional Answers beginning on page AA1.

1.

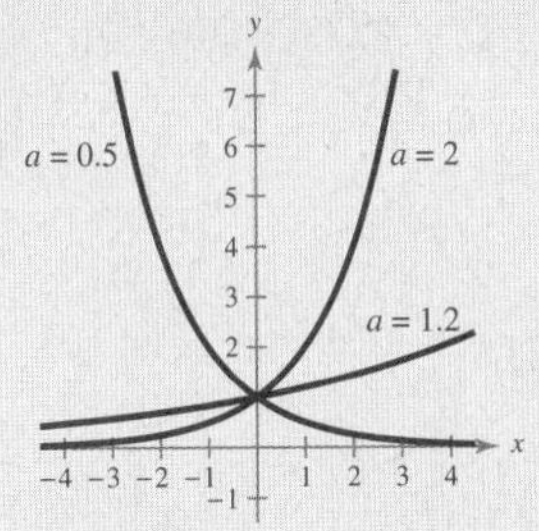

$y = 0.5^x$ and $y = 1.2^x$

$0 < a \le e^{1/e}$

2.

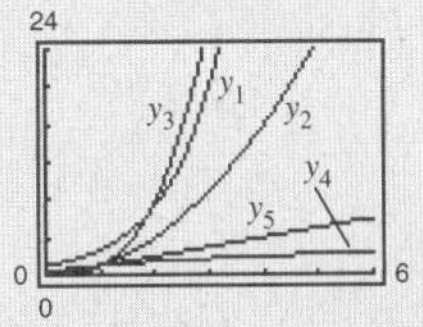

y_1 increases at the fastest rate. (*Note:* One of the intersection points of $y = e^x$ and $y = x^3$ is approximately (4.536, 93), and past this point $e^x > x^3$. This is not shown on the graph above.)

3. As $x \to \infty$, the graph of e^x increases at a greater rate than the graph of x^n.

7. (a)

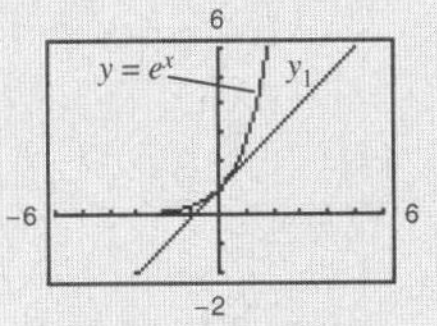

(b)

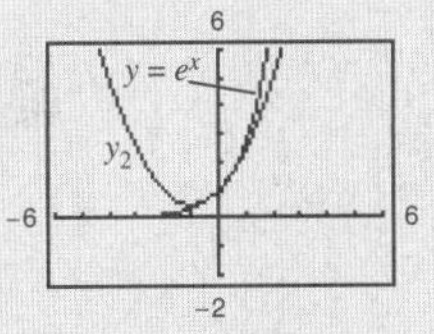

(c)

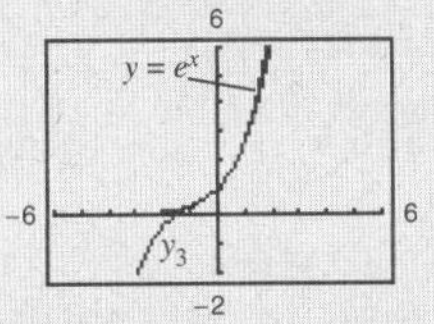

8. $y_4 = 1 + \dfrac{x}{1!} + \dfrac{x^2}{2!} + \dfrac{x^3}{3!} + \dfrac{x^4}{4!}$

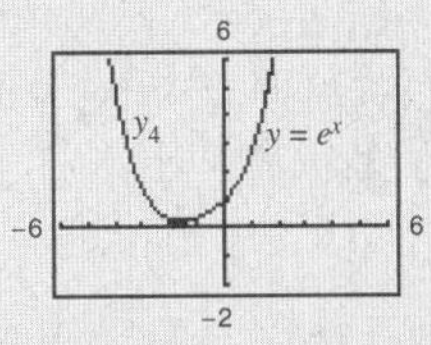

The pattern implies that

$$e^x = 1 + \frac{x}{1!} + \frac{x^2}{2!} + \frac{x^3}{3!} + \cdots.$$

14. A lab culture initially contains 500 bacteria. Two hours later, the number of bacteria has decreased to 200. Find the exponential decay model of the form

$B = B_0 a^{kt}$ $\quad B = 500\left(\frac{2}{5}\right)^{t/2}$

that can be used to approximate the number of bacteria after t hours.

15. The table shows the colonial population estimates of the American colonies from 1700 to 1780. (Source: U.S. Census Bureau)

Year	Population
1700	250,900
1710	331,700
1720	466,200
1730	629,400
1740	905,600
1750	1,170,800
1760	1,593,600
1770	2,148,100
1780	2,780,400

See margin.

In each of the following, let y represent the population in the year t, with $t = 0$ corresponding to 1700.

(a) Use the *regression* feature of a graphing utility to find an exponential model for the data.

(b) Use the *regression* feature of the graphing utility to find a quadratic model for the data.

(c) Use the graphing utility to plot the data and the models from parts (a) and (b) in the same viewing window.

(d) Which model is a better fit for the data? Would you use this model to predict the population of the United States in 2015? Explain your reasoning.

16. Show that $\dfrac{\log_a x}{\log_{a/b} x} = 1 + \log_a \dfrac{1}{b}$. Answers will vary.

17. Solve $(\ln x)^2 = \ln x^2$. $1, e^2$

18. Use a graphing utility to compare the graph of the function $y = \ln x$ with the graph of each given function. See margin.

(a) $y_1 = x - 1$

(b) $y_2 = (x - 1) - \frac{1}{2}(x - 1)^2$

(c) $y_3 = (x - 1) - \frac{1}{2}(x - 1)^2 + \frac{1}{3}(x - 1)^3$

19. Identify the pattern of successive polynomials given in Exercise 18. Extend the pattern one more term and compare the graph of the resulting polynomial function with the graph of $y = \ln x$. What do you think the pattern implies? See margin.

20. Using

$y = ab^x$ and $y = ax^b$ See margin.

take the natural logarithm of each side of each equation. What are the slope and y-intercept of the line relating x and $\ln y$ for $y = ab^x$? What are the slope and y-intercept of the line relating $\ln x$ and $\ln y$ for $y = ax^b$?

In Exercises 21 and 22, use the model

$y = 80.4 - 11 \ln x, \quad 100 \le x \le 1500$

which approximates the minimum required ventilation rate in terms of the air space per child in a public school classroom. In the model, x is the air space per child in cubic feet and y is the ventilation rate per child in cubic feet per minute.

21. Use a graphing utility to graph the model and approximate the required ventilation rate if there is 300 cubic feet of air space per child. See margin.

22. A classroom is designed for 30 students. The air conditioning system in the room has the capacity of moving 450 cubic feet of air per minute.

(a) Determine the ventilation rate per child, assuming that the room is filled to capacity. $15 \text{ ft}^3/\text{min}$

(b) Estimate the air space required per child. 382.0 ft^3

(c) Determine the minimum number of square feet of floor space required for the room if the ceiling height is 30 feet. 382.0 ft^2

In Exercises 23–26, (a) use a graphing utility to create a scatter plot of the data, (b) decide whether the data could best be modeled by a linear model, an exponential model, or a logarithmic model, (c) explain why you chose the model you did in part (b), (d) use the *regression* feature of a graphing utility to find the model you chose in part (b) for the data and graph the model with the scatter plot, and (e) determine how well the model you chose fits the data.

23. (1, 2.0), (1.5, 3.5), (2, 4.0), (4, 5.8), (6, 7.0), (8, 7.8)

24. (1, 4.4), (1.5, 4.7), (2, 5.5), (4, 9.9), (6, 18.1), (8, 33.0)

25. (1, 7.5), (1.5, 7.0), (2, 6.8), (4, 5.0), (6, 3.5), (8, 2.0)

26. (1, 5.0), (1.5, 6.0), (2, 6.4), (4, 7.8), (6, 8.6), (8, 9.0)

23–26. See margin.

15. (a) $y_1 = 252{,}606(1.0310)^t$

(b) $y_2 = 400.88t^2 - 1464.6t + 291{,}782$

(c)

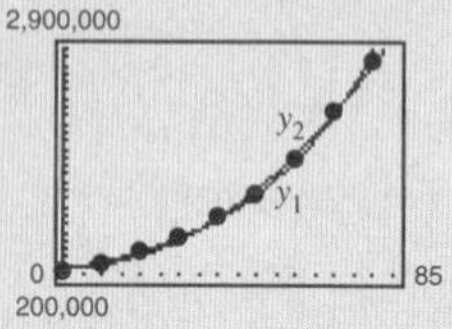

(d) The exponential model is a better fit. No, because the model is rapidly approaching infinity.

18. (a)

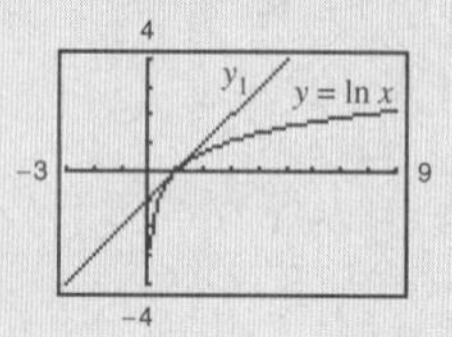

(b)

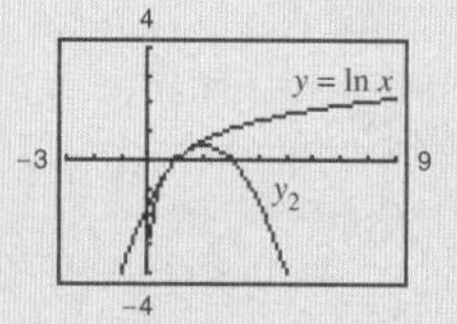

(c)

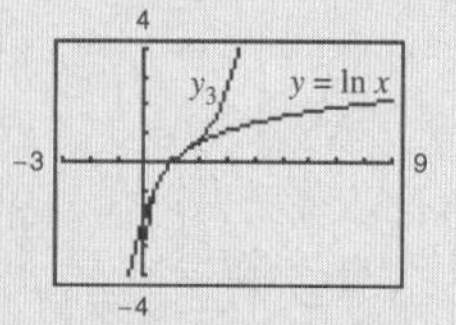

20. Slope $= \ln b$; y-intercept: $(0, \ln a)$

Slope $= b$; y-intercept: $(0, \ln a)$

21.

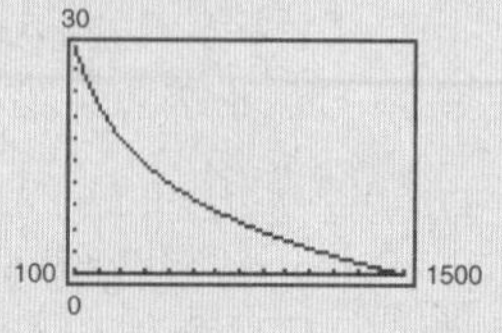

$17.7 \text{ ft}^3/\text{min}$

23. (a)

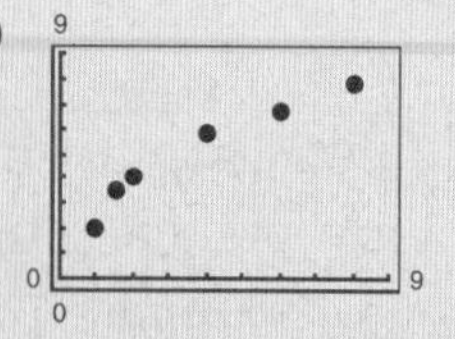

(b)–(e) Answers will vary.

24. (a)

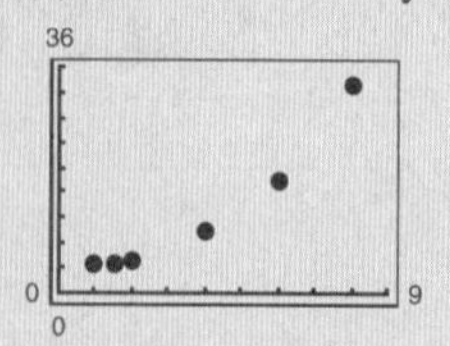

(b)–(e) Answers will vary.

25. (a)

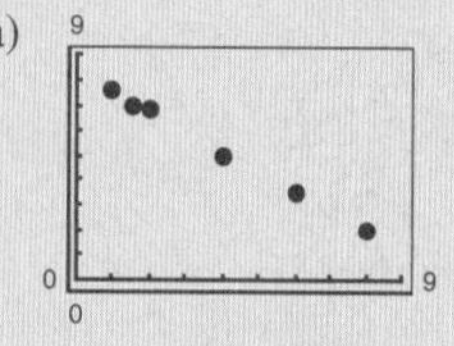

(b)–(e) Answers will vary.

26. (a)

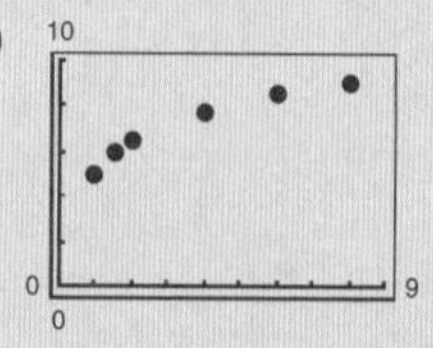

(b)–(e) Answers will vary.

19. See Additional Answers beginning on page AA1.

Pacing and Assignment Guide 4

REGULAR SCHEDULE

Lesson	Day	AVERAGE	ADVANCED
4.1	Day 1	pp. 288–289 Exs. 1–6, 13–21 odd, 28, 29, 32, 37, 41–57 odd, 63, 65, 75–85 odd	pp. 288–289 Exs. 14–20 even, 24–38 even, 44, 48–62 even, 68, 70, 74, 82–88 even
	Day 2	pp. 288, 290–191 Exs. 7–10, 89, 94–96, 99–109 odd, 112, 114, 117, 121–123	pp. 290–291 Exs. 90, 92, 94, 100, 102–104, 106–118 even, 119, 124–127
4.2	Day 1	pp. 297–298 Exs. 1–4, 5–25 odd, 28, 29, 35, 39–45 odd, 49, 53, 60–65, 72	pp. 297–298 Exs. 1–4, 6–18 even, 32–42 even, 46, 48, 54–58 even, 59, 60, 65, 66, 69, 70, 72
4.3	Day 1	pp. 306–307 Exs. 5, 9–15 odd, 22, 24, 25–31 odd, 32, 37–43 odd, 57–61 odd	pp. 306–307 Exs. 6–18 even, 24–30 even, 34–46 even, 58–62 even
	Day 2	pp. 307–309 Exs. 47–55 odd, 63–66, 70, 71, 73, 76, 77–81 odd, 84, 85	pp. 307–309 Exs. 50–56 even, 64–72 even, 74–76, 78–88 even
4.4	Day 1	pp. 316–317 Exs. 1–7, 9–13 odd, 19–23, 27, 31–39 odd, 45, 47, 51–57 odd, 63, 67	pp. 316–317 Exs. 1–7, 10–18 even, 19–22, 28–38 even, 44–48 even, 52–56 even, 66–68
	Day 2	pp. 317–318 Exs. 71–77 odd, 81–97 odd, 98, 102–104, 106	pp. 317–318 Exs. 70–96 even, 97, 98, 100–102, 105–107
4.5	Day 1	pp. 326–329 Exs. 7–13 odd, 21–27 odd, 37, 45, 47, 51, 63, 67, 69, 73, 77–87 odd, 90, 93, 95–97, 101	pp. 326–329 Exs. 10–14 even, 18, 22–32 even, 38, 52–68 even, 74–80 even, 84–94 even, 98–102 even, 103
4.6	Day 1	pp. 337–340 Exs. 9–15, 21, 29, 43, 44, 49, 53, 57, 61, 69, 73–77, 81, 87–93 odd, 96–98	pp. 337–340 Exs. 9–14, 16, 24–32 even, 40, 48, 50, 54–66 even, 72–76, 78, 84–88 even, 92–95, 98, 104
4.7	Day 1	pp. 347–350 Exs. 1–4, 5–11 odd, 19, 22, 23–27 odd, 41, 43, 47, 85, 87, 91, 105, 111, 112	pp. 347–350 Exs. 1–4, 12–22 even, 32–42 even, 44–48, 88–94 even, 106, 108, 109, 115–118, 122–132 even
	Day 2	pp. 347–350 Exs. 51–59 odd, 69–83 odd, 89, 97, 99, 107, 108, 113–115, 135, 137	pp. 347–350 Exs. 50–54 even, 62–72 even, 76–82 even, 89, 98, 100, 104, 107, 110, 135, 136
4.8	Day 1	pp. 357–359 Exs. 5–17 odd, 19–21, 24, 26, 29, 30, 35, 36, 39–45 odd	pp. 357–359 Exs. 8–18 even, 20–22, 25, 27, 30, 34, 36, 38, 40–42, 44, 46
	Day 2	pp. 360–361 Exs. 47–51 odd, 55, 58, 59, 61–64, 68–70	pp. 360–361 Exs. 48–52 even, 56, 59, 60–63, 65, 66, 68–70
Review	Day 1	pp. 364–366 Exs. 1, 7, 11, 13, 17, 21–23, 25, 29, 33, 41, 45, 49–57 odd, 63, 65, 71, 79, 87–95 odd, 100, 103, 105, 111, 119, 123, 129, 141–145 odd	pp. 364–366 Exs. 4, 6, 10, 16–20 even, 21, 24, 26, 30, 34, 42, 46, 50–58 even, 64, 66, 78, 80, 88, 92, 93, 98, 102–106 even, 112, 120, 124–130 even, 140–148 even
Assess	Day 1	Chapter 4 Test	Chapter 4 Test
Yearly Pacing		Chapter 4 Total – 15 days	Remaining – 111 days

BLOCK SCHEDULE

DAY 1	DAY 2	DAY 3	DAY 4	DAY 5	DAY 6	DAY 7	DAY 8
4.1	**4.2**	**4.3 (CONT.)**	**4.4 (CONT.)**	**4.6**	**4.7 (CONT.)**	**4.8 (CONT.)**	**ASSESS**
pp. 288–291 Exs. 1–10, 13–21 odd, 28, 29, 32, 37, 41–57 odd, 63, 65, 75–85 odd, 89, 94–96, 99–109 odd, 112, 114, 117, 121–123	pp. 297–298 Exs. 1–4, 5–25 odd, 28, 29, 35, 39–45 odd, 49, 53, 60–65, 72	pp. 307–309 Exs. 47–55 odd, 63–66, 70, 71, 73, 76, 77–81 odd, 84, 85	pp. 317–318 Exs. 71–77 odd, 81–97 odd, 98, 102–104, 106	pp. 337–340 Exs. 9–15, 21, 29, 43, 44, 49, 53, 57, 61, 69, 73–77, 81, 87–93 odd, 96–98	pp. 347–350 Exs. 51–59 odd, 69–83 odd, 89, 97, 99, 107, 108, 113–115, 135, 137	pp. 360–361 Exs. 47–51 odd, 55, 58, 59, 61–64, 68–70	Chapter 4 Test
	4.3	**4.4**	**4.5**	**4.7**	**4.8**	**REVIEW**	
	pp. 306–307 Exs. 5, 9–15 odd, 22, 24, 25–31 odd, 32, 37–43 odd, 57–61 odd	pp. 316–317 Exs. 1–7, 9–13 odd, 19–23, 27, 31–39 odd, 45, 47, 51–57 odd, 63, 67	pp. 326–329 Exs. 7–13 odd, 21–27 odd, 37, 45, 47, 51, 63, 67, 69, 73, 77–87 odd, 90, 93, 95–97, 101	pp. 347–350 Exs. 1–4, 5–11 odd, 19, 22, 23–27 odd, 41, 43, 47, 85, 87, 91, 105, 111, 112	pp. 357–359 Exs. 5–17 odd, 19–21, 24, 26, 29, 30, 35, 36, 39–45 odd	pp. 364–366 Exs. 1, 7, 11, 13, 17, 21–23, 25, 29, 33, 41, 45, 49–57 odd, 63, 65, 71, 79, 87–95 odd, 100, 103, 105, 111, 119, 123, 129, 141–145 odd	Begin Chapter 5

Yearly Pacing Chapter 4 Total – 7.5 days Remaining – 55.5 days

4

Trigonometry

In Mathematics

Trigonometry is used to find relationships between the sides and angles of triangles, and to write trigonometric functions as models of real-life quantities.

In Real Life

Trigonometric functions are used to model quantities that are periodic. For instance, throughout the day, the depth of water at the end of a dock in Bar Harbor, Maine varies with the tides. The depth can be modeled by a trigonometric function. (See Example 7, page 325.)

Andre Jenny/Alamy

IN CAREERS

There are many careers that use trigonometry. Several are listed below.

- Biologist
  Exercise 70, page 308
- Meteorologist
  Exercise 99, page 318
- Mechanical Engineer
  Exercise 95, page 339
- Surveyor
  Exercise 41, page 359

PLAN AND PREPARE

Main Ideas

In Chapter 4, students learn how to evaluate and graph the trigonometric functions, their inverses, and reciprocals. The chapter begins by introducing radian measure and the definition of trigonometric functions on the unit circle. Students then learn how to find trigonometric ratios of an acute angle by drawing a right triangle and of any angle by drawing a unit circle and a reference angle. They also learn how to graph trigonometric functions and to identify the basic characteristics of the trigonometric functions, their reciprocals, and inverses. Finally, students use trigonometric ratios to solve problems in a variety of contexts such as mechanics, biology, and navigation.

Chapter Planning Guide

Chapter Resources

- Complete Solutions Guide

Interactive Technology

- Instructor Success Organizer
- Notetaking Guide IAE
- Instructional DVDs
- Animated Precalculus
- PowerLecture with ExamView

4.1 Radian and Degree Measure

What you should learn

- Describe angles.
- Use radian measure.
- Use degree measure.
- Use angles to model and solve real-life problems.

Why you should learn it

You can use angles to model and solve real-life problems. For instance, in Exercise 119 on page 291, you are asked to use angles to find the speed of a bicycle.

© Wolfgang Rattay/Reuters/Corbis

Angles

As derived from the Greek language, the word **trigonometry** means "measurement of triangles." Initially, trigonometry dealt with relationships among the sides and angles of triangles and was used in the development of astronomy, navigation, and surveying. With the development of calculus and the physical sciences in the 17th century, a different perspective arose—one that viewed the classic trigonometric relationships as *functions* with the set of real numbers as their domains. Consequently, the applications of trigonometry expanded to include a vast number of physical phenomena involving rotations and vibrations. These phenomena include sound waves, light rays, planetary orbits, vibrating strings, pendulums, and orbits of atomic particles.

The approach in this text incorporates *both* perspectives, starting with angles and their measure.

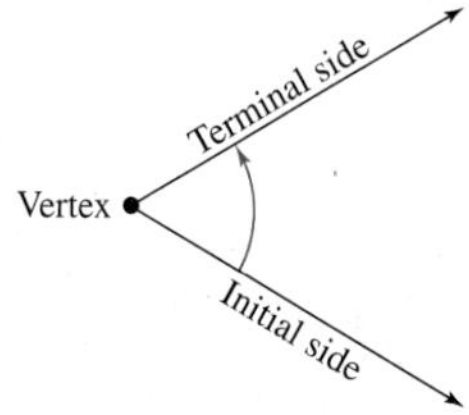

Angle
FIGURE 4.1

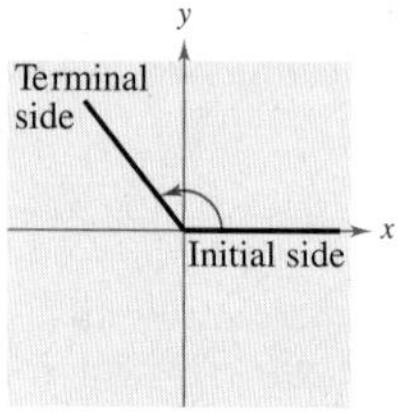

Angle in standard position
FIGURE 4.2

An **angle** is determined by rotating a ray (half-line) about its endpoint. The starting position of the ray is the **initial side** of the angle, and the position after rotation is the **terminal side,** as shown in Figure 4.1. The endpoint of the ray is the **vertex** of the angle. This perception of an angle fits a coordinate system in which the origin is the vertex and the initial side coincides with the positive x-axis. Such an angle is in **standard position,** as shown in Figure 4.2. **Positive angles** are generated by counterclockwise rotation, and **negative angles** by clockwise rotation, as shown in Figure 4.3. Angles are labeled with Greek letters α (alpha), β (beta), and θ (theta), as well as uppercase letters A, B, and C. In Figure 4.4, note that angles α and β have the same initial and terminal sides. Such angles are **coterminal.**

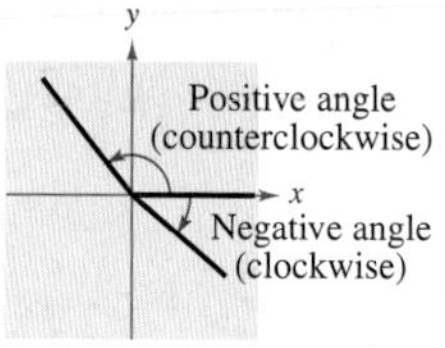

FIGURE 4.3

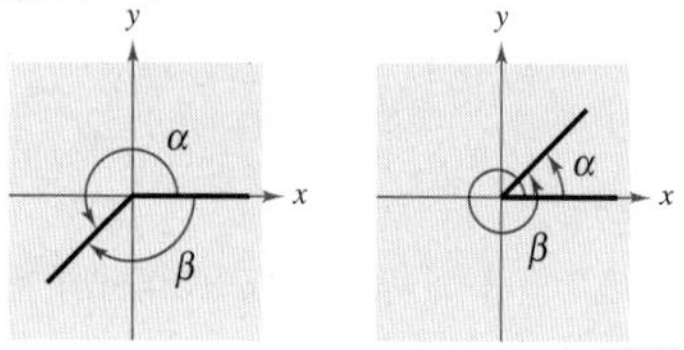

FIGURE 4.4 Coterminal angles

1 PLAN AND PREPARE

Warm-up Exercises

Transparency Available
Available at the Instructor's companion site.

Notetaking Guide

Transparency Available
Promotes interactive learning and notetaking skills. Available at the Instructor's companion site.

Animated Precalculus

An **Animated Precalculus** tutorial is available at the Student companion site for **Section 4.1.**

Pacing

Average: 2 days
Advanced: 2 days
Block: 1 block

2 FOCUS AND MOTIVATE

Essential Question

How do you describe angles and angular movement? **Tell students that they will learn how to answer this question by studying radian and degree measure, motion along a circular arc, and area of a sector.**

Resource Planning Guide

Chapter Resources

- Complete Solutions Guide

Workbooks

- Notetaking Guide
- Student Solutions Guide

Interactive Technology

- Instructor Success Organizer
- Notetaking Guide IAE
- Instructional DVDs
- Animated Precalculus
- PowerLecture with ExamView

Radian Measure

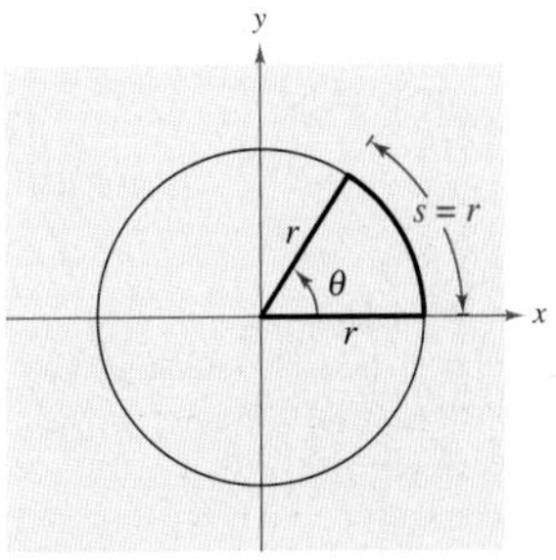

Arc length = radius when $\theta = 1$ radian
FIGURE 4.5

The **measure of an angle** is determined by the amount of rotation from the initial side to the terminal side. One way to measure angles is in *radians*. This type of measure is especially useful in calculus. To define a radian, you can use a **central angle** of a circle, one whose vertex is the center of the circle, as shown in Figure 4.5.

> **Definition of Radian**
>
> One **radian** is the measure of a central angle θ that intercepts an arc s equal in length to the radius r of the circle. See Figure 4.5. Algebraically, this means that
>
> $$\theta = \frac{s}{r}$$
>
> where θ is measured in radians.

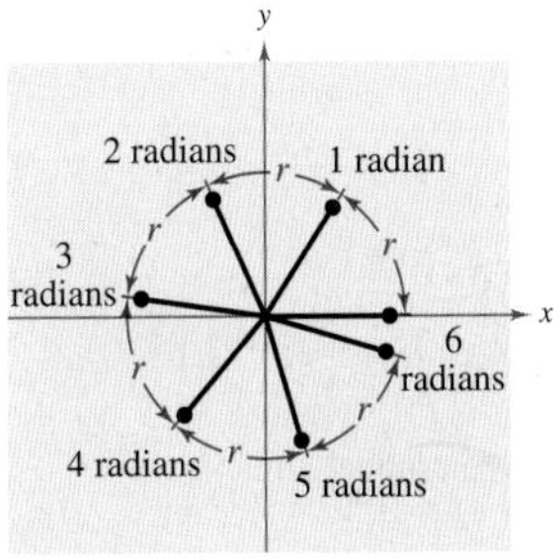

FIGURE 4.6

Because the circumference of a circle is $2\pi r$ units, it follows that a central angle of one full revolution (counterclockwise) corresponds to an arc length of

$$s = 2\pi r.$$

Moreover, because $2\pi \approx 6.28$, there are just over six radius lengths in a full circle, as shown in Figure 4.6. Because the units of measure for s and r are the same, the ratio s/r has no units—it is simply a real number.

Because the radian measure of an angle of one full revolution is 2π, you can obtain the following.

$$\frac{1}{2}\text{ revolution} = \frac{2\pi}{2} = \pi \text{ radians}$$

$$\frac{1}{4}\text{ revolution} = \frac{2\pi}{4} = \frac{\pi}{2} \text{ radians}$$

$$\frac{1}{6}\text{ revolution} = \frac{2\pi}{6} = \frac{\pi}{3} \text{ radians}$$

These and other common angles are shown in Figure 4.7.

> **Study Tip**
>
> One revolution around a circle of radius r corresponds to an angle of 2π radians because
>
> $$\theta = \frac{s}{r} = \frac{2\pi r}{r} = 2\pi \text{ radians.}$$

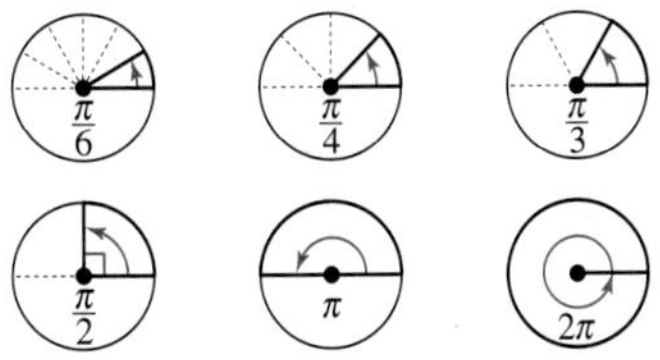

FIGURE 4.7

Recall that the four quadrants in a coordinate system are numbered I, II, III, and IV. Figure 4.8 on page 282 shows which angles between 0 and 2π lie in each of the four quadrants. Note that angles between 0 and $\pi/2$ are **acute** angles and angles between $\pi/2$ and π are **obtuse** angles.

3 TEACH

Extra Example 1

a. For the positive angle $\frac{9\pi}{4}$, subtract 2π to obtain a coterminal angle.

$\frac{\pi}{4}$

b. For the positive angle $\frac{5\pi}{6}$, subtract 2π to obtain a coterminal angle.

$-\frac{7\pi}{6}$

c. For the negative angle $-\frac{3\pi}{4}$, add 2π to find a coterminal angle.

$\frac{5\pi}{4}$

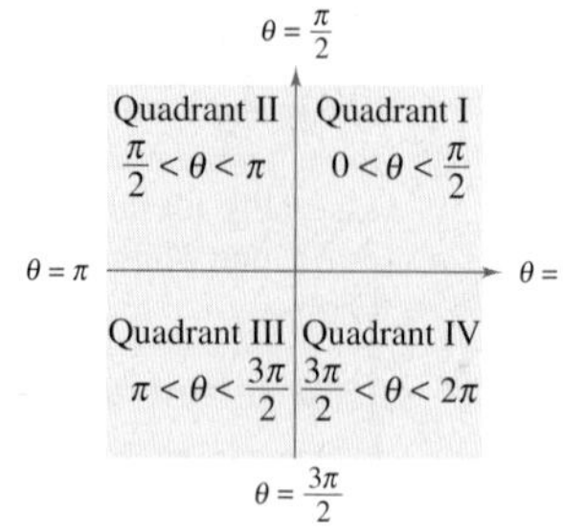

FIGURE 4.8

Study Tip

The phrase "the terminal side of θ lies in a quadrant" is often abbreviated by simply saying that "θ lies in a quadrant." The terminal sides of the "quadrant angles" 0, $\pi/2$, π, and $3\pi/2$ do not lie within quadrants.

Two angles are coterminal if they have the same initial and terminal sides. For instance, the angles 0 and 2π are coterminal, as are the angles $\pi/6$ and $13\pi/6$. You can find an angle that is coterminal to a given angle θ by adding or subtracting 2π (one revolution), as demonstrated in Example 1. A given angle θ has infinitely many coterminal angles. For instance, $\theta = \pi/6$ is coterminal with

$$\frac{\pi}{6} + 2n\pi$$

where n is an integer.

Algebra Help

You can review operations involving fractions in Appendix A.1.

Example 1 Sketching and Finding Coterminal Angles

a. For the positive angle $13\pi/6$, subtract 2π to obtain a coterminal angle

$$\frac{13\pi}{6} - 2\pi = \frac{\pi}{6}.$$ See Figure 4.9.

b. For the positive angle $3\pi/4$, subtract 2π to obtain a coterminal angle

$$\frac{3\pi}{4} - 2\pi = -\frac{5\pi}{4}.$$ See Figure 4.10.

c. For the negative angle $-2\pi/3$, add 2π to obtain a coterminal angle

$$-\frac{2\pi}{3} + 2\pi = \frac{4\pi}{3}.$$ See Figure 4.11.

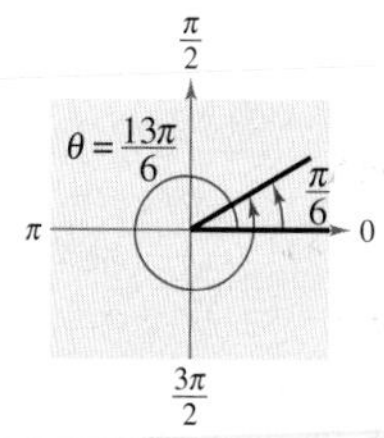

FIGURE 4.9

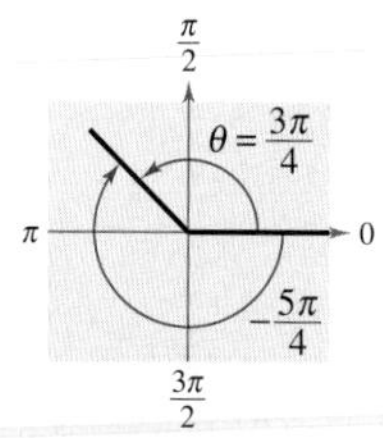

FIGURE 4.10

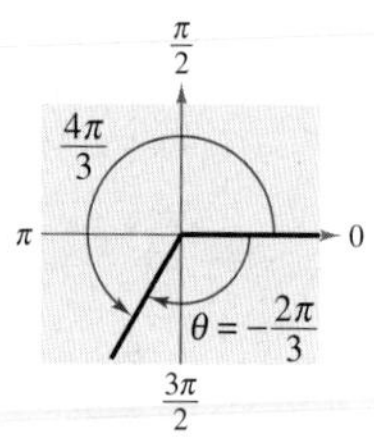

FIGURE 4.11

CHECKPoint Now try Exercise 27.

Differentiated Instruction

Kinesthetic Learners For Example 1, have students cover the three figures at the bottom of the page with a piece of paper. Direct them to refer to the common angles shown on page 281 to assist them in sketching the three angles. After students have sketched the angles, have them remove the piece of paper and check their angles.

Two positive angles α and β are **complementary** (complements of each other) if their sum is $\pi/2$. Two positive angles are **supplementary** (supplements of each other) if their sum is π. See Figure 4.12.

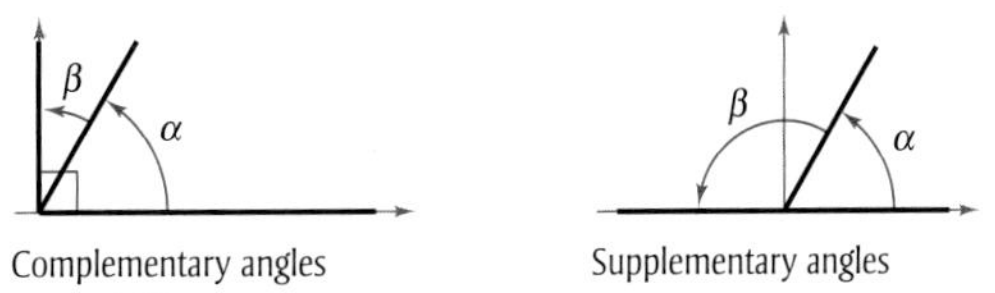

FIGURE 4.12

Example 2 Complementary and Supplementary Angles

If possible, find the complement and the supplement of (a) $2\pi/5$ and (b) $4\pi/5$.

Solution

a. The complement of $2\pi/5$ is

$$\frac{\pi}{2} - \frac{2\pi}{5} = \frac{5\pi}{10} - \frac{4\pi}{10} = \frac{\pi}{10}.$$

The supplement of $2\pi/5$ is

$$\pi - \frac{2\pi}{5} = \frac{5\pi}{5} - \frac{2\pi}{5} = \frac{3\pi}{5}.$$

b. Because $4\pi/5$ is greater than $\pi/2$, it has no complement. (Remember that complements are *positive* angles.) The supplement is

$$\pi - \frac{4\pi}{5} = \frac{5\pi}{5} - \frac{4\pi}{5} = \frac{\pi}{5}.$$

CHECK*Point* Now try Exercise 31.

Degree Measure

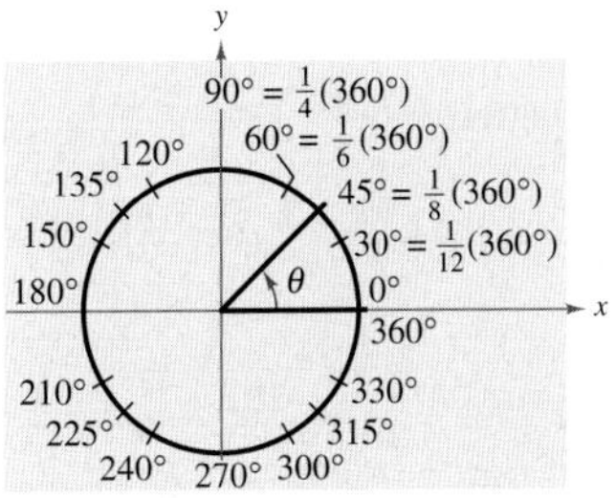

FIGURE 4.13

A second way to measure angles is in terms of **degrees,** denoted by the symbol °. A measure of one degree (1°) is equivalent to a rotation of $\frac{1}{360}$ of a complete revolution about the vertex. To measure angles, it is convenient to mark degrees on the circumference of a circle, as shown in Figure 4.13. So, a full revolution (counterclockwise) corresponds to 360°, a half revolution to 180°, a quarter revolution to 90°, and so on.

Because 2π radians corresponds to one complete revolution, degrees and radians are related by the equations

$$360° = 2\pi \text{ rad} \qquad \text{and} \qquad 180° = \pi \text{ rad}.$$

From the latter equation, you obtain

$$1° = \frac{\pi}{180} \text{ rad} \qquad \text{and} \qquad 1 \text{ rad} = \left(\frac{180°}{\pi}\right)$$

which lead to the conversion rules at the top of the next page.

Extra Example 2

If possible, find the complement and the supplement of the angle.

a. $\frac{\pi}{6}$

Complement: $\frac{\pi}{3}$**; supplement:** $\frac{5\pi}{6}$

b. $\frac{5\pi}{6}$

No complement; supplement: $\frac{\pi}{6}$

Extra Example 3

Express each of the following angles in radian measure as a multiple of π. (Do not use a calculator.)

a. 60°

$\frac{\pi}{3}$ **radians**

b. 320°

$\frac{16\pi}{9}$ **radians**

c. $-30°$

$-\frac{\pi}{6}$ **radians**

Avoiding Common Errors

The radian is a new unit of measure for most students. Converting from degrees to radians and vice versa should help students become familiar with radian measure.

Extra Example 4

Express the following angles in degree measure. (Do not use a calculator.)

a. $\frac{\pi}{6}$

30°

b. $\frac{5\pi}{3}$

300°

c. 3 radians

171.89°

TECHNOLOGY

With calculators it is convenient to use *decimal* degrees to denote fractional parts of degrees. Historically, however, fractional parts of degrees were expressed in *minutes* and *seconds*, using the prime (′) and double prime (″) notations, respectively. That is,

$$1' = \text{one minute} = \tfrac{1}{60}(1°)$$

$$1'' = \text{one second} = \tfrac{1}{3600}(1°).$$

Consequently, an angle of 64 degrees, 32 minutes, and 47 seconds is represented by $\theta = 64°\,32'\,47''$. Many calculators have special keys for converting an angle in degrees, minutes, and seconds (D° M′ S″) to decimal degree form, and vice versa.

Conversions Between Degrees and Radians

1. To convert degrees to radians, multiply degrees by $\dfrac{\pi \text{ rad}}{180°}$.
2. To convert radians to degrees, multiply radians by $\dfrac{180°}{\pi \text{ rad}}$.

To apply these two conversion rules, use the basic relationship π rad = 180°. (See Figure 4.14.)

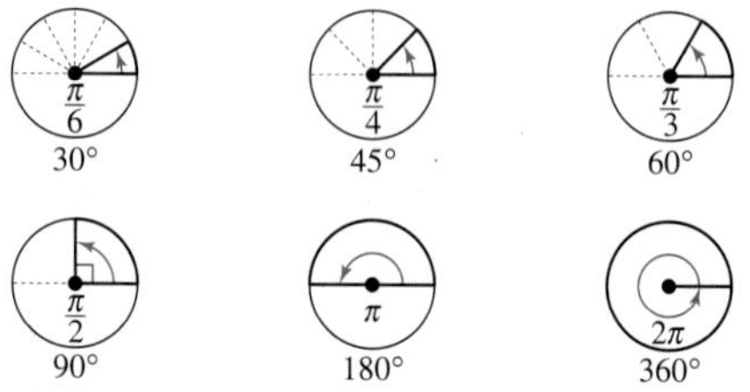

FIGURE 4.14

When no units of angle measure are specified, *radian measure is implied*. For instance, if you write $\theta = 2$, you imply that $\theta = 2$ radians.

Example 3 Converting from Degrees to Radians

a. $135° = (135 \text{ deg})\left(\dfrac{\pi \text{ rad}}{180 \text{ deg}}\right) = \dfrac{3\pi}{4}$ radians   Multiply by $\pi/180$.

b. $540° = (540 \text{ deg})\left(\dfrac{\pi \text{ rad}}{180 \text{ deg}}\right) = 3\pi$ radians   Multiply by $\pi/180$.

c. $-270° = (-270 \text{ deg})\left(\dfrac{\pi \text{ rad}}{180 \text{ deg}}\right) = -\dfrac{3\pi}{2}$ radians   Multiply by $\pi/180$.

CHECK *Point* Now try Exercise 57.

Example 4 Converting from Radians to Degrees

a. $-\dfrac{\pi}{2} \text{ rad} = \left(-\dfrac{\pi}{2} \text{ rad}\right)\left(\dfrac{180 \text{ deg}}{\pi \text{ rad}}\right) = -90°$ Multiply by $180/\pi$.

b. $\dfrac{9\pi}{2} \text{ rad} = \left(\dfrac{9\pi}{2} \text{ rad}\right)\left(\dfrac{180 \text{ deg}}{\pi \text{ rad}}\right) = 810°$ Multiply by $180/\pi$.

c. $2 \text{ rad} = (2 \text{ rad})\left(\dfrac{180 \text{ deg}}{\pi \text{ rad}}\right) = \dfrac{360°}{\pi} \approx 114.59°$ Multiply by $180/\pi$.

CHECK *Point* Now try Exercise 61.

If you have a calculator with a "radian-to-degree" conversion key, try using it to verify the result shown in part (b) of Example 4.

Applications

The *radian measure* formula, $\theta = s/r$, can be used to measure arc length along a circle.

Arc Length

For a circle of radius r, a central angle θ intercepts an arc of length s given by

$$s = r\theta \qquad \text{Length of circular arc}$$

where θ is measured in radians. Note that if $r = 1$, then $s = \theta$, and the radian measure of θ equals the arc length.

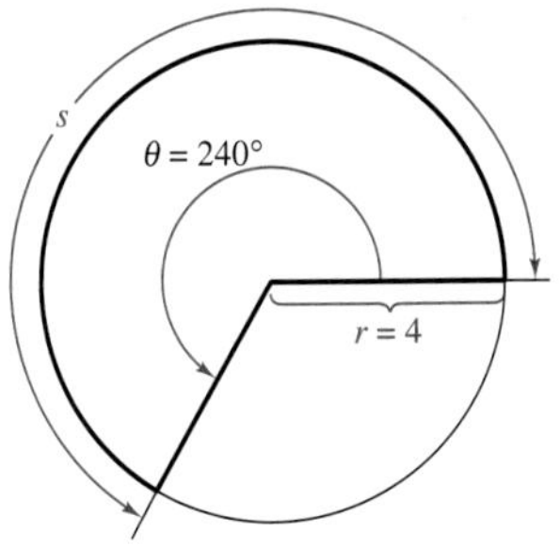

FIGURE 4.15

Example 5 Finding Arc Length

A circle has a radius of 4 inches. Find the length of the arc intercepted by a central angle of 240°, as shown in Figure 4.15.

Solution

To use the formula $s = r\theta$, first convert 240° to radian measure.

$$240° = (240\ \text{deg})\left(\frac{\pi\ \text{rad}}{180\ \text{deg}}\right)$$

$$= \frac{4\pi}{3}\ \text{radians}$$

Then, using a radius of $r = 4$ inches, you can find the arc length to be

$$s = r\theta$$

$$= 4\left(\frac{4\pi}{3}\right)$$

$$= \frac{16\pi}{3} \approx 16.76\ \text{inches.}$$

Note that the units for $r\theta$ are determined by the units for r because θ is given in radian measure, which has no units.

CHECK**Point** Now try Exercise 89.

Extra Example 5

A circle has a radius of 27 inches. Find the length of the arc intercepted by a central angle of 160°.

≈ 75.40 inches

The formula for the length of a circular arc can be used to analyze the motion of a particle moving at a *constant speed* along a circular path.

Linear and Angular Speeds

Consider a particle moving at a constant speed along a circular arc of radius r. If s is the length of the arc traveled in time t, then the **linear speed** v of the particle is

$$\text{Linear speed } v = \frac{\text{arc length}}{\text{time}} = \frac{s}{t}.$$

Moreover, if θ is the angle (in radian measure) corresponding to the arc length s, then the **angular speed** ω (the lowercase Greek letter omega) of the particle is

$$\text{Angular speed } \omega = \frac{\text{central angle}}{\text{time}} = \frac{\theta}{t}.$$

Study Tip

Linear speed measures how fast the particle moves, and angular speed measures how fast the angle changes. By dividing the formula for arc length by t, you can establish a relationship between linear speed v and angular speed ω, as shown.

$$s = r\theta$$

$$\frac{s}{t} = \frac{r\theta}{t}$$

$$v = r\omega$$

Extra Example 6

The second hand of a clock is 8 centimeters long. Find the linear speed of the tip of this second hand as it passes around the clock face.

≈ 0.8378 centimeter per second

Extra Example 7

The circular blade on a saw rotates at 2400 revolutions per minute.

a. Find the angular speed in radians per second.

80π radians per second

b. The blade has a radius of 4 inches. Find the linear speed of a blade tip in inches per second.

≈ 1005 inches per second

FIGURE 4.16

Example 6 Finding Linear Speed

The second hand of a clock is 10.2 centimeters long, as shown in Figure 4.16. Find the linear speed of the tip of this second hand as it passes around the clock face.

Solution

In one revolution, the arc length traveled is

$$s = 2\pi r$$

$$= 2\pi(10.2) \qquad \text{Substitute for } r.$$

$$= 20.4\pi \text{ centimeters.}$$

The time required for the second hand to travel this distance is

$$t = 1 \text{ minute} = 60 \text{ seconds.}$$

So, the linear speed of the tip of the second hand is

$$\text{Linear speed} = \frac{s}{t}$$

$$= \frac{20.4\pi \text{ centimeters}}{60 \text{ seconds}}$$

$$\approx 1.068 \text{ centimeters per second.}$$

CHECKPoint Now try Exercise 111.

FIGURE 4.17

Example 7 Finding Angular and Linear Speeds

The blades of a wind turbine are 116 feet long (see Figure 4.17). The propeller rotates at 15 revolutions per minute.

a. Find the angular speed of the propeller in radians per minute.

b. Find the linear speed of the tips of the blades.

Solution

a. Because each revolution generates 2π radians, it follows that the propeller turns $(15)(2\pi) = 30\pi$ radians per minute. In other words, the angular speed is

$$\text{Angular speed} = \frac{\theta}{t}$$

$$= \frac{30\pi \text{ radians}}{1 \text{ minute}} = 30\pi \text{ radians per minute.}$$

b. The linear speed is

$$\text{Linear speed} = \frac{s}{t}$$

$$= \frac{r\theta}{t}$$

$$= \frac{(116)(30\pi) \text{ feet}}{1 \text{ minute}} \approx 10{,}933 \text{ feet per minute.}$$

CHECKPoint Now try Exercise 113.

A **sector** of a circle is the region bounded by two radii of the circle and their intercepted arc (see Figure 4.18).

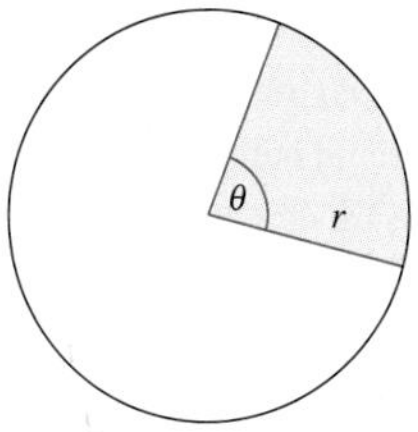

FIGURE 4.18

> **Area of a Sector of a Circle**
>
> For a circle of radius r, the area A of a sector of the circle with central angle θ is given by
>
> $$A = \frac{1}{2}r^2\theta$$
>
> where θ is measured in radians.

Example 8 Area of a Sector of a Circle

A sprinkler on a golf course fairway sprays water over a distance of 70 feet and rotates through an angle of 120° (see Figure 4.19). Find the area of the fairway watered by the sprinkler.

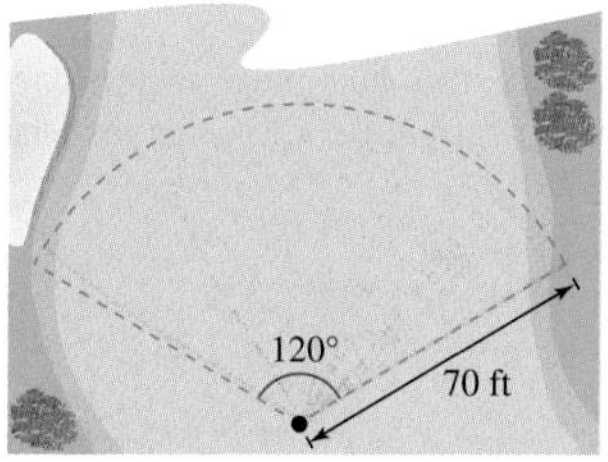

FIGURE 4.19

Solution

First convert 120° to radian measure as follows.

$$\theta = 120°$$

$$= (120 \text{ deg})\left(\frac{\pi \text{ rad}}{180 \text{ deg}}\right) \quad \text{Multiply by } \pi/180.$$

$$= \frac{2\pi}{3} \text{ radians}$$

Then, using $\theta = 2\pi/3$ and $r = 70$, the area is

$$A = \frac{1}{2}r^2\theta \quad \text{Formula for the area of a sector of a circle}$$

$$= \frac{1}{2}(70)^2\left(\frac{2\pi}{3}\right) \quad \text{Substitute for } r \text{ and } \theta.$$

$$= \frac{4900\pi}{3} \quad \text{Simplify.}$$

$$\approx 5131 \text{ square feet.} \quad \text{Simplify.}$$

CHECK*Point* Now try Exercise 117.

Extra Example 8

A sprinkler on a golf course is set to spray water over a distance of 75 feet and rotates through an angle of 135°. Find the area of the fairway watered by the sprinkler.

6627 square feet

Closing the Lesson

Have students summarize the major points of the lesson and answer the Essential Question: How do you describe angles and angular movement?

- **Use radians and degrees and proper vocabulary to describe and compare angles in standard position.**
- **Convert from degrees to radians and from radians to degrees.**
- **Use radian measure θ to find arc length s in a circle of radius r, using the equation $s = r\theta$.**
- **Find linear or angular speed along a circular arc by dividing arc length or central angle by time.**
- **Find the area A of a sector with central angle θ and radius r, using the equation $A = \frac{1}{2}r^2\theta$.**

4 PRACTICE AND APPLY

Assignment Guide

Transparencies Available
Available at the Instructor's companion site.

Average:
Day 1: pp. 288–289
Exs. 1–6, 13–21 odd, 28, 29, 32, 37, 41–57 odd, 63, 65, 75–85 odd
Day 2: pp. 288, 290–291
Exs. 7–10, 89, 94–96, 99–109 odd, 112, 114, 117, 121–123

Advanced:
Day 1: pp. 288–289
Exs. 14–20 even, 24–38 even, 44, 48–62 even, 68, 70, 74, 82–88 even
Day 2: pp. 290–291
Exs. 90, 92, 94, 100, 102–104, 106–118 even, 119, 124–127

Block:
pp. 288–291
Exs. 1–10, 13–21 odd, 28, 29, 32, 37, 41–57 odd, 63, 65, 75–85 odd, 89, 94–96, 99–109 odd, 112, 114, 117, 121–123

4.1 EXERCISES

See www.CalcChat.com for worked-out solutions to odd-numbered exercises.

VOCABULARY: Fill in the blanks.

1. ________ means "measurement of triangles." Trigonometry
2. An _angle_ is determined by rotating a ray about its endpoint.
3. Two angles that have the same initial and terminal sides are _coterminal_
4. One _radian_ is the measure of a central angle that intercepts an arc equal to the radius of the circle.
5. Angles that measure between 0 and $\pi/2$ are _acute_ angles, and angles that measure between $\pi/2$ and π are _obtuse_ angles.
6. Two positive angles that have a sum of $\pi/2$ are ________ angles, whereas two positive angles that have a sum of π are ________ angles. complementary; supplementary
7. The angle measure that is equivalent to a rotation of $\frac{1}{360}$ of a complete revolution about an angle's vertex is one _degree_.
8. 180 degrees = _π_ radians.
9. The _linear_ speed of a particle is the ratio of arc length to time traveled, and the _angular_ speed of a particle is the ratio of central angle to time traveled.
10. The area A of a sector of a circle with radius r and central angle θ, where θ is measured in radians, is given by the formula ________. $A = \frac{1}{2}r^2\theta$

SKILLS AND APPLICATIONS

In Exercises 11–16, estimate the angle to the nearest one-half radian.

11. 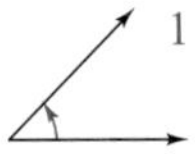

12. 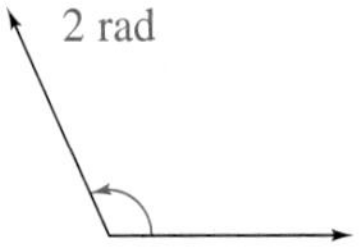

13. 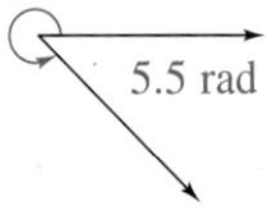

14. 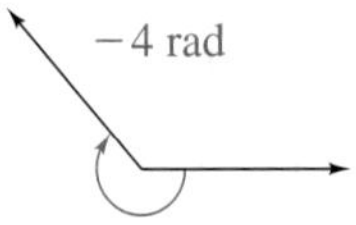

15. 

16. 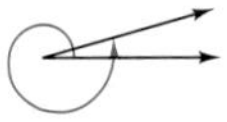

In Exercises 17–22, determine the quadrant in which each angle lies. (The angle measure is given in radians.)

17. (a) $\frac{\pi}{4}$ I (b) $\frac{5\pi}{4}$ III
18. (a) $\frac{11\pi}{8}$ III (b) $\frac{9\pi}{8}$ III
19. (a) $-\frac{\pi}{6}$ IV (b) $-\frac{\pi}{3}$ IV
20. (a) $-\frac{5\pi}{6}$ III (b) $-\frac{11\pi}{9}$ II
21. (a) 3.5 III (b) 2.25 II
22. (a) 6.02 IV (b) −4.25 II

In Exercises 23–26, sketch each angle in standard position. 23–26. See margin.

23. (a) $\frac{\pi}{3}$ (b) $-\frac{2\pi}{3}$
24. (a) $-\frac{7\pi}{4}$ (b) $\frac{5\pi}{2}$
25. (a) $\frac{11\pi}{6}$ (b) −3
26. (a) 4 (b) 7π

In Exercises 27–30, determine two coterminal angles (one positive and one negative) for each angle. Give your answers in radians. 27–30. See margin.

27. (a) 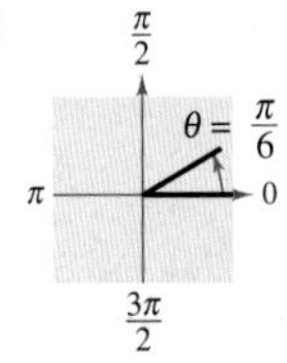

(b) 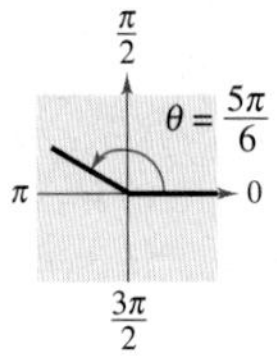

28. (a) 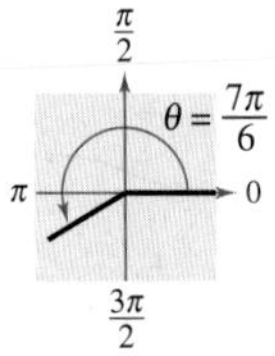

(b) 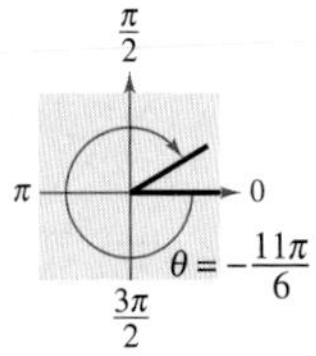

29. (a) $\theta = \frac{2\pi}{3}$ (b) $\theta = \frac{\pi}{12}$
30. (a) $\theta = -\frac{9\pi}{4}$ (b) $\theta = -\frac{2\pi}{15}$

23. (a) 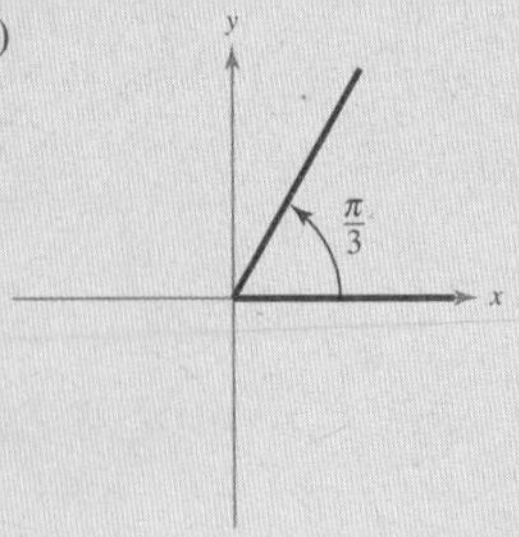

(b) 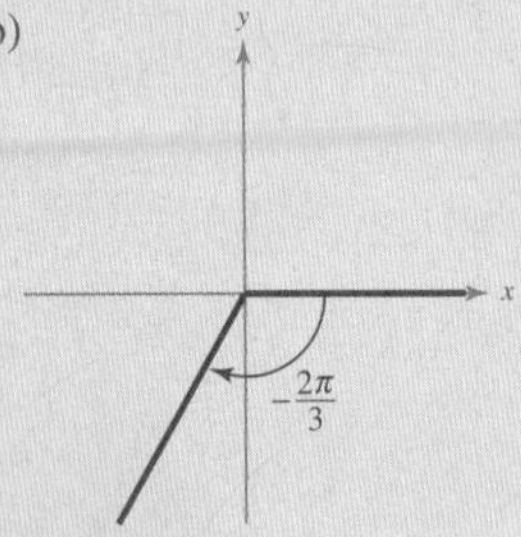

24. (a) 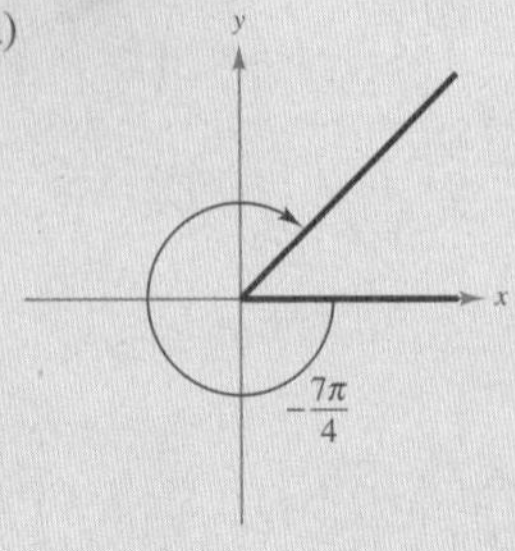

(b) 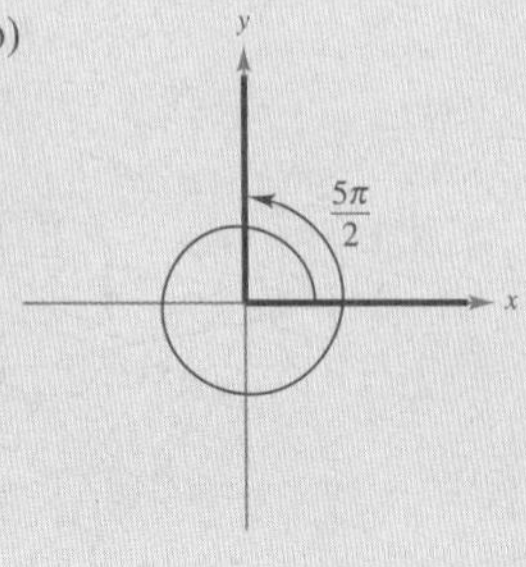

25. (a) 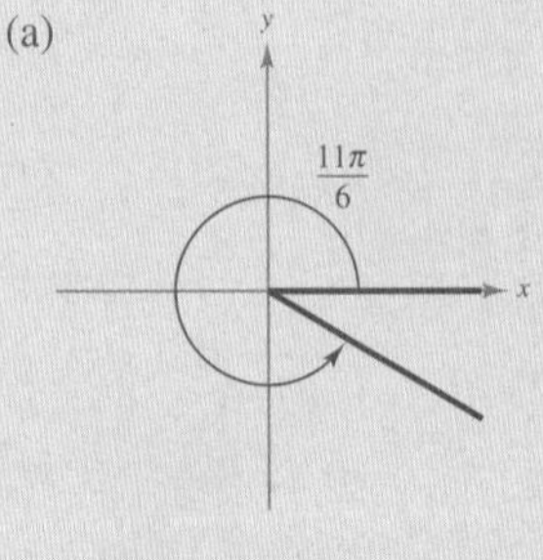

(b) 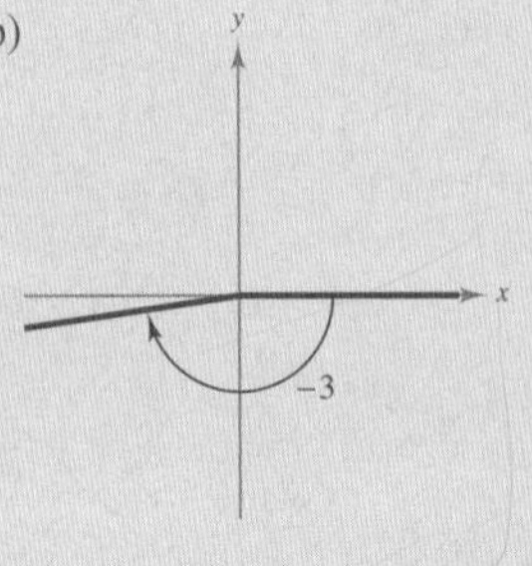

26–30. See Additional Answers beginning on page AA1.

In Exercises 31–34, find (if possible) the complement and supplement of each angle. 31–34. See margin.

31. (a) $\pi/3$ (b) $\pi/4$ **32.** (a) $\pi/12$ (b) $11\pi/12$

33. (a) 1 (b) 2 **34.** (a) 3 (b) 1.5

In Exercises 35–40, estimate the number of degrees in the angle. Use a protractor to check your answer.

35. 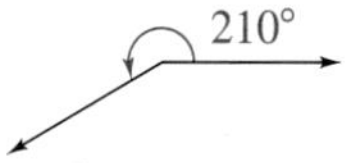 210°

36. 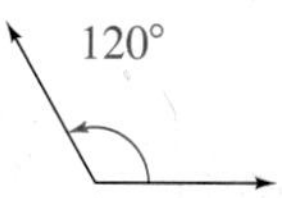 120°

37. 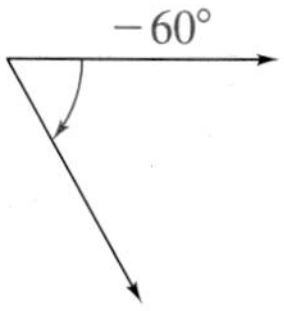 −60°

38. 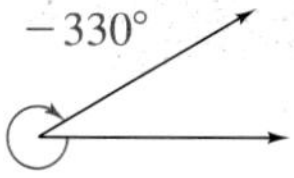 −330°

39.  165°

40. 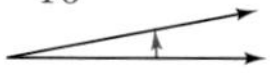 10°

In Exercises 41–44, determine the quadrant in which each angle lies.

41. (a) 130° II (b) 285° IV

42. (a) 8.3° I (b) 257° 30′ III

43. (a) −132° 50′ III (b) −336° I

44. (a) −260° II (b) −3.4° IV

In Exercises 45–48, sketch each angle in standard position.

45. (a) 90° (b) 180° **46.** (a) 270° (b) 120°

47. (a) −30° (b) −135°

48. (a) −750° (b) −600° 45–48. See margin.

In Exercises 49–52, determine two coterminal angles (one positive and one negative) for each angle. Give your answers in degrees. 49–52. See margin.

49. (a) 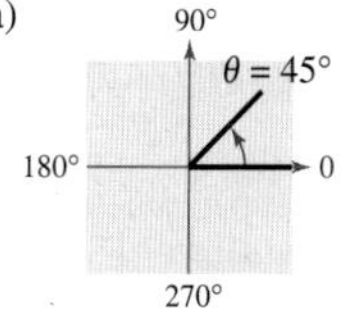

(b) 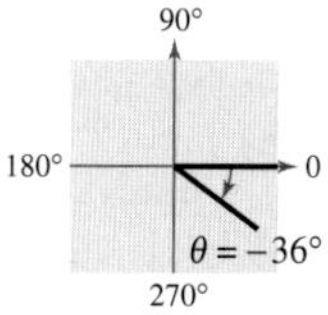

50. (a) 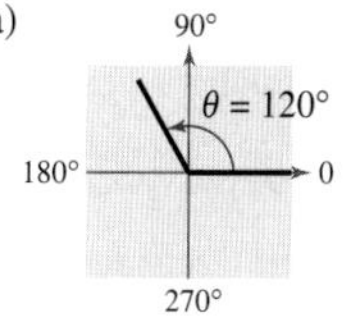

(b) 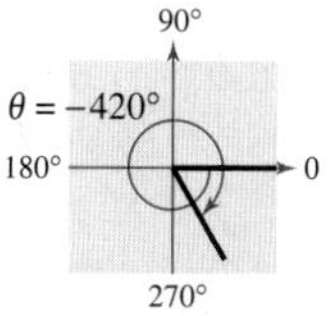

51. (a) $\theta = 240°$ (b) $\theta = -180°$

52. (a) $\theta = -390°$ (b) $\theta = 230°$

In Exercises 53–56, find (if possible) the complement and supplement of each angle. 53–56. See margin.

53. (a) 18° (b) 85° **54.** (a) 46° (b) 93°

55. (a) 150° (b) 79° **56.** (a) 130° (b) 170°

In Exercises 57–60, rewrite each angle in radian measure as a multiple of π. (Do not use a calculator.) 57–60. See margin.

57. (a) 30° (b) 45° **58.** (a) 315° (b) 120°

59. (a) −20° (b) −60° **60.** (a) −270° (b) 144°

In Exercises 61–64, rewrite each angle in degree measure. (Do not use a calculator.)

61. (a) $\frac{3\pi}{2}$ 270° (b) $\frac{7\pi}{6}$ 210° **62.** (a) $-\frac{7\pi}{12}$ −105° (b) $\frac{\pi}{9}$ 20°

63. (a) $\frac{5\pi}{4}$ 225° (b) $-\frac{7\pi}{3}$ −420° **64.** (a) $\frac{11\pi}{6}$ 330° (b) $\frac{34\pi}{15}$ 408°

In Exercises 65–72, convert the angle measure from degrees to radians. Round to three decimal places.

65. 45° 0.785 **66.** 87.4° 1.525

67. −216.35° −3.776 **68.** −48.27° −0.842

69. 532° 9.285 **70.** 345° 6.021

71. −0.83° −0.014 **72.** 0.54° 0.009

In Exercises 73–80, convert the angle measure from radians to degrees. Round to three decimal places.

73. $\pi/7$ 25.714° **74.** $5\pi/11$ 81.818°

75. $15\pi/8$ 337.500° **76.** $13\pi/2$ 1170.000°

77. -4.2π −756.000° **78.** 4.8π 864.000°

79. −2 −114.592° **80.** −0.57 −32.659°

In Exercises 81–84, convert each angle measure to decimal degree form without using a calculator. Then check your answers using a calculator.

81. (a) 54° 45′ (b) −128° 30′ (a) 54.75° (b) −128.5°

82. (a) 245° 10′ (b) 2° 12′ (a) 245.167° (b) 2.2°

83. (a) 85° 18′ 30″ (b) 330° 25″ (a) 85.308° (b) 330.007°

84. (a) −135° 36″ (b) −408° 16′ 20″ (a) −135.01° (b) −408.272°

In Exercises 85–88, convert each angle measure to degrees, minutes, and seconds without using a calculator. Then check your answers using a calculator.

85. (a) 240.6° 240° 36′ (b) −145.8° −145° 48′

86. (a) −345.12° (b) 0.45° (a) −345° 7′ 12″ (b) 0° 27′

87. (a) 2.5° 2° 30′ (b) −3.58° −3° 34′ 48″

88. (a) −0.36° −0° 21′ 36″ (b) 0.79° 0° 47′ 24″

31. (a) Complement: $\frac{\pi}{6}$

Supplement: $\frac{2\pi}{3}$

(b) Complement: $\frac{\pi}{4}$

Supplement: $\frac{3\pi}{4}$

32. (a) Complement: $\frac{5\pi}{12}$

Supplement: $\frac{11\pi}{12}$

(b) Complement: none

Supplement: $\frac{\pi}{12}$

33. (a) Complement: $\frac{\pi}{2} - 1 \approx 0.57$

Supplement: $\pi - 1 \approx 2.14$

(b) Complement: none

Supplement: $\pi - 2 \approx 1.14$

34. (a) Complement: none

Supplement: $\pi - 3 \approx 0.14$

(b) Complement: $\frac{\pi}{2} - 1.5 \approx 0.07$

Supplement: $\pi - 1.5 \approx 1.64$

45. (a) 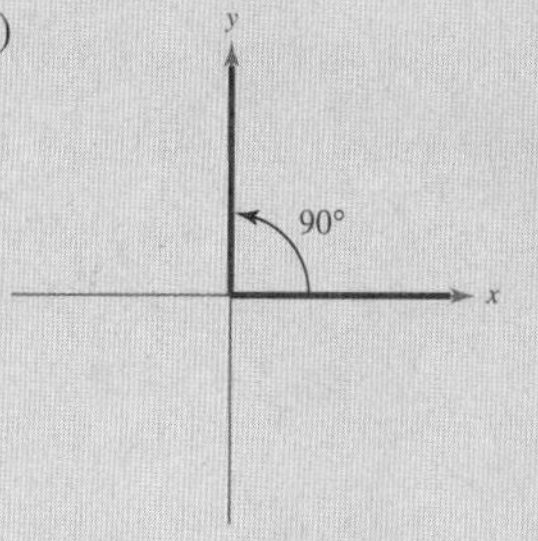

(b) 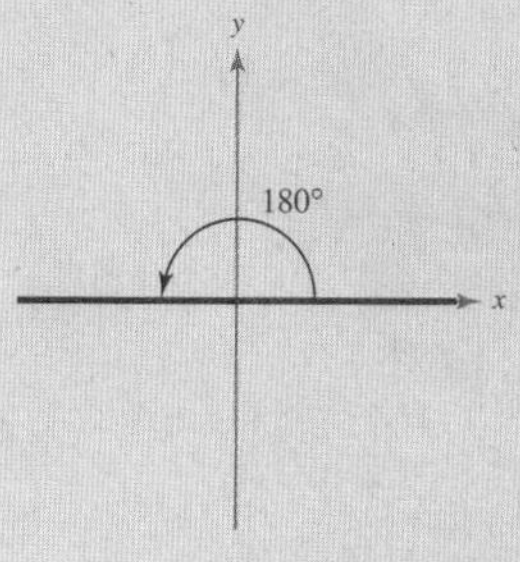

46. (a) 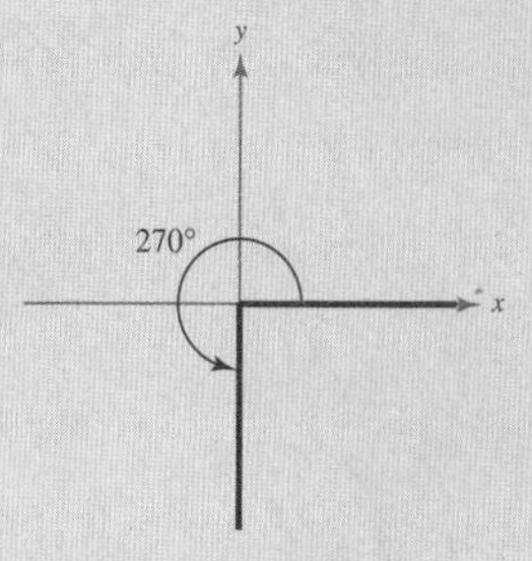

46. (b) 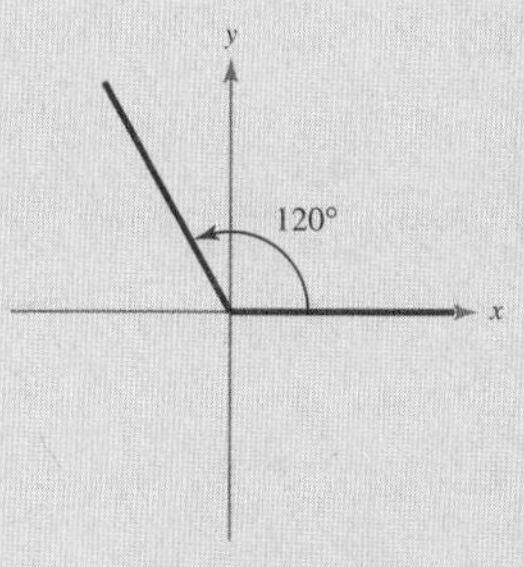

47. (a) 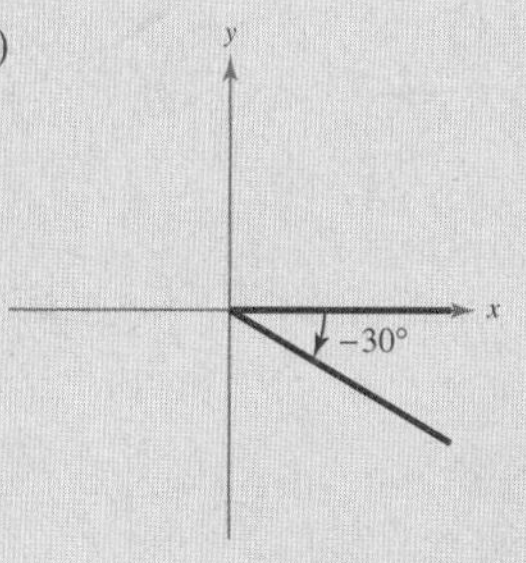

(b) 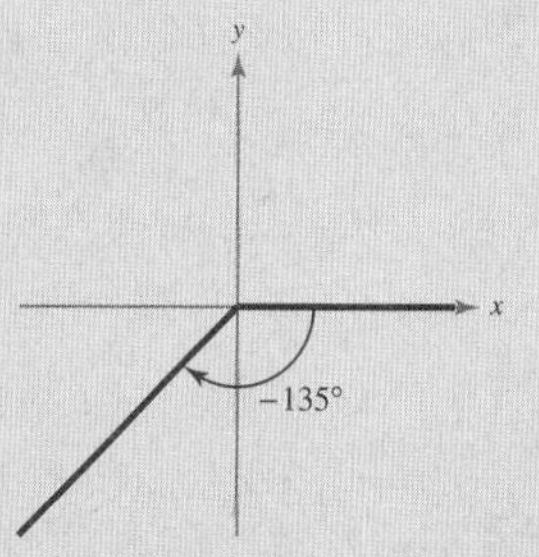

48–60. See Additional Answers beginning on page AA1.

107. 0.071 rad $\approx$ 4.04°
108. 0.063 rad $\approx$ 3.59°
111. (a) $10{,}000\pi$ rad/min $\approx$ 31,415.93 rad/min

In Exercises 89–92, find the length of the arc on a circle of radius r intercepted by a central angle θ.

Radius r	*Central Angle θ*
89. 15 inches	120° 10π in. $\approx$ 31.42 in.
90. 9 feet	60° 3π ft $\approx$ 9.42 ft
91. 3 meters	150° 2.5π m $\approx$ 7.85 m
92. 20 centimeters	45° 5π cm $\approx$ 15.71 cm

In Exercises 93–96, find the radian measure of the central angle of a circle of radius r that intercepts an arc of length s.

Radius r	*Arc Length s*
93. 4 inches	18 inches $\frac{9}{2}$ rad
94. 14 feet	8 feet $\frac{4}{7}$ rad
95. 25 centimeters	10.5 centimeters $\frac{21}{50}$ rad
96. 80 kilometers	150 kilometers $\frac{15}{8}$ rad

In Exercises 97–100, use the given arc length and radius to find the angle θ (in radians).

97.
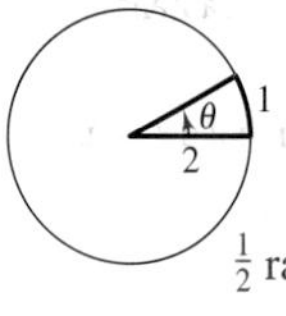

$\frac{1}{2}$ rad

98.
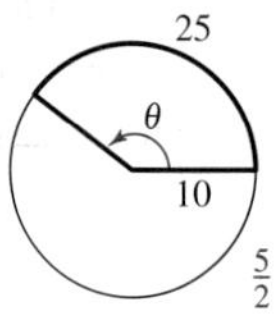

$\frac{5}{2}$ rad

99.
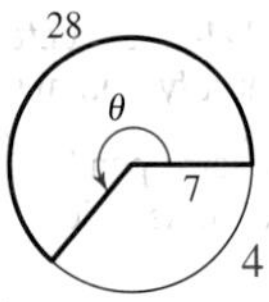

4 rad

100.
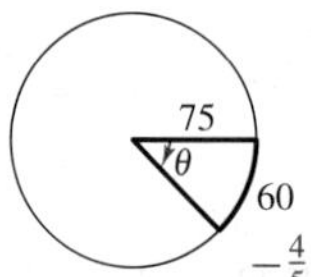

$-\frac{4}{5}$ rad

In Exercises 101–104, find the area of the sector of the circle with radius r and central angle θ.

Radius r	*Central Angle θ*
101. 6 inches	$\pi/3$ 6π in.^{2} $\approx$ 18.85 in.^{2}
102. 12 millimeters	$\pi/4$ 18π mm^2 $\approx$ 56.55 mm^2
103. 2.5 feet	225° 12.27 ft^2
104. 1.4 miles	330° 5.64 mi^2

DISTANCE BETWEEN CITIES In Exercises 105 and 106, find the distance between the cities. Assume that Earth is a sphere of radius 4000 miles and that the cities are on the same longitude (one city is due north of the other).

City	*Latitude*
105. Dallas, Texas 591.3 mi	32° 47′ 39″ N
Omaha, Nebraska	41° 15′ 50″ N

City 686.2 mi	*Latitude*
106. San Francisco, California	37° 47′ 36″ N
Seattle, Washington	47° 37′ 18″ N

107. DIFFERENCE IN LATITUDES Assuming that Earth is a sphere of radius 6378 kilometers, what is the difference in the latitudes of Syracuse, New York and Annapolis, Maryland, where Syracuse is about 450 kilometers due north of Annapolis? 107–108. See margin.

108. DIFFERENCE IN LATITUDES Assuming that Earth is a sphere of radius 6378 kilometers, what is the difference in the latitudes of Lynchburg, Virginia and Myrtle Beach, South Carolina, where Lynchburg is about 400 kilometers due north of Myrtle Beach?

109. INSTRUMENTATION The pointer on a voltmeter is 6 centimeters in length (see figure). Find the angle through which the pointer rotates when it moves 2.5 centimeters on the scale. $\frac{5}{12}$ rad

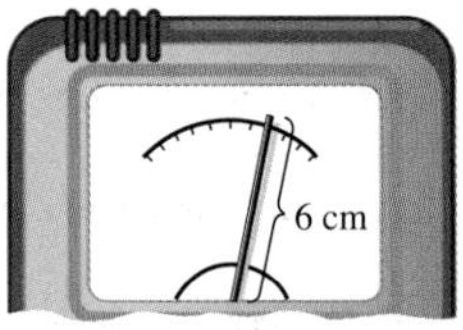

FIGURE FOR 109

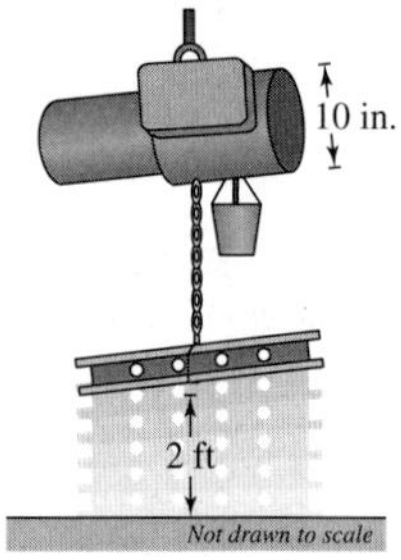

FIGURE FOR 110

110. ELECTRIC HOIST An electric hoist is being used to lift a beam (see figure). The diameter of the drum on the hoist is 10 inches, and the beam must be raised 2 feet. Find the number of degrees through which the drum must rotate. 275°

111. LINEAR AND ANGULAR SPEEDS A circular power saw has a $7\frac{1}{4}$-inch-diameter blade that rotates at 5000 revolutions per minute.

(a) Find the angular speed of the saw blade in radians per minute. See margin.

(b) Find the linear speed (in feet per minute) of one of the 24 cutting teeth as they contact the wood being cut. 9490.23 ft/min

112. LINEAR AND ANGULAR SPEEDS A carousel with a 50-foot diameter makes 4 revolutions per minute.

(a) Find the angular speed of the carousel in radians per minute. 8π rad/min $\approx$ 25.13 rad/min

(b) Find the linear speed (in feet per minute) of the platform rim of the carousel.

200π ft/min $\approx$ 628.3 ft/min

113. LINEAR AND ANGULAR SPEEDS The diameter of a DVD is approximately 12 centimeters. The drive motor of the DVD player is controlled to rotate precisely between 200 and 500 revolutions per minute, depending on what track is being read.

(a) Find an interval for the angular speed of a DVD as it rotates. $[400\pi, 1000\pi]$ rad/min

(b) Find an interval for the linear speed of a point on the outermost track as the DVD rotates. See margin.

114. ANGULAR SPEED A two-inch-diameter pulley on an electric motor that runs at 1700 revolutions per minute is connected by a belt to a four-inch-diameter pulley on a saw arbor.

(a) Find the angular speed (in radians per minute) of each pulley. 3400π rad/min; 1700π rad/min

(b) Find the revolutions per minute of the saw. See margin.

115. ANGULAR SPEED A car is moving at a rate of 65 miles per hour, and the diameter of its wheels is 2 feet.

(a) Find the number of revolutions per minute the wheels are rotating. 910.37 revolutions/min

(b) Find the angular speed of the wheels in radians per minute. 5720 rad/min

116. ANGULAR SPEED A computerized spin balance machine rotates a 25-inch-diameter tire at 480 revolutions per minute. See margin.

(a) Find the road speed (in miles per hour) at which the tire is being balanced.

(b) At what rate should the spin balance machine be set so that the tire is being tested for 55 miles per hour?

117. AREA A sprinkler on a golf green is set to spray water over a distance of 15 meters and to rotate through an angle of 140°. Draw a diagram that shows the region that can be irrigated with the sprinkler. Find the area of the region. See margin.

118. AREA A car's rear windshield wiper rotates 125°. The total length of the wiper mechanism is 25 inches and wipes the windshield over a distance of 14 inches. Find the area covered by the wiper. See margin.

119. SPEED OF A BICYCLE The radii of the pedal sprocket, the wheel sprocket, and the wheel of the bicycle in the figure are 4 inches, 2 inches, and 14 inches, respectively. A cyclist is pedaling at a rate of 1 revolution per second. See margin.

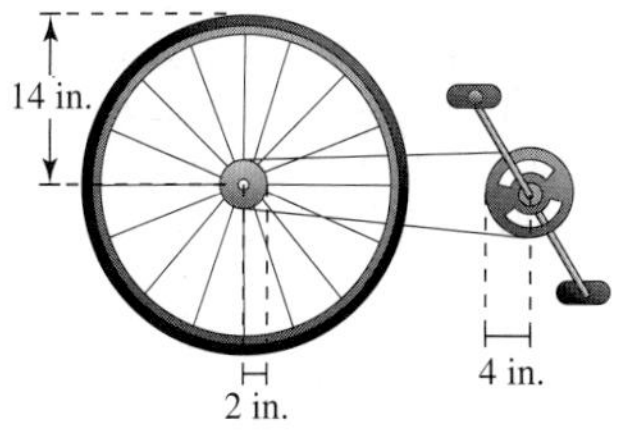

(a) Find the speed of the bicycle in feet per second and miles per hour.

(b) Use your result from part (a) to write a function for the distance d (in miles) a cyclist travels in terms of the number n of revolutions of the pedal sprocket.

(c) Write a function for the distance d (in miles) a cyclist travels in terms of the time t (in seconds). Compare this function with the function from part (b).

(d) Classify the types of functions you found in parts (b) and (c). Explain your reasoning.

120. CAPSTONE Write a short paper in your own words explaining the meaning of each of the following concepts to a classmate. Answers will vary.

(a) an angle in standard position

(b) positive and negative angles

(c) coterminal angles

(d) angle measure in degrees and radians

(e) obtuse and acute angles

(f) complementary and supplementary angles

EXPLORATION

121–123. See margin.

TRUE OR FALSE? In Exercises 121–123, determine whether the statement is true or false. Justify your answer.

121. A measurement of 4 radians corresponds to two complete revolutions from the initial side to the terminal side of an angle.

122. The difference between the measures of two coterminal angles is always a multiple of 360° if expressed in degrees and is always a multiple of 2π radians if expressed in radians.

123. An angle that measures $-1260°$ lies in Quadrant III.

124. THINK ABOUT IT A fan motor turns at a given angular speed. How does the speed of the tips of the blades change if a fan of greater diameter is installed on the motor? Explain. See margin.

125. THINK ABOUT IT Is a degree or a radian the larger unit of measure? Explain. Radian. 1 rad $\approx 57.3°$

126. WRITING If the radius of a circle is increasing and the magnitude of a central angle is held constant, how is the length of the intercepted arc changing? Explain your reasoning. See margin.

127. PROOF Prove that the area of a circular sector of radius r with central angle θ is $A = \frac{1}{2}\theta r^2$, where θ is measured in radians. Proof

5 ASSESS AND RETEACH

Daily Homework Quiz

Transparency Available
Available at the Instructor's companion site.

113. (b) $[2400\pi, 6000\pi]$ cm/min

114. (b) 850 revolutions/min

116. (a) 35.70 mi/h

(b) 739.50 revolutions/min

117.

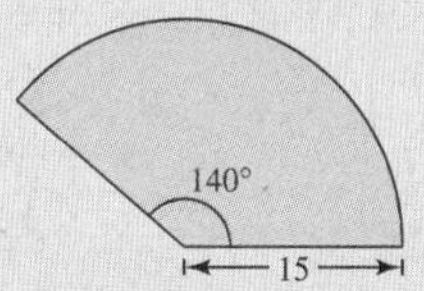

$A = 87.5\pi \text{ m}^2 \approx 274.89 \text{ m}^2$

118. $A = 175\pi \text{ in.}^2 \approx 549.8 \text{ in.}^2$

119. (a) $\frac{14\pi}{3}$ ft/sec $\approx$ 10 mi/h

(b) $d = \frac{7\pi}{7920}n$

(c) $d = \frac{7\pi}{7920}t$

(d) The functions are both linear.

121. False. A measurement of 4π radians corresponds to two complete revolutions from the initial side to the terminal side of an angle.

122. True. Let α and β represent coterminal angles, and let n represent an integer.

$\alpha = \beta + n(360°)$

$\alpha - \beta = n(360°)$

123. False. The terminal side of the angle lies on the x-axis.

124. The speed increases. The linear velocity is proportional to the radius.

126. The arc length is increasing. If θ is constant, the length of the arc is proportional to the radius ($s = r\theta$).

1 PLAN AND PREPARE

Warm-up Exercises

Transparency Available
Available at the Instructor's companion site.

Notetaking Guide

Transparency Available
Promotes interactive learning and notetaking skills.
Available at the Instructor's companion site.

Animated Precalculus

An **Animated Precalculus** tutorial is available at the Student companion site for **Section 4.2.**

Pacing

Average: 1 day
Advanced: 1 day
Block: 0.5 block with 4.3

2 FOCUS AND MOTIVATE

Essential Question

How do you evaluate trigonometric functions by using the unit circle?
Tell students that they will learn how to answer this question by defining trigonometric functions, locating points on the unit circle, and studying the period of sine and cosine.

4.2 TRIGONOMETRIC FUNCTIONS: THE UNIT CIRCLE

What you should learn

- Identify a unit circle and describe its relationship to real numbers.
- Evaluate trigonometric functions using the unit circle.
- Use the domain and period to evaluate sine and cosine functions.
- Use a calculator to evaluate trigonometric functions.

Why you should learn it

Trigonometric functions are used to model the movement of an oscillating weight. For instance, in Exercise 60 on page 298, the displacement from equilibrium of an oscillating weight suspended by a spring is modeled as a function of time.

Richard Megna/Fundamental Photographs

The Unit Circle

The two historical perspectives of trigonometry incorporate different methods for introducing the trigonometric functions. Our first introduction to these functions is based on the unit circle.

Consider the **unit circle** given by

$$x^2 + y^2 = 1 \qquad \text{Unit circle}$$

as shown in Figure 4.20.

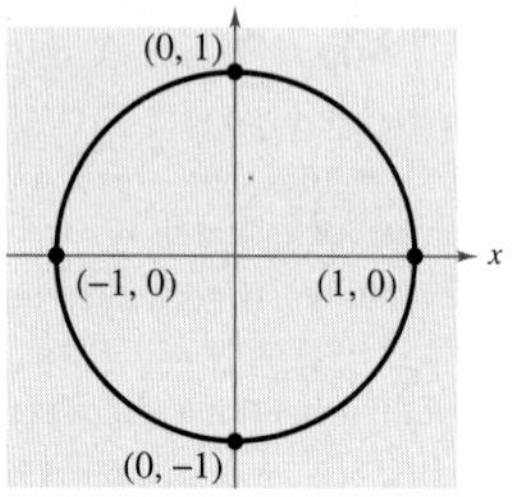

FIGURE 4.20

Imagine that the real number line is wrapped around this circle, with positive numbers corresponding to a counterclockwise wrapping and negative numbers corresponding to a clockwise wrapping, as shown in Figure 4.21.

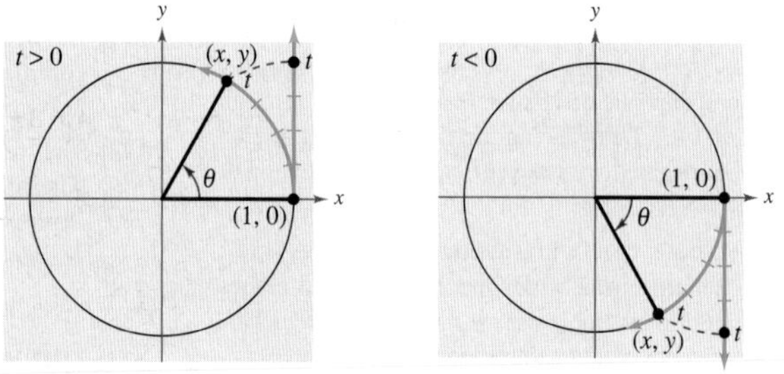

FIGURE 4.21

As the real number line is wrapped around the unit circle, each real number t corresponds to a point (x, y) on the circle. For example, the real number 0 corresponds to the point $(1, 0)$. Moreover, because the unit circle has a circumference of 2π, the real number 2π also corresponds to the point $(1, 0)$.

In general, each real number t also corresponds to a central angle θ (in standard position) whose radian measure is t. With this interpretation of t, the arc length formula $s = r\theta$ (with $r = 1$) indicates that the real number t is the (directional) length of the arc intercepted by the angle θ, given in radians.

Resource Planning Guide

Chapter Resources
- Complete Solutions Guide

Workbooks
- Notetaking Guide
- Student Solutions Guide

Interactive Technology
- Instructor Success Organizer
- Notetaking Guide IAE
- Instructional DVDs
- Animated Precalculus
- PowerLecture with ExamView

The Trigonometric Functions

From the preceding discussion, it follows that the coordinates x and y are two functions of the real variable t. You can use these coordinates to define the six trigonometric functions of t.

sine **cosecant** **cosine** **secant** **tangent** **cotangent**

These six functions are normally abbreviated sin, csc, cos, sec, tan, and cot, respectively.

Study Tip

Note in the definition at the right that the functions in the second row are the *reciprocals* of the corresponding functions in the first row.

Definitions of Trigonometric Functions

Let t be a real number and let (x, y) be the point on the unit circle corresponding to t.

$$\sin t = y \qquad \cos t = x \qquad \tan t = \frac{y}{x}, \quad x \neq 0$$

$$\csc t = \frac{1}{y}, \quad y \neq 0 \qquad \sec t = \frac{1}{x}, \quad x \neq 0 \qquad \cot t = \frac{x}{y}, \quad y \neq 0$$

In the definitions of the trigonometric functions, note that the tangent and secant are not defined when $x = 0$. For instance, because $t = \pi/2$ corresponds to $(x, y) = (0, 1)$, it follows that $\tan(\pi/2)$ and $\sec(\pi/2)$ are *undefined*. Similarly, the cotangent and cosecant are not defined when $y = 0$. For instance, because $t = 0$ corresponds to $(x, y) = (1, 0)$, cot 0 and csc 0 are *undefined*.

In Figure 4.22, the unit circle has been divided into eight equal arcs, corresponding to t-values of

$$0, \frac{\pi}{4}, \frac{\pi}{2}, \frac{3\pi}{4}, \pi, \frac{5\pi}{4}, \frac{3\pi}{2}, \frac{7\pi}{4}, \text{ and } 2\pi.$$

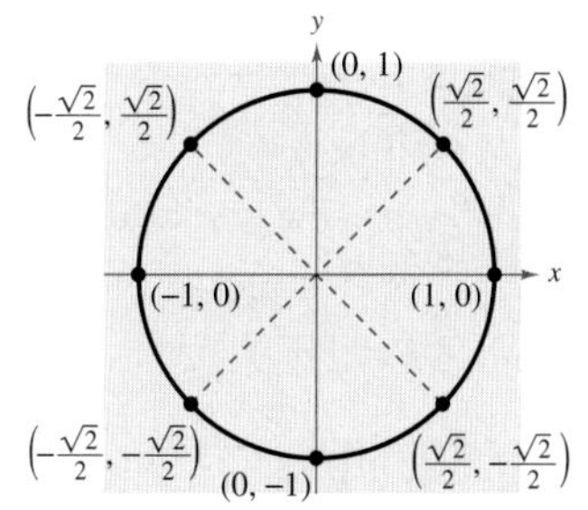

FIGURE 4.22

Similarly, in Figure 4.23, the unit circle has been divided into 12 equal arcs, corresponding to t-values of

$$0, \frac{\pi}{6}, \frac{\pi}{3}, \frac{\pi}{2}, \frac{2\pi}{3}, \frac{5\pi}{6}, \pi, \frac{7\pi}{6}, \frac{4\pi}{3}, \frac{3\pi}{2}, \frac{5\pi}{3}, \frac{11\pi}{6}, \text{ and } 2\pi.$$

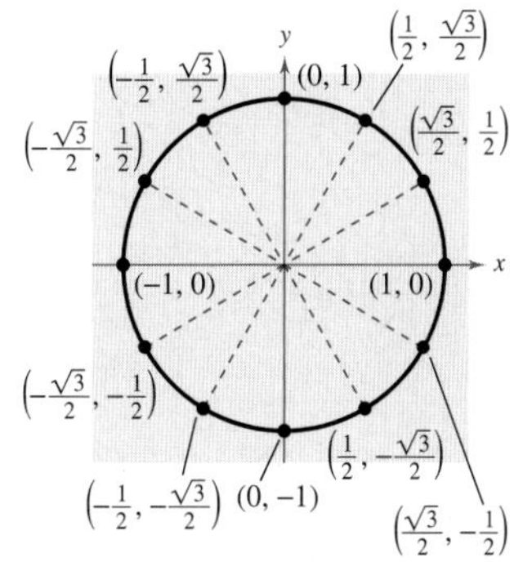

FIGURE 4.23

To verify the points on the unit circle in Figure 4.22, note that $\left(\frac{\sqrt{2}}{2}, \frac{\sqrt{2}}{2}\right)$ also lies on the line $y = x$. So, substituting x for y in the equation of the unit circle produces the following.

$$x^2 + x^2 = 1 \quad \Longrightarrow \quad 2x^2 = 1 \quad \Longrightarrow \quad x^2 = \frac{1}{2} \quad \Longrightarrow \quad x = \pm\frac{\sqrt{2}}{2}$$

Because the point is in the first quadrant, $x = \frac{\sqrt{2}}{2}$ and because $y = x$, you also have $y = \frac{\sqrt{2}}{2}$. You can use similar reasoning to verify the rest of the points in Figure 4.22 and the points in Figure 4.23.

Using the (x, y) coordinates in Figures 4.22 and 4.23, you can evaluate the trigonometric functions for common t-values. This procedure is demonstrated in Examples 1, 2, and 3. You should study and learn these exact function values for common t-values because they will help you in later sections to perform calculations.

3 TEACH

Extra Example 1

Evaluate the six trigonometric functions at each real number.

a. $t = \frac{2\pi}{3}$

$\sin\frac{2\pi}{3} = \frac{\sqrt{3}}{2}$, $\cos\frac{2\pi}{3} = -\frac{1}{2}$,

$\tan\frac{2\pi}{3} = -\sqrt{3}$, $\cot\frac{2\pi}{3} = -\frac{\sqrt{3}}{3}$,

$\sec\frac{2\pi}{3} = -2$, $\csc\frac{2\pi}{3} = \frac{2\sqrt{3}}{3}$

b. $t = \frac{4\pi}{3}$

$\sin\frac{4\pi}{3} = -\frac{\sqrt{3}}{2}$, $\cos\frac{4\pi}{3} = -\frac{1}{2}$,

$\tan\frac{4\pi}{3} = \sqrt{3}$, $\cot\frac{4\pi}{3} = \frac{\sqrt{3}}{3}$,

$\sec\frac{4\pi}{3} = -2$, $\csc\frac{4\pi}{3} = -\frac{2\sqrt{3}}{3}$

c. $t = 2\pi$

$\sin 2\pi = 0$, $\cos 2\pi = 1$, $\tan 2\pi = 0$, $\cot 2\pi$ is undefined, $\sec 2\pi = 1$, $\csc 2\pi$ is undefined

d. $t = \frac{\pi}{2}$

$\sin\frac{\pi}{2} = 1$, $\cos\frac{\pi}{2} = 0$,

$\tan\frac{\pi}{2}$ is undefined, $\cot\frac{\pi}{2} = 0$,

$\sec\frac{\pi}{2}$ is undefined, $\csc\frac{\pi}{2} = 1$

Algebra Help

You can review dividing fractions and rationalizing denominators in Appendix A.1 and Appendix A.2, respectively.

Example 1 Evaluating Trigonometric Functions

Evaluate the six trigonometric functions at each real number.

a. $t = \frac{\pi}{6}$ **b.** $t = \frac{5\pi}{4}$ **c.** $t = 0$ **d.** $t = \pi$

Solution

For each t-value, begin by finding the corresponding point (x, y) on the unit circle. Then use the definitions of trigonometric functions listed on page 293.

a. $t = \frac{\pi}{6}$ corresponds to the point $(x, y) = \left(\frac{\sqrt{3}}{2}, \frac{1}{2}\right)$.

$$\sin\frac{\pi}{6} = y = \frac{1}{2} \qquad \csc\frac{\pi}{6} = \frac{1}{y} = \frac{1}{1/2} = 2$$

$$\cos\frac{\pi}{6} = x = \frac{\sqrt{3}}{2} \qquad \sec\frac{\pi}{6} = \frac{1}{x} = \frac{2}{\sqrt{3}} = \frac{2\sqrt{3}}{3}$$

$$\tan\frac{\pi}{6} = \frac{y}{x} = \frac{1/2}{\sqrt{3}/2} = \frac{1}{\sqrt{3}} = \frac{\sqrt{3}}{3} \qquad \cot\frac{\pi}{6} = \frac{x}{y} = \frac{\sqrt{3}/2}{1/2} = \sqrt{3}$$

b. $t = \frac{5\pi}{4}$ corresponds to the point $(x, y) = \left(-\frac{\sqrt{2}}{2}, -\frac{\sqrt{2}}{2}\right)$.

$$\sin\frac{5\pi}{4} = y = -\frac{\sqrt{2}}{2} \qquad \csc\frac{5\pi}{4} = \frac{1}{y} = -\frac{2}{\sqrt{2}} = -\sqrt{2}$$

$$\cos\frac{5\pi}{4} = x = -\frac{\sqrt{2}}{2} \qquad \sec\frac{5\pi}{4} = \frac{1}{x} = -\frac{2}{\sqrt{2}} = -\sqrt{2}$$

$$\tan\frac{5\pi}{4} = \frac{y}{x} = \frac{-\sqrt{2}/2}{-\sqrt{2}/2} = 1 \qquad \cot\frac{5\pi}{4} = \frac{x}{y} = \frac{-\sqrt{2}/2}{-\sqrt{2}/2} = 1$$

c. $t = 0$ corresponds to the point $(x, y) = (1, 0)$.

$$\sin 0 = y = 0 \qquad \csc 0 = \frac{1}{y} \text{ is undefined.}$$

$$\cos 0 = x = 1 \qquad \sec 0 = \frac{1}{x} = \frac{1}{1} = 1$$

$$\tan 0 = \frac{y}{x} = \frac{0}{1} = 0 \qquad \cot 0 = \frac{x}{y} \text{ is undefined.}$$

d. $t = \pi$ corresponds to the point $(x, y) = (-1, 0)$.

$$\sin\pi = y = 0 \qquad \csc\pi = \frac{1}{y} \text{ is undefined.}$$

$$\cos\pi = x = -1 \qquad \sec\pi = \frac{1}{x} = \frac{1}{-1} = -1$$

$$\tan\pi = \frac{y}{x} = \frac{0}{-1} = 0 \qquad \cot\pi = \frac{x}{y} \text{ is undefined.}$$

CHECKPoint Now try Exercise 23.

Example 2 Evaluating Trigonometric Functions

Evaluate the six trigonometric functions at $t = -\frac{\pi}{3}$.

Solution

Moving *clockwise* around the unit circle, it follows that $t = -\pi/3$ corresponds to the point $(x, y) = \left(1/2, -\sqrt{3}/2\right)$.

$$\sin\left(-\frac{\pi}{3}\right) = -\frac{\sqrt{3}}{2} \qquad \csc\left(-\frac{\pi}{3}\right) = -\frac{2}{\sqrt{3}} = -\frac{2\sqrt{3}}{3}$$

$$\cos\left(-\frac{\pi}{3}\right) = \frac{1}{2} \qquad \sec\left(-\frac{\pi}{3}\right) = 2$$

$$\tan\left(-\frac{\pi}{3}\right) = \frac{-\sqrt{3}/2}{1/2} = -\sqrt{3} \qquad \cot\left(-\frac{\pi}{3}\right) = \frac{1/2}{-\sqrt{3}/2} = -\frac{1}{\sqrt{3}} = -\frac{\sqrt{3}}{3}$$

CHECK*Point* Now try Exercise 33.

Domain and Period of Sine and Cosine

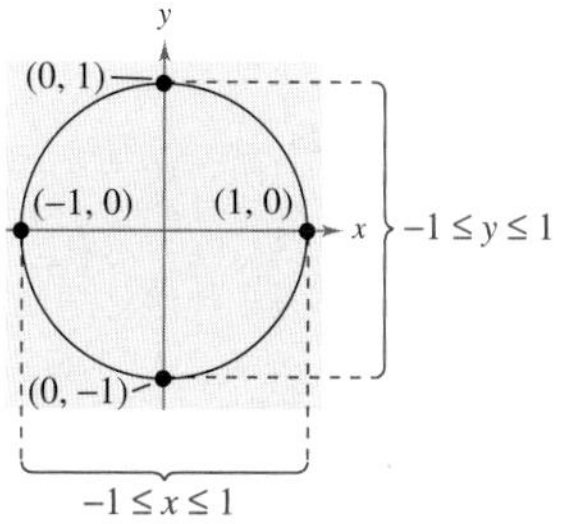

FIGURE 4.24

The *domain* of the sine and cosine functions is the set of all real numbers. To determine the *range* of these two functions, consider the unit circle shown in Figure 4.24. By definition, $\sin t = y$ and $\cos t = x$. Because (x, y) is on the unit circle, you know that $-1 \le y \le 1$ and $-1 \le x \le 1$. So, the values of sine and cosine also range between -1 and 1.

$$-1 \le y \le 1 \qquad \text{and} \qquad -1 \le x \le 1$$
$$-1 \le \sin t \le 1 \qquad\qquad -1 \le \cos t \le 1$$

Adding 2π to each value of t in the interval $[0, 2\pi]$ completes a second revolution around the unit circle, as shown in Figure 4.25. The values of $\sin(t + 2\pi)$ and $\cos(t + 2\pi)$ correspond to those of $\sin t$ and $\cos t$. Similar results can be obtained for repeated revolutions (positive or negative) on the unit circle. This leads to the general result

$$\sin(t + 2\pi n) = \sin t$$

and

$$\cos(t + 2\pi n) = \cos t$$

for any integer n and real number t. Functions that behave in such a repetitive (or cyclic) manner are called **periodic.**

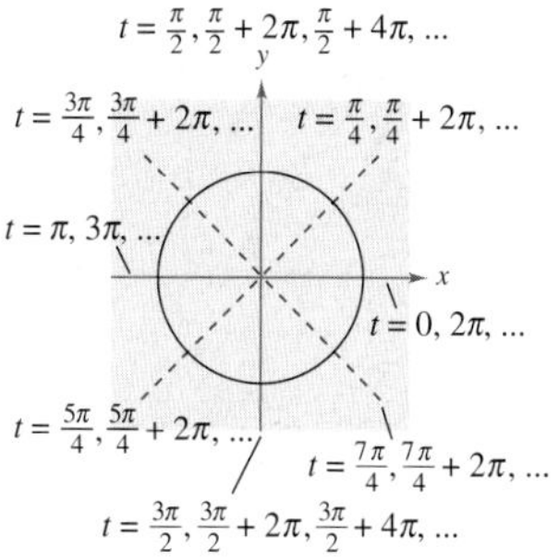

FIGURE 4.25

Definition of Periodic Function

A function f is **periodic** if there exists a positive real number c such that

$$f(t + c) = f(t)$$

for all t in the domain of f. The smallest number c for which f is periodic is called the **period** of f.

Extra Example 2

Evaluate (if possible) the six trigonometric functions of $t = -\frac{2\pi}{3}$.

$\sin\left(-\frac{2\pi}{3}\right) = -\frac{\sqrt{3}}{2}$,

$\cos\left(-\frac{2\pi}{3}\right) = -\frac{1}{2}$,

$\tan\left(-\frac{2\pi}{3}\right) = \sqrt{3}$,

$\cot\left(-\frac{2\pi}{3}\right) = \frac{\sqrt{3}}{3}$,

$\sec\left(-\frac{2\pi}{3}\right) = -2$,

$\csc\left(-\frac{2\pi}{3}\right) = -\frac{2\sqrt{3}}{3}$

Differentiated Instruction

English Language Learners Point out to students learning English that *periodic* is an adjective and that *period* is a noun. Explain that the most common definition of *period* is a unit of time. Discuss with students how the words *period* and *periodic* are related in common speech and how they are related in mathematical definitions.

Extra Example 3

Find the following.

a. $\cos \frac{9\pi}{3}$

−1

b. $\sin\left(-\frac{11\pi}{2}\right)$

1

c. If $\tan(t) = \frac{2}{3}$, find $\tan(-t)$.

$-\frac{2}{3}$

Extra Example 4

Use a calculator to evaluate.

a. $\sin \frac{5\pi}{7}$

0.7818

b. csc 2

1.0998

Avoiding Common Errors

When calculating reciprocal functions on a calculator, students should be careful not to confuse reciprocal with inverse (for example, $\sin^{-1} \theta$). Students can avoid this error by rewriting the expression in terms of sine, cosine, or tangent before evaluating.

Example:

$$\sec\left(\frac{\pi}{5}\right) = \frac{1}{\cos(\pi/5)} \approx 1.2361$$

Closing the Lesson

Have students summarize the major points of the lesson and answer the Essential Question: How do you evaluate trigonometric functions by using the unit circle?

- **Use definitions and points on the unit circle to evaluate trigonometric functions for $-2\pi < t < 2\pi$.**
- **Recognize that cosine and secant functions are even and that sine, cosecant, tangent, and cotangent functions are odd.**
- **Use the definition of a periodic function to evaluate trigonometric functions for $t \le -2\pi$ or $t \ge 2\pi$.**

Recall from Section 1.5 that a function f is *even* if $f(-t) = f(t)$, and is *odd* if $f(-t) = -f(t)$.

Even and Odd Trigonometric Functions

The cosine and secant functions are *even*.

$\cos(-t) = \cos t \qquad \sec(-t) = \sec t$

The sine, cosecant, tangent, and cotangent functions are *odd*.

$\sin(-t) = -\sin t \qquad \csc(-t) = -\csc t$

$\tan(-t) = -\tan t \qquad \cot(-t) = -\cot t$

Example 3 Using the Period to Evaluate the Sine and Cosine

a. Because $\frac{13\pi}{6} = 2\pi + \frac{\pi}{6}$, you have $\sin \frac{13\pi}{6} = \sin\left(2\pi + \frac{\pi}{6}\right) = \sin \frac{\pi}{6} = \frac{1}{2}$.

b. Because $-\frac{7\pi}{2} = -4\pi + \frac{\pi}{2}$, you have

$$\cos\left(-\frac{7\pi}{2}\right) = \cos\left(-4\pi + \frac{\pi}{2}\right) = \cos \frac{\pi}{2} = 0.$$

c. For $\sin t = \frac{4}{5}$, $\sin(-t) = -\frac{4}{5}$ because the sine function is odd.

CHECKPoint Now try Exercise 37.

Study Tip

From the definition of periodic function, it follows that the sine and cosine functions are periodic and have a period of 2π. The other four trigonometric functions are also periodic, and will be discussed further in Section 4.6.

Evaluating Trigonometric Functions with a Calculator

When evaluating a trigonometric function with a calculator, you need to set the calculator to the desired *mode* of measurement (*degree* or *radian*).

Most calculators do not have keys for the cosecant, secant, and cotangent functions. To evaluate these functions, you can use the x^{-1} key with their respective reciprocal functions sine, cosine, and tangent. For instance, to evaluate $\csc(\pi/8)$, use the fact that

$$\csc \frac{\pi}{8} = \frac{1}{\sin(\pi/8)}$$

and enter the following keystroke sequence in *radian* mode.

(SIN (π ÷ 8)) x^{-1} ENTER Display 2.6131259

TECHNOLOGY

When evaluating trigonometric functions with a calculator, remember to enclose all fractional angle measures in parentheses. For instance, if you want to evaluate *sin t* for $t = \pi/6$, you should enter

SIN (π ÷ 6) ENTER.

These keystrokes yield the correct value of 0.5. Note that some calculators automatically place a left parenthesis after trigonometric functions. Check the user's guide for your calculator for specific keystrokes on how to evaluate trigonometric functions.

Example 4 Using a Calculator

Function	*Mode*	*Calculator Keystrokes*	*Display*
a. $\sin \frac{2\pi}{3}$	Radian	SIN (2 π ÷ 3) ENTER	0.8660254
b. cot 1.5	Radian	(TAN (1.5)) x^{-1} ENTER	0.0709148

CHECKPoint Now try Exercise 55.

4.2 EXERCISES

See www.CalcChat.com for worked-out solutions to odd-numbered exercises.

VOCABULARY: Fill in the blanks.

1. Each real number t corresponds to a point (x, y) on the __unit__ __circle__.
2. A function f is __periodic__ if there exists a positive real number c such that $f(t + c) = f(t)$ for all t in the domain of f.
3. The smallest number c for which a function f is periodic is called the __period__ of f.
4. A function f is __odd__ if $f(-t) = -f(t)$ and __even__ if $f(-t) = f(t)$.

SKILLS AND APPLICATIONS

5–8. See margin.

In Exercises 5–8, determine the exact values of the six trigonometric functions of the real number t.

5.

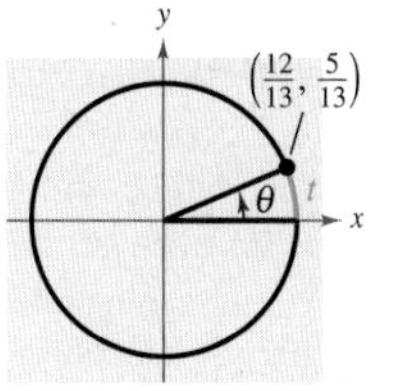

6.

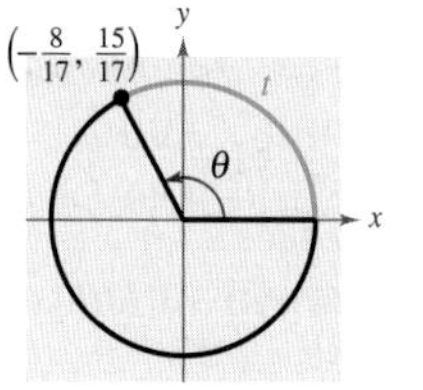

7.

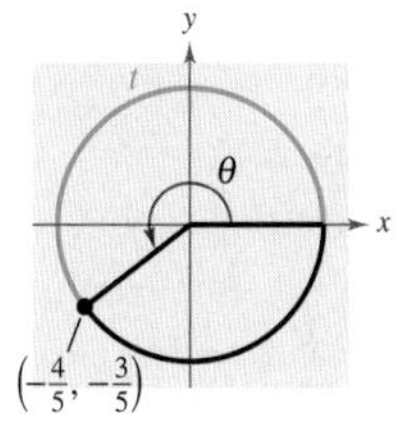

8.

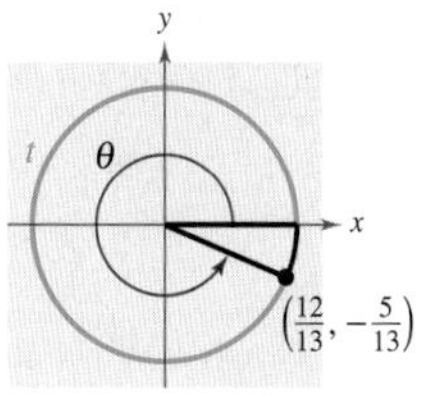

In Exercises 9–16, find the point (x, y) on the unit circle that corresponds to the real number t.

9. $t = \frac{\pi}{2}$ $(0, 1)$
10. $t = \pi$ $(-1, 0)$
11. $t = \frac{\pi}{4}$ $\left(\frac{\sqrt{2}}{2}, \frac{\sqrt{2}}{2}\right)$
12. $t = \frac{\pi}{3}$ $\left(\frac{1}{2}, \frac{\sqrt{3}}{2}\right)$
13. $t = \frac{5\pi}{6}$ $\left(-\frac{\sqrt{3}}{2}, \frac{1}{2}\right)$
14. $t = \frac{3\pi}{4}$ $\left(-\frac{\sqrt{2}}{2}, \frac{\sqrt{2}}{2}\right)$
15. $t = \frac{4\pi}{3}$ $\left(-\frac{1}{2}, -\frac{\sqrt{3}}{2}\right)$
16. $t = \frac{5\pi}{3}$ $\left(\frac{1}{2}, -\frac{\sqrt{3}}{2}\right)$

In Exercises 17–26, evaluate (if possible) the sine, cosine, and tangent of the real number. 17–25. See margin.

17. $t = \frac{\pi}{4}$
18. $t = \frac{\pi}{3}$
19. $t = -\frac{\pi}{6}$
20. $t = -\frac{\pi}{4}$
21. $t = -\frac{7\pi}{4}$
22. $t = -\frac{4\pi}{3}$
23. $t = \frac{11\pi}{6}$
24. $t = \frac{5\pi}{3}$
25. $t = -\frac{3\pi}{2}$
26. $t = -2\pi$ $\sin(-2\pi) = 0$, $\cos(-2\pi) = 1$, $\tan(-2\pi) = 0$

In Exercises 27–34, evaluate (if possible) the six trigonometric functions of the real number. 27–34. See margin.

27. $t = \frac{2\pi}{3}$
28. $t = \frac{5\pi}{6}$
29. $t = \frac{4\pi}{3}$
30. $t = \frac{7\pi}{4}$
31. $t = \frac{3\pi}{4}$
32. $t = \frac{3\pi}{2}$
33. $t = -\frac{\pi}{2}$
34. $t = -\pi$

In Exercises 35–42, evaluate the trigonometric function using its period as an aid. 35–42. See margin.

35. $\sin 4\pi$
36. $\cos 3\pi$
37. $\cos \frac{7\pi}{3}$
38. $\sin \frac{9\pi}{4}$
39. $\cos \frac{17\pi}{4}$
40. $\sin \frac{19\pi}{6}$
41. $\sin\left(-\frac{8\pi}{3}\right)$
42. $\cos\left(-\frac{9\pi}{4}\right)$

In Exercises 43–48, use the value of the trigonometric function to evaluate the indicated functions.

43. $\sin t = \frac{1}{2}$
    (a) $\sin(-t)$ (a) $-\frac{1}{2}$
    (b) $\csc(-t)$ (b) -2
44. $\sin(-t) = \frac{3}{8}$
    (a) $\sin t$ (a) $-\frac{3}{8}$
    (b) $\csc t$ (b) $-\frac{8}{3}$
45. $\cos(-t) = -\frac{1}{5}$
    (a) $\cos t$ (a) $-\frac{1}{5}$
    (b) $\sec(-t)$ (b) -5
46. $\cos t = -\frac{3}{4}$
    (a) $\cos(-t)$ (a) $-\frac{3}{4}$
    (b) $\sec(-t)$ (b) $-\frac{4}{3}$
47. $\sin t = \frac{4}{5}$
    (a) $\sin(\pi - t)$ (a) $\frac{4}{5}$
    (b) $\sin(t + \pi)$ (b) $-\frac{4}{5}$
48. $\cos t = \frac{4}{5}$
    (a) $\cos(\pi - t)$ (a) $-\frac{4}{5}$
    (b) $\cos(t + \pi)$ (b) $-\frac{4}{5}$

4 PRACTICE AND APPLY

Assignment Guide

Transparencies Available
Available at the Instructor's companion site.

Average:
Day 1: pp. 297–298
Exs. 1–4, 5–25 odd, 28, 29, 35, 39–45 odd, 49, 53, 60–65, 72

Advanced:
Day 1: pp. 297–298
Exs. 1–4, 6–18 even, 32–42 even, 46, 48, 54–58 even, 59, 60, 65, 66, 69, 70, 72

Block:
pp. 297–298
Exs. 1–4, 5–25 odd, 28, 29, 35, 39–45 odd, 49, 53, 60–65, 72 (with 4.3)

5. $\sin t = \frac{5}{13}$ $\csc t = \frac{13}{5}$
   $\cos t = \frac{12}{13}$ $\sec t = \frac{13}{12}$
   $\tan t = \frac{5}{12}$ $\cot t = \frac{12}{5}$
6. $\sin t = \frac{15}{17}$ $\csc t = \frac{17}{15}$
   $\cos t = -\frac{8}{17}$ $\sec t = -\frac{17}{8}$
   $\tan t = -\frac{15}{8}$ $\cot t = -\frac{8}{15}$
7. $\sin t = -\frac{3}{5}$ $\csc t = -\frac{5}{3}$
   $\cos t = -\frac{4}{5}$ $\sec t = -\frac{5}{4}$
   $\tan t = \frac{3}{4}$ $\cot t = \frac{4}{3}$
8. $\sin t = -\frac{5}{13}$ $\csc t = -\frac{13}{5}$
   $\cos t = \frac{12}{13}$ $\sec t = \frac{13}{12}$
   $\tan t = -\frac{5}{12}$ $\cot t = -\frac{12}{5}$

17. $\sin \frac{\pi}{4} = \frac{\sqrt{2}}{2}$, $\cos \frac{\pi}{4} = \frac{\sqrt{2}}{2}$, $\tan \frac{\pi}{4} = 1$
18. $\sin \frac{\pi}{3} = \frac{\sqrt{3}}{2}$, $\cos \frac{\pi}{3} = \frac{1}{2}$, $\tan \frac{\pi}{3} = \sqrt{3}$
19. $\sin\left(-\frac{\pi}{6}\right) = -\frac{1}{2}$, $\cos\left(-\frac{\pi}{6}\right) = \frac{\sqrt{3}}{2}$, $\tan\left(-\frac{\pi}{6}\right) = -\frac{\sqrt{3}}{3}$
20. $\sin\left(-\frac{\pi}{4}\right) = -\frac{\sqrt{2}}{2}$, $\cos\left(-\frac{\pi}{4}\right) = \frac{\sqrt{2}}{2}$, $\tan\left(-\frac{\pi}{4}\right) = -1$

21. $\sin\left(-\frac{7\pi}{4}\right) = \frac{\sqrt{2}}{2}$, $\cos\left(-\frac{7\pi}{4}\right) = \frac{\sqrt{2}}{2}$, $\tan\left(-\frac{7\pi}{4}\right) = 1$
22. $\sin\left(-\frac{4\pi}{3}\right) = \frac{\sqrt{3}}{2}$, $\cos\left(-\frac{4\pi}{3}\right) = -\frac{1}{2}$, $\tan\left(-\frac{4\pi}{3}\right) = -\sqrt{3}$
23. $\sin \frac{11\pi}{6} = -\frac{1}{2}$, $\cos \frac{11\pi}{6} = \frac{\sqrt{3}}{2}$, $\tan \frac{11\pi}{6} = -\frac{\sqrt{3}}{3}$
24. $\sin \frac{5\pi}{3} = -\frac{\sqrt{3}}{2}$, $\cos \frac{5\pi}{3} = \frac{1}{2}$, $\tan \frac{5\pi}{3} = -\sqrt{3}$

25, 27–42. See Additional Answers beginning on page AA1.

5 ASSESS AND RETEACH

Daily Homework Quiz

Transparency Available
Available at the Instructor's companion site.

59. (a) 0.25 ft (b) 0.02 ft
(c) −0.25 ft
60. (a) See below.
61. False. $\sin(-t) = -\sin(t)$ means that the function is odd, not that the sine of a negative angle is a negative number.
62. True. The tangent function has a period of π.
63. False. The real number 0 corresponds to the point (1, 0).
69. It is an odd function.
71. (a)

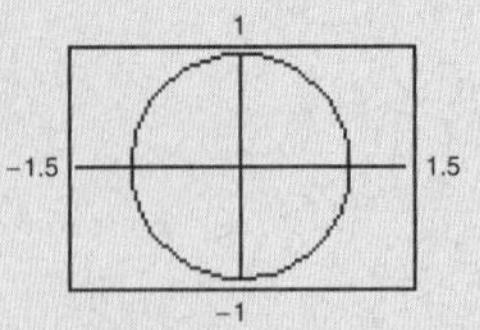

Circle of radius 1 centered at (0, 0)
(b) The t-values represent the central angle in radians. The x- and y-values represent the location in the coordinate plane.
(c) $-1 \le x \le 1, -1 \le y \le 1$

In Exercises 49–58, use a calculator to evaluate the trigonometric function. Round your answer to four decimal places. (Be sure the calculator is set in the correct angle mode.)

49. $\sin \frac{\pi}{4}$ 0.7071
50. $\tan \frac{\pi}{3}$ 1.7321
51. $\cot \frac{\pi}{4}$ 1.0000
52. $\csc \frac{2\pi}{3}$ 1.1547
53. $\cos(-1.7)$ −0.1288
54. $\cos(-2.5)$ −0.8011
55. $\csc 0.8$ 1.3940
56. $\sec 1.8$ −4.4014
57. $\sec(-22.8)$ −1.4486
58. $\cot(-0.9)$ −0.7936

59. **HARMONIC MOTION** The displacement from equilibrium of an oscillating weight suspended by a spring is given by $y(t) = \frac{1}{4}\cos 6t$, where y is the displacement (in feet) and t is the time (in seconds). Find the displacements when (a) $t = 0$, (b) $t = \frac{1}{4}$, and (c) $t = \frac{1}{2}$. See margin.

60. **HARMONIC MOTION** The displacement from equilibrium of an oscillating weight suspended by a spring and subject to the damping effect of friction is given by $y(t) = \frac{1}{4}e^{-t}\cos 6t$, where y is the displacement (in feet) and t is the time (in seconds).

(a) Complete the table. See margin.

t	0	$\frac{1}{4}$	$\frac{1}{2}$	$\frac{3}{4}$	1
y					

(b) Use the *table* feature of a graphing utility to approximate the time when the weight reaches equilibrium. $t \approx 5.5$

(c) What appears to happen to the displacement as t increases? The displacement decreases.

EXPLORATION

TRUE OR FALSE? In Exercises 61–64, determine whether the statement is true or false. Justify your answer.

61. Because $\sin(-t) = -\sin t$, it can be said that the sine of a negative angle is a negative number.

62. $\tan a = \tan(a - 6\pi)$ 61–63. See margin.

63. The real number 0 corresponds to the point (0, 1) on the unit circle.

64. $\cos\left(-\frac{7\pi}{2}\right) = \cos\left(\pi + \frac{\pi}{2}\right)$ True

65. Let (x_1, y_1) and (x_2, y_2) be points on the unit circle corresponding to $t = t_1$ and $t = \pi - t_1$, respectively.

(a) Identify the symmetry of the points (x_1, y_1) and (x_2, y_2). y-axis symmetry

(b) Make a conjecture about any relationship between $\sin t_1$ and $\sin(\pi - t_1)$. $\sin t_1 = \sin(\pi - t_1)$

(c) Make a conjecture about any relationship between $\cos t_1$ and $\cos(\pi - t_1)$. $\cos(\pi - t_1) = -\cos t_1$

66. Use the unit circle to verify that the cosine and secant functions are even and that the sine, cosecant, tangent, and cotangent functions are odd. Answers will vary.

67. Verify that $\cos 2t \ne 2\cos t$ by approximating $\cos 1.5$ and $2\cos 0.75$. Answers will vary.

68. Verify that $\sin(t_1 + t_2) \ne \sin t_1 + \sin t_2$ by approximating $\sin 0.25$, $\sin 0.75$, and $\sin 1$. Answers will vary.

69. **THINK ABOUT IT** Because $f(t) = \sin t$ is an odd function and $g(t) = \cos t$ is an even function, what can be said about the function $h(t) = f(t)g(t)$? See margin.

70. **THINK ABOUT IT** Because $f(t) = \sin t$ and $g(t) = \tan t$ are odd functions, what can be said about the function $h(t) = f(t)g(t)$? It is an even function.

71. **GRAPHICAL ANALYSIS** With your graphing utility in *radian* and *parametric* modes, enter the equations

$X_{1T} = \cos T$ and $Y_{1T} = \sin T$

and use the following settings.

Tmin = 0, Tmax = 6.3, Tstep = 0.1
Xmin = −1.5, Xmax = 1.5, Xscl = 1
Ymin = −1, Ymax = 1, Yscl = 1 See margin.

(a) Graph the entered equations and describe the graph.

(b) Use the *trace* feature to move the cursor around the graph. What do the t-values represent? What do the x- and y-values represent?

(c) What are the least and greatest values of x and y?

72. **CAPSTONE** A student you are tutoring has used a unit circle divided into 8 equal parts to complete the table for selected values of t. What is wrong?

t	0	$\frac{\pi}{4}$	$\frac{\pi}{2}$	$\frac{3\pi}{4}$	π
x	1	$\frac{\sqrt{2}}{2}$	0	$-\frac{\sqrt{2}}{2}$	−1
y	0	$\frac{\sqrt{2}}{2}$	1	$\frac{\sqrt{2}}{2}$	0
$\sin t$	1	$\frac{\sqrt{2}}{2}$	0	$-\frac{\sqrt{2}}{2}$	−1
$\cos t$	0	$\frac{\sqrt{2}}{2}$	1	$\frac{\sqrt{2}}{2}$	0
$\tan t$	Undef.	1	0	−1	Undef.

See margin.

60. (a)

t	0	$\frac{1}{4}$	$\frac{1}{2}$	$\frac{3}{4}$	1
y	0.25	0.0138	−0.1501	−0.0249	0.0883

72. See Additional Answers beginning on page AA1.

4.3 Right Triangle Trigonometry

What you should learn

- Evaluate trigonometric functions of acute angles.
- Use fundamental trigonometric identities.
- Use a calculator to evaluate trigonometric functions.
- Use trigonometric functions to model and solve real-life problems.

Why you should learn it

Trigonometric functions are often used to analyze real-life situations. For instance, in Exercise 76 on page 309, you can use trigonometric functions to find the height of a helium-filled balloon.

Joseph Sohm/Visions of America/Corbis

The Six Trigonometric Functions

Our second look at the trigonometric functions is from a *right triangle* perspective. Consider a right triangle, with one acute angle labeled θ, as shown in Figure 4.26. Relative to the angle θ, the three sides of the triangle are the **hypotenuse,** the **opposite side** (the side opposite the angle θ), and the **adjacent side** (the side adjacent to the angle θ).

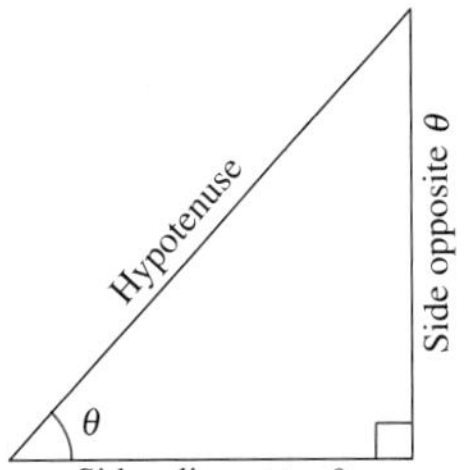

FIGURE 4.26

Using the lengths of these three sides, you can form six ratios that define the six trigonometric functions of the acute angle θ.

sine cosecant cosine secant tangent cotangent

In the following definitions, it is important to see that $0° < \theta < 90°$ (θ lies in the first quadrant) and that for such angles the value of each trigonometric function is *positive*.

Right Triangle Definitions of Trigonometric Functions

Let θ be an *acute* angle of a right triangle. The six trigonometric functions of the angle θ are defined as follows. (Note that the functions in the second row are the *reciprocals* of the corresponding functions in the first row.)

$$\sin\theta = \frac{\text{opp}}{\text{hyp}} \qquad \cos\theta = \frac{\text{adj}}{\text{hyp}} \qquad \tan\theta = \frac{\text{opp}}{\text{adj}}$$

$$\csc\theta = \frac{\text{hyp}}{\text{opp}} \qquad \sec\theta = \frac{\text{hyp}}{\text{adj}} \qquad \cot\theta = \frac{\text{adj}}{\text{opp}}$$

The abbreviations opp, adj, and hyp represent the lengths of the three sides of a right triangle.

opp = the length of the side *opposite* θ

adj = the length of the side *adjacent to* θ

hyp = the length of the *hypotenuse*

1 PLAN AND PREPARE

Warm-up Exercises

Transparency Available
Available at the Instructor's companion site.

Notetaking Guide

Transparency Available
Promotes interactive learning and notetaking skills. Available at the Instructor's companion site.

Animated Precalculus

An **Animated Precalculus** tutorial is available at the Student companion site for **Section 4.3.**

Pacing

Average: 2 days
Advanced: 2 days
Block: 0.5 block with 4.2
0.5 block with 4.4

2 FOCUS AND MOTIVATE

Essential Question

How do you use trigonometry to find unknown side lengths and angles in right triangles? **Tell students that they will learn how to answer this question by studying right triangle definitions of and identities between trigonometric functions.**

Resource Planning Guide

Chapter Resources

- Complete Solutions Guide

Workbooks

- Notetaking Guide
- Student Solutions Guide

Interactive Technology

- Instructor Success Organizer
- Notetaking Guide IAE
- Instructional DVDs
- Animated Precalculus
- PowerLecture with ExamView

3 TEACH

Extra Example 1

Find the values of the six trigonometric functions of θ as shown in the figure.

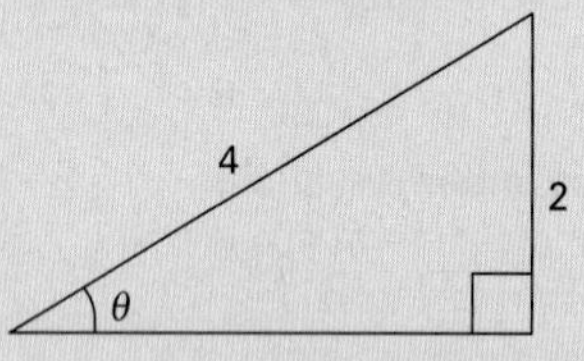

$\sin\theta = \frac{1}{2}$, $\cos\theta = \frac{\sqrt{3}}{2}$,

$\tan\theta = \frac{\sqrt{3}}{3}$, $\cot\theta = \sqrt{3}$,

$\sec\theta = \frac{2\sqrt{3}}{3}$, $\csc\theta = 2$

Extra Example 2

Find the values of cot 45°, sec 45°, and csc 45°.

1, $\sqrt{2}$, $\sqrt{2}$

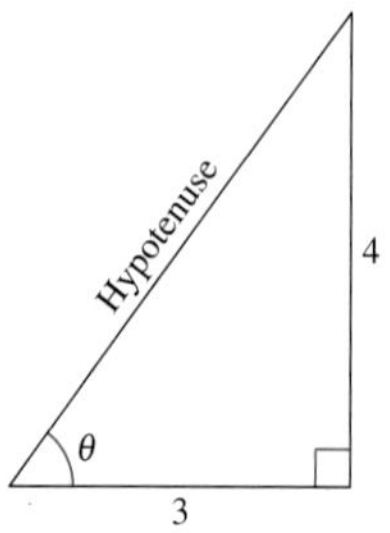

FIGURE 4.27

Example 1 Evaluating Trigonometric Functions

Use the triangle in Figure 4.27 to find the values of the six trigonometric functions of θ.

Solution

By the Pythagorean Theorem, $(\text{hyp})^2 = (\text{opp})^2 + (\text{adj})^2$, it follows that

$$\begin{aligned} \text{hyp} &= \sqrt{4^2 + 3^2} \\ &= \sqrt{25} \\ &= 5. \end{aligned}$$

So, the six trigonometric functions of θ are

$$\sin\theta = \frac{\text{opp}}{\text{hyp}} = \frac{4}{5} \qquad \csc\theta = \frac{\text{hyp}}{\text{opp}} = \frac{5}{4}$$

$$\cos\theta = \frac{\text{adj}}{\text{hyp}} = \frac{3}{5} \qquad \sec\theta = \frac{\text{hyp}}{\text{adj}} = \frac{5}{3}$$

$$\tan\theta = \frac{\text{opp}}{\text{adj}} = \frac{4}{3} \qquad \cot\theta = \frac{\text{adj}}{\text{opp}} = \frac{3}{4}.$$

CHECKPoint Now try Exercise 7.

Algebra Help

You can review the Pythagorean Theorem in Section 1.1.

HISTORICAL NOTE

Georg Joachim Rhaeticus (1514–1574) was the leading Teutonic mathematical astronomer of the 16th century. He was the first to define the trigonometric functions as ratios of the sides of a right triangle.

In Example 1, you were given the lengths of two sides of the right triangle, but not the angle θ. Often, you will be asked to find the trigonometric functions of a *given* acute angle θ. To do this, construct a right triangle having θ as one of its angles.

Example 2 Evaluating Trigonometric Functions of 45°

Find the values of sin 45°, cos 45°, and tan 45°.

Solution

Construct a right triangle having 45° as one of its acute angles, as shown in Figure 4.28. Choose the length of the adjacent side to be 1. From geometry, you know that the other acute angle is also 45°. So, the triangle is isosceles and the length of the opposite side is also 1. Using the Pythagorean Theorem, you find the length of the hypotenuse to be $\sqrt{2}$.

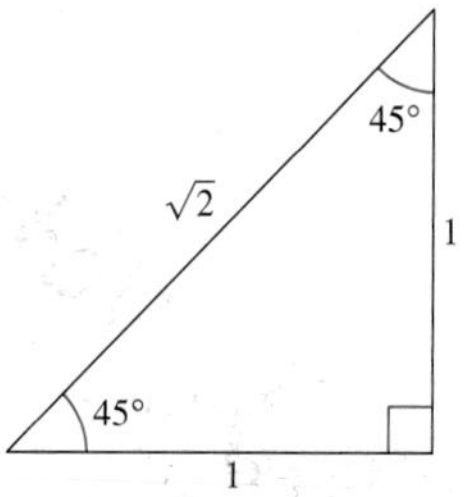

FIGURE 4.28

$$\sin 45^\circ = \frac{\text{opp}}{\text{hyp}} = \frac{1}{\sqrt{2}} = \frac{\sqrt{2}}{2}$$

$$\cos 45^\circ = \frac{\text{adj}}{\text{hyp}} = \frac{1}{\sqrt{2}} = \frac{\sqrt{2}}{2}$$

$$\tan 45^\circ = \frac{\text{opp}}{\text{adj}} = \frac{1}{1} = 1$$

CHECKPoint Now try Exercise 23.

Differentiated Instruction

Inclusion Some students will benefit from a review of the Pythagorean Theorem. Direct their attention to the right triangle in Example 1, and have students use the Pythagorean Theorem to write three equations that model the length of the hypotenuse, the opposite side, and the adjacent side—$(\text{hyp})^2 = (\text{opp})^2 + (\text{adj})^2$, $(\text{opp})^2 = (\text{hyp})^2 - (\text{adj})^2$, and $(\text{adj})^2 = (\text{hyp})^2 - (\text{opp})^2$.

Study Tip

Because the angles 30°, 45°, and 60° ($\pi/6$, $\pi/4$, and $\pi/3$) occur frequently in trigonometry, you should learn to construct the triangles shown in Figures 4.28 and 4.29.

Example 3 Evaluating Trigonometric Functions of 30° and 60°

Use the equilateral triangle shown in Figure 4.29 to find the values of sin 60°, cos 60°, sin 30°, and cos 30°.

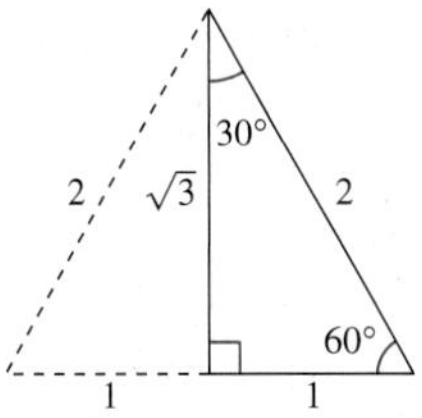

FIGURE 4.29

Solution

Use the Pythagorean Theorem and the equilateral triangle in Figure 4.29 to verify the lengths of the sides shown in the figure. For $\theta = 60°$, you have adj $= 1$, opp $= \sqrt{3}$, and hyp $= 2$. So,

$$\sin 60° = \frac{\text{opp}}{\text{hyp}} = \frac{\sqrt{3}}{2} \quad \text{and} \quad \cos 60° = \frac{\text{adj}}{\text{hyp}} = \frac{1}{2}.$$

For $\theta = 30°$, adj $= \sqrt{3}$, opp $= 1$, and hyp $= 2$. So,

$$\sin 30° = \frac{\text{opp}}{\text{hyp}} = \frac{1}{2} \quad \text{and} \quad \cos 30° = \frac{\text{adj}}{\text{hyp}} = \frac{\sqrt{3}}{2}.$$

CHECKPoint Now try Exercise 27.

TECHNOLOGY

You can use a calculator to convert the answers in Example 3 to decimals. However, the radical form is the exact value and in most cases, the exact value is preferred.

Extra Example 3

Use the equilateral triangle shown to find the values of tan 60°, cot 60°, tan 30°, and cot 30°.

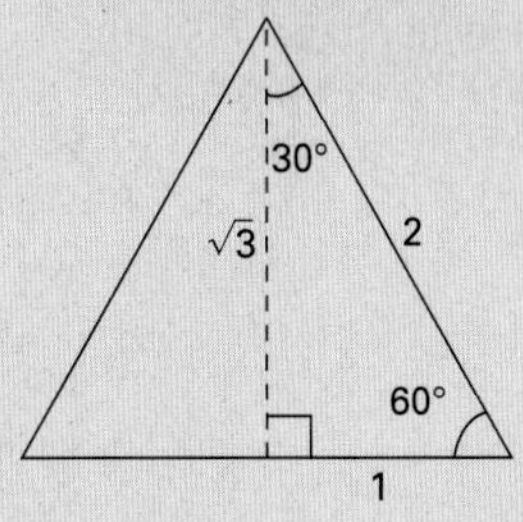

$\sqrt{3}, \frac{\sqrt{3}}{3}, \frac{\sqrt{3}}{3}, \sqrt{3}$

Sines, Cosines, and Tangents of Special Angles

$$\sin 30° = \sin\frac{\pi}{6} = \frac{1}{2} \qquad \cos 30° = \cos\frac{\pi}{6} = \frac{\sqrt{3}}{2} \qquad \tan 30° = \tan\frac{\pi}{6} = \frac{\sqrt{3}}{3}$$

$$\sin 45° = \sin\frac{\pi}{4} = \frac{\sqrt{2}}{2} \qquad \cos 45° = \cos\frac{\pi}{4} = \frac{\sqrt{2}}{2} \qquad \tan 45° = \tan\frac{\pi}{4} = 1$$

$$\sin 60° = \sin\frac{\pi}{3} = \frac{\sqrt{3}}{2} \qquad \cos 60° = \cos\frac{\pi}{3} = \frac{1}{2} \qquad \tan 60° = \tan\frac{\pi}{3} = \sqrt{3}$$

In the box, note that $\sin 30° = \frac{1}{2} = \cos 60°$. This occurs because 30° and 60° are complementary angles. In general, it can be shown from the right triangle definitions that *cofunctions of complementary angles are equal*. That is, if θ is an acute angle, the following relationships are true.

$$\sin(90° - \theta) = \cos\theta \qquad \cos(90° - \theta) = \sin\theta$$

$$\tan(90° - \theta) = \cot\theta \qquad \cot(90° - \theta) = \tan\theta$$

$$\sec(90° - \theta) = \csc\theta \qquad \csc(90° - \theta) = \sec\theta$$

Cofunction Identity

Extra Example 4
Let θ be an acute angle such that $\cos \theta = 0.96$. Find the values of (a) $\sin \theta$ and (b) $\tan \theta$, using trigonometric identities.
0.28; $0.291\overline{6}$

Trigonometric Identities

In trigonometry, a great deal of time is spent studying relationships between trigonometric functions (identities).

Fundamental Trigonometric Identities

Reciprocal Identities

$$\sin \theta = \frac{1}{\csc \theta} \qquad \cos \theta = \frac{1}{\sec \theta} \qquad \tan \theta = \frac{1}{\cot \theta}$$

$$\csc \theta = \frac{1}{\sin \theta} \qquad \sec \theta = \frac{1}{\cos \theta} \qquad \cot \theta = \frac{1}{\tan \theta}$$

Quotient Identities

$$\tan \theta = \frac{\sin \theta}{\cos \theta} \qquad \cot \theta = \frac{\cos \theta}{\sin \theta}$$

Pythagorean Identities

$$\sin^2 \theta + \cos^2 \theta = 1 \qquad 1 + \tan^2 \theta = \sec^2 \theta$$

$$1 + \cot^2 \theta = \csc^2 \theta$$

Note that $\sin^2 \theta$ represents $(\sin \theta)^2$, $\cos^2 \theta$ represents $(\cos \theta)^2$, and so on.

Example 4 Applying Trigonometric Identities

Let θ be an acute angle such that $\sin \theta = 0.6$. Find the values of (a) $\cos \theta$ and (b) $\tan \theta$ using trigonometric identities.

Solution

a. To find the value of $\cos \theta$, use the Pythagorean identity

$$\sin^2 \theta + \cos^2 \theta = 1.$$

So, you have

$$(0.6)^2 + \cos^2 \theta = 1 \qquad \text{Substitute 0.6 for } \sin \theta.$$

$$\cos^2 \theta = 1 - (0.6)^2 = 0.64 \qquad \text{Subtract } (0.6)^2 \text{ from each side.}$$

$$\cos \theta = \sqrt{0.64} = 0.8. \qquad \text{Extract the positive square root.}$$

b. Now, knowing the sine and cosine of θ, you can find the tangent of θ to be

$$\tan \theta = \frac{\sin \theta}{\cos \theta} = \frac{0.6}{0.8} = 0.75.$$

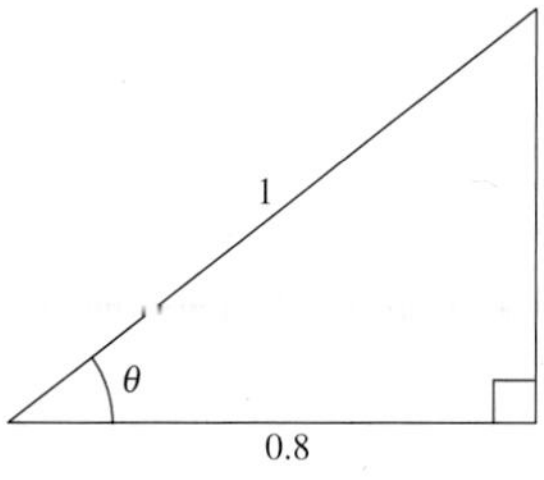

FIGURE 4.30

Use the definitions of $\cos \theta$ and $\tan \theta$, and the triangle shown in Figure 4.30, to check these results.

CHECKPoint Now try Exercise 33.

Example 5 Applying Trigonometric Identities

Let θ be an acute angle such that $\tan \theta = 3$. Find the values of (a) $\cot \theta$ and (b) $\sec \theta$ using trigonometric identities.

Solution

a. $\cot \theta = \dfrac{1}{\tan \theta}$ — Reciprocal identity

$\cot \theta = \dfrac{1}{3}$

b. $\sec^2 \theta = 1 + \tan^2 \theta$ — Pythagorean identity

$\sec^2 \theta = 1 + 3^2$

$\sec^2 \theta = 10$

$\sec \theta = \sqrt{10}$

Use the definitions of $\cot \theta$ and $\sec \theta$, and the triangle shown in Figure 4.31, to check these results.

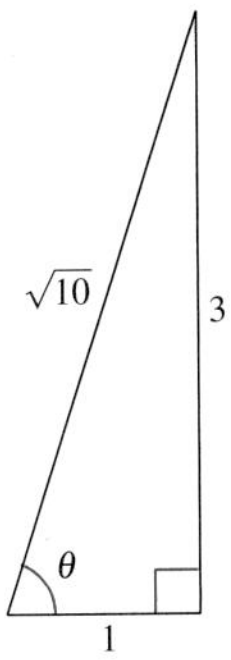

FIGURE 4.31

CHECKPoint Now try Exercise 35.

Evaluating Trigonometric Functions with a Calculator

To use a calculator to evaluate trigonometric functions of angles measured in degrees, first set the calculator to *degree* mode and then proceed as demonstrated in Section 4.2. For instance, you can find values of cos 28° and sec 28° as follows.

	Function	*Mode*	*Calculator Keystrokes*	*Display*
a.	cos 28°	Degree	[COS] 28 [ENTER]	0.8829476
b.	sec 28°	Degree	[(] [COS] [(] 28 [)] [)] [x^{-1}] [ENTER]	1.1325701

Throughout this text, angles are assumed to be measured in radians unless noted otherwise. For example, sin 1 means the sine of 1 radian and sin 1° means the sine of 1 degree.

Study Tip

You can also use the reciprocal identities for sine, cosine, and tangent to evaluate the cosecant, secant, and cotangent functions with a calculator. For instance, you could use the following keystroke sequence to evaluate sec 28°.

1 [÷] [COS] 28 [ENTER]

The calculator should display 1.1325701.

Example 6 Using a Calculator

Use a calculator to evaluate $\sec(5° \, 40' \, 12'')$.

Solution

Begin by converting to decimal degree form. [Recall that $1' = \frac{1}{60}(1°)$ and $1'' = \frac{1}{3600}(1°)$].

$$5° \, 40' \, 12'' = 5° + \left(\frac{40}{60}\right)° + \left(\frac{12}{3600}\right)° = 5.67°$$

Then, use a calculator to evaluate sec 5.67°.

Function	*Calculator Keystrokes*	*Display*
$\sec(5° \, 40' \, 12'') = \sec 5.67°$	[(] [COS] [(] 5.67 [)] [)] [x^{-1}] [ENTER]	1.0049166

CHECKPoint Now try Exercise 51.

Extra Example 5

Let β be an acute angle such that $\tan \beta = 4$. Find the values of (a) $\cot \beta$ and (b) $\sec \beta$, using trigonometric identities.

$\frac{1}{4}$; $\sqrt{17}$

Extra Example 6

Use a calculator to evaluate $\csc(34° \, 30' \, 36'')$.

1.7651

Avoiding Common Errors

Students should check to see whether their calculators are set to the correct mode *(radian* or *degree)* before using them to evaluate a trigonometric function.

Extra Example 7

A biologist wants to know the width *w* of a river in order to properly set instruments for studying the pollutants in the water. From point *A*, the biologist walks downstream 70 feet and sights to point *C* (see figure). From this sighting, it is determined that $\theta = 54°$. How wide is the river?

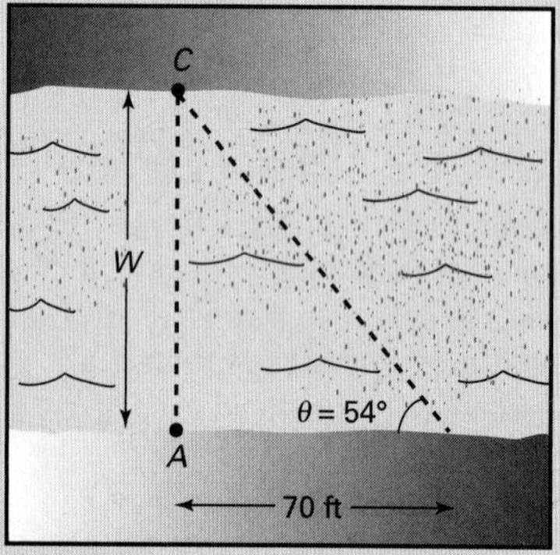

≈ **96 feet**

Extra Example 8

A 12-meter flagpole casts a 12-meter shadow, as shown in the figure. Find θ, the angle of elevation to the sun.

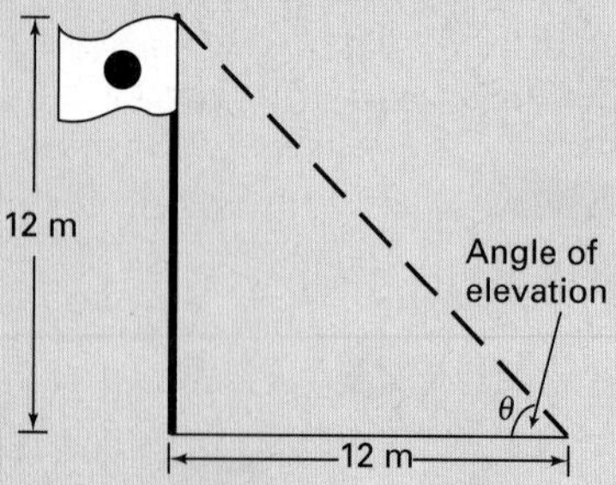

45°

Applications Involving Right Triangles

Many applications of trigonometry involve a process called **solving right triangles.** In this type of application, you are usually given one side of a right triangle and one of the acute angles and are asked to find one of the other sides, *or* you are given two sides and are asked to find one of the acute angles.

In Example 7, the angle you are given is the **angle of elevation,** which represents the angle from the horizontal upward to an object. For objects that lie below the horizontal, it is common to use the term **angle of depression,** as shown in Figure 4.32.

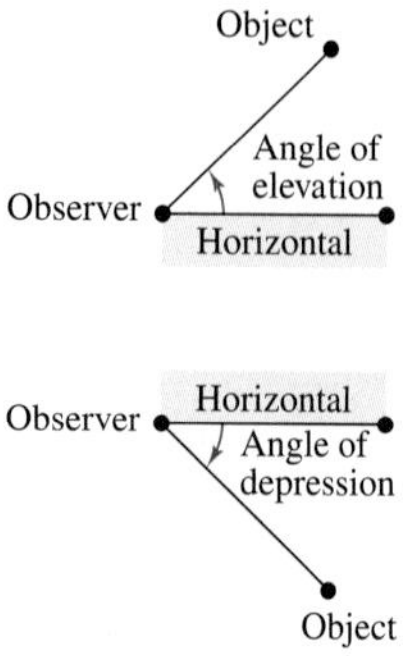

FIGURE 4.32

Example 7 Using Trigonometry to Solve a Right Triangle

A surveyor is standing 115 feet from the base of the Washington Monument, as shown in Figure 4.33. The surveyor measures the angle of elevation to the top of the monument as 78.3°. How tall is the Washington Monument?

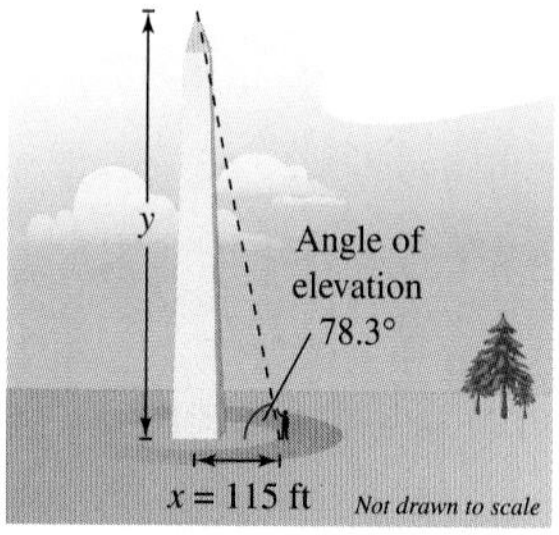

FIGURE 4.33

Solution

From Figure 4.33, you can see that

$$\tan 78.3° = \frac{\text{opp}}{\text{adj}} = \frac{y}{x}$$

where $x = 115$ and y is the height of the monument. So, the height of the Washington Monument is

$$y = x \tan 78.3° \approx 115(4.82882) \approx 555 \text{ feet.}$$

CHECKPoint Now try Exercise 67.

Example 8 Using Trigonometry to Solve a Right Triangle

A historic lighthouse is 200 yards from a bike path along the edge of a lake. A walkway to the lighthouse is 400 yards long. Find the acute angle θ between the bike path and the walkway, as illustrated in Figure 4.34.

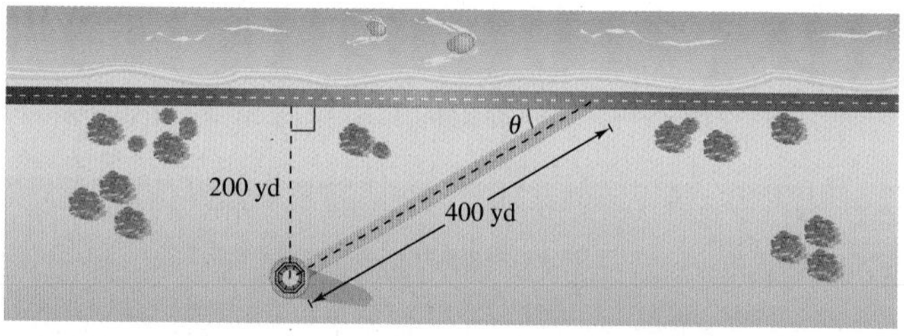

FIGURE 4.34

Solution

From Figure 4.34, you can see that the sine of the angle θ is

$$\sin \theta = \frac{\text{opp}}{\text{hyp}} = \frac{200}{400} = \frac{1}{2}.$$

Now you should recognize that $\theta = 30°$.

CHECKPoint Now try Exercise 69.

By now you are able to recognize that $\theta = 30°$ is the acute angle that satisfies the equation $\sin \theta = \frac{1}{2}$. Suppose, however, that you were given the equation $\sin \theta = 0.6$ and were asked to find the acute angle θ. Because

$$\sin 30° = \frac{1}{2}$$
$$= 0.5000$$

and

$$\sin 45° = \frac{1}{\sqrt{2}}$$
$$\approx 0.7071$$

you might guess that θ lies somewhere between 30° and 45°. In a later section, you will study a method by which a more precise value of θ can be determined.

Example 9 Solving a Right Triangle

Find the length c of the skateboard ramp shown in Figure 4.35.

FIGURE 4.35

Solution

From Figure 4.35, you can see that

$$\sin 18.4° = \frac{\text{opp}}{\text{hyp}}$$
$$= \frac{4}{c}.$$

So, the length of the skateboard ramp is

$$c = \frac{4}{\sin 18.4°}$$
$$\approx \frac{4}{0.3156}$$
$$\approx 12.7 \text{ feet.}$$

CHECKPoint Now try Exercise 71.

Extra Example 9

A ramp $17\frac{1}{2}$ feet in length rises to a loading platform that is $3\frac{1}{2}$ feet off the ground (see figure). Find the angle θ that the ramp makes with the ground.

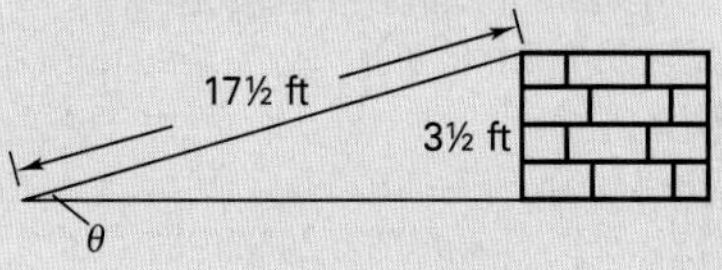

$\approx 12°$

Closing the Lesson

Have students summarize the major points of the lesson and answer the Essential Question: How do you use trigonometry to find unknown side lengths and angles in right triangles?

- **Use the right triangle definitions to express trigonometric functions as ratios between side lengths of a right triangle.**
- **Evaluate trigonometric functions of 30°, 45°, and 60° by using the side lengths of unit 30°-60°-90° and 45°-45°-90° triangles.**
- **Use fundamental trigonometric identities to find an unknown trigonometric ratio when another is given.**

4 PRACTICE AND APPLY

Assignment Guide

Transparencies Available
Available at the Instructor's companion site.

Average:
Day 1: pp. 306–307
Exs. 5, 9–15 odd, 22, 24, 25–31 odd, 32, 37–43 odd, 57–61 odd
Day 2: pp. 307–309
Exs. 47–55 odd, 63–66, 70, 71, 73, 76, 77–81 odd, 84, 85

Advanced:
Day 1: pp. 306–307
Exs. 6–18 even, 24–30 even, 34–46 even, 58–62 even
Day 2: pp. 307–309
Exs. 50–56 even, 64–72 even, 74–76, 78–88 even

Block:
pp. 306–307
Exs. 5, 9–15 odd, 22, 24, 25–31 odd, 32, 37–43 odd, 57–61 odd (with 4.2)
pp. 307–309
Exs. 47–55 odd, 63–66, 70, 71, 73, 76, 77–81 odd, 84, 85 (with 4.4)

5. $\sin\theta = \frac{3}{5}$ $\csc\theta = \frac{5}{3}$
$\cos\theta = \frac{4}{5}$ $\sec\theta = \frac{5}{4}$
$\tan\theta = \frac{3}{4}$ $\cot\theta = \frac{4}{3}$

6. $\sin\theta = \frac{5}{13}$ $\csc\theta = \frac{13}{5}$
$\cos\theta = \frac{12}{13}$ $\sec\theta = \frac{13}{12}$
$\tan\theta = \frac{5}{12}$ $\cot\theta = \frac{12}{5}$

7. $\sin\theta = \frac{9}{41}$ $\csc\theta = \frac{41}{9}$
$\cos\theta = \frac{40}{41}$ $\sec\theta = \frac{41}{40}$
$\tan\theta = \frac{9}{40}$ $\cot\theta = \frac{40}{9}$

8. $\sin\theta = \sqrt{2}/2$ $\csc\theta = \sqrt{2}$
$\cos\theta = \sqrt{2}/2$ $\sec\theta = \sqrt{2}$
$\tan\theta = 1$ $\cot\theta = 1$

9. $\sin\theta = \frac{8}{17}$ $\csc\theta = \frac{17}{8}$
$\cos\theta = \frac{15}{17}$ $\sec\theta = \frac{17}{15}$
$\tan\theta = \frac{8}{15}$ $\cot\theta = \frac{15}{8}$
The triangles are similar, and corresponding sides are proportional.

10. $\sin\theta = \frac{3}{5}$ $\csc\theta = \frac{5}{3}$
$\cos\theta = \frac{4}{5}$ $\sec\theta = \frac{5}{4}$
$\tan\theta = \frac{3}{4}$ $\cot\theta = \frac{4}{3}$
The triangles are similar, and corresponding sides are proportional.

4.3 EXERCISES

See www.CalcChat.com for worked-out solutions to odd-numbered exercises.

VOCABULARY

1. Match the trigonometric function with its right triangle definition.

(a) Sine v (b) Cosine iv (c) Tangent vi (d) Cosecant iii (e) Secant i (f) Cotangent ii

(i) $\frac{\text{hypotenuse}}{\text{adjacent}}$ (ii) $\frac{\text{adjacent}}{\text{opposite}}$ (iii) $\frac{\text{hypotenuse}}{\text{opposite}}$ (iv) $\frac{\text{adjacent}}{\text{hypotenuse}}$ (v) $\frac{\text{opposite}}{\text{hypotenuse}}$ (vi) $\frac{\text{opposite}}{\text{adjacent}}$

In Exercises 2–4, fill in the blanks.

2. Relative to the angle θ, the three sides of a right triangle are the opposite side, the adjacent side, and the ________. hypotenuse

3. Cofunctions of ________ angles are equal. complementary

4. An angle that measures from the horizontal upward to an object is called the angle of elevation, whereas an angle that measures from the horizontal downward to an object is called the angle of depression

SKILLS AND APPLICATIONS

In Exercises 5–8, find the exact values of the six trigonometric functions of the angle θ shown in the figure. (Use the Pythagorean Theorem to find the third side of the triangle.) 5–8. See margin.

5.
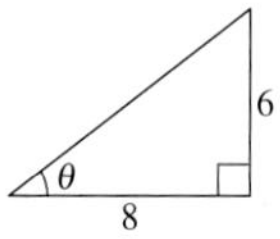

6.
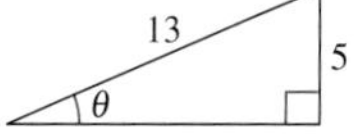

7.
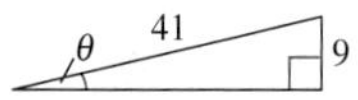

8.
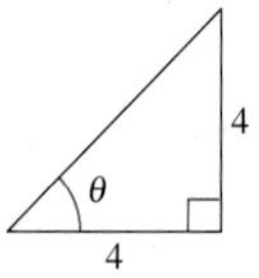

In Exercises 9–12, find the exact values of the six trigonometric functions of the angle θ for each of the two triangles. Explain why the function values are the same. 9–12. See margin.

9.
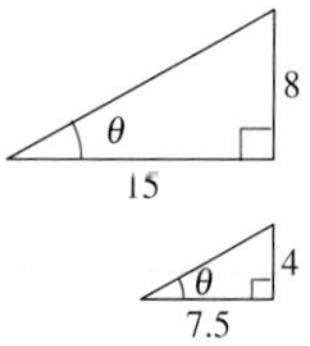

10.
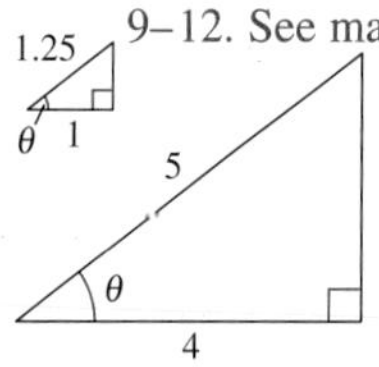

11.
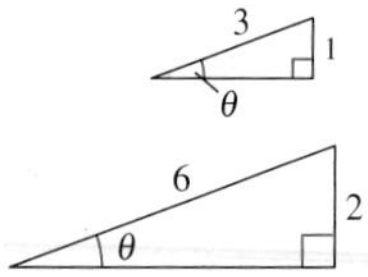

12.
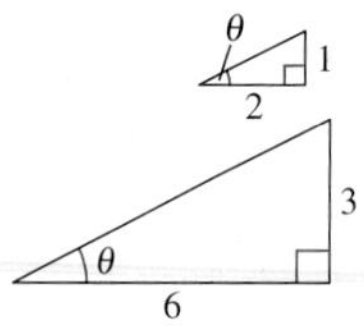

In Exercises 13–20, sketch a right triangle corresponding to the trigonometric function of the acute angle θ. Use the Pythagorean Theorem to determine the third side and then find the other five trigonometric functions of θ.

13. $\tan\theta = \frac{3}{4}$ **14.** $\cos\theta = \frac{5}{6}$ 13–20. See margin.

15. $\sec\theta = \frac{3}{2}$ **16.** $\tan\theta = \frac{4}{5}$

17. $\sin\theta = \frac{1}{5}$ **18.** $\sec\theta = \frac{17}{7}$

19. $\cot\theta = 3$ **20.** $\csc\theta = 9$

In Exercises 21–30, construct an appropriate triangle to complete the table. ($0° \le \theta \le 90°, 0 \le \theta \le \pi/2$)

	Function	*θ (deg)*	*θ (rad)*	*Function Value*
21.	sin	30°		
22.	cos	45°		
23.	sec	45°	$\frac{\pi}{4}$	$\sqrt{2}$
24.	tan	60°	$\frac{\pi}{3}$	$\sqrt{3}$
25.	cot	60°	$\frac{\pi}{3}$	$\frac{\sqrt{3}}{3}$
26.	csc	45°	$\frac{\pi}{4}$	$\sqrt{2}$
27.	csc	30°	$\frac{\pi}{6}$	2
28.	sin	45°	$\frac{\pi}{4}$	$\frac{\sqrt{2}}{2}$
29.	cot	45°	$\frac{\pi}{4}$	1
30.	tan	30°	$\frac{\pi}{6}$	$\frac{\sqrt{3}}{3}$

21–22. See margin.

11. $\sin\theta = \dfrac{1}{3}$ $\csc\theta = 3$
$\cos\theta = \dfrac{2\sqrt{2}}{3}$ $\sec\theta = \dfrac{3\sqrt{2}}{4}$
$\tan\theta = \dfrac{\sqrt{2}}{4}$ $\cot\theta = 2\sqrt{2}$
The triangles are similar, and corresponding sides are proportional.

12. $\sin\theta = \dfrac{\sqrt{5}}{5}$ $\csc\theta = \sqrt{5}$
$\cos\theta = \dfrac{2\sqrt{5}}{5}$ $\sec\theta = \dfrac{\sqrt{5}}{2}$
$\tan\theta = \dfrac{1}{2}$ $\cot\theta = 2$
The triangles are similar, and corresponding sides are proportional.

21. $\dfrac{\pi}{6}; \dfrac{1}{2}$

22. $\dfrac{\pi}{4}; \dfrac{\sqrt{2}}{2}$

13–20. See Additional Answers beginning on page AA1.

In Exercises 31–36, use the given function value(s), and trigonometric identities (including the cofunction identities), to find the indicated trigonometric functions. 31–36. See margin.

31. $\sin 60° = \frac{\sqrt{3}}{2}$, $\cos 60° = \frac{1}{2}$

(a) $\sin 30°$ (b) $\cos 30°$

(c) $\tan 60°$ (d) $\cot 60°$

32. $\sin 30° = \frac{1}{2}$, $\tan 30° = \frac{\sqrt{3}}{3}$

(a) $\csc 30°$ (b) $\cot 60°$

(c) $\cos 30°$ (d) $\cot 30°$

33. $\cos \theta = \frac{1}{3}$

(a) $\sin \theta$ (b) $\tan \theta$

(c) $\sec \theta$ (d) $\csc(90° - \theta)$

34. $\sec \theta = 5$

(a) $\cos \theta$ (b) $\cot \theta$

(c) $\cot(90° - \theta)$ (d) $\sin \theta$

35. $\cot \alpha = 5$

(a) $\tan \alpha$ (b) $\csc \alpha$

(c) $\cot(90° - \alpha)$ (d) $\cos \alpha$

36. $\cos \beta = \frac{\sqrt{7}}{4}$

(a) $\sec \beta$ (b) $\sin \beta$

(c) $\cot \beta$ (d) $\sin(90° - \beta)$

In Exercises 37–46, use trigonometric identities to transform the left side of the equation into the right side ($0 < \theta < \pi/2$). 37–46. Answers will vary.

37. $\tan \theta \cot \theta = 1$

38. $\cos \theta \sec \theta = 1$

39. $\tan \alpha \cos \alpha = \sin \alpha$

40. $\cot \alpha \sin \alpha = \cos \alpha$

41. $(1 + \sin \theta)(1 - \sin \theta) = \cos^2 \theta$

42. $(1 + \cos \theta)(1 - \cos \theta) = \sin^2 \theta$

43. $(\sec \theta + \tan \theta)(\sec \theta - \tan \theta) = 1$

44. $\sin^2 \theta - \cos^2 \theta = 2 \sin^2 \theta - 1$

45. $\frac{\sin \theta}{\cos \theta} + \frac{\cos \theta}{\sin \theta} = \csc \theta \sec \theta$

46. $\frac{\tan \beta + \cot \beta}{\tan \beta} = \csc^2 \beta$

In Exercises 47–56, use a calculator to evaluate each function. Round your answers to four decimal places. (Be sure the calculator is in the correct angle mode.)

47. (a) $\sin 10°$ 0.1736 (b) $\cos 80°$ 0.1736

48. (a) $\tan 23.5°$ 0.4348 (b) $\cot 66.5°$ 0.4348

49. (a) $\sin 16.35°$ 0.2815 (b) $\csc 16.35°$ 3.5523

50. (a) $\cot 79.56°$ 0.1843 (b) $\sec 79.56°$ 5.5186

51. (a) $\cos 4° 50' 15''$ (b) $\sec 4° 50' 15''$ See margin.

52. (a) $\sec 42° 12'$ 1.3499 (b) $\csc 48° 7'$ 1.3432

53. (a) $\cot 11° 15'$ 5.0273 (b) $\tan 11° 15'$ 0.1989

54. (a) $\sec 56° 8' 10''$ (b) $\cos 56° 8' 10''$ See margin.

55. (a) $\csc 32° 40' 3''$ (b) $\tan 44° 28' 16''$ See margin.

56. (a) $\sec(\frac{9}{5} \cdot 20 + 32)°$ 2.6695 (b) $\cot(\frac{9}{5} \cdot 30 + 32)°$ 0.0699

In Exercises 57–62, find the values of θ in degrees ($0° < \theta < 90°$) and radians ($0 < \theta < \pi/2$) without the aid of a calculator. 57–62. See margin.

57. (a) $\sin \theta = \frac{1}{2}$ (b) $\csc \theta = 2$

58. (a) $\cos \theta = \frac{\sqrt{2}}{2}$ (b) $\tan \theta = 1$

59. (a) $\sec \theta = 2$ (b) $\cot \theta = 1$

60. (a) $\tan \theta = \sqrt{3}$ (b) $\cos \theta = \frac{1}{2}$

61. (a) $\csc \theta = \frac{2\sqrt{3}}{3}$ (b) $\sin \theta = \frac{\sqrt{2}}{2}$

62. (a) $\cot \theta = \frac{\sqrt{3}}{3}$ (b) $\sec \theta = \sqrt{2}$

In Exercises 63–66, solve for x, y, or r as indicated.

63. Solve for y. $9\sqrt{3}$

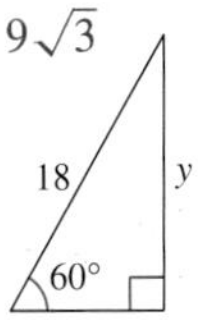

64. Solve for x. $30\sqrt{3}$

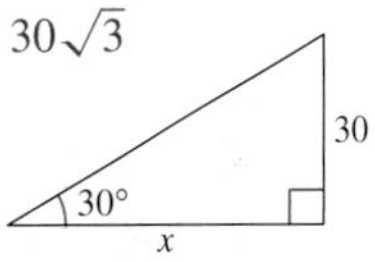

65. Solve for x. $\frac{32\sqrt{3}}{3}$

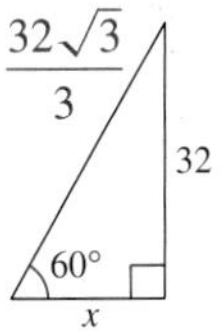

66. Solve for r. $20\sqrt{2}$

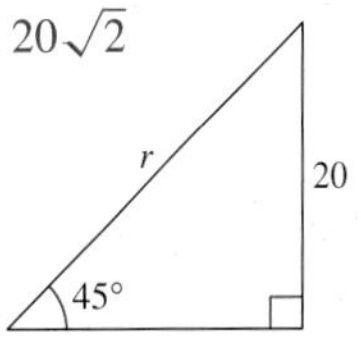

67. EMPIRE STATE BUILDING You are standing 45 meters from the base of the Empire State Building. You estimate that the angle of elevation to the top of the 86th floor (the observatory) is 82°. If the total height of the building is another 123 meters above the 86th floor, what is the approximate height of the building? One of your friends is on the 86th floor. What is the distance between you and your friend? 443.2 m; 323.3 m

31. (a) $\frac{1}{2}$ (b) $\frac{\sqrt{3}}{2}$ (c) $\sqrt{3}$ (d) $\frac{\sqrt{3}}{3}$

32. (a) 2 (b) $\frac{\sqrt{3}}{3}$ (c) $\frac{\sqrt{3}}{2}$ (d) $\sqrt{3}$

33. (a) $\frac{2\sqrt{2}}{3}$ (b) $2\sqrt{2}$ (c) 3 (d) 3

34. (a) $\frac{1}{5}$ (b) $\frac{\sqrt{6}}{12}$ (c) $2\sqrt{6}$ (d) $\frac{2\sqrt{6}}{5}$

35. (a) $\frac{1}{5}$ (b) $\sqrt{26}$ (c) $\frac{1}{5}$ (d) $\frac{5\sqrt{26}}{26}$

36. (a) $\frac{4\sqrt{7}}{7}$ (b) $\frac{3}{4}$ (c) $\frac{\sqrt{7}}{3}$ (d) $\frac{\sqrt{7}}{4}$

51. (a) 0.9964 (b) 1.0036

54. (a) 1.7946 (b) 0.5572

55. (a) 1.8527 (b) 0.9817

57. (a) $30° = \frac{\pi}{6}$ (b) $30° = \frac{\pi}{6}$

58. (a) $45° = \frac{\pi}{4}$ (b) $45° = \frac{\pi}{4}$

59. (a) $60° = \frac{\pi}{3}$ (b) $45° = \frac{\pi}{4}$

60. (a) $60° = \frac{\pi}{3}$ (b) $60° = \frac{\pi}{3}$

61. (a) $60° = \frac{\pi}{3}$ (b) $45° = \frac{\pi}{4}$

62. (a) $60° = \frac{\pi}{3}$ (b) $45° = \frac{\pi}{4}$

63. 15.5885
64. 51.9165
65. 18.4752
66. 28.2843

68. (a)

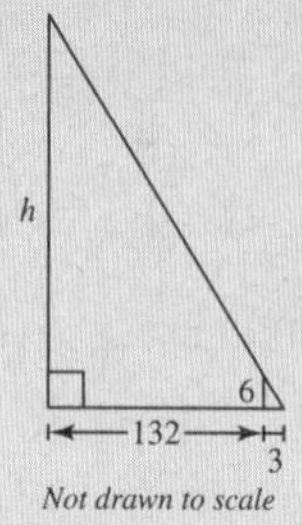

(b) $\tan\theta = \frac{6}{3} = \frac{h}{135}$

68. HEIGHT A six-foot person walks from the base of a broadcasting tower directly toward the tip of the shadow cast by the tower. When the person is 132 feet from the tower and 3 feet from the tip of the shadow, the person's shadow starts to appear beyond the tower's shadow.

(a) Draw a right triangle that gives a visual representation of the problem. Show the known quantities of the triangle and use a variable to indicate the height of the tower. See margin.

(b) Use a trigonometric function to write an equation involving the unknown quantity. See margin.

(c) What is the height of the tower? 270 ft

69. ANGLE OF ELEVATION You are skiing down a mountain with a vertical height of 1500 feet. The distance from the top of the mountain to the base is 3000 feet. What is the angle of elevation from the base to the top of the mountain? $30° = \pi/6$

70. WIDTH OF A RIVER A biologist wants to know the width w of a river so that instruments for studying the pollutants in the water can be set properly. From point A, the biologist walks downstream 100 feet and sights to point C (see figure). From this sighting, it is determined that $\theta = 54°$. How wide is the river? 137.6 ft

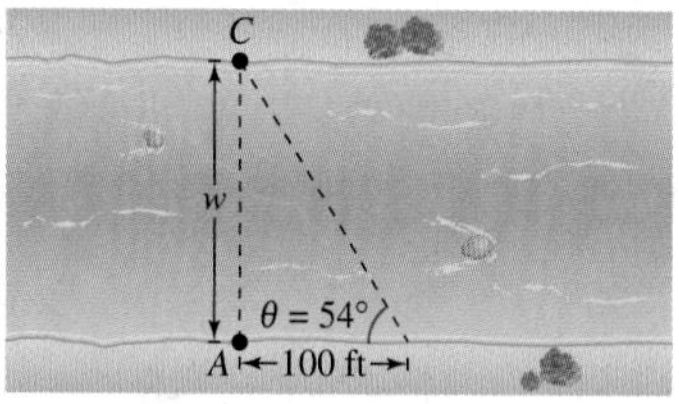

71. LENGTH A guy wire runs from the ground to a cell tower. The wire is attached to the cell tower 150 feet above the ground. The angle formed between the wire and the ground is 43° (see figure).

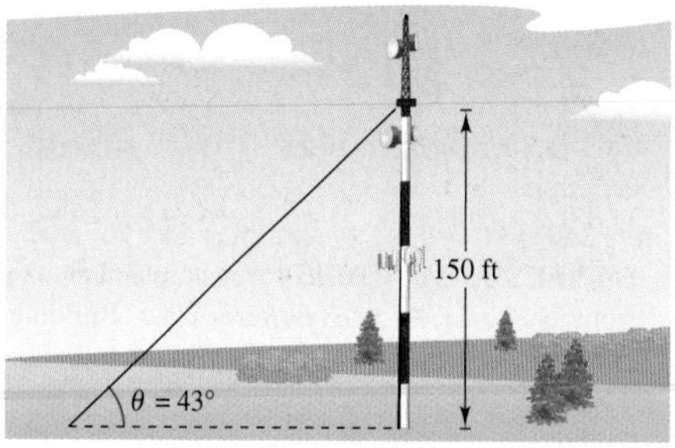

(a) How long is the guy wire? 219.9 ft

(b) How far from the base of the tower is the guy wire anchored to the ground? 160.9 ft

72. HEIGHT OF A MOUNTAIN In traveling across flat land, you notice a mountain directly in front of you. Its angle of elevation (to the peak) is 3.5°. After you drive 13 miles closer to the mountain, the angle of elevation is 9°. Approximate the height of the mountain. 1.3 mi

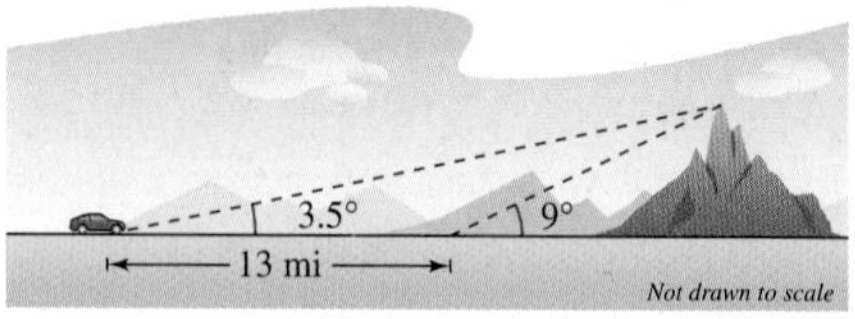

73. MACHINE SHOP CALCULATIONS A steel plate has the form of one-fourth of a circle with a radius of 60 centimeters. Two two-centimeter holes are to be drilled in the plate positioned as shown in the figure. Find the coordinates of the center of each hole.

$(x_1, y_1) = (28\sqrt{3}, 28)$

$(x_2, y_2) = (28, 28\sqrt{3})$

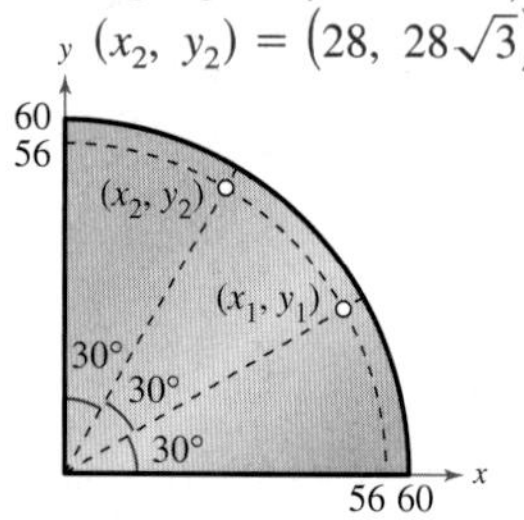

FIGURE FOR 73

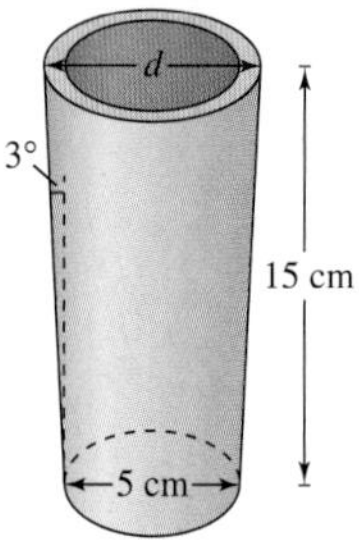

FIGURE FOR 74

74. MACHINE SHOP CALCULATIONS A tapered shaft has a diameter of 5 centimeters at the small end and is 15 centimeters long (see figure). The taper is 3°. Find the diameter d of the large end of the shaft. 6.57 cm

75. GEOMETRY Use a compass to sketch a quarter of a circle of radius 10 centimeters. Using a protractor, construct an angle of 20° in standard position (see figure). Drop a perpendicular line from the point of intersection of the terminal side of the angle and the arc of the circle. By actual measurement, calculate the coordinates (x, y) of the point of intersection and use these measurements to approximate the six trigonometric functions of a 20° angle.

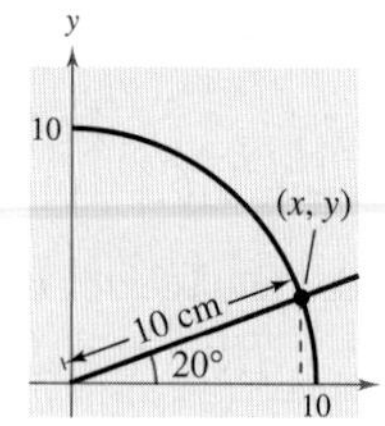

$\sin 20° \approx 0.34$, $\cos 20° \approx 0.94$, $\tan 20° \approx 0.36$, $\csc 20° \approx 2.92$, $\sec 20° \approx 1.06$, $\cot 20° \approx 2.75$

76. HEIGHT A 20-meter line is used to tether a helium-filled balloon. Because of a breeze, the line makes an angle of approximately 85° with the ground.

(a) Draw a right triangle that gives a visual representation of the problem. Show the known quantities of the triangle and use a variable to indicate the height of the balloon. See margin.

(b) Use a trigonometric function to write an equation involving the unknown quantity. See margin.

(c) What is the height of the balloon? 19.9 m

(d) The breeze becomes stronger and the angle the balloon makes with the ground decreases. How does this affect the triangle you drew in part (a)? See margin.

(e) Complete the table, which shows the heights (in meters) of the balloon for decreasing angle measures θ.

Angle, θ	80°	70°	60°	50°
Height	19.7	18.8	17.3	15.3

Angle, θ	40°	30°	20°	10°
Height	12.9	10.0	6.8	3.5

(f) As the angle the balloon makes with the ground approaches 0°, how does this affect the height of the balloon? Draw a right triangle to explain your reasoning. See margin.

EXPLORATION

77–82. See margin.

TRUE OR FALSE? In Exercises 77–82, determine whether the statement is true or false. Justify your answer.

77. $\sin 60° \csc 60° = 1$

78. $\sec 30° = \csc 60°$

79. $\sin 45° + \cos 45° = 1$

80. $\cot^2 10° - \csc^2 10° = -1$

81. $\dfrac{\sin 60°}{\sin 30°} = \sin 2°$

82. $\tan[(5°)^2] = \tan^2 5°$

83. THINK ABOUT IT

(a) Complete the table. See margin.

θ	0.1	0.2	0.3	0.4	0.5
$\sin\theta$					

(b) Is θ or $\sin\theta$ greater for θ in the interval (0, 0.5]? θ

(c) As θ approaches 0, how do θ and $\sin\theta$ compare? Explain.

As $\theta \to 0$, $\sin\theta \to 0$ and $\dfrac{\theta}{\sin\theta} \to 1$.

84. THINK ABOUT IT

(a) Complete the table. See margin.

θ	0°	18°	36°	54°	72°	90°
$\sin\theta$						
$\cos\theta$						

(b) Discuss the behavior of the sine function for θ in the range from 0° to 90°. Increasing function

(c) Discuss the behavior of the cosine function for θ in the range from 0° to 90°. Decreasing function

(d) Use the definitions of the sine and cosine functions to explain the results of parts (b) and (c). See margin.

85. WRITING In right triangle trigonometry, explain why $\sin 30° = \frac{1}{2}$ regardless of the size of the triangle.

86. GEOMETRY Use the equilateral triangle shown in Figure 4.29 and similar triangles to verify the points in Figure 4.23 (in Section 4.2) that do not lie on the axes.

87. THINK ABOUT IT You are given only the value $\tan\theta$. Is it possible to find the value of $\sec\theta$ without finding the measure of θ? Explain. 85–87. See margin.

88. CAPSTONE The Johnstown Inclined Plane in Pennsylvania is one of the longest and steepest hoists in the world. The railway cars travel a distance of 896.5 feet at an angle of approximately 35.4°, rising to a height of 1693.5 feet above sea level.

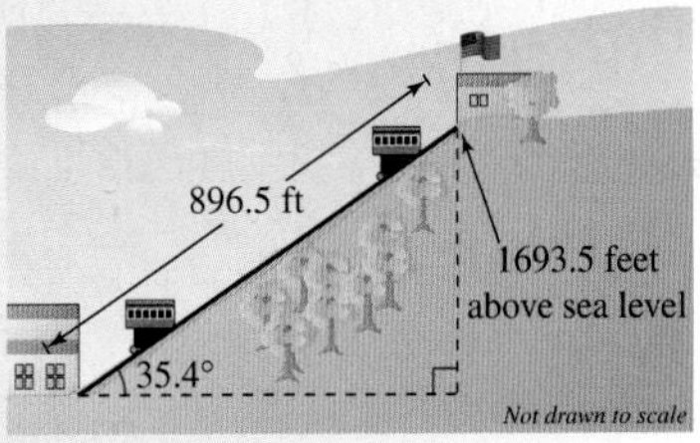

(a) Find the vertical rise of the inclined plane. 519.33 ft

(b) Find the elevation of the lower end of the inclined plane. 1174.17 ft

(c) The cars move up the mountain at a rate of 300 feet per minute. Find the rate at which they rise vertically. 173.11 ft/min

5 ASSESS AND RETEACH

Daily Homework Quiz

Transparency Available

Available at the Instructor's companion site.

76. (a)

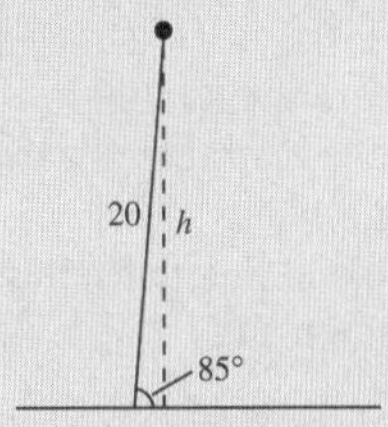

(b) $\sin 85° = \dfrac{h}{20}$

(d) The side of the triangle labeled h will become shorter.

(f) As $\theta \to 0°$, $h \to 0$.

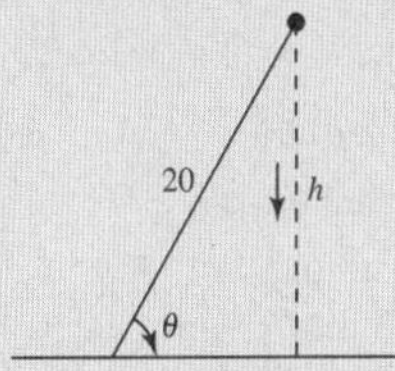

77. True, $\csc x = \dfrac{1}{\sin x}$.

78. True, $\sec x = \csc(90° - x)$.

79. False, $\dfrac{\sqrt{2}}{2} + \dfrac{\sqrt{2}}{2} \neq 1$.

80. True, $\cot^2\theta - \csc^2\theta = -1$ for all θ.

81. False, $1.7321 \neq 0.0349$.

82. False, $\tan 25° \neq (\tan 5°)(\tan 5°)$.

83. (a) See below.

84. (a), (d) See below.

85. Corresponding sides of similar triangles are proportional.

86. Sample answer:

$x = \cos 30° = \dfrac{\sqrt{3}}{2}$

$y = \sin 30° = \dfrac{1}{2} \Rightarrow \left(\dfrac{\sqrt{3}}{2}, \dfrac{1}{2}\right)$

$x = \cos 60° = \dfrac{1}{2}$

$y = \sin 60° = \dfrac{\sqrt{3}}{2} \Rightarrow \left(\dfrac{1}{2}, \dfrac{\sqrt{3}}{2}\right)$

Signs change depending on what quadrant the point lies in.

87. Yes, $\tan\theta$ is equal to opp/adj. You can find the value of the hypotenuse by the Pythagorean Theorem, then you can find $\sec\theta$, which is equal to hyp/adj.

83. (a)

θ	0.1	0.2	0.3	0.4	0.5
$\sin\theta$	0.0998	0.1987	0.2955	0.3894	0.4794

84. (a)

θ	0°	18°	36°	54°	72°	90°
$\sin\theta$	0	0.3090	0.5878	0.8090	0.9511	1
$\cos\theta$	1	0.9511	0.8090	0.5878	0.3090	0

(d) As the angle increases, the length of the side opposite the angle increases relative to the length of the hypotenuse and the length of the side adjacent to the angle decreases relative to the length of the hypotenuse. Thus, the sine increases and the cosine decreases.

1 PLAN AND PREPARE

Warm-up Exercises

Transparency Available
Available at the Instructor's companion site.

Notetaking Guide

Transparency Available
Promotes interactive learning and notetaking skills. Available at the Instructor's companion site.

Animated Precalculus

An **Animated Precalculus** tutorial is available at the Student companion site for **Section 4.4.**

Pacing

Average: 2 days
Advanced: 2 days
Block: 0.5 block with 4.3
0.5 block with 4.5

2 FOCUS AND MOTIVATE

Essential Question

How do you evaluate trigonometric functions of any angle? **Tell students that they will learn how to answer this question by studying the definitions of trigonometric functions and by using acute angles formed by a terminal side and the x-axis.**

4.4 Trigonometric Functions of Any Angle

What you should learn

- Evaluate trigonometric functions of any angle.
- Find reference angles.
- Evaluate trigonometric functions of real numbers.

Why you should learn it

You can use trigonometric functions to model and solve real-life problems. For instance, in Exercise 99 on page 318, you can use trigonometric functions to model the monthly normal temperatures in New York City and Fairbanks, Alaska.

James Urbach/SuperStock

Introduction

In Section 4.3, the definitions of trigonometric functions were restricted to acute angles. In this section, the definitions are extended to cover *any* angle. If θ is an *acute* angle, these definitions coincide with those given in the preceding section.

Definitions of Trigonometric Functions of Any Angle

Let θ be an angle in standard position with (x, y) a point on the terminal side of θ and $r = \sqrt{x^2 + y^2} \neq 0$.

$$\sin \theta = \frac{y}{r} \qquad \cos \theta = \frac{x}{r}$$

$$\tan \theta = \frac{y}{x}, \quad x \neq 0 \qquad \cot \theta = \frac{x}{y}, \quad y \neq 0$$

$$\sec \theta = \frac{r}{x}, \quad x \neq 0 \qquad \csc \theta = \frac{r}{y}, \quad y \neq 0$$

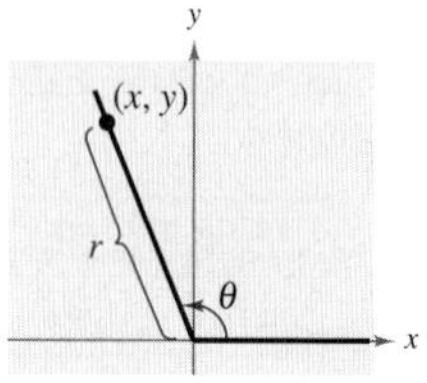

Because $r = \sqrt{x^2 + y^2}$ *cannot* be zero, it follows that the sine and cosine functions are defined for any real value of θ. However, if $x = 0$, the tangent and secant of θ are undefined. For example, the tangent of 90° is undefined. Similarly, if $y = 0$, the cotangent and cosecant of θ are undefined.

Example 1 Evaluating Trigonometric Functions

Let $(-3, 4)$ be a point on the terminal side of θ. Find the sine, cosine, and tangent of θ.

Solution

Referring to Figure 4.36, you can see that $x = -3$, $y = 4$, and

$$r = \sqrt{x^2 + y^2} = \sqrt{(-3)^2 + 4^2} = \sqrt{25} = 5.$$

So, you have the following.

$$\sin \theta = \frac{y}{r} = \frac{4}{5} \qquad \cos \theta = \frac{x}{r} = -\frac{3}{5} \qquad \tan \theta = \frac{y}{x} = -\frac{4}{3}$$

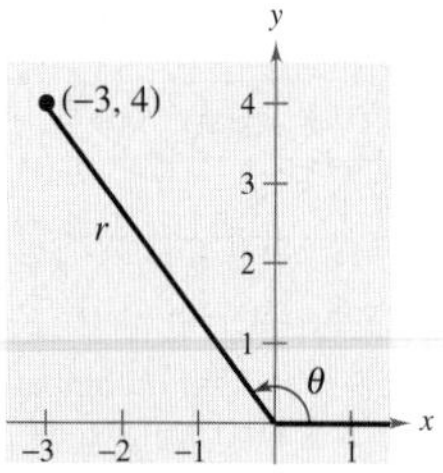

FIGURE 4.36

CHECKPoint Now try Exercise 9.

Algebra Help

The formula $r = \sqrt{x^2 + y^2}$ is a result of the Distance Formula. You can review the Distance Formula in Section 1.1.

Resource Planning Guide

Chapter Resources
- Complete Solutions Guide

Workbooks
- Notetaking Guide
- Student Solutions Guide

Interactive Technology
- Instructor Success Organizer
- Notetaking Guide IAE
- Instructional DVDs
- Animated Precalculus
- PowerLecture with ExamView

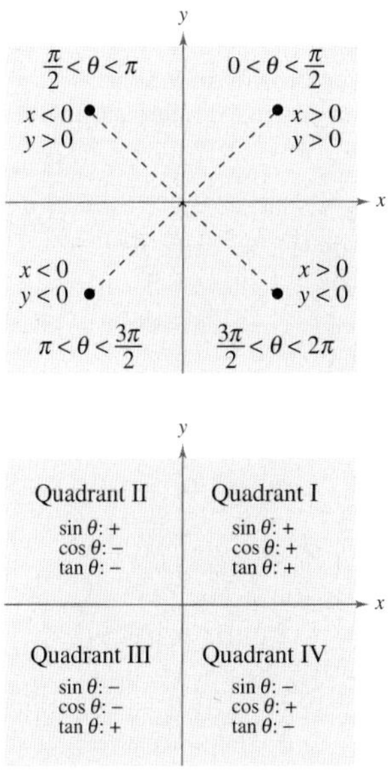

FIGURE 4.37

The *signs* of the trigonometric functions in the four quadrants can be determined from the definitions of the functions. For instance, because $\cos\theta = x/r$, it follows that $\cos\theta$ is positive wherever $x > 0$, which is in Quadrants I and IV. (Remember, r is always positive.) In a similar manner, you can verify the results shown in Figure 4.37.

Example 2 Evaluating Trigonometric Functions

Given $\tan\theta = -\frac{5}{4}$ and $\cos\theta > 0$, find $\sin\theta$ and $\sec\theta$.

Solution

Note that θ lies in Quadrant IV because that is the only quadrant in which the tangent is negative and the cosine is positive. Moreover, using

$$\tan\theta = \frac{y}{x} = -\frac{5}{4}$$

and the fact that y is negative in Quadrant IV, you can let $y = -5$ and $x = 4$. So, $r = \sqrt{16 + 25} = \sqrt{41}$ and you have

$$\sin\theta = \frac{y}{r} = \frac{-5}{\sqrt{41}} \approx -0.7809$$

$$\sec\theta = \frac{r}{x} = \frac{\sqrt{41}}{4} \approx 1.6008.$$

CHECK*Point* Now try Exercise 23.

Example 3 Trigonometric Functions of Quadrant Angles

Evaluate the cosine and tangent functions at the four quadrant angles $0, \frac{\pi}{2}, \pi$, and $\frac{3\pi}{2}$.

Solution

To begin, choose a point on the terminal side of each angle, as shown in Figure 4.38. For each of the four points, $r = 1$, and you have the following.

$$\cos 0 = \frac{x}{r} = \frac{1}{1} = 1 \qquad \tan 0 = \frac{y}{x} = \frac{0}{1} = 0 \qquad (x, y) = (1, 0)$$

$$\cos\frac{\pi}{2} = \frac{x}{r} = \frac{0}{1} = 0 \qquad \tan\frac{\pi}{2} = \frac{y}{x} = \frac{1}{0} \Rightarrow \text{undefined} \qquad (x, y) = (0, 1)$$

$$\cos\pi = \frac{x}{r} = \frac{-1}{1} = -1 \qquad \tan\pi = \frac{y}{x} = \frac{0}{-1} = 0 \qquad (x, y) = (-1, 0)$$

$$\cos\frac{3\pi}{2} = \frac{x}{r} = \frac{0}{1} = 0 \qquad \tan\frac{3\pi}{2} = \frac{y}{x} = \frac{-1}{0} \Rightarrow \text{undefined} \qquad (x, y) = (0, -1)$$

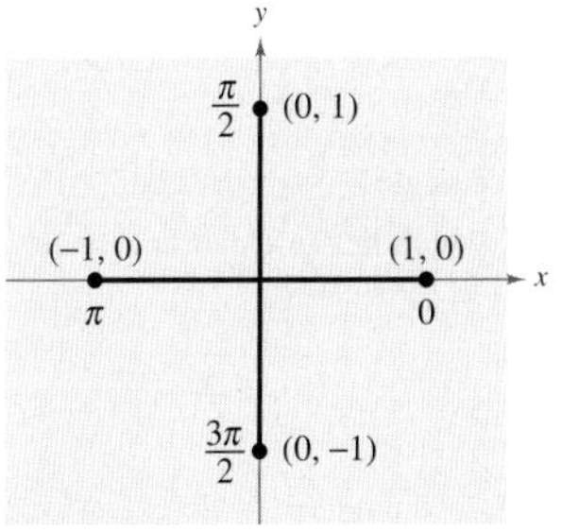

FIGURE 4.38

CHECK*Point* Now try Exercise 37.

3 TEACH

Extra Example 1

Let $(-2, 3)$ be a point on the terminal side of θ. Find the sine, cosine, and tangent of θ.

$\sin\theta = \frac{3\sqrt{13}}{13}$, $\cos\theta = -\frac{2\sqrt{13}}{13}$, $\tan\theta = -\frac{3}{2}$

Extra Example 2

Given $\sin\theta = \frac{4}{5}$ and $\tan\theta < 0$, find $\cos\theta$ and $\csc\theta$.

$-\frac{3}{5}, \frac{5}{4}$

Extra Example 3

Evaluate the cosecant and cotangent functions at $0, \frac{\pi}{2}, \pi$, and $\frac{3\pi}{2}$.

csc 0: undefined, $\csc\frac{\pi}{2} = 1$,

csc π: undefined, $\csc\frac{3\pi}{2} = -1$;

cot 0: undefined, $\cot\frac{\pi}{2} = 0$,

cot π: undefined, $\cot\frac{3\pi}{2} = 0$

Extra Example 4

Find the reference angle θ'.

a. $\theta = 213°$

33°

b. $\theta = 1.7$

1.4416

c. $\theta = 144°$

36°

Reference Angles

The values of the trigonometric functions of angles greater than 90° (or less than 0°) can be determined from their values at corresponding acute angles called **reference angles.**

Definition of Reference Angle

Let θ be an angle in standard position. Its **reference angle** is the acute angle θ' formed by the terminal side of θ and the horizontal axis.

Figure 4.39 shows the reference angles for θ in Quadrants II, III, and IV.

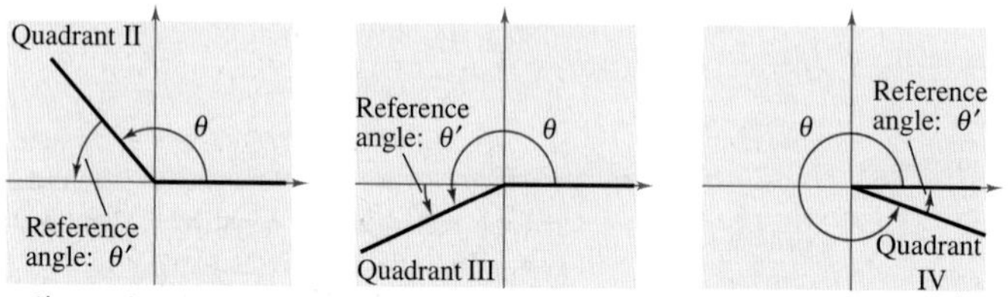

$\theta' = \pi - \theta$ (radians) $\quad$ $\theta' = \theta - \pi$ (radians) $\quad$ $\theta' = 2\pi - \theta$ (radians)

$\theta' = 180° - \theta$ (degrees) $\quad$ $\theta' = \theta - 180°$ (degrees) $\quad$ $\theta' = 360° - \theta$ (degrees)

FIGURE 4.39

Example 4 Finding Reference Angles

Find the reference angle θ'.

a. $\theta = 300°$ **b.** $\theta = 2.3$ **c.** $\theta = -135°$

Solution

a. Because 300° lies in Quadrant IV, the angle it makes with the x-axis is

$$\theta' = 360° - 300°$$
$$= 60°. \quad \text{Degrees}$$

Figure 4.40 shows the angle $\theta = 300°$ and its reference angle $\theta' = 60°$.

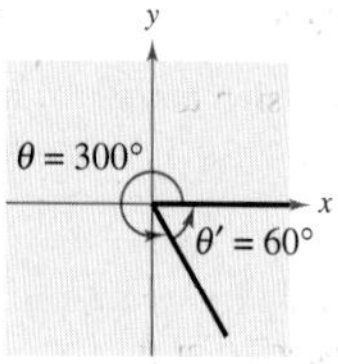

FIGURE 4.40

b. Because 2.3 lies between $\pi/2 \approx 1.5708$ and $\pi \approx 3.1416$, it follows that it is in Quadrant II and its reference angle is

$$\theta' = \pi - 2.3$$
$$\approx 0.8416. \quad \text{Radians}$$

Figure 4.41 shows the angle $\theta = 2.3$ and its reference angle $\theta' = \pi - 2.3$.

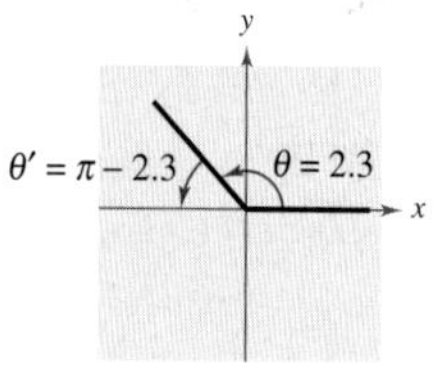

FIGURE 4.41

c. First, determine that $-135°$ is coterminal with 225°, which lies in Quadrant III. So, the reference angle is

$$\theta' = 225° - 180°$$
$$= 45°. \quad \text{Degrees}$$

Figure 4.42 shows the angle $\theta = -135°$ and its reference angle $\theta' = 45°$.

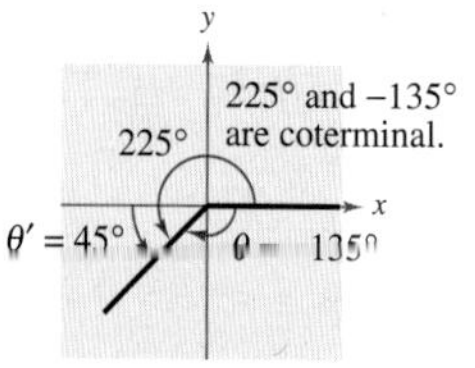

FIGURE 4.42

CHECK*Point* Now try Exercise 45.

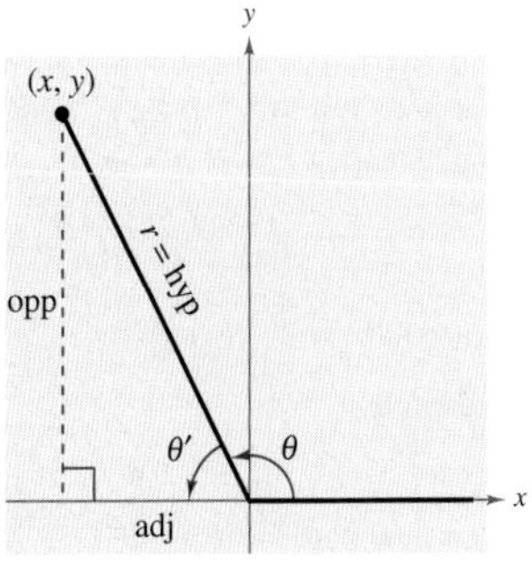

opp = |y|, adj = |x|
FIGURE 4.43

Trigonometric Functions of Real Numbers

To see how a reference angle is used to evaluate a trigonometric function, consider the point (x, y) on the terminal side of θ, as shown in Figure 4.43. By definition, you know that

$$\sin\theta = \frac{y}{r} \quad \text{and} \quad \tan\theta = \frac{y}{x}.$$

For the right triangle with acute angle θ' and sides of lengths $|x|$ and $|y|$, you have

$$\sin\theta' = \frac{\text{opp}}{\text{hyp}} = \frac{|y|}{r}$$

and

$$\tan\theta' = \frac{\text{opp}}{\text{adj}} = \frac{|y|}{|x|}.$$

So, it follows that $\sin\theta$ and $\sin\theta'$ are equal, *except possibly in sign*. The same is true for $\tan\theta$ and $\tan\theta'$ *and* for the other four trigonometric functions. In all cases, the sign of the function value can be determined by the quadrant in which θ lies.

Evaluating Trigonometric Functions of Any Angle

To find the value of a trigonometric function of any angle θ:

1. Determine the function value for the associated reference angle θ'.
2. Depending on the quadrant in which θ lies, affix the appropriate sign to the function value.

By using reference angles and the special angles discussed in the preceding section, you can greatly extend the scope of *exact* trigonometric values. For instance, knowing the function values of 30° means that you know the function values of all angles for which 30° is a reference angle. For convenience, the table below shows the exact values of the trigonometric functions of special angles and quadrant angles.

Study Tip

Learning the table of values at the right is worth the effort because doing so will increase both your efficiency and your confidence. Here is a pattern for the sine function that may help you remember the values.

θ	0°	30°	45°	60°	90°
$\sin\theta$	$\frac{\sqrt{0}}{2}$	$\frac{\sqrt{1}}{2}$	$\frac{\sqrt{2}}{2}$	$\frac{\sqrt{3}}{2}$	$\frac{\sqrt{4}}{2}$

Reverse the order to get cosine values of the same angles.

Trigonometric Values of Common Angles

θ (degrees)	0°	30°	45°	60°	90°	180°	270°
θ (radians)	0	$\frac{\pi}{6}$	$\frac{\pi}{4}$	$\frac{\pi}{3}$	$\frac{\pi}{2}$	π	$\frac{3\pi}{2}$
$\sin\theta$	0	$\frac{1}{2}$	$\frac{\sqrt{2}}{2}$	$\frac{\sqrt{3}}{2}$	1	0	-1
$\cos\theta$	1	$\frac{\sqrt{3}}{2}$	$\frac{\sqrt{2}}{2}$	$\frac{1}{2}$	0	-1	0
$\tan\theta$	0	$\frac{\sqrt{3}}{3}$	1	$\sqrt{3}$	Undef.	0	Undef.

Extra Example 5

Evaluate.

a. $\sin \frac{5\pi}{3}$

$-\frac{\sqrt{3}}{2}$

b. $\cos(-60°)$

$\frac{1}{2}$

c. $\tan \frac{11\pi}{6}$

$-\frac{\sqrt{3}}{3}$

Example 5 Using Reference Angles

Evaluate each trigonometric function.

a. $\cos \frac{4\pi}{3}$ **b.** $\tan(-210°)$ **c.** $\csc \frac{11\pi}{4}$

Solution

a. Because $\theta = 4\pi/3$ lies in Quadrant III, the reference angle is

$$\theta' = \frac{4\pi}{3} - \pi = \frac{\pi}{3}$$

as shown in Figure 6.41. Moreover, the cosine is negative in Quadrant III, so

$$\cos \frac{4\pi}{3} = (-) \cos \frac{\pi}{3}$$
$$= -\frac{1}{2}.$$

b. Because $-210° + 360° = 150°$, it follows that $-210°$ is coterminal with the second-quadrant angle $150°$. So, the reference angle is $\theta' = 180° - 150° = 30°$, as shown in Figure 4.45. Finally, because the tangent is negative in Quadrant II, you have

$$\tan(-210°) = (-) \tan 30°$$
$$= -\frac{\sqrt{3}}{3}.$$

c. Because $(11\pi/4) - 2\pi = 3\pi/4$, it follows that $11\pi/4$ is coterminal with the second-quadrant angle $3\pi/4$. So, the reference angle is $\theta' = \pi - (3\pi/4) = \pi/4$, as shown in Figure 4.46. Because the cosecant is positive in Quadrant II, you have

$$\csc \frac{11\pi}{4} = (+) \csc \frac{\pi}{4}$$
$$= \frac{1}{\sin(\pi/4)}$$
$$= \sqrt{2}.$$

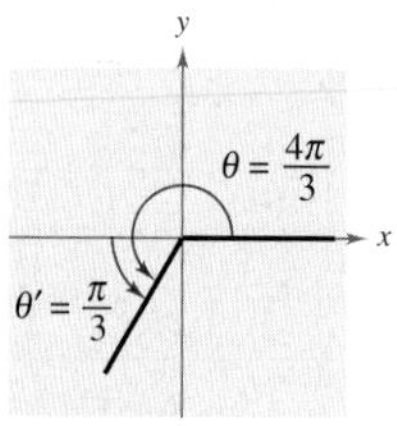

FIGURE 4.44

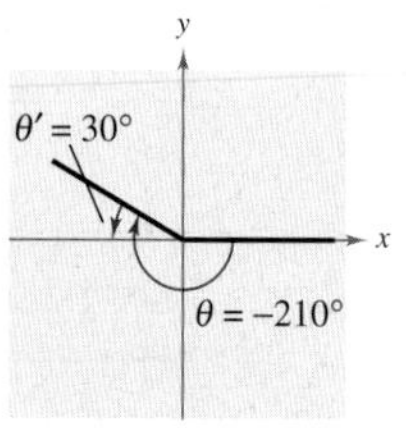

FIGURE 4.45

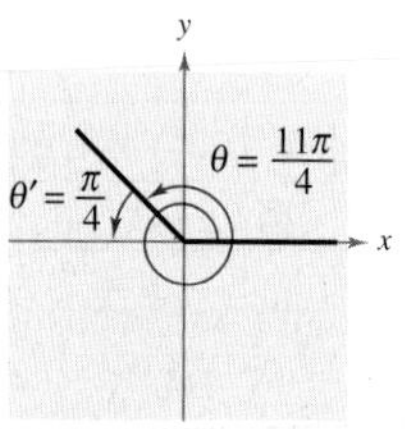

FIGURE 4.46

CHECK *Point* Now try Exercise 59.

Example 6 Using Trigonometric Identities

Let θ be an angle in Quadrant II such that $\sin\theta = \frac{1}{3}$. Find (a) $\cos\theta$ and (b) $\tan\theta$ by using trigonometric identities.

Solution

a. Using the Pythagorean identity $\sin^2\theta + \cos^2\theta = 1$, you obtain

$$\left(\frac{1}{3}\right)^2 + \cos^2\theta = 1 \qquad \text{Substitute } \tfrac{1}{3} \text{ for } \sin\theta.$$

$$\cos^2\theta = 1 - \frac{1}{9} = \frac{8}{9}.$$

Because $\cos\theta < 0$ in Quadrant II, you can use the negative root to obtain

$$\cos\theta = -\frac{\sqrt{8}}{\sqrt{9}} = -\frac{2\sqrt{2}}{3}.$$

b. Using the trigonometric identity $\tan\theta = \dfrac{\sin\theta}{\cos\theta}$, you obtain

$$\tan\theta = \frac{1/3}{-2\sqrt{2}/3} \qquad \text{Substitute for } \sin\theta \text{ and } \cos\theta.$$

$$= -\frac{1}{2\sqrt{2}}$$

$$= -\frac{\sqrt{2}}{4}.$$

CHECK*Point* Now try Exercise 69.

You can use a calculator to evaluate trigonometric functions, as shown in the next example.

Example 7 Using a Calculator

Use a calculator to evaluate each trigonometric function.

a. cot 410° **b.** $\sin(-7)$ **c.** $\sec\dfrac{\pi}{9}$

Solution

Function	*Mode*	*Calculator Keystrokes*	*Display*
a. cot 410°	Degree	(TAN (410)) x⁻¹ ENTER	0.8390996
b. $\sin(-7)$	Radian	SIN ((-) 7) ENTER	−0.6569866
c. $\sec\dfrac{\pi}{9}$	Radian	(COS (π ÷ 9)) x⁻¹ ENTER	1.0641778

CHECK*Point* Now try Exercise 79.

Extra Example 6

Let θ be an angle in Quadrant III such that $\sin\theta = -\frac{5}{13}$. Find (a) $\sec\theta$ and (b) $\tan\theta$ by using trigonometric identities.

$-\frac{13}{12}, \frac{5}{12}$

Extra Example 7

Use a calculator to evaluate each trigonometric function.

a. cot 375°

3.7321

b. $\sin(-4.1)$

0.8183

c. $\sec\dfrac{3\pi}{8}$

2.6131

Avoiding Common Errors

Remind students to rewrite problems containing cosecant, secant, or cotangent in terms of sine, cosine, or tangent before evaluating. When using a calculator to evaluate these functions, students should also be reminded that $\csc\theta = (\sin\theta)^{-1} \neq \sin^{-1}\theta$.

Closing the Lesson

Have students summarize the major points of the lesson and answer the Essential Question: How do you evaluate trigonometric functions of any angle?

- **Use the definitions of trigonometric ratios to calculate ratios, given the coordinates of a point and its distance from the origin.**
- **Identify the reference angle for a given angle by finding the acute angle between the terminal side and the *x*-axis.**
- **Evaluate trigonometric functions by calculating the function value for the reference angle and adjusting the sign as necessary, depending on the quadrant.**

4 PRACTICE AND APPLY

Assignment Guide

Transparencies Available
Available at the Instructor's companion site.

Average:

Day 1: pp. 316–317
Exs. 1–7, 9–13 odd, 19–23, 27, 31–39 odd, 45, 47, 51–57 odd, 63, 67

Day 2: pp. 317–318
Exs. 71–77 odd, 81–97 odd, 98, 102–104, 106

Advanced:

Day 1: pp. 316–317
Exs. 1–7, 10–18 even, 19–22, 28–38 even, 44–48 even, 52–56 even, 66–68

Day 2: pp. 317–318
Exs. 70–96 even, 97, 98, 100–102, 105–107

Block:

pp. 316–317
Exs. 1–7, 9–13 odd, 19–23, 27, 31–39 odd, 45, 47, 51–57 odd, 63, 67 (with 4.3)

pp. 317–318
Exs. 71–77 odd, 81–97 odd, 98, 102–104, 106 (with 4.5)

4.4 EXERCISES

See www.CalcChat.com for worked-out solutions to odd-numbered exercises.

VOCABULARY: Fill in the blanks.

In Exercises 1–6, let θ be an angle in standard position, with (x, y) a point on the terminal side of θ and $r = \sqrt{x^2 + y^2} \neq 0$.

1. $\sin\theta =$ ____ $\frac{y}{r}$ **2.** $\frac{r}{y} =$ ____ $\csc\theta$

3. $\tan\theta =$ ____ $\frac{y}{x}$ **4.** $\sec\theta =$ ____ $\frac{r}{x}$

5. $\frac{x}{r} =$ ____ $\cos\theta$ **6.** $\frac{x}{y} =$ ____ $\cot\theta$

7. Because $r = \sqrt{x^2 + y^2}$ cannot be ____ zero, the sine and cosine functions are ____ defined for any real value of θ.

8. The acute positive angle that is formed by the terminal side of the angle θ and the horizontal axis is called the ________ angle of θ and is denoted by θ'. reference

SKILLS AND APPLICATIONS

In Exercises 9–12, determine the exact values of the six trigonometric functions of the angle θ. 9–12. See margin.

9. (a)
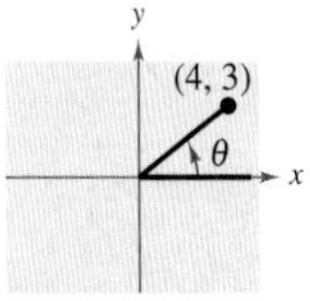

(b)
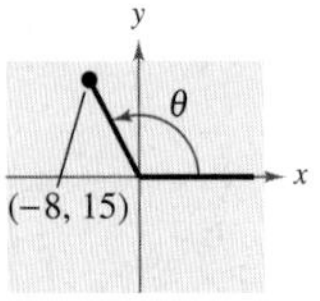

10. (a)
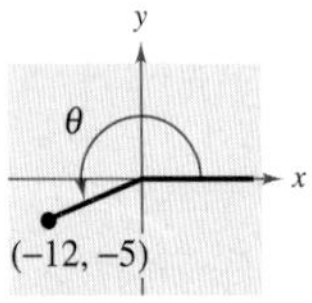

(b)
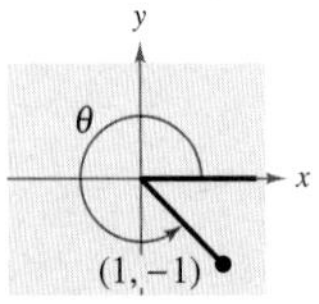

11. (a)
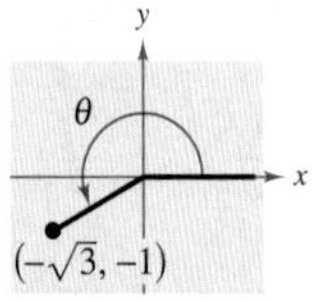

(b)
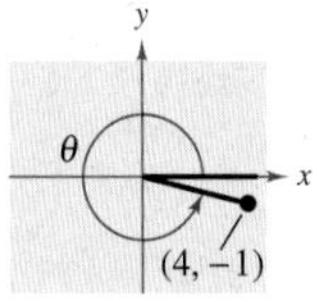

12. (a)
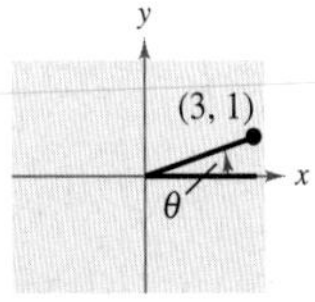

(b)
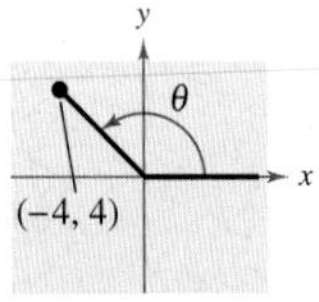

In Exercises 13–18, the point is on the terminal side of an angle in standard position. Determine the exact values of the six trigonometric functions of the angle. 13–18. See margin.

13. $(5, 12)$ **14.** $(8, 15)$

15. $(-5, -2)$ **16.** $(-4, 10)$

17. $(-5.4, 7.2)$ **18.** $(3\frac{1}{2}, -7\frac{3}{4})$

In Exercises 19–22, state the quadrant in which θ lies.

19. $\sin\theta > 0$ and $\cos\theta > 0$ I

20. $\sin\theta < 0$ and $\cos\theta < 0$ III

21. $\sin\theta > 0$ and $\cos\theta < 0$ II

22. $\sec\theta > 0$ and $\cot\theta < 0$ IV

In Exercises 23–32, find the values of the six trigonometric functions of θ with the given constraint. 23–32. See margin.

	Function Value	*Constraint*
23.	$\tan\theta = -\frac{15}{8}$	$\sin\theta > 0$
24.	$\cos\theta = \frac{8}{17}$	$\tan\theta < 0$
25.	$\sin\theta = \frac{3}{5}$	θ lies in Quadrant II.
26.	$\cos\theta = -\frac{4}{5}$	θ lies in Quadrant III.
27.	$\cot\theta = -3$	$\cos\theta > 0$
28.	$\csc\theta = 4$	$\cot\theta < 0$
29.	$\sec\theta = -2$	$\sin\theta < 0$
30.	$\sin\theta = 0$	$\sec\theta = -1$
31.	$\cot\theta$ is undefined.	$\pi/2 \le \theta \le 3\pi/2$
32.	$\tan\theta$ is undefined.	$\pi \le \theta \le 2\pi$

In Exercises 33–36, the terminal side of θ lies on the given line in the specified quadrant. Find the values of the six trigonometric functions of θ by finding a point on the line. 33–36. See margin.

	Line	*Quadrant*
33.	$y = -x$	II
34.	$y = \frac{1}{3}x$	III
35.	$2x - y = 0$	III
36.	$4x + 3y = 0$	IV

9. (a) $\sin\theta = \frac{3}{5}$ $\csc\theta = \frac{5}{3}$
$\cos\theta = \frac{4}{5}$ $\sec\theta = \frac{5}{4}$
$\tan\theta = \frac{3}{4}$ $\cot\theta = \frac{4}{3}$
(b) $\sin\theta = \frac{15}{17}$ $\csc\theta = \frac{17}{15}$
$\cos\theta = -\frac{8}{17}$ $\sec\theta = -\frac{17}{8}$
$\tan\theta = -\frac{15}{8}$ $\cot\theta = -\frac{8}{15}$

10. (a) $\sin\theta = -\frac{5}{13}$ $\csc\theta = -\frac{13}{5}$
$\cos\theta = -\frac{12}{13}$ $\sec\theta = -\frac{13}{12}$
$\tan\theta = \frac{5}{12}$ $\cot\theta = \frac{12}{5}$
(b) $\sin\theta = -\frac{\sqrt{2}}{2}$ $\csc\theta = -\sqrt{2}$
$\cos\theta = \frac{\sqrt{2}}{2}$ $\sec\theta = \sqrt{2}$
$\tan\theta = -1$ $\cot\theta = -1$

11. (a) $\sin\theta = -\frac{1}{2}$ $\csc\theta = -2$
$\cos\theta = -\frac{\sqrt{3}}{2}$ $\sec\theta = -\frac{2\sqrt{3}}{3}$
$\tan\theta = \frac{\sqrt{3}}{3}$ $\cot\theta = \sqrt{3}$
(b) $\sin\theta = -\frac{\sqrt{17}}{17}$ $\csc\theta = -\sqrt{17}$
$\cos\theta = \frac{4\sqrt{17}}{17}$ $\sec\theta = \frac{\sqrt{17}}{4}$
$\tan\theta = -\frac{1}{4}$ $\cot\theta = -4$

12. (a) $\sin\theta = \frac{\sqrt{10}}{10}$ $\csc\theta = \sqrt{10}$
$\cos\theta = \frac{3\sqrt{10}}{10}$ $\sec\theta = \frac{\sqrt{10}}{3}$
$\tan\theta = \frac{1}{3}$ $\cot\theta = 3$
(b) $\sin\theta = \frac{\sqrt{2}}{2}$ $\csc\theta = \sqrt{2}$
$\cos\theta = -\frac{\sqrt{2}}{2}$ $\sec\theta = -\sqrt{2}$
$\tan\theta = -1$ $\cot\theta = -1$

13–18, 23–36. See Additional Answers beginning on page AA1.

In Exercises 37–44, evaluate the trigonometric function of the quadrant angle.

37. $\sin \pi$ 0

38. $\csc \dfrac{3\pi}{2}$ -1

39. $\sec \dfrac{3\pi}{2}$ Undefined

40. $\sec \pi$ -1

41. $\sin \dfrac{\pi}{2}$ 1

42. $\cot \pi$ Undefined

43. $\csc \pi$ Undefined

44. $\cot \dfrac{\pi}{2}$ 0

In Exercises 45–52, find the reference angle θ', and sketch θ and θ' in standard position. 45–52. See margin.

45. $\theta = 160°$

46. $\theta = 309°$

47. $\theta = -125°$

48. $\theta = -215°$

49. $\theta = \dfrac{2\pi}{3}$

50. $\theta = \dfrac{7\pi}{6}$

51. $\theta = 4.8$

52. $\theta = 11.6$

In Exercises 53–68, evaluate the sine, cosine, and tangent of the angle without using a calculator. 53–68. See margin.

53. $225°$

54. $300°$

55. $750°$

56. $-405°$

57. $-150°$

58. $-840°$

59. $\dfrac{2\pi}{3}$

60. $\dfrac{3\pi}{4}$

61. $\dfrac{5\pi}{4}$

62. $\dfrac{7\pi}{6}$

63. $-\dfrac{\pi}{6}$

64. $-\dfrac{\pi}{2}$

65. $\dfrac{9\pi}{4}$

66. $\dfrac{10\pi}{3}$

67. $-\dfrac{3\pi}{2}$

68. $-\dfrac{23\pi}{4}$

In Exercises 69–74, find the indicated trigonometric value in the specified quadrant. 69–74. See margin.

Function	*Quadrant*	*Trigonometric Value*
69. $\sin \theta = -\frac{3}{5}$	IV	$\cos \theta$
70. $\cot \theta = -3$	II	$\sin \theta$
71. $\tan \theta = \frac{3}{2}$	III	$\sec \theta$
72. $\csc \theta = -2$	IV	$\cot \theta$
73. $\cos \theta = \frac{5}{8}$	I	$\sec \theta$
74. $\sec \theta = -\frac{9}{4}$	III	$\tan \theta$

In Exercises 75–90, use a calculator to evaluate the trigonometric function. Round your answer to four decimal places. (Be sure the calculator is set in the correct angle mode.)

75. $\sin 10°$ 0.1736

76. $\sec 225°$ -1.4142

77. $\cos(-110°)$ -0.3420

78. $\csc(-330°)$ 2.0000

79. $\tan 304°$ -1.4826

80. $\cot 178°$ -28.6363

81. $\sec 72°$ 3.2361

82. $\tan(-188°)$ -0.1405

83. $\tan 4.5$ 4.6373

84. $\cot 1.35$ 0.2245

85. $\tan \dfrac{\pi}{9}$ 0.3640

86. $\tan\left(-\dfrac{\pi}{9}\right)$ -0.3640

87. $\sin(-0.65)$ -0.6052

88. $\sec 0.29$ 1.0436

89. $\cot\left(-\dfrac{11\pi}{8}\right)$ -0.4142

90. $\csc\left(-\dfrac{15\pi}{14}\right)$ 4.4940

In Exercises 91–96, find two solutions of the equation. Give your answers in degrees ($0° \le \theta < 360°$) and in radians ($0 \le \theta < 2\pi$). Do not use a calculator. 91–96. See margin.

91. (a) $\sin \theta = \frac{1}{2}$ (b) $\sin \theta = -\frac{1}{2}$

92. (a) $\cos \theta = \dfrac{\sqrt{2}}{2}$ (b) $\cos \theta = -\dfrac{\sqrt{2}}{2}$

93. (a) $\csc \theta = \dfrac{2\sqrt{3}}{3}$ (b) $\cot \theta = -1$

94. (a) $\sec \theta = 2$ (b) $\sec \theta = -2$

95. (a) $\tan \theta = 1$ (b) $\cot \theta = -\sqrt{3}$

96. (a) $\sin \theta = \dfrac{\sqrt{3}}{2}$ (b) $\sin \theta = -\dfrac{\sqrt{3}}{2}$

97. DISTANCE An airplane, flying at an altitude of 6 miles, is on a flight path that passes directly over an observer (see figure). If θ is the angle of elevation from the observer to the plane, find the distance d from the observer to the plane when (a) $\theta = 30°$, (b) $\theta = 90°$, and (c) $\theta = 120°$.
(a) 12 mi (b) 6 mi (c) 6.9 mi

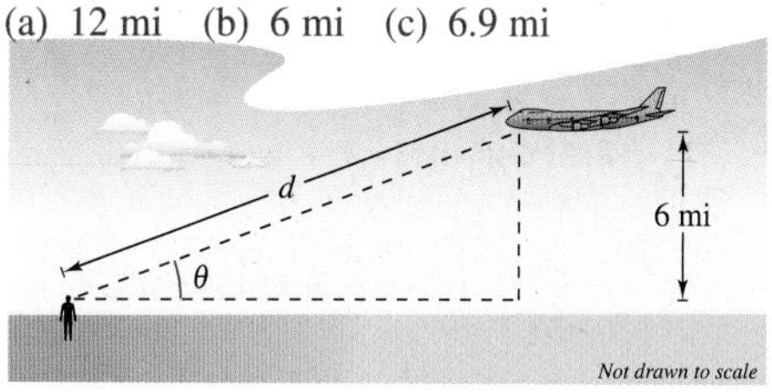

98. HARMONIC MOTION The displacement from equilibrium of an oscillating weight suspended by a spring is given by $y(t) = 2 \cos 6t$, where y is the displacement (in centimeters) and t is the time (in seconds). Find the displacement when (a) $t = 0$, (b) $t = \frac{1}{4}$, and (c) $t = \frac{1}{2}$.
(a) 2 cm (b) 0.14 cm (c) -1.98 cm

45. $\theta' = 20°$

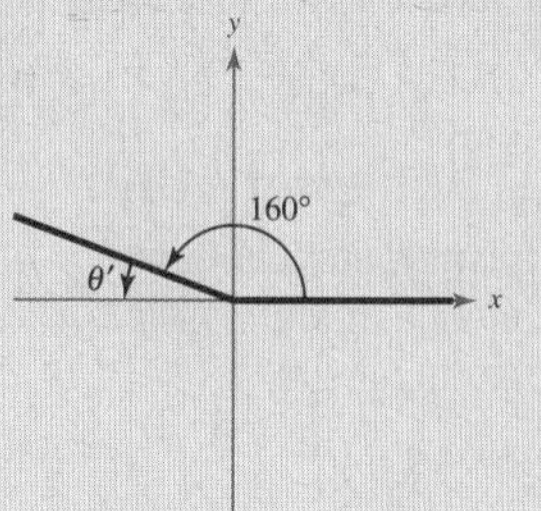

46. $\theta' = 51°$

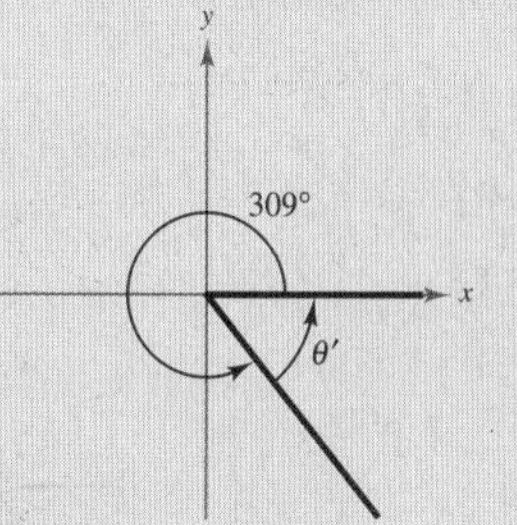

47. $\theta' = 55°$

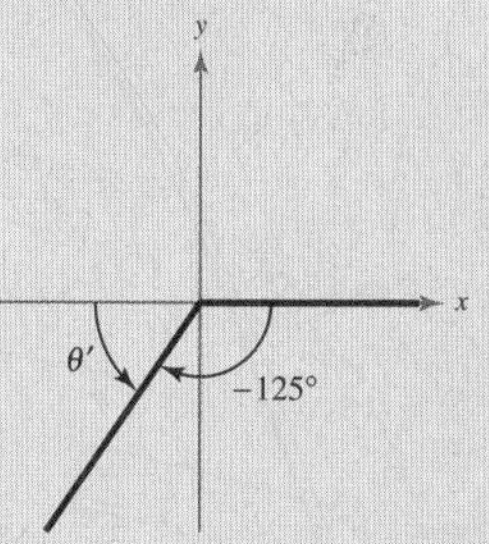

48. $\theta' = 35°$

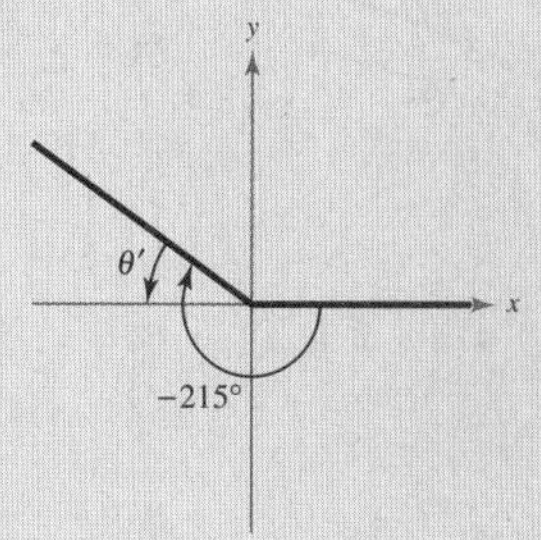

49. $\theta' = \dfrac{\pi}{3}$

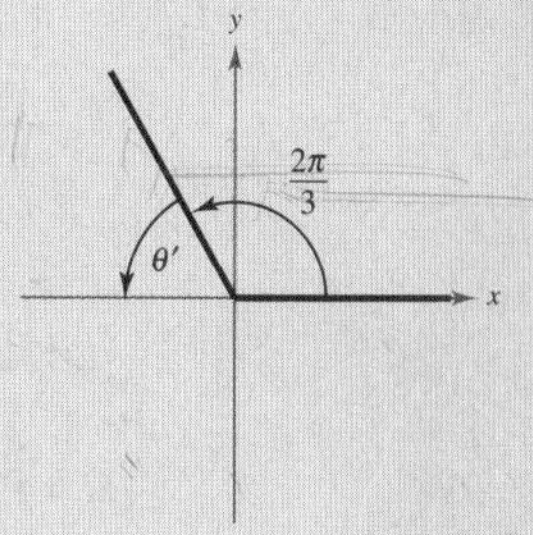

50. $\theta' = \dfrac{\pi}{6}$

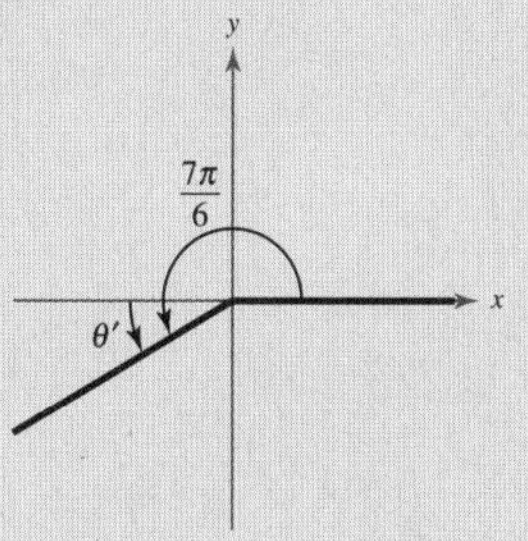

51. $\theta' = 2\pi - 4.8$

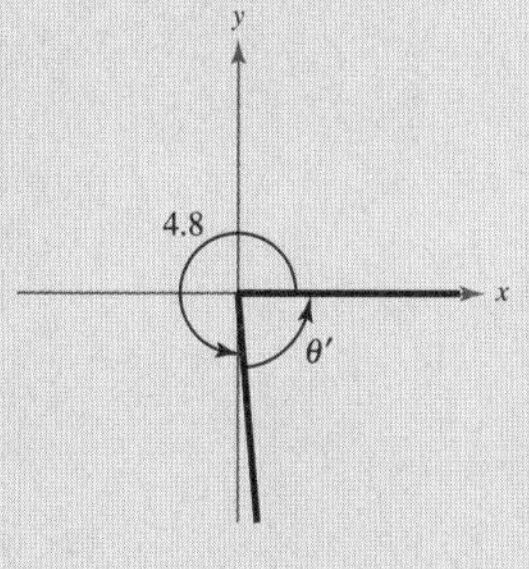

52. $\theta' = 4\pi - 11.6$

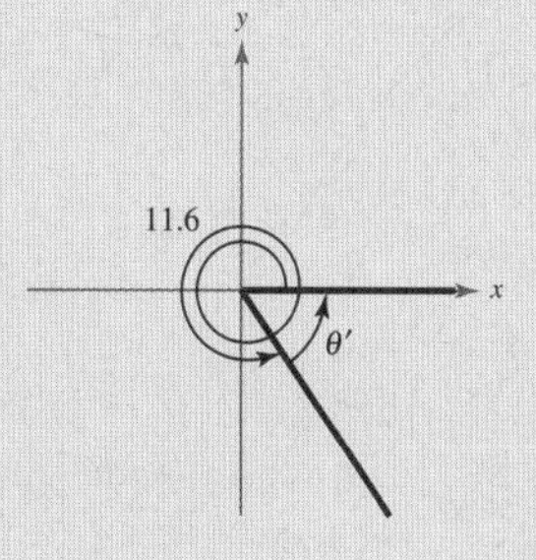

53–74, 91–96. See Additional Answers beginning on page AA1.

5 ASSESS AND RETEACH

Daily Homework Quiz

Transparency Available

Available at the Instructor's companion site.

99. See below.

100. (a) 26,134 units
(b) 31,438 units
(c) 21,452 units
(d) 26,756 units

104. False. For θ in Quadrant II, $\theta' = 180° - \theta$. For θ in Quadrant III, $\theta' = \theta - 180°$. For θ in Quadrant IV, $\theta' = 360° - \theta$.

105. As θ increases from 0° to 90°, x decreases from 12 cm to 0 cm and y increases from 0 cm to 12 cm. Therefore, $\sin \theta = y/12$ increases from 0 to 1 and $\cos \theta = x/12$ decreases from 1 to 0. Thus, $\tan \theta = y/x$ increases without bound. When $\theta = 90°$, the tangent is undefined.

107. (a) $\sin t = y$, $\cos t = x$
(b) $r = 1$ because it is a unit circle.

99. DATA ANALYSIS: METEOROLOGY The table shows the monthly normal temperatures (in degrees Fahrenheit) for selected months in New York City (N) and Fairbanks, Alaska (F). (Source: National Climatic Data Center) See margin.

Month	New York City, N	Fairbanks, F
January	33	−10
April	52	32
July	77	62
October	58	24
December	38	−6

(a) Use the *regression* feature of a graphing utility to find a model of the form $y = a \sin(bt + c) + d$ for each city. Let t represent the month, with $t = 1$ corresponding to January.

(b) Use the models from part (a) to find the monthly normal temperatures for the two cities in February, March, May, June, August, September, and November.

(c) Compare the models for the two cities.

100. SALES A company that produces snowboards, which are seasonal products, forecasts monthly sales over the next 2 years to be $S = 23.1 + 0.442t + 4.3 \cos(\pi t/6)$, where S is measured in thousands of units and t is the time in months, with $t = 1$ representing January 2010. Predict sales for each of the following months.

(a) February 2010 (b) February 2011
(c) June 2010 (d) June 2011 See margin.

101. HARMONIC MOTION The displacement from equilibrium of an oscillating weight suspended by a spring and subject to the damping effect of friction is given by $y(t) = 2e^{-t} \cos 6t$, where y is the displacement (in centimeters) and t is the time (in seconds). Find the displacement when (a) $t = 0$, (b) $t = \frac{1}{4}$, and (c) $t = \frac{1}{2}$.
(a) 2 cm
(b) 0.11 cm
(c) −1.2 cm

102. ELECTRIC CIRCUITS The current I (in amperes) when 100 volts is applied to a circuit is given by $I = 5e^{-2t} \sin t$, where t is the time (in seconds) after the voltage is applied. Approximate the current at $t = 0.7$ second after the voltage is applied. 0.79 ampere

EXPLORATION

TRUE OR FALSE? In Exercises 103 and 104, determine whether the statement is true or false. Justify your answer.

103. In each of the four quadrants, the signs of the secant function and sine function will be the same.

False. In each of the four quadrants, the signs of the secant function and the cosine function will be the same, because these functions are reciprocals of each other.

104. To find the reference angle for an angle θ (given in degrees), find the integer n such that $0 \le 360°n - \theta \le 360°$. The difference $360°n - \theta$ is the reference angle. See margin.

105. WRITING Consider an angle in standard position with $r = 12$ centimeters, as shown in the figure. Write a short paragraph describing the changes in the values of x, y, $\sin \theta$, $\cos \theta$, and $\tan \theta$ as θ increases continuously from 0° to 90°. See margin.

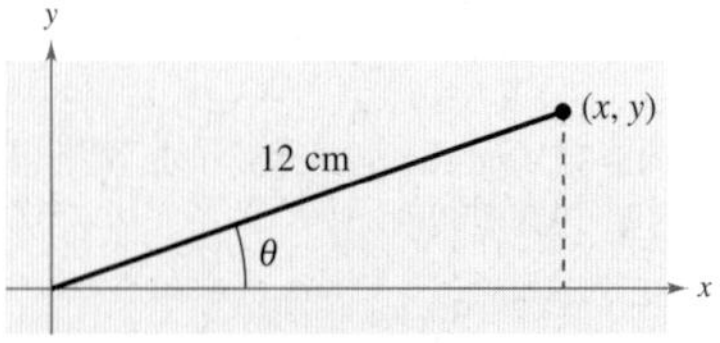

106. CAPSTONE Write a short paper in your own words explaining to a classmate how to evaluate the six trigonometric functions of any angle θ in standard position. Include an explanation of reference angles and how to use them, the signs of the functions in each of the four quadrants, and the trigonometric values of common angles. Be sure to include figures or diagrams in your paper. Answers will vary.

107. THINK ABOUT IT The figure shows point $P(x, y)$ on a unit circle and right triangle OAP.

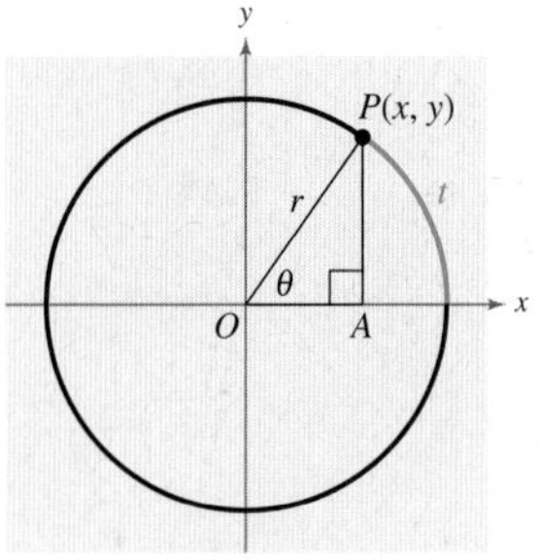

(a) Find $\sin t$ and $\cos t$ using the unit circle definitions of sine and cosine (from Section 4.2). See margin.

(b) What is the value of r? Explain. See margin.

(c) Use the definitions of sine and cosine given in this section to find $\sin \theta$ and $\cos \theta$. Write your answers in terms of x and y. $\sin \theta = y$, $\cos \theta = x$

(d) Based on your answers to parts (a) and (c), what can you conclude?
$\sin t = \sin \theta$ and $\cos t = \cos \theta$.

99. (a) $N = 22.099 \sin(0.522t - 2.219) + 55.008$
$F = 36.641 \sin(0.502t - 1.831) + 25.610$
(b) February: $N = 34.6°$, $F = -1.4°$
March: $N = 41.6°$, $F = 13.9°$
May: $N = 63.4°$, $F = 48.6°$
June: $N = 72.5°$, $F = 59.5°$
August: $N = 75.5°$, $F = 55.6°$
September: $N = 68.6°$, $F = 41.7°$
November: $N = 46.8°$, $F = 6.5°$
(c) Answers will vary.

4.5 Graphs of Sine and Cosine Functions

What you should learn

- Sketch the graphs of basic sine and cosine functions.
- Use amplitude and period to help sketch the graphs of sine and cosine functions.
- Sketch translations of the graphs of sine and cosine functions.
- Use sine and cosine functions to model real-life data.

Why you should learn it

Sine and cosine functions are often used in scientific calculations. For instance, in Exercise 87 on page 328, you can use a trigonometric function to model the airflow of your respiratory cycle.

Basic Sine and Cosine Curves

In this section, you will study techniques for sketching the graphs of the sine and cosine functions. The graph of the sine function is a **sine curve.** In Figure 4.47, the black portion of the graph represents one period of the function and is called **one cycle** of the sine curve. The gray portion of the graph indicates that the basic sine curve repeats indefinitely in the positive and negative directions. The graph of the cosine function is shown in Figure 4.48.

Recall from Section 4.2 that the domain of the sine and cosine functions is the set of all real numbers. Moreover, the range of each function is the interval $[-1, 1]$, and each function has a period of 2π. Do you see how this information is consistent with the basic graphs shown in Figures 4.47 and 4.48?

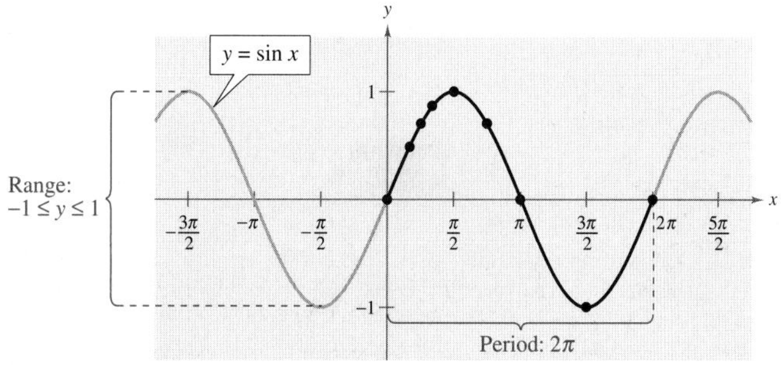

FIGURE 4.47

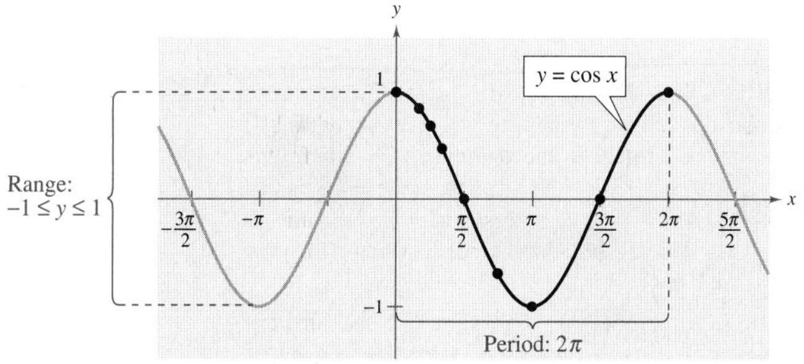

FIGURE 4.48

Note in Figures 4.47 and 4.48 that the sine curve is symmetric with respect to the *origin*, whereas the cosine curve is symmetric with respect to the *y-axis*. These properties of symmetry follow from the fact that the sine function is odd and the cosine function is even.

1 PLAN AND PREPARE

Warm-up Exercises

Transparency Available
Available at the Instructor's companion site.

Notetaking Guide

Transparency Available
Promotes interactive learning and notetaking skills. Available at the Instructor's companion site.

Animated Precalculus

An **Animated Precalculus** tutorial is available at the Student companion site for **Section 4.5.**

Pacing

Average: 1 day
Advanced: 1 day
Block: 0.5 block with 4.4

2 FOCUS AND MOTIVATE

Essential Question

How do you sketch the graphs of sine and cosine functions? **Tell students that they will learn how to answer this question by studying the basic characteristics of sine and cosine graphs and applying transformations to the basic graphs.**

Resource Planning Guide

Chapter Resources

- Complete Solutions Guide

Workbooks

- Notetaking Guide
- Student Solutions Guide

Interactive Technology

- Instructor Success Organizer
- Notetaking Guide IAE
- Instructional DVDs
- Animated Precalculus
- PowerLecture with ExamView

3 TEACH

Extra Example 1

Sketch the graph of $y = 3\cos x$ on the interval $[-\pi/2, 9\pi/2]$.

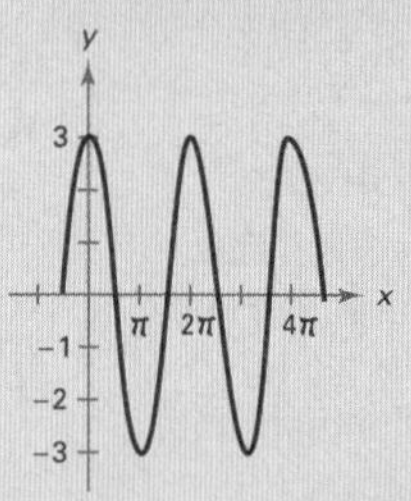

To sketch the graphs of the basic sine and cosine functions by hand, it helps to note five **key points** in one period of each graph: the *intercepts*, *maximum points*, and *minimum points* (see Figure 4.49).

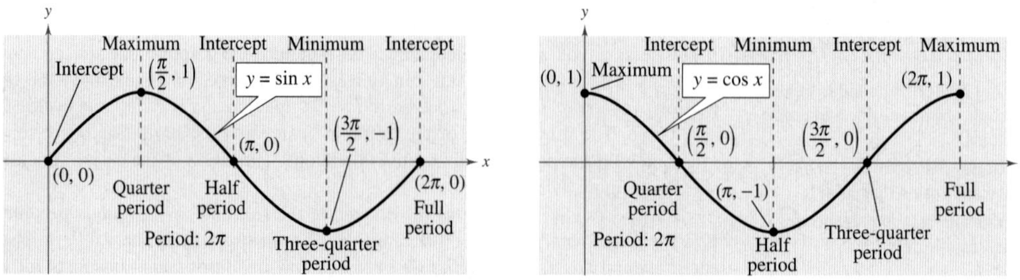

FIGURE 4.49

Example 1 Using Key Points to Sketch a Sine Curve

Sketch the graph of $y = 2\sin x$ on the interval $[-\pi, 4\pi]$.

Solution

Note that

$$y = 2\sin x = 2(\sin x)$$

indicates that the y-values for the key points will have twice the magnitude of those on the graph of $y = \sin x$. Divide the period 2π into four equal parts to get the key points for $y = 2\sin x$.

Intercept	*Maximum*	*Intercept*	*Minimum*	*Intercept*
$(0, 0)$,	$\left(\frac{\pi}{2}, 2\right)$,	$(\pi, 0)$,	$\left(\frac{3\pi}{2}, -2\right)$,	and $(2\pi, 0)$

By connecting these key points with a smooth curve and extending the curve in both directions over the interval $[-\pi, 4\pi]$, you obtain the graph shown in Figure 4.50.

TECHNOLOGY

When using a graphing utility to graph trigonometric functions, pay special attention to the viewing window you use. For instance, try graphing $y = [\sin(10x)]/10$ in the standard viewing window in *radian* mode. What do you observe? Use the *zoom* feature to find a viewing window that displays a good view of the graph.

No graph is visible. Try $-\pi \le x \le \pi$ and $-0.5 \le y \le 0.5$ as a viewing window.

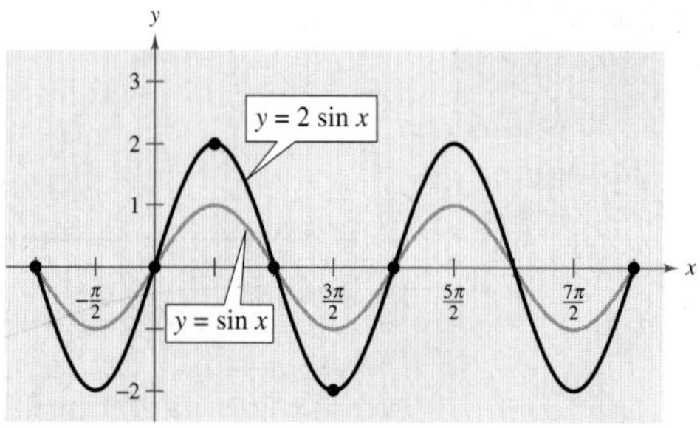

FIGURE 4.50

CHECK Point Now try Exercise 39.

Amplitude and Period

In the remainder of this section you will study the graphic effect of each of the constants a, b, c, and d in equations of the forms

$$y = d + a\sin(bx - c)$$

and

$$y = d + a\cos(bx - c).$$

A quick review of the transformations you studied in Section 1.7 should help in this investigation.

The constant factor a in $y = a\sin x$ acts as a *scaling factor*—a *vertical stretch* or *vertical shrink* of the basic sine curve. If $|a| > 1$, the basic sine curve is stretched, and if $|a| < 1$, the basic sine curve is shrunk. The result is that the graph of $y = a\sin x$ ranges between $-a$ and a instead of between -1 and 1. The absolute value of a is the **amplitude** of the function $y = a\sin x$. The range of the function $y = a\sin x$ for $a > 0$ is $-a \le y \le a$.

Definition of Amplitude of Sine and Cosine Curves

The **amplitude** of $y = a\sin x$ and $y = a\cos x$ represents half the distance between the maximum and minimum values of the function and is given by

$$\text{Amplitude} = |a|.$$

Example 2 Scaling: Vertical Shrinking and Stretching

On the same coordinate axes, sketch the graph of each function.

a. $y = \dfrac{1}{2}\cos x$ **b.** $y = 3\cos x$

Solution

a. Because the amplitude of $y = \frac{1}{2}\cos x$ is $\frac{1}{2}$, the maximum value is $\frac{1}{2}$ and the minimum value is $-\frac{1}{2}$. Divide one cycle, $0 \le x \le 2\pi$, into four equal parts to get the key points

Maximum	*Intercept*	*Minimum*	*Intercept*		*Maximum*
$\left(0, \frac{1}{2}\right)$,	$\left(\frac{\pi}{2}, 0\right)$,	$\left(\pi, -\frac{1}{2}\right)$,	$\left(\frac{3\pi}{2}, 0\right)$,	and	$\left(2\pi, \frac{1}{2}\right)$.

b. A similar analysis shows that the amplitude of $y = 3\cos x$ is 3, and the key points are

Maximum	*Intercept*	*Minimum*	*Intercept*		*Maximum*
$(0, 3)$,	$\left(\frac{\pi}{2}, 0\right)$,	$(\pi, -3)$,	$\left(\frac{3\pi}{2}, 0\right)$,	and	$(2\pi, 3)$.

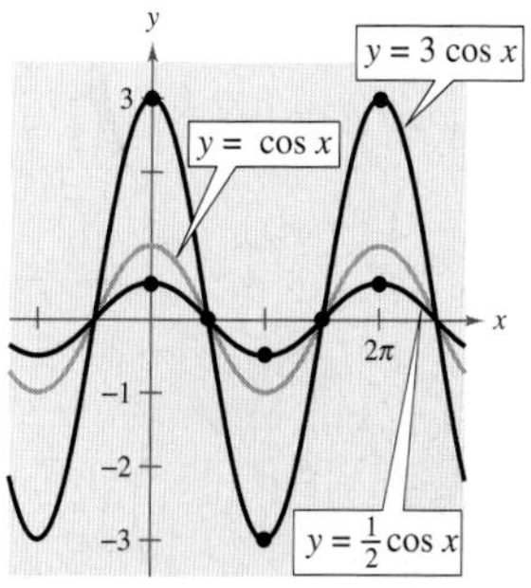

FIGURE 4.51

The graphs of these two functions are shown in Figure 4.51. Notice that the graph of $y = \frac{1}{2}\cos x$ is a vertical *shrink* of the graph of $y = \cos x$ and the graph of $y = 3\cos x$ is a vertical *stretch* of the graph of $y = \cos x$.

CHECKPoint Now try Exercise 41.

Extra Example 2

On the same coordinate axes, sketch the graphs of $f(x) = 2\sin x$ and $g(x) = \frac{1}{3}\sin x$.

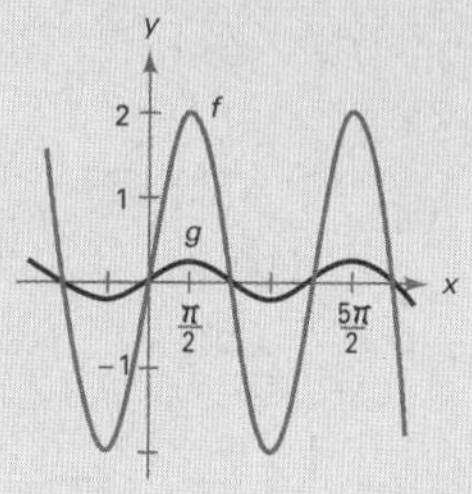

Extra Example 3

Sketch the graph of $y = \cos \frac{x}{2}$.

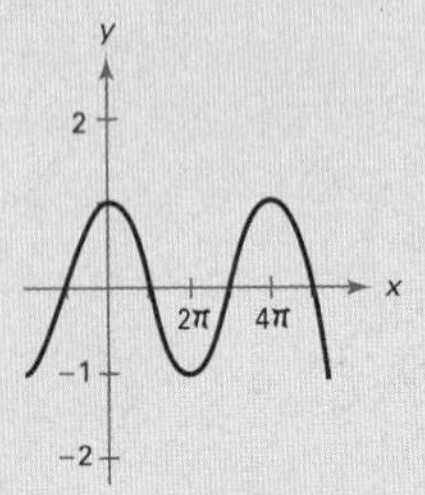

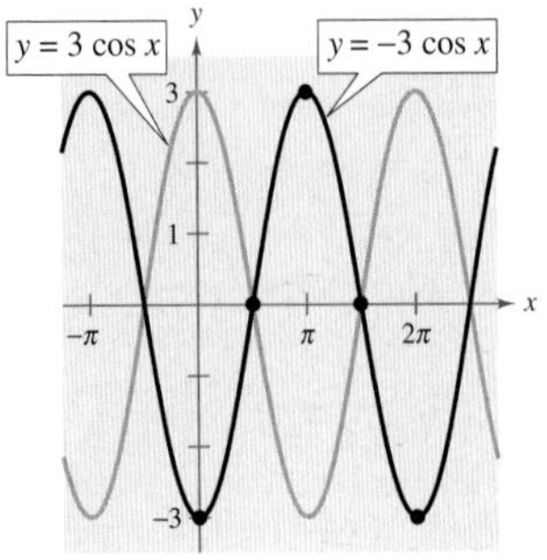

FIGURE 4.52

You know from Section 1.7 that the graph of $y = -f(x)$ is a **reflection** in the x-axis of the graph of $y = f(x)$. For instance, the graph of $y = -3 \cos x$ is a reflection of the graph of $y = 3 \cos x$, as shown in Figure 4.52.

Because $y = a \sin x$ completes one cycle from $x = 0$ to $x = 2\pi$, it follows that $y = a \sin bx$ completes one cycle from $x = 0$ to $x = 2\pi/b$.

Period of Sine and Cosine Functions

Let b be a positive real number. The **period** of $y = a \sin bx$ and $y = a \cos bx$ is given by

$$\text{Period} = \frac{2\pi}{b}.$$

Note that if $0 < b < 1$, the period of $y = a \sin bx$ is greater than 2π and represents a *horizontal stretching* of the graph of $y = a \sin x$. Similarly, if $b > 1$, the period of $y = a \sin bx$ is less than 2π and represents a *horizontal shrinking* of the graph of $y = a \sin x$. If b is negative, the identities $\sin(-x) = -\sin x$ and $\cos(-x) = \cos x$ are used to rewrite the function.

Example 3 Scaling: Horizontal Stretching

Sketch the graph of $y = \sin \frac{x}{2}$.

Solution

The amplitude is 1. Moreover, because $b = \frac{1}{2}$, the period is

$$\frac{2\pi}{b} = \frac{2\pi}{\frac{1}{2}} = 4\pi. \qquad \text{Substitute for } b.$$

Now, divide the period-interval $[0, 4\pi]$ into four equal parts with the values π, 2π, and 3π to obtain the key points on the graph.

Intercept	*Maximum*	*Intercept*	*Minimum*		*Intercept*
$(0, 0)$,	$(\pi, 1)$,	$(2\pi, 0)$,	$(3\pi, -1)$,	and	$(4\pi, 0)$

The graph is shown in Figure 4.53.

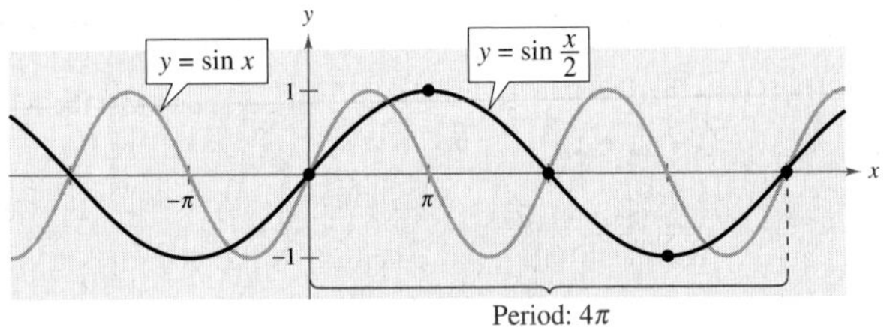

FIGURE 4.53

CHECKPoint Now try Exercise 43.

Study Tip

In general, to divide a period-interval into four equal parts, successively add "period/4," starting with the left endpoint of the interval. For instance, for the period-interval $[-\pi/6, \pi/2]$ of length $2\pi/3$, you would successively add

$$\frac{2\pi/3}{4} = \frac{\pi}{6}$$

to get $-\pi/6, 0, \pi/6, \pi/3$, and $\pi/2$ as the x-values for the key points on the graph.

Translations of Sine and Cosine Curves

> *Algebra Help*
>
> You can review the techniques for shifting, reflecting, and stretching graphs in Section 1.7.

The constant c in the general equations

$$y = a\sin(bx - c) \quad \text{and} \quad y = a\cos(bx - c)$$

creates a *horizontal translation* (shift) of the basic sine and cosine curves. Comparing $y = a\sin bx$ with $y = a\sin(bx - c)$, you find that the graph of $y = a\sin(bx - c)$ completes one cycle from $bx - c = 0$ to $bx - c = 2\pi$. By solving for x, you can find the interval for one cycle to be

$$\underbrace{\frac{c}{b}}_{\text{Left endpoint}} \le x \le \underbrace{\frac{c}{b} + \underbrace{\frac{2\pi}{b}}_{\text{Period}}}_{\text{Right endpoint}}.$$

This implies that the period of $y = a\sin(bx - c)$ is $2\pi/b$, and the graph of $y = a\sin bx$ is shifted by an amount c/b. The number c/b is the **phase shift.**

> **Graphs of Sine and Cosine Functions**
>
> The graphs of $y = a\sin(bx - c)$ and $y = a\cos(bx - c)$ have the following characteristics. (Assume $b > 0$.)
>
> $$\text{Amplitude} = |a| \qquad \text{Period} = \frac{2\pi}{b}$$
>
> The left and right endpoints of a one-cycle interval can be determined by solving the equations $bx - c = 0$ and $bx - c = 2\pi$.

Extra Example 4

Sketch the graph of

$$y = 2\sin\left(x - \frac{\pi}{2}\right).$$

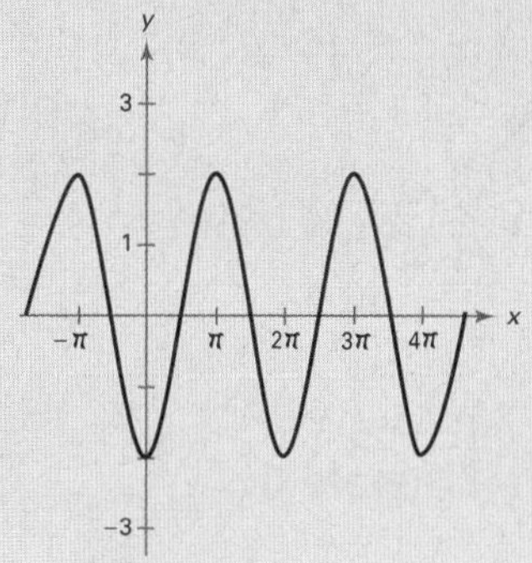

Example 4 Horizontal Translation

Analyze the graph of $y = \frac{1}{2}\sin\left(x - \frac{\pi}{3}\right)$.

Algebraic Solution

The amplitude is $\frac{1}{2}$ and the period is 2π. By solving the equations

$$x - \frac{\pi}{3} = 0 \quad \Longrightarrow \quad x = \frac{\pi}{3}$$

and

$$x - \frac{\pi}{3} = 2\pi \quad \Longrightarrow \quad x = \frac{7\pi}{3}$$

you see that the interval $[\pi/3, 7\pi/3]$ corresponds to one cycle of the graph. Dividing this interval into four equal parts produces the key points

Intercept	*Maximum*	*Intercept*	*Minimum*		*Intercept*
$\left(\frac{\pi}{3}, 0\right)$,	$\left(\frac{5\pi}{6}, \frac{1}{2}\right)$,	$\left(\frac{4\pi}{3}, 0\right)$,	$\left(\frac{11\pi}{6}, -\frac{1}{2}\right)$,	and	$\left(\frac{7\pi}{3}, 0\right)$.

CHECKPoint Now try Exercise 49.

Graphical Solution

Use a graphing utility set in *radian* mode to graph $y = (1/2)\sin(x - \pi/3)$, as shown in Figure 4.54. Use the *minimum, maximum,* and *zero* or *root* features of the graphing utility to approximate the key points (1.05, 0), (2.62, 0.5), (4.19, 0), (5.76, −0.5), and (7.33, 0).

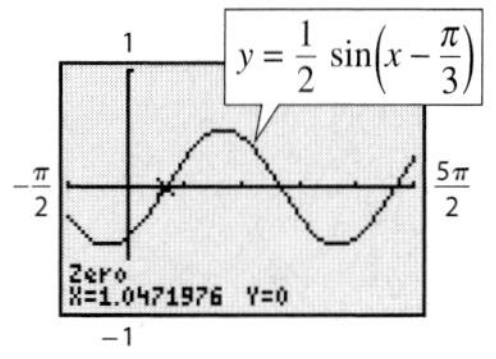

FIGURE 4.54

Extra Example 5

Sketch the graph of

$y = -\frac{1}{2}\sin(\pi x + \pi).$

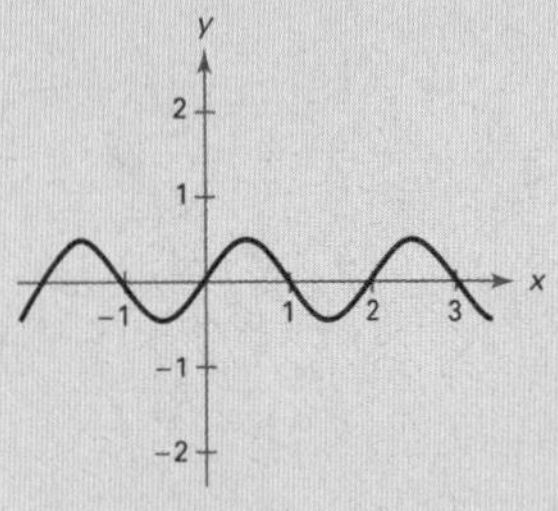

Extra Example 6

Sketch the graph of $y = 2\cos x - 5$.

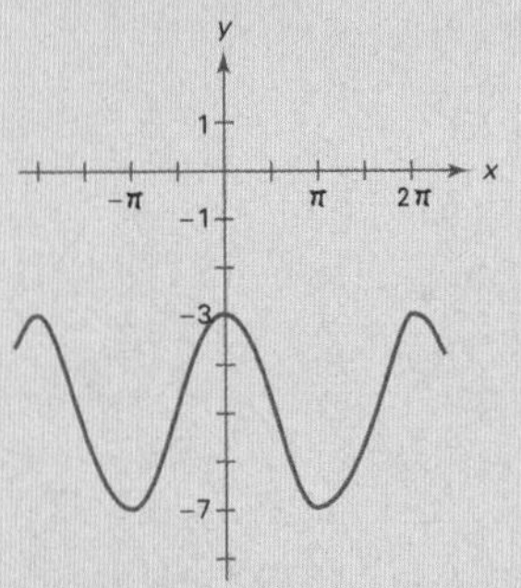

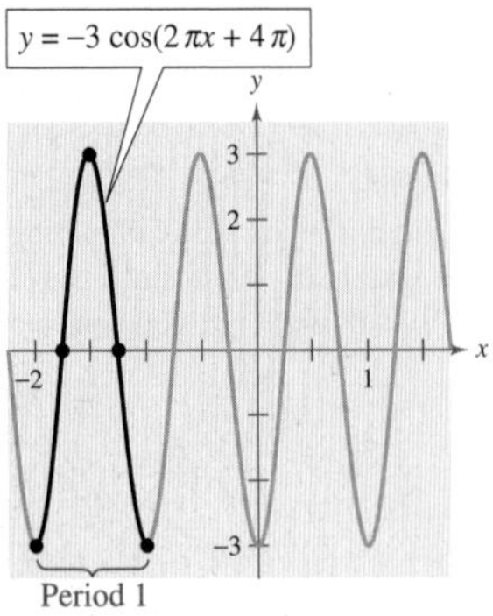

FIGURE 4.55

Example 5 Horizontal Translation

Sketch the graph of

$$y = -3\cos(2\pi x + 4\pi).$$

Solution

The amplitude is 3 and the period is $2\pi/2\pi = 1$. By solving the equations

$$2\pi x + 4\pi = 0$$
$$2\pi x = -4\pi$$
$$x = -2$$

and

$$2\pi x + 4\pi = 2\pi$$
$$2\pi x = -2\pi$$
$$x = -1$$

you see that the interval $[-2, -1]$ corresponds to one cycle of the graph. Dividing this interval into four equal parts produces the key points

Minimum	*Intercept*	*Maximum*	*Intercept*		*Minimum*
$(-2, -3)$,	$\left(-\frac{7}{4}, 0\right)$,	$\left(-\frac{3}{2}, 3\right)$,	$\left(-\frac{5}{4}, 0\right)$,	and	$(-1, -3)$.

The graph is shown in Figure 4.55.

CHECKPoint Now try Exercise 51.

The final type of transformation is the *vertical translation* caused by the constant d in the equations

$$y = d + a\sin(bx - c)$$

and

$$y = d + a\cos(bx - c).$$

The shift is d units upward for $d > 0$ and d units downward for $d < 0$. In other words, the graph oscillates about the horizontal line $y = d$ instead of about the x-axis.

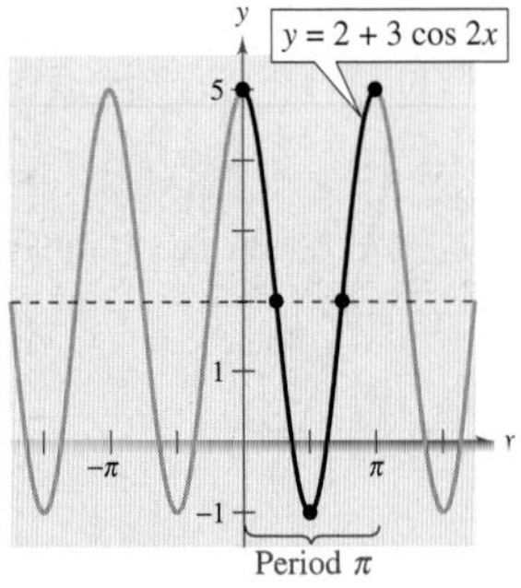

FIGURE 4.56

Example 6 Vertical Translation

Sketch the graph of

$$y = 2 + 3\cos 2x.$$

Solution

The amplitude is 3 and the period is π. The key points over the interval $[0, \pi]$ are

$$(0, 5), \quad \left(\frac{\pi}{4}, 2\right), \quad \left(\frac{\pi}{2}, -1\right), \quad \left(\frac{3\pi}{4}, 2\right), \quad \text{and} \quad (\pi, 5).$$

The graph is shown in Figure 4.56. Compared with the graph of $f(x) = 3\cos 2x$, the graph of $y = 2 + 3\cos 2x$ is shifted upward two units.

CHECKPoint Now try Exercise 57.

Mathematical Modeling

Sine and cosine functions can be used to model many real-life situations, including electric currents, musical tones, radio waves, tides, and weather patterns.

Time, t	Depth, y
Midnight	3.4
2 A.M.	8.7
4 A.M.	11.3
6 A.M.	9.1
8 A.M.	3.8
10 A.M.	0.1
Noon	1.2

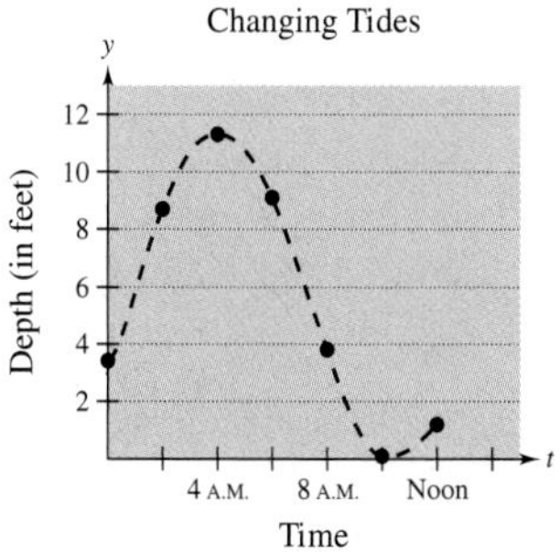

FIGURE 4.57

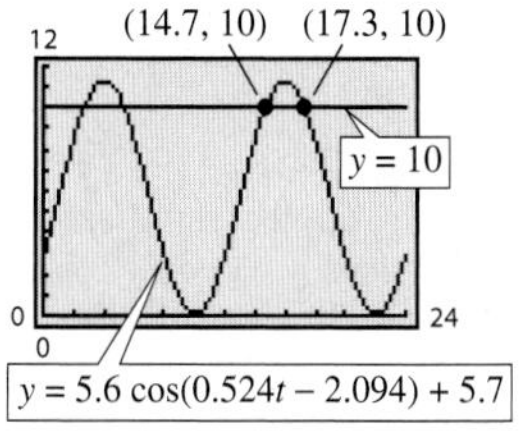

FIGURE 4.58

Example 7 Finding a Trigonometric Model

Throughout the day, the depth of water at the end of a dock in Bar Harbor, Maine varies with the tides. The table shows the depths (in feet) at various times during the morning. (Source: Nautical Software, Inc.)

a. Use a trigonometric function to model the data.

b. Find the depths at 9 A.M. and 3 P.M.

c. A boat needs at least 10 feet of water to moor at the dock. During what times in the afternoon can it safely dock?

Solution

a. Begin by graphing the data, as shown in Figure 4.57. You can use either a sine or a cosine model. Suppose you use a cosine model of the form

$$y = a\cos(bt - c) + d.$$

The difference between the maximum height and the minimum height of the graph is twice the amplitude of the function. So, the amplitude is

$$a = \frac{1}{2}[(\text{maximum depth}) - (\text{minimum depth})] = \frac{1}{2}(11.3 - 0.1) = 5.6.$$

The cosine function completes one half of a cycle between the times at which the maximum and minimum depths occur. So, the period is

$$p = 2[(\text{time of min. depth}) - (\text{time of max. depth})] = 2(10 - 4) = 12$$

which implies that $b = 2\pi/p \approx 0.524$. Because high tide occurs 4 hours after midnight, consider the left endpoint to be $c/b = 4$, so $c \approx 2.094$. Moreover, because the average depth is $\frac{1}{2}(11.3 + 0.1) = 5.7$, it follows that $d = 5.7$. So, you can model the depth with the function given by

$$y = 5.6\cos(0.524t - 2.094) + 5.7.$$

b. The depths at 9 A.M. and 3 P.M. are as follows.

$$y = 5.6\cos(0.524 \cdot 9 - 2.094) + 5.7$$
$$\approx 0.84 \text{ foot} \qquad \text{9 A.M.}$$
$$y = 5.6\cos(0.524 \cdot 15 - 2.094) + 5.7$$
$$\approx 10.57 \text{ feet} \qquad \text{3 P.M.}$$

c. To find out when the depth y is at least 10 feet, you can graph the model with the line $y = 10$ using a graphing utility, as shown in Figure 4.58. Using the *intersect* feature, you can determine that the depth is at least 10 feet between 2:42 P.M. ($t \approx 14.7$) and 5:18 P.M. ($t \approx 17.3$).

CHECK*Point* Now try Exercise 91.

Extra Example 7

The normal monthly temperatures in degrees Fahrenheit in Albany, NY, for six months are given in the table.

x (month)	y (temperature)
Jan	21
Mar	34
May	58
Jul	72
Sep	61
Nov	40

a. Use a trigonometric function to model this data.

$$y = 25.5\cos\left(\frac{\pi}{6}x - \pi\right) + 46.5$$

b. Find the normal temperature in December.

24°

c. A painting company will accept exterior jobs only when the normal temperature is 64 degrees or higher. During what months will this company accept exterior jobs?

The company will accept exterior jobs from about mid-May through mid-August.

Closing the Lesson

Have students summarize the major points of the lesson and answer the Essential Question: How do you sketch the graphs of sine and cosine functions?

- **Recognize the shape and key points of sine and cosine graphs.**
- **Find the amplitude and vertical shift of a transformed sine or cosine function by finding its vertical stretch factor and center between maximum and minimum values.**
- **Find the period and phase shift of a transformed function $f(x) = a\sin(bx - c)$ or $f(x) = a\cos(bx - c)$ by finding the one-cycle interval given by x-values satisfying $bx - c = 0$ and $bx - c = 2\pi$.**

4 PRACTICE AND APPLY

Assignment Guide

Transparencies Available
Available at the Instructor's companion site.

Average:
Day 1: pp. 326–329
Exs. 7–13 odd, 21–27 odd, 37, 45, 47, 51, 63, 67, 69, 73, 77–87 odd, 90, 93, 95–97, 101

Advanced:
Day 1: pp. 326–329
Exs. 10–14 even, 18, 22–32 even, 38, 52–68 even, 74–80 even, 84–94 even, 98–102 even, 103

Block:
pp. 326–329
Exs. 7–13 odd, 21–27 odd, 37, 45, 47, 51, 63, 67, 69, 73, 77–87 odd, 90, 93, 95–97, 101 (with 4.4)

4.5 EXERCISES

See www.CalcChat.com for worked-out solutions to odd-numbered exercises.

VOCABULARY: Fill in the blanks.

1. One period of a sine or cosine function is called one __cycle__ of the sine or cosine curve.
2. The ________ of a sine or cosine curve represents half the distance between the maximum and minimum values of the function. amplitude
3. For the function given by $y = a\sin(bx - c)$, $\frac{c}{b}$ represents the __phase__ __shift__ of the graph of the function.
4. For the function given by $y = d + a\cos(bx - c)$, d represents a ________ ________ of the graph of the function. vertical translation

SKILLS AND APPLICATIONS

5–16. See margin.

In Exercises 5–18, find the period and amplitude.

5. $y = 2\sin 5x$

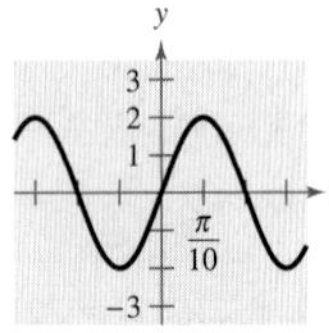

6. $y = 3\cos 2x$

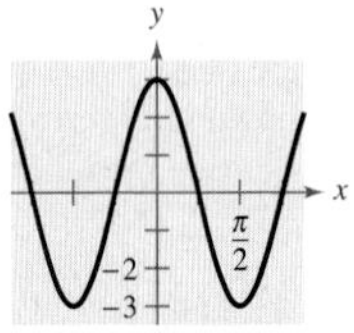

7. $y = \frac{3}{4}\cos\frac{x}{2}$

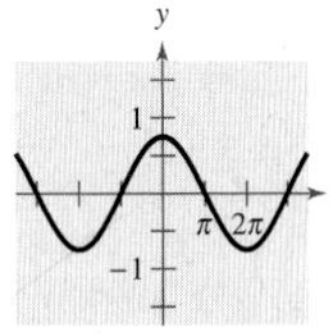

8. $y = -3\sin\frac{x}{3}$

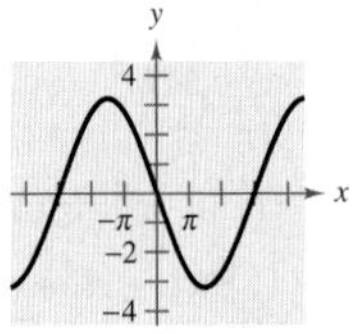

9. $y = \frac{1}{2}\sin\frac{\pi x}{3}$

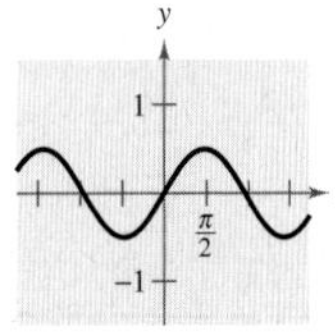

10. $y = \frac{3}{2}\cos\frac{\pi x}{2}$

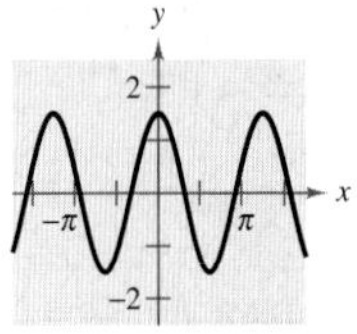

11. $y = -4\sin x$
12. $y = -\cos\frac{2x}{3}$
13. $y = 3\sin 10x$
14. $y = \frac{1}{5}\sin 6x$
15. $y = \frac{5}{3}\cos\frac{4x}{5}$
16. $y = \frac{5}{2}\cos\frac{x}{4}$
17. $y = \frac{1}{4}\sin 2\pi x$
    Period: 1; Amplitude: $\frac{1}{4}$
18. $y = \frac{2}{3}\cos\frac{\pi x}{10}$
    Period: 20; Amplitude: $\frac{2}{3}$

In Exercises 19–26, describe the relationship between the graphs of f and g. Consider amplitude, period, and shifts. 19–26. See margin.

19. $f(x) = \sin x$
    $g(x) = \sin(x - \pi)$
20. $f(x) = \cos x$
    $g(x) = \cos(x + \pi)$
21. $f(x) = \cos 2x$
    $g(x) = -\cos 2x$
22. $f(x) = \sin 3x$
    $g(x) = \sin(-3x)$
23. $f(x) = \cos x$
    $g(x) = \cos 2x$
24. $f(x) = \sin x$
    $g(x) = \sin 3x$
25. $f(x) = \sin 2x$
    $g(x) = 3 + \sin 2x$
26. $f(x) = \cos 4x$
    $g(x) = -2 + \cos 4x$

In Exercises 27–30, describe the relationship between the graphs of f and g. Consider amplitude, period, and shifts. 27–30. See margin.

27.

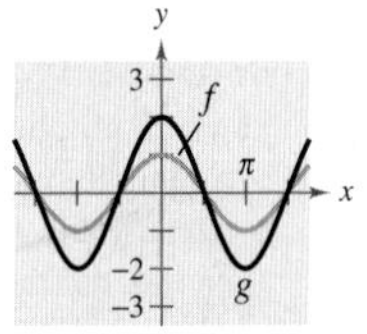

28.

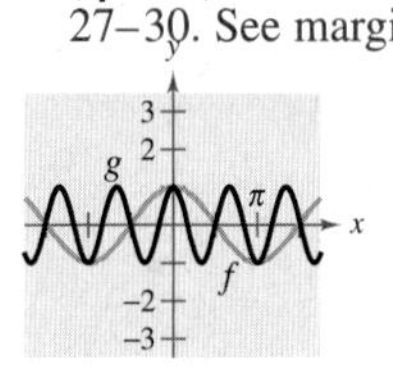

29.

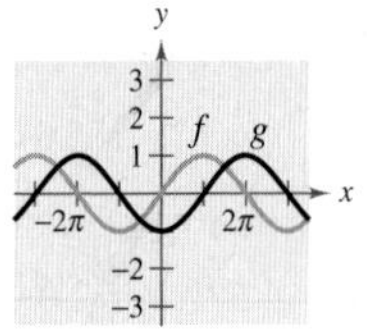

30.

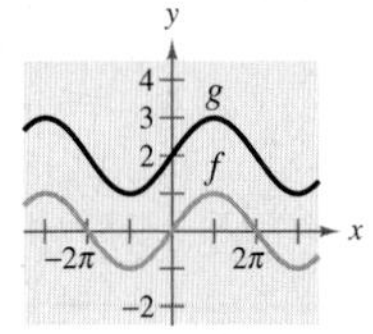

In Exercises 31–38, graph f and g on the same set of coordinate axes. (Include two full periods.) 31–34. See margin.

31. $f(x) = -2\sin x$
    $g(x) = 4\sin x$
32. $f(x) = \sin x$
    $g(x) = \sin\frac{x}{3}$
33. $f(x) = \cos x$
    $g(x) = 2 + \cos x$
34. $f(x) = 2\cos 2x$
    $g(x) = -\cos 4x$

5. Period: $\frac{2\pi}{5}$; Amplitude: 2
6. Period: π; Amplitude: 3
7. Period: 4π; Amplitude: $\frac{3}{4}$
8. Period: 6π; Amplitude: 3
9. Period: 6; Amplitude: $\frac{1}{2}$
10. Period: 4; Amplitude: $\frac{3}{2}$
11. Period: 2π; Amplitude: 4
12. Period: 3π; Amplitude: 1
13. Period: $\frac{\pi}{5}$; Amplitude: 3
14. Period: $\frac{\pi}{3}$; Amplitude: $\frac{1}{5}$
15. Period: $\frac{5\pi}{2}$; Amplitude: $\frac{5}{3}$
16. Period: 8π; Amplitude: $\frac{5}{2}$
19. g is a shift of f π units to the right.
20. g is a shift of f π units to the left.
21. g is a reflection of f in the x-axis.
22. g is a reflection of f in the y-axis.
23. The period of f is twice the period of g.
24. The period of g is one-third the period of f.
25. g is a shift of f three units upward.
26. g is a shift of f two units downward.
27. The graph of g has twice the amplitude of the graph of f.
28. The period of g is one-third the period of f.
29. The graph of g is a horizontal shift of the graph of f π units to the right.
30. g is a shift of f two units upward.

31.

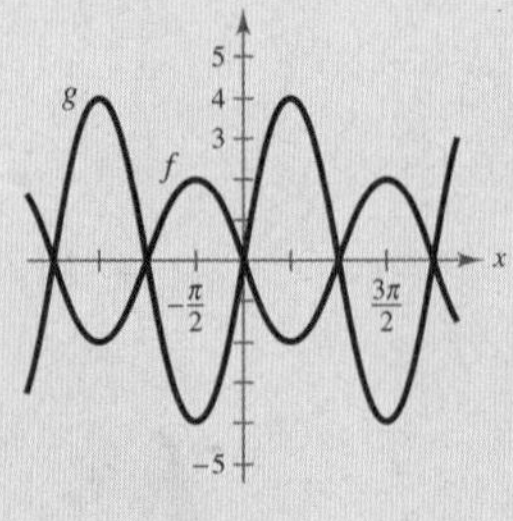

32.

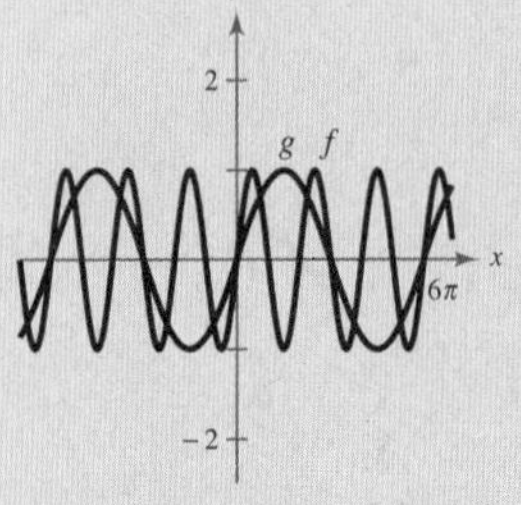

33–34. See Additional Answers beginning on page AA1.

35. $f(x) = -\frac{1}{2}\sin\frac{x}{2}$ **36.** $f(x) = 4\sin\pi x$

35–38. See margin.

$g(x) = 3 - \frac{1}{2}\sin\frac{x}{2}$ $g(x) = 4\sin\pi x - 3$

37. $f(x) = 2\cos x$ **38.** $f(x) = -\cos x$

$g(x) = 2\cos(x + \pi)$ $g(x) = -\cos(x - \pi)$

In Exercises 39–60, sketch the graph of the function. (Include two full periods.) 39–60. See margin.

39. $y = 5\sin x$ **40.** $y = \frac{1}{4}\sin x$

41. $y = \frac{1}{3}\cos x$ **42.** $y = 4\cos x$

43. $y = \cos\frac{x}{2}$ **44.** $y = \sin 4x$

45. $y = \cos 2\pi x$ **46.** $y = \sin\frac{\pi x}{4}$

47. $y = -\sin\frac{2\pi x}{3}$ **48.** $y = -10\cos\frac{\pi x}{6}$

49. $y = \sin\left(x - \frac{\pi}{2}\right)$ **50.** $y = \sin(x - 2\pi)$

51. $y = 3\cos(x + \pi)$ **52.** $y = 4\cos\left(x + \frac{\pi}{4}\right)$

53. $y = 2 - \sin\frac{2\pi x}{3}$ **54.** $y = -3 + 5\cos\frac{\pi t}{12}$

55. $y = 2 + \frac{1}{10}\cos 60\pi x$ **56.** $y = 2\cos x - 3$

57. $y = 3\cos(x + \pi) - 3$ **58.** $y = 4\cos\left(x + \frac{\pi}{4}\right) + 4$

59. $y = \frac{2}{3}\cos\left(\frac{x}{2} - \frac{\pi}{4}\right)$ **60.** $y = -3\cos(6x + \pi)$

In Exercises 61–66, g is related to a parent function $f(x) = \sin(x)$ or $f(x) = \cos(x)$. (a) Describe the sequence of transformations from f to g. (b) Sketch the graph of g. (c) Use function notation to write g in terms of f. 61–66. See margin.

61. $g(x) = \sin(4x - \pi)$ **62.** $g(x) = \sin(2x + \pi)$

63. $g(x) = \cos(x - \pi) + 2$ **64.** $g(x) = 1 + \cos(x + \pi)$

65. $g(x) = 2\sin(4x - \pi) - 3$ **66.** $g(x) = 4 - \sin(2x + \pi)$

In Exercises 67–72, use a graphing utility to graph the function. Include two full periods. Be sure to choose an appropriate viewing window. 67–72. See margin.

67. $y = -2\sin(4x + \pi)$ **68.** $y = -4\sin\left(\frac{2}{3}x - \frac{\pi}{3}\right)$

69. $y = \cos\left(2\pi x - \frac{\pi}{2}\right) + 1$

70. $y = 3\cos\left(\frac{\pi x}{2} + \frac{\pi}{2}\right) - 2$

71. $y = -0.1\sin\left(\frac{\pi x}{10} + \pi\right)$ **72.** $y = \frac{1}{100}\sin 120\pi t$

GRAPHICAL REASONING In Exercises 73–76, find a and d for the function $f(x) = a\cos x + d$ such that the graph of f matches the figure.

73.

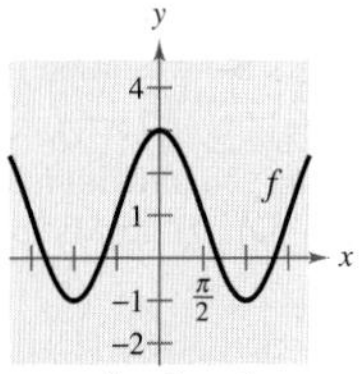

$a = 2, d = 1$

74.

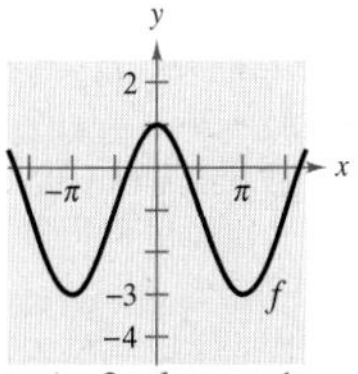

$a = 2, d = -1$

75.

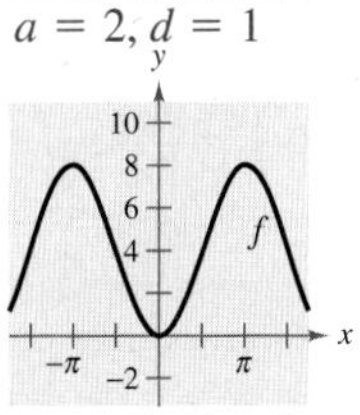

$a = -4, d = 4$

76.

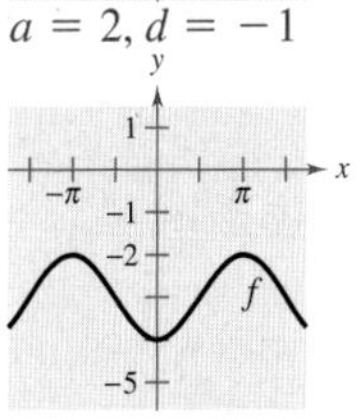

$a = -1, d = -3$

GRAPHICAL REASONING In Exercises 77–80, find a, b, and c for the function $f(x) = a\sin(bx - c)$ such that the graph of f matches the figure.

77.

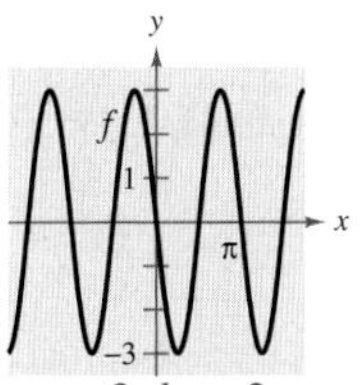

$a = -3, b = 2, c = 0$

78.

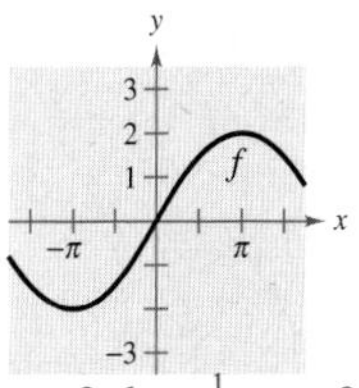

$a = 2, b = \frac{1}{2}, c = 0$

79.

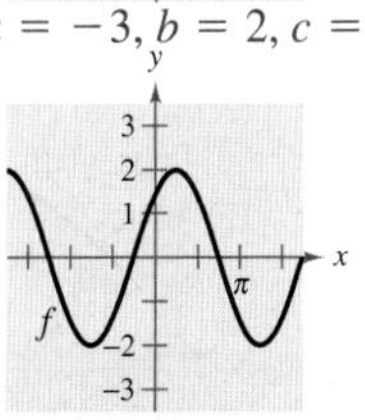

See margin.

80.

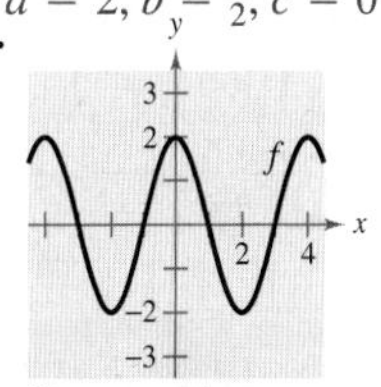

See margin.

In Exercises 81 and 82, use a graphing utility to graph y_1 and y_2 in the interval $[-2\pi, 2\pi]$. Use the graphs to find real numbers x such that $y_1 = y_2$. 81–82. See margin.

81. $y_1 = \sin x$ **82.** $y_1 = \cos x$

$y_2 = -\frac{1}{2}$ $y_2 = -1$

In Exercises 83–86, write an equation for the function that is described by the given characteristics.

83. A sine curve with a period of π, an amplitude of 2, a right phase shift of $\pi/2$, and a vertical translation up 1 unit $y = 1 + 2\sin(2x - \pi)$

35.

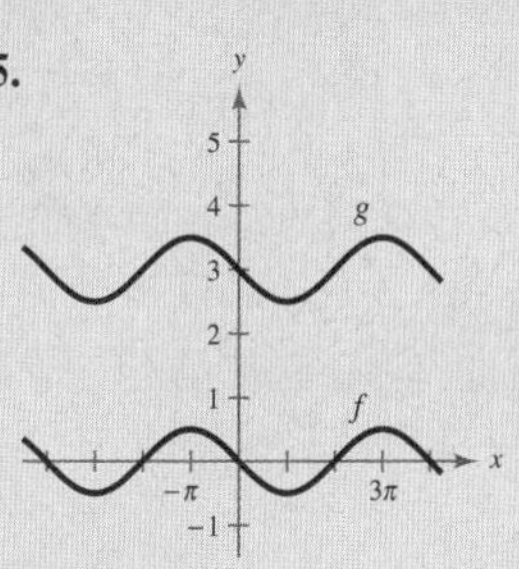

36.

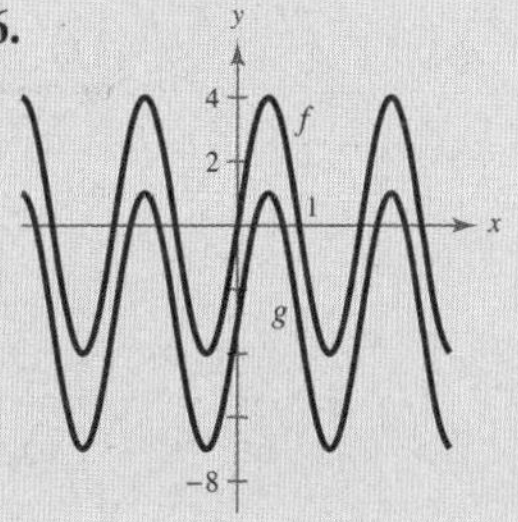

37.

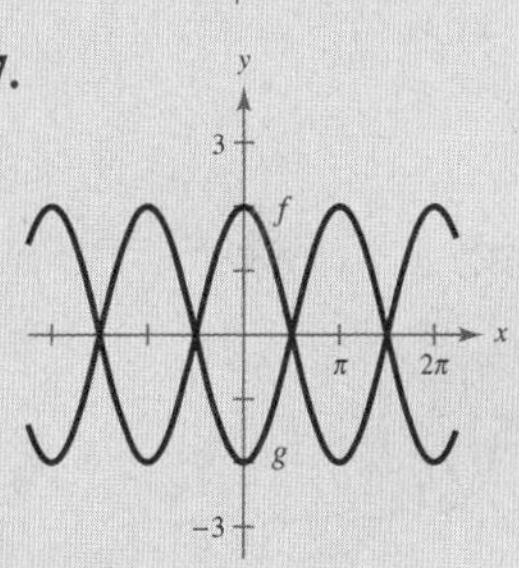

38.

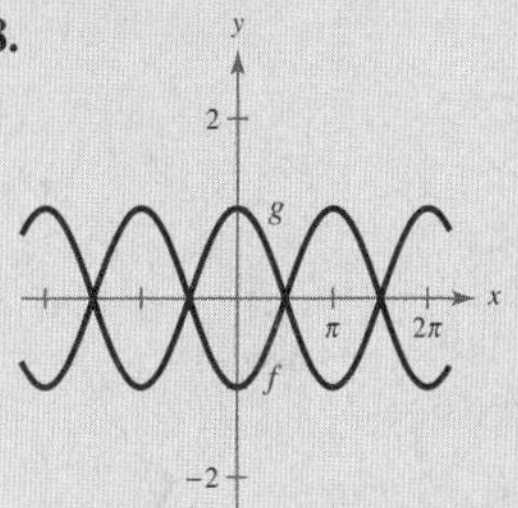

39.

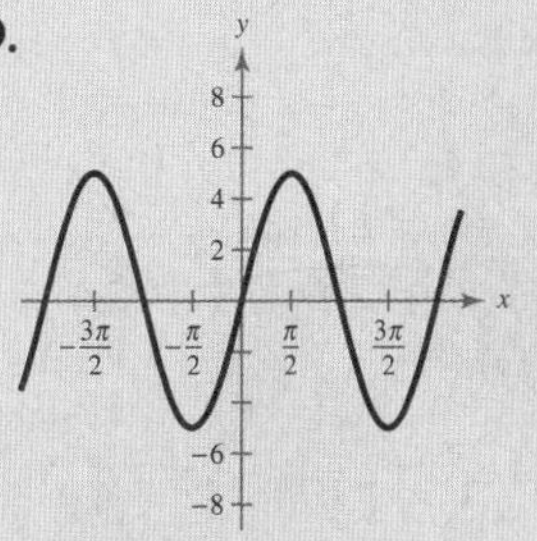

40.

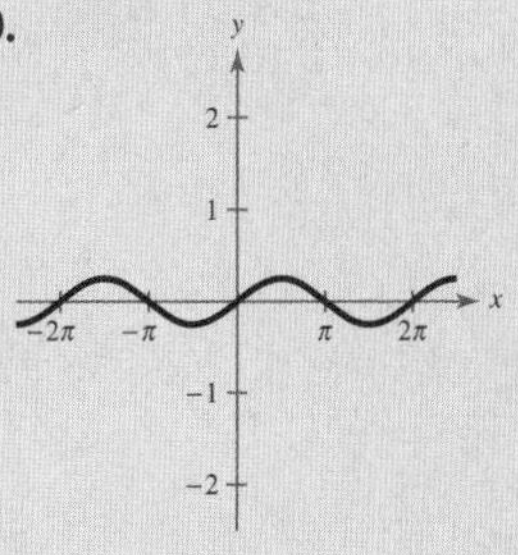

41.

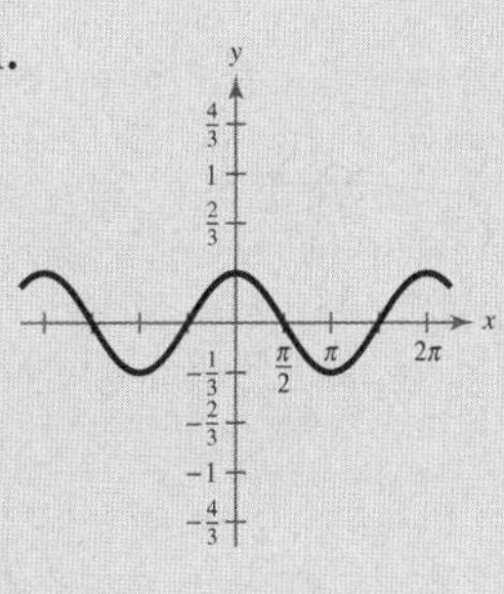

42.

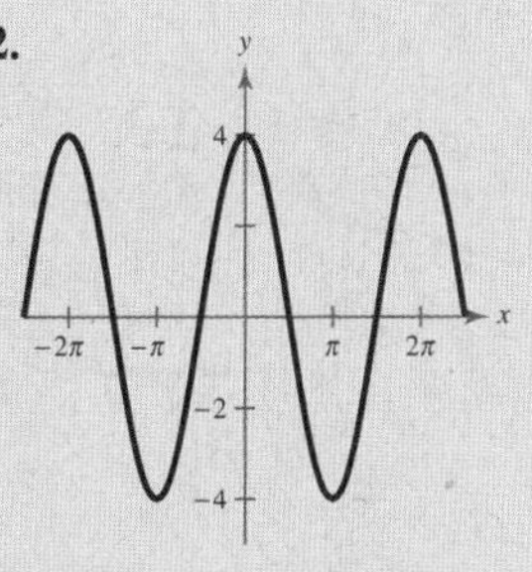

43.

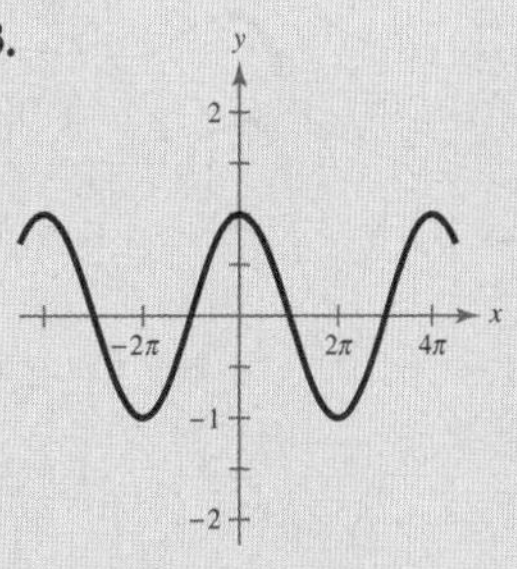

44–72, 79–82. See Additional Answers beginning on page AA1.

84. A sine curve with a period of 4π, an amplitude of 3, a left phase shift of $\pi/4$, and a vertical translation down 1 unit See margin.

85. A cosine curve with a period of π, an amplitude of 1, a left phase shift of π, and a vertical translation down $\frac{3}{2}$ units $y = \cos(2x + 2\pi) - \frac{3}{2}$

86. A cosine curve with a period of 4π, an amplitude of 3, a right phase shift of $\pi/2$, and a vertical translation up 2 units $y = 2 + 3\cos\left(\frac{1}{2}x - \frac{\pi}{4}\right)$

87. RESPIRATORY CYCLE For a person at rest, the velocity v (in liters per second) of airflow during a respiratory cycle (the time from the beginning of one breath to the beginning of the next) is given by $v = 0.85 \sin \frac{\pi t}{3}$, where t is the time (in seconds). (Inhalation occurs when $v > 0$, and exhalation occurs when $v < 0$.)

(a) Find the time for one full respiratory cycle. 6 sec

(b) Find the number of cycles per minute. 10 cycles/min

(c) Sketch the graph of the velocity function. See margin.

88. RESPIRATORY CYCLE After exercising for a few minutes, a person has a respiratory cycle for which the velocity of airflow is approximated by $v = 1.75 \sin \frac{\pi t}{2}$, where t is the time (in seconds). (Inhalation occurs when $v > 0$, and exhalation occurs when $v < 0$.)

(a) Find the time for one full respiratory cycle. 4 sec

(b) Find the number of cycles per minute. 15 cycles/min

(c) Sketch the graph of the velocity function. See margin.

89. DATA ANALYSIS: METEOROLOGY The table shows the maximum daily high temperatures in Las Vegas L and International Falls I (in degrees Fahrenheit) for month t, with $t = 1$ corresponding to January. (Source: National Climatic Data Center) See margin.

Month, t	Las Vegas, L	International Falls, I
1	57.1	13.8
2	63.0	22.4
3	69.5	34.9
4	78.1	51.5
5	87.8	66.6
6	98.9	74.2
7	104.1	78.6
8	101.8	76.3
9	93.8	64.7
10	80.8	51.7
11	66.0	32.5
12	57.3	18.1

(a) A model for the temperature in Las Vegas is given by

$$L(t) = 80.60 + 23.50\cos\left(\frac{\pi t}{6} - 3.67\right).$$

Find a trigonometric model for International Falls.

(b) Use a graphing utility to graph the data points and the model for the temperatures in Las Vegas. How well does the model fit the data?

(c) Use a graphing utility to graph the data points and the model for the temperatures in International Falls. How well does the model fit the data?

(d) Use the models to estimate the average maximum temperature in each city. Which term of the models did you use? Explain.

(e) What is the period of each model? Are the periods what you expected? Explain.

(f) Which city has the greater variability in temperature throughout the year? Which factor of the models determines this variability? Explain.

90. HEALTH The function given by

$$P = 100 - 20\cos\frac{5\pi t}{3}$$ (b) 50 heartbeats/min

approximates the blood pressure P (in millimeters of mercury) at time t (in seconds) for a person at rest.

(a) Find the period of the function. $\frac{6}{5}$ sec

(b) Find the number of heartbeats per minute.

91. PIANO TUNING When tuning a piano, a technician strikes a tuning fork for the A above middle C and sets up a wave motion that can be approximated by $y = 0.001 \sin 880\pi t$, where t is the time (in seconds).

(a) What is the period of the function? $\frac{1}{440}$ sec

(b) The frequency f is given by $f = 1/p$. What is the frequency of the note? 440 cycles/sec

92. DATA ANALYSIS: ASTRONOMY The percents y (in decimal form) of the moon's face that was illuminated on day x in the year 2009, where $x = 1$ represents January 1, are shown in the table. (Source: U.S. Naval Observatory)

x	y
4	0.5
11	1.0
18	0.5
26	0.0
33	0.5
40	1.0

84. $y = 3\sin\left(\frac{1}{2}x + \frac{\pi}{8}\right) - 1$

87. (c)

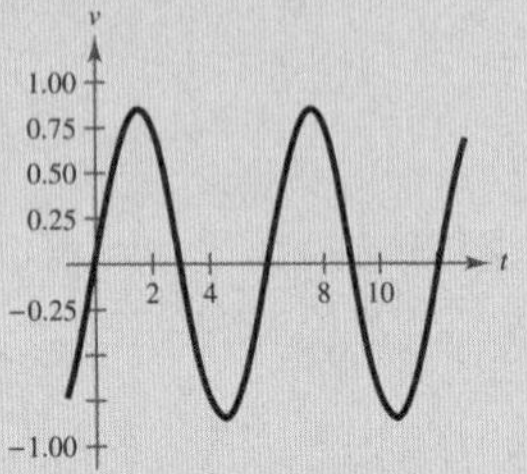

88. (c)

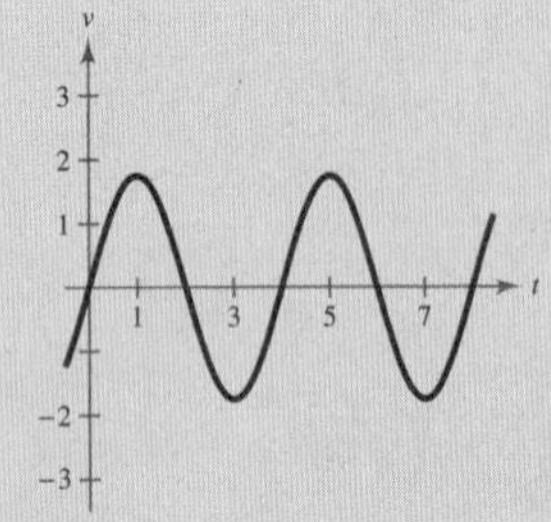

89. (a) $I(t) = 46.2 + 32.4\cos\left(\frac{\pi t}{6} - 3.67\right)$

(b)

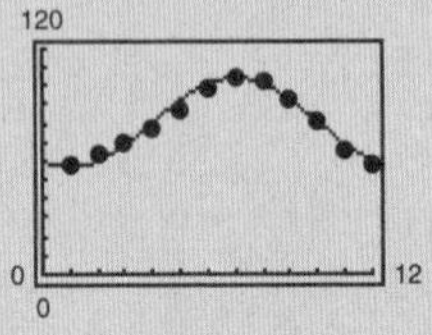

The model fits the data well.

(c)

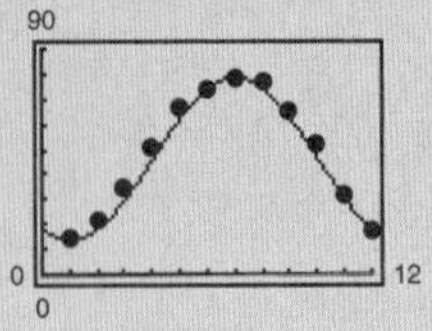

The model fits the data well.

(d) Las Vegas: 80.6°; International Falls: 46.2° The constant term gives the annual average temperature.

(e) 12; yes; One full period is one year.

(f) International Falls; amplitude; The greater the amplitude, the greater the variability in temperature.

(a) Create a scatter plot of the data. (a)–(c). See margin.

(b) Find a trigonometric model that fits the data.

(c) Add the graph of your model in part (b) to the scatter plot. How well does the model fit the data?

(d) What is the period of the model? 29

(e) Estimate the moon's percent illumination for March 12, 2009. 89%

93. FUEL CONSUMPTION The daily consumption C (in gallons) of diesel fuel on a farm is modeled by

$$C = 30.3 + 21.6 \sin\left(\frac{2\pi t}{365} + 10.9\right)$$

where t is the time (in days), with $t = 1$ corresponding to January 1. See margin.

(a) What is the period of the model? Is it what you expected? Explain.

(b) What is the average daily fuel consumption? Which term of the model did you use? Explain.

(c) Use a graphing utility to graph the model. Use the graph to approximate the time of the year when consumption exceeds 40 gallons per day.

94. FERRIS WHEEL A Ferris wheel is built such that the height h (in feet) above ground of a seat on the wheel at time t (in seconds) can be modeled by

$$h(t) = 53 + 50 \sin\left(\frac{\pi}{10}t - \frac{\pi}{2}\right).$$ See margin.

(a) Find the period of the model. What does the period tell you about the ride?

(b) Find the amplitude of the model. What does the amplitude tell you about the ride?

(c) Use a graphing utility to graph one cycle of the model.

EXPLORATION

95–97. See margin.

TRUE OR FALSE? In Exercises 95–97, determine whether the statement is true or false. Justify your answer.

95. The graph of the function given by $f(x) = \sin(x + 2\pi)$ translates the graph of $f(x) = \sin x$ exactly one period to the right so that the two graphs look identical.

96. The function given by $y = \frac{1}{2}\cos 2x$ has an amplitude that is twice that of the function given by $y = \cos x$.

97. The graph of $y = -\cos x$ is a reflection of the graph of $y = \sin(x + \pi/2)$ in the x-axis.

98. WRITING Sketch the graph of $y = \cos bx$ for $b = \frac{1}{2}$, 2, and 3. How does the value of b affect the graph? How many complete cycles occur between 0 and 2π for each value of b? See margin.

99. WRITING Sketch the graph of $y = \sin(x - c)$ for $c = -\pi/4$, 0, and $\pi/4$. How does the value of c affect the graph? See margin.

100. CAPSTONE Use a graphing utility to graph the function given by $y = d + a\sin(bx - c)$, for several different values of a, b, c, and d. Write a paragraph describing the changes in the graph corresponding to changes in each constant. Answers will vary.

CONJECTURE In Exercises 101 and 102, graph f and g on the same set of coordinate axes. Include two full periods. Make a conjecture about the functions. 101–102. See margin.

101. $f(x) = \sin x, \quad g(x) = \cos\left(x - \frac{\pi}{2}\right)$

102. $f(x) = \sin x, \quad g(x) = -\cos\left(x + \frac{\pi}{2}\right)$

103. Using calculus, it can be shown that the sine and cosine functions can be approximated by the polynomials

$$\sin x \approx x - \frac{x^3}{3!} + \frac{x^5}{5!} \quad \text{and} \quad \cos x \approx 1 - \frac{x^2}{2!} + \frac{x^4}{4!}$$

where x is in radians. See margin.

(a) Use a graphing utility to graph the sine function and its polynomial approximation in the same viewing window. How do the graphs compare?

(b) Use a graphing utility to graph the cosine function and its polynomial approximation in the same viewing window. How do the graphs compare?

(c) Study the patterns in the polynomial approximations of the sine and cosine functions and predict the next term in each. Then repeat parts (a) and (b). How did the accuracy of the approximations change when an additional term was added?

104. Use the polynomial approximations of the sine and cosine functions in Exercise 103 to approximate the following function values. Compare the results with those given by a calculator. Is the error in the approximation the same in each case? Explain.

(a) $\sin \frac{1}{2}$ (b) $\sin 1$ (c) $\sin \frac{\pi}{6}$ See margin.

(d) $\cos(-0.5)$ (e) $\cos 1$ (f) $\cos \frac{\pi}{4}$

PROJECT: METEOROLOGY To work an extended application analyzing the mean monthly temperature and mean monthly precipitation in Honolulu, Hawaii, visit this text's website at *academic.cengage.com*. (Data Source: National Climatic Data Center)

5 ASSESS AND RETEACH

Daily Homework Quiz

Transparency Available
Available at the Instructor's companion site.

92. (a)

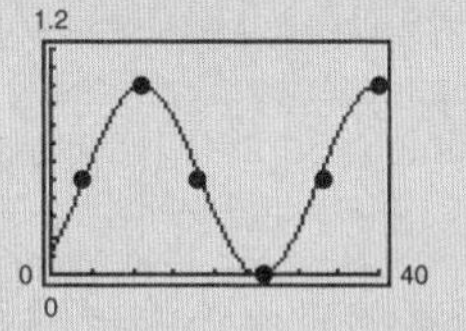

(b) $y = 0.5\sin(0.22x - 0.82) + 0.5$

(c) The model fits the data well.

93. (a) 365; Yes, because there are 365 days in a year.

(b) 30.3 gal; the constant term

(c)

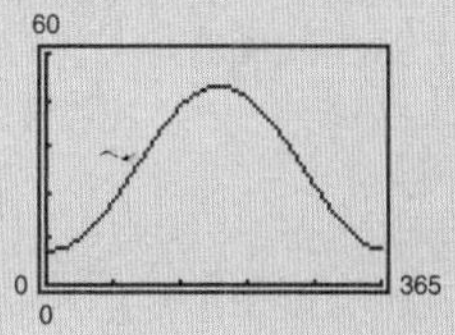

$124 < t < 252$

94. (a) 20 sec; It takes 20 seconds to complete one revolution on the Ferris wheel.

(b) 50 ft; The diameter of the Ferris wheel is 100 feet.

(c)

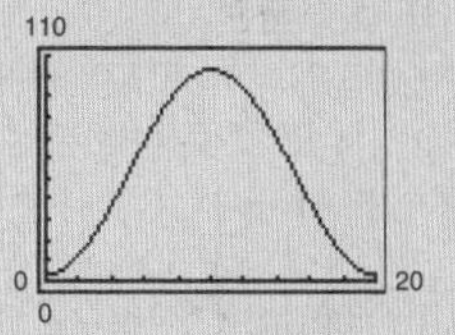

95. False. The graph of $f(x) = \sin(x + 2\pi)$ translates the graph of $f(x) = \sin x$ exactly one period to the left so that the two graphs look identical.

96. False. The function $y = \frac{1}{2}\cos 2x$ has an amplitude that is one-half that of $y = \cos x$. For $y = a\cos bx$, the amplitude is $|a|$.

97. True. Because $\cos x = \sin\left(x + \frac{\pi}{2}\right)$, $y = -\cos x$ is a reflection in the x-axis of $y = \sin\left(x + \frac{\pi}{2}\right)$.

101.

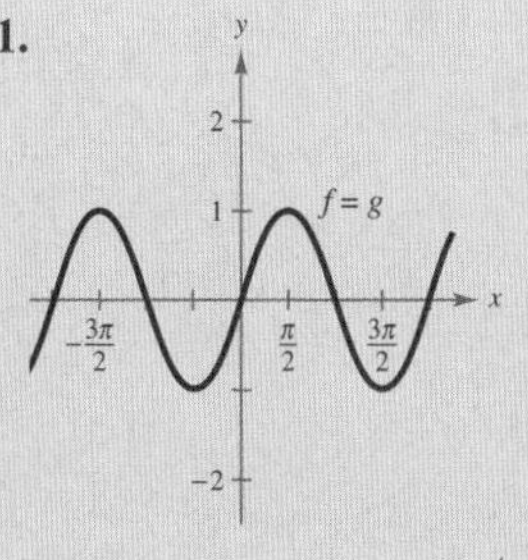

Conjecture: $\sin x = \cos\left(x - \frac{\pi}{2}\right)$

102.

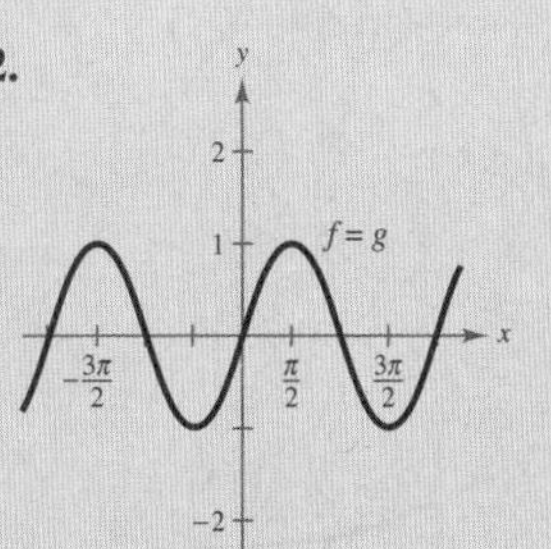

Conjecture: $\sin x = -\cos\left(x + \frac{\pi}{2}\right)$

98–99, 103–104. See Additional Answers beginning on page AA1.

1 PLAN AND PREPARE

Warm-up Exercises

Transparency Available
Available at the Instructor's companion site.

Notetaking Guide

Transparency Available
Promotes interactive learning and notetaking skills.
Available at the Instructor's companion site.

Animated Precalculus

An **Animated Precalculus** tutorial is available at the Student companion site for **Section 4.6.**

Pacing

Average: 1 day
Advanced: 1 day
Block: 0.5 block with 4.7

2 FOCUS AND MOTIVATE

Essential Question

How do you sketch the graphs of other trigonometric functions?
Tell students that they will learn how to answer this question by plotting values and identifying the basic characteristics of tangent, cotangent, secant, cosecant, and damped trigonometric graphs.

4.6 GRAPHS OF OTHER TRIGONOMETRIC FUNCTIONS

What you should learn

- Sketch the graphs of tangent functions.
- Sketch the graphs of cotangent functions.
- Sketch the graphs of secant and cosecant functions.
- Sketch the graphs of damped trigonometric functions.

Why you should learn it

Graphs of trigonometric functions can be used to model real-life situations such as the distance from a television camera to a unit in a parade, as in Exercise 92 on page 339.

Alan Pappe/Photodisc/Getty Images

Algebra Help

- You can review odd and even functions in Section 1.5.
- You can review symmetry of a graph in Section 1.2.
- You can review trigonometric identities in Section 4.3.
- You can review asymptotes in Section 2.6.
- You can review domain and range of a function in Section 1.4.
- You can review intercepts of a graph in Section 1.2.

Graph of the Tangent Function

Recall that the tangent function is odd. That is, $\tan(-x) = -\tan x$. Consequently, the graph of $y = \tan x$ is symmetric with respect to the origin. You also know from the identity $\tan x = \sin x/\cos x$ that the tangent is undefined for values at which $\cos x = 0$. Two such values are $x = \pm\pi/2 \approx \pm 1.5708$.

x	$-\frac{\pi}{2}$	-1.57	-1.5	$-\frac{\pi}{4}$	0	$\frac{\pi}{4}$	1.5	1.57	$\frac{\pi}{2}$
$\tan x$	Undef.	-1255.8	-14.1	-1	0	1	14.1	1255.8	Undef.

As indicated in the table, $\tan x$ increases without bound as x approaches $\pi/2$ from the left, and decreases without bound as x approaches $-\pi/2$ from the right. So, the graph of $y = \tan x$ has *vertical asymptotes* at $x = \pi/2$ and $x = -\pi/2$, as shown in Figure 4.59. Moreover, because the period of the tangent function is π, vertical asymptotes also occur when $x = \pi/2 + n\pi$, where n is an integer. The domain of the tangent function is the set of all real numbers other than $x = \pi/2 + n\pi$, and the range is the set of all real numbers.

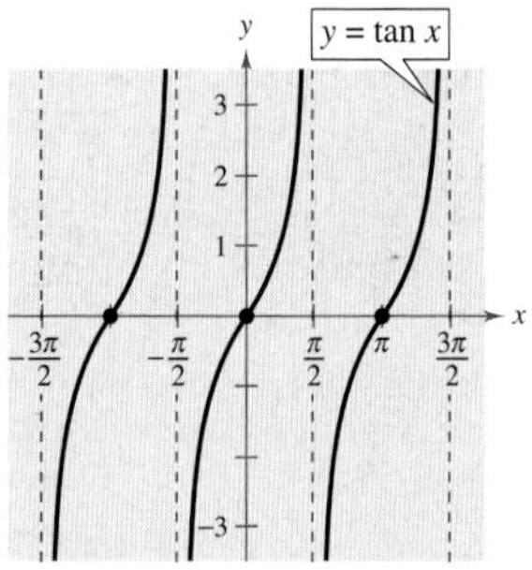

PERIOD: π
DOMAIN: ALL $x \neq \frac{\pi}{2} + n\pi$
RANGE: $(-\infty, \infty)$
VERTICAL ASYMPTOTES: $x = \frac{\pi}{2} + n\pi$
SYMMETRY: ORIGIN

FIGURE 4.59

Sketching the graph of $y = a\tan(bx - c)$ is similar to sketching the graph of $y = a\sin(bx - c)$ in that you locate key points that identify the intercepts and asymptotes. Two consecutive vertical asymptotes can be found by solving the equations

$$bx - c = -\frac{\pi}{2} \quad \text{and} \quad bx - c = \frac{\pi}{2}.$$

The midpoint between two consecutive vertical asymptotes is an x-intercept of the graph. The period of the function $y = a\tan(bx - c)$ is the distance between two consecutive vertical asymptotes. The amplitude of a tangent function is not defined. After plotting the asymptotes and the x-intercept, plot a few additional points between the two asymptotes and sketch one cycle. Finally, sketch one or two additional cycles to the left and right.

Resource Planning Guide

Chapter Resources

- Complete Solutions Guide

Workbooks

- Notetaking Guide
- Student Solutions Guide

Interactive Technology

- Instructor Success Organizer
- Notetaking Guide IAE
- Instructional DVDs
- Animated Precalculus
- PowerLecture with ExamView

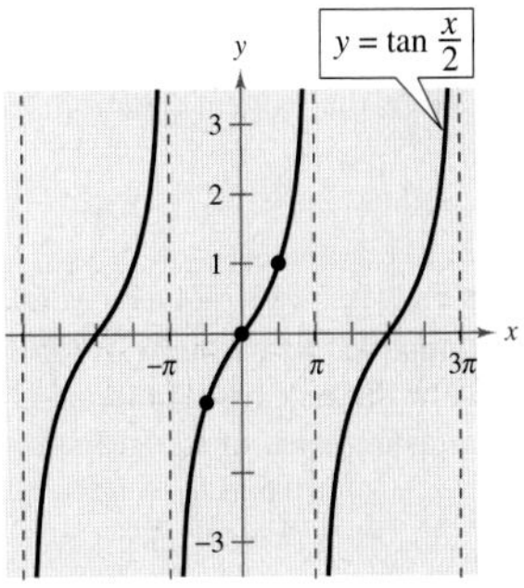

FIGURE 4.60

Example 1 Sketching the Graph of a Tangent Function

Sketch the graph of $y = \tan(x/2)$.

Solution

By solving the equations

$$\frac{x}{2} = -\frac{\pi}{2} \quad \text{and} \quad \frac{x}{2} = \frac{\pi}{2}$$

$$x = -\pi \qquad\qquad x = \pi$$

you can see that two consecutive vertical asymptotes occur at $x = -\pi$ and $x = \pi$. Between these two asymptotes, plot a few points, including the x-intercept, as shown in the table. Three cycles of the graph are shown in Figure 4.60.

x	$-\pi$	$-\frac{\pi}{2}$	0	$\frac{\pi}{2}$	π
$\tan\frac{x}{2}$	Undef.	-1	0	1	Undef.

CHECK**Point** Now try Exercise 15.

Example 2 Sketching the Graph of a Tangent Function

Sketch the graph of $y = -3 \tan 2x$.

Solution

By solving the equations

$$2x = -\frac{\pi}{2} \quad \text{and} \quad 2x = \frac{\pi}{2}$$

$$x = -\frac{\pi}{4} \qquad\qquad x = \frac{\pi}{4}$$

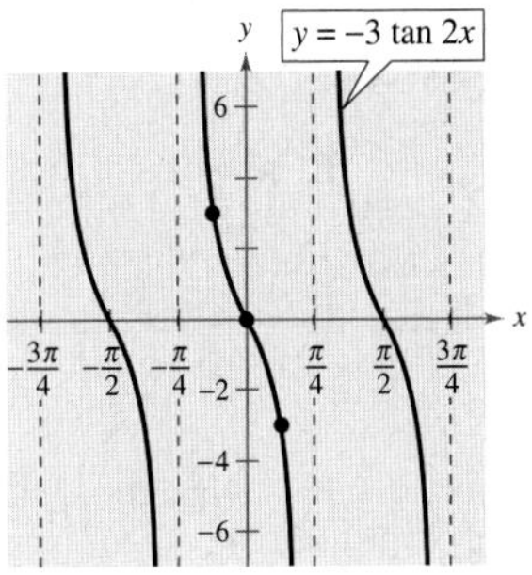

FIGURE 4.61

you can see that two consecutive vertical asymptotes occur at $x = -\pi/4$ and $x = \pi/4$. Between these two asymptotes, plot a few points, including the x-intercept, as shown in the table. Three cycles of the graph are shown in Figure 4.61.

x	$-\frac{\pi}{4}$	$-\frac{\pi}{8}$	0	$\frac{\pi}{8}$	$\frac{\pi}{4}$
$-3 \tan 2x$	Undef.	3	0	-3	Undef.

By comparing the graphs in Examples 1 and 2, you can see that the graph of $y = a \tan(bx - c)$ increases between consecutive vertical asymptotes when $a > 0$, and decreases between consecutive vertical asymptotes when $a < 0$. In other words, the graph for $a < 0$ is a reflection in the x-axis of the graph for $a > 0$.

CHECK**Point** Now try Exercise 17.

3 TEACH

Extra Example 1

Sketch the graph of $y = \tan \frac{x}{4}$.

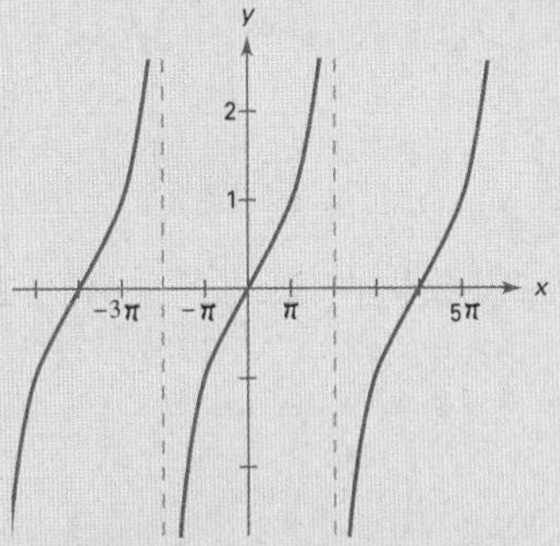

Extra Example 2

Sketch the graph of $y = \tan 2x$.

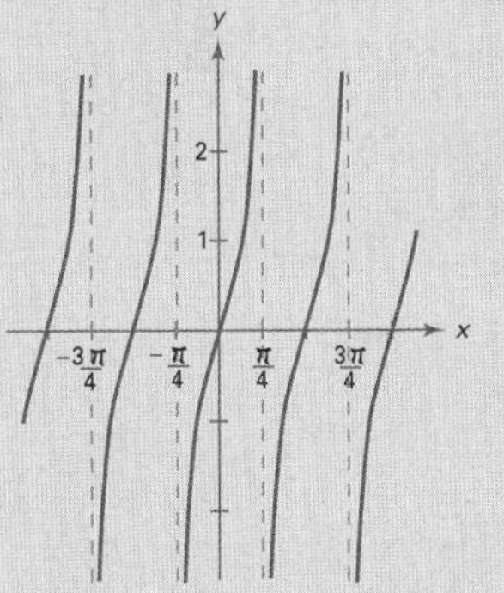

Extra Example 3

Sketch the graph of $y = \cot \frac{x}{4}$.

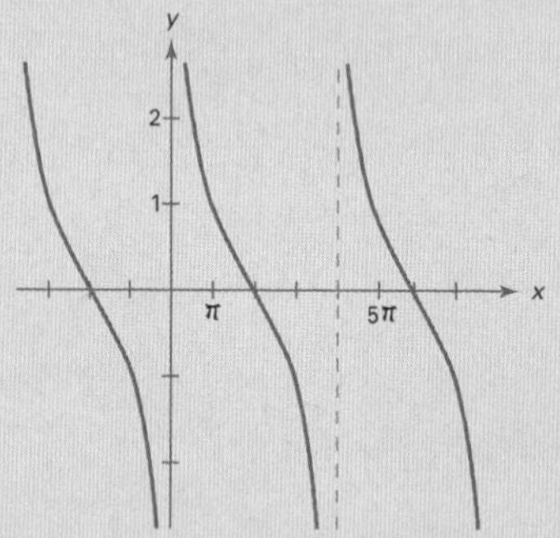

Graph of the Cotangent Function

The graph of the cotangent function is similar to the graph of the tangent function. It also has a period of π. However, from the identity

$$y = \cot x = \frac{\cos x}{\sin x}$$

you can see that the cotangent function has vertical asymptotes when $\sin x$ is zero, which occurs at $x = n\pi$, where n is an integer. The graph of the cotangent function is shown in Figure 4.62. Note that two consecutive vertical asymptotes of the graph of $y = a\cot(bx - c)$ can be found by solving the equations $bx - c = 0$ and $bx - c = \pi$.

TECHNOLOGY

Some graphing utilities have difficulty graphing trigonometric functions that have vertical asymptotes. Your graphing utility may connect parts of the graphs of tangent, cotangent, secant, and cosecant functions that are not supposed to be connected. To eliminate this problem, change the mode of the graphing utility to *dot* mode.

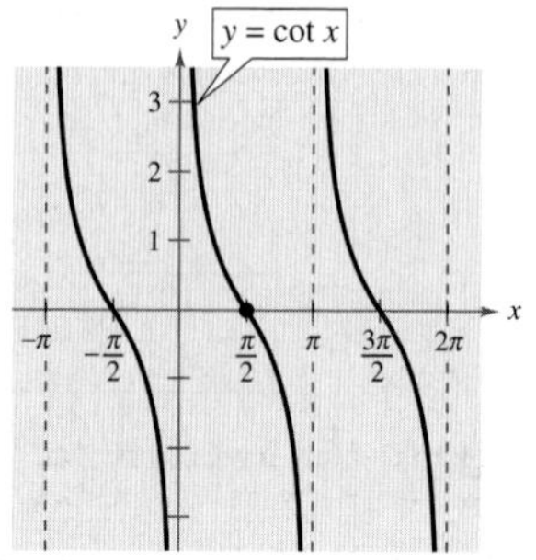

FIGURE 4.62

PERIOD: π
DOMAIN: ALL $x \neq n\pi$
RANGE: $(-\infty, \infty)$
VERTICAL ASYMPTOTES: $x = n\pi$
SYMMETRY: ORIGIN

Example 3 Sketching the Graph of a Cotangent Function

Sketch the graph of $y = 2\cot \frac{x}{3}$.

Solution

By solving the equations

$$\frac{x}{3} = 0 \quad \text{and} \quad \frac{x}{3} = \pi$$

$$x = 0 \qquad\qquad x = 3\pi$$

you can see that two consecutive vertical asymptotes occur at $x = 0$ and $x = 3\pi$. Between these two asymptotes, plot a few points, including the x-intercept, as shown in the table. Three cycles of the graph are shown in Figure 4.63. Note that the period is 3π, the distance between consecutive asymptotes.

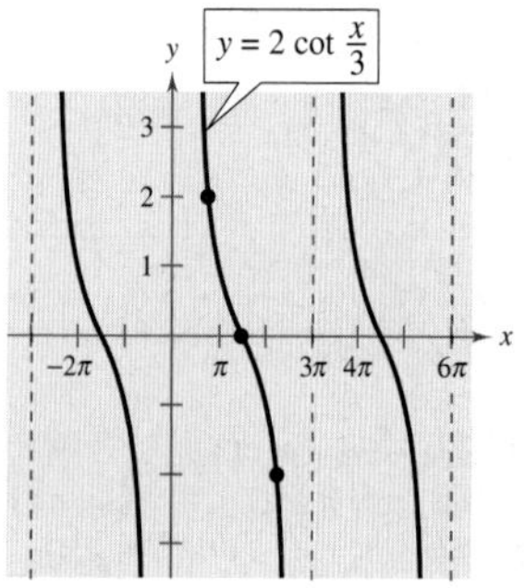

FIGURE 4.63

x	0	$\frac{3\pi}{4}$	$\frac{3\pi}{2}$	$\frac{9\pi}{4}$	3π
$2\cot\frac{x}{3}$	Undef.	2	0	-2	Undef.

CHECKPoint Now try Exercise 27.

Graphs of the Reciprocal Functions

The graphs of the two remaining trigonometric functions can be obtained from the graphs of the sine and cosine functions using the reciprocal identities

$$\csc x = \frac{1}{\sin x} \quad \text{and} \quad \sec x = \frac{1}{\cos x}.$$

For instance, at a given value of x, the y-coordinate of $\sec x$ is the reciprocal of the y-coordinate of $\cos x$. Of course, when $\cos x = 0$, the reciprocal does not exist. Near such values of x, the behavior of the secant function is similar to that of the tangent function. In other words, the graphs of

$$\tan x = \frac{\sin x}{\cos x} \quad \text{and} \quad \sec x = \frac{1}{\cos x}$$

have vertical asymptotes at $x = \pi/2 + n\pi$, where n is an integer, and the cosine is zero at these x-values. Similarly,

$$\cot x = \frac{\cos x}{\sin x} \quad \text{and} \quad \csc x = \frac{1}{\sin x}$$

have vertical asymptotes where $\sin x = 0$—that is, at $x = n\pi$.

To sketch the graph of a secant or cosecant function, you should first make a sketch of its reciprocal function. For instance, to sketch the graph of $y = \csc x$, first sketch the graph of $y = \sin x$. Then take reciprocals of the y-coordinates to obtain points on the graph of $y = \csc x$. This procedure is used to obtain the graphs shown in Figure 4.64.

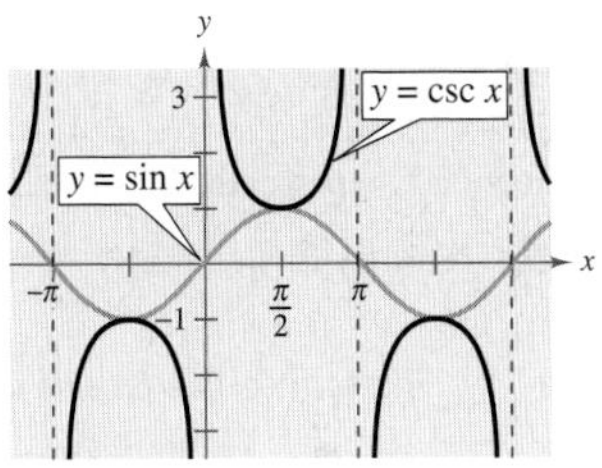

PERIOD: 2π
DOMAIN: ALL $x \neq n\pi$
RANGE: $(-\infty, -1] \cup [1, \infty)$
VERTICAL ASYMPTOTES: $x = n\pi$
SYMMETRY: ORIGIN

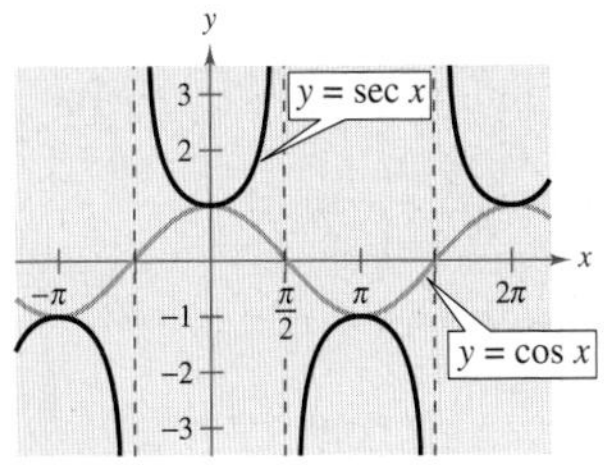

PERIOD: 2π
DOMAIN: ALL $x \neq \frac{\pi}{2} + n\pi$
RANGE: $(-\infty, -1] \cup [1, \infty)$
VERTICAL ASYMPTOTES: $x = \frac{\pi}{2} + n\pi$
SYMMETRY: y-AXIS

FIGURE 4.64

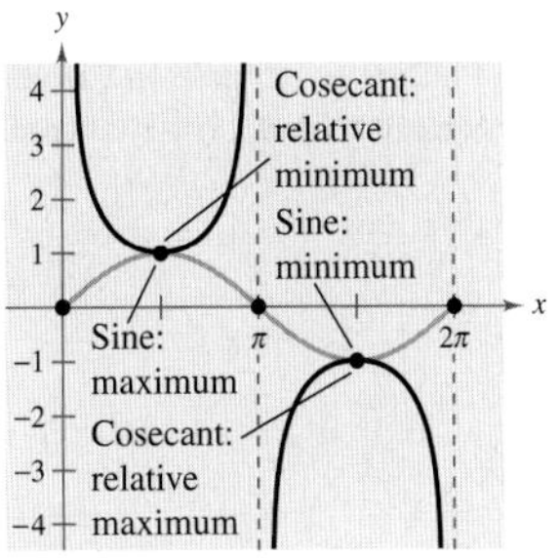

FIGURE 4.65

In comparing the graphs of the cosecant and secant functions with those of the sine and cosine functions, note that the "hills" and "valleys" are interchanged. For example, a hill (or maximum point) on the sine curve corresponds to a valley (a relative minimum) on the cosecant curve, and a valley (or minimum point) on the sine curve corresponds to a hill (a relative maximum) on the cosecant curve, as shown in Figure 4.65. Additionally, x-intercepts of the sine and cosine functions become vertical asymptotes of the cosecant and secant functions, respectively (see Figure 4.65).

Extra Example 4

Sketch the graph of

$y = 2\csc\left(x + \frac{\pi}{2}\right)$.

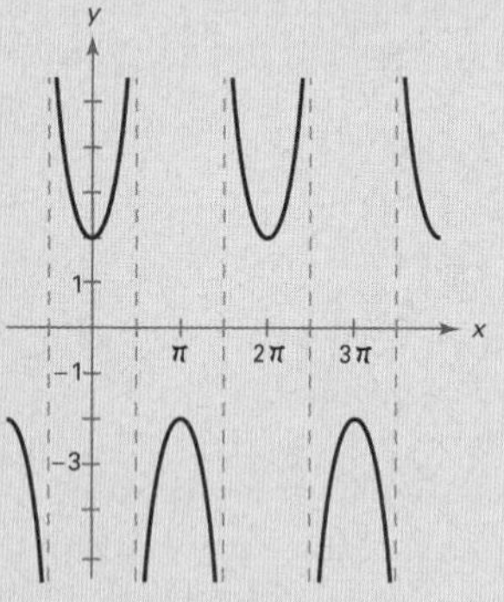

Extra Example 5

Sketch the graph of $y = \sec \pi x$.

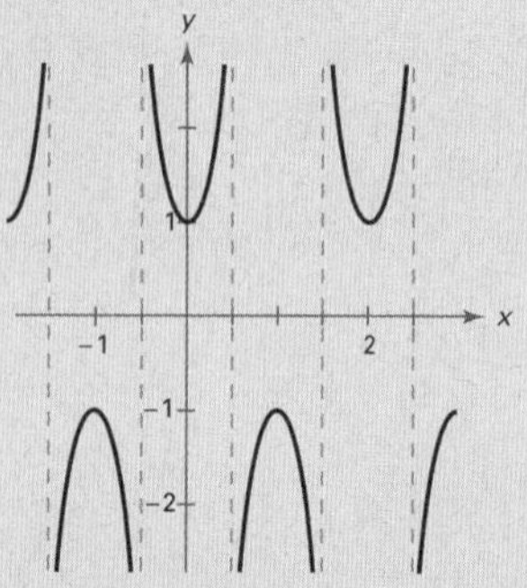

Avoiding Common Errors

Secant and cosecant functions can be graphed with a graphing utility by entering the equations Y=1/cos(X) and Y=1/sin(X), respectively. On many graphing calculators, doing so can produce a vertical line between the hills and valleys. Students should note that this line is a result of the calculator's trying to connect values on the screen and is not part of the graph. The line can be eliminated by setting the mode to DOT.

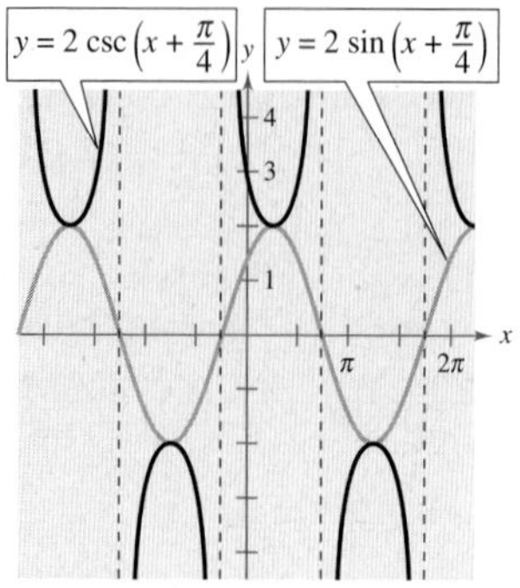

FIGURE 4.66

Example 4 Sketching the Graph of a Cosecant Function

Sketch the graph of $y = 2\csc\left(x + \frac{\pi}{4}\right)$.

Solution

Begin by sketching the graph of

$$y = 2\sin\left(x + \frac{\pi}{4}\right).$$

For this function, the amplitude is 2 and the period is 2π. By solving the equations

$$x + \frac{\pi}{4} = 0 \qquad \text{and} \qquad x + \frac{\pi}{4} = 2\pi$$

$$x = -\frac{\pi}{4} \qquad\qquad x = \frac{7\pi}{4}$$

you can see that one cycle of the sine function corresponds to the interval from $x = -\pi/4$ to $x = 7\pi/4$. The graph of this sine function is represented by the gray curve in Figure 4.66. Because the sine function is zero at the midpoint and endpoints of this interval, the corresponding cosecant function

$$y = 2\csc\left(x + \frac{\pi}{4}\right)$$

$$= 2\left(\frac{1}{\sin[x + (\pi/4)]}\right)$$

has vertical asymptotes at $x = -\pi/4$, $x = 3\pi/4$, $x = 7\pi/4$, etc. The graph of the cosecant function is represented by the black curve in Figure 4.66.

CHECKPoint Now try Exercise 33.

Example 5 Sketching the Graph of a Secant Function

Sketch the graph of $y = \sec 2x$.

Solution

Begin by sketching the graph of $y = \cos 2x$, as indicated by the gray curve in Figure 4.67. Then, form the graph of $y = \sec 2x$ as the black curve in the figure. Note that the x-intercepts of $y = \cos 2x$

$$\left(-\frac{\pi}{4}, 0\right), \quad \left(\frac{\pi}{4}, 0\right), \quad \left(\frac{3\pi}{4}, 0\right), \ldots$$

correspond to the vertical asymptotes

$$x = -\frac{\pi}{4}, \quad x = \frac{\pi}{4}, \quad x = \frac{3\pi}{4}, \ldots$$

of the graph of $y = \sec 2x$. Moreover, notice that the period of $y = \cos 2x$ and $y = \sec 2x$ is π.

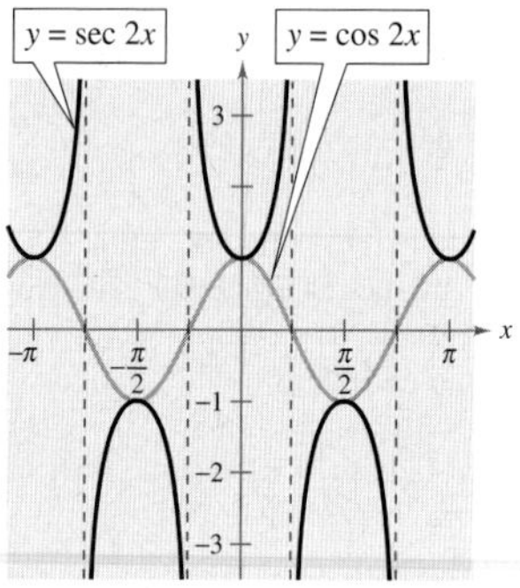

FIGURE 4.67

CHECKPoint Now try Exercise 35.

Damped Trigonometric Graphs

A *product* of two functions can be graphed using properties of the individual functions. For instance, consider the function

$$f(x) = x \sin x$$

as the product of the functions $y = x$ and $y = \sin x$. Using properties of absolute value and the fact that $|\sin x| \le 1$, you have $0 \le |x||\sin x| \le |x|$. Consequently,

$$-|x| \le x \sin x \le |x|$$

which means that the graph of $f(x) = x \sin x$ lies between the lines $y = -x$ and $y = x$. Furthermore, because

$$f(x) = x \sin x = \pm x \quad \text{at} \quad x = \frac{\pi}{2} + n\pi$$

and

$$f(x) = x \sin x = 0 \quad \text{at} \quad x = n\pi$$

the graph of f touches the line $y = -x$ or the line $y = x$ at $x = \pi/2 + n\pi$ and has x-intercepts at $x = n\pi$. A sketch of f is shown in Figure 4.68. In the function $f(x) = x \sin x$, the factor x is called the **damping factor.**

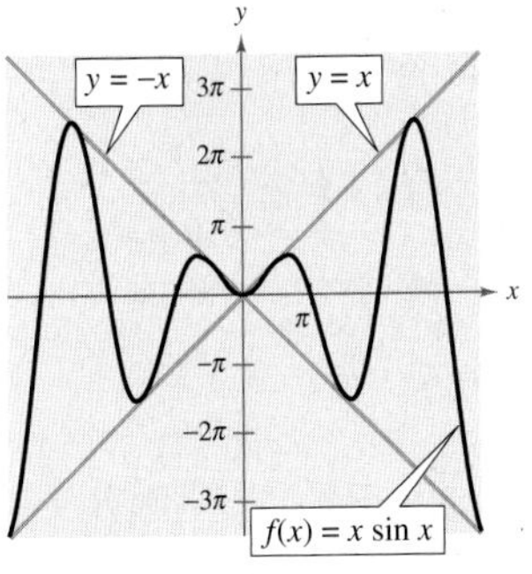

FIGURE 4.68

Study Tip

Do you see why the graph of $f(x) = x \sin x$ touches the lines $y = \pm x$ at $x = \pi/2 + n\pi$ and why the graph has x-intercepts at $x = n\pi$? Recall that the sine function is equal to 1 at $\pi/2$, $3\pi/2, 5\pi/2, \ldots$ (odd multiples of $\pi/2$) and is equal to 0 at π, $2\pi, 3\pi, \ldots$ (multiples of π).

Example 6 Damped Sine Wave

Sketch the graph of $f(x) = e^{-x} \sin 3x$.

Solution

Consider $f(x)$ as the product of the two functions

$$y = e^{-x} \quad \text{and} \quad y = \sin 3x$$

each of which has the set of real numbers as its domain. For any real number x, you know that $e^{-x} \ge 0$ and $|\sin 3x| \le 1$. So, $e^{-x}|\sin 3x| \le e^{-x}$, which means that

$$-e^{-x} \le e^{-x} \sin 3x \le e^{-x}.$$

Furthermore, because

$$f(x) = e^{-x} \sin 3x = \pm e^{-x} \quad \text{at} \quad x = \frac{\pi}{6} + \frac{n\pi}{3}$$

and

$$f(x) = e^{-x} \sin 3x = 0 \quad \text{at} \quad x = \frac{n\pi}{3}$$

the graph of f touches the curves $y = -e^{-x}$ and $y = e^{-x}$ at $x = \pi/6 + n\pi/3$ and has intercepts at $x = n\pi/3$. A sketch is shown in Figure 4.69.

CHECKPoint Now try Exercise 65.

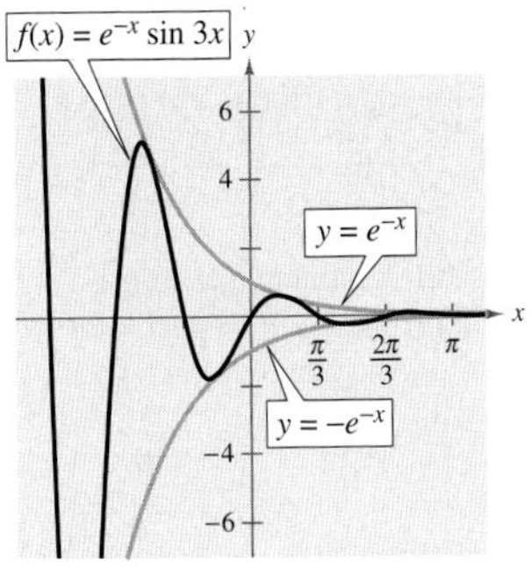

FIGURE 4.69

Extra Example 6

Sketch the graph of $f(x) = e^x \sin 4x$.

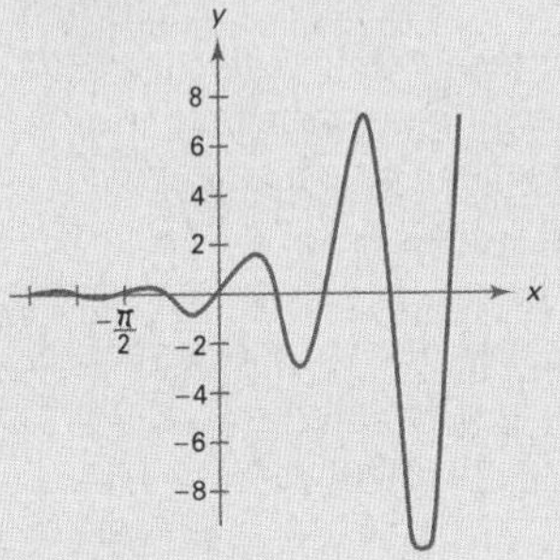

Figure 4.70 summarizes the characteristics of the six basic trigonometric functions.

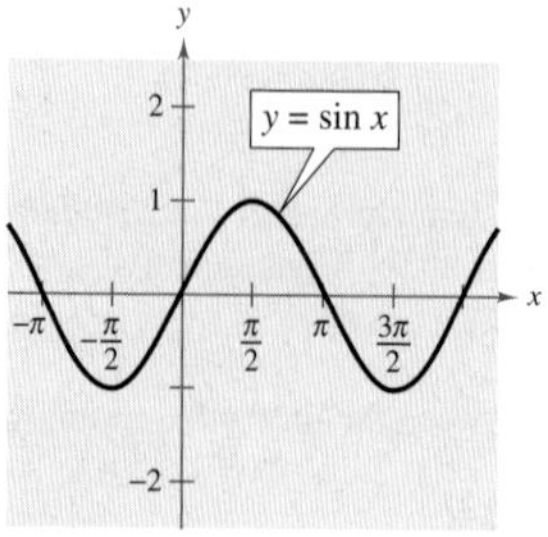

DOMAIN: $(-\infty, \infty)$
RANGE: $[-1, 1]$
PERIOD: 2π

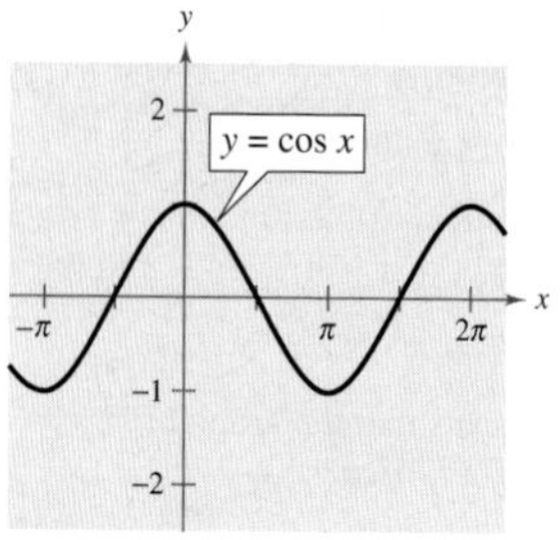

DOMAIN: $(-\infty, \infty)$
RANGE: $[-1, 1]$
PERIOD: 2π

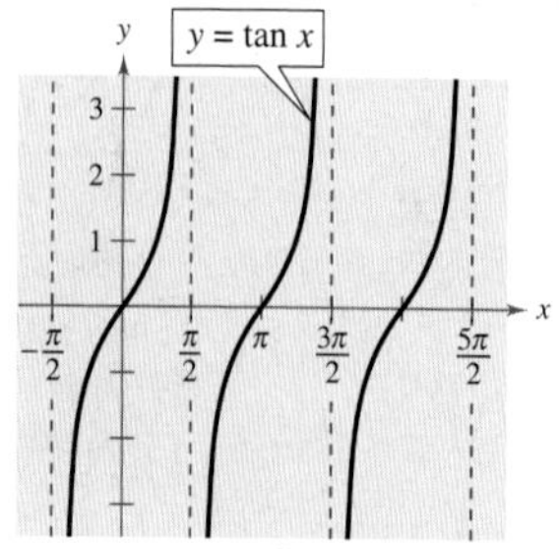

DOMAIN: ALL $x \neq \frac{\pi}{2} + n\pi$
RANGE: $(-\infty, \infty)$
PERIOD: π

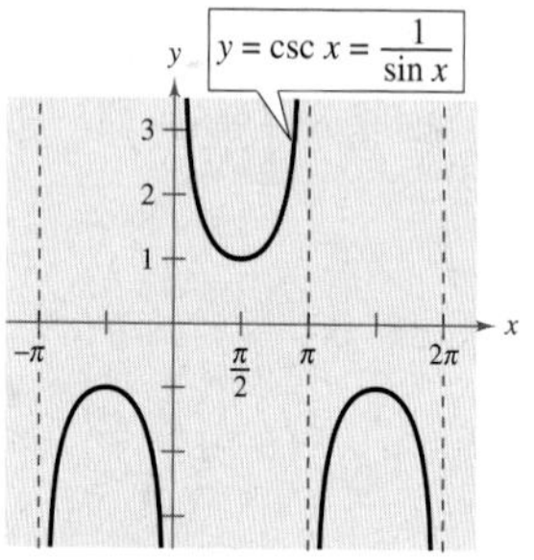

DOMAIN: ALL $x \neq n\pi$
RANGE: $(-\infty, -1] \cup [1, \infty)$
PERIOD: 2π

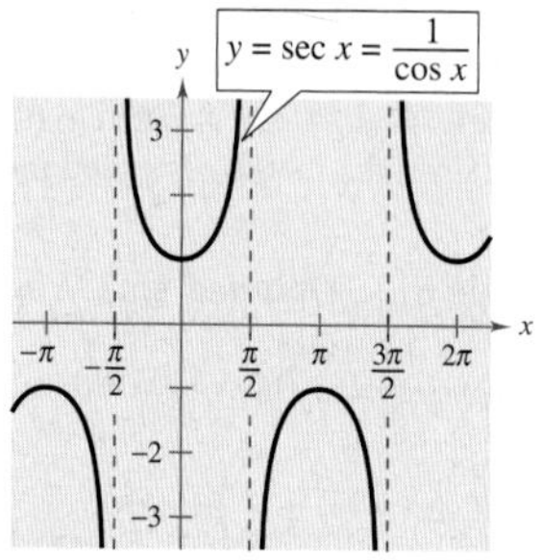

DOMAIN: ALL $x \neq \frac{\pi}{2} + n\pi$
RANGE: $(-\infty, -1] \cup [1, \infty)$
PERIOD: 2π

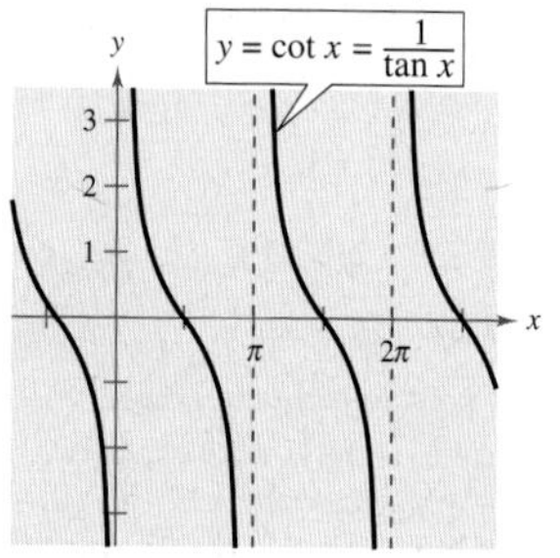

DOMAIN: ALL $x \neq n\pi$
RANGE: $(-\infty, \infty)$
PERIOD: π

FIGURE 4.70

CLASSROOM DISCUSSION

Combining Trigonometric Functions Recall from Section 1.8 that functions can be combined arithmetically. This also applies to trigonometric functions. For each of the functions

$$h(x) = x + \sin x \quad \text{and} \quad h(x) = \cos x - \sin 3x$$

(a) identify two simpler functions f and g that comprise the combination, (b) use a table to show how to obtain the numerical values of $h(x)$ from the numerical values of $f(x)$ and $g(x)$, and (c) use graphs of f and g to show how the graph of h may be formed.

Can you find functions

$$f(x) = d + a\sin(bx + c) \quad \text{and} \quad g(x) = d + a\cos(bx + c)$$

such that $f(x) + g(x) = 0$ for all x? See margin.

Closing the Lesson

Have students summarize the major points of the lesson and answer the Essential Question: How do you sketch the graphs of other trigonometric functions?

- **Identify intercepts, vertical asymptotes, and shape of tangent, cotangent, secant, and cosecant graphs.**
- **Explain the relationship between graphs of reciprocal functions sine and cosecant and cosine and secant.**
- **Sketch the graph of a damped trigonometric function by plotting the damping factor x or e^{-x} and its reflection in the x-axis and sketching the trigonometric function stretched between the two.**

Classroom Discussion

$h(x) = x + \sin x$

(a) $f(x) = x$ and $g(x) = \sin x$

(b) Tables will vary. See example below.

(c) A graph of h can be formed by adding the graphs of f and g point by point.

$h(x) = \cos x - \sin 3x$

(a) $f(x) = \cos x$ and $g(x) = \sin 3x$

(b) Tables will vary. See example below.

(c) A graph of h can be formed by subtracting the graph of g from the graph of f point by point.

Examples will vary. One example is $f(x) = \sin x$ and $g(x) = \cos\left(x + \frac{\pi}{2}\right)$.

(b) Example of table for $h(x) = x + \sin x$

x	-3	-2	-1	0	1	2	3
$f(x) = x$	-3	-2	-1	0	1	2	3
$g(x) = \sin x$	-0.14112	-0.90930	-0.84147	0	0.84147	0.90930	0.14112
$h(x) = f(x) + g(x)$	-3.14112	-2.90930	-1.84147	0	1.84147	2.90930	3.14112

(b) Example of table for $h(x) = \cos x - \sin 3x$

x	-3	-2	-1	0	1	2	3
$f(x) = \cos x$	-0.98999	-0.41615	0.54030	1	0.54030	-0.41615	-0.98999
$g(x) = \sin 3x$	-0.41212	0.27942	-0.14112	0	0.14112	-0.27942	0.41212
$h(x) = f(x) - g(x)$	-0.57787	-0.69557	0.68142	1	0.39918	-0.13673	-1.40211

4.6 EXERCISES

See www.CalcChat.com for worked-out solutions to odd-numbered exercises.

VOCABULARY: Fill in the blanks.

1. The tangent, cotangent, and cosecant functions are ___odd___, so the graphs of these functions have symmetry with respect to the ___origin___.
2. The graphs of the tangent, cotangent, secant, and cosecant functions all have ___vertical___ asymptotes.
3. To sketch the graph of a secant or cosecant function, first make a sketch of its corresponding ________ function. reciprocal
4. For the functions given by $f(x) = g(x) \cdot \sin x$, $g(x)$ is called the ___damping___ factor of the function $f(x)$.
5. The period of $y = \tan x$ is ___π___.
6. The domain of $y = \cot x$ is all real numbers such that ___$x \neq n\pi$___.
7. The range of $y = \sec x$ is ________. $(-\infty, -1] \cup [1, \infty)$
8. The period of $y = \csc x$ is ___2π___.

SKILLS AND APPLICATIONS

In Exercises 9–14, match the function with its graph. State the period of the function. [The graphs are labeled (a), (b), (c), (d), (e), and (f).]

(a)

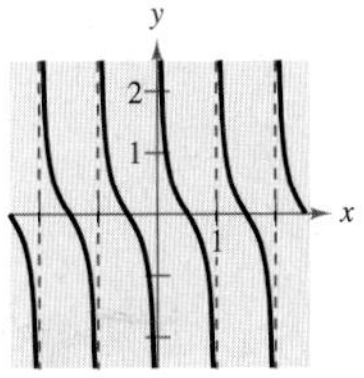

(b)

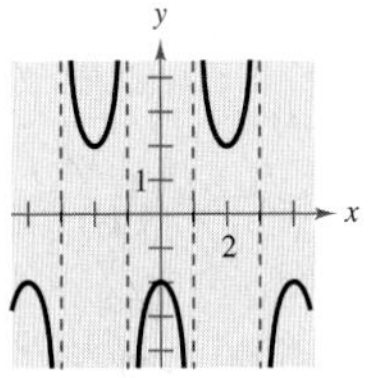

(c)

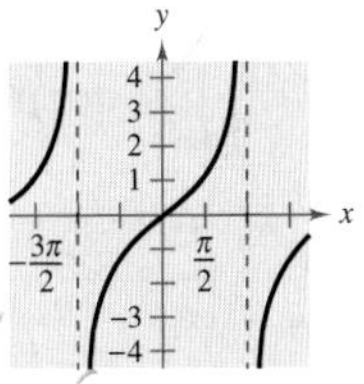

(d)

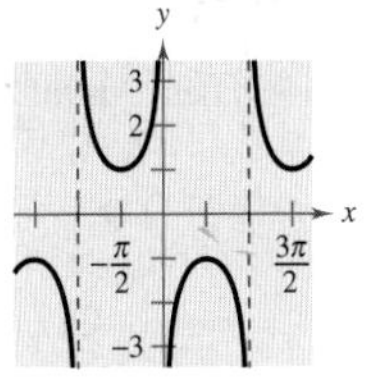

(e)

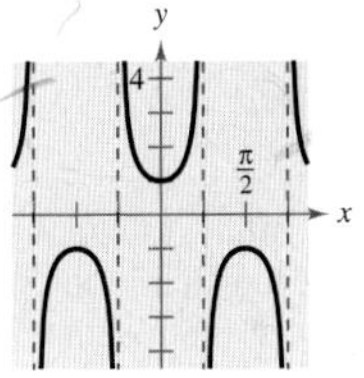

(f)

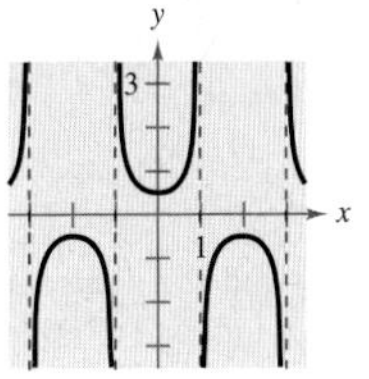

9. $y = \sec 2x$ e, π
10. $y = \tan \dfrac{x}{2}$ c, 2π
11. $y = \dfrac{1}{2} \cot \pi x$ a, 1
12. $y = -\csc x$ d, 2π
13. $y = \dfrac{1}{2} \sec \dfrac{\pi x}{2}$ f, 4
14. $y = -2 \sec \dfrac{\pi x}{2}$ b, 4

In Exercises 15–38, sketch the graph of the function. Include two full periods. 15–38. See margin.

15. $y = \dfrac{1}{3} \tan x$
16. $y = \tan 4x$
17. $y = -2 \tan 3x$
18. $y = -3 \tan \pi x$
19. $y = -\frac{1}{2} \sec x$
20. $y = \frac{1}{4} \sec x$
21. $y = \csc \pi x$
22. $y = 3 \csc 4x$
23. $y = \frac{1}{2} \sec \pi x$
24. $y = -2 \sec 4x + 2$
25. $y = \csc \dfrac{x}{2}$
26. $y = \csc \dfrac{x}{3}$
27. $y = 3 \cot 2x$
28. $y = 3 \cot \dfrac{\pi x}{2}$
29. $y = 2 \sec 3x$
30. $y = -\frac{1}{2} \tan x$
31. $y = \tan \dfrac{\pi x}{4}$
32. $y = \tan(x + \pi)$
33. $y = 2 \csc(x - \pi)$
34. $y = \csc(2x - \pi)$
35. $y = 2 \sec(x + \pi)$
36. $y = -\sec \pi x + 1$
37. $y = \dfrac{1}{4} \csc\left(x + \dfrac{\pi}{4}\right)$
38. $y = 2 \cot\left(x + \dfrac{\pi}{2}\right)$

In Exercises 39–48, use a graphing utility to graph the function. Include two full periods. 39–48. See margin.

39. $y = \tan \dfrac{x}{3}$
40. $y = -\tan 2x$
41. $y = -2 \sec 4x$
42. $y = \sec \pi x$
43. $y = \tan\left(x - \dfrac{\pi}{4}\right)$
44. $y = \dfrac{1}{4} \cot\left(x - \dfrac{\pi}{2}\right)$
45. $y = -\csc(4x - \pi)$
46. $y = 2 \sec(2x - \pi)$
47. $y = 0.1 \tan\left(\dfrac{\pi x}{4} + \dfrac{\pi}{4}\right)$
48. $y = \dfrac{1}{3} \sec\left(\dfrac{\pi x}{2} + \dfrac{\pi}{2}\right)$

4 PRACTICE AND APPLY

Assignment Guide

Transparencies Available
Available at the Instructor's companion site.

Average:
Day 1: pp. 337–340
Exs. 9–15, 21, 29, 43, 44, 49, 53, 57, 61, 69, 73–77, 81, 87–93 odd, 96–98

Advanced:
Day 1: pp. 337–340
Exs. 9–14, 16, 24–32 even, 40, 48, 50, 54–66 even, 72–76, 78, 84–88 even, 92–95, 98, 104

Block:
pp. 337–340
Exs. 9–15, 21, 29, 43, 44, 49, 53, 57, 61, 69, 73–77, 81, 87–93 odd, 96–98 (with 4.7)

15.

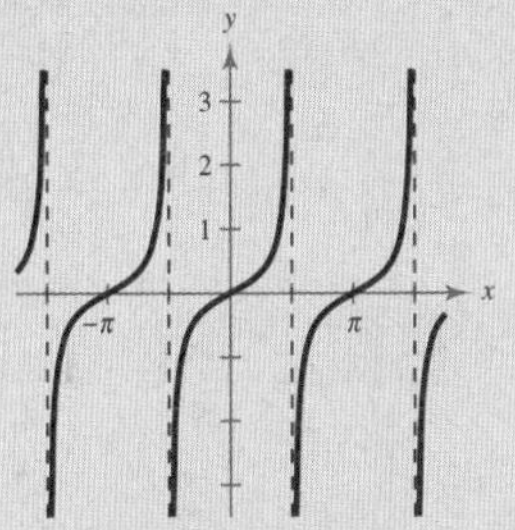

16.

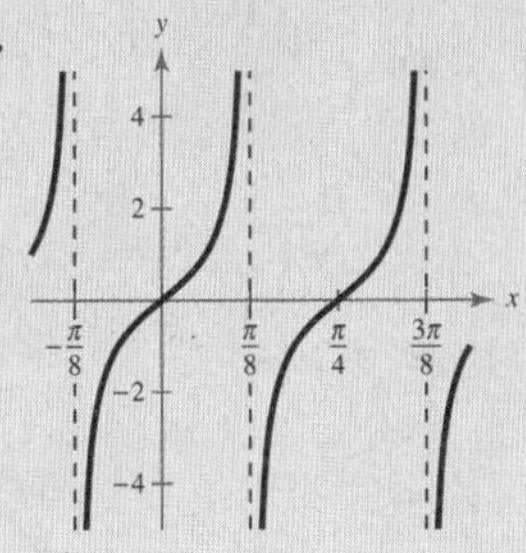

17.

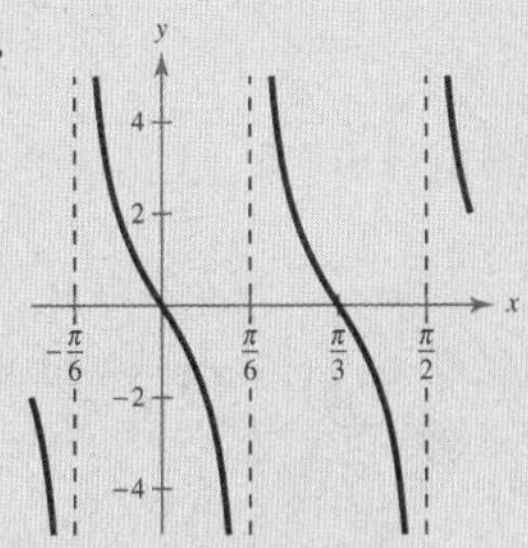

18.

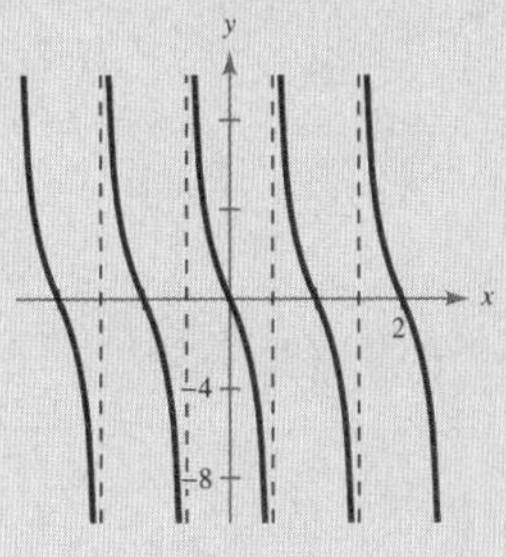

19.

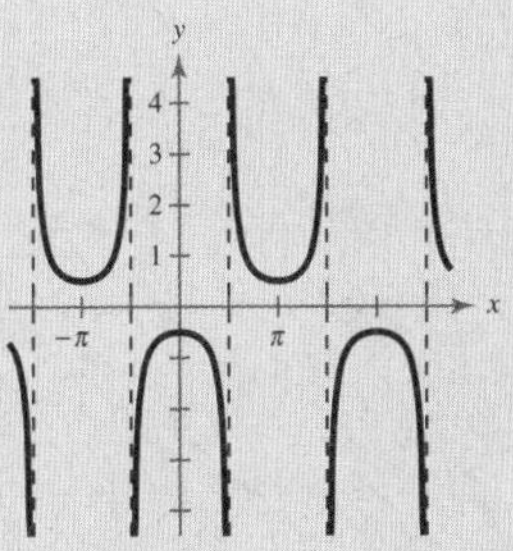

20.

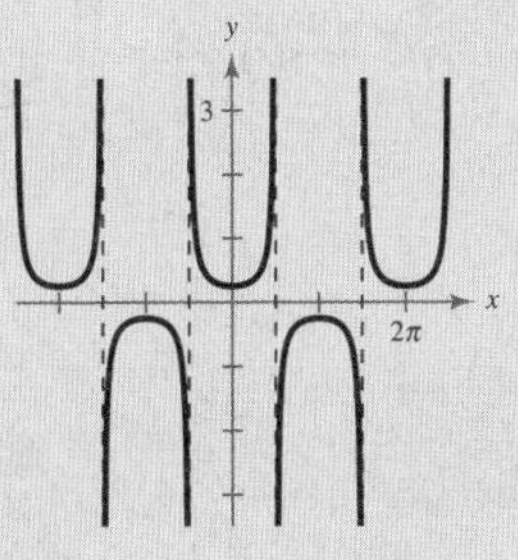

21.

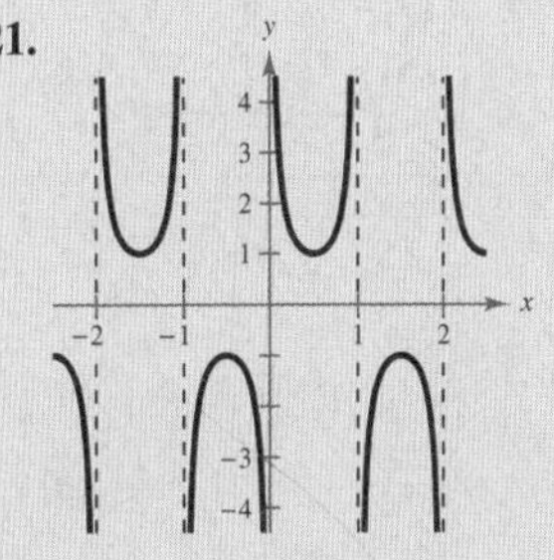

22–48. See Additional Answers beginning on page AA1.

In Exercises 49–56, use a graph to solve the equation on the interval $[-2\pi, 2\pi]$. 49–56. See margin.

49. $\tan x = 1$ **50.** $\tan x = \sqrt{3}$

51. $\cot x = -\frac{\sqrt{3}}{3}$ **52.** $\cot x = 1$

53. $\sec x = -2$ **54.** $\sec x = 2$

55. $\csc x = \sqrt{2}$ **56.** $\csc x = -\frac{2\sqrt{3}}{3}$

In Exercises 57–64, use the graph of the function to determine whether the function is even, odd, or neither. Verify your answer algebraically.

57. $f(x) = \sec x$ Even **58.** $f(x) = \tan x$ Odd

59. $g(x) = \cot x$ Odd **60.** $g(x) = \csc x$ Odd

61. $f(x) = x + \tan x$ Odd **62.** $f(x) = x^2 - \sec x$ Even

63. $g(x) = x \csc x$ Even **64.** $g(x) = x^2 \cot x$ Odd

65. GRAPHICAL REASONING Consider the functions given by

$$f(x) = 2 \sin x \quad \text{and} \quad g(x) = \frac{1}{2} \csc x$$

on the interval $(0, \pi)$. See margin.

(a) Graph f and g in the same coordinate plane.

(b) Approximate the interval in which $f > g$.

(c) Describe the behavior of each of the functions as x approaches π. How is the behavior of g related to the behavior of f as x approaches π?

66. GRAPHICAL REASONING Consider the functions given by

$$f(x) = \tan \frac{\pi x}{2} \quad \text{and} \quad g(x) = \frac{1}{2} \sec \frac{\pi x}{2}$$

on the interval $(-1, 1)$. See margin.

(a) Use a graphing utility to graph f and g in the same viewing window.

(b) Approximate the interval in which $f < g$.

(c) Approximate the interval in which $2f < 2g$. How does the result compare with that of part (b)? Explain.

In Exercises 67–72, use a graphing utility to graph the two equations in the same viewing window. Use the graphs to determine whether the expressions are equivalent. Verify the results algebraically. 67–72. See margin.

67. $y_1 = \sin x \csc x, \quad y_2 = 1$

68. $y_1 = \sin x \sec x, \quad y_2 = \tan x$

69. $y_1 = \frac{\cos x}{\sin x}, \quad y_2 = \cot x$

70. $y_1 = \tan x \cot^2 x, \quad y_2 = \cot x$

71. $y_1 = 1 + \cot^2 x, \quad y_2 = \csc^2 x$

72. $y_1 = \sec^2 x - 1, \quad y_2 = \tan^2 x$

In Exercises 73–76, match the function with its graph. Describe the behavior of the function as x approaches zero. [The graphs are labeled (a), (b), (c), and (d).]

(a)

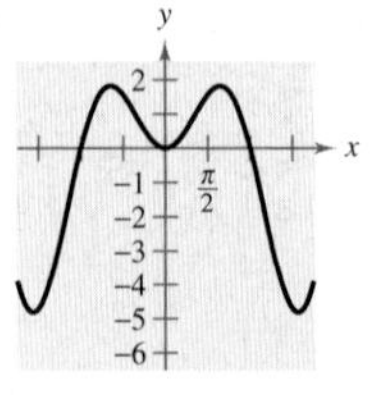

(b)

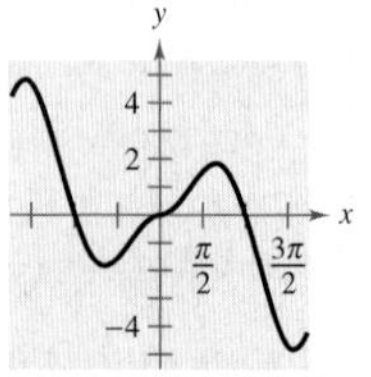

(c)

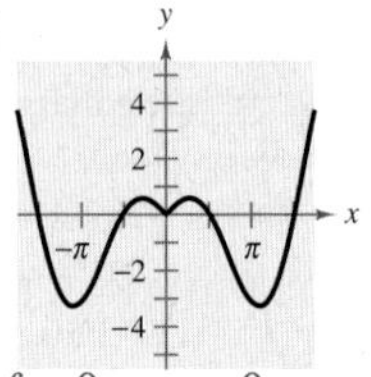

(d)

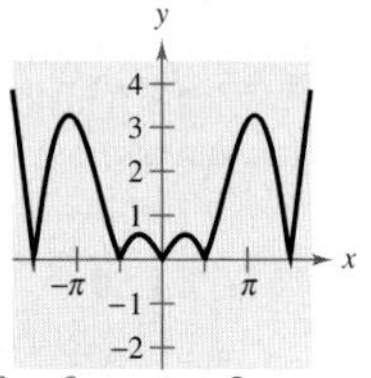

d, $f \to 0$ as $x \to 0$. a, $f \to 0$ as $x \to 0$.

73. $f(x) = |x \cos x|$ **74.** $f(x) = x \sin x$

75. $g(x) = |x| \sin x$ **76.** $g(x) = |x| \cos x$

b, $g \to 0$ as $x \to 0$. c, $g \to 0$ as $x \to 0$.

CONJECTURE In Exercises 77–80, graph the functions f and g. Use the graphs to make a conjecture about the relationship between the functions. 77–80. See margin.

77. $f(x) = \sin x + \cos\left(x + \frac{\pi}{2}\right), \quad g(x) = 0$

78. $f(x) = \sin x - \cos\left(x + \frac{\pi}{2}\right), \quad g(x) = 2 \sin x$

79. $f(x) = \sin^2 x, \quad g(x) = \frac{1}{2}(1 - \cos 2x)$

80. $f(x) = \cos^2 \frac{\pi x}{2}, \quad g(x) = \frac{1}{2}(1 + \cos \pi x)$

In Exercises 81–84, use a graphing utility to graph the function and the damping factor of the function in the same viewing window. Describe the behavior of the function as x increases without bound. 81–84. See margin.

81. $g(x) = e^{-x^2/2} \sin x$ **82.** $f(x) = e^{-x} \cos x$

83. $f(x) = 2^{-x/4} \cos \pi x$ **84.** $h(x) = 2^{-x^2/4} \sin x$

In Exercises 85–86, use a graphing utility to graph the function. Describe the behavior of the function as x approaches zero. 85–86. See margin.

85. $y = \frac{6}{x} + \cos x, \quad x > 0$ **86.** $y = \frac{4}{x} + \sin 2x, \quad x > 0$

49. $-\frac{7\pi}{4}, -\frac{3\pi}{4}, \frac{\pi}{4}, \frac{5\pi}{4}$

50. $-\frac{5\pi}{3}, -\frac{2\pi}{3}, \frac{\pi}{3}, \frac{4\pi}{3}$

51. $-\frac{4\pi}{3}, -\frac{\pi}{3}, \frac{2\pi}{3}, \frac{5\pi}{3}$

52. $-\frac{7\pi}{4}, -\frac{3\pi}{4}, \frac{\pi}{4}, \frac{5\pi}{4}$

53. $-\frac{4\pi}{3}, -\frac{2\pi}{3}, \frac{2\pi}{3}, \frac{4\pi}{3}$

54. $-\frac{5\pi}{3}, -\frac{\pi}{3}, \frac{\pi}{3}, \frac{5\pi}{3}$

55. $-\frac{7\pi}{4}, -\frac{5\pi}{4}, \frac{\pi}{4}, \frac{3\pi}{4}$

56. $-\frac{2\pi}{3}, -\frac{\pi}{3}, \frac{4\pi}{3}, \frac{5\pi}{3}$

65. (a)

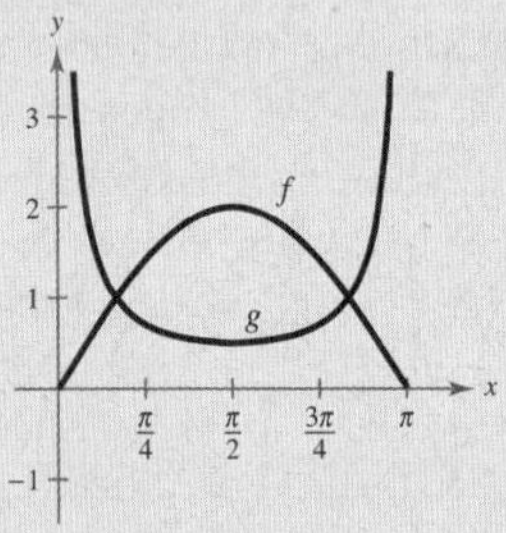

(b) $\frac{\pi}{6} < x < \frac{5\pi}{6}$

(c) f approaches 0 and g approaches $+\infty$ because the cosecant is the reciprocal of the sine.

66. (a)

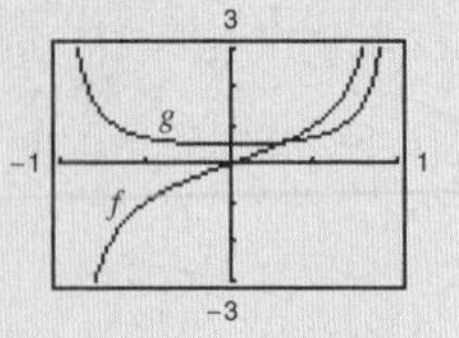

(b) $\left(-1, \frac{1}{3}\right)$

(c) $\left(-1, \frac{1}{3}\right)$; The intervals are the same.

67.

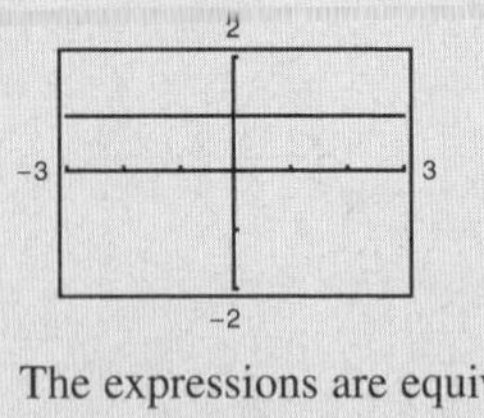

The expressions are equivalent except when $\sin x = 0$, y_1 is undefined.

68.

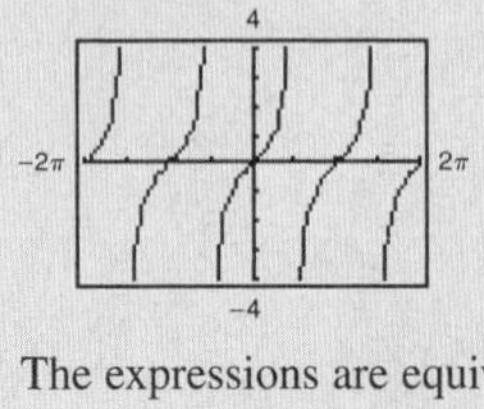

The expressions are equivalent.

69.

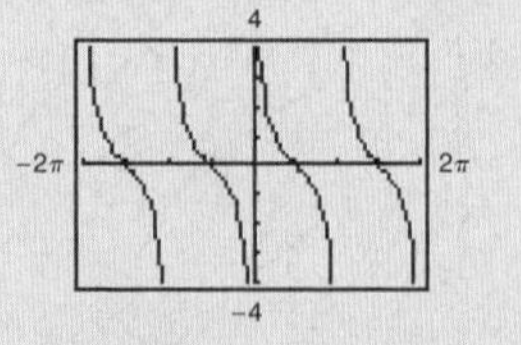

The expressions are equivalent.

70.

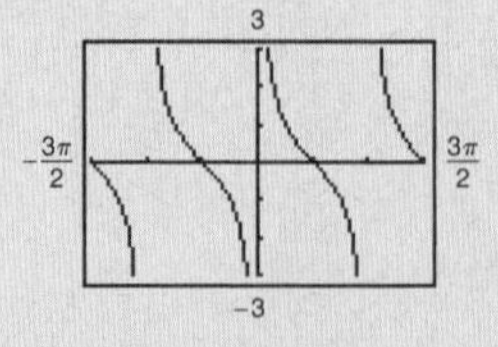

The expressions are equivalent except when $\cot x = 0$, y_1 is undefined.

71.

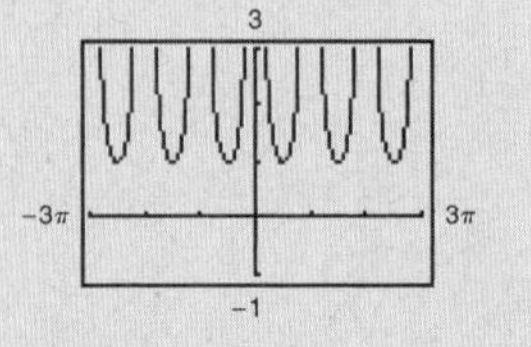

The expressions are equivalent.

72, 77–86. See Additional Answers beginning on page AA1.

87–90. See margin.

87. $g(x) = \dfrac{\sin x}{x}$ **88.** $f(x) = \dfrac{1 - \cos x}{x}$

89. $f(x) = \sin \dfrac{1}{x}$ **90.** $h(x) = x \sin \dfrac{1}{x}$

91. DISTANCE A plane flying at an altitude of 7 miles above a radar antenna will pass directly over the radar antenna (see figure). Let d be the ground distance from the antenna to the point directly under the plane and let x be the angle of elevation to the plane from the antenna. (d is positive as the plane approaches the antenna.) Write d as a function of x and graph the function over the interval $0 < x < \pi$. See margin.

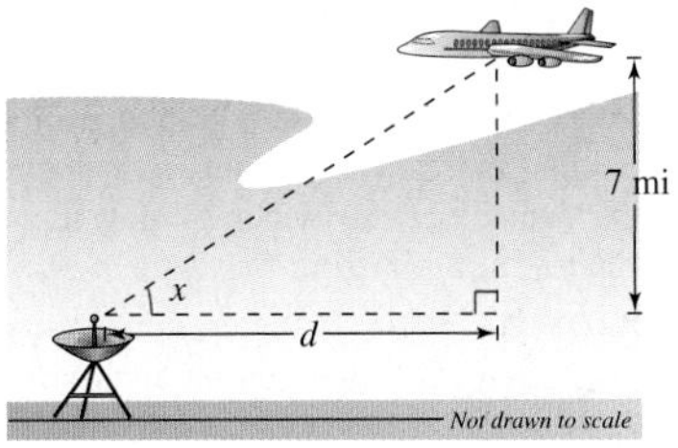

92. TELEVISION COVERAGE A television camera is on a reviewing platform 27 meters from the street on which a parade will be passing from left to right (see figure). Write the distance d from the camera to a particular unit in the parade as a function of the angle x, and graph the function over the interval $-\pi/2 < x < \pi/2$. (Consider x as negative when a unit in the parade approaches from the left.) See margin.

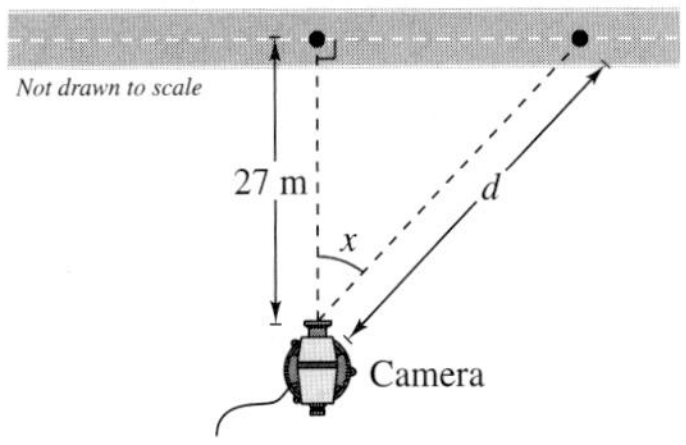

93. METEOROLOGY The normal monthly high temperatures H (in degrees Fahrenheit) in Erie, Pennsylvania are approximated by

$$H(t) = 56.94 - 20.86 \cos(\pi t/6) - 11.58 \sin(\pi t/6)$$

and the normal monthly low temperatures L are approximated by

$$L(t) = 41.80 - 17.13 \cos(\pi t/6) - 13.39 \sin(\pi t/6)$$

where t is the time (in months), with $t = 1$ corresponding to January (see figure). (Source: National Climatic Data Center)

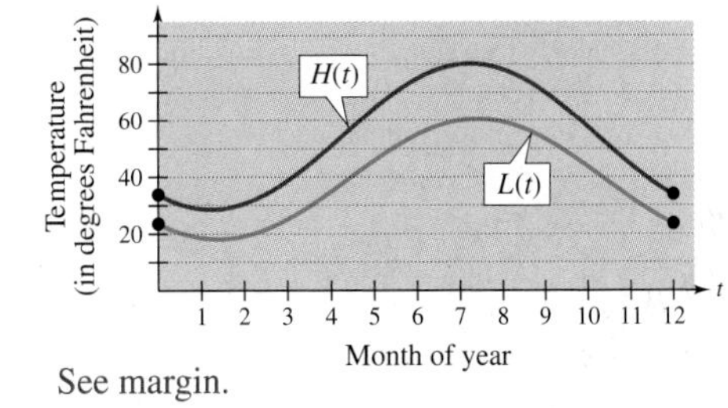

See margin.

(a) What is the period of each function?

(b) During what part of the year is the difference between the normal high and normal low temperatures greatest? When is it smallest?

(c) The sun is northernmost in the sky around June 21, but the graph shows the warmest temperatures at a later date. Approximate the lag time of the temperatures relative to the position of the sun.

94. SALES The projected monthly sales S (in thousands of units) of lawn mowers (a seasonal product) are modeled by $S = 74 + 3t - 40 \cos(\pi t/6)$, where t is the time (in months), with $t = 1$ corresponding to January. Graph the sales function over 1 year. See margin.

95. HARMONIC MOTION An object weighing W pounds is suspended from the ceiling by a steel spring (see figure). The weight is pulled downward (positive direction) from its equilibrium position and released. The resulting motion of the weight is described by the function $y = \frac{1}{2}e^{-t/4} \cos 4t,\ t > 0$, where y is the distance (in feet) and t is the time (in seconds).

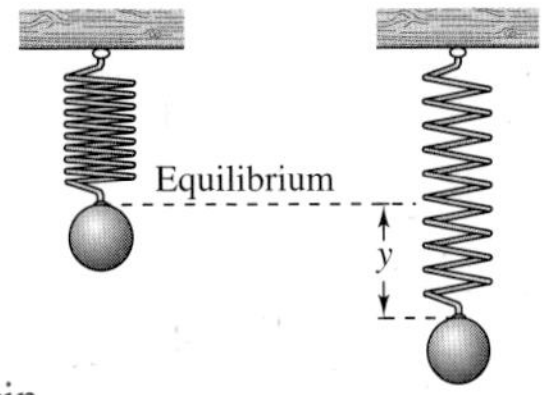

See margin.

(a) Use a graphing utility to graph the function.

(b) Describe the behavior of the displacement function for increasing values of time t.

EXPLORATION

96–97. See margin.

TRUE OR FALSE? In Exercises 96 and 97, determine whether the statement is true or false. Justify your answer.

96. The graph of $y = \csc x$ can be obtained on a calculator by graphing the reciprocal of $y = \sin x$.

97. The graph of $y = \sec x$ can be obtained on a calculator by graphing a translation of the reciprocal of $y = \sin x$.

87.

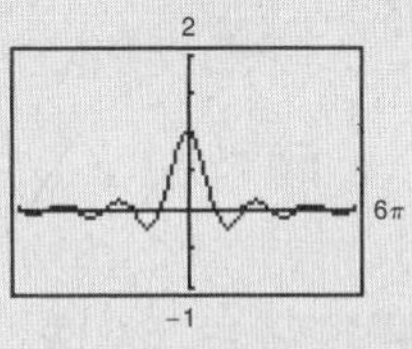

As $x \to 0$, $g(x) \to 1$.

88.

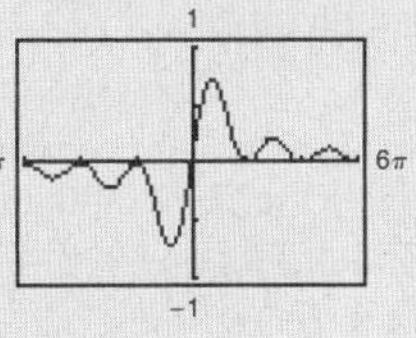

As $x \to 0$, $f(x) \to 0$.

89.

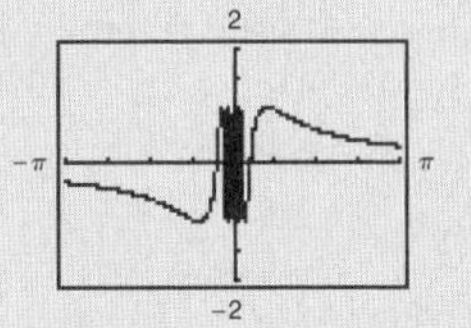

As $x \to 0$, $f(x)$ oscillates between 1 and -1.

90.

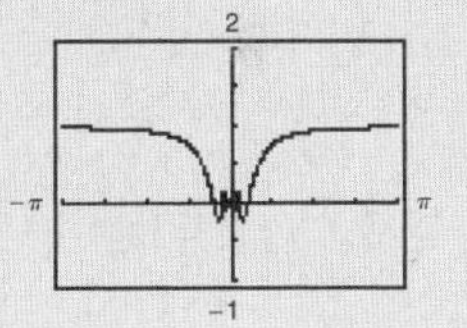

As $x \to 0$, $h(x) \to 0$.

91. $d = 7 \cot x$

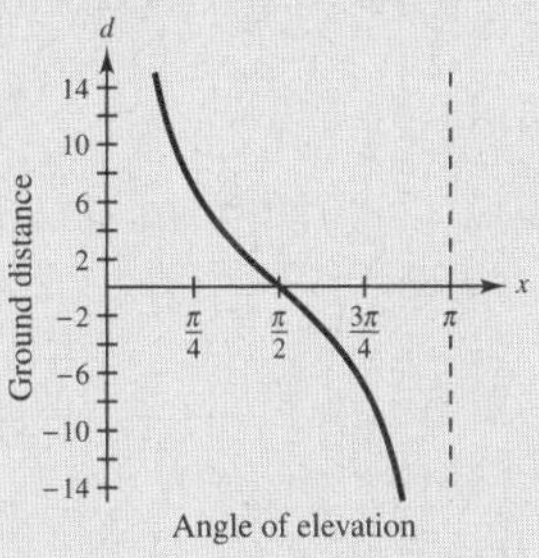

92. $d = 27 \sec x$

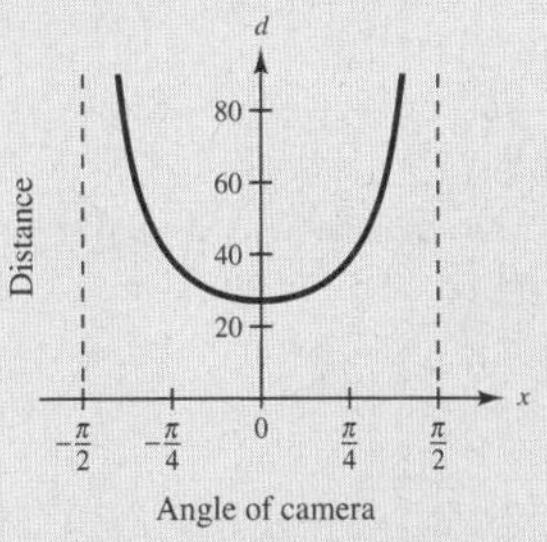

93. (a) Period of $H(t)$: 12 mo
Period of $L(t)$: 12 mo
(b) Summer; winter
(c) About 0.5 mo

94.

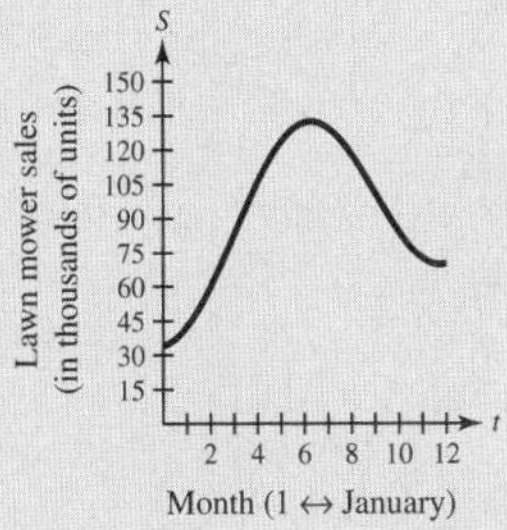

95. (a)

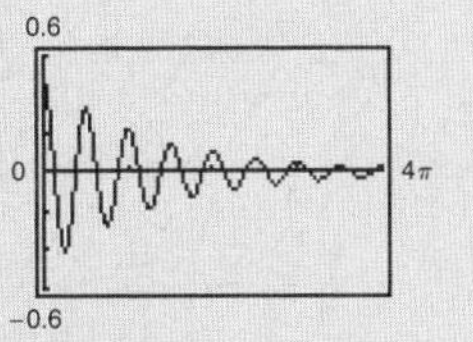

(b) y approaches 0 as t increases.

96. True. For a given value of x, the y-coordinate of $\csc x$ is the reciprocal of the y-coordinate of $\sin x$.

97. True. $y = \sec x$ is equal to $y = 1/\cos x$, and if the reciprocal of $y = \sin x$ is translated $\pi/2$ units to the left, then

$$\frac{1}{\sin\left(x + \dfrac{\pi}{2}\right)} = \frac{1}{\cos x} = \sec x.$$

5 ASSESS AND RETEACH

Daily Homework Quiz

Transparency Available
Available at the Instructor's companion site.

98. (a) (i) $f(x) = \tan 2x$; The period is $\pi/2$ and the graph is increasing on $(-\pi/4, \pi/4)$.
(b) (ii) $f(x) = \csc 4x$; The period is $\pi/2$ and the graph has vertical asymptotes at multiples of $\pi/4$.

99. (a) As $x \to \frac{\pi^+}{2}$, $f(x) \to -\infty$.
(b) As $x \to \frac{\pi^-}{2}$, $f(x) \to \infty$.
(c) As $x \to -\frac{\pi^+}{2}$, $f(x) \to -\infty$.
(d) As $x \to -\frac{\pi^-}{2}$, $f(x) \to \infty$.

100. (a) As $x \to \frac{\pi^+}{2}$, $f(x) \to -\infty$.
(b) As $x \to \frac{\pi^-}{2}$, $f(x) \to \infty$.
(c) As $x \to -\frac{\pi^+}{2}$, $f(x) \to \infty$.
(d) As $x \to -\frac{\pi^-}{2}$, $f(x) \to -\infty$.

101. (a) As $x \to 0^+$, $f(x) \to \infty$.
(b) As $x \to 0^-$, $f(x) \to -\infty$.
(c) As $x \to \pi^+$, $f(x) \to \infty$.
(d) As $x \to \pi^-$, $f(x) \to -\infty$.

102. (a) As $x \to 0^+$, $f(x) \to \infty$.
(b) As $x \to 0^-$, $f(x) \to -\infty$.
(c) As $x \to \pi^+$, $f(x) \to -\infty$.
(d) As $x \to \pi^-$, $f(x) \to \infty$.

103. (a)

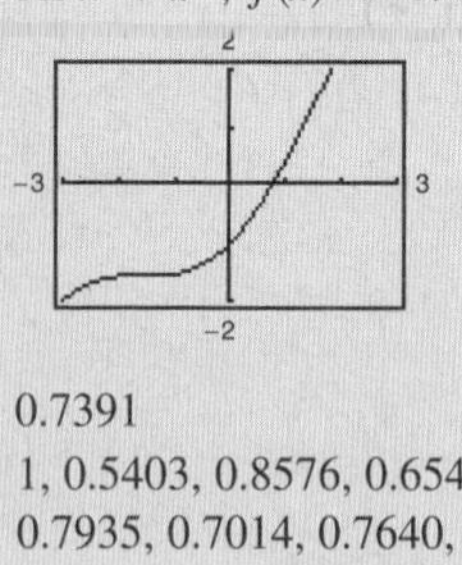

0.7391

(b) 1, 0.5403, 0.8576, 0.6543, 0.7935, 0.7014, 0.7640, 0.7221, 0.7504, 0.7314, . . . ; 0.7391

104.

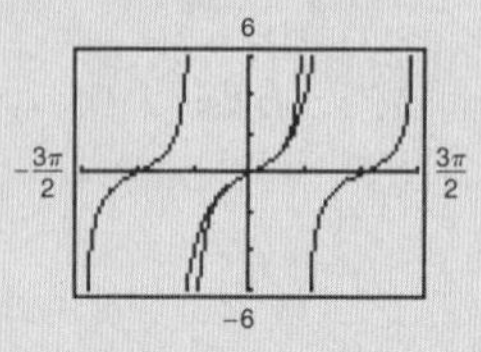

The graphs appear to coincide on the interval $-1.1 \le x \le 1.1$.

105.

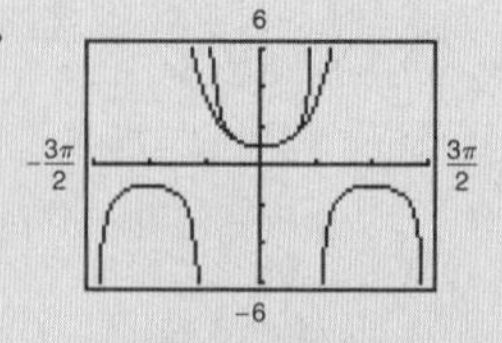

The graphs appear to coincide on the interval $-1.1 \le x \le 1.1$.

106. See Additional Answers beginning on page AA1.

---

98. CAPSTONE Determine which function is represented by the graph. Do not use a calculator. Explain your reasoning. See margin.

(a)

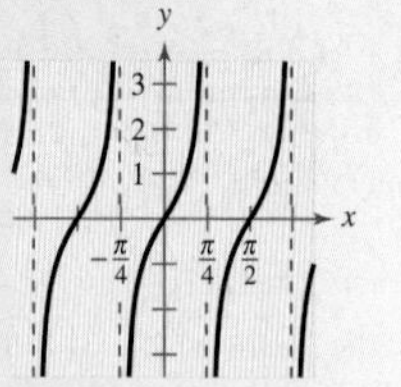

(b)

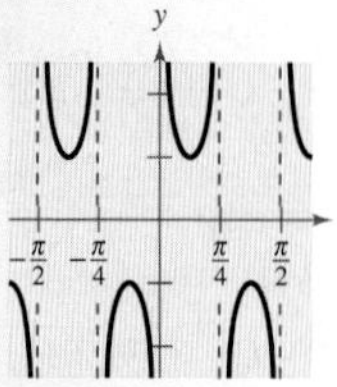

(a)	(b)
(i) $f(x) = \tan 2x$	(i) $f(x) = \sec 4x$
(ii) $f(x) = \tan(x/2)$	(ii) $f(x) = \csc 4x$
(iii) $f(x) = 2 \tan x$	(iii) $f(x) = \csc(x/4)$
(iv) $f(x) = -\tan 2x$	(iv) $f(x) = \sec(x/4)$
(v) $f(x) = -\tan(x/2)$	(v) $f(x) = \csc(4x - \pi)$

In Exercises 99 and 100, use a graphing utility to graph the function. Use the graph to determine the behavior of the function as $x \to c$. 99–100. See margin.

(a) $x \to \frac{\pi^+}{2}$ (as x approaches $\frac{\pi}{2}$ from the right)

(b) $x \to \frac{\pi^-}{2}$ (as x approaches $\frac{\pi}{2}$ from the left)

(c) $x \to -\frac{\pi^+}{2}$ (as x approaches $-\frac{\pi}{2}$ from the right)

(d) $x \to -\frac{\pi^-}{2}$ (as x approaches $-\frac{\pi}{2}$ from the left)

99. $f(x) = \tan x$ **100.** $f(x) = \sec x$

In Exercises 101 and 102, use a graphing utility to graph the function. Use the graph to determine the behavior of the function as $x \to c$. 101–102. See margin.

(a) As $x \to 0^+$, the value of $f(x) \to$ ▮.
(b) As $x \to 0^-$, the value of $f(x) \to$ ▮.
(c) As $x \to \pi^+$, the value of $f(x) \to$ ▮.
(d) As $x \to \pi^-$, the value of $f(x) \to$ ▮.

101. $f(x) = \cot x$ **102.** $f(x) = \csc x$

103. THINK ABOUT IT Consider the function given by $f(x) = x - \cos x$. See margin.

(a) Use a graphing utility to graph the function and verify that there exists a zero between 0 and 1. Use the graph to approximate the zero.

(b) Starting with $x_0 = 1$, generate a sequence $x_1, x_2, x_3, \ldots$, where $x_n = \cos(x_{n-1})$. For example,

$$x_0 = 1$$
$$x_1 = \cos(x_0)$$
$$x_2 = \cos(x_1)$$
$$x_3 = \cos(x_2)$$
$$\vdots$$

What value does the sequence approach?

104. APPROXIMATION Using calculus, it can be shown that the tangent function can be approximated by the polynomial

$$\tan x \approx x + \frac{2x^3}{3!} + \frac{16x^5}{5!}$$

where x is in radians. Use a graphing utility to graph the tangent function and its polynomial approximation in the same viewing window. How do the graphs compare? See margin.

105. APPROXIMATION Using calculus, it can be shown that the secant function can be approximated by the polynomial

$$\sec x \approx 1 + \frac{x^2}{2!} + \frac{5x^4}{4!}$$

where x is in radians. Use a graphing utility to graph the secant function and its polynomial approximation in the same viewing window. How do the graphs compare? See margin.

106. PATTERN RECOGNITION See margin.

(a) Use a graphing utility to graph each function.

$$y_1 = \frac{4}{\pi}\left(\sin \pi x + \frac{1}{3}\sin 3\pi x\right)$$

$$y_2 = \frac{4}{\pi}\left(\sin \pi x + \frac{1}{3}\sin 3\pi x + \frac{1}{5}\sin 5\pi x\right)$$

(b) Identify the pattern started in part (a) and find a function y_3 that continues the pattern one more term. Use a graphing utility to graph y_3.

(c) The graphs in parts (a) and (b) approximate the periodic function in the figure. Find a function y_4 that is a better approximation.

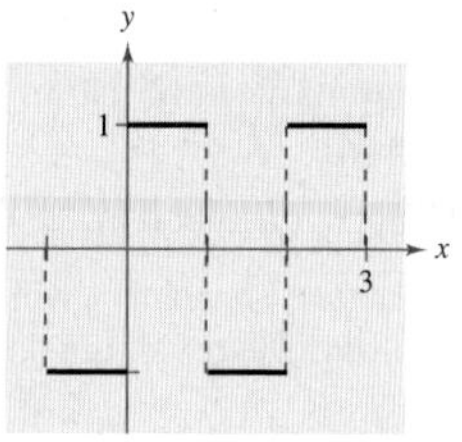

4.7 Inverse Trigonometric Functions

What you should learn

- Evaluate and graph the inverse sine function.
- Evaluate and graph the other inverse trigonometric functions.
- Evaluate and graph the compositions of trigonometric functions.

Why you should learn it

You can use inverse trigonometric functions to model and solve real-life problems. For instance, in Exercise 106 on page 349, an inverse trigonometric function can be used to model the angle of elevation from a television camera to a space shuttle launch.

Inverse Sine Function

Recall from Section 1.9 that, for a function to have an inverse function, it must be one-to-one—that is, it must pass the Horizontal Line Test. From Figure 4.71, you can see that $y = \sin x$ does not pass the test because different values of x yield the same y-value.

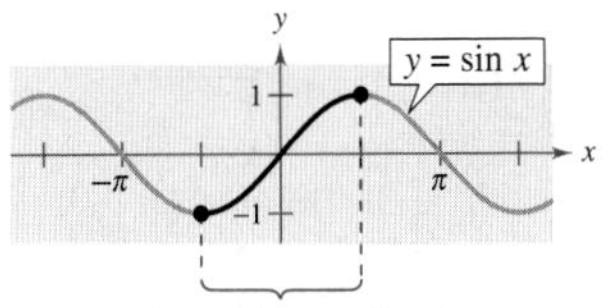

FIGURE 4.71

However, if you restrict the domain to the interval $-\pi/2 \le x \le \pi/2$ (corresponding to the black portion of the graph in Figure 4.71), the following properties hold.

1. On the interval $[-\pi/2, \pi/2]$, the function $y = \sin x$ is increasing.
2. On the interval $[-\pi/2, \pi/2]$, $y = \sin x$ takes on its full range of values, $-1 \le \sin x \le 1$.
3. On the interval $[-\pi/2, \pi/2]$, $y = \sin x$ is one-to-one.

So, on the restricted domain $-\pi/2 \le x \le \pi/2$, $y = \sin x$ has a unique inverse function called the **inverse sine function.** It is denoted by

$$y = \arcsin x \quad \text{or} \quad y = \sin^{-1} x.$$

The notation $\sin^{-1} x$ is consistent with the inverse function notation $f^{-1}(x)$. The $\arcsin x$ notation (read as "the arcsine of x") comes from the association of a central angle with its intercepted *arc length* on a unit circle. So, $\arcsin x$ means the angle (or arc) whose sine is x. Both notations, $\arcsin x$ and $\sin^{-1} x$, are commonly used in mathematics, so remember that $\sin^{-1} x$ denotes the *inverse* sine function rather than $1/\sin x$. The values of $\arcsin x$ lie in the interval $-\pi/2 \le \arcsin x \le \pi/2$. The graph of $y = \arcsin x$ is shown in Example 2.

Study Tip

When evaluating the inverse sine function, it helps to remember the phrase "the arcsine of x is the angle (or number) whose sine is x."

Definition of Inverse Sine Function

The **inverse sine function** is defined by

$$y = \arcsin x \quad \text{if and only if} \quad \sin y = x$$

where $-1 \le x \le 1$ and $-\pi/2 \le y \le \pi/2$. The domain of $y = \arcsin x$ is $[-1, 1]$, and the range is $[-\pi/2, \pi/2]$.

1 Plan and Prepare

Warm-up Exercises

Transparency Available
Available at the Instructor's companion site.

Notetaking Guide

Transparency Available
Promotes interactive learning and notetaking skills.
Available at the Instructor's companion site.

Animated Precalculus

An **Animated Precalculus** tutorial is available at the Student companion site for **Section 4.7.**

Pacing

Average: 2 days
Advanced: 2 days
Block: 0.5 block with 4.6
0.5 block with 4.8

2 Focus and Motivate

Essential Question

How do you evaluate and graph the inverses of trigonometric functions? **Tell students that they will learn how to answer this question by studying the definitions of inverse trigonometric functions and plotting points.**

Resource Planning Guide

Chapter Resources

- Complete Solutions Guide

Workbooks

- Notetaking Guide
- Student Solutions Guide

Interactive Technology

- Instructor Success Organizer
- Notetaking Guide IAE
- Instructional DVDs
- Animated Precalculus
- PowerLecture with ExamView

3 TEACH

Extra Example 1

If possible, find the exact value.

a. $\arcsin(-1)$

$-\frac{\pi}{2}$

b. $\sin^{-1}\left(\frac{1}{2}\right)$

$\frac{\pi}{6}$

c. $\sin^{-1}(\sqrt{3})$

No solution

Extra Example 2

Sketch a graph of $y = \arcsin 2x$.

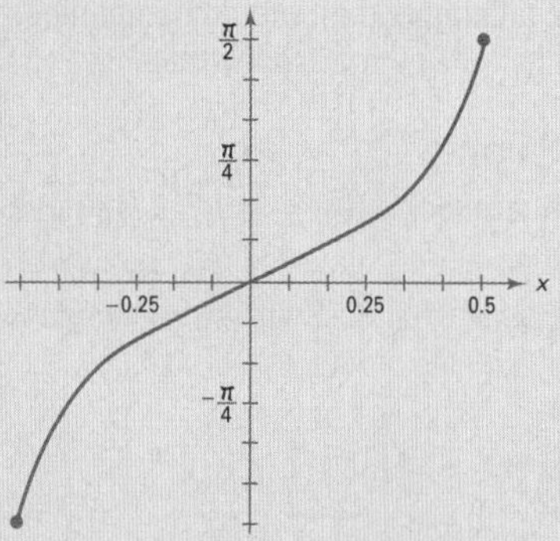

Study Tip

As with the trigonometric functions, much of the work with the inverse trigonometric functions can be done by *exact* calculations rather than by calculator approximations. Exact calculations help to increase your understanding of the inverse functions by relating them to the right triangle definitions of the trigonometric functions.

Example 1 Evaluating the Inverse Sine Function

If possible, find the exact value.

a. $\arcsin\left(-\frac{1}{2}\right)$ **b.** $\sin^{-1}\frac{\sqrt{3}}{2}$ **c.** $\sin^{-1}2$

Solution

a. Because $\sin\left(-\frac{\pi}{6}\right) = -\frac{1}{2}$ for $-\frac{\pi}{2} \le y \le \frac{\pi}{2}$, it follows that

$$\arcsin\left(-\frac{1}{2}\right) = -\frac{\pi}{6}. \qquad \text{Angle whose sine is } -\tfrac{1}{2}$$

b. Because $\sin\frac{\pi}{3} = \frac{\sqrt{3}}{2}$ for $-\frac{\pi}{2} \le y \le \frac{\pi}{2}$, it follows that

$$\sin^{-1}\frac{\sqrt{3}}{2} = \frac{\pi}{3}. \qquad \text{Angle whose sine is } \sqrt{3}/2$$

c. It is not possible to evaluate $y = \sin^{-1}x$ when $x = 2$ because there is no angle whose sine is 2. Remember that the domain of the inverse sine function is $[-1, 1]$.

CHECKPoint Now try Exercise 5.

Example 2 Graphing the Arcsine Function

Sketch a graph of

$$y = \arcsin x.$$

Solution

By definition, the equations $y = \arcsin x$ and $\sin y = x$ are equivalent for $-\pi/2 \le y \le \pi/2$. So, their graphs are the same. From the interval $[-\pi/2, \pi/2]$, you can assign values to y in the second equation to make a table of values. Then plot the points and draw a smooth curve through the points.

y	$-\frac{\pi}{2}$	$-\frac{\pi}{4}$	$-\frac{\pi}{6}$	0	$\frac{\pi}{6}$	$\frac{\pi}{4}$	$\frac{\pi}{2}$
$x = \sin y$	-1	$-\frac{\sqrt{2}}{2}$	$-\frac{1}{2}$	0	$\frac{1}{2}$	$\frac{\sqrt{2}}{2}$	1

The resulting graph for $y = \arcsin x$ is shown in Figure 4.72. Note that it is the reflection (in the line $y = x$) of the black portion of the graph in Figure 4.71. Be sure you see that Figure 4.72 shows the *entire* graph of the inverse sine function. Remember that the domain of $y = \arcsin x$ is the closed interval $[-1, 1]$ and the range is the closed interval $[-\pi/2, \pi/2]$.

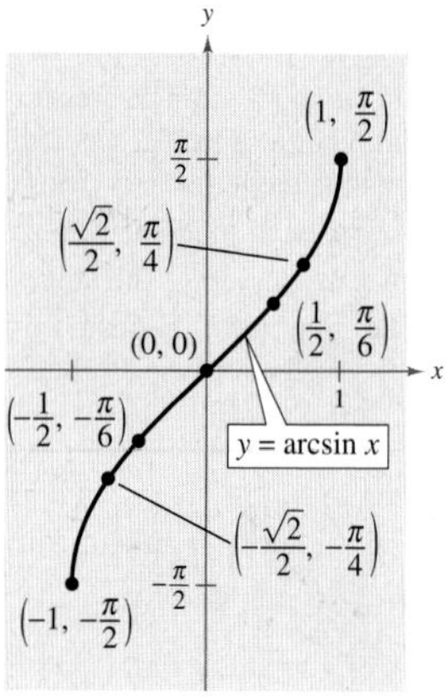

FIGURE 4.72

CHECKPoint Now try Exercise 21.

Other Inverse Trigonometric Functions

The cosine function is decreasing and one-to-one on the interval $0 \le x \le \pi$, as shown in Figure 4.73.

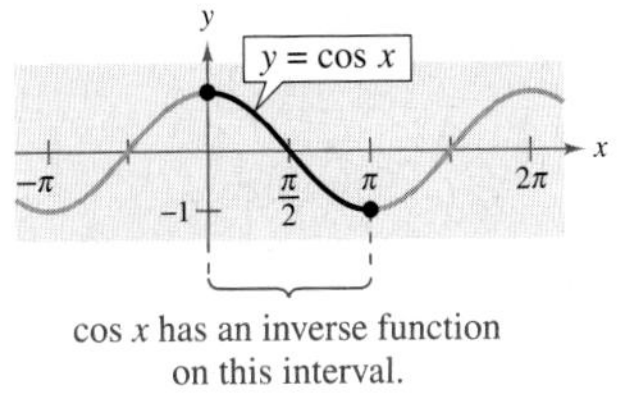

FIGURE 4.73

Consequently, on this interval the cosine function has an inverse function—the **inverse cosine function**—denoted by

$$y = \arccos x \qquad \text{or} \qquad y = \cos^{-1} x.$$

Similarly, you can define an **inverse tangent function** by restricting the domain of $y = \tan x$ to the interval $(-\pi/2, \pi/2)$. The following list summarizes the definitions of the three most common inverse trigonometric functions. The remaining three are defined in Exercises 115–117.

Definitions of the Inverse Trigonometric Functions

Function	*Domain*	*Range*
$y = \arcsin x$ if and only if $\sin y = x$	$-1 \le x \le 1$	$-\dfrac{\pi}{2} \le y \le \dfrac{\pi}{2}$
$y = \arccos x$ if and only if $\cos y = x$	$-1 \le x \le 1$	$0 \le y \le \pi$
$y = \arctan x$ if and only if $\tan y = x$	$-\infty < x < \infty$	$-\dfrac{\pi}{2} < y < \dfrac{\pi}{2}$

The graphs of these three inverse trigonometric functions are shown in Figure 4.74.

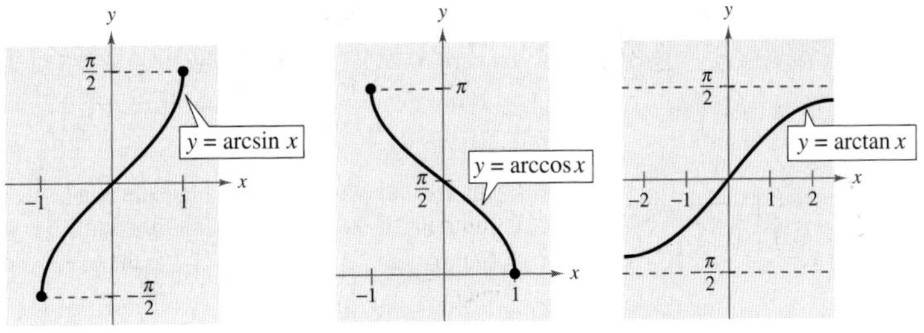

DOMAIN: $[-1, 1]$
RANGE: $\left[-\frac{\pi}{2}, \frac{\pi}{2}\right]$

DOMAIN: $[-1, 1]$
RANGE: $[0, \pi]$

DOMAIN: $(-\infty, \infty)$
RANGE: $\left(-\frac{\pi}{2}, \frac{\pi}{2}\right)$

FIGURE 4.74

Extra Example 3

Find the exact value.

a. $\arccos \frac{\sqrt{3}}{2}$

$\frac{\pi}{6}$

b. $\cos^{-1}(-0.5)$

$\frac{2\pi}{3}$

c. arctan (1)

$\frac{\pi}{4}$

d. $\tan^{-1}\left(\frac{\sqrt{3}}{3}\right)$

$\frac{\pi}{6}$

Avoiding Common Errors

Remind students that the range of each inverse trigonometric function is limited to allow it to be a function. Students should know these ranges well to ensure that their answers are within the correct range. Referencing the graphs can help students visualize the range of each function.

Extra Example 4

Use a calculator to approximate the value, if possible.

a. arctan 4.84

1.3671

b. arccos(−0.349)

1.9273

c. $\sin^{-1}(-1.1)$

No solution

Example 3 Evaluating Inverse Trigonometric Functions

Find the exact value.

a. $\arccos \frac{\sqrt{2}}{2}$ **b.** $\cos^{-1}(-1)$

c. arctan 0 **d.** $\tan^{-1}(-1)$

Solution

a. Because $\cos(\pi/4) = \sqrt{2}/2$, and $\pi/4$ lies in $[0, \pi]$, it follows that

$$\arccos \frac{\sqrt{2}}{2} = \frac{\pi}{4}. \quad \text{Angle whose cosine is } \sqrt{2}/2$$

b. Because $\cos \pi = -1$, and π lies in $[0, \pi]$, it follows that

$$\cos^{-1}(-1) = \pi. \quad \text{Angle whose cosine is } -1$$

c. Because $\tan 0 = 0$, and 0 lies in $(-\pi/2, \pi/2)$, it follows that

$$\arctan 0 = 0. \quad \text{Angle whose tangent is } 0$$

d. Because $\tan(-\pi/4) = -1$, and $-\pi/4$ lies in $(-\pi/2, \pi/2)$, it follows that

$$\tan^{-1}(-1) = -\frac{\pi}{4}. \quad \text{Angle whose tangent is } -1$$

CHECKPoint Now try Exercise 15.

Example 4 Calculators and Inverse Trigonometric Functions

Use a calculator to approximate the value (if possible).

a. arctan(−8.45)

b. $\sin^{-1} 0.2447$

c. arccos 2

Solution

Function	*Mode*	*Calculator Keystrokes*
a. arctan(−8.45)	Radian	TAN⁻¹ ((−) 8.45) ENTER

From the display, it follows that $\arctan(-8.45) \approx -1.453001$.

b. $\sin^{-1} 0.2447$	Radian	SIN⁻¹ (0.2447) ENTER

From the display, it follows that $\sin^{-1} 0.2447 \approx 0.2472103$.

c. arccos 2	Radian	COS⁻¹ (2) ENTER

In *real number* mode, the calculator should display an *error message* because the domain of the inverse cosine function is $[-1, 1]$.

CHECKPoint Now try Exercise 29.

WARNING/CAUTION

Remember that the domain of the inverse sine function and the inverse cosine function is $[-1, 1]$, as indicated in Example 4(c).

In Example 4, if you had set the calculator to *degree* mode, the displays would have been in degrees rather than radians. This convention is peculiar to calculators. By definition, the values of inverse trigonometric functions are *always in radians*.

Compositions of Functions

Algebra Help

You can review the composition of functions in Section 1.8.

Recall from Section 1.9 that for all x in the domains of f and f^{-1}, inverse functions have the properties

$$f(f^{-1}(x)) = x \quad \text{and} \quad f^{-1}(f(x)) = x.$$

Inverse Properties of Trigonometric Functions

If $-1 \le x \le 1$ and $-\pi/2 \le y \le \pi/2$, then

$$\sin(\arcsin x) = x \quad \text{and} \quad \arcsin(\sin y) = y.$$

If $-1 \le x \le 1$ and $0 \le y \le \pi$, then

$$\cos(\arccos x) = x \quad \text{and} \quad \arccos(\cos y) = y.$$

If x is a real number and $-\pi/2 < y < \pi/2$, then

$$\tan(\arctan x) = x \quad \text{and} \quad \arctan(\tan y) = y.$$

Keep in mind that these inverse properties do not apply for arbitrary values of x and y. For instance,

$$\arcsin\left(\sin \frac{3\pi}{2}\right) = \arcsin(-1) = -\frac{\pi}{2} \neq \frac{3\pi}{2}.$$

In other words, the property

$$\arcsin(\sin y) = y$$

is not valid for values of y outside the interval $[-\pi/2, \pi/2]$.

Example 5 Using Inverse Properties

If possible, find the exact value.

a. $\tan[\arctan(-5)]$ **b.** $\arcsin\left(\sin \frac{5\pi}{3}\right)$ **c.** $\cos(\cos^{-1} \pi)$

Solution

a. Because -5 lies in the domain of the arctan function, the inverse property applies, and you have

$$\tan[\arctan(-5)] = -5.$$

b. In this case, $5\pi/3$ does not lie within the range of the arcsine function, $-\pi/2 \le y \le \pi/2$. However, $5\pi/3$ is coterminal with

$$\frac{5\pi}{3} - 2\pi = -\frac{\pi}{3}$$

which does lie in the range of the arcsine function, and you have

$$\arcsin\left(\sin \frac{5\pi}{3}\right) = \arcsin\left[\sin\left(-\frac{\pi}{3}\right)\right] = -\frac{\pi}{3}.$$

c. The expression $\cos(\cos^{-1} \pi)$ is not defined because $\cos^{-1} \pi$ is not defined. Remember that the domain of the inverse cosine function is $[-1, 1]$.

CHECKPoint Now try Exercise 49.

Extra Example 5

If possible, find the exact value.

a. $\tan[\arctan(-14)]$

-14

b. $\sin(\arcsin \pi)$

No solution

c. $\cos[\arccos(0.54)]$

0.54

Extra Example 6

Find the exact value.

a. $\cos\left[\arctan\left(-\frac{3}{4}\right)\right]$

$\frac{4}{5}$

b. $\sin\left[\arccos\left(\frac{2}{3}\right)\right]$

$\frac{\sqrt{5}}{3}$

Extra Example 7

Write each of the following as an algebraic expression in x.

a. $\sec(\arctan x)$

$\sqrt{x^2 + 1}$

b. $\tan(\arccos 2x)$

$\frac{\sqrt{1 - 4x^2}}{2x}, 0 < x \le \frac{1}{2}$

Closing the Lesson

Have students summarize the major points of the lesson and answer the Essential Question: How do you evaluate and graph the inverses of trigonometric functions?

- **Recognize the characteristics of arcsine, arccosine, and arctangent compared with inverses sine, cosine, and tangent, including domain and range.**
- **Use a calculator or knowledge of common trigonometric ratios to find the value of inverse trigonometric functions.**
- **Use definitions of inverse functions to evaluate compositions of trigonometric functions and their inverses.**

Example 6 shows how to use right triangles to find exact values of compositions of inverse functions. Then, Example 7 shows how to use right triangles to convert a trigonometric expression into an algebraic expression. This conversion technique is used frequently in calculus.

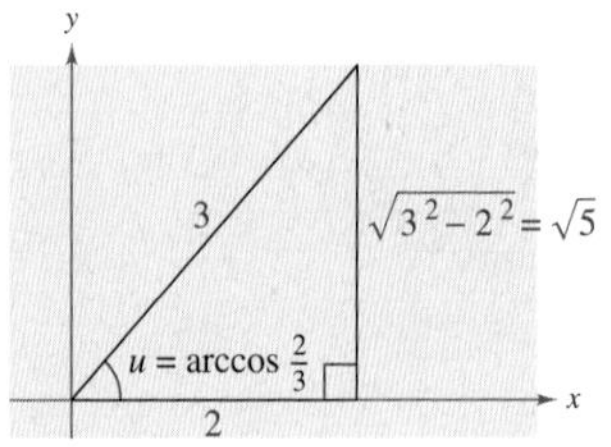

Angle whose cosine is $\frac{2}{3}$

FIGURE 4.75

Example 6 Evaluating Compositions of Functions

Find the exact value.

a. $\tan\left(\arccos\frac{2}{3}\right)$ **b.** $\cos\left[\arcsin\left(-\frac{3}{5}\right)\right]$

Solution

a. If you let $u = \arccos\frac{2}{3}$, then $\cos u = \frac{2}{3}$. Because $\cos u$ is positive, u is a *first*-quadrant angle. You can sketch and label angle u as shown in Figure 4.75. Consequently,

$$\tan\left(\arccos\frac{2}{3}\right) = \tan u = \frac{\text{opp}}{\text{adj}} = \frac{\sqrt{5}}{2}.$$

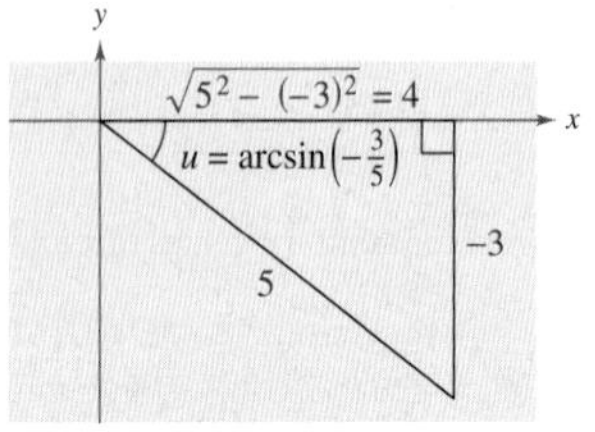

Angle whose sine is $-\frac{3}{5}$

FIGURE 4.76

b. If you let $u = \arcsin\left(-\frac{3}{5}\right)$, then $\sin u = -\frac{3}{5}$. Because $\sin u$ is negative, u is a *fourth*-quadrant angle. You can sketch and label angle u as shown in Figure 4.76. Consequently,

$$\cos\left[\arcsin\left(-\frac{3}{5}\right)\right] = \cos u = \frac{\text{adj}}{\text{hyp}} = \frac{4}{5}.$$

CHECKPoint Now try Exercise 57.

Example 7 Some Problems from Calculus

Write each of the following as an algebraic expression in x.

a. $\sin(\arccos 3x)$, $0 \le x \le \frac{1}{3}$ **b.** $\cot(\arccos 3x)$, $0 \le x < \frac{1}{3}$

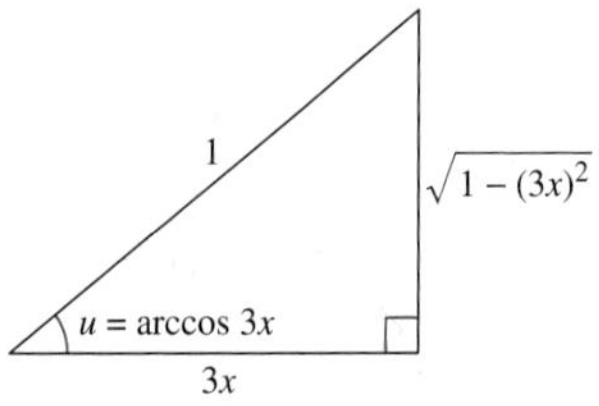

Angle whose cosine is $3x$

FIGURE 4.77

Solution

If you let $u = \arccos 3x$, then $\cos u = 3x$, where $-1 \le 3x \le 1$. Because

$$\cos u = \frac{\text{adj}}{\text{hyp}} = \frac{3x}{1}$$

you can sketch a right triangle with acute angle u, as shown in Figure 4.77. From this triangle, you can easily convert each expression to algebraic form.

a. $\sin(\arccos 3x) = \sin u = \frac{\text{opp}}{\text{hyp}} = \sqrt{1 - 9x^2}, \quad 0 \le x \le \frac{1}{3}$

b. $\cot(\arccos 3x) = \cot u = \frac{\text{adj}}{\text{opp}} = \frac{3x}{\sqrt{1 - 9x^2}}, \quad 0 \le x < \frac{1}{3}$

CHECKPoint Now try Exercise 67.

In Example 7, similar arguments can be made for x-values lying in the interval $\left[-\frac{1}{3}, 0\right]$.

4.7 EXERCISES

See www.CalcChat.com for worked-out solutions to odd-numbered exercises.

VOCABULARY: Fill in the blanks.

	Function	*Alternative Notation*	*Domain*	*Range*
1.	$y = \arcsin x$	$y = \sin^{-1} x$	$-1 \le x \le 1$	$-\frac{\pi}{2} \le y \le \frac{\pi}{2}$
2.	$y = \arccos x$	$y = \cos^{-1} x$	$-1 \le x \le 1$	$0 \le y \le \pi$
3.	$y = \arctan x$	$y = \tan^{-1} x$	$-\infty < x < \infty$	$-\frac{\pi}{2} < y < \frac{\pi}{2}$

4. Without restrictions, no trigonometric function has a(n) inverse function.

SKILLS AND APPLICATIONS

In Exercises 5–20, evaluate the expression without using a calculator. 5–10, 13–14. See margin.

5. $\arcsin \frac{1}{2}$ **6.** $\arcsin 0$

7. $\arccos \frac{1}{2}$ **8.** $\arccos 0$

9. $\arctan \frac{\sqrt{3}}{3}$ **10.** $\arctan(1)$

11. $\cos^{-1}\left(-\frac{\sqrt{3}}{2}\right)$ $\frac{5\pi}{6}$ **12.** $\sin^{-1}\left(-\frac{\sqrt{2}}{2}\right)$ $-\frac{\pi}{4}$

13. $\arctan(-\sqrt{3})$ **14.** $\arctan \sqrt{3}$

15. $\arccos\left(-\frac{1}{2}\right)$ $\frac{2\pi}{3}$ **16.** $\arcsin \frac{\sqrt{2}}{2}$ $\frac{\pi}{4}$

17. $\sin^{-1}\left(-\frac{\sqrt{3}}{2}\right)$ $-\frac{\pi}{3}$ **18.** $\tan^{-1}\left(-\frac{\sqrt{3}}{3}\right)$ $-\frac{\pi}{6}$

19. $\tan^{-1} 0$ 0 **20.** $\cos^{-1} 1$ 0

In Exercises 21 and 22, use a graphing utility to graph f, g, and $y = x$ in the same viewing window to verify geometrically that g is the inverse function of f. (Be sure to restrict the domain of f properly.) 21–22. See margin.

21. $f(x) = \sin x$, $g(x) = \arcsin x$

22. $f(x) = \tan x$, $g(x) = \arctan x$

In Exercises 23–40, use a calculator to evaluate the expression. Round your result to two decimal places.

23. $\arccos 0.37$ 1.19 **24.** $\arcsin 0.65$ 0.71

25. $\arcsin(-0.75)$ −0.85 **26.** $\arccos(-0.7)$ 2.35

27. $\arctan(-3)$ −1.25 **28.** $\arctan 25$ 1.53

29. $\sin^{-1} 0.31$ 0.32 **30.** $\cos^{-1} 0.26$ 1.31

31. $\arccos(-0.41)$ 1.99 **32.** $\arcsin(-0.125)$ −0.13

33. $\arctan 0.92$ 0.74 **34.** $\arctan 2.8$ 1.23

35. $\arcsin \frac{7}{8}$ 1.07 **36.** $\arccos\left(-\frac{1}{3}\right)$ 1.91

37. $\tan^{-1} \frac{19}{4}$ 1.36 **38.** $\tan^{-1}\left(-\frac{95}{7}\right)$ −1.50

39. $\tan^{-1}(-\sqrt{372})$ −1.52 **40.** $\tan^{-1}(-\sqrt{2165})$ −1.55

In Exercises 41 and 42, determine the missing coordinates of the points on the graph of the function. 41–42. See margin.

41.

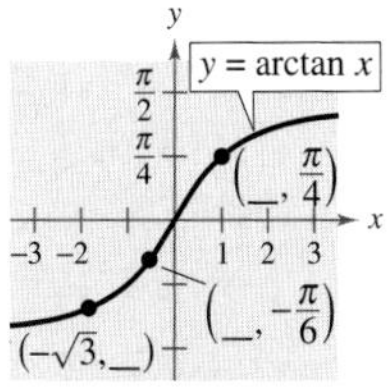

42.

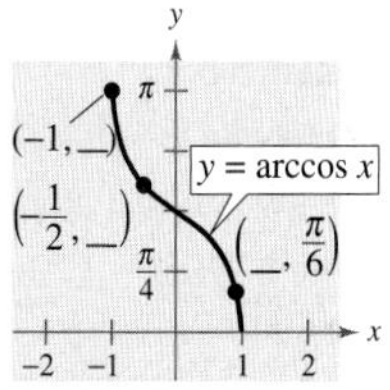

In Exercises 43–48, use an inverse trigonometric function to write θ as a function of x. 43–48. See margin.

43.

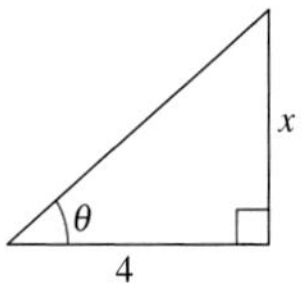

44.

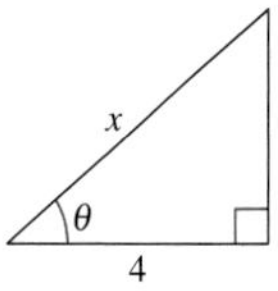

45.

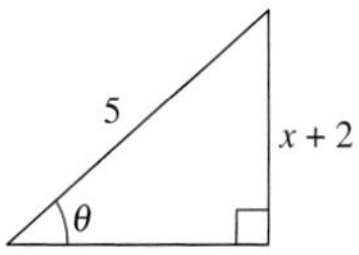

46.

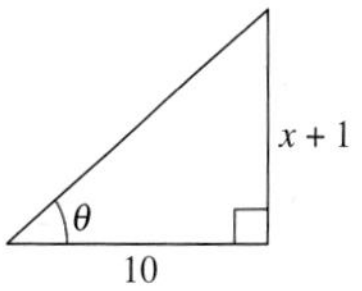

47.

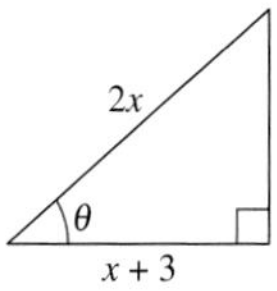

48.

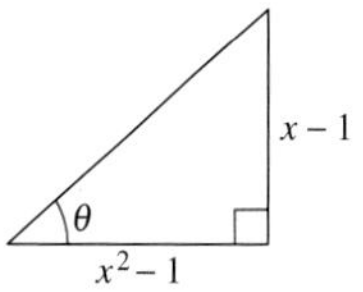

In Exercises 49–54, use the properties of inverse trigonometric functions to evaluate the expression.

49. $\sin(\arcsin 0.3)$ 0.3 **50.** $\tan(\arctan 45)$ 45

51. $\cos[\arccos(-0.1)]$ −0.1 **52.** $\sin[\arcsin(-0.2)]$ −0.2

53. $\arcsin(\sin 3\pi)$ 0 **54.** $\arccos\left(\cos \frac{7\pi}{2}\right)$ $\frac{\pi}{2}$

41. $-\frac{\pi}{3}, -\frac{\sqrt{3}}{3}, 1$

42. $\pi, \frac{2\pi}{3}, \frac{\sqrt{3}}{2}$

43. $\theta = \arctan \frac{x}{4}$

44. $\theta = \arccos \frac{4}{x}$

45. $\theta = \arcsin \frac{x+2}{5}$

46. $\theta = \arctan \frac{x+1}{10}$

47. $\theta = \arccos \frac{x+3}{2x}$

48. $\theta = \arctan \frac{1}{x+1}$, $x \ne 1$

4 PRACTICE AND APPLY

Assignment Guide

Transparencies Available
Available at the Instructor's companion site.

Average:

Day 1: pp. 347–350
Exs. 1–4, 5–11 odd, 19, 22, 23–27 odd, 41, 43, 47, 85, 87, 91, 105, 111, 112

Day 2: pp. 347–350
Exs. 51–59 odd, 69–83 odd, 89, 97, 99, 107, 108, 113–115, 135, 137

Advanced:

Day 1: pp. 347–350
Exs. 1–4, 12–20 even, 22, 32–42 even, 44–48, 88–94 even, 106, 108, 109, 115–118, 122–132 even

Day 2: pp. 347–350
Exs. 50–54 even, 62–72 even, 76–82 even, 89, 98, 100, 104, 107, 110, 135, 136

Block:

pp. 347–350
Exs. 1–4, 5–11 odd, 19, 22, 23–27 odd, 41, 43, 47, 85, 87, 91, 105, 111, 112 (with 4.6)

pp. 347–350
Exs. 51–59 odd, 69–83 odd, 89, 97, 99, 107, 108, 113–115, 135, 137 (with 4.8)

5. $\frac{\pi}{6}$ **6.** 0

7. $\frac{\pi}{3}$ **8.** $\frac{\pi}{2}$

9. $\frac{\pi}{6}$ **10.** $\frac{\pi}{4}$

13. $-\frac{\pi}{3}$ **14.** $\frac{\pi}{3}$

21.

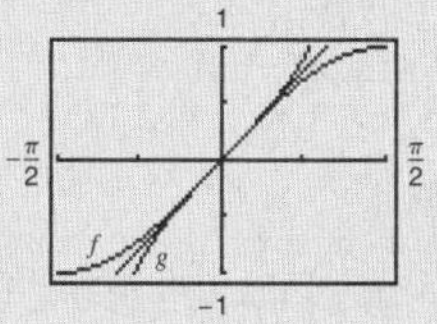

22.

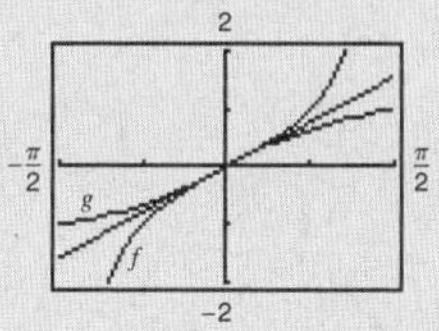

In Exercises 55–66, find the exact value of the expression. (*Hint:* Sketch a right triangle.) 61–63. See margin.

55. $\sin\left(\arctan \frac{3}{4}\right)$ $\frac{3}{5}$

56. $\sec\left(\arcsin \frac{4}{5}\right)$ $\frac{5}{3}$

57. $\cos(\tan^{-1} 2)$ $\frac{\sqrt{5}}{5}$

58. $\sin\left(\cos^{-1} \frac{\sqrt{5}}{5}\right)$ $\frac{2\sqrt{5}}{5}$

59. $\cos\left(\arcsin \frac{5}{13}\right)$ $\frac{12}{13}$

60. $\csc\left[\arctan\left(-\frac{5}{12}\right)\right]$ $-\frac{13}{5}$

61. $\sec\left[\arctan\left(-\frac{3}{5}\right)\right]$

62. $\tan\left[\arcsin\left(-\frac{3}{4}\right)\right]$

63. $\sin\left[\arccos\left(-\frac{2}{3}\right)\right]$

64. $\cot\left(\arctan \frac{5}{8}\right)$ $\frac{8}{5}$

65. $\csc\left[\cos^{-1}\left(\frac{\sqrt{3}}{2}\right)\right]$ 2

66. $\sec\left[\sin^{-1}\left(-\frac{\sqrt{2}}{2}\right)\right]$ $\sqrt{2}$

In Exercises 67–76, write an algebraic expression that is equivalent to the expression. (*Hint:* Sketch a right triangle, as demonstrated in Example 7.)

67. $\cot(\arctan x)$ See margin.

68. $\sin(\arctan x)$ See margin.

69. $\cos(\arcsin 2x)$ $\sqrt{1-4x^2}$

70. $\sec(\arctan 3x)$ $\sqrt{9x^2+1}$

71. $\sin(\arccos x)$ $\sqrt{1-x^2}$

72. $\sec[\arcsin(x-1)]$ See margin.

73. $\tan\left(\arccos \frac{x}{3}\right)$ $\frac{\sqrt{9-x^2}}{x}$

74. $\cot\left(\arctan \frac{1}{x}\right)$ x

75. $\csc\left(\arctan \frac{x}{\sqrt{2}}\right)$ $\frac{\sqrt{x^2+2}}{x}$

76. $\cos\left(\arcsin \frac{x-h}{r}\right)$ $\frac{\sqrt{r^2-(x-h)^2}}{r}$

In Exercises 77 and 78, use a graphing utility to graph f and g in the same viewing window to verify that the two functions are equal. Explain why they are equal. Identify any asymptotes of the graphs. 77–78. See margin.

77. $f(x) = \sin(\arctan 2x)$, $g(x) = \frac{2x}{\sqrt{1+4x^2}}$

78. $f(x) = \tan\left(\arccos \frac{x}{2}\right)$, $g(x) = \frac{\sqrt{4-x^2}}{x}$

In Exercises 79–82, fill in the blank.

79. $\arctan \frac{9}{x} = \arcsin(\quad)$, $x \neq 0$ See margin.

80. $\arcsin \frac{\sqrt{36-x^2}}{6} = \arccos(\quad)$, $0 \le x \le 6$ $\frac{x}{6}$

81. $\arccos \frac{3}{\sqrt{x^2-2x+10}} = \arcsin(\quad)$ $\frac{|x-1|}{\sqrt{x^2-2x+10}}$

82. $\arccos \frac{x-2}{2} = \arctan(\quad)$, $|x-2| \le 2$ See margin.

In Exercises 83 and 84, sketch a graph of the function and compare the graph of g with the graph of $f(x) = \arcsin x$.

83. $g(x) = \arcsin(x-1)$ 83–84. See margin.

84. $g(x) = \arcsin \frac{x}{2}$

In Exercises 85–90, sketch a graph of the function.

85. $y = 2 \arccos x$ 85–90. See margin.

86. $g(t) = \arccos(t+2)$

87. $f(x) = \arctan 2x$

88. $f(x) = \frac{\pi}{2} + \arctan x$

89. $h(v) = \tan(\arccos v)$

90. $f(x) = \arccos \frac{x}{4}$

In Exercises 91–96, use a graphing utility to graph the function. 91–96. See margin.

91. $f(x) = 2 \arccos(2x)$

92. $f(x) = \pi \arcsin(4x)$

93. $f(x) = \arctan(2x-3)$

94. $f(x) = -3 + \arctan(\pi x)$

95. $f(x) = \pi - \sin^{-1}\left(\frac{2}{3}\right)$

96. $f(x) = \frac{\pi}{2} + \cos^{-1}\left(\frac{1}{\pi}\right)$

In Exercises 97 and 98, write the function in terms of the sine function by using the identity

$$A \cos \omega t + B \sin \omega t = \sqrt{A^2+B^2} \sin\left(\omega t + \arctan \frac{A}{B}\right).$$

Use a graphing utility to graph both forms of the function. What does the graph imply? 97–98. See margin.

97. $f(t) = 3 \cos 2t + 3 \sin 2t$

98. $f(t) = 4 \cos \pi t + 3 \sin \pi t$

In Exercises 99–104, fill in the blank. If not possible, state the reason. (*Note:* The notation $x \to c^+$ indicates that x approaches c from the right and $x \to c^-$ indicates that x approaches c from the left.)

99. As $x \to 1^-$, the value of $\arcsin x \to$ ___. $\frac{\pi}{2}$

100. As $x \to 1^-$, the value of $\arccos x \to$ ___. 0

---

61. $\frac{\sqrt{34}}{5}$ **62.** $-\frac{3\sqrt{7}}{7}$

63. $\frac{\sqrt{5}}{3}$ **67.** $\frac{1}{x}$

68. $\frac{x}{\sqrt{x^2+1}}$ **72.** $\frac{1}{\sqrt{2x-x^2}}$

77.

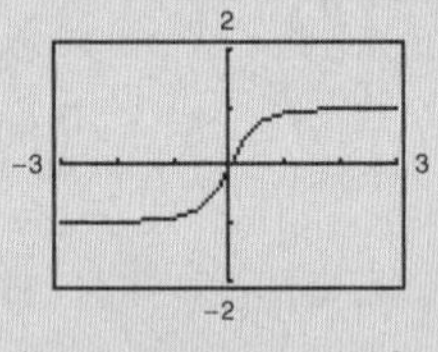

Asymptotes: $y = \pm 1$

78.

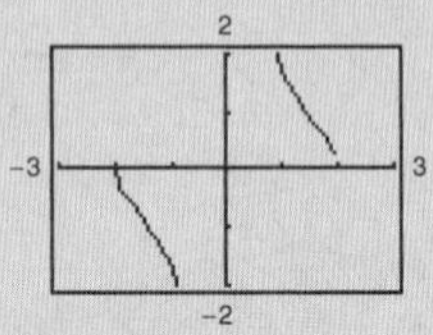

Asymptote: $x = 0$

79. $\frac{9}{\sqrt{x^2+81}}$, $x > 0$; $\frac{-9}{\sqrt{x^2+81}}$, $x < 0$

82. $\frac{\sqrt{4x-x^2}}{x-2}$

83.

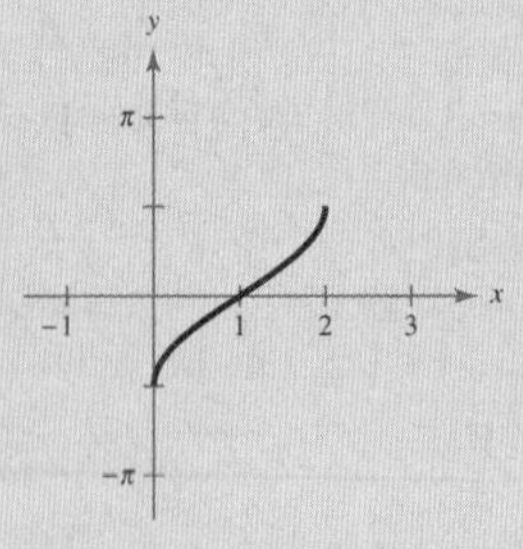

The graph of g is a horizontal shift one unit to the right of f.

84.

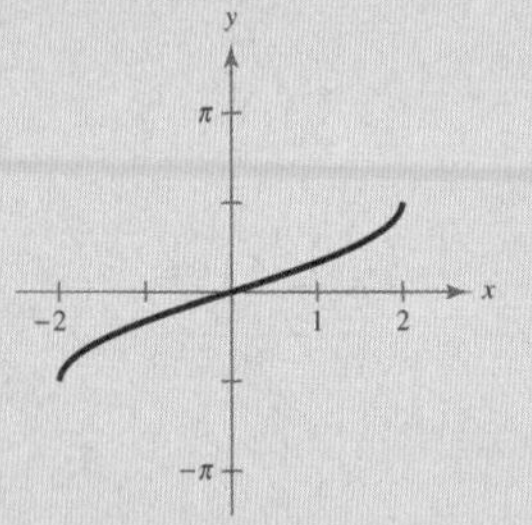

The graph of g is a horizontal stretch of the graph of f.

85.

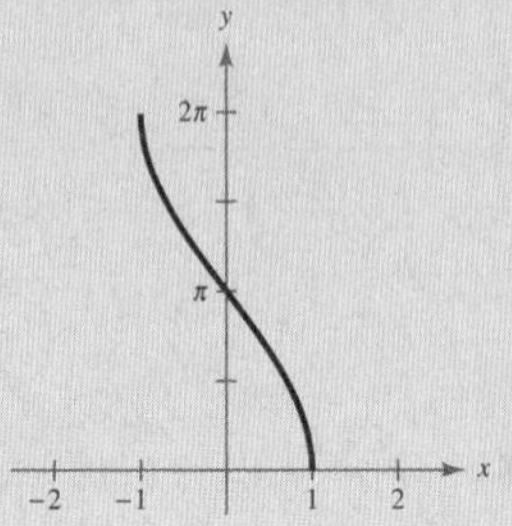

86.

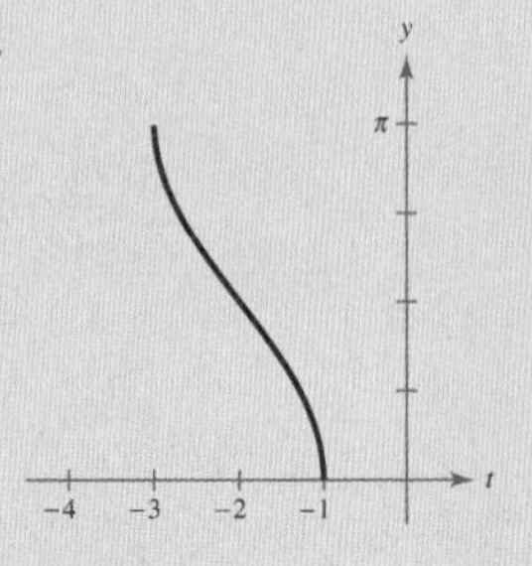

87.

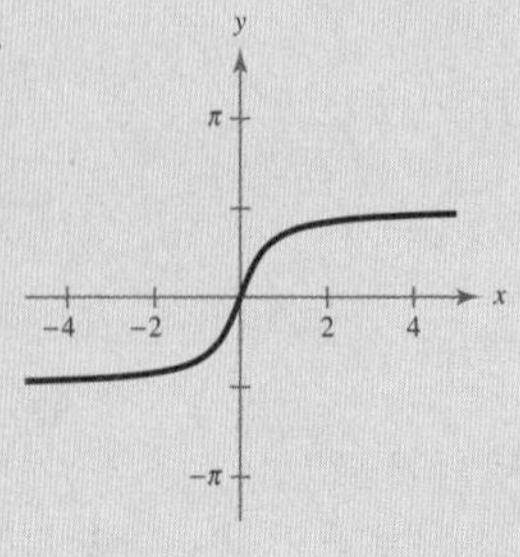

88.

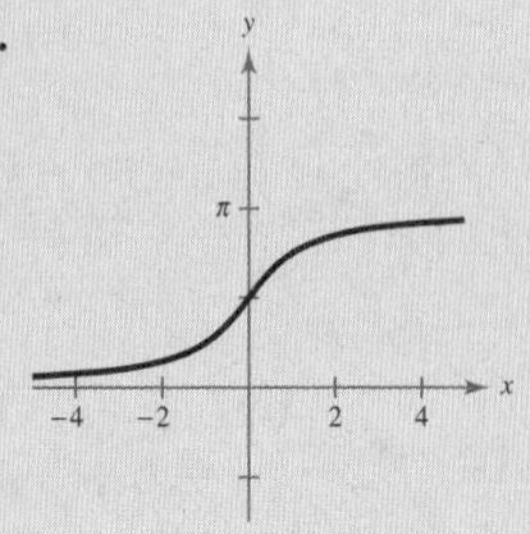

89–97. See page 349.
98. See Additional Answers beginning on page AA1.

101. As $x \to \infty$, the value of $\arctan x \to$ ▢. $\dfrac{\pi}{2}$

102. As $x \to -1^+$, the value of $\arcsin x \to$ ▢. See margin.

103. As $x \to -1^+$, the value of $\arccos x \to$ ▢. π

104. As $x \to -\infty$, the value of $\arctan x \to$ ▢. $-\dfrac{\pi}{2}$

105. DOCKING A BOAT A boat is pulled in by means of a winch located on a dock 5 feet above the deck of the boat (see figure). Let θ be the angle of elevation from the boat to the winch and let s be the length of the rope from the winch to the boat.

(a) $\theta = \arcsin \dfrac{5}{s}$ (b) 0.13, 0.25

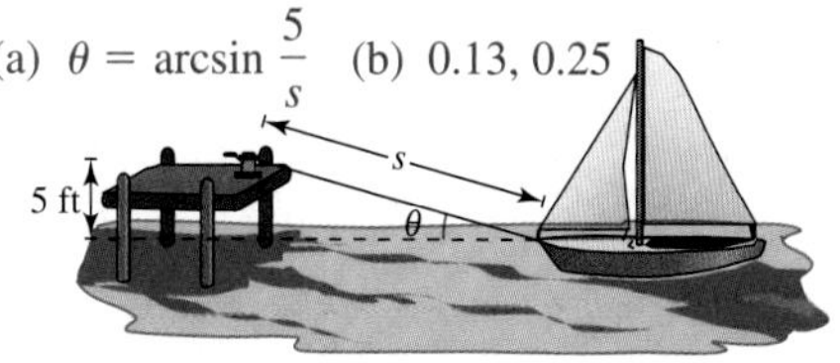

(a) Write θ as a function of s.

(b) Find θ when $s = 40$ feet and $s = 20$ feet.

106. PHOTOGRAPHY A television camera at ground level is filming the lift-off of a space shuttle at a point 750 meters from the launch pad (see figure). Let θ be the angle of elevation to the shuttle and let s be the height of the shuttle.

(a) $\theta = \arctan \dfrac{s}{750}$ (b) 21.8°, 58.0°

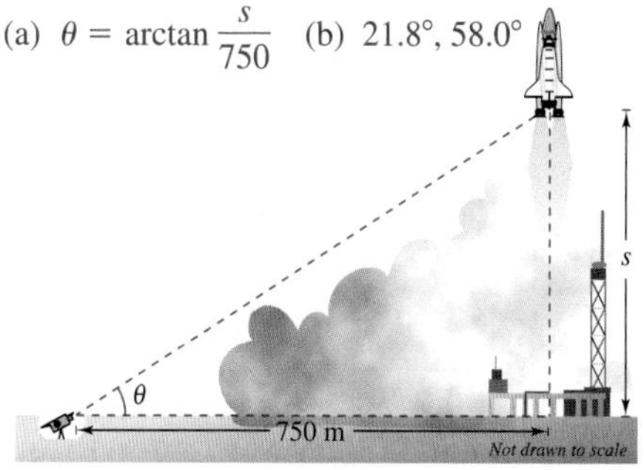

(a) Write θ as a function of s.

(b) Find θ when $s = 300$ meters and $s = 1200$ meters.

107. PHOTOGRAPHY A photographer is taking a picture of a three-foot-tall painting hung in an art gallery. The camera lens is 1 foot below the lower edge of the painting (see figure). The angle β subtended by the camera lens x feet from the painting is See margin.

$$\beta = \arctan \frac{3x}{x^2 + 4}, \quad x > 0.$$

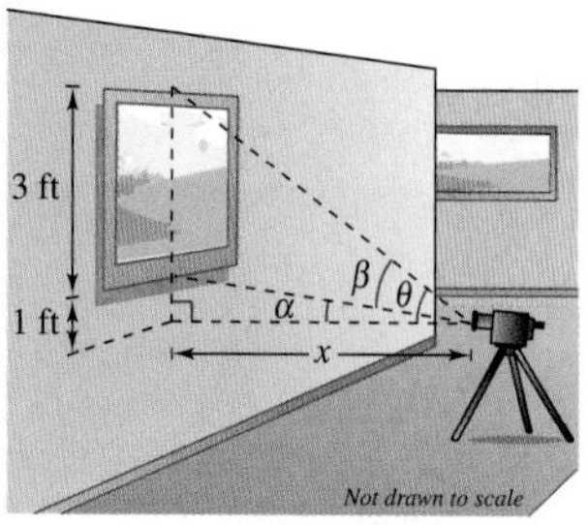

(a) Use a graphing utility to graph β as a function of x.

(b) Move the cursor along the graph to approximate the distance from the picture when β is maximum.

(c) Identify the asymptote of the graph and discuss its meaning in the context of the problem.

108. GRANULAR ANGLE OF REPOSE Different types of granular substances naturally settle at different angles when stored in cone-shaped piles. This angle θ is called the *angle of repose* (see figure). When rock salt is stored in a cone-shaped pile 11 feet high, the diameter of the pile's base is about 34 feet. (Source: Bulk-Store Structures, Inc.)

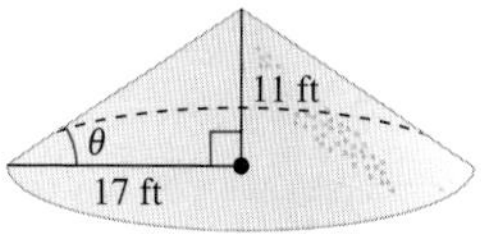

(a) Find the angle of repose for rock salt. $\theta \approx 32.9°$

(b) How tall is a pile of rock salt that has a base diameter of 40 feet? 12.94 ft

109. GRANULAR ANGLE OF REPOSE When whole corn is stored in a cone-shaped pile 20 feet high, the diameter of the pile's base is about 82 feet.

(a) Find the angle of repose for whole corn. $\theta \approx 26.0°$

(b) How tall is a pile of corn that has a base diameter of 100 feet? 24.4 ft

110. ANGLE OF ELEVATION An airplane flies at an altitude of 6 miles toward a point directly over an observer. Consider θ and x as shown in the figure.

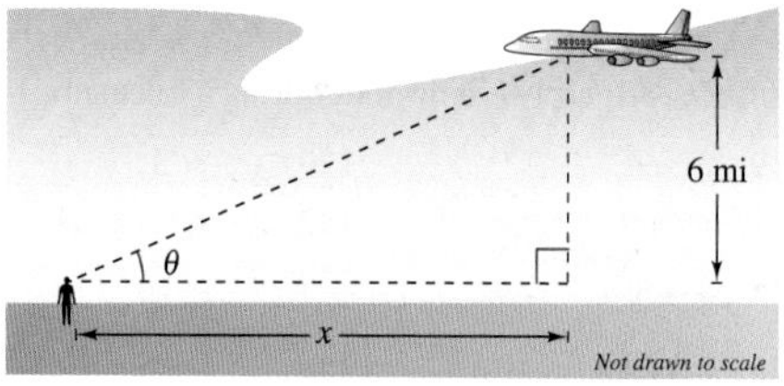

(a) Write θ as a function of x. $\theta = \arctan \dfrac{6}{x}$

(b) Find θ when $x = 7$ miles and $x = 1$ mile. 40.6°, 80.5°

89.

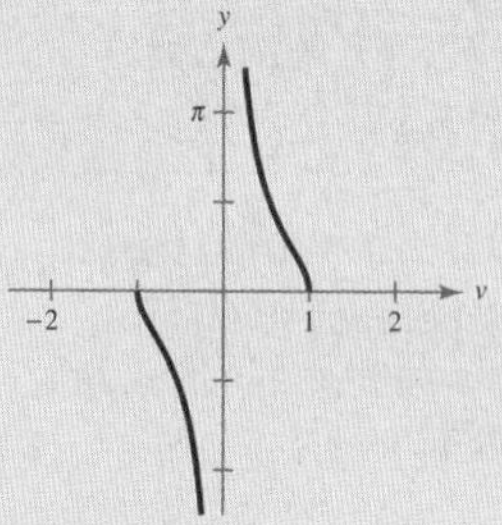

90.

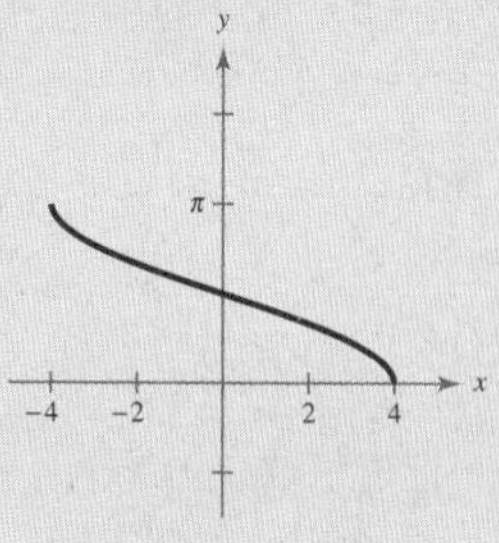

91.

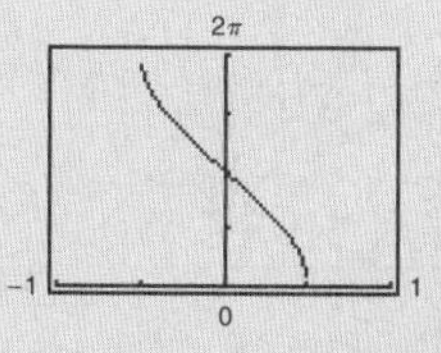

92.

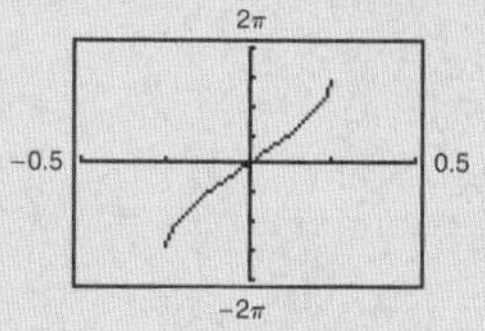

93.

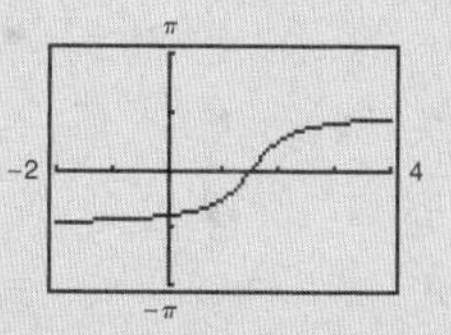

94.

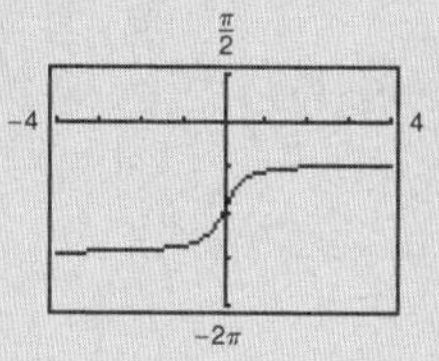

95.

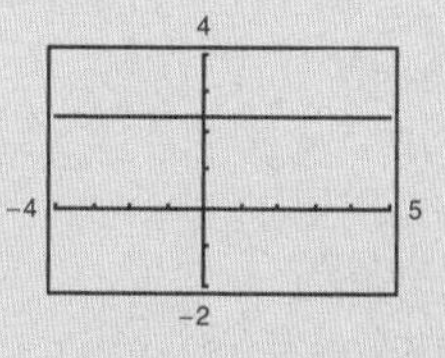

96.

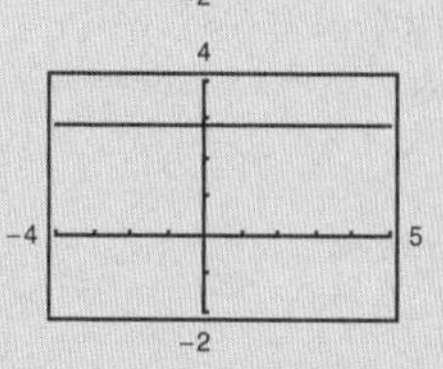

97. $3\sqrt{2} \sin\left(2t + \dfrac{\pi}{4}\right)$

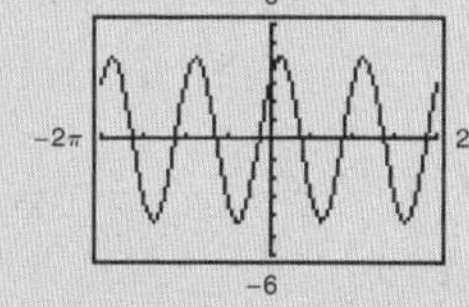

The graph implies that the identity is true.

102. $-\dfrac{\pi}{2}$

107. (a)

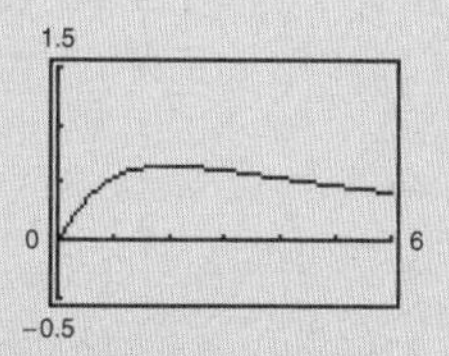

(b) 2 ft

(c) $\beta = 0$; As x increases, β approaches 0.

5 ASSESS AND RETEACH

Daily Homework Quiz

Transparency Available

Available at the Instructor's companion site.

112. False. $\frac{5\pi}{6}$ is not in the range of the arcsine.

113. False. $\frac{5\pi}{4}$ is not in the range of the arctangent.

115. Domain: $(-\infty, \infty)$
Range: $(0, \pi)$

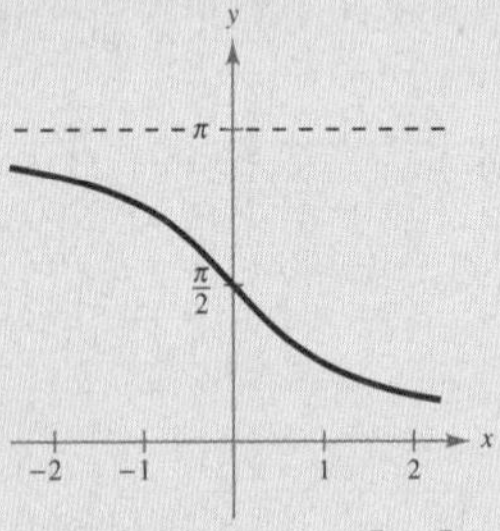

116. Domain: $(-\infty, -1] \cup [1, \infty)$
Range: $[0, \pi/2) \cup (\pi/2, \pi]$

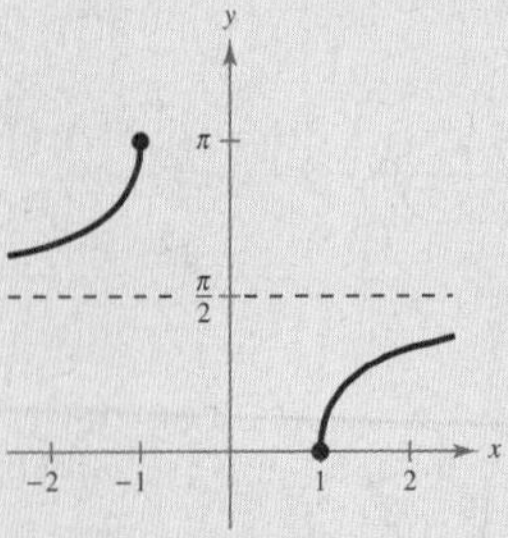

117. Domain: $(-\infty, -1] \cup [1, \infty)$
Range: $[-\pi/2, 0) \cup (0, \pi/2]$

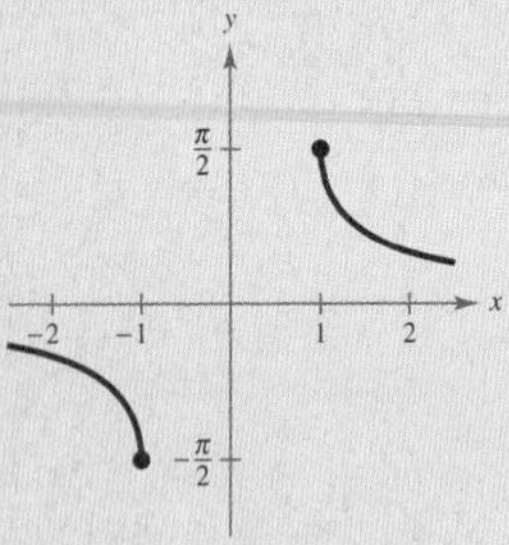

111. SECURITY PATROL A security car with its spotlight on is parked 20 meters from a warehouse. Consider θ and x as shown in the figure.

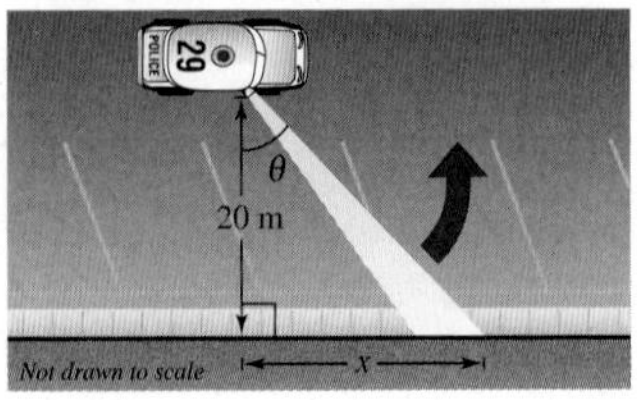

(a) Write θ as a function of x. $\theta = \arctan \frac{x}{20}$

(b) Find θ when $x = 5$ meters and $x = 12$ meters. 14.0°, 31.0°

EXPLORATION

TRUE OR FALSE? In Exercises 112–114, determine whether the statement is true or false. Justify your answer.

112. $\sin \frac{5\pi}{6} = \frac{1}{2}$ ⟹ $\arcsin \frac{1}{2} = \frac{5\pi}{6}$ 112–113. See margin.

113. $\tan \frac{5\pi}{4} = 1$ ⟹ $\arctan 1 = \frac{5\pi}{4}$

114. $\arctan x = \frac{\arcsin x}{\arccos x}$ False. The graphs are not the same.

115. Define the inverse cotangent function by restricting the domain of the cotangent function to the interval $(0, \pi)$, and sketch its graph. See margin.

116. Define the inverse secant function by restricting the domain of the secant function to the intervals $[0, \pi/2)$ and $(\pi/2, \pi]$, and sketch its graph. See margin.

117. Define the inverse cosecant function by restricting the domain of the cosecant function to the intervals $[-\pi/2, 0)$ and $(0, \pi/2]$, and sketch its graph. See margin.

118. CAPSTONE Use the results of Exercises 115–117 to explain how to graph (a) the inverse cotangent function, (b) the inverse secant function, and (c) the inverse cosecant function on a graphing utility. Answers will vary.

In Exercises 119–126, use the results of Exercises 115–117 to evaluate each expression without using a calculator.

119. $\operatorname{arcsec} \sqrt{2}$ $\frac{\pi}{4}$

120. $\operatorname{arcsec} 1$ 0

121. $\operatorname{arccot}(-1)$

122. $\operatorname{arccot}(-\sqrt{3})$ 121–124. See margin.

123. $\operatorname{arccsc} 2$

124. $\operatorname{arccsc}(-1)$

125. $\operatorname{arccsc}\left(\frac{2\sqrt{3}}{3}\right)$ $\frac{\pi}{3}$

126. $\operatorname{arcsec}\left(-\frac{2\sqrt{3}}{3}\right)$ $\frac{5\pi}{6}$

In Exercises 127–134, use the results of Exercises 115–117 and a calculator to approximate the value of the expression. Round your result to two decimal places.

127. $\operatorname{arcsec} 2.54$ 1.17

128. $\operatorname{arcsec}(-1.52)$ 2.29

129. $\operatorname{arccot} 5.25$ 0.19

130. $\operatorname{arccot}(-10)$ 3.04

131. $\operatorname{arccot} \frac{5}{3}$ 0.54

132. $\operatorname{arccot}\left(-\frac{16}{7}\right)$ 2.73

133. $\operatorname{arccsc}\left(-\frac{25}{3}\right)$ −0.12

134. $\operatorname{arccsc}(-12)$ −0.08

135. AREA In calculus, it is shown that the area of the region bounded by the graphs of $y = 0$, $y = 1/(x^2 + 1)$, $x = a$, and $x = b$ is given by

Area $= \arctan b - \arctan a$

(see figure). Find the area for the following values of a and b.

(a) $a = 0, b = 1$ (b) $a = -1, b = 1$
(c) $a = 0, b = 3$ (d) $a = -1, b = 3$

(a) $\frac{\pi}{4}$
(b) $\frac{\pi}{2}$
(c) 1.25
(d) 2.03

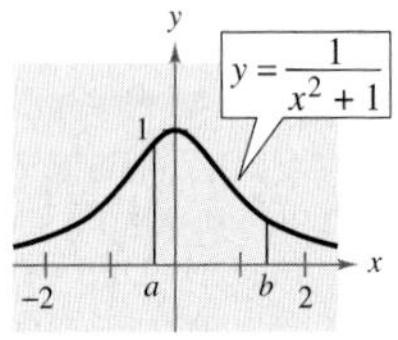

136. THINK ABOUT IT Use a graphing utility to graph the functions

$f(x) = \sqrt{x}$ and $g(x) = 6 \arctan x$. See margin.

For $x > 0$, it appears that $g > f$. Explain why you know that there exists a positive real number a such that $g < f$ for $x > a$. Approximate the number a.

137. THINK ABOUT IT Consider the functions given by

$f(x) = \sin x$ and $f^{-1}(x) = \arcsin x$. See margin.

(a) Use a graphing utility to graph the composite functions $f \circ f^{-1}$ and $f^{-1} \circ f$.

(b) Explain why the graphs in part (a) are not the graph of the line $y = x$. Why do the graphs of $f \circ f^{-1}$ and $f^{-1} \circ f$ differ?

138. PROOF Prove each identity.

(a) $\arcsin(-x) = -\arcsin x$ (a)–(e). Proofs

(b) $\arctan(-x) = -\arctan x$

(c) $\arctan x + \arctan \frac{1}{x} = \frac{\pi}{2}, \quad x > 0$

(d) $\arcsin x + \arccos x = \frac{\pi}{2}$

(e) $\arcsin x = \arctan \frac{x}{\sqrt{1 - x^2}}$

121. $\frac{3\pi}{4}$ **122.** $\frac{5\pi}{6}$

123. $\frac{\pi}{6}$ **124.** $-\frac{\pi}{2}$

136.

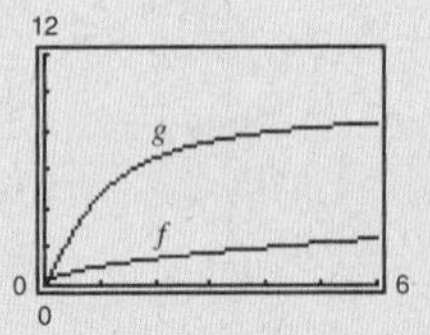

As x increases to infinity, g approaches 3π, but f has no maximum.
$a \approx 87.54$

137. (a) $f \circ f^{-1}$ $f^{-1} \circ f$

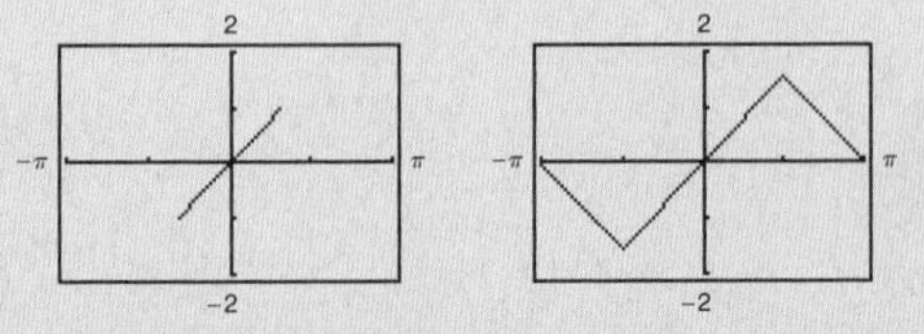

(b) The domains and ranges of the functions are restricted. The graphs of $f \circ f^{-1}$ and $f^{-1} \circ f$ differ because of the domains and ranges of f and f^{-1}.

4.8 Applications and Models

What you should learn

- Solve real-life problems involving right triangles.
- Solve real-life problems involving directional bearings.
- Solve real-life problems involving harmonic motion.

Why you should learn it

Right triangles often occur in real-life situations. For instance, in Exercise 65 on page 361, right triangles are used to determine the shortest grain elevator for a grain storage bin on a farm.

Applications Involving Right Triangles

In this section, the three angles of a right triangle are denoted by the letters A, B, and C (where C is the right angle), and the lengths of the sides opposite these angles by the letters a, b, and c (where c is the hypotenuse).

Example 1 Solving a Right Triangle

Solve the right triangle shown in Figure 4.78 for all unknown sides and angles.

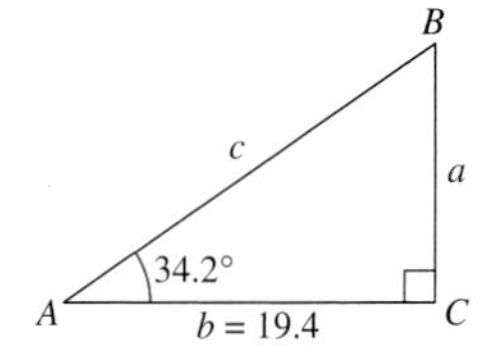

FIGURE 4.78

Solution

Because $C = 90°$, it follows that $A + B = 90°$ and $B = 90° - 34.2° = 55.8°$. To solve for a, use the fact that

$$\tan A = \frac{\text{opp}}{\text{adj}} = \frac{a}{b} \quad \Longrightarrow \quad a = b \tan A.$$

So, $a = 19.4 \tan 34.2° \approx 13.18$. Similarly, to solve for c, use the fact that

$$\cos A = \frac{\text{adj}}{\text{hyp}} = \frac{b}{c} \quad \Longrightarrow \quad c = \frac{b}{\cos A}.$$

So, $c = \dfrac{19.4}{\cos 34.2°} \approx 23.46.$

CHECKPoint Now try Exercise 5.

Example 2 Finding a Side of a Right Triangle

A safety regulation states that the maximum angle of elevation for a rescue ladder is 72°. A fire department's longest ladder is 110 feet. What is the maximum safe rescue height?

Solution

A sketch is shown in Figure 4.79. From the equation $\sin A = a/c$, it follows that

$$a = c \sin A = 110 \sin 72° \approx 104.6.$$

So, the maximum safe rescue height is about 104.6 feet above the height of the fire truck.

CHECKPoint Now try Exercise 19.

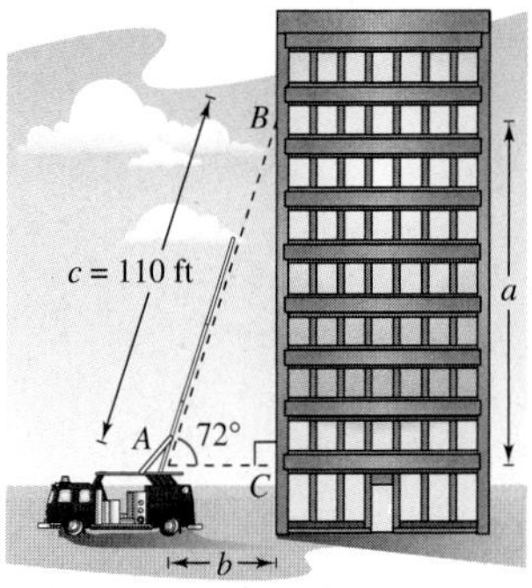

FIGURE 4.79

1 PLAN AND PREPARE

Warm-up Exercises

Transparency Available
Available at the Instructor's companion site.

Notetaking Guide

Transparency Available
Promotes interactive learning and notetaking skills. Available at the Instructor's companion site.

Animated Precalculus

An **Animated Precalculus** tutorial is available at the Student companion site for **Section 4.8.**

Pacing

Average: 2 days
Advanced: 2 days
Block: 0.5 block with 4.7
0.5 block with Review

2 FOCUS AND MOTIVATE

Essential Question

How do you use trigonometric functions to solve real-life problems? **Tell students that they will learn how to answer this question by studying real-life problems involving right triangles, directional bearings, and harmonic motion.**

Resource Planning Guide

Chapter Resources
- Complete Solutions Guide

Workbooks
- Notetaking Guide
- Student Solutions Guide

Interactive Technology
- Instructor Success Organizer
- Notetaking Guide IAE
- Instructional DVDs
- Animated Precalculus
- PowerLecture with ExamView

Example 3 Finding a Side of a Right Triangle

At a point 200 feet from the base of a building, the angle of elevation to the *bottom* of a smokestack is 35°, whereas the angle of elevation to the *top* is 53°, as shown in Figure 4.80. Find the height s of the smokestack alone.

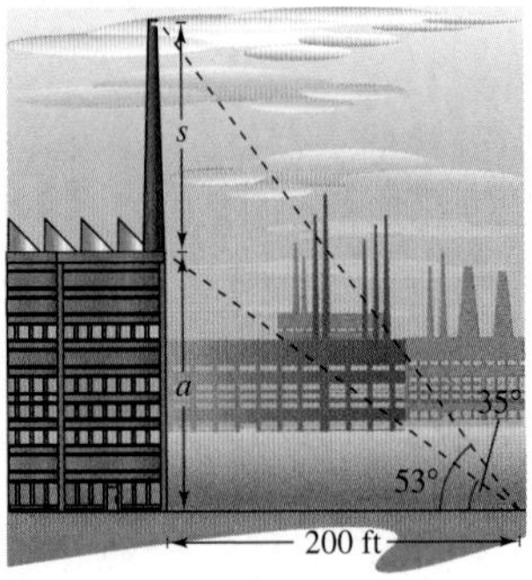

FIGURE 4.80

Solution

Note from Figure 4.80 that this problem involves two right triangles. For the smaller right triangle, use the fact that

$$\tan 35° = \frac{a}{200}$$

to conclude that the height of the building is

$$a = 200 \tan 35°.$$

For the larger right triangle, use the equation

$$\tan 53° = \frac{a + s}{200}$$

to conclude that $a + s = 200 \tan 53°$. So, the height of the smokestack is

$$\begin{aligned} s &= 200 \tan 53° - a \\ &= 200 \tan 53° - 200 \tan 35° \\ &\approx 125.4 \text{ feet.} \end{aligned}$$

CHECKPoint Now try Exercise 23.

Example 4 Finding an Acute Angle of a Right Triangle

A swimming pool is 20 meters long and 12 meters wide. The bottom of the pool is slanted so that the water depth is 1.3 meters at the shallow end and 4 meters at the deep end, as shown in Figure 4.81. Find the angle of depression of the bottom of the pool.

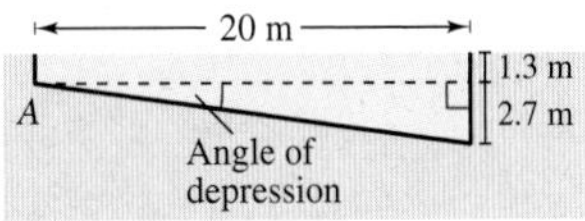

FIGURE 4.81

Solution

Using the tangent function, you can see that

$$\begin{aligned} \tan A &= \frac{\text{opp}}{\text{adj}} \\ &= \frac{2.7}{20} \\ &= 0.135. \end{aligned}$$

So, the angle of depression is

$$\begin{aligned} A &= \arctan 0.135 \\ &\approx 0.13419 \text{ radian} \\ &\approx 7.69°. \end{aligned}$$

CHECKPoint Now try Exercise 29.

3 TEACH

Extra Example 1

Solve the right triangle shown in the figure, where $A = 20°$ and $b = 15$. (Round to two decimal places.)

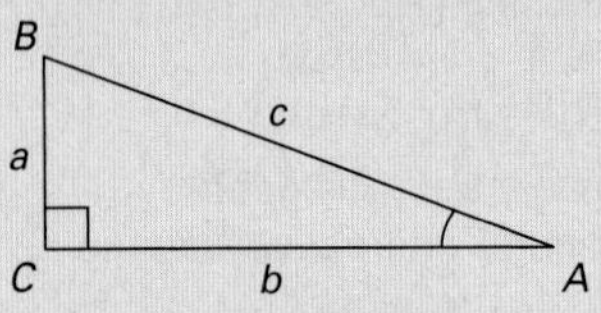

$a = 5.46$, $c = 15.95$, $B = 70°$

Extra Example 2

A ladder 16 feet long leans against the side of a house. Find the height h from the top of the ladder to the ground if the angle of elevation of the ladder is 74°.

15.4 feet

Extra Example 3

From a point 65 feet in front of a church, the angles of elevation to the base of the steeple and the top of the steeple are 35° and 43°, respectively. Find the height of the steeple.

15.1 feet

Extra Example 4

From the time a small airplane is 100 feet high and 1600 ground feet from its landing runway, the plane descends in a straight line to the runway. Determine the plane's angle of descent.

See below.

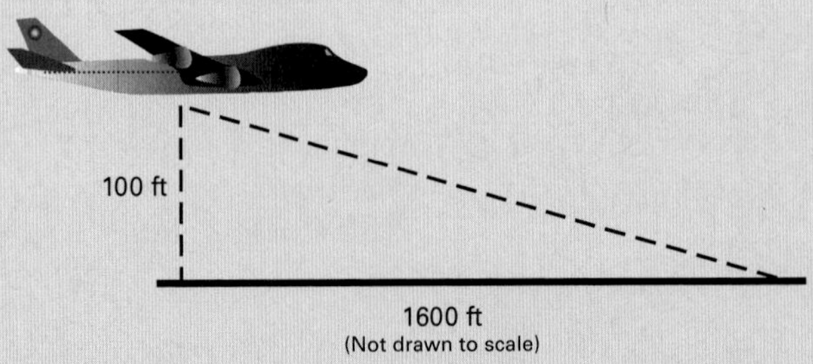

3.58°

Trigonometry and Bearings

In surveying and navigation, directions can be given in terms of **bearings.** A bearing measures the acute angle that a path or line of sight makes with a fixed north-south line, as shown in Figure 4.82. For instance, the bearing S 35° E in Figure 4.82 means 35 degrees east of south.

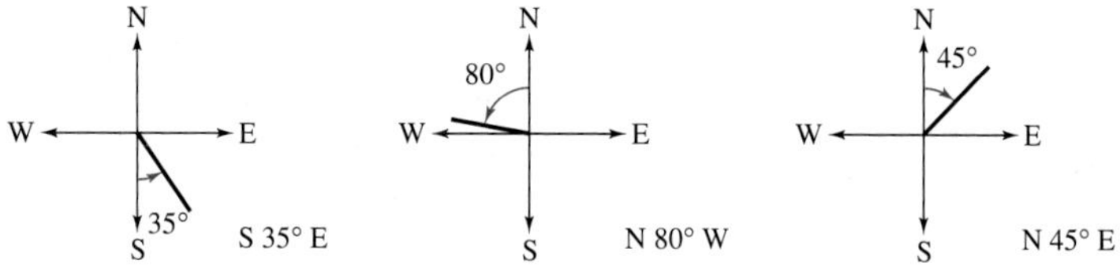

FIGURE 4.82

Example 5 Finding Directions in Terms of Bearings

A ship leaves port at noon and heads due west at 20 knots, or 20 nautical miles (nm) per hour. At 2 P.M. the ship changes course to N 54° W, as shown in Figure 4.83. Find the ship's bearing and distance from the port of departure at 3 P.M.

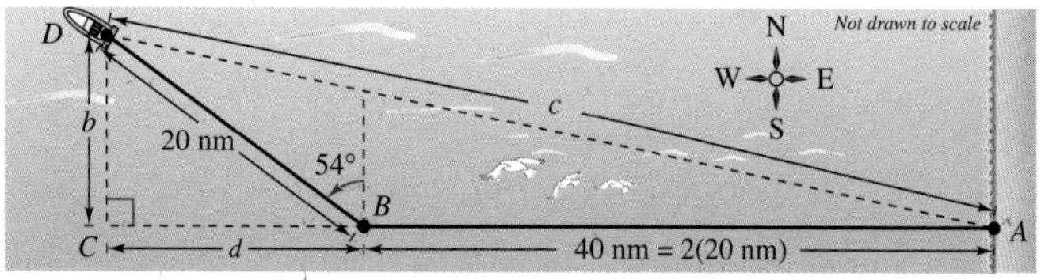

FIGURE 4.83

Solution

For triangle BCD, you have $B = 90° - 54° = 36°$. The two sides of this triangle can be determined to be

$$b = 20 \sin 36° \qquad \text{and} \qquad d = 20 \cos 36°.$$

For triangle ACD, you can find angle A as follows.

$$\tan A = \frac{b}{d + 40} = \frac{20 \sin 36°}{20 \cos 36° + 40} \approx 0.2092494$$

$$A \approx \arctan 0.2092494 \approx 11.82°$$

The angle with the north-south line is $90° - 11.82° = 78.18°$. So, the bearing of the ship is N 78.18° W. Finally, from triangle ACD, you have $\sin A = b/c$, which yields

$$c = \frac{b}{\sin A} = \frac{20 \sin 36°}{\sin 11.82°}$$

$$\approx 57.4 \text{ nautical miles.} \qquad \text{Distance from port}$$

CHECKPoint Now try Exercise 37.

Study Tip

In *air navigation*, bearings are measured in degrees *clockwise* from north. Examples of air navigation bearings are shown below.

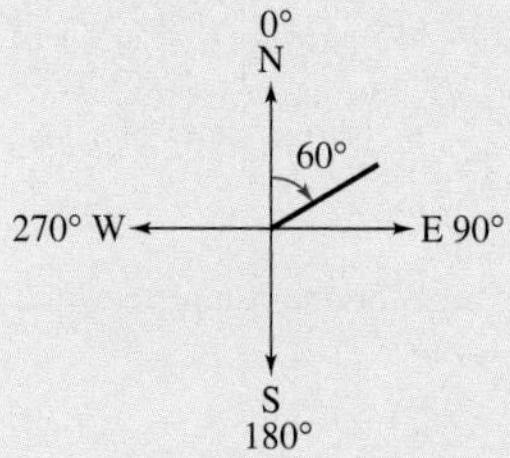

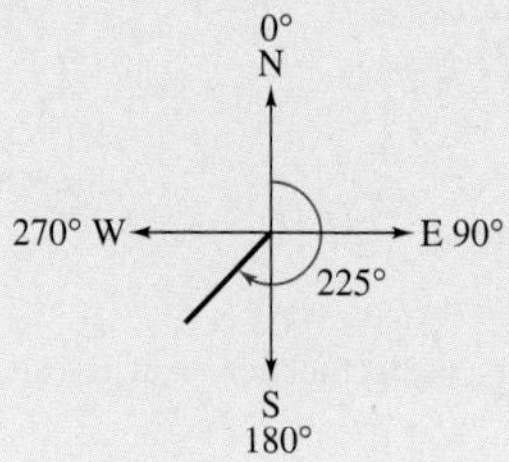

Extra Example 5

A sailboat leaves a pier and heads due west at 8 knots. After 15 minutes the sailboat tacks, changing course to N 16° W at 10 knots. Find the sailboat's bearing and distance from the pier after 12 minutes on this course.

See below.

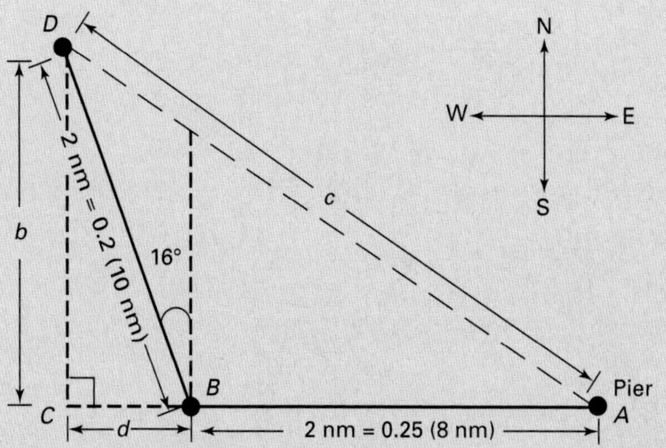

N 53.0° W, 3.2 nautical miles

Harmonic Motion

The periodic nature of the trigonometric functions is useful for describing the motion of a point on an object that vibrates, oscillates, rotates, or is moved by wave motion.

For example, consider a ball that is bobbing up and down on the end of a spring, as shown in Figure 4.84. Suppose that 10 centimeters is the maximum distance the ball moves vertically upward or downward from its equilibrium (at rest) position. Suppose further that the time it takes for the ball to move from its maximum displacement above zero to its maximum displacement below zero and back again is $t = 4$ seconds. Assuming the ideal conditions of perfect elasticity and no friction or air resistance, the ball would continue to move up and down in a uniform and regular manner.

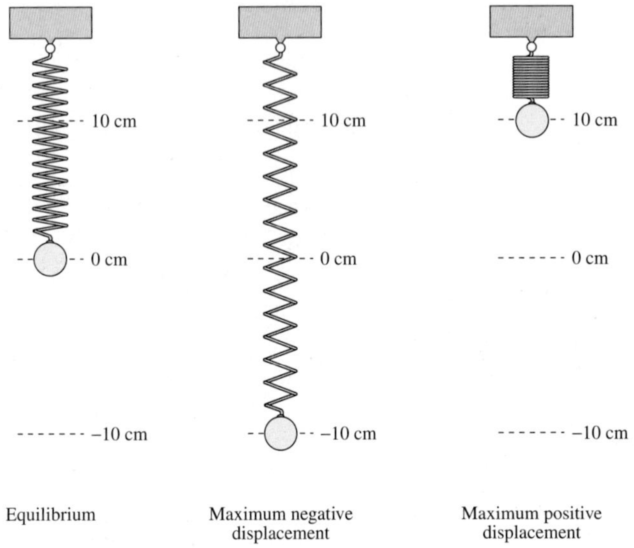

FIGURE 4.84

From this spring you can conclude that the period (time for one complete cycle) of the motion is

Period = 4 seconds

its amplitude (maximum displacement from equilibrium) is

Amplitude = 10 centimeters

and its **frequency** (number of cycles per second) is

$$\text{Frequency} = \frac{1}{4} \text{ cycle per second.}$$

Motion of this nature can be described by a sine or cosine function, and is called **simple harmonic motion.**

Definition of Simple Harmonic Motion

A point that moves on a coordinate line is said to be in **simple harmonic motion** if its distance d from the origin at time t is given by either

$$d = a \sin \omega t \qquad \text{or} \qquad d = a \cos \omega t$$

where a and ω are real numbers such that $\omega > 0$. The motion has amplitude $|a|$, period $\dfrac{2\pi}{\omega}$, and frequency $\dfrac{\omega}{2\pi}$.

Example 6 Simple Harmonic Motion

Write the equation for the simple harmonic motion of the ball described in Figure 4.84, where the period is 4 seconds. What is the frequency of this harmonic motion?

Solution

Because the spring is at equilibrium ($d = 0$) when $t = 0$, you use the equation

$$d = a \sin \omega t.$$

Moreover, because the maximum displacement from zero is 10 and the period is 4, you have

$$\text{Amplitude} = |a| = 10$$

$$\text{Period} = \frac{2\pi}{\omega} = 4 \quad \Longrightarrow \quad \omega = \frac{\pi}{2}.$$

Consequently, the equation of motion is

$$d = 10 \sin \frac{\pi}{2} t.$$

Note that the choice of $a = 10$ or $a = -10$ depends on whether the ball initially moves up or down. The frequency is

$$\text{Frequency} = \frac{\omega}{2\pi}$$

$$= \frac{\pi/2}{2\pi}$$

$$= \frac{1}{4} \text{ cycle per second.}$$

CHECKPoint Now try Exercise 53.

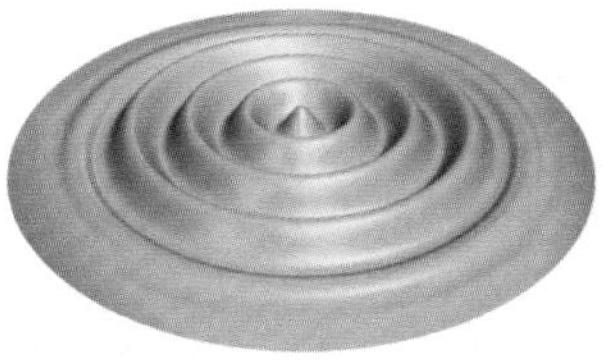

FIGURE 4.85

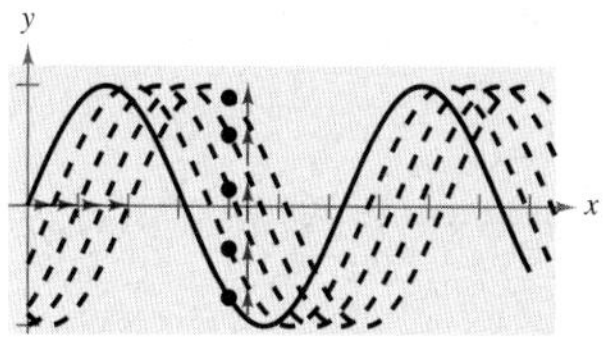

FIGURE 4.86

One illustration of the relationship between sine waves and harmonic motion can be seen in the wave motion resulting when a stone is dropped into a calm pool of water. The waves move outward in roughly the shape of sine (or cosine) waves, as shown in Figure 4.85. As an example, suppose you are fishing and your fishing bob is attached so that it does not move horizontally. As the waves move outward from the dropped stone, your fishing bob will move up and down in simple harmonic motion, as shown in Figure 4.86.

Extra Example 6

Find a model for simple harmonic motion that satisfies the specified conditions.

Displacement $t = 0$	0
Amplitude	4 cm
Period	6 sec

$d = 4 \sin \dfrac{\pi}{3} t$ or $d = -4 \sin \dfrac{\pi}{3} t$

What is the frequency of this harmonic motion?

$\dfrac{1}{6}$ cycle per second

Example 7 Simple Harmonic Motion

Given the equation for simple harmonic motion

$$d = 6\cos\frac{3\pi}{4}t$$

find (a) the maximum displacement, (b) the frequency, (c) the value of d when $t = 4$, and (d) the least positive value of t for which $d = 0$.

Algebraic Solution

The given equation has the form $d = a\cos\omega t$, with $a = 6$ and $\omega = 3\pi/4$.

a. The maximum displacement (from the point of equilibrium) is given by the amplitude. So, the maximum displacement is 6.

b.
$$\text{Frequency} = \frac{\omega}{2\pi} = \frac{3\pi/4}{2\pi} = \frac{3}{8} \text{ cycle per unit of time}$$

c.
$$d = 6\cos\left[\frac{3\pi}{4}(4)\right] = 6\cos 3\pi = 6(-1) = -6$$

d. To find the least positive value of t for which $d = 0$, solve the equation

$$d = 6\cos\frac{3\pi}{4}t = 0.$$

First divide each side by 6 to obtain

$$\cos\frac{3\pi}{4}t = 0.$$

This equation is satisfied when

$$\frac{3\pi}{4}t = \frac{\pi}{2}, \frac{3\pi}{2}, \frac{5\pi}{2}, \ldots.$$

Multiply these values by $4/(3\pi)$ to obtain

$$t = \frac{2}{3}, 2, \frac{10}{3}, \ldots.$$

So, the least positive value of t is $t = \frac{2}{3}$.

CHECKPoint Now try Exercise 57.

Graphical Solution

Use a graphing utility set in *radian* mode to graph

$$y = 6\cos\frac{3\pi}{4}x.$$

a. Use the *maximum* feature of the graphing utility to estimate that the maximum displacement from the point of equilibrium $y = 0$ is 6, as shown in Figure 4.87.

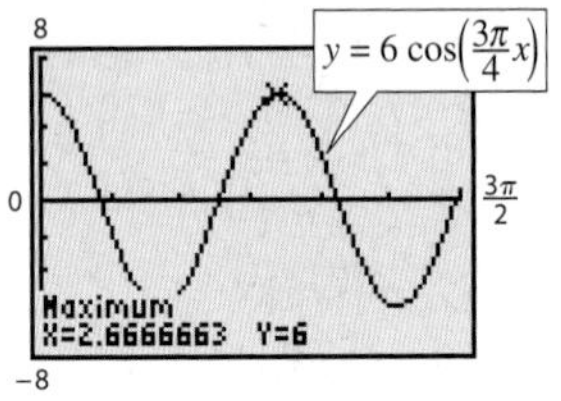

FIGURE 4.87

b. The period is the time for the graph to complete one cycle, which is $x \approx 2.667$. You can estimate the frequency as follows.

$$\text{Frequency} \approx \frac{1}{2.667} \approx 0.375 \text{ cycle per unit of time}$$

c. Use the *trace* or *value* feature to estimate that the value of y when $x = 4$ is $y = -6$, as shown in Figure 4.88.

d. Use the *zero* or *root* feature to estimate that the least positive value of x for which $y = 0$ is $x \approx 0.6667$, as shown in Figure 4.89.

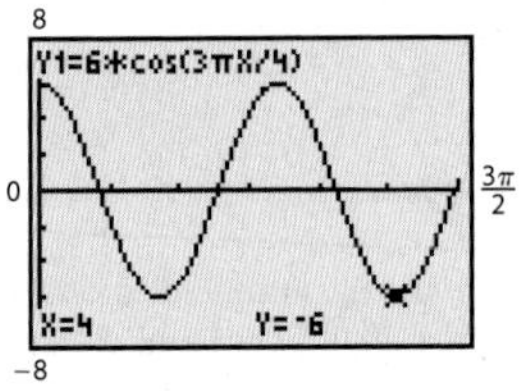

FIGURE 4.88

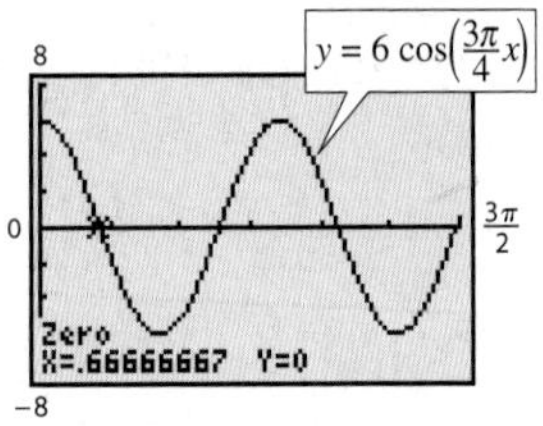

FIGURE 4.89

Extra Example 7

Given the equation for simple harmonic motion $d = 4\cos 6\pi t$,

a. Find the maximum displacement.
4

b. Find the frequency.
3 cycles per unit of time

c. Find the value of d when $t = 4$.
4

d. Find the least positive value of t for which $d = 0$.
$\frac{1}{12}$

Closing the Lesson

Have students summarize the major points of the lesson and answer the Essential Question: How do you use trigonometric functions to solve real-life problems?

- Solve real-life problems involving right triangles by using trigonometric ratios to find unknown sides and angles.
- Use trigonometric ratios and angles measured relative to the north-south line to solve problems involving navigation.
- Model and solve problems involving simple harmonic motion by relating characteristics of a harmonic motion experiment to the basic characteristics of sine and cosine functions.

4.8 EXERCISES

See www.CalcChat.com for worked-out solutions to odd-numbered exercises.

VOCABULARY: Fill in the blanks.

1. A bearing measures the acute angle a path or line of sight makes with a fixed north-south line.
2. A point that moves on a coordinate line is said to be in simple harmonic motion if its distance d from the origin at time t is given by either $d = a \sin \omega t$ or $d = a \cos \omega t$.
3. The time for one complete cycle of a point in simple harmonic motion is its period.
4. The number of cycles per second of a point in simple harmonic motion is its frequency

SKILLS AND APPLICATIONS

In Exercises 5–14, solve the right triangle shown in the figure for all unknown sides and angles. Round your answers to two decimal places. 5–14. See margin.

5. $A = 30°$, $b = 3$
6. $B = 54°$, $c = 15$
7. $B = 71°$, $b = 24$
8. $A = 8.4°$, $a = 40.5$
9. $a = 3$, $b = 4$
10. $a = 25$, $c = 35$
11. $b = 16$, $c = 52$
12. $b = 1.32$, $c = 9.45$
13. $A = 12°15'$, $c = 430.5$
14. $B = 65°12'$, $a = 14.2$

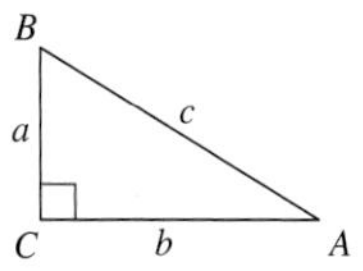

FIGURE FOR 5–14

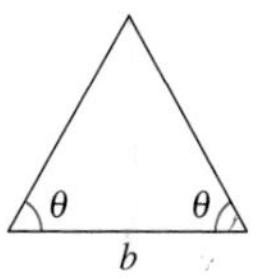

FIGURE FOR 15–18

In Exercises 15–18, find the altitude of the isosceles triangle shown in the figure. Round your answers to two decimal places.

15. $\theta = 45°$, $b = 6$ 3.00
16. $\theta = 18°$, $b = 10$ 1.62
17. $\theta = 32°$, $b = 8$ 2.50
18. $\theta = 27°$, $b = 11$ 2.80

19. **LENGTH** The sun is 25° above the horizon. Find the length of a shadow cast by a building that is 100 feet tall (see figure). 214.45 ft

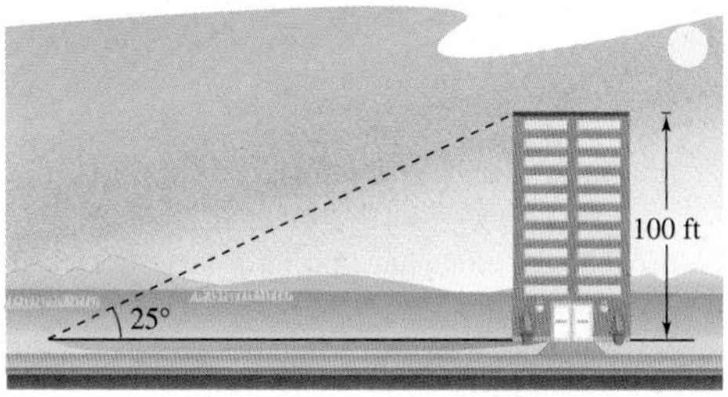

20. **LENGTH** The sun is 20° above the horizon. Find the length of a shadow cast by a park statue that is 12 feet tall. 32.97 ft

21. 19.7 ft

21. **HEIGHT** A ladder 20 feet long leans against the side of a house. Find the height from the top of the ladder to the ground if the angle of elevation of the ladder is 80°.
22. **HEIGHT** The length of a shadow of a tree is 125 feet when the angle of elevation of the sun is 33°. Approximate the height of the tree. 81.2 ft
23. **HEIGHT** From a point 50 feet in front of a church, the angles of elevation to the base of the steeple and the top of the steeple are 35° and 47° 40′, respectively. Find the height of the steeple. 19.9 ft
24. **DISTANCE** An observer in a lighthouse 350 feet above sea level observes two ships directly offshore. The angles of depression to the ships are 4° and 6.5° (see figure). How far apart are the ships? 1933.3 ft

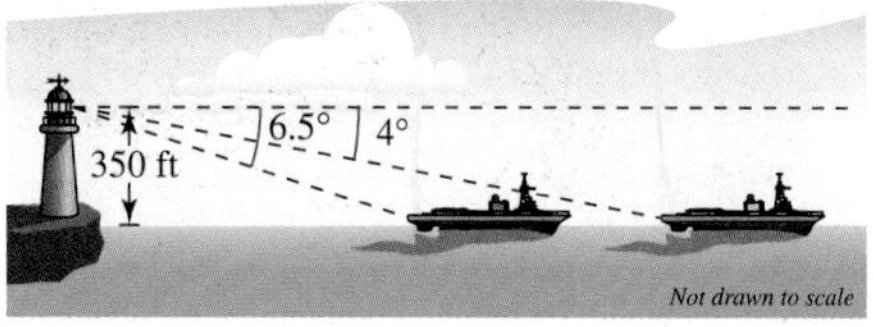

25. **DISTANCE** A passenger in an airplane at an altitude of 10 kilometers sees two towns directly to the east of the plane. The angles of depression to the towns are 28° and 55° (see figure). How far apart are the towns? 11.8 km

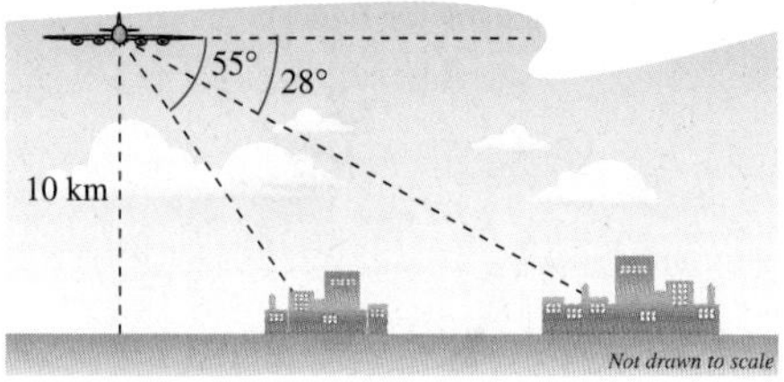

4 PRACTICE AND APPLY

Assignment Guide

Transparencies Available
Available at the Instructor's companion site.

Average:
Day 1: pp. 357–359
Exs. 5–17 odd, 19–21, 24, 26, 29, 30, 35, 36, 39–45 odd
Day 2: pp. 360–361
Exs. 47–51 odd, 55, 58, 59, 61–64, 68–70

Advanced:
Day 1: pp. 357–359
Exs. 8–18 even, 20–22, 25, 27, 30, 34, 36, 38, 40–42, 44, 46
Day 2: pp. 360–361
Exs. 48–52 even, 56, 59, 60–63, 65, 66, 68–70

Block:
pp. 357–359
Exs. 5–17 odd, 19–21, 24, 26, 29, 30, 35, 36, 39–45 odd (with 4.7)
pp. 360–361
Exs. 47–51 odd, 55, 58, 59, 61–64, 68–70 (with review)

5. $a \approx 1.73$, $c \approx 3.46$, $B = 60°$
6. $a \approx 8.82$, $b \approx 12.14$, $A = 36°$
7. $a \approx 8.26$, $c \approx 25.38$, $A = 19°$
8. $b \approx 274.27$, $c \approx 277.24$, $B = 81.6°$
9. $c = 5$, $A \approx 36.87°$, $B \approx 53.13°$
10. $b \approx 24.49$, $A \approx 45.58°$, $B \approx 44.42°$
11. $a \approx 49.48$, $A \approx 72.08°$, $B \approx 17.92°$
12. $a \approx 9.36$, $A \approx 81.97°$, $B \approx 8.03°$
13. $a \approx 91.34$, $b \approx 420.70$, $B = 77°45'$
14. $b \approx 30.73$, $c \approx 33.85$, $A = 24°48'$

26. About 3.23 mi or about 17,054 ft

28. (a)

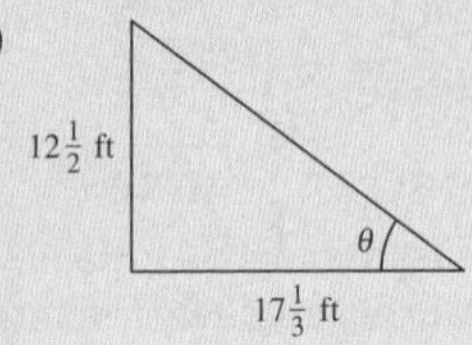

(b) $\tan\theta = \dfrac{12\frac{1}{2}}{17\frac{1}{3}}$

31. (a) $\sqrt{h^2 + 34h + 10,289}$

(b) $\theta = \arccos\left(\dfrac{100}{l}\right)$

32. (b) $\arctan\left(\dfrac{25.98}{d}\right)$

26. **ALTITUDE** You observe a plane approaching overhead and assume that its speed is 550 miles per hour. The angle of elevation of the plane is 16° at one time and 57° one minute later. Approximate the altitude of the plane. See margin.

27. **ANGLE OF ELEVATION** An engineer erects a 75-foot cellular telephone tower. Find the angle of elevation to the top of the tower at a point on level ground 50 feet from its base. 56.3°

28. **ANGLE OF ELEVATION** The height of an outdoor basketball backboard is $12\frac{1}{2}$ feet, and the backboard casts a shadow $17\frac{1}{3}$ feet long.

(a) Draw a right triangle that gives a visual representation of the problem. Label the known and unknown quantities. See margin.

(b) Use a trigonometric function to write an equation involving the unknown quantity. See margin.

(c) Find the angle of elevation of the sun. 35.8°

29. **ANGLE OF DEPRESSION** A cellular telephone tower that is 150 feet tall is placed on top of a mountain that is 1200 feet above sea level. What is the angle of depression from the top of the tower to a cell phone user who is 5 horizontal miles away and 400 feet above sea level? 2.06°

30. **ANGLE OF DEPRESSION** A Global Positioning System satellite orbits 12,500 miles above Earth's surface (see figure). Find the angle of depression from the satellite to the horizon. Assume the radius of Earth is 4000 miles. 75.97°

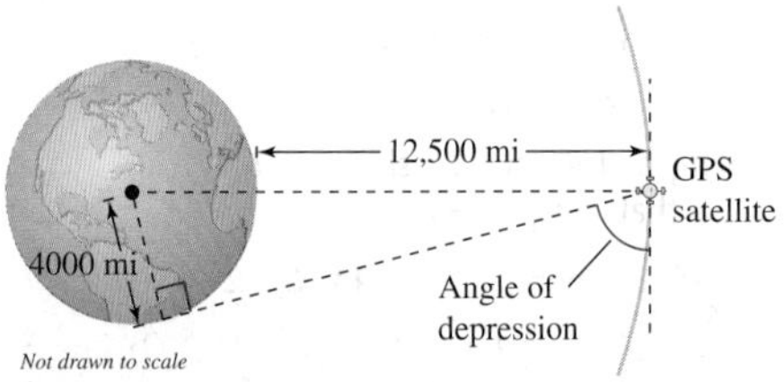

31. **HEIGHT** You are holding one of the tethers attached to the top of a giant character balloon in a parade. Before the start of the parade the balloon is upright and the bottom is floating approximately 20 feet above ground level. You are standing approximately 100 feet ahead of the balloon (see figure).

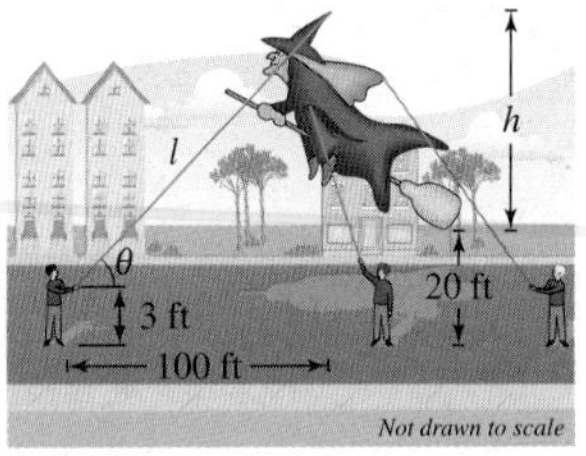

(a) Find the length l of the tether you are holding in terms of h, the height of the balloon from top to bottom. See margin.

(b) Find an expression for the angle of elevation θ from you to the top of the balloon. See margin.

(c) Find the height h of the balloon if the angle of elevation to the top of the balloon is 35°. 53.02 ft

32. **HEIGHT** The designers of a water park are creating a new slide and have sketched some preliminary drawings. The length of the ladder is 30 feet, and its angle of elevation is 60° (see figure).

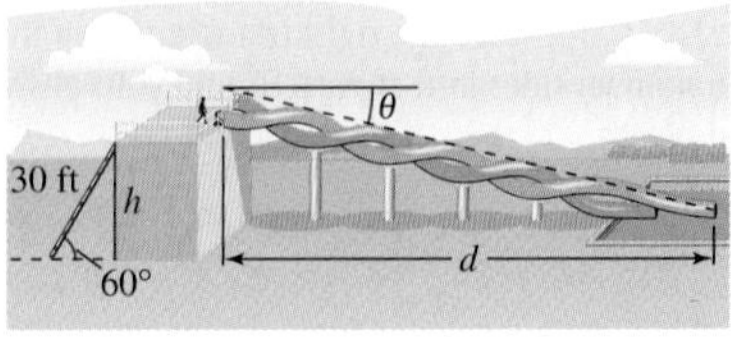

(a) Find the height h of the slide. About 25.98 ft

(b) Find the angle of depression θ from the top of the slide to the end of the slide at the ground in terms of the horizontal distance d the rider travels. See margin.

(c) The angle of depression of the ride is bounded by safety restrictions to be no less than 25° and not more than 30°. Find an interval for how far the rider travels horizontally. $45.0 \text{ ft} \le d \le 55.7 \text{ ft}$

33. **SPEED ENFORCEMENT** A police department has set up a speed enforcement zone on a straight length of highway. A patrol car is parked parallel to the zone, 200 feet from one end and 150 feet from the other end (see figure).

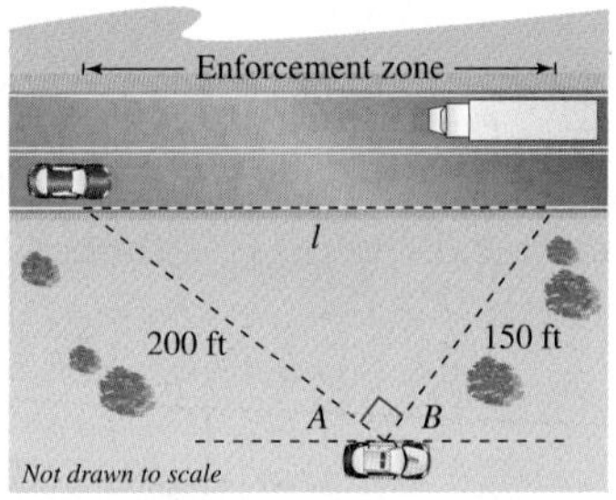

(a) Find the length l of the zone and the measures of the angles A and B (in degrees).

(b) Find the minimum amount of time (in seconds) it takes for a vehicle to pass through the zone without exceeding the posted speed limit of 35 miles per hour.

(a) $l = 250$ ft, $A \approx 36.87°$, $B \approx 53.13°$

(b) 4.87 sec

34. AIRPLANE ASCENT During takeoff, an airplane's angle of ascent is 18° and its speed is 275 feet per second.

(a) Find the plane's altitude after 1 minute. 5099 ft

(b) How long will it take the plane to climb to an altitude of 10,000 feet? 117.7 sec

35. NAVIGATION An airplane flying at 600 miles per hour has a bearing of 52°. After flying for 1.5 hours, how far north and how far east will the plane have traveled from its point of departure? See margin.

36. NAVIGATION A jet leaves Reno, Nevada and is headed toward Miami, Florida at a bearing of 100°. The distance between the two cities is approximately 2472 miles.

(a) How far north and how far west is Reno relative to Miami? 429.26 mi north; 2434.44 mi east

(b) If the jet is to return directly to Reno from Miami, at what bearing should it travel? 280°

37. NAVIGATION A ship leaves port at noon and has a bearing of S 29° W. The ship sails at 20 knots. See margin.

(a) How many nautical miles south and how many nautical miles west will the ship have traveled by 6:00 P.M.?

(b) At 6:00 P.M., the ship changes course to due west. Find the ship's bearing and distance from the port of departure at 7:00 P.M.

38. NAVIGATION A privately owned yacht leaves a dock in Myrtle Beach, South Carolina and heads toward Freeport in the Bahamas at a bearing of S 1.4° E. The yacht averages a speed of 20 knots over the 428 nautical-mile trip. See margin.

(a) How long will it take the yacht to make the trip?

(b) How far east and south is the yacht after 12 hours?

(c) If a plane leaves Myrtle Beach to fly to Freeport, what bearing should be taken?

39. NAVIGATION A ship is 45 miles east and 30 miles south of port. The captain wants to sail directly to port. What bearing should be taken? N 56.31° W

40. NAVIGATION An airplane is 160 miles north and 85 miles east of an airport. The pilot wants to fly directly to the airport. What bearing should be taken? 208°

41. SURVEYING A surveyor wants to find the distance across a swamp (see figure). The bearing from A to B is N 32° W. The surveyor walks 50 meters from A, and at the point C the bearing to B is N 68° W. Find (a) the bearing from A to C and (b) the distance from A to B.

(a) N 58° E (b) 68.82 m

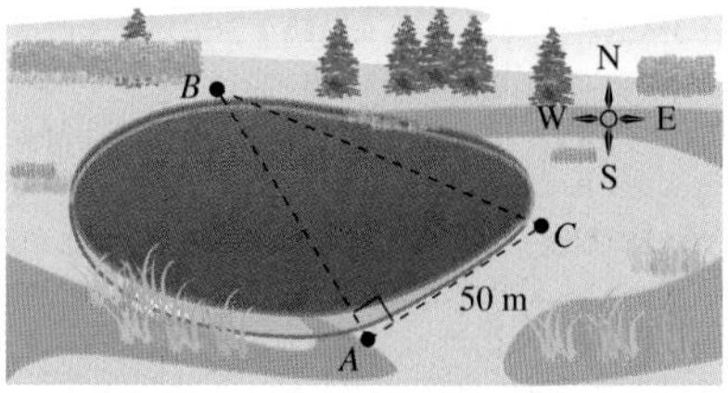

FIGURE FOR 41

42. LOCATION OF A FIRE Two fire towers are 30 kilometers apart, where tower A is due west of tower B. A fire is spotted from the towers, and the bearings from A and B are N 76° E and N 56° W, respectively (see figure). Find the distance d of the fire from the line segment AB. $d \approx 5.46$ km

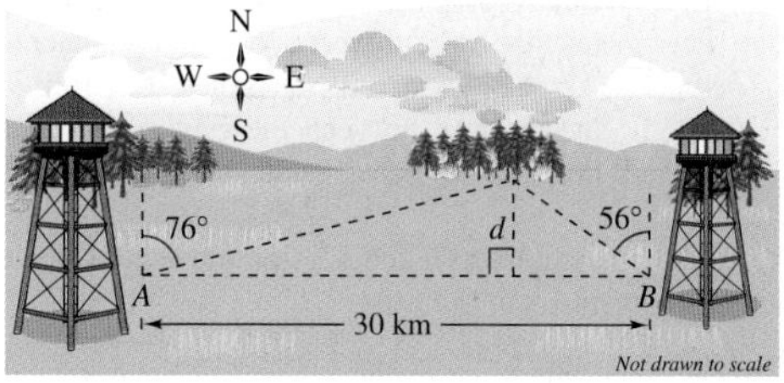

GEOMETRY In Exercises 43 and 44, find the angle α between two nonvertical lines L_1 and L_2. The angle α satisfies the equation

$$\tan \alpha = \left| \frac{m_2 - m_1}{1 + m_2 m_1} \right|$$

where m_1 and m_2 are the slopes of L_1 and L_2, respectively. (Assume that $m_1 m_2 \neq -1$.)

43. L_1: $3x - 2y = 5$ 78.7°
L_2: $x + y = 1$

44. L_1: $2x - y = 8$ 52.1°
L_2: $x - 5y = -4$

45. GEOMETRY Determine the angle between the diagonal of a cube and the diagonal of its base, as shown in the figure. 35.3°

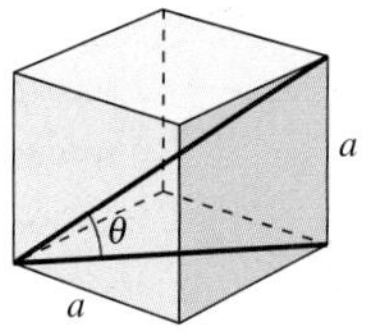

FIGURE FOR 45

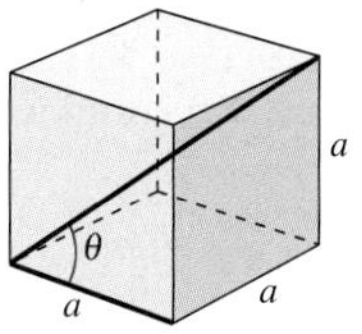

FIGURE FOR 46

46. GEOMETRY Determine the angle between the diagonal of a cube and its edge, as shown in the figure. 54.7°

35. 554 mi north; 709 mi east

37. (a) 104.95 nautical mi south; 58.18 nautical mi west

(b) S 36.7° W; distance = 130.9 nautical mi

38. (a) 21.4 h

(b) 5.86 nautical mi east; 239.93 nautical mi south

(c) 178.6°

53. $d = 4\sin(\pi t)$

54. $d = 3\sin\left(\dfrac{\pi t}{3}\right)$

55. $d = 3\cos\left(\dfrac{4\pi t}{3}\right)$

56. $d = 2\cos\left(\dfrac{\pi t}{5}\right)$

57. (a) 9 (b) $\frac{3}{5}$
(c) 9 (d) $\frac{5}{12}$

58. (a) $\frac{1}{2}$ (b) 10
(c) $\frac{1}{2}$ (d) $\frac{1}{40}$

59. (a) $\frac{1}{4}$ (b) 3
(c) 0 (d) $\frac{1}{6}$

60. (a) $\frac{1}{64}$ (b) 396
(c) 0 (d) $\frac{1}{792}$

61. $\omega = 528\pi$

62. $d = \dfrac{7}{4}\cos\dfrac{\pi t}{5}$

63. (a)

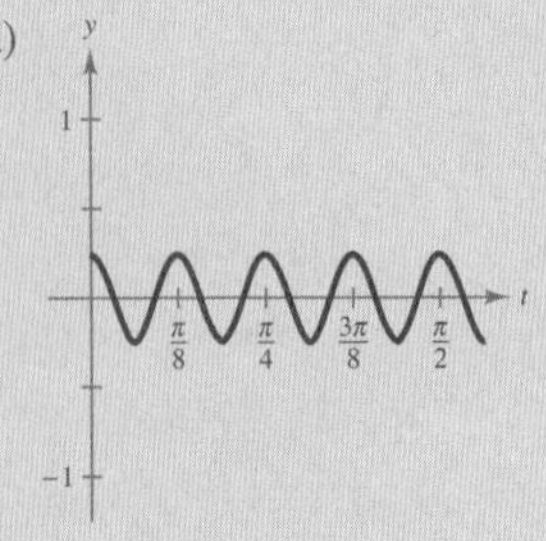

(b) $\dfrac{\pi}{8}$ (c) $\dfrac{\pi}{32}$

64. (a) See table below.
(b) See table below.
83.14 ft²
(c) $A = 64(1 + \cos\theta)(\sin\theta)$
(d)

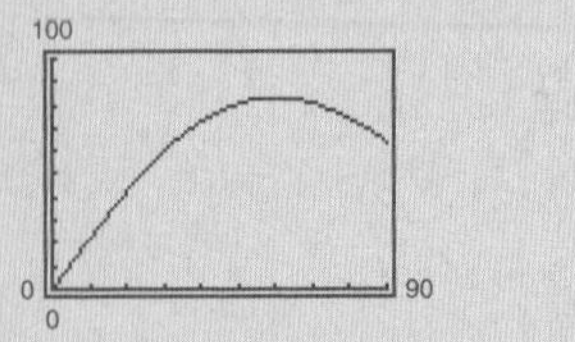

About 83.1 ft² when $\theta = 60°$
The answers are the same.

47. GEOMETRY Find the length of the sides of a regular pentagon inscribed in a circle of radius 25 inches. 29.4 in.

48. GEOMETRY Find the length of the sides of a regular hexagon inscribed in a circle of radius 25 inches. 25 in.

49. HARDWARE Write the distance y across the flat sides of a hexagonal nut as a function of r (see figure).
$y = \sqrt{3}r$

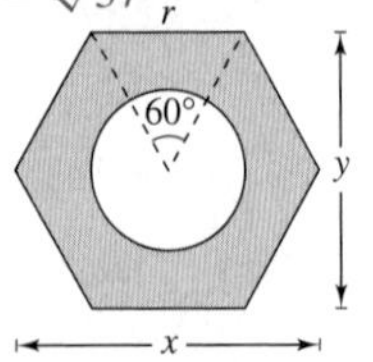

FIGURE FOR 49

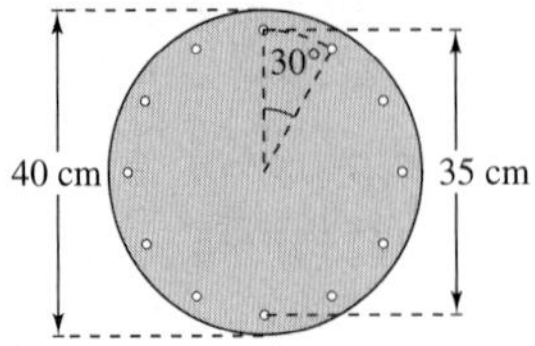

FIGURE FOR 50

50. BOLT HOLES The figure shows a circular piece of sheet metal that has a diameter of 40 centimeters and contains 12 equally-spaced bolt holes. Determine the straight-line distance between the centers of consecutive bolt holes. 9.06 cm

TRUSSES In Exercises 51 and 52, find the lengths of all the unknown members of the truss.

51. $a \approx 12.2,\ b \approx 7$

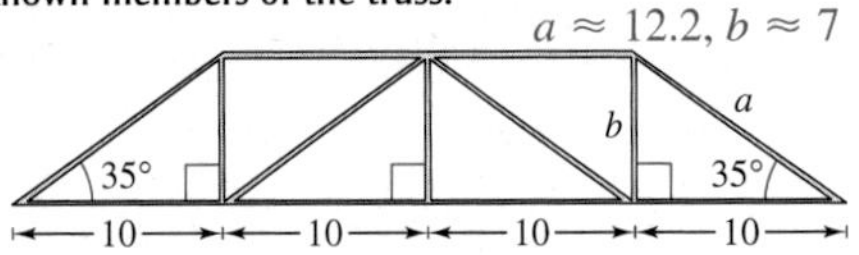

52.

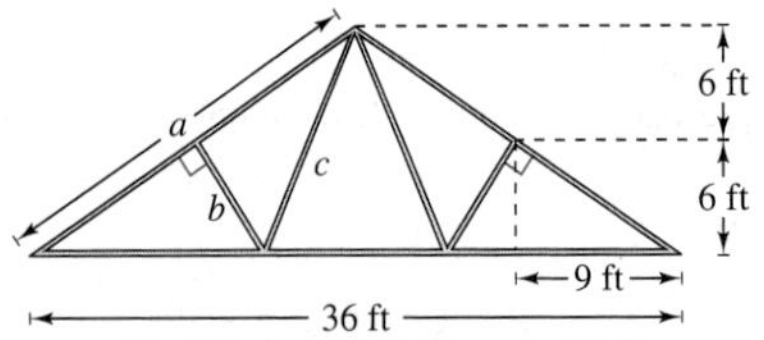

$a \approx 21.6$ ft, $b \approx 7.2$ ft, $c \approx 13$ ft

HARMONIC MOTION In Exercises 53–56, find a model for simple harmonic motion satisfying the specified conditions. 53–56. See margin.

	Displacement ($t = 0$)	Amplitude	Period
53.	0	4 centimeters	2 seconds
54.	0	3 meters	6 seconds
55.	3 inches	3 inches	1.5 seconds
56.	2 feet	2 feet	10 seconds

HARMONIC MOTION In Exercises 57–60, for the simple harmonic motion described by the trigonometric function, find (a) the maximum displacement, (b) the frequency, (c) the value of d when $t = 5$, and (d) the least positive value of t for which $d = 0$. Use a graphing utility to verify your results. 57–60. See margin.

57. $d = 9\cos\dfrac{6\pi}{5}t$ **58.** $d = \dfrac{1}{2}\cos 20\pi t$

59. $d = \dfrac{1}{4}\sin 6\pi t$ **60.** $d = \dfrac{1}{64}\sin 792\pi t$

61. See margin.

61. TUNING FORK A point on the end of a tuning fork moves in simple harmonic motion described by $d = a\sin\omega t$. Find ω given that the tuning fork for middle C has a frequency of 264 vibrations per second.

62. WAVE MOTION A buoy oscillates in simple harmonic motion as waves go past. It is noted that the buoy moves a total of 3.5 feet from its low point to its high point (see figure), and that it returns to its high point every 10 seconds. Write an equation that describes the motion of the buoy if its high point is at $t = 0$. See margin.

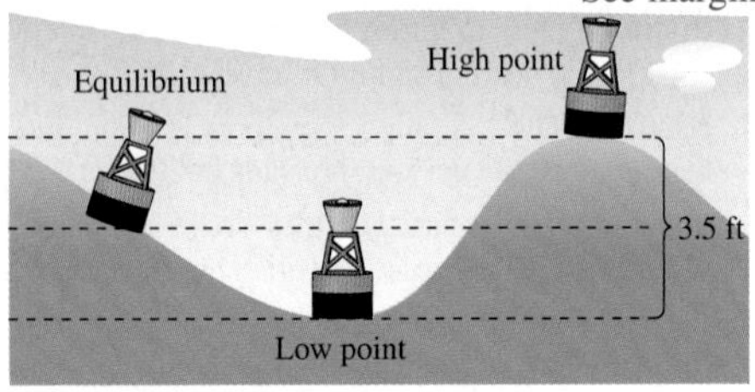

63. OSCILLATION OF A SPRING A ball that is bobbing up and down on the end of a spring has a maximum displacement of 3 inches. Its motion (in ideal conditions) is modeled by $y = \frac{1}{4}\cos 16t\ (t > 0)$, where y is measured in feet and t is the time in seconds. See margin.

(a) Graph the function.

(b) What is the period of the oscillations?

(c) Determine the first time the weight passes the point of equilibrium ($y = 0$).

64. NUMERICAL AND GRAPHICAL ANALYSIS The cross section of an irrigation canal is an isosceles trapezoid of which 3 of the sides are 8 feet long (see figure). The objective is to find the angle θ that maximizes the area of the cross section. [*Hint:* The area of a trapezoid is $(h/2)(b_1 + b_2)$.]

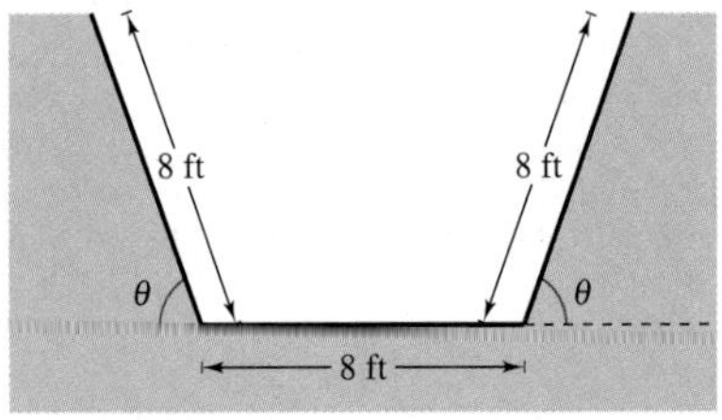

64. (a)

Base 1	Base 2	Altitude	Area
8	8 + 16 cos 30°	8 sin 30°	59.7
8	8 + 16 cos 40°	8 sin 40°	72.7
8	8 + 16 cos 50°	8 sin 50°	80.5
8	8 + 16 cos 60°	8 sin 60°	83.1
8	8 + 16 cos 70°	8 sin 70°	80.7
8	8 + 16 cos 80°	8 sin 80°	74.0
8	8 + 16 cos 90°	8 sin 90°	64.0

(b)

Base 1	Base 2	Altitude	Area
8	8 + 16 cos 56°	8 sin 56°	82.73
8	8 + 16 cos 57°	8 sin 57°	82.91
8	8 + 16 cos 58°	8 sin 58°	83.04
8	8 + 16 cos 59°	8 sin 59°	83.11
8	8 + 16 cos 60°	8 sin 60°	83.14
8	8 + 16 cos 61°	8 sin 61°	83.11
8	8 + 16 cos 62°	8 sin 62°	83.04

See page 360.

(a) Complete seven additional rows of the table.

Base 1	Base 2	Altitude	Area
8	$8 + 16 \cos 10°$	$8 \sin 10°$	22.1
8	$8 + 16 \cos 20°$	$8 \sin 20°$	42.5

(b) Use a graphing utility to generate additional rows of the table. Use the table to estimate the maximum cross-sectional area.

(c) Write the area A as a function of θ.

(d) Use a graphing utility to graph the function. Use the graph to estimate the maximum cross-sectional area. How does your estimate compare with that of part (b)?

65. NUMERICAL AND GRAPHICAL ANALYSIS A 2-meter-high fence is 3 meters from the side of a grain storage bin. A grain elevator must reach from ground level outside the fence to the storage bin (see figure). The objective is to determine the shortest elevator that meets the constraints. See margin.

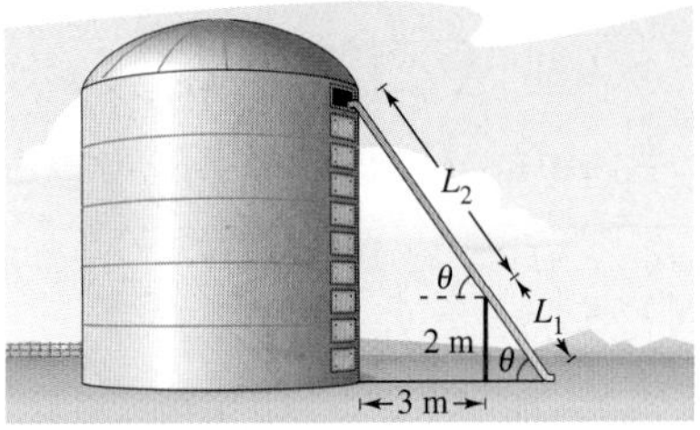

(a) Complete four rows of the table.

θ	L_1	L_2	$L_1 + L_2$
0.1	$\frac{2}{\sin 0.1}$	$\frac{3}{\cos 0.1}$	23.0
0.2	$\frac{2}{\sin 0.2}$	$\frac{3}{\cos 0.2}$	13.1

(b) Use a graphing utility to generate additional rows of the table. Use the table to estimate the minimum length of the elevator.

(c) Write the length $L_1 + L_2$ as a function of θ.

(d) Use a graphing utility to graph the function. Use the graph to estimate the minimum length. How does your estimate compare with that of part (b)?

66. DATA ANALYSIS The table shows the average sales S (in millions of dollars) of an outerwear manufacturer for each month t, where $t = 1$ represents January.

Time, t	1	2	3	4	5	6
Sales, S	13.46	11.15	8.00	4.85	2.54	1.70

Time, t	7	8	9	10	11	12
Sales, S	2.54	4.85	8.00	11.15	13.46	14.30

See margin.

(a) Create a scatter plot of the data.

(b) Find a trigonometric model that fits the data. Graph the model with your scatter plot. How well does the model fit the data?

(c) What is the period of the model? Do you think it is reasonable given the context? Explain your reasoning.

(d) Interpret the meaning of the model's amplitude in the context of the problem.

67. DATA ANALYSIS The number of hours H of daylight in Denver, Colorado on the 15th of each month are: 1(9.67), 2(10.72), 3(11.92), 4(13.25), 5(14.37), 6(14.97), 7(14.72), 8(13.77), 9(12.48), 10(11.18), 11(10.00), 12(9.38). The month is represented by t, with $t = 1$ corresponding to January. A model for the data is given by

$$H(t) = 12.13 + 2.77 \sin[(\pi t/6) - 1.60].$$ See margin.

(a) Use a graphing utility to graph the data points and the model in the same viewing window.

(b) What is the period of the model? Is it what you expected? Explain.

(c) What is the amplitude of the model? What does it represent in the context of the problem? Explain.

EXPLORATION

68. CAPSTONE While walking across flat land, you notice a wind turbine tower of height h feet directly in front of you. The angle of elevation to the top of the tower is A degrees. After you walk d feet closer to the tower, the angle of elevation increases to B degrees.

(a) Draw a diagram to represent the situation.

(b) Write an expression for the height h of the tower in terms of the angles A and B and the distance d.

See margin.

TRUE OR FALSE? In Exercises 69 and 70, determine whether the statement is true or false. Justify your answer.

69. The Leaning Tower of Pisa is not vertical, but if you know the angle of elevation θ to the top of the tower when you stand d feet away from it, you can find its height h using the formula $h = d \tan \theta$. See margin.

70. N 24° E means 24 degrees north of east.

False. N 24° E means 24 degrees east of north.

65(a)–(b). See Additional Answers beginning on page AA1.

5 ASSESS AND RETEACH

Daily Homework Quiz

Transparency Available
Available at the Instructor's companion site.

65. (c) $L = L_1 + L_2 = \frac{2}{\sin \theta} + \frac{3}{\cos \theta}$

(d)

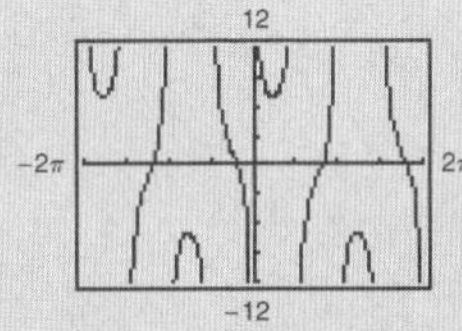

7.0 m; The answers are the same.

66. (a)

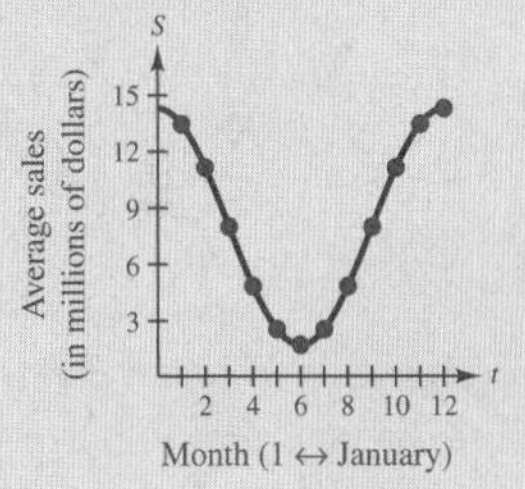

(b) $S = 8 + 6.3 \cos\left(\frac{\pi}{6}t\right)$ or

$S = 8 + 6.3 \sin\left(\frac{\pi}{6}t + \frac{\pi}{2}\right)$

The model is a good fit.

(c) 12. Yes, sales of outerwear are seasonal.

(d) Maximum displacement from average sales of $8 million

67. (a)

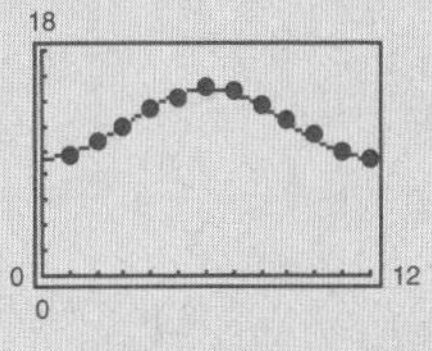

(b) 12; Yes, there are 12 months in a year.

(c) 2.77; The maximum change in the number of hours of daylight

68. (a)

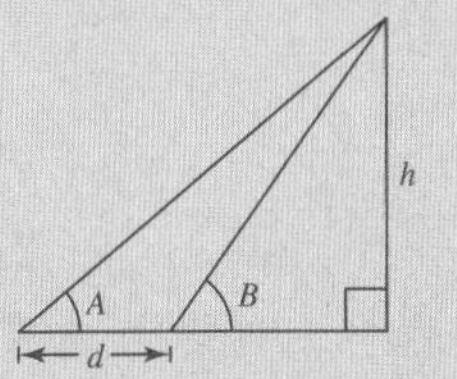

(b) $h = \frac{d \tan A \tan B}{\tan B - \tan A}$

69. False. The scenario does not create a right triangle because the tower is not vertical.

4 Chapter Summary

	What Did You Learn?	Explanation/Examples	Review Exercises
Section 4.1	Describe angles *(p. 280)*.	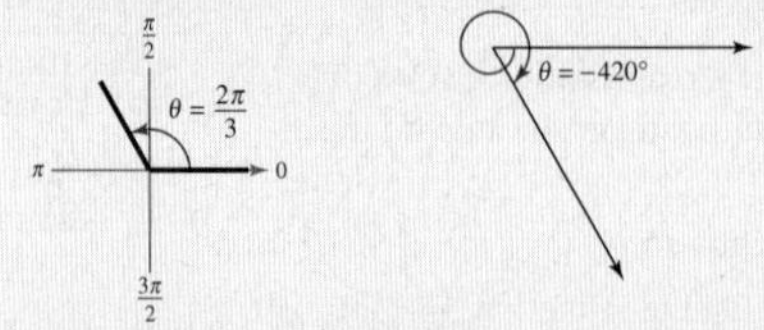	1–8
	Convert between degrees and radians *(p. 284)*.	To convert degrees to radians, multiply degrees by $(\pi \text{ rad})/180°$. To convert radians to degrees, multiply radians by $180°/(\pi \text{ rad})$.	9–20
	Use angles to model and solve real-life problems *(p. 285)*.	Angles can be used to find the length of a circular arc and the area of a sector of a circle. (See Examples 5 and 8.)	21–24
Section 4.2	Identify a unit circle and describe its relationship to real numbers *(p. 292)*.	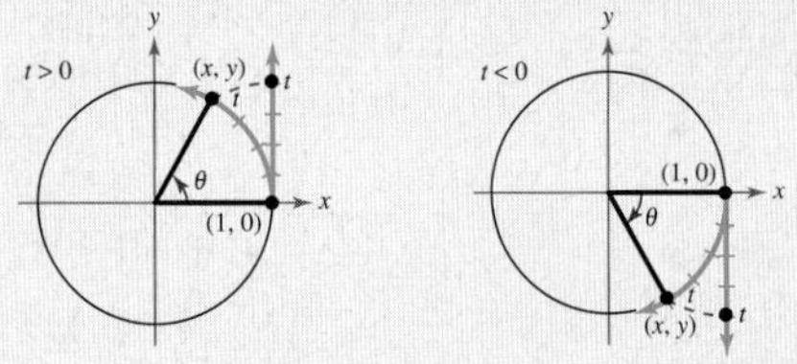	25–28
	Evaluate trigonometric functions using the unit circle *(p. 293)*.	$t = \frac{2\pi}{3}$ corresponds to $(x, y) = \left(-\frac{1}{2}, \frac{\sqrt{3}}{2}\right)$. So $\cos\frac{2\pi}{3} = -\frac{1}{2}$, $\sin\frac{2\pi}{3} = \frac{\sqrt{3}}{2}$, and $\tan\frac{2\pi}{3} = -\sqrt{3}$.	29–32
	Use domain and period to evaluate sine and cosine functions *(p. 295)*.	Because $\frac{9\pi}{4} = 2\pi + \frac{\pi}{4}$, $\sin\frac{9\pi}{4} = \sin\frac{\pi}{4} = \frac{\sqrt{2}}{2}$.	33–36
	Use a calculator to evaluate trigonometric functions *(p. 296)*.	$\sin\frac{3\pi}{8} \approx 0.9239$, $\cot(-1.2) \approx -0.3888$	37–40
Section 4.3	Evaluate trigonometric functions of acute angles *(p. 299)*.	$\sin\theta = \frac{\text{opp}}{\text{hyp}}$, $\cos\theta = \frac{\text{adj}}{\text{hyp}}$, $\tan\theta = \frac{\text{opp}}{\text{adj}}$ $\csc\theta = \frac{\text{hyp}}{\text{opp}}$, $\sec\theta = \frac{\text{hyp}}{\text{adj}}$, $\cot\theta = \frac{\text{adj}}{\text{opp}}$	41, 42
	Use fundamental trigonometric identities *(p. 302)*.	$\sin\theta = \frac{1}{\csc\theta}$, $\tan\theta = \frac{\sin\theta}{\cos\theta}$, $\sin^2\theta + \cos^2\theta = 1$	43–46
	Use a calculator to evaluate trigonometric functions *(p. 303)*.	$\tan 34.7° \approx 0.6924$, $\csc 29° 15' \approx 2.0466$	47–54
	Use trigonometric functions to model and solve real-life problems *(p. 304)*.	Trigonometric functions can be used to find the height of a monument, the angle between two paths, and the length of a ramp. (See Examples 7–9.)	55, 56

	What Did You Learn?	Explanation/Examples	Review Exercises
Section 4.4	Evaluate trigonometric functions of any angle *(p. 310)*.	Let (3, 4) be a point on the terminal side of θ. Then $\sin\theta = \frac{4}{5}$, $\cos\theta = \frac{3}{5}$, and $\tan\theta = \frac{4}{3}$.	57–70
	Find reference angles *(p. 312)*.	Let θ be an angle in standard position. Its reference angle is the acute angle θ' formed by the terminal side of θ and the horizontal axis.	71–74
	Evaluate trigonometric functions of real numbers *(p. 313)*.	$\cos\frac{7\pi}{3} = \frac{1}{2}$ because $\theta' = \frac{7\pi}{3} - 2\pi = \frac{\pi}{3}$. So, $\cos\frac{7\pi}{3} = \cos\frac{\pi}{3} = \frac{1}{2}$.	75–84
Section 4.5	Sketch the graphs of sine and cosine functions using amplitude and period *(p. 319)*.	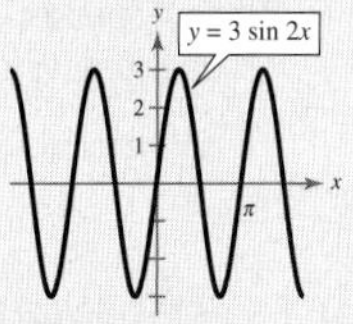 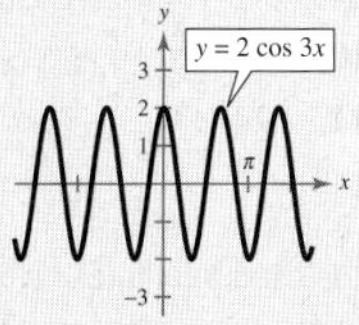	85–88
	Sketch translations of the graphs of sine and cosine functions *(p. 323)*.	For $y = d + a\sin(bx - c)$ and $y = d + a\cos(bx - c)$, the constant c creates a horizontal translation. The constant d creates a vertical translation. (See Examples 4–6.)	89–92
	Use sine and cosine functions to model real-life data *(p. 325)*.	A cosine function can be used to model the depth of the water at the end of a dock at various times. (See Example 7.)	93, 94
Section 4.6	Sketch the graphs of tangent *(p. 330)*, cotangent *(p. 332)*, secant *(p. 333)*, and cosecant *(p. 333)*, functions.	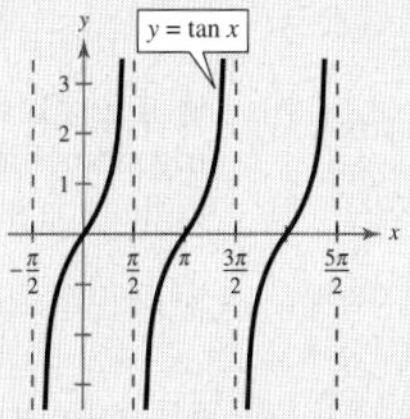 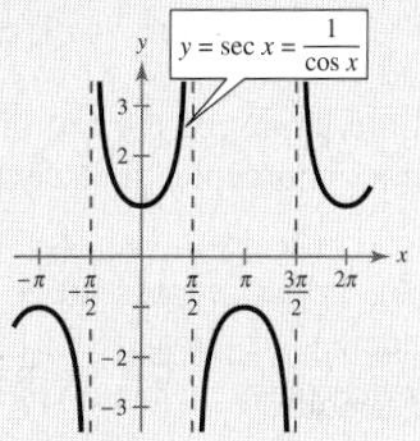	95–102
	Sketch the graphs of damped trigonometric functions *(p. 335)*.	For $f(x) = x\cos 2x$ and $g(x) = \log x \sin 4x$, the factors x and $\log x$ are called damping factors.	103, 104
Section 4.7	Evaluate and graph inverse trigonometric functions *(p. 341)*.	$\sin^{-1}\frac{1}{2} = \frac{\pi}{6}$, $\cos^{-1}\left(-\frac{\sqrt{2}}{2}\right) = \frac{3\pi}{4}$, $\tan^{-1}\sqrt{3} = \frac{\pi}{3}$	105–122, 131–138
	Evaluate and graph the compositions of trigonometric functions *(p. 345)*.	$\cos[\arctan(5/12)] = 12/13$, $\sin(\sin^{-1} 0.4) = 0.4$	123–130
Section 4.8	Solve real-life problems involving right triangles *(p. 351)*.	A trigonometric function can be used to find the height of a smokestack on top of a building. (See Example 3.)	139, 140
	Solve real-life problems involving directional bearings *(p. 353)*.	Trigonometric functions can be used to find a ship's bearing and distance from a port at a given time. (See Example 5.)	141
	Solve real-life problems involving harmonic motion *(p. 354)*.	Sine or cosine functions can be used to describe the motion of an object that vibrates, oscillates, rotates, or is moved by wave motion. (See Examples 6 and 7.)	142

4 REVIEW EXERCISES

See www.CalcChat.com for worked-out solutions to odd-numbered exercises.

4.1 In Exercises 1–8, (a) sketch the angle in standard position, (b) determine the quadrant in which the angle lies, and (c) determine one positive and one negative coterminal angle.

1. $15\pi/4$ **2.** $2\pi/9$ 1–8. See margin.
3. $-4\pi/3$ **4.** $-23\pi/3$
5. $70°$ **6.** $280°$
7. $-110°$ **8.** $-405°$

In Exercises 9–12, convert the angle measure from degrees to radians. Round your answer to three decimal places.

9. $450°$ 7.854 **10.** $-112.5°$ -1.963
11. $-33° 45'$ -0.589 **12.** $197° 17'$ 3.443

In Exercises 13–16, convert the angle measure from radians to degrees. Round your answer to three decimal places.

13. $3\pi/10$ 54.000° **14.** $-11\pi/6$ $-330.000°$
15. -3.5 $-200.535°$ **16.** 5.7 326.586°

In Exercises 17–20, convert each angle measure to degrees, minutes, and seconds without using a calculator.

17. 198.4° 198° 24′ **18.** $-70.2°$ $-70°$ 12′
19. 0.65° 0° 39′ **20.** $-5.96°$ $-5°$ 57′ 36″

21. ARC LENGTH Find the length of the arc on a circle with a radius of 20 inches intercepted by a central angle of 138°. 48.17 in.

22. PHONOGRAPH Phonograph records are vinyl discs that rotate on a turntable. A typical record album is 12 inches in diameter and plays at $33\frac{1}{3}$ revolutions per minute.
(a) What is the angular speed of a record album? $66\frac{2}{3}\pi$ rad/min
(b) What is the linear speed of the outer edge of a record album? 400π in./min

23. CIRCULAR SECTOR Find the area of the sector of a circle with a radius of 18 inches and central angle $\theta = 120°$. Area ≈ 339.29 in.²

24. CIRCULAR SECTOR Find the area of the sector of a circle with a radius of 6.5 millimeters and central angle $\theta = 5\pi/6$. Area ≈ 55.31 mm²

4.2 In Exercises 25–28, find the point (x, y) on the unit circle that corresponds to the real number t. 25–26. See margin.

25. $t = 2\pi/3$ **26.** $t = 7\pi/4$
27. $t = 7\pi/6$ **28.** $t = -4\pi/3$
$\left(-\frac{\sqrt{3}}{2}, -\frac{1}{2}\right)$ $\left(-\frac{1}{2}, \frac{\sqrt{3}}{2}\right)$

In Exercises 29–32, evaluate (if possible) the six trigonometric functions of the real number. 29–32. See margin.

29. $t = 7\pi/6$ **30.** $t = 3\pi/4$
31. $t = -2\pi/3$ **32.** $t = 2\pi$

In Exercises 33–36, evaluate the trigonometric function using its period as an aid. 33–36. See margin.

33. $\sin(11\pi/4)$ **34.** $\cos 4\pi$
35. $\sin(-17\pi/6)$ **36.** $\cos(-13\pi/3)$

In Exercises 37–40, use a calculator to evaluate the trigonometric function. Round your answer to four decimal places.

37. tan 33 -75.3130 **38.** csc 10.5 -1.1368
39. $\sec(12\pi/5)$ 3.2361 **40.** $\sin(-\pi/9)$ -0.3420

4.3 In Exercises 41 and 42, find the exact values of the six trigonometric functions of the angle θ shown in the figure. 41–42. See margin.

41.
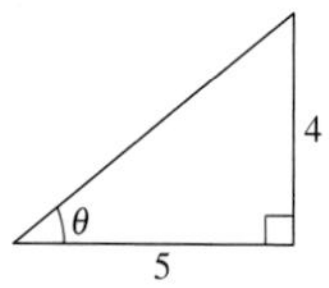

42.
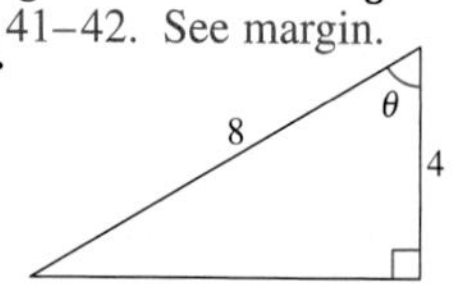

In Exercises 43–46, use the given function value and trigonometric identities (including the cofunction identities) to find the indicated trigonometric functions. 43–46. See margin.

43. $\sin\theta = \frac{1}{3}$	(a) $\csc\theta$	(b) $\cos\theta$
	(c) $\sec\theta$	(d) $\tan\theta$
44. $\tan\theta = 4$	(a) $\cot\theta$	(b) $\sec\theta$
	(c) $\cos\theta$	(d) $\csc\theta$
45. $\csc\theta = 4$	(a) $\sin\theta$	(b) $\cos\theta$
	(c) $\sec\theta$	(d) $\tan\theta$
46. $\csc\theta = 5$	(a) $\sin\theta$	(b) $\cot\theta$
	(c) $\tan\theta$	(d) $\sec(90° - \theta)$

In Exercises 47–54, use a calculator to evaluate the trigonometric function. Round your answer to four decimal places.

47. tan 33° 0.6494 **48.** csc 11° 5.2408
49. sin 34.2° 0.5621 **50.** sec 79.3° 5.3860
51. cot 15° 14′ 3.6722 **52.** csc 44° 35′ 1.4246
53. tan 31° 24′ 5″ 0.6104 **54.** cos 78° 11′ 58″ 0.2045

55. RAILROAD GRADE A train travels 3.5 kilometers on a straight track with a grade of 1° 10′ (see figure on the next page). What is the vertical rise of the train in that distance? 71.3 m

25. $\left(-\frac{1}{2}, \frac{\sqrt{3}}{2}\right)$

26. $\left(\frac{\sqrt{2}}{2}, -\frac{\sqrt{2}}{2}\right)$

29. $\sin\frac{7\pi}{6} = -\frac{1}{2}$
$\cos\frac{7\pi}{6} = -\frac{\sqrt{3}}{2}$
$\tan\frac{7\pi}{6} = \frac{\sqrt{3}}{3}$
$\csc\frac{7\pi}{6} = -2$
$\sec\frac{7\pi}{6} = -\frac{2\sqrt{3}}{3}$
$\cot\frac{7\pi}{6} = \sqrt{3}$

30. $\sin\frac{3\pi}{4} = \frac{\sqrt{2}}{2}$
$\cos\frac{3\pi}{4} = -\frac{\sqrt{2}}{2}$
$\tan\frac{3\pi}{4} = -1$
$\csc\frac{3\pi}{4} = \sqrt{2}$
$\sec\frac{3\pi}{4} = -\sqrt{2}$
$\cot\frac{3\pi}{4} = -1$

31. $\sin\left(-\frac{2\pi}{3}\right) = -\frac{\sqrt{3}}{2}$
$\cos\left(-\frac{2\pi}{3}\right) = -\frac{1}{2}$
$\tan\left(-\frac{2\pi}{3}\right) = \sqrt{3}$
$\csc\left(-\frac{2\pi}{3}\right) = -\frac{2\sqrt{3}}{3}$
$\sec\left(-\frac{2\pi}{3}\right) = -2$
$\cot\left(-\frac{2\pi}{3}\right) = \frac{\sqrt{3}}{3}$

32. $\sin 2\pi = 0$
$\cos 2\pi = 1$
$\tan 2\pi = 0$
$\csc 2\pi$ is undefined.
$\sec 2\pi = 1$
$\cot 2\pi$ is undefined.

33. $\sin\frac{11\pi}{4} = \sin\frac{3\pi}{4} = \frac{\sqrt{2}}{2}$

34. $\cos 4\pi = \cos 0 = 1$

35. $\sin\left(-\frac{17\pi}{6}\right) = \sin\frac{7\pi}{6} = -\frac{1}{2}$

36. $\cos\left(-\frac{13\pi}{3}\right) = \cos\frac{5\pi}{3} = \frac{1}{2}$

41. $\sin\theta = \frac{4\sqrt{41}}{41}$ $\csc\theta = \frac{\sqrt{41}}{4}$
$\cos\theta = \frac{5\sqrt{41}}{41}$ $\sec\theta = \frac{\sqrt{41}}{5}$
$\tan\theta = \frac{4}{5}$ $\cot\theta = \frac{5}{4}$

42. $\sin\theta = \frac{\sqrt{3}}{2}$ $\csc\theta = \frac{2\sqrt{3}}{3}$
$\cos\theta = \frac{1}{2}$ $\sec\theta = 2$
$\tan\theta = \sqrt{3}$ $\cot\theta = \frac{\sqrt{3}}{3}$

43. (a) 3 (b) $\frac{2\sqrt{2}}{3}$ (c) $\frac{3\sqrt{2}}{4}$ (d) $\frac{\sqrt{2}}{4}$

44. (a) $\frac{1}{4}$ (b) $\sqrt{17}$ (c) $\frac{\sqrt{17}}{17}$ (d) $\frac{\sqrt{17}}{4}$

45. (a) $\frac{1}{4}$ (b) $\frac{\sqrt{15}}{4}$ (c) $\frac{4\sqrt{15}}{15}$ (d) $\frac{\sqrt{15}}{15}$

46. (a) $\frac{1}{5}$ (b) $2\sqrt{6}$ (c) $\frac{\sqrt{6}}{12}$ (d) 5

1–8. See Additional Answers beginning on page AA1.

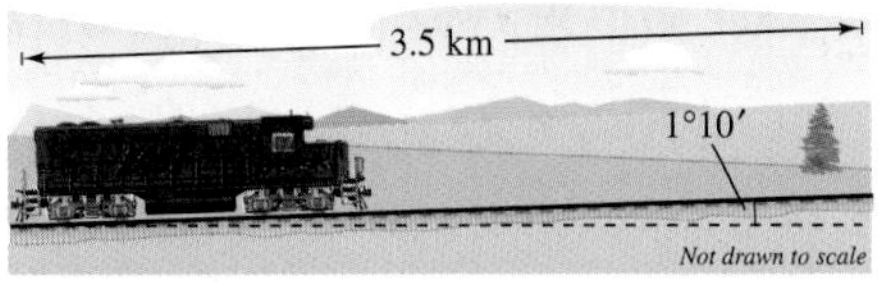

FIGURE FOR 55

56. GUY WIRE A guy wire runs from the ground to the top of a 25-foot telephone pole. The angle formed between the wire and the ground is 52°. How far from the base of the pole is the wire attached to the ground? 19.5 ft

4.4 **In Exercises 57–64, the point is on the terminal side of an angle θ in standard position. Determine the exact values of the six trigonometric functions of the angle θ.** 57–64. See margin.

57. $(12, 16)$ **58.** $(3, -4)$

59. $\left(\frac{2}{3}, \frac{5}{2}\right)$ **60.** $\left(-\frac{10}{3}, -\frac{2}{3}\right)$

61. $(-0.5, 4.5)$ **62.** $(0.3, 0.4)$

63. $(x, 4x),\ x > 0$ **64.** $(-2x, -3x),\ x > 0$

In Exercises 65–70, find the values of the remaining five trigonometric functions of θ. 65–70. See margin.

Function Value	*Constraint*
65. $\sec\theta = \frac{6}{5}$	$\tan\theta < 0$
66. $\csc\theta = \frac{3}{2}$	$\cos\theta < 0$
67. $\sin\theta = \frac{3}{8}$	$\cos\theta < 0$
68. $\tan\theta = \frac{5}{4}$	$\cos\theta < 0$
69. $\cos\theta = -\frac{2}{5}$	$\sin\theta > 0$
70. $\sin\theta = -\frac{1}{2}$	$\cos\theta > 0$

In Exercises 71–74, find the reference angle θ' and sketch θ and θ' in standard position. 71–74. See margin.

71. $\theta = 264°$ **72.** $\theta = 635°$

73. $\theta = -6\pi/5$ **74.** $\theta = 17\pi/3$

In Exercises 75–80, evaluate the sine, cosine, and tangent of the angle without using a calculator. 75–80. See margin.

75. $\pi/3$ **76.** $\pi/4$

77. $-7\pi/3$ **78.** $-5\pi/4$

79. $495°$ **80.** $-150°$

In Exercises 81–84, use a calculator to evaluate the trigonometric function. Round your answer to four decimal places.

81. $\sin 4$ −0.7568 **82.** $\cot(-4.8)$ 0.0878

83. $\sin(12\pi/5)$ 0.9511 **84.** $\tan(-25\pi/7)$ 4.3813

4.5 **In Exercises 85–92, sketch the graph of the function. Include two full periods.** 85–92. See margin.

85. $y = \sin 6x$ **86.** $y = -\cos 3x$

87. $f(x) = 5\sin(2x/5)$ **88.** $f(x) = 8\cos(-x/4)$

89. $y = 5 + \sin x$ **90.** $y = -4 - \cos\pi x$

91. $g(t) = \frac{5}{2}\sin(t - \pi)$ **92.** $g(t) = 3\cos(t + \pi)$

93. SOUND WAVES Sound waves can be modeled by sine functions of the form $y = a \sin bx$, where x is measured in seconds.

(a) Write an equation of a sound wave whose amplitude is 2 and whose period is $\frac{1}{264}$ second. $y = 2\sin 528\pi x$

(b) What is the frequency of the sound wave described in part (a)? 264 cycles/sec

94. DATA ANALYSIS: METEOROLOGY The times S of sunset (Greenwich Mean Time) at 40° north latitude on the 15th of each month are: 1(16:59), 2(17:35), 3(18:06), 4(18:38), 5(19:08), 6(19:30), 7(19:28), 8(18:57), 9(18:09), 10(17:21), 11(16:44), 12(16:36). The month is represented by t, with $t = 1$ corresponding to January. A model (in which minutes have been converted to the decimal parts of an hour) for the data is $S(t) = 18.09 + 1.41\sin[(\pi t/6) + 4.60]$. See margin.

(a) Use a graphing utility to graph the data points and the model in the same viewing window.

(b) What is the period of the model? Is it what you expected? Explain.

(c) What is the amplitude of the model? What does it represent in the model? Explain.

4.6 **In Exercises 95–102, sketch a graph of the function. Include two full periods.** 95–102. See margin.

95. $f(x) = 3\tan 2x$ **96.** $f(t) = \tan\left(t + \frac{\pi}{2}\right)$

97. $f(x) = \frac{1}{2}\cot x$ **98.** $g(t) = 2\cot 2t$

99. $f(x) = 3\sec x$ **100.** $h(t) = \sec\left(t - \frac{\pi}{4}\right)$

101. $f(x) = \frac{1}{2}\csc\frac{x}{2}$ **102.** $f(t) = 3\csc\left(2t + \frac{\pi}{4}\right)$

In Exercises 103 and 104, use a graphing utility to graph the function and the damping factor of the function in the same viewing window. Describe the behavior of the function as x increases without bound. 103–104. See margin.

103. $f(x) = x\cos x$ **104.** $g(x) = x^4\cos x$

4.7 **In Exercises 105–110, evaluate the expression. If necessary, round your answer to two decimal places.** 105–106. See margin.

105. $\arcsin\left(-\frac{1}{2}\right)$ **106.** $\arcsin(-1)$

107. $\arcsin 0.4$ 0.41 **108.** $\arcsin 0.213$ 0.21

109. $\sin^{-1}(-0.44)$ −0.46 **110.** $\sin^{-1} 0.89$ 1.10

57. $\sin\theta = \frac{4}{5}$, $\cos\theta = \frac{3}{5}$, $\tan\theta = \frac{4}{3}$, $\csc\theta = \frac{5}{4}$, $\sec\theta = \frac{5}{3}$, $\cot\theta = \frac{3}{4}$

58. $\sin\theta = -\frac{4}{5}$, $\cos\theta = \frac{3}{5}$, $\tan\theta = -\frac{4}{3}$, $\csc\theta = -\frac{5}{4}$, $\sec\theta = \frac{5}{3}$, $\cot\theta = -\frac{3}{4}$

59. $\sin\theta = \frac{15\sqrt{241}}{241}$, $\cos\theta = \frac{4\sqrt{241}}{241}$, $\tan\theta = \frac{15}{4}$, $\csc\theta = \frac{\sqrt{241}}{15}$, $\sec\theta = \frac{\sqrt{241}}{4}$, $\cot\theta = \frac{4}{15}$

60. $\sin\theta = -\frac{\sqrt{26}}{26}$, $\cos\theta = -\frac{5\sqrt{26}}{26}$, $\tan\theta = \frac{1}{5}$, $\csc\theta = -\sqrt{26}$, $\sec\theta = -\frac{\sqrt{26}}{5}$, $\cot\theta = 5$

61. $\sin\theta = \frac{9\sqrt{82}}{82}$, $\csc\theta = \frac{\sqrt{82}}{9}$, $\cos\theta = \frac{-\sqrt{82}}{82}$, $\sec\theta = -\sqrt{82}$, $\tan\theta = -9$, $\cot\theta = -\frac{1}{9}$

62. $\sin\theta = \frac{4}{5}$, $\csc\theta = \frac{5}{4}$, $\cos\theta = \frac{3}{5}$, $\sec\theta = \frac{5}{3}$, $\tan\theta = \frac{4}{3}$, $\cot\theta = \frac{3}{4}$

63. $\sin\theta = \frac{4\sqrt{17}}{17}$, $\csc\theta = \frac{\sqrt{17}}{4}$, $\cos\theta = \frac{\sqrt{17}}{17}$, $\sec\theta = \sqrt{17}$, $\tan\theta = 4$, $\cot\theta = \frac{1}{4}$

64. $\sin\theta = -\frac{3\sqrt{13}}{13}$, $\cos\theta = -\frac{2\sqrt{13}}{13}$, $\tan\theta = \frac{3}{2}$, $\csc\theta = -\frac{\sqrt{13}}{3}$, $\sec\theta = -\frac{\sqrt{13}}{2}$, $\cot\theta = \frac{2}{3}$

65. $\sin\theta = -\frac{\sqrt{11}}{6}$, $\cos\theta = \frac{5}{6}$, $\tan\theta = -\frac{\sqrt{11}}{5}$, $\csc\theta = -\frac{6\sqrt{11}}{11}$, $\cot\theta = -\frac{5\sqrt{11}}{11}$

66. $\sin\theta = \frac{2}{3}$, $\cos\theta = -\frac{\sqrt{5}}{3}$, $\tan\theta = -\frac{2\sqrt{5}}{5}$, $\sec\theta = -\frac{3\sqrt{5}}{5}$, $\cot\theta = -\frac{\sqrt{5}}{2}$

67. $\cos\theta = -\frac{\sqrt{55}}{8}$, $\tan\theta = -\frac{3\sqrt{55}}{55}$, $\csc\theta = \frac{8}{3}$, $\sec\theta = -\frac{8\sqrt{55}}{55}$, $\cot\theta = -\frac{\sqrt{55}}{3}$

68. $\sin\theta = -\frac{5\sqrt{41}}{41}$, $\cos\theta = -\frac{4\sqrt{41}}{41}$, $\csc\theta = -\frac{\sqrt{41}}{5}$, $\sec\theta = -\frac{\sqrt{41}}{4}$, $\cot\theta = \frac{4}{5}$

69–80, 85–92, 94–106. See Additional Answers beginning on page AA1.

In Exercises 111–114, evaluate the expression without using a calculator. 111–114. See margin.

111. $\arccos(-\sqrt{2}/2)$ **112.** $\arccos(\sqrt{2}/2)$

113. $\cos^{-1}(-1)$ **114.** $\cos^{-1}(\sqrt{3}/2)$

In Exercises 115–118, use a calculator to evaluate the expression. Round your answer to two decimal places.

115. $\arccos 0.324$ 1.24 **116.** $\arccos(-0.888)$ 2.66

117. $\tan^{-1}(-1.5)$ -0.98 **118.** $\tan^{-1} 8.2$ 1.45

In Exercises 119–122, use a graphing utility to graph the function. 119–122. See margin.

119. $f(x) = 2 \arcsin x$ **120.** $f(x) = 3 \arccos x$

121. $f(x) = \arctan(x/2)$ **122.** $f(x) = -\arcsin 2x$

In Exercises 123–128, find the exact value of the expression.

123. $\cos\left(\arctan \frac{3}{4}\right)$ $\frac{4}{5}$ **124.** $\tan\left(\arccos \frac{3}{5}\right)$ $\frac{4}{3}$

125. $\sec\left(\tan^{-1} \frac{12}{5}\right)$ $\frac{13}{5}$ **126.** $\sec\left[\sin^{-1}\left(-\frac{1}{4}\right)\right]$ See margin.

127. $\cot\left(\arctan \frac{7}{10}\right)$ $\frac{10}{7}$ **128.** $\cot\left[\arcsin\left(-\frac{12}{13}\right)\right]$ $-\frac{5}{12}$

In Exercises 129 and 130, write an algebraic expression that is equivalent to the expression. 129–130. See margin.

129. $\tan[\arccos(x/2)]$ **130.** $\sec[\arcsin(x-1)]$

In Exercises 131–134, evaluate each expression without using a calculator.

131. $\operatorname{arccot} \sqrt{3}$ $\frac{\pi}{6}$ **132.** $\operatorname{arcsec}(-1)$ π

133. $\operatorname{arcsec}(-\sqrt{2})$ $\frac{3\pi}{4}$ **134.** $\operatorname{arccsc} 1$ $\frac{\pi}{2}$

In Exercises 135–138, use a calculator to approximate the value of the expression. Round your result to two decimal places.

135. $\operatorname{arccot}(10.5)$ 0.09 **136.** $\operatorname{arcsec}(-7.5)$ 1.70

137. $\operatorname{arcsec}\left(-\frac{5}{2}\right)$ 1.98 **138.** $\operatorname{arccsc}(-2.01)$ -0.52

4.8 **139. ANGLE OF ELEVATION** The height of a radio transmission tower is 70 meters, and it casts a shadow of length 30 meters. Draw a diagram and find the angle of elevation of the sun. See margin.

140. HEIGHT Your football has landed at the edge of the roof of your school building. When you are 25 feet from the base of the building, the angle of elevation to your football is 21°. How high off the ground is your football? 9.6 ft

141. DISTANCE From city A to city B, a plane flies 650 miles at a bearing of 48°. From city B to city C, the plane flies 810 miles at a bearing of 115°. Find the distance from city A to city C and the bearing from city A to city C. 1221 mi, 85.6°

142. WAVE MOTION Your fishing bobber oscillates in simple harmonic motion from the waves in the lake where you fish. Your bobber moves a total of 1.5 inches from its high point to its low point and returns to its high point every 3 seconds. Write an equation modeling the motion of your bobber if it is at its high point at time $t = 0$. $d = 0.75 \cos\left(\frac{2\pi t}{3}\right)$

EXPLORATION

143–144. See margin.

TRUE OR FALSE? In Exercises 143 and 144, determine whether the statement is true or false. Justify your answer.

143. $y = \sin \theta$ is not a function because $\sin 30° = \sin 150°$.

144. Because $\tan 3\pi/4 = -1$, $\arctan(-1) = 3\pi/4$.

145. See margin.

145. WRITING Describe the behavior of $f(\theta) = \sec \theta$ at the zeros of $g(\theta) = \cos \theta$. Explain your reasoning.

146. CONJECTURE See margin.

(a) Use a graphing utility to complete the table.

θ	0.1	0.4	0.7	1.0	1.3
$\tan\left(\theta - \frac{\pi}{2}\right)$					
$-\cot \theta$					

(b) Make a conjecture about the relationship between $\tan[\theta - (\pi/2)]$ and $-\cot \theta$.

147. WRITING When graphing the sine and cosine functions, determining the amplitude is part of the analysis. Explain why this is not true for the other four trigonometric functions. See margin.

148. OSCILLATION OF A SPRING A weight is suspended from a ceiling by a steel spring. The weight is lifted (positive direction) from the equilibrium position and released. The resulting motion of the weight is modeled by $y = Ae^{-kt} \cos bt = \frac{1}{5}e^{-t/10} \cos 6t$, where y is the distance in feet from equilibrium and t is the time in seconds. The graph of the function is shown in the figure. For each of the following, describe the change in the system without graphing the resulting function.

(a) A is changed from $\frac{1}{5}$ to $\frac{1}{3}$. (a) The displacement is increased.

(b) k is changed from $\frac{1}{10}$ to $\frac{1}{3}$. (b) The friction damps the oscillations more quickly.

(c) b is changed from 6 to 9.

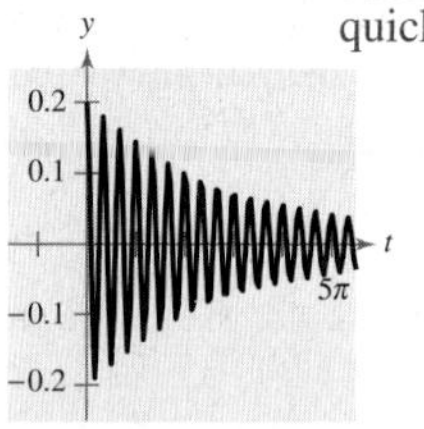

(c) The frequency of the oscillations increases.

111. $\frac{3\pi}{4}$ **112.** $\frac{\pi}{4}$

113. π **114.** $\frac{\pi}{6}$

119.

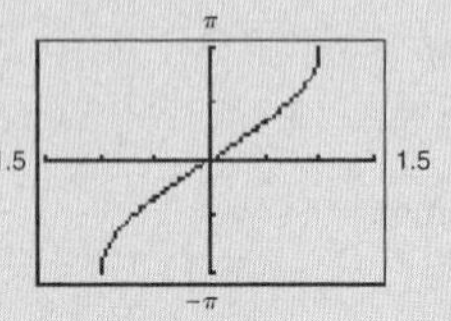

120.

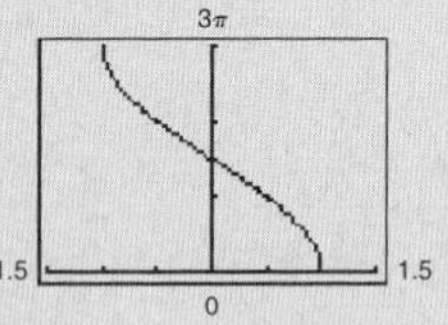

121.

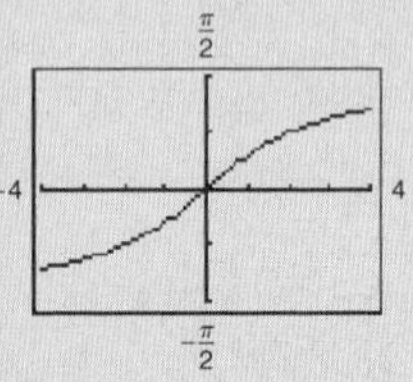

122.

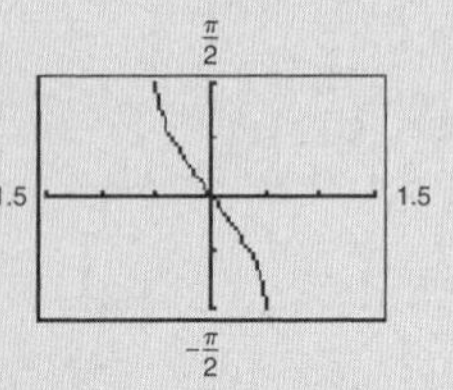

126. $\frac{4\sqrt{15}}{15}$ **129.** $\frac{\sqrt{4 - x^2}}{x}$

130. $\frac{1}{\sqrt{x(2 - x)}}$

139.

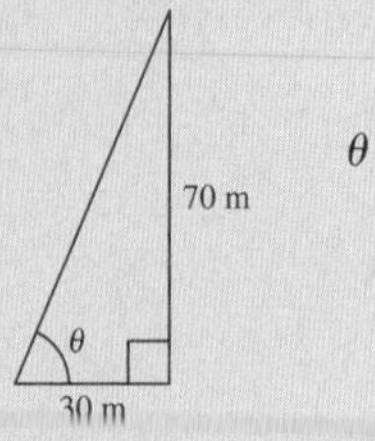

$\theta \approx 66.8°$

143. False. For each θ there corresponds exactly one value of y.

144. False. $3\pi/4$ is not in the range of the arctangent function.

145. The function is undefined because $\sec \theta = 1/\cos \theta$.

146. (a)

θ	0.1	0.4	0.7
$\tan\left(\theta - \frac{\pi}{2}\right)$	-9.9666	-2.3652	-1.1872
$-\cot \theta$	-9.9666	-2.3652	-1.1872

θ	1.0	1.3
$\tan\left(\theta - \frac{\pi}{2}\right)$	-0.6421	-0.2776
$-\cot \theta$	-0.6421	-0.2776

(b) $\tan\left(\theta - \frac{\pi}{2}\right) = -\cot \theta$

147. The ranges of the other four trigonometric functions are $(-\infty, \infty)$ or $(-\infty, -1] \cup [1, \infty)$.

4 CHAPTER TEST

See www.CalcChat.com for worked-out solutions to odd-numbered exercises.

Take this test as you would take a test in class. When you are finished, check your work against the answers given in the back of the book.

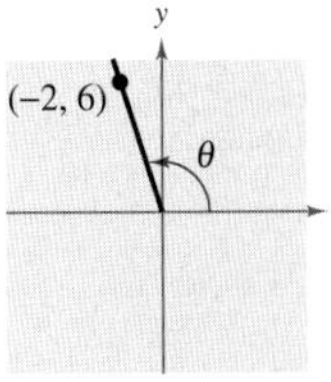

FIGURE FOR 4

1. Consider an angle that measures $\frac{5\pi}{4}$ radians.
   (a) Sketch the angle in standard position. See margin.
   (b) Determine two coterminal angles (one positive and one negative). $\frac{13\pi}{4}, -\frac{3\pi}{4}$
   (c) Convert the angle to degree measure. $225°$
2. A truck is moving at a rate of 105 kilometers per hour, and the diameter of its wheels is 1 meter. Find the angular speed of the wheels in radians per minute.
3. A water sprinkler sprays water on a lawn over a distance of 25 feet and rotates through an angle of 130°. Find the area of the lawn watered by the sprinkler.
4. Find the exact values of the six trigonometric functions of the angle θ shown in the figure.
5. Given that $\tan\theta = \frac{3}{2}$, find the other five trigonometric functions of θ. 2–6. See margin.
6. Determine the reference angle θ' for the angle $\theta = 205°$ and sketch θ and θ' in standard position.
7. Determine the quadrant in which θ lies if $\sec\theta < 0$ and $\tan\theta > 0$. Quadrant III
8. Find two exact values of θ in degrees $(0 \le \theta < 360°)$ if $\cos\theta = -\sqrt{3}/2$. (Do not use a calculator.) $150°, 210°$
9. Use a calculator to approximate two values of θ in radians $(0 \le \theta < 2\pi)$ if $\csc\theta = 1.030$. Round the results to two decimal places. 1.33, 1.81

In Exercises 10 and 11, find the remaining five trigonometric functions of θ satisfying the conditions. 10–11. See margin.

10. $\cos\theta = \frac{3}{5}, \quad \tan\theta < 0$
11. $\sec\theta = -\frac{29}{20}, \quad \sin\theta > 0$

In Exercises 12 and 13, sketch the graph of the function. (Include two full periods.) 12–13. See margin.

12. $g(x) = -2\sin\left(x - \frac{\pi}{4}\right)$
13. $f(\alpha) = \frac{1}{2}\tan 2\alpha$

In Exercises 14 and 15, use a graphing utility to graph the function. If the function is periodic, find its period. 14–15. See margin.

14. $y = \sin 2\pi x + 2\cos \pi x$
15. $y = 6e^{-0.12t}\cos(0.25t), \quad 0 \le t \le 32$

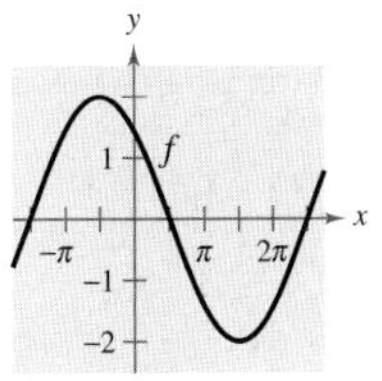

FIGURE FOR 16

16. Find a, b, and c for the function $f(x) = a\sin(bx + c)$ such that the graph of f matches the figure. See margin.
17. Find the exact value of $\cot\left(\arcsin\frac{3}{8}\right)$ without the aid of a calculator. $\frac{\sqrt{55}}{3}$
18. Graph the function $f(x) = 2\arcsin\left(\frac{1}{2}x\right)$. See margin.
19. A plane is 90 miles south and 110 miles east of London Heathrow Airport. What bearing should be taken to fly directly to the airport? $309.3°$
20. Write the equation for the simple harmonic motion of a ball on a spring that starts at its lowest point of 6 inches below equilibrium, bounces to its maximum height of 6 inches above equilibrium, and returns to its lowest point in a total of 2 seconds. $d = -6\cos\pi t$

1. (a)

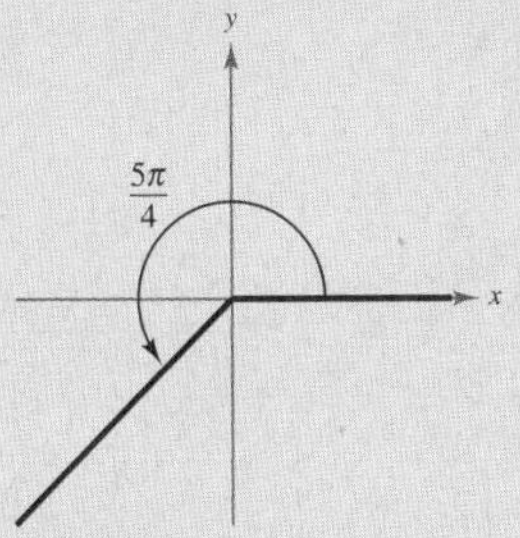

2. 3500 rad/min

3. About 709.04 ft²

4. $\sin\theta = \frac{3\sqrt{10}}{10}$
$\cos\theta = -\frac{\sqrt{10}}{10}$
$\tan\theta = -3$
$\csc\theta = \frac{\sqrt{10}}{3}$
$\sec\theta = -\sqrt{10}$
$\cot\theta = -\frac{1}{3}$

5. For $0 \le \theta < \frac{\pi}{2}$:
$\sin\theta = \frac{3\sqrt{13}}{13}$
$\cos\theta = \frac{2\sqrt{13}}{13}$
$\csc\theta = \frac{\sqrt{13}}{3}$
$\sec\theta = \frac{\sqrt{13}}{2}$
$\cot\theta = \frac{2}{3}$

For $\pi \le \theta < \frac{3\pi}{2}$:
$\sin\theta = -\frac{3\sqrt{13}}{13}$
$\cos\theta = -\frac{2\sqrt{13}}{13}$
$\csc\theta = -\frac{\sqrt{13}}{3}$
$\sec\theta = -\frac{\sqrt{13}}{2}$
$\cot\theta = \frac{2}{3}$

6. $\theta' = 25°$

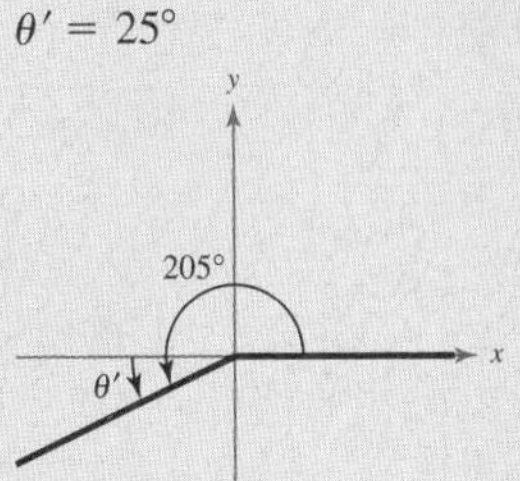

10. $\sin\theta = -\frac{4}{5}$
$\tan\theta = -\frac{4}{3}$
$\csc\theta = -\frac{5}{4}$
$\sec\theta = \frac{5}{3}$
$\cot\theta = -\frac{3}{4}$

11. $\sin\theta = \frac{21}{29}$
$\cos\theta = -\frac{20}{29}$
$\tan\theta = -\frac{21}{20}$
$\csc\theta = \frac{29}{21}$
$\cot\theta = -\frac{20}{21}$

12.

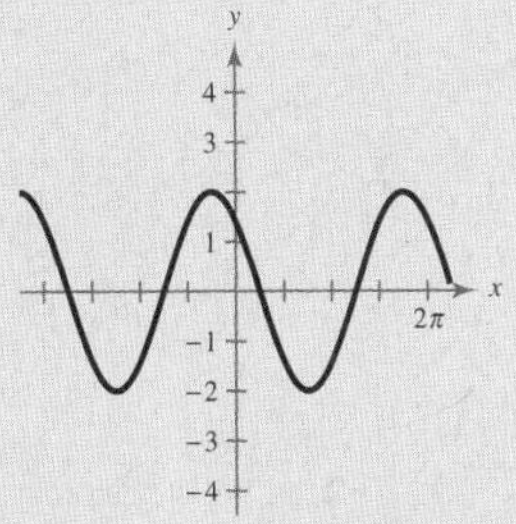

13.

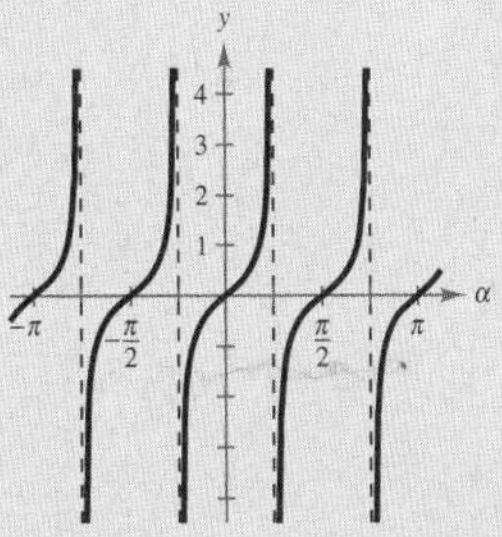

14–16, 18. See Additional Answers beginning on page AA1.

PROOFS IN MATHEMATICS

The Pythagorean Theorem

The Pythagorean Theorem is one of the most famous theorems in mathematics. More than 100 different proofs now exist. James A. Garfield, the twentieth president of the United States, developed a proof of the Pythagorean Theorem in 1876. His proof, shown below, involved the fact that a trapezoid can be formed from two congruent right triangles and an isosceles right triangle.

The Pythagorean Theorem

In a right triangle, the sum of the squares of the lengths of the legs is equal to the square of the length of the hypotenuse, where a and b are the legs and c is the hypotenuse.

$$a^2 + b^2 = c^2$$

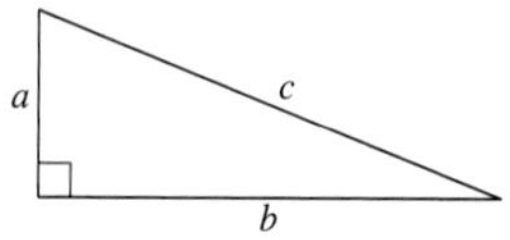

Proof

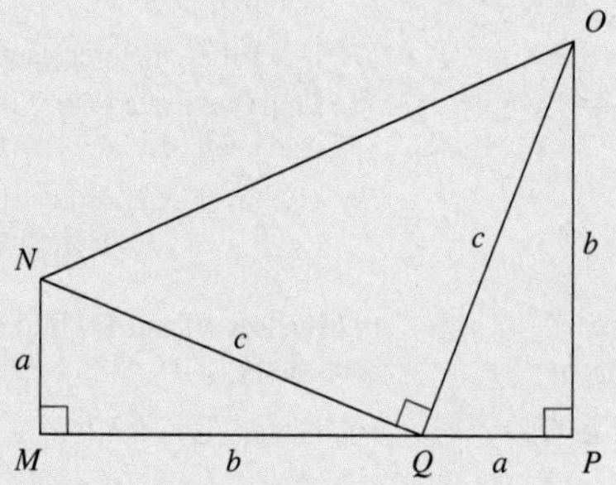

Area of trapezoid $MNOP$ = Area of $\triangle MNQ$ + Area of $\triangle PQO$ + Area of $\triangle NOQ$

$$\frac{1}{2}(a + b)(a + b) = \frac{1}{2}ab + \frac{1}{2}ab + \frac{1}{2}c^2$$

$$\frac{1}{2}(a + b)(a + b) = ab + \frac{1}{2}c^2$$

$$(a + b)(a + b) = 2ab + c^2$$

$$a^2 + 2ab + b^2 = 2ab + c^2$$

$$a^2 + b^2 = c^2$$

368

PROBLEM SOLVING

This collection of thought-provoking and challenging exercises further explores and expands upon concepts learned in this chapter.

1. The restaurant at the top of the Space Needle in Seattle, Washington is circular and has a radius of 47.25 feet. The dining part of the restaurant revolves, making about one complete revolution every 48 minutes. A dinner party was seated at the edge of the revolving restaurant at 6:45 P.M. and was finished at 8:57 P.M. See margin.

(a) Find the angle through which the dinner party rotated.

(b) Find the distance the party traveled during dinner.

2. A bicycle's gear ratio is the number of times the freewheel turns for every one turn of the chainwheel (see figure). The table shows the numbers of teeth in the freewheel and chainwheel for the first five gears of an 18-speed touring bicycle. The chainwheel completes one rotation for each gear. Find the angle through which the freewheel turns for each gear. Give your answers in both degrees and radians. See margin.

Gear number	Number of teeth in freewheel	Number of teeth in chainwheel
1	32	24
2	26	24
3	22	24
4	32	40
5	19	24

3. A surveyor in a helicopter is trying to determine the width of an island, as shown in the figure.

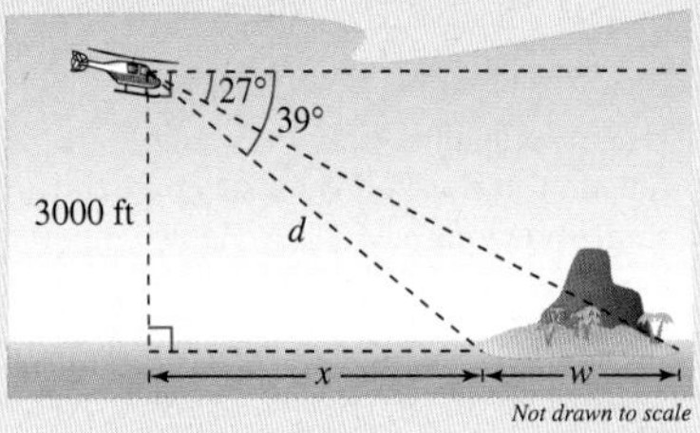

(a) What is the shortest distance d the helicopter would have to travel to land on the island? 4767 ft

(b) What is the horizontal distance x that the helicopter would have to travel before it would be directly over the nearer end of the island? 3705 ft

(c) Find the width w of the island. Explain how you obtained your answer. See margin.

4. Use the figure below.

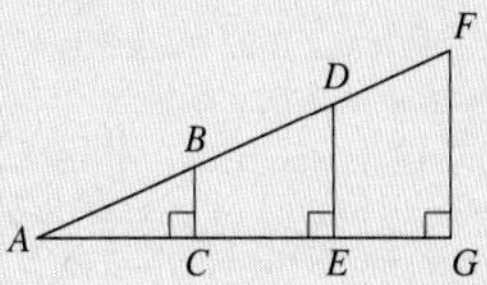

(a) Explain why $\triangle ABC$, $\triangle ADE$, and $\triangle AFG$ are similar triangles. Answers will vary.

(b) What does similarity imply about the ratios

$\frac{BC}{AB}, \frac{DE}{AD},$ and $\frac{FG}{AF}$? The ratios are equal.

(c) Does the value of $\sin A$ depend on which triangle from part (a) is used to calculate it? Would the value of $\sin A$ change if it were found using a different right triangle that was similar to the three given triangles? No; No

(d) Do your conclusions from part (c) apply to the other five trigonometric functions? Explain. See margin.

5. Use a graphing utility to graph h, and use the graph to decide whether h is even, odd, or neither. See margin.

(a) $h(x) = \cos^2 x$

(b) $h(x) = \sin^2 x$

6. If f is an even function and g is an odd function, use the results of Exercise 5 to make a conjecture about h, where

(a) $h(x) = [f(x)]^2$ $h(x)$ is even.

(b) $h(x) = [g(x)]^2$. $h(x)$ is even.

7. The model for the height h (in feet) of a Ferris wheel car is

$h = 50 + 50 \sin 8\pi t$

where t is the time (in minutes). (The Ferris wheel has a radius of 50 feet.) This model yields a height of 50 feet when $t = 0$. Alter the model so that the height of the car is 1 foot when $t = 0$.

$$h = 51 - 50 \sin\left(8\pi t + \frac{\pi}{2}\right)$$

1. (a) $\frac{11\pi}{2}$ rad or 990°

(b) About 816.42 ft

2. Gear 1: 270°, $\frac{3\pi}{2}$ rad

Gear 2: About 332.3°, $\frac{24\pi}{13}$ rad

Gear 3: About 392.7°, $\frac{24\pi}{11}$ rad

Gear 4: 450°, $\frac{5\pi}{2}$ rad

Gear 5: About 454.7°, $\frac{48\pi}{19}$ rad

3. (c) $w = 2183$ ft,

$\tan 63° = \frac{w + 3705}{3000}$

4. (d) Yes, because all six trigonometric functions are ratios of right triangles.

5. (a)

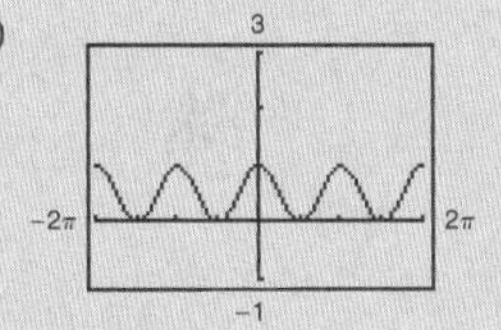

Even

(b)

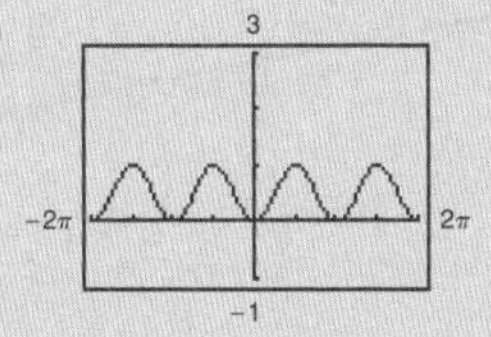

Even

369

8. The pressure P (in millimeters of mercury) against the walls of the blood vessels of a patient is modeled by

$$P = 100 - 20\cos\left(\frac{8\pi}{3}t\right)$$

where t is time (in seconds). See margin.

(a) Use a graphing utility to graph the model.

(b) What is the period of the model? What does the period tell you about this situation?

(c) What is the amplitude of the model? What does it tell you about this situation?

(d) If one cycle of this model is equivalent to one heartbeat, what is the pulse of this patient?

(e) If a physician wants this patient's pulse rate to be 64 beats per minute or less, what should the period be? What should the coefficient of t be?

9. A popular theory that attempts to explain the ups and downs of everyday life states that each of us has three cycles, called biorhythms, which begin at birth. These three cycles can be modeled by sine waves.

$$\text{Physical (23 days): } P = \sin\frac{2\pi t}{23}, \quad t \geq 0$$

$$\text{Emotional (28 days): } E = \sin\frac{2\pi t}{28}, \quad t \geq 0$$

$$\text{Intellectual (33 days): } I = \sin\frac{2\pi t}{33}, \quad t \geq 0$$

where t is the number of days since birth. Consider a person who was born on July 20, 1988. See margin.

(a) Use a graphing utility to graph the three models in the same viewing window for $7300 \leq t \leq 7380$.

(b) Describe the person's biorhythms during the month of September 2008.

(c) Calculate the person's three energy levels on September 22, 2008.

10. (a) Use a graphing utility to graph the functions given by

$$f(x) = 2\cos 2x + 3\sin 3x \quad \text{and}$$

$$g(x) = 2\cos 2x + 3\sin 4x. \text{ (a)–(c). See margin.}$$

(b) Use the graphs from part (a) to find the period of each function.

(c) If α and β are positive integers, is the function given by $h(x) = A\cos\alpha x + B\sin\beta x$ periodic? Explain your reasoning.

11. Two trigonometric functions f and g have periods of 2, and their graphs intersect at $x = 5.35$.

(a) Give one smaller and one larger positive value of x at which the functions have the same value. 3.35, 7.35

(b) Determine one negative value of x at which the graphs intersect. -0.65

(c) Is it true that $f(13.35) = g(-4.65)$? Explain your reasoning. See margin.

12. The function f is periodic, with period c. So, $f(t + c) = f(t)$. Are the following equal? Explain.

(a) $f(t - 2c) = f(t)$ Equal; two-period shift

(b) $f\left(t + \frac{1}{2}c\right) = f\left(\frac{1}{2}t\right)$ See margin.

(c) $f\left(\frac{1}{2}(t + c)\right) = f\left(\frac{1}{2}t\right)$ See margin.

13. If you stand in shallow water and look at an object below the surface of the water, the object will look farther away from you than it really is. This is because when light rays pass between air and water, the water refracts, or bends, the light rays. The index of refraction for water is 1.333. This is the ratio of the sine of θ_1 and the sine of θ_2 (see figure).

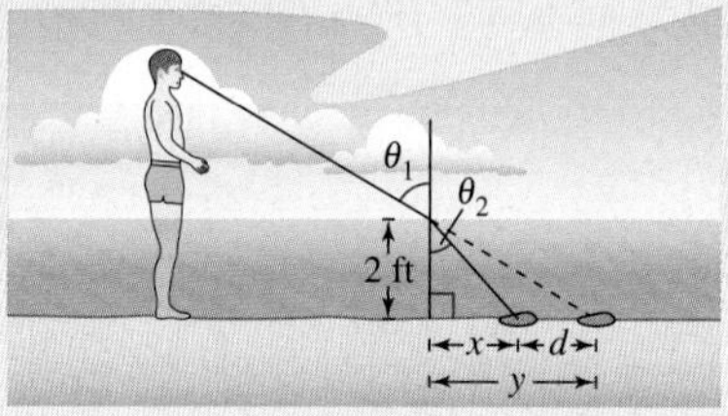

(a) You are standing in water that is 2 feet deep and are looking at a rock at angle $\theta_1 = 60°$ (measured from a line perpendicular to the surface of the water). Find θ_2. 40.5°

(b) Find the distances x and y. See margin.

(c) Find the distance d between where the rock is and where it appears to be. About 1.75 ft

(d) What happens to d as you move closer to the rock? Explain your reasoning. See margin.

14. In calculus, it can be shown that the arctangent function can be approximated by the polynomial

$$\arctan x \approx x - \frac{x^3}{3} + \frac{x^5}{5} - \frac{x^7}{7}$$

where x is in radians. See margin.

(a) Use a graphing utility to graph the arctangent function and its polynomial approximation in the same viewing window. How do the graphs compare?

(b) Study the pattern in the polynomial approximation of the arctangent function and guess the next term. Then repeat part (a). How does the accuracy of the approximation change when additional terms are added?

8. (a)

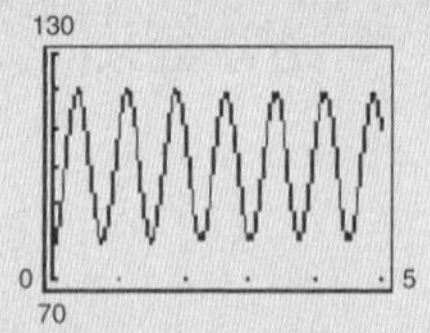

(b) Period $= \frac{3}{4}$ sec; Answers will vary.

(c) 20 mm; Answers will vary.

(d) 80 beats/min

(e) Period $= \dfrac{15}{16}$ sec; $\dfrac{32\pi}{15}$

9. (a)

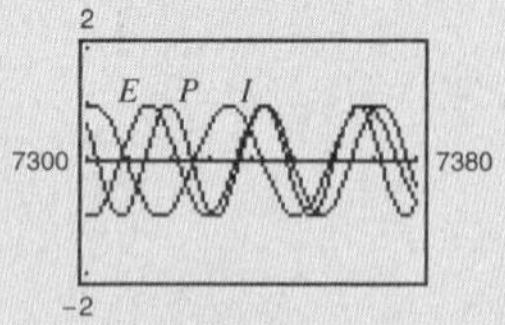

(b)

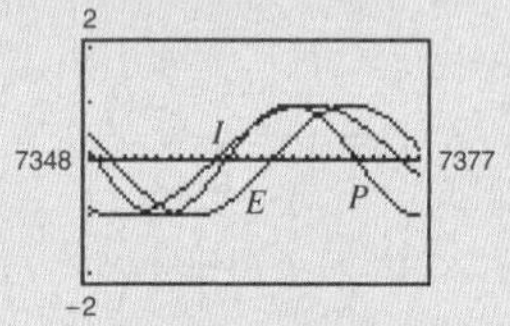

All three drop earlier in the month, then peak toward the middle of the month, and drop again toward the latter part of the month.

(c) $P(7369) = 0.631$
$E(7369) = 0.901$
$I(7369) = 0.945$

10. (a)

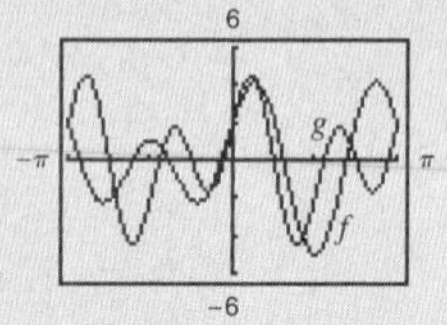

(b) Period of f: 2π;
Period of g: π

(c) Yes, because the sine and cosine functions are periodic.

11. (c) Yes. There is a difference of nine periods between the values.

12. (b) Not equal; $f\left(t + \frac{1}{2}c\right)$ is a horizontal translation and $f\left(\frac{1}{2}t\right)$ is a period change.

(c) Not equal; For example, $\sin\left[\frac{1}{2}(\pi + 2\pi)\right] \neq \sin\left(\frac{1}{2}\pi\right)$.

13. (b) $x \approx 1.71$ ft; $y \approx 3.46$ ft

(d) As you move closer to the rock, d must get smaller and smaller. The angles θ_1 and θ_2 will decrease along with the distance y, so d will decrease.

14. (a)

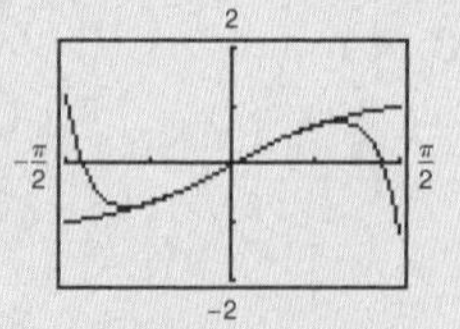

The approximation is accurate over the interval $-1 \leq x \leq 1$.

(b) $x^9/9$

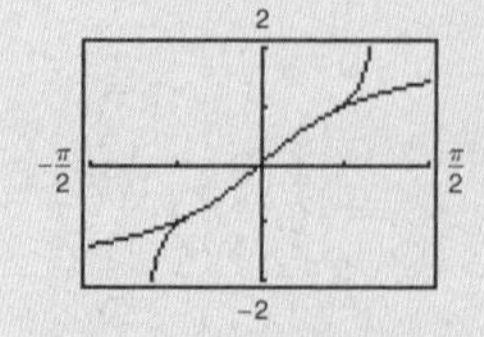

The accuracy improves.

REGULAR SCHEDULE

Lesson	Day	AVERAGE	ADVANCED
5.1	Day 1	pp. 377–378 Exs. 11–15 odd, 18, 19, 25–37, 45–57 odd, 67, 69, 73	pp. 377–378 Exs. 12–16 even, 17, 22, 24–36, 42–46 even, 52–58 even, 62–74 even
	Day 2	pp. 378–379 Exs. 77, 82, 83, 85, 89, 93–109 odd, 114, 117–123 odd, 127–129, 131, 133, 137, 142	pp. 378–379 Exs. 76, 80, 84, 88, 90, 94, 100–110 even, 117, 118–124 even, 130–134 even, 135, 136, 138, 142
5.2	Day 1	pp. 385–386 Exs. 13–25 odd, 29–39 odd, 42, 43, 45, 51, 55, 59, 62, 65–69 odd, 71–73	pp. 385–386 Exs. 11, 12, 20–26 even, 30–42 even, 46, 52, 56, 58, 64–70 even, 71, 72, 74, 78
5.3	Day 1	p. 394 Exs. 1–4, 5–9 odd, 14, 16, 19–29 odd, 34, 36	p. 394 Exs. 1–4, 8–16 even, 22–32 even, 36, 38
	Day 2	pp. 394–397 Exs. 40, 41, 45, 49, 53, 59, 67–75 odd, 85, 88, 89–99 odd, 100	pp. 394–397 Exs. 42–48 even, 54, 60–64 even, 72–86 even, 87, 88–94 even, 97, 98, 102, 104
5.4	Day 1	p. 402 Exs. 1–6, 9–13 odd, 17, 21, 25, 29–35 odd, 39–45 odd, 53, 55, 59	p. 402 Exs. 1–6, 8, 12, 14, 18, 24, 26, 30–44 even, 48–60 even
	Day 2	pp. 403–404 Exs. 63–69 odd, 72, 73, 81–89 odd, 91–95, 99, 103–107 odd	pp. 403–404 Exs. 62–68 even, 73, 74, 78–82 even, 86, 88, 89, 90–100 even, 104–108 even, 109, 112
5.5	Day 1	pp. 413–414 Exs. 1–4, 11, 13, 17, 21–25 odd, 29, 31, 37–41 odd, 49, 51, 111, 115, 118	pp. 413–414 Exs. 12–22 even, 26, 28, 31, 40–52 even, 56, 58, 112, 113, 116
	Day 2	pp. 413–415 Exs. 5–10, 53, 55, 59, 65–69 odd, 73, 79, 81, 85, 91, 97, 99, 103, 107, 122, 123, 125, 137	pp. 413–415 Exs. 56–60 even, 66–70 even, 74, 80, 84, 88–92 even, 98, 100, 104, 108, 110, 120–126 even, 130, 132, 136, 138
Review	Day 1	pp. 418–420 Exs. 7–11 odd, 21–25 odd, 33–39 odd, 43, 47, 53, 57, 61, 65, 71, 77–87 odd, 91, 95, 99, 101, 105, 109, 110, 115, 119–123 odd	pp. 418–420 Exs. 4–10 even, 16, 22–26 even, 32–38 even, 46, 50, 54, 58, 62–66 even, 74, 76, 80, 86, 90, 92, 98–102 even, 106, 111–114, 120, 124
Assess	Day 1	Chapter 5 Test	Chapter 5 Test

Yearly Pacing Chapter 5 Total – 11 days Remaining – 100 days

BLOCK SCHEDULE

DAY 1	DAY 2	DAY 3	DAY 4	DAY 5	DAY 6
ASSESS	5.1 (CONT.)	5.3	5.4	5.5	REVIEW
Chapter 4 Test	pp. 378–379 Exs. 77, 82, 83, 85, 89, 93–109 odd, 114, 117–123 odd, 127–129, 131, 133, 137, 142	pp. 394–397 Exs. 1–4, 5–9 odd, 14, 16, 19–29 odd, 34, 36, 40, 41, 45, 49, 53, 59, 67–75 odd, 85, 88, 89–99 odd, 100	pp. 402–404 Exs. 1–6, 9–13 odd, 17, 21, 25, 29–35 odd, 39–45 odd, 53, 55, 59, 63–69 odd, 72, 73, 81–89 odd, 91–95, 99, 103–107 odd	pp. 413–415 Exs. 1–11, 13, 17, 21–25 odd, 29, 31, 37–41 odd, 49–55 odd, 59, 65–69 odd, 73, 79, 81, 85, 91, 97, 99, 103, 107, 111, 115, 118, 122, 123, 125, 137	pp. 418–420 Exs. 7–11 odd, 21–25 odd, 33–39 odd, 43, 47, 53, 57, 61, 65, 71, 77–87 odd, 91, 95, 99, 101, 105, 109, 110, 115, 119–123 odd
5.1	5.2				ASSESS
pp. 377–378 Exs. 11–15 odd, 18, 19, 25–37, 45–57 odd, 67, 69, 73	pp. 385–386 Exs. 13–25 odd, 29–39 odd, 42, 43, 45, 51, 55, 59, 62, 65–69 odd, 71–73				Chapter 5 Test

Yearly Pacing Chapter 5 Total – 5.5 days Remaining – 50 days

5

Analytic Trigonometry

In Mathematics

Analytic trigonometry is used to simplify trigonometric expressions and solve trigonometric equations.

In Real Life

Analytic trigonometry is used to model real-life phenomena. For instance, when an airplane travels faster than the speed of sound, the sound waves form a cone behind the airplane. Concepts of trigonometry can be used to describe the apex angle of the cone. (See Exercise 137, page 415.)

Christopher Pasatier/Reuters/Landov

IN CAREERS

There are many careers that use analytic trigonometry. Several are listed below.

- Mechanical Engineer
  Exercise 89, page 396
- Physicist
  Exercise 90, page 403
- Athletic Trainer
  Exercise 135, page 415
- Physical Therapist
  Exercise 8, page 425

PLAN AND PREPARE

Main Ideas

In Chapter 5, students learn strategies for simplifying expressions and solving equations by using trigonometric identities. First, students learn how trigonometric functions can be rewritten by using identities and how to verify identities. Next, students learn how to solve trigonometric equations written in quadratic form and equations containing more than one angle. Then they study equations containing sums and differences of angles. Finally, students rewrite trigonometric expressions that contain functions of multiple or half-angles and that involve squares or products of trigonometric functions.

Chapter Planning Guide

Chapter Resources

- Complete Solutions Guide

Interactive Technology

- Instructor Success Organizer
- Notetaking Guide IAE
- Instructional DVDs
- Animated Precalculus
- PowerLecture with ExamView

371

1 PLAN AND PREPARE

Warm-up Exercises

Transparency Available
Available at the Instructor's companion site.

Notetaking Guide

Transparency Available
Promotes interactive learning and notetaking skills.
Available at the Instructor's companion site.

Animated Precalculus

An **Animated Precalculus** tutorial is available at the Student companion site for **Section 5.1.**

Pacing

Average: 2 days
Advanced: 2 days
Block: 0.5 block with Chapter 4 Test
0.5 block with 5.2

2 FOCUS AND MOTIVATE

Essential Question

How do you rewrite trigonometric expressions in order to simplify and evaluate functions? **Tell students that they will learn how to answer this question by studying the fundamental trigonometric identities and using them to simplify trigonometric expressions.**

5.1 Using Fundamental Identities

What you should learn

- Recognize and write the fundamental trigonometric identities.
- Use the fundamental trigonometric identities to evaluate trigonometric functions, simplify trigonometric expressions, and rewrite trigonometric expressions.

Why you should learn it

Fundamental trigonometric identities can be used to simplify trigonometric expressions. For instance, in Exercise 123 on page 379, you can use trigonometric identities to simplify an expression for the coefficient of friction.

Introduction

In Chapter 4, you studied the basic definitions, properties, graphs, and applications of the individual trigonometric functions. In this chapter, you will learn how to use the fundamental identities to do the following.

1. Evaluate trigonometric functions.
2. Simplify trigonometric expressions.
3. Develop additional trigonometric identities.
4. Solve trigonometric equations.

Fundamental Trigonometric Identities

Reciprocal Identities

$$\sin u = \frac{1}{\csc u} \qquad \cos u = \frac{1}{\sec u} \qquad \tan u = \frac{1}{\cot u}$$

$$\csc u = \frac{1}{\sin u} \qquad \sec u = \frac{1}{\cos u} \qquad \cot u = \frac{1}{\tan u}$$

Quotient Identities

$$\tan u = \frac{\sin u}{\cos u} \qquad \cot u = \frac{\cos u}{\sin u}$$

Pythagorean Identities

$$\sin^2 u + \cos^2 u = 1 \qquad 1 + \tan^2 u = \sec^2 u \qquad 1 + \cot^2 u = \csc^2 u$$

Cofunction Identities

$$\sin\left(\frac{\pi}{2} - u\right) = \cos u \qquad \cos\left(\frac{\pi}{2} - u\right) = \sin u$$

$$\tan\left(\frac{\pi}{2} - u\right) = \cot u \qquad \cot\left(\frac{\pi}{2} - u\right) = \tan u$$

$$\sec\left(\frac{\pi}{2} - u\right) = \csc u \qquad \csc\left(\frac{\pi}{2} - u\right) = \sec u$$

Even/Odd Identities

$$\sin(-u) = -\sin u \qquad \cos(-u) = \cos u \qquad \tan(-u) = -\tan u$$

$$\csc(-u) = -\csc u \qquad \sec(-u) = \sec u \qquad \cot(-u) = -\cot u$$

Study Tip

You should learn the fundamental trigonometric identities well, because they are used frequently in trigonometry and they will also appear later in calculus. Note that u can be an angle, a real number, or a variable.

Pythagorean identities are sometimes used in radical form such as

$$\sin u = \pm\sqrt{1 - \cos^2 u}$$

or

$$\tan u = \pm\sqrt{\sec^2 u - 1}$$

where the sign depends on the choice of u.

Resource Planning Guide

Chapter Resources
- Complete Solutions Guide

Workbooks
- Notetaking Guide
- Student Solutions Guide

Interactive Technology
- Instructor Success Organizer
- Notetaking Guide IAE
- Instructional DVDs
- Animated Precalculus
- PowerLecture with ExamView

Using the Fundamental Identities

One common application of trigonometric identities is to use given values of trigonometric functions to evaluate other trigonometric functions.

Example 1 Using Identities to Evaluate a Function

Use the values $\sec u = -\frac{3}{2}$ and $\tan u > 0$ to find the values of all six trigonometric functions.

Solution

Using a reciprocal identity, you have

$$\cos u = \frac{1}{\sec u} = \frac{1}{-3/2} = -\frac{2}{3}.$$

Using a Pythagorean identity, you have

$$\sin^2 u = 1 - \cos^2 u \qquad \text{Pythagorean identity}$$

$$= 1 - \left(-\frac{2}{3}\right)^2 \qquad \text{Substitute } -\tfrac{2}{3} \text{ for } \cos u.$$

$$= 1 - \frac{4}{9} = \frac{5}{9}. \qquad \text{Simplify.}$$

Because $\sec u < 0$ and $\tan u > 0$, it follows that u lies in Quadrant III. Moreover, because $\sin u$ is negative when u is in Quadrant III, you can choose the negative root and obtain $\sin u = -\sqrt{5}/3$. Now, knowing the values of the sine and cosine, you can find the values of all six trigonometric functions.

$$\sin u = -\frac{\sqrt{5}}{3} \qquad \csc u = \frac{1}{\sin u} = -\frac{3}{\sqrt{5}} = -\frac{3\sqrt{5}}{5}$$

$$\cos u = -\frac{2}{3} \qquad \sec u = \frac{1}{\cos u} = -\frac{3}{2}$$

$$\tan u = \frac{\sin u}{\cos u} = \frac{-\sqrt{5}/3}{-2/3} = \frac{\sqrt{5}}{2} \qquad \cot u = \frac{1}{\tan u} = \frac{2}{\sqrt{5}} = \frac{2\sqrt{5}}{5}$$

CHECKPoint Now try Exercise 21.

Example 2 Simplifying a Trigonometric Expression

Simplify $\sin x \cos^2 x - \sin x$.

Solution

First factor out a common monomial factor and then use a fundamental identity.

$$\sin x \cos^2 x - \sin x = \sin x(\cos^2 x - 1) \qquad \text{Factor out common monomial factor.}$$

$$= -\sin x(1 - \cos^2 x) \qquad \text{Factor out } -1.$$

$$= -\sin x(\sin^2 x) \qquad \text{Pythagorean identity}$$

$$= -\sin^3 x \qquad \text{Multiply.}$$

CHECKPoint Now try Exercise 59.

TECHNOLOGY

You can use a graphing utility to check the result of Example 2. To do this, graph

$y_1 = \sin x \cos^2 x - \sin x$

and

$y_2 = -\sin^3 x$

in the same viewing window, as shown below. Because Example 2 shows the equivalence algebraically and the two graphs appear to coincide, you can conclude that the expressions are equivalent.

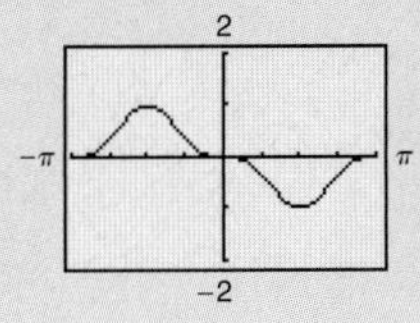

3 TEACH

Extra Example 1

Use the values $\sin x = \frac{1}{2}$ and $\cos x > 0$ to find the values of all six trigonometric functions.

$\sin x = \frac{1}{2}, \cos x = \frac{\sqrt{3}}{2},$

$\tan x = \frac{\sqrt{3}}{3}, \cot x = \sqrt{3},$

$\sec x = \frac{2\sqrt{3}}{3}, \csc x = 2$

Extra Example 2

Simplify $\cos^2 x \csc x - \csc x$.

$-\sin x$

Avoiding Common Errors

When simplifying expressions, remind students that any new value introduced must be a known trigonometric identity or an algebraic identity. For example, it is not acceptable to multiply an expression only by $\sin x$, but the expression can be multiplied by

$\frac{\sin x}{\sin x} = 1.$

Extra Example 3

Factor each expression.

a. $1 - \cos^2 x$

$(1 - \cos x)(1 + \cos x)$

b. $2\csc^2 x - 7\csc x + 6$

$(2\csc x - 3)(\csc x - 2)$

Extra Example 4

Factor $\sec^2 x + 3\tan x + 1$.

$(\tan x + 2)(\tan x + 1)$

Extra Example 5

Simplify $\csc t - \cos t \cot t$.

$\sin t$

When factoring trigonometric expressions, it is helpful to find a special polynomial factoring form that fits the expression, as shown in Example 3.

Example 3 Factoring Trigonometric Expressions

Factor each expression.

a. $\sec^2 \theta - 1$ **b.** $4\tan^2 \theta + \tan \theta - 3$

Solution

a. This expression has the form $u^2 - v^2$, which is the difference of two squares. It factors as

$$\sec^2 \theta - 1 = (\sec \theta - 1)(\sec \theta + 1).$$

b. This expression has the polynomial form $ax^2 + bx + c$, and it factors as

$$4\tan^2 \theta + \tan \theta - 3 = (4\tan \theta - 3)(\tan \theta + 1).$$

CHECK*Point* Now try Exercise 61.

Algebra Help

In Example 3, you need to be able to factor the difference of two squares and factor a trinomial. You can review the techniques for factoring in Appendix A.3.

On occasion, factoring or simplifying can best be done by first rewriting the expression in terms of just *one* trigonometric function or in terms of *sine and cosine only*. These strategies are shown in Examples 4 and 5, respectively.

Example 4 Factoring a Trigonometric Expression

Factor $\csc^2 x - \cot x - 3$.

Solution

Use the identity $\csc^2 x = 1 + \cot^2 x$ to rewrite the expression in terms of the cotangent.

$$\csc^2 x - \cot x - 3 = (1 + \cot^2 x) - \cot x - 3 \qquad \text{Pythagorean identity}$$

$$= \cot^2 x - \cot x - 2 \qquad \text{Combine like terms.}$$

$$= (\cot x - 2)(\cot x + 1) \qquad \text{Factor.}$$

CHECK*Point* Now try Exercise 65.

Example 5 Simplifying a Trigonometric Expression

Simplify $\sin t + \cot t \cos t$.

Solution

Begin by rewriting $\cot t$ in terms of sine and cosine.

$$\sin t + \cot t \cos t = \sin t + \left(\frac{\cos t}{\sin t}\right)\cos t \qquad \text{Quotient identity}$$

$$= \frac{\sin^2 t + \cos^2 t}{\sin t} \qquad \text{Add fractions.}$$

$$= \frac{1}{\sin t} \qquad \text{Pythagorean identity}$$

$$= \csc t \qquad \text{Reciprocal identity}$$

CHECK*Point* Now try Exercise 71.

Study Tip

Remember that when adding rational expressions, you must first find the least common denominator (LCD). In Example 5, the LCD is $\sin t$.

Example 6 Adding Trigonometric Expressions

Perform the addition and simplify.

$$\frac{\sin\theta}{1+\cos\theta}+\frac{\cos\theta}{\sin\theta}$$

Solution

$$\frac{\sin\theta}{1+\cos\theta}+\frac{\cos\theta}{\sin\theta}=\frac{(\sin\theta)(\sin\theta)+(\cos\theta)(1+\cos\theta)}{(1+\cos\theta)(\sin\theta)}$$

$$=\frac{\sin^2\theta+\cos^2\theta+\cos\theta}{(1+\cos\theta)(\sin\theta)}$$ Multiply.

$$=\frac{\cancel{1+\cos\theta}}{\cancel{(1+\cos\theta)}(\sin\theta)}$$ Pythagorean identity: $\sin^2\theta+\cos^2\theta=1$

$$=\frac{1}{\sin\theta}$$ Divide out common factor.

$$=\csc\theta$$ Reciprocal identity

CHECKPoint Now try Exercise 75.

The next two examples involve techniques for rewriting expressions in forms that are used in calculus.

Example 7 Rewriting a Trigonometric Expression

Rewrite $\dfrac{1}{1+\sin x}$ so that it is *not* in fractional form.

Solution

From the Pythagorean identity $\cos^2 x = 1-\sin^2 x = (1-\sin x)(1+\sin x)$, you can see that multiplying both the numerator and the denominator by $(1-\sin x)$ will produce a monomial denominator.

$$\frac{1}{1+\sin x}=\frac{1}{1+\sin x}\cdot\frac{1-\sin x}{1-\sin x}$$ Multiply numerator and denominator by $(1-\sin x)$.

$$=\frac{1-\sin x}{1-\sin^2 x}$$ Multiply.

$$=\frac{1-\sin x}{\cos^2 x}$$ Pythagorean identity

$$=\frac{1}{\cos^2 x}-\frac{\sin x}{\cos^2 x}$$ Write as separate fractions.

$$=\frac{1}{\cos^2 x}-\frac{\sin x}{\cos x}\cdot\frac{1}{\cos x}$$ Product of fractions

$$=\sec^2 x-\tan x\sec x$$ Reciprocal and quotient identities

CHECKPoint Now try Exercise 81.

Extra Example 6

Perform the addition and simplify $\dfrac{1}{1+\sin\theta}+\dfrac{1}{1-\sin\theta}$.

$2\sec^2\theta$

Extra Example 7

Rewrite $\dfrac{\cos^2 y}{1-\sin y}$ so that it is *not* in fractional form.

$1+\sin y$

Extra Example 8

Use the substitution $x = 5 \sin \theta$, $0 < \theta < \frac{\pi}{2}$ to write $\sqrt{25 - x^2}$ as a trigonometric function of θ.

$5 \cos \theta$

Extra Example 9

Rewrite $\ln|\sec \theta| + \ln|\cot \theta|$ as a single logarithm and simplify the result.

$\ln|\csc \theta|$

Closing the Lesson

Have students summarize the major points of the lesson and answer the Essential Question: How do you rewrite trigonometric expressions in order to simplify and evaluate trigonometric functions?

Use the fundamental trigonometric identities to

- **simplify trigonometric expressions,**
- **evaluate trigonometric functions,**
- **solve trigonometric equations, and**
- **develop additional trigonometric identities.**

Example 8 Trigonometric Substitution

Use the substitution $x = 2 \tan \theta$, $0 < \theta < \pi/2$, to write

$$\sqrt{4 + x^2}$$

as a trigonometric function of θ.

Solution

Begin by letting $x = 2 \tan \theta$. Then, you can obtain

$\sqrt{4 + x^2} = \sqrt{4 + (2 \tan \theta)^2}$	Substitute $2 \tan \theta$ for x.
$= \sqrt{4 + 4 \tan^2 \theta}$	Rule of exponents
$= \sqrt{4(1 + \tan^2 \theta)}$	Factor.
$= \sqrt{4 \sec^2 \theta}$	Pythagorean identity
$= 2 \sec \theta.$	$\sec \theta > 0$ for $0 < \theta < \pi/2$

CHECK*Point* Now try Exercise 93.

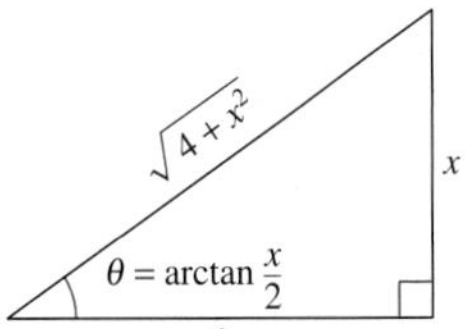

Angle whose tangent is $\pi/2$.
FIGURE 5.1

Figure 5.1 shows the right triangle illustration of the trigonometric substitution $x = 2 \tan \theta$ in Example 8. You can use this triangle to check the solution of Example 8. For $0 < \theta < \pi/2$, you have

$$\text{opp} = x, \quad \text{adj} = 2, \quad \text{and} \quad \text{hyp} = \sqrt{4 + x^2}.$$

With these expressions, you can write the following.

$$\sec \theta = \frac{\text{hyp}}{\text{adj}}$$

$$\sec \theta = \frac{\sqrt{4 + x^2}}{2}$$

$$2 \sec \theta = \sqrt{4 + x^2}$$

So, the solution checks.

Example 9 Rewriting a Logarithmic Expression

Rewrite $\ln|\csc \theta| + \ln|\tan \theta|$ as a single logarithm and simplify the result.

Solution

$\ln|\csc \theta| + \ln|\tan \theta| = \ln|\csc \theta \tan \theta|$	Product Property of Logarithms
$= \ln\left\lvert\frac{1}{\sin \theta} \cdot \frac{\sin \theta}{\cos \theta}\right\rvert$	Reciprocal and quotient identities
$= \ln\left\lvert\frac{1}{\cos \theta}\right\rvert$	Simplify.
$= \ln|\sec \theta|$	Reciprocal identity

CHECK*Point* Now try Exercise 113.

Algebra Help

Recall that for positive real numbers u and v,

$$\ln u + \ln v = \ln(uv).$$

You can review the properties of logarithms in Section 3.3.

Differentiated Instruction

Auditory Learners To simplify expressions in the exercises, students will need to use the fundamental trigonometric identities. Instruct them to read each identity aloud so that they can hear how it is used in the expression. Naming each identity as it is implemented will help students better remember the case in which each identity is used.

5.1 EXERCISES

See www.CalcChat.com for worked-out solutions to odd-numbered exercises.

VOCABULARY: Fill in the blank to complete the trigonometric identity.

1. $\dfrac{\sin u}{\cos u} = $ tan u
2. $\dfrac{1}{\csc u} = $ sin u
3. $\dfrac{1}{\tan u} = $ cot u
4. $\dfrac{1}{\cos u} = $ sec u
5. $1 + $ $\cot^2 u$ $= \csc^2 u$
6. $1 + \tan^2 u = $ $\sec^2 u$
7. $\sin\left(\dfrac{\pi}{2} - u\right) = $ cos u
8. $\sec\left(\dfrac{\pi}{2} - u\right) = $ csc u
9. $\cos(-u) = $ cos u
10. $\tan(-u) = $ $-\tan u$

SKILLS AND APPLICATIONS

In Exercises 11–24, use the given values to evaluate (if possible) all six trigonometric functions. 11–24. See margin.

11. $\sin x = \frac{1}{2}, \quad \cos x = \frac{\sqrt{3}}{2}$
12. $\tan x = \frac{\sqrt{3}}{3}, \quad \cos x = -\frac{\sqrt{3}}{2}$
13. $\sec \theta = \sqrt{2}, \quad \sin \theta = -\frac{\sqrt{2}}{2}$
14. $\csc \theta = \frac{25}{7}, \quad \tan \theta = \frac{7}{24}$
15. $\tan x = \frac{8}{15}, \quad \sec x = -\frac{17}{15}$
16. $\cot \phi = -3, \quad \sin \phi = \frac{\sqrt{10}}{10}$
17. $\sec \phi = \frac{3}{2}, \quad \csc \phi = -\frac{3\sqrt{5}}{5}$
18. $\cos\left(\frac{\pi}{2} - x\right) = \frac{3}{5}, \quad \cos x = \frac{4}{5}$
19. $\sin(-x) = -\frac{1}{3}, \quad \tan x = -\frac{\sqrt{2}}{4}$
20. $\sec x = 4, \quad \sin x > 0$
21. $\tan \theta = 2, \quad \sin \theta < 0$
22. $\csc \theta = -5, \quad \cos \theta < 0$
23. $\sin \theta = -1, \quad \cot \theta = 0$
24. $\tan \theta$ is undefined, $\quad \sin \theta > 0$

In Exercises 25–30, match the trigonometric expression with one of the following.

(a) $\sec x$	(b) -1	(c) $\cot x$
(d) 1	(e) $-\tan x$	(f) $\sin x$

25. $\sec x \cos x$ d
26. $\tan x \csc x$ a
27. $\cot^2 x - \csc^2 x$ b
28. $(1 - \cos^2 x)(\csc x)$ f
29. $\dfrac{\sin(-x)}{\cos(-x)}$ e
30. $\dfrac{\sin[(\pi/2) - x]}{\cos[(\pi/2) - x]}$ c

In Exercises 31–36, match the trigonometric expression with one of the following.

(a) $\csc x$	(b) $\tan x$	(c) $\sin^2 x$
(d) $\sin x \tan x$	(e) $\sec^2 x$	(f) $\sec^2 x + \tan^2 x$

31. $\sin x \sec x$ b
32. $\cos^2 x(\sec^2 x - 1)$ c
33. $\sec^4 x - \tan^4 x$ f
34. $\cot x \sec x$ a
35. $\dfrac{\sec^2 x - 1}{\sin^2 x}$ e
36. $\dfrac{\cos^2[(\pi/2) - x]}{\cos x}$ d

In Exercises 37–58, use the fundamental identities to simplify the expression. There is more than one correct form of each answer.

37. $\cot \theta \sec \theta$ $\csc \theta$
38. $\cos \beta \tan \beta$ $\sin \beta$
39. $\tan(-x) \cos x$ $-\sin x$
40. $\sin x \cot(-x)$ $-\cos x$
41. $\sin \phi(\csc \phi - \sin \phi)$ $\cos^2 \phi$
42. $\sec^2 x(1 - \sin^2 x)$ 1
43. $\dfrac{\cot x}{\csc x}$ $\cos x$
44. $\dfrac{\csc \theta}{\sec \theta}$ $\cot \theta$
45. $\dfrac{1 - \sin^2 x}{\csc^2 x - 1}$ $\sin^2 x$
46. $\dfrac{1}{\tan^2 x + 1}$ $\cos^2 x$
47. $\dfrac{\tan \theta \cot \theta}{\sec \theta}$ $\cos \theta$
48. $\dfrac{\sin \theta \csc \theta}{\tan \theta}$ $\cot \theta$
49. $\sec \alpha \cdot \dfrac{\sin \alpha}{\tan \alpha}$ 1
50. $\dfrac{\tan^2 \theta}{\sec^2 \theta}$ $\sin^2 \theta$
51. $\cos\left(\dfrac{\pi}{2} - x\right)\sec x$ $\tan x$
52. $\cot\left(\dfrac{\pi}{2} - x\right)\cos x$ $\sin x$
53. $\dfrac{\cos^2 y}{1 - \sin y}$ $1 + \sin y$
54. $\cos t(1 + \tan^2 t)$ $\sec t$
55. $\sin \beta \tan \beta + \cos \beta$ $\sec \beta$
56. $\csc \phi \tan \phi + \sec \phi$ $2 \sec \phi$
57. $\cot u \sin u + \tan u \cos u$ $\cos u + \sin u$
58. $\sin \theta \sec \theta + \cos \theta \csc \theta$ $\csc \theta \sec \theta$

4 PRACTICE AND APPLY

Assignment Guide

Transparencies Available
Available at the Instructor's companion site.

Average:
Day 1: pp. 377–378
Exs. 11–15 odd, 18, 19, 25–37, 45–57 odd, 67, 69, 73
Day 2: pp. 378–379
Exs. 77, 82, 83, 85, 89, 93–109 odd, 114, 117–123 odd, 127–129, 131, 133, 137, 142

Advanced:
Day 1: pp. 377–378
Exs. 12–16 even, 17, 22, 24–36, 42–46 even, 52–58 even, 62–74 even
Day 2: pp. 378–379
Exs. 76, 80, 84, 88, 90, 94, 100–110 even, 117, 118–124 even, 130–134 even, 135, 136, 138, 142

Block:
pp. 377–378
Exs. 11–15 odd, 18, 19, 25–37, 45–57 odd, 67, 69, 73 (with Chapter 4 Test)
pp. 378–379
Exs. 77, 82, 83, 85, 89, 93–109 odd, 114, 117–123 odd, 127–129, 131, 133, 137, 142 (with 5.2)

11. $\sin x = \frac{1}{2}$, $\cos x = \frac{\sqrt{3}}{2}$, $\tan x = \frac{\sqrt{3}}{3}$, $\csc x = 2$, $\sec x = \frac{2\sqrt{3}}{3}$, $\cot x = \sqrt{3}$

12. $\sin x = -\frac{1}{2}$, $\cos x = -\frac{\sqrt{3}}{2}$, $\tan x = \frac{\sqrt{3}}{3}$, $\csc x = -2$, $\sec x = -\frac{2\sqrt{3}}{3}$, $\cot x = \sqrt{3}$

13. $\sin \theta = -\frac{\sqrt{2}}{2}$, $\cos \theta = \frac{\sqrt{2}}{2}$, $\tan \theta = -1$, $\csc \theta = -\sqrt{2}$, $\sec \theta = \sqrt{2}$, $\cot \theta = -1$

14. $\sin \theta = \frac{7}{25}$, $\cos \theta = \frac{24}{25}$, $\tan \theta = \frac{7}{24}$, $\csc \theta = \frac{25}{7}$, $\sec \theta = \frac{25}{24}$, $\cot \theta = \frac{24}{7}$

15. $\sin x = -\frac{8}{17}$, $\cos x = -\frac{15}{17}$, $\tan x = \frac{8}{15}$, $\csc x = -\frac{17}{8}$, $\sec x = -\frac{17}{15}$, $\cot x = \frac{15}{8}$

16. $\sin \phi = \frac{\sqrt{10}}{10}$, $\cos \phi = -\frac{3\sqrt{10}}{10}$, $\tan \phi = -\frac{1}{3}$, $\csc \phi = \sqrt{10}$, $\sec \phi = -\frac{\sqrt{10}}{3}$, $\cot \phi = -3$

17–24. See Additional Answers beginning on page AA1.

59. $\sin^2 x$
60. $\cos^2 x$
61. $\sin^2 x \tan^2 x$
65. $\sec^4 x$
66. $\sin^4 x$
67. $\sin^2 x - \cos^2 x$
68. $\sec^2 x + \tan^2 x$
75. $2 \csc^2 x$
76. $-2 \cot^2 x$
77. $2 \sec x$
78. $2 \csc x$
85. See below.
86. See below.
105. $3 \cos \theta = 3$
$\sin \theta = 0$
$\cos \theta = 1$
106. $6 \cos \theta = 3$
$\sin \theta = \pm\frac{\sqrt{3}}{2}$
$\cos \theta = \frac{1}{2}$
107. $4 \sin \theta = 2\sqrt{2}$
$\sin \theta = \frac{\sqrt{2}}{2}$
$\cos \theta = \frac{\sqrt{2}}{2}$
108. $10 \sin \theta = -5\sqrt{3}$
$\sin \theta = -\frac{\sqrt{3}}{2}$
$\cos \theta = \frac{1}{2}$
110. $\frac{\pi}{2} \le \theta \le \frac{3\pi}{2}$
111. $0 \le \theta < \frac{\pi}{2}, \frac{3\pi}{2} < \theta < 2\pi$

In Exercises 59–70, factor the expression and use the fundamental identities to simplify. There is more than one correct form of each answer. 59–61, 65–68. See margin.

59. $\tan^2 x - \tan^2 x \sin^2 x$
60. $\sin^2 x \csc^2 x - \sin^2 x$
61. $\sin^2 x \sec^2 x - \sin^2 x$
62. $\cos^2 x + \cos^2 x \tan^2 x$ 1
63. $\frac{\sec^2 x - 1}{\sec x - 1}$ $\sec x + 1$
64. $\frac{\cos^2 x - 4}{\cos x - 2}$ $\cos x + 2$
65. $\tan^4 x + 2 \tan^2 x + 1$
66. $1 - 2 \cos^2 x + \cos^4 x$
67. $\sin^4 x - \cos^4 x$
68. $\sec^4 x - \tan^4 x$
69. $\csc^3 x - \csc^2 x - \csc x + 1$ $\cot^2 x(\csc x - 1)$
70. $\sec^3 x - \sec^2 x - \sec x + 1$ $\tan^2 x(\sec x - 1)$

In Exercises 71–74, perform the multiplication and use the fundamental identities to simplify. There is more than one correct form of each answer.

71. $(\sin x + \cos x)^2$ $1 + 2 \sin x \cos x$
72. $(\cot x + \csc x)(\cot x - \csc x)$ -1
73. $(2 \csc x + 2)(2 \csc x - 2)$ $4 \cot^2 x$
74. $(3 - 3 \sin x)(3 + 3 \sin x)$ $9 \cos^2 x$

In Exercises 75–80, perform the addition or subtraction and use the fundamental identities to simplify. There is more than one correct form of each answer. 75–78. See margin.

75. $\frac{1}{1 + \cos x} + \frac{1}{1 - \cos x}$
76. $\frac{1}{\sec x + 1} - \frac{1}{\sec x - 1}$
77. $\frac{\cos x}{1 + \sin x} + \frac{1 + \sin x}{\cos x}$
78. $\frac{\tan x}{1 + \sec x} + \frac{1 + \sec x}{\tan x}$
79. $\tan x + \frac{\cos x}{1 + \sin x}$ $\sec x$
80. $\tan x - \frac{\sec^2 x}{\tan x}$ $-\cot x$

In Exercises 81–84, rewrite the expression so that it is not in fractional form. There is more than one correct form of each answer.

81. $\frac{\sin^2 y}{1 - \cos y}$ $1 + \cos y$
82. $\frac{5}{\tan x + \sec x}$ $5(\sec x - \tan x)$
83. $\frac{3}{\sec x - \tan x}$ $3(\sec x + \tan x)$
84. $\frac{\tan^2 x}{\csc x + 1}$ $\tan^4 x(\csc x - 1)$

NUMERICAL AND GRAPHICAL ANALYSIS In Exercises 85–88, use a graphing utility to complete the table and graph the functions. Make a conjecture about y_1 and y_2.

x	0.2	0.4	0.6	0.8	1.0	1.2	1.4
y_1							
y_2							

85–88. See margin.

85. $y_1 = \cos\left(\frac{\pi}{2} - x\right), \quad y_2 = \sin x$
86. $y_1 = \sec x - \cos x, \quad y_2 = \sin x \tan x$
87. $y_1 = \frac{\cos x}{1 - \sin x}, \quad y_2 = \frac{1 + \sin x}{\cos x}$
88. $y_1 = \sec^4 x - \sec^2 x, \quad y_2 = \tan^2 x + \tan^4 x$

In Exercises 89–92, use a graphing utility to determine which of the six trigonometric functions is equal to the expression. Verify your answer algebraically.

89. $\cos x \cot x + \sin x$ $\csc x$
90. $\sec x \csc x - \tan x$ $\cot x$
91. $\frac{1}{\sin x}\left(\frac{1}{\cos x} - \cos x\right)$ $\tan x$
92. $\frac{1}{2}\left(\frac{1 + \sin \theta}{\cos \theta} + \frac{\cos \theta}{1 + \sin \theta}\right)$ $\sec \theta$

In Exercises 93–104, use the trigonometric substitution to write the algebraic expression as a trigonometric function of θ, where $0 < \theta < \pi/2$.

93. $\sqrt{9 - x^2}, \quad x = 3 \cos \theta$ $3 \sin \theta$
94. $\sqrt{64 - 16x^2}, \quad x = 2 \cos \theta$ $8 \sin \theta$
95. $\sqrt{16 - x^2}, \quad x = 4 \sin \theta$ $4 \cos \theta$
96. $\sqrt{49 - x^2}, \quad x = 7 \sin \theta$ $7 \cos \theta$
97. $\sqrt{x^2 - 9}, \quad x = 3 \sec \theta$ $3 \tan \theta$
98. $\sqrt{x^2 - 4}, \quad x = 2 \sec \theta$ $2 \tan \theta$
99. $\sqrt{x^2 + 25}, \quad x = 5 \tan \theta$ $5 \sec \theta$
100. $\sqrt{x^2 + 100}, \quad x = 10 \tan \theta$ $10 \sec \theta$
101. $\sqrt{4x^2 + 9}, \quad 2x = 3 \tan \theta$ $3 \sec \theta$
102. $\sqrt{9x^2 + 25}, \quad 3x = 5 \tan \theta$ $5 \sec \theta$
103. $\sqrt{2 - x^2}, \quad x = \sqrt{2} \sin \theta$ $\sqrt{2} \cos \theta$
104. $\sqrt{10 - x^2}, \quad x = \sqrt{10} \sin \theta$ $\sqrt{10} \cos \theta$

In Exercises 105–108, use the trigonometric substitution to write the algebraic equation as a trigonometric equation of θ, where $-\pi/2 < \theta < \pi/2$. Then find $\sin \theta$ and $\cos \theta$. 105–108. See margin.

105. $3 = \sqrt{9 - x^2}, \quad x = 3 \sin \theta$
106. $3 = \sqrt{36 - x^2}, \quad x = 6 \sin \theta$
107. $2\sqrt{2} = \sqrt{16 - 4x^2}, \quad x = 2 \cos \theta$
108. $-5\sqrt{3} = \sqrt{100 - x^2}, \quad x = 10 \cos \theta$

In Exercises 109–112, use a graphing utility to solve the equation for θ, where $0 \le \theta < 2\pi$.

109. $\sin \theta = \sqrt{1 - \cos^2 \theta}$ $0 \le \theta \le \pi$
110. $\cos \theta = -\sqrt{1 - \sin^2 \theta}$
111. $\sec \theta = \sqrt{1 + \tan^2 \theta}$
110–111. See margin.
112. $\csc \theta = \sqrt{1 + \cot^2 \theta}$ $0 < \theta < \pi$

85.

x	0.2	0.4	0.6	0.8	1.0	1.2	1.4
y_1	0.1987	0.3894	0.5646	0.7174	0.8415	0.9320	0.9854
y_2	0.1987	0.3894	0.5646	0.7174	0.8415	0.9320	0.9854

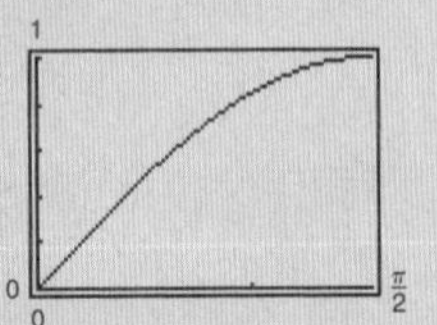

$y_1 = y_2$

86.

x	0.2	0.4	0.6	0.8	1.0	1.2	1.4
y_1	0.0403	0.1646	0.3863	0.7386	1.3105	2.3973	5.7135
y_2	0.0403	0.1646	0.3863	0.7386	1.3105	2.3973	5.7135

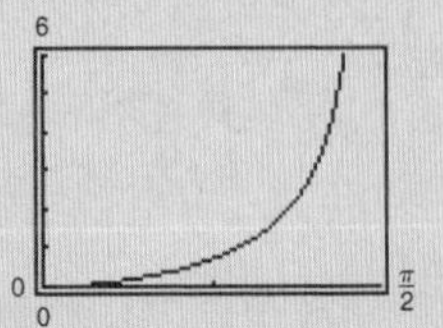

$y_1 = y_2$

87–88. See Additional Answers beginning on page AA1.

In Exercises 113–118, rewrite the expression as a single logarithm and simplify the result. 113–116. See margin.

113. $\ln|\cos x| - \ln|\sin x|$ **114.** $\ln|\sec x| + \ln|\sin x|$

115. $\ln|\sin x| + \ln|\cot x|$ **116.** $\ln|\tan x| + \ln|\csc x|$

117. $\ln|\cot t| + \ln(1 + \tan^2 t)$ $\ln|\csc t \sec t|$

118. $\ln(\cos^2 t) + \ln(1 + \tan^2 t)$ 0

In Exercises 119–122, use a calculator to demonstrate the identity for each value of θ. 119–122. See margin.

119. $\csc^2 \theta - \cot^2 \theta = 1$

(a) $\theta = 132°$ (b) $\theta = \dfrac{2\pi}{7}$

120. $\tan^2 \theta + 1 = \sec^2 \theta$

(a) $\theta = 346°$ (b) $\theta = 3.1$

121. $\cos\left(\dfrac{\pi}{2} - \theta\right) = \sin \theta$

(a) $\theta = 80°$ (b) $\theta = 0.8$

122. $\sin(-\theta) = -\sin \theta$

(a) $\theta = 250°$ (b) $\theta = \frac{1}{2}$

123. FRICTION The forces acting on an object weighing W units on an inclined plane positioned at an angle of θ with the horizontal (see figure) are modeled by

$$\mu W \cos \theta = W \sin \theta$$

where μ is the coefficient of friction. Solve the equation for μ and simplify the result. $\mu = \tan \theta$

124. RATE OF CHANGE The rate of change of the function $f(x) = -x + \tan x$ is given by the expression $-1 + \sec^2 x$. Show that this expression can also be written as $\tan^2 x$. Answers will vary.

125. RATE OF CHANGE The rate of change of the function $f(x) = \sec x + \cos x$ is given by the expression $\sec x \tan x - \sin x$. Show that this expression can also be written as $\sin x \tan^2 x$. Answers will vary.

126. RATE OF CHANGE The rate of change of the function $f(x) = -\csc x - \sin x$ is given by the expression $\csc x \cot x - \cos x$. Show that this expression can also be written as $\cos x \cot^2 x$. Answers will vary.

EXPLORATION

127–128. See margin.

TRUE OR FALSE? In Exercises 127 and 128, determine whether the statement is true or false. Justify your answer.

127. The even and odd trigonometric identities are helpful for determining whether the value of a trigonometric function is positive or negative.

128. A cofunction identity can be used to transform a tangent function so that it can be represented by a cosecant function.

In Exercises 129–132, fill in the blanks. (*Note:* The notation $x \to c^+$ indicates that x approaches c from the right and $x \to c^-$ indicates that x approaches c from the left.)

129. As $x \to \dfrac{\pi}{2}^-$, $\sin x \to$ ____ and $\csc x \to$ ____. 1, 1

130. As $x \to 0^+$, $\cos x \to$ ____ and $\sec x \to$ ____. 1, 1

131. As $x \to \dfrac{\pi}{2}^-$, $\tan x \to$ ____ and $\cot x \to$ ____. ∞, 0

132. As $x \to \pi^+$, $\sin x \to$ ____ and $\csc x \to$ ____. 0, $-\infty$

In Exercises 133–138, determine whether or not the equation is an identity, and give a reason for your answer.

133. $\cos \theta = \sqrt{1 - \sin^2 \theta}$ **134.** $\cot \theta = \sqrt{\csc^2 \theta + 1}$

135. $\dfrac{(\sin k\theta)}{(\cos k\theta)} = \tan \theta$, k is a constant.

133–138. See margin.

136. $\dfrac{1}{(5 \cos \theta)} = 5 \sec \theta$

137. $\sin \theta \csc \theta = 1$ **138.** $\csc^2 \theta = 1$

139. Use the trigonometric substitution $u = a \sin \theta$, where $-\pi/2 < \theta < \pi/2$ and $a > 0$, to simplify the expression $\sqrt{a^2 - u^2}$. $a \cos \theta$

140. Use the trigonometric substitution $u = a \tan \theta$, where $-\pi/2 < \theta < \pi/2$ and $a > 0$, to simplify the expression $\sqrt{a^2 + u^2}$. $a \sec \theta$

141. Use the trigonometric substitution $u = a \sec \theta$, where $0 < \theta < \pi/2$ and $a > 0$, to simplify the expression $\sqrt{u^2 - a^2}$. $a \tan \theta$

142. CAPSTONE (a)–(b). Answers will vary.

(a) Use the definitions of sine and cosine to derive the Pythagorean identity $\sin^2 \theta + \cos^2 \theta = 1$.

(b) Use the Pythagorean identity $\sin^2 \theta + \cos^2 \theta = 1$ to derive the other Pythagorean identities, $1 + \tan^2 \theta = \sec^2 \theta$ and $1 + \cot^2 \theta = \csc^2 \theta$. Discuss how to remember these identities and other fundamental identities.

5 ASSESS AND RETEACH

Daily Homework Quiz

Transparency Available

Available at the Instructor's companion site.

113. $\ln|\cot x|$

114. $\ln|\tan x|$

115. $\ln|\cos x|$

116. $\ln|\sec x|$

119. See below.

120. See below.

121. (a) $\cos(90° - 80°) = \sin 80° \approx 0.9848$

(b) $\cos\left(\dfrac{\pi}{2} - 0.8\right) = \sin 0.8 \approx 0.7174$

122. (a) $\sin(-250°) = -\sin 250° \approx 0.9397$

(b) $\sin\left(-\frac{1}{2}\right) = -\sin\left(\frac{1}{2}\right) \approx -0.4794$

127. True. For example, $\sin(-x) = -\sin x$.

128. False. A cofunction identity can be used to transform a tangent function so that it can be represented by a cotangent function.

133. Not an identity because $\cos \theta = \pm\sqrt{1 - \sin^2 \theta}$

134. Not an identity because $\cot \theta = \pm\sqrt{\csc^2 \theta - 1}$

135. Not an identity because $\dfrac{\sin k\theta}{\cos k\theta} = \tan k\theta$

136. Not an identity because $\dfrac{5}{\cos \theta} \neq \dfrac{1}{5 \cos \theta}$

137. An identity because $\sin \theta \cdot \dfrac{1}{\sin \theta} = 1$

138. Not an identity because $\dfrac{1}{\sin \theta} \neq 1$

119. (a) $\csc^2 132° - \cot^2 132° \approx 1.8107 - 0.8107 = 1$

(b) $\csc^2 \dfrac{2\pi}{7} - \cot^2 \dfrac{2\pi}{7} \approx 1.6360 - 0.6360 = 1$

120. (a) $(\tan 346°)^2 + 1 = (\sec 346°)^2 \approx 1.0622$

(b) $(\tan 3.1)^2 + 1 = (\sec 3.1)^2 \approx 1.0017$

5.2 Verifying Trigonometric Identities

What you should learn

- Verify trigonometric identities.

Why you should learn it

You can use trigonometric identities to rewrite trigonometric equations that model real-life situations. For instance, in Exercise 70 on page 386, you can use trigonometric identities to simplify the equation that models the length of a shadow cast by a gnomon (a device used to tell time).

Robert W. Ginn/PhotoEdit

Introduction

In this section, you will study techniques for verifying trigonometric identities. In the next section, you will study techniques for solving trigonometric equations. The key to verifying identities *and* solving equations is the ability to use the fundamental identities and the rules of algebra to rewrite trigonometric expressions.

Remember that a *conditional equation* is an equation that is true for only some of the values in its domain. For example, the conditional equation

$$\sin x = 0 \qquad \text{Conditional equation}$$

is true only for $x = n\pi$, where n is an integer. When you find these values, you are *solving* the equation.

On the other hand, an equation that is true for all real values in the domain of the variable is an *identity*. For example, the familiar equation

$$\sin^2 x = 1 - \cos^2 x \qquad \text{Identity}$$

is true for all real numbers x. So, it is an identity.

Verifying Trigonometric Identities

Although there are similarities, verifying that a trigonometric equation is an identity is quite different from solving an equation. There is no well-defined set of rules to follow in verifying trigonometric identities, and the process is best learned by practice.

Guidelines for Verifying Trigonometric Identities

1. Work with one side of the equation at a time. It is often better to work with the more complicated side first.
2. Look for opportunities to factor an expression, add fractions, square a binomial, or create a monomial denominator.
3. Look for opportunities to use the fundamental identities. Note which functions are in the final expression you want. Sines and cosines pair up well, as do secants and tangents, and cosecants and cotangents.
4. If the preceding guidelines do not help, try converting all terms to sines and cosines.
5. Always try *something*. Even paths that lead to dead ends provide insights.

Verifying trigonometric identities is a useful process if you need to convert a trigonometric expression into a form that is more useful algebraically. When you verify an identity, you cannot *assume* that the two sides of the equation are equal because you are trying to verify that they *are* equal. As a result, when verifying identities, you cannot use operations such as adding the same quantity to each side of the equation or cross multiplication.

1 PLAN AND PREPARE

Warm-up Exercises

Transparency Available
Available at the Instructor's companion site.

Notetaking Guide

Transparency Available
Promotes interactive learning and notetaking skills. Available at the Instructor's companion site.

Animated Precalculus

An **Animated Precalculus** tutorial is available at the Student companion site for **Section 5.2.**

Pacing

Average: 1 day
Advanced: 1 day
Block: 0.5 block with 5.1

2 FOCUS AND MOTIVATE

Essential Question

How do you verify a trigonometric identity? **Tell students that they will learn how to answer this question by rewriting at least one side of the identity, using the fundamental trigonometric identities.**

Resource Planning Guide

Chapter Resources

- Complete Solutions Guide

Workbooks

- Notetaking Guide
- Student Solutions Guide

Interactive Technology

- Instructor Success Organizer
- Notetaking Guide IAE
- Instructional DVDs
- Animated Precalculus
- PowerLecture with ExamView

Example 1 Verifying a Trigonometric Identity

Verify the identity $(\sec^2 \theta - 1)/\sec^2 \theta = \sin^2 \theta$.

Solution

The left side is more complicated, so start with it.

$$\frac{\sec^2 \theta - 1}{\sec^2 \theta} = \frac{(\tan^2 \theta + 1) - 1}{\sec^2 \theta} \qquad \text{Pythagorean identity}$$

$$= \frac{\tan^2 \theta}{\sec^2 \theta} \qquad \text{Simplify.}$$

$$= \tan^2 \theta(\cos^2 \theta) \qquad \text{Reciprocal identity}$$

$$= \frac{\sin^2 \theta}{\cancel{(\cos^2 \theta)}}\cancel{(\cos^2 \theta)} \qquad \text{Quotient identity}$$

$$= \sin^2 \theta \qquad \text{Simplify.}$$

Notice how the identity is verified. You start with the left side of the equation (the more complicated side) and use the fundamental trigonometric identities to simplify it until you obtain the right side.

CHECKPoint Now try Exercise 15.

> **WARNING / CAUTION**
> Remember that an identity is only true for all real values in the domain of the variable. For instance, in Example 1 the identity is not true when $\theta = \pi/2$ because $\sec^2 \theta$ is not defined when $\theta = \pi/2$.

There can be more than one way to verify an identity. Here is another way to verify the identity in Example 1.

$$\frac{\sec^2 \theta - 1}{\sec^2 \theta} = \frac{\sec^2 \theta}{\sec^2 \theta} - \frac{1}{\sec^2 \theta} \qquad \text{Rewrite as the difference of fractions.}$$

$$= 1 - \cos^2 \theta \qquad \text{Reciprocal identity}$$

$$= \sin^2 \theta \qquad \text{Pythagorean identity}$$

Example 2 Verifying a Trigonometric Identity

Verify the identity $2\sec^2 \alpha = \dfrac{1}{1 - \sin \alpha} + \dfrac{1}{1 + \sin \alpha}$.

Algebraic Solution

The right side is more complicated, so start with it.

$$\frac{1}{1 - \sin \alpha} + \frac{1}{1 + \sin \alpha} = \frac{1 + \sin \alpha + 1 - \sin \alpha}{(1 - \sin \alpha)(1 + \sin \alpha)} \qquad \text{Add fractions.}$$

$$= \frac{2}{1 - \sin^2 \alpha} \qquad \text{Simplify.}$$

$$= \frac{2}{\cos^2 \alpha} \qquad \text{Pythagorean identity}$$

$$= 2\sec^2 \alpha \qquad \text{Reciprocal identity}$$

Numerical Solution

Use the *table* feature of a graphing utility set in *radian* mode to create a table that shows the values of $y_1 = 2/\cos^2 x$ and $y_2 = 1/(1 - \sin x) + 1/(1 + \sin x)$ for different values of x, as shown in Figure 5.2. From the table, you can see that the values appear to be identical, so $2\sec^2 x = 1/(1 - \sin x) + 1/(1 + \sin x)$ appears to be an identity.

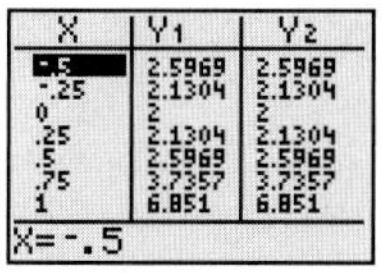

FIGURE 5.2

CHECKPoint Now try Exercise 31.

3 TEACH

Extra Example 1

Verify the identity $\dfrac{\sin^2 \theta + \cos^2 \theta}{\cos^2 \theta \sec^2 \theta} = 1$.

$$\frac{\sin^2 \theta + \cos^2 \theta}{\cos^2 \theta \sec^2 \theta} = \frac{1}{\cos^2 \theta \sec^2 \theta}$$

$$= \frac{\cos^2 \theta}{\cos^2 \theta}$$

$$= 1$$

Avoiding Common Errors

Students often try to verify identities by using methods learned for solving equations. Emphasize that identities are not conditional equations but actually two equivalent expressions. Either side must be worked on separately as an expression. Each step should have a justifiable reason for the changes made. Writing the reasons can help students understand the process.

Extra Example 2

Verify the identity

$$\frac{1}{1 - \cos \beta} + \frac{1}{1 + \cos \beta} = 2\csc^2 \beta.$$

$$\frac{1}{1 - \cos \beta} + \frac{1}{1 + \cos \beta}$$

$$= \frac{1 + \cos \beta + 1 - \cos \beta}{(1 - \cos \beta)(1 + \cos \beta)}$$

$$= \frac{2}{1 - \cos^2 \beta}$$

$$= \frac{2}{\sin^2 \beta}$$

$$= 2\csc^2 \beta$$

Extra Example 3

Verify the identity
$(\sec^2 x - 1)(\sin^2 x - 1) = -\sin^2 x.$

$$\begin{aligned}(\sec^2 x - 1)(\sin^2 x - 1) &= (\tan^2 x)(-\cos^2 x)\\ &= -\frac{\sin^2 x \cos^2 x}{\cos^2 x}\\ &= -\sin^2 x\end{aligned}$$

Extra Example 4

Verify the identity
$\csc x - \sin x = \cos x \cot x.$

$$\begin{aligned}\csc x - \sin x &= \frac{1}{\sin x} - \sin x\\ &= \frac{1 - \sin^2 x}{\sin x}\\ &= \frac{\cos^2 x}{\sin x}\\ &= \cos x \cdot \frac{\cos x}{\sin x}\\ &= \cos x \cot x\end{aligned}$$

Example 3 Verifying a Trigonometric Identity

Verify the identity $(\tan^2 x + 1)(\cos^2 x - 1) = -\tan^2 x$.

Algebraic Solution

By applying identities before multiplying, you obtain the following.

$$\begin{aligned}(\tan^2 x + 1)(\cos^2 x - 1) &= (\sec^2 x)(-\sin^2 x) && \text{Pythagorean identities}\\ &= -\frac{\sin^2 x}{\cos^2 x} && \text{Reciprocal identity}\\ &= -\left(\frac{\sin x}{\cos x}\right)^2 && \text{Rule of exponents}\\ &= -\tan^2 x && \text{Quotient identity}\end{aligned}$$

Graphical Solution

Use a graphing utility set in *radian* mode to graph the left side of the identity $y_1 = (\tan^2 x + 1)(\cos^2 x - 1)$ and the right side of the identity $y_2 = -\tan^2 x$ in the same viewing window, as shown in Figure 5.3. (Select the *line* style for y_1 and the *path* style for y_2.) Because the graphs appear to coincide, $(\tan^2 x + 1)(\cos^2 x - 1) = -\tan^2 x$ appears to be an identity.

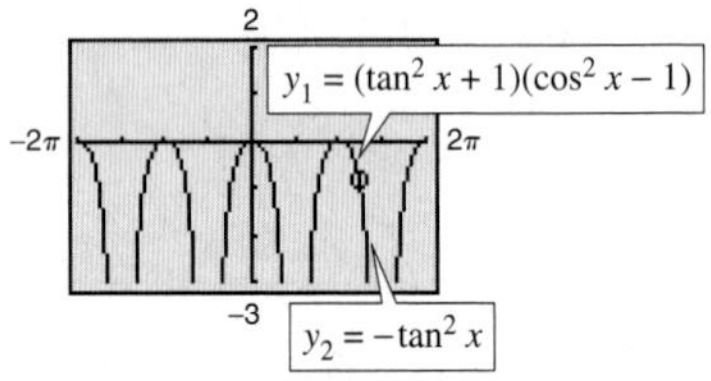

FIGURE 5.3

CHECKPoint Now try Exercise 53.

Example 4 Converting to Sines and Cosines

Verify the identity $\tan x + \cot x = \sec x \csc x$.

Solution

Try converting the left side into sines and cosines.

$$\begin{aligned}\tan x + \cot x &= \frac{\sin x}{\cos x} + \frac{\cos x}{\sin x} && \text{Quotient identities}\\ &= \frac{\sin^2 x + \cos^2 x}{\cos x \sin x} && \text{Add fractions.}\\ &= \frac{1}{\cos x \sin x} && \text{Pythagorean identity}\\ &= \frac{1}{\cos x} \cdot \frac{1}{\sin x} && \text{Product of fractions.}\\ &= \sec x \csc x && \text{Reciprocal identities}\end{aligned}$$

CHECKPoint Now try Exercise 25.

WARNING/CAUTION

Although a graphing utility can be useful in helping to verify an identity, you must use algebraic techniques to produce a *valid* proof.

Recall from algebra that *rationalizing the denominator* using conjugates is, on occasion, a powerful simplification technique. A related form of this technique, shown below, works for simplifying trigonometric expressions as well.

$$\frac{1}{1 - \cos x} = \frac{1}{1 - \cos x}\left(\frac{1 + \cos x}{1 + \cos x}\right) = \frac{1 + \cos x}{1 - \cos^2 x} = \frac{1 + \cos x}{\sin^2 x}$$
$$= \csc^2 x(1 + \cos x)$$

This technique is demonstrated in the next example.

Study Tip

As shown at the right, $\csc^2 x(1 + \cos x)$ is considered a simplified form of $1/(1 - \cos x)$ because the expression does not contain any fractions.

Example 5 Verifying a Trigonometric Identity

Verify the identity $\sec x + \tan x = \dfrac{\cos x}{1 - \sin x}$.

Algebraic Solution

Begin with the *right* side because you can create a monomial denominator by multiplying the numerator and denominator by $1 + \sin x$.

$$\frac{\cos x}{1 - \sin x} = \frac{\cos x}{1 - \sin x}\left(\frac{1 + \sin x}{1 + \sin x}\right) \quad \text{Multiply numerator and denominator by } 1 + \sin x.$$

$$= \frac{\cos x + \cos x \sin x}{1 - \sin^2 x} \quad \text{Multiply.}$$

$$= \frac{\cos x + \cos x \sin x}{\cos^2 x} \quad \text{Pythagorean identity}$$

$$= \frac{\cos x}{\cos^2 x} + \frac{\cos x \sin x}{\cos^2 x} \quad \text{Write as separate fractions.}$$

$$= \frac{1}{\cos x} + \frac{\sin x}{\cos x} \quad \text{Simplify.}$$

$$= \sec x + \tan x \quad \text{Identities}$$

CHECKPoint Now try Exercise 59.

Graphical Solution

Use a graphing utility set in the *radian* and *dot* modes to graph $y_1 = \sec x + \tan x$ and $y_2 = \cos x/(1 - \sin x)$ in the same viewing window, as shown in Figure 5.4. Because the graphs appear to coincide, $\sec x + \tan x = \cos x/(1 - \sin x)$ appears to be an identity.

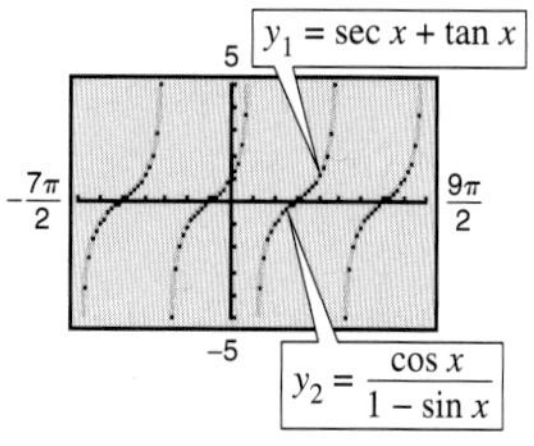

FIGURE 5.4

In Examples 1 through 5, you have been verifying trigonometric identities by working with one side of the equation and converting to the form given on the other side. On occasion, it is practical to work with each side *separately*, to obtain one common form equivalent to both sides. This is illustrated in Example 6.

Example 6 Working with Each Side Separately

Verify the identity $\dfrac{\cot^2 \theta}{1 + \csc \theta} = \dfrac{1 - \sin \theta}{\sin \theta}$.

Algebraic Solution

Working with the left side, you have

$$\frac{\cot^2 \theta}{1 + \csc \theta} = \frac{\csc^2 \theta - 1}{1 + \csc \theta} \quad \text{Pythagorean identity}$$

$$= \frac{(\csc \theta - 1)\cancel{(\csc \theta + 1)}}{\cancel{1 + \csc \theta}} \quad \text{Factor.}$$

$$= \csc \theta - 1. \quad \text{Simplify.}$$

Now, simplifying the right side, you have

$$\frac{1 - \sin \theta}{\sin \theta} = \frac{1}{\sin \theta} - \frac{\sin \theta}{\sin \theta} \quad \text{Write as separate fractions.}$$

$$= \csc \theta - 1. \quad \text{Reciprocal identity}$$

The identity is verified because both sides are equal to $\csc \theta - 1$.

CHECKPoint Now try Exercise 19.

Numerical Solution

Use the *table* feature of a graphing utility set in *radian* mode to create a table that shows the values of $y_1 = \cot^2 x/(1 + \csc x)$ and $y_2 = (1 - \sin x)/\sin x$ for different values of x, as shown in Figure 5.5. From the table you can see that the values appear to be identical, so $\cot^2 x/(1 + \csc x) = (1 - \sin x)/\sin x$ appears to be an identity.

X	Y1	Y2
-.5	-3.086	-3.086
-.25	-5.042	-5.042
0	ERROR	ERROR
.25	3.042	3.042
.5	1.0858	1.0858
.75	.46705	.46705
	.1884	.1884

X=1

FIGURE 5.5

Extra Example 5

Verify the identity

$$\csc \beta + \cot \beta = \frac{\sin \beta}{1 - \cos \beta}.$$

$$\frac{\sin \beta}{1 - \cos \beta} \cdot \frac{1 + \cos \beta}{1 + \cos \beta}$$

$$= \frac{\sin \beta(1 + \cos \beta)}{1 - \cos^2 \beta}$$

$$= \frac{\sin \beta(1 + \cos \beta)}{\sin^2 \beta}$$

$$= \frac{1 + \cos \beta}{\sin \beta}$$

$$= \frac{1}{\sin \beta} + \frac{\cos \beta}{\sin \beta}$$

$$= \csc \beta + \cot \beta$$

Extra Example 6

Verify the identity

$$\frac{\tan^2 \theta}{1 + \sec \theta} = \frac{1 - \cos \theta}{\cos \theta}.$$

Left side:

$$\frac{\tan^2 \theta}{1 + \sec \theta} = \frac{\sec^2 \theta - 1}{1 + \sec \theta}$$

$$= \frac{(\sec \theta - 1)(\sec \theta + 1)}{(1 + \sec \theta)}$$

$$= \sec \theta - 1$$

Right side:

$$\frac{1 - \cos \theta}{\cos \theta} = \frac{1}{\cos \theta} - \frac{\cos \theta}{\cos \theta}$$

$$= \sec \theta - 1$$

Extra Example 7

Verify each identity.

a. $\tan^3 x = \tan x \sec^2 x - \tan x$

$\tan^3 x = (\tan x)(\tan^2 x)$

$= \tan x(\sec^2 x - 1)$

$= \tan x \sec^2 x - \tan x$

b. $\cos^3 x \sin^4 x = (\sin^4 x - \sin^6 x)\cos x$

$\cos^3 x \sin^4 x$

$= \cos^2 x \sin^4 x \cos x$

$= (1 - \sin^2 x)\sin^4 x \cos x$

$= (\sin^4 x - \sin^6 x)\cos x$

c. $\cot^4 x \csc x = \cot^2 x(\csc^3 x - \csc x)$

$\cot^4 x \csc x$

$= \cot^2 x \cot^2 x \csc x$

$= \cot^2 x(\csc^2 x - 1)\csc x$

$= \cot^2 x(\csc^3 x - \csc x)$

Closing the Lesson

Have students summarize the major points of the lesson and answer the Essential Question: How do you verify a trigonometric identity?

- **Operate on one side of an identity at a time.**
- **Use the fundamental trigonometric identities to simplify the more complicated side of an identity.**
- **Use previously studied algebraic techniques, such as factoring, squaring a binomial, adding fractions, or creating a monomial denominator.**
- **Look for ways to simplify the expressions by writing different trigonometric terms as one or two ratios (e.g., as sine and cosine).**

In Example 7, powers of trigonometric functions are rewritten as more complicated sums of products of trigonometric functions. This is a common procedure used in calculus.

Example 7 Three Examples from Calculus

Verify each identity.

a. $\tan^4 x = \tan^2 x \sec^2 x - \tan^2 x$

b. $\sin^3 x \cos^4 x = (\cos^4 x - \cos^6 x) \sin x$

c. $\csc^4 x \cot x = \csc^2 x(\cot x + \cot^3 x)$

Solution

a. $\tan^4 x = (\tan^2 x)(\tan^2 x)$ — Write as separate factors.

$= \tan^2 x(\sec^2 x - 1)$ — Pythagorean identity

$= \tan^2 x \sec^2 x - \tan^2 x$ — Multiply.

b. $\sin^3 x \cos^4 x = \sin^2 x \cos^4 x \sin x$ — Write as separate factors.

$= (1 - \cos^2 x) \cos^4 x \sin x$ — Pythagorean identity

$= (\cos^4 x - \cos^6 x) \sin x$ — Multiply.

c. $\csc^4 x \cot x = \csc^2 x \csc^2 x \cot x$ — Write as separate factors.

$= \csc^2 x(1 + \cot^2 x) \cot x$ — Pythagorean identity

$= \csc^2 x(\cot x + \cot^3 x)$ — Multiply.

CHECK*Point* Now try Exercise 63.

Classroom Discussion

Error Analysis You are tutoring a student in trigonometry. One of the homework problems your student encounters asks whether the following statement is an identity.

$$\tan^2 x \sin^2 x \stackrel{?}{=} \frac{5}{6} \tan^2 x$$

Your student does not attempt to verify the equivalence algebraically, but mistakenly uses only a graphical approach. Using range settings of

Xmin $= -3\pi$	Ymin $= -20$
Xmax $= 3\pi$	Ymax $= 20$
Xscl $= \pi/2$	Yscl $= 1$

your student graphs both sides of the expression on a graphing utility and concludes that the statement is an identity.

What is wrong with your student's reasoning? Explain. Discuss the limitations of verifying identities graphically.

This particular set of range settings actually shows the statement's left side and right side as coinciding, when an algebraic verification shows that they are not equal (using a different set of range settings will confirm this). A trigonometric identity should always be verified algebraically first, and then graphically. Showing that the graphs of the left and right sides of a statement appear to coincide is not strong enough proof to conclude that the statement is an identity.

5.2 EXERCISES

See www.CalcChat.com for worked-out solutions to odd-numbered exercises.

VOCABULARY

In Exercises 1 and 2, fill in the blanks.

1. An equation that is true for all real values in its domain is called an identity.
2. An equation that is true for only some values in its domain is called a conditional equation

In Exercises 3–8, fill in the blank to complete the trigonometric identity.

3. $\dfrac{1}{\cot u} = \underline{\tan u}$

4. $\dfrac{\cos u}{\sin u} = \underline{\cot u}$

5. $\sin^2 u + \underline{\cos^2 u} = 1$

6. $\cos\left(\dfrac{\pi}{2} - u\right) = \underline{\sin u}$

7. $\csc(-u) = \underline{-\csc u}$

8. $\sec(-u) = \underline{\sec u}$

SKILLS AND APPLICATIONS

In Exercises 9–50, verify the identity. 9–50. Answers will vary.

9. $\tan t \cot t = 1$
10. $\sec y \cos y = 1$
11. $\cot^2 y(\sec^2 y - 1) = 1$
12. $\cos x + \sin x \tan x = \sec x$
13. $(1 + \sin \alpha)(1 - \sin \alpha) = \cos^2 \alpha$
14. $\cos^2 \beta - \sin^2 \beta = 2\cos^2 \beta - 1$
15. $\cos^2 \beta - \sin^2 \beta = 1 - 2\sin^2 \beta$
16. $\sin^2 \alpha - \sin^4 \alpha = \cos^2 \alpha - \cos^4 \alpha$
17. $\dfrac{\tan^2 \theta}{\sec \theta} = \sin \theta \tan \theta$
18. $\dfrac{\cot^3 t}{\csc t} = \cos t(\csc^2 t - 1)$
19. $\dfrac{\cot^2 t}{\csc t} = \dfrac{1 - \sin^2 t}{\sin t}$
20. $\dfrac{1}{\tan \beta} + \tan \beta = \dfrac{\sec^2 \beta}{\tan \beta}$
21. $\sin^{1/2} x \cos x - \sin^{5/2} x \cos x = \cos^3 x\sqrt{\sin x}$
22. $\sec^6 x(\sec x \tan x) - \sec^4 x(\sec x \tan x) = \sec^5 x \tan^3 x$
23. $\dfrac{\cot x}{\sec x} = \csc x - \sin x$
24. $\dfrac{\sec \theta - 1}{1 - \cos \theta} = \sec \theta$
25. $\csc x - \sin x = \cos x \cot x$
26. $\sec x - \cos x = \sin x \tan x$
27. $\dfrac{1}{\tan x} + \dfrac{1}{\cot x} = \tan x + \cot x$
28. $\dfrac{1}{\sin x} - \dfrac{1}{\csc x} = \csc x - \sin x$
29. $\dfrac{1 + \sin \theta}{\cos \theta} + \dfrac{\cos \theta}{1 + \sin \theta} = 2\sec \theta$
30. $\dfrac{\cos \theta \cot \theta}{1 - \sin \theta} - 1 = \csc \theta$
31. $\dfrac{1}{\cos x + 1} + \dfrac{1}{\cos x - 1} = -2\csc x \cot x$
32. $\cos x - \dfrac{\cos x}{1 - \tan x} = \dfrac{\sin x \cos x}{\sin x - \cos x}$
33. $\tan\left(\dfrac{\pi}{2} - \theta\right)\tan \theta = 1$
34. $\dfrac{\cos[(\pi/2) - x]}{\sin[(\pi/2) - x]} = \tan x$
35. $\dfrac{\tan x \cot x}{\cos x} = \sec x$
36. $\dfrac{\csc(-x)}{\sec(-x)} = -\cot x$
37. $(1 + \sin y)[1 + \sin(-y)] = \cos^2 y$
38. $\dfrac{\tan x + \tan y}{1 - \tan x \tan y} = \dfrac{\cot x + \cot y}{\cot x \cot y - 1}$
39. $\dfrac{\tan x + \cot y}{\tan x \cot y} = \tan y + \cot x$
40. $\dfrac{\cos x - \cos y}{\sin x + \sin y} + \dfrac{\sin x - \sin y}{\cos x + \cos y} = 0$
41. $\sqrt{\dfrac{1 + \sin \theta}{1 - \sin \theta}} = \dfrac{1 + \sin \theta}{|\cos \theta|}$
42. $\sqrt{\dfrac{1 - \cos \theta}{1 + \cos \theta}} = \dfrac{1 - \cos \theta}{|\sin \theta|}$
43. $\cos^2 \beta + \cos^2\left(\dfrac{\pi}{2} - \beta\right) = 1$
44. $\sec^2 y - \cot^2\left(\dfrac{\pi}{2} - y\right) = 1$
45. $\sin t \csc\left(\dfrac{\pi}{2} - t\right) = \tan t$
46. $\sec^2\left(\dfrac{\pi}{2} - x\right) - 1 = \cot^2 x$
47. $\tan(\sin^{-1} x) = \dfrac{x}{\sqrt{1 - x^2}}$
48. $\cos(\sin^{-1} x) = \sqrt{1 - x^2}$
49. $\tan\left(\sin^{-1}\dfrac{x - 1}{4}\right) = \dfrac{x - 1}{\sqrt{16 - (x - 1)^2}}$
50. $\tan\left(\cos^{-1}\dfrac{x + 1}{2}\right) = \dfrac{\sqrt{4 - (x + 1)^2}}{x + 1}$

4 PRACTICE AND APPLY

Assignment Guide

Transparencies Available
Available at the Instructor's companion site.

Average:
Day 1: pp. 385–386
Exs. 13–25 odd, 29–39 odd, 42, 43, 45, 51, 55, 59, 62, 65–69 odd, 71–73

Advanced:
Day 1: pp. 385–386
Exs. 11, 12, 20–26 even, 30–42 even, 46, 52, 56, 58, 64–70 even, 71, 72, 74, 78

Block:
pp. 385–386
Exs. 13–25 odd, 29–39 odd, 42, 43, 45, 51, 55, 59, 62, 65–69 odd, 71–73 (with 5.1)

5 ASSESS AND RETEACH

Daily Homework Quiz

Transparency Available
Available at the Instructor's companion site.

51. In the first line, $\cot(x)$ is substituted for $\cot(-x)$, which is incorrect; $\cot(-x) = -\cot(x)$.

52. In the first line, the following incorrect substitutions are made: $\sec(-\theta) = -\sec(\theta)$ and $\sin(-\theta) = \sin(\theta)$.
The correct substitutions are: $\sec(-\theta) = \sec(\theta)$ and $\sin(-\theta) = -\sin(\theta)$.

53. (a)

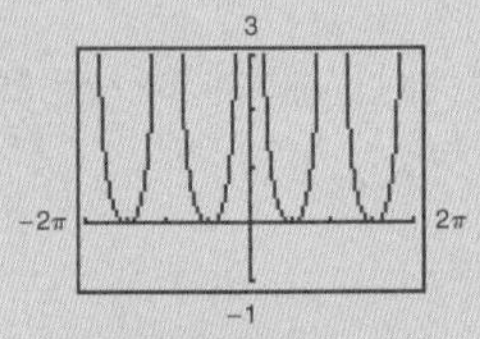

(b)

X	Y1	Y2
-3	49.214	49.214
-2	.20945	.20945
-1	.41228	.41228
0	ERROR	ERROR
1	.41228	.41228
2	.20945	.20945
3	49.214	49.214

X=-3

Identity

(c) Answers will vary.

54. (a)

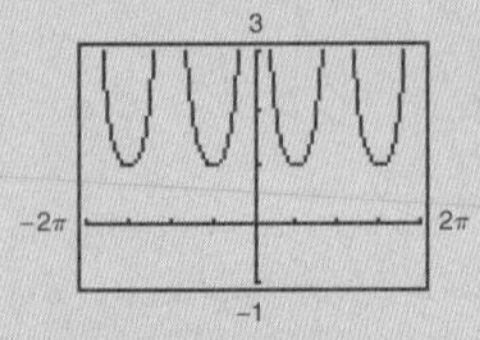

(b)

X	Y1	Y2
-3	50.214	50.214
-2	1.2095	1.2095
-1	1.4123	1.4123
0	ERROR	ERROR
1	1.4123	1.4123
2	1.2095	1.2095
3	50.214	50.214

X=-3

Identity

(c) Answers will vary.

55. (a)

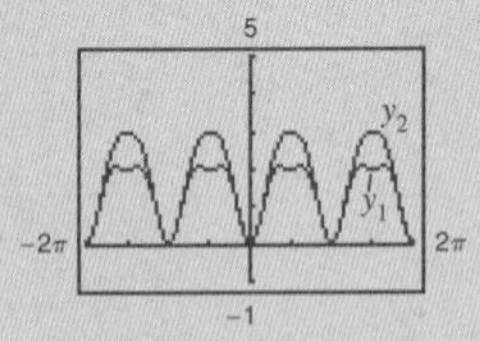

(b)

X	Y1	Y2
-4.712	2	3
-3.142	0	0
-1.571	2	3
0	0	0
1.5708	2	3
3.1416	0	0
4.7124	2	3

X=-4.71238898038

Not an identity

(c) Answers will vary.

ERROR ANALYSIS In Exercises 51 and 52, describe the error(s). 51–52. See margin.

51. $(1 + \tan x)[1 + \cot(-x)]$
$= (1 + \tan x)(1 + \cot x)$
$= 1 + \cot x + \tan x + \tan x \cot x$
$= 1 + \cot x + \tan x + 1$
$= 2 + \cot x + \tan x$

52. $\dfrac{1 + \sec(-\theta)}{\sin(-\theta) + \tan(-\theta)} = \dfrac{1 - \sec \theta}{\sin \theta - \tan \theta}$
$= \dfrac{1 - \sec \theta}{(\sin \theta)[1 - (1/\cos \theta)]}$
$= \dfrac{1 - \sec \theta}{\sin \theta(1 - \sec \theta)}$
$= \dfrac{1}{\sin \theta} = \csc \theta$

In Exercises 53–60, (a) use a graphing utility to graph each side of the equation to determine whether the equation is an identity, (b) use the *table* feature of a graphing utility to determine whether the equation is an identity, and (c) confirm the results of parts (a) and (b) algebraically. 53–60. See margin.

53. $(1 + \cot^2 x)(\cos^2 x) = \cot^2 x$

54. $\csc x(\csc x - \sin x) + \dfrac{\sin x - \cos x}{\sin x} + \cot x = \csc^2 x$

55. $2 + \cos^2 x - 3 \cos^4 x = \sin^2 x(3 + 2 \cos^2 x)$

56. $\tan^4 x + \tan^2 x - 3 = \sec^2 x(4 \tan^2 x - 3)$

57. $\csc^4 x - 2 \csc^2 x + 1 = \cot^4 x$

58. $(\sin^4 \beta - 2 \sin^2 \beta + 1) \cos \beta = \cos^5 \beta$

59. $\dfrac{1 + \cos x}{\sin x} = \dfrac{\sin x}{1 - \cos x}$

60. $\dfrac{\cot \alpha}{\csc \alpha + 1} = \dfrac{\csc \alpha + 1}{\cot \alpha}$

In Exercises 61–64, verify the identity. 61–64. Answers will vary.

61. $\tan^5 x = \tan^3 x \sec^2 x - \tan^3 x$

62. $\sec^4 x \tan^2 x = (\tan^2 x + \tan^4 x) \sec^2 x$

63. $\cos^3 x \sin^2 x = (\sin^2 x - \sin^4 x) \cos x$

64. $\sin^4 x + \cos^4 x = 1 - 2 \cos^2 x + 2 \cos^4 x$

In Exercises 65–68, use the cofunction identities to evaluate the expression without using a calculator.

65. $\sin^2 25° + \sin^2 65°$ 1

66. $\cos^2 55° + \cos^2 35°$ 1

67. $\cos^2 20° + \cos^2 52° + \cos^2 38° + \cos^2 70°$ 2

68. $\tan^2 63° + \cot^2 16° - \sec^2 74° - \csc^2 27°$ −2

69. **RATE OF CHANGE** The rate of change of the function $f(x) = \sin x + \csc x$ with respect to change in the variable x is given by the expression $\cos x - \csc x \cot x$. Show that the expression for the rate of change can also be $-\cos x \cot^2 x$. Answers will vary.

70. **SHADOW LENGTH** The length s of a shadow cast by a vertical gnomon (a device used to tell time) of height h when the angle of the sun above the horizon is θ (see figure) can be modeled by the equation

$$s = \frac{h \sin(90° - \theta)}{\sin \theta}.$$

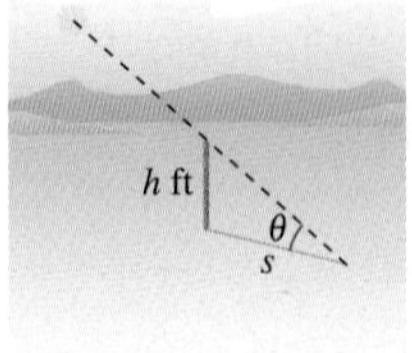

Answers will vary.

(a) Verify that the equation for s is equal to $h \cot \theta$.

(b) Use a graphing utility to complete the table. Let $h = 5$ feet.

θ	15°	30°	45°	60°	75°	90°
s	18.66	8.66	5	2.89	1.34	0

(c) Use your table from part (b) to determine the angles of the sun that result in the maximum and minimum lengths of the shadow. Maximum: 15°; Minimum: 90°

(d) Based on your results from part (c), what time of day do you think it is when the angle of the sun above the horizon is 90°? Noon

EXPLORATION

TRUE OR FALSE? In Exercises 71 and 72, determine whether the statement is true or false. Justify your answer.

71. There can be more than one way to verify a trigonometric identity. 71–72. See margin.

72. The equation $\sin^2 \theta + \cos^2 \theta = 1 + \tan^2 \theta$ is an identity because $\sin^2(0) + \cos^2(0) = 1$ and $1 + \tan^2(0) = 1$.

THINK ABOUT IT In Exercises 73–77, explain why the equation is not an identity and find one value of the variable for which the equation is not true. 73–77. See margin.

73. $\sin \theta = \sqrt{1 - \cos^2 \theta}$

74. $\tan \theta = \sqrt{\sec^2 \theta - 1}$

75. $1 - \cos \theta = \sin \theta$

76. $\csc \theta - 1 = \cot \theta$

77. $1 + \tan \theta = \sec \theta$

78. **CAPSTONE** Write a short paper in your own words explaining to a classmate the difference between a trigonometric identity and a conditional equation. Include suggestions on how to verify a trigonometric identity. Answers will vary.

56. (a)

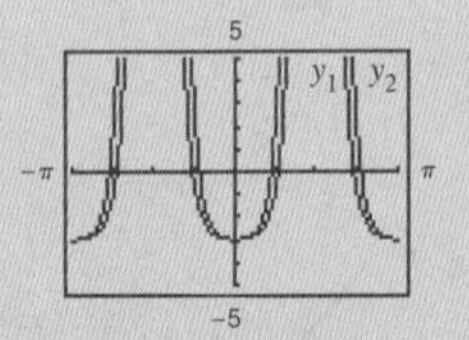

(b)

X	Y1	Y2
-3	-2.979	-2.978
-2	24.569	92.954
-1	5.3087	22.958
0	-3	-3
1	5.3087	22.958
2	24.569	92.954
3	-2.979	-2.978

X=-3

Not an identity

(c) Answers will vary.

57. (a)

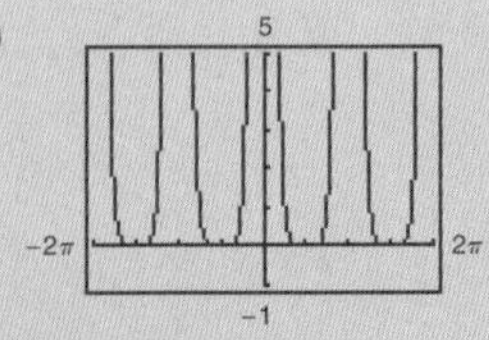

(b)

X	Y1	Y2
-3	2422	2422
-2	.04387	.04387
-1	.16998	.16998
0	ERROR	ERROR
1	.16998	.16998
2	.04387	.04387
3	2422	2422

X=-3

Identity

(c) Answers will vary.

58–60, 71–77. See Additional Answers beginning on page AA1.

5.3 SOLVING TRIGONOMETRIC EQUATIONS

What you should learn

- Use standard algebraic techniques to solve trigonometric equations.
- Solve trigonometric equations of quadratic type.
- Solve trigonometric equations involving multiple angles.
- Use inverse trigonometric functions to solve trigonometric equations.

Why you should learn it

You can use trigonometric equations to solve a variety of real-life problems. For instance, in Exercise 92 on page 396, you can solve a trigonometric equation to help answer questions about monthly sales of skiing equipment.

Tom Stillo/Index Stock Imagery/Photo Library

Introduction

To solve a trigonometric equation, use standard algebraic techniques such as collecting like terms and factoring. Your preliminary goal in solving a trigonometric equation is to *isolate* the trigonometric function in the equation. For example, to solve the equation $2 \sin x = 1$, divide each side by 2 to obtain

$$\sin x = \frac{1}{2}.$$

To solve for x, note in Figure 5.6 that the equation $\sin x = \frac{1}{2}$ has solutions $x = \pi/6$ and $x = 5\pi/6$ in the interval $[0, 2\pi)$. Moreover, because $\sin x$ has a period of 2π, there are infinitely many other solutions, which can be written as

$$x = \frac{\pi}{6} + 2n\pi \quad \text{and} \quad x = \frac{5\pi}{6} + 2n\pi \qquad \text{General solution}$$

where n is an integer, as shown in Figure 5.6.

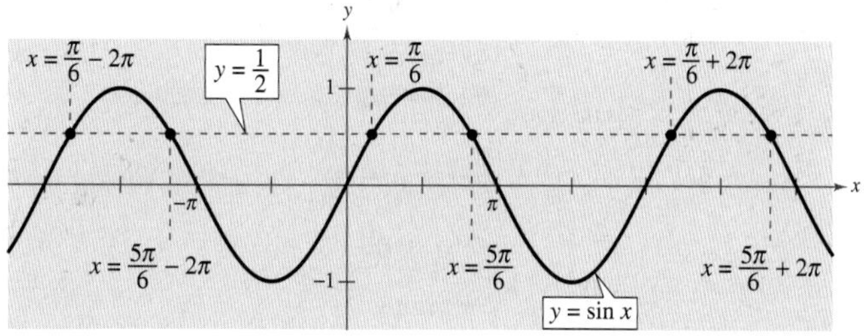

FIGURE 5.6

Another way to show that the equation $\sin x = \frac{1}{2}$ has infinitely many solutions is indicated in Figure 5.7. Any angles that are coterminal with $\pi/6$ or $5\pi/6$ will also be solutions of the equation.

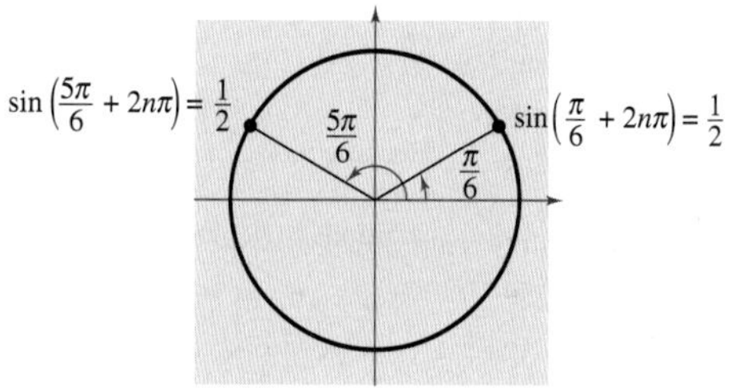

FIGURE 5.7

When solving trigonometric equations, you should write your answer(s) using exact values rather than decimal approximations.

1 PLAN AND PREPARE

Warm-up Exercises

Transparency Available
Available at the Instructor's companion site.

Notetaking Guide

Transparency Available
Promotes interactive learning and notetaking skills. Available at the Instructor's companion site.

Animated Precalculus

An **Animated Precalculus** tutorial is available at the Student companion site for **Section 5.3.**

Pacing

Average: 2 days
Advanced: 2 days
Block: 1 block

2 FOCUS AND MOTIVATE

Essential Question

How do you solve trigonometric equations written in quadratic form or containing more than one angle?
Tell students that they will learn how to answer this question by relating previously studied algebraic techniques to trigonometry.

Resource Planning Guide

Chapter Resources

- Complete Solutions Guide

Workbooks

- Notetaking Guide
- Student Solutions Guide

Interactive Technology

- Instructor Success Organizer
- Notetaking Guide IAE
- Instructional DVDs
- Animated Precalculus
- PowerLecture with ExamView

3 TEACH

Extra Example 1

Solve $\sin x - \sqrt{2} = -\sin x$.

$x = \frac{\pi}{4} + 2n\pi$ and $x = \frac{3\pi}{4} + 2n\pi$, where n is an integer.

Avoiding Common Errors

Students often miss solutions to trigonometric equations by failing to include possible solutions in all quadrants. These must be checked against the range of the function and the interval specified. If no interval is stated, solutions must include multiples beyond the first period.

Extra Example 2

Solve $4\sin^2 x - 3 = 0$.

$x = \frac{\pi}{3} + n\pi$ and $x = \frac{2\pi}{3} + n\pi$, where n is an integer.

Example 1 Collecting Like Terms

Solve $\sin x + \sqrt{2} = -\sin x$.

Solution

Begin by rewriting the equation so that $\sin x$ is isolated on one side of the equation.

$$\sin x + \sqrt{2} = -\sin x \qquad \text{Write original equation.}$$

$$\sin x + \sin x + \sqrt{2} = 0 \qquad \text{Add } \sin x \text{ to each side.}$$

$$\sin x + \sin x = -\sqrt{2} \qquad \text{Subtract } \sqrt{2} \text{ from each side.}$$

$$2\sin x = -\sqrt{2} \qquad \text{Combine like terms.}$$

$$\sin x = -\frac{\sqrt{2}}{2} \qquad \text{Divide each side by 2.}$$

Because $\sin x$ has a period of 2π, first find all solutions in the interval $[0, 2\pi)$. These solutions are $x = 5\pi/4$ and $x = 7\pi/4$. Finally, add multiples of 2π to each of these solutions to get the general form

$$x = \frac{5\pi}{4} + 2n\pi \quad \text{and} \quad x = \frac{7\pi}{4} + 2n\pi \qquad \text{General solution}$$

where n is an integer.

CHECKPoint Now try Exercise 11.

Example 2 Extracting Square Roots

Solve $3\tan^2 x - 1 = 0$.

Solution

Begin by rewriting the equation so that $\tan x$ is isolated on one side of the equation.

$$3\tan^2 x - 1 = 0 \qquad \text{Write original equation.}$$

$$3\tan^2 x = 1 \qquad \text{Add 1 to each side.}$$

$$\tan^2 x = \frac{1}{3} \qquad \text{Divide each side by 3.}$$

$$\tan x = \pm\frac{1}{\sqrt{3}} = \pm\frac{\sqrt{3}}{3} \qquad \text{Extract square roots.}$$

Because $\tan x$ has a period of π, first find all solutions in the interval $[0, \pi)$. These solutions are $x = \pi/6$ and $x = 5\pi/6$. Finally, add multiples of π to each of these solutions to get the general form

$$x = \frac{\pi}{6} + n\pi \quad \text{and} \quad x = \frac{5\pi}{6} + n\pi \qquad \text{General solution}$$

where n is an integer.

CHECKPoint Now try Exercise 15.

WARNING / CAUTION

When you extract square roots, make sure you account for both the positive and negative solutions.

The equations in Examples 1 and 2 involved only one trigonometric function. When two or more functions occur in the same equation, collect all terms on one side and try to separate the functions by factoring or by using appropriate identities. This may produce factors that yield no solutions, as illustrated in Example 3.

Example 3 Factoring

Solve $\cot x \cos^2 x = 2 \cot x$.

Solution

Begin by rewriting the equation so that all terms are collected on one side of the equation.

$$\cot x \cos^2 x = 2 \cot x \quad \text{Write original equation.}$$

$$\cot x \cos^2 x - 2 \cot x = 0 \quad \text{Subtract } 2 \cot x \text{ from each side.}$$

$$\cot x(\cos^2 x - 2) = 0 \quad \text{Factor.}$$

By setting each of these factors equal to zero, you obtain

$$\cot x = 0 \quad \text{and} \quad \cos^2 x - 2 = 0$$

$$x = \frac{\pi}{2} \qquad \cos^2 x = 2$$

$$\cos x = \pm\sqrt{2}.$$

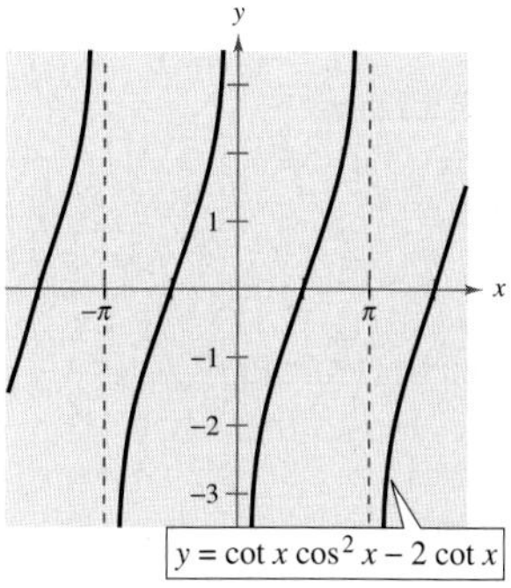

FIGURE 5.8

The equation $\cot x = 0$ has the solution $x = \pi/2$ [in the interval $(0, \pi)$]. No solution is obtained for $\cos x = \pm\sqrt{2}$ because $\pm\sqrt{2}$ are outside the range of the cosine function. Because $\cot x$ has a period of π, the general form of the solution is obtained by adding multiples of π to $x = \pi/2$, to get

$$x = \frac{\pi}{2} + n\pi \quad \text{General solution}$$

where n is an integer. You can confirm this graphically by sketching the graph of $y = \cot x \cos^2 x - 2 \cot x$, as shown in Figure 5.8. From the graph you can see that the x-intercepts occur at $-3\pi/2$, $-\pi/2$, $\pi/2$, $3\pi/2$, and so on. These x-intercepts correspond to the solutions of $\cot x \cos^2 x - 2 \cot x = 0$.

CHECK*Point* Now try Exercise 19.

Extra Example 3
Solve $\sin^2 x = 2 \sin x$.
$x = n\pi$, where n is an integer.

Equations of Quadratic Type

Many trigonometric equations are of quadratic type $ax^2 + bx + c = 0$. Here are a couple of examples.

Quadratic in sin x	*Quadratic in sec x*
$2 \sin^2 x - \sin x - 1 = 0$	$\sec^2 x - 3 \sec x - 2 = 0$
$2(\sin x)^2 - \sin x - 1 = 0$	$(\sec x)^2 - 3(\sec x) - 2 = 0$

Algebra Help

You can review the techniques for solving quadratic equations in Appendix A.5.

To solve equations of this type, factor the quadratic or, if this is not possible, use the Quadratic Formula.

Extra Example 4

Find all solutions of $2\sin^2 x - 3\sin x + 1 = 0$ in the interval $[0, 2\pi)$.

$x = \frac{\pi}{6}, x = \frac{5\pi}{6}$, and $x = \frac{\pi}{2}$

Extra Example 5

Solve $3\sec^2 x - 2\tan^2 x - 4 = 0$.

$x = \frac{\pi}{4} + n\pi$ and $x = \frac{3\pi}{4} + n\pi$, where n is an integer.

Example 4 Factoring an Equation of Quadratic Type

Find all solutions of $2\sin^2 x - \sin x - 1 = 0$ in the interval $[0, 2\pi)$.

Algebraic Solution

Begin by treating the equation as a quadratic in $\sin x$ and factoring.

$2\sin^2 x - \sin x - 1 = 0$ Write original equation.

$(2\sin x + 1)(\sin x - 1) = 0$ Factor.

Setting each factor equal to zero, you obtain the following solutions in the interval $[0, 2\pi)$.

$2\sin x + 1 = 0$ and $\sin x - 1 = 0$

$\sin x = -\frac{1}{2}$ $\qquad$ $\sin x = 1$

$x = \frac{7\pi}{6}, \frac{11\pi}{6}$ $\qquad$ $x = \frac{\pi}{2}$

Graphical Solution

Use a graphing utility set in *radian* mode to graph $y = 2\sin^2 x - \sin x - 1$ for $0 \le x < 2\pi$, as shown in Figure 5.9. Use the *zero* or *root* feature or the *zoom* and *trace* features to approximate the x-intercepts to be

$$x \approx 1.571 \approx \frac{\pi}{2}, \quad x \approx 3.665 \approx \frac{7\pi}{6}, \quad \text{and} \quad x \approx 5.760 \approx \frac{11\pi}{6}.$$

These values are the approximate solutions of $2\sin^2 x - \sin x - 1 = 0$ in the interval $[0, 2\pi)$.

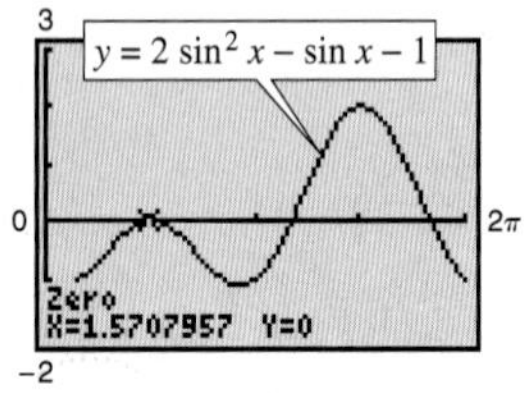

FIGURE 5.9

CHECK Point Now try Exercise 33.

Example 5 Rewriting with a Single Trigonometric Function

Solve $2\sin^2 x + 3\cos x - 3 = 0$.

Solution

This equation contains both sine and cosine functions. You can rewrite the equation so that it has only cosine functions by using the identity $\sin^2 x = 1 - \cos^2 x$.

$2\sin^2 x + 3\cos x - 3 = 0$ Write original equation.

$2(1 - \cos^2 x) + 3\cos x - 3 = 0$ Pythagorean identity

$2\cos^2 x - 3\cos x + 1 = 0$ Multiply each side by -1.

$(2\cos x - 1)(\cos x - 1) = 0$ Factor.

Set each factor equal to zero to find the solutions in the interval $[0, 2\pi)$.

$2\cos x - 1 = 0 \Rightarrow \cos x = \frac{1}{2} \Rightarrow x = \frac{\pi}{3}, \frac{5\pi}{3}$

$\cos x - 1 = 0 \Rightarrow \cos x = 1 \Rightarrow x = 0$

Because $\cos x$ has a period of 2π, the general form of the solution is obtained by adding multiples of 2π to get

$x = 2n\pi, \quad x = \frac{\pi}{3} + 2n\pi, \quad x = \frac{5\pi}{3} + 2n\pi$ General solution

where n is an integer.

CHECK Point Now try Exercise 35.

Sometimes you must square each side of an equation to obtain a quadratic, as demonstrated in the next example. Because this procedure can introduce extraneous solutions, you should check any solutions in the original equation to see whether they are valid or extraneous.

Example 6 Squaring and Converting to Quadratic Type

Find all solutions of $\cos x + 1 = \sin x$ in the interval $[0, 2\pi)$.

Solution

It is not clear how to rewrite this equation in terms of a single trigonometric function. Notice what happens when you square each side of the equation.

$\cos x + 1 = \sin x$	Write original equation.
$\cos^2 x + 2\cos x + 1 = \sin^2 x$	Square each side.
$\cos^2 x + 2\cos x + 1 = 1 - \cos^2 x$	Pythagorean identity
$\cos^2 x + \cos^2 x + 2\cos x + 1 - 1 = 0$	Rewrite equation.
$2\cos^2 x + 2\cos x = 0$	Combine like terms.
$2\cos x(\cos x + 1) = 0$	Factor.

Setting each factor equal to zero produces

$2\cos x = 0$ and $\cos x + 1 = 0$

$\cos x = 0$ $\qquad$ $\cos x = -1$

$x = \dfrac{\pi}{2}, \dfrac{3\pi}{2}$ $\qquad$ $x = \pi.$

Because you squared the original equation, check for extraneous solutions.

Check $x = \pi/2$

$\cos\dfrac{\pi}{2} + 1 \stackrel{?}{=} \sin\dfrac{\pi}{2}$ Substitute $\pi/2$ for x.

$0 + 1 = 1$ Solution checks. ✓

Check $x = 3\pi/2$

$\cos\dfrac{3\pi}{2} + 1 \stackrel{?}{=} \sin\dfrac{3\pi}{2}$ Substitute $3\pi/2$ for x.

$0 + 1 \neq -1$ Solution does not check.

Check $x = \pi$

$\cos\pi + 1 \stackrel{?}{=} \sin\pi$ Substitute π for x.

$-1 + 1 = 0$ Solution checks. ✓

Of the three possible solutions, $x = 3\pi/2$ is extraneous. So, in the interval $[0, 2\pi)$, the only two solutions are $x = \pi/2$ and $x = \pi$.

CHECKPoint Now try Exercise 37.

Study Tip

You square each side of the equation in Example 6 because the squares of the sine and cosine functions are related by a Pythagorean identity. The same is true for the squares of the secant and tangent functions and for the squares of the cosecant and cotangent functions.

Extra Example 6

Find all of the solutions of $\sin x + 1 = \cos x$ in the interval $[0, 2\pi)$.

$x = 0$ and $x = \dfrac{3\pi}{2}$

Extra Example 7

Find all solutions of $\sin 2x - \frac{\sqrt{3}}{2} = 0$.

$x = \frac{\pi}{6} + n\pi$ and $x = \frac{\pi}{3} + n\pi$, where n is an integer.

Extra Example 8

Find all solutions of $\tan \frac{x}{2} - 1 = 0$.

$x = \frac{\pi}{2} + 2n\pi$, where n is an integer.

Functions Involving Multiple Angles

The next two examples involve trigonometric functions of multiple angles of the forms $\sin ku$ and $\cos ku$. To solve equations of these forms, first solve the equation for ku, then divide your result by k.

Example 7 Functions of Multiple Angles

Solve $2 \cos 3t - 1 = 0$.

Solution

$2 \cos 3t - 1 = 0$ Write original equation.

$2 \cos 3t = 1$ Add 1 to each side.

$\cos 3t = \frac{1}{2}$ Divide each side by 2.

In the interval $[0, 2\pi)$, you know that $3t = \pi/3$ and $3t = 5\pi/3$ are the only solutions, so, in general, you have

$$3t = \frac{\pi}{3} + 2n\pi \quad \text{and} \quad 3t = \frac{5\pi}{3} + 2n\pi.$$

Dividing these results by 3, you obtain the general solution

$$t = \frac{\pi}{9} + \frac{2n\pi}{3} \quad \text{and} \quad t = \frac{5\pi}{9} + \frac{2n\pi}{3}$$ General solution

where n is an integer.

CHECK*Point* Now try Exercise 39.

Example 8 Functions of Multiple Angles

Solve $3 \tan \frac{x}{2} + 3 = 0$.

Solution

$3 \tan \frac{x}{2} + 3 = 0$ Write original equation.

$3 \tan \frac{x}{2} = -3$ Subtract 3 from each side.

$\tan \frac{x}{2} = -1$ Divide each side by 3.

In the interval $[0, \pi)$, you know that $x/2 = 3\pi/4$ is the only solution, so, in general, you have

$$\frac{x}{2} = \frac{3\pi}{4} + n\pi.$$

Multiplying this result by 2, you obtain the general solution

$$x = \frac{3\pi}{2} + 2n\pi$$ General solution

where n is an integer.

CHECK*Point* Now try Exercise 43.

Using Inverse Functions

In the next example, you will see how inverse trigonometric functions can be used to solve an equation.

Example 9 Using Inverse Functions

Solve $\sec^2 x - 2\tan x = 4$.

Solution

$$\sec^2 x - 2\tan x = 4 \qquad \text{Write original equation.}$$

$$1 + \tan^2 x - 2\tan x - 4 = 0 \qquad \text{Pythagorean identity}$$

$$\tan^2 x - 2\tan x - 3 = 0 \qquad \text{Combine like terms.}$$

$$(\tan x - 3)(\tan x + 1) = 0 \qquad \text{Factor.}$$

Setting each factor equal to zero, you obtain two solutions in the interval $(-\pi/2, \pi/2)$. [Recall that the range of the inverse tangent function is $(-\pi/2, \pi/2)$.]

$$\tan x - 3 = 0 \qquad \text{and} \qquad \tan x + 1 = 0$$

$$\tan x = 3 \qquad \tan x = -1$$

$$x = \arctan 3 \qquad x = -\frac{\pi}{4}$$

Finally, because $\tan x$ has a period of π, you obtain the general solution by adding multiples of π

$$x = \arctan 3 + n\pi \qquad \text{and} \qquad x = -\frac{\pi}{4} + n\pi \qquad \text{General solution}$$

where n is an integer. You can use a calculator to approximate the value of arctan 3.

CHECK*Point* Now try Exercise 63.

Classroom Discussion

Equations with No Solutions One of the following equations has solutions and the other two do not. Which two equations do not have solutions?

a. $\sin^2 x - 5\sin x + 6 = 0$

b. $\sin^2 x - 4\sin x + 6 = 0$

c. $\sin^2 x - 5\sin x - 6 = 0$

Equations a and b

Find conditions involving the constants b and c that will guarantee that the equation

$$\sin^2 x + b\sin x + c = 0$$

has at least one solution on some interval of length 2π.

Either $-2 \le \sqrt{b^2 - 4c} + b \le 2$ or $-2 \le \sqrt{b^2 - 4c} - b \le 2$ must be true.

Extra Example 9

Find all solutions of $4\tan^2 x + 5\tan x = 6$.

$x = \arctan\left(\frac{3}{4}\right) + n\pi$ **and** $x = \arctan(-2) + n\pi$, **where** n **is an integer.**

Closing the Lesson

Have students summarize the major points of the lesson and answer the Essential Question: How do you solve trigonometric equations written in quadratic form or containing more than one angle?

- **Solve trigonometric equations by converting the equation to quadratic form and factoring.**
- **Solve trigonometric equations of the forms sin ku and cos ku by solving for u and identifying all of the values for which this is true over the given interval.**
- **Use inverse functions to solve trigonometric equations.**

4 PRACTICE AND APPLY

Assignment Guide

Transparencies Available
Available at the Instructor's companion site.

Average:
Day 1: p. 394
Exs. 1–4, 5–9 odd, 14, 16, 19–29 odd, 34, 36
Day 2: pp. 394–397
Exs. 40, 41, 45, 49, 53, 59, 67–75 odd, 85, 88, 89–99 odd, 100

Advanced:
Day 1: p. 394
Exs. 1–4, 8–16 even, 22–32 even, 36, 38
Day 2: pp. 394–397
Exs. 42–48 even, 54, 60–64 even, 72–86 even, 87, 88–94 even, 97, 98, 102, 104

Block:
pp. 394–397
Exs. 1–4, 5–9 odd, 14, 16, 19–29 odd, 34, 36, 40, 41, 45, 49, 53, 59, 67–75 odd, 85, 88, 89–99 odd, 100

5.3 EXERCISES

See www.CalcChat.com for worked-out solutions to odd-numbered exercises.

VOCABULARY: Fill in the blanks.

1. When solving a trigonometric equation, the preliminary goal is to __isolate__ the trigonometric function involved in the equation.
2. The equation $2\sin\theta + 1 = 0$ has the solutions $\theta = \frac{7\pi}{6} + 2n\pi$ and $\theta = \frac{11\pi}{6} + 2n\pi$, which are called __general__ solutions.
3. The equation $2\tan^2 x - 3\tan x + 1 = 0$ is a trigonometric equation that is of ________ type. quadratic
4. A solution of an equation that does not satisfy the original equation is called an ________ solution. extraneous

SKILLS AND APPLICATIONS

In Exercises 5–10, verify that the *x*-values are solutions of the equation. 5–10. Answers will vary.

5. $2\cos x - 1 = 0$
   (a) $x = \frac{\pi}{3}$ (b) $x = \frac{5\pi}{3}$
6. $\sec x - 2 = 0$
   (a) $x = \frac{\pi}{3}$ (b) $x = \frac{5\pi}{3}$
7. $3\tan^2 2x - 1 = 0$
   (a) $x = \frac{\pi}{12}$ (b) $x = \frac{5\pi}{12}$
8. $2\cos^2 4x - 1 = 0$
   (a) $x = \frac{\pi}{16}$ (b) $x = \frac{3\pi}{16}$
9. $2\sin^2 x - \sin x - 1 = 0$
   (a) $x = \frac{\pi}{2}$ (b) $x = \frac{7\pi}{6}$
10. $\csc^4 x - 4\csc^2 x = 0$
   (a) $x = \frac{\pi}{6}$ (b) $x = \frac{5\pi}{6}$

In Exercises 11–24, solve the equation. 11–24. See margin.

11. $2\cos x + 1 = 0$
12. $2\sin x + 1 = 0$
13. $\sqrt{3}\csc x - 2 = 0$
14. $\tan x + \sqrt{3} = 0$
15. $3\sec^2 x - 4 = 0$
16. $3\cot^2 x - 1 = 0$
17. $\sin x(\sin x + 1) = 0$
18. $(3\tan^2 x - 1)(\tan^2 x - 3) = 0$
19. $4\cos^2 x - 1 = 0$
20. $\sin^2 x = 3\cos^2 x$
21. $2\sin^2 2x = 1$
22. $\tan^2 3x = 3$
23. $\tan 3x(\tan x - 1) = 0$
24. $\cos 2x(2\cos x + 1) = 0$

In Exercises 25–38, find all solutions of the equation in the interval $[0, 2\pi)$.

25. $\cos^3 x = \cos x$ $0, \frac{\pi}{2}, \pi, \frac{3\pi}{2}$
26. $\sec^2 x - 1 = 0$ $0, \pi$

27–38. See margin.

27. $3\tan^3 x = \tan x$
28. $2\sin^2 x = 2 + \cos x$
29. $\sec^2 x - \sec x = 2$
30. $\sec x\csc x = 2\csc x$
31. $2\sin x + \csc x = 0$
32. $\sec x + \tan x = 1$
33. $2\cos^2 x + \cos x - 1 = 0$
34. $2\sin^2 x + 3\sin x + 1 = 0$
35. $2\sec^2 x + \tan^2 x - 3 = 0$
36. $\cos x + \sin x\tan x = 2$
37. $\csc x + \cot x = 1$
38. $\sin x - 2 = \cos x - 2$

In Exercises 39–44, solve the multiple-angle equation. 39–44. See margin.

39. $\cos 2x = \frac{1}{2}$
40. $\sin 2x = -\frac{\sqrt{3}}{2}$
41. $\tan 3x = 1$
42. $\sec 4x = 2$
43. $\cos\frac{x}{2} = \frac{\sqrt{2}}{2}$
44. $\sin\frac{x}{2} = -\frac{\sqrt{3}}{2}$

In Exercises 45–48, find the *x*-intercepts of the graph.

45. $y = \sin\frac{\pi x}{2} + 1$ $3 + 4n$

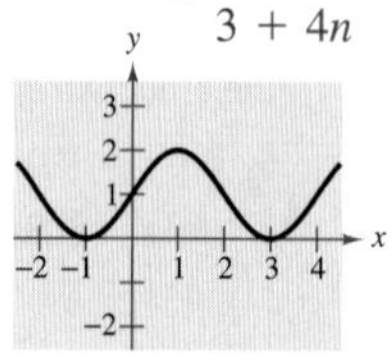

46. $y = \sin\pi x + \cos\pi x$ $\frac{3}{4} + n$

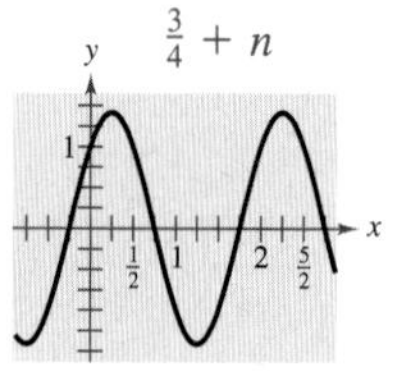

47. $y = \tan^2\left(\frac{\pi x}{6}\right) - 3$

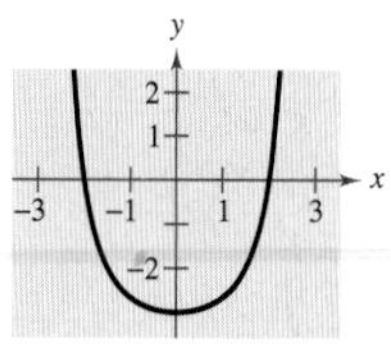

$-2 + 6n, 2 + 6n$

48. $y = \sec^4\left(\frac{\pi x}{8}\right) - 4$

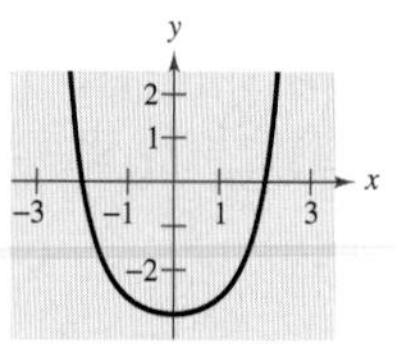

$-2 + 8n, 2 + 8n$

11. $\frac{2\pi}{3} + 2n\pi, \frac{4\pi}{3} + 2n\pi$
12. $\frac{7\pi}{6} + 2n\pi, \frac{11\pi}{6} + 2n\pi$
13. $\frac{\pi}{3} + 2n\pi, \frac{2\pi}{3} + 2n\pi$
14. $\frac{2\pi}{3} + n\pi$
15. $\frac{\pi}{6} + n\pi, \frac{5\pi}{6} + n\pi$
16. $\frac{\pi}{3} + n\pi, \frac{2\pi}{3} + n\pi$
17. $n\pi, \frac{3\pi}{2} + 2n\pi$
18. $\frac{\pi}{6} + n\pi, \frac{5\pi}{6} + n\pi, \frac{\pi}{3} + n\pi, \frac{2\pi}{3} + n\pi$
19. $\frac{\pi}{3} + n\pi, \frac{2\pi}{3} + n\pi$
20. $\frac{\pi}{3} + n\pi, \frac{2\pi}{3} + n\pi$
21. $\frac{\pi}{8} + \frac{n\pi}{2}, \frac{3\pi}{8} + \frac{n\pi}{2}$
22. $\frac{\pi}{9} + \frac{n\pi}{3}, \frac{2\pi}{9} + \frac{n\pi}{3}$
23. $\frac{n\pi}{3}, \frac{\pi}{4} + n\pi$
24. $\frac{\pi}{4} + \frac{n\pi}{2}, \frac{2\pi}{3} + 2n\pi, \frac{4\pi}{3} + 2n\pi$

27. $0, \pi, \frac{\pi}{6}, \frac{5\pi}{6}, \frac{7\pi}{6}, \frac{11\pi}{6}$
28. $\frac{\pi}{2}, \frac{3\pi}{2}, \frac{2\pi}{3}, \frac{4\pi}{3}$
29. $\frac{\pi}{3}, \frac{5\pi}{3}, \pi$
30. $\frac{\pi}{3}, \frac{5\pi}{3}$
31. No solution
32. 0
33. $\pi, \frac{\pi}{3}, \frac{5\pi}{3}$
34. $\frac{7\pi}{6}, \frac{3\pi}{2}, \frac{11\pi}{6}$
35. $\frac{\pi}{6}, \frac{5\pi}{6}, \frac{7\pi}{6}, \frac{11\pi}{6}$
36. $\frac{\pi}{3}, \frac{5\pi}{3}$
37. $\frac{\pi}{2}$
38. $\frac{\pi}{4}, \frac{5\pi}{4}$
39. $\frac{\pi}{6} + n\pi, \frac{5\pi}{6} + n\pi$
40. $\frac{2\pi}{3} + n\pi, \frac{5\pi}{6} + n\pi$
41. $\frac{\pi}{12} + \frac{n\pi}{3}$
42. $\frac{\pi}{12} + \frac{n\pi}{2}, \frac{5\pi}{12} + \frac{n\pi}{2}$
43. $\frac{\pi}{2} + 4n\pi, \frac{7\pi}{2} + 4n\pi$
44. $\frac{8\pi}{3} + 4n\pi, \frac{10\pi}{3} + 4n\pi$

In Exercises 49–58, use a graphing utility to approximate the solutions (to three decimal places) of the equation in the interval $[0, 2\pi)$.

49. $2\sin x + \cos x = 0$ 2.678, 5.820

50. $4\sin^3 x + 2\sin^2 x - 2\sin x - 1 = 0$ 50–54. See margin.

51. $\dfrac{1+\sin x}{\cos x} + \dfrac{\cos x}{1+\sin x} = 4$

52. $\dfrac{\cos x \cot x}{1 - \sin x} = 3$

53. $x\tan x - 1 = 0$

54. $x\cos x - 1 = 0$

55. $\sec^2 x + 0.5\tan x - 1 = 0$ 0, 2.678, 3.142, 5.820

56. $\csc^2 x + 0.5\cot x - 5 = 0$ 0.515, 2.726, 3.657, 5.868

57. $2\tan^2 x + 7\tan x - 15 = 0$ 0.983, 1.768, 4.124, 4.910

58. $6\sin^2 x - 7\sin x + 2 = 0$ 0.524, 0.730, 2.412, 2.618

In Exercises 59–62, use the Quadratic Formula to solve the equation in the interval $[0, 2\pi)$. Then use a graphing utility to approximate the angle x. 59–61. See margin.

59. $12\sin^2 x - 13\sin x + 3 = 0$

60. $3\tan^2 x + 4\tan x - 4 = 0$

61. $\tan^2 x + 3\tan x + 1 = 0$

62. $4\cos^2 x - 4\cos x - 1 = 0$ 1.7794, 4.5038

In Exercises 63–74, use inverse functions where needed to find all solutions of the equation in the interval $[0, 2\pi)$.

63. $\tan^2 x + \tan x - 12 = 0$ 63–70, 72–73. See margin.

64. $\tan^2 x - \tan x - 2 = 0$

65. $\tan^2 x - 6\tan x + 5 = 0$

66. $\sec^2 x + \tan x - 3 = 0$

67. $2\cos^2 x - 5\cos x + 2 = 0$

68. $2\sin^2 x - 7\sin x + 3 = 0$

69. $\cot^2 x - 9 = 0$

70. $\cot^2 x - 6\cot x + 5 = 0$

71. $\sec^2 x - 4\sec x = 0$ $\arccos\left(\frac{1}{4}\right), 2\pi - \arccos\left(\frac{1}{4}\right)$

72. $\sec^2 x + 2\sec x - 8 = 0$

73. $\csc^2 x + 3\csc x - 4 = 0$

74. $\csc^2 x - 5\csc x = 0$ $\arcsin\left(-\frac{1}{5}\right) + \pi, \arcsin\left(\frac{1}{5}\right)$

In Exercises 75–78, use a graphing utility to approximate the solutions (to three decimal places) of the equation in the given interval.

75. $3\tan^2 x + 5\tan x - 4 = 0, \quad \left[-\frac{\pi}{2}, \frac{\pi}{2}\right]$ −1.154, 0.534

76. $\cos^2 x - 2\cos x - 1 = 0, \quad [0, \pi]$ 1.998

77. $4\cos^2 x - 2\sin x + 1 = 0, \quad \left[-\frac{\pi}{2}, \frac{\pi}{2}\right]$ 1.110

78. $2\sec^2 x + \tan x - 6 = 0, \quad \left[-\frac{\pi}{2}, \frac{\pi}{2}\right]$ −1.035, 0.870

In Exercises 79–84, (a) use a graphing utility to graph the function and approximate the maximum and minimum points on the graph in the interval $[0, 2\pi)$, and (b) solve the trigonometric equation and demonstrate that its solutions are the x-coordinates of the maximum and minimum points of f. (Calculus is required to find the trigonometric equation.) 79–84. See margin.

Function	*Trigonometric Equation*
79. $f(x) = \sin^2 x + \cos x$	$2\sin x\cos x - \sin x = 0$
80. $f(x) = \cos^2 x - \sin x$	$-2\sin x\cos x - \cos x = 0$
81. $f(x) = \sin x + \cos x$	$\cos x - \sin x = 0$
82. $f(x) = 2\sin x + \cos 2x$	$2\cos x - 4\sin x\cos x = 0$
83. $f(x) = \sin x\cos x$	$-\sin^2 x + \cos^2 x = 0$
84. $f(x) = \sec x + \tan x - x$	$\sec x\tan x + \sec^2 x - 1 = 0$

FIXED POINT In Exercises 85 and 86, find the smallest positive fixed point of the function f. [A *fixed point* of a function f is a real number c such that $f(c) = c$.]

85. $f(x) = \tan\dfrac{\pi x}{4}$ 1

86. $f(x) = \cos x$ 0.739

87. **GRAPHICAL REASONING** Consider the function given by

$$f(x) = \cos\frac{1}{x}$$

and its graph shown in the figure.

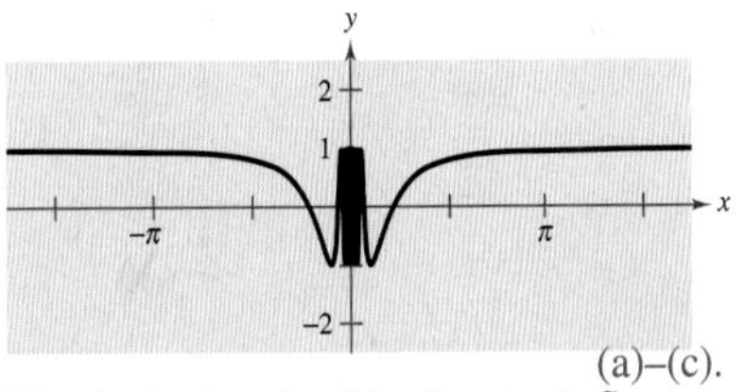

(a)–(c).

(a) What is the domain of the function? See margin.

(b) Identify any symmetry and any asymptotes of the graph.

(c) Describe the behavior of the function as $x \to 0$.

(d) How many solutions does the equation

$$\cos\frac{1}{x} = 0$$ Infinitely many solutions; $\dfrac{2}{2n\pi + \pi}$

have in the interval $[-1, 1]$? Find the solutions.

(e) Does the equation $\cos(1/x) = 0$ have a greatest solution? If so, approximate the solution. If not, explain why. Yes, 0.6366

50. 0.785, 2.356, 3.665, 3.927, 5.498, 5.760

51. 1.047, 5.236

52. 0.524, 2.618

53. 0.860, 3.426

54. 4.917

59. 0.3398, 0.8481, 2.2935, 2.8018

60. 0.5880, 2.0344, 3.7296, 5.1760

61. 1.9357, 2.7767, 5.0773, 5.9183

63. $\arctan(-4) + \pi$, $\arctan(-4) + 2\pi$, $\arctan 3$, $\arctan 3 + \pi$

64. $\frac{3\pi}{4}, \frac{7\pi}{4}$, $\arctan 2$, $\arctan 2 + \pi$

65. $\frac{\pi}{4}, \frac{5\pi}{4}$, $\arctan 5$, $\arctan 5 + \pi$

66. $\arctan(-2) + \pi$, $\arctan(-2) + 2\pi$, $\frac{\pi}{4}, \frac{5\pi}{4}$

67. $\frac{\pi}{3}, \frac{5\pi}{3}$

68. $\frac{\pi}{6}, \frac{5\pi}{6}$

70. $\frac{\pi}{4}, \frac{5\pi}{4}$, $\arctan\left(\frac{1}{5}\right)$, $\arctan\left(\frac{1}{5}\right) + \pi$

72. $\frac{\pi}{3}, \frac{5\pi}{3}$, $\arccos\left(-\frac{1}{4}\right)$, $2\pi - \arccos\left(-\frac{1}{4}\right)$

73. $\frac{\pi}{2}$, $\arcsin\left(-\frac{1}{4}\right) + 2\pi$, $\arcsin\left(\frac{1}{4}\right) + \pi$

79. (a)

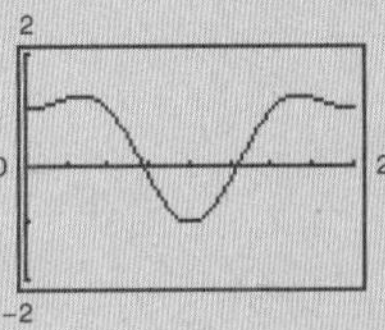

Maximum: (1.0472, 1.25)
Maximum: (5.2360, 1.25)
Minimum: (0, 1)
Minimum: (3.1416, −1)

(b) $\frac{\pi}{3} \approx 1.0472$
$\frac{5\pi}{3} \approx 5.2360$
0
$\pi \approx 3.1416$

80. (a)

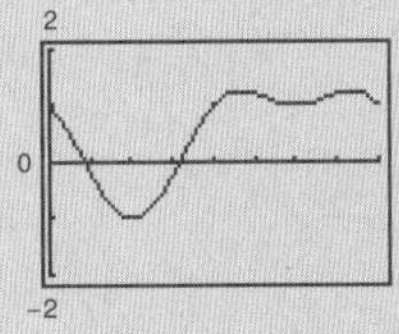

Maximum: (3.6652, 1.25)
Maximum: (5.7596, 1.25)
Minimum: (1.5708, −1)
Minimum: (4.7124, 1)

(b) $\frac{7\pi}{6} \approx 3.6652$
$\frac{11\pi}{6} \approx 5.7596$
$\frac{\pi}{2} \approx 1.5708$
$\frac{3\pi}{2} \approx 4.7124$

81. (a)

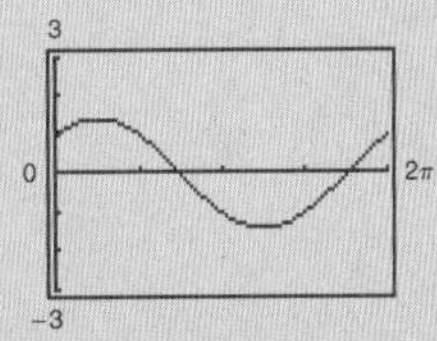

Maximum: (0.7854, 1.4142)
Minimum: (3.9270, −1.4142)

(b) $\frac{\pi}{4} \approx 0.7854$
$\frac{5\pi}{4} \approx 3.9270$

69, 82–84, 87(a)–(c). See Additional Answers beginning on page AA1.

90.

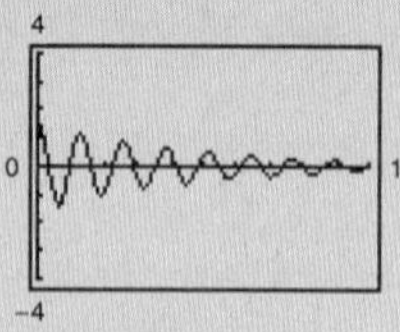

1.96 sec

88. GRAPHICAL REASONING Consider the function given by $f(x) = (\sin x)/x$ and its graph shown in the figure.

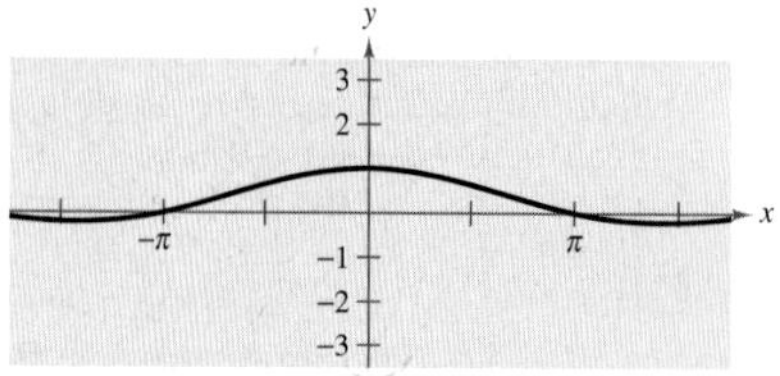

(a) What is the domain of the function? All real numbers x except $x = 0$

(b) Identify any symmetry and any asymptotes of the graph. y-axis symmetry

(c) Describe the behavior of the function as $x \to 0$. y approaches 1.

(d) How many solutions does the equation

$$\frac{\sin x}{x} = 0 \quad \text{Four solutions: } \pm\pi, \pm 2\pi$$

have in the interval $[-8, 8]$? Find the solutions.

89. HARMONIC MOTION A weight is oscillating on the end of a spring (see figure). The position of the weight relative to the point of equilibrium is given by $y = \frac{1}{12}(\cos 8t - 3 \sin 8t)$, where y is the displacement (in meters) and t is the time (in seconds). Find the times when the weight is at the point of equilibrium ($y = 0$) for $0 \le t \le 1$. 0.04 sec, 0.43 sec, 0.83 sec

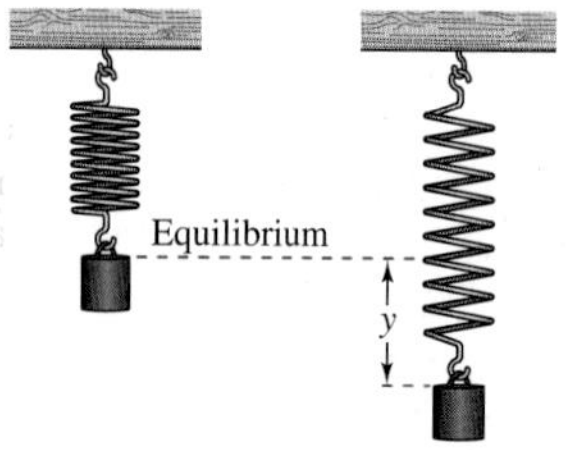

90. DAMPED HARMONIC MOTION The displacement from equilibrium of a weight oscillating on the end of a spring is given by $y = 1.56e^{-0.22t}\cos 4.9t$, where y is the displacement (in feet) and t is the time (in seconds). Use a graphing utility to graph the displacement function for $0 \le t \le 10$. Find the time beyond which the displacement does not exceed 1 foot from equilibrium. See margin.

91. SALES The monthly sales S (in thousands of units) of a seasonal product are approximated by

$$S = 74.50 + 43.75 \sin \frac{\pi t}{6}$$

where t is the time (in months), with $t = 1$ corresponding to January. Determine the months in which sales exceed 100,000 units. February, March, and April

92. SALES The monthly sales S (in hundreds of units) of skiing equipment at a sports store are approximated by

$$S = 58.3 + 32.5 \cos \frac{\pi t}{6}$$

where t is the time (in months), with $t = 1$ corresponding to January. Determine the months in which sales exceed 7500 units. January, November, December

93. PROJECTILE MOTION A batted baseball leaves the bat at an angle of θ with the horizontal and an initial velocity of $v_0 = 100$ feet per second. The ball is caught by an outfielder 300 feet from home plate (see figure). Find θ if the range r of a projectile is given by $r = \frac{1}{32}v_0^2 \sin 2\theta$. 36.9°, 53.1°

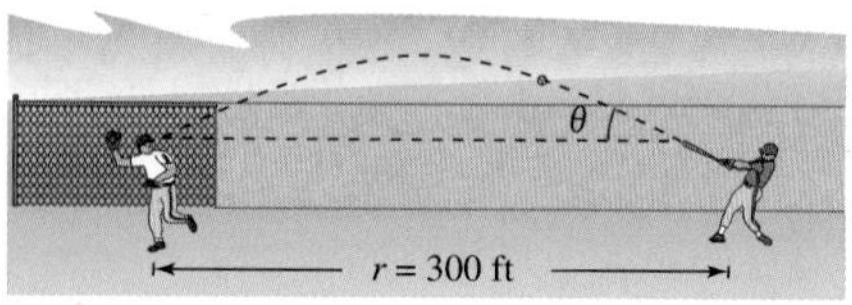

Not drawn to scale

94. PROJECTILE MOTION A sharpshooter intends to hit a target at a distance of 1000 yards with a gun that has a muzzle velocity of 1200 feet per second (see figure). Neglecting air resistance, determine the gun's minimum angle of elevation θ if the range r is given by

$$r = \frac{1}{32}v_0^2 \sin 2\theta. \quad 1.9°$$

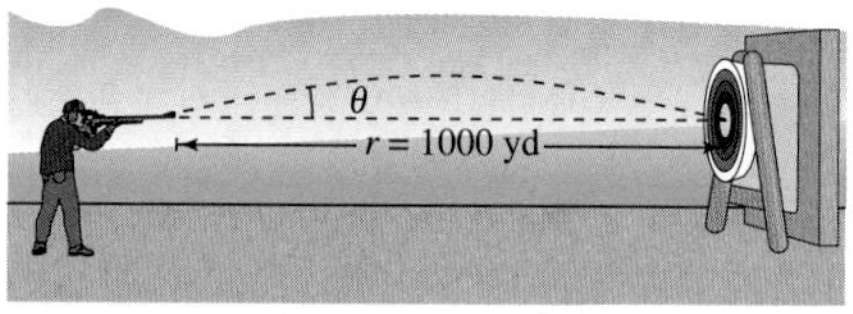

Not drawn to scale

95. FERRIS WHEEL A Ferris wheel is built such that the height h (in feet) above ground of a seat on the wheel at time t (in minutes) can be modeled by

$$h(t) = 53 + 50 \sin\left(\frac{\pi}{16}t - \frac{\pi}{2}\right).$$

The wheel makes one revolution every 32 seconds. The ride begins when $t = 0$. $t = 8$ sec and $t = 24$ sec

(a) During the first 32 seconds of the ride, when will a person on the Ferris wheel be 53 feet above ground?

(b) When will a person be at the top of the Ferris wheel for the first time during the ride? If the ride lasts 160 seconds, how many times will a person be at the top of the ride, and at what times?
5 times: $t = 16, 48, 80, 112, 144$ sec

96. DATA ANALYSIS: METEOROLOGY The table shows the average daily high temperatures in Houston H (in degrees Fahrenheit) for month t, with $t = 1$ corresponding to January. (Source: National Climatic Data Center) See margin.

Month, t	Houston, H
1	62.3
2	66.5
3	73.3
4	79.1
5	85.5
6	90.7
7	93.6
8	93.5
9	89.3
10	82.0
11	72.0
12	64.6

(a) Create a scatter plot of the data.

(b) Find a cosine model for the temperatures in Houston.

(c) Use a graphing utility to graph the data points and the model for the temperatures in Houston. How well does the model fit the data?

(d) What is the overall average daily high temperature in Houston?

(e) Use a graphing utility to describe the months during which the average daily high temperature is above 86°F and below 86°F.

97. GEOMETRY The area of a rectangle (see figure) inscribed in one arc of the graph of $y = \cos x$ is given by $A = 2x \cos x, 0 < x < \pi/2$. See margin.

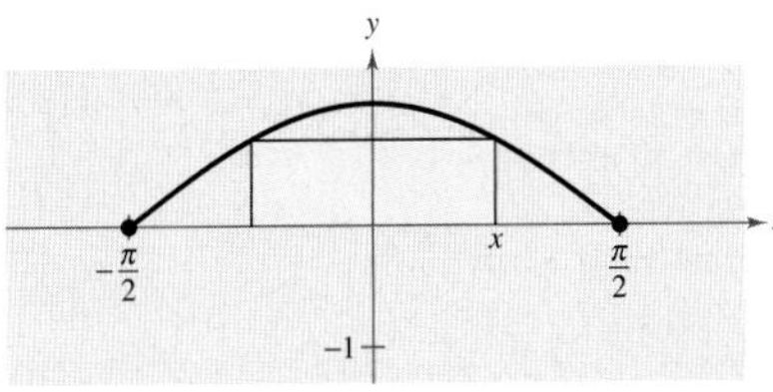

(a) Use a graphing utility to graph the area function, and approximate the area of the largest inscribed rectangle.

(b) Determine the values of x for which $A \geq 1$.

98. QUADRATIC APPROXIMATION Consider the function given by $f(x) = 3 \sin(0.6x - 2)$.

(a) Approximate the zero of the function in the interval $[0, 6]$. $\frac{10}{3}$

(b) A quadratic approximation agreeing with f at $x = 5$ is $g(x) = -0.45x^2 + 5.52x - 13.70$. Use a graphing utility to graph f and g in the same viewing window. Describe the result. See margin.

(c) Use the Quadratic Formula to find the zeros of g. Compare the zero in the interval $[0, 6]$ with the result of part (a). 3.46, 8.81
3.46 is close to the zero of f in the interval $[0, 6]$.

EXPLORATION

99–100. See margin.

TRUE OR FALSE? In Exercises 99 and 100, determine whether the statement is true or false. Justify your answer.

99. The equation $2 \sin 4t - 1 = 0$ has four times the number of solutions in the interval $[0, 2\pi)$ as the equation $2 \sin t - 1 = 0$.

100. If you correctly solve a trigonometric equation to the statement $\sin x = 3.4$, then you can finish solving the equation by using an inverse function.

101. THINK ABOUT IT Explain what would happen if you divided each side of the equation $\cot x \cos^2 x = 2 \cot x$ by $\cot x$. Is this a correct method to use when solving equations? See margin.

102. GRAPHICAL REASONING Use a graphing utility to confirm the solutions found in Example 6 in two different ways. See margin.

(a) Graph both sides of the equation and find the x-coordinates of the points at which the graphs intersect.

Left side: $y = \cos x + 1$

Right side: $y = \sin x$

(b) Graph the equation $y = \cos x + 1 - \sin x$ and find the x-intercepts of the graph. Do both methods produce the same x-values? Which method do you prefer? Explain.

103. Explain in your own words how knowledge of algebra is important when solving trigonometric equations. Answers will vary.

104. CAPSTONE Consider the equation $2 \sin x - 1 = 0$. Explain the similarities and differences between finding all solutions in the interval $\left[0, \frac{\pi}{2}\right)$, finding all solutions in the interval $[0, 2\pi)$, and finding the general solution. See margin.

PROJECT: METEOROLOGY To work an extended application analyzing the normal daily high temperatures in Phoenix and in Seattle, visit this text's website at *academic.cengage.com*. (Data Source: NOAA)

5 ASSESS AND RETEACH

Daily Homework Quiz

Transparency Available
Available at the Instructor's companion site.

96. (a) and (c)

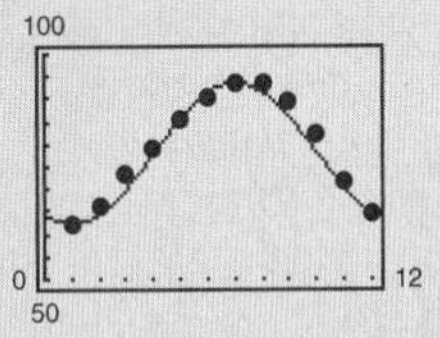

The model fits the data well.

(b) $H = 15.65 \cos\left(\frac{\pi}{6}t - \frac{7\pi}{6}\right) + 77.95$

(d) 77.95°F

(e) Above 86°: June through September
Below 86°: October through May

97. (a)

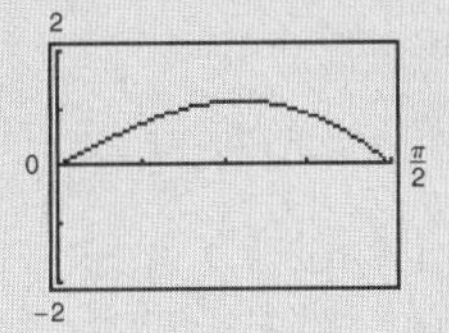

$A \approx 1.12$

(b) $0.6 < x < 1.1$

98. (b)

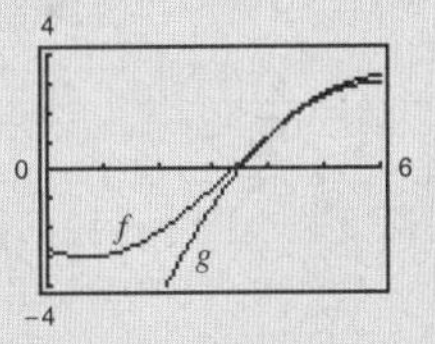

For $3.5 \leq x \leq 6$, the approximation appears to be good.

99. True. The first equation has a smaller period than the second equation, so it will have more solutions in the interval $[0, 2\pi)$.

100. False. There is no value of x for which $\sin x = 3.4$.

101. The equation would become $\cos^2 x = 2$; this is not the correct method to use when solving equations.

102. (a)

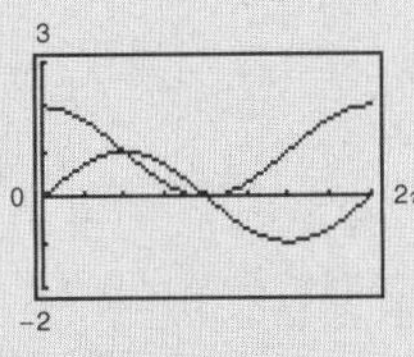

Graphs intersect when $x = \frac{\pi}{2}$ and $x = \pi$.

(b)

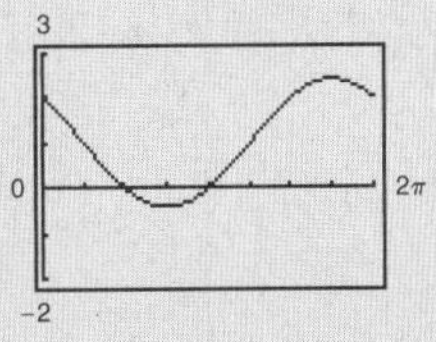

x-intercepts: $\left(\frac{\pi}{2}, 0\right)$, $(\pi, 0)$

Both methods produce the same x-values.

104. See Additional Answers beginning on page AA1.

1 PLAN AND PREPARE

Warm-up Exercises

Transparency Available
Available at the Instructor's companion site.

Notetaking Guide

Transparency Available
Promotes interactive learning and notetaking skills.
Available at the Instructor's companion site.

Animated Precalculus

An **Animated Precalculus** tutorial is available at the Student companion site for **Section 5.4.**

Pacing

Average: 2 days
Advanced: 2 days
Block: 1 block

2 FOCUS AND MOTIVATE

Essential Question

How do you simplify expressions and solve equations that contain sums or differences of angles?
Tell students that they will learn how to answer this question by studying the sum and difference formulas and their use in solving problems.

5.4 SUM AND DIFFERENCE FORMULAS

What you should learn

- Use sum and difference formulas to evaluate trigonometric functions, verify identities, and solve trigonometric equations.

Why you should learn it

You can use identities to rewrite trigonometric expressions. For instance, in Exercise 89 on page 403, you can use an identity to rewrite a trigonometric expression in a form that helps you analyze a harmonic motion equation.

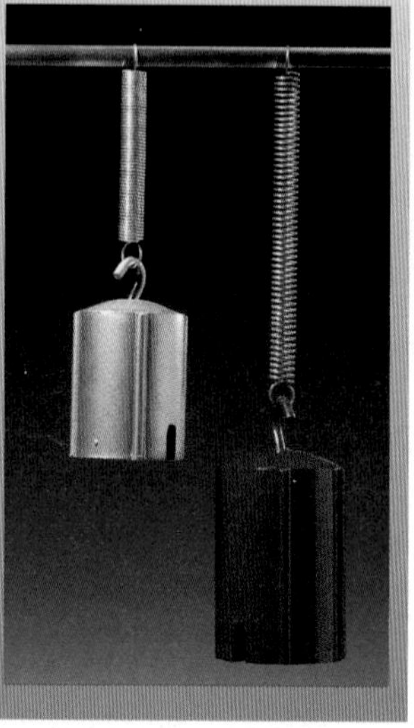

Richard Megna/Fundamental Photographs

Using Sum and Difference Formulas

In this and the following section, you will study the uses of several trigonometric identities and formulas.

> **Sum and Difference Formulas**
>
> $\sin(u + v) = \sin u \cos v + \cos u \sin v$
>
> $\sin(u - v) = \sin u \cos v - \cos u \sin v$
>
> $\cos(u + v) = \cos u \cos v - \sin u \sin v$
>
> $\cos(u - v) = \cos u \cos v + \sin u \sin v$
>
> $\tan(u + v) = \dfrac{\tan u + \tan v}{1 - \tan u \tan v}$ $\qquad$ $\tan(u - v) = \dfrac{\tan u - \tan v}{1 + \tan u \tan v}$

For a proof of the sum and difference formulas, see Proofs in Mathematics on page 422.

Examples 1 and 2 show how **sum and difference formulas** can be used to find exact values of trigonometric functions involving sums or differences of special angles.

Example 1 Evaluating a Trigonometric Function

Find the exact value of $\sin \frac{\pi}{12}$.

Solution

To find the *exact* value of $\sin \frac{\pi}{12}$, use the fact that

$$\frac{\pi}{12} = \frac{\pi}{3} - \frac{\pi}{4}.$$

Consequently, the formula for $\sin(u - v)$ yields

$$\begin{aligned}\sin \frac{\pi}{12} &= \sin\left(\frac{\pi}{3} - \frac{\pi}{4}\right)\\ &= \sin \frac{\pi}{3} \cos \frac{\pi}{4} - \cos \frac{\pi}{3} \sin \frac{\pi}{4}\\ &= \frac{\sqrt{3}}{2}\left(\frac{\sqrt{2}}{2}\right) - \frac{1}{2}\left(\frac{\sqrt{2}}{2}\right)\\ &= \frac{\sqrt{6} - \sqrt{2}}{4}.\end{aligned}$$

Try checking this result on your calculator. You will find that $\sin \frac{\pi}{12} \approx 0.259$.

CHECKPoint Now try Exercise 7.

Resource Planning Guide

Chapter Resources
- Complete Solutions Guide

Workbooks
- Notetaking Guide
- Student Solutions Guide

Interactive Technology
- Instructor Success Organizer
- Notetaking Guide IAE
- Instructional DVDs
- Animated Precalculus
- PowerLecture with ExamView

Study Tip

Another way to solve Example 2 is to use the fact that $75° = 120° - 45°$ together with the formula for $\cos(u - v)$.

Example 2 Evaluating a Trigonometric Function

Find the exact value of $\cos 75°$.

Solution

Using the fact that $75° = 30° + 45°$, together with the formula for $\cos(u + v)$, you obtain

$$\begin{aligned}\cos 75° &= \cos(30° + 45°)\\ &= \cos 30° \cos 45° - \sin 30° \sin 45°\\ &= \frac{\sqrt{3}}{2}\left(\frac{\sqrt{2}}{2}\right) - \frac{1}{2}\left(\frac{\sqrt{2}}{2}\right) = \frac{\sqrt{6} - \sqrt{2}}{4}.\end{aligned}$$

CHECKPoint Now try Exercise 11.

Example 3 Evaluating a Trigonometric Expression

Find the exact value of $\sin(u + v)$ given

$$\sin u = \frac{4}{5}, \text{ where } 0 < u < \frac{\pi}{2}, \quad \text{and} \quad \cos v = -\frac{12}{13}, \text{ where } \frac{\pi}{2} < v < \pi.$$

Solution

Because $\sin u = 4/5$ and u is in Quadrant I, $\cos u = 3/5$, as shown in Figure 5.10. Because $\cos v = -12/13$ and v is in Quadrant II, $\sin v = 5/13$, as shown in Figure 5.11. You can find $\sin(u + v)$ as follows.

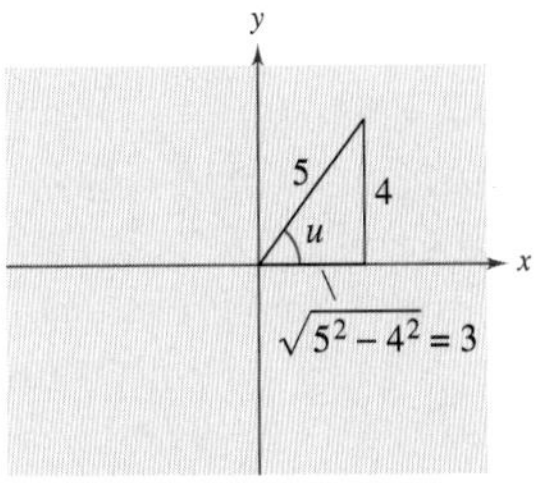

FIGURE 5.10

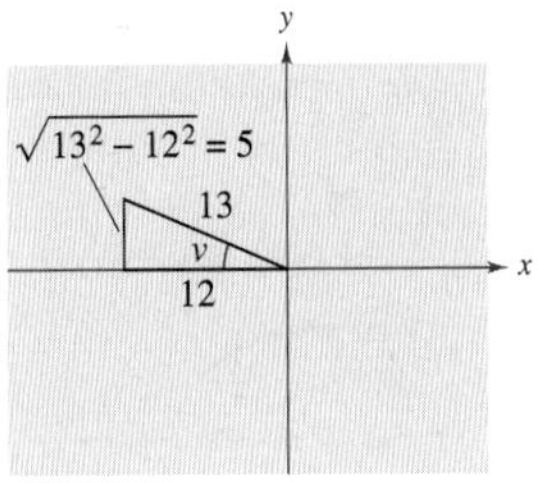

FIGURE 5.11

$$\begin{aligned}\sin(u + v) &= \sin u \cos v + \cos u \sin v\\ &= \left(\frac{4}{5}\right)\left(-\frac{12}{13}\right) + \left(\frac{3}{5}\right)\left(\frac{5}{13}\right)\\ &= -\frac{48}{65} + \frac{15}{65}\\ &= -\frac{33}{65}\end{aligned}$$

CHECKPoint Now try Exercise 43.

Example 4 An Application of a Sum Formula

Write $\cos(\arctan 1 + \arccos x)$ as an algebraic expression.

Solution

This expression fits the formula for $\cos(u + v)$. Angles $u = \arctan 1$ and $v = \arccos x$ are shown in Figure 5.12. So

$$\begin{aligned}\cos(u + v) &= \cos(\arctan 1)\cos(\arccos x) - \sin(\arctan 1)\sin(\arccos x)\\ &= \frac{1}{\sqrt{2}} \cdot x - \frac{1}{\sqrt{2}} \cdot \sqrt{1 - x^2}\\ &= \frac{x - \sqrt{1 - x^2}}{\sqrt{2}}.\end{aligned}$$

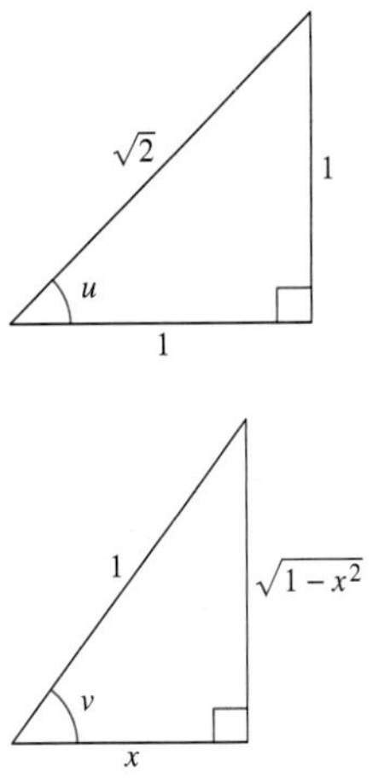

FIGURE 5.12

CHECKPoint Now try Exercise 57.

3 TEACH

Extra Example 1

Find the exact value of $\cos \frac{\pi}{12}$.

$\frac{\sqrt{2} + \sqrt{6}}{4}$

Avoiding Common Errors

When working with sum and difference formulas, students need to be careful with radical operations. Although a calculator gives an approximate decimal answer, the exact value requires the radical form.

Extra Example 2

Find the exact value of $\sin 75°$.

$\frac{\sqrt{2} + \sqrt{6}}{4}$

Extra Example 3

Find the exact value of $\cos(u + v)$ given $\sin u = \frac{7}{25}$, where $0 < u < \frac{\pi}{2}$, and $\cos v = -\frac{4}{5}$, where $\frac{\pi}{2} < v < \pi$.

$-\frac{117}{125}$

Extra Example 4

Write $\sin(\arctan 1 + \arccos x)$ as an algebraic expression.

$\frac{x + \sqrt{1 - x^2}}{\sqrt{2}}$

Extra Example 5

Prove the cofunction identity $\sin\left(x - \frac{\pi}{2}\right) = -\cos x$.

$$\begin{aligned}\sin\left(x - \frac{\pi}{2}\right) &= (\sin x)\cos\frac{\pi}{2} - (\cos x)\sin\frac{\pi}{2}\\ &= \sin x(0) - \cos x(1)\\ &= -\cos x\end{aligned}$$

Extra Example 6

Simplify each expression.

a. $\sin\left(\frac{3\pi}{2} - \theta\right)$

$-\cos\theta$

b. $\tan\left(\theta - \frac{\pi}{4}\right)$

$\frac{\tan\theta - 1}{\tan\theta + 1}$

HISTORICAL NOTE

The Granger Collection, New York

Hipparchus, considered the most eminent of Greek astronomers, was born about 190 B.C. in Nicaea. He was credited with the invention of trigonometry. He also derived the sum and difference formulas for $\sin(A \pm B)$ and $\cos(A \pm B)$.

Example 5 shows how to use a difference formula to prove the cofunction identity

$$\cos\left(\frac{\pi}{2} - x\right) = \sin x.$$

Example 5 Proving a Cofunction Identity

Prove the cofunction identity $\cos\left(\frac{\pi}{2} - x\right) = \sin x$.

Solution

Using the formula for $\cos(u - v)$, you have

$$\begin{aligned}\cos\left(\frac{\pi}{2} - x\right) &= \cos\frac{\pi}{2}\cos x + \sin\frac{\pi}{2}\sin x\\ &= (0)(\cos x) + (1)(\sin x)\\ &= \sin x.\end{aligned}$$

CHECKPoint Now try Exercise 61.

Sum and difference formulas can be used to rewrite expressions such as

$$\sin\left(\theta + \frac{n\pi}{2}\right) \quad \text{and} \quad \cos\left(\theta + \frac{n\pi}{2}\right), \quad \text{where } n \text{ is an integer}$$

as expressions involving only $\sin\theta$ or $\cos\theta$. The resulting formulas are called **reduction formulas.**

Example 6 Deriving Reduction Formulas

Simplify each expression.

a. $\cos\left(\theta - \frac{3\pi}{2}\right)$ **b.** $\tan(\theta + 3\pi)$

Solution

a. Using the formula for $\cos(u - v)$, you have

$$\begin{aligned}\cos\left(\theta - \frac{3\pi}{2}\right) &= \cos\theta\cos\frac{3\pi}{2} + \sin\theta\sin\frac{3\pi}{2}\\ &= (\cos\theta)(0) + (\sin\theta)(-1)\\ &= -\sin\theta.\end{aligned}$$

b. Using the formula for $\tan(u + v)$, you have

$$\begin{aligned}\tan(\theta + 3\pi) &= \frac{\tan\theta + \tan 3\pi}{1 - \tan\theta\tan 3\pi}\\ &= \frac{\tan\theta + 0}{1 - (\tan\theta)(0)}\\ &= \tan\theta.\end{aligned}$$

CHECKPoint Now try Exercise 73.

Example 7 Solving a Trigonometric Equation

Find all solutions of $\sin\left(x + \frac{\pi}{4}\right) + \sin\left(x - \frac{\pi}{4}\right) = -1$ in the interval $[0, 2\pi)$.

Algebraic Solution

Using sum and difference formulas, rewrite the equation as

$$\sin x \cos \frac{\pi}{4} + \cos x \sin \frac{\pi}{4} + \sin x \cos \frac{\pi}{4} - \cos x \sin \frac{\pi}{4} = -1$$

$$2 \sin x \cos \frac{\pi}{4} = -1$$

$$2(\sin x)\left(\frac{\sqrt{2}}{2}\right) = \frac{1}{2}$$

$$\sin x = -\frac{1}{\sqrt{2}}$$

$$\sin x = -\frac{\sqrt{2}}{2}.$$

So, the only solutions in the interval $[0, 2\pi)$ are

$$x = \frac{5\pi}{4} \quad \text{and} \quad x = \frac{7\pi}{4}.$$

Graphical Solution

Sketch the graph of

$$y = \sin\left(x + \frac{\pi}{4}\right) + \sin\left(x - \frac{\pi}{4}\right) + 1 \text{ for } 0 \le x < 2\pi.$$

as shown in Figure 5.13. From the graph you can see that the x-intercepts are $5\pi/4$ and $7\pi/4$. So, the solutions in the interval $[0, 2\pi)$ are

$$x = \frac{5\pi}{4} \quad \text{and} \quad x = \frac{7\pi}{4}.$$

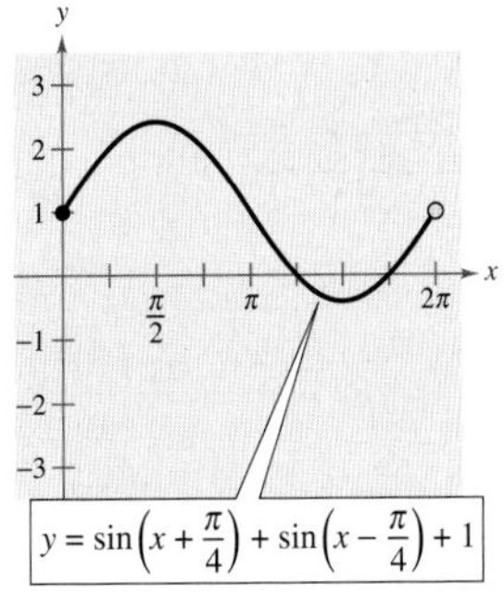

FIGURE 5.13

CHECKPoint Now try Exercise 79.

The next example was taken from calculus. It is used to derive the derivative of the sine function.

Example 8 An Application from Calculus

Verify that $\frac{\sin(x + h) - \sin x}{h} = (\cos x)\left(\frac{\sin h}{h}\right) - (\sin x)\left(\frac{1 - \cos h}{h}\right)$ where $h \neq 0$.

Solution

Using the formula for $\sin(u + v)$, you have

$$\frac{\sin(x + h) - \sin x}{h} = \frac{\sin x \cos h + \cos x \sin h - \sin x}{h}$$

$$= \frac{\cos x \sin h - \sin x(1 - \cos h)}{h}$$

$$= (\cos x)\left(\frac{\sin h}{h}\right) - (\sin x)\left(\frac{1 - \cos h}{h}\right).$$

CHECKPoint Now try Exercise 105.

Extra Example 7

Find all of the solutions of

$\sin\left(x + \frac{\pi}{2}\right) + \sin\left(x - \frac{3\pi}{2}\right) = 1$

in the interval $[0, 2\pi)$.

$x = \frac{\pi}{3}$ and $x = \frac{5\pi}{3}$

Extra Example 8

Verify that $\frac{\cos(x + h) - \cos x}{h} =$

$\cos x\left(\frac{\cos h - 1}{h}\right) - \sin x\left(\frac{\sin h}{h}\right).$

See below.

Closing the Lesson

Have students summarize the major points of the lesson and answer the Essential Question: How do you simplify expressions and solve equations that contain sums or differences of angles?

Use the sum and difference formulas to

- **evaluate trigonometric functions,**
- **verify identities, and**
- **solve equations.**

Answer for Extra Example 8

$$\frac{\cos(x + h) - \cos x}{h} = \frac{\cos x \cos h - \sin x \sin h - \cos x}{h}$$

$$= \frac{\cos x \cos h - \cos x - \sin x \sin h}{h}$$

$$= \cos x\left(\frac{\cos h - 1}{h}\right) - \sin x\left(\frac{\sin h}{h}\right)$$

4 PRACTICE AND APPLY

Assignment Guide

Transparencies Available
Available at the Instructor's companion site.

Average:
Day 1: p. 402
Exs. 1–6, 9–13 odd, 17, 21, 25, 29–35 odd, 39–45 odd, 53, 55, 59
Day 2: pp. 403–404
Exs. 63–69 odd, 72, 73, 81–89 odd, 91–95, 99, 103–107 odd

Advanced:
Day 1: p. 402
Exs. 1–6, 8, 12, 14, 18, 24, 26, 30–44 even, 48–60 even
Day 2: pp. 403–404
Exs. 62–68 even, 73, 74, 78–82 even, 86, 88, 89, 90–100 even, 104–108 even, 109, 112

Block:
pp. 402–404
Exs. 1–6, 9–13 odd, 17, 21, 25, 29–35 odd, 39–45 odd, 53, 55, 59, 63–69 odd, 72, 73, 81–89 odd, 91–95, 99, 103–107 odd

5.4 EXERCISES

See www.CalcChat.com for worked-out solutions to odd-numbered exercises.

VOCABULARY: Fill in the blank.

1. $\sin(u - v) =$ ________ $\sin u \cos v - \cos u \sin v$
2. $\cos(u + v) =$ ________ $\cos u \cos v - \sin u \sin v$
3. $\tan(u + v) =$ See margin.
4. $\sin(u + v) =$ ________ $\sin u \cos v + \cos u \sin v$
5. $\cos(u - v) =$ ________ $\cos u \cos v + \sin u \sin v$
6. $\tan(u - v) =$ ________ $\dfrac{\tan u - \tan v}{1 + \tan u \tan v}$

SKILLS AND APPLICATIONS

7–12. See margin.

In Exercises 7–12, find the exact value of each expression.

7. (a) $\cos\left(\frac{\pi}{4} + \frac{\pi}{3}\right)$ (b) $\cos\frac{\pi}{4} + \cos\frac{\pi}{3}$
8. (a) $\sin\left(\frac{3\pi}{4} + \frac{5\pi}{6}\right)$ (b) $\sin\frac{3\pi}{4} + \sin\frac{5\pi}{6}$
9. (a) $\sin\left(\frac{7\pi}{6} - \frac{\pi}{3}\right)$ (b) $\sin\frac{7\pi}{6} - \sin\frac{\pi}{3}$
10. (a) $\cos(120° + 45°)$ (b) $\cos 120° + \cos 45°$
11. (a) $\sin(135° - 30°)$ (b) $\sin 135° - \cos 30°$
12. (a) $\sin(315° - 60°)$ (b) $\sin 315° - \sin 60°$

In Exercises 13–28, find the exact values of the sine, cosine, and tangent of the angle. 13–28. See margin.

13. $\frac{11\pi}{12} = \frac{3\pi}{4} + \frac{\pi}{6}$
14. $\frac{7\pi}{12} = \frac{\pi}{3} + \frac{\pi}{4}$
15. $\frac{17\pi}{12} = \frac{9\pi}{4} - \frac{5\pi}{6}$
16. $-\frac{\pi}{12} = \frac{\pi}{6} - \frac{\pi}{4}$
17. $105° = 60° + 45°$
18. $165° = 135° + 30°$
19. $195° = 225° - 30°$
20. $255° = 300° - 45°$
21. $\frac{13\pi}{12}$
22. $-\frac{7\pi}{12}$
23. $-\frac{13\pi}{12}$
24. $\frac{5\pi}{12}$
25. $285°$
26. $-105°$
27. $-165°$
28. $15°$

In Exercises 29–36, write the expression as the sine, cosine, or tangent of an angle.

29. $\sin 3 \cos 1.2 - \cos 3 \sin 1.2$ $\sin 1.8$
30. $\cos\frac{\pi}{7}\cos\frac{\pi}{5} - \sin\frac{\pi}{7}\sin\frac{\pi}{5}$ $\cos\frac{12\pi}{35}$
31. $\sin 60° \cos 15° + \cos 60° \sin 15°$ $\sin 75°$
32. $\cos 130° \cos 40° - \sin 130° \sin 40°$ $\cos 170°$
33. $\dfrac{\tan 45° - \tan 30°}{1 + \tan 45° \tan 30°}$ $\tan 15°$
34. $\dfrac{\tan 140° - \tan 60°}{1 + \tan 140° \tan 60°}$ $\tan 80°$
35. $\dfrac{\tan 2x + \tan x}{1 - \tan 2x \tan x}$ $\tan 3x$
36. $\cos 3x \cos 2y + \sin 3x \sin 2y$ $\cos(3x - 2y)$

In Exercises 37–42, find the exact value of the expression.

37. $\sin\frac{\pi}{12}\cos\frac{\pi}{4} + \cos\frac{\pi}{12}\sin\frac{\pi}{4}$ $\frac{\sqrt{3}}{2}$
38. $\cos\frac{\pi}{16}\cos\frac{3\pi}{16} - \sin\frac{\pi}{16}\sin\frac{3\pi}{16}$ $\frac{\sqrt{2}}{2}$
39. $\sin 120° \cos 60° - \cos 120° \sin 60°$ $\frac{\sqrt{3}}{2}$
40. $\cos 120° \cos 30° + \sin 120° \sin 30°$ 0
41. $\dfrac{\tan(5\pi/6) - \tan(\pi/6)}{1 + \tan(5\pi/6)\tan(\pi/6)}$ $-\sqrt{3}$
42. $\dfrac{\tan 25° + \tan 110°}{1 - \tan 25° \tan 110°}$ -1

In Exercises 43–50, find the exact value of the trigonometric function given that $\sin u = \frac{5}{13}$ and $\cos v = -\frac{3}{5}$. (Both u and v are in Quadrant II.)

43. $\sin(u + v)$ $-\frac{63}{65}$
44. $\cos(u - v)$ $\frac{56}{65}$
45. $\cos(u + v)$ $\frac{16}{65}$
46. $\sin(v - u)$ $-\frac{33}{65}$
47. $\tan(u + v)$ $-\frac{63}{16}$
48. $\csc(u - v)$ $\frac{65}{33}$
49. $\sec(v - u)$ $\frac{65}{56}$
50. $\cot(u + v)$ $-\frac{16}{63}$

In Exercises 51–56, find the exact value of the trigonometric function given that $\sin u = -\frac{7}{25}$ and $\cos v = -\frac{4}{5}$. (Both u and v are in Quadrant III.)

51. $\cos(u + v)$ $\frac{3}{5}$
52. $\sin(u + v)$ $\frac{4}{5}$
53. $\tan(u - v)$ $-\frac{44}{117}$
54. $\cot(v - u)$ $\frac{117}{44}$
55. $\csc(u - v)$ $-\frac{125}{44}$
56. $\sec(v - u)$ $\frac{125}{117}$

In Exercises 57–60, write the trigonometric expression as an algebraic expression.

57. $\sin(\arcsin x + \arccos x)$ 1
58. $\sin(\arctan 2x - \arccos x)$ See margin.
59. $\cos(\arccos x + \arcsin x)$ 0
60. $\cos(\arccos x - \arctan x)$ See margin.

3. $\dfrac{\tan u + \tan v}{1 - \tan u \tan v}$

7. (a) $\dfrac{\sqrt{2} - \sqrt{6}}{4}$ (b) $\dfrac{\sqrt{2} + 1}{2}$

8. (a) $-\dfrac{\sqrt{6} + \sqrt{2}}{4}$ (b) $\dfrac{\sqrt{2} + 1}{2}$

9. (a) $\dfrac{1}{2}$ (b) $\dfrac{-\sqrt{3} - 1}{2}$

10. (a) $\dfrac{-\sqrt{2} - \sqrt{6}}{4}$ (b) $\dfrac{-1 + \sqrt{2}}{2}$

11. (a) $\dfrac{\sqrt{6} + \sqrt{2}}{4}$ (b) $\dfrac{\sqrt{2} - \sqrt{3}}{2}$

12. (a) $\dfrac{-2 - \sqrt{6}}{4}$ (b) $\dfrac{-\sqrt{2} - \sqrt{3}}{2}$

13. $\sin\frac{11\pi}{12} = \frac{\sqrt{2}}{4}(\sqrt{3} - 1)$
$\cos\frac{11\pi}{12} = -\frac{\sqrt{2}}{4}(\sqrt{3} + 1)$
$\tan\frac{11\pi}{12} = -2 + \sqrt{3}$

14. $\sin\frac{7\pi}{12} = \frac{\sqrt{2}}{4}(\sqrt{3} + 1)$
$\cos\frac{7\pi}{12} = \frac{\sqrt{2}}{4}(1 - \sqrt{3})$
$\tan\frac{7\pi}{12} = -2 - \sqrt{3}$

15. $\sin\frac{17\pi}{12} = -\frac{\sqrt{2}}{4}(\sqrt{3} + 1)$
$\cos\frac{17\pi}{12} = \frac{\sqrt{2}}{4}(1 - \sqrt{3})$
$\tan\frac{17\pi}{12} = 2 + \sqrt{3}$

16. $\sin\left(-\frac{\pi}{12}\right) = \frac{\sqrt{2}}{4}(1 - \sqrt{3})$
$\cos\left(-\frac{\pi}{12}\right) = \frac{\sqrt{2}}{4}(\sqrt{3} + 1)$
$\tan\left(-\frac{\pi}{12}\right) = -2 + \sqrt{3}$

17. $\sin 105° = \frac{\sqrt{2}}{4}(\sqrt{3} + 1)$
$\cos 105° = \frac{\sqrt{2}}{4}(1 - \sqrt{3})$
$\tan 105° = -2 - \sqrt{3}$

18. $\sin 165° = \frac{\sqrt{2}}{4}(\sqrt{3} - 1)$
$\cos 165° = -\frac{\sqrt{2}}{4}(\sqrt{3} + 1)$
$\tan 165° = -2 + \sqrt{3}$

19. $\sin 195° = \frac{\sqrt{2}}{4}(1 - \sqrt{3})$
$\cos 195° = -\frac{\sqrt{2}}{4}(\sqrt{3} + 1)$
$\tan 195° = 2 - \sqrt{3}$

20–28, 58, 60. See page 403.

In Exercises 61–70, prove the identity. 61–70. Proofs

61. $\sin\left(\frac{\pi}{2} - x\right) = \cos x$ **62.** $\sin\left(\frac{\pi}{2} + x\right) = \cos x$

63. $\sin\left(\frac{\pi}{6} + x\right) = \frac{1}{2}(\cos x + \sqrt{3}\sin x)$

64. $\cos\left(\frac{5\pi}{4} - x\right) = -\frac{\sqrt{2}}{2}(\cos x + \sin x)$

65. $\cos(\pi - \theta) + \sin\left(\frac{\pi}{2} + \theta\right) = 0$

66. $\tan\left(\frac{\pi}{4} - \theta\right) = \frac{1 - \tan\theta}{1 + \tan\theta}$

67. $\cos(x + y)\cos(x - y) = \cos^2 x - \sin^2 y$

68. $\sin(x + y)\sin(x - y) = \sin^2 x - \sin^2 y$

69. $\sin(x + y) + \sin(x - y) = 2\sin x\cos y$

70. $\cos(x + y) + \cos(x - y) = 2\cos x\cos y$

In Exercises 71–74, simplify the expression algebraically and use a graphing utility to confirm your answer graphically.

71. $\cos\left(\frac{3\pi}{2} - x\right)$ $-\sin x$ **72.** $\cos(\pi + x)$ $-\cos x$

73. $\sin\left(\frac{3\pi}{2} + \theta\right)$ $-\cos\theta$ **74.** $\tan(\pi + \theta)$ $\tan\theta$

In Exercises 75–84, find all solutions of the equation in the interval $[0, 2\pi)$.

75. $\sin(x + \pi) - \sin x + 1 = 0$ 75–78. See margin.

76. $\sin(x + \pi) - \sin x - 1 = 0$

77. $\cos(x + \pi) - \cos x - 1 = 0$

78. $\cos(x + \pi) - \cos x + 1 = 0$

79. $\sin\left(x + \frac{\pi}{6}\right) - \sin\left(x - \frac{\pi}{6}\right) = \frac{1}{2}$ $\frac{\pi}{3}, \frac{5\pi}{3}$

80. $\sin\left(x + \frac{\pi}{3}\right) + \sin\left(x - \frac{\pi}{3}\right) = 1$ $\frac{\pi}{2}$

81. $\cos\left(x + \frac{\pi}{4}\right) - \cos\left(x - \frac{\pi}{4}\right) = 1$ $\frac{5\pi}{4}, \frac{7\pi}{4}$

82. $\tan(x + \pi) + 2\sin(x + \pi) = 0$ $0, \frac{\pi}{3}, \pi, \frac{5\pi}{3}$

83. $\sin\left(x + \frac{\pi}{2}\right) - \cos^2 x = 0$ $0, \frac{\pi}{2}, \frac{3\pi}{2}$

84. $\cos\left(x - \frac{\pi}{2}\right) + \sin^2 x = 0$ $0, \pi, \frac{3\pi}{2}$

In Exercises 85–88, use a graphing utility to approximate the solutions in the interval $[0, 2\pi)$.

85. $\cos\left(x + \frac{\pi}{4}\right) + \cos\left(x - \frac{\pi}{4}\right) = 1$ $\frac{\pi}{4}, \frac{7\pi}{4}$

86. $\tan(x + \pi) - \cos\left(x + \frac{\pi}{2}\right) = 0$ $0, \pi$

87. $\sin\left(x + \frac{\pi}{2}\right) + \cos^2 x = 0$ $\frac{\pi}{2}, \pi, \frac{3\pi}{2}$

88. $\cos\left(x - \frac{\pi}{2}\right) - \sin^2 x = 0$ $0, \frac{\pi}{2}, \pi$

89. HARMONIC MOTION A weight is attached to a spring suspended vertically from a ceiling. When a driving force is applied to the system, the weight moves vertically from its equilibrium position, and this motion is modeled by

$$y = \frac{1}{3}\sin 2t + \frac{1}{4}\cos 2t$$

where y is the distance from equilibrium (in feet) and t is the time (in seconds). See margin.

(a) Use the identity

$$a\sin B\theta + b\cos B\theta = \sqrt{a^2 + b^2}\sin(B\theta + C)$$

where $C = \arctan(b/a)$, $a > 0$, to write the model in the form $y = \sqrt{a^2 + b^2}\sin(Bt + C)$.

(b) Find the amplitude of the oscillations of the weight.

(c) Find the frequency of the oscillations of the weight.

90. STANDING WAVES The equation of a standing wave is obtained by adding the displacements of two waves traveling in opposite directions (see figure). Assume that each of the waves has amplitude A, period T, and wavelength λ. If the models for these waves are

$$y_1 = A\cos 2\pi\left(\frac{t}{T} - \frac{x}{\lambda}\right) \quad \text{and} \quad y_2 = A\cos 2\pi\left(\frac{t}{T} + \frac{x}{\lambda}\right)$$

show that

$$y_1 + y_2 = 2A\cos\frac{2\pi t}{T}\cos\frac{2\pi x}{\lambda}.$$ Answers will vary.

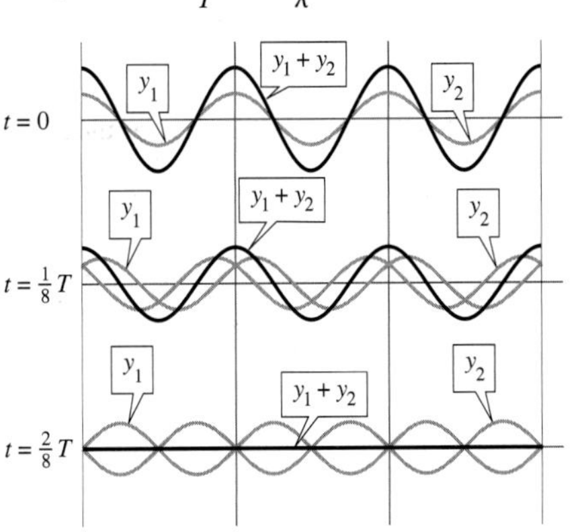

20. $\sin 255° = -\frac{\sqrt{2}}{4}(\sqrt{3} + 1)$
$\cos 255° = \frac{\sqrt{2}}{4}(1 - \sqrt{3})$
$\tan 255° = 2 + \sqrt{3}$

21. $\sin\frac{13\pi}{12} = \frac{\sqrt{2}}{4}(1 - \sqrt{3})$
$\cos\frac{13\pi}{12} = -\frac{\sqrt{2}}{4}(1 + \sqrt{3})$
$\tan\frac{13\pi}{12} = 2 - \sqrt{3}$

22. $\sin\left(-\frac{7\pi}{12}\right) = -\frac{\sqrt{2}}{4}(\sqrt{3} + 1)$
$\cos\left(-\frac{7\pi}{12}\right) = \frac{\sqrt{2}}{4}(1 - \sqrt{3})$
$\tan\left(-\frac{7\pi}{12}\right) = 2 + \sqrt{3}$

23. $\sin\left(-\frac{13\pi}{12}\right) = \frac{\sqrt{2}}{4}(\sqrt{3} - 1)$
$\cos\left(-\frac{13\pi}{12}\right) = -\frac{\sqrt{2}}{4}(\sqrt{3} + 1)$
$\tan\left(-\frac{13\pi}{12}\right) = -2 + \sqrt{3}$

24. $\sin\frac{5\pi}{12} = \frac{\sqrt{2}}{4}(1 + \sqrt{3})$
$\cos\frac{5\pi}{12} = \frac{\sqrt{2}}{4}(\sqrt{3} - 1)$
$\tan\frac{5\pi}{12} = \sqrt{3} + 2$

25. $\sin 285° = -\frac{\sqrt{2}}{4}(\sqrt{3} + 1)$
$\cos 285° = \frac{\sqrt{2}}{4}(\sqrt{3} - 1)$
$\tan 285° = -(2 + \sqrt{3})$

26. $\sin(-105°) = -\frac{\sqrt{2}}{4}(\sqrt{3} + 1)$
$\cos(-105°) = \frac{\sqrt{2}}{4}(1 - \sqrt{3})$
$\tan(-105°) = 2 + \sqrt{3}$

27. $\sin(-165°) = -\frac{\sqrt{2}}{4}(\sqrt{3} - 1)$
$\cos(-165°) = -\frac{\sqrt{2}}{4}(1 + \sqrt{3})$
$\tan(-165°) = 2 - \sqrt{3}$

28. $\sin 15° = \frac{\sqrt{2}}{4}(\sqrt{3} - 1)$
$\cos 15° = \frac{\sqrt{2}}{4}(1 + \sqrt{3})$
$\tan 15° = 2 - \sqrt{3}$

58. $\frac{2x^2 - \sqrt{1 - x^2}}{\sqrt{4x^2 + 1}}$

60. $\frac{x + x\sqrt{1 - x^2}}{\sqrt{x^2 + 1}}$

75. $\frac{\pi}{6}, \frac{5\pi}{6}$ **76.** $\frac{7\pi}{6}, \frac{11\pi}{6}$

77. $\frac{2\pi}{3}, \frac{4\pi}{3}$ **78.** $\frac{\pi}{3}, \frac{5\pi}{3}$

89. (a) $y = \frac{5}{12}\sin(2t + 0.6435)$

(b) $\frac{5}{12}$ ft (c) $\frac{1}{\pi}$ cycle/sec

EXPLORATION

91–94. See margin.

TRUE OR FALSE? In Exercises 91–94, determine whether the statement is true or false. Justify your answer.

91. $\sin(u \pm v) = \sin u \cos v \pm \cos u \sin v$

92. $\cos(u \pm v) = \cos u \cos v \pm \sin u \sin v$

93. $\tan\left(x - \frac{\pi}{4}\right) = \frac{\tan x + 1}{1 - \tan x}$

94. $\sin\left(x - \frac{\pi}{2}\right) = -\cos x$

95–98. Answers will vary.

In Exercises 95–98, verify the identity.

95. $\cos(n\pi + \theta) = (-1)^n \cos \theta$, n is an integer

96. $\sin(n\pi + \theta) = (-1)^n \sin \theta$, n is an integer

97. $a \sin B\theta + b \cos B\theta = \sqrt{a^2 + b^2} \sin(B\theta + C)$, where $C = \arctan(b/a)$ and $a > 0$

98. $a \sin B\theta + b \cos B\theta = \sqrt{a^2 + b^2} \cos(B\theta - C)$, where $C = \arctan(a/b)$ and $b > 0$

In Exercises 99–102, use the formulas given in Exercises 97 and 98 to write the trigonometric expression in the following forms. 99–102. See margin.

(a) $\sqrt{a^2 + b^2} \sin(B\theta + C)$ (b) $\sqrt{a^2 + b^2} \cos(B\theta - C)$

99. $\sin \theta + \cos \theta$

100. $3 \sin 2\theta + 4 \cos 2\theta$

101. $12 \sin 3\theta + 5 \cos 3\theta$

102. $\sin 2\theta + \cos 2\theta$

In Exercises 103 and 104, use the formulas given in Exercises 97 and 98 to write the trigonometric expression in the form $a \sin B\theta + b \cos B\theta$. 103–104. See margin.

103. $2 \sin\left(\theta + \frac{\pi}{4}\right)$

104. $5 \cos\left(\theta - \frac{\pi}{4}\right)$

105. Verify the following identity used in calculus. Answers will vary.

$$\frac{\cos(x + h) - \cos x}{h} = \frac{\cos x(\cos h - 1)}{h} - \frac{\sin x \sin h}{h}$$

106. Let $x = \pi/6$ in the identity in Exercise 105 and define the functions f and g as follows. See margin.

$$f(h) = \frac{\cos[(\pi/6) + h] - \cos(\pi/6)}{h}$$

$$g(h) = \cos \frac{\pi}{6}\left(\frac{\cos h - 1}{h}\right) - \sin \frac{\pi}{6}\left(\frac{\sin h}{h}\right)$$

(a) What are the domains of the functions f and g?

(b) Use a graphing utility to complete the table.

h	0.5	0.2	0.1	0.05	0.02	0.01
$f(h)$						
$g(h)$						

(c) Use a graphing utility to graph the functions f and g.

(d) Use the table and the graphs to make a conjecture about the values of the functions f and g as $h \to 0$.

In Exercises 107 and 108, use the figure, which shows two lines whose equations are $y_1 = m_1x + b_1$ and $y_2 = m_2x + b_2$. Assume that both lines have positive slopes. Derive a formula for the angle between the two lines. Then use your formula to find the angle between the given pair of lines.

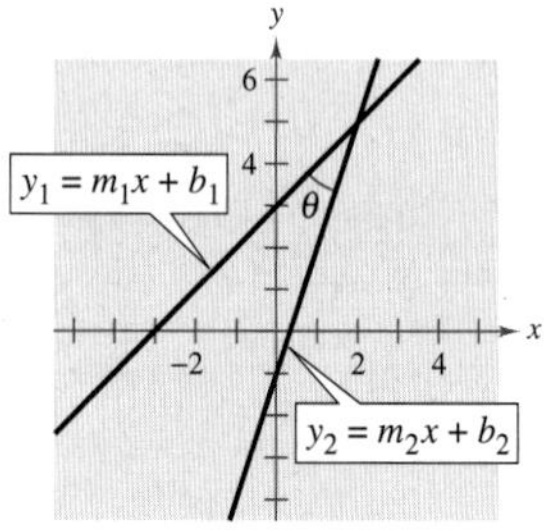

107. $y = x$ and $y = \sqrt{3}x$ 15°

108. $y = x$ and $y = \frac{1}{\sqrt{3}}x$ 15°

In Exercises 109 and 110, use a graphing utility to graph y_1 and y_2 in the same viewing window. Use the graphs to determine whether $y_1 = y_2$. Explain your reasoning. 109–110. See margin.

109. $y_1 = \cos(x + 2)$, $y_2 = \cos x + \cos 2$

110. $y_1 = \sin(x + 4)$, $y_2 = \sin x + \sin 4$

111. PROOF Proofs

(a) Write a proof of the formula for $\sin(u + v)$.

(b) Write a proof of the formula for $\sin(u - v)$.

112. CAPSTONE Give an example to justify each statement. See margin.

(a) $\sin(u + v) \neq \sin u + \sin v$

(b) $\sin(u - v) \neq \sin u - \sin v$

(c) $\cos(u + v) \neq \cos u + \cos v$

(d) $\cos(u - v) \neq \cos u - \cos v$

(e) $\tan(u + v) \neq \tan u + \tan v$

(f) $\tan(u - v) \neq \tan u - \tan v$

5 ASSESS AND RETEACH

Daily Homework Quiz

Transparency Available
Available at the Instructor's companion site.

93. False. $\tan\left(x - \frac{\pi}{4}\right) = \frac{\tan x - 1}{1 + \tan x}$

99. (a) $\sqrt{2} \sin\left(\theta + \frac{\pi}{4}\right)$
(b) $\sqrt{2} \cos\left(\theta - \frac{\pi}{4}\right)$

100. (a) $5 \sin(2\theta + 0.9273)$
(b) $5 \cos(2\theta - 0.6435)$

101. (a) $13 \sin(3\theta + 0.3948)$
(b) $13 \cos(3\theta - 1.1760)$

102. (a) $\sqrt{2} \sin\left(2\theta + \frac{\pi}{4}\right)$
(b) $\sqrt{2} \cos\left(2\theta - \frac{\pi}{4}\right)$

103. $\sqrt{2} \sin \theta + \sqrt{2} \cos \theta$

104. $\frac{5\sqrt{2}}{2} \sin \theta + \frac{5\sqrt{2}}{2} \cos \theta$

106. (a) All real numbers h except $h = 0$

(b)

h	0.5	0.2	0.1
$f(h)$	-0.69	-0.58	-0.54
$g(h)$	-0.69	-0.58	-0.54

h	0.05	0.02	0.01
$f(h)$	-0.52	-0.51	-0.50
$g(h)$	-0.52	-0.51	-0.50

(c)

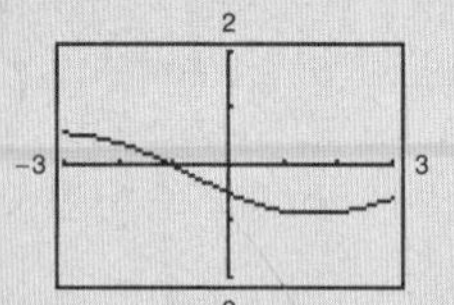

(d) As $h \to 0$, the function $f(h)$ approaches -0.5 and the function $g(h)$ approaches -0.5.

109.

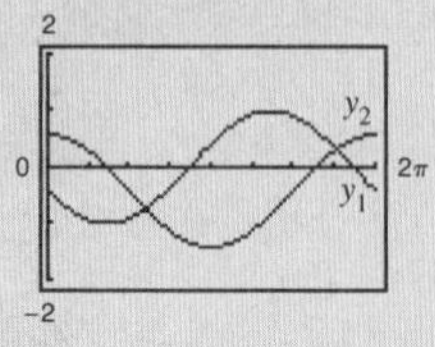

No, $y_1 \neq y_2$ because their graphs are different.

110.

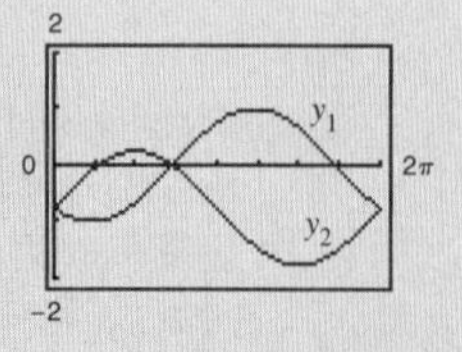

No, $y_1 \neq y_2$ because their graphs are different.

112. Answers will vary. Sample answers:

(a) $u = \pi, v = \frac{3\pi}{2}$ (b) $u = \frac{\pi}{2}, v = \frac{\pi}{4}$

(c) $u = \frac{\pi}{2}, v = \pi$ (d) $u = 2\pi, v = \frac{\pi}{2}$

(e) $u = \frac{\pi}{3}, v = \frac{5\pi}{6}$ (f) $u = \frac{\pi}{3}, v = \frac{\pi}{6}$

91–92, 94. See Additional Answers beginning on page AA1.

5.5 MULTIPLE-ANGLE AND PRODUCT-TO-SUM FORMULAS

What you should learn

- Use multiple-angle formulas to rewrite and evaluate trigonometric functions.
- Use power-reducing formulas to rewrite and evaluate trigonometric functions.
- Use half-angle formulas to rewrite and evaluate trigonometric functions.
- Use product-to-sum and sum-to-product formulas to rewrite and evaluate trigonometric functions.
- Use trigonometric formulas to rewrite real-life models.

Why you should learn it

You can use a variety of trigonometric formulas to rewrite trigonometric functions in more convenient forms. For instance, in Exercise 135 on page 415, you can use a double-angle formula to determine at what angle an athlete must throw a javelin.

Mark Dadswell/Getty Images

Multiple-Angle Formulas

In this section, you will study four other categories of trigonometric identities.

1. The first category involves *functions of multiple angles* such as $\sin ku$ and $\cos ku$.
2. The second category involves *squares of trigonometric functions* such as $\sin^2 u$.
3. The third category involves *functions of half-angles* such as $\sin(u/2)$.
4. The fourth category involves *products of trigonometric functions* such as $\sin u \cos v$.

You should learn the **double-angle formulas** because they are used often in trigonometry and calculus. For proofs of these formulas, see Proofs in Mathematics on page 423.

Double-Angle Formulas

$$\sin 2u = 2\sin u \cos u$$

$$\tan 2u = \frac{2\tan u}{1-\tan^2 u}$$

$$\cos 2u = \cos^2 u - \sin^2 u$$
$$= 2\cos^2 u - 1$$
$$= 1 - 2\sin^2 u$$

Example 1 Solving a Multiple-Angle Equation

Solve $2\cos x + \sin 2x = 0$.

Solution

Begin by rewriting the equation so that it involves functions of x (rather than $2x$). Then factor and solve.

$2\cos x + \sin 2x = 0$ Write original equation.

$2\cos x + 2\sin x\cos x = 0$ Double-angle formula

$2\cos x(1 + \sin x) = 0$ Factor.

$2\cos x = 0$ and $1 + \sin x = 0$ Set factors equal to zero.

$x = \frac{\pi}{2}, \frac{3\pi}{2}$ $x = \frac{3\pi}{2}$ Solutions in $[0, 2\pi)$

So, the general solution is

$$x = \frac{\pi}{2} + 2n\pi \quad \text{and} \quad x = \frac{3\pi}{2} + 2n\pi$$

where n is an integer. Try verifying these solutions graphically.

CHECKPoint Now try Exercise 19.

1 PLAN AND PREPARE

Warm-up Exercises

Transparency Available
Available at the Instructor's companion site.

Notetaking Guide

Transparency Available
Promotes interactive learning and notetaking skills. Available at the Instructor's companion site.

Animated Precalculus

An **Animated Precalculus** tutorial is available at the Student companion site for **Section 5.5.**

Pacing

Average: 2 days
Advanced: 2 days
Block: 1 block

2 FOCUS AND MOTIVATE

Essential Question

How do you rewrite trigonometric expressions that contain functions of multiple or half-angles, or functions that involve squares or products of trigonometric expressions? **Tell students that they will learn how to answer this question by studying double-angle, power-reducing, half-angle, and product-to-sum formulas.**

Resource Planning Guide

Chapter Resources
- Complete Solutions Guide

Workbooks
- Notetaking Guide
- Student Solutions Guide

Interactive Technology
- Instructor Success Organizer
- Notetaking Guide IAE
- Instructional DVDs
- Animated Precalculus
- PowerLecture with ExamView

3 TEACH

Extra Example 1

Solve $\cos 2x + \cos x = 0$.

$x = \frac{\pi}{3} + 2n\pi$, $x = \frac{5\pi}{3} + 2n\pi$, **and** $x = \pi + 2n\pi$, **where n is an integer.**

Extra Example 2

Use a double-angle formula to rewrite the equation $g(x) = 3 - 6\sin^2 x$. Then sketch the graph of the equation over the interval $[0, 2\pi]$.

$g(x) = 3\cos 2x$

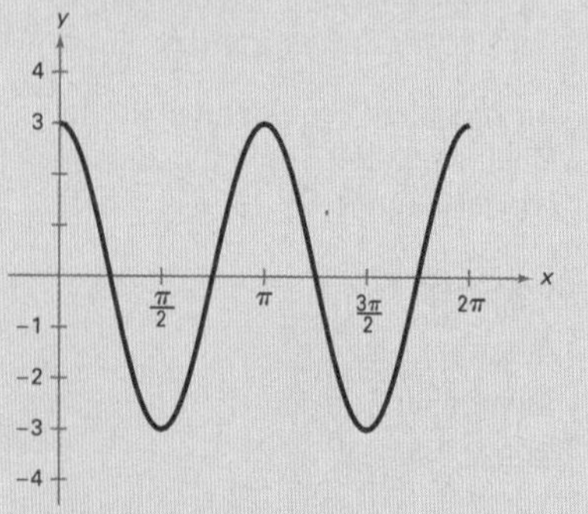

Extra Example 3

Use $\sin u = \frac{3}{5}$, $0 < u < \frac{\pi}{2}$, to find $\sin 2u$, $\cos 2u$, and $\tan 2u$.

$\sin 2u = \frac{24}{25}$, $\cos 2u = \frac{7}{25}$, $\tan 2u = \frac{24}{7}$

Example 2 Using Double-Angle Formulas to Analyze Graphs

Use a double-angle formula to rewrite the equation

$$y = 4\cos^2 x - 2.$$

Then sketch the graph of the equation over the interval $[0, 2\pi]$.

Solution

Using the double-angle formula for $\cos 2u$, you can rewrite the original equation as

$$y = 4\cos^2 x - 2 \qquad \text{Write original equation.}$$

$$= 2(2\cos^2 x - 1) \qquad \text{Factor.}$$

$$= 2\cos 2x. \qquad \text{Use double-angle formula.}$$

Using the techniques discussed in Section 4.5, you can recognize that the graph of this function has an amplitude of 2 and a period of π. The key points in the interval $[0, \pi]$ are as follows.

Maximum	Intercept	Minimum	Intercept	Maximum
$(0, 2)$	$\left(\frac{\pi}{4}, 0\right)$	$\left(\frac{\pi}{2}, -2\right)$	$\left(\frac{3\pi}{4}, 0\right)$	$(\pi, 2)$

Two cycles of the graph are shown in Figure 5.14.

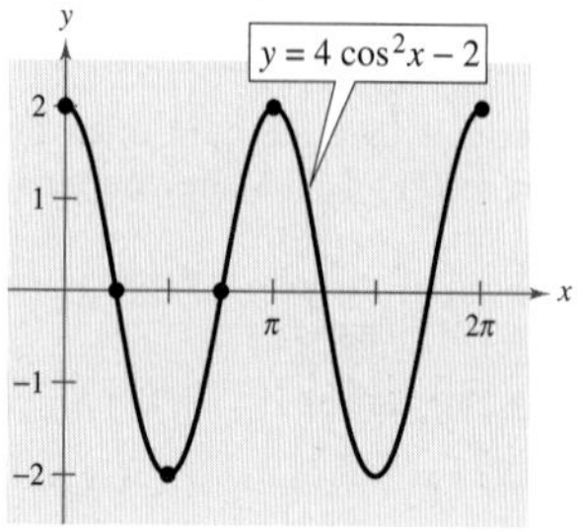

FIGURE 5.14

CHECKPoint Now try Exercise 33.

Example 3 Evaluating Functions Involving Double Angles

Use the following to find $\sin 2\theta$, $\cos 2\theta$, and $\tan 2\theta$.

$$\cos\theta = \frac{5}{13}, \qquad \frac{3\pi}{2} < \theta < 2\pi$$

Solution

From Figure 5.15, you can see that $\sin\theta = y/r = -12/13$. Consequently, using each of the double-angle formulas, you can write

$$\sin 2\theta = 2\sin\theta\cos\theta = 2\left(-\frac{12}{13}\right)\left(\frac{5}{13}\right) = -\frac{120}{169}$$

$$\cos 2\theta = 2\cos^2\theta - 1 = 2\left(\frac{25}{169}\right) - 1 = -\frac{119}{169}$$

$$\tan 2\theta = \frac{\sin 2\theta}{\cos 2\theta} = \frac{120}{119}.$$

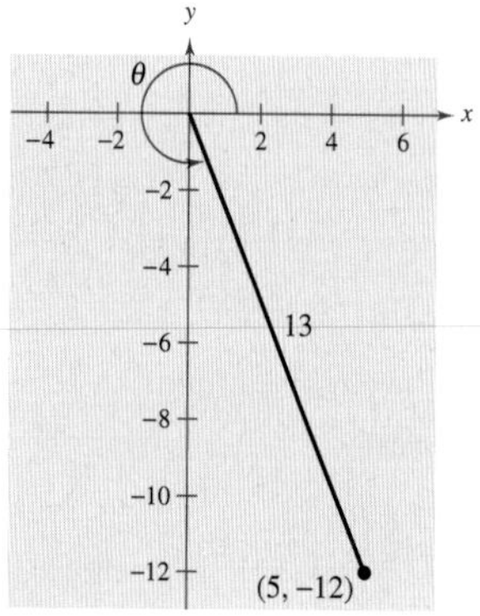

FIGURE 5.15

CHECKPoint Now try Exercise 37.

The double-angle formulas are not restricted to angles 2θ and θ. Other *double* combinations, such as 4θ and 2θ or 6θ and 3θ, are also valid. Here are two examples.

$$\sin 4\theta = 2\sin 2\theta\cos 2\theta \quad \text{and} \quad \cos 6\theta = \cos^2 3\theta - \sin^2 3\theta$$

By using double-angle formulas together with the sum formulas given in the preceding section, you can form other multiple-angle formulas.

Example 4 Deriving a Triple-Angle Formula

$$\begin{aligned}
\sin 3x &= \sin(2x + x) \\
&= \sin 2x \cos x + \cos 2x \sin x \\
&= 2 \sin x \cos x \cos x + (1 - 2 \sin^2 x) \sin x \\
&= 2 \sin x \cos^2 x + \sin x - 2 \sin^3 x \\
&= 2 \sin x(1 - \sin^2 x) + \sin x - 2 \sin^3 x \\
&= 2 \sin x - 2 \sin^3 x + \sin x - 2 \sin^3 x \\
&= 3 \sin x - 4 \sin^3 x
\end{aligned}$$

CHECKPoint Now try Exercise 117.

Power-Reducing Formulas

The double-angle formulas can be used to obtain the following **power-reducing formulas.** Example 5 shows a typical power reduction that is used in calculus.

Power-Reducing Formulas

$$\sin^2 u = \frac{1 - \cos 2u}{2} \qquad \cos^2 u = \frac{1 + \cos 2u}{2} \qquad \tan^2 u = \frac{1 - \cos 2u}{1 + \cos 2u}$$

For a proof of the power-reducing formulas, see Proofs in Mathematics on page 423.

Example 5 Reducing a Power

Rewrite $\sin^4 x$ as a sum of first powers of the cosines of multiple angles.

Solution

Note the repeated use of power-reducing formulas.

$\sin^4 x = (\sin^2 x)^2$	Property of exponents
$= \left(\frac{1 - \cos 2x}{2}\right)^2$	Power-reducing formula
$= \frac{1}{4}(1 - 2 \cos 2x + \cos^2 2x)$	Expand.
$= \frac{1}{4}\left(1 - 2 \cos 2x + \frac{1 + \cos 4x}{2}\right)$	Power-reducing formula
$= \frac{1}{4} - \frac{1}{2} \cos 2x + \frac{1}{8} + \frac{1}{8} \cos 4x$	Distributive Property
$= \frac{1}{8}(3 - 4 \cos 2x + \cos 4x)$	Factor out common factor.

CHECKPoint Now try Exercise 43.

Extra Example 4

Derive a triple-angle formula for $\cos 3x$.

$$\begin{aligned}
\cos 3x &= \cos(2x + x) \\
&= \cos 2x \cos x - \sin 2x \sin x \\
&= (2 \cos^2 x - 1) \cos x - (2 \sin x \cos x) \sin x \\
&= 2 \cos^3 x - \cos x - 2 \sin^2 x \cos x \\
&= 2 \cos^3 x - \cos x - 2(1 - \cos^2 x) \cos x \\
&= 2 \cos^3 x - \cos x - 2 \cos x + 2 \cos^3 x \\
&= 4 \cos^3 x - 3 \cos x
\end{aligned}$$

Extra Example 5

Rewrite $\tan^4 x$ as a quotient of first powers of the cosines of multiple angles.

$$\frac{3 - 4 \cos 2x + \cos 4x}{3 + 4 \cos 2x + \cos 4x}$$

Extra Example 6

Find the exact value of cos 105°.

$-\frac{\sqrt{2-\sqrt{3}}}{2}$

Half-Angle Formulas

You can derive some useful alternative forms of the power-reducing formulas by replacing u with $u/2$. The results are called **half-angle formulas.**

Half-Angle Formulas

$$\sin \frac{u}{2} = \pm\sqrt{\frac{1-\cos u}{2}}$$

$$\cos \frac{u}{2} = \pm\sqrt{\frac{1+\cos u}{2}}$$

$$\tan \frac{u}{2} = \frac{1-\cos u}{\sin u} = \frac{\sin u}{1+\cos u}$$

The signs of $\sin \frac{u}{2}$ and $\cos \frac{u}{2}$ depend on the quadrant in which $\frac{u}{2}$ lies.

Example 6 Using a Half-Angle Formula

Find the exact value of sin 105°.

Solution

Begin by noting that 105° is half of 210°. Then, using the half-angle formula for $\sin(u/2)$ and the fact that 105° lies in Quadrant II, you have

$$\begin{aligned}\sin 105° &= \sqrt{\frac{1-\cos 210°}{2}}\\ &= \sqrt{\frac{1-(-\cos 30°)}{2}}\\ &= \sqrt{\frac{1+(\sqrt{3}/2)}{2}}\\ &= \frac{\sqrt{2+\sqrt{3}}}{2}.\end{aligned}$$

The positive square root is chosen because $\sin\theta$ is positive in Quadrant II.

CHECKPoint Now try Exercise 59.

Study Tip

To find the exact value of a trigonometric function with an angle measure in D°M′S″ form using a half-angle formula, first convert the angle measure to decimal degree form. Then multiply the resulting angle measure by 2.

Use your calculator to verify the result obtained in Example 6. That is, evaluate sin 105° and $\left(\sqrt{2+\sqrt{3}}\right)/2$.

$$\sin 105° \approx 0.9659258$$

$$\frac{\sqrt{2+\sqrt{3}}}{2} \approx 0.9659258$$

You can see that both values are approximately 0.9659258.

Example 7 Solving a Trigonometric Equation

Find all solutions of $2 - \sin^2 x = 2\cos^2 \frac{x}{2}$ in the interval $[0, 2\pi)$.

Algebraic Solution

$2 - \sin^2 x = 2\cos^2 \frac{x}{2}$ — Write original equation.

$2 - \sin^2 x = 2\left(\pm\sqrt{\frac{1+\cos x}{2}}\right)^2$ — Half-angle formula

$2 - \sin^2 x = 2\left(\frac{1+\cos x}{2}\right)$ — Simplify.

$2 - \sin^2 x = 1 + \cos x$ — Simplify.

$2 - (1 - \cos^2 x) = 1 + \cos x$ — Pythagorean identity

$\cos^2 x - \cos x = 0$ — Simplify.

$\cos x(\cos x - 1) = 0$ — Factor.

By setting the factors $\cos x$ and $\cos x - 1$ equal to zero, you find that the solutions in the interval $[0, 2\pi)$ are

$$x = \frac{\pi}{2}, \quad x = \frac{3\pi}{2}, \quad \text{and} \quad x = 0.$$

CHECKPoint Now try Exercise 77.

Graphical Solution

Use a graphing utility set in *radian* mode to graph $y = 2 - \sin^2 x - 2\cos^2(x/2)$, as shown in Figure 5.16. Use the *zero* or *root* feature or the *zoom* and *trace* features to approximate the x-intercepts in the interval $[0, 2\pi)$ to be

$$x = 0, x \approx 1.571 \approx \frac{\pi}{2}, \text{ and } x \approx 4.712 \approx \frac{3\pi}{2}.$$

These values are the approximate solutions of $2 - \sin^2 x - 2\cos^2(x/2) = 0$ in the interval $[0, 2\pi)$.

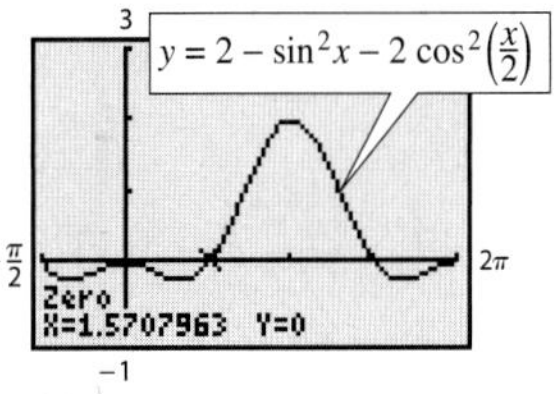

FIGURE 5.16

Product-to-Sum Formulas

Each of the following **product-to-sum formulas** can be verified using the sum and difference formulas discussed in the preceding section.

Product-to-Sum Formulas

$$\sin u \sin v = \frac{1}{2}[\cos(u - v) - \cos(u + v)]$$

$$\cos u \cos v = \frac{1}{2}[\cos(u - v) + \cos(u + v)]$$

$$\sin u \cos v = \frac{1}{2}[\sin(u + v) + \sin(u - v)]$$

$$\cos u \sin v = \frac{1}{2}[\sin(u + v) - \sin(u - v)]$$

Product-to-sum formulas are used in calculus to evaluate integrals involving the products of sines and cosines of two different angles.

Extra Example 7

Find all solutions of $\cos^2 x = \sin^2 \frac{x}{2}$ in the interval $[0, 2\pi)$.

$x = \frac{\pi}{3}, x = \frac{5\pi}{3}$, and $x = \pi$

Avoiding Common Errors

Students must be careful when reducing trigonometric functions. A common error is to rewrite $2\cos^2 \frac{x}{2}$ as $\cos^2 x$.

The correct identity is

$$2\cos^2 \frac{x}{2} = 2\left(\frac{1+\cos x}{2}\right).$$

Extra Example 8
Rewrite $\sin 5\theta \cos 3\theta$ as a sum or difference.

$\frac{1}{2}(\sin 8\theta + \sin 2\theta)$

Extra Example 9
Find the exact value of $\sin 195° + \sin 105°$.

$\frac{\sqrt{2}}{2}$

Example 8 Writing Products as Sums

Rewrite the product $\cos 5x \sin 4x$ as a sum or difference.

Solution

Using the appropriate product-to-sum formula, you obtain

$$\cos 5x \sin 4x = \tfrac{1}{2}[\sin(5x + 4x) - \sin(5x - 4x)]$$
$$= \tfrac{1}{2}\sin 9x - \tfrac{1}{2}\sin x.$$

CHECKPoint Now try Exercise 85.

Occasionally, it is useful to reverse the procedure and write a sum of trigonometric functions as a product. This can be accomplished with the following **sum-to-product formulas.**

Sum-to-Product Formulas

$$\sin u + \sin v = 2\sin\left(\frac{u+v}{2}\right)\cos\left(\frac{u-v}{2}\right)$$

$$\sin u - \sin v = 2\cos\left(\frac{u+v}{2}\right)\sin\left(\frac{u-v}{2}\right)$$

$$\cos u + \cos v = 2\cos\left(\frac{u+v}{2}\right)\cos\left(\frac{u-v}{2}\right)$$

$$\cos u - \cos v = -2\sin\left(\frac{u+v}{2}\right)\sin\left(\frac{u-v}{2}\right)$$

For a proof of the sum-to-product formulas, see Proofs in Mathematics on page 424.

Example 9 Using a Sum-to-Product Formula

Find the exact value of $\cos 195° + \cos 105°$.

Solution

Using the appropriate sum-to-product formula, you obtain

$$\cos 195° + \cos 105° = 2\cos\left(\frac{195° + 105°}{2}\right)\cos\left(\frac{195° - 105°}{2}\right)$$
$$= 2\cos 150° \cos 45°$$
$$= 2\left(-\frac{\sqrt{3}}{2}\right)\left(\frac{\sqrt{2}}{2}\right)$$
$$= -\frac{\sqrt{6}}{2}.$$

CHECKPoint Now try Exercise 99.

Example 10 Solving a Trigonometric Equation

Solve $\sin 5x + \sin 3x = 0$.

Algebraic Solution

$$\sin 5x + \sin 3x = 0 \qquad \text{Write original equation.}$$

$$2\sin\left(\frac{5x + 3x}{2}\right)\cos\left(\frac{5x - 3x}{2}\right) = 0 \qquad \text{Sum-to-product formula}$$

$$2\sin 4x \cos x = 0 \qquad \text{Simplify.}$$

By setting the factor $2 \sin 4x$ equal to zero, you can find that the solutions in the interval $[0, 2\pi)$ are

$$x = 0, \frac{\pi}{4}, \frac{\pi}{2}, \frac{3\pi}{4}, \pi, \frac{5\pi}{4}, \frac{3\pi}{2}, \frac{7\pi}{4}.$$

The equation $\cos x = 0$ yields no additional solutions, so you can conclude that the solutions are of the form

$$x = \frac{n\pi}{4}$$

where n is an integer.

Graphical Solution

Sketch the graph of

$$y = \sin 5x + \sin 3x,$$

as shown in Figure 5.17. From the graph you can see that the x-intercepts occur at multiples of $\pi/4$. So, you can conclude that the solutions are of the form

$$x = \frac{n\pi}{4}$$

where n is an integer.

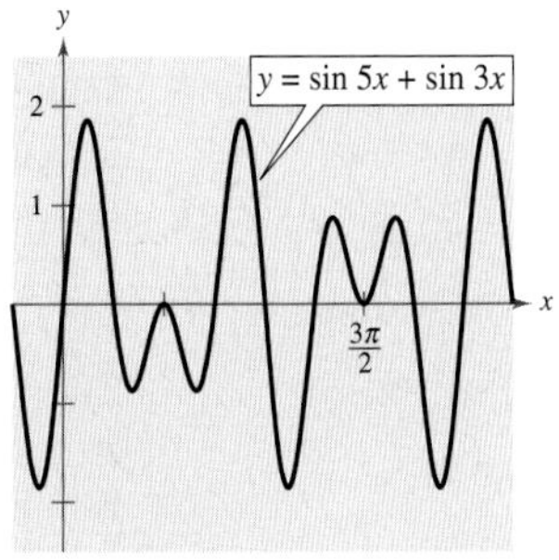

FIGURE 5.17

CHECK**Point** Now try Exercise 103.

Example 11 Verifying a Trigonometric Identity

Verify the identity $\dfrac{\sin 3x - \sin x}{\cos x + \cos 3x} = \tan x$.

Solution

Using appropriate sum-to-product formulas, you have

$$\frac{\sin 3x - \sin x}{\cos x + \cos 3x} = \frac{2\cos\left(\frac{3x + x}{2}\right)\sin\left(\frac{3x - x}{2}\right)}{2\cos\left(\frac{x + 3x}{2}\right)\cos\left(\frac{x - 3x}{2}\right)}$$

$$= \frac{2\cos(2x)\sin x}{2\cos(2x)\cos(-x)}$$

$$= \frac{\sin x}{\cos(-x)}$$

$$= \frac{\sin x}{\cos x} = \tan x.$$

CHECK**Point** Now try Exercise 121.

Extra Example 10

Solve $\sin 4x - \sin 2x = 0$.

$x = n\pi$ and $x = \dfrac{(2n + 1)\pi}{6}$, where n is an integer.

Extra Example 11

Verify the identity $\dfrac{\sin 6x + \sin 4x}{\cos 6x + \cos 4x} = \tan 5x$.

$$\frac{\sin 6x + \sin 4x}{\cos 6x + \cos 4x} = \frac{2\sin\left(\frac{6x + 4x}{2}\right)\cos\left(\frac{6x - 4x}{2}\right)}{2\cos\left(\frac{6x + 4x}{2}\right)\cos\left(\frac{6x - 4x}{2}\right)}$$

$$= \frac{2\sin 5x \cos x}{2\cos 5x \cos x}$$

$$= \tan 5x$$

Application

Example 12 Projectile Motion

Ignoring air resistance, the range of a projectile fired at an angle θ with the horizontal and with an initial velocity of v_0 feet per second is given by

$$r = \frac{1}{16}v_0^2 \sin\theta\cos\theta$$

where r is the horizontal distance (in feet) that the projectile will travel. A place kicker for a football team can kick a football from ground level with an initial velocity of 80 feet per second (see Figure 5.18).

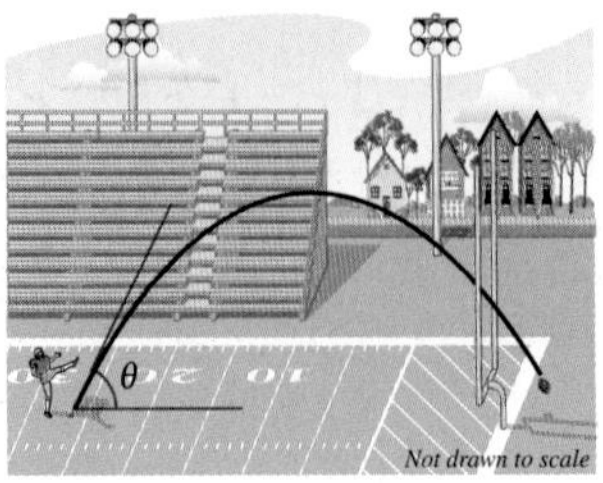

FIGURE 5.18

a. Write the projectile motion model in a simpler form.

b. At what angle must the player kick the football so that the football travels 200 feet?

c. For what angle is the horizontal distance the football travels a maximum?

Solution

a. You can use a double-angle formula to rewrite the projectile motion model as

$$r = \frac{1}{32}v_0^2(2\sin\theta\cos\theta) \qquad \text{Rewrite original projectile motion model.}$$

$$= \frac{1}{32}v_0^2\sin 2\theta. \qquad \text{Rewrite model using a double-angle formula.}$$

b.

$$r = \frac{1}{32}v_0^2\sin 2\theta \qquad \text{Write projectile motion model.}$$

$$200 = \frac{1}{32}(80)^2\sin 2\theta \qquad \text{Substitute 200 for } r \text{ and 80 for } v_0.$$

$$200 = 200\sin 2\theta \qquad \text{Simplify.}$$

$$1 = \sin 2\theta \qquad \text{Divide each side by 200.}$$

You know that $2\theta = \pi/2$, so dividing this result by 2 produces $\theta = \pi/4$. Because $\pi/4 = 45°$, you can conclude that the player must kick the football at an angle of 45° so that the football will travel 200 feet.

c. From the model $r = 200\sin 2\theta$ you can see that the amplitude is 200. So the maximum range is $r = 200$ feet. From part (b), you know that this corresponds to an angle of 45°. Therefore, kicking the football at an angle of 45° will produce a maximum horizontal distance of 200 feet.

CHECK*Point* Now try Exercise 135.

Classroom Discussion

Deriving an Area Formula Describe how you can use a double-angle formula or a half-angle formula to derive a formula for the area of an isosceles triangle. Use a labeled sketch to illustrate your derivation. Then write two examples that show how your formula can be used. See margin. Examples will vary.

Extra Example 12

Ignoring air resistance, the range of a projectile fired at an angle θ with the horizontal and with an initial velocity of v_0 feet per second is given by $r = \frac{1}{16}v_0^2\sin\theta\cos\theta$, where r is the horizontal distance (in feet) that the projectile will travel. A place kicker for a football team can kick a football from ground level with an initial velocity of 78 feet per second.

a. At what angle must the player kick the football so that it travels 188 feet?

40.71° or 49.29°

b. For what angle is the horizontal distance the football travels a maximum?

45°

Closing the Lesson

Have students summarize the major points of the lesson and answer the Essential Question: How do you rewrite trigonometric expressions that contain functions of multiple or half-angles, or functions that involve squares or products of trigonometric expressions?

- **Use double-angle or half-angle formulas to rewrite equations so that they contain functions of x rather than functions of $2x$ or $\frac{x}{2}$.**
- **Use power-reducing formulas to write powers of trigonometric functions in lower degrees.**
- **Use the sum-to-product and product-to-sum formulas to write sums of trigonometric functions as products and vice versa.**

Classroom Discussion

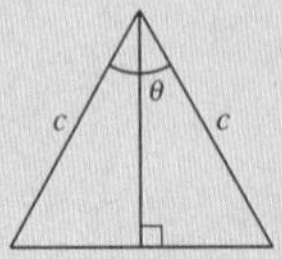

Let c be the length of the two equal sides of an isosceles triangle, and let θ be the angle between the two equal sides.

$$\begin{aligned}
\text{Area} &= \left(\frac{1}{2}\text{base}\right)(\text{height})\\
&= \left(c\sin\frac{\theta}{2}\right)\left(c\cos\frac{\theta}{2}\right)\\
&= c^2\sqrt{\frac{1-\cos\theta}{2}}\sqrt{\frac{1+\cos\theta}{2}}\\
&= c^2\sqrt{\frac{1-\cos^2\theta}{4}}\\
&= \frac{1}{2}c^2\sqrt{\sin^2\theta}\\
&= \frac{1}{2}c^2\sin\theta
\end{aligned}$$

Differentiated Instruction

Kinesthetic Learners After students have completed Example 12, take them outside with a football to recreate the problem. Assume the initial velocity to be 60 feet per second. Mark the point from which the ball is kicked and measure where it lands (first bounce). Then substitute these numbers in the equation to find the angle at which the football was kicked.

5.5 EXERCISES

See www.CalcChat.com for worked-out solutions to odd-numbered exercises.

VOCABULARY: Fill in the blank to complete the trigonometric formula.

1. $\sin 2u = \underline{2 \sin u \cos u}$
2. $\dfrac{1 + \cos 2u}{2} = \underline{\cos^2 u}$
3. $\cos 2u = \underline{\text{See margin.}}$
4. $\dfrac{1 - \cos 2u}{1 + \cos 2u} = \underline{\tan^2 u}$
5. $\sin \dfrac{u}{2} = \underline{\qquad}$ $\pm\sqrt{\dfrac{1 - \cos u}{2}}$
6. $\tan \dfrac{u}{2} = \underline{\qquad}$ $\dfrac{1 - \cos u}{\sin u} = \dfrac{\sin u}{1 + \cos u}$
7. $\cos u \cos v = \underline{\text{See margin.}}$
8. $\sin u \cos v = \underline{\frac{1}{2}[\sin(u + v) + \sin(u - v)]}$
9. $\sin u + \sin v = \underline{\text{See margin.}}$
10. $\cos u - \cos v = \underline{\qquad}$ $-2 \sin\left(\dfrac{u+v}{2}\right) \sin\left(\dfrac{u-v}{2}\right)$

SKILLS AND APPLICATIONS

In Exercises 11–18, use the figure to find the exact value of the trigonometric function.

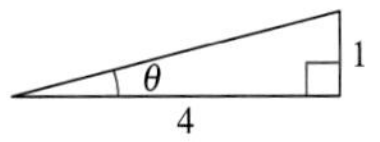

11. $\cos 2\theta$ $\frac{15}{17}$
12. $\sin 2\theta$ $\frac{8}{17}$
13. $\tan 2\theta$ $\frac{8}{15}$
14. $\sec 2\theta$ $\frac{17}{15}$
15. $\csc 2\theta$ $\frac{17}{8}$
16. $\cot 2\theta$ $\frac{15}{8}$
17. $\sin 4\theta$ $\frac{240}{289}$
18. $\tan 4\theta$ $\frac{240}{161}$

In Exercises 19–28, find the exact solutions of the equation in the interval $[0, 2\pi)$. 19–28. See margin.

19. $\sin 2x - \sin x = 0$
20. $\sin 2x + \cos x = 0$
21. $4 \sin x \cos x = 1$
22. $\sin 2x \sin x = \cos x$
23. $\cos 2x - \cos x = 0$
24. $\cos 2x + \sin x = 0$
25. $\sin 4x = -2 \sin 2x$
26. $(\sin 2x + \cos 2x)^2 = 1$
27. $\tan 2x - \cot x = 0$
28. $\tan 2x - 2 \cos x = 0$

In Exercises 29–36, use a double-angle formula to rewrite the expression.

29. $6 \sin x \cos x$ $3 \sin 2x$
30. $\sin x \cos x$ $\frac{1}{2} \sin 2x$
31. $6 \cos^2 x - 3$ $3 \cos 2x$
32. $\cos^2 x - \frac{1}{2}$ $\frac{1}{2} \cos 2x$
33. $4 - 8 \sin^2 x$ $4 \cos 2x$
34. $10 \sin^2 x - 5$ $-5 \cos 2x$
35. $(\cos x + \sin x)(\cos x - \sin x)$ $\cos 2x$
36. $(\sin x - \cos x)(\sin x + \cos x)$ $-\cos 2x$

In Exercises 37–42, find the exact values of $\sin 2u$, $\cos 2u$, and $\tan 2u$ using the double-angle formulas.

37. $\sin u = -\frac{3}{5}$, $\frac{3\pi}{2} < u < 2\pi$ $\sin 2u = -\frac{24}{25}$, $\cos 2u = \frac{7}{25}$, $\tan 2u = -\frac{24}{7}$
38. $\cos u = -\frac{4}{5}$, $\frac{\pi}{2} < u < \pi$ $\sin 2u = -\frac{24}{25}$, $\cos 2u = \frac{7}{25}$, $\tan 2u = -\frac{24}{7}$
39. $\tan u = \frac{3}{5}$, $0 < u < \frac{\pi}{2}$ $\sin 2u = \frac{15}{17}$, $\cos 2u = \frac{8}{17}$, $\tan 2u = \frac{15}{8}$
40. $\cot u = \sqrt{2}$, $\pi < u < \frac{3\pi}{2}$
41. $\sec u = -2$, $\frac{\pi}{2} < u < \pi$ 40–42. See margin.
42. $\csc u = 3$, $\frac{\pi}{2} < u < \pi$

In Exercises 43–52, use the power-reducing formulas to rewrite the expression in terms of the first power of the cosine. 43–52. See margin.

43. $\cos^4 x$
44. $\sin^4 2x$
45. $\cos^4 2x$
46. $\sin^8 x$
47. $\tan^4 2x$
48. $\sin^2 x \cos^4 x$
49. $\sin^2 2x \cos^2 2x$
50. $\tan^2 2x \cos^4 2x$
51. $\sin^4 x \cos^2 x$
52. $\sin^4 x \cos^4 x$

In Exercises 53–58, use the figure to find the exact value of the trigonometric function.

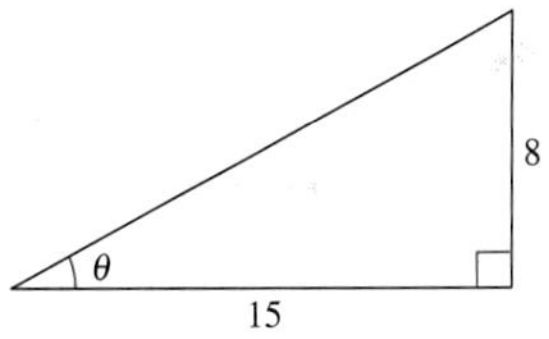

53. $\cos \frac{\theta}{2}$ $\frac{4\sqrt{17}}{17}$
54. $\sin \frac{\theta}{2}$ $\frac{\sqrt{17}}{17}$
55. $\tan \frac{\theta}{2}$ $\frac{1}{4}$
56. $\sec \frac{\theta}{2}$ $\frac{\sqrt{17}}{4}$
57. $\csc \frac{\theta}{2}$ $\sqrt{17}$
58. $\cot \frac{\theta}{2}$ 4

40. $\sin 2u = \dfrac{2\sqrt{2}}{3}$, $\cos 2u = \dfrac{1}{3}$, $\tan 2u = 2\sqrt{2}$

41. $\sin 2u = -\dfrac{\sqrt{3}}{2}$, $\cos 2u = -\dfrac{1}{2}$, $\tan 2u = \sqrt{3}$

42. $\sin 2u = -\dfrac{4\sqrt{2}}{9}$, $\cos 2u = \dfrac{7}{9}$, $\tan 2u = -\dfrac{4\sqrt{2}}{7}$

43. $\frac{1}{8}(3 + 4 \cos 2x + \cos 4x)$

44. $\frac{1}{8}(3 - 4 \cos 4x + \cos 8x)$

45. $\frac{1}{8}(3 + 4 \cos 4x + \cos 8x)$

46. $\frac{1}{128}(35 - 48 \cos 2x + 28 \cos 4x - 16 \cos 2x \cos 4x + \cos 8x)$

47. $\dfrac{(3 - 4 \cos 4x + \cos 8x)}{(3 + 4 \cos 4x + \cos 8x)}$

48. $\frac{1}{16}(1 + \cos 2x - \cos 4x - \cos 2x \cos 4x)$

49. $\frac{1}{8}(1 - \cos 8x)$

50. $\frac{1}{8}(1 - \cos 8x)$

51. $\frac{1}{16}(1 - \cos 2x - \cos 4x + \cos 2x \cos 4x)$

52. $\frac{1}{128}(3 - 4 \cos 4x + \cos 8x)$

4 PRACTICE AND APPLY

Assignment Guide

Transparencies Available
Available at the Instructor's companion site.

Average:
Day 1: pp. 413–414
Exs. 1–4, 11, 13, 17, 21–25 odd, 29, 31, 37–41 odd, 49, 51, 111, 115, 118
Day 2: pp. 413–415
Exs. 5–10, 53, 55, 59, 65–69 odd, 73, 79, 81, 85, 91, 97, 99, 103, 107, 122, 123, 125, 137

Advanced:
Day 1: pp. 413–414
Exs. 12–22 even, 26, 28, 31, 40–52 even, 56, 58, 112, 113, 116
Day 2: pp. 413–415
Exs. 56–60 even, 66–70 even, 74, 80, 84, 88–92 even, 98, 100, 104, 108, 110, 120–126 even, 130, 132, 136, 138

Block:
pp. 413–415
Exs. 1–11, 13, 17, 21–25 odd, 29, 31, 37–41 odd, 49–55 odd, 59, 65–69 odd, 73, 79, 81, 85, 91, 97, 99, 103, 107, 111, 115, 118, 122, 123, 125, 137

3. $\cos^2 u - \sin^2 u = 2 \cos^2 u - 1 = 1 - 2 \sin^2 u$

7. $\frac{1}{2}[\cos(u - v) + \cos(u + v)]$

9. $2 \sin\left(\dfrac{u+v}{2}\right) \cos\left(\dfrac{u-v}{2}\right)$

19. $0, \frac{\pi}{3}, \pi, \frac{5\pi}{3}$

20. $\frac{\pi}{2}, \frac{7\pi}{6}, \frac{3\pi}{2}, \frac{11\pi}{6}$

21. $\frac{\pi}{12}, \frac{5\pi}{12}, \frac{13\pi}{12}, \frac{17\pi}{12}$

22. $\frac{\pi}{2}, \frac{3\pi}{2}, \frac{\pi}{4}, \frac{3\pi}{4}, \frac{5\pi}{4}, \frac{7\pi}{4}$

23. $0, \frac{2\pi}{3}, \frac{4\pi}{3}$

24. $\frac{\pi}{2}, \frac{7\pi}{6}, \frac{11\pi}{6}$

25. $0, \frac{\pi}{2}, \pi, \frac{3\pi}{2}$

26. $0, \frac{\pi}{4}, \frac{\pi}{2}, \frac{3\pi}{4}, \pi, \frac{5\pi}{4}, \frac{3\pi}{2}, \frac{7\pi}{4}$

27. $\frac{\pi}{2}, \frac{\pi}{6}, \frac{5\pi}{6}, \frac{7\pi}{6}, \frac{3\pi}{2}, \frac{11\pi}{6}$

28. $\frac{\pi}{6}, \frac{\pi}{2}, \frac{5\pi}{6}, \frac{3\pi}{2}$

In Exercises 59–66, use the half-angle formulas to determine the exact values of the sine, cosine, and tangent of the angle.

59. $75°$ **60.** $165°$ 59–66. See margin.

61. $112° 30'$ **62.** $67° 30'$

63. $\pi/8$ **64.** $\pi/12$

65. $3\pi/8$ **66.** $7\pi/12$

In Exercises 67–72, (a) determine the quadrant in which $u/2$ lies, and (b) find the exact values of $\sin(u/2)$, $\cos(u/2)$, and $\tan(u/2)$ using the half-angle formulas. 67–72. See margin.

67. $\cos u = \frac{7}{25}, \quad 0 < u < \frac{\pi}{2}$

68. $\sin u = \frac{5}{13}, \quad \frac{\pi}{2} < u < \pi$

69. $\tan u = -\frac{5}{12}, \quad \frac{3\pi}{2} < u < 2\pi$

70. $\cot u = 3, \quad \pi < u < \frac{3\pi}{2}$

71. $\csc u = -\frac{5}{3}, \quad \pi < u < \frac{3\pi}{2}$

72. $\sec u = \frac{7}{2}, \quad \frac{3\pi}{2} < u < 2\pi$

In Exercises 73–76, use the half-angle formulas to simplify the expression.

73. $\sqrt{\frac{1 - \cos 6x}{2}}$ $|\sin 3x|$ **74.** $\sqrt{\frac{1 + \cos 4x}{2}}$ $|\cos 2x|$

75. $-\sqrt{\frac{1 - \cos 8x}{1 + \cos 8x}}$ $-|\tan 4x|$ **76.** $-\sqrt{\frac{1 - \cos(x - 1)}{2}}$ See margin.

In Exercises 77–80, find all solutions of the equation in the interval $[0, 2\pi)$. Use a graphing utility to graph the equation and verify the solutions. 77–80. See margin.

77. $\sin \frac{x}{2} + \cos x = 0$ **78.** $\sin \frac{x}{2} + \cos x - 1 = 0$

79. $\cos \frac{x}{2} - \sin x = 0$ **80.** $\tan \frac{x}{2} - \sin x = 0$

In Exercises 81–90, use the product-to-sum formulas to write the product as a sum or difference. 81–88. See margin.

81. $\sin \frac{\pi}{3} \cos \frac{\pi}{6}$ **82.** $4 \cos \frac{\pi}{3} \sin \frac{5\pi}{6}$

83. $10 \cos 75° \cos 15°$ **84.** $6 \sin 45° \cos 15°$

85. $\sin 5\theta \sin 3\theta$ **86.** $3 \sin(-4\alpha) \sin 6\alpha$

87. $7 \cos(-5\beta) \sin 3\beta$ **88.** $\cos 2\theta \cos 4\theta$

89. $\sin(x + y) \sin(x - y)$ $\frac{1}{2}(\cos 2y - \cos 2x)$ **90.** $\sin(x + y) \cos(x - y)$ $\frac{1}{2}(\sin 2x + \sin 2y)$

In Exercises 91–98, use the sum-to-product formulas to write the sum or difference as a product. 91–96. See margin.

91. $\sin 3\theta + \sin \theta$ **92.** $\sin 5\theta - \sin 3\theta$

93. $\cos 6x + \cos 2x$ **94.** $\cos x + \cos 4x$

95. $\sin(\alpha + \beta) - \sin(\alpha - \beta)$ **96.** $\cos(\phi + 2\pi) + \cos \phi$

97. $\cos\left(\theta + \frac{\pi}{2}\right) - \cos\left(\theta - \frac{\pi}{2}\right)$ $-2 \sin \theta \sin \frac{\pi}{2} = -2 \sin \theta$

98. $\sin\left(x + \frac{\pi}{2}\right) + \sin\left(x - \frac{\pi}{2}\right)$ $2 \sin x \cos \frac{\pi}{2} = 0$

In Exercises 99–102, use the sum-to-product formulas to find the exact value of the expression.

99. $\sin 75° + \sin 15°$ $\frac{\sqrt{6}}{2}$ **100.** $\cos 120° + \cos 60°$ 0

101. $\cos \frac{3\pi}{4} - \cos \frac{\pi}{4}$ $-\sqrt{2}$ **102.** $\sin \frac{5\pi}{4} - \sin \frac{3\pi}{4}$ $-\sqrt{2}$

In Exercises 103–106, find all solutions of the equation in the interval $[0, 2\pi)$. Use a graphing utility to graph the equation and verify the solutions. 103–106. See margin.

103. $\sin 6x + \sin 2x = 0$ **104.** $\cos 2x - \cos 6x = 0$

105. $\frac{\cos 2x}{\sin 3x - \sin x} - 1 = 0$ **106.** $\sin^2 3x - \sin^2 x = 0$

In Exercises 107–110, use the figure to find the exact value of the trigonometric function.

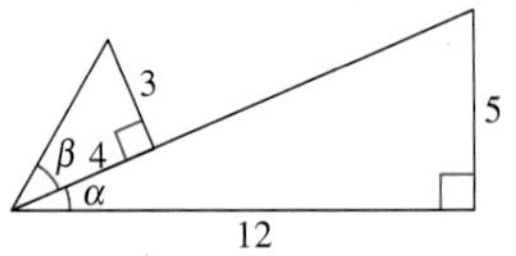

107. $\sin 2\alpha$ $\frac{120}{169}$ **108.** $\cos 2\beta$ $\frac{7}{25}$

109. $\cos(\beta/2)$ $\frac{3\sqrt{10}}{10}$ **110.** $\sin(\alpha + \beta)$ $\frac{56}{65}$

In Exercises 111–124, verify the identity.

111. $\csc 2\theta = \frac{\csc \theta}{2 \cos \theta}$ **112.** $\sec 2\theta = \frac{\sec^2 \theta}{2 - \sec^2 \theta}$

113. $\sin \frac{\alpha}{3} \cos \frac{\alpha}{3} = \frac{1}{2} \sin \frac{2\alpha}{3}$ **114.** $\frac{\cos 3\beta}{\cos \beta} = 1 - 4 \sin^2 \beta$

115. $1 + \cos 10y = 2 \cos^2 5y$ 111–120. Answers will vary.

116. $\cos^4 x - \sin^4 x = \cos 2x$

117. $\cos 4\alpha = \cos^2 2\alpha - \sin^2 2\alpha$

118. $(\sin x + \cos x)^2 = 1 + \sin 2x$

119. $\tan \frac{u}{2} = \csc u - \cot u$

120. $\sec \frac{u}{2} = \pm\sqrt{\frac{2 \tan u}{\tan u + \sin u}}$

59. $\sin 75° = \frac{1}{2}\sqrt{2 + \sqrt{3}}$
$\cos 75° = \frac{1}{2}\sqrt{2 - \sqrt{3}}$
$\tan 75° = 2 + \sqrt{3}$

60. $\sin 165° = \frac{1}{2}\sqrt{2 - \sqrt{3}}$
$\cos 165° = -\frac{1}{2}\sqrt{2 + \sqrt{3}}$
$\tan 165° = \sqrt{3} - 2$

61. $\sin 112° 30' = \frac{1}{2}\sqrt{2 + \sqrt{2}}$
$\cos 112° 30' = -\frac{1}{2}\sqrt{2 - \sqrt{2}}$
$\tan 112° 30' = -1 - \sqrt{2}$

62. $\sin 67° 30' = \frac{1}{2}\sqrt{2 + \sqrt{2}}$
$\cos 67° 30' = \frac{1}{2}\sqrt{2 - \sqrt{2}}$
$\tan 67° 30' = 1 + \sqrt{2}$

63. $\sin \frac{\pi}{8} = \frac{1}{2}\sqrt{2 - \sqrt{2}}$
$\cos \frac{\pi}{8} = \frac{1}{2}\sqrt{2 + \sqrt{2}}$
$\tan \frac{\pi}{8} = \sqrt{2} - 1$

64. $\sin \frac{\pi}{12} = \frac{1}{2}\sqrt{2 - \sqrt{3}}$
$\cos \frac{\pi}{12} = \frac{1}{2}\sqrt{2 + \sqrt{3}}$
$\tan \frac{\pi}{12} = 2 - \sqrt{3}$

65. $\sin \frac{3\pi}{8} = \frac{1}{2}\sqrt{2 + \sqrt{2}}$
$\cos \frac{3\pi}{8} = \frac{1}{2}\sqrt{2 - \sqrt{2}}$
$\tan \frac{3\pi}{8} = \sqrt{2} + 1$

66. $\sin \frac{7\pi}{12} = \frac{1}{2}\sqrt{2 + \sqrt{3}}$
$\cos \frac{7\pi}{12} = -\frac{1}{2}\sqrt{2 - \sqrt{3}}$
$\tan \frac{7\pi}{12} = -2 - \sqrt{3}$

67. (a) Quadrant I
(b) $\sin \frac{u}{2} = \frac{3}{5}$
$\cos \frac{u}{2} = \frac{4}{5}$
$\tan \frac{u}{2} = \frac{3}{4}$

68. (a) Quadrant I
(b) $\sin \frac{u}{2} = \frac{5\sqrt{26}}{26}$
$\cos \frac{u}{2} = \frac{\sqrt{26}}{26}$
$\tan \frac{u}{2} = 5$

69. (a) Quadrant II
(b) $\sin \frac{u}{2} = \frac{\sqrt{26}}{26}$
$\cos \frac{u}{2} = -\frac{5\sqrt{26}}{26}$
$\tan \frac{u}{2} = -\frac{1}{5}$

70. (a) Quadrant II
(b) $\sin \frac{u}{2} = \frac{1}{2}\sqrt{\frac{10 + 3\sqrt{10}}{5}}$
$\cos \frac{u}{2} = -\frac{1}{2}\sqrt{\frac{10 - 3\sqrt{10}}{5}}$
$\tan \frac{u}{2} = -3 - \sqrt{10}$

71. (a) Quadrant II
(b) $\sin \frac{u}{2} = \frac{3\sqrt{10}}{10}$, $\cos \frac{u}{2} = -\frac{\sqrt{10}}{10}$, $\tan \frac{u}{2} = -3$

72. (a) Quadrant II
(b) $\sin \frac{u}{2} = \frac{\sqrt{70}}{14}$
$\cos \frac{u}{2} = -\frac{3\sqrt{14}}{14}$
$\tan \frac{u}{2} = -\frac{\sqrt{5}}{3}$

76. $-\left|\sin\left(\frac{x - 1}{2}\right)\right|$

77. π

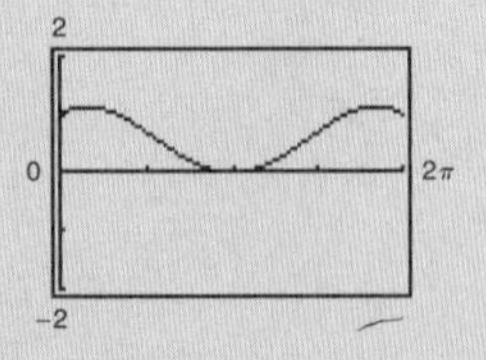

78–88, 91–96, 103–106. See Additional Answers beginning on page AA1.

121. $\dfrac{\cos 4x + \cos 2x}{\sin 4x + \sin 2x} = \cot 3x$ 121–124. Answers will vary.

122. $\dfrac{\sin x \pm \sin y}{\cos x + \cos y} = \tan \dfrac{x \pm y}{2}$

123. $\sin\left(\dfrac{\pi}{6} + x\right) + \sin\left(\dfrac{\pi}{6} - x\right) = \cos x$

124. $\cos\left(\dfrac{\pi}{3} + x\right) + \cos\left(\dfrac{\pi}{3} - x\right) = \cos x$

In Exercises 125–128, use a graphing utility to verify the identity. Confirm that it is an identity algebraically.

125. $\cos 3\beta = \cos^3 \beta - 3 \sin^2 \beta \cos \beta$ 125–128. See margin.

126. $\sin 4\beta = 4 \sin \beta \cos \beta(1 - 2 \sin^2 \beta)$

127. $(\cos 4x - \cos 2x)/(2 \sin 3x) = -\sin x$

128. $(\cos 3x - \cos x)/(\sin 3x - \sin x) = -\tan 2x$

In Exercises 129 and 130, graph the function by hand in the interval $[0, 2\pi]$ by using the power-reducing formulas.

129. $f(x) = \sin^2 x$

130. $f(x) = \cos^2 x$ 129–130. See margin.

In Exercises 131–134, write the trigonometric expression as an algebraic expression.

131. $\sin(2 \arcsin x)$ $2x\sqrt{1 - x^2}$

132. $\cos(2 \arccos x)$ $2x^2 - 1$

133. $\cos(2 \arcsin x)$ $1 - 2x^2$

134. $\sin(2 \arccos x)$ $2x\sqrt{1 - x^2}$

135. **PROJECTILE MOTION** The range of a projectile fired at an angle θ with the horizontal and with an initial velocity of v_0 feet per second is

$$r = \frac{1}{32} v_0^2 \sin 2\theta$$ 23.85°

where r is measured in feet. An athlete throws a javelin at 75 feet per second. At what angle must the athlete throw the javelin so that the javelin travels 130 feet?

136. **RAILROAD TRACK** When two railroad tracks merge, the overlapping portions of the tracks are in the shapes of circular arcs (see figure). The radius of each arc r (in feet) and the angle θ are related by

$$\frac{x}{2} = 2r \sin^2 \frac{\theta}{2}.$$

Write a formula for x in terms of $\cos \theta$. $x = 2r(1 - \cos \theta)$

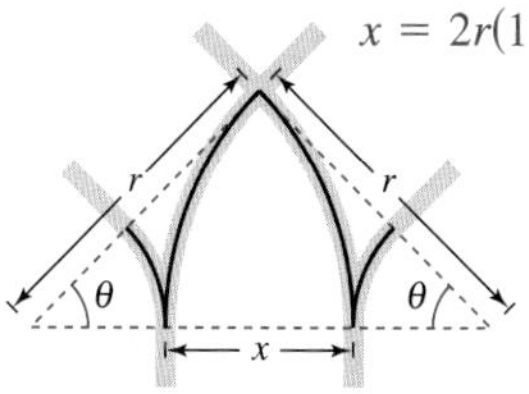

137. **MACH NUMBER** The mach number M of an airplane is the ratio of its speed to the speed of sound. When an airplane travels faster than the speed of sound, the sound waves form a cone behind the airplane (see figure). The mach number is related to the apex angle θ of the cone by $\sin(\theta/2) = 1/M$.

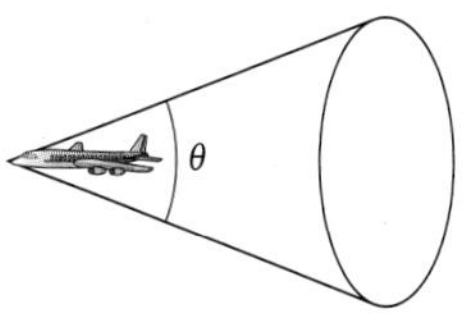

(a) Find the angle θ that corresponds to a mach number of 1. π

(b) Find the angle θ that corresponds to a mach number of 4.5. 0.4482

(c) The speed of sound is about 760 miles per hour. Determine the speed of an object with the mach numbers from parts (a) and (b). 760 mi/h; 3420 mi/h

(d) Rewrite the equation in terms of θ. $\theta = 2 \sin^{-1}\left(\dfrac{1}{M}\right)$

EXPLORATION

138. **CAPSTONE** Consider the function given by $f(x) = \sin^4 x + \cos^4 x$. See margin.

(a) Use the power-reducing formulas to write the function in terms of cosine to the first power.

(b) Determine another way of rewriting the function. Use a graphing utility to rule out incorrectly rewritten functions.

(c) Add a trigonometric term to the function so that it becomes a perfect square trinomial. Rewrite the function as a perfect square trinomial minus the term that you added. Use a graphing utility to rule out incorrectly rewritten functions.

(d) Rewrite the result of part (c) in terms of the sine of a double angle. Use a graphing utility to rule out incorrectly rewritten functions.

(e) When you rewrite a trigonometric expression, the result may not be the same as a friend's. Does this mean that one of you is wrong? Explain.

TRUE OR FALSE? In Exercises 139 and 140, determine whether the statement is true or false. Justify your answer.

139. Because the sine function is an odd function, for a negative number u, $\sin 2u = -2 \sin u \cos u$.

140. $\sin \dfrac{u}{2} = -\sqrt{\dfrac{1 - \cos u}{2}}$ when u is in the second quadrant. 139–140. See margin.

5 ASSESS AND RETEACH

Daily Homework Quiz

Transparency Available

Available at the Instructor's companion site.

125.

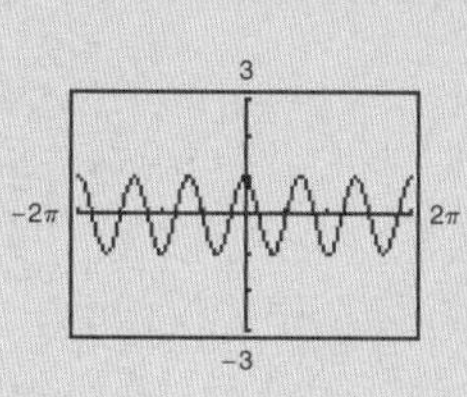

126.

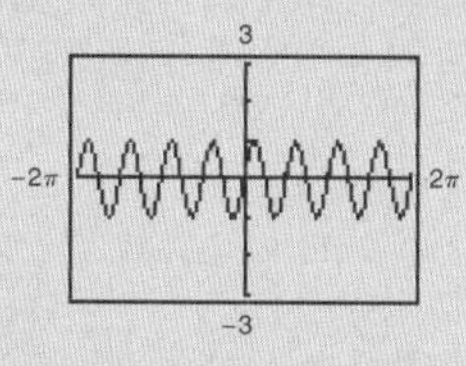

127.

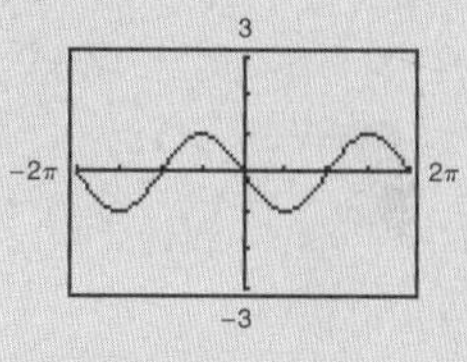

128.

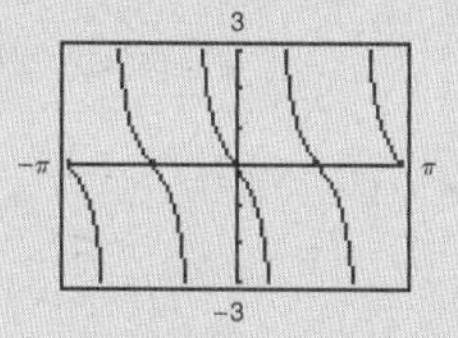

129.

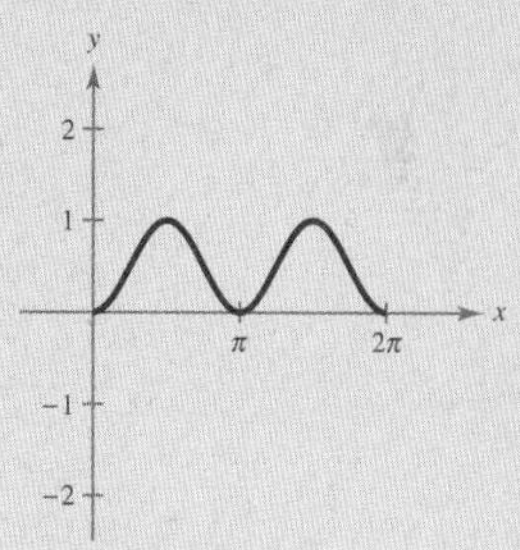

130.

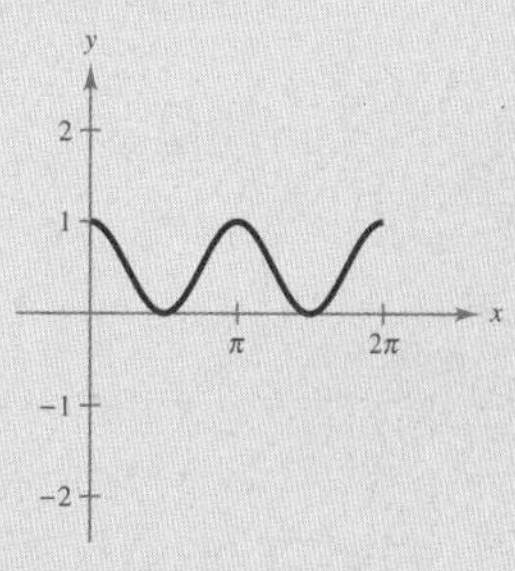

138. (a) $\frac{1}{4}(3 + \cos 4x)$
(b) $2 \cos^4 x - 2 \cos^2 x + 1$
(c) $1 - 2 \sin^2 x \cos^2 x$
(d) $1 - \frac{1}{2} \sin^2 2x$
(e) No. There is often more than one way to rewrite a trigonometric expression.

139. False. For $u < 0$,

$$\begin{aligned} \sin 2u &= -\sin(-2u) \\ &= -2 \sin(-u) \cos(-u) \\ &= -2(-\sin u) \cos u \\ &= 2 \sin u \cos u. \end{aligned}$$

140. False. If $90° < u < 180°$, $\dfrac{u}{2}$ is in the first quadrant and

$$\sin \frac{u}{2} = \sqrt{\frac{1 - \cos u}{2}}.$$

5 Chapter Summary

	What Did You Learn?	Explanation/Examples	Review Exercises
Section 5.1	Recognize and write the fundamental trigonometric identities *(p. 372).*	**Reciprocal Identities** $\sin u = 1/\csc u$ $\cos u = 1/\sec u$ $\tan u = 1/\cot u$ $\csc u = 1/\sin u$ $\sec u = 1/\cos u$ $\cot u = 1/\tan u$ **Quotient Identities:** $\tan u = \dfrac{\sin u}{\cos u}$, $\cot u = \dfrac{\cos u}{\sin u}$ **Pythagorean Identities:** $\sin^2 u + \cos^2 u = 1$, $1 + \tan^2 u = \sec^2 u$, $1 + \cot^2 u = \csc^2 u$ **Cofunction Identities** $\sin[(\pi/2) - u] = \cos u$ $\cos[(\pi/2) - u] = \sin u$ $\tan[(\pi/2) - u] = \cot u$ $\cot[(\pi/2) - u] = \tan u$ $\sec[(\pi/2) - u] = \csc u$ $\csc[(\pi/2) - u] = \sec u$ **Even/Odd Identities** $\sin(-u) = -\sin u$ $\cos(-u) = \cos u$ $\tan(-u) = -\tan u$ $\csc(-u) = -\csc u$ $\sec(-u) = \sec u$ $\cot(-u) = -\cot u$	1–6
	Use the fundamental trigonometric identities to evaluate trigonometric functions, and simplify and rewrite trigonometric expressions *(p. 373).*	In some cases, when factoring or simplifying trigonometric expressions, it is helpful to rewrite the expression in terms of just *one* trigonometric function or in terms of *sine and cosine only.*	7–28
Section 5.2	Verify trigonometric identities *(p. 380).*	**Guidelines for Verifying Trigonometric Identities** **1.** Work with one side of the equation at a time. **2.** Look to factor an expression, add fractions, square a binomial, or create a monomial denominator. **3.** Look to use the fundamental identities. Note which functions are in the final expression you want. Sines and cosines pair up well, as do secants and tangents, and cosecants and cotangents. **4.** If the preceding guidelines do not help, try converting all terms to sines and cosines. **5.** Always try *something.*	29–36
Section 5.3	Use standard algebraic techniques to solve trigonometric equations *(p. 387).*	Use standard algebraic techniques such as collecting like terms, extracting square roots, and factoring to solve trigonometric equations.	37–42
	Solve trigonometric equations of quadratic type *(p. 389).*	To solve trigonometric equations of quadratic type $ax^2 + bx + c = 0$, factor the quadratic or, if this is not possible, use the Quadratic Formula.	43–46
	Solve trigonometric equations involving multiple angles *(p. 392).*	To solve equations that contain forms such as $\sin ku$ or $\cos ku$, first solve the equation for ku, then divide your result by k.	47–52
	Use inverse trigonometric functions to solve trigonometric equations *(p. 393).*	After factoring an equation and setting the factors equal to 0, you may get an equation such as $\tan x - 3 = 0$. In this case, use inverse trigonometric functions to solve. (See Example 9.)	53–56

	What Did You Learn?	Explanation/Examples	Review Exercises
Section 5.4	Use sum and difference formulas to evaluate trigonometric functions, verify identities, and solve trigonometric equations *(p. 398).*	**Sum and Difference Formulas** $\sin(u + v) = \sin u \cos v + \cos u \sin v$ $\sin(u - v) = \sin u \cos v - \cos u \sin v$ $\cos(u + v) = \cos u \cos v - \sin u \sin v$ $\cos(u - v) = \cos u \cos v + \sin u \sin v$ $\tan(u + v) = \dfrac{\tan u + \tan v}{1 - \tan u \tan v}$ $\tan(u - v) = \dfrac{\tan u - \tan v}{1 + \tan u \tan v}$	57–80
Section 5.5	Use multiple-angle formulas to rewrite and evaluate trigonometric functions *(p. 405).*	**Double-Angle Formulas** $\sin 2u = 2 \sin u \cos u$ $\cos 2u = \cos^2 u - \sin^2 u$ $= 2\cos^2 u - 1$ $\tan 2u = \dfrac{2 \tan u}{1 - \tan^2 u}$ $= 1 - 2\sin^2 u$	81–86
	Use power-reducing formulas to rewrite and evaluate trigonometric functions *(p. 407).*	**Power-Reducing Formulas** $\sin^2 u = \dfrac{1 - \cos 2u}{2}$, $\cos^2 u = \dfrac{1 + \cos 2u}{2}$ $\tan^2 u = \dfrac{1 - \cos 2u}{1 + \cos 2u}$	87–90
	Use half-angle formulas to rewrite and evaluate trigonometric functions *(p. 408).*	**Half-Angle Formulas** $\sin \dfrac{u}{2} = \pm\sqrt{\dfrac{1 - \cos u}{2}}$, $\cos \dfrac{u}{2} = \pm\sqrt{\dfrac{1 + \cos u}{2}}$ $\tan \dfrac{u}{2} = \dfrac{1 - \cos u}{\sin u} = \dfrac{\sin u}{1 + \cos u}$ The signs of $\sin(u/2)$ and $\cos(u/2)$ depend on the quadrant in which $u/2$ lies.	91–100
	Use product-to-sum formulas *(p. 409)* and sum-to-product formulas *(p. 410)* to rewrite and evaluate trigonometric functions.	**Product-to-Sum Formulas** $\sin u \sin v = (1/2)[\cos(u - v) - \cos(u + v)]$ $\cos u \cos v = (1/2)[\cos(u - v) + \cos(u + v)]$ $\sin u \cos v = (1/2)[\sin(u + v) + \sin(u - v)]$ $\cos u \sin v = (1/2)[\sin(u + v) - \sin(u - v)]$ **Sum-to-Product Formulas** $\sin u + \sin v = 2 \sin\left(\dfrac{u + v}{2}\right)\cos\left(\dfrac{u - v}{2}\right)$ $\sin u - \sin v = 2 \cos\left(\dfrac{u + v}{2}\right)\sin\left(\dfrac{u - v}{2}\right)$ $\cos u + \cos v = 2 \cos\left(\dfrac{u + v}{2}\right)\cos\left(\dfrac{u - v}{2}\right)$ $\cos u - \cos v = -2 \sin\left(\dfrac{u + v}{2}\right)\sin\left(\dfrac{u - v}{2}\right)$	101–108
	Use trigonometric formulas to rewrite real-life models *(p. 412).*	A trigonometric formula can be used to rewrite the projectile motion model $r = (1/16)v_0^2 \sin \theta \cos \theta$. (See Example 12.)	109–114

5 REVIEW EXERCISES

See www.CalcChat.com for worked-out solutions to odd-numbered exercises.

5.1 In Exercises 1–6, name the trigonometric function that is equivalent to the expression.

1. $\dfrac{\sin x}{\cos x}$ $\tan x$
2. $\dfrac{1}{\sin x}$ $\csc x$
3. $\dfrac{1}{\sec x}$ $\cos x$
4. $\dfrac{1}{\tan x}$ $\cot x$
5. $\sqrt{\cot^2 x + 1}$ $|\csc x|$
6. $\sqrt{1 + \tan^2 x}$ $|\sec x|$

In Exercises 7–10, use the given values and trigonometric identities to evaluate (if possible) all six trigonometric functions. 7–10. See margin.

7. $\sin x = \frac{5}{13}$, $\cos x = \frac{12}{13}$
8. $\tan \theta = \dfrac{2}{3}$, $\sec \theta = \dfrac{\sqrt{13}}{3}$
9. $\sin\left(\dfrac{\pi}{2} - x\right) = \dfrac{\sqrt{2}}{2}$, $\sin x = -\dfrac{\sqrt{2}}{2}$
10. $\csc\left(\dfrac{\pi}{2} - \theta\right) = 9$, $\sin \theta = \dfrac{4\sqrt{5}}{9}$

In Exercises 11–24, use the fundamental trigonometric identities to simplify the expression.

11. $\dfrac{1}{\cot^2 x + 1}$ $\sin^2 x$
12. $\dfrac{\tan \theta}{1 - \cos^2 \theta}$ $\sec \theta \csc \theta$
13. $\tan^2 x(\csc^2 x - 1)$ 1
14. $\cot^2 x(\sin^2 x)$ $\cos^2 x$
15. $\dfrac{\sin\left(\dfrac{\pi}{2} - \theta\right)}{\sin \theta}$ $\cot \theta$
16. $\dfrac{\cot\left(\dfrac{\pi}{2} - u\right)}{\cos u}$ $\tan u \sec u$
17. $\dfrac{\sin^2 \theta + \cos^2 \theta}{\sin \theta}$ $\csc \theta$
18. $\dfrac{\sec^2(-\theta)}{\csc^2 \theta}$ $\tan^2 \theta$
19. $\cos^2 x + \cos^2 x \cot^2 x$
20. $\tan^2 \theta \csc^2 \theta - \tan^2 \theta$ 1
21. $(\tan x + 1)^2 \cos x$
22. $(\sec x - \tan x)^2$
23. $\dfrac{1}{\csc \theta + 1} - \dfrac{1}{\csc \theta - 1}$
24. $\dfrac{\tan^2 x}{1 + \sec x}$ 19, 21–24. See margin.

In Exercises 25 and 26, use the trigonometric substitution to write the algebraic expression as a trigonometric function of θ, where $0 < \theta < \pi/2$.

25. $\sqrt{25 - x^2}$, $x = 5 \sin \theta$ $5 \cos \theta$
26. $\sqrt{x^2 - 16}$, $x = 4 \sec \theta$ $4 \tan \theta$

27. **RATE OF CHANGE** The rate of change of the function $f(x) = \csc x - \cot x$ is given by the expression $\csc^2 x - \csc x \cot x$. Show that this expression can also be written as

$$\frac{1 - \cos x}{\sin^2 x}.$$ Answers will vary.

28. **RATE OF CHANGE** The rate of change of the function $f(x) = 2\sqrt{\sin x}$ is given by the expression $\sin^{-1/2} x \cos x$. Show that this expression can also be written as $\cot x \sqrt{\sin x}$. Answers will vary.

5.2 In Exercises 29–36, verify the identity. 29–36. Answers will vary.

29. $\cos x(\tan^2 x + 1) = \sec x$
30. $\sec^2 x \cot x - \cot x = \tan x$
31. $\sec\left(\dfrac{\pi}{2} - \theta\right) = \csc \theta$
32. $\cot\left(\dfrac{\pi}{2} - x\right) = \tan x$
33. $\dfrac{1}{\tan \theta \csc \theta} = \cos \theta$
34. $\dfrac{1}{\tan x \csc x \sin x} = \cot x$
35. $\sin^5 x \cos^2 x = (\cos^2 x - 2\cos^4 x + \cos^6 x) \sin x$
36. $\cos^3 x \sin^2 x = (\sin^2 x - \sin^4 x) \cos x$

5.3 In Exercises 37–42, solve the equation. 37–42. See margin.

37. $\sin x = \sqrt{3} - \sin x$
38. $4 \cos \theta = 1 + 2 \cos \theta$
39. $3\sqrt{3} \tan u = 3$
40. $\frac{1}{2} \sec x - 1 = 0$
41. $3 \csc^2 x = 4$
42. $4 \tan^2 u - 1 = \tan^2 u$

In Exercises 43–52, find all solutions of the equation in the interval $[0, 2\pi)$. 43–45. See margin.

43. $2 \cos^2 x - \cos x = 1$
44. $2 \sin^2 x - 3 \sin x = -1$
45. $\cos^2 x + \sin x = 1$
46. $\sin^2 x + 2 \cos x = 2$ 0
47. $2 \sin 2x - \sqrt{2} = 0$ See margin.
48. $2 \cos \dfrac{x}{2} + 1 = 0$ $\dfrac{4\pi}{3}$
49. $3 \tan^2\left(\dfrac{x}{3}\right) - 1 = 0$ $\dfrac{\pi}{2}$
50. $\sqrt{3} \tan 3x = 0$
51. $\cos 4x(\cos x - 1) = 0$ 50–51. See margin.
52. $3 \csc^2 5x = -4$ No solution

In Exercises 53–56, use inverse functions where needed to find all solutions of the equation in the interval $[0, 2\pi)$.

53. $\sin^2 x - 2 \sin x = 0$ $0, \pi$
54. $2 \cos^2 x + 3 \cos x = 0$
55. $\tan^2 \theta + \tan \theta - 6 = 0$
56. $\sec^2 x + 6 \tan x + 4 = 0$ 54–56. See margin.

5.4 In Exercises 57–60, find the exact values of the sine, cosine, and tangent of the angle. 57–60. See margin.

57. $285° = 315° - 30°$
58. $345° = 300° + 45°$
59. $\dfrac{25\pi}{12} = \dfrac{11\pi}{6} + \dfrac{\pi}{4}$
60. $\dfrac{19\pi}{12} = \dfrac{11\pi}{6} - \dfrac{\pi}{4}$

---

7. $\tan x = \frac{5}{12}$, $\csc x = \frac{13}{5}$, $\sec x = \frac{13}{12}$, $\cot x = \frac{12}{5}$
8. $\sin \theta = \dfrac{2\sqrt{13}}{13}$, $\cos \theta = \dfrac{3\sqrt{13}}{13}$, $\csc \theta = \dfrac{\sqrt{13}}{2}$, $\cot \theta = \dfrac{3}{2}$
9. $\cos x = \dfrac{\sqrt{2}}{2}$, $\tan x = -1$, $\csc x = -\sqrt{2}$, $\sec x = \sqrt{2}$, $\cot x = -1$
10. $\cos \theta = \dfrac{1}{9}$, $\tan \theta = 4\sqrt{5}$, $\csc \theta = \dfrac{9\sqrt{5}}{20}$, $\sec \theta = 9$, $\cot \theta = \dfrac{\sqrt{5}}{20}$
19. $\cot^2 x$
21. $\sec x + 2 \sin x$
22. $2 \tan^2 x - 2 \sec x \tan x + 1$
23. $-2 \tan^2 \theta$
24. $\sec x - 1$
37. $\dfrac{\pi}{3} + 2n\pi, \dfrac{2\pi}{3} + 2n\pi$
38. $\dfrac{\pi}{3} + 2n\pi, \dfrac{5\pi}{3} + 2n\pi$
39. $\dfrac{\pi}{6} + n\pi$
40. $\dfrac{\pi}{3} + 2n\pi, \dfrac{5\pi}{3} + 2n\pi$
41. $\dfrac{\pi}{3} + n\pi, \dfrac{2\pi}{3} + n\pi$
42. $\dfrac{\pi}{6} + n\pi, \dfrac{5\pi}{6} + n\pi$
43. $0, \dfrac{2\pi}{3}, \dfrac{4\pi}{3}$
44. $\dfrac{\pi}{6}, \dfrac{\pi}{2}, \dfrac{5\pi}{6}$
45. $0, \dfrac{\pi}{2}, \pi$
47. $\dfrac{\pi}{8}, \dfrac{3\pi}{8}, \dfrac{9\pi}{8}, \dfrac{11\pi}{8}$
50. $0, \dfrac{\pi}{3}, \dfrac{2\pi}{3}, \pi, \dfrac{4\pi}{3}, \dfrac{5\pi}{3}$
51. $0, \dfrac{\pi}{8}, \dfrac{3\pi}{8}, \dfrac{5\pi}{8}, \dfrac{7\pi}{8}, \dfrac{9\pi}{8}, \dfrac{11\pi}{8}, \dfrac{13\pi}{8}, \dfrac{15\pi}{8}$
54. $\dfrac{\pi}{2}, \dfrac{3\pi}{2}$
55. $\arctan(-3) + \pi$, $\arctan(-3) + 2\pi$, $\arctan 2$, $\arctan 2 + \pi$
56. $\dfrac{3\pi}{4}, \dfrac{7\pi}{4}$, $\arctan(-5) + \pi$, $\arctan(-5) + 2\pi$
57. $\sin 285° = -\dfrac{\sqrt{2}}{4}(\sqrt{3} + 1)$, $\cos 285° = \dfrac{\sqrt{2}}{4}(\sqrt{3} - 1)$, $\tan 285° = -2 - \sqrt{3}$
58. $\sin 345° = \dfrac{\sqrt{2}}{4}(1 - \sqrt{3})$, $\cos 345° = \dfrac{\sqrt{2}}{4}(1 + \sqrt{3})$, $\tan 345° = -2 + \sqrt{3}$
59. $\sin \dfrac{25\pi}{12} = \dfrac{\sqrt{2}}{4}(\sqrt{3} - 1)$, $\cos \dfrac{25\pi}{12} = \dfrac{\sqrt{2}}{4}(\sqrt{3} + 1)$, $\tan \dfrac{25\pi}{12} = 2 - \sqrt{3}$
60. $\sin \dfrac{19\pi}{12} = -\dfrac{\sqrt{2}}{4}(\sqrt{3} + 1)$, $\cos \dfrac{19\pi}{12} = \dfrac{\sqrt{2}}{4}(\sqrt{3} - 1)$, $\tan \dfrac{19\pi}{12} = -2 - \sqrt{3}$

In Exercises 61–64, write the expression as the sine, cosine, or tangent of an angle.

61. $\sin 60° \cos 45° - \cos 60° \sin 45°$ $\sin 15°$

62. $\cos 45° \cos 120° - \sin 45° \sin 120°$ $\cos 165°$

63. $\dfrac{\tan 25° + \tan 10°}{1 - \tan 25° \tan 10°}$ $\tan 35°$

64. $\dfrac{\tan 68° - \tan 115°}{1 + \tan 68° \tan 115°}$ $\tan(-47°)$

In Exercises 65–70, find the exact value of the trigonometric function given that $\tan u = \frac{3}{4}$ and $\cos v = -\frac{4}{5}$. (u is in Quadrant I and v is in Quadrant III.)

65. $\sin(u + v)$ $-\frac{24}{25}$ **66.** $\tan(u + v)$ $\frac{24}{7}$

67. $\cos(u - v)$ -1 **68.** $\sin(u - v)$ 0

69. $\cos(u + v)$ $-\frac{7}{25}$ **70.** $\tan(u - v)$ 0

In Exercises 71–76, verify the identity.

71. $\cos\left(x + \frac{\pi}{2}\right) = -\sin x$ **72.** $\sin\left(x - \frac{3\pi}{2}\right) = \cos x$

73. $\tan\left(x - \frac{\pi}{2}\right) = -\cot x$ **74.** $\tan(\pi - x) = -\tan x$

75. $\cos 3x = 4\cos^3 x - 3\cos x$

76. $\dfrac{\sin(\alpha - \beta)}{\sin(\alpha + \beta)} = \dfrac{\tan \alpha - \tan \beta}{\tan \alpha + \tan \beta}$

71–76. Answers will vary.

In Exercises 77–80, find all solutions of the equation in the interval $[0, 2\pi)$.

77. $\sin\left(x + \frac{\pi}{4}\right) - \sin\left(x - \frac{\pi}{4}\right) = 1$ $\frac{\pi}{4}, \frac{7\pi}{4}$

78. $\cos\left(x + \frac{\pi}{6}\right) - \cos\left(x - \frac{\pi}{6}\right) = 1$ $\frac{3\pi}{2}$

79. $\sin\left(x + \frac{\pi}{2}\right) - \sin\left(x - \frac{\pi}{2}\right) = \sqrt{3}$ $\frac{\pi}{6}, \frac{11\pi}{6}$

80. $\cos\left(x + \frac{3\pi}{4}\right) - \cos\left(x - \frac{3\pi}{4}\right) = 0$ $0, \pi$

5.5 In Exercises 81–84, find the exact values of $\sin 2u$, $\cos 2u$, and $\tan 2u$ using the double-angle formulas. 81–84. See margin.

81. $\sin u = -\frac{4}{5}, \quad \pi < u < \frac{3\pi}{2}$

82. $\cos u = -\frac{2}{\sqrt{5}}, \quad \frac{\pi}{2} < u < \pi$

83. $\sec u = -3, \quad \frac{\pi}{2} < u < \pi$

84. $\cot u = 2, \quad \pi < u < \frac{3\pi}{2}$

In Exercises 85 and 86, use double-angle formulas to verify the identity algebraically and use a graphing utility to confirm your result graphically. 85–86. See margin.

85. $\sin 4x = 8\cos^3 x \sin x - 4\cos x \sin x$

86. $\tan^2 x = \dfrac{1 - \cos 2x}{1 + \cos 2x}$

In Exercises 87–90, use the power-reducing formulas to rewrite the expression in terms of the first power of the cosine. 87–90. See margin.

87. $\tan^2 2x$ **88.** $\cos^2 3x$

89. $\sin^2 x \tan^2 x$ **90.** $\cos^2 x \tan^2 x$

In Exercises 91–94, use the half-angle formulas to determine the exact values of the sine, cosine, and tangent of the angle.

91. $-75°$ **92.** $15°$

93. $\frac{19\pi}{12}$ **94.** $-\frac{17\pi}{12}$

91–94. See margin.

In Exercises 95–98, (a) determine the quadrant in which $u/2$ lies, and (b) find the exact values of $\sin(u/2)$, $\cos(u/2)$, and $\tan(u/2)$ using the half-angle formulas. 95–98. See margin.

95. $\sin u = \frac{7}{25}, \quad 0 < u < \pi/2$

96. $\tan u = \frac{4}{3}, \quad \pi < u < 3\pi/2$

97. $\cos u = -\frac{2}{7}, \quad \pi/2 < u < \pi$

98. $\sec u = -6, \quad \pi/2 < u < \pi$

In Exercises 99 and 100, use the half-angle formulas to simplify the expression.

99. $-\sqrt{\dfrac{1 + \cos 10x}{2}}$ $-|\cos 5x|$ **100.** $\dfrac{\sin 6x}{1 + \cos 6x}$ $\tan 3x$

In Exercises 101–104, use the product-to-sum formulas to write the product as a sum or difference.

101. $\cos \frac{\pi}{6} \sin \frac{\pi}{6}$ 101–102. See margin. **102.** $6 \sin 15° \sin 45°$

103. $\cos 4\theta \sin 6\theta$ $\frac{1}{2}[\sin 10\theta - \sin(-2\theta)]$ **104.** $2 \sin 7\theta \cos 3\theta$ $\sin 10\theta + \sin 4\theta$

In Exercises 105–108, use the sum-to-product formulas to write the sum or difference as a product.

105. $\sin 4\theta - \sin 8\theta$ $2\cos 6\theta \sin(-2\theta)$

106. $\cos 6\theta + \cos 5\theta$ See margin.

107. $\cos\left(x + \frac{\pi}{6}\right) - \cos\left(x - \frac{\pi}{6}\right)$ $-2\sin x \sin \frac{\pi}{6}$

108. $\sin\left(x + \frac{\pi}{4}\right) - \sin\left(x - \frac{\pi}{4}\right)$ $2\cos x \sin \frac{\pi}{4}$

81. $\sin 2u = \frac{24}{25}$
$\cos 2u = -\frac{7}{25}$
$\tan 2u = -\frac{24}{7}$

82. $\sin 2u = -\frac{4}{5}$
$\cos 2u = \frac{3}{5}$
$\tan 2u = -\frac{4}{3}$

83. $\sin 2u = -\dfrac{4\sqrt{2}}{9}$
$\cos 2u = -\dfrac{7}{9}$
$\tan 2u = \dfrac{4\sqrt{2}}{7}$

84. $\sin 2u = \frac{4}{5}$
$\cos 2u = \frac{3}{5}$
$\tan 2u = \frac{4}{3}$

85.

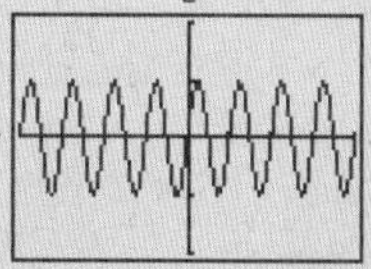

86.

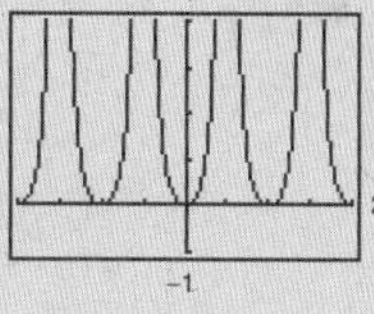

87. $\dfrac{1 - \cos 4x}{1 + \cos 4x}$

88. $\dfrac{1 + \cos 6x}{2}$

89. $\dfrac{3 - 4\cos 2x + \cos 4x}{4(1 + \cos 2x)}$

90. $\dfrac{1 - \cos 2x}{2}$

91. $\sin(-75°) = -\frac{1}{2}\sqrt{2 + \sqrt{3}}$
$\cos(-75°) = \frac{1}{2}\sqrt{2 - \sqrt{3}}$
$\tan(-75°) = -2 - \sqrt{3}$

92. $\sin 15° = \frac{1}{2}\sqrt{2 - \sqrt{3}}$
$\cos 15° = \frac{1}{2}\sqrt{2 + \sqrt{3}}$
$\tan 15° = 2 - \sqrt{3}$

93. $\sin \frac{19\pi}{12} = -\frac{1}{2}\sqrt{2 + \sqrt{3}}$
$\cos \frac{19\pi}{12} = \frac{1}{2}\sqrt{2 - \sqrt{3}}$
$\tan \frac{19\pi}{12} = -2 - \sqrt{3}$

94. $\sin\left(-\frac{17\pi}{12}\right) = \frac{1}{2}\sqrt{2 + \sqrt{3}}$
$\cos\left(-\frac{17\pi}{12}\right) = -\frac{1}{2}\sqrt{2 - \sqrt{3}}$
$\tan\left(-\frac{17\pi}{12}\right) = -2 - \sqrt{3}$

95. (a) Quadrant I
(b) $\sin \frac{u}{2} = \frac{\sqrt{2}}{10}$
$\cos \frac{u}{2} = \frac{7\sqrt{2}}{10}$
$\tan \frac{u}{2} = \frac{1}{7}$

96. (a) Quadrant II
(b) $\sin \frac{u}{2} = \frac{2\sqrt{5}}{5}$
$\cos \frac{u}{2} = -\frac{\sqrt{5}}{5}$
$\tan \frac{u}{2} = -2$

97. (a) Quadrant I
(b) $\sin \frac{u}{2} = \frac{3\sqrt{14}}{14}$
$\cos \frac{u}{2} = \frac{\sqrt{70}}{14}$
$\tan \frac{u}{2} = \frac{3\sqrt{5}}{5}$

98. (a) Quadrant I
(b) $\sin \frac{u}{2} = \sqrt{\frac{7}{12}} = \frac{\sqrt{21}}{6}$
$\cos \frac{u}{2} = \sqrt{\frac{5}{12}} = \frac{\sqrt{15}}{6}$
$\tan \frac{u}{2} = \sqrt{\frac{7}{5}} = \frac{\sqrt{35}}{5}$

106. $2\cos \frac{11\theta}{2} \cos \frac{\theta}{2}$

101–102. See Additional Answers beginning on page AA1.

109. PROJECTILE MOTION A baseball leaves the hand of the player at first base at an angle of θ with the horizontal and at an initial velocity of $v_0 = 80$ feet per second. The ball is caught by the player at second base 100 feet away. Find θ if the range r of a projectile is

$$r = \frac{1}{32}v_0^2 \sin 2\theta.$$ $\theta = 15°$ or $\dfrac{\pi}{12}$

110. GEOMETRY A trough for feeding cattle is 4 meters long and its cross sections are isosceles triangles with the two equal sides being $\frac{1}{2}$ meter (see figure). The angle between the two sides is θ. See margin.

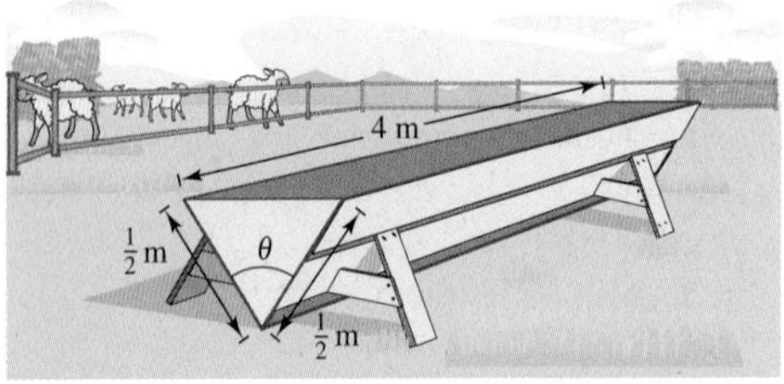

(a) Write the trough's volume as a function of $\theta/2$.

(b) Write the volume of the trough as a function of θ and determine the value of θ such that the volume is maximum.

HARMONIC MOTION In Exercises 111–114, use the following information. A weight is attached to a spring suspended vertically from a ceiling. When a driving force is applied to the system, the weight moves vertically from its equilibrium position, and this motion is described by the model $y = 1.5 \sin 8t - 0.5 \cos 8t$, where y is the distance from equilibrium (in feet) and t is the time (in seconds).

111. Use a graphing utility to graph the model. See margin.

112. Write the model in the form See margin.

$$y = \sqrt{a^2 + b^2}\sin(Bt + C).$$

113. $\frac{1}{2}\sqrt{10}$ ft

113. Find the amplitude of the oscillations of the weight.

114. Find the frequency of the oscillations of the weight. $\dfrac{4}{\pi}$ cycles/sec

EXPLORATION

TRUE OR FALSE? In Exercises 115–118, determine whether the statement is true or false. Justify your answer. 115–117. See margin.

115. If $\dfrac{\pi}{2} < \theta < \pi$, then $\cos\dfrac{\theta}{2} < 0$.

116. $\sin(x + y) = \sin x + \sin y$

117. $4 \sin(-x)\cos(-x) = -2 \sin 2x$

118. $4 \sin 45° \cos 15° = 1 + \sqrt{3}$
True by a product-to-sum formula

119. List the reciprocal identities, quotient identities, and Pythagorean identities from memory. See margin.

120. THINK ABOUT IT If a trigonometric equation has an infinite number of solutions, is it true that the equation is an identity? Explain. See margin.

121. THINK ABOUT IT Explain why you know from observation that the equation $a \sin x - b = 0$ has no solution if $|a| < |b|$. $-1 \le \sin x \le 1$ for all x

122. SURFACE AREA The surface area of a honeycomb is given by the equation

$$S = 6hs + \frac{3}{2}s^2\left(\frac{\sqrt{3} - \cos\theta}{\sin\theta}\right),\quad 0 < \theta \le 90°$$

where $h = 2.4$ inches, $s = 0.75$ inch, and θ is the angle shown in the figure.

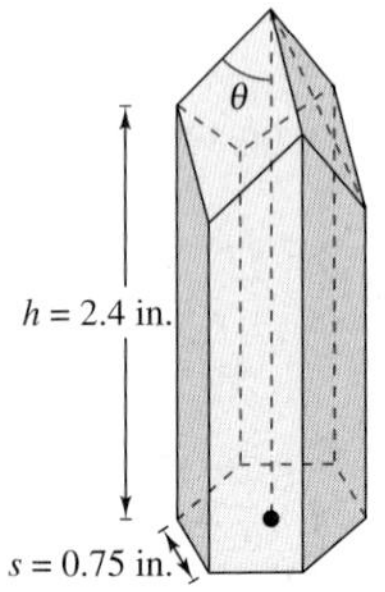

(a) For what value(s) of θ is the surface area 12 square inches? 49.91479°, 59.86118°

(b) What value of θ gives the minimum surface area? 54.735616°

In Exercises 123 and 124, use the graphs of y_1 and y_2 to determine how to change one function to form the identity $y_1 = y_2$.

123. $y_1 = \sec^2\left(\dfrac{\pi}{2} - x\right)$

$y_2 = \cot^2 x$

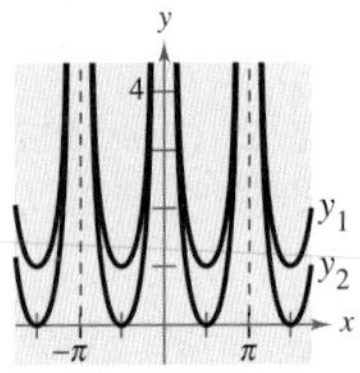

$y_1 = y_2 + 1$

124. $y_1 = \dfrac{\cos 3x}{\cos x}$

$y_2 = (2 \sin x)^2$

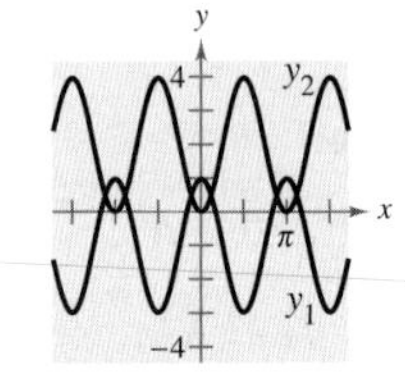

$y_1 = 1 - y_2$

In Exercises 125 and 126, use the *zero* or *root* feature of a graphing utility to approximate the zeros of the function.

125. $y = \sqrt{x + 3} + 4 \cos x$ $-1.8431, 2.1758, 3.9903, 8.8935, 9.8820$

126. $y = 2 - \dfrac{1}{2}x^2 + 3 \sin\dfrac{\pi x}{2}$
$-3.1395, -2.0000, -0.4378, 2.0000$

117. True. $4 \sin(-x)\cos(-x) = 4(-\sin x)\cos x$
$= -4 \sin x \cos x$
$= -2(2 \sin x \cos x)$
$= -2 \sin 2x$

110. (a) $V = \sin\dfrac{\theta}{2}\cos\dfrac{\theta}{2}$ m^3

(b) $V = \dfrac{1}{2}\sin\theta$ m^3

Volume is maximum when $\theta = \dfrac{\pi}{2}$.

111.

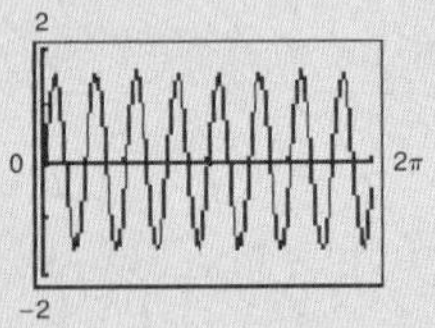

112. $y = \frac{1}{2}\sqrt{10}\sin\left(8t - \arctan\frac{1}{3}\right)$

115. False. If $(\pi/2) < \theta < \pi$, then $\cos(\theta/2) > 0$. The sign of $\cos(\theta/2)$ depends on the quadrant in which $\theta/2$ lies.

116. False. Using the sum and difference formula, $\sin(x + y) = \sin x \cos y + \cos x \sin y$.

117. See below.

119. Reciprocal identities:

$\sin\theta = \dfrac{1}{\csc\theta}$, $\cos\theta = \dfrac{1}{\sec\theta}$,

$\tan\theta = \dfrac{1}{\cot\theta}$, $\csc\theta = \dfrac{1}{\sin\theta}$,

$\sec\theta = \dfrac{1}{\cos\theta}$, $\cot\theta = \dfrac{1}{\tan\theta}$

Quotient identities:

$\tan\theta = \dfrac{\sin\theta}{\cos\theta}$, $\cot\theta = \dfrac{\cos\theta}{\sin\theta}$

Pythagorean identities:

$\sin^2\theta + \cos^2\theta = 1$,
$1 + \tan^2\theta = \sec^2\theta$,
$1 + \cot^2\theta = \csc^2\theta$

120. No. For an equation to be an identity, the equation must be true for all real numbers x. $\sin\theta = \frac{1}{2}$ has an infinite number of solutions but is not an identity.

5 CHAPTER TEST

See www.CalcChat.com for worked-out solutions to odd-numbered exercises.

Take this test as you would take a test in class. When you are finished, check your work against the answers given in the back of the book.

1. If $\tan\theta = \frac{6}{5}$ and $\cos\theta < 0$, use the fundamental identities to evaluate all six trigonometric functions of θ. See margin.
2. Use the fundamental identities to simplify $\csc^2\beta(1 - \cos^2\beta)$. 1
3. Factor and simplify $\dfrac{\sec^4 x - \tan^4 x}{\sec^2 x + \tan^2 x}$. 1
4. Add and simplify $\dfrac{\cos\theta}{\sin\theta} + \dfrac{\sin\theta}{\cos\theta}$. 4. $\csc\theta\sec\theta$
5. Determine the values of θ, $0 \le \theta < 2\pi$, for which $\tan\theta = -\sqrt{\sec^2\theta - 1}$ is true.
6. Use a graphing utility to graph the functions $y_1 = \cos x + \sin x\tan x$ and $y_2 = \sec x$. Make a conjecture about y_1 and y_2. Verify the result algebraically.

5–6. See margin.

In Exercises 7–12, verify the identity. 7–12. Answers will vary.

7. $\sin\theta\sec\theta = \tan\theta$
8. $\sec^2 x\tan^2 x + \sec^2 x = \sec^4 x$
9. $\dfrac{\csc\alpha + \sec\alpha}{\sin\alpha + \cos\alpha} = \cot\alpha + \tan\alpha$
10. $\tan\left(x + \dfrac{\pi}{2}\right) = -\cot x$
11. $\sin(n\pi + \theta) = (-1)^n\sin\theta$, n is an integer.
12. $(\sin x + \cos x)^2 = 1 + \sin 2x$
13. Rewrite $\sin^4\dfrac{x}{2}$ in terms of the first power of the cosine. $\frac{1}{8}(3 - 4\cos x + \cos 2x)$
14. Use a half-angle formula to simplify the expression $\sin 4\theta/(1 + \cos 4\theta)$. $\tan 2\theta$
15. Write $4\sin 3\theta\cos 2\theta$ as a sum or difference. $2(\sin 5\theta + \sin\theta)$
16. Write $\cos 3\theta - \cos\theta$ as a product. $-2\sin 2\theta\sin\theta$

In Exercises 17–20, find all solutions of the equation in the interval $[0, 2\pi)$.

17. $\tan^2 x + \tan x = 0$ 17–20. See margin.
18. $\sin 2\alpha - \cos\alpha = 0$
19. $4\cos^2 x - 3 = 0$
20. $\csc^2 x - \csc x - 2 = 0$
21. Use a graphing utility to approximate the solutions of the equation $5\sin x - x = 0$ accurate to three decimal places. $-2.596, 0, 2.596$
22. Find the exact value of $\cos 105°$ using the fact that $105° = 135° - 30°$. See margin.
23. Use the figure to find the exact values of $\sin 2u$, $\cos 2u$, and $\tan 2u$. See margin.

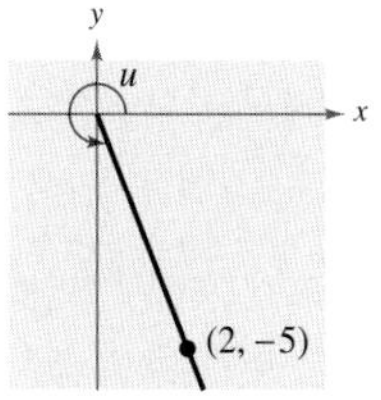

FIGURE FOR 23

24. Cheyenne, Wyoming has a latitude of 41°N. At this latitude, the position of the sun at sunrise can be modeled by

$$D = 31\sin\left(\frac{2\pi}{365}t - 1.4\right)$$

where t is the time (in days) and $t = 1$ represents January 1. In this model, D represents the number of degrees north or south of due east that the sun rises. Use a graphing utility to determine the days on which the sun is more than 20° north of due east at sunrise. Day 123 to day 223

25. The heights h (in feet) of two people in different seats on a Ferris wheel can be modeled by See margin.

$$h_1 = 28\cos 10t + 38 \quad\text{and}\quad h_2 = 28\cos\left[10\left(t - \frac{\pi}{6}\right)\right] + 38,\ 0 \le t \le 2$$

where t is the time (in minutes). When are the two people at the same height?

1. $\sin\theta = -\dfrac{6\sqrt{61}}{61}$

$\cos\theta = -\dfrac{5\sqrt{61}}{61}$

$\tan\theta = \dfrac{6}{5}$

$\csc\theta = -\dfrac{\sqrt{61}}{6}$

$\sec\theta = -\dfrac{\sqrt{61}}{5}$

$\cot\theta = \dfrac{5}{6}$

5. $\theta = 0, \dfrac{\pi}{2} < \theta \le \pi, \dfrac{3\pi}{2} < \theta < 2\pi$

6.

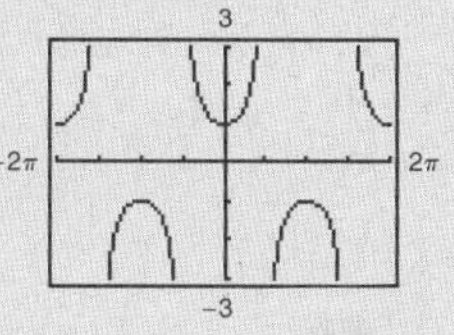

$y_1 = y_2$

17. $0, \dfrac{3\pi}{4}, \pi, \dfrac{7\pi}{4}$

18. $\dfrac{\pi}{6}, \dfrac{\pi}{2}, \dfrac{5\pi}{6}, \dfrac{3\pi}{2}$

19. $\dfrac{\pi}{6}, \dfrac{5\pi}{6}, \dfrac{7\pi}{6}, \dfrac{11\pi}{6}$

20. $\dfrac{\pi}{6}, \dfrac{5\pi}{6}, \dfrac{3\pi}{2}$

22. $\dfrac{\sqrt{2} - \sqrt{6}}{4}$

23. See below.

25. $t = 0.26$ min
0.58 min
0.89 min
1.20 min
1.52 min
1.83 min

23. $\sin 2u = -\frac{20}{29}$, $\cos 2u = -\frac{21}{29}$, $\tan 2u = \frac{20}{21}$

PROOFS IN MATHEMATICS

Sum and Difference Formulas *(p. 398)*

$\sin(u + v) = \sin u \cos v + \cos u \sin v$

$\sin(u - v) = \sin u \cos v - \cos u \sin v$

$\cos(u + v) = \cos u \cos v - \sin u \sin v$

$\cos(u - v) = \cos u \cos v + \sin u \sin v$

$\tan(u + v) = \dfrac{\tan u + \tan v}{1 - \tan u \tan v}$

$\tan(u - v) = \dfrac{\tan u - \tan v}{1 + \tan u \tan v}$

Proof

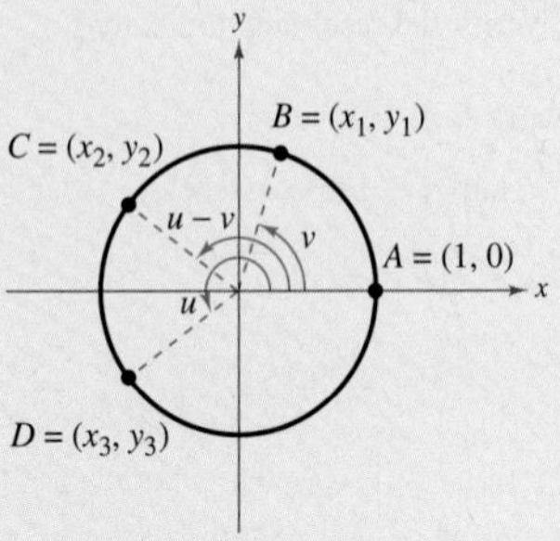

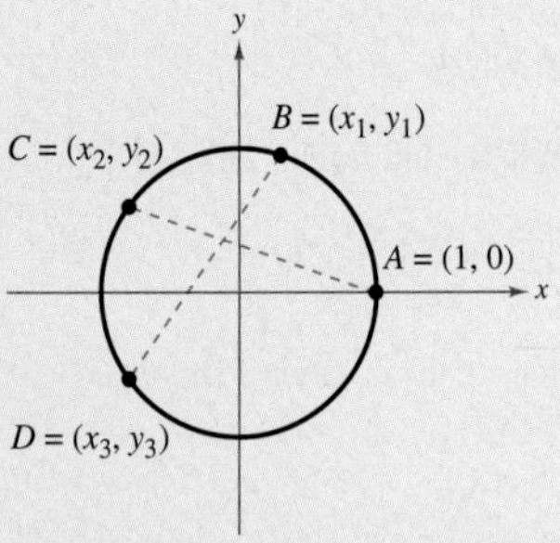

You can use the figures at the left for the proofs of the formulas for $\cos(u \pm v)$. In the top figure, let A be the point $(1, 0)$ and then use u and v to locate the points $B = (x_1, y_1)$, $C = (x_2, y_2)$, and $D = (x_3, y_3)$ on the unit circle. So, $x_i^2 + y_i^2 = 1$ for $i = 1, 2$, and 3. For convenience, assume that $0 < v < u < 2\pi$. In the bottom figure, note that arcs AC and BD have the same length. So, line segments AC and BD are also equal in length, which implies that

$$\sqrt{(x_2 - 1)^2 + (y_2 - 0)^2} = \sqrt{(x_3 - x_1)^2 + (y_3 - y_1)^2}$$

$$x_2^2 - 2x_2 + 1 + y_2^2 = x_3^2 - 2x_1x_3 + x_1^2 + y_3^2 - 2y_1y_3 + y_1^2$$

$$(x_2^2 + y_2^2) + 1 - 2x_2 = (x_3^2 + y_3^2) + (x_1^2 + y_1^2) - 2x_1x_3 - 2y_1y_3$$

$$1 + 1 - 2x_2 = 1 + 1 - 2x_1x_3 - 2y_1y_3$$

$$x_2 = x_3x_1 + y_3y_1.$$

Finally, by substituting the values $x_2 = \cos(u - v)$, $x_3 = \cos u$, $x_1 = \cos v$, $y_3 = \sin u$, and $y_1 = \sin v$, you obtain $\cos(u - v) = \cos u \cos v + \sin u \sin v$. The formula for $\cos(u + v)$ can be established by considering $u + v = u - (-v)$ and using the formula just derived to obtain

$$\cos(u + v) = \cos[u - (-v)] = \cos u \cos(-v) + \sin u \sin(-v)$$

$$= \cos u \cos v - \sin u \sin v.$$

You can use the sum and difference formulas for sine and cosine to prove the formulas for $\tan(u \pm v)$.

$$\tan(u \pm v) = \frac{\sin(u \pm v)}{\cos(u \pm v)}$$ Quotient identity

$$= \frac{\sin u \cos v \pm \cos u \sin v}{\cos u \cos v \mp \sin u \sin v}$$ Sum and difference formulas

$$= \frac{\dfrac{\sin u \cos v \pm \cos u \sin v}{\cos u \cos v}}{\dfrac{\cos u \cos v \mp \sin u \sin v}{\cos u \cos v}}$$ Divide numerator and denominator by $\cos u \cos v$.

422

$$= \frac{\dfrac{\sin u \cos v}{\cos u \cos v} \pm \dfrac{\cos u \sin v}{\cos u \cos v}}{\dfrac{\cos u \cos v}{\cos u \cos v} \mp \dfrac{\sin u \sin v}{\cos u \cos v}}$$ Write as separate fractions.

$$= \frac{\dfrac{\sin u}{\cos u} \pm \dfrac{\sin v}{\cos v}}{1 \mp \dfrac{\sin u}{\cos u} \cdot \dfrac{\sin v}{\cos v}}$$ Product of fractions

$$= \frac{\tan u \pm \tan v}{1 \mp \tan u \tan v}$$ Quotient identity

---

Trigonometry and Astronomy

Trigonometry was used by early astronomers to calculate measurements in the universe. Trigonometry was used to calculate the circumference of Earth and the distance from Earth to the moon. Another major accomplishment in astronomy using trigonometry was computing distances to stars.

Double-Angle Formulas (p. 405)

$$\sin 2u = 2 \sin u \cos u \qquad \cos 2u = \cos^2 u - \sin^2 u$$

$$\tan 2u = \frac{2 \tan u}{1 - \tan^2 u} \qquad = 2\cos^2 u - 1 = 1 - 2\sin^2 u$$

Proof

To prove all three formulas, let $v = u$ in the corresponding sum formulas.

$$\sin 2u = \sin(u + u) = \sin u \cos u + \cos u \sin u = 2 \sin u \cos u$$

$$\cos 2u = \cos(u + u) = \cos u \cos u - \sin u \sin u = \cos^2 u - \sin^2 u$$

$$\tan 2u = \tan(u + u) = \frac{\tan u + \tan u}{1 - \tan u \tan u} = \frac{2 \tan u}{1 - \tan^2 u}$$

Power-Reducing Formulas (p. 407)

$$\sin^2 u = \frac{1 - \cos 2u}{2} \qquad \cos^2 u = \frac{1 + \cos 2u}{2} \qquad \tan^2 u = \frac{1 - \cos 2u}{1 + \cos 2u}$$

Proof

To prove the first formula, solve for $\sin^2 u$ in the double-angle formula $\cos 2u = 1 - 2\sin^2 u$, as follows.

$$\cos 2u = 1 - 2\sin^2 u$$ Write double-angle formula.

$$2\sin^2 u = 1 - \cos 2u$$ Subtract $\cos 2u$ from and add $2 \sin^2 u$ to each side.

$$\sin^2 u = \frac{1 - \cos 2u}{2}$$ Divide each side by 2.

423

In a similar way you can prove the second formula, by solving for $\cos^2 u$ in the double-angle formula

$$\cos 2u = 2\cos^2 u - 1.$$

To prove the third formula, use a quotient identity, as follows.

$$\tan^2 u = \frac{\sin^2 u}{\cos^2 u} = \frac{\dfrac{1 - \cos 2u}{2}}{\dfrac{1 + \cos 2u}{2}} = \frac{1 - \cos 2u}{1 + \cos 2u}$$

Sum-to-Product Formulas *(p. 410)*

$$\sin u + \sin v = 2\sin\left(\frac{u+v}{2}\right)\cos\left(\frac{u-v}{2}\right)$$

$$\sin u - \sin v = 2\cos\left(\frac{u+v}{2}\right)\sin\left(\frac{u-v}{2}\right)$$

$$\cos u + \cos v = 2\cos\left(\frac{u+v}{2}\right)\cos\left(\frac{u-v}{2}\right)$$

$$\cos u - \cos v = -2\sin\left(\frac{u+v}{2}\right)\sin\left(\frac{u-v}{2}\right)$$

Proof

To prove the first formula, let $x = u + v$ and $y = u - v$. Then substitute $u = (x + y)/2$ and $v = (x - y)/2$ in the product-to-sum formula.

$$\sin u \cos v = \frac{1}{2}[\sin(u+v) + \sin(u-v)]$$

$$\sin\left(\frac{x+y}{2}\right)\cos\left(\frac{x-y}{2}\right) = \frac{1}{2}(\sin x + \sin y)$$

$$2\sin\left(\frac{x+y}{2}\right)\cos\left(\frac{x-y}{2}\right) = \sin x + \sin y$$

The other sum-to-product formulas can be proved in a similar manner.

424

PROBLEM SOLVING

This collection of thought-provoking and challenging exercises further explores and expands upon concepts learned in this chapter.

1. (a) Write each of the other trigonometric functions of θ in terms of $\sin\theta$. See margin.
   (b) Write each of the other trigonometric functions of θ in terms of $\cos\theta$. See margin.

2. Verify that for all integers n,

$$\cos\left[\frac{(2n+1)\pi}{2}\right] = 0.$$ Answers will vary.

3. Verify that for all integers n,

$$\sin\left[\frac{(12n+1)\pi}{6}\right] = \frac{1}{2}.$$ Answers will vary.

4. A particular sound wave is modeled by See margin.

$$p(t) = \frac{1}{4\pi}(p_1(t) + 30p_2(t) + p_3(t) + p_5(t) + 30p_6(t))$$

where $p_n(t) = \frac{1}{n}\sin(524n\pi t)$, and t is the time (in seconds).

   (a) Find the sine components $p_n(t)$ and use a graphing utility to graph each component. Then verify the graph of p that is shown.

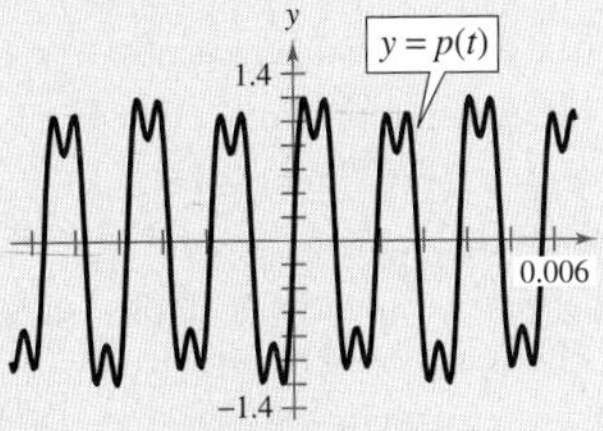

   (b) Find the period of each sine component of p. Is p periodic? If so, what is its period?
   (c) Use the *zero* or *root* feature or the *zoom* and *trace* features of a graphing utility to find the t-intercepts of the graph of p over one cycle.
   (d) Use the *maximum* and *minimum* features of a graphing utility to approximate the absolute maximum and absolute minimum values of p over one cycle.

5. Three squares of side s are placed side by side (see figure). Make a conjecture about the relationship between the sum $u + v$ and w. Prove your conjecture by using the identity for the tangent of the sum of two angles. $u + v = w$

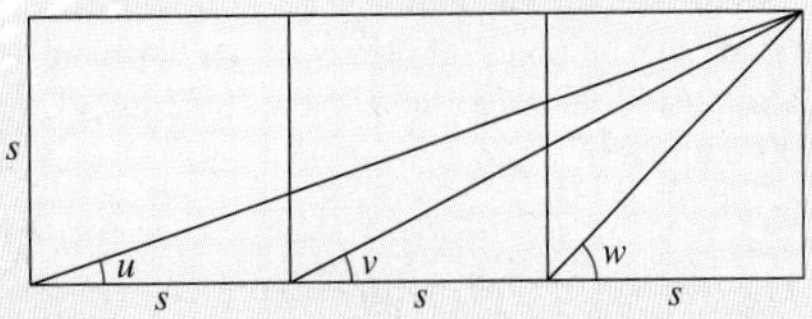

FIGURE FOR 5

6. The path traveled by an object (neglecting air resistance) that is projected at an initial height of h_0 feet, an initial velocity of v_0 feet per second, and an initial angle θ is given by

$$y = -\frac{16}{v_0^2\cos^2\theta}x^2 + (\tan\theta)x + h_0$$

where x and y are measured in feet. Find a formula for the maximum height of an object projected from ground level at velocity v_0 and angle θ. To do this, find half of the horizontal distance

$$\frac{1}{32}v_0^2\sin 2\theta$$

and then substitute it for x in the general model for the path of a projectile (where $h_0 = 0$). $y = \frac{1}{64}v_0^2\sin^2\theta$

7. Use the figure to derive the formulas for

$$\sin\frac{\theta}{2},\ \cos\frac{\theta}{2},\ \text{and}\ \tan\frac{\theta}{2}$$

where θ is an acute angle. See margin.

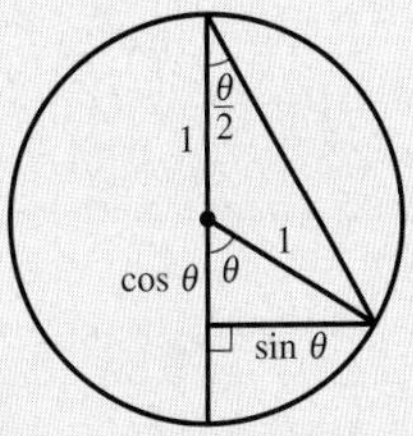

8. The force F (in pounds) on a person's back when he or she bends over at an angle θ is modeled by

$$F = \frac{0.6W\sin(\theta + 90°)}{\sin 12°}$$

where W is the person's weight (in pounds). See margin.

   (a) Simplify the model.
   (b) Use a graphing utility to graph the model, where $W = 185$ and $0° < \theta < 90°$.
   (c) At what angle is the force a maximum? At what angle is the force a minimum?

1. (a) $\cos\theta = \pm\sqrt{1-\sin^2\theta}$

$\tan\theta = \pm\frac{\sin\theta}{\sqrt{1-\sin^2\theta}}$

$\cot\theta = \pm\frac{\sqrt{1-\sin^2\theta}}{\sin\theta}$

$\sec\theta = \pm\frac{1}{\sqrt{1-\sin^2\theta}}$

$\csc\theta = \frac{1}{\sin\theta}$

(b) $\sin\theta = \pm\sqrt{1-\cos^2\theta}$

$\tan\theta = \pm\frac{\sqrt{1-\cos^2\theta}}{\cos\theta}$

$\csc\theta = \pm\frac{1}{\sqrt{1-\cos^2\theta}}$

$\sec\theta = \frac{1}{\cos\theta}$

$\cot\theta = \pm\frac{\cos\theta}{\sqrt{1-\cos^2\theta}}$

4. (a) $p_1(t) = \sin(524\pi t)$

$p_2(t) = \frac{1}{2}\sin(1048\pi t)$

$p_3(t) = \frac{1}{3}\sin(1572\pi t)$

$p_5(t) = \frac{1}{5}\sin(2620\pi t)$

$p_6(t) = \frac{1}{6}\sin(3144\pi t)$

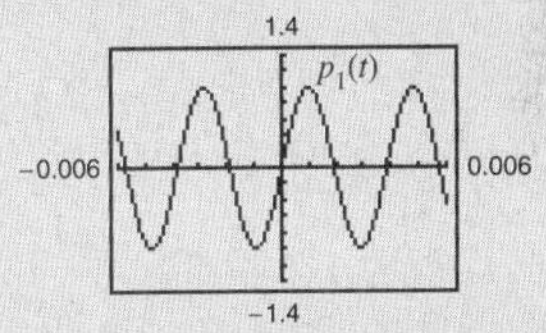

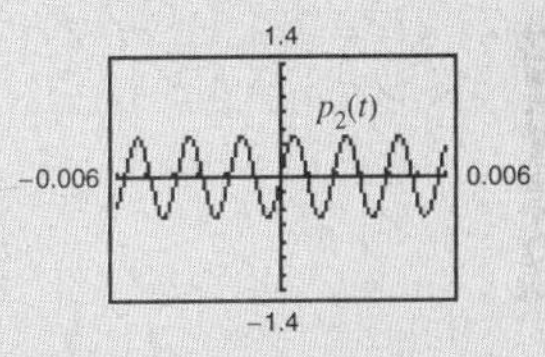

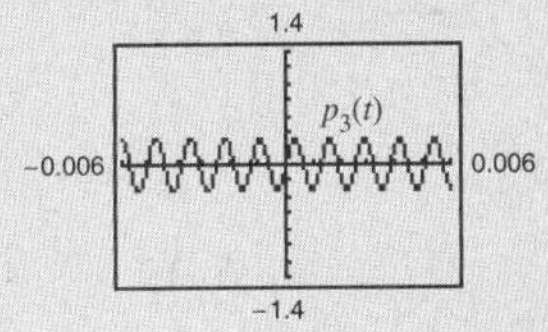

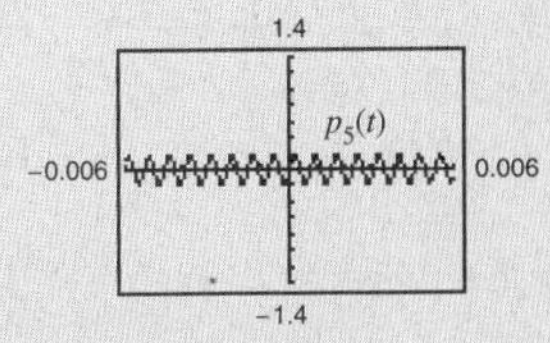

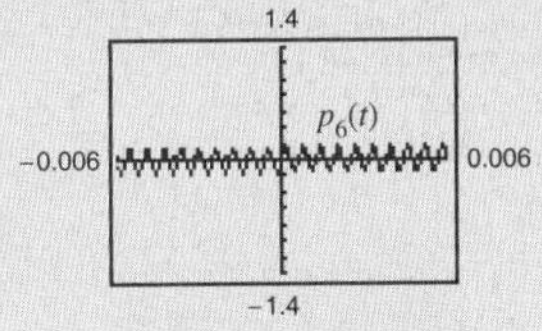

(b) $p_1: \frac{1}{262}$ $p_5: \frac{1}{1310}$

$p_2: \frac{1}{524}$ $p_6: \frac{1}{1572}$

$p_3: \frac{1}{786}$

p is periodic with period $\frac{1}{262}$.

4. (c) (0, 0), (0.00096, 0), (0.00191, 0) (0.00285, 0), (0.00382, 0)
   (d) Maximum: (0.00024, 1.19524)
   Minimum: (0.00357, −1.19525)

7. $\sin\frac{\theta}{2} = \sqrt{\frac{1-\cos\theta}{2}}$

$\cos\frac{\theta}{2} = \sqrt{\frac{1+\cos\theta}{2}}$

$\tan\frac{\theta}{2} = \frac{\sin\theta}{1+\cos\theta}$

8. (a) $F = \frac{0.6\,W\cos\theta}{\sin 12°}$
   (b)

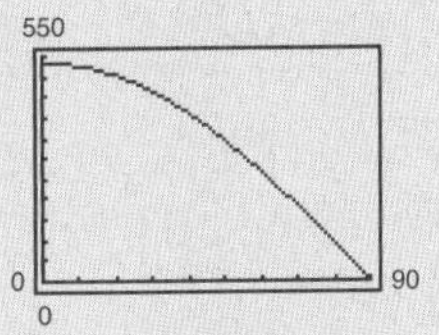

   (c) Maximum: $\theta = 0°$
   Minimum: $\theta = 90°$

9. (a)

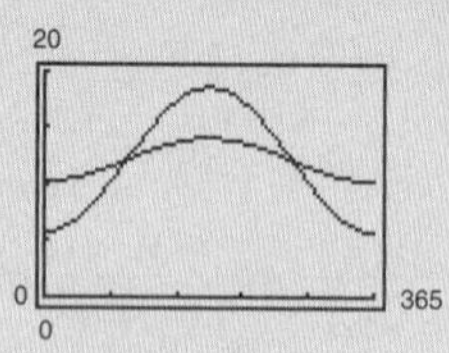

(b) $t \approx 91$ (April 1)
$t \approx 274$ (October 1)

(c) Seward; The amplitudes: 6.4 and 1.9

(d) 365.2 days

10. (a) High tides: 6:12 A.M., 6:36 P.M.
Low tides: 12:00 A.M., 12:24 P.M.

(b) The water depth never falls below 7 feet.

(c)

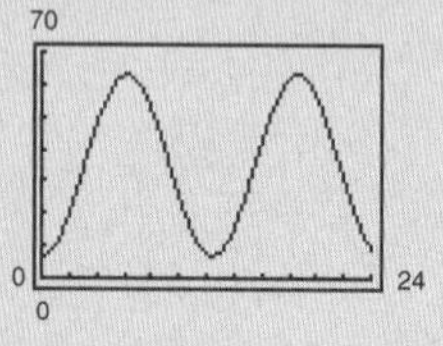

11. (a) $\frac{\pi}{6} \le x \le \frac{5\pi}{6}$

(b) $\frac{2\pi}{3} \le x \le \frac{4\pi}{3}$

(c) $\frac{\pi}{2} < x < \pi, \frac{3\pi}{2} < x < 2\pi$

(d) $0 \le x \le \frac{\pi}{4}, \frac{5\pi}{4} \le x \le 2\pi$

12. (a) $n = \frac{1}{2}\left(\cot\frac{\theta}{2} + \sqrt{3}\right)$

(b) $\theta \approx 76.5°$

9. The number of hours of daylight that occur at any location on Earth depends on the time of year and the latitude of the location. The following equations model the numbers of hours of daylight in Seward, Alaska (60° latitude) and New Orleans, Louisiana (30° latitude).

$$D = 12.2 - 6.4\cos\left[\frac{\pi(t + 0.2)}{182.6}\right] \quad \text{Seward}$$

$$D = 12.2 - 1.9\cos\left[\frac{\pi(t + 0.2)}{182.6}\right] \quad \text{New Orleans}$$

In these models, D represents the number of hours of daylight and t represents the day, with $t = 0$ corresponding to January 1. See margin.

(a) Use a graphing utility to graph both models in the same viewing window. Use a viewing window of $0 \le t \le 365$.

(b) Find the days of the year on which both cities receive the same amount of daylight.

(c) Which city has the greater variation in the number of daylight hours? Which constant in each model would you use to determine the difference between the greatest and least numbers of hours of daylight?

(d) Determine the period of each model.

10. The tide, or depth of the ocean near the shore, changes throughout the day. The water depth d (in feet) of a bay can be modeled by

$$d = 35 - 28\cos\frac{\pi}{6.2}t$$

where t is the time in hours, with $t = 0$ corresponding to 12:00 A.M. See margin.

(a) Algebraically find the times at which the high and low tides occur.

(b) Algebraically find the time(s) at which the water depth is 3.5 feet.

(c) Use a graphing utility to verify your results from parts (a) and (b).

11. Find the solution of each inequality in the interval $[0, 2\pi]$. See margin.

(a) $\sin x \ge 0.5$ (b) $\cos x \le -0.5$

(c) $\tan x < \sin x$ (d) $\cos x \ge \sin x$

12. The index of refraction n of a transparent material is the ratio of the speed of light in a vacuum to the speed of light in the material. Some common materials and their indices are air (1.00), water (1.33), and glass (1.50). Triangular prisms are often used to measure the index of refraction based on the formula

$$n = \frac{\sin\left(\frac{\theta}{2} + \frac{\alpha}{2}\right)}{\sin\frac{\theta}{2}}.$$

For the prism shown in the figure, $\alpha = 60°$. See margin.

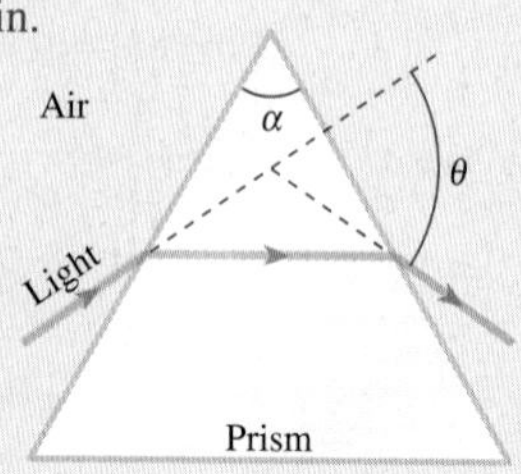

(a) Write the index of refraction as a function of $\cot(\theta/2)$.

(b) Find θ for a prism made of glass.

13. (a) Write a sum formula for $\sin(u + v + w)$.

(b) Write a sum formula for $\tan(u + v + w)$. See margin.

14. (a) Derive a formula for $\cos 3\theta$.

(b) Derive a formula for $\cos 4\theta$. See margin.

15. The heights h (in inches) of pistons 1 and 2 in an automobile engine can be modeled by

$$h_1 = 3.75\sin 733t + 7.5$$

and

$$h_2 = 3.75\sin 733\left(t + \frac{4\pi}{3}\right) + 7.5$$

where t is measured in seconds. See margin.

(a) Use a graphing utility to graph the heights of these two pistons in the same viewing window for $0 \le t \le 1$.

(b) How often are the pistons at the same height?

13. (a) $\sin(u + v + w) = \sin u\cos v\cos w - \sin u\sin v\sin w + \cos u\sin v\cos w + \cos u\cos v\sin w$

(b) $\tan(u + v + w) = \dfrac{\tan u + \tan v + \tan w - \tan u\tan v\tan w}{1 - \tan u\tan v - \tan u\tan w - \tan v\tan w}$

14. (a) $\cos 3\theta = \cos\theta - 4\sin^2\theta\cos\theta$

(b) $\cos 4\theta = \cos^4\theta - 6\sin^2\theta\cos^2\theta + \sin^4\theta$

15. (a)

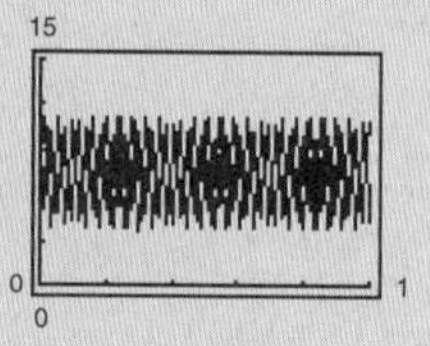

(b) 233.3 times/sec

Pacing and Assignment Guide 6

REGULAR SCHEDULE

Lesson	Day	AVERAGE	ADVANCED
6.1	Day 1	pp. 434–436 Exs. 1–4, 7–11 odd, 17–23 odd, 26–30 even, 35, 40, 43, 47, 51–53, 57–60	pp. 434–436 Exs. 1–4, 6–12 even, 20, 24, 30–38 even, 42–50 even, 51, 52, 56–60, 62
6.2	Day 1	pp. 441–444 Exs. 1–4, 6, 9, 13, 15, 21–27 odd, 33, 41, 45, 47, 51–55 odd, 58, 61–65 odd, 74	pp. 441–444 Exs. 1–4, 10, 14, 16, 22–30 even, 34–38 even, 42–52 even, 55–57, 60, 67, 69, 74, 76
6.3	Day 1	pp. 454–455 Exs. 1–6, 12, 15, 17, 21–29 odd, 32, 35–39 odd, 43–53 odd, 57, 60, 62	pp. 454–455 Exs. 1–3, 12–20 even, 24–30 even, 33, 34–40 even, 46–54 even, 58, 60, 61
	Day 2	pp. 454–457 Exs. 7–10, 65, 67–69, 73–87 odd, 91, 94, 99, 103–109 odd, 112	pp. 454–457 Exs. 7–10, 64, 66, 70–76 even, 80–92 even, 100–112 even, 113
6.4	Day 1	pp. 465–466 Exs. 1–4, 9, 13, 15, 19–33 odd, 39, 41, 45–51 odd, 54, 55	pp. 465–466 Exs. 1–4, 10–18 even, 22–28 even, 32, 34, 40, 42, 46–58 even
	Day 2	pp. 465–467 Exs. 5, 6, 61–73 odd, 76, 78, 79, 81, 87, 88, 90, 92	pp. 465–467 Exs. 5, 6, 62–76 even, 79, 80, 82, 87, 89, 90
6.5	Day 1	pp. 476–477 Exs. 1, 2, 9–15 odd, 19–27 odd, 31–35 odd, 39–43 odd, 48, 49, 51, 57, 59, 63	pp. 476–477 Exs. 1, 2, 10–16 even, 22, 24, 28–38 even, 42, 44, 48–54 even, 55, 58, 60, 64
	Day 2	pp. 476–477 Exs. 3, 4, 65, 67, 68, 73–77 odd, 81–89 odd, 93, 95, 100, 103, 105, 108, 111, 116	pp. 476–477 Exs. 3, 4, 66, 68, 72–76 even, 80–88 even, 98, 101, 104, 106, 107, 110, 114, 116
Review	Day 1	pp. 480–483 Exs. 5, 7, 17–21 odd, 27, 31, 33, 37, 39, 45–51 odd, 55, 59, 65–71 odd, 75–79 odd, 83, 91, 95, 99, 103, 105, 109, 115, 119, 123, 127, 129, 143, 147	pp. 480–483 Exs. 4, 10, 18–22 even, 28, 32, 34, 38, 46–52 even, 56, 64, 68, 70, 74–80 even, 86–92 even, 96, 102–106 even, 110, 116, 120, 124, 126, 130, 144, 146, 147
Assess	Day 1	Chapter 6 Test	Chapter 6 Test

Yearly Pacing Chapter 6 Total – 10 days Remaining – 90 days

BLOCK SCHEDULE

DAY 1	DAY 2	DAY 3	DAY 4	DAY 5
6.1	6.3	6.4	6.5	REVIEW
pp. 434–436 Exs. 1–4, 7–11 odd, 17–23 odd, 26–30 even, 35, 40, 43, 47, 51–53, 57–60	pp. 454–457 Exs. 1–10, 12, 15, 17, 21–29 odd, 32, 35–39 odd, 43–53 odd, 57, 60, 62, 65, 67–69, 73–87 odd, 91, 94, 99, 103–109 odd, 112	pp. 465–467 Exs. 1–6, 9, 13, 15, 19–33 odd, 39, 41, 45–51 odd, 54, 55, 61–73 odd, 76, 78, 79, 81, 87, 88, 90, 92	pp. 476–477 Exs. 1–4, 9–15 odd, 19–27 odd, 31–35 odd, 39–43 odd, 48, 49, 51, 57, 59, 63–67 odd, 68, 73–77 odd, 81–89 odd, 93, 95, 100, 103, 105, 108, 111, 116	pp. 480–483 Exs. 5, 7, 17–21 odd, 27, 31, 33, 37, 39, 45–51 odd, 55, 59, 65–71 odd, 75–79 odd, 83, 91, 95, 99, 103, 105, 109, 115, 119, 123, 127, 129, 143, 147
6.2				ASSESS
pp. 441–444 Exs. 1–4, 6, 9, 13, 15, 21–27 odd, 33, 41, 45, 47, 51–55 odd, 58, 61–65 odd, 74				Chapter 6 Test

Yearly Pacing Chapter 6 Total – 5 days Remaining – 45 days

Additional Topics in Trigonometry

6

In Mathematics

Trigonometry is used to solve triangles, represent vectors, and to write trigonometric forms of complex numbers.

In Real Life

Trigonometry is used to find areas, estimate heights, and represent vectors involving force, velocity, and other quantities. For instance, trigonometry and vectors can be used to find the tension in the tow lines as a loaded barge is being towed by two tugboats. (See Exercise 93, page 456.)

Luca Tettoni/Terra/Corbis

IN CAREERS

There are many careers that use trigonometry. Several are listed below.

- Pilot
  Exercise 51, page 435
- Civil Engineer
  Exercise 55, page 443
- Awning Designer
  Exercise 58, page 443
- Landscaper
  Exercise 4, page 491

PLAN AND PREPARE

Main Ideas

In Chapter 6, students learn how to apply trigonometry to oblique triangles, vectors, and complex numbers. They begin the chapter by learning how to find side lengths, angles, and areas of oblique triangles by using the Law of Sines and the Law of Cosines. They then study vectors and vector notation, using trigonometry to solve real-world problems such as finding force on an inclined ramp or a wind-adjusted bearing in airplane navigation. Finally, students learn how to write and perform operations on complex numbers in trigonometric form.

Chapter Planning Guide

Chapter Resources
- Complete Solutions Guide

Interactive Technology
- Instructor Success Organizer
- Notetaking Guide IAE
- Instructional DVDs
- Animated Precalculus
- PowerLecture with ExamView

1 PLAN AND PREPARE

Warm-up Exercises

Transparency Available
Available at the Instructor's companion site.

Notetaking Guide

Transparency Available
Promotes interactive learning and notetaking skills.
Available at the Instructor's companion site.

Animated Precalculus

An **Animated Precalculus** tutorial is available at the Student companion site for **Section 6.1.**

Pacing

Average: 1 day
Advanced: 1 day
Block: 0.5 block with 6.2

2 FOCUS AND MOTIVATE

Essential Question

How do you use trigonometry to solve and find the areas of oblique triangles? **Tell students that they will learn how to answer this question by using the relationships between angles in a triangle and the lengths of the sides opposite them.**

Resource Planning Guide

Chapter Resources
- Complete Solutions Guide

Workbooks
- Notetaking Guide
- Student Solutions Guide

Interactive Technology
- Instructor Success Organizer
- Notetaking Guide IAE
- Instructional DVDs
- Animated Precalculus
- PowerLecture with ExamView

6.1 LAW OF SINES

What you should learn

- Use the Law of Sines to solve oblique triangles (AAS or ASA).
- Use the Law of Sines to solve oblique triangles (SSA).
- Find the areas of oblique triangles.
- Use the Law of Sines to model and solve real-life problems.

Why you should learn it

You can use the Law of Sines to solve real-life problems involving oblique triangles. For instance, in Exercise 53 on page 436, you can use the Law of Sines to determine the distance from a boat to the shoreline.

Introduction

In Chapter 4, you studied techniques for solving right triangles. In this section and the next, you will solve **oblique triangles**—triangles that have no right angles. As standard notation, the angles of a triangle are labeled A, B, and C, and their opposite sides are labeled a, b, and c, as shown in Figure 6.1.

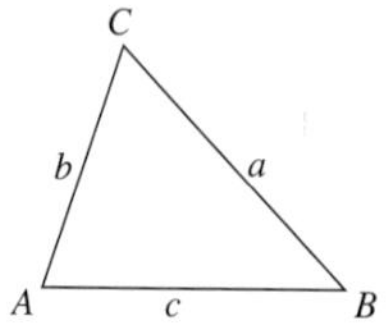

FIGURE 6.1

To solve an oblique triangle, you need to know the measure of at least one side and any two other measures of the triangle—either two sides, two angles, or one angle and one side. This breaks down into the following four cases.

1. Two angles and any side (AAS or ASA)
2. Two sides and an angle opposite one of them (SSA)
3. Three sides (SSS)
4. Two sides and their included angle (SAS)

The first two cases can be solved using the **Law of Sines,** whereas the last two cases require the Law of Cosines (see Section 6.2).

Law of Sines

If ABC is a triangle with sides a, b, and c, then

$$\frac{a}{\sin A} = \frac{b}{\sin B} = \frac{c}{\sin C}.$$

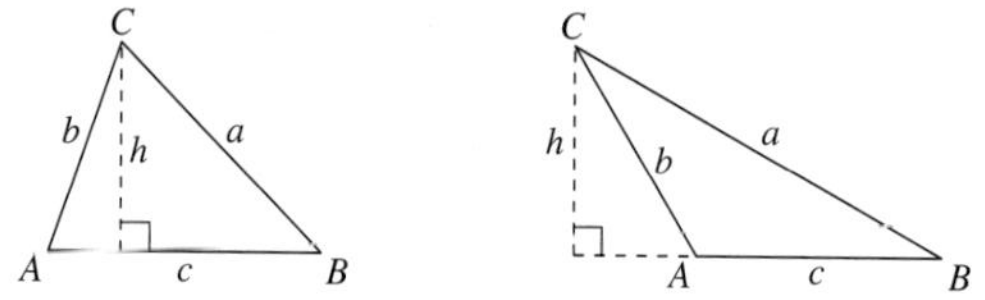

A is acute. *A* is obtuse.

The Law of Sines can also be written in the reciprocal form

$$\frac{\sin A}{a} = \frac{\sin B}{b} = \frac{\sin C}{c}.$$

For a proof of the Law of Sines, see Proofs in Mathematics on page 487.

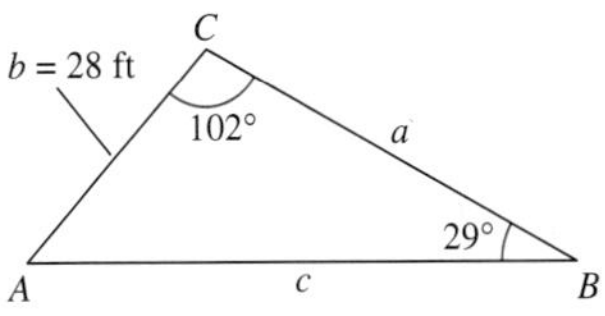

FIGURE 6.2

Study Tip

When solving triangles, a careful sketch is useful as a quick test for the feasibility of an answer. Remember that the longest side lies opposite the largest angle, and the shortest side lies opposite the smallest angle.

Example 1 Given Two Angles and One Side—AAS

For the triangle in Figure 6.2, $C = 102°$, $B = 29°$, and $b = 28$ feet. Find the remaining angle and sides.

Solution

The third angle of the triangle is

$$A = 180° - B - C$$
$$= 180° - 29° - 102°$$
$$= 49°.$$

By the Law of Sines, you have

$$\frac{a}{\sin A} = \frac{b}{\sin B} = \frac{c}{\sin C}.$$

Using $b = 28$ produces

$$a = \frac{b}{\sin B}(\sin A) = \frac{28}{\sin 29°}(\sin 49°) \approx 43.59 \text{ feet}$$

and

$$c = \frac{b}{\sin B}(\sin C) = \frac{28}{\sin 29°}(\sin 102°) \approx 56.49 \text{ feet.}$$

CHECKPoint Now try Exercise 5.

Example 2 Given Two Angles and One Side—ASA

A pole tilts *toward* the sun at an 8° angle from the vertical, and it casts a 22-foot shadow. The angle of elevation from the tip of the shadow to the top of the pole is 43°. How tall is the pole?

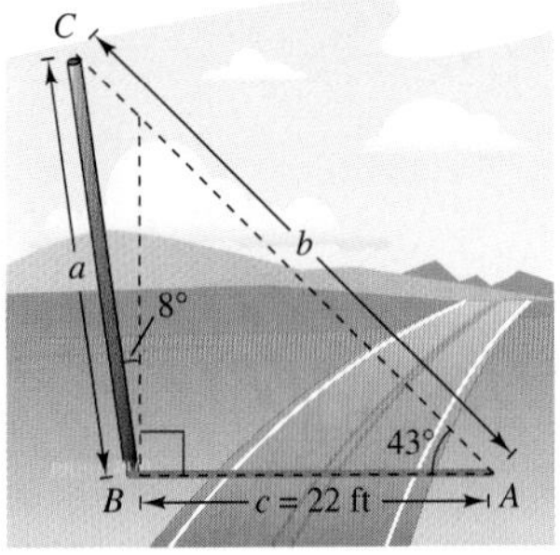

FIGURE 6.3

Solution

From Figure 6.3, note that $A = 43°$ and $B = 90° + 8° = 98°$. So, the third angle is

$$C = 180° - A - B$$
$$= 180° - 43° - 98°$$
$$= 39°.$$

By the Law of Sines, you have

$$\frac{a}{\sin A} = \frac{c}{\sin C}.$$

Because $c = 22$ feet, the length of the pole is

$$a = \frac{c}{\sin C}(\sin A) = \frac{22}{\sin 39°}(\sin 43°) \approx 23.84 \text{ feet.}$$

CHECKPoint Now try Exercise 45.

For practice, try reworking Example 2 for a pole that tilts *away from* the sun under the same conditions.

3 TEACH

Extra Example 1

For triangle ABC, $A = 30°$, $B = 45°$, and $a = 32$ feet. Find the remaining angles and sides.

$C = 105°$, $b \approx 45.25$ feet, $c \approx 61.82$ feet

Extra Example 2

Because of prevailing winds, a tree grew so that it was leaning 6° from the vertical. At a point 30 meters from the tree, the angle of elevation to the top of the tree is 22.5°. Find the height h of the tree.

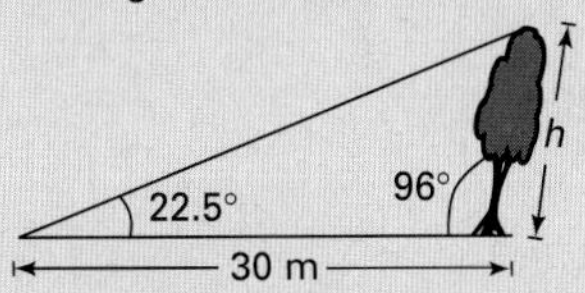

$\approx$ 13.1 meters

Extra Example 3
For triangle ABC, $a = 12$ inches, $b = 5$ inches, and $A = 31°$. Find the remaining sides and angles.
$B \approx 12.39°$, $C \approx 136.61°$, $c \approx 16$ inches

The Ambiguous Case (SSA)

In Examples 1 and 2, you saw that two angles and one side determine a unique triangle. However, if two sides and one opposite angle are given, three possible situations can occur: (1) no such triangle exists, (2) one such triangle exists, or (3) two distinct triangles may satisfy the conditions.

The Ambiguous Case (SSA)

Consider a triangle in which you are given a, b, and A. $(h = b \sin A)$

	A is acute.	A is acute.	A is acute.	A is acute.	A is obtuse.	A is obtuse.
Sketch	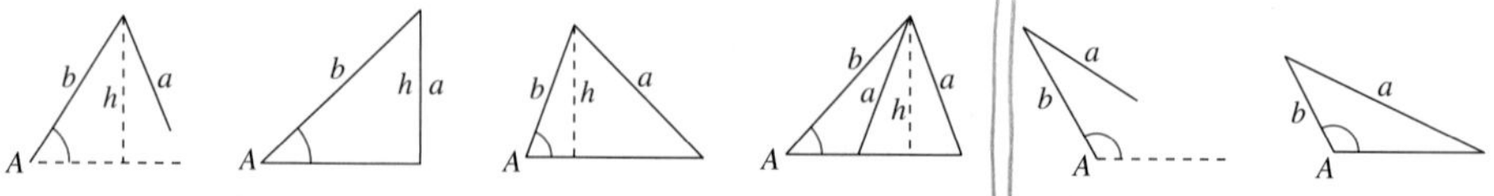					
Necessary condition	$a < h$	$a = h$	$a \geq b$	$h < a < b$	$a \leq b$	$a > b$
Triangles possible	None	One	One	Two	None	One

Example 3 Single-Solution Case—SSA

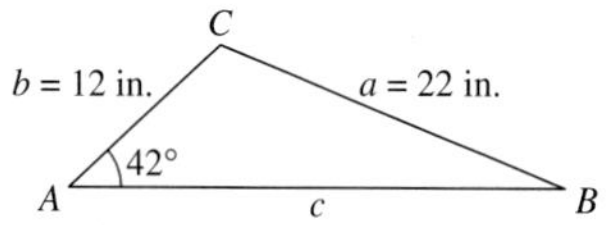

One solution: $a \geq b$
FIGURE 6.4

For the triangle in Figure 6.4, $a = 22$ inches, $b = 12$ inches, and $A = 42°$. Find the remaining side and angles.

Solution

By the Law of Sines, you have

$$\frac{\sin B}{b} = \frac{\sin A}{a} \qquad \text{Reciprocal form}$$

$$\sin B = b\left(\frac{\sin A}{a}\right) \qquad \text{Multiply each side by } b.$$

$$\sin B = 12\left(\frac{\sin 42°}{22}\right) \qquad \text{Substitute for } A, a, \text{ and } b.$$

$$B \approx 21.41°. \qquad B \text{ is acute.}$$

Now, you can determine that

$$C \approx 180° - 42° - 21.41° = 116.59°.$$

Then, the remaining side is

$$\frac{c}{\sin C} = \frac{a}{\sin A}$$

$$c = \frac{a}{\sin A}(\sin C) = \frac{22}{\sin 42°}(\sin 116.59°) \approx 29.40 \text{ inches.}$$

CHECKPoint Now try Exercise 25.

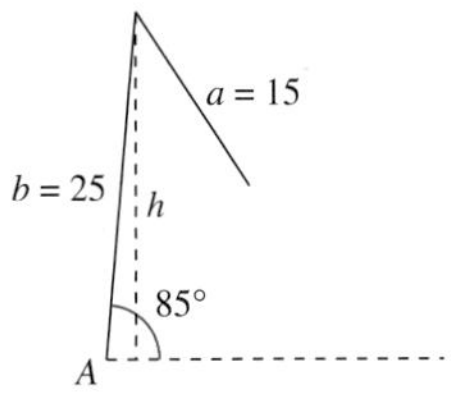

No solution: $a < h$

FIGURE 6.5

Example 4 No-Solution Case—SSA

Show that there is no triangle for which $a = 15$, $b = 25$, and $A = 85°$.

Solution

Begin by making the sketch shown in Figure 6.5. From this figure it appears that no triangle is formed. You can verify this using the Law of Sines.

$$\frac{\sin B}{b} = \frac{\sin A}{a}$$ Reciprocal form

$$\sin B = b\left(\frac{\sin A}{a}\right)$$ Multiply each side by b.

$$\sin B = 25\left(\frac{\sin 85°}{15}\right) \approx 1.660 > 1$$

This contradicts the fact that $|\sin B| \le 1$. So, no triangle can be formed having sides $a = 15$ and $b = 25$ and an angle of $A = 85°$.

CHECKPoint Now try Exercise 27.

Example 5 Two-Solution Case—SSA

Find two triangles for which $a = 12$ meters, $b = 31$ meters, and $A = 20.5°$.

Solution

By the Law of Sines, you have

$$\frac{\sin B}{b} = \frac{\sin A}{a}$$ Reciprocal form

$$\sin B = b\left(\frac{\sin A}{a}\right) = 31\left(\frac{\sin 20.5°}{12}\right) \approx 0.9047.$$

There are two angles, $B_1 \approx 64.8°$ and $B_2 \approx 180° - 64.8° = 115.2°$, between 0° and 180° whose sine is 0.9047. For $B_1 \approx 64.8°$, you obtain

$$C \approx 180° - 20.5° - 64.8° = 94.7°$$

$$c = \frac{a}{\sin A}(\sin C) = \frac{12}{\sin 20.5°}(\sin 94.7°) \approx 34.15 \text{ meters.}$$

For $B_2 \approx 115.2°$, you obtain

$$C \approx 180° - 20.5° - 115.2° = 44.3°$$

$$c = \frac{a}{\sin A}(\sin C) = \frac{12}{\sin 20.5°}(\sin 44.3°) \approx 23.93 \text{ meters.}$$

The resulting triangles are shown in Figure 6.6.

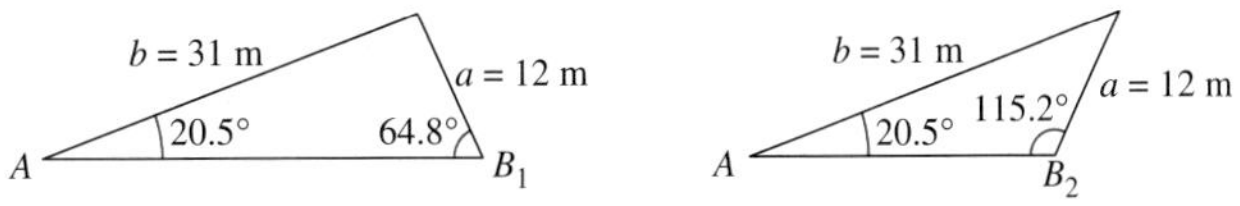

FIGURE 6.6

CHECKPoint Now try Exercise 29.

Extra Example 4

Show that there is no triangle for which $A = 60°$, $a = 4$, and $b = 14$.

$$\frac{4}{\sin 60°} = \frac{14}{\sin B}$$

$$\sin B = \frac{14 \sin 60°}{4} \approx 3.03$$

This contradicts $|\sin B| \le 1$. Therefore, no triangle can be formed.

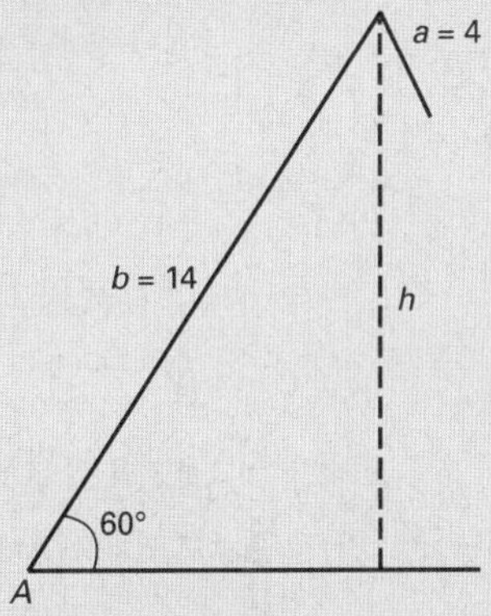

Extra Example 5

Find two triangles for which $A = 58°$, $a = 4.5$, and $b = 5$.

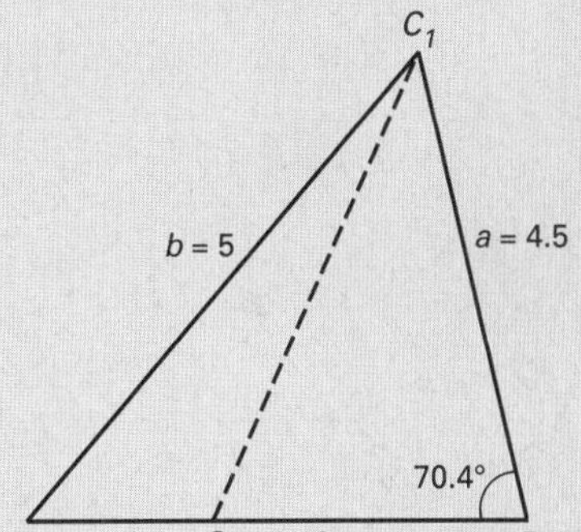

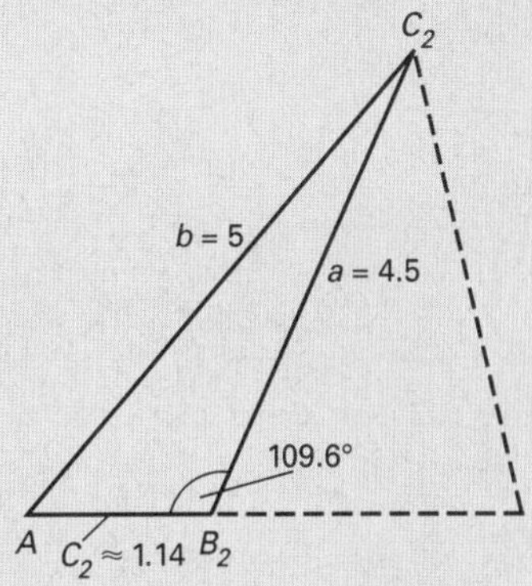

Avoiding Common Errors

The ambiguous case for the Law of Sines is often overlooked, especially in application problems. An application problem can have no solution, one solution, or two possible solutions if the given information fits the SSA pattern. Encourage students to draw a sketch to help them identify which case applies.

Extra Example 6

Find the area of a triangular lot containing side lengths that measure 24 yards and 18 yards and form an angle of 80°.

≈ 212.7 square yards

Study Tip

To see how to obtain the height of the obtuse triangle in Figure 6.7, notice the use of the reference angle $180° - A$ and the difference formula for sine, as follows.

$$\begin{aligned} h &= b\sin(180° - A) \\ &= b(\sin 180° \cos A \\ &\quad - \cos 180° \sin A) \\ &= b[0 \cdot \cos A - (-1) \cdot \sin A] \\ &= b \sin A \end{aligned}$$

Area of an Oblique Triangle

The procedure used to prove the Law of Sines leads to a simple formula for the area of an oblique triangle. Referring to Figure 6.7, note that each triangle has a height of $h = b \sin A$. Consequently, the area of each triangle is

$$\text{Area} = \frac{1}{2}(\text{base})(\text{height}) = \frac{1}{2}(c)(b\sin A) = \frac{1}{2}bc\sin A.$$

By similar arguments, you can develop the formulas

$$\text{Area} = \frac{1}{2}ab\sin C = \frac{1}{2}ac\sin B.$$

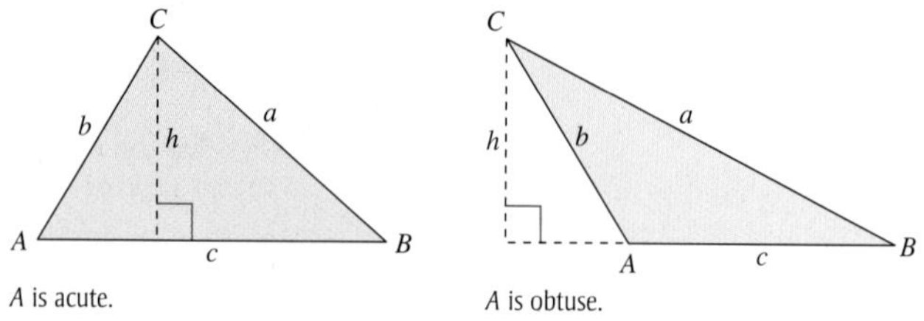

FIGURE 6.7

Area of an Oblique Triangle

The area of any triangle is one-half the product of the lengths of two sides times the sine of their included angle. That is,

$$\text{Area} = \frac{1}{2}bc\sin A = \frac{1}{2}ab\sin C = \frac{1}{2}ac\sin B.$$

Note that if angle A is 90°, the formula gives the area for a right triangle:

$$\text{Area} = \frac{1}{2}bc(\sin 90°) = \frac{1}{2}bc = \frac{1}{2}(\text{base})(\text{height}). \qquad \sin 90° = 1$$

Similar results are obtained for angles C and B equal to 90°.

Example 6 Finding the Area of a Triangular Lot

Find the area of a triangular lot having two sides of lengths 90 meters and 52 meters and an included angle of 102°.

Solution

Consider $a = 90$ meters, $b = 52$ meters, and angle $C = 102°$, as shown in Figure 6.8. Then, the area of the triangle is

$$\text{Area} = \frac{1}{2}ab\sin C = \frac{1}{2}(90)(52)(\sin 102°) \approx 2289 \text{ square meters.}$$

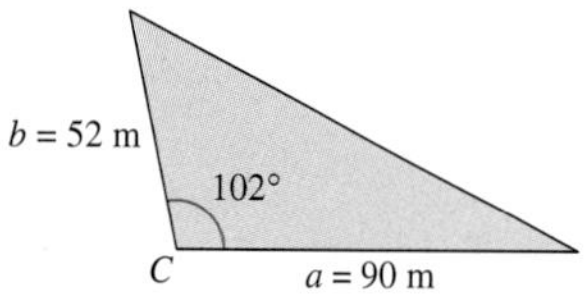

FIGURE 6.8

CHECKPoint Now try Exercise 39.

Application

Example 7 An Application of the Law of Sines

The course for a boat race starts at point A in Figure 6.9 and proceeds in the direction S 52° W to point B, then in the direction S 40° E to point C, and finally back to A. Point C lies 8 kilometers directly south of point A. Approximate the total distance of the race course.

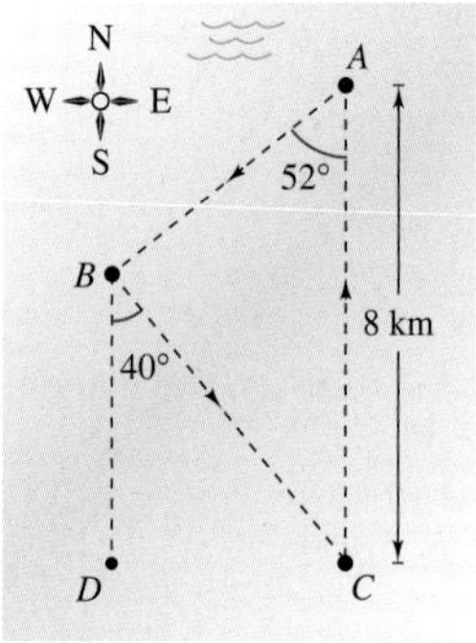

FIGURE 6.9

Solution

Because lines BD and AC are parallel, it follows that $\angle BCA \cong \angle CBD$. Consequently, triangle ABC has the measures shown in Figure 6.10. The measure of angle B is $180° - 52° - 40° = 88°$. Using the Law of Sines,

$$\frac{a}{\sin 52°} = \frac{b}{\sin 88°} = \frac{c}{\sin 40°}.$$

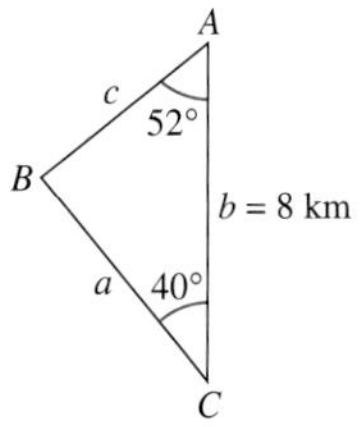

FIGURE 6.10

Because $b = 8$,

$$a = \frac{8}{\sin 88°}(\sin 52°) \approx 6.308$$

and

$$c = \frac{8}{\sin 88°}(\sin 40°) \approx 5.145.$$

The total length of the course is approximately

$$\text{Length} \approx 8 + 6.308 + 5.145$$
$$= 19.453 \text{ kilometers.}$$

CHECK*Point* Now try Exercise 49.

Classroom Discussion

Using the Law of Sines In this section, you have been using the Law of Sines to solve *oblique* triangles. Can the Law of Sines also be used to solve a right triangle? If so, write a short paragraph explaining how to use the Law of Sines to solve each triangle. Is there an easier way to solve these triangles?

a. (AAS)

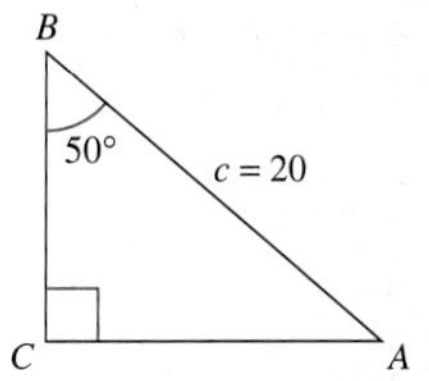

b. (ASA)

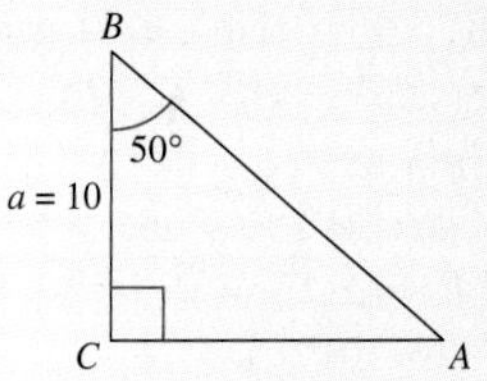

Yes

a. $A = 40°$, $a \approx 12.86$, $b \approx 15.32$ **b.** $A = 40°$, $b \approx 11.92$, $c \approx 15.56$

Answers will vary. It is probably easier to use the right triangle definitions of sine, cosine, and tangent to solve the triangle.

Extra Example 7

On a small lake, a person swims from point *A* to point *B* at a bearing of N 28° E. The person then swims to point *C* at a bearing of N 58° W. Point *C* is 800 meters due north of point *A*. How many total meters does the person swim?

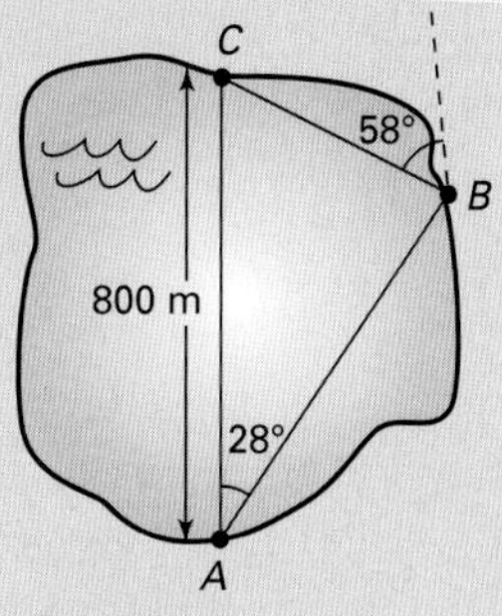

≈ 1056 meters

Closing the Lesson

Have students summarize the major points of the lesson and answer the Essential Question: How do you use trigonometry to solve and find the areas of oblique triangles?

- **Use the Law of Sines to find unknown angles and side lengths in cases AAS, ASA, and SSA.**
- **Recognize situations in which the ambiguous case SSA produces no solution, one solution, or two solutions.**
- **Find the area of a triangle by multiplying one-half the product of the lengths of two sides by the sine of their included angle.**

6.1 EXERCISES

See www.CalcChat.com for worked-out solutions to odd-numbered exercises.

VOCABULARY: Fill in the blanks.

1. An oblique triangle is a triangle that has no right angle.
2. For triangle ABC, the Law of Sines is given by $\dfrac{a}{\sin A} = \dfrac{b}{\sin B} = \dfrac{c}{\sin C}$.
3. Two angles and one side determine a unique triangle.
4. The area of an oblique triangle is given by $\frac{1}{2}bc \sin A = \frac{1}{2}ab \sin C = \frac{1}{2}ac \sin B$.

SKILLS AND APPLICATIONS

In Exercises 5–24, use the Law of Sines to solve the triangle. Round your answers to two decimal places.

5.
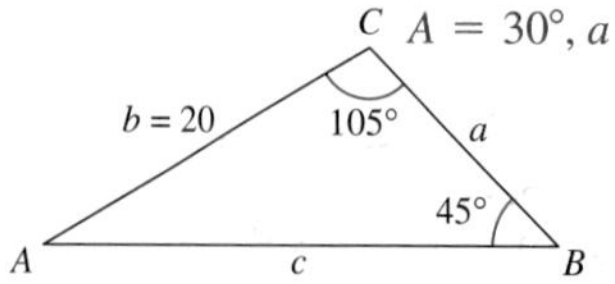

$A = 30°, a \approx 14.14, c \approx 27.32$

6.
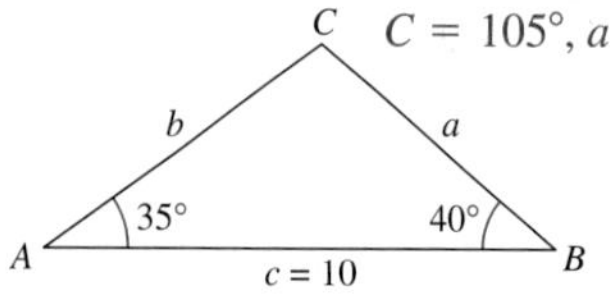

$C = 105°, a \approx 5.94, b \approx 6.65$

7.
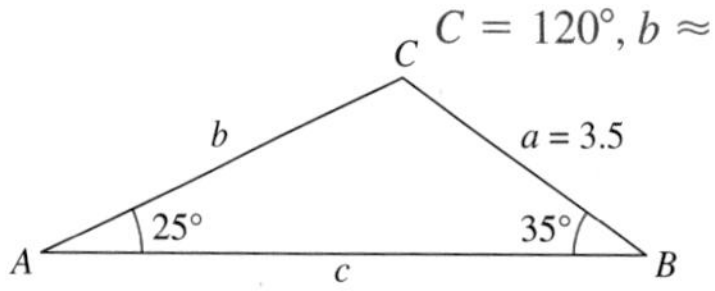

$C = 120°, b \approx 4.75, c \approx 7.17$

8.
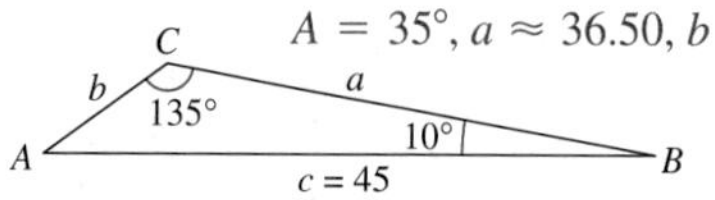

$A = 35°, a \approx 36.50, b \approx 11.05$

9. $A = 102.4°$, $C = 16.7°$, $a = 21.6$ 9–18. See margin.
10. $A = 24.3°$, $C = 54.6°$, $c = 2.68$
11. $A = 83° 20'$, $C = 54.6°$, $c = 18.1$
12. $A = 5° 40'$, $B = 8° 15'$, $b = 4.8$
13. $A = 35°$, $B = 65°$, $c = 10$
14. $A = 120°$, $B = 45°$, $c = 16$
15. $A = 55°$, $B = 42°$, $c = \frac{3}{4}$
16. $B = 28°$, $C = 104°$, $a = 3\frac{5}{8}$
17. $A = 36°$, $a = 8$, $b = 5$
18. $A = 60°$, $a = 9$, $c = 10$
19. $B = 15° 30'$, $a = 4.5$, $b = 6.8$
    $A \approx 10°11'$, $C \approx 154°19'$, $c \approx 11.03$
20. $B = 2° 45'$, $b = 6.2$, $c = 5.8$ 20–24. See margin.
21. $A = 145°$, $a = 14$, $b = 4$
22. $A = 100°$, $a = 125$, $c = 10$
23. $A = 110° 15'$, $a = 48$, $b = 16$
24. $C = 95.20°$, $a = 35$, $c = 50$

In Exercises 25–34, use the Law of Sines to solve (if possible) the triangle. If two solutions exist, find both. Round your answers to two decimal places.

25. $A = 110°$, $a = 125$, $b = 100$ See margin.
26. $A = 110°$, $a = 125$, $b = 200$ No solution
27. $A = 76°$, $a = 18$, $b = 20$ No solution
28. $A = 76°$, $a = 34$, $b = 21$ See margin.
29. $A = 58°$, $a = 11.4$, $b = 12.8$ See margin.
30. $A = 58°$, $a = 4.5$, $b = 12.8$ No solution
31. $A = 120°$, $a = b = 25$ No solution
32. $A = 120°$, $a = 25$, $b = 24$ See margin.
33. $A = 45°$, $a = b = 1$ See margin.
34. $A = 25° 4'$, $a = 9.5$, $b = 22$ See margin.

In Exercises 35–38, find values for b such that the triangle has (a) one solution, (b) two solutions, and (c) no solution.

35. $A = 36°$, $a = 5$ 35–38. See margin.
36. $A = 60°$, $a = 10$
37. $A = 10°$, $a = 10.8$
38. $A = 88°$, $a = 315.6$

In Exercises 39–44, find the area of the triangle having the indicated angle and sides.

39. $C = 120°$, $a = 4$, $b = 6$ 10.4
40. $B = 130°$, $a = 62$, $c = 20$ 474.9
41. $A = 43° 45'$, $b = 57$, $c = 85$ 1675.2
42. $A = 5° 15'$, $b = 4.5$, $c = 22$ 4.5
43. $B = 72° 30'$, $a = 105$, $c = 64$ 3204.5
44. $C = 84° 30'$, $a = 16$, $b = 20$ 159.3

4 PRACTICE AND APPLY

Assignment Guide

Transparencies Available
Available at the Instructor's companion site.

Average:
Day 1: pp. 434–436
Exs. 1–4, 7–11 odd, 17–23 odd, 26–30 even, 35, 40, 43, 47, 51–53, 57–60

Advanced:
Day 1: pp. 434–436
Exs. 1–4, 6–12 even, 20, 24, 30–38 even, 42–50 even, 51, 52, 56, 57–60, 62

Block:
pp. 434–436
Exs. 1–4, 7–11 odd, 17–23 odd, 26–30 even, 35, 40, 43, 47, 51–53, 57–60 (with 6.2)

9. $B = 60.9°, b \approx 19.32, c \approx 6.36$
10. $B = 101.1°, a \approx 1.35, b \approx 3.23$
11. $B = 42°4', a \approx 22.05, b \approx 14.88$
12. $C = 166°5', a \approx 3.30, c \approx 8.05$
13. $C = 80°,\ a \approx 5.82,\ b \approx 9.20$
14. $C = 15°,\ a \approx 53.54,\ b \approx 43.71$
15. $C = 83°, a \approx 0.62, b \approx 0.51$
16. $A = 48°, b \approx 2.29, c \approx 4.73$
17. $B \approx 21.55°, C \approx 122.45°, c \approx 11.49$
18. Two solutions:
$B \approx 45.79°, C \approx 74.21°, b \approx 7.45$
$B \approx 14.21°, C \approx 105.79°, b \approx 2.55$
20. $A \approx 174°41', C \approx 2°34', a \approx 11.99$
21. $B \approx 9.43°,\ C = 25.57°,\ c \approx 10.53$
22. $B \approx 75.48°, C \approx 4.52°, b \approx 122.87$
23. $B \approx 18°13', C \approx 51°32', c \approx 40.06$
24. $A \approx 44.20°,\ B \approx 40.60°,\ b \approx 32.67$
25. $B \approx 48.74°, C \approx 21.26°, c \approx 48.23$
28. $B \approx 36.82°, C \approx 67.18°, c \approx 32.30$
29. Two solutions:
$B \approx 72.21°, C \approx 49.79°, c \approx 10.27$
$B \approx 107.79°, C \approx 14.21°, c \approx 3.30$
32. $B \approx 56.24°,\ C \approx 3.76°,\ c \approx 1.89$
33. $B = 45°,\ C = 90°,\ c \approx 1.41$
34. Two solutions:
$B \approx 78.85°,\ C \approx 76.08°,\ c \approx 21.76$
$B \approx 101.15°,\ C \approx 53.78°,\ c \approx 18.09$
35. (a) $b \le 5,\ b = \dfrac{5}{\sin 36°}$ (b) $5 < b < \dfrac{5}{\sin 36°}$
(c) $b > \dfrac{5}{\sin 36°}$
36. (a) $b \le 10, b = \dfrac{10}{\sin 60°}$
(b) $10 < b < \dfrac{10}{\sin 60°}$ (c) $b > \dfrac{10}{\sin 60°}$
37. (a) $b \le 10.8, b = \dfrac{10.8}{\sin 10°}$
(b) $10.8 < b < \dfrac{10.8}{\sin 10°}$ (c) $b > \dfrac{10.8}{\sin 10°}$
38. (a) $b \le 315.6, b = \dfrac{315.6}{\sin 88°}$
(b) $315.6 < b < \dfrac{315.6}{\sin 88°}$
(c) $b > \dfrac{315.6}{\sin 88°}$

45. HEIGHT Because of prevailing winds, a tree grew so that it was leaning 4° from the vertical. At a point 40 meters from the tree, the angle of elevation to the top of the tree is 30° (see figure). Find the height h of the tree. 24.1 m

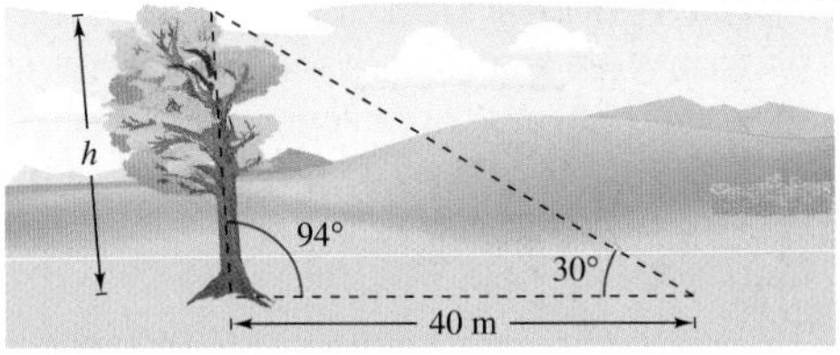

46. HEIGHT A flagpole at a right angle to the horizontal is located on a slope that makes an angle of 12° with the horizontal. The flagpole's shadow is 16 meters long and points directly up the slope. The angle of elevation from the tip of the shadow to the sun is 20°.

(a) Draw a triangle to represent the situation. Show the known quantities on the triangle and use a variable to indicate the height of the flagpole.

(b) Write an equation that can be used to find the height of the flagpole. (a)–(b). See margin.

(c) Find the height of the flagpole. 9 m

47. ANGLE OF ELEVATION A 10-meter utility pole casts a 17-meter shadow directly down a slope when the angle of elevation of the sun is 42° (see figure). Find θ, the angle of elevation of the ground. 16.1°

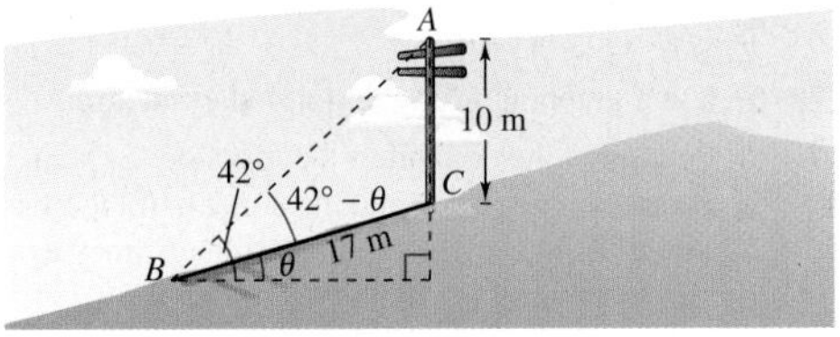

48. FLIGHT PATH A plane flies 500 kilometers with a bearing of 316° from Naples to Elgin (see figure). The plane then flies 720 kilometers from Elgin to Canton (Canton is due west of Naples). Find the bearing of the flight from Elgin to Canton. 240°

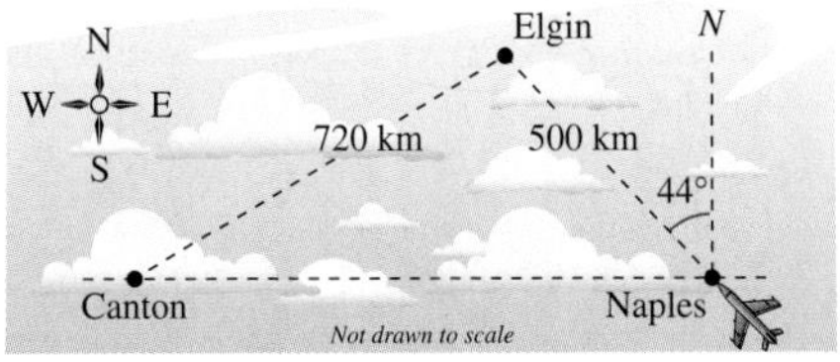

49. BRIDGE DESIGN A bridge is to be built across a small lake from a gazebo to a dock (see figure). The bearing from the gazebo to the dock is S 41° W. From a tree 100 meters from the gazebo, the bearings to the gazebo and the dock are S 74° E and S 28° E, respectively. Find the distance from the gazebo to the dock. 77 m

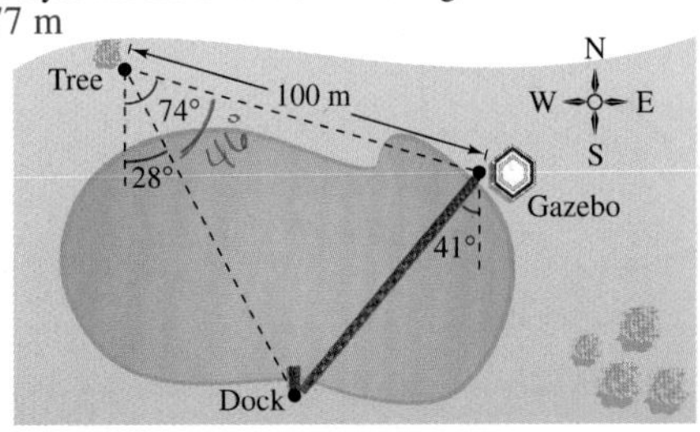

50. RAILROAD TRACK DESIGN The circular arc of a railroad curve has a chord of length 3000 feet corresponding to a central angle of 40°.

(a) Draw a diagram that visually represents the situation. Show the known quantities on the diagram and use the variables r and s to represent the radius of the arc and the length of the arc, respectively. See margin.

(b) Find the radius r of the circular arc. 4385.71 ft

(c) Find the length s of the circular arc. 3061.80 ft

51. GLIDE PATH A pilot has just started on the glide path for landing at an airport with a runway of length 9000 feet. The angles of depression from the plane to the ends of the runway are 17.5° and 18.8°.

(a) Draw a diagram that visually represents the situation. See margin.

(b) Find the air distance the plane must travel until touching down on the near end of the runway. 22.6 mi

(c) Find the ground distance the plane must travel until touching down. 21.4 mi

(d) Find the altitude of the plane when the pilot begins the descent. 7.3 mi

52. LOCATING A FIRE The bearing from the Pine Knob fire tower to the Colt Station fire tower is N 65° E, and the two towers are 30 kilometers apart. A fire spotted by rangers in each tower has a bearing of N 80° E from Pine Knob and S 70° E from Colt Station (see figure). Find the distance of the fire from each tower. See margin.

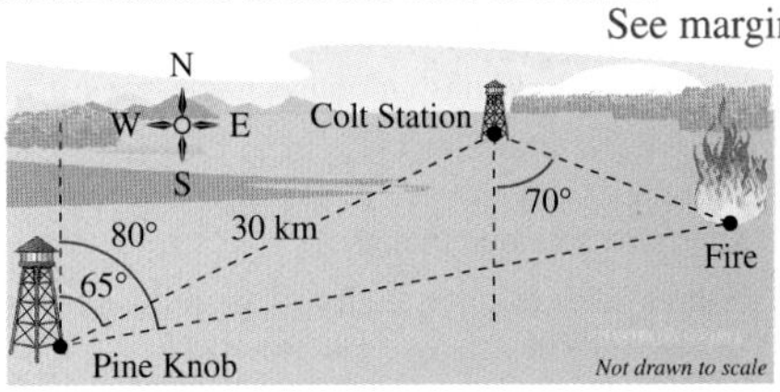

46. (a)

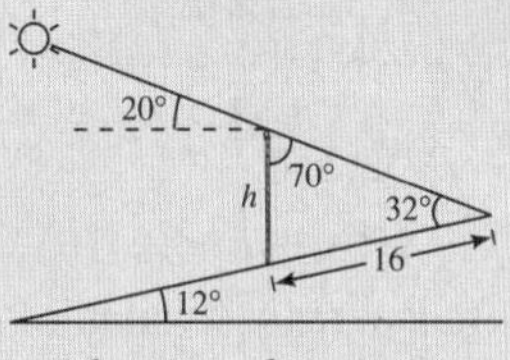

(b) $\dfrac{16}{\sin 70°} = \dfrac{h}{\sin 32°}$

50. (a)

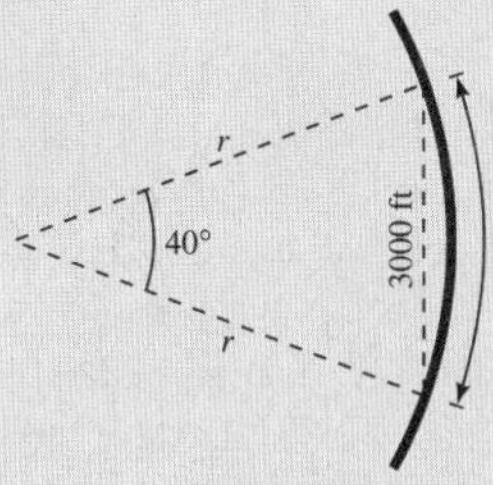

51. (a)

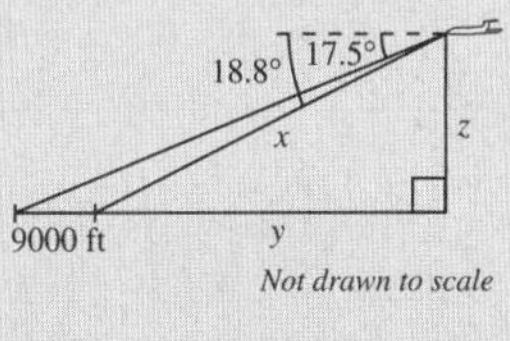

52. From Pine Knob: 42.4 km
From Colt Station: 15.5 km

53. DISTANCE A boat is sailing due east parallel to the shoreline at a speed of 10 miles per hour. At a given time, the bearing to the lighthouse is S 70° E, and 15 minutes later the bearing is S 63° E (see figure). The lighthouse is located at the shoreline. What is the distance from the boat to the shoreline? 3.2 mi

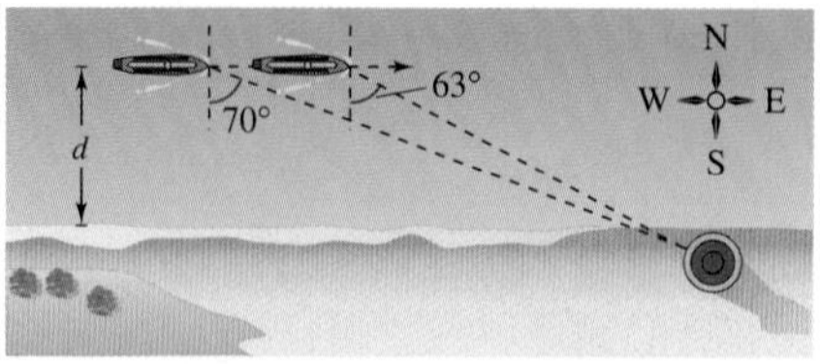

54. DISTANCE A family is traveling due west on a road that passes a famous landmark. At a given time the bearing to the landmark is N 62° W, and after the family travels 5 miles farther the bearing is N 38° W. What is the closest the family will come to the landmark while on the road? 4.55 mi

55. ALTITUDE The angles of elevation to an airplane from two points A and B on level ground are 55° and 72°, respectively. The points A and B are 2.2 miles apart, and the airplane is east of both points in the same vertical plane. Find the altitude of the plane. 5.86 mi

56. DISTANCE The angles of elevation θ and ϕ to an airplane from the airport control tower and from an observation post 2 miles away are being continuously monitored (see figure). Write an equation giving the distance d between the plane and observation post in terms of θ and ϕ. $d = \dfrac{2 \sin \theta}{\sin(\phi - \theta)}$

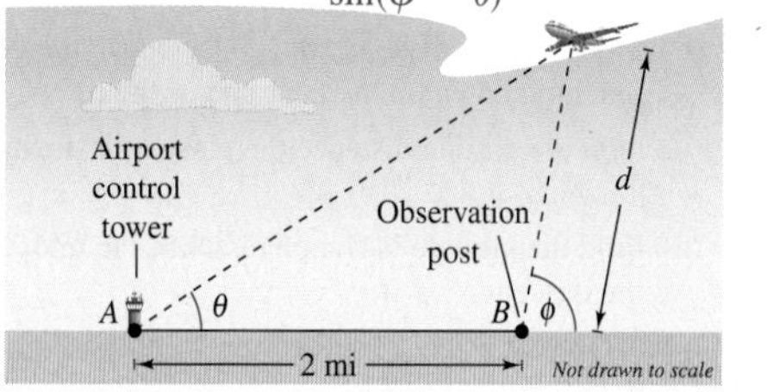

EXPLORATION

TRUE OR FALSE? In Exercises 57–59, determine whether the statement is true or false. Justify your answer. 57–59. See margin.

57. If a triangle contains an obtuse angle, then it must be oblique.

58. Two angles and one side of a triangle do not necessarily determine a unique triangle.

59. If three sides or three angles of an oblique triangle are known, then the triangle can be solved.

60. GRAPHICAL AND NUMERICAL ANALYSIS In the figure, α and β are positive angles.

(a) Write α as a function of β. $\alpha = \arcsin(0.5 \sin \beta)$

(b) Use a graphing utility to graph the function in part (a). Determine its domain and range.

(c) Use the result of part (a) to write c as a function of β. (b)–(e). See margin.

(d) Use a graphing utility to graph the function in part (c). Determine its domain and range.

(e) Complete the table. What can you infer?

β	0.4	0.8	1.2	1.6	2.0	2.4	2.8
α							
c							

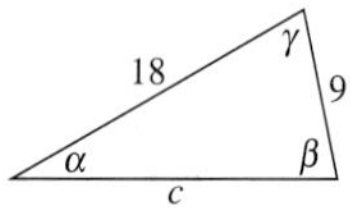

FIGURE FOR 60

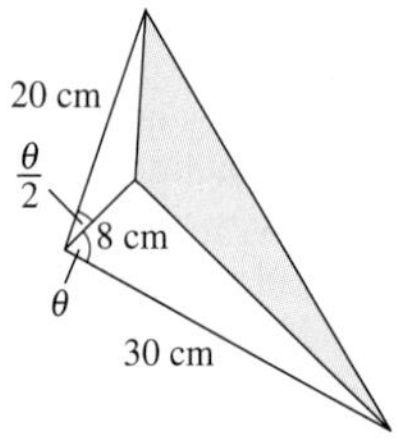

FIGURE FOR 61

61. GRAPHICAL ANALYSIS See margin.

(a) Write the area A of the shaded region in the figure as a function of θ.

(b) Use a graphing utility to graph the function.

(c) Determine the domain of the function. Explain how the area of the region and the domain of the function would change if the eight-centimeter line segment were decreased in length.

62. CAPSTONE In the figure, a triangle is to be formed by drawing a line segment of length a from (4, 3) to the positive x-axis. For what value(s) of a can you form (a) one triangle, (b) two triangles, and (c) no triangles? Explain your reasoning.

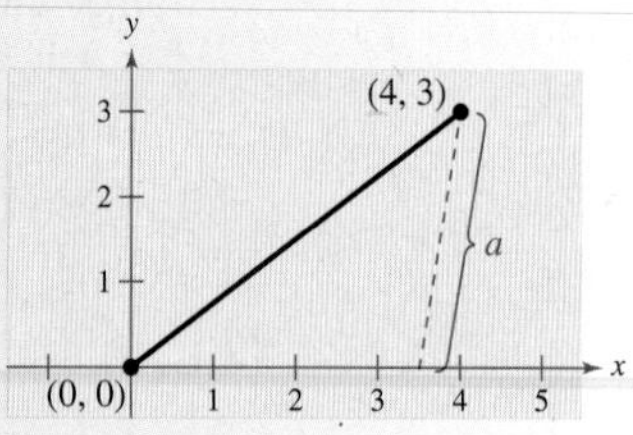

(a) $a \ge 5$, $a = 3$ (b) $3 < a < 5$
(c) $a < 3$
Explanations will vary.

5 ASSESS AND RETEACH

Daily Homework Quiz

Transparency Available
Available at the Instructor's companion site.

57. True. If an angle of a triangle is obtuse (greater than 90°), then the other two angles must be acute and therefore less than 90°. The triangle is oblique.

58. False. Two angles and one side determine a unique triangle, while two sides and one opposite angle do not necessarily determine a unique triangle.

59. False. If just three angles are known, the triangle cannot be solved.

60. (b)

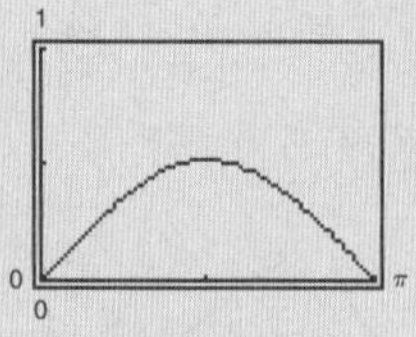

Domain: $0 < \beta < \pi$

Range: $0 < \alpha < \dfrac{\pi}{6}$

(c) See below.

(d)

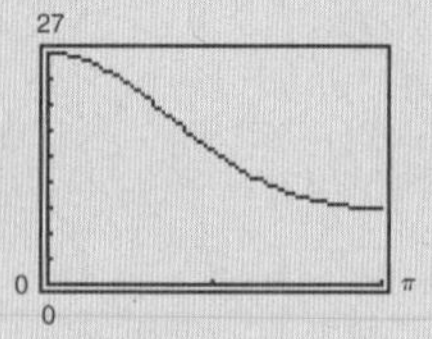

Domain: $0 < \beta < \pi$

Range: $9 < c < 27$

(e) See below.

61. (a) See below.

(b)

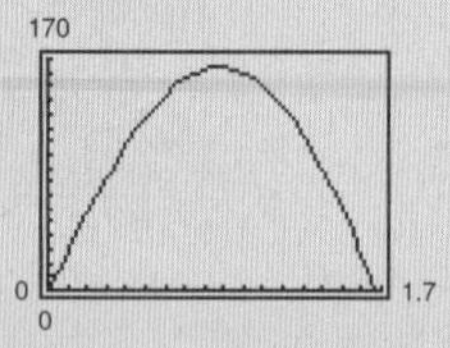

(c) Domain: $0 \le \theta \le 1.6690$
The domain would increase in length and the area would have a greater maximum value.

60. (c) $c = \dfrac{18 \sin[\pi - \beta - \arcsin(0.5 \sin \beta)]}{\sin \beta}$

(e)

β	0.4	0.8	1.2	1.6	2.0	2.4	2.8
α	0.1960	0.3669	0.4848	0.5234	0.4720	0.3445	0.1683
c	25.95	23.07	19.19	15.33	12.29	10.31	9.27

As β increases from 0 to π, α increases and then decreases, and c decreases from 27 to 9.

61. (a) $A = 20\left(15 \sin \dfrac{3\theta}{2} - 4 \sin \dfrac{\theta}{2} - 6 \sin \theta\right)$

6.2 Law of Cosines

What you should learn

- Use the Law of Cosines to solve oblique triangles (SSS or SAS).
- Use the Law of Cosines to model and solve real-life problems.
- Use Heron's Area Formula to find the area of a triangle.

Why you should learn it

You can use the Law of Cosines to solve real-life problems involving oblique triangles. For instance, in Exercise 52 on page 443, you can use the Law of Cosines to approximate how far a baseball player has to run to make a catch.

Daniel Bendjy/istockphoto.com

Introduction

Two cases remain in the list of conditions needed to solve an oblique triangle—SSS and SAS. If you are given three sides (SSS), or two sides and their included angle (SAS), none of the ratios in the Law of Sines would be complete. In such cases, you can use the **Law of Cosines.**

Law of Cosines

Standard Form	*Alternative Form*
$a^2 = b^2 + c^2 - 2bc \cos A$	$\cos A = \dfrac{b^2 + c^2 - a^2}{2bc}$
$b^2 = a^2 + c^2 - 2ac \cos B$	$\cos B = \dfrac{a^2 + c^2 - b^2}{2ac}$
$c^2 = a^2 + b^2 - 2ab \cos C$	$\cos C = \dfrac{a^2 + b^2 - c^2}{2ab}$

For a proof of the Law of Cosines, see Proofs in Mathematics on page 488.

Example 1 Three Sides of a Triangle—SSS

Find the three angles of the triangle in Figure 6.11.

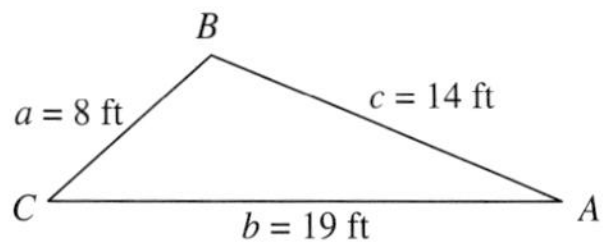

FIGURE 6.11

Solution

It is a good idea first to find the angle opposite the longest side—side b in this case. Using the alternative form of the Law of Cosines, you find that

$$\cos B = \frac{a^2 + c^2 - b^2}{2ac} = \frac{8^2 + 14^2 - 19^2}{2(8)(14)} \approx -0.45089.$$

Because $\cos B$ is negative, you know that B is an *obtuse* angle given by $B \approx 116.80°$. At this point, it is simpler to use the Law of Sines to determine A.

$$\sin A = a\left(\frac{\sin B}{b}\right) \approx 8\left(\frac{\sin 116.80°}{19}\right) \approx 0.37583$$

You know that A must be acute because B is obtuse, and a triangle can have, at most, one obtuse angle. So, $A \approx 22.08°$ and $C \approx 180° - 22.08° - 116.80° = 41.12°$.

CHECK*Point* Now try Exercise 5.

1 PLAN AND PREPARE

Warm-up Exercises

Transparency Available
Available at the Instructor's companion site.

Notetaking Guide

Transparency Available
Promotes interactive learning and notetaking skills. Available at the Instructor's companion site.

Animated Precalculus

An **Animated Precalculus** tutorial is available at the Student companion site for **Section 6.2.**

Pacing

Average: 1 day
Advanced: 1 day
Block: 0.5 block with 6.1

2 FOCUS AND MOTIVATE

Essential Question

How do you use trigonometry to solve and find the areas of oblique triangles? **Tell students that they will learn how to answer this question by using the relationships between an angle in a triangle and the lengths of the sides of the triangle.**

Resource Planning Guide

Chapter Resources

- Complete Solutions Guide

Workbooks

- Notetaking Guide
- Student Solutions Guide

Interactive Technology

- Instructor Success Organizer
- Notetaking Guide IAE
- Instructional DVDs
- Animated Precalculus
- PowerLecture with ExamView

Do you see why it was wise to find the largest angle *first* in Example 1? Knowing the cosine of an angle, you can determine whether the angle is acute or obtuse. That is,

$\cos\theta > 0 \quad \text{for} \quad 0° < \theta < 90°$ Acute

$\cos\theta < 0 \quad \text{for} \quad 90° < \theta < 180°.$ Obtuse

So, in Example 1, once you found that angle B was obtuse, you knew that angles A and C were both acute. If the largest angle is acute, the remaining two angles are acute also.

Example 2 Two Sides and the Included Angle—SAS

Find the remaining angles and side of the triangle in Figure 6.12.

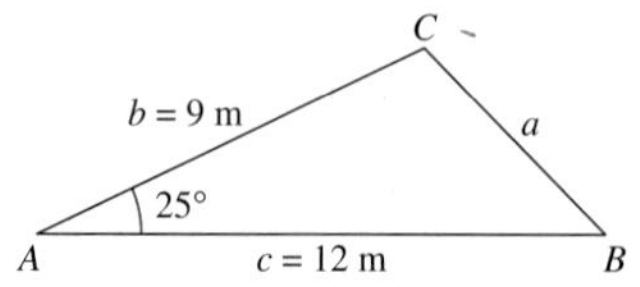

FIGURE 6.12

Solution

Use the Law of Cosines to find the unknown side a in the figure.

$$a^2 = b^2 + c^2 - 2bc\cos A$$

$$a^2 = 9^2 + 12^2 - 2(9)(12)\cos 25°$$

$$a^2 \approx 29.2375$$

$$a \approx 5.4072$$

Because $a \approx 5.4072$ meters, you now know the ratio $(\sin A)/a$ and you can use the reciprocal form of the Law of Sines to solve for B.

$$\frac{\sin B}{b} = \frac{\sin A}{a}$$

$$\sin B = b\left(\frac{\sin A}{a}\right)$$

$$= 9\left(\frac{\sin 25}{5.4072}\right)$$

$$\approx 0.7034$$

There are two angles between 0° and 180° whose sine is 0.7034, $B_1 \approx 44.7°$ and $B_2 \approx 180° - 44.7° = 135.3°$.

For $B_1 \approx 44.7°$,

$$C_1 \approx 180° - 25° - 44.7° = 110.3°.$$

For $B_2 \approx 135.3°$,

$$C_2 \approx 180° - 25° - 135.3° = 19.7°.$$

Because side c is the longest side of the triangle, C must be the largest angle of the triangle. So, $B \approx 44.7°$ and $C \approx 110.3°$.

CHECKPoint Now try Exercise 7.

Study Tip

When solving an oblique triangle given three sides, you use the alternative form of the Law of Cosines to solve for an angle. When solving an oblique triangle given two sides and their included angle, you use the standard form of the Law of Cosines to solve for an unknown.

3 TEACH

Extra Example 1

Find the three angles of triangle *ABC*.

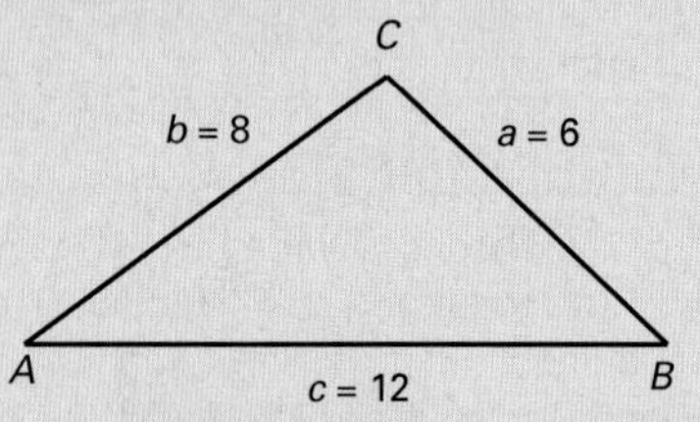

$A \approx 26.38°$, $B \approx 36.34°$, $C \approx 117.28°$

Extra Example 2

Find the remaining angles and side of triangle *ABC*.

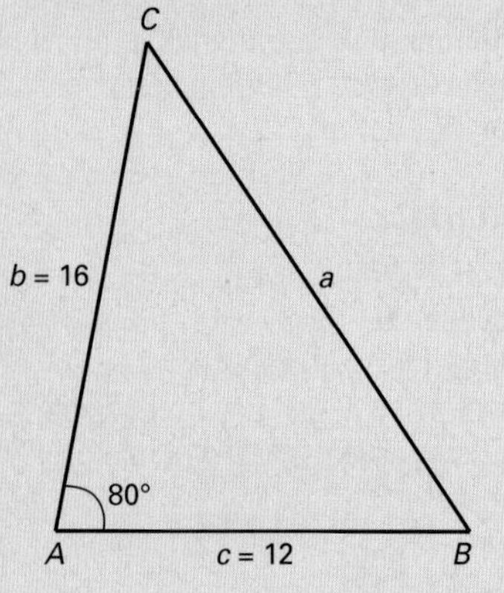

$a \approx 18.26$, $C \approx 40.33°$, $B \approx 59.65°$

Applications

Example 3 An Application of the Law of Cosines

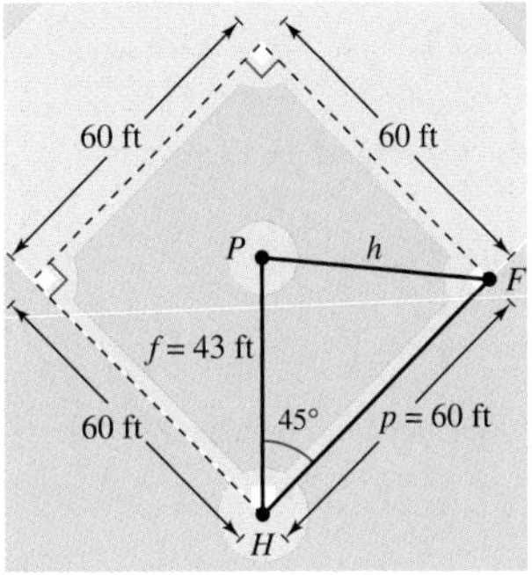

FIGURE 6.13

The pitcher's mound on a women's softball field is 43 feet from home plate and the distance between the bases is 60 feet, as shown in Figure 6.13. (The pitcher's mound is not halfway between home plate and second base.) How far is the pitcher's mound from first base?

Solution

In triangle HPF, $H = 45°$ (line HP bisects the right angle at H), $f = 43$, and $p = 60$. Using the Law of Cosines for this SAS case, you have

$$h^2 = f^2 + p^2 - 2fp \cos H$$

$$= 43^2 + 60^2 - 2(43)(60)\cos 45° \approx 1800.3.$$

So, the approximate distance from the pitcher's mound to first base is

$$h \approx \sqrt{1800.3} \approx 42.43 \text{ feet.}$$

CHECKPoint Now try Exercise 43.

Example 4 An Application of the Law of Cosines

A ship travels 60 miles due east, then adjusts its course northward, as shown in Figure 6.14. After traveling 80 miles in that direction, the ship is 139 miles from its point of departure. Describe the bearing from point B to point C.

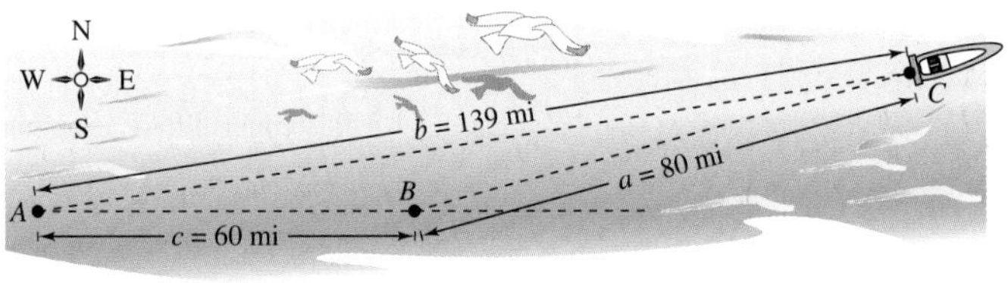

FIGURE 6.14

Solution

You have $a = 80$, $b = 139$, and $c = 60$. So, using the alternative form of the Law of Cosines, you have

$$\cos B = \frac{a^2 + c^2 - b^2}{2ac}$$

$$= \frac{80^2 + 60^2 - 139^2}{2(80)(60)}$$

$$\approx -0.97094.$$

So, $B \approx \arccos(-0.97094) \approx 166.15°$, and thus the bearing measured from due north from point B to point C is

$$166.15° - 90° = 76.15°, \text{ or N } 76.15° \text{ E.}$$

CHECKPoint Now try Exercise 49.

Extra Example 3

In a softball game, a batter hits the ball to center field. The center fielder then throws the ball to third base as shown. The distance from the center fielder to home plate is 240 feet. The distance between the bases is 60 feet. How far did the center fielder throw the ball?

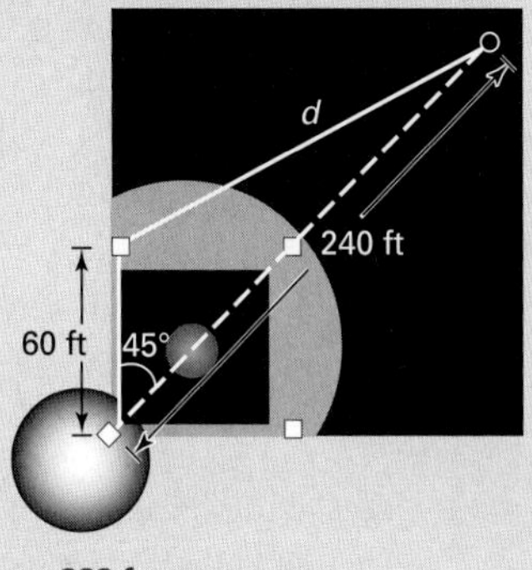

≈ 202 feet

Extra Example 4

A ship travels 40 miles due east and then changes direction. When the ship has traveled 30 miles at this heading, it is 56 miles from its point of departure. Describe the bearing from point B to point C in the figure.

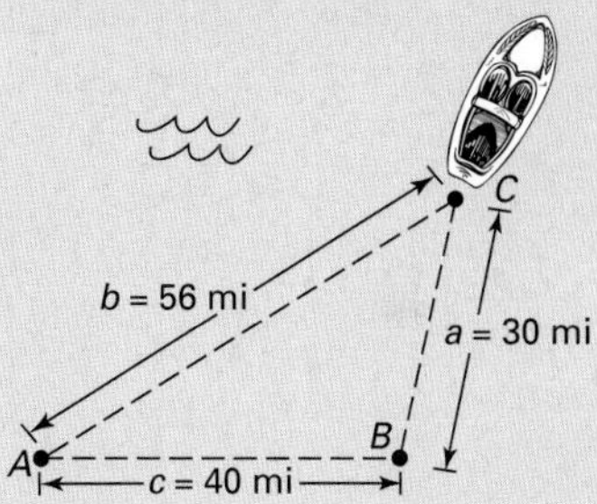

Measured from due north, the bearing from point B to point C is $105.37° - 90° \approx 15.37°$, or N 15.4° E.

Heron's Area Formula

HISTORICAL NOTE

Heron of Alexandria (c. 100 B.C.) was a Greek geometer and inventor. His works describe how to find the areas of triangles, quadrilaterals, regular polygons having 3 to 12 sides, and circles as well as the surface areas and volumes of three-dimensional objects.

The Law of Cosines can be used to establish the following formula for the area of a triangle. This formula is called **Heron's Area Formula** after the Greek mathematician Heron (c. 100 B.C.).

Heron's Area Formula

Given any triangle with sides of lengths a, b, and c, the area of the triangle is

$$\text{Area} = \sqrt{s(s-a)(s-b)(s-c)}$$

where $s = (a + b + c)/2$.

For a proof of Heron's Area Formula, see Proofs in Mathematics on page 489.

Example 5 Using Heron's Area Formula

Find the area of a triangle having sides of lengths $a = 43$ meters, $b = 53$ meters, and $c = 72$ meters.

Solution

Because $s = (a + b + c)/2 = 168/2 = 84$, Heron's Area Formula yields

$$\begin{aligned}\text{Area} &= \sqrt{s(s-a)(s-b)(s-c)}\\ &= \sqrt{84(41)(31)(12)}\\ &\approx 1131.89 \text{ square meters.}\end{aligned}$$

CHECKPoint Now try Exercise 59.

You have now studied three different formulas for the area of a triangle.

Standard Formula: $\text{Area} = \frac{1}{2}bh$

Oblique Triangle: $\text{Area} = \frac{1}{2}bc \sin A = \frac{1}{2}ab \sin C = \frac{1}{2}ac \sin B$

Heron's Area Formula: $\text{Area} = \sqrt{s(s-a)(s-b)(s-c)}$

Classroom Discussion

The Area of a Triangle Use the most appropriate formula to find the area of each triangle below. Show your work and give your reasons for choosing each formula.

See margin.

a.

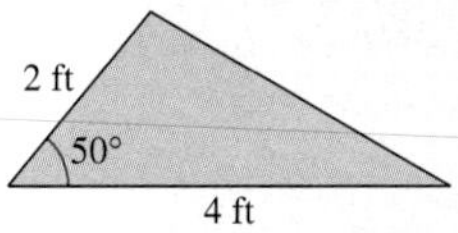

b.

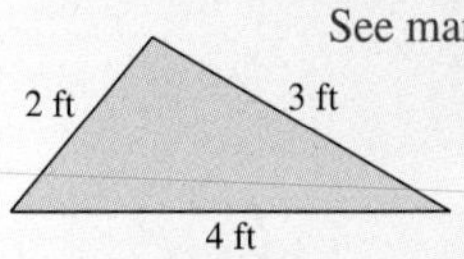

c.

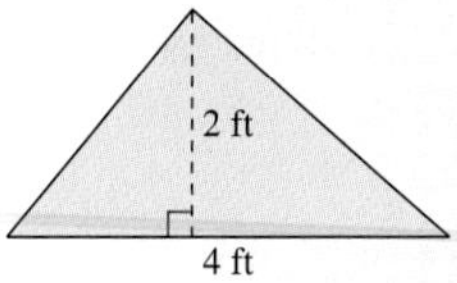

d.

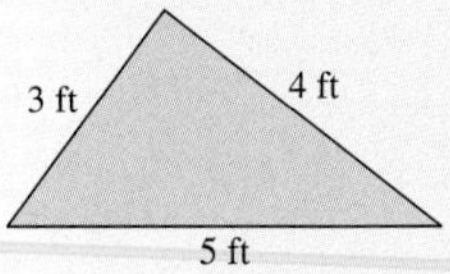

Extra Example 5

Find the area of a triangle having sides of lengths $a = 5$ feet, $b = 9$ feet, and $c = 8$ feet.

≈ 19.90 square feet

Closing the Lesson

Have students summarize the major points of the lesson and answer the Essential Question: How do you use trigonometry to solve and find the areas of oblique triangles?

- **Use the Law of Cosines to find unknown angles and side lengths in cases SSS and SAS.**
- **Find the area of any triangle by using Heron's formula $A = \sqrt{s(s-a)(s-b)(s-c)}$, where $s = (a + b + c) \div 2$.**

Classroom Discussion

a. $\text{Area} = \frac{1}{2}(2)(4)\sin 50° \approx 3.064 \text{ ft}^2$

b. $\text{Area} = \sqrt{\frac{9}{2}\left(\frac{9}{2}-2\right)\left(\frac{9}{2}-3\right)\left(\frac{9}{2}-4\right)} \approx 2.905 \text{ ft}^2$

c. $\text{Area} = \frac{1}{2}(2)(4) = 4 \text{ ft}^2$

d.

$\text{Area} = \sqrt{6(6-3)(6-4)(6-5)} = 6 \text{ ft}^2$

Differentiated Instruction

Visual Learners For Example 5, instruct students to sketch the given triangle in millimeters. Have them label sides a, b, and c and use Heron's Area Formula to find the area. Next, direct them to use a ruler to find the height of the triangle. Then, to check their work, have them use the formula $A = \frac{1}{2}bh$ to find the area of the triangle.

6.2 EXERCISES

See www.CalcChat.com for worked-out solutions to odd-numbered exercises.

VOCABULARY: Fill in the blanks.

1. If you are given three sides of a triangle, you would use the Law of <u>Cosines</u> to find the three angles of the triangle.
2. If you are given two angles and any side of a triangle, you would use the Law of <u>Sines</u> to solve the triangle.
3. The standard form of the Law of Cosines for $\cos B = \frac{a^2 + c^2 - b^2}{2ac}$ is $b^2 = a^2 + c^2 - 2ac \cos B$.
4. The Law of Cosines can be used to establish a formula for finding the area of a triangle called <u>Heron's Area</u> Formula.

SKILLS AND APPLICATIONS

5–20. See margin.

In Exercises 5–20, use the Law of Cosines to solve the triangle. Round your answers to two decimal places.

5. 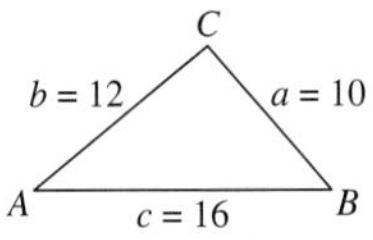

6. 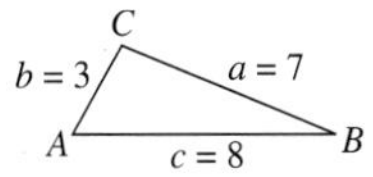

7. 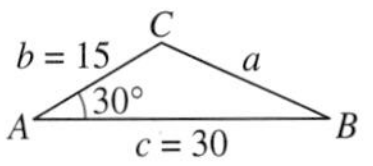

8. 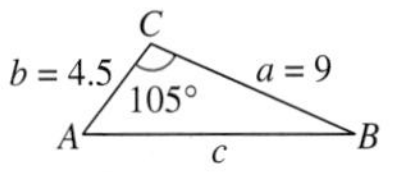

9. $a = 11, \quad b = 15, \quad c = 21$
10. $a = 55, \quad b = 25, \quad c = 72$
11. $a = 75.4, \quad b = 52, \quad c = 52$
12. $a = 1.42, \quad b = 0.75, \quad c = 1.25$
13. $A = 120°, \quad b = 6, \quad c = 7$
14. $A = 48°, \quad b = 3, \quad c = 14$
15. $B = 10° 35', \quad a = 40, \quad c = 30$
16. $B = 75° 20', \quad a = 6.2, \quad c = 9.5$
17. $B = 125° 40', \quad a = 37, \quad c = 37$
18. $C = 15° 15', \quad a = 7.45, \quad b = 2.15$
19. $C = 43°, \quad a = \frac{4}{9}, \quad b = \frac{7}{9}$
20. $C = 101°, \quad a = \frac{3}{8}, \quad b = \frac{3}{4}$

In Exercises 21–26, complete the table by solving the parallelogram shown in the figure. (The lengths of the diagonals are given by c and d.)

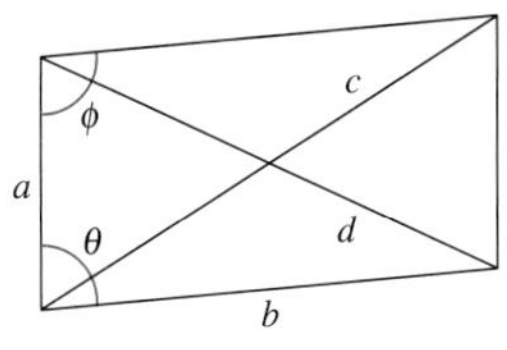

	a	b	c	d	θ	ϕ
21.	5	8	12.07	5.69	45°	135°
22.	25	35	52.20	31.22	60°	120°
23.	10	14	20	13.86	68.2°	111.8°
24.	40	60	63.23	80	104.5°	75.5°
25.	15	16.96	25	20	77.2°	102.8°
26.	35.18	25	50	35	68.7°	111.3°

In Exercises 27–32, determine whether the Law of Sines or the Law of Cosines is needed to solve the triangle. Then solve the triangle. 27–32. See margin.

27. $a = 8, \quad c = 5, \quad B = 40°$
28. $a = 10, \quad b = 12, \quad C = 70°$
29. $A = 24°, \quad a = 4, \quad b = 18$
30. $a = 11, \quad b = 13, \quad c = 7$
31. $A = 42°, \quad B = 35°, \quad c = 1.2$
32. $a = 160, \quad B = 12°, \quad C = 7°$

In Exercises 33–40, use Heron's Area Formula to find the area of the triangle.

33. $a = 8, \quad b = 12, \quad c = 17$ 43.52
34. $a = 33, \quad b = 36, \quad c = 25$ 399.04
35. $a = 2.5, \quad b = 10.2, \quad c = 9$ 10.4
36. $a = 75.4, \quad b = 52, \quad c = 52$ 1350.2
37. $a = 12.32, \quad b = 8.46, \quad c = 15.05$ 52.11
38. $a = 3.05, \quad b = 0.75, \quad c = 2.45$ 0.61
39. $a = 1, \quad b = \frac{1}{2}, \quad c = \frac{3}{4}$ 0.18
40. $a = \frac{3}{5}, \quad b = \frac{5}{8}, \quad c = \frac{3}{8}$ 0.11

27. Law of Cosines; $A \approx 102.44°, \ C \approx 37.56°, \ b \approx 5.26$
28. Law of Cosines; $A \approx 47.56°, \ B \approx 62.44°, \ c \approx 12.72$
29. Law of Sines; No solution
30. Law of Cosines; $A \approx 57.79°, \ B \approx 89.63°, \ C \approx 32.58°$
31. Law of Sines; $C = 103°, \ a \approx 0.82, \ b \approx 0.71$
32. Law of Sines; $A = 161°, \ b \approx 102.18, \ c \approx 59.89$

4 PRACTICE AND APPLY

Assignment Guide

Transparencies Available
Available at the Instructor's companion site.

Average:
Day 1: pp. 441–444
Exs. 1–4, 6, 9, 13, 15, 21–27 odd, 33, 41, 45, 47, 51–55 odd, 58, 61–65 odd, 74

Advanced:
Day 1: pp. 441–444
Exs. 1–4, 10, 14, 16, 22–30 even, 34–38 even, 42–52 even, 55–57, 60, 67, 69, 74, 76

Block:
pp. 441–444
Exs. 1–4, 6, 9, 13, 15, 21–27 odd, 33, 41, 45, 47, 51–55 odd, 58, 61–65 odd, 74 (with 6.1)

5. $A \approx 38.62°, B \approx 48.51°, C \approx 92.87°$
6. $A \approx 60°, B \approx 21.79°, C \approx 98.21°$
7. $B \approx 23.79°, C \approx 126.21°, a \approx 18.59$
8. $A \approx 51.87°, B \approx 23.13°, c \approx 11.06$
9. $A \approx 30.11°, B \approx 43.16°, C \approx 106.73°$
10. $A \approx 39.35°, B \approx 16.75°, C \approx 123.90°$
11. $A \approx 92.94°, B \approx 43.53°, C \approx 43.53°$
12. $A \approx 86.68°, B \approx 31.82°, C \approx 61.50°$
13. $B \approx 27.46°, C \approx 32.54°, a \approx 11.27$
14. $B \approx 10.53°, C \approx 121.47°, a \approx 12.20$
15. $A \approx 141°45', C \approx 27°40', b \approx 11.87$
16. $A \approx 37°6', C \approx 67°34', b \approx 9.94$
17. $A = 27°10', C = 27°10', b \approx 65.84$
18. $A \approx 158°17', B \approx 6°28', c \approx 5.41$
19. $A \approx 33.80°, B \approx 103.20°, c \approx 0.54$
20. $A \approx 24.15°, B \approx 54.85°, c \approx 0.90$

41.

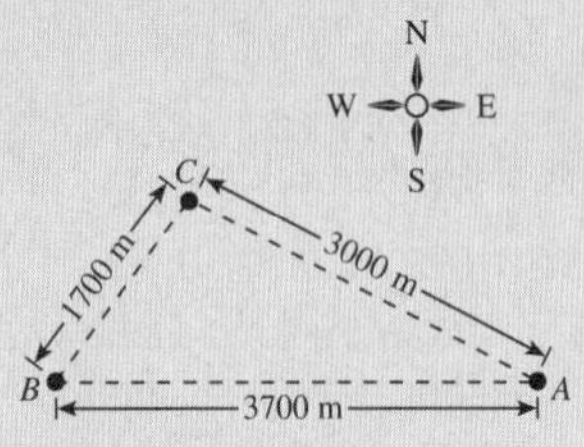

N 37.1° E, S 63.1° E

42.

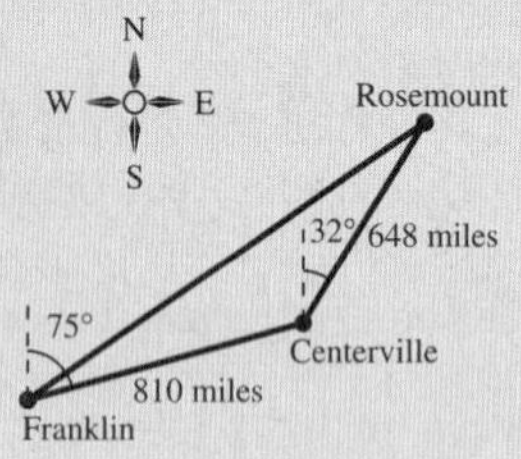

1357.8 mi, 56°

41. **NAVIGATION** A boat race runs along a triangular course marked by buoys A, B, and C. The race starts with the boats headed west for 3700 meters. The other two sides of the course lie to the north of the first side, and their lengths are 1700 meters and 3000 meters. Draw a figure that gives a visual representation of the situation, and find the bearings for the last two legs of the race. See margin.

42. **NAVIGATION** A plane flies 810 miles from Franklin to Centerville with a bearing of 75°. Then it flies 648 miles from Centerville to Rosemount with a bearing of 32°. Draw a figure that visually represents the situation, and find the straight-line distance and bearing from Franklin to Rosemount. See margin.

43. **SURVEYING** To approximate the length of a marsh, a surveyor walks 250 meters from point A to point B, then turns 75° and walks 220 meters to point C (see figure). Approximate the length AC of the marsh. 373.3 m

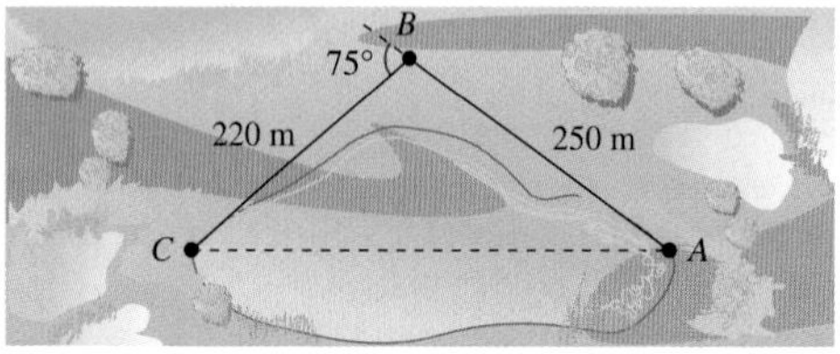

44. **SURVEYING** A triangular parcel of land has 115 meters of frontage, and the other boundaries have lengths of 76 meters and 92 meters. What angles does the frontage make with the two other boundaries? 41.2°, 52.9°

45. **SURVEYING** A triangular parcel of ground has sides of lengths 725 feet, 650 feet, and 575 feet. Find the measure of the largest angle. 72.3°

46. **STREETLIGHT DESIGN** Determine the angle θ in the design of the streetlight shown in the figure. 127.2°

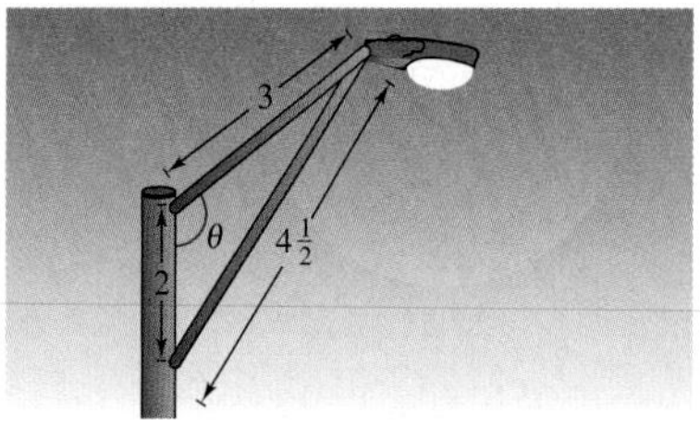

47. **DISTANCE** Two ships leave a port at 9 A.M. One travels at a bearing of N 53° W at 12 miles per hour, and the other travels at a bearing of S 67° W at 16 miles per hour. Approximate how far apart they are at noon that day. 43.3 mi

48. **LENGTH** A 100-foot vertical tower is to be erected on the side of a hill that makes a 6° angle with the horizontal (see figure). Find the length of each of the two guy wires that will be anchored 75 feet uphill and downhill from the base of the tower. 131.1 ft, 118.6 ft

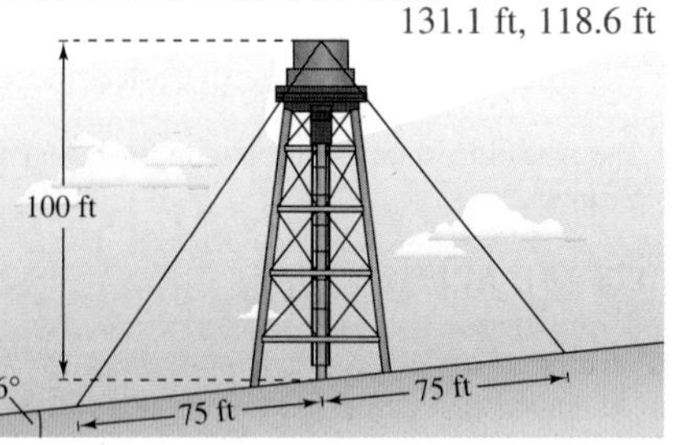

49. **NAVIGATION** On a map, Orlando is 178 millimeters due south of Niagara Falls, Denver is 273 millimeters from Orlando, and Denver is 235 millimeters from Niagara Falls (see figure).

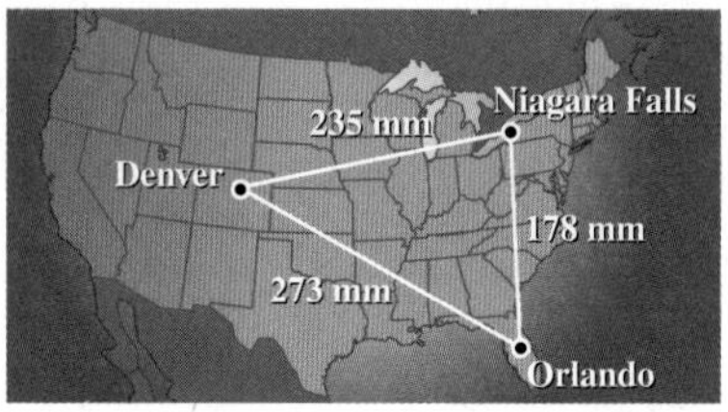

(a) Find the bearing of Denver from Orlando. N 58.4° W

(b) Find the bearing of Denver from Niagara Falls. S 81.5° W

50. **NAVIGATION** On a map, Minneapolis is 165 millimeters due west of Albany, Phoenix is 216 millimeters from Minneapolis, and Phoenix is 368 millimeters from Albany (see figure). (a) N 59.7° E (b) N 72.8° E

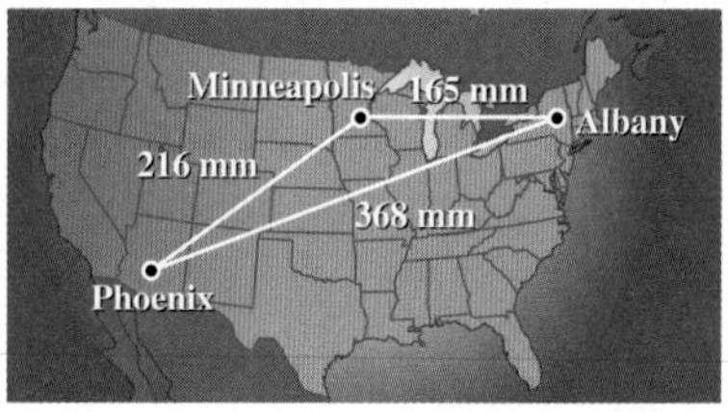

(a) Find the bearing of Minneapolis from Phoenix.

(b) Find the bearing of Albany from Phoenix.

51. **BASEBALL** On a baseball diamond with 90-foot sides, the pitcher's mound is 60.5 feet from home plate. How far is it from the pitcher's mound to third base? 63.7 ft

52. BASEBALL The baseball player in center field is playing approximately 330 feet from the television camera that is behind home plate. A batter hits a fly ball that goes to the wall 420 feet from the camera (see figure). The camera turns 8° to follow the play. Approximately how far does the center fielder have to run to make the catch? 103.9 ft

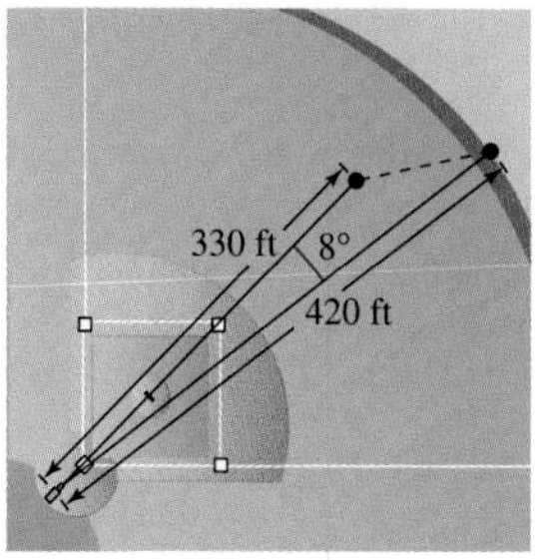

53. AIRCRAFT TRACKING To determine the distance between two aircraft, a tracking station continuously determines the distance to each aircraft and the angle A between them (see figure). Determine the distance a between the planes when $A = 42°$, $b = 35$ miles, and $c = 20$ miles. 24.2 mi

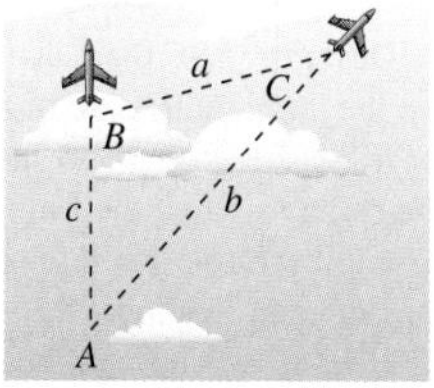

54. AIRCRAFT TRACKING Use the figure for Exercise 53 to determine the distance a between the planes when $A = 11°$, $b = 20$ miles, and $c = 20$ miles. 3.8 mi

55. TRUSSES Q is the midpoint of the line segment $\overline{PR}$ in the truss rafter shown in the figure. What are the lengths of the line segments $\overline{PQ}$, $\overline{QS}$, and $\overline{RS}$?

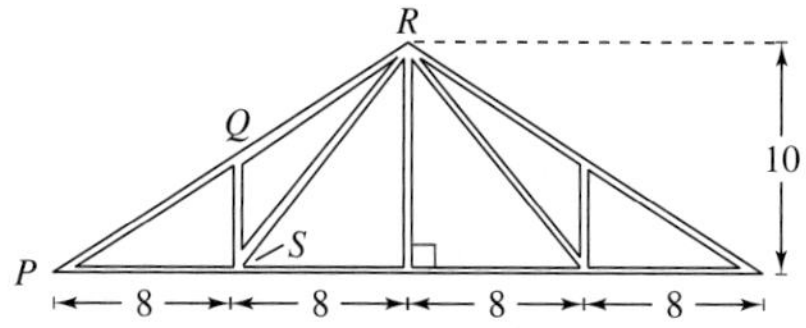

$\overline{PQ} \approx 9.4$, $\overline{QS} = 5$, $\overline{RS} \approx 12.8$

See margin.
56. ENGINE DESIGN An engine has a seven-inch connecting rod fastened to a crank (see figure).

(a) Use the Law of Cosines to write an equation giving the relationship between x and θ.

(b) Write x as a function of θ. (Select the sign that yields positive values of x.)

(c) Use a graphing utility to graph the function in part (b).

(d) Use the graph in part (c) to determine the maximum distance the piston moves in one cycle.

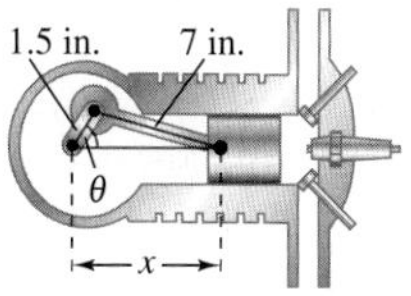

FIGURE FOR 56

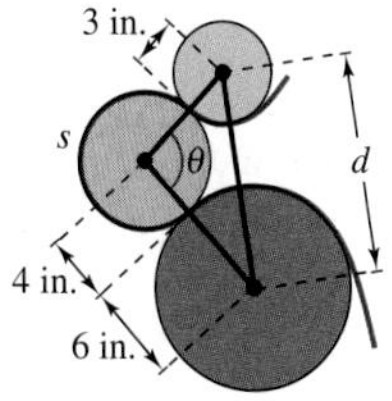

FIGURE FOR 57

57. PAPER MANUFACTURING In a process with continuous paper, the paper passes across three rollers of radii 3 inches, 4 inches, and 6 inches (see figure). The centers of the three-inch and six-inch rollers are d inches apart, and the length of the arc in contact with the paper on the four-inch roller is s inches. Complete the table. See margin.

d (inches)	9	10	12	13	14	15	16
θ (degrees)							
s (inches)							

58. AWNING DESIGN A retractable awning above a patio door lowers at an angle of 50° from the exterior wall at a height of 10 feet above the ground (see figure). No direct sunlight is to enter the door when the angle of elevation of the sun is greater than 70°. What is the length x of the awning? 3.95 ft

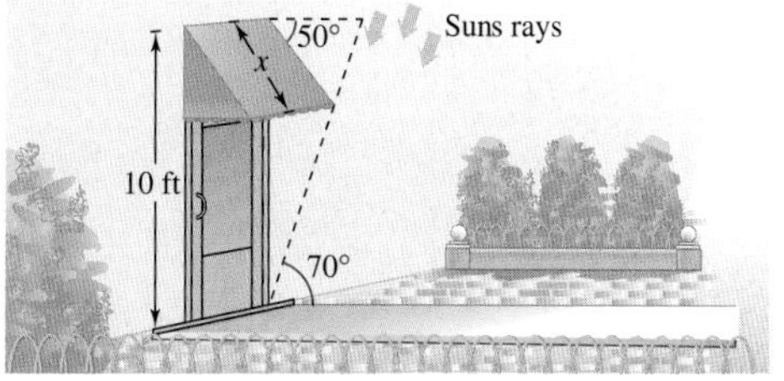

59. GEOMETRY The lengths of the sides of a triangular parcel of land are approximately 200 feet, 500 feet, and 600 feet. Approximate the area of the parcel. 46,837.5 ft^2

56. (a) $x^2 - 3x\cos\theta - 46.75 = 0$

(b) $x = \frac{1}{2}\left(3\cos\theta + \sqrt{9\cos^2\theta + 187}\right)$

(c)

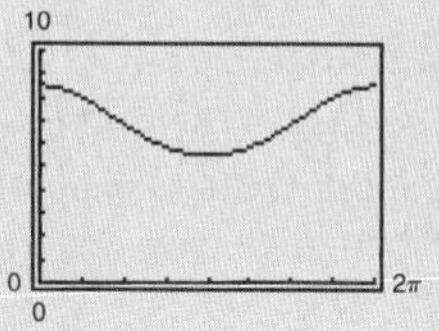

(d) 8.5 in.

57.

d (inches)	9	10	12	13	14	15	16
θ (degrees)	60.9°	69.5°	88.0°	98.2°	109.6°	122.9°	139.8°
s (inches)	20.88	20.28	18.99	18.28	17.48	16.55	15.37

5 ASSESS AND RETEACH

Daily Homework Quiz

Transparency Available
Available at the Instructor's companion site.

63. False. For s to be the average of the lengths of the three sides of the triangle, s would be equal to $(a + b + c)/3$.
64. False. To solve an SSA triangle, the Law of Sines is needed.
65. No. The three side lengths do not form a triangle.
66. No. The Law of Sines is used to solve ASA triangles.
68. (a) 570.60 (b) 5909.20 (c) 177.09
70. $c^2 = a^2 + b^2$; The Pythagorean Theorem is a special case of the Law of Cosines.
71. Either; Because A is obtuse, there is only one solution for B or C.
72. To solve the triangle using the Law of Cosines, substitute values into $a^2 = b^2 + c^2 - 2bc \cos A$. After simplifying, you get a quadratic equation to solve for c. Using the Law of Sines will give the same result as using the Law of Cosines. Sample answer: An advantage of using the Law of Cosines is that it is easier to choose the correct value to avoid the ambiguous case, but its disadvantage is that it is more complicated with computations. The opposite is true for the Law of Sines.
73. The Law of Cosines can be used to solve the single-solution case of SSA. There is no method that can solve the no-solution case of SSA.
74. (a) Law of Sines
(b) Law of Sines
(c) Law of Cosines
(d) Law of Sines
(e) Law of Sines
(f) Law of Cosines

60. GEOMETRY A parking lot has the shape of a parallelogram (see figure). The lengths of two adjacent sides are 70 meters and 100 meters. The angle between the two sides is 70°. What is the area of the parking lot? 6577.8 m^2

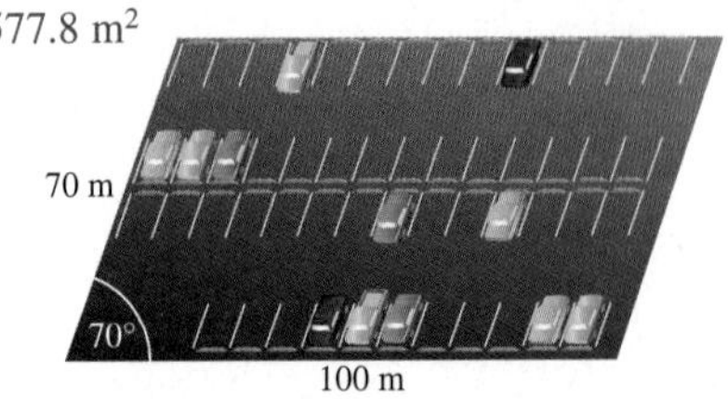

61. GEOMETRY You want to buy a triangular lot measuring 510 yards by 840 yards by 1120 yards. The price of the land is \$2000 per acre. How much does the land cost? (*Hint:* 1 acre = 4840 square yards) \$83,336.37

62. GEOMETRY You want to buy a triangular lot measuring 1350 feet by 1860 feet by 2490 feet. The price of the land is \$2200 per acre. How much does the land cost? (*Hint:* 1 acre = 43,560 square feet) \$62,340.71

EXPLORATION

63–66. See margin.

TRUE OR FALSE? In Exercises 63 and 64, determine whether the statement is true or false. Justify your answer.

63. In Heron's Area Formula, s is the average of the lengths of the three sides of the triangle.

64. In addition to SSS and SAS, the Law of Cosines can be used to solve triangles with SSA conditions.

65. WRITING A triangle has side lengths of 10 centimeters, 16 centimeters, and 5 centimeters. Can the Law of Cosines be used to solve the triangle? Explain.

66. WRITING Given a triangle with $b = 47$ meters, $A = 87°$, and $C = 110°$, can the Law of Cosines be used to solve the triangle? Explain.

67. CIRCUMSCRIBED AND INSCRIBED CIRCLES Let R and r be the radii of the circumscribed and inscribed circles of a triangle ABC, respectively (see figure), and let $s = \dfrac{a + b + c}{2}$.

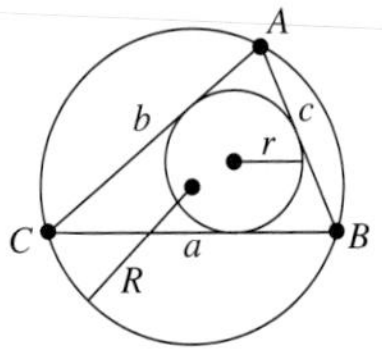

(a) Prove that $2R = \dfrac{a}{\sin A} = \dfrac{b}{\sin B} = \dfrac{c}{\sin C}$. Proof

(b) Prove that $r = \sqrt{\dfrac{(s - a)(s - b)(s - c)}{s}}$. Proof

CIRCUMSCRIBED AND INSCRIBED CIRCLES In Exercises 68 and 69, use the results of Exercise 67.

68. Given a triangle with $a = 25$, $b = 55$, and $c = 72$, find the areas of (a) the triangle, (b) the circumscribed circle, and (c) the inscribed circle. See margin.

69. Find the length of the largest circular running track that can be built on a triangular piece of property with sides of lengths 200 feet, 250 feet, and 325 feet. 405.2 ft

70. THINK ABOUT IT What familiar formula do you obtain when you use the third form of the Law of Cosines $c^2 = a^2 + b^2 - 2ab \cos C$, and you let $C = 90°$? What is the relationship between the Law of Cosines and this formula? See margin.

71. THINK ABOUT IT In Example 2, suppose $A = 115°$. After solving for a, which angle would you solve for next, B or C? Are there two possible solutions for that angle? If so, how can you determine which angle is the correct solution? See margin.

72. WRITING Describe how the Law of Cosines can be used to solve the ambiguous case of the oblique triangle ABC, where $a = 12$ feet, $b = 30$ feet, and $A = 20°$. Is the result the same as when the Law of Sines is used to solve the triangle? Describe the advantages and the disadvantages of each method. See margin.

73. WRITING In Exercise 72, the Law of Cosines was used to solve a triangle in the two-solution case of SSA. Can the Law of Cosines be used to solve the no-solution and single-solution cases of SSA? Explain. See margin.

74. CAPSTONE Determine whether the Law of Sines or the Law of Cosines is needed to solve the triangle.

(a) A, C, and a (b) a, c, and C
(c) b, c, and A (d) A, B, and c
(e) b, c, and C (f) a, b, and c
See margin.

75. PROOF Use the Law of Cosines to prove that

Proof $\dfrac{1}{2}bc(1 + \cos A) = \dfrac{a + b + c}{2} \cdot \dfrac{-a + b + c}{2}$.

76. PROOF Use the Law of Cosines to prove that

$\dfrac{1}{2}bc(1 - \cos A) = \dfrac{a - b + c}{2} \cdot \dfrac{a + b - c}{2}$.

Proof

6.3 VECTORS IN THE PLANE

What you should learn

- Represent vectors as directed line segments.
- Write the component forms of vectors.
- Perform basic vector operations and represent them graphically.
- Write vectors as linear combinations of unit vectors.
- Find the direction angles of vectors.
- Use vectors to model and solve real-life problems.

Why you should learn it

You can use vectors to model and solve real-life problems involving magnitude and direction. For instance, in Exercise 102 on page 457, you can use vectors to determine the true direction of a commercial jet.

Introduction

Quantities such as force and velocity involve both *magnitude* and *direction* and cannot be completely characterized by a single real number. To represent such a quantity, you can use a **directed line segment,** as shown in Figure 6.15. The directed line segment $\overrightarrow{PQ}$ has **initial point** P and **terminal point** Q. Its **magnitude** (or length) is denoted by $\|\overrightarrow{PQ}\|$ and can be found using the Distance Formula.

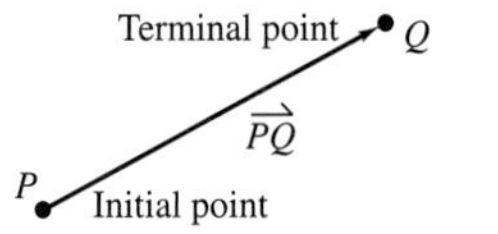

FIGURE 6.15

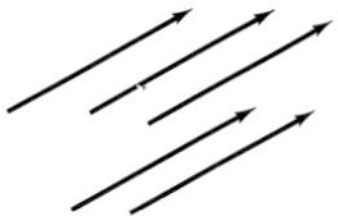
FIGURE 6.16

Two directed line segments that have the same magnitude and direction are equivalent. For example, the directed line segments in Figure 6.16 are all equivalent. The set of all directed line segments that are equivalent to the directed line segment $\overrightarrow{PQ}$ is a **vector v in the plane,** written $\mathbf{v} = \overrightarrow{PQ}$. Vectors are denoted by lowercase, boldface letters such as **u**, **v**, and **w**.

Example 1 Vector Representation by Directed Line Segments

Let **u** be represented by the directed line segment from $P(0, 0)$ to $Q(3, 2)$, and let **v** be represented by the directed line segment from $R(1, 2)$ to $S(4, 4)$, as shown in Figure 6.17. Show that **u** and **v** are equivalent.

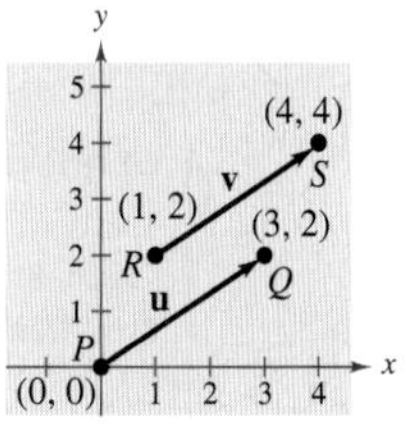

FIGURE 6.17

Solution

From the Distance Formula, it follows that $\overrightarrow{PQ}$ and $\overrightarrow{RS}$ have the *same magnitude*.

$$\|\overrightarrow{PQ}\| = \sqrt{(3-0)^2 + (2-0)^2} = \sqrt{13} \qquad \|\overrightarrow{RS}\| = \sqrt{(4-1)^2 + (4-2)^2} = \sqrt{13}$$

Moreover, both line segments have the *same direction* because they are both directed toward the upper right on lines having a slope of

$$\frac{4-2}{4-1} = \frac{2-0}{3-0} = \frac{2}{3}.$$

Because $\overrightarrow{PQ}$ and $\overrightarrow{RS}$ have the same magnitude and direction, **u** and **v** are equivalent.

CHECKPoint Now try Exercise 11.

1 PLAN AND PREPARE

Warm-up Exercises

Transparency Available
Available at the Instructor's companion site.

Notetaking Guide

Transparency Available
Promotes interactive learning and notetaking skills.
Available at the Instructor's companion site.

Animated Precalculus

An **Animated Precalculus** tutorial is available at the Student companion site for **Section 6.3.**

Pacing

Average: 2 days
Advanced: 2 days
Block: 1 block

2 FOCUS AND MOTIVATE

Essential Question

How do you represent and perform operations with vector quantities? **Tell students that they will learn how to answer this question by studying the definitions and properties of vectors and vector operations.**

Resource Planning Guide

Chapter Resources
- Complete Solutions Guide

Workbooks
- Notetaking Guide
- Student Solutions Guide

Interactive Technology
- Instructor Success Organizer
- Notetaking Guide IAE
- Instructional DVDs
- Animated Precalculus
- PowerLecture with ExamView

3 TEACH

Extra Example 1

Let **u** be represented by the directed line segment from $P = (0, 0)$ to $Q = (3, 1)$, and let **v** be represented by the directed line segment from $R = (2, 2)$ to $S = (5, 3)$. Show that **u** and **v** are equivalent.

$\overrightarrow{PQ}$ and $\overrightarrow{RS}$ have the *same* magnitude.

$$\|\overrightarrow{PQ}\| = \sqrt{(3-0)^2 + (1-0)^2} = \sqrt{10}$$

$$\|\overrightarrow{RS}\| = \sqrt{(5-2)^2 + (3-2)^2} = \sqrt{10}$$

Also, both line segments have the *same direction* because they are both directed toward the upper right on lines having a slope of $\frac{1}{3}$. So, $\overrightarrow{PQ}$ and $\overrightarrow{RS}$ have the same length and direction, and it follows that u and v are equivalent.

Extra Example 2

Find the component form and magnitude of the vector **v** that has the initial point $(-2, 3)$ and terminal point $(-7, 9)$.

Component form: $\langle -5, 6\rangle$; Magnitude: $\sqrt{61} \approx 7.81$

Avoiding Common Errors

Emphasize to students that the component form represents a family of vectors. The vector $\mathbf{v} = \langle 1, 3\rangle$ can be considered a vector with initial point (0, 0) and terminal point (1, 3) as well as a vector with initial point (0, −1) and terminal point (1, 2) and other equivalent vectors.

Component Form of a Vector

The directed line segment whose initial point is the origin is often the most convenient representative of a set of equivalent directed line segments. This representative of the vector **v** is in **standard position.**

A vector whose initial point is the origin (0, 0) can be uniquely represented by the coordinates of its terminal point (v_1, v_2). This is the **component form of a vector v,** written as $\mathbf{v} = \langle v_1, v_2\rangle$. The coordinates v_1 and v_2 are the *components* of **v**. If both the initial point and the terminal point lie at the origin, **v** is the **zero vector** and is denoted by $\mathbf{0} = \langle 0, 0\rangle$.

TECHNOLOGY

You can graph vectors with a graphing utility by graphing directed line segments. Consult the user's guide for your graphing utility for specific instructions.

Component Form of a Vector

The component form of the vector with initial point $P(p_1, p_2)$ and terminal point $Q(q_1, q_2)$ is given by

$$\overrightarrow{PQ} = \langle q_1 - p_1, q_2 - p_2\rangle = \langle v_1, v_2\rangle = \mathbf{v}.$$

The **magnitude** (or length) of **v** is given by

$$\|\mathbf{v}\| = \sqrt{(q_1 - p_1)^2 + (q_2 - p_2)^2} = \sqrt{v_1^2 + v_2^2}.$$

If $\|\mathbf{v}\| = 1$, **v** is a **unit vector.** Moreover, $\|\mathbf{v}\| = 0$ if and only if **v** is the zero vector **0**.

Two vectors $\mathbf{u} = \langle u_1, u_2\rangle$ and $\mathbf{v} = \langle v_1, v_2\rangle$ are *equal* if and only if $u_1 = v_1$ and $u_2 = v_2$. For instance, in Example 1, the vector **u** from $P(0, 0)$ to $Q(3, 2)$ is $\mathbf{u} = \overrightarrow{PQ} = \langle 3 - 0, 2 - 0\rangle = \langle 3, 2\rangle$, and the vector **v** from $R(1, 2)$ to $S(4, 4)$ is $\mathbf{v} = \overrightarrow{RS} = \langle 4 - 1, 4 - 2\rangle = \langle 3, 2\rangle$.

Example 2 Finding the Component Form of a Vector

Find the component form and magnitude of the vector **v** that has initial point $(4, -7)$ and terminal point $(-1, 5)$.

Algebraic Solution

Let

$$P(4, -7) = (p_1, p_2)$$

and

$$Q(-1, 5) = (q_1, q_2).$$

Then, the components of $\mathbf{v} = \langle v_1, v_2\rangle$ are

$$v_1 = q_1 - p_1 = -1 - 4 = -5$$

$$v_2 = q_2 - p_2 = 5 - (-7) = 12.$$

So, $\mathbf{v} = \langle -5, 12\rangle$ and the magnitude of **v** is

$$\|\mathbf{v}\| = \sqrt{(-5)^2 + 12^2} = \sqrt{169} = 13.$$

CHECKPoint Now try Exercise 19.

Graphical Solution

Use centimeter graph paper to plot the points $P(4, -7)$ and $Q(-1, 5)$. Carefully sketch the vector **v**. Use the sketch to find the components of $\mathbf{v} = \langle v_1, v_2\rangle$. Then use a centimeter ruler to find the magnitude of **v**.

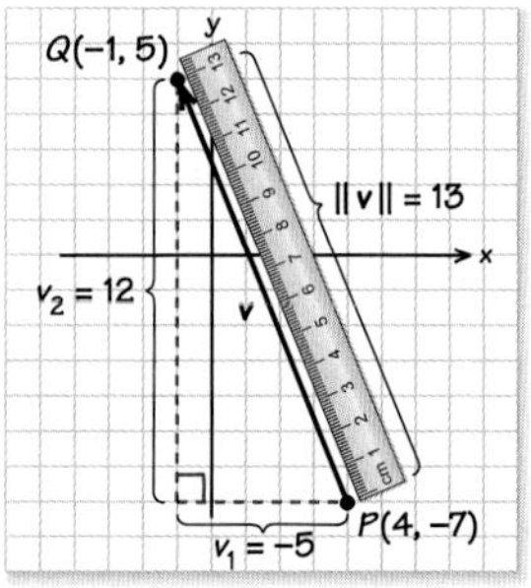

FIGURE 6.18

Figure 6.18 shows that the components of **v** are $v_1 = -5$ and $v_2 = 12$, so $\mathbf{v} = \langle -5, 12\rangle$. Figure 6.18 also shows that the magnitude of **v** is $\|\mathbf{v}\| = 13$.

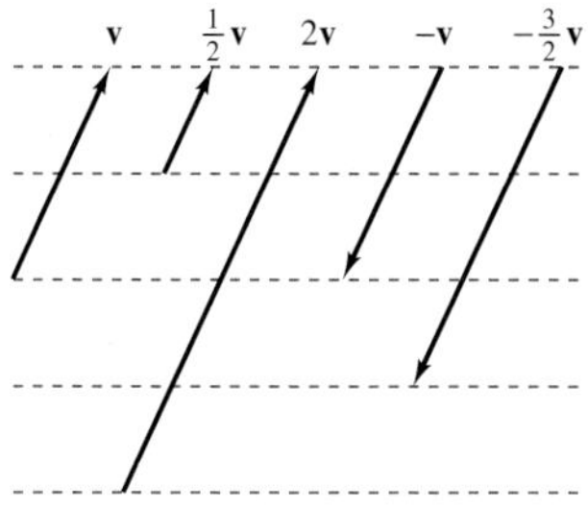

FIGURE 6.19

Vector Operations

The two basic vector operations are **scalar multiplication** and **vector addition.** In operations with vectors, numbers are usually referred to as **scalars.** In this text, scalars will always be real numbers. Geometrically, the product of a vector **v** and a scalar k is the vector that is $|k|$ times as long as **v**. If k is positive, $k\mathbf{v}$ has the same direction as **v**, and if k is negative, $k\mathbf{v}$ has the direction opposite that of **v**, as shown in Figure 6.19.

To add two vectors **u** and **v** geometrically, first position them (without changing their lengths or directions) so that the initial point of the second vector **v** coincides with the terminal point of the first vector **u**. The sum $\mathbf{u} + \mathbf{v}$ is the vector formed by joining the initial point of the first vector **u** with the terminal point of the second vector **v**, as shown in Figure 6.20. This technique is called the **parallelogram law** for vector addition because the vector $\mathbf{u} + \mathbf{v}$, often called the **resultant** of vector addition, is the diagonal of a parallelogram having adjacent sides **u** and **v**.

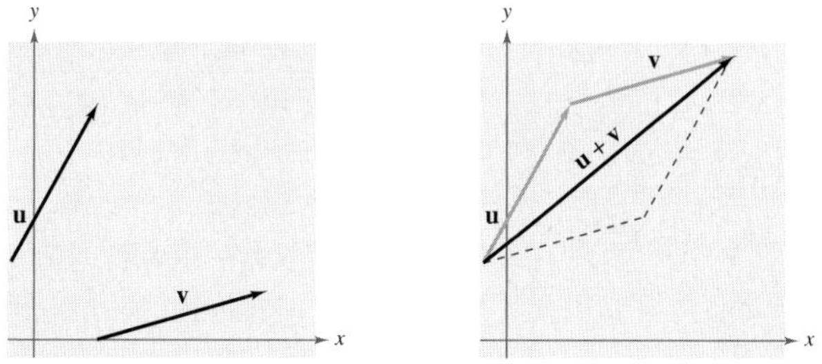

FIGURE 6.20

Definitions of Vector Addition and Scalar Multiplication

Let $\mathbf{u} = \langle u_1, u_2 \rangle$ and $\mathbf{v} = \langle v_1, v_2 \rangle$ be vectors and let k be a scalar (a real number). Then the *sum* of **u** and **v** is the vector

$$\mathbf{u} + \mathbf{v} = \langle u_1 + v_1, u_2 + v_2 \rangle \qquad \text{Sum}$$

and the *scalar multiple* of k times **u** is the vector

$$k\mathbf{u} = k\langle u_1, u_2 \rangle = \langle ku_1, ku_2 \rangle. \qquad \text{Scalar multiple}$$

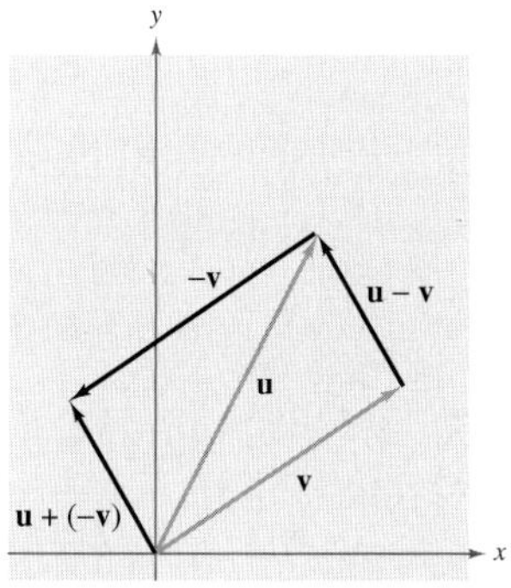

$\mathbf{u} - \mathbf{v} = \mathbf{u} + (-\mathbf{v})$
FIGURE 6.21

The **negative** of $\mathbf{v} = \langle v_1, v_2 \rangle$ is

$$-\mathbf{v} = (-1)\mathbf{v}$$

$$= \langle -v_1, -v_2 \rangle \qquad \text{Negative}$$

and the **difference** of **u** and **v** is

$$\mathbf{u} - \mathbf{v} = \mathbf{u} + (-\mathbf{v}) \qquad \text{Add } (-\mathbf{v}). \text{ See Figure 6.21.}$$

$$= \langle u_1 - v_1, u_2 - v_2 \rangle. \qquad \text{Difference}$$

To represent $\mathbf{u} - \mathbf{v}$ geometrically, you can use directed line segments with the *same* initial point. The difference $\mathbf{u} - \mathbf{v}$ is the vector from the terminal point of **v** to the terminal point of **u**, which is equal to $\mathbf{u} + (-\mathbf{v})$, as shown in Figure 6.21.

Differentiated Instruction

Inclusion and Kinesthetic Learners To help students grasp the concept of adding vectors, designate north, south, east, and west in the classroom. Instruct students to walk a number of steps in one direction and then a number of steps in another direction, such as 12 steps east, 5 steps south. Then have them find the shortest distance between the beginning point and ending points. Discuss how both direction and magnitude are important in describing a vector.

Extra Example 3

Let **u** = ⟨1, 2⟩ and **v** = ⟨3, 1⟩, and find each of the following vectors.

a. **u** + **v**

⟨4, 3⟩

b. **u** − **v**

⟨−2, 1⟩

c. 2**u** − 3**v**

⟨−7, 1⟩

The component definitions of vector addition and scalar multiplication are illustrated in Example 3. In this example, notice that each of the vector operations can be interpreted geometrically.

Example 3 Vector Operations

Let $\mathbf{v} = \langle -2, 5\rangle$ and $\mathbf{w} = \langle 3, 4\rangle$, and find each of the following vectors.

a. $2\mathbf{v}$ **b.** $\mathbf{w} - \mathbf{v}$ **c.** $\mathbf{v} + 2\mathbf{w}$

Solution

a. Because $\mathbf{v} = \langle -2, 5\rangle$, you have

$$\begin{aligned} 2\mathbf{v} &= 2\langle -2, 5\rangle \\ &= \langle 2(-2), 2(5)\rangle \\ &= \langle -4, 10\rangle. \end{aligned}$$

A sketch of $2\mathbf{v}$ is shown in Figure 6.22.

b. The difference of $\mathbf{w}$ and $\mathbf{v}$ is

$$\begin{aligned} \mathbf{w} - \mathbf{v} &= \langle 3, 4\rangle - \langle -2, 5\rangle \\ &= \langle 3 - (-2), 4 - 5\rangle \\ &= \langle 5, -1\rangle. \end{aligned}$$

A sketch of $\mathbf{w} - \mathbf{v}$ is shown in Figure 6.23. Note that the figure shows the vector difference $\mathbf{w} - \mathbf{v}$ as the sum $\mathbf{w} + (-\mathbf{v})$.

c. The sum of $\mathbf{v}$ and $2\mathbf{w}$ is

$$\begin{aligned} \mathbf{v} + 2\mathbf{w} &= \langle -2, 5\rangle + 2\langle 3, 4\rangle \\ &= \langle -2, 5\rangle + \langle 2(3), 2(4)\rangle \\ &= \langle -2, 5\rangle + \langle 6, 8\rangle \\ &= \langle -2 + 6, 5 + 8\rangle \\ &= \langle 4, 13\rangle. \end{aligned}$$

A sketch of $\mathbf{v} + 2\mathbf{w}$ is shown in Figure 6.24.

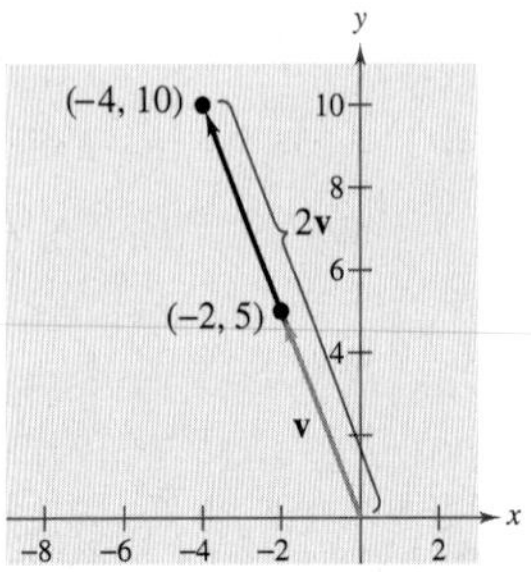

FIGURE 6.22

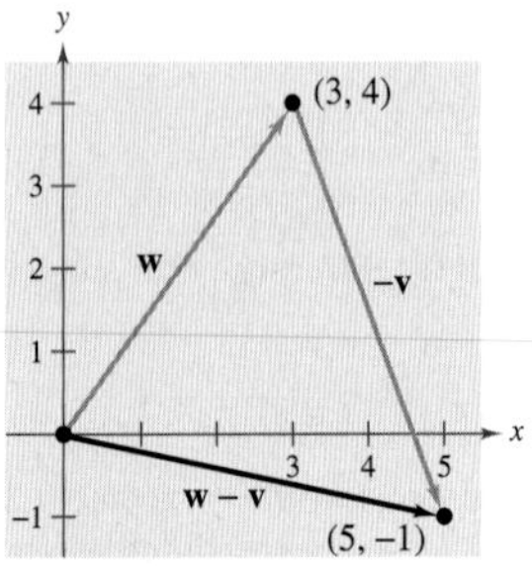

FIGURE 6.23

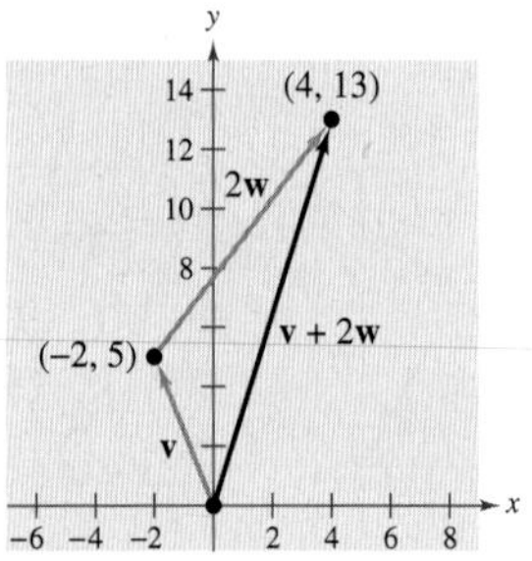

FIGURE 6.24

CHECKPoint Now try Exercise 31.

Vector addition and scalar multiplication share many of the properties of ordinary arithmetic.

Properties of Vector Addition and Scalar Multiplication

Let **u**, **v**, and **w** be vectors and let c and d be scalars. Then the following properties are true.

1. $\mathbf{u} + \mathbf{v} = \mathbf{v} + \mathbf{u}$ **2.** $(\mathbf{u} + \mathbf{v}) + \mathbf{w} = \mathbf{u} + (\mathbf{v} + \mathbf{w})$

3. $\mathbf{u} + \mathbf{0} = \mathbf{u}$ **4.** $\mathbf{u} + (-\mathbf{u}) = \mathbf{0}$

5. $c(d\mathbf{u}) = (cd)\mathbf{u}$ **6.** $(c + d)\mathbf{u} = c\mathbf{u} + d\mathbf{u}$

7. $c(\mathbf{u} + \mathbf{v}) = c\mathbf{u} + c\mathbf{v}$ **8.** $1(\mathbf{u}) = \mathbf{u},\ \ 0(\mathbf{u}) = \mathbf{0}$

9. $\|c\mathbf{v}\| = |c|\,\|\mathbf{v}\|$

Property 9 can be stated as follows: the magnitude of the vector $c\mathbf{v}$ is the absolute value of c times the magnitude of **v**.

Unit Vectors

In many applications of vectors, it is useful to find a unit vector that has the same direction as a given nonzero vector **v**. To do this, you can divide **v** by its magnitude to obtain

$$\mathbf{u} = \text{unit vector} = \frac{\mathbf{v}}{\|\mathbf{v}\|} = \left(\frac{1}{\|\mathbf{v}\|}\right)\mathbf{v}. \qquad \text{Unit vector in direction of } \mathbf{v}$$

Note that **u** is a scalar multiple of **v**. The vector **u** has a magnitude of 1 and the same direction as **v**. The vector **u** is called a **unit vector in the direction of v**.

Example 4 Finding a Unit Vector

Find a unit vector in the direction of $\mathbf{v} = \langle -2, 5\rangle$ and verify that the result has a magnitude of 1.

Solution

The unit vector in the direction of **v** is

$$\frac{\mathbf{v}}{\|\mathbf{v}\|} = \frac{\langle -2, 5\rangle}{\sqrt{(-2)^2 + (5)^2}}$$

$$= \frac{1}{\sqrt{29}}\langle -2, 5\rangle$$

$$= \left\langle \frac{-2}{\sqrt{29}}, \frac{5}{\sqrt{29}} \right\rangle.$$

This vector has a magnitude of 1 because

$$\sqrt{\left(\frac{-2}{\sqrt{29}}\right)^2 + \left(\frac{5}{\sqrt{29}}\right)^2} = \sqrt{\frac{4}{29} + \frac{25}{29}} = \sqrt{\frac{29}{29}} = 1.$$

CHECKPoint Now try Exercise 41.

HISTORICAL NOTE

The Granger Collection

William Rowan Hamilton (1805–1865), an Irish mathematician, did some of the earliest work with vectors. Hamilton spent many years developing a system of vector-like quantities called quaternions. Although Hamilton was convinced of the benefits of quaternions, the operations he defined did not produce good models for physical phenomena. It was not until the latter half of the nineteenth century that the Scottish physicist James Maxwell (1831–1879) restructured Hamilton's quaternions in a form useful for representing physical quantities such as force, velocity, and acceleration.

Extra Example 4

Find a unit vector in the direction of $\mathbf{v} = \langle 7, -3\rangle$ and verify that the result has magnitude 1.

$\left\langle \frac{7}{\sqrt{58}}, \frac{-3}{\sqrt{58}} \right\rangle;$

$\sqrt{\left(\frac{7}{\sqrt{58}}\right)^2 + \left(\frac{-3}{\sqrt{58}}\right)^2} =$

$\sqrt{\frac{49}{58} + \frac{9}{58}} = \sqrt{\frac{58}{58}} = 1$

Extra Example 5

Let **u** be the vector with initial point $(-2, 6)$ and terminal point $(-8, 3)$. Write **u** as a linear combination of the standard unit vectors **i** and **j**.

$\mathbf{u} = -6\mathbf{i} - 3\mathbf{j}$

Extra Example 6

Let $\mathbf{u} = \mathbf{i} + \mathbf{j}$ and $\mathbf{v} = 5\mathbf{i} - 3\mathbf{j}$. Find $2\mathbf{u} - 3\mathbf{v}$.

$-13\mathbf{i} + 11\mathbf{j}$

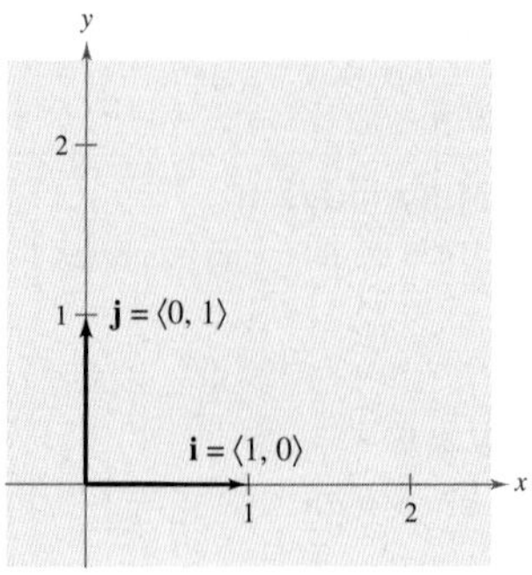

FIGURE 6.25

The unit vectors $\langle 1, 0\rangle$ and $\langle 0, 1\rangle$ are called the **standard unit vectors** and are denoted by

$$\mathbf{i} = \langle 1, 0\rangle \quad \text{and} \quad \mathbf{j} = \langle 0, 1\rangle$$

as shown in Figure 6.25. (Note that the lowercase letter **i** is written in boldface to distinguish it from the imaginary number $i = \sqrt{-1}$.) These vectors can be used to represent any vector $\mathbf{v} = \langle v_1, v_2\rangle$, as follows.

$$\begin{aligned}\mathbf{v} &= \langle v_1, v_2\rangle \\ &= v_1\langle 1, 0\rangle + v_2\langle 0, 1\rangle \\ &= v_1\mathbf{i} + v_2\mathbf{j}\end{aligned}$$

The scalars v_1 and v_2 are called the **horizontal** and **vertical components of v**, respectively. The vector sum

$$v_1\mathbf{i} + v_2\mathbf{j}$$

is called a **linear combination** of the vectors **i** and **j**. Any vector in the plane can be written as a linear combination of the standard unit vectors **i** and **j**.

Example 5 Writing a Linear Combination of Unit Vectors

Let **u** be the vector with initial point $(2, -5)$ and terminal point $(-1, 3)$. Write **u** as a linear combination of the standard unit vectors **i** and **j**.

Solution

Begin by writing the component form of the vector **u**.

$$\begin{aligned}\mathbf{u} &= \langle -1 - 2, 3 - (-5)\rangle \\ &= \langle -3, 8\rangle \\ &= -3\mathbf{i} + 8\mathbf{j}\end{aligned}$$

This result is shown graphically in Figure 6.26.

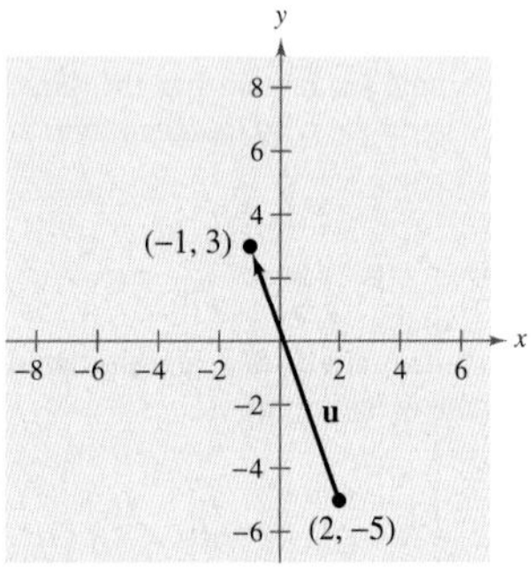

FIGURE 6.26

CHECKPoint Now try Exercise 53.

Example 6 Vector Operations

Let $\mathbf{u} = -3\mathbf{i} + 8\mathbf{j}$ and let $\mathbf{v} = 2\mathbf{i} - \mathbf{j}$. Find $2\mathbf{u} - 3\mathbf{v}$.

Solution

You could solve this problem by converting **u** and **v** to component form. This, however, is not necessary. It is just as easy to perform the operations in unit vector form.

$$\begin{aligned}2\mathbf{u} - 3\mathbf{v} &= 2(-3\mathbf{i} + 8\mathbf{j}) - 3(2\mathbf{i} - \mathbf{j}) \\ &= -6\mathbf{i} + 16\mathbf{j} - 6\mathbf{i} + 3\mathbf{j} \\ &= -12\mathbf{i} + 19\mathbf{j}\end{aligned}$$

CHECKPoint Now try Exercise 59.

Direction Angles

If **u** is a *unit vector* such that θ is the angle (measured counterclockwise) from the positive x-axis to **u**, the terminal point of **u** lies on the unit circle and you have

$$\mathbf{u} = \langle x, y\rangle = \langle\cos\theta, \sin\theta\rangle = (\cos\theta)\mathbf{i} + (\sin\theta)\mathbf{j}$$

as shown in Figure 6.27. The angle θ is the **direction angle** of the vector **u**.

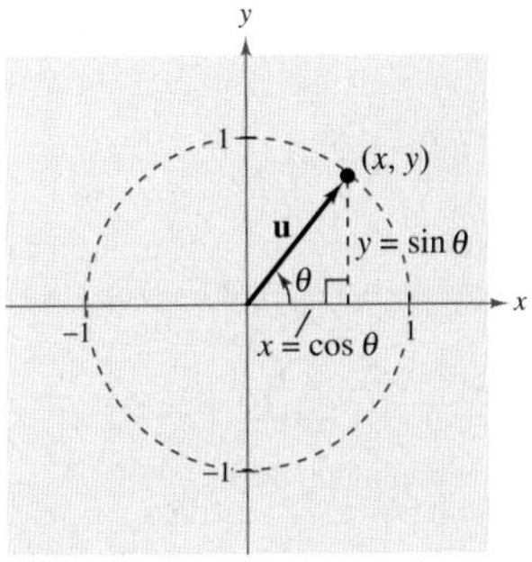

$\|\mathbf{u}\| = 1$

FIGURE 6.27

Suppose that **u** is a unit vector with direction angle θ. If $\mathbf{v} = a\mathbf{i} + b\mathbf{j}$ is any vector that makes an angle θ with the positive x-axis, it has the same direction as **u** and you can write

$$\mathbf{v} = \|\mathbf{v}\|\langle\cos\theta, \sin\theta\rangle$$
$$= \|\mathbf{v}\|(\cos\theta)\mathbf{i} + \|\mathbf{v}\|(\sin\theta)\mathbf{j}.$$

Because $\mathbf{v} = a\mathbf{i} + b\mathbf{j} = \|\mathbf{v}\|(\cos\theta)\mathbf{i} + \|\mathbf{v}\|(\sin\theta)\mathbf{j}$, it follows that the direction angle θ for **v** is determined from

$$\tan\theta = \frac{\sin\theta}{\cos\theta} \qquad \text{Quotient identity}$$

$$= \frac{\|\mathbf{v}\|\sin\theta}{\|\mathbf{v}\|\cos\theta} \qquad \text{Multiply numerator and denominator by } \|\mathbf{v}\|.$$

$$= \frac{b}{a}. \qquad \text{Simplify.}$$

Example 7 Finding Direction Angles of Vectors

Find the direction angle of each vector.

a. $\mathbf{u} = 3\mathbf{i} + 3\mathbf{j}$

b. $\mathbf{v} = 3\mathbf{i} - 4\mathbf{j}$

Solution

a. The direction angle is

$$\tan\theta = \frac{b}{a} = \frac{3}{3} = 1.$$

So, $\theta = 45°$, as shown in Figure 6.28.

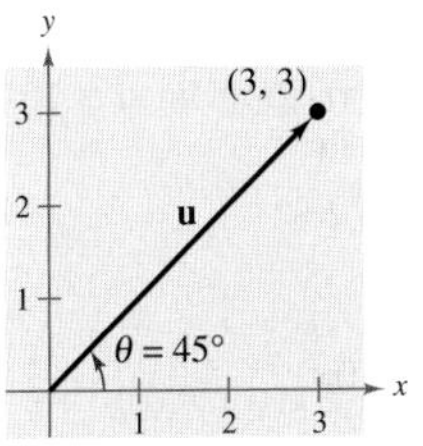

FIGURE 6.28

b. The direction angle is

$$\tan\theta = \frac{b}{a} = \frac{-4}{3}.$$

Moreover, because $\mathbf{v} = 3\mathbf{i} - 4\mathbf{j}$ lies in Quadrant IV, θ lies in Quadrant IV and its reference angle is

$$\theta = \left|\arctan\left(-\frac{4}{3}\right)\right| \approx |-53.13°| = 53.13°.$$

So, it follows that $\theta \approx 360° - 53.13° = 306.87°$, as shown in Figure 6.29.

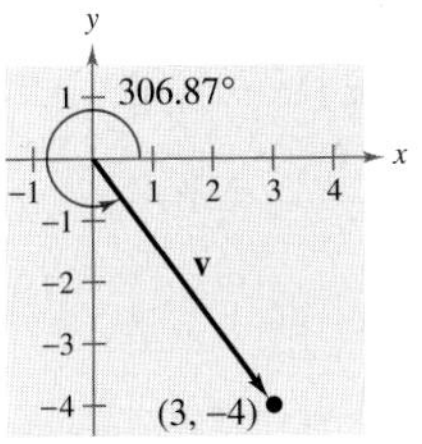

FIGURE 6.29

CHECKPoint Now try Exercise 63.

Extra Example 7

Find the direction angle of each vector.

a. $\mathbf{v} = -6\mathbf{i} + 6\mathbf{j}$

135°

b. $\mathbf{v} = -7\mathbf{i} - 4\mathbf{j}$

≈ 209.7°

Extra Example 8

Find the component form of the vector that represents the velocity of an airplane descending at a speed of 100 miles per hour at an angle 45° below the horizontal.

$\langle -50\sqrt{2}, -50\sqrt{2} \rangle$

Extra Example 9

A force of 500 pounds is required to pull a boat and trailer up a ramp inclined at 12° from the horizontal. Find the combined weight of the boat and trailer.

≈ 2405 pounds

Applications of Vectors

Example 8 Finding the Component Form of a Vector

Find the component form of the vector that represents the velocity of an airplane descending at a speed of 150 miles per hour at an angle 20° below the horizontal, as shown in Figure 6.30.

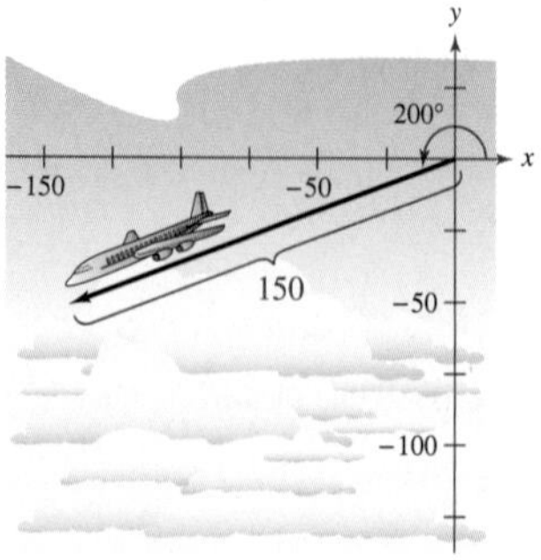

FIGURE 6.30

Solution

The velocity vector **v** has a magnitude of 150 and a direction angle of $\theta = 200°$.

$$\begin{aligned}\mathbf{v} &= \|\mathbf{v}\|(\cos\theta)\mathbf{i} + \|\mathbf{v}\|(\sin\theta)\mathbf{j}\\ &= 150(\cos 200°)\mathbf{i} + 150(\sin 200°)\mathbf{j}\\ &\approx 150(-0.9397)\mathbf{i} + 150(-0.3420)\mathbf{j}\\ &\approx -140.96\mathbf{i} - 51.30\mathbf{j}\\ &= \langle -140.96, -51.30\rangle\end{aligned}$$

You can check that **v** has a magnitude of 150, as follows.

$$\begin{aligned}\|\mathbf{v}\| &\approx \sqrt{(-140.96)^2 + (-51.30)^2}\\ &\approx \sqrt{19{,}869.72 + 2631.69}\\ &= \sqrt{22{,}501.41} \approx 150\end{aligned}$$

CHECK*Point* Now try Exercise 83.

Example 9 Using Vectors to Determine Weight

A force of 600 pounds is required to pull a boat and trailer up a ramp inclined at 15° from the horizontal. Find the combined weight of the boat and trailer.

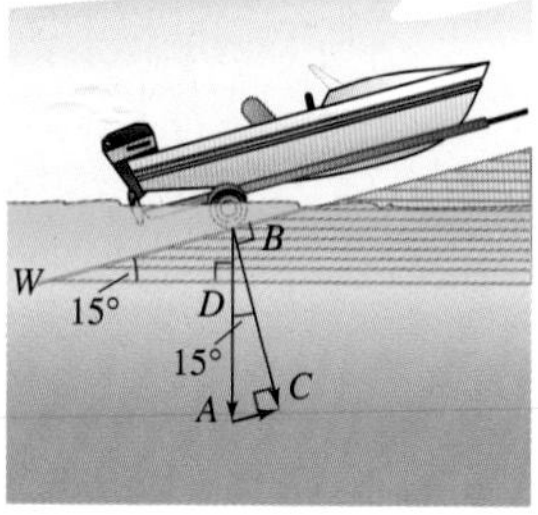

FIGURE 6.31

Solution

Based on Figure 6.31, you can make the following observations.

$\|\overrightarrow{BA}\|$ = force of gravity = combined weight of boat and trailer

$\|\overrightarrow{BC}\|$ = force against ramp

$\|\overrightarrow{AC}\|$ = force required to move boat up ramp = 600 pounds

By construction, triangles *BWD* and *ABC* are similar. Therefore, angle *ABC* is 15°. So, in triangle *ABC* you have

$$\begin{aligned}\sin 15° &= \frac{\|\overrightarrow{AC}\|}{\|\overrightarrow{BA}\|}\\ \sin 15° &= \frac{600}{\|\overrightarrow{BA}\|}\\ \|\overrightarrow{BA}\| &= \frac{600}{\sin 15°}\\ \|\overrightarrow{BA}\| &\approx 2318.\end{aligned}$$

Consequently, the combined weight is approximately 2318 pounds. (In Figure 6.31, note that $\overrightarrow{AC}$ is parallel to the ramp.)

CHECK*Point* Now try Exercise 95.

Example 10 Using Vectors to Find Speed and Direction

Study Tip

Recall from Section 4.8 that in air navigation, bearings can be measured in degrees clockwise from north.

An airplane is traveling at a speed of 500 miles per hour with a bearing of 330° at a fixed altitude with a negligible wind velocity as shown in Figure 6.32(a). When the airplane reaches a certain point, it encounters a wind with a velocity of 70 miles per hour in the direction N 45° E, as shown in Figure 6.32(b). What are the resultant speed and direction of the airplane?

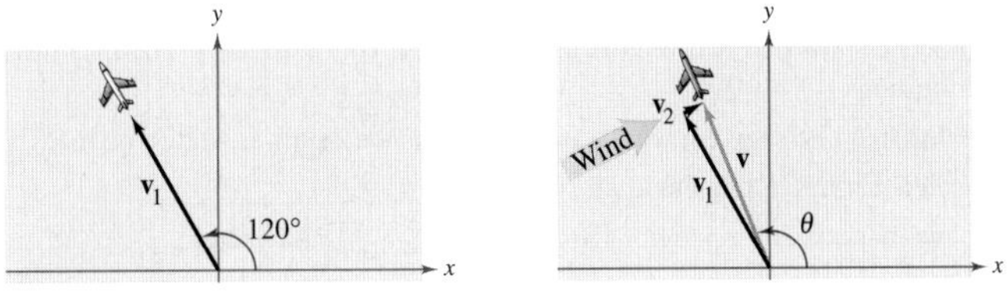

(a) (b)

FIGURE 6.32

Solution

Using Figure 6.32, the velocity of the airplane (alone) is

$$\mathbf{v}_1 = 500\langle \cos 120°, \sin 120° \rangle$$
$$= \langle -250, 250\sqrt{3} \rangle$$

and the velocity of the wind is

$$\mathbf{v}_2 = 70\langle \cos 45°, \sin 45° \rangle$$
$$= \langle 35\sqrt{2}, 35\sqrt{2} \rangle.$$

So, the velocity of the airplane (in the wind) is

$$\mathbf{v} = \mathbf{v}_1 + \mathbf{v}_2$$
$$= \langle -250 + 35\sqrt{2}, 250\sqrt{3} + 35\sqrt{2} \rangle$$
$$\approx \langle -200.5, 482.5 \rangle$$

and the resultant speed of the airplane is

$$\|\mathbf{v}\| \approx \sqrt{(-200.5)^2 + (482.5)^2}$$
$$\approx 522.5 \text{ miles per hour.}$$

Finally, if θ is the direction angle of the flight path, you have

$$\tan\theta \approx \frac{482.5}{-200.5}$$
$$\approx -2.4065$$

which implies that

$$\theta \approx 180° + \arctan(-2.4065) \approx 180° - 67.4° = 112.6°.$$

So, the true direction of the airplane is approximately

$$270° + (180° - 112.6°) = 337.4°.$$

CHECK*Point* Now try Exercise 101.

Extra Example 10

An airplane is traveling at a speed of 724 kilometers per hour at a bearing of N 30° E. If the wind velocity is 32 kilometers per hour from the west, find the resultant speed and direction of the plane.

≈ 740.5 kilometers per hour at an angle of about 32.14°

Closing the Lesson

Have students summarize the major points of the lesson and answer the Essential Question: How do you represent and perform operations with vector quantities?

- **Represent vector $\langle v_1, v_2 \rangle$ in standard position on the coordinate plane and find its magnitude by using the distance formula.**
- **Perform scalar multiplication of a vector by multiplying each of the vector's components by a scalar quantity.**
- **Perform addition of two vectors by adding their components to form a vector sum.**
- **Represent a vector as a sum of unit vectors i and j.**
- **Use trigonometric ratios to find vector angles, given vectors in component form or vice versa.**

4 PRACTICE AND APPLY

Assignment Guide

Transparencies Available
Available at the Instructor's companion site.

Average:
Day 1: pp. 454–455
Exs. 1–6, 12, 15, 17, 21–29 odd, 32, 35–39 odd, 43–53 odd, 57, 60, 62
Day 2: pp. 454–457
Exs. 7–10, 65, 67–69, 73–87 odd, 91, 94, 99, 103–109 odd, 112

Advanced:
Day 1: pp. 454–455
Exs. 1–3, 12–20 even, 24–30 even, 33, 34–40 even, 46–54 even, 58, 60, 61
Day 2: pp. 454–457
Exs. 7–10, 64, 66, 70–76 even, 80–92 even, 100–112 even, 113

Block:
pp. 454–457
Exs. 1–10, 12, 15, 17, 21–29 odd, 32, 35–39 odd, 43–53 odd, 57, 60, 62, 65, 67–69, 73–87 odd, 91, 94, 99, 103–109 odd, 112

6.3 EXERCISES

See www.CalcChat.com for worked-out solutions to odd-numbered exercises.

VOCABULARY: Fill in the blanks.

1. A directed line segment can be used to represent a quantity that involves both magnitude and direction.
2. The directed line segment $\overrightarrow{PQ}$ has initial point P and terminal point Q.
3. The ________ of the directed line segment $\overrightarrow{PQ}$ is denoted by $\|\overrightarrow{PQ}\|$. magnitude
4. The set of all directed line segments that are equivalent to a given directed line segment $\overrightarrow{PQ}$ is a vector **v** in the plane.
5. In order to show that two vectors are equivalent, you must show that they have the same magnitude and the same direction.
6. The directed line segment whose initial point is the origin is said to be in standard position.
7. A vector that has a magnitude of 1 is called a unit vector.
8. The two basic vector operations are scalar ________ and vector ________. multiplication; addition
9. The vector **u** + **v** is called the ________ of vector addition. resultant
10. The vector sum $v_1\mathbf{i} + v_2\mathbf{j}$ is called a ________ ________ of the vectors **i** and **j**, and the scalars v_1 and v_2 are called the ________ and ________ components of **v**, respectively. linear combination; horizontal; vertical

SKILLS AND APPLICATIONS

11–12. See margin.

In Exercises 11 and 12, show that u and v are equivalent.

11.

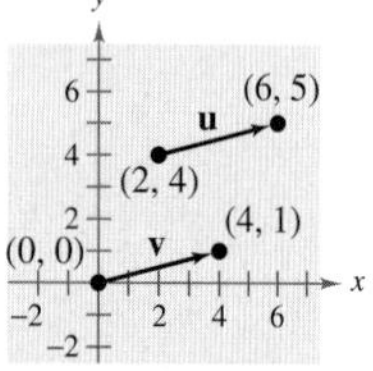

12.

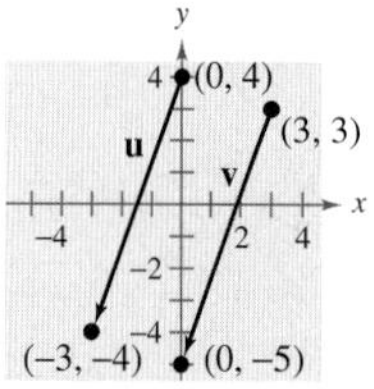

In Exercises 13–24, find the component form and the magnitude of the vector v. 13–14. See margin.

13.

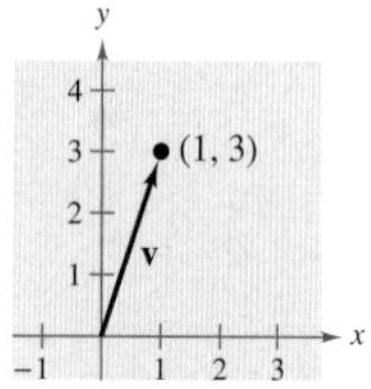

14.

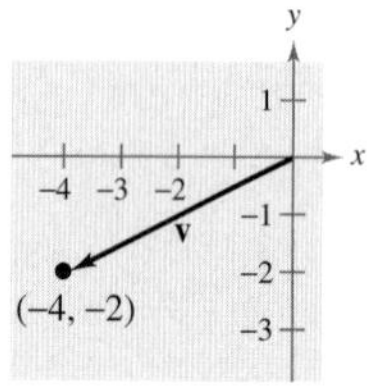

15.

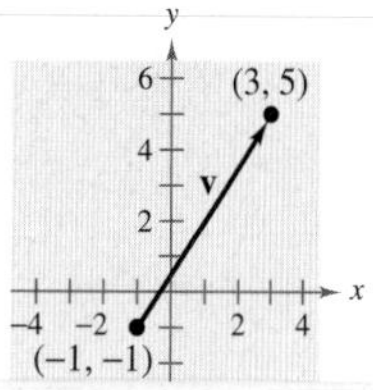

$\mathbf{v} = \langle 4, 6\rangle; \|\mathbf{v}\| = 2\sqrt{13}$

16.

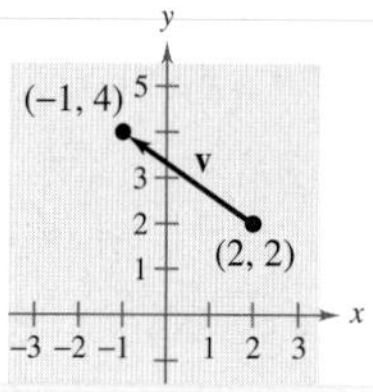

$\mathbf{v} = \langle -3, 2\rangle; \|\mathbf{v}\| = \sqrt{13}$

17. $\mathbf{v} = \langle 0, 5\rangle; \|\mathbf{v}\| = 5$

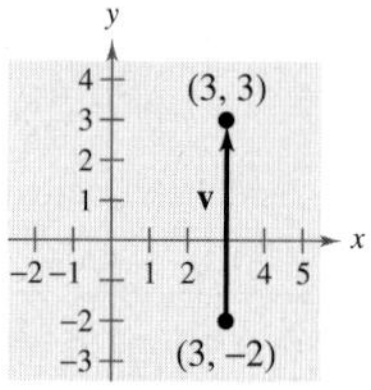

18. $\mathbf{v} = \langle 7, 0\rangle; \|\mathbf{v}\| = 7$

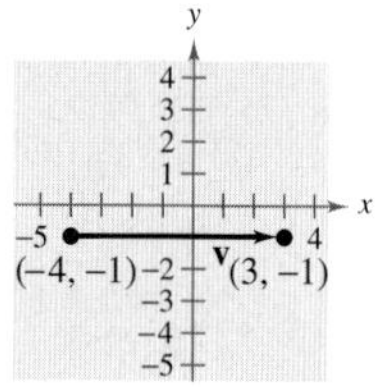

	Initial Point	*Terminal Point*
19.	$(-3, -5)$	$(5, 1)$ $\mathbf{v} = \langle 8, 6\rangle; \|\mathbf{v}\| = 10$
20.	$(-2, 7)$	$(5, -17)$ $\mathbf{v} = \langle 7, -24\rangle; \|\mathbf{v}\| = 25$
21.	$(1, 3)$	$(-8, -9)$ See margin.
22.	$(1, 11)$	$(9, 3)$ $\mathbf{v} = \langle 8, -8\rangle; \|\mathbf{v}\| = 8\sqrt{2}$
23.	$(-1, 5)$	$(15, 12)$ See margin.
24.	$(-3, 11)$	$(9, 40)$ See margin.

In Exercises 25–30, use the figure to sketch a graph of the specified vector. To print an enlarged copy of the graph, go to the website *www.mathgraphs.com*. 25–30. See margin.

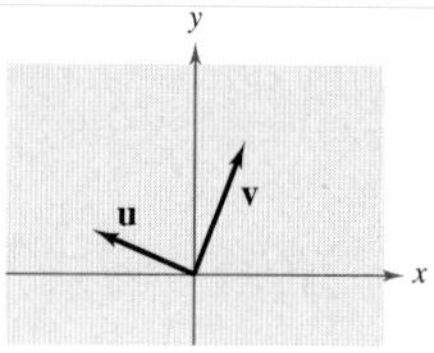

25. $-\mathbf{v}$
26. $5\mathbf{v}$
27. $\mathbf{u} + \mathbf{v}$
28. $\mathbf{u} + 2\mathbf{v}$
29. $\mathbf{u} - \mathbf{v}$
30. $\mathbf{v} - \frac{1}{2}\mathbf{u}$

11. $\|\mathbf{u}\| = \|\mathbf{v}\| = \sqrt{17}$, $\text{slope}_\mathbf{u} = \text{slope}_\mathbf{v} = \frac{1}{4}$
u and **v** have the same magnitude and direction, so they are equal.
12. $\|\mathbf{u}\| = \|\mathbf{v}\| = \sqrt{73}$, $\text{slope}_\mathbf{u} = \text{slope}_\mathbf{v} = \frac{8}{3}$
u and **v** have the same magnitude and direction, so they are equal.
13. $\mathbf{v} = \langle 1, 3\rangle, \|\mathbf{v}\| = \sqrt{10}$
14. $\mathbf{v} = \langle -4, -2\rangle; \|\mathbf{v}\| = 2\sqrt{5}$
21. $\mathbf{v} = \langle -9, -12\rangle; \|\mathbf{v}\| = 15$
23. $\mathbf{v} = \langle 16, 7\rangle; \|\mathbf{v}\| = \sqrt{305}$
24. $\mathbf{v} = \langle 12, 29\rangle; \|\mathbf{v}\| = \sqrt{985}$
25.

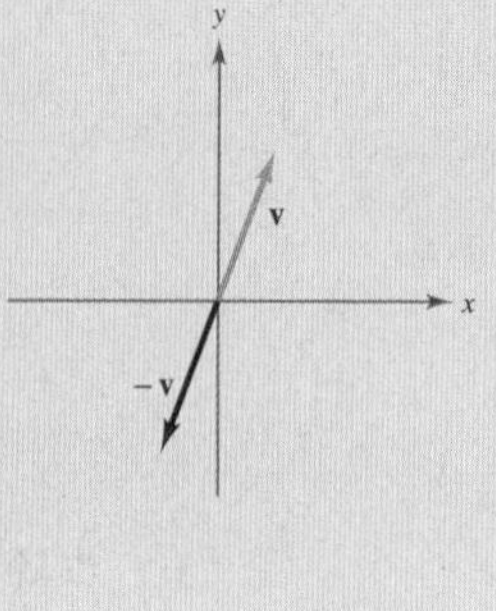

26.

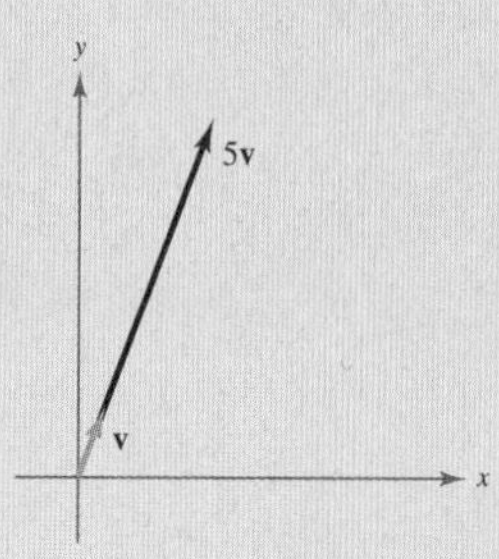

27.

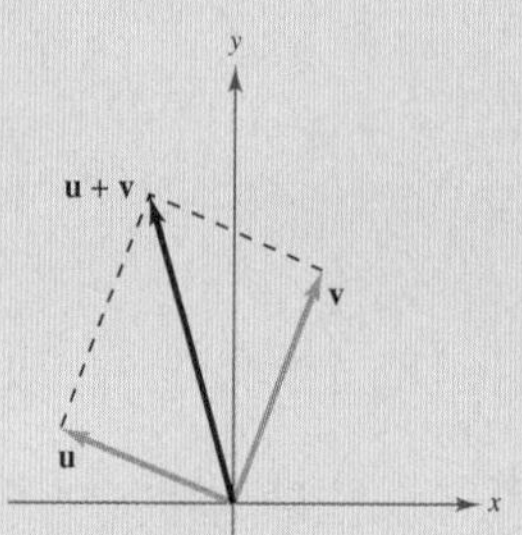

28.

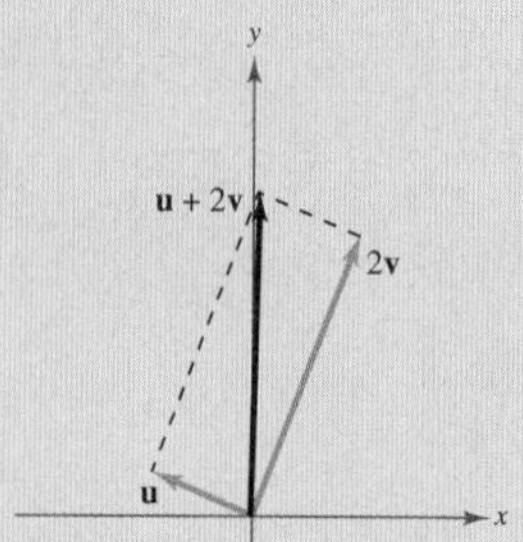

29–30. See Additional Answers beginning on page AA1.

31–38. See margin.
In Exercises 31–38, find (a) $\mathbf{u}+\mathbf{v}$, (b) $\mathbf{u}-\mathbf{v}$, and (c) $2\mathbf{u}-3\mathbf{v}$, Then sketch each resultant vector.

31. $\mathbf{u}=\langle 2,1\rangle,\ \mathbf{v}=\langle 1,3\rangle$ **32.** $\mathbf{u}=\langle 2,3\rangle,\ \mathbf{v}=\langle 4,0\rangle$

33. $\mathbf{u}=\langle -5,3\rangle,\ \mathbf{v}=\langle 0,0\rangle$ **34.** $\mathbf{u}=\langle 0,0\rangle,\ \mathbf{v}=\langle 2,1\rangle$

35. $\mathbf{u}=\mathbf{i}+\mathbf{j},\ \mathbf{v}=2\mathbf{i}-3\mathbf{j}$

36. $\mathbf{u}=-2\mathbf{i}+\mathbf{j},\ \mathbf{v}=3\mathbf{j}$

37. $\mathbf{u}=2\mathbf{i},\ \mathbf{v}=\mathbf{j}$ **38.** $\mathbf{u}=2\mathbf{j},\ \mathbf{v}=3\mathbf{i}$

41–44, 47–48. See margin.
In Exercises 39–48, find a unit vector in the direction of the given vector. Verify that the result has a magnitude of 1.

39. $\mathbf{u}=\langle 3,0\rangle$ $\langle 1,0\rangle$ **40.** $\mathbf{u}=\langle 0,-2\rangle$ $\langle 0,-1\rangle$

41. $\mathbf{v}=\langle -2,2\rangle$ **42.** $\mathbf{v}=\langle 5,-12\rangle$

43. $\mathbf{v}=\mathbf{i}+\mathbf{j}$ **44.** $\mathbf{v}=6\mathbf{i}-2\mathbf{j}$

45. $\mathbf{w}=4\mathbf{j}$ $\mathbf{j}$ **46.** $\mathbf{w}=-6\mathbf{i}$ $-\mathbf{i}$

47. $\mathbf{w}=\mathbf{i}-2\mathbf{j}$ **48.** $\mathbf{w}=7\mathbf{j}-3\mathbf{i}$

In Exercises 49–52, find the vector $\mathbf{v}$ with the given magnitude and the same direction as $\mathbf{u}$. 50–52. See margin.

	Magnitude		*Direction*
49.	$\lVert\mathbf{v}\rVert=10$	$\mathbf{v}=\langle -6,8\rangle$	$\mathbf{u}=\langle -3,4\rangle$
50.	$\lVert\mathbf{v}\rVert=3$		$\mathbf{u}=\langle -12,-5\rangle$
51.	$\lVert\mathbf{v}\rVert=9$		$\mathbf{u}=\langle 2,5\rangle$
52.	$\lVert\mathbf{v}\rVert=8$		$\mathbf{u}=\langle 3,3\rangle$

In Exercises 53–56, the initial and terminal points of a vector are given. Write a linear combination of the standard unit vectors $\mathbf{i}$ and $\mathbf{j}$.

	Initial Point	*Terminal Point*	
53.	$(-2,1)$	$(3,-2)$	$5\mathbf{i}-3\mathbf{j}$
54.	$(0,-2)$	$(3,6)$	$3\mathbf{i}+8\mathbf{j}$
55.	$(-6,4)$	$(0,1)$	$6\mathbf{i}-3\mathbf{j}$
56.	$(-1,-5)$	$(2,3)$	$3\mathbf{i}+8\mathbf{j}$

In Exercises 57–62, find the component form of $\mathbf{v}$ and sketch the specified vector operations geometrically, where $\mathbf{u}=2\mathbf{i}-\mathbf{j}$, and $\mathbf{w}=\mathbf{i}+2\mathbf{j}$. 57–62. See margin.

57. $\mathbf{v}=\frac{3}{2}\mathbf{u}$ **58.** $\mathbf{v}=\frac{3}{4}\mathbf{w}$

59. $\mathbf{v}=\mathbf{u}+2\mathbf{w}$ **60.** $\mathbf{v}=-\mathbf{u}+\mathbf{w}$

61. $\mathbf{v}=\frac{1}{2}(3\mathbf{u}+\mathbf{w})$ **62.** $\mathbf{v}=\mathbf{u}-2\mathbf{w}$

In Exercises 63–66, find the magnitude and direction angle of the vector $\mathbf{v}$.

63. $\mathbf{v}=6\mathbf{i}-6\mathbf{j}$ $\lVert\mathbf{v}\rVert=6\sqrt{2};\ \theta=315^\circ$ **64.** $\mathbf{v}=-5\mathbf{i}+4\mathbf{j}$ $\lVert\mathbf{v}\rVert=\sqrt{41};\ \theta=141.3^\circ$

65. $\mathbf{v}=3(\cos 60^\circ\mathbf{i}+\sin 60^\circ\mathbf{j})$ $\lVert\mathbf{v}\rVert=3;\ \theta=60^\circ$

66. $\mathbf{v}=8(\cos 135^\circ\mathbf{i}+\sin 135^\circ\mathbf{j})$ $\lVert\mathbf{v}\rVert=8;\ \theta=135^\circ$

In Exercises 67–74, find the component form of $\mathbf{v}$ given its magnitude and the angle it makes with the positive x-axis. Sketch $\mathbf{v}$. 67–74. See margin.

	Magnitude	*Angle*
67.	$\lVert\mathbf{v}\rVert=3$	$\theta=0^\circ$
68.	$\lVert\mathbf{v}\rVert=1$	$\theta=45^\circ$
69.	$\lVert\mathbf{v}\rVert=\frac{7}{2}$	$\theta=150^\circ$
70.	$\lVert\mathbf{v}\rVert=\frac{3}{4}$	$\theta=150^\circ$
71.	$\lVert\mathbf{v}\rVert=2\sqrt{3}$	$\theta=45^\circ$
72.	$\lVert\mathbf{v}\rVert=4\sqrt{3}$	$\theta=90^\circ$
73.	$\lVert\mathbf{v}\rVert=3$	$\mathbf{v}$ in the direction $3\mathbf{i}+4\mathbf{j}$
74.	$\lVert\mathbf{v}\rVert=2$	$\mathbf{v}$ in the direction $\mathbf{i}+3\mathbf{j}$

In Exercises 75–78, find the component form of the sum of $\mathbf{u}$ and $\mathbf{v}$ with direction angles $\theta_{\mathbf{u}}$ and $\theta_{\mathbf{v}}$.

	Magnitude	*Angle*	
75.	$\lVert\mathbf{u}\rVert=5$	$\theta_{\mathbf{u}}=0^\circ$	$\langle 5,5\rangle$
	$\lVert\mathbf{v}\rVert=5$	$\theta_{\mathbf{v}}=90^\circ$	
76.	$\lVert\mathbf{u}\rVert=4$	$\theta_{\mathbf{u}}=60^\circ$	$\langle 2,4+2\sqrt{3}\rangle$
	$\lVert\mathbf{v}\rVert=4$	$\theta_{\mathbf{v}}=90^\circ$	
77.	$\lVert\mathbf{u}\rVert=20$	$\theta_{\mathbf{u}}=45^\circ$	$\langle 10\sqrt{2}-50,10\sqrt{2}\rangle$
	$\lVert\mathbf{v}\rVert=50$	$\theta_{\mathbf{v}}=180^\circ$	
78.	$\lVert\mathbf{u}\rVert=50$	$\theta_{\mathbf{u}}=30^\circ$	$\langle 33.04,53.19\rangle$
	$\lVert\mathbf{v}\rVert=30$	$\theta_{\mathbf{v}}=110^\circ$	

In Exercises 79 and 80, use the Law of Cosines to find the angle α between the vectors. (Assume $0^\circ\le\alpha\le 180^\circ$.)

79. $\mathbf{v}=\mathbf{i}+\mathbf{j},\quad \mathbf{w}=2\mathbf{i}-2\mathbf{j}$ 90°

80. $\mathbf{v}=\mathbf{i}+2\mathbf{j},\quad \mathbf{w}=2\mathbf{i}-\mathbf{j}$ 90°

RESULTANT FORCE In Exercises 81 and 82, find the angle between the forces given the magnitude of their resultant. (*Hint:* Write force 1 as a vector in the direction of the positive x-axis and force 2 as a vector at an angle θ with the positive x-axis.)

	Force 1	*Force 2*	*Resultant Force*	
81.	45 pounds	60 pounds	90 pounds	62.7°
82.	3000 pounds	1000 pounds	3750 pounds	47.4°

83. VELOCITY A gun with a muzzle velocity of 1200 feet per second is fired at an angle of 6° above the horizontal. Find the vertical and horizontal components of the velocity. See margin.

84. Detroit Tigers pitcher Joel Zumaya was recorded throwing a pitch at a velocity of 104 miles per hour. If he threw the pitch at an angle of 35° below the horizontal, find the vertical and horizontal components of the velocity. (Source: Damon Lichtenwalner, Baseball Info Solutions)
Vertical ≈ -59.7 mi/h, Horizontal ≈ 85.2 mi/h

31. (a) $\langle 3,4\rangle$

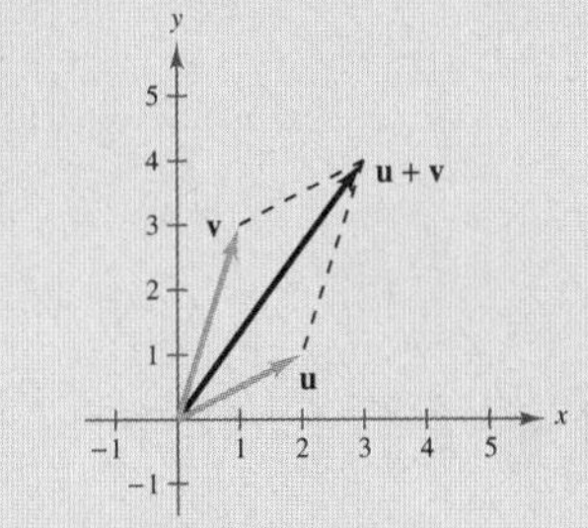

(b) $\langle 1,-2\rangle$

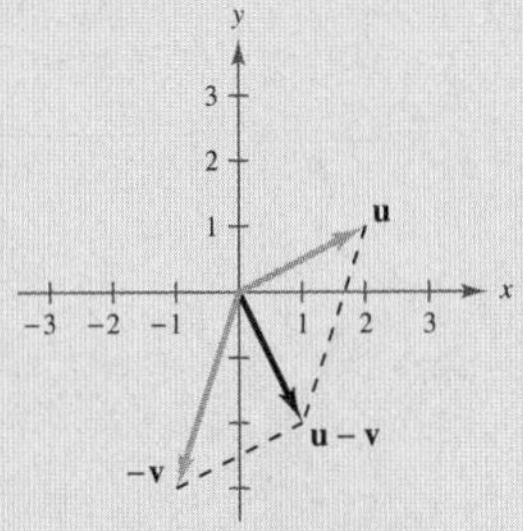

(c) $\langle 1,-7\rangle$

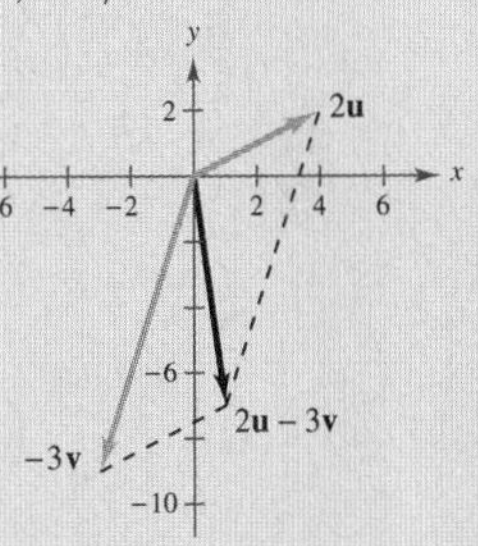

32. (a) $\langle 6,3\rangle$

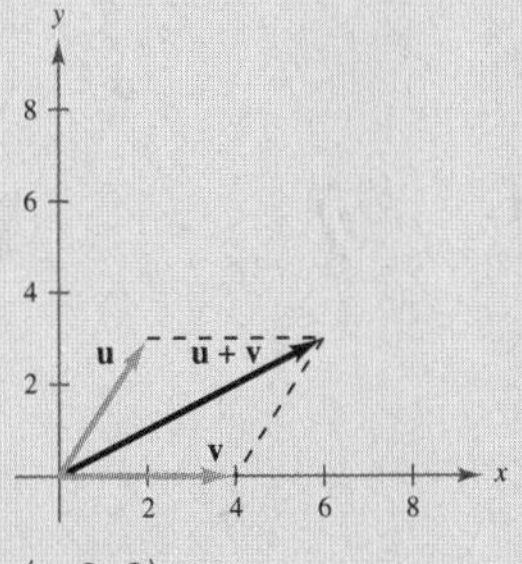

(b) $\langle -2,3\rangle$

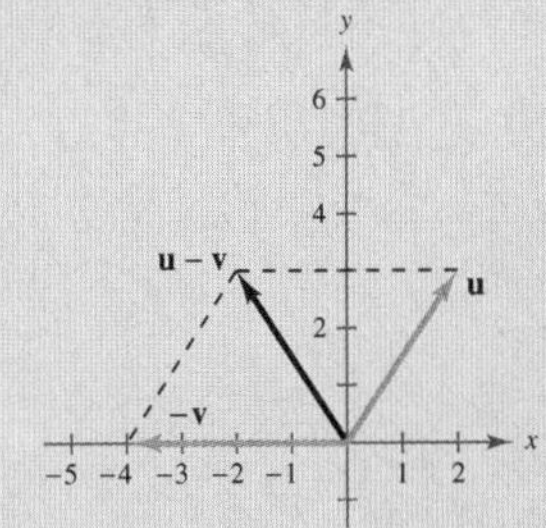

(c) $\langle -8,6\rangle$

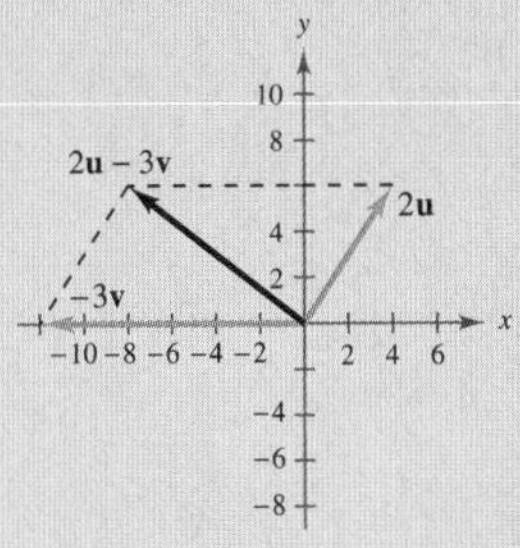

41. $\left\langle -\frac{\sqrt{2}}{2},\frac{\sqrt{2}}{2}\right\rangle$ **42.** $\left\langle \frac{5}{13},-\frac{12}{13}\right\rangle$

43. $\frac{\sqrt{2}}{2}\mathbf{i}+\frac{\sqrt{2}}{2}\mathbf{j}$

44. $\frac{3\sqrt{10}}{10}\mathbf{i}-\frac{\sqrt{10}}{10}\mathbf{j}$

47. $\frac{\sqrt{5}}{5}\mathbf{i}-\frac{2\sqrt{5}}{5}\mathbf{j}$

48. $-\frac{3\sqrt{58}}{58}\mathbf{i}+\frac{7\sqrt{58}}{58}\mathbf{j}$

50. $\mathbf{v}=\left\langle -\frac{36}{13},-\frac{15}{13}\right\rangle$

51. $\mathbf{v}=\left\langle \frac{18\sqrt{29}}{29},\frac{45\sqrt{29}}{29}\right\rangle$

52. $\mathbf{v}=\langle 4\sqrt{2},4\sqrt{2}\rangle$

83. Vertical ≈ 125.4 ft/sec,
Horizontal ≈ 1193.4 ft/sec

33–38, 57–62, 67–74. See Additional Answers beginning on page AA1.

94. 

53.2 lb

85. RESULTANT FORCE Forces with magnitudes of 125 newtons and 300 newtons act on a hook (see figure). The angle between the two forces is 45°. Find the direction and magnitude of the resultant of these forces. 12.8°; 398.32 N

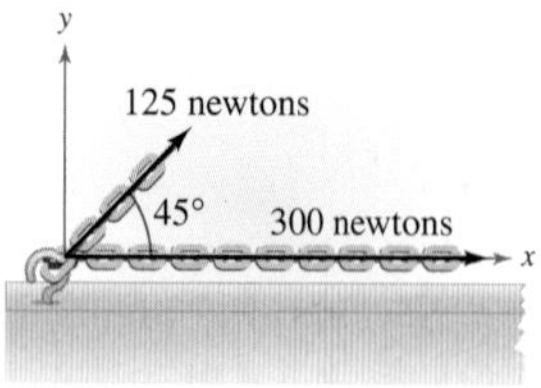

FIGURE FOR 85

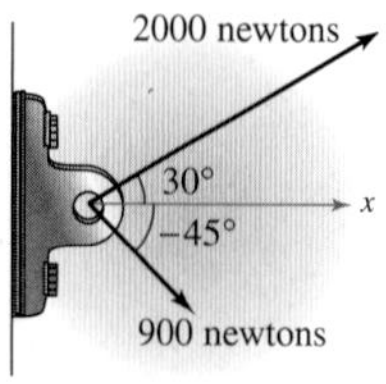

FIGURE FOR 86

86. RESULTANT FORCE Forces with magnitudes of 2000 newtons and 900 newtons act on a machine part at angles of 30° and −45°, respectively, with the x-axis (see figure). Find the direction and magnitude of the resultant of these forces. 8.7°; 2396.2 N

87. RESULTANT FORCE Three forces with magnitudes of 75 pounds, 100 pounds, and 125 pounds act on an object at angles of 30°, 45°, and 120°, respectively, with the positive x-axis. Find the direction and magnitude of the resultant of these forces. 71.3°; 228.5 lb

88. RESULTANT FORCE Three forces with magnitudes of 70 pounds, 40 pounds, and 60 pounds act on an object at angles of −30°, 45°, and 135°, respectively, with the positive x-axis. Find the direction and magnitude of the resultant of these forces. 37.5°; 58.6 lb

89. A traffic light weighing 12 pounds is suspended by two cables (see figure). Find the tension in each cable. 17.5 lb

90. Repeat Exercise 89 if $\theta_1 = 40°$ and $\theta_2 = 35°$. $T_L \approx 10.2$ lb, $T_R \approx 9.5$ lb

CABLE TENSION In Exercises 91 and 92, use the figure to determine the tension in each cable supporting the load.

91. 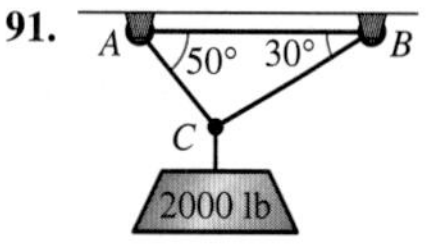

$T_{AC} \approx 1758.8$ lb
$T_{BC} \approx 1305.4$ lb

92. 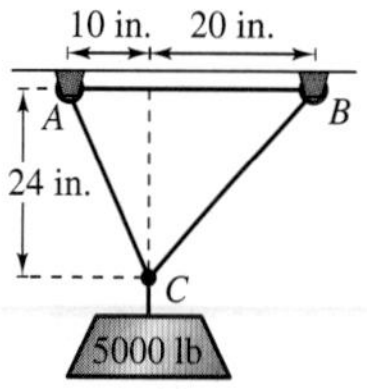

$T_{AC} \approx 3611.1$ lb
$T_{BC} \approx 2169.5$ lb

93. TOW LINE TENSION A loaded barge is being towed by two tugboats, and the magnitude of the resultant is 6000 pounds directed along the axis of the barge (see figure). Find the tension in the tow lines if they each make an 18° angle with the axis of the barge. 3154.4 lb

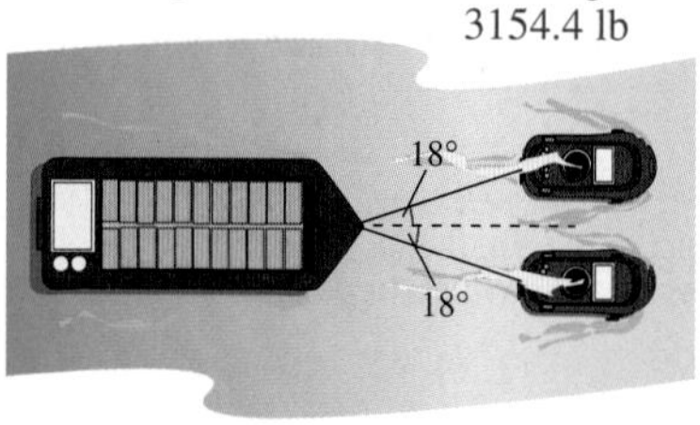

94. ROPE TENSION To carry a 100-pound cylindrical weight, two people lift on the ends of short ropes that are tied to an eyelet on the top center of the cylinder. Each rope makes a 20° angle with the vertical. Draw a figure that gives a visual representation of the situation, and find the tension in the ropes. See margin.

In Exercises 95–98, a force of F pounds is required to pull an object weighing W pounds up a ramp inclined at θ degrees from the horizontal. 97. 19.5°

95. Find F if $W = 100$ pounds and $\theta = 12°$. 20.8 lb

96. Find W if $F = 600$ pounds and $\theta = 14°$. 2480.1 lb

97. Find θ if $F = 5000$ pounds and $W = 15{,}000$ pounds.

98. Find F if $W = 5000$ pounds and $\theta = 26°$. 2191.9 lb

99. WORK A heavy object is pulled 30 feet across a floor, using a force of 100 pounds. The force is exerted at an angle of 50° above the horizontal (see figure). Find the work done. (Use the formula for work, $W = FD$, where F is the component of the force in the direction of motion and D is the distance.) 1928.4 ft-lb

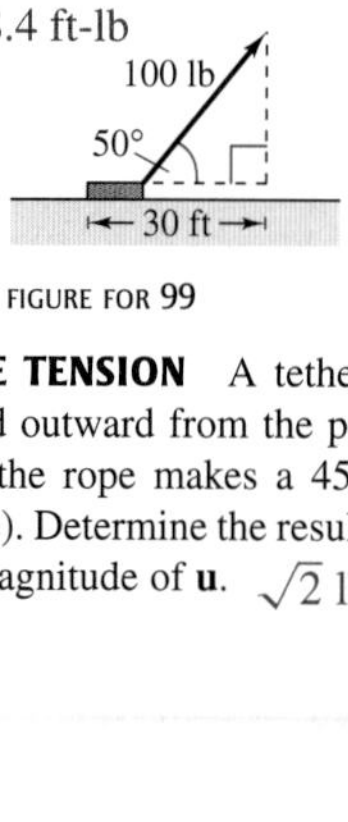

FIGURE FOR 99

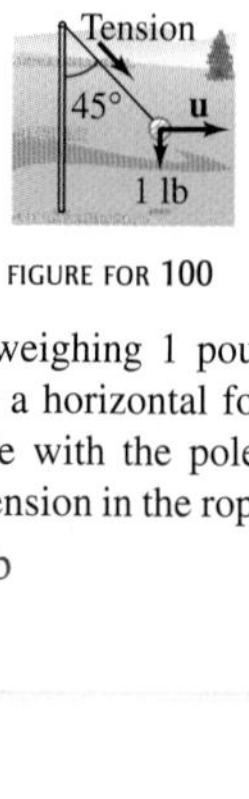

FIGURE FOR 100

100. ROPE TENSION A tetherball weighing 1 pound is pulled outward from the pole by a horizontal force **u** until the rope makes a 45° angle with the pole (see figure). Determine the resulting tension in the rope and the magnitude of **u**. $\sqrt{2}$ lb; 1 lb

101. NAVIGATION An airplane is flying in the direction of 148°, with an airspeed of 875 kilometers per hour. Because of the wind, its groundspeed and direction are 800 kilometers per hour and 140°, respectively (see figure). Find the direction and speed of the wind. N 21.4° E; 138.7 km/h

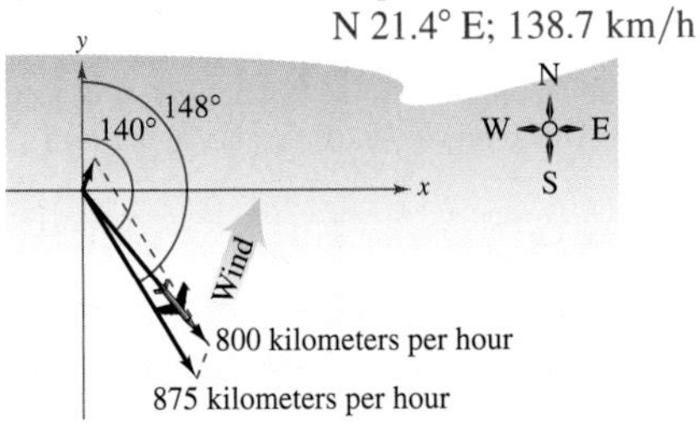

102. NAVIGATION A commercial jet is flying from Miami to Seattle. The jet's velocity with respect to the air is 580 miles per hour, and its bearing is 332°. The wind, at the altitude of the plane, is blowing from the southwest with a velocity of 60 miles per hour.

(a) Draw a figure that gives a visual representation of the situation. See margin.

(b) Write the velocity of the wind as a vector in component form. $60\langle\cos 45°, \sin 45°\rangle$

(c) Write the velocity of the jet relative to the air in component form. $580\langle\cos 118°, \sin 118°\rangle$

(d) What is the speed of the jet with respect to the ground? 600.3 mi/h

(e) What is the true direction of the jet? 337.5°

EXPLORATION

TRUE OR FALSE? In Exercises 103–110, use the figure to determine whether the statement is true or false. Justify your answer. 103–108. See margin.

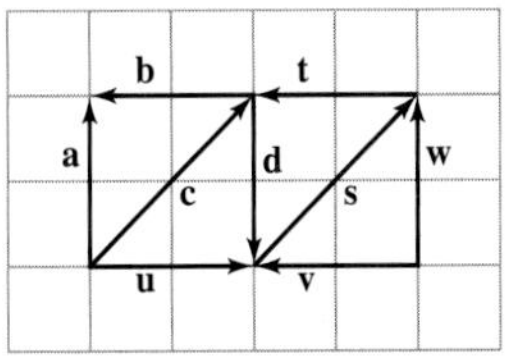

103. $\mathbf{a} = -\mathbf{d}$

104. $\mathbf{c} = \mathbf{s}$

105. $\mathbf{a} + \mathbf{u} = \mathbf{c}$

106. $\mathbf{v} + \mathbf{w} = -\mathbf{s}$

107. $\mathbf{a} + \mathbf{w} = -2\mathbf{d}$

108. $\mathbf{a} + \mathbf{d} = \mathbf{0}$

109. $\mathbf{u} - \mathbf{v} = -2(\mathbf{b} + \mathbf{t})$
False. $\mathbf{u} - \mathbf{v} = -(\mathbf{b} + \mathbf{t})$

110. $\mathbf{t} - \mathbf{w} = \mathbf{b} - \mathbf{a}$
True. $\mathbf{a} = \mathbf{w}$ and $\mathbf{b} = \mathbf{t}$

111. PROOF Prove that $(\cos\theta)\mathbf{i} + (\sin\theta)\mathbf{j}$ is a unit vector for any value of θ. Proof

112. CAPSTONE The initial and terminal points of vector $\mathbf{v}$ are $(3, -4)$ and $(9, 1)$, respectively.

(a) Write $\mathbf{v}$ in component form. $\mathbf{v} = \langle 6, 5\rangle$

(b) Write $\mathbf{v}$ as the linear combination of the standard unit vectors $\mathbf{i}$ and $\mathbf{j}$. $6\mathbf{i} + 5\mathbf{j}$

(c) Sketch $\mathbf{v}$ with its initial point at the origin. See margin.

(d) Find the magnitude of $\mathbf{v}$. $\|\mathbf{v}\| = \sqrt{61}$

113. GRAPHICAL REASONING Consider two forces

$\mathbf{F}_1 = \langle 10, 0\rangle$ and $\mathbf{F}_2 = 5\langle\cos\theta, \sin\theta\rangle$. See margin.

(a) Find $\|\mathbf{F}_1 + \mathbf{F}_2\|$ as a function of θ.

(b) Use a graphing utility to graph the function in part (a) for $0 \le \theta < 2\pi$.

(c) Use the graph in part (b) to determine the range of the function. What is its maximum, and for what value of θ does it occur? What is its minimum, and for what value of θ does it occur?

(d) Explain why the magnitude of the resultant is never 0.

114. TECHNOLOGY Write a program for your graphing utility that graphs two vectors and their difference given the vectors in component form. Answers will vary.

In Exercises 115 and 116, use the program in Exercise 114 to find the difference of the vectors shown in the figure.

115.

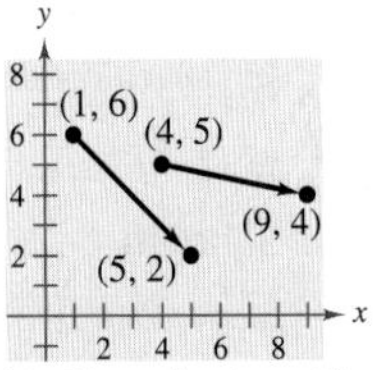

$\langle 1, 3\rangle$ or $\langle -1, -3\rangle$

116.

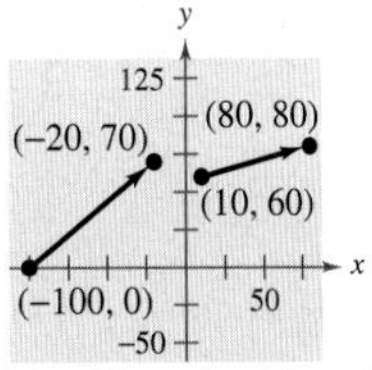

$\langle 10, 50\rangle$ or $\langle -10, -50\rangle$

117. WRITING In your own words, state the difference between a scalar and a vector. Give examples of each.

118. WRITING Give geometric descriptions of the operations of addition of vectors and multiplication of a vector by a scalar. 117–118. Answers will vary.

119. WRITING Identify the quantity as a scalar or as a vector. Explain your reasoning. See margin.

(a) The muzzle velocity of a bullet

(b) The price of a company's stock

(c) The air temperature in a room

(d) The weight of an automobile

5 ASSESS AND RETEACH

Daily Homework Quiz

Transparency Available
Available at the Instructor's companion site.

102. (a)

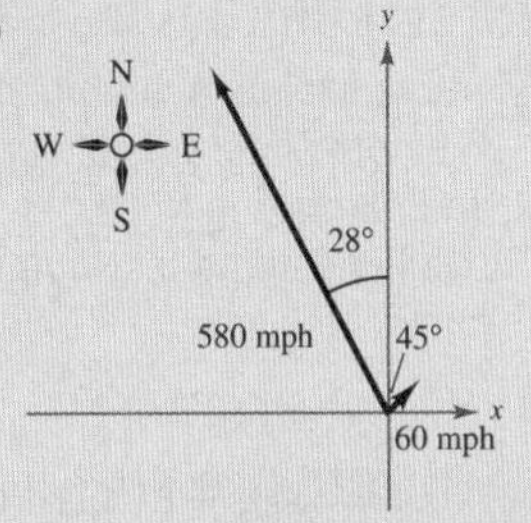

103. True. The magnitudes are equal and the directions are opposite.

104. True. The vectors have the same magnitude and direction.

105. True. $\mathbf{a} - \mathbf{b} = \mathbf{c}$ and $\mathbf{u} = -\mathbf{b}$

106. False. $\mathbf{v} - \mathbf{w} = -\mathbf{s}$

107. True. $\mathbf{a} = -\mathbf{d}$, $\mathbf{w} = -\mathbf{d}$

108. True. $\mathbf{a} = -\mathbf{d}$

112. (c)

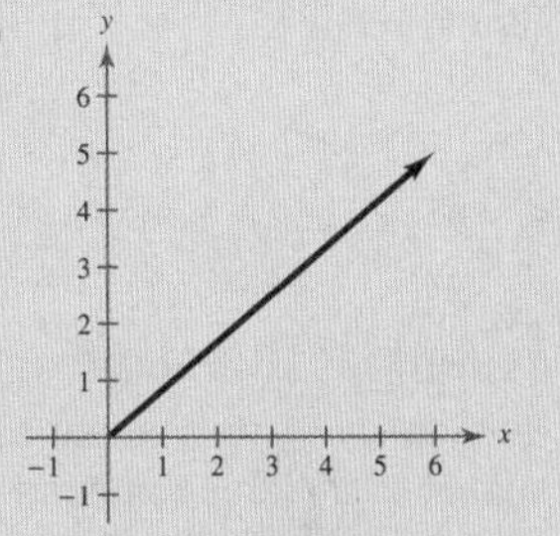

113. (a) $5\sqrt{5 + 4\cos\theta}$

(b)

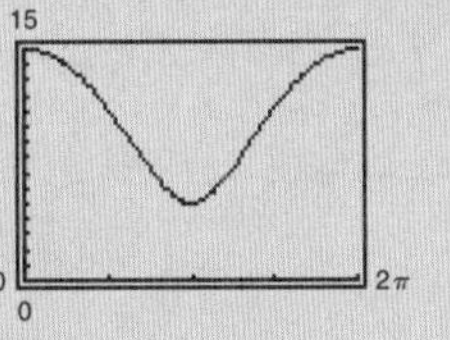

(c) Range: $[5, 15]$
Maximum is 15 when $\theta = 0$.
Minimum is 5 when $\theta = \pi$.

(d) The magnitudes of $\mathbf{F}_1$ and $\mathbf{F}_2$ are not the same.

119. (a) Vector. Velocity has both magnitude and direction.

(b) Scalar. Price has only magnitude.

(c) Scalar. Temperature has only magnitude.

(d) Vector. Weight has both magnitude and direction.

1 PLAN AND PREPARE

Warm-up Exercises

Transparency Available
Available at the Instructor's companion site.

Notetaking Guide

Transparency Available
Promotes interactive learning and notetaking skills. Available at the Instructor's companion site.

Animated Precalculus

An **Animated Precalculus** tutorial is available at the Student companion site for **Section 6.4.**

Pacing

Average: 2 days
Advanced: 2 days
Block: 1 block

2 FOCUS AND MOTIVATE

Essential Question

How do you write a vector as the sum of two vector components?
Tell students that they will learn how to answer this question by studying the dot product and angle between vectors as well as by representing a vector as the sum of two perpendicular component vectors.

Resource Planning Guide

Chapter Resources
- Complete Solutions Guide

Workbooks
- Notetaking Guide
- Student Solutions Guide

Interactive Technology
- Instructor Success Organizer
- Notetaking Guide IAE
- Instructional DVDs
- Animated Precalculus
- PowerLecture with ExamView

6.4 Vectors and Dot Products

What you should learn

- Find the dot product of two vectors and use the properties of the dot product.
- Find the angle between two vectors and determine whether two vectors are orthogonal.
- Write a vector as the sum of two vector components.
- Use vectors to find the work done by a force.

Why you should learn it

You can use the dot product of two vectors to solve real-life problems involving two vector quantities. For instance, in Exercise 76 on page 466, you can use the dot product to find the force necessary to keep a sport utility vehicle from rolling down a hill.

The Dot Product of Two Vectors

So far you have studied two vector operations—vector addition and multiplication by a scalar—each of which yields another vector. In this section, you will study a third vector operation, the **dot product.** This product yields a scalar, rather than a vector.

Definition of the Dot Product

The **dot product** of $\mathbf{u} = \langle u_1, u_2 \rangle$ and $\mathbf{v} = \langle v_1, v_2 \rangle$ is

$$\mathbf{u} \cdot \mathbf{v} = u_1v_1 + u_2v_2.$$

Properties of the Dot Product

Let **u**, **v**, and **w** be vectors in the plane or in space and let c be a scalar.

1. $\mathbf{u} \cdot \mathbf{v} = \mathbf{v} \cdot \mathbf{u}$
2. $\mathbf{0} \cdot \mathbf{v} = 0$
3. $\mathbf{u} \cdot (\mathbf{v} + \mathbf{w}) = \mathbf{u} \cdot \mathbf{v} + \mathbf{u} \cdot \mathbf{w}$
4. $\mathbf{v} \cdot \mathbf{v} = \|\mathbf{v}\|^2$
5. $c(\mathbf{u} \cdot \mathbf{v}) = c\mathbf{u} \cdot \mathbf{v} = \mathbf{u} \cdot c\mathbf{v}$

For proofs of the properties of the dot product, see Proofs in Mathematics on page 490.

Example 1 Finding Dot Products

Find each dot product.

a. $\langle 4, 5 \rangle \cdot \langle 2, 3 \rangle$ **b.** $\langle 2, -1 \rangle \cdot \langle 1, 2 \rangle$ **c.** $\langle 0, 3 \rangle \cdot \langle 4, -2 \rangle$

Solution

a. $\langle 4, 5 \rangle \cdot \langle 2, 3 \rangle = 4(2) + 5(3) = 8 + 15 = 23$

b. $\langle 2, -1 \rangle \cdot \langle 1, 2 \rangle = 2(1) + (-1)(2) = 2 - 2 = 0$

c. $\langle 0, 3 \rangle \cdot \langle 4, -2 \rangle = 0(4) + 3(-2) = 0 - 6 = -6$

CHECKPoint Now try Exercise 7.

In Example 1, be sure you see that the dot product of two vectors is a scalar (a real number), not a vector. Moreover, notice that the dot product can be positive, zero, or negative.

Example 2 Using Properties of Dot Products

Let $\mathbf{u} = \langle -1, 3\rangle$, $\mathbf{v} = \langle 2, -4\rangle$, and $\mathbf{w} = \langle 1, -2\rangle$. Find each dot product.

a. $(\mathbf{u} \cdot \mathbf{v})\mathbf{w}$

b. $\mathbf{u} \cdot 2\mathbf{v}$

Solution

Begin by finding the dot product of **u** and **v**.

$$\begin{aligned}\mathbf{u} \cdot \mathbf{v} &= \langle -1, 3\rangle \cdot \langle 2, -4\rangle \\ &= (-1)(2) + 3(-4) \\ &= -14\end{aligned}$$

a. $$\begin{aligned}(\mathbf{u} \cdot \mathbf{v})\mathbf{w} &= -14\langle 1, -2\rangle \\ &= \langle -14, 28\rangle\end{aligned}$$

b. $$\begin{aligned}\mathbf{u} \cdot 2\mathbf{v} &= 2(\mathbf{u} \cdot \mathbf{v}) \\ &= 2(-14) \\ &= -28\end{aligned}$$

Notice that the product in part (a) is a vector, whereas the product in part (b) is a scalar. Can you see why?

CHECK*Point* Now try Exercise 17.

Example 3 Dot Product and Magnitude

The dot product of **u** with itself is 5. What is the magnitude of **u**?

Solution

Because $\|\mathbf{u}\|^2 = \mathbf{u} \cdot \mathbf{u}$ and $\mathbf{u} \cdot \mathbf{u} = 5$, it follows that

$$\begin{aligned}\|\mathbf{u}\| &= \sqrt{\mathbf{u} \cdot \mathbf{u}} \\ &= \sqrt{5}.\end{aligned}$$

CHECK*Point* Now try Exercise 25.

The Angle Between Two Vectors

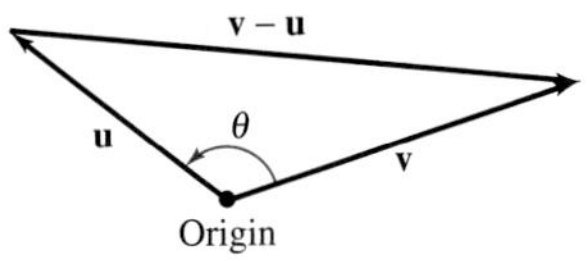

FIGURE 6.33

The **angle between two nonzero vectors** is the angle θ, $0 \le \theta \le \pi$, between their respective standard position vectors, as shown in Figure 6.33. This angle can be found using the dot product.

Angle Between Two Vectors

If θ is the angle between two nonzero vectors **u** and **v**, then

$$\cos\theta = \frac{\mathbf{u} \cdot \mathbf{v}}{\|\mathbf{u}\|\,\|\mathbf{v}\|}.$$

For a proof of the angle between two vectors, see Proofs in Mathematics on page 490.

3 TEACH

Extra Example 1

Find each dot product.

a. $\langle 3, 4\rangle \cdot \langle 2, -3\rangle$

−6

b. $\langle 2, 2\rangle \cdot \langle 1, -1\rangle$

0

c. $\langle 0, 4\rangle \cdot \langle 3, -2\rangle$

−8

Extra Example 2

Let $\mathbf{u} = \langle 3, 4\rangle$, $\mathbf{v} = \langle -2, 6\rangle$, and $\mathbf{w} = \langle 1, -1\rangle$. Find each of the following.

a. $(\mathbf{u} \cdot \mathbf{v})\mathbf{w}$

$\langle 18, -18\rangle$

b. $\mathbf{u} \cdot 2\mathbf{w}$

−2

Extra Example 3

The dot product of **u** with itself is 7. What is the magnitude of **u**?

$\sqrt{7}$

Extra Example 4

Find the angle θ between $\mathbf{u} = \langle 3, 0 \rangle$ and $\mathbf{v} = \langle 1, 6 \rangle$.

$\theta \approx 80.54°$

Example 4 Finding the Angle Between Two Vectors

Find the angle θ between $\mathbf{u} = \langle 4, 3 \rangle$ and $\mathbf{v} = \langle 3, 5 \rangle$.

Solution

The two vectors and θ are shown in Figure 6.34.

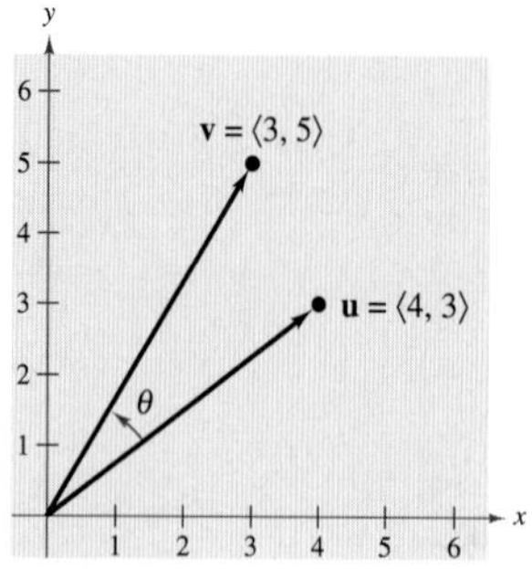

FIGURE 6.34

$$\cos \theta = \frac{\mathbf{u} \cdot \mathbf{v}}{\|\mathbf{u}\| \ \|\mathbf{v}\|}$$

$$= \frac{\langle 4, 3 \rangle \cdot \langle 3, 5 \rangle}{\|\langle 4, 3 \rangle\| \ \|\langle 3, 5 \rangle\|}$$

$$= \frac{27}{5\sqrt{34}}$$

This implies that the angle between the two vectors is

$$\theta = \arccos \frac{27}{5\sqrt{34}} \approx 22.2°.$$

CHECK *Point* Now try Exercise 35.

Rewriting the expression for the angle between two vectors in the form

$\mathbf{u} \cdot \mathbf{v} = \|\mathbf{u}\| \ \|\mathbf{v}\| \cos \theta$ Alternative form of dot product

produces an alternative way to calculate the dot product. From this form, you can see that because $\|\mathbf{u}\|$ and $\|\mathbf{v}\|$ are always positive, $\mathbf{u} \cdot \mathbf{v}$ and $\cos \theta$ will always have the same sign. Figure 6.35 shows the five possible orientations of two vectors.

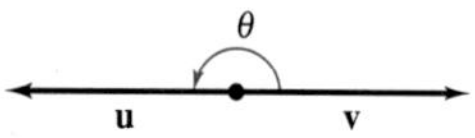

$\theta = \pi$
$\cos \theta = -1$
Opposite Direction

FIGURE 6.35

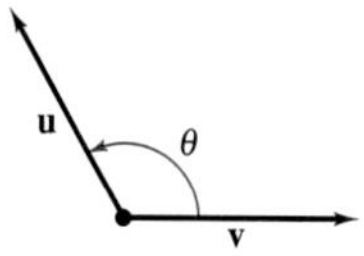

$\frac{\pi}{2} < \theta < \pi$
$-1 < \cos \theta < 0$
Obtuse Angle

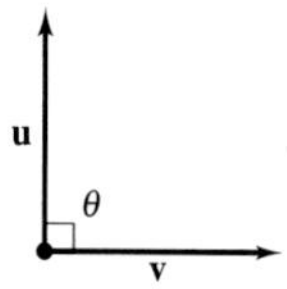

$\theta = \frac{\pi}{2}$
$\cos \theta = 0$
90° Angle

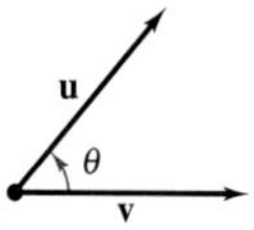

$0 < \theta < \frac{\pi}{2}$
$0 < \cos \theta < 1$
Acute Angle

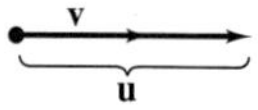

$\theta = 0$
$\cos \theta = 1$
Same Direction

Definition of Orthogonal Vectors

The vectors **u** and **v** are **orthogonal** if $\mathbf{u} \cdot \mathbf{v} = 0$.

The terms *orthogonal* and *perpendicular* mean essentially the same thing—meeting at right angles. Note that the zero vector is orthogonal to every vector **u**, because $\mathbf{0} \cdot \mathbf{u} = 0$.

TECHNOLOGY

The graphing utility program, Finding the Angle Between Two Vectors, found on the website for this text at *academic.cengage.com*, graphs two vectors $\mathbf{u} = \langle a, b \rangle$ and $\mathbf{v} = \langle c, d \rangle$ in standard position and finds the measure of the angle between them. Use the program to verify the solutions for Examples 4 and 5.

Example 5 Determining Orthogonal Vectors

Are the vectors $\mathbf{u} = \langle 2, -3 \rangle$ and $\mathbf{v} = \langle 6, 4 \rangle$ orthogonal?

Solution

Find the dot product of the two vectors.

$$\mathbf{u} \cdot \mathbf{v} = \langle 2, -3 \rangle \cdot \langle 6, 4 \rangle = 2(6) + (-3)(4) = 0$$

Because the dot product is 0, the two vectors are orthogonal (see Figure 6.36).

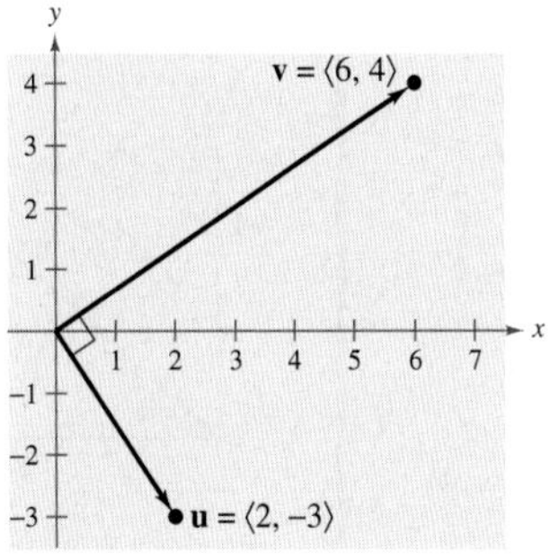

FIGURE 6.36

CHECKPoint Now try Exercise 53.

Extra Example 5

Are the vectors $\mathbf{u} = \langle -12, 30 \rangle$ and $\mathbf{v} = \left\langle \frac{5}{4}, \frac{1}{2} \right\rangle$ orthogonal?

Yes, because $\mathbf{u} \cdot \mathbf{v} = 0$.

Finding Vector Components

You have already seen applications in which two vectors are added to produce a resultant vector. Many applications in physics and engineering pose the reverse problem—decomposing a given vector into the sum of two **vector components.**

Consider a boat on an inclined ramp, as shown in Figure 6.37. The force $\mathbf{F}$ due to gravity pulls the boat *down* the ramp and *against* the ramp. These two orthogonal forces, $\mathbf{w}_1$ and $\mathbf{w}_2$, are vector components of $\mathbf{F}$. That is,

$$\mathbf{F} = \mathbf{w}_1 + \mathbf{w}_2. \qquad \text{Vector components of } \mathbf{F}$$

The negative of component $\mathbf{w}_1$ represents the force needed to keep the boat from rolling down the ramp, whereas $\mathbf{w}_2$ represents the force that the tires must withstand against the ramp. A procedure for finding $\mathbf{w}_1$ and $\mathbf{w}_2$ is shown on the following page.

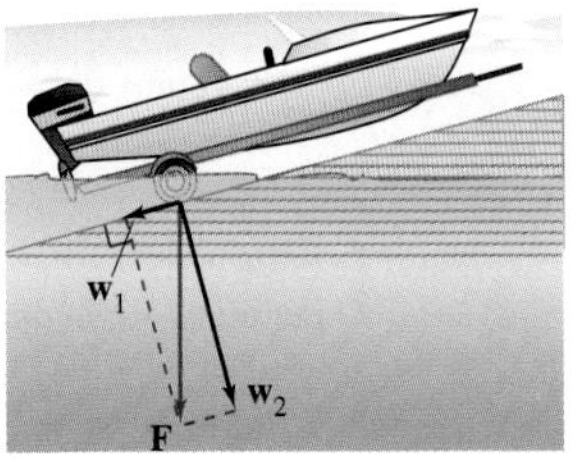

FIGURE 6.37

Definition of Vector Components

Let **u** and **v** be nonzero vectors such that

$$\mathbf{u} = \mathbf{w}_1 + \mathbf{w}_2$$

where $\mathbf{w}_1$ and $\mathbf{w}_2$ are orthogonal and $\mathbf{w}_1$ is parallel to (or a scalar multiple of) **v**, as shown in Figure 6.38. The vectors $\mathbf{w}_1$ and $\mathbf{w}_2$ are called **vector components** of **u**. The vector $\mathbf{w}_1$ is the **projection** of **u** onto **v** and is denoted by

$$\mathbf{w}_1 = \text{proj}_{\mathbf{v}}\mathbf{u}.$$

The vector $\mathbf{w}_2$ is given by $\mathbf{w}_2 = \mathbf{u} - \mathbf{w}_1$.

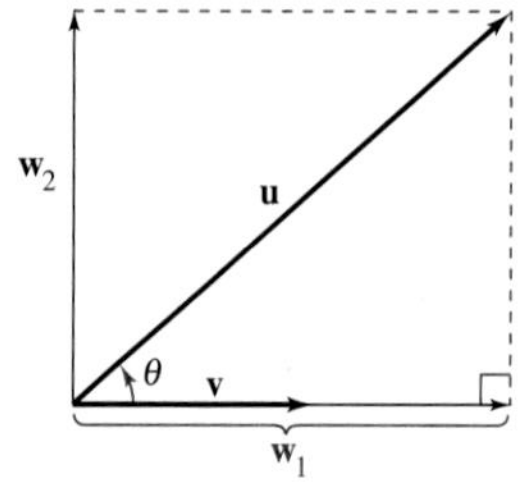

θ is acute.

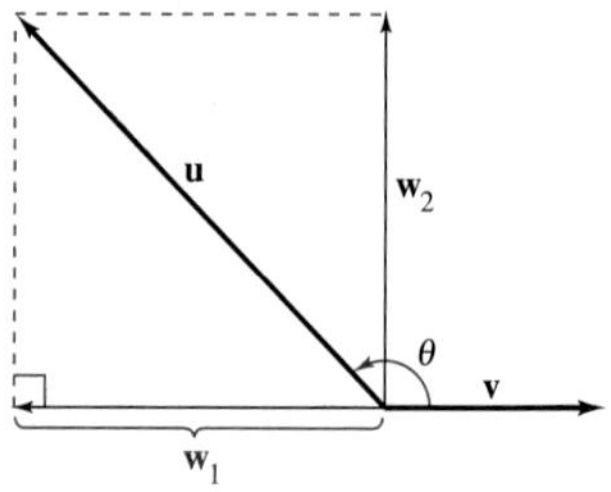

θ is obtuse.

FIGURE 6.38

From the definition of vector components, you can see that it is easy to find the component $\mathbf{w}_2$ once you have found the projection of **u** onto **v**. To find the projection, you can use the dot product, as follows.

$$\mathbf{u} = \mathbf{w}_1 + \mathbf{w}_2 = c\mathbf{v} + \mathbf{w}_2 \qquad \mathbf{w}_1 \text{ is a scalar multiple of } \mathbf{v}.$$

$$\mathbf{u} \cdot \mathbf{v} = (c\mathbf{v} + \mathbf{w}_2) \cdot \mathbf{v} \qquad \text{Take dot product of each side with } \mathbf{v}.$$

$$= c\mathbf{v} \cdot \mathbf{v} + \mathbf{w}_2 \cdot \mathbf{v}$$

$$= c\|\mathbf{v}\|^2 + 0 \qquad \mathbf{w}_2 \text{ and } \mathbf{v} \text{ are orthogonal.}$$

So,

$$c = \frac{\mathbf{u} \cdot \mathbf{v}}{\|\mathbf{v}\|^2}$$

and

$$\mathbf{w}_1 = \text{proj}_{\mathbf{v}}\mathbf{u} = c\mathbf{v} = \frac{\mathbf{u} \cdot \mathbf{v}}{\|\mathbf{v}\|^2}\mathbf{v}.$$

Projection of u onto v

Let **u** and **v** be nonzero vectors. The projection of **u** onto **v** is

$$\text{proj}_{\mathbf{v}}\mathbf{u} = \left(\frac{\mathbf{u} \cdot \mathbf{v}}{\|\mathbf{v}\|^2}\right)\mathbf{v}.$$

Example 6 Decomposing a Vector into Components

Find the projection of $\mathbf{u} = \langle 3, -5\rangle$ onto $\mathbf{v} = \langle 6, 2\rangle$. Then write $\mathbf{u}$ as the sum of two orthogonal vectors, one of which is $\text{proj}_{\mathbf{v}}\mathbf{u}$.

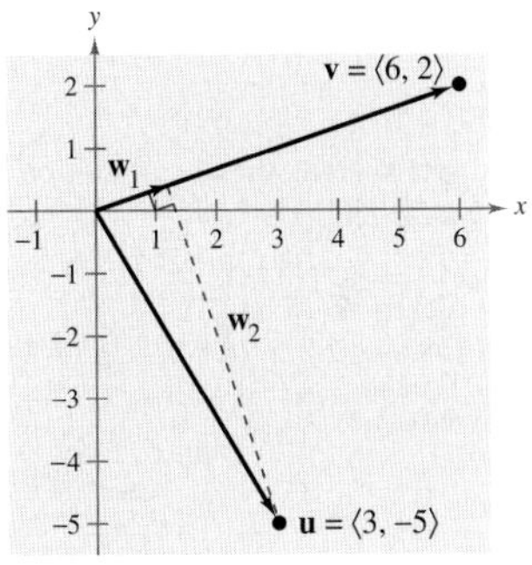

FIGURE 6.39

Solution

The projection of $\mathbf{u}$ onto $\mathbf{v}$ is

$$\mathbf{w}_1 = \text{proj}_{\mathbf{v}}\mathbf{u} = \left(\frac{\mathbf{u}\cdot\mathbf{v}}{\|\mathbf{v}\|^2}\right)\mathbf{v} = \left(\frac{8}{40}\right)\langle 6, 2\rangle = \left\langle \frac{6}{5}, \frac{2}{5}\right\rangle$$

as shown in Figure 6.39. The other component, $\mathbf{w}_2$, is

$$\mathbf{w}_2 = \mathbf{u} - \mathbf{w}_1 = \langle 3, -5\rangle - \left\langle \frac{6}{5}, \frac{2}{5}\right\rangle = \left\langle \frac{9}{5}, -\frac{27}{5}\right\rangle.$$

So,

$$\mathbf{u} = \mathbf{w}_1 + \mathbf{w}_2 = \left\langle \frac{6}{5}, \frac{2}{5}\right\rangle + \left\langle \frac{9}{5}, -\frac{27}{5}\right\rangle = \langle 3, -5\rangle.$$

CHECK*Point* Now try Exercise 59.

Example 7 Finding a Force

A 200-pound cart sits on a ramp inclined at 30°, as shown in Figure 6.40. What force is required to keep the cart from rolling down the ramp?

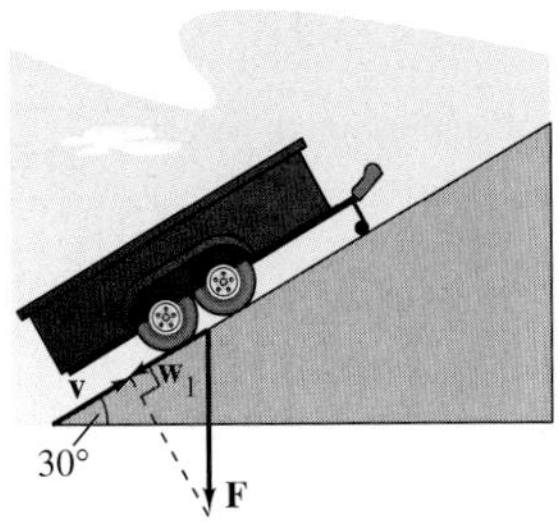

FIGURE 6.40

Solution

Because the force due to gravity is vertical and downward, you can represent the gravitational force by the vector

$$\mathbf{F} = -200\mathbf{j}. \qquad \text{Force due to gravity}$$

To find the force required to keep the cart from rolling down the ramp, project $\mathbf{F}$ onto a unit vector $\mathbf{v}$ in the direction of the ramp, as follows.

$$\mathbf{v} = (\cos 30°)\mathbf{i} + (\sin 30°)\mathbf{j} = \frac{\sqrt{3}}{2}\mathbf{i} + \frac{1}{2}\mathbf{j} \qquad \text{Unit vector along ramp}$$

Therefore, the projection of $\mathbf{F}$ onto $\mathbf{v}$ is

$$\begin{aligned}\mathbf{w}_1 &= \text{proj}_{\mathbf{v}}\mathbf{F}\\ &= \left(\frac{\mathbf{F}\cdot\mathbf{v}}{\|\mathbf{v}\|^2}\right)\mathbf{v}\\ &= (\mathbf{F}\cdot\mathbf{v})\mathbf{v}\\ &= (-200)\left(\frac{1}{2}\right)\mathbf{v}\\ &= -100\left(\frac{\sqrt{3}}{2}\mathbf{i} + \frac{1}{2}\mathbf{j}\right).\end{aligned}$$

The magnitude of this force is 100, and so a force of 100 pounds is required to keep the cart from rolling down the ramp.

CHECK*Point* Now try Exercise 75.

Extra Example 6

Find the projection of $\mathbf{u} = \langle 3, 4\rangle$ onto $\mathbf{v} = \langle 8, 2\rangle$. Then write $\mathbf{u}$ as the sum of two orthogonal vectors, one of which is $\text{proj}_{\mathbf{v}}\,\mathbf{u}$.

$$\mathbf{w}_1 = \text{proj}_{\mathbf{v}}\mathbf{u} = \left\langle \frac{64}{17}, \frac{16}{17}\right\rangle$$

$$\mathbf{w}_2 = \mathbf{u} - \mathbf{w}_1 = \left\langle -\frac{13}{17}, \frac{52}{17}\right\rangle$$

$$\mathbf{u} = \mathbf{w}_1 + \mathbf{w}_2 = \langle 3, 4\rangle$$

Avoiding Common Errors

Dot products and scalar multiplication are easily confused. Students should use caution when evaluating longer expressions. For example, when a projection of $\mathbf{u}$ onto $\mathbf{v}$ is calculated, the first factor $\frac{\mathbf{u}\cdot\mathbf{v}}{\|\mathbf{v}\|^2}$ yields a scalar. The scalar is then multiplied by a vector, yielding a vector.

Extra Example 7

A truck with a gross weight of 36,000 pounds is parked on a hill inclined at 10°. Assume that the only force to overcome is the force of gravity. Find the force required to keep the truck from rolling down the hill.

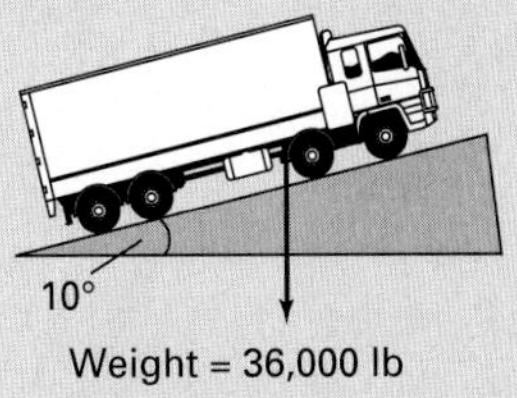

≈ 6251.3 pounds

Extra Example 8

To slide an object across a floor, a person pulls a rope with a constant force of 25 pounds at a constant angle of 30° above the horizontal. Find the work done if the object is dragged 40 feet.

≈ 866 foot-pounds

Closing the Lesson

Have students summarize the major points of the lesson and answer the Essential Question: How do you write a vector as the sum of two vector components?

- **Find the dot product of and angle between two vectors.**
- **Determine whether vectors are orthogonal by finding their dot product.**
- **Find the projection of vector u onto vector v by using the formula $\text{proj}_{\mathbf{v}}\mathbf{u} = \left(\dfrac{\mathbf{u}\cdot\mathbf{v}}{\|\mathbf{v}\|^2}\right)\mathbf{v}$.**
- **Find components of a vector by finding its projection onto a second vector and then finding the difference between the projection and the original vector.**

Work

The work W done by a *constant* force $\mathbf{F}$ acting along the line of motion of an object is given by

$$W = (\text{magnitude of force})(\text{distance}) = \|\mathbf{F}\|\,\|\overrightarrow{PQ}\|$$

as shown in Figure 6.41. If the constant force $\mathbf{F}$ is not directed along the line of motion, as shown in Figure 6.42, the work W done by the force is given by

$$W = \|\text{proj}_{\overrightarrow{PQ}}\mathbf{F}\|\,\|\overrightarrow{PQ}\| \qquad \text{Projection form for work}$$

$$= (\cos\theta)\|\mathbf{F}\|\,\|\overrightarrow{PQ}\| \qquad \|\text{proj}_{\overrightarrow{PQ}}\mathbf{F}\| = (\cos\theta)\|\mathbf{F}\|$$

$$= \mathbf{F}\cdot\overrightarrow{PQ}. \qquad \text{Alternative form of dot product}$$

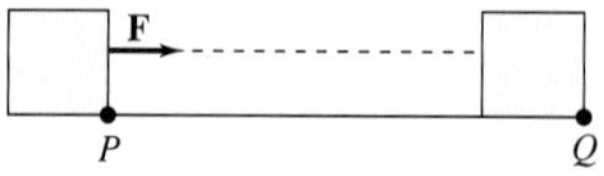

Force acts along the line of motion.
FIGURE 6.41

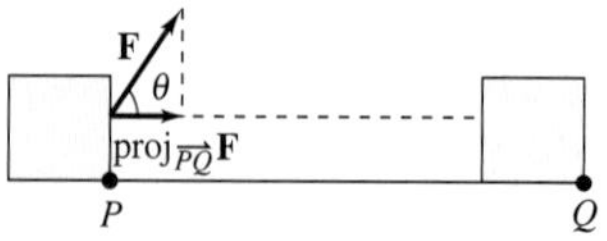

Force acts at angle θ with the line of motion.
FIGURE 6.42

This notion of work is summarized in the following definition.

Definition of Work

The **work** W done by a constant force $\mathbf{F}$ as its point of application moves along the vector $\overrightarrow{PQ}$ is given by either of the following.

1. $W = \|\text{proj}_{\overrightarrow{PQ}}\mathbf{F}\|\,\|\overrightarrow{PQ}\|$ — Projection form
2. $W = \mathbf{F}\cdot\overrightarrow{PQ}$ — Dot product form

Example 8 Finding Work

To close a sliding barn door, a person pulls on a rope with a constant force of 50 pounds at a constant angle of 60°, as shown in Figure 6.43. Find the work done in moving the barn door 12 feet to its closed position.

FIGURE 6.43

Solution

Using a projection, you can calculate the work as follows.

$$W = \|\text{proj}_{\overrightarrow{PQ}}\mathbf{F}\|\,\|\overrightarrow{PQ}\| \qquad \text{Projection form for work}$$

$$= (\cos 60°)\|\mathbf{F}\|\,\|\overrightarrow{PQ}\|$$

$$= \frac{1}{2}(50)(12) = 300 \text{ foot-pounds}$$

So, the work done is 300 foot-pounds. You can verify this result by finding the vectors $\mathbf{F}$ and $\overrightarrow{PQ}$ and calculating their dot product.

CHECKPoint Now try Exercise 79.

6.4 EXERCISES

See www.CalcChat.com for worked-out solutions to odd-numbered exercises.

VOCABULARY: Fill in the blanks.

1. The ___dot___ ___product___ of two vectors yields a scalar, rather than a vector.
2. The dot product of $\mathbf{u} = \langle u_1, u_2 \rangle$ and $\mathbf{v} = \langle v_1, v_2 \rangle$ is $\mathbf{u} \cdot \mathbf{v} =$ ___$u_1v_1 + u_2v_2$___.
3. If θ is the angle between two nonzero vectors $\mathbf{u}$ and $\mathbf{v}$, then $\cos\theta =$ ___$\dfrac{\mathbf{u} \cdot \mathbf{v}}{\|\mathbf{u}\|\,\|\mathbf{v}\|}$___.
4. The vectors $\mathbf{u}$ and $\mathbf{v}$ are ___orthogonal___ if $\mathbf{u} \cdot \mathbf{v} = 0$.
5. The projection of $\mathbf{u}$ onto $\mathbf{v}$ is given by $\text{proj}_{\mathbf{v}}\mathbf{u} =$ ___$\left(\dfrac{\mathbf{u} \cdot \mathbf{v}}{\|\mathbf{v}\|^2}\right)\mathbf{v}$___.
6. The work W done by a constant force $\mathbf{F}$ as its point of application moves along the vector $\overrightarrow{PQ}$ is given by $W =$ ___$\|\text{proj}_{\overrightarrow{PQ}}\mathbf{F}\|\,\|\overrightarrow{PQ}\|$___ or $W =$ ___$\mathbf{F} \cdot \overrightarrow{PQ}$___.

SKILLS AND APPLICATIONS

In Exercises 7–14, find the dot product of $\mathbf{u}$ and $\mathbf{v}$.

7. $\mathbf{u} = \langle 7, 1 \rangle$, $\mathbf{v} = \langle -3, 2 \rangle$ -19
8. $\mathbf{u} = \langle 6, 10 \rangle$, $\mathbf{v} = \langle -2, 3 \rangle$ 18
9. $\mathbf{u} = \langle -4, 1 \rangle$, $\mathbf{v} = \langle 2, -3 \rangle$ -11
10. $\mathbf{u} = \langle -2, 5 \rangle$, $\mathbf{v} = \langle -1, -8 \rangle$ -38
11. $\mathbf{u} = 4\mathbf{i} - 2\mathbf{j}$, $\mathbf{v} = \mathbf{i} - \mathbf{j}$ 6
12. $\mathbf{u} = 3\mathbf{i} + 4\mathbf{j}$, $\mathbf{v} = 7\mathbf{i} - 2\mathbf{j}$ 13
13. $\mathbf{u} = 3\mathbf{i} + 2\mathbf{j}$, $\mathbf{v} = -2\mathbf{i} - 3\mathbf{j}$ -12
14. $\mathbf{u} = \mathbf{i} - 2\mathbf{j}$, $\mathbf{v} = -2\mathbf{i} + \mathbf{j}$ -4

In Exercises 15–24, use the vectors $\mathbf{u} = \langle 3, 3 \rangle$, $\mathbf{v} = \langle -4, 2 \rangle$, and $\mathbf{w} = \langle 3, -1 \rangle$ to find the indicated quantity. State whether the result is a vector or a scalar. 17, 19–21. See margin.

15. $\mathbf{u} \cdot \mathbf{u}$ 18; scalar
16. $3\mathbf{u} \cdot \mathbf{v}$ -18; scalar
17. $(\mathbf{u} \cdot \mathbf{v})\mathbf{v}$
18. $(\mathbf{v} \cdot \mathbf{u})\mathbf{w}$ $\langle -18, 6 \rangle$; vector
19. $(3\mathbf{w} \cdot \mathbf{v})\mathbf{u}$
20. $(\mathbf{u} \cdot 2\mathbf{v})\mathbf{w}$
21. $\|\mathbf{w}\| - 1$
22. $2 - \|\mathbf{u}\|$ $2 - 3\sqrt{2}$; scalar
23. $(\mathbf{u} \cdot \mathbf{v}) - (\mathbf{u} \cdot \mathbf{w})$ -12; scalar
24. $(\mathbf{v} \cdot \mathbf{u}) - (\mathbf{w} \cdot \mathbf{v})$ 8; scalar

In Exercises 25–30, use the dot product to find the magnitude of $\mathbf{u}$.

25. $\mathbf{u} = \langle -8, 15 \rangle$ 17
26. $\mathbf{u} = \langle 4, -6 \rangle$ $2\sqrt{13}$
27. $\mathbf{u} = 20\mathbf{i} + 25\mathbf{j}$ $5\sqrt{41}$
28. $\mathbf{u} = 12\mathbf{i} - 16\mathbf{j}$ 20
29. $\mathbf{u} = 6\mathbf{j}$ 6
30. $\mathbf{u} = -21\mathbf{i}$ 21

In Exercises 31–40, find the angle θ between the vectors.

31. $\mathbf{u} = \langle 1, 0 \rangle$, $\mathbf{v} = \langle 0, -2 \rangle$ $90°$
32. $\mathbf{u} = \langle 3, 2 \rangle$, $\mathbf{v} = \langle 4, 0 \rangle$ $33.69°$
33. $\mathbf{u} = 3\mathbf{i} + 4\mathbf{j}$, $\mathbf{v} = -2\mathbf{j}$ $143.13°$
34. $\mathbf{u} = 2\mathbf{i} - 3\mathbf{j}$, $\mathbf{v} = \mathbf{i} - 2\mathbf{j}$ $7.13°$
35. $\mathbf{u} = 2\mathbf{i} - \mathbf{j}$, $\mathbf{v} = 6\mathbf{i} + 4\mathbf{j}$ $60.26°$
36. $\mathbf{u} = -6\mathbf{i} - 3\mathbf{j}$, $\mathbf{v} = -8\mathbf{i} + 4\mathbf{j}$ $53.13°$
37. $\mathbf{u} = 5\mathbf{i} + 5\mathbf{j}$, $\mathbf{v} = -6\mathbf{i} + 6\mathbf{j}$ $90°$
38. $\mathbf{u} = 2\mathbf{i} - 3\mathbf{j}$, $\mathbf{v} = 4\mathbf{i} + 3\mathbf{j}$ $93.18°$
39. $\mathbf{u} = \cos\left(\dfrac{\pi}{3}\right)\mathbf{i} + \sin\left(\dfrac{\pi}{3}\right)\mathbf{j}$, $\mathbf{v} = \cos\left(\dfrac{3\pi}{4}\right)\mathbf{i} + \sin\left(\dfrac{3\pi}{4}\right)\mathbf{j}$ $\dfrac{5\pi}{12}$
40. $\mathbf{u} = \cos\left(\dfrac{\pi}{4}\right)\mathbf{i} + \sin\left(\dfrac{\pi}{4}\right)\mathbf{j}$, $\mathbf{v} = \cos\left(\dfrac{\pi}{2}\right)\mathbf{i} + \sin\left(\dfrac{\pi}{2}\right)\mathbf{j}$ $\dfrac{\pi}{4}$

In Exercises 41–44, graph the vectors and find the degree measure of the angle θ between the vectors. 41–44. See margin.

41. $\mathbf{u} = 3\mathbf{i} + 4\mathbf{j}$, $\mathbf{v} = -7\mathbf{i} + 5\mathbf{j}$
42. $\mathbf{u} = 6\mathbf{i} + 3\mathbf{j}$, $\mathbf{v} = -4\mathbf{i} + 4\mathbf{j}$
43. $\mathbf{u} = 5\mathbf{i} + 5\mathbf{j}$, $\mathbf{v} = -8\mathbf{i} + 8\mathbf{j}$
44. $\mathbf{u} = 2\mathbf{i} - 3\mathbf{j}$, $\mathbf{v} = 8\mathbf{i} + 3\mathbf{j}$

In Exercises 45–48, use vectors to find the interior angles of the triangle with the given vertices. 45–46. See margin.

45. $(1, 2), (3, 4), (2, 5)$
46. $(-3, -4), (1, 7), (8, 2)$
47. $(-3, 0), (2, 2), (0, 6)$ $41.63°, 53.13°, 85.24°$
48. $(-3, 5), (-1, 9), (7, 9)$ $21.80°, 41.63°, 116.57°$

In Exercises 49–52, find $\mathbf{u} \cdot \mathbf{v}$, where θ is the angle between $\mathbf{u}$ and $\mathbf{v}$.

49. $\|\mathbf{u}\| = 4$, $\|\mathbf{v}\| = 10$, $\theta = \dfrac{2\pi}{3}$ -20
50. $\|\mathbf{u}\| = 100$, $\|\mathbf{v}\| = 250$, $\theta = \dfrac{\pi}{6}$ $12{,}500\sqrt{3}$
51. $\|\mathbf{u}\| = 9$, $\|\mathbf{v}\| = 36$, $\theta = \dfrac{3\pi}{4}$ -229.1
52. $\|\mathbf{u}\| = 4$, $\|\mathbf{v}\| = 12$, $\theta = \dfrac{\pi}{3}$ 24

4 PRACTICE AND APPLY

Assignment Guide

Transparencies Available
Available at the Instructor's companion site.

Average:
Day 1: pp. 465–466
Exs. 1–4, 9, 13, 15, 19–33 odd, 39, 41, 45–51 odd, 54, 55
Day 2: pp. 465–467
Exs. 5, 6, 61–73 odd, 76, 78, 79, 81, 87, 88, 90, 92

Advanced:
Day 1: pp. 465–466
Exs. 1–4, 10–18 even, 22–28 even, 32, 34, 40, 42, 46–58 even
Day 2: pp. 465–467
Exs. 5, 6, 62–76 even, 79, 80, 82, 87, 89, 90

Block:
pp. 465–467
Exs. 1–6, 9, 13, 15, 19–33 odd, 39, 41, 45–51 odd, 54, 55, 61–73 odd, 76, 78, 79, 81, 87, 88, 90, 92

17. $\langle 24, -12 \rangle$; vector
19. $\langle -126, -126 \rangle$; vector
20. $\langle -36, 12 \rangle$; vector
21. $\sqrt{10} - 1$; scalar

41.
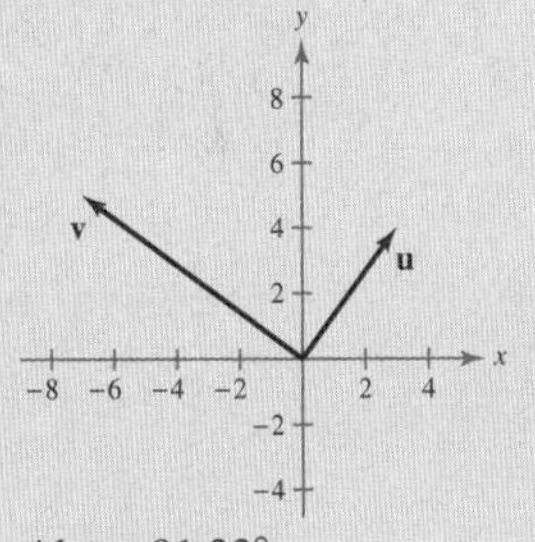
About 91.33°

42.
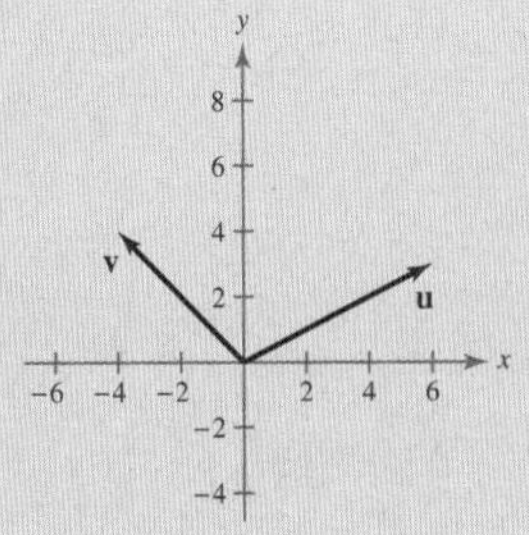
About 108.43°

43.
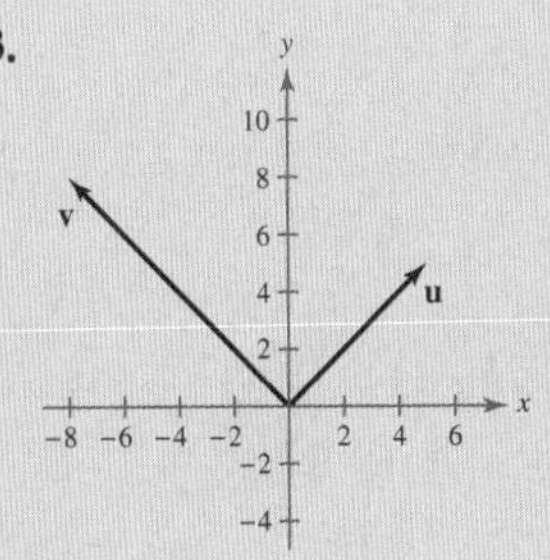
90°

44.
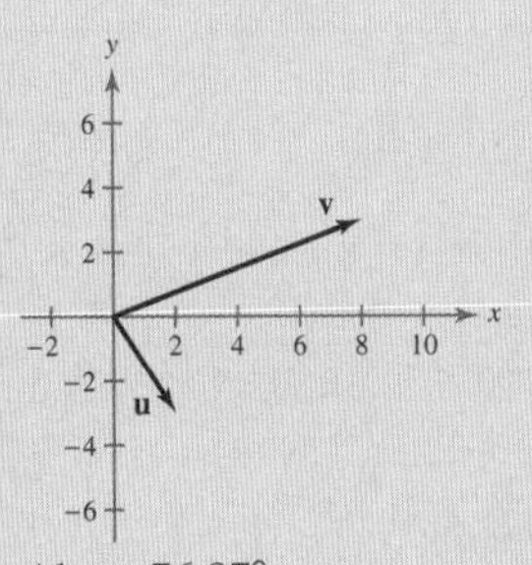
About 76.87°

45. 26.57°, 63.43°, 90°
46. 41.41°, 64.14°, 74.45°

59. $\frac{1}{37}\langle 84, 14\rangle, \frac{1}{37}\langle -10, 60\rangle$
60. $\langle 0, 0\rangle, \langle 4, 2\rangle$
61. $\frac{45}{229}\langle 2, 15\rangle, \frac{6}{229}\langle -15, 2\rangle$
62. $\frac{14}{17}\langle -4, -1\rangle, \frac{5}{17}\langle 1, -4\rangle$
67. $\langle -5, 3\rangle, \langle 5, -3\rangle$
68. $\langle 3, 8\rangle, \langle -3, -8\rangle$
69. $\frac{2}{3}\mathbf{i} + \frac{1}{2}\mathbf{j}, -\frac{2}{3}\mathbf{i} - \frac{1}{2}\mathbf{j}$
70. $3\mathbf{i} - \frac{5}{2}\mathbf{j}, -3\mathbf{i} + \frac{5}{2}\mathbf{j}$
73. (a) \$892,901.50
This value gives the total revenue that can be earned by selling all of the cellular phones.
74. (a) \$11,877.50
This value gives the total revenue earned by selling the hot dogs and hamburgers.

In Exercises 53–58, determine whether **u** and **v** are orthogonal, parallel, or neither.

53. $\mathbf{u} = \langle -12, 30\rangle$
$\mathbf{v} = \langle \frac{1}{2}, -\frac{5}{4}\rangle$ Parallel

54. $\mathbf{u} = \langle 3, 15\rangle$
$\mathbf{v} = \langle -1, 5\rangle$ Neither

55. $\mathbf{u} = \frac{1}{4}(3\mathbf{i} - \mathbf{j})$
$\mathbf{v} = 5\mathbf{i} + 6\mathbf{j}$ Neither

56. $\mathbf{u} = \mathbf{i}$
$\mathbf{v} = -2\mathbf{i} + 2\mathbf{j}$ Neither

57. $\mathbf{u} = 2\mathbf{i} - 2\mathbf{j}$
$\mathbf{v} = -\mathbf{i} - \mathbf{j}$ Orthogonal

58. $\mathbf{u} = \langle \cos\theta, \sin\theta\rangle$
$\mathbf{v} = \langle \sin\theta, -\cos\theta\rangle$ Orthogonal

In Exercises 59–62, find the projection of **u** onto **v**. Then write **u** as the sum of two orthogonal vectors, one of which is $\text{proj}_{\mathbf{v}}\mathbf{u}$. 59–62. See margin.

59. $\mathbf{u} = \langle 2, 2\rangle$
$\mathbf{v} = \langle 6, 1\rangle$

60. $\mathbf{u} = \langle 4, 2\rangle$
$\mathbf{v} = \langle 1, -2\rangle$

61. $\mathbf{u} = \langle 0, 3\rangle$
$\mathbf{v} = \langle 2, 15\rangle$

62. $\mathbf{u} = \langle -3, -2\rangle$
$\mathbf{v} = \langle -4, -1\rangle$

In Exercises 63–66, use the graph to determine mentally the projection of **u** onto **v**. (The coordinates of the terminal points of the vectors in standard position are given.) Use the formula for the projection of **u** onto **v** to verify your result.

63. $\langle 3, 2\rangle$

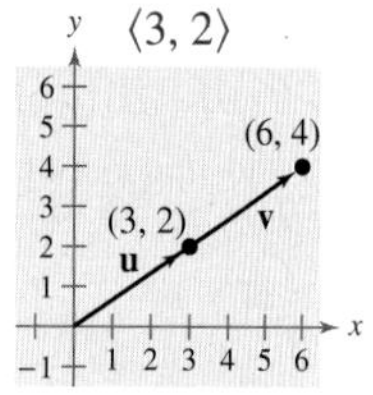

64. $\langle -3, -2\rangle$

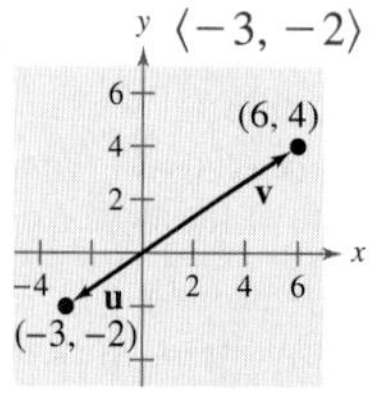

65. $\langle 0, 0\rangle$

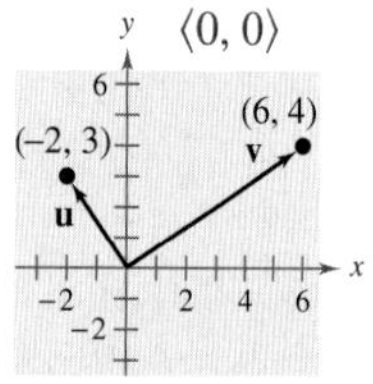

66. $\langle 0, 0\rangle$

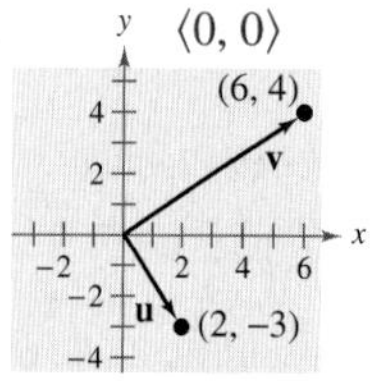

In Exercises 67–70, find two vectors in opposite directions that are orthogonal to the vector **u**. (There are many correct answers.) 67–70. See margin.

67. $\mathbf{u} = \langle 3, 5\rangle$

68. $\mathbf{u} = \langle -8, 3\rangle$

69. $\mathbf{u} = \frac{1}{2}\mathbf{i} - \frac{2}{3}\mathbf{j}$

70. $\mathbf{u} = -\frac{5}{2}\mathbf{i} - 3\mathbf{j}$

WORK In Exercises 71 and 72, find the work done in moving a particle from P to Q if the magnitude and direction of the force are given by **v**.

71. $P(0, 0)$, $Q(4, 7)$, $\mathbf{v} = \langle 1, 4\rangle$ 32

72. $P(1, 3)$, $Q(-3, 5)$, $\mathbf{v} = -2\mathbf{i} + 3\mathbf{j}$ 14

73. **REVENUE** The vector $\mathbf{u} = \langle 4600, 5250\rangle$ gives the numbers of units of two models of cellular phones produced by a telecommunications company. The vector $\mathbf{v} = \langle 79.99, 99.99\rangle$ gives the prices (in dollars) of the two models of cellular phones, respectively.
(a) Find the dot product $\mathbf{u} \cdot \mathbf{v}$ and interpret the result in the context of the problem. See margin.
(b) Identify the vector operation used to increase the prices by 5%. $1.05\mathbf{v}$

74. **REVENUE** The vector $\mathbf{u} = \langle 3140, 2750\rangle$ gives the numbers of hamburgers and hot dogs, respectively, sold at a fast-food stand in one month. The vector $\mathbf{v} = \langle 2.25, 1.75\rangle$ gives the prices (in dollars) of the food items.
(a) Find the dot product $\mathbf{u} \cdot \mathbf{v}$ and interpret the result in the context of the problem. See margin.
(b) Identify the vector operation used to increase the prices by 2.5%. $1.025\mathbf{v}$

75. **BRAKING LOAD** A truck with a gross weight of 30,000 pounds is parked on a slope of $d°$ (see figure). Assume that the only force to overcome is the force of gravity.

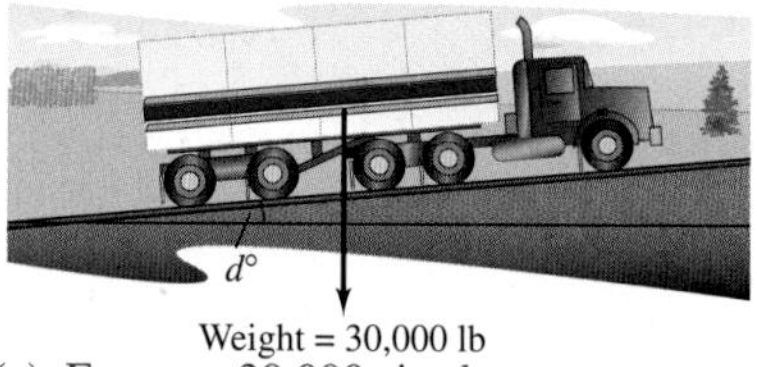

(a) Force = 30,000 sin d
(a) Find the force required to keep the truck from rolling down the hill in terms of the slope d.
(b) Use a graphing utility to complete the table. See margin.

d	0°	1°	2°	3°	4°	5°
Force						

d	6°	7°	8°	9°	10°
Force					

(c) Find the force perpendicular to the hill when $d = 5°$. 29,885.8 lb

76. **BRAKING LOAD** A sport utility vehicle with a gross weight of 5400 pounds is parked on a slope of 10°. Assume that the only force to overcome is the force of gravity. Find the force required to keep the vehicle from rolling down the hill. Find the force perpendicular to the hill. 937.7 lb; 5318.0 lb

75. (b)

d	0°	1°	2°	3°	4°	5°
Force	0	523.6	1047.0	1570.1	2092.7	2614.7

d	6°	7°	8°	9°	10°
Force	3135.9	3656.1	4175.2	4693.0	5209.4

77. WORK Determine the work done by a person lifting a 245-newton bag of sugar 3 meters. 735 N-m

78. WORK Determine the work done by a crane lifting a 2400-pound car 5 feet. 12,000 ft-lb

79. WORK A force of 45 pounds exerted at an angle of 30° above the horizontal is required to slide a table across a floor (see figure). The table is dragged 20 feet. Determine the work done in sliding the table. 779.4 ft-lb

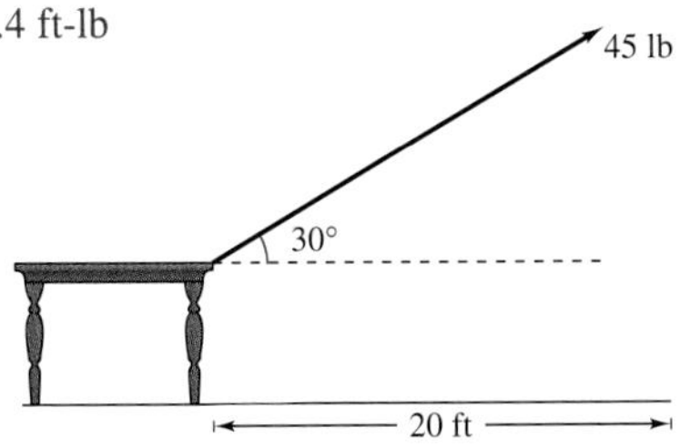

80. WORK A tractor pulls a log 800 meters, and the tension in the cable connecting the tractor and log is approximately 15,691 newtons. The direction of the force is 35° above the horizontal. Approximate the work done in pulling the log. 10,282,651.78 N-m

81. WORK One of the events in a local strongman contest is to pull a cement block 100 feet. One competitor pulls the block by exerting a force of 250 pounds on a rope attached to the block at an angle of 30° with the horizontal (see figure). Find the work done in pulling the block. 21,650.64 ft-lb

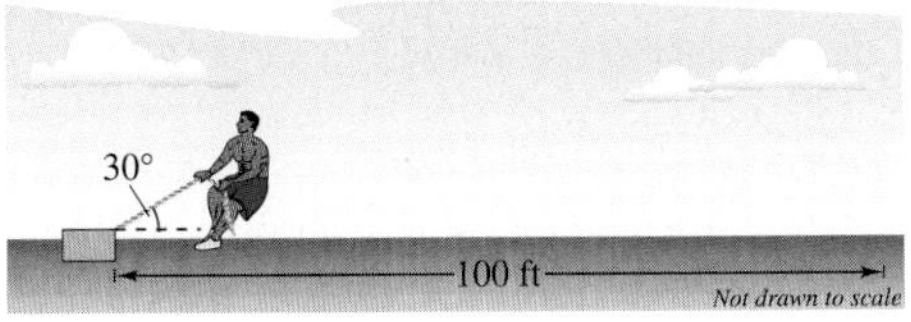

82. WORK A toy wagon is pulled by exerting a force of 25 pounds on a handle that makes a 20° angle with the horizontal (see figure). Find the work done in pulling the wagon 50 feet. 1174.62 ft-lb

83. PROGRAMMING Given vectors **u** and **v** in component form, write a program for your graphing utility in which the output is (a) $\|\mathbf{u}\|$, (b) $\|\mathbf{v}\|$, and (c) the angle between **u** and **v**. Answers will vary.

84. PROGRAMMING Use the program you wrote in Exercise 83 to find the angle between the given vectors.

(a) $\mathbf{u} = \langle 8, -4 \rangle$ and $\mathbf{v} = \langle 2, 5 \rangle$ 94.76°

(b) $\mathbf{u} = \langle 2, -6 \rangle$ and $\mathbf{v} = \langle 4, 1 \rangle$ 85.60°

85. PROGRAMMING Given vectors **u** and **v** in component form, write a program for your graphing utility in which the output is the component form of the projection of **u** onto **v**. Answers will vary.

86. PROGRAMMING Use the program you wrote in Exercise 85 to find the projection of **u** onto **v** for the given vectors.

(a) $\mathbf{u} = \langle 5, 6 \rangle$ and $\mathbf{v} = \langle -1, 3 \rangle$ $\langle -1.3, 3.9 \rangle$

(b) $\mathbf{u} = \langle 3, -2 \rangle$ and $\mathbf{v} = \langle -2, 1 \rangle$ $\langle 3.2, -1.6 \rangle$

EXPLORATION

TRUE OR FALSE? In Exercises 87 and 88, determine whether the statement is true or false. Justify your answer.

87. See margin.

87. The work W done by a constant force **F** acting along the line of motion of an object is represented by a vector.

88. A sliding door moves along the line of vector $\overrightarrow{PQ}$. If a force is applied to the door along a vector that is orthogonal to $\overrightarrow{PQ}$, then no work is done.

True. $\cos 90° = 0$

89. PROOF Use vectors to prove that the diagonals of a rhombus are perpendicular. Proof

90. CAPSTONE What is known about θ, the angle between two nonzero vectors **u** and **v**, under each condition (see figure)? See margin.

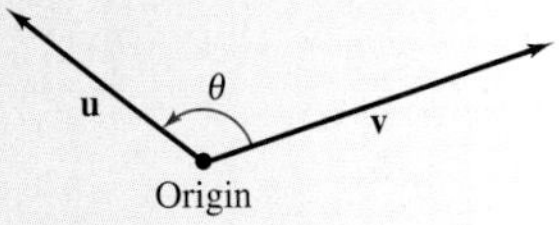

(a) $\mathbf{u} \cdot \mathbf{v} = 0$ (b) $\mathbf{u} \cdot \mathbf{v} > 0$ (c) $\mathbf{u} \cdot \mathbf{v} < 0$

91. THINK ABOUT IT What can be said about the vectors **u** and **v** under each condition? See margin.

(a) The projection of **u** onto **v** equals **u**.

(b) The projection of **u** onto **v** equals **0**.

92. PROOF Prove the following. Proof

$$\|\mathbf{u} - \mathbf{v}\|^2 = \|\mathbf{u}\|^2 + \|\mathbf{v}\|^2 - 2\mathbf{u} \cdot \mathbf{v}$$

93. PROOF Prove that if **u** is a unit vector and θ is the angle between **u** and **i**, then $\mathbf{u} = \cos\theta\mathbf{i} + \sin\theta\mathbf{j}$. Proof

94. PROOF Prove that if **u** is a unit vector and θ is the angle between **u** and **j**, then

$$\mathbf{u} = \cos\left(\frac{\pi}{2} - \theta\right)\mathbf{i} + \sin\left(\frac{\pi}{2} - \theta\right)\mathbf{j}.$$ Proof

5 ASSESS AND RETEACH

Daily Homework Quiz

Transparency Available

Available at the Instructor's companion site.

87. False. Work is represented by a scalar.

90. (a) $\theta = \frac{\pi}{2}$

(b) $0 \le \theta < \frac{\pi}{2}$

(c) $\frac{\pi}{2} < \theta \le \pi$

91. (a) **u** and **v** are parallel.

(b) **u** and **v** are orthogonal.

1 PLAN AND PREPARE

Warm-up Exercises

Transparency Available
Available at the Instructor's companion site.

Notetaking Guide

Transparency Available
Promotes interactive learning and notetaking skills. Available at the Instructor's companion site.

Animated Precalculus

An **Animated Precalculus** tutorial is available at the Student companion site for **Section 6.5.**

Pacing

Average: 2 days
Advanced: 2 days
Block: 1 block

2 FOCUS AND MOTIVATE

Essential Question

How do you represent complex numbers and perform operations on them by using trigonometry?
Tell students that they will learn how to answer this question by representing complex numbers on the complex plane and by operating on complex numbers in trigonometric form.

6.5 TRIGONOMETRIC FORM OF A COMPLEX NUMBER

What you should learn

- Plot complex numbers in the complex plane and find absolute values of complex numbers.
- Write the trigonometric forms of complex numbers.
- Multiply and divide complex numbers written in trigonometric form.
- Use DeMoivre's Theorem to find powers of complex numbers.
- Find *n*th roots of complex numbers.

Why you should learn it

You can use the trigonometric form of a complex number to perform operations with complex numbers. For instance, in Exercises 99–106 on page 477, you can use the trigonometric forms of complex numbers to help you solve polynomial equations.

The Complex Plane

Just as real numbers can be represented by points on the real number line, you can represent a complex number

$$z = a + bi$$

as the point (a, b) in a coordinate plane (the **complex plane**). The horizontal axis is called the **real axis** and the vertical axis is called the **imaginary axis,** as shown in Figure 6.44.

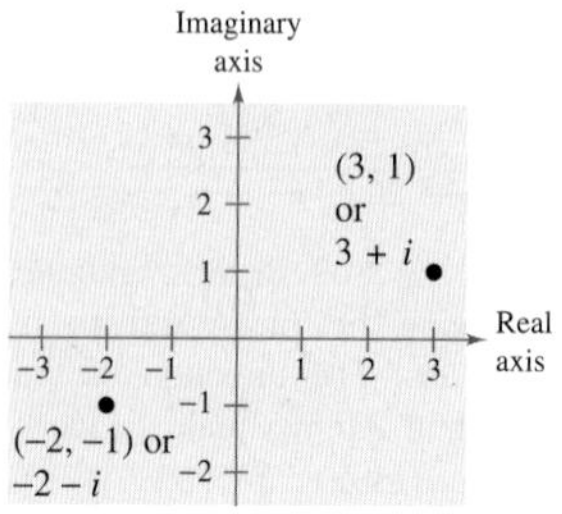

FIGURE 6.44

The **absolute value** of the complex number $a + bi$ is defined as the distance between the origin (0, 0) and the point (a, b).

Definition of the Absolute Value of a Complex Number

The **absolute value** of the complex number $z = a + bi$ is

$$|a + bi| = \sqrt{a^2 + b^2}.$$

If the complex number $a + bi$ is a real number (that is, if $b = 0$), then this definition agrees with that given for the absolute value of a real number

$$|a + 0i| = \sqrt{a^2 + 0^2} = |a|.$$

Example 1 Finding the Absolute Value of a Complex Number

Plot $z = -2 + 5i$ and find its absolute value.

Solution

The number is plotted in Figure 6.45. It has an absolute value of

$$|z| = \sqrt{(-2)^2 + 5^2}$$
$$= \sqrt{29}.$$

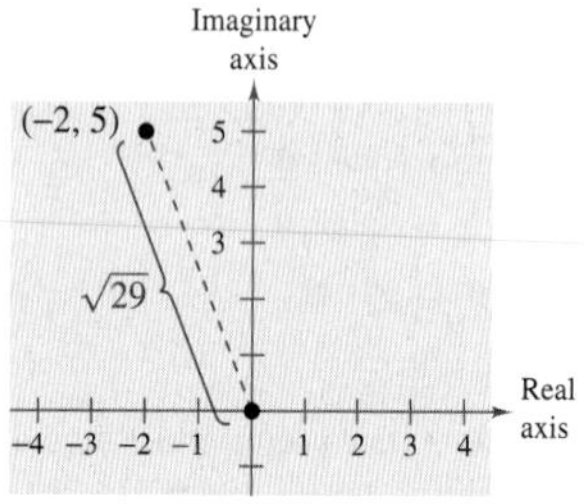

FIGURE 6.45

CHECK*Point* Now try Exercise 9.

Resource Planning Guide

Chapter Resources
- Complete Solutions Guide

Workbooks
- Notetaking Guide
- Student Solutions Guide

Interactive Technology
- Instructor Success Organizer
- Notetaking Guide IAE
- Instructional DVDs
- Animated Precalculus
- PowerLecture with ExamView

Trigonometric Form of a Complex Number

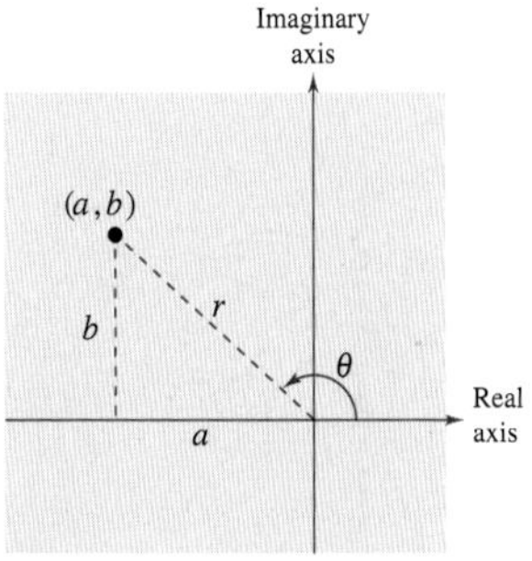

FIGURE 6.46

In Section 2.4, you learned how to add, subtract, multiply, and divide complex numbers. To work effectively with *powers* and *roots* of complex numbers, it is helpful to write complex numbers in trigonometric form. In Figure 6.46, consider the nonzero complex number $a + bi$. By letting θ be the angle from the positive real axis (measured counterclockwise) to the line segment connecting the origin and the point (a, b), you can write

$$a = r\cos\theta \quad \text{and} \quad b = r\sin\theta$$

where $r = \sqrt{a^2 + b^2}$. Consequently, you have

$$a + bi = (r\cos\theta) + (r\sin\theta)i$$

from which you can obtain the **trigonometric form of a complex number.**

Trigonometric Form of a Complex Number

The **trigonometric form** of the complex number $z = a + bi$ is

$$z = r(\cos\theta + i\sin\theta)$$

where $a = r\cos\theta$, $b = r\sin\theta$, $r = \sqrt{a^2 + b^2}$, and $\tan\theta = b/a$. The number r is the **modulus** of z, and θ is called an **argument** of z.

The trigonometric form of a complex number is also called the *polar form*. Because there are infinitely many choices for θ, the trigonometric form of a complex number is not unique. Normally, θ is restricted to the interval $0 \le \theta < 2\pi$, although on occasion it is convenient to use $\theta < 0$.

Example 2 Writing a Complex Number in Trigonometric Form

Write the complex number $z = -2 - 2\sqrt{3}i$ in trigonometric form.

Solution

The absolute value of z is

$$r = \left|-2 - 2\sqrt{3}i\right| = \sqrt{(-2)^2 + \left(-2\sqrt{3}\right)^2} = \sqrt{16} = 4$$

and the reference angle θ' is given by

$$\tan\theta' = \frac{b}{a} = \frac{-2\sqrt{3}}{-2} = \sqrt{3}.$$

Because $\tan(\pi/3) = \sqrt{3}$ and because $z = -2 - 2\sqrt{3}i$ lies in Quadrant III, you choose θ to be $\theta = \pi + \pi/3 = 4\pi/3$. So, the trigonometric form is

$$z = r(\cos\theta + i\sin\theta)$$

$$= 4\left(\cos\frac{4\pi}{3} + i\sin\frac{4\pi}{3}\right).$$

See Figure 6.47.

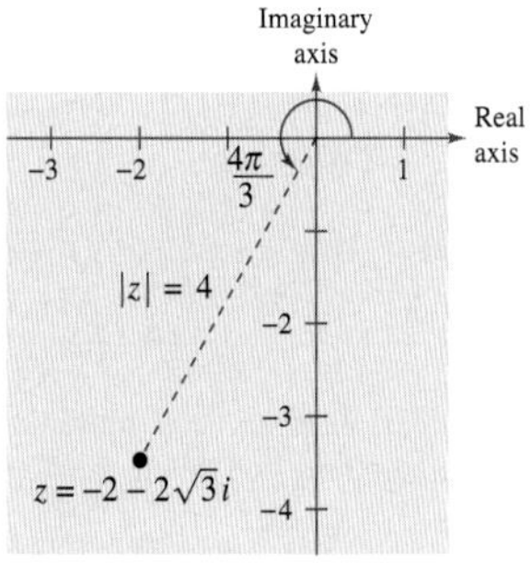

FIGURE 6.47

CHECKPoint Now try Exercise 17.

3 TEACH

Extra Example 1

Plot $z = 3 - 4i$ and find its absolute value.

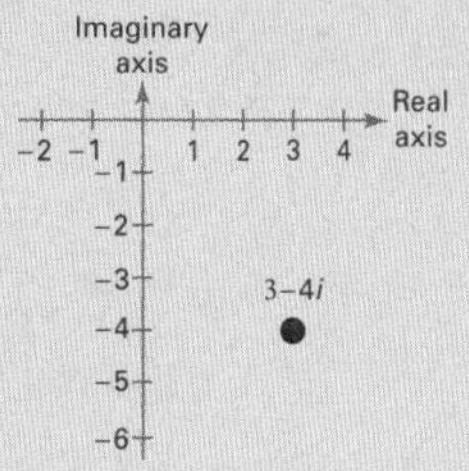

5

Extra Example 2

Write the complex number $z = 6 - 6i$ in trigonometric form.

$$z = 6\sqrt{2}\left(\cos\frac{7\pi}{4} + i\sin\frac{7\pi}{4}\right)$$

Avoiding Common Errors

Calculator errors often occur during conversion of a point in the complex plane to a trigonometric form. Students should be aware that the $\tan^{-1}$ function key will give an angle restricted to quadrant IV or I. The argument of the answer must be adjusted to reflect the quadrant containing the signs for the complex number or point.

Extra Example 3

Write the complex number $z = 8\left(\cos\frac{2\pi}{3} + i\sin\frac{2\pi}{3}\right)$ in standard form $a + bi$.

$-4 + 4\sqrt{3}i$

TECHNOLOGY

A graphing utility can be used to convert a complex number in trigonometric (or polar) form to standard form. For specific keystrokes, see the user's manual for your graphing utility.

Example 3 Writing a Complex Number in Standard Form

Write the complex number in standard form $a + bi$.

$$z = \sqrt{8}\left[\cos\left(-\frac{\pi}{3}\right) + i\sin\left(-\frac{\pi}{3}\right)\right]$$

Solution

Because $\cos\left(-\frac{\pi}{3}\right) = \frac{1}{2}$ and $\sin\left(-\frac{\pi}{3}\right) = -\frac{\sqrt{3}}{2}$, you can write

$$\begin{aligned} z &= \sqrt{8}\left[\cos\left(-\frac{\pi}{3}\right) + i\sin\left(-\frac{\pi}{3}\right)\right] \\ &= 2\sqrt{2}\left(\frac{1}{2} - \frac{\sqrt{3}}{2}i\right) \\ &= \sqrt{2} - \sqrt{6}i. \end{aligned}$$

CHECK*Point* Now try Exercise 35.

Multiplication and Division of Complex Numbers

The trigonometric form adapts nicely to multiplication and division of complex numbers. Suppose you are given two complex numbers

$$z_1 = r_1(\cos\theta_1 + i\sin\theta_1) \quad \text{and} \quad z_2 = r_2(\cos\theta_2 + i\sin\theta_2).$$

The product of z_1 and z_2 is given by

$$\begin{aligned} z_1z_2 &= r_1r_2(\cos\theta_1 + i\sin\theta_1)(\cos\theta_2 + i\sin\theta_2) \\ &= r_1r_2[(\cos\theta_1\cos\theta_2 - \sin\theta_1\sin\theta_2) + i(\sin\theta_1\cos\theta_2 + \cos\theta_1\sin\theta_2)]. \end{aligned}$$

Using the sum and difference formulas for cosine and sine, you can rewrite this equation as

$$z_1z_2 = r_1r_2[\cos(\theta_1 + \theta_2) + i\sin(\theta_1 + \theta_2)].$$

This establishes the first part of the following rule. The second part is left for you to verify (see Exercise 109).

Product and Quotient of Two Complex Numbers

Let $z_1 = r_1(\cos\theta_1 + i\sin\theta_1)$ and $z_2 = r_2(\cos\theta_2 + i\sin\theta_2)$ be complex numbers.

$$z_1z_2 = r_1r_2[\cos(\theta_1 + \theta_2) + i\sin(\theta_1 + \theta_2)] \qquad \text{Product}$$

$$\frac{z_1}{z_2} = \frac{r_1}{r_2}[\cos(\theta_1 - \theta_2) + i\sin(\theta_1 - \theta_2)], \quad z_2 \neq 0 \qquad \text{Quotient}$$

Note that this rule says that to *multiply* two complex numbers you multiply moduli and add arguments, whereas to *divide* two complex numbers you divide moduli and subtract arguments.

Example 4 Multiplying Complex Numbers

Find the product z_1z_2 of the complex numbers.

$$z_1 = 2\left(\cos\frac{2\pi}{3} + i\sin\frac{2\pi}{3}\right) \qquad z_2 = 8\left(\cos\frac{11\pi}{6} + i\sin\frac{11\pi}{6}\right)$$

Solution

$$z_1z_2 = 2\left(\cos\frac{2\pi}{3} + i\sin\frac{2\pi}{3}\right)\cdot 8\left(\cos\frac{11\pi}{6} + i\sin\frac{11\pi}{6}\right)$$

$$= 16\left[\cos\left(\frac{2\pi}{3} + \frac{11\pi}{6}\right) + i\sin\left(\frac{2\pi}{3} + \frac{11\pi}{6}\right)\right]$$ Multiply moduli and add arguments.

$$= 16\left(\cos\frac{5\pi}{2} + i\sin\frac{5\pi}{2}\right)$$

$$= 16\left(\cos\frac{\pi}{2} + i\sin\frac{\pi}{2}\right)$$ $\frac{5\pi}{2}$ and $\frac{\pi}{2}$ are coterminal.

$$= 16[0 + i(1)]$$

$$= 16i$$

TECHNOLOGY

Some graphing utilities can multiply and divide complex numbers in trigonometric form. If you have access to such a graphing utility, use it to find z_1z_2 and z_1/z_2 in Examples 4 and 5.

You can check this result by first converting the complex numbers to the standard forms $z_1 = -1 + \sqrt{3}i$ and $z_2 = 4\sqrt{3} - 4i$ and then multiplying algebraically, as in Section 2.4.

$$z_1z_2 = \left(-1 + \sqrt{3}i\right)\left(4\sqrt{3} - 4i\right)$$

$$= -4\sqrt{3} + 4i + 12i + 4\sqrt{3}$$

$$= 16i$$

CHECK**Point** Now try Exercise 47.

Example 5 Dividing Complex Numbers

Find the quotient z_1/z_2 of the complex numbers.

$$z_1 = 24(\cos 300° + i\sin 300°) \qquad z_2 = 8(\cos 75° + i\sin 75°)$$

Solution

$$\frac{z_1}{z_2} = \frac{24(\cos 300° + i\sin 300°)}{8(\cos 75° + i\sin 75°)}$$

$$= \frac{24}{8}[\cos(300° - 75°) + i\sin(300° - 75°)]$$ Divide moduli and subtract arguments.

$$= 3(\cos 225° + i\sin 225°)$$

$$= 3\left[\left(-\frac{\sqrt{2}}{2}\right) + i\left(-\frac{\sqrt{2}}{2}\right)\right]$$

$$= -\frac{3\sqrt{2}}{2} - \frac{3\sqrt{2}}{2}i$$

CHECK**Point** Now try Exercise 53.

Extra Example 4

Find the product z_1z_2 of the complex numbers $z_1 = 3\left(\cos\frac{\pi}{3} + i\sin\frac{\pi}{3}\right)$ and $z_2 = 4\left(\cos\frac{\pi}{6} + i\sin\frac{\pi}{6}\right)$.

$12i$

Extra Example 5

Find the quotient $\frac{z_1}{z_2}$ of the complex numbers $z_1 = \cos 40° + i\sin 40°$ and $z_2 = \cos 10° + i\sin 10°$.

$\frac{\sqrt{3}}{2} + \frac{1}{2}i$

Extra Example 6

Use DeMoivre's Theorem to find $(1 + i)^6$.

$-8i$

Powers of Complex Numbers

The trigonometric form of a complex number is used to raise a complex number to a power. To accomplish this, consider repeated use of the multiplication rule.

$$z = r(\cos\theta + i\sin\theta)$$
$$z^2 = r(\cos\theta + i\sin\theta)r(\cos\theta + i\sin\theta) = r^2(\cos 2\theta + i\sin 2\theta)$$
$$z^3 = r^2(\cos 2\theta + i\sin 2\theta)r(\cos\theta + i\sin\theta) = r^3(\cos 3\theta + i\sin 3\theta)$$
$$z^4 = r^4(\cos 4\theta + i\sin 4\theta)$$
$$z^5 = r^5(\cos 5\theta + i\sin 5\theta)$$
$$\vdots$$

This pattern leads to DeMoivre's Theorem, which is named after the French mathematician Abraham DeMoivre (1667–1754).

HISTORICAL NOTE

Abraham DeMoivre (1667–1754) is remembered for his work in probability theory and DeMoivre's Theorem. His book *The Doctrine of Chances* (published in 1718) includes the theory of recurring series and the theory of partial fractions.

DeMoivre's Theorem

If $z = r(\cos\theta + i\sin\theta)$ is a complex number and n is a positive integer, then

$$\begin{aligned} z^n &= [r(\cos\theta + i\sin\theta)]^n \\ &= r^n(\cos n\theta + i\sin n\theta). \end{aligned}$$

Example 6 Finding Powers of a Complex Number

Use DeMoivre's Theorem to find $(-1 + \sqrt{3}i)^{12}$.

Solution

First convert the complex number to trigonometric form using

$$r = \sqrt{(-1)^2 + (\sqrt{3})^2} = 2 \quad \text{and} \quad \theta = \arctan\frac{\sqrt{3}}{-1} = \frac{2\pi}{3}.$$

So, the trigonometric form is

$$z = -1 + \sqrt{3}i = 2\left(\cos\frac{2\pi}{3} + i\sin\frac{2\pi}{3}\right).$$

Then, by DeMoivre's Theorem, you have

$$\begin{aligned} (-1 + \sqrt{3}i)^{12} &= \left[2\left(\cos\frac{2\pi}{3} + i\sin\frac{2\pi}{3}\right)\right]^{12} \\ &= 2^{12}\left[\cos\frac{12(2\pi)}{3} + i\sin\frac{12(2\pi)}{3}\right] \\ &= 4096(\cos 8\pi + i\sin 8\pi) \\ &= 4096(1 + 0) \\ &= 4096. \end{aligned}$$

CHECKPoint Now try Exercise 69.

Roots of Complex Numbers

Recall that a consequence of the Fundamental Theorem of Algebra is that a polynomial equation of degree n has n solutions in the complex number system. So, the equation $x^6 = 1$ has six solutions, and in this particular case you can find the six solutions by factoring and using the Quadratic Formula.

$$\begin{aligned} x^6 - 1 &= (x^3 - 1)(x^3 + 1) \\ &= (x - 1)(x^2 + x + 1)(x + 1)(x^2 - x + 1) = 0 \end{aligned}$$

Consequently, the solutions are

$$x = \pm 1, \qquad x = \frac{-1 \pm \sqrt{3}i}{2}, \qquad \text{and} \qquad x = \frac{1 \pm \sqrt{3}i}{2}.$$

Each of these numbers is a sixth root of 1. In general, an ***n*th root of a complex number** is defined as follows.

> **Definition of an *n*th Root of a Complex Number**
>
> The complex number $u = a + bi$ is an ***n*th root** of the complex number z if
>
> $$z = u^n = (a + bi)^n.$$

To find a formula for an nth root of a complex number, let u be an nth root of z, where

$$u = s(\cos \beta + i \sin \beta)$$

and

$$z = r(\cos \theta + i \sin \theta).$$

By DeMoivre's Theorem and the fact that $u^n = z$, you have

$$s^n(\cos n\beta + i \sin n\beta) = r(\cos \theta + i \sin \theta).$$

Taking the absolute value of each side of this equation, it follows that $s^n = r$. Substituting back into the previous equation and dividing by r, you get

$$\cos n\beta + i \sin n\beta = \cos \theta + i \sin \theta.$$

So, it follows that

$$\cos n\beta = \cos \theta \qquad \text{and} \qquad \sin n\beta = \sin \theta.$$

Because both sine and cosine have a period of 2π, these last two equations have solutions if and only if the angles differ by a multiple of 2π. Consequently, there must exist an integer k such that

$$\begin{aligned} n\beta &= \theta + 2\pi k \\ \beta &= \frac{\theta + 2\pi k}{n}. \end{aligned}$$

By substituting this value of β into the trigonometric form of u, you get the result stated on the following page.

Extra Example 7

Find all the fourth roots of 1.

$k = 0$: 1; $k = 1$: i; $k = 2$: -1; $k = 3$: $-i$

Finding nth Roots of a Complex Number

For a positive integer n, the complex number $z = r(\cos\theta + i\sin\theta)$ has exactly n distinct nth roots given by

$$\sqrt[n]{r}\left(\cos\frac{\theta + 2\pi k}{n} + i\sin\frac{\theta + 2\pi k}{n}\right)$$

where $k = 0, 1, 2, \ldots, n - 1$.

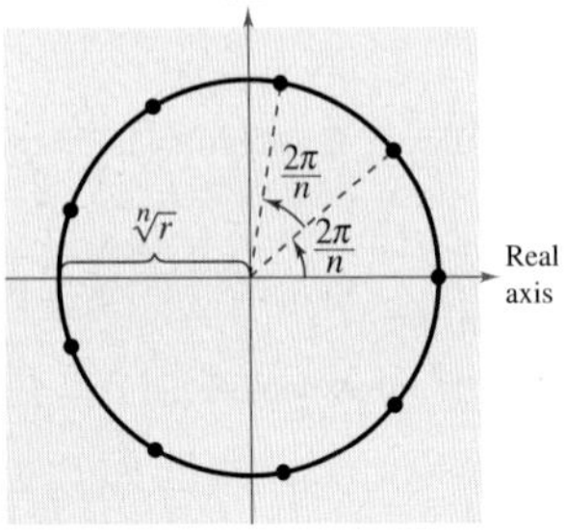

FIGURE 6.48

When k exceeds $n - 1$, the roots begin to repeat. For instance, if $k = n$, the angle

$$\frac{\theta + 2\pi n}{n} = \frac{\theta}{n} + 2\pi$$

is coterminal with θ/n, which is also obtained when $k = 0$.

The formula for the nth roots of a complex number z has a nice geometrical interpretation, as shown in Figure 6.48. Note that because the nth roots of z all have the same magnitude $\sqrt[n]{r}$, they all lie on a circle of radius $\sqrt[n]{r}$ with center at the origin. Furthermore, because successive nth roots have arguments that differ by $2\pi/n$, the n roots are equally spaced around the circle.

You have already found the sixth roots of 1 by factoring and by using the Quadratic Formula. Example 7 shows how you can solve the same problem with the formula for nth roots.

Example 7 Finding the nth Roots of a Real Number

Find all sixth roots of 1.

Solution

First write 1 in the trigonometric form $1 = 1(\cos 0 + i\sin 0)$. Then, by the nth root formula, with $n = 6$ and $r = 1$, the roots have the form

$$\sqrt[6]{1}\left(\cos\frac{0 + 2\pi k}{6} + i\sin\frac{0 + 2\pi k}{6}\right) = \cos\frac{\pi k}{3} + i\sin\frac{\pi k}{3}.$$

So, for $k = 0, 1, 2, 3, 4,$ and 5, the sixth roots are as follows. (See Figure 6.49.)

$$\cos 0 + i\sin 0 = 1$$

$$\cos\frac{\pi}{3} + i\sin\frac{\pi}{3} = \frac{1}{2} + \frac{\sqrt{3}}{2}i$$ Increment by $\frac{2\pi}{n} = \frac{2\pi}{6} = \frac{\pi}{3}$

$$\cos\frac{2\pi}{3} + i\sin\frac{2\pi}{3} = -\frac{1}{2} + \frac{\sqrt{3}}{2}i$$

$$\cos\pi + i\sin\pi = -1$$

$$\cos\frac{4\pi}{3} + i\sin\frac{4\pi}{3} = -\frac{1}{2} - \frac{\sqrt{3}}{2}i$$

$$\cos\frac{5\pi}{3} + i\sin\frac{5\pi}{3} = \frac{1}{2} - \frac{\sqrt{3}}{2}i$$

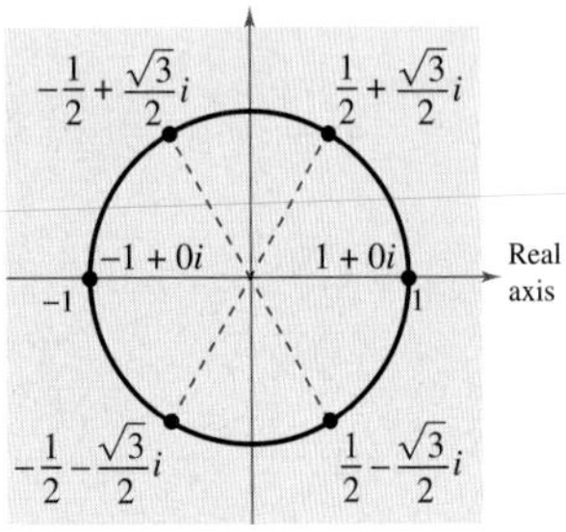

FIGURE 6.49

CHECK*Point* Now try Exercise 91.

In Figure 6.49, notice that the roots obtained in Example 7 all have a magnitude of 1 and are equally spaced around the unit circle. Also notice that the complex roots occur in conjugate pairs, as discussed in Section 2.5. The n distinct nth roots of 1 are called the ***n*th roots of unity.**

Example 8 Finding the *n*th Roots of a Complex Number

Find the three cube roots of $z = -2 + 2i$.

Solution

Because z lies in Quadrant II, the trigonometric form of z is

$$z = -2 + 2i$$
$$= \sqrt{8}\,(\cos 135^\circ + i \sin 135^\circ). \qquad \theta = \arctan\left(\frac{2}{-2}\right) = 135^\circ$$

By the formula for nth roots, the cube roots have the form

$$\sqrt[6]{8}\left(\cos\frac{135^\circ + 360^\circ k}{3} + i \sin\frac{135^\circ + 360^\circ k}{3}\right).$$

Finally, for $k = 0, 1,$ and 2, you obtain the roots

$$\sqrt[6]{8}\left(\cos\frac{135^\circ + 360^\circ(0)}{3} + i \sin\frac{135^\circ + 360^\circ(0)}{3}\right) = \sqrt{2}(\cos 45^\circ + i \sin 45^\circ)$$
$$= 1 + i$$

$$\sqrt[6]{8}\left(\cos\frac{135^\circ + 360^\circ(1)}{3} + i \sin\frac{135^\circ + 360^\circ(1)}{3}\right) = \sqrt{2}(\cos 165^\circ + i \sin 165^\circ)$$
$$\approx -1.3660 + 0.3660i$$

$$\sqrt[6]{8}\left(\cos\frac{135^\circ + 360^\circ(2)}{3} + i \sin\frac{135^\circ + 360^\circ(2)}{3}\right) = \sqrt{2}(\cos 285^\circ + i \sin 285^\circ)$$
$$\approx 0.3660 - 1.3660i.$$

See Figure 6.50.

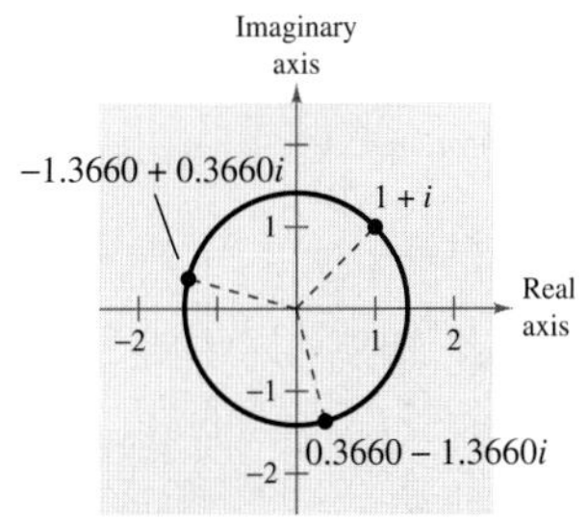

FIGURE 6.50

CHECKPoint Now try Exercise 97.

Study Tip

Note in Example 8 that the absolute value of z is

$$r = |-2 + 2i|$$
$$= \sqrt{(-2)^2 + 2^2}$$
$$= \sqrt{8}$$

and the angle θ is given by

$$\tan\theta = \frac{b}{a} = \frac{2}{-2} = -1.$$

Classroom Discussion

A Famous Mathematical Formula The famous formula

$$e^{a+bi} = e^a(\cos b + i \sin b)$$

is called Euler's Formula, after the Swiss mathematician Leonhard Euler (1707–1783). Although the interpretation of this formula is beyond the scope of this text, we decided to include it because it gives rise to one of the most wonderful equations in mathematics.

$$e^{\pi i} + 1 = 0$$

This elegant equation relates the five most famous numbers in mathematics—0, 1, π, e, and i—in a single equation. Show how Euler's Formula can be used to derive this equation. See margin.

Extra Example 8

Find the three cube roots of $z = -6 + 6i$.

$k = 0$: $\approx 1.4422 + 1.4422i$

$k = 1$: $\approx -1.9701 + 0.59279i$

$k = 2$: $\approx 0.52790 - 1.9701i$

Closing the Lesson

Have students summarize the major points of the lesson and answer the Essential Question: How do you represent complex numbers and perform operations on them by using trigonometry?

- **Plot a complex number $a + bi$ as the point (a, b) on the complex plane, and find its absolute value by finding the distance between (a, b) and the origin.**
- **Write a complex number in trigonometric form $z = r(\cos\theta + i \sin\theta)$.**
- **Use trigonometric formulas to find the product or quotient of two complex numbers.**
- **Use DeMoivre's Theorem to find powers and roots of complex numbers.**

Classroom Discussion

$e^{a+bi} = e^a(\cos b + i \sin b)$

Let $a = 0$ and $b = \pi$.

$$e^{0+\pi i} = e^0(\cos\pi + i \sin\pi)$$
$$e^{\pi i} = -1$$
$$e^{\pi i} + 1 = 0$$

4 PRACTICE AND APPLY

Assignment Guide

Transparencies Available
Available at the Instructor's companion site.

Average:
Day 1: pp. 476–477
Exs. 1, 2, 9–15 odd, 19–27 odd, 31–35 odd, 39–43 odd, 48, 49, 51, 57, 59, 63
Day 2: pp. 476–477
Exs. 3, 4, 65, 67, 68, 73–77 odd, 81–89 odd, 93, 95, 100, 103, 105, 108, 111, 116

Advanced:
Day 1: pp. 476–477
Exs. 1, 2, 10–16 even, 22, 24, 28–38 even, 42, 44, 48–54 even, 55, 58, 60, 64
Day 2: pp. 476–477
Exs. 3, 4, 66, 68, 72–76 even, 80–88 even, 98, 101, 104, 106, 107, 110, 114, 116

Block:
pp. 476–477
Exs. 1–4, 9–15 odd, 19–27 odd, 31–35 odd, 39–43 odd, 48, 49, 51, 57, 59, 63–67 odd, 68, 73–77 odd, 81–89 odd, 93, 95, 100, 103, 105, 108, 111, 116

6.5 EXERCISES

See www.CalcChat.com for worked-out solutions to odd-numbered exercises.

VOCABULARY: Fill in the blanks.

1. The absolute value of a complex number $a + bi$ is the distance between the origin $(0, 0)$ and the point (a, b).
2. The trigonometric form of a complex number $z = a + bi$ is given by $z = r(\cos\theta + i\sin\theta)$, where r is the modulus of z and θ is the argument of z.
3. ________ Theorem states that if $z = r(\cos\theta + i\sin\theta)$ is a complex number and n is a positive integer, then $z^n = r^n(\cos n\theta + i\sin n\theta)$. DeMoivre's
4. The complex number $u = a + bi$ is an nth root of the complex number z if $z = u^n = (a + bi)^n$.

SKILLS AND APPLICATIONS

In Exercises 5–10, plot the complex number and find its absolute value. 5–10. See margin.

5. $-6 + 8i$
6. $5 - 12i$
7. $-7i$
8. -7
9. $4 - 6i$
10. $-8 + 3i$

In Exercises 11–14, write the complex number in trigonometric form. 11–14. See margin.

11. 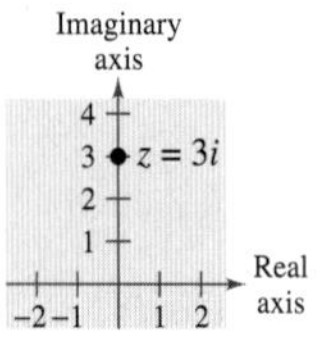

12. 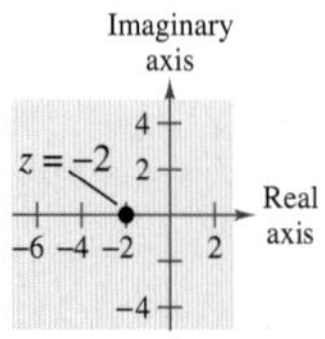

13. 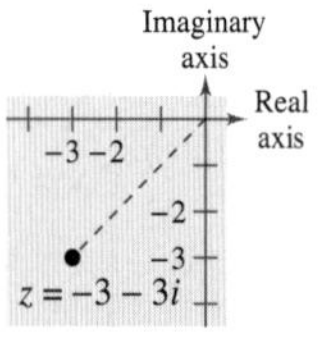

14. 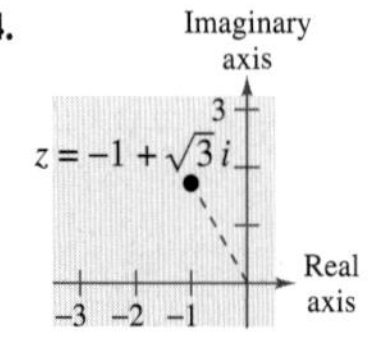

15–32. See margin.
In Exercises 15–32, represent the complex number graphically, and find the trigonometric form of the number.

15. $1 + i$
16. $5 - 5i$
17. $1 - \sqrt{3}i$
18. $4 - 4\sqrt{3}i$
19. $-2(1 + \sqrt{3}i)$
20. $\frac{5}{2}(\sqrt{3} - i)$
21. $-5i$
22. $12i$
23. $-7 + 4i$
24. $3 - i$
25. 2
26. 4
27. $2\sqrt{2} - i$
28. $-3 - i$
29. $5 + 2i$
30. $8 + 3i$
31. $-8 - 5\sqrt{3}i$
32. $-9 - 2\sqrt{10}i$

33–42. See margin.
In Exercises 33–42, find the standard form of the complex number. Then represent the complex number graphically.

33. $2(\cos 60° + i\sin 60°)$
34. $5(\cos 135° + i\sin 135°)$
35. $\sqrt{48}[\cos(-30°) + i\sin(-30°)]$
36. $\sqrt{8}(\cos 225° + i\sin 225°)$
37. $\frac{9}{4}\left(\cos\frac{3\pi}{4} + i\sin\frac{3\pi}{4}\right)$
38. $6\left(\cos\frac{5\pi}{12} + i\sin\frac{5\pi}{12}\right)$
39. $7(\cos 0 + i\sin 0)$
40. $8\left(\cos\frac{\pi}{2} + i\sin\frac{\pi}{2}\right)$
41. $5[\cos(198°\,45') + i\sin(198°\,45')]$
42. $9.75[\cos(280°\,30') + i\sin(280°\,30')]$

In Exercises 43–46, use a graphing utility to represent the complex number in standard form. 43–46. See margin.

43. $5\left(\cos\frac{\pi}{9} + i\sin\frac{\pi}{9}\right)$
44. $10\left(\cos\frac{2\pi}{5} + i\sin\frac{2\pi}{5}\right)$
45. $2(\cos 155° + i\sin 155°)$
46. $9(\cos 58° + i\sin 58°)$

In Exercises 47–58, perform the operation and leave the result in trigonometric form. 47–58. See margin.

47. $\left[2\left(\cos\frac{\pi}{4} + i\sin\frac{\pi}{4}\right)\right]\left[6\left(\cos\frac{\pi}{12} + i\sin\frac{\pi}{12}\right)\right]$
48. $\left[\frac{3}{4}\left(\cos\frac{\pi}{3} + i\sin\frac{\pi}{3}\right)\right]\left[4\left(\cos\frac{3\pi}{4} + i\sin\frac{3\pi}{4}\right)\right]$
49. $\left[\frac{5}{3}(\cos 120° + i\sin 120°)\right]\left[\frac{2}{3}(\cos 30° + i\sin 30°)\right]$
50. $\left[\frac{1}{2}(\cos 100° + i\sin 100°)\right]\left[\frac{4}{5}(\cos 300° + i\sin 300°)\right]$
51. $(\cos 80° + i\sin 80°)(\cos 330° + i\sin 330°)$
52. $(\cos 5° + i\sin 5°)(\cos 20° + i\sin 20°)$
53. $\dfrac{3(\cos 50° + i\sin 50°)}{9(\cos 20° + i\sin 20°)}$
54. $\dfrac{\cos 120° + i\sin 120°}{2(\cos 40° + i\sin 40°)}$
55. $\dfrac{\cos\pi + i\sin\pi}{\cos(\pi/3) + i\sin(\pi/3)}$
56. $\dfrac{5(\cos 4.3 + i\sin 4.3)}{4(\cos 2.1 + i\sin 2.1)}$
57. $\dfrac{12(\cos 92° + i\sin 92°)}{2(\cos 122° + i\sin 122°)}$
58. $\dfrac{6(\cos 40° + i\sin 40°)}{7(\cos 100° + i\sin 100°)}$

5. 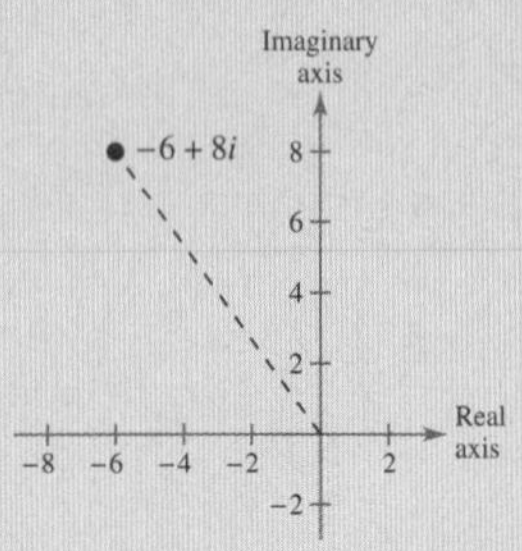

10

6. 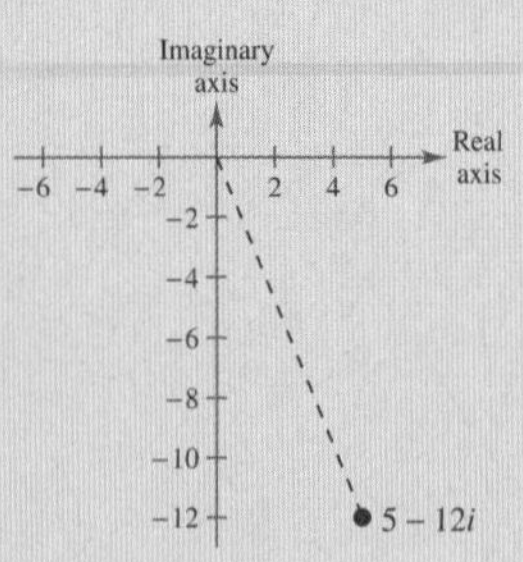

13

7. 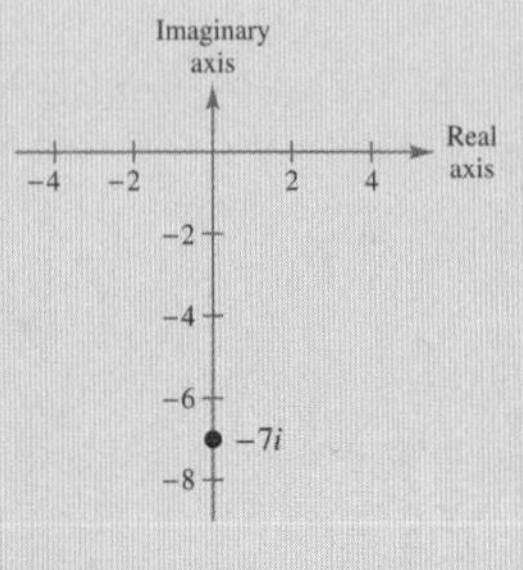

7

8. 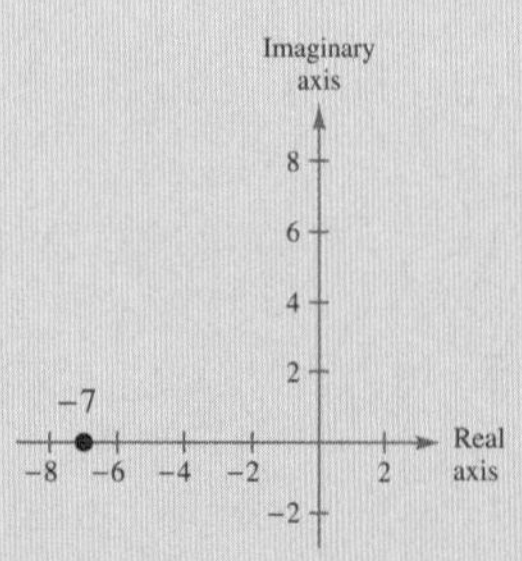

7

9. 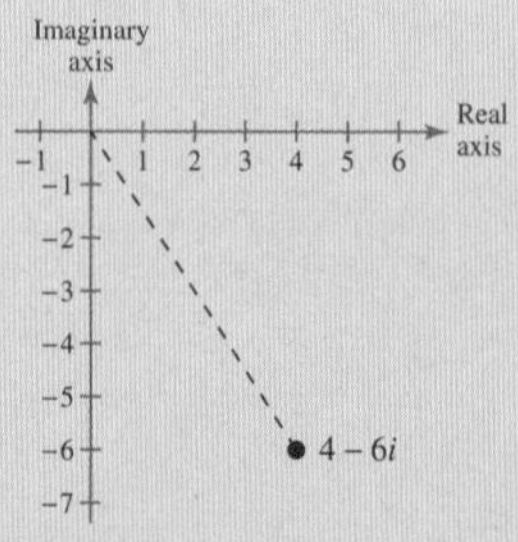

$2\sqrt{13}$

10. 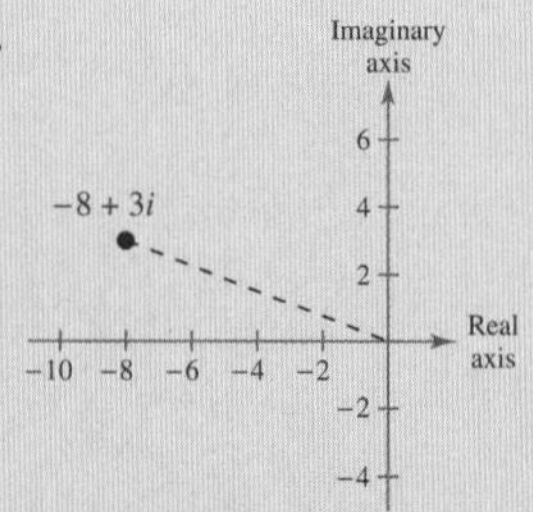

$\sqrt{73}$

11–58. See Additional Answers beginning on page AA1.

In Exercises 59–64, (a) write the trigonometric forms of the complex numbers, (b) perform the indicated operation using the trigonometric forms, and (c) perform the indicated operation using the standard forms, and check your result with that of part (b). 59–64. See margin.

59. $(2 + 2i)(1 - i)$ **60.** $(\sqrt{3} + i)(1 + i)$

61. $-2i(1 + i)$ **62.** $3i(1 - \sqrt{2}i)$

63. $\dfrac{3 + 4i}{1 - \sqrt{3}i}$ **64.** $\dfrac{1 + \sqrt{3}i}{6 - 3i}$

In Exercises 65 and 66, represent the powers z, z^2, z^3, and z^4 graphically. Describe the pattern. 65–66. See margin.

65. $z = \dfrac{\sqrt{2}}{2}(1 + i)$ **66.** $z = \dfrac{1}{2}(1 + \sqrt{3}i)$

In Exercises 67–82, use DeMoivre's Theorem to find the indicated power of the complex number. Write the result in standard form. 71, 73–74, 77, 81. See margin.

67. $(1 + i)^5$ $-4 - 4i$ **68.** $(2 + 2i)^6$ $-512i$

69. $(-1 + i)^6$ $8i$ **70.** $(3 - 2i)^8$ $-239 + 28{,}560i$

71. $2(\sqrt{3} + i)^{10}$ **72.** $4(1 - \sqrt{3}i)^3$ -32

73. $[5(\cos 20° + i \sin 20°)]^3$ **74.** $[3(\cos 60° + i \sin 60°)]^4$

75. $\left(\cos \dfrac{\pi}{4} + i \sin \dfrac{\pi}{4}\right)^{12}$ -1 **76.** $\left[2\left(\cos \dfrac{\pi}{2} + i \sin \dfrac{\pi}{2}\right)\right]^8$ 256

77. $[5(\cos 3.2 + i \sin 3.2)]^4$ **78.** $(\cos 0 + i \sin 0)^{20}$ 1

79. $(3 - 2i)^5$ $-597 - 122i$ **80.** $(\sqrt{5} - 4i)^3$ $-43\sqrt{5} + 4i$

81. $[3(\cos 15° + i \sin 15°)]^4$ **82.** $\left[2\left(\cos \dfrac{\pi}{8} + i \sin \dfrac{\pi}{8}\right)\right]^6$ $-32\sqrt{2} + 32\sqrt{2}i$

In Exercises 83–98, (a) use the formula on page 474 to find the indicated roots of the complex number, (b) represent each of the roots graphically, and (c) write each of the roots in standard form. 83–98. See margin.

83. Square roots of $5(\cos 120° + i \sin 120°)$

84. Square roots of $16(\cos 60° + i \sin 60°)$

85. Cube roots of $8\left(\cos \dfrac{2\pi}{3} + i \sin \dfrac{2\pi}{3}\right)$

86. Fifth roots of $32\left(\cos \dfrac{5\pi}{6} + i \sin \dfrac{5\pi}{6}\right)$

87. Cube roots of $-\frac{125}{2}(1 + \sqrt{3}i)$

88. Cube roots of $-4\sqrt{2}(-1 + i)$

89. Square roots of $-25i$ **90.** Fourth roots of $625i$

91. Fourth roots of 16 **92.** Fourth roots of i

93. Fifth roots of 1 **94.** Cube roots of 1000

95. Cube roots of -125 **96.** Fourth roots of -4

97. Fifth roots of $4(1 - i)$ **98.** Sixth roots of $64i$

In Exercises 99–106, use the formula on page 474 to find all the solutions of the equation and represent the solutions graphically. 99–106. See margin.

99. $x^4 + i = 0$ **100.** $x^3 + 1 = 0$

101. $x^5 + 243 = 0$ **102.** $x^3 - 27 = 0$

103. $x^4 + 16i = 0$ **104.** $x^6 + 64i = 0$

105. $x^3 - (1 - i) = 0$ **106.** $x^4 + (1 + i) = 0$

EXPLORATION

107–108. See margin.

TRUE OR FALSE? In Exercises 107 and 108, determine whether the statement is true or false. Justify your answer.

107. Geometrically, the nth roots of any complex number z are all equally spaced around the unit circle centered at the origin.

108. The product of two complex numbers is zero only when the modulus of one (or both) of the complex numbers is zero.

109. Given two complex numbers $z_1 = r_1(\cos \theta_1 + i \sin \theta_1)$ and $z_2 = r_2(\cos \theta_2 + i \sin \theta_2)$, $z_2 \neq 0$, show that

$$\frac{z_1}{z_2} = \frac{r_1}{r_2}[\cos(\theta_1 - \theta_2) + i \sin(\theta_1 - \theta_2)].$$ Answers will vary.

110. Show that $\bar{z} = r[\cos(-\theta) + i \sin(-\theta)]$ is the complex conjugate of $z = r(\cos \theta + i \sin \theta)$. Answers will vary.

111. Use the trigonometric forms of z and $\bar{z}$ in Exercise 110 to find (a) $z\bar{z}$ and (b) $z/\bar{z}$, $\bar{z} \neq 0$. See margin.

112. Show that the negative of $z = r(\cos \theta + i \sin \theta)$ is $-z = r[\cos(\theta + \pi) + i \sin(\theta + \pi)]$. Answers will vary.

113. Show that $\frac{1}{2}(1 - \sqrt{3}i)$ is a ninth root of -1. See margin.

114. Show that $2^{-1/4}(1 - i)$ is a fourth root of -2. See margin.

115. THINK ABOUT IT Explain how you can use DeMoivre's Theorem to solve the polynomial equation $x^4 + 16 = 0$. [*Hint:* Write -16 as $16(\cos \pi + i \sin \pi)$.] See margin.

116. CAPSTONE Use the graph of the roots of a complex number. See margin.

(a) Write each of the roots in trigonometric form.

(b) Identify the complex number whose roots are given. Use a graphing utility to verify your results.

(i)

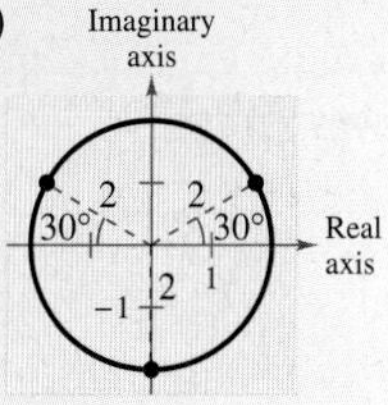

(ii)

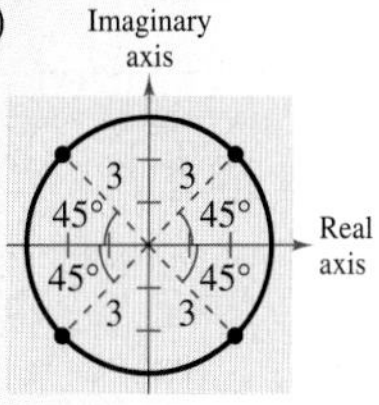

5 ASSESS AND RETEACH

Daily Homework Quiz

Transparency Available

Available at the Instructor's companion site.

65.

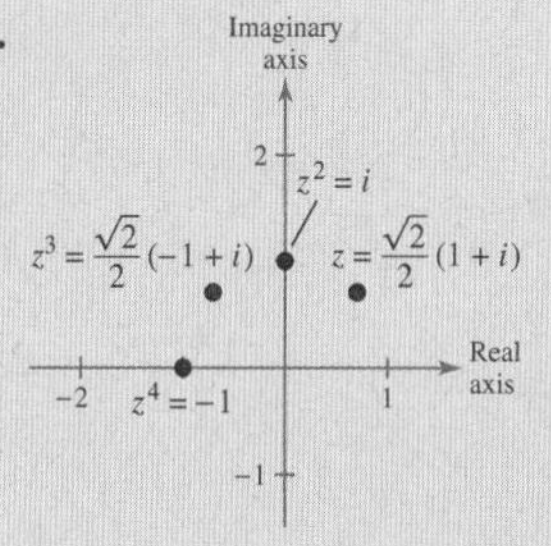

The absolute value of each is 1, and the consecutive powers of z are each 45° apart.

66.

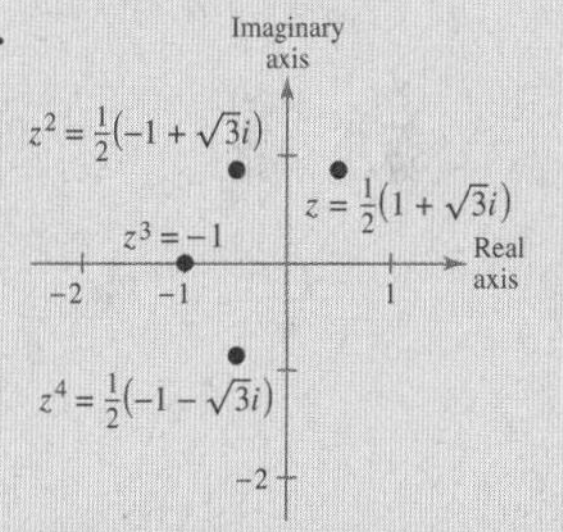

The absolute value of each is 1, and the consecutive powers of z are each $\pi/3$ radians apart.

71. $1024 - 1024\sqrt{3}i$

73. $\dfrac{125}{2} + \dfrac{125\sqrt{3}}{2}i$

74. $-\dfrac{81}{2} - \dfrac{81\sqrt{3}}{2}i$

77. $608.0 + 144.7i$

81. $\dfrac{81}{2} + \dfrac{81\sqrt{3}}{2}i$

83. (a) $\sqrt{5}(\cos 60° + i \sin 60°)$
$\sqrt{5}(\cos 240° + i \sin 240°)$

(b)

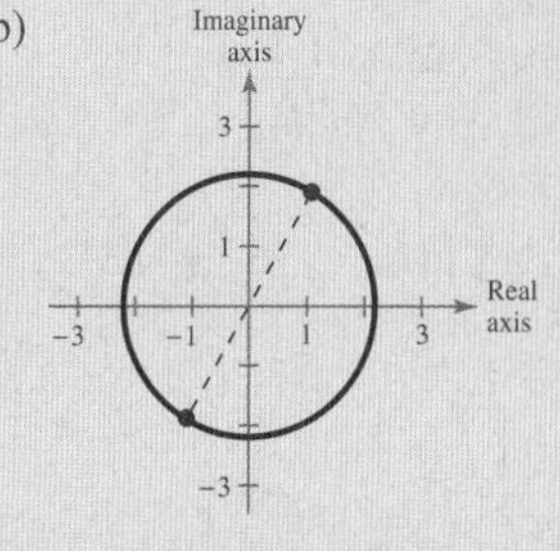

(c) $\dfrac{\sqrt{5}}{2} + \dfrac{\sqrt{15}}{2}i,\ -\dfrac{\sqrt{5}}{2} - \dfrac{\sqrt{15}}{2}i$

84. (a) $4(\cos 30° + i \sin 30°)$
$4(\cos 210° + i \sin 210°)$

(b)

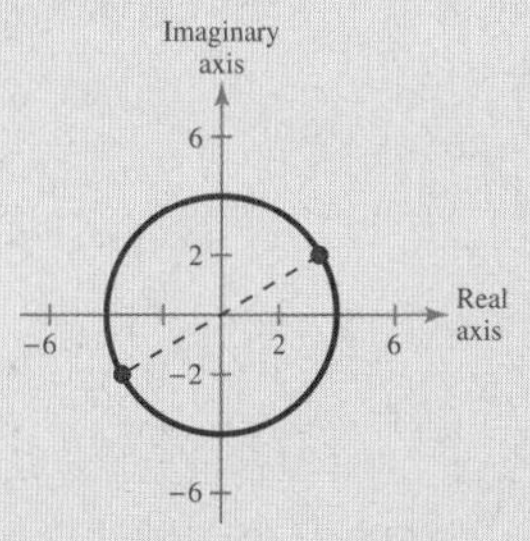

(c) $2\sqrt{3} + 2i,\ -2\sqrt{3} - 2i$

107. False. They are equally spaced around the circle centered at the origin with radius $\sqrt[n]{r}$.

108. True.
$z_1z_2 = r_1r_2[\cos(\theta_1 + \theta_2) + i \sin(\theta_1 + \theta_2)] = 0$ if and only if $r_1 = 0$ and/or $r_2 = 0$.

111. (a) r^2 (b) $\cos 2\theta + i \sin 2\theta$

113–114. Answers will vary.

59–64, 85–106, 115–116. See Additional Answers beginning on page AA1.

6 Chapter Summary

	What Did You Learn?	Explanation/Examples	Review Exercises
Section 6.1	Use the Law of Sines to solve oblique triangles (AAS or ASA) *(p. 428).*	**Law of Sines** If ABC is a triangle with sides a, b, and c, then $\dfrac{a}{\sin A} = \dfrac{b}{\sin B} = \dfrac{c}{\sin C}$. 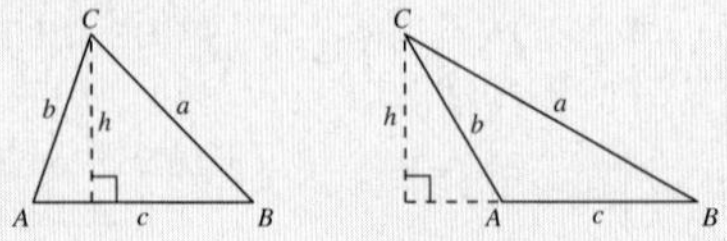 A is acute. A is obtuse.	1–12
	Use the Law of Sines to solve oblique triangles (SSA) *(p. 430).*	If two sides and one opposite angle are given, three possible situations can occur: (1) no such triangle exists (see Example 4), (2) one such triangle exists (see Example 3), or (3) two distinct triangles may satisfy the conditions. (see Example 5).	1–12
	Find the areas of oblique triangles *(p. 432).*	The area of any triangle is one-half the product of the lengths of two sides times the sine of their included angle. That is, Area $= \frac{1}{2}bc \sin A = \frac{1}{2}ab \sin C = \frac{1}{2}ac \sin B$.	13–16
	Use the Law of Sines to model and solve real-life problems *(p. 433).*	The Law of Sines can be used to approximate the total distance of a boat race course. (See Example 7.)	17–20
Section 6.2	Use the Law of Cosines to solve oblique triangles (SSS or SAS) *(p. 437).*	**Law of Cosines** *Standard Form* / *Alternative Form* $a^2 = b^2 + c^2 - 2bc \cos A$ $\cos A = \dfrac{b^2 + c^2 - a^2}{2bc}$ $b^2 = a^2 + c^2 - 2ac \cos B$ $\cos B = \dfrac{a^2 + c^2 - b^2}{2ac}$ $c^2 = a^2 + b^2 - 2ab \cos C$ $\cos C = \dfrac{a^2 + b^2 - c^2}{2ab}$	21–30
	Use the Law of Cosines to model and solve real-life problems *(p. 439).*	The Law of Cosines can be used to find the distance between a pitcher's mound and first base on a women's softball field. (See Example 3.)	35–38
	Use Heron's Area Formula to find the area of a triangle *(p. 440).*	**Heron's Area Formula:** Given any triangle with sides of lengths a, b, and c, the area of the triangle is Area $= \sqrt{s(s-a)(s-b)(s-c)}$, where $s = (a + b + c)/2$.	39–42
Section 6.3	Represent vectors as directed line segments *(p. 445).*	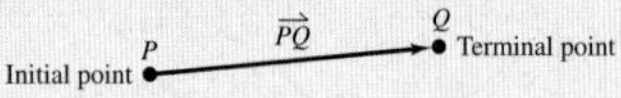	43, 44
	Write the component forms of vectors *(p. 446).*	The component form of the vector with initial point $P(p_1, p_2)$ and terminal point $Q(q_1, q_2)$ is given by $\overrightarrow{PQ} = \langle q_1 - p_1, q_2 - p_2 \rangle = \langle v_1, v_2 \rangle = \mathbf{v}$.	45–50

	What Did You Learn?	Explanation/Examples	Review Exercises
Section 6.3	Perform basic vector operations and represent them graphically *(p. 447).*	Let $\mathbf{u} = \langle u_1, u_2 \rangle$ and $\mathbf{v} = \langle v_1, v_2 \rangle$ be vectors and let k be a scalar (a real number). $\mathbf{u} + \mathbf{v} = \langle u_1 + v_1, u_2 + v_2 \rangle$ $\quad k\mathbf{u} = \langle ku_1, ku_2 \rangle$ $-\mathbf{v} = \langle -v_1, -v_2 \rangle$ $\quad \mathbf{u} - \mathbf{v} = \langle u_1 - v_1, u_2 - v_2 \rangle$	51–62
	Write vectors as linear combinations of unit vectors *(p. 449).*	$\mathbf{v} = \langle v_1, v_2 \rangle = v_1\langle 1, 0 \rangle + v_2\langle 0, 1 \rangle = v_1\mathbf{i} + v_2\mathbf{j}$ The scalars v_1 and v_2 are the horizontal and vertical components of $\mathbf{v}$, respectively. The vector sum $v_1\mathbf{i} + v_2\mathbf{j}$ is the linear combination of the vectors $\mathbf{i}$ and $\mathbf{j}$.	63–68
	Find the direction angles of vectors *(p. 451).*	If $\mathbf{u} = 2i + 2j$, then the direction angle is $\tan \theta = 2/2 = 1$. So, $\theta = 45°$.	69–74
	Use vectors to model and solve real-life problems *(p. 452).*	Vectors can be used to find the resultant speed and direction of an airplane. (See Example 10.)	75–78
Section 6.4	Find the dot product of two vectors and use the properties of the dot product *(p. 458).*	The dot product of $\mathbf{u} = \langle u_1, u_2 \rangle$ and $\mathbf{v} = \langle v_1, v_2 \rangle$ is $\mathbf{u} \cdot \mathbf{v} = u_1v_1 + u_2v_2$.	79–90
	Find the angle between two vectors and determine whether two vectors are orthogonal *(p. 459).*	If θ is the angle between two nonzero vectors $\mathbf{u}$ and $\mathbf{v}$, then $\cos \theta = \dfrac{\mathbf{u} \cdot \mathbf{v}}{\\|\mathbf{u}\\| \\|\mathbf{v}\\|}$. Vectors $\mathbf{u}$ and $\mathbf{v}$ are orthogonal if $\mathbf{u} \cdot \mathbf{v} = 0$.	91–98
	Write a vector as the sum of two vector components *(p. 461).*	Many applications in physics and engineering require the decomposition of a given vector into the sum of two vector components. (See Example 7.)	99–102
	Use vectors to find the work done by a force *(p. 464).*	The work W done by a constant force $\mathbf{F}$ as its point of application moves along the vector $\overrightarrow{PQ}$ is given by either of the following. **1.** $W = \\|\text{proj}_{\overrightarrow{PQ}}\mathbf{F}\\| \\|\overrightarrow{PQ}\\|$ $\quad$ **2.** $W = \mathbf{F} \cdot \overrightarrow{PQ}$	103–106
Section 6.5	Plot complex numbers in the complex plane and find absolute values of complex numbers *(p. 468).*	A complex number $z = a + bi$ can be represented as the point (a, b) in the complex plane. The horizontal axis is the real axis and the vertical axis is the imaginary axis. The absolute value of $z = a + bi$ is $\|a + bi\| = \sqrt{a^2 + b^2}$.	107–112
	Write the trigonometric forms of complex numbers *(p. 469).*	The trigonometric form of the complex number $z = a + bi$ is $z = r(\cos \theta + i \sin \theta)$ where $a = r \cos \theta$, $b = r \sin \theta$, $r = \sqrt{a^2 + b^2}$, and $\tan \theta = b/a$.	113–118
	Multiply and divide complex numbers written in trigonometric form *(p. 470).*	Let $z_1 = r_1(\cos \theta_1 + i \sin \theta_1)$ and $z_2 = r_2(\cos \theta_2 + i \sin \theta_2)$. $z_1z_2 = r_1r_2[\cos(\theta_1 + \theta_2) + i \sin(\theta_1 + \theta_2)]$ $z_1/z_2 = (r_1/r_2)[\cos(\theta_1 - \theta_2) + i \sin(\theta_1 - \theta_2)], \quad z_2 \neq 0$	119, 120
	Use DeMoivre's Theorem to find powers of complex numbers *(p. 472).*	**DeMoivre's Theorem:** If $z = r(\cos \theta + i \sin \theta)$ is a complex number and n is a positive integer, then $z^n = [r(\cos \theta + i \sin \theta)]^n = r^n(\cos n\theta + i \sin n\theta)$.	121–124
	Find nth roots of complex numbers *(p. 473).*	The complex number $u = a + bi$ is an nth root of the complex number z if $z = u^n = (a + bi)^n$.	125–134

1. $C = 72°, b \approx 12.21, c \approx 12.36$
2. $C = 37°, b = 43.48, c = 30.52$
3. $A = 26°, a \approx 24.89, c \approx 56.23$
4. $A = 150°, a \approx 48.24, b \approx 16.75$
5. $C = 66°, a \approx 2.53, b \approx 9.11$
6. $C = 40°, a \approx 162.42,$ $b \approx 115.29$
7. $B = 108°, a \approx 11.76, c \approx 21.49$
8. $A = 80°, b \approx 334.95,$ $c \approx 219.04$
9. $A \approx 20.41°, C \approx 9.59°,$ $a \approx 20.92$
10. No solution
11. $B \approx 39.48°, C \approx 65.52°,$ $c \approx 48.24$
12. Two solutions:
    $A \approx 40.92°, C \approx 114.08°,$
    $c \approx 8.64$
    $A \approx 139.08°, C \approx 15.92°,$
    $c \approx 2.60$
23. $A \approx 16.99°, B \approx 26.00°,$ $C \approx 137.01°$
24. $A \approx 35.32°, B \approx 22.67°,$ $C \approx 122.01°$
25. $A \approx 29.92°, B \approx 86.18°,$ $C \approx 63.90°$
26. $A \approx 101.47°, B \approx 31.73°,$ $C \approx 46.80°$
27. $A = 36°, C = 36°, b \approx 17.80$
28. $A \approx 9.90°, C \approx 20.10°,$ $b \approx 29.09$
29. $A \approx 45.76°, B \approx 91.24°,$ $c \approx 21.42$
30. $B \approx 35.20°, C \approx 82.80°,$ $a \approx 17.37$
31. Law of Sines; $A \approx 77.52°, B \approx 38.48°,$ $a \approx 14.12$
32. Law of Cosines; $A \approx 51.21°, C \approx 76.79°,$ $b \approx 4.05$
33. Law of Cosines; $A \approx 28.62°, B \approx 33.56°,$ $C \approx 117.82°$

6 REVIEW EXERCISES

See www.CalcChat.com for worked-out solutions to odd-numbered exercises.

6.1 **In Exercises 1–12, use the Law of Sines to solve (if possible) the triangle. If two solutions exist, find both. Round your answers to two decimal places.** 1–12. See margin.

1.

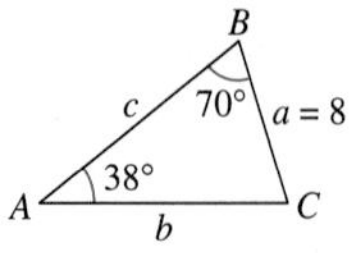

2.

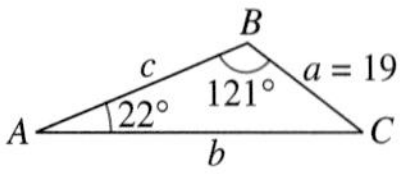

3. $B = 72°, \; C = 82°, \; b = 54$
4. $B = 10°, \; C = 20°, \; c = 33$
5. $A = 16°, \; B = 98°, \; c = 8.4$
6. $A = 95°, \; B = 45°, \; c = 104.8$
7. $A = 24°, \; C = 48°, \; b = 27.5$
8. $B = 64°, \; C = 36°, \; a = 367$
9. $B = 150°, \; b = 30, \; c = 10$
10. $B = 150°, \; a = 10, \; b = 3$
11. $A = 75°, \; a = 51.2, \; b = 33.7$
12. $B = 25°, \; a = 6.2, \; b = 4$

In Exercises 13–16, find the area of the triangle having the indicated angle and sides.

13. $A = 33°, \; b = 7, \; c = 10$ 19.06
14. $B = 80°, \; a = 4, \; c = 8$ 15.8
15. $C = 119°, \; a = 18, \; b = 6$ 47.23
16. $A = 11°, \; b = 22, \; c = 21$ 44.1

17. **HEIGHT** From a certain distance, the angle of elevation to the top of a building is 17°. At a point 50 meters closer to the building, the angle of elevation is 31°. Approximate the height of the building. 31.1 m

18. **GEOMETRY** Find the length of the side w of the parallelogram. 4.8

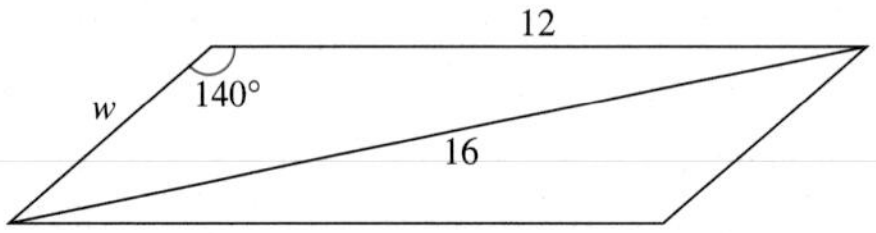

19. **HEIGHT** A tree stands on a hillside of slope 28° from the horizontal. From a point 75 feet down the hill, the angle of elevation to the top of the tree is 45° (see figure). Find the height of the tree. 31.01 ft

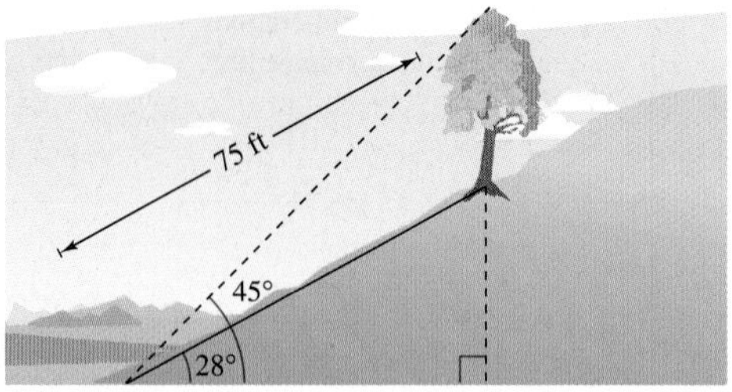

FIGURE FOR 19

20. **RIVER WIDTH** A surveyor finds that a tree on the opposite bank of a river flowing due east has a bearing of N 22° 30′ E from a certain point and a bearing of N 15° W from a point 400 feet downstream. Find the width of the river. 586.4 ft

6.2 **In Exercises 21–30, use the Law of Cosines to solve the triangle. Round your answers to two decimal places.**

21.

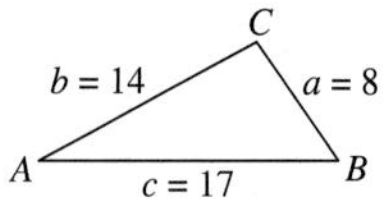

$A \approx 27.81°, B \approx 54.75°,$ $C \approx 97.44°$

22.

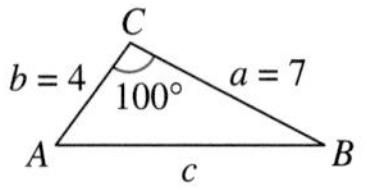

$A \approx 52.95°, B \approx 27.05°,$ $c \approx 8.64$

23. $a = 6, \; b = 9, \; c = 14$ 23–30. See margin.
24. $a = 75, \; b = 50, \; c = 110$
25. $a = 2.5, \; b = 5.0, \; c = 4.5$
26. $a = 16.4, \; b = 8.8, \; c = 12.2$
27. $B = 108°, \; a = 11, \; c = 11$
28. $B = 150°, \; a = 10, \; c = 20$
29. $C = 43°, \; a = 22.5, \; b = 31.4$
30. $A = 62°, \; b = 11.34, \; c = 19.52$

In Exercises 31–34, determine whether the Law of Sines or the Law of Cosines is needed to solve the triangle. Then solve the triangle. 31–33. See margin.

31. $b = 9, \; c = 13, \; C = 64°$
32. $a = 4, \; c = 5, \; B = 52°$
33. $a = 13, \; b = 15, \; c = 24$
34. $A = 44°, \; B = 31°, \; c = 2.8$
    Law of Sines;
    $C = 105°, a \approx 2.01, b \approx 1.49$

35. GEOMETRY The lengths of the diagonals of a parallelogram are 10 feet and 16 feet. Find the lengths of the sides of the parallelogram if the diagonals intersect at an angle of 28°. About 4.3 ft, about 12.6 ft

36. GEOMETRY The lengths of the diagonals of a parallelogram are 30 meters and 40 meters. Find the lengths of the sides of the parallelogram if the diagonals intersect at an angle of 34°. About 11.3 m, about 33.5 m

37. SURVEYING To approximate the length of a marsh, a surveyor walks 425 meters from point A to point B. Then the surveyor turns 65° and walks 300 meters to point C (see figure). Approximate the length AC of the marsh. 615.1 m

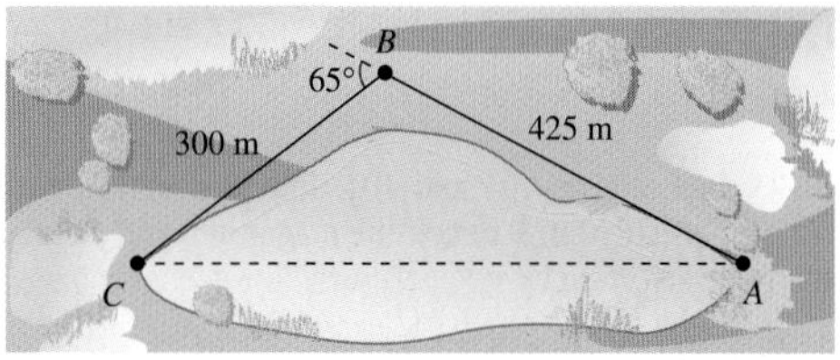

38. NAVIGATION Two planes leave an airport at approximately the same time. One is flying 425 miles per hour at a bearing of 355°, and the other is flying 530 miles per hour at a bearing of 67°. Draw a figure that gives a visual representation of the situation and determine the distance between the planes after they have flown for 2 hours. See margin.

In Exercises 39–42, use Heron's Area Formula to find the area of the triangle.

39. $a = 3,\ b = 6,\ c = 8$ 7.64

40. $a = 15,\ b = 8,\ c = 10$ 36.98

41. $a = 12.3,\ b = 15.8,\ c = 3.7$ 8.36

42. $a = \frac{4}{5},\ b = \frac{3}{4},\ c = \frac{5}{8}$ 0.22

6.3 In Exercises 43 and 44, show that **u** and **v** are equivalent.

43.

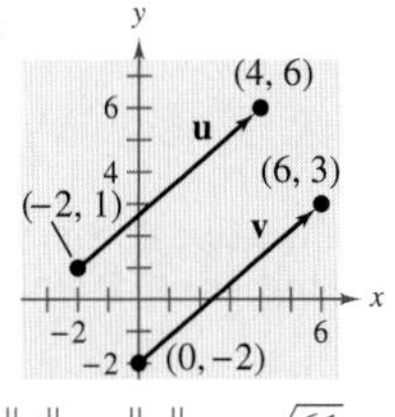

$\|\mathbf{u}\| = \|\mathbf{v}\| = \sqrt{61}$, $\text{slope}_{\mathbf{u}} = \text{slope}_{\mathbf{v}} = \frac{5}{6}$

44.

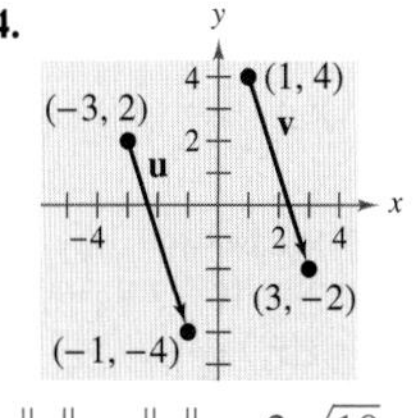

$\|\mathbf{u}\| = \|\mathbf{v}\| = 2\sqrt{10}$, $\text{slope}_{\mathbf{u}} = \text{slope}_{\mathbf{v}} = -3$

In Exercises 45–50, find the component form of the vector **v** satisfying the conditions.

45. $\langle 7, -5\rangle$

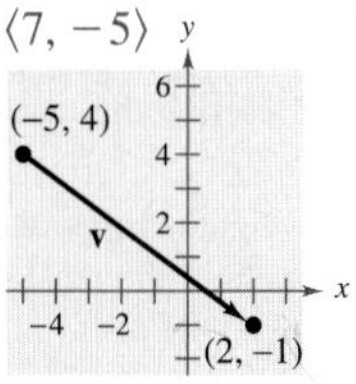

46. $\langle 6, \frac{5}{2}\rangle$

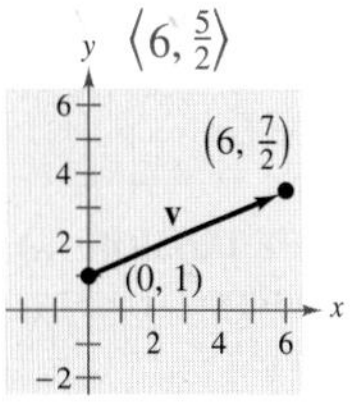

47. Initial point: (0, 10); terminal point: (7, 3) $\langle 7, -7\rangle$

48. Initial point: (1, 5); terminal point: (15, 9) $\langle 14, 4\rangle$

49. $\|\mathbf{v}\| = 8,\quad \theta = 120°$ $\langle -4, 4\sqrt{3}\rangle$

50. $\|\mathbf{v}\| = \frac{1}{2},\quad \theta = 225°$ $\left\langle -\frac{\sqrt{2}}{4}, -\frac{\sqrt{2}}{4}\right\rangle$

In Exercises 51–58, find (a) **u** + **v**, (b) **u** − **v**, (c) 4**u**, and (d) 3**v** + 5**u**. 51–58. See margin.

51. $\mathbf{u} = \langle -1, -3\rangle,\ \mathbf{v} = \langle -3, 6\rangle$

52. $\mathbf{u} = \langle 4, 5\rangle,\ \mathbf{v} = \langle 0, -1\rangle$

53. $\mathbf{u} = \langle -5, 2\rangle,\ \mathbf{v} = \langle 4, 4\rangle$

54. $\mathbf{u} = \langle 1, -8\rangle,\ \mathbf{v} = \langle 3, -2\rangle$

55. $\mathbf{u} = 2\mathbf{i} - \mathbf{j},\ \mathbf{v} = 5\mathbf{i} + 3\mathbf{j}$

56. $\mathbf{u} = -7\mathbf{i} - 3\mathbf{j},\ \mathbf{v} = 4\mathbf{i} - \mathbf{j}$

57. $\mathbf{u} = 4\mathbf{i},\ \mathbf{v} = -\mathbf{i} + 6\mathbf{j}$

58. $\mathbf{u} = -6\mathbf{j},\ \mathbf{v} = \mathbf{i} + \mathbf{j}$

In Exercises 59–62, find the component form of **w** and sketch the specified vector operations geometrically, where **u** = 6**i** − 5**j** and **v** = 10**i** + 3**j**. 59–62. See margin.

59. $\mathbf{w} = 2\mathbf{u} + \mathbf{v}$

60. $\mathbf{w} = 4\mathbf{u} - 5\mathbf{v}$

61. $\mathbf{w} = 3\mathbf{v}$

62. $\mathbf{w} = \frac{1}{2}\mathbf{v}$

In Exercises 63–66, write vector **u** as a linear combination of the standard unit vectors **i** and **j**.

63. $\mathbf{u} = \langle -1, 5\rangle$ $-\mathbf{i} + 5\mathbf{j}$

64. $\mathbf{u} = \langle -6, -8\rangle$ $-6\mathbf{i} - 8\mathbf{j}$

65. **u** has initial point (3, 4) and terminal point (9, 8). $6\mathbf{i} + 4\mathbf{j}$

66. **u** has initial point (−2, 7) and terminal point (5, −9). $7\mathbf{i} - 16\mathbf{j}$

In Exercises 67 and 68, write the vector **v** in the form $\|\mathbf{v}\|(\cos\theta\mathbf{i} + \sin\theta\mathbf{j})$.

67. $\mathbf{v} = -10\mathbf{i} + 10\mathbf{j}$ $10\sqrt{2}(\cos 135°\mathbf{i} + \sin 135°\mathbf{j})$

68. $\mathbf{v} = 4\mathbf{i} - \mathbf{j}$ $\sqrt{17}(\cos 346°\mathbf{i} + \sin 346°\mathbf{j})$

In Exercises 69–74, find the magnitude and the direction angle of the vector **v**.

69. $\mathbf{v} = 7(\cos 60°\mathbf{i} + \sin 60°\mathbf{j})$ $\|\mathbf{v}\| = 7;\ \theta = 60°$

70. $\mathbf{v} = 3(\cos 150°\mathbf{i} + \sin 150°\mathbf{j})$ $\|\mathbf{v}\| = 3;\ \theta = 150°$

71. $\mathbf{v} = 5\mathbf{i} + 4\mathbf{j}$ $\|\mathbf{v}\| = \sqrt{41};\ \theta = 38.7°$

72. $\mathbf{v} = -4\mathbf{i} + 7\mathbf{j}$ $\|\mathbf{v}\| = \sqrt{65};\ \theta = 119.7°$

38.

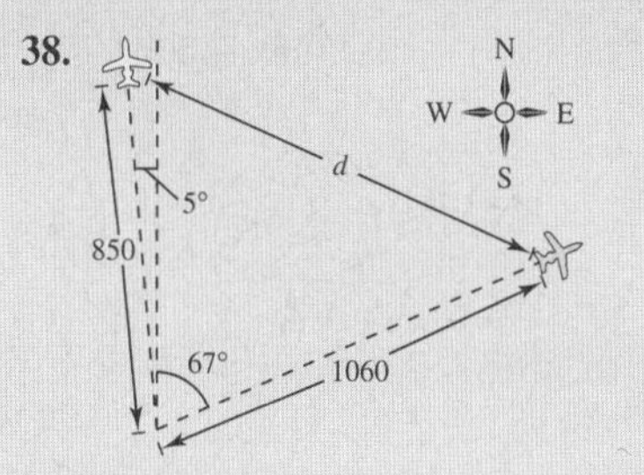

1135.5 mi

51. (a) $\langle -4, 3\rangle$ (b) $\langle 2, -9\rangle$ (c) $\langle -4, -12\rangle$ (d) $\langle -14, 3\rangle$

52. (a) $\langle 4, 4\rangle$ (b) $\langle 4, 6\rangle$ (c) $\langle 16, 20\rangle$ (d) $\langle 20, 22\rangle$

53. (a) $\langle -1, 6\rangle$ (b) $\langle -9, -2\rangle$ (c) $\langle -20, 8\rangle$ (d) $\langle -13, 22\rangle$

54. (a) $\langle 4, -10\rangle$ (b) $\langle -2, -6\rangle$ (c) $\langle 4, -32\rangle$ (d) $\langle 14, -46\rangle$

55. (a) $7\mathbf{i} + 2\mathbf{j}$ (b) $-3\mathbf{i} - 4\mathbf{j}$ (c) $8\mathbf{i} - 4\mathbf{j}$ (d) $25\mathbf{i} + 4\mathbf{j}$

56. (a) $-3\mathbf{i} - 4\mathbf{j}$ (b) $-11\mathbf{i} - 2\mathbf{j}$ (c) $-28\mathbf{i} - 12\mathbf{j}$ (d) $-23\mathbf{i} - 18\mathbf{j}$

57. (a) $3\mathbf{i} + 6\mathbf{j}$ (b) $5\mathbf{i} - 6\mathbf{j}$ (c) $16\mathbf{i}$ (d) $17\mathbf{i} + 18\mathbf{j}$

58. (a) $\mathbf{i} - 5\mathbf{j}$ (b) $-\mathbf{i} - 7\mathbf{j}$ (c) $-24\mathbf{j}$ (d) $3\mathbf{i} - 27\mathbf{j}$

59. $\langle 22, -7\rangle$

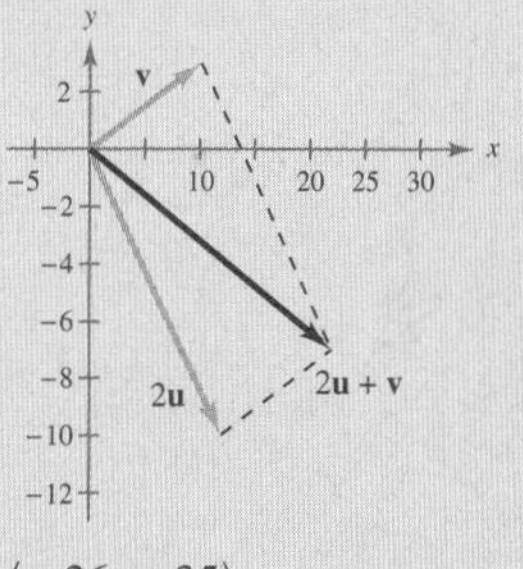

60. $\langle -26, -35\rangle$

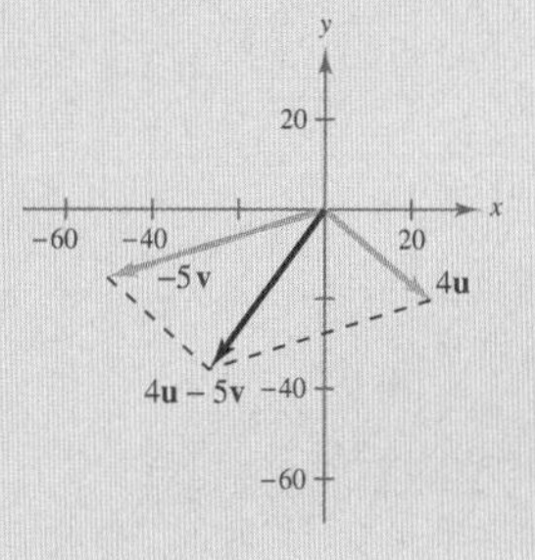

61. $\langle 30, 9\rangle$

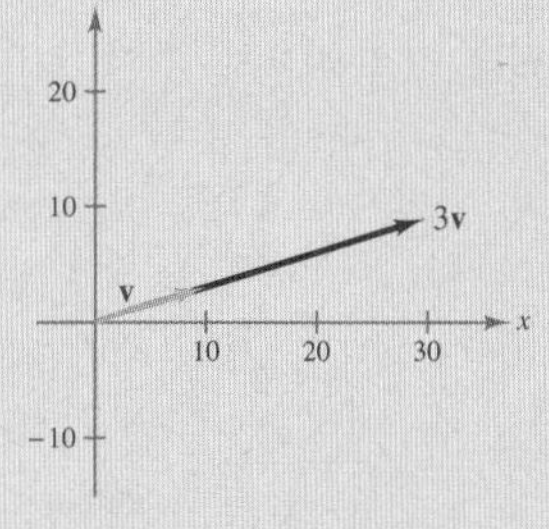

62. $\langle 5, \frac{3}{2}\rangle$

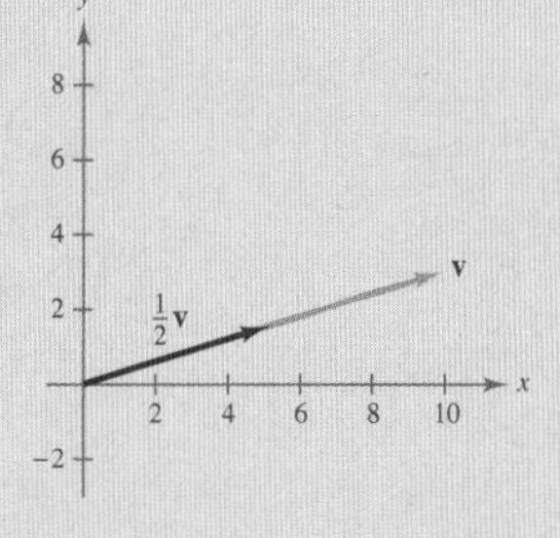

73. $\mathbf{v} = -3\mathbf{i} - 3\mathbf{j}$
$\|\mathbf{v}\| = 3\sqrt{2};\ \theta = 225^\circ$

74. $\mathbf{v} = 8\mathbf{i} - \mathbf{j}$
$\|\mathbf{v}\| = \sqrt{65};\ \theta = 352.9^\circ$

75. RESULTANT FORCE Forces with magnitudes of 85 pounds and 50 pounds act on a single point. The angle between the forces is 15°. Describe the resultant force. See margin.

76. ROPE TENSION A 180-pound weight is supported by two ropes, as shown in the figure. Find the tension in each rope. 180 lb each

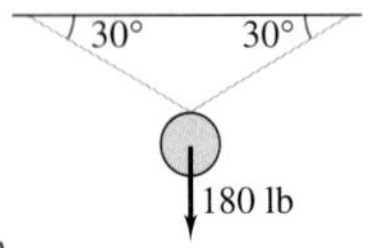

77–78. See margin.

77. NAVIGATION An airplane has an airspeed of 430 miles per hour at a bearing of 135°. The wind velocity is 35 miles per hour in the direction of N 30°E. Find the resultant speed and direction of the airplane.

78. NAVIGATION An airplane has an airspeed of 724 kilometers per hour at a bearing of 30°. The wind velocity is 32 kilometers per hour from the west. Find the resultant speed and direction of the airplane.

6.4 In Exercises 79–82, find the dot product of **u** and **v**.

79. $\mathbf{u} = \langle 6, 7\rangle$, $\mathbf{v} = \langle -3, 9\rangle$ 45

80. $\mathbf{u} = \langle -7, 12\rangle$, $\mathbf{v} = \langle -4, -14\rangle$ -140

81. $\mathbf{u} = 3\mathbf{i} + 7\mathbf{j}$, $\mathbf{v} = 11\mathbf{i} - 5\mathbf{j}$ -2

82. $\mathbf{u} = -7\mathbf{i} + 2\mathbf{j}$, $\mathbf{v} = 16\mathbf{i} - 12\mathbf{j}$ -136

In Exercises 83–90, use the vectors $\mathbf{u} = \langle -4, 2\rangle$ and $\mathbf{v} = \langle 5, 1\rangle$ to find the indicated quantity. State whether the result is a vector or a scalar. 85, 87–88. See margin.

83. $2\mathbf{u}\cdot\mathbf{u}$ 40; scalar

84. $3\mathbf{u}\cdot\mathbf{v}$ -54; scalar

85. $4 - \|\mathbf{u}\|$

86. $\|\mathbf{v}\|^2$ 26; scalar

87. $\mathbf{u}(\mathbf{u}\cdot\mathbf{v})$

88. $(\mathbf{u}\cdot\mathbf{v})\mathbf{v}$

89. $(\mathbf{u}\cdot\mathbf{u}) - (\mathbf{u}\cdot\mathbf{v})$ 38; scalar

90. $(\mathbf{v}\cdot\mathbf{v}) - (\mathbf{v}\cdot\mathbf{u})$ 44; scalar

In Exercises 91–94, find the angle θ between the vectors.

91. $\mathbf{u} = \cos\frac{7\pi}{4}\mathbf{i} + \sin\frac{7\pi}{4}\mathbf{j}$, $\mathbf{v} = \cos\frac{5\pi}{6}\mathbf{i} + \sin\frac{5\pi}{6}\mathbf{j}$ $\frac{11\pi}{12}$

92. $\mathbf{u} = \cos 45^\circ\mathbf{i} + \sin 45^\circ\mathbf{j}$, $\mathbf{v} = \cos 300^\circ\mathbf{i} + \sin 300^\circ\mathbf{j}$ 105°

93. $\mathbf{u} = \langle 2\sqrt{2}, -4\rangle$, $\mathbf{v} = \langle -\sqrt{2}, 1\rangle$ 160.5°

94. $\mathbf{u} = \langle 3, \sqrt{3}\rangle$, $\mathbf{v} = \langle 4, 3\sqrt{3}\rangle$ 22.4°

In Exercises 95–98, determine whether **u** and **v** are orthogonal, parallel, or neither.

95. $\mathbf{u} = \langle -3, 8\rangle$, $\mathbf{v} = \langle 8, 3\rangle$ Orthogonal

96. $\mathbf{u} = \langle \frac{1}{4}, -\frac{1}{2}\rangle$, $\mathbf{v} = \langle -2, 4\rangle$ Parallel

97. $\mathbf{u} = -\mathbf{i}$, $\mathbf{v} = \mathbf{i} + 2\mathbf{j}$ Neither

98. $\mathbf{u} = -2\mathbf{i} + \mathbf{j}$, $\mathbf{v} = 3\mathbf{i} + 6\mathbf{j}$ Orthogonal

In Exercises 99–102, find the projection of **u** onto **v**. Then write **u** as the sum of two orthogonal vectors, one of which is $\text{proj}_{\mathbf{v}}\mathbf{u}$.

99. $\mathbf{u} = \langle -4, 3\rangle$, $\mathbf{v} = \langle -8, -2\rangle$ $-\frac{13}{17}\langle 4, 1\rangle, \frac{16}{17}\langle -1, 4\rangle$

100. $\mathbf{u} = \langle 5, 6\rangle$, $\mathbf{v} = \langle 10, 0\rangle$ $\langle 5, 0\rangle, \langle 0, 6\rangle$

101. $\mathbf{u} = \langle 2, 7\rangle$, $\mathbf{v} = \langle 1, -1\rangle$ $\frac{5}{2}\langle -1, 1\rangle, \frac{9}{2}\langle 1, 1\rangle$

102. $\mathbf{u} = \langle -3, 5\rangle$, $\mathbf{v} = \langle -5, 2\rangle$ $\frac{25}{29}\langle -5, 2\rangle, \frac{19}{29}\langle 2, 5\rangle$

WORK In Exercises 103 and 104, find the work done in moving a particle from P to Q if the magnitude and direction of the force are given by **v**.

103. $P(5, 3)$, $Q(8, 9)$, $\mathbf{v} = \langle 2, 7\rangle$ 48

104. $P(-2, -9)$, $Q(-12, 8)$, $\mathbf{v} = 3\mathbf{i} - 6\mathbf{j}$ -132

105. 72,000 ft-lb

105. WORK Determine the work done (in foot-pounds) by a crane lifting an 18,000-pound truck 48 inches.

106. WORK A mover exerts a horizontal force of 25 pounds on a crate as it is pushed up a ramp that is 12 feet long and inclined at an angle of 20° above the horizontal. Find the work done in pushing the crate. 281.9 ft-lb

6.5 In Exercises 107–112, plot the complex number and find its absolute value. 107–112. See margin.

107. $7i$

108. $-6i$

109. $5 + 3i$

110. $-10 - 4i$

111. $\sqrt{2} - \sqrt{2}i$

112. $-\sqrt{2} + \sqrt{2}i$

In Exercises 113–118, write the complex number in trigonometric form. 113–118. See margin.

113. $4i$

114. -7

115. $5 - 5i$

116. $5 + 12i$

117. $-5 - 12i$

118. $-3\sqrt{3} + 3i$

In Exercises 119 and 120, (a) write the two complex numbers in trigonometric form, and (b) use the trigonometric forms to find z_1z_2 and z_1/z_2, where $z_2 \neq 0$. 119–120. See margin.

119. $z_1 = 2\sqrt{3} - 2i$, $z_2 = -10i$

120. $z_1 = -3(1 + i)$, $z_2 = 2(\sqrt{3} + i)$

75. The resultant force is 133.92 pounds and 5.6° from the 85-pound force.

77. 422.30 mi/h; 130.4°

78. 740.5 km/h; 32.1°

85. $4 - 2\sqrt{5}$; scalar

87. $\langle 72, -36\rangle$; vector

88. $\langle -90, -18\rangle$; vector

107.

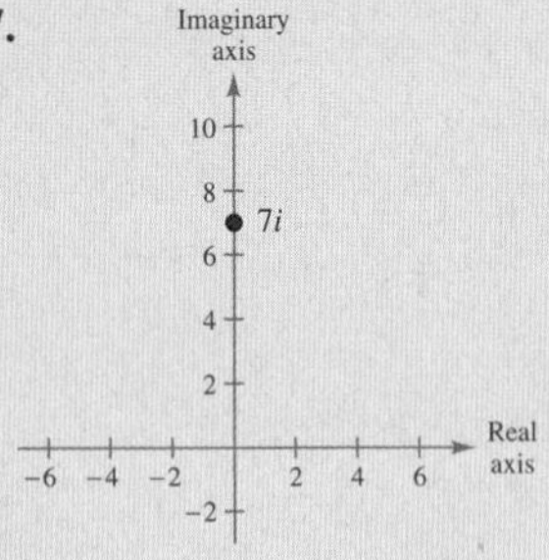

7

108.

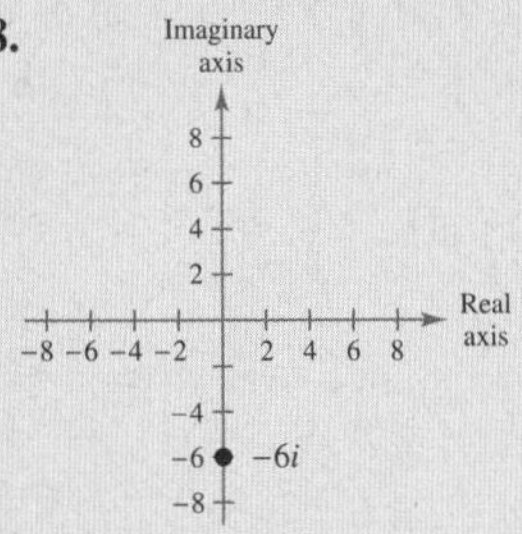

6

109.

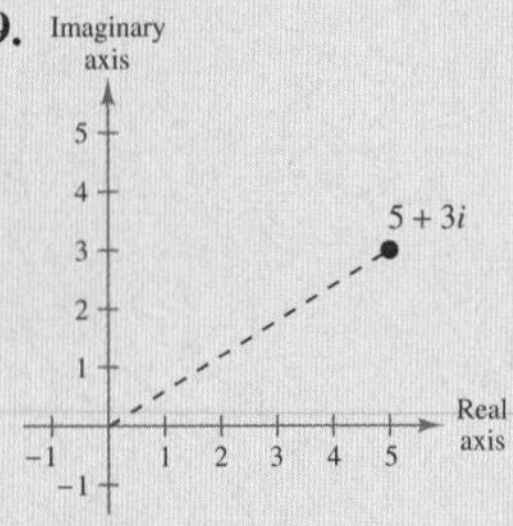

$\sqrt{34}$

110.

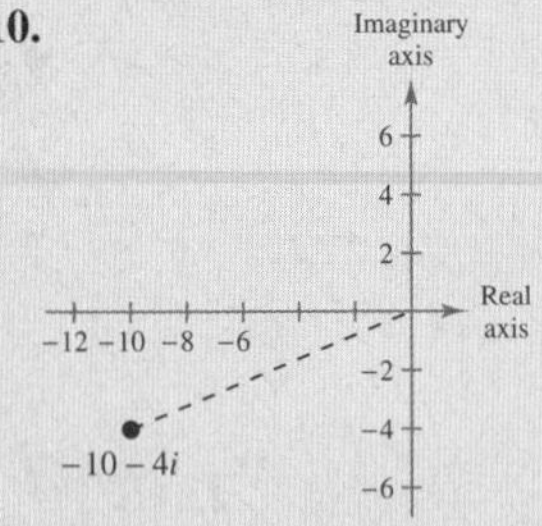

$2\sqrt{29}$

111.

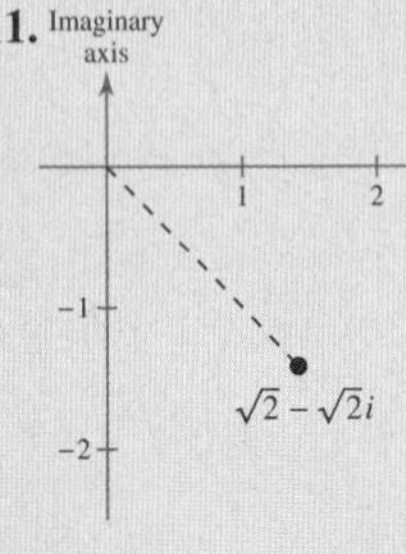

2

112.

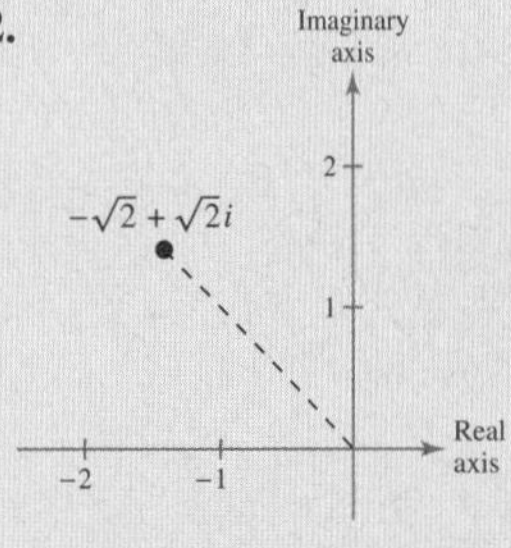

2

113. $4\left(\cos\frac{\pi}{2} + i\sin\frac{\pi}{2}\right)$

114. $7(\cos\pi + i\sin\pi)$

115. $5\sqrt{2}\left(\cos\frac{7\pi}{4} + i\sin\frac{7\pi}{4}\right)$

116. $13(\cos 1.176 + i\sin 1.176)$

117. $13(\cos 4.32 + i\sin 4.32)$

118. $6\left(\cos\frac{5\pi}{6} + i\sin\frac{5\pi}{6}\right)$

119–120. See Additional Answers beginning on page AA1.

In Exercises 121–124, use DeMoivre's Theorem to find the indicated power of the complex number. Write the result in standard form.

121. $\left[5\left(\cos\frac{\pi}{12} + i\sin\frac{\pi}{12}\right)\right]^4$ $\frac{625}{2} + \frac{625\sqrt{3}}{2}i$

122. $\left[2\left(\cos\frac{4\pi}{15} + i\sin\frac{4\pi}{15}\right)\right]^5$ $-16 - 16\sqrt{3}i$

123. $(2 + 3i)^6$ $2035 - 828i$

124. $(1 - i)^8$ 16

In Exercises 125–128, (a) use the formula on page 474 to find the indicated roots of the complex number, (b) represent each of the roots graphically, and (c) write each of the roots in standard form. 125–128. See margin.

125. Sixth roots of $-729i$

126. Fourth roots of $256i$

127. Cube roots of 8

128. Fifth roots of -1024

In Exercises 129–134, use the formula on page 474 to find all solutions of the equation and represent the solutions graphically. 129–134. See margin.

129. $x^4 + 81 = 0$

130. $x^5 - 32 = 0$

131. $x^3 + 8i = 0$

132. $x^4 - 64i = 0$

133. $x^5 + x^3 - x^2 - 1 = 0$

134. $x^5 + 4x^3 - 8x^2 - 32 = 0$

EXPLORATION

135–139. See margin.

TRUE OR FALSE? In Exercises 135–139, determine whether the statement is true or false. Justify your answer.

135. The Law of Sines is true if one of the angles in the triangle is a right angle.

136. When the Law of Sines is used, the solution is always unique.

137. If **u** is a unit vector in the direction of **v**, then $\mathbf{v} = \|\mathbf{v}\|\mathbf{u}$.

138. If $\mathbf{v} = a\mathbf{i} + b\mathbf{j} = \mathbf{0}$, then $a = -b$.

139. $x = \sqrt{3} + i$ is a solution of the equation $x^2 - 8i = 0$.

140. State the Law of Sines from memory. See margin.

141. State the Law of Cosines from memory. See margin.

142. What characterizes a vector in the plane? See margin.

143. Which vectors in the figure appear to be equivalent? A and C

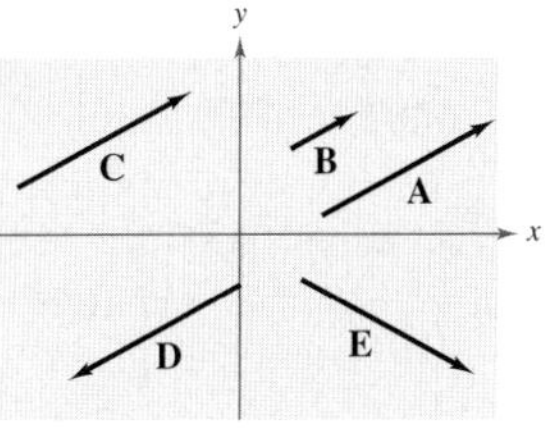

See margin.

144. The vectors **u** and **v** have the same magnitudes in the two figures. In which figure will the magnitude of the sum be greater? Give a reason for your answer.

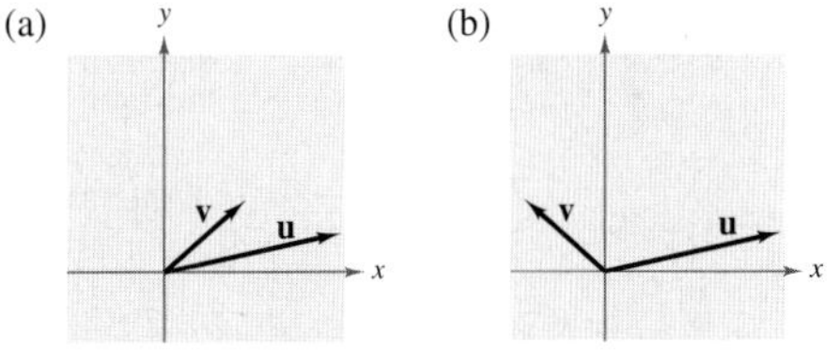

145. Give a geometric description of the scalar multiple $k\mathbf{u}$ of the vector **u**, for $k > 0$ and for $k < 0$. See margin.

146. Give a geometric description of the sum of the vectors **u** and **v**. See margin.

GRAPHICAL REASONING In Exercises 147 and 148, use the graph of the roots of a complex number. 147–148. See margin.

(a) Write each of the roots in trigonometric form.

(b) Identify the complex number whose roots are given. Use a graphing utility to verify your results.

147.

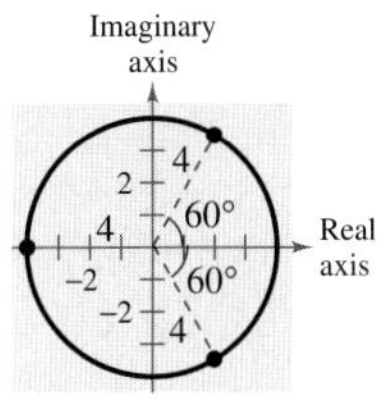

148.

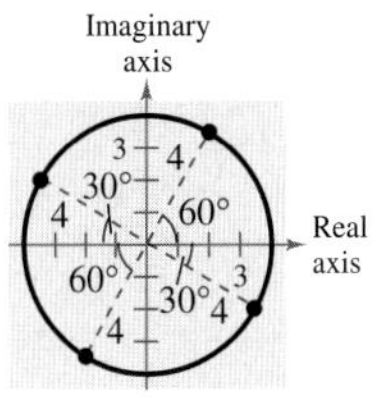

149. The figure shows z_1 and z_2. Describe z_1z_2 and z_1/z_2. See margin.

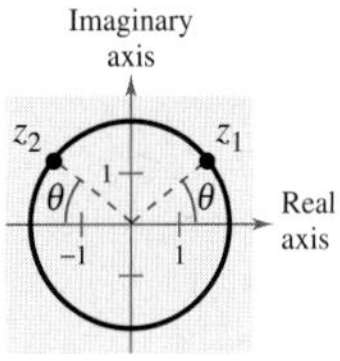

150. One of the fourth roots of a complex number z is shown in the figure.

(a) How many roots are not shown? 3 roots

(b) Describe the other roots. On the circle 120°, 210°, and 300° from the positive x-axis

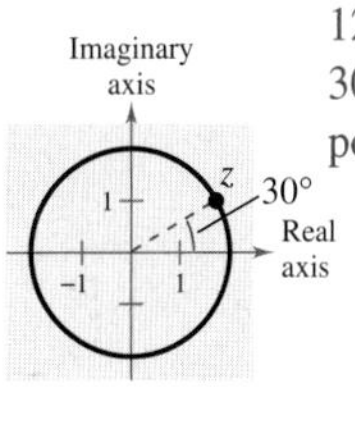

135. True. Sin 90° is defined in the Law of Sines.

136. False. There may be no solution, one solution, or two solutions.

137. True. By definition, $\mathbf{u} = \frac{\mathbf{v}}{\|\mathbf{v}\|}$, so $\mathbf{v} = \|\mathbf{v}\|\mathbf{u}$.

138. False. If $\mathbf{v} = a\mathbf{i} + b\mathbf{j} = \mathbf{0}$, then $a = b = 0$.

139. False. The solutions to $x^2 - 8i = 0$ are $x = 2 + 2i$ and $x = -2 - 2i$.

140. $\frac{a}{\sin A} = \frac{b}{\sin B} = \frac{c}{\sin C}$

141. $a^2 = b^2 + c^2 - 2bc\cos A$, $b^2 = a^2 + c^2 - 2ac\cos B$, $c^2 = a^2 + b^2 - 2ab\cos C$

142. Direction and magnitude

144. a; The angle between the vectors is acute.

145. If $k > 0$, the direction is the same and the magnitude is k times as great. If $k < 0$, the result is a vector in the opposite direction and the magnitude is $|k|$ times as great.

146. The diagonal of the parallelogram with **u** and **v** as its adjacent sides

147. (a) $4(\cos 60° + i\sin 60°)$
$4(\cos 180° + i\sin 180°)$
$4(\cos 300° + i\sin 300°)$
(b) -64

148. (a) $4(\cos 60° + i\sin 60°)$
$4(\cos 150° + i\sin 150°)$
$4(\cos 240° + i\sin 240°)$
$4(\cos 330° + i\sin 330°)$
(b) $-128 - 128\sqrt{3}i$

149. $z_1z_2 = -4$;

$$\frac{z_1}{z_2} = \cos(2\theta - \pi) + i\sin(2\theta - \pi) = -\cos 2\theta - i\sin 2\theta$$

125–134. See Additional Answers beginning on page AA1.

6 CHAPTER TEST

See www.CalcChat.com for worked-out solutions to odd-numbered exercises.

Take this test as you would take a test in class. When you are finished, check your work against the answers given in the back of the book.

In Exercises 1–6, use the information to solve (if possible) the triangle. If two solutions exist, find both solutions. Round your answers to two decimal places. 1–6. See margin.

1. $A = 24°,\ B = 68°,\ a = 12.2$
2. $B = 110°,\ C = 28°,\ a = 15.6$
3. $A = 24°,\ a = 11.2,\ b = 13.4$
4. $a = 4.0,\ b = 7.3,\ c = 12.4$
5. $B = 100°,\ a = 15,\ b = 23$
6. $C = 121°,\ a = 34,\ b = 55$

7. A triangular parcel of land has borders of lengths 60 meters, 70 meters, and 82 meters. Find the area of the parcel of land. $2052.5\ \text{m}^2$

8. An airplane flies 370 miles from point A to point B with a bearing of 24°. It then flies 240 miles from point B to point C with a bearing of 37° (see figure). Find the distance and bearing from point A to point C. 606.3 mi; 29.1°

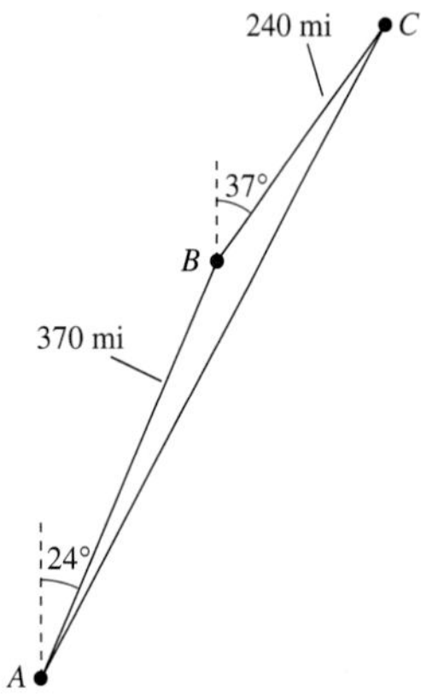

FIGURE FOR 8

In Exercises 9 and 10, find the component form of the vector v satisfying the given conditions.

9. Initial point of **v**: $(-3, 7)$; terminal point of **v**: $(11, -16)$ $\langle 14, -23\rangle$

10. Magnitude of **v**: $\|\mathbf{v}\| = 12$; direction of **v**: $\mathbf{u} = \langle 3, -5\rangle$ $\left\langle \frac{18\sqrt{34}}{17}, -\frac{30\sqrt{34}}{17}\right\rangle$

In Exercises 11–14, u = ⟨2, 7⟩ and v = ⟨−6, 5⟩. Find the resultant vector and sketch its graph. 11–14. See margin.

11. $\mathbf{u} + \mathbf{v}$
12. $\mathbf{u} - \mathbf{v}$
13. $5\mathbf{u} - 3\mathbf{v}$
14. $4\mathbf{u} + 2\mathbf{v}$

15. Find a unit vector in the direction of $\mathbf{u} = \langle 24, -7\rangle$. $\left\langle \frac{24}{25}, -\frac{7}{25}\right\rangle$

16. Forces with magnitudes of 250 pounds and 130 pounds act on an object at angles of 45° and −60°, respectively, with the x-axis. Find the direction and magnitude of the resultant of these forces. 14.9°; 250.15 lb

17. Find the angle between the vectors $\mathbf{u} = \langle -1, 5\rangle$ and $\mathbf{v} = \langle 3, -2\rangle$. 135°

18. Are the vectors $\mathbf{u} = \langle 6, -10\rangle$ and $\mathbf{v} = \langle 5, 3\rangle$ orthogonal? Yes

19. Find the projection of $\mathbf{u} = \langle 6, 7\rangle$ onto $\mathbf{v} = \langle -5, -1\rangle$. Then write **u** as the sum of two orthogonal vectors. $\frac{37}{26}\langle 5, 1\rangle$; $\frac{29}{26}\langle -1, 5\rangle$

20. A 500-pound motorcycle is headed up a hill inclined at 12°. What force is required to keep the motorcycle from rolling down the hill when stopped at a red light? 20. About 104 lb

21. Write the complex number $z = 5 - 5i$ in trigonometric form. See margin.

22. Write the complex number $z = 6(\cos 120° + i \sin 120°)$ in standard form. $-3 + 3\sqrt{3}i$

In Exercises 23 and 24, use DeMoivre's Theorem to find the indicated power of the complex number. Write the result in standard form.

23. $\left[3\left(\cos\frac{7\pi}{6} + i \sin\frac{7\pi}{6}\right)\right]^8$ See margin.
24. $(3 - 3i)^6$ $5832i$

25. Find the fourth roots of $256(1 + \sqrt{3}i)$. See margin.

26. Find all solutions of the equation $x^3 - 27i = 0$ and represent the solutions graphically. See margin.

---

1. $C = 88°,\ b \approx 27.81,\ c \approx 29.98$
2. $A = 42°,\ b \approx 21.91,\ c \approx 10.95$
3. Two solutions:
$B \approx 29.12°,\ C \approx 126.88°,\ c \approx 22.03$
$B \approx 150.88°,\ C \approx 5.12°,\ c \approx 2.46$
4. No solution
5. $A \approx 39.96°,\ C \approx 40.04°,\ c \approx 15.02$
6. $A \approx 21.90°,\ B \approx 37.10°,\ c \approx 78.15$
11. $\langle -4, 12\rangle$

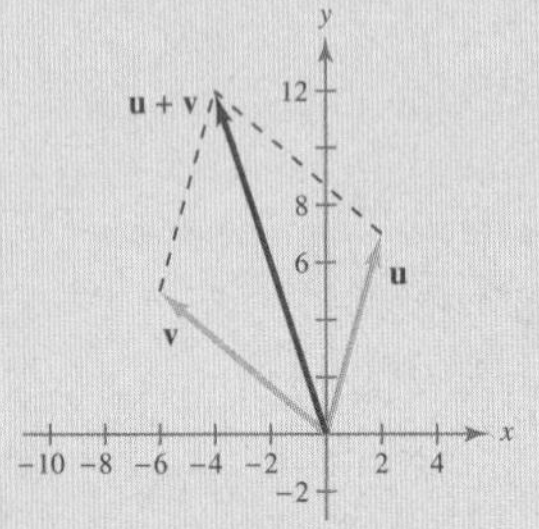

12. $\langle 8, 2\rangle$

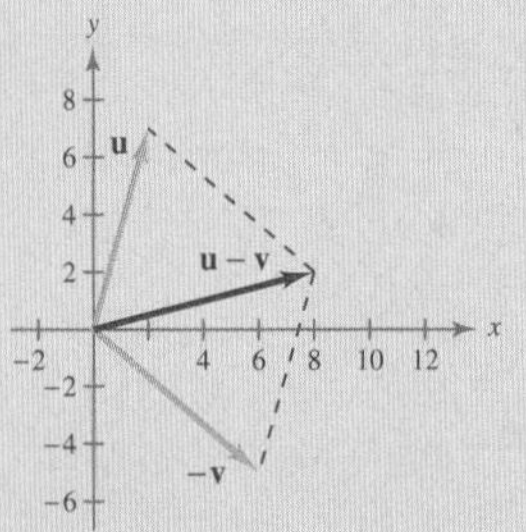

13. $\langle 28, 20\rangle$

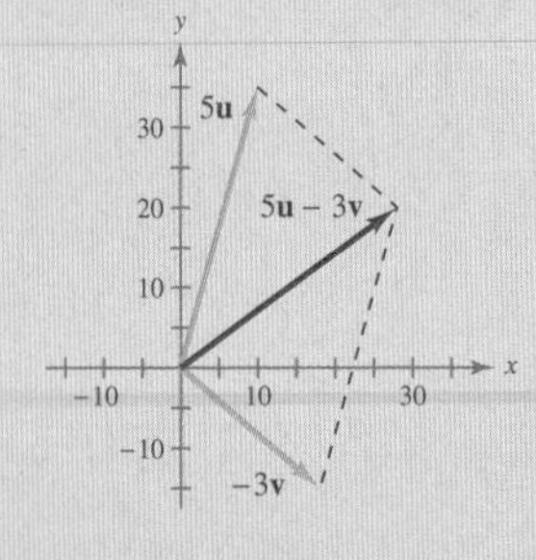

14. $\langle -4, 38\rangle$

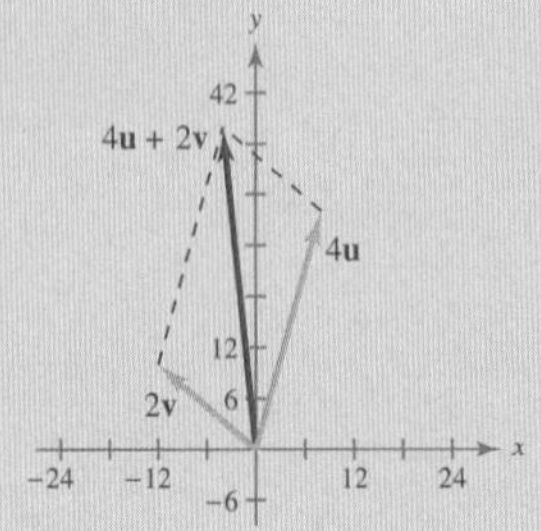

21. $5\sqrt{2}\left(\cos\frac{7\pi}{4} + i \sin\frac{7\pi}{4}\right)$

23. $-\frac{6561}{2} - \frac{6561\sqrt{3}}{2}i$

25. $4\sqrt[4]{2}\left(\cos\frac{\pi}{12} + i \sin\frac{\pi}{12}\right)$
$4\sqrt[4]{2}\left(\cos\frac{7\pi}{12} + i \sin\frac{7\pi}{12}\right)$
$4\sqrt[4]{2}\left(\cos\frac{13\pi}{12} + i \sin\frac{13\pi}{12}\right)$
$4\sqrt[4]{2}\left(\cos\frac{19\pi}{12} + i \sin\frac{19\pi}{12}\right)$

26. $3\left(\cos\frac{\pi}{6} + i \sin\frac{\pi}{6}\right)$
$3\left(\cos\frac{5\pi}{6} + i \sin\frac{5\pi}{6}\right)$
$3\left(\cos\frac{3\pi}{2} + i \sin\frac{3\pi}{2}\right)$

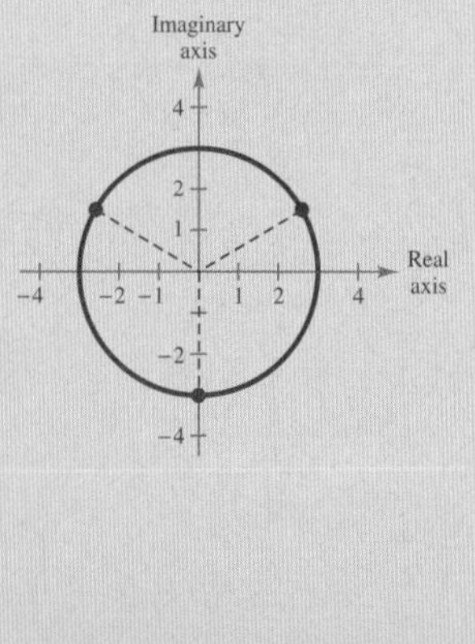

6 CUMULATIVE TEST FOR CHAPTERS 4–6

See www.CalcChat.com for worked-out solutions to odd-numbered exercises.

Take this test as you would take a test in class. When you are finished, check your work against the answers given in the back of the book.

1. Consider the angle $\theta = -120°$.
   (a) Sketch the angle in standard position. See margin.
   (b) Determine a coterminal angle in the interval $[0°, 360°)$. $240°$
   (c) Convert the angle to radian measure. $-\frac{2\pi}{3}$
   (d) Find the reference angle θ'. $60°$
   (e) Find the exact values of the six trigonometric functions of θ. See margin.
2. Convert the angle $\theta = -1.45$ radians to degrees. Round the answer to one decimal place. $-83.1°$
3. Find $\cos\theta$ if $\tan\theta = -\frac{21}{20}$ and $\sin\theta < 0$. $\frac{20}{29}$

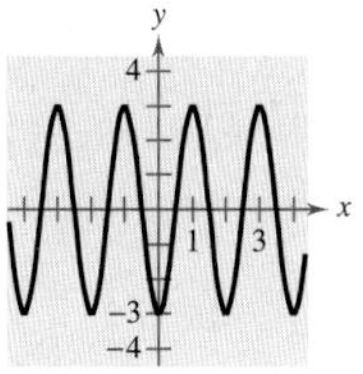

FIGURE FOR 7

In Exercises 4–6, sketch the graph of the function. (Include two full periods.) 4–6. See margin.

4. $f(x) = 3 - 2\sin\pi x$
5. $g(x) = \frac{1}{2}\tan\left(x - \frac{\pi}{2}\right)$
6. $h(x) = -\sec(x + \pi)$
7. Find a, b, and c such that the graph of the function $h(x) = a\cos(bx + c)$ matches the graph in the figure. $a = -3, b = \pi, c = 0$
8. Sketch the graph of the function $f(x) = \frac{1}{2}x\sin x$ over the interval $-3\pi \le x \le 3\pi$. See margin.

In Exercises 9 and 10, find the exact value of the expression without using a calculator.

9. $\tan(\arctan 4.9)$ 4.9
10. $\tan\left(\arcsin\frac{3}{5}\right)$ $\frac{3}{4}$
11. Write an algebraic expression equivalent to $\sin(\arccos 2x)$. $\sqrt{1 - 4x^2}$
12. Use the fundamental identities to simplify: $\cos\left(\frac{\pi}{2} - x\right)\csc x$. 1
13. Subtract and simplify: $\frac{\sin\theta - 1}{\cos\theta} - \frac{\cos\theta}{\sin\theta - 1}$. $2\tan\theta$

In Exercises 14–16, verify the identity. 14–16. Answers will vary.

14. $\cot^2\alpha(\sec^2\alpha - 1) = 1$
15. $\sin(x + y)\sin(x - y) = \sin^2 x - \sin^2 y$
16. $\sin^2 x\cos^2 x = \frac{1}{8}(1 - \cos 4x)$

In Exercises 17 and 18, find all solutions of the equation in the interval $[0, 2\pi)$.

17. $2\cos^2\beta - \cos\beta = 0$ $\frac{\pi}{3}, \frac{\pi}{2}, \frac{3\pi}{2}, \frac{5\pi}{3}$
18. $3\tan\theta - \cot\theta = 0$ $\frac{\pi}{6}, \frac{5\pi}{6}, \frac{7\pi}{6}, \frac{11\pi}{6}$
19. Use the Quadratic Formula to solve the equation in the interval $[0, 2\pi)$: $\sin^2 x + 2\sin x + 1 = 0$. $\frac{3\pi}{2}$
20. Given that $\sin u = \frac{12}{13}$, $\cos v = \frac{3}{5}$, and angles u and v are both in Quadrant I, find $\tan(u - v)$. $\frac{16}{63}$
21. If $\tan\theta = \frac{1}{2}$, find the exact value of $\tan(2\theta)$. $\frac{4}{3}$
22. If $\tan\theta = \frac{4}{3}$, find the exact value of $\sin\frac{\theta}{2}$.
   $\frac{\sqrt{5}}{5}, \frac{2\sqrt{5}}{5}$

1. (a)

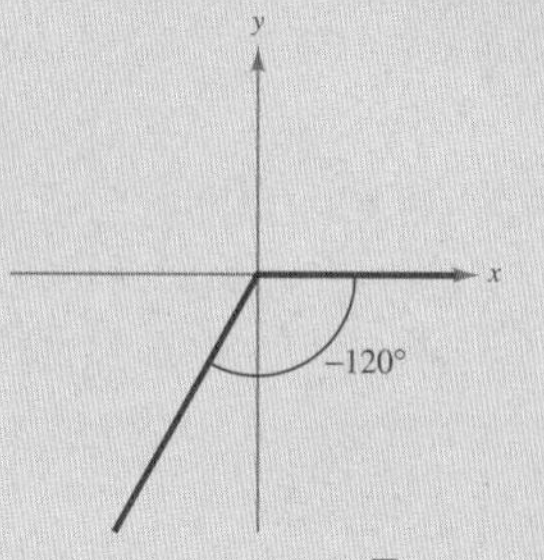

(e) $\sin(-120°) = -\frac{\sqrt{3}}{2}$

$\cos(-120°) = -\frac{1}{2}$

$\tan(-120°) = \sqrt{3}$

$\csc(-120°) = -\frac{2\sqrt{3}}{3}$

$\sec(-120°) = -2$

$\cot(-120°) = \frac{\sqrt{3}}{3}$

4.

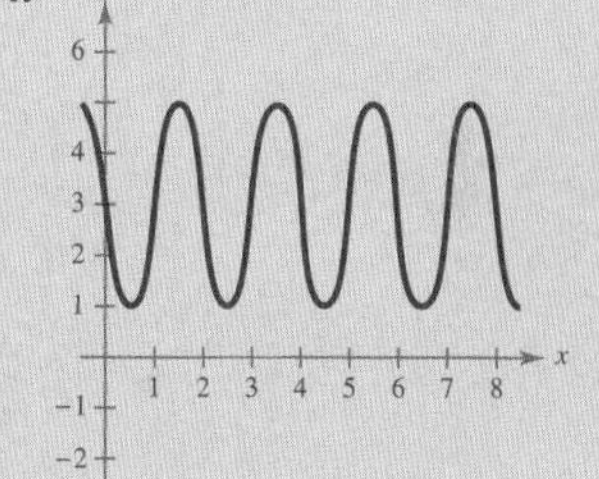

5.

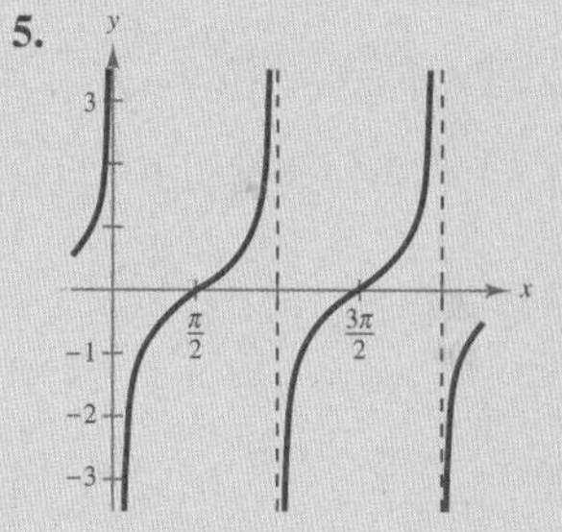

6.

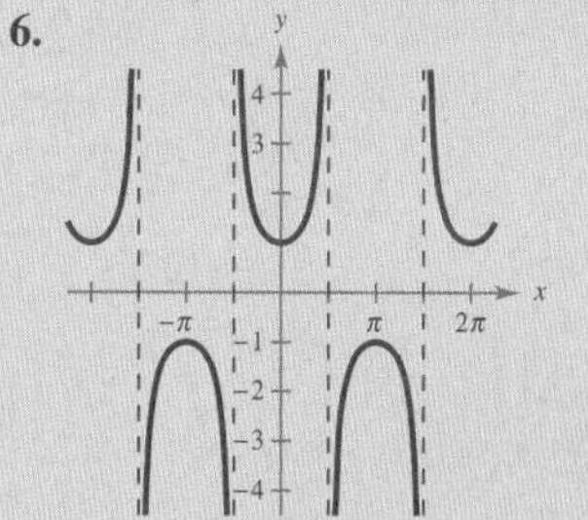

8.

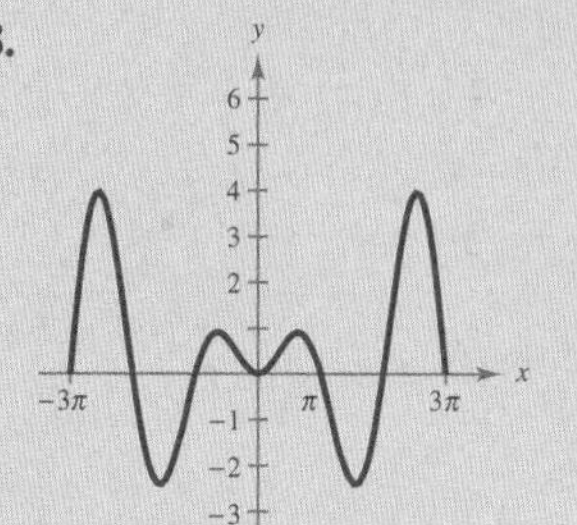

23. Write the product $5 \sin \frac{3\pi}{4} \cdot \cos \frac{7\pi}{4}$ as a sum or difference. $\frac{5}{2}\left(\sin \frac{5\pi}{2} - \sin \pi\right)$

24. Write $\cos 9x - \cos 7x$ as a product. $-2 \sin 8x \sin x$

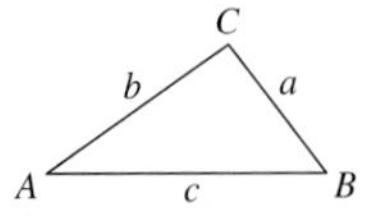

FIGURE FOR 25–28

In Exercises 25–28, use the information to solve the triangle shown in the figure. Round your answers to two decimal places. 25–28. See margin.

25. $A = 30°,\ a = 9,\ b = 8$

26. $A = 30°,\ b = 8,\ c = 10$

27. $A = 30°,\ C = 90°,\ b = 10$

28. $a = 4.7,\ b = 8.1,\ c = 10.3$

In Exercises 29 and 30, determine whether the Law of Sines or the Law of Cosines is needed to solve the triangle. Then solve the triangle. 29–30. See margin.

29. $A = 45°,\ B = 26°,\ c = 20$

30. $a = 1.2,\ b = 10,\ C = 80°$

31. Two sides of a triangle have lengths 7 inches and 12 inches. Their included angle measures 99°. Find the area of the triangle. 41.48 in.^{2}

32. 599.09 m^2

32. Find the area of a triangle with sides of lengths 30 meters, 41 meters, and 45 meters.

33. Write the vector $\mathbf{u} = \langle 7, 8 \rangle$ as a linear combination of the standard unit vectors $\mathbf{i}$ and $\mathbf{j}$. $7\mathbf{i} + 8\mathbf{j}$

34. Find a unit vector in the direction of $\mathbf{v} = \mathbf{i} + \mathbf{j}$. $\left\langle \frac{\sqrt{2}}{2}, \frac{\sqrt{2}}{2} \right\rangle$

35. Find $\mathbf{u} \cdot \mathbf{v}$ for $\mathbf{u} = 3\mathbf{i} + 4\mathbf{j}$ and $\mathbf{v} = \mathbf{i} - 2\mathbf{j}$. -5

36. Find the projection of $\mathbf{u} = \langle 8, -2 \rangle$ onto $\mathbf{v} = \langle 1, 5 \rangle$. Then write $\mathbf{u}$ as the sum of two orthogonal vectors. $-\frac{1}{13}\langle 1, 5 \rangle;\ \frac{21}{13}\langle 5, -1 \rangle$

37. Write the complex number $-2 + 2i$ in trigonometric form. See margin.

38. Find the product of $[4(\cos 30° + i \sin 30°)][6(\cos 120° + i \sin 120°)]$. Write the answer in standard form. $-12\sqrt{3} + 12i$

39. Find the three cube roots of 1. See margin.

40. Find all the solutions of the equation $x^5 + 243 = 0$. See margin.

41. A ceiling fan with 21-inch blades makes 63 revolutions per minute. Find the angular speed of the fan in radians per minute. Find the linear speed of the tips of the blades in inches per minute. About 395.8 rad/min; about 8312.7 in./min

42. Find the area of the sector of a circle with a radius of 12 yards and a central angle of 105°. 42π yd^2 $\approx$ 131.95 yd^2

43. From a point 200 feet from a flagpole, the angles of elevation to the bottom and top of the flag are 16° 45′ and 18°, respectively. Approximate the height of the flag to the nearest foot. 5 ft

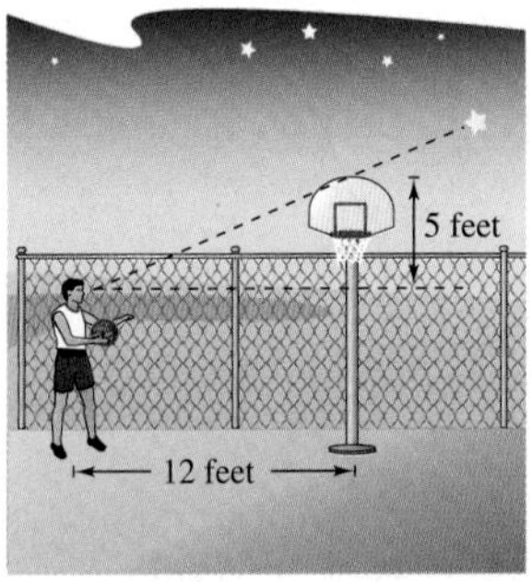

FIGURE FOR 44

44. To determine the angle of elevation of a star in the sky, you get the star in your line of vision with the backboard of a basketball hoop that is 5 feet higher than your eyes (see figure). Your horizontal distance from the backboard is 12 feet. What is the angle of elevation of the star? 22.6°

45. Write a model for a particle in simple harmonic motion with a displacement of 4 inches and a period of 8 seconds. See margin.

46. An airplane's velocity with respect to the air is 500 kilometers per hour, with a bearing of 30°. The wind at the altitude of the plane has a velocity of 50 kilometers per hour with a bearing of N 60° E. What is the true direction of the plane, and what is its speed relative to the ground? 32.6°; 543.9 km/h

47. A force of 85 pounds exerted at an angle of 60° above the horizontal is required to slide an object across a floor. The object is dragged 10 feet. Determine the work done in sliding the object. 425 ft-lb

25. $B \approx 26.39°,\ C \approx 123.61°,\ c \approx 14.99$

26. $B \approx 52.48°,\ C \approx 97.52°,\ a \approx 5.04$

27. $B = 60°,\ a \approx 5.77,\ c \approx 11.55$

28. $A \approx 26.28°,\ B \approx 49.74°,\ C \approx 103.98°$

29. Law of Sines; $C = 109°,\ a \approx 14.96,\ b \approx 9.27$

30. Law of Cosines; $A \approx 6.75°,\ B \approx 93.25°,\ c \approx 9.86$

37. $2\sqrt{2}\left(\cos \frac{3\pi}{4} + i \sin \frac{3\pi}{4}\right)$

39. $\cos 0 + i \sin 0 = 1$

$\cos \frac{2\pi}{3} + i \sin \frac{2\pi}{3} = -\frac{1}{2} + \frac{\sqrt{3}}{2}i$

$\cos \frac{4\pi}{3} + i \sin \frac{4\pi}{3} = -\frac{1}{2} - \frac{\sqrt{3}}{2}i$

40. $3\left(\cos \frac{\pi}{5} + i \sin \frac{\pi}{5}\right)$

$3\left(\cos \frac{3\pi}{5} + i \sin \frac{3\pi}{5}\right)$

$3(\cos \pi + i \sin \pi)$

$3\left(\cos \frac{7\pi}{5} + i \sin \frac{7\pi}{5}\right)$

$3\left(\cos \frac{9\pi}{5} + i \sin \frac{9\pi}{5}\right)$

45. $d = 4 \cos \frac{\pi}{4} t$

Law of Sines (p. 428)

If ABC is a triangle with sides a, b, and c, then

$$\frac{a}{\sin A} = \frac{b}{\sin B} = \frac{c}{\sin C}.$$

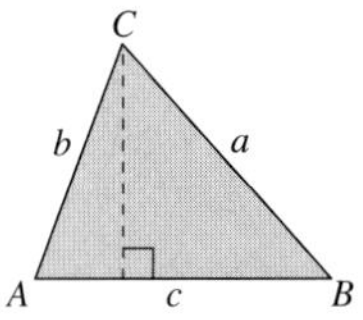

A is acute.

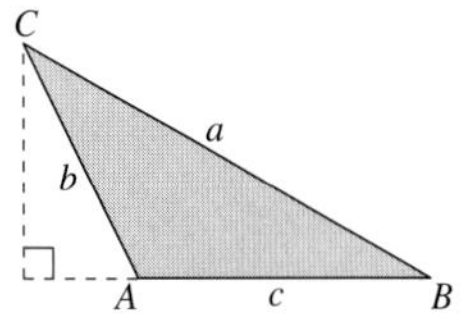

A is obtuse.

Proof

Let h be the altitude of either triangle found in the figure above. Then you have

$$\sin A = \frac{h}{b} \quad \text{or} \quad h = b \sin A$$

$$\sin B = \frac{h}{a} \quad \text{or} \quad h = a \sin B.$$

Equating these two values of h, you have

$$a \sin B = b \sin A \quad \text{or} \quad \frac{a}{\sin A} = \frac{b}{\sin B}.$$

Note that $\sin A \neq 0$ and $\sin B \neq 0$ because no angle of a triangle can have a measure of $0°$ or $180°$. In a similar manner, construct an altitude from vertex B to side AC (extended in the obtuse triangle), as shown at the left. Then you have

$$\sin A = \frac{h}{c} \quad \text{or} \quad h = c \sin A$$

$$\sin C = \frac{h}{a} \quad \text{or} \quad h = a \sin C.$$

Equating these two values of h, you have

$$a \sin C = c \sin A \quad \text{or} \quad \frac{a}{\sin A} = \frac{c}{\sin C}.$$

By the Transitive Property of Equality you know that

$$\frac{a}{\sin A} = \frac{b}{\sin B} = \frac{c}{\sin C}.$$

So, the Law of Sines is established.

Law of Tangents

Besides the Law of Sines and the Law of Cosines, there is also a Law of Tangents, which was developed by Francois Viète (1540–1603). The Law of Tangents follows from the Law of Sines and the sum-to-product formulas for sine and is defined as follows.

$$\frac{a+b}{a-b} = \frac{\tan[(A+B)/2]}{\tan[(A-B)/2]}$$

The Law of Tangents can be used to solve a triangle when two sides and the included angle are given (SAS). Before calculators were invented, the Law of Tangents was used to solve the SAS case instead of the Law of Cosines, because computation with a table of tangent values was easier.

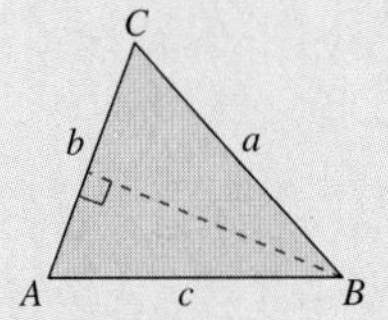

A is acute.

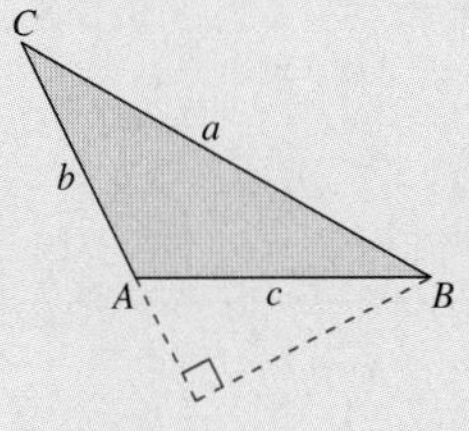

A is obtuse.

487

Law of Cosines (p. 437)

Standard Form	Alternative Form
$a^2 = b^2 + c^2 - 2bc \cos A$	$\cos A = \dfrac{b^2 + c^2 - a^2}{2bc}$
$b^2 = a^2 + c^2 - 2ac \cos B$	$\cos B = \dfrac{a^2 + c^2 - b^2}{2ac}$
$c^2 = a^2 + b^2 - 2ab \cos C$	$\cos C = \dfrac{a^2 + b^2 - c^2}{2ab}$

Proof

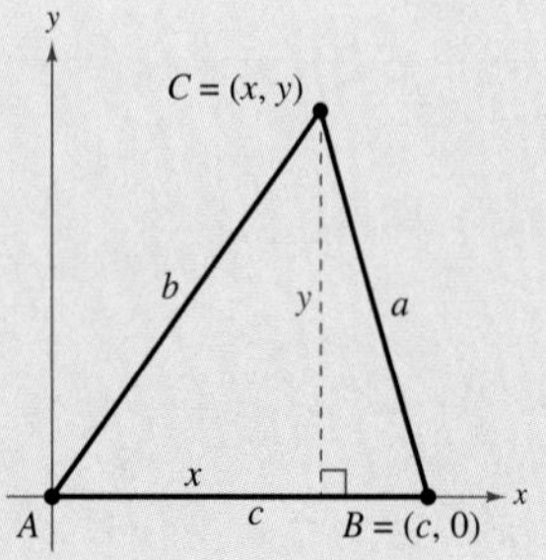

To prove the first formula, consider the top triangle at the left, which has three acute angles. Note that vertex B has coordinates $(c, 0)$. Furthermore, C has coordinates (x, y), where $x = b \cos A$ and $y = b \sin A$. Because a is the distance from vertex C to vertex B, it follows that

$$a = \sqrt{(x - c)^2 + (y - 0)^2} \qquad \text{Distance Formula}$$
$$a^2 = (x - c)^2 + (y - 0)^2 \qquad \text{Square each side.}$$
$$a^2 = (b \cos A - c)^2 + (b \sin A)^2 \qquad \text{Substitute for } x \text{ and } y.$$
$$a^2 = b^2 \cos^2 A - 2bc \cos A + c^2 + b^2 \sin^2 A \qquad \text{Expand.}$$
$$a^2 = b^2(\sin^2 A + \cos^2 A) + c^2 - 2bc \cos A \qquad \text{Factor out } b^2.$$
$$a^2 = b^2 + c^2 - 2bc \cos A. \qquad \sin^2 A + \cos^2 A = 1$$

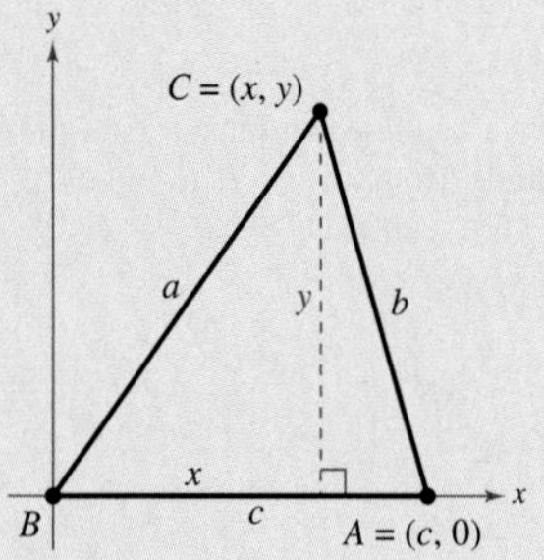

To prove the second formula, consider the bottom triangle at the left, which also has three acute angles. Note that vertex A has coordinates $(c, 0)$. Furthermore, C has coordinates (x, y), where $x = a \cos B$ and $y = a \sin B$. Because b is the distance from vertex C to vertex A, it follows that

$$b = \sqrt{(x - c)^2 + (y - 0)^2} \qquad \text{Distance Formula}$$
$$b^2 = (x - c)^2 + (y - 0)^2 \qquad \text{Square each side.}$$
$$b^2 = (a \cos B - c)^2 + (a \sin B)^2 \qquad \text{Substitute for } x \text{ and } y.$$
$$b^2 = a^2 \cos^2 B - 2ac \cos B + c^2 + a^2 \sin^2 B \qquad \text{Expand.}$$
$$b^2 = a^2(\sin^2 B + \cos^2 B) + c^2 - 2ac \cos B \qquad \text{Factor out } a^2.$$
$$b^2 = a^2 + c^2 - 2ac \cos B. \qquad \sin^2 B + \cos^2 B = 1$$

A similar argument is used to establish the third formula.

488

Heron's Area Formula (p. 440)

Given any triangle with sides of lengths a, b, and c, the area of the triangle is

$$\text{Area} = \sqrt{s(s-a)(s-b)(s-c)}$$

where $s = \dfrac{a+b+c}{2}$.

Proof

From Section 6.1, you know that

$$\text{Area} = \frac{1}{2}bc \sin A \qquad \text{Formula for the area of an oblique triangle}$$

$$(\text{Area})^2 = \frac{1}{4}b^2c^2 \sin^2 A \qquad \text{Square each side.}$$

$$\text{Area} = \sqrt{\frac{1}{4}b^2c^2 \sin^2 A} \qquad \text{Take the square root of each side.}$$

$$= \sqrt{\frac{1}{4}b^2c^2(1 - \cos^2 A)} \qquad \text{Pythagorean Identity}$$

$$= \sqrt{\left[\frac{1}{2}bc(1 + \cos A)\right]\left[\frac{1}{2}bc(1 - \cos A)\right]}. \qquad \text{Factor.}$$

Using the Law of Cosines, you can show that

$$\frac{1}{2}bc(1 + \cos A) = \frac{a+b+c}{2} \cdot \frac{-a+b+c}{2}$$

and

$$\frac{1}{2}bc(1 - \cos A) = \frac{a-b+c}{2} \cdot \frac{a+b-c}{2}.$$

Letting $s = (a + b + c)/2$, these two equations can be rewritten as

$$\frac{1}{2}bc(1 + \cos A) = s(s-a)$$

and

$$\frac{1}{2}bc(1 - \cos A) = (s-b)(s-c).$$

By substituting into the last formula for area, you can conclude that

$$\text{Area} = \sqrt{s(s-a)(s-b)(s-c)}.$$

489

Properties of the Dot Product (p. 458)

Let **u**, **v**, and **w** be vectors in the plane or in space and let c be a scalar.

1. $\mathbf{u} \cdot \mathbf{v} = \mathbf{v} \cdot \mathbf{u}$
2. $\mathbf{0} \cdot \mathbf{v} = 0$
3. $\mathbf{u} \cdot (\mathbf{v} + \mathbf{w}) = \mathbf{u} \cdot \mathbf{v} + \mathbf{u} \cdot \mathbf{w}$
4. $\mathbf{v} \cdot \mathbf{v} = \|\mathbf{v}\|^2$
5. $c(\mathbf{u} \cdot \mathbf{v}) = c\mathbf{u} \cdot \mathbf{v} = \mathbf{u} \cdot c\mathbf{v}$

Proof

Let $\mathbf{u} = \langle u_1, u_2 \rangle$, $\mathbf{v} = \langle v_1, v_2 \rangle$, $\mathbf{w} = \langle w_1, w_2 \rangle$, $\mathbf{0} = \langle 0, 0 \rangle$, and let c be a scalar.

1. $\mathbf{u} \cdot \mathbf{v} = u_1v_1 + u_2v_2 = v_1u_1 + v_2u_2 = \mathbf{v} \cdot \mathbf{u}$
2. $\mathbf{0} \cdot \mathbf{v} = 0 \cdot v_1 + 0 \cdot v_2 = 0$
3. $$\begin{aligned}\mathbf{u} \cdot (\mathbf{v} + \mathbf{w}) &= \mathbf{u} \cdot \langle v_1 + w_1, v_2 + w_2 \rangle \\ &= u_1(v_1 + w_1) + u_2(v_2 + w_2) \\ &= u_1v_1 + u_1w_1 + u_2v_2 + u_2w_2 \\ &= (u_1v_1 + u_2v_2) + (u_1w_1 + u_2w_2) = \mathbf{u} \cdot \mathbf{v} + \mathbf{u} \cdot \mathbf{w}\end{aligned}$$
4. $\mathbf{v} \cdot \mathbf{v} = v_1^2 + v_2^2 = \left(\sqrt{v_1^2 + v_2^2}\right)^2 = \|\mathbf{v}\|^2$
5. $$\begin{aligned}c(\mathbf{u} \cdot \mathbf{v}) &= c(\langle u_1, u_2 \rangle \cdot \langle v_1, v_2 \rangle) \\ &= c(u_1v_1 + u_2v_2) \\ &= (cu_1)v_1 + (cu_2)v_2 \\ &= \langle cu_1, cu_2 \rangle \cdot \langle v_1, v_2 \rangle \\ &= c\mathbf{u} \cdot \mathbf{v}\end{aligned}$$

Angle Between Two Vectors (p. 459)

If θ is the angle between two nonzero vectors **u** and **v**, then $\cos\theta = \dfrac{\mathbf{u} \cdot \mathbf{v}}{\|\mathbf{u}\|\,\|\mathbf{v}\|}$.

Proof

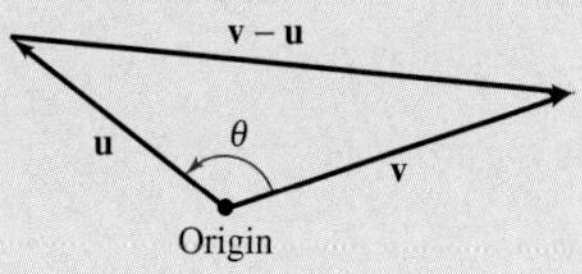

Consider the triangle determined by vectors **u**, **v**, and **v** − **u**, as shown in the figure. By the Law of Cosines, you can write

$$\begin{aligned}\|\mathbf{v} - \mathbf{u}\|^2 &= \|\mathbf{u}\|^2 + \|\mathbf{v}\|^2 - 2\|\mathbf{u}\|\,\|\mathbf{v}\|\cos\theta \\ (\mathbf{v} - \mathbf{u}) \cdot (\mathbf{v} - \mathbf{u}) &= \|\mathbf{u}\|^2 + \|\mathbf{v}\|^2 - 2\|\mathbf{u}\|\,\|\mathbf{v}\|\cos\theta \\ (\mathbf{v} - \mathbf{u}) \cdot \mathbf{v} - (\mathbf{v} - \mathbf{u}) \cdot \mathbf{u} &= \|\mathbf{u}\|^2 + \|\mathbf{v}\|^2 - 2\|\mathbf{u}\|\,\|\mathbf{v}\|\cos\theta \\ \mathbf{v} \cdot \mathbf{v} - \mathbf{u} \cdot \mathbf{v} - \mathbf{v} \cdot \mathbf{u} + \mathbf{u} \cdot \mathbf{u} &= \|\mathbf{u}\|^2 + \|\mathbf{v}\|^2 - 2\|\mathbf{u}\|\,\|\mathbf{v}\|\cos\theta \\ \|\mathbf{v}\|^2 - 2\mathbf{u} \cdot \mathbf{v} + \|\mathbf{u}\|^2 &= \|\mathbf{u}\|^2 + \|\mathbf{v}\|^2 - 2\|\mathbf{u}\|\,\|\mathbf{v}\|\cos\theta \\ \cos\theta &= \frac{\mathbf{u} \cdot \mathbf{v}}{\|\mathbf{u}\|\,\|\mathbf{v}\|}.\end{aligned}$$

490

PROBLEM SOLVING

This collection of thought-provoking and challenging exercises further explores and expands upon concepts learned in this chapter.

1. In the figure, a beam of light is directed at the blue mirror, reflected to the red mirror, and then reflected back to the blue mirror. Find the distance PT that the light travels from the red mirror back to the blue mirror. 2.01 ft

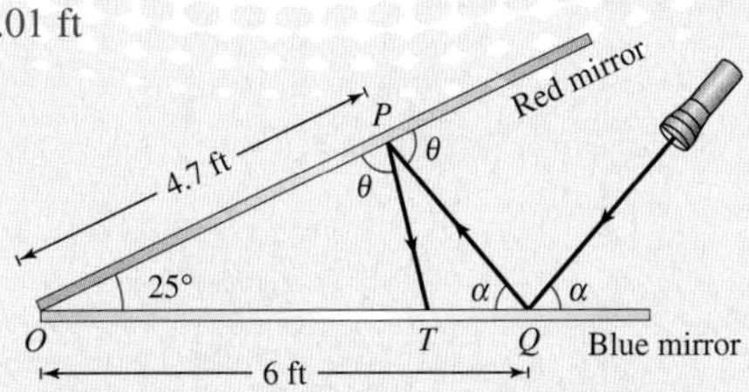

2. A triathlete sets a course to swim S 25° E from a point on shore to a buoy $\frac{3}{4}$ mile away. After swimming 300 yards through a strong current, the triathlete is off course at a bearing of S 35° E. Find the bearing and distance the triathlete needs to swim to correct her course.

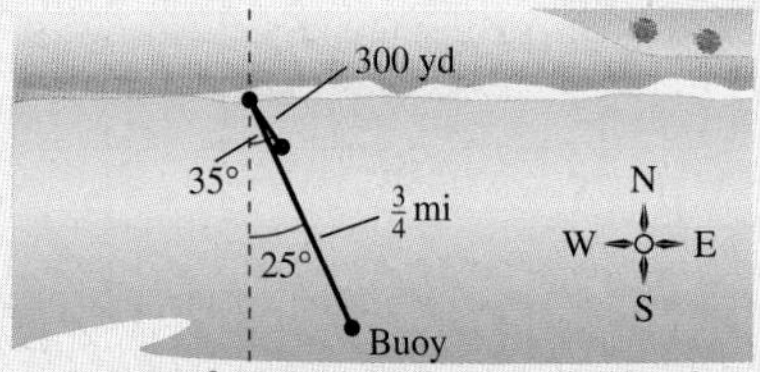

S 22.09° E; 1025.88 yd or 0.58 mi

3. A hiking party is lost in a national park. Two ranger stations have received an emergency SOS signal from the party. Station B is 75 miles due east of station A. The bearing from station A to the signal is S 60° E and the bearing from station B to the signal is S 75° W.

(a) Draw a diagram that gives a visual representation of the problem. (a)–(b). See margin.

(b) Find the distance from each station to the SOS signal.

(c) A rescue party is in the park 20 miles from station A at a bearing of S 80° E. Find the distance and the bearing the rescue party must travel to reach the lost hiking party. 11.03 mi; S 21.7° E

4. You are seeding a triangular courtyard. One side of the courtyard is 52 feet long and another side is 46 feet long. The angle opposite the 52-foot side is 65°.

(a) Draw a diagram that gives a visual representation of the situation. See margin.

(b) How long is the third side of the courtyard? 50.5 ft

(c) One bag of grass seed covers an area of 50 square feet. How many bags of grass seed will you need to cover the courtyard? 22 bags

5. For each pair of vectors, find the following. See margin.

(i) $\|\mathbf{u}\|$ (ii) $\|\mathbf{v}\|$ (iii) $\|\mathbf{u}+\mathbf{v}\|$

(iv) $\left\|\frac{\mathbf{u}}{\|\mathbf{u}\|}\right\|$ (v) $\left\|\frac{\mathbf{v}}{\|\mathbf{v}\|}\right\|$ (vi) $\left\|\frac{\mathbf{u}+\mathbf{v}}{\|\mathbf{u}+\mathbf{v}\|}\right\|$

(a) $\mathbf{u} = \langle 1, -1 \rangle$, $\mathbf{v} = \langle -1, 2 \rangle$ (b) $\mathbf{u} = \langle 0, 1 \rangle$, $\mathbf{v} = \langle 3, -3 \rangle$

(c) $\mathbf{u} = \langle 1, \frac{1}{2} \rangle$, $\mathbf{v} = \langle 2, 3 \rangle$ (d) $\mathbf{u} = \langle 2, -4 \rangle$, $\mathbf{v} = \langle 5, 5 \rangle$

6. A skydiver is falling at a constant downward velocity of 120 miles per hour. In the figure, vector **u** represents the skydiver's velocity. A steady breeze pushes the skydiver to the east at 40 miles per hour. Vector **v** represents the wind velocity.

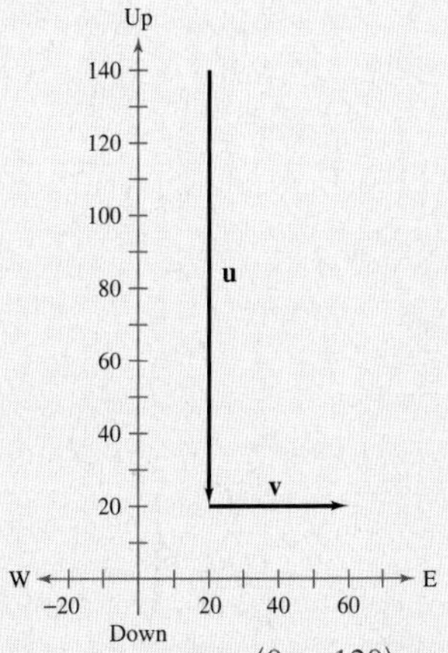

$\mathbf{u} = \langle 0, -120 \rangle$, $\mathbf{v} = \langle 40, 0 \rangle$

(a) Write the vectors **u** and **v** in component form.

(b) Let $\mathbf{s} = \mathbf{u} + \mathbf{v}$. Use the figure to sketch **s**. To print an enlarged copy of the graph, go to the website *www.mathgraphs.com*. (b)–(c). See margin.

(c) Find the magnitude of **s**. What information does the magnitude give you about the skydiver's fall?

(d) If there were no wind, the skydiver would fall in a path perpendicular to the ground. At what angle to the ground is the path of the skydiver when the skydiver is affected by the 40-mile-per-hour wind from due west? 71.57°

(e) The skydiver is blown to the west at 30 miles per hour. Draw a new figure that gives a visual representation of the problem and find the skydiver's new velocity. See margin.

3. (a)

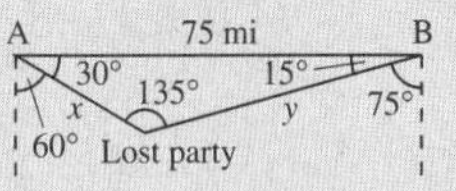

(b) Station A: 27.45 mi; Station B: 53.03 mi

4. (a)

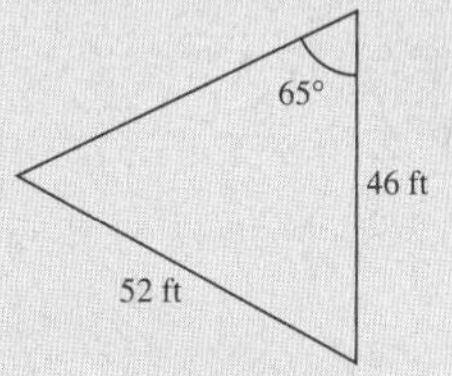

5. (a) (i) $\sqrt{2}$ (iv) 1
(ii) $\sqrt{5}$ (v) 1
(iii) 1 (vi) 1
(b) (i) 1 (iv) 1
(ii) $3\sqrt{2}$ (v) 1
(iii) $\sqrt{13}$ (vi) 1
(c) (i) $\frac{\sqrt{5}}{2}$ (iv) 1
(ii) $\sqrt{13}$ (v) 1
(iii) $\frac{\sqrt{85}}{2}$ (vi) 1
(d) (i) $2\sqrt{5}$ (iv) 1
(ii) $5\sqrt{2}$ (v) 1
(iii) $5\sqrt{2}$ (vi) 1

6. (b)

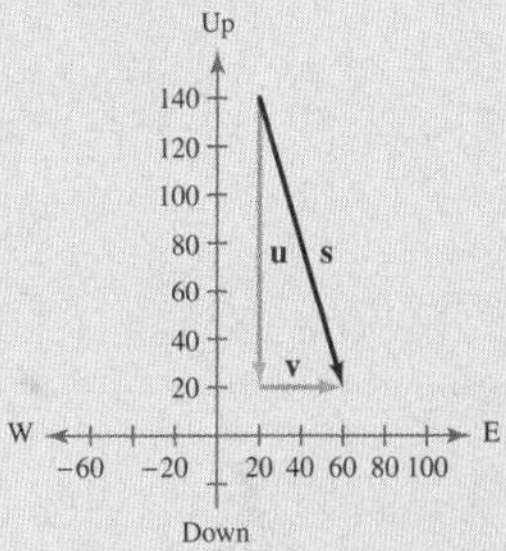

(c) 126.5 miles per hour; The magnitude gives the actual rate of the skydiver's fall.

(e)

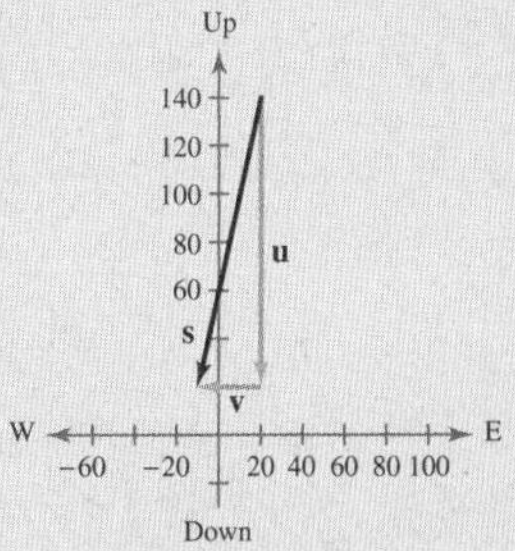

123.7 mi/h

8. $\mathbf{u} \cdot \mathbf{v} = 0$ and $\mathbf{u} \cdot \mathbf{w} = 0$

$\mathbf{u} \cdot (c\mathbf{v} + d\mathbf{w})$
$= \mathbf{u} \cdot c\mathbf{v} + \mathbf{u} \cdot d\mathbf{w}$
$= c(\mathbf{u} \cdot \mathbf{v}) + d(\mathbf{u} \cdot \mathbf{w})$
$= 0$

9. (a)

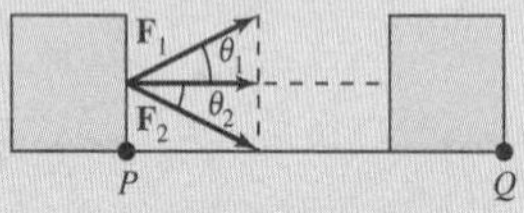

The amount of work done by $\mathbf{F}_1$ is equal to the amount of work done by $\mathbf{F}_2$.

(b)

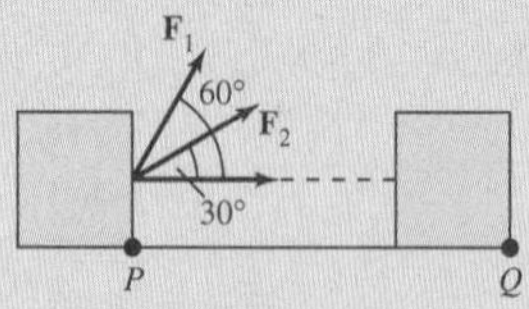

The amount of work done by $\mathbf{F}_2$ is $\sqrt{3}$ times as great as the amount of work done by $\mathbf{F}_1$.

10. (a) See below.

(b) No. Find the square root of the sum of the squares of the vertical and horizontal components.

7. Write the vector $\mathbf{w}$ in terms of $\mathbf{u}$ and $\mathbf{v}$, given that the terminal point of $\mathbf{w}$ bisects the line segment (see figure).

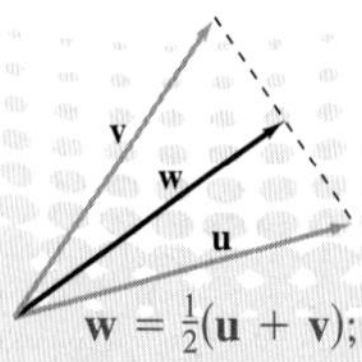

$\mathbf{w} = \frac{1}{2}(\mathbf{u} + \mathbf{v});\ \mathbf{w} = \frac{1}{2}(\mathbf{v} - \mathbf{u})$

8. Prove that if $\mathbf{u}$ is orthogonal to $\mathbf{v}$ and $\mathbf{w}$, then $\mathbf{u}$ is orthogonal to

$c\mathbf{v} + d\mathbf{w}$

for any scalars c and d (see figure). See margin.

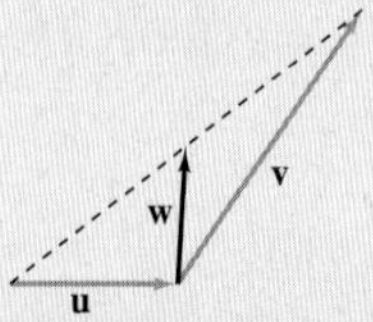

9. Two forces of the same magnitude $\mathbf{F}_1$ and $\mathbf{F}_2$ act at angles θ_1 and θ_2, respectively. Use a diagram to compare the work done by $\mathbf{F}_1$ with the work done by $\mathbf{F}_2$ in moving along the vector PQ if See margin.

(a) $\theta_1 = -\theta_2$

(b) $\theta_1 = 60°$ and $\theta_2 = 30°$.

10. Four basic forces are in action during flight: weight, lift, thrust, and drag. To fly through the air, an object must overcome its own *weight*. To do this, it must create an upward force called *lift*. To generate lift, a forward motion called *thrust* is needed. The thrust must be great enough to overcome air resistance, which is called *drag*.

For a commercial jet aircraft, a quick climb is important to maximize efficiency because the performance of an aircraft at high altitudes is enhanced. In addition, it is necessary to clear obstacles such as buildings and mountains and to reduce noise in residential areas. In the diagram, the angle θ is called the climb angle. The velocity of the plane can be represented by a vector $\mathbf{v}$ with a vertical component $\|\mathbf{v}\| \sin \theta$ (called climb speed) and a horizontal component $\|\mathbf{v}\| \cos \theta$, where $\|\mathbf{v}\|$ is the speed of the plane.

When taking off, a pilot must decide how much of the thrust to apply to each component. The more the thrust is applied to the horizontal component, the faster the airplane will gain speed. The more the thrust is applied to the vertical component, the quicker the airplane will climb.

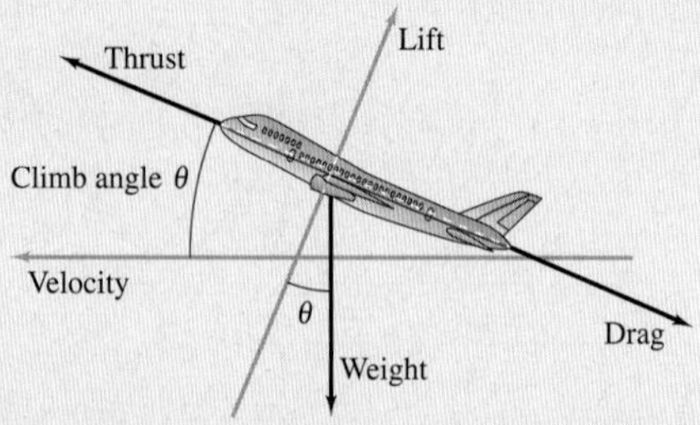

FIGURE FOR 10

(a)–(b). See margin.

(a) Complete the table for an airplane that has a speed of $\|\mathbf{v}\| = 100$ miles per hour.

θ	0.5°	1.0°	1.5°	2.0°	2.5°	3.0°
$\|\mathbf{v}\| \sin \theta$						
$\|\mathbf{v}\| \cos \theta$						

(b) Does an airplane's speed equal the sum of the vertical and horizontal components of its velocity? If not, how could you find the speed of an airplane whose velocity components were known?

(c) Use the result of part (b) to find the speed of an airplane with the given velocity components.

(i) $\|\mathbf{v}\| \sin \theta = 5.235$ miles per hour
$\|\mathbf{v}\| \cos \theta = 149.909$ miles per hour

(ii) $\|\mathbf{v}\| \sin \theta = 10.463$ miles per hour
$\|\mathbf{v}\| \cos \theta = 149.634$ miles per hour

(i) 150 mi/h (ii) 150 mi/h

10. (a)

θ	0.5°	1.0°	1.5°	2.0°	2.5°	3.0°
$\|\mathbf{v}\| \sin \theta$	0.873	1.745	2.618	3.490	4.362	5.234
$\|\mathbf{v}\| \cos \theta$	99.996	99.985	99.966	99.939	99.905	99.863

REGULAR SCHEDULE

Lesson	Day	AVERAGE	ADVANCED
7.1	Day 1	pp. 501–504 Exs. 1–4, 7–9, 12–23, 26, 27, 29, 32, 85, 86	pp. 501–504 Exs. 1–4, 8–14 even, 18, 20, 26–34 even, 85, 86, 90, 91
	Day 2	pp. 501–504 Exs. 5, 6, 35, 37, 41, 47–51 odd, 55, 61, 65, 68, 70, 71, 73, 79–83 odd, 91	pp. 501–504 Exs. 5, 6, 38, 40, 46–50 even, 54, 58, 60, 64–74 even, 78–84 even
7.2	Day 1	pp. 513–514 Exs. 1, 2, 5–11 odd, 14, 16–19, 21, 22, 26, 27, 29, 35–41 odd	pp. 513–514 Exs. 1, 2, 6–12 even, 18–20, 22–30 even, 36–42 even
	Day 2	pp. 513–516 Exs. 3, 4, 44, 46, 49–59 odd, 63–65, 68–71	pp. 513–516 Exs. 3, 4, 44, 47, 48–60 even, 61, 65, 66, 68, 70–72
7.3	Day 1	pp. 525–529 Exs. 1–4, 7–17 odd, 20, 23, 27–31 odd, 36–41 odd, 85, 89–91	pp. 525–529 Exs. 1–4, 8–18 even, 22–32 even, 38–42 even, 86, 88, 94
	Day 2	pp. 525–529 Exs. 5, 6, 43, 47, 51, 55, 59, 62, 63–75 odd, 79, 83, 93	pp. 525–529 Exs. 5, 6, 44–50 even, 56, 57, 60–78 even, 82, 84, 92, 94
7.4	Day 1	pp. 536–537 Exs. 1–4, 6–8, 11, 15, 19, 23–31 odd, 39–45 odd, 51, 53, 57, 59, 63–67 odd	pp. 536–537 Exs. 1–4, 6–8, 12, 16–20 even, 24, 30, 36–46 even, 52, 58–70 even, 71
7.5	Day 1	pp. 545–546 Exs. 1–3, 8, 10, 11, 13, 17–29 odd, 33–39 odd, 61–69 odd	pp. 545–546 Exs. 1–3, 8–14 even, 18–24 even, 28–40 even, 62–70 even
	Day 2	pp. 545–548 Exs. 4–6, 42, 45, 46, 51, 55, 73, 76, 77–81 odd, 86–88, 91–94	pp. 545–548 Exs. 4–6, 44, 45, 48–52 even, 56, 74–78 even, 82, 85, 87, 88, 90–94
7.6	Day 1	pp. 555–557 Exs. 1–8, 11, 14, 15, 17, 21, 25, 29, 30, 33, 35, 39, 43–47 odd, 48	pp. 555–557 Exs. 1–6, 10, 12, 16, 18, 24, 26, 30–40 even, 44, 48
Review	Day 1	pp. 560–564 Exs. 1, 5, 11, 15–25 odd, 29, 33, 37, 39, 43, 49, 51, 57, 61, 67, 71, 79, 83, 87–93 odd, 99, 105, 107, 111, 115	pp. 560–564 Exs. 2, 10, 12, 18–26 even, 32, 36–46 even, 50, 54–58 even, 64, 66, 70, 80, 84, 88, 90, 94, 100, 103, 110, 112, 116
Assess	Day 1	Chapter 7 Test	Chapter 7 Test

Yearly Pacing Chapter 7 Total – 12 days Remaining – 78 days

BLOCK SCHEDULE

DAY 1	DAY 2	DAY 3	DAY 4	DAY 5	DAY 6
7.1	7.2	7.3	7.4	7.5 (CONT.)	REVIEW
pp. 501–504 Exs. 1–9, 12–23, 26, 27, 29, 32, 35, 37, 41, 47–51 odd, 55, 61, 65, 68, 70, 71, 73, 79–83 odd, 85, 86, 91	pp. 513–516 Exs. 1–4, 5–11 odd, 14, 16–19, 21, 22, 26, 27, 29, 35–41 odd, 44, 46, 49–59 odd, 63–65, 68–71	pp. 525–529 Exs. 1–6, 7–17 odd, 20, 23, 27–31 odd, 36–43 odd, 47, 51, 55, 59, 62, 63–75 odd, 79, 83, 85, 89–91, 93	pp. 536–537 Exs. 1–4, 6–8, 11, 15, 19, 23–31 odd, 39–45 odd, 51, 53, 57, 59, 63–67 odd	pp. 545–548 Exs. 4–6, 42, 45, 46, 51, 55, 73, 76, 77–81 odd, 86–88, 91–94	pp. 560–564 Exs. 1, 5, 11, 15–25 odd, 29, 33, 37, 39, 43, 49, 51, 57, 61, 67, 71, 79, 83, 87–93 odd, 99, 105, 107, 111, 115
			7.5	7.6	ASSESS
			pp. 545–546 Exs. 1–3, 8, 10, 11, 13, 17–29 odd, 33–39 odd, 61–69 odd	pp. 555–557 Exs. 1–8, 11, 14, 15, 17, 21, 25, 29, 30, 33, 35, 39, 43–47 odd, 48	Chapter 7 Test

Yearly Pacing Chapter 7 Total – 6 days Remaining – 39 days

Systems of Equations and Inequalities

7

In Mathematics

You can use a system of equations to solve a problem involving two or more equations.

In Real Life

Systems of equations and inequalities are used to determine the correct amounts to use in making an acid mixture, how much to invest in different funds, a break-even point for a business, and many other real-life applications. Systems of equations are also used to find least squares regression parabolas. For instance, a wildlife management team can use a system to model the reproduction rates of deer. (See Exercise 81, page 528.)

Krzysztof Wiktor/Shutterstock

IN CAREERS

There are many careers that use systems of equations and inequalities. Several are listed below.

- Economist
  Exercise 72, page 503
- Investor
  Exercises 53 and 54, page 515
- Dietitian
  Example 9, page 544
- Concert Promoter
  Exercise 78, page 546

1 PLAN AND PREPARE

Main Ideas

In Chapter 7, students learn to solve systems of equations and inequalities. The chapter begins by introducing techniques to solve systems of equations by the methods of substitution and elimination and to check solutions numerically and graphically. Students learn to apply Gaussian elimination to solve more complicated systems. They apply the technique to find partial fraction decompositions of rational functions. The chapter concludes with students learning how to find the solution of a system of inequalities and to use linear programming to optimize a linear function, given a set of constraints.

Chapter Planning Guide

Chapter Resources

- Complete Solutions Guide

Interactive Technology

- Instructor Success Organizer
- Notetaking Guide IAE
- Instructional DVDs
- Animated Precalculus
- PowerLecture with ExamView

493

7.1 Linear and Nonlinear Systems of Equations

1 Plan and Prepare

Warm-up Exercises

Transparency Available
Available at the Instructor's companion site.

Notetaking Guide

Transparency Available
Promotes interactive learning and notetaking skills.
Available at the Instructor's companion site.

Animated Precalculus

An **Animated Precalculus** tutorial is available at the Student companion site for **Section 7.1.**

Pacing

Average: 2 days
Advanced: 2 days
Block: 1 block

2 Focus and Motivate

Essential Question

How do you use the method of substitution and graphing to solve systems of equations? **Tell students that they will learn how to answer this question by manipulating linear and nonlinear equations algebraically and graphically.**

What you should learn

- Use the method of substitution to solve systems of linear equations in two variables.
- Use the method of substitution to solve systems of nonlinear equations in two variables.
- Use a graphical approach to solve systems of equations in two variables.
- Use systems of equations to model and solve real-life problems.

Why you should learn it

Graphs of systems of equations help you solve real-life problems. For instance, in Exercise 75 on page 503, you can use the graph of a system of equations to approximate when the consumption of wind energy surpassed the consumption of solar energy.

© M. Sinibaldi/Corbis

The Method of Substitution

Up to this point in the text, most problems have involved either a function of one variable or a single equation in two variables. However, many problems in science, business, and engineering involve two or more equations in two or more variables. To solve such problems, you need to find solutions of a **system of equations.** Here is an example of a system of two equations in two unknowns.

$$\begin{cases} 2x + y = 5 & \text{Equation 1} \\ 3x - 2y = 4 & \text{Equation 2} \end{cases}$$

A **solution** of this system is an ordered pair that satisfies each equation in the system. Finding the set of all solutions is called **solving the system of equations.** For instance, the ordered pair $(2, 1)$ is a solution of this system. To check this, you can substitute 2 for x and 1 for y in *each* equation.

Check (2, 1) in Equation 1 and Equation 2:

$2x + y = 5$ Write Equation 1.

$2(2) + 1 \stackrel{?}{=} 5$ Substitute 2 for x and 1 for y.

$4 + 1 = 5$ Solution checks in Equation 1. ✓

$3x - 2y = 4$ Write Equation 2.

$3(2) - 2(1) \stackrel{?}{=} 4$ Substitute 2 for x and 1 for y.

$6 - 2 = 4$ Solution checks in Equation 2. ✓

In this chapter, you will study four ways to solve systems of equations, beginning with the **method of substitution.**

Method	*Section*	*Type of System*
1. Substitution	7.1	Linear or nonlinear, two variables
2. Graphical method	7.1	Linear or nonlinear, two variables
3. Elimination	7.2	Linear, two variables
4. Gaussian elimination	7.3	Linear, three or more variables

Method of Substitution

1. *Solve* one of the equations for one variable in terms of the other.
2. *Substitute* the expression found in Step 1 into the other equation to obtain an equation in one variable.
3. *Solve* the equation obtained in Step 2.
4. *Back-substitute* the value obtained in Step 3 into the expression obtained in Step 1 to find the value of the other variable.
5. *Check* that the solution satisfies *each* of the original equations.

Resource Planning Guide

Chapter Resources
- Complete Solutions Guide

Workbooks
- Notetaking Guide
- Student Solutions Guide

Interactive Technology
- Instructor Success Organizer
- Notetaking Guide IAE
- Instructional DVDs
- Animated Precalculus
- PowerLecture with ExamView

Example 1 Solving a System of Equations by Substitution

Solve the system of equations.

$$\begin{cases} x + y = 4 & \text{Equation 1} \\ x - y = 2 & \text{Equation 2} \end{cases}$$

Solution

Begin by solving for y in Equation 1.

$y = 4 - x$ Solve for y in Equation 1.

Next, substitute this expression for y into Equation 2 and solve the resulting single-variable equation for x.

$x - y = 2$ Write Equation 2.

$x - (4 - x) = 2$ Substitute $4 - x$ for y.

$x - 4 + x = 2$ Distributive Property

$2x = 6$ Combine like terms.

$x = 3$ Divide each side by 2.

Finally, you can solve for y by *back-substituting* $x = 3$ into the equation $y = 4 - x$, to obtain

$y = 4 - x$ Write revised Equation 1.

$y = 4 - 3$ Substitute 3 for x.

$y = 1.$ Solve for y.

The solution is the ordered pair (3, 1). You can check this solution as follows.

Check

Substitute (3, 1) into Equation 1:

$x + y = 4$ Write Equation 1.

$3 + 1 \stackrel{?}{=} 4$ Substitute for x and y.

$4 = 4$ Solution checks in Equation 1. ✓

Substitute (3, 1) into Equation 2:

$x - y = 2$ Write Equation 2.

$3 - 1 \stackrel{?}{=} 2$ Substitute for x and y.

$2 = 2$ Solution checks in Equation 2. ✓

Because (3, 1) satisfies both equations in the system, it is a solution of the system of equations.

CHECKPoint Now try Exercise 11.

The term *back-substitution* implies that you work *backwards*. First you solve for one of the variables, and then you substitute that value *back* into one of the equations in the system to find the value of the other variable.

Algebra Help

You can review the techniques for solving different types of equations in Appendix A.5.

WARNING / CAUTION

Because many steps are required to solve a system of equations, it is very easy to make errors in arithmetic. So, you should always check your solution by substituting it into *each* equation in the original system.

3 TEACH

Extra Example 1

Solve the system of equations.

$$\begin{cases} x - y = 0 \\ 5x - 3y = 6 \end{cases}$$

(3, 3)

Differentiated Instruction

Auditory Learners For Example 1, have each student work with a partner. Have one cover the solution while the other instructs the partner on how to solve the system of equations by giving directions based on the instructions in the solution. Have students switch roles to work through Example 3 on page 497.

Extra Example 2

A total of $25,000 is invested in two funds paying 7% and 4% simple interest. The yearly interest is $1405. How much is invested at each rate?

$13,500 is invested at 7% and $11,500 is invested at 4%.

Example 2 Solving a System by Substitution

A total of $12,000 is invested in two funds paying 5% and 3% simple interest. (Recall that the formula for simple interest is $I = Prt$, where P is the principal, r is the annual interest rate, and t is the time.) The yearly interest is $500. How much is invested at each rate?

Solution

Verbal Model: 5% fund + 3% fund = Total investment

5% interest + 3% interest = Total interest

Labels:

Amount in 5% fund $= x$	(dollars)
Interest for 5% fund $= 0.05x$	(dollars)
Amount in 3% fund $= y$	(dollars)
Interest for 3% fund $= 0.03y$	(dollars)
Total investment $= 12{,}000$	(dollars)
Total interest $= 500$	(dollars)

System: $\begin{cases} x + y = 12{,}000 & \text{Equation 1} \\ 0.05x + 0.03y = 500 & \text{Equation 2} \end{cases}$

To begin, it is convenient to multiply each side of Equation 2 by 100. This eliminates the need to work with decimals.

$100(0.05x + 0.03y) = 100(500)$ Multiply each side by 100.

$5x + 3y = 50{,}000$ Revised Equation 2

To solve this system, you can solve for x in Equation 1.

$x = 12{,}000 - y$ Revised Equation 1

Then, substitute this expression for x into revised Equation 2 and solve the resulting equation for y.

$5x + 3y = 50{,}000$ Write revised Equation 2.

$5(12{,}000 - y) + 3y = 50{,}000$ Substitute $12{,}000 - y$ for x.

$60{,}000 - 5y + 3y = 50{,}000$ Distributive Property

$-2y = -10{,}000$ Combine like terms.

$y = 5000$ Divide each side by -2.

Next, back-substitute the value $y = 5000$ to solve for x.

$x = 12{,}000 - y$ Write revised Equation 1.

$x = 12{,}000 - 5000$ Substitute 5000 for y.

$x = 7000$ Simplify.

The solution is (7000, 5000). So, $7000 is invested at 5% and $5000 is invested at 3%. Check this in the original system.

CHECKPoint Now try Exercise 25.

Study Tip

When using the method of substitution, it does not matter which variable you choose to solve for first. Whether you solve for y first or x first, you will obtain the same solution. When making your choice, you should choose the variable and equation that are easier to work with. For instance, in Example 2, solving for x in Equation 1 is easier than solving for x in Equation 2.

TECHNOLOGY

One way to check the answers you obtain in this section is to use a graphing utility. For instance, enter the two equations in Example 2

$y_1 = 12{,}000 - x$

$y_2 = \dfrac{500 - 0.05x}{0.03}$

and find an appropriate viewing window that shows where the two lines intersect. Then use the *intersect* feature or the *zoom* and *trace* features to find the point of intersection. Does this point agree with the solution obtained at the right?

The point of intersection (7000, 5000) agrees with the solution.

Nonlinear Systems of Equations

The equations in Examples 1 and 2 are linear. The method of substitution can also be used to solve systems in which one or both of the equations are nonlinear.

Example 3 Substitution: Two-Solution Case

Solve the system of equations.

$$\begin{cases} 3x^2 + 4x - y = 7 & \text{Equation 1} \\ 2x - y = -1 & \text{Equation 2} \end{cases}$$

Solution

Begin by solving for y in Equation 2 to obtain $y = 2x + 1$. Next, substitute this expression for y into Equation 1 and solve for x.

$3x^2 + 4x - (2x + 1) = 7$ Substitute $2x + 1$ for y in Equation 1.

$3x^2 + 2x - 1 = 7$ Simplify.

$3x^2 + 2x - 8 = 0$ Write in general form.

$(3x - 4)(x + 2) = 0$ Factor.

$x = \frac{4}{3}, -2$ Solve for x.

Back-substituting these values of x to solve for the corresponding values of y produces the solutions $\left(\frac{4}{3}, \frac{11}{3}\right)$ and $(-2, -3)$. Check these in the original system.

CHECKPoint Now try Exercise 31.

Algebra Help

You can review the techniques for factoring in Appendix A.3.

When using the method of substitution, you may encounter an equation that has no solution, as shown in Example 4.

Example 4 Substitution: No-Real-Solution Case

Solve the system of equations.

$$\begin{cases} -x + y = 4 & \text{Equation 1} \\ x^2 + y = 3 & \text{Equation 2} \end{cases}$$

Solution

Begin by solving for y in Equation 1 to obtain $y = x + 4$. Next, substitute this expression for y into Equation 2 and solve for x.

$x^2 + (x + 4) = 3$ Substitute $x + 4$ for y in Equation 2.

$x^2 + x + 1 = 0$ Simplify.

$x = \dfrac{-1 \pm \sqrt{-3}}{2}$ Use the Quadratic Formula.

Because the discriminant is negative, the equation $x^2 + x + 1 = 0$ has no (real) solution. So, the original system has no (real) solution.

CHECKPoint Now try Exercise 33.

Extra Example 3

Solve the system of equations.

$$\begin{cases} -2x + y = 5 \\ x^2 + 3x - y = 1 \end{cases}$$

(2, 9), (−3, −1)

Extra Example 4

Solve the system of equations.

$$\begin{cases} 2x - y = -3 \\ 2x^2 + 4x - y^2 = 0 \end{cases}$$

No (real) solution

Extra Example 5

Solve the system of equations.

$$\begin{cases} -4x + y = 1 \\ 3x + y = 15 \end{cases}$$

(2, 9)

Avoiding Common Errors

Students should be reminded that not all equations are functions. When using a graphing utility to graph equations that are not functions, students should graph the equation as two separate parts. For example, the graph of $x^2 - y^2 = 4$ will show the entire hyperbola only when graphed as $y_1 = \sqrt{4 - x^2}$ and $y_2 = -\sqrt{4 - x^2}$. Without graphing both equations, some solutions may be lost.

Technology

(2, 0); (0, −1), (2, 1); None

TECHNOLOGY

Most graphing utilities have built-in features that approximate the point(s) of intersection of two graphs. Typically, you must enter the equations of the graphs and visually locate a point of intersection before using the *intersect* feature.

Use this feature to find the points of intersection of the graphs in Figures 7.1 to 7.3. Be sure to adjust your viewing window so that you see all the points of intersection.

See margin.

Algebra Help

You can review the techniques for graphing equations in Section 1.2.

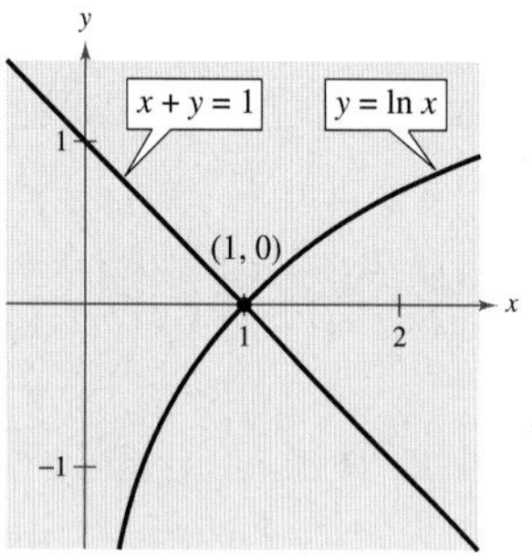

FIGURE 7.4

Graphical Approach to Finding Solutions

From Examples 2, 3, and 4, you can see that a system of two equations in two unknowns can have exactly one solution, more than one solution, or no solution. By using a **graphical method,** you can gain insight about the number of solutions and the location(s) of the solution(s) of a system of equations by graphing each of the equations in the same coordinate plane. The solutions of the system correspond to the **points of intersection** of the graphs. For instance, the two equations in Figure 7.1 graph as two lines with a *single point* of intersection; the two equations in Figure 7.2 graph as a parabola and a line with *two points* of intersection; and the two equations in Figure 7.3 graph as a line and a parabola that have *no points* of intersection.

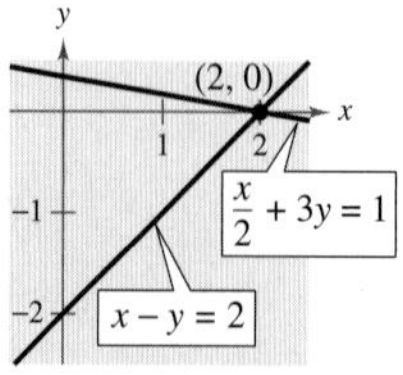

One intersection point

FIGURE 7.1

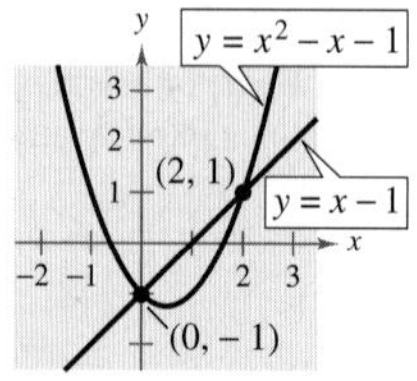

Two intersection points

FIGURE 7.2

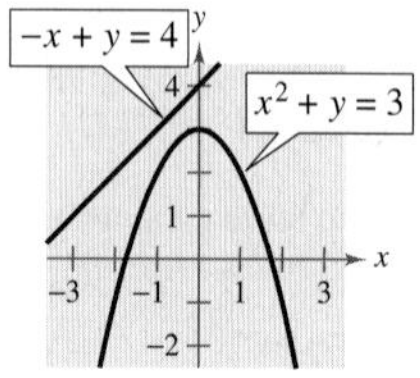

No intersection points

FIGURE 7.3

Example 5 Solving a System of Equations Graphically

Solve the system of equations.

$$\begin{cases} y = \ln x & \text{Equation 1} \\ x + y = 1 & \text{Equation 2} \end{cases}$$

Solution

Sketch the graphs of the two equations. From the graphs of these equations, it is clear that there is only one point of intersection and that $(1, 0)$ is the solution point (see Figure 7.4). You can check this solution as follows.

Check (1, 0) in Equation 1:

$y = \ln x$ — Write Equation 1.

$0 = \ln 1$ — Substitute for x and y.

$0 = 0$ — Solution checks in Equation 1. ✓

Check (1, 0) in Equation 2:

$x + y = 1$ — Write Equation 2.

$1 + 0 = 1$ — Substitute for x and y.

$1 = 1$ — Solution checks in Equation 2. ✓

CHECKPoint Now try Exercise 39.

Example 5 shows the value of a graphical approach to solving systems of equations in two variables. Notice what would happen if you tried only the substitution method in Example 5. You would obtain the equation $x + \ln x = 1$. It would be difficult to solve this equation for x using standard algebraic techniques.

Applications

The total cost C of producing x units of a product typically has two components—the initial cost and the cost per unit. When enough units have been sold so that the total revenue R equals the total cost C, the sales are said to have reached the **break-even point.** You will find that the break-even point corresponds to the point of intersection of the cost and revenue curves.

Example 6 Break-Even Analysis

A shoe company invests $300,000 in equipment to produce a new line of athletic footwear. Each pair of shoes costs $5 to produce and is sold for $60. How many pairs of shoes must be sold before the business breaks even?

Algebraic Solution

The total cost of producing x units is

$$\text{Total cost} = \text{Cost per unit} \cdot \text{Number of units} + \text{Initial cost}$$

$$C = 5x + 300{,}000. \qquad \text{Equation 1}$$

The revenue obtained by selling x units is

$$\text{Total revenue} = \text{Price per unit} \cdot \text{Number of units}$$

$$R = 60x. \qquad \text{Equation 2}$$

Because the break-even point occurs when $R = C$, you have $C = 60x$, and the system of equations to solve is

$$\begin{cases} C = 5x + 300{,}000 \\ C = 60x \end{cases}.$$

Solve by substitution.

$60x = 5x + 300{,}000$ Substitute $60x$ for C in Equation 1.

$55x = 300{,}000$ Subtract $5x$ from each side.

$x \approx 5455$ Divide each side by 55.

So, the company must sell about 5455 pairs of shoes to break even.

Graphical Solution

The total cost of producing x units is

$$\text{Total cost} = \text{Cost per unit} \cdot \text{Number of units} + \text{Initial cost}$$

$$C = 5x + 300{,}000. \qquad \text{Equation 1}$$

The revenue obtained by selling x units is

$$\text{Total revenue} = \text{Price per unit} \cdot \text{Number of units}$$

$$R = 60x. \qquad \text{Equation 2}$$

Because the break-even point occurs when $R = C$, you have $C = 60x$, and the system of equations to solve is

$$\begin{cases} C = 5x + 300{,}000 \\ C = 60x \end{cases}.$$

Use a graphing utility to graph $y_1 = 5x + 300{,}000$ and $y_2 = 60x$ in the same viewing window. Use the *intersect* feature or the *zoom* and *trace* features of the graphing utility to approximate the point of intersection of the graphs. The point of intersection (break-even point) occurs at $x \approx 5455$, as shown in Figure 7.5. So, the company must sell about 5455 pairs of shoes to break even.

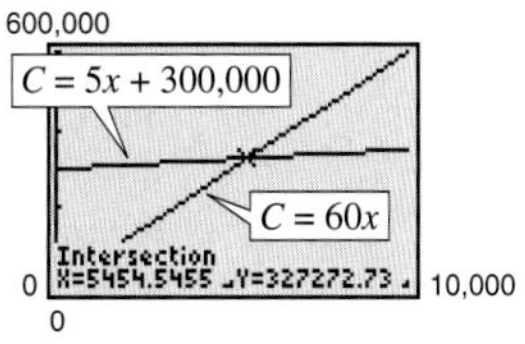

FIGURE 7.5

CHECKPoint Now try Exercise 67.

Another way to view the solution in Example 6 is to consider the profit function

$$P = R - C.$$

The break-even point occurs when the profit is 0, which is the same as saying that $R = C$.

Extra Example 6

A small business has an initial investment of $6000. The unit cost of the product is $23.20, and the selling price is $35.20. How many units must be sold to break even?

500 units

Example 7 Movie Ticket Sales

The weekly ticket sales for a new comedy movie decreased each week. At the same time, the weekly ticket sales for a new drama movie increased each week. Models that approximate the weekly ticket sales S (in millions of dollars) for each movie are

$$\begin{cases} S = 60 - 8x & \text{Comedy} \\ S = 10 + 4.5x & \text{Drama} \end{cases}$$

where x represents the number of weeks each movie was in theaters, with $x = 0$ corresponding to the ticket sales during the opening weekend. After how many weeks will the ticket sales for the two movies be equal?

Algebraic Solution

Because the second equation has already been solved for S in terms of x, substitute this value into the first equation and solve for x, as follows.

$10 + 4.5x = 60 - 8x$ Substitute for S in Equation 1.

$4.5x + 8x = 60 - 10$ Add $8x$ and -10 to each side.

$12.5x = 50$ Combine like terms.

$x = 4$ Divide each side by 12.5.

So, the weekly ticket sales for the two movies will be equal after 4 weeks.

Numerical Solution

You can create a table of values for each model to determine when the ticket sales for the two movies will be equal.

Number of weeks, x	0	1	2	3	4	5	6
Sales, S (comedy)	60	52	44	36	28	20	12
Sales, S (drama)	10	14.5	19	23.5	28	32.5	37

So, from the table above, you can see that the weekly ticket sales for the two movies will be equal after 4 weeks.

CHECKPoint Now try Exercise 69.

Classroom Discussion

Interpreting Points of Intersection You plan to rent a 14-foot truck for a two-day local move. At truck rental agency A, you can rent a truck for \$29.95 per day plus \$0.49 per mile. At agency B, you can rent a truck for \$50 per day plus \$0.25 per mile.

a. Write a total cost equation in terms of x and y for the total cost of renting the truck from each agency.

b. Use a graphing utility to graph the two equations in the same viewing window and find the point of intersection. Interpret the meaning of the point of intersection in the context of the problem.

c. Which agency should you choose if you plan to travel a total of 100 miles during the two-day move? Why?

d. How does the situation change if you plan to drive 200 miles during the two-day move?

See margin.

Extra Example 7

From 2001 to 2008, the population of City A was increasing at a faster rate than was the population of City B. Models that approximate the two populations P (in thousands) are

$$\begin{cases} P = 4947.3 + 95t \\ P = 5118 + 41.4t \end{cases}$$

where t represents the number of years since 2001. According to these two models, when would you expect the populations of these two cities to be equal?

The populations should be equal at $t = 3.2$ years, which was sometime in 2004.

Closing the Lesson

Have students summarize the major points of the lesson and answer the Essential Question: How do you use the method of substitution and graphing to solve systems of equations?

- **Use the method of substitution to solve a system of equations by first solving one equation for one variable and then substituting the expression into the other equation.**
- **Use graphing to solve a system of equations by graphing each equation in order to identify intersection points.**
- **Verify solutions of systems of equations by substituting the solutions into the original equations.**

Classroom Discussion

a. Agency A cost equation:
$y = 59.90 + 0.49x$
Agency B cost equation:
$y = 100 + 0.25x$

b.

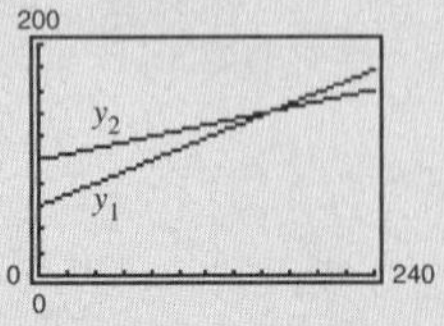

Point of intersection: (167.08, 141.77). This gives the point at which the plans from both agencies cost the same (\$141.77 for 167.08 miles).

c. Agency A. If you plan to drive the truck less than 167 miles, it is less expensive to choose Agency A.

d. Agency B. If you plan to drive more than 167 miles, choose Agency B.

7.1 EXERCISES

See www.CalcChat.com for worked-out solutions to odd-numbered exercises.

VOCABULARY: Fill in the blanks.

1. A set of two or more equations in two or more variables is called a ___system___ of ___equations___.
2. A ___solution___ of a system of equations is an ordered pair that satisfies each equation in the system.
3. Finding the set of all solutions to a system of equations is called ___solving___ the system of equations.
4. The first step in solving a system of equations by the method of ________ is to solve one of the equations for one variable in terms of the other variable. substitution
5. Graphically, the solution of a system of two equations is the ___point___ of ___intersection___ of the graphs of the two equations.
6. In business applications, the point at which the revenue equals costs is called the ________ point. break-even

SKILLS AND APPLICATIONS

In Exercises 7–10, determine whether each ordered pair is a solution of the system of equations. 7–10. See margin.

7. $\begin{cases} 2x - y = 4 \\ 8x + y = -9 \end{cases}$ (a) $(0, -4)$ (b) $(-2, 7)$ (c) $\left(\frac{3}{2}, -1\right)$ (d) $\left(-\frac{1}{2}, -5\right)$

8. $\begin{cases} 4x^2 + y = 3 \\ -x - y = 11 \end{cases}$ (a) $(2, -13)$ (b) $(2, -9)$ (c) $\left(-\frac{3}{2}, -\frac{31}{3}\right)$ (d) $\left(-\frac{7}{4}, -\frac{37}{4}\right)$

9. $\begin{cases} y = -4e^x \\ 7x - y = 4 \end{cases}$ (a) $(-4, 0)$ (b) $(0, -4)$ (c) $(0, -2)$ (d) $(-1, -3)$

10. $\begin{cases} -\log x + 3 = y \\ \frac{1}{9}x + y = \frac{28}{9} \end{cases}$ (a) $\left(9, \frac{37}{9}\right)$ (b) $(10, 2)$ (c) $(1, 3)$ (d) $(2, 4)$

In Exercises 11–20, solve the system by the method of substitution. Check your solution(s) graphically.

11. $\begin{cases} 2x + y = 6 \\ -x + y = 0 \end{cases}$

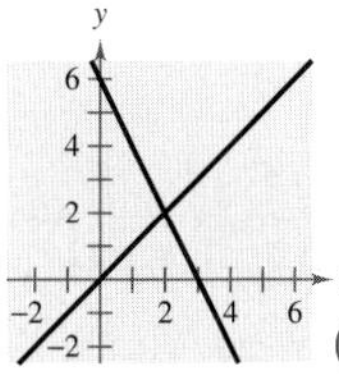

$(2, 2)$

12. $\begin{cases} x - 4y = -11 \\ x + 3y = 3 \end{cases}$

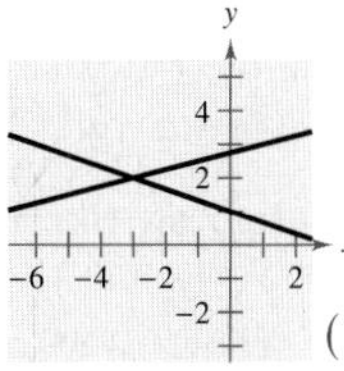

$(-3, 2)$

13. $\begin{cases} x - y = -4 \\ x^2 - y = -2 \end{cases}$

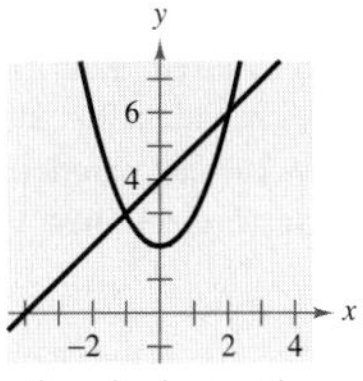

$(2, 6), (-1, 3)$

14. $\begin{cases} 3x + y = 2 \\ x^3 - 2 + y = 0 \end{cases}$

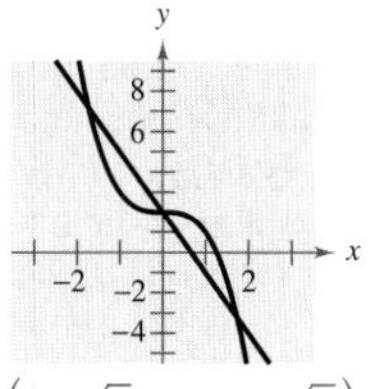

$\left(-\sqrt{3}, 2 + 3\sqrt{3}\right)$, $(0, 2)$, $\left(\sqrt{3}, 2 - 3\sqrt{3}\right)$

15–20. See margin.

15. $\begin{cases} -\frac{1}{2}x + y = -\frac{5}{2} \\ x^2 + y^2 = 25 \end{cases}$

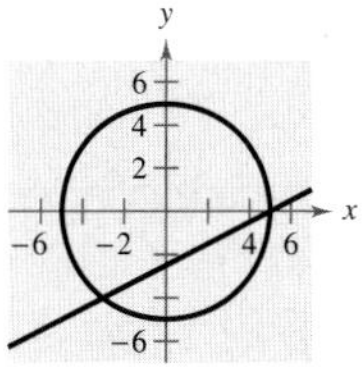

16. $\begin{cases} x + y = 0 \\ x^3 - 5x - y = 0 \end{cases}$

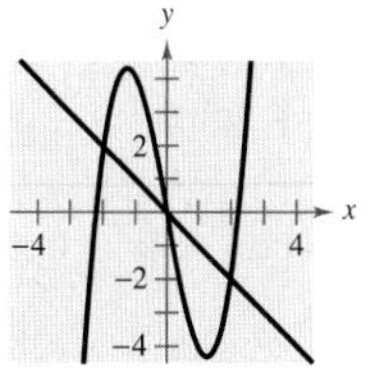

17. $\begin{cases} x^2 + y = 0 \\ x^2 - 4x - y = 0 \end{cases}$

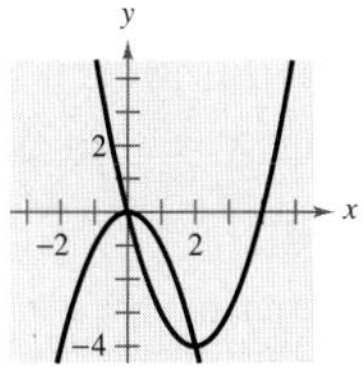

18. $\begin{cases} y = -2x^2 + 2 \\ y = 2(x^4 - 2x^2 + 1) \end{cases}$

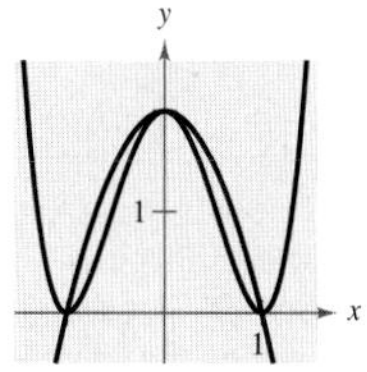

19. $\begin{cases} y = x^3 - 3x^2 + 1 \\ y = x^2 - 3x + 1 \end{cases}$

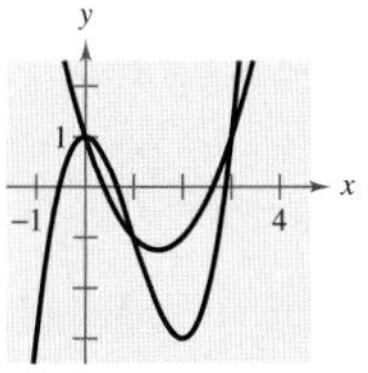

20. $\begin{cases} y = x^3 - 3x^2 + 4 \\ y = -2x + 4 \end{cases}$

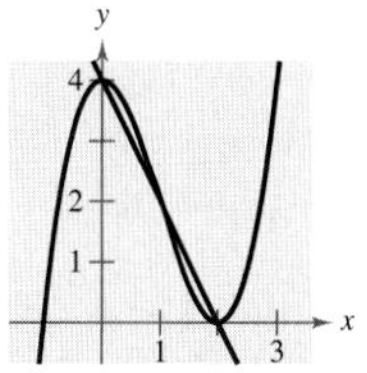

In Exercises 21–34, solve the system by the method of substitution.

21. $\begin{cases} x - y = 2 \\ 6x - 5y = 16 \end{cases}$ $(6, 4)$

22. $\begin{cases} x + 4y = 3 \\ 2x - 7y = -24 \end{cases}$ $(-5, 2)$

23. $\begin{cases} 2x - y + 2 = 0 \\ 4x + y - 5 = 0 \end{cases}$ $\left(\frac{1}{2}, 3\right)$

24. $\begin{cases} 6x - 3y - 4 = 0 \\ x + 2y - 4 = 0 \end{cases}$ $\left(\frac{4}{3}, \frac{4}{3}\right)$

4 PRACTICE AND APPLY

Assignment Guide

Transparencies Available
Available at the Instructor's companion site.

Average:
Day 1: pp. 501–504
Exs. 1–4, 7–9, 12–23, 26, 27, 29, 32, 85, 86
Day 2: pp. 501–504
Exs. 5, 6, 35, 37, 41, 47–51 odd, 55, 61, 65, 68, 70, 71, 73, 79–83 odd, 91

Advanced:
Day 1: pp. 501–504
Exs. 1–4, 8–14 even, 18, 20, 26–34 even, 85, 86, 90, 91
Day 2: pp. 501–504
Exs. 5, 6, 38, 40, 46–50 even, 54, 58, 60, 64–74 even, 78–84 even

Block:
pp. 501–504
Exs. 1–9, 12–23, 26, 27, 29, 32, 35, 37, 41, 47–51 odd, 55, 61, 65, 68, 70, 71, 73, 79–83 odd, 85, 86, 91

7. (a) No (b) No (c) No (d) Yes
8. (a) Yes (b) No (c) No (d) Yes
9. (a) No (b) Yes (c) No (d) No
10. (a) No (b) Yes (c) Yes (d) No
15. $(-3, -4), (5, 0)$
16. $(0, 0), (2, -2), (-2, 2)$
17. $(0, 0), (2, -4)$
18. $(0, 2), (1, 0), (-1, 0)$
19. $(0, 1), (1, -1), (3, 1)$
20. $(0, 4), (1, 2), (2, 0)$

25. $\begin{cases} 1.5x + 0.8y = 2.3 \\ 0.3x - 0.2y = 0.1 \end{cases}$ $(1, 1)$

26. $\begin{cases} 0.5x + 3.2y = 9.0 \\ 0.2x - 1.6y = -3.6 \end{cases}$ $\left(2, \frac{5}{2}\right)$

27. $\begin{cases} \frac{1}{5}x + \frac{1}{2}y = 8 \\ x + y = 20 \end{cases}$ $\left(\frac{20}{3}, \frac{40}{3}\right)$

28. $\begin{cases} \frac{1}{2}x + \frac{3}{4}y = 10 \\ \frac{3}{4}x - y = 4 \end{cases}$ $\left(\frac{208}{17}, \frac{88}{17}\right)$

29. $\begin{cases} 6x + 5y = -3 \\ -x - \frac{5}{6}y = -7 \end{cases}$ No solution

30. $\begin{cases} -\frac{2}{3}x + y = 2 \\ 2x - 3y = 6 \end{cases}$ No solution

31. $\begin{cases} x^2 - y = 0 \\ 2x + y = 0 \end{cases}$ $(-2, 4), (0, 0)$

32. $\begin{cases} x - 2y = 0 \\ 3x - y^2 = 0 \end{cases}$ $(0, 0), (12, 6)$

33. $\begin{cases} x - y = -1 \\ x^2 - y = -4 \end{cases}$ No solution

34. $\begin{cases} y = -x \\ y = x^3 + 3x^2 + 2x \end{cases}$ $(0, 0)$

In Exercises 35–48, solve the system graphically. 35–48. See margin.

35. $\begin{cases} -x + 2y = -2 \\ 3x + y = 20 \end{cases}$

36. $\begin{cases} x + y = 0 \\ 3x - 2y = 5 \end{cases}$

37. $\begin{cases} x - 3y = -3 \\ 5x + 3y = -6 \end{cases}$

38. $\begin{cases} -x + 2y = -7 \\ x - y = 2 \end{cases}$

39. $\begin{cases} x + y = 4 \\ x^2 + y^2 - 4x = 0 \end{cases}$

40. $\begin{cases} -x + y = 3 \\ x^2 - 6x - 27 + y^2 = 0 \end{cases}$

41. $\begin{cases} x - y + 3 = 0 \\ x^2 - 4x + 7 = y \end{cases}$

42. $\begin{cases} y^2 - 4x + 11 = 0 \\ -\frac{1}{2}x + y = -\frac{1}{2} \end{cases}$

43. $\begin{cases} 7x + 8y = 24 \\ x - 8y = 8 \end{cases}$

44. $\begin{cases} x - y = 0 \\ 5x - 2y = 6 \end{cases}$

45. $\begin{cases} 3x - 2y = 0 \\ x^2 - y^2 = 4 \end{cases}$

46. $\begin{cases} 2x - y + 3 = 0 \\ x^2 + y^2 - 4x = 0 \end{cases}$

47. $\begin{cases} x^2 + y^2 = 25 \\ 3x^2 - 16y = 0 \end{cases}$

48. $\begin{cases} x^2 + y^2 = 25 \\ (x - 8)^2 + y^2 = 41 \end{cases}$

49–54. See margin.

In Exercises 49–54, use a graphing utility to solve the system of equations. Find the solution(s) accurate to two decimal places.

49. $\begin{cases} y = e^x \\ x - y + 1 = 0 \end{cases}$

50. $\begin{cases} y = -4e^{-x} \\ y + 3x + 8 = 0 \end{cases}$

51. $\begin{cases} x + 2y = 8 \\ y = \log_2 x \end{cases}$

52. $\begin{cases} y + 2 = \ln(x - 1) \\ 3y + 2x = 9 \end{cases}$

53. $\begin{cases} x^2 + y^2 = 169 \\ x^2 - 8y = 104 \end{cases}$

54. $\begin{cases} x^2 + y^2 = 4 \\ 2x^2 - y = 2 \end{cases}$

In Exercises 55–64, solve the system graphically or algebraically. Explain your choice of method.

55. $\begin{cases} y = 2x \\ y = x^2 + 1 \end{cases}$ $(1, 2)$

56. $\begin{cases} x^2 + y^2 = 25 \\ 2x + y = 10 \end{cases}$ $(3, 4), (5, 0)$

57. $\begin{cases} x - 2y = 4 \\ x^2 - y = 0 \end{cases}$ No solution

58. $\begin{cases} y = (x + 1)^3 \\ y = \sqrt{x - 1} \end{cases}$ No solution

59. $\begin{cases} y - e^{-x} = 1 \\ y - \ln x = 3 \end{cases}$ $(0.287, 1.751)$

60. $\begin{cases} x^2 + y = 4 \\ e^x - y = 0 \end{cases}$ $(-1.96, 0.14), (1.06, 2.88)$

61–63. See margin.

61. $\begin{cases} y = x^4 - 2x^2 + 1 \\ y = 1 - x^2 \end{cases}$

62. $\begin{cases} y = x^3 - 2x^2 + x - 1 \\ y = -x^2 + 3x - 1 \end{cases}$

63. $\begin{cases} xy - 1 = 0 \\ 2x - 4y + 7 = 0 \end{cases}$

64. $\begin{cases} x - 2y = 1 \\ y = \sqrt{x - 1} \end{cases}$ $(1, 0), (5, 2)$

BREAK-EVEN ANALYSIS In Exercises 65 and 66, find the sales necessary to break even ($R = C$) for the cost C of producing x units and the revenue R obtained by selling x units. (Round to the nearest whole unit.)

65. $C = 8650x + 250{,}000$, $R = 9950x$ 192 units

66. $C = 5.5\sqrt{x} + 10{,}000$, $R = 3.29x$ 3133 units

67. **BREAK-EVEN ANALYSIS** A small software company invests \$25,000 to produce a software package that will sell for \$69.95. Each unit can be produced for \$45.25.
   (a) How many units must be sold to break even? 1013 units
   (b) How many units must be sold to make a profit of \$100,000? 5061 units

68. **BREAK-EVEN ANALYSIS** A small fast-food restaurant invests \$10,000 to produce a new food item that will sell for \$3.99. Each item can be produced for \$1.90.
   (a) How many items must be sold to break even? 4785 items
   (b) How many items must be sold to make a profit of \$12,000? 10,527 items

69. **DVD RENTALS** The weekly rentals for a newly released DVD of an animated film at a local video store decreased each week. At the same time, the weekly rentals for a newly released DVD of a horror film increased each week. Models that approximate the weekly rentals R for each DVD are

$$\begin{cases} R = 360 - 24x & \text{Animated film} \\ R = 24 + 18x & \text{Horror film} \end{cases}$$

where x represents the number of weeks each DVD was in the store, with $x = 1$ corresponding to the first week.
   (a) After how many weeks will the rentals for the two movies be equal? (a) 8 weeks (b) See margin.
   (b) Use a table to solve the system of equations numerically. Compare your result with that of part (a).

70. **SALES** The total weekly sales for a newly released portable media player (PMP) increased each week. At the same time, the total weekly sales for another newly released PMP decreased each week. Models that approximate the total weekly sales S (in thousands of units) for each PMP are

$$\begin{cases} S = 15x + 50 & \text{PMP 1} \\ S = -20x + 190 & \text{PMP 2} \end{cases}$$

where x represents the number of weeks each PMP was in stores, with $x = 0$ corresponding to the PMP sales on the day each PMP was first released in stores.

35. $(6, 2)$ 36. $(1, -1)$
37. $\left(-\frac{3}{2}, \frac{1}{2}\right)$ 38. $(-3, -5)$
39. $(2, 2), (4, 0)$
40. $(-3, 0), (3, 6)$
41. $(1, 4), (4, 7)$
42. $(3, 1), (15, 7)$
43. $\left(4, -\frac{1}{2}\right)$ 44. $(2, 2)$
45. No solution 46. No solution
47. $(4, 3), (-4, 3)$
48. $(3, 4), (3, -4)$

49. 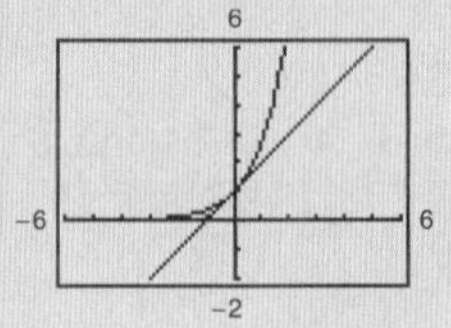
$(0, 1)$

50. 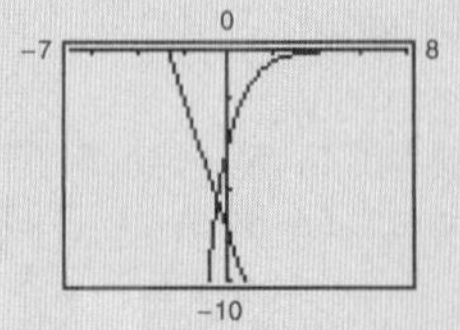
$(-0.49, -6.53)$

51. 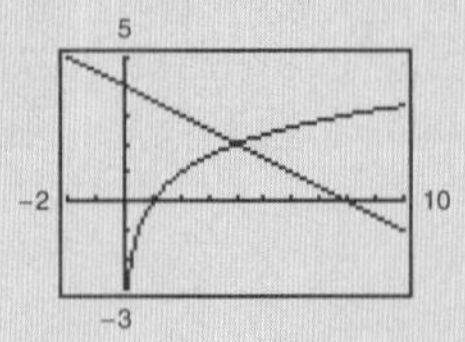
$(4, 2)$

52. 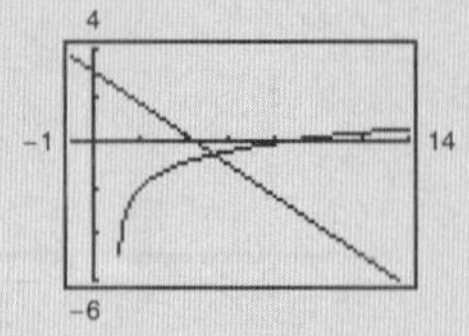
$(5.31, -0.54)$

53. 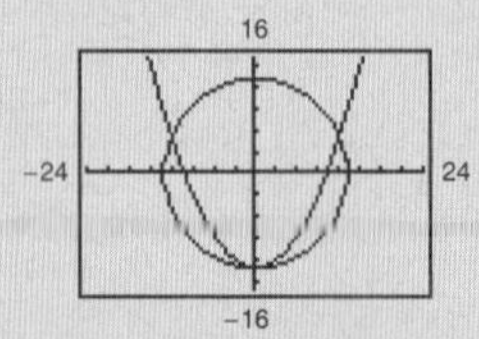
$(0, -13), (\pm 12, 5)$

54. 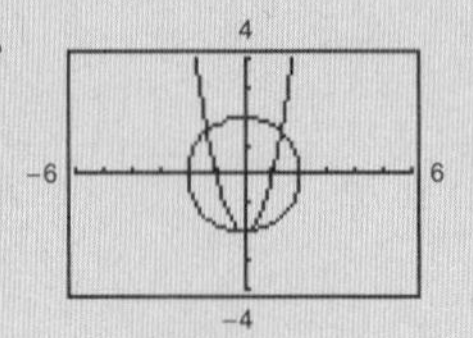
$(0, -2), (\pm 1.32, 1.50)$

61. $(-1, 0), (0, 1), (1, 0)$
62. $(0, -1), (2, 1), (-1, -5)$
63. $\left(\frac{1}{2}, 2\right), \left(-4, -\frac{1}{4}\right)$

69. (b)

	1	2	3	4
$360 - 24x$	336	312	288	264
$24 + 18x$	42	60	78	96

	5	6	7	8
$360 - 24x$	240	216	192	168
$24 + 18x$	114	132	150	168

(a) After how many weeks will the sales for the two PMPs be equal? 4 weeks (b) See margin.

(b) Use a table to solve the system of equations numerically. Compare your result with that of part (a).

71. **CHOICE OF TWO JOBS** You are offered two jobs selling dental supplies. One company offers a straight commission of 6% of sales. The other company offers a salary of \$500 per week plus 3% of sales. How much would you have to sell in a week in order to make the straight commission offer better? More than \$16,666.67

72. **SUPPLY AND DEMAND** The supply and demand curves for a business dealing with wheat are

Supply: $p = 1.45 + 0.00014x^2$

Demand: $p = (2.388 - 0.007x)^2$

where p is the price in dollars per bushel and x is the quantity in bushels per day. Use a graphing utility to graph the supply and demand equations and find the market equilibrium. (The market equilibrium is the point of intersection of the graphs for $x > 0$.) See margin.

73. **INVESTMENT PORTFOLIO** A total of \$25,000 is invested in two funds paying 6% and 8.5% simple interest. (The 6% investment has a lower risk.) The investor wants a yearly interest income of \$2000 from the two investments.

(a) Write a system of equations in which one equation represents the total amount invested and the other equation represents the \$2000 required in interest. Let x and y represent the amounts invested at 6% and 8.5%, respectively. See margin.

(b) Use a graphing utility to graph the two equations in the same viewing window. As the amount invested at 6% increases, how does the amount invested at 8.5% change? How does the amount of interest income change? Explain. See margin.

(c) What amount should be invested at 6% to meet the requirement of \$2000 per year in interest? \$5000

74. **LOG VOLUME** You are offered two different rules for estimating the number of board feet in a 16-foot log. (A board foot is a unit of measure for lumber equal to a board 1 foot square and 1 inch thick.) The first rule is the *Doyle Log Rule* and is modeled by $V_1 = (D - 4)^2$, $5 \le D \le 40$, and the other is the *Scribner Log Rule* and is modeled by $V_2 = 0.79D^2 - 2D - 4$, $5 \le D \le 40$, where D is the diameter (in inches) of the log and V is its volume (in board feet).

(a) Use a graphing utility to graph the two log rules in the same viewing window. See margin.

(b) For what diameter do the two scales agree? 24.7 in.

(c) You are selling large logs by the board foot. Which scale would you use? Explain your reasoning. Doyle Log Rule; For large logs, the Doyle Log Rule gives a greater volume for a given diameter.

75. **DATA ANALYSIS: RENEWABLE ENERGY** The table shows the consumption C (in trillions of Btus) of solar energy and wind energy in the United States from 1998 through 2006. (Source: Energy Information Administration) (a)–(c). See margin.

Year	Solar, C	Wind, C
1998	70	31
1999	69	46
2000	66	57
2001	65	70
2002	64	105
2003	64	115
2004	65	142
2005	66	178
2006	72	264

(a) Use the *regression* feature of a graphing utility to find a cubic model for the solar energy consumption data and a quadratic model for the wind energy consumption data. Let t represent the year, with $t = 8$ corresponding to 1998.

(b) Use a graphing utility to graph the data and the two models in the same viewing window.

(c) Use the graph from part (b) to approximate the point of intersection of the graphs of the models. Interpret your answer in the context of the problem.

(d) Describe the behavior of each model. Do you think the models can be used to predict consumption of solar energy and wind energy in the United States for future years? Explain. (d)–(e). Answers will vary.

(e) Use your school's library, the Internet, or some other reference source to research the advantages and disadvantages of using renewable energy.

76. **DATA ANALYSIS: POPULATION** The table shows the populations P (in millions) of Georgia, New Jersey, and North Carolina from 2002 through 2007. (Source: U.S. Census Bureau)

Year	Georgia, G	New Jersey, J	North Carolina, N
2002	8.59	8.56	8.32
2003	8.74	8.61	8.42
2004	8.92	8.64	8.54
2005	9.11	8.66	8.68
2006	9.34	8.67	8.87
2007	9.55	8.69	9.06

70. (b) See below.

72.
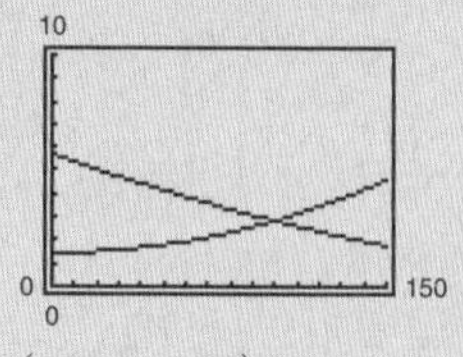

(99.99, 2.85)

73. (a) $\begin{cases} x + y = 25{,}000 \\ 0.06x + 0.085y = 2{,}000 \end{cases}$

(b)
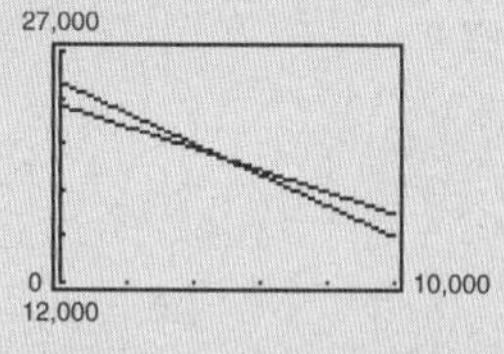

Decreases; Interest is fixed.

74. (a)
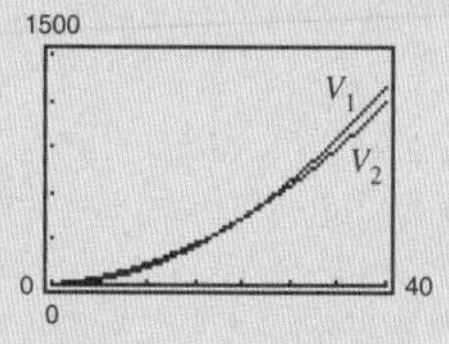

70. (b)

	1	2	3	4
$15x + 50$	65	80	95	110
$-20x + 190$	170	150	130	110

75. (a) Solar: $0.0598t^3 - 1.719t^2 + 14.66t + 32.2$
Wind: $3.237t^2 - 51.97t + 247.9$

(b)
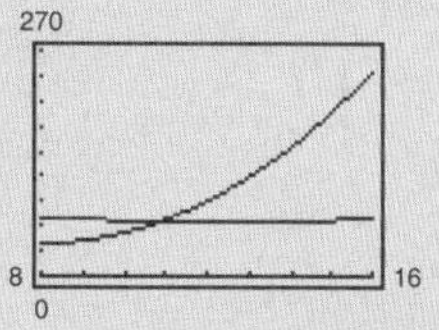

(c) Point of intersection: (10.9, 65.26); Consumption of solar and wind energy are equal at this point in time in the year 2000.

(a)–(d). See margin.

(a) Use the *regression* feature of a graphing utility to find linear models for each set of data. Let t represent the year, with $t = 2$ corresponding to 2002.

(b) Use a graphing utility to graph the data and the models in the same viewing window.

(c) Use the graph from part (b) to approximate any points of intersection of the graphs of the models. Interpret the points of intersection in the context of the problem.

(d) Verify your answers from part (c) algebraically.

77. DATA ANALYSIS: TUITION The table shows the average costs (in dollars) of one year's tuition for public and private universities in the United States from 2000 through 2006. (Source: U.S. National Center for Education Statistics)

Year	Public universities	Private universities
2000	2506	14,081
2001	2562	15,000
2002	2700	15,742
2003	2903	16,383
2004	3319	17,327
2005	3629	18,154
2006	3874	18,862

(a) Use the *regression* feature of a graphing utility to find a quadratic model T_1 for tuition at public universities and a linear model T_2 for tuition at private universities. Let t represent the year, with $t = 0$ corresponding to 2000. (a)–(b). See margin.

(b) Use a graphing utility to graph the data and the two models in the same viewing window.

(c) Use the graph from part (b) to determine the year after 2006 in which tuition at public universities will exceed tuition at private universities. 2038

(d) Verify your answer from part (c) algebraically. 2038

GEOMETRY In Exercises 78–82, find the dimensions of the rectangle meeting the specified conditions.

78. The perimeter is 56 meters and the length is 4 meters greater than the width. 12 m × 16 m

79. The perimeter is 280 centimeters and the width is 20 centimeters less than the length. 60 cm × 80 cm

80. The perimeter is 42 inches and the width is three-fourths the length. 9 in. × 12 in.

81. The perimeter is 484 feet and the length is $4\frac{1}{2}$ times the width. 44 ft × 198 ft

82. The perimeter is 30.6 millimeters and the length is 2.4 times the width. 4.5 mm × 10.8 mm

83. GEOMETRY What are the dimensions of a rectangular tract of land if its perimeter is 44 kilometers and its area is 120 square kilometers? 10 km × 12 km

84. GEOMETRY What are the dimensions of an isosceles right triangle with a two-inch hypotenuse and an area of 1 square inch? $\sqrt{2}$ in. × $\sqrt{2}$ in. × 2 in.

EXPLORATION

85–86. See margin.

TRUE OR FALSE? In Exercises 85 and 86, determine whether the statement is true or false. Justify your answer.

85. In order to solve a system of equations by substitution, you must always solve for y in one of the two equations and then back-substitute.

86. If a system consists of a parabola and a circle, then the system can have at most two solutions.

87. GRAPHICAL REASONING Use a graphing utility to graph $y_1 = 4 - x$ and $y_2 = x - 2$ in the same viewing window. Use the *zoom* and *trace* features to find the coordinates of the point of intersection. What is the relationship between the point of intersection and the solution found in Example 1? See margin.

88. GRAPHICAL REASONING Use a graphing utility to graph the two equations in Example 3, $y_1 = 3x^2 + 4x - 7$ and $y_2 = 2x + 1$, in the same viewing window. How many solutions do you think this system has? Repeat this experiment for the equations in Example 4. How many solutions does this system have? Explain your reasoning. See margin.

89. THINK ABOUT IT When solving a system of equations by substitution, how do you recognize that the system has no solution? See margin.

90. CAPSTONE Consider the system of equations

$$\begin{cases} ax + by = c \\ dx + ey = f \end{cases}.$$

Answers will vary.

(a) Find values for a, b, c, d, e, and f so that the system has one distinct solution. (There is more than one correct answer.)

(b) Explain how to solve the system in part (a) by the method of substitution and graphically.

(c) Write a brief paragraph describing any advantages of the method of substitution over the graphical method of solving a system of equations.

91. Find equations of lines whose graphs intersect the graph of the parabola $y = x^2$ at (a) two points, (b) one point, and (c) no points. (There is more than one correct answer.) Use graphs to support your answers.
(a) $y = 2x$ (b) $y = 0$ (c) $y = x - 2$

5 ASSESS AND RETEACH

Daily Homework Quiz

Transparency Available
Available at the Instructor's companion site.

76. (a) Georgia: $0.194t + 8.17$
New Jersey: $0.024t + 8.53$
North Carolina: $0.148t + 7.98$

(b)

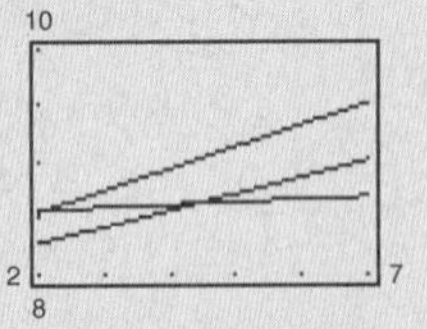

(c) Point of intersection: (2.12, 8.58); Georgia's population exceeded New Jersey's after this point in time in 2002.
Point of intersection: (4.44, 8.64); North Carolina's population exceeded New Jersey's after this point in time in 2004.

(d) (2.12, 8.58), (4.44, 8.64)

77. (a)
$T_1 = 26.560t^2 + 85.54t + 2468.5$
$T_2 = 794.14t + 14{,}124.6$

(b)

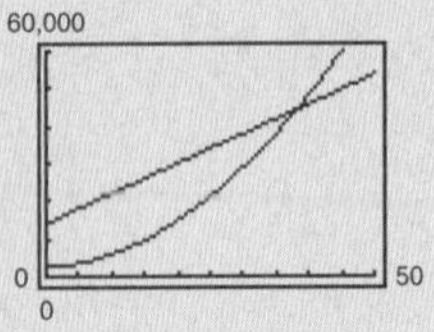

85. False. To solve a system of equations by substitution, you can solve for either variable in one of the two equations and then back-substitute.

86. False. The system can have at most four solutions because a parabola and a circle can intersect at most four times.

87.

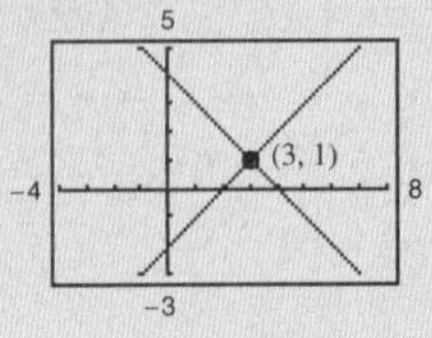

(3, 1); The point of intersection is equal to the solution found in Example 1.

88.

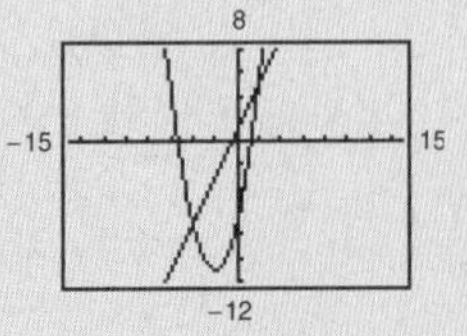

Two solutions

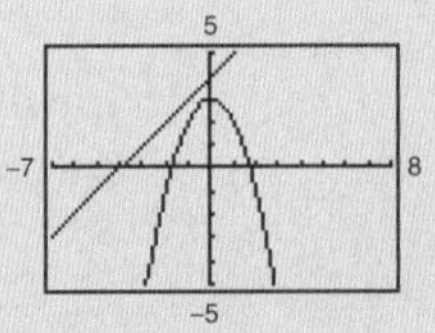

No real solution

The number of points of intersection of the graph of a system of equations is the number of solutions the system has.

89. For a linear system, the result will be a contradictory equation such as $0 = N$, where N is a nonzero real number. For a nonlinear system, there may be an equation with imaginary solutions.

7.2 TWO-VARIABLE LINEAR SYSTEMS

What you should learn

- Use the method of elimination to solve systems of linear equations in two variables.
- Interpret graphically the numbers of solutions of systems of linear equations in two variables.
- Use systems of linear equations in two variables to model and solve real-life problems.

Why you should learn it

You can use systems of equations in two variables to model and solve real-life problems. For instance, in Exercise 61 on page 515, you will solve a system of equations to find a linear model that represents the relationship between wheat yield and amount of fertilizer applied.

The Method of Elimination

In Section 7.1, you studied two methods for solving a system of equations: substitution and graphing. Now you will study the **method of elimination.** The key step in this method is to obtain, for one of the variables, coefficients that differ only in sign so that *adding* the equations eliminates the variable.

$3x + 5y = 7$	Equation 1
$-3x - 2y = -1$	Equation 2
$3y = 6$	Add equations.

Note that by adding the two equations, you eliminate the x-terms and obtain a single equation in y. Solving this equation for y produces $y = 2$, which you can then back-substitute into one of the original equations to solve for x.

Example 1 Solving a System of Equations by Elimination

Solve the system of linear equations.

$$\begin{cases} 3x + 2y = 4 & \text{Equation 1} \\ 5x - 2y = 12 & \text{Equation 2} \end{cases}$$

Solution

Because the coefficients of y differ only in sign, you can eliminate the y-terms by adding the two equations.

$3x + 2y = 4$	Write Equation 1.
$5x - 2y = 12$	Write Equation 2.
$8x = 16$	Add equations.
$x = 2$	Solve for x.

By back-substituting $x = 2$ into Equation 1, you can solve for y.

$3x + 2y = 4$	Write Equation 1.
$3(2) + 2y = 4$	Substitute 2 for x.
$6 + 2y = 4$	Simplify.
$y = -1$	Solve for y.

The solution is $(2, -1)$. Check this in the original system, as follows.

Check

$3(2) + 2(-1) \stackrel{?}{=} 4$	Substitute into Equation 1.
$6 - 2 = 4$	Equation 1 checks. ✓
$5(2) - 2(-1) \stackrel{?}{=} 12$	Substitute into Equation 2.
$10 + 2 = 12$	Equation 2 checks. ✓

CHECKPoint Now try Exercise 13.

1 PLAN AND PREPARE

Warm-up Exercises

Transparency Available
Available at the Instructor's companion site.

Notetaking Guide

Transparency Available
Promotes interactive learning and notetaking skills. Available at the Instructor's companion site.

Animated Precalculus

An **Animated Precalculus** tutorial is available at the Student companion site for **Section 7.2.**

Pacing

Average: 2 days
Advanced: 2 days
Block: 1 block

2 FOCUS AND MOTIVATE

Essential Question

How do you use the method of elimination to solve systems of equations? **Tell students that they will learn how to answer this question by combining multiples of equations to eliminate variables and studying the graphical interpretations of solutions.**

Resource Planning Guide

Chapter Resources
- Complete Solutions Guide

Workbooks
- Notetaking Guide
- Student Solutions Guide

Interactive Technology
- Instructor Success Organizer
- Notetaking Guide IAE
- Instructional DVDs
- Animated Precalculus
- PowerLecture with ExamView

3 TEACH

Extra Example 1

Solve the system of linear equations.

$$\begin{cases} 2x + y = -1 \\ 2x - y = -7 \end{cases}$$

$(-2, 3)$

Extra Example 2

Solve the system of linear equations.

$$\begin{cases} 2x + y = 1 \\ 6x - 3y = 6 \end{cases}$$

$\left(\frac{3}{4}, -\frac{1}{2}\right)$

Avoiding Common Errors

When multiplying an equation, students often forget to multiply the constant as well as the coefficients. Remind students that they must multiply each term on both sides of the equation in order to maintain equality. For instance, in Example 2, students often rewrite the equation $5x + y = -1$ as $20x + 4y = -1$, rather than the correct equation $20x + 4y = -4$.

Method of Elimination

To use the **method of elimination** to solve a system of two linear equations in x and y, perform the following steps.

1. *Obtain coefficients* for x (or y) that differ only in sign by multiplying all terms of one or both equations by suitably chosen constants.
2. *Add* the equations to eliminate one variable.
3. *Solve* the equation obtained in Step 2.
4. *Back-substitute* the value obtained in Step 3 into either of the original equations and solve for the other variable.
5. *Check* that the solution satisfies *each* of the original equations.

Example 2 Solving a System of Equations by Elimination

Solve the system of linear equations.

$$\begin{cases} 2x - 4y = -7 & \text{Equation 1} \\ 5x + y = -1 & \text{Equation 2} \end{cases}$$

Solution

For this system, you can obtain coefficients that differ only in sign by multiplying Equation 2 by 4.

$2x - 4y = -7 \Rightarrow 2x - 4y = -7$ Write Equation 1.

$5x + y = -1 \Rightarrow 20x + 4y = -4$ Multiply Equation 2 by 4.

$22x = -11$ Add equations.

$x = -\frac{1}{2}$ Solve for x.

By back-substituting $x = -\frac{1}{2}$ into Equation 1, you can solve for y.

$2x - 4y = -7$ Write Equation 1.

$2\left(-\frac{1}{2}\right) - 4y = -7$ Substitute $-\frac{1}{2}$ for x.

$-4y = -6$ Combine like terms.

$y = \frac{3}{2}$ Solve for y.

The solution is $\left(-\frac{1}{2}, \frac{3}{2}\right)$. Check this in the original system, as follows.

Check

$2x - 4y = -7$ Write original Equation 1.

$2\left(-\frac{1}{2}\right) - 4\left(\frac{3}{2}\right) \stackrel{?}{=} -7$ Substitute into Equation 1.

$-1 - 6 = -7$ Equation 1 checks. ✓

$5x + y = -1$ Write original Equation 2.

$5\left(-\frac{1}{2}\right) + \frac{3}{2} \stackrel{?}{=} -1$ Substitute into Equation 2.

$-\frac{5}{2} + \frac{3}{2} = -1$ Equation 2 checks. ✓

CHECKPoint Now try Exercise 15.

In Example 2, the two systems of linear equations (the original system and the system obtained by multiplying by constants)

$$\begin{cases} 2x - 4y = -7 \\ 5x + y = -1 \end{cases} \quad \text{and} \quad \begin{cases} 2x - 4y = -7 \\ 20x + 4y = -4 \end{cases}$$

are called **equivalent systems** because they have precisely the same solution set. The operations that can be performed on a system of linear equations to produce an equivalent system are (1) interchanging any two equations, (2) multiplying an equation by a nonzero constant, and (3) adding a multiple of one equation to any other equation in the system.

Example 3 Solving the System of Equations by Elimination

Solve the system of linear equations.

$$\begin{cases} 5x + 3y = 9 & \text{Equation 1} \\ 2x - 4y = 14 & \text{Equation 2} \end{cases}$$

Algebraic Solution

You can obtain coefficients that differ only in sign by multiplying Equation 1 by 4 and multiplying Equation 2 by 3.

$5x + 3y = 9 \Rightarrow 20x + 12y = 36$ Multiply Equation 1 by 4.

$2x - 4y = 14 \Rightarrow 6x - 12y = 42$ Multiply Equation 2 by 3.

$26x = 78$ Add equations.

$x = 3$ Solve for x.

By back-substituting $x = 3$ into Equation 2, you can solve for y.

$2x - 4y = 14$ Write Equation 2.

$2(3) - 4y = 14$ Substitute 3 for x.

$-4y = 8$ Combine like terms.

$y = -2$ Solve for y.

The solution is $(3, -2)$. Check this in the original system.

Graphical Solution

Solve each equation for y. Then use a graphing utility to graph $y_1 = -\frac{5}{3}x + 3$ and $y_2 = \frac{1}{2}x - \frac{7}{2}$ in the same viewing window. Use the *intersect* feature or the *zoom* and *trace* features to approximate the point of intersection of the graphs. From the graph in Figure 7.6, you can see that the point of intersection is $(3, -2)$. You can determine that this is the exact solution by checking $(3, -2)$ in both equations.

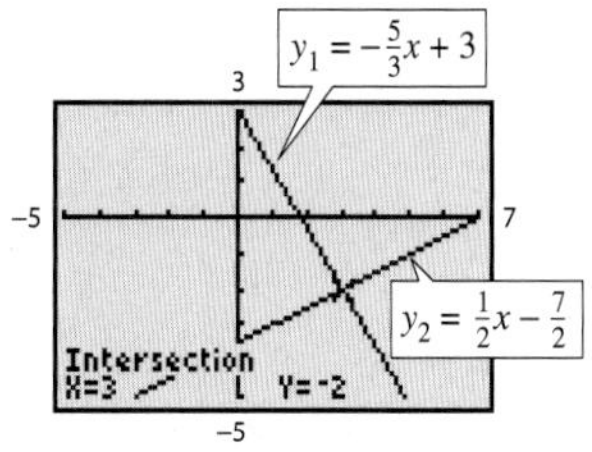

FIGURE 7.6

CHECK Point Now try Exercise 17.

You can check the solution from Example 3 as follows.

$5(3) + 3(-2) \stackrel{?}{=} 9$ Substitute 3 for x and -2 for y in Equation 1.

$15 - 6 = 9$ Equation 1 checks. ✓

$2(3) - 4(-2) \stackrel{?}{=} 14$ Substitute 3 for x and -2 for y in Equation 2.

$6 + 8 = 14$ Equation 2 checks. ✓

Keep in mind that the terminology and methods discussed in this section apply only to systems of *linear* equations.

Extra Example 3

Solve the system of linear equations.

$$\begin{cases} 3x + 2y = 7 \\ 2x + 5y = 1 \end{cases}$$

$(3, -1)$

Differentiated Instruction

English Language Learners Explain to students who may be learning English that the prefix *in-* means "not," as in *not consistent* and *not dependent*. Discuss with students how they can use the meaning of the prefix to help them remember the mathematical meanings of consistent, inconsistent, dependent, and independent.

Extra Example 4

Match each system of linear equations with its graph in the figure. Describe the number of solutions, and state whether the system is consistent or inconsistent.

a. $\begin{cases} -2x + 3y = 6 \\ 4x - 6y = -3 \end{cases}$

ii; no solution; inconsistent

b. $\begin{cases} -2x + 3y = 6 \\ -6x + 9y = 18 \end{cases}$

i; infinitely many solutions; consistent

c. $\begin{cases} -2x + 3y = 6 \\ x + 3y = 15 \end{cases}$

iii; one solution; consistent

i.

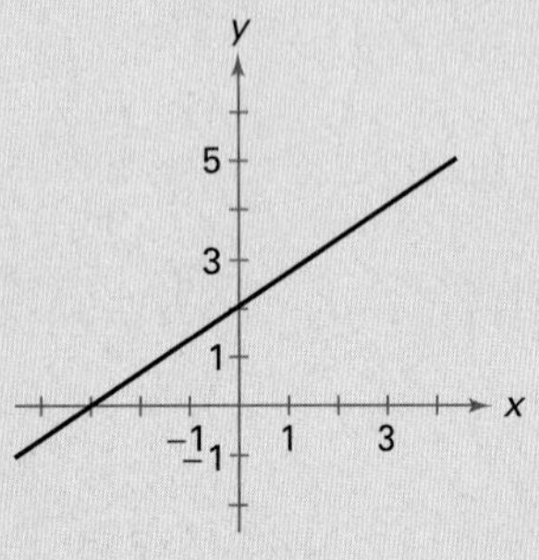

ii.

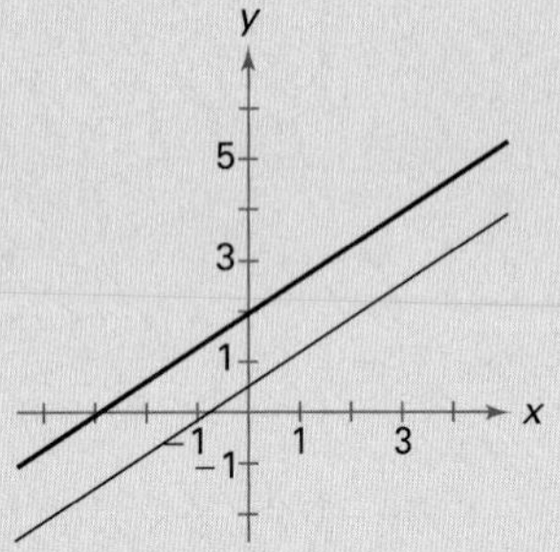

iii.

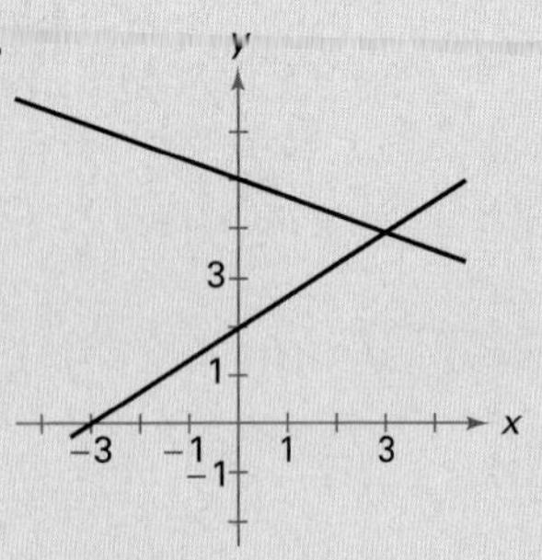

Graphical Interpretation of Solutions

It is possible for a *general* system of equations to have exactly one solution, two or more solutions, or no solution. If a system of *linear* equations has two different solutions, it must have an *infinite* number of solutions.

Graphical Interpretations of Solutions

For a system of two linear equations in two variables, the number of solutions is one of the following.

Number of Solutions	*Graphical Interpretation*	*Slopes of Lines*
1. Exactly one solution	The two lines intersect at one point.	The slopes of the two lines are not equal.
2. Infinitely many solutions	The two lines coincide (are identical).	The slopes of the two lines are equal.
3. No solution	The two lines are parallel.	The slopes of the two lines are equal.

A system of linear equations is **consistent** if it has at least one solution. A consistent system with exactly one solution is *independent*, whereas a consistent system with infinitely many solutions is *dependent*. A system is **inconsistent** if it has no solution.

Example 4 Recognizing Graphs of Linear Systems

Match each system of linear equations with its graph in Figure 7.7. Describe the number of solutions and state whether the system is consistent or inconsistent.

a. $\begin{cases} 2x - 3y = 3 \\ -4x + 6y = 6 \end{cases}$ **b.** $\begin{cases} 2x - 3y = 3 \\ x + 2y = 5 \end{cases}$ **c.** $\begin{cases} 2x - 3y = 3 \\ -4x + 6y = -6 \end{cases}$

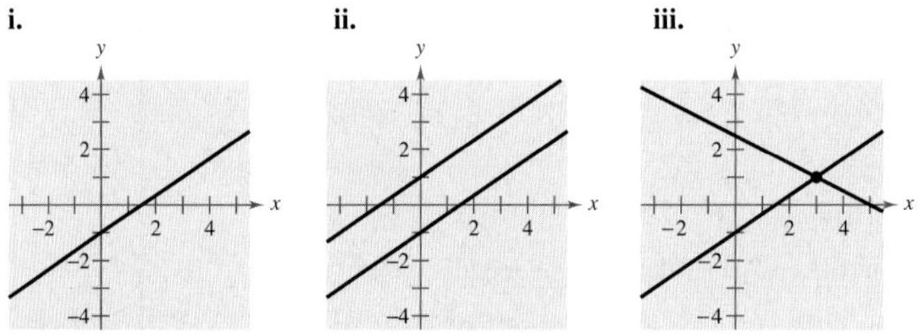

FIGURE 7.7

Study Tip

A comparison of the slopes of two lines gives useful information about the number of solutions of the corresponding system of equations. To solve a system of equations graphically, it helps to begin by writing the equations in slope-intercept form. Try doing this for the systems in Example 4.

Solution

a. The graph of system (a) is a pair of parallel lines (ii). The lines have no point of intersection, so the system has no solution. The system is inconsistent.

b. The graph of system (b) is a pair of intersecting lines (iii). The lines have one point of intersection, so the system has exactly one solution. The system is consistent.

c. The graph of system (c) is a pair of lines that coincide (i). The lines have infinitely many points of intersection, so the system has infinitely many solutions. The system is consistent.

CHECKPoint Now try Exercises 31–34.

In Examples 5 and 6, note how you can use the method of elimination to determine that a system of linear equations has no solution or infinitely many solutions.

Example 5 No-Solution Case: Method of Elimination

Solve the system of linear equations.

$$\begin{cases} x - 2y = 3 & \text{Equation 1} \\ -2x + 4y = 1 & \text{Equation 2} \end{cases}$$

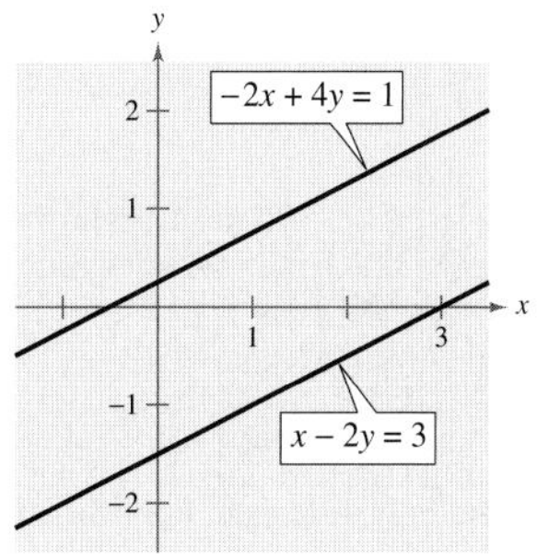

FIGURE 7.8

Solution

To obtain coefficients that differ only in sign, you can multiply Equation 1 by 2.

$$x - 2y = 3 \Rightarrow 2x - 4y = 6 \quad \text{Multiply Equation 1 by 2.}$$

$$-2x + 4y = 1 \Rightarrow \underline{-2x + 4y = 1} \quad \text{Write Equation 2}$$

$$0 = 7 \quad \text{False statement}$$

Because there are no values of x and y for which $0 = 7$, you can conclude that the system is inconsistent and has no solution. The lines corresponding to the two equations in this system are shown in Figure 7.8. Note that the two lines are parallel and therefore have no point of intersection.

CHECKPoint Now try Exercise 21.

In Example 5, note that the occurrence of a false statement, such as $0 = 7$, indicates that the system has no solution. In the next example, note that the occurrence of a statement that is true for all values of the variables, such as $0 = 0$, indicates that the system has infinitely many solutions.

Example 6 Many-Solution Case: Method of Elimination

Solve the system of linear equations.

$$\begin{cases} 2x - y = 1 & \text{Equation 1} \\ 4x - 2y = 2 & \text{Equation 2} \end{cases}$$

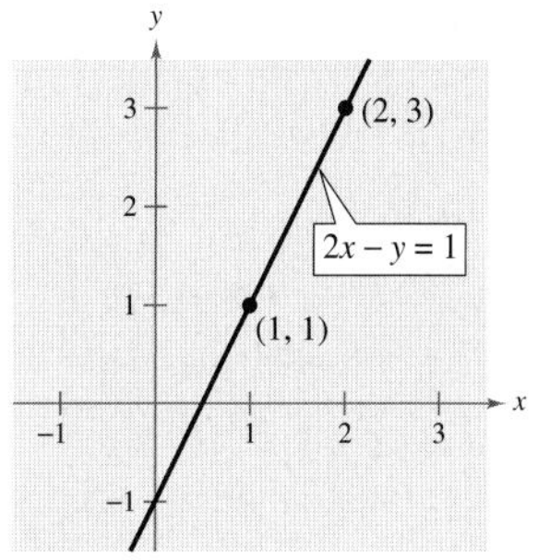

FIGURE 7.9

Solution

To obtain coefficients that differ only in sign, you can multiply Equation 1 by -2.

$$2x - y = 1 \Rightarrow -4x + 2y = -2 \quad \text{Multiply Equation 1 by } -2.$$

$$4x - 2y = 2 \Rightarrow \underline{4x - 2y = 2} \quad \text{Write Equation 2.}$$

$$0 = 0 \quad \text{Add equations.}$$

Because the two equations are equivalent (have the same solution set), you can conclude that the system has infinitely many solutions. The solution set consists of all points (x, y) lying on the line $2x - y = 1$, as shown in Figure 7.9. Letting $x = a$, where a is any real number, you can see that the solutions of the system are $(a, 2a - 1)$.

CHECKPoint Now try Exercise 23.

Extra Example 5

Solve the system of linear equations.

$$\begin{cases} 6x - 5y = 3 \\ -12x + 10y = 5 \end{cases}$$

No solution; inconsistent

Extra Example 6

Solve the system of linear equations.

$$\begin{cases} \frac{1}{2}x - \frac{1}{8}y = -\frac{3}{8} \\ -4x + y = 3 \end{cases}$$

The solution set consists of all points lying on the line $-4x + y = 3$.

Extra Example 7

Solve the system of linear equations.

$$\begin{cases} 0.03x + 0.04y = 0.75 \\ 0.02x + 0.06y = 0.90 \end{cases}$$

(9, 12)

TECHNOLOGY

The general solution of the linear system

$$\begin{cases} ax + by = c \\ dx + ey = f \end{cases}$$

is

$$x = \frac{ce - bf}{ae - bd}$$

and

$$y = \frac{af - cd}{ae - bd}.$$

If $ae - bd = 0$, the system does not have a unique solution. A graphing utility program (called Systems of Linear Equations) for solving such a system can be found at the website for this text at *academic.cengage.com*. Try using the program for your graphing utility to solve the system in Example 7.

Example 7 illustrates a strategy for solving a system of linear equations that has decimal coefficients.

Example 7 A Linear System Having Decimal Coefficients

Solve the system of linear equations.

$$\begin{cases} 0.02x - 0.05y = -0.38 & \text{Equation 1} \\ 0.03x + 0.04y = 1.04 & \text{Equation 2} \end{cases}$$

Solution

Because the coefficients in this system have two decimal places, you can begin by multiplying each equation by 100. This produces a system in which the coefficients are all integers.

$$\begin{cases} 2x - 5y = -38 & \text{Revised Equation 1} \\ 3x + 4y = 104 & \text{Revised Equation 2} \end{cases}$$

Now, to obtain coefficients that differ only in sign, multiply Equation 1 by 3 and multiply Equation 2 by -2.

$$2x - 5y = -38 \quad \Rightarrow \quad 6x - 15y = -114 \qquad \text{Multiply Equation 1 by 3.}$$

$$3x + 4y = 104 \quad \Rightarrow \quad -6x - 8y = -208 \qquad \text{Multiply Equation 2 by } -2.$$

$$-23y = -322 \qquad \text{Add equations.}$$

So, you can conclude that

$$y = \frac{-322}{-23}$$

$$= 14.$$

Back-substituting $y = 14$ into revised Equation 2 produces the following.

$$3x + 4y = 104 \qquad \text{Write revised Equation 2.}$$

$$3x + 4(14) = 104 \qquad \text{Substitute 14 for } y.$$

$$3x = 48 \qquad \text{Combine like terms.}$$

$$x = 16 \qquad \text{Solve for } x.$$

The solution is (16, 14). Check this in the original system, as follows.

Check

$$0.02x - 0.05y = -0.38 \qquad \text{Write original Equation 1.}$$

$$0.02(16) - 0.05(14) \stackrel{?}{=} -0.38 \qquad \text{Substitute into Equation 1.}$$

$$0.32 - 0.70 = -0.38 \qquad \text{Equation 1 checks. } \checkmark$$

$$0.03x + 0.04y = 1.04 \qquad \text{Write original Equation 2.}$$

$$0.03(16) + 0.04(14) \stackrel{?}{=} 1.04 \qquad \text{Substitute into Equation 2.}$$

$$0.48 + 0.56 = 1.04 \qquad \text{Equation 2 checks. } \checkmark$$

CHECKPoint Now try Exercise 25.

Applications

At this point, you may be asking the question "How can I tell which application problems can be solved using a system of linear equations?" The answer comes from the following considerations.

1. Does the problem involve more than one unknown quantity?

2. Are there two (or more) equations or conditions to be satisfied?

If one or both of these situations occur, the appropriate mathematical model for the problem may be a system of linear equations.

Example 8 An Application of a Linear System

An airplane flying into a headwind travels the 2000-mile flying distance between Chicopee, Massachusetts and Salt Lake City, Utah in 4 hours and 24 minutes. On the return flight, the same distance is traveled in 4 hours. Find the airspeed of the plane and the speed of the wind, assuming that both remain constant.

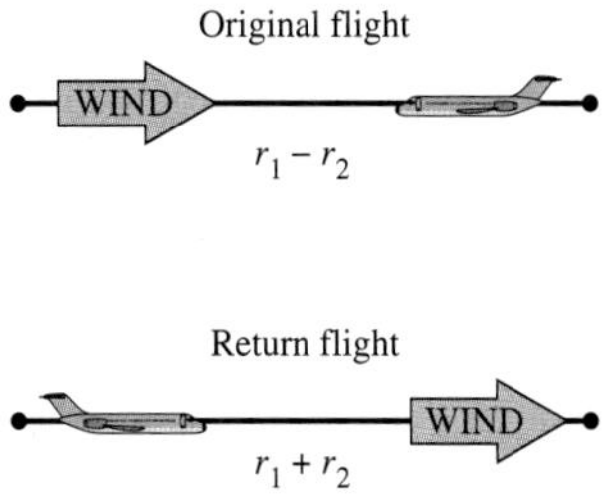

FIGURE 7.10

Solution

The two unknown quantities are the speeds of the wind and the plane. If r_1 is the speed of the plane and r_2 is the speed of the wind, then

$r_1 - r_2 =$ speed of the plane against the wind

$r_1 + r_2 =$ speed of the plane with the wind

as shown in Figure 7.10. Using the formula distance = (rate)(time) for these two speeds, you obtain the following equations.

$$2000 = (r_1 - r_2)\left(4 + \frac{24}{60}\right)$$

$$2000 = (r_1 + r_2)(4)$$

These two equations simplify as follows.

$$\begin{cases} 5000 = 11r_1 - 11r_2 & \text{Equation 1} \\ 500 = r_1 + r_2 & \text{Equation 2} \end{cases}$$

To solve this system by elimination, multiply Equation 2 by 11.

$5000 = 11r_1 - 11r_2$	⇨	$5000 = 11r_1 - 11r_2$	Write Equation 1.
$500 = r_1 + r_2$	⇨	$5500 = 11r_1 + 11r_2$	Multiply Equation 2 by 11.
		$10{,}500 = 22r_1$	Add equations.

So,

$$r_1 = \frac{10{,}500}{22} = \frac{5250}{11} \approx 477.27 \text{ miles per hour} \qquad \text{Speed of plane}$$

and

$$r_2 = 500 - \frac{5250}{11} = \frac{250}{11} \approx 22.73 \text{ miles per hour.} \qquad \text{Speed of wind}$$

Check this solution in the original statement of the problem.

CHECK**Point** Now try Exercise 43.

Extra Example 8

An airplane flying into a headwind travels the 1650-mile flying distance between two cities in 3 hours and 18 minutes. On the return flight, the distance is traveled in 3 hours. Find the air speed of the plane and the speed of the wind, assuming that both remain constant.

Air speed = 525 miles per hour; wind speed = 25 miles per hour

Extra Example 9

Find the point of equilibrium of the supply and demand equations.

$$\begin{cases} p = 81 - 0.55x & \text{Demand equation} \\ p = 0.125x & \text{Supply equation} \end{cases}$$

(120, 15)

Closing the Lesson

Have students summarize the major points of the lesson and answer the Essential Question: How do you use the method of elimination to solve systems of equations?

- **Use the method of elimination to solve systems of equations by multiplying one or both equations by suitably chosen constants, adding the equations to eliminate a variable, and back-substituting to solve for the remaining variable.**
- **Recognize systems of equations that have no solution by seeing that their graphs form parallel lines and that the method of elimination produces a false statement.**
- **Recognize systems of equations that have exactly one solution by seeing that their graphs intersect at exactly one point and that the method of elimination produces exactly one value for each variable.**
- **Recognize systems of equations that have infinitely many solutions by seeing that their graphs are the same line and that the method of elimination produces a statement that is always true, regardless of the values of the variables.**

In a free market, the demands for many products are related to the prices of the products. As the prices decrease, the demands by consumers increase and the amounts that producers are able or willing to supply decrease.

Example 9 Finding the Equilibrium Point

The demand and supply equations for a new type of personal digital assistant are

$$\begin{cases} p = 150 - 0.00001x & \text{Demand equation} \\ p = 60 + 0.00002x & \text{Supply equation} \end{cases}$$

where p is the price in dollars and x represents the number of units. Find the equilibrium point for this market. The **equilibrium point** is the price p and number of units x that satisfy both the demand and supply equations.

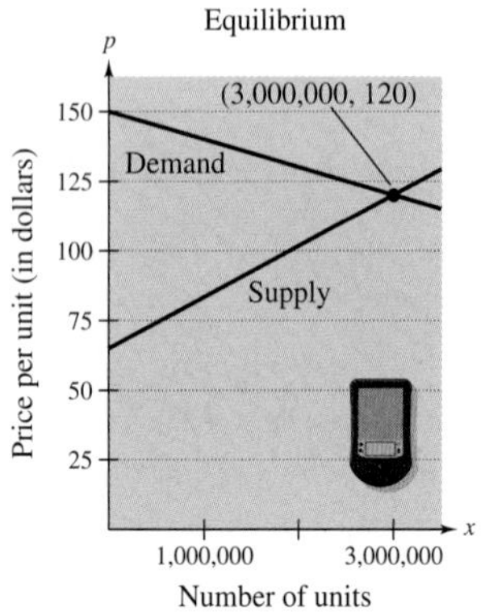

FIGURE 7.11

Solution

Because p is written in terms of x, begin by substituting the value of p given in the supply equation into the demand equation.

$$p = 150 - 0.00001x \quad \text{Write demand equation.}$$

$$60 + 0.00002x = 150 - 0.00001x \quad \text{Substitute } 60 + 0.00002x \text{ for } p.$$

$$0.00003x = 90 \quad \text{Combine like terms.}$$

$$x = 3{,}000{,}000 \quad \text{Solve for } x.$$

So, the equilibrium point occurs when the demand and supply are each 3 million units. (See Figure 7.11.) The price that corresponds to this x-value is obtained by back-substituting $x = 3{,}000{,}000$ into either of the original equations. For instance, back-substituting into the demand equation produces

$$\begin{aligned} p &= 150 - 0.00001(3{,}000{,}000) \\ &= 150 - 30 \\ &= \$120. \end{aligned}$$

The solution is (3,000,000, 120). You can check this as follows.

Check

Substitute (3,000,000, 120) into the demand equation.

$$p = 150 - 0.00001x \quad \text{Write demand equation.}$$

$$120 \stackrel{?}{=} 150 - 0.00001(3{,}000{,}000) \quad \text{Substitute 120 for } p \text{ and 3,000,000 for } x.$$

$$120 = 120 \quad \text{Solution checks in demand equation. ✓}$$

Substitute (3,000,000, 120) into the supply equation.

$$p = 60 + 0.00002x \quad \text{Write supply equation.}$$

$$120 \stackrel{?}{=} 60 + 0.00002(3{,}000{,}000) \quad \text{Substitute 120 for } p \text{ and 3,000,000 for } x.$$

$$120 = 120 \quad \text{Solution checks in supply equation. ✓}$$

CHECKPoint Now try Exercise 45.

7.2 EXERCISES

See www.CalcChat.com for worked-out solutions to odd-numbered exercises.

VOCABULARY: Fill in the blanks.

1. The first step in solving a system of equations by the method of ________ is to obtain coefficients for x (or y) that differ only in sign. elimination
2. Two systems of equations that have the same solution set are called ________ systems. equivalent
3. A system of linear equations that has at least one solution is called ________, whereas a system of linear equations that has no solution is called ________. consistent; inconsistent
4. In business applications, the ________ ________ is defined as the price p and the number of units x that satisfy both the demand and supply equations. equilibrium point

SKILLS AND APPLICATIONS

In Exercises 5–12, solve the system by the method of elimination. Label each line with its equation. To print an enlarged copy of the graph, go to the website *www.mathgraphs.com*. 5–12. See margin.

5. $\begin{cases} 2x + y = 5 \\ x - y = 1 \end{cases}$

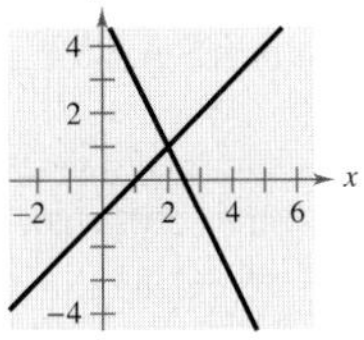

6. $\begin{cases} x + 3y = 1 \\ -x + 2y = 4 \end{cases}$

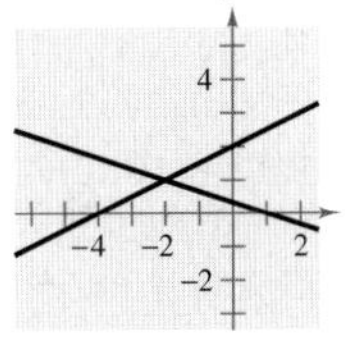

7. $\begin{cases} x + y = 0 \\ 3x + 2y = 1 \end{cases}$

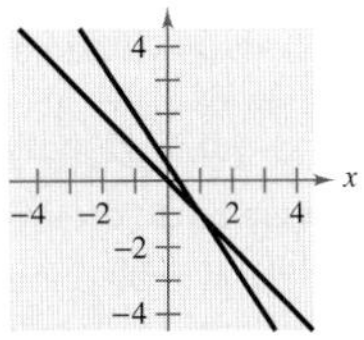

8. $\begin{cases} 2x - y = -3 \\ 4x + 3y = -21 \end{cases}$

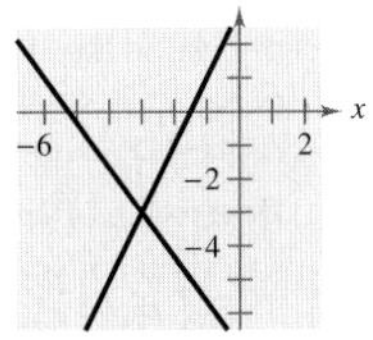

9. $\begin{cases} x - y = 2 \\ -2x + 2y = 5 \end{cases}$

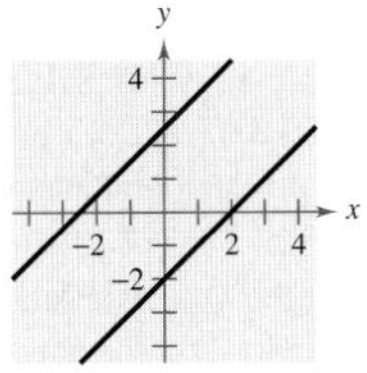

10. $\begin{cases} 3x + 2y = 3 \\ 6x + 4y = 14 \end{cases}$

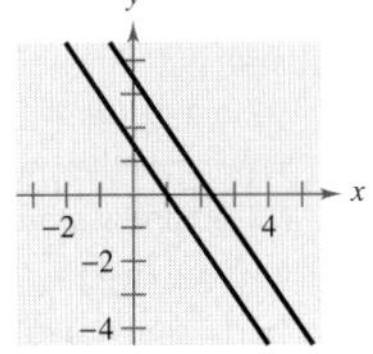

11. $\begin{cases} 3x - 2y = 5 \\ -6x + 4y = -10 \end{cases}$

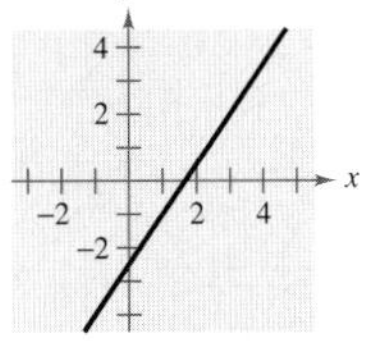

12. $\begin{cases} 9x - 3y = -15 \\ -3x + y = 5 \end{cases}$

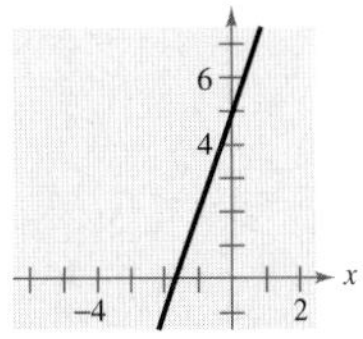

In Exercises 13–30, solve the system by the method of elimination and check any solutions algebraically.

13. $\begin{cases} x + 2y = 6 \\ x - 2y = 2 \end{cases}$ $(4, 1)$
14. $\begin{cases} 3x - 5y = 8 \\ 2x + 5y = 22 \end{cases}$ $(6, 2)$
15. $\begin{cases} 5x + 3y = 6 \\ 3x - y = 5 \end{cases}$ $\left(\frac{3}{2}, -\frac{1}{2}\right)$
16. $\begin{cases} x + 5y = 10 \\ 3x - 10y = -5 \end{cases}$ $\left(3, \frac{7}{5}\right)$
17. $\begin{cases} 3x + 2y = 10 \\ 2x + 5y = 3 \end{cases}$ $(4, -1)$
18. $\begin{cases} 2r + 4s = 5 \\ 16r + 50s = 55 \end{cases}$ $\left(\frac{5}{6}, \frac{5}{6}\right)$
19. $\begin{cases} 5u + 6v = 24 \\ 3u + 5v = 18 \end{cases}$ $\left(\frac{12}{7}, \frac{18}{7}\right)$
20. $\begin{cases} 3x + 11y = 4 \\ -2x - 5y = 9 \end{cases}$ $(-17, 5)$
21. $\begin{cases} \frac{9}{5}x + \frac{6}{5}y = 4 \\ 9x + 6y = 3 \end{cases}$ No solution
22. $\begin{cases} \frac{3}{4}x + y = \frac{1}{8} \\ \frac{9}{4}x + 3y = \frac{3}{8} \end{cases}$ 22–26. See margin.
23. $\begin{cases} -5x + 6y = -3 \\ 20x - 24y = 12 \end{cases}$
24. $\begin{cases} 7x + 8y = 6 \\ -14x - 16y = -12 \end{cases}$
25. $\begin{cases} 0.2x - 0.5y = -27.8 \\ 0.3x + 0.4y = 68.7 \end{cases}$
26. $\begin{cases} 0.05x - 0.03y = 0.21 \\ 0.07x + 0.02y = 0.16 \end{cases}$
27. $\begin{cases} 4b + 3m = 3 \\ 3b + 11m = 13 \end{cases}$ $\left(-\frac{6}{35}, \frac{43}{35}\right)$
28. $\begin{cases} 2x + 5y = 8 \\ 5x + 8y = 10 \end{cases}$ $\left(-\frac{14}{9}, \frac{20}{9}\right)$
29. $\begin{cases} \dfrac{x+3}{4} + \dfrac{y-1}{3} = 1 \\ 2x - y = 12 \end{cases}$ $(5, -2)$
30. $\begin{cases} \dfrac{x-1}{2} + \dfrac{y+2}{3} = 4 \\ x - 2y = 5 \end{cases}$ $(7, 1)$

4 PRACTICE AND APPLY

Assignment Guide

Transparencies Available
Available at the Instructor's companion site.

Average:
Day 1: pp. 513–514
Exs. 1, 2, 5–11 odd, 14, 16–19, 21, 22, 26, 27, 29, 35–41 odd
Day 2: pp. 513–516
Exs. 3, 4, 44, 46, 49–59 odd, 63–65, 68–71

Advanced:
Day 1: pp. 513–514
Exs. 1, 2, 6–12 even, 18–20, 22–30 even, 36–42 even
Day 2: pp. 513–516
Exs. 3, 4, 44, 47, 48–60 even, 61, 65, 66, 68, 70–72

Block:
pp. 513–516
Exs. 1–4, 5–11 odd, 14, 16–19, 21, 22, 26, 27, 29, 35–41 odd, 44, 46, 49–59 odd, 63–65, 68–71

5. $(2, 1)$

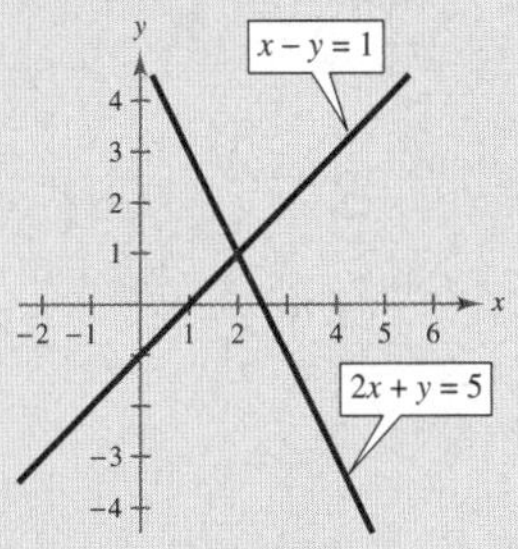

6. $(-2, 1)$

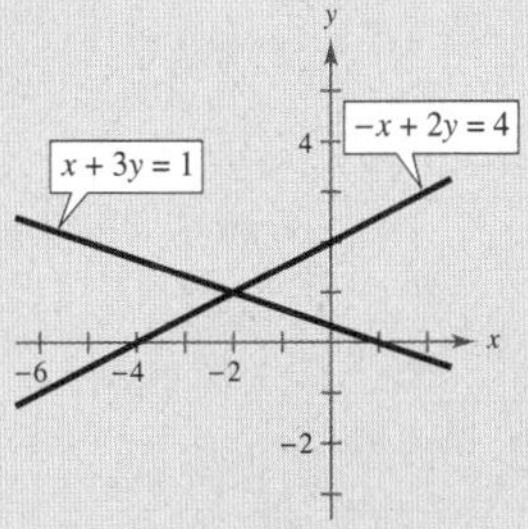

8. $(-3, -3)$

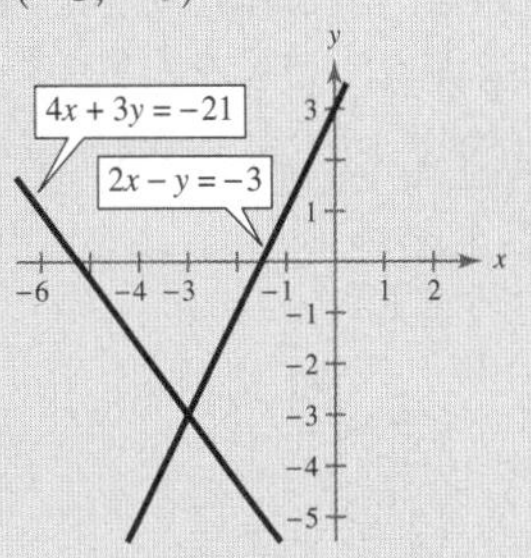

9. No solution

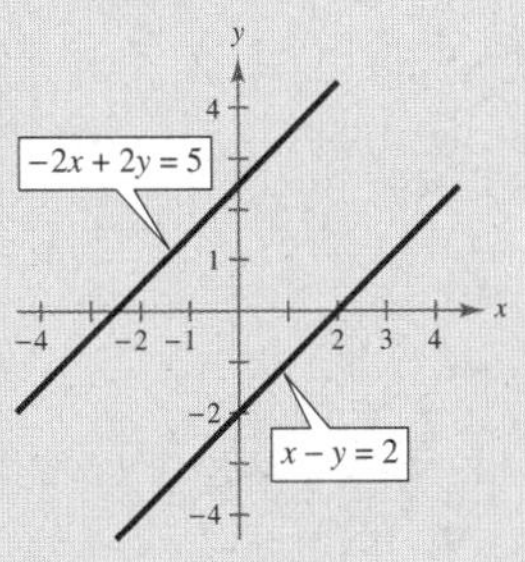

10. No solution

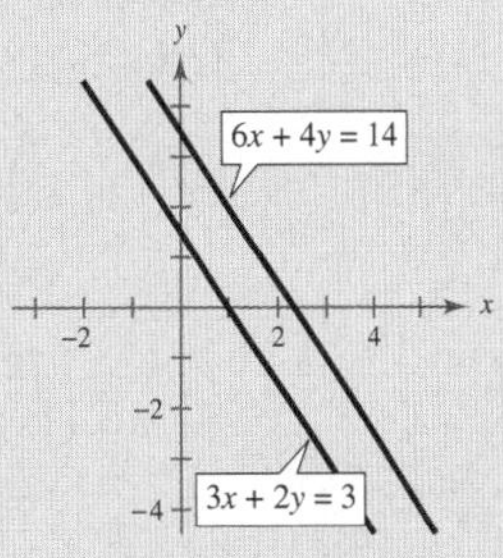

7. $(1, -1)$

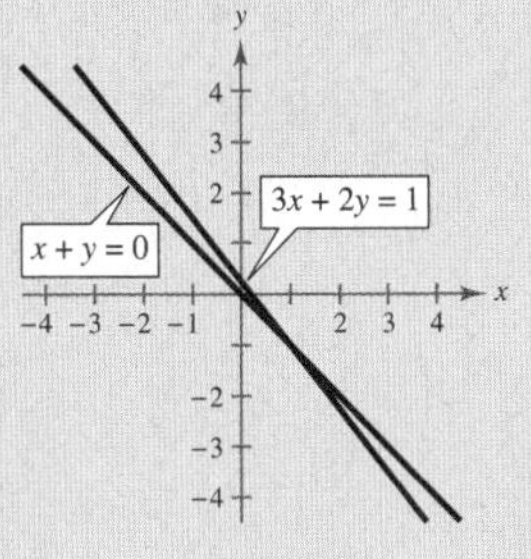

11–12, 22–26. See Additional Answers beginning on page AA1.

31. b; one solution; consistent

32. c; one solution; consistent

33. a; infinitely many solutions; consistent

34. d; no solutions; inconsistent

43. 550 mi/h, 50 mi/h

49. Cheeseburger: 300 calories; French fries: 230 calories

50. Apple juice: 95.5 mg; Orange juice: 81.9 mg

51. (a) $\begin{cases} x + y = 30 \\ 0.25x + 0.5y = 12 \end{cases}$

(b) 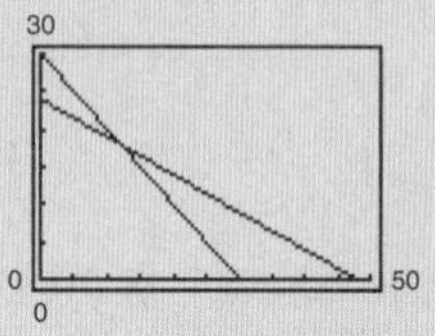

Decreases

(c) 25% solution: 12 L; 50% solution: 18 L

52. (a) $\begin{cases} x + y = 500 \\ 87x + 92y = 44{,}500 \end{cases}$

(b) 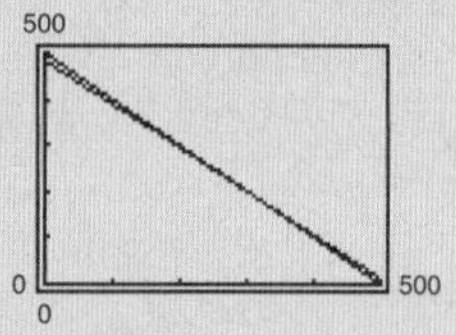

Decreases

In Exercises 31–34, match the system of linear equations with its graph. Describe the number of solutions and state whether the system is consistent or inconsistent. [The graphs are labeled (a), (b), (c) and (d).] 31–34. See margin.

(a)

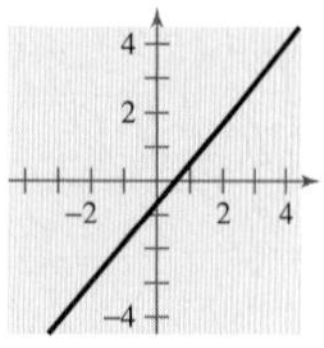

(b)

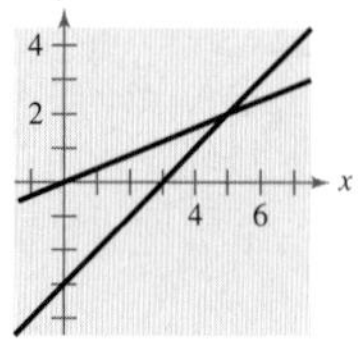

(c)

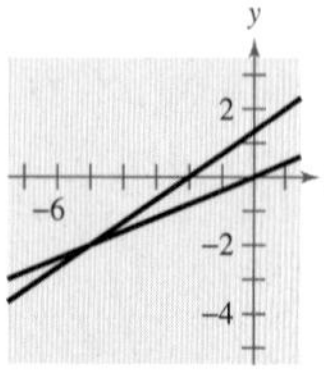

(d)

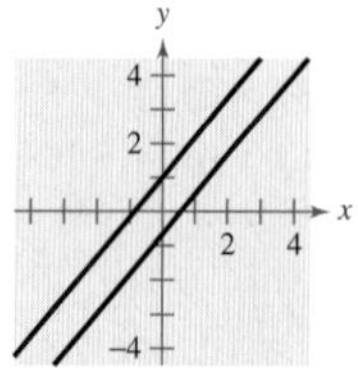

31. $\begin{cases} 2x - 5y = 0 \\ x - y = 3 \end{cases}$

32. $\begin{cases} 2x - 5y = 0 \\ 2x - 3y = -4 \end{cases}$

33. $\begin{cases} -7x + 6y = -4 \\ 14x - 12y = 8 \end{cases}$

34. $\begin{cases} 7x - 6y = -6 \\ -7x + 6y = -4 \end{cases}$

In Exercises 35–42, use any method to solve the system.

35. $\begin{cases} 3x - 5y = 7 \\ 2x + y = 9 \end{cases}$ $(4, 1)$

36. $\begin{cases} -x + 3y = 17 \\ 4x + 3y = 7 \end{cases}$ $(-2, 5)$

37. $\begin{cases} y = 2x - 5 \\ y = 5x - 11 \end{cases}$ $(2, -1)$

38. $\begin{cases} 7x + 3y = 16 \\ y = x + 2 \end{cases}$ $(1, 3)$

39. $\begin{cases} x - 5y = 21 \\ 6x + 5y = 21 \end{cases}$ $(6, -3)$

40. $\begin{cases} y = -2x - 17 \\ y = 2 - 3x \end{cases}$ $(19, -55)$

41. $\begin{cases} -5x + 9y = 13 \\ y = x - 4 \end{cases}$ $\left(\frac{49}{4}, \frac{33}{4}\right)$

42. $\begin{cases} 4x - 3y = 6 \\ -5x + 7y = -1 \end{cases}$ $(3, 2)$

43. AIRPLANE SPEED An airplane flying into a headwind travels the 1800-mile flying distance between Pittsburgh, Pennsylvania and Phoenix, Arizona in 3 hours and 36 minutes. On the return flight, the distance is traveled in 3 hours. Find the airspeed of the plane and the speed of the wind, assuming that both remain constant. See margin.

44. AIRPLANE SPEED Two planes start from Los Angeles International Airport and fly in opposite directions. The second plane starts $\frac{1}{2}$ hour after the first plane, but its speed is 80 kilometers per hour faster. Find the airspeed of each plane if 2 hours after the first plane departs the planes are 3200 kilometers apart.
First plane: 880 km/h;
Second plane: 960 km/h

SUPPLY AND DEMAND In Exercises 45–48, find the equilibrium point of the demand and supply equations. The equilibrium point is the price p and number of units x that satisfy both the demand and supply equations.

	Demand	*Supply*	
45.	$p = 500 - 0.4x$	$p = 380 + 0.1x$	$(240, 404)$
46.	$p = 100 - 0.05x$	$p = 25 + 0.1x$	$(500, 75)$
47.	$p = 140 - 0.00002x$	$p = 80 + 0.00001x$	$(2{,}000{,}000, 100)$
48.	$p = 400 - 0.0002x$	$p = 225 + 0.0005x$	$(250{,}000, 350)$

49. NUTRITION Two cheeseburgers and one small order of French fries from a fast-food restaurant contain a total of 830 calories. Three cheeseburgers and two small orders of French fries contain a total of 1360 calories. Find the caloric content of each item. See margin.

50. NUTRITION One eight-ounce glass of apple juice and one eight-ounce glass of orange juice contain a total of 177.4 milligrams of vitamin C. Two eight-ounce glasses of apple juice and three eight-ounce glasses of orange juice contain a total of 436.7 milligrams of vitamin C. How much vitamin C is in an eight-ounce glass of each type of juice? See margin.

51. ACID MIXTURE Thirty liters of a 40% acid solution is obtained by mixing a 25% solution with a 50% solution.

(a) Write a system of equations in which one equation represents the amount of final mixture required and the other represents the percent of acid in the final mixture. Let x and y represent the amounts of the 25% and 50% solutions, respectively.

(b) Use a graphing utility to graph the two equations in part (a) in the same viewing window. As the amount of the 25% solution increases, how does the amount of the 50% solution change? (a)–(c). See margin.

(c) How much of each solution is required to obtain the specified concentration of the final mixture?

52. FUEL MIXTURE Five hundred gallons of 89-octane gasoline is obtained by mixing 87-octane gasoline with 92-octane gasoline.

(a) Write a system of equations in which one equation represents the amount of final mixture required and the other represents the amounts of 87- and 92-octane gasolines in the final mixture. Let x and y represent the numbers of gallons of 87-octane and 92-octane gasolines, respectively. See margin.

(b) Use a graphing utility to graph the two equations in part (a) in the same viewing window. As the amount of 87-octane gasoline increases, how does the amount of 92-octane gasoline change? See margin.

(c) How much of each type of gasoline is required to obtain the 500 gallons of 89-octane gasoline?
87-octane: 300 gal; 92-octane: 200 gal

53. INVESTMENT PORTFOLIO A total of \$24,000 is invested in two corporate bonds that pay 3.5% and 5% simple interest. The investor wants an annual interest income of \$930 from the investments. What amount should be invested in the 3.5% bond? \$18,000

54. INVESTMENT PORTFOLIO A total of \$32,000 is invested in two municipal bonds that pay 5.75% and 6.25% simple interest. The investor wants an annual interest income of \$1900 from the investments. What amount should be invested in the 5.75% bond? \$20,000

55. PRESCRIPTIONS The numbers of prescriptions P (in thousands) filled at two pharmacies from 2006 through 2010 are shown in the table.

Year	Pharmacy A	Pharmacy B
2006	19.2	20.4
2007	19.6	20.8
2008	20.0	21.1
2009	20.6	21.5
2010	21.3	22.0

(a) Use a graphing utility to create a scatter plot of the data for pharmacy A and use the *regression* feature to find a linear model. Let t represent the year, with $t = 6$ corresponding to 2006. Repeat the procedure for pharmacy B. See margin.

(b) Assuming the numbers for the given five years are representative of future years, will the number of prescriptions filled at pharmacy A ever exceed the number of prescriptions filled at pharmacy B? If so, when? Yes, in the year 2015

56. DATA ANALYSIS A store manager wants to know the demand for a product as a function of the price. The daily sales for different prices of the product are shown in the table.

Price, x	Demand, y
\$1.00	45
\$1.20	37
\$1.50	23

(a) Find the least squares regression line $y = ax + b$ for the data by solving the system for a and b.

$$\begin{cases} 3.00b + 3.70a = 105.00 \\ 3.70b + 4.69a = 123.90 \end{cases}$$ $y = -44.21x + 89.53$

(b) Use the regression feature of a graphing utility to confirm the result in part (a). $y = -44.21x + 89.53$

(c) Use the graphing utility to plot the data and graph the linear model from part (a) in the same viewing window. See margin.

(d) Use the linear model from part (a) to predict the demand when the price is \$1.75. 12 units

FITTING A LINE TO DATA In Exercises 57–60, find the least squares regression line $y = ax + b$ for the points

$(x_1, y_1), (x_2, y_2), \ldots, (x_n, y_n)$

by solving the system for a and b.

$$nb + \left(\sum_{i=1}^{n} x_i\right)a = \left(\sum_{i=1}^{n} y_i\right)$$

$$\left(\sum_{i=1}^{n} x_i\right)b + \left(\sum_{i=1}^{n} x_i^2\right)a = \left(\sum_{i=1}^{n} x_i y_i\right)$$

Then use a graphing utility to confirm the result. (If you are unfamiliar with summation notation, look at the discussion in Section 9.1 or in Appendix B at the website for this text at *academic.cengage.com*.)

57. $y = 0.97x + 2.1$

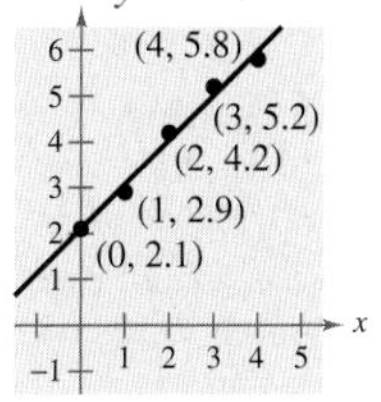

58. $y = -0.58x + 5.4$

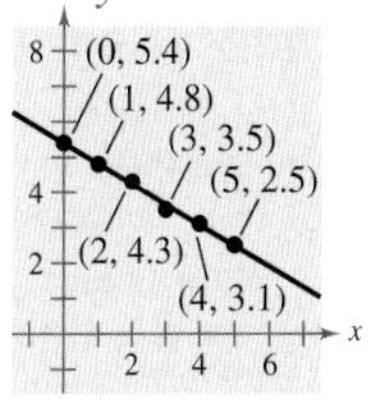

59. (0, 8), (1, 6), (2, 4), (3, 2) $y = -2x + 8$

60. (1, 0.0), (2, 1.1), (3, 2.3), (4, 3.8), (5, 4.0), (6, 5.5), (7, 6.7), (8, 6.9) $y = 1.025x - 0.825$

61. DATA ANALYSIS An agricultural scientist used four test plots to determine the relationship between wheat yield y (in bushels per acre) and the amount of fertilizer x (in hundreds of pounds per acre). The results are shown in the table.

Fertilizer, x	Yield, y
1.0	32
1.5	41
2.0	48
2.5	53

(a) Use the technique demonstrated in Exercises 57–60 to set up a system of equations for the data and to find the least squares regression line $y = ax + b$. $y = 14x + 19$

(b) Use the linear model to predict the yield for a fertilizer application of 160 pounds per acre. 41.4 bushels/acre

55. (a)

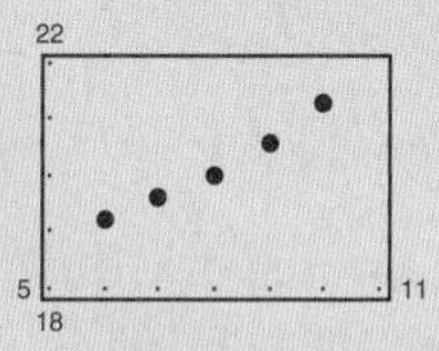

Pharmacy A: $P = 0.52t + 16.0$

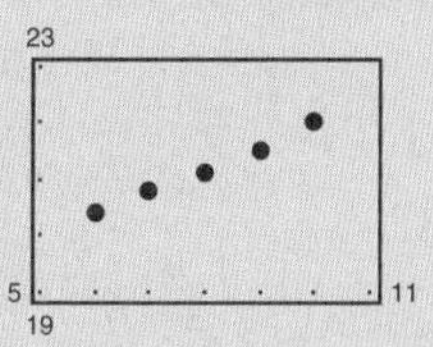

Pharmacy B: $P = 0.39t + 18.0$

56. (c)

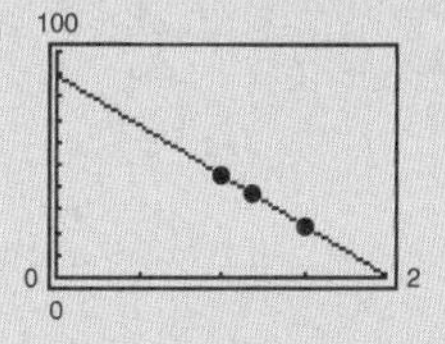

5 ASSESS AND RETEACH

Daily Homework Quiz

Transparency Available
Available at the Instructor's companion site.

62. (c) See below.

(f) Answers will vary. Sample answer: No, the budget probably will not continue to increase at the same rate.

63. False. Two lines that coincide have infinitely many points of intersection.

64. False. Solving a system of equations algebraically will always give an exact solution.

65. No. Two lines will intersect only once or will coincide, and if they coincide the system will have infinitely many solutions.

68. (a) $\begin{cases} y = 5x + 1 \\ y = x - 5 \end{cases}$

The slopes are different, giving one point of intersection and one solution.

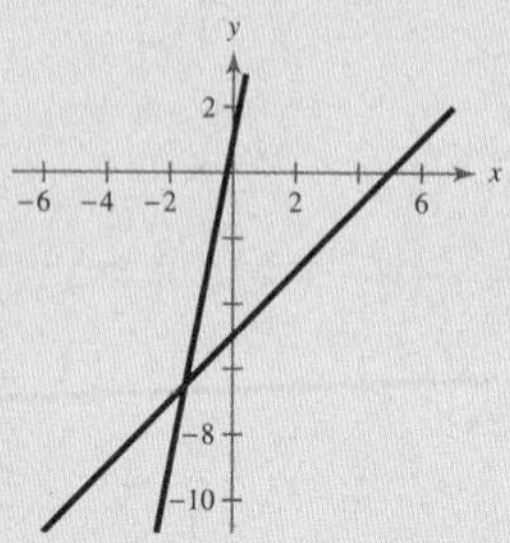

(b) $\begin{cases} y = \frac{4}{3}x - \frac{1}{3} \\ y = \frac{4}{3}x - \frac{1}{3} \end{cases}$

The slopes are equal and the lines have infinitely many intersection points and solutions because they are the same line.

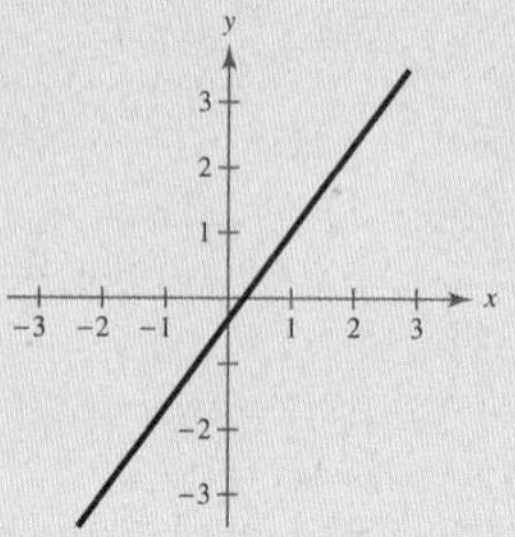

(c) $\begin{cases} y = -\frac{1}{2}x + \frac{3}{2} \\ y = -\frac{1}{2}x - 4 \end{cases}$

The slopes are equal but there are no intersection points or solutions because the lines are parallel.

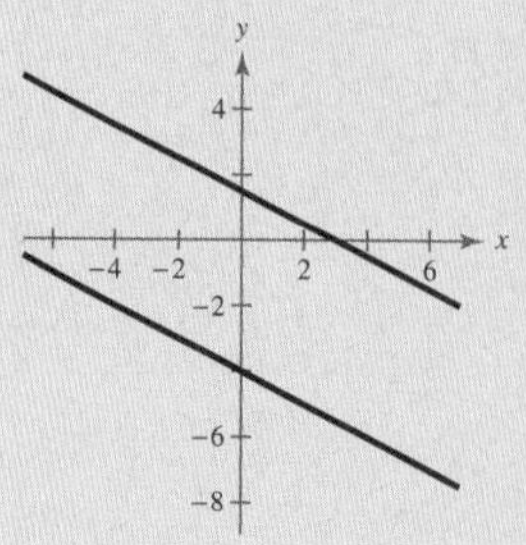

62. DEFENSE DEPARTMENT OUTLAYS The table shows the total national outlays y for defense functions (in billions of dollars) for the years 2000 through 2007. (Source: U.S. Office of Management and Budget)

Year	Outlays, y
2000	294.4
2001	304.8
2002	348.5
2003	404.8
2004	455.8
2005	495.3
2006	521.8
2007	552.6

(a) Use the technique demonstrated in Exercises 57–60 to set up a system of equations for the data and to find the least squares regression line $y = at + b$. Let t represent the year, with $t = 0$ corresponding to 2000. (a) and (b). $y = 40.28t + 281.3$

(b) Use the *regression* feature of a graphing utility to find a linear model for the data. How does this model compare with the model obtained in part (a)?

(c) Use the linear model to create a table of estimated values of y. Compare the estimated values with the actual data. See margin.

(d) Use the linear model to estimate the total national outlay for 2008. 603.54

(e) Use the Internet, your school's library, or some other reference source to find the total national outlay for 2008. How does this value compare with your answer in part (d)? Answers will vary.

(f) Is the linear model valid for long-term predictions of total national outlays? Explain. See margin.

EXPLORATION

63–64. See margin.

TRUE OR FALSE? In Exercises 63 and 64, determine whether the statement is true or false. Justify your answer.

63. If two lines do not have exactly one point of intersection, then they must be parallel.

64. Solving a system of equations graphically will always give an exact solution.

65. WRITING Briefly explain whether or not it is possible for a consistent system of linear equations to have exactly two solutions. See margin.

66. THINK ABOUT IT Give examples of a system of linear equations that has (a) no solution and (b) an infinite number of solutions.
(a) $\begin{cases} x + y = 10 \\ x + y = 20 \end{cases}$ (b) $\begin{cases} x + y = 3 \\ 2x + 2y = 6 \end{cases}$

67. COMPARING METHODS Use the method of substitution to solve the system in Example 1. Is the method of substitution or the method of elimination easier? Explain.
The method of elimination is much easier.

68. CAPSTONE Rewrite each system of equations in slope-intercept form and sketch the graph of each system. What is the relationship among the slopes of the two lines, the number of points of intersection, and the number of solutions? See margin.

(a) $\begin{cases} 5x - y = -1 \\ -x + y = -5 \end{cases}$ (b) $\begin{cases} 4x - 3y = 1 \\ -8x + 6y = -2 \end{cases}$

(c) $\begin{cases} x + 2y = 3 \\ x + 2y = -8 \end{cases}$

THINK ABOUT IT In Exercises 69 and 70, the graphs of the two equations appear to be parallel. Yet, when the system is solved algebraically, you find that the system does have a solution. Find the solution and explain why it does not appear on the portion of the graph that is shown.

69. $\begin{cases} 100y - x = 200 \\ 99y - x = -198 \end{cases}$ **70.** $\begin{cases} 21x - 20y = 0 \\ 13x - 12y = 120 \end{cases}$

69–70. See margin.

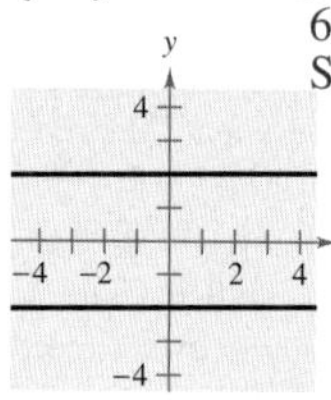

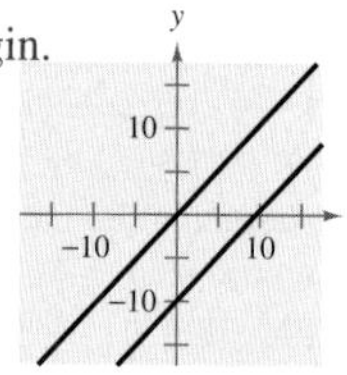

In Exercises 71 and 72, find the value of k such that the system of linear equations is inconsistent.

71. $\begin{cases} 4x - 8y = -3 \\ 2x + ky = 16 \end{cases}$ $k = -4$ **72.** $\begin{cases} 15x + 3y = 6 \\ -10x + ky = 9 \end{cases}$ $k = -2$

ADVANCED APPLICATIONS In Exercises 73 and 74, solve the system of equations for u and v. While solving for these variables, consider the transcendental functions as constants. (Systems of this type are found in a course in differential equations.)

73. $\begin{cases} u \sin x + v \cos x = 0 \\ u \cos x - v \sin x = \sec x \end{cases}$ $u = 1, v = -\tan x$

74. $\begin{cases} u \cos 2x + v \sin 2x = 0 \\ u(-2 \sin 2x) + v(2 \cos 2x) = \csc x \end{cases}$ $u = -\frac{1}{2}$, $v = \frac{1}{2} \cot 2x$

PROJECT: COLLEGE EXPENSES To work an extended application analyzing the average undergraduate tuition, room, and board charges at private degree-granting institutions in the United States from 1990 through 2007, visit this text's website at *academic.cengage.com*. (Data Source: U.S. Dept. of Education)

69. (39,600, 398). It is necessary to change the scale on the axes to see the point of intersection.

70. (300, 315). It is necessary to change the scale on the axes to see the point of intersection.

62. (c)

Year	2000	2001	2002	2003
y	281.3	321.58	361.86	402.14

Year	2004	2005	2006	2007
y	442.42	482.7	522.98	563.26

7.3 Multivariable Linear Systems

What you should learn

- Use back-substitution to solve linear systems in row-echelon form.
- Use Gaussian elimination to solve systems of linear equations.
- Solve nonsquare systems of linear equations.
- Use systems of linear equations in three or more variables to model and solve real-life problems.

Why you should learn it

Systems of linear equations in three or more variables can be used to model and solve real-life problems. For instance, in Exercise 83 on page 529, a system of equations can be used to determine the combination of scoring plays in Super Bowl XLIII.

Harry E. Walker/MCT/Landov

Row-Echelon Form and Back-Substitution

The method of elimination can be applied to a system of linear equations in more than two variables. In fact, this method easily adapts to computer use for solving linear systems with dozens of variables.

When elimination is used to solve a system of linear equations, the goal is to rewrite the system in a form to which back-substitution can be applied. To see how this works, consider the following two systems of linear equations.

System of Three Linear Equations in Three Variables: (See Example 3.)

$$\begin{cases} x - 2y + 3z = 9 \\ -x + 3y = -4 \\ 2x - 5y + 5z = 17 \end{cases}$$

Equivalent System in Row-Echelon Form: (See Example 1.)

$$\begin{cases} x - 2y + 3z = 9 \\ y + 3z = 5 \\ z = 2 \end{cases}$$

The second system is said to be in **row-echelon form,** which means that it has a "stair-step" pattern with leading coefficients of 1. After comparing the two systems, it should be clear that it is easier to solve the system in row-echelon form, using back-substitution.

Example 1 Using Back-Substitution in Row-Echelon Form

Solve the system of linear equations.

$$\begin{cases} x - 2y + 3z = 9 & \text{Equation 1} \\ y + 3z = 5 & \text{Equation 2} \\ z = 2 & \text{Equation 3} \end{cases}$$

Solution

From Equation 3, you know the value of z. To solve for y, substitute $z = 2$ into Equation 2 to obtain

$y + 3(2) = 5$ Substitute 2 for z.

$y = -1.$ Solve for y.

Then substitute $y = -1$ and $z = 2$ into Equation 1 to obtain

$x - 2(-1) + 3(2) = 9$ Substitute -1 for y and 2 for z.

$x = 1.$ Solve for x.

The solution is $x = 1$, $y = -1$, and $z = 2$, which can be written as the **ordered triple** $(1, -1, 2)$. Check this in the original system of equations.

CHECK *Point* Now try Exercise 11.

1 PLAN AND PREPARE

Warm-up Exercises

Transparency Available
Available at the Instructor's companion site.

Notetaking Guide

Transparency Available
Promotes interactive learning and notetaking skills.
Available at the Instructor's companion site.

Animated Precalculus

An **Animated Precalculus** tutorial is available at the Student companion site for **Section 7.3.**

Pacing

Average: 2 days
Advanced: 2 days
Block: 1 block

2 FOCUS AND MOTIVATE

Essential Question

How do you solve systems of linear equations in more than two variables? **Tell students that they will learn how to answer this question by studying how the method of elimination can be used to solve systems in three variables.**

Resource Planning Guide

Chapter Resources
- Complete Solutions Guide

Workbooks
- Notetaking Guide
- Student Solutions Guide

Interactive Technology
- Instructor Success Organizer
- Notetaking Guide IAE
- Instructional DVDs
- Animated Precalculus
- PowerLecture with ExamView

3 TEACH

Extra Example 1

Solve the system of linear equations.

$$\begin{cases} 2x - y + 5z = 22 \\ \quad\ \ y + 3z = 6 \\ \qquad\quad z = 3 \end{cases}$$

(2, −3, 3)

Extra Example 2

Solve the system of linear equations.

$$\begin{cases} 2x + y = 90 \\ x + 2y = 90 \end{cases}$$

(30, 30)

HISTORICAL NOTE

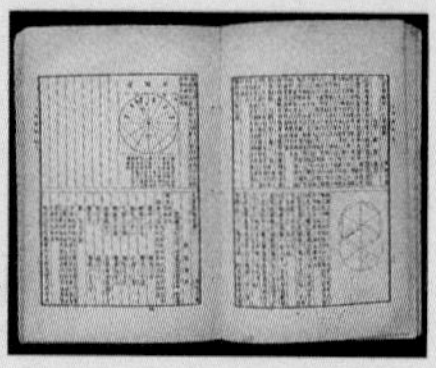

Christopher Liu/China Stock

One of the most influential Chinese mathematics books was the *Chui-chang suan-shu* or *Nine Chapters on the Mathematical Art* (written in approximately 250 B.C.). Chapter Eight of the *Nine Chapters* contained solutions of systems of linear equations using positive and negative numbers. One such system was as follows.

$$\begin{cases} 3x + 2y + z = 39 \\ 2x + 3y + z = 34 \\ x + 2y + 3z = 26 \end{cases}$$

This system was solved using column operations on a matrix. Matrices (plural for matrix) will be discussed in the next chapter.

Gaussian Elimination

Two systems of equations are *equivalent* if they have the same solution set. To solve a system that is not in row-echelon form, first convert it to an *equivalent* system that is in row-echelon form by using the following operations.

Operations That Produce Equivalent Systems

Each of the following **row operations** on a system of linear equations produces an *equivalent* system of linear equations.

1. Interchange two equations.
2. Multiply one of the equations by a nonzero constant.
3. Add a multiple of one of the equations to another equation to replace the latter equation.

To see how this is done, take another look at the method of elimination, as applied to a system of two linear equations.

Example 2 Using Gaussian Elimination to Solve a System

Solve the system of linear equations.

$$\begin{cases} 3x - 2y = -1 & \text{Equation 1} \\ x - y = 0 & \text{Equation 2} \end{cases}$$

Solution

There are two strategies that seem reasonable: eliminate the variable x or eliminate the variable y. The following steps show how to use the first strategy.

$$\begin{cases} x - y = 0 \\ 3x - 2y = -1 \end{cases}$$ Interchange the two equations in the system.

$$\begin{cases} -3x + 3y = 0 \\ 3x - 2y = -1 \end{cases}$$ Multiply the first equation by -3.

$$\begin{array}{r} -3x + 3y = 0 \\ 3x - 2y = -1 \\ \hline y = -1 \end{array}$$ Add the multiple of the first equation to the second equation to obtain a new second equation.

$$\begin{cases} x - y = 0 \\ y = -1 \end{cases}$$ New system in row-echelon form

Notice in the first step that interchanging rows is an easy way of obtaining a leading coefficient of 1. Now back-substitute $y = -1$ into Equation 2 and solve for x.

$x - (-1) = 0$ Substitute -1 for y.

$x = -1$ Solve for x.

The solution is $x = -1$ and $y = -1$, which can be written as the ordered pair $(-1, -1)$.

CHECK Point Now try Exercise 19.

Rewriting a system of linear equations in row-echelon form usually involves a chain of equivalent systems, each of which is obtained by using one of the three basic row operations listed on the previous page. This process is called **Gaussian elimination,** after the German mathematician Carl Friedrich Gauss (1777–1855).

WARNING / CAUTION

Arithmetic errors are often made when performing elementary row operations. You should note the operation performed in each step so that you can go back and check your work.

Example 3 Using Gaussian Elimination to Solve a System

Solve the system of linear equations.

$$\begin{cases} x - 2y + 3z = 9 & \text{Equation 1} \\ -x + 3y = -4 & \text{Equation 2} \\ 2x - 5y + 5z = 17 & \text{Equation 3} \end{cases}$$

Solution

Because the leading coefficient of the first equation is 1, you can begin by saving the x at the upper left and eliminating the other x-terms from the first column.

$$\begin{aligned} x - 2y + 3z &= 9 && \text{Write Equation 1.} \\ -x + 3y &= -4 && \text{Write Equation 2.} \\ \hline y + 3z &= 5 && \text{Add Equation 1 to Equation 2.} \end{aligned}$$

$$\begin{cases} x - 2y + 3z = 9 \\ y + 3z = 5 \\ 2x - 5y + 5z = 17 \end{cases}$$

Adding the first equation to the second equation produces a new second equation.

$$\begin{aligned} -2x + 4y - 6z &= -18 && \text{Multiply Equation 1 by } -2. \\ 2x - 5y + 5z &= 17 && \text{Write Equation 3.} \\ \hline -y - z &= -1 && \text{Add revised Equation 1 to Equation 3.} \end{aligned}$$

$$\begin{cases} x - 2y + 3z = 9 \\ y + 3z = 5 \\ -y - z = -1 \end{cases}$$

Adding -2 times the first equation to the third equation produces a new third equation.

Now that all but the first x have been eliminated from the first column, go to work on the second column. (You need to eliminate y from the third equation.)

$$\begin{cases} x - 2y + 3z = 9 \\ y + 3z = 5 \\ 2z = 4 \end{cases}$$

Adding the second equation to the third equation produces a new third equation.

Finally, you need a coefficient of 1 for z in the third equation.

$$\begin{cases} x - 2y + 3z = 9 \\ y + 3z = 5 \\ z = 2 \end{cases}$$

Multiplying the third equation by $\frac{1}{2}$ produces a new third equation.

This is the same system that was solved in Example 1, and, as in that example, you can conclude that the solution is

$x = 1, \quad y = -1, \quad$ and $\quad z = 2.$

CHECKPoint Now try Exercise 21.

Extra Example 3

Solve the system of linear equations.

$$\begin{cases} x + y + z = 6 \\ 2x - y + z = 3 \\ 3x + y - z = 2 \end{cases}$$

(1, 2, 3)

Extra Example 4

Solve the system of linear equations.

$$\begin{cases} 3x - 2y + 4z = 1 \\ x + y - 2z = 3 \\ 2x - 3y + 6z = 8 \end{cases}$$

No solution, inconsistent

Avoiding Common Errors

Students often encounter confusion when attempting to solve an inconsistent system of equations. Remind students that equivalent equations in a system will yield an infinite number of solutions and that equations with equal coefficients but differing constant terms will yield no solutions.

The next example involves an inconsistent system—one that has no solution. The key to recognizing an inconsistent system is that at some stage in the elimination process you obtain a false statement such as $0 = -2$.

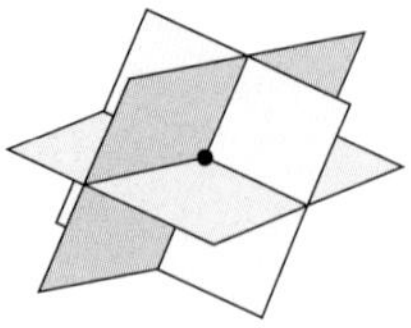

Solution: one point
FIGURE 7.12

Example 4 An Inconsistent System

Solve the system of linear equations.

$$\begin{cases} x - 3y + z = 1 & \text{Equation 1} \\ 2x - y - 2z = 2 & \text{Equation 2} \\ x + 2y - 3z = -1 & \text{Equation 3} \end{cases}$$

Solution

$$\begin{cases} x - 3y + z = 1 \\ 5y - 4z = 0 \\ x + 2y - 3z = -1 \end{cases}$$

Adding -2 times the first equation to the second equation produces a new second equation.

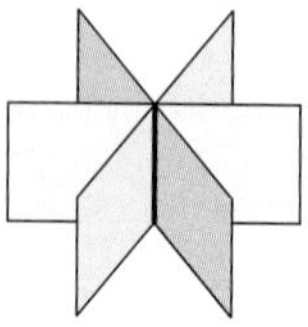

Solution: one line
FIGURE 7.13

$$\begin{cases} x - 3y + z = 1 \\ 5y - 4z = 0 \\ 5y - 4z = -2 \end{cases}$$

Adding -1 times the first equation to the third equation produces a new third equation.

$$\begin{cases} x - 3y + z = 1 \\ 5y - 4z = 0 \\ 0 = -2 \end{cases}$$

Adding -1 times the second equation to the third equation produces a new third equation.

Because $0 = -2$ is a false statement, you can conclude that this system is inconsistent and has no solution. Moreover, because this system is equivalent to the original system, you can conclude that the original system also has no solution.

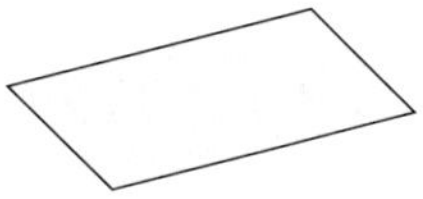

Solution: one plane
FIGURE 7.14

CHECK *Point* Now try Exercise 25.

As with a system of linear equations in two variables, the solution(s) of a system of linear equations in more than two variables must fall into one of three categories.

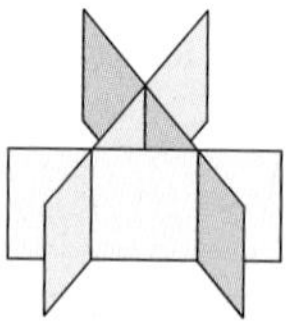

Solution: none
FIGURE 7.15

The Number of Solutions of a Linear System

For a system of linear equations, exactly one of the following is true.

1. There is exactly one solution.
2. There are infinitely many solutions.
3. There is no solution.

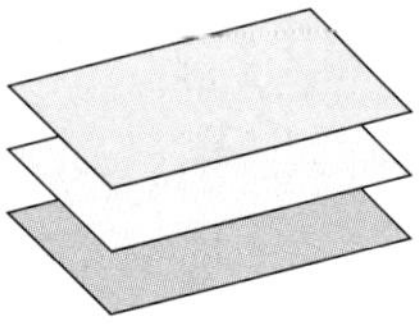

Solution: none
FIGURE 7.16

In Section 7.2, you learned that a system of two linear equations in two variables can be represented graphically as a pair of lines that are intersecting, coincident, or parallel. A system of three linear equations in three variables has a similar graphical representation—it can be represented as three planes in space that intersect in one point (exactly one solution) [see Figure 7.12], intersect in a line or a plane (infinitely many solutions) [see Figures 7.13 and 7.14], or have no points common to all three planes (no solution) [see Figures 7.15 and 7.16].

Example 5 A System with Infinitely Many Solutions

Solve the system of linear equations.

$$\begin{cases} x + y - 3z = -1 & \text{Equation 1} \\ y - z = 0 & \text{Equation 2} \\ -x + 2y = 1 & \text{Equation 3} \end{cases}$$

Solution

$$\begin{cases} x + y - 3z = -1 \\ y - z = 0 \\ 3y - 3z = 0 \end{cases}$$

Adding the first equation to the third equation produces a new third equation.

$$\begin{cases} x + y - 3z = -1 \\ y - z = 0 \\ 0 = 0 \end{cases}$$

Adding -3 times the second equation to the third equation produces a new third equation.

This result means that Equation 3 depends on Equations 1 and 2 in the sense that it gives no additional information about the variables. Because $0 = 0$ is a true statement, you can conclude that this system will have infinitely many solutions. However, it is incorrect to say simply that the solution is "infinite." You must also specify the correct form of the solution. So, the original system is equivalent to the system

$$\begin{cases} x + y - 3z = -1 \\ y - z = 0 \end{cases}.$$

In the last equation, solve for y in terms of z to obtain $y = z$. Back-substituting $y = z$ in the first equation produces $x = 2z - 1$. Finally, letting $z = a$, where a is a real number, the solutions to the given system are all of the form $x = 2a - 1$, $y = a$, and $z = a$. So, every ordered triple of the form

$(2a - 1, a, a)$ $\quad$ *a is a real number.*

is a solution of the system.

CHECK Point Now try Exercise 29.

> **Study Tip**
>
> In Example 5, x and y are solved in terms of the third variable z. To write the correct form of the solution to the system that does not use any of the three variables of the system, let a represent any real number and let $z = a$. Then solve for x and y. The solution can then be written in terms of a, which is not one of the variables of the system.

In Example 5, there are other ways to write the same infinite set of solutions. For instance, letting $x = b$, the solutions could have been written as

$\left(b, \frac{1}{2}(b + 1), \frac{1}{2}(b + 1)\right).$ $\quad$ *b is a real number.*

To convince yourself that this description produces the same set of solutions, consider the following.

Substitution	*Solution*	
$a = 0$	$(2(0) - 1, 0, 0) = (-1, 0, 0)$	Same solution
$b = -1$	$\left(-1, \frac{1}{2}(-1 + 1), \frac{1}{2}(-1 + 1)\right) = (-1, 0, 0)$	
$a = 1$	$(2(1) - 1, 1, 1) = (1, 1, 1)$	Same solution
$b = 1$	$\left(1, \frac{1}{2}(1 + 1), \frac{1}{2}(1 + 1)\right) = (1, 1, 1)$	
$a = 2$	$(2(2) - 1, 2, 2) = (3, 2, 2)$	Same solution
$b = 3$	$\left(3, \frac{1}{2}(3 + 1), \frac{1}{2}(3 + 1)\right) = (3, 2, 2)$	

> **Study Tip**
>
> When comparing descriptions of an infinite solution set, keep in mind that there is more than one way to describe the set.

Extra Example 5

Solve the system of linear equations.

$$\begin{cases} x + 2y - 7z = -4 \\ 2x + 3y + z = 5 \\ 3x + 7y - 36z = -25 \end{cases}$$

$(-23a + 22, 15a - 13, a)$, where a is a real number.

Extra Example 6

Solve the system of linear equations.

$$\begin{cases} x - y + 4z = 3 \\ 4x \quad\quad - z = 0 \end{cases}$$

$(a, 17a - 3, 4a)$, where a is a real number.

Nonsquare Systems

So far, each system of linear equations you have looked at has been *square*, which means that the number of equations is equal to the number of variables. In a **nonsquare** system, the number of equations differs from the number of variables. A system of linear equations cannot have a unique solution unless there are at least as many equations as there are variables in the system.

Example 6 A System with Fewer Equations than Variables

Solve the system of linear equations.

$$\begin{cases} x - 2y + z = 2 & \text{Equation 1} \\ 2x - y - z = 1 & \text{Equation 2} \end{cases}$$

Solution

Begin by rewriting the system in row-echelon form.

$$\begin{cases} x - 2y + z = 2 \\ \quad 3y - 3z = -3 \end{cases}$$

Adding -2 times the first equation to the second equation produces a new second equation.

$$\begin{cases} x - 2y + z = 2 \\ \quad y - z = -1 \end{cases}$$

Multiplying the second equation by $\frac{1}{3}$ produces a new second equation.

Solve for y in terms of z, to obtain

$$y = z - 1.$$

By back-substituting $y = z - 1$ into Equation 1, you can solve for x, as follows.

$$x - 2y + z = 2 \quad \text{Write Equation 1.}$$

$$x - 2(z - 1) + z = 2 \quad \text{Substitute } z - 1 \text{ for } y \text{ in Equation 1.}$$

$$x - 2z + 2 + z = 2 \quad \text{Distributive Property}$$

$$x = z \quad \text{Solve for } x.$$

Finally, by letting $z = a$, where a is a real number, you have the solution

$$x = a, \quad y = a - 1, \quad \text{and} \quad z = a.$$

So, every ordered triple of the form

$$(a, a - 1, a) \quad a \text{ is a real number.}$$

is a solution of the system. Because there were originally three variables and only two equations, the system cannot have a unique solution.

CHECKPoint Now try Exercise 33.

In Example 6, try choosing some values of a to obtain different solutions of the system, such as (1, 0, 1), (2, 1, 2), and (3, 2, 3). Then check each of the solutions in the original system to verify that they are solutions of the original system.

Applications

Example 7 Vertical Motion

The height at time t of an object that is moving in a (vertical) line with constant acceleration a is given by the **position equation**

$$s = \frac{1}{2}at^2 + v_0t + s_0.$$

The height s is measured in feet, the acceleration a is measured in feet per second squared, t is measured in seconds, v_0 is the initial velocity (at $t = 0$), and s_0 is the initial height. Find the values of a, v_0, and s_0 if $s = 52$ at $t = 1$, $s = 52$ at $t = 2$, and $s = 20$ at $t = 3$, and interpret the result. (See Figure 7.17.)

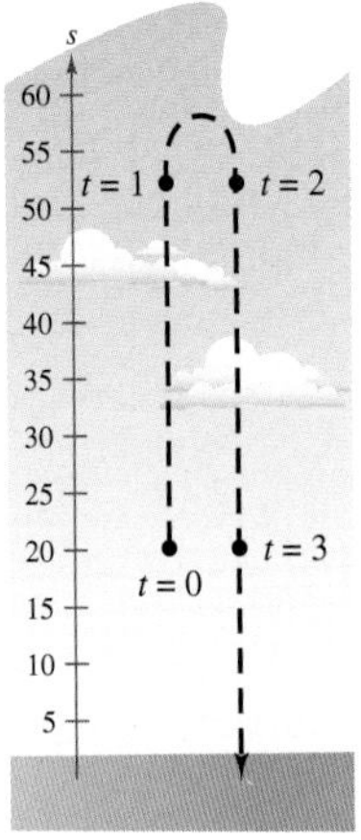

FIGURE 7.17

Solution

By substituting the three values of t and s into the position equation, you can obtain three linear equations in a, v_0, and s_0.

When $t = 1$: $\frac{1}{2}a(1)^2 + v_0(1) + s_0 = 52$ ⟹ $a + 2v_0 + 2s_0 = 104$

When $t = 2$: $\frac{1}{2}a(2)^2 + v_0(2) + s_0 = 52$ ⟹ $2a + 2v_0 + s_0 = 52$

When $t = 3$: $\frac{1}{2}a(3)^2 + v_0(3) + s_0 = 20$ ⟹ $9a + 6v_0 + 2s_0 = 40$

This produces the following system of linear equations.

$$\begin{cases} a + 2v_0 + 2s_0 = 104 \\ 2a + 2v_0 + s_0 = 52 \\ 9a + 6v_0 + 2s_0 = 40 \end{cases}$$

Now solve the system using Gaussian elimination.

$$\begin{cases} a + 2v_0 + 2s_0 = 104 \\ -2v_0 - 3s_0 = -156 \\ 9a + 6v_0 + 2s_0 = 40 \end{cases}$$

Adding -2 times the first equation to the second equation produces a new second equation.

$$\begin{cases} a + 2v_0 + 2s_0 = 104 \\ -2v_0 - 3s_0 = -156 \\ -12v_0 - 16s_0 = -896 \end{cases}$$

Adding -9 times the first equation to the third equation produces a new third equation.

$$\begin{cases} a + 2v_0 + 2s_0 = 104 \\ -2v_0 - 3s_0 = -156 \\ 2s_0 = 40 \end{cases}$$

Adding -6 times the second equation to the third equation produces a new third equation.

$$\begin{cases} a + 2v_0 + 2s_0 = 104 \\ v_0 + \frac{3}{2}s_0 = 78 \\ s_0 = 20 \end{cases}$$

Multiplying the second equation by $-\frac{1}{2}$ produces a new second equation and multiplying the third equation by $\frac{1}{2}$ produces a new third equation.

So, the solution of this system is $a = -32$, $v_0 = 48$, and $s_0 = 20$, which can be written as $(-32, 48, 20)$. This solution results in a position equation of $s = -16t^2 + 48t + 20$ and implies that the object was thrown upward at a velocity of 48 feet per second from a height of 20 feet.

CHECKPoint Now try Exercise 45.

Extra Example 7

Find the position equation $s = \frac{1}{2}at^2 + v_0t + s_0$ for an object at the given heights moving vertically at the specified times.

At $t = 1$ second, $s = 104$ feet.

At $t = 2$ seconds, $s = 76$ feet.

At $t = 3$ seconds, $s = 16$ feet.

$s = -16t^2 + 20t + 100$

Extra Example 8

Find a quadratic equation, $y = ax^2 + bx + c$, whose graph passes through the points $(0, 0)$, $(3, -3)$, and $(6, 0)$.

$y = \frac{1}{3}x^2 - 2x$

Extra Example 9

A small business borrowed \$30,000 to renovate its building. Some of the money was borrowed at 7%, some at 9%, and some at 12%. The amount borrowed at 9% was \$1000 greater than the amount borrowed at 12%. How much was borrowed at each rate if the total interest owed for the first year was \$2960?

\$5000 was borrowed at 7%, \$13,000 at 9%, and \$12,000 at 12%.

Closing the Lesson

Have students summarize the major points of the lesson and answer the Essential Question: How do you solve systems of linear equations in more than two variables?

- **Write a system of equations in row-echelon form using Gaussian elimination by interchanging equations, multiplying equations by constants, and replacing an equation with the sum of multiples of equations.**
- **Use back-substitution to solve a system of equations written in row-echelon form.**
- **Recognize situations in which there is exactly one, infinitely many, or no solutions of a linear system.**
- **Find solutions of nonsquare systems by using Gaussian elimination and writing the values of each variable in terms of a single variable.**

Example 8 Data Analysis: Curve-Fitting

Find a quadratic equation

$$y = ax^2 + bx + c$$

whose graph passes through the points $(-1, 3)$, $(1, 1)$, and $(2, 6)$.

Solution

Because the graph of $y = ax^2 + bx + c$ passes through the points $(-1, 3)$, $(1, 1)$, and $(2, 6)$, you can write the following.

When $x = -1$, $y = 3$: $a(-1)^2 + b(-1) + c = 3$

When $x = 1$, $y = 1$: $a(1)^2 + b(1) + c = 1$

When $x = 2$, $y = 6$: $a(2)^2 + b(2) + c = 6$

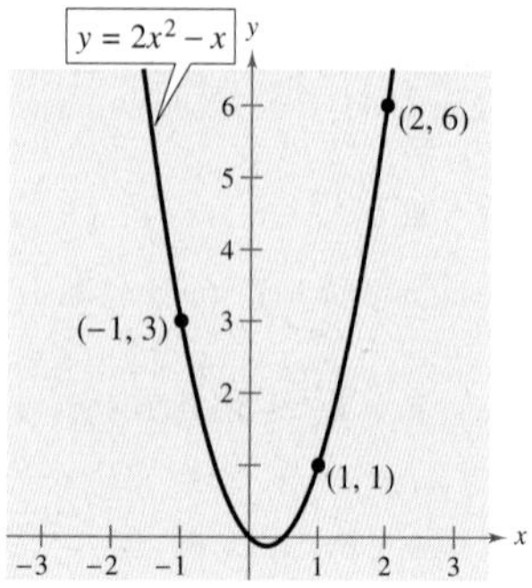

FIGURE 7.18

This produces the following system of linear equations.

$$\begin{cases} a - b + c = 3 & \text{Equation 1} \\ a + b + c = 1 & \text{Equation 2} \\ 4a + 2b + c = 6 & \text{Equation 3} \end{cases}$$

The solution of this system is $a = 2$, $b = -1$, and $c = 0$. So, the equation of the parabola is $y = 2x^2 - x$, as shown in Figure 7.18.

CHECKPoint Now try Exercise 49.

Example 9 Investment Analysis

An inheritance of \$12,000 was invested among three funds: a money-market fund that paid 3% annually, municipal bonds that paid 4% annually, and mutual funds that paid 7% annually. The amount invested in mutual funds was \$4000 more than the amount invested in municipal bonds. The total interest earned during the first year was \$670. How much was invested in each type of fund?

Solution

Let x, y, and z represent the amounts invested in the money-market fund, municipal bonds, and mutual funds, respectively. From the given information, you can write the following equations.

$$\begin{cases} x + y + z = 12{,}000 & \text{Equation 1} \\ z = y + 4000 & \text{Equation 2} \\ 0.03x + 0.04y + 0.07z = 670 & \text{Equation 3} \end{cases}$$

Rewriting this system in standard form without decimals produces the following.

$$\begin{cases} x + y + z = 12{,}000 & \text{Equation 1} \\ -y + z = 4{,}000 & \text{Equation 2} \\ 3x + 4y + 7z = 67{,}000 & \text{Equation 3} \end{cases}$$

Using Gaussian elimination to solve this system yields $x = 2000$, $y = 3000$, and $z = 7000$. So, \$2000 was invested in the money-market fund, \$3000 was invested in municipal bonds, and \$7000 was invested in mutual funds.

CHECKPoint Now try Exercise 61.

7.3 EXERCISES

See www.CalcChat.com for worked-out solutions to odd-numbered exercises.

VOCABULARY: Fill in the blanks.

1. A system of equations that is in ________ form has a "stair-step" pattern with leading coefficients of 1. row-echelon
2. A solution to a system of three linear equations in three unknowns can be written as an ordered triple, which has the form (x, y, z).
3. The process used to write a system of linear equations in row-echelon form is called ________ elimination. Gaussian
4. Interchanging two equations of a system of linear equations is a row operation that produces an equivalent system.
5. A system of equations is called nonsquare if the number of equations differs from the number of variables in the system.
6. The equation $s = \frac{1}{2}at^2 + v_0t + s_0$ is called the position equation, and it models the height s of an object at time t that is moving in a vertical line with a constant acceleration a.

SKILLS AND APPLICATIONS

In Exercises 7–10, determine whether each ordered triple is a solution of the system of equations.

7. $\begin{cases} 6x - y + z = -1 \\ 4x - 3z = -19 \\ 2y + 5z = 25 \end{cases}$

(a) $(2, 0, -2)$ No (b) $(-3, 0, 5)$ No
(c) $(0, -1, 4)$ No (d) $(-1, 0, 5)$ Yes

8. $\begin{cases} 3x + 4y - z = 17 \\ 5x - y + 2z = -2 \\ 2x - 3y + 7z = -21 \end{cases}$

(a) $(3, -1, 2)$ No (b) $(1, 3, -2)$ Yes
(c) $(4, 1, -3)$ No (d) $(1, -2, 2)$ No

9. $\begin{cases} 4x + y - z = 0 \\ -8x - 6y + z = -\frac{7}{4} \\ 3x - y = -\frac{9}{4} \end{cases}$

(a) $\left(\frac{1}{2}, -\frac{3}{4}, -\frac{7}{4}\right)$ No (b) $\left(-\frac{3}{2}, \frac{5}{4}, -\frac{5}{4}\right)$ No
(c) $\left(-\frac{1}{2}, \frac{3}{4}, -\frac{5}{4}\right)$ Yes (d) $\left(-\frac{1}{2}, \frac{1}{6}, -\frac{3}{4}\right)$ No

10. $\begin{cases} -4x - y - 8z = -6 \\ y + z = 0 \\ 4x - 7y = 6 \end{cases}$

(a) $(-2, -2, 2)$ Yes (b) $\left(-\frac{33}{2}, -10, 10\right)$ No
(c) $\left(\frac{1}{8}, -\frac{1}{2}, \frac{1}{2}\right)$ No (d) $\left(-\frac{11}{2}, -4, 4\right)$ Yes

In Exercises 11–16, use back-substitution to solve the system of linear equations. 11–12. See margin.

11. $\begin{cases} 2x - y + 5z = 24 \\ y + 2z = 6 \\ z = 8 \end{cases}$

12. $\begin{cases} 4x - 3y - 2z = 21 \\ 6y - 5z = -8 \\ z = -2 \end{cases}$

13. $\begin{cases} 2x + y - 3z = 10 \\ y + z = 12 \\ z = 2 \end{cases}$ $(3, 10, 2)$

14. $\begin{cases} x - y + 2z = 22 \\ 3y - 8z = -9 \\ z = -3 \end{cases}$ $(17, -11, -3)$

15. $\begin{cases} 4x - 2y + z = 8 \\ -y + z = 4 \\ z = 11 \end{cases}$ $\left(\frac{11}{4}, 7, 11\right)$

16. $\begin{cases} 5x - 8z = 22 \\ 3y - 5z = 10 \\ z = -4 \end{cases}$ $\left(-2, -\frac{10}{3}, -4\right)$

In Exercises 17 and 18, perform the row operation and write the equivalent system. 17–18. See margin.

17. Add Equation 1 to Equation 2.

$\begin{cases} x - 2y + 3z = 5 & \text{Equation 1} \\ -x + 3y - 5z = 4 & \text{Equation 2} \\ 2x - 3z = 0 & \text{Equation 3} \end{cases}$

What did this operation accomplish?

18. Add -2 times Equation 1 to Equation 3.

$\begin{cases} x - 2y + 3z = 5 & \text{Equation 1} \\ -x + 3y - 5z = 4 & \text{Equation 2} \\ 2x - 3z = 0 & \text{Equation 3} \end{cases}$

What did this operation accomplish?

In Exercises 19–44, solve the system of linear equations and check any solution algebraically. 19–26. See margin.

19. $\begin{cases} x + y + z = 7 \\ 2x - y + z = 9 \\ 3x - z = 10 \end{cases}$

20. $\begin{cases} x + y + z = 5 \\ x - 2y + 4z = 13 \\ 3y + 4z = 13 \end{cases}$

21. $\begin{cases} 2x + 2z = 2 \\ 5x + 3y = 4 \\ 3y - 4z = 4 \end{cases}$

22. $\begin{cases} 2x + 4y + z = 1 \\ x - 2y - 3z = 2 \\ x + y - z = -1 \end{cases}$

23. $\begin{cases} 6y + 4z = -12 \\ 3x + 3y = 9 \\ 2x - 3z = 10 \end{cases}$

24. $\begin{cases} 2x + 4y - z = 7 \\ 2x - 4y + 2z = -6 \\ x + 4y + z = 0 \end{cases}$

25. $\begin{cases} 2x + y - z = 7 \\ x - 2y + 2z = -9 \\ 3x - y + z = 5 \end{cases}$

26. $\begin{cases} 5x - 3y + 2z = 3 \\ 2x + 4y - z = 7 \\ x - 11y + 4z = 3 \end{cases}$

4 PRACTICE AND APPLY

Assignment Guide

Transparencies Available
Available at the Instructor's companion site.

Average:
Day 1: pp. 525–529
Exs. 1–4, 7–17 odd, 20, 23, 27–31 odd, 36–41 odd, 85, 89–91
Day 2: pp. 525–529
Exs. 5, 6, 43, 47, 51, 55, 59, 62, 63–75 odd, 79, 83, 93

Advanced:
Day 1: pp. 525–529
Exs. 1–4, 8–18 even, 22–32 even, 38–42 even, 86, 88, 94
Day 2: pp. 525–529
Exs. 5, 6, 44–50 even, 56, 57, 60–78 even, 82, 84, 92, 94

Block:
pp. 525–529
Exs. 1–6, 7–17 odd, 20, 23, 27–31 odd, 36–43 odd, 47, 51, 55, 59, 62, 63–75 odd, 79, 83, 85, 89–91, 93

11. $(-13, -10, 8)$
12. $(2, -3, -2)$
17. $\begin{cases} x - 2y + 3z = 5 \\ y - 2z = 9 \\ 2x - 3z = 0 \end{cases}$
First step in putting the system in row-echelon form.
18. $\begin{cases} x - 2y + 3z = 5 \\ -x + 3y - 5z = 4 \\ 4y - 9z = -10 \end{cases}$
Eliminated the x-term from the third equation.
19. $(4, 1, 2)$
20. $\left(\frac{5}{3}, \frac{1}{3}, 3\right)$
21. $(-4, 8, 5)$
22. $(5, -3, 3)$
23. $(5, -2, 0)$
24. $\left(1, \frac{1}{2}, -3\right)$
25. No solution
26. No solution

27–28. See margin.

27. $\begin{cases} 3x - 5y + 5z = 1 \\ 5x - 2y + 3z = 0 \\ 7x - y + 3z = 0 \end{cases}$

28. $\begin{cases} 2x + y + 3z = 1 \\ 2x + 6y + 8z = 3 \\ 6x + 8y + 18z = 5 \end{cases}$

29. $\begin{cases} x + 2y - 7z = -4 \\ 2x + y + z = 13 \\ 3x + 9y - 36z = -33 \end{cases}$ $(-3a + 10,\ 5a - 7,\ a)$

30. $\begin{cases} 2x + y - 3z = 4 \\ 4x + 2z = 10 \\ -2x + 3y - 13z = -8 \end{cases}$ $\left(-\frac{1}{2}a + \frac{5}{2},\ 4a - 1,\ a\right)$

31–34. See margin.

31. $\begin{cases} 3x - 3y + 6z = 6 \\ x + 2y - z = 5 \\ 5x - 8y + 13z = 7 \end{cases}$

32. $\begin{cases} x + 2z = 5 \\ 3x - y - z = 1 \\ 6x - y + 5z = 16 \end{cases}$

33. $\begin{cases} x - 2y + 5z = 2 \\ 4x - z = 0 \end{cases}$

34. $\begin{cases} x - 3y + 2z = 18 \\ 5x - 13y + 12z = 80 \end{cases}$

35. $\begin{cases} 2x - 3y + z = -2 \\ -4x + 9y = 7 \end{cases}$ $\left(-\frac{3}{2}a + \frac{1}{2},\ -\frac{2}{3}a + 1,\ a\right)$

36. $\begin{cases} 2x + 3y + 3z = 7 \\ 4x + 18y + 15z = 44 \end{cases}$ $\left(-\frac{3}{8}a - \frac{1}{4},\ -\frac{3}{4}a + \frac{5}{2},\ a\right)$

37. $\begin{cases} x + 3w = 4 \\ 2y - z - w = 0 \\ 3y - 2w = 1 \\ 2x - y + 4z = 5 \end{cases}$ $(1, 1, 1, 1)$

38. $\begin{cases} x + y + z + w = 6 \\ 2x + 3y - w = 0 \\ -3x + 4y + z + 2w = 4 \\ x + 2y - z + w = 0 \end{cases}$ $(1, 0, 3, 2)$

39–44. See margin.

39. $\begin{cases} x + 4z = 1 \\ x + y + 10z = 10 \\ 2x - y + 2z = -5 \end{cases}$

40. $\begin{cases} 2x - 2y - 6z = -4 \\ -3x + 2y + 6z = 1 \\ x - y - 5z = -3 \end{cases}$

41. $\begin{cases} 2x + 3y = 0 \\ 4x + 3y - z = 0 \\ 8x + 3y + 3z = 0 \end{cases}$

42. $\begin{cases} 4x + 3y + 17z = 0 \\ 5x + 4y + 22z = 0 \\ 4x + 2y + 19z = 0 \end{cases}$

43. $\begin{cases} 12x + 5y + z = 0 \\ 23x + 4y - z = 0 \end{cases}$

44. $\begin{cases} 2x - y - z = 0 \\ -2x + 6y + 4z = 2 \end{cases}$

VERTICAL MOTION In Exercises 45–48, an object moving vertically is at the given heights at the specified times. Find the position equation $s = \frac{1}{2}at^2 + v_0t + s_0$ for the object.

45. At $t = 1$ second, $s = 128$ feet $s = -16t^2 + 144$
At $t = 2$ seconds, $s = 80$ feet
At $t = 3$ seconds, $s = 0$ feet

46. At $t = 1$ second, $s = 32$ feet $s = -16t^2 + 48t$
At $t = 2$ seconds, $s = 32$ feet
At $t = 3$ seconds, $s = 0$ feet

$s = -16t^2 - 32t + 400$

47. At $t = 1$ second, $s = 352$ feet
At $t = 2$ seconds, $s = 272$ feet
At $t = 3$ seconds, $s = 160$ feet

48. At $t = 1$ second, $s = 132$ feet
At $t = 2$ seconds, $s = 100$ feet
At $t = 3$ seconds, $s = 36$ feet

$s = -16t^2 + 16t + 132$

In Exercises 49–54, find the equation of the parabola

$y = ax^2 + bx + c$ 49–54. See margin.

that passes through the points. To verify your result, use a graphing utility to plot the points and graph the parabola.

49. $(0, 0), (2, -2), (4, 0)$ **50.** $(0, 3), (1, 4), (2, 3)$
51. $(2, 0), (3, -1), (4, 0)$ **52.** $(1, 3), (2, 2), (3, -3)$
53. $\left(\frac{1}{2}, 1\right), (1, 3), (2, 13)$
54. $(-2, -3), (-1, 0), \left(\frac{1}{2}, -3\right)$

In Exercises 55–58, find the equation of the circle

$x^2 + y^2 + Dx + Ey + F = 0$

that passes through the points. To verify your result, use a graphing utility to plot the points and graph the circle.

55–58. See margin.

55. $(0, 0), (5, 5), (10, 0)$
56. $(0, 0), (0, 6), (3, 3)$
57. $(-3, -1), (2, 4), (-6, 8)$
58. $(0, 0), (0, -2), (3, 0)$

59. SPORTS In Super Bowl I, on January 15, 1967, the Green Bay Packers defeated the Kansas City Chiefs by a score of 35 to 10. The total points scored came from 13 different scoring plays, which were a combination of touchdowns, extra-point kicks, and field goals, worth 6, 1, and 3 points, respectively. The same number of touchdowns and extra-point kicks were scored. There were six times as many touchdowns as field goals. How many touchdowns, extra-point kicks, and field goals were scored during the game? (Source: Super Bowl.com) See margin.

60. SPORTS In the 2008 Women's NCAA Final Four Championship game, the University of Tennessee Lady Volunteers defeated the University of Stanford Cardinal by a score of 64 to 48. The Lady Volunteers won by scoring a combination of two-point baskets, three-point baskets, and one-point free throws. The number of two-point baskets was two more than the number of free throws. The number of free throws was two more than five times the number of three-point baskets. What combination of scoring accounted for the Lady Volunteers' 64 points? (Source: National Collegiate Athletic Association)
19 two-point baskets, 3 three-point baskets, 17 one-point free throws

27. $\left(-\frac{1}{2}, 1, \frac{3}{2}\right)$ **28.** $\left(\frac{3}{10}, \frac{2}{5}, 0\right)$
31. $(-a + 3,\ a + 1,\ a)$
32. $(-2a + 5,\ -7a + 14,\ a)$
33. $(2a,\ 21a - 1,\ 8a)$
34. $(-5a + 3,\ -a - 5,\ a)$
39. No solution **40.** $\left(3, \frac{7}{2}, \frac{1}{2}\right)$
41. $(0, 0, 0)$ **42.** $(0, 0, 0)$
43. $(9a,\ -35a,\ 67a)$
44. $\left(\frac{1}{5}a + \frac{1}{5},\ -\frac{3}{5}a + \frac{2}{5},\ a\right)$

49. $y = \frac{1}{2}x^2 - 2x$

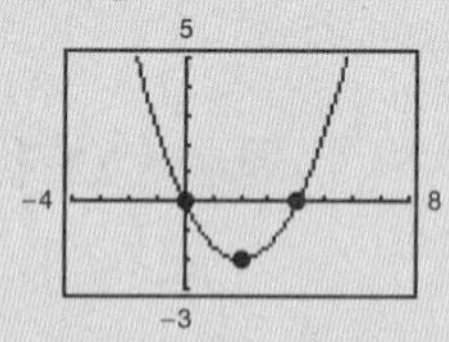

50. $y = -x^2 + 2x + 3$

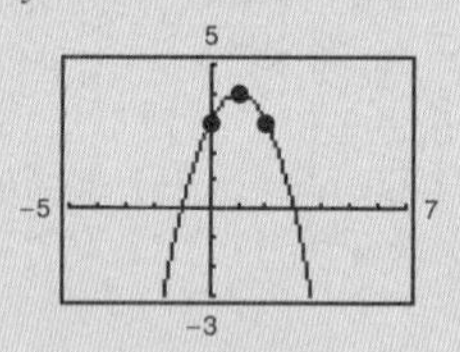

51. $y = x^2 - 6x + 8$

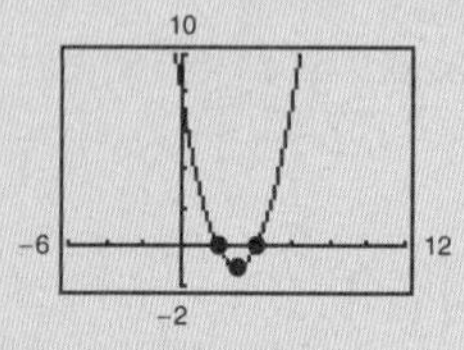

52. $y = -2x^2 + 5x$

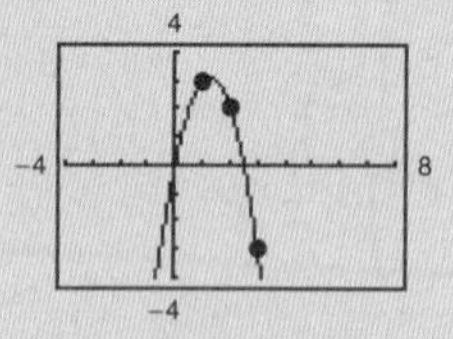

53. $y = 4x^2 - 2x + 1$

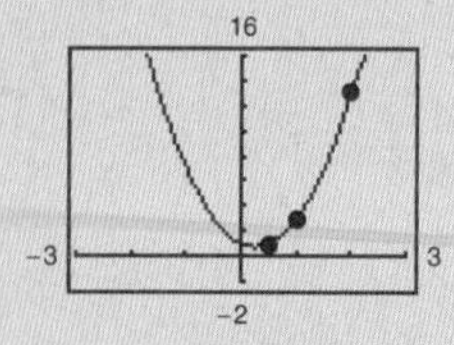

54. $y = -2x^2 - 3x - 1$

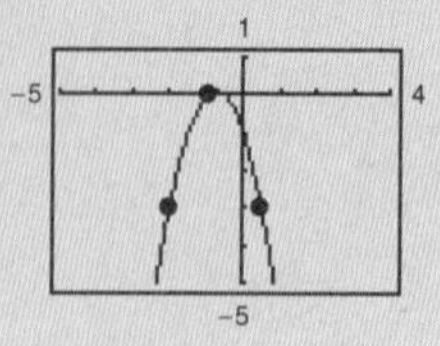

55. $x^2 + y^2 - 10x = 0$

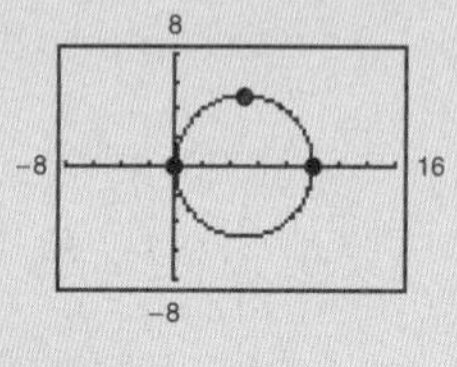

56. $x^2 + y^2 - 6y = 0$

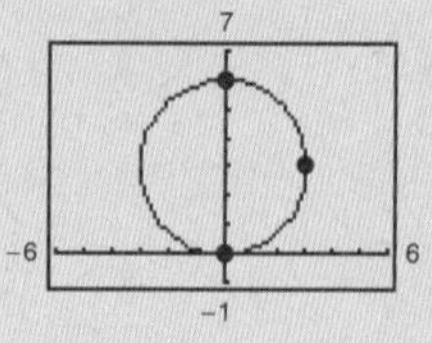

57. $x^2 + y^2 + 6x - 8y = 0$

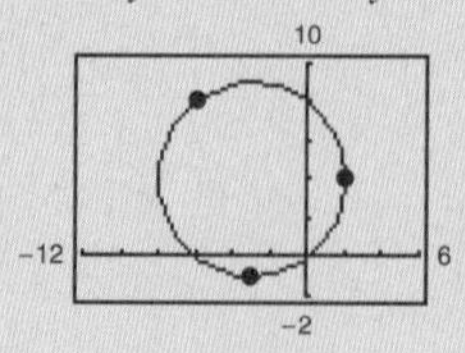

58. $x^2 + y^2 - 3x + 2y = 0$

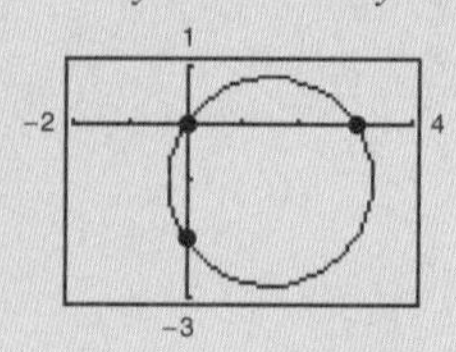

59. 6 touchdowns, 6 extra-point kicks, 1 field goal

61. FINANCE A small corporation borrowed $775,000 to expand its clothing line. Some of the money was borrowed at 8%, some at 9%, and some at 10%. How much was borrowed at each rate if the annual interest owed was $67,500 and the amount borrowed at 8% was four times the amount borrowed at 10%? See margin.

62. FINANCE A small corporation borrowed $800,000 to expand its line of toys. Some of the money was borrowed at 8%, some at 9%, and some at 10%. How much was borrowed at each rate if the annual interest owed was $67,000 and the amount borrowed at 8% was five times the amount borrowed at 10%? See margin.

INVESTMENT PORTFOLIO In Exercises 63 and 64, consider an investor with a portfolio totaling $500,000 that is invested in certificates of deposit, municipal bonds, blue-chip stocks, and growth or speculative stocks. How much is invested in each type of investment? 63–64. See margin.

63. The certificates of deposit pay 3% annually, and the municipal bonds pay 5% annually. Over a five-year period, the investor expects the blue-chip stocks to return 8% annually and the growth stocks to return 10% annually. The investor wants a combined annual return of 5% and also wants to have only one-fourth of the portfolio invested in stocks.

64. The certificates of deposit pay 2% annually, and the municipal bonds pay 4% annually. Over a five-year period, the investor expects the blue-chip stocks to return 10% annually and the growth stocks to return 14% annually. The investor wants a combined annual return of 6% and also wants to have only one-fourth of the portfolio invested in stocks.

65. AGRICULTURE A mixture of 5 pounds of fertilizer A, 13 pounds of fertilizer B, and 4 pounds of fertilizer C provides the optimal nutrients for a plant. Commercial brand X contains equal parts of fertilizer B and fertilizer C. Commercial brand Y contains one part of fertilizer A and two parts of fertilizer B. Commercial brand Z contains two parts of fertilizer A, five parts of fertilizer B, and two parts of fertilizer C. How much of each fertilizer brand is needed to obtain the desired mixture? See margin.

66. AGRICULTURE A mixture of 12 liters of chemical A, 16 liters of chemical B, and 26 liters of chemical C is required to kill a destructive crop insect. Commercial spray X contains 1, 2, and 2 parts, respectively, of these chemicals. Commercial spray Y contains only chemical C. Commercial spray Z contains only chemicals A and B in equal amounts. How much of each type of commercial spray is needed to get the desired mixture? See margin.

48 ft, 35 ft, 27 ft

67. GEOMETRY The perimeter of a triangle is 110 feet. The longest side of the triangle is 21 feet longer than the shortest side. The sum of the lengths of the two shorter sides is 14 feet more than the length of the longest side. Find the lengths of the sides of the triangle.

68. GEOMETRY The perimeter of a triangle is 180 feet. The longest side of the triangle is 9 feet shorter than twice the shortest side. The sum of the lengths of the two shorter sides is 30 feet more than the length of the longest side. Find the lengths of the sides of the triangle. 75 ft, 63 ft, 42 ft

In Exercises 69 and 70, find the values of x, y, and z in the figure.

69.

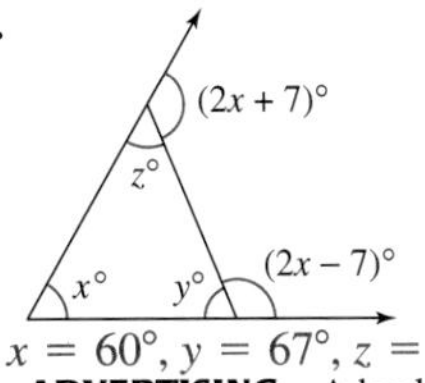

$x = 60°, y = 67°, z = 53°$

70.

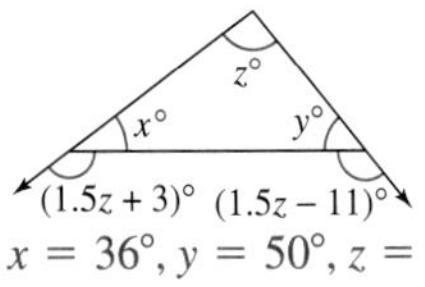

$x = 36°, y = 50°, z = 94°$

71. ADVERTISING A health insurance company advertises on television, on radio, and in the local newspaper. The marketing department has an advertising budget of $42,000 per month. A television ad costs $1000, a radio ad costs $200, and a newspaper ad costs $500. The department wants to run 60 ads per month, and have as many television ads as radio and newspaper ads combined. How many of each type of ad can the department run each month? See margin.

72. RADIO You work as a disc jockey at your college radio station. You are supposed to play 32 songs within two hours. You are to choose the songs from the latest rock, dance, and pop albums. You want to play twice as many rock songs as pop songs and four more pop songs than dance songs. How many of each type of song will you play? Rock = 18, Dance = 5, Pop = 9

73. ACID MIXTURE A chemist needs 10 liters of a 25% acid solution. The solution is to be mixed from three solutions whose concentrations are 10%, 20%, and 50%. How many liters of each solution will satisfy each condition? See margin.

(a) Use 2 liters of the 50% solution.

(b) Use as little as possible of the 50% solution.

(c) Use as much as possible of the 50% solution.

74. ACID MIXTURE A chemist needs 12 gallons of a 20% acid solution. The solution is to be mixed from three solutions whose concentrations are 10%, 15%, and 25%. How many gallons of each solution will satisfy each condition? See margin.

(a) Use 4 gallons of the 25% solution.

(b) Use as little as possible of the 25% solution.

(c) Use as much as possible of the 25% solution.

61. $300,000 at 8%
$400,000 at 9%
$75,000 at 10%

62. $625,000 at 8%
$50,000 at 9%
$125,000 at 10%

63. $187{,}500 + s$ in certificates of deposit
$187{,}500 - s$ in municipal bonds
$125{,}000 - s$ in blue-chip stocks
s in growth stocks

64. $-125{,}000 + 2s$ in certificates of deposit
$500{,}000 - 2s$ in municipal bonds
$125{,}000 - s$ in blue-chip stocks
s in growth stocks

65. Brand X = 4 lb
Brand Y = 9 lb
Brand Z = 9 lb

66. 20 L of spray X
18 L of spray Y
16 L of spray Z

71. Television = 30 ads
Radio = 10 ads
Newspaper = 20 ads

73. (a) 1 L of 10%, 7 L of 20%, 2 L of 50%
(b) 0 L of 10%, $8\frac{1}{3}$ L of 20%, $1\frac{2}{3}$ L of 50%
(c) $6\frac{1}{4}$ L of 10%, 0 L of 20%, $3\frac{3}{4}$ L of 50%

74. (a) Not possible
(b) 0 gal of 10%, 6 gal of 15%, 6 gal of 25%
(c) 4 gal of 10%, 0 gal of 15%, 8 gal of 25%

77. $y = -\frac{5}{24}x^2 - \frac{3}{10}x + \frac{41}{6}$

81. (b)

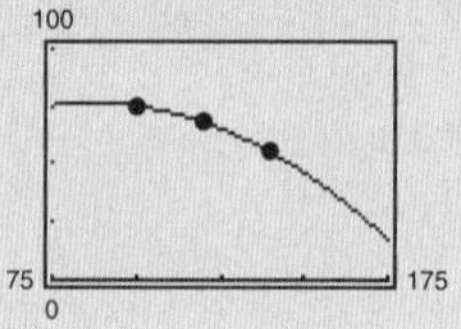

75. ELECTRICAL NETWORK Applying Kirchhoff's Laws to the electrical network in the figure, the currents I_1, I_2, and I_3 are the solution of the system

$$\begin{cases} I_1 - I_2 + I_3 = 0 \\ 3I_1 + 2I_2 = 7 \\ 2I_2 + 4I_3 = 8 \end{cases}$$

find the currents. $I_1 = 1, I_2 = 2, I_3 = 1$

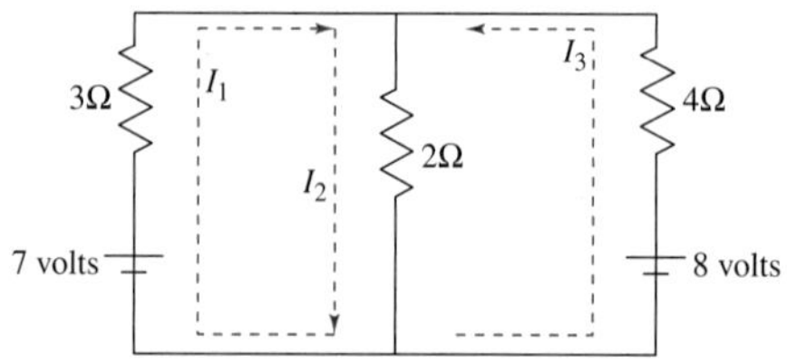

76. PULLEY SYSTEM A system of pulleys is loaded with 128-pound and 32-pound weights (see figure). The tensions t_1 and t_2 in the ropes and the acceleration a of the 32-pound weight are found by solving the system of equations

$$\begin{cases} t_1 - 2t_2 = 0 \\ t_1 - 2a = 128 \\ t_2 + a = 32 \end{cases}$$

where t_1 and t_2 are measured in pounds and a is measured in feet per second squared.

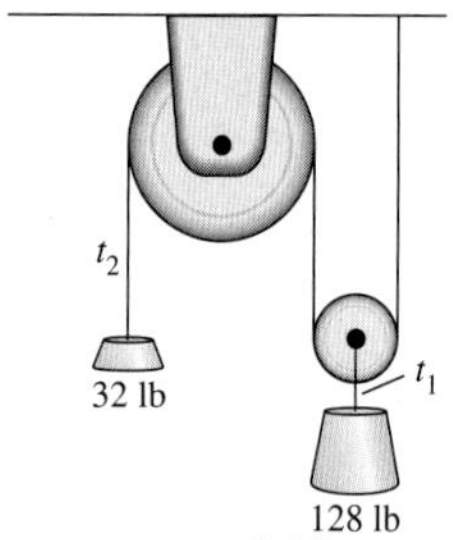

(a) Solve this system. $t_1 = 96$ lb, $t_2 = 48$ lb, $a = -16$ ft/sec^2

(b) The 32-pound weight in the pulley system is replaced by a 64-pound weight. The new pulley system will be modeled by the following system of equations.

$$\begin{cases} t_1 - 2t_2 = 0 \\ t_1 - 2a = 128 \\ t_2 + a = 64 \end{cases}$$

Solve this system and use your answer for the acceleration to describe what (if anything) is happening in the pulley system.

$t_1 = 128$ lb, $t_2 = 64$ lb, $a = 0$ ft/sec^2
The system is stable.

FITTING A PARABOLA In Exercises 77–80, find the least squares regression parabola $y = ax^2 + bx + c$ for the points $(x_1, y_1), (x_2, y_2), \ldots, (x_n, y_n)$ by solving the following system of linear equations for a, b, and c. Then use the *regression* feature of a graphing utility to confirm the result. (If you are unfamiliar with summation notation, look at the discussion in Section 9.1 or in Appendix B at the website for this text at *academic.cengage.com*.)

$$nc + \left(\sum_{i=1}^{n} x_i\right)b + \left(\sum_{i=1}^{n} x_i^2\right)a = \sum_{i=1}^{n} y_i$$

$$\left(\sum_{i=1}^{n} x_i\right)c + \left(\sum_{i=1}^{n} x_i^2\right)b + \left(\sum_{i=1}^{n} x_i^3\right)a = \sum_{i=1}^{n} x_i y_i$$

$$\left(\sum_{i=1}^{n} x_i^2\right)c + \left(\sum_{i=1}^{n} x_i^3\right)b + \left(\sum_{i=1}^{n} x_i^4\right)a = \sum_{i=1}^{n} x_i^2 y_i$$

77. See margin.

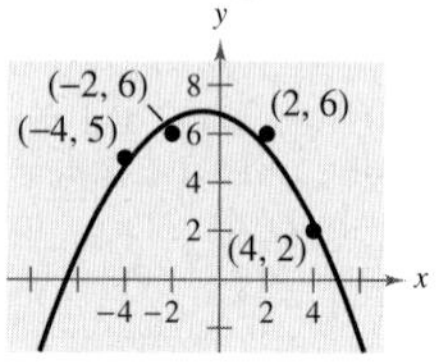

78. $y = \frac{3}{7}x^2 + \frac{6}{5}x + \frac{26}{35}$

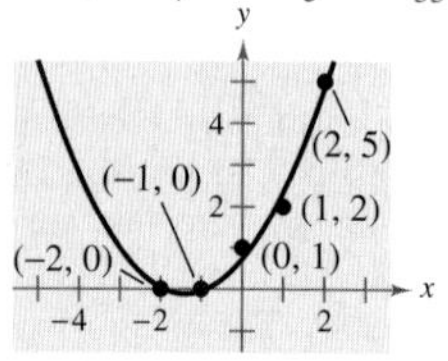

79. $y = x^2 - x$

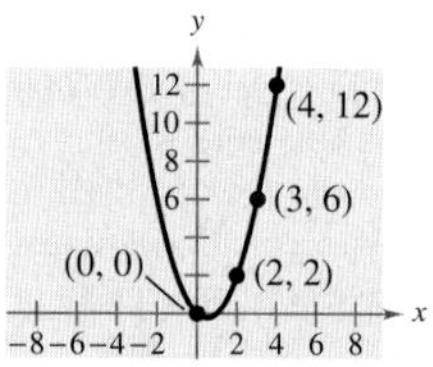

80. $y = -\frac{5}{4}x^2 + \frac{9}{20}x + \frac{199}{20}$

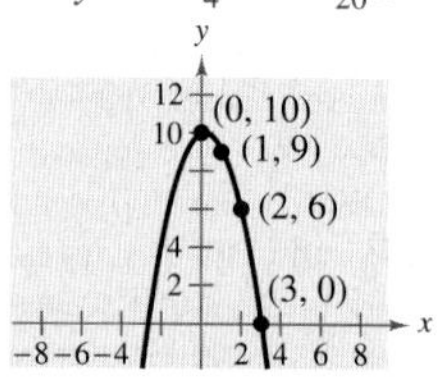

81. DATA ANALYSIS: WILDLIFE A wildlife management team studied the reproduction rates of deer in three tracts of a wildlife preserve. Each tract contained 5 acres. In each tract, the number of females x, and the percent of females y that had offspring the following year, were recorded. The results are shown in the table.

Number, x	Percent, y
100	75
120	68
140	55

(a) Use the technique demonstrated in Exercises 77–80 to set up a system of equations for the data and to find a least squares regression parabola that models the data. $y = -0.0075x^2 + 1.3x + 20$

(b) Use a graphing utility to graph the parabola and the data in the same viewing window. See margin.

(c) Use the model to create a table of estimated values of y. Compare the estimated values with the actual data. See margin.

(d) Use the model to estimate the percent of females that had offspring when there were 170 females. (d) 24.25%

(e) Use the model to estimate the number of females when 40% of the females had offspring. 156 females

82. DATA ANALYSIS: STOPPING DISTANCE In testing a new automobile braking system, the speed x (in miles per hour) and the stopping distance y (in feet) were recorded in the table.

Speed, x	Stopping distance, y
30	55
40	105
50	188

(a) Use the technique demonstrated in Exercises 77–80 to set up a system of equations for the data and to find a least squares regression parabola that models the data. $y = 0.165x^2 - 6.55x + 103$

(b) Graph the parabola and the data on the same set of axes. See margin.

(c) Use the model to estimate the stopping distance when the speed is 70 miles per hour. 453 ft

83. SPORTS In Super Bowl XLIII, on February 1, 2009, the Pittsburgh Steelers defeated the Arizona Cardinals by a score of 27 to 23. The total points scored came from 15 different scoring plays, which were a combination of touchdowns, extra-point kicks, field goals, and safeties, worth 6, 1, 3, and 2 points, respectively. There were three times as many touchdowns as field goals, and the number of extra-point kicks was equal to the number of touchdowns. How many touchdowns, extra-point kicks, field goals, and safeties were scored during the game? (Source: National Football League) See margin.

84. SPORTS In the 2008 Armed Forces Bowl, the University of Houston defeated the Air Force Academy by a score of 34 to 28. The total points scored came from 18 different scoring plays, which were a combination of touchdowns, extra-point kicks, field goals, and two-point conversions, worth 6, 1, 3, and 2 points, respectively. The number of touchdowns was one more than the number of extra-point kicks, and there were four times as many field goals as two-point conversions. How many touchdowns, extra-point kicks, field goals, and two-point conversions were scored during the game? (Source: ESPN.com)

7 touchdowns, 6 extra-point kicks, 4 field goals, 1 two-point conversion

ADVANCED APPLICATIONS In Exercises 85–88, find values of x, y, and λ that satisfy the system. These systems arise in certain optimization problems in calculus, and λ is called a Lagrange multiplier. 85–88. See margin.

85. $\begin{cases} y + \lambda = 0 \\ x + \lambda = 0 \\ x + y - 10 = 0 \end{cases}$

86. $\begin{cases} 2x + \lambda = 0 \\ 2y + \lambda = 0 \\ x + y - 4 = 0 \end{cases}$

87. $\begin{cases} 2x - 2x\lambda = 0 \\ -2y + \lambda = 0 \\ y - x^2 = 0 \end{cases}$

88. $\begin{cases} 2 + 2y + 2\lambda = 0 \\ 2x + 1 + \lambda = 0 \\ 2x + y - 100 = 0 \end{cases}$

EXPLORATION

TRUE OR FALSE? In Exercises 89 and 90, determine whether the statement is true or false. Justify your answer.

89. The system

$$\begin{cases} x + 3y - 6z = -16 \\ 2y - z = -1 \\ z = 3 \end{cases}$$

is in row-echelon form. False. Equation 2 does not have a leading coefficient of 1.

90. If a system of three linear equations is inconsistent, then its graph has no points common to all three equations. See margin.

91. THINK ABOUT IT Are the following two systems of equations equivalent? Give reasons for your answer.

$$\begin{cases} x + 3y - z = 6 \\ 2x - y + 2z = 1 \\ 3x + 2y - z = 2 \end{cases} \qquad \begin{cases} x + 3y - z = 6 \\ -7y + 4z = 1 \\ -7y - 4z = -16 \end{cases}$$

No. Answers will vary.

92. CAPSTONE Find values of a, b, and c (if possible) such that the system of linear equations has (a) a unique solution, (b) no solution, and (c) an infinite number of solutions.

$$\begin{aligned} x + y \quad &= 2 \\ y + z &= 2 \\ x \quad + z &= 2 \\ ax + by + cz &= 0 \end{aligned}$$

(a) $a = 1, b = 1, c = -2$
(b) $a = 1, b = 1, c = 2$
(c) Not possible

In Exercises 93–96, find two systems of linear equations that have the ordered triple as a solution. (There are many correct answers.) 93–96. See margin.

93. $(3, -4, 2)$ **94.** $(-5, -2, 1)$

95. $\left(-6, -\frac{1}{2}, -\frac{7}{4}\right)$ **96.** $\left(-\frac{3}{2}, 4, -7\right)$

PROJECT: EARNINGS PER SHARE To work an extended application analyzing the earnings per share for Wal-Mart Stores, Inc. from 1992 through 2007, visit this text's website at *academic.cengage.com*. (Data Source: Wal-Mart Stores, Inc.)

5 ASSESS AND RETEACH

Daily Homework Quiz

Transparency Available
Available at the Instructor's companion site.

81. (c)

x	100	120	140
y	75	68	55

The values are the same.

82. (b)

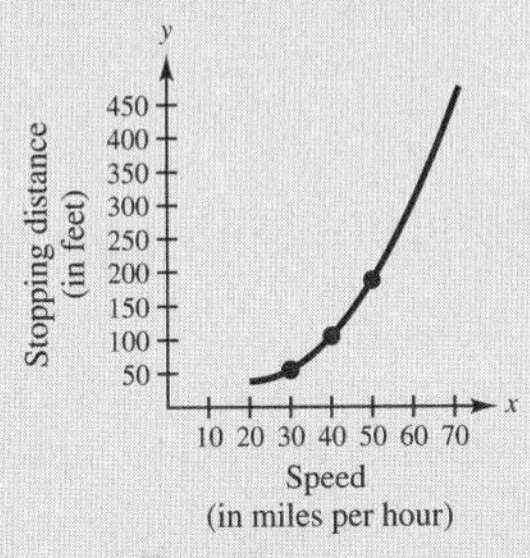

83. 6 touchdowns, 6 extra-point kicks, 2 field goals, 1 safety

85. $x = 5, y = 5, \lambda = -5$

86. $x = 2, y = 2, \lambda = -4$

87. $x = \pm\frac{\sqrt{2}}{2}, y = \frac{1}{2}, \lambda = 1$ or $x = 0, y = 0, \lambda = 0$

88. $x = 25, y = 50, \lambda = -51$

90. True. If a system of three linear equations is inconsistent, then it has no points in common to all three equations.

93. Sample answers:

$$\begin{cases} 2x + y - z = 0 \\ y + 2z = 0 \\ -x + 2y + z = -9 \end{cases}$$

$$\begin{cases} x + y + z = 1 \\ 2x - z = 4 \\ 4y + 8z = 0 \end{cases}$$

94. Sample answers:

$$\begin{cases} x + y + z = -6 \\ -2x - y + 3z = 15 \\ x + 4y - z = -14 \end{cases}$$

$$\begin{cases} 2x - y - z = -9 \\ -x + 2y + 2z = 3 \\ -3x + y - 2z = 11 \end{cases}$$

95. Sample answers:

$$\begin{cases} x + 2y + 4z = -14 \\ x - 12y = 0 \\ x - 8z = 8 \end{cases}$$

$$\begin{cases} 4x - 2y - 8z = -9 \\ -x + 4z = -1 \\ -7y + 2z = 0 \end{cases}$$

96. Sample answers:

$$\begin{cases} 2x - y + 3z = -28 \\ -6x + 4y + z = 18 \\ -4x - 2y - 3z = 19 \end{cases}$$

$$\begin{cases} 4x + y - 2z = 12 \\ 4y + 2z = 2 \\ -2x + y + z = 0 \end{cases}$$

1 PLAN AND PREPARE

Warm-up Exercises

Transparency Available
Available at the Instructor's companion site.

Notetaking Guide

Transparency Available
Promotes interactive learning and notetaking skills.
Available at the Instructor's companion site.

Animated Precalculus

An **Animated Precalculus** tutorial is available at the Student companion site for **Section 7.4.**

Pacing

Average: 1 day
Advanced: 1 day
Block: 0.5 block with 7.5

2 FOCUS AND MOTIVATE

Essential Question

How do you write a rational expression as the sum of two or more simpler rational expressions?
Tell students that they will learn how to answer this question by studying algebraic techniques for finding the numerators and denominators of a partial fraction decomposition.

Resource Planning Guide

Chapter Resources
- Complete Solutions Guide

Workbooks
- Notetaking Guide
- Student Solutions Guide

Interactive Technology
- Instructor Success Organizer
- Notetaking Guide IAE
- Instructional DVDs
- Animated Precalculus
- PowerLecture with ExamView

7.4 PARTIAL FRACTIONS

What you should learn
- Recognize partial fraction decompositions of rational expressions.
- Find partial fraction decompositions of rational expressions.

Why you should learn it

Partial fractions can help you analyze the behavior of a rational function. For instance, in Exercise 62 on page 537, you can analyze the exhaust temperatures of a diesel engine using partial fractions.

© Michael Rosenfeld/Getty Images

Algebra Help

You can review how to find the degree of a polynomial (such as $x - 3$ and $x + 2$) in Appendix A.3.

Study Tip

Appendix A.4 shows you how to combine expressions such as

$$\frac{1}{x-2} + \frac{-1}{x+3} = \frac{5}{(x-2)(x+3)}.$$

The method of partial fraction decomposition shows you how to reverse this process and write

$$\frac{5}{(x-2)(x+3)} = \frac{1}{x-2} + \frac{-1}{x+3}.$$

Introduction

In this section, you will learn to write a rational expression as the sum of two or more simpler rational expressions. For example, the rational expression

$$\frac{x+7}{x^2 - x - 6}$$

can be written as the sum of two fractions with first-degree denominators. That is,

$$\overbrace{\frac{x+7}{x^2-x-6} = \underbrace{\frac{2}{x-3}}_{\text{Partial fraction}} + \underbrace{\frac{-1}{x+2}}_{\text{Partial fraction}}}^{\text{Partial fraction decomposition of } \frac{x+7}{x^2-x-6}}.$$

Each fraction on the right side of the equation is a **partial fraction,** and together they make up the **partial fraction decomposition** of the left side.

Decomposition of $N(x)/D(x)$ into Partial Fractions

1. *Divide if improper:* If $N(x)/D(x)$ is an improper fraction [degree of $N(x) \geq$ degree of $D(x)$], divide the denominator into the numerator to obtain
$$\frac{N(x)}{D(x)} = (\text{polynomial}) + \frac{N_1(x)}{D(x)}$$
and apply Steps 2, 3, and 4 below to the proper rational expression $N_1(x)/D(x)$. Note that $N_1(x)$ is the remainder from the division of $N(x)$ by $D(x)$.
2. *Factor the denominator:* Completely factor the denominator into factors of the form
$$(px + q)^m \quad \text{and} \quad (ax^2 + bx + c)^n$$
where $(ax^2 + bx + c)$ is irreducible.
3. *Linear factors:* For *each* factor of the form $(px + q)^m$, the partial fraction decomposition must include the following sum of m fractions.
$$\frac{A_1}{(px+q)} + \frac{A_2}{(px+q)^2} + \cdots + \frac{A_m}{(px+q)^m}$$
4. *Quadratic factors:* For *each* factor of the form $(ax^2 + bx + c)^n$, the partial fraction decomposition must include the following sum of n fractions.
$$\frac{B_1x + C_1}{ax^2 + bx + c} + \frac{B_2x + C_2}{(ax^2 + bx + c)^2} + \cdots + \frac{B_nx + C_n}{(ax^2 + bx + c)^n}$$

Partial Fraction Decomposition

Algebraic techniques for determining the constants in the numerators of partial fractions are demonstrated in the examples that follow. Note that the techniques vary slightly, depending on the type of factors of the denominator: linear or quadratic, distinct or repeated.

Example 1 Distinct Linear Factors

Write the partial fraction decomposition of $\dfrac{x+7}{x^2-x-6}$.

Solution

The expression is proper, so be sure to factor the denominator. Because $x^2 - x - 6 = (x-3)(x+2)$, you should include one partial fraction with a constant numerator for each linear factor of the denominator. Write the form of the decomposition as follows.

$$\frac{x+7}{x^2-x-6} = \frac{A}{x-3} + \frac{B}{x+2}$$ Write form of decomposition.

Multiplying each side of this equation by the least common denominator, $(x-3)(x+2)$, leads to the **basic equation**

$$x + 7 = A(x+2) + B(x-3).$$ Basic equation

Because this equation is true for all x, you can substitute any *convenient* values of x that will help determine the constants A and B. Values of x that are especially convenient are ones that make the factors $(x+2)$ and $(x-3)$ equal to zero. For instance, let $x = -2$. Then

$$-2 + 7 = A(-2+2) + B(-2-3)$$ Substitute -2 for x.

$$5 = A(0) + B(-5)$$

$$5 = -5B$$

$$-1 = B.$$

To solve for A, let $x = 3$ and obtain

$$3 + 7 = A(3+2) + B(3-3)$$ Substitute 3 for x.

$$10 = A(5) + B(0)$$

$$10 = 5A$$

$$2 = A.$$

So, the partial fraction decomposition is

$$\frac{x+7}{x^2-x-6} = \frac{2}{x-3} + \frac{-1}{x+2}.$$

Check this result by combining the two partial fractions on the right side of the equation, or by using your graphing utility.

CHECKPoint Now try Exercise 23.

TECHNOLOGY

You can use a graphing utility to check the decomposition found in Example 1. To do this, graph

$$y_1 = \frac{x+7}{x^2-x-6}$$

and

$$y_2 = \frac{2}{x-3} + \frac{-1}{x+2}$$

in the same viewing window. The graphs should be identical, as shown below.

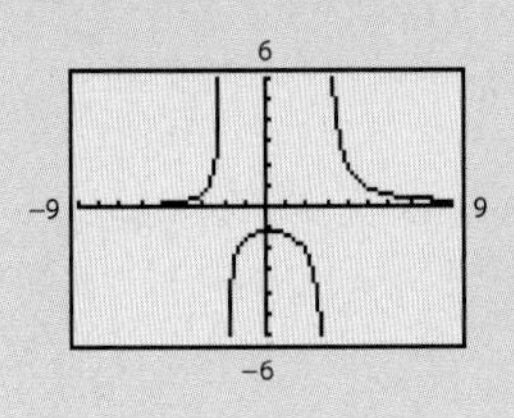

3 TEACH

Extra Example 1

Write the partial fraction decomposition of $\dfrac{x+8}{x^2+6x+8}$.

$\dfrac{3}{x+2} + \dfrac{-2}{x+4}$

Extra Example 2

Write the partial fraction decomposition of $\dfrac{3x^2 - x + 5}{x^3 - 2x^2 + x}$.

$\dfrac{5}{x} + \dfrac{-2}{x-1} + \dfrac{7}{(x-1)^2}$

Avoiding Common Errors

Students often neglect to write fractions with lesser powers of a factor when setting up the partial fraction decomposition. Remind students that when factors are repeated in the denominator, students should be careful to write a fraction for each power up to the highest power of the factor. Students should check their answer and their understanding by recombining the partial fractions in their answer to obtain the original fraction.

The next example shows how to find the partial fraction decomposition of a rational expression whose denominator has a *repeated* linear factor.

Example 2 Repeated Linear Factors

Write the partial fraction decomposition of $\dfrac{x^4 + 2x^3 + 6x^2 + 20x + 6}{x^3 + 2x^2 + x}$.

Algebra Help

You can review long division of polynomials in Section 2.3. You can review factoring of polynomials in Appendix A.3.

Solution

This rational expression is improper, so you should begin by dividing the numerator by the denominator to obtain

$$x + \frac{5x^2 + 20x + 6}{x^3 + 2x^2 + x}.$$

Because the denominator of the remainder factors as

$$x^3 + 2x^2 + x = x(x^2 + 2x + 1) = x(x+1)^2$$

you should include one partial fraction with a constant numerator for each power of x and $(x + 1)$ and write the form of the decomposition as follows.

$$\frac{5x^2 + 20x + 6}{x(x+1)^2} = \frac{A}{x} + \frac{B}{x+1} + \frac{C}{(x+1)^2}$$ Write form of decomposition.

Multiplying by the LCD, $x(x + 1)^2$, leads to the basic equation

$$5x^2 + 20x + 6 = A(x+1)^2 + Bx(x+1) + Cx.$$ Basic equation

WARNING/CAUTION

To obtain the basic equation, be sure to multiply *each* fraction in the form of the decomposition by the LCD.

Letting $x = -1$ eliminates the A- and B-terms and yields

$$5(-1)^2 + 20(-1) + 6 = A(-1+1)^2 + B(-1)(-1+1) + C(-1)$$
$$5 - 20 + 6 = 0 + 0 - C$$
$$C = 9.$$

Letting $x = 0$ eliminates the B- and C-terms and yields

$$5(0)^2 + 20(0) + 6 = A(0+1)^2 + B(0)(0+1) + C(0)$$
$$6 = A(1) + 0 + 0$$
$$6 = A.$$

At this point, you have exhausted the most convenient choices for x, so to find the value of B, use *any other value* for x along with the known values of A and C. So, using $x = 1$, $A = 6$, and $C = 9$,

$$5(1)^2 + 20(1) + 6 = 6(1+1)^2 + B(1)(1+1) + 9(1)$$
$$31 = 6(4) + 2B + 9$$
$$-2 = 2B$$
$$-1 = B.$$

So, the partial fraction decomposition is

$$\frac{x^4 + 2x^3 + 6x^2 + 20x + 6}{x^3 + 2x^2 + x} = x + \frac{6}{x} + \frac{-1}{x+1} + \frac{9}{(x+1)^2}.$$

CHECKPoint Now try Exercise 49.

The procedure used to solve for the constants in Examples 1 and 2 works well when the factors of the denominator are linear. However, when the denominator contains irreducible quadratic factors, you should use a different procedure, which involves writing the right side of the basic equation in polynomial form and *equating the coefficients* of like terms. Then you can use a system of equations to solve for the coefficients.

Example 3 Distinct Linear and Quadratic Factors

Write the partial fraction decomposition of

$$\frac{3x^2 + 4x + 4}{x^3 + 4x}.$$

Solution

This expression is proper, so factor the denominator. Because the denominator factors as

$$x^3 + 4x = x(x^2 + 4)$$

you should include one partial fraction with a constant numerator and one partial fraction with a linear numerator and write the form of the decomposition as follows.

$$\frac{3x^2 + 4x + 4}{x^3 + 4x} = \frac{A}{x} + \frac{Bx + C}{x^2 + 4}$$ Write form of decomposition.

Multiplying by the LCD, $x(x^2 + 4)$, yields the basic equation

$$3x^2 + 4x + 4 = A(x^2 + 4) + (Bx + C)x.$$ Basic equation

Expanding this basic equation and collecting like terms produces

$$3x^2 + 4x + 4 = Ax^2 + 4A + Bx^2 + Cx$$

$$= (A + B)x^2 + Cx + 4A.$$ Polynomial form

Finally, because two polynomials are equal if and only if the coefficients of like terms are equal, you can equate the coefficients of like terms on opposite sides of the equation.

$$3x^2 + 4x + 4 = (A + B)x^2 + Cx + 4A$$ Equate coefficients of like terms.

You can now write the following system of linear equations.

$$\begin{cases} A + B = 3 & \text{Equation 1} \\ C = 4 & \text{Equation 2} \\ 4A = 4 & \text{Equation 3} \end{cases}$$

From this system you can see that $A = 1$ and $C = 4$. Moreover, substituting $A = 1$ into Equation 1 yields

$$1 + B = 3 \Longrightarrow B = 2.$$

So, the partial fraction decomposition is

$$\frac{3x^2 + 4x + 4}{x^3 + 4x} = \frac{1}{x} + \frac{2x + 4}{x^2 + 4}.$$

CHECKPoint Now try Exercise 33.

HISTORICAL NOTE

The Granger Collection

John Bernoulli (1667–1748), a Swiss mathematician, introduced the method of partial fractions and was instrumental in the early development of calculus. Bernoulli was a professor at the University of Basel and taught many outstanding students, the most famous of whom was Leonhard Euler.

Extra Example 3

Write the partial fraction decomposition of $\dfrac{5x^2 - x + 27}{x^3 + 9x}$.

$\dfrac{3}{x} + \dfrac{2x - 1}{x^2 + 9}$

Extra Example 4

Write the partial fraction decomposition of $\dfrac{6x^3 + 16x}{(x^2 + 3)^2}$.

$\dfrac{6x}{x^2 + 3} + \dfrac{-2x}{(x^2 + 3)^2}$

The next example shows how to find the partial fraction decomposition of a rational expression whose denominator has a *repeated* quadratic factor.

Example 4 Repeated Quadratic Factors

Write the partial fraction decomposition of $\dfrac{8x^3 + 13x}{(x^2 + 2)^2}$.

Solution

Include one partial fraction with a linear numerator for each power of $(x^2 + 2)$.

$$\frac{8x^3 + 13x}{(x^2 + 2)^2} = \frac{Ax + B}{x^2 + 2} + \frac{Cx + D}{(x^2 + 2)^2} \qquad \text{Write form of decomposition.}$$

Multiplying by the LCD, $(x^2 + 2)^2$, yields the basic equation

$$8x^3 + 13x = (Ax + B)(x^2 + 2) + Cx + D \qquad \text{Basic equation}$$
$$= Ax^3 + 2Ax + Bx^2 + 2B + Cx + D$$
$$= Ax^3 + Bx^2 + (2A + C)x + (2B + D). \qquad \text{Polynomial form}$$

Equating coefficients of like terms on opposite sides of the equation

$$8x^3 + 0x^2 + 13x + 0 = Ax^3 + Bx^2 + (2A + C)x + (2B + D)$$

produces the following system of linear equations.

$$\begin{cases} A = 8 & \text{Equation 1} \\ B = 0 & \text{Equation 2} \\ 2A + C = 13 & \text{Equation 3} \\ 2B + D = 0 & \text{Equation 4} \end{cases}$$

Finally, use the values $A = 8$ and $B = 0$ to obtain the following.

$$2(8) + C = 13 \qquad \text{Substitute 8 for } A \text{ in Equation 3.}$$
$$C = -3$$

$$2(0) + D = 0 \qquad \text{Substitute 0 for } B \text{ in Equation 4.}$$
$$D = 0$$

So, using $A = 8$, $B = 0$, $C = -3$, and $D = 0$, the partial fraction decomposition is

$$\frac{8x^3 + 13x}{(x^2 + 2)^2} = \frac{8x}{x^2 + 2} + \frac{-3x}{(x^2 + 2)^2}.$$

Check this result by combining the two partial fractions on the right side of the equation, or by using your graphing utility.

CHECK*Point* Now try Exercise 55.

Guidelines for Solving the Basic Equation

Linear Factors

1. Substitute the *zeros* of the distinct linear factors into the basic equation.
2. For repeated linear factors, use the coefficients determined in Step 1 to rewrite the basic equation. Then substitute *other* convenient values of x and solve for the remaining coefficients.

Quadratic Factors

1. Expand the basic equation.
2. Collect terms according to powers of x.
3. Equate the coefficients of like terms to obtain equations involving A, B, C, and so on.
4. Use a system of linear equations to solve for $A, B, C, \ldots$.

Keep in mind that for *improper* rational expressions such as

$$\frac{N(x)}{D(x)} = \frac{2x^3 + x^2 - 7x + 7}{x^2 + x - 2}$$

you must first divide before applying partial fraction decomposition.

Classroom Discussion

Error Analysis You are tutoring a student in algebra. In trying to find a partial fraction decomposition, the student writes the following.

$$\frac{x^2+1}{x(x-1)} = \frac{A}{x} + \frac{B}{x-1}$$

$$\frac{x^2+1}{x(x-1)} = \frac{A(x-1)}{x(x-1)} + \frac{Bx}{x(x-1)}$$

$$x^2 + 1 = A(x-1) + Bx \qquad \text{Basic equation}$$

By substituting $x = 0$ and $x = 1$ into the basic equation, the student concludes that $A = -1$ and $B = 2$. However, in checking this solution, the student obtains the following.

$$\frac{-1}{x} + \frac{2}{x-1} = \frac{(-1)(x-1) + 2(x)}{x(x-1)}$$

$$= \frac{x+1}{x(x-1)}$$

$$\neq \frac{x^2+1}{x(x-1)}$$

What is wrong? See margin.

Closing the Lesson

Have students summarize the major points of the lesson and answer the Essential Question: How do you write a rational expression as the sum of two or more simpler rational expressions?

- **Factor the denominator of the rational expression to determine the denominators of the partial fraction decomposition.**
- **For each factor of the denominator and each lesser power of each factor, write one denominator of the partial fraction decomposition.**
- **For linear or quadratic denominators, write unknown numerators that are constant or linear, respectively.**
- **Write and solve the basic equation to find the numerators and the completed partial fraction decomposition.**

Classroom Discussion

Because $\frac{x^2+1}{x(x-1)}$ is an improper fraction, the student should have begun by dividing to obtain $\frac{x^2+1}{x(x-1)} = 1 + \frac{x+1}{x(x-1)}$, and should then have decomposed $\frac{x+1}{x(x-1)}$ into its partial fractions by the usual methods.

4 PRACTICE AND APPLY

Assignment Guide

Transparencies Available
Available at the Instructor's companion site.

Average:
Day 1: pp. 536–537
Exs. 1–4, 6–8, 11, 15, 19, 23–31 odd, 39–45 odd, 51, 53, 57, 59, 63–67 odd

Advanced:
Day 1: pp. 536–537
Exs. 1–4, 6–8, 12, 16–20 even, 24, 30, 36–46 even, 52, 58–70 even, 71

Block:
pp. 536–537
Exs. 1–4, 6–8, 11, 15, 19, 23–31 odd, 39–45 odd, 51, 53, 57, 59, 63–67 odd (with 7.5)

10. $\dfrac{A}{x+3} + \dfrac{B}{x+1}$

11. $\dfrac{A}{x} + \dfrac{B}{x^2} + \dfrac{C}{x-7}$

12. $\dfrac{A}{x} + \dfrac{B}{x^2} + \dfrac{C}{4x+11}$

13. $\dfrac{A}{x-5} + \dfrac{B}{(x-5)^2} + \dfrac{C}{(x-5)^3}$

14. See below.

17. $\dfrac{A}{x} + \dfrac{Bx+C}{x^2+1} + \dfrac{Dx+E}{(x^2+1)^2}$

18. $\dfrac{A}{x} + \dfrac{B}{x^2} + \dfrac{C}{3x-1} + \dfrac{D}{(3x-1)^2}$

25. $\dfrac{1}{2}\left(\dfrac{1}{x-1} - \dfrac{1}{x+1}\right)$

26. $\dfrac{1}{6}\left(\dfrac{1}{2x-3} - \dfrac{1}{2x+3}\right)$

27. $-\dfrac{3}{x} - \dfrac{1}{x+2} + \dfrac{5}{x-2}$

28. $\dfrac{1}{18}\left(-\dfrac{4}{x} - \dfrac{1}{x+3} + \dfrac{5}{x-3}\right)$

29. $\dfrac{3}{x-3} + \dfrac{9}{(x-3)^2}$

30. $\dfrac{2}{x-1} - \dfrac{1}{(x-1)^2}$

31. $\dfrac{3}{x} - \dfrac{1}{x^2} + \dfrac{1}{x+1}$

32. $\dfrac{2}{x} + \dfrac{1}{x^2} - \dfrac{2}{x-1} + \dfrac{7}{(x-1)^2}$

33. $\dfrac{3}{x} - \dfrac{2x-2}{x^2+1}$

34. $\dfrac{2}{3}\left(\dfrac{1}{x-1} - \dfrac{x-1}{x^2+x+1}\right)$

35. $-\dfrac{1}{x-1} + \dfrac{x+2}{x^2-2}$

7.4 EXERCISES

See www.CalcChat.com for worked-out solutions to odd-numbered exercises.

VOCABULARY: Fill in the blanks.

1. The process of writing a rational expression as the sum or difference of two or more simpler rational expressions is called ______ ______ ______. partial fraction decomposition
2. If the degree of the numerator of a rational expression is greater than or equal to the degree of the denominator, then the fraction is called improper.
3. Each fraction on the right side of the equation $\dfrac{x-1}{x^2-8x+15} = \dfrac{-1}{x-3} + \dfrac{2}{x-5}$ is a partial fraction.
4. The basic equation is obtained after multiplying each side of the partial fraction decomposition form by the least common denominator.

SKILLS AND APPLICATIONS

In Exercises 5–8, match the rational expression with the form of its decomposition. [The decompositions are labeled (a), (b), (c), and (d).]

(a) $\dfrac{A}{x} + \dfrac{B}{x+2} + \dfrac{C}{x-2}$ (b) $\dfrac{A}{x} + \dfrac{B}{x-4}$

(c) $\dfrac{A}{x} + \dfrac{B}{x^2} + \dfrac{C}{x-4}$ (d) $\dfrac{A}{x} + \dfrac{Bx+C}{x^2+4}$

5. $\dfrac{3x-1}{x(x-4)}$ b
6. $\dfrac{3x-1}{x^2(x-4)}$ c
7. $\dfrac{3x-1}{x(x^2+4)}$ d
8. $\dfrac{3x-1}{x(x^2-4)}$ a

In Exercises 9–18, write the form of the partial fraction decomposition of the rational expression. Do not solve for the constants.

9. $\dfrac{3}{x^2-2x}$ $\dfrac{A}{x} + \dfrac{B}{x-2}$
10. $\dfrac{x-2}{x^2+4x+3}$
11. $\dfrac{9}{x^3-7x^2}$
12. $\dfrac{x^2-3x+2}{4x^3+11x^2}$
13. $\dfrac{4x^2+3}{(x-5)^3}$
14. $\dfrac{6x+5}{(x+2)^4}$
15. $\dfrac{2x-3}{x^3+10x}$ $\dfrac{A}{x} + \dfrac{Bx+C}{x^2+10}$
16. $\dfrac{x-6}{2x^3+8x}$ $\dfrac{A}{2x} + \dfrac{Bx+C}{x^2+4}$
17. $\dfrac{x-1}{x(x^2+1)^2}$
18. $\dfrac{x+4}{x^2(3x-1)^2}$

10–14, 17–18. See margin.

In Exercises 19–42, write the partial fraction decomposition of the rational expression. Check your result algebraically.

19. $\dfrac{1}{x^2+x}$ $\dfrac{1}{x} - \dfrac{1}{x+1}$
20. $\dfrac{3}{x^2-3x}$ $\dfrac{1}{x-3} - \dfrac{1}{x}$
21. $\dfrac{1}{2x^2+x}$ $\dfrac{1}{x} - \dfrac{2}{2x+1}$
22. $\dfrac{5}{x^2+x-6}$ $\dfrac{1}{x-2} - \dfrac{1}{x+3}$
23. $\dfrac{3}{x^2+x-2}$ $\dfrac{1}{x-1} - \dfrac{1}{x+2}$
24. $\dfrac{x+1}{x^2-x-6}$ $\dfrac{1}{5}\left(\dfrac{4}{x-3} + \dfrac{1}{x+2}\right)$

25–42. See margin.

25. $\dfrac{1}{x^2-1}$
26. $\dfrac{1}{4x^2-9}$
27. $\dfrac{x^2+12x+12}{x^3-4x}$
28. $\dfrac{x+2}{x(x^2-9)}$
29. $\dfrac{3x}{(x-3)^2}$
30. $\dfrac{2x-3}{(x-1)^2}$
31. $\dfrac{4x^2+2x-1}{x^2(x+1)}$
32. $\dfrac{6x^2+1}{x^2(x-1)^2}$
33. $\dfrac{x^2+2x+3}{x^3+x}$
34. $\dfrac{2x}{x^3-1}$
35. $\dfrac{x}{x^3-x^2-2x+2}$
36. $\dfrac{x+6}{x^3-3x^2-4x+12}$
37. $\dfrac{2x^2+x+8}{(x^2+4)^2}$
38. $\dfrac{x^2}{x^4-2x^2-8}$
39. $\dfrac{x}{16x^4-1}$
40. $\dfrac{3}{x^4+x}$
41. $\dfrac{x^2+5}{(x+1)(x^2-2x+3)}$
42. $\dfrac{x^2-4x+7}{(x+1)(x^2-2x+3)}$

In Exercises 43–50, write the partial fraction decomposition of the improper rational expression. 43–48. See margin.

43. $\dfrac{x^2-x}{x^2+x+1}$
44. $\dfrac{x^2-4x}{x^2+x+6}$
45. $\dfrac{2x^3-x^2+x+5}{x^2+3x+2}$
46. $\dfrac{x^3+2x^2-x+1}{x^2+3x-4}$
47. $\dfrac{x^4}{(x-1)^3}$
48. $\dfrac{16x^4}{(2x-1)^3}$
49. $\dfrac{x^4+2x^3+4x^2+8x+2}{x^3+2x^2+x}$ $x + \dfrac{2}{x} + \dfrac{1}{x+1} + \dfrac{3}{(x+1)^2}$
50. $\dfrac{2x^4+8x^3+7x^2-7x-12}{x^3+4x^2+4x}$ $2x - \dfrac{3}{x} + \dfrac{2}{x+2} + \dfrac{1}{(x+2)^2}$

36. $\dfrac{1}{5}\left(\dfrac{9}{x-3} + \dfrac{1}{x+2} - \dfrac{10}{x-2}\right)$

37. $\dfrac{2}{x^2+4} + \dfrac{x}{(x^2+4)^2}$

38. $\dfrac{1}{6}\left(\dfrac{2}{x^2+2} - \dfrac{1}{x+2} + \dfrac{1}{x-2}\right)$

39. $\dfrac{1}{8}\left(\dfrac{1}{2x+1} + \dfrac{1}{2x-1} - \dfrac{4x}{4x^2+1}\right)$

40. $\dfrac{3}{x} - \dfrac{1}{x+1} - \dfrac{2x-1}{x^2-x+1}$

41. $\dfrac{1}{x+1} + \dfrac{2}{x^2-2x+3}$

42. $\dfrac{2}{x+1} - \dfrac{x-1}{x^2-2x+3}$

14. $\dfrac{A}{x+2} + \dfrac{B}{(x+2)^2} + \dfrac{C}{(x+2)^3} + \dfrac{D}{(x+2)^4}$

43–48. See Additional Answers beginning on page AA1.

In Exercises 51–58, write the partial fraction decomposition of the rational expression. Use a graphing utility to check your result. 51–58. See margin.

51. $\dfrac{5-x}{2x^2+x-1}$ **52.** $\dfrac{3x^2-7x-2}{x^3-x}$

53. $\dfrac{4x^2-1}{2x(x+1)^2}$ **54.** $\dfrac{3x+1}{2x^3+3x^2}$

55. $\dfrac{x^2+x+2}{(x^2+2)^2}$ **56.** $\dfrac{x^3}{(x+2)^2(x-2)^2}$

57. $\dfrac{2x^3-4x^2-15x+5}{x^2-2x-8}$ **58.** $\dfrac{x^3-x+3}{x^2+x-2}$

GRAPHICAL ANALYSIS In Exercises 59 and 60, (a) write the partial fraction decomposition of the rational function, (b) identify the graph of the rational function and the graph of each term of its decomposition, and (c) state any relationship between the vertical asymptotes of the graph of the rational function and the vertical asymptotes of the graphs of the terms of the decomposition. To print an enlarged copy of the graph, go to the website *www.mathgraphs.com*. 59–60. See margin.

59. $y = \dfrac{x-12}{x(x-4)}$ **60.** $y = \dfrac{2(4x-3)}{x^2-9}$

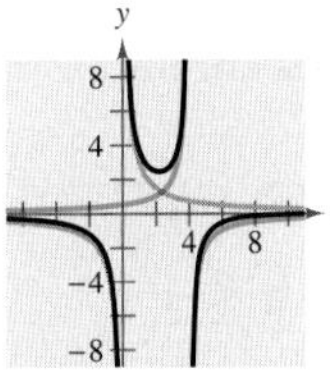

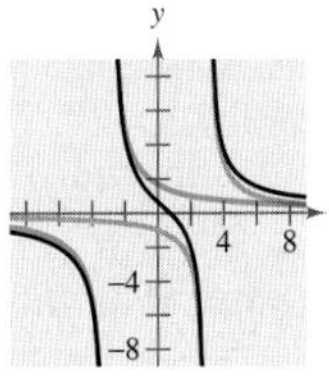

61. ENVIRONMENT The predicted cost C (in thousands of dollars) for a company to remove $p\%$ of a chemical from its waste water is given by the model

$$C = \frac{120p}{10{,}000-p^2}, \quad 0 \le p < 100. \quad \frac{60}{100-p} - \frac{60}{100+p}$$

Write the partial fraction decomposition for the rational function. Verify your result by using the *table* feature of a graphing utility to create a table comparing the original function with the partial fractions.

62. THERMODYNAMICS The magnitude of the range R of exhaust temperatures (in degrees Fahrenheit) in an experimental diesel engine is approximated by the model

$$R = \frac{5000(4-3x)}{(11-7x)(7-4x)}, \quad 0 < x \le 1$$

where x is the relative load (in foot-pounds).

(a) Write the partial fraction decomposition of the equation.
$\dfrac{5000}{7-4x} - \dfrac{5000}{11-7x}, \quad 0 < x \le 1$

(b) The decomposition in part (a) is the difference of two fractions. The absolute values of the terms give the expected maximum and minimum temperatures of the exhaust gases for different loads.

Ymax = |1st term| Ymin = |2nd term|

Write the equations for Ymax and Ymin. See margin.

(c) Use a graphing utility to graph each equation from part (b) in the same viewing window. See margin.

(d) Determine the expected maximum and minimum temperatures for a relative load of 0.5.
Max = 1000°F, Min ≈ 666.7°F

EXPLORATION

TRUE OR FALSE? In Exercises 63–65, determine whether the statement is true or false. Justify your answer.
63–64. See margin.

63. For the rational expression $\dfrac{x}{(x+10)(x-10)^2}$, the partial fraction decomposition is of the form $\dfrac{A}{x+10} + \dfrac{B}{(x-10)^2}$.

64. For the rational expression $\dfrac{2x+3}{x^2(x+2)^2}$, the partial fraction decomposition is of the form $\dfrac{Ax+B}{x^2} + \dfrac{Cx+D}{(x+2)^2}$.

65. When writing the partial fraction decomposition of the expression $\dfrac{x^3+x-2}{x^2-5x-14}$, the first step is to divide the numerator by the denominator.
True. The expression is an improper rational expression.

66. CAPSTONE Explain the similarities and differences in finding the partial fraction decompositions of proper rational expressions whose denominators factor into (a) distinct linear factors, (b) distinct quadratic factors, (c) repeated factors, and (d) linear and quadratic factors.
Answers will vary.

In Exercises 67–70, write the partial fraction decomposition of the rational expression. Check your result algebraically. Then assign a value to the constant *a* to check the result graphically.

67. $\dfrac{1}{a^2-x^2}$ See margin. **68.** $\dfrac{1}{x(x+a)}$ $\dfrac{1}{a}\left(\dfrac{1}{x} - \dfrac{1}{x+a}\right)$

69. $\dfrac{1}{y(a-y)}$ See margin. **70.** $\dfrac{1}{(x+1)(a-x)}$ See margin.

71. WRITING Describe two ways of solving for the constants in a partial fraction decomposition.
Answers will vary. Sample answer: You can substitute any convenient values of x that will help determine the constants. You can also find the basic equation, expand it, then equate coefficients of like terms.

5 ASSESS AND RETEACH

Daily Homework Quiz
Transparency Available
Available at the Instructor's companion site.

51. $\dfrac{3}{2x-1} - \dfrac{2}{x+1}$

52. $\dfrac{2}{x} + \dfrac{4}{x+1} - \dfrac{3}{x-1}$

53. $\dfrac{1}{2}\left[-\dfrac{1}{x} + \dfrac{5}{x+1} - \dfrac{3}{(x+1)^2}\right]$

54. $\dfrac{1}{9}\left(\dfrac{7}{x} + \dfrac{3}{x^2} - \dfrac{14}{2x+3}\right)$

55. $\dfrac{1}{x^2+2} + \dfrac{x}{(x^2+2)^2}$

57. $2x + \dfrac{1}{2}\left(\dfrac{3}{x-4} - \dfrac{1}{x+2}\right)$

58. $x - 1 + \dfrac{1}{x+2} + \dfrac{1}{x-1}$

59. (a) $\dfrac{3}{x} - \dfrac{2}{x-4}$

(b) $y = \dfrac{x-12}{x(x-4)}$

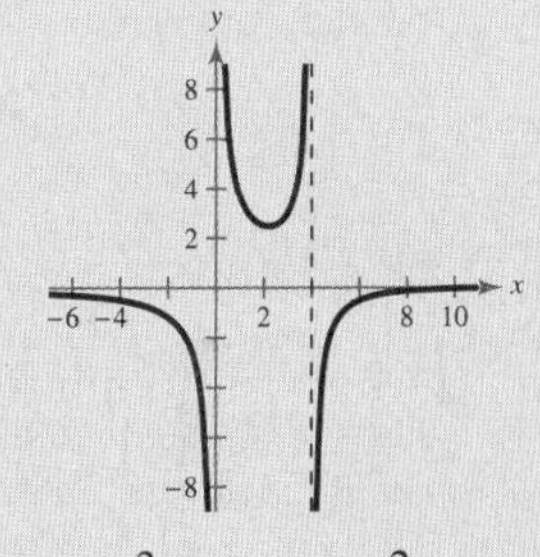

$y = \dfrac{3}{x}$, $y = -\dfrac{2}{x-4}$

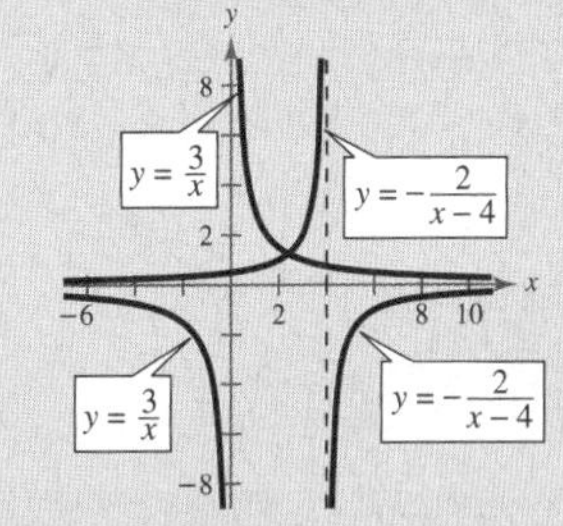

(c) The vertical asymptotes are the same.

60. (a) $\dfrac{3}{x-3} + \dfrac{5}{x+3}$

60. (b) $y = \dfrac{2(4x-3)}{x^2-9}$

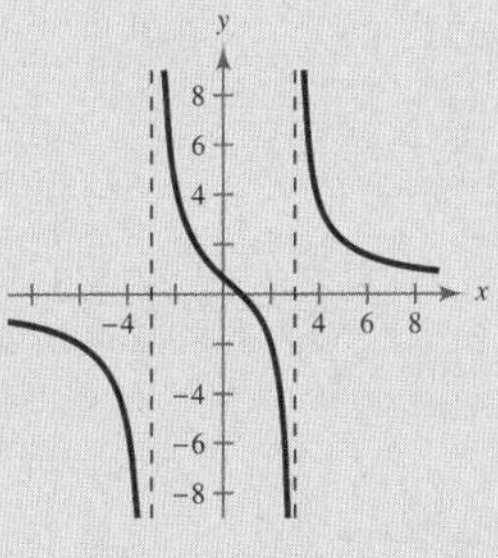

$y = \dfrac{3}{x-3}$, $y = \dfrac{5}{x+3}$

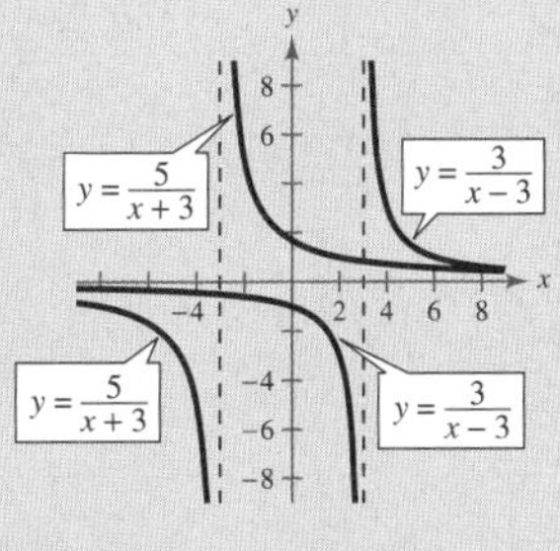

(c) The vertical asymptotes are the same.

62. (b) Ymax $= \left|\dfrac{5000}{7-4x}\right|$,

Ymin $= \left|\dfrac{5000}{11-7x}\right|$

(c)

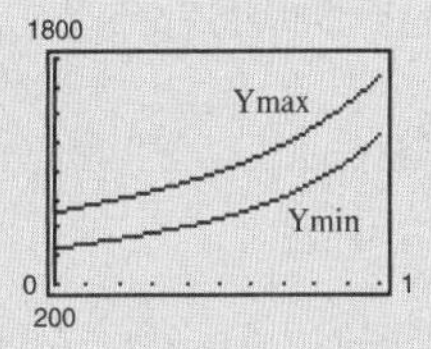

56, 63–64, 67, 69–70. See Additional Answers beginning on page AA1.

1 PLAN AND PREPARE

Warm-up Exercises

Transparency Available
Available at the Instructor's companion site.

Notetaking Guide

Transparency Available
Promotes interactive learning and notetaking skills.
Available at the Instructor's companion site.

Animated Precalculus

An **Animated Precalculus** tutorial is available at the Student companion site for **Section 7.5.**

Pacing

Average: 2 days
Advanced: 2 days
Block: 0.5 block with 7.4
0.5 block with 7.6

2 FOCUS AND MOTIVATE

Essential Question

How do you find the solution of a system of inequalities? **Tell students that they will learn how to answer this question by graphing the equations corresponding to each inequality and identifying the regions that satisfy the inequalities.**

7.5 SYSTEMS OF INEQUALITIES

What you should learn

- Sketch the graphs of inequalities in two variables.
- Solve systems of inequalities.
- Use systems of inequalities in two variables to model and solve real-life problems.

Why you should learn it

You can use systems of inequalities in two variables to model and solve real-life problems. For instance, in Exercise 83 on page 547, you will use a system of inequalities to analyze the retail sales of prescription drugs.

Jon Feingersh/Masterfile

The Graph of an Inequality

The statements $3x - 2y < 6$ and $2x^2 + 3y^2 \geq 6$ are inequalities in two variables. An ordered pair (a, b) is a **solution of an inequality** in x and y if the inequality is true when a and b are substituted for x and y, respectively. The **graph of an inequality** is the collection of all solutions of the inequality. To sketch the graph of an inequality, begin by sketching the graph of the *corresponding equation.* The graph of the equation will normally separate the plane into two or more regions. In each such region, one of the following must be true.

1. *All* points in the region are solutions of the inequality.
2. *No* point in the region is a solution of the inequality.

So, you can determine whether the points in an entire region satisfy the inequality by simply testing *one* point in the region.

Sketching the Graph of an Inequality in Two Variables

1. Replace the inequality sign by an equal sign, and sketch the graph of the resulting equation. (Use a dashed line for < or > and a solid line for ≤ or ≥.)
2. Test one point in each of the regions formed by the graph in Step 1. If the point satisfies the inequality, shade the entire region to denote that every point in the region satisfies the inequality.

Example 1 Sketching the Graph of an Inequality

Sketch the graph of $y \geq x^2 - 1$.

Solution

Begin by graphing the corresponding equation $y = x^2 - 1$, which is a parabola, as shown in Figure 7.19. By testing a point *above* the parabola $(0, 0)$ and a point *below* the parabola $(0, -2)$, you can see that the points that satisfy the inequality are those lying above (or on) the parabola.

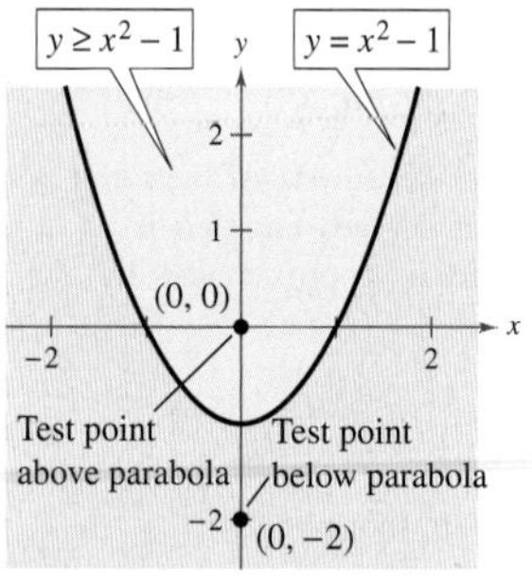

FIGURE 7.19

CHECKPoint Now try Exercise 7.

WARNING/CAUTION

Be careful when you are sketching the graph of an inequality in two variables. A dashed line means that all points on the line or curve *are not* solutions of the inequality. A solid line means that all points on the line or curve *are* solutions of the inequality.

Resource Planning Guide

Chapter Resources
- Complete Solutions Guide

Workbooks
- Notetaking Guide
- Student Solutions Guide

Interactive Technology
- Instructor Success Organizer
- Notetaking Guide IAE
- Instructional DVDs
- Animated Precalculus
- PowerLecture with ExamView

Algebra Help

You can review the properties of inequalities in Appendix A.6.

The inequality in Example 1 is a nonlinear inequality in two variables. Most of the following examples involve **linear inequalities** such as $ax + by < c$ (a and b are not both zero). The graph of a linear inequality is a half-plane lying on one side of the line $ax + by = c$.

Example 2 Sketching the Graph of a Linear Inequality

Sketch the graph of each linear inequality.

a. $x > -2$ **b.** $y \le 3$

Solution

a. The graph of the corresponding equation $x = -2$ is a vertical line. The points that satisfy the inequality $x > -2$ are those lying to the right of this line, as shown in Figure 7.20.

b. The graph of the corresponding equation $y = 3$ is a horizontal line. The points that satisfy the inequality $y \le 3$ are those lying below (or on) this line, as shown in Figure 7.21.

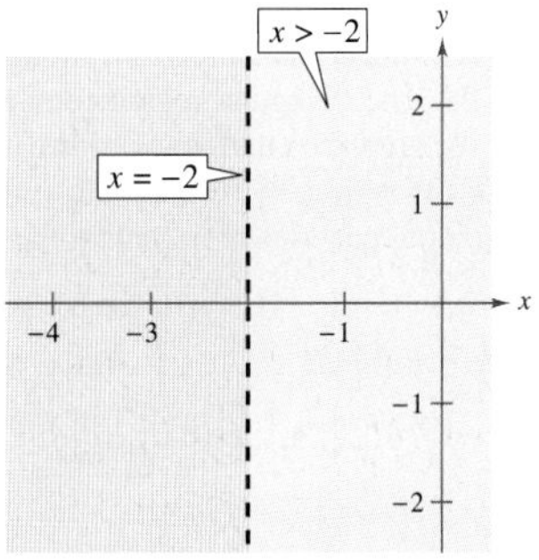

FIGURE 7.20

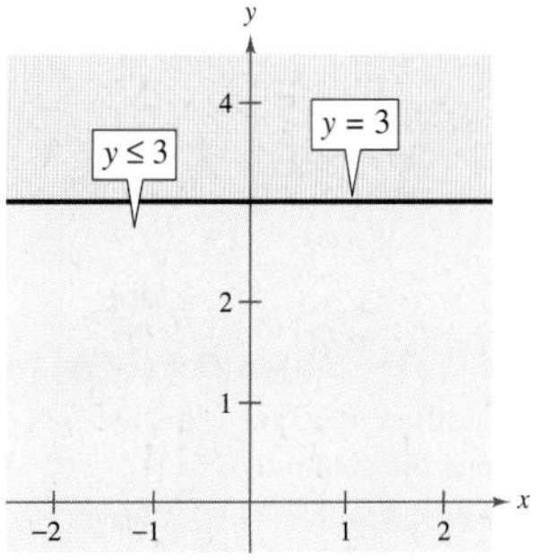

FIGURE 7.21

CHECK Point Now try Exercise 9.

TECHNOLOGY

A graphing utility can be used to graph an inequality or a system of inequalities. For instance, to graph $y \ge x - 2$, enter $y = x - 2$ and use the *shade* feature of the graphing utility to shade the correct part of the graph. You should obtain the graph below. Consult the user's guide for your graphing utility for specific keystrokes.

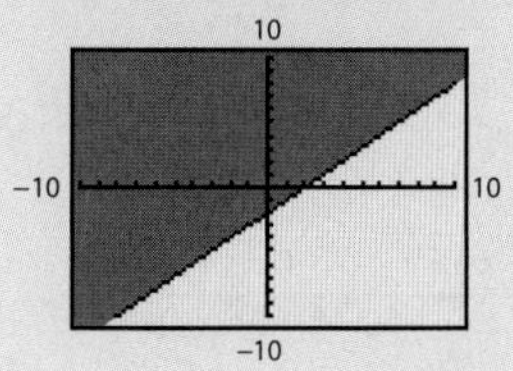

Example 3 Sketching the Graph of a Linear Inequality

Sketch the graph of $x - y < 2$.

Solution

The graph of the corresponding equation $x - y = 2$ is a line, as shown in Figure 7.22. Because the origin $(0, 0)$ satisfies the inequality, the graph consists of the half-plane lying above the line. (Try checking a point below the line. Regardless of which point you choose, you will see that it does not satisfy the inequality.)

CHECK Point Now try Exercise 15.

To graph a linear inequality, it can help to write the inequality in slope-intercept form. For instance, by writing $x - y < 2$ in the form

$$y > x - 2$$

you can see that the solution points lie *above* the line $x - y = 2$ (or $y = x - 2$), as shown in Figure 7.22.

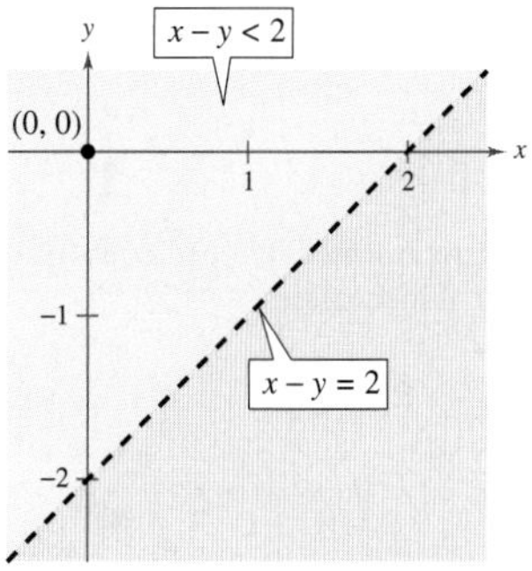

FIGURE 7.22

3 TEACH

Extra Example 1

Sketch the graph of $y \le x^2 + 1$.

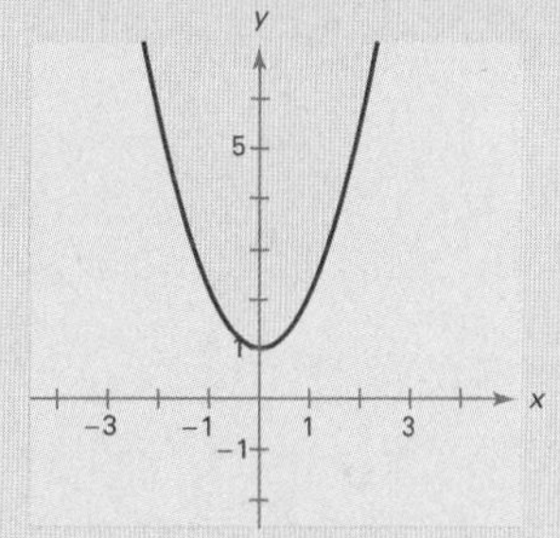

Extra Example 2

Sketch the graph of each inequality.

a. $x \ge 3$ **b.** $y < -1$

a.

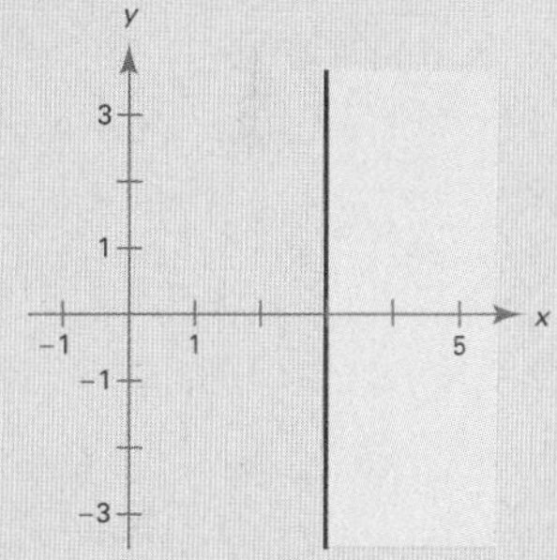

b.

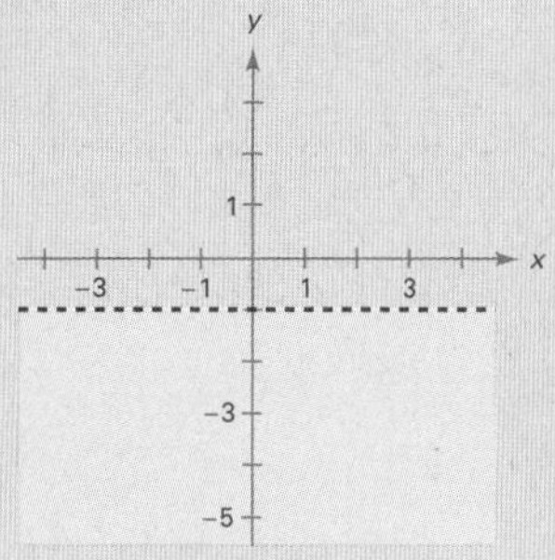

Extra Example 3

Sketch the graph of $x + y > -2$.

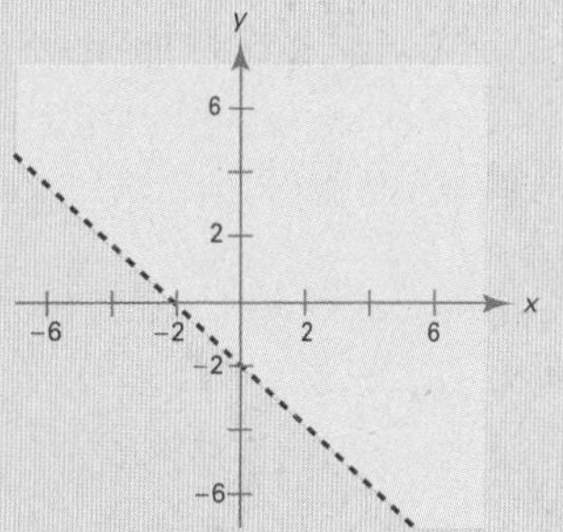

Differentiated Instruction

Visual Learners To give students additional practice in identifying the graph of an inequality, show them several graphs of inequalities along with the inequalities represented. Have students shade the region of each graph where all points are solutions of the inequality. Ask students to determine whether the line should be dashed or solid, given the inequality.

Extra Example 4

Sketch the graph and label the vertices of the solution of the system of inequalities.

$$\begin{cases} x + y \geq 1 \\ -x + y \geq 1 \\ y \leq 2 \end{cases}$$

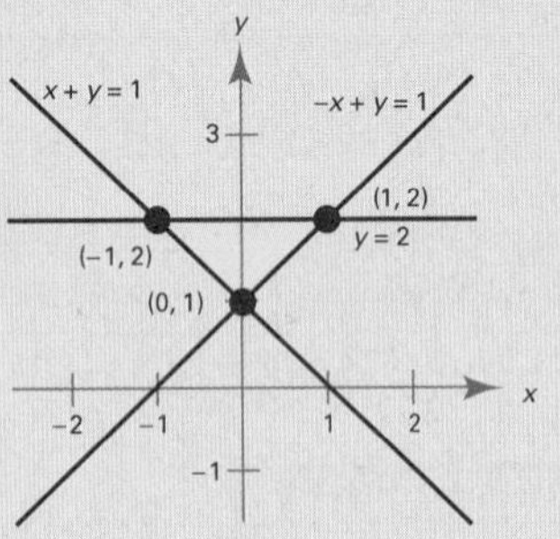

Systems of Inequalities

Many practical problems in business, science, and engineering involve systems of linear inequalities. A **solution** of a system of inequalities in x and y is a point (x, y) that satisfies each inequality in the system.

To sketch the graph of a system of inequalities in two variables, first sketch the graph of each individual inequality (on the same coordinate system) and then find the region that is *common* to every graph in the system. This region represents the **solution set** of the system. For systems of *linear inequalities*, it is helpful to find the vertices of the solution region.

Example 4 Solving a System of Inequalities

Sketch the graph (and label the vertices) of the solution set of the system.

$$\begin{cases} x - y < 2 & \text{Inequality 1} \\ x > -2 & \text{Inequality 2} \\ y \leq 3 & \text{Inequality 3} \end{cases}$$

Solution

The graphs of these inequalities are shown in Figures 7.22, 7.20, and 7.21, respectively, on page 539. The triangular region common to all three graphs can be found by superimposing the graphs on the same coordinate system, as shown in Figure 7.23. To find the vertices of the region, solve the three systems of corresponding equations obtained by taking *pairs* of equations representing the boundaries of the individual regions.

Study Tip

Using different colored pencils to shade the solution of each inequality in a system will make identifying the solution of the system of inequalities easier.

Vertex A: $(-2, -4)$ $\begin{cases} x - y = 2 \\ x = -2 \end{cases}$

Vertex B: $(5, 3)$ $\begin{cases} x - y = 2 \\ y = 3 \end{cases}$

Vertex C: $(-2, 3)$ $\begin{cases} x = -2 \\ y = 3 \end{cases}$

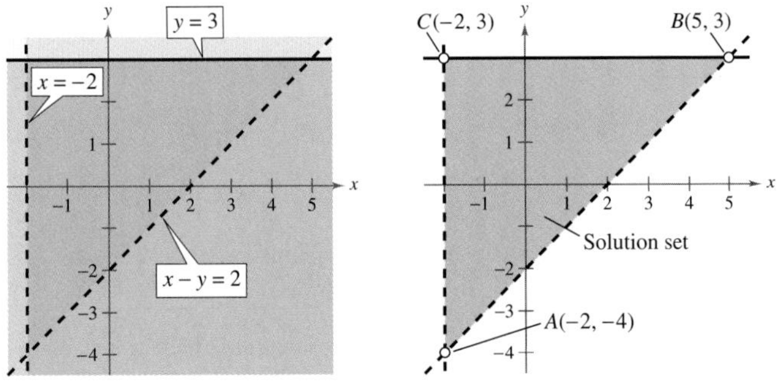

FIGURE 7.23

Note in Figure 7.23 that the vertices of the region are represented by open dots. This means that the vertices *are not* solutions of the system of inequalities.

CHECK Point Now try Exercise 41.

For the triangular region shown in Figure 7.23, each point of intersection of a pair of boundary lines corresponds to a vertex. With more complicated regions, two border lines can sometimes intersect at a point that is not a vertex of the region, as shown in Figure 7.24. To keep track of which points of intersection are actually vertices of the region, you should sketch the region and refer to your sketch as you find each point of intersection.

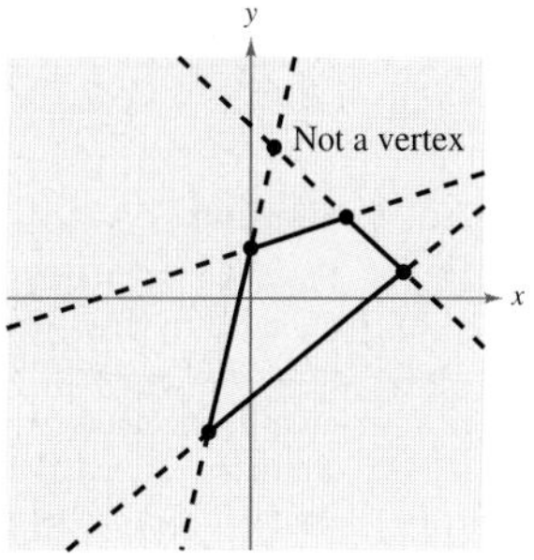

FIGURE 7.24

Example 5 Solving a System of Inequalities

Sketch the region containing all points that satisfy the system of inequalities.

$$\begin{cases} x^2 - y \le 1 & \text{Inequality 1} \\ -x + y \le 1 & \text{Inequality 2} \end{cases}$$

Solution

As shown in Figure 7.25, the points that satisfy the inequality

$$x^2 - y \le 1 \qquad \text{Inequality 1}$$

are the points lying above (or on) the parabola given by

$$y = x^2 - 1. \qquad \text{Parabola}$$

The points satisfying the inequality

$$-x + y \le 1 \qquad \text{Inequality 2}$$

are the points lying below (or on) the line given by

$$y = x + 1. \qquad \text{Line}$$

To find the points of intersection of the parabola and the line, solve the system of corresponding equations.

$$\begin{cases} x^2 - y = 1 \\ -x + y = 1 \end{cases}$$

Using the method of substitution, you can find the solutions to be $(-1, 0)$ and $(2, 3)$. So, the region containing all points that satisfy the system is indicated by the shaded region in Figure 7.25.

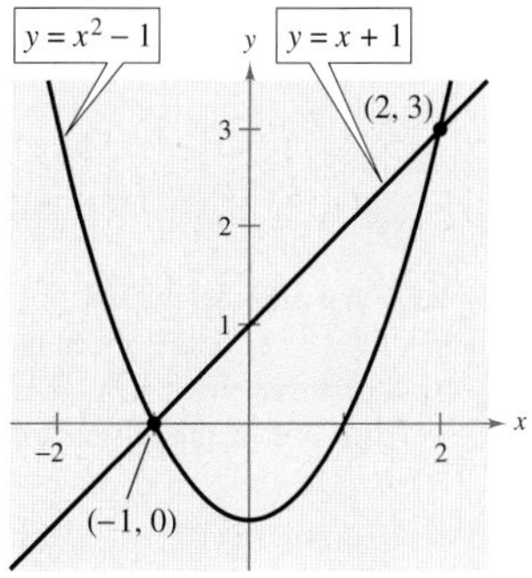

FIGURE 7.25

CHECKPoint Now try Exercise 43.

Extra Example 5

Sketch the region containing all points that satisfy the system of inequalities.

$$\begin{cases} x < 2 - y \\ x > y^2 \end{cases}$$

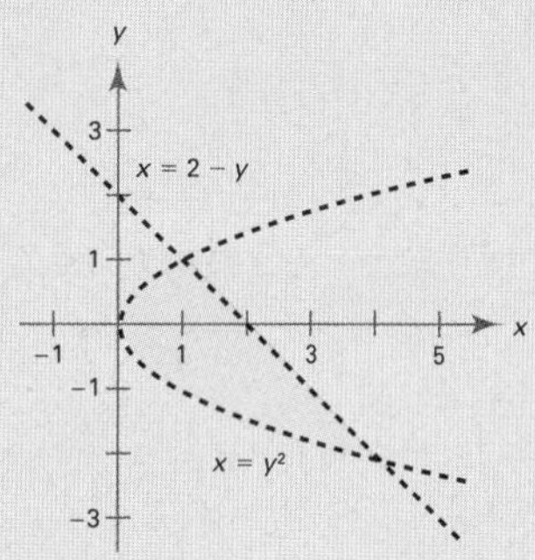

When solving a system of inequalities, you should be aware that the system might have no solution *or* it might be represented by an unbounded region in the plane. These two possibilities are shown in Examples 6 and 7.

Example 6 A System with No Solution

Sketch the solution set of the system of inequalities.

$$\begin{cases} x + y > 3 & \text{Inequality 1} \\ x + y < -1 & \text{Inequality 2} \end{cases}$$

Solution

From the way the system is written, it is clear that the system has no solution, because the quantity $(x + y)$ cannot be both less than -1 and greater than 3. Graphically, the inequality $x + y > 3$ is represented by the half-plane lying above the line $x + y = 3$, and the inequality $x + y < -1$ is represented by the half-plane lying below the line $x + y = -1$, as shown in Figure 7.26. These two half-planes have no points in common. So, the system of inequalities has no solution.

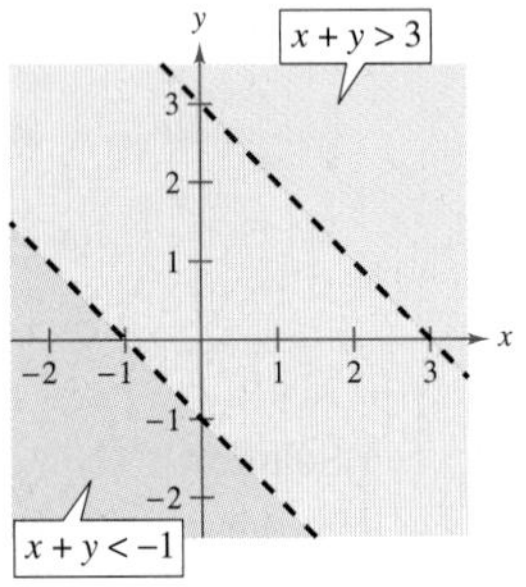

FIGURE 7.26

CHECKPoint Now try Exercise 45.

Example 7 An Unbounded Solution Set

Sketch the solution set of the system of inequalities.

$$\begin{cases} x + \ \ y < 3 & \text{Inequality 1} \\ x + 2y > 3 & \text{Inequality 2} \end{cases}$$

Solution

The graph of the inequality $x + y < 3$ is the half-plane that lies below the line $x + y = 3$, as shown in Figure 7.27. The graph of the inequality $x + 2y > 3$ is the half-plane that lies above the line $x + 2y = 3$. The intersection of these two half-planes is an *infinite wedge* that has a vertex at $(3, 0)$. So, the solution set of the system of inequalities is unbounded.

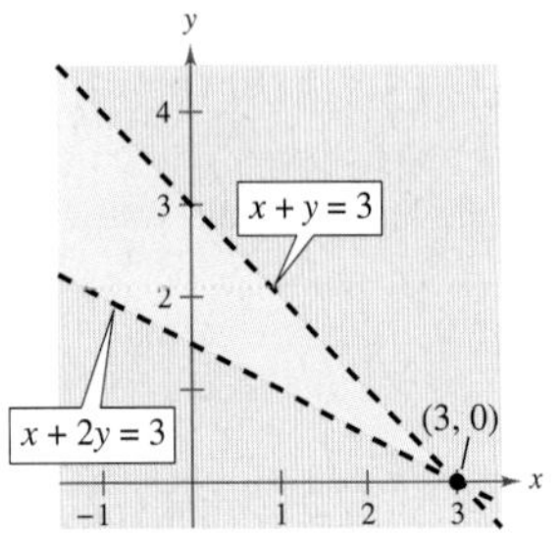

FIGURE 7.27

CHECKPoint Now try Exercise 47.

Extra Example 6

Sketch the solution set of the system of inequalities.

$$\begin{cases} y > 2x + 3 \\ y < 2x - 1 \end{cases}$$

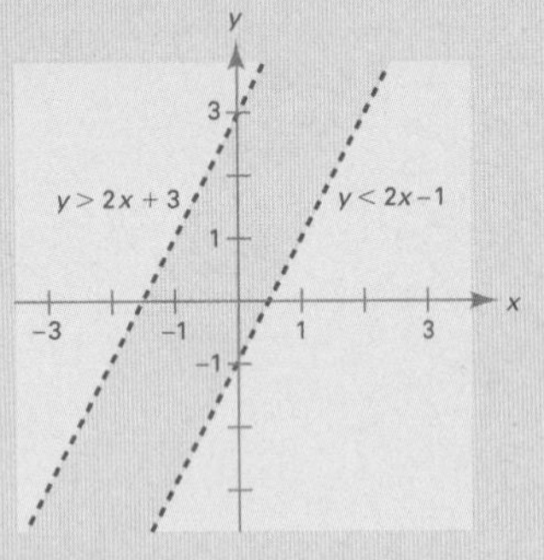

No solution

Extra Example 7

Sketch the solution set of the system of inequalities.

$$\begin{cases} y \ge x^2 \\ y > x + 2 \end{cases}$$

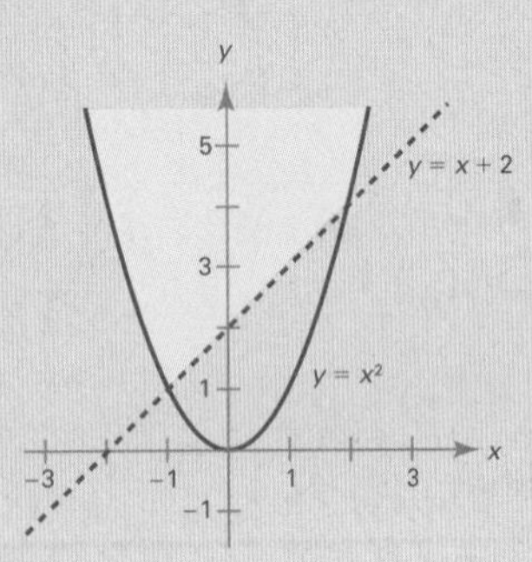

Applications

Example 9 in Section 7.2 discussed the *equilibrium point* for a system of demand and supply equations. The next example discusses two related concepts that economists call **consumer surplus** and **producer surplus.** As shown in Figure 7.28, the consumer surplus is defined as the area of the region that lies *below* the demand curve, *above* the horizontal line passing through the equilibrium point, and to the right of the p-axis. Similarly, the producer surplus is defined as the area of the region that lies *above* the supply curve, *below* the horizontal line passing through the equilibrium point, and to the right of the p-axis. The consumer surplus is a measure of the amount that consumers would have been willing to pay *above what they actually paid*, whereas the producer surplus is a measure of the amount that producers would have been willing to receive *below what they actually received.*

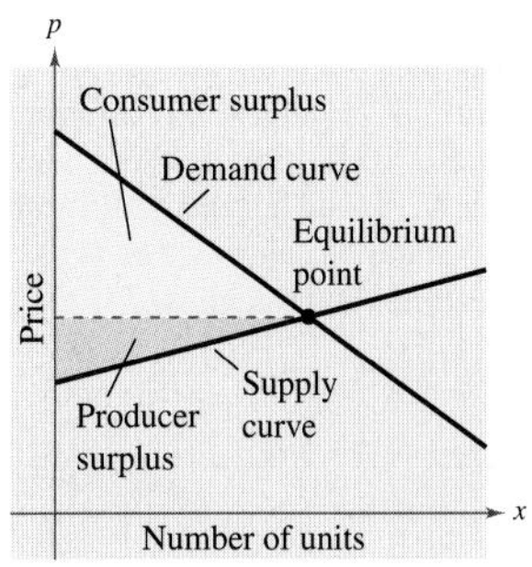

FIGURE 7.28

Example 8 Consumer Surplus and Producer Surplus

The demand and supply equations for a new type of personal digital assistant are given by

$$\begin{cases} p = 150 - 0.00001x & \text{Demand equation} \\ p = 60 + 0.00002x & \text{Supply equation} \end{cases}$$

where p is the price (in dollars) and x represents the number of units. Find the consumer surplus and producer surplus for these two equations.

Solution

Begin by finding the equilibrium point (when supply and demand are equal) by solving the equation

$$60 + 0.00002x = 150 - 0.00001x.$$

In Example 9 in Section 7.2, you saw that the solution is $x = 3{,}000{,}000$ units, which corresponds to an equilibrium price of $p = \$120$. So, the consumer surplus and producer surplus are the areas of the following triangular regions.

Consumer Surplus *Producer Surplus*

$$\begin{cases} p \le 150 - 0.00001x \\ p \ge 120 \\ x \ge 0 \end{cases} \qquad \begin{cases} p \ge 60 + 0.00002x \\ p \le 120 \\ x \ge 0 \end{cases}$$

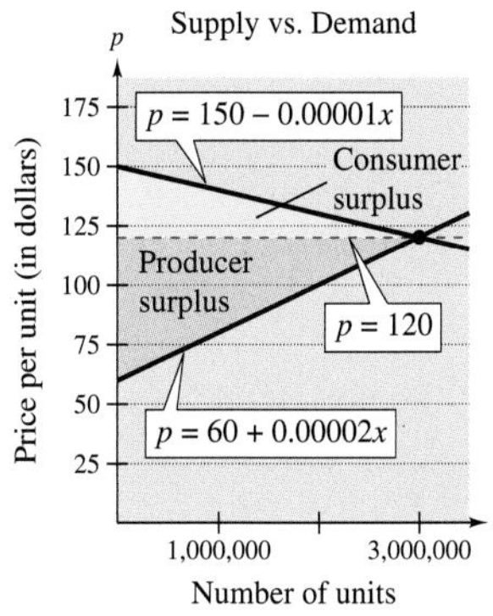

FIGURE 7.29

In Figure 7.29, you can see that the consumer and producer surpluses are defined as the areas of the shaded triangles.

$$\text{Consumer surplus} = \frac{1}{2}(\text{base})(\text{height})$$

$$= \frac{1}{2}(3{,}000{,}000)(30) = \$45{,}000{,}000$$

$$\text{Producer surplus} = \frac{1}{2}(\text{base})(\text{height})$$

$$= \frac{1}{2}(3{,}000{,}000)(60) = \$90{,}000{,}000$$

CHECKPoint Now try Exercise 71.

Extra Example 8

Find the consumer surplus and producer surplus for the demand and supply equations.

$$\begin{cases} p = 81 - 0.55x \\ p = 0.125x \end{cases}$$

Consumer surplus = \$3960; producer surplus = \$900

Example 9 Nutrition

The liquid portion of a diet is to provide at least 300 calories, 36 units of vitamin A, and 90 units of vitamin C. A cup of dietary drink X provides 60 calories, 12 units of vitamin A, and 10 units of vitamin C. A cup of dietary drink Y provides 60 calories, 6 units of vitamin A, and 30 units of vitamin C. Set up a system of linear inequalities that describes how many cups of each drink should be consumed each day to meet or exceed the minimum daily requirements for calories and vitamins.

Solution

Begin by letting x and y represent the following.

$x =$ number of cups of dietary drink X

$y =$ number of cups of dietary drink Y

To meet or exceed the minimum daily requirements, the following inequalities must be satisfied.

$$\begin{cases} 60x + 60y \geq 300 & \text{Calories} \\ 12x + 6y \geq 36 & \text{Vitamin A} \\ 10x + 30y \geq 90 & \text{Vitamin C} \\ x \geq 0 & \\ y \geq 0 & \end{cases}$$

The last two inequalities are included because x and y cannot be negative. The graph of this system of inequalities is shown in Figure 7.30. (More is said about this application in Example 6 in Section 7.6.)

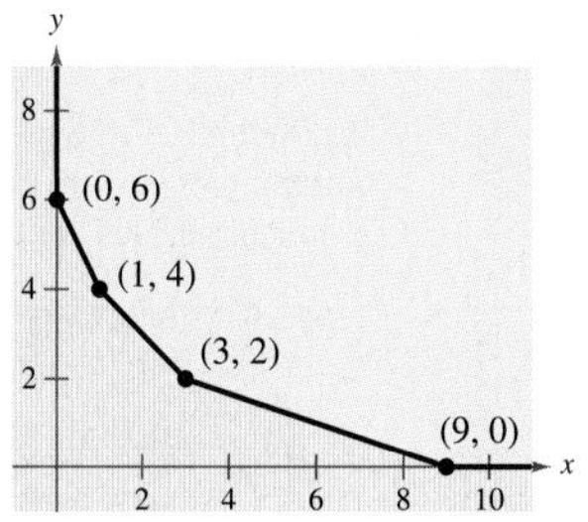

FIGURE 7.30

CHECK Point Now try Exercise 75.

Classroom Discussion

Creating a System of Inequalities Plot the points (0, 0), (4, 0), (3, 2), and (0, 2) in a coordinate plane. Draw the quadrilateral that has these four points as its vertices. Write a system of linear inequalities that has the quadrilateral as its solution. Explain how you found the system of inequalities. See margin.

Extra Example 9

A dietitian is asked to design a special diet supplement with two different foods. Each ounce of food X contains 20 units of calcium, 15 units of iron, and 10 units of vitamin B. Each ounce of food Y contains 10 units of calcium, 10 units of iron, and 20 units of vitamin B. The minimum daily requirements of the diet are 280 units of calcium, 160 units of iron, and 180 units of vitamin B. Find and graph a system of inequalities describing the different amounts of food X and food Y that can be used.

$x =$ number of ounces of food X

$y =$ number of ounces of food Y

$$\begin{cases} \text{Calcium: } 20x + 10y \geq 280 \\ \text{Iron: } 15x + 10y \geq 160 \\ \text{Vitamin B: } 10x + 20y \geq 180 \\ x \geq 0 \\ y \geq 0 \end{cases}$$

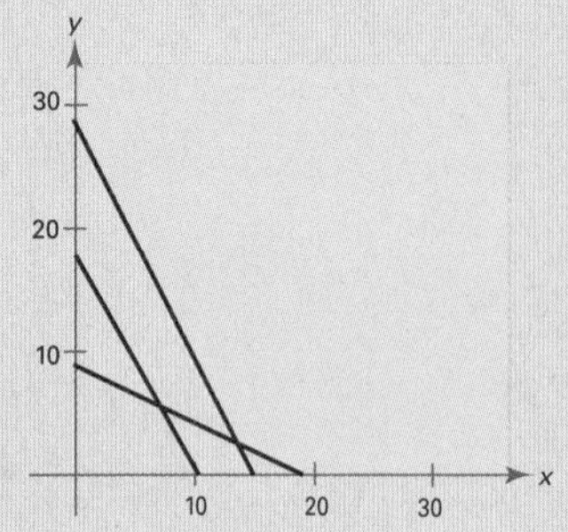

Closing the Lesson

Have students summarize the major points of the lesson and answer the Essential Question: How do you find the solution of a system of inequalities?

- **Graph an inequality by replacing the inequality sign with an equal sign, graphing the resulting equation, and shading the regions on the graph that satisfy the inequality.**
- **Find the solution set of a system of inequalities by graphing each inequality, labeling vertices, and shading the region that is common to each inequality.**
- **Show whether vertices and edges are included or excluded by using closed or open dots and solid or dashed lines.**

Classroom Discussion

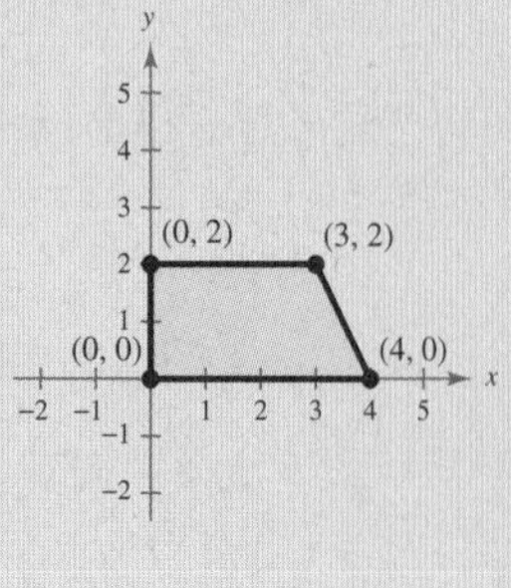

$$\begin{cases} 0 \leq y \leq 2 \\ x \geq 0 \\ y \leq -2x + 8 \end{cases}$$

7.5 EXERCISES

See www.CalcChat.com for worked-out solutions to odd-numbered exercises.

VOCABULARY: Fill in the blanks.

1. An ordered pair (a, b) is a solution of an inequality in x and y if the inequality is true when a and b are substituted for x and y, respectively.
2. The graph of an inequality is the collection of all solutions of the inequality.
3. The graph of a linear inequality is a half-plane lying on one side of the line $ax + by = c$.
4. A solution of a system of inequalities in x and y is a point (x, y) that satisfies each inequality in the system.
5. A solution set of a system of inequalities in two variables is the region common to the graphs of every inequality in the system.
6. The area of the region that lies below the demand curve, above the horizontal line passing through the equilibrium point, to the right of the p-axis is called the consumer surplus.

SKILLS AND APPLICATIONS

In Exercises 7–20, sketch the graph of the inequality.

7–20. See margin.

7. $y < 5 - x^2$
8. $y^2 - x < 0$
9. $x \geq 6$
10. $x < -4$
11. $y > -7$
12. $10 \geq y$
13. $y < 2 - x$
14. $y > 4x - 3$
15. $2y - x \geq 4$
16. $5x + 3y \geq -15$
17. $(x + 1)^2 + (y - 2)^2 < 9$
18. $(x - 1)^2 + (y - 4)^2 > 9$
19. $y \leq \dfrac{1}{1 + x^2}$
20. $y > \dfrac{-15}{x^2 + x + 4}$

In Exercises 21–32, use a graphing utility to graph the inequality. 21–32. See margin.

21. $y < \ln x$
22. $y \geq -2 - \ln(x + 3)$
23. $y < 4^{-x-5}$
24. $y \leq 2^{2x-0.5} - 7$
25. $y \geq \frac{5}{9}x - 2$
26. $y \leq 6 - \frac{3}{2}x$
27. $y < -3.8x + 1.1$
28. $y \geq -20.74 + 2.66x$
29. $x^2 + 5y - 10 \leq 0$
30. $2x^2 - y - 3 > 0$
31. $\frac{5}{2}y - 3x^2 - 6 \geq 0$
32. $-\frac{1}{10}x^2 - \frac{3}{8}y < -\frac{1}{4}$

In Exercises 33–36, write an inequality for the shaded region shown in the figure.

33.

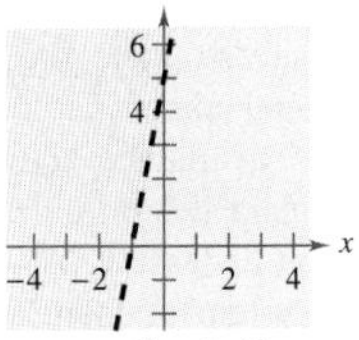

$y < 5x + 5$

34.

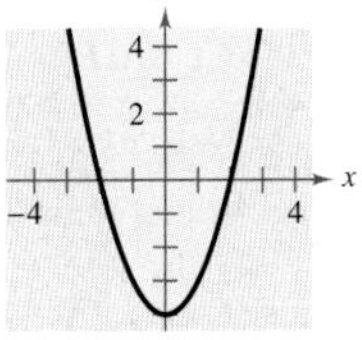

$y \geq x^2 - 4$

35.

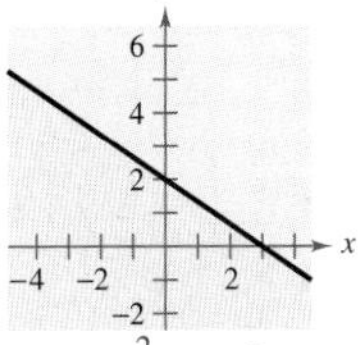

$y \geq -\frac{2}{3}x + 2$

36.

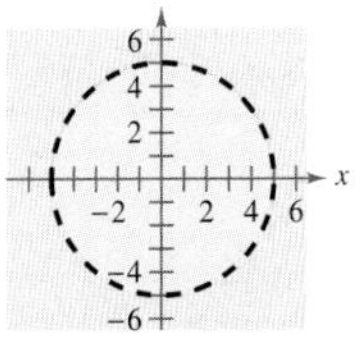

$x^2 + y^2 < 25$

In Exercises 37–40, determine whether each ordered pair is a solution of the system of linear inequalities.

37. $\begin{cases} x \geq -4 \\ y > -3 \\ y \leq -8x - 3 \end{cases}$ (a) $(0, 0)$ No (b) $(-1, -3)$ No (c) $(-4, 0)$ Yes (d) $(-3, 11)$ Yes

38. $\begin{cases} -2x + 5y \geq 3 \\ y < 4 \\ -4x + 2y < 7 \end{cases}$ (a) $(0, 2)$ Yes (b) $(-6, 4)$ No (c) $(-8, -2)$ No (d) $(-3, 2)$ No

39. $\begin{cases} 3x + y > 1 \\ -y - \frac{1}{2}x^2 \leq -4 \\ -15x + 4y > 0 \end{cases}$ (a) $(0, 10)$ Yes (b) $(0, -1)$ No (c) $(2, 9)$ Yes (d) $(-1, 6)$ Yes

40. $\begin{cases} x^2 + y^2 \geq 36 \\ -3x + y \leq 10 \\ \frac{2}{3}x - y \geq 5 \end{cases}$ (a) $(-1, 7)$ No (b) $(-5, 1)$ No (c) $(6, 0)$ No (d) $(4, -8)$ Yes

In Exercises 41–54, sketch the graph and label the vertices of the solution set of the system of inequalities.

41–44. See margin.

41. $\begin{cases} x + y \leq 1 \\ -x + y \leq 1 \\ y \geq 0 \end{cases}$

42. $\begin{cases} 3x + 4y < 12 \\ x > 0 \\ y > 0 \end{cases}$

43. $\begin{cases} x^2 + y \leq 7 \\ x \geq -2 \\ y \geq 0 \end{cases}$

44. $\begin{cases} 4x^2 + y \geq 2 \\ x \leq 1 \\ y \leq 1 \end{cases}$

4 PRACTICE AND APPLY

Assignment Guide

Transparencies Available
Available at the Instructor's companion site.

Average:
Day 1: pp. 545–546
Exs. 1–3, 8, 10, 11, 13, 17–29 odd, 33–39 odd, 61–69 odd
Day 2: pp. 545–548
Exs. 4–6, 42, 45, 46, 51, 55, 73, 76, 77–81 odd, 86–88, 91–94

Advanced:
Day 1: pp. 545–546
Exs. 1–3, 8–14 even, 18–24 even, 28–40 even, 62–70 even
Day 2: pp. 545–548
Exs. 4–6, 44, 45, 48–52 even, 56, 74–78 even, 82, 85, 87, 88, 90, 91–94

Block:
pp. 545–546
Exs. 1–3, 8, 10, 11, 13, 17–29 odd, 33–39 odd, 61–69 odd (with 7.4)
pp. 545–548
Exs. 4–6, 42, 45, 46, 51, 55, 73, 76, 77–81 odd, 86–88, 91–94 (with 7.6)

7.

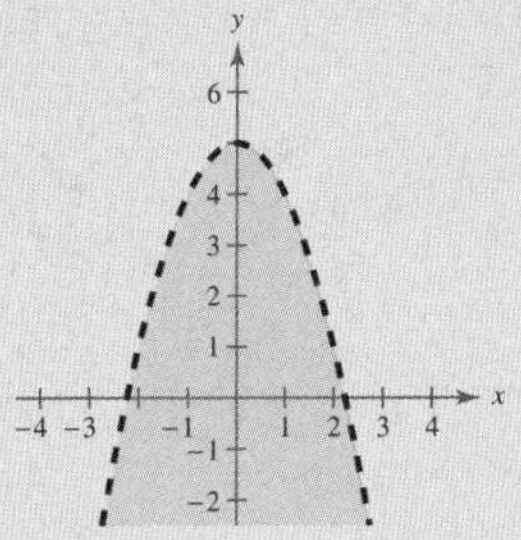

8.

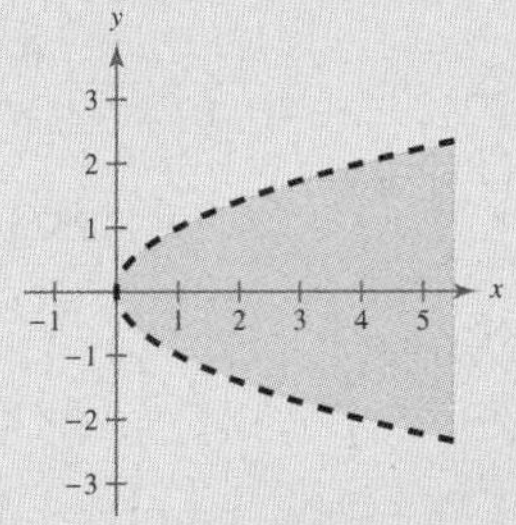

9.

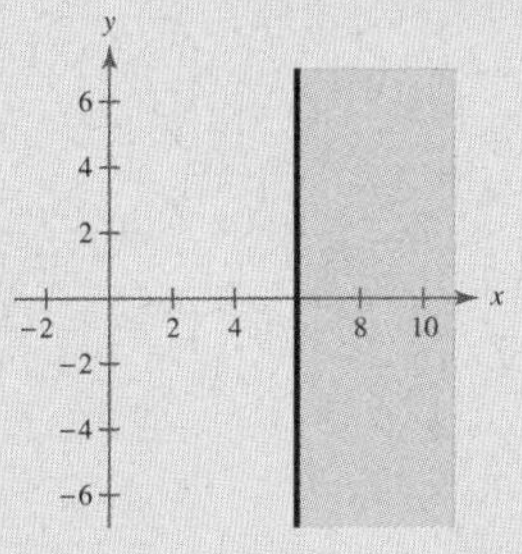

10.

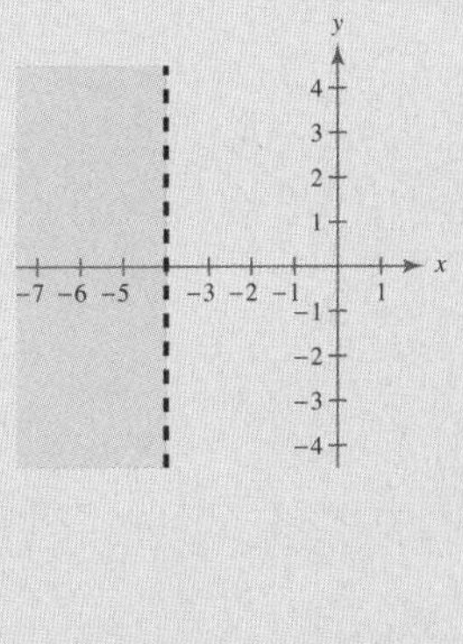

11.

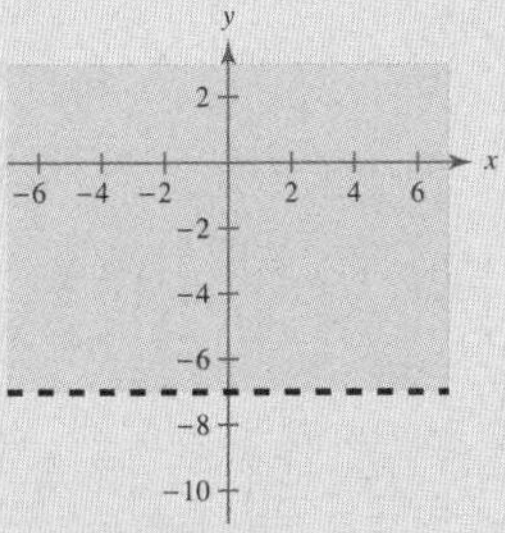

12.

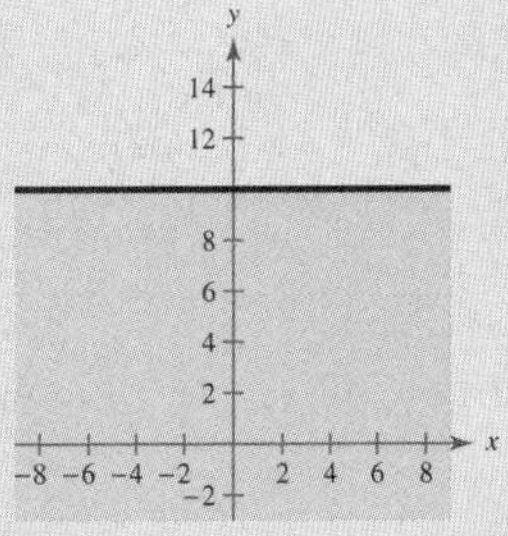

13–32, 41–44. See Additional Answers beginning on page AA1.

45–54. See margin.

45. $\begin{cases} 2x + y > 2 \\ 6x + 3y < 2 \end{cases}$

46. $\begin{cases} x - 7y > -36 \\ 5x + 2y > 5 \\ 6x - 5y > 6 \end{cases}$

47. $\begin{cases} -3x + 2y < 6 \\ x - 4y > -2 \\ 2x + y < 3 \end{cases}$

48. $\begin{cases} x - 2y < -6 \\ 5x - 3y > -9 \end{cases}$

49. $\begin{cases} x > y^2 \\ x < y + 2 \end{cases}$

50. $\begin{cases} x - y^2 > 0 \\ x - y > 2 \end{cases}$

51. $\begin{cases} x^2 + y^2 \le 36 \\ x^2 + y^2 \ge 9 \end{cases}$

52. $\begin{cases} x^2 + y^2 \le 25 \\ 4x - 3y \le 0 \end{cases}$

53. $\begin{cases} 3x + 4 \ge y^2 \\ x - y < 0 \end{cases}$

54. $\begin{cases} x < 2y - y^2 \\ 0 < x + y \end{cases}$

In Exercises 55–60, use a graphing utility to graph the solution set of the system of inequalities. 55–60. See margin.

55. $\begin{cases} y \le \sqrt{3x} + 1 \\ y \ge x^2 + 1 \end{cases}$

56. $\begin{cases} y < -x^2 + 2x + 3 \\ y > x^2 - 4x + 3 \end{cases}$

57. $\begin{cases} y < x^3 - 2x + 1 \\ y > -2x \\ x \le 1 \end{cases}$

58. $\begin{cases} y \ge x^4 - 2x^2 + 1 \\ y \le 1 - x^2 \end{cases}$

59. $\begin{cases} x^2y \ge 1 \\ 0 < x \le 4 \\ y \le 4 \end{cases}$

60. $\begin{cases} y \le e^{-x^2/2} \\ y \ge 0 \\ -2 \le x \le 2 \end{cases}$

In Exercises 61–70, derive a set of inequalities to describe the region. 61–70. See margin.

61.

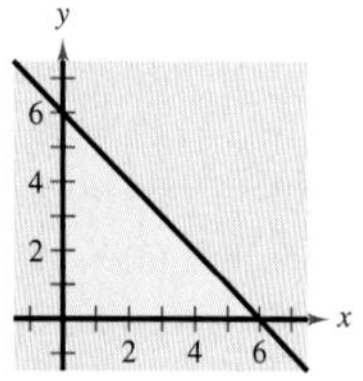

62.

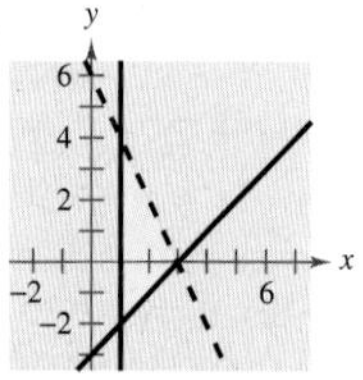

63.

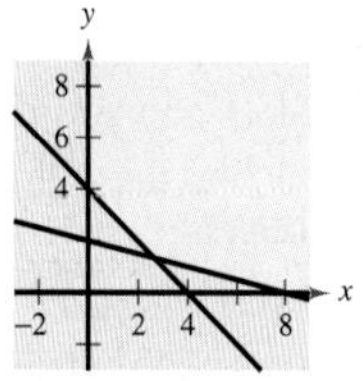

64.

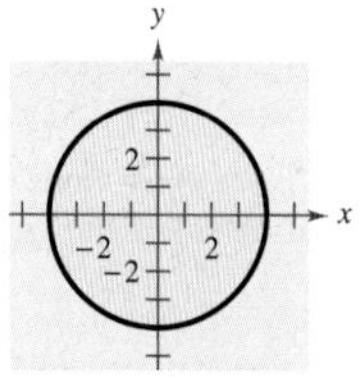

65.

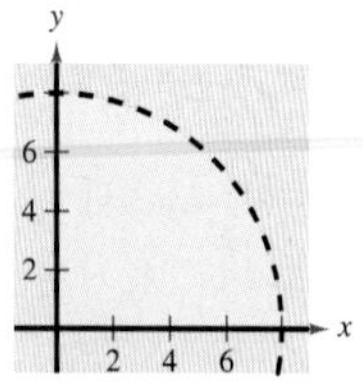

66.

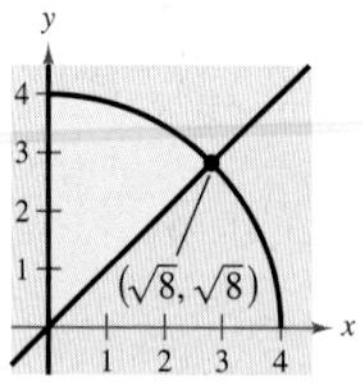

67. Rectangle: vertices at (4, 3), (9, 3), (9, 9), (4, 9)

68. Parallelogram: vertices at (0, 0), (4, 0), (1, 4), (5, 4)

69. Triangle: vertices at (0, 0), (6, 0), (1, 5)

70. Triangle: vertices at (−1, 0), (1, 0), (0, 1)

SUPPLY AND DEMAND In Exercises 71–74, (a) graph the systems representing the consumer surplus and producer surplus for the supply and demand equations and (b) find the consumer surplus and producer surplus. 71–74. See margin.

	Demand	*Supply*
71.	$p = 50 - 0.5x$	$p = 0.125x$
72.	$p = 100 - 0.05x$	$p = 25 + 0.1x$
73.	$p = 140 - 0.00002x$	$p = 80 + 0.00001x$
74.	$p = 400 - 0.0002x$	$p = 225 + 0.0005x$

75. PRODUCTION A furniture company can sell all the tables and chairs it produces. Each table requires 1 hour in the assembly center and $1\frac{1}{3}$ hours in the finishing center. Each chair requires $1\frac{1}{2}$ hours in the assembly center and $1\frac{1}{2}$ hours in the finishing center. The company's assembly center is available 12 hours per day, and its finishing center is available 15 hours per day. Find and graph a system of inequalities describing all possible production levels. See margin.

76. INVENTORY A store sells two models of laptop computers. Because of the demand, the store stocks at least twice as many units of model A as of model B. The costs to the store for the two models are \$800 and \$1200, respectively. The management does not want more than \$20,000 in computer inventory at any one time, and it wants at least four model A laptop computers and two model B laptop computers in inventory at all times. Find and graph a system of inequalities describing all possible inventory levels. See margin.

77. INVESTMENT ANALYSIS A person plans to invest up to \$20,000 in two different interest-bearing accounts. Each account is to contain at least \$5000. Moreover, the amount in one account should be at least twice the amount in the other account. Find and graph a system of inequalities to describe the various amounts that can be deposited in each account. See margin.

78. TICKET SALES For a concert event, there are \$30 reserved seat tickets and \$20 general admission tickets. There are 2000 reserved seats available, and fire regulations limit the number of paid ticket holders to 3000. The promoter must take in at least \$75,000 in ticket sales. Find and graph a system of inequalities describing the different numbers of tickets that can be sold. See margin.

45.

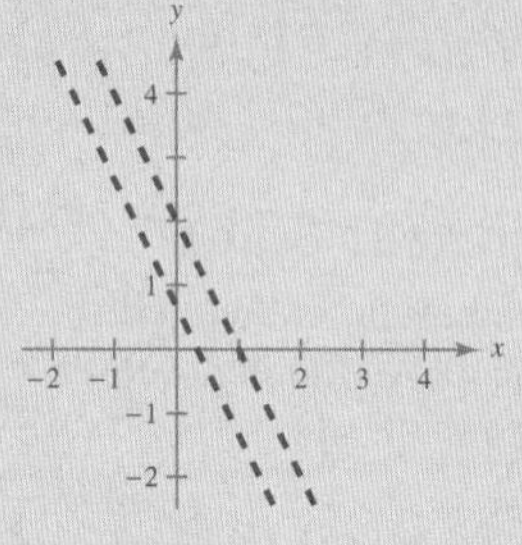

No solution

46.

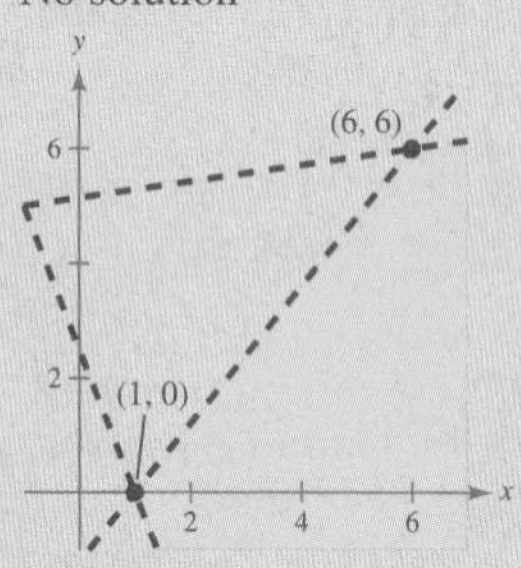

47.

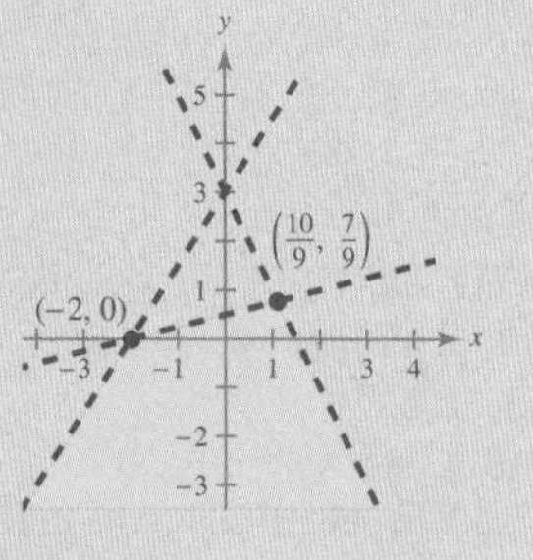

48.

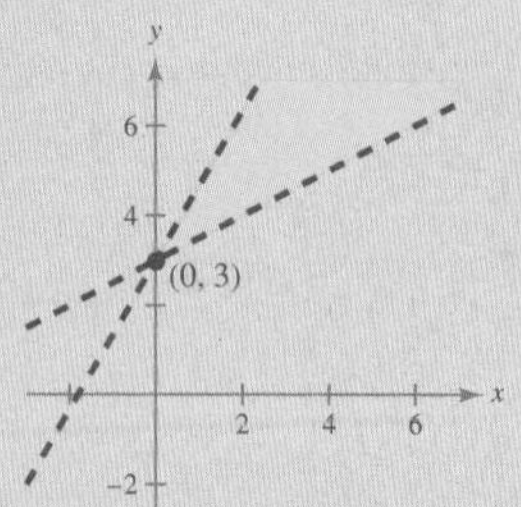

49.

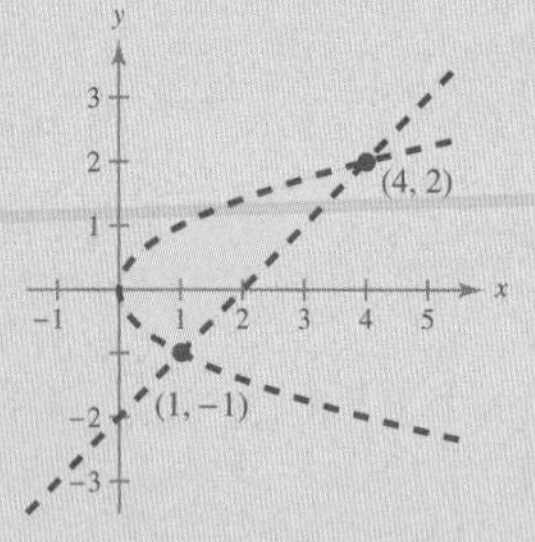

50.

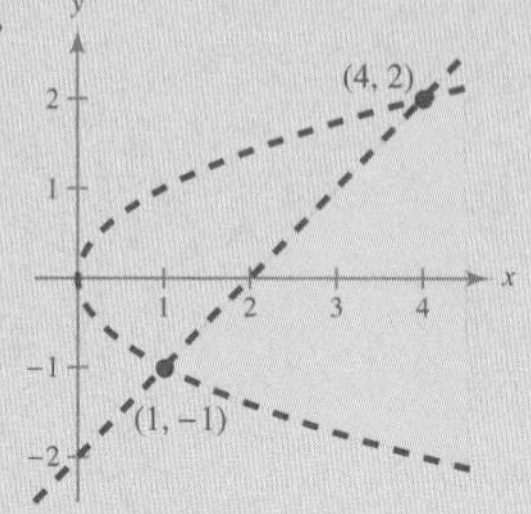

51.

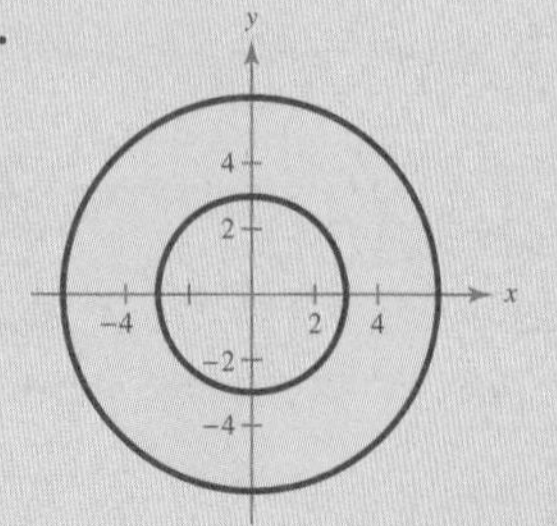

52.

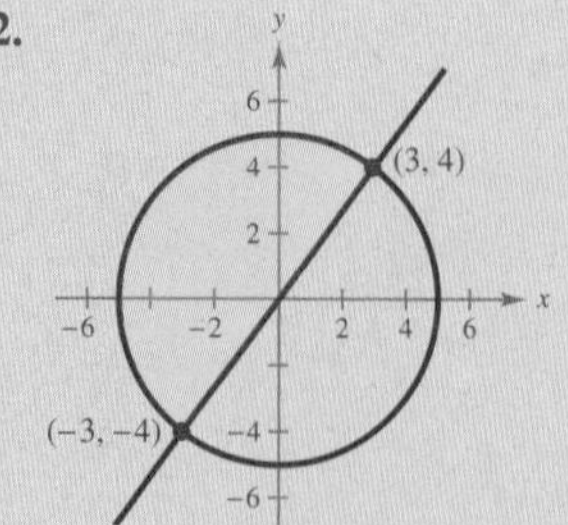

53.

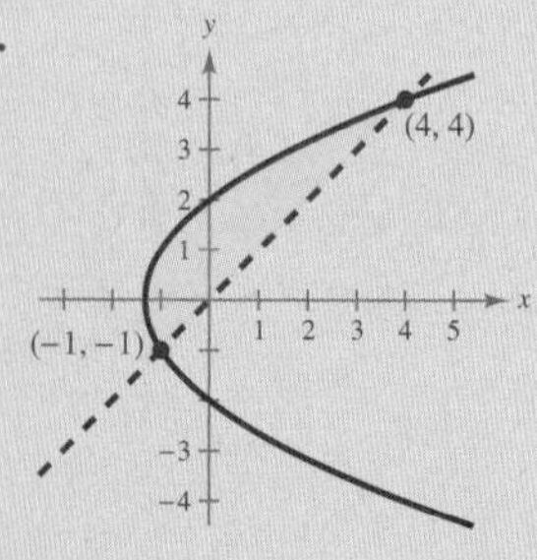

54–78. See Additional Answers beginning on page AA1.

79. SHIPPING A warehouse supervisor is told to ship at least 50 packages of gravel that weigh 55 pounds each and at least 40 bags of stone that weigh 70 pounds each. The maximum weight capacity of the truck to be used is 7500 pounds. Find and graph a system of inequalities describing the numbers of bags of stone and gravel that can be shipped. See margin.

80. TRUCK SCHEDULING A small company that manufactures two models of exercise machines has an order for 15 units of the standard model and 16 units of the deluxe model. The company has trucks of two different sizes that can haul the products, as shown in the table.

Truck	Standard	Deluxe
Large	6	3
Medium	4	6

Find and graph a system of inequalities describing the numbers of trucks of each size that are needed to deliver the order. See margin.

81. NUTRITION A dietitian is asked to design a special dietary supplement using two different foods. Each ounce of food X contains 20 units of calcium, 15 units of iron, and 10 units of vitamin B. Each ounce of food Y contains 10 units of calcium, 10 units of iron, and 20 units of vitamin B. The minimum daily requirements of the diet are 300 units of calcium, 150 units of iron, and 200 units of vitamin B.

(a) Write a system of inequalities describing the different amounts of food X and food Y that can be used. See margin.

(b) Sketch a graph of the region corresponding to the system in part (a). See margin.

(c) Find two solutions of the system and interpret their meanings in the context of the problem. Answers will vary.

82. HEALTH A person's maximum heart rate is $220 - x$, where x is the person's age in years for $20 \le x \le 70$. When a person exercises, it is recommended that the person strive for a heart rate that is at least 50% of the maximum and at most 75% of the maximum. (Source: American Heart Association)

(a) Write a system of inequalities that describes the exercise target heart rate region. See margin.

(b) Sketch a graph of the region in part (a). See margin.

(c) Find two solutions to the system and interpret their meanings in the context of the problem. Answers will vary.

83. DATA ANALYSIS: PRESCRIPTION DRUGS The table shows the retail sales y (in billions of dollars) of prescription drugs in the United States from 2000 through 2007. (Source: National Association of Chain Drug Stores)

Year	Retail sales, y
2000	145.6
2001	161.3
2002	182.7
2003	204.2
2004	220.1
2005	232.0
2006	250.6
2007	259.4

$y = 16.75t + 148.4$

(a) Use the *regression* feature of a graphing utility to find a linear model for the data. Let t represent the year, with $t = 0$ corresponding to 2000.

(b) The total retail sales of prescription drugs in the United States during this eight-year period can be approximated by finding the area of the trapezoid bounded by the linear model you found in part (a) and the lines $y = 0, t = -0.5$, and $t = 7.5$. Use a graphing utility to graph this region. See margin.

(c) Use the formula for the area of a trapezoid to approximate the total retail sales of prescription drugs. \$1656.2 billion

84. DATA ANALYSIS: MERCHANDISE The table shows the retail sales y (in millions of dollars) for Aeropostale, Inc. from 2000 through 2007. (Source: Aeropostale, Inc.)

Year	Retail sales, y
2000	213.4
2001	304.8
2002	550.9
2003	734.9
2004	964.2
2005	1204.3
2006	1413.2
2007	1590.9

(a) Use the *regression* feature of a graphing utility to find a linear model for the data. Let t represent the year, with $t = 0$ corresponding to 2000. See margin.

(b) The total retail sales for Aeropostale during this eight-year period can be approximated by finding the area of the trapezoid bounded by the linear model you found in part (a) and the lines $y = 0$, $t = -0.5$, and $t = 7.5$. Use a graphing utility to graph this region. See margin.

(c) Use the formula for the area of a trapezoid to approximate the total retail sales for Aeropostale. \$6976.8 million

79. $\begin{cases} 55x + 70y \le 7500 \\ x \ge 50 \\ y \ge 40 \end{cases}$

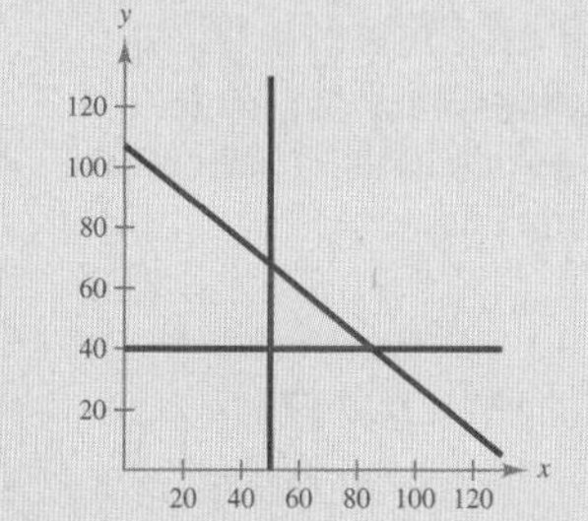

80. $\begin{cases} 6x + 4y \ge 15 \\ 3x + 6y \ge 16 \\ x \ge 0 \\ y \ge 0 \end{cases}$

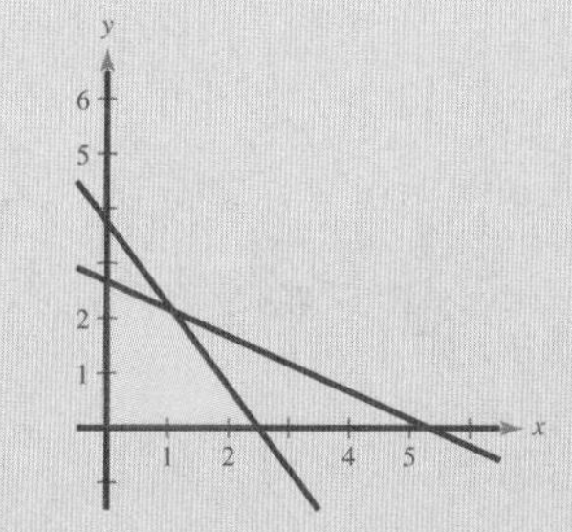

81. (a) $\begin{cases} 20x + 10y \ge 300 \\ 15x + 10y \ge 150 \\ 10x + 20y \ge 200 \\ x \ge 0 \\ y \ge 0 \end{cases}$

(b)

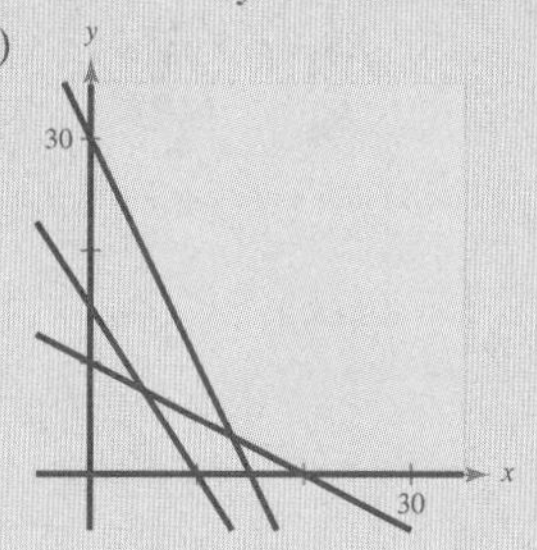

82. (a) $y \ge 0.5(220 - x)$
$y \le 0.75(220 - x)$
$x \ge 20$
$x \le 70$

(b)

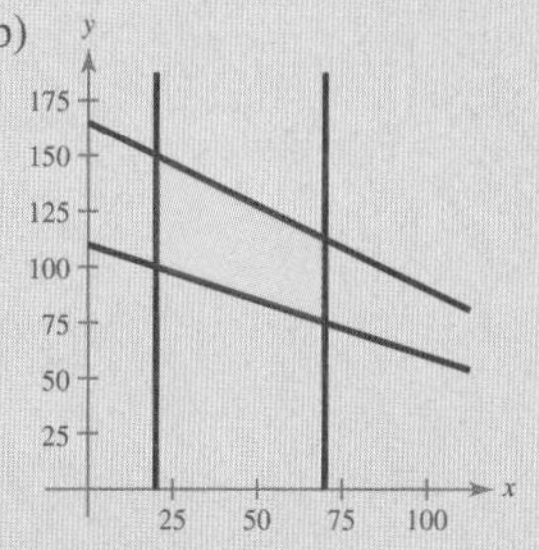

83. (b)

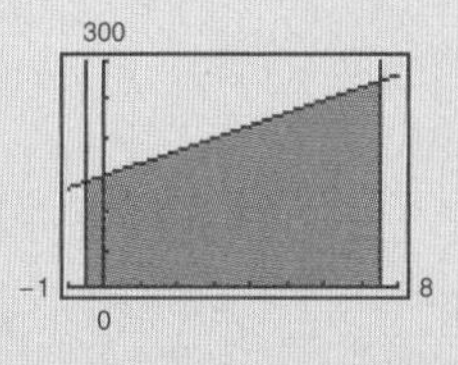

84. (a) $y = 206.83t + 148.2$

(b)

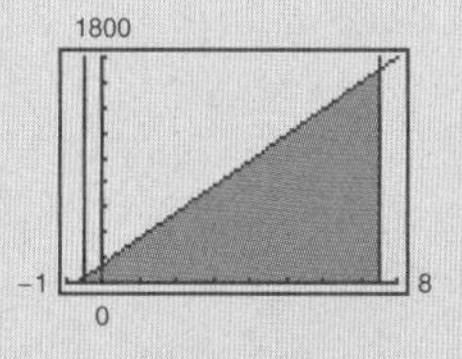

5 ASSESS AND RETEACH

Daily Homework Quiz

Transparency Available
Available at the Instructor's companion site.

85. (a) $\begin{cases} xy \geq 500 \\ 2x + \pi y \geq 125 \\ x \geq 0 \\ y \geq 0 \end{cases}$

(b)

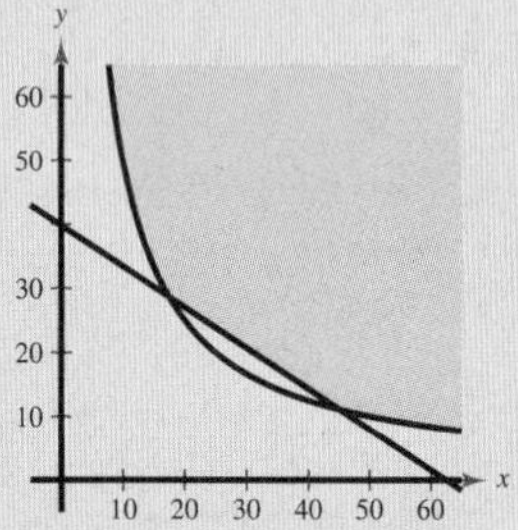

87. False. The graph shows the solution of the system

$\begin{cases} y < 6 \\ -4x - 9y < 6. \\ 3x + y^2 \geq 2 \end{cases}$

89. (a) $\begin{cases} \pi y^2 - \pi x^2 \geq 10 \\ y > x \\ x > 0 \end{cases}$

(b)

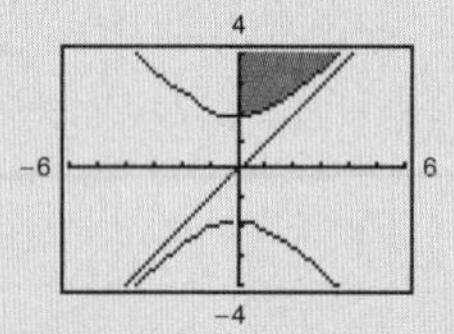

(c) The line is an asymptote to the boundary. The larger the circles, the closer the radii can be while still satisfying the constraint.

85. PHYSICAL FITNESS FACILITY An indoor running track is to be constructed with a space for exercise equipment inside the track (see figure). The track must be at least 125 meters long, and the exercise space must have an area of at least 500 square meters. See margin.

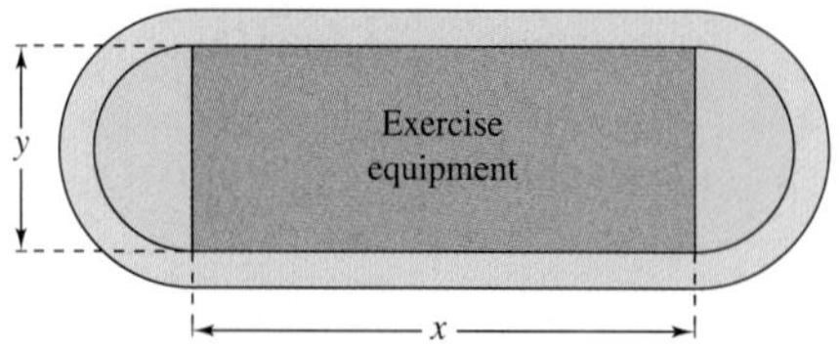

(a) Find a system of inequalities describing the requirements of the facility.

(b) Graph the system from part (a).

EXPLORATION

TRUE OR FALSE? In Exercises 86 and 87, determine whether the statement is true or false. Justify your answer.

86. The area of the figure defined by the system

$\begin{cases} x \geq -3 \\ x \leq 6 \\ y \leq 5 \\ y \geq -6 \end{cases}$ True. The figure is a rectangle with a length of 9 units and a width of 11 units.

is 99 square units.

87. The graph below shows the solution of the system

$\begin{cases} y \leq 6 \\ -4x - 9y > 6. \\ 3x + y^2 \geq 2 \end{cases}$ See margin.

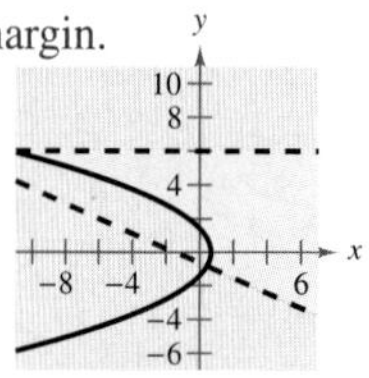

88. CAPSTONE

(a) Explain the difference between the graphs of the inequality $x \leq -5$ on the real number line and on the rectangular coordinate system.

(b) After graphing the boundary of the inequality $x + y < 3$, explain how you decide on which side of the boundary the solution set of the inequality lies.

(a) The graph is a half-line on the real number line; on the rectangular coordinate system, the graph is a half-plane.

(b) Test a point on each side of the line. Because the origin (0, 0) satisfies the inequality, the solution set of the inequality lies below the line.

89. GRAPHICAL REASONING Two concentric circles have radii x and y, where $y > x$. The area between the circles must be at least 10 square units. See margin.

(a) Find a system of inequalities describing the constraints on the circles.

(b) Use a graphing utility to graph the system of inequalities in part (a). Graph the line $y = x$ in the same viewing window.

(c) Identify the graph of the line in relation to the boundary of the inequality. Explain its meaning in the context of the problem.

90. The graph of the solution of the inequality $x + 2y < 6$ is shown in the figure. Describe how the solution set would change for each of the following.

(a) $x + 2y \leq 6$ (a) The boundary would be included in the solution.

(b) $x + 2y > 6$

(b) The solution would be the half-plane on the opposite side of the boundary.

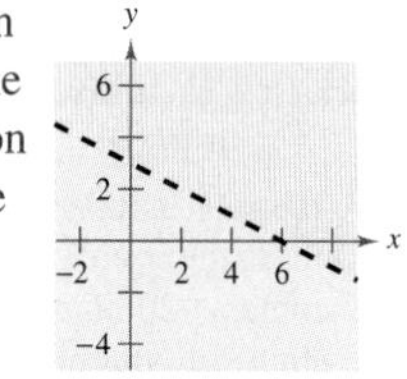

In Exercises 91–94, match the system of inequalities with the graph of its solution. [The graphs are labeled (a), (b), (c), and (d).]

(a)

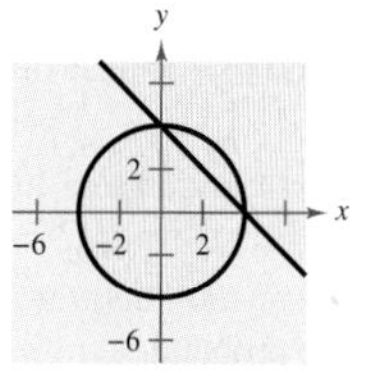

(b)

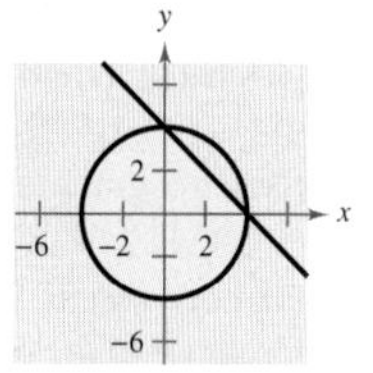

(c)

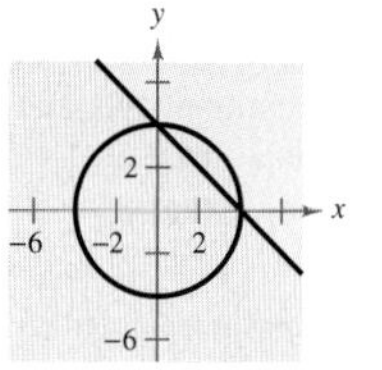

(d)

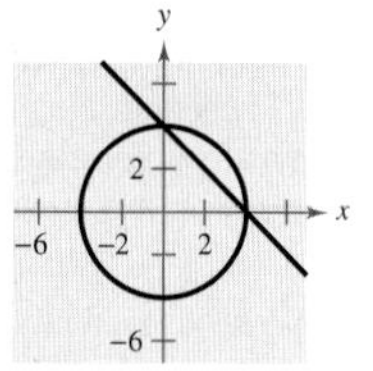

91. $\begin{cases} x^2 + y^2 \leq 16 \\ x + y \geq 4 \end{cases}$ d

92. $\begin{cases} x^2 + y^2 \leq 16 \\ x + y \leq 4 \end{cases}$ b

93. $\begin{cases} x^2 + y^2 \geq 16 \\ x + y \geq 4 \end{cases}$ c

94. $\begin{cases} x^2 + y^2 \geq 16 \\ x + y \leq 4 \end{cases}$ a

7.6 Linear Programming

What you should learn

- Solve linear programming problems.
- Use linear programming to model and solve real-life problems.

Why you should learn it

Linear programming is often useful in making real-life economic decisions. For example, Exercise 42 on page 557 shows how you can determine the optimal cost of a blend of gasoline and compare it with the national average.

Tim Boyle/Getty Images

Linear Programming: A Graphical Approach

Many applications in business and economics involve a process called **optimization,** in which you are asked to find the minimum or maximum value of a quantity. In this section, you will study an optimization strategy called **linear programming.**

A two-dimensional linear programming problem consists of a linear **objective function** and a system of linear inequalities called **constraints.** The objective function gives the quantity that is to be maximized (or minimized), and the constraints determine the set of **feasible solutions.** For example, suppose you are asked to maximize the value of

$z = ax + by$ Objective function

subject to a set of constraints that determines the shaded region in Figure 7.31.

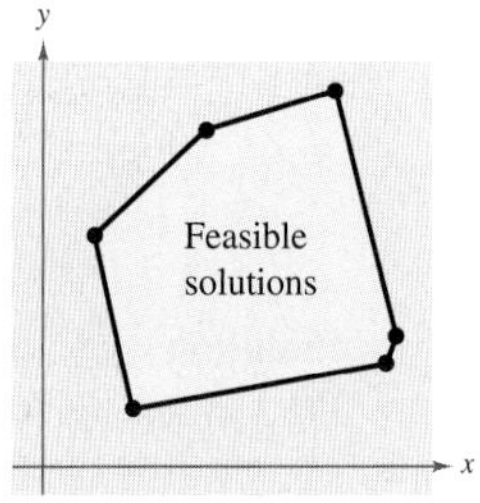

FIGURE 7.31

Because every point in the shaded region satisfies each constraint, it is not clear how you should find the point that yields a maximum value of z. Fortunately, it can be shown that if there is an optimal solution, it must occur at one of the vertices. This means that *you can find the maximum value of z by testing z at each of the vertices.*

Optimal Solution of a Linear Programming Problem

If a linear programming problem has a solution, it must occur at a vertex of the set of feasible solutions. If there is more than one solution, at least one of them must occur at such a vertex. In either case, the value of the objective function is unique.

Some guidelines for solving a linear programming problem in two variables are listed at the top of the next page.

1 PLAN AND PREPARE

Warm-up Exercises

Transparency Available
Available at the Instructor's companion site.

Notetaking Guide

Transparency Available
Promotes interactive learning and notetaking skills. Available at the Instructor's companion site.

Animated Precalculus

An **Animated Precalculus** tutorial is available at the Student companion site for **Section 7.6.**

Pacing

Average: 1 day
Advanced: 1 day
Block: 0.5 block with 7.5

2 FOCUS AND MOTIVATE

Essential Question

How do you find the maximum or minimum value of a function if there are linear constraints on the values of the variables in the function?
Tell students that they will learn how to answer this question by using linear programming, a technique that involves graphing constraints as inequalities and testing points within the solution set.

Resource Planning Guide

Chapter Resources
- Complete Solutions Guide

Workbooks
- Notetaking Guide
- Student Solutions Guide

Interactive Technology
- Instructor Success Organizer
- Notetaking Guide IAE
- Instructional DVDs
- Animated Precalculus
- PowerLecture with ExamView

3 TEACH

Extra Example 1

Find the maximum value of

$z = 4x + 5y$

subject to the following constraints.

$$\left.\begin{aligned} x &\ge 0 \\ y &\ge 0 \\ x + y &\le 6 \end{aligned}\right\}$$

Maximum value of z at (0, 6): 30

Avoiding Common Errors

Students often confuse the terminology in linear programming. Remind students that constraint equations always reflect given conditions or information and that linear programming identifies the point at which the objective function is at a maximum or minimum value, given the constraints.

Solving a Linear Programming Problem

1. Sketch the region corresponding to the system of constraints. (The points inside or on the boundary of the region are *feasible solutions.*)
2. Find the vertices of the region.
3. Test the objective function at each of the vertices and select the values of the variables that optimize the objective function. For a bounded region, both a minimum and a maximum value will exist. (For an unbounded region, *if* an optimal solution exists, it will occur at a vertex.)

Example 1 Solving a Linear Programming Problem

Find the maximum value of

$$z = 3x + 2y \qquad \text{Objective function}$$

subject to the following constraints.

$$\left.\begin{aligned} x &\ge 0 \\ y &\ge 0 \\ x + 2y &\le 4 \\ x - y &\le 1 \end{aligned}\right\} \qquad \text{Constraints}$$

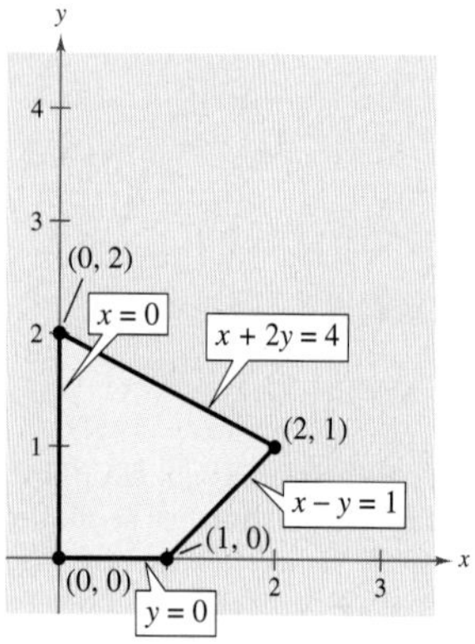

FIGURE 7.32

Solution

The constraints form the region shown in Figure 7.32. At the four vertices of this region, the objective function has the following values.

At (0, 0): $z = 3(0) + 2(0) = 0$

At (0, 2): $z = 3(0) + 2(2) = 4$

At (2, 1): $z = 3(2) + 2(1) = 8$ — Maximum value of z

At (1, 0): $z = 3(1) + 2(0) = 3$

So, the maximum value of z is 8, and this occurs when $x = 2$ and $y = 1$.

CHECK*Point* Now try Exercise 9.

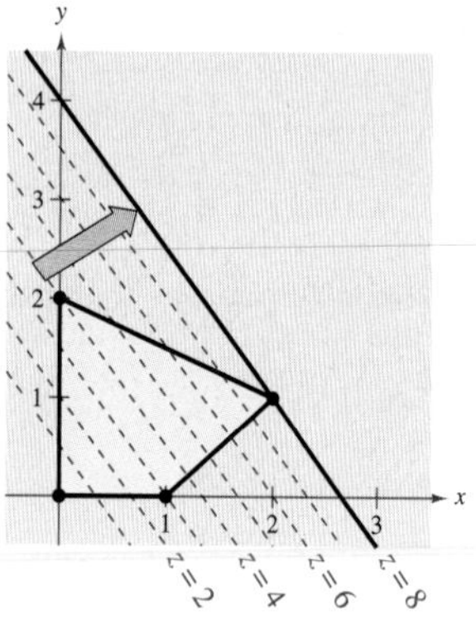

FIGURE 7.33

In Example 1, try testing some of the *interior* points in the region. You will see that the corresponding values of z are less than 8. Here are some examples.

At (1, 1): $z = 3(1) + 2(1) = 5$ At $\left(\frac{1}{2}, \frac{3}{2}\right)$: $z = 3\left(\frac{1}{2}\right) + 2\left(\frac{3}{2}\right) = \frac{9}{2}$

To see why the maximum value of the objective function in Example 1 must occur at a vertex, consider writing the objective function in slope-intercept form

$$y = -\frac{3}{2}x + \frac{z}{2} \qquad \text{Family of lines}$$

where $z/2$ is the y-intercept of the objective function. This equation represents a family of lines, each of slope $-\frac{3}{2}$. Of these infinitely many lines, you want the one that has the largest z-value while still intersecting the region determined by the constraints. In other words, of all the lines whose slope is $-\frac{3}{2}$, you want the one that has the largest y-intercept *and* intersects the given region, as shown in Figure 7.33. From the graph, you can see that such a line will pass through one (or more) of the vertices of the region.

The next example shows that the same basic procedure can be used to solve a problem in which the objective function is to be *minimized.*

Example 2 Minimizing an Objective Function

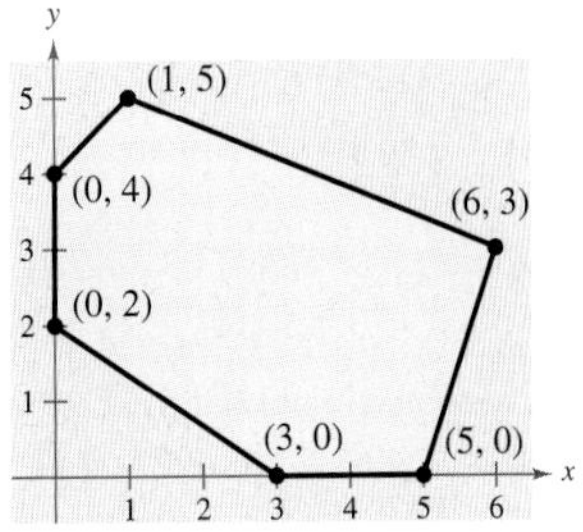

FIGURE 7.34

Find the minimum value of

$$z = 5x + 7y \quad \text{Objective function}$$

where $x \geq 0$ and $y \geq 0$, subject to the following constraints.

$$\left.\begin{aligned} 2x + 3y &\geq 6 \\ 3x - y &\leq 15 \\ -x + y &\leq 4 \\ 2x + 5y &\leq 27 \end{aligned}\right\} \quad \text{Constraints}$$

Solution

The region bounded by the constraints is shown in Figure 7.34. By testing the objective function at each vertex, you obtain the following.

At (0, 2): $z = 5(0) + 7(2) = 14$ Minimum value of z

At (0, 4): $z = 5(0) + 7(4) = 28$

At (1, 5): $z = 5(1) + 7(5) = 40$

At (6, 3): $z = 5(6) + 7(3) = 51$

At (5, 0): $z = 5(5) + 7(0) = 25$

At (3, 0): $z = 5(3) + 7(0) = 15$

So, the minimum value of z is 14, and this occurs when $x = 0$ and $y = 2$.

CHECKPoint Now try Exercise 11.

HISTORICAL NOTE

George Dantzig (1914–2005) was the first to propose the simplex method, or linear programming, in 1947. This technique defined the steps needed to find the optimal solution to a complex multivariable problem.

Example 3 Maximizing an Objective Function

Find the maximum value of

$$z = 5x + 7y \quad \text{Objective function}$$

where $x \geq 0$ and $y \geq 0$, subject to the following constraints.

$$\left.\begin{aligned} 2x + 3y &\geq 6 \\ 3x - y &\leq 15 \\ -x + y &\leq 4 \\ 2x + 5y &\leq 27 \end{aligned}\right\} \quad \text{Constraints}$$

Solution

This linear programming problem is identical to that given in Example 2 above, *except* that the objective function is maximized instead of minimized. Using the values of z at the vertices shown above, you can conclude that the maximum value of z is

$$z = 5(6) + 7(3) = 51$$

and occurs when $x = 6$ and $y = 3$.

CHECKPoint Now try Exercise 13.

Extra Example 2

Find the minimum value of

$z = 12x + 8y$

subject to the following constraints.

$$\left.\begin{aligned} 0 \leq x &\leq 60 \\ 0 \leq y &\leq 45 \\ 5x + 6y &\leq 420 \\ 2x + y &\geq 20 \end{aligned}\right\}$$

Minimum value at (10, 0): 120

Extra Example 3

Find the maximum value of

$z = 12x + 8y$

subject to the following constraints.

$$\left.\begin{aligned} 0 \leq x &\leq 60 \\ 0 \leq y &\leq 45 \\ 5x + 6y &\leq 420 \end{aligned}\right\}$$

Maximum value at (60, 20): 880

Extra Example 4

Find the maximum value of

$z = 3x + 7y$

subject to the following constraints.

$$\begin{cases} x \ge 0 \\ y \ge 0 \\ x + y \ge 8 \\ 3x + 5y \ge 30 \end{cases}$$

No maximum value

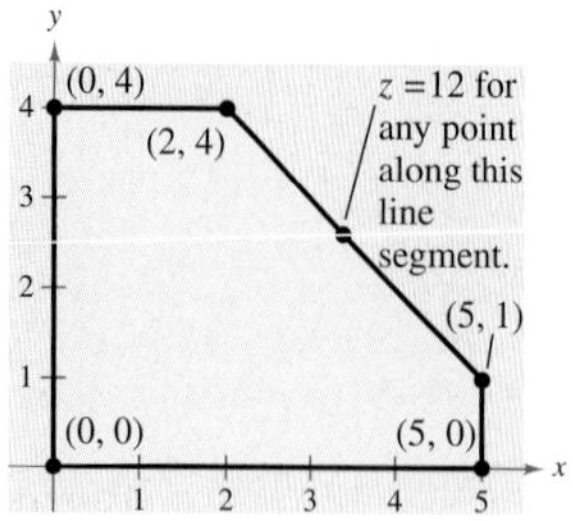

FIGURE 7.35

It is possible for the maximum (or minimum) value in a linear programming problem to occur at *two* different vertices. For instance, at the vertices of the region shown in Figure 7.35, the objective function

$z = 2x + 2y$ Objective function

has the following values.

At (0, 0): $z = 2(0) + 2(0) = 0$

At (0, 4): $z = 2(0) + 2(4) = 8$

At (2, 4): $z = 2(2) + 2(4) = 12$ Maximum value of z

At (5, 1): $z = 2(5) + 2(1) = 12$ Maximum value of z

At (5, 0): $z = 2(5) + 2(0) = 10$

In this case, you can conclude that the objective function has a maximum value not only at the vertices (2, 4) and (5, 1); it also has a maximum value (of 12) at *any point on the line segment connecting these two vertices.* Note that the objective function in slope-intercept form $y = -x + \frac{1}{2}z$ has the same slope as the line through the vertices (2, 4) and (5, 1).

Some linear programming problems have no optimal solutions. This can occur if the region determined by the constraints is *unbounded.* Example 4 illustrates such a problem.

Algebra Help

The slope m of the nonvertical line through the points (x_1, y_1) and (x_2, y_2) is

$$m = \frac{y_2 - y_1}{x_2 - x_1}$$

where $x_1 \ne x_2$.

Example 4 An Unbounded Region

Find the maximum value of

$z = 4x + 2y$ Objective function

where $x \ge 0$ and $y \ge 0$, subject to the following constraints.

$$\begin{cases} x + 2y \ge 4 \\ 3x + y \ge 7 \\ -x + 2y \le 7 \end{cases}$$ Constraints

Solution

The region determined by the constraints is shown in Figure 7.36. For this unbounded region, there is no maximum value of z. To see this, note that the point $(x, 0)$ lies in the region for all values of $x \ge 4$. Substituting this point into the objective function, you get

$z = 4(x) + 2(0) = 4x.$

By choosing x to be large, you can obtain values of z that are as large as you want. So, there is no maximum value of z. However, there *is* a minimum value of z.

At (1, 4): $z = 4(1) + 2(4) = 12$

At (2, 1): $z = 4(2) + 2(1) = 10$ Minimum value of z

At (4, 0): $z = 4(4) + 2(0) = 16$

So, the minimum value of z is 10, and this occurs when $x = 2$ and $y = 1$.

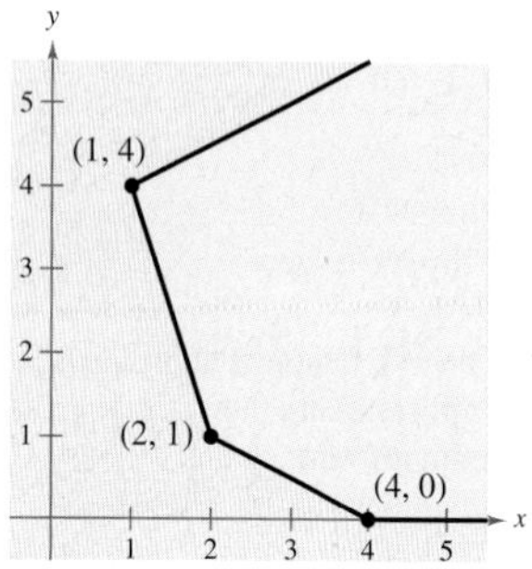

FIGURE 7.36

CHECK Point Now try Exercise 15.

Applications

Example 5 shows how linear programming can be used to find the maximum profit in a business application.

Example 5 Optimal Profit

A candy manufacturer wants to maximize the combined profit for two types of boxed chocolates. A box of chocolate covered creams yields a profit of \$1.50 per box, and a box of chocolate covered nuts yields a profit of \$2.00 per box. Market tests and available resources have indicated the following constraints.

1. The combined production level should not exceed 1200 boxes per month.
2. The demand for a box of chocolate covered nuts is no more than half the demand for a box of chocolate covered creams.
3. The production level for chocolate covered creams should be less than or equal to 600 boxes plus three times the production level for chocolate covered nuts.

What is the maximum monthly profit? How many boxes of each type should be produced per month to yield the maximum profit?

Solution

Let x be the number of boxes of chocolate covered creams and let y be the number of boxes of chocolate covered nuts. So, the objective function (for the combined profit) is given by

$$P = 1.5x + 2y.$$ Objective function

The three constraints translate into the following linear inequalities.

1. $x + y \le 1200$ ⟹ $x + y \le 1200$
2. $y \le \frac{1}{2}x$ ⟹ $-x + 2y \le 0$
3. $x \le 600 + 3y$ ⟹ $x - 3y \le 600$

Because neither x nor y can be negative, you also have the two additional constraints of $x \ge 0$ and $y \ge 0$. Figure 7.37 shows the region determined by the constraints. To find the maximum monthly profit, test the values of P at the vertices of the region.

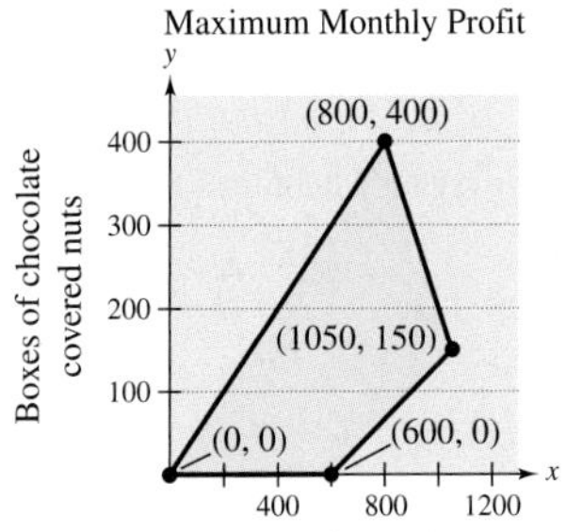

FIGURE 7.37

At $(0, 0)$: $P = 1.5(0) + 2(0) = 0$

At $(800, 400)$: $P = 1.5(800) + 2(400) = 2000$ Maximum profit

At $(1050, 150)$: $P = 1.5(1050) + 2(150) = 1875$

At $(600, 0)$: $P = 1.5(600) + 2(0) = 900$

So, the maximum monthly profit is \$2000, and it occurs when the monthly production consists of 800 boxes of chocolate covered creams and 400 boxes of chocolate covered nuts.

CHECKPoint Now try Exercise 35.

In Example 5, if the manufacturer improved the production of chocolate covered creams so that they yielded a profit of \$2.50 per unit, the maximum monthly profit could then be found using the objective function $P = 2.5x + 2y$. By testing the values of P at the vertices of the region, you would find that the maximum monthly profit was \$2925 and that it occurred when $x = 1050$ and $y = 150$.

Extra Example 5

A company makes two models of compact disc players at costs of \$250 and \$400. The \$250 model yields a profit of \$45, and the \$400 model yields a profit of \$50. A merchant who sells the compact disc players estimates that the total monthly demand will not exceed 250 units. The merchant does not want to invest more than \$70,000 in inventory for these products. Find the number of units of each model that should be stocked in order to maximize profit.

To maximize the profit, the merchant should stock 200 units of the model costing \$250 and 50 units of the model costing \$400. The maximum profit would be \$11,500.

Extra Example 6

A pet store mixes two brands of dog food. Brand X costs \$5 per bag and contains two units of nutritional element A, two units of element B, and two units of element C. Brand Y costs \$4 per bag and contains one unit of nutritional element A, nine units of element B, and three units of element C. The minimum requirements of nutrients A, B, and C are 12 units, 36 units, and 24 units, respectively. Find the number of bags of each brand that should be mixed to produce a mixture having a minimum cost.

To minimize cost, use three bags of Brand X and six bags of Brand Y for a total cost of \$39.

Closing the Lesson

Have students summarize the major points of the lesson and answer the Essential Question: How do you find the maximum or minimum value of a function if there are linear constraints on the values of the variables in the function?

- **Find the set of feasible solutions of a system of constraints by finding the solution set of the corresponding system of inequalities.**
- **Optimize a given function over the constraints by finding the value of the function at each vertex of the feasible region.**

Classroom Discussion

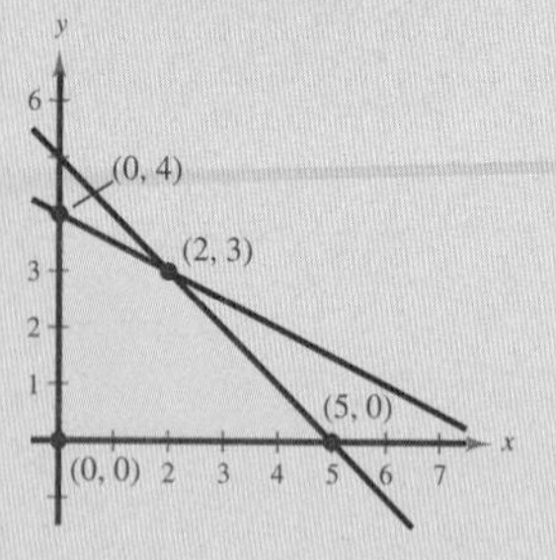

Answers are not unique.

a. $z = -x + y$ **b.** $z = 2x + 3y$
c. $z = x - y$ **d.** $z = -x - y$

Example 6 Optimal Cost

The liquid portion of a diet is to provide at least 300 calories, 36 units of vitamin A, and 90 units of vitamin C. A cup of dietary drink X costs \$0.12 and provides 60 calories, 12 units of vitamin A, and 10 units of vitamin C. A cup of dietary drink Y costs \$0.15 and provides 60 calories, 6 units of vitamin A, and 30 units of vitamin C. How many cups of each drink should be consumed each day to obtain an optimal cost and still meet the daily requirements?

Solution

As in Example 9 in Section 7.5, let x be the number of cups of dietary drink X and let y be the number of cups of dietary drink Y.

$$\left.\begin{array}{ll} \text{For calories:} & 60x + 60y \geq 300 \\ \text{For vitamin A:} & 12x + 6y \geq 36 \\ \text{For vitamin C:} & 10x + 30y \geq 90 \\ & x \geq 0 \\ & y \geq 0 \end{array}\right\} \quad \text{Constraints}$$

The cost C is given by $C = 0.12x + 0.15y$. Objective function

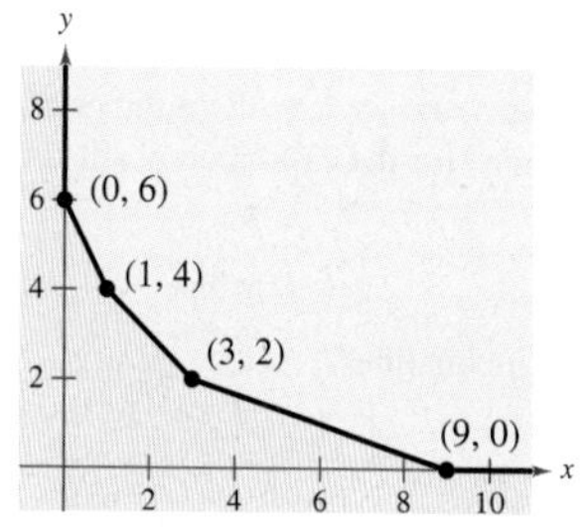

FIGURE 7.38

The graph of the region corresponding to the constraints is shown in Figure 7.38. Because you want to incur as little cost as possible, you want to determine the *minimum* cost. To determine the minimum cost, test C at each vertex of the region.

At $(0, 6)$: $C = 0.12(0) + 0.15(6) = 0.90$
At $(1, 4)$: $C = 0.12(1) + 0.15(4) = 0.72$
At $(3, 2)$: $C = 0.12(3) + 0.15(2) = 0.66$ Minimum value of C
At $(9, 0)$: $C = 0.12(9) + 0.15(0) = 1.08$

So, the minimum cost is \$0.66 per day, and this occurs when 3 cups of drink X and 2 cups of drink Y are consumed each day.

CHECKPoint Now try Exercise 37.

Classroom Discussion

Creating a Linear Programming Problem Sketch the region determined by the following constraints.

$$\left.\begin{array}{r} x + 2y \leq 8 \\ x + y \leq 5 \\ x \geq 0 \\ y \geq 0 \end{array}\right\} \quad \text{Constraints}$$

Find, if possible, an objective function of the form $z = ax + by$ that has a maximum at each indicated vertex of the region.

a. $(0, 4)$ b. $(2, 3)$ c. $(5, 0)$ d. $(0, 0)$

Explain how you found each objective function. See margin.

7.6 EXERCISES

See www.CalcChat.com for worked-out solutions to odd-numbered exercises.

VOCABULARY: Fill in the blanks.

1. In the process called ________, you are asked to find the maximum or minimum value of a quantity. optimization
2. One type of optimization strategy is called linear programming.
3. The objective function of a linear programming problem gives the quantity that is to be maximized or minimized.
4. The ________ of a linear programming problem determine the set of feasible solutions. constraints; feasible solutions
5. The feasible solutions are inside or on the boundary of the region corresponding to a system of constraints.
6. If a linear programming problem has a solution, it must occur at a vertex of the set of feasible solutions.

SKILLS AND APPLICATIONS

In Exercises 7–12, find the minimum and maximum values of the objective function and where they occur, subject to the indicated constraints. (For each exercise, the graph of the region determined by the constraints is provided.)

7. Objective function:
$z = 4x + 3y$
Constraints:
$x \geq 0$
$y \geq 0$
$x + y \leq 5$

Minimum at (0, 0): 0
Maximum at (5, 0): 20

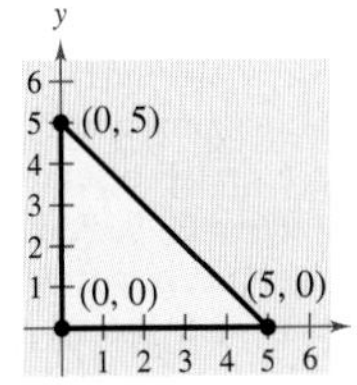

8. Objective function:
$z = 2x + 8y$
Constraints:
$x \geq 0$
$y \geq 0$
$2x + y \leq 4$

Minimum at (0, 0): 0
Maximum at (0, 4): 32

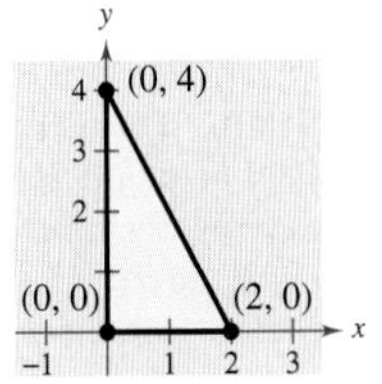

9. Objective function:
$z = 2x + 5y$
Constraints:
$x \geq 0$
$y \geq 0$
$x + 3y \leq 15$
$4x + y \leq 16$

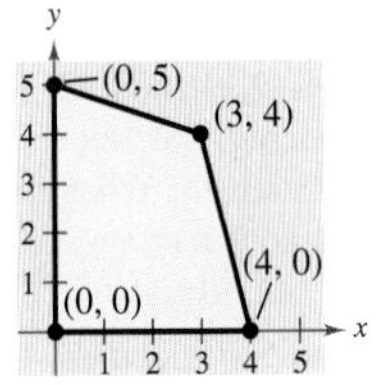

Minimum at (0, 0): 0
Maximum at (3, 4): 26

10. Objective function:
$z = 4x + 5y$
Constraints:
$x \geq 0$
$2x + 3y \geq 6$
$3x - y \leq 9$
$x + 4y \leq 16$

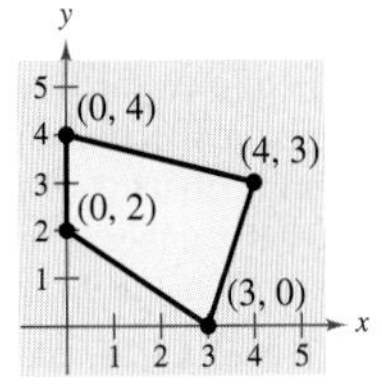

Minimum at (0, 2): 10
Maximum at (4, 3): 31

11–12. See margin.

11. Objective function:
$z = 10x + 7y$
Constraints:
$0 \leq x \leq 60$
$0 \leq y \leq 45$
$5x + 6y \leq 420$

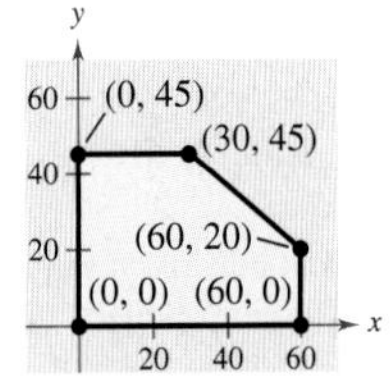

12. Objective function:
$z = 40x + 45y$
Constraints:
$x \geq 0$
$y \geq 0$
$8x + 9y \leq 7200$
$8x + 9y \geq 3600$

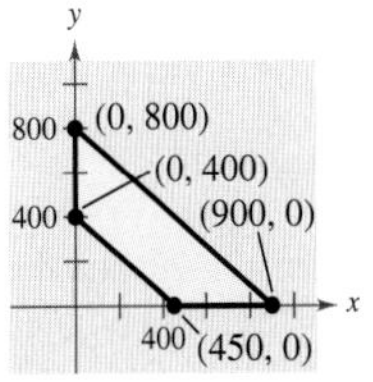

In Exercises 13–16, sketch the region determined by the constraints. Then find the minimum and maximum values of the objective function (if possible) and where they occur, subject to the indicated constraints. 13–16. See margin.

13. Objective function:
$z = 3x + 2y$
Constraints:
$x \geq 0$
$y \geq 0$
$5x + 2y \leq 20$
$5x + y \geq 10$

14. Objective function:
$z = 5x + \frac{1}{2}y$
Constraints:
$x \geq 0$
$y \geq 0$
$\frac{1}{2}x + y \leq 8$
$x + \frac{1}{2}y \geq 4$

15. Objective function:
$z = 4x + 5y$
Constraints:
$x \geq 0$
$y \geq 0$
$x + y \geq 8$
$3x + 5y \geq 30$

16. Objective function:
$z = 5x + 4y$
Constraints:
$x \geq 0$
$y \geq 0$
$2x + 2y \geq 10$
$x + 2y \geq 6$

4 PRACTICE AND APPLY

Assignment Guide

Transparencies Available
Available at the Instructor's companion site.

Average:
Day 1: pp. 555–557
Exs. 1–8, 11, 14, 15, 17, 21, 25, 29, 30, 33, 35, 39, 43–47 odd, 48

Advanced:
Day 1: pp. 555–557
Exs. 1–6, 10, 12, 16, 18, 24, 26, 30–40 even, 44, 48

Block:
pp. 555–557
Exs. 1–8, 11, 14, 15, 17, 21, 25, 29, 30, 33, 35, 39, 43–47 odd, 48 (with 7.5)

11. Minimum at (0, 0): 0
Maximum at (60, 20): 740

12. Minimum at any point on the line segment connecting (0, 400) and (450, 0): 18,000
Maximum at any point on the line segment connecting (0, 800) and (900, 0): 36,000

13.

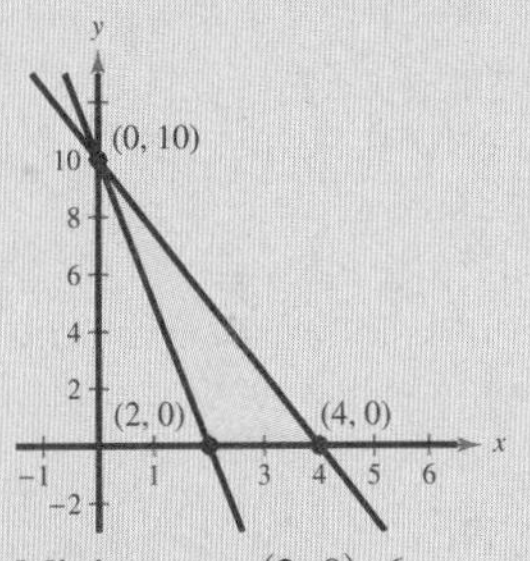

Minimum at (2, 0): 6
Maximum at (0, 10): 20

14.

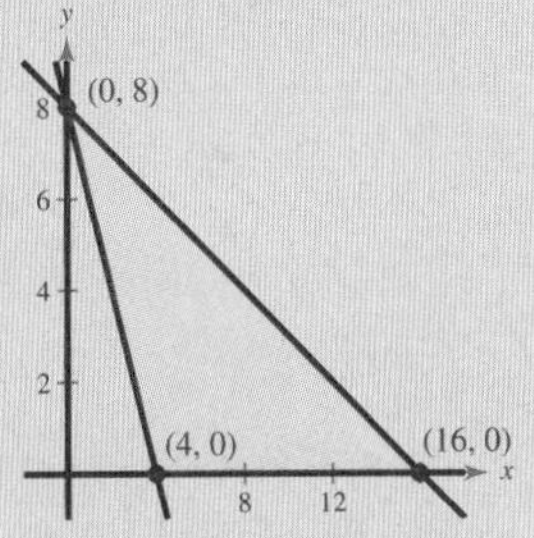

Minimum at (0, 8): 4
Maximum at (16, 0): 80

15.

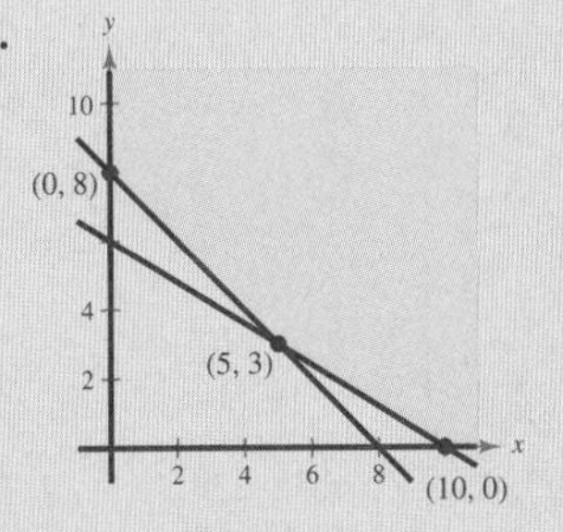

Minimum at (5, 3): 35
No maximum

16.

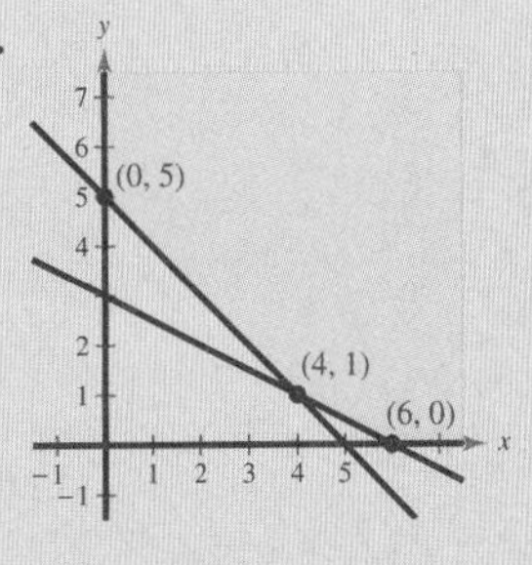

Minimum at (0, 5): 20
No maximum

In Exercises 17–20, use a graphing utility to graph the region determined by the constraints. Then find the minimum and maximum values of the objective function and where they occur, subject to the constraints. 17–20. See margin.

17. Objective function:
$z = 3x + y$
Constraints:
$x \geq 0$
$y \geq 0$
$x + 4y \leq 60$
$3x + 2y \geq 48$

18. Objective function:
$z = x$
Constraints:
$x \geq 0$
$y \geq 0$
$2x + 3y \leq 60$
$2x + y \leq 28$
$4x + y \leq 48$

19. Objective function:
$z = x + 4y$
Constraints:
(See Exercise 17.)

20. Objective function:
$z = y$
Constraints:
(See Exercise 18.)

21–24. See margin.

In Exercises 21–24, find the minimum and maximum values of the objective function and where they occur, subject to the constraints $x \geq 0$, $y \geq 0$, $3x + y \leq 15$, and $4x + 3y \leq 30$.

21. $z = 2x + y$
22. $z = 5x + y$
23. $z = x + y$
24. $z = 3x + y$

In Exercises 25–28, find the minimum and maximum values of the objective function and where they occur, subject to the constraints $x \geq 0$, $y \geq 0$, $x + 4y \leq 20$, $x + y \leq 18$, and $2x + 2y \leq 21$. 25–28. See below.

25. $z = x + 5y$
26. $z = 2x + 4y$
27. $z = 4x + 5y$
28. $z = 4x + y$

In Exercises 29–34, the linear programming problem has an unusual characteristic. Sketch a graph of the solution region for the problem and describe the unusual characteristic. Find the minimum and maximum values of the objective function (if possible) and where they occur. 29–34. See margin.

29. Objective function:
$z = 2.5x + y$
Constraints:
$x \geq 0$
$y \geq 0$
$3x + 5y \leq 15$
$5x + 2y \leq 10$

30. Objective function:
$z = x + y$
Constraints:
$x \geq 0$
$y \geq 0$
$-x + y \leq 1$
$-x + 2y \leq 4$

25. Minimum at (0, 0): 0; Maximum at (0, 5): 25
26. Minimum at (0, 0): 0; Maximum at $\left(\frac{22}{3}, \frac{19}{6}\right)$: $\frac{82}{3}$
27. Minimum at (0, 0): 0; Maximum at $\left(\frac{22}{3}, \frac{19}{6}\right)$: $\frac{271}{6}$
28. Minimum at (0, 0): 0; Maximum at $\left(\frac{21}{2}, 0\right)$: 42

31. Objective function:
$z = -x + 2y$
Constraints:
$x \geq 0$
$y \geq 0$
$x \leq 10$
$x + y \leq 7$

32. Objective function:
$z = x + y$
Constraints:
$x \geq 0$
$y \geq 0$
$-x + y \leq 0$
$-3x + y \geq 3$

33. Objective function:
$z = 3x + 4y$
Constraints:
$x \geq 0$
$y \geq 0$
$x + y \leq 1$
$2x + y \leq 4$

34. Objective function:
$z = x + 2y$
Constraints:
$x \geq 0$
$y \geq 0$
$x + 2y \leq 4$
$2x + y \leq 4$

35. OPTIMAL PROFIT A merchant plans to sell two models of MP3 players at prices of \$225 and \$250. The \$225 model yields a profit of \$30 per unit and the \$250 model yields a profit of \$31 per unit. The merchant estimates that the total monthly demand will not exceed 275 units. The merchant does not want to invest more than \$63,000 in inventory for these products. What is the optimal inventory level for each model? What is the optimal profit? See margin.

36. OPTIMAL PROFIT A manufacturer produces two models of elliptical cross-training exercise machines. The times for assembling, finishing, and packaging model X are 3 hours, 3 hours, and 0.8 hour, respectively. The times for model Y are 4 hours, 2.5 hours, and 0.4 hour. The total times available for assembling, finishing, and packaging are 6000 hours, 4200 hours, and 950 hours, respectively. The profits per unit are \$300 for model X and \$375 for model Y. What is the optimal production level for each model? What is the optimal profit? See margin.

37. OPTIMAL COST An animal shelter mixes two brands of dog food. Brand X costs \$25 per bag and contains two units of nutritional element A, two units of element B, and two units of element C. Brand Y costs \$20 per bag and contains one unit of nutritional element A, nine units of element B, and three units of element C. The minimum required amounts of nutrients A, B, and C are 12 units, 36 units, and 24 units, respectively. What is the optimal number of bags of each brand that should be mixed? What is the optimal cost? See margin.

38. OPTIMAL COST A humanitarian agency can use two models of vehicles for a refugee rescue mission. Each model A vehicle costs \$1000 and each model B vehicle costs \$1500. Mission strategies and objectives indicate the following constraints.

17.
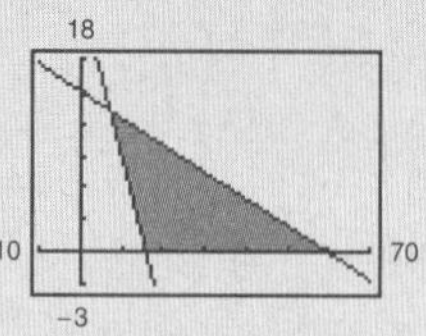

Minimum at (7.2, 13.2): 34.8
Maximum at (60, 0): 180

18.
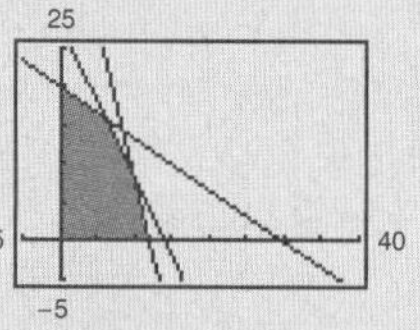

Minimum at any point on the line segment connecting (0, 0) and (0, 20): 0
Maximum at (12, 0): 12

19.
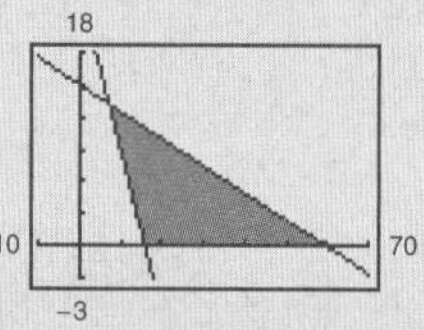

Minimum at (16, 0): 16
Maximum at any point on the line segment connecting (7.2, 13.2) and (60, 0): 60

20.
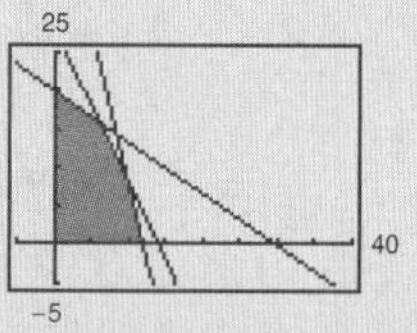

Minimum at any point on the line segment connecting (0, 0) and (12, 0): 0
Maximum at (0, 20): 20

21. Minimum at (0, 0): 0
Maximum at (3, 6): 12

22. Minimum at (0, 0): 0
Maximum at (5, 0): 25

23. Minimum at (0, 0): 0
Maximum at (0, 10): 10

24. Minimum at (0, 0): 0
Maximum at any point on the line segment connecting (3, 6) and (5, 0): 15

29.
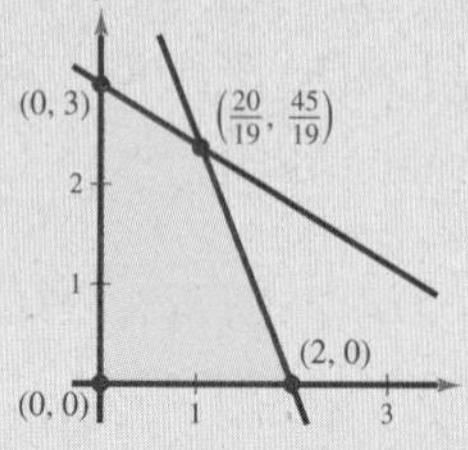

The maximum, 5, occurs at any point on the line segment connecting (2, 0) and $\left(\frac{20}{19}, \frac{45}{19}\right)$.
Minimum at (0, 0): 0

30.
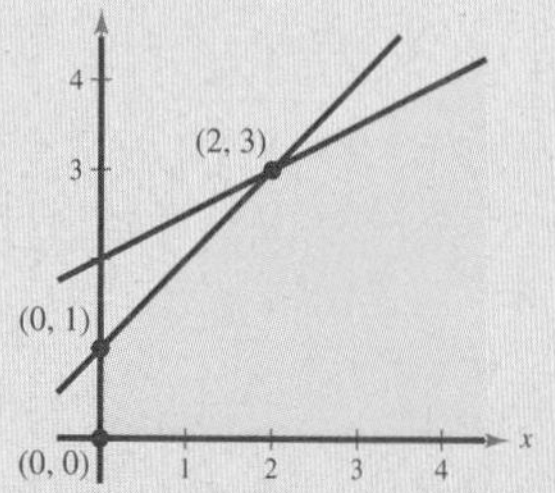

The constraints do not form a closed set of points. Therefore, $z = x + y$ is unbounded.
Minimum at (0, 0): 0

31.
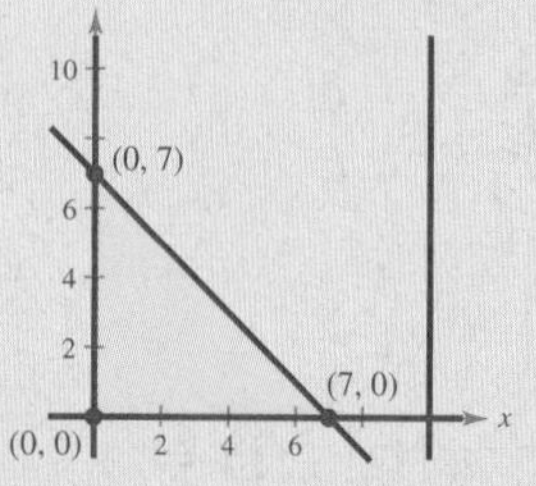

The constraint $x \leq 10$ is extraneous. Minimum at (7, 0): −7; maximum at (0, 7): 14

32–37. See Additional Answers beginning on page AA1.

- A total of at least 20 vehicles must be used.
- A model A vehicle can hold 45 boxes of supplies. A model B vehicle can hold 30 boxes of supplies. The agency must deliver at least 690 boxes of supplies to the refugee camp.
- A model A vehicle can hold 20 refugees. A model B vehicle can hold 32 refugees. The agency must rescue at least 520 refugees. See margin.

What is the optimal number of vehicles of each model that should be used? What is the optimal cost?

39. OPTIMAL REVENUE An accounting firm has 780 hours of staff time and 272 hours of reviewing time available each week. The firm charges \$1600 for an audit and \$250 for a tax return. Each audit requires 60 hours of staff time and 16 hours of review time. Each tax return requires 10 hours of staff time and 4 hours of review time. What numbers of audits and tax returns will yield an optimal revenue? What is the optimal revenue? See margin.

40. OPTIMAL REVENUE The accounting firm in Exercise 39 lowers its charge for an audit to \$1400. What numbers of audits and tax returns will yield an optimal revenue? What is the optimal revenue? See margin.

41. MEDIA SELECTION A company has budgeted a maximum of \$1,000,000 for national advertising of an allergy medication. Each minute of television time costs \$100,000 and each one-page newspaper ad costs \$20,000. Each television ad is expected to be viewed by 20 million viewers, and each newspaper ad is expected to be seen by 5 million readers. The company's market research department recommends that at most 80% of the advertising budget be spent on television ads. What is the optimal amount that should be spent on each type of ad? What is the optimal total audience? See margin.

42. OPTIMAL COST According to AAA (Automobile Association of America), on March 27, 2009, the national average price per gallon of regular unleaded (87-octane) gasoline was \$2.03, and the price of premium unleaded (93-octane) gasoline was \$2.23.

(a) Write an objective function that models the cost of the blend of mid-grade unleaded gasoline (89-octane).

(b) Determine the constraints for the objective function in part (a). (a)–(d). See margin.

(c) Sketch a graph of the region determined by the constraints from part (b).

(d) Determine the blend of regular and premium unleaded gasoline that results in an optimal cost of mid-grade unleaded gasoline.

(e) What is the optimal cost? \$2.10/gal

(f) Is the cost lower than the national average of \$2.15 per gallon for mid-grade unleaded gasoline? Yes

43. INVESTMENT PORTFOLIO An investor has up to \$250,000 to invest in two types of investments. Type A pays 8% annually and type B pays 10% annually. To have a well-balanced portfolio, the investor imposes the following conditions. At least one-fourth of the total portfolio is to be allocated to type A investments and at least one-fourth of the portfolio is to be allocated to type B investments. What is the optimal amount that should be invested in each type of investment? What is the optimal return? See margin.

44. INVESTMENT PORTFOLIO An investor has up to \$450,000 to invest in two types of investments. Type A pays 6% annually and type B pays 10% annually. To have a well-balanced portfolio, the investor imposes the following conditions. At least one-half of the total portfolio is to be allocated to type A investments and at least one-fourth of the portfolio is to be allocated to type B investments. What is the optimal amount that should be invested in each type of investment? What is the optimal return? See margin.

EXPLORATION

45–47. See margin.

TRUE OR FALSE? In Exercises 45–47, determine whether the statement is true or false. Justify your answer.

45. If an objective function has a maximum value at the vertices (4, 7) and (8, 3), you can conclude that it also has a maximum value at the points (4.5, 6.5) and (7.8, 3.2).

46. If an objective function has a minimum value at the vertex (20, 0), you can conclude that it also has a minimum value at the point (0, 0).

47. When solving a linear programming problem, if the objective function has a maximum value at more than one vertex, you can assume that there are an infinite number of points that will produce the maximum value.

48. CAPSTONE Using the constraint region shown below, determine which of the following objective functions has (a) a maximum at vertex *A*, (b) a maximum at vertex *B*, (c) a maximum at vertex *C*, and (d) a minimum at vertex *C*.

(i) $z = 2x + y$

(ii) $z = 2x - y$

(iii) $z = -x + 2y$

(a) iii (b) i

(c) ii (d) iii

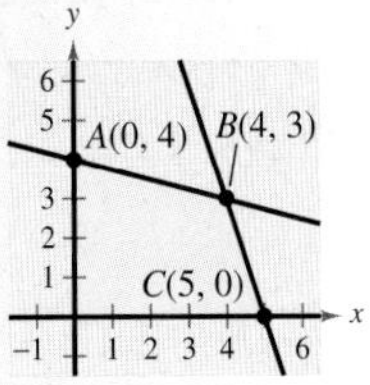

5 ASSESS AND RETEACH

Daily Homework Quiz

Transparency Available

Available at the Instructor's companion site.

38. 10 model A vehicles
10 model B vehicles
Optimal cost: \$25,000

39. 13 audits
0 tax returns
Optimal revenue: \$20,800

40. 5 audits
48 tax returns
Optimal revenue: \$19,000

41. \$0 on TV ads
\$1,000,000 on newspaper ads
Optimal audience:
250 million people

42. (a) $C = 2.03x + 2.23y$

(b)
$$x + y = 1$$
$$87x + 93y = 89$$
$$x \ge 0$$
$$y \ge 0$$

(c)

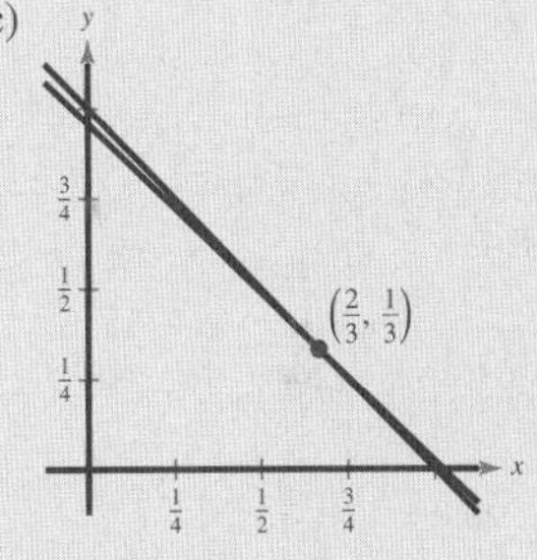

(d) $\frac{2}{3}$ gal of 87-octane and $\frac{1}{3}$ gal of 93-octane

43. \$62,500 to type A
\$187,500 to type B
Optimal return: \$23,750

44. \$225,000 to type A
\$225,000 to type B
Optimal return: \$36,000

45. True. The objective function has a maximum value at any point on the line segment connecting the two vertices.

46. False. (0, 0) may not be a feasible solution.

47. True. If an objective function has a maximum value at more than one vertex, then any point on the line segment connecting the points will produce the maximum value.

7 Chapter Summary

	What Did You Learn?	Explanation/Examples	Review Exercises
Section 7.1	Use the method of substitution to solve systems of linear equations in two variables *(p. 494)*.	**Method of Substitution** **1.** *Solve* one of the equations for one variable in terms of the other. **2.** *Substitute* the expression found in Step 1 into the other equation to obtain an equation in one variable. **3.** *Solve* the equation obtained in Step 2. **4.** *Back-substitute* the value obtained in Step 3 into the expression obtained in Step 1 to find the value of the other variable. **5.** *Check* that the solution satisfies *each* of the original equations.	1–6
	Use the method of substitution to solve systems of nonlinear equations in two variables *(p. 497)*.	The method of substitution (see steps above) can be used to solve systems in which one or both of the equations are nonlinear. (See Examples 3 and 4.)	7–10
	Use a graphical approach to solve systems of equations in two variables *(p. 498)*.	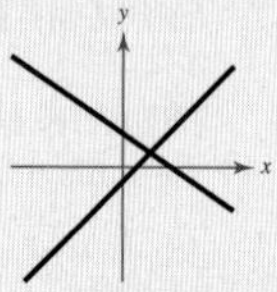 One intersection point 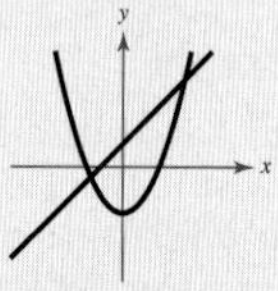 Two intersection points 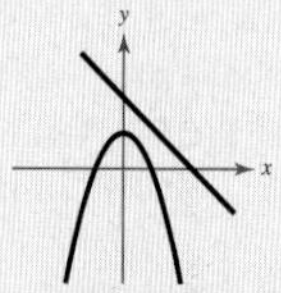 No intersection points	11–18
	Use systems of equations to model and solve real-life problems *(p. 499)*.	A system of equations can be used to find the break-even point for a company. (See Example 6.)	19–24
Section 7.2	Use the method of elimination to solve systems of linear equations in two variables *(p. 505)*.	**Method of Elimination** **1.** *Obtain coefficients* for x (or y) that differ only in sign. **2.** *Add* the equations to eliminate one variable. **3.** *Solve* the equation obtained in Step 2. **4.** *Back-substitute* the value obtained in Step 3 into either of the original equations and solve for the other variable. **5.** *Check* that the solution satisfies *each* of the original equations.	25–32
	Interpret graphically the numbers of solutions of systems of linear equations in two variables *(p. 508)*.	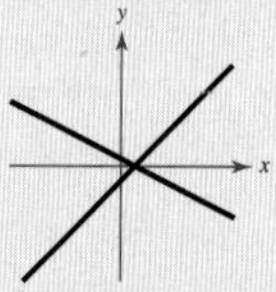 Lines intersect at one point; exactly one solution 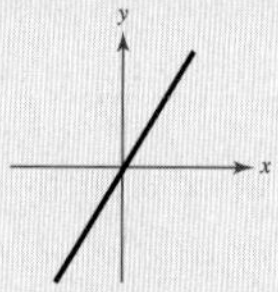 Lines coincide; infinitely many solutions 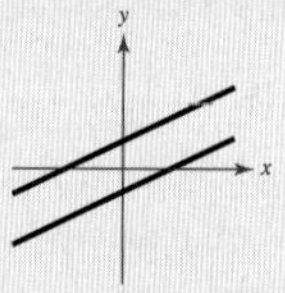 Lines are parallel; no solution	33–36
	Use systems of linear equations in two variables to model and solve real-life problems *(p. 511)*.	A system of linear equations in two variables can be used to find the equilibrium point for a particular market. (See Example 9.)	37, 38

	What Did You Learn?	Explanation/Examples	Review Exercises
Section 7.3	Use back-substitution to solve linear systems in row-echelon form *(p. 517).*	$\begin{cases} x - 2y + 3z = 9 \\ -x + 3y = -4 \\ 2x - 5y + 5z = 17 \end{cases} \rightarrow$ **Row-Echelon Form** $\begin{cases} x - 2y + 3z = 9 \\ y + 3z = 5 \\ z = 2 \end{cases}$	39–42
	Use Gaussian elimination to solve systems of linear equations *(p. 518).*	To produce an equivalent system of linear equations, use row operations by (1) interchanging two equations, (2) multiplying one equation by a nonzero constant, or (3) adding a multiple of one of the equations to another equation to replace the latter equation.	43–48
	Solve nonsquare systems of linear equations *(p. 522).*	In a nonsquare system, the number of equations differs from the number of variables. A system of linear equations cannot have a unique solution unless there are at least as many equations as there are variables.	49, 50
	Use systems of linear equations in three or more variables to model and solve real-life problems *(p. 523).*	A system of linear equations in three variables can be used to find the position equation of an object that is moving in a (vertical) line with constant acceleration. (See Example 7.)	51–60
Section 7.4	Recognize partial fraction decompositions of rational expressions *(p. 530).*	$\dfrac{9}{x^3 - 6x^2} = \dfrac{9}{x^2(x - 6)} = \dfrac{A}{x} + \dfrac{B}{x^2} + \dfrac{C}{x - 6}$	61–64
	Find partial fraction decompositions of rational expressions *(p. 531).*	The techniques used for determining constants in the numerators of partial fractions vary slightly, depending on the type of factors of the denominator: linear or quadratic, distinct or repeated.	65–72
Section 7.5	Sketch the graphs of inequalities in two variables *(p. 538).*	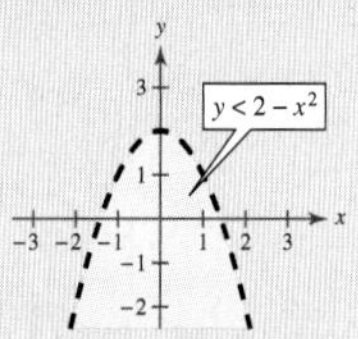 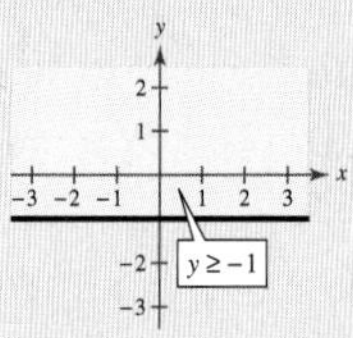	73–78
	Solve systems of inequalities *(p. 540).*	$\begin{cases} x^2 + y \le 5 \\ x \ge -1 \\ y \ge 0 \end{cases}$ 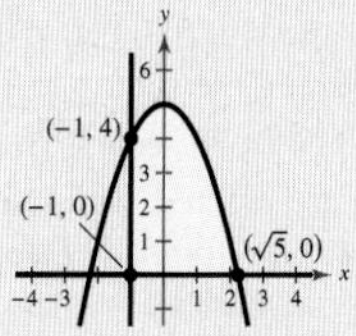	79–86
	Use systems of inequalities in two variables to model and solve real-life problems *(p. 543).*	A system of inequalities in two variables can be used to find the consumer surplus and producer surplus for given demand and supply functions. (See Example 8.)	87–92
Section 7.6	Solve linear programming problems *(p. 549).*	To solve a linear programming problem, (1) sketch the region corresponding to the system of constraints, (2) find the vertices of the region, and (3) test the objective function at each of the vertices and select the values of the variables that optimize the objective function.	93–98
	Use linear programming to model and solve real-life problems *(p. 553).*	Linear programming can be used to find the maximum profit in business applications. (See Example 5.)	99–103

4. $\left(-1, -\frac{2}{3}\right)$
5. (0.25, 0.625)
15.
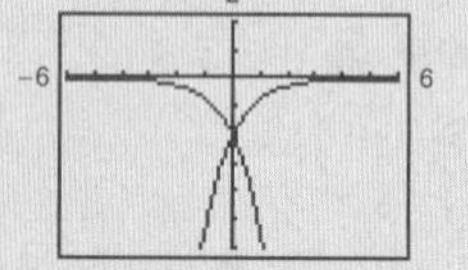

(0, −2)
16.
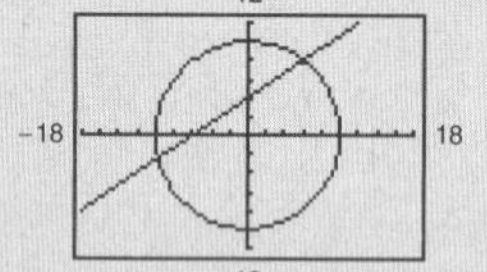

(6, 8), (−9.69, −2.46)
17.
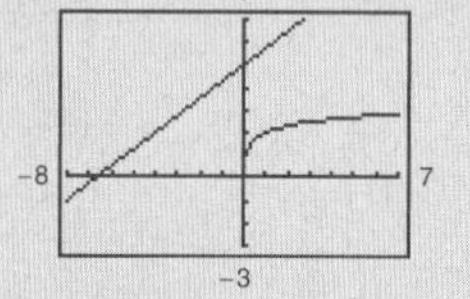

No solution
18.
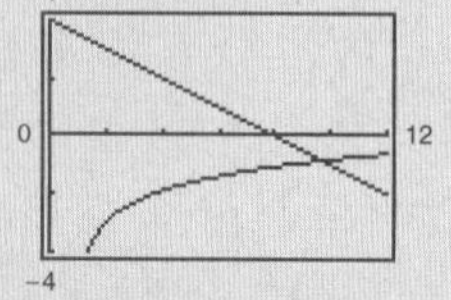

(9.68, −0.84)
24.
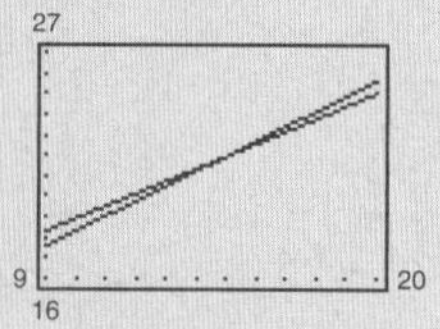

The BMI for males exceeds the BMI for females after age 15.
25. $\left(\frac{5}{2}, 3\right)$
26. $\left(\frac{3}{10}, \frac{2}{5}\right)$
27. (−0.5, 0.8)
28. $\left(\frac{1}{3}, -\frac{1}{2}\right)$
29. (0, 0)
30. (−3, 7)
31. $\left(\frac{8}{5}a + \frac{14}{5}, a\right)$
32. No solution

7 REVIEW EXERCISES

See www.CalcChat.com for worked-out solutions to odd-numbered exercises.

7.1 In Exercises 1–10, solve the system by the method of substitution. 4–5. See margin.

1. $\begin{cases} x + y = 2 \\ x - y = 0 \end{cases}$ (1, 1)
2. $\begin{cases} 2x - 3y = 3 \\ x - y = 0 \end{cases}$ (−3, −3)
3. $\begin{cases} 4x - y - 1 = 0 \\ 8x + y - 17 = 0 \end{cases}$ $\left(\frac{3}{2}, 5\right)$
4. $\begin{cases} 10x + 6y + 14 = 0 \\ x + 9y + 7 = 0 \end{cases}$
5. $\begin{cases} 0.5x + y = 0.75 \\ 1.25x - 4.5y = -2.5 \end{cases}$
6. $\begin{cases} -x + \frac{2}{5}y = \frac{3}{5} \\ -x + \frac{1}{5}y = -\frac{4}{5} \end{cases}$ $\left(\frac{11}{5}, 7\right)$
7. $\begin{cases} x^2 - y^2 = 9 \\ x - y = 1 \end{cases}$ (5, 4)
8. $\begin{cases} x^2 + y^2 = 169 \\ 3x + 2y = 39 \end{cases}$ (13, 0), (5, 12)
9. $\begin{cases} y = 2x^2 \\ y = x^4 - 2x^2 \end{cases}$ (0, 0), (2, 8), (−2, 8)
10. $\begin{cases} x = y + 3 \\ x = y^2 + 1 \end{cases}$ (5, 2), (2, −1)

In Exercises 11–14, solve the system graphically.

11. $\begin{cases} 2x - y = 10 \\ x + 5y = -6 \end{cases}$ (4, −2)
12. $\begin{cases} 8x - 3y = -3 \\ 2x + 5y = 28 \end{cases}$ (1.5, 5)
13. $\begin{cases} y = 2x^2 - 4x + 1 \\ y = x^2 - 4x + 3 \end{cases}$ (1.41, −0.66), (−1.41, 10.66)
14. $\begin{cases} y^2 - 2y + x = 0 \\ x + y = 0 \end{cases}$ (0, 0), (−3, 3)

In Exercises 15–18, use a graphing utility to solve the system of equations. Find the solution accurate to two decimal places. 15–18. See margin.

15. $\begin{cases} y = -2e^{-x} \\ 2e^x + y = 0 \end{cases}$
16. $\begin{cases} x^2 + y^2 = 100 \\ 2x - 3y = -12 \end{cases}$
17. $\begin{cases} y = 2 + \log x \\ y = \frac{3}{4}x + 5 \end{cases}$
18. $\begin{cases} y = \ln(x - 1) - 3 \\ y = 4 - \frac{1}{2}x \end{cases}$

19. **BREAK-EVEN ANALYSIS** You set up a scrapbook business and make an initial investment of \$50,000. The unit cost of a scrapbook kit is \$12 and the selling price is \$25. How many kits must you sell to break even? 3847 units

20. **CHOICE OF TWO JOBS** You are offered two sales jobs at a pharmaceutical company. One company offers an annual salary of \$55,000 plus a year-end bonus of 1.5% of your total sales. The other company offers an annual salary of \$52,000 plus a year-end bonus of 2% of your total sales. What amount of sales will make the second offer better? Explain. Sales greater than \$600,000

21. **GEOMETRY** The perimeter of a rectangle is 480 meters and its length is 150% of its width. Find the dimensions of the rectangle. 96 m × 144 m

22. **GEOMETRY** The perimeter of a rectangle is 68 feet and its width is $\frac{8}{9}$ times its length. Find the dimensions of the rectangle. 16 ft × 18 ft

23. **GEOMETRY** The perimeter of a rectangle is 40 inches. The area of the rectangle is 96 square inches. Find the dimensions of the rectangle. 8 in. × 12 in.

24. **BODY MASS INDEX** Body Mass Index (BMI) is a measure of body fat based on height and weight. The 75th percentile BMI for females, ages 9 to 20, is growing more slowly than that for males of the same age range. Models that represent the 75th percentile BMI for males and females, ages 9 to 20, are given by

$B = 0.73a + 11$ Males

$B = 0.61a + 12.8$ Females

where B is the BMI (kg/m^2) and a represents the age, with $a = 9$ corresponding to 9 years of age. Use a graphing utility to determine whether the BMI for males ever exceeds the BMI for females. (Source: National Center for Health Statistics) See margin.

7.2 In Exercises 25–32, solve the system by the method of elimination. 25–32. See margin.

25. $\begin{cases} 2x - y = 2 \\ 6x + 8y = 39 \end{cases}$
26. $\begin{cases} 40x + 30y = 24 \\ 20x - 50y = -14 \end{cases}$
27. $\begin{cases} 0.2x + 0.3y = 0.14 \\ 0.4x + 0.5y = 0.20 \end{cases}$
28. $\begin{cases} 12x + 42y = -17 \\ 30x - 18y = 19 \end{cases}$
29. $\begin{cases} 3x - 2y = 0 \\ 3x + 2(y + 5) = 10 \end{cases}$
30. $\begin{cases} 7x + 12y = 63 \\ 2x + 3(y + 2) = 21 \end{cases}$
31. $\begin{cases} 1.25x - 2y = 3.5 \\ 5x - 8y = 14 \end{cases}$
32. $\begin{cases} 1.5x + 2.5y = 8.5 \\ 6x + 10y = 24 \end{cases}$

In Exercises 33–36, match the system of linear equations with its graph. Describe the number of solutions and state whether the system is consistent or inconsistent. [The graphs are labeled (a), (b), (c), and (d).]

(a)
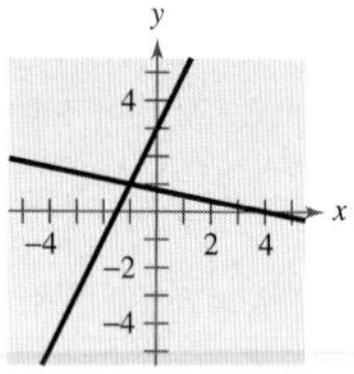

(b)
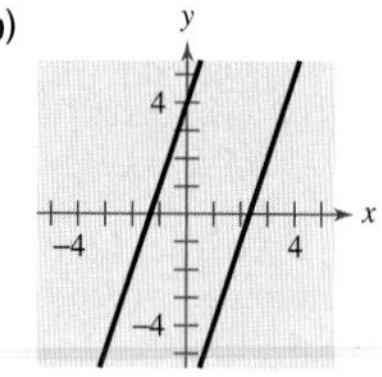

(c)

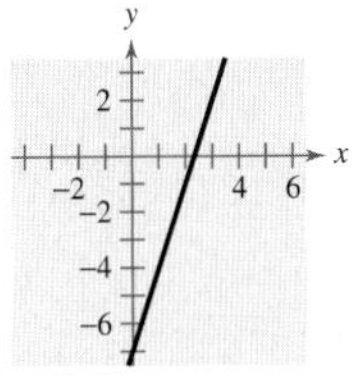

(d)

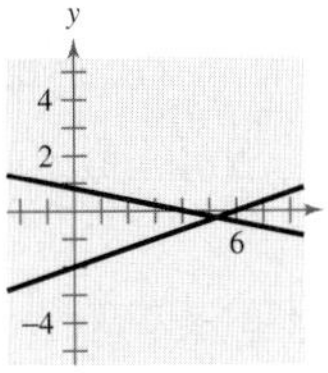

33–36. See margin.

33. $\begin{cases} x + 5y = 4 \\ x - 3y = 6 \end{cases}$

34. $\begin{cases} -3x + y = -7 \\ 9x - 3y = 21 \end{cases}$

35. $\begin{cases} 3x - y = 7 \\ -6x + 2y = 8 \end{cases}$

36. $\begin{cases} 2x - y = -3 \\ x + 5y = 4 \end{cases}$

SUPPLY AND DEMAND In Exercises 37 and 38, find the equilibrium point of the demand and supply equations.

	Demand $\left(\frac{500{,}000}{7}, \frac{159}{7}\right)$	*Supply*
37.	$p = 37 - 0.0002x$	$p = 22 + 0.00001x$
38.	$p = 120 - 0.0001x$	$p = 45 + 0.0002x$

(250,000, 95)

7.3 In Exercises 39–42, use back-substitution to solve the system of linear equations. 39–40. See margin.

39. $\begin{cases} x - 4y + 3z = 3 \\ -y + z = -1 \\ z = -5 \end{cases}$

40. $\begin{cases} x - 7y + 8z = 85 \\ y - 9z = -35 \\ z = 3 \end{cases}$

41. $\begin{cases} 4x - 3y - 2z = -65 \\ 8y - 7z = -14 \\ z = 10 \end{cases}$ $(-6, 7, 10)$

42. $\begin{cases} 5x - 7z = 9 \\ 3y - 8z = -4 \\ z = -7 \end{cases}$ $(-8, -20, -7)$

In Exercises 43–48, use Gaussian elimination to solve the system of equations.

43. $\begin{cases} x + 2y + 6z = 4 \\ -3x + 2y - z = -4 \\ 4x + 2z = 16 \end{cases}$ $\left(\frac{24}{5}, \frac{22}{5}, -\frac{8}{5}\right)$

44. $\begin{cases} x + 3y - z = 13 \\ 2x - 5z = 23 \\ 4x - y - 2z = 14 \end{cases}$ $\left(\frac{38}{17}, \frac{40}{17}, -\frac{63}{17}\right)$

45. $\begin{cases} x - 2y + z = -6 \\ 2x - 3y = -7 \\ -x + 3y - 3z = 11 \end{cases}$ $(3a + 4, 2a + 5, a)$

46. $\begin{cases} 2x + 6z = -9 \\ 3x - 2y + 11z = -16 \\ 3x - y + 7z = -11 \end{cases}$ $\left(-\frac{3}{4}, 0, -\frac{5}{4}\right)$

47. $\begin{cases} x + 4w = 1 \\ 3y + z - w = 4 \\ 2y - 3w = 2 \\ 4x - y + 2z = 5 \end{cases}$ $(1, 1, 1, 0)$

48. $\begin{cases} x + y + z + w = 6 \\ 3x + 4y - w = 3 \\ -2x + 3y + z + 3w = 6 \\ x + 4y - z + 2w = 7 \end{cases}$ $(2, 0, 1, 3)$

In Exercises 49 and 50, solve the nonsquare system of equations.

49. $\begin{cases} 5x - 12y + 7z = 16 \\ 3x - 7y + 4z = 9 \end{cases}$ $(a - 4, a - 3, a)$

50. $\begin{cases} 2x + 5y - 19z = 34 \\ 3x + 8y - 31z = 54 \end{cases}$ $(-3a + 2, 5a + 6, a)$

In Exercises 51 and 52, find the equation of the parabola $y = ax^2 + bx + c$ that passes through the points. To verify your result, use a graphing utility to plot the points and graph the parabola. 51–52. See margin.

51.

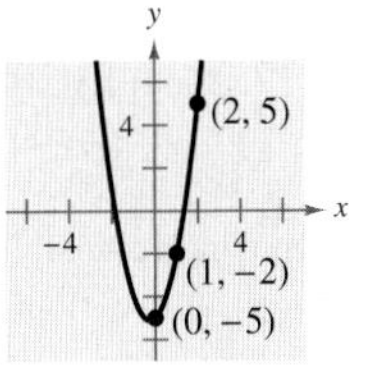

52.

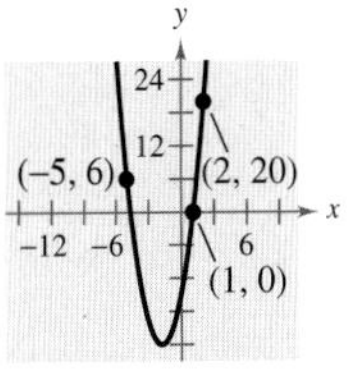

In Exercises 53 and 54, find the equation of the circle

$x^2 + y^2 + Dx + Ey + F = 0$ 53–54. See margin.

that passes through the points. To verify your result, use a graphing utility to plot the points and graph the circle.

53.

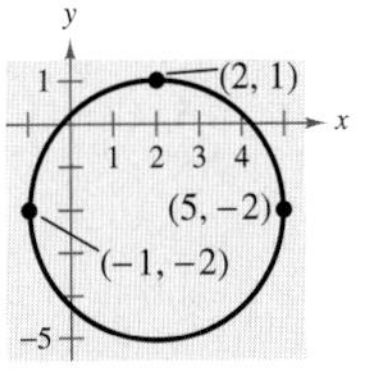

54.

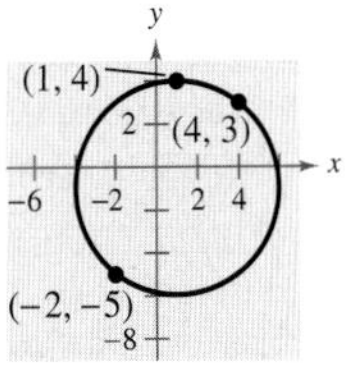

55. DATA ANALYSIS: ONLINE SHOPPING The table shows the projected online retail sales y (in billions of dollars) in the United States from 2010 through 2012. (Source: Forrester Research, Inc.)

Year	Online retail sales, y
2010	267.8
2011	301.0
2012	334.7

(a) Use the technique demonstrated in Exercises 77–80 in Section 7.3 to set up a system of equations for the data and to find a least squares regression parabola that models the data. Let x represent the year, with $x = 10$ corresponding to 2010. (a)–(b). See margin.

(b) Use a graphing utility to graph the parabola and the data in the same viewing window. How well does the model fit the data?

(c) Use the model to estimate the online retail sales in the United States in 2015. Does your answer seem reasonable? $438.8 billion; yes

33. d, one solution, consistent
34. c, infinitely many solutions, consistent
35. b, no solution, inconsistent
36. a, one solution, consistent
39. $(2, -4, -5)$
40. $(5, -8, 3)$
51. $y = 2x^2 + x - 5$
52. $y = 3x^2 + 11x - 14$
53. $x^2 + y^2 - 4x + 4y - 1 = 0$
54. $x^2 + y^2 - 2x + 2y - 23 = 0$
55. (a) $y = 0.25x^2 + 27.95x - 36.7$
(b)

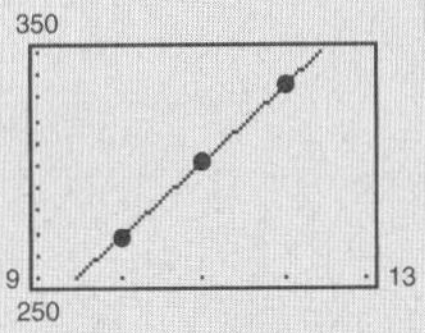

The model is a good fit.

56. AGRICULTURE A mixture of 6 gallons of chemical A, 8 gallons of chemical B, and 13 gallons of chemical C is required to kill a destructive crop insect. Commercial spray X contains 1, 2, and 2 parts, respectively, of these chemicals. Commercial spray Y contains only chemical C. Commercial spray Z contains chemicals A, B, and C in equal amounts. How much of each type of commercial spray is needed to get the desired mixture? See margin.

57. INVESTMENT ANALYSIS An inheritance of \$40,000 was divided among three investments yielding \$3500 in interest per year. The interest rates for the three investments were 7%, 9%, and 11%. Find the amount placed in each investment if the second and third were \$3000 and \$5000 less than the first, respectively. See margin.

58. VERTICAL MOTION An object moving vertically is at the given heights at the specified times. Find the position equation

$s = \frac{1}{2}at^2 + v_0t + s_0$

for the object.

(a) $s = -16t^2 + 150$

(b) $s = -16t^2 - 20t + 220$

(a) At $t = 1$ second, $s = 134$ feet
At $t = 2$ seconds, $s = 86$ feet
At $t = 3$ seconds, $s = 6$ feet

(b) At $t = 1$ second, $s = 184$ feet
At $t = 2$ seconds, $s = 116$ feet
At $t = 3$ seconds, $s = 16$ feet

59. SPORTS Pebble Beach Golf Links in Pebble Beach, California is an 18-hole course that consists of par-3 holes, par-4 holes, and par-5 holes. There are two more par-4 holes than twice the number of par-5 holes, and the number of par-3 holes is equal to the number of par-5 holes. Find the numbers of par-3, par-4, and par-5 holes on the course. (Source: Pebble Beach Resorts)

60. SPORTS St Andrews Golf Course in St Andrews, Scotland is one of the oldest golf courses in the world. It is an 18-hole course that consists of par-3 holes, par-4 holes, and par-5 holes. There are seven times as many par-4 holes as par-5 holes, and the sum of the numbers of par-3 and par-5 holes is four. Find the numbers of par-3, par-4, and par-5 holes on the course. (Source: St Andrews Links Trust) 59–60. See margin.

7.4 In Exercises 61–64, write the form of the partial fraction decomposition for the rational expression. Do not solve for the constants.

61. $\dfrac{3}{x^2 + 20x}$ $\quad \dfrac{A}{x} + \dfrac{B}{x + 20}$

62. $\dfrac{x - 8}{x^2 - 3x - 28}$ $\quad \dfrac{A}{x - 7} + \dfrac{B}{x + 4}$

63. $\dfrac{3x - 4}{x^3 - 5x^2}$ $\quad \dfrac{A}{x} + \dfrac{B}{x^2} + \dfrac{C}{x - 5}$

64. $\dfrac{x - 2}{x(x^2 + 2)^2}$ $\quad \dfrac{A}{x} + \dfrac{Bx + C}{x^2 + 2} + \dfrac{Dx + E}{(x^2 + 2)^2}$

In Exercises 65–72, write the partial fraction decomposition of the rational expression. 65–72. See margin.

65. $\dfrac{4 - x}{x^2 + 6x + 8}$

66. $\dfrac{-x}{x^2 + 3x + 2}$

67. $\dfrac{x^2}{x^2 + 2x - 15}$

68. $\dfrac{9}{x^2 - 9}$

69. $\dfrac{x^2 + 2x}{x^3 - x^2 + x - 1}$

70. $\dfrac{4x}{3(x - 1)^2}$

71. $\dfrac{3x^2 + 4x}{(x^2 + 1)^2}$

72. $\dfrac{4x^2}{(x - 1)(x^2 + 1)}$

7.5 In Exercises 73–78, sketch the graph of the inequality. 73–78. See margin.

73. $y \le 5 - \frac{1}{2}x$

74. $3y - x \ge 7$

75. $y - 4x^2 > -1$

76. $y \le \dfrac{3}{x^2 + 2}$

77. $(x - 1)^2 + (y - 3)^2 < 16$

78. $x^2 + (y + 5)^2 > 1$

In Exercises 79–86, sketch the graph and label the vertices of the solution set of the system of inequalities. 79–86. See margin.

79. $\begin{cases} x + 2y \le 160 \\ 3x + y \le 180 \\ x \ge 0 \\ y \ge 0 \end{cases}$

80. $\begin{cases} 2x + 3y \le 24 \\ 2x + y \le 16 \\ x \ge 0 \\ y \ge 0 \end{cases}$

81. $\begin{cases} 3x + 2y \ge 24 \\ x + 2y \ge 12 \\ 2 \le x \le 15 \\ y \le 15 \end{cases}$

82. $\begin{cases} 2x + y \ge 16 \\ x + 3y \ge 18 \\ 0 \le x \le 25 \\ 0 \le y \le 25 \end{cases}$

83. $\begin{cases} y < x + 1 \\ y > x^2 - 1 \end{cases}$

84. $\begin{cases} y \le 6 - 2x - x^2 \\ y \ge x + 6 \end{cases}$

85. $\begin{cases} 2x - 3y \ge 0 \\ 2x - y \le 8 \\ y \ge 0 \end{cases}$

86. $\begin{cases} x^2 + y^2 \le 9 \\ (x - 3)^2 + y^2 \le 9 \end{cases}$

56. 10 gal of spray X
5 gal of spray Y
12 gal of spray Z

57. \$16,000 at 7%
\$13,000 at 9%
\$11,000 at 11%

59. 4 par-3 holes, 10 par-4 holes, 4 par-5 holes

60. 2 par-3 holes, 14 par-4 holes, 2 par-5 holes

65. $\dfrac{3}{x + 2} - \dfrac{4}{x + 4}$

66. $\dfrac{1}{x + 1} - \dfrac{2}{x + 2}$

67. $1 - \dfrac{25}{8(x + 5)} + \dfrac{9}{8(x - 3)}$

68. $\dfrac{1}{2}\left(\dfrac{3}{x - 3} - \dfrac{3}{x + 3}\right)$

69. $\dfrac{1}{2}\left(\dfrac{3}{x - 1} - \dfrac{x - 3}{x^2 + 1}\right)$

70. $\dfrac{4}{3(x - 1)} + \dfrac{4}{3(x - 1)^2}$

71. $\dfrac{3}{x^2 + 1} + \dfrac{4x - 3}{(x^2 + 1)^2}$

72. $2\left(\dfrac{1}{x - 1} + \dfrac{x + 1}{x^2 + 1}\right)$

73.

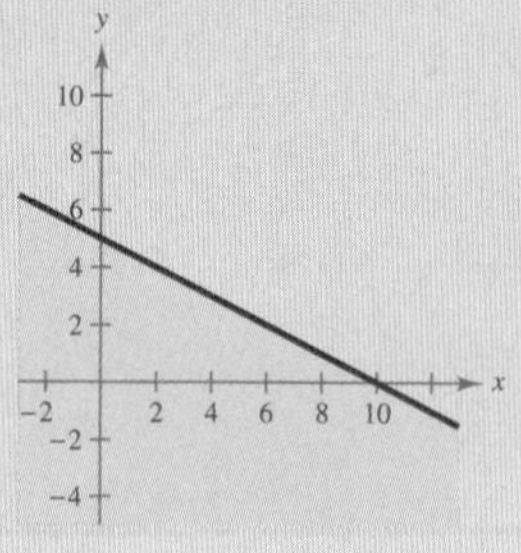

74.

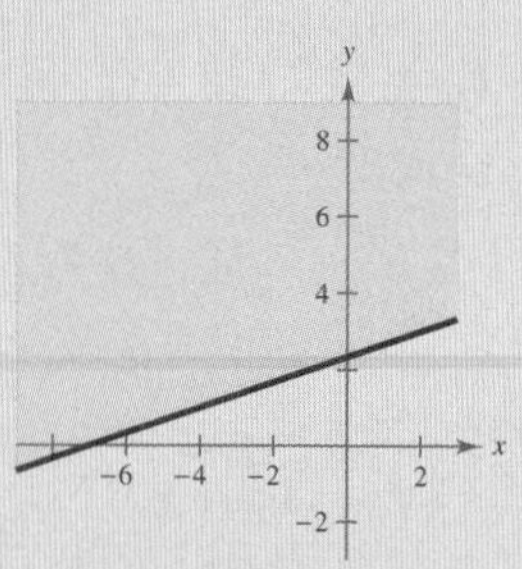

75.

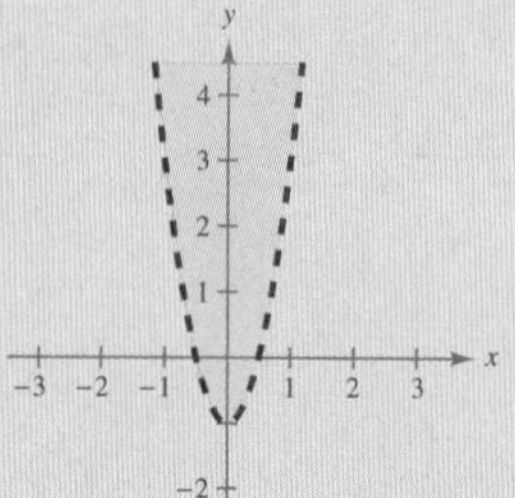

76.

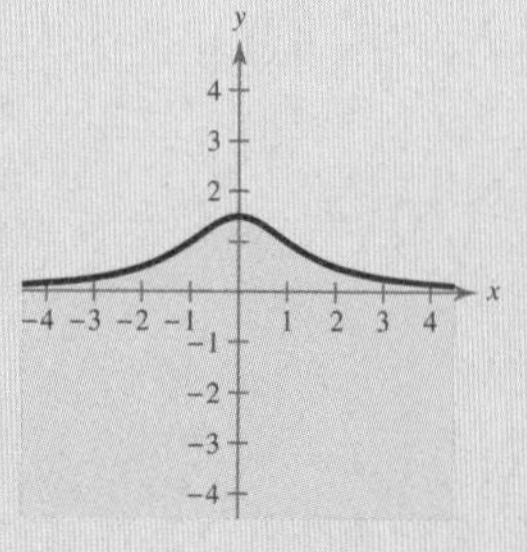

77.

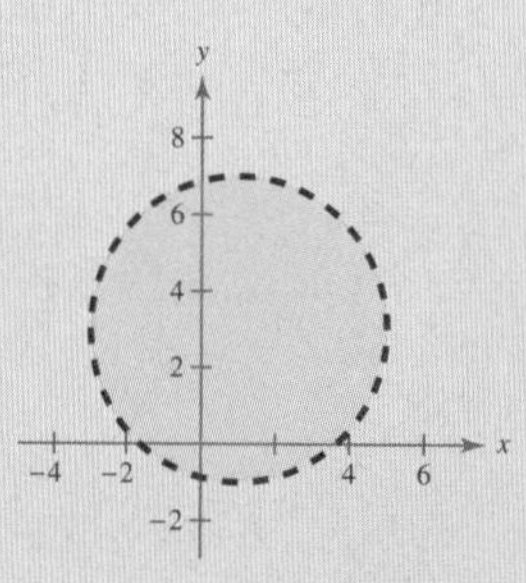

78.

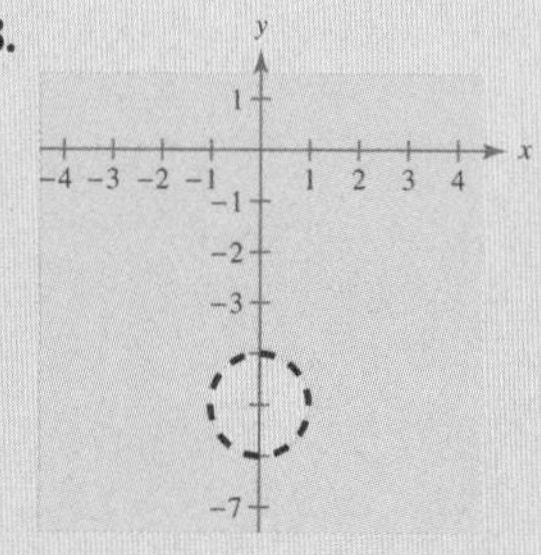

79–86. See Additional Answers beginning on page AA1.

87. INVENTORY COSTS A warehouse operator has 24,000 square feet of floor space in which to store two products. Each unit of product I requires 20 square feet of floor space and costs \$12 per day to store. Each unit of product II requires 30 square feet of floor space and costs \$8 per day to store. The total storage cost per day cannot exceed \$12,400. Find and graph a system of inequalities describing all possible inventory levels. See margin.

88. NUTRITION A dietitian is asked to design a special dietary supplement using two different foods. Each ounce of food X contains 12 units of calcium, 10 units of iron, and 20 units of vitamin B. Each ounce of food Y contains 15 units of calcium, 20 units of iron, and 12 units of vitamin B. The minimum daily requirements of the diet are 300 units of calcium, 280 units of iron, and 300 units of vitamin B. See margin.

(a) Write a system of inequalities describing the different amounts of food X and food Y that can be used.

(b) Sketch a graph of the region in part (a).

(c) Find two solutions to the system and interpret their meanings in the context of the problem.

SUPPLY AND DEMAND In Exercises 89 and 90, (a) graph the systems representing the consumer surplus and producer surplus for the supply and demand equations and (b) find the consumer surplus and producer surplus. 89–90. See margin.

	Demand	*Supply*
89.	$p = 160 - 0.0001x$	$p = 70 + 0.0002x$
90.	$p = 130 - 0.0002x$	$p = 30 + 0.0003x$

91. GEOMETRY Derive a set of inequalities to describe the region of a rectangle with vertices at (3, 1), (7, 1), (7, 10), and (3, 10). See below.

92. DATA ANALYSIS: COMPUTER SALES The table shows the sales y (in billions of dollars) for Dell, Inc. from 2000 through 2007. (Source: Dell, Inc.) See margin.

Year	Sales, y
2000	31.9
2001	31.2
2002	35.4
2003	41.4
2004	49.2
2005	55.9
2006	57.4
2007	61.1

(a) Use the *regression* feature of a graphing utility to find a linear model for the data. Let t represent the year, with $t = 0$ corresponding to 2000.

(b) The total sales for Dell during this eight-year period can be approximated by finding the area of the trapezoid bounded by the linear model you found in part (a) and the lines $y = 0$, $t = -0.5$, and $t = 7.5$. Use a graphing utility to graph this region.

(c) Use the formula for the area of a trapezoid to approximate the total retail sales for Dell.

7.6 **In Exercises 93–98, sketch the region determined by the constraints. Then find the minimum and maximum values of the objective function (if possible) and where they occur, subject to the indicated constraints.** 93–98. See margin.

93. Objective function:
$z = 3x + 4y$
Constraints:
$x \ge 0$
$y \ge 0$
$2x + 5y \le 50$
$4x + y \le 28$

94. Objective function:
$z = 10x + 7y$
Constraints:
$x \ge 0$
$y \ge 0$
$2x + y \ge 100$
$x + y \ge 75$

95. Objective function:
$z = 1.75x + 2.25y$
Constraints:
$x \ge 0$
$y \ge 0$
$2x + y \ge 25$
$3x + 2y \ge 45$

96. Objective function:
$z = 50x + 70y$
Constraints:
$x \ge 0$
$y \ge 0$
$x + 2y \le 1500$
$5x + 2y \le 3500$

97. Objective function:
$z = 5x + 11y$
Constraints:
$x \ge 0$
$y \ge 0$
$x + 3y \le 12$
$3x + 2y \le 15$

98. Objective function:
$z = -2x + y$
Constraints:
$x \ge 0$
$y \ge 0$
$x + y \ge 7$
$5x + 2y \ge 20$

99. OPTIMAL REVENUE A student is working part time as a hairdresser to pay college expenses. The student may work no more than 24 hours per week. Haircuts cost \$25 and require an average of 20 minutes, and permanents cost \$70 and require an average of 1 hour and 10 minutes. What combination of haircuts and/or permanents will yield an optimal revenue? What is the optimal revenue?
72 haircuts, 0 permanents; Optimal revenue: \$1800

91. $\begin{cases} x \ge 3 \\ x \le 7 \\ y \ge 1 \\ y \le 10 \end{cases}$

92. (a) $y = 4.82t + 28.6$

(b)
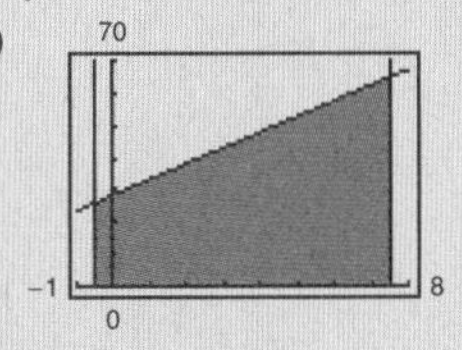

(c) \$363.76 billion

93.
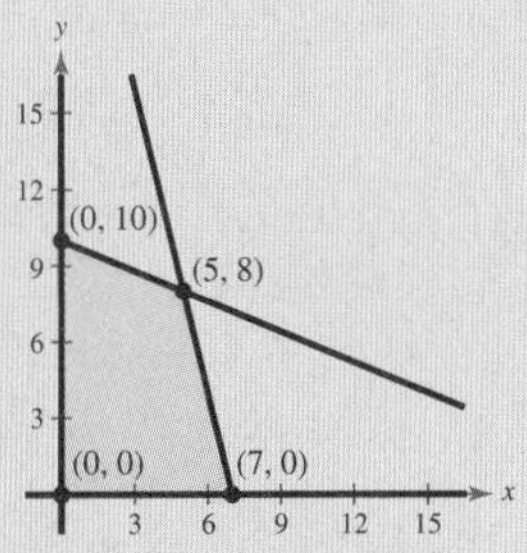

Minimum at (0, 0): 0
Maximum at (5, 8): 47

94.
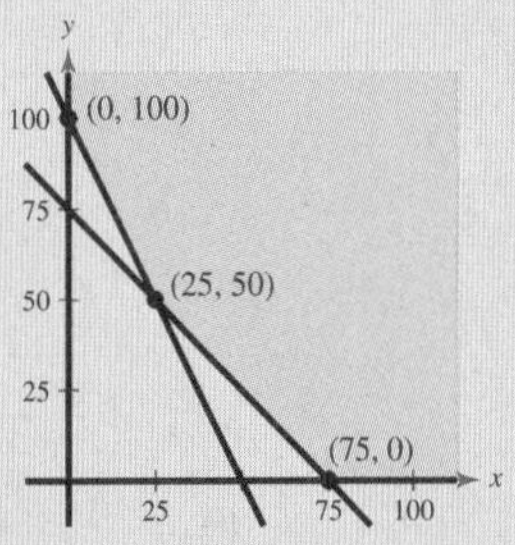

Minimum at (25, 50): 600
No maximum

95–98. See Additional Answers beginning on page AA1.

87. $\begin{cases} 20x + 30y \le 24{,}000 \\ 12x + 8y \le 12{,}400 \\ x \ge 0 \\ y \ge 0 \end{cases}$

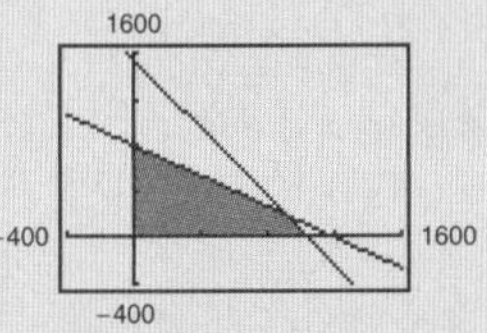

88. (a) x = food X, y = food Y

$\begin{cases} 12x + 15y \ge 300 \\ 10x + 20y \ge 280 \\ 20x + 12y \ge 300 \\ x \ge 0 \\ y \ge 0 \end{cases}$

(b)
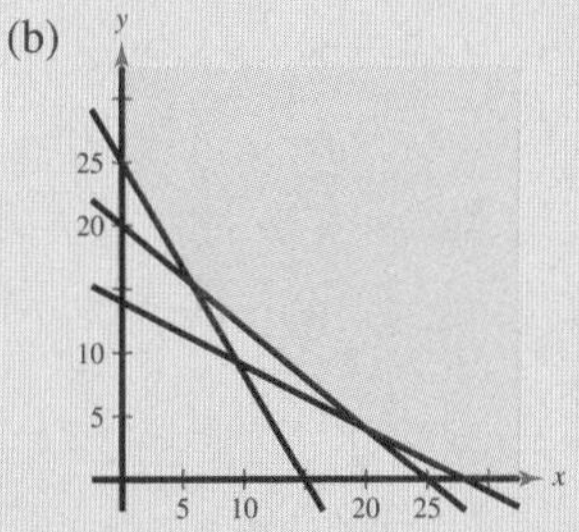

(c) Answers will vary. Sample answer: (15, 8) and (16, 9)

89. (a)
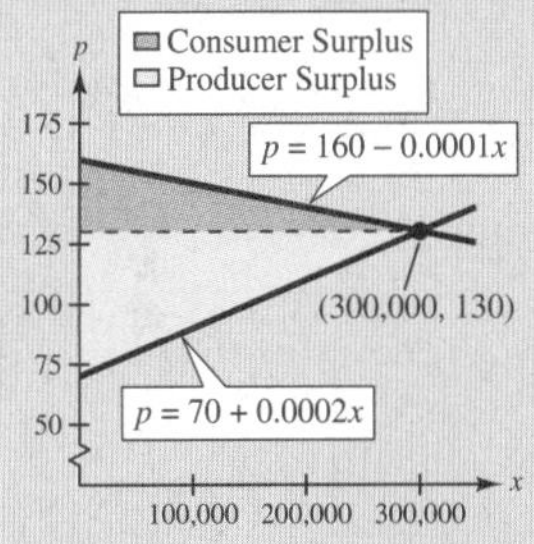

(b) Consumer surplus: \$4,500,000
Producer surplus: \$9,000,000

90. (a)
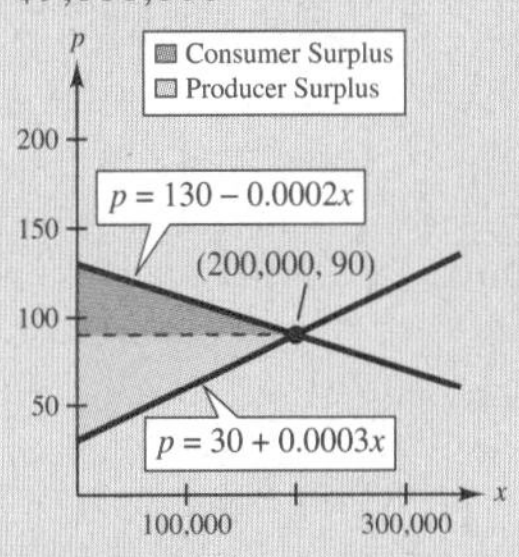

(b) Consumer surplus: \$4,000,000
Producer surplus: \$6,000,000

100. 5 walking shoes
2 running shoes
Optimal profit: \$138

101. 750 units of model A
1000 units of model B
Optimal profit: \$83,750

103. $\frac{2}{3}$ regular unleaded
$\frac{1}{3}$ premium unleaded
Optimal cost: \$1.93

106. False. An objective function can have no maximum value, one point where a maximum value occurs, or an infinite number of points where a maximum value occurs.

107. $\begin{cases} 4x + y = -22 \\ \frac{1}{2}x + y = 6 \end{cases}$

108. $\begin{cases} x - y = 9 \\ 3x + y = 11 \end{cases}$

109. $\begin{cases} 3x + y = 7 \\ -6x + 3y = 1 \end{cases}$

110. $\begin{cases} x + 5y = 9 \\ x + 10y = 20 \end{cases}$

111. $\begin{cases} x + y + z = 6 \\ x + y - z = 0 \\ x - y - z = 2 \end{cases}$

112. $\begin{cases} x - 2y + z = -7 \\ 2x + y - 4z = -25 \\ -x + 3y - z = 12 \end{cases}$

113. $\begin{cases} 2x + 2y - 3z = 7 \\ x - 2y + z = 4 \\ -x + 4y - z = -1 \end{cases}$

114. $\begin{cases} 2x + y + 4z = -6 \\ -4x + 2y + 4z = -5 \\ 4x - y + z = -\frac{3}{4} \end{cases}$

115. An inconsistent system of linear equations has no solution.

100. OPTIMAL PROFIT A shoe manufacturer produces a walking shoe and a running shoe yielding profits of \$18 and \$24, respectively. Each shoe must go through three processes, for which the required times per unit are shown in the table.

	Process I	Process II	Process III
Hours for walking shoe	4	1	1
Hours for running shoe	2	2	1
Hours available per day	24	9	8

What is the optimal production level for each type of shoe? What is the optimal profit? See margin.

101. OPTIMAL PROFIT A manufacturer produces two models of bicycles. The times (in hours) required for assembling, painting, and packaging each model are shown in the table.

Process	Hours, model A	Hours, model B
Assembling	2	2.5
Painting	4	1
Packaging	1	0.75

The total times available for assembling, painting, and packaging are 4000 hours, 4800 hours, and 1500 hours, respectively. The profits per unit are \$45 for model A and \$50 for model B. What is the optimal production level for each model? What is the optimal profit? See margin.

102. OPTIMAL COST A pet supply company mixes two brands of dry dog food. Brand X costs \$15 per bag and contains eight units of nutritional element A, one unit of nutritional element B, and two units of nutritional element C. Brand Y costs \$30 per bag and contains two units of nutritional element A, one unit of nutritional element B, and seven units of nutritional element C. Each bag of mixed dog food must contain at least 16 units, 5 units, and 20 units of nutritional elements A, B, and C, respectively. Find the numbers of bags of brands X and Y that should be mixed to produce a mixture meeting the minimum nutritional requirements and having an optimal cost. What is the optimal cost?

3 bags of brand X
2 bags of brand Y
Optimal cost: \$105

103. OPTIMAL COST Regular unleaded gasoline and premium unleaded gasoline have octane ratings of 87 and 93, respectively. For the week of March 23, 2009, regular unleaded gasoline in Houston, Texas averaged \$1.85 per gallon. For the same week, premium unleaded gasoline averaged \$2.10 per gallon. Determine the blend of regular and premium unleaded gasoline that results in an optimal cost of mid-grade unleaded (89-octane) gasoline. What is the optimal cost? (Source: Energy Information Administration)
See margin.

EXPLORATION

TRUE OR FALSE? In Exercises 104–106, determine whether the statement is true or false. Justify your answer.

104. If a system of equations consists of a circle and a parabola, it is possible for the system to have three solutions. True. The system can have from 0 to 4 solutions.

105. The system

$\begin{cases} y \le 5 \\ y \ge -2 \\ y \ge \frac{7}{2}x - 9 \\ y \ge -\frac{7}{2}x + 26 \end{cases}$

False. To represent a region covered by an isosceles trapezoid, the last two inequality signs should be $\le$.

represents the region covered by an isosceles trapezoid.

106. It is possible for an objective function of a linear programming problem to have exactly 10 maximum value points. See margin.

In Exercises 107–110, find a system of linear equations having the ordered pair as a solution. (There are many correct answers.) 107–110. See margin.

107. $(-8, 10)$
108. $(5, -4)$
109. $\left(\frac{4}{3}, 3\right)$
110. $\left(-2, \frac{11}{5}\right)$

In Exercises 111–114, find a system of linear equations having the ordered triple as a solution. (There are many correct answers.) 111–114. See margin.

111. $(4, -1, 3)$
112. $(-3, 5, 6)$
113. $\left(5, \frac{3}{2}, 2\right)$
114. $\left(-\frac{1}{2}, -2, -\frac{3}{4}\right)$

115. WRITING Explain what is meant by an inconsistent system of linear equations. See margin.

116. How can you tell graphically that a system of linear equations in two variables has no solution? Give an example.
The lines are distinct and parallel.
$\begin{cases} x + 2y = 3 \\ 2x + 4y = 9 \end{cases}$

7 CHAPTER TEST

See www.CalcChat.com for worked-out solutions to odd-numbered exercises.

Take this test as you would take a test in class. When you are finished, check your work against the answers given in the back of the book.

In Exercises 1–3, solve the system by the method of substitution.

1. $\begin{cases} x + y = -9 \\ 5x - 8y = 20 \end{cases}$ $(-4, -5)$

2. $\begin{cases} y = x - 1 \\ y = (x - 1)^3 \end{cases}$ $(0, -1), (1, 0), (2, 1)$

3. $\begin{cases} 2x - y^2 = 0 \\ x - y = 4 \end{cases}$ $(8, 4), (2, -2)$

In Exercises 4–6, solve the system graphically. 4–6. See margin.

4. $\begin{cases} 3x - 6y = 0 \\ 3x + 6y = 18 \end{cases}$

5. $\begin{cases} y = 9 - x^2 \\ y = x + 3 \end{cases}$

6. $\begin{cases} y - \ln x = 12 \\ 7x - 2y + 11 = -6 \end{cases}$

In Exercises 7–10, solve the linear system by the method of elimination.

7. $\begin{cases} 3x + 4y = -26 \\ 7x - 5y = 11 \end{cases}$ $(-2, -5)$

8. $\begin{cases} 1.4x - y = 17 \\ 0.8x + 6y = -10 \end{cases}$ $(10, -3)$

9. $\begin{cases} x - 2y + 3z = 11 \\ 2x - z = 3 \\ 3y + z = -8 \end{cases}$ $(2, -3, 1)$

10. $\begin{cases} 3x + 2y + z = 17 \\ -x + y + z = 4 \\ x - y - z = 3 \end{cases}$ No solution

11–14. See margin.

In Exercises 11–14, write the partial fraction decomposition of the rational expression.

11. $\dfrac{2x + 5}{x^2 - x - 2}$ **12.** $\dfrac{3x^2 - 2x + 4}{x^2(2 - x)}$ **13.** $\dfrac{x^2 + 5}{x^3 - x}$ **14.** $\dfrac{x^2 - 4}{x^3 + 2x}$

In Exercises 15–17, sketch the graph and label the vertices of the solution of the system of inequalities. 15–17. See margin.

15. $\begin{cases} 2x + y \le 4 \\ 2x - y \ge 0 \\ x \ge 0 \end{cases}$

16. $\begin{cases} y < -x^2 + x + 4 \\ y > 4x \end{cases}$

17. $\begin{cases} x^2 + y^2 \le 36 \\ x \ge 2 \\ y \ge -4 \end{cases}$

18. Find the maximum and minimum values of the objective function $z = 20x + 12y$, and where they occur, subject to the following constraints.

$$\left.\begin{aligned} x &\ge 0 \\ y &\ge 0 \\ x + 4y &\le 32 \\ 3x + 2y &\le 36 \end{aligned}\right\} \text{Constraints}$$

18. Maximum at (12, 0): 240; Minimum at (0, 0): 0

19. \$24,000 in 4% fund; \$26,000 in 5.5% fund

19. A total of \$50,000 is invested in two funds paying 4% and 5.5% simple interest. The yearly interest is \$2390. How much is invested at each rate?

20. Find the equation of the parabola $y = ax^2 + bx + c$ passing through the points $(0, 6)$, $(-2, 2)$, and $(3, \frac{9}{2})$. $y = -\frac{1}{2}x^2 + x + 6$

21. A manufacturer produces two types of television stands. The amounts (in hours) of time for assembling, staining, and packaging the two models are shown in the table at the left. The total amounts of time available for assembling, staining, and packaging are 4000, 8950, and 2650 hours, respectively. The profits per unit are \$30 (model I) and \$40 (model II). What is the optimal inventory level for each model? What is the optimal profit? 0 units of model I; 5300 units of model II
Optimal profit: \$212,000

	Model I	Model II
Assembling	0.5	0.75
Staining	2.0	1.5
Packaging	0.5	0.5

TABLE FOR 21

4.

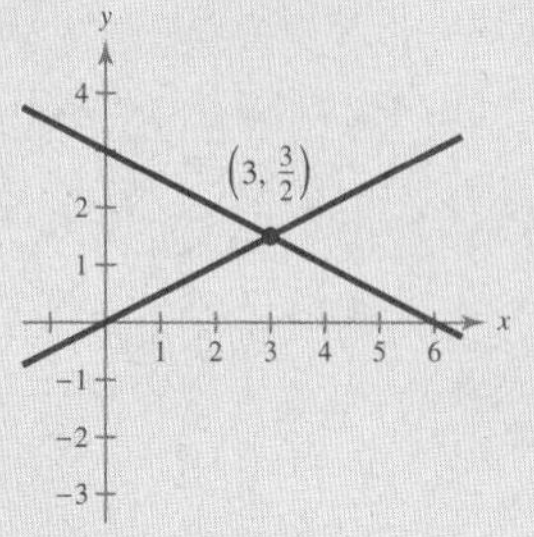

$(3, \frac{3}{2})$

5.

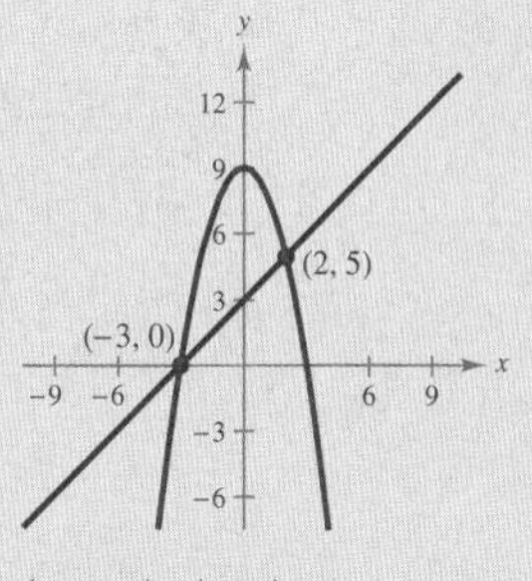

$(-3, 0), (2, 5)$

6.

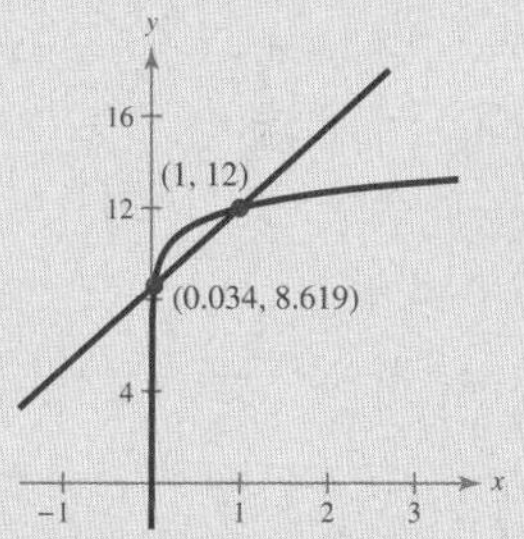

$(1, 12), (0.034, 8.619)$

11. $-\dfrac{1}{x + 1} + \dfrac{3}{x - 2}$

12. $\dfrac{2}{x^2} + \dfrac{3}{2 - x}$

13. $-\dfrac{5}{x} + \dfrac{3}{x + 1} + \dfrac{3}{x - 1}$

14. $-\dfrac{2}{x} + \dfrac{3x}{x^2 + 2}$

15.

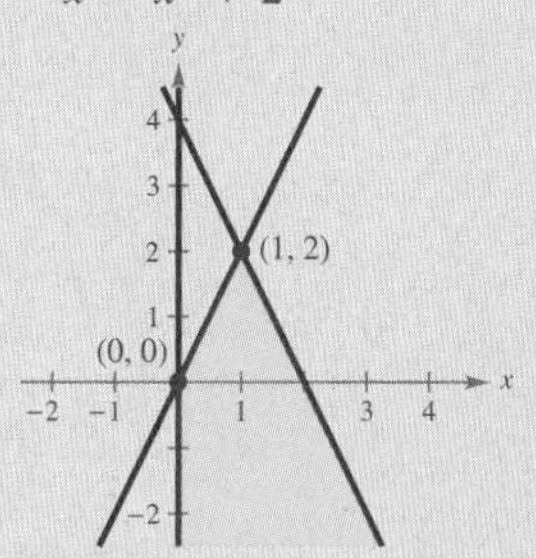

16.

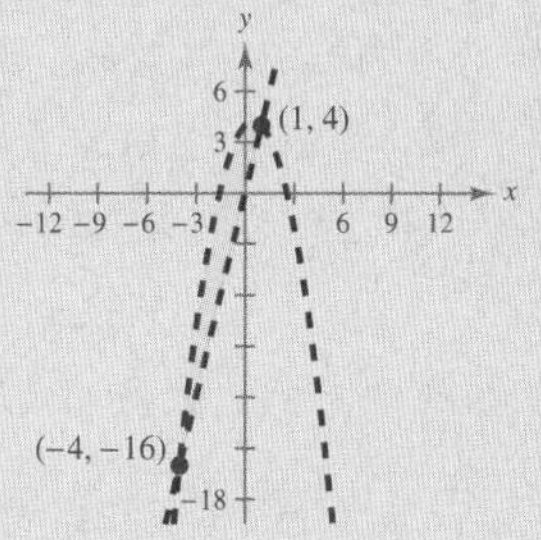

17.

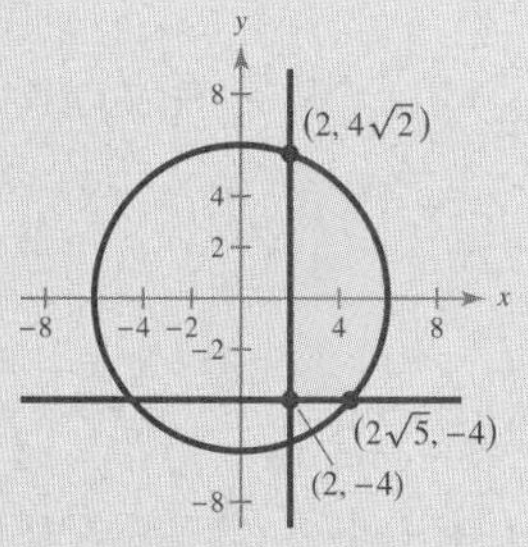

PROOFS IN MATHEMATICS

An **indirect proof** can be useful in proving statements of the form "p implies q." Recall that the conditional statement $p \rightarrow q$ is false only when p is true and q is false. To prove a conditional statement indirectly, assume that p is true and q is false. If this assumption leads to an impossibility, then you have proved that the conditional statement is true. An indirect proof is also called a **proof by contradiction.**

You can use an indirect proof to prove the following conditional statement,

"If a is a positive integer and a^2 is divisible by 2, then a is divisible by 2,"

as follows. First, assume that p, "a is a positive integer and a^2 is divisible by 2," is true and q, "a is divisible by 2," is false. This means that a is not divisible by 2. If so, a is odd and can be written as $a = 2n + 1$, where n is an integer.

$a = 2n + 1$ — Definition of an odd integer

$a^2 = 4n^2 + 4n + 1$ — Square each side.

$a^2 = 2(2n^2 + 2n) + 1$ — Distributive Property

So, by the definition of an odd integer, a^2 is odd. This contradicts the assumption, and you can conclude that a is divisible by 2.

Example Using an Indirect Proof

Use an indirect proof to prove that $\sqrt{2}$ is an irrational number.

Solution

Begin by assuming that $\sqrt{2}$ is *not* an irrational number. Then $\sqrt{2}$ can be written as the quotient of two integers a and $b (b \neq 0)$ that have no common factors.

$\sqrt{2} = \frac{a}{b}$ — Assume that $\sqrt{2}$ is a rational number.

$2 = \frac{a^2}{b^2}$ — Square each side.

$2b^2 = a^2$ — Multiply each side by b^2.

This implies that 2 is a factor of a^2. So, 2 is also a factor of a, and a can be written as $2c$, where c is an integer.

$2b^2 = (2c)^2$ — Substitute $2c$ for a.

$2b^2 = 4c^2$ — Simplify.

$b^2 = 2c^2$ — Divide each side by 2.

This implies that 2 is a factor of b^2 and also a factor of b. So, 2 is a factor of both a and b. This contradicts the assumption that a and b have no common factors. So, you can conclude that $\sqrt{2}$ is an irrational number.

566

PROBLEM SOLVING

This collection of thought-provoking and challenging exercises further explores and expands upon concepts learned in this chapter.

1. A theorem from geometry states that if a triangle is inscribed in a circle such that one side of the triangle is a diameter of the circle, then the triangle is a right triangle. Show that this theorem is true for the circle See margin.

$$x^2 + y^2 = 100$$

and the triangle formed by the lines

$$y = 0,\ y = \tfrac{1}{2}x + 5, \text{ and } y = -2x + 20.$$

2. Find k_1 and k_2 such that the system of equations has an infinite number of solutions. $k_1 = -\frac{10}{3}, k_2 = \frac{16}{3}$

$$\begin{cases} 3x - 5y = 8 \\ 2x + k_1 y = k_2 \end{cases}$$

3. Consider the following system of linear equations in x and y. $ad \neq bc$

$$\begin{cases} ax + by = e \\ cx + dy = f \end{cases}$$

Under what conditions will the system have exactly one solution?

4. Graph the lines determined by each system of linear equations. Then use Gaussian elimination to solve each system. At each step of the elimination process, graph the corresponding lines. What do you observe? See margin.

(a) $\begin{cases} x - 4y = -3 \\ 5x - 6y = 13 \end{cases}$

(b) $\begin{cases} 2x - 3y = 7 \\ -4x + 6y = -14 \end{cases}$

5. A system of two equations in two unknowns is solved and has a finite number of solutions. Determine the maximum number of solutions of the system satisfying each condition.

(a) Both equations are linear. One

(b) One equation is linear and the other is quadratic. Two

(c) Both equations are quadratic. Four

6. In the 2008 presidential election, approximately 125.2 million voters divided their votes between Barack Obama and John McCain. Obama received approximately 8.5 million more votes than McCain. Write and solve a system of equations to find the total number of votes cast for each candidate. Let D represent the number of votes cast for Obama, and let R represent the number of votes cast for McCain. (Source: CNN.com)

$D + R = 125{,}200{,}000$

$D - R = 8{,}500{,}000$

Barack Obama: 66,850,000

John McCain: 58,350,000

7. The Vietnam Veterans Memorial (or "The Wall") in Washington, D.C. was designed by Maya Ying Lin when she was a student at Yale University. This monument has two vertical, triangular sections of black granite with a common side (see figure). The bottom of each section is level with the ground. The tops of the two sections can be approximately modeled by the equations

$$-2x + 50y = 505 \quad \text{and} \quad 2x + 50y = 505$$

when the x-axis is superimposed at the base of the wall. Each unit in the coordinate system represents 1 foot. How high is the memorial at the point where the two sections meet? How long is each section?
10.1 ft; About 252.7 ft

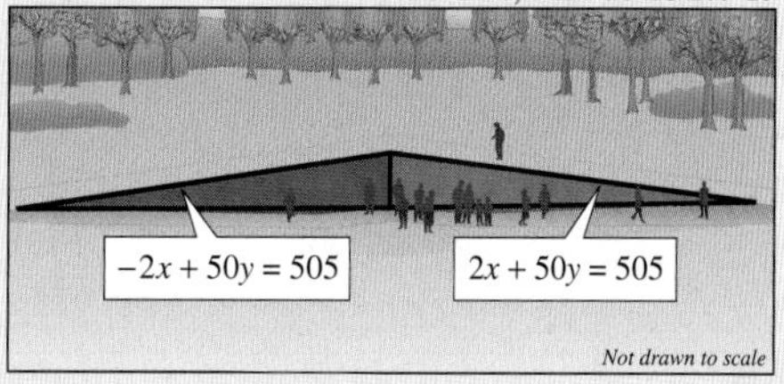

8. Weights of atoms and molecules are measured in atomic mass units (u). A molecule of C_2H_6 (ethane) is made up of two carbon atoms and six hydrogen atoms and weighs 30.070 u. A molecule of C_3H_8 (propane) is made up of three carbon atoms and eight hydrogen atoms and weighs 44.097 u. Find the weights of a carbon atom and a hydrogen atom. Carbon: 12.011 u; Hydrogen: 1.008 u

9. Connecting a DVD player to a television set requires a cable with special connectors at both ends. You buy a six-foot cable for \$15.50 and a three-foot cable for \$10.25. Assuming that the cost of a cable is the sum of the cost of the two connectors and the cost of the cable itself, what is the cost of a four-foot cable? Explain your reasoning. \$12.00

10. A hotel 35 miles from an airport runs a shuttle service to and from the airport. The 9:00 A.M. bus leaves for the airport traveling at 30 miles per hour. The 9:15 A.M. bus leaves for the airport traveling at 40 miles per hour. Write a system of linear equations that represents distance as a function of time for each bus. Graph and solve the system. How far from the airport will the 9:15 A.M. bus catch up to the 9:00 A.M. bus? See margin.

10. $\begin{cases} d_1 = 30t \\ d_2 = 40\left(t - \frac{1}{4}\right) \end{cases}$

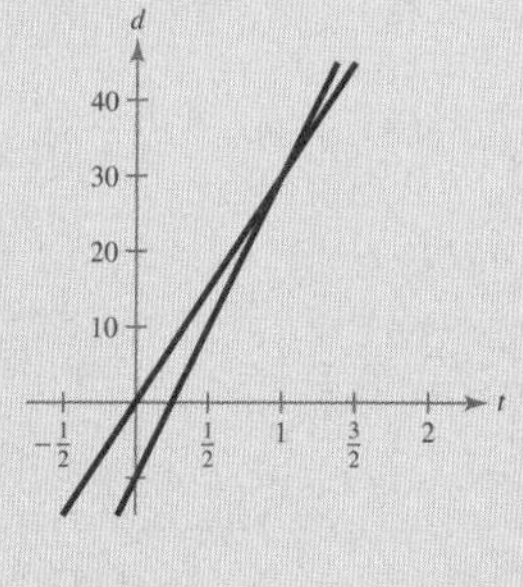

(1, 30); 5 mi

1.

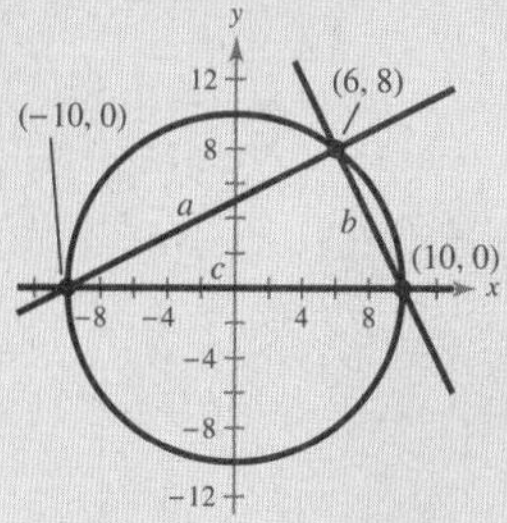

$a = 8\sqrt{5}, b = 4\sqrt{5}, c = 20$

$(8\sqrt{5})^2 + (4\sqrt{5})^2 = 20^2$

Therefore, the triangle is a right triangle.

4. (a)

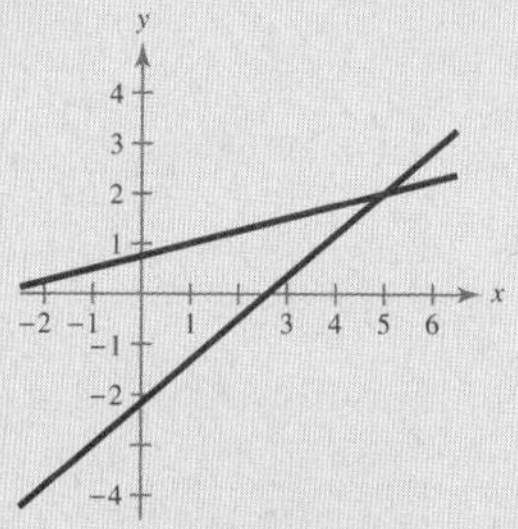

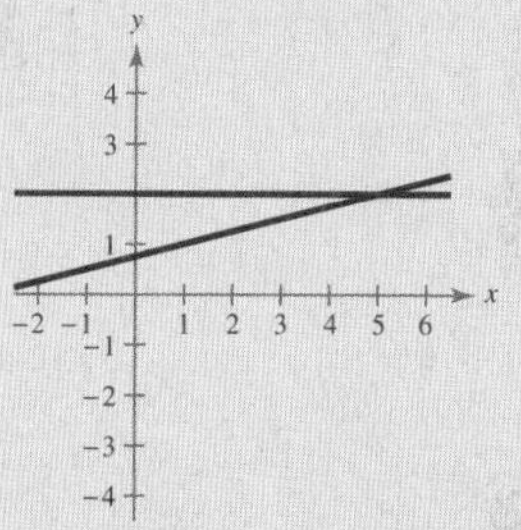

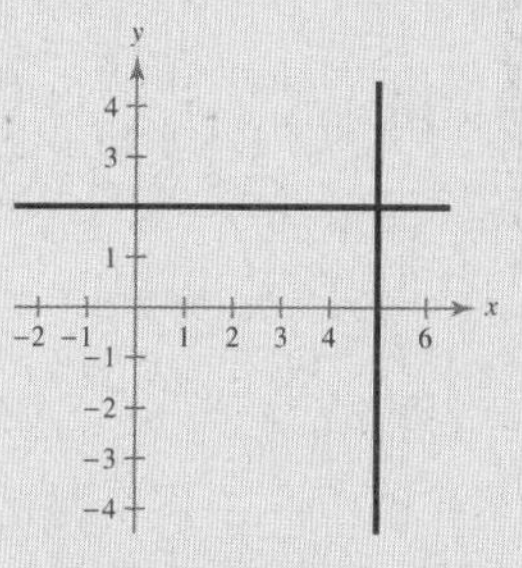

(5, 2)

Answers will vary.

(b)

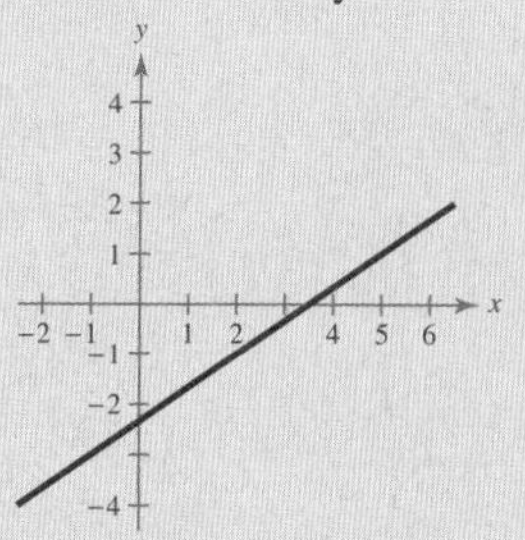

$\left(\frac{3}{2}a + \frac{7}{2}, a\right)$

Answers will vary.

13. (a) $\left(\dfrac{-5a+16}{6}, \dfrac{5a-16}{6}, a\right)$

(b) $\left(\dfrac{-11a+36}{14}, \dfrac{13a-40}{14}, a\right)$

(c) $(-a+3, a-3, a)$

(d) Infinitely many

15. $\begin{cases} a + t \le 32 \\ 0.15a \ge 1.9 \\ 193a + 772t \ge 11{,}000 \end{cases}$

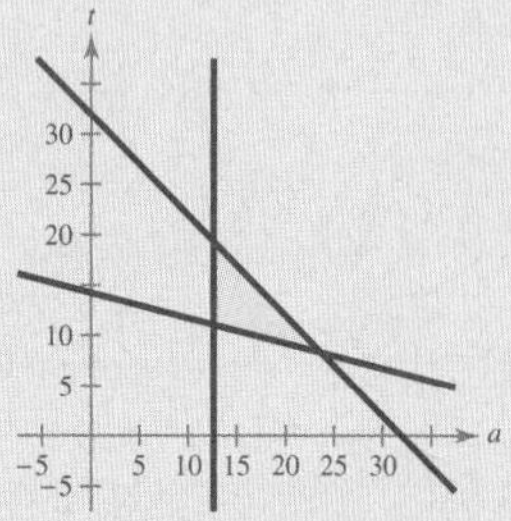

16. (a) $\begin{cases} y \ge 3.65x + 91 \\ y \le 4.85x + 119 \\ x \ge 0 \\ y \ge 91 \end{cases}$

(b)

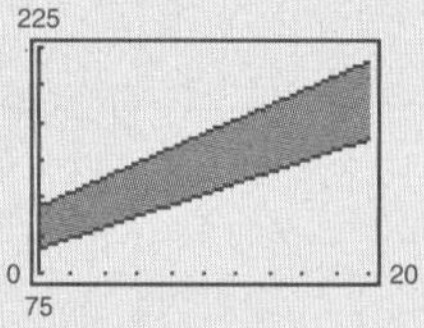

17. (a) $\begin{cases} x + y \le 200 \\ x \ge 60 \\ 0 < y \le 130 \end{cases}$

(b)

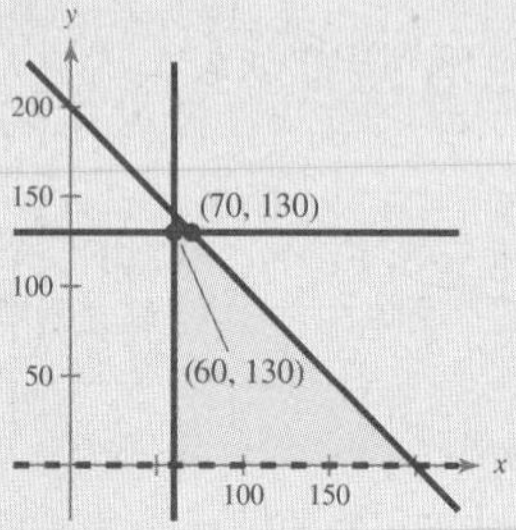

(c) No, because the total cholesterol is greater than 200 milligrams per deciliter.

(d) LDL: 135 mg/dL, HDL: 65 mg/dL, LDL + HDL: 200 mg/dL

(e) $(75, 105)$; $\frac{180}{75} = 2.4 < 5$; Answers will vary.

11. Solve each system of equations by letting $X = 1/x$, $Y = 1/y$, and $Z = 1/z$.

(a) $\begin{cases} \dfrac{12}{x} - \dfrac{12}{y} = 7 \\ \dfrac{3}{x} + \dfrac{4}{y} = 0 \end{cases}$ $(3, -4)$

(b) $\begin{cases} \dfrac{2}{x} + \dfrac{1}{y} - \dfrac{3}{z} = 4 \\ \dfrac{4}{x} + \dfrac{2}{z} = 10 \\ -\dfrac{2}{x} + \dfrac{3}{y} - \dfrac{13}{z} = -8 \end{cases}$ $\left(\dfrac{2}{-a+5}, \dfrac{1}{4a-1}, \dfrac{1}{a}\right)$

12. What values should be given to a, b, and c so that the linear system shown has $(-1, 2, -3)$ as its only solution? $a = 12, b = -4, c = 10$

$$\begin{cases} x + 2y - 3z = a & \text{Equation 1} \\ -x - y + z = b & \text{Equation 2} \\ 2x + 3y - 2z = c & \text{Equation 3} \end{cases}$$

13. The following system has one solution: $x = 1$, $y = -1$, and $z = 2$.

$$\begin{cases} 4x - 2y + 5z = 16 \\ x + y = 0 \\ -x - 3y + 2z = 6 \end{cases}$$

Solve the system given by (a) Equation 1 and Equation 2, (b) Equation 1 and Equation 3, and (c) Equation 2 and Equation 3. (d) How many solutions does each of these systems have? See margin.

14. Solve the system of linear equations algebraically.

$$\begin{aligned} x_1 - x_2 + 2x_3 + 2x_4 + 6x_5 &= 6 \\ 3x_1 - 2x_2 + 4x_3 + 4x_4 + 12x_5 &= 14 \\ -x_2 - x_3 - x_4 - 3x_5 &= -3 \\ 2x_1 - 2x_2 + 4x_3 + 5x_4 + 15x_5 &= 10 \\ 2x_1 - 2x_2 + 4x_3 + 4x_4 + 13x_5 &= 13 \end{aligned}$$

$x_1 = 2$; $x_2 = \frac{2}{3}$; $x_3 = \frac{13}{3}$; $x_4 = -5$; $x_5 = 1$

15. Each day, an average adult moose can process about 32 kilograms of terrestrial vegetation (twigs and leaves) and aquatic vegetation. From this food, it needs to obtain about 1.9 grams of sodium and 11,000 calories of energy. Aquatic vegetation has about 0.15 gram of sodium per kilogram and about 193 calories of energy per kilogram, whereas terrestrial vegetation has minimal sodium and about four times as much energy as aquatic vegetation. Write and graph a system of inequalities that describes the amounts t and a of terrestrial and aquatic vegetation, respectively, for the daily diet of an average adult moose. (Source: Biology by Numbers) See margin.

16. For a healthy person who is 4 feet 10 inches tall, the recommended minimum weight is about 91 pounds and increases by about 3.65 pounds for each additional inch of height. The recommended maximum weight is about 119 pounds and increases by about 4.85 pounds for each additional inch of height. (Source: U.S. Department of Agriculture)

(a) Let x be the number of inches by which a person's height exceeds 4 feet 10 inches and let y be the person's weight in pounds. Write a system of inequalities that describes the possible values of x and y for a healthy person. See margin.

(b) Use a graphing utility to graph the system of inequalities from part (a). See margin.

(c) What is the recommended weight range for someone 6 feet tall? $142.1 \text{ lb} \le y \le 186.9 \text{ lb}$

17. The cholesterol in human blood is necessary, but too much cholesterol can lead to health problems. A blood cholesterol test gives three readings: LDL ("bad") cholesterol, HDL ("good") cholesterol, and total cholesterol (LDL + HDL). It is recommended that your LDL cholesterol level be less than 130 milligrams per deciliter, your HDL cholesterol level be at least 60 milligrams per deciliter, and your total cholesterol level be no more than 200 milligrams per deciliter. (Source: American Heart Association) See margin.

(a) Write a system of linear inequalities for the recommended cholesterol levels. Let x represent HDL cholesterol and let y represent LDL cholesterol.

(b) Graph the system of inequalities from part (a). Label any vertices of the solution region.

(c) Are the following cholesterol levels within recommendations? Explain your reasoning.

LDL: 120 milligrams per deciliter

HDL: 90 milligrams per deciliter

Total: 210 milligrams per deciliter

(d) Give an example of cholesterol levels in which the LDL cholesterol level is too high but the HDL and total cholesterol levels are acceptable.

(e) Another recommendation is that the ratio of total cholesterol to HDL cholesterol be less than 5. Find a point in your solution region from part (b) that meets this recommendation, and explain why it meets the recommendation.

REGULAR SCHEDULE

Lesson	Day	AVERAGE	ADVANCED
8.1	Day 1	pp. 579–581 Exs. 1–6, 9–15 odd, 19–27 odd, 33, 35, 36, 40, 55, 57	pp. 579–581 Exs. 1–6, 10–18 even, 22–40 even, 56, 58
	Day 2	pp. 579–581 Exs. 7, 8, 42, 43–47 odd, 51, 53, 59–67 odd, 71, 73	pp. 579–581 Exs. 7, 8, 42–44, 46–52 even, 60–76 even
	Day 3	pp. 581–583 Exs. 79, 81, 85, 93–107 odd, 111, 113, 116–120, 122, 123	pp. 581–583 Exs. 80, 82, 86, 92–108 even, 112, 114, 115, 119–123
8.2	Day 1	pp. 594–595 Exs. 1–3, 8, 9, 11, 15, 16, 17–23 odd, 25–27, 29, 30	pp. 594–595 Exs. 1–3, 8–16 even, 17, 18–24 even, 26–28, 30, 32
	Day 2	pp. 594–596 Exs. 4–6, 33, 34–38 even, 41, 43, 47–49, 52, 53, 55	pp. 594–596 Exs. 4–6, 34–40 even, 44–46, 48–56 even
	Day 3	pp. 596–598 Exs. 57, 59, 63–67 odd, 68, 70, 71–77 odd, 78, 79–85 odd, 89, 91	pp. 596–598 Exs. 58–68 even, 70–72, 74, 76–78, 80–86 even, 90–94 even
8.3	Day 1	p. 605 Exs. 1–4, 6–8, 9–17 odd, 20–23, 25, 27, 33	p. 605 Exs. 1–4, 6–14 even, 18–26 even, 32, 34
	Day 2	pp. 605–607 Exs. 37–41 odd, 45, 49–61 odd, 66, 67, 69, 76–78	pp. 605–607 Exs. 38–46 even, 52–62 even, 67, 68, 75, 76, 81
8.4	Day 1	pp. 613–614 Exs. 1–3, 5, 7, 11, 15–27 odd, 30, 31, 63, 65, 71, 73	pp. 613–614 Exs. 1–3, 6–12 even, 16–32 even, 64, 66, 72, 74
	Day 2	pp. 613–615 Exs. 4, 33, 35, 39, 41, 47, 55, 59, 67, 69, 75–85 odd, 91, 92, 95–99 odd, 100	pp. 613–615 Exs. 4, 36–42 even, 50, 56, 60, 68, 70, 76–86 even, 94–100 even
8.5	Day 1	pp. 625–626 Exs. 1–3, 9, 11, 15, 17, 21, 23, 27–37 odd, 41–45 odd, 49, 51	pp. 625–626 Exs. 1–3, 8, 14–18 even, 22, 24, 28–38 even, 42–46 even, 50, 52
	Day 2	pp. 625–627 Exs. 4–6, 56, 58, 59, 61, 62, 65, 67, 71–74, 76	pp. 625–627 Exs. 4–6, 56, 59, 60–68 even, 69, 71–74, 76
Review	Day 1	pp. 630–634 Exs. 5–11 odd, 15, 21, 33–37 odd, 41, 45, 49, 51, 57, 60, 65, 69–73 odd, 77, 85, 93, 105, 113–119 odd, 129, 133, 137, 139, 143, 147, 150, 152	pp. 630–634 Exs. 4–12 even, 18, 20, 28, 34–38 even, 42, 48–52 even, 56, 62, 66, 70–74 even, 78, 86, 102, 114–120 even, 130, 136–140 even, 144, 148, 151, 153
Assess	Day 1	Chapter 8 Test	Chapter 8 Test
Yearly Pacing		Chapter 8 Total – 14 days	Remaining – 64 days

BLOCK SCHEDULE

DAY 1	DAY 2	DAY 3	DAY 4	DAY 5	DAY 6	DAY 7
8.1	**8.1 (CONT.)**	**8.2 (CONT.)**	**8.3**	**8.4**	**8.5**	**REVIEW**
pp. 579–581 Exs. 1–8, 9–15 odd, 19–27 odd, 33, 35, 36, 40, 42, 43–47 odd, 51–67 odd, 71, 73	pp. 581–583 Exs. 79, 81, 85, 93–107 odd, 111, 113, 116–120, 122, 123	pp. 594–598 Exs. 4–6, 33, 34–38 even, 41, 43, 47–49, 52, 53, 55–59 odd, 63–67 odd, 68, 70, 71–77 odd, 78, 79–85 odd, 89, 91	pp. 605–607 Exs. 1–4, 6–8, 9–17 odd, 20–23, 25, 27, 33, 37–41 odd, 45, 49–61 odd, 66, 67, 69, 76–78	pp. 613–615 Exs. 1–5, 7, 11, 15–27 odd, 30, 31–35 odd, 39, 41, 47, 55, 59, 63–85 odd, 91, 92, 95–99 odd, 100	pp. 625–627 Exs. 1–6, 9, 11, 15, 17, 21, 23, 27–37 odd, 41–45 odd, 49, 51, 56, 58, 59, 61, 62, 65, 67, 71–74, 76	pp. 630–634 Exs. 5–11 odd, 15, 21, 33–37 odd, 41, 45, 49, 51, 57, 60, 65, 69–73 odd, 77, 85, 93, 105, 113–119 odd, 129, 133, 137, 139, 143, 147, 150, 152
	8.2					**ASSESS**
	pp. 594–595 Exs. 1–3, 8, 9, 11, 15, 16, 17–23 odd, 25–27, 29, 30					Chapter 8 Test

Yearly Pacing Chapter 8 Total – 7 days Remaining – 32 days

Matrices and Determinants

8

In Mathematics

Matrices are used to model and solve a variety of problems. For instance, you can use matrices to solve systems of linear equations.

In Real Life

Matrices are used to model inventory levels, electrical networks, investment portfolios, and other real-life situations. For instance, you can use a matrix to model the number of people in the United States who participate in snowboarding. (See Exercise 114, page 583.)

Graham Heywood/istockphoto.com

IN CAREERS

There are many careers that use matrices. Several are listed below.

- Bank Teller
  Exercise 110, page 582
- Political Analyst
  Exercise 70, page 597
- Small Business Owner
  Exercises 69–72, pages 606 and 607
- Florist
  Exercise 74, page 607

PLAN AND PREPARE

Main Ideas

In Chapter 8, students learn to write matrices, perform matrix operations, and use matrices to solve problems. Students first learn how to solve a system of equations by writing and operating on the system in matrix form. After studying addition and multiplication of matrices, they then learn how to find the inverse of a matrix and use the inverse to solve systems of equations. Next, students learn to find the determinant of a square matrix. The chapter concludes by applying matrices to applications including Cramer's Rule, finding areas of triangles, and encoding messages.

Chapter Planning Guide

Chapter Resources

- Complete Solutions Guide

Interactive Technology

- Instructor Success Organizer
- Notetaking Guide IAE
- Instructional DVDs
- Animated Precalculus
- PowerLecture with ExamView

1 PLAN AND PREPARE

Warm-up Exercises

Transparency Available
Available at the Instructor's companion site.

Notetaking Guide

Transparency Available
Promotes interactive learning and notetaking skills.
Available at the Instructor's companion site.

Animated Precalculus

An **Animated Precalculus** tutorial is available at the Student companion site for **Section 8.1.**

Pacing

Average: 3 days
Advanced: 3 days
Block: 1 block
0.5 block with 8.2

2 FOCUS AND MOTIVATE

Essential Question

How do you use matrices to solve systems of equations?
Tell students that they will learn how to answer this question by representing systems of equations in matrix form and by manipulating matrices to find solutions.

8.1 MATRICES AND SYSTEMS OF EQUATIONS

What you should learn

- Write matrices and identify their orders.
- Perform elementary row operations on matrices.
- Use matrices and Gaussian elimination to solve systems of linear equations.
- Use matrices and Gauss-Jordan elimination to solve systems of linear equations.

Why you should learn it

You can use matrices to solve systems of linear equations in two or more variables. For instance, in Exercise 113 on page 582, you will use a matrix to find a model for the path of a ball thrown by a baseball player.

Foto Agency/PhotoLibrary

Matrices

In this section, you will study a streamlined technique for solving systems of linear equations. This technique involves the use of a rectangular array of real numbers called a **matrix.** The plural of matrix is *matrices.*

> **Definition of Matrix**
>
> If m and n are positive integers, an $m \times n$ (read "m by n") matrix is a rectangular array
>
> $$\begin{array}{l} \\ \text{Row 1} \\ \text{Row 2} \\ \text{Row 3} \\ \vdots \\ \text{Row } m \end{array} \begin{array}{c} \begin{array}{ccccc} \text{Column 1} & \text{Column 2} & \text{Column 3} & \cdots & \text{Column } n \end{array} \\ \begin{bmatrix} a_{11} & a_{12} & a_{13} & \cdots & a_{1n} \\ a_{21} & a_{22} & a_{23} & \cdots & a_{2n} \\ a_{31} & a_{32} & a_{33} & \cdots & a_{3n} \\ \vdots & \vdots & \vdots & & \vdots \\ a_{m1} & a_{m2} & a_{m3} & \cdots & a_{mn} \end{bmatrix} \end{array}$$
>
> in which each **entry,** a_{ij}, of the matrix is a number. An $m \times n$ matrix has m rows and n columns. Matrices are usually denoted by capital letters.

The entry in the ith row and jth column is denoted by the *double subscript* notation a_{ij}. For instance, a_{23} refers to the entry in the second row, third column. A matrix having m rows and n columns is said to be of **order** $m \times n$. If $m = n$, the matrix is **square** of order $m \times m$ (or $n \times n$). For a square matrix, the entries $a_{11}, a_{22}, a_{33}, \ldots$ are the **main diagonal** entries.

Example 1 Order of Matrices

Determine the order of each matrix.

a. $[2]$ **b.** $\begin{bmatrix} 1 & -3 & 0 & \frac{1}{2} \end{bmatrix}$

c. $\begin{bmatrix} 0 & 0 \\ 0 & 0 \end{bmatrix}$ **d.** $\begin{bmatrix} 5 & 0 \\ 2 & -2 \\ -7 & 4 \end{bmatrix}$

Solution

a. This matrix has *one* row and *one* column. The order of the matrix is 1×1.

b. This matrix has *one* row and *four* columns. The order of the matrix is 1×4.

c. This matrix has *two* rows and *two* columns. The order of the matrix is 2×2.

d. This matrix has *three* rows and *two* columns. The order of the matrix is 3×2.

CHECK*Point* Now try Exercise 9.

A matrix that has only one row is called a **row matrix,** and a matrix that has only one column is called a **column matrix.**

Resource Planning Guide

Chapter Resources
- Complete Solutions Guide

Workbooks
- Notetaking Guide
- Student Solutions Guide

Interactive Technology
- Instructor Success Organizer
- Notetaking Guide IAE
- Instructional DVDs
- Animated Precalculus
- PowerLecture with ExamView

A matrix derived from a system of linear equations (each written in standard form with the constant term on the right) is the **augmented matrix** of the system. Moreover, the matrix derived from the coefficients of the system (but not including the constant terms) is the **coefficient matrix** of the system.

System:
$$\begin{cases} x - 4y + 3z = 5 \\ -x + 3y - z = -3 \\ 2x \qquad - 4z = 6 \end{cases}$$

Augmented Matrix:
$$\begin{bmatrix} 1 & -4 & 3 & \vdots & 5 \\ -1 & 3 & -1 & \vdots & -3 \\ 2 & 0 & -4 & \vdots & 6 \end{bmatrix}$$

Coefficient Matrix:
$$\begin{bmatrix} 1 & -4 & 3 \\ -1 & 3 & -1 \\ 2 & 0 & -4 \end{bmatrix}$$

Study Tip

The vertical dots in an augmented matrix separate the coefficients of the linear system from the constant terms.

Note the use of 0 for the missing coefficient of the y-variable in the third equation, and also note the fourth column of constant terms in the augmented matrix.

When forming either the coefficient matrix or the augmented matrix of a system, you should begin by vertically aligning the variables in the equations and using zeros for the coefficients of the missing variables.

Example 2 Writing an Augmented Matrix

Write the augmented matrix for the system of linear equations.

$$\begin{cases} x + 3y - w = 9 \\ -y + 4z + 2w = -2 \\ x - 5z - 6w = 0 \\ 2x + 4y - 3z = 4 \end{cases}$$

What is the order of the augmented matrix?

Solution

Begin by rewriting the linear system and aligning the variables.

$$\begin{cases} x + 3y \qquad\qquad - w = 9 \\ \quad -y + 4z + 2w = -2 \\ x \qquad - 5z - 6w = 0 \\ 2x + 4y - 3z \qquad = 4 \end{cases}$$

Next, use the coefficients and constant terms as the matrix entries. Include zeros for the coefficients of the missing variables.

$$\begin{matrix} R_1 \\ R_2 \\ R_3 \\ R_4 \end{matrix} \begin{bmatrix} 1 & 3 & 0 & -1 & \vdots & 9 \\ 0 & -1 & 4 & 2 & \vdots & -2 \\ 1 & 0 & -5 & -6 & \vdots & 0 \\ 2 & 4 & -3 & 0 & \vdots & 4 \end{bmatrix}$$

The augmented matrix has four rows and five columns, so it is a 4×5 matrix. The notation R_n is used to designate each row in the matrix. For example, Row 1 is represented by R_1.

CHECKPoint Now try Exercise 17.

3 TEACH

Extra Example 1

Determine the order of each matrix.

a. $[-4]$

1×1

b. $\begin{bmatrix} 0 \\ -6 \\ 15 \end{bmatrix}$

3×1

c. $\begin{bmatrix} 3 & 1 & 0 \\ -9 & 7 & 4 \\ -2 & 2 & 6 \end{bmatrix}$

3×3

d. $\begin{bmatrix} -1 & 4 & 11 & 0 \\ 6 & 3 & -5 & 7 \end{bmatrix}$

2×4

Extra Example 2

Write the augmented matrix for the system of linear equations.

$$\begin{cases} x + y + z = 2 \\ 2x - y + 3z = -1 \\ -x + 2y - z = 4 \end{cases}$$

$$\begin{bmatrix} 1 & 1 & 1 & \vdots & 2 \\ 2 & -1 & 3 & \vdots & -1 \\ -1 & 2 & -1 & \vdots & 4 \end{bmatrix}$$

Elementary Row Operations

In Section 7.3, you studied three operations that can be used on a system of linear equations to produce an equivalent system.

1. Interchange two equations.
2. Multiply an equation by a nonzero constant.
3. Add a multiple of an equation to another equation.

In matrix terminology, these three operations correspond to **elementary row operations.** An elementary row operation on an augmented matrix of a given system of linear equations produces a new augmented matrix corresponding to a new (but equivalent) system of linear equations. Two matrices are **row-equivalent** if one can be obtained from the other by a sequence of elementary row operations.

Elementary Row Operations

1. Interchange two rows.
2. Multiply a row by a nonzero constant.
3. Add a multiple of a row to another row.

Although elementary row operations are simple to perform, they involve a lot of arithmetic. Because it is easy to make a mistake, you should get in the habit of noting the elementary row operations performed in each step so that you can go back and check your work.

Example 3 Elementary Row Operations

a. Interchange the first and second rows of the original matrix.

Original Matrix $\begin{bmatrix} 0 & 1 & 3 & 4 \\ -1 & 2 & 0 & 3 \\ 2 & -3 & 4 & 1 \end{bmatrix}$ *New Row-Equivalent Matrix* $\begin{matrix} R_2 \\ R_1 \\ \end{matrix}\begin{bmatrix} -1 & 2 & 0 & 3 \\ 0 & 1 & 3 & 4 \\ 2 & -3 & 4 & 1 \end{bmatrix}$

b. Multiply the first row of the original matrix by $\frac{1}{2}$.

Original Matrix $\begin{bmatrix} 2 & -4 & 6 & -2 \\ 1 & 3 & -3 & 0 \\ 5 & -2 & 1 & 2 \end{bmatrix}$ *New Row-Equivalent Matrix* $\begin{matrix} \frac{1}{2}R_1 \rightarrow \\ \\ \end{matrix}\begin{bmatrix} 1 & -2 & 3 & -1 \\ 1 & 3 & -3 & 0 \\ 5 & -2 & 1 & 2 \end{bmatrix}$

c. Add -2 times the first row of the original matrix to the third row.

Original Matrix $\begin{bmatrix} 1 & 2 & -4 & 3 \\ 0 & 3 & -2 & -1 \\ 2 & 1 & 5 & -2 \end{bmatrix}$ *New Row-Equivalent Matrix* $\begin{matrix} \\ \\ -2R_1 + R_3 \rightarrow \end{matrix}\begin{bmatrix} 1 & 2 & -4 & 3 \\ 0 & 3 & -2 & -1 \\ 0 & -3 & 13 & -8 \end{bmatrix}$

Note that the elementary row operation is written beside the row that is *changed.*

CHECKPoint Now try Exercise 37.

TECHNOLOGY

Most graphing utilities can perform elementary row operations on matrices. Consult the user's guide for your graphing utility for specific keystrokes.

After performing a row operation, the new row-equivalent matrix that is displayed on your graphing utility is stored in the *answer* variable. You should use the *answer* variable and not the original matrix for subsequent row operations.

Extra Example 3

Perform the following row operations on the given matrix.

a. Interchange the first and third rows of the original matrix.

$\begin{bmatrix} 1 & 3 & 4 & 0 \\ 0 & 3 & -1 & 2 \\ 1 & 2 & -3 & 4 \end{bmatrix}$

$\begin{bmatrix} 1 & 2 & -3 & 4 \\ 0 & 3 & -1 & 2 \\ 1 & 3 & 4 & 0 \end{bmatrix}$

b. Multiply the second row of the original matrix by $-\frac{1}{2}$.

$\begin{bmatrix} 1 & 0 & 3 & 6 \\ 2 & -8 & 4 & 0 \\ 5 & 7 & 9 & 4 \end{bmatrix}$

$\begin{bmatrix} 1 & 0 & 3 & 6 \\ -1 & 4 & -2 & 0 \\ 5 & 7 & 9 & 4 \end{bmatrix}$

c. Add -3 times the first row of the original matrix to the second row.

$\begin{bmatrix} 4 & 5 & 9 & -1 \\ 0 & 5 & 2 & 3 \\ -2 & 7 & -3 & 1 \end{bmatrix}$

$\begin{bmatrix} 4 & 5 & 9 & -1 \\ -12 & -10 & -25 & 6 \\ -2 & 7 & -3 & 1 \end{bmatrix}$

In Example 3 in Section 7.3, you used Gaussian elimination with back-substitution to solve a system of linear equations. The next example demonstrates the matrix version of Gaussian elimination. The two methods are essentially the same. The basic difference is that with matrices you do not need to keep writing the variables.

Example 4 Comparing Linear Systems and Matrix Operations

Linear System

$$\begin{cases} x - 2y + 3z = 9 \\ -x + 3y = -4 \\ 2x - 5y + 5z = 17 \end{cases}$$

Associated Augmented Matrix

$$\begin{bmatrix} 1 & -2 & 3 & \vdots & 9 \\ -1 & 3 & 0 & \vdots & -4 \\ 2 & -5 & 5 & \vdots & 17 \end{bmatrix}$$

Add the first equation to the second equation.

$$\begin{cases} x - 2y + 3z = 9 \\ y + 3z = 5 \\ 2x - 5y + 5z = 17 \end{cases}$$

Add the first row to the second row ($R_1 + R_2$).

$$\begin{matrix} \\ R_1 + R_2 \rightarrow \\ \\ \end{matrix} \begin{bmatrix} 1 & -2 & 3 & \vdots & 9 \\ 0 & 1 & 3 & \vdots & 5 \\ 2 & -5 & 5 & \vdots & 17 \end{bmatrix}$$

Add -2 times the first equation to the third equation.

$$\begin{cases} x - 2y + 3z = 9 \\ y + 3z = 5 \\ -y - z = -1 \end{cases}$$

Add -2 times the first row to the third row ($-2R_1 + R_3$).

$$\begin{matrix} \\ \\ -2R_1 + R_3 \rightarrow \end{matrix} \begin{bmatrix} 1 & -2 & 3 & \vdots & 9 \\ 0 & 1 & 3 & \vdots & 5 \\ 0 & -1 & -1 & \vdots & -1 \end{bmatrix}$$

Add the second equation to the third equation.

$$\begin{cases} x - 2y + 3z = 9 \\ y + 3z = 5 \\ 2z = 4 \end{cases}$$

Add the second row to the third row ($R_2 + R_3$).

$$\begin{matrix} \\ \\ R_2 + R_3 \rightarrow \end{matrix} \begin{bmatrix} 1 & -2 & 3 & \vdots & 9 \\ 0 & 1 & 3 & \vdots & 5 \\ 0 & 0 & 2 & \vdots & 4 \end{bmatrix}$$

Multiply the third equation by $\frac{1}{2}$.

$$\begin{cases} x - 2y + 3z = 9 \\ y + 3z = 5 \\ z = 2 \end{cases}$$

Multiply the third row by $\frac{1}{2}$ ($\frac{1}{2}R_3$).

$$\begin{matrix} \\ \\ \frac{1}{2}R_3 \rightarrow \end{matrix} \begin{bmatrix} 1 & -2 & 3 & \vdots & 9 \\ 0 & 1 & 3 & \vdots & 5 \\ 0 & 0 & 1 & \vdots & 2 \end{bmatrix}$$

At this point, you can use back-substitution to find x and y.

$y + 3(2) = 5$ Substitute 2 for z.

$y = -1$ Solve for y.

$x - 2(-1) + 3(2) = 9$ Substitute -1 for y and 2 for z.

$x = 1$ Solve for x.

The solution is $x = 1$, $y = -1$, and $z = 2$.

CHECK *Point* Now try Exercise 39.

WARNING / CAUTION

Arithmetic errors are often made when elementary row operations are performed. Note the operation you perform in each step so that you can go back and check your work.

Study Tip

Remember that you should check a solution by substituting the values of x, y, and z into each equation of the original system. For example, you can check the solution to Example 4 as follows.

Equation 1:
$1 - 2(-1) + 3(2) = 9$ ✓

Equation 2:
$-1 + 3(-1) = -4$ ✓

Equation 3:
$2(1) - 5(-1) + 5(2) = 17$ ✓

Extra Example 4

Solve the system.

$$\begin{cases} x + 3y + 4z = 7 \\ 2x + 7y + 5z = 10 \\ 3x + 10y + 4z = 27 \end{cases}$$

$x = 45$, $y = -10$, $z = -2$

Extra Example 5

Determine whether each matrix is in row-echelon form. If it is, determine whether the matrix is in reduced row-echelon form.

a. $\begin{bmatrix} 1 & 0 & -2 & 4 \\ 0 & 1 & 11 & 3 \\ 0 & 0 & 0 & 0 \end{bmatrix}$

Reduced row-echelon form

b. $\begin{bmatrix} 1 & 3 & 4 & -2 \\ 0 & 0 & 0 & 0 \\ 0 & 1 & 6 & -1 \end{bmatrix}$

Not in row-echelon form because the row of all zeros does not occur at the bottom of the matrix

c. $\begin{bmatrix} 1 & 2 & 3 & 4 \\ 0 & 1 & 5 & 0 \\ 0 & 0 & 1 & 7 \\ 0 & 0 & 0 & 0 \end{bmatrix}$

Row-echelon form

d. $\begin{bmatrix} 1 & 2 & -5 & 3 & 9 \\ 0 & 0 & 1 & 4 & -1 \\ 0 & 0 & 0 & 1 & 6 \\ 0 & 0 & 0 & 0 & 1 \end{bmatrix}$

Row-echelon form

e. $\begin{bmatrix} 1 & 2 & -1 & 8 \\ 0 & 3 & 1 & -4 \\ 0 & 0 & 1 & 3 \end{bmatrix}$

Not in row-echelon form because the first entry in the second row is not a leading 1

f. $\begin{bmatrix} 0 & 1 & 4 & 0 \\ 0 & 0 & 1 & -6 \\ 0 & 0 & 0 & 0 \end{bmatrix}$

Row-echelon form

The last matrix in Example 4 is said to be in **row-echelon form.** The term *echelon* refers to the stair-step pattern formed by the nonzero elements of the matrix. To be in this form, a matrix must have the following properties.

Row-Echelon Form and Reduced Row-Echelon Form

A matrix in **row-echelon form** has the following properties.

1. Any rows consisting entirely of zeros occur at the bottom of the matrix.
2. For each row that does not consist entirely of zeros, the first nonzero entry is 1 (called a **leading 1**).
3. For two successive (nonzero) rows, the leading 1 in the higher row is farther to the left than the leading 1 in the lower row.

A matrix in *row-echelon form* is in **reduced row-echelon form** if every column that has a leading 1 has zeros in every position above and below its leading 1.

It is worth noting that the row-echelon form of a matrix is not unique. That is, two different sequences of elementary row operations may yield different row-echelon forms. However, the *reduced* row-echelon form of a given matrix is unique.

Example 5 Row-Echelon Form

Determine whether each matrix is in row-echelon form. If it is, determine whether the matrix is in reduced row-echelon form.

a. $\begin{bmatrix} 1 & 2 & -1 & 4 \\ 0 & 1 & 0 & 3 \\ 0 & 0 & 1 & -2 \end{bmatrix}$ b. $\begin{bmatrix} 1 & 2 & -1 & 2 \\ 0 & 0 & 0 & 0 \\ 0 & 1 & 2 & -4 \end{bmatrix}$

c. $\begin{bmatrix} 1 & -5 & 2 & -1 & 3 \\ 0 & 0 & 1 & 3 & -2 \\ 0 & 0 & 0 & 1 & 4 \\ 0 & 0 & 0 & 0 & 1 \end{bmatrix}$ d. $\begin{bmatrix} 1 & 0 & 0 & -1 \\ 0 & 1 & 0 & 2 \\ 0 & 0 & 1 & 3 \\ 0 & 0 & 0 & 0 \end{bmatrix}$

e. $\begin{bmatrix} 1 & 2 & -3 & 4 \\ 0 & 2 & 1 & -1 \\ 0 & 0 & 1 & -3 \end{bmatrix}$ f. $\begin{bmatrix} 0 & 1 & 0 & 5 \\ 0 & 0 & 1 & 3 \\ 0 & 0 & 0 & 0 \end{bmatrix}$

Solution

The matrices in (a), (c), (d), and (f) are in row-echelon form. The matrices in (d) and (f) are in *reduced* row-echelon form because every column that has a leading 1 has zeros in every position above and below its leading 1. The matrix in (b) is not in row-echelon form because a row of all zeros does not occur at the bottom of the matrix. The matrix in (e) is not in row-echelon form because the first nonzero entry in Row 2 is not a leading 1.

CHECKPoint Now try Exercise 41.

Every matrix is row-equivalent to a matrix in row-echelon form. For instance, in Example 5, you can change the matrix in part (e) to row-echelon form by multiplying its second row by $\frac{1}{2}$.

Gaussian Elimination with Back-Substitution

Gaussian elimination with back-substitution works well for solving systems of linear equations by hand or with a computer. For this algorithm, the order in which the elementary row operations are performed is important. You should operate from left to right by columns, using elementary row operations to obtain zeros in all entries directly below the leading 1's.

Example 6 Gaussian Elimination with Back-Substitution

Solve the system $\begin{cases} y + z - 2w = -3 \\ x + 2y - z = 2 \\ 2x + 4y + z - 3w = -2 \\ x - 4y - 7z - w = -19 \end{cases}$.

Solution

$$\left[\begin{array}{cccc:c} 0 & 1 & 1 & -2 & -3 \\ 1 & 2 & -1 & 0 & 2 \\ 2 & 4 & 1 & -3 & -2 \\ 1 & -4 & -7 & -1 & -19 \end{array}\right]$$

Write augmented matrix.

$$\begin{array}{r} R_2 \\ R_1 \\ \\ \\ \end{array}\left[\begin{array}{cccc:c} 1 & 2 & -1 & 0 & 2 \\ 0 & 1 & 1 & -2 & -3 \\ 2 & 4 & 1 & -3 & -2 \\ 1 & -4 & -7 & -1 & -19 \end{array}\right]$$

Interchange R_1 and R_2 so first column has leading 1 in upper left corner.

$$\begin{array}{r} \\ \\ -2R_1 + R_3 \rightarrow \\ -R_1 + R_4 \rightarrow \end{array}\left[\begin{array}{cccc:c} 1 & 2 & -1 & 0 & 2 \\ 0 & 1 & 1 & -2 & -3 \\ 0 & 0 & 3 & -3 & -6 \\ 0 & -6 & -6 & -1 & -21 \end{array}\right]$$

Perform operations on R_3 and R_4 so first column has zeros below its leading 1.

$$\begin{array}{r} \\ \\ \\ 6R_2 + R_4 \rightarrow \end{array}\left[\begin{array}{cccc:c} 1 & 2 & -1 & 0 & 2 \\ 0 & 1 & 1 & -2 & -3 \\ 0 & 0 & 3 & -3 & -6 \\ 0 & 0 & 0 & -13 & -39 \end{array}\right]$$

Perform operations on R_4 so second column has zeros below its leading 1.

$$\begin{array}{r} \\ \\ \frac{1}{3}R_3 \rightarrow \\ -\frac{1}{13}R_4 \rightarrow \end{array}\left[\begin{array}{cccc:c} 1 & 2 & -1 & 0 & 2 \\ 0 & 1 & 1 & -2 & -3 \\ 0 & 0 & 1 & -1 & -2 \\ 0 & 0 & 0 & 1 & 3 \end{array}\right]$$

Perform operations on R_3 and R_4 so third and fourth columns have leading 1's.

The matrix is now in row-echelon form, and the corresponding system is

$$\begin{cases} x + 2y - z = 2 \\ y + z - 2w = -3 \\ z - w = -2 \\ w = 3 \end{cases}.$$

Using back-substitution, you can determine that the solution is $x = -1$, $y = 2$, $z = 1$, and $w = 3$.

CHECKPoint Now try Exercise 63.

Extra Example 6

Solve the system.

$$\begin{cases} 2x - y + z = 7 \\ x + y - z + 3w = -4 \\ x - 4y + 3z - 2w = 18 \\ y + z - w = 1 \end{cases}$$

(1, −2, 3, 0)

Extra Example 7

Solve the system.

$$\begin{cases} x + y - z = 7 \\ x + z = 2 \\ 2x + 4y - z = 10 \\ x - y + 4z = -5 \end{cases}$$

No solution, inconsistent

The procedure for using Gaussian elimination with back-substitution is summarized below.

Gaussian Elimination with Back-Substitution

1. Write the augmented matrix of the system of linear equations.
2. Use elementary row operations to rewrite the augmented matrix in row-echelon form.
3. Write the system of linear equations corresponding to the matrix in row-echelon form, and use back-substitution to find the solution.

When solving a system of linear equations, remember that it is possible for the system to have no solution. If, in the elimination process, you obtain a row of all zeros except for the last entry, it is unnecessary to continue the elimination process. You can simply conclude that the system has no solution, or is *inconsistent.*

Example 7 A System with No Solution

Solve the system $\begin{cases} x - y + 2z = 4 \\ x + z = 6 \\ 2x - 3y + 5z = 4 \\ 3x + 2y - z = 1 \end{cases}$.

Solution

$$\begin{bmatrix} 1 & -1 & 2 & \vdots & 4 \\ 1 & 0 & 1 & \vdots & 6 \\ 2 & -3 & 5 & \vdots & 4 \\ 3 & 2 & -1 & \vdots & 1 \end{bmatrix}$$ Write augmented matrix.

$$\begin{matrix} \\ -R_1 + R_2 \rightarrow \\ -2R_1 + R_3 \rightarrow \\ -3R_1 + R_4 \rightarrow \end{matrix} \begin{bmatrix} 1 & -1 & 2 & \vdots & 4 \\ 0 & 1 & -1 & \vdots & 2 \\ 0 & -1 & 1 & \vdots & -4 \\ 0 & 5 & -7 & \vdots & -11 \end{bmatrix}$$ Perform row operations.

$$\begin{matrix} \\ \\ R_2 + R_3 \rightarrow \\ \\ \end{matrix} \begin{bmatrix} 1 & -1 & 2 & \vdots & 4 \\ 0 & 1 & -1 & \vdots & 2 \\ 0 & 0 & 0 & \vdots & -2 \\ 0 & 5 & -7 & \vdots & -11 \end{bmatrix}$$ Perform row operations.

Note that the third row of this matrix consists entirely of zeros except for the last entry. This means that the original system of linear equations is inconsistent. You can see why this is true by converting back to a system of linear equations.

$$\begin{cases} x - y + 2z = 4 \\ y - z = 2 \\ 0 = -2 \\ 5y - 7z = -11 \end{cases}$$

Because the third equation is not possible, the system has no solution.

CHECKPoint Now try Exercise 81.

Gauss-Jordan Elimination

With Gaussian elimination, elementary row operations are applied to a matrix to obtain a (row-equivalent) row-echelon form of the matrix. A second method of elimination, called **Gauss-Jordan elimination,** after Carl Friedrich Gauss and Wilhelm Jordan (1842–1899), continues the reduction process until a *reduced* row-echelon form is obtained. This procedure is demonstrated in Example 8.

Example 8 Gauss-Jordan Elimination

Use Gauss-Jordan elimination to solve the system $\begin{cases} x - 2y + 3z = 9 \\ -x + 3y = -4. \\ 2x - 5y + 5z = 17 \end{cases}$

Solution

In Example 4, Gaussian elimination was used to obtain the row-echelon form of the linear system above.

$$\begin{bmatrix} 1 & -2 & 3 & \vdots & 9 \\ 0 & 1 & 3 & \vdots & 5 \\ 0 & 0 & 1 & \vdots & 2 \end{bmatrix}$$

Now, apply elementary row operations until you obtain zeros above each of the leading 1's, as follows.

$$\begin{matrix} 2R_2 + R_1 \rightarrow \\ \\ \\ \end{matrix} \begin{bmatrix} 1 & 0 & 9 & \vdots & 19 \\ 0 & 1 & 3 & \vdots & 5 \\ 0 & 0 & 1 & \vdots & 2 \end{bmatrix}$$

Perform operations on R_1 so second column has a zero above its leading 1.

$$\begin{matrix} -9R_3 + R_1 \rightarrow \\ -3R_3 + R_2 \rightarrow \\ \\ \end{matrix} \begin{bmatrix} 1 & 0 & 0 & \vdots & 1 \\ 0 & 1 & 0 & \vdots & -1 \\ 0 & 0 & 1 & \vdots & 2 \end{bmatrix}$$

Perform operations on R_1 and R_2 so third column has zeros above its leading 1.

The matrix is now in reduced row-echelon form. Converting back to a system of linear equations, you have

$$\begin{cases} x = 1 \\ y = -1. \\ z = 2 \end{cases}$$

Now you can simply read the solution, $x = 1$, $y = -1$, and $z = 2$, which can be written as the ordered triple $(1, -1, 2)$.

CHECKPoint Now try Exercise 71.

The elimination procedures described in this section sometimes result in fractional coefficients. For instance, in the elimination procedure for the system

$$\begin{cases} 2x - 5y + 5z = 17 \\ 3x - 2y + 3z = 11 \\ -3x + 3y = -6 \end{cases}$$

you may be inclined to multiply the first row by $\frac{1}{2}$ to produce a leading 1, which will result in working with fractional coefficients. You can sometimes avoid fractions by judiciously choosing the order in which you apply elementary row operations.

TECHNOLOGY

For a demonstration of a graphical approach to Gauss-Jordan elimination on a 2 × 3 matrix, see the Visualizing Row Operations Program available for several models of graphing calculators at the website for this text at *academic.cengage.com*.

Study Tip

The advantage of using Gauss-Jordan elimination to solve a system of linear equations is that the solution of the system is easily found without using back-substitution, as illustrated in Example 8.

Extra Example 8

Use Gauss-Jordan elimination to solve the system.

$$\begin{cases} x - 3z = -5 \\ 3x + y - 2z = -4 \\ 2x + 2y + z = -2 \end{cases}$$

(1, −3, 2)

Extra Example 9

Solve the system.

$$\begin{cases} x + y + 5z = -3 \\ -x - 2y - 8z = 5 \\ -x \quad\quad - 2z = 1 \end{cases}$$

$(-2a - 1, -3a - 2, a)$, where a is a real number

Closing the Lesson

Have students summarize the major points of the lesson and answer the Essential Question: How do you use matrices to solve systems of equations?

- **Represent a system of equations in matrix form by using an augmented matrix containing the coefficients and constants of the system written in standard form.**
- **Perform elementary row operations in order to write equivalent systems of equations.**
- **Solve systems of equations written in augmented matrix form by rewriting the matrix in row-echelon form and using back-substitution or by rewriting the matrix in reduced row-echelon form.**

Recall from Chapter 7 that when there are fewer equations than variables in a system of equations, then the system has either no solution or infinitely many solutions.

Example 9 A System with an Infinite Number of Solutions

Solve the system.

$$\begin{cases} 2x + 4y - 2z = 0 \\ 3x + 5y \quad\quad = 1 \end{cases}$$

Solution

$$\begin{bmatrix} 2 & 4 & -2 & \vdots & 0 \\ 3 & 5 & 0 & \vdots & 1 \end{bmatrix}$$

$$\tfrac{1}{2}R_1 \rightarrow \begin{bmatrix} 1 & 2 & -1 & \vdots & 0 \\ 3 & 5 & 0 & \vdots & 1 \end{bmatrix}$$

$$-3R_1 + R_2 \rightarrow \begin{bmatrix} 1 & 2 & -1 & \vdots & 0 \\ 0 & -1 & 3 & \vdots & 1 \end{bmatrix}$$

$$-R_2 \rightarrow \begin{bmatrix} 1 & 2 & -1 & \vdots & 0 \\ 0 & 1 & -3 & \vdots & -1 \end{bmatrix}$$

$$-2R_2 + R_1 \rightarrow \begin{bmatrix} 1 & 0 & 5 & \vdots & 2 \\ 0 & 1 & -3 & \vdots & -1 \end{bmatrix}$$

The corresponding system of equations is

$$\begin{cases} x + 5z = 2 \\ y - 3z = -1 \end{cases}.$$

Solving for x and y in terms of z, you have

$x = -5z + 2$ and $y = 3z - 1$.

To write a solution of the system that does not use any of the three variables of the system, let a represent any real number and let

$z = a$.

Now substitute a for z in the equations for x and y.

$x = -5z + 2 = -5a + 2$

$y = 3z - 1 = 3a - 1$

So, the solution set can be written as an ordered triple with the form

$(-5a + 2, 3a - 1, a)$

where a is any real number. Remember that a solution set of this form represents an infinite number of solutions. Try substituting values for a to obtain a few solutions. Then check each solution in the original system of equations.

CHECKPoint Now try Exercise 79.

Study Tip

In Example 9, x and y are solved for in terms of the third variable z. To write a solution of the system that does not use any of the three variables of the system, let a represent any real number and let $z = a$. Then solve for x and y. The solution can then be written in terms of a, which is not one of the variables of the system.

8.1 EXERCISES

See www.CalcChat.com for worked-out solutions to odd-numbered exercises.

VOCABULARY: Fill in the blanks.

1. A rectangular array of real numbers that can be used to solve a system of linear equations is called a matrix.
2. A matrix is square if the number of rows equals the number of columns.
3. For a square matrix, the entries $a_{11}, a_{22}, a_{33}, \ldots, a_{nn}$ are the main diagonal entries.
4. A matrix with only one row is called a row matrix, and a matrix with only one column is called a column matrix.
5. The matrix derived from a system of linear equations is called the ________ matrix of the system. augmented
6. The matrix derived from the coefficients of a system of linear equations is called the coefficient matrix of the system.
7. Two matrices are called ________ if one of the matrices can be obtained from the other by a sequence of elementary row operations. row-equivalent
8. A matrix in row-echelon form is in reduced row-echelon form if every column that has a leading 1 has zeros in every position above and below its leading 1.

SKILLS AND APPLICATIONS

In Exercises 9–14, determine the order of the matrix.

9. $\begin{bmatrix} 7 & 0 \end{bmatrix}$ 1×2

10. $\begin{bmatrix} 5 & -3 & 8 & 7 \end{bmatrix}$ 1×4

11. $\begin{bmatrix} 2 \\ 36 \\ 3 \end{bmatrix}$ 3×1

12. $\begin{bmatrix} -3 & 7 & 15 & 0 \\ 0 & 0 & 3 & 3 \\ 1 & 1 & 6 & 7 \end{bmatrix}$ 3×4

13. $\begin{bmatrix} 33 & 45 \\ -9 & 20 \end{bmatrix}$ 2×2

14. $\begin{bmatrix} -7 & 6 & 4 \\ 0 & -5 & 1 \end{bmatrix}$ 2×3

In Exercises 15–20, write the augmented matrix for the system of linear equations. 15–20. See margin.

15. $\begin{cases} 4x - 3y = -5 \\ -x + 3y = 12 \end{cases}$

16. $\begin{cases} 7x + 4y = 22 \\ 5x - 9y = 15 \end{cases}$

17. $\begin{cases} x + 10y - 2z = 2 \\ 5x - 3y + 4z = 0 \\ 2x + y = 6 \end{cases}$

18. $\begin{cases} -x - 8y + 5z = 8 \\ -7x - 15z = -38 \\ 3x - y + 8z = 20 \end{cases}$

19. $\begin{cases} 7x - 5y + z = 13 \\ 19x - 8z = 10 \end{cases}$

20. $\begin{cases} 9x + 2y - 3z = 20 \\ -25y + 11z = -5 \end{cases}$

In Exercises 21–26, write the system of linear equations represented by the augmented matrix. (Use variables x, y, z, and w, if applicable.) 21–26. See margin.

21. $\left[\begin{array}{cc:c} 1 & 2 & 7 \\ 2 & -3 & 4 \end{array}\right]$

22. $\left[\begin{array}{cc:c} 7 & -5 & 0 \\ 8 & 3 & -2 \end{array}\right]$

23. $\left[\begin{array}{ccc:c} 2 & 0 & 5 & -12 \\ 0 & 1 & -2 & 7 \\ 6 & 3 & 0 & 2 \end{array}\right]$

24. $\left[\begin{array}{ccc:c} 4 & -5 & -1 & 18 \\ -11 & 0 & 6 & 25 \\ 3 & 8 & 0 & -29 \end{array}\right]$

25. $\left[\begin{array}{cccc:c} 9 & 12 & 3 & 0 & 0 \\ -2 & 18 & 5 & 2 & 10 \\ 1 & 7 & -8 & 0 & -4 \\ 3 & 0 & 2 & 0 & -10 \end{array}\right]$

26. $\left[\begin{array}{cccc:c} 6 & 2 & -1 & -5 & -25 \\ -1 & 0 & 7 & 3 & 7 \\ 4 & -1 & -10 & 6 & 23 \\ 0 & 8 & 1 & -11 & -21 \end{array}\right]$

In Exercises 27–34, fill in the blank(s) using elementary row operations to form a row-equivalent matrix. 27–30. See margin.

27. $\begin{bmatrix} 1 & 4 & 3 \\ 2 & 10 & 5 \end{bmatrix}$
$\begin{bmatrix} 1 & 4 & 3 \\ 0 & \square & -1 \end{bmatrix}$

28. $\begin{bmatrix} 3 & 6 & 8 \\ 4 & -3 & 6 \end{bmatrix}$
$\begin{bmatrix} 1 & \square & \frac{8}{3} \\ 4 & -3 & 6 \end{bmatrix}$

29. $\begin{bmatrix} 1 & 1 & 1 \\ 5 & -2 & 4 \end{bmatrix}$
$\begin{bmatrix} 1 & 1 & 1 \\ 0 & \square & -1 \end{bmatrix}$

30. $\begin{bmatrix} -3 & 3 & 12 \\ 18 & -8 & 4 \end{bmatrix}$
$\begin{bmatrix} 1 & -1 & \square \\ 18 & -8 & 4 \end{bmatrix}$

31. $\begin{bmatrix} 1 & 5 & 4 & -1 \\ 0 & 1 & -2 & 2 \\ 0 & 0 & 1 & -7 \end{bmatrix}$
$\begin{bmatrix} 1 & 0 & \square & \square \\ 0 & 1 & -2 & 2 \\ 0 & 0 & 1 & -7 \end{bmatrix}$
$\begin{bmatrix} 1 & 0 & 14 & -11 \\ 0 & 1 & -2 & 2 \\ 0 & 0 & 1 & -7 \end{bmatrix}$

32. $\begin{bmatrix} 1 & 0 & 6 & 1 \\ 0 & -1 & 0 & 7 \\ 0 & 0 & -1 & 3 \end{bmatrix}$
$\begin{bmatrix} 1 & 0 & 6 & 1 \\ 0 & 1 & 0 & \square \\ 0 & 0 & 1 & \square \end{bmatrix}$
$\begin{bmatrix} 1 & 0 & 6 & 1 \\ 0 & 1 & 0 & -7 \\ 0 & 0 & 1 & -3 \end{bmatrix}$

4 PRACTICE AND APPLY

Assignment Guide

Transparencies Available
Available at the Instructor's companion site.

Average:

Day 1: pp. 579–581
Exs. 1–6, 9–15 odd, 19–27 odd, 33, 35, 36, 40, 55, 57

Day 2: pp. 579–581
Exs. 7, 8, 42, 43–47 odd, 51, 53, 59–67 odd, 71, 73

Day 3: pp. 581–583
Exs. 79, 81, 85, 93–107 odd, 111, 113, 116–120, 122, 123

Advanced:

Day 1: pp. 579–581
Exs. 1–6, 10–18 even, 22–40 even, 56, 58

Day 2: pp. 579–581
Exs. 7, 8, 42–44, 46–52 even, 60–76 even

Day 3: pp. 581–583
Exs. 80, 82, 86, 92–108 even, 112, 114, 115, 119–123

Block:

pp. 579–581
Exs. 1–8, 9–15 odd, 19–27 odd, 33, 35, 36, 40, 42, 43–47 odd, 51–67 odd, 71, 73

pp. 581–583
Exs. 79, 81, 85, 93–107 odd, 111, 113, 116–120, 122, 123 (with 8.2)

15. $\left[\begin{array}{cc:c} 4 & -3 & -5 \\ -1 & 3 & 12 \end{array}\right]$

16. $\left[\begin{array}{cc:c} 7 & 4 & 22 \\ 5 & -9 & 15 \end{array}\right]$

17. $\left[\begin{array}{ccc:c} 1 & 10 & -2 & 2 \\ 5 & -3 & 4 & 0 \\ 2 & 1 & 0 & 6 \end{array}\right]$

18. $\left[\begin{array}{ccc:c} -1 & -8 & 5 & 8 \\ -7 & 0 & -15 & -38 \\ 3 & -1 & 8 & 20 \end{array}\right]$

19. $\left[\begin{array}{ccc:c} 7 & -5 & 1 & 13 \\ 19 & 0 & -8 & 10 \end{array}\right]$

20. $\left[\begin{array}{ccc:c} 9 & 2 & -3 & 20 \\ 0 & -25 & 11 & -5 \end{array}\right]$

21. $\begin{cases} x + 2y = 7 \\ 2x - 3y = 4 \end{cases}$

22. $\begin{cases} 7x - 5y = 0 \\ 8x + 3y = -2 \end{cases}$

23. $\begin{cases} 2x + 5z = -12 \\ y - 2z = 7 \\ 6x + 3y = 2 \end{cases}$

24. $\begin{cases} 4x - 5y - z = 18 \\ -11x + 6z = 25 \\ 3x + 8y = -29 \end{cases}$

25. $\begin{cases} 9x + 12y + 3z = 0 \\ -2x + 18y + 5z + 2w = 10 \\ x + 7y - 8z = -4 \\ 3x + 2z = -10 \end{cases}$

26. $\begin{cases} 6x + 2y - z - 5w = -25 \\ -x + 7z + 3w = 7 \\ 4x - y - 10z + 6w = 23 \\ 8y + z - 11w = -21 \end{cases}$

27. $\begin{bmatrix} 1 & 4 & 3 \\ 0 & 2 & -1 \end{bmatrix}$

28. $\begin{bmatrix} 1 & 2 & \frac{8}{3} \\ 4 & -3 & 6 \end{bmatrix}$

29. $\begin{bmatrix} 1 & 1 & 1 \\ 0 & -7 & -1 \end{bmatrix}$

30. $\begin{bmatrix} 1 & -1 & -4 \\ 18 & -8 & 4 \end{bmatrix}$

33–34. See margin.

33. $\begin{bmatrix} 1 & 1 & 4 & -1 \\ 3 & 8 & 10 & 3 \\ -2 & 1 & 12 & 6 \end{bmatrix}$

$\begin{bmatrix} 1 & 1 & 4 & -1 \\ 0 & 5 & \square & \square \\ 0 & 3 & \square & \square \end{bmatrix}$

$\begin{bmatrix} 1 & 1 & 4 & -1 \\ 0 & 1 & -\frac{2}{5} & \frac{6}{5} \\ 0 & 3 & \square & \square \end{bmatrix}$

34. $\begin{bmatrix} 2 & 4 & 8 & 3 \\ 1 & -1 & -3 & 2 \\ 2 & 6 & 4 & 9 \end{bmatrix}$

$\begin{bmatrix} 1 & \square & \square & \square \\ 1 & -1 & -3 & 2 \\ 2 & 6 & 4 & 9 \end{bmatrix}$

$\begin{bmatrix} 1 & 2 & 4 & \frac{3}{2} \\ 0 & \square & -7 & \frac{1}{2} \\ 0 & 2 & \square & \square \end{bmatrix}$

In Exercises 35–38, identify the elementary row operation(s) being performed to obtain the new row-equivalent matrix. 35–38. See margin.

Original Matrix / *New Row-Equivalent Matrix*

35. $\begin{bmatrix} -2 & 5 & 1 \\ 3 & -1 & -8 \end{bmatrix}$ $\quad \begin{bmatrix} 13 & 0 & -39 \\ 3 & -1 & -8 \end{bmatrix}$

Original Matrix / *New Row-Equivalent Matrix*

36. $\begin{bmatrix} 3 & -1 & -4 \\ -4 & 3 & 7 \end{bmatrix}$ $\quad \begin{bmatrix} 3 & -1 & -4 \\ 5 & 0 & -5 \end{bmatrix}$

Original Matrix / *New Row-Equivalent Matrix*

37. $\begin{bmatrix} 0 & -1 & -5 & 5 \\ -1 & 3 & -7 & 6 \\ 4 & -5 & 1 & 3 \end{bmatrix}$ $\quad \begin{bmatrix} -1 & 3 & -7 & 6 \\ 0 & -1 & -5 & 5 \\ 0 & 7 & -27 & 27 \end{bmatrix}$

Original Matrix / *New Row-Equivalent Matrix*

38. $\begin{bmatrix} -1 & -2 & 3 & -2 \\ 2 & -5 & 1 & -7 \\ 5 & 4 & -7 & 6 \end{bmatrix}$ $\quad \begin{bmatrix} -1 & -2 & 3 & -2 \\ 0 & -9 & 7 & -11 \\ 0 & -6 & 8 & -4 \end{bmatrix}$

39. Perform the sequence of row operations on the matrix. What did the operations accomplish? See margin.

$\begin{bmatrix} 1 & 2 & 3 \\ 2 & -1 & -4 \\ 3 & 1 & -1 \end{bmatrix}$

(a) Add -2 times R_1 to R_2.
(b) Add -3 times R_1 to R_3.
(c) Add -1 times R_2 to R_3.
(d) Multiply R_2 by $-\frac{1}{5}$.
(e) Add -2 times R_2 to R_1.

40. Perform the sequence of row operations on the matrix. What did the operations accomplish? See margin.

$\begin{bmatrix} 7 & 1 \\ 0 & 2 \\ -3 & 4 \\ 4 & 1 \end{bmatrix}$

(a) Add R_3 to R_4.
(b) Interchange R_1 and R_4.
(c) Add 3 times R_1 to R_3.
(d) Add -7 times R_1 to R_4.
(e) Multiply R_2 by $\frac{1}{2}$.
(f) Add the appropriate multiples of R_2 to R_1, R_3, and R_4.

In Exercises 41–44, determine whether the matrix is in row-echelon form. If it is, determine if it is also in reduced row-echelon form. 41–42. Reduced row-echelon form

41. $\begin{bmatrix} 1 & 0 & 0 & 0 \\ 0 & 1 & 1 & 5 \\ 0 & 0 & 0 & 0 \end{bmatrix}$ **42.** $\begin{bmatrix} 1 & 3 & 0 & 0 \\ 0 & 0 & 1 & 8 \\ 0 & 0 & 0 & 0 \end{bmatrix}$

43. $\begin{bmatrix} 1 & 0 & 0 & 1 \\ 0 & 1 & 0 & -1 \\ 0 & 0 & 0 & 2 \end{bmatrix}$ Not in row-echelon form **44.** $\begin{bmatrix} 1 & 0 & 1 & 0 \\ 0 & 1 & 0 & 2 \\ 0 & 0 & 1 & 0 \end{bmatrix}$ Row-echelon form

In Exercises 45–48, write the matrix in row-echelon form. (Remember that the row-echelon form of a matrix is not unique.) 45–48. See margin.

45. $\begin{bmatrix} 1 & 1 & 0 & 5 \\ -2 & -1 & 2 & -10 \\ 3 & 6 & 7 & 14 \end{bmatrix}$ **46.** $\begin{bmatrix} 1 & 2 & -1 & 3 \\ 3 & 7 & -5 & 14 \\ -2 & -1 & -3 & 8 \end{bmatrix}$

47. $\begin{bmatrix} 1 & -1 & -1 & 1 \\ 5 & -4 & 1 & 8 \\ -6 & 8 & 18 & 0 \end{bmatrix}$ **48.** $\begin{bmatrix} 1 & -3 & 0 & -7 \\ -3 & 10 & 1 & 23 \\ 4 & -10 & 2 & -24 \end{bmatrix}$

In Exercises 49–54, use the matrix capabilities of a graphing utility to write the matrix in *reduced* row-echelon form.

49. $\begin{bmatrix} 3 & 3 & 3 \\ -1 & 0 & -4 \\ 2 & 4 & -2 \end{bmatrix}$ See margin. **50.** $\begin{bmatrix} 1 & 3 & 2 \\ 5 & 15 & 9 \\ 2 & 6 & 10 \end{bmatrix}$ $\begin{bmatrix} 1 & 3 & 0 \\ 0 & 0 & 1 \\ 0 & 0 & 0 \end{bmatrix}$

51. $\begin{bmatrix} 1 & 2 & 3 & -5 \\ 1 & 2 & 4 & -9 \\ -2 & -4 & -4 & 3 \\ 4 & 8 & 11 & -14 \end{bmatrix}$ $\begin{bmatrix} 1 & 2 & 0 & 0 \\ 0 & 0 & 1 & 0 \\ 0 & 0 & 0 & 1 \\ 0 & 0 & 0 & 0 \end{bmatrix}$

52. $\begin{bmatrix} -2 & 3 & -1 & -2 \\ 4 & -2 & 5 & 8 \\ 1 & 5 & -2 & 0 \\ 3 & 8 & -10 & -30 \end{bmatrix}$ $\begin{bmatrix} 1 & 0 & 0 & 0 \\ 0 & 1 & 0 & 0 \\ 0 & 0 & 1 & 0 \\ 0 & 0 & 0 & 1 \end{bmatrix}$

53. $\begin{bmatrix} -3 & 5 & 1 & 12 \\ 1 & -1 & 1 & 4 \end{bmatrix}$ **54.** $\begin{bmatrix} 5 & 1 & 2 & 4 \\ -1 & 5 & 10 & -32 \end{bmatrix}$

53–54. See margin.

In Exercises 55–58, write the system of linear equations represented by the augmented matrix. Then use back-substitution to solve. (Use variables *x*, *y*, and *z*, if applicable.)

55. $\left[\begin{array}{cc:c} 1 & -2 & 4 \\ 0 & 1 & -3 \end{array}\right]$

$\begin{cases} x - 2y = 4 \\ y = -3 \end{cases}$

$(-2, -3)$

56. $\left[\begin{array}{cc:c} 1 & 5 & 0 \\ 0 & 1 & -1 \end{array}\right]$

$\begin{cases} x + 5y = 0 \\ y = -1 \end{cases}$

$(5, -1)$

33. $\begin{bmatrix} 1 & 1 & 4 & -1 \\ 0 & 5 & -2 & 6 \\ 0 & 3 & 20 & 4 \end{bmatrix}$ $\begin{bmatrix} 1 & 1 & 4 & -1 \\ 0 & 1 & -\frac{2}{5} & \frac{6}{5} \\ 0 & 3 & 20 & 4 \end{bmatrix}$

34. $\begin{bmatrix} 1 & 2 & 4 & \frac{3}{2} \\ 1 & -1 & -3 & 2 \\ 2 & 6 & 4 & 9 \end{bmatrix}$ $\begin{bmatrix} 1 & 2 & 4 & \frac{3}{2} \\ 0 & -3 & -7 & \frac{1}{2} \\ 0 & 2 & -4 & 6 \end{bmatrix}$

35. Add 5 times Row 2 to Row 1.
36. Add 3 times Row 1 to Row 2.
37. Interchange Row 1 and Row 2. Add 4 times new Row 1 to Row 3.
38. Add 2 times Row 1 to Row 2. Add 5 times Row 1 to Row 3.

39. (a) $\begin{bmatrix} 1 & 2 & 3 \\ 0 & -5 & -10 \\ 3 & 1 & -1 \end{bmatrix}$
(b) $\begin{bmatrix} 1 & 2 & 3 \\ 0 & -5 & -10 \\ 0 & -5 & -10 \end{bmatrix}$
(c) $\begin{bmatrix} 1 & 2 & 3 \\ 0 & -5 & -10 \\ 0 & 0 & 0 \end{bmatrix}$
(d) $\begin{bmatrix} 1 & 2 & 3 \\ 0 & 1 & 2 \\ 0 & 0 & 0 \end{bmatrix}$
(e) $\begin{bmatrix} 1 & 0 & -1 \\ 0 & 1 & 2 \\ 0 & 0 & 0 \end{bmatrix}$

The matrix is in reduced row-echelon form.

40. (a) $\begin{bmatrix} 7 & 1 \\ 0 & 2 \\ -3 & 4 \\ 1 & 5 \end{bmatrix}$ (b) $\begin{bmatrix} 1 & 5 \\ 0 & 2 \\ -3 & 4 \\ 7 & 1 \end{bmatrix}$
(c) $\begin{bmatrix} 1 & 5 \\ 0 & 2 \\ 0 & 19 \\ 7 & 1 \end{bmatrix}$ (d) $\begin{bmatrix} 1 & 5 \\ 0 & 2 \\ 0 & 19 \\ 0 & -34 \end{bmatrix}$
(e) $\begin{bmatrix} 1 & 5 \\ 0 & 1 \\ 0 & 19 \\ 0 & -34 \end{bmatrix}$ (f) $\begin{bmatrix} 1 & 0 \\ 0 & 1 \\ 0 & 0 \\ 0 & 0 \end{bmatrix}$

The matrix is in reduced row-echelon form.

45. $\begin{bmatrix} 1 & 1 & 0 & 5 \\ 0 & 1 & 2 & 0 \\ 0 & 0 & 1 & -1 \end{bmatrix}$

46. $\begin{bmatrix} 1 & 2 & -1 & 3 \\ 0 & 1 & -2 & 5 \\ 0 & 0 & 1 & -1 \end{bmatrix}$

47. $\begin{bmatrix} 1 & -1 & -1 & 1 \\ 0 & 1 & 6 & 3 \\ 0 & 0 & 0 & 0 \end{bmatrix}$

48. $\begin{bmatrix} 1 & -3 & 0 & -7 \\ 0 & 1 & 1 & 2 \\ 0 & 0 & 0 & 0 \end{bmatrix}$

49. $\begin{bmatrix} 1 & 0 & 0 \\ 0 & 1 & 0 \\ 0 & 0 & 1 \end{bmatrix}$

53. $\begin{bmatrix} 1 & 0 & 3 & 16 \\ 0 & 1 & 2 & 12 \end{bmatrix}$

54. $\begin{bmatrix} 1 & 0 & 0 & 2 \\ 0 & 1 & 2 & -6 \end{bmatrix}$

57–58. See margin.

57. $\left[\begin{array}{rrrcr} 1 & -1 & 2 & \vdots & 4 \\ 0 & 1 & -1 & \vdots & 2 \\ 0 & 0 & 1 & \vdots & -2 \end{array}\right]$ **58.** $\left[\begin{array}{rrrcr} 1 & 2 & -2 & \vdots & -1 \\ 0 & 1 & 1 & \vdots & 9 \\ 0 & 0 & 1 & \vdots & -3 \end{array}\right]$

In Exercises 59–62, an augmented matrix that represents a system of linear equations (in variables x, y, and z, if applicable) has been reduced using Gauss-Jordan elimination. Write the solution represented by the augmented matrix.

59. $\left[\begin{array}{rrcr} 1 & 0 & \vdots & 3 \\ 0 & 1 & \vdots & -4 \end{array}\right]$ **60.** $\left[\begin{array}{rrcr} 1 & 0 & \vdots & -6 \\ 0 & 1 & \vdots & 10 \end{array}\right]$

61. $\left[\begin{array}{rrrcr} 1 & 0 & 0 & \vdots & -4 \\ 0 & 1 & 0 & \vdots & -10 \\ 0 & 0 & 1 & \vdots & 4 \end{array}\right]$ **62.** $\left[\begin{array}{rrrcr} 1 & 0 & 0 & \vdots & 5 \\ 0 & 1 & 0 & \vdots & -3 \\ 0 & 0 & 1 & \vdots & 0 \end{array}\right]$ 59–62. See margin.

In Exercises 63–84, use matrices to solve the system of equations (if possible). Use Gaussian elimination with back-substitution or Gauss-Jordan elimination. 63–82. See margin.

63. $\begin{cases} x + 2y = 7 \\ 2x + y = 8 \end{cases}$ **64.** $\begin{cases} 2x + 6y = 16 \\ 2x + 3y = 7 \end{cases}$

65. $\begin{cases} 3x - 2y = -27 \\ x + 3y = 13 \end{cases}$ **66.** $\begin{cases} -x + y = 4 \\ 2x - 4y = -34 \end{cases}$

67. $\begin{cases} -2x + 6y = -22 \\ x + 2y = -9 \end{cases}$ **68.** $\begin{cases} 5x - 5y = -5 \\ -2x - 3y = 7 \end{cases}$

69. $\begin{cases} 8x - 4y = 7 \\ 5x + 2y = 1 \end{cases}$ **70.** $\begin{cases} x - 3y = 5 \\ -2x + 6y = -10 \end{cases}$

71. $\begin{cases} x - 3z = -2 \\ 3x + y - 2z = 5 \\ 2x + 2y + z = 4 \end{cases}$ **72.** $\begin{cases} 2x - y + 3z = 24 \\ 2y - z = 14 \\ 7x - 5y = 6 \end{cases}$

73. $\begin{cases} -x + y - z = -14 \\ 2x - y + z = 21 \\ 3x + 2y + z = 19 \end{cases}$ **74.** $\begin{cases} 2x + 2y - z = 2 \\ x - 3y + z = -28 \\ -x + y = 14 \end{cases}$

75. $\begin{cases} x + 2y - 3z = -28 \\ 4y + 2z = 0 \\ -x + y - z = -5 \end{cases}$ **76.** $\begin{cases} 3x - 2y + z = 15 \\ -x + y + 2z = -10 \\ x - y - 4z = 14 \end{cases}$

77. $\begin{cases} x + 2y = 0 \\ -x - y = 0 \end{cases}$ **78.** $\begin{cases} x + 2y = 0 \\ 2x + 4y = 0 \end{cases}$

79. $\begin{cases} x + 2y + z = 8 \\ 3x + 7y + 6z = 26 \end{cases}$ **80.** $\begin{cases} x + y + 4z = 5 \\ 2x + y - z = 9 \end{cases}$

81. $\begin{cases} -x + y = -22 \\ 3x + 4y = 4 \\ 4x - 8y = 32 \end{cases}$ **82.** $\begin{cases} x + 2y = 0 \\ x + y = 6 \\ 3x - 2y = 8 \end{cases}$

83. $\begin{cases} 3x + 2y - z + w = 0 \\ x - y + 4z + 2w = 25 \\ -2x + y + 2z - w = 2 \\ x + y + z + w = 6 \end{cases}$ $(3, -2, 5, 0)$

84. $\begin{cases} x - 4y + 3z - 2w = 9 \\ 3x - 2y + z - 4w = -13 \\ -4x + 3y - 2z + w = -4 \\ -2x + y - 4z + 3w = -10 \end{cases}$ $(-1, 0, 6, 4)$

In Exercises 85–90, use the matrix capabilities of a graphing utility to reduce the augmented matrix corresponding to the system of equations, and solve the system.

85. $\begin{cases} 3x + 3y + 12z = 6 \\ x + y + 4z = 2 \\ 2x + 5y + 20z = 10 \\ -x + 2y + 8z = 4 \end{cases}$ **86.** $\begin{cases} 2x + 10y + 2z = 6 \\ x + 5y + 2z = 6 \\ x + 5y + z = 3 \\ -3x - 15y - 3z = -9 \end{cases}$

87. $\begin{cases} 2x + y - z + 2w = -6 \\ 3x + 4y + w = 1 \\ x + 5y + 2z + 6w = -3 \\ 5x + 2y - z - w = 3 \end{cases}$

85. $(0, 2 - 4a, a)$
86. $(-5a, a, 3)$
87. $(1, 0, 4, -2)$

88. $\begin{cases} x + 2y + 2z + 4w = 11 \\ 3x + 6y + 5z + 12w = 30 \\ x + 3y - 3z + 2w = -5 \\ 6x - y - z + w = -9 \end{cases}$ $(-1, 1, 3, 1)$

89. $\begin{cases} x + y + z + w = 0 \\ 2x + 3y + z - 2w = 0 \\ 3x + 5y + z = 0 \end{cases}$ $(-2a, a, a, 0)$

90. $\begin{cases} x + 2y + z + 3w = 0 \\ x - y + w = 0 \\ y - z + 2w = 0 \end{cases}$ $(-2a, -a, a, a)$

In Exercises 91–94, determine whether the two systems of linear equations yield the same solution. If so, find the solution using matrices. 91–94. See margin.

91. (a) $\begin{cases} x - 2y + z = -6 \\ y - 5z = 16 \\ z = -3 \end{cases}$ (b) $\begin{cases} x + y - 2z = 6 \\ y + 3z = -8 \\ z = -3 \end{cases}$

92. (a) $\begin{cases} x - 3y + 4z = -11 \\ y - z = -4 \\ z = 2 \end{cases}$ (b) $\begin{cases} x + 4y = -11 \\ y + 3z = 4 \\ z = 2 \end{cases}$

93. (a) $\begin{cases} x - 4y + 5z = 27 \\ y - 7z = -54 \\ z = 8 \end{cases}$ (b) $\begin{cases} x - 6y + z = 15 \\ y + 5z = 42 \\ z = 8 \end{cases}$

94. (a) $\begin{cases} x + 3y - z = 19 \\ y + 6z = -18 \\ z = -4 \end{cases}$ (b) $\begin{cases} x - y + 3z = -15 \\ y - 2z = 14 \\ z = -4 \end{cases}$

In Exercises 95–98, use a system of equations to find the quadratic function $f(x) = ax^2 + bx + c$ that satisfies the equations. Solve the system using matrices.

95. $f(1) = 1, f(2) = -1, f(3) = -5$ $f(x) = -x^2 + x + 1$

96. $f(1) = 2, f(2) = 9, f(3) = 20$ $f(x) = 2x^2 + x - 1$

57. $\begin{cases} x - y + 2z = 4 \\ y - z = 2 \\ z = -2 \end{cases}$
$(8, 0, -2)$

58. $\begin{cases} x + 2y - 2z = -1 \\ y + z = 9 \\ z = -3 \end{cases}$
$(-31, 12, -3)$

59. $(3, -4)$
60. $(-6, 10)$
61. $(-4, -10, 4)$
62. $(5, -3, 0)$
63. $(3, 2)$
64. $(-1, 3)$
65. $(-5, 6)$
66. $(9, 13)$
67. $(-1, -4)$
68. $(-2, -1)$
69. $\left(\frac{1}{2}, -\frac{3}{4}\right)$
70. $(3a + 5, a)$
71. $(4, -3, 2)$
72. $(8, 10, 6)$
73. $(7, -3, 4)$
74. $(-6, 8, 2)$
75. $(-4, -3, 6)$
76. $(5, -1, -2)$
77. $(0, 0)$
78. $(-2a, a)$
79. $(5a + 4, -3a + 2, a)$
80. $(5a + 4, -9a + 1, a)$
81. Inconsistent
82. Inconsistent
91. Yes; $(-1, 1, -3)$
92. No
93. No
94. No

99. $f(x) = x^3 - 2x^2 + x - 1$

100. $f(x) = x^3 + 2x^2 - x + 2$

101. $f(x) = x^3 - 2x^2 - 4x + 1$

102. $f(x) = x^3 - x^2 + 2x - 1$

103. $\begin{bmatrix} 1 & 3 & \frac{3}{2} & \vdots & 4 \\ 0 & 1 & \frac{7}{4} & \vdots & -\frac{3}{2} \\ 0 & 0 & 1 & \vdots & 2 \end{bmatrix}$, $\begin{bmatrix} 1 & 3 & 1 & \vdots & 3 \\ 0 & 1 & 2 & \vdots & -1 \\ 0 & 0 & 1 & \vdots & 2 \end{bmatrix}$

105–106. See below.

108. \$100,000 at 9%
\$250,000 at 10%
\$150,000 at 12%

109. $\begin{cases} x + 5y + 10z + 20w = 95 \\ x + y + z + w = 26 \\ y - 4z = 0 \\ x - 2y = -1 \end{cases}$

\$1 bills: 15
\$5 bills: 8
\$10 bills: 2
\$20 bills: 1

110. $\begin{cases} x + 5y + 10z + 20w = 2600 \\ x + y + z + w = 235 \\ -2x + w = 0 \\ -x + y = 10 \end{cases}$

\$1 bills: 50
\$5 bills: 60
\$10 bills: 25
\$20 bills: 100

97. $f(-2) = -15, f(-1) = 7, f(1) = -3$ $f(x) = -9x^2 - 5x + 11$

98. $f(-2) = -3, f(1) = -3, f(2) = -11$ $f(x) = -2x^2 - 2x + 1$

In Exercises 99–102, use a system of equations to find the cubic function $f(x) = ax^3 + bx^2 + cx + d$ that satisfies the equations. Solve the system using matrices. 99–102. See margin.

99. $f(-1) = -5$, $f(1) = -1$, $f(2) = 1$, $f(3) = 11$

100. $f(-1) = 4$, $f(1) = 4$, $f(2) = 16$, $f(3) = 44$

101. $f(-2) = -7$, $f(-1) = 2$, $f(1) = -4$, $f(2) = -7$

102. $f(-2) = -17$, $f(-1) = -5$, $f(1) = 1$, $f(2) = 7$

103. Use the system

$$\begin{cases} x + 3y + z = 3 \\ x + 5y + 5z = 1 \\ 2x + 6y + 3z = 8 \end{cases}$$

to write two different matrices in row-echelon form that yield the same solution. See margin.

104. ELECTRICAL NETWORK The currents in an electrical network are given by the solution of the system

$$\begin{cases} I_1 - I_2 + I_3 = 0 \\ 3I_1 + 4I_2 = 18 \\ I_2 + 3I_3 = 6 \end{cases}$$ $I_1 = 2, I_2 = 3, I_3 = 1$

where I_1, I_2, and I_3 are measured in amperes. Solve the system of equations using matrices.

105. PARTIAL FRACTIONS Use a system of equations to write the partial fraction decomposition of the rational expression. Solve the system using matrices. See margin.

$$\frac{4x^2}{(x+1)^2(x-1)} = \frac{A}{x-1} + \frac{B}{x+1} + \frac{C}{(x+1)^2}$$

106. PARTIAL FRACTIONS Use a system of equations to write the partial fraction decomposition of the rational expression. Solve the system using matrices. See margin.

$$\frac{8x^2}{(x-1)^2(x+1)} = \frac{A}{x+1} + \frac{B}{x-1} + \frac{C}{(x-1)^2}$$

107. FINANCE A small shoe corporation borrowed \$1,500,000 to expand its line of shoes. Some of the money was borrowed at 7%, some at 8%, and some at 10%. Use a system of equations to determine how much was borrowed at each rate if the annual interest was \$130,500 and the amount borrowed at 10% was 4 times the amount borrowed at 7%. Solve the system using matrices. \$150,000 at 7%
\$750,000 at 8%
\$600,000 at 10%

108. FINANCE A small software corporation borrowed \$500,000 to expand its software line. Some of the money was borrowed at 9%, some at 10%, and some at 12%. Use a system of equations to determine how much was borrowed at each rate if the annual interest was \$52,000 and the amount borrowed at 10% was $2\frac{1}{2}$ times the amount borrowed at 9%. Solve the system using matrices. See margin.

109. TIPS A food server examines the amount of money earned in tips after working an 8-hour shift. The server has a total of \$95 in denominations of \$1, \$5, \$10, and \$20 bills. The total number of paper bills is 26. The number of \$5 bills is 4 times the number of \$10 bills, and the number of \$1 bills is 1 less than twice the number of \$5 bills. Write a system of linear equations to represent the situation. Then use matrices to find the number of each denomination. See margin.

110. BANKING A bank teller is counting the total amount of money in a cash drawer at the end of a shift. There is a total of \$2600 in denominations of \$1, \$5, \$10, and \$20 bills The total number of paper bills is 235. The number of \$20 bills is twice the number of \$1 bills, and the number of \$5 bills is 10 more than the number of \$1 bills. Write a system of linear equations to represent the situation. Then use matrices to find the number of each denomination. See margin.

In Exercises 111 and 112, use a system of equations to find the equation of the parabola $y = ax^2 + bx + c$ that passes through the points. Solve the system using matrices. Use a graphing utility to verify your results.

111.

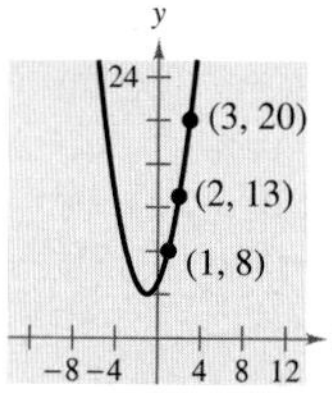

$y = x^2 + 2x + 5$

112.

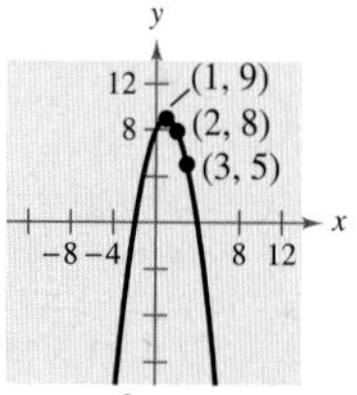

$y = -x^2 + 2x + 8$

113. MATHEMATICAL MODELING A video of the path of a ball thrown by a baseball player was analyzed with a grid covering the TV screen. The tape was paused three times, and the position of the ball was measured each time. The coordinates obtained are shown in the table. (x and y are measured in feet.)

Horizontal distance, x	Height, y
0	5.0
15	9.6
30	12.4

105. $\dfrac{4x^2}{(x+1)^2(x-1)} = \dfrac{1}{x-1} + \dfrac{3}{x+1} - \dfrac{2}{(x+1)^2}$

106. $\dfrac{8x^2}{(x-1)^2(x+1)} = \dfrac{2}{x+1} + \dfrac{6}{x-1} + \dfrac{4}{(x-1)^2}$

(a)–(e). See margin.
(a) Use a system of equations to find the equation of the parabola $y = ax^2 + bx + c$ that passes through the three points. Solve the system using matrices.
(b) Use a graphing utility to graph the parabola.
(c) Graphically approximate the maximum height of the ball and the point at which the ball struck the ground.
(d) Analytically find the maximum height of the ball and the point at which the ball struck the ground.
(e) Compare your results from parts (c) and (d).

114. DATA ANALYSIS: SNOWBOARDERS The table shows the numbers of people y (in millions) in the United States who participated in snowboarding in selected years from 2003 to 2007. (Source: National Sporting Goods Association) See margin.

Year	Number, y
2003	6.3
2005	6.0
2007	5.1

(a) Use a system of equations to find the equation of the parabola $y = at^2 + bt + c$ that passes through the points. Let t represent the year, with $t = 3$ corresponding to 2003. Solve the system using matrices.
(b) Use a graphing utility to graph the parabola.
(c) Use the equation in part (a) to estimate the number of people who participated in snowboarding in 2009. Does your answer seem reasonable? Explain.
(d) Do you believe that the equation can be used for years far beyond 2007? Explain.

NETWORK ANALYSIS **In Exercises 115 and 116, answer the questions about the specified network. (In a network it is assumed that the total flow into each junction is equal to the total flow out of each junction.)** 115–116. See margin.

115. Water flowing through a network of pipes (in thousands of cubic meters per hour) is shown in the figure.

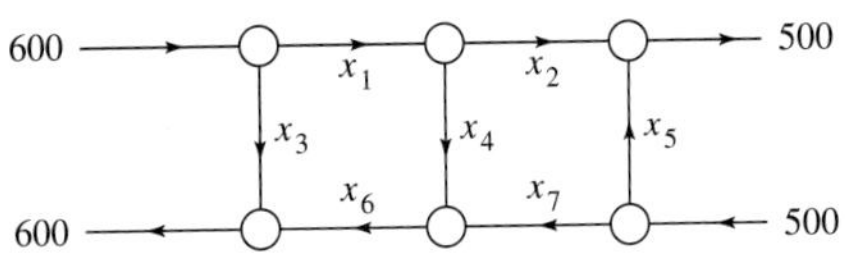

(a) Solve this system using matrices for the water flow represented by x_i, $i = 1, 2, \ldots, 7$.
(b) Find the network flow pattern when $x_6 = 0$ and $x_7 = 0$.
(c) Find the network flow pattern when $x_5 = 400$ and $x_6 = 500$.

116. The flow of traffic (in vehicles per hour) through a network of streets is shown in the figure.

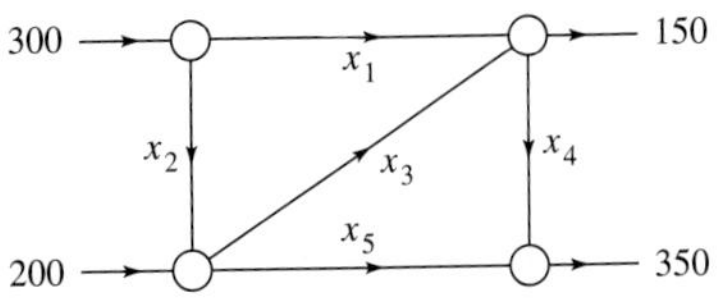

(a) Solve this system using matrices for the traffic flow represented by x_i, $i = 1, 2, \ldots, 5$.
(b) Find the traffic flow when $x_2 = 200$ and $x_3 = 50$.
(c) Find the traffic flow when $x_2 = 150$ and $x_3 = 0$.

EXPLORATION

TRUE OR FALSE? **In Exercises 117 and 118, determine whether the statement is true or false. Justify your answer.**

117. $\begin{bmatrix} 5 & 0 & -2 & 7 \\ -1 & 3 & -6 & 0 \end{bmatrix}$ is a 4×2 matrix. False. It is a 2×4 matrix.

118. The method of Gaussian elimination reduces a matrix until a reduced row-echelon form is obtained. See margin.

119. THINK ABOUT IT The augmented matrix below represents system of linear equations (in variables x, y, and z) that has been reduced using Gauss-Jordan elimination. Write a system of equations with nonzero coefficients that is represented by the reduced matrix. (There are many correct answers.) See margin.

$$\left[\begin{array}{ccc|c} 1 & 0 & 3 & -2 \\ 0 & 1 & 4 & 1 \\ 0 & 0 & 0 & 0 \end{array}\right]$$

120. THINK ABOUT IT See margin.
(a) Describe the row-echelon form of an augmented matrix that corresponds to a system of linear equations that is inconsistent.
(b) Describe the row-echelon form of an augmented matrix that corresponds to a system of linear equations that has an infinite number of solutions.

121. Describe the three elementary row operations that can be performed on an augmented matrix. See margin.

122. CAPSTONE In your own words, describe the difference between a matrix in row-echelon form and a matrix in reduced row-echelon form. Include an example of each to support your explanation. See margin.

123. What is the relationship between the three elementary row operations performed on an augmented matrix and the operations that lead to equivalent systems of equations? They are the same.

119. Answers will vary. For example:
$$\begin{cases} x + y + 7z = -1 \\ x + 2y + 11z = 0 \\ 2x + y + 10z = -3 \end{cases}$$

120. (a) There exists a row with all zeros except for the entry in the last column.
(b) There are fewer rows with nonzero entries than there are variables, and no row has the first nonzero value in the last column.

121. Interchange two rows.
Multiply a row by a nonzero constant.
Add a multiple of a row to another row.

122. A matrix in reduced row-echelon form has zeros above and below the leading 1's. A matrix in row-echelon form may have any real numbers above the leading 1's. Examples will vary.

5 ASSESS AND RETEACH

Daily Homework Quiz

Transparency Available
Available at the Instructor's companion site.

113. (a) $y = -0.004x^2 + 0.367x + 5$
(b)

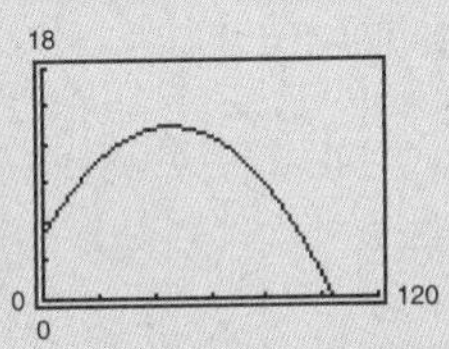

(c) 13 ft, 104 ft
(d) 13.418 ft, 103.793 ft
(e) The results are similar.

114. (a) $y = -0.075t^2 + 0.45t + 5.625$
(b)

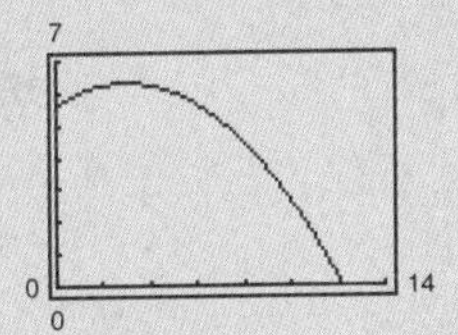

(c) 3.6 million; The model is probably not very reasonable outside the data set.
(d) No, because the model will eventually hit negative numbers.

115. (a) $x_1 = s$, $x_2 = t$, $x_3 = 600 - s$, $x_4 = s - t$, $x_5 = 500 - t$, $x_6 = s$, $x_7 = t$
(b) $x_1 = 0$, $x_2 = 0$, $x_3 = 600$, $x_4 = 0$, $x_5 = 500$, $x_6 = 0$, $x_7 = 0$
(c) $x_1 = 500$, $x_2 = 100$, $x_3 = 100$, $x_4 = 400$, $x_5 = 400$, $x_6 = 500$, $x_7 = 100$

116. (a) $x_1 = 500 - s - t$, $x_2 = -200 + s + t$, $x_3 = s$, $x_4 = 350 - t$, $x_5 = t$
(b) $x_1 = 100$, $x_2 = 200$, $x_3 = 50$, $x_4 = 0$, $x_5 = 350$
(c) $x_1 = 150$, $x_2 = 150$, $x_3 = 0$, $x_4 = 0$, $x_5 = 350$

118. False. Gaussian elimination reduces a matrix until a row-echelon form is obtained; Gauss-Jordan elimination reduces a matrix until a reduced row-echelon form is obtained.

1 PLAN AND PREPARE

Warm-up Exercises

Transparency Available
Available at the Instructor's companion site.

Notetaking Guide

Transparency Available
Promotes interactive learning and notetaking skills.
Available at the Instructor's companion site.

Animated Precalculus

An **Animated Precalculus** tutorial is available at the Student companion site for **Section 8.2.**

Pacing

Average: 3 days
Advanced: 3 days
Block: 0.5 block with 8.1
1 block

2 FOCUS AND MOTIVATE

Essential Question

How do you perform operations on matrices? **Tell students that they will learn how to answer this question by studying the definitions of matrix addition, scalar multiplication, and matrix multiplication.**

8.2 OPERATIONS WITH MATRICES

What you should learn

- Decide whether two matrices are equal.
- Add and subtract matrices and multiply matrices by scalars.
- Multiply two matrices.
- Use matrix operations to model and solve real-life problems.

Why you should learn it

Matrix operations can be used to model and solve real-life problems. For instance, in Exercise 76 on page 598, matrix operations are used to analyze annual health care costs.

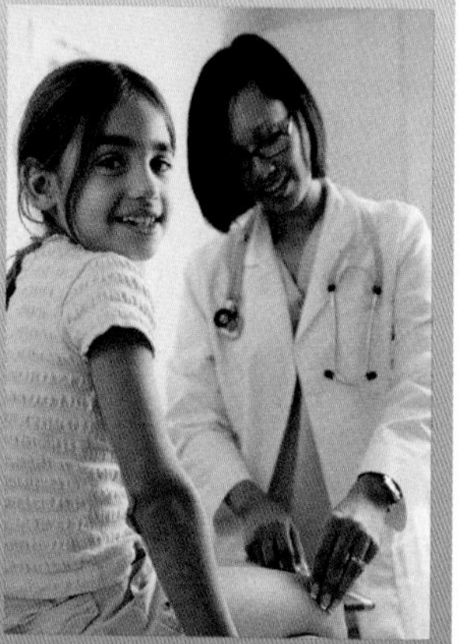
© Royalty-Free/Corbis

Equality of Matrices

In Section 8.1, you used matrices to solve systems of linear equations. There is a rich mathematical theory of matrices, and its applications are numerous. This section and the next two introduce some fundamentals of matrix theory. It is standard mathematical convention to represent matrices in any of the following three ways.

Representation of Matrices

1. A matrix can be denoted by an uppercase letter such as A, B, or C.
2. A matrix can be denoted by a representative element enclosed in brackets, such as $[a_{ij}]$, $[b_{ij}]$, or $[c_{ij}]$.
3. A matrix can be denoted by a rectangular array of numbers such as

$$A = [a_{ij}] = \begin{bmatrix} a_{11} & a_{12} & a_{13} & \cdots & a_{1n} \\ a_{21} & a_{22} & a_{23} & \cdots & a_{2n} \\ a_{31} & a_{32} & a_{33} & \cdots & a_{3n} \\ \vdots & \vdots & \vdots & & \vdots \\ a_{m1} & a_{m2} & a_{m3} & \cdots & a_{mn} \end{bmatrix}.$$

Two matrices $A = [a_{ij}]$ and $B = [b_{ij}]$ are **equal** if they have the same order ($m \times n$) and $a_{ij} = b_{ij}$ for $1 \le i \le m$ and $1 \le j \le n$. In other words, two matrices are equal if their corresponding entries are equal.

Example 1 Equality of Matrices

Solve for a_{11}, a_{12}, a_{21}, and a_{22} in the following matrix equation.

$$\begin{bmatrix} a_{11} & a_{12} \\ a_{21} & a_{22} \end{bmatrix} = \begin{bmatrix} 2 & -1 \\ -3 & 0 \end{bmatrix}$$

Solution

Because two matrices are equal only if their corresponding entries are equal, you can conclude that

$$a_{11} = 2, \quad a_{12} = -1, \quad a_{21} = -3, \quad \text{and} \quad a_{22} = 0.$$

CHECK*Point* Now try Exercise 7.

Be sure you see that for two matrices to be equal, they must have the same order *and* their corresponding entries must be equal. For instance,

$$\begin{bmatrix} 2 & -1 \\ \sqrt{4} & \frac{1}{2} \end{bmatrix} = \begin{bmatrix} 2 & -1 \\ 2 & 0.5 \end{bmatrix} \quad \text{but} \quad \begin{bmatrix} 2 & -1 \\ 3 & 4 \\ 0 & 0 \end{bmatrix} \neq \begin{bmatrix} 2 & -1 \\ 3 & 4 \end{bmatrix}.$$

Resource Planning Guide

Chapter Resources
- Complete Solutions Guide

Workbooks
- Notetaking Guide
- Student Solutions Guide

Interactive Technology
- Instructor Success Organizer
- Notetaking Guide IAE
- Instructional DVDs
- Animated Precalculus
- PowerLecture with ExamView

Matrix Addition and Scalar Multiplication

In this section, three basic matrix operations will be covered. The first two are matrix addition and scalar multiplication. With matrix addition, you can add two matrices (of the same order) by adding their corresponding entries.

Definition of Matrix Addition

If $A = [a_{ij}]$ and $B = [b_{ij}]$ are matrices of order $m \times n$, their sum is the $m \times n$ matrix given by

$$A + B = [a_{ij} + b_{ij}].$$

The sum of two matrices of different orders is undefined.

HISTORICAL NOTE

The Granger Collection

Arthur Cayley (1821–1895), a British mathematician, invented matrices around 1858. Cayley was a Cambridge University graduate and a lawyer by profession. His groundbreaking work on matrices was begun as he studied the theory of transformations. Cayley also was instrumental in the development of determinants. Cayley and two American mathematicians, Benjamin Peirce (1809–1880) and his son Charles S. Peirce (1839–1914), are credited with developing "matrix algebra."

Example 2 Addition of Matrices

a. $\begin{bmatrix} -1 & 2 \\ 0 & 1 \end{bmatrix} + \begin{bmatrix} 1 & 3 \\ -1 & 2 \end{bmatrix} = \begin{bmatrix} -1+1 & 2+3 \\ 0+(-1) & 1+2 \end{bmatrix}$

$= \begin{bmatrix} 0 & 5 \\ -1 & 3 \end{bmatrix}$

b. $\begin{bmatrix} 0 & 1 & -2 \\ 1 & 2 & 3 \end{bmatrix} + \begin{bmatrix} 0 & 0 & 0 \\ 0 & 0 & 0 \end{bmatrix} = \begin{bmatrix} 0 & 1 & -2 \\ 1 & 2 & 3 \end{bmatrix}$

c. $\begin{bmatrix} 1 \\ -3 \\ -2 \end{bmatrix} + \begin{bmatrix} -1 \\ 3 \\ 2 \end{bmatrix} = \begin{bmatrix} 0 \\ 0 \\ 0 \end{bmatrix}$

d. The sum of

$$A = \begin{bmatrix} 2 & 1 & 0 \\ 4 & 0 & -1 \\ 3 & -2 & 2 \end{bmatrix} \quad \text{and}$$

$$B = \begin{bmatrix} 0 & 1 \\ -1 & 3 \\ 2 & 4 \end{bmatrix}$$

is undefined because A is of order 3×3 and B is of order 3×2.

CHECKPoint Now try Exercise 13(a).

In operations with matrices, numbers are usually referred to as **scalars.** In this text, scalars will always be real numbers. You can multiply a matrix A by a scalar c by multiplying each entry in A by c.

Definition of Scalar Multiplication

If $A = [a_{ij}]$ is an $m \times n$ matrix and c is a scalar, the **scalar multiple** of A by c is the $m \times n$ matrix given by

$$cA = [ca_{ij}].$$

3 TEACH

Extra Example 1

Solve for a_{11}, a_{12}, a_{21}, and a_{22} in the following matrix.

$$\begin{bmatrix} a_{11} & a_{12} \\ a_{21} & a_{22} \end{bmatrix} = \begin{bmatrix} -3 & -2 \\ 7 & 13 \end{bmatrix}$$

$a_{11} = -3$, $a_{12} = -2$, $a_{21} = 7$, $a_{22} = 13$

Extra Example 2

Evaluate.

a. $\begin{bmatrix} 4 & -1 \\ 2 & -3 \end{bmatrix} + \begin{bmatrix} 2 & -1 \\ 0 & 6 \end{bmatrix}$

$\begin{bmatrix} 6 & -2 \\ 2 & 3 \end{bmatrix}$

b. $\begin{bmatrix} 1 & 5 & -3 \\ 0 & 2 & 7 \end{bmatrix} + \begin{bmatrix} 0 & 0 & 0 \\ -3 & 4 & 1 \end{bmatrix}$

$\begin{bmatrix} 1 & 5 & -3 \\ -3 & 6 & 8 \end{bmatrix}$

c. $\begin{bmatrix} 4 \\ -6 \\ 0 \end{bmatrix} + \begin{bmatrix} -2 \\ 3 \\ 1 \end{bmatrix}$

$\begin{bmatrix} 2 \\ -3 \\ 1 \end{bmatrix}$

d. $\begin{bmatrix} 1 & 2 & 3 \\ 0 & 4 & 5 \\ 1 & 6 & 7 \end{bmatrix} + \begin{bmatrix} -3 & 1 \\ 4 & 7 \\ -5 & 0 \end{bmatrix}$

The sum of these matrices is undefined because they do not have the same order.

Extra Example 3

If $A = \begin{bmatrix} 4 & -1 \\ 0 & 4 \\ -3 & 8 \end{bmatrix}$ and $B = \begin{bmatrix} 0 & 4 \\ -1 & 3 \\ 1 & 7 \end{bmatrix}$, find the following matrices.

a. $-3A$

$$\begin{bmatrix} -12 & 3 \\ 0 & -12 \\ 9 & -24 \end{bmatrix}$$

b. $2B$

$$\begin{bmatrix} 0 & 8 \\ -2 & 6 \\ 2 & 14 \end{bmatrix}$$

c. $-3A + 2B$

$$\begin{bmatrix} -12 & 11 \\ -2 & -6 \\ 11 & -10 \end{bmatrix}$$

The symbol $-A$ represents the negation of A, which is the scalar product $(-1)A$. Moreover, if A and B are of the same order, then $A - B$ represents the sum of A and $(-1)B$. That is,

$$A - B = A + (-1)B. \quad \text{Subtraction of matrices}$$

The order of operations for matrix expressions is similar to that for real numbers. In particular, you perform scalar multiplication before matrix addition and subtraction, as shown in Example 3(c).

Example 3 Scalar Multiplication and Matrix Subtraction

For the following matrices, find (a) $3A$, (b) $-B$, and (c) $3A - B$.

$$A = \begin{bmatrix} 2 & 2 & 4 \\ -3 & 0 & -1 \\ 2 & 1 & 2 \end{bmatrix} \quad \text{and} \quad B = \begin{bmatrix} 2 & 0 & 0 \\ 1 & -4 & 3 \\ -1 & 3 & 2 \end{bmatrix}$$

Solution

a. $3A = 3\begin{bmatrix} 2 & 2 & 4 \\ -3 & 0 & -1 \\ 2 & 1 & 2 \end{bmatrix}$ Scalar multiplication

$= \begin{bmatrix} 3(2) & 3(2) & 3(4) \\ 3(-3) & 3(0) & 3(-1) \\ 3(2) & 3(1) & 3(2) \end{bmatrix}$ Multiply each entry by 3.

$= \begin{bmatrix} 6 & 6 & 12 \\ -9 & 0 & -3 \\ 6 & 3 & 6 \end{bmatrix}$ Simplify.

b. $-B = (-1)\begin{bmatrix} 2 & 0 & 0 \\ 1 & -4 & 3 \\ -1 & 3 & 2 \end{bmatrix}$ Definition of negation

$= \begin{bmatrix} -2 & 0 & 0 \\ -1 & 4 & -3 \\ 1 & -3 & -2 \end{bmatrix}$ Multiply each entry by -1.

c. $3A - B = \begin{bmatrix} 6 & 6 & 12 \\ -9 & 0 & -3 \\ 6 & 3 & 6 \end{bmatrix} - \begin{bmatrix} 2 & 0 & 0 \\ 1 & -4 & 3 \\ -1 & 3 & 2 \end{bmatrix}$ Matrix subtraction

$= \begin{bmatrix} 4 & 6 & 12 \\ -10 & 4 & -6 \\ 7 & 0 & 4 \end{bmatrix}$ Subtract corresponding entries.

CHECKPoint Now try Exercise 13(b), (c), and (d).

It is often convenient to rewrite the scalar multiple cA by factoring c out of every entry in the matrix. For instance, in the following example, the scalar $\frac{1}{2}$ has been factored out of the matrix.

$$\begin{bmatrix} \frac{1}{2} & -\frac{3}{2} \\ \frac{5}{2} & \frac{1}{2} \end{bmatrix} = \begin{bmatrix} \frac{1}{2}(1) & \frac{1}{2}(-3) \\ \frac{1}{2}(5) & \frac{1}{2}(1) \end{bmatrix} = \frac{1}{2}\begin{bmatrix} 1 & -3 \\ 5 & 1 \end{bmatrix}$$

Differentiated Instruction

Auditory Learners Students must be careful to make correct calculations on all numbers in the matrices when multiplying and subtracting. Encourage them to say each calculation aloud as they make it, such as "3 times 2 equals 6," or "−1 times 2 is −2." This step will act as a check to make sure that they have completed the calculation correctly.

Algebra Help

You can review the properties of addition and multiplication of real numbers (and other properties of real numbers) in Appendix A.1.

The properties of matrix addition and scalar multiplication are similar to those of addition and multiplication of real numbers.

Properties of Matrix Addition and Scalar Multiplication

Let A, B, and C be $m \times n$ matrices and let c and d be scalars.

1. $A + B = B + A$	Commutative Property of Matrix Addition
2. $A + (B + C) = (A + B) + C$	Associative Property of Matrix Addition
3. $(cd)A = c(dA)$	Associative Property of Scalar Multiplication
4. $1A = A$	Scalar Identity Property
5. $c(A + B) = cA + cB$	Distributive Property
6. $(c + d)A = cA + dA$	Distributive Property

Note that the Associative Property of Matrix Addition allows you to write expressions such as $A + B + C$ without ambiguity because the same sum occurs no matter how the matrices are grouped. This same reasoning applies to sums of four or more matrices.

Example 4 Addition of More than Two Matrices

By adding corresponding entries, you obtain the following sum of four matrices.

$$\begin{bmatrix} 1 \\ 2 \\ -3 \end{bmatrix} + \begin{bmatrix} -1 \\ -1 \\ 2 \end{bmatrix} + \begin{bmatrix} 0 \\ 1 \\ 4 \end{bmatrix} + \begin{bmatrix} 2 \\ -3 \\ -2 \end{bmatrix} = \begin{bmatrix} 2 \\ -1 \\ 1 \end{bmatrix}$$

CHECKPoint Now try Exercise 19.

Example 5 Using the Distributive Property

Perform the indicated matrix operations.

$$3\left(\begin{bmatrix} -2 & 0 \\ 4 & 1 \end{bmatrix} + \begin{bmatrix} 4 & -2 \\ 3 & 7 \end{bmatrix}\right)$$

Solution

$$3\left(\begin{bmatrix} -2 & 0 \\ 4 & 1 \end{bmatrix} + \begin{bmatrix} 4 & -2 \\ 3 & 7 \end{bmatrix}\right) = 3\begin{bmatrix} -2 & 0 \\ 4 & 1 \end{bmatrix} + 3\begin{bmatrix} 4 & -2 \\ 3 & 7 \end{bmatrix}$$

$$= \begin{bmatrix} -6 & 0 \\ 12 & 3 \end{bmatrix} + \begin{bmatrix} 12 & -6 \\ 9 & 21 \end{bmatrix}$$

$$= \begin{bmatrix} 6 & -6 \\ 21 & 24 \end{bmatrix}$$

CHECKPoint Now try Exercise 21.

In Example 5, you could add the two matrices first and then multiply the matrix by 3, as follows. Notice that you obtain the same result.

$$3\left(\begin{bmatrix} -2 & 0 \\ 4 & 1 \end{bmatrix} + \begin{bmatrix} 4 & -2 \\ 3 & 7 \end{bmatrix}\right) = 3\begin{bmatrix} 2 & -2 \\ 7 & 8 \end{bmatrix} = \begin{bmatrix} 6 & -6 \\ 21 & 24 \end{bmatrix}$$

TECHNOLOGY

Most graphing utilities have the capability of performing matrix operations. Consult the user's guide for your graphing utility for specific keystrokes. Try using a graphing utility to find the sum of the matrices

$$A = \begin{bmatrix} 2 & -3 \\ -1 & 0 \end{bmatrix}$$

and

$$B = \begin{bmatrix} -1 & 4 \\ 2 & -5 \end{bmatrix}.$$

$$A + B = \begin{bmatrix} 1 & 1 \\ 1 & -5 \end{bmatrix}$$

Extra Example 4

For the following matrices, find $A + B + C + D$.

$$A = \begin{bmatrix} 4 \\ -1 \\ 2 \end{bmatrix}, B = \begin{bmatrix} 0 \\ 2 \\ 0 \end{bmatrix},$$

$$C = \begin{bmatrix} -3 \\ -1 \\ -2 \end{bmatrix}, D = \begin{bmatrix} -3 \\ 5 \\ 2 \end{bmatrix}$$

$$\begin{bmatrix} -2 \\ 5 \\ 2 \end{bmatrix}$$

Extra Example 5

Perform the indicated matrix operations.

$$2\left(\begin{bmatrix} 1 & 3 \\ -2 & 2 \end{bmatrix} + \begin{bmatrix} -4 & 0 \\ -3 & 1 \end{bmatrix}\right)$$

$$\begin{bmatrix} -6 & 6 \\ -10 & 6 \end{bmatrix}$$

Extra Example 6

Solve for X in the equation $2X - 2A = B$, where

$$A = \begin{bmatrix} 0 & 3 \\ 2 & 0 \\ -4 & -1 \end{bmatrix} \text{ and } B = \begin{bmatrix} -4 & -8 \\ -2 & 0 \\ 14 & -6 \end{bmatrix}.$$

$$X = \begin{bmatrix} -2 & -1 \\ 1 & 0 \\ 3 & -4 \end{bmatrix}$$

One important property of addition of real numbers is that the number 0 is the additive identity. That is, $c + 0 = c$ for any real number c. For matrices, a similar property holds. That is, if A is an $m \times n$ matrix and O is the $m \times n$ **zero matrix** consisting entirely of zeros, then $A + O = A$.

In other words, O is the **additive identity** for the set of all $m \times n$ matrices. For example, the following matrices are the additive identities for the sets of all 2×3 and 2×2 matrices.

$$\underbrace{O = \begin{bmatrix} 0 & 0 & 0 \\ 0 & 0 & 0 \end{bmatrix}}_{2 \times 3 \text{ zero matrix}} \quad \text{and} \quad \underbrace{O = \begin{bmatrix} 0 & 0 \\ 0 & 0 \end{bmatrix}}_{2 \times 2 \text{ zero matrix}}$$

The algebra of real numbers and the algebra of matrices have many similarities. For example, compare the following solutions.

WARNING / CAUTION

Remember that matrices are denoted by capital letters. So, when you solve for X, you are solving for a *matrix* that makes the matrix equation true.

Real Numbers (Solve for x.)	*m × n Matrices (Solve for X.)*
$x + a = b$	$X + A = B$
$x + a + (-a) = b + (-a)$	$X + A + (-A) = B + (-A)$
$x + 0 = b - a$	$X + O = B - A$
$x = b - a$	$X = B - A$

The algebra of real numbers and the algebra of matrices also have important differences, which will be discussed later.

Example 6 Solving a Matrix Equation

Solve for X in the equation $3X + A = B$, where

$$A = \begin{bmatrix} 1 & -2 \\ 0 & 3 \end{bmatrix} \quad \text{and} \quad B = \begin{bmatrix} -3 & 4 \\ 2 & 1 \end{bmatrix}.$$

Solution

Begin by solving the matrix equation for X to obtain

$$3X = B - A$$

$$X = \frac{1}{3}(B - A).$$

Now, using the matrices A and B, you have

$$X = \frac{1}{3}\left(\begin{bmatrix} -3 & 4 \\ 2 & 1 \end{bmatrix} - \begin{bmatrix} 1 & -2 \\ 0 & 3 \end{bmatrix}\right) \qquad \text{Substitute the matrices.}$$

$$= \frac{1}{3}\begin{bmatrix} -4 & 6 \\ 2 & -2 \end{bmatrix} \qquad \text{Subtract matrix } A \text{ from matrix } B.$$

$$= \begin{bmatrix} -\frac{4}{3} & 2 \\ \frac{2}{3} & -\frac{2}{3} \end{bmatrix}. \qquad \text{Multiply the matrix by } \tfrac{1}{3}.$$

CHECKPoint Now try Exercise 31.

Matrix Multiplication

Another basic matrix operation is **matrix multiplication.** At first glance, the definition may seem unusual. You will see later, however, that this definition of the product of two matrices has many practical applications.

Definition of Matrix Multiplication

If $A = [a_{ij}]$ is an $m \times n$ matrix and $B = [b_{ij}]$ is an $n \times p$ matrix, the product AB is an $m \times p$ matrix

$$AB = [c_{ij}]$$

where $c_{ij} = a_{i1}b_{1j} + a_{i2}b_{2j} + a_{i3}b_{3j} + \cdots + a_{in}b_{nj}$.

The definition of matrix multiplication indicates a *row-by-column* multiplication, where the entry in the ith row and jth column of the product AB is obtained by multiplying the entries in the ith row of A by the corresponding entries in the jth column of B and then adding the results. So for the product of two matrices to be defined, the number of columns of the first matrix must equal the number of rows of the second matrix. The general pattern for matrix multiplication is as follows.

$$\begin{bmatrix} a_{11} & a_{12} & a_{13} & \cdots & a_{1n} \\ a_{21} & a_{22} & a_{23} & \cdots & a_{2n} \\ a_{31} & a_{32} & a_{33} & \cdots & a_{3n} \\ \vdots & \vdots & \vdots & & \vdots \\ a_{i1} & a_{i2} & a_{i3} & \cdots & a_{in} \\ \vdots & \vdots & \vdots & & \vdots \\ a_{m1} & a_{m2} & a_{m3} & \cdots & a_{mn} \end{bmatrix} \begin{bmatrix} b_{11} & b_{12} & \cdots & b_{1j} & \cdots & b_{1p} \\ b_{21} & b_{22} & \cdots & b_{2j} & \cdots & b_{2p} \\ b_{31} & b_{32} & \cdots & b_{3j} & \cdots & b_{3p} \\ \vdots & \vdots & & \vdots & & \vdots \\ b_{n1} & b_{n2} & \cdots & b_{nj} & \cdots & b_{np} \end{bmatrix} = \begin{bmatrix} c_{11} & c_{12} & \cdots & c_{1j} & \cdots & c_{1p} \\ c_{21} & c_{22} & \cdots & c_{2j} & \cdots & c_{2p} \\ \vdots & \vdots & & \vdots & & \vdots \\ c_{i1} & c_{i2} & \cdots & c_{ij} & \cdots & c_{ip} \\ \vdots & \vdots & & \vdots & & \vdots \\ c_{m1} & c_{m2} & \cdots & c_{mj} & \cdots & c_{mp} \end{bmatrix}$$

$$a_{i1}b_{1j} + a_{i2}b_{2j} + a_{i3}b_{3j} + \cdots + a_{in}b_{nj} = c_{ij}$$

Example 7 **Finding the Product of Two Matrices**

Find the product AB using $A = \begin{bmatrix} -1 & 3 \\ 4 & -2 \\ 5 & 0 \end{bmatrix}$ and $B = \begin{bmatrix} -3 & 2 \\ -4 & 1 \end{bmatrix}$.

Solution

To find the entries of the product, multiply each row of A by each column of B.

$$AB = \begin{bmatrix} -1 & 3 \\ 4 & -2 \\ 5 & 0 \end{bmatrix} \begin{bmatrix} -3 & 2 \\ -4 & 1 \end{bmatrix}$$

$$= \begin{bmatrix} (-1)(-3) + (3)(-4) & (-1)(2) + (3)(1) \\ (4)(-3) + (-2)(-4) & (4)(2) + (-2)(1) \\ (5)(-3) + (0)(-4) & (5)(2) + (0)(1) \end{bmatrix}$$

$$= \begin{bmatrix} -9 & 1 \\ -4 & 6 \\ -15 & 10 \end{bmatrix}$$

CHECKPoint Now try Exercise 35.

Study Tip

In Example 7, the product AB is defined because the number of columns of A is equal to the number of rows of B. Also, note that the product AB has order 3×2.

Extra Example 7

Find the product AB, where

$A = \begin{bmatrix} -1 & 4 \\ 2 & 0 \\ 1 & 2 \end{bmatrix}$ and $B = \begin{bmatrix} 1 & -2 \\ 0 & 7 \end{bmatrix}$.

$\begin{bmatrix} -1 & 30 \\ 2 & -4 \\ 1 & 12 \end{bmatrix}$

Avoiding Common Errors

Students often make mistakes when aligning entries in matrix multiplication. One method of finding AB is to write the first column of B above the first row of A; the number of entries must match. The matching numbers are multiplied, and then the products are added. This sum becomes the first entry of the answer. Finding this sum for each row will generate the first column of the answer. The remaining columns in the answer are calculated by repeating the procedure with each remaining column of B.

Extra Example 8

Find the product AB, where

$$A = \begin{bmatrix} 4 & 0 & 0 \\ 0 & -9 & 0 \\ 0 & 0 & 5 \end{bmatrix} \text{ and}$$

$$B = \begin{bmatrix} \frac{1}{4} & 0 & 0 \\ 0 & -\frac{1}{9} & 0 \\ 0 & 0 & \frac{1}{2} \end{bmatrix}.$$

$$\begin{bmatrix} 1 & 0 & 0 \\ 0 & 1 & 0 \\ 0 & 0 & \frac{5}{2} \end{bmatrix}$$

Extra Example 9

Find the product and dimension of each of the following.

a. $\underset{2 \times 2}{\begin{bmatrix} 0 & 1 \\ 7 & 2 \end{bmatrix}} \underset{2 \times 3}{\begin{bmatrix} 0 & 3 & -2 \\ 2 & 1 & 4 \end{bmatrix}}$

$\underset{2 \times 3}{\begin{bmatrix} 2 & 1 & 4 \\ 4 & 23 & -6 \end{bmatrix}}$

b. $\underset{3 \times 2}{\begin{bmatrix} 2 & 1 \\ -4 & 0 \\ 1 & 3 \end{bmatrix}} \underset{2 \times 1}{\begin{bmatrix} 3 \\ -1 \end{bmatrix}}$

$\underset{3 \times 1}{\begin{bmatrix} 5 \\ -12 \\ 0 \end{bmatrix}}$

c. $\underset{2 \times 3}{\begin{bmatrix} 0 & 2 & 4 \\ -1 & 1 & 2 \end{bmatrix}} \underset{2 \times 3}{\begin{bmatrix} 2 & -4 & 5 \\ 0 & 9 & 3 \end{bmatrix}}$

This operation is undefined because the matrices do not have compatible orders for matrix multiplication.

Be sure you understand that for the product of two matrices to be defined, the number of *columns* of the first matrix must equal the number of *rows* of the second matrix. That is, the middle two indices must be the same. The outside two indices give the order of the product, as shown below.

$$\underset{m \times n}{A} \times \underset{n \times p}{B} = \underset{m \times p}{AB}$$

Equal (middle indices n and n)

Order of AB (outside indices m and p)

Example 8 Finding the Product of Two Matrices

Find the product AB where

$$A = \begin{bmatrix} 1 & 0 & 3 \\ 2 & -1 & -2 \end{bmatrix} \quad \text{and} \quad B = \begin{bmatrix} -2 & 4 \\ 1 & 0 \\ -1 & 1 \end{bmatrix}.$$

Solution

Note that the order of A is 2×3 and the order of B is 3×2. So, the product AB has order 2×2.

$$AB = \begin{bmatrix} 1 & 0 & 3 \\ 2 & -1 & -2 \end{bmatrix} \begin{bmatrix} -2 & 4 \\ 1 & 0 \\ -1 & 1 \end{bmatrix}$$

$$= \begin{bmatrix} 1(-2) + 0(1) + 3(-1) & 1(4) + 0(0) + 3(1) \\ 2(-2) + (-1)(1) + (-2)(-1) & 2(4) + (-1)(0) + (-2)(1) \end{bmatrix}$$

$$= \begin{bmatrix} -5 & 7 \\ -3 & 6 \end{bmatrix}$$

CHECKPoint Now try Exercise 33.

Example 9 Patterns in Matrix Multiplication

a. $\underset{2 \times 2}{\begin{bmatrix} 3 & 4 \\ -2 & 5 \end{bmatrix}} \underset{2 \times 2}{\begin{bmatrix} 1 & 0 \\ 0 & 1 \end{bmatrix}} = \underset{2 \times 2}{\begin{bmatrix} 3 & 4 \\ -2 & 5 \end{bmatrix}}$

b. $\underset{3 \times 3}{\begin{bmatrix} 6 & 2 & 0 \\ 3 & -1 & 2 \\ 1 & 4 & 6 \end{bmatrix}} \underset{3 \times 1}{\begin{bmatrix} 1 \\ 2 \\ -3 \end{bmatrix}} = \underset{3 \times 1}{\begin{bmatrix} 10 \\ -5 \\ -9 \end{bmatrix}}$

c. The product AB for the following matrices is not defined.

$$\underset{3 \times 2}{A = \begin{bmatrix} -2 & 1 \\ 1 & -3 \\ 1 & 4 \end{bmatrix}} \quad \text{and} \quad \underset{3 \times 4}{B = \begin{bmatrix} -2 & 3 & 1 & 4 \\ 0 & 1 & -1 & 2 \\ 2 & -1 & 0 & 1 \end{bmatrix}}$$

CHECKPoint Now try Exercise 39.

Example 10 Patterns in Matrix Multiplication

a. $\underset{1\times 3}{\begin{bmatrix} 1 & -2 & -3 \end{bmatrix}} \underset{3\times 1}{\begin{bmatrix} 2 \\ -1 \\ 1 \end{bmatrix}} = \underset{1\times 1}{[1]}$

b. $\underset{3\times 1}{\begin{bmatrix} 2 \\ -1 \\ 1 \end{bmatrix}} \underset{1\times 3}{\begin{bmatrix} 1 & -2 & -3 \end{bmatrix}} = \underset{3\times 3}{\begin{bmatrix} 2 & -4 & -6 \\ -1 & 2 & 3 \\ 1 & -2 & -3 \end{bmatrix}}$

CHECKPoint Now try Exercise 51.

In Example 10, note that the two products are different. Even if both AB and BA are defined, matrix multiplication is not, in general, commutative. That is, for most matrices, $AB \neq BA$. This is one way in which the algebra of real numbers and the algebra of matrices differ.

Properties of Matrix Multiplication

Let A, B, and C be matrices and let c be a scalar.

1. $A(BC) = (AB)C$ — Associative Property of Matrix Multiplication
2. $A(B + C) = AB + AC$ — Distributive Property
3. $(A + B)C = AC + BC$ — Distributive Property
4. $c(AB) = (cA)B = A(cB)$ — Associative Property of Scalar Multiplication

Definition of Identity Matrix

The $n \times n$ matrix that consists of 1's on its main diagonal and 0's elsewhere is called the **identity matrix of order $n \times n$** and is denoted by

$$I_n = \begin{bmatrix} 1 & 0 & 0 & \cdots & 0 \\ 0 & 1 & 0 & \cdots & 0 \\ 0 & 0 & 1 & \cdots & 0 \\ \vdots & \vdots & \vdots & & \vdots \\ 0 & 0 & 0 & \cdots & 1 \end{bmatrix}. \quad \text{Identity matrix}$$

Note that an identity matrix must be *square*. When the order is understood to be $n \times n$, you can denote I_n simply by I.

If A is an $n \times n$ matrix, the identity matrix has the property that $AI_n = A$ and $I_nA = A$. For example,

$$\begin{bmatrix} 3 & -2 & 5 \\ 1 & 0 & 4 \\ -1 & 2 & -3 \end{bmatrix}\begin{bmatrix} 1 & 0 & 0 \\ 0 & 1 & 0 \\ 0 & 0 & 1 \end{bmatrix} = \begin{bmatrix} 3 & -2 & 5 \\ 1 & 0 & 4 \\ -1 & 2 & -3 \end{bmatrix} \quad AI = A$$

and

$$\begin{bmatrix} 1 & 0 & 0 \\ 0 & 1 & 0 \\ 0 & 0 & 1 \end{bmatrix}\begin{bmatrix} 3 & -2 & 5 \\ 1 & 0 & 4 \\ -1 & 2 & -3 \end{bmatrix} = \begin{bmatrix} 3 & -2 & 5 \\ 1 & 0 & 4 \\ -1 & 2 & -3 \end{bmatrix}. \quad IA = A$$

Extra Example 10

Find the product and the dimension of each of the following.

a. $\underset{1\times 4}{\begin{bmatrix} 0 & 1 & 5 & -3 \end{bmatrix}} \underset{4\times 1}{\begin{bmatrix} 3 \\ 5 \\ -1 \\ 2 \end{bmatrix}}$

$\underset{1\times 1}{[-6]}$

b. $\underset{4\times 1}{\begin{bmatrix} 0 \\ 1 \\ 4 \\ -2 \end{bmatrix}} \underset{1\times 4}{\begin{bmatrix} -1 & 2 & 0 & 3 \end{bmatrix}}$

$\underset{4\times 4}{\begin{bmatrix} 0 & 0 & 0 & 0 \\ -1 & 2 & 0 & 3 \\ -4 & 8 & 0 & 12 \\ 2 & -4 & 0 & -6 \end{bmatrix}}$

Extra Example 11

Consider the system of linear equations.

$$\begin{cases} -x_1 + 3x_2 = 3 \\ x_1 - x_2 = 3 \end{cases}$$

a. Write this system as a matrix equation, $AX = B$.

$$\begin{bmatrix} -1 & 3 \\ 1 & -1 \end{bmatrix}\begin{bmatrix} x_1 \\ x_2 \end{bmatrix} = \begin{bmatrix} 3 \\ 3 \end{bmatrix}$$

b. Use Gauss-Jordan elimination on the augmented matrix $[A \vdots B]$ to solve for the matrix X.

$$X = \begin{bmatrix} x_1 \\ x_2 \end{bmatrix} = \begin{bmatrix} 6 \\ 3 \end{bmatrix}$$

Applications

Matrix multiplication can be used to represent a system of linear equations. Note how the system

$$\begin{cases} a_{11}x_1 + a_{12}x_2 + a_{13}x_3 = b_1 \\ a_{21}x_1 + a_{22}x_2 + a_{23}x_3 = b_2 \\ a_{31}x_1 + a_{32}x_2 + a_{33}x_3 = b_3 \end{cases}$$

can be written as the matrix equation $AX = B$, where A is the *coefficient matrix* of the system, and X and B are column matrices.

$$\begin{bmatrix} a_{11} & a_{12} & a_{13} \\ a_{21} & a_{22} & a_{23} \\ a_{31} & a_{32} & a_{33} \end{bmatrix}\begin{bmatrix} x_1 \\ x_2 \\ x_3 \end{bmatrix} = \begin{bmatrix} b_1 \\ b_2 \\ b_3 \end{bmatrix}$$

$$A \qquad \times \quad X \quad = \quad B$$

Study Tip

The column matrix B is also called a *constant* matrix. Its entries are the constant terms in the system of equations.

Example 11 Solving a System of Linear Equations

Consider the following system of linear equations.

$$\begin{cases} x_1 - 2x_2 + x_3 = -4 \\ x_2 + 2x_3 = 4 \\ 2x_1 + 3x_2 - 2x_3 = 2 \end{cases}$$

a. Write this system as a matrix equation, $AX = B$.

b. Use Gauss-Jordan elimination on the augmented matrix $[A \vdots B]$ to solve for the matrix X.

Study Tip

The notation $[A \vdots B]$ represents the augmented matrix formed when matrix B is adjoined to matrix A. The notation $[I \vdots X]$ represents the reduced row-echelon form of the augmented matrix that yields the *solution* of the system.

Solution

a. In matrix form, $AX = B$, the system can be written as follows.

$$\begin{bmatrix} 1 & -2 & 1 \\ 0 & 1 & 2 \\ 2 & 3 & -2 \end{bmatrix}\begin{bmatrix} x_1 \\ x_2 \\ x_3 \end{bmatrix} = \begin{bmatrix} -4 \\ 4 \\ 2 \end{bmatrix}$$

b. The augmented matrix is formed by adjoining matrix B to matrix A.

$$[A \vdots B] = \left[\begin{array}{ccc:c} 1 & -2 & 1 & -4 \\ 0 & 1 & 2 & 4 \\ 2 & 3 & -2 & 2 \end{array}\right]$$

Using Gauss-Jordan elimination, you can rewrite this equation as

$$[I \vdots X] = \left[\begin{array}{ccc:c} 1 & 0 & 0 & -1 \\ 0 & 1 & 0 & 2 \\ 0 & 0 & 1 & 1 \end{array}\right]$$

So, the solution of the system of linear equations is $x_1 = -1$, $x_2 = 2$, and $x_3 = 1$, and the solution of the matrix equation is

$$X = \begin{bmatrix} x_1 \\ x_2 \\ x_3 \end{bmatrix} = \begin{bmatrix} -1 \\ 2 \\ 1 \end{bmatrix}.$$

CHECKPoint Now try Exercise 61.

Example 12 Softball Team Expenses

Two softball teams submit equipment lists to their sponsors.

	Women's Team	*Men's Team*
Bats	12	15
Balls	45	38
Gloves	15	17

Each bat costs \$80, each ball costs \$6, and each glove costs \$60. Use matrices to find the total cost of equipment for each team.

Solution

The equipment lists E and the costs per item C can be written in matrix form as

$$E = \begin{bmatrix} 12 & 15 \\ 45 & 38 \\ 15 & 17 \end{bmatrix}$$

and

$$C = \begin{bmatrix} 80 & 6 & 60 \end{bmatrix}.$$

The total cost of equipment for each team is given by the product

$$CE = \begin{bmatrix} 80 & 6 & 60 \end{bmatrix}\begin{bmatrix} 12 & 15 \\ 45 & 38 \\ 15 & 17 \end{bmatrix}$$

$$= \begin{bmatrix} 80(12) + 6(45) + 60(15) & 80(15) + 6(38) + 60(17) \end{bmatrix}$$

$$= \begin{bmatrix} 2130 & 2448 \end{bmatrix}.$$

So, the total cost of equipment for the women's team is \$2130 and the total cost of equipment for the men's team is \$2448.

CHECKPoint Now try Exercise 69.

Study Tip

Notice in Example 12 that you cannot find the total cost using the product EC because EC is not defined. That is, the number of columns of E (2 columns) does not equal the number of rows of C (1 row).

Classroom Discussion

Problem Posing Write a matrix multiplication application problem that uses the matrix

$$A = \begin{bmatrix} 20 & 42 & 33 \\ 17 & 30 & 50 \end{bmatrix}.$$ Problems will vary.

Exchange problems with another student in your class. Form the matrices that represent the problem, and solve the problem. Interpret your solution in the context of the problem. Check with the creator of the problem to see if you are correct. Discuss other ways to represent and/or approach the problem.

Extra Example 12

A fruit grower raises two crops, which are shipped to three outlets. The list below shows how many units of each crop are shipped to each outlet.

	Outlet I	Outlet II	Outlet III
Crop 1	100	75	75
Crop 2	125	150	100

The profit per unit for Crop 1 is \$3.75, and the profit per unit for Crop 2 is \$7.00. Find the profits for each of the outlets.

Outlet I has a profit of \$1250, Outlet II has a profit of \$1331.25, and Outlet III has a profit of \$981.25.

Closing the Lesson

Have students summarize the major points of the lesson and answer the Essential Question: How do you perform operations on matrices?

- **Find the sum of two matrices of the same order by adding their corresponding entries to form a new matrix of the same order.**
- **Find the product of a matrix with a scalar quantity by multiplying each matrix entry by the quantity.**
- **Find the product of matrix A and matrix B by finding matrix C whose entries c_{ij} are calculated by multiplying entries in the ith row of A by corresponding entries in the jth column of B and adding the results.**
- **Identify and apply properties of matrix addition, scalar multiplication, matrix multiplication, and the identity matrix.**

4 PRACTICE AND APPLY

Assignment Guide

Transparencies Available
Available at the Instructor's companion site.

Average:
Day 1: pp. 594–595
Exs. 1–3, 8, 9, 11, 15, 16, 17–23 odd, 25–27, 29, 30
Day 2: pp. 594–596
Exs. 4–6, 33, 34–38 even, 41, 43, 47–49, 52, 53, 55
Day 3: pp. 596–598
Exs. 57, 59, 63–67 odd, 68, 70, 71–77 odd, 78, 79–85 odd, 89, 91

Advanced:
Day 1: pp. 594–595
Exs. 1–3, 8–16 even, 17, 18–24 even, 26–28, 30, 32
Day 2: pp. 594–596
Exs. 4–6, 34–40 even, 44–46, 48–56 even
Day 3: pp. 596–598
Exs. 58–68 even, 70–72, 74, 76–78, 80–86 even, 90–94 even

Block:
pp. 594–595
Exs. 1–3, 8, 9, 11, 15, 16, 17–23 odd, 25–27, 29, 30 (with 8.1)
pp. 594–598
Exs. 4–6, 33, 34–38 even, 41, 43, 47–49, 52, 53, 55–59 odd, 63–67 odd, 68, 70, 71–77 odd, 78, 79–85 odd, 89, 91

8.2 EXERCISES

See www.CalcChat.com for worked-out solutions to odd-numbered exercises.

VOCABULARY

In Exercises 1–4, fill in the blanks.

1. Two matrices are **equal** if all of their corresponding entries are equal.
2. When performing matrix operations, real numbers are often referred to as **scalars**.
3. A matrix consisting entirely of zeros is called a **zero** matrix and is denoted by **O**.
4. The $n \times n$ matrix consisting of 1's on its main diagonal and 0's elsewhere is called the **identity** matrix of order $n \times n$.

In Exercises 5 and 6, match the matrix property with the correct form. A, B, and C are matrices of order $m \times n$, and c and d are scalars.

5. (a) $1A = A$ (i) Distributive Property
(b) $A + (B + C) = (A + B) + C$ (ii) Commutative Property of Matrix Addition
(c) $(c + d)A = cA + dA$ (iii) Scalar Identity Property
(d) $(cd)A = c(dA)$ (iv) Associative Property of Matrix Addition
(e) $A + B = B + A$ (v) Associative Property of Scalar Multiplication

6. (a) $A + O = A$ (i) Distributive Property
(b) $c(AB) = A(cB)$ (ii) Additive Identity of Matrix Addition
(c) $A(B + C) = AB + AC$ (iii) Associative Property of Matrix Multiplication
(d) $A(BC) = (AB)C$ (iv) Associative Property of Scalar Multiplication

SKILLS AND APPLICATIONS

In Exercises 7–10, find x and y. 7–10. See margin.

7. $\begin{bmatrix} x & -2 \\ 7 & y \end{bmatrix} = \begin{bmatrix} -4 & -2 \\ 7 & 22 \end{bmatrix}$

8. $\begin{bmatrix} -5 & x \\ y & 8 \end{bmatrix} = \begin{bmatrix} -5 & 13 \\ 12 & 8 \end{bmatrix}$

9. $\begin{bmatrix} 16 & 4 & 5 & 4 \\ -3 & 13 & 15 & 6 \\ 0 & 2 & 4 & 0 \end{bmatrix} = \begin{bmatrix} 16 & 4 & 2x+1 & 4 \\ -3 & 13 & 15 & 3x \\ 0 & 2 & 3y-5 & 0 \end{bmatrix}$

10. $\begin{bmatrix} x+2 & 8 & -3 \\ 1 & 2y & 2x \\ 7 & -2 & y+2 \end{bmatrix} = \begin{bmatrix} 2x+6 & 8 & -3 \\ 1 & 18 & -8 \\ 7 & -2 & 11 \end{bmatrix}$

In Exercises 11–18, if possible, find (a) $A + B$, (b) $A - B$, (c) $3A$, and (d) $3A - 2B$. 11–13. See margin.

11. $A = \begin{bmatrix} 1 & -1 \\ 2 & -1 \end{bmatrix}, \quad B = \begin{bmatrix} 2 & -1 \\ -1 & 8 \end{bmatrix}$

12. $A = \begin{bmatrix} 1 & 2 \\ 2 & 1 \end{bmatrix}, \quad B = \begin{bmatrix} -3 & -2 \\ 4 & 2 \end{bmatrix}$

13. $A = \begin{bmatrix} 8 & -1 \\ 2 & 3 \\ -4 & 5 \end{bmatrix}, \quad B = \begin{bmatrix} 1 & 6 \\ -1 & -5 \\ 1 & 10 \end{bmatrix}$

14. $A = \begin{bmatrix} 1 & -1 & 3 \\ 0 & 6 & 9 \end{bmatrix}, \quad B = \begin{bmatrix} -2 & 0 & -5 \\ -3 & 4 & -7 \end{bmatrix}$
(a) $\begin{bmatrix} -1 & -1 & -2 \\ -3 & 10 & 2 \end{bmatrix}$ (b) $\begin{bmatrix} 3 & -1 & 8 \\ 3 & 2 & 16 \end{bmatrix}$
(c) $\begin{bmatrix} 3 & -3 & 9 \\ 0 & 18 & 27 \end{bmatrix}$ (d) $\begin{bmatrix} 7 & -3 & 19 \\ 6 & 10 & 41 \end{bmatrix}$

15. $A = \begin{bmatrix} 4 & 5 & -1 & 3 & 4 \\ 1 & 2 & -2 & -1 & 0 \end{bmatrix}$, 15–18. See margin.
$B = \begin{bmatrix} 1 & 0 & -1 & 1 & 0 \\ -6 & 8 & 2 & -3 & -7 \end{bmatrix}$

16. $A = \begin{bmatrix} -1 & 4 & 0 \\ 3 & -2 & 2 \\ 5 & 4 & -1 \\ 0 & 8 & -6 \\ -4 & -1 & 0 \end{bmatrix}, \quad B = \begin{bmatrix} -3 & 5 & 1 \\ 2 & -4 & -7 \\ 10 & -9 & -1 \\ 3 & 2 & -4 \\ 0 & 1 & -2 \end{bmatrix}$

17. $A = \begin{bmatrix} 6 & 0 & 3 \\ -1 & -4 & 0 \end{bmatrix}, \quad B = \begin{bmatrix} 8 & -1 \\ 4 & -3 \end{bmatrix}$

18. $A = \begin{bmatrix} 3 \\ 2 \\ -1 \end{bmatrix}, \quad B = \begin{bmatrix} -4 & 6 & 2 \end{bmatrix}$

In Exercises 19–24, evaluate the expression. 19–20. See margin.

19. $\begin{bmatrix} -5 & 0 \\ 3 & -6 \end{bmatrix} + \begin{bmatrix} 7 & 1 \\ -2 & -1 \end{bmatrix} + \begin{bmatrix} -10 & -8 \\ 14 & 6 \end{bmatrix}$

20. $\begin{bmatrix} 6 & 8 \\ -1 & 0 \end{bmatrix} + \begin{bmatrix} 0 & 5 \\ -3 & -1 \end{bmatrix} + \begin{bmatrix} -11 & -7 \\ 2 & -1 \end{bmatrix}$

21. $4\left(\begin{bmatrix} -4 & 0 & 1 \\ 0 & 2 & 3 \end{bmatrix} - \begin{bmatrix} 2 & 1 & -2 \\ 3 & -6 & 0 \end{bmatrix}\right)$
$\begin{bmatrix} -24 & -4 & 12 \\ -12 & 32 & 12 \end{bmatrix}$

7. $x = -4, y = 22$
8. $x = 13, y = 12$
9. $x = 2, y = 3$
10. $x = -4, y = 9$

11. (a) $\begin{bmatrix} 3 & -2 \\ 1 & 7 \end{bmatrix}$ (b) $\begin{bmatrix} -1 & 0 \\ 3 & -9 \end{bmatrix}$
(c) $\begin{bmatrix} 3 & -3 \\ 6 & -3 \end{bmatrix}$ (d) $\begin{bmatrix} -1 & -1 \\ 8 & -19 \end{bmatrix}$

12. (a) $\begin{bmatrix} -2 & 0 \\ 6 & 3 \end{bmatrix}$ (b) $\begin{bmatrix} 4 & 4 \\ -2 & -1 \end{bmatrix}$
(c) $\begin{bmatrix} 3 & 6 \\ 6 & 3 \end{bmatrix}$ (d) $\begin{bmatrix} 9 & 10 \\ -2 & -1 \end{bmatrix}$

13. (a) $\begin{bmatrix} 9 & 5 \\ 1 & -2 \\ -3 & 15 \end{bmatrix}$ (b) $\begin{bmatrix} 7 & -7 \\ 3 & 8 \\ -5 & -5 \end{bmatrix}$
(c) $\begin{bmatrix} 24 & -3 \\ 6 & 9 \\ -12 & 15 \end{bmatrix}$ (d) $\begin{bmatrix} 22 & -15 \\ 8 & 19 \\ -14 & -5 \end{bmatrix}$

15. (a) $\begin{bmatrix} 5 & 5 & -2 & 4 & 4 \\ -5 & 10 & 0 & -4 & -7 \end{bmatrix}$
(b) $\begin{bmatrix} 3 & 5 & 0 & 2 & 4 \\ 7 & -6 & -4 & 2 & 7 \end{bmatrix}$
(c) $\begin{bmatrix} 12 & 15 & -3 & 9 & 12 \\ 3 & 6 & -6 & -3 & 0 \end{bmatrix}$
(d) $\begin{bmatrix} 10 & 15 & -1 & 7 & 12 \\ 15 & -10 & -10 & 3 & 14 \end{bmatrix}$

17. (a), (b), and (d) not possible
(c) $\begin{bmatrix} 18 & 0 & 9 \\ -3 & -12 & 0 \end{bmatrix}$

18. (a), (b), and (d) not possible (c) $\begin{bmatrix} 9 \\ 6 \\ -3 \end{bmatrix}$

19. $\begin{bmatrix} -8 & -7 \\ 15 & -1 \end{bmatrix}$ 20. $\begin{bmatrix} -5 & 6 \\ -2 & -2 \end{bmatrix}$

16. See Additional Answers beginning on page AA1.

22–24. See margin.

22. $\frac{1}{2}([5\quad -2\quad 4\quad 0] + [14\quad 6\quad -18\quad 9])$

23. $-3\left(\begin{bmatrix}0&-3\\7&2\end{bmatrix}+\begin{bmatrix}-6&3\\8&1\end{bmatrix}\right)-2\begin{bmatrix}4&-4\\7&-9\end{bmatrix}$

24. $-\begin{bmatrix}4&11\\-2&-1\\9&3\end{bmatrix}+\frac{1}{6}\left(\begin{bmatrix}-5&-1\\3&4\\0&13\end{bmatrix}+\begin{bmatrix}7&5\\-9&-1\\6&-1\end{bmatrix}\right)$

In Exercises 25–28, use the matrix capabilities of a graphing utility to evaluate the expression. Round your results to three decimal places, if necessary. 25–28. See margin.

25. $\frac{3}{7}\begin{bmatrix}2&5\\-1&-4\end{bmatrix}+6\begin{bmatrix}-3&0\\2&2\end{bmatrix}$

26. $55\left(\begin{bmatrix}14&-11\\-22&19\end{bmatrix}+\begin{bmatrix}-22&20\\13&6\end{bmatrix}\right)$

27. $-\begin{bmatrix}3.211&6.829\\-1.004&4.914\\0.055&-3.889\end{bmatrix}-\begin{bmatrix}-1.630&-3.090\\5.256&8.335\\-9.768&4.251\end{bmatrix}$

28. $-\begin{bmatrix}10&15\\-20&10\\12&4\end{bmatrix}+\frac{1}{8}\left(\begin{bmatrix}-13&11\\7&0\\6&9\end{bmatrix}+\begin{bmatrix}-3&13\\-3&8\\-14&15\end{bmatrix}\right)$

In Exercises 29–32, solve for X in the equation, given

$A=\begin{bmatrix}-2&-1\\1&0\\3&-4\end{bmatrix}$ and $B=\begin{bmatrix}0&3\\2&0\\-4&-1\end{bmatrix}$. 29–32. See margin.

29. $X = 3A - 2B$ **30.** $2X = 2A - B$

31. $2X + 3A = B$ **32.** $2A + 4B = -2X$

In Exercises 33–40, if possible, find AB and state the order of the result.

33. $A=\begin{bmatrix}2&1\\-3&4\\1&6\end{bmatrix},\ B=\begin{bmatrix}0&-1&0\\4&0&2\\8&-1&7\end{bmatrix}$ Not possible

34. $A=\begin{bmatrix}0&-1&2\\6&0&3\\7&-1&8\end{bmatrix},\ B=\begin{bmatrix}2&-1\\4&-5\\1&6\end{bmatrix}$ 34–36. See margin.

35. $A=\begin{bmatrix}-1&6\\-4&5\\0&3\end{bmatrix},\ B=\begin{bmatrix}2&3\\0&9\end{bmatrix}$

36. $A=\begin{bmatrix}1&0&0\\0&4&0\\0&0&-2\end{bmatrix},\ B=\begin{bmatrix}3&0&0\\0&-1&0\\0&0&5\end{bmatrix}$

37. $A=\begin{bmatrix}5&0&0\\0&-8&0\\0&0&7\end{bmatrix},\ B=\begin{bmatrix}\frac{1}{5}&0&0\\0&-\frac{1}{8}&0\\0&0&\frac{1}{2}\end{bmatrix}$

$\begin{bmatrix}1&0&0\\0&1&0\\0&0&\frac{7}{2}\end{bmatrix}$ Order: 3×3

38. $A=\begin{bmatrix}0&0&5\\0&0&-3\\0&0&4\end{bmatrix},\ B=\begin{bmatrix}6&-11&4\\8&16&4\\0&0&0\end{bmatrix}$ See margin.

39. $A=\begin{bmatrix}10\\12\end{bmatrix},\ B=[6\quad -2\quad 1\quad 6]$ See margin.

40. $A=\begin{bmatrix}1&0&3&-2\\6&13&8&-17\end{bmatrix},\ B=\begin{bmatrix}1&6\\4&2\end{bmatrix}$ Not possible

In Exercises 41–46, use the matrix capabilities of a graphing utility to find AB, if possible. 41–43. See margin.

41. $A=\begin{bmatrix}7&5&-4\\-2&5&1\\10&-4&-7\end{bmatrix},\ B=\begin{bmatrix}2&-2&3\\8&1&4\\-4&2&-8\end{bmatrix}$

42. $A=\begin{bmatrix}11&-12&4\\14&10&12\\6&-2&9\end{bmatrix},\ B=\begin{bmatrix}12&10\\-5&12\\15&16\end{bmatrix}$

43. $A=\begin{bmatrix}-3&8&-6&8\\-12&15&9&6\\5&-1&1&5\end{bmatrix},\ B=\begin{bmatrix}3&1&6\\24&15&14\\16&10&21\\8&-4&10\end{bmatrix}$

44. $A=\begin{bmatrix}-2&4&8\\21&5&6\\13&2&6\end{bmatrix},\ B=\begin{bmatrix}2&0\\-7&15\\32&14\\0.5&1.6\end{bmatrix}$ Not possible

45. $A=\begin{bmatrix}9&10&-38&18\\100&-50&250&75\end{bmatrix},$ Not possible

$B=\begin{bmatrix}52&-85&27&45\\40&-35&60&82\end{bmatrix}$

46. $A=\begin{bmatrix}16&-18\\-4&13\\-9&21\end{bmatrix},\ B=\begin{bmatrix}-7&20&-1\\7&15&26\end{bmatrix}$ See margin.

In Exercises 47–52, if possible, find (a) AB, (b) BA, and (c) A^2. (*Note:* $A^2 = AA$.) 47–51. See margin.

47. $A=\begin{bmatrix}1&2\\4&2\end{bmatrix},\ B=\begin{bmatrix}2&-1\\-1&8\end{bmatrix}$

48. $A=\begin{bmatrix}6&3\\-2&-4\end{bmatrix},\ B=\begin{bmatrix}-2&0\\2&4\end{bmatrix}$

49. $A=\begin{bmatrix}3&-1\\1&3\end{bmatrix},\ B=\begin{bmatrix}1&-3\\3&1\end{bmatrix}$

50. $A=\begin{bmatrix}1&-1\\1&1\end{bmatrix},\ B=\begin{bmatrix}1&3\\-3&1\end{bmatrix}$

51. $A=\begin{bmatrix}7\\8\\-1\end{bmatrix},\ B=[1\quad 1\quad 2]$

52. $A=[3\quad 2\quad 1],\ B=\begin{bmatrix}2\\3\\0\end{bmatrix}$ (a) $[12]$ (b) $\begin{bmatrix}6&4&2\\9&6&3\\0&0&0\end{bmatrix}$ (c) Not possible

47. (a) $\begin{bmatrix}0&15\\6&12\end{bmatrix}$ (b) $\begin{bmatrix}-2&2\\31&14\end{bmatrix}$ (c) $\begin{bmatrix}9&6\\12&12\end{bmatrix}$

48. (a) $\begin{bmatrix}-6&12\\-4&-16\end{bmatrix}$ (b) $\begin{bmatrix}-12&-6\\4&-10\end{bmatrix}$ (c) $\begin{bmatrix}30&6\\-4&10\end{bmatrix}$

49. (a) $\begin{bmatrix}0&-10\\10&0\end{bmatrix}$ (b) $\begin{bmatrix}0&-10\\10&0\end{bmatrix}$ (c) $\begin{bmatrix}8&-6\\6&8\end{bmatrix}$

50. (a) $\begin{bmatrix}4&2\\-2&4\end{bmatrix}$ (b) $\begin{bmatrix}4&2\\-2&4\end{bmatrix}$ (c) $\begin{bmatrix}0&-2\\2&0\end{bmatrix}$

51. (a) $\begin{bmatrix}7&7&14\\8&8&16\\-1&-1&-2\end{bmatrix}$ (b) $[13]$ (c) Not possible

22. $\begin{bmatrix}\frac{19}{2}&2&-7&\frac{9}{2}\end{bmatrix}$

23. $\begin{bmatrix}10&8\\-59&9\end{bmatrix}$

24. $\begin{bmatrix}-\frac{11}{3}&-\frac{31}{3}\\1&\frac{3}{2}\\-8&-1\end{bmatrix}$

25. $\begin{bmatrix}-17.143&2.143\\11.571&10.286\end{bmatrix}$

26. $\begin{bmatrix}-440&495\\-495&1375\end{bmatrix}$

27. $\begin{bmatrix}-1.581&-3.739\\-4.252&-13.249\\9.713&-0.362\end{bmatrix}$

28. $\begin{bmatrix}-12&-12\\20.5&-9\\-13&-1\end{bmatrix}$

29. $\begin{bmatrix}-6&-9\\-1&0\\17&-10\end{bmatrix}$ **30.** $\begin{bmatrix}-2&-\frac{5}{2}\\0&0\\5&-\frac{7}{2}\end{bmatrix}$

31. $\begin{bmatrix}3&3\\-\frac{1}{2}&0\\-\frac{13}{2}&\frac{11}{2}\end{bmatrix}$ **32.** $\begin{bmatrix}2&-5\\-5&0\\5&6\end{bmatrix}$

34. $\begin{bmatrix}-2&17\\15&12\\18&46\end{bmatrix}$ Order: 3×2

35. $\begin{bmatrix}-2&51\\-8&33\\0&27\end{bmatrix}$ Order: 3×2

36. $\begin{bmatrix}3&0&0\\0&-4&0\\0&0&-10\end{bmatrix}$ Order: 3×3

38. $\begin{bmatrix}0&0&0\\0&0&0\\0&0&0\end{bmatrix}$ Order: 3×3

39. $\begin{bmatrix}60&-20&10&60\\72&-24&12&72\end{bmatrix}$

Order: 2×4

41. $\begin{bmatrix}70&-17&73\\32&11&6\\16&-38&70\end{bmatrix}$

42. $\begin{bmatrix}252&30\\298&452\\217&180\end{bmatrix}$

43. $\begin{bmatrix}151&25&48\\516&279&387\\47&-20&87\end{bmatrix}$

46. $\begin{bmatrix}-238&50&-484\\119&115&342\\210&135&555\end{bmatrix}$

In Exercises 53–56, evaluate the expression. Use the matrix capabilities of a graphing utility to verify your answer.

53. $\begin{bmatrix} 3 & 1 \\ 0 & -2 \end{bmatrix}\begin{bmatrix} 1 & 0 \\ -2 & 2 \end{bmatrix}\begin{bmatrix} 1 & 0 \\ 2 & 4 \end{bmatrix}$ $\quad \begin{bmatrix} 5 & 8 \\ -4 & -16 \end{bmatrix}$

54. $-3\left(\begin{bmatrix} 6 & 5 & -1 \\ 1 & -2 & 0 \end{bmatrix}\begin{bmatrix} 0 & 3 \\ -1 & -3 \\ 4 & 1 \end{bmatrix}\right)$ $\quad \begin{bmatrix} 27 & -6 \\ -6 & -27 \end{bmatrix}$

55. $\begin{bmatrix} 0 & 2 & -2 \\ 4 & 1 & 2 \end{bmatrix}\left(\begin{bmatrix} 4 & 0 \\ 0 & -1 \\ -1 & 2 \end{bmatrix} + \begin{bmatrix} -2 & 3 \\ -3 & 5 \\ 0 & -3 \end{bmatrix}\right)$ $\quad \begin{bmatrix} -4 & 10 \\ 3 & 14 \end{bmatrix}$

56. $\begin{bmatrix} 3 \\ -1 \\ 5 \\ 7 \end{bmatrix}([5 \quad -6] + [7 \quad -1] + [-8 \quad 9])$ $\quad \begin{bmatrix} 12 & 6 \\ -4 & -2 \\ 20 & 10 \\ 28 & 14 \end{bmatrix}$

In Exercises 57–64, (a) write the system of linear equations as a matrix equation, $AX = B$, and (b) use Gauss-Jordan elimination on the augmented matrix $[A \vdots B]$ to solve for the matrix X. 57–64. See margin.

57. $\begin{cases} -x_1 + x_2 = 4 \\ -2x_1 + x_2 = 0 \end{cases}$

58. $\begin{cases} 2x_1 + 3x_2 = 5 \\ x_1 + 4x_2 = 10 \end{cases}$

59. $\begin{cases} -2x_1 - 3x_2 = -4 \\ 6x_1 + x_2 = -36 \end{cases}$

60. $\begin{cases} -4x_1 + 9x_2 = -13 \\ x_1 - 3x_2 = 12 \end{cases}$

61. $\begin{cases} x_1 - 2x_2 + 3x_3 = 9 \\ -x_1 + 3x_2 - x_3 = -6 \\ 2x_1 - 5x_2 + 5x_3 = 17 \end{cases}$

62. $\begin{cases} x_1 + x_2 - 3x_3 = -1 \\ -x_1 + 2x_2 = 1 \\ x_1 - x_2 + x_3 = 2 \end{cases}$

63. $\begin{cases} x_1 - 5x_2 + 2x_3 = -20 \\ -3x_1 + x_2 - x_3 = 8 \\ -2x_2 + 5x_3 = -16 \end{cases}$

64. $\begin{cases} x_1 - x_2 + 4x_3 = 17 \\ x_1 + 3x_2 = -11 \\ -6x_2 + 5x_3 = 40 \end{cases}$

65. MANUFACTURING A corporation has three factories, each of which manufactures acoustic guitars and electric guitars. The number of guitars produced at factory j in one day is represented by a_{ij} in the matrix

$$A = \begin{bmatrix} 70 & 50 & 25 \\ 35 & 100 & 70 \end{bmatrix}. \quad \begin{bmatrix} 84 & 60 & 30 \\ 42 & 120 & 84 \end{bmatrix}$$

Find the production levels if production is increased by 20%.

66. MANUFACTURING A corporation has four factories, each of which manufactures sport utility vehicles and pickup trucks. The number of units of vehicle i produced at factory j in one day is represented by a_{ij} in the matrix

$$A = \begin{bmatrix} 100 & 90 & 70 & 30 \\ 40 & 20 & 60 & 60 \end{bmatrix}. \quad \begin{bmatrix} 110 & 99 & 77 & 33 \\ 44 & 22 & 66 & 66 \end{bmatrix}$$

Find the production levels if production is increased by 10%.

67. AGRICULTURE A fruit grower raises two crops, apples and peaches. Each of these crops is sent to three different outlets for sale. These outlets are The Farmer's Market, The Fruit Stand, and The Fruit Farm. The numbers of bushels of apples sent to the three outlets are 125, 100, and 75, respectively. The numbers of bushels of peaches sent to the three outlets are 100, 175, and 125, respectively. The profit per bushel for apples is \$3.50 and the profit per bushel for peaches is \$6.00.

(a) Write a matrix A that represents the number of bushels of each crop i that are shipped to each outlet j. State what each entry a_{ij} of the matrix represents.

(b) Write a matrix B that represents the profit per bushel of each fruit. State what each entry b_{ij} of the matrix represents. (a)–(c). See margin.

(c) Find the product BA and state what each entry of the matrix represents.

68. REVENUE An electronics manufacturer produces three models of LCD televisions, which are shipped to two warehouses. The numbers of units of model i that are shipped to warehouse j are represented by a_{ij} in the matrix

$$A = \begin{bmatrix} 5{,}000 & 4{,}000 \\ 6{,}000 & 10{,}000 \\ 8{,}000 & 5{,}000 \end{bmatrix}.$$

The prices per unit are represented by the matrix

$$B = [\$699.95 \quad \$899.95 \quad \$1099.95].$$

Compute BA and interpret the result. See margin.

69. INVENTORY A company sells five models of computers through three retail outlets. The inventories are represented by S.

Outlet	Model A	Model B	Model C	Model D	Model E
1	3	2	2	3	0
2	0	2	3	4	3
3	4	2	1	3	2

$$S = \begin{bmatrix} 3 & 2 & 2 & 3 & 0 \\ 0 & 2 & 3 & 4 & 3 \\ 4 & 2 & 1 & 3 & 2 \end{bmatrix}$$

The wholesale and retail prices are represented by T.

Model	Price: Wholesale	Price: Retail
A	\$840	\$1100
B	\$1200	\$1350
C	\$1450	\$1650
D	\$2650	\$3000
E	\$3050	\$3200

$$T = \begin{bmatrix} \$840 & \$1100 \\ \$1200 & \$1350 \\ \$1450 & \$1650 \\ \$2650 & \$3000 \\ \$3050 & \$3200 \end{bmatrix}$$

Compute ST and interpret the result. See margin.

57. (a) $\begin{bmatrix} -1 & 1 \\ -2 & 1 \end{bmatrix}\begin{bmatrix} x_1 \\ x_2 \end{bmatrix} = \begin{bmatrix} 4 \\ 0 \end{bmatrix}$ (b) $\begin{bmatrix} 4 \\ 8 \end{bmatrix}$

58. (a) $\begin{bmatrix} 2 & 3 \\ 1 & 4 \end{bmatrix}\begin{bmatrix} x_1 \\ x_2 \end{bmatrix} = \begin{bmatrix} 5 \\ 10 \end{bmatrix}$ (b) $\begin{bmatrix} -2 \\ 3 \end{bmatrix}$

59. (a) $\begin{bmatrix} -2 & -3 \\ 6 & 1 \end{bmatrix}\begin{bmatrix} x_1 \\ x_2 \end{bmatrix} = \begin{bmatrix} -4 \\ -36 \end{bmatrix}$ (b) $\begin{bmatrix} -7 \\ 6 \end{bmatrix}$

60. (a) $\begin{bmatrix} -4 & 9 \\ 1 & -3 \end{bmatrix}\begin{bmatrix} x_1 \\ x_2 \end{bmatrix} = \begin{bmatrix} -13 \\ 12 \end{bmatrix}$ (b) $\begin{bmatrix} -23 \\ -\frac{35}{3} \end{bmatrix}$

61. (a) $\begin{bmatrix} 1 & -2 & 3 \\ -1 & 3 & -1 \\ 2 & -5 & 5 \end{bmatrix}\begin{bmatrix} x_1 \\ x_2 \\ x_3 \end{bmatrix} = \begin{bmatrix} 9 \\ -6 \\ 17 \end{bmatrix}$ (b) $\begin{bmatrix} 1 \\ -1 \\ 2 \end{bmatrix}$

62. (a) $\begin{bmatrix} 1 & 1 & -3 \\ -1 & 2 & 0 \\ 1 & -1 & 1 \end{bmatrix}\begin{bmatrix} x_1 \\ x_2 \\ x_3 \end{bmatrix} = \begin{bmatrix} -1 \\ 1 \\ 2 \end{bmatrix}$ (b) $\begin{bmatrix} 2 \\ \frac{3}{2} \\ \frac{3}{2} \end{bmatrix}$

63. (a) $\begin{bmatrix} 1 & -5 & 2 \\ -3 & 1 & -1 \\ 0 & -2 & 5 \end{bmatrix}\begin{bmatrix} x_1 \\ x_2 \\ x_3 \end{bmatrix} = \begin{bmatrix} -20 \\ 8 \\ -16 \end{bmatrix}$ (b) $\begin{bmatrix} -1 \\ 3 \\ -2 \end{bmatrix}$

64. (a) $\begin{bmatrix} 1 & -1 & 4 \\ 1 & 3 & 0 \\ 0 & -6 & 5 \end{bmatrix}\begin{bmatrix} x_1 \\ x_2 \\ x_3 \end{bmatrix} = \begin{bmatrix} 17 \\ -11 \\ 40 \end{bmatrix}$ (b) $\begin{bmatrix} 4 \\ -5 \\ 2 \end{bmatrix}$

67. (a) $A = \begin{bmatrix} 125 & 100 & 75 \\ 100 & 175 & 125 \end{bmatrix}$

The entries represent the numbers of bushels of each crop that are shipped to each outlet.

(b) $B = [\$3.50 \quad \$6.00]$

The entries represent the profits per bushel of each crop.

(c) $BA = [\$1037.50 \quad \$1400 \quad \$1012.50]$

The entries represent the profits from both crops at each of the three outlets.

68. $[\$17{,}699{,}050 \quad \$17{,}299{,}050]$

The entries represent the costs of the three models of the LCD televisions at the two warehouses.

69. $\begin{bmatrix} \$15{,}770 & \$18{,}300 \\ \$26{,}500 & \$29{,}250 \\ \$21{,}260 & \$24{,}150 \end{bmatrix}$

The entries represent the wholesale and retail values of the inventories at the three outlets.

70. VOTING PREFERENCES The matrix

$$P = \overset{\text{From}}{\begin{matrix} \text{R} & \text{D} & \text{I} \end{matrix}}$$

$$P = \begin{bmatrix} 0.6 & 0.1 & 0.1 \\ 0.2 & 0.7 & 0.1 \\ 0.2 & 0.2 & 0.8 \end{bmatrix} \begin{matrix} \text{R} \\ \text{D} \\ \text{I} \end{matrix} \Bigg\} \text{To}$$

is called a *stochastic matrix*. Each entry $p_{ij}\,(i \neq j)$ represents the proportion of the voting population that changes from party i to party j, and p_{ii} represents the proportion that remains loyal to the party from one election to the next. Compute and interpret P^2. See margin.

71. VOTING PREFERENCES Use a graphing utility to find P^3, P^4, P^5, P^6, P^7, and P^8 for the matrix given in Exercise 70. Can you detect a pattern as P is raised to higher powers? See margin.

72. LABOR/WAGE REQUIREMENTS A company that manufactures boats has the following labor-hour and wage requirements.

Labor per boat

Department: Cutting, Assembly, Packaging

$$S = \begin{bmatrix} 1.0\text{ h} & 0.5\text{ h} & 0.2\text{ h} \\ 1.6\text{ h} & 1.0\text{ h} & 0.2\text{ h} \\ 2.5\text{ h} & 2.0\text{ h} & 1.4\text{ h} \end{bmatrix} \begin{matrix} \text{Small} \\ \text{Medium} \\ \text{Large} \end{matrix} \Bigg\} \text{Boat size}$$

Wages per hour

Plant: A, B

$$T = \begin{bmatrix} \$15 & \$13 \\ \$12 & \$11 \\ \$11 & \$10 \end{bmatrix} \begin{matrix} \text{Cutting} \\ \text{Assembly} \\ \text{Packaging} \end{matrix} \Bigg\} \text{Department}$$

Compute ST and interpret the result. See margin.

73. PROFIT At a local dairy mart, the numbers of gallons of skim milk, 2% milk, and whole milk sold over the weekend are represented by A.

Columns: Skim milk, 2% milk, Whole milk

$$A = \begin{bmatrix} 40 & 64 & 52 \\ 60 & 82 & 76 \\ 76 & 96 & 84 \end{bmatrix} \begin{matrix} \text{Friday} \\ \text{Saturday} \\ \text{Sunday} \end{matrix}$$

The selling prices (in dollars per gallon) and the profits (in dollars per gallon) for the three types of milk sold by the dairy mart are represented by B.

Columns: Selling price, Profit

$$B = \begin{bmatrix} \$3.45 & \$1.20 \\ \$3.65 & \$1.30 \\ \$3.85 & \$1.45 \end{bmatrix} \begin{matrix} \text{Skim milk} \\ \text{2\% milk} \\ \text{Whole milk} \end{matrix}$$

(a) Compute AB and interpret the result. See margin.

(b) Find the dairy mart's total profit from milk sales for the weekend. \$833.20

74. PROFIT At a convenience store, the numbers of gallons of 87-octane, 89-octane, and 93-octane gasoline sold over the weekend are represented by A.

Octane: 87, 89, 93

$$A = \begin{bmatrix} 580 & 840 & 320 \\ 560 & 420 & 160 \\ 860 & 1020 & 540 \end{bmatrix} \begin{matrix} \text{Friday} \\ \text{Saturday} \\ \text{Sunday} \end{matrix}$$

The selling prices (in dollars per gallon) and the profits (in dollars per gallon) for the three grades of gasoline sold by the convenience store are represented by B.

Columns: Selling price, Profit

$$B = \begin{bmatrix} \$2.00 & \$0.08 \\ \$2.10 & \$0.09 \\ \$2.20 & \$0.10 \end{bmatrix} \begin{matrix} 87 \\ 89 \\ 93 \end{matrix} \Bigg\} \text{Octane}$$

(a) Compute AB and interpret the result. See margin.

(b) Find the convenience store's profit from gasoline sales for the weekend. \$467.20

75. EXERCISE The numbers of calories burned by individuals of different body weights performing different types of aerobic exercises for a 20-minute time period are shown in matrix A.

Calories burned: 120-lb person, 150-lb person

$$A = \begin{bmatrix} 109 & 136 \\ 127 & 159 \\ 64 & 79 \end{bmatrix} \begin{matrix} \text{Bicycling} \\ \text{Jogging} \\ \text{Walking} \end{matrix}$$

(a) A 120-pound person and a 150-pound person bicycled for 40 minutes, jogged for 10 minutes, and walked for 60 minutes. Organize the time they spent exercising in a matrix B. $\begin{bmatrix} 2 & 0.5 & 3 \end{bmatrix}$

(b) Compute BA and interpret the result.

120 lb, 150 lb

$\begin{bmatrix} 473.5 & 588.5 \end{bmatrix}$

The entries represent the total calories burned.

70. $\begin{bmatrix} 0.40 & 0.15 & 0.15 \\ 0.28 & 0.53 & 0.17 \\ 0.32 & 0.32 & 0.68 \end{bmatrix}$

P^2 gives the proportions of the voting population that changed parties or remained loyal to their parties from the first election to the third.

71. $P^3 = \begin{bmatrix} 0.300 & 0.175 & 0.175 \\ 0.308 & 0.433 & 0.217 \\ 0.392 & 0.392 & 0.608 \end{bmatrix}$

$P^4 = \begin{bmatrix} 0.250 & 0.188 & 0.188 \\ 0.315 & 0.377 & 0.248 \\ 0.435 & 0.435 & 0.565 \end{bmatrix}$

$P^5 = \begin{bmatrix} 0.225 & 0.194 & 0.194 \\ 0.314 & 0.345 & 0.267 \\ 0.461 & 0.461 & 0.539 \end{bmatrix}$

$P^6 = \begin{bmatrix} 0.213 & 0.197 & 0.197 \\ 0.311 & 0.326 & 0.280 \\ 0.477 & 0.477 & 0.523 \end{bmatrix}$

$P^7 = \begin{bmatrix} 0.206 & 0.198 & 0.198 \\ 0.308 & 0.316 & 0.288 \\ 0.486 & 0.486 & 0.514 \end{bmatrix}$

$P^8 = \begin{bmatrix} 0.203 & 0.199 & 0.199 \\ 0.305 & 0.309 & 0.292 \\ 0.492 & 0.492 & 0.508 \end{bmatrix}$

Approaches the matrix

$\begin{bmatrix} 0.2 & 0.2 & 0.2 \\ 0.3 & 0.3 & 0.3 \\ 0.5 & 0.5 & 0.5 \end{bmatrix}$

72. $\begin{bmatrix} 23.2 & 20.5 \\ 38.2 & 33.8 \\ 76.9 & 68.5 \end{bmatrix}$

The entries represent the labor costs at each plant for each size of boat.

73. (a) Sales \$, Profit

$\begin{bmatrix} 571.8 & 206.6 \\ 798.9 & 288.8 \\ 936 & 337.8 \end{bmatrix}$

The entries represent the total sales and profits for milk on Friday, Saturday, and Sunday.

74. (a) Sales \$, Profit

$\begin{bmatrix} 3628 & 154 \\ 2354 & 98.6 \\ 5050 & 214.6 \end{bmatrix}$

The entries represent the total sales and profits for gasoline on Friday, Saturday, and Sunday.

76. **HEALTH CARE** The health care plans offered this year by a local manufacturing plant are as follows. For individuals, the comprehensive plan costs \$694.32, the HMO standard plan costs \$451.80, and the HMO Plus plan costs \$489.48. For families, the comprehensive plan costs \$1725.36, the HMO standard plan costs \$1187.76, and the HMO Plus plan costs \$1248.12. The plant expects the costs of the plans to change next year as follows. For individuals, the costs for the comprehensive, HMO standard, and HMO Plus plans will be \$683.91, \$463.10, and \$499.27, respectively. For families, the costs for the comprehensive, HMO standard, and HMO Plus plans will be \$1699.48, \$1217.45, and \$1273.08, respectively. See margin.

(a) Organize the information using two matrices A and B, where A represents the health care plan costs for this year and B represents the health care plan costs for next year. State what each entry of each matrix represents.

(b) Compute $A - B$ and interpret the result.

(c) The employees receive monthly paychecks from which the health care plan costs are deducted. Use the matrices from part (a) to write matrices that show how much will be deducted from each employees' paycheck this year and next year.

(d) Suppose instead that the costs of the health care plans increase by 4% next year. Write a matrix that shows the new monthly payments.

EXPLORATION

77–78. See margin.

TRUE OR FALSE? In Exercises 77 and 78, determine whether the statement is true or false. Justify your answer.

77. Two matrices can be added only if they have the same order.

78. Matrix multiplication is commutative.

THINK ABOUT IT In Exercises 79–86, let matrices A, B, C, and D be of orders 2×3, 2×3, 3×2, and 2×2, respectively. Determine whether the matrices are of proper order to perform the operation(s). If so, give the order of the answer.

79. $A + 2C$ Not possible
80. $B - 3C$ Not possible
81. AB Not possible
82. BC 2×2
83. $BC - D$ 2×2
84. $CB - D$ Not possible
85. $D(A - 3B)$ 2×3
86. $(BC - D)A$ 2×3

87. Consider matrices A, B, and C below. Perform the indicated operations and compare the results.

$$A = \begin{bmatrix} 3 & -1 \\ 4 & 7 \end{bmatrix}, \quad B = \begin{bmatrix} -2 & 0 \\ 8 & 1 \end{bmatrix}, \quad C = \begin{bmatrix} 5 & 2 \\ 2 & -6 \end{bmatrix}$$

See margin.

(a) Find $A + B$ and $B + A$.

(b) Find $A + B$, then add C to the resulting matrix. Find $B + C$, then add A to the resulting matrix.

(c) Find $2A$ and $2B$, then add the two resulting matrices. Find $A + B$, then multiply the resulting matrix by 2.

88. Use the following matrices to find AB, BA, $(AB)C$, and $A(BC)$. What do your results tell you about matrix multiplication, commutativity, and associativity?

$$A = \begin{bmatrix} 1 & 2 \\ 3 & 4 \end{bmatrix}, \quad B = \begin{bmatrix} 0 & 1 \\ 2 & 3 \end{bmatrix}, \quad C = \begin{bmatrix} 3 & 0 \\ 0 & 1 \end{bmatrix}$$ See margin.

89. **THINK ABOUT IT** If a, b, and c are real numbers such that $c \neq 0$ and $ac = bc$, then $a = b$. However, if A, B, and C are nonzero matrices such that $AC = BC$, then A is *not necessarily* equal to B. Illustrate this using the following matrices. See margin.

$$A = \begin{bmatrix} 0 & 1 \\ 0 & 1 \end{bmatrix}, \quad B = \begin{bmatrix} 1 & 0 \\ 1 & 0 \end{bmatrix}, \quad C = \begin{bmatrix} 2 & 3 \\ 2 & 3 \end{bmatrix}$$

90. **THINK ABOUT IT** If a and b are real numbers such that $ab = 0$, then $a = 0$ or $b = 0$. However, if A and B are matrices such that $AB = O$, it is *not necessarily* true that $A = O$ or $B = O$. Illustrate this using the following matrices.

$$A = \begin{bmatrix} 3 & 3 \\ 4 & 4 \end{bmatrix}, \quad B = \begin{bmatrix} 1 & -1 \\ -1 & 1 \end{bmatrix}$$ See margin.

91. Let A and B be unequal diagonal matrices of the same order. (A **diagonal matrix** is a square matrix in which each entry not on the main diagonal is zero.) Determine the products AB for several pairs of such matrices. Make a conjecture about a quick rule for such products. See margin.

92. Let $i = \sqrt{-1}$ and let

$$A = \begin{bmatrix} i & 0 \\ 0 & i \end{bmatrix} \quad \text{and} \quad B = \begin{bmatrix} 0 & -i \\ i & 0 \end{bmatrix}.$$ See margin.

(a) Find A^2, A^3, and A^4. Identify any similarities with i^2, i^3, and i^4.

(b) Find and identify B^2.

93. Find two matrices A and B such that $AB = BA$. Answers will vary.

94. **CAPSTONE** Let matrices A and B be of orders 3×2 and 2×2, respectively. Answer the following questions and explain your reasoning.

(a) Is it possible that $A = B$?

(b) Is $A + B$ defined?

(c) Is AB defined? If so, is it possible that $AB = BA$?

(a) No, they have different orders.
(b) No, they have different orders.
(c) Yes; No, BA is undefined.

5 ASSESS AND RETEACH

Daily Homework Quiz

Transparency Available

Available at the Instructor's companion site.

76. (a) $A: \begin{bmatrix} 694.32 & 1725.36 \\ 451.8 & 1187.76 \\ 489.48 & 1248.12 \end{bmatrix}$

$B: \begin{bmatrix} 683.91 & 1699.48 \\ 463.1 & 1217.45 \\ 499.27 & 1273.08 \end{bmatrix}$

Each entry represents the cost of a plan.

(b) $\begin{bmatrix} 10.41 & 25.88 \\ -11.3 & -29.69 \\ -9.79 & -24.96 \end{bmatrix}$

Employees choosing the comprehensive plan have a decrease in cost, while those choosing one of the other two plans have an increase in cost.

(c) $A: \begin{bmatrix} 57.86 & 143.78 \\ 37.65 & 98.98 \\ 40.79 & 104.01 \end{bmatrix}$

$B: \begin{bmatrix} 56.99 & 141.62 \\ 38.59 & 101.45 \\ 41.61 & 106.09 \end{bmatrix}$

(d) $\begin{bmatrix} 60.17 & 149.53 \\ 39.16 & 102.94 \\ 42.42 & 108.17 \end{bmatrix}$

77. True. The sum of two matrices of different orders is undefined.

78. False. For most matrices, $AB \neq BA$.

87. (a) $A + B = \begin{bmatrix} 1 & -1 \\ 12 & 8 \end{bmatrix}$, $B + A = \begin{bmatrix} 1 & -1 \\ 12 & 8 \end{bmatrix}$

(b) $(A + B) + C = \begin{bmatrix} 6 & 1 \\ 14 & 2 \end{bmatrix}$, $(B + C) + A = \begin{bmatrix} 6 & 1 \\ 14 & 2 \end{bmatrix}$

(c) $2A + 2B = \begin{bmatrix} 2 & -2 \\ 24 & 16 \end{bmatrix}$, $2(A + B) = \begin{bmatrix} 2 & -2 \\ 24 & 16 \end{bmatrix}$

88. $AB = \begin{bmatrix} 4 & 7 \\ 8 & 15 \end{bmatrix}$, $BA = \begin{bmatrix} 3 & 4 \\ 11 & 16 \end{bmatrix}$

$(AB)C = \begin{bmatrix} 12 & 7 \\ 24 & 15 \end{bmatrix}$, $A(BC) = \begin{bmatrix} 12 & 7 \\ 24 & 15 \end{bmatrix}$

Matrix multiplication is associative but not commutative.

89. $AC = BC = \begin{bmatrix} 2 & 3 \\ 2 & 3 \end{bmatrix}$

90. $AB = \begin{bmatrix} 0 & 0 \\ 0 & 0 \end{bmatrix}$

$AB = O$ and neither A nor B is O.

91. AB is a diagonal matrix whose entries are the products of the corresponding entries of A and B.

92. (a) $A^2 = \begin{bmatrix} -1 & 0 \\ 0 & -1 \end{bmatrix}$ and $i^2 = -1$

$A^3 = \begin{bmatrix} -i & 0 \\ 0 & -i \end{bmatrix}$ and $i^3 = -i$

$A^4 = \begin{bmatrix} 1 & 0 \\ 0 & 1 \end{bmatrix}$ and $i^4 = 1$

(b) $B^2 = \begin{bmatrix} 1 & 0 \\ 0 & 1 \end{bmatrix} = I$, the identity matrix

8.3 THE INVERSE OF A SQUARE MATRIX

What you should learn

- Verify that two matrices are inverses of each other.
- Use Gauss-Jordan elimination to find the inverses of matrices.
- Use a formula to find the inverses of 2×2 matrices.
- Use inverse matrices to solve systems of linear equations.

Why you should learn it

You can use inverse matrices to model and solve real-life problems. For instance, in Exercise 75 on page 607, an inverse matrix is used to find a quadratic model for the enrollment projections for public universities in the United States.

Alberto L. Pomares/istockphoto.com

The Inverse of a Matrix

This section further develops the algebra of matrices. To begin, consider the real number equation $ax = b$. To solve this equation for x, multiply each side of the equation by a^{-1} (provided that $a \neq 0$).

$$ax = b$$
$$(a^{-1}a)x = a^{-1}b$$
$$(1)x = a^{-1}b$$
$$x = a^{-1}b$$

The number a^{-1} is called the *multiplicative inverse of a* because $a^{-1}a = 1$. The definition of the multiplicative **inverse of a matrix** is similar.

> **Definition of the Inverse of a Square Matrix**
>
> Let A be an $n \times n$ matrix and let I_n be the $n \times n$ identity matrix. If there exists a matrix A^{-1} such that
>
> $$AA^{-1} = I_n = A^{-1}A$$
>
> then A^{-1} is called the **inverse** of A. The symbol A^{-1} is read "A inverse."

Example 1 The Inverse of a Matrix

Show that B is the inverse of A, where

$$A = \begin{bmatrix} -1 & 2 \\ -1 & 1 \end{bmatrix} \quad \text{and} \quad B = \begin{bmatrix} 1 & -2 \\ 1 & -1 \end{bmatrix}.$$

Solution

To show that B is the inverse of A, show that $AB = I = BA$, as follows.

$$AB = \begin{bmatrix} -1 & 2 \\ -1 & 1 \end{bmatrix}\begin{bmatrix} 1 & -2 \\ 1 & -1 \end{bmatrix} = \begin{bmatrix} -1+2 & 2-2 \\ -1+1 & 2-1 \end{bmatrix} = \begin{bmatrix} 1 & 0 \\ 0 & 1 \end{bmatrix}$$

$$BA = \begin{bmatrix} 1 & -2 \\ 1 & -1 \end{bmatrix}\begin{bmatrix} -1 & 2 \\ -1 & 1 \end{bmatrix} = \begin{bmatrix} -1+2 & 2-2 \\ -1+1 & 2-1 \end{bmatrix} = \begin{bmatrix} 1 & 0 \\ 0 & 1 \end{bmatrix}$$

As you can see, $AB = I = BA$. This is an example of a square matrix that has an inverse. Note that not all square matrices have inverses.

CHECKPoint Now try Exercise 5.

Recall that it is not always true that $AB = BA$, even if both products are defined. However, if A and B are both square matrices and $AB = I_n$, it can be shown that $BA = I_n$. So, in Example 1, you need only to check that $AB = I_2$.

1 PLAN AND PREPARE

Warm-up Exercises

Transparency Available
Available at the Instructor's companion site.

Notetaking Guide

Transparency Available
Promotes interactive learning and notetaking skills.
Available at the Instructor's companion site.

Animated Precalculus

An **Animated Precalculus** tutorial is available at the Student companion site for **Section 8.3.**

Pacing

Average: 2 days
Advanced: 2 days
Block: 1 block

2 FOCUS AND MOTIVATE

Essential Question

How do you find and use the inverse of a square matrix? **Tell students that they will learn how to answer this question by studying the definition of inverse, methods for calculating it, and its application in solving systems of equations.**

Resource Planning Guide

Chapter Resources
- Complete Solutions Guide

Workbooks
- Notetaking Guide
- Student Solutions Guide

Interactive Technology
- Instructor Success Organizer
- Notetaking Guide IAE
- Instructional DVDs
- Animated Precalculus
- PowerLecture with ExamView

3 TEACH

Extra Example 1

Show that B is the inverse of A, where $A = \begin{bmatrix} 2 & -1 \\ -3 & 1 \end{bmatrix}$ and $B = \begin{bmatrix} -1 & -1 \\ -3 & -2 \end{bmatrix}$.

See below.

Extra Example 2

Find the inverse of $A = \begin{bmatrix} 1 & -2 \\ -1 & 3 \end{bmatrix}$.

$A^{-1} = \begin{bmatrix} 3 & 2 \\ 1 & 1 \end{bmatrix}$

Finding Inverse Matrices

If a matrix A has an inverse, A is called **invertible** (or **nonsingular**); otherwise, A is called **singular.** A nonsquare matrix cannot have an inverse. To see this, note that if A is of order $m \times n$ and B is of order $n \times m$ (where $m \neq n$), the products AB and BA are of different orders and so cannot be equal to each other. Not all square matrices have inverses (see the matrix at the bottom of page 602). If, however, a matrix does have an inverse, that inverse is unique. Example 2 shows how to use a system of equations to find the inverse of a matrix.

Example 2 Finding the Inverse of a Matrix

Find the inverse of

$$A = \begin{bmatrix} 1 & 4 \\ -1 & -3 \end{bmatrix}.$$

Solution

To find the inverse of A, try to solve the matrix equation $AX = I$ for X.

$$\underset{A}{\begin{bmatrix} 1 & 4 \\ -1 & -3 \end{bmatrix}} \underset{X}{\begin{bmatrix} x_{11} & x_{12} \\ x_{21} & x_{22} \end{bmatrix}} = \underset{I}{\begin{bmatrix} 1 & 0 \\ 0 & 1 \end{bmatrix}}$$

$$\begin{bmatrix} x_{11} + 4x_{21} & x_{12} + 4x_{22} \\ -x_{11} - 3x_{21} & -x_{12} - 3x_{22} \end{bmatrix} = \begin{bmatrix} 1 & 0 \\ 0 & 1 \end{bmatrix}$$

Equating corresponding entries, you obtain two systems of linear equations.

$$\begin{cases} x_{11} + 4x_{21} = 1 \\ -x_{11} - 3x_{21} = 0 \end{cases}$$ Linear system with two variables, x_{11} and x_{21}.

$$\begin{cases} x_{12} + 4x_{22} = 0 \\ -x_{12} - 3x_{22} = 1 \end{cases}$$ Linear system with two variables, x_{12} and x_{22}.

Solve the first system using elementary row operations to determine that $x_{11} = -3$ and $x_{21} = 1$. From the second system you can determine that $x_{12} = -4$ and $x_{22} = 1$. Therefore, the inverse of A is

$$X = A^{-1} = \begin{bmatrix} -3 & -4 \\ 1 & 1 \end{bmatrix}.$$

You can use matrix multiplication to check this result.

Check

$$AA^{-1} = \begin{bmatrix} 1 & 4 \\ -1 & -3 \end{bmatrix}\begin{bmatrix} -3 & -4 \\ 1 & 1 \end{bmatrix} = \begin{bmatrix} 1 & 0 \\ 0 & 1 \end{bmatrix} \checkmark$$

$$A^{-1}A = \begin{bmatrix} -3 & -4 \\ 1 & 1 \end{bmatrix}\begin{bmatrix} 1 & 4 \\ -1 & -3 \end{bmatrix} = \begin{bmatrix} 1 & 0 \\ 0 & 1 \end{bmatrix} \checkmark$$

CHECKPoint Now try Exercise 15.

$$AB = \begin{bmatrix} 2 & -1 \\ -3 & 1 \end{bmatrix}\begin{bmatrix} -1 & -1 \\ -3 & -2 \end{bmatrix} = \begin{bmatrix} 2(-1) + (-1)(-3) & 2(-1) + (-1)(-2) \\ -3(-1) + 1(-3) & -3(-1) + 1(-2) \end{bmatrix} = \begin{bmatrix} 1 & 0 \\ 0 & 1 \end{bmatrix}$$

$$BA = \begin{bmatrix} -1 & -1 \\ -3 & -2 \end{bmatrix}\begin{bmatrix} 2 & -1 \\ -3 & 1 \end{bmatrix} = \begin{bmatrix} -1(2) + (-1)(-3) & -1(-1) + (-1)(1) \\ -3(2) + (-2)(-3) & -3(-1) + (-2)(1) \end{bmatrix} = \begin{bmatrix} 1 & 0 \\ 0 & 1 \end{bmatrix}$$

In Example 2, note that the two systems of linear equations have the *same coefficient matrix* A. Rather than solve the two systems represented by

$$\begin{bmatrix} 1 & 4 & \vdots & 1 \\ -1 & -3 & \vdots & 0 \end{bmatrix}$$

and

$$\begin{bmatrix} 1 & 4 & \vdots & 0 \\ -1 & -3 & \vdots & 1 \end{bmatrix}$$

separately, you can solve them *simultaneously* by *adjoining* the identity matrix to the coefficient matrix to obtain

$$\overbrace{\begin{bmatrix} 1 & 4 \\ -1 & -3 \end{bmatrix}}^{A} \begin{matrix} \vdots \\ \vdots \end{matrix} \overbrace{\begin{bmatrix} 1 & 0 \\ 0 & 1 \end{bmatrix}}^{I}.$$

This "doubly augmented" matrix can be represented as $[A \;\vdots\; I]$. By applying Gauss-Jordan elimination to this matrix, you can solve *both* systems with a single elimination process.

$$\begin{bmatrix} 1 & 4 & \vdots & 1 & 0 \\ -1 & -3 & \vdots & 0 & 1 \end{bmatrix}$$

$$R_1 + R_2 \rightarrow \begin{bmatrix} 1 & 4 & \vdots & 1 & 0 \\ 0 & 1 & \vdots & 1 & 1 \end{bmatrix}$$

$$-4R_2 + R_1 \rightarrow \begin{bmatrix} 1 & 0 & \vdots & -3 & -4 \\ 0 & 1 & \vdots & 1 & 1 \end{bmatrix}$$

So, from the "doubly augmented" matrix $[A \;\vdots\; I]$, you obtain the matrix $[I \;\vdots\; A^{-1}]$.

$$\overbrace{\begin{bmatrix} 1 & 4 \\ -1 & -3 \end{bmatrix}}^{A} \begin{matrix} \vdots \\ \vdots \end{matrix} \overbrace{\begin{bmatrix} 1 & 0 \\ 0 & 1 \end{bmatrix}}^{I} \Rightarrow \overbrace{\begin{bmatrix} 1 & 0 \\ 0 & 1 \end{bmatrix}}^{I} \begin{matrix} \vdots \\ \vdots \end{matrix} \overbrace{\begin{bmatrix} -3 & -4 \\ 1 & 1 \end{bmatrix}}^{A^{-1}}$$

This procedure (or algorithm) works for any square matrix that has an inverse.

TECHNOLOGY

Most graphing utilities can find the inverse of a square matrix. To do so, you may have to use the inverse key x^{-1}. Consult the user's guide for your graphing utility for specific keystrokes.

Finding an Inverse Matrix

Let A be a square matrix of order n.

1. Write the $n \times 2n$ matrix that consists of the given matrix A on the left and the $n \times n$ identity matrix I on the right to obtain $[A \;\vdots\; I]$.
2. If possible, row reduce A to I using elementary row operations on the *entire* matrix $[A \;\vdots\; I]$. The result will be the matrix $[I \;\vdots\; A^{-1}]$. If this is not possible, A is not invertible.
3. Check your work by multiplying to see that $AA^{-1} = I = A^{-1}A$.

Extra Example 3

Find the inverse of $A = \begin{bmatrix} 1 & 1 & 1 \\ 3 & 5 & 4 \\ 0 & -1 & 0 \end{bmatrix}$.

$$A^{-1} = \begin{bmatrix} 4 & -1 & -1 \\ 0 & 0 & -1 \\ -3 & 1 & 2 \end{bmatrix}$$

Example 3 Finding the Inverse of a Matrix

Find the inverse of $A = \begin{bmatrix} 1 & -1 & 0 \\ 1 & 0 & -1 \\ 6 & -2 & -3 \end{bmatrix}$.

Solution

Begin by adjoining the identity matrix to A to form the matrix

$$[A \,\vdots\, I] = \left[\begin{array}{ccc:ccc} 1 & -1 & 0 & 1 & 0 & 0 \\ 1 & 0 & -1 & 0 & 1 & 0 \\ 6 & -2 & -3 & 0 & 0 & 1 \end{array}\right].$$

Use elementary row operations to obtain the form $[I \,\vdots\, A^{-1}]$, as follows.

$$\begin{array}{r} \\ -R_1 + R_2 \rightarrow \\ -6R_1 + R_3 \rightarrow \end{array} \left[\begin{array}{ccc:ccc} 1 & -1 & 0 & 1 & 0 & 0 \\ 0 & 1 & -1 & -1 & 1 & 0 \\ 0 & 4 & -3 & -6 & 0 & 1 \end{array}\right]$$

$$\begin{array}{r} R_2 + R_1 \rightarrow \\ \\ -4R_2 + R_3 \rightarrow \end{array} \left[\begin{array}{ccc:ccc} 1 & 0 & -1 & 0 & 1 & 0 \\ 0 & 1 & -1 & -1 & 1 & 0 \\ 0 & 0 & 1 & -2 & -4 & 1 \end{array}\right]$$

$$\begin{array}{r} R_3 + R_1 \rightarrow \\ R_3 + R_2 \rightarrow \\ \\ \end{array} \left[\begin{array}{ccc:ccc} 1 & 0 & 0 & -2 & -3 & 1 \\ 0 & 1 & 0 & -3 & -3 & 1 \\ 0 & 0 & 1 & -2 & -4 & 1 \end{array}\right] = [I \,\vdots\, A^{-1}]$$

So, the matrix A is invertible and its inverse is

$$A^{-1} = \begin{bmatrix} -2 & -3 & 1 \\ -3 & -3 & 1 \\ -2 & -4 & 1 \end{bmatrix}.$$

Confirm this result by multiplying A and A^{-1} to obtain I, as follows.

Check

$$AA^{-1} = \begin{bmatrix} 1 & -1 & 0 \\ 1 & 0 & -1 \\ 6 & -2 & -3 \end{bmatrix} \begin{bmatrix} -2 & -3 & 1 \\ -3 & -3 & 1 \\ -2 & -4 & 1 \end{bmatrix} = \begin{bmatrix} 1 & 0 & 0 \\ 0 & 1 & 0 \\ 0 & 0 & 1 \end{bmatrix} = I$$

WARNING/CAUTION

Be sure to check your solution because it is easy to make algebraic errors when using elementary row operations.

CHECKPoint Now try Exercise 19.

The process shown in Example 3 applies to any $n \times n$ matrix A. When using this algorithm, if the matrix A does not reduce to the identity matrix, then A does not have an inverse. For instance, the following matrix has no inverse.

$$A = \begin{bmatrix} 1 & 2 & 0 \\ 3 & -1 & 2 \\ -2 & 3 & -2 \end{bmatrix}$$

To confirm that matrix A above has no inverse, adjoin the identity matrix to A to form $[A \,\vdots\, I]$ and perform elementary row operations on the matrix. After doing so, you will see that it is impossible to obtain the identity matrix I on the left. Therefore, A is not invertible.

The Inverse of a 2 × 2 Matrix

Using Gauss-Jordan elimination to find the inverse of a matrix works well (even as a computer technique) for matrices of order 3 × 3 or greater. For 2 × 2 matrices, however, many people prefer to use a formula for the inverse rather than Gauss-Jordan elimination. This simple formula, which works *only* for 2 × 2 matrices, is explained as follows. If A is a 2 × 2 matrix given by

$$A = \begin{bmatrix} a & b \\ c & d \end{bmatrix}$$

then A is invertible if and only if $ad - bc \neq 0$. Moreover, if $ad - bc \neq 0$, the inverse is given by

$$A^{-1} = \frac{1}{ad - bc}\begin{bmatrix} d & -b \\ -c & a \end{bmatrix}.$$ Formula for inverse of matrix A

The denominator $ad - bc$ is called the **determinant** of the 2 × 2 matrix A. You will study determinants in the next section.

Example 4 Finding the Inverse of a 2 × 2 Matrix

If possible, find the inverse of each matrix.

a. $A = \begin{bmatrix} 3 & -1 \\ -2 & 2 \end{bmatrix}$

b. $B = \begin{bmatrix} 3 & -1 \\ -6 & 2 \end{bmatrix}$

Solution

a. For the matrix A, apply the formula for the inverse of a 2 × 2 matrix to obtain

$$\begin{aligned} ad - bc &= (3)(2) - (-1)(-2) \\ &= 4. \end{aligned}$$

Because this quantity is not zero, the inverse is formed by interchanging the entries on the main diagonal, changing the signs of the other two entries, and multiplying by the scalar $\frac{1}{4}$, as follows.

$$A^{-1} = \frac{1}{4}\begin{bmatrix} 2 & 1 \\ 2 & 3 \end{bmatrix}$$ Substitute for a, b, c, d, and the determinant.

$$= \begin{bmatrix} \frac{1}{2} & \frac{1}{4} \\ \frac{1}{2} & \frac{3}{4} \end{bmatrix}$$ Multiply by the scalar $\frac{1}{4}$.

b. For the matrix B, you have

$$\begin{aligned} ad - bc &= (3)(2) - (-1)(-6) \\ &= 0 \end{aligned}$$

which means that B is not invertible.

CHECKPoint Now try Exercise 35.

Extra Example 4

If possible, find the inverse of each matrix.

a. $A = \begin{bmatrix} 5 & -1 \\ 3 & 4 \end{bmatrix}$

$$A^{-1} = \begin{bmatrix} \frac{4}{23} & \frac{1}{23} \\ -\frac{3}{23} & \frac{5}{23} \end{bmatrix}$$

b. $B = \begin{bmatrix} 2 & -4 \\ -2 & 4 \end{bmatrix}$

Matrix B is not invertible because the determinant is equal to 0.

Systems of Linear Equations

You know that a system of linear equations can have exactly one solution, infinitely many solutions, or no solution. If the coefficient matrix A of a *square* system (a system that has the same number of equations as variables) is invertible, the system has a unique solution, which is defined as follows.

A System of Equations with a Unique Solution

If A is an invertible matrix, the system of linear equations represented by $AX = B$ has a unique solution given by

$$X = A^{-1}B.$$

Example 5 Solving a System Using an Inverse Matrix

You are going to invest \$10,000 in AAA-rated bonds, AA-rated bonds, and B-rated bonds and want an annual return of \$730. The average yields are 6% on AAA bonds, 7.5% on AA bonds, and 9.5% on B bonds. You will invest twice as much in AAA bonds as in B bonds. Your investment can be represented as

$$\begin{cases} x + y + z = 10{,}000 \\ 0.06x + 0.075y + 0.095z = 730 \\ x - 2z = 0 \end{cases}$$

where x, y, and z represent the amounts invested in AAA, AA, and B bonds, respectively. Use an inverse matrix to solve the system.

Solution

Begin by writing the system in the matrix form $AX = B$.

$$\begin{bmatrix} 1 & 1 & 1 \\ 0.06 & 0.075 & 0.095 \\ 1 & 0 & -2 \end{bmatrix}\begin{bmatrix} x \\ y \\ z \end{bmatrix} = \begin{bmatrix} 10{,}000 \\ 730 \\ 0 \end{bmatrix}$$

Then, use Gauss-Jordan elimination to find A^{-1}.

$$A^{-1} = \begin{bmatrix} 15 & -200 & -2 \\ -21.5 & 300 & 3.5 \\ 7.5 & -100 & -1.5 \end{bmatrix}$$

Finally, multiply B by A^{-1} on the left to obtain the solution.

$$X = A^{-1}B$$

$$= \begin{bmatrix} 15 & -200 & -2 \\ -21.5 & 300 & 3.5 \\ 7.5 & -100 & -1.5 \end{bmatrix}\begin{bmatrix} 10{,}000 \\ 730 \\ 0 \end{bmatrix} = \begin{bmatrix} 4000 \\ 4000 \\ 2000 \end{bmatrix}$$

The solution of the system is $x = 4000$, $y = 4000$, and $z = 2000$. So, you will invest \$4000 in AAA bonds, \$4000 in AA bonds, and \$2000 in B bonds.

CHECK *Point* Now try Exercise 65.

TECHNOLOGY

To solve a system of equations with a graphing utility, enter the matrices A and B in the matrix editor. Then, using the inverse key, solve for X.

A x^{-1} B ENTER

The screen will display the solution, matrix X.

Extra Example 5

You invest \$15,000 in AAA-rated bonds, AA-rated bonds, and B-rated bonds and want an annual return of \$1140. The average yields are 6.5% on AAA bonds, 7% on AA bonds, and 9% on B bonds. You invest twice as much in AAA bonds as in AA bonds. Your investment can be represented as

$$\begin{cases} x + y + z = 15{,}000 \\ 0.065x + 0.07y + 0.09z = 1140 \\ x - 2y = 0 \end{cases}$$

where x, y, and z represent the amounts invested in AAA, AA, and B bonds, respectively. How much have you invested in each bond? Use an inverse matrix to solve the system.

AAA: \$6000, AA: \$3000, B: \$6000

Closing the Lesson

Have students summarize the major points of the lesson and answer the Essential Question: How do you find and use the inverse of a square matrix?

- **Find the inverse of a square matrix A by creating an augmented matrix $[A \vdots I]$ and converting it to matrix $[I \vdots A^{-1}]$ by using elementary row operations.**
- **Recall the formula for finding the inverse of a 2×2 matrix.**
- **Solve a system of equations in matrix form by multiplying the inverse of the coefficient matrix by the constant matrix.**

8.3 EXERCISES

See www.CalcChat.com for worked-out solutions to odd-numbered exercises.

VOCABULARY: Fill in the blanks.

1. In a square matrix, the number of rows equals the number of columns.
2. If there exists an $n \times n$ matrix A^{-1} such that $AA^{-1} = I_n = A^{-1}A$, then A^{-1} is called the inverse of A.
3. If a matrix A has an inverse, it is called invertible or ________; if it does not have an inverse, it is called singular. 3. nonsingular;
4. If A is an invertible matrix, the system of linear equations represented by $AX = B$ has a unique solution given by $X =$ $A^{-1}B$.

SKILLS AND APPLICATIONS

In Exercises 5–12, show that B is the inverse of A.

5–12. $AB = I$ and $BA = I$

5. $A = \begin{bmatrix} 2 & 1 \\ 5 & 3 \end{bmatrix}, B = \begin{bmatrix} 3 & -1 \\ -5 & 2 \end{bmatrix}$

6. $A = \begin{bmatrix} 1 & -1 \\ -1 & 2 \end{bmatrix}, B = \begin{bmatrix} 2 & 1 \\ 1 & 1 \end{bmatrix}$

7. $A = \begin{bmatrix} 1 & 2 \\ 3 & 4 \end{bmatrix}, B = \begin{bmatrix} -2 & 1 \\ \frac{3}{2} & -\frac{1}{2} \end{bmatrix}$

8. $A = \begin{bmatrix} 1 & -1 \\ 2 & 3 \end{bmatrix}, B = \begin{bmatrix} \frac{3}{5} & \frac{1}{5} \\ -\frac{2}{5} & \frac{1}{5} \end{bmatrix}$

9. $A = \begin{bmatrix} 2 & -17 & 11 \\ -1 & 11 & -7 \\ 0 & 3 & -2 \end{bmatrix}, B = \begin{bmatrix} 1 & 1 & 2 \\ 2 & 4 & -3 \\ 3 & 6 & -5 \end{bmatrix}$

10. $A = \begin{bmatrix} -4 & 1 & 5 \\ -1 & 2 & 4 \\ 0 & -1 & -1 \end{bmatrix}, B = \begin{bmatrix} -\frac{1}{2} & 1 & \frac{3}{2} \\ \frac{1}{4} & -1 & -\frac{11}{4} \\ -\frac{1}{4} & 1 & \frac{7}{4} \end{bmatrix}$

11. $A = \begin{bmatrix} -2 & 2 & 3 \\ 1 & -1 & 0 \\ 0 & 1 & 4 \end{bmatrix}, B = \frac{1}{3}\begin{bmatrix} -4 & -5 & 3 \\ -4 & -8 & 3 \\ 1 & 2 & 0 \end{bmatrix}$

12. $A = \begin{bmatrix} -1 & 1 & 0 & -1 \\ 1 & -1 & 1 & 0 \\ -1 & 1 & 2 & 0 \\ 0 & -1 & 1 & 1 \end{bmatrix},$

$B = \frac{1}{3}\begin{bmatrix} -3 & 1 & 1 & -3 \\ -3 & -1 & 2 & -3 \\ 0 & 1 & 1 & 0 \\ -3 & -2 & 1 & 0 \end{bmatrix}$

In Exercises 13–24, find the inverse of the matrix (if it exists).

13. $\begin{bmatrix} 2 & 0 \\ 0 & 3 \end{bmatrix}$ $\begin{bmatrix} \frac{1}{2} & 0 \\ 0 & \frac{1}{3} \end{bmatrix}$

14. $\begin{bmatrix} 1 & 2 \\ 3 & 7 \end{bmatrix}$ $\begin{bmatrix} 7 & -2 \\ -3 & 1 \end{bmatrix}$

15. $\begin{bmatrix} 1 & -2 \\ 2 & -3 \end{bmatrix}$ $\begin{bmatrix} -3 & 2 \\ -2 & 1 \end{bmatrix}$

16. $\begin{bmatrix} -7 & 33 \\ 4 & -19 \end{bmatrix}$ $\begin{bmatrix} -19 & -33 \\ -4 & -7 \end{bmatrix}$

17. $\begin{bmatrix} 3 & 1 \\ 4 & 2 \end{bmatrix}$ $\begin{bmatrix} 1 & -\frac{1}{2} \\ -2 & \frac{3}{2} \end{bmatrix}$

18. $\begin{bmatrix} 4 & -1 \\ -3 & 1 \end{bmatrix}$ $\begin{bmatrix} 1 & 1 \\ 3 & 4 \end{bmatrix}$

19–24. See margin.

19. $\begin{bmatrix} 1 & 1 & 1 \\ 3 & 5 & 4 \\ 3 & 6 & 5 \end{bmatrix}$

20. $\begin{bmatrix} 1 & 2 & 2 \\ 3 & 7 & 9 \\ -1 & -4 & -7 \end{bmatrix}$

21. $\begin{bmatrix} -5 & 0 & 0 \\ 2 & 0 & 0 \\ -1 & 5 & 7 \end{bmatrix}$

22. $\begin{bmatrix} 1 & 0 & 0 \\ 3 & 0 & 0 \\ 2 & 5 & 5 \end{bmatrix}$

23. $\begin{bmatrix} -8 & 0 & 0 & 0 \\ 0 & 1 & 0 & 0 \\ 0 & 0 & 4 & 0 \\ 0 & 0 & 0 & -5 \end{bmatrix}$

24. $\begin{bmatrix} 1 & 3 & -2 & 0 \\ 0 & 2 & 4 & 6 \\ 0 & 0 & -2 & 1 \\ 0 & 0 & 0 & 5 \end{bmatrix}$

In Exercises 25–34, use the matrix capabilities of a graphing utility to find the inverse of the matrix (if it exists). 25–34. See margin.

25. $\begin{bmatrix} 1 & 2 & -1 \\ 3 & 7 & -10 \\ -5 & -7 & -15 \end{bmatrix}$

26. $\begin{bmatrix} 10 & 5 & -7 \\ -5 & 1 & 4 \\ 3 & 2 & -2 \end{bmatrix}$

27. $\begin{bmatrix} 1 & 1 & 2 \\ 3 & 1 & 0 \\ -2 & 0 & 3 \end{bmatrix}$

28. $\begin{bmatrix} 3 & 2 & 2 \\ 2 & 2 & 2 \\ -4 & 4 & 3 \end{bmatrix}$

29. $\begin{bmatrix} -\frac{1}{2} & \frac{3}{4} & \frac{1}{4} \\ 1 & 0 & -\frac{3}{2} \\ 0 & -1 & \frac{1}{2} \end{bmatrix}$

30. $\begin{bmatrix} -\frac{5}{6} & \frac{1}{3} & \frac{11}{6} \\ 0 & \frac{2}{3} & 2 \\ 1 & -\frac{1}{2} & -\frac{5}{2} \end{bmatrix}$

31. $\begin{bmatrix} 0.1 & 0.2 & 0.3 \\ -0.3 & 0.2 & 0.2 \\ 0.5 & 0.4 & 0.4 \end{bmatrix}$

32. $\begin{bmatrix} 0.6 & 0 & -0.3 \\ 0.7 & -1 & 0.2 \\ 1 & 0 & -0.9 \end{bmatrix}$

33. $\begin{bmatrix} -1 & 0 & 1 & 0 \\ 0 & 2 & 0 & -1 \\ 2 & 0 & -1 & 0 \\ 0 & -1 & 0 & 1 \end{bmatrix}$

34. $\begin{bmatrix} 1 & -2 & -1 & -2 \\ 3 & -5 & -2 & -3 \\ 2 & -5 & -2 & -5 \\ -1 & 4 & 4 & 11 \end{bmatrix}$

In Exercises 35–40, use the formula on page 603 to find the inverse of the 2×2 matrix (if it exists).

35. $\begin{bmatrix} 2 & 3 \\ -1 & 5 \end{bmatrix}$ $\begin{bmatrix} \frac{5}{13} & -\frac{3}{13} \\ \frac{1}{13} & \frac{2}{13} \end{bmatrix}$

36. $\begin{bmatrix} 1 & -2 \\ -3 & 2 \end{bmatrix}$ $\begin{bmatrix} -\frac{1}{2} & -\frac{1}{2} \\ -\frac{3}{4} & -\frac{1}{4} \end{bmatrix}$

37. $\begin{bmatrix} -4 & -6 \\ 2 & 3 \end{bmatrix}$
Does not exist

38. $\begin{bmatrix} -12 & 3 \\ 5 & -2 \end{bmatrix}$
$\begin{bmatrix} -\frac{2}{9} & -\frac{1}{3} \\ -\frac{5}{9} & -\frac{4}{3} \end{bmatrix}$

4 PRACTICE AND APPLY

Assignment Guide

Transparencies Available
Available at the Instructor's companion site.

Average:
Day 1: p. 605
Exs. 1–4, 6–8, 9–17 odd, 20–23, 25, 27, 33
Day 2: p. 605–607
Exs. 37–41 odd, 45, 49–61 odd, 66, 67, 69, 76–78

Advanced:
Day 1: p. 605
Exs. 1–4, 6–14 even, 18–26 even, 32, 34
Day 2: pp. 605–607
Exs. 38–46 even, 52–62 even, 67, 68, 75, 76, 81

Block:
pp. 605–607
Exs. 1–4, 6–8, 9–17 odd, 20–23, 25, 27, 33, 37–41 odd, 45, 49–61 odd, 66, 67, 69, 76–78

19. $\begin{bmatrix} 1 & 1 & -1 \\ -3 & 2 & -1 \\ 3 & -3 & 2 \end{bmatrix}$

20. $\begin{bmatrix} -13 & 6 & 4 \\ 12 & -5 & -3 \\ -5 & 2 & 1 \end{bmatrix}$

21. Does not exist

22. Does not exist

23. $\begin{bmatrix} -\frac{1}{8} & 0 & 0 & 0 \\ 0 & 1 & 0 & 0 \\ 0 & 0 & \frac{1}{4} & 0 \\ 0 & 0 & 0 & -\frac{1}{5} \end{bmatrix}$

24. $\begin{bmatrix} 1 & -\frac{3}{2} & -4 & \frac{13}{5} \\ 0 & \frac{1}{2} & 1 & -\frac{4}{5} \\ 0 & 0 & -\frac{1}{2} & \frac{1}{10} \\ 0 & 0 & 0 & \frac{1}{5} \end{bmatrix}$

25. $\begin{bmatrix} -175 & 37 & -13 \\ 95 & -20 & 7 \\ 14 & -3 & 1 \end{bmatrix}$

26. $\begin{bmatrix} -10 & -4 & 27 \\ 2 & 1 & -5 \\ -13 & -5 & 35 \end{bmatrix}$

27. $\begin{bmatrix} -1.5 & 1.5 & 1 \\ 4.5 & -3.5 & -3 \\ -1 & 1 & 1 \end{bmatrix}$

28. $\begin{bmatrix} 1 & -1 & 0 \\ 7 & -8.5 & 1 \\ -8 & 10 & -1 \end{bmatrix}$

29. $\begin{bmatrix} -12 & -5 & -9 \\ -4 & -2 & -4 \\ -8 & -4 & -6 \end{bmatrix}$

30. Does not exist

31. $\begin{bmatrix} 0 & -1.\overline{81} & 0.\overline{90} \\ -10 & 5 & 5 \\ 10 & -2.\overline{72} & -3.\overline{63} \end{bmatrix}$

32. $\begin{bmatrix} 3.75 & 0 & -1.25 \\ 3.458\overline{3} & -1 & -1.375 \\ 4.1\overline{6} & 0 & -2.5 \end{bmatrix}$

33. $\begin{bmatrix} 1 & 0 & 1 & 0 \\ 0 & 1 & 0 & 1 \\ 2 & 0 & 1 & 0 \\ 0 & 1 & 0 & 2 \end{bmatrix}$

34. $\begin{bmatrix} -24 & 7 & 1 & -2 \\ -10 & 3 & 0 & -1 \\ -29 & 7 & 3 & -2 \\ 12 & -3 & -1 & 1 \end{bmatrix}$

39. $\begin{bmatrix} \frac{7}{2} & -\frac{3}{4} \\ \frac{1}{5} & \frac{4}{5} \end{bmatrix}$ $\begin{bmatrix} \frac{16}{59} & \frac{15}{59} \\ -\frac{4}{59} & \frac{70}{59} \end{bmatrix}$

40. $\begin{bmatrix} -\frac{1}{4} & \frac{9}{4} \\ \frac{5}{3} & \frac{8}{9} \end{bmatrix}$ $\begin{bmatrix} -\frac{32}{143} & \frac{81}{143} \\ \frac{60}{143} & \frac{9}{143} \end{bmatrix}$

In Exercises 41–44, use the inverse matrix found in Exercise 15 to solve the system of linear equations.

41. $\begin{cases} x - 2y = 5 \\ 2x - 3y = 10 \end{cases}$ $(5, 0)$

42. $\begin{cases} x - 2y = 0 \\ 2x - 3y = 3 \end{cases}$ $(6, 3)$

43. $\begin{cases} x - 2y = 4 \\ 2x - 3y = 2 \end{cases}$ $(-8, -6)$

44. $\begin{cases} x - 2y = 1 \\ 2x - 3y = -2 \end{cases}$ $(-7, -4)$

In Exercises 45 and 46, use the inverse matrix found in Exercise 19 to solve the system of linear equations.

45. $\begin{cases} x + y + z = 0 \\ 3x + 5y + 4z = 5 \\ 3x + 6y + 5z = 2 \end{cases}$ $(3, 8, -11)$

46. $\begin{cases} x + y + z = -1 \\ 3x + 5y + 4z = 2 \\ 3x + 6y + 5z = 0 \end{cases}$ $(1, 7, -9)$

In Exercises 47 and 48, use the inverse matrix found in Exercise 34 to solve the system of linear equations.

47. $\begin{cases} x_1 - 2x_2 - x_3 - 2x_4 = 0 \\ 3x_1 - 5x_2 - 2x_3 - 3x_4 = 1 \\ 2x_1 - 5x_2 - 2x_3 - 5x_4 = -1 \\ -x_1 + 4x_2 + 4x_3 + 11x_4 = 2 \end{cases}$ $(2, 1, 0, 0)$

48. $\begin{cases} x_1 - 2x_2 - x_3 - 2x_4 = 1 \\ 3x_1 - 5x_2 - 2x_3 - 3x_4 = -2 \\ 2x_1 - 5x_2 - 2x_3 - 5x_4 = 0 \\ -x_1 + 4x_2 + 4x_3 + 11x_4 = -3 \end{cases}$ $(-32, -13, -37, 15)$

In Exercises 49 and 50, use a graphing utility to solve the system of linear equations using an inverse matrix.

49. $\begin{aligned} x_1 + 2x_2 - x_3 + 3x_4 - x_5 &= -3 \\ x_1 - 3x_2 + x_3 + 2x_4 - x_5 &= -3 \\ 2x_1 + x_2 + x_3 - 3x_4 + x_5 &= 6 \\ x_1 - x_2 + 2x_3 + x_4 - x_5 &= 2 \\ 2x_1 + x_2 - x_3 + 2x_4 + x_5 &= -3 \end{aligned}$ $(0, 1, 2, -1, 0)$

50. $\begin{aligned} x_1 + x_2 - x_3 + 3x_4 - x_5 &= 3 \\ 2x_1 + x_2 + x_3 + x_4 + x_5 &= 4 \\ x_1 + x_2 - x_3 + 2x_4 - x_5 &= 3 \\ 2x_1 + x_2 + 4x_3 + x_4 - x_5 &= -1 \\ 3x_1 + x_2 + x_3 - 2x_4 + x_5 &= 5 \end{aligned}$ $(1, 2, -1, 0, 1)$

In Exercises 51–58, use an inverse matrix to solve (if possible) the system of linear equations.

51. $\begin{cases} 3x + 4y = -2 \\ 5x + 3y = 4 \end{cases}$ $(2, -2)$

52. $\begin{cases} 18x + 12y = 13 \\ 30x + 24y = 23 \end{cases}$ $\left(\frac{1}{2}, \frac{1}{3}\right)$

53. $\begin{cases} -0.4x + 0.8y = 1.6 \\ 2x - 4y = 5 \end{cases}$ No solution

54. $\begin{cases} 0.2x - 0.6y = 2.4 \\ -x + 1.4y = -8.8 \end{cases}$ $(6, -2)$

55. $\begin{cases} -\frac{1}{4}x + \frac{3}{8}y = -2 \\ \frac{3}{2}x + \frac{3}{4}y = -12 \end{cases}$ $(-4, -8)$

56. $\begin{cases} \frac{5}{6}x - y = -20 \\ \frac{4}{3}x - \frac{7}{2}y = -51 \end{cases}$ $(-12, 10)$

57. $\begin{cases} 4x - y + z = -5 \\ 2x + 2y + 3z = 10 \\ 5x - 2y + 6z = 1 \end{cases}$ $(-1, 3, 2)$

58. $\begin{cases} 4x - 2y + 3z = -2 \\ 2x + 2y + 5z = 16 \\ 8x - 5y - 2z = 4 \end{cases}$ $(5, 8, -2)$

In Exercises 59–62, use the matrix capabilities of a graphing utility to solve (if possible) the system of linear equations.

59. $\begin{cases} 5x - 3y + 2z = 2 \\ 2x + 2y - 3z = 3 \\ x - 7y + 8z = -4 \end{cases}$

60. $\begin{cases} 2x + 3y + 5z = 4 \\ 3x + 5y + 9z = 7 \\ 5x + 9y + 17z = 13 \end{cases}$

59–60. See margin.

61. $\begin{cases} 3x - 2y + z = -29 \\ -4x + y - 3z = 37 \\ x - 5y + z = -24 \end{cases}$ $(-7, 3, -2)$

62. $\begin{cases} -8x + 7y - 10z = -151 \\ 12x + 3y - 5z = 86 \\ 15x - 9y + 2z = 187 \end{cases}$ $(10, -3, 5)$

In Exercises 63 and 64, show that the matrix is invertible and find its inverse. 63–64. See margin.

63. $A = \begin{bmatrix} \sin\theta & \cos\theta \\ -\cos\theta & \sin\theta \end{bmatrix}$

64. $A = \begin{bmatrix} \sec\theta & \tan\theta \\ \tan\theta & \sec\theta \end{bmatrix}$

INVESTMENT PORTFOLIO In Exercises 65–68, consider a person who invests in AAA-rated bonds, A-rated bonds, and B-rated bonds. The average yields are 6.5% on AAA bonds, 7% on A bonds, and 9% on B bonds. The person invests twice as much in B bonds as in A bonds. Let x, y, and z represent the amounts invested in AAA, A, and B bonds, respectively.

$$\begin{cases} x + y + z = \textbf{(total investment)} \\ 0.065x + 0.07y + 0.09z = \textbf{(annual return)} \\ 2y - z = 0 \end{cases}$$

Use the inverse of the coefficient matrix of this system to find the amount invested in each type of bond. 65–68. See margin.

	Total Investment	*Annual Return*
65.	$10,000	$705
66.	$10,000	$760
67.	$12,000	$835
68.	$500,000	$38,000

PRODUCTION In Exercises 69–72, a small home business creates muffins, bones, and cookies for dogs. In addition to other ingredients, each muffin requires 2 units of beef, 3 units of chicken, and 2 units of liver. Each bone requires 1 unit of beef, 1 unit of chicken, and 1 unit of liver. Each cookie requires 2 units of beef, 1 unit of chicken, and 1.5 units of liver. Find the numbers of muffins, bones, and cookies that the company can create with the given amounts of ingredients.

59. $\left(\frac{5}{16}a + \frac{13}{16}, \frac{19}{16}a + \frac{11}{16}, a\right)$

60. $(2a - 1, -3a + 2, a)$

63. $A^{-1} = \begin{bmatrix} \sin\theta & -\cos\theta \\ \cos\theta & \sin\theta \end{bmatrix}$

64. $A^{-1} = \begin{bmatrix} \sec\theta & -\tan\theta \\ -\tan\theta & \sec\theta \end{bmatrix}$

65. $7000 in AAA-rated bonds
$1000 in A-rated bonds
$2000 in B-rated bonds

66. $4000 in AAA-rated bonds
$2000 in A-rated bonds
$4000 in B-rated bonds

67. $9000 in AAA-rated bonds
$1000 in A-rated bonds
$2000 in B-rated bonds

68. $200,000 in AAA-rated bonds
$100,000 in A-rated bonds
$200,000 in B-rated bonds

69–72. See margin.

69. 700 units of beef
500 units of chicken
600 units of liver

70. 525 units of beef
480 units of chicken
500 units of liver

71. 800 units of beef
750 units of chicken
725 units of liver

72. 1000 units of beef
950 units of chicken
900 units of liver

73. COFFEE A coffee manufacturer sells a 10-pound package that contains three flavors of coffee for \$26. French vanilla coffee costs \$2 per pound, hazelnut flavored coffee costs \$2.50 per pound, and Swiss chocolate flavored coffee costs \$3 per pound. The package contains the same amount of hazelnut as Swiss chocolate. Let f represent the number of pounds of French vanilla, h represent the number of pounds of hazelnut, and s represent the number of pounds of Swiss chocolate. See margin.

(a) Write a system of linear equations that represents the situation.

(b) Write a matrix equation that corresponds to your system.

(c) Solve your system of linear equations using an inverse matrix. Find the number of pounds of each flavor of coffee in the 10-pound package.

74. FLOWERS A florist is creating 10 centerpieces for the tables at a wedding reception. Roses cost \$2.50 each, lilies cost \$4 each, and irises cost \$2 each. The customer has a budget of \$300 allocated for the centerpieces and wants each centerpiece to contain 12 flowers, with twice as many roses as the number of irises and lilies combined.

(a) Write a system of linear equations that represents the situation. (a)–(c). See margin.

(b) Write a matrix equation that corresponds to your system.

(c) Solve your system of linear equations using an inverse matrix. Find the number of flowers of each type that the florist can use to create the 10 centerpieces.

75. ENROLLMENT The table shows the enrollment projections (in millions) for public universities in the United States for the years 2010 through 2012. (Source: U.S. National Center for Education Statistics, *Digest of Education Statistics*) See margin.

Year	Enrollment projections
2010	13.89
2011	14.04
2012	14.20

(a) The data can be modeled by the quadratic function $y = at^2 + bt + c$. Create a system of linear equations for the data. Let t represent the year, with $t = 10$ corresponding to 2010.

(b) Use the matrix capabilities of a graphing utility to find the inverse matrix to solve the system from part (a) and find the least squares regression parabola $y = at^2 + bt + c$.

(c) Use the graphing utility to graph the parabola with the data.

(d) Do you believe the model is a reasonable predictor of future enrollments? Explain.

EXPLORATION

76. CAPSTONE If A is a 2×2 matrix $A = \begin{bmatrix} a & b \\ c & d \end{bmatrix}$, then A is invertible if and only if $ad - bc \neq 0$. If $ad - bc \neq 0$, verify that the inverse is

$$A^{-1} = \frac{1}{ad - bc}\begin{bmatrix} d & -b \\ -c & a \end{bmatrix}.$$ Answers will vary.

77–78. See margin.

TRUE OR FALSE? In Exercises 77 and 78, determine whether the statement is true or false. Justify your answer.

77. Multiplication of an invertible matrix and its inverse is commutative.

78. If you multiply two square matrices and obtain the identity matrix, you can assume that the matrices are inverses of one another.

79. WRITING Explain how to determine whether the inverse of a 2×2 matrix exists. If so, explain how to find the inverse. Answers will vary.

80. WRITING Explain in your own words how to write a system of three linear equations in three variables as a matrix equation, $AX = B$, as well as how to solve the system using an inverse matrix. Answers will vary.

81. Consider matrices of the form

$$A = \begin{bmatrix} a_{11} & 0 & 0 & 0 & \cdots & 0 \\ 0 & a_{22} & 0 & 0 & \cdots & 0 \\ 0 & 0 & a_{33} & 0 & \cdots & 0 \\ \vdots & \vdots & \vdots & \vdots & \cdots & \vdots \\ 0 & 0 & 0 & 0 & \cdots & a_{nn} \end{bmatrix}.$$

(a) Write a 2×2 matrix and a 3×3 matrix in the form of A. Find the inverse of each. Answers will vary.

(b) Use the result of part (a) to make a conjecture about the inverses of matrices in the form of A. See margin.

PROJECT: VIEWING TELEVISION To work an extended application analyzing the average amounts of time spent viewing television in the United States, visit this text's website at *academic.cengage.com*. (Data Source: The Nielsen Company)

81. (b)

$$A^{-1} = \begin{bmatrix} \frac{1}{a_{11}} & 0 & 0 & \cdots & 0 \\ 0 & \frac{1}{a_{22}} & 0 & \cdots & 0 \\ 0 & 0 & \frac{1}{a_{33}} & \cdots & 0 \\ \vdots & \vdots & \vdots & \cdots & \vdots \\ 0 & 0 & 0 & \cdots & \frac{1}{a_{nn}} \end{bmatrix}$$

5 ASSESS AND RETEACH

Daily Homework Quiz

Transparency Available
Available at the Instructor's companion site.

69. 0 muffins, 300 bones, 200 cookies

70. 5 muffins, 415 bones, 50 cookies

71. 100 muffins, 300 bones, 150 cookies

72. 150 muffins, 300 bones, 200 cookies

73. (a) $\begin{cases} 2f + 2.5h + 3s = 26 \\ f + h + s = 10 \\ h - s = 0 \end{cases}$

(b) $\begin{bmatrix} 2 & 2.5 & 3 \\ 1 & 1 & 1 \\ 0 & 1 & -1 \end{bmatrix}\begin{bmatrix} f \\ h \\ s \end{bmatrix} = \begin{bmatrix} 26 \\ 10 \\ 0 \end{bmatrix}$

(c) 2 pounds of French vanilla, 4 pounds of hazelnut, 4 pounds of Swiss chocolate

74. (a) $\begin{cases} 2.5r + 4l + 2i = 300 \\ -r + 2l + 2i = 0 \\ r + l + i = 120 \end{cases}$

(b) $\begin{bmatrix} 2.5 & 4 & 2 \\ -1 & 2 & 2 \\ 1 & 1 & 1 \end{bmatrix}\begin{bmatrix} r \\ l \\ i \end{bmatrix} = \begin{bmatrix} 300 \\ 0 \\ 120 \end{bmatrix}$

(c) 80 roses, 10 lilies, 30 irises

75. (a) $\begin{cases} 100a + 10b + c = 13.89 \\ 121a + 11b + c = 14.04 \\ 144a + 12b + c = 14.20 \end{cases}$

(b) $y = 0.005t^2 + 0.045t + 12.94$

(c)
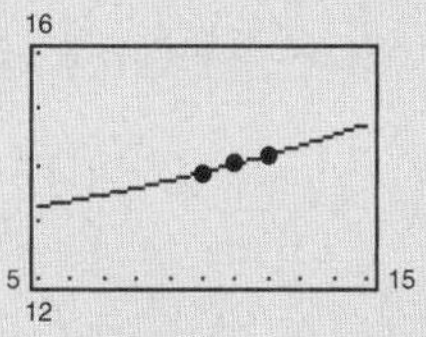

(d) For the immediate future it is, but not for long-term predictions.

77. True. If B is the inverse of A, then $AB = I = BA$.

78. True. If A and B are both square matrices and $AB = I_n$, it can be shown that $BA = I_n$.

1 PLAN AND PREPARE

Warm-up Exercises

Transparency Available
Available at the Instructor's companion site.

Notetaking Guide

Transparency Available
Promotes interactive learning and notetaking skills. Available at the Instructor's companion site.

Animated Precalculus

An **Animated Precalculus** tutorial is available at the Student companion site for **Section 8.4.**

Pacing

Average: 2 days
Advanced: 2 days
Block: 1 block

2 FOCUS AND MOTIVATE

Essential Question

How do you find the determinant of a square matrix? **Tell students that they will learn how to answer this question by learning how to calculate the determinant of a 2 × 2 matrix and how to find the minors and cofactors of a matrix.**

8.4 THE DETERMINANT OF A SQUARE MATRIX

What you should learn

- Find the determinants of 2 × 2 matrices.
- Find minors and cofactors of square matrices.
- Find the determinants of square matrices.

Why you should learn it

Determinants are often used in other branches of mathematics. For instance, Exercises 85–90 on page 615 show some types of determinants that are useful when changes in variables are made in calculus.

The Determinant of a 2×2 Matrix

Every *square* matrix can be associated with a real number called its **determinant.** Determinants have many uses, and several will be discussed in this and the next section. Historically, the use of determinants arose from special number patterns that occur when systems of linear equations are solved. For instance, the system

$$\begin{cases} a_1x + b_1y = c_1 \\ a_2x + b_2y = c_2 \end{cases}$$

has a solution

$$x = \frac{c_1b_2 - c_2b_1}{a_1b_2 - a_2b_1} \quad \text{and} \quad y = \frac{a_1c_2 - a_2c_1}{a_1b_2 - a_2b_1}$$

provided that $a_1b_2 - a_2b_1 \neq 0$. Note that the denominators of the two fractions are the same. This denominator is called the *determinant* of the coefficient matrix of the system.

Coefficient Matrix	*Determinant*
$A = \begin{bmatrix} a_1 & b_1 \\ a_2 & b_2 \end{bmatrix}$	$\det(A) = a_1b_2 - a_2b_1$

The determinant of the matrix A can also be denoted by vertical bars on both sides of the matrix, as indicated in the following definition.

> **Definition of the Determinant of a 2×2 Matrix**
>
> The **determinant** of the matrix
>
> $$A = \begin{bmatrix} a_1 & b_1 \\ a_2 & b_2 \end{bmatrix}$$
>
> is given by
>
> $$\det(A) = |A| = \begin{vmatrix} a_1 & b_1 \\ a_2 & b_2 \end{vmatrix} = a_1b_2 - a_2b_1.$$

In this text, $\det(A)$ and $|A|$ are used interchangeably to represent the determinant of A. Although vertical bars are also used to denote the absolute value of a real number, the context will show which use is intended.

A convenient method for remembering the formula for the determinant of a 2×2 matrix is shown in the following diagram.

$$\det(A) = \begin{vmatrix} a_1 & b_1 \\ a_2 & b_2 \end{vmatrix} = a_1b_2 - a_2b_1$$

Note that the determinant is the difference of the products of the two diagonals of the matrix.

Resource Planning Guide

Chapter Resources

- Complete Solutions Guide

Workbooks

- Notetaking Guide
- Student Solutions Guide

Interactive Technology

- Instructor Success Organizer
- Notetaking Guide IAE
- Instructional DVDs
- Animated Precalculus
- PowerLecture with ExamView

Example 1 The Determinant of a 2 × 2 Matrix

Find the determinant of each matrix.

a. $A = \begin{bmatrix} 2 & -3 \\ 1 & 2 \end{bmatrix}$

b. $B = \begin{bmatrix} 2 & 1 \\ 4 & 2 \end{bmatrix}$

c. $C = \begin{bmatrix} 0 & \frac{3}{2} \\ 2 & 4 \end{bmatrix}$

Solution

a. $\det(A) = \begin{vmatrix} 2 & -3 \\ 1 & 2 \end{vmatrix}$

$= 2(2) - 1(-3)$

$= 4 + 3 = 7$

b. $\det(B) = \begin{vmatrix} 2 & 1 \\ 4 & 2 \end{vmatrix}$

$= 2(2) - 4(1)$

$= 4 - 4 = 0$

c. $\det(C) = \begin{vmatrix} 0 & \frac{3}{2} \\ 2 & 4 \end{vmatrix}$

$= 0(4) - 2\left(\frac{3}{2}\right)$

$= 0 - 3 = -3$

CHECKPoint Now try Exercise 9.

Notice in Example 1 that the determinant of a matrix can be positive, zero, or negative.

The determinant of a matrix of order 1 × 1 is defined simply as the entry of the matrix. For instance, if $A = [-2]$, then $\det(A) = -2$.

TECHNOLOGY

Most graphing utilities can evaluate the determinant of a matrix. For instance, you can evaluate the determinant of

$$A = \begin{bmatrix} 2 & -3 \\ 1 & 2 \end{bmatrix}$$

by entering the matrix as [*A*] and then choosing the *determinant* feature. The result should be 7, as in Example 1(a). Try evaluating the determinants of other matrices. Consult the user's guide for your graphing utility for specific keystrokes.

3 TEACH

Extra Example 1

Find the determinant of each matrix.

a. $A = \begin{bmatrix} 2 & -1 \\ 3 & 5 \end{bmatrix}$

13

b. $B = \begin{bmatrix} 1 & 0 \\ -4 & 5 \end{bmatrix}$

5

c. $C = \begin{bmatrix} 3 & -3 \\ -2 & 2 \end{bmatrix}$

0

Minors and Cofactors

To define the determinant of a square matrix of order 3×3 or higher, it is convenient to introduce the concepts of **minors** and **cofactors.**

Minors and Cofactors of a Square Matrix

If A is a square matrix, the **minor** M_{ij} of the entry a_{ij} is the determinant of the matrix obtained by deleting the ith row and jth column of A. The **cofactor** C_{ij} of the entry a_{ij} is

$$C_{ij} = (-1)^{i+j} M_{ij}.$$

Sign Pattern for Cofactors

$$\begin{bmatrix} + & - & + \\ - & + & - \\ + & - & + \end{bmatrix}$$

3×3 matrix

$$\begin{bmatrix} + & - & + & - \\ - & + & - & + \\ + & - & + & - \\ - & + & - & + \end{bmatrix}$$

4×4 matrix

$$\begin{bmatrix} + & - & + & - & + & \cdots \\ - & + & - & + & - & \cdots \\ + & - & + & - & + & \cdots \\ - & + & - & + & - & \cdots \\ + & - & + & - & + & \cdots \\ \vdots & \vdots & \vdots & \vdots & \vdots & \end{bmatrix}$$

$n \times n$ matrix

In the sign pattern for cofactors at the left, notice that *odd* positions (where $i + j$ is odd) have negative signs and *even* positions (where $i + j$ is even) have positive signs.

Example 2 Finding the Minors and Cofactors of a Matrix

Find all the minors and cofactors of

$$A = \begin{bmatrix} 0 & 2 & 1 \\ 3 & -1 & 2 \\ 4 & 0 & 1 \end{bmatrix}.$$

Solution

To find the minor M_{11}, delete the first row and first column of A and evaluate the determinant of the resulting matrix.

$$\begin{bmatrix} 0 & 2 & 1 \\ 3 & -1 & 2 \\ 4 & 0 & 1 \end{bmatrix}, \quad M_{11} = \begin{vmatrix} -1 & 2 \\ 0 & 1 \end{vmatrix} = -1(1) - 0(2) = -1$$

Similarly, to find M_{12}, delete the first row and second column.

$$\begin{bmatrix} 0 & 2 & 1 \\ 3 & -1 & 2 \\ 4 & 0 & 1 \end{bmatrix}, \quad M_{12} = \begin{vmatrix} 3 & 2 \\ 4 & 1 \end{vmatrix} = 3(1) - 4(2) = -5$$

Continuing this pattern, you obtain the minors.

$M_{11} = -1 \quad M_{12} = -5 \quad M_{13} = 4$

$M_{21} = 2 \quad M_{22} = -4 \quad M_{23} = -8$

$M_{31} = 5 \quad M_{32} = -3 \quad M_{33} = -6$

Now, to find the cofactors, combine these minors with the checkerboard pattern of signs for a 3×3 matrix shown at the upper left.

$C_{11} = -1 \quad C_{12} = 5 \quad C_{13} = 4$

$C_{21} = -2 \quad C_{22} = -4 \quad C_{23} = 8$

$C_{31} = 5 \quad C_{32} = 3 \quad C_{33} = -6$

CHECKPoint Now try Exercise 29.

Extra Example 2

Find all the minors and cofactors of

$$A = \begin{bmatrix} 3 & -2 & 4 \\ 3 & 2 & 1 \\ -1 & 3 & 6 \end{bmatrix}.$$

$M_{11} = 9, M_{12} = 19, M_{13} = 11$

$M_{21} = -24, M_{22} = 22, M_{23} = 7$

$M_{31} = -10, M_{32} = -9, M_{33} = 12$

$C_{11} = 9, C_{12} = -19, C_{13} = 11$

$C_{21} = 24, C_{22} = 22, C_{23} = -7$

$C_{31} = -10, C_{32} = 9, C_{33} = 12$

The Determinant of a Square Matrix

The definition below is called *inductive* because it uses determinants of matrices of order $n - 1$ to define determinants of matrices of order n.

Determinant of a Square Matrix

If A is a square matrix (of order 2×2 or greater), the determinant of A is the sum of the entries in any row (or column) of A multiplied by their respective cofactors. For instance, expanding along the first row yields

$$|A| = a_{11}C_{11} + a_{12}C_{12} + \cdot \cdot \cdot + a_{1n}C_{1n}.$$

Applying this definition to find a determinant is called **expanding by cofactors.**

Try checking that for a 2×2 matrix

$$A = \begin{bmatrix} a_1 & b_1 \\ a_2 & b_2 \end{bmatrix}$$

this definition of the determinant yields $|A| = a_1b_2 - a_2b_1$, as previously defined.

Example 3 The Determinant of a Matrix of Order 3 × 3

Find the determinant of

$$A = \begin{bmatrix} 0 & 2 & 1 \\ 3 & -1 & 2 \\ 4 & 0 & 1 \end{bmatrix}.$$

Solution

Note that this is the same matrix that was in Example 2. There you found the cofactors of the entries in the first row to be

$$C_{11} = -1, \quad C_{12} = 5, \quad \text{and} \quad C_{13} = 4.$$

So, by the definition of a determinant, you have

$$\begin{aligned} |A| &= a_{11}C_{11} + a_{12}C_{12} + a_{13}C_{13} && \text{First-row expansion} \\ &= 0(-1) + 2(5) + 1(4) \\ &= 14. \end{aligned}$$

CHECKPoint Now try Exercise 39.

In Example 3, the determinant was found by expanding by the cofactors in the first row. You could have used any row or column. For instance, you could have expanded along the second row to obtain

$$\begin{aligned} |A| &= a_{21}C_{21} + a_{22}C_{22} + a_{23}C_{23} && \text{Second-row expansion} \\ &= 3(-2) + (-1)(-4) + 2(8) \\ &= 14. \end{aligned}$$

Extra Example 3

Find the determinant of

$$A = \begin{bmatrix} 3 & 4 & -2 \\ 3 & 5 & 0 \\ -1 & 4 & 1 \end{bmatrix}.$$

−31

Extra Example 4

Find the determinant of

$$A = \begin{bmatrix} 2 & 6 & -4 & 2 \\ 2 & -2 & 3 & 6 \\ 1 & 5 & 0 & 1 \\ 3 & 1 & 0 & -5 \end{bmatrix}.$$

704

Avoiding Common Errors

When expanding a determinant by using cofactors, students often have trouble deciding which column or row to use. Students should be reminded that the rows or columns with zero elements will usually reduce work by eliminating the necessity of calculating all of the cofactors.

Closing the Lesson

Have students summarize the major points of the lesson and answer the Essential Question: How do you find the determinant of a square matrix?

- **Calculate the determinant of a 2×2 matrix by finding the difference of the products of the diagonals.**
- **Find a cofactor C_{ij} of a square matrix by eliminating row i and column j, finding the determinant of the matrix that remains, and giving it the appropriate sign.**
- **Find the determinant of a square matrix by finding the sum of the products found by multiplying each entry in any row by its specific cofactor.**

When expanding by cofactors, you do not need to find cofactors of zero entries, because zero times its cofactor is zero.

$$a_{ij}C_{ij} = (0)C_{ij} = 0$$

So, the row (or column) containing the most zeros is usually the best choice for expansion by cofactors. This is demonstrated in the next example.

Example 4 The Determinant of a Matrix of Order 4 × 4

Find the determinant of

$$A = \begin{bmatrix} 1 & -2 & 3 & 0 \\ -1 & 1 & 0 & 2 \\ 0 & 2 & 0 & 3 \\ 3 & 4 & 0 & 2 \end{bmatrix}.$$

Solution

After inspecting this matrix, you can see that three of the entries in the third column are zeros. So, you can eliminate some of the work in the expansion by using the third column.

$$|A| = 3(C_{13}) + 0(C_{23}) + 0(C_{33}) + 0(C_{43})$$

Because C_{23}, C_{33}, and C_{43} have zero coefficients, you need only find the cofactor C_{13}. To do this, delete the first row and third column of A and evaluate the determinant of the resulting matrix.

$$C_{13} = (-1)^{1+3}\begin{vmatrix} -1 & 1 & 2 \\ 0 & 2 & 3 \\ 3 & 4 & 2 \end{vmatrix} \qquad \text{Delete 1st row and 3rd column.}$$

$$= \begin{vmatrix} -1 & 1 & 2 \\ 0 & 2 & 3 \\ 3 & 4 & 2 \end{vmatrix} \qquad \text{Simplify.}$$

Expanding by cofactors in the second row yields

$$C_{13} = 0(-1)^3\begin{vmatrix} 1 & 2 \\ 4 & 2 \end{vmatrix} + 2(-1)^4\begin{vmatrix} -1 & 2 \\ 3 & 2 \end{vmatrix} + 3(-1)^5\begin{vmatrix} -1 & 1 \\ 3 & 4 \end{vmatrix}$$

$$= 0 + 2(1)(-8) + 3(-1)(-7)$$

$$= 5.$$

So, you obtain

$$|A| = 3C_{13}$$

$$= 3(5)$$

$$= 15.$$

CHECKPoint Now try Exercise 49.

Try using a graphing utility to confirm the result of Example 4.

Differentiated Instruction

Inclusion Some students may have difficulty moving from finding the determinant of a 2×2 matrix to finding the determinant of a 3×3 or 4×4 matrix. Write a 2×2 matrix on the board. Have students give direction on how to find the determinant. Assist students as needed. Then, add a column and a row to the matrix to make it a 3×3. Work with students to find the determinant. When that is done, increase the matrix to 4×4 and help students find the determinant.

8.4 EXERCISES

See www.CalcChat.com for worked-out solutions to odd-numbered exercises.

VOCABULARY: Fill in the blanks.

1. Both det(A) and $|A|$ represent the ________ of the matrix A. determinant
2. The _minor_ M_{ij} of the entry a_{ij} is the determinant of the matrix obtained by deleting the ith row and jth column of the square matrix A.
3. The _cofactor_ C_{ij} of the entry a_{ij} of the square matrix A is given by $(-1)^{i+j}M_{ij}$.
4. The method of finding the determinant of a matrix of order 2×2 or greater is called ________ by ________. expanding; cofactors

SKILLS AND APPLICATIONS

In Exercises 5–20, find the determinant of the matrix.

5. $[4]$ 4
6. $[-10]$ -10
7. $\begin{bmatrix} 8 & 4 \\ 2 & 3 \end{bmatrix}$ 16
8. $\begin{bmatrix} -9 & 0 \\ 6 & 2 \end{bmatrix}$ -18
9. $\begin{bmatrix} 6 & 2 \\ -5 & 3 \end{bmatrix}$ 28
10. $\begin{bmatrix} 3 & -3 \\ 4 & -8 \end{bmatrix}$ -12
11. $\begin{bmatrix} -7 & 0 \\ 3 & 0 \end{bmatrix}$ 0
12. $\begin{bmatrix} 4 & -3 \\ 0 & 0 \end{bmatrix}$ 0
13. $\begin{bmatrix} 2 & 6 \\ 0 & 3 \end{bmatrix}$ 6
14. $\begin{bmatrix} 2 & -3 \\ -6 & 9 \end{bmatrix}$ 0
15. $\begin{bmatrix} -3 & -2 \\ -6 & -1 \end{bmatrix}$ -9
16. $\begin{bmatrix} 4 & 7 \\ -2 & 5 \end{bmatrix}$ 34
17. $\begin{bmatrix} -7 & 6 \\ \frac{1}{2} & 3 \end{bmatrix}$ -24
18. $\begin{bmatrix} 0 & 6 \\ -3 & 2 \end{bmatrix}$ 18
19. $\begin{bmatrix} -\frac{1}{2} & \frac{1}{3} \\ -6 & \frac{1}{3} \end{bmatrix}$ $\frac{11}{6}$
20. $\begin{bmatrix} \frac{2}{3} & \frac{4}{3} \\ -1 & -\frac{1}{3} \end{bmatrix}$ $\frac{10}{9}$

In Exercises 21–24, use the matrix capabilities of a graphing utility to find the determinant of the matrix.

21. $\begin{bmatrix} 0.3 & 0.2 & 0.2 \\ 0.2 & 0.2 & 0.2 \\ -0.4 & 0.4 & 0.3 \end{bmatrix}$ -0.002
22. $\begin{bmatrix} 0.1 & 0.2 & 0.3 \\ -0.3 & 0.2 & 0.2 \\ 0.5 & 0.4 & 0.4 \end{bmatrix}$ -0.022
23. $\begin{bmatrix} 0.9 & 0.7 & 0 \\ -0.1 & 0.3 & 1.3 \\ -2.2 & 4.2 & 6.1 \end{bmatrix}$ -4.842
24. $\begin{bmatrix} 0.1 & 0.1 & -4.3 \\ 7.5 & 6.2 & 0.7 \\ 0.3 & 0.6 & -1.2 \end{bmatrix}$ -11.217

In Exercises 25–32, find all (a) minors and (b) cofactors of the matrix. 25–32. See margin.

25. $\begin{bmatrix} 4 & 5 \\ 3 & -6 \end{bmatrix}$
26. $\begin{bmatrix} 0 & 10 \\ 3 & -4 \end{bmatrix}$
27. $\begin{bmatrix} 3 & 1 \\ -2 & -4 \end{bmatrix}$
28. $\begin{bmatrix} -6 & 5 \\ 7 & -2 \end{bmatrix}$
29. $\begin{bmatrix} 4 & 0 & 2 \\ -3 & 2 & 1 \\ 1 & -1 & 1 \end{bmatrix}$
30. $\begin{bmatrix} 1 & -1 & 0 \\ 3 & 2 & 5 \\ 4 & -6 & 4 \end{bmatrix}$
31. $\begin{bmatrix} -4 & 6 & 3 \\ 7 & -2 & 8 \\ 1 & 0 & -5 \end{bmatrix}$
32. $\begin{bmatrix} -2 & 9 & 4 \\ 7 & -6 & 0 \\ 6 & 7 & -6 \end{bmatrix}$

In Exercises 33–38, find the determinant of the matrix by the method of expansion by cofactors. Expand using the indicated row or column.

33. $\begin{bmatrix} -3 & 2 & 1 \\ 4 & 5 & 6 \\ 2 & -3 & 1 \end{bmatrix}$
(a) Row 1 -75
(b) Column 2 -75

34. $\begin{bmatrix} -3 & 4 & 2 \\ 6 & 3 & 1 \\ 4 & -7 & -8 \end{bmatrix}$
(a) Row 2 151
(b) Column 3 151

35. $\begin{bmatrix} 5 & 0 & -3 \\ 0 & 12 & 4 \\ 1 & 6 & 3 \end{bmatrix}$
(a) Row 2 96
(b) Column 2 96

36. $\begin{bmatrix} 10 & -5 & 5 \\ 30 & 0 & 10 \\ 0 & 10 & 1 \end{bmatrix}$
(a) Row 3 650
(b) Column 1 650

37. $\begin{bmatrix} 6 & 0 & -3 & 5 \\ 4 & 13 & 6 & -8 \\ -1 & 0 & 7 & 4 \\ 8 & 6 & 0 & 2 \end{bmatrix}$
(a) Row 2 170
(b) Column 2 170

38. $\begin{bmatrix} 10 & 8 & 3 & -7 \\ 4 & 0 & 5 & -6 \\ 0 & 3 & 2 & 7 \\ 1 & 0 & -3 & 2 \end{bmatrix}$
(a) Row 3 -1167
(b) Column 1 -1167

In Exercises 39–54, find the determinant of the matrix. Expand by cofactors on the row or column that appears to make the computations easiest.

39. $\begin{bmatrix} 2 & -1 & 0 \\ 4 & 2 & 1 \\ 4 & 2 & 1 \end{bmatrix}$ 0
40. $\begin{bmatrix} -2 & 2 & 3 \\ 1 & -1 & 0 \\ 0 & 1 & 4 \end{bmatrix}$ 3
41. $\begin{bmatrix} 6 & 3 & -7 \\ 0 & 0 & 0 \\ 4 & -6 & 3 \end{bmatrix}$ 0
42. $\begin{bmatrix} 1 & 1 & 2 \\ 3 & 1 & 0 \\ -2 & 0 & 3 \end{bmatrix}$ -2
43. $\begin{bmatrix} -1 & 8 & -3 \\ 0 & 3 & -6 \\ 0 & 0 & 3 \end{bmatrix}$ -9
44. $\begin{bmatrix} 1 & 0 & 0 \\ -1 & -1 & 0 \\ 4 & 11 & 5 \end{bmatrix}$ -5

4 PRACTICE AND APPLY

Assignment Guide

Transparencies Available
Available at the Instructor's companion site.

Average:
Day 1: pp. 613–614
Exs. 1–3, 5, 7, 11, 15–27 odd, 30, 31, 63, 65, 71, 73
Day 2: pp. 613–615
Exs. 4, 33, 35, 39, 41, 47, 55, 59, 67, 69, 75–85 odd, 91, 92, 95–99 odd, 100

Advanced:
Day 1: pp. 613–614
Exs. 1–3, 6–12 even, 16–32 even, 64, 66, 72, 74
Day 2: pp. 613–615
Exs. 4, 36–42 even, 50, 56, 60, 68, 70, 76–86 even, 94–100 even

Block:
pp. 613–615
Exs. 1–5, 7, 11, 15–27 odd, 30, 31–35 odd, 39, 41, 47, 55, 59, 63–85 odd, 91, 92, 95–99 odd, 100

25. (a) $M_{11} = -6, M_{12} = 3, M_{21} = 5, M_{22} = 4$
(b) $C_{11} = -6, C_{12} = -3, C_{21} = -5, C_{22} = 4$

26. (a) $M_{11} = -4, M_{12} = 3, M_{21} = 10, M_{22} = 0$
(b) $C_{11} = -4, C_{12} = -3, C_{21} = -10, C_{22} = 0$

27. (a) $M_{11} = -4, M_{12} = -2, M_{21} = 1, M_{22} = 3$
(b) $C_{11} = -4, C_{12} = 2, C_{21} = -1, C_{22} = 3$

28. (a) $M_{11} = -2, M_{12} = 7, M_{21} = 5, M_{22} = -6$
(b) $C_{11} = -2, C_{12} = -7, C_{21} = -5, C_{22} = -6$

29. (a) $M_{11} = 3, M_{12} = -4, M_{13} = 1, M_{21} = 2, M_{22} = 2, M_{23} = -4, M_{31} = -4, M_{32} = 10, M_{33} = 8$
(b) $C_{11} = 3, C_{12} = 4, C_{13} = 1, C_{21} = -2, C_{22} = 2, C_{23} = 4, C_{31} = -4, C_{32} = -10, C_{33} = 8$

30. (a) $M_{11} = 38, M_{12} = -8, M_{13} = -26, M_{21} = -4, M_{22} = 4, M_{23} = -2, M_{31} = -5, M_{32} = 5, M_{33} = 5$

30. (b) $C_{11} = 38, C_{12} = 8, C_{13} = -26, C_{21} = 4, C_{22} = 4, C_{23} = 2, C_{31} = -5, C_{32} = -5, C_{33} = 5$

31. (a) $M_{11} = 10, M_{12} = -43, M_{13} = 2, M_{21} = -30, M_{22} = 17, M_{23} = -6, M_{31} = 54, M_{32} = -53, M_{33} = -34$
(b) $C_{11} = 10, C_{12} = 43, C_{13} = 2, C_{21} = 30, C_{22} = 17, C_{23} = 6, C_{31} = 54, C_{32} = 53, C_{33} = -34$

32. (a) $M_{11} = 36, M_{12} = -42, M_{13} = 85, M_{21} = -82, M_{22} = -12, M_{23} = -68, M_{31} = 24, M_{32} = -28, M_{33} = -51$
(b) $C_{11} = 36, C_{12} = 42, C_{13} = 85, C_{21} = 82, C_{22} = -12, C_{23} = 68, C_{31} = 24, C_{32} = 28, C_{33} = -51$

63. (a) -3 (b) -2
(c) $\begin{bmatrix} -2 & 0 \\ 0 & -3 \end{bmatrix}$ (d) 6

64. (a) 0 (b) -1
(c) $\begin{bmatrix} -2 & -5 \\ 4 & 10 \end{bmatrix}$ (d) 0

65. (a) -8 (b) 0
(c) $\begin{bmatrix} -4 & 4 \\ 1 & -1 \end{bmatrix}$ (d) 0

66. (a) -17 (b) -6
(c) $\begin{bmatrix} 4 & 22 \\ -1 & 20 \end{bmatrix}$ (d) 102

67. (a) -21 (b) -19
(c) $\begin{bmatrix} 7 & 1 & 4 \\ -8 & 9 & -3 \\ 7 & -3 & 9 \end{bmatrix}$
(d) 399

68. (a) -23 (b) 1
(c) $\begin{bmatrix} -9 & 4 & 1 \\ -5 & -10 & 6 \\ 4 & -1 & -1 \end{bmatrix}$
(d) -23

69. (a) 2 (b) -6
(c) $\begin{bmatrix} 1 & 4 & 3 \\ -1 & 0 & 3 \\ 0 & 2 & 0 \end{bmatrix}$
(d) -12

70. (a) 0 (b) -7
(c) $\begin{bmatrix} 7 & -4 & 9 \\ 8 & -6 & 3 \\ 6 & -2 & 15 \end{bmatrix}$
(d) 0

79. $x = 1 \pm \sqrt{2}$
80. $x = -2, 1$
81. $x = -1, 4$
82. $x = -1, 3$
83. $x = -1, -4$
84. $x = -2, 3$

45. $\begin{vmatrix} 1 & 4 & -2 \\ 3 & 2 & 0 \\ -1 & 4 & 3 \end{vmatrix}$ -58 **46.** $\begin{vmatrix} 2 & -1 & 3 \\ 1 & 4 & 4 \\ 1 & 0 & 2 \end{vmatrix}$ 2

47. $\begin{vmatrix} 2 & 4 & 6 \\ 0 & 3 & 1 \\ 0 & 0 & -5 \end{vmatrix}$ -30 **48.** $\begin{vmatrix} -3 & 0 & 0 \\ 7 & 11 & 0 \\ 1 & 2 & 2 \end{vmatrix}$ -66

49. $\begin{vmatrix} 2 & 6 & 6 & 2 \\ 2 & 7 & 3 & 6 \\ 1 & 5 & 0 & 1 \\ 3 & 7 & 0 & 7 \end{vmatrix}$ -168 **50.** $\begin{vmatrix} 3 & 6 & -5 & 4 \\ -2 & 0 & 6 & 0 \\ 1 & 1 & 2 & 2 \\ 0 & 3 & -1 & -1 \end{vmatrix}$ -108

51. $\begin{vmatrix} 5 & 3 & 0 & 6 \\ 4 & 6 & 4 & 12 \\ 0 & 2 & -3 & 4 \\ 0 & 1 & -2 & 2 \end{vmatrix}$ 0 **52.** $\begin{vmatrix} 1 & 4 & 3 & 2 \\ -5 & 6 & 2 & 1 \\ 0 & 0 & 0 & 0 \\ 3 & -2 & 1 & 5 \end{vmatrix}$ 0

53. $\begin{vmatrix} 3 & 2 & 4 & -1 & 5 \\ -2 & 0 & 1 & 3 & 2 \\ 1 & 0 & 0 & 4 & 0 \\ 6 & 0 & 2 & -1 & 0 \\ 3 & 0 & 5 & 1 & 0 \end{vmatrix}$ 412

54. $\begin{vmatrix} 5 & 2 & 0 & 0 & -2 \\ 0 & 1 & 4 & 3 & 2 \\ 0 & 0 & 2 & 6 & 3 \\ 0 & 0 & 3 & 4 & 1 \\ 0 & 0 & 0 & 0 & 2 \end{vmatrix}$ -100

In Exercises 55–62, use the matrix capabilities of a graphing utility to evaluate the determinant.

55. $\begin{vmatrix} 3 & 8 & -7 \\ 0 & -5 & 4 \\ 8 & 1 & 6 \end{vmatrix}$ -126 **56.** $\begin{vmatrix} 5 & -8 & 0 \\ 9 & 7 & 4 \\ -8 & 7 & 1 \end{vmatrix}$ 223

57. $\begin{vmatrix} 7 & 0 & -14 \\ -2 & 5 & 4 \\ -6 & 2 & 12 \end{vmatrix}$ 0 **58.** $\begin{vmatrix} 3 & 0 & 0 \\ -2 & 5 & 0 \\ 12 & 5 & 7 \end{vmatrix}$ 105

59. $\begin{vmatrix} 1 & -1 & 8 & 4 \\ 2 & 6 & 0 & -4 \\ 2 & 0 & 2 & 6 \\ 0 & 2 & 8 & 0 \end{vmatrix}$ -336 **60.** $\begin{vmatrix} 0 & -3 & 8 & 2 \\ 8 & 1 & -1 & 6 \\ -4 & 6 & 0 & 9 \\ -7 & 0 & 0 & 14 \end{vmatrix}$ 7441

61. $\begin{vmatrix} 3 & -2 & 4 & 3 & 1 \\ -1 & 0 & 2 & 1 & 0 \\ 5 & -1 & 0 & 3 & 2 \\ 4 & 7 & -8 & 0 & 0 \\ 1 & 2 & 3 & 0 & 2 \end{vmatrix}$ 410

62. $\begin{vmatrix} -2 & 0 & 0 & 0 & 0 \\ 0 & 3 & 0 & 0 & 0 \\ 0 & 0 & -1 & 0 & 0 \\ 0 & 0 & 0 & 2 & 0 \\ 0 & 0 & 0 & 0 & -4 \end{vmatrix}$ -48

In Exercises 63–70, find (a) $|A|$, (b) $|B|$, (c) AB, and (d) $|AB|$.

63–70. See margin.

63. $A = \begin{bmatrix} -1 & 0 \\ 0 & 3 \end{bmatrix}$, $B = \begin{bmatrix} 2 & 0 \\ 0 & -1 \end{bmatrix}$

64. $A = \begin{bmatrix} -2 & 1 \\ 4 & -2 \end{bmatrix}$, $B = \begin{bmatrix} 1 & 2 \\ 0 & -1 \end{bmatrix}$

65. $A = \begin{bmatrix} 4 & 0 \\ 3 & -2 \end{bmatrix}$, $B = \begin{bmatrix} -1 & 1 \\ -2 & 2 \end{bmatrix}$

66. $A = \begin{bmatrix} 5 & 4 \\ 3 & -1 \end{bmatrix}$, $B = \begin{bmatrix} 0 & 6 \\ 1 & -2 \end{bmatrix}$

67. $A = \begin{bmatrix} 0 & 1 & 2 \\ -3 & -2 & 1 \\ 0 & 4 & 1 \end{bmatrix}$, $B = \begin{bmatrix} 3 & -2 & 0 \\ 1 & -1 & 2 \\ 3 & 1 & 1 \end{bmatrix}$

68. $A = \begin{bmatrix} 3 & 2 & 0 \\ -1 & -3 & 4 \\ -2 & 0 & 1 \end{bmatrix}$, $B = \begin{bmatrix} -3 & 0 & 1 \\ 0 & 2 & -1 \\ -2 & -1 & 1 \end{bmatrix}$

69. $A = \begin{bmatrix} -1 & 2 & 1 \\ 1 & 0 & 1 \\ 0 & 1 & 0 \end{bmatrix}$, $B = \begin{bmatrix} -1 & 0 & 0 \\ 0 & 2 & 0 \\ 0 & 0 & 3 \end{bmatrix}$

70. $A = \begin{bmatrix} 2 & 0 & 1 \\ 1 & -1 & 2 \\ 3 & 1 & 0 \end{bmatrix}$, $B = \begin{bmatrix} 2 & -1 & 4 \\ 0 & 1 & 3 \\ 3 & -2 & 1 \end{bmatrix}$

In Exercises 71–76, evaluate the determinant(s) to verify the equation. 71–76. Answers will vary.

71. $\begin{vmatrix} w & x \\ y & z \end{vmatrix} = -\begin{vmatrix} y & z \\ w & x \end{vmatrix}$ **72.** $\begin{vmatrix} w & cx \\ y & cz \end{vmatrix} = c\begin{vmatrix} w & x \\ y & z \end{vmatrix}$

73. $\begin{vmatrix} w & x \\ y & z \end{vmatrix} = \begin{vmatrix} w & x + cw \\ y & z + cy \end{vmatrix}$

74. $\begin{vmatrix} w & x \\ cw & cx \end{vmatrix} = 0$

75. $\begin{vmatrix} 1 & x & x^2 \\ 1 & y & y^2 \\ 1 & z & z^2 \end{vmatrix} = (y - x)(z - x)(z - y)$

76. $\begin{vmatrix} a + b & a & a \\ a & a + b & a \\ a & a & a + b \end{vmatrix} = b^2(3a + b)$

In Exercises 77–84, solve for x. 79–84. See margin.

77. $\begin{vmatrix} x & 2 \\ 1 & x \end{vmatrix} = 2$ $x = \pm 2$ **78.** $\begin{vmatrix} x & 4 \\ -1 & x \end{vmatrix} = 20$ $x = \pm 4$

79. $\begin{vmatrix} x & 1 \\ 2 & x - 2 \end{vmatrix} = -1$ **80.** $\begin{vmatrix} x + 1 & 2 \\ -1 & x \end{vmatrix} = 4$

81. $\begin{vmatrix} x - 1 & 2 \\ 3 & x - 2 \end{vmatrix} = 0$ **82.** $\begin{vmatrix} x - 2 & -1 \\ -3 & x \end{vmatrix} = 0$

83. $\begin{vmatrix} x + 3 & 2 \\ 1 & x + 2 \end{vmatrix} = 0$ **84.** $\begin{vmatrix} x + 4 & -2 \\ 7 & x - 5 \end{vmatrix} = 0$

In Exercises 85–90, evaluate the determinant in which the entries are functions. Determinants of this type occur when changes of variables are made in calculus.

85. $\begin{vmatrix} 4u & -1 \\ -1 & 2v \end{vmatrix}$ $8uv - 1$ **86.** $\begin{vmatrix} 3x^2 & -3y^2 \\ 1 & 1 \end{vmatrix}$ $3x^2 + 3y^2$

87. $\begin{vmatrix} e^{2x} & e^{3x} \\ 2e^{2x} & 3e^{3x} \end{vmatrix}$ e^{5x} **88.** $\begin{vmatrix} e^{-x} & xe^{-x} \\ -e^{-x} & (1-x)e^{-x} \end{vmatrix}$ e^{-2x}

89. $\begin{vmatrix} x & \ln x \\ 1 & 1/x \end{vmatrix}$ $1 - \ln x$ **90.** $\begin{vmatrix} x & x \ln x \\ 1 & 1 + \ln x \end{vmatrix}$ x

EXPLORATION

91–92. See margin.

TRUE OR FALSE? In Exercises 91 and 92, determine whether the statement is true or false. Justify your answer.

91. If a square matrix has an entire row of zeros, the determinant will always be zero.

92. If two columns of a square matrix are the same, the determinant of the matrix will be zero.

93. Find square matrices A and B to demonstrate that $|A + B| \neq |A| + |B|$. Answers will vary.

94. Consider square matrices in which the entries are consecutive integers. An example of such a matrix is

$$\begin{bmatrix} 4 & 5 & 6 \\ 7 & 8 & 9 \\ 10 & 11 & 12 \end{bmatrix}.$$

(a) See margin.
(b) Answers will vary.

(a) Use a graphing utility to evaluate the determinants of four matrices of this type. Make a conjecture based on the results.

(b) Verify your conjecture.

95. See margin.

95. WRITING Write a brief paragraph explaining the difference between a square matrix and its determinant.

96. THINK ABOUT IT If A is a matrix of order 3×3 such that $|A| = 5$, is it possible to find $|2A|$? Explain.
Yes. $|2A| = 8|A| = 8(5) = 40$

PROPERTIES OF DETERMINANTS In Exercises 97–99, a property of determinants is given (A and B are square matrices). State how the property has been applied to the given determinants and use a graphing utility to verify the results. 97–99. See margin.

97. If B is obtained from A by interchanging two rows of A or interchanging two columns of A, then $|B| = -|A|$.

(a) $\begin{vmatrix} 1 & 3 & 4 \\ -7 & 2 & -5 \\ 6 & 1 & 2 \end{vmatrix} = -\begin{vmatrix} 1 & 4 & 3 \\ -7 & -5 & 2 \\ 6 & 2 & 1 \end{vmatrix}$

(b) $\begin{vmatrix} 1 & 3 & 4 \\ -2 & 2 & 0 \\ 1 & 6 & 2 \end{vmatrix} = -\begin{vmatrix} 1 & 6 & 2 \\ -2 & 2 & 0 \\ 1 & 3 & 4 \end{vmatrix}$

98. If B is obtained from A by adding a multiple of a row of A to another row of A or by adding a multiple of a column of A to another column of A, then $|B| = |A|$.

(a) $\begin{vmatrix} 1 & -3 \\ 5 & 2 \end{vmatrix} = \begin{vmatrix} 1 & -3 \\ 0 & 17 \end{vmatrix}$

(b) $\begin{vmatrix} 5 & 4 & 2 \\ 2 & -3 & 4 \\ 7 & 6 & 3 \end{vmatrix} = \begin{vmatrix} 1 & 10 & -6 \\ 2 & -3 & 4 \\ 7 & 6 & 3 \end{vmatrix}$

99. If B is obtained from A by multiplying a row by a nonzero constant c or by multiplying a column by a nonzero constant c, then $|B| = c|A|$.

(a) $\begin{vmatrix} 5 & 10 \\ 2 & -3 \end{vmatrix} = 5\begin{vmatrix} 1 & 2 \\ 2 & -3 \end{vmatrix}$

(b) $\begin{vmatrix} 1 & 8 & -3 \\ 3 & -12 & 6 \\ 7 & 4 & 9 \end{vmatrix} = 12\begin{vmatrix} 1 & 2 & -1 \\ 3 & -3 & 2 \\ 7 & 1 & 3 \end{vmatrix}$

100. CAPSTONE If A is an $n \times n$ matrix, explain how to find the following. See margin.

(a) The minor M_{ij} of the entry a_{ij}

(b) The cofactor C_{ij} of the entry a_{ij}

(c) The determinant of A

In Exercises 101–104, evaluate the determinant.

101. $\begin{vmatrix} 1 & 0 & 0 \\ 0 & 5 & 0 \\ 0 & 0 & 2 \end{vmatrix}$ 10 **102.** $\begin{vmatrix} -2 & 0 & 0 & 0 \\ 0 & 2 & 0 & 0 \\ 0 & 0 & 1 & 0 \\ 0 & 0 & 0 & 3 \end{vmatrix}$ -12

103. $\begin{vmatrix} -1 & 2 & -5 \\ 0 & 3 & 4 \\ 0 & 0 & 3 \end{vmatrix}$ -9 **104.** $\begin{vmatrix} 1 & 0 & 0 \\ -4 & -1 & 0 \\ 5 & 1 & 5 \end{vmatrix}$ -5

105. See margin.

105. CONJECTURE A **triangular matrix** is a square matrix with all zero entries either below or above its main diagonal. A square matrix is **upper triangular** if it has all zero entries below its main diagonal and is **lower triangular** if it has all zero entries above its main diagonal. A matrix that is both upper and lower triangular is called diagonal. That is, a **diagonal matrix** is a square matrix in which all entries above and below the main diagonal are zero. In Exercises 101–104, you evaluated the determinants of triangular matrices. Make a conjecture based on your results.

106. Use the matrix capabilities of a graphing utility to find the determinant of A. What message appears on the screen? Why does the graphing utility display this message?

$$A = \begin{bmatrix} 1 & 2 \\ -1 & 0 \\ 3 & -2 \end{bmatrix}$$

An error message appears because the matrix is not square.

5 ASSESS AND RETEACH

Daily Homework Quiz

Transparency Available
Available at the Instructor's companion site.

91. True. If an entire row is zero, then each cofactor in the expansion is multiplied by zero.

92. True. If a square matrix has two columns that are equal, then elementary column operations can be used to create a column with all zeros.

94. (a) For an $n \times n$ matrix $(n > 2)$ with consecutive integer entries, the determinant appears to be 0.

95. A square matrix is a square array of numbers. The determinant of a square matrix is a real number.

97. (a) Columns 2 and 3 of A were interchanged.
$|A| = -115 = -|B|$
(b) Rows 1 and 3 of A were interchanged.
$|A| = -40 = -|B|$

98. (a) Add -5 times Row 1 to Row 2.
$|A| = 17 = |B|$
(b) Add -2 times Row 2 to Row 1.
$|A| = -11 = |B|$

99. (a) Multiply Row 1 by 5.
(b) Multiply Column 2 by 4 and Column 3 by 3.

100. See below.

105. The determinant of a triangular matrix is the product of the terms in the diagonal.

100. (a) Take the determinant of the $(n-1) \times (n-1)$ matrix that is left after deleting the ith row and jth column.
(b) If $i + j$ is odd, then $C_{ij} = -M_{ij}$. If $i + j$ is even, then $C_{ij} = M_{ij}$.
(c) $|A| = a_{11}C_{11} + a_{12}C_{12} + \ldots + a_{1n}C_{1n}$

1 PLAN AND PREPARE

Warm-up Exercises

Transparency Available
Available at the Instructor's companion site.

Notetaking Guide

Transparency Available
Promotes interactive learning and notetaking skills. Available at the Instructor's companion site.

Animated Precalculus

An **Animated Precalculus** tutorial is available at the Student companion site for **Section 8.5.**

Pacing

Average: 2 days
Advanced: 2 days
Block: 1 block

2 FOCUS AND MOTIVATE

Essential Question

How do you use matrices to solve systems of equations, find areas of triangles, and write coded messages? **Tell students that they will learn how to answer this question by studying Cramer's Rule, formulas for using the determinant in geometry, and a technique for using matrix multiplication to code messages.**

8.5 Applications of Matrices and Determinants

What you should learn

- Use Cramer's Rule to solve systems of linear equations.
- Use determinants to find the areas of triangles.
- Use a determinant to test for collinear points and find an equation of a line passing through two points.
- Use matrices to encode and decode messages.

Why you should learn it

You can use Cramer's Rule to solve real-life problems. For instance, in Exercise 69 on page 627, Cramer's Rule is used to find a quadratic model for the per capita consumption of bottled water in the United States.

MAFORD/istockphoto.com

Cramer's Rule

So far, you have studied three methods for solving a system of linear equations: substitution, elimination with equations, and elimination with matrices. In this section, you will study one more method, **Cramer's Rule,** named after Gabriel Cramer (1704–1752). This rule uses determinants to write the solution of a system of linear equations. To see how Cramer's Rule works, take another look at the solution described at the beginning of Section 8.4. There, it was pointed out that the system

$$\begin{cases} a_1x + b_1y = c_1 \\ a_2x + b_2y = c_2 \end{cases}$$

has a solution

$$x = \frac{c_1b_2 - c_2b_1}{a_1b_2 - a_2b_1} \quad \text{and} \quad y = \frac{a_1c_2 - a_2c_1}{a_1b_2 - a_2b_1}$$

provided that $a_1b_2 - a_2b_1 \neq 0$. Each numerator and denominator in this solution can be expressed as a determinant, as follows.

$$x = \frac{c_1b_2 - c_2b_1}{a_1b_2 - a_2b_1} = \frac{\begin{vmatrix} c_1 & b_1 \\ c_2 & b_2 \end{vmatrix}}{\begin{vmatrix} a_1 & b_1 \\ a_2 & b_2 \end{vmatrix}} \qquad y = \frac{a_1c_2 - a_2c_1}{a_1b_2 - a_2b_1} = \frac{\begin{vmatrix} a_1 & c_1 \\ a_2 & c_2 \end{vmatrix}}{\begin{vmatrix} a_1 & b_1 \\ a_2 & b_2 \end{vmatrix}}$$

Relative to the original system, the denominator for x and y is simply the determinant of the *coefficient* matrix of the system. This determinant is denoted by D. The numerators for x and y are denoted by D_x and D_y, respectively. They are formed by using the column of constants as replacements for the coefficients of x and y, as follows.

Coefficient Matrix	D	D_x	D_y
$\begin{bmatrix} a_1 & b_1 \\ a_2 & b_2 \end{bmatrix}$	$\begin{vmatrix} a_1 & b_1 \\ a_2 & b_2 \end{vmatrix}$	$\begin{vmatrix} c_1 & b_1 \\ c_2 & b_2 \end{vmatrix}$	$\begin{vmatrix} a_1 & c_1 \\ a_2 & c_2 \end{vmatrix}$

For example, given the system

$$\begin{cases} 2x - 5y = 3 \\ -4x + 3y = 8 \end{cases}$$

the coefficient matrix, D, D_x, and D_y are as follows.

Coefficient Matrix	D	D_x	D_y
$\begin{bmatrix} 2 & -5 \\ -4 & 3 \end{bmatrix}$	$\begin{vmatrix} 2 & -5 \\ -4 & 3 \end{vmatrix}$	$\begin{vmatrix} 3 & -5 \\ 8 & 3 \end{vmatrix}$	$\begin{vmatrix} 2 & 3 \\ -4 & 8 \end{vmatrix}$

Resource Planning Guide

Chapter Resources
- Complete Solutions Guide

Workbooks
- Notetaking Guide
- Student Solutions Guide

Interactive Technology
- Instructor Success Organizer
- Notetaking Guide IAE
- Instructional DVDs
- Animated Precalculus
- PowerLecture with ExamView

Cramer's Rule generalizes easily to systems of n equations in n variables. The value of each variable is given as the quotient of two determinants. The denominator is the determinant of the coefficient matrix, and the numerator is the determinant of the matrix formed by replacing the column corresponding to the variable (being solved for) with the column representing the constants. For instance, the solution for x_3 in the following system is shown.

$$\begin{cases} a_{11}x_1 + a_{12}x_2 + a_{13}x_3 = b_1 \\ a_{21}x_1 + a_{22}x_2 + a_{23}x_3 = b_2 \\ a_{31}x_1 + a_{32}x_2 + a_{33}x_3 = b_3 \end{cases} \qquad x_3 = \frac{|A_3|}{|A|} = \frac{\begin{vmatrix} a_{11} & a_{12} & b_1 \\ a_{21} & a_{22} & b_2 \\ a_{31} & a_{32} & b_3 \end{vmatrix}}{\begin{vmatrix} a_{11} & a_{12} & a_{13} \\ a_{21} & a_{22} & a_{23} \\ a_{31} & a_{32} & a_{33} \end{vmatrix}}$$

Cramer's Rule

If a system of n linear equations in n variables has a coefficient matrix A with a nonzero determinant $|A|$, the solution of the system is

$$x_1 = \frac{|A_1|}{|A|}, \quad x_2 = \frac{|A_2|}{|A|}, \quad . \ . \ . \ , \quad x_n = \frac{|A_n|}{|A|}$$

where the ith column of A_i is the column of constants in the system of equations. If the determinant of the coefficient matrix is zero, the system has either no solution or infinitely many solutions.

Example 1 Using Cramer's Rule for a 2 × 2 System

Use Cramer's Rule to solve the system of linear equations.

$$\begin{cases} 4x - 2y = 10 \\ 3x - 5y = 11 \end{cases}$$

Solution

To begin, find the determinant of the coefficient matrix.

$$D = \begin{vmatrix} 4 & -2 \\ 3 & -5 \end{vmatrix} = -20 - (-6) = -14$$

Because this determinant is not zero, you can apply Cramer's Rule.

$$x = \frac{D_x}{D} = \frac{\begin{vmatrix} 10 & -2 \\ 11 & -5 \end{vmatrix}}{-14} = \frac{-50 - (-22)}{-14} = \frac{-28}{-14} = 2$$

$$y = \frac{D_y}{D} = \frac{\begin{vmatrix} 4 & 10 \\ 3 & 11 \end{vmatrix}}{-14} = \frac{44 - 30}{-14} = \frac{14}{-14} = -1$$

So, the solution is $x = 2$ and $y = -1$. Check this in the original system.

CHECKPoint Now try Exercise 7.

3 TEACH

Extra Example 1

Use Cramer's Rule to solve the following system of linear equations.

$$\begin{cases} 3x + 4y = 1 \\ 5x + 3y = 9 \end{cases}$$

(3, −2)

Extra Example 2

Use Cramer's Rule to solve the following system of linear equations.

$$\begin{cases} 4x - y + z = 12 \\ 2x + 2y + 3z = 1 \\ 5x - 2y + 6z = 22 \end{cases}$$

(2, −3, 1)

Avoiding Common Errors

When applying Cramer's Rule to linear equations, students should make sure that each equation is expressed with the variables in the correct order and that any missing variable is denoted by a corresponding zero in the matrix.

For example:

the system $\begin{cases} 3x - 5z = 10 \\ 2y - x = 5 \\ y + 6z = 2 \end{cases}$

produces coefficient matrix

$$\begin{bmatrix} 3 & 0 & -5 \\ -1 & 2 & 0 \\ 0 & 1 & 6 \end{bmatrix}.$$

Example 2 Using Cramer's Rule for a 3 × 3 System

Use Cramer's Rule to solve the system of linear equations.

$$\begin{cases} -x + 2y - 3z = 1 \\ 2x + z = 0 \\ 3x - 4y + 4z = 2 \end{cases}$$

Solution

To find the determinant of the coefficient matrix

$$\begin{bmatrix} -1 & 2 & -3 \\ 2 & 0 & 1 \\ 3 & -4 & 4 \end{bmatrix}$$

expand along the second row, as follows.

$$D = 2(-1)^3\begin{vmatrix} 2 & -3 \\ -4 & 4 \end{vmatrix} + 0(-1)^4\begin{vmatrix} -1 & -3 \\ 3 & 4 \end{vmatrix} + 1(-1)^5\begin{vmatrix} -1 & 2 \\ 3 & -4 \end{vmatrix}$$

$$= -2(-4) + 0 - 1(-2)$$

$$= 10$$

Because this determinant is not zero, you can apply Cramer's Rule.

$$x = \frac{D_x}{D} = \frac{\begin{vmatrix} 1 & 2 & -3 \\ 0 & 0 & 1 \\ 2 & -4 & 4 \end{vmatrix}}{10} = \frac{8}{10} = \frac{4}{5}$$

$$y = \frac{D_y}{D} = \frac{\begin{vmatrix} -1 & 1 & -3 \\ 2 & 0 & 1 \\ 3 & 2 & 4 \end{vmatrix}}{10} = \frac{-15}{10} = -\frac{3}{2}$$

$$z = \frac{D_z}{D} = \frac{\begin{vmatrix} -1 & 2 & 1 \\ 2 & 0 & 0 \\ 3 & -4 & 2 \end{vmatrix}}{10} = \frac{-16}{10} = -\frac{8}{5}$$

The solution is $\left(\frac{4}{5}, -\frac{3}{2}, -\frac{8}{5}\right)$. Check this in the original system as follows.

Check

$-\left(\frac{4}{5}\right) + 2\left(-\frac{3}{2}\right) - 3\left(-\frac{8}{5}\right) \stackrel{?}{=} 1$	Substitute into Equation 1.
$-\frac{4}{5} - 3 + \frac{24}{5} = 1$	Equation 1 checks. ✓
$2\left(\frac{4}{5}\right) + \left(-\frac{8}{5}\right) \stackrel{?}{=} 0$	Substitute into Equation 2.
$\frac{8}{5} - \frac{8}{5} = 0$	Equation 2 checks. ✓
$3\left(\frac{4}{5}\right) - 4\left(-\frac{3}{2}\right) + 4\left(-\frac{8}{5}\right) \stackrel{?}{=} 2$	Substitute into Equation 3.
$\frac{12}{5} + 6 - \frac{32}{5} = 2$	Equation 3 checks. ✓

CHECKPoint Now try Exercise 13.

Remember that Cramer's Rule does not apply when the determinant of the coefficient matrix is zero. This would create division by zero, which is undefined.

Area of a Triangle

Another application of matrices and determinants is finding the area of a triangle whose vertices are given as points in a coordinate plane.

> **Area of a Triangle**
>
> The area of a triangle with vertices (x_1, y_1), (x_2, y_2), and (x_3, y_3) is
>
> $$\text{Area} = \pm\frac{1}{2}\begin{vmatrix} x_1 & y_1 & 1 \\ x_2 & y_2 & 1 \\ x_3 & y_3 & 1 \end{vmatrix}$$
>
> where the symbol $\pm$ indicates that the appropriate sign should be chosen to yield a positive area.

Example 3 Finding the Area of a Triangle

Find the area of a triangle whose vertices are $(1, 0)$, $(2, 2)$, and $(4, 3)$, as shown in Figure 8.1.

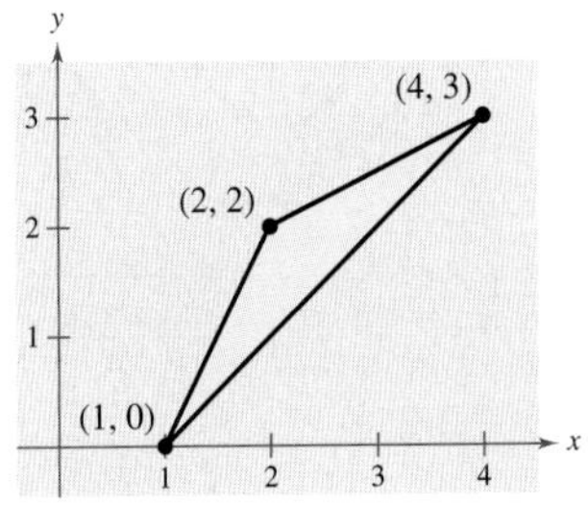

FIGURE 8.1

Solution

Let $(x_1, y_1) = (1, 0)$, $(x_2, y_2) = (2, 2)$, and $(x_3, y_3) = (4, 3)$. Then, to find the area of the triangle, evaluate the determinant.

$$\begin{vmatrix} x_1 & y_1 & 1 \\ x_2 & y_2 & 1 \\ x_3 & y_3 & 1 \end{vmatrix} = \begin{vmatrix} 1 & 0 & 1 \\ 2 & 2 & 1 \\ 4 & 3 & 1 \end{vmatrix}$$

$$= 1(-1)^2\begin{vmatrix} 2 & 1 \\ 3 & 1 \end{vmatrix} + 0(-1)^3\begin{vmatrix} 2 & 1 \\ 4 & 1 \end{vmatrix} + 1(-1)^4\begin{vmatrix} 2 & 2 \\ 4 & 3 \end{vmatrix}$$

$$= 1(-1) + 0 + 1(-2)$$

$$= -3.$$

Using this value, you can conclude that the area of the triangle is

$$\text{Area} = -\frac{1}{2}\begin{vmatrix} 1 & 0 & 1 \\ 2 & 2 & 1 \\ 4 & 3 & 1 \end{vmatrix} \qquad \text{Choose } (-) \text{ so that the area is positive.}$$

$$= -\frac{1}{2}(-3)$$

$$= \frac{3}{2} \text{ square units.}$$

CHECKPoint Now try Exercise 25.

Extra Example 3

Find the area of a triangle whose vertices are (0, 0), (4, 1), and (2, 5).

9 square units

Extra Example 4

Determine whether the points (3, −1), (0, −3), and (9, 3) are collinear.

The points are collinear.

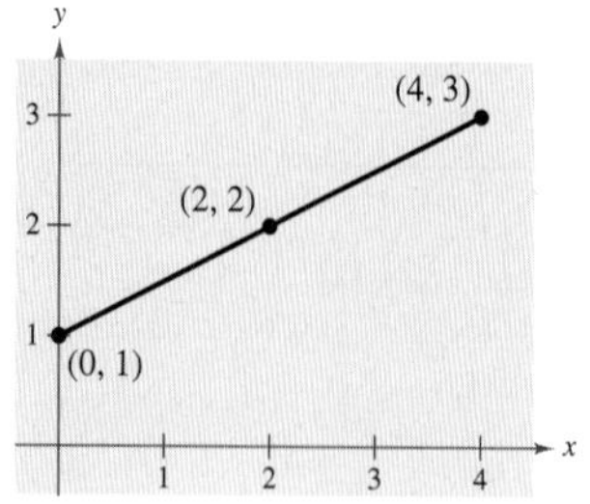

FIGURE 8.2

Lines in a Plane

What if the three points in Example 3 had been on the same line? What would have happened had the area formula been applied to three such points? The answer is that the determinant would have been zero. Consider, for instance, the three collinear points (0, 1), (2, 2), and (4, 3), as shown in Figure 8.2. The area of the "triangle" that has these three points as vertices is

$$\frac{1}{2}\begin{vmatrix} 0 & 1 & 1 \\ 2 & 2 & 1 \\ 4 & 3 & 1 \end{vmatrix} = \frac{1}{2}\left[0(-1)^2\begin{vmatrix} 2 & 1 \\ 3 & 1 \end{vmatrix} + 1(-1)^3\begin{vmatrix} 2 & 1 \\ 4 & 1 \end{vmatrix} + 1(-1)^4\begin{vmatrix} 2 & 2 \\ 4 & 3 \end{vmatrix}\right]$$

$$= \frac{1}{2}[0 - 1(-2) + 1(-2)]$$

$$= 0.$$

The result is generalized as follows.

Test for Collinear Points

Three points (x_1, y_1), (x_2, y_2), and (x_3, y_3) are **collinear** (lie on the same line) if and only if

$$\begin{vmatrix} x_1 & y_1 & 1 \\ x_2 & y_2 & 1 \\ x_3 & y_3 & 1 \end{vmatrix} = 0.$$

Example 4 Testing for Collinear Points

Determine whether the points (−2, −2), (1, 1), and (7, 5) are collinear. (See Figure 8.3.)

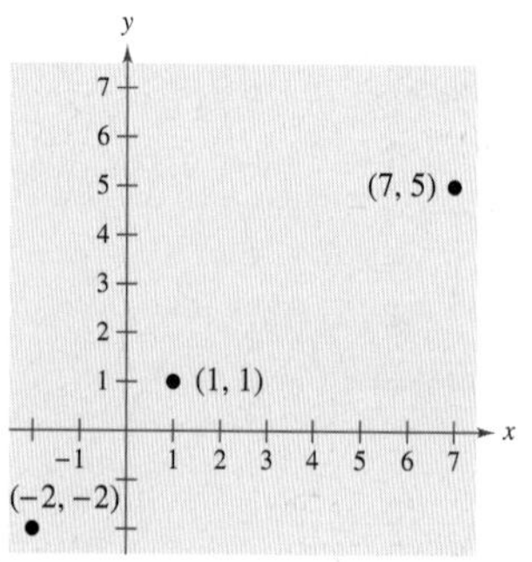

FIGURE 8.3

Solution

Letting $(x_1, y_1) = (-2, -2)$, $(x_2, y_2) = (1, 1)$, and $(x_3, y_3) = (7, 5)$, you have

$$\begin{vmatrix} x_1 & y_1 & 1 \\ x_2 & y_2 & 1 \\ x_3 & y_3 & 1 \end{vmatrix} = \begin{vmatrix} -2 & -2 & 1 \\ 1 & 1 & 1 \\ 7 & 5 & 1 \end{vmatrix}$$

$$= -2(-1)^2\begin{vmatrix} 1 & 1 \\ 5 & 1 \end{vmatrix} + (-2)(-1)^3\begin{vmatrix} 1 & 1 \\ 7 & 1 \end{vmatrix} + 1(-1)^4\begin{vmatrix} 1 & 1 \\ 7 & 5 \end{vmatrix}$$

$$= -2(-4) + 2(-6) + 1(-2)$$

$$= -6.$$

Because the value of this determinant is *not* zero, you can conclude that the three points do not lie on the same line. Moreover, the area of the triangle with vertices at these points is $\left(-\frac{1}{2}\right)(-6) = 3$ square units.

CHECKPoint Now try Exercise 39.

The test for collinear points can be adapted to another use. That is, if you are given two points on a rectangular coordinate system, you can find an equation of the line passing through the two points, as follows.

Two-Point Form of the Equation of a Line

An equation of the line passing through the distinct points (x_1, y_1) and (x_2, y_2) is given by

$$\begin{vmatrix} x & y & 1 \\ x_1 & y_1 & 1 \\ x_2 & y_2 & 1 \end{vmatrix} = 0.$$

Example 5 Finding an Equation of a Line

Find an equation of the line passing through the two points $(2, 4)$ and $(-1, 3)$, as shown in Figure 8.4.

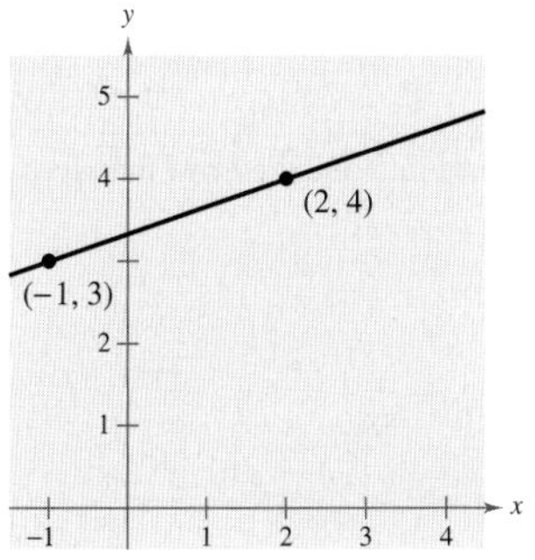

FIGURE 8.4

Solution

Let $(x_1, y_1) = (2, 4)$ and $(x_2, y_2) = (-1, 3)$. Applying the determinant formula for the equation of a line produces

$$\begin{vmatrix} x & y & 1 \\ 2 & 4 & 1 \\ -1 & 3 & 1 \end{vmatrix} = 0.$$

To evaluate this determinant, you can expand by cofactors along the first row to obtain the following.

$$x(-1)^2\begin{vmatrix} 4 & 1 \\ 3 & 1 \end{vmatrix} + y(-1)^3\begin{vmatrix} 2 & 1 \\ -1 & 1 \end{vmatrix} + 1(-1)^4\begin{vmatrix} 2 & 4 \\ -1 & 3 \end{vmatrix} = 0$$

$$x(1)(1) + y(-1)(3) + (1)(1)(10) = 0$$

$$x - 3y + 10 = 0$$

So, an equation of the line is

$$x - 3y + 10 = 0.$$

CHECKPoint Now try Exercise 47.

Note that this method of finding the equation of a line works for all lines, including horizontal and vertical lines. For instance, the equation of the vertical line through $(2, 0)$ and $(2, 2)$ is

$$\begin{vmatrix} x & y & 1 \\ 2 & 0 & 1 \\ 2 & 2 & 1 \end{vmatrix} = 0$$

$$4 - 2x = 0$$

$$x = 2.$$

Extra Example 5

Find an equation of the line passing through the two points (0, 0) and (4, 5).

$5x - 4y = 0$

Extra Example 6

Write the uncoded row matrices of order 1×3 for the message

LANDING SUCCESSFUL.

$[12\ \ 1\ \ 14]\ [4\ \ 9\ \ 14]\ [7\ \ 0\ \ 19]$

$[21\ \ 3\ \ 3]\ [5\ \ 19\ \ 19]\ [6\ \ 21\ \ 12]$

Cryptography

A **cryptogram** is a message written according to a secret code. (The Greek word *kryptos* means "hidden.") Matrix multiplication can be used to encode and decode messages. To begin, you need to assign a number to each letter in the alphabet (with 0 assigned to a blank space), as follows.

0 = _	9 = I	18 = R
1 = A	10 = J	19 = S
2 = B	11 = K	20 = T
3 = C	12 = L	21 = U
4 = D	13 = M	22 = V
5 = E	14 = N	23 = W
6 = F	15 = O	24 = X
7 = G	16 = P	25 = Y
8 = H	17 = Q	26 = Z

Then the message is converted to numbers and partitioned into **uncoded row matrices,** each having n entries, as demonstrated in Example 6.

Example 6 Forming Uncoded Row Matrices

Write the uncoded row matrices of order 1×3 for the message

MEET ME MONDAY.

Solution

Partitioning the message (including blank spaces, but ignoring punctuation) into groups of three produces the following uncoded row matrices.

[13 5 5]	[20 0 13]	[5 0 13]	[15 14 4]	[1 25 0]
M E E	T _ M	E _ M	O N D	A Y _

Note that a blank space is used to fill out the last uncoded row matrix.

CHECK*Point* Now try Exercise 55(a).

To encode a message, use the techniques demonstrated in Section 8.3 to choose an $n \times n$ invertible matrix such as

$$A = \begin{bmatrix} 1 & -2 & 2 \\ -1 & 1 & 3 \\ 1 & -1 & -4 \end{bmatrix}$$

and multiply the uncoded row matrices by A (on the right) to obtain **coded row matrices.** Here is an example.

Uncoded Matrix *Encoding Matrix A* *Coded Matrix*

$$[13 \quad 5 \quad 5] \begin{bmatrix} 1 & -2 & 2 \\ -1 & 1 & 3 \\ 1 & -1 & -4 \end{bmatrix} = [13 \quad -26 \quad 21]$$

Example 7 Encoding a Message

Use the following invertible matrix to encode the message MEET ME MONDAY.

$$A = \begin{bmatrix} 1 & -2 & 2 \\ -1 & 1 & 3 \\ 1 & -1 & -4 \end{bmatrix}$$

Solution

The coded row matrices are obtained by multiplying each of the uncoded row matrices found in Example 6 by the matrix A, as follows.

Uncoded Matrix *Encoding Matrix A* *Coded Matrix*

$$[13 \quad 5 \quad 5] \begin{bmatrix} 1 & -2 & 2 \\ -1 & 1 & 3 \\ 1 & -1 & -4 \end{bmatrix} = [13 \quad -26 \quad 21]$$

$$[20 \quad 0 \quad 13] \begin{bmatrix} 1 & -2 & 2 \\ -1 & 1 & 3 \\ 1 & -1 & -4 \end{bmatrix} = [33 \quad -53 \quad -12]$$

$$[5 \quad 0 \quad 13] \begin{bmatrix} 1 & -2 & 2 \\ -1 & 1 & 3 \\ 1 & -1 & -4 \end{bmatrix} = [18 \quad -23 \quad -42]$$

$$[15 \quad 14 \quad 4] \begin{bmatrix} 1 & -2 & 2 \\ -1 & 1 & 3 \\ 1 & -1 & -4 \end{bmatrix} = [5 \quad -20 \quad 56]$$

$$[1 \quad 25 \quad 0] \begin{bmatrix} 1 & -2 & 2 \\ -1 & 1 & 3 \\ 1 & -1 & -4 \end{bmatrix} = [-24 \quad 23 \quad 77]$$

So, the sequence of coded row matrices is

$$[13 \ -26 \ 21][33 \ -53 \ -12][18 \ -23 \ -42][5 \ -20 \ 56][-24 \ 23 \ 77].$$

Finally, removing the matrix notation produces the following cryptogram.

13 −26 21 33 −53 −12 18 −23 −42 5 −20 56 −24 23 77

CHECKPoint Now try Exercise 55(b).

For those who do not know the encoding matrix A, decoding the cryptogram found in Example 7 is difficult. But for an authorized receiver who knows the encoding matrix A, decoding is simple. The receiver just needs to multiply the coded row matrices by A^{-1} (on the right) to retrieve the uncoded row matrices. Here is an example.

$$\underbrace{[13 \quad -26 \quad 21]}_{\text{Coded}} \underbrace{\begin{bmatrix} -1 & -10 & -8 \\ -1 & -6 & -5 \\ 0 & -1 & -1 \end{bmatrix}}_{A^{-1}} = \underbrace{[13 \quad 5 \quad 5]}_{\text{Uncoded}}$$

Extra Example 7

Use the following matrix to encode the message LANDING SUCCESSFUL.

$$A = \begin{bmatrix} 1 & 2 & 2 \\ 3 & 7 & 9 \\ -1 & -4 & -7 \end{bmatrix}$$

Use the uncoded row matrices from Extra Example 6.

1 −25 −65 17 15 −9
−12 −62 −119 27 51 48
43 67 48 57 111 117

Extra Example 8

Use the inverse of the matrix

$$A = \begin{bmatrix} 1 & 2 & 2 \\ 3 & 7 & 9 \\ -1 & -4 & -7 \end{bmatrix}$$ to decode

the cryptogram: 42 88 101 88 201 251 30 33 0 26 56 64.

ENEMY FOUND

Closing the Lesson

Have students summarize the major points of the lesson and answer the Essential Question: How do you use matrices to solve systems of equations, find areas of triangles, and write coded messages?

- **Use Cramer's Rule to find the solution of a system of equations.**
- **Use a determinant to test whether three points in a coordinate plane are collinear and, if not, to find the area of the triangle they form.**
- **Use matrix multiplication to encode and decode a numerical message, given an invertible encoding matrix.**

HISTORICAL NOTE

Bettmann/Corbis

During World War II, Navajo soldiers created a code using their native language to send messages between battalions. Native words were assigned to represent characters in the English alphabet, and they created a number of expressions for important military terms, such as *iron-fish* to mean *submarine*. Without the Navajo Code Talkers, the Second World War might have had a very different outcome.

Example 8 Decoding a Message

Use the inverse of the matrix

$$A = \begin{bmatrix} 1 & -2 & 2 \\ -1 & 1 & 3 \\ 1 & -1 & -4 \end{bmatrix}$$

to decode the cryptogram

13 −26 21 33 −53 −12 18 −23 −42 5 −20 56 −24 23 77.

Solution

First find A^{-1} by using the techniques demonstrated in Section 8.3. A^{-1} is the decoding matrix. Then partition the message into groups of three to form the coded row matrices. Finally, multiply each coded row matrix by A^{-1} (on the right).

Coded Matrix *Decoding Matrix* A^{-1} *Decoded Matrix*

$$[13 \quad -26 \quad 21] \begin{bmatrix} -1 & -10 & -8 \\ -1 & -6 & -5 \\ 0 & -1 & -1 \end{bmatrix} = [13 \quad 5 \quad 5]$$

$$[33 \quad -53 \quad -12] \begin{bmatrix} -1 & -10 & -8 \\ -1 & -6 & -5 \\ 0 & -1 & -1 \end{bmatrix} = [20 \quad 0 \quad 13]$$

$$[18 \quad -23 \quad -42] \begin{bmatrix} -1 & -10 & -8 \\ -1 & -6 & -5 \\ 0 & -1 & -1 \end{bmatrix} = [5 \quad 0 \quad 13]$$

$$[5 \quad -20 \quad 56] \begin{bmatrix} -1 & -10 & -8 \\ -1 & -6 & -5 \\ 0 & -1 & -1 \end{bmatrix} = [15 \quad 14 \quad 4]$$

$$[-24 \quad 23 \quad 77] \begin{bmatrix} -1 & -10 & -8 \\ -1 & -6 & -5 \\ 0 & -1 & -1 \end{bmatrix} = [1 \quad 25 \quad 0]$$

So, the message is as follows.

[13	5	5]	[20	0	13]	[5	0	13]	[15	14	4]	[1	25	0]
M	E	E	T	_	M	E	_	M	O	N	D	A	Y	_

CHECKPoint Now try Exercise 63.

CLASSROOM DISCUSSION

Cryptography Use your school's library, the Internet, or some other reference source to research information about another type of cryptography. Write a short paragraph describing how mathematics is used to code and decode messages.

Answers will vary.

8.5 EXERCISES

See www.CalcChat.com for worked-out solutions to odd-numbered exercises.

VOCABULARY: Fill in the blanks.

1. The method of using determinants to solve a system of linear equations is called Cramer's Rule.
2. Three points are collinear if the points lie on the same line.
3. The area A of a triangle with vertices (x_1, y_1), (x_2, y_2), and (x_3, y_3) is given by ______. $A = \pm\frac{1}{2}\begin{vmatrix} x_1 & y_1 & 1 \\ x_2 & y_2 & 1 \\ x_3 & y_3 & 1 \end{vmatrix}$
4. A message written according to a secret code is called a cryptogram.
5. To encode a message, choose an invertible matrix A and multiply the uncoded row matrices by A (on the right) to obtain coded row matrices.
6. If a message is encoded using an invertible matrix A, then the message can be decoded by multiplying the coded row matrices by A^{-1} (on the right).

SKILLS AND APPLICATIONS

In Exercises 7–16, use Cramer's Rule to solve (if possible) the system of equations. 7–16. See margin.

7. $\begin{cases} -7x + 11y = -1 \\ 3x - 9y = 9 \end{cases}$
8. $\begin{cases} 4x - 3y = -10 \\ 6x + 9y = 12 \end{cases}$
9. $\begin{cases} 3x + 2y = -2 \\ 6x + 4y = 4 \end{cases}$
10. $\begin{cases} 6x - 5y = 17 \\ -13x + 3y = -76 \end{cases}$
11. $\begin{cases} -0.4x + 0.8y = 1.6 \\ 0.2x + 0.3y = 2.2 \end{cases}$
12. $\begin{cases} 2.4x - 1.3y = 14.63 \\ -4.6x + 0.5y = -11.51 \end{cases}$
13. $\begin{cases} 4x - y + z = -5 \\ 2x + 2y + 3z = 10 \\ 5x - 2y + 6z = 1 \end{cases}$
14. $\begin{cases} 4x - 2y + 3z = -2 \\ 2x + 2y + 5z = 16 \\ 8x - 5y - 2z = 4 \end{cases}$
15. $\begin{cases} x + 2y + 3z = -3 \\ -2x + y - z = 6 \\ 3x - 3y + 2z = -11 \end{cases}$
16. $\begin{cases} 5x - 4y + z = -14 \\ -x + 2y - 2z = 10 \\ 3x + y + z = 1 \end{cases}$

In Exercises 17–20, use a graphing utility and Cramer's Rule to solve (if possible) the system of equations. 17–20. See margin.

17. $\begin{cases} 3x + 3y + 5z = 1 \\ 3x + 5y + 9z = 2 \\ 5x + 9y + 17z = 4 \end{cases}$
18. $\begin{cases} x + 2y - z = -7 \\ 2x - 2y - 2z = -8 \\ -x + 3y + 4z = 8 \end{cases}$
19. $\begin{cases} 2x - y + z = 5 \\ x - 2y - z = 1 \\ 3x + y + z = 4 \end{cases}$
20. $\begin{cases} 3x - y - 3z = 1 \\ 2x + y + 2z = -4 \\ x + y - z = 5 \end{cases}$

In Exercises 21–32, use a determinant and the given vertices of a triangle to find the area of the triangle.

21. 7

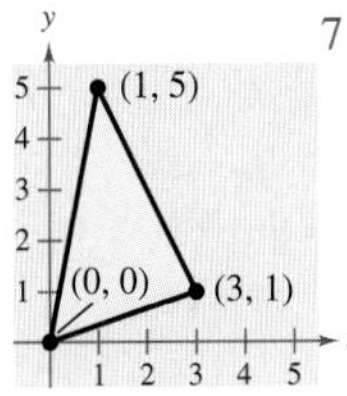

22. $\frac{33}{2}$

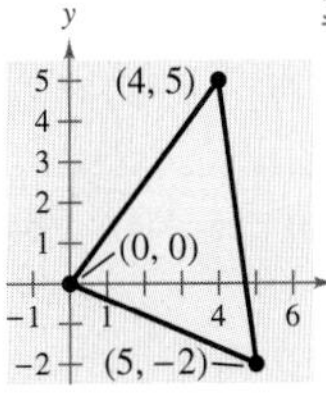

23. 14

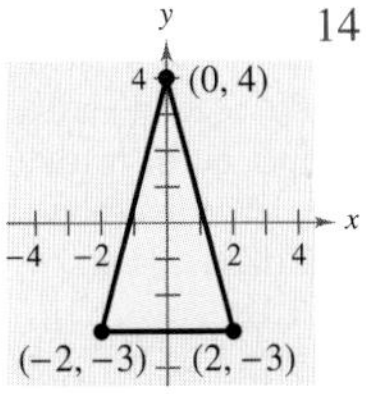

24. $\frac{31}{2}$

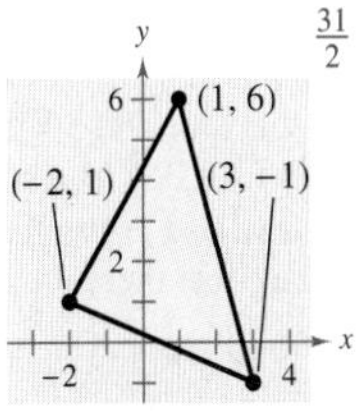

25. $\frac{33}{8}$

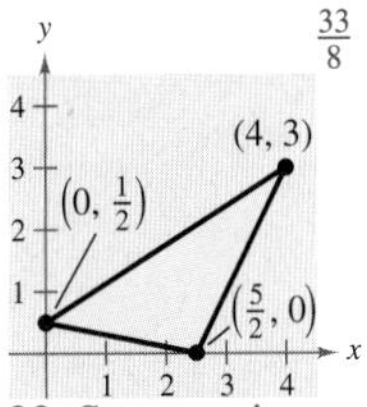

26. 55

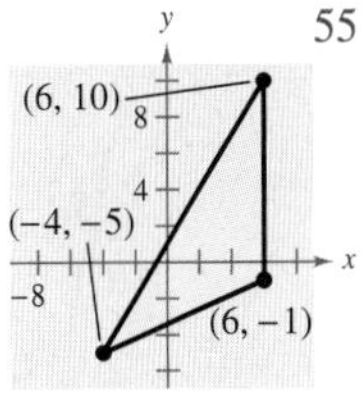

27–32. See margin.

27. $(-2, 4), (2, 3), (-1, 5)$
28. $(0, -2), (-1, 4), (3, 5)$
29. $(-3, 5), (2, 6), (3, -5)$
30. $(-2, 4), (1, 5), (3, -2)$
31. $(-4, 2), (0, \frac{7}{2}), (3, -\frac{1}{2})$
32. $(\frac{9}{2}, 0), (2, 6), (0, -\frac{3}{2})$

In Exercises 33 and 34, find a value of y such that the triangle with the given vertices has an area of 4 square units.

33. $(-5, 1), (0, 2), (-2, y)$ $y = \frac{16}{5}$ or $y = 0$
34. $(-4, 2), (-3, 5), (-1, y)$ $y = 19$ or $y = 3$

In Exercises 35 and 36, find a value of y such that the triangle with the given vertices has an area of 6 square units.

35. $(-2, -3), (1, -1), (-8, y)$ $y = -3$ or $y = -11$
36. $(1, 0), (5, -3), (-3, y)$ $y = 6$ or $y = 0$

37. **AREA OF A REGION** A large region of forest has been infested with gypsy moths. The region is roughly triangular, as shown in the figure on the next page. From the northernmost vertex A of the region, the distances to the other vertices are 25 miles south and 10 miles east (for vertex B), and 20 miles south and 28 miles east (for vertex C). Use a graphing utility to approximate the number of square miles in this region. 250 mi²

4 PRACTICE AND APPLY

Assignment Guide

Transparencies Available
Available at the Instructor's companion site.

Average:
Day 1: pp. 625–626
Exs. 1–3, 9, 11, 15, 17, 21, 23, 27–37 odd, 41–45 odd, 49, 51
Day 2: pp. 625–627
Exs. 4–6, 56, 58, 59, 61, 62, 65, 67, 71–74, 76

Advanced:
Day 1: pp. 625–626
Exs. 1–3, 8, 14–18 even, 22, 24, 28–38 even, 42–46 even, 50, 52
Day 2: pp. 625–627
Exs. 4–6, 56, 59, 60–68 even, 69, 71–74, 76

Block:
pp. 625–627
Exs. 1–6, 9, 11, 15, 17, 21, 23, 27–37 odd, 41–45 odd, 49, 51, 56, 58, 59, 61, 62, 65, 67, 71–74, 76

7. $(-3, -2)$
8. $(-1, 2)$
9. Not possible
10. $(7, 5)$
11. $(\frac{32}{7}, \frac{30}{7})$
12. $(\frac{8}{5}, -\frac{83}{10})$
13. $(-1, 3, 2)$
14. $(5, 8, -2)$
15. $(-2, 1, -1)$
16. $(0, 3, -2)$
17. $(0, -\frac{1}{2}, \frac{1}{2})$
18. $(-3, -1, 2)$
19. $(1, -1, 2)$
20. $(-\frac{9}{8}, \frac{7}{2}, -\frac{21}{8})$
27. $\frac{5}{2}$ 28. $\frac{25}{2}$
29. 28 30. $\frac{23}{2}$
31. $\frac{41}{4}$ 32. $\frac{123}{8}$

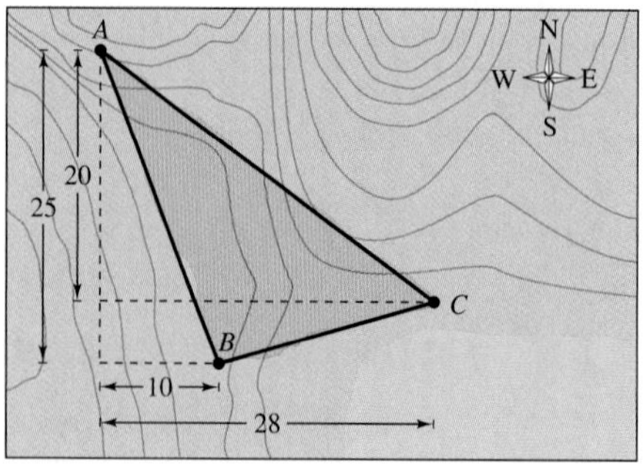

FIGURE FOR 37

38. AREA OF A REGION You own a triangular tract of land, as shown in the figure. To estimate the number of square feet in the tract, you start at one vertex, walk 65 feet east and 50 feet north to the second vertex, and then walk 85 feet west and 30 feet north to the third vertex. Use a graphing utility to determine how many square feet there are in the tract of land. 3100 ft^2

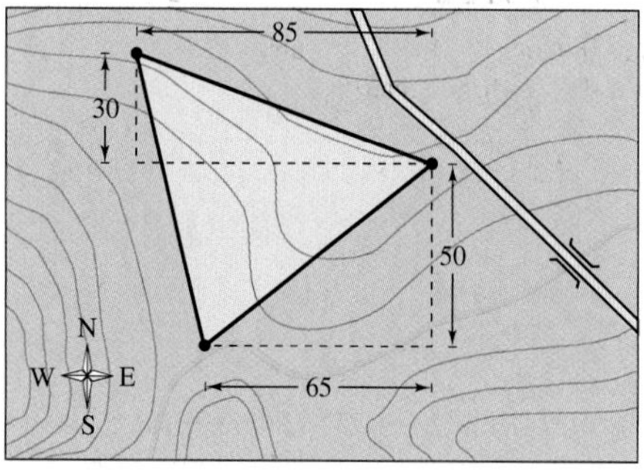

In Exercises 39–44, use a determinant to determine whether the points are collinear. 39–44. See margin.

39. $(3, -1), (0, -3), (12, 5)$ **40.** $(3, -5), (6, 1), (4, 2)$

41. $\left(2, -\frac{1}{2}\right), (-4, 4), (6, -3)$ **42.** $\left(0, \frac{1}{2}\right), (2, -1), \left(-4, \frac{7}{2}\right)$

43. $(0, 2), (1, 2.4), (-1, 1.6)$ **44.** $(2, 3), (3, 3.5), (-1, 2)$

In Exercises 45 and 46, find y such that the points are collinear.

45. $(2, -5), (4, y), (5, -2)$ $y = -3$ **46.** $(-6, 2), (-5, y), (-3, 5)$ $y = 3$

In Exercises 47–52, use a determinant to find an equation of the line passing through the points. 47–52. See margin.

47. $(0, 0), (5, 3)$ **48.** $(0, 0), (-2, 2)$

49. $(-4, 3), (2, 1)$ **50.** $(10, 7), (-2, -7)$

51. $\left(-\frac{1}{2}, 3\right), \left(\frac{5}{2}, 1\right)$ **52.** $\left(\frac{2}{3}, 4\right), (6, 12)$

In Exercises 53 and 54, (a) write the uncoded 1×2 row matrices for the message. (b) Then encode the message using the encoding matrix. 53–54. See margin.

Message	*Encoding Matrix*
53. COME HOME SOON	$\begin{bmatrix} 1 & 2 \\ 3 & 5 \end{bmatrix}$
54. HELP IS ON THE WAY	$\begin{bmatrix} -2 & 3 \\ -1 & 1 \end{bmatrix}$

In Exercises 55 and 56, (a) write the uncoded 1×3 row matrices for the message. (b) Then encode the message using the encoding matrix. 55–56. See margin.

Message	*Encoding Matrix*
55. CALL ME TOMORROW	$\begin{bmatrix} 1 & -1 & 0 \\ 1 & 0 & -1 \\ -6 & 2 & 3 \end{bmatrix}$
56. PLEASE SEND MONEY	$\begin{bmatrix} 4 & 2 & 1 \\ -3 & -3 & -1 \\ 3 & 2 & 1 \end{bmatrix}$

In Exercises 57–60, write a cryptogram for the message using the matrix A. 57–60. See margin.

$$A = \begin{bmatrix} 1 & 2 & 2 \\ 3 & 7 & 9 \\ -1 & -4 & -7 \end{bmatrix}$$

57. LANDING SUCCESSFUL

58. ICEBERG DEAD AHEAD

59. HAPPY BIRTHDAY

60. OPERATION OVERLOAD

In Exercises 61–64, use A^{-1} to decode the cryptogram.

61. $A = \begin{bmatrix} 1 & 2 \\ 3 & 5 \end{bmatrix}$ HAPPY NEW YEAR

11 21 64 112 25 50 29 53 23 46
40 75 55 92

62. $A = \begin{bmatrix} 2 & 3 \\ 3 & 4 \end{bmatrix}$ TO BE OR NOT TO BE

85 120 6 8 10 15 84 117 42 56 90
125 60 80 30 45 19 26

63. $A = \begin{bmatrix} 1 & -1 & 0 \\ 1 & 0 & -1 \\ -6 & 2 & 3 \end{bmatrix}$ CLASS IS CANCELED

9 −1 −9 38 −19 −19 28 −9 −19
−80 25 41 −64 21 31 9 −5 −4

39. Collinear
40. Not collinear
41. Not collinear
42. Collinear
43. Collinear
44. Not collinear
47. $3x - 5y = 0$
48. $x + y = 0$
49. $x + 3y - 5 = 0$
50. $7x - 6y - 28 = 0$
51. $2x + 3y - 8 = 0$
52. $3x - 2y + 6 = 0$
53. (a) Uncoded: [3 15], [13 5], [0 8], [15 13], [5 0], [19 15], [15 14]
(b) Encoded: 48 81 28 51 24 40 54 95 5 10 64 113 57 100
54. (a) Uncoded: [8 5], [12 16], [0 9], [19 0], [15 14], [0 20], [8 5], [0 23], [1 25]
(b) Encoded:
−21 29 −40 52
−9 9 −38 57
−44 59 −20 20
−21 29 −23
23 −27 28
55. (a) Uncoded: [3 1 12], [12 0 13], [5 0 20], [15 13 15], [18 18 15], [23 0 0]
(b) Encoded: −68 21 35
−66 14 39 −115
35 60 −62 15
32 −54 12 27
23 −23 0
56. (a) Uncoded: [16 12 5], [1 19 5], [0 19 5], [14 4 0], [13 15 14], [5 25 0]
(b) Encoded: 43 6 9 −38
−45 −13 −42 −47
−14 44 16 10 49 9
12 −55 −65 −20
57. 1 −25 −65 17 15
−9 −12 −62 −119
27 51 48 43 67
48 57 111 117
58. 13 19 10 −1 −33
−77 3 −2 −14
4 1 −9 −5 −25
−47 4 1 −9
59. −5 −41 −87 91
207 257 11 −5
−41 40 80
84 76 177 227
60. 58 122 139 1 −37 −95 40 67 55 23 17
−19 47 88 88 14 21 11

64. $A = \begin{bmatrix} 3 & -4 & 2 \\ 0 & 2 & 1 \\ 4 & -5 & 3 \end{bmatrix}$ HAVE A GREAT WEEKEND

112 −140 83 19 −25 13 72 −76 61 95
−118 71 20 21 38 35 −23 36 42 −48 32

In Exercises 65 and 66, decode the cryptogram by using the inverse of the matrix A.

$$A = \begin{bmatrix} 1 & 2 & 2 \\ 3 & 7 & 9 \\ -1 & -4 & -7 \end{bmatrix}$$

65. 20 17 −15 −12 −56 −104 1 −25 −65
62 143 181 SEND PLANES

66. 13 −9 −59 61 112 106 −17 −73 −131 11
24 29 65 144 172 RETURN AT DAWN

67. The following cryptogram was encoded with a 2×2 matrix.

8 21 −15 −10 −13 −13 5 10 5 25 5 19
−1 6 20 40 −18 −18 1 16

The last word of the message is _RON. What is the message? MEET ME TONIGHT RON

68. The following cryptogram was encoded with a 2×2 matrix.

5 2 25 11 −2 −7 −15 −15 32 14 −8
−13 38 19 −19 −19 37 16

The last word of the message is _SUE. What is the message? CANCEL ORDERS SUE

69. DATA ANALYSIS: BOTTLED WATER The table shows the per capita consumption of bottled water y (in gallons) in the United States from 2000 through 2007. (Source: Economic Research Service, U.S. Department of Agriculture) See margin.

Year	Consumption, y
2000	16.7
2001	18.2
2002	20.1
2003	21.6
2004	23.2
2005	25.5
2006	27.7
2007	29.1

(a) Use the technique demonstrated in Exercises 77–80 in Section 7.3 to create a system of linear equations for the data. Let t represent the year, with $t = 0$ corresponding to 2000.

(b) Use Cramer's Rule to solve the system from part (a) and find the least squares regression parabola $y = at^2 + bt + c$.

(c) Use a graphing utility to graph the parabola from part (b).

(d) Use the graph from part (c) to estimate when the per capita consumption of bottled water will exceed 35 gallons.

70. HAIR PRODUCTS A hair product company sells three types of hair products for \$30, \$20, and \$10 per unit. In one year, the total revenue for the three products was \$800,000, which corresponded to the sale of 40,000 units. The company sold half as many units of the \$30 product as units of the \$20 product. Use Cramer's Rule to solve a system of linear equations to find how many units of each product were sold. 10,000 units at \$30, 20,000 units at \$20, 10,000 units at \$10

EXPLORATION

71–74. See margin.

TRUE OR FALSE? In Exercises 71–74, determine whether the statement is true or false. Justify your answer.

71. In Cramer's Rule, the numerator is the determinant of the coefficient matrix.

72. You cannot use Cramer's Rule when solving a system of linear equations if the determinant of the coefficient matrix is zero.

73. In a system of linear equations, if the determinant of the coefficient matrix is zero, the system has no solution.

74. The points $(-5, -13)$, $(0, 2)$, and $(3, 11)$ are collinear.

75. WRITING Use your school's library, the Internet, or some other reference source to research a few current real-life uses of cryptography. Write a short summary of these uses. Include a description of how messages are encoded and decoded in each case. Answers will vary.

76. CAPSTONE

(a) State Cramer's Rule for solving a system of linear equations. See margin.

(b) At this point in the text, you have learned several methods for solving systems of linear equations. Briefly describe which method(s) you find easiest to use and which method(s) you find most difficult to use. Answers will vary.

77. Use determinants to find the area of a triangle with vertices $(3, -1)$, $(7, -1)$, and $(7, 5)$. Confirm your answer by plotting the points in a coordinate plane and using the formula

Area $= \frac{1}{2}$(base)(height). 12

5 ASSESS AND RETEACH

Daily Homework Quiz

Transparency Available
Available at the Instructor's companion site.

69. See below.

71. False. The denominator is the determinant of the coefficient matrix.

72. True. If the determinant of the coefficient matrix is zero, then the solution of the system would result in division by zero, which is undefined.

73. False. If the determinant of the coefficient matrix is zero, the system has either no solution or infinitely many solutions.

74. True. $\begin{vmatrix} -5 & -13 & 1 \\ 0 & 2 & 1 \\ 3 & 11 & 1 \end{vmatrix} = 0$

69. (a) $\begin{cases} 8c + 28b + 140a = 182.1 \\ 28c + 140b + 784a = 713.4 \\ 140c + 784b + 4676a = 3724.8 \end{cases}$

(b) $y = 0.034t^2 + 1.57t + 16.66$

(c)

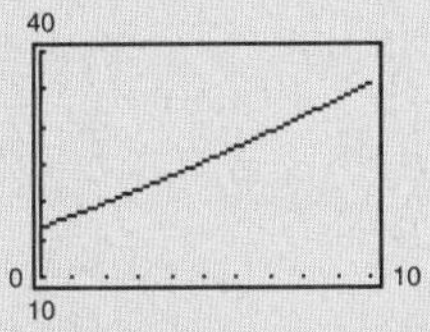

(d) 2009

76. (a) If a system of n linear equations in n variables has a coefficient matrix A with a nonzero determinant $|A|$, the solution of the system is

$$x_1 = \frac{|A_1|}{|A|},\ x_2 = \frac{|A_2|}{|A|}, \ldots, x_n = \frac{|A_n|}{|A|}$$

where the ith column of A_i is the column of constants in the system of equations. If the determinant of the coefficient matrix is zero, the system has either no solution or infinitely many solutions.

8 Chapter Summary

	What Did You Learn?	Explanation/Examples	Review Exercises
Section 8.1	Write matrices and identify their orders *(p. 570)*.	$\begin{bmatrix} -1 & 1 \\ 4 & 7 \end{bmatrix}$ 2×2; $\begin{bmatrix} -2 & 3 & 0 \end{bmatrix}$ 1×3; $\begin{bmatrix} 4 & -3 \\ 5 & 0 \\ -2 & 1 \end{bmatrix}$ 3×2; $\begin{bmatrix} 8 \\ -8 \end{bmatrix}$ 2×1	1–8
	Perform elementary row operations on matrices *(p. 572)*.	**Elementary Row Operations** **1.** Interchange two rows. **2.** Multiply a row by a nonzero constant. **3.** Add a multiple of a row to another row.	9, 10
	Use matrices and Gaussian elimination to solve systems of linear equations *(p. 575)*.	**Gaussian Elimination with Back-Substitution** **1.** Write the augmented matrix of the system of linear equations. **2.** Use elementary row operations to rewrite the augmented matrix in row-echelon form. **3.** Write the system of linear equations corresponding to the matrix in row-echelon form, and use back-substitution to find the solution.	11–28
	Use matrices and Gauss-Jordan elimination to solve systems of linear equations *(p. 577)*.	Gauss-Jordan elimination continues the reduction process on a matrix in row-echelon form until a *reduced* row-echelon form is obtained. (See Example 8.)	29–36
Section 8.2	Decide whether two matrices are equal *(p. 584)*.	Two matrices are equal if their corresponding entries are equal.	37–40
	Add and subtract matrices and multiply matrices by scalars *(p. 585)*.	**Definition of Matrix Addition** If $A = [a_{ij}]$ and $B = [b_{ij}]$ are matrices of order $m \times n$, their sum is the $m \times n$ matrix given by $A + B = [a_{ij} + b_{ij}]$. **Definition of Scalar Multiplication** If $A = [a_{ij}]$ is an $m \times n$ matrix and c is a scalar, the scalar multiple of A by c is the $m \times n$ matrix given by $cA = [c_{ij}]$	41–54
	Multiply two matrices *(p. 589)*.	**Matrix Multiplication** If $A = [a_{ij}]$ is an $m \times n$ matrix and $B = [b_{ij}]$ is an $n \times p$ matrix, the product AB is an $m \times p$ matrix $AB = [c_{ij}]$ where $c_{ij} = a_{i1}b_{1j} + a_{i2}b_{2j} + a_{i3}b_{3j} + \cdot \cdot \cdot + a_{in}b_{nj}$.	55–68
	Use matrix operations to model and solve real-life problems *(p. 592)*.	Matrix operations can be used to find the total cost of equipment for two softball teams. (See Example 12.)	69–72
Section 8.3	Verify that two matrices are inverses of each other *(p. 599)*.	**Inverse of a Square Matrix** Let A be an $n \times n$ matrix and let I_n be the $n \times n$ identity matrix. If there exists a matrix A^{-1} such that $AA^{-1} = I_n = A^{-1}A$ then A^{-1} is the inverse of A.	73–76

	What Did You Learn?	Explanation/Examples	Review Exercises
Section 8.3	Use Gauss-Jordan elimination to find the inverses of matrices *(p. 600)*.	**Finding an Inverse Matrix** Let A be a square matrix of order n. **1.** Write the $n \times 2n$ matrix that consists of the given matrix A on the left and the $n \times n$ identity matrix I on the right to obtain $[A \vdots I]$. **2.** If possible, row reduce A to I using elementary row operations on the *entire* matrix $[A \vdots I]$. The result will be the matrix $[I \vdots A^{-1}]$. If this is not possible, A is not invertible. **3.** Check your work to see that $AA^{-1} = I = A^{-1}A$.	77–84
	Use a formula to find the inverses of 2×2 matrices *(p. 603)*.	If $A = \begin{bmatrix} a & b \\ c & d \end{bmatrix}$ and $ad - bc \neq 0$, then $A^{-1} = \dfrac{1}{ad - bc}\begin{bmatrix} d & -b \\ -c & a \end{bmatrix}.$	85–92
	Use inverse matrices to solve systems of linear equations *(p. 604)*.	If A is an invertible matrix, the system of linear equations represented by $AX = B$ has a unique solution given by $X = A^{-1}B$.	93–110
Section 8.4	Find the determinants of 2×2 matrices *(p. 608)*.	The determinant of the matrix $A = \begin{bmatrix} a_1 & b_1 \\ a_2 & b_2 \end{bmatrix}$ is given by $\det(A) = \lvert A \rvert = \begin{vmatrix} a_1 & b_1 \\ a_2 & b_2 \end{vmatrix} = a_1b_2 - a_2b_1.$	111–114
	Find minors and cofactors of square matrices *(p. 610)*.	If A is a square matrix, the minor M_{ij} of the entry a_{ij} is the determinant of the matrix obtained by deleting the ith row and jth column of A. The cofactor C_{ij} of the entry a_{ij} is $C_{ij} = (-1)^{i+j}M_{ij}$.	115–118
	Find the determinants of square matrices *(p. 611)*.	If A is a square matrix (of order 2×2 or greater), the determinant of A is the sum of the entries in any row (or column) of A multiplied by their respective cofactors.	119–128
Section 8.5	Use Cramer's Rule to solve systems of linear equations *(p. 616)*.	Cramer's Rule uses determinants to write the solution of a system of linear equations.	129–132
	Use determinants to find the areas of triangles *(p. 619)*.	The area of a triangle with vertices (x_1, y_1), (x_2, y_2), and (x_3, y_3) is $\text{Area} = \pm\dfrac{1}{2}\begin{vmatrix} x_1 & y_1 & 1 \\ x_2 & y_2 & 1 \\ x_3 & y_3 & 1 \end{vmatrix}$ where the symbol $\pm$ indicates that the appropriate sign should be chosen to yield a positive area.	133–136
	Use a determinant to test for collinear points and find an equation of a line passing through two points *(p. 620)*.	Three points (x_1, y_1), (x_2, y_2), and (x_3, y_3) are collinear (lie on the same line) if and only if $\begin{vmatrix} x_1 & y_1 & 1 \\ x_2 & y_2 & 1 \\ x_3 & y_3 & 1 \end{vmatrix} = 0.$	137–142
	Use matrices to encode and decode messages *(p. 622)*.	The inverse of a matrix can be used to decode a cryptogram. (See Example 8.)	143–146

5. $\begin{bmatrix} 3 & -10 & \vdots & 15 \\ 5 & 4 & \vdots & 22 \end{bmatrix}$

6. $\begin{bmatrix} 8 & -7 & 4 & \vdots & 12 \\ 3 & -5 & 2 & \vdots & 20 \\ 5 & 3 & -3 & \vdots & 26 \end{bmatrix}$

7. $\begin{cases} 5x + y + 7z = -9 \\ 4x + 2y = 10 \\ 9x + 4y + 2z = 3 \end{cases}$

8. $\begin{cases} 13x + 16y + 7z + 3w = 2 \\ x + 21y + 8z + 5w = 12 \\ 4x + 10y - 4z + 3w = -1 \end{cases}$

9. $\begin{bmatrix} 1 & 2 & 3 \\ 0 & 1 & 1 \\ 0 & 0 & 1 \end{bmatrix}$

10. $\begin{bmatrix} 1 & 2 & 4 \\ 0 & 1 & \frac{10}{7} \\ 0 & 0 & 0 \end{bmatrix}$

11. $\begin{cases} x + 2y + 3z = 9 \\ y - 2z = 2 \\ z = 0 \end{cases}$
$(5, 2, 0)$

12. $\begin{cases} x + 3y - 9z = 4 \\ y - z = 10 \\ z = -2 \end{cases}$
$(-38, 8, -2)$

13. $\begin{cases} x - 5y + 4z = 1 \\ y + 2z = 3 \\ z = 4 \end{cases}$
$(-40, -5, 4)$

14. $\begin{cases} x - 8y = -2 \\ y - z = -7 \\ z = 1 \end{cases}$
$(-50, -6, 1)$

15. $(10, -12)$
16. $(-9, -4)$
17. $\left(-\frac{1}{5}, \frac{7}{10}\right)$
18. $\left(\frac{3}{5}, \frac{1}{2}\right)$
19. Inconsistent
20. $(2a - 3, a)$
21. $(1, -2, 2)$
22. $(-4, 0, 8)$
23. $\left(-2a + \frac{3}{2}, 2a + 1, a\right)$
24. Inconsistent
25. $(5, 2, -6)$
26. $\left(\frac{1}{2}, -\frac{1}{3}, 1\right)$

8 REVIEW EXERCISES

See www.CalcChat.com for worked-out solutions to odd-numbered exercises.

8.1 In Exercises 1–4, determine the order of the matrix.

1. $\begin{bmatrix} -4 \\ 0 \\ 5 \end{bmatrix}$ 3×1

2. $\begin{bmatrix} 3 & -1 & 0 & 6 \\ -2 & 7 & 1 & 4 \end{bmatrix}$ 2×4

3. $[3]$ 1×1

4. $[6 \quad 2 \quad -5 \quad 8 \quad 0]$ 1×5

In Exercises 5 and 6, write the augmented matrix for the system of linear equations. 5–6. See margin.

5. $\begin{cases} 3x - 10y = 15 \\ 5x + 4y = 22 \end{cases}$

6. $\begin{cases} 8x - 7y + 4z = 12 \\ 3x - 5y + 2z = 20 \\ 5x + 3y - 3z = 26 \end{cases}$

In Exercises 7 and 8, write the system of linear equations represented by the augmented matrix. (Use variables x, y, z, and w, if applicable.) 7–8. See margin.

7. $\begin{bmatrix} 5 & 1 & 7 & \vdots & -9 \\ 4 & 2 & 0 & \vdots & 10 \\ 9 & 4 & 2 & \vdots & 3 \end{bmatrix}$

8. $\begin{bmatrix} 13 & 16 & 7 & 3 & \vdots & 2 \\ 1 & 21 & 8 & 5 & \vdots & 12 \\ 4 & 10 & -4 & 3 & \vdots & -1 \end{bmatrix}$

In Exercises 9 and 10, write the matrix in row-echelon form. (Remember that the row-echelon form of a matrix is not unique.) 9–10. See margin.

9. $\begin{bmatrix} 0 & 1 & 1 \\ 1 & 2 & 3 \\ 2 & 2 & 2 \end{bmatrix}$

10. $\begin{bmatrix} 4 & 8 & 16 \\ 3 & -1 & 2 \\ -2 & 10 & 12 \end{bmatrix}$

In Exercises 11–14, write the system of linear equations represented by the augmented matrix. Then use back-substitution to solve the system. (Use variables x, y, and z.) 11–14. See margin.

11. $\begin{bmatrix} 1 & 2 & 3 & \vdots & 9 \\ 0 & 1 & -2 & \vdots & 2 \\ 0 & 0 & 1 & \vdots & 0 \end{bmatrix}$

12. $\begin{bmatrix} 1 & 3 & -9 & \vdots & 4 \\ 0 & 1 & -1 & \vdots & 10 \\ 0 & 0 & 1 & \vdots & -2 \end{bmatrix}$

13. $\begin{bmatrix} 1 & -5 & 4 & \vdots & 1 \\ 0 & 1 & 2 & \vdots & 3 \\ 0 & 0 & 1 & \vdots & 4 \end{bmatrix}$

14. $\begin{bmatrix} 1 & -8 & 0 & \vdots & -2 \\ 0 & 1 & -1 & \vdots & -7 \\ 0 & 0 & 1 & \vdots & 1 \end{bmatrix}$

15–26. See margin.

In Exercises 15–28, use matrices and Gaussian elimination with back-substitution to solve the system of equations (if possible).

15. $\begin{cases} 5x + 4y = 2 \\ -x + y = -22 \end{cases}$

16. $\begin{cases} 2x - 5y = 2 \\ 3x - 7y = 1 \end{cases}$

17. $\begin{cases} 0.3x - 0.1y = -0.13 \\ 0.2x - 0.3y = -0.25 \end{cases}$

18. $\begin{cases} 0.2x - 0.1y = 0.07 \\ 0.4x - 0.5y = -0.01 \end{cases}$

19. $\begin{cases} -x + 2y = 3 \\ 2x - 4y = 6 \end{cases}$

20. $\begin{cases} -x + 2y = 3 \\ 2x - 4y = -6 \end{cases}$

21. $\begin{cases} x - 2y + z = 7 \\ 2x + y - 2z = -4 \\ -x + 3y + 2z = -3 \end{cases}$

22. $\begin{cases} x - 2y + z = 4 \\ 2x + y - 2z = -24 \\ -x + 3y + 2z = 20 \end{cases}$

23. $\begin{cases} 2x + y + 2z = 4 \\ 2x + 2y = 5 \\ 2x - y + 6z = 2 \end{cases}$

24. $\begin{cases} x + 2y + 6z = 1 \\ 2x + 5y + 15z = 4 \\ 3x + y + 3z = -6 \end{cases}$

25. $\begin{cases} 2x + 3y + z = 10 \\ 2x - 3y - 3z = 22 \\ 4x - 2y + 3z = -2 \end{cases}$

26. $\begin{cases} 2x + 3y + 3z = 3 \\ 6x + 6y + 12z = 13 \\ 12x + 9y - z = 2 \end{cases}$

27. $\begin{cases} 2x + y + z = 6 \\ -2y + 3z - w = 9 \\ 3x + 3y - 2z - 2w = -11 \\ x + z + 3w = 14 \end{cases}$ $(1, 0, 4, 3)$

28. $\begin{cases} x + 2y + w = 3 \\ -3y + 3z = 0 \\ 4x + 4y + z + 2w = 0 \\ 2x + z = 3 \end{cases}$ Inconsistent

In Exercises 29–34, use matrices and Gauss-Jordan elimination to solve the system of equations.

29. $\begin{cases} x + 2y - z = 3 \\ x - y - z = -3 \\ 2x + y + 3z = 10 \end{cases}$

30. $\begin{cases} x - 3y + z = 2 \\ 3x - y - z = -6 \\ -x + y - 3z = -2 \end{cases}$

31. $\begin{cases} -x + y + 2z = 1 \\ 2x + 3y + z = -2 \\ 5x + 4y + 2z = 4 \end{cases}$

29. $(1, 2, 2)$
30. $(-2, -1, 1)$
31. $(2, -3, 3)$

32. $\begin{cases} 4x + 4y + 4z = 5 \\ 4x - 2y - 8z = 1 \\ 5x + 3y + 8z = 6 \end{cases}$ $\left(\frac{31}{42}, \frac{5}{14}, \frac{13}{84}\right)$

33. $\begin{cases} 2x - y + 9z = -8 \\ -x - 3y + 4z = -15 \\ 5x + 2y - z = 17 \end{cases}$ $(2, 3, -1)$

34. $\begin{cases} -3x + y + 7z = -20 \\ 5x - 2y - z = 34 \\ -x + y + 4z = -8 \end{cases}$ $(6, -2, 0)$

In Exercises 35 and 36, use the matrix capabilities of a graphing utility to reduce the augmented matrix corresponding to the system of equations, and solve the system.

35. $\begin{cases} 3x - y + 5z - 2w = -44 \\ x + 6y + 4z - w = 1 \\ 5x - y + z + 3w = -15 \\ 4y - z - 8w = 58 \end{cases}$ (2, 6, −10, −3)

36. $\begin{cases} 4x + 12y + 2z = 20 \\ x + 6y + 4z = 12 \\ x + 6y + z = 8 \\ -2x - 10y - 2z = -10 \end{cases}$ Inconsistent

8.2 In Exercises 37–40, find *x* and *y*.

37. $\begin{bmatrix} -1 & x \\ y & 9 \end{bmatrix} = \begin{bmatrix} -1 & 12 \\ -7 & 9 \end{bmatrix}$ $x = 12, y = -7$

38. $\begin{bmatrix} -1 & 0 \\ x & 5 \\ -4 & y \end{bmatrix} = \begin{bmatrix} -1 & 0 \\ 8 & 5 \\ -4 & 0 \end{bmatrix}$ $x = 8, y = 0$

39. $\begin{bmatrix} x+3 & -4 & 4y \\ 0 & -3 & 2 \\ -2 & y+5 & 6x \end{bmatrix} = \begin{bmatrix} 5x-1 & -4 & 44 \\ 0 & -3 & 2 \\ -2 & 16 & 6 \end{bmatrix}$ $x = 1, y = 11$

40. $\begin{bmatrix} -9 & 4 & 2 & -5 \\ 0 & -3 & 7 & -4 \\ 6 & -1 & 1 & 0 \end{bmatrix} = \begin{bmatrix} -9 & 4 & x-10 & -5 \\ 0 & -3 & 7 & 2y \\ \frac{1}{2}x & -1 & 1 & 0 \end{bmatrix}$
$x = 12, y = -2$

In Exercises 41–44, if possible, find (a) $A + B$, (b) $A - B$, (c) $4A$, and (d) $A + 3B$. 41–43. See margin.

41. $A = \begin{bmatrix} 2 & -2 \\ 3 & 5 \end{bmatrix}$, $B = \begin{bmatrix} -3 & 10 \\ 12 & 8 \end{bmatrix}$

42. $A = \begin{bmatrix} 4 & 3 \\ -6 & 1 \\ 10 & 1 \end{bmatrix}$, $B = \begin{bmatrix} 3 & 11 \\ 15 & 25 \\ 20 & 29 \end{bmatrix}$

43. $A = \begin{bmatrix} 5 & 4 \\ -7 & 2 \\ 11 & 2 \end{bmatrix}$, $B = \begin{bmatrix} 0 & 3 \\ 4 & 12 \\ 20 & 40 \end{bmatrix}$

44. $A = \begin{bmatrix} 6 & -5 & 7 \end{bmatrix}$, $B = \begin{bmatrix} -1 \\ 4 \\ 8 \end{bmatrix}$ (a), (b), and (d) not possible (c) $\begin{bmatrix} 24 & -20 & 28 \end{bmatrix}$

In Exercises 45–48, perform the matrix operations. If it is not possible, explain why.

45. $\begin{bmatrix} 7 & 3 \\ -1 & 5 \end{bmatrix} + \begin{bmatrix} 10 & -20 \\ 14 & -3 \end{bmatrix}$ $\begin{bmatrix} 17 & -17 \\ 13 & 2 \end{bmatrix}$

46. $\begin{bmatrix} -11 & 16 & 19 \\ -7 & -2 & 1 \end{bmatrix} - \begin{bmatrix} 6 & 0 \\ 8 & -4 \\ -2 & 10 \end{bmatrix}$ Not possible. The matrices are not of the same order.

47. $-2\begin{bmatrix} 1 & 2 \\ 5 & -4 \\ 6 & 0 \end{bmatrix} + 8\begin{bmatrix} 7 & 1 \\ 1 & 2 \\ 1 & 4 \end{bmatrix}$ $\begin{bmatrix} 54 & 4 \\ -2 & 24 \\ -4 & 32 \end{bmatrix}$

48. $-\begin{bmatrix} 8 & -1 & 8 \\ -2 & 4 & 12 \\ 0 & -6 & 0 \end{bmatrix} - 5\begin{bmatrix} -2 & 0 & -4 \\ 3 & -1 & 1 \\ 6 & 12 & -8 \end{bmatrix}$ See margin.

In Exercises 49 and 50, use the matrix capabilities of a graphing utility to evaluate the expression.

49. $3\begin{bmatrix} 8 & -2 & 5 \\ 1 & 3 & -1 \end{bmatrix} + 6\begin{bmatrix} 4 & -2 & -3 \\ 2 & 7 & 6 \end{bmatrix}$ $\begin{bmatrix} 48 & -18 & -3 \\ 15 & 51 & 33 \end{bmatrix}$

50. $-5\begin{bmatrix} 2 & 0 \\ 7 & -2 \\ 8 & 2 \end{bmatrix} + 4\begin{bmatrix} 4 & -2 \\ 6 & 11 \\ -1 & 3 \end{bmatrix}$ $\begin{bmatrix} 6 & -8 \\ -11 & 54 \\ -44 & 2 \end{bmatrix}$

In Exercises 51–54, solve for *X* in the equation, given

$A = \begin{bmatrix} -4 & 0 \\ 1 & -5 \\ -3 & 2 \end{bmatrix}$ and $B = \begin{bmatrix} 1 & 2 \\ -2 & 1 \\ 4 & 4 \end{bmatrix}$. 51–54. See margin.

51. $X = 2A - 3B$

52. $6X = 4A + 3B$

53. $3X + 2A = B$

54. $2A - 5B = 3X$

In Exercises 55–58, find *AB*, if possible.

55. $A = \begin{bmatrix} 2 & -2 \\ 3 & 5 \end{bmatrix}$, $B = \begin{bmatrix} -3 & 10 \\ 12 & 8 \end{bmatrix}$ $\begin{bmatrix} -30 & 4 \\ 51 & 70 \end{bmatrix}$

56. $A = \begin{bmatrix} 5 & 4 \\ -7 & 2 \\ 11 & 2 \end{bmatrix}$, $B = \begin{bmatrix} 4 & 12 \\ 20 & 40 \\ 15 & 30 \end{bmatrix}$ See margin.

57. $A = \begin{bmatrix} 5 & 4 \\ -7 & 2 \\ 11 & 2 \end{bmatrix}$, $B = \begin{bmatrix} 4 & 12 \\ 20 & 40 \end{bmatrix}$ $\begin{bmatrix} 100 & 220 \\ 12 & -4 \\ 84 & 212 \end{bmatrix}$

58. $A = \begin{bmatrix} 6 & -5 & 7 \end{bmatrix}$, $B = \begin{bmatrix} -1 \\ 4 \\ 8 \end{bmatrix}$ $[30]$

In Exercises 59–66, perform the matrix operations, if possible. If it is not possible, explain why.

59. $\begin{bmatrix} 1 & 2 \\ 5 & -4 \\ 6 & 0 \end{bmatrix}\begin{bmatrix} 6 & -2 & 8 \\ 4 & 0 & 0 \end{bmatrix}$ $\begin{bmatrix} 14 & -2 & 8 \\ 14 & -10 & 40 \\ 36 & -12 & 48 \end{bmatrix}$

60. $\begin{bmatrix} 1 & 5 & 6 \\ 2 & -4 & 0 \end{bmatrix}\begin{bmatrix} 6 & -2 & 8 \\ 4 & 0 & 0 \end{bmatrix}$ See margin.

61. $\begin{bmatrix} 1 & 5 & 6 \\ 2 & -4 & 0 \end{bmatrix}\begin{bmatrix} 6 & 4 \\ -2 & 0 \\ 8 & 0 \end{bmatrix}$ $\begin{bmatrix} 44 & 4 \\ 20 & 8 \end{bmatrix}$

62. $\begin{bmatrix} 1 & 3 & 2 \\ 0 & 2 & -4 \\ 0 & 0 & 3 \end{bmatrix}\begin{bmatrix} 4 & -3 & 2 \\ 0 & 3 & -1 \\ 0 & 0 & 2 \end{bmatrix}$ $\begin{bmatrix} 4 & 6 & 3 \\ 0 & 6 & -10 \\ 0 & 0 & 6 \end{bmatrix}$

41. (a) $\begin{bmatrix} -1 & 8 \\ 15 & 13 \end{bmatrix}$ (b) $\begin{bmatrix} 5 & -12 \\ -9 & -3 \end{bmatrix}$
(c) $\begin{bmatrix} 8 & -8 \\ 12 & 20 \end{bmatrix}$ (d) $\begin{bmatrix} -7 & 28 \\ 39 & 29 \end{bmatrix}$

42. (a) $\begin{bmatrix} 7 & 14 \\ 9 & 26 \\ 30 & 30 \end{bmatrix}$ (b) $\begin{bmatrix} 1 & -8 \\ -21 & -24 \\ -10 & -28 \end{bmatrix}$
(c) $\begin{bmatrix} 16 & 12 \\ -24 & 4 \\ 40 & 4 \end{bmatrix}$ (d) $\begin{bmatrix} 13 & 36 \\ 39 & 76 \\ 70 & 88 \end{bmatrix}$

43. (a) $\begin{bmatrix} 5 & 7 \\ -3 & 14 \\ 31 & 42 \end{bmatrix}$
(b) $\begin{bmatrix} 5 & 1 \\ -11 & -10 \\ -9 & -38 \end{bmatrix}$
(c) $\begin{bmatrix} 20 & 16 \\ -28 & 8 \\ 44 & 8 \end{bmatrix}$ (d) $\begin{bmatrix} 5 & 13 \\ 5 & 38 \\ 71 & 122 \end{bmatrix}$

48. $\begin{bmatrix} 2 & 1 & 12 \\ -13 & 1 & -17 \\ -30 & -54 & 40 \end{bmatrix}$

51. $\begin{bmatrix} -11 & -6 \\ 8 & -13 \\ -18 & -8 \end{bmatrix}$

52. $\begin{bmatrix} -\frac{13}{6} & 1 \\ -\frac{1}{3} & -\frac{17}{6} \\ 0 & \frac{10}{3} \end{bmatrix}$ **53.** $\begin{bmatrix} 3 & \frac{2}{3} \\ -\frac{4}{3} & \frac{11}{3} \\ \frac{10}{3} & 0 \end{bmatrix}$

54. $\begin{bmatrix} -\frac{13}{3} & -\frac{10}{3} \\ 4 & -5 \\ -\frac{26}{3} & -\frac{16}{3} \end{bmatrix}$

56. Not possible. The number of columns of *A* does not equal the number of rows of *B*.

60. Not possible. The number of columns of the first matrix does not equal the number of rows of the second matrix.

63. $\begin{bmatrix} 1 & 2 & -1 \\ 0 & 4 & -2 \\ 1 & 1 & 3 \end{bmatrix} \begin{bmatrix} 1 & -1 & 2 \end{bmatrix}$ See margin.

64. $\begin{bmatrix} 4 & -2 & 6 \end{bmatrix} \begin{bmatrix} -2 & 1 \\ 0 & -3 \\ 2 & 0 \end{bmatrix}$ $\begin{bmatrix} 4 & 10 \end{bmatrix}$

65. $\begin{bmatrix} 2 & 1 \\ 6 & 0 \end{bmatrix} \left(\begin{bmatrix} 4 & 2 \\ -3 & 1 \end{bmatrix} + \begin{bmatrix} -2 & 4 \\ 0 & 4 \end{bmatrix} \right)$ $\begin{bmatrix} 1 & 17 \\ 12 & 36 \end{bmatrix}$

66. $-3 \begin{bmatrix} 1 & -1 \\ 4 & 2 \end{bmatrix} \left(\begin{bmatrix} 0 & 3 \\ 1 & 2 \end{bmatrix} \begin{bmatrix} 1 & 0 \\ 5 & -3 \end{bmatrix} \right)$ $\begin{bmatrix} -12 & 9 \\ -246 & 144 \end{bmatrix}$

In Exercises 67 and 68, use the matrix capabilities of a graphing utility to find the product.

67. $\begin{bmatrix} 4 & 1 \\ 11 & -7 \\ 12 & 3 \end{bmatrix} \begin{bmatrix} 3 & -5 & 6 \\ 2 & -2 & -2 \end{bmatrix}$ $\begin{bmatrix} 14 & -22 & 22 \\ 19 & -41 & 80 \\ 42 & -66 & 66 \end{bmatrix}$

68. $\begin{bmatrix} -2 & 3 & 10 \\ 4 & -2 & 2 \end{bmatrix} \begin{bmatrix} 1 & 1 \\ -5 & 2 \\ 3 & 2 \end{bmatrix}$ $\begin{bmatrix} 13 & 24 \\ 20 & 4 \end{bmatrix}$

69. **MANUFACTURING** A tire corporation has three factories, each of which manufactures two models of tires. The number of units of model i produced at factory j in one day is represented by a_{ij} in the matrix

$$A = \begin{bmatrix} 80 & 120 & 140 \\ 40 & 100 & 80 \end{bmatrix}.$$ $\begin{bmatrix} 76 & 114 & 133 \\ 38 & 95 & 76 \end{bmatrix}$

Find the production levels if production is decreased by 5%.

70. **MANUFACTURING** A power tool company has four manufacturing plants, each of which produces three types of cordless power tools. The number of units of cordless power tool i produced at plant j in one day is represented by a_{ij} in the matrix

$$A = \begin{bmatrix} 80 & 70 & 90 & 40 \\ 50 & 30 & 80 & 20 \\ 90 & 60 & 100 & 50 \end{bmatrix}.$$ $\begin{bmatrix} 96 & 84 & 108 & 48 \\ 60 & 36 & 96 & 24 \\ 108 & 72 & 120 & 60 \end{bmatrix}$

Find the production levels if production is increased by 20%.

71. **MANUFACTURING** An electronics manufacturing company produces three different models of headphones that are shipped to two warehouses. The number of units of model i that are shipped to warehouse j is represented by a_{ij} in the matrix See margin.

$$A = \begin{bmatrix} 8200 & 7400 \\ 6500 & 9800 \\ 5400 & 4800 \end{bmatrix}.$$

The price per unit is represented by the matrix

$B = [\$79.99 \quad \$109.95 \quad \$189.99]$.

Compute BA and interpret the result.

72. **CELL PHONE CHARGES** The pay-as-you-go charges (in dollars per minute) of two cellular telephone companies for calls inside the coverage area, regional roaming calls, and calls outside the coverage area are represented by C.

$$C = \begin{bmatrix} 0.07 & 0.095 \\ 0.10 & 0.08 \\ 0.28 & 0.25 \end{bmatrix} \begin{matrix} \text{Inside} \\ \text{Regional roaming} \\ \text{Outside} \end{matrix} \Bigg\} \text{ Coverage area}$$

(Columns: Company A, B)

Each month, you plan to use 120 minutes on calls inside the coverage area, 80 minutes on regional roaming calls, and 20 minutes on calls outside the coverage area.

(a) Write a matrix T that represents the times spent on the phone for each type of call. T: $[120 \quad 80 \quad 20]$

(b) Compute TC and interpret the result. See margin.

8.3 In Exercises 73–76, show that B is the inverse of A.

73. $A = \begin{bmatrix} -4 & -1 \\ 7 & 2 \end{bmatrix}$, $B = \begin{bmatrix} -2 & -1 \\ 7 & 4 \end{bmatrix}$ 73–76. $AB = I$ and $BA = I$

74. $A = \begin{bmatrix} 5 & -1 \\ 11 & -2 \end{bmatrix}$, $B = \begin{bmatrix} -2 & 1 \\ -11 & 5 \end{bmatrix}$

75. $A = \begin{bmatrix} 1 & 1 & 0 \\ 1 & 0 & 1 \\ 6 & 2 & 3 \end{bmatrix}$, $B = \begin{bmatrix} -2 & -3 & 1 \\ 3 & 3 & -1 \\ 2 & 4 & -1 \end{bmatrix}$

76. $A = \begin{bmatrix} 1 & -1 & 0 \\ -1 & 0 & -1 \\ 8 & -4 & 2 \end{bmatrix}$, $B = \begin{bmatrix} -2 & 1 & \frac{1}{2} \\ -3 & 1 & \frac{1}{2} \\ 2 & -2 & -\frac{1}{2} \end{bmatrix}$

77–80. See margin.

In Exercises 77–80, find the inverse of the matrix (if it exists).

77. $\begin{bmatrix} -6 & 5 \\ -5 & 4 \end{bmatrix}$

78. $\begin{bmatrix} -3 & -5 \\ 2 & 3 \end{bmatrix}$

79. $\begin{bmatrix} 2 & 0 & 3 \\ -1 & 1 & 1 \\ 2 & -2 & 1 \end{bmatrix}$

80. $\begin{bmatrix} 0 & -2 & 1 \\ -5 & -2 & -3 \\ 7 & 3 & 4 \end{bmatrix}$

81–84. See margin.

In Exercises 81–84, use the matrix capabilities of a graphing utility to find the inverse of the matrix (if it exists).

81. $\begin{bmatrix} -1 & -2 & -2 \\ 3 & 7 & 9 \\ 1 & 4 & 7 \end{bmatrix}$

82. $\begin{bmatrix} 1 & 4 & 6 \\ 2 & -3 & 1 \\ -1 & 18 & 16 \end{bmatrix}$

83. $\begin{bmatrix} 1 & 3 & 1 & 6 \\ 4 & 4 & 2 & 6 \\ 3 & 4 & 1 & 2 \\ -1 & 2 & -1 & -2 \end{bmatrix}$

84. $\begin{bmatrix} 8 & 0 & 2 & 8 \\ 4 & -2 & 0 & -2 \\ 1 & 2 & 1 & 4 \\ -1 & 4 & 1 & 1 \end{bmatrix}$

63. Not possible. The number of columns of the first matrix does not equal the number of rows of the second matrix.

71. [\$2,396,539 \$2,581,388]
The merchandise shipped to warehouse 1 is worth \$2,396,539 and the merchandise shipped to warehouse 2 is worth \$2,581,388.

72. (b) A B
$[22 \quad 22.8]$
Shows total costs of calls.

77. $\begin{bmatrix} 4 & -5 \\ 5 & -6 \end{bmatrix}$

78. $\begin{bmatrix} 3 & 5 \\ -2 & -3 \end{bmatrix}$

79. $\begin{bmatrix} \frac{1}{2} & -1 & -\frac{1}{2} \\ \frac{1}{2} & -\frac{2}{3} & -\frac{5}{6} \\ 0 & \frac{2}{3} & \frac{1}{3} \end{bmatrix}$

80. $\begin{bmatrix} 1 & 11 & 8 \\ -1 & -7 & -5 \\ -1 & -14 & -10 \end{bmatrix}$

81. $\begin{bmatrix} 13 & 6 & -4 \\ -12 & -5 & 3 \\ 5 & 2 & -1 \end{bmatrix}$

82. Does not exist

83. $\begin{bmatrix} -3 & 6 & -5.5 & 3.5 \\ 1 & -2 & 2 & -1 \\ 7 & -15 & 14.5 & -9.5 \\ -1 & 2.5 & -2.5 & 1.5 \end{bmatrix}$

84. $\begin{bmatrix} -2.5 & 3 & 7 & -2 \\ -4 & 4.5 & 11 & -3 \\ 14.5 & -16 & -40 & 12 \\ -1 & 1 & 3 & -1 \end{bmatrix}$

In Exercises 85–92, use the formula below to find the inverse of the matrix, if it exists. 85–92. See margin.

$$A^{-1} = \frac{1}{ad - bc}\begin{bmatrix} d & -b \\ -c & a \end{bmatrix}$$

85. $\begin{bmatrix} -7 & 2 \\ -8 & 2 \end{bmatrix}$ **86.** $\begin{bmatrix} 10 & 4 \\ 7 & 3 \end{bmatrix}$

87. $\begin{bmatrix} -12 & 6 \\ 10 & -5 \end{bmatrix}$ **88.** $\begin{bmatrix} -18 & -15 \\ -6 & -5 \end{bmatrix}$

89. $\begin{bmatrix} -\frac{1}{2} & 20 \\ \frac{3}{10} & -6 \end{bmatrix}$ **90.** $\begin{bmatrix} -\frac{3}{4} & \frac{5}{2} \\ -\frac{4}{5} & -\frac{8}{3} \end{bmatrix}$

91. $\begin{bmatrix} 0.5 & 0.1 \\ -0.2 & -0.4 \end{bmatrix}$ **92.** $\begin{bmatrix} 1.6 & -3.2 \\ 1.2 & -2.4 \end{bmatrix}$

In Exercises 93–104, use an inverse matrix to solve (if possible) the system of linear equations. 93–100. See margin.

93. $\begin{cases} -x + 4y = 8 \\ 2x - 7y = -5 \end{cases}$ **94.** $\begin{cases} 5x - y = 13 \\ -9x + 2y = -24 \end{cases}$

95. $\begin{cases} -3x + 10y = 8 \\ 5x - 17y = -13 \end{cases}$ **96.** $\begin{cases} 4x - 2y = -10 \\ -19x + 9y = 47 \end{cases}$

97. $\begin{cases} \frac{1}{2}x + \frac{1}{3}y = 2 \\ -3x + 2y = 0 \end{cases}$ **98.** $\begin{cases} -\frac{5}{6}x + \frac{3}{8}y = -2 \\ 4x - 3y = 0 \end{cases}$

99. $\begin{cases} 0.3x + 0.7y = 10.2 \\ 0.4x + 0.6y = 7.6 \end{cases}$ **100.** $\begin{cases} 3.5x - 4.5y = 8 \\ 2.5x - 7.5y = 25 \end{cases}$

101. $\begin{cases} 3x + 2y - z = 6 \\ x - y + 2z = -1 \\ 5x + y + z = 7 \end{cases}$ $(2, -1, -2)$

102. $\begin{cases} -x + 4y - 2z = 12 \\ 2x - 9y + 5z = -25 \\ -x + 5y - 4z = 10 \end{cases}$ $(-2, 4, 3)$

103. $\begin{cases} -2x + y + 2z = -13 \\ -x - 4y + z = -11 \\ -y - z = 0 \end{cases}$ $(6, 1, -1)$

104. $\begin{cases} 3x - y + 5z = -14 \\ -x + y + 6z = 8 \\ -8x + 4y - z = 44 \end{cases}$ $(-3, 5, 0)$

105–108. See margin.

In Exercises 105–110, use the matrix capabilities of a graphing utility to solve (if possible) the system of linear equations.

105. $\begin{cases} x + 2y = -1 \\ 3x + 4y = -5 \end{cases}$ **106.** $\begin{cases} x + 3y = 23 \\ -6x + 2y = -18 \end{cases}$

107. $\begin{cases} \frac{6}{5}x - \frac{4}{7}y = \frac{6}{5} \\ -\frac{12}{5}x + \frac{12}{7}y = -\frac{17}{5} \end{cases}$ **108.** $\begin{cases} 5x + 10y = 7 \\ 2x + y = -98 \end{cases}$

109. $\begin{cases} -3x - 3y - 4z = 2 \\ y + z = -1 \\ 4x + 3y + 4z = -1 \end{cases}$ $(1, 1, -2)$

110. $\begin{cases} x - 3y - 2z = 8 \\ -2x + 7y + 3z = -19 \\ x - y - 3z = 3 \end{cases}$ $(4, -2, 1)$

8.4 In Exercises 111–114, find the determinant of the matrix.

111. $\begin{bmatrix} 8 & 5 \\ 2 & -4 \end{bmatrix}$ -42 **112.** $\begin{bmatrix} -9 & 11 \\ 7 & -4 \end{bmatrix}$ -41

113. $\begin{bmatrix} 50 & -30 \\ 10 & 5 \end{bmatrix}$ 550 **114.** $\begin{bmatrix} 14 & -24 \\ 12 & -15 \end{bmatrix}$ 78

In Exercises 115–118, find all (a) minors and (b) cofactors of the matrix. 115–118. See margin.

115. $\begin{bmatrix} 2 & -1 \\ 7 & 4 \end{bmatrix}$ **116.** $\begin{bmatrix} 3 & 6 \\ 5 & -4 \end{bmatrix}$

117. $\begin{bmatrix} 3 & 2 & -1 \\ -2 & 5 & 0 \\ 1 & 8 & 6 \end{bmatrix}$ **118.** $\begin{bmatrix} 8 & 3 & 4 \\ 6 & 5 & -9 \\ -4 & 1 & 2 \end{bmatrix}$

In Exercises 119–128, find the determinant of the matrix. Expand by cofactors on the row or column that appears to make the computations easiest.

119. $\begin{bmatrix} -2 & 0 & 0 \\ 2 & -1 & 0 \\ -1 & 1 & -3 \end{bmatrix}$ -6 **120.** $\begin{bmatrix} 0 & 1 & -2 \\ 0 & 1 & 2 \\ -1 & -1 & 3 \end{bmatrix}$ -4

121. $\begin{bmatrix} 4 & 1 & -1 \\ 2 & 3 & 2 \\ 1 & -1 & 0 \end{bmatrix}$ 15 **122.** $\begin{bmatrix} -1 & -2 & 1 \\ 2 & 3 & 0 \\ -5 & -1 & 3 \end{bmatrix}$ 16

123. $\begin{bmatrix} -2 & 4 & 1 \\ -6 & 0 & 2 \\ 5 & 3 & 4 \end{bmatrix}$ 130 **124.** $\begin{bmatrix} 1 & 1 & 4 \\ -4 & 1 & 2 \\ 0 & 1 & -1 \end{bmatrix}$ -23

125. $\begin{bmatrix} 1 & 2 & -1 & 0 \\ 1 & 2 & -4 & 1 \\ 2 & -4 & -3 & 1 \\ 2 & 0 & 0 & 0 \end{bmatrix}$ -8 **126.** $\begin{bmatrix} 1 & -2 & 1 & 2 \\ 4 & 1 & 4 & 1 \\ 2 & 3 & 3 & 0 \\ 0 & -2 & -4 & 2 \end{bmatrix}$ 56

127. $\begin{bmatrix} 3 & 0 & -4 & 0 \\ 0 & 8 & 1 & 2 \\ 6 & 1 & 8 & 2 \\ 0 & 3 & -4 & 1 \end{bmatrix}$ 279 **128.** $\begin{bmatrix} -5 & 6 & 0 & 0 \\ 0 & 1 & -1 & 2 \\ -3 & 4 & -5 & 1 \\ 1 & 6 & 0 & 3 \end{bmatrix}$ -255

8.5 In Exercises 129–132, use Cramer's Rule to solve (if possible) the system of equations.

129. $\begin{cases} 5x - 2y = 6 \\ -11x + 3y = -23 \end{cases}$ $(4, 7)$ **130.** $\begin{cases} 3x + 8y = -7 \\ 9x - 5y = 37 \end{cases}$ $(3, -2)$

131. $\begin{cases} -2x + 3y - 5z = -11 \\ 4x - y + z = -3 \\ -x - 4y + 6z = 15 \end{cases}$ $(-1, 4, 5)$

85. $\begin{bmatrix} 1 & -1 \\ 4 & -\frac{7}{2} \end{bmatrix}$

86. $\begin{bmatrix} \frac{3}{2} & -2 \\ -\frac{7}{2} & 5 \end{bmatrix}$

87. Does not exist

88. Does not exist

89. $\begin{bmatrix} 2 & \frac{20}{3} \\ \frac{1}{10} & \frac{1}{6} \end{bmatrix}$

90. $\begin{bmatrix} -\frac{2}{3} & -\frac{5}{8} \\ \frac{1}{5} & -\frac{3}{16} \end{bmatrix}$

91. $\begin{bmatrix} \frac{20}{9} & \frac{5}{9} \\ -\frac{10}{9} & -\frac{25}{9} \end{bmatrix}$

92. Does not exist

93. $(36, 11)$

94. $(2, -3)$

95. $(-6, -1)$

96. $(-2, 1)$

97. $(2, 3)$

98. $(6, 8)$

99. $(-8, 18)$

100. $(-3.5, -4.5)$

105. $(-3, 1)$

106. $(5, 6)$

107. $\left(\frac{1}{6}, -\frac{7}{4}\right)$

108. $(-65.8, 33.6)$

115. (a) $M_{11} = 4, M_{12} = 7,$
$M_{21} = -1, M_{22} = 2$
(b) $C_{11} = 4, C_{12} = -7,$
$C_{21} = 1, C_{22} = 2$

116. (a) $M_{11} = -4, M_{12} = 5,$
$M_{21} = 6, M_{22} = 3$
(b) $C_{11} = -4, C_{12} = -5,$
$C_{21} = -6, C_{22} = 3$

117. (a) $M_{11} = 30, M_{12} = -12,$
$M_{13} = -21, M_{21} = 20,$
$M_{22} = 19, M_{23} = 22,$
$M_{31} = 5, M_{32} = -2,$
$M_{33} = 19$
(b) $C_{11} = 30, C_{12} = 12,$
$C_{13} = -21, C_{21} = -20,$
$C_{22} = 19, C_{23} = -22,$
$C_{31} = 5, C_{32} = 2, C_{33} = 19$

118. (a) $M_{11} = 19, M_{12} = -24, M_{13} = 26, M_{21} = 2,$
$M_{22} = 32, M_{23} = 20, M_{31} = -47, M_{32} = -96,$
$M_{33} = 22$
(b) $C_{11} = 19, C_{12} = 24, C_{13} = 26, C_{21} = -2,$
$C_{22} = 32, C_{23} = -20, C_{31} = -47, C_{32} = 96,$
$C_{33} = 22$

139. $x - 2y + 4 = 0$

140. $3x + 2y - 16 = 0$

141. $2x + 6y - 13 = 0$

142. $10x - 5y + 9 = 0$

143. (a) Uncoded: [12 15 15], [11 0 15], [21 20 0], [2 5 12], [15 23 0]

(b) Encoded: −21 6 0 −68 8 45 102 −42 −60 −53 20 21 99 −30 −69

144. (a) Uncoded: [8 5 1], [4 0 4], [21 5 0], [23 5 19], [20 0 0]

(b) Encoded: 22 47 54 0 −8 −20 36 77 87 19 5 −42 20 40 40

147. False. The matrix must be square.

148. True. This is the correct sum of the two determinants.

149. An error message appears because $1(6) - (-2)(-3) = 0$.

150. The matrix must be square and its determinant nonzero.

151. If A is a square matrix, the cofactor C_{ij} of the entry a_{ij} is $(-1)^{i+j}M_{ij}$, where M_{ij} is the determinant obtained by deleting the ith row and jth column of A. The determinant of A is the sum of the entries of any row or column of A multiplied by their respective cofactors.

152. No. The first two matrices describe a system of equations with one solution. The third matrix describes a system with infinitely many solutions.

153. The part of the matrix corresponding to the coefficients of the system reduces to a matrix in which the number of rows with nonzero entries is the same as the number of variables.

132. $\begin{cases} 5x - 2y + z = 15 \\ 3x - 3y - z = -7 \\ 2x - y - 7z = -3 \end{cases}$ (6, 8, 1)

In Exercises 133–136, use a determinant and the given vertices of a triangle to find the area of the triangle.

133. 16

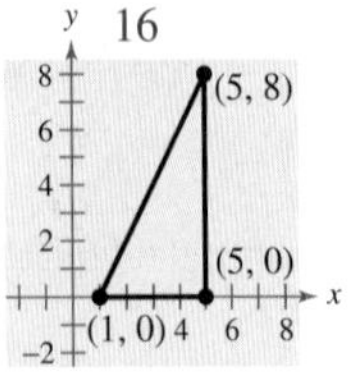

134. 24

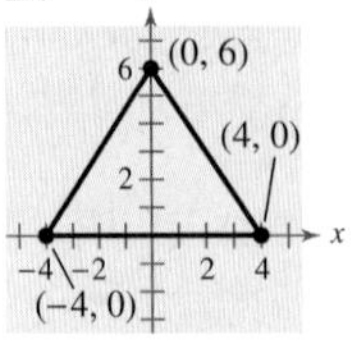

135. 10

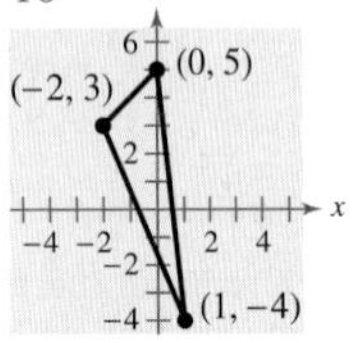

136. $\frac{25}{8}$

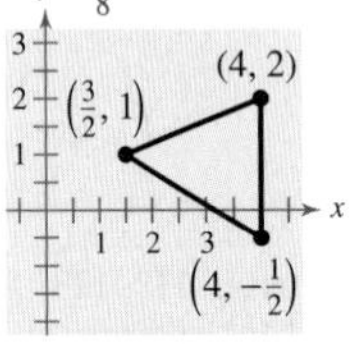

In Exercises 137 and 138, use a determinant to determine whether the points are collinear.

137. $(-1, 7), (3, -9), (-3, 15)$ Collinear

138. $(0, -5), (-2, -6), (8, -1)$ Collinear

In Exercises 139–142, use a determinant to find an equation of the line passing through the points. 139–142. See margin.

139. $(-4, 0), (4, 4)$

140. $(2, 5), (6, -1)$

141. $\left(-\frac{5}{2}, 3\right), \left(\frac{7}{2}, 1\right)$

142. $(-0.8, 0.2), (0.7, 3.2)$

In Exercises 143 and 144, (a) write the uncoded 1×3 row matrices for the message, and (b) encode the message using the encoding matrix. 143–144. See margin.

Message	*Encoding Matrix*
143. LOOK OUT BELOW	$\begin{bmatrix} 2 & -2 & 0 \\ 3 & 0 & -3 \\ -6 & 2 & 3 \end{bmatrix}$
144. HEAD DUE WEST	$\begin{bmatrix} 1 & 2 & 2 \\ 3 & 7 & 9 \\ -1 & -4 & -7 \end{bmatrix}$

In Exercises 145 and 146, decode the cryptogram by using the inverse of the matrix

$$A = \begin{bmatrix} -5 & 4 & -3 \\ 10 & -7 & 6 \\ 8 & -6 & 5 \end{bmatrix}.$$

145. −5 11 −2 370 −265 225 −57 48 −33 32 −15 20 245 −171 147 SEE YOU FRIDAY

146. 145 −105 92 264 −188 160 23 −16 15 129 −84 78 −9 8 −5 159 −118 100 219 −152 133 370 −265 225 −105 84 −63 MAY THE FORCE BE WITH YOU

EXPLORATION

147–148. See margin.

TRUE OR FALSE? In Exercises 147 and 148, determine whether the statement is true or false. Justify your answer.

147. It is possible to find the determinant of a 4×5 matrix.

148. $\begin{vmatrix} a_{11} & a_{12} & a_{13} \\ a_{21} & a_{22} & a_{23} \\ a_{31} + c_1 & a_{32} + c_2 & a_{33} + c_3 \end{vmatrix} =$

$\begin{vmatrix} a_{11} & a_{12} & a_{13} \\ a_{21} & a_{22} & a_{23} \\ a_{31} & a_{32} & a_{33} \end{vmatrix} + \begin{vmatrix} a_{11} & a_{12} & a_{13} \\ a_{21} & a_{22} & a_{23} \\ c_1 & c_2 & c_3 \end{vmatrix}$

149. Use the matrix capabilities of a graphing utility to find the inverse of the matrix

$$A = \begin{bmatrix} 1 & -3 \\ -2 & 6 \end{bmatrix}.$$

149–150. See margin.

What message appears on the screen? Why does the graphing utility display this message?

150. Under what conditions does a matrix have an inverse?

151. WRITING What is meant by the cofactor of an entry of a matrix? How are cofactors used to find the determinant of the matrix? See margin.

152. Three people were asked to solve a system of equations using an augmented matrix. Each person reduced the matrix to row-echelon form. The reduced matrices were

$$\begin{bmatrix} 1 & 2 & \vdots & 3 \\ 0 & 1 & \vdots & 1 \end{bmatrix}, \begin{bmatrix} 1 & 0 & \vdots & 1 \\ 0 & 1 & \vdots & 1 \end{bmatrix},$$

and

$$\begin{bmatrix} 1 & 2 & \vdots & 3 \\ 0 & 0 & \vdots & 0 \end{bmatrix}.$$

Can all three be right? Explain. See margin.

153. THINK ABOUT IT Describe the row-echelon form of an augmented matrix that corresponds to a system of linear equations that has a unique solution. See margin.

154. Solve the equation for λ.

$$\begin{vmatrix} 2 - \lambda & 5 \\ 3 & -8 - \lambda \end{vmatrix} = 0$$

$\lambda = \pm 2\sqrt{10} - 3$

8 CHAPTER TEST

See www.CalcChat.com for worked-out solutions to odd-numbered exercises.

Take this test as you would take a test in class. When you are finished, check your work against the answers given in the back of the book.

In Exercises 1 and 2, write the matrix in reduced row-echelon form.

1. $\begin{bmatrix} 1 & -1 & 5 \\ 6 & 2 & 3 \\ 5 & 3 & -3 \end{bmatrix}$ $\begin{bmatrix} 1 & 0 & 0 \\ 0 & 1 & 0 \\ 0 & 0 & 1 \end{bmatrix}$

2. $\begin{bmatrix} 1 & 0 & -1 & 2 \\ -1 & 1 & 1 & -3 \\ 1 & 1 & -1 & 1 \\ 3 & 2 & -3 & 4 \end{bmatrix}$ See margin.

3. Write the augmented matrix corresponding to the system of equations and solve the system.

$$\begin{cases} 4x + 3y - 2z = 14 \\ -x - y + 2z = -5 \\ 3x + y - 4z = 8 \end{cases} \quad \begin{bmatrix} 4 & 3 & -2 & \vdots & 14 \\ -1 & -1 & 2 & \vdots & -5 \\ 3 & 1 & -4 & \vdots & 8 \end{bmatrix}, \left(1, 3, -\tfrac{1}{2}\right)$$

4. Find (a) $A - B$, (b) $3A$, (c) $3A - 2B$, and (d) AB (if possible).

$$A = \begin{bmatrix} 6 & 5 \\ -5 & -5 \end{bmatrix}, \quad B = \begin{bmatrix} 5 & 0 \\ -5 & -1 \end{bmatrix}$$ See margin.

In Exercises 5 and 6, find the inverse of the matrix (if it exists).

5. $\begin{bmatrix} -4 & 3 \\ 5 & -2 \end{bmatrix}$ $\begin{bmatrix} \frac{2}{7} & \frac{3}{7} \\ \frac{5}{7} & \frac{4}{7} \end{bmatrix}$

6. $\begin{bmatrix} -2 & 4 & -6 \\ 2 & 1 & 0 \\ 4 & -2 & 5 \end{bmatrix}$ $\begin{bmatrix} -\frac{5}{2} & 4 & -3 \\ 5 & -7 & 6 \\ 4 & -6 & 5 \end{bmatrix}$

7. Use the result of Exercise 5 to solve the system.

$$\begin{cases} -4x + 3y = 6 \\ 5x - 2y = 24 \end{cases}$$ $(12, 18)$

In Exercises 8–10, evaluate the determinant of the matrix.

8. $\begin{bmatrix} -6 & 4 \\ 10 & 12 \end{bmatrix}$ -112

9. $\begin{bmatrix} \frac{5}{2} & \frac{13}{4} \\ -8 & \frac{6}{5} \end{bmatrix}$ 29

10. $\begin{bmatrix} 6 & -7 & 2 \\ 3 & -2 & 0 \\ 1 & 5 & 1 \end{bmatrix}$ 43

In Exercises 11 and 12, use Cramer's Rule to solve (if possible) the system of equations.

11. $\begin{cases} 7x + 6y = 9 \\ -2x - 11y = -49 \end{cases}$ $(-3, 5)$

12. $\begin{cases} 6x - y + 2z = -4 \\ -2x + 3y - z = 10 \\ 4x - 4y + z = -18 \end{cases}$ $(-2, 4, 6)$

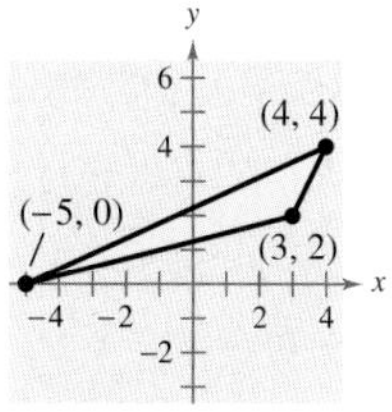

FIGURE FOR 13

13. Use a determinant to find the area of the triangle in the figure. 7

14. Find the uncoded 1×3 row matrices for the message KNOCK ON WOOD. Then encode the message using the matrix A below.

$$A = \begin{bmatrix} 1 & -1 & 0 \\ 1 & 0 & -1 \\ 6 & -2 & -3 \end{bmatrix}$$ See margin.

15. One hundred liters of a 50% solution is obtained by mixing a 60% solution with a 20% solution. How many liters of each solution must be used to obtain the desired mixture? 75 L of 60% solution, 25 L of 20% solution

2. $\begin{bmatrix} 1 & 0 & -1 & 2 \\ 0 & 1 & 0 & -1 \\ 0 & 0 & 0 & 0 \\ 0 & 0 & 0 & 0 \end{bmatrix}$

4. (a) $\begin{bmatrix} 1 & 5 \\ 0 & -4 \end{bmatrix}$

(b) $\begin{bmatrix} 18 & 15 \\ -15 & -15 \end{bmatrix}$

(c) $\begin{bmatrix} 8 & 15 \\ -5 & -13 \end{bmatrix}$

(d) $\begin{bmatrix} 5 & -5 \\ 0 & 5 \end{bmatrix}$

14. Uncoded: [11 14 15], [3 11 0], [15 14 0], [23 15 15], [4 0 0]
Encoded: 115 −41 −59 14 −3 −11 29 −15 −14 128 −53 −60 4 −4 0

PROOFS IN MATHEMATICS

Proofs without words are pictures or diagrams that give a visual understanding of why a theorem or statement is true. They can also provide a starting point for writing a formal proof. The following proof shows that a 2×2 determinant is the area of a parallelogram.

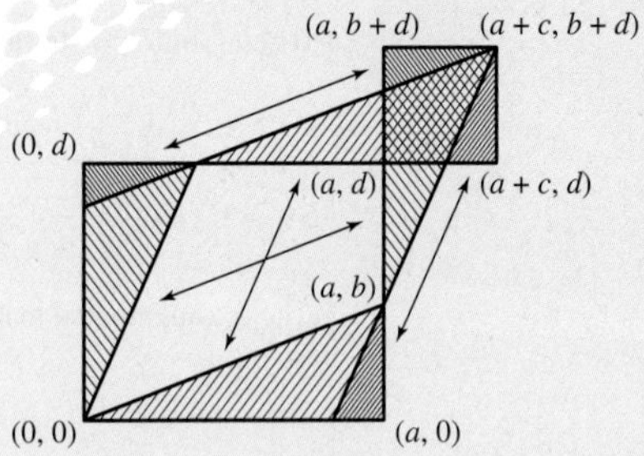

$$\begin{vmatrix} a & b \\ c & d \end{vmatrix} = ad - bc = \|▭\| - \|□\| = \|▱\|$$

The following is a color-coded version of the proof along with a brief explanation of why this proof works.

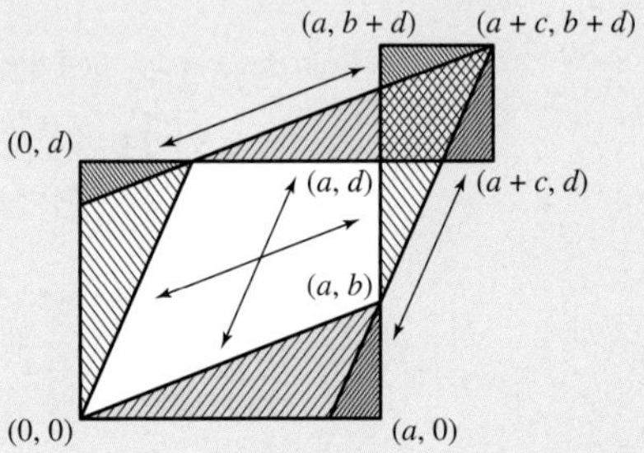

$$\begin{vmatrix} a & b \\ c & d \end{vmatrix} = ad - bc = \|▭\| - \|□\| = \|▱\|$$

Area of ▭ = Area of orange △ + Area of yellow △ + Area of blue △ +
Area of pink △ + Area of white quadrilateral

Area of □ = Area of orange △ + Area of pink △ + Area of green quadrilateral

Area of ▱ = Area of white quadrilateral + Area of blue △ + Area of yellow △ −
Area of green quadrilateral
= Area of ▭ − Area of □

From "Proof Without Words" by Solomon W. Golomb, *Mathematics Magazine*, March 1985, Vol. 58, No. 2, pg. 107. Reprinted with permission.

636

PROBLEM SOLVING

This collection of thought-provoking and challenging exercises further explores and expands upon concepts learned in this chapter.

1. The columns of matrix T show the coordinates of the vertices of a triangle. Matrix A is a transformation matrix.

$$A = \begin{bmatrix} 0 & -1 \\ 1 & 0 \end{bmatrix} \quad T = \begin{bmatrix} 1 & 2 & 3 \\ 1 & 4 & 2 \end{bmatrix}$$ See margin.

(a) Find AT and AAT. Then sketch the original triangle and the two transformed triangles. What transformation does A represent?

(b) Given the triangle determined by AAT, describe the transformation process that produces the triangle determined by AT and then the triangle determined by T.

2. The matrices show the number of people (in thousands) who lived in each region of the United States in 2000 and the number of people (in thousands) projected to live in each region in 2015. The regional populations are separated into three age categories. (Source: U.S. Census Bureau) See margin.

2000

	0–17	18–64	65 +
Northeast	13,048	33,174	7,372
Midwest	16,648	39,486	8,259
South	25,567	62,232	12,438
Mountain	4,935	11,208	2,030
Pacific	12,097	28,037	4,892

2015

	0–17	18–64	65 +
Northeast	12,441	35,288	8,837
Midwest	16,363	42,249	9,957
South	29,372	73,495	17,574
Mountain	6,016	14,231	3,338
Pacific	12,826	33,294	7,085

(a) The total population in 2000 was approximately 281,422,000 and the projected total population in 2015 is 322,366,000. Rewrite the matrices to give the information as percents of the total population.

(b) Write a matrix that gives the projected change in the percent of the population in each region and age group from 2000 to 2015.

(c) Based on the result of part (b), which region(s) and age group(s) are projected to show relative growth from 2000 to 2015?

3. Determine whether the matrix is idempotent. A square matrix is **idempotent** if $A^2 = A$.

(a) $\begin{bmatrix} 1 & 0 \\ 0 & 0 \end{bmatrix}$ Yes (b) $\begin{bmatrix} 0 & 1 \\ 1 & 0 \end{bmatrix}$ No

(c) $\begin{bmatrix} 2 & 3 \\ -1 & -2 \end{bmatrix}$ No (d) $\begin{bmatrix} 2 & 3 \\ 1 & 2 \end{bmatrix}$ No

4. Let $A = \begin{bmatrix} 1 & 2 \\ -2 & 1 \end{bmatrix}$. See margin.

(a) Show that $A^2 - 2A + 5I = O$, where I is the identity matrix of order 2.

(b) Show that $A^{-1} = \frac{1}{5}(2I - A)$.

(c) Show in general that for any square matrix satisfying

$$A^2 - 2A + 5I = O$$

the inverse of A is given by

$$A^{-1} = \tfrac{1}{5}(2I - A).$$

5. Two competing companies offer satellite television to a city with 100,000 households. Gold Satellite System has 25,000 subscribers and Galaxy Satellite Network has 30,000 subscribers. (The other 45,000 households do not subscribe.) The percent changes in satellite subscriptions each year are shown in the matrix below. See margin.

Percent Changes

Percent Changes	From Gold	From Galaxy	From Nonsubscriber
To Gold	0.70	0.15	0.15
To Galaxy	0.20	0.80	0.15
To Nonsubscriber	0.10	0.05	0.70

(a) Find the number of subscribers each company will have in 1 year using matrix multiplication. Explain how you obtained your answer.

(b) Find the number of subscribers each company will have in 2 years using matrix multiplication. Explain how you obtained your answer.

(c) Find the number of subscribers each company will have in 3 years using matrix multiplication. Explain how you obtained your answer.

(d) What is happening to the number of subscribers to each company? What is happening to the number of nonsubscribers?

6. Find x such that the matrix is equal to its own inverse.

$$A = \begin{bmatrix} 3 & x \\ -2 & -3 \end{bmatrix} \quad x = 4$$

7. Find x such that the matrix is singular.

$$A = \begin{bmatrix} 4 & x \\ -2 & -3 \end{bmatrix} \quad x = 6$$

8. Find an example of a singular 2×2 matrix satisfying $A^2 = A$.

Answers will vary. For example: $A = \begin{bmatrix} 1 & 1 \\ 0 & 0 \end{bmatrix}$

1. (a) $AT = \begin{bmatrix} -1 & -4 & -2 \\ 1 & 2 & 3 \end{bmatrix}$

$AAT = \begin{bmatrix} -1 & -2 & -3 \\ -1 & -4 & -2 \end{bmatrix}$

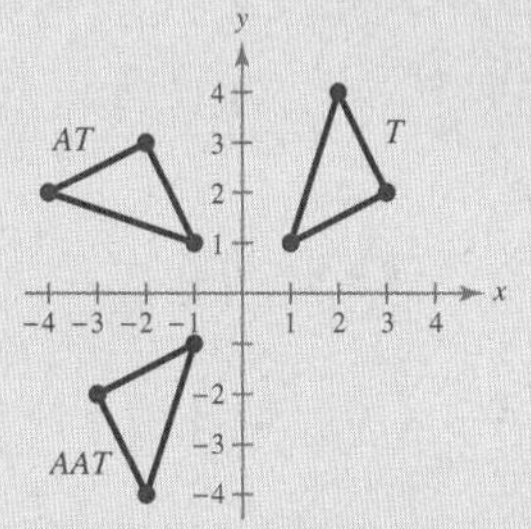

A represents a counterclockwise rotation.

(b) AAT is rotated clockwise 90° to obtain AT. AT is then rotated clockwise 90° to obtain T.

2. See below.

5. (a) Gold Satellite System: 28,750 subscribers

Galaxy Satellite Network: 35,750 subscribers

Nonsubscribers: 35,500

Answers will vary.

(b) Gold Satellite System: 30,813 subscribers

Galaxy Satellite Network: 39,675 subscribers

Nonsubscribers: 29,513

Answers will vary.

(c) Gold Satellite System: 31,947 subscribers

Galaxy Satellite Network: 42,329 subscribers

Nonsubscribers: 25,724

Answers will vary.

(d) Satellite companies are increasing the number of subscribers, while the nonsubscribers are decreasing.

2. (a)

2000

	0–17	18–64	65+
Northeast	4.64	11.79	2.62
Midwest	5.92	14.03	2.93
South	9.08	22.11	4.42
Mountain	1.75	3.98	0.72
Pacific	4.30	9.96	1.74

2015

	0–17	18–64	65+
Northeast	3.86	10.95	2.74
Midwest	5.08	13.11	3.09
South	9.11	22.80	5.45
Mountain	1.87	4.41	1.04
Pacific	3.98	10.33	2.20

(b)

	0–17	18–64	65+
Northeast	−0.78	−0.84	0.12
Midwest	−0.84	−0.92	0.16
South	0.03	0.69	1.03
Mountain	0.12	0.43	0.32
Pacific	−0.32	0.37	0.46

(c) The South and Mountain regions and the 65+ age group show relative growth.

4. See Additional Answers beginning on page AA1.

12. $\begin{vmatrix} x & 0 & 0 & d \\ -1 & x & 0 & c \\ 0 & -1 & x & b \\ 0 & 0 & -1 & a \end{vmatrix}$

13. Sulfur: 32 atomic mass units
Nitrogen: 14 atomic mass units
Fluorine: 19 atomic mass units

14. Transformer: \$10.00
Foot of wire: \$0.20
Light: \$1.00

15. $A^T = \begin{bmatrix} -1 & 2 \\ 1 & 0 \\ -2 & 1 \end{bmatrix}$

$B^T = \begin{bmatrix} -3 & 1 & 1 \\ 0 & 2 & -1 \end{bmatrix}$

$(AB)^T = \begin{bmatrix} 2 & -5 \\ 4 & -1 \end{bmatrix} = B^TA^T$

16. REMEMBER SEPTEMBER THE ELEVENTH

18. See below.

20. (a) Answers will vary.
(b) Squaring the 2×2 matrix yields the zero matrix. Cubing the 3×3 matrix yields the zero matrix.
(c) A^4 is the zero matrix.
(d) A^n is the zero matrix.

9. Verify the following equation.

$$\begin{vmatrix} 1 & 1 & 1 \\ a & b & c \\ a^2 & b^2 & c^2 \end{vmatrix} = (a - b)(b - c)(c - a)$$

9–11. Answers will vary.

10. Verify the following equation.

$$\begin{vmatrix} 1 & 1 & 1 \\ a & b & c \\ a^3 & b^3 & c^3 \end{vmatrix} = (a - b)(b - c)(c - a)(a + b + c)$$

11. Verify the following equation.

$$\begin{vmatrix} x & 0 & c \\ -1 & x & b \\ 0 & -1 & a \end{vmatrix} = ax^2 + bx + c$$

12. See margin.

12. Use the equation given in Exercise 11 as a model to find a determinant that is equal to $ax^3 + bx^2 + cx + d$.

13. The atomic masses of three compounds are shown in the table. Use a linear system and Cramer's Rule to find the atomic masses of sulfur (S), nitrogen (N), and fluorine (F). See margin.

Compound	Formula	Atomic Mass
Tetrasulfur tetranitride	S_4N_4	184
Sulfur hexafluoride	SF_6	146
Dinitrogen tetrafluoride	N_2F_4	104

14. A walkway lighting package includes a transformer, a certain length of wire, and a certain number of lights on the wire. The price of each lighting package depends on the length of wire and the number of lights on the wire. Use the following information to find the cost of a transformer, the cost per foot of wire, and the cost of a light. Assume that the cost of each item is the same in each lighting package. See margin.

- A package that contains a transformer, 25 feet of wire, and 5 lights costs \$20.
- A package that contains a transformer, 50 feet of wire, and 15 lights costs \$35.
- A package that contains a transformer, 100 feet of wire, and 20 lights costs \$50.

15. The **transpose** of a matrix, denoted A^T, is formed by writing its columns as rows. Find the transpose of each matrix and verify that $(AB)^T = B^TA^T$. See margin.

$$A = \begin{bmatrix} -1 & 1 & -2 \\ 2 & 0 & 1 \end{bmatrix}, \quad B = \begin{bmatrix} -3 & 0 \\ 1 & 2 \\ 1 & -1 \end{bmatrix}$$

16. Use the inverse of matrix A to decode the cryptogram.

$$A = \begin{bmatrix} 1 & -2 & 2 \\ 1 & 1 & -3 \\ 1 & -1 & 4 \end{bmatrix}$$

23 13 −34 31 −34 63 25 −17 61
24 14 −37 41 −17 −8 20 −29 40
38 −56 116 13 −11 1 22 −3 −6
41 −53 85 28 −32 16 See margin.

17. A code breaker intercepted the encoded message below.

45 −35 38 −30 18 −18 35 −30 81 −60
42 −28 75 −55 2 −2 22 −21 15
−10

Let

$$A^{-1} = \begin{bmatrix} w & x \\ y & z \end{bmatrix}. \qquad \text{(a) } A^{-1} = \begin{bmatrix} 1 & -2 \\ 1 & -3 \end{bmatrix}$$

(a) You know that $[45 \quad -35]A^{-1} = [10 \quad 15]$ and that $[38 \quad -30]A^{-1} = [8 \quad 14]$, where A^{-1} is the inverse of the encoding matrix A. Write and solve two systems of equations to find w, x, y, and z.

(b) Decode the message. JOHN RETURN TO BASE

18. Let

$$A = \begin{bmatrix} 6 & 4 & 1 \\ 0 & 2 & 3 \\ 1 & 1 & 2 \end{bmatrix}.$$

Use a graphing utility to find A^{-1}. Compare $|A^{-1}|$ with $|A|$. Make a conjecture about the determinant of the inverse of a matrix. See margin.

19. Let A be an $n \times n$ matrix each of whose rows adds up to zero. Find $|A|$. $|A| = 0$

20. Consider matrices of the form See margin.

$$A = \begin{bmatrix} 0 & a_{12} & a_{13} & a_{14} & \cdots & a_{1n} \\ 0 & 0 & a_{23} & a_{24} & \cdots & a_{2n} \\ 0 & 0 & 0 & a_{34} & \cdots & a_{3n} \\ \vdots & \vdots & \vdots & \vdots & \cdots & \vdots \\ 0 & 0 & 0 & 0 & \cdots & a_{(n-1)n} \\ 0 & 0 & 0 & 0 & \cdots & 0 \end{bmatrix}.$$

(a) Write a 2×2 matrix and a 3×3 matrix in the form of A.

(b) Use a graphing utility to raise each of the matrices to higher powers. Describe the result.

(c) Use the result of part (b) to make a conjecture about powers of A if A is a 4×4 matrix. Use a graphing utility to test your conjecture.

(d) Use the results of parts (b) and (c) to make a conjecture about powers of A if A is an $n \times n$ matrix.

18. $A^{-1} = \begin{bmatrix} 0.0625 & -0.4375 & 0.625 \\ 0.1875 & 0.6875 & -1.125 \\ -0.125 & -0.125 & 0.75 \end{bmatrix}$

$|A^{-1}| = \dfrac{1}{16}, |A| = 16$

$|A^{-1}| = \dfrac{1}{|A|}$

REGULAR SCHEDULE

Lesson	Day	AVERAGE	ADVANCED
9.1	Day 1	pp. 647–648 Exs. 1–3, 11–15 odd, 19, 21, 27–37 odd, 41, 43–46, 49, 51, 55–61 odd	pp. 647–648 Exs. 1–3, 12–16 even, 20, 24–28 even, 34–42 even, 43–46, 52, 54, 58, 62
	Day 2	pp. 647–648 Exs. 4–7, 65–69 odd, 73–79 odd, 83, 86, 87–93 odd, 97, 103–111 odd	pp. 647–648 Exs. 4–7, 64–78 even, 82–88 even, 92–98 even, 104–112 even
	Day 3	pp. 647–650 Exs. 8, 114–116, 117–121 odd, 122, 123, 127–131, 135–138, 140	pp. 647–650 Exs. 8, 114–120 even, 122–124, 126–140 even
9.2	Day 1	p. 657 Exs. 7–11 odd, 15–23 odd, 27–37 odd, 41–45 odd, 48, 49, 51, 55	p. 657 Exs. 8–12 even, 13, 16–22 even, 26–40 even, 44–50 even, 54–58 even
	Day 2	pp. 658–660 Exs. 61–67 odd, 71, 75, 77, 81, 83, 89–95 odd, 98, 101, 105–107, 109, 110, 113	pp. 658–660 Exs. 60–66 even, 72–86 even, 90–100 even, 104, 108–112, 114
9.3	Day 1	pp. 667–668 Exs. 1–3, 7–15 odd, 19–29 odd, 33, 37–41 odd, 47–51 odd, 57–61, 65	pp. 667–668 Exs. 1–3, 8–16 even, 22–32 even, 36–44 even, 48, 52, 54, 57–60, 62, 66
	Day 2	pp. 667–668 Exs. 4, 67, 69, 75–83 odd, 87–91 odd, 95–107	pp. 667–668 Exs. 4, 70–80 even, 84–92 even, 96–110 even
	Day 3	pp. 668–670 Exs. 111, 114–117, 123–133 odd, 137, 138, 141	pp. 668–670 Exs. 112–114, 116, 118–120, 122–142 even
9.4	Day 1	pp. 679–680 Exs. 1, 2, 7, 9, 13, 15, 18, 21–35 odd, 39, 41, 45, 47	pp. 679–680 Exs. 1, 2, 6–16 even, 22–36 even, 40, 42, 46, 48
	Day 2	pp. 679–680 Exs. 3, 4, 49–53 odd, 57–61 odd, 65–69 odd, 75, 81–85	pp. 679–680 Exs. 3, 4, 50–56 even, 60–70 even, 74, 79–85
9.5	Day 1	pp. 686–687 Exs. 1–4, 7, 9, 13, 17–29 odd, 33–43 odd, 61, 63, 73, 75	pp. 686–687 Exs. 1–4, 8, 10, 14–18 even, 22–30 even, 34–44 even, 62, 64, 74, 78
	Day 2	pp. 686–688 Exs. 69, 71, 79, 83–87 odd, 93–96, 99–101, 103	pp. 686–688 Exs. 48–54 even, 58–64 even, 70, 72, 80–90 even, 91, 93–95, 98–100, 102, 104
9.6	Day 1	pp. 696–697 Exs. 1–3, 7, 9, 10, 12, 15, 17, 21–27 odd, 31–39 odd, 40, 43, 45, 48, 49	pp. 696–697 Exs. 1–3, 8–14 even, 20–28 even, 32–40 even, 44–50 even
	Day 2	pp. 696–698 Exs. 4–6, 63–73 odd, 74, 87–90, 91–95 odd, 96	pp. 696–698 Exs. 4–6, 64–76 even, 87–90, 92–96 even, 97
9.7	Day 1	pp. 707–709 Exs. 1–4, 9–12, 13–19 odd, 22, 23, 26–29, 31–33, 35–41 odd, 45, 48, 49–51	pp. 707–709 Exs. 1–4, 10–20 even, 22–24, 28–30, 32–34, 36–42 even, 46, 48, 50–52
	Day 2	pp. 707–711 Exs. 5–8, 53–55, 58, 64, 67–69, 71–75	pp. 707–711 Exs. 5–8, 54–56, 58, 64, 66, 67, 69–75
Review	Day 1	pp. 714–715 Exs. 3–6, 9–15 odd, 19–33 odd, 37–41 odd, 45–55 odd, 59, 61, 65–71 odd	pp. 714–715 Exs. 2–6 even, 12–16 even, 20–34 even, 38–42 even, 46–58 even, 62–72 even
	Day 2	pp. 715–716 Exs. 73, 77–83 odd, 87–107 odd, 109–111, 113–116, 118, 120	pp. 715–716 Exs. 74–84 even, 88–108 even, 110–117, 119, 120
Assess	Day 1	Chapter 9 Test	Chapter 9 Test
Yearly Pacing	Chapter 9 Total – 19 days	Remaining – 45 days	

BLOCK SCHEDULE

DAY 1	DAY 2	DAY 3	DAY 4	DAY 5
9.1	**9.1 (CONT.)**	**9.2 (CONT.)**	**9.3 (CONT.)**	**9.4**
pp. 647–648 Exs. 1–7, 11–15 odd, 19, 21, 27–37 odd, 41, 43–46, 49, 51, 55–61 odd, 65–69 odd, 73–79 odd, 83, 86, 87–93 odd, 97, 103–111 odd	pp. 647–650 Exs. 8, 114–116, 117–121 odd, 122, 123, 127–131, 135–138, 140	pp. 658–660 Exs. 61–67 odd, 71, 75, 77, 81, 83, 89–95 odd, 98, 101, 105–107, 109, 110, 113	pp. 667–670 Exs. 4, 67, 69, 75–83 odd, 87–91 odd, 95–107, 111, 114–117, 123–133 odd, 137, 138, 141	pp. 679–680 Exs. 1–4, 7, 9, 13, 15, 18, 21–35 odd, 39, 41, 45–53 odd, 57–61 odd, 65–69 odd, 75, 81–85
	9.2	**9.3**		
	p. 657 Exs. 7–11 odd, 15–23 odd, 27–37 odd, 41–45 odd, 48, 49, 51, 55	pp. 667–668 Exs. 1–3, 7–15 odd, 19–29 odd, 33, 37–41 odd, 47–51 odd, 57–61, 65		

DAY 6	DAY 7	DAY 8	DAY 9	DAY 10
9.5	**9.6**	**9.7**	**REVIEW**	**ASSESS**
pp. 686–688 Exs. 1–4, 7, 9, 13, 17–29 odd, 33–43 odd, 61, 63, 69–75 odd, 79, 83–87 odd, 93–96, 99–101, 103	pp. 696–698 Exs. 1–7, 9, 10, 12, 15, 17, 21–27 odd, 31–39 odd, 40, 43, 45, 48, 49, 63–73 odd, 74, 87–90, 91–95 odd, 96	pp. 707–711 Exs. 1–12, 13–19 odd, 22, 23, 26–29, 31–33, 35–41 odd, 45, 48, 49–51, 53–55, 58, 64, 67–69, 71–75	pp. 714–716 Exs. 3–6, 9–15 odd, 19–33 odd, 37–41 odd, 45–55 odd, 59, 61, 65–73 odd, 77–83 odd, 87–107 odd, 109–111, 113–116, 118, 120	Chapter 9 Test
				10.1
				Begin Chapter 10

Yearly Pacing Chapter 9 Total – 9.5 days Remaining – 22.5 days

9

Sequences, Series, and Probability

In Mathematics

Sequences and series are used to describe algebraic patterns. Mathematical induction is used to prove formulas. The Binomial Theorem is used to calculate binomial coefficients. Probability theory is used to determine the likelihood of an event.

In Real Life

The concepts discussed in this chapter are used to model depreciation, sales, compound interest, population growth, and other real-life applications. For instance, the federal debt of the United States can be modeled by a sequence, which can then be used to identify patterns in the data. (See Exercise 125, page 649.)

Jonathan Larsen/Shutterstock

IN CAREERS

There are many careers that use the concepts presented in this chapter. Several are listed below.

- Public Finance Economist
  Exercises 127–130, page 669
- Professional Poker Player
  Example 9, page 695
- Quality Assurance Technician
  Example 11, page 706
- Survey Researcher
  Exercise 45, page 708

PLAN AND PREPARE

Main Ideas

In Chapter 9, students analyze sequences and series, expand binomials, and determine the probability of events. The chapter first introduces methods of representing sequences and series, including summation notation. Students then model and find sums of arithmetic and geometric sequences. Mathematical induction is introduced as a method to prove summation formulas. Students then expand binomials by using Pascal's Triangle and the Binomial Theorem. The chapter concludes with probability, a concept that challenges students to count possible outcomes and determine the probability of multiple events.

Chapter Planning Guide

Chapter Resources

- Complete Solutions Guide

Interactive Technology

- Instructor Success Organizer
- Notetaking Guide IAE
- Instructional DVDs
- Animated Precalculus
- PowerLecture with ExamView

9.1 SEQUENCES AND SERIES

What you should learn

- Use sequence notation to write the terms of sequences.
- Use factorial notation.
- Use summation notation to write sums.
- Find the sums of series.
- Use sequences and series to model and solve real-life problems.

Why you should learn it

Sequences and series can be used to model real-life problems. For instance, in Exercise 123 on page 649, sequences are used to model the numbers of Best Buy stores from 2002 through 2007.

Scott Olson/Getty Images

Sequences

In mathematics, the word *sequence* is used in much the same way as in ordinary English. Saying that a collection is listed in *sequence* means that it is ordered so that it has a first member, a second member, a third member, and so on. Two examples are 1, 2, 3, 4, . . . and 1, 3, 5, 7, ...

Mathematically, you can think of a sequence as a *function* whose domain is the set of positive integers.

$$f(1) = a_1,\ f(2) = a_2,\ f(3) = a_3,\ f(4) = a_4, \ldots,\ f(n) = a_n, \ldots$$

Rather than using function notation, however, sequences are usually written using subscript notation, as indicated in the following definition.

> **Definition of Sequence**
>
> An **infinite sequence** is a function whose domain is the set of positive integers. The function values
>
> $$a_1, a_2, a_3, a_4, \ldots, a_n, \ldots$$
>
> are the **terms** of the sequence. If the domain of the function consists of the first n positive integers only, the sequence is a **finite sequence.**

On occasion it is convenient to begin subscripting a sequence with 0 instead of 1 so that the terms of the sequence become $a_0, a_1, a_2, a_3, \ldots$. When this is the case, the domain includes 0.

Example 1 Writing the Terms of a Sequence

Write the first four terms of the sequences given by

a. $a_n = 3n - 2$ **b.** $a_n = 3 + (-1)^n$.

Solution

a. The first four terms of the sequence given by $a_n = 3n - 2$ are

$a_1 = 3(1) - 2 = 1$ 1st term

$a_2 = 3(2) - 2 = 4$ 2nd term

$a_3 = 3(3) - 2 = 7$ 3rd term

$a_4 = 3(4) - 2 = 10.$ 4th term

b. The first four terms of the sequence given by $a_n = 3 + (-1)^n$ are

$a_1 = 3 + (-1)^1 = 3 - 1 = 2$ 1st term

$a_2 = 3 + (-1)^2 = 3 + 1 = 4$ 2nd term

$a_3 = 3 + (-1)^3 = 3 - 1 = 2$ 3rd term

$a_4 = 3 + (-1)^4 = 3 + 1 = 4.$ 4th term

CHECKPoint Now try Exercise 9.

> **Study Tip**
>
> The subscripts of a sequence make up the domain of the sequence and serve to identify the locations of terms within the sequence. For example, a_4 is the fourth term of the sequence, and a_n is the nth term of the sequence. Any variable can be used as a subscript. The most commonly used variable subscripts in sequence and series notation are i, j, k, and n.

1 PLAN AND PREPARE

Warm-up Exercises

Transparency Available
Available at the Instructor's companion site.

Notetaking Guide

Transparency Available
Promotes interactive learning and notetaking skills.
Available at the Instructor's companion site.

Animated Precalculus

An **Animated Precalculus** tutorial is available at the Student companion site for **Section 9.1.**

Pacing

Average: 3 days
Advanced: 3 days
Block: 1 block
0.5 block with 9.2

2 FOCUS AND MOTIVATE

Essential Question

How do you represent a sequence of numbers or the sum of a sequence? **Tell students that they will learn how to answer this question by studying factorial and summation notation.**

Resource Planning Guide

Chapter Resources
- Complete Solutions Guide

Workbooks
- Notetaking Guide
- Student Solutions Guide

Interactive Technology
- Instructor Success Organizer
- Notetaking Guide IAE
- Instructional DVDs
- Animated Precalculus
- PowerLecture with ExamView

Example 2 A Sequence Whose Terms Alternate in Sign

Write the first five terms of the sequence given by $a_n = \frac{(-1)^n}{2n + 1}$.

Solution

The first five terms of the sequence are as follows.

$$a_1 = \frac{(-1)^1}{2(1) + 1} = \frac{-1}{2 + 1} = -\frac{1}{3} \qquad \text{1st term}$$

$$a_2 = \frac{(-1)^2}{2(2) + 1} = \frac{1}{4 + 1} = \frac{1}{5} \qquad \text{2nd term}$$

$$a_3 = \frac{(-1)^3}{2(3) + 1} = \frac{-1}{6 + 1} = -\frac{1}{7} \qquad \text{3rd term}$$

$$a_4 = \frac{(-1)^4}{2(4) + 1} = \frac{1}{8 + 1} = \frac{1}{9} \qquad \text{4th term}$$

$$a_5 = \frac{(-1)^5}{2(5) + 1} = \frac{-1}{10 + 1} = -\frac{1}{11} \qquad \text{5th term}$$

CHECK*Point* Now try Exercise 25.

Simply listing the first few terms is not sufficient to define a unique sequence—the nth term *must be given*. To see this, consider the following sequences, both of which have the same first three terms.

$$\frac{1}{2}, \frac{1}{4}, \frac{1}{8}, \frac{1}{16}, \ldots, \frac{1}{2^n}, \ldots$$

$$\frac{1}{2}, \frac{1}{4}, \frac{1}{8}, \frac{1}{15}, \ldots, \frac{6}{(n + 1)(n^2 - n + 6)}, \ldots$$

Example 3 Finding the nth Term of a Sequence

Write an expression for the apparent nth term (a_n) of each sequence.

a. $1, 3, 5, 7, \ldots$ **b.** $2, -5, 10, -17, \ldots$

Solution

a. n: 1 2 3 4 . . . n

Terms: 1 3 5 7 . . . a_n

Apparent pattern: Each term is 1 less than twice n, which implies that

$$a_n = 2n - 1.$$

b. n: 1 2 3 4 . . . n

Terms: 2 −5 10 −17 . . . a_n

Apparent pattern: The terms have alternating signs with those in the even positions being negative. Each term is 1 more than the square of n, which implies that

$$a_n = (-1)^{n+1}(n^2 + 1)$$

CHECK*Point* Now try Exercise 47.

TECHNOLOGY

To graph a sequence using a graphing utility, set the mode to *sequence* and *dot* and enter the sequence. The graph of the sequence in Example 3(a) is shown below. You can use the *trace* feature or *value* feature to identify the terms.

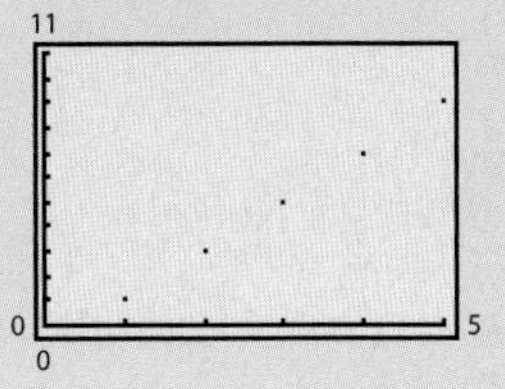

3 TEACH

Extra Example 1

Write the first five terms of each sequence.

a. $a_n = 2n + 1$

3, 5, 7, 9, 11

b. $a_n = 2 - (-1)^n$

3, 1, 3, 1, 3

Extra Example 2

Write the first five terms of

$$a_n = \frac{2 + (-1)^n}{n}.$$

$$\mathbf{1, \frac{3}{2}, \frac{1}{3}, \frac{3}{4}, \frac{1}{5}}$$

Extra Example 3

Write an expression for the most apparent nth term of each sequence.

a. 1, 5, 9, 13, 17, . . .

$a_n = 4n - 3$

b. 2, −9, 28, −65, 126

$a_n = (-1)^{n-1}(n^3 + 1)$

Extra Example 4

Write the first five terms of the recursively-defined sequence.

$a_1 = 6,\ a_{k+1} = a_k + 1$

6, 7, 8, 9, 10

Some sequences are defined **recursively.** To define a sequence recursively, you need to be given one or more of the first few terms. All other terms of the sequence are then defined using previous terms. A well-known recursive sequence is the Fibonacci sequence shown in Example 4.

Example 4 The Fibonacci Sequence: A Recursive Sequence

The Fibonacci sequence is defined recursively, as follows.

$$a_0 = 1,\ a_1 = 1,\ a_k = a_{k-2} + a_{k-1}, \text{ where } k \geq 2$$

Write the first six terms of this sequence.

Solution

$a_0 = 1$ — 0th term is given.

$a_1 = 1$ — 1st term is given.

$a_2 = a_{2-2} + a_{2-1} = a_0 + a_1 = 1 + 1 = 2$ — Use recursion formula.

$a_3 = a_{3-2} + a_{3-1} = a_1 + a_2 = 1 + 2 = 3$ — Use recursion formula.

$a_4 = a_{4-2} + a_{4-1} = a_2 + a_3 = 2 + 3 = 5$ — Use recursion formula.

$a_5 = a_{5-2} + a_{5-1} = a_3 + a_4 = 3 + 5 = 8$ — Use recursion formula.

CHECK*Point* Now try Exercise 65.

Factorial Notation

Some very important sequences in mathematics involve terms that are defined with special types of products called **factorials.**

Definition of Factorial

If n is a positive integer, $\boldsymbol{n}$ **factorial** is defined as

$$n! = 1 \cdot 2 \cdot 3 \cdot 4 \cdot \cdot \cdot (n - 1) \cdot n.$$

As a special case, zero factorial is defined as $0! = 1$.

Here are some values of $n!$ for the first several nonnegative integers. Notice that $0!$ is 1 by definition.

$0! = 1$

$1! = 1$

$2! = 1 \cdot 2 - 2$

$3! = 1 \cdot 2 \cdot 3 = 6$

$4! = 1 \cdot 2 \cdot 3 \cdot 4 = 24$

$5! = 1 \cdot 2 \cdot 3 \cdot 4 \cdot 5 = 120$

The value of n does not have to be very large before the value of $n!$ becomes extremely large. For instance, $10! = 3{,}628{,}800$.

Factorials follow the same conventions for order of operations as do exponents. For instance,

$$2n! = 2(n!) = 2(1 \cdot 2 \cdot 3 \cdot 4 \cdot \cdot \cdot n)$$

whereas $(2n)! = 1 \cdot 2 \cdot 3 \cdot 4 \cdot \cdot \cdot 2n$.

Example 5 Writing the Terms of a Sequence Involving Factorials

Write the first five terms of the sequence given by

$$a_n = \frac{2^n}{n!}.$$

Begin with $n = 0$.

Algebraic Solution

$a_0 = \frac{2^0}{0!} = \frac{1}{1} = 1$ 0th term

$a_1 = \frac{2^1}{1!} = \frac{2}{1} = 2$ 1st term

$a_2 = \frac{2^2}{2!} = \frac{4}{2} = 2$ 2nd term

$a_3 = \frac{2^3}{3!} = \frac{8}{6} = \frac{4}{3}$ 3rd term

$a_4 = \frac{2^4}{4!} = \frac{16}{24} = \frac{2}{3}$ 4th term

CHECKPoint Now try Exercise 71.

Numerical Solution

Set your graphing utility to *sequence* mode. Enter the sequence into your graphing utility, as shown in Figure 9.1. Use the *table* feature (in *ask* mode) to create a table showing the terms of the sequence u_n for $n = 0, 1, 2, 3,$ and 4.

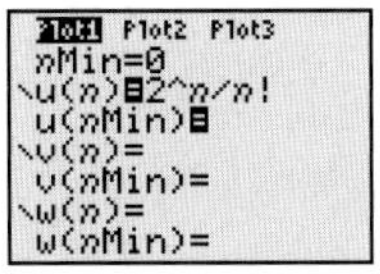

FIGURE 9.1

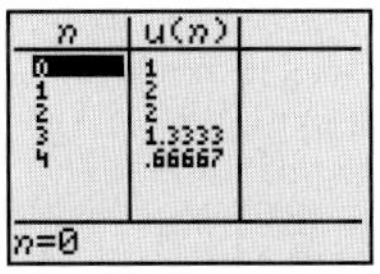

FIGURE 9.2

From Figure 9.2, you can estimate the first five terms of the sequence as follows.

$$u_0 = 1, \; u_1 = 2, \; u_2 = 2, \; u_3 \approx 1.3333 \approx \tfrac{4}{3}, \; u_4 \approx 0.66667 \approx \tfrac{2}{3}$$

When working with fractions involving factorials, you will often find that the fractions can be reduced to simplify the computations.

Example 6 Evaluating Factorial Expressions

Evaluate each factorial expression.

a. $\frac{8!}{2! \cdot 6!}$ **b.** $\frac{2! \cdot 6!}{3! \cdot 5!}$ **c.** $\frac{n!}{(n-1)!}$

Solution

a. $\frac{8!}{2! \cdot 6!} = \frac{\cancel{1 \cdot 2 \cdot 3 \cdot 4 \cdot 5 \cdot 6} \cdot 7 \cdot 8}{1 \cdot 2 \cdot \cancel{1 \cdot 2 \cdot 3 \cdot 4 \cdot 5 \cdot 6}} = \frac{7 \cdot 8}{2} = 28$

b. $\frac{2! \cdot 6!}{3! \cdot 5!} = \frac{\cancel{1 \cdot 2} \cdot \cancel{1 \cdot 2 \cdot 3 \cdot 4 \cdot 5} \cdot 6}{\cancel{1 \cdot 2} \cdot 3 \cdot \cancel{1 \cdot 2 \cdot 3 \cdot 4 \cdot 5}} = \frac{6}{3} = 2$

c. $\frac{n!}{(n-1)!} = \frac{\cancel{1 \cdot 2 \cdot 3 \cdots (n-1)} \cdot n}{\cancel{1 \cdot 2 \cdot 3 \cdots (n-1)}} = n$

CHECKPoint Now try Exercise 81.

Algebra Help

Note in Example 6(a) that you can simplify the computation as follows.

$$\frac{8!}{2! \cdot 6!} = \frac{8 \cdot 7 \cdot \cancel{6!}}{2! \cdot \cancel{6!}}$$

$$= \frac{8 \cdot 7}{2 \cdot 1} = 28$$

Extra Example 5

Write the first five terms of the sequence given by $a_n = \frac{3^n + 1}{n!}$. Begin with $n = 0$. Then graph the terms on a set of coordinate axes.

$2, 4, 5, \frac{14}{3}, \frac{41}{12}$

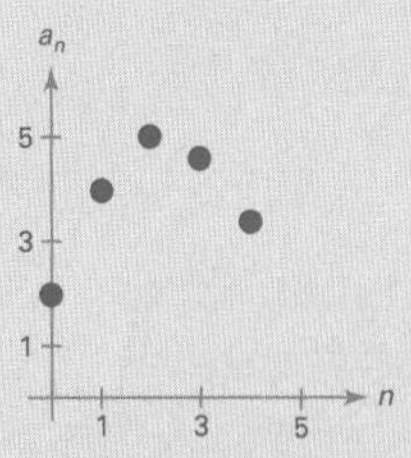

Extra Example 6

Evaluate each factorial expression.

a. $\frac{9!}{3!7!}$

12

b. $\frac{3!8!}{4!4!}$

420

c. $\frac{(n+1)!}{n!}$

$n + 1$

Differentiated Instruction

Visual Learners To assist visual learners in grasping the concept of factorials, encourage them to write out factorials in their calculations until they have memorized the basics. In Example 5, have them write 3! as $1 \cdot 2 \cdot 3$ and 4! as $1 \cdot 2 \cdot 3 \cdot 4$. Repeating this process will help students understand factorials and begin to recognize values for basic factorials.

Extra Example 7

Find each sum.

a. $\sum_{i=1}^{4}(4i + 1)$

44

b. $\sum_{k=2}^{5}(2 + k^3)$

232

c. $\sum_{i=1}^{6}\frac{2}{i!}$

≈ 3.43611

Avoiding Common Errors

Students often make errors by using an incorrect upper or lower limit in summation notation. Remind students to confirm that the lower limit creates the correct value for the first term and that the value reflects the correct sign pattern if a power of a negative number is included in the expression. Reading and writing these limits correctly will help students solve problems involving upper and lower limits in calculus.

TECHNOLOGY

Most graphing utilities are able to sum the first n terms of a sequence. Check your user's guide for a *sum sequence* feature or a *series* feature.

Study Tip

Summation notation is an instruction to add the terms of a sequence. From the definition at the right, the upper limit of summation tells you where to end the sum. Summation notation helps you generate the appropriate terms of the sequence prior to finding the actual sum, which may be unclear.

Summation Notation

There is a convenient notation for the sum of the terms of a finite sequence. It is called **summation notation** or **sigma notation** because it involves the use of the uppercase Greek letter sigma, written as Σ.

Definition of Summation Notation

The sum of the first n terms of a sequence is represented by

$$\sum_{i=1}^{n} a_i = a_1 + a_2 + a_3 + a_4 + \cdots + a_n$$

where i is called the **index of summation,** n is the **upper limit of summation,** and 1 is the **lower limit of summation.**

Example 7 Summation Notation for a Sum

Find each sum.

a. $\sum_{i=1}^{5} 3i$ b. $\sum_{k=3}^{6}(1 + k^2)$ c. $\sum_{i=0}^{8}\frac{1}{i!}$

Solution

a. $$\sum_{i=1}^{5} 3i = 3(1) + 3(2) + 3(3) + 3(4) + 3(5)$$
$$= 3(1 + 2 + 3 + 4 + 5)$$
$$= 3(15)$$
$$= 45$$

b. $$\sum_{k=3}^{6}(1 + k^2) = (1 + 3^2) + (1 + 4^2) + (1 + 5^2) + (1 + 6^2)$$
$$= 10 + 17 + 26 + 37$$
$$= 90$$

c. $$\sum_{i=0}^{8}\frac{1}{i!} = \frac{1}{0!} + \frac{1}{1!} + \frac{1}{2!} + \frac{1}{3!} + \frac{1}{4!} + \frac{1}{5!} + \frac{1}{6!} + \frac{1}{7!} + \frac{1}{8!}$$
$$= 1 + 1 + \frac{1}{2} + \frac{1}{6} + \frac{1}{24} + \frac{1}{120} + \frac{1}{720} + \frac{1}{5040} + \frac{1}{40{,}320}$$
$$\approx 2.71828$$

For this summation, note that the sum is very close to the irrational number $e \approx 2.718281828$. It can be shown that as more terms of the sequence whose nth term is $1/n!$ are added, the sum becomes closer and closer to e.

CHECKPoint Now try Exercise 85.

In Example 7, note that the lower limit of a summation does not have to be 1. Also note that the index of summation does not have to be the letter i. For instance, in part (b), the letter k is the index of summation.

Study Tip

Variations in the upper and lower limits of summation can produce quite different-looking summation notations for *the same sum*. For example, the following two sums have the same terms.

$$\sum_{i=1}^{3} 3(2^i) = 3(2^1 + 2^2 + 2^3)$$

$$\sum_{i=0}^{2} 3(2^{i+1}) = 3(2^1 + 2^2 + 2^3)$$

Properties of Sums

1. $\sum_{i=1}^{n} c = cn,\quad c$ is a constant.
2. $\sum_{i=1}^{n} ca_i = c\sum_{i=1}^{n} a_i,\quad c$ is a constant.
3. $\sum_{i=1}^{n} (a_i + b_i) = \sum_{i=1}^{n} a_i + \sum_{i=1}^{n} b_i$
4. $\sum_{i=1}^{n} (a_i - b_i) = \sum_{i=1}^{n} a_i - \sum_{i=1}^{n} b_i$

For proofs of these properties, see Proofs in Mathematics on page 720.

Series

Many applications involve the sum of the terms of a finite or infinite sequence. Such a sum is called a **series.**

Definition of Series

Consider the infinite sequence $a_1, a_2, a_3, \ldots, a_i, \ldots$.

1. The sum of the first n terms of the sequence is called a **finite series** or the ***n*th partial sum** of the sequence and is denoted by

$$a_1 + a_2 + a_3 + \cdots + a_n = \sum_{i=1}^{n} a_i.$$

2. The sum of all the terms of the infinite sequence is called an **infinite series** and is denoted by

$$a_1 + a_2 + a_3 + \cdots + a_i + \cdots = \sum_{i=1}^{\infty} a_i.$$

Example 8 Finding the Sum of a Series

For the series $\sum_{i=1}^{\infty} \frac{3}{10^i}$, find (a) the third partial sum and (b) the sum.

Solution

a. The third partial sum is

$$\sum_{i=1}^{3} \frac{3}{10^i} = \frac{3}{10^1} + \frac{3}{10^2} + \frac{3}{10^3} = 0.3 + 0.03 + 0.003 = 0.333.$$

b. The sum of the series is

$$\sum_{i=1}^{\infty} \frac{3}{10^i} = \frac{3}{10^1} + \frac{3}{10^2} + \frac{3}{10^3} + \frac{3}{10^4} + \frac{3}{10^5} + \cdots$$

$$= 0.3 + 0.03 + 0.003 + 0.0003 + 0.00003 + \cdots$$

$$= 0.33333\ldots = \frac{1}{3}.$$

CHECKPoint Now try Exercise 113.

Extra Example 8

For the series $\sum_{n=1}^{\infty} \frac{5}{10^n}$, find (a) the third partial sum and (b) the sum.

$0.555;\ 0.55555\ldots = \frac{5}{9}$

Extra Example 9

A deposit of \$1500 is made in an account that earns 2.5% interest compounded monthly. The balance in the account after n months is given by

$$A_n = 1500\left(1 + \frac{0.025}{12}\right)^n,$$

$n = 0, 1, 2, \ldots$.

a. Write the first three terms of the sequence.

\$1500, \$1503.13, \$1506.26

b. Find the balance in the account after four years by computing the 48th term of the sequence.

\$1657.58

Extra Example 10

The number of employees in physicians' offices in the United States from 2002 through 2007 is approximated by the model $a_n = 2.52n^2 + 24.8n + 1908$, $n = 0, 1, \ldots, 7$, where a_n is the number of employees (in thousands) and n represents the year, with $n = 2$ corresponding to 2002. Find the last three terms of this sequence, which represent the number of U.S. physicians' office employees for the years 2005 through 2007. (Source: U.S. Bureau of Labor Statistics)

2,095,000; 2,147,520; 2,205,080

Closing the Lesson

Have students summarize the major points of the lesson and answer the Essential Question: How do you represent a sequence of numbers or the sum of a sequence?

- **Write, simplify, and evaluate expressions containing $n!$ by using the definition of factorial.**
- **Use summation notation to represent the sum of a finite or infinite sequence.**
- **Recognize properties of sums.**

Applications

Sequences have many applications in business and science. Two such applications are illustrated in Examples 9 and 10.

Example 9 Compound Interest

A deposit of \$5000 is made in an account that earns 3% interest compounded quarterly. The balance in the account after n quarters is given by

$$A_n = 5000\left(1 + \frac{0.03}{4}\right)^n, \quad n = 0, 1, 2, \ldots.$$

a. Write the first three terms of the sequence.

b. Find the balance in the account after 10 years by computing the 40th term of the sequence.

Solution

a. The first three terms of the sequence are as follows.

$$A_0 = 5000\left(1 + \frac{0.03}{4}\right)^0 = \$5000.00 \qquad \text{Original deposit}$$

$$A_1 = 5000\left(1 + \frac{0.03}{4}\right)^1 = \$5037.50 \qquad \text{First-quarter balance}$$

$$A_2 = 5000\left(1 + \frac{0.03}{4}\right)^2 = \$5075.28 \qquad \text{Second-quarter balance}$$

b. The 40th term of the sequence is

$$A_{40} = 5000\left(1 + \frac{0.03}{4}\right)^{40} = \$6741.74. \qquad \text{Ten-year balance}$$

CHECK*Point* Now try Exercise 121.

Example 10 Population of the United States

For the years 1980 through 2007, the resident population of the United States can be approximated by the model

$$a_n = 226.6 + 2.33n + 0.019n^2, \quad n = 0, 1, \ldots, 27$$

where a_n is the population (in millions) and n represents the year, with $n = 0$ corresponding to 1980. Find the last five terms of this finite sequence, which represent the U.S. population for the years 2003 through 2007. (Source: U.S. Census Bureau)

Solution

The last five terms of this finite sequence are as follows.

$$a_{23} = 226.6 + 2.33(23) + 0.019(23)^2 \approx 290.2 \qquad \text{2003 population}$$

$$a_{24} = 226.6 + 2.33(24) + 0.019(24)^2 \approx 293.5 \qquad \text{2004 population}$$

$$a_{25} = 226.6 + 2.33(25) + 0.019(25)^2 \approx 296.7 \qquad \text{2005 population}$$

$$a_{26} = 226.6 + 2.33(26) + 0.019(26)^2 \approx 300.0 \qquad \text{2006 population}$$

$$a_{27} = 226.6 + 2.33(27) + 0.019(27)^2 \approx 303.4 \qquad \text{2007 population}$$

CHECK*Point* Now try Exercise 125.

9.1 EXERCISES

See www.CalcChat.com for worked-out solutions to odd-numbered exercises.

VOCABULARY: Fill in the blanks.

1. An infinite sequence is a function whose domain is the set of positive integers.
2. The function values $a_1, a_2, a_3, a_4, \ldots$ are called the terms of a sequence.
3. A sequence is a finite sequence if the domain of the function consists only of the first n positive integers.
4. If you are given one or more of the first few terms of a sequence, and all other terms of the sequence are defined using previous terms, then the sequence is said to be defined recursively
5. If n is a positive integer, n factorial is defined as $n! = 1 \cdot 2 \cdot 3 \cdot 4 \cdots (n-1) \cdot n$.
6. The notation used to represent the sum of the terms of a finite sequence is summation notation or sigma notation.
7. For the sum $\sum_{i=1}^{n} a_i$, i is called the index of summation, n is the upper limit of summation, and 1 is the lower limit of summation.
8. The sum of the terms of a finite or infinite sequence is called a series.

SKILLS AND APPLICATIONS

In Exercises 9–32, write the first five terms of the sequence. (Assume that n begins with 1.) 9–32. See margin.

9. $a_n = 2n + 5$
10. $a_n = 4n - 7$
11. $a_n = 2^n$
12. $a_n = \left(\frac{1}{2}\right)^n$
13. $a_n = (-2)^n$
14. $a_n = \left(-\frac{1}{2}\right)^n$
15. $a_n = \dfrac{n+2}{n}$
16. $a_n = \dfrac{n}{n+2}$
17. $a_n = \dfrac{6n}{3n^2 - 1}$
18. $a_n = \dfrac{2n}{n^2 + 1}$
19. $a_n = \dfrac{1 + (-1)^n}{n}$
20. $a_n = 1 + (-1)^n$
21. $a_n = 2 - \dfrac{1}{3^n}$
22. $a_n = \dfrac{2^n}{3^n}$
23. $a_n = \dfrac{1}{n^{3/2}}$
24. $a_n = \dfrac{10}{n^{2/3}}$
25. $a_n = \dfrac{(-1)^n}{n^2}$
26. $a_n = (-1)^n\left(\dfrac{n}{n+1}\right)$
27. $a_n = \frac{2}{3}$
28. $a_n = 0.3$
29. $a_n = n(n-1)(n-2)$
30. $a_n = n(n^2 - 6)$
31. $a_n = \dfrac{(-1)^{n+1}}{n^2 + 1}$
32. $a_n = \dfrac{(-1)^{n+1}}{2n + 1}$

In Exercises 33–36, find the indicated term of the sequence.

33. $a_n = (-1)^n(3n - 2)$
$a_{25} =$ -73
34. $a_n = (-1)^{n-1}[n(n-1)]$
$a_{16} =$ -240
35. $a_n = \dfrac{4n}{2n^2 - 3}$
$a_{11} =$ $\frac{44}{239}$
36. $a_n = \dfrac{4n^2 - n + 3}{n(n-1)(n+2)}$
$a_{13} =$ $\frac{37}{130}$

In Exercises 37–42, use a graphing utility to graph the first 10 terms of the sequence. (Assume that n begins with 1.) 37–42. See margin.

37. $a_n = \dfrac{2}{3}n$
38. $a_n = 2 - \dfrac{4}{n}$
39. $a_n = 16(-0.5)^{n-1}$
40. $a_n = 8(0.75)^{n-1}$
41. $a_n = \dfrac{2n}{n+1}$
42. $a_n = \dfrac{3n^2}{n^2 + 1}$

In Exercises 43–46, match the sequence with the graph of its first 10 terms. [The graphs are labeled (a), (b), (c), and (d).]

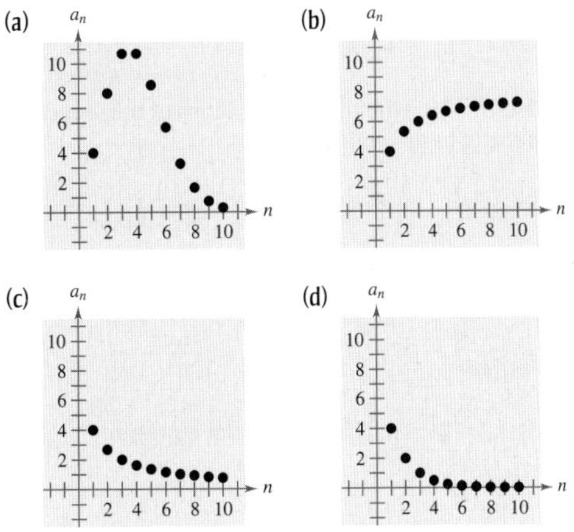

43. $a_n = \dfrac{8}{n+1}$ c
44. $a_n = \dfrac{8n}{n+1}$ b
45. $a_n = 4(0.5)^{n-1}$ d
46. $a_n = \dfrac{4^n}{n!}$ a

4 PRACTICE AND APPLY

Assignment Guide

Transparencies Available
Available at the Instructor's companion site.

Average:
Day 1: pp. 647–648
Exs. 1–3, 11–15 odd, 19, 21, 27–37 odd, 41, 43–46, 49, 51, 55–61 odd
Day 2: pp. 647–648
Exs. 4–7, 65–69 odd, 73–79 odd, 83, 86, 87–93 odd, 97, 103–111 odd
Day 3: pp. 647–650
Exs. 8, 114–116, 117–121 odd, 122, 123, 127–131, 135–138, 140

Advanced:
Day 1: pp. 647–648
Exs. 1–3, 12–16 even, 20, 24–28 even, 34–42 even, 43–46, 52, 54, 58, 62
Day 2: pp. 647–648
Exs. 4–7, 64–78 even, 82–88 even, 92–98 even, 104–112 even
Day 3: pp. 647–650
Exs. 8, 114–120 even, 122–124, 126–140 even

Block:
pp. 647–648
Exs. 1–7, 11–15 odd, 19, 21, 27–37 odd, 41, 43–46, 49, 51, 55–61 odd, 65–69 odd, 73–79 odd, 83, 86, 87–93 odd, 97, 103–111 odd
pp. 647–650
Exs. 8, 114–116, 117–121 odd, 122, 123, 127–131, 135–138, 140 (with 9.2)

9. 7, 9, 11, 13, 15
10. $-3, 1, 5, 9, 13$
11. 2, 4, 8, 16, 32
12. $\frac{1}{2}, \frac{1}{4}, \frac{1}{8}, \frac{1}{16}, \frac{1}{32}$
13. $-2, 4, -8, 16, -32$
14. $-\frac{1}{2}, \frac{1}{4}, -\frac{1}{8}, \frac{1}{16}, -\frac{1}{32}$
15. $3, 2, \frac{5}{3}, \frac{3}{2}, \frac{7}{5}$
16. $\frac{1}{3}, \frac{1}{2}, \frac{3}{5}, \frac{2}{3}, \frac{5}{7}$
17. $3, \frac{12}{11}, \frac{9}{13}, \frac{24}{47}, \frac{15}{37}$
18. $1, \frac{4}{5}, \frac{3}{5}, \frac{8}{17}, \frac{5}{13}$
19. $0, 1, 0, \frac{1}{2}, 0$
20. 0, 2, 0, 2, 0
21. $\frac{5}{3}, \frac{17}{9}, \frac{53}{27}, \frac{161}{81}, \frac{485}{243}$
22. $\frac{2}{3}, \frac{4}{9}, \frac{8}{27}, \frac{16}{81}, \frac{32}{243}$
23. $1, \dfrac{1}{2^{3/2}}, \dfrac{1}{3^{3/2}}, \dfrac{1}{8}, \dfrac{1}{5^{3/2}}$
24. $10, \dfrac{10}{\sqrt[3]{4}}, \dfrac{10}{\sqrt[3]{9}}, \dfrac{10}{\sqrt[3]{16}}, \dfrac{10}{\sqrt[3]{25}}$
25. $-1, \frac{1}{4}, -\frac{1}{9}, \frac{1}{16}, -\frac{1}{25}$
26. $-\frac{1}{2}, \frac{2}{3}, -\frac{3}{4}, \frac{4}{5}, -\frac{5}{6}$
27. $\frac{2}{3}, \frac{2}{3}, \frac{2}{3}, \frac{2}{3}, \frac{2}{3}$
28. 0.3, 0.3, 0.3, 0.3, 0.3
29. 0, 0, 6, 24, 60
30. $-5, -4, 9, 40, 95$
31. $\frac{1}{2}, -\frac{1}{5}, \frac{1}{10}, -\frac{1}{17}, \frac{1}{26}$
32. $\frac{1}{3}, -\frac{1}{5}, \frac{1}{7}, -\frac{1}{9}, \frac{1}{11}$

37.
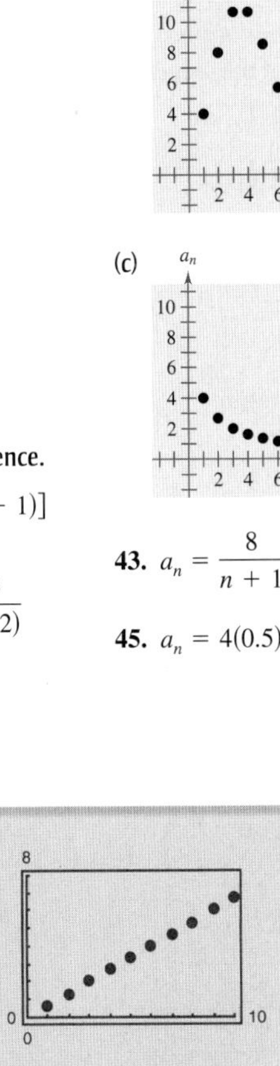

38.
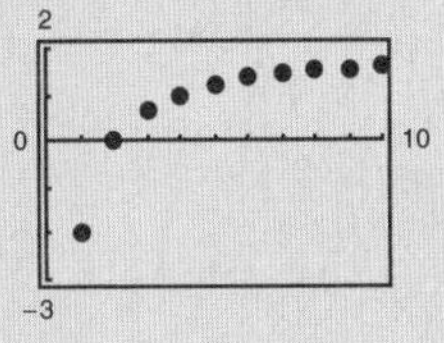

39.
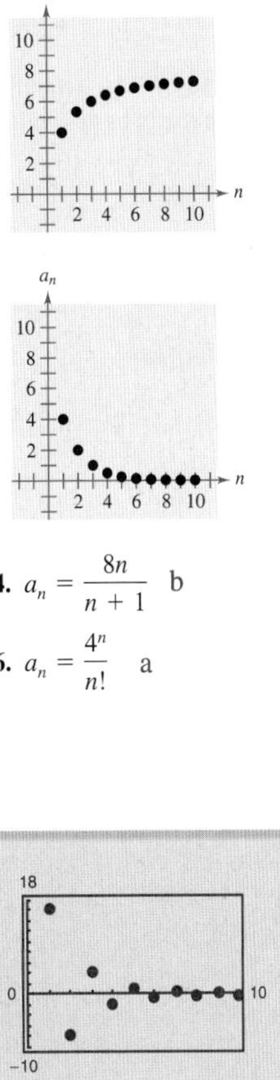

40.
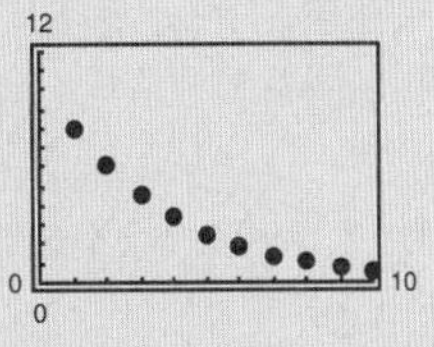

41–42. See Additional Answers beginning on page AA1.

47–62. See margin.

In Exercises 47–62, write an expression for the apparent nth term of the sequence. (Assume that n begins with 1.)

47. $1, 4, 7, 10, 13, \ldots$

48. $3, 7, 11, 15, 19, \ldots$

49. $0, 3, 8, 15, 24, \ldots$

50. $2, -4, 6, -8, 10, \ldots$

51. $-\frac{2}{3}, \frac{3}{4}, -\frac{4}{5}, \frac{5}{6}, -\frac{6}{7}, \ldots$

52. $\frac{1}{2}, -\frac{1}{4}, \frac{1}{8}, -\frac{1}{16}, \ldots$

53. $\frac{2}{1}, \frac{3}{3}, \frac{4}{5}, \frac{5}{7}, \frac{6}{9}, \ldots$

54. $\frac{1}{3}, \frac{2}{9}, \frac{4}{27}, \frac{8}{81}, \ldots$

55. $1, \frac{1}{4}, \frac{1}{9}, \frac{1}{16}, \frac{1}{25}, \ldots$

56. $1, \frac{1}{2}, \frac{1}{6}, \frac{1}{24}, \frac{1}{120}, \ldots$

57. $1, -1, 1, -1, 1, \ldots$

58. $1, 2, \frac{2^2}{2}, \frac{2^3}{6}, \frac{2^4}{24}, \frac{2^5}{120}, \ldots$

59. $1, 3, 1, 3, 1, \ldots$

60. $3, \frac{3}{2}, 1, \frac{3}{4}, \frac{3}{5}, \ldots$

61. $1 + \frac{1}{1}, 1 + \frac{1}{2}, 1 + \frac{1}{3}, 1 + \frac{1}{4}, 1 + \frac{1}{5}, \ldots$

62. $1 + \frac{1}{2}, 1 + \frac{3}{4}, 1 + \frac{7}{8}, 1 + \frac{15}{16}, 1 + \frac{31}{32}, \ldots$

In Exercises 63–66, write the first five terms of the sequence defined recursively.

63. $a_1 = 28, \quad a_{k+1} = a_k - 4$ 28, 24, 20, 16, 12

64. $a_1 = 15, \quad a_{k+1} = a_k + 3$ 15, 18, 21, 24, 27

65. $a_1 = 3, \quad a_{k+1} = 2(a_k - 1)$ 3, 4, 6, 10, 18

66. $a_1 = 32, \quad a_{k+1} = \frac{1}{2}a_k$ 32, 16, 8, 4, 2

In Exercises 67–70, write the first five terms of the sequence defined recursively. Use the pattern to write the nth term of the sequence as a function of n. (Assume that n begins with 1.)

67. $a_1 = 6, \quad a_{k+1} = a_k + 2$ 67. 6, 8, 10, 12, 14; $a_n = 2n + 4$

68. $a_1 = 25, \quad a_{k+1} = a_k - 5$ 68. 25, 20, 15, 10, 5; $a_n = 30 - 5n$

69. $a_1 = 81, \quad a_{k+1} = \frac{1}{3}a_k$

70. $a_1 = 14, \quad a_{k+1} = (-2)a_k$

69–70. See margin.

In Exercises 71–76, write the first five terms of the sequence. (Assume that n begins with 0.)

71. $a_n = \dfrac{1}{n!}$ $1, 1, \frac{1}{2}, \frac{1}{6}, \frac{1}{24}$

72. $a_n = \dfrac{n!}{2n + 1}$ $1, \frac{1}{3}, \frac{2}{5}, \frac{6}{7}, \frac{8}{3}$

73. $a_n = \dfrac{1}{(n + 1)!}$ See margin.

74. $a_n = \dfrac{n^2}{(n + 1)!}$ $0, \frac{1}{2}, \frac{2}{3}, \frac{3}{8}, \frac{2}{15}$

75. $a_n = \dfrac{(-1)^{2n}}{(2n)!}$ $1, \frac{1}{2}, \frac{1}{24}, \frac{1}{720}, \frac{1}{40{,}320}$

76. $a_n = \dfrac{(-1)^{2n+1}}{(2n + 1)!}$ $-1, -\frac{1}{6}, -\frac{1}{120}, -\frac{1}{5040}, -\frac{1}{362{,}880}$

In Exercises 77–84, simplify the factorial expression.

77. $\dfrac{4!}{6!}$ $\frac{1}{30}$

78. $\dfrac{5!}{8!}$ $\frac{1}{336}$

79. $\dfrac{12!}{4! \cdot 8!}$ 495

80. $\dfrac{10! \cdot 3!}{4! \cdot 6!}$ 1260

81. $\dfrac{(n + 1)!}{n!}$ $n + 1$

82. $\dfrac{(n + 2)!}{n!}$ $(n + 2)(n + 1)$

83. $\dfrac{(2n - 1)!}{(2n + 1)!}$ $\dfrac{1}{2n(2n + 1)}$

84. $\dfrac{(3n + 1)!}{(3n)!}$ $3n + 1$

In Exercises 85–96, find the sum.

85. $\sum_{i=1}^{5} (2i + 1)$ 35

86. $\sum_{i=1}^{6} (3i - 1)$ 57

87. $\sum_{k=1}^{4} 10$ 40

88. $\sum_{k=1}^{5} 6$ 30

89. $\sum_{i=0}^{4} i^2$ 30

90. $\sum_{i=0}^{5} 3i^2$ 165

91. $\sum_{k=0}^{3} \dfrac{1}{k^2 + 1}$ $\frac{9}{5}$

92. $\sum_{j=3}^{5} \dfrac{1}{j^2 - 3}$ $\frac{124}{429}$

93. $\sum_{k=2}^{5} (k + 1)^2(k - 3)$ 88

94. $\sum_{i=1}^{4} [(i - 1)^2 + (i + 1)^3]$ 238

95. $\sum_{i=1}^{4} 2^i$ 30

96. $\sum_{j=0}^{4} (-2)^j$ 11

In Exercises 97–102, use a calculator to find the sum.

97. $\sum_{n=0}^{5} \dfrac{1}{2n + 1}$ $\frac{6508}{3465}$

98. $\sum_{j=1}^{10} \dfrac{3}{j + 1}$ 6.06

99. $\sum_{k=0}^{4} \dfrac{(-1)^k}{k + 1}$ $\frac{47}{60}$

100. $\sum_{k=0}^{4} \dfrac{(-1)^k}{k!}$ $\frac{3}{8}$

101. $\sum_{n=0}^{25} \dfrac{1}{4^n}$ 1.33

102. $\sum_{n=0}^{25} \dfrac{1}{5^{n+1}}$ 0.25

In Exercises 103–112, use sigma notation to write the sum.

103–112. See margin.

103. $\dfrac{1}{3(1)} + \dfrac{1}{3(2)} + \dfrac{1}{3(3)} + \cdots + \dfrac{1}{3(9)}$

104. $\dfrac{5}{1 + 1} + \dfrac{5}{1 + 2} + \dfrac{5}{1 + 3} + \cdots + \dfrac{5}{1 + 15}$

105. $\left[2\left(\frac{1}{8}\right) + 3\right] + \left[2\left(\frac{2}{8}\right) + 3\right] + \cdots + \left[2\left(\frac{8}{8}\right) + 3\right]$

106. $\left[1 - \left(\frac{1}{6}\right)^2\right] + \left[1 - \left(\frac{2}{6}\right)^2\right] + \cdots + \left[1 - \left(\frac{6}{6}\right)^2\right]$

107. $3 - 9 + 27 - 81 + 243 - 729$

108. $1 - \frac{1}{2} + \frac{1}{4} - \frac{1}{8} + \cdots - \frac{1}{128}$

109. $\dfrac{1}{1^2} - \dfrac{1}{2^2} + \dfrac{1}{3^2} - \dfrac{1}{4^2} + \cdots - \dfrac{1}{20^2}$

110. $\dfrac{1}{1 \cdot 3} + \dfrac{1}{2 \cdot 4} + \dfrac{1}{3 \cdot 5} + \cdots + \dfrac{1}{10 \cdot 12}$

111. $\frac{1}{4} + \frac{3}{8} + \frac{7}{16} + \frac{15}{32} + \frac{31}{64}$

112. $\frac{1}{2} + \frac{2}{4} + \frac{6}{8} + \frac{24}{16} + \frac{120}{32} + \frac{720}{64}$

In Exercises 113–116, find the indicated partial sum of the series.

113. $\sum_{i=1}^{\infty} 5\left(\frac{1}{2}\right)^i$ $\frac{75}{16}$

Fourth partial sum

114. $\sum_{i=1}^{\infty} 2\left(\frac{1}{3}\right)^i$ $\frac{242}{243}$

Fifth partial sum

115. $\sum_{n=1}^{\infty} 4\left(-\frac{1}{2}\right)^n$ $-\frac{3}{2}$

Third partial sum

116. $\sum_{n=1}^{\infty} 8\left(-\frac{1}{4}\right)^n$ $-\frac{51}{32}$

Fourth partial sum

47. $a_n = 3n - 2$

48. $a_n = 4n - 1$

49. $a_n = n^2 - 1$

50. $a_n = (-1)^{n+1}(2n)$

51. $a_n = \dfrac{(-1)^n(n + 1)}{n + 2}$

52. $a_n = \dfrac{(-1)^{n+1}}{2^n}$

53. $a_n = \dfrac{n + 1}{2n - 1}$

54. $a_n = \dfrac{2^{n-1}}{3^n}$

55. $a_n = \dfrac{1}{n^2}$

56. $a_n = \dfrac{1}{n!}$

57. $a_n = (-1)^{n+1}$

58. $a_n = \dfrac{2^{n-1}}{(n - 1)!}$

59. $a_n = (-1)^n + 2$

60. $a_n = \dfrac{3}{n}$

61. $a_n = 1 + \dfrac{1}{n}$

62. $a_n = 1 + \dfrac{2^n - 1}{2^n}$

69. 81, 27, 9, 3, 1

$a_n = \dfrac{243}{3^n}$

70. 14, −28, 56, −112, 224

$a_n = 14(-2)^{n-1}$

73. $1, \frac{1}{2}, \frac{1}{6}, \frac{1}{24}, \frac{1}{120}$

103. $\sum_{i=1}^{9} \dfrac{1}{3i}$

104. $\sum_{i=1}^{15} \dfrac{5}{1 + i}$

105. $\sum_{i=1}^{8} \left[2\left(\dfrac{i}{8}\right) + 3\right]$

106. $\sum_{i=1}^{6} \left[1 - \left(\dfrac{i}{6}\right)^2\right]$

107. $\sum_{i=1}^{6} (-1)^{i+1}3^i$

108. $\sum_{i=0}^{7} \left(-\dfrac{1}{2}\right)^i$

109. $\sum_{i=1}^{20} \dfrac{(-1)^{i+1}}{i^2}$

110. $\sum_{i=1}^{10} \dfrac{1}{i(i + 2)}$

111. $\sum_{i=1}^{5} \dfrac{2^i - 1}{2^{i+1}}$

112. $\sum_{i=1}^{6} \dfrac{i!}{2^i}$

In Exercises 117–120, find the sum of the infinite series.

117. $\sum_{i=1}^{\infty} 6\left(\frac{1}{10}\right)^i$ $\frac{2}{3}$

118. $\sum_{k=1}^{\infty} \left(\frac{1}{10}\right)^k$ $\frac{1}{9}$

119. $\sum_{k=1}^{\infty} 7\left(\frac{1}{10}\right)^k$ $\frac{7}{9}$

120. $\sum_{i=1}^{\infty} 2\left(\frac{1}{10}\right)^i$ $\frac{2}{9}$

121. COMPOUND INTEREST You deposit \$25,000 in an account that earns 7% interest compounded monthly. The balance in the account after n months is given by

$$A_n = 25{,}000\left(1 + \frac{0.07}{12}\right)^n, \quad n = 1, 2, 3, \ldots.$$

See margin.

(a) Write the first six terms of the sequence.

(b) Find the balance in the account after 5 years by computing the 60th term of the sequence.

(c) Is the balance after 10 years twice the balance after 5 years? Explain.

122. COMPOUND INTEREST A deposit of \$10,000 is made in an account that earns 8.5% interest compounded quarterly. The balance in the account after n quarters is given by

$$A_n = 10{,}000\left(1 + \frac{0.085}{4}\right)^n, \quad n = 1, 2, 3, \ldots.$$

See margin.

(a) Write the first eight terms of the sequence.

(b) Find the balance in the account after 10 years by computing the 40th term of the sequence.

(c) Is the balance after 20 years twice the balance after 10 years? Explain.

123. DATA ANALYSIS: NUMBER OF STORES The table shows the numbers a_n of Best Buy stores from 2002 through 2007. (Source: Best Buy Company, Inc.)

Year	Number of stores, a_n
2002	548
2003	595
2004	668
2005	786
2006	822
2007	923

(a) Use the *regression* feature of a graphing utility to find a linear sequence that models the data. Let n represent the year, with $n = 2$ corresponding to 2002. $b_n = 76.4n + 380$

(b) Use the *regression* feature of a graphing utility to find a quadratic sequence that models the data.

$c_n = 2.18n^2 + 56.8n + 418$

(c) Evaluate the sequences from parts (a) and (b) for $n = 2, 3, \ldots, 7$. Compare these values with those shown in the table. Which model is a better fit for the data? Explain. See margin.

(d) Which model do you think would better predict the number of Best Buy stores in the future? Use the model you chose to predict the number of Best Buy stores in 2013. The quadratic model; 1524

124. MEDICINE The numbers a_n (in thousands) of AIDS cases reported from 2000 through 2007 can be approximated by the model

$$a_n = 0.0768n^3 - 3.150n^2 + 41.56n - 136.4,$$

$$n = 10, 11, \ldots, 17$$

where n is the year, with $n = 10$ corresponding to 2000. (Source: U.S. Centers for Disease Control and Prevention) See margin.

(a) Find the terms of this finite sequence. Use the *statistical plotting* feature of a graphing utility to construct a bar graph that represents the sequence.

(b) What does the graph in part (a) say about reported cases of AIDS?

125. FEDERAL DEBT From 1995 to 2007, the federal debt of the United States rose from almost \$5 trillion to almost \$9 trillion. The federal debt a_n (in billions of dollars) from 1995 through 2007 is approximated by the model

$$a_n = 1.0904n^3 - 6.348n^2 + 41.76n + 4871.3,$$

$$n = 5, 6, \ldots, 17$$

See margin.

where n is the year, with $n = 5$ corresponding to 1995. (Source: U.S. Office of Management and Budget)

(a) Find the terms of this finite sequence. Use the *statistical plotting* feature of a graphing utility to construct a bar graph that represents the sequence.

(b) What does the pattern in the bar graph in part (a) say about the future of the federal debt?

126. REVENUE The revenues a_n (in millions of dollars) of Amazon.com from 2001 through 2008 are shown in the figure on the next page. The revenues can be approximated by the model

$$a_n = 296.477n^2 - 469.11n + 3606.2,$$

$$n = 1, 2, \ldots, 8$$

where n is the year, with $n = 1$ corresponding to 2001. Use this model to approximate the total revenue from 2001 through 2008. Compare this sum with the result of adding the revenues shown in the figure on the next page. (Source: Amazon.com)

\$72,443 million

123. (c)

n	2	3	4	5	6	7
a_n	548	595	668	786	822	923
b_n	533	609	686	762	838	915
c_n	540	608	680	757	837	922

The quadratic model fits better.

121. (a) $A_1 = \$25{,}145.83$, $A_2 = \$25{,}292.52$, $A_3 = \$25{,}440.06$, $A_4 = \$25{,}588.46$, $A_5 = \$25{,}737.72$, $A_6 = \$25{,}887.86$

(b) \$35,440.63

(c) No; $A_{120} = \$50{,}241.53$

122. (a) $A_1 = \$10{,}212.50$, $A_2 = \$10{,}429.52$, $A_3 = \$10{,}651.14$, $A_4 = \$10{,}877.48$, $A_5 = \$11{,}108.63$, $A_6 = \$11{,}344.68$, $A_7 = \$11{,}585.76$, $A_8 = \$11{,}831.96$

(b) \$23,189.04

(c) No; $A_{80} = \$53{,}773.16$

123. (c) See below.

124. (a) $a_{10} = 41$, $a_{11} = 41.83$, $a_{12} = 41.43$, $a_{13} = 40.26$, $a_{14} = 38.78$, $a_{15} = 37.45$, $a_{16} = 36.73$, $a_{17} = 37.09$

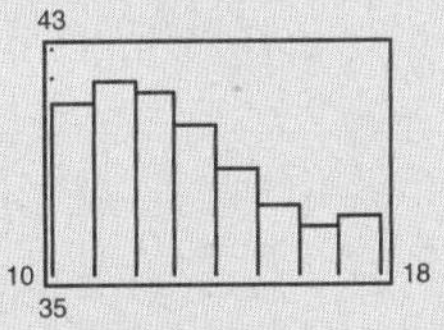

(b) The number of cases fluctuates.

125. (a) $a_5 = \$5057.7$, $a_6 = \$5128.9$, $a_7 = \$5226.6$, $a_8 = \$5357.4$, $a_9 = \$5527.9$, $a_{10} = \$5744.5$, $a_{11} = \$6013.9$, $a_{12} = \$6342.5$, $a_{13} = \$6737.0$, $a_{14} = \$7203.8$, $a_{15} = \$7749.5$, $a_{16} = \$8380.7$, $a_{17} = \$9103.8$

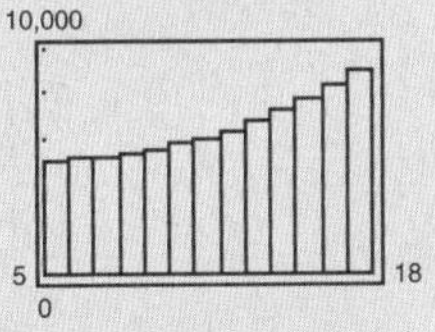

(b) The federal debt is increasing.

5 ASSESS AND RETEACH

Daily Homework Quiz

Transparency Available
Available at the Instructor's companion site.

128. See below.

135. $x, \frac{x^2}{2}, \frac{x^3}{6}, \frac{x^4}{24}, \frac{x^5}{120}$

136. $-\frac{x^3}{3}, \frac{x^5}{5}, -\frac{x^7}{7}, \frac{x^9}{9}, -\frac{x^{11}}{11}$

137. $-\frac{x^2}{2}, \frac{x^4}{24}, -\frac{x^6}{720}, \frac{x^8}{40{,}320}, -\frac{x^{10}}{3{,}628{,}800}$

138. $-\frac{x^3}{6}, \frac{x^5}{120}, -\frac{x^7}{5040}, \frac{x^9}{362{,}880}, -\frac{x^{11}}{39{,}916{,}800}$

141. (a)

Number of blue cube faces	0	1	2	3
$3 \times 3 \times 3$	1	6	12	8

(b)

Number of blue cube faces	0	1	2	3
$4 \times 4 \times 4$	8	24	24	8
$5 \times 5 \times 5$	27	54	36	8
$6 \times 6 \times 6$	64	96	48	8

(c) The different columns change at different rates.

(d) See below.

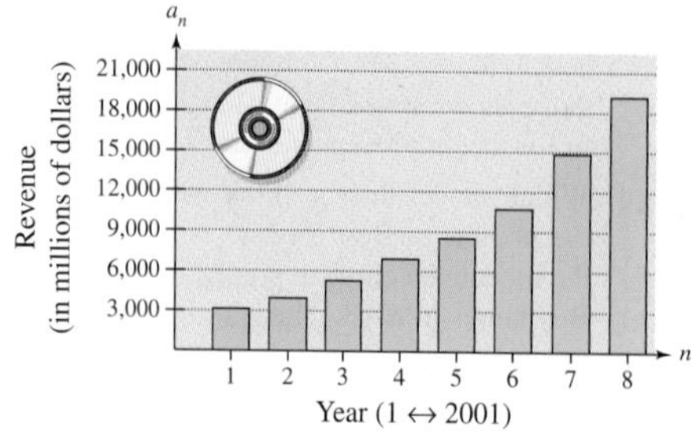

FIGURE FOR 126

EXPLORATION

TRUE OR FALSE? In Exercises 127 and 128, determine whether the statement is true or false. Justify your answer.

127. $\sum_{i=1}^{4}(i^2 + 2i) = \sum_{i=1}^{4} i^2 + 2\sum_{i=1}^{4} i$ True by the Properties of Sums

128. $\sum_{j=1}^{4} 2^j = \sum_{j=3}^{6} 2^{j-2}$ See margin.

FIBONACCI SEQUENCE In Exercises 129 and 130, use the Fibonacci sequence. (See Example 4.)

129. Write the first 12 terms of the Fibonacci sequence a_n and the first 10 terms of the sequence given by

$$b_n = \frac{a_{n+1}}{a_n}, \quad n \geq 1.$$

1, 1, 2, 3, 5, 8, 13, 21, 34, 55, 89, 144; 1, 2, $\frac{3}{2}, \frac{5}{3}, \frac{8}{5}, \frac{13}{8}, \frac{21}{13}, \frac{34}{21}, \frac{55}{34}, \frac{89}{55}$

130. Using the definition for b_n in Exercise 129, show that b_n can be defined recursively by

$$b_n = 1 + \frac{1}{b_{n-1}}.$$ Answers will vary.

ARITHMETIC MEAN In Exercises 131–134, use the following definition of the arithmetic mean $\bar{x}$ of a set of n measurements $x_1, x_2, x_3, \ldots, x_n$.

$$\bar{x} = \frac{1}{n}\sum_{i=1}^{n} x_i$$

131. Find the arithmetic mean of the six checking account balances \$327.15, \$785.69, \$433.04, \$265.38, \$604.12, and \$590.30. Use the statistical capabilities of a graphing utility to verify your result. \$500.95

132. Find the arithmetic mean of the following prices per gallon for regular unleaded gasoline at five gasoline stations in a city: \$1.899, \$1.959, \$1.919, \$1.939, and \$1.999. Use the statistical capabilities of a graphing utility to verify your result. \$1.943

133. PROOF Prove that $\sum_{i=1}^{n}(x_i - \bar{x}) = 0$. 133–134. Proofs

134. PROOF Prove that $\sum_{i=1}^{n}(x_i - \bar{x})^2 = \sum_{i=1}^{n} x_i^2 - \frac{1}{n}\left(\sum_{i=1}^{n} x_i\right)^2$.

In Exercises 135–138, find the first five terms of the sequence. 135–138. See margin.

135. $a_n = \frac{x^n}{n!}$

136. $a_n = \frac{(-1)^n x^{2n+1}}{2n+1}$

137. $a_n = \frac{(-1)^n x^{2n}}{(2n)!}$

138. $a_n = \frac{(-1)^n x^{2n+1}}{(2n+1)!}$

139. Write out the first five terms of the sequence whose nth term is

$$a_n = \frac{(-1)^{n+1}}{2n+1}.$$

$\frac{1}{3}, -\frac{1}{5}, \frac{1}{7}, -\frac{1}{9}, \frac{1}{11}$; No, the signs are opposite.

Are they the same as the first five terms of the sequence in Example 2? If not, how do they differ?

140. CAPSTONE In your own words, explain the difference between a sequence and a series. Provide examples of each. Answers will vary.

141. A $3 \times 3 \times 3$ cube is created using 27 unit cubes (a unit cube has a length, width, and height of 1 unit), and only the faces of each cube that are visible are painted blue, as shown in the figure.

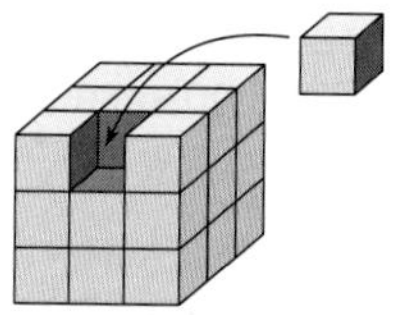

See margin.

(a) Complete the table to determine how many unit cubes of the $3 \times 3 \times 3$ cube have 0 blue faces, 1 blue face, 2 blue faces, and 3 blue faces.

Number of blue cube faces	0	1	2	3
$3 \times 3 \times 3$				

(b) Do the same for a $4 \times 4 \times 4$ cube, a $5 \times 5 \times 5$ cube, and a $6 \times 6 \times 6$ cube. Add your results to the table above.

(c) What type of pattern do you observe in the table?

(d) Write a formula you could use to determine the column values for an $n \times n \times n$ cube.

128. True. The sums are equal because $2^1 + 2^2 + 2^3 + 2^4 = 2^{3-2} + 2^{4-2} + 2^{5-2} + 2^{6-2}$.

141. (d)

Number of blue cube faces	0	1	2	3
$n \times n \times n$	$(n-2)^3$	$6(n-2)^2$	$12(n-2)$	8

9.2 Arithmetic Sequences and Partial Sums

What you should learn

- Recognize, write, and find the nth terms of arithmetic sequences.
- Find nth partial sums of arithmetic sequences.
- Use arithmetic sequences to model and solve real-life problems.

Why you should learn it

Arithmetic sequences have practical real-life applications. For instance, in Exercise 91 on page 658, an arithmetic sequence is used to model the seating capacity of an auditorium.

Arithmetic Sequences

A sequence whose consecutive terms have a common difference is called an **arithmetic sequence.**

Definition of Arithmetic Sequence

A sequence is **arithmetic** if the differences between consecutive terms are the same. So, the sequence

$$a_1, a_2, a_3, a_4, \ldots, a_n, \ldots$$

is arithmetic if there is a number d such that

$$a_2 - a_1 = a_3 - a_2 = a_4 - a_3 = \cdots = d.$$

The number d is the **common difference** of the arithmetic sequence.

Example 1 Examples of Arithmetic Sequences

a. The sequence whose nth term is $4n + 3$ is arithmetic. For this sequence, the common difference between consecutive terms is 4.

$$\underbrace{7, 11}_{11 - 7 = 4}, 15, 19, \ldots, 4n + 3, \ldots \qquad \text{Begin with } n = 1.$$

b. The sequence whose nth term is $7 - 5n$ is arithmetic. For this sequence, the common difference between consecutive terms is -5.

$$\underbrace{2, -3}_{-3 - 2 = -5}, -8, -13, \ldots, 7 - 5n, \ldots \qquad \text{Begin with } n = 1.$$

c. The sequence whose nth term is $\frac{1}{4}(n + 3)$ is arithmetic. For this sequence, the common difference between consecutive terms is $\frac{1}{4}$.

$$\underbrace{1, \frac{5}{4}}_{\frac{5}{4} - 1 = \frac{1}{4}}, \frac{3}{2}, \frac{7}{4}, \ldots, \frac{n + 3}{4}, \ldots \qquad \text{Begin with } n = 1.$$

CHECK*Point* Now try Exercise 5.

The sequence $1, 4, 9, 16, \ldots,$ whose nth term is n^2, is *not* arithmetic. The difference between the first two terms is

$$a_2 - a_1 = 4 - 1 = 3$$

but the difference between the second and third terms is

$$a_3 - a_2 = 9 - 4 = 5.$$

1 PLAN AND PREPARE

Warm-up Exercises

Transparency Available
Available at the Instructor's companion site.

Notetaking Guide

Transparency Available
Promotes interactive learning and notetaking skills. Available at the Instructor's companion site.

Animated Precalculus

An **Animated Precalculus** tutorial is available at the Student companion site for **Section 9.2.**

Pacing

Average: 2 days
Advanced: 2 days
Block: 0.5 block with 9.1
0.5 block with 9.3

2 FOCUS AND MOTIVATE

Essential Question

How do you find the nth term or partial sum of an arithmetic sequence? **Tell students that they will learn how to answer this question by studying list, formula, and recursive formula representations of arithmetic sequences.**

Resource Planning Guide

Chapter Resources
- Complete Solutions Guide

Workbooks
- Notetaking Guide
- Student Solutions Guide

Interactive Technology
- Instructor Success Organizer
- Notetaking Guide IAE
- Instructional DVDs
- Animated Precalculus
- PowerLecture with ExamView

3 TEACH

Extra Example 1

For each of the arithmetic sequences, find the common difference.

a. $5, 8, 11, 14, 17, \ldots, 3n + 2$
 3

b. $9, 5, 1, -3, -7, \ldots, 13 - 4n$
 −4

c. $1, \frac{7}{6}, \frac{4}{3}, \frac{3}{2}, \frac{5}{3}, \ldots, \frac{n+5}{6}$
 $\frac{1}{6}$

Extra Example 2

Find a formula for the nth term of the arithmetic sequence whose common difference is 5 and whose first term is −1.

$a_n = 5n - 6$

Avoiding Common Errors

Students sometimes mistake the first term of an arithmetic sequence for the y-intercept of the corresponding linear function. Remind students that the y-intercept can be found by subtracting the common difference from the first term. An organized list similar to the one in the solution to Example 2 can be used to confirm that the equation produces the correct sequence.

The *n*th Term of an Arithmetic Sequence

The nth term of an arithmetic sequence has the form

$$a_n = a_1 + (n - 1)d$$

where d is the common difference between consecutive terms of the sequence and a_1 is the first term.

Study Tip

The nth term of an arithmetic sequence can be derived from the pattern below.

$a_1 = a_1$	1st term
$a_2 = a_1 + d$	2nd term
$a_3 = a_1 + 2d$	3rd term
$a_4 = a_1 + 3d$	4th term
$a_5 = a_1 + 4d$	5th term
1 less	
⋮	
$a_n = a_1 + (n - 1)d$	nth term
1 less	

Example 2 Finding the *n*th Term of an Arithmetic Sequence

Find a formula for the nth term of the arithmetic sequence whose common difference is 3 and whose first term is 2.

Solution

You know that the formula for the nth term is of the form $a_n = a_1 + (n - 1)d$. Moreover, because the common difference is $d = 3$ and the first term is $a_1 = 2$, the formula must have the form

$$a_n = 2 + 3(n - 1). \qquad \text{Substitute 2 for } a_1 \text{ and 3 for } d.$$

So, the formula for the nth term is

$$a_n = 3n - 1.$$

The sequence therefore has the following form.

$$2, 5, 8, 11, 14, \ldots, 3n - 1, \ldots$$

CHECKPoint Now try Exercise 25.

Study Tip

You can find a_1 in Example 3 by using the nth term of an arithmetic sequence, as follows.

$$a_n = a_1 + (n - 1)d$$
$$a_4 = a_1 + (4 - 1)d$$
$$20 = a_1 + (4 - 1)5$$
$$20 = a_1 + 15$$
$$5 = a_1$$

Example 3 Writing the Terms of an Arithmetic Sequence

The fourth term of an arithmetic sequence is 20, and the 13th term is 65. Write the first 11 terms of this sequence.

Solution

You know that $a_4 = 20$ and $a_{13} = 65$. So, you must add the common difference d nine times to the fourth term to obtain the 13th term. Therefore, the fourth and 13th terms of the sequence are related by

$$a_{13} = a_4 + 9d. \qquad a_4 \text{ and } a_{13} \text{ are nine terms apart.}$$

Using $a_4 = 20$ and $a_{13} = 65$, you can conclude that $d = 5$, which implies that the sequence is as follows.

a_1	a_2	a_3	a_4	a_5	a_6	a_7	a_8	a_9	a_{10}	a_{11} . . .
5	10	15	20	25	30	35	40	45	50	55 . . .

CHECKPoint Now try Exercise 39.

If you know the nth term of an arithmetic sequence *and* you know the common difference of the sequence, you can find the $(n + 1)$th term by using the *recursion formula*

$$a_{n+1} = a_n + d. \qquad \text{Recursion formula}$$

With this formula, you can find any term of an arithmetic sequence, *provided* that you know the preceding term. For instance, if you know the first term, you can find the second term. Then, knowing the second term, you can find the third term, and so on.

Example 4 Using a Recursion Formula

Find the ninth term of the arithmetic sequence that begins with 2 and 9.

Solution

For this sequence, the common difference is

$$d = 9 - 2 = 7.$$

There are two ways to find the ninth term. One way is simply to write out the first nine terms (by repeatedly adding 7).

2, 9, 16, 23, 30, 37, 44, 51, 58

Another way to find the ninth term is to first find a formula for the nth term. Because the common difference is $d = 7$ and the first term is $a_1 = 2$, the formula must have the form

$$a_n = 2 + 7(n - 1). \qquad \text{Substitute 2 for } a_1 \text{ and 7 for } d.$$

Therefore, a formula for the nth term is

$$a_n = 7n - 5$$

which implies that the ninth term is

$$a_9 = 7(9) - 5 = 58.$$

CHECKPoint Now try Exercise 47.

Extra Example 3

The eighth term of an arithmetic sequence is 25, and the 12th term is 41. Write the first five terms of this sequence.

−3, 1, 5, 9, 13

Extra Example 4

Find the tenth term of the arithmetic sequence that begins with 8 and 20.

116

Extra Example 5

Find the sum: 40 + 37 + 34 + 31 + 28 + 25 + 22.

217

Extra Example 6

Find the sum of the given integers.

a. 1 to 35

630

b. 1 to 57

1653

The Sum of a Finite Arithmetic Sequence

There is a simple formula for the *sum* of a finite arithmetic sequence.

WARNING / CAUTION

Note that this formula works only for *arithmetic* sequences.

The Sum of a Finite Arithmetic Sequence

The sum of a finite arithmetic sequence with n terms is

$$S_n = \frac{n}{2}(a_1 + a_n).$$

For a proof of this formula for the sum of a finite arithmetic sequence, see Proofs in Mathematics on page 721.

Example 5 Finding the Sum of a Finite Arithmetic Sequence

Find the sum: 1 + 3 + 5 + 7 + 9 + 11 + 13 + 15 + 17 + 19.

Solution

To begin, notice that the sequence is arithmetic (with a common difference of 2). Moreover, the sequence has 10 terms. So, the sum of the sequence is

$$S_n = \frac{n}{2}(a_1 + a_n) \qquad \text{Formula for the sum of an arithmetic sequence}$$

$$= \frac{10}{2}(1 + 19) \qquad \text{Substitute 10 for } n\text{, 1 for } a_1\text{, and 19 for } a_n.$$

$$= 5(20) = 100. \qquad \text{Simplify.}$$

CHECKPoint Now try Exercise 51.

Example 6 Finding the Sum of a Finite Arithmetic Sequence

Find the sum of the integers (a) from 1 to 100 and (b) from 1 to N.

Solution

a. The integers from 1 to 100 form an arithmetic sequence that has 100 terms. So, you can use the formula for the sum of an arithmetic sequence, as follows.

$$S_n = 1 + 2 + 3 + 4 + 5 + 6 + \cdots + 99 + 100$$

$$= \frac{n}{2}(a_1 + a_n) \qquad \text{Formula for sum of an arithmetic sequence}$$

$$= \frac{100}{2}(1 + 100) \qquad \text{Substitute 100 for } n\text{, 1 for } a_1\text{, 100 for } a_n.$$

$$= 50(101) = 5050 \qquad \text{Simplify.}$$

b. $S_n = 1 + 2 + 3 + 4 + \cdots + N$

$$= \frac{n}{2}(a_1 + a_n) \qquad \text{Formula for sum of an arithmetic sequence}$$

$$= \frac{N}{2}(1 + N) \qquad \text{Substitute } N \text{ for } n\text{, 1 for } a_1\text{, and } N \text{ for } a_n.$$

CHECKPoint Now try Exercise 55.

HISTORICAL NOTE

A teacher of Carl Friedrich Gauss (1777–1855) asked him to add all the integers from 1 to 100. When Gauss returned with the cheorrect answer after only a few moments, the teacher could only look at him in astounded silence. This is what Gauss did:

$$\begin{aligned} S_n &= 1 + 2 + 3 + \cdots + 100 \\ S_n &= 100 + 99 + 98 + \cdots + 1 \\ \hline 2S_n &= 101 + 101 + 101 + \cdots + 101 \\ S_n &= \frac{100 \times 101}{2} = 5050 \end{aligned}$$

The sum of the first n terms of an infinite sequence is the *nth partial sum*. The nth partial sum can be found by using the formula for the sum of a finite arithmetic sequence.

Example 7 Finding a Partial Sum of an Arithmetic Sequence

Find the 150th partial sum of the arithmetic sequence

$5, 16, 27, 38, 49, ...$

Solution

For this arithmetic sequence, $a_1 = 5$ and $d = 16 - 5 = 11$. So,

$$a_n = 5 + 11(n - 1)$$

and the nth term is $a_n = 11n - 6$. Therefore, $a_{150} = 11(150) - 6 = 1644$, and the sum of the first 150 terms is

$$S_{150} = \frac{n}{2}(a_1 + a_{150}) \qquad \text{nth partial sum formula}$$

$$= \frac{150}{2}(5 + 1644) \qquad \text{Substitute 150 for } n\text{, 5 for } a_1\text{, and 1644 for } a_{150}.$$

$$= 75(1649) \qquad \text{Simplify.}$$

$$= 123{,}675. \qquad \text{nth partial sum}$$

CHECKPoint Now try Exercise 69.

Applications

Example 8 Prize Money

In a golf tournament, the 16 golfers with the lowest scores win cash prizes. First place receives a cash prize of \$1000, second place receives \$950, third place receives \$900, and so on. What is the total amount of prize money?

Solution

The cash prizes awarded form an arithmetic sequence in which the first term is $a_1 = 1000$ and the common difference is $d = -50$. Because

$$a_n = 1000 + (-50)(n - 1)$$

you can determine that the formula for the nth term of the sequence is $a_n = -50n + 1050$. So, the 16th term of the sequence is $a_{16} = -50(16) + 1050 = 250$, and the total amount of prize money is

$$S_{16} = 1000 + 950 + 900 + \cdot \cdot \cdot + 250$$

$$S_{16} = \frac{n}{2}(a_1 + a_{16}) \qquad \text{nth partial sum formula}$$

$$= \frac{16}{2}(1000 + 250) \qquad \text{Substitute 16 for } n\text{, 1000 for } a_1\text{, and 250 for } a_{16}.$$

$$= 8(1250) = \$10{,}000. \qquad \text{Simplify.}$$

CHECKPoint Now try Exercise 97.

Extra Example 7

Find the 50th partial sum of the arithmetic sequence

$-6, -2, 2, 6, ...$

4600

Extra Example 8

Determine the seating capacity of an auditorium with 30 rows of seats if there are 20 seats in the first row, 22 seats in the second row, 24 seats in the third row, and so on.

1470 seats

Extra Example 9

Consider a job offer with a starting salary of $32,500 and an annual raise of $2500. Determine the total compensation from the company through six full years of employment.
$232,500

Closing the Lesson

Have students summarize the major points of the lesson and answer the Essential Question: How do you find the *n*th term or partial sum of an arithmetic sequence?

- **Use the formula $a_n = dn + c$ or the recursion formula $a_{n+1} = a_n + d$ to represent the *n*th term of an arithmetic sequence with starting value *c* and common difference *d*.**
- **Find the sum of a finite difference by using the formula $S_n = \frac{n}{2}(a_1 + a_n)$.**

Classroom Discussion

a. $-7, -4, -1, 2, 5, 8, 11$; $a_{n+1} = a_n + 3$
b. $17, 23, 29, 35, 41, 47, 53, 59, 65, 71$; $a_{n+1} = a_n + 6$
c. Not possible
d. $4, 7.5, 11, 14.5, 18, 21.5, 25, 28.5, 32, 35.5, 39$; $a_{n+1} = a_n + 3.5$
e. Not possible

Example 9 Total Sales

A small business sells $10,000 worth of skin care products during its first year. The owner of the business has set a goal of increasing annual sales by $7500 each year for 9 years. Assuming that this goal is met, find the total sales during the first 10 years this business is in operation.

Solution

The annual sales form an arithmetic sequence in which $a_1 = 10{,}000$ and $d = 7500$. So,

$$a_n = 10{,}000 + 7500(n - 1)$$

and the nth term of the sequence is

$$a_n = 7500n + 2500.$$

This implies that the 10th term of the sequence is

$$a_{10} = 7500(10) + 2500$$
$$= 77{,}500.$$ See Figure 9.3.

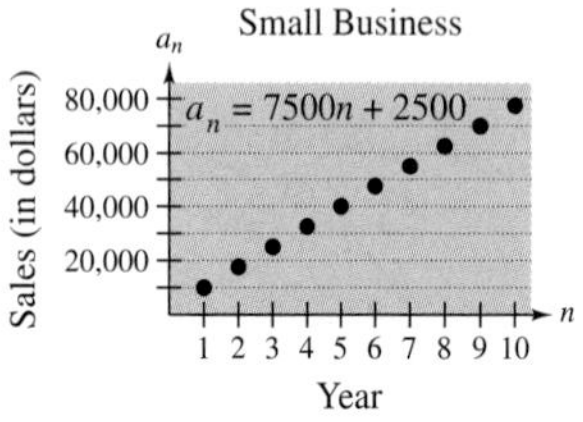

FIGURE 9.3

The sum of the first 10 terms of the sequence is

$$S_{10} = \frac{n}{2}(a_1 + a_{10})$$ *n*th partial sum formula

$$= \frac{10}{2}(10{,}000 + 77{,}500)$$ Substitute 10 for n, 10,000 for a_1, and 77,500 for a_{10}.

$$= 5(87{,}500)$$ Simplify.

$$= 437{,}500.$$ Simplify.

So, the total sales for the first 10 years will be $437,500.

CHECK*Point* Now try Exercise 99.

Classroom Discussion

Numerical Relationships Decide whether it is possible to fill in the blanks in each of the sequences such that the resulting sequence is arithmetic. If so, find a recursion formula for the sequence. See margin.

a. -7, ▭, ▭, ▭, ▭, ▭, 11
b. 17, ▭, ▭, ▭, ▭, ▭, ▭, ▭, ▭, 71
c. 2, 6, ▭, ▭, 162
d. 4, 7.5, ▭, ▭, ▭, ▭, ▭, ▭, ▭, ▭, 39
e. 8, 12, ▭, ▭, ▭, 60.75

9.2 EXERCISES

See www.CalcChat.com for worked-out solutions to odd-numbered exercises.

VOCABULARY: Fill in the blanks.

1. A sequence is called an arithmetic sequence if the differences between consecutive terms are the same. This difference is called the common difference.
2. The nth term of an arithmetic sequence has the form $a_n = a_1 + (n-1)d$.
3. If you know the nth term of an arithmetic sequence *and* you know the common difference of the sequence, you can find the $(n+1)$th term by using the recursion formula $a_{n+1} = a_n + d$.
4. The formula $S_n = \frac{n}{2}(a_1 + a_n)$ can be used to find the sum of the first n terms of an arithmetic sequence, called the sum of a finite arithmetic sequence.

SKILLS AND APPLICATIONS

In Exercises 5–14, determine whether the sequence is arithmetic. If so, find the common difference. 5–10. See margin.

5. $10, 8, 6, 4, 2, \ldots$
6. $4, 9, 14, 19, 24, \ldots$
7. $1, 2, 4, 8, 16, \ldots$
8. $80, 40, 20, 10, 5, \ldots$
9. $\frac{9}{4}, 2, \frac{7}{4}, \frac{3}{2}, \frac{5}{4}, \ldots$
10. $3, \frac{5}{2}, 2, \frac{3}{2}, 1, \ldots$
11. $3.7, 4.3, 4.9, 5.5, 6.1, \ldots$ Arithmetic sequence, $d = 0.6$
12. $5.3, 5.7, 6.1, 6.5, 6.9, \ldots$ Arithmetic sequence, $d = 0.4$
13. $\ln 1, \ln 2, \ln 3, \ln 4, \ln 5, \ldots$ Not an arithmetic sequence
14. $1^2, 2^2, 3^2, 4^2, 5^2, \ldots$ Not an arithmetic sequence

In Exercises 15–22, write the first five terms of the sequence. Determine whether the sequence is arithmetic. If so, find the common difference. (Assume that n begins with 1.) 15–22. See margin.

15. $a_n = 5 + 3n$
16. $a_n = 100 - 3n$
17. $a_n = 3 - 4(n-2)$
18. $a_n = 1 + (n-1)4$
19. $a_n = (-1)^n$
20. $a_n = 2^{n-1}$
21. $a_n = \frac{(-1)^n 3}{n}$
22. $a_n = (2^n)n$

In Exercises 23–32, find a formula for a_n for the arithmetic sequence. 23–32. See margin.

23. $a_1 = 1, d = 3$
24. $a_1 = 15, d = 4$
25. $a_1 = 100, d = -8$
26. $a_1 = 0, d = -\frac{2}{3}$
27. $4, \frac{3}{2}, -1, -\frac{7}{2}, \ldots$
28. $10, 5, 0, -5, -10, \ldots$
29. $a_1 = 5, a_4 = 15$
30. $a_1 = -4, a_5 = 16$
31. $a_3 = 94, a_6 = 85$
32. $a_5 = 190, a_{10} = 115$

In Exercises 33–40, write the first five terms of the arithmetic sequence.

33. $a_1 = 5, d = 6$ $\quad 5, 11, 17, 23, 29$
34. $a_1 = 5, d = -\frac{3}{4}$ $\quad 5, \frac{17}{4}, \frac{7}{2}, \frac{11}{4}, 2$
35. $a_1 = -2.6, d = -0.4$ $\quad -2.6, -3.0, -3.4, -3.8, -4.2$
36. $a_1 = 16.5, d = 0.25$ $\quad 16.5, 16.75, 17, 17.25, 17.5$
37. $a_1 = 2, a_{12} = 46$ $\quad 2, 6, 10, 14, 18$
38. $a_4 = 16, a_{10} = 46$ $\quad 1, 6, 11, 16, 21$
39. $a_8 = 26, a_{12} = 42$ $\quad -2, 2, 6, 10, 14$
40. $a_3 = 19, a_{15} = -1.7$ $\quad 22.45, 20.725, 19, 17.275, 15.55$

In Exercises 41–46, write the first five terms of the arithmetic sequence defined recursively.

41. $a_1 = 15, \quad a_{n+1} = a_n + 4$ $\quad 15, 19, 23, 27, 31$
42. $a_1 = 6, \quad a_{n+1} = a_n + 5$ $\quad 6, 11, 16, 21, 26$
43. $a_1 = 200, \quad a_{n+1} = a_n - 10$ $\quad 200, 190, 180, 170, 160$
44. $a_1 = 72, \quad a_{n+1} = a_n - 6$ $\quad 72, 66, 60, 54, 48$
45. $a_1 = \frac{5}{8}, \quad a_{n+1} = a_n - \frac{1}{8}$ $\quad \frac{5}{8}, \frac{1}{2}, \frac{3}{8}, \frac{1}{4}, \frac{1}{8}$
46. $a_1 = 0.375, \quad a_{n+1} = a_n + 0.25$ $\quad 0.375, 0.625, 0.875, 1.125, 1.375$

In Exercises 47–50, the first two terms of the arithmetic sequence are given. Find the missing term.

47. $a_1 = 5, a_2 = 11, a_{10} = \square$ $\quad 59$
48. $a_1 = 3, a_2 = 13, a_9 = \square$ $\quad 83$
49. $a_1 = 4.2, a_2 = 6.6, a_7 = \square$ $\quad 18.6$
50. $a_1 = -0.7, a_2 = -13.8, a_8 = \square$ $\quad -92.4$

In Exercises 51–58, find the sum of the finite arithmetic sequence.

51. $2 + 4 + 6 + 8 + 10 + 12 + 14 + 16 + 18 + 20$ $\quad 110$
52. $1 + 4 + 7 + 10 + 13 + 16 + 19$ $\quad 70$
53. $-1 + (-3) + (-5) + (-7) + (-9)$ $\quad -25$
54. $-5 + (-3) + (-1) + 1 + 3 + 5$ $\quad 0$
55. Sum of the first 50 positive even integers $\quad 2550$
56. Sum of the first 100 positive odd integers $\quad 10,000$
57. Sum of the integers from -100 to 30 $\quad -4585$
58. Sum of the integers from -10 to 50 $\quad 1220$

23. $a_n = 3n - 2$
24. $a_n = 4n + 11$
25. $a_n = -8n + 108$
26. $a_n = -\frac{2}{3}n + \frac{2}{3}$
27. $a_n = -\frac{5}{2}n + \frac{13}{2}$
28. $a_n = -5n + 15$
29. $a_n = \frac{10}{3}n + \frac{5}{3}$
30. $a_n = 5n - 9$
31. $a_n = -3n + 103$
32. $a_n = -15n + 265$

4 PRACTICE AND APPLY

Assignment Guide

Transparencies Available
Available at the Instructor's companion site.

Average:
Day 1: p. 657
Exs. 7–11 odd, 15–23 odd, 27–37 odd, 41–45 odd, 48, 49, 51, 55
Day 2: pp. 658–660
Exs. 61–67 odd, 71, 75, 77, 81, 83, 89–95 odd, 98, 101, 105–107, 109, 110, 113

Advanced:
Day 1: p. 657
Exs. 8–12 even, 13, 16–22 even, 26–40 even, 44–50 even, 54–58 even
Day 2: pp. 658–660
Exs. 60–66 even, 72–86 even, 90–100 even, 104, 108–112, 114

Block:
p. 657
Exs. 7–11 odd, 15–23 odd, 27–37 odd, 41–45 odd, 48, 49, 51, 55 (with 9.1)
pp. 658–660
Exs. 61–67 odd, 71, 75, 77, 81, 83, 89–95 odd, 98, 101, 105–107, 109, 110, 113 (with 9.3)

5. Arithmetic sequence, $d = -2$
6. Arithmetic sequence, $d = 5$
7. Not an arithmetic sequence
8. Not an arithmetic sequence
9. Arithmetic sequence, $d = -\frac{1}{4}$
10. Arithmetic sequence, $d = -\frac{1}{2}$
15. $8, 11, 14, 17, 20$
Arithmetic sequence, $d = 3$
16. $97, 94, 91, 88, 85$
Arithmetic sequence, $d = -3$
17. $7, 3, -1, -5, -9$
Arithmetic sequence, $d = -4$
18. $1, 5, 9, 13, 17$
Arithmetic sequence, $d = 4$
19. $-1, 1, -1, 1, -1$
Not an arithmetic sequence
20. $1, 2, 4, 8, 16$
Not an arithmetic sequence
21. $-3, \frac{3}{2}, -1, \frac{3}{4}, -\frac{3}{5}$
Not an arithmetic sequence
22. $2, 8, 24, 64, 160$
Not an arithmetic sequence

79.
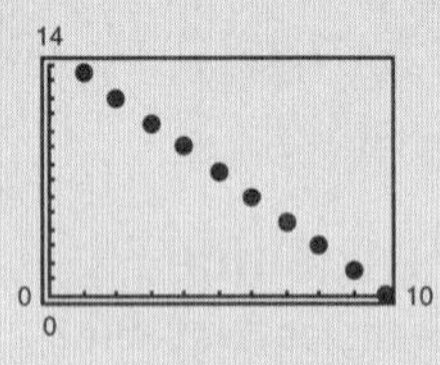

80.
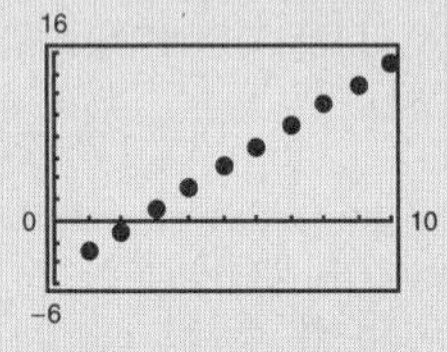

81.
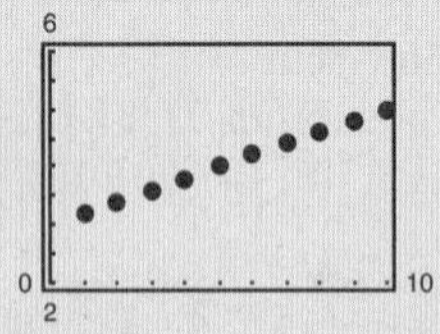

82.
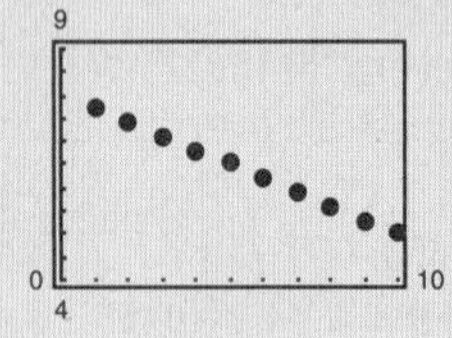

In Exercises 59–66, find the indicated nth partial sum of the arithmetic sequence.

59. $8, 20, 32, 44, \ldots, \quad n = 10$ 620

60. $-6, -2, 2, 6, \ldots, \quad n = 50$ 4600

61. $4.2, 3.7, 3.2, 2.7, \ldots, \quad n = 12$ 17.4

62. $0.5, 1.3, 2.1, 2.9, \ldots, \quad n = 10$ 41

63. $40, 37, 34, 31, \ldots, \quad n = 10$ 265

64. $75, 70, 65, 60, \ldots, \quad n = 25$ 375

65. $a_1 = 100, \; a_{25} = 220, \quad n = 25$ 4000

66. $a_1 = 15, \; a_{100} = 307, \quad n = 100$ 16,100

In Exercises 67–74, find the partial sum.

67. $\sum_{n=1}^{50} n$ 1275

68. $\sum_{n=1}^{100} 2n$ 10,100

69. $\sum_{n=10}^{100} 6n$ 30,030

70. $\sum_{n=51}^{100} 7n$ 26,425

71. $\sum_{n=11}^{30} n - \sum_{n=1}^{10} n$ 355

72. $\sum_{n=51}^{100} n - \sum_{n=1}^{50} n$ 2500

73. $\sum_{n=1}^{500} (n + 8)$ 129,250

74. $\sum_{n=1}^{250} (1000 - n)$ 218,625

In Exercises 75–78, match the arithmetic sequence with its graph. [The graphs are labeled (a), (b), (c), and (d).]

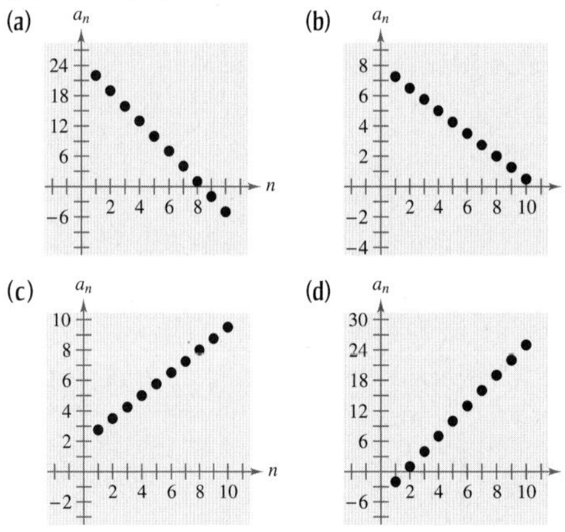

75. $a_n = -\frac{3}{4}n + 8$ b

76. $a_n = 3n - 5$ d

77. $a_n = 2 + \frac{3}{4}n$ c

78. $a_n = 25 - 3n$ a

In Exercises 79–82, use a graphing utility to graph the first 10 terms of the sequence. (Assume that n begins with 1.)

79. $a_n = 15 - \frac{3}{2}n$

80. $a_n = -5 + 2n$

81. $a_n = 0.2n + 3$

82. $a_n = -0.3n + 8$

79–82. See margin.

In Exercises 83–88, use a graphing utility to find the partial sum.

83. $\sum_{n=1}^{20} (2n + 1)$ 440

84. $\sum_{n=0}^{50} (50 - 2n)$ 0

85. $\sum_{n=1}^{100} \frac{n + 1}{2}$ 2575

86. $\sum_{n=0}^{100} \frac{4 - n}{4}$ -1161.5

87. $\sum_{i=1}^{60} \left(250 - \frac{2}{5}i\right)$ 14,268

88. $\sum_{j=1}^{200} (10.5 + 0.025j)$ 2602.5

JOB OFFER In Exercises 89 and 90, consider a job offer with the given starting salary and the given annual raise.

(a) Determine the salary during the sixth year of employment.

(b) Determine the total compensation from the company through six full years of employment.

	Starting Salary	*Annual Raise*
89.	\$32,500 (a) \$40,000	\$1500 (b) \$217,500
90.	\$36,800 (a) \$45,550	\$1750 (b) \$247,050

91. **SEATING CAPACITY** Determine the seating capacity of an auditorium with 30 rows of seats if there are 20 seats in the first row, 24 seats in the second row, 28 seats in the third row, and so on. 2340 seats

92. **SEATING CAPACITY** Determine the seating capacity of an auditorium with 36 rows of seats if there are 15 seats in the first row, 18 seats in the second row, 21 seats in the third row, and so on. 2430 seats

93. **BRICK PATTERN** A brick patio has the approximate shape of a trapezoid (see figure). The patio has 18 rows of bricks. The first row has 14 bricks and the 18th row has 31 bricks. How many bricks are in the patio? 405 bricks

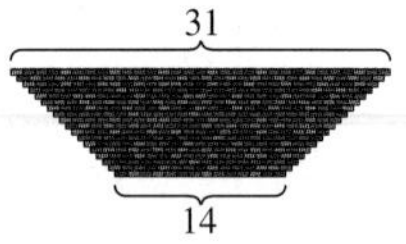

FIGURE FOR 93

FIGURE FOR 94

94. BRICK PATTERN A triangular brick wall is made by cutting some bricks in half to use in the first column of every other row (see figure on the previous page). The wall has 28 rows. The top row is one-half brick wide and the bottom row is 14 bricks wide. How many bricks are used in the finished wall? 203 bricks

95. FALLING OBJECT An object with negligible air resistance is dropped from a plane. During the first second of fall, the object falls 4.9 meters; during the second second, it falls 14.7 meters; during the third second, it falls 24.5 meters; during the fourth second, it falls 34.3 meters. If this arithmetic pattern continues, how many meters will the object fall in 10 seconds? 490 m

96. FALLING OBJECT An object with negligible air resistance is dropped from the top of the Sears Tower in Chicago at a height of 1454 feet. During the first second of fall, the object falls 16 feet; during the second second, it falls 48 feet; during the third second, it falls 80 feet; during the fourth second, it falls 112 feet. If this arithmetic pattern continues, how many feet will the object fall in 7 seconds? 784 ft

97. PRIZE MONEY A county fair is holding a baked goods competition in which the top eight bakers receive cash prizes. First place receives a cash prize of \$200, second place receives \$175, third place receives \$150, and so on.

(a) Write a sequence a_n that represents the cash prize awarded in terms of the place n in which the baked good places. $a_n = -25n + 225$

(b) Find the total amount of prize money awarded at the competition. \$900

98. PRIZE MONEY A city bowling league is holding a tournament in which the top 12 bowlers with the highest three-game totals are awarded cash prizes. First place will win \$1200, second place \$1100, third place \$1000, and so on.

(a) Write a sequence a_n that represents the cash prize awarded in terms of the place n in which the bowler finishes. $a_n = 1300 - 100n$

(b) Find the total amount of prize money awarded at the tournament. \$7800

99. TOTAL PROFIT A small snowplowing company makes a profit of \$8000 during its first year. The owner of the company sets a goal of increasing profit by \$1500 each year for 5 years. Assuming that this goal is met, find the total profit during the first 6 years of this business. What kinds of economic factors could prevent the company from meeting its profit goal? Are there any other factors that could prevent the company from meeting its goal? Explain.

\$70,500; Answers will vary.

100. TOTAL SALES An entrepreneur sells \$15,000 worth of sports memorabilia during one year and sets a goal of increasing annual sales by \$5000 each year for 9 years. Assuming that this goal is met, find the total sales during the first 10 years of this business. What kinds of economic factors could prevent the business from meeting its goals? \$375,000; Answers will vary.

101. BORROWING MONEY You borrowed \$2000 from a friend to purchase a new laptop computer and have agreed to pay back the loan with monthly payments of \$200 plus 1% interest on the unpaid balance.

(a) Find the first six monthly payments you will make, and the unpaid balance after each month. See margin.

(b) Find the total amount of interest paid over the term of the loan. \$110

102. BORROWING MONEY You borrowed \$5000 from your parents to purchase a used car. The arrangements of the loan are such that you will make payments of \$250 per month plus 1% interest on the unpaid balance.

(a) Find the first year's monthly payments you will make, and the unpaid balance after each month.

(b) Find the total amount of interest paid over the term of the loan. (a) See margin. (b) \$525.00

103. DATA ANALYSIS: PERSONAL INCOME The table shows the per capita personal income a_n in the United States from 2002 through 2008. (Source: U.S. Bureau of Economic Analysis)

Year	Per capita personal income, a_n
2002	\$30,834
2003	\$31,519
2004	\$33,159
2005	\$34,691
2006	\$36,791
2007	\$38,654
2008	\$39,742

(a) Find an arithmetic sequence that models the data. Let n represent the year, with $n = 2$ corresponding to 2002. $a_n = 1594n + 27{,}087$

(b) Use a graphing utility to graph the terms of the finite sequence you found in part (a). See margin.

(c) Use the sequence from part (a) to estimate the per capita personal income in 2009. \$41,433

(d) Use your school's library, the Internet, or some other reference source to find the actual per capita personal income in 2009, and compare this value with the estimate from part (c).

Answers will vary.

101. (a)

Month	1	2	3
Monthly payment	\$220	\$218	\$216
Unpaid balance	\$1800	\$1600	\$1400

Month	4	5	6
Monthly payment	\$214	\$212	\$210
Unpaid balance	\$1200	\$1000	\$800

102. (a) See below.

103. (b)

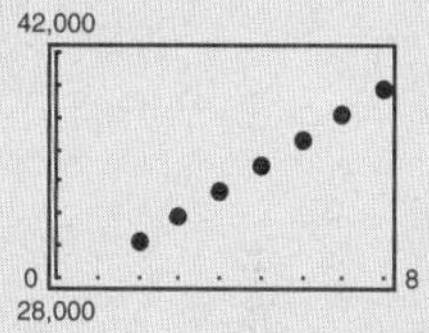

102. (a)

Month	1	2	3	4	5	6
Payment	\$300.00	\$297.50	\$295.00	\$292.50	\$290.00	\$287.50
Unpaid balance	\$4750	\$4500	\$4250	\$4000	\$3750	\$3500

Month	7	8	9	10	11	12
Payment	\$285.00	\$282.50	\$280.00	\$277.50	\$275.00	\$272.50
Unpaid balance	\$3250	\$3000	\$2750	\$2500	\$2250	\$2000

104. DATA ANALYSIS: SALES The table shows the sales a_n (in billions of dollars) for Coca-Cola Enterprises, Inc. from 2000 through 2007. (Source: Coca-Cola Enterprises, Inc.)

Year	Sales, a_n
2000	14.8
2001	15.7
2002	16.9
2003	17.3
2004	18.2
2005	18.7
2006	19.8
2007	20.9

(a) Construct a bar graph showing the annual sales from 2000 through 2007. See margin.

(b) Find an arithmetic sequence that models the data. Let n represent the year, with $n = 0$ corresponding to 2000. $a_n = 0.87n + 14.8$

(c) Use a graphing utility to graph the terms of the finite sequence you found in part (b). See margin.

(d) Use summation notation to represent the *total* sales from 2000 through 2007. Find the total sales. $\sum_{n=0}^{7} (0.87n + 14.8) = 142.8$

EXPLORATION

105–106. See margin.

TRUE OR FALSE? In Exercises 105 and 106, determine whether the statement is true or false. Justify your answer.

105. Given an arithmetic sequence for which only the first two terms are known, it is possible to find the nth term.

106. If the only known information about a finite arithmetic sequence is its first term and its last term, then it is possible to find the sum of the sequence.

In Exercises 107 and 108, find the first 10 terms of the sequence.

107. $a_1 = x, d = 2x$ $x, 3x, 5x, 7x, 9x, 11x, 13x, 15x, 17x, 19x$

108. $a_1 = -y, d = 5y$ $-y, 4y, 9y, 14y, 19y, 24y, 29y, 34y, 39y, 44y$

109. WRITING Explain how to use the first two terms of an arithmetic sequence to find the nth term. See margin.

110. CAPSTONE In your own words, describe the characteristics of an arithmetic sequence. Give an example of a sequence that is arithmetic and a sequence that is *not* arithmetic. Answers will vary.

111. (a) Graph the first 10 terms of the arithmetic sequence $a_n = 2 + 3n$. (a)–(d). See margin.

(b) Graph the equation of the line $y = 3x + 2$.

(c) Discuss any differences between the graph of

$$a_n = 2 + 3n$$

and the graph of

$$y = 3x + 2.$$

(d) Compare the slope of the line in part (b) with the common difference of the sequence in part (a). What can you conclude about the slope of a line and the common difference of an arithmetic sequence?

112. PATTERN RECOGNITION See margin.

(a) Compute the following sums of consecutive positive odd integers.

$1 + 3 = \square$

$1 + 3 + 5 = \square$

$1 + 3 + 5 + 7 = \square$

$1 + 3 + 5 + 7 + 9 = \square$

$1 + 3 + 5 + 7 + 9 + 11 = \square$

(b) Use the sums in part (a) to make a conjecture about the sums of consecutive positive odd integers. Check your conjecture for the sum

$1 + 3 + 5 + 7 + 9 + 11 + 13 = \square$.

(c) Verify your conjecture algebraically.

113. THINK ABOUT IT The sum of the first 20 terms of an arithmetic sequence with a common difference of 3 is 650. Find the first term. 4

114. THINK ABOUT IT The sum of the first n terms of an arithmetic sequence with first term a_1 and common difference d is S_n. Determine the sum if each term is increased by 5. Explain. $S_n + 5n$; Explanations will vary.

PROJECT: HOUSING PRICES To work an extended application analyzing the median sales prices of new, privately owned, single-family homes sold in the United States from 1991 through 2007, visit this text's website at *academic.cengage.com*. (Data Source: U.S. Census Bureau)

5 ASSESS AND RETEACH

Daily Homework Quiz

Transparency Available
Available at the Instructor's companion site.

104. (a)

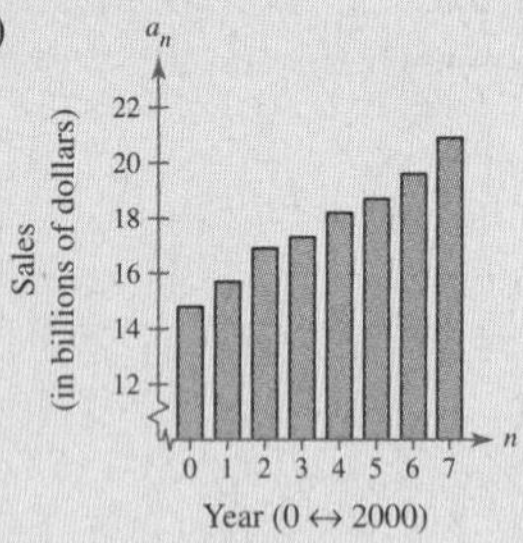

(c)

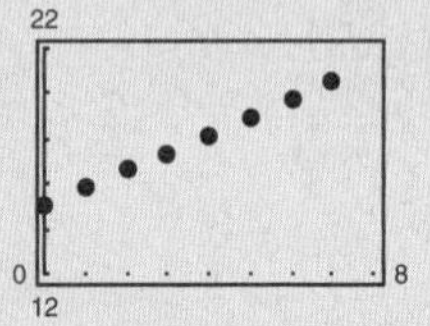

105. True. Given a_1 and a_2, $d = a_2 - a_1$ and $a_n = a_1 + (n - 1)d$.

106. True by the formula for the sum of a finite arithmetic sequence

$$S_n = \frac{n}{2}(a_1 + a_n).$$

109. Add the first term to $(n - 1)$ times the common difference.

111. (a)

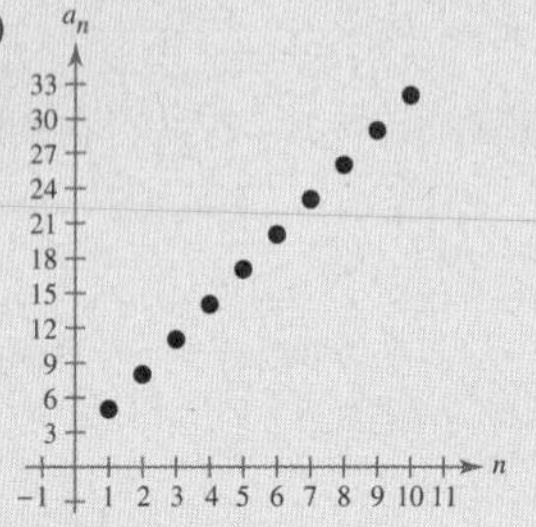

(b)

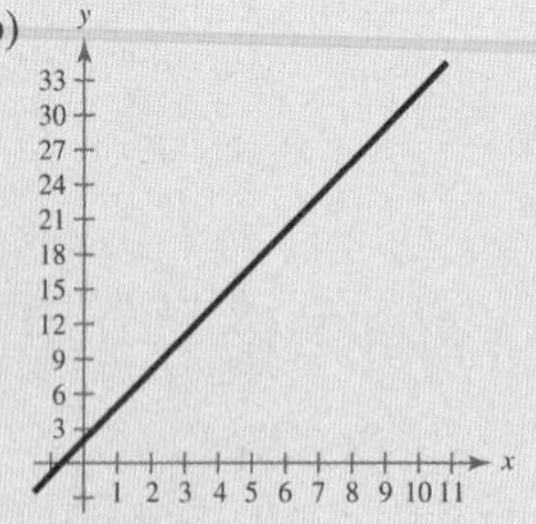

(c) The graph of $y = 3x + 2$ contains all points on the line. The graph of $a_n = 2 + 3n$ contains only points at the positive integers.

(d) The slope of the line and the common difference of the arithmetic sequence are equal.

112. (a) 4, 9, 16, 25, 36

(b) $S_n = n^2$; $S_7 = 49 = 7^2$

(c) $\frac{n}{2}[1 + (2n - 1)] = n^2$

9.3 Geometric Sequences and Series

What you should learn

- Recognize, write, and find the nth terms of geometric sequences.
- Find the sum of a finite geometric sequence.
- Find the sum of an infinite geometric series.
- Use geometric sequences to model and solve real-life problems.

Why you should learn it

Geometric sequences can be used to model and solve real-life problems. For instance, in Exercise 113 on page 668, you will use a geometric sequence to model the population of China.

© Bob Krist/Corbis

Geometric Sequences

In Section 9.2, you learned that a sequence whose consecutive terms have a common *difference* is an arithmetic sequence. In this section, you will study another important type of sequence called a **geometric sequence.** Consecutive terms of a geometric sequence have a common *ratio.*

> **Definition of Geometric Sequence**
>
> A sequence is **geometric** if the ratios of consecutive terms are the same. So, the sequence $a_1, a_2, a_3, a_4, . . . , a_n, . . .$ is geometric if there is a number r such that
>
> $$\frac{a_2}{a_1} = \frac{a_3}{a_2} = \frac{a_4}{a_3} = \cdot \cdot \cdot = r, \quad r \neq 0.$$
>
> The number r is the **common ratio** of the sequence.

Example 1 Examples of Geometric Sequences

a. The sequence whose nth term is 2^n is geometric. For this sequence, the common ratio of consecutive terms is 2.

$$2, 4, 8, 16, . . . , 2^n, . . . \qquad \text{Begin with } n = 1.$$

$$\frac{4}{2} = 2$$

b. The sequence whose nth term is $4(3^n)$ is geometric. For this sequence, the common ratio of consecutive terms is 3.

$$12, 36, 108, 324, . . . , 4(3^n), . . . \qquad \text{Begin with } n = 1.$$

$$\frac{36}{12} = 3$$

c. The sequence whose nth term is $\left(-\frac{1}{3}\right)^n$ is geometric. For this sequence, the common ratio of consecutive terms is $-\frac{1}{3}$.

$$-\frac{1}{3}, \frac{1}{9}, -\frac{1}{27}, \frac{1}{81}, . . . , \left(-\frac{1}{3}\right)^n, . . . \qquad \text{Begin with } n = 1.$$

$$\frac{1/9}{-1/3} = -\frac{1}{3}$$

CHECKPoint Now try Exercise 5.

In Example 1, notice that each of the geometric sequences has an nth term that is of the form ar^n, where the common ratio of the sequence is r. A geometric sequence may be thought of as an exponential function whose domain is the set of natural numbers.

WARNING / CAUTION

Be sure you understand that the sequence 1, 4, 9, 16, . . . , whose nth term is n^2, is *not* geometric. The ratio of the second term to the first term is

$$\frac{a_2}{a_1} = \frac{4}{1} = 4$$

but the ratio of the third term to the second term is

$$\frac{a_3}{a_2} = \frac{9}{4}.$$

1 PLAN AND PREPARE

Warm-up Exercises

Transparency Available
Available at the Instructor's companion site.

Notetaking Guide

Transparency Available
Promotes interactive learning and notetaking skills. Available at the Instructor's companion site.

Animated Precalculus

An **Animated Precalculus** tutorial is available at the Student companion site for **Section 9.3.**

Pacing

Average: 3 days
Advanced: 3 days
Block: 0.5 block with 9.2
1 block

2 FOCUS AND MOTIVATE

Essential Question

How do you find terms and sums of geometric sequences? **Tell students that they will learn how to answer this question by studying formulas to find the nth terms and sums of geometric sequences and series.**

Resource Planning Guide

Chapter Resources
- Complete Solutions Guide

Workbooks
- Notetaking Guide
- Student Solutions Guide

Interactive Technology
- Instructor Success Organizer
- Notetaking Guide IAE
- Instructional DVDs
- Animated Precalculus
- PowerLecture with ExamView

> **The *n*th Term of a Geometric Sequence**
>
> The *n*th term of a geometric sequence has the form
>
> $$a_n = a_1 r^{n-1}$$
>
> where r is the common ratio of consecutive terms of the sequence. So, every geometric sequence can be written in the following form.
>
> $$\begin{array}{cccccccc} a_1, & a_2, & a_3, & a_4, & a_5, \ldots\ldots, & & a_n, \ldots\ldots \\ \downarrow & \downarrow & \downarrow & \downarrow & \downarrow & & \downarrow & \\ a_1, & a_1 r, & a_1 r^2, & a_1 r^3, & a_1 r^4, \ldots, & & a_1 r^{n-1}, \ldots & \end{array}$$

If you know the nth term of a geometric sequence, you can find the $(n + 1)$th term by multiplying by r. That is, $a_{n+1} = a_n r$.

Example 2 Finding the Terms of a Geometric Sequence

Write the first five terms of the geometric sequence whose first term is $a_1 = 3$ and whose common ratio is $r = 2$. Then graph the terms on a set of coordinate axes.

Solution

Starting with 3, repeatedly multiply by 2 to obtain the following.

$a_1 = 3$	1st term	$a_4 = 3(2^3) = 24$	4th term
$a_2 = 3(2^1) = 6$	2nd term	$a_5 = 3(2^4) = 48$	5th term
$a_3 = 3(2^2) = 12$	3rd term		

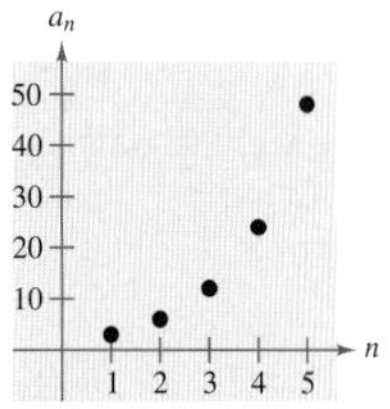

FIGURE 9.4

Figure 9.4 shows the first five terms of this geometric sequence.

CHECKPoint Now try Exercise 17.

Example 3 Finding a Term of a Geometric Sequence

Find the 15th term of the geometric sequence whose first term is 20 and whose common ratio is 1.05.

Algebraic Solution

$a_{15} = a_1 r^{n-1}$	Formula for geometric sequence
$= 20(1.05)^{15-1}$	Substitute 20 for a_1, 1.05 for r, and 15 for n.
≈ 39.60	Use a calculator.

CHECKPoint Now try Exercise 35.

Numerical Solution

For this sequence, $r = 1.05$ and $a_1 = 20$. So, $a_n = 20(1.05)^{n-1}$. Use the *table* feature of a graphing utility to create a table that shows the values of $u_n = 20(1.05)^{n-1}$ for $n = 1$ through $n = 15$. From Figure 9.5, the number in the 15th row is approximately 39.60, so the 15th term of the geometric sequence is about 39.60.

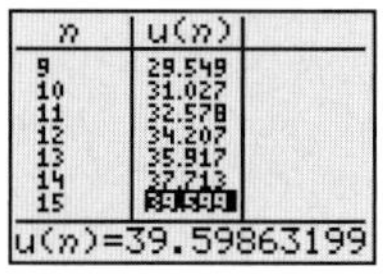

FIGURE 9.5

3 TEACH

Extra Example 1

For each of the geometric sequences, find the common ratio.

a. $3, 9, 27, 81, 243, \ldots, 3^n$

3

b. $10, 20, 40, 80, 160, \ldots, 5(2^n)$

2

c. $-\frac{1}{4}, \frac{1}{16}, -\frac{1}{64}, \frac{1}{256}, -\frac{1}{1024}, \ldots, \left(-\frac{1}{4}\right)^n$

$-\frac{1}{4}$

Avoiding Common Errors

Students often assume that sequences are either arithmetic or geometric. Remind them that many sequences do not meet the conditions for either of these types. To determine whether a sequence is arithmetic or geometric, students should check to see whether the difference or ratio remains constant for all given terms.

Extra Example 2

Write the first five terms of the geometric sequence whose first term is $a_1 = 2$ and whose common ratio is $r = 4$. Then graph the terms on a set of coordinate axes.

2, 8, 32, 128, 512

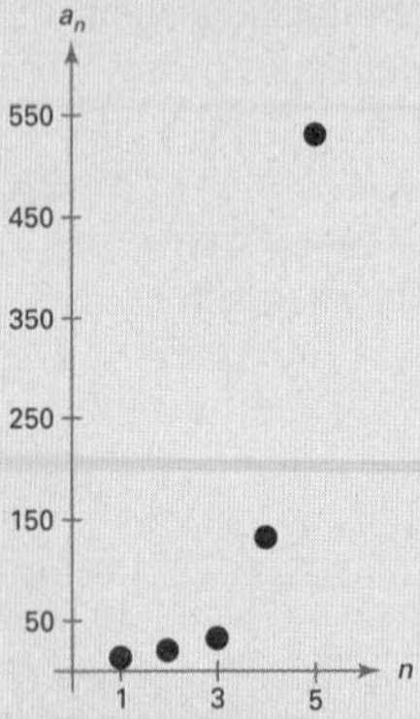

Extra Example 3

Find the ninth term of the geometric sequence whose first term is 4 and whose common ratio is $\frac{1}{2}$.

$\frac{1}{64}$

Example 4 Finding a Term of a Geometric Sequence

Find the 12th term of the geometric sequence

$5, 15, 45, \ldots .$

Solution

The common ratio of this sequence is

$$r = \frac{15}{5} = 3.$$

Because the first term is $a_1 = 5$, you can determine the 12th term $(n = 12)$ to be

$$\begin{aligned} a_n &= a_1 r^{n-1} && \text{Formula for geometric sequence} \\ a_{12} &= 5(3)^{12-1} && \text{Substitute 5 for } a_1\text{, 3 for } r\text{, and 12 for } n. \\ &= 5(177{,}147) && \text{Use a calculator.} \\ &= 885{,}735. && \text{Simplify.} \end{aligned}$$

CHECKPoint Now try Exercise 45.

If you know *any* two terms of a geometric sequence, you can use that information to find a formula for the nth term of the sequence.

Example 5 Finding a Term of a Geometric Sequence

The fourth term of a geometric sequence is 125, and the 10th term is $125/64$. Find the 14th term. (Assume that the terms of the sequence are positive.)

Solution

The 10th term is related to the fourth term by the equation

$$a_{10} = a_4 r^6 \qquad \text{Multiply fourth term by } r^{10-4}.$$

Because $a_{10} = 125/64$ and $a_4 = 125$, you can solve for r as follows.

$$\begin{aligned} \frac{125}{64} &= 125r^6 && \text{Substitute } \tfrac{125}{64} \text{ for } a_{10} \text{ and 125 for } a_4. \\ \frac{1}{64} &= r^6 && \text{Divide each side by 125.} \\ \frac{1}{2} &= r && \text{Take the sixth root of each side.} \end{aligned}$$

You can obtain the 14th term by multiplying the 10th term by r^4.

$$\begin{aligned} a_{14} &= a_{10} r^4 && \text{Multiply the 10th term by } r^{14-10}. \\ &= \frac{125}{64}\left(\frac{1}{2}\right)^4 && \text{Substitute } \tfrac{125}{64} \text{ for } a_{10} \text{ and } \tfrac{1}{2} \text{ for } r. \\ &= \frac{125}{64}\left(\frac{1}{16}\right) && \text{Evaluate power.} \\ &= \frac{125}{1024} && \text{Simplify.} \end{aligned}$$

CHECKPoint Now try Exercise 53.

Algebra Help

Remember that r is the common ratio of consecutive terms of a geometric sequence. So, in Example 5,

$$\begin{aligned} a_{10} &= a_1 r^9 \\ &= a_1 \cdot r \cdot r \cdot r \cdot r^6 \\ &= a_1 \cdot \frac{a_2}{a_1} \cdot \frac{a_3}{a_2} \cdot \frac{a_4}{a_3} \cdot r^6 \\ &= a_4 r^6. \end{aligned}$$

Extra Example 4

Find the 10th term of the geometric sequence $6, -2, \frac{2}{3}, \ldots .$

$-\frac{2}{6561}$

Extra Example 5

The second term of a geometric sequence is -18, and the fifth term is $\frac{2}{3}$. Find the sixth term.

$-\frac{2}{9}$

Extra Example 6

Find the sum $\sum_{n=1}^{7} 2^{n-1}$.

127

The Sum of a Finite Geometric Sequence

The formula for the sum of a *finite* geometric sequence is as follows.

> **The Sum of a Finite Geometric Sequence**
>
> The sum of the finite geometric sequence
>
> $$a_1,\ a_1r,\ a_1r^2,\ a_1r^3,\ a_1r^4, \ldots, a_1r^{n-1}$$
>
> with common ratio $r \neq 1$ is given by $S_n = \sum_{i=1}^{n} a_1r^{i-1} = a_1\left(\frac{1-r^n}{1-r}\right)$.

For a proof of this formula for the sum of a finite geometric sequence, see Proofs in Mathematics on page 721.

Example 6 Finding the Sum of a Finite Geometric Sequence

Find the sum $\sum_{i=1}^{12} 4(0.3)^{i-1}$.

Solution

By writing out a few terms, you have

$$\sum_{i=1}^{12} 4(0.3)^{i-1} = 4(0.3)^0 + 4(0.3)^1 + 4(0.3)^2 + \cdots + 4(0.3)^{11}.$$

Now, because $a_1 = 4$, $r = 0.3$, and $n = 12$, you can apply the formula for the sum of a finite geometric sequence to obtain

$$S_n = a_1\left(\frac{1-r^n}{1-r}\right) \qquad \text{Formula for the sum of a sequence}$$

$$\sum_{i=1}^{12} 4(0.3)^{i-1} = 4\left[\frac{1-(0.3)^{12}}{1-0.3}\right] \qquad \text{Substitute 4 for } a_1\text{, 0.3 for } r\text{, and 12 for } n.$$

$$\approx 5.714. \qquad \text{Use a calculator.}$$

CHECKPoint Now try Exercise 71.

When using the formula for the sum of a finite geometric sequence, be careful to check that the sum is of the form

$$\sum_{i=1}^{n} a_1\, r^{i-1}. \qquad \text{Exponent for } r \text{ is } i-1.$$

If the sum is not of this form, you must adjust the formula. For instance, if the sum in Example 6 were $\sum_{i=1}^{12} 4(0.3)^i$, then you would evaluate the sum as follows.

$$\sum_{i=1}^{12} 4(0.3)^i = 4(0.3) + 4(0.3)^2 + 4(0.3)^3 + \cdots + 4(0.3)^{12}$$

$$= 4(0.3) + [4(0.3)](0.3) + [4(0.3)](0.3)^2 + \cdots + [4(0.3)](0.3)^{11}$$

$$= 4(0.3)\left[\frac{1-(0.3)^{12}}{1-0.3}\right] \approx 1.714 \qquad a_1 = 4(0.3),\ r = 0.3,\ n = 12$$

Geometric Series

The summation of the terms of an infinite geometric *sequence* is called an **infinite geometric series** or simply a **geometric series.**

The formula for the sum of a *finite* geometric *sequence* can, depending on the value of r, be extended to produce a formula for the sum of an *infinite* geometric *series*. Specifically, if the common ratio r has the property that $|r| < 1$, it can be shown that r^n becomes arbitrarily close to zero as n increases without bound. Consequently,

$$a_1\left(\frac{1-r^n}{1-r}\right) \longrightarrow a_1\left(\frac{1-0}{1-r}\right) \quad \text{as} \quad n \longrightarrow \infty.$$

This result is summarized as follows.

The Sum of an Infinite Geometric Series

If $|r| < 1$, the infinite geometric series

$$a_1 + a_1r + a_1r^2 + a_1r^3 + \cdot \cdot \cdot + a_1r^{n-1} + \cdot \cdot \cdot$$

has the sum

$$S = \sum_{i=0}^{\infty} a_1r^i = \frac{a_1}{1-r}.$$

Note that if $|r| \geq 1$, the series does not have a sum.

Example 7 Finding the Sum of an Infinite Geometric Series

Find each sum.

a. $\displaystyle\sum_{n=0}^{\infty} 4(0.6)^n$

b. $3 + 0.3 + 0.03 + 0.003 + \cdot \cdot \cdot$

Solution

a. $\displaystyle\sum_{n=0}^{\infty} 4(0.6)^n = 4 + 4(0.6) + 4(0.6)^2 + 4(0.6)^3 + \cdot \cdot \cdot + 4(0.6)^n + \cdot \cdot \cdot$

$$= \frac{4}{1-0.6} \qquad \frac{a_1}{1-r}$$

$$= 10$$

b. $3 + 0.3 + 0.03 + 0.003 + \cdot \cdot \cdot = 3 + 3(0.1) + 3(0.1)^2 + 3(0.1)^3 + \cdot \cdot \cdot$

$$= \frac{3}{1-0.1} \qquad \frac{a_1}{1-r}$$

$$= \frac{10}{3}$$

$$\approx 3.33$$

CHECK*Point* Now try Exercise 93.

Extra Example 7

Find each sum.

a. $\displaystyle\sum_{n=0}^{\infty} 5\left(\frac{1}{2}\right)^n$

10

b. $5 + 0.5 + 0.05 + 0.005 + \cdots$

$\frac{50}{9}$

Extra Example 8

A deposit of $100 is made on the first day of each month in a savings account that pays 6% interest, compounded monthly. Find the balance of this annuity after 4 years.
$5436.83

Closing the Lesson

Have students summarize the major points of the lesson and answer the Essential Question: How do you find terms and sums of geometric sequences?

- **Use the formula $a_n = a_1 r^{n-1}$ to represent the nth term of a geometric sequence with starting value a_1 and common ratio r.**
- **Use the formula**
$$S_n = \sum_{i=1}^{n} a_1 r^{i-1} = a_1\left(\frac{1-r^n}{1-r}\right)$$
to find the sum of a finite geometric sequence.
- **Use the formula**
$$S = \sum_{i=0}^{\infty} a_1 r^i = \frac{a_1}{1-r}$$
to find the sum of a geometric series.

Classroom Discussion

Sequences will vary. One possibility (in inches, when starting with an 8-foot piece of string) is: 96, 48, 24, 12, 6, 3, $1\frac{1}{2}$, $\frac{3}{4}$, $\frac{3}{8}$, $\frac{3}{16}$, $\frac{3}{32}$, $\frac{3}{64}$ (and can go no further).

Formula: $a_n = 96\left(\frac{1}{2}\right)^{n-1}$

You could theoretically make an infinite number of cuts, but realistically the string would become so small that it would be impossible to cut.

Study Tip

Recall from Section 3.1 that the formula for compound interest (for n compoundings per year) is

$$A = P\left(1 + \frac{r}{n}\right)^{nt}.$$

So, in Example 8, $50 is the principal P, 0.06 is the interest rate r, 12 is the number of compoundings per year n, and 2 is the time t in years. If you substitute these values into the formula, you obtain

$$A = 50\left(1 + \frac{0.06}{12}\right)^{12(2)}$$
$$= 50\left(1 + \frac{0.06}{12}\right)^{24}.$$

Application

Example 8 Increasing Annuity

A deposit of $50 is made on the first day of each month in an account that pays 6% interest, compounded monthly. What is the balance at the end of 2 years? (This type of savings plan is called an **increasing annuity.**)

Solution

The first deposit will gain interest for 24 months, and its balance will be

$$A_{24} = 50\left(1 + \frac{0.06}{12}\right)^{24}$$
$$= 50(1.005)^{24}.$$

The second deposit will gain interest for 23 months, and its balance will be

$$A_{23} = 50\left(1 + \frac{0.06}{12}\right)^{23}$$
$$= 50(1.005)^{23}.$$

The last deposit will gain interest for only 1 month, and its balance will be

$$A_1 = 50\left(1 + \frac{0.06}{12}\right)^{1}$$
$$= 50(1.005).$$

The total balance in the annuity will be the sum of the balances of the 24 deposits. Using the formula for the sum of a finite geometric sequence, with $A_1 = 50(1.005)$ and $r = 1.005$, you have

$$S_{24} = 50(1.005)\left[\frac{1-(1.005)^{24}}{1-1.005}\right]$$ Substitute 50(1.005) for A_1, 1.005 for r, and 24 for n.

$$= \$1277.96.$$ Simplify.

CHECKPoint Now try Exercise 121.

Classroom Discussion

An Experiment You will need a piece of string or yarn, a pair of scissors, and a tape measure. Measure out any length of string at least 5 feet long. Double over the string and cut it in half. Take one of the resulting halves, double it over, and cut it in half. Continue this process until you are no longer able to cut a length of string in half. How many cuts were you able to make? Construct a sequence of the resulting string lengths after each cut, starting with the original length of the string. Find a formula for the nth term of this sequence. How many cuts could you theoretically make? Discuss why you were not able to make that many cuts. See margin.

9.3 EXERCISES

See www.CalcChat.com for worked-out solutions to odd-numbered exercises.

VOCABULARY: Fill in the blanks.

1. A sequence is called a $\underline{\text{geometric}}$ sequence if the ratios between consecutive terms are the same. This ratio is called the $\underline{\text{common}}$ ratio.
2. The nth term of a geometric sequence has the form $\underline{a_n = a_1 r^{n-1}}$.
3. The formula for the sum of a finite geometric sequence is given by $\underline{S_n = a_1\left(\frac{1-r^n}{1-r}\right)}$.
4. The sum of the terms of an infinite geometric sequence is called a $\underline{\text{geometric series}}$.

SKILLS AND APPLICATIONS

In Exercises 5–16, determine whether the sequence is geometric. If so, find the common ratio. 5–16. See margin.

5. $2, 10, 50, 250, \ldots$
6. $7, 21, 63, 189, \ldots$
7. $3, 12, 21, 30, \ldots$
8. $25, 20, 15, 10, \ldots$
9. $1, -\frac{1}{2}, \frac{1}{4}, -\frac{1}{8}, \ldots$
10. $5, 1, 0.2, 0.04, \ldots$
11. $\frac{1}{8}, \frac{1}{4}, \frac{1}{2}, 1, \ldots$
12. $9, -6, 4, -\frac{8}{3}, \ldots$
13. $1, \frac{1}{2}, \frac{1}{3}, \frac{1}{4}, \ldots$
14. $\frac{1}{5}, \frac{2}{7}, \frac{3}{9}, \frac{4}{11}, \ldots$
15. $1, -\sqrt{7}, 7, -7\sqrt{7}, \ldots$
16. $2, \frac{4}{\sqrt{3}}, \frac{8}{3}, \frac{16}{3\sqrt{3}}, \ldots$

In Exercises 17–28, write the first five terms of the geometric sequence. 17–28. See margin.

17. $a_1 = 4, r = 3$
18. $a_1 = 8, r = 2$
19. $a_1 = 1, r = \frac{1}{2}$
20. $a_1 = 1, r = \frac{1}{3}$
21. $a_1 = 5, r = -\frac{1}{10}$
22. $a_1 = 6, r = -\frac{1}{4}$
23. $a_1 = 1, r = e$
24. $a_1 = 2, r = \pi$
25. $a_1 = 3, r = \sqrt{5}$
26. $a_1 = 4, r = -\frac{1}{\sqrt{2}}$
27. $a_1 = 2, r = \frac{x}{4}$
28. $a_1 = 5, r = 2x$

In Exercises 29–34, write the first five terms of the geometric sequence. Determine the common ratio and write the nth term of the sequence as a function of n. 29–34. See margin.

29. $a_1 = 64, \quad a_{k+1} = \frac{1}{2}a_k$
30. $a_1 = 81, \quad a_{k+1} = \frac{1}{3}a_k$
31. $a_1 = 9, \quad a_{k+1} = 2a_k$
32. $a_1 = 5, \quad a_{k+1} = -2a_k$
33. $a_1 = 6, \quad a_{k+1} = -\frac{3}{2}a_k$
34. $a_1 = 80, \quad a_{k+1} = -\frac{1}{2}a_k$

In Exercises 35–44, write an expression for the nth term of the geometric sequence. Then find the indicated term.

35. $a_1 = 4, r = \frac{1}{2}, n = 10$
36. $a_1 = 5, r = \frac{7}{2}, n = 8$
37. $a_1 = 6, r = -\frac{1}{3}, n = 12$
38. $a_1 = 64, r = -\frac{1}{4}, n = 10$
39. $a_1 = 100, r = e^x, n = 9$
40. $a_1 = 1, r = e^{-x}, n = 4$
41. $a_1 = 1, r = \sqrt{2}, n = 12$
42. $a_1 = 1, r = \sqrt{3}, n = 8$
43. $a_1 = 500, r = 1.02, n = 40$ 35–44. See margin.
44. $a_1 = 1000, r = 1.005, n = 60$

In Exercises 45–56, find the indicated nth term of the geometric sequence.

45. 9th term: $11, 33, 99, \ldots$ $a_9 = 72{,}171$
46. 7th term: $3, 36, 432, \ldots$ $a_7 = 8{,}957{,}952$
47. 10th term: $5, 30, 180, \ldots$ $a_{10} = 50{,}388{,}480$
48. 22nd term: $4, 8, 16, \ldots$ $a_{22} = 8{,}388{,}608$
49. 8th term: $\frac{1}{2}, -\frac{1}{8}, \frac{1}{32}, -\frac{1}{128}, \ldots$ $a_8 = -\frac{1}{32{,}768}$
50. 7th term: $\frac{8}{5}, -\frac{16}{25}, \frac{32}{125}, -\frac{64}{625}, \ldots$ $a_7 = \frac{512}{78{,}125}$
51. 3rd term: $a_1 = 16, a_4 = \frac{27}{4}$ $a_3 = 9$
52. 1st term: $a_2 = 3, a_5 = \frac{3}{64}$ $a_1 = 12$
53. 6th term: $a_4 = -18, a_7 = \frac{2}{3}$ $a_6 = -2$
54. 7th term: $a_3 = \frac{16}{3}, a_5 = \frac{64}{27}$ $a_7 = \frac{256}{243}$
55. 5th term: $a_2 = 2, a_3 = -\sqrt{2}$ 55. $a_5 = -\frac{1}{\sqrt{2}}$
56. 9th term: $a_3 = 11, a_4 = -11\sqrt{11}$ $a_9 = 14{,}641$

In Exercises 57–60, match the geometric sequence with its graph. [The graphs are labeled (a), (b), (c), and (d).]

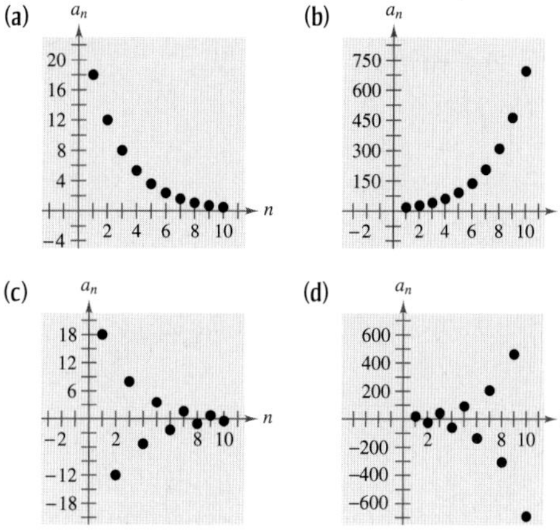

57. $a_n = 18\left(\frac{2}{3}\right)^{n-1}$ a
58. $a_n = 18\left(-\frac{2}{3}\right)^{n-1}$ c
59. $a_n = 18\left(\frac{3}{2}\right)^{n-1}$ b
60. $a_n = 18\left(-\frac{3}{2}\right)^{n-1}$ d

4 PRACTICE AND APPLY

Assignment Guide

Transparencies Available
Available at the Instructor's companion site.

Average:
Day 1: pp. 667–668
Exs. 1–3, 7–15 odd, 19–29 odd, 33, 37–41 odd, 47–51 odd, 57–61, 65
Day 2: pp. 667–668
Exs. 4, 67, 69, 75–83 odd, 87–91 odd, 95–107
Day 3: pp. 668–670
Exs. 111, 114–117, 123–133 odd, 137, 138, 141

Advanced:
Day 1: pp. 667–668
Exs. 1–3, 8–16 even, 22–32 even, 36–44 even, 48, 52, 54, 57–60, 62, 66
Day 2: pp. 667–668
Exs. 4, 70–80 even, 84–92 even, 96–110 even
Day 3: pp. 668–670
Exs. 112–114, 116, 118–120, 122–142 even

Block:
pp. 667–668
Exs. 1–3, 7–15 odd, 19–29 odd, 33, 37–41 odd, 47–51 odd, 57–61, 65 (with 9.2)
pp. 667–670
Exs. 4, 67, 69, 75–83 odd, 87–91 odd, 95–107, 111, 114–117, 123–133 odd, 137, 138, 141

5. Geometric sequence, $r = 5$
6. Geometric sequence, $r = 3$
7. Not a geometric sequence
8. Not a geometric sequence
9. Geometric sequence, $r = -\frac{1}{2}$
10. Geometric sequence, $r = 0.2$
11. Geometric sequence, $r = 2$
12. Geometric sequence, $r = -\frac{2}{3}$
13. Not a geometric sequence
14. Not a geometric sequence
15. Geometric sequence, $r = -\sqrt{7}$
16. Geometric sequence, $r = \frac{2}{\sqrt{3}}$
17. $4, 12, 36, 108, 324$
18. $8, 16, 32, 64, 128$
19. $1, \frac{1}{2}, \frac{1}{4}, \frac{1}{8}, \frac{1}{16}$
20. $1, \frac{1}{3}, \frac{1}{9}, \frac{1}{27}, \frac{1}{81}$
21. $5, -\frac{1}{2}, \frac{1}{20}, -\frac{1}{200}, \frac{1}{2000}$
22. $6, -\frac{3}{2}, \frac{3}{8}, -\frac{3}{32}, \frac{3}{128}$
23. $1, e, e^2, e^3, e^4$
24. $2, 2\pi, 2\pi^2, 2\pi^3, 2\pi^4$
25. $3, 3\sqrt{5}, 15, 15\sqrt{5}, 75$
26. $4, -2\sqrt{2}, 2, -\sqrt{2}, 1$
27. $2, \frac{x}{2}, \frac{x^2}{8}, \frac{x^3}{32}, \frac{x^4}{128}$
28. $5, 10x, 20x^2, 40x^3, 80x^4$
29. $64, 32, 16, 8, 4; r = \frac{1}{2}; a_n = 128\left(\frac{1}{2}\right)^n$
30. $81, 27, 9, 3, 1; r = \frac{1}{3}; a_n = 243\left(\frac{1}{3}\right)^n$
31. $9, 18, 36, 72, 144; r = 2; a_n = \frac{9}{2}(2)^n$
32. $5, -10, 20, -40, 80; r = -2; a_n = -\frac{5}{2}(-2)^n$
33. $6, -9, \frac{27}{2}, -\frac{81}{4}, \frac{243}{8}; r = -\frac{3}{2}; a_n = -4\left(-\frac{3}{2}\right)^n$
34. $80, -40, 20, -10, 5; r = -\frac{1}{2}; a_n = -160\left(-\frac{1}{2}\right)^n$
35. $a_n = 4\left(\frac{1}{2}\right)^{n-1}; \frac{1}{128}$
36. $a_n = 5\left(\frac{7}{2}\right)^{n-1}; \frac{4{,}117{,}715}{128}$
37. $a_n = 6\left(-\frac{1}{3}\right)^{n-1}; -\frac{2}{59{,}049}$
38. $a_n = 64\left(-\frac{1}{4}\right)^{n-1}; -\frac{1}{4096}$
39. $a_n = 100e^{x(n-1)}; 100e^{8x}$
40. $a_n = e^{-x(n-1)}; e^{-3x}$
41. $a_n = \left(\sqrt{2}\right)^{n-1}; 32\sqrt{2}$
42. $a_n = \left(\sqrt{3}\right)^{n-1}; 27\sqrt{3}$
43. $a_n = 500(1.02)^{n-1}$; About 1082.372
44. $a_n = 1000(1.005)^{n-1}$; About 1342.139

In Exercises 61–66, use a graphing utility to graph the first 10 terms of the sequence. 61–66. See margin.

61. $a_n = 12(-0.75)^{n-1}$ **62.** $a_n = 10(1.5)^{n-1}$

63. $a_n = 12(-0.4)^{n-1}$ **64.** $a_n = 20(-1.25)^{n-1}$

65. $a_n = 2(1.3)^{n-1}$ **66.** $a_n = 10(1.2)^{n-1}$

In Exercises 67–86, find the sum of the finite geometric sequence.

67. $\sum_{n=1}^{7} 4^{n-1}$ 5461 **68.** $\sum_{n=1}^{10} \left(\frac{3}{2}\right)^{n-1}$ $\frac{58{,}025}{512}$

69. $\sum_{n=1}^{6} (-7)^{n-1}$ $-14{,}706$ **70.** $\sum_{n=1}^{8} 5\left(-\frac{5}{2}\right)^{n-1}$ $-\frac{278{,}835}{128}$

71. $\sum_{i=1}^{7} 64\left(-\frac{1}{2}\right)^{i-1}$ 43 **72.** $\sum_{i=1}^{10} 2\left(\frac{1}{4}\right)^{i-1}$ 2.667

73. $\sum_{i=1}^{6} 32\left(\frac{1}{4}\right)^{i-1}$ $\frac{1365}{32}$ **74.** $\sum_{i=1}^{12} 16\left(\frac{1}{2}\right)^{i-1}$ $\frac{4095}{128}$

75. $\sum_{n=0}^{20} 3\left(\frac{3}{2}\right)^{n}$ 29,921.311 **76.** $\sum_{n=0}^{40} 5\left(\frac{3}{5}\right)^{n}$ 12.500

77. $\sum_{n=0}^{15} 2\left(\frac{4}{3}\right)^{n}$ 592.647 **78.** $\sum_{n=0}^{20} 10\left(\frac{1}{5}\right)^{n}$ 12.500

79. $\sum_{n=0}^{5} 300(1.06)^{n}$ 2092.596 **80.** $\sum_{n=0}^{6} 500(1.04)^{n}$ 3949.147

81. $\sum_{n=0}^{40} 2\left(-\frac{1}{4}\right)^{n}$ 1.600 **82.** $\sum_{n=0}^{50} 10\left(\frac{2}{3}\right)^{n-1}$ 45.000

83. $\sum_{i=1}^{10} 8\left(-\frac{1}{4}\right)^{i-1}$ 6.400 **84.** $\sum_{i=0}^{25} 8\left(-\frac{1}{2}\right)^{i}$ 5.333

85. $\sum_{i=1}^{10} 5\left(-\frac{1}{3}\right)^{i-1}$ 3.750 **86.** $\sum_{i=1}^{100} 15\left(\frac{2}{3}\right)^{i-1}$ 45.000

In Exercises 87–92, use summation notation to write the sum. 87–92. See margin.

87. $10 + 30 + 90 + \cdots + 7290$

88. $9 + 18 + 36 + \cdots + 1152$

89. $2 - \frac{1}{2} + \frac{1}{8} - \cdots + \frac{1}{2048}$

90. $15 - 3 + \frac{3}{5} - \cdots - \frac{3}{625}$

91. $0.1 + 0.4 + 1.6 + \cdots + 102.4$

92. $32 + 24 + 18 + \cdots + 10.125$

In Exercises 93–106, find the sum of the infinite geometric series.

93. $\sum_{n=0}^{\infty} \left(\frac{1}{2}\right)^{n}$ 2 **94.** $\sum_{n=0}^{\infty} 2\left(\frac{2}{3}\right)^{n}$ 6

95. $\sum_{n=0}^{\infty} \left(-\frac{1}{2}\right)^{n}$ $\frac{2}{3}$ **96.** $\sum_{n=0}^{\infty} 2\left(-\frac{2}{3}\right)^{n}$ $\frac{6}{5}$

97. $\sum_{n=0}^{\infty} 4\left(\frac{1}{4}\right)^{n}$ $\frac{16}{3}$ **98.** $\sum_{n=0}^{\infty} \left(\frac{1}{10}\right)^{n}$ $\frac{10}{9}$

99. $\sum_{n=0}^{\infty} (0.4)^{n}$ $\frac{5}{3}$ **100.** $\sum_{n=0}^{\infty} 4(0.2)^{n}$ 5

101. $\sum_{n=0}^{\infty} -3(0.9)^{n}$ -30 **102.** $\sum_{n=0}^{\infty} -10(0.2)^{n}$ $-\frac{25}{2}$

103. $8 + 6 + \frac{9}{2} + \frac{27}{8} + \cdots$ **104.** $9 + 6 + 4 + \frac{8}{3} + \cdots$

105. $\frac{1}{9} - \frac{1}{3} + 1 - 3 + \cdots$

106. $-\frac{125}{36} + \frac{25}{6} - 5 + 6 - \cdots$

103. 32

104. 27

105–106. Undefined

In Exercises 107–110, find the rational number representation of the repeating decimal.

107. $0.\overline{36}$ $\frac{4}{11}$ **108.** $0.\overline{297}$ $\frac{11}{37}$

109. $0.3\overline{18}$ $\frac{7}{22}$ **110.** $1.3\overline{8}$ $\frac{25}{18}$

GRAPHICAL REASONING In Exercises 111 and 112, use a graphing utility to graph the function. Identify the horizontal asymptote of the graph and determine its relationship to the sum. 111–112. See margin.

111. $f(x) = 6\left[\frac{1-(0.5)^x}{1-(0.5)}\right]$, $\sum_{n=0}^{\infty} 6\left(\frac{1}{2}\right)^n$

112. $f(x) = 2\left[\frac{1-(0.8)^x}{1-(0.8)}\right]$, $\sum_{n=0}^{\infty} 2\left(\frac{4}{5}\right)^n$

113. DATA ANALYSIS: POPULATION The table shows the mid-year populations a_n of China (in millions) from 2002 through 2008. (Source: U.S. Census Bureau)
(a)–(c). See margin.

Year	Population, a_n
2002	1284.3
2003	1291.5
2004	1298.8
2005	1306.3
2006	1314.0
2007	1321.9
2008	1330.0

(a) Use the *exponential regression* feature of a graphing utility to find a geometric sequence that models the data. Let n represent the year, with $n = 2$ corresponding to 2002.

(b) Use the sequence from part (a) to describe the rate at which the population of China is growing.

(c) Use the sequence from part (a) to predict the population of China in 2015. The U.S. Census Bureau predicts the population of China will be 1393.4 million in 2015. How does this value compare with your prediction?

(d) Use the sequence from part (a) to determine when the population of China will reach 1.35 billion.
2010

61.

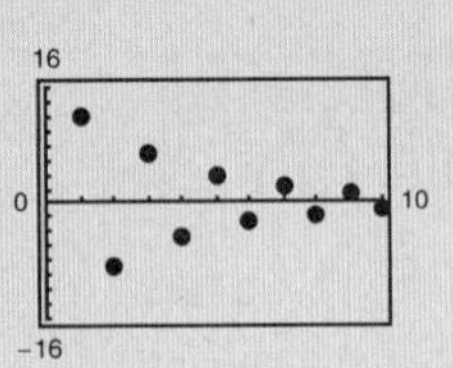

62.

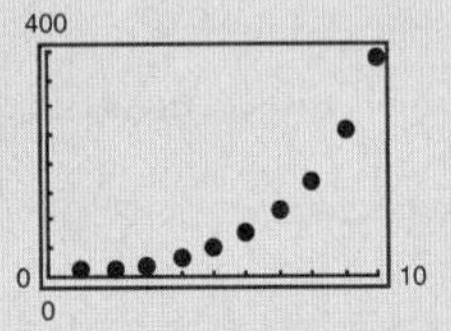

63.

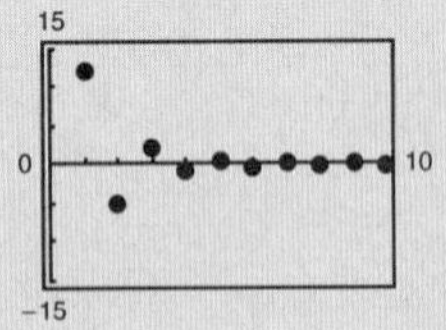

64.

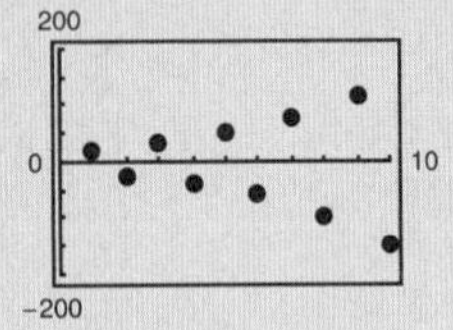

65.

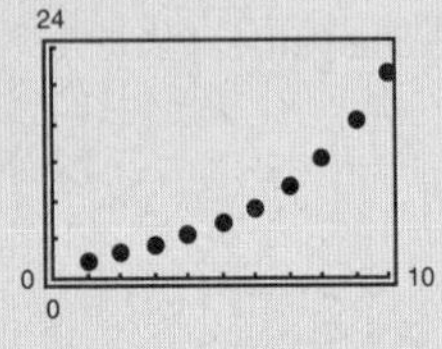

66.

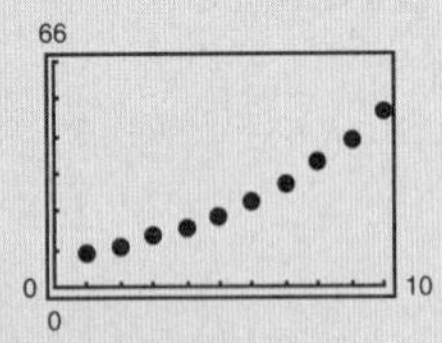

87. $\sum_{n=1}^{7} 10(3)^{n-1}$

88. $\sum_{n=1}^{8} 9(2)^{n-1}$

89. $\sum_{n=1}^{7} 2\left(-\frac{1}{4}\right)^{n-1}$

90. $\sum_{n=1}^{6} 15\left(-\frac{1}{5}\right)^{n-1}$

91. $\sum_{n=1}^{6} 0.1(4)^{n-1}$

92. $\sum_{n=1}^{5} 32\left(\frac{3}{4}\right)^{n-1}$

111.

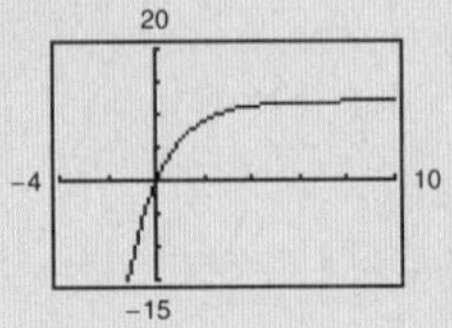

Horizontal asymptote: $y = 12$
Corresponds to the sum of the series

112.

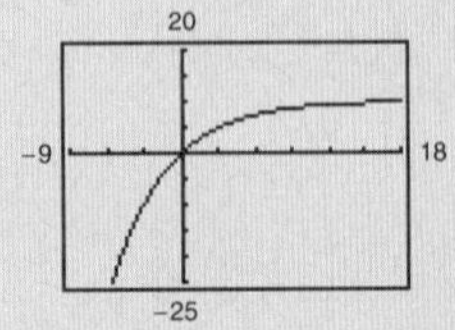

Horizontal asymptote: $y = 10$
Corresponds to the sum of the series

113. (a) $a_n = 1269.10(1.006)^n$
(b) The population is growing at a rate of 0.6% per year.
(c) 1388.2 million. This value is close to the prediction.

114–115. See margin.

114. COMPOUND INTEREST A principal of \$5000 is invested at 6% interest. Find the amount after 10 years if the interest is compounded (a) annually, (b) semiannually, (c) quarterly, (d) monthly, and (e) daily.

115. COMPOUND INTEREST A principal of \$2500 is invested at 2% interest. Find the amount after 20 years if the interest is compounded (a) annually, (b) semiannually, (c) quarterly, (d) monthly, and (e) daily.

116. DEPRECIATION A tool and die company buys a machine for \$175,000 and it depreciates at a rate of 30% per year. (In other words, at the end of each year the depreciated value is 70% of what it was at the beginning of the year.) Find the depreciated value of the machine after 5 full years. \$29,412.25

117. ANNUITIES A deposit of \$100 is made at the beginning of each month in an account that pays 6% interest, compounded monthly. The balance A in the account at the end of 5 years is

$$A = 100\left(1 + \frac{0.06}{12}\right)^1 + \cdot \cdot \cdot + 100\left(1 + \frac{0.06}{12}\right)^{60}.$$

Find A. \$7011.89

118. ANNUITIES A deposit of \$50 is made at the beginning of each month in an account that pays 8% interest, compounded monthly. The balance A in the account at the end of 5 years is

$$A = 50\left(1 + \frac{0.08}{12}\right)^1 + \cdot \cdot \cdot + 50\left(1 + \frac{0.08}{12}\right)^{60}.$$

Find A. \$3698.34

119. ANNUITIES A deposit of P dollars is made at the beginning of each month in an account with an annual interest rate r, compounded monthly. The balance A after t years is

$$A = P\left(1 + \frac{r}{12}\right) + P\left(1 + \frac{r}{12}\right)^2 + \cdot \cdot \cdot + P\left(1 + \frac{r}{12}\right)^{12t}.$$

Show that the balance is

$$A = P\left[\left(1 + \frac{r}{12}\right)^{12t} - 1\right]\left(1 + \frac{12}{r}\right).$$ Answers will vary.

120. ANNUITIES A deposit of P dollars is made at the beginning of each month in an account with an annual interest rate r, compounded continuously. The balance A after t years is

$$A = Pe^{r/12} + Pe^{2r/12} + \cdot \cdot \cdot + Pe^{12tr/12}.$$

Show that the balance is $A = \dfrac{Pe^{r/12}(e^{rt} - 1)}{e^{r/12} - 1}$.

Answers will vary.

ANNUITIES In Exercises 121–124, consider making monthly deposits of P dollars in a savings account with an annual interest rate r. Use the results of Exercises 119 and 120 to find the balance A after t years if the interest is compounded (a) monthly and (b) continuously. 121–124. See margin.

121. $P = \$50,\ r = 5\%,\ t = 20$ years

122. $P = \$75,\ r = 3\%,\ t = 25$ years

123. $P = \$100,\ r = 2\%,\ t = 40$ years

124. $P = \$20,\ r = 4.5\%,\ t = 50$ years

125. ANNUITIES Consider an initial deposit of P dollars in an account with an annual interest rate r, compounded monthly. At the end of each month, a withdrawal of W dollars will occur and the account will be depleted in t years. The amount of the initial deposit required is

$$P = W\left(1 + \frac{r}{12}\right)^{-1} + W\left(1 + \frac{r}{12}\right)^{-2} + \cdot \cdot \cdot + W\left(1 + \frac{r}{12}\right)^{-12t}.$$

Show that the initial deposit is

$$P = W\left(\frac{12}{r}\right)\left[1 - \left(1 + \frac{r}{12}\right)^{-12t}\right].$$ Answers will vary.

126. ANNUITIES Determine the amount required in a retirement account for an individual who retires at age 65 and wants an income of \$2000 from the account each month for 20 years. Use the result of Exercise 125 and assume that the account earns 9% compounded monthly. \$222,289.91

MULTIPLIER EFFECT In Exercises 127–130, use the following information. A tax rebate has been given to property owners by the state government with the anticipation that each property owner will spend approximately $p\%$ of the rebate, and in turn each recipient of this amount will spend $p\%$ of what they receive, and so on. Economists refer to this exchange of money and its circulation within the economy as the "multiplier effect." The multiplier effect operates on the idea that the expenditures of one individual become the income of another individual. For the given tax rebate, find the total amount put back into the state's economy, if this effect continues without end.

	Tax rebate	$p\%$	
127.	\$400	75%	\$1600
128.	\$250	80%	\$1250
129.	\$600	72.5%	About \$2181.82
130.	\$450	77.5%	\$2000

114. (a) \$8954.24
(b) \$9030.56
(c) \$9070.09
(d) \$9096.98
(e) \$9110.14

115. (a) \$3714.87
(b) \$3722.16
(c) \$3725.85
(d) \$3728.32
(e) \$3729.52

121. (a) \$20,637.32
(b) \$20,662.37

122. (a) \$33,534.21
(b) \$33,551.91

123. (a) \$73,565.97
(b) \$73,593.75

124. (a) \$45,224.39
(b) \$45,352.85

5 ASSESS AND RETEACH

Daily Homework Quiz

Transparency Available
Available at the Instructor's companion site.

132. $273\frac{8}{9}$ in.^{2}

133. \$5,435,989.84

135. (a) 3208.53 ft; 2406.4 ft; 5614.93 ft
(b) 5950 ft

137. False. A sequence is geometric if the ratios of consecutive terms are the same.

138. False. $a_n = a_1 r^{n-1}$

139. (a)

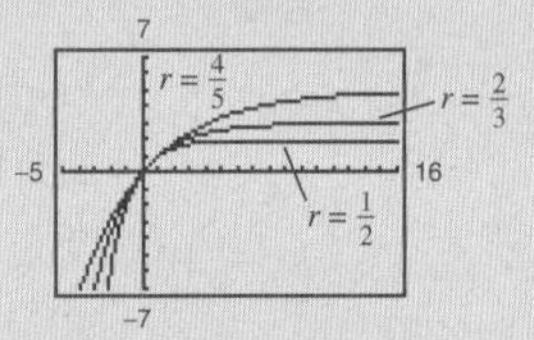

As $x \to \infty$, $y \to \dfrac{1}{1-r}$.

(b)

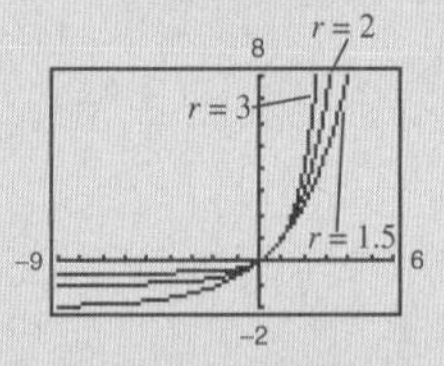

As $x \to \infty$, $y \to \infty$.

141. Given a real number r between -1 and 1, as the exponent n increases, r^n approaches zero.

131. GEOMETRY The sides of a square are 16 inches in length. A new square is formed by connecting the midpoints of the sides of the original square, and two of the resulting triangles are shaded (see figure). If this process is repeated five more times, determine the total area of the shaded region. 126 in.^{2}

132. GEOMETRY The sides of a square are 27 inches in length. New squares are formed by dividing the original square into nine squares. The center square is then shaded (see figure). If this process is repeated three more times, determine the total area of the shaded region. See margin.

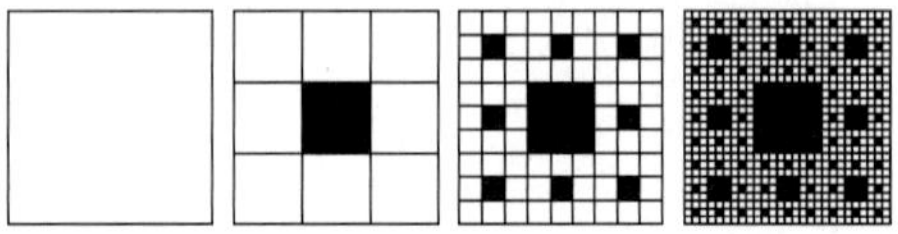

133. SALARY An investment firm has a job opening with a salary of \$45,000 for the first year. Suppose that during the next 39 years, there is a 5% raise each year. Find the total compensation over the 40-year period. See margin.

134. SALARY A technology services company has a job opening with a salary of \$52,700 for the first year. Suppose that during the next 24 years, there is a 3% raise each year. Find the total compensation over the 25-year period. \$1,921,403.23

135. DISTANCE A bungee jumper is jumping off the New River Gorge Bridge in West Virginia, which has a height of 876 feet. The cord stretches 850 feet and the jumper rebounds 75% of the distance fallen. See margin.

(a) After jumping and rebounding 10 times, how far has the jumper traveled downward? How far has the jumper traveled upward? What is the total distance traveled downward and upward?

(b) Approximate the total distance, both downward and upward, that the jumper travels before coming to rest.

136. DISTANCE A ball is dropped from a height of 16 feet. Each time it drops h feet, it rebounds $0.81h$ feet.

(a) Find the total vertical distance traveled by the ball.

(b) The ball takes the following times (in seconds) for each fall. (a) 152.42 ft (b) 19 sec

$s_1 = -16t^2 + 16, \qquad s_1 = 0 \text{ if } t = 1$

$s_2 = -16t^2 + 16(0.81), \qquad s_2 = 0 \text{ if } t = 0.9$

$s_3 = -16t^2 + 16(0.81)^2, \qquad s_3 = 0 \text{ if } t = (0.9)^2$

$s_4 = -16t^2 + 16(0.81)^3, \qquad s_4 = 0 \text{ if } t = (0.9)^3$

$\vdots \qquad\qquad \vdots$

$s_n = -16t^2 + 16(0.81)^{n-1}, \qquad s_n = 0 \text{ if } t = (0.9)^{n-1}$

Beginning with s_2, the ball takes the same amount of time to bounce up as it does to fall, and so the total time elapsed before it comes to rest is

$$t = 1 + 2\sum_{n=1}^{\infty} (0.9)^n.$$

Find this total time.

EXPLORATION

137–138. See margin.

TRUE OR FALSE? In Exercises 137 and 138, determine whether the statement is true or false. Justify your answer.

137. A sequence is geometric if the ratios of consecutive differences of consecutive terms are the same.

138. You can find the nth term of a geometric sequence by multiplying its common ratio by the first term of the sequence raised to the $(n-1)$th power.

139. GRAPHICAL REASONING Consider the graph of

$$y = \left(\frac{1 - r^x}{1 - r}\right).$$ See margin.

(a) Use a graphing utility to graph y for $r = \frac{1}{2}, \frac{2}{3}$, and $\frac{4}{5}$. What happens as $x \to \infty$?

(b) Use a graphing utility to graph y for $r = 1.5$, 2, and 3. What happens as $x \to \infty$?

140. CAPSTONE (a)–(b). Answers will vary.

(a) Write a brief paragraph that describes the similarities and differences between a geometric sequence and a geometric series. Give an example of each.

(b) Write a brief paragraph that describes the difference between a finite geometric series and an infinite geometric series. Is it always possible to find the sum of a finite geometric series? Is it always possible to find the sum of an infinite geometric series? Explain.

141. WRITING Write a brief paragraph explaining why the terms of a geometric sequence decrease in magnitude when $-1 < r < 1$. See margin.

142. Find two different geometric series with sums of 4. Answers will vary.

PROJECT: HOUSING VACANCIES To work an extended application analyzing the numbers of vacant houses in the United States from 1990 through 2007, visit this text's website at *academic.cengage.com*. (Data Source: U.S. Census Bureau)

9.4 MATHEMATICAL INDUCTION

What you should learn

- Use mathematical induction to prove statements involving a positive integer n.
- Recognize patterns and write the nth term of a sequence.
- Find the sums of powers of integers.
- Find finite differences of sequences.

Why you should learn it

Finite differences can be used to determine what type of model can be used to represent a sequence. For instance, in Exercise 79 on page 680, you will use finite differences to find a model that represents the numbers of Alaskan residents from 2002 through 2007.

Jeff Schultz/PhotoLibrary

Introduction

In this section, you will study a form of mathematical proof called **mathematical induction.** It is important that you see clearly the logical need for it, so take a closer look at the problem discussed in Example 5 in Section 9.2.

$$S_1 = 1 = 1^2$$
$$S_2 = 1 + 3 = 2^2$$
$$S_3 = 1 + 3 + 5 = 3^2$$
$$S_4 = 1 + 3 + 5 + 7 = 4^2$$
$$S_5 = 1 + 3 + 5 + 7 + 9 = 5^2$$

Judging from the pattern formed by these first five sums, it appears that the sum of the first n odd integers is

$$S_n = 1 + 3 + 5 + 7 + 9 + \cdot \cdot \cdot + (2n - 1) = n^2.$$

Although this particular formula *is* valid, it is important for you to see that recognizing a pattern and then simply *jumping to the conclusion* that the pattern must be true for all values of n is *not* a logically valid method of proof. There are many examples in which a pattern appears to be developing for small values of n and then at some point the pattern fails. One of the most famous cases of this was the conjecture by the French mathematician Pierre de Fermat (1601–1665), who speculated that all numbers of the form

$$F_n = 2^{2^n} + 1, \quad n = 0, 1, 2, . . .$$

are prime. For $n = 0, 1, 2, 3$, and 4, the conjecture is true.

$$F_0 = 3$$
$$F_1 = 5$$
$$F_2 = 17$$
$$F_3 = 257$$
$$F_4 = 65{,}537$$

The size of the next Fermat number ($F_5 = 4{,}294{,}967{,}297$) is so great that it was difficult for Fermat to determine whether it was prime or not. However, another well-known mathematician, Leonhard Euler (1707–1783), later found the factorization

$$F_5 = 4{,}294{,}967{,}297$$
$$= 641(6{,}700{,}417)$$

which proved that F_5 is not prime and therefore Fermat's conjecture was false.

Just because a rule, pattern, or formula seems to work for several values of n, you cannot simply decide that it is valid for all values of n without going through a *legitimate proof.* Mathematical induction is one method of proof.

1 PLAN AND PREPARE

Warm-up Exercises

Transparency Available
Available at the Instructor's companion site.

Notetaking Guide

Transparency Available
Promotes interactive learning and notetaking skills.
Available at the Instructor's companion site.

Animated Precalculus

An **Animated Precalculus** tutorial is available at the Student companion site for **Section 9.4.**

Pacing

Average: 2 days
Advanced: 2 days
Block: 1 block

2 FOCUS AND MOTIVATE

Essential Question

How do you use mathematical induction to find and prove formulas for sums of sequences and series?
Tell students that they will learn how to answer this question by testing whether the truth of one term implies the truth of the next term.

Resource Planning Guide

Chapter Resources
- Complete Solutions Guide

Workbooks
- Notetaking Guide
- Student Solutions Guide

Interactive Technology
- Instructor Success Organizer
- Notetaking Guide IAE
- Instructional DVDs
- Animated Precalculus
- PowerLecture with ExamView

3 TEACH

Extra Example 1

Find the statement P_{k+1} for each given statement P_k.

a. $P_k = \dfrac{6}{k(k+3)}$

$P_{k+1} = \dfrac{6}{(k+1)(k+4)}$

b. $P_k: S_k = 2 + 5 + 8 + \cdots + [3(k-1) - 2] + (3k - 2)$

$P_{k+1}: S_{k+1} = 2 + 5 + 8 + \cdots + (3k-2) + (3k+1)$

c. $P_k: k + 4 < 6k^2$

$P_{k+1}: k + 5 < 6(k^2 + 2k + 1)$

d. $P_k: 4^k \geq 3k + 1$

$P_{k+1}: 4^{k+1} \geq 3k + 4$

Avoiding Common Errors

Most errors in proof by mathematical induction occur when writing and simplifying S_{k+1}. Students should be careful to preserve operations when substituting. To help students avoid these errors, you may wish to review procedures for expanding powers and combining algebraic fractions.

Study Tip

It is important to recognize that in order to prove a statement by induction, both parts of the Principle of Mathematical Induction are necessary.

The Principle of Mathematical Induction

Let P_n be a statement involving the positive integer n. If

1. P_1 is true, and
2. for every positive integer k, the truth of P_k implies the truth of P_{k+1}

then the statement P_n must be true for all positive integers n.

To apply the Principle of Mathematical Induction, you need to be able to determine the statement P_{k+1} for a given statement P_k. To determine P_{k+1}, substitute the quantity $k + 1$ for k in the statement P_k.

Example 1 A Preliminary Example

Find the statement P_{k+1} for each given statement P_k.

a. $P_k: S_k = \dfrac{k^2(k+1)^2}{4}$

b. $P_k: S_k = 1 + 5 + 9 + \cdots + [4(k-1) - 3] + (4k - 3)$

c. $P_k: k + 3 < 5k^2$

d. $P_k: 3^k \geq 2k + 1$

Solution

a. $P_{k+1}: S_{k+1} = \dfrac{(k+1)^2(k+1+1)^2}{4}$ Replace k by $k + 1$.

$= \dfrac{(k+1)^2(k+2)^2}{4}$ Simplify.

b. $P_{k+1}: S_{k+1} = 1 + 5 + 9 + \cdots + \{4[(k+1) - 1] - 3\} + [4(k+1) - 3]$

$= 1 + 5 + 9 + \cdots + (4k - 3) + (4k + 1)$

c. $P_{k+1}: (k+1) + 3 < 5(k+1)^2$

$k + 4 < 5(k^2 + 2k + 1)$

d. $P_{k+1}: 3^{k+1} \geq 2(k+1) + 1$

$3^{k+1} \geq 2k + 3$

CHECKPoint Now try Exercise 5.

A well-known illustration used to explain why the Principle of Mathematical Induction works is the unending line of dominoes (see Figure 9.6). If the line actually contains infinitely many dominoes, it is clear that you could not knock the entire line down by knocking down only *one domino* at a time. However, suppose it were true that each domino would knock down the next one as it fell. Then you could knock them all down simply by pushing the first one and starting a chain reaction. Mathematical induction works in the same way. If the truth of P_k implies the truth of P_{k+1} and if P_1 is true, the chain reaction proceeds as follows: P_1 implies P_2, P_2 implies P_3, P_3 implies P_4, and so on.

FIGURE 9.6

When using mathematical induction to prove a *summation* formula (such as the one in Example 2), it is helpful to think of S_{k+1} as

$$S_{k+1} = S_k + a_{k+1}$$

where a_{k+1} is the $(k + 1)$th term of the original sum.

Example 2 Using Mathematical Induction

Use mathematical induction to prove the following formula.

$$\begin{aligned} S_n &= 1 + 3 + 5 + 7 + \cdot \cdot \cdot + (2n - 1) \\ &= n^2 \end{aligned}$$

Solution

Mathematical induction consists of two distinct parts. First, you must show that the formula is true when $n = 1$.

1. When $n = 1$, the formula is valid, because

$$S_1 = 1 = 1^2.$$

The second part of mathematical induction has two steps. The first step is to *assume* that the formula is valid for some integer k. The second step is to use this assumption to prove that the formula is valid for the *next* integer, $k + 1$.

2. Assuming that the formula

$$\begin{aligned} S_k &= 1 + 3 + 5 + 7 + \cdot \cdot \cdot + (2k - 1) \\ &= k^2 \end{aligned}$$

is true, you must show that the formula $S_{k+1} = (k + 1)^2$ is true.

$$\begin{aligned} S_{k+1} &= 1 + 3 + 5 + 7 + \cdot \cdot \cdot + (2k - 1) + [2(k + 1) - 1] \\ &= [1 + 3 + 5 + 7 + \cdot \cdot \cdot + (2k - 1)] + (2k + 2 - 1) \\ &= S_k + (2k + 1) \qquad \text{Group terms to form } S_k. \\ &= k^2 + 2k + 1 \qquad \text{Replace } S_k \text{ by } k^2. \\ &= (k + 1)^2 \end{aligned}$$

Combining the results of parts (1) and (2), you can conclude by mathematical induction that the formula is valid for all positive integer values of n.

CHECKPoint Now try Exercise 11.

It occasionally happens that a statement involving natural numbers is not true for the first $k - 1$ positive integers but is true for all values of $n \geq k$. In these instances, you use a slight variation of the Principle of Mathematical Induction in which you verify P_k rather than P_1. This variation is called the *Extended Principle of Mathematical Induction*. To see the validity of this, note from Figure 9.6 that all but the first $k - 1$ dominoes can be knocked down by knocking over the kth domino. This suggests that you can prove a statement P_n to be true for $n \geq k$ by showing that P_k is true and that P_k implies P_{k+1}. In Exercises 25–30 of this section, you are asked to apply this extension of mathematical induction.

Extra Example 2

Use mathematical induction to prove the following formula.

$5 + 7 + 9 + 11 + 13 + \cdots + (3 + 2n)$
$= n(n + 4)$

1. When $n = 1$, $S_1 = 5 = 1(1 + 4)$.

2. Assume that

$$\begin{aligned} S_{k+1} &= 5 + 7 + 9 + 11 + 13 + \cdots + (3 + 2k) \\ &= k(k + 4). \end{aligned}$$

Then, show that

$$S_{k+1} = (k + 1)(k + 5).$$

$$\begin{aligned} S_{k+1} &= 5 + 7 + 9 + 11 + 13 + \cdots + (3 + 2k) + [3 + 2(k + 1)] \\ &= S_k + (2k + 5) \\ &= k(k + 4) + (2k + 5) \\ &= k^2 + 6k + 5 \\ &= (k + 1)(k + 5) \end{aligned}$$

By mathematical induction, the formula is valid for all positive integer values of n.

Extra Example 3

Use mathematical induction to prove the following formula.

$1(1-1)+2(2-1)+3(3-1)+\cdots+n(n-1)=\dfrac{n(n-1)(n+1)}{3}$

1. When $n=1$,
$$S_1=\frac{1(1-1)(1+1)}{3}=0.$$

2. Assume that
$$S_k=1(1-1)+2(2-1)+3(3-1)+\cdots+k(k-1)=\frac{k(k-1)(k+1)}{3}.$$
Then show that
$$S_{k+1}=\frac{(k+1)k(k+2)}{3}.$$
$$\begin{aligned}S_{k+1}&=1(1-1)+2(2-1)+3(3-1)+\cdots+k(k-1)+(k+1)k\\&=S_k+k(k+1)\\&=\frac{k(k-1)(k+1)}{3}+\frac{3k(k+1)}{3}\\&=\frac{k(k-1)(k+1)+3k(k+1)}{3}\\&=\frac{k(k^2-1)+3k^2+3k}{3}\\&=\frac{k^3+3k^2+2k}{3}\\&=\frac{k(k^2+3k+2)}{3}\\&=\frac{k(k+1)(k+2)}{3}\end{aligned}$$

By mathematical induction, this formula is valid for all positive integer values of *n*.

Example 3 Using Mathematical Induction

Use mathematical induction to prove the formula

$$S_n=1^2+2^2+3^2+4^2+\cdots+n^2=\frac{n(n+1)(2n+1)}{6}$$

for all integers $n\ge 1$.

Solution

1. When $n=1$, the formula is valid, because
$$S_1=1^2=\frac{1(2)(3)}{6}.$$

2. Assuming that
$$S_k=1^2+2^2+3^2+4^2+\cdots+k^2=\frac{k(k+1)(2k+1)}{6}\qquad a_k=k^2$$
you must show that
$$S_{k+1}=\frac{(k+1)(k+1+1)[2(k+1)+1]}{6}=\frac{(k+1)(k+2)(2k+3)}{6}.$$
To do this, write the following.
$$\begin{aligned}S_{k+1}&=S_k+a_{k+1}\\&=(1^2+2^2+3^2+4^2+\cdots+k^2)+(k+1)^2 && \text{Substitute for } S_k.\\&=\frac{k(k+1)(2k+1)}{6}+(k+1)^2 && \text{By assumption}\\&=\frac{k(k+1)(2k+1)+6(k+1)^2}{6} && \text{Combine fractions.}\\&=\frac{(k+1)[k(2k+1)+6(k+1)]}{6} && \text{Factor.}\\&=\frac{(k+1)(2k^2+7k+6)}{6} && \text{Simplify.}\\&=\frac{(k+1)(k+2)(2k+3)}{6} && S_k \text{ implies } S_{k+1}.\end{aligned}$$

Combining the results of parts (1) and (2), you can conclude by mathematical induction that the formula is valid for *all* integers $n\ge 1$.

CHECKPoint Now try Exercise 17.

Study Tip

Remember that when adding rational expressions, you must first find the least common denominator (LCD). In Example 3, the LCD is 6.

When proving a formula using mathematical induction, the only statement that you need to verify is P_1. As a check, however, it is a good idea to try verifying some of the other statements. For instance, in Example 3, try verifying P_2 and P_3.

Example 4 Proving an Inequality by Mathematical Induction

Prove that $n < 2^n$ for all positive integers n.

Solution

1. For $n = 1$ and $n = 2$, the statement is true because

$$1 < 2^1 \quad \text{and} \quad 2 < 2^2.$$

2. Assuming that

$$k < 2^k$$

you need to show that $k + 1 < 2^{k+1}$. For $n = k$, you have

$$2^{k+1} = 2(2^k) > 2(k) = 2k. \qquad \text{By assumption}$$

Because $2k = k + k > k + 1$ for all $k > 1$, it follows that

$$2^{k+1} > 2k > k + 1 \quad \text{or} \quad k + 1 < 2^{k+1}.$$

Combining the results of parts (1) and (2), you can conclude by mathematical induction that $n < 2^n$ for all integers $n \geq 1$.

CHECKPoint Now try Exercise 25.

Study Tip

To check a result that you have proved by mathematical induction, it helps to list the statement for several values of n. For instance, in Example 4, you could list

$1 < 2^1 = 2$, $2 < 2^2 = 4$,

$3 < 2^3 = 8$, $4 < 2^4 = 16$,

$5 < 2^5 = 32$, $6 < 2^6 = 64$.

From this list, your intuition confirms that the statement $n < 2^n$ is reasonable.

Example 5 Proving Factors by Mathematical Induction

Prove that 3 is a factor of $4^n - 1$ for all positive integers n.

Solution

1. For $n = 1$, the statement is true because

$$4^1 - 1 = 3.$$

So, 3 is a factor.

2. Assuming that 3 is a factor of $4^k - 1$, you must show that 3 is a factor of $4^{k+1} - 1$. To do this, write the following.

$$4^{k+1} - 1 = 4^{k+1} - 4^k + 4^k - 1 \qquad \text{Subtract and add } 4^k.$$

$$= 4^k(4 - 1) + (4^k - 1) \qquad \text{Regroup terms.}$$

$$= 4^k \cdot 3 + (4^k - 1) \qquad \text{Simplify.}$$

Because 3 is a factor of $4^k \cdot 3$ and 3 is also a factor of $4^k - 1$, it follows that 3 is a factor of $4^{k+1} - 1$. Combining the results of parts (1) and (2), you can conclude by mathematical induction that 3 is a factor of $4^n - 1$ for all positive integers n.

CHECKPoint Now try Exercise 37.

Pattern Recognition

Although choosing a formula on the basis of a few observations does *not* guarantee the validity of the formula, pattern recognition *is* important. Once you have a pattern or formula that you think works, you can try using mathematical induction to prove your formula.

Extra Example 4

Prove that $(n + 1)! > 2^n$ for all integers n such that $n \geq 2$.

1. When $n = 2$, $3! = 6$ and $2^2 = 4$, thus $3! > 2^2$.

2. Assume $(k + 1)! > 2^k$, $k \geq 2$. Then, show that $(k + 2)! > 2^{k+1}$. $(k + 2)! = (k + 1)!(k + 2) > 2^k(2)$ because $k + 2 > 2$. Thus, $(k + 2)! > 2^{k+1}$.

Therefore, by mathematical induction, the formula is valid for all integers n such that $n \geq 2$.

Extra Example 5

Prove that 4 is a factor of $5^n - 1$ for all positive integers n.

1. For $n = 1$, the statement is true because $5^1 - 1 = 4$, so 4 is a factor.

2. Assume that 4 is a factor of $5^k - 1$. Show that 4 is a factor of $5^{k+1} - 1$.

$$5^{k+1} - 1 = 5^{k+1} - 5^k + 5^k - 1$$
$$= 5^k(5 - 1) + (5^k - 1)$$
$$= 5^k(4) + (5^k - 1)$$

Because 4 is a factor of $5^k(4)$ and 4 is also a factor of $5^k - 1$, it follows that 4 is a factor of $5^{k+1} - 1$.

Therefore, by mathematical induction, 4 is a factor of $5^n - 1$ for all positive integers n.

Extra Example 6

Find the formula for the finite sum and prove its validity.

$3 + 7 + 11 + 15 + \cdots + 4n - 1$

$$S_k = 3 + 7 + 11 + 15 + \cdots + 4k - 1k = k(2k + 1)$$

To prove the hypothesis, show validity for $n = k + 1$.

$$\begin{aligned} S_{k+1} &= [3 + 7 + 11 + 15 + \cdots + 4k - 1] + 4k + 3 \\ &= k(2k + 1) + 4k + 3 \\ &= 2k^2 + k + 4k + 3 \\ &= 2k^2 + 5k + 3 \\ &= (k + 1)(2k + 3) \end{aligned}$$

So, the hypothesis is valid.

Finding a Formula for the *n*th Term of a Sequence

To find a formula for the nth term of a sequence, consider these guidelines.

1. Calculate the first several terms of the sequence. It is often a good idea to write the terms in both simplified and factored forms.
2. Try to find a recognizable pattern for the terms and write a formula for the nth term of the sequence. This is your *hypothesis* or *conjecture*. You might try computing one or two more terms in the sequence to test your hypothesis.
3. Use mathematical induction to prove your hypothesis.

Example 6 Finding a Formula for a Finite Sum

Find a formula for the finite sum and prove its validity.

$$\frac{1}{1 \cdot 2} + \frac{1}{2 \cdot 3} + \frac{1}{3 \cdot 4} + \frac{1}{4 \cdot 5} + \cdots + \frac{1}{n(n+1)}$$

Solution

Begin by writing out the first few sums.

$$S_1 = \frac{1}{1 \cdot 2} = \frac{1}{2} = \frac{1}{1+1}$$

$$S_2 = \frac{1}{1 \cdot 2} + \frac{1}{2 \cdot 3} = \frac{4}{6} = \frac{2}{3} = \frac{2}{2+1}$$

$$S_3 = \frac{1}{1 \cdot 2} + \frac{1}{2 \cdot 3} + \frac{1}{3 \cdot 4} = \frac{9}{12} = \frac{3}{4} = \frac{3}{3+1}$$

$$S_4 = \frac{1}{1 \cdot 2} + \frac{1}{2 \cdot 3} + \frac{1}{3 \cdot 4} + \frac{1}{4 \cdot 5} = \frac{48}{60} = \frac{4}{5} = \frac{4}{4+1}$$

From this sequence, it appears that the formula for the kth sum is

$$S_k = \frac{1}{1 \cdot 2} + \frac{1}{2 \cdot 3} + \frac{1}{3 \cdot 4} + \frac{1}{4 \cdot 5} + \cdots + \frac{1}{k(k+1)} = \frac{k}{k+1}.$$

To prove the validity of this hypothesis, use mathematical induction. Note that you have already verified the formula for $n = 1$, so you can begin by assuming that the formula is valid for $n = k$ and trying to show that it is valid for $n = k + 1$.

$$S_{k+1} = \left[\frac{1}{1 \cdot 2} + \frac{1}{2 \cdot 3} + \frac{1}{3 \cdot 4} + \frac{1}{4 \cdot 5} + \cdots + \frac{1}{k(k+1)}\right] + \frac{1}{(k+1)(k+2)}$$

$$= \frac{k}{k+1} + \frac{1}{(k+1)(k+2)} \qquad \text{By assumption}$$

$$= \frac{k(k+2)+1}{(k+1)(k+2)} = \frac{k^2+2k+1}{(k+1)(k+2)} = \frac{(k+1)^2}{(k+1)(k+2)} = \frac{k+1}{k+2}$$

So, by mathematical induction, you can conclude that the hypothesis is valid.

CHECKPoint Now try Exercise 43.

Sums of Powers of Integers

The formula in Example 3 is one of a collection of useful summation formulas. This and other formulas dealing with the sums of various powers of the first n positive integers are as follows.

Sums of Powers of Integers

1. $1 + 2 + 3 + 4 + \cdots + n = \dfrac{n(n+1)}{2}$

2. $1^2 + 2^2 + 3^2 + 4^2 + \cdots + n^2 = \dfrac{n(n+1)(2n+1)}{6}$

3. $1^3 + 2^3 + 3^3 + 4^3 + \cdots + n^3 = \dfrac{n^2(n+1)^2}{4}$

4. $1^4 + 2^4 + 3^4 + 4^4 + \cdots + n^4 = \dfrac{n(n+1)(2n+1)(3n^2+3n-1)}{30}$

5. $1^5 + 2^5 + 3^5 + 4^5 + \cdots + n^5 = \dfrac{n^2(n+1)^2(2n^2+2n-1)}{12}$

Example 7 Finding a Sum of Powers of Integers

Find each sum.

a. $\displaystyle\sum_{i=1}^{7} i^3 = 1^3 + 2^3 + 3^3 + 4^3 + 5^3 + 6^3 + 7^3$

b. $\displaystyle\sum_{i=1}^{4} (6i - 4i^2)$

Solution

a. Using the formula for the sum of the cubes of the first n positive integers, you obtain

$$\sum_{i=1}^{7} i^3 = 1^3 + 2^3 + 3^3 + 4^3 + 5^3 + 6^3 + 7^3$$

$$= \frac{7^2(7+1)^2}{4} = \frac{49(64)}{4} = 784. \qquad \text{Formula 3}$$

b.
$$\sum_{i=1}^{4} (6i - 4i^2) = \sum_{i=1}^{4} 6i - \sum_{i=1}^{4} 4i^2$$

$$= 6\sum_{i=1}^{4} i - 4\sum_{i=1}^{4} i^2$$

$$= 6\left[\frac{4(4+1)}{2}\right] - 4\left[\frac{4(4+1)(8+1)}{6}\right] \qquad \text{Formulas 1 and 2}$$

$$= 6(10) - 4(30)$$

$$= 60 - 120 = -60$$

CHECK*Point* Now try Exercise 55.

Extra Example 7

Find each sum.

a. $\displaystyle\sum_{i=1}^{8} i^4$

8772

b. $\displaystyle\sum_{i=1}^{5} (3i^2 - 5i)$

90

Extra Example 8

Find a quadratic model for the sequence 0, 4, 10, 18, 28, ...

$a_n = n^2 + n - 2$

Closing the Lesson

Have students summarize the major points of the lesson and answer the Essential Question: How do you use mathematical induction to find and prove formulas for sums of sequences and series?

- **Use mathematical induction to prove the validity of a statement P_k by first showing that P_1 is true and then showing that if P_k is true, P_{k+1} must also be true.**
- **Find a formula for the nth term of a sequence by calculating the first several terms in the sequence, making a hypothesis that fits the data, and proving the hypothesis by using mathematical induction.**
- **Use the method of finite differences to find a polynomial equation for a sequence.**

Study Tip

For a linear model, the *first* differences should be the same nonzero number. For a quadratic model, the *second* differences are the same nonzero number.

Finite Differences

The **first differences** of a sequence are found by subtracting consecutive terms. The **second differences** are found by subtracting consecutive first differences. The first and second differences of the sequence 3, 5, 8, 12, 17, 23, . . . are as follows.

n:	1		2		3		4		5		6
a_n:	3		5		8		12		17		23
First differences:		2		3		4		5		6	
Second differences:			1		1		1		1		

For this sequence, the second differences are all the same. When this happens, the sequence has a perfect *quadratic* model. If the first differences are all the same, the sequence has a *linear* model. That is, it is arithmetic.

Example 8 Finding a Quadratic Model

Find the quadratic model for the sequence

3, 5, 8, 12, 17, 23, ...

Solution

You know from the second differences shown above that the model is quadratic and has the form

$$a_n = an^2 + bn + c.$$

By substituting 1, 2, and 3 for n, you can obtain a system of three linear equations in three variables.

$a_1 = a(1)^2 + b(1) + c = 3$ Substitute 1 for n.

$a_2 = a(2)^2 + b(2) + c = 5$ Substitute 2 for n.

$a_3 = a(3)^2 + b(3) + c = 8$ Substitute 3 for n.

You now have a system of three equations in a, b, and c.

$$\begin{cases} a + b + c = 3 & \text{Equation 1} \\ 4a + 2b + c = 5 & \text{Equation 2} \\ 9a + 3b + c = 8 & \text{Equation 3} \end{cases}$$

Using the techniques discussed in Chapter 7, you can find the solution to be $a = \frac{1}{2}$, $b = \frac{1}{2}$, and $c = 2$. So, the quadratic model is

$$a_n = \frac{1}{2}n^2 + \frac{1}{2}n + 2.$$

Try checking the values of a_1, a_2, and a_3.

CHECKPoint Now try Exercise 73.

9.4 EXERCISES

See www.CalcChat.com for worked-out solutions to odd-numbered exercises.

VOCABULARY: Fill in the blanks.

1. The first step in proving a formula by mathematical induction is to show that the formula is true when $n = 1$.
2. The first differences of a sequence are found by subtracting consecutive terms.
3. A sequence is an arithmetic sequence if the first differences are all the same nonzero number.
4. If the second differences of a sequence are all the same nonzero number, then the sequence has a perfect quadratic model.

SKILLS AND APPLICATIONS

In Exercises 5–10, find P_{k+1} for the given P_k. 5–10. See margin.

5. $P_k = \dfrac{5}{k(k+1)}$
6. $P_k = \dfrac{1}{2(k+2)}$
7. $P_k = \dfrac{k^2(k+3)^2}{6}$
8. $P_k = \dfrac{k}{3}(2k+1)$
9. $P_k = \dfrac{3}{(k+2)(k+3)}$
10. $P_k = \dfrac{k^2}{2(k+1)^2}$

In Exercises 11–24, use mathematical induction to prove the formula for every positive integer n. 11–24. Proofs

11. $2 + 4 + 6 + 8 + \cdots + 2n = n(n+1)$
12. $3 + 7 + 11 + 15 + \cdots + (4n-1) = n(2n+1)$
13. $2 + 7 + 12 + 17 + \cdots + (5n-3) = \dfrac{n}{2}(5n-1)$
14. $1 + 4 + 7 + 10 + \cdots + (3n-2) = \dfrac{n}{2}(3n-1)$
15. $1 + 2 + 2^2 + 2^3 + \cdots + 2^{n-1} = 2^n - 1$
16. $2(1 + 3 + 3^2 + 3^3 + \cdots + 3^{n-1}) = 3^n - 1$
17. $1 + 2 + 3 + 4 + \cdots + n = \dfrac{n(n+1)}{2}$
18. $1^3 + 2^3 + 3^3 + 4^3 + \cdots + n^3 = \dfrac{n^2(n+1)^2}{4}$
19. $1^2 + 3^2 + 5^2 + \cdots + (2n-1)^2 = \dfrac{n(2n-1)(2n+1)}{3}$
20. $\left(1+\dfrac{1}{1}\right)\left(1+\dfrac{1}{2}\right)\left(1+\dfrac{1}{3}\right)\cdots\left(1+\dfrac{1}{n}\right) = n+1$
21. $\displaystyle\sum_{i=1}^{n} i^5 = \dfrac{n^2(n+1)^2(2n^2+2n-1)}{12}$
22. $\displaystyle\sum_{i=1}^{n} i^4 = \dfrac{n(n+1)(2n+1)(3n^2+3n-1)}{30}$
23. $\displaystyle\sum_{i=1}^{n} i(i+1) = \dfrac{n(n+1)(n+2)}{3}$
24. $\displaystyle\sum_{i=1}^{n} \dfrac{1}{(2i-1)(2i+1)} = \dfrac{n}{2n+1}$

In Exercises 25–30, prove the inequality for the indicated integer values of n. 25–30. Proofs

25. $n! > 2^n, \quad n \ge 4$
26. $\left(\frac{4}{3}\right)^n > n, \quad n \ge 7$
27. $\dfrac{1}{\sqrt{1}} + \dfrac{1}{\sqrt{2}} + \dfrac{1}{\sqrt{3}} + \cdots + \dfrac{1}{\sqrt{n}} > \sqrt{n}, \quad n \ge 2$
28. $\left(\dfrac{x}{y}\right)^{n+1} < \left(\dfrac{x}{y}\right)^n, \quad n \ge 1$ and $0 < x < y$
29. $(1+a)^n \ge na, \quad n \ge 1$ and $a > 0$
30. $2n^2 > (n+1)^2, \quad n \ge 3$

In Exercises 31–42, use mathematical induction to prove the property for all positive integers n. 31–42. Proofs

31. $(ab)^n = a^n b^n$
32. $\left(\dfrac{a}{b}\right)^n = \dfrac{a^n}{b^n}$
33. If $x_1 \ne 0, x_2 \ne 0, \ldots, x_n \ne 0$, then $(x_1x_2x_3 \cdots x_n)^{-1} = x_1^{-1}x_2^{-1}x_3^{-1} \cdots x_n^{-1}$.
34. If $x_1 > 0, x_2 > 0, \ldots, x_n > 0$, then $\ln(x_1x_2 \cdots x_n) = \ln x_1 + \ln x_2 + \cdots + \ln x_n$.
35. Generalized Distributive Law: $x(y_1 + y_2 + \cdots + y_n) = xy_1 + xy_2 + \cdots + xy_n$
36. $(a+bi)^n$ and $(a-bi)^n$ are complex conjugates for all $n \ge 1$.
37. A factor of $(n^3 + 3n^2 + 2n)$ is 3.
38. A factor of $(n^3 - n + 3)$ is 3.
39. A factor of $(n^4 - n + 4)$ is 2.
40. A factor of $(2^{2n+1} + 1)$ is 3.
41. A factor of $(2^{4n-2} + 1)$ is 5.
42. A factor of $(2^{2n-1} + 3^{2n-1})$ is 5.

In Exercises 43–48, find a formula for the sum of the first n terms of the sequence. 43–44. See margin.

43. $1, 5, 9, 13, \ldots$
44. $25, 22, 19, 16, \ldots$
45. $1, \frac{9}{10}, \frac{81}{100}, \frac{729}{1000}, \ldots$ $\quad S_n = 10 - 10\left(\dfrac{9}{10}\right)^n$
46. $3, -\frac{9}{2}, \frac{27}{4}, -\frac{81}{8}, \ldots$ $\quad S_n = \dfrac{6}{5}\left[1 - \left(-\dfrac{3}{2}\right)^n\right]$

4 PRACTICE AND APPLY

Assignment Guide

Transparencies Available
Available at the Instructor's companion site.

Average:
Day 1: pp. 679–680
Exs. 1, 2, 7, 9, 13, 15, 18, 21–35 odd, 39, 41, 45, 47
Day 2: pp. 679–680
Exs. 3, 4, 49–53 odd, 57–61 odd, 65–69 odd, 75, 81–85

Advanced:
Day 1: pp. 679–680
Exs. 1, 2, 6–16 even, 22–36 even, 40, 42, 46, 48
Day 2: pp. 679–680
Exs. 3, 4, 50–56 even, 60–70 even, 74, 79–85

Block:
pp. 679–680
Exs. 1–4, 7, 9, 13, 15, 18, 21–35 odd, 39, 41, 45–53 odd, 57–61 odd, 65–69 odd, 75, 81–85

5. $\dfrac{5}{(k+1)(k+2)}$
6. $\dfrac{1}{2(k+3)}$
7. $\dfrac{(k+1)^2(k+4)^2}{6}$
8. $\dfrac{k+1}{3}(2k+3)$
9. $\dfrac{3}{(k+3)(k+4)}$
10. $\dfrac{(k+1)^2}{2(k+2)^2}$
43. $S_n = n(2n-1)$
44. $S_n = \dfrac{n}{2}(-3n+53)$

47. $\frac{1}{4}, \frac{1}{12}, \frac{1}{24}, \frac{1}{40}, \ldots, \frac{1}{2n(n+1)}, \ldots$ 47–48. See margin.

48. $\frac{1}{2 \cdot 3}, \frac{1}{3 \cdot 4}, \frac{1}{4 \cdot 5}, \frac{1}{5 \cdot 6}, \ldots, \frac{1}{(n+1)(n+2)}, \ldots$

In Exercises 49–58, find the sum using the formulas for the sums of powers of integers.

49. $\sum_{n=1}^{15} n$ 120

50. $\sum_{n=1}^{30} n$ 465

51. $\sum_{n=1}^{6} n^2$ 91

52. $\sum_{n=1}^{10} n^3$ 3025

53. $\sum_{n=1}^{5} n^4$ 979

54. $\sum_{n=1}^{8} n^5$ 61,776

55. $\sum_{n=1}^{6} (n^2 - n)$ 70

56. $\sum_{n=1}^{20} (n^3 - n)$ 43,890

57. $\sum_{i=1}^{6} (6i - 8i^3)$ −3402

58. $\sum_{j=1}^{10} \left(3 - \frac{1}{2}j + \frac{1}{2}j^2\right)$ 195

In Exercises 59–64, decide whether the sequence can be represented perfectly by a linear or a quadratic model. If so, find the model.

59. 5, 13, 21, 29, 37, 45, . . . Linear; $a_n = 8n - 3$

60. 2, 9, 16, 23, 30, 37, . . . Linear; $a_n = 7n - 5$

61. 6, 15, 30, 51, 78, 111, . . . Quadratic; $a_n = 3n^2 + 3$

62. 0, 6, 16, 30, 48, 70, . . . Quadratic; $a_n = 2n^2 - 2$

63. −2, 1, 6, 13, 22, 33, . . . Quadratic; $a_n = n^2 - 3$

64. −1, 8, 23, 44, 71, 104, . . . Quadratic; $a_n = 3n^2 - 4$

In Exercises 65–72, write the first six terms of the sequence beginning with the given term. Then calculate the first and second differences of the sequence. State whether the sequence has a linear model, a quadratic model, or neither. 65–72. See margin.

65. $a_1 = 0$
$a_n = a_{n-1} + 3$

66. $a_1 = 2$
$a_n = a_{n-1} + 2$

67. $a_1 = 3$
$a_n = a_{n-1} - n$

68. $a_2 = -3$
$a_n = -2a_{n-1}$

69. $a_0 = 2$
$a_n = (a_{n-1})^2$

70. $a_0 = 0$
$a_n = a_{n-1} + n$

71. $a_1 = 2$
$a_n = n - a_{n-1}$

72. $a_1 = 0$
$a_n = a_{n-1} + 2n$

In Exercises 73–78, find a quadratic model for the sequence with the indicated terms.

73. $a_0 = 3,\ a_1 = 3,\ a_4 = 15$ $a_n = n^2 - n + 3$

74. $a_0 = 7,\ a_1 = 6,\ a_3 = 10$ $a_n = n^2 - 2n + 7$

75. $a_0 = -3,\ a_2 = 1,\ a_4 = 9$ $a_n = \frac{1}{2}n^2 + n - 3$

76. $a_0 = 3,\ a_2 = 0,\ a_6 = 36$ $a_n = \frac{7}{4}n^2 - 5n + 3$

77. $a_1 = 0,\ a_2 = 8,\ a_4 = 30$ $a_n = n^2 + 5n - 6$

78. $a_0 = -3,\ a_2 = -5,\ a_6 = -57$ $a_n = -2n^2 + 3n - 3$

79. DATA ANALYSIS: RESIDENTS The table shows the numbers a_n (in thousands) of Alaskan residents from 2002 through 2007. (Source: U.S. Census Bureau)

Year	Number of residents, a_n
2002	643
2003	651
2004	662
2005	669
2006	677
2007	683

(a) Find the first differences of the data shown in the table. (a) 8, 11, 7, 8, 6 (b) See margin.

(b) Use your results from part (a) to determine whether a linear model can be used to approximate the data. If so, find a model algebraically. Let n represent the year, with $n = 2$ corresponding to 2002.

(c) Use the *regression* feature of a graphing utility to find a linear model for the data. Compare this model with the one from part (b). $a_n = 8.1n + 628$

(d) Use the models found in parts (b) and (c) to estimate the number of residents in 2013. How do these values compare? See margin.

EXPLORATION

80. CAPSTONE In your own words, explain what is meant by a proof by mathematical induction. Answers will vary.

81–85. See margin.

TRUE OR FALSE? In Exercises 81–85, determine whether the statement is true or false. Justify your answer.

81. If the statement P_1 is true but the true statement P_6 does *not* imply that the statement P_7 is true, then P_n is not necessarily true for all positive integers n.

82. If the statement P_k is true and P_k implies P_{k+1}, then P_1 is also true.

83. If the second differences of a sequence are all zero, then the sequence is arithmetic.

84. A sequence with n terms has $n - 1$ second differences.

85. If a sequence is arithmetic, then the first differences of the sequence are all zero.

5 ASSESS AND RETEACH

Daily Homework Quiz

Transparency Available
Available at the Instructor's companion site.

47. $S_n = \frac{n}{2(n+1)}$

48. $S_n = \frac{n}{2(n+2)}$

65. 0, 3, 6, 9, 12, 15
First differences: 3, 3, 3, 3, 3
Second differences: 0, 0, 0, 0
Linear

66. 2, 4, 6, 8, 10, 12
First differences: 2, 2, 2, 2, 2
Second differences: 0, 0, 0, 0
Linear

67. 3, 1, −2, −6, −11, −17
First differences: −2, −3, −4, −5, −6
Second differences: −1, −1, −1, −1
Quadratic

68. −3, 6, −12, 24, −48, 96
First differences: 9, −18, 36, −72, 144
Second differences: −27, 54, −108, 216
Neither

69. 2, 4, 16, 256, 65,536, 4,294,967,296
First differences: 2, 12, 240, 65,280, 4,294,901,760
Second differences: 10, 228, 65,040, 4,294,836,480
Neither

70. 0, 1, 3, 6, 10, 15
First differences: 1, 2, 3, 4, 5
Second differences: 1, 1, 1, 1
Quadratic

71. 2, 0, 3, 1, 4, 2
First differences: −2, 3, −2, 3, −2
Second differences: 5, −5, 5, −5
Neither

72. 0, 4, 10, 18, 28, 40
First differences: 4, 6, 8, 10, 12
Second differences: 2, 2, 2, 2
Quadratic

79. (b) A linear model can be used. $a_n = 8n + 627$
(d) Part (b): $a_n = 731$; Part (c): $a_n = 733.3$
The values are very similar.

81. True. P_7 may be false.

82. False. P_1 must be proven to be true.

83. True. If the second differences are all zero, then the first differences are all the same and the sequence is arithmetic.

84. False. A sequence with n terms has $n - 2$ second differences.

85. False. A sequence that is arithmetic has second differences equal to zero.

9.5 The Binomial Theorem

What you should learn

- Use the Binomial Theorem to calculate binomial coefficients.
- Use Pascal's Triangle to calculate binomial coefficients.
- Use binomial coefficients to write binomial expansions.

Why you should learn it

You can use binomial coefficients to model and solve real-life problems. For instance, in Exercise 91 on page 687, you will use binomial coefficients to write the expansion of a model that represents the average dollar amounts of child support collected per case in the United States.

Binomial Coefficients

Recall that a *binomial* is a polynomial that has two terms. In this section, you will study a formula that provides a quick method of raising a binomial to a power. To begin, look at the expansion of $(x + y)^n$ for several values of n.

$$(x + y)^0 = 1$$
$$(x + y)^1 = x + y$$
$$(x + y)^2 = x^2 + 2xy + y^2$$
$$(x + y)^3 = x^3 + 3x^2y + 3xy^2 + y^3$$
$$(x + y)^4 = x^4 + 4x^3y + 6x^2y^2 + 4xy^3 + y^4$$
$$(x + y)^5 = x^5 + 5x^4y + 10x^3y^2 + 10x^2y^3 + 5xy^4 + y^5$$

There are several observations you can make about these expansions.

1. In each expansion, there are $n + 1$ terms.
2. In each expansion, x and y have symmetrical roles. The powers of x decrease by 1 in successive terms, whereas the powers of y increase by 1.
3. The sum of the powers of each term is n. For instance, in the expansion of $(x + y)^5$, the sum of the powers of each term is 5.

$$(x + y)^5 = x^5 + \overbrace{5x^4y^1}^{4+1=5} + \overbrace{10x^3y^2}^{3+2=5} + 10x^2y^3 + 5x^1y^4 + y^5$$

4. The coefficients increase and then decrease in a symmetric pattern.

The coefficients of a binomial expansion are called **binomial coefficients.** To find them, you can use the **Binomial Theorem.**

> **The Binomial Theorem**
>
> In the expansion of $(x + y)^n$
>
> $$(x + y)^n = x^n + nx^{n-1}y + \cdots + {}_nC_r\, x^{n-r}y^r + \cdots + nxy^{n-1} + y^n$$
>
> the coefficient of $x^{n-r}y^r$ is
>
> $${}_nC_r = \frac{n!}{(n-r)!r!}.$$
>
> The symbol $\binom{n}{r}$ is often used in place of ${}_nC_r$ to denote binomial coefficients.

For a proof of the Binomial Theorem, see Proofs in Mathematics on page 722.

1 PLAN AND PREPARE

Warm-up Exercises

Transparency Available
Available at the Instructor's companion site.

Notetaking Guide

Transparency Available
Promotes interactive learning and notetaking skills. Available at the Instructor's companion site.

Animated Precalculus

An **Animated Precalculus** tutorial is available at the Student companion site for **Section 9.5.**

Pacing

Average: 2 days
Advanced: 2 days
Block: 1 block

2 FOCUS AND MOTIVATE

Essential Question

How do you find the expansion of a binomial $(x + y)^n$? **Tell students that they will learn how to answer this question by studying a formula for binomial coefficients and the relationship between a binomial expansion and Pascal's Triangle.**

Resource Planning Guide

Chapter Resources
- Complete Solutions Guide

Workbooks
- Notetaking Guide
- Student Solutions Guide

Interactive Technology
- Instructor Success Organizer
- Notetaking Guide IAE
- Instructional DVDs
- Animated Precalculus
- PowerLecture with ExamView

3 TEACH

Extra Example 1

Find each binomial coefficient.

a. ${}_9C_2$

36

b. $\binom{11}{4}$

330

c. ${}_8C_0$

1

d. $\binom{5}{5}$

1

Extra Example 2

Find each binomial coefficient.

a. ${}_8C_5$

56

b. $\binom{8}{3}$

56

c. ${}_{14}C_1$

14

d. $\binom{14}{13}$

14

TECHNOLOGY

Most graphing calculators are programmed to evaluate ${}_nC_r$. Consult the user's guide for your calculator and then evaluate ${}_8C_5$. You should get an answer of 56.

Example 1 Finding Binomial Coefficients

Find each binomial coefficient.

a. ${}_8C_2$ **b.** $\binom{10}{3}$ **c.** ${}_7C_0$ **d.** $\binom{8}{8}$

Solution

a. $${}_8C_2 = \frac{8!}{6! \cdot 2!} = \frac{(8 \cdot 7) \cdot \cancel{6!}}{\cancel{6!} \cdot 2!} = \frac{8 \cdot 7}{2 \cdot 1} = 28$$

b. $$\binom{10}{3} = \frac{10!}{7! \cdot 3!} = \frac{(10 \cdot 9 \cdot 8) \cdot \cancel{7!}}{\cancel{7!} \cdot 3!} = \frac{10 \cdot 9 \cdot 8}{3 \cdot 2 \cdot 1} = 120$$

c. $${}_7C_0 = \frac{\cancel{7!}}{\cancel{7!} \cdot 0!} = 1$$ **d.** $$\binom{8}{8} = \frac{\cancel{8!}}{0! \cdot \cancel{8!}} = 1$$

CHECKPoint Now try Exercise 5.

When $r \neq 0$ and $r \neq n$, as in parts (a) and (b) above, there is a simple pattern for evaluating binomial coefficients that works because there will always be factorial terms that divide out from the expression.

$${}_8C_2 = \frac{\overbrace{8 \cdot 7}^{\text{2 factors}}}{\underbrace{2 \cdot 1}_{\text{2 factors}}} \quad \text{and} \quad \binom{10}{3} = \frac{\overbrace{10 \cdot 9 \cdot 8}^{\text{3 factors}}}{\underbrace{3 \cdot 2 \cdot 1}_{\text{3 factors}}}$$

Example 2 Finding Binomial Coefficients

Find each binomial coefficient.

a. ${}_7C_3$ **b.** $\binom{7}{4}$ **c.** ${}_{12}C_1$ **d.** $\binom{12}{11}$

Solution

a. $${}_7C_3 = \frac{7 \cdot \cancel{6} \cdot 5}{\cancel{3} \cdot \cancel{2} \cdot 1} = 35$$

b. $$\binom{7}{4} = \frac{7 \cdot \cancel{6} \cdot 5 \cdot \cancel{4}}{\cancel{4} \cdot \cancel{3} \cdot \cancel{2} \cdot 1} = 35$$

c. $${}_{12}C_1 = \frac{12}{1} = 12$$

d. $$\binom{12}{11} = \frac{12!}{1! \cdot 11!} = \frac{(12) \cdot \cancel{11!}}{1! \cdot \cancel{11!}} = \frac{12}{1} = 12$$

CHECKPoint Now try Exercise 11.

It is not a coincidence that the results in parts (a) and (b) of Example 2 are the same and that the results in parts (c) and (d) are the same. In general, it is true that

$${}_nC_r = {}_nC_{n-r}.$$

This shows the symmetric property of binomial coefficients that was identified earlier.

Pascal's Triangle

There is a convenient way to remember the pattern for binomial coefficients. By arranging the coefficients in a triangular pattern, you obtain the following array, which is called **Pascal's Triangle.** This triangle is named after the famous French mathematician Blaise Pascal (1623–1662).

```
                  1
                1   1
              1   2   1
            1   3   3   1
          1   4   6   4   1
        1   5  10  10   5   1            4 + 6 = 10
      1   6  15  20  15   6   1
    1   7  21  35  35  21   7   1        15 + 6 = 21
```

The first and last numbers in each row of Pascal's Triangle are 1. Every other number in each row is formed by adding the two numbers immediately above the number. Pascal noticed that numbers in this triangle are precisely the same numbers that are the coefficients of binomial expansions, as follows.

$$(x+y)^0 = 1 \qquad \text{0th row}$$

$$(x+y)^1 = 1x + 1y \qquad \text{1st row}$$

$$(x+y)^2 = 1x^2 + 2xy + 1y^2 \qquad \text{2nd row}$$

$$(x+y)^3 = 1x^3 + 3x^2y + 3xy^2 + 1y^3 \qquad \text{3rd row}$$

$$(x+y)^4 = 1x^4 + 4x^3y + 6x^2y^2 + 4xy^3 + 1y^4 \qquad \vdots$$

$$(x+y)^5 = 1x^5 + 5x^4y + 10x^3y^2 + 10x^2y^3 + 5xy^4 + 1y^5$$

$$(x+y)^6 = 1x^6 + 6x^5y + 15x^4y^2 + 20x^3y^3 + 15x^2y^4 + 6xy^5 + 1y^6$$

$$(x+y)^7 = 1x^7 + 7x^6y + 21x^5y^2 + 35x^4y^3 + 35x^3y^4 + 21x^2y^5 + 7xy^6 + 1y^7$$

The top row in Pascal's Triangle is called the *zeroth row* because it corresponds to the binomial expansion $(x+y)^0 = 1$. Similarly, the next row is called the *first row* because it corresponds to the binomial expansion $(x+y)^1 = 1(x) + 1(y)$. In general, the *nth row* in Pascal's Triangle gives the coefficients of $(x+y)^n$.

Example 3 Using Pascal's Triangle

Use the seventh row of Pascal's Triangle to find the binomial coefficients.

$_8C_0, {}_8C_1, {}_8C_2, {}_8C_3, {}_8C_4, {}_8C_5, {}_8C_6, {}_8C_7, {}_8C_8$

Solution

```
   1     7     21    35    35    21    7     1
  / \   / \   /  \  /  \  /  \  /  \  / \   / \
 1    8     28    56    70    56    28    8    1
 |    |     |     |     |     |     |     |    |
8C0  8C1   8C2   8C3   8C4   8C5   8C6   8C7  8C8
```

CHECKPoint Now try Exercise 15.

Extra Example 3

Use the fifth row of Pascal's Triangle to find the binomial coefficients.

$_6C_0, {}_6C_1, {}_6C_2, {}_6C_3, {}_6C_4, {}_6C_5, {}_6C_6$

1, 6, 15, 20, 15, 6, 1

Extra Example 4

Write the expansion for the expression $(x + 2)^4$.

$x^4 + 8x^3 + 24x^2 + 32x + 16$

Avoiding Common Errors

Most errors in binomial expansion involve the powers of the terms. Students should confirm that the power of the leading term is less than the number of terms and that the two powers in each term (before any simplification) add to the original power of the binomial.

Extra Example 5

Write the expansion for each expression.

a. $(y - 2)^4$

$y^4 - 8y^3 + 24y^2 - 32y + 16$

b. $(2x - y)^4$

$16x^4 - 32x^3y + 24x^2y^2 - 8xy^3 + y^4$

HISTORICAL NOTE

Precious Mirror "Pascal's" Triangle and forms of the Binomial Theorem were known in Eastern cultures prior to the Western "discovery" of the theorem. A Chinese text entitled *Precious Mirror* contains a triangle of binomial expansions through the eighth power.

Algebra Help

The property of exponents

$$(ab)^m = a^m b^m$$

is used in the solutions to Example 5. For instance, in Example 5(a)

$$(2x)^4 = 2^4x^4 = 16x^4.$$

You can review properties of exponents in Appendix A.2.

Binomial Expansions

As mentioned at the beginning of this section, when you write out the coefficients for a binomial that is raised to a power, you are **expanding a binomial.** The formulas for binomial coefficients give you an easy way to expand binomials, as demonstrated in the next four examples.

Example 4 Expanding a Binomial

Write the expansion of the expression

$$(x + 1)^3.$$

Solution

The binomial coefficients from the third row of Pascal's Triangle are

1, 3, 3, 1.

So, the expansion is as follows.

$$(x + 1)^3 = (1)x^3 + (3)x^2(1) + (3)x(1^2) + (1)(1^3)$$
$$= x^3 + 3x^2 + 3x + 1$$

CHECK*Point* Now try Exercise 19.

To expand binomials representing *differences* rather than sums, you alternate signs. Here are two examples.

$$(x - 1)^3 = x^3 - 3x^2 + 3x - 1$$
$$(x - 1)^4 = x^4 - 4x^3 + 6x^2 - 4x + 1$$

Example 5 Expanding a Binomial

Write the expansion of each expression.

a. $(2x - 3)^4$

b. $(x - 2y)^4$

Solution

The binomial coefficients from the fourth row of Pascal's Triangle are

1, 4, 6, 4, 1.

So, the expansions are as follows.

a. $(2x - 3)^4 = (1)(2x)^4 - (4)(2x)^3(3) + (6)(2x)^2(3^2) - (4)(2x)(3^3) + (1)(3^4)$
$= 16x^4 - 96x^3 + 216x^2 - 216x + 81$

b. $(x - 2y)^4 = (1)x^4 - (4)x^3(2y) + (6)x^2(2y)^2 - (4)x(2y)^3 + (1)(2y)^4$
$= x^4 - 8x^3y + 24x^2y^2 - 32xy^3 + 16y^4$

CHECK*Point* Now try Exercise 31.

TECHNOLOGY

You can use a graphing utility to check the expansion in Example 6. Graph the original binomial expression and the expansion in the same viewing window. The graphs should coincide, as shown below.

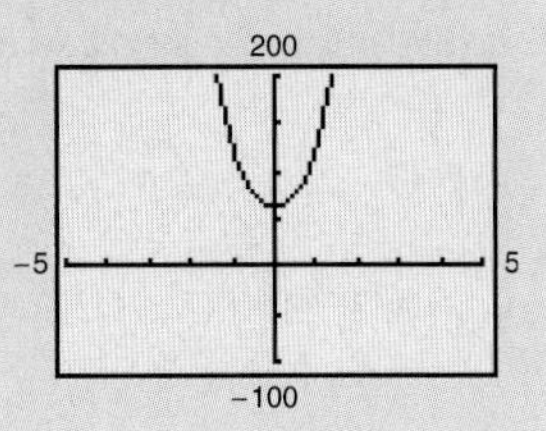

Example 6 Expanding a Binomial

Write the expansion of $(x^2 + 4)^3$.

Solution

Use the third row of Pascal's Triangle, as follows.

$$(x^2 + 4)^3 = (1)(x^2)^3 + (3)(x^2)^2(4) + (3)x^2(4^2) + (1)(4^3)$$
$$= x^6 + 12x^4 + 48x^2 + 64$$

CHECKPoint Now try Exercise 33.

Sometimes you will need to find a specific term in a binomial expansion. Instead of writing out the entire expansion, you can use the fact that, from the Binomial Theorem, the $(r + 1)$th term is ${}_nC_r x^{n-r} y^r$.

Example 7 Finding a Term in a Binomial Expansion

a. Find the sixth term of $(a + 2b)^8$.

b. Find the coefficient of the term a^6b^5 in the expansion of $(3a - 2b)^{11}$.

Solution

a. Remember that the formula is for the $(r + 1)$th term, so r is one less than the number of the term you need. So, to find the sixth term in this binomial expansion, use $r = 5$, $n = 8$, $x = a$, and $y = 2b$, as shown.

$${}_8C_5 a^{8-5}(2b)^5 = 56 \cdot a^3 \cdot (2b)^5 = 56(2^5)a^3b^5 = 1792a^3b^5.$$

b. In this case, $n = 11$, $r = 5$, $x = 3a$, and $y = -2b$. Substitute these values to obtain

$${}_nC_r x^{n-r} y^r = {}_{11}C_5(3a)^6(-2b)^5$$
$$= (462)(729a^6)(-32b^5)$$
$$= -10{,}777{,}536a^6b^5.$$

So, the coefficient is $-10{,}777{,}536$.

CHECKPoint Now try Exercise 47.

CLASSROOM DISCUSSION

Error Analysis You are a math instructor and receive the following solutions from one of your students on a quiz. Find the error(s) in each solution. Discuss ways that your student could avoid the error(s) in the future. See margin.

a. Find the second term in the expansion of $(2x - 3y)^5$.

~~$5(2x)^4(3y)^2 = 720x^4y^2$~~

b. Find the fourth term in the expansion of $\left(\frac{1}{2}x + 7y\right)^6$.

~~${}_6C_4\left(\frac{1}{2}x\right)^2(7y)^4 = 9003.75x^2y^4$~~

Extra Example 6

Write the expansion for $(3 - x^2)^4$.

$81 - 108x^2 + 54x^4 - 12x^6 + x^8$

Extra Example 7

a. Find the fifth term of $(a + 2b)^8$.

$1120a^4b^4$

b. Find the coefficient of the term a^4b^7 in the expansion of $(2a - 3b)^{11}$.

$11{,}547{,}360$

Closing the Lesson

Have students summarize the major points of the lesson and answer the Essential Question: How do you find the expansion of a binomial $(x + y)^n$?

- **Find the coefficients in a binomial expansion by using the formula** $${}_nC_r = \frac{n!}{(n - r)!r!}.$$
- **Use the nth row of Pascal's Triangle to identify the coefficients of an nth degree binomial expansion.**
- **Use Pascal's Triangle and the Binomial Theorem to write the expansion of binomials.**

Classroom Discussion

a. Student used the wrong sign and raised $3y$ to the incorrect power in the expansion. Correct solution: $-5(2x)^4(3y)^1 = -240x^4y$

b. Student gave the fifth term instead of the fourth term. Correct solution:

$${}_6C_3\left(\frac{1}{2}x\right)^3(7y)^3 = 20\left(\frac{1}{2}x\right)^3(7y)^3$$
$$= 857.5x^3y^3$$

4 PRACTICE AND APPLY

Assignment Guide

Transparencies Available
Available at the Instructor's companion site.

Average:
Day 1: pp. 686–687
Exs. 1–4, 7, 9, 13, 17–29 odd, 33–43 odd, 61, 63, 73, 75
Day 2: pp. 686–688
Exs. 69, 71, 79, 83–87 odd, 93–96, 99–101, 103

Advanced:
Day 1: pp. 686–687
Exs. 1–4, 8, 10, 14–18 even, 22–30 even, 34–44 even, 62, 64, 74, 78
Day 2: pp. 686–688
Exs. 48–54 even, 58–64 even, 70, 72, 80–90 even, 91, 93–95, 98–100, 102, 104

Block:
pp. 686–688
Exs. 1–4, 7, 9, 13, 17–29 odd, 33–43 odd, 61, 63, 69–75 odd, 79, 83–87 odd, 93–96, 99–101, 103

9.5 EXERCISES

See www.CalcChat.com for worked-out solutions to odd-numbered exercises.

VOCABULARY: Fill in the blanks.

1. The coefficients of a binomial expansion are called binomial coefficients.
2. To find binomial coefficients, you can use the Binomial Theorem or Pascal's Triangle.
3. The notation used to denote a binomial coefficient is ________ or ________.
4. When you write out the coefficients for a binomial that is raised to a power, you are expanding a binomial.

3. $\binom{n}{r}$; ${}_nC_r$

SKILLS AND APPLICATIONS

In Exercises 5–14, calculate the binomial coefficient.

5. ${}_5C_3$ 10
6. ${}_8C_6$ 28
7. ${}_{12}C_0$ 1
8. ${}_{20}C_{20}$ 1
9. ${}_{20}C_{15}$ 15,504
10. ${}_{12}C_5$ 792
11. $\binom{10}{4}$ 210
12. $\binom{10}{6}$ 210
13. $\binom{100}{98}$ 4950
14. $\binom{100}{2}$ 4950

In Exercises 15–18, evaluate using Pascal's Triangle.

15. $\binom{6}{5}$ 6
16. $\binom{9}{6}$ 84
17. ${}_7C_4$ 35
18. ${}_{10}C_2$ 45

In Exercises 19–40, use the Binomial Theorem to expand and simplify the expression. 19–40. See margin.

19. $(x + 1)^4$
20. $(x + 1)^6$
21. $(a + 6)^4$
22. $(a + 5)^5$
23. $(y - 4)^3$
24. $(y - 2)^5$
25. $(x + y)^5$
26. $(c + d)^3$
27. $(2x + y)^3$
28. $(7a + b)^3$
29. $(r + 3s)^6$
30. $(x + 2y)^4$
31. $(3a - 4b)^5$
32. $(2x - 5y)^5$
33. $(x^2 + y^2)^4$
34. $(x^2 + y^2)^6$
35. $\left(\frac{1}{x} + y\right)^5$
36. $\left(\frac{1}{x} + 2y\right)^6$
37. $\left(\frac{2}{x} - y\right)^4$
38. $\left(\frac{2}{x} - 3y\right)^5$
39. $2(x - 3)^4 + 5(x - 3)^2$
40. $(4x - 1)^3 - 2(4x - 1)^4$

In Exercises 41–44, expand the binomial by using Pascal's Triangle to determine the coefficients. 41–44. See margin.

41. $(2t - s)^5$
42. $(3 - 2z)^4$
43. $(x + 2y)^5$
44. $(3v + 2)^6$

In Exercises 45–52, find the specified nth term in the expansion of the binomial. 45–52. See margin.

45. $(x + y)^{10}$, $n = 4$
46. $(x - y)^6$, $n = 7$
47. $(x - 6y)^5$, $n = 3$
48. $(x - 10z)^7$, $n = 4$
49. $(4x + 3y)^9$, $n = 8$
50. $(5a + 6b)^5$, $n = 5$
51. $(10x - 3y)^{12}$, $n = 10$
52. $(7x + 2y)^{15}$, $n = 7$

In Exercises 53–60, find the coefficient a of the term in the expansion of the binomial.

Binomial	*Term*	
53. $(x + 3)^{12}$	ax^5	1,732,104
54. $(x^2 + 3)^{12}$	ax^8	3,247,695
55. $(4x - y)^{10}$	ax^2y^8	720
56. $(x - 2y)^{10}$	ax^8y^2	180
57. $(2x - 5y)^9$	ax^4y^5	−6,300,000
58. $(3x - 4y)^8$	ax^6y^2	326,592
59. $(x^2 + y)^{10}$	ax^8y^6	210
60. $(z^2 - t)^{10}$	az^4t^8	45

In Exercises 61–66, use the Binomial Theorem to expand and simplify the expression.

61. $(\sqrt{x} + 5)^3$ $x^{3/2} + 15x + 75x^{1/2} + 125$
62. $(2\sqrt{t} - 1)^3$ $8t^{3/2} - 12t + 6t^{1/2} - 1$
63. $(x^{2/3} - y^{1/3})^3$ $x^2 - 3x^{4/3}y^{1/3} + 3x^{2/3}y^{2/3} - y$
64. $(u^{3/5} + 2)^5$
65. $(3\sqrt{t} + \sqrt[4]{t})^4$ 64–66. See margin.
66. $(x^{3/4} - 2x^{5/4})^4$

In Exercises 67–72, expand the expression in the difference quotient and simplify. 67–72. See margin.

$$\frac{f(x + h) - f(x)}{h} \quad \text{Difference quotient}$$

67. $f(x) = x^3$
68. $f(x) = x^4$
69. $f(x) = x^6$
70. $f(x) = x^8$
71. $f(x) = \sqrt{x}$
72. $f(x) = \frac{1}{x}$

19. $x^4 + 4x^3 + 6x^2 + 4x + 1$
20–22. See below.
23. $y^3 - 12y^2 + 48y - 64$
24–25. See below.
26. $c^3 + 3c^2d + 3cd^2 + d^3$
27. $8x^3 + 12x^2y + 6xy^2 + y^3$
28. $343a^3 + 147a^2b + 21ab^2 + b^3$
29–35. See below.
37. $\frac{16}{x^4} - \frac{32y}{x^3} + \frac{24y^2}{x^2} - \frac{8y^3}{x} + y^4$
38–40. See below.
45. $120x^7y^3$
46. y^6
47. $360x^3y^2$
48. $-35{,}000x^4z^3$
49. $1{,}259{,}712x^2y^7$
50. $32{,}400ab^4$
51. $-4{,}330{,}260{,}000y^9x^3$
52. $1.293 \times 10^{13}x^9y^6$
67. $3x^2 + 3xh + h^2$, $h \neq 0$
68. $4x^3 + 6x^2h + 4xh^2 + h^3$, $h \neq 0$
71. $\frac{1}{\sqrt{x + h} + \sqrt{x}}$, $h \neq 0$
72. $-\frac{1}{x(x + h)}$, $h \neq 0$

20. $x^6 + 6x^5 + 15x^4 + 20x^3 + 15x^2 + 6x + 1$
21. $a^4 + 24a^3 + 216a^2 + 864a + 1296$
22. $a^5 + 25a^4 + 250a^3 + 1250a^2 + 3125a + 3125$
24. $y^5 - 10y^4 + 40y^3 - 80y^2 + 80y - 32$
25. $x^5 + 5x^4y + 10x^3y^2 + 10x^2y^3 + 5xy^4 + y^5$
29. $r^6 + 18r^5s + 135r^4s^2 + 540r^3s^3 + 1215r^2s^4 + 1458rs^5 + 729s^6$
30. $x^4 + 8x^3y + 24x^2y^2 + 32xy^3 + 16y^4$
31. $243a^5 - 1620a^4b + 4320a^3b^2 - 5760a^2b^3 + 3840ab^4 - 1024b^5$
32. $32x^5 - 400x^4y + 2000x^3y^2 - 5000x^2y^3 + 6250xy^4 - 3125y^5$
33. $x^8 + 4x^6y^2 + 6x^4y^4 + 4x^2y^6 + y^8$
34. $x^{12} + 6x^{10}y^2 + 15x^8y^4 + 20x^6y^6 + 15x^4y^8 + 6x^2y^{10} + y^{12}$
35. $\frac{1}{x^5} + \frac{5y}{x^4} + \frac{10y^2}{x^3} + \frac{10y^3}{x^2} + \frac{5y^4}{x} + y^5$
38. $\frac{32}{x^5} - \frac{240y}{x^4} + \frac{720y^2}{x^3} - \frac{1080y^3}{x^2} + \frac{810y^4}{x} - 243y^5$
39. $2x^4 - 24x^3 + 113x^2 - 246x + 207$
40. $-512x^4 + 576x^3 - 240x^2 + 44x - 3$

36, 41–44, 64–66, 69, 70. See Additional Answers beginning on page AA1.

In Exercises 73–78, use the Binomial Theorem to expand the complex number. Simplify your result.

73. $(1 + i)^4$ -4 **74.** $(2 - i)^5$ $-38 - 41i$

75. $(2 - 3i)^6$ $2035 + 828i$ **76.** $(5 + \sqrt{-9})^3$ $-10 + 198i$

77. $\left(-\frac{1}{2} + \frac{\sqrt{3}}{2}i\right)^3$ 1 **78.** $(5 - \sqrt{3}i)^4$ $184 - 440\sqrt{3}i$

APPROXIMATION In Exercises 79–82, use the Binomial Theorem to approximate the quantity accurate to three decimal places. For example, in Exercise 79, use the expansion

$$(1.02)^8 = (1 + 0.02)^8 = 1 + 8(0.02) + 28(0.02)^2 + \cdot \cdot \cdot .$$

79. $(1.02)^8$ 1.172 **80.** $(2.005)^{10}$ 1049.890

81. $(2.99)^{12}$ 510,568.785 **82.** $(1.98)^9$ 467.721

GRAPHICAL REASONING In Exercises 83 and 84, use a graphing utility to graph f and g in the same viewing window. What is the relationship between the two graphs? Use the Binomial Theorem to write the polynomial function g in standard form. 83–84. See margin.

83. $f(x) = x^3 - 4x$, $g(x) = f(x + 4)$

84. $f(x) = -x^4 + 4x^2 - 1$, $g(x) = f(x - 3)$

PROBABILITY In Exercises 85–88, consider n independent trials of an experiment in which each trial has two possible outcomes: "success" or "failure." The probability of a success on each trial is p, and the probability of a failure is $q = 1 - p$. In this context, the term ${}_nC_k\, p^k q^{n-k}$ in the expansion of $(p + q)^n$ gives the probability of k successes in the n trials of the experiment.

85. A fair coin is tossed seven times. To find the probability of obtaining four heads, evaluate the term

$${}_7C_4\left(\tfrac{1}{2}\right)^4\left(\tfrac{1}{2}\right)^3$$

in the expansion of $\left(\frac{1}{2} + \frac{1}{2}\right)^7$. 0.273

86. The probability of a baseball player getting a hit during any given time at bat is $\frac{1}{4}$. To find the probability that the player gets three hits during the next 10 times at bat, evaluate the term

$${}_{10}C_3\left(\tfrac{1}{4}\right)^3\left(\tfrac{3}{4}\right)^7$$

in the expansion of $\left(\frac{1}{4} + \frac{3}{4}\right)^{10}$. 0.250

87. The probability of a sales representative making a sale with any one customer is $\frac{1}{3}$. The sales representative makes eight contacts a day. To find the probability of making four sales, evaluate the term

$${}_8C_4\left(\tfrac{1}{3}\right)^4\left(\tfrac{2}{3}\right)^4$$

in the expansion of $\left(\frac{1}{3} + \frac{2}{3}\right)^8$. 0.171

88. To find the probability that the sales representative in Exercise 87 makes four sales if the probability of a sale with any one customer is $\frac{1}{2}$, evaluate the term

$${}_8C_4\left(\tfrac{1}{2}\right)^4\left(\tfrac{1}{2}\right)^4$$

in the expansion of $\left(\frac{1}{2} + \frac{1}{2}\right)^8$. 0.273

89. FINDING A PATTERN Describe the pattern formed by the sums of the numbers along the diagonal segments of Pascal's Triangle (see figure).

Fibonnaci sequence

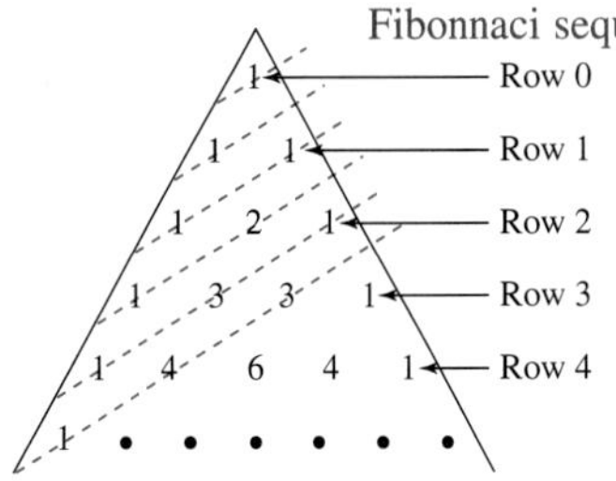

90. FINDING A PATTERN Use each of the encircled groups of numbers in the figure to form a 2 × 2 matrix. Find the determinant of each matrix. Describe the pattern.

See margin.

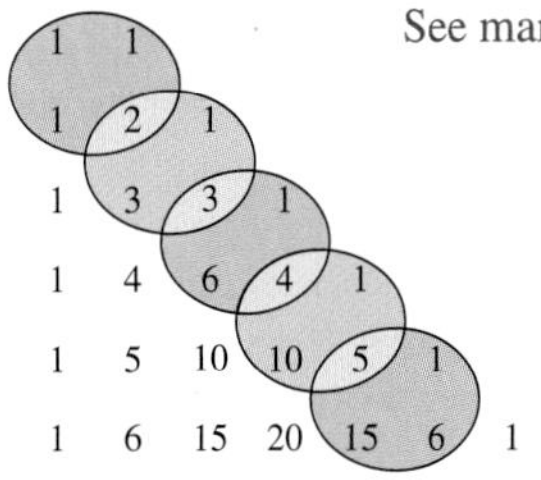

91. CHILD SUPPORT The average dollar amounts $f(t)$ of child support collected per case in the United States from 2000 through 2007 can be approximated by the model

$$f(t) = -4.702t^2 + 110.18t + 1026.7, \quad 0 \le t \le 7$$

where t represents the year, with $t = 0$ corresponding to 2000. (Source: U.S. Department of Health and Human Services)

(a) You want to adjust the model so that $t = 0$ corresponds to 2005 rather than 2000. To do this, you shift the graph of f five units *to the left* to obtain $g(t) = f(t + 5)$. Write $g(t)$ in standard form.

(b) Use a graphing utility to graph f and g in the same viewing window. (a)–(b). See margin.

(c) Use the graphs to estimate when the average child support collections exceeded \$1525. 2007

83.

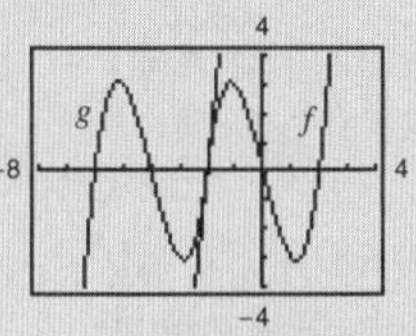

g is shifted four units to the left of f.

$g(x) = x^3 + 12x^2 + 44x + 48$

84.

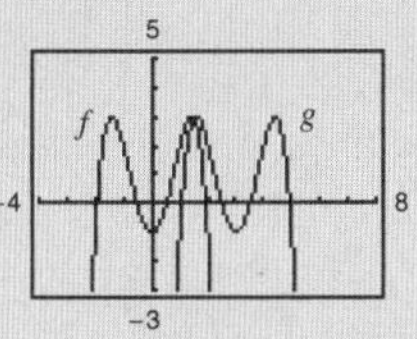

g is shifted three units to the right of f.

$g(x) = -x^4 + 12x^3 - 50x^2 + 84x - 46$

90. The determinants are 1, 3, 6, 10, 15, . . . , which constitute one of the diagonals of Pascal's Triangle.

91. (a) See below.

(b)

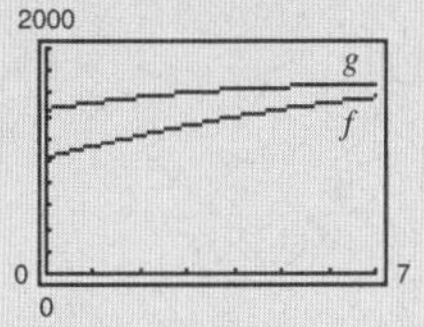

91. (a) $g(t) = -4.702t^2 + 63.16t + 1460.05$

5 ASSESS AND RETEACH

Daily Homework Quiz

Transparency Available
Available at the Instructor's companion site.

93. True. The coefficients from the Binomial Theorem can be used to find the numbers in Pascal's Triangle.

94. False. Expanding binomials that represent differences is accurate. The coefficients have alternating signs.

95. False. The coefficient of the x^{10}-term is 1,732,104 and the coefficient of the x^{14}-term is 192,456.

96. The first and last numbers in each row are 1. Every other number in each row is formed by adding the two numbers immediately above the number.

97. See below.

99.

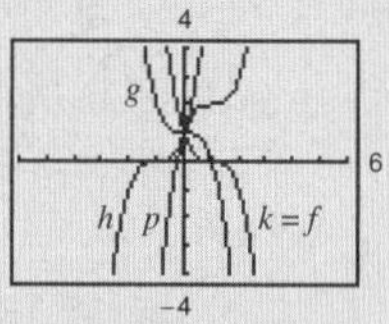

$k(x)$ is the expansion of $f(x)$.

105.

n	r	${}_nC_r$	${}_nC_{n-r}$
9	5	126	126
7	1	7	7
12	4	495	495
6	0	1	1
10	7	120	120

${}_nC_r = {}_nC_{n-r}$
This illustrates the symmetry of Pascal's Triangle.

92. DATA ANALYSIS: ELECTRICITY The table shows the average prices $f(t)$ (in cents per kilowatt hour) of residential electricity in the United States from 2000 through 2007. (Source: Energy Information Administration)

(a)–(d). See margin.

Year	Average price, $f(t)$
2000	8.24
2001	8.58
2002	8.44
2003	8.72
2004	8.95
2005	9.45
2006	10.40
2007	10.64

(a) Use the *regression* feature of a graphing utility to find a cubic model for the data. Let t represent the year, with $t = 0$ corresponding to 2000.

(b) Use the graphing utility to plot the data and the model in the same viewing window.

(c) You want to adjust the model so that $t = 0$ corresponds to 2005 rather than 2000. To do this, you shift the graph of f five units *to the left* to obtain $g(t) = f(t + 5)$. Write $g(t)$ in standard form.

(d) Use the graphing utility to graph g in the same viewing window as f.

(e) Use both models to estimate the average price in 2008. Do you obtain the same answer? 11.54; yes

(f) Do your answers to part (e) seem reasonable? Explain. Yes, the price seems reasonable.

(g) What factors do you think may have contributed to the change in the average price? Answers will vary.

EXPLORATION

93–95. See margin.

TRUE OR FALSE? In Exercises 93–95, determine whether the statement is true or false. Justify your answer.

93. The Binomial Theorem could be used to produce each row of Pascal's Triangle.

94. A binomial that represents a difference cannot always be accurately expanded using the Binomial Theorem.

95. The x^{10}-term and the x^{14}-term of the expansion of $(x^2 + 3)^{12}$ have identical coefficients.

96. WRITING In your own words, explain how to form the rows of Pascal's Triangle. See margin.

97. Form rows 8–10 of Pascal's Triangle. See margin.

98. THINK ABOUT IT How many terms are in the expansion of $(x + y)^n$? $n + 1$ terms

99. GRAPHICAL REASONING Which two functions have identical graphs, and why? Use a graphing utility to graph the functions in the given order and in the same viewing window. Compare the graphs. See margin.

(a) $f(x) = (1 - x)^3$

(b) $g(x) = 1 - x^3$

(c) $h(x) = 1 + 3x + 3x^2 + x^3$

(d) $k(x) = 1 - 3x + 3x^2 - x^3$

(e) $p(x) = 1 + 3x - 3x^2 + x^3$

100. CAPSTONE How do the expansions of $(x + y)^n$ and $(x - y)^n$ differ? Support your explanation with an example. Answers will vary.

PROOF In Exercises 101–104, prove the property for all integers r and n where $0 \le r \le n$. 101–104. Proofs

101. ${}_nC_r = {}_nC_{n-r}$

102. ${}_nC_0 - {}_nC_1 + {}_nC_2 - \cdots \pm {}_nC_n = 0$

103. ${}_{n+1}C_r = {}_nC_r + {}_nC_{r-1}$

104. The sum of the numbers in the nth row of Pascal's Triangle is 2^n.

105. Complete the table and describe the result. See margin.

n	r	${}_nC_r$	${}_nC_{n-r}$
9	5		
7	1		
12	4		
6	0		
10	7		

What characteristic of Pascal's Triangle is illustrated by this table?

106. Another form of the Binomial Theorem is

$$(x + y)^n = x^n + \frac{nx^{n-1}y}{1!} + \frac{n(n-1)x^{n-2}y^2}{2!} + \frac{n(n-1)(n-2)x^{n-3}y^3}{3!} + \cdots + y^n.$$

Use this form of the Binomial Theorem to expand and simplify each expression. See margin.

(a) $(2x + 3)^6$

(b) $(x + ay)^4$

(c) $(x - ay)^5$

(d) $(1 + x)^{12}$

97.

1 8 28 56 70 56 28 8 1
1 9 36 84 126 126 84 36 9 1
1 10 45 120 210 252 210 120 45 10 1

106. (a) $64x^6 + 576x^5 + 2160x^4 + 4320x^3 + 4860x^2 + 2916x + 729$

(b) $x^4 + 4ayx^3 + 6a^2y^2x^2 + 4a^3y^3x + a^4y^4$

(c) $x^5 - 5ayx^4 + 10a^2y^2x^3 - 10a^3y^3x^2 + 5a^4y^4x - a^5y^5$

(d) $x^{12} + 12x^{11} + 66x^{10} + 220x^9 + 495x^8 + 792x^7 + 924x^6 + 792x^5 + 495x^4 + 220x^3 + 66x^2 + 12x + 1$

92(a)–(d). See Additional Answers beginning on page AA1.

9.6 Counting Principles

What you should learn

- Solve simple counting problems.
- Use the Fundamental Counting Principle to solve counting problems.
- Use permutations to solve counting problems.
- Use combinations to solve counting problems.

Why you should learn it

You can use counting principles to solve counting problems that occur in real life. For instance, in Exercise 78 on page 698, you are asked to use counting principles to determine the number of possible ways of selecting the winning numbers in the Powerball lottery.

© Michael Simpson/Getty Images

Simple Counting Problems

This section and Section 9.7 present a brief introduction to some of the basic counting principles and their application to probability. In Section 9.7, you will see that much of probability has to do with counting the number of ways an event can occur. The following two examples describe simple counting problems.

Example 1 Selecting Pairs of Numbers at Random

Eight pieces of paper are numbered from 1 to 8 and placed in a box. One piece of paper is drawn from the box, its number is written down, and the piece of paper is *replaced in the box*. Then, a second piece of paper is drawn from the box, and its number is written down. Finally, the two numbers are added together. How many different ways can a sum of 12 be obtained?

Solution

To solve this problem, count the different ways that a sum of 12 can be obtained using two numbers from 1 to 8.

First number	4	5	6	7	8
Second number	8	7	6	5	4

From this list, you can see that a sum of 12 can occur in five different ways.

CHECK*Point* Now try Exercise 11.

Example 2 Selecting Pairs of Numbers at Random

Eight pieces of paper are numbered from 1 to 8 and placed in a box. Two pieces of paper are drawn from the box *at the same time*, and the numbers on the pieces of paper are written down and totaled. How many different ways can a sum of 12 be obtained?

Solution

To solve this problem, count the different ways that a sum of 12 can be obtained *using two different numbers* from 1 to 8.

First number	4	5	7	8
Second number	8	7	5	4

So, a sum of 12 can be obtained in four different ways.

CHECK*Point* Now try Exercise 13.

The difference between the counting problems in Examples 1 and 2 can be described by saying that the random selection in Example 1 occurs **with replacement,** whereas the random selection in Example 2 occurs **without replacement,** which eliminates the possibility of choosing two 6's.

1 PLAN AND PREPARE

Warm-up Exercises

Transparency Available
Available at the Instructor's companion site.

Notetaking Guide

Transparency Available
Promotes interactive learning and notetaking skills.
Available at the Instructor's companion site.

Animated Precalculus

An **Animated Precalculus** tutorial is available at the Student companion site for **Section 9.6.**

Pacing

Average: 2 days
Advanced: 2 days
Block: 1 block

2 FOCUS AND MOTIVATE

Essential Question

How do you count the number of ways in which an event can occur?
Tell students that they will learn how to answer this question by using the Fundamental Counting Principle and the definitions of permutation and combination.

Resource Planning Guide

Chapter Resources
- Complete Solutions Guide

Workbooks
- Notetaking Guide
- Student Solutions Guide

Interactive Technology
- Instructor Success Organizer
- Notetaking Guide IAE
- Instructional DVDs
- Animated Precalculus
- PowerLecture with ExamView

3 TEACH

Extra Example 1

Determine in how many ways a computer can randomly generate two integers from 1 to 12 whose sum is 6.

5

Extra Example 2

Determine in how many ways a computer can randomly generate two *distinct* integers from 1 to 12 whose sum is 10.

8

Extra Example 3

A combination lock will open when the right choice of three numbers (from 1 to 30, inclusive) is selected. How many different lock combinations are possible?

27,000

Extra Example 4

In a certain state, each automobile license plate number consists of two letters followed by a four-digit number. How many distinct license plate numbers can be formed?

6,760,000

The Fundamental Counting Principle

Examples 1 and 2 describe simple counting problems in which you can *list* each possible way that an event can occur. When it is possible, this is always the best way to solve a counting problem. However, some events can occur in so many different ways that it is not feasible to write out the entire list. In such cases, you must rely on formulas and counting principles. The most important of these is the **Fundamental Counting Principle.**

Fundamental Counting Principle

Let E_1 and E_2 be two events. The first event E_1 can occur in m_1 different ways. After E_1 has occurred, E_2 can occur in m_2 different ways. The number of ways that the two events can occur is $m_1 \cdot m_2$.

The Fundamental Counting Principle can be extended to three or more events. For instance, the number of ways that three events E_1, E_2, and E_3 can occur is $m_1 \cdot m_2 \cdot m_3$.

Example 3 Using the Fundamental Counting Principle

How many different pairs of letters from the English alphabet are possible?

Solution

There are two events in this situation. The first event is the choice of the first letter, and the second event is the choice of the second letter. Because the English alphabet contains 26 letters, it follows that the number of two-letter pairs is

$$26 \cdot 26 = 676.$$

CHECK *Point* Now try Exercise 19.

Example 4 Using the Fundamental Counting Principle

Telephone numbers in the United States currently have 10 digits. The first three are the *area code* and the next seven are the *local telephone number*. How many different telephone numbers are possible within each area code? (Note that at this time, a local telephone number cannot begin with 0 or 1.)

Solution

Because the first digit of a local telephone number cannot be 0 or 1, there are only eight choices for the first digit. For each of the other six digits, there are 10 choices.

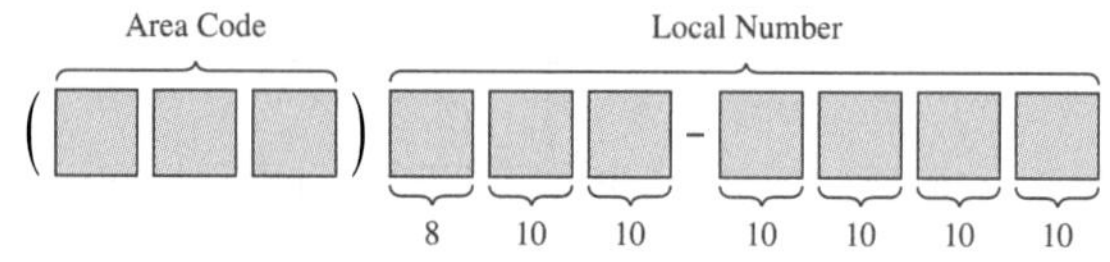

So, the number of local telephone numbers that are possible *within* each area code is

$$8 \cdot 10 \cdot 10 \cdot 10 \cdot 10 \cdot 10 \cdot 10 = 8{,}000{,}000.$$

CHECK *Point* Now try Exercise 25.

Permutations

One important application of the Fundamental Counting Principle is in determining the number of ways that n elements can be arranged (in order). An ordering of n elements is called a **permutation** of the elements.

Definition of Permutation

A **permutation** of n different elements is an ordering of the elements such that one element is first, one is second, one is third, and so on.

Example 5 Finding the Number of Permutations of n Elements

How many permutations are possible for the letters A, B, C, D, E, and F?

Solution

Consider the following reasoning.

First position: Any of the *six* letters
Second position: Any of the remaining *five* letters
Third position: Any of the remaining *four* letters
Fourth position: Any of the remaining *three* letters
Fifth position: Either of the remaining *two* letters
Sixth position: The *one* remaining letter

So, the numbers of choices for the six positions are as follows.

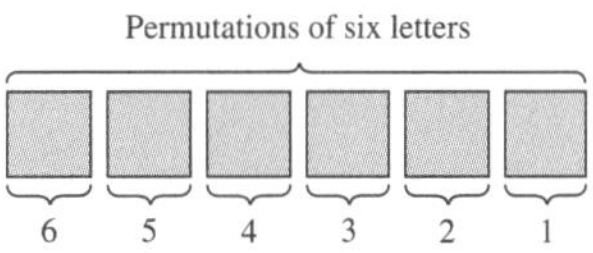

The total number of permutations of the six letters is

$$6! = 6 \cdot 5 \cdot 4 \cdot 3 \cdot 2 \cdot 1$$
$$= 720.$$

CHECKPoint Now try Exercise 39.

Number of Permutations of n Elements

The number of permutations of n elements is

$$n \cdot (n-1) \cdot \cdot \cdot 4 \cdot 3 \cdot 2 \cdot 1 = n!.$$

In other words, there are $n!$ different ways that n elements can be ordered.

Extra Example 5

In how many ways can eight children line up in a row?
40,320

Differentiated Instruction

Kinesthetic Learners For Example 5, have students write each one of the letters A, B, C, D, E, and F on a separate piece of paper. Then have students randomly draw a letter from the group for the first position. Point out that now only five letters remain from which students may draw for the second position. Have students continue to draw letters at random until they have completed one permutation of the six letters.

Extra Example 6

A coin club has five members. In how many ways can a president and a vice-president be selected from its members?

20

Vaughn Youtz/Newsmakers/Getty Images

Eleven thoroughbred racehorses hold the title of Triple Crown winner for winning the Kentucky Derby, the Preakness, and the Belmont Stakes in the same year. Forty-nine horses have won two out of the three races.

Example 6 Counting Horse Race Finishes

Eight horses are running in a race. In how many different ways can these horses come in first, second, and third? (Assume that there are no ties.)

Solution

Here are the different possibilities.

Win (first position): *Eight* choices

Place (second position): *Seven* choices

Show (third position): *Six* choices

Using the Fundamental Counting Principle, multiply these three numbers together to obtain the following.

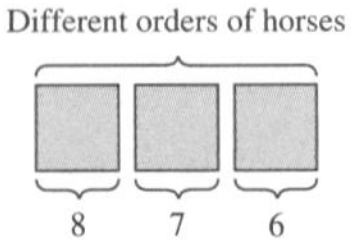

So, there are $8 \cdot 7 \cdot 6 = 336$ different orders.

CHECK***Point*** Now try Exercise 41.

It is useful, on occasion, to order a *subset* of a collection of elements rather than the entire collection. For example, you might want to choose and order r elements out of a collection of n elements. Such an ordering is called a **permutation of n elements taken r at a time.**

TECHNOLOGY

Most graphing calculators are programmed to evaluate ${}_nP_r$. Consult the user's guide for your calculator and then evaluate ${}_8P_5$. You should get an answer of 6720.

Permutations of n Elements Taken r at a Time

The number of permutations of n elements taken r at a time is

$$
\begin{aligned}
{}_nP_r &= \frac{n!}{(n-r)!} \\
&= n(n-1)(n-2) \cdot \cdot \cdot (n-r+1).
\end{aligned}
$$

Using this formula, you can rework Example 6 to find that the number of permutations of eight horses taken three at a time is

$$
\begin{aligned}
{}_8P_3 &= \frac{8!}{(8-3)!} \\
&= \frac{8!}{5!} \\
&= \frac{8 \cdot 7 \cdot 6 \cdot \cancel{5!}}{\cancel{5!}} \\
&= 336
\end{aligned}
$$

which is the same answer obtained in the example.

Remember that for permutations, order is important. So, if you are looking at the possible permutations of the letters A, B, C, and D taken three at a time, the permutations (A, B, D) and (B, A, D) are counted as different because the *order* of the elements is different.

Suppose, however, that you are asked to find the possible permutations of the letters A, A, B, and C. The total number of permutations of the four letters would be ${}_4P_4 = 4!$. However, not all of these arrangements would be *distinguishable* because there are two A's in the list. To find the number of distinguishable permutations, you can use the following formula.

Distinguishable Permutations

Suppose a set of n objects has n_1 of one kind of object, n_2 of a second kind, n_3 of a third kind, and so on, with

$$n = n_1 + n_2 + n_3 + \cdot \cdot \cdot + n_k.$$

Then the number of **distinguishable permutations** of the n objects is

$$\frac{n!}{n_1! \cdot n_2! \cdot n_3! \cdot \cdot \cdot \cdot \cdot n_k!}.$$

Example 7 Distinguishable Permutations

In how many distinguishable ways can the letters in BANANA be written?

Solution

This word has six letters, of which three are A's, two are N's, and one is a B. So, the number of distinguishable ways the letters can be written is

$$\frac{n!}{n_1! \cdot n_2! \cdot n_3!} = \frac{6!}{3! \cdot 2! \cdot 1!}$$

$$= \frac{6 \cdot 5 \cdot 4 \cdot \cancel{3!}}{\cancel{3!} \cdot 2!}$$

$$= 60.$$

The 60 different distinguishable permutations are as follows.

AAABNN	AAANBN	AAANNB	AABANN	AABNAN	AABNNA
AANABN	AANANB	AANBAN	AANBNA	AANNAB	AANNBA
ABAANN	ABANAN	ABANNA	ABNAAN	ABNANA	ABNNAA
ANAABN	ANAANB	ANABAN	ANABNA	ANANAB	ANANBA
ANBAAN	ANBANA	ANBNAA	ANNAAB	ANNABA	ANNBAA
BAAANN	BAANAN	BAANNA	BANAAN	BANANA	BANNAA
BNAAAN	BNAANA	BNANAA	BNNAAA	NAAABN	NAAANB
NAABAN	NAABNA	NAANAB	NAANBA	NABAAN	NABANA
NABNAA	NANAAB	NANABA	NANBAA	NBAAAN	NBAANA
NBANAA	NBNAAA	NNAAAB	NNAABA	NNABAA	NNBAAA

CHECKPoint Now try Exercise 43.

Extra Example 7

Find the number of distinguishable permutations of this group of letters: A, A, E, E, E, J, P, P, R.

15,120

Extra Example 8

In how many different ways can two letters be chosen from the letters A, B, C, D, E, F, and G? (The order of the two letters is not important.)

21

Combinations

When you count the number of possible permutations of a set of elements, order is important. As a final topic in this section, you will look at a method of selecting subsets of a larger set in which order is *not* important. Such subsets are called **combinations of *n* elements taken *r* at a time.** For instance, the combinations

$$\{A, B, C\} \quad \text{and} \quad \{B, A, C\}$$

are equivalent because both sets contain the same three elements, and the order in which the elements are listed is not important. So, you would count only one of the two sets. A common example of how a combination occurs is a card game in which the player is free to reorder the cards after they have been dealt.

Example 8 Combinations of *n* Elements Taken *r* at a Time

In how many different ways can three letters be chosen from the letters A, B, C, D, and E? (The order of the three letters is not important.)

Solution

The following subsets represent the different combinations of three letters that can be chosen from the five letters.

$\{A, B, C\}$ $\{A, B, D\}$
$\{A, B, E\}$ $\{A, C, D\}$
$\{A, C, E\}$ $\{A, D, E\}$
$\{B, C, D\}$ $\{B, C, E\}$
$\{B, D, E\}$ $\{C, D, E\}$

From this list, you can conclude that there are 10 different ways that three letters can be chosen from five letters.

CHECK*Point* Now try Exercise 61.

Combinations of *n* Elements Taken *r* at a Time

The number of combinations of n elements taken r at a time is

$$_nC_r = \frac{n!}{(n-r)!r!}$$

which is equivalent to $_nC_r = \frac{_nP_r}{r!}$.

Note that the formula for $_nC_r$ is the same one given for binomial coefficients. To see how this formula is used, solve the counting problem in Example 8. In that problem, you are asked to find the number of combinations of five elements taken three at a time. So, $n = 5$, $r = 3$, and the number of combinations is

$$_5C_3 = \frac{5!}{2!3!} = \frac{5 \cdot \overset{2}{\cancel{4}} \cdot \cancel{3!}}{\cancel{2} \cdot 1 \cdot \cancel{3!}} = 10$$

which is the same answer obtained in Example 8.

A ♥	A ♦	A ♣	A ♠
2 ♥	2 ♦	2 ♣	2 ♠
3 ♥	3 ♦	3 ♣	3 ♠
4 ♥	4 ♦	4 ♣	4 ♠
5 ♥	5 ♦	5 ♣	5 ♠
6 ♥	6 ♦	6 ♣	6 ♠
7 ♥	7 ♦	7 ♣	7 ♠
8 ♥	8 ♦	8 ♣	8 ♠
9 ♥	9 ♦	9 ♣	9 ♠
10 ♥	10 ♦	10 ♣	10 ♠
J ♥	J ♦	J ♣	J ♠
Q ♥	Q ♦	Q ♣	Q ♠
K ♥	K ♦	K ♣	K ♠

Standard deck of playing cards
FIGURE 9.7

Example 9 Counting Card Hands

A standard poker hand consists of five cards dealt from a deck of 52 (see Figure 9.7). How many different poker hands are possible? (After the cards are dealt, the player may reorder them, and so order is not important.)

Solution

You can find the number of different poker hands by using the formula for the number of combinations of 52 elements taken five at a time, as follows.

$$\begin{aligned} {}_{52}C_5 &= \frac{52!}{(52-5)!5!} \\ &= \frac{52!}{47!5!} \\ &= \frac{52 \cdot 51 \cdot 50 \cdot 49 \cdot 48 \cdot \cancel{47!}}{5 \cdot 4 \cdot 3 \cdot 2 \cdot 1 \cdot \cancel{47!}} \\ &= 2{,}598{,}960 \end{aligned}$$

CHECKPoint Now try Exercise 63.

Example 10 Forming a Team

You are forming a 12-member swim team from 10 girls and 15 boys. The team must consist of five girls and seven boys. How many different 12-member teams are possible?

Solution

There are ${}_{10}C_5$ ways of choosing five girls. There are ${}_{15}C_7$ ways of choosing seven boys. By the Fundamental Counting Principal, there are ${}_{10}C_5 \cdot {}_{15}C_7$ ways of choosing five girls and seven boys.

$$\begin{aligned} {}_{10}C_5 \cdot {}_{15}C_7 &= \frac{10!}{5! \cdot 5!} \cdot \frac{15!}{8! \cdot 7!} \\ &= 252 \cdot 6435 \\ &= 1{,}621{,}620 \end{aligned}$$

So, there are 1,621,620 12-member swim teams possible.

CHECKPoint Now try Exercise 71.

When solving problems involving counting principles, you need to be able to distinguish among the various counting principles in order to determine which is necessary to solve the problem correctly. To do this, ask yourself the following questions.

1. Is the order of the elements important? *Permutation*
2. Are the chosen elements a subset of a larger set in which order is not important? *Combination*
3. Does the problem involve two or more separate events? *Fundamental Counting Principle*

Extra Example 9

For a certain experiment, four students are randomly selected from a class of 20. How many different groups of four students are possible?

4845

Extra Example 10

You are forming a 10-person committee from 9 women and 12 men. The committee must consist of 5 women and 5 men. How many different 10-member committees are possible?

99,792

Closing the Lesson

Have students summarize the major points of the lesson and answer the Essential Question: How do you count the number of ways in which an event can occur?

- **To find the number of ways in which two or more events can occur sequentially, multiply the number of ways in which each event can occur.**
- **Determine in how many different ways a subset of objects can be chosen from a set and ordered by determining the number of permutations.**
- **Determine in how many different ways a subset of objects can be chosen from a set by determining the number of combinations.**

4 PRACTICE AND APPLY

Assignment Guide

Transparencies Available
Available at the Instructor's companion site.

Average:
Day 1: pp. 696–697
Exs. 1–3, 7, 9, 10, 12, 15, 17, 21–27 odd, 31–39 odd, 40, 43, 45, 48, 49
Day 2: pp. 696–698
Exs. 4–6, 63–73 odd, 74, 87–90, 91–95 odd, 96

Advanced:
Day 1: pp. 696–697
Exs. 1–3, 8–14 even, 20–28 even, 32–40 even, 44–50 even
Day 2: pp. 696–698
Exs. 4–6, 64–76 even, 87–90, 92–96 even, 97

Block:
pp. 696–698
Exs. 1–7, 9, 10, 12, 15, 17, 21–27 odd, 31–39 odd, 40, 43, 45, 48, 49, 63–73 odd, 74, 87–90, 91–95 odd, 96

9.6 EXERCISES

See www.CalcChat.com for worked-out solutions to odd-numbered exercises.

VOCABULARY: Fill in the blanks.

1. The ________ ________ ________ states that if there are m_1 ways for one event to occur and m_2 ways for a second event to occur, there are $m_1 \cdot m_2$ ways for both events to occur. Fundamental Counting Principle
2. An ordering of n elements is called a ________ of the elements. permutation
3. The number of permutations of n elements taken r at a time is given by the formula ________. ${}_nP_r = \dfrac{n!}{(n-r)!}$
4. The number of ________ ________ of n objects is given by $\dfrac{n!}{n_1!n_2!n_3! \cdot \cdot \cdot n_k!}$. distinguishable permutations
5. When selecting subsets of a larger set in which order is not important, you are finding the number of ________ of n elements taken r at a time. combinations
6. The number of combinations of n elements taken r at a time is given by the formula ________. ${}_nC_r = \dfrac{n!}{(n-r)!r!}$

SKILLS AND APPLICATIONS

RANDOM SELECTION In Exercises 7–14, determine the number of ways a computer can randomly generate one or more such integers from 1 through 12.

7. An odd integer 6
8. An even integer 6
9. A prime integer 5
10. An integer that is greater than 9 3
11. An integer that is divisible by 4 3
12. An integer that is divisible by 3 4
13. Two *distinct* integers whose sum is 9 8
14. Two *distinct* integers whose sum is 8 6

15. **ENTERTAINMENT SYSTEMS** A customer can choose one of three amplifiers, one of two compact disc players, and one of five speaker models for an entertainment system. Determine the number of possible system configurations. 30
16. **JOB APPLICANTS** A college needs two additional faculty members: a chemist and a statistician. In how many ways can these positions be filled if there are five applicants for the chemistry position and three applicants for the statistics position? 15
17. **COURSE SCHEDULE** A college student is preparing a course schedule for the next semester. The student may select one of two mathematics courses, one of three science courses, and one of five courses from the social sciences and humanities. How many schedules are possible? 30
18. **AIRCRAFT BOARDING** Eight people are boarding an aircraft. Two have tickets for first class and board before those in the economy class. In how many ways can the eight people board the aircraft? 1440
19. **TRUE-FALSE EXAM** In how many ways can a six-question true-false exam be answered? (Assume that no questions are omitted.) 64
20. **TRUE-FALSE EXAM** In how many ways can a 12-question true-false exam be answered? (Assume that no questions are omitted.) 4096
21. **LICENSE PLATE NUMBERS** In the state of Pennsylvania, each standard automobile license plate number consists of three letters followed by a four-digit number. How many distinct license plate numbers can be formed in Pennsylvania? 175,760,000
22. **LICENSE PLATE NUMBERS** In a certain state, each automobile license plate number consists of two letters followed by a four-digit number. To avoid confusion between "O" and "zero" and between "I" and "one," the letters "O" and "I" are not used. How many distinct license plate numbers can be formed in this state? 5,760,000
23. **THREE-DIGIT NUMBERS** How many three-digit numbers can be formed under each condition?
    (a) The leading digit cannot be zero. 900
    (b) The leading digit cannot be zero and no repetition of digits is allowed. 648
    (c) The leading digit cannot be zero and the number must be a multiple of 5. 180
    (d) The number is at least 400. 600
24. **FOUR-DIGIT NUMBERS** How many four-digit numbers can be formed under each condition?
    (a) The leading digit cannot be zero. 9000
    (b) The leading digit cannot be zero and no repetition of digits is allowed. 4536
    (c) The leading digit cannot be zero and the number must be less than 5000. 4000
    (d) The leading digit cannot be zero and the number must be even. 4500
25. **COMBINATION LOCK** A combination lock will open when the right choice of three numbers (from 1 to 40, inclusive) is selected. How many different lock combinations are possible? 64,000

26. **COMBINATION LOCK** A combination lock will open when the right choice of three numbers (from 1 to 50, inclusive) is selected. How many different lock combinations are possible? 125,000

27. **CONCERT SEATS** Four couples have reserved seats in a row for a concert. In how many different ways can they be seated if (a) 40,320 (b) 384
(a) there are no seating restrictions?
(b) the two members of each couple wish to sit together?

28. **SINGLE FILE** In how many orders can four girls and four boys walk through a doorway single file if
(a) there are no restrictions? 40,320
(b) the girls walk through before the boys? 576

In Exercises 29–34, evaluate $_nP_r$.

29. $_4P_4$ 24
30. $_5P_5$ 120
31. $_8P_3$ 336
32. $_{20}P_2$ 380
33. $_5P_4$ 120
34. $_7P_4$ 840

In Exercises 35–38, evaluate $_nP_r$ using a graphing utility.

35. $_{20}P_5$ 1,860,480
36. $_{100}P_5$ 9,034,502,400
37. $_{100}P_3$ 970,200
38. $_{10}P_8$ 1,814,400

39. **POSING FOR A PHOTOGRAPH** In how many ways can five children posing for a photograph line up in a row? 120

40. **RIDING IN A CAR** In how many ways can six people sit in a six-passenger car? 720

41. **CHOOSING OFFICERS** From a pool of 12 candidates, the offices of president, vice-president, secretary, and treasurer will be filled. In how many different ways can the offices be filled? 11,880

42. **ASSEMBLY LINE PRODUCTION** There are four processes involved in assembling a product, and these processes can be performed in any order. The management wants to test each order to determine which is the least time-consuming. How many different orders will have to be tested? 24

In Exercises 43–46, find the number of distinguishable permutations of the group of letters.

43. A, A, G, E, E, E, M 420
44. B, B, B, T, T, T, T, T 56
45. A, L, G, E, B, R, A 2520
46. M, I, S, S, I, S, S, I, P, P, I 34,650

47. Write all permutations of the letters A, B, C, and D. See margin.

48. Write all permutations of the letters A, B, C, and D if the letters B and C must remain between the letters A and D. ABCD, DBCA, ACBD, DCBA

49. **BATTING ORDER** A baseball coach is creating a nine-player batting order by selecting from a team of 15 players. How many different batting orders are possible? 1,816,214,400

50. **ATHLETICS** Eight sprinters have qualified for the finals in the 100-meter dash at the NCAA national track meet. In how many ways can the sprinters come in first, second, and third? (Assume there are no ties.) 336

In Exercises 51–56, evaluate $_nC_r$ using the formula from this section.

51. $_5C_2$ 10
52. $_6C_3$ 20
53. $_4C_1$ 4
54. $_5C_1$ 5
55. $_{25}C_0$ 1
56. $_{20}C_0$ 1

In Exercises 57–60, evaluate $_nC_r$ using a graphing utility.

57. $_{20}C_4$ 4845
58. $_{10}C_7$ 120
59. $_{42}C_5$ 850,668
60. $_{50}C_6$ 15,890,700

61. Write all possible selections of two letters that can be formed from the letters A, B, C, D, E, and F. (The order of the two letters is not important.) See margin.

62. **FORMING AN EXPERIMENTAL GROUP** In order to conduct an experiment, five students are randomly selected from a class of 20. How many different groups of five students are possible? 15,504

63. **JURY SELECTION** From a group of 40 people, a jury of 12 people is to be selected. In how many different ways can the jury be selected? 5,586,853,480

64. **COMMITTEE MEMBERS** A U.S. Senate Committee has 14 members. Assuming party affiliation was not a factor in selection, how many different committees were possible from the 100 U.S. senators? 64–66. See margin.

65. **LOTTERY CHOICES** In the Massachusetts Mass Cash game, a player chooses five distinct numbers from 1 to 35. In how many ways can a player select the five numbers?

66. **LOTTERY CHOICES** In the Louisiana Lotto game, a player chooses six distinct numbers from 1 to 40. In how many ways can a player select the six numbers?

67. **DEFECTIVE UNITS** A shipment of 25 television sets contains three defective units. In how many ways can a vending company purchase four of these units and receive (a) all good units, (b) two good units, and (c) at least two good units? (a) 7315 (b) 693 (c) 12,628

68. **INTERPERSONAL RELATIONSHIPS** The complexity of interpersonal relationships increases dramatically as the size of a group increases. Determine the numbers of different two-person relationships in groups of people of sizes (a) 3, (b) 8, (c) 12, and (d) 20.
(a) 3 (b) 28 (c) 66 (d) 190

47. ABCD, ABDC, ACBD, ACDB, ADBC, ADCB, BACD, BADC, CABD, CADB, DABC, DACB, BCAD, BDAC, CBAD, CDAB, DBAC, DCAB, BCDA, BDCA, CBDA, CDBA, DBCA, DCBA

61. AB, AC, AD, AE, AF, BC, BD, BE, BF, CD, CE, CF, DE, DF, EF

64. 4.42×10^{16}

65. 324,632

66. 3,838,380

5 ASSESS AND RETEACH

Daily Homework Quiz

Transparency Available
Available at the Instructor's companion site.

69. (a) 3744 (b) 24
70. (a) 495 (b) 210
78. (c) There are 45,057,474 possible winning numbers in the state lottery, which is less than the possible number of winning Powerball numbers.
79. $n = 5$ or $n = 6$
80. $n = 9$ or $n = 10$
81. $n = 10$
82. $n = 12$
83. $n = 3$
84. $n = 2$
85. $n = 2$
86. $n = 5$
87. False. It is an example of a combination.
88. True by the definition of the Fundamental Counting Principle.
90. ${}_{10}P_6 > {}_{10}C_6$. Changing the order of any of the six elements selected results in a different permutation but the same combination.
96. (a) Permutations because order matters.
(b) Combinations because order does not matter.
(c) Permutations because order matters.
(d) Combinations because order does not matter.
97. The symbol ${}_nP_r$ denotes the number of ways to choose and order r elements out of a collection of n elements.

69. **POKER HAND** You are dealt five cards from an ordinary deck of 52 playing cards. In how many ways can you get (a) a full house and (b) a five-card combination containing two jacks and three aces? (A full house consists of three of one kind and two of another. For example, A-A-A-5-5 and K-K-K-10-10 are full houses.)

70. **JOB APPLICANTS** A clothing manufacturer interviews 12 people for four openings in the human resources department of the company. Five of the 12 people are women. If all 12 are qualified, in how many ways can the employer fill the four positions if (a) the selection is random and (b) exactly two women are selected?

69–70. See margin.

71. **FORMING A COMMITTEE** A six-member research committee at a local college is to be formed having one administrator, three faculty members, and two students. There are seven administrators, 12 faculty members, and 20 students in contention for the committee. How many six-member committees are possible? 292,600

72. **LAW ENFORCEMENT** A police department uses computer imaging to create digital photographs of alleged perpetrators from eyewitness accounts. One software package contains 195 hairlines, 99 sets of eyes and eyebrows, 89 noses, 105 mouths, and 74 chins and cheek structures.
(a) Find the possible number of different faces that the software could create. $1.335(10)^{10}$
(b) An eyewitness can clearly recall the hairline and eyes and eyebrows of a suspect. How many different faces can be produced with this information? 691,530

GEOMETRY In Exercises 73–76, find the number of diagonals of the polygon. (A line segment connecting any two nonadjacent vertices is called a *diagonal* of the polygon.)

73. Pentagon 5
74. Hexagon 9
75. Octagon 20
76. Decagon (10 sides) 35

77. **GEOMETRY** Three points that are not collinear determine three lines. How many lines are determined by nine points, no three of which are collinear? 36

78. **LOTTERY** Powerball is a lottery game that is operated by the Multi-State Lottery Association and is played in 30 states, Washington D.C., and the U.S. Virgin Islands. The game is played by drawing five white balls out of a drum of 59 white balls (numbered 1–59) and one red powerball out of a drum of 39 red balls (numbered 1–39). The jackpot is won by matching all five white balls in any order and the red powerball.
(a) Find the possible number of winning Powerball numbers. 195,249,054
(b) Find the possible number of winning Powerball numbers if the jackpot is won by matching all five white balls in order and the red power ball. 1
(c) Compare the results of part (a) with a state lottery in which a jackpot is won by matching six balls from a drum of 59 balls. See margin.

In Exercises 79–86, solve for n. 79–86. See margin.

79. $14 \cdot {}_nP_3 = {}_{n+2}P_4$
80. ${}_nP_5 = 18 \cdot {}_{n-2}P_4$
81. ${}_nP_4 = 10 \cdot {}_{n-1}P_3$
82. ${}_nP_6 = 12 \cdot {}_{n-1}P_5$
83. ${}_{n+1}P_3 = 4 \cdot {}_nP_2$
84. ${}_{n+2}P_3 = 6 \cdot {}_{n+2}P_1$
85. $4 \cdot {}_{n+1}P_2 = {}_{n+2}P_3$
86. $5 \cdot {}_{n-1}P_1 = {}_nP_2$

EXPLORATION

87–88. See margin.

TRUE OR FALSE? In Exercises 87 and 88, determine whether the statement is true or false. Justify your answer.

87. The number of letter pairs that can be formed in any order from any two of the first 13 letters in the alphabet (A–M) is an example of a permutation.

88. The number of permutations of n elements can be determined by using the Fundamental Counting Principle.

89. What is the relationship between ${}_nC_r$ and ${}_nC_{n-r}$? 89. They are equal.

90. Without calculating the numbers, determine which of the following is greater. Explain. See margin.
(a) The number of combinations of 10 elements taken six at a time
(b) The number of permutations of 10 elements taken six at a time

PROOF In Exercises 91–94, prove the identity. 91–94. Proofs

91. ${}_nP_{n-1} = {}_nP_n$
92. ${}_nC_n = {}_nC_0$
93. ${}_nC_{n-1} = {}_nC_1$
94. ${}_nC_r = \dfrac{{}_nP_r}{r!}$

95. **THINK ABOUT IT** Can your calculator evaluate ${}_{100}P_{80}$? If not, explain why.
No. For some calculators the number is too great.

96. **CAPSTONE** Decide whether each scenario should be counted using permutations or combinations. Explain your reasoning. (Do not calculate.)
(a) Number of ways 10 people can line up in a row for concert tickets. (a)–(d). See margin.
(b) Number of different arrangements of three types of flowers from an array of 20 types.
(c) Number of four-digit pin numbers for a debit card.
(d) Number of two-scoop ice cream sundaes created from 31 different flavors.

97. **WRITING** Explain in words the meaning of ${}_nP_r$.
See margin.

9.7 PROBABILITY

What you should learn

- Find the probabilities of events.
- Find the probabilities of mutually exclusive events.
- Find the probabilities of independent events.
- Find the probability of the complement of an event.

Why you should learn it

Probability applies to many games of chance. For instance, in Exercise 67 on page 710, you will calculate probabilities that relate to the game of roulette.

Hank de Lespinasse/Tips Images/
The Image Bank/Getty Images

The Probability of an Event

Any happening for which the result is uncertain is called an **experiment.** The possible results of the experiment are **outcomes,** the set of all possible outcomes of the experiment is the **sample space** of the experiment, and any subcollection of a sample space is an **event.**

For instance, when a six-sided die is tossed, the sample space can be represented by the numbers 1 through 6. For this experiment, each of the outcomes is *equally likely*.

To describe sample spaces in such a way that each outcome is equally likely, you must sometimes distinguish between or among various outcomes in ways that appear artificial. Example 1 illustrates such a situation.

Example 1 Finding a Sample Space

Find the sample space for each of the following.

a. One coin is tossed.

b. Two coins are tossed.

c. Three coins are tossed.

Solution

a. Because the coin will land either heads up (denoted by H) or tails up (denoted by T), the sample space is

$$S = \{H, T\}.$$

b. Because either coin can land heads up or tails up, the possible outcomes are as follows.

$HH =$ heads up on both coins

$HT =$ heads up on first coin and tails up on second coin

$TH =$ tails up on first coin and heads up on second coin

$TT =$ tails up on both coins

So, the sample space is

$$S = \{HH, HT, TH, TT\}.$$

Note that this list distinguishes between the two cases HT and TH, even though these two outcomes appear to be similar.

c. Following the notation of part (b), the sample space is

$$S = \{HHH, HHT, HTH, HTT, THH, THT, TTH, TTT\}.$$

Note that this list distinguishes among the cases HHT, HTH, and THH, and among the cases HTT, THT, and TTH.

CHECKPoint Now try Exercise 9.

1 PLAN AND PREPARE

Warm-up Exercises

Transparency Available
Available at the Instructor's companion site.

Notetaking Guide

Transparency Available
Promotes interactive learning and notetaking skills.
Available at the Instructor's companion site.

Animated Precalculus

An **Animated Precalculus** tutorial is available at the Student companion site for **Section 9.7.**

Pacing

Average: 2 days
Advanced: 2 days
Block: 1 block

2 FOCUS AND MOTIVATE

Essential Question

How do you find the probability that a series of events will occur? **Tell students that they will learn how to answer this question by identifying outcomes and analyzing situations involving independent, mutually exclusive, and complementary events.**

Resource Planning Guide

Chapter Resources
- Complete Solutions Guide

Workbooks
- Notetaking Guide
- Student Solutions Guide

Interactive Technology
- Instructor Success Organizer
- Notetaking Guide IAE
- Instructional DVDs
- Animated Precalculus
- PowerLecture with ExamView

3 TEACH

Extra Example 1

Find the sample space for each of the following.

a. A letter is chosen randomly from the alphabet.
S = {A, B, C, D, E, F, G, H, I, J, K, L, M, N, O, P, Q, R, S, T, U, V, W, X, Y, Z}

b. A six-sided die is tossed.
S = {1, 2, 3, 4, 5, 6}

c. A coin is flipped once, and a six-sided die is tossed once.
S = {H1, H2, H3, H4, H5, H6, T1, T2, T3, T4, T5, T6}

Extra Example 2

a. Two coins are tossed. What is the probability that one will land heads up and that the other will land tails up?
$\frac{1}{2}$

b. A card is drawn from a standard deck of playing cards. What is the probability that the card is a heart?
$\frac{1}{4}$

To calculate the probability of an event, count the number of outcomes in the event and in the sample space. The *number of outcomes* in event E is denoted by $n(E)$, and the number of outcomes in the sample space S is denoted by $n(S)$. The probability that event E will occur is given by $n(E)/n(S)$.

The Probability of an Event

If an event E has $n(E)$ equally likely outcomes and its sample space S has $n(S)$ equally likely outcomes, the **probability** of event E is

$$P(E) = \frac{n(E)}{n(S)}.$$

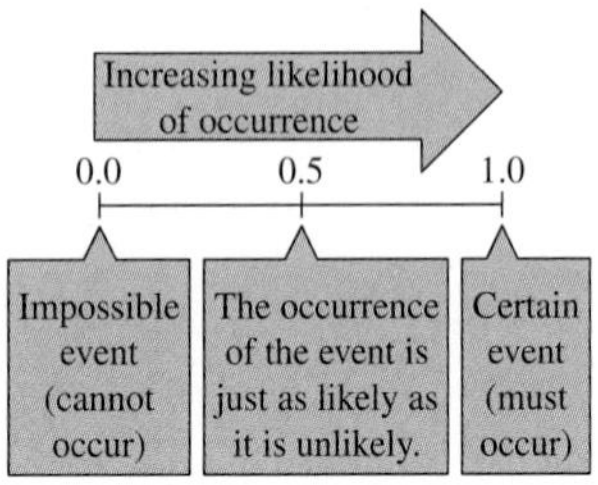

FIGURE 9.8

Because the number of outcomes in an event must be less than or equal to the number of outcomes in the sample space, the probability of an event must be a number between 0 and 1. That is,

$$0 \le P(E) \le 1$$

as indicated in Figure 9.8. If $P(E) = 0$, event E *cannot occur*, and E is called an **impossible event.** If $P(E) = 1$, event E *must occur*, and E is called a **certain event.**

Example 2 Finding the Probability of an Event

a. Two coins are tossed. What is the probability that both land heads up?

b. A card is drawn from a standard deck of playing cards. What is the probability that it is an ace?

Solution

a. Following the procedure in Example 1(b), let

$$E = \{HH\}$$

and

$$S = \{HH, HT, TH, TT\}.$$

The probability of getting two heads is

$$P(E) = \frac{n(E)}{n(S)} = \frac{1}{4}.$$

b. Because there are 52 cards in a standard deck of playing cards and there are four aces (one in each suit), the probability of drawing an ace is

$$P(E) = \frac{n(E)}{n(S)} = \frac{4}{52} = \frac{1}{13}.$$

Study Tip

You can write a probability as a fraction, a decimal, or a percent. For instance, in Example 2(a), the probability of getting two heads can be written as $\frac{1}{4}$, 0.25, or 25%.

CHECKPoint Now try Exercise 15.

FIGURE 9.9

Example 3 Finding the Probability of an Event

Two six-sided dice are tossed. What is the probability that the total of the two dice is 7? (See Figure 9.9.)

Solution

Because there are six possible outcomes on each die, you can use the Fundamental Counting Principle to conclude that there are $6 \cdot 6$ or 36 different outcomes when two dice are tossed. To find the probability of rolling a total of 7, you must first count the number of ways in which this can occur.

First die	Second die
1	6
2	5
3	4
4	3
5	2
6	1

So, a total of 7 can be rolled in six ways, which means that the probability of rolling a 7 is

$$P(E) = \frac{n(E)}{n(S)} = \frac{6}{36} = \frac{1}{6}.$$

CHECKPoint Now try Exercise 25.

Study Tip

You could have written out each sample space in Examples 2(b) and 3 and simply counted the outcomes in the desired events. For larger sample spaces, however, you should use the counting principles discussed in Section 9.6.

Example 4 Finding the Probability of an Event

Twelve-sided dice, as shown in Figure 9.10, can be constructed (in the shape of regular dodecahedrons) such that each of the numbers from 1 to 6 appears twice on each die. Prove that these dice can be used in any game requiring ordinary six-sided dice without changing the probabilities of the various outcomes.

Solution

For an ordinary six-sided die, each of the numbers 1, 2, 3, 4, 5, and 6 occurs only once, so the probability of any particular number coming up is

$$P(E) = \frac{n(E)}{n(S)} = \frac{1}{6}.$$

For one of the 12-sided dice, each number occurs twice, so the probability of any particular number coming up is

$$P(E) = \frac{n(E)}{n(S)} = \frac{2}{12} = \frac{1}{6}.$$

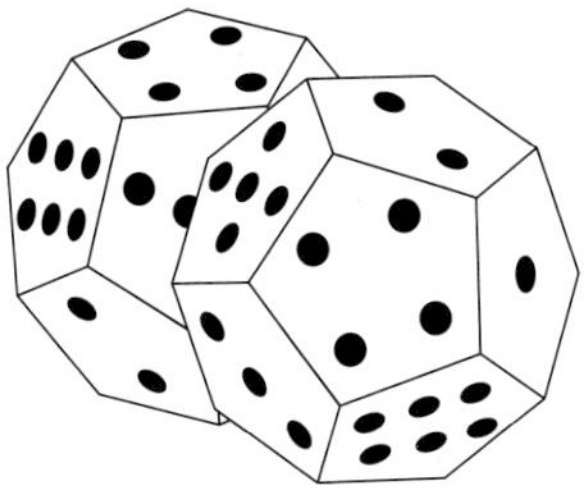

FIGURE 9.10

CHECKPoint Now try Exercise 27.

Extra Example 3

A six-sided die is tossed twice. What is the probability that the total of the two tosses is 5?

$\frac{1}{9}$

Extra Example 4

Show that the probability of drawing a card that is a heart from a standard deck of playing cards is the same as the probability of drawing the ace of hearts from the set consisting of the aces of hearts, diamonds, clubs, and spades.

Drawing a heart:

$P(E) = \frac{n(E)}{n(S)} = \frac{13}{52} = \frac{1}{4}$; drawing the ace of hearts: $P(E) = \frac{n(E)}{n(S)} = \frac{1}{4}$

Extra Example 5

A class is given a list of 20 study problems from which 10 will be part of an upcoming exam. If a given student knows how to solve 17 of the problems, find the probability that the student will be able to correctly answer all 10 questions on the exam.

$\frac{2}{19}$

Extra Example 6

A college sends a survey to selected members of the class of 2009. Of the 1354 people who graduated that year, 672 are female graduates and 682 are male graduates. If a graduate is selected at random, what is the probability that the person is female?

$\frac{672}{1354} = \frac{336}{677}$

Example 5 The Probability of Winning a Lottery

In Arizona's The Pick game, a player chooses six different numbers from 1 to 44. If these six numbers match the six numbers drawn (in any order) by the lottery commission, the player wins (or shares) the top prize. What is the probability of winning the top prize if the player buys one ticket?

Solution

To find the number of elements in the sample space, use the formula for the number of combinations of 44 elements taken six at a time.

$$n(S) = {}_{44}C_6 = \frac{44 \cdot 43 \cdot 42 \cdot 41 \cdot 40 \cdot 39}{6 \cdot 5 \cdot 4 \cdot 3 \cdot 2 \cdot 1} = 7{,}059{,}052$$

If a person buys only one ticket, the probability of winning is

$$P(E) = \frac{n(E)}{n(S)} = \frac{1}{7{,}059{,}052}.$$

CHECKPoint Now try Exercise 31.

Example 6 Random Selection

The numbers of colleges and universities in various regions of the United States in 2007 are shown in Figure 9.11. One institution is selected at random. What is the probability that the institution is in one of the three southern regions? (Source: National Center for Education Statistics)

Solution

From the figure, the total number of colleges and universities is 4309. Because there are $738 + 276 + 406 = 1420$ colleges and universities in the three southern regions, the probability that the institution is in one of these regions is

$$P(E) = \frac{n(E)}{n(S)} = \frac{1420}{4309} \approx 0.330.$$

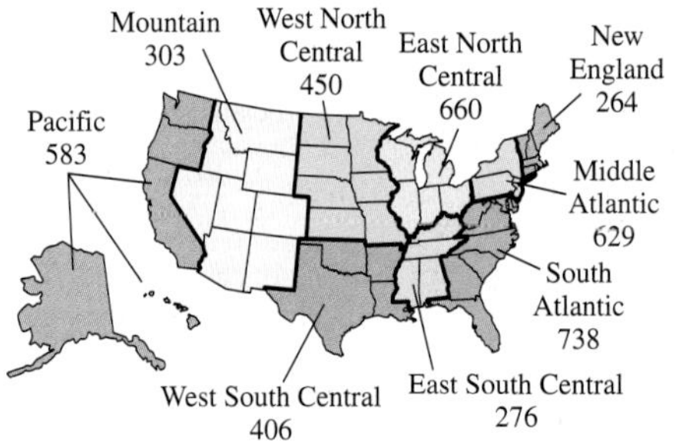

FIGURE 9.11

CHECKPoint Now try Exercise 43.

Mutually Exclusive Events

Two events A and B (from the same sample space) are **mutually exclusive** if A and B have no outcomes in common. In the terminology of sets, the intersection of A and B is the empty set, which implies that

$$P(A \cap B) = 0.$$

For instance, if two dice are tossed, the event A of rolling a total of 6 and the event B of rolling a total of 9 are mutually exclusive. To find the probability that one or the other of two mutually exclusive events will occur, you can *add* their individual probabilities.

Probability of the Union of Two Events

If A and B are events in the same sample space, the probability of A or B occurring is given by

$$P(A \cup B) = P(A) + P(B) - P(A \cap B).$$

If A and B are mutually exclusive, then

$$P(A \cup B) = P(A) + P(B).$$

Example 7 The Probability of a Union of Events

One card is selected from a standard deck of 52 playing cards. What is the probability that the card is either a heart or a face card?

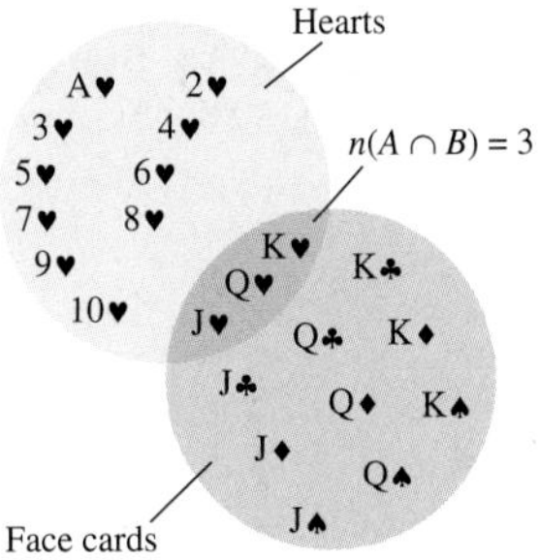

FIGURE 9.12

Solution

Because the deck has 13 hearts, the probability of selecting a heart (event A) is

$$P(A) = \frac{13}{52}.$$

Similarly, because the deck has 12 face cards, the probability of selecting a face card (event B) is

$$P(B) = \frac{12}{52}.$$

Because three of the cards are hearts *and* face cards (see Figure 9.12), it follows that

$$P(A \cap B) = \frac{3}{52}.$$

Finally, applying the formula for the probability of the union of two events, you can conclude that the probability of selecting a heart or a face card is

$$P(A \cup B) = P(A) + P(B) - P(A \cap B)$$

$$= \frac{13}{52} + \frac{12}{52} - \frac{3}{52} = \frac{22}{52} \approx 0.423.$$

CHECKPoint Now try Exercise 57.

Extra Example 7

One card is selected from a standard deck of 52 playing cards. What is the probability that the card is either a club or an ace?

$\frac{16}{52} = \frac{2}{7}$

Extra Example 8

A wind turbine plant has a total of 158 wage and salary workers. The circle graph gives the age profile of these workers.

Age of Wage and Salary Workers

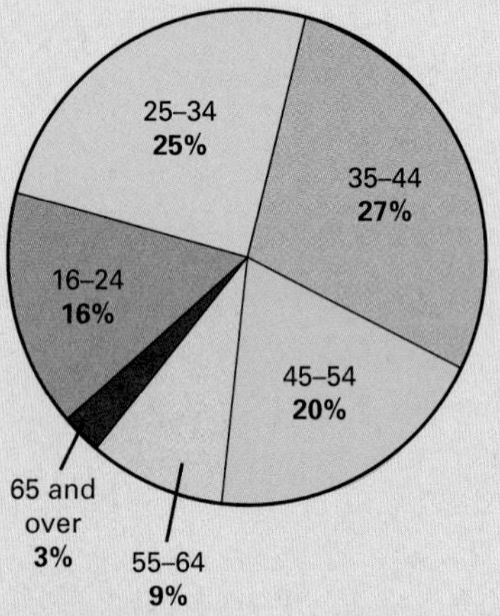

a. What is the probability that a person selected at random from the plant is in the 35–44 age group?

27%

b. What is the probability that a person selected at random from the plant is in the 35–54 age group?

47%

Example 8 Probability of Mutually Exclusive Events

The personnel department of a company has compiled data on the numbers of employees who have been with the company for various periods of time. The results are shown in the table.

Years of Service	Number of employees
0–4	157
5–9	89
10–14	74
15–19	63
20–24	42
25–29	38
30–34	37
35–39	21
40–44	8

If an employee is chosen at random, what is the probability that the employee has (a) 4 or fewer years of service and (b) 9 or fewer years of service?

Solution

a. To begin, add the number of employees to find that the total is 529. Next, let event A represent choosing an employee with 0 to 4 years of service. Then the probability of choosing an employee who has 4 or fewer years of service is

$$P(A) = \frac{157}{529} \approx 0.297.$$

b. Let event B represent choosing an employee with 5 to 9 years of service. Then

$$P(B) = \frac{89}{529}.$$

Because event A from part (a) and event B have no outcomes in common, you can conclude that these two events are mutually exclusive and that

$$\begin{aligned} P(A \cup B) &= P(A) + P(B) \\ &= \frac{157}{529} + \frac{89}{529} \\ &= \frac{246}{529} \\ &\approx 0.465. \end{aligned}$$

So, the probability of choosing an employee who has 9 or fewer years of service is about 0.465.

CHECKPoint Now try Exercise 59.

Independent Events

Two events are **independent** if the occurrence of one has no effect on the occurrence of the other. For instance, rolling a total of 12 with two six-sided dice has no effect on the outcome of future rolls of the dice. To find the probability that two independent events will occur, *multiply* the probabilities of each.

> **Probability of Independent Events**
>
> If A and B are independent events, the probability that both A and B will occur is
>
> $$P(A \text{ and } B) = P(A) \cdot P(B).$$

Example 9 Probability of Independent Events

A random number generator on a computer selects three integers from 1 to 20. What is the probability that all three numbers are less than or equal to 5?

Solution

The probability of selecting a number from 1 to 5 is

$$P(A) = \frac{5}{20} = \frac{1}{4}.$$

So, the probability that all three numbers are less than or equal to 5 is

$$P(A) \cdot P(A) \cdot P(A) = \left(\frac{1}{4}\right)\left(\frac{1}{4}\right)\left(\frac{1}{4}\right)$$

$$= \frac{1}{64}.$$

CHECK**Point** Now try Exercise 61.

Example 10 Probability of Independent Events

In 2009, approximately 13% of the adult population of the United States got most of their news from the Internet. In a survey, 10 people were chosen at random from the adult population. What is the probability that all 10 got most of their news from the Internet? (Source: CBS News/New York Times Poll)

Solution

Let A represent choosing an adult who gets most of his or her news from the Internet. The probability of choosing an adult who got most of his or her news from the Internet is 0.13, the probability of choosing a second adult who got most of his or her news from the Internet is 0.13, and so on. Because these events are independent, you can conclude that the probability that all 10 people got most of their news from the Internet is

$$[P(A)]^{10} = (0.13)^{10} \approx 0.000000001.$$

CHECK**Point** Now try Exercise 63.

Extra Example 9

Two integers from 1 to 30 are chosen by a random number generator. What is the probability that both numbers are less than 12?

$\frac{121}{900}$

Avoiding Common Errors

Students sometimes neglect to classify the type of events correctly before applying probability rules. When they are calculating $P(A \text{ or } B)$, remind students to first classify A and B as mutually exclusive or as having common outcomes. When they calculate $P(A \text{ and } B)$, remind students to verify that A and B are independent.

Extra Example 10

A sales representative makes a sale at approximately one-third of all calls. If, on a given day, the representative contacts five potential clients, what is the probability that a sale will be made with each of the five contacts?

$\frac{1}{243}$

Extra Example 11

A sales representative makes a sale at approximately one-third of all calls. If, on a given day, the representative contacts five potential clients, what is the probability that a sale will be made with at least one contact?

$\frac{211}{243}$

Closing the Lesson

Have students summarize the major points of the lesson and answer the Essential Question: How do you find the probability that a series of events will occur?

- **Find the probability of an event by dividing the number of outcomes making up the event by the number of outcomes in the sample space.**
- **Find the probability that a series of mutually exclusive events within the same sample space will occur by adding their individual probabilities.**
- **Find the probability that a series of independent events will occur by multiplying their individual probabilities.**
- **Find the probability that the complement of an event will occur by subtracting the probability of the event from 1.**

The Complement of an Event

The **complement of an event** A is the collection of all outcomes in the sample space that are *not* in A. The complement of event A is denoted by A'. Because $P(A \text{ or } A') = 1$ and because A and A' are mutually exclusive, it follows that $P(A) + P(A') = 1$. So, the probability of A' is

$$P(A') = 1 - P(A).$$

For instance, if the probability of *winning* a certain game is

$$P(A) = \frac{1}{4}$$

the probability of *losing* the game is

$$P(A') = 1 - \frac{1}{4}$$

$$= \frac{3}{4}.$$

Probability of a Complement

Let A be an event and let A' be its complement. If the probability of A is $P(A)$, the probability of the complement is

$$P(A') = 1 - P(A).$$

Example 11 Finding the Probability of a Complement

A manufacturer has determined that a machine averages one faulty unit for every 1000 it produces. What is the probability that an order of 200 units will have one or more faulty units?

Solution

To solve this problem as stated, you would need to find the probabilities of having exactly one faulty unit, exactly two faulty units, exactly three faulty units, and so on. However, using complements, you can simply find the probability that all units are perfect and then subtract this value from 1. Because the probability that any given unit is perfect is 999/1000, the probability that all 200 units are perfect is

$$P(A) = \left(\frac{999}{1000}\right)^{200}$$

$$\approx 0.819.$$

So, the probability that at least one unit is faulty is

$$P(A') = 1 - P(A)$$

$$\approx 1 - 0.819$$

$$= 0.181.$$

CHECKPoint Now try Exercise 65.

9.7 EXERCISES

See www.CalcChat.com for worked-out solutions to odd-numbered exercises.

VOCABULARY

In Exercises 1–7, fill in the blanks.

1. An ________ is an event whose result is uncertain, and the possible results of the event are called ________. experiment; outcomes
2. The set of all possible outcomes of an experiment is called the ________. sample space
3. To determine the ________ of an event, you can use the formula $P(E) = \frac{n(E)}{n(S)}$, where $n(E)$ is the number of outcomes in the event and $n(S)$ is the number of outcomes in the sample space. probability
4. If $P(E) = 0$, then E is an ________ event, and if $P(E) = 1$, then E is a ________ event. impossible; certain
5. If two events from the same sample space have no outcomes in common, then the two events are ________. mutually exclusive
6. If the occurrence of one event has no effect on the occurrence of a second event, then the events are ________. independent
7. The ________ of an event A is the collection of all outcomes in the sample space that are not in A. complement
8. Match the probability formula with the correct probability name.
   - (a) Probability of the union of two events
   - (b) Probability of mutually exclusive events
   - (c) Probability of independent events
   - (d) Probability of a complement
   - (i) $P(A \cup B) = P(A) + P(B)$
   - (ii) $P(A') = 1 - P(A)$
   - (iii) $P(A \cup B) = P(A) + P(B) - P(A \cap B)$
   - (iv) $P(A \text{ and } B) = P(A) \cdot P(B)$

   Answer: (a)–(iii), (b)–(i), (c)–(iv), (d)–(ii)

SKILLS AND APPLICATIONS

In Exercises 9–14, determine the sample space for the experiment. 9–14. See margin.

9. A coin and a six-sided die are tossed.
10. A six-sided die is tossed twice and the sum of the results is recorded.
11. A taste tester has to rank three varieties of yogurt, A, B, and C, according to preference.
12. Two marbles are selected (without replacement) from a bag containing two red marbles, two blue marbles, and one yellow marble. The color of each marble is recorded.
13. Two county supervisors are selected from five supervisors, A, B, C, D, and E, to study a recycling plan.
14. A sales representative makes presentations about a product in three homes per day. In each home, there may be a sale (denote by S) or there may be no sale (denote by F).

TOSSING A COIN In Exercises 15–20, find the probability for the experiment of tossing a coin three times. Use the sample space $S = \{HHH, HHT, HTH, HTT, THH, THT, TTH, TTT\}$.

15. The probability of getting exactly one tail $\frac{3}{8}$
16. The probability of getting exactly two tails $\frac{3}{8}$
17. The probability of getting a head on the first toss $\frac{1}{2}$
18. The probability of getting a tail on the last toss $\frac{1}{2}$
19. The probability of getting at least one head $\frac{7}{8}$
20. The probability of getting at least two heads $\frac{1}{2}$

DRAWING A CARD In Exercises 21–24, find the probability for the experiment of selecting one card from a standard deck of 52 playing cards.

21. The card is a face card. $\frac{3}{13}$
22. The card is not a face card. $\frac{10}{13}$
23. The card is a red face card. $\frac{3}{26}$
24. The card is a 9 or lower. (Aces are low.) $\frac{9}{13}$

TOSSING A DIE In Exercises 25–30, find the probability for the experiment of tossing a six-sided die twice.

25. The sum is 6. $\frac{5}{36}$
26. The sum is at least 8. $\frac{5}{12}$
27. The sum is less than 11. $\frac{11}{12}$
28. The sum is 2, 3, or 12. $\frac{1}{9}$
29. The sum is odd and no more than 7. $\frac{1}{3}$
30. The sum is odd or prime. $\frac{19}{36}$

DRAWING MARBLES In Exercises 31–34, find the probability for the experiment of drawing two marbles (without replacement) from a bag containing one green, two yellow, and three red marbles.

31. Both marbles are red. $\frac{1}{5}$
32. Both marbles are yellow. $\frac{1}{15}$
33. Neither marble is yellow. $\frac{2}{5}$
34. The marbles are of different colors. $\frac{11}{15}$

4 PRACTICE AND APPLY

Assignment Guide

Transparencies Available
Available at the Instructor's companion site.

Average:
Day 1: pp. 707–709
Exs. 1–4, 9–12, 13–19 odd, 22, 23, 26–29, 31–33, 35–41 odd, 45, 48, 49–51
Day 2: pp. 707–711
Exs. 5–8, 53–55, 58, 64, 67–69, 71–75

Advanced:
Day 1: pp. 707–709
Exs. 1–4, 10–20 even, 22–24, 28–30, 32–34, 36–42 even, 46, 48, 50–52
Day 2: pp. 707–711
Exs. 5–8, 54–56, 58, 64, 66, 67, 69–75

Block:
pp. 707–711
Exs. 1–12, 13–19 odd, 22, 23, 26–29, 31–33, 35–41 odd, 45, 48, 49–51, 53–55, 58, 64, 67–69, 71–75

9. $\{(H, 1), (H, 2), (H, 3), (H, 4), (H, 5), (H, 6), (T, 1), (T, 2), (T, 3), (T, 4), (T, 5), (T, 6)\}$
10. $\{2, 3, \ldots, 12\}$
11. {ABC, ACB, BAC, BCA, CAB, CBA}
12. {(red, red), (red, blue), (red, yellow), (blue, blue), (blue, yellow)}
13. {AB, AC, AD, AE, BC, BD, BE, CD, CE, DE}
14. {SSS, SSF, SFS, SFF, FSS, FSF, FFS, FFF}

In Exercises 35–38, you are given the probability that an event *will* happen. Find the probability that the event *will not* happen.

35. $P(E) = 0.87$ 0.13

36. $P(E) = 0.36$ 0.64

37. $P(E) = \frac{1}{4}$ $\frac{3}{4}$

38. $P(E) = \frac{2}{3}$ $\frac{1}{3}$

In Exercises 39–42, you are given the probability that an event *will not* happen. Find the probability that the event *will* happen.

39. $P(E') = 0.23$ 0.77

40. $P(E') = 0.92$ 0.08

41. $P(E') = \frac{17}{35}$ $\frac{18}{35}$

42. $P(E') = \frac{61}{100}$ $\frac{39}{100}$

43. GRAPHICAL REASONING In 2008, there were approximately 8.92 million unemployed workers in the United States. The circle graph shows the age profile of these unemployed workers. (Source: U.S. Bureau of Labor Statistics)

Ages of Unemployed Workers

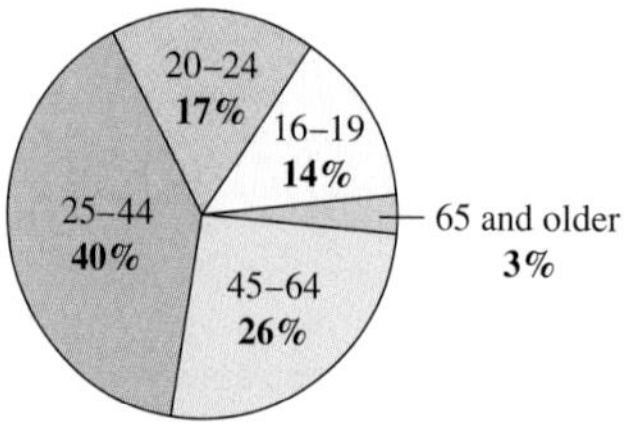

(a) Estimate the number of unemployed workers in the 16–19 age group. 1.25 million

(b) What is the probability that a person selected at random from the population of unemployed workers is in the 25–44 age group? $\frac{2}{5}$

(c) What is the probability that a person selected at random from the population of unemployed workers is in the 45–64 age group? $\frac{13}{50}$

(d) What is the probability that a person selected at random from the population of unemployed workers is 45 or older? $\frac{29}{100}$

44. GRAPHICAL REASONING The educational attainment of the United States population age 25 years or older in 2007 is shown in the circle graph. Use the fact that the population of people 25 years or older was approximately 194.32 million in 2007. (Source: U.S. Census Bureau)

Educational Attainment

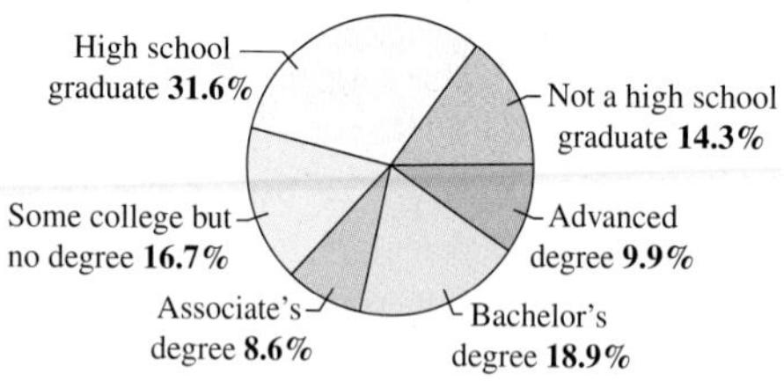

(a) Estimate the number of people 25 years or older who have high school diplomas. 166.53 million

(b) Estimate the number of people 25 years or older who have advanced degrees. 19.24 million

(c) Find the probability that a person 25 years or older selected at random has earned a Bachelor's degree or higher. 0.288

(d) Find the probability that a person 25 years or older selected at random has earned a high school diploma or gone on to post-secondary education. 0.857

(e) Find the probability that a person 25 years or older selected at random has earned an Associate's degree or higher. 0.374

45. GRAPHICAL REASONING The figure shows the results of a recent survey in which 1011 adults were asked to grade U.S. public schools. (Source: Phi Delta Kappa/Gallup Poll)

Grading Public Schools

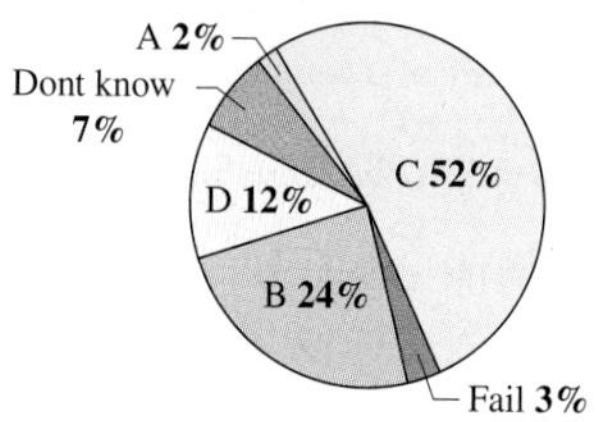

(a) Estimate the number of adults who gave U.S. public schools a B. 243

(b) An adult is selected at random. What is the probability that the adult will give the U.S. public schools an A? $\frac{1}{50}$

(c) An adult is selected at random. What is the probability the adult will give the U.S. public schools a C or a D? $\frac{16}{25}$

46. GRAPHICAL REASONING The figure shows the results of a survey in which auto racing fans listed their favorite type of racing. (Source: ESPN Sports Poll/TNS Sports)

Favorite Type of Racing

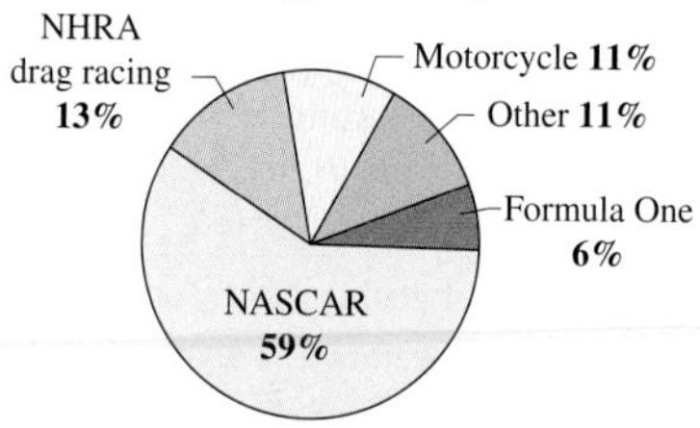

(a) What is the probability that an auto racing fan selected at random lists NASCAR racing as his or her favorite type of racing? $\frac{59}{100}$

(b) What is the probability that an auto racing fan selected at random lists Formula One or motorcycle racing as his or her favorite type of racing? $\frac{17}{100}$

(c) What is the probability that an auto racing fan selected at random does *not* list NHRA drag racing as his or her favorite type of racing? $\frac{87}{100}$

47. DATA ANALYSIS A study of the effectiveness of a flu vaccine was conducted with a sample of 500 people. Some participants in the study were given no vaccine, some were given one injection, and some were given two injections. The results of the study are listed in the table.

	No vaccine	One injection	Two injections	Total
Flu	7	2	13	22
No flu	149	52	277	478
Total	156	54	290	500

A person is selected at random from the sample. Find the specified probability.

(a) The person had two injections. 58%

(b) The person did not get the flu. 95.6%

(c) The person got the flu and had one injection. 0.4%

48. DATA ANALYSIS One hundred college students were interviewed to determine their political party affiliations and whether they favored a balanced-budget amendment to the Constitution. The results of the study are listed in the table, where D represents Democrat and R represents Republican.

	Favor	Not favor	Unsure	Total
D	23	25	7	55
R	32	9	4	45
Total	55	34	11	100

A person is selected at random from the sample. Find the probability that the described person is selected.

(a) A person who doesn't favor the amendment 34%

(b) A Republican 45%

(c) A Democrat who favors the amendment 23%

49. ALUMNI ASSOCIATION A college sends a survey to selected members of the class of 2009. Of the 1254 people who graduated that year, 672 are women, of whom 124 went on to graduate school. Of the 582 male graduates, 198 went on to graduate school. An alumni member is selected at random. What are the probabilities that the person is (a) female, (b) male, and (c) female and did not attend graduate school?

(a) $\frac{112}{209}$ (b) $\frac{97}{209}$ (c) $\frac{274}{627}$

50. EDUCATION In a high school graduating class of 128 students, 52 are on the honor roll. Of these, 48 are going on to college; of the other 76 students, 56 are going on to college. A student is selected at random from the class. What is the probability that the person chosen is (a) going to college, (b) not going to college, and (c) not going to college and on the honor roll? See margin.

51. WINNING AN ELECTION Three people have been nominated for president of a class. From a poll, it is estimated that the first candidate has a 37% chance of winning and the second candidate has a 44% chance of winning. What is the probability that the third candidate will win? 19%

52. PAYROLL ERROR The employees of a company work in six departments: 31 are in sales, 54 are in research, 42 are in marketing, 20 are in engineering, 47 are in finance, and 58 are in production. One employee's paycheck is lost. What is the probability that the employee works in the research department? $\frac{3}{14}$

In Exercises 53–60, the sample spaces are large and you should use the counting principles discussed in Section 9.6.

53. PREPARING FOR A TEST A class is given a list of 20 study problems, from which 10 will be part of an upcoming exam. A student knows how to solve 15 of the problems. Find the probabilities that the student will be able to answer (a) all 10 questions on the exam, (b) exactly eight questions on the exam, and (c) at least nine questions on the exam. 53–54. See margin.

54. PAYROLL MIX-UP Five paychecks and envelopes are addressed to five different people. The paychecks are randomly inserted into the envelopes. What are the probabilities that (a) exactly one paycheck will be inserted in the correct envelope and (b) at least one paycheck will be inserted in the correct envelope?

55. GAME SHOW On a game show, you are given five digits to arrange in the proper order to form the price of a car. If you are correct, you win the car. What is the probability of winning, given the following conditions?

(a) You guess the position of each digit. $\frac{1}{120}$

(b) You know the first digit and guess the positions of the other digits. $\frac{1}{24}$

56. CARD GAME The deck for a card game is made up of 108 cards. Twenty-five each are red, yellow, blue, and green, and eight are wild cards. Each player is randomly dealt a seven-card hand.

(a) What is the probability that a hand will contain exactly two wild cards? 0.076

(b) What is the probability that a hand will contain two wild cards, two red cards, and three blue cards? 0.00069

50. (a) $\frac{13}{16}$ (b) $\frac{3}{16}$ (c) $\frac{1}{32}$
53. (a) $\frac{21}{1292}$ (b) $\frac{225}{646}$ (c) $\frac{49}{323}$
54. (a) $\frac{3}{8}$ (b) $\frac{19}{30}$

61. (a) $\frac{1}{4}$ (b) $\frac{1}{2}$
(c) $\frac{841}{1600}$ (d) $\frac{1}{40}$

62. (a) $\frac{1}{4}$ (b) $\frac{1}{2}$
(c) $\frac{841}{6400}$ (d) $\frac{1}{80}$

65. (a) 0.9702 (b) 0.9998
(c) 0.0002

66. (a) 0.81 (b) 0.01 (c) 0.99

57. **DRAWING A CARD** One card is selected at random from an ordinary deck of 52 playing cards. Find the probabilities that (a) the card is an even-numbered card, (b) the card is a heart or a diamond, and (c) the card is a nine or a face card. (a) $\frac{5}{13}$ (b) $\frac{1}{2}$ (c) $\frac{4}{13}$

58. **POKER HAND** Five cards are drawn from an ordinary deck of 52 playing cards. What is the probability that the hand drawn is a full house? (A full house is a hand that consists of two of one kind and three of another kind.) $\frac{6}{4165}$

59. **DEFECTIVE UNITS** A shipment of 12 microwave ovens contains three defective units. A vending company has ordered four of these units, and because each is identically packaged, the selection will be random. What are the probabilities that (a) all four units are good, (b) exactly two units are good, and (c) at least two units are good? (a) $\frac{14}{55}$ (b) $\frac{12}{55}$ (c) $\frac{54}{55}$

60. **PIN CODES** ATM personal identification number (PIN) codes typically consist of four-digit sequences of numbers. Find the probability that if you forget your PIN, you can guess the correct sequence (a) at random and (b) if you recall the first two digits. (a) $\frac{1}{10,000}$ (b) $\frac{1}{100}$

61. **RANDOM NUMBER GENERATOR** Two integers from 1 through 40 are chosen by a random number generator. What are the probabilities that (a) the numbers are both even, (b) one number is even and one is odd, (c) both numbers are less than 30, and (d) the same number is chosen twice? See margin.

62. **RANDOM NUMBER GENERATOR** Repeat Exercise 61 for a random number generator that chooses two integers from 1 through 80. See margin.

63. **FLEXIBLE WORK HOURS** In a survey, people were asked if they would prefer to work flexible hours—even if it meant slower career advancement—so they could spend more time with their families. The results of the survey are shown in the figure. Three people from the survey were chosen at random. What is the probability that all three people would prefer flexible work hours? 0.4746

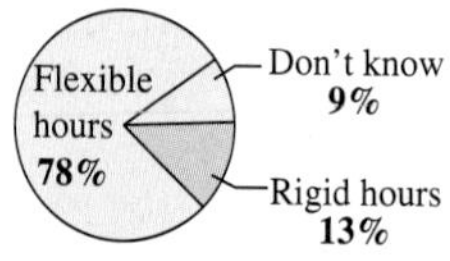

64. **CONSUMER AWARENESS** Suppose that the methods used by shoppers to pay for merchandise are as shown in the circle graph. Two shoppers are chosen at random. What is the probability that both shoppers paid for their purchases only in cash? 0.1024

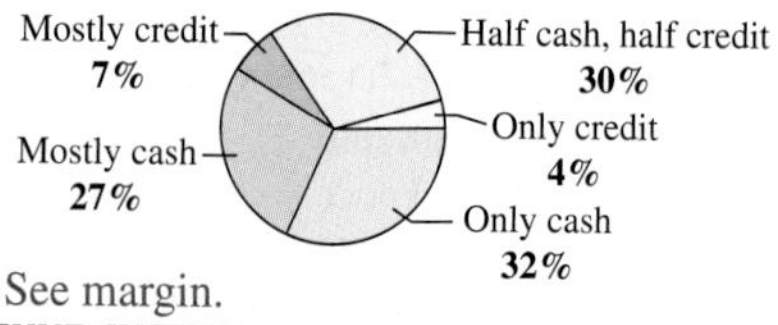

65–66. See margin.

65. **BACKUP SYSTEM** A space vehicle has an independent backup system for one of its communication networks. The probability that either system will function satisfactorily during a flight is 0.985. What are the probabilities that during a given flight (a) both systems function satisfactorily, (b) at least one system functions satisfactorily, and (c) both systems fail?

66. **BACKUP VEHICLE** A fire company keeps two rescue vehicles. Because of the demand on the vehicles and the chance of mechanical failure, the probability that a specific vehicle is available when needed is 90%. The availability of one vehicle is independent of the availability of the other. Find the probabilities that (a) both vehicles are available at a given time, (b) neither vehicle is available at a given time, and (c) at least one vehicle is available at a given time.

67. **ROULETTE** American roulette is a game in which a wheel turns on a spindle and is divided into 38 pockets. Thirty-six of the pockets are numbered 1–36, of which half are red and half are black. Two of the pockets are green and are numbered 0 and 00 (see figure). The dealer spins the wheel and a small ball in opposite directions. As the ball slows to a stop, it has an equal probability of landing in any of the numbered pockets.

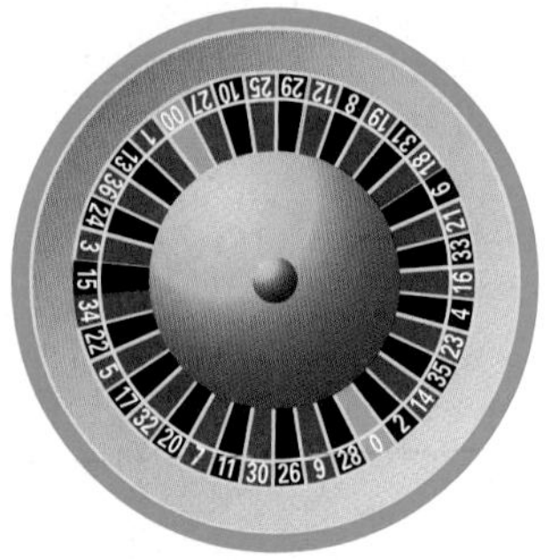

(a) Find the probability of landing in the number 00 pocket. $\frac{1}{38}$

(b) Find the probability of landing in a red pocket. $\frac{9}{19}$

(c) Find the probability of landing in a green pocket or a black pocket. $\frac{10}{19}$

(d) Find the probability of landing in the number 14 pocket on two consecutive spins. $\frac{1}{1444}$

(e) Find the probability of landing in a red pocket on three consecutive spins. $\frac{729}{6859}$

68. A BOY OR A GIRL? Assume that the probability of the birth of a child of a particular sex is 50%. In a family with four children, what are the probabilities that (a) all the children are boys, (b) all the children are the same sex, and (c) there is at least one boy? See margin.

69. GEOMETRY You and a friend agree to meet at your favorite fast-food restaurant between 5:00 and 6:00 P.M. The one who arrives first will wait 15 minutes for the other, and then will leave (see figure). What is the probability that the two of you will actually meet, assuming that your arrival times are random within the hour? $\frac{7}{16}$

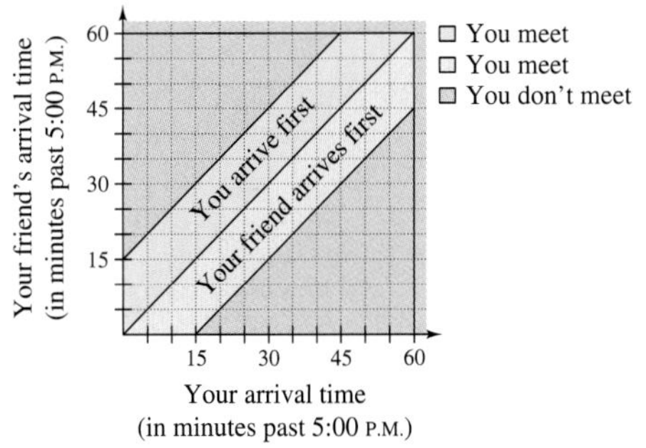

70. ESTIMATING π A coin of diameter d is dropped onto a paper that contains a grid of squares d units on a side (see figure).

(a) Find the probability that the coin covers a vertex of one of the squares on the grid. $\pi/4$

(b) Perform the experiment 100 times and use the results to approximate π. Approximations will vary.

EXPLORATION

TRUE OR FALSE? In Exercises 71 and 72, determine whether the statement is true or false. Justify your answer.

71. If A and B are independent events with nonzero probabilities, then A can occur when B occurs.

True. Two events are independent if the occurrence of one has no effect on the occurrence of the other.

72. Rolling a number less than 3 on a normal six-sided die has a probability of $\frac{1}{3}$. The complement of this event is to roll a number greater than 3, and its probability is $\frac{1}{2}$. See margin.

73. PATTERN RECOGNITION Consider a group of n people.

(a) Explain why the following pattern gives the probabilities that the n people have distinct birthdays. See margin.

$$n = 2: \quad \frac{365}{365} \cdot \frac{364}{365} = \frac{365 \cdot 364}{365^2}$$

$$n = 3: \quad \frac{365}{365} \cdot \frac{364}{365} \cdot \frac{363}{365} = \frac{365 \cdot 364 \cdot 363}{365^3}$$

(b) Use the pattern in part (a) to write an expression for the probability that $n = 4$ people have distinct birthdays. $\frac{365}{365} \cdot \frac{364}{365} \cdot \frac{363}{365} \cdot \frac{362}{365}$

(c) Let P_n be the probability that the n people have distinct birthdays. Verify that this probability can be obtained recursively by Answers will vary.

$$P_1 = 1 \text{ and } P_n = \frac{365 - (n - 1)}{365} P_{n-1}.$$

(d) Explain why $Q_n = 1 - P_n$ gives the probability that at least two people in a group of n people have the same birthday. See margin.

(e) Use the results of parts (c) and (d) to complete the table. See margin.

n	10	15	20	23	30	40	50
P_n							
Q_n							

(f) How many people must be in a group so that the probability of at least two of them having the same birthday is greater than $\frac{1}{2}$? Explain. 23; $Q_n > 0.5$ for $n \geq 23$.

74. CAPSTONE Write a short paragraph defining the following. See margin.

(a) Sample space of an experiment

(b) Event

(c) The probability of an event E in a sample space S

(d) The probability of the complement of E

75. See margin.

75. THINK ABOUT IT A weather forecast indicates that the probability of rain is 40%. What does this mean?

76. Toss two coins 100 times and write down the number of heads that occur on each toss (0, 1, or 2). How many times did two heads occur? How many times would you expect two heads to occur if you did the experiment 1000 times? Answers will vary; 250

5 ASSESS AND RETEACH

Daily Homework Quiz

Transparency Available

Available at the Instructor's companion site.

68. (a) $\frac{1}{16}$ (b) $\frac{1}{8}$ (c) $\frac{15}{16}$

72. False. The complement of the event is to roll a number greater than or equal to 3, and its probability is $\frac{2}{3}$.

73. (a) As you consider successive people with distinct birthdays, the probabilities must decrease to take into account the birth dates already used. Because the birth dates of people are independent events, multiply the respective probabilities of distinct birthdays.

(d) Q_n is the probability that the birthdays are *not* distinct, which is equivalent to at least two people having the same birthday.

(e) See below.

74. (a) The set of all possible outcomes of an experiment

(b) Any subcollection of a sample space

(c) If an event E has $n(E)$ equally likely outcomes and its sample space S has $n(S)$ equally likely outcomes, the probability of event E is

$$P(E) = \frac{n(E)}{n(S)}.$$

(d) $P(E') = 1 - P(E)$

75. Meteorological records indicate that over an extended period of time with similar weather conditions it will rain 40% of the time.

73. (e)

n	10	15	20	23	30	40	50
P_n	0.88	0.75	0.59	0.49	0.29	0.11	0.03
Q_n	0.12	0.25	0.41	0.51	0.71	0.89	0.97

9 Chapter Summary

	What Did You Learn?	Explanation/Examples	Review Exercises
Section 9.1	Use sequence notation to write the terms of sequences *(p. 640)*.	$a_n = 7n - 4$; $a_1 = 7(1) - 4 = 3$, $a_2 = 7(2) - 4 = 10$, $a_3 = 7(3) - 4 = 17$, $a_4 = 7(4) - 4 = 24$	1–8
	Use factorial notation *(p. 642)*.	If n is a positive integer, $n! = 1 \cdot 2 \cdot 3 \cdot 4 \cdot \cdot \cdot (n - 1) \cdot n$.	9–12
	Use summation notation to write sums *(p. 644)*.	The sum of the first n terms of a sequence is represented by $\sum_{i=1}^{n} a_i = a_1 + a_2 + a_3 + a_4 + \cdot \cdot \cdot + a_n$.	13–20
	Find the sums of series *(p. 645)*.	$\sum_{i=1}^{\infty} \frac{5}{10^i} = \frac{5}{10^1} + \frac{5}{10^2} + \frac{5}{10^3} + \frac{5}{10^4} + \frac{5}{10^5} + \cdot \cdot \cdot$ $= 0.5 + 0.05 + 0.005 + 0.0005 + 0.00005 + \cdot \cdot \cdot$ $= 0.55555 \ldots = \frac{5}{9}$	21, 22
	Use sequences and series to model and solve real-life problems *(p. 646)*.	A sequence can be used to model the resident population of the United States from 1980 through 2007. (See Example 10.)	23, 24
Section 9.2	Recognize, write, and find the *n*th terms of arithmetic sequences *(p. 651)*.	$a_n = 9n + 5$; $a_1 = 9(1) + 5 = 14$, $a_2 = 9(2) + 5 = 23$, $a_3 = 9(3) + 5 = 32$, $a_4 = 9(4) + 5 = 41$	25–38
	Find *n*th partial sums of arithmetic sequences *(p. 654)*.	The sum of a finite arithmetic sequence with n terms is $S_n = (n/2)(a_1 + a_n)$.	39–44
	Use arithmetic sequences to model and solve real-life problems *(p. 655)*.	An arithmetic sequence can be used to find the total amount of prize money awarded at a golf tournament. (See Example 8.)	45, 46
Section 9.3	Recognize, write, and find the *n*th terms of geometric sequences *(p. 661)*.	$a_n = 3(4^n)$; $a_1 = 3(4^1) = 12$, $a_2 = 3(4^2) = 48$, $a_3 = 3(4^3) = 192$, $a_4 = 3(4^4) = 768$	47–58
	Find the sum of a finite geometric sequence *(p. 664)*.	The sum of the finite geometric sequence $a_1, a_1r, a_1r^2, \ldots, a_1r^{n-1}$ with common ratio $r \neq 1$ is given by $S_n = \sum_{i=1}^{n} a_1r^{i-1} = a_1\left(\frac{1 - r^n}{1 - r}\right)$.	59–66
	Find the sum of an infinite geometric series *(p. 665)*.	If $\lvert r \rvert < 1$, the infinite geometric series $a_1 + a_1r + a_1r^2 + \cdot \cdot \cdot + a_1r^{n-1} + \cdot \cdot \cdot$ has the sum $S = \sum_{i=0}^{\infty} a_1r^i = \frac{a_1}{1 - r}$.	67–70
	Use geometric sequences to model and solve real-life problems *(p. 666)*.	A finite geometric sequence can be used to find the balance in an annuity at the end of two years. (See Example 8.)	71, 72
Section 9.4	Use mathematical induction to prove statements involving a positive integer *n* *(p. 671)*.	Let P_n be a statement involving the positive integer n. If (1) P_1 is true, and (2) for every positive integer k, the truth of P_k implies the truth of P_{k+1}, then the statement P_n must be true for all positive integers n.	73–76

	What Did You Learn?	Explanation/Examples	Review Exercises
Section 9.4	Recognize patterns and write the *n*th term of a sequence *(p. 675).*	To find a formula for the *n*th term of a sequence, (1) calculate the first several terms of the sequence, (2) try to find a pattern for the terms and write a formula (hypothesis) for the *n*th term of the sequence, and (3) use mathematical induction to prove your hypothesis.	77–80
	Find the sums of powers of integers *(p. 677).*	$\sum_{i=1}^{8} i^2 = \frac{n(n+1)(2n+1)}{6} = \frac{8(8+1)(16+1)}{6} = 204$	81, 82
	Find finite differences of sequences *(p. 678).*	The first differences of a sequence are found by subtracting consecutive terms. The second differences are found by subtracting consecutive first differences.	83–86
Section 9.5	Use the Binomial Theorem to calculate binomial coefficients *(p. 681).*	**The Binomial Theorem:** In the expansion of $(x + y)^n = x^n + nx^{n-1}y + \cdots + {}_nC_r x^{n-r}y^r + \cdots + nxy^{n-1} + y^n$, the coefficient of $x^{n-r}y^r$ is ${}_nC_r = \frac{n!}{(n-r)!r!}$.	87, 88
	Use Pascal's Triangle to calculate binomial coefficients *(p. 683).*	First several rows of Pascal's triangle: 1; 1 1; 1 2 1; 1 3 3 1; 1 4 6 4 1	89, 90
	Use binomial coefficients to write binomial expansions *(p. 684).*	$(x + 1)^3 = x^3 + 3x^2 + 3x + 1$ $(x - 1)^4 = x^4 - 4x^3 + 6x^2 - 4x + 1$	91–96
Section 9.6	Solve simple counting problems *(p. 689).*	A computer randomly generates an integer from 1 through 15. The computer can generate an integer that is divisible by 3 in 5 ways (3, 6, 9, 12, and 15).	97, 98
	Use the Fundamental Counting Principle to solve counting problems *(p. 690).*	**Fundamental Counting Principle:** Let E_1 and E_2 be two events. The first event E_1 can occur in m_1 different ways. After E_1 has occurred, E_2 can occur in m_2 different ways. The number of ways that the two events can occur is $m_1 \cdot m_2$.	99, 100
	Use permutations to solve counting problems *(p. 691).*	The number of permutations of n elements taken r at a time is ${}_nP_r = n!/(n - r)!$.	101, 102
	Use combinations to solve counting problems *(p. 694).*	The number of combinations of n elements taken r at a time is ${}_nC_r = n!/[(n - r)!r!]$, or ${}_nC_r = {}_nP_r/r!$.	103, 104
Section 9.7	Find the probabilities of events *(p. 699).*	If an event E has $n(E)$ equally likely outcomes and its sample space S has $n(S)$ equally likely outcomes, the probability of event E is $P(E) = n(E)/n(S)$.	105, 106
	Find the probabilities of mutually exclusive events *(p. 703).*	If A and B are events in the same sample space, the probability of A or B occurring is $P(A \cup B) = P(A) + (B) - P(A \cap B)$. If A and B are mutually exclusive, $P(A \cup B) = P(A) + P(B)$.	107, 108
	Find the probabilities of independent events *(p. 705).*	If A and B are independent events, the probability that both A and B will occur is $P(A \text{ and } B) = P(A) \cdot P(B)$.	109, 110
	Find the probability of the complement of an event *(p. 706).*	Let A be an event and let A' be its complement. If the probability of A is $P(A)$, the probability of the complement is $P(A') = 1 - P(A)$.	111, 112

5. $a_n = 2(-1)^n$
6. $a_n = n^2 - 2$
7. $a_n = \dfrac{4}{n}$
8. $a_n = \dfrac{(-1)^{n+1}}{n}$

23. (a) $A_1 = \$10{,}066.67$, $A_2 = \$10{,}133.78$, $A_3 = \$10{,}201.34$, $A_4 = \$10{,}269.35$, $A_5 = \$10{,}337.81$, $A_6 = \$10{,}406.73$, $A_7 = \$10{,}476.10$, $A_8 = \$10{,}545.95$, $A_9 = \$10{,}616.25$, $A_{10} = \$10{,}687.03$

24. $a_9 = 35.82$, $a_{10} = 38.00$, $a_{11} = 40.22$, $a_{12} = 42.48$, $a_{13} = 44.78$, $a_{14} = 47.12$, $a_{15} = 49.50$, $a_{16} = 51.92$, $a_{17} = 54.38$

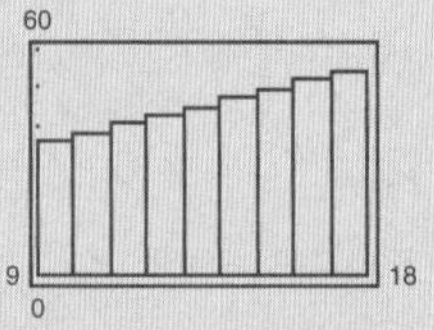

25. Arithmetic sequence, $d = -7$
26. Not an arithmetic sequence
27. Arithmetic sequence, $d = \frac{1}{2}$
28. Arithmetic sequence, $d = -\frac{1}{16}$
33. $a_n = 12n - 5$
34. $a_n = -5n + 33$
35. $a_n = 3ny - 2y$
36. $a_n = nx - 3x$
37. $a_n = -7n + 107$
38. $a_n = -\frac{1}{3}n + \frac{31}{3}$

9 REVIEW EXERCISES

See www.CalcChat.com for worked-out solutions to odd-numbered exercises.

9.1 In Exercises 1–4, write the first five terms of the sequence. (Assume that n begins with 1.)

1. $a_n = 2 + \dfrac{6}{n}$ $\quad 8, 5, 4, \frac{7}{2}, \frac{16}{5}$
2. $a_n = \dfrac{(-1)^n 5n}{2n - 1}$ $\quad -5, \frac{10}{3}, -3, \frac{20}{7}, -\frac{25}{9}$
3. $a_n = \dfrac{72}{n!}$ $\quad 72, 36, 12, 3, \frac{3}{5}$
4. $a_n = n(n - 1)$ $\quad 0, 2, 6, 12, 20$

In Exercises 5–8, write an expression for the apparent nth term of the sequence. (Assume that n begins with 1.) 5–8. See margin.

5. $-2, 2, -2, 2, -2, \dots$
6. $-1, 2, 7, 14, 23, \dots$
7. $4, 2, \frac{4}{3}, 1, \frac{4}{5}, \dots$
8. $1, -\frac{1}{2}, \frac{1}{3}, -\frac{1}{4}, \frac{1}{5}, \dots$

In Exercises 9–12, simplify the factorial expression.

9. $9!$ $\quad 362{,}880$
10. $4! \cdot 0!$ $\quad 24$
11. $\dfrac{3! \cdot 5!}{6!}$ $\quad 1$
12. $\dfrac{7! \cdot 6!}{6! \cdot 8!}$ $\quad \frac{1}{8}$

In Exercises 13–18, find the sum.

13. $\displaystyle\sum_{i=1}^{6} 8$ $\quad 48$
14. $\displaystyle\sum_{k=2}^{5} 4k$ $\quad 56$
15. $\displaystyle\sum_{j=1}^{4} \frac{6}{j^2}$ $\quad \frac{205}{24}$
16. $\displaystyle\sum_{i=1}^{8} \frac{i}{i + 1}$ $\quad 6.17$
17. $\displaystyle\sum_{k=1}^{10} 2k^3$ $\quad 6050$
18. $\displaystyle\sum_{j=0}^{4} (j^2 + 1)$ $\quad 35$

In Exercises 19 and 20, use sigma notation to write the sum.

19. $\dfrac{1}{2(1)} + \dfrac{1}{2(2)} + \dfrac{1}{2(3)} + \cdots + \dfrac{1}{2(20)}$ $\quad \displaystyle\sum_{k=1}^{20} \frac{1}{2k}$
20. $\dfrac{1}{2} + \dfrac{2}{3} + \dfrac{3}{4} + \cdots + \dfrac{9}{10}$ $\quad \displaystyle\sum_{k=1}^{9} \frac{k}{k + 1}$

In Exercises 21 and 22, find the sum of the infinite series.

21. $\displaystyle\sum_{i=1}^{\infty} \frac{4}{10^i}$ $\quad \frac{4}{9}$
22. $\displaystyle\sum_{k=1}^{\infty} \frac{2}{100^k}$ $\quad \frac{2}{99}$

23. **COMPOUND INTEREST** A deposit of \$10,000 is made in an account that earns 8% interest compounded monthly. The balance in the account after n months is given by

$$A_n = 10{,}000\left(1 + \frac{0.08}{12}\right)^n, \quad n = 1, 2, 3, \dots$$

(a) Write the first 10 terms of this sequence. See margin.

(b) Find the balance in this account after 10 years by finding the 120th term of the sequence. $A_{120} = \$22{,}196.40$

24. **LOTTERY TICKET SALES** The total sales a_n (in billions of dollars) of lottery tickets in the United States from 1999 through 2007 can be approximated by the model

$$a_n = 0.02n^2 + 1.8n + 18, \quad n = 9, 10, \dots, 17$$

where n is the year, with $n = 9$ corresponding to 1999. Find the terms of this finite sequence. Use a graphing utility to construct a bar graph that represents the sequence. (Source: TLF Publications, Inc.) See margin.

9.2 In Exercises 25–28, determine whether the sequence is arithmetic. If so, find the common difference. 25–28. See margin.

25. $6, -1, -8, -15, -22, \dots$
26. $0, 1, 3, 6, 10, \dots$
27. $\frac{1}{2}, 1, \frac{3}{2}, 2, \frac{5}{2}, \dots$
28. $1, \frac{15}{16}, \frac{7}{8}, \frac{13}{16}, \frac{3}{4}, \dots$

In Exercises 29–32, write the first five terms of the arithmetic sequence.

29. $a_1 = 3, d = 11$ $\quad 3, 14, 25, 36, 47$
30. $a_1 = 6, d = -2$ $\quad 6, 4, 2, 0, -2$
31. $a_1 = 25, a_{k+1} = a_k + 3$ $\quad 25, 28, 31, 34, 37$
32. $a_1 = 4.2, a_{k+1} = a_k + 0.4$ $\quad 4.2, 4.6, 5.0, 5.4, 5.8$

In Exercises 33–38, find a formula for a_n for the arithmetic sequence. 33–38. See margin.

33. $a_1 = 7, d = 12$
34. $a_1 = 28, d = -5$
35. $a_1 = y, d = 3y$
36. $a_1 = -2x, d = x$
37. $a_2 = 93, a_6 = 65$
38. $a_7 = 8, a_{13} = 6$

39. Find the sum of the first 100 positive multiples of 7.
40. Find the sum of the integers from 40 to 90 (inclusive).

39. 35,350 $\quad$ 40. 3315

In Exercises 41–44, find the partial sum.

41. $\displaystyle\sum_{j=1}^{10} (2j - 3)$ $\quad 80$
42. $\displaystyle\sum_{j=1}^{8} (20 - 3j)$ $\quad 52$
43. $\displaystyle\sum_{k=1}^{11} \left(\frac{2}{3}k + 4\right)$ $\quad 88$
44. $\displaystyle\sum_{k=1}^{25} \left(\frac{3k + 1}{4}\right)$ $\quad 250$

45. **JOB OFFER** The starting salary for an accountant is \$43,800 with a guaranteed salary increase of \$1950 per year. Determine (a) the salary during the fifth year and (b) the total compensation through five full years of employment. (a) \$51,600 (b) \$238,500

46. **BALING HAY** In the first two trips baling hay around a large field, a farmer obtains 123 bales and 112 bales, respectively. Because each round gets shorter, the farmer estimates that the same pattern will continue. Estimate the total number of bales made if the farmer takes another six trips around the field. 676 bales

9.3 In Exercises 47–50, determine whether the sequence is geometric. If so, find the common ratio. 47–50. See margin.

47. 6, 12, 24, 48, . . .
48. 54, −18, 6, −2, . . .
49. $\frac{1}{5}, -\frac{3}{5}, \frac{9}{5}, -\frac{27}{5}, \ldots$
50. $\frac{1}{4}, \frac{2}{5}, \frac{3}{6}, \frac{4}{7}, \ldots$

In Exercises 51–54, write the first five terms of the geometric sequence. 51–54. See margin.

51. $a_1 = 4,\ r = -\frac{1}{4}$
52. $a_1 = 2,\ r = 15$
53. $a_1 = 9,\ a_3 = 4$
54. $a_1 = 2,\ a_3 = 12$

In Exercises 55–58, write an expression for the nth term of the geometric sequence. Then find the 10th term of the sequence. 55–58. See margin.

55. $a_1 = 18,\ a_2 = -9$
56. $a_3 = 6,\ a_4 = 1$
57. $a_1 = 100,\ r = 1.05$
58. $a_1 = 5,\ r = 0.2$

In Exercises 59–64, find the sum of the finite geometric sequence.

59. $\sum_{i=1}^{7} 2^{i-1}$ 127
60. $\sum_{i=1}^{5} 3^{i-1}$ 121
61. $\sum_{i=1}^{4} \left(\frac{1}{2}\right)^{i}$ $\frac{15}{16}$
62. $\sum_{i=1}^{6} \left(\frac{1}{3}\right)^{i-1}$ $\frac{364}{243}$
63. $\sum_{i=1}^{5} (2)^{i-1}$ 31
64. $\sum_{i=1}^{4} 6(3)^{i}$ 720

In Exercises 65 and 66, use a graphing utility to find the sum of the finite geometric sequence.

65. $\sum_{i=1}^{10} 10\left(\frac{3}{5}\right)^{i-1}$ 24.85
66. $\sum_{i=1}^{15} 20(0.2)^{i-1}$ 25

In Exercises 67–70, find the sum of the infinite geometric series.

67. $\sum_{i=1}^{\infty} \left(\frac{7}{8}\right)^{i-1}$ 8
68. $\sum_{i=1}^{\infty} (0.5)^{i-1}$ 2
69. $\sum_{k=1}^{\infty} 4\left(\frac{2}{3}\right)^{k-1}$ 12
70. $\sum_{k=1}^{\infty} 1.3\left(\frac{1}{10}\right)^{k-1}$ $\frac{13}{9}$

71. **DEPRECIATION** A paper manufacturer buys a machine for \$120,000. During the next 5 years, it will depreciate at a rate of 30% per year. (In other words, at the end of each year the depreciated value will be 70% of what it was at the beginning of the year.)
(a) Find the formula for the nth term of a geometric sequence that gives the value of the machine t full years after it was purchased. $a_n = 120{,}000(0.7)^n$
(b) Find the depreciated value of the machine after 5 full years. \$20,168.40

72. **ANNUITY** You deposit \$800 in an account at the beginning of each month for 10 years. The account pays 6% compounded monthly. What will your balance be at the end of 10 years? What would the balance be if the interest were compounded continuously? \$131,758.99; \$131,868.13

9.4 In Exercises 73–76, use mathematical induction to prove the formula for every positive integer n. 73–76. Proofs

73. $3 + 5 + 7 + \cdots + (2n + 1) = n(n + 2)$
74. $1 + \frac{3}{2} + 2 + \frac{5}{2} + \cdots + \frac{1}{2}(n + 1) = \frac{n}{4}(n + 3)$
75. $\sum_{i=0}^{n-1} ar^i = \frac{a(1 - r^n)}{1 - r}$
76. $\sum_{k=0}^{n-1} (a + kd) = \frac{n}{2}[2a + (n - 1)d]$

In Exercises 77–80, find a formula for the sum of the first n terms of the sequence. 77–80. See margin.

77 9, 13, 17, 21, . . .
78. 68, 60, 52, 44, . . .
79. $1, \frac{3}{5}, \frac{9}{25}, \frac{27}{125}, \ldots$
80. $12, -1, \frac{1}{12}, -\frac{1}{144}, \ldots$

In Exercises 81 and 82, find the sum using the formulas for the sums of powers of integers.

81. $\sum_{n=1}^{50} n$ 1275
82. $\sum_{n=1}^{6} (n^5 - n^2)$ 12,110

In Exercises 83–86, write the first five terms of the sequence beginning with the given term. Then calculate the first and second differences of the sequence. State whether the sequence has a linear model, a quadratic model, or neither. 83–86. See margin.

83. $a_1 = 5$, $a_n = a_{n-1} + 5$
84. $a_1 = -3$, $a_n = a_{n-1} - 2n$
85. $a_1 = 16$, $a_n = a_{n-1} - 1$
86. $a_0 = 0$, $a_n = n - a_{n-1}$

9.5 In Exercises 87 and 88, use the Binomial Theorem to calculate the binomial coefficient.

87. ${}_6C_4$ 15
88. ${}_{12}C_3$ 220

In Exercises 89 and 90, use Pascal's Triangle to calculate the binomial coefficient.

89. $\binom{8}{6}$ 28
90. $\binom{9}{4}$ 126

In Exercises 91–96, use the Binomial Theorem to expand and simplify the expression. (Remember that $i = \sqrt{-1}$.) 91–96. See margin.

91. $(x + 4)^4$
92. $(x - 3)^6$
93. $(a - 3b)^5$
94. $(3x + y^2)^7$
95. $(5 + 2i)^4$
96. $(4 - 5i)^3$

47. Geometric sequence, $r = 2$
48. Geometric sequence, $r = -\frac{1}{3}$
49. Geometric sequence, $r = -3$
50. Not a geometric sequence
51. $4, -1, \frac{1}{4}, -\frac{1}{16}, \frac{1}{64}$
52. 2, 30, 450, 6750, 101,250
53. $9, 6, 4, \frac{8}{3}, \frac{16}{9}$ or $9, -6, 4, -\frac{8}{3}, \frac{16}{9}$
54. $2, 2\sqrt{6}, 12, 12\sqrt{6}, 72$ or $2, -2\sqrt{6}, 12, -12\sqrt{6}, 72$
55. $a_n = 18\left(-\frac{1}{2}\right)^{n-1}$; $-\frac{9}{512}$
56. $a_n = 216\left(\frac{1}{6}\right)^{n-1}$; $\frac{1}{46{,}656}$
57. $a_n = 100(1.05)^{n-1}$; About 155.133
58. $a_n = 5(0.2)^{n-1}$; 0.00000256
77. $S_n = n(2n + 7)$
78. $S_n = 4n(18 - n)$
79. $S_n = \frac{5}{2}\left[1 - \left(\frac{3}{5}\right)^n\right]$
80. $S_n = \frac{144}{13}\left[1 - \left(-\frac{1}{12}\right)^n\right]$
83. 5, 10, 15, 20, 25
First differences: 5, 5, 5, 5
Second differences: 0, 0, 0
Linear
84. −3, −7, −13, −21, −31
First differences: −4, −6, −8, −10
Second differences: −2, −2, −2
Quadratic
85. 16, 15, 14, 13, 12
First differences: −1, −1, −1, −1
Second differences: 0, 0, 0
Linear
86. 0, 1, 1, 2, 2
First differences: 1, 0, 1, 0
Second differences: −1, 1, −1
Neither

91. $x^4 + 16x^3 + 96x^2 + 256x + 256$
92. $x^6 - 18x^5 + 135x^4 - 540x^3 + 1215x^2 - 1458x + 729$
93. $a^5 - 15a^4b + 90a^3b^2 - 270a^2b^3 + 405ab^4 - 243b^5$
94. $2187x^7 + 5103x^6y^2 + 5103x^5y^4 + 2835x^4y^6 + 945x^3y^8 + 189x^2y^{10} + 21xy^{12} + y^{14}$
95. $41 + 840i$
96. $-236 - 115i$

113. See below.
114. True by Properties of Sums
115. True by Properties of Sums
116. See below.
117. The set of natural numbers
118. In the sequence in part (a), the odd-numbered terms are negative, whereas in the sequence in part (b), the even-numbered terms are negative.
119. Each term of the sequence is defined in terms of preceding terms.

9.6 **97. NUMBERS IN A HAT** Slips of paper numbered 1 through 14 are placed in a hat. In how many ways can you draw two numbers with replacement that total 12? 11

98. SHOPPING A customer in an electronics store can choose one of six speaker systems, one of five DVD players, and one of six plasma televisions to design a home theater system. How many systems can be designed? 180

99. TELEPHONE NUMBERS The same three-digit prefix is used for all of the telephone numbers in a small town. How many different telephone numbers are possible by changing only the last four digits? 10,000

100. COURSE SCHEDULE A college student is preparing a course schedule for the next semester. The student may select one of three mathematics courses, one of four science courses, and one of six history courses. How many schedules are possible? 72

101. RACE There are 10 bicyclists entered in a race. In how many different ways could the top 3 places be decided? 720

102. JURY SELECTION A group of potential jurors has been narrowed down to 32 people. In how many ways can a jury of 12 people be selected? 225,792,840

103. APPAREL You have eight different suits to choose from to take on a trip. How many combinations of three suits could you take on your trip? 56

104. MENU CHOICES A local sub shop offers five different breads, four different meats, three different cheeses, and six different vegetables. You can choose one bread and any number of the other items. Find the total number of combinations of sandwiches possible. 40,960

9.7 **105. APPAREL** A man has five pairs of socks, of which no two pairs are the same color. He randomly selects two socks from a drawer. What is the probability that he gets a matched pair? $\frac{1}{9}$

106. BOOKSHELF ORDER A child returns a five-volume set of books to a bookshelf. The child is not able to read, and so cannot distinguish one volume from another. What is the probability that the books are shelved in the correct order? $\frac{1}{120}$

107. STUDENTS BY CLASS At a particular university, the number of students in the four classes are broken down by percents, as shown in the table.

Class	Percent
Freshmen	31
Sophomores	26
Juniors	25
Seniors	18

A single student is picked randomly by lottery for a cash scholarship. What is the probability that the scholarship winner is

(a) a junior or senior? 43%

(b) a freshman, sophomore, or junior? 82%

108. DATA ANALYSIS A sample of college students, faculty, and administration were asked whether they favored a proposed increase in the annual activity fee to enhance student life on campus. The results are listed in the table.

	Students	Faculty	Admin.	Total
Favor	237	37	18	292
Oppose	163	38	7	208
Total	400	75	25	500

A person is selected at random from the sample. Find each specified probability.

(a) The person is not in favor of the proposal. 41.6%

(b) The person is a student. 80%

(c) The person is a faculty member and is in favor of the proposal. 7.4%

109. TOSSING A DIE A six-sided die is tossed four times. What is the probability of getting a 5 on each roll? $\frac{1}{1296}$

110. TOSSING A DIE A six-sided die is tossed six times. What is the probability that each side appears exactly once? $\frac{5}{324}$

111. DRAWING A CARD You randomly select a card from a 52-card deck. What is the probability that the card is not a club? $\frac{3}{4}$

112. TOSSING A COIN Find the probability of obtaining at least one tail when a coin is tossed five times. $\frac{31}{32}$

EXPLORATION

113–116. See margin.

TRUE OR FALSE? In Exercises 113–116, determine whether the statement is true or false. Justify your answer.

113. $\dfrac{(n+2)!}{n!} = (n+2)(n+1)$

114. $\displaystyle\sum_{i=1}^{5} (i^3 + 2i) = \sum_{i=1}^{5} i^3 + \sum_{i=1}^{5} 2i$

115. $\displaystyle\sum_{k=1}^{8} 3k = 3\sum_{k=1}^{8} k$

116. $\displaystyle\sum_{j=1}^{6} 2^j = \sum_{j=3}^{8} 2^{j-2}$

117. THINK ABOUT IT An infinite sequence is a function. What is the domain of the function? See margin.

118. THINK ABOUT IT How do the two sequences differ?

118–119. See margin.

(a) $a_n = \dfrac{(-1)^n}{n}$ (b) $a_n = \dfrac{(-1)^{n+1}}{n}$

119. WRITING Explain what is meant by a recursion formula.

120. WRITING Write a brief paragraph explaining how to identify the graph of an arithmetic sequence and the graph of a geometric sequence. Answers will vary.

113. True. $\dfrac{(n+2)!}{n!} = \dfrac{(n+2)(n+1)n!}{n!} = (n+2)(n+1)$

116. True. The sums are equal because
$2^1 + 2^2 + 2^3 + 2^4 + 2^5 + 2^6 = 2^{3-2} + 2^{4-2} + 2^{5-2} + 2^{6-2} + 2^{7-2} + 2^{8-2}.$

11. See below.

9 Chapter Test

See www.CalcChat.com for worked-out solutions to odd-numbered exercises.

Take this test as you would take a test in class. When you are finished, check your work against the answers given in the back of the book.

1. Write the first five terms of the sequence $a_n = \dfrac{(-1)^n}{3n+2}$. (Assume that n begins with 1.) $-\frac{1}{5}, \frac{1}{8}, -\frac{1}{11}, \frac{1}{14}, -\frac{1}{17}$

2. Write an expression for the nth term of the sequence.

$$\frac{3}{1!}, \frac{4}{2!}, \frac{5}{3!}, \frac{6}{4!}, \frac{7}{5!}, \ldots \quad a_n = \frac{n+2}{n!}$$

3. Find the next three terms of the series. Then find the sixth partial sum of the series.

$8 + 21 + 34 + 47 + \cdots$ 60, 73, 86; 243

4. The fifth term of an arithmetic sequence is 5.4, and the 12th term is 11.0. Find the nth term. $a_n = 0.8n + 1.4$

5. The second term of a geometric sequence is 28, and the sixth term is 7168. Find the nth term. $a_n = 7(4)^{n-1}$

6. Write the first five terms of the sequence $a_n = 5(2)^{n-1}$. (Assume that n begins with 1.) 5, 10, 20, 40, 80

In Exercises 7–9, find the sum.

7. $\displaystyle\sum_{i=1}^{50} (2i^2 + 5)$ 86,100 **8.** $\displaystyle\sum_{n=1}^{9} (12n - 7)$ 477 **9.** $\displaystyle\sum_{i=1}^{\infty} 4\left(\tfrac{1}{2}\right)^i$ 4

10. Use mathematical induction to prove the formula. Proof

$$5 + 10 + 15 + \cdots + 5n = \frac{5n(n+1)}{2}$$

11. Use the Binomial Theorem to expand and simplify (a) $(x + 6y)^4$ and (b) $3(x-2)^5 + 4(x-2)^3$. See margin.

12. Find the coefficient of the term a^4b^3 in the expansion of $(3a - 2b)^7$. $-22,680$

In Exercises 13 and 14, evaluate each expression.

13. (a) ${}_9P_2$ (b) ${}_{70}P_3$ (a) 72 (b) 328,440

14. (a) ${}_{11}C_4$ (b) ${}_{66}C_4$ (a) 330 (b) 720,720

15. How many distinct license plates can be issued consisting of one letter followed by a three-digit number? 26,000

16. Eight people are going for a ride in a boat that seats eight people. One person will drive, and only three of the remaining people are willing to ride in the two bow seats. How many seating arrangements are possible? 720

17. You attend a karaoke night and hope to hear your favorite song. The karaoke song book has 300 different songs (your favorite song is among them). Assuming that the singers are equally likely to pick any song and no song is repeated, what is the probability that your favorite song is one of the 20 that you hear that night? $\frac{1}{15}$

18. You are with three of your friends at a party. Names of all of the 30 guests are placed in a hat and drawn randomly to award four door prizes. Each guest is limited to one prize. What is the probability that you and your friends win all four of the prizes? $\frac{1}{27,405}$

19. The weather report calls for a 90% chance of snow. According to this report, what is the probability that it will *not* snow? 10%

11. (a) $x^4 + 24x^3y + 216x^2y^2 + 864xy^3 + 1296y^4$
(b) $3x^5 - 30x^4 + 124x^3 - 264x^2 + 288x - 128$

9 CUMULATIVE TEST FOR CHAPTERS 7–9

See www.CalcChat.com for worked-out solutions to odd-numbered exercises.

Take this test as you would take a test in class. When you are finished, check your work against the answers given in the back of the book.

In Exercises 1–4, solve the system by the specified method.

1. Substitution

$$\begin{cases} y = 3 - x^2 \\ 2(y - 2) = x - 1 \end{cases}$$ $(1, 2), \left(-\frac{3}{2}, \frac{3}{4}\right)$

2. Elimination

$$\begin{cases} x + 3y = -6 \\ 2x + 4y = -10 \end{cases}$$ $(-3, -1)$

3. Elimination

$$\begin{cases} -2x + 4y - z = -16 \\ x - 2y + 2z = 5 \\ x - 3y - z = 13 \end{cases}$$ $(5, -2, -2)$

4. Gauss-Jordan Elimination

$$\begin{cases} x + 3y - 2z = -7 \\ -2x + y - z = -5 \\ 4x + y + z = 3 \end{cases}$$ $(1, -2, 1)$

In Exercises 5 and 6, sketch the graph of the solution set of the system of inequalities.

5–6. See margin.

5. $\begin{cases} 2x + y \geq -3 \\ x - 3y \leq 2 \end{cases}$

6. $\begin{cases} x - y > 6 \\ 5x + 2y < 10 \end{cases}$

7. Sketch the region determined by the constraints. Then find the minimum and maximum values, and where they occur, of the objective function $z = 3x + 2y$, subject to the indicated constraints. See margin.

$$x + 4y \leq 20$$
$$2x + y \leq 12$$
$$x \geq 0$$
$$y \geq 0$$

8. See margin.

8. A custom-blend bird seed is to be mixed from seed mixtures costing \$0.75 per pound and \$1.25 per pound. How many pounds of each seed mixture are used to make 200 pounds of custom-blend bird seed costing \$0.95 per pound?

9. Find the equation of the parabola $y = ax^2 + bx + c$ passing through the points (0, 6), (2, 3), and (4, 2). $y = \frac{1}{4}x^2 - 2x + 6$

$$\begin{cases} -x + 2y - z = 9 \\ 2x - y + 2z = -9 \\ 3x + 3y - 4z = 7 \end{cases}$$

SYSTEM FOR 10 AND 11

In Exercises 10 and 11, use the system of equations at the left. 10–11. See margin.

10. Write the augmented matrix corresponding to the system of equations.

11. Solve the system using the matrix found in Exercise 10 and Gauss-Jordan elimination.

In Exercises 12–17, perform the operations using the following matrices. 12–17. See margin.

$$A = \begin{bmatrix} 3 & 0 \\ -1 & 4 \end{bmatrix}, \quad B = \begin{bmatrix} -2 & 5 \\ 0 & -1 \end{bmatrix}$$

12. $A + B$

13. $-8B$

14. $2A - 5B$

15. AB

16. A^2

17. $BA - B^2$

$$\begin{bmatrix} 7 & 1 & 0 \\ -2 & 4 & -1 \\ 3 & 8 & 5 \end{bmatrix}$$

MATRIX FOR 18

18. Find the determinant of the matrix at the left. 203

19. Find the inverse of the matrix (if it exists): $\begin{bmatrix} 1 & 2 & -1 \\ 3 & 7 & -10 \\ -5 & -7 & -15 \end{bmatrix}$.

$$\begin{bmatrix} -175 & 37 & -13 \\ 95 & -20 & 7 \\ 14 & -3 & 1 \end{bmatrix}$$

5.

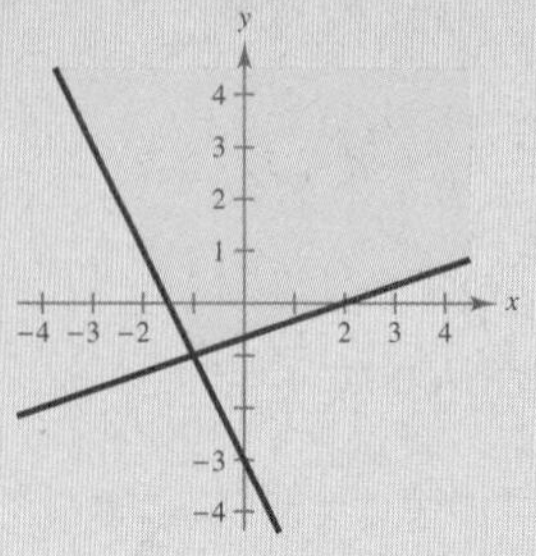

6.

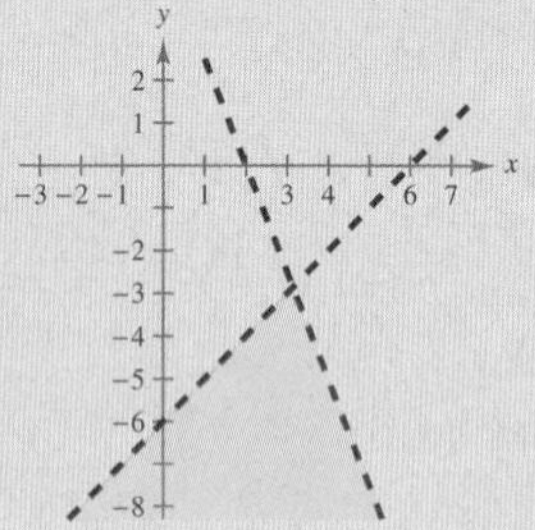

7.

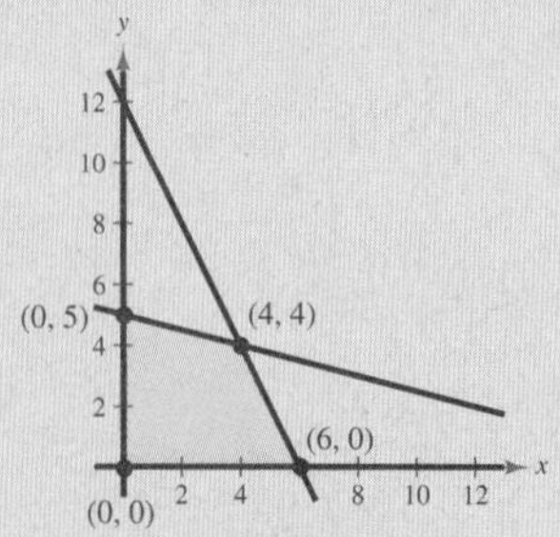

Maximum at (4, 4): $z = 20$

Minimum at (0, 0): $z = 0$

8. \$0.75 mixture: 120 lb; \$1.25 mixture: 80 lb

10. $\begin{bmatrix} -1 & 2 & -1 & \vdots & 9 \\ 2 & -1 & 2 & \vdots & -9 \\ 3 & 3 & -4 & \vdots & 7 \end{bmatrix}$

11. $(-2, 3, -1)$

12. $\begin{bmatrix} 1 & 5 \\ -1 & 3 \end{bmatrix}$

13. $\begin{bmatrix} 16 & -40 \\ 0 & 8 \end{bmatrix}$

14. $\begin{bmatrix} 16 & -25 \\ -2 & 13 \end{bmatrix}$

15. $\begin{bmatrix} -6 & 15 \\ 2 & -9 \end{bmatrix}$

16. $\begin{bmatrix} 9 & 0 \\ -7 & 16 \end{bmatrix}$

17. $\begin{bmatrix} -15 & 35 \\ 1 & -5 \end{bmatrix}$

Age group	Gym shoes	Jogging shoes	Walking shoes
14–17	0.09	0.09	0.03
18–24	0.06	0.10	0.05
25–34	0.12	0.25	0.12

MATRIX FOR 20

20. The percents (by age group) of the total amounts spent on three types of footwear in a recent year are shown in the matrix. The total amounts (in millions) spent by each age group on the three types of footwear were \$442.20 (14–17 age group), \$466.57 (18–24 age group), and \$1088.09 (25–34 age group). How many dollars worth of gym shoes, jogging shoes, and walking shoes were sold that year? (Source: National Sporting Goods Association) See margin.

20. Gym shoes: \$2042 million
Jogging shoes: \$1733 million
Walking shoes: \$3415 million

In Exercises 21 and 22, use Cramer's Rule to solve the system of equations.

21. $\begin{cases} 8x - 3y = -52 \\ 3x + 5y = 5 \end{cases}$ $(-5, 4)$

22. $\begin{cases} 5x + 4y + 3z = 7 \\ -3x - 8y + 7z = -9 \\ 7x - 5y - 6z = -53 \end{cases}$ $(-3, 4, 2)$

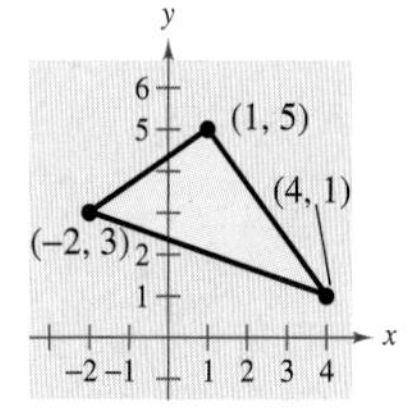

FIGURE FOR 23

23. Find the area of the triangle shown in the figure. 9

24. Write the first five terms of the sequence $a_n = \dfrac{(-1)^{n+1}}{2n + 3}$. (Assume that n begins with 1.) $\frac{1}{5}, -\frac{1}{7}, \frac{1}{9}, -\frac{1}{11}, \frac{1}{13}$

25. Write an expression for the nth term of the sequence.

$\dfrac{2!}{4}, \dfrac{3!}{5}, \dfrac{4!}{6}, \dfrac{5!}{7}, \dfrac{6!}{8}, \ldots$ $a_n = \dfrac{(n + 1)!}{n + 3}$

26. Find the sum of the first 16 terms of the arithmetic sequence 6, 18, 30, 42, ... 1536

27. The sixth term of an arithmetic sequence is 20.6, and the ninth term is 30.2.

(a) Find the 20th term. 65.4

(b) Find the nth term. $a_n = 3.2n + 1.4$

28. Write the first five terms of the sequence $a_n = 3(2)^{n-1}$. (Assume that n begins with 1.) 3, 6, 12, 24, 48

29. Find the sum: $\sum_{i=0}^{\infty} 1.3\left(\frac{1}{10}\right)^{i-1}$. $\frac{130}{9}$

30. Use mathematical induction to prove the formula

$3 + 7 + 11 + 15 + \cdots + (4n - 1) = n(2n + 1)$. Proof

31. Use the Binomial Theorem to expand and simplify $(w - 9)^4$.
$w^4 - 36w^3 + 486w^2 - 2916w + 6561$

In Exercises 32–35, evaluate the expression.

32. ${}_{14}P_3$ 2184 **33.** ${}_{25}P_2$ 600 **34.** $\binom{8}{4}$ 70 **35.** ${}_{11}C_6$ 462

In Exercises 36 and 37, find the number of distinguishable permutations of the group of letters.

36. B, A, S, K, E, T, B, A, L, L 453,600

37. A, N, T, A, R, C, T, I, C, A 151,200

38. A personnel manager at a department store has 10 applicants to fill three different sales positions. In how many ways can this be done, assuming that all the applicants are qualified for any of the three positions? 720

39. On a game show, the digits 3, 4, and 5 must be arranged in the proper order to form the price of an appliance. If the digits are arranged correctly, the contestant wins the appliance. What is the probability of winning if the contestant knows that the price is at least \$400? $\frac{1}{4}$

PROOFS IN MATHEMATICS

Properties of Sums *(p. 645)*

1. $\sum_{i=1}^{n} c = cn, \quad c$ is a constant.

2. $\sum_{i=1}^{n} ca_i = c\sum_{i=1}^{n} a_i, \quad c$ is a constant.

3. $\sum_{i=1}^{n} (a_i + b_i) = \sum_{i=1}^{n} a_i + \sum_{i=1}^{n} b_i$

4. $\sum_{i=1}^{n} (a_i - b_i) = \sum_{i=1}^{n} a_i - \sum_{i=1}^{n} b_i$

Infinite Series

The study of infinite series was considered a novelty in the fourteenth century. Logician Richard Suiseth, whose nickname was Calculator, solved this problem.

If throughout the first half of a given time interval a variation continues at a certain intensity; throughout the next quarter of the interval at double the intensity; throughout the following eighth at triple the intensity and so ad infinitum; The average intensity for the whole interval will be the intensity of the variation during the second subinterval (or double the intensity).

This is the same as saying that the sum of the infinite series

$$\frac{1}{2} + \frac{2}{4} + \frac{3}{8} + \cdots + \frac{n}{2^n} + \cdots$$

is 2.

Proof

Each of these properties follows directly from the properties of real numbers.

1. $\sum_{i=1}^{n} c = c + c + c + \cdots + c = cn \qquad n \text{ terms}$

The Distributive Property is used in the proof of Property 2.

2. $$\begin{aligned}\sum_{i=1}^{n} ca_i &= ca_1 + ca_2 + ca_3 + \cdots + ca_n \\ &= c(a_1 + a_2 + a_3 + \cdots + a_n) \\ &= c\sum_{i=1}^{n} a_i\end{aligned}$$

The proof of Property 3 uses the Commutative and Associative Properties of Addition.

3. $$\begin{aligned}\sum_{i=1}^{n} (a_i + b_i) &= (a_1 + b_1) + (a_2 + b_2) + (a_3 + b_3) + \cdots + (a_n + b_n) \\ &= (a_1 + a_2 + a_3 + \cdots + a_n) + (b_1 + b_2 + b_3 + \cdots + b_n) \\ &= \sum_{i=1}^{n} a_i + \sum_{i=1}^{n} b_i\end{aligned}$$

The proof of Property 4 uses the Commutative and Associative Properties of Addition and the Distributive Property.

4. $$\begin{aligned}\sum_{i=1}^{n} (a_i - b_i) &= (a_1 - b_1) + (a_2 - b_2) + (a_3 - b_3) + \cdots + (a_n - b_n) \\ &= (a_1 + a_2 + a_3 + \cdots + a_n) + (-b_1 - b_2 - b_3 - \cdots - b_n) \\ &= (a_1 + a_2 + a_3 + \cdots + a_n) - (b_1 + b_2 + b_3 + \cdots + b_n) \\ &= \sum_{i=1}^{n} a_i - \sum_{i=1}^{n} b_i\end{aligned}$$

720

The Sum of a Finite Arithmetic Sequence (p. 654)

The sum of a finite arithmetic sequence with n terms is

$$S_n = \frac{n}{2}(a_1 + a_n).$$

Proof

Begin by generating the terms of the arithmetic sequence in two ways. In the first way, repeatedly add d to the first term to obtain

$$\begin{aligned} S_n &= a_1 + a_2 + a_3 + \cdot \cdot \cdot + a_{n-2} + a_{n-1} + a_n \\ &= a_1 + [a_1 + d] + [a_1 + 2d] + \cdot \cdot \cdot + [a_1 + (n-1)d]. \end{aligned}$$

In the second way, repeatedly subtract d from the nth term to obtain

$$\begin{aligned} S_n &= a_n + a_{n-1} + a_{n-2} + \cdot \cdot \cdot + a_3 + a_2 + a_1 \\ &= a_n + [a_n - d] + [a_n - 2d] + \cdot \cdot \cdot + [a_n - (n-1)d]. \end{aligned}$$

If you add these two versions of S_n, the multiples of d subtract out and you obtain

$$2S_n = (a_1 + a_n) + (a_1 + a_n) + (a_1 + a_n) + \cdot \cdot \cdot + (a_1 + a_n) \qquad n \text{ terms}$$

$$2S_n = n(a_1 + a_n)$$

$$S_n = \frac{n}{2}(a_1 + a_n).$$

The Sum of a Finite Geometric Sequence (p. 664)

The sum of the finite geometric sequence

$$a_1,\ a_1r,\ a_1r^2,\ a_1r^3,\ a_1r^4,\ .\ .\ .\ ,\ a_1r^{n-1}$$

with common ratio $r \neq 1$ is given by $S_n = \sum_{i=1}^{n} a_1r^{i-1} = a_1\left(\frac{1-r^n}{1-r}\right)$.

Proof

$$S_n = a_1 + a_1r + a_1r^2 + \cdot \cdot \cdot + a_1r^{n-2} + a_1r^{n-1}$$

$$rS_n = a_1r + a_1r^2 + a_1r^3 + \cdot \cdot \cdot + a_1r^{n-1} + a_1r^n \qquad \text{Multiply by } r.$$

Subtracting the second equation from the first yields

$$S_n - rS_n = a_1 - a_1r^n.$$

So, $S_n(1 - r) = a_1(1 - r^n)$, and, because $r \neq 1$, you have $S_n = a_1\left(\frac{1-r^n}{1-r}\right)$.

721

The Binomial Theorem *(p. 681)*

In the expansion of $(x + y)^n$

$$(x + y)^n = x^n + nx^{n-1}y + \cdot \cdot \cdot + {}_nC_r\, x^{n-r}y^r + \cdot \cdot \cdot + nxy^{n-1} + y^n$$

the coefficient of $x^{n-r}y^r$ is

$${}_nC_r = \frac{n!}{(n - r)!r!}.$$

Proof

The Binomial Theorem can be proved quite nicely using mathematical induction. The steps are straightforward but look a little messy, so only an outline of the proof is presented.

1. If $n = 1$, you have $(x + y)^1 = x^1 + y^1 = {}_1C_0x + {}_1C_1y$, and the formula is valid.
2. Assuming that the formula is true for $n = k$, the coefficient of $x^{k-r}y^r$ is

$${}_kC_r = \frac{k!}{(k - r)!r!} = \frac{k(k - 1)(k - 2) \cdot \cdot \cdot (k - r + 1)}{r!}.$$

To show that the formula is true for $n = k + 1$, look at the coefficient of $x^{k+1-r}y^r$ in the expansion of

$$(x + y)^{k+1} = (x + y)^k(x + y).$$

From the right-hand side, you can determine that the term involving $x^{k+1-r}y^r$ is the sum of two products.

$$({}_kC_rx^{k-r}y^r)(x) + ({}_kC_{r-1}x^{k+1-r}y^{r-1})(y)$$

$$= \left[\frac{k!}{(k - r)!r!} + \frac{k!}{(k + 1 - r)!(r - 1)!}\right]x^{k+1-r}y^r$$

$$= \left[\frac{(k + 1 - r)k!}{(k + 1 - r)!r!} + \frac{k!r}{(k + 1 - r)!r!}\right]x^{k+1-r}y^r$$

$$= \left[\frac{k!(k + 1 - r + r)}{(k + 1 - r)!r!}\right]x^{k+1-r}y^r$$

$$= \left[\frac{(k + 1)!}{(k + 1 - r)!r!}\right]x^{k+1-r}y^r$$

$$= {}_{k+1}C_rx^{k+1-r}y^r$$

So, by mathematical induction, the Binomial Theorem is valid for all positive integers n.

722

PROBLEM SOLVING

This collection of thought-provoking and challenging exercises further explores and expands upon concepts learned in this chapter.

1. Let $x_0 = 1$ and consider the sequence x_n given by

$$x_n = \frac{1}{2}x_{n-1} + \frac{1}{x_{n-1}}, \quad n = 1, 2, \ldots$$

Use a graphing utility to compute the first 10 terms of the sequence and make a conjecture about the value of x_n as n approaches infinity. See margin.

2. Consider the sequence

$$a_n = \frac{n+1}{n^2+1}.$$ See margin.

(a) Use a graphing utility to graph the first 10 terms of the sequence.

(b) Use the graph from part (a) to estimate the value of a_n as n approaches infinity.

(c) Complete the table.

n	1	10	100	1000	10,000
a_n					

(d) Use the table from part (c) to determine (if possible) the value of a_n as n approaches infinity.

3. Consider the sequence

$$a_n = 3 + (-1)^n.$$

(a) Use a graphing utility to graph the first 10 terms of the sequence. See margin.

(b) Use the graph from part (a) to describe the behavior of the graph of the sequence. If n is odd, $a_n = 2$, and if n is even, $a_n = 4$.

(c) Complete the table.

n	1	10	101	1000	10,001
a_n	2	4	2	4	2

(d) Use the table from part (c) to determine (if possible) the value of a_n as n approaches infinity. See margin.

4. The following operations are performed on each term of an arithmetic sequence. Determine if the resulting sequence is arithmetic, and if so, state the common difference. See margin.

(a) A constant C is added to each term.

(b) Each term is multiplied by a nonzero constant C.

(c) Each term is squared.

5. The following sequence of perfect squares is not arithmetic.

1, 4, 9, 16, 25, 36, 49, 64, 81, . . .

However, you can form a related sequence that is arithmetic by finding the differences of consecutive terms. See margin.

(a) Write the first eight terms of the related arithmetic sequence described above. What is the nth term of this sequence?

(b) Describe how you can find an arithmetic sequence that is related to the following sequence of perfect cubes.

1, 8, 27, 64, 125, 216, 343, 512, 729, . . .

(c) Write the first seven terms of the related sequence in part (b) and find the nth term of the sequence.

(d) Describe how you can find the arithmetic sequence that is related to the following sequence of perfect fourth powers.

1, 16, 81, 256, 625, 1296, 2401, 4096, 6561, . . .

(e) Write the first six terms of the related sequence in part (d) and find the nth term of the sequence.

6. Can the Greek hero Achilles, running at 20 feet per second, ever catch a tortoise, starting 20 feet ahead of Achilles and running at 10 feet per second? The Greek mathematician Zeno said no. When Achilles runs 20 feet, the tortoise will be 10 feet ahead. Then, when Achilles runs 10 feet, the tortoise will be 5 feet ahead. Achilles will keep cutting the distance in half but will never catch the tortoise. The table shows Zeno's reasoning. From the table you can see that both the distances and the times required to achieve them form infinite geometric series. Using the table, show that both series have finite sums. What do these sums represent? See margin.

Distance (in feet)	Time (in seconds)
20	1
10	0.5
5	0.25
2.5	0.125
1.25	0.0625
0.625	0.03125

7. Recall that a *fractal* is a geometric figure that consists of a pattern that is repeated infinitely on a smaller and smaller scale. A well-known fractal is called the *Sierpinski Triangle*. In the first stage, the midpoints of the three sides are used to create the vertices of a new triangle, which is then removed, leaving three triangles. The first three stages are shown on the next page. Note that each remaining triangle is similar to the original triangle. Assume that the length of each side of the original triangle is one unit. See page 724.

2. (c)

n	1	10	100	1000	10,000
a_n	1	0.1089	0.0101	0.0010	0.0001

1. 1, 1.5, $1.41\overline{6}$, 1.414215686, 1.414213562, 1.414213562, . . .
x_n approaches $\sqrt{2}$.

2. (a)

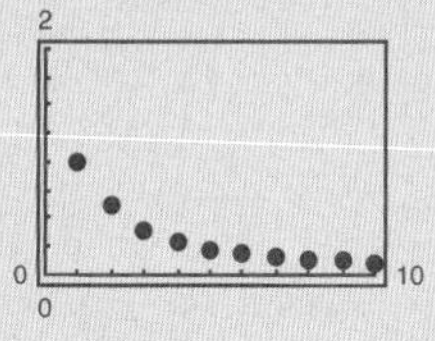

(b) 0

(c) See below.

(d) 0

3. (a)

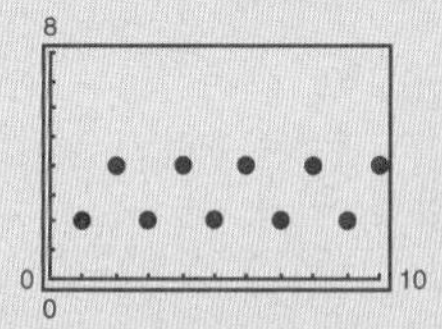

(d) It is not possible to find the value of a_n as n approaches infinity.

4. (a) Arithmetic sequence, difference $= d$

(b) Arithmetic sequence, difference $= dC$

(c) Not an arithmetic sequence

5. (a) 3, 5, 7, 9, 11, 13, 15, 17
$a_n = 2n + 1$

(b) To obtain the arithmetic sequence, find the differences of consecutive terms of the sequence of perfect cubes. Then find the differences of consecutive terms of the resulting sequence.

(c) 12, 18, 24, 30, 36, 42, 48
$a_n = 6n + 6$

(d) To obtain the arithmetic sequence, find the third sequence obtained by taking the differences of consecutive terms in consecutive sequences.

(e) 60, 84, 108, 132, 156, 180
$a_n = 24n + 36$

6. $s_d = \dfrac{a_1}{1-r} = \dfrac{20}{1-\frac{1}{2}} = 40$

This represents the total distance Achilles ran.

$s_t = \dfrac{a_1}{1-r} = \dfrac{1}{1-\frac{1}{2}} = 2$

This represents the total amount of time Achilles ran.

8. (a) 7, 22, 11, 34, 17, 52, 26, 13, 40, 20, 10, 5, 16, 8, 4, 2, 1, 4, 2, 1
(b) $a_1 = 4$: 4, 2, 1, 4, 2, 1, 4, 2, 1, 4
$a_1 = 5$: 5, 16, 8, 4, 2, 1, 4, 2, 1, 4
$a_1 = 12$: 12, 6, 3, 10, 5, 16, 8, 4, 2, 1
Eventually, the terms repeat: 4, 2, 1

10. (a) P_n is true for integers $n \geq 3$.
(b) P_n is true for integers $1 \leq n \leq 50$.
(c) P_1, P_2, and P_3 are true.
(d) P_{2n} is true for any positive integer n.

12. (c)
$$P(E) = \frac{\text{odds in favors of } E}{\text{odds in favor of } E + 1}$$
(d) Odds in favor of event
$$E = \frac{P(E)}{P(E')}$$

Write a formula that describes the side length of the triangles that will be generated in the nth stage. Write a formula for the area of the triangles that will be generated in the nth stage. $S_n = \left(\frac{1}{2}\right)^{n-1}$, $A_n = \frac{\sqrt{3}}{4}S_n^2$

FIGURE FOR 7

8. You can define a sequence using a piecewise formula. The following is an example of a piecewise-defined sequence.

$$a_1 = 7,\ a_n = \begin{cases} \dfrac{a_{n-1}}{2}, & \text{if } a_{n-1} \text{ is even} \\ 3a_{n-1} + 1, & \text{if } a_{n-1} \text{ is odd} \end{cases}$$ See margin.

(a) Write the first 20 terms of the sequence.

(b) Find the first 10 terms of the sequences for which $a_1 = 4$, $a_1 = 5$, and $a_1 = 12$ (using a_n as defined above). What conclusion can you make about the behavior of each sequence?

9. The numbers 1, 5, 12, 22, 35, 51, . . . are called pentagonal numbers because they represent the numbers of dots used to make pentagons, as shown below. Use mathematical induction to prove that the nth pentagonal number P_n is given by

$$P_n = \frac{n(3n-1)}{2}.$$ Proof

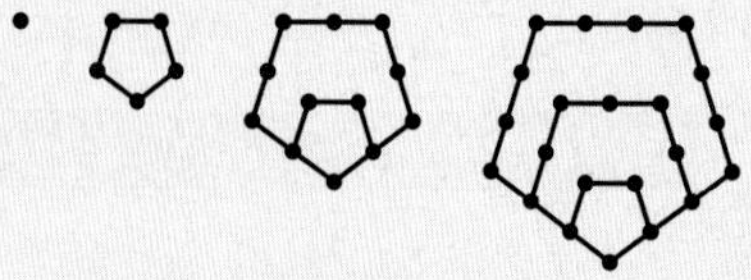

10. What conclusion can be drawn from the following information about the sequence of statements P_n?

(a) P_3 is true and P_k implies P_{k+1}. See margin.

(b) $P_1, P_2, P_3, \ldots, P_{50}$ are all true.

(c) P_1, P_2, and P_3 are all true, but the truth of P_k does not imply that P_{k+1} is true.

(d) P_2 is true and P_{2k} implies P_{2k+2}.

11. Let $f_1, f_2, \ldots, f_n, \ldots$ be the Fibonacci sequence.

(a) Use mathematical induction to prove that

$$f_1 + f_2 + \cdots + f_n = f_{n+2} - 1.$$ Proof

(b) Find the sum of the first 20 terms of the Fibonacci sequence. 17,710

12. The odds in favor of an event occurring are the ratio of the probability that the event will occur to the probability that the event will not occur. The reciprocal of this ratio represents the odds against the event occurring.

(a) Six of the marbles in a bag are red. The odds against choosing a red marble are 4 to 1. How many marbles are in the bag? 30 marbles

(b) A bag contains three blue marbles and seven yellow marbles. What are the odds in favor of choosing a blue marble? What are the odds against choosing a blue marble? 3 to 7; 7 to 3

(c) Write a formula for converting the odds in favor of an event to the probability of the event. See margin.

(d) Write a formula for converting the probability of an event to the odds in favor of the event. See margin.

13. You are taking a test that contains only multiple choice questions (there are five choices for each question). You are on the last question and you know that the answer is not B or D, but you are not sure about answers A, C, and E. What is the probability that you will get the right answer if you take a guess? $\frac{1}{3}$

14. A dart is thrown at the circular target shown below. The dart is equally likely to hit any point inside the target. What is the probability that it hits the region outside the triangle? $\frac{\pi - 1}{\pi}$

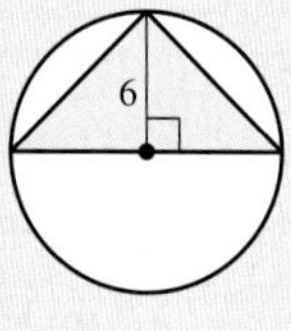

15. An event A has n possible outcomes, which have the values $x_1, x_2, \ldots, x_n$. The probabilities of the n outcomes occurring are $p_1, p_2, \ldots, p_n$. The **expected value** V of an event A is the sum of the products of the outcomes' probabilities and their values,

$$V = p_1x_1 + p_2x_2 + \cdots + p_nx_n.$$

(a) To win California's Super Lotto Plus game, you must match five different numbers chosen from the numbers 1 to 47, plus one Mega number chosen from the numbers 1 to 27. You purchase a ticket for \$1. If the jackpot for the next drawing is \$12,000,000, what is the expected value of the ticket? $-\$0.71$

(b) You are playing a dice game in which you need to score 60 points to win. On each turn, you roll two six-sided dice. Your score for the turn is 0 if the dice do not show the same number, and the product of the numbers on the dice if they do show the same number. What is the expected value of each turn? How many turns will it take on average to score 60 points? 2.53, 24 turns

Pacing and Assignment Guide 10

REGULAR SCHEDULE

Lesson	Day	AVERAGE	ADVANCED
10.1	Day 1	pp. 730–731 Exs. 1–3, 5–13 odd, 17, 19, 23, 25, 31–35 odd, 37–39, 42, 43–49 odd	pp. 730–731 Exs. 1–3, 6–12 even, 24–30 even, 35–40, 42–50 even
	Day 2	pp. 730–732 Exs. 4, 51, 55–57, 60, 61–67 odd, 69–72, 75	pp. 730–732 Exs. 4, 52, 56–66 even, 68–74
10.2	Day 1	pp. 738–739 Exs. 1–5, 9–12, 13–17 odd, 19–21, 25–31 odd, 35–41 odd, 45–53 odd, 57, 59	pp. 738–739 Exs. 1–5, 9–12, 14–18 even, 19, 20–30 even, 38–50 even, 54–60 even
	Day 2	pp. 738–741 Exs. 6–8, 61, 63, 67, 69, 72, 73, 77–83 odd, 84, 86	pp. 738–741 Exs. 6–8, 62–74 even, 78–82 even, 83–88
10.3	Day 1	pp. 748–749 Exs. 1–3, 5–10, 11–27 odd	pp. 748–749 Exs. 1–3, 5–10, 12–28 even
	Day 2	pp. 748–750 Exs. 4, 29–45 odd, 49, 50, 53–63 odd, 67–69, 71, 73, 74, 76	pp. 748–750 Exs. 4, 30–46 even, 50–68 even, 70–75, 78
10.4	Day 1	pp. 758–759 Exs. 1–10, 15–18, 21–33 odd, 37–41 odd	pp. 758–759 Exs. 1–8, 12–28 even, 34–42 even
	Day 2	pp. 759–760 Exs. 45–51 odd, 54, 55–59 odd, 63–71 odd, 73–79	pp. 759–760 Exs. 44–56 even, 60–72 even, 73–76, 78–80
10.5	Day 1	pp. 767–768 Exs. 1, 2, 5–9 odd, 14, 15, 17, 18, 23, 24, 37–40, 51, 55	pp. 767–768 Exs. 1, 2, 6–14 even, 15, 16–26 even, 37–42, 52, 56
	Day 2	pp. 767–768 Exs. 3, 4, 27–31 odd, 45–49 odd, 57–67 odd, 71–73	pp. 767–768 Exs. 3, 4, 28, 32–36 even, 44–50 even, 58–70 even, 71, 72, 74, 75
10.6	Day 1	pp. 774–775 Exs. 1–4, 6, 7–15 odd, 19–27 odd, 29–32, 33–39 odd	pp. 774–775 Exs. 1–4, 6–16 even, 20–28 even, 29–32, 36–40 even
	Day 2	pp. 775–776 Exs. 43, 45, 49–55 odd, 57–61, 63, 65, 68–71	pp. 775–776 Exs. 44, 46, 50–56 even, 57–60, 62, 63, 64–68 even, 69, 70, 72, 74
10.7	Day 1	p. 781 Exs. 1–4, 8, 10, 15–17, 19–21, 26, 27–31 odd, 37, 39, 42–47, 51, 57–61	p. 781 Exs. 1–4, 8, 10, 16–18, 20–22, 26–28, 30, 32, 41, 44–52 even, 53, 58–62
	Day 2	pp. 781–782 Exs. 65–79 odd, 85–105 odd, 119–122, 124	p. 782 Exs. 68–82 even, 90–100 even, 104–108 even, 119–124, 126
10.8	Day 1	p. 789 Exs. 1–12, 13–17 odd, 19–21, 23, 25, 28, 29, 31, 36–38, 40, 44–46	p. 789 Exs. 1–12, 14–18, 20–22, 24–30 even, 31, 32, 34, 36–38, 40–48 even
	Day 2	pp. 789–790 Exs. 49–67 odd, 69–71, 73–75, 77, 80	pp. 789–790 Exs. 50–68 even, 69, 70, 72–74, 76–78, 81, 82
10.9	Day 1	pp. 795–796 Exs. 1–5, 7, 9–14, 17–21 odd, 25–35 odd, 41–51 odd	pp. 795–796 Exs. 1–4, 6, 8–14, 18–26 even, 30–54 even
	Day 2	pp. 796–797 Exs. 55, 56, 57–65 odd, 67–70, 72, 73–81 odd	pp. 796–797 Exs. 55, 56–64 even, 66–70, 72–82 even
Review	Day 1	pp. 800–801 Exs. 1–5 odd, 9–13 odd, 17–23 odd, 26, 27–47 odd, 49–51	pp. 800–801 Exs. 2–6 even, 10–14 even, 18–24 even, 25, 28–44 even, 46–48, 50–52
	Day 2	pp. 801–802 Exs. 53–65 odd, 71, 75–87 odd, 91, 95, 99–111 odd, 113–117	pp. 801–802 Exs. 54–66 even, 70, 76–88 even, 92, 96, 100–112 even, 113–117
Assess	Day 1	Chapter 10 Test	Chapter 10 Test

Yearly Pacing Chapter 10 Total – 21 days Remaining – 24 days

BLOCK SCHEDULE

DAY 1	DAY 2	DAY 3	DAY 4	DAY 5	DAY 6
ASSESS	**10.1 (CONT.)**	**10.2 (CONT.)**	**10.3 (CONT.)**	**10.4 (CONT.)**	**10.5 (CONT.)**
Chapter 9 Test	pp. 730–732 Exs. 4, 51, 55–57, 60, 61–67 odd, 69–72, 75	pp. 738–741 Exs. 6–8, 61, 63, 67, 69, 72, 73, 77–83 odd, 84, 86	pp. 748–750 Exs. 4, 29–45 odd, 49, 50, 53–63 odd, 67–69, 71, 73, 74, 76	pp. 759–760 Exs. 45–51 odd, 54, 55–59 odd, 63–71 odd, 73–79	pp. 767–768 Exs. 3, 4, 27–31 odd, 45–49 odd, 57–67 odd, 71–73
10.1	**10.2**	**10.3**	**10.4**	**10.5**	**10.6**
pp. 730–731 Exs. 1–3, 5–13 odd, 17, 19, 23, 25, 31–35 odd, 37–39, 42, 43–49 odd	pp. 738–739 Exs. 1–5, 9–12, 13–17 odd, 19–21, 25–31 odd, 35–41 odd, 45–53 odd, 57, 59	pp. 748–749 Exs. 1–3, 5–10, 11–27 odd	pp. 758–759 Exs. 1–10, 15–18, 21–33 odd, 37–41 odd	pp. 767–768 Exs. 1, 2, 5–9 odd, 14, 15, 17, 18, 23, 24, 37–40, 51, 55	pp. 774–775 Exs. 1–4, 6, 7–15 odd, 19–27 odd, 29–32, 33–39 odd

DAY 7	DAY 8	DAY 9	DAY 10	DAY 11
10.6 (CONT.)	**10.7 (CONT.)**	**10.8 (CONT.)**	**10.9 (CONT.)**	**REVIEW (CONT.)**
pp. 775–776 Exs. 43, 45, 49–55 odd, 57–61, 63, 65, 68–71	pp. 781–782 Exs. 65–79 odd, 85–105 odd, 119–122, 124	pp. 789–790 Exs. 49–67 odd, 69–71, 73–75, 77, 80	pp. 796–797 Exs. 55, 56, 57–65 odd, 67–70, 72, 73–81 odd	pp. 801–802 Exs. 53–65 odd, 71, 75–87 odd, 91, 95, 99–111 odd, 113–117
10.7	**10.8**	**10.9**	**REVIEW**	**ASSESS**
p. 781 Exs. 1–4, 8, 10, 15–17, 19–21, 26, 27–31 odd, 37, 39, 42–47, 51, 57–61	p. 789 Exs. 1–12, 13–17 odd, 19–21, 23, 25, 28, 29, 31, 36–38, 40, 44–46	pp. 795–796 Exs. 1–5, 7, 9–14, 17–21 odd, 25–35 odd, 41–51 odd	pp. 800–801 Exs.1–5 odd, 9–13 odd, 17–23 odd, 26, 27–47 odd, 49–51	Chapter 10 Test

Yearly Pacing Chapter 10 Total – 10.5 days Remaining – 12 days

Topics in Analytic Geometry

10

In Mathematics

A conic is a collection of points satisfying a geometric property.

In Real Life

Conics are used as models in construction, planetary orbits, radio navigation, and projectile motion. For instance, you can use conics to model the orbits of the planets as they move about the sun. Using the techniques presented in this chapter, you can determine the distances between the planets and the center of the sun. (See Exercises 55–62, page 796.)

Mike Agliolo/Photo Researchers, Inc.

IN CAREERS

There are many careers that use conics and other topics in analytic geometry. Several are listed below.

- Home Contractor
  Exercise 69, page 732
- Civil Engineer
  Exercises 73 and 74, page 740
- Artist
  Exercise 51, page 759
- Astronomer
  Exercises 63 and 64, page 796

PLAN AND PREPARE

Main Ideas

In Chapter 10, students work with conic sections and equations in parametric and polar form. The chapter begins by introducing analysis of lines with trigonometry and a distance formula. Students then solve problems involving conic sections, eventually classifying a conic by its equation in general form. Students also learn to rotate a conic section in order to simplify its equation. The chapter then introduces parametric and polar forms for writing and graphing equations. Students end the chapter by using polar coordinates to represent and solve problems involving conic sections.

Chapter Planning Guide

Chapter Resources
- Complete Solutions Guide

Interactive Technology
- Instructor Success Organizer
- Notetaking Guide IAE
- Instructional DVDs
- Animated Precalculus
- PowerLecture with ExamView

10.1 LINES

What you should learn

- Find the inclination of a line.
- Find the angle between two lines.
- Find the distance between a point and a line.

Why you should learn it

The inclination of a line can be used to measure heights indirectly. For instance, in Exercise 70 on page 732, the inclination of a line can be used to determine the change in elevation from the base to the top of the Falls Incline Railway in Niagara Falls, Ontario, Canada.

JTB Photo/Japan Travel Bureau/PhotoLibrary

Inclination of a Line

In Section 1.3, you learned that the graph of the linear equation

$$y = mx + b$$

is a nonvertical line with slope m and y-intercept $(0, b)$. There, the slope of a line was described as the rate of change in y with respect to x. In this section, you will look at the slope of a line in terms of the angle of inclination of the line.

Every nonhorizontal line must intersect the x-axis. The angle formed by such an intersection determines the **inclination** of the line, as specified in the following definition.

> **Definition of Inclination**
>
> The **inclination** of a nonhorizontal line is the positive angle θ (less than π) measured counterclockwise from the x-axis to the line. (See Figure 10.1.)

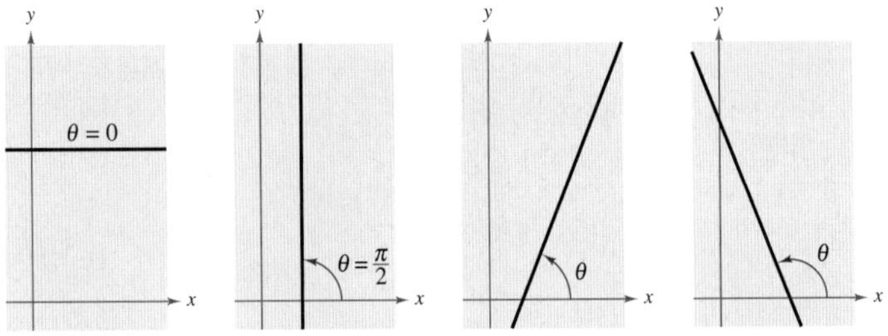

FIGURE 10.1

The inclination of a line is related to its slope in the following manner.

> **Inclination and Slope**
>
> If a nonvertical line has inclination θ and slope m, then
>
> $$m = \tan \theta.$$

For a proof of this relation between inclination and slope, see Proofs in Mathematics on page 804.

1 PLAN AND PREPARE

Warm-up Exercises

Transparency Available
Available at the Instructor's companion site.

Notetaking Guide

Transparency Available
Promotes interactive learning and notetaking skills.
Available at the Instructor's companion site.

Animated Precalculus

An **Animated Precalculus** tutorial is available at the Student companion site for **Section 10.1.**

Pacing

Average: 2 days
Advanced: 2 days
Block: 0.5 block with Chapter 9 Test
0.5 block with 10.2

2 FOCUS AND MOTIVATE

Essential Question

How do you find the angle of inclination of a line and the distance between a point and a line? **Tell students that they will learn how to answer this question by using trigonometry and a distance formula.**

Resource Planning Guide

Chapter Resources
- Complete Solutions Guide

Workbooks
- Notetaking Guide
- Student Solutions Guide

Interactive Technology
- Instructor Success Organizer
- Notetaking Guide IAE
- Instructional DVDs
- Animated Precalculus
- PowerLecture with ExamView

Example 1 Finding the Inclination of a Line

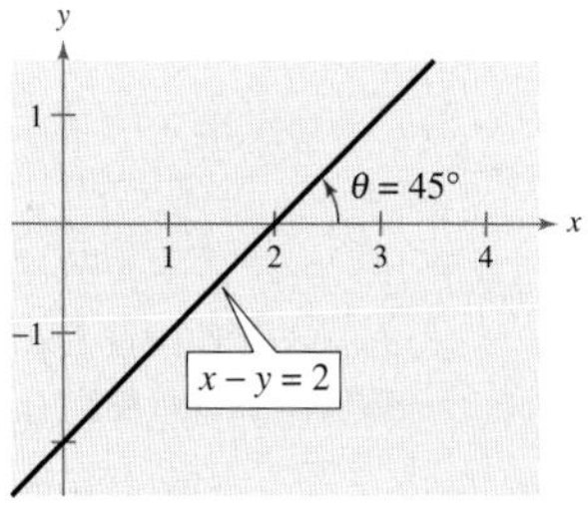

FIGURE 10.2

Find the inclination of the line $x - y = 2$.

Solution

The slope of this line is $m = 1$. So, its inclination is determined from the equation

$$\tan\theta = 1.$$

From Figure 10.2, it follows that $0 < \theta < \frac{\pi}{2}$. This means that

$$\theta = \arctan 1$$
$$= \frac{\pi}{4}.$$

The angle of inclination is $\frac{\pi}{4}$ radian or 45°.

CHECKPoint Now try Exercise 27.

Example 2 Finding the Inclination of a Line

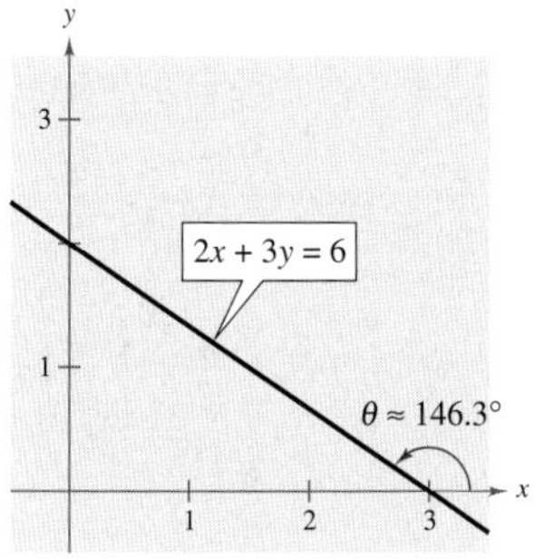

FIGURE 10.3

Find the inclination of the line $2x + 3y = 6$.

Solution

The slope of this line is $m = -\frac{2}{3}$. So, its inclination is determined from the equation

$$\tan\theta = -\frac{2}{3}.$$

From Figure 10.3, it follows that $\frac{\pi}{2} < \theta < \pi$. This means that

$$\theta = \pi + \arctan\left(-\frac{2}{3}\right)$$
$$\approx \pi + (-0.588)$$
$$= \pi - 0.588$$
$$\approx 2.554.$$

The angle of inclination is about 2.554 radians or about 146.3°.

CHECKPoint Now try Exercise 33.

The Angle Between Two Lines

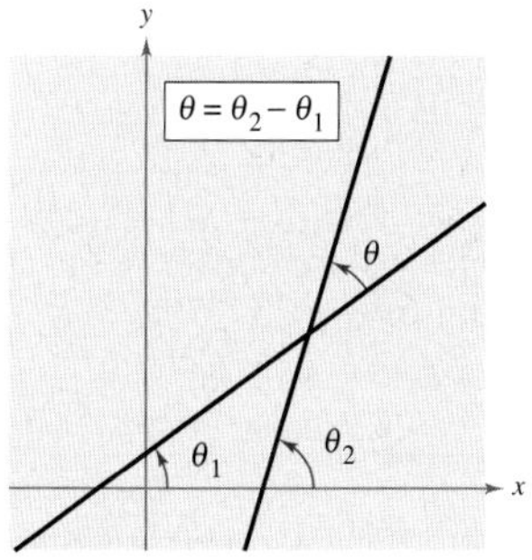

FIGURE 10.4

Two distinct lines in a plane are either parallel or intersecting. If they intersect and are nonperpendicular, their intersection forms two pairs of opposite angles. One pair is acute and the other pair is obtuse. The smaller of these angles is called the **angle between the two lines.** As shown in Figure 10.4, you can use the inclinations of the two lines to find the angle between the two lines. If two lines have inclinations θ_1 and θ_2, where $\theta_1 < \theta_2$ and $\theta_2 - \theta_1 < \pi/2$, the angle between the two lines is

$$\theta = \theta_2 - \theta_1.$$

3 TEACH

Extra Example 1

Find the inclination of the line $\sqrt{3}x - 3y + 3 = 0$.

$\frac{\pi}{6}$ radian, or 30°

Extra Example 2

Find the inclination of the line $5x - y + 3 = 0$.

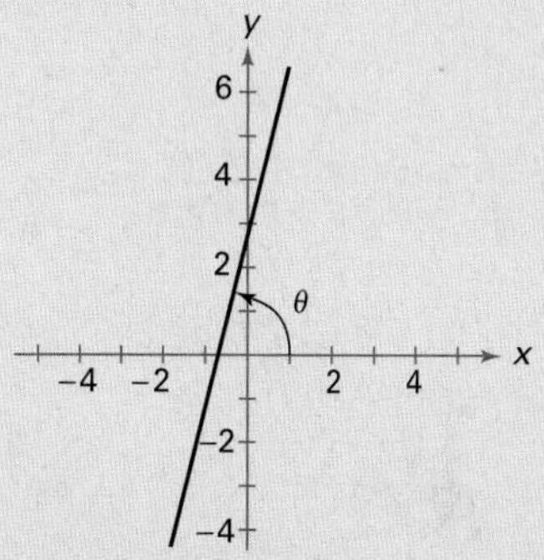

1.373 radians or 78.7°

Avoiding Common Errors

Students sometimes forget that the angle of inclination θ is always considered positive. If a line has a positive slope, then $0° < \theta < 90°$. If a line has a negative slope, then $90° < \theta < 180°$. In order to find the angle of a line with a negative slope, remind students that they can use $\tan^{-1}$ on a graphing calculator and then add π radians or 180° to the result.

Extra Example 3

Find the angle between the two lines.

Line 1: $2x + y = 4$

Line 2: $x - y = 2$

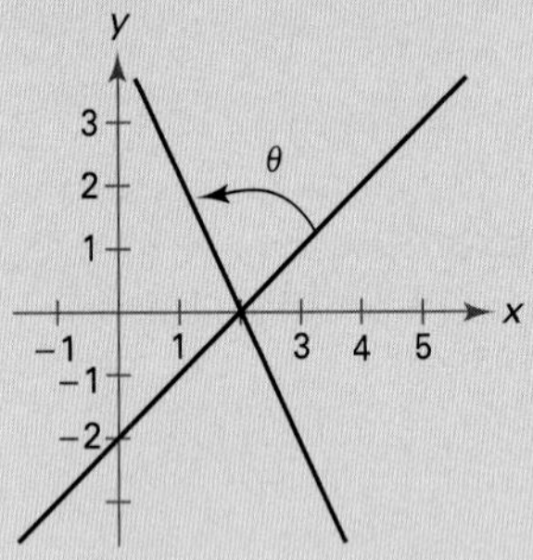

≈ 1.249 radians or ≈ 71.6°

You can use the formula for the tangent of the difference of two angles

$$\tan \theta = \tan(\theta_2 - \theta_1)$$

$$= \frac{\tan \theta_2 - \tan \theta_1}{1 + \tan \theta_1 \tan \theta_2}$$

to obtain the formula for the angle between two lines.

> **Angle Between Two Lines**
>
> If two nonperpendicular lines have slopes m_1 and m_2, the angle between the two lines is
>
> $$\tan \theta = \left|\frac{m_2 - m_1}{1 + m_1 m_2}\right|.$$

Example 3 Finding the Angle Between Two Lines

Find the angle between the two lines.

Line 1: $2x - y - 4 = 0$ *Line 2:* $3x + 4y - 12 = 0$

Solution

The two lines have slopes of $m_1 = 2$ and $m_2 = -\frac{3}{4}$, respectively. So, the tangent of the angle between the two lines is

$$\tan \theta = \left|\frac{m_2 - m_1}{1 + m_1 m_2}\right| = \left|\frac{(-3/4) - 2}{1 + (2)(-3/4)}\right| = \left|\frac{-11/4}{-2/4}\right| = \frac{11}{2}.$$

Finally, you can conclude that the angle is

$$\theta = \arctan \frac{11}{2} \approx 1.391 \text{ radians} \approx 79.70°$$

as shown in Figure 10.5.

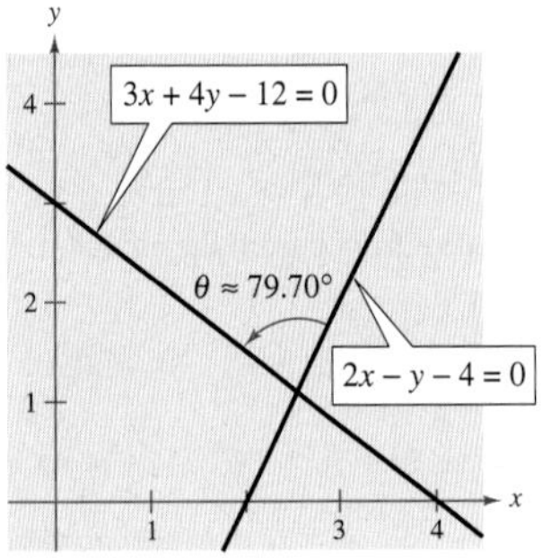

FIGURE 10.5

CHECKPoint Now try Exercise 41.

The Distance Between a Point and a Line

Finding the distance between a line and a point not on the line is an application of perpendicular lines. This distance is defined as the length of the perpendicular line segment joining the point and the line, as shown in Figure 10.6.

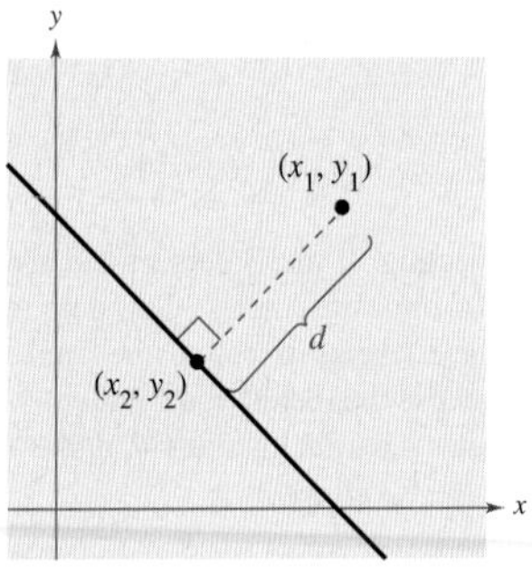

FIGURE 10.6

> **Distance Between a Point and a Line**
>
> The distance between the point (x_1, y_1) and the line $Ax + By + C = 0$ is
>
> $$d = \frac{|Ax_1 + By_1 + C|}{\sqrt{A^2 + B^2}}.$$

Remember that the values of A, B, and C in this distance formula correspond to the general equation of a line, $Ax + By + C = 0$. For a proof of this formula for the distance between a point and a line, see Proofs in Mathematics on page 804.

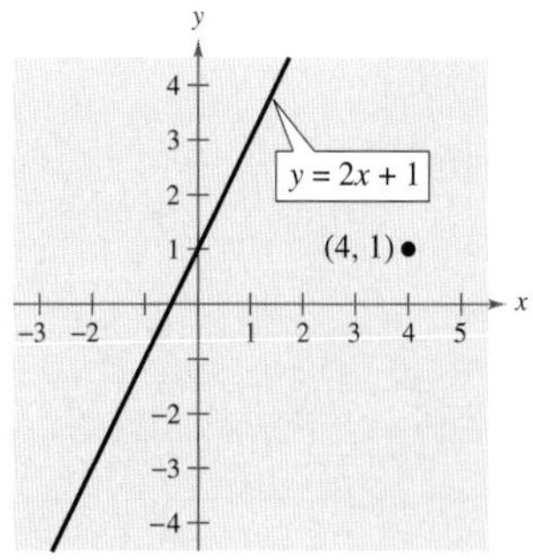

FIGURE 10.7

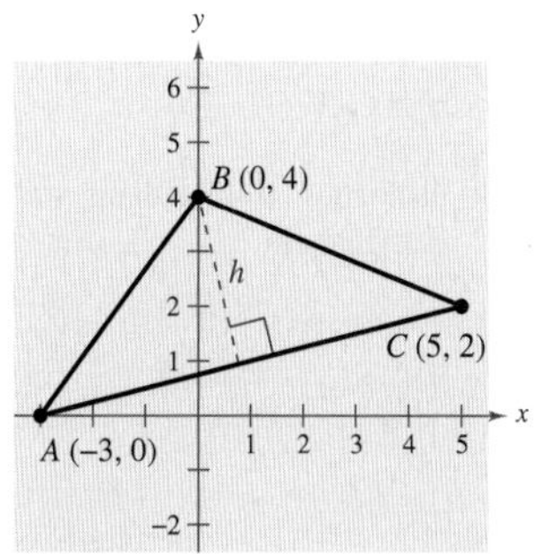

FIGURE 10.8

Example 4 Finding the Distance Between a Point and a Line

Find the distance between the point (4, 1) and the line $y = 2x + 1$.

Solution

The general form of the equation is $-2x + y - 1 = 0$. So, the distance between the point and the line is

$$d = \frac{|-2(4) + 1(1) + (-1)|}{\sqrt{(-2)^2 + 1^2}} = \frac{8}{\sqrt{5}} \approx 3.58 \text{ units.}$$

The line and the point are shown in Figure 10.7.

CHECKPoint Now try Exercise 53.

Example 5 An Application of Two Distance Formulas

Figure 10.8 shows a triangle with vertices $A(-3, 0)$, $B(0, 4)$, and $C(5, 2)$.

a. Find the altitude h from vertex B to side AC.

b. Find the area of the triangle.

Solution

a. To find the altitude, use the formula for the distance between line AC and the point (0, 4). The equation of line AC is obtained as follows.

$$\textit{Slope: } m = \frac{2 - 0}{5 - (-3)} = \frac{2}{8} = \frac{1}{4}$$

$$\textit{Equation: } y - 0 = \frac{1}{4}(x + 3) \qquad \text{Point-slope form}$$

$$4y = x + 3 \qquad \text{Multiply each side by 4.}$$

$$x - 4y + 3 = 0 \qquad \text{General form}$$

So, the distance between this line and the point (0, 4) is

$$\text{Altitude} = h = \frac{|1(0) + (-4)(4) + 3|}{\sqrt{1^2 + (-4)^2}} = \frac{13}{\sqrt{17}} \text{ units.}$$

b. Using the formula for the distance between two points, you can find the length of the base AC to be

$$b = \sqrt{[5 - (-3)]^2 + (2 - 0)^2} \qquad \text{Distance Formula}$$

$$= \sqrt{8^2 + 2^2} \qquad \text{Simplify.}$$

$$= 2\sqrt{17} \text{ units.} \qquad \text{Simplify.}$$

Finally, the area of the triangle in Figure 10.8 is

$$A = \frac{1}{2}bh \qquad \text{Formula for the area of a triangle}$$

$$= \frac{1}{2}(2\sqrt{17})\left(\frac{13}{\sqrt{17}}\right) \qquad \text{Substitute for } b \text{ and } h.$$

$$= 13 \text{ square units.} \qquad \text{Simplify.}$$

CHECKPoint Now try Exercise 59.

Extra Example 4

Find the distance between the point (0, 2) and the line $4x + 3y = 0$.

$\frac{6}{5} = 1.2$ units

Extra Example 5

Consider a triangle with vertices $A(0, 0)$, $B(1, 5)$, and $C(3, 1)$.

a. Find the altitude from vertex B to side AC.

$\frac{14}{\sqrt{10}} = \frac{7\sqrt{10}}{5}$ units

b. Find the area of the triangle.

7 square units

Closing the Lesson

Have students summarize the major points of the lesson and answer the Essential Question: How do you find the angle of inclination of a line and the distance between a point and a line?

- **Find the angle of inclination of a line by using the relationship $m = \tan\theta$.**
- **Find the angle between two lines by finding the difference between the angle of inclination of each line or by using the formula $\tan\theta = \left|\frac{m_2 - m_1}{1 + m_1 m_2}\right|$, where m_1 and m_2 are the slopes of each line.**
- **Find the distance between a point (x_1, y_1) and line $Ax + By + C = 0$ by using the formula $d = \frac{|Ax_1 + By_1 + C|}{\sqrt{A^2 + B^2}}$.**

4 PRACTICE AND APPLY

Assignment Guide

Transparencies Available
Available at the Instructor's companion site.

Average:
Day 1: pp. 730–731
Exs. 1–3, 5–13 odd, 17, 19, 23, 25, 31–35 odd, 37–39, 42, 43–49 odd
Day 2: pp. 730–732
Exs. 4, 51, 55–57, 60, 61–67 odd, 69–72, 75

Advanced:
Day 1: pp. 730–731
Exs. 1–3, 6–12 even, 24–30 even, 35–40, 42–50 even
Day 2: pp. 730–732
Exs. 4, 52, 56–66 even, 68–74

Block:
pp. 730–731
Exs. 1–3, 5–13 odd, 17, 19, 23, 25, 31–35 odd, 37–39, 42, 43–49 odd (with Chapter 9 Test)
pp. 730–732
Exs. 4, 51, 55–57, 60, 61–67 odd, 69–72, 75 (with 10.2)

19. $\frac{\pi}{6}$ rad, 30°

20. $\frac{\pi}{3}$ rad, 60°

21. $\frac{5\pi}{6}$ rad, 150°

22. $\frac{2\pi}{3}$ rad, 120°

27. $\frac{3\pi}{4}$ rad, 135°

28. $\frac{\pi}{6}$ rad, 30°

29. $\frac{\pi}{4}$ rad, 45°

30. $\frac{\pi}{3}$ rad, 60°

31. $\frac{5\pi}{6}$ rad, 150°

32. $\frac{2\pi}{3}$ rad, 120°

10.1 EXERCISES

See www.CalcChat.com for worked-out solutions to odd-numbered exercises.

VOCABULARY: Fill in the blanks.

1. The ________ of a nonhorizontal line is the positive angle θ (less than π) measured counterclockwise from the x-axis to the line. inclination
2. If a nonvertical line has inclination θ and slope m, then $m =$ ___$\tan\theta$___ .
3. If two nonperpendicular lines have slopes m_1 and m_2, the angle between the two lines is $\tan\theta =$ $\left|\frac{m_2 - m_1}{1 + m_1 m_2}\right|$
4. The distance between the point (x_1, y_1) and the line $Ax + By + C = 0$ is given by $d =$ ________ . $\frac{|Ax_1 + By_1 + C|}{\sqrt{A^2 + B^2}}$

SKILLS AND APPLICATIONS

In Exercises 5–12, find the slope of the line with inclination θ.

5. $\frac{\sqrt{3}}{3}$

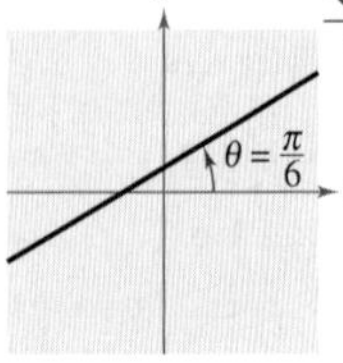

6. 1

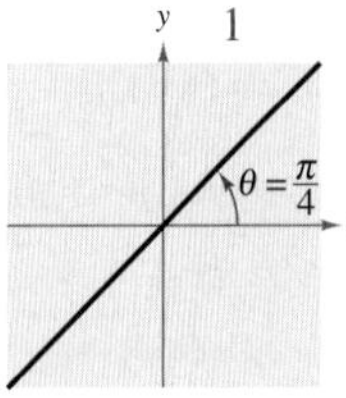

7. -1

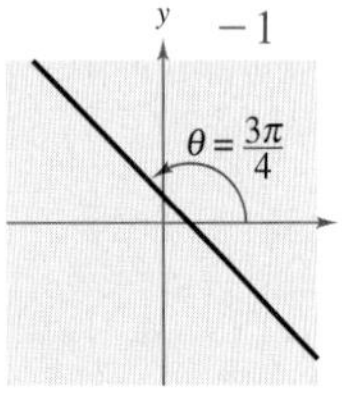

8. $-\sqrt{3}$

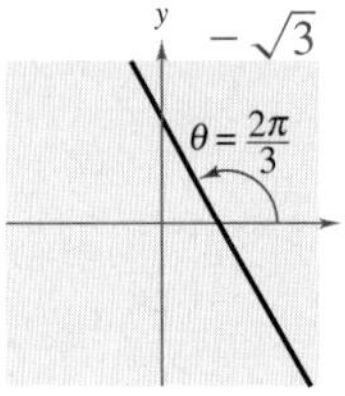

9. $\theta = \frac{\pi}{3}$ radians $\sqrt{3}$
10. $\theta = \frac{5\pi}{6}$ radians $-\frac{\sqrt{3}}{3}$
11. $\theta = 1.27$ radians 3.2236
12. $\theta = 2.88$ radians -0.2677

In Exercises 13–18, find the inclination θ (in radians and degrees) of the line with a slope of m.

13. $m = -1$ $\frac{3\pi}{4}$ rad, 135°
14. $m = -2$ 2.0344 rad, 116.6°
15. $m = 1$
16. $m = 2$ 1.1071 rad, 63.4°
17. $m = \frac{3}{4}$ 0.6435 rad, 36.9°
18. $m = -\frac{5}{2}$ 1.9513 rad, 111.8°

15. $\frac{\pi}{4}$ rad, 45°

In Exercises 19–26, find the inclination θ (in radians and degrees) of the line passing through the points.

19–22. See margin.

19. $(\sqrt{3}, 2), (0, 1)$
20. $(1, 2\sqrt{3}), (0, \sqrt{3})$
21. $(-\sqrt{3}, -1), (0, -2)$
22. $(3, \sqrt{3}), (6, -2\sqrt{3})$
23. $(6, 1), (10, 8)$ 1.0517 rad, 60.3°
24. $(12, 8), (-4, -3)$ 0.6023 rad, 34.5°
25. $(-2, 20), (10, 0)$ 2.1112 rad, 121.0°
26. $(0, 100), (50, 0)$ 2.0344 rad, 116.6°

In Exercises 27–36, find the inclination θ (in radians and degrees) of the line. 27–32. See margin.

27. $2x + 2y - 5 = 0$
28. $x - \sqrt{3}y + 1 = 0$
29. $3x - 3y + 1 = 0$
30. $\sqrt{3}x - y + 2 = 0$
31. $x + \sqrt{3}y + 2 = 0$
32. $-2\sqrt{3}x - 2y = 0$
33. $6x - 2y + 8 = 0$ 1.2490 rad, 71.6°
34. $4x + 5y - 9 = 0$ 2.4669 rad, 141.3°
35. $5x + 3y = 0$ 2.1112 rad, 121.0°
36. $2x - 6y - 12 = 0$ 0.3218 rad, 18.4°

In Exercises 37–46, find the angle θ (in radians and degrees) between the lines.

37. $3x + y = 3$
$x - y = 2$

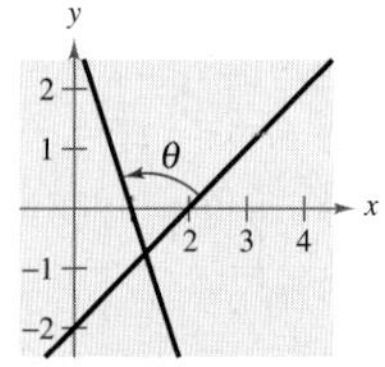

1.1071 rad, 63.4°

38. $x + 3y = 2$
$x - 2y = -3$

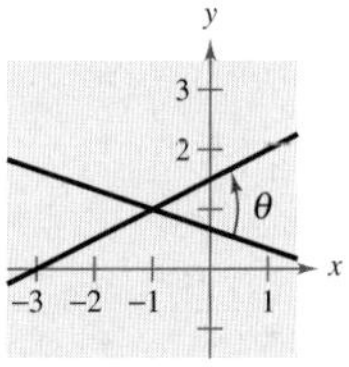

$\frac{\pi}{4}$ rad, 45°

39. $x - y = 0$
$3x - 2y = -1$

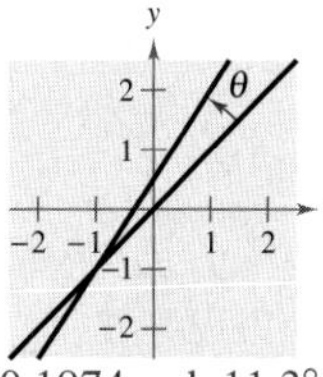

0.1974 rad, $11.3°$

40. $2x - y = 2$
$4x + 3y = 24$

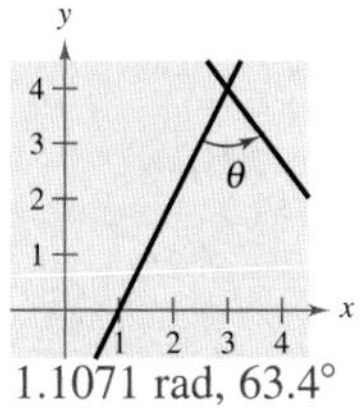

1.1071 rad, $63.4°$

41. $x - 2y = 7$
$6x + 2y = 5$ 1.4289 rad, $81.9°$

42. $5x + 2y = 16$
$3x - 5y = -1$ 1.4109 rad, $80.8°$

43. $x + 2y = 8$
$x - 2y = 2$ 0.9273 rad, $53.1°$

44. $3x - 5y = 3$
$3x + 5y = 12$ 1.0808 rad, $61.9°$

45. $0.05x - 0.03y = 0.21$
$0.07x + 0.02y = 0.16$ 0.8187 rad, $46.9°$

46. $0.02x - 0.05y = -0.19$
$0.03x + 0.04y = 0.52$ 1.0240 rad, $58.7°$

ANGLE MEASUREMENT In Exercises 47–50, find the slope of each side of the triangle and use the slopes to find the measures of the interior angles. 47–50. See margin.

47.

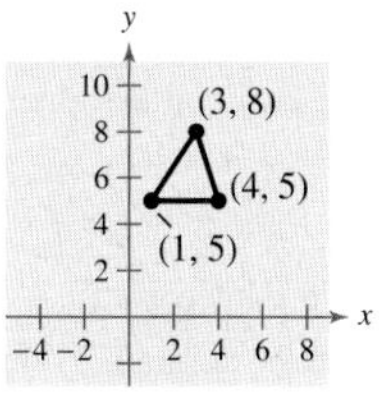

48.

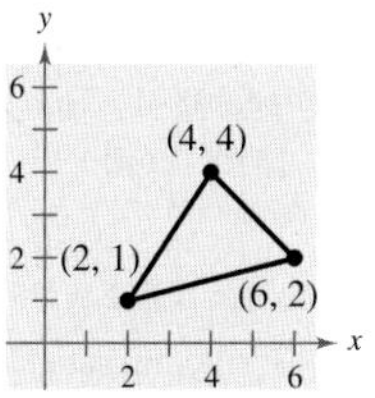

49.

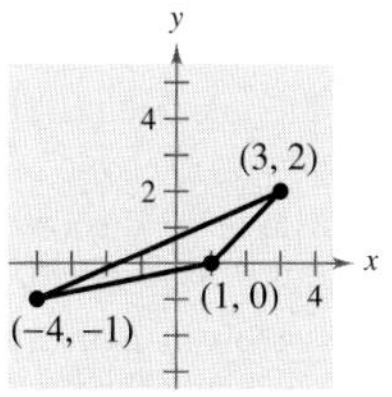

50.

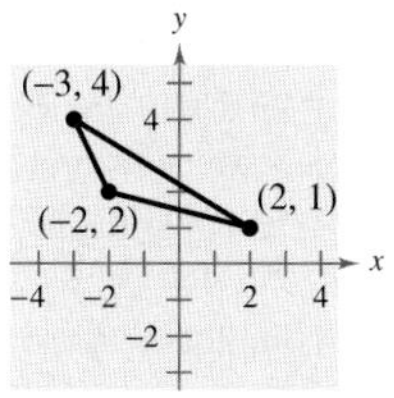

In Exercises 51–58, find the distance between the point and the line.

	Point	*Line*	
51.	(0, 0)	$4x + 3y = 0$	0
52.	(0, 0)	$2x - y = 4$	$\frac{4\sqrt{5}}{5} \approx 1.7889$
53.	(2, 3)	$3x + y = 1$	$\frac{4\sqrt{10}}{5} \approx 2.5298$
54.	$(-2, 1)$	$x - y = 2$	$\frac{5\sqrt{2}}{2} \approx 3.5355$
55.	(6, 2)	$x + 1 = 0$	7
56.	(2, 1)	$-2x + y - 2 = 0$	$\sqrt{5} \approx 2.2361$
57.	(0, 8)	$6x - y = 0$	See margin.
58.	(4, 2)	$x - y = 20$	$9\sqrt{2} \approx 12.7279$

In Exercises 59–62, the points represent the vertices of a triangle. (a) Draw triangle ABC in the coordinate plane, (b) find the altitude from vertex B of the triangle to side AC, and (c) find the area of the triangle. 59–62. See margin.

59. $A = (0, 0)$, $B = (1, 4)$, $C = (4, 0)$

60. $A = (0, 0)$, $B = (4, 5)$, $C = (5, -2)$

61. $A = \left(-\frac{1}{2}, \frac{1}{2}\right)$, $B = (2, 3)$, $C = \left(\frac{5}{2}, 0\right)$

62. $A = (-4, -5)$, $B = (3, 10)$, $C = (6, 12)$

In Exercises 63 and 64, find the distance between the parallel lines.

63. $x + y = 1$
$x + y = 5$ $2\sqrt{2}$

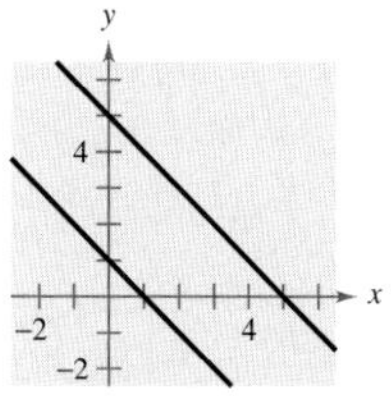

64. $3x - 4y = 1$
$3x - 4y = 10$ $\frac{9}{5}$

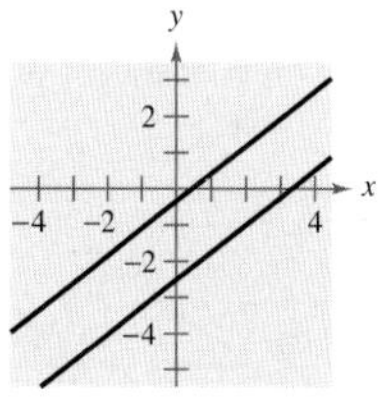

65. ROAD GRADE A straight road rises with an inclination of 0.10 radian from the horizontal (see figure). Find the slope of the road and the change in elevation over a two-mile stretch of the road. 0.1003, 1054 ft

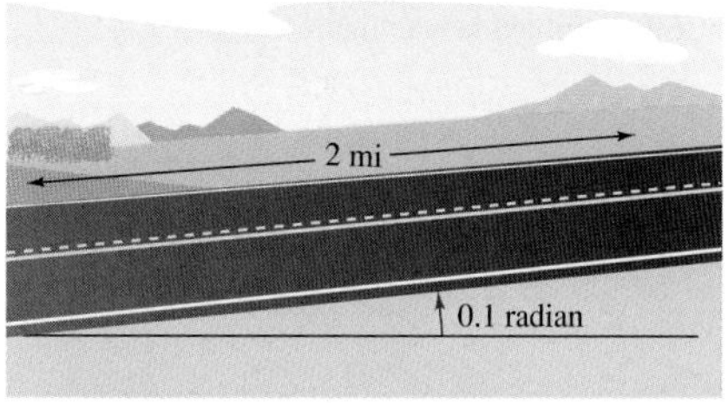

66. ROAD GRADE A straight road rises with an inclination of 0.20 radian from the horizontal. Find the slope of the road and the change in elevation over a one-mile stretch of the road. 0.2027, 1049 ft

47–50. See below.

57. $\frac{8\sqrt{37}}{37} \approx 1.3152$

59. (a)

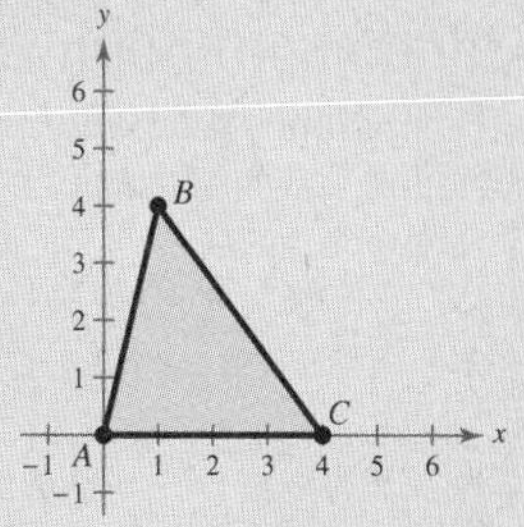

(b) 4 (c) 8

60. (a)

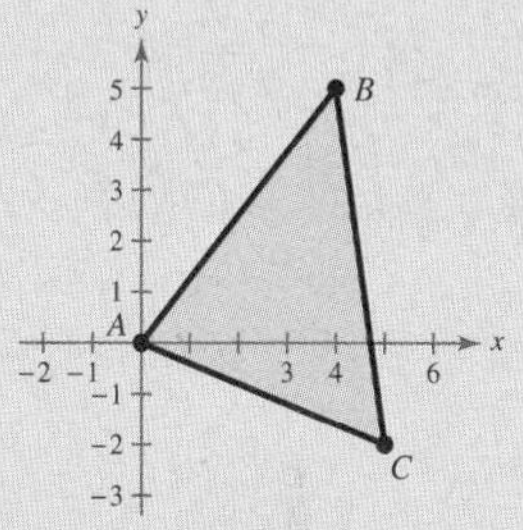

(b) $\frac{33\sqrt{29}}{29}$ (c) $\frac{33}{2}$

61. (a)

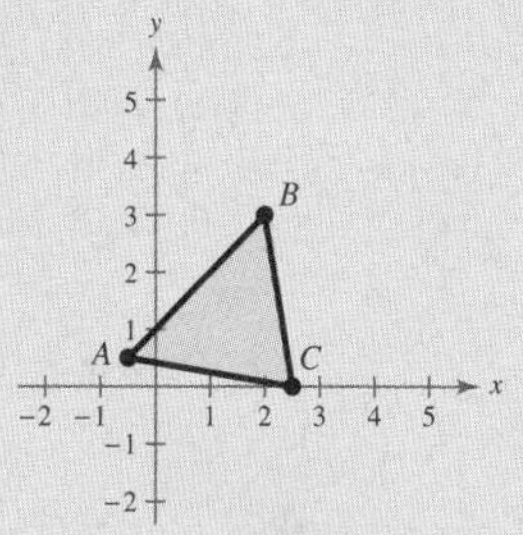

(b) $\frac{35\sqrt{37}}{74}$ (c) $\frac{35}{8}$

62. (a)

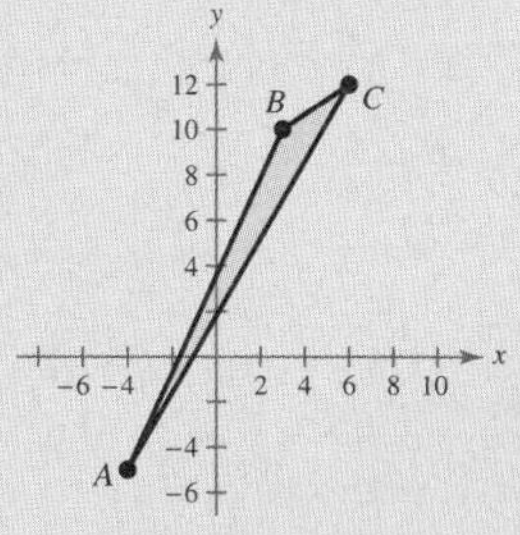

(b) $\frac{31\sqrt{389}}{389}$ (c) $\frac{31}{2}$

47. $(1, 5) \leftrightarrow (4, 5)$: slope $= 0$
$(4, 5) \leftrightarrow (3, 8)$: slope $= -3$
$(3, 8) \leftrightarrow (1, 5)$: slope $= \frac{3}{2}$
$(1, 5)$: $56.3°$; $(4, 5)$: $71.6°$; $(3, 8)$: $52.1°$

48. $(2, 1) \leftrightarrow (4, 4)$: slope $= \frac{3}{2}$
$(4, 4) \leftrightarrow (6, 2)$: slope $= -1$
$(6, 2) \leftrightarrow (2, 1)$: slope $= \frac{1}{4}$
$(2, 1)$: $42.3°$; $(4, 4)$: $78.7°$; $(6, 2)$: $59.0°$

49. $(-4, -1) \leftrightarrow (3, 2)$: slope $= \frac{3}{7}$
$(3, 2) \leftrightarrow (1, 0)$: slope $= 1$
$(1, 0) \leftrightarrow (-4, -1)$: slope $= \frac{1}{5}$
$(-4, -1)$: $11.9°$; $(3, 2)$: $21.8°$; $(1, 0)$: $146.3°$

50. $(-2, 2) \leftrightarrow (-3, 4)$: slope $= -2$
$(-3, 4) \leftrightarrow (2, 1)$: slope $= -\frac{3}{5}$
$(2, 1) \leftrightarrow (-2, 2)$: slope $= -\frac{1}{4}$
$(-3, 4)$: $32.5°$; $(2, 1)$: $16.9°$; $(-2, 2)$: $130.6°$

67. PITCH OF A ROOF A roof has a rise of 3 feet for every horizontal change of 5 feet (see figure). Find the inclination of the roof. $31.0°$

68. CONVEYOR DESIGN A moving conveyor is built so that it rises 1 meter for each 3 meters of horizontal travel.

(a) Draw a diagram that gives a visual representation of the problem. See margin.

(b) Find the inclination of the conveyor. $18.4°$

(c) The conveyor runs between two floors in a factory. The distance between the floors is 5 meters. Find the length of the conveyor. 15.8 m

69. TRUSS Find the angles α and β shown in the drawing of the roof truss. $\alpha \approx 33.69°$; $\beta \approx 56.31°$

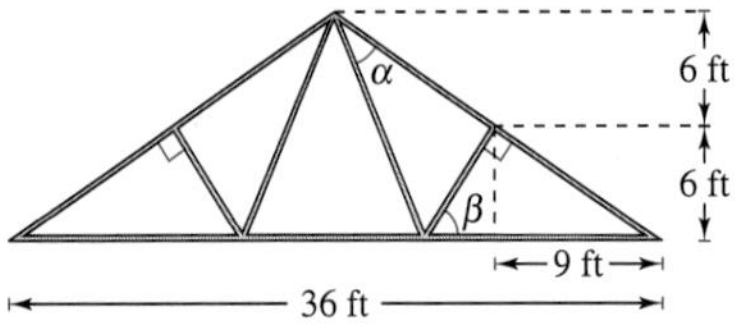

70. The Falls Incline Railway in Niagara Falls, Ontario, Canada is an inclined railway that was designed to carry people from the City of Niagara Falls to Queen Victoria Park. The railway is approximately 170 feet long with a 36% uphill grade (see figure).

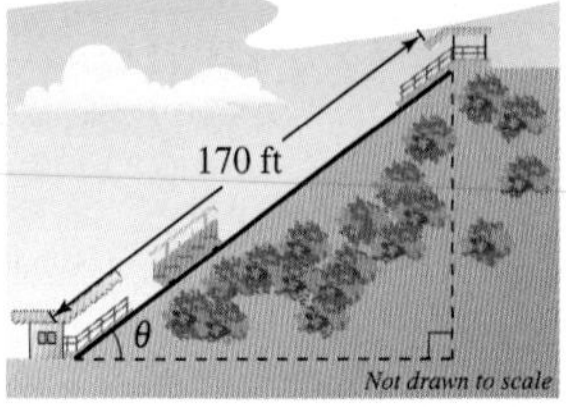

(a) Find the inclination θ of the railway. 0.3456 rad, $19.8°$

(b) Find the change in elevation from the base to the top of the railway. 57.6 ft

(c) Using the origin of a rectangular coordinate system as the base of the inclined plane, find the equation of the line that models the railway track. $y = 0.36x$

(d) Sketch a graph of the equation you found in part (c). See margin.

EXPLORATION

71–72. See margin.

TRUE OR FALSE? In Exercises 71 and 72, determine whether the statement is true or false. Justify your answer.

71. A line that has an inclination greater than $\pi/2$ radians has a negative slope.

72. To find the angle between two lines whose angles of inclination θ_1 and θ_2 are known, substitute θ_1 and θ_2 for m_1 and m_2, respectively, in the formula for the angle between two lines.

73. Consider a line with slope m and y-intercept $(0, 4)$.

(a) Write the distance d between the origin and the line as a function of m. (a) $d = \dfrac{4}{\sqrt{m^2 + 1}}$

(b) Graph the function in part (a). See margin.

(c) Find the slope that yields the maximum distance between the origin and the line. $m = 0$

(d) Find the asymptote of the graph in part (b) and interpret its meaning in the context of the problem. See margin.

74. CAPSTONE Discuss why the inclination of a line can be an angle that is larger than $\pi/2$, but the angle between two lines cannot be larger than $\pi/2$. Decide whether the following statement is true or false: "The inclination of a line is the angle between the line and the x-axis." Explain. See margin.

75. Consider a line with slope m and y-intercept $(0, 4)$.

(a) Write the distance d between the point $(3, 1)$ and the line as a function of m. (a)–(b).

(b) Graph the function in part (a). See margin.

(c) Find the slope that yields the maximum distance between the point and the line. $m = 1$

(d) Is it possible for the distance to be 0? If so, what is the slope of the line that yields a distance of 0?

(e) Find the asymptote of the graph in part (b) and interpret its meaning in the context of the problem.

(d) Yes. $m = -1$

(e) $d = 3$. As the line approaches the vertical, the distance approaches 3.

5 ASSESS AND RETEACH

Daily Homework Quiz

Transparency Available

Available at the Instructor's companion site.

68. (a)

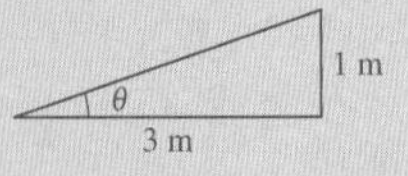

70. (d)

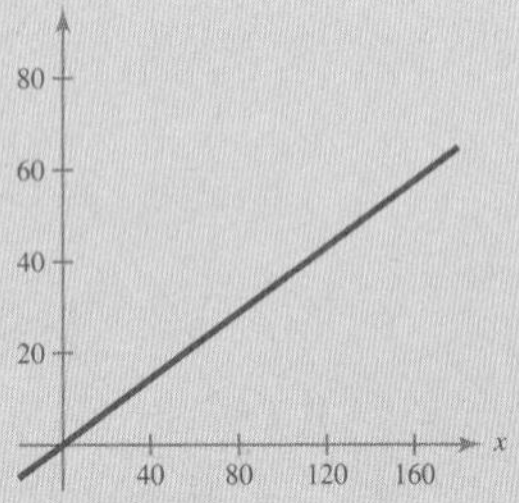

71. True. The inclination of a line is related to its slope by $m = \tan\theta$. If the angle is greater than $\pi/2$ but less than π, then the angle is in the second quadrant, where the tangent function is negative.

72. False. Substitute $\tan\theta_1$ and $\tan\theta_2$ for m_1 and m_2 in the formula for the angle between two lines.

73. (b)

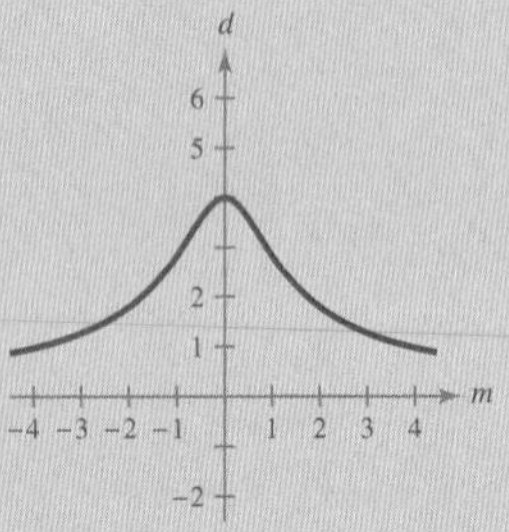

(d) The graph has a horizontal asymptote of $d = 0$. As the slope becomes larger, the distance between the origin and the line, $y = mx + 4$, becomes smaller and approaches 0.

74. Answers will vary; False. The inclination is the *positive angle measured counterclockwise* from the x-axis, not necessarily the angle between the line and the x-axis.

75. (a) $d = \dfrac{3|m + 1|}{\sqrt{m^2 + 1}}$

(b)

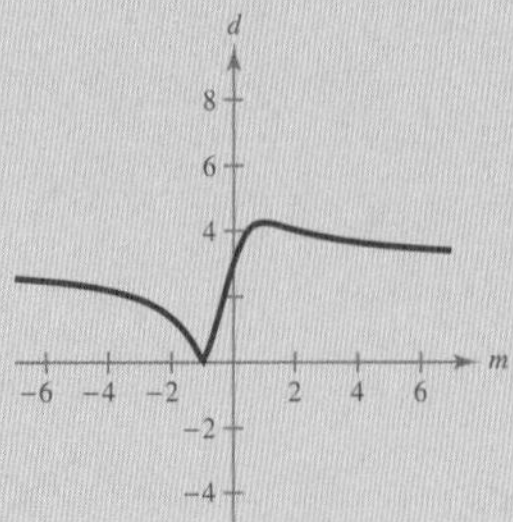

10.2 INTRODUCTION TO CONICS: PARABOLAS

What you should learn

- Recognize a conic as the intersection of a plane and a double-napped cone.
- Write equations of parabolas in standard form and graph parabolas.
- Use the reflective property of parabolas to solve real-life problems.

Why you should learn it

Parabolas can be used to model and solve many types of real-life problems. For instance, in Exercise 71 on page 739, a parabola is used to model the cables of the Golden Gate Bridge.

Cosmo Condina/The Image Bank/ Getty Images

Conics

Conic sections were discovered during the classical Greek period, 600 to 300 B.C. The early Greeks were concerned largely with the geometric properties of conics. It was not until the 17th century that the broad applicability of conics became apparent and played a prominent role in the early development of calculus.

A **conic section** (or simply **conic**) is the intersection of a plane and a double-napped cone. Notice in Figure 10.9 that in the formation of the four basic conics, the intersecting plane does not pass through the vertex of the cone. When the plane does pass through the vertex, the resulting figure is a **degenerate conic,** as shown in Figure 10.10.

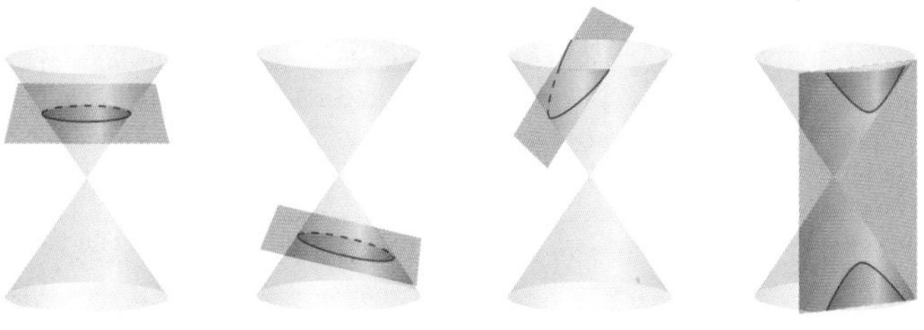

Circle Ellipse Parabola Hyperbola

FIGURE 10.9 Basic Conics

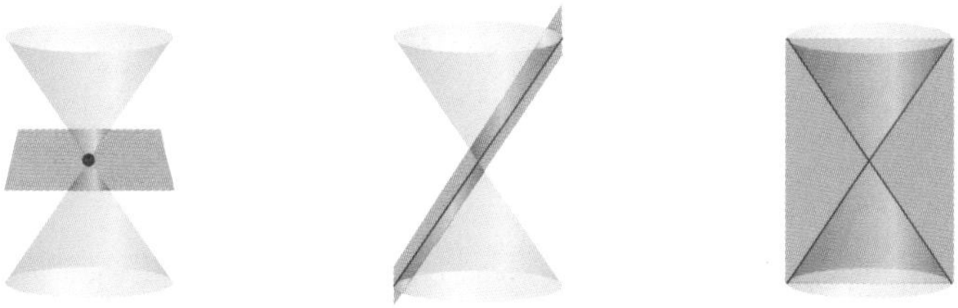

Point Line Two Intersecting Lines

FIGURE 10.10 Degenerate Conics

There are several ways to approach the study of conics. You could begin by defining conics in terms of the intersections of planes and cones, as the Greeks did, or you could define them algebraically, in terms of the general second-degree equation

$$Ax^2 + Bxy + Cy^2 + Dx + Ey + F = 0.$$

However, you will study a third approach, in which each of the conics is defined as a **locus** (collection) of points satisfying a geometric property. For example, in Section 1.2, you learned that a circle is defined as the collection of all points (x, y) that are equidistant from a fixed point (h, k). This leads to the standard form of the equation of a circle

$$(x - h)^2 + (y - k)^2 = r^2. \qquad \text{Equation of circle}$$

1 PLAN AND PREPARE

Warm-up Exercises

Transparency Available
Available at the Instructor's companion site.

Notetaking Guide

Transparency Available
Promotes interactive learning and notetaking skills. Available at the Instructor's companion site.

Animated Precalculus

An **Animated Precalculus** tutorial is available at the Student companion site for **Section 10.2.**

Pacing

Average: 2 days
Advanced: 2 days
Block: 0.5 block with 10.1
0.5 block with 10.3

2 FOCUS AND MOTIVATE

Essential Question

How do you recognize each conic section and solve problems involving parabolas? **Tell students that they will learn how to answer this question by studying the basic form of each conic section and the key characteristics of a parabola.**

Resource Planning Guide

Chapter Resources
- Complete Solutions Guide

Workbooks
- Notetaking Guide
- Student Solutions Guide

Interactive Technology
- Instructor Success Organizer
- Notetaking Guide IAE
- Instructional DVDs
- Animated Precalculus
- PowerLecture with ExamView

Avoiding Common Errors

Students often become confused because the standard form $(x - h)^2 = 4p(y - k)$ and the quadratic form $y = a(x - h)^2 + k$ for a parabola are similar. Show students that these forms are different because the coefficient is written with the linear term in the standard form and with the squared term in the quadratic form. Note that $a = \frac{1}{4p}$.

Parabolas

In Section 2.1, you learned that the graph of the quadratic function

$$f(x) = ax^2 + bx + c$$

is a parabola that opens upward or downward. The following definition of a parabola is more general in the sense that it is independent of the orientation of the parabola.

Definition of Parabola

A **parabola** is the set of all points (x, y) in a plane that are equidistant from a fixed line **(directrix)** and a fixed point **(focus)** not on the line.

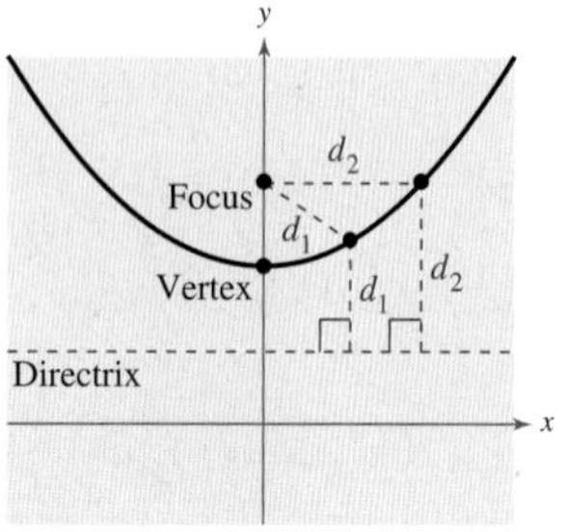

FIGURE 10.11 Parabola

The midpoint between the focus and the directrix is called the **vertex,** and the line passing through the focus and the vertex is called the **axis** of the parabola. Note in Figure 10.11 that a parabola is symmetric with respect to its axis. Using the definition of a parabola, you can derive the following **standard form** of the equation of a parabola whose directrix is parallel to the x-axis or to the y-axis.

Standard Equation of a Parabola

The **standard form of the equation of a parabola** with vertex at (h, k) is as follows.

$(x - h)^2 = 4p(y - k),\ p \neq 0$ Vertical axis, directrix: $y = k - p$

$(y - k)^2 = 4p(x - h),\ p \neq 0$ Horizontal axis, directrix: $x = h - p$

The focus lies on the axis p units (*directed distance*) from the vertex. If the vertex is at the origin $(0, 0)$, the equation takes one of the following forms.

$x^2 = 4py$ Vertical axis

$y^2 = 4px$ Horizontal axis

See Figure 10.12.

For a proof of the standard form of the equation of a parabola, see Proofs in Mathematics on page 805.

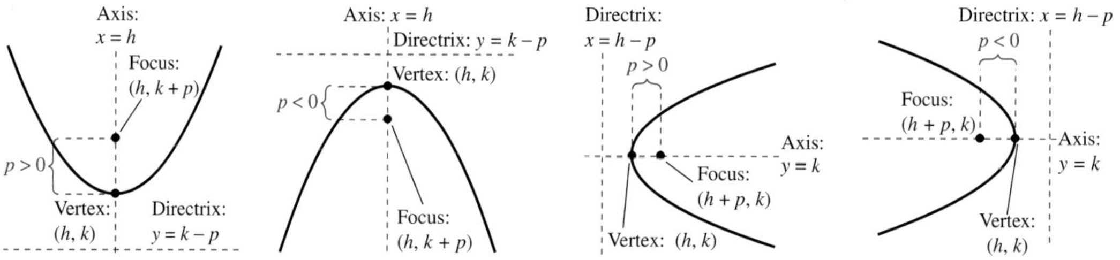

(a) $(x - h)^2 = 4p(y - k)$ Vertical axis: $p > 0$

(b) $(x - h)^2 = 4p(y - k)$ Vertical axis: $p < 0$

(c) $(y - k)^2 = 4p(x - h)$ Horizontal axis: $p > 0$

(d) $(y - k)^2 = 4p(x - h)$ Horizontal axis: $p < 0$

FIGURE 10.12

TECHNOLOGY

Use a graphing utility to confirm the equation found in Example 1. In order to graph the equation, you may have to use two separate equations:

$y_1 = \sqrt{8x}$ Upper part

and

$y_2 = -\sqrt{8x}.$ Lower part

Example 1 Vertex at the Origin

Find the standard equation of the parabola with vertex at the origin and focus $(2, 0)$.

Solution

The axis of the parabola is horizontal, passing through $(0, 0)$ and $(2, 0)$, as shown in Figure 10.13.

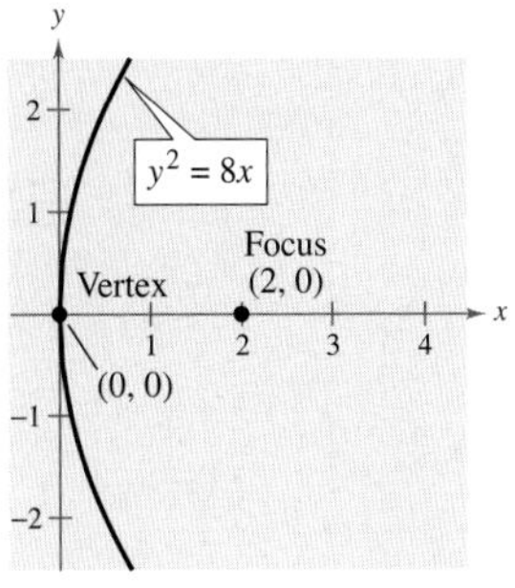

FIGURE 10.13

The standard form is $y^2 = 4px$, where $h = 0$, $k = 0$, and $p = 2$. So, the equation is $y^2 = 8x$.

CHECKPoint Now try Exercise 23.

Algebra Help

The technique of completing the square is used to write the equation in Example 2 in standard form. You can review completing the square in Appendix A.5.

Example 2 Finding the Focus of a Parabola

Find the focus of the parabola given by $y = -\frac{1}{2}x^2 - x + \frac{1}{2}$.

Solution

To find the focus, convert to standard form by completing the square.

$y = -\frac{1}{2}x^2 - x + \frac{1}{2}$	Write original equation.
$-2y = x^2 + 2x - 1$	Multiply each side by –2.
$1 - 2y = x^2 + 2x$	Add 1 to each side.
$1 + 1 - 2y = x^2 + 2x + 1$	Complete the square.
$2 - 2y = x^2 + 2x + 1$	Combine like terms.
$-2(y - 1) = (x + 1)^2$	Standard form

Comparing this equation with

$$(x - h)^2 = 4p(y - k)$$

you can conclude that $h = -1, k = 1$, and $p = -\frac{1}{2}$. Because p is negative, the parabola opens downward, as shown in Figure 10.14. So, the focus of the parabola is $(h, k + p) = \left(-1, \frac{1}{2}\right)$.

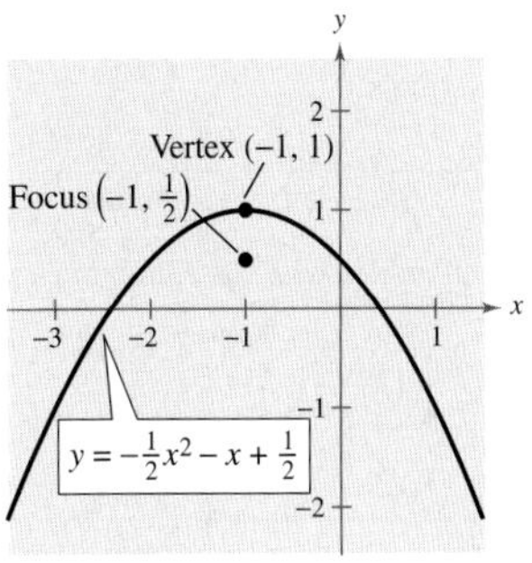

FIGURE 10.14

CHECKPoint Now try Exercise 43.

3 TEACH

Extra Example 1

Find the standard equation of the parabola with vertex (3, 2) and focus (1, 2).

$(y - 2)^2 = -8(x - 3)$

Extra Example 2

Find the focus of the parabola given by $y = -\frac{1}{6}(x^2 + 4x - 2)$.

$\left(-2, -\frac{1}{2}\right)$

Extra Example 3

Find the standard form of the equation of the parabola with vertex (1, 3) and focus (1, 5). Then write the quadratic form of the equation.

$(x - 1)^2 = 8(y - 3)$;

$\frac{1}{8}(x^2 - 2x + 25) = y$

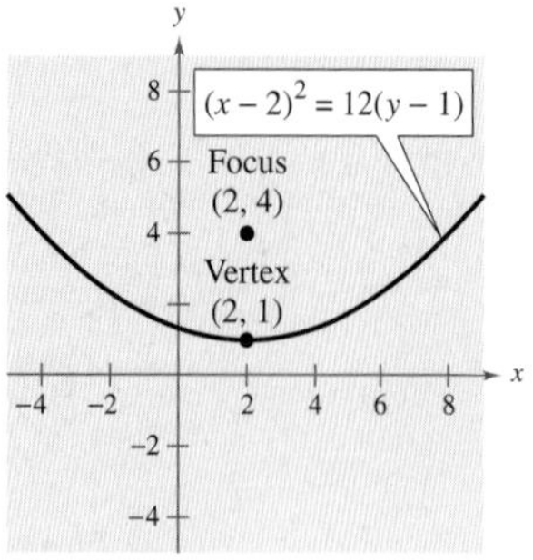

FIGURE 10.15

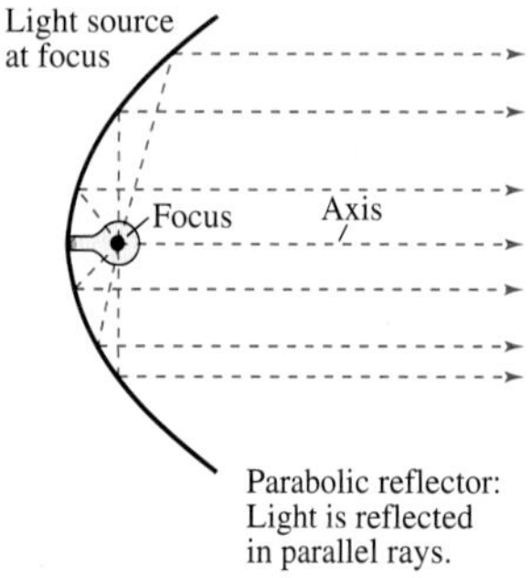

FIGURE 10.16

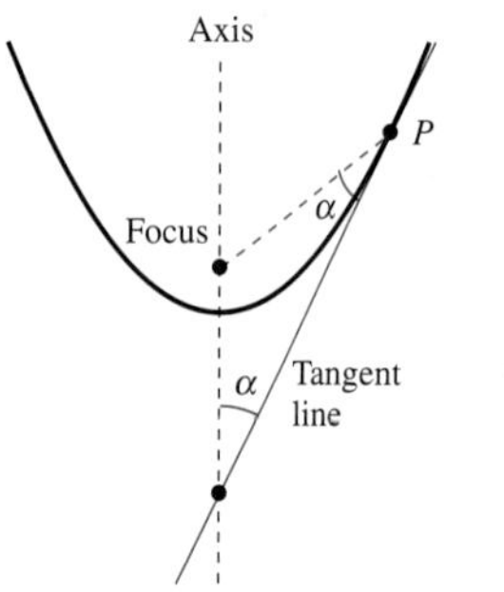

FIGURE 10.17

Example 3 Finding the Standard Equation of a Parabola

Find the standard form of the equation of the parabola with vertex (2, 1) and focus (2, 4). Then write the quadratic form of the equation.

Solution

Because the axis of the parabola is vertical, passing through (2, 1) and (2, 4), consider the equation

$$(x - h)^2 = 4p(y - k)$$

where $h = 2$, $k = 1$, and $p = 4 - 1 = 3$. So, the standard form is

$$(x - 2)^2 = 12(y - 1).$$

You can obtain the more common quadratic form as follows.

$$(x - 2)^2 = 12(y - 1) \quad \text{Write original equation.}$$

$$x^2 - 4x + 4 = 12y - 12 \quad \text{Multiply.}$$

$$x^2 - 4x + 16 = 12y \quad \text{Add 12 to each side.}$$

$$\frac{1}{12}(x^2 - 4x + 16) = y \quad \text{Divide each side by 12.}$$

The graph of this parabola is shown in Figure 10.15.

CHECKPoint Now try Exercise 55.

Application

A line segment that passes through the focus of a parabola and has endpoints on the parabola is called a **focal chord.** The specific focal chord perpendicular to the axis of the parabola is called the **latus rectum.**

Parabolas occur in a wide variety of applications. For instance, a parabolic reflector can be formed by revolving a parabola around its axis. The resulting surface has the property that all incoming rays parallel to the axis are reflected through the focus of the parabola. This is the principle behind the construction of the parabolic mirrors used in reflecting telescopes. Conversely, the light rays emanating from the focus of a parabolic reflector used in a flashlight are all parallel to one another, as shown in Figure 10.16.

A line is **tangent** to a parabola at a point on the parabola if the line intersects, but does not cross, the parabola at the point. Tangent lines to parabolas have special properties related to the use of parabolas in constructing reflective surfaces.

Reflective Property of a Parabola

The tangent line to a parabola at a point P makes equal angles with the following two lines (see Figure 10.17).

1. The line passing through P and the focus
2. The axis of the parabola

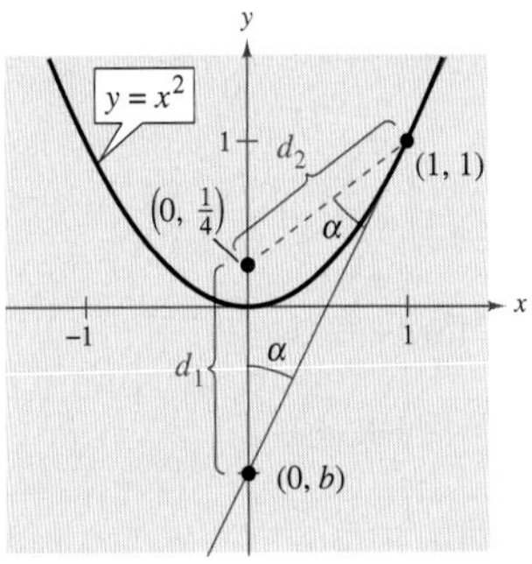

FIGURE 10.18

Example 4 Finding the Tangent Line at a Point on a Parabola

Find the equation of the tangent line to the parabola given by $y = x^2$ at the point $(1, 1)$.

Solution

For this parabola, $p = \frac{1}{4}$ and the focus is $\left(0, \frac{1}{4}\right)$, as shown in Figure 10.18. You can find the y-intercept $(0, b)$ of the tangent line by equating the lengths of the two sides of the isosceles triangle shown in Figure 10.18:

$$d_1 = \frac{1}{4} - b$$

and

$$d_2 = \sqrt{(1 - 0)^2 + \left[1 - \left(\frac{1}{4}\right)\right]^2} = \frac{5}{4}.$$

Note that $d_1 = \frac{1}{4} - b$ rather than $b - \frac{1}{4}$. The order of subtraction for the distance is important because the distance must be positive. Setting $d_1 = d_2$ produces

$$\frac{1}{4} - b = \frac{5}{4}$$

$$b = -1.$$

So, the slope of the tangent line is

$$m = \frac{1 - (-1)}{1 - 0} = 2$$

and the equation of the tangent line in slope-intercept form is

$$y = 2x - 1.$$

CHECK Point Now try Exercise 65.

TECHNOLOGY

Use a graphing utility to confirm the result of Example 4. By graphing

$y_1 = x^2$ and $y_2 = 2x - 1$

in the same viewing window, you should be able to see that the line touches the parabola at the point $(1, 1)$.

Algebra Help

You can review techniques for writing linear equations in Section 1.3.

Classroom Discussion

Satellite Dishes Cross sections of satellite dishes are parabolic in shape. Use the figure shown to write a paragraph explaining why satellite dishes are parabolic.
See margin.

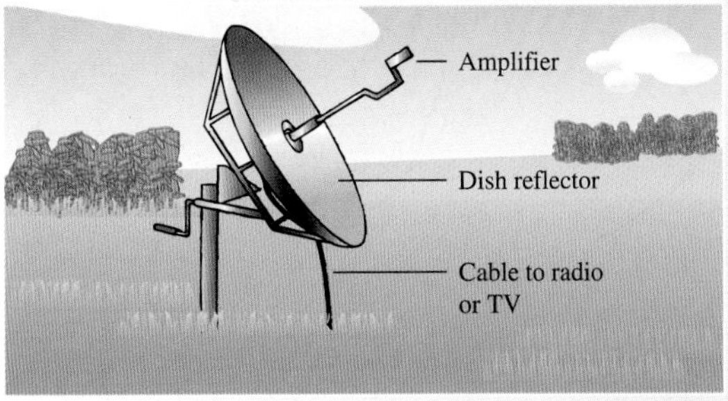

Extra Example 4

Find the equation of the tangent line to the parabola given by $x^2 = 2y$ at the point $\left(3, \frac{9}{2}\right)$.

$y = 3x - \frac{9}{2}$

Closing the Lesson

Have students summarize the major points of the lesson and answer the Essential Question: How do you recognize each conic section and solve problems involving parabolas?

- **Describe how each conic section can be formed by the intersection of a plane with a double-napped cone.**
- **Use the locus definition of a parabola and its equation in standard form to describe a parabola in terms of its vertex, focus, and directrix.**
- **Use the locus definition of a parabola and the distance formula to find the equation for a line tangent to a parabola at a given point.**
- **Use the reflective properties of a parabola to solve real-life problems.**

Classroom Discussion

When a television signal hits the antenna dish, the parabolic shape of the dish reflects the signal inward to the focus of the parabola. The signal is then transferred to the receiving equipment.

10.2 EXERCISES

See www.CalcChat.com for worked-out solutions to odd-numbered exercises.

VOCABULARY: Fill in the blanks.

1. A conic is the intersection of a plane and a double-napped cone.
2. When a plane passes through the vertex of a double-napped cone, the intersection is a degenerate conic.
3. A collection of points satisfying a geometric property can also be referred to as a locus of points.
4. A parabola is defined as the set of all points (x, y) in a plane that are equidistant from a fixed line, called the directrix, and a fixed point, called the focus, not on the line.
5. The line that passes through the focus and the vertex of a parabola is called the axis of the parabola.
6. The vertex of a parabola is the midpoint between the focus and the directrix.
7. A line segment that passes through the focus of a parabola and has endpoints on the parabola is called a focal chord.
8. A line is tangent to a parabola at a point on the parabola if the line intersects, but does not cross, the parabola at the point.

SKILLS AND APPLICATIONS

In Exercises 9–12, describe in words how a plane could intersect with the double-napped cone shown to form the conic section. 9–12. See margin.

9. Circle
10. Ellipse
11. Parabola
12. Hyperbola

In Exercises 13–18, match the equation with its graph. [The graphs are labeled (a), (b), (c), (d), (e), and (f).]

(a)

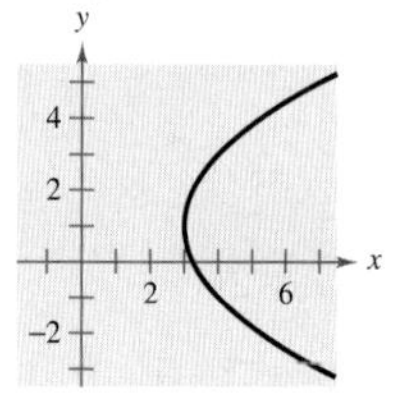

(b)

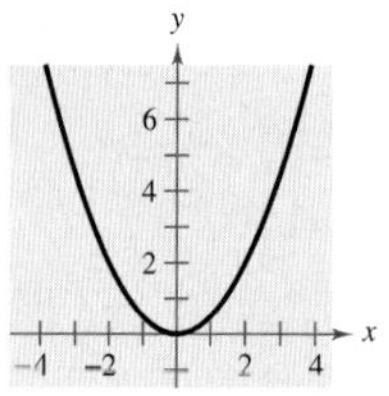

(c)

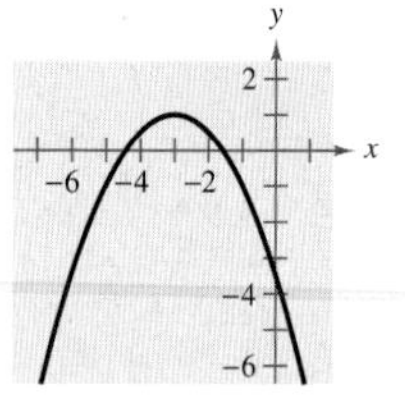

(d)

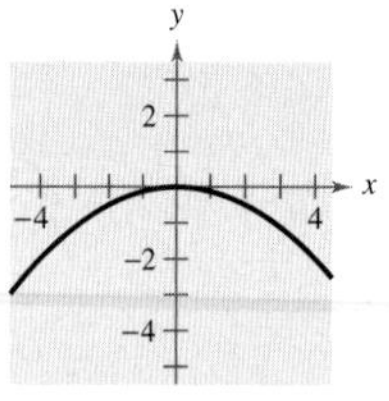

(e)

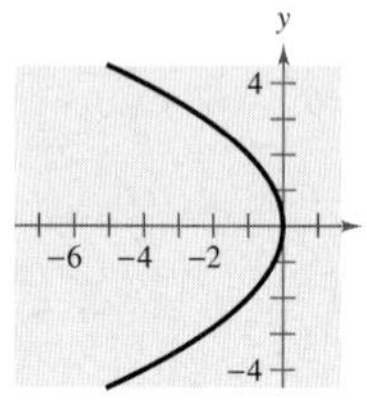

(f)

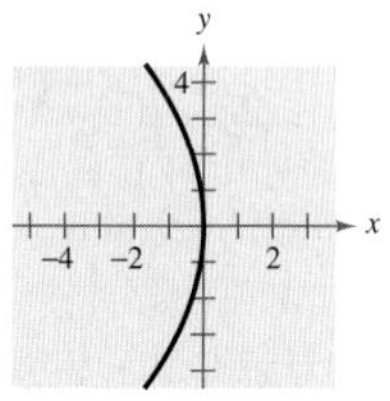

13. $y^2 = -4x$ e
14. $x^2 = 2y$ b
15. $x^2 = -8y$ d
16. $y^2 = -12x$ f
17. $(y - 1)^2 = 4(x - 3)$ a
18. $(x + 3)^2 = -2(y - 1)$ c

In Exercises 19–32, find the standard form of the equation of the parabola with the given characteristic(s) and vertex at the origin. 19–32. See margin.

19.

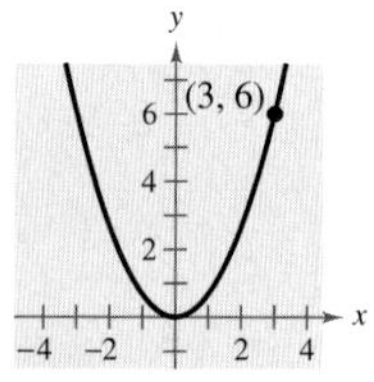

20.

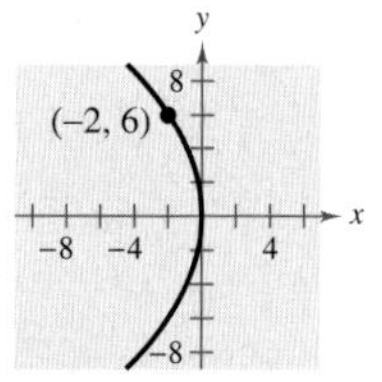

21. Focus: $\left(0, \frac{1}{2}\right)$
22. Focus: $\left(-\frac{3}{2}, 0\right)$
23. Focus: $(-2, 0)$
24. Focus: $(0, -2)$
25. Directrix: $y = 1$
26. Directrix: $y = -2$
27. Directrix: $x = -1$
28. Directrix: $x = 3$
29. Vertical axis and passes through the point $(4, 6)$
30. Vertical axis and passes through the point $(-3, -3)$
31. Horizontal axis and passes through the point $(-2, 5)$
32. Horizontal axis and passes through the point $(3, -2)$

4 PRACTICE AND APPLY

Assignment Guide

Transparencies Available
Available at the Instructor's companion site.

Average:
Day 1: pp. 738–739
Exs. 1–5, 9–12, 13–17 odd, 19–21, 25–31 odd, 35–41 odd, 45–53 odd, 57, 59
Day 2: pp. 738–741
Exs. 6–8, 61, 63, 67, 69, 72, 73, 77–83 odd, 84, 86

Advanced:
Day 1: pp. 738–739
Exs. 1–5, 9–12, 14–18 even, 19, 20–30 even, 38–50 even, 54–60 even
Day 2: pp. 738–741
Exs. 6–8, 62–74 even, 78–82 even, 83–88

Block:
pp. 738–739
Exs. 1–5, 9–12, 13–17 odd, 19–21, 25–31 odd, 35–41 odd, 45–53 odd, 57, 59 (with 10.1)
pp. 738–741
Exs. 6–8, 61, 63, 67, 69, 72, 73, 77–83 odd, 84, 86 (with 10.3)

9. A circle is formed when a plane intersects the top or bottom half of a double-napped cone and is perpendicular to the axis of the cone.
10. An ellipse is formed when a plane intersects only the top or bottom half of a double-napped cone but is not parallel or perpendicular to the axis of the cone, is not parallel to the side of the cone, and does not intersect the vertex.
11. A parabola is formed when a plane intersects the top or bottom half of a double-napped cone, is parallel to the side of the cone, and does not intersect the vertex.
12. A hyperbola is formed when a plane intersects both halves of a double-napped cone, is parallel to the axis of the cone, and does not intersect the vertex.

19. $x^2 = \frac{3}{2}y$
20. $y^2 = -18x$
21. $x^2 = 2y$
22. $y^2 = -6x$
23. $y^2 = -8x$
24. $x^2 = -8y$
25. $x^2 = -4y$
26. $x^2 = 8y$
27. $y^2 = 4x$
28. $y^2 = -12x$
29. $x^2 = \frac{8}{3}y$
30. $x^2 = -3y$
31. $y^2 = -\frac{25}{2}x$
32. $y^2 = \frac{4}{3}x$

In Exercises 33–46, find the vertex, focus, and directrix of the parabola, and sketch its graph. 33–46. See margin.

33. $y = \frac{1}{2}x^2$ **34.** $y = -2x^2$

35. $y^2 = -6x$ **36.** $y^2 = 3x$

37. $x^2 + 6y = 0$ **38.** $x + y^2 = 0$

39. $(x - 1)^2 + 8(y + 2) = 0$

40. $(x + 5) + (y - 1)^2 = 0$

41. $(x + 3)^2 = 4\left(y - \frac{3}{2}\right)$ **42.** $\left(x + \frac{1}{2}\right)^2 = 4(y - 1)$

43. $y = \frac{1}{4}(x^2 - 2x + 5)$ **44.** $x = \frac{1}{4}(y^2 + 2y + 33)$

45. $y^2 + 6y + 8x + 25 = 0$

46. $y^2 - 4y - 4x = 0$

47–50. See margin.

In Exercises 47–50, find the vertex, focus, and directrix of the parabola. Use a graphing utility to graph the parabola.

47. $x^2 + 4x + 6y - 2 = 0$ **48.** $x^2 - 2x + 8y + 9 = 0$

49. $y^2 + x + y = 0$ **50.** $y^2 - 4x - 4 = 0$

In Exercises 51–60, find the standard form of the equation of the parabola with the given characteristics.

51. $(x - 3)^2 = -(y - 1)$

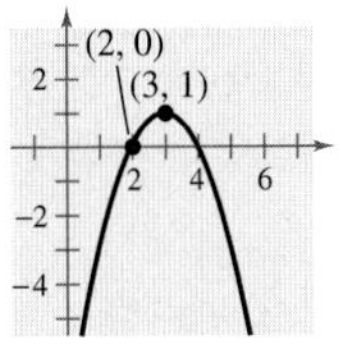

52. $(y - 3)^2 = -2(x - 5)$

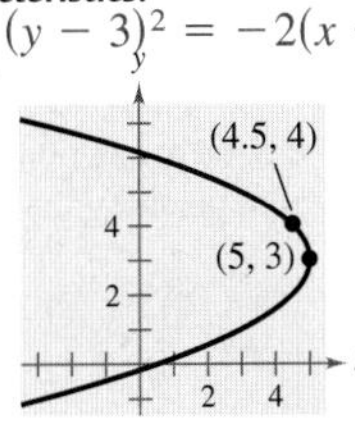

53. $y^2 = 4(x + 4)$

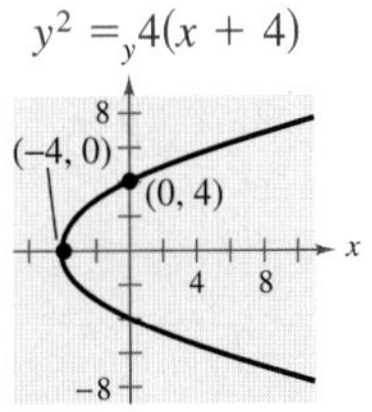

54. $(x - 3)^2 = 3(y + 3)$

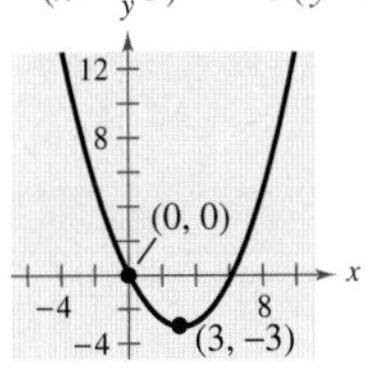

55. Vertex: (4, 3); focus: (6, 3) $(y - 3)^2 = 8(x - 4)$

56. Vertex: $(-1, 2)$; focus: $(-1, 0)$ $(x + 1)^2 = -8(y - 2)$

57. Vertex: (0, 2); directrix: $y = 4$ $x^2 = -8(y - 2)$

58. Vertex: (1, 2); directrix: $y = -1$ $(x - 1)^2 = 12(y - 2)$

59. Focus: (2, 2); directrix: $x = -2$ $(y - 2)^2 = 8x$

60. Focus: (0, 0); directrix: $y = 8$ $x^2 = -16(y - 4)$

In Exercises 61 and 62, change the equation of the parabola so that its graph matches the description.

61. $(y - 3)^2 = 6(x + 1)$; upper half of parabola $y = \sqrt{6(x + 1)} + 3$

62. $(y + 1)^2 = 2(x - 4)$; lower half of parabola $y = -\sqrt{2(x - 4)} - 1$

In Exercises 63 and 64, the equations of a parabola and a tangent line to the parabola are given. Use a graphing utility to graph both equations in the same viewing window. Determine the coordinates of the point of tangency.

	Parabola	*Tangent Line*
63.	$y^2 - 8x = 0$	$x - y + 2 = 0$
64.	$x^2 + 12y = 0$	$x + y - 3 = 0$

63–64. See margin.

In Exercises 65–68, find an equation of the tangent line to the parabola at the given point, and find the x-intercept of the line. 65–68. See margin.

65. $x^2 = 2y$, $(4, 8)$ **66.** $x^2 = 2y$, $\left(-3, \frac{9}{2}\right)$

67. $y = -2x^2$, $(-1, -2)$ **68.** $y = -2x^2$, $(2, -8)$

69. REVENUE The revenue R (in dollars) generated by the sale of x units of a patio furniture set is given by

$$(x - 106)^2 = -\frac{4}{5}(R - 14{,}045).$$ See margin.

Use a graphing utility to graph the function and approximate the number of sales that will maximize revenue.

70. REVENUE The revenue R (in dollars) generated by the sale of x units of a digital camera is given by

$$(x - 135)^2 = -\frac{5}{7}(R - 25{,}515).$$ See margin.

Use a graphing utility to graph the function and approximate the number of sales that will maximize revenue.

71. SUSPENSION BRIDGE Each cable of the Golden Gate Bridge is suspended (in the shape of a parabola) between two towers that are 1280 meters apart. The top of each tower is 152 meters above the roadway. The cables touch the roadway midway between the towers.

(a) Draw a sketch of the bridge. Locate the origin of a rectangular coordinate system at the center of the roadway. Label the coordinates of the known points. See margin.

(b) Write an equation that models the cables.

(c) Complete the table by finding the height y of the suspension cables over the roadway at a distance of x meters from the center of the bridge.

(b) $y = \dfrac{19x^2}{51{,}200}$

Distance, x	Height, y
0	0
100	3.71
250	23.19
400	59.38
500	92.77

33. Vertex: (0, 0)
Focus: $\left(0, \frac{1}{2}\right)$
Directrix: $y = -\frac{1}{2}$

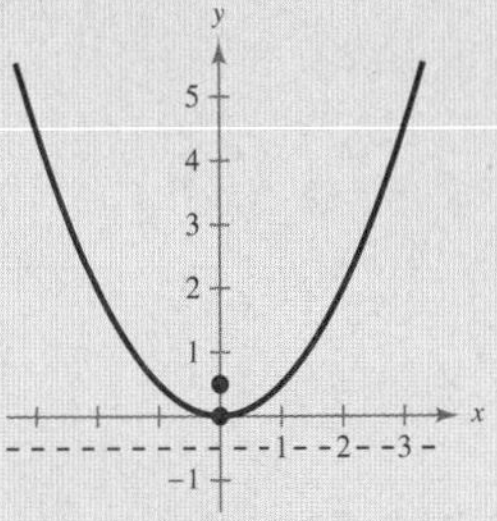

34. Vertex: (0, 0)
Focus: $\left(0, -\frac{1}{8}\right)$
Directrix: $y = \frac{1}{8}$

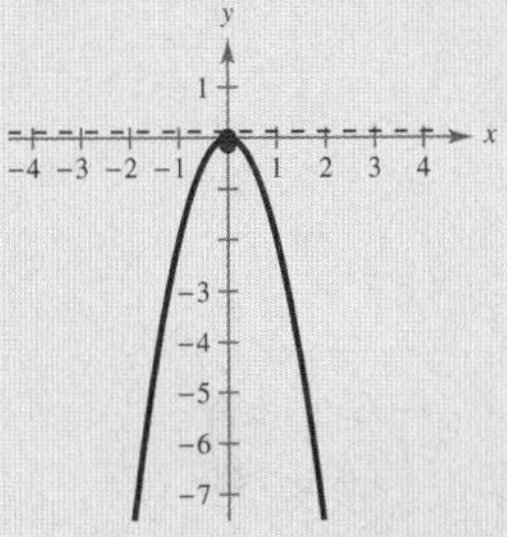

35. Vertex: (0, 0)
Focus: $\left(-\frac{3}{2}, 0\right)$
Directrix: $x = \frac{3}{2}$

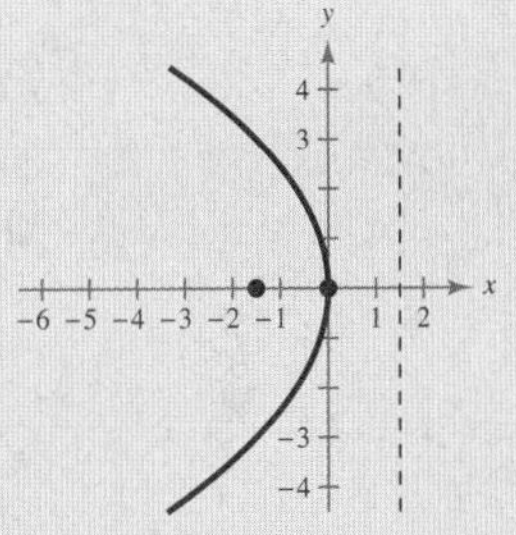

36. Vertex: (0, 0)
Focus: $\left(\frac{3}{4}, 0\right)$
Directrix: $x = -\frac{3}{4}$

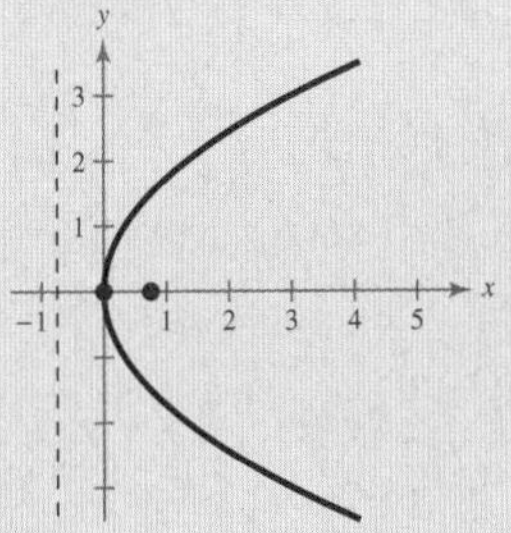

37. Vertex: (0, 0)
Focus: $\left(0, -\frac{3}{2}\right)$
Directrix: $y = \frac{3}{2}$

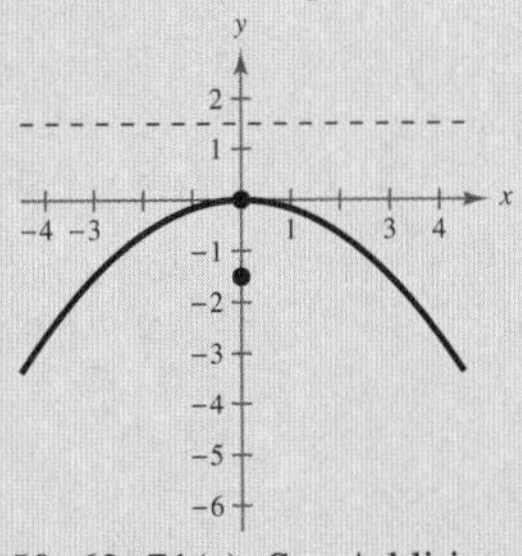

38. Vertex: (0, 0)
Focus: $\left(-\frac{1}{4}, 0\right)$
Directrix: $x = \frac{1}{4}$

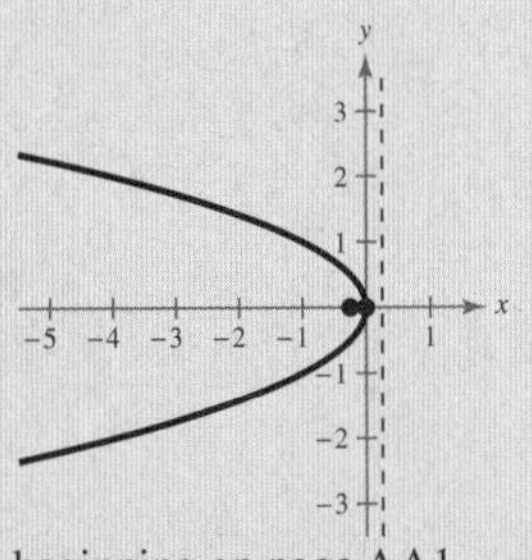

39. Vertex: $(1, -2)$
Focus: $(1, -4)$
Directrix: $y = 0$

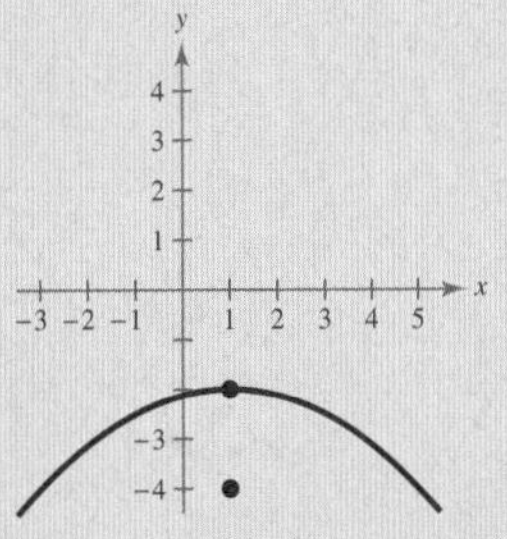

40–50, 63–71(a). See Additional Answers beginning on page AA1.

75. (a) $x^2 = 180{,}000y$
(b) $300\sqrt{2}$ cm ≈ 424.26 cm

76. (a) $x^2 = \dfrac{640{,}000}{3}y$
(b) $\dfrac{800\sqrt{3}}{3}$ cm ≈ 461.88 cm

72. SATELLITE DISH The receiver in a parabolic satellite dish is 4.5 feet from the vertex and is located at the focus (see figure). Write an equation for a cross section of the reflector. (Assume that the dish is directed upward and the vertex is at the origin.) $y = \frac{1}{18}x^2$

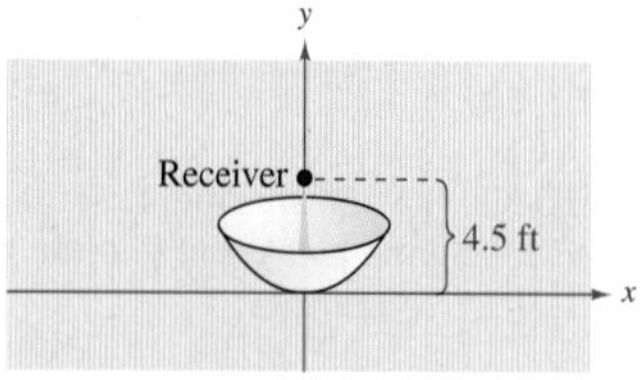

73. ROAD DESIGN Roads are often designed with parabolic surfaces to allow rain to drain off. A particular road that is 32 feet wide is 0.4 foot higher in the center than it is on the sides (see figure).

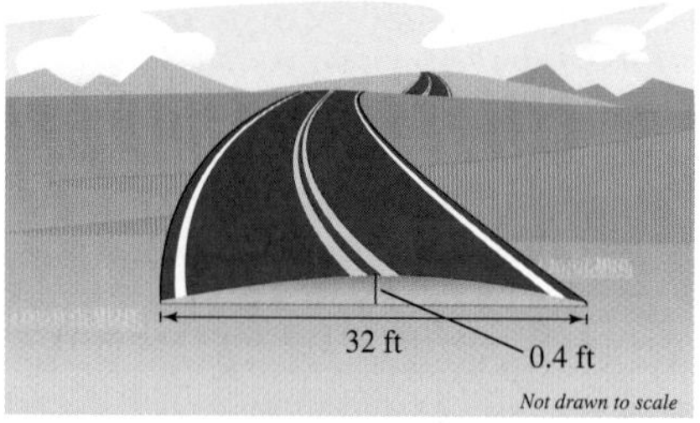

Cross section of road surface

(a) Find an equation of the parabola that models the road surface. (Assume that the origin is at the center of the road.) $y = -\frac{1}{640}x^2$

(b) How far from the center of the road is the road surface 0.1 foot lower than in the middle? 8 ft

74. HIGHWAY DESIGN Highway engineers design a parabolic curve for an entrance ramp from a straight street to an interstate highway (see figure). Find an equation of the parabola. $y^2 = 640x$

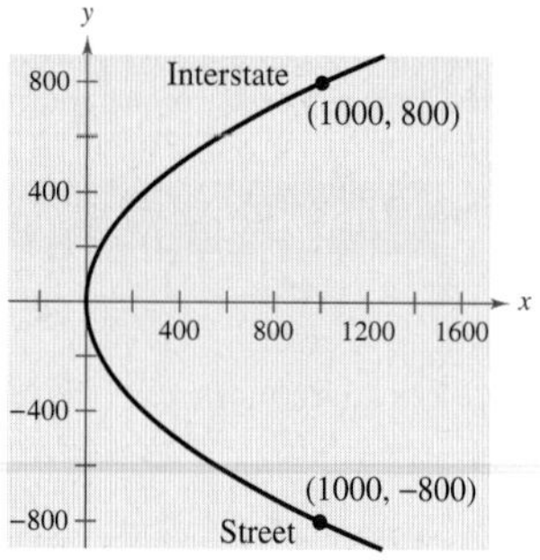

75. BEAM DEFLECTION A simply supported beam is 12 meters long and has a load at the center (see figure). The deflection of the beam at its center is 2 centimeters. Assume that the shape of the deflected beam is parabolic.

(a) Write an equation of the parabola. (Assume that the origin is at the center of the deflected beam.)

(b) How far from the center of the beam is the deflection equal to 1 centimeter? (a)–(b). See margin.

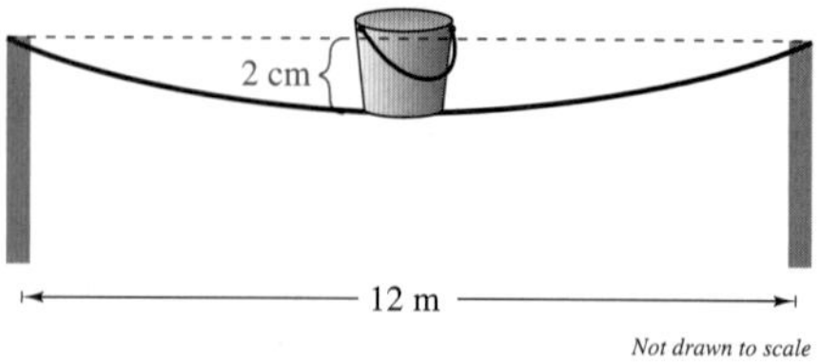

76. BEAM DEFLECTION Repeat Exercise 75 if the length of the beam is 16 meters and the deflection of the beam at the center is 3 centimeters. See margin.

77. FLUID FLOW Water is flowing from a horizontal pipe 48 feet above the ground. The falling stream of water has the shape of a parabola whose vertex $(0, 48)$ is at the end of the pipe (see figure). The stream of water strikes the ground at the point $(10\sqrt{3}, 0)$. Find the equation of the path taken by the water. $x^2 = -\frac{25}{4}(y - 48)$

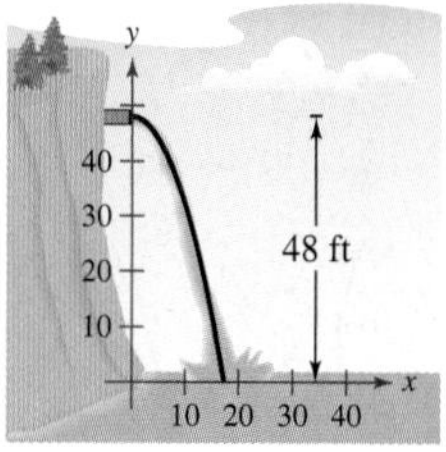

FIGURE FOR 77

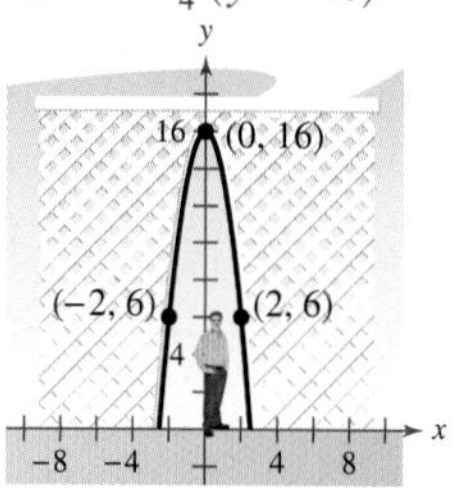

FIGURE FOR 78

78. LATTICE ARCH A parabolic lattice arch is 16 feet high at the vertex. At a height of 6 feet, the width of the lattice arch is 4 feet (see figure). How wide is the lattice arch at ground level? About 5.06 ft

79. SATELLITE ORBIT A satellite in a 100-mile-high circular orbit around Earth has a velocity of approximately 17,500 miles per hour. If this velocity is multiplied by $\sqrt{2}$, the satellite will have the minimum velocity necessary to escape Earth's gravity and it will follow a parabolic path with the center of Earth as the focus (see figure on the next page).

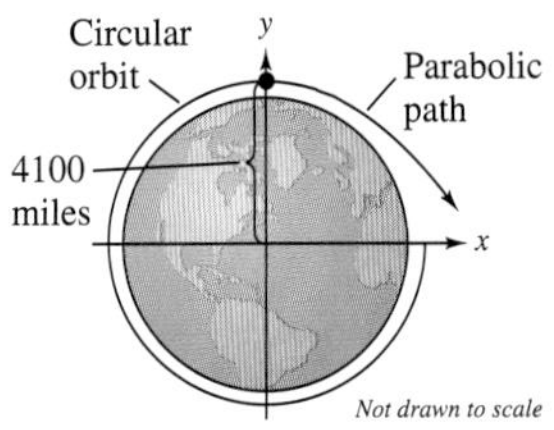

FIGURE FOR 79 See margin.

(a) Find the escape velocity of the satellite.

(b) Find an equation of the parabolic path of the satellite (assume that the radius of Earth is 4000 miles).

80. PATH OF A SOFTBALL The path of a softball is modeled by $-12.5(y - 7.125) = (x - 6.25)^2$, where the coordinates x and y are measured in feet, with $x = 0$ corresponding to the position from which the ball was thrown. See margin.

(a) Use a graphing utility to graph the trajectory of the softball.

(b) Use the *trace* feature of the graphing utility to approximate the highest point and the range of the trajectory.

PROJECTILE MOTION In Exercises 81 and 82, consider the path of a projectile projected horizontally with a velocity of v feet per second at a height of s feet, where the model for the path is

$$x^2 = -\frac{v^2}{16}(y - s).$$

In this model (in which air resistance is disregarded), y is the height (in feet) of the projectile and x is the horizontal distance (in feet) the projectile travels.

81. A ball is thrown from the top of a 100-foot tower with a velocity of 28 feet per second. $x^2 = -49(y - 100)$

(a) Find the equation of the parabolic path.

(b) How far does the ball travel horizontally before striking the ground? 70 ft

82. A cargo plane is flying at an altitude of 30,000 feet and a speed of 540 miles per hour. A supply crate is dropped from the plane. How many *feet* will the crate travel horizontally before it hits the ground? 34,294.6 ft

EXPLORATION

83–84. See margin.

TRUE OR FALSE? In Exercises 83 and 84, determine whether the statement is true or false. Justify your answer.

83. It is possible for a parabola to intersect its directrix.

84. If the vertex and focus of a parabola are on a horizontal line, then the directrix of the parabola is vertical.

85. Let (x_1, y_1) be the coordinates of a point on the parabola $x^2 = 4py$. The equation of the line tangent to the parabola at the point is

$$y - y_1 = \frac{x_1}{2p}(x - x_1).$$

What is the slope of the tangent line? $m = \dfrac{x_1}{2p}$

86. CAPSTONE Explain what each of the following equations represents, and how equations (a) and (b) are equivalent. See margin.

(a) $y = a(x - h)^2 + k, \quad a \neq 0$

(b) $(x - h)^2 = 4p(y - k), \quad p \neq 0$

(c) $(y - k)^2 = 4p(x - h), \quad p \neq 0$

87. GRAPHICAL REASONING Consider the parabola $x^2 = 4py$. See margin.

(a) Use a graphing utility to graph the parabola for $p = 1$, $p = 2$, $p = 3$, and $p = 4$. Describe the effect on the graph when p increases.

(b) Locate the focus for each parabola in part (a).

(c) For each parabola in part (a), find the length of the latus rectum (see figure). How can the length of the latus rectum be determined directly from the standard form of the equation of the parabola?

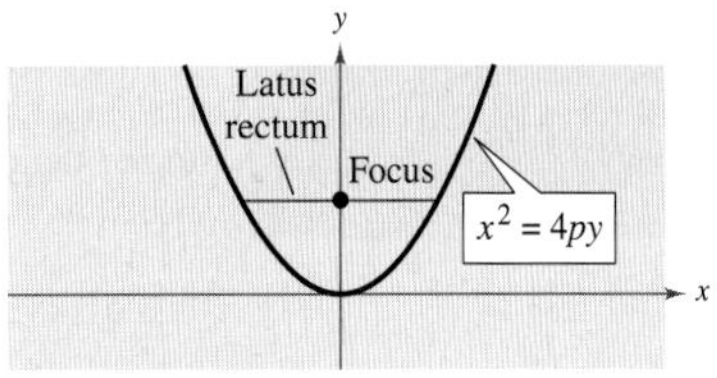

(d) Explain how the result of part (c) can be used as a sketching aid when graphing parabolas.

88. GEOMETRY The area of the shaded region in the figure is $A = \frac{8}{3}p^{1/2}b^{3/2}$. See margin.

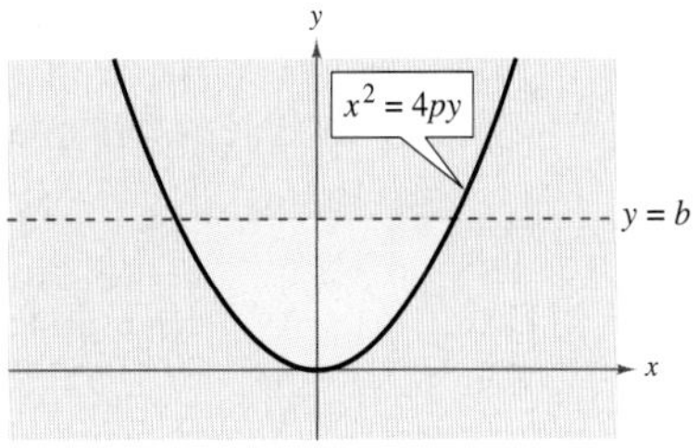

(a) Find the area when $p = 2$ and $b = 4$.

(b) Give a geometric explanation of why the area approaches 0 as p approaches 0.

5 ASSESS AND RETEACH

Daily Homework Quiz

Transparency Available
Available at the Instructor's companion site.

79.
(a) $17{,}500\sqrt{2}$ mi/h $\approx 24{,}750$ mi/h
(b) $x^2 = -16{,}400(y - 4100)$

80. (a)

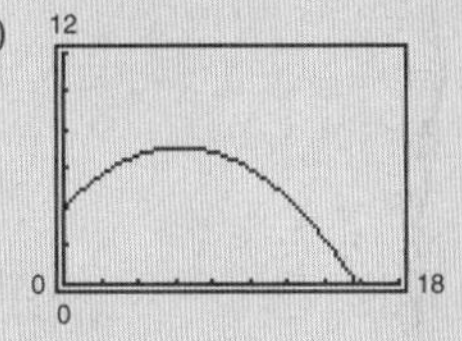

(b) Highest point: (6.25, 7.125)
Range: 15.69 ft

83. False. If the graph crossed the directrix, there would exist points closer to the directrix than the focus.

84. True. If the axis (line connecting the vertex and focus) is horizontal, then the directrix must be vertical.

86. Both (a) and (b) are parabolas with vertical axes, while (c) is a parabola with a horizontal axis. Equations (a) and (b) are equivalent if $p = 1/(4a)$.

87. (a)

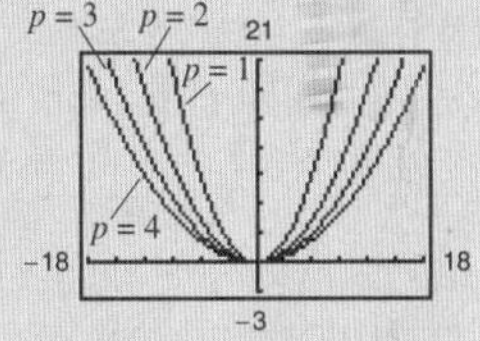

As p increases, the graph becomes wider.
(b) (0, 1), (0, 2), (0, 3), (0, 4)
(c) 4, 8, 12, 16; $4|p|$
(d) It is an easy way to determine two additional points on the graph.

88. (a) $\dfrac{64\sqrt{2}}{3} \approx 30.17$
(b) As p approaches zero, the parabola becomes narrower and narrower, thus the area becomes smaller and smaller.

1 PLAN AND PREPARE

Warm-up Exercises

Transparency Available
Available at the Instructor's companion site.

Notetaking Guide

Transparency Available
Promotes interactive learning and notetaking skills.
Available at the Instructor's companion site.

Animated Precalculus

An **Animated Precalculus** tutorial is available at the Student companion site for **Section 10.3.**

Pacing

Average: 2 days
Advanced: 2 days
Block: 0.5 block with 10.2
0.5 block with 10.4

2 FOCUS AND MOTIVATE

Essential Question

How do you solve problems involving ellipses? **Tell students that they will learn how to answer this question by studying the key characteristics of an ellipse.**

10.3 ELLIPSES

What you should learn

- Write equations of ellipses in standard form and graph ellipses.
- Use properties of ellipses to model and solve real-life problems.
- Find eccentricities of ellipses.

Why you should learn it

Ellipses can be used to model and solve many types of real-life problems. For instance, in Exercise 65 on page 749, an ellipse is used to model the orbit of Halley's comet.

Harvard College Observatory/Photo Researchers, Inc.

Introduction

The second type of conic is called an **ellipse,** and is defined as follows.

> **Definition of Ellipse**
>
> An **ellipse** is the set of all points (x, y) in a plane, the sum of whose distances from two distinct fixed points **(foci)** is constant. See Figure 10.19.

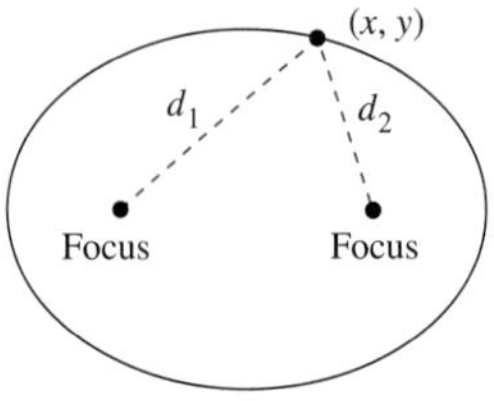

$d_1 + d_2$ is constant.

FIGURE 10.19

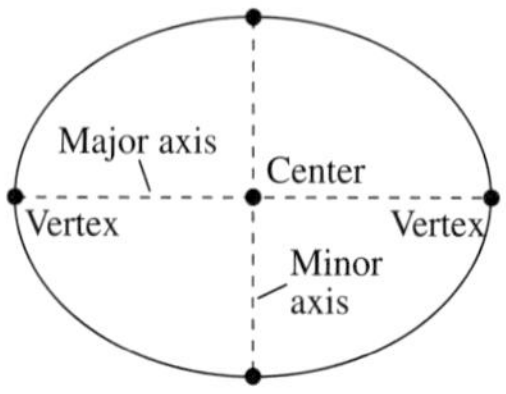

FIGURE 10.20

The line through the foci intersects the ellipse at two points called **vertices.** The chord joining the vertices is the **major axis,** and its midpoint is the **center** of the ellipse. The chord perpendicular to the major axis at the center is the **minor axis** of the ellipse. See Figure 10.20.

You can visualize the definition of an ellipse by imagining two thumbtacks placed at the foci, as shown in Figure 10.21. If the ends of a fixed length of string are fastened to the thumbtacks and the string is *drawn taut* with a pencil, the path traced by the pencil will be an ellipse.

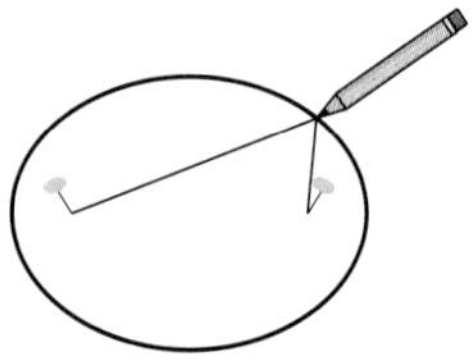

FIGURE 10.21

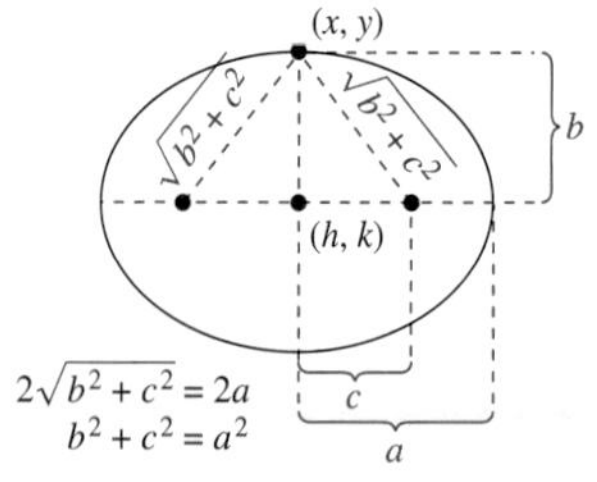

FIGURE 10.22

To derive the standard form of the equation of an ellipse, consider the ellipse in Figure 10.22 with the following points: center, (h, k); vertices, $(h \pm a, k)$; foci, $(h \pm c, k)$. Note that the center is the midpoint of the segment joining the foci. The sum of the distances from any point on the ellipse to the two foci is constant. Using a vertex point, this constant sum is

$$(a + c) + (a - c) = 2a \qquad \text{Length of major axis}$$

or simply the length of the major axis. Now, if you let (x, y) be *any* point on the ellipse, the sum of the distances between (x, y) and the two foci must also be $2a$.

Resource Planning Guide

Chapter Resources
- Complete Solutions Guide

Workbooks
- Notetaking Guide
- Student Solutions Guide

Interactive Technology
- Instructor Success Organizer
- Notetaking Guide IAE
- Instructional DVDs
- Animated Precalculus
- PowerLecture with ExamView

That is,

$$\sqrt{[x - (h - c)]^2 + (y - k)^2} + \sqrt{[x - (h + c)]^2 + (y - k)^2} = 2a$$

which, after expanding and regrouping, reduces to

$$(a^2 - c^2)(x - h)^2 + a^2(y - k)^2 = a^2(a^2 - c^2).$$

Finally, in Figure 10.22, you can see that

$$b^2 = a^2 - c^2$$

which implies that the equation of the ellipse is

$$b^2(x - h)^2 + a^2(y - k)^2 = a^2b^2$$

$$\frac{(x - h)^2}{a^2} + \frac{(y - k)^2}{b^2} = 1.$$

You would obtain a similar equation in the derivation by starting with a vertical major axis. Both results are summarized as follows.

Study Tip

Consider the equation of the ellipse

$$\frac{(x - h)^2}{a^2} + \frac{(y - k)^2}{b^2} = 1.$$

If you let $a = b$, then the equation can be rewritten as

$$(x - h)^2 + (y - k)^2 = a^2$$

which is the standard form of the equation of a circle with radius $r = a$ (see Section 1.2). Geometrically, when $a = b$ for an ellipse, the major and minor axes are of equal length, and so the graph is a circle.

Standard Equation of an Ellipse

The **standard form of the equation of an ellipse,** with center (h, k) and major and minor axes of lengths $2a$ and $2b$, respectively, where $0 < b < a$, is

$$\frac{(x - h)^2}{a^2} + \frac{(y - k)^2}{b^2} = 1 \qquad \text{Major axis is horizontal.}$$

$$\frac{(x - h)^2}{b^2} + \frac{(y - k)^2}{a^2} = 1. \qquad \text{Major axis is vertical.}$$

The foci lie on the major axis, c units from the center, with $c^2 = a^2 - b^2$. If the center is at the origin $(0, 0)$, the equation takes one of the following forms.

$$\frac{x^2}{a^2} + \frac{y^2}{b^2} = 1 \qquad \text{Major axis is horizontal.}$$

$$\frac{x^2}{b^2} + \frac{y^2}{a^2} = 1 \qquad \text{Major axis is vertical.}$$

Figure 10.23 shows both the horizontal and vertical orientations for an ellipse.

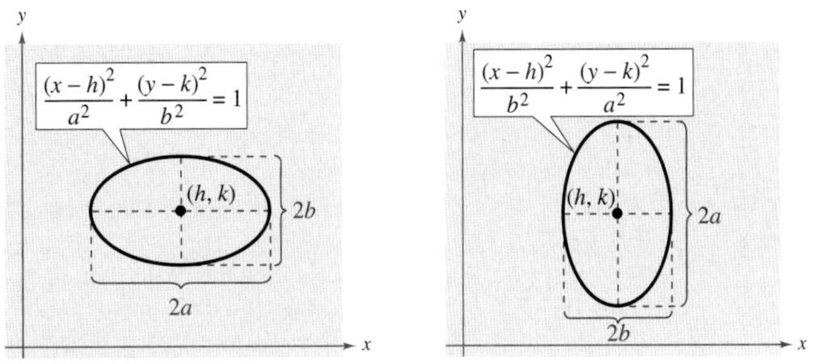

Major axis is horizontal. Major axis is vertical.

FIGURE 10.23

Example 1 Finding the Standard Equation of an Ellipse

Find the standard form of the equation of the ellipse having foci at $(0, 1)$ and $(4, 1)$ and a major axis of length 6, as shown in Figure 10.24.

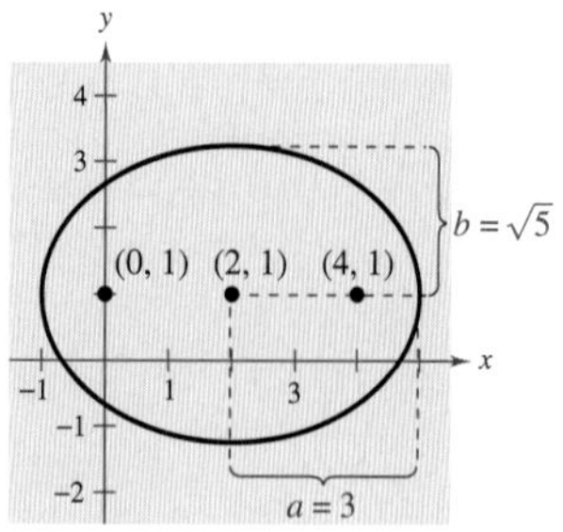

FIGURE 10.24

Solution

Because the foci occur at $(0, 1)$ and $(4, 1)$, the center of the ellipse is $(2, 1)$ and the distance from the center to one of the foci is $c = 2$. Because $2a = 6$, you know that $a = 3$. Now, from $c^2 = a^2 - b^2$, you have

$$b = \sqrt{a^2 - c^2} = \sqrt{3^2 - 2^2} = \sqrt{5}.$$

Because the major axis is horizontal, the standard equation is

$$\frac{(x-2)^2}{3^2} + \frac{(y-1)^2}{(\sqrt{5})^2} = 1.$$

This equation simplifies to

$$\frac{(x-2)^2}{9} + \frac{(y-1)^2}{5} = 1.$$

CHECKPoint Now try Exercise 23.

Example 2 Sketching an Ellipse

Sketch the ellipse given by $x^2 + 4y^2 + 6x - 8y + 9 = 0$.

Solution

Begin by writing the original equation in standard form. In the fourth step, note that 9 and 4 are added to *both* sides of the equation when completing the squares.

$$x^2 + 4y^2 + 6x - 8y + 9 = 0$$ Write original equation.

$$(x^2 + 6x + \quad) + (4y^2 - 8y + \quad) = -9$$ Group terms.

$$(x^2 + 6x + \quad) + 4(y^2 - 2y + \quad) = -9$$ Factor 4 out of y-terms.

$$(x^2 + 6x + 9) + 4(y^2 - 2y + 1) = -9 + 9 + 4(1)$$

$$(x+3)^2 + 4(y-1)^2 = 4$$ Write in completed square form.

$$\frac{(x+3)^2}{4} + \frac{(y-1)^2}{1} = 1$$ Divide each side by 4.

$$\frac{(x+3)^2}{2^2} + \frac{(y-1)^2}{1^2} = 1$$ Write in standard form.

From this standard form, it follows that the center is $(h, k) = (-3, 1)$. Because the denominator of the x-term is $a^2 = 2^2$, the endpoints of the major axis lie two units to the right and left of the center. Similarly, because the denominator of the y-term is $b^2 = 1^2$, the endpoints of the minor axis lie one unit up and down from the center. Now, from $c^2 = a^2 - b^2$, you have $c = \sqrt{2^2 - 1^2} = \sqrt{3}$. So, the foci of the ellipse are $(-3 - \sqrt{3}, 1)$ and $(-3 + \sqrt{3}, 1)$. The ellipse is shown in Figure 10.25.

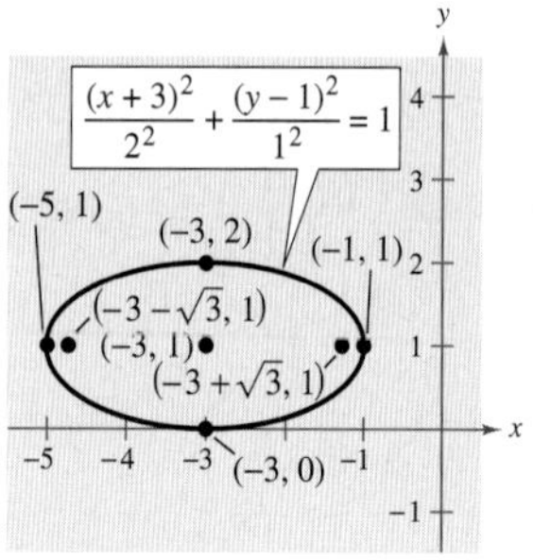

FIGURE 10.25

CHECKPoint Now try Exercise 47.

3 TEACH

Extra Example 1

Find the standard form of the equation of the ellipse having foci at $(-2, 2)$ and $(4, 2)$ and a major axis of length 10.

$$\frac{(x-1)^2}{25} + \frac{(y-2)^2}{16} = 1$$

Extra Example 2

Sketch the graph of the ellipse given by $9x^2 + 4y^2 + 36x - 8y + 4 = 0$.

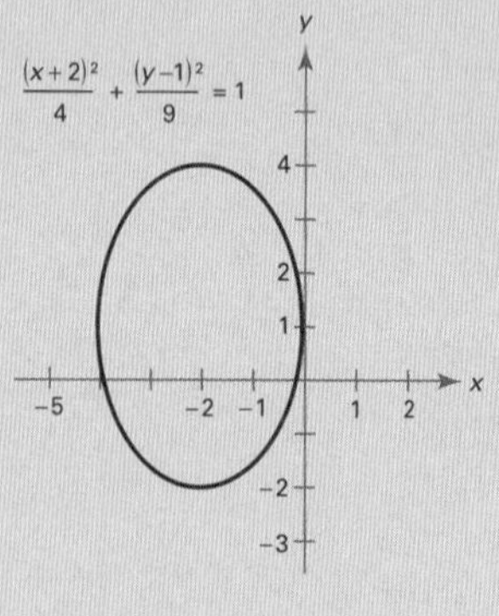

Avoiding Common Errors

Remind students that they must complete the square for both variables when writing the equation in standard form. Students should also make sure that they compensate for the number introduced multiplied by the coefficient for each variable. They can do this by adding this amount to the other side of the equation.

Example 3 Analyzing an Ellipse

Find the center, vertices, and foci of the ellipse $4x^2 + y^2 - 8x + 4y - 8 = 0$.

Solution

By completing the square, you can write the original equation in standard form.

$$4x^2 + y^2 - 8x + 4y - 8 = 0 \qquad \text{Write original equation.}$$

$$(4x^2 - 8x + \quad) + (y^2 + 4y + \quad) = 8 \qquad \text{Group terms.}$$

$$4(x^2 - 2x + \quad) + (y^2 + 4y + \quad) = 8 \qquad \text{Factor 4 out of } x\text{-terms.}$$

$$4(x^2 - 2x + 1) + (y^2 + 4y + 4) = 8 + 4(1) + 4$$

$$4(x - 1)^2 + (y + 2)^2 = 16 \qquad \text{Write in completed square form.}$$

$$\frac{(x - 1)^2}{4} + \frac{(y + 2)^2}{16} = 1 \qquad \text{Divide each side by 16.}$$

$$\frac{(x - 1)^2}{2^2} + \frac{(y + 2)^2}{4^2} = 1 \qquad \text{Write in standard form.}$$

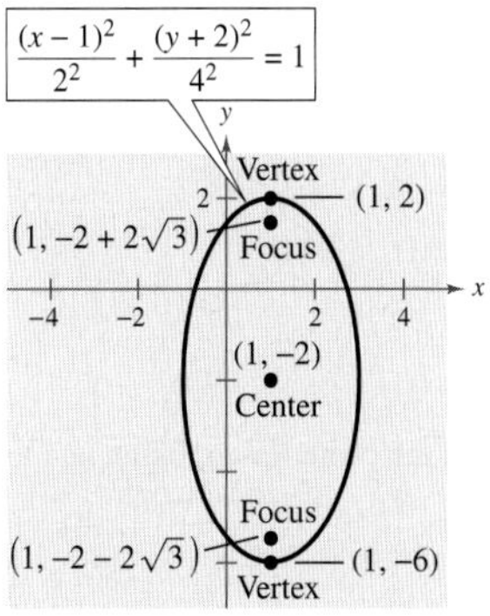

FIGURE 10.26

The major axis is vertical, where $h = 1$, $k = -2$, $a = 4$, $b = 2$, and

$$c = \sqrt{a^2 - b^2} = \sqrt{16 - 4} = \sqrt{12} = 2\sqrt{3}.$$

So, you have the following.

Center: $(1, -2)$ Vertices: $(1, -6)$, $(1, 2)$ Foci: $(1, -2 - 2\sqrt{3})$, $(1, -2 + 2\sqrt{3})$

The graph of the ellipse is shown in Figure 10.26.

CHECKPoint Now try Exercise 51.

TECHNOLOGY

You can use a graphing utility to graph an ellipse by graphing the upper and lower portions in the same viewing window. For instance, to graph the ellipse in Example 3, first solve for y to get

$$y_1 = -2 + 4\sqrt{1 - \frac{(x - 1)^2}{4}} \quad \text{and} \quad y_2 = -2 - 4\sqrt{1 - \frac{(x - 1)^2}{4}}.$$

Use a viewing window in which $-6 \le x \le 9$ and $-7 \le y \le 3$. You should obtain the graph shown below.

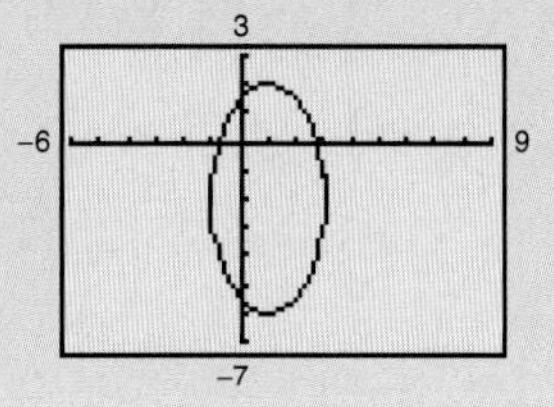

Extra Example 3

Find the center, vertices, and foci of the ellipse given by $16x^2 + 25y^2 - 32x - 50y + 16 = 0$.

Center: $(1, 1)$; Foci: $(\frac{7}{4}, 1)$, $(\frac{1}{4}, 1)$;

Vertices: $(\frac{9}{4}, 1)$, $(-\frac{1}{4}, 1)$

Extra Example 4

The first artificial satellite to orbit Earth was *Sputnik I* (launched by Russia in 1957). Its orbit was elliptical with the center of Earth at one focus. The major and minor axes of the orbit had lengths of 13,906 kilometers and 13,887 kilometers, respectively. Find the apogee and perigee from Earth's center to the satellite. Use these to find the least distance and greatest distance of the satellite from Earth's surface in this orbit (Earth has a radius of 6378 kilometers).

Apogee: 7316 kilometers; perigee: 6590 kilometers; greatest distance: 938 kilometers; least distance: 212 kilometers

Application

Ellipses have many practical and aesthetic uses. For instance, machine gears, supporting arches, and acoustic designs often involve elliptical shapes. The orbits of satellites and planets are also ellipses. Example 4 investigates the elliptical orbit of the moon about Earth.

Example 4 An Application Involving an Elliptical Orbit

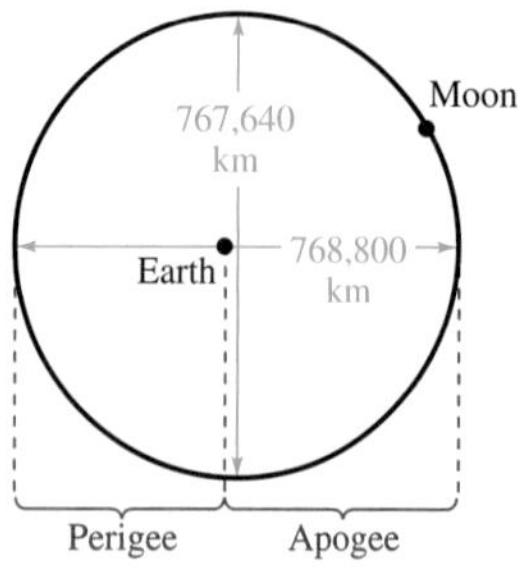

FIGURE 10.27

The moon travels about Earth in an elliptical orbit with Earth at one focus, as shown in Figure 10.27. The major and minor axes of the orbit have lengths of 768,800 kilometers and 767,640 kilometers, respectively. Find the greatest and smallest distances (the *apogee* and *perigee*, respectively) from Earth's center to the moon's center.

Solution

Because $2a = 768{,}800$ and $2b = 767{,}640$, you have

$$a = 384{,}400 \text{ and } b = 383{,}820$$

which implies that

$$c = \sqrt{a^2 - b^2}$$
$$= \sqrt{384{,}400^2 - 383{,}820^2}$$
$$\approx 21{,}108.$$

So, the greatest distance between the center of Earth and the center of the moon is

$$a + c \approx 384{,}400 + 21{,}108 = 405{,}508 \text{ kilometers}$$

and the smallest distance is

$$a - c \approx 384{,}400 - 21{,}108 = 363{,}292 \text{ kilometers.}$$

CHECKPoint Now try Exercise 65.

WARNING/CAUTION

Note in Example 4 and Figure 10.27 that Earth *is not* the center of the moon's orbit.

Eccentricity

One of the reasons it was difficult for early astronomers to detect that the orbits of the planets are ellipses is that the foci of the planetary orbits are relatively close to their centers, and so the orbits are nearly circular. To measure the ovalness of an ellipse, you can use the concept of **eccentricity.**

Definition of Eccentricity

The **eccentricity** e of an ellipse is given by the ratio

$$e = \frac{c}{a}.$$

Note that $0 < e < 1$ for *every* ellipse.

To see how this ratio is used to describe the shape of an ellipse, note that because the foci of an ellipse are located along the major axis between the vertices and the center, it follows that

$$0 < c < a.$$

For an ellipse that is nearly circular, the foci are close to the center and the ratio c/a is small, as shown in Figure 10.28. On the other hand, for an elongated ellipse, the foci are close to the vertices and the ratio c/a is close to 1, as shown in Figure 10.29.

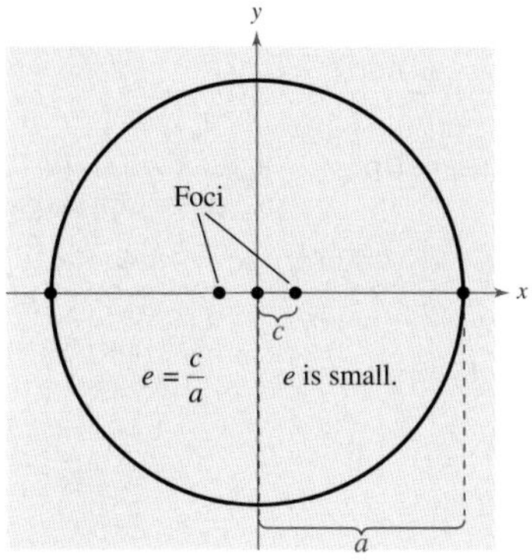

FIGURE 10.28

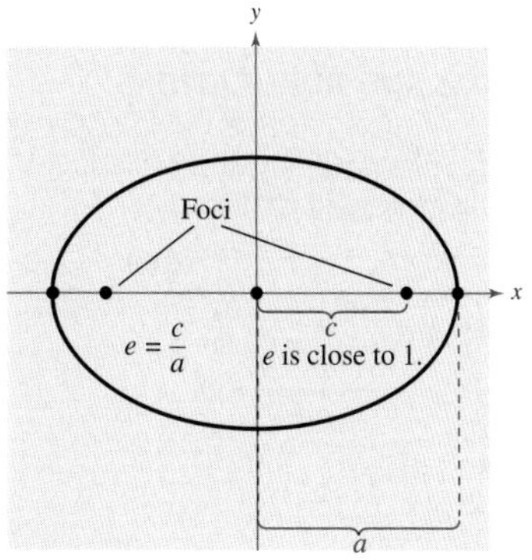

FIGURE 10.29

The time it takes Saturn to orbit the sun is about 29.4 Earth years.

The orbit of the moon has an eccentricity of $e \approx 0.0549$, and the eccentricities of the eight planetary orbits are as follows.

Mercury:	$e \approx 0.2056$	Jupiter:	$e \approx 0.0484$
Venus:	$e \approx 0.0068$	Saturn:	$e \approx 0.0542$
Earth:	$e \approx 0.0167$	Uranus:	$e \approx 0.0472$
Mars:	$e \approx 0.0934$	Neptune:	$e \approx 0.0086$

Classroom Discussion

Ellipses and Circles

a. Show that the equation of an ellipse can be written as

$$\frac{(x-h)^2}{a^2} + \frac{(y-k)^2}{a^2(1-e^2)} = 1.$$

b. For the equation in part (a), let $a = 4$, $h = 1$, and $k = 2$, and use a graphing utility to graph the ellipse for $e = 0.95$, $e = 0.75$, $e = 0.5$, $e = 0.25$, and $e = 0.1$. Discuss the changes in the shape of the ellipse as e approaches 0.

c. Make a conjecture about the shape of the graph in part (b) when $e = 0$. What is the equation of this ellipse? What is another name for an ellipse with an eccentricity of 0? See margin.

Closing the Lesson

Have students summarize the major points of the lesson and answer the Essential Question: How do you solve problems involving ellipses?

- **Describe an ellipse as the locus of points, the sum of whose distances from two distinct fixed points is constant.**
- **Write the standard form of the equation of an ellipse, using its center, vertices, and major and minor axes.**
- **Find the distance c from the center to the foci of an ellipse with major and minor axes of lengths $2a$ and $2b$, respectively, by using the Pythagorean Theorem or the equation $c = \sqrt{a^2 - b^2}$.**
- **Find the ovalness of an ellipse by calculating its eccentricity.**

Classroom Discussion

a. Answers will vary.

b.

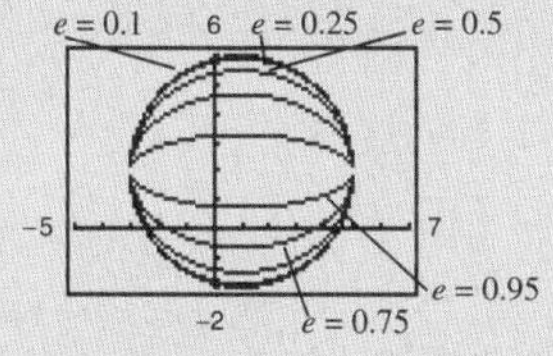

As e approaches 0, the shape of the ellipse approaches the shape of a circle.

c. When $e = 0$, the graph of the equation is circular. The equation of the ellipse is

$$\frac{(x-h)^2}{a^2} + \frac{(y-k)^2}{a^2} = 1,$$

otherwise known as the equation of a circle.

10.3 EXERCISES

See www.CalcChat.com for worked-out solutions to odd-numbered exercises.

VOCABULARY: Fill in the blanks.

1. An ellipse is the set of all points (x, y) in a plane, the sum of whose distances from two distinct fixed points, called foci, is constant.
2. The chord joining the vertices of an ellipse is called the major axis, and its midpoint is the center of the ellipse.
3. The chord perpendicular to the major axis at the center of the ellipse is called the minor axis of the ellipse.
4. The concept of ________ is used to measure the ovalness of an ellipse. eccentricity

SKILLS AND APPLICATIONS

In Exercises 5–10, match the equation with its graph. [The graphs are labeled (a), (b), (c), (d), (e), and (f).]

(a)

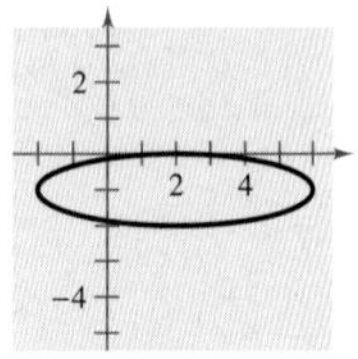

(b)

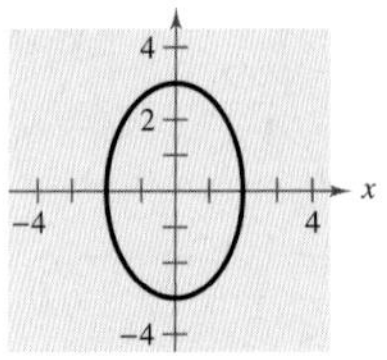

(c)

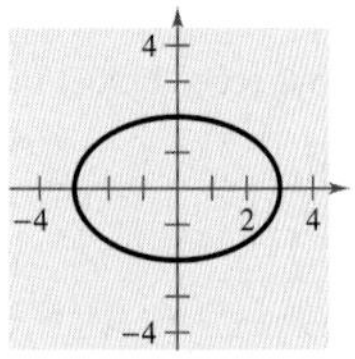

(d)

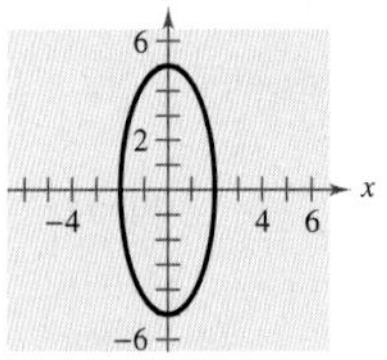

(e)

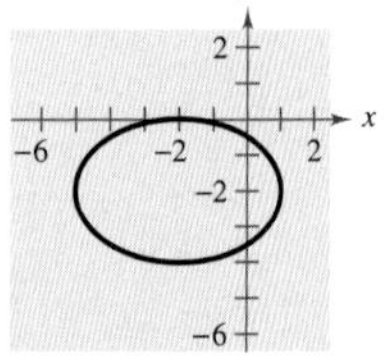

(f)

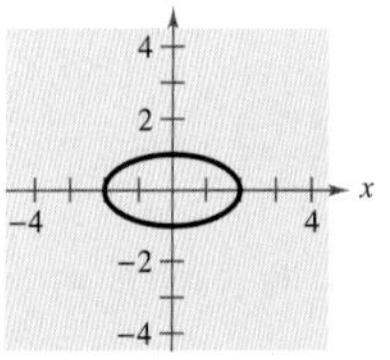

5. $\frac{x^2}{4} + \frac{y^2}{9} = 1$ b
6. $\frac{x^2}{9} + \frac{y^2}{4} = 1$ c
7. $\frac{x^2}{4} + \frac{y^2}{25} = 1$ d
8. $\frac{x^2}{4} + y^2 = 1$ f
9. $\frac{(x-2)^2}{16} + (y+1)^2 = 1$ a
10. $\frac{(x+2)^2}{9} + \frac{(y+2)^2}{4} = 1$ e

In Exercises 11–18, find the standard form of the equation of the ellipse with the given characteristics and center at the origin.

11–18. See margin.

11.

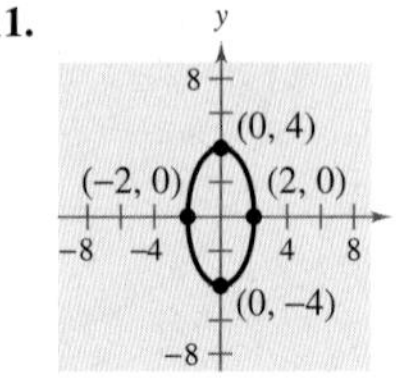

12.

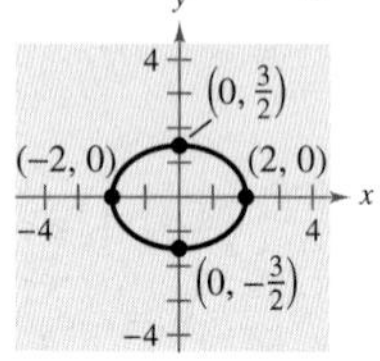

13. Vertices: $(\pm 7, 0)$; foci: $(\pm 2, 0)$
14. Vertices: $(0, \pm 8)$; foci: $(0, \pm 4)$
15. Foci: $(\pm 5, 0)$; major axis of length 14
16. Foci: $(\pm 2, 0)$; major axis of length 10
17. Vertices: $(0, \pm 5)$; passes through the point $(4, 2)$
18. Vertical major axis; passes through the points $(0, 6)$ and $(3, 0)$

In Exercises 19–28, find the standard form of the equation of the ellipse with the given characteristics.

19–26. See margin.

19.

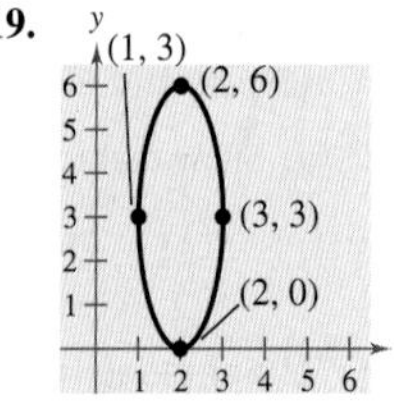

20.

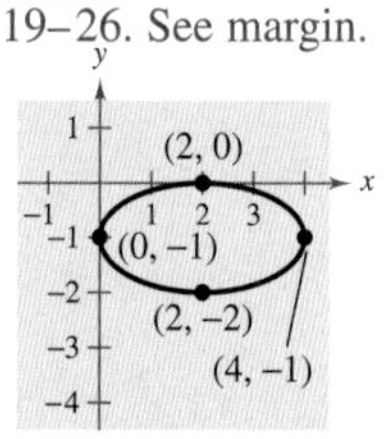

21. Vertices: $(0, 2), (8, 2)$; minor axis of length 2
22. Foci: $(0, 0), (4, 0)$; major axis of length 6
23. Foci: $(0, 0), (0, 8)$; major axis of length 16
24. Center: $(2, -1)$; vertex: $(2, \frac{1}{2})$; minor axis of length 2
25. Center: $(0, 4)$; $a = 2c$; vertices: $(-4, 4), (4, 4)$
26. Center: $(3, 2)$; $a = 3c$; foci: $(1, 2), (5, 2)$

4 PRACTICE AND APPLY

Assignment Guide

Transparencies Available
Available at the Instructor's companion site.

Average:
Day 1: pp. 748–749
Exs. 1–3, 5–10, 11–27 odd
Day 2: pp. 748–750
Exs. 4, 29–45 odd, 49, 50, 53–63 odd, 67–69, 71, 73, 74, 76

Advanced:
Day 1: pp. 748–749
Exs. 1–3, 5–10, 12–28 even
Day 2: pp. 748–750
Exs. 4, 30–46 even, 50–68 even, 70–75, 78

Block:
pp. 748–749
Exs. 1–3, 5–10, 11–27 odd (with 10.2)
pp. 748–750
Exs. 4, 29–45 odd, 49, 50, 53–63 odd, 67–69, 71, 73, 74, 76 (with 10.4)

11. $\frac{x^2}{4} + \frac{y^2}{16} = 1$
12. $\frac{x^2}{4} + \frac{4y^2}{9} = 1$
13. $\frac{x^2}{49} + \frac{y^2}{45} = 1$
14. $\frac{x^2}{48} + \frac{y^2}{64} = 1$
15. $\frac{x^2}{49} + \frac{y^2}{24} = 1$
16. $\frac{x^2}{25} + \frac{y^2}{21} = 1$
17. $\frac{21x^2}{400} + \frac{y^2}{25} = 1$
18. $\frac{x^2}{9} + \frac{y^2}{36} = 1$
19. $\frac{(x-2)^2}{1} + \frac{(y-3)^2}{9} = 1$
20. $\frac{(x-2)^2}{4} + \frac{(y+1)^2}{1} = 1$
21. $\frac{(x-4)^2}{16} + \frac{(y-2)^2}{1} = 1$
22. $\frac{(x-2)^2}{9} + \frac{y^2}{5} = 1$
23. $\frac{x^2}{48} + \frac{(y-4)^2}{64} = 1$
24. $\frac{(x-2)^2}{1} + \frac{4(y+1)^2}{9} = 1$
25. $\frac{x^2}{16} + \frac{(y-4)^2}{12} = 1$
26. $\frac{(x-3)^2}{36} + \frac{(y-2)^2}{32} = 1$

27. Vertices: (0, 2), (4, 2); endpoints of the minor axis: (2, 3), (2, 1) 27–28. See margin.

28. Vertices: (5, 0), (5, 12); endpoints of the minor axis: (1, 6), (9, 6)

In Exercises 29–52, identify the conic as a circle or an ellipse. Then find the center, radius, vertices, foci, and eccentricity of the conic (if applicable), and sketch its graph. 29–52. See margin.

29. $\frac{x^2}{25} + \frac{y^2}{16} = 1$

30. $\frac{x^2}{16} + \frac{y^2}{81} = 1$

31. $\frac{x^2}{25} + \frac{y^2}{25} = 1$

32. $\frac{x^2}{9} + \frac{y^2}{9} = 1$

33. $\frac{x^2}{5} + \frac{y^2}{9} = 1$

34. $\frac{x^2}{64} + \frac{y^2}{28} = 1$

35. $\frac{(x-4)^2}{16} + \frac{(y+1)^2}{25} = 1$

36. $\frac{(x+3)^2}{12} + \frac{(y-2)^2}{16} = 1$

37. $\frac{x^2}{4/9} + \frac{(y+1)^2}{4/9} = 1$

38. $\frac{(x+5)^2}{9/4} + (y-1)^2 = 1$

39. $(x+2)^2 + \frac{(y+4)^2}{1/4} = 1$

40. $\frac{(x-3)^2}{25/4} + \frac{(y-1)^2}{25/4} = 1$

41. $9x^2 + 4y^2 + 36x - 24y + 36 = 0$

42. $9x^2 + 4y^2 - 54x + 40y + 37 = 0$

43. $x^2 + y^2 - 2x + 4y - 31 = 0$

44. $x^2 + 5y^2 - 8x - 30y - 39 = 0$

45. $3x^2 + y^2 + 18x - 2y - 8 = 0$

46. $6x^2 + 2y^2 + 18x - 10y + 2 = 0$

47. $x^2 + 4y^2 - 6x + 20y - 2 = 0$

48. $x^2 + y^2 - 4x + 6y - 3 = 0$

49. $9x^2 + 9y^2 + 18x - 18y + 14 = 0$

50. $16x^2 + 25y^2 - 32x + 50y + 16 = 0$

51. $9x^2 + 25y^2 - 36x - 50y + 60 = 0$

52. $16x^2 + 16y^2 - 64x + 32y + 55 = 0$

In Exercises 53–56, use a graphing utility to graph the ellipse. Find the center, foci, and vertices. (Recall that it may be necessary to solve the equation for *y* and obtain two equations.) 53–56. See margin.

53. $5x^2 + 3y^2 = 15$

54. $3x^2 + 4y^2 = 12$

55. $12x^2 + 20y^2 - 12x + 40y - 37 = 0$

56. $36x^2 + 9y^2 + 48x - 36y - 72 = 0$

In Exercises 57–60, find the eccentricity of the ellipse.

57. $\frac{x^2}{4} + \frac{y^2}{9} = 1$ $\frac{\sqrt{5}}{3}$

58. $\frac{x^2}{25} + \frac{y^2}{36} = 1$ $\frac{\sqrt{11}}{6}$

59. $x^2 + 9y^2 - 10x + 36y + 52 = 0$ 59. $\frac{2\sqrt{2}}{3}$

60. $4x^2 + 3y^2 - 8x + 18y + 19 = 0$ $\frac{1}{2}$

61. Find an equation of the ellipse with vertices $(\pm 5, 0)$ and eccentricity $e = \frac{3}{5}$. See margin.

62. Find an equation of the ellipse with vertices $(0, \pm 8)$ and eccentricity $e = \frac{1}{2}$. See margin.

63. **ARCHITECTURE** A semielliptical arch over a tunnel for a one-way road through a mountain has a major axis of 50 feet and a height at the center of 10 feet.

(a) Draw a rectangular coordinate system on a sketch of the tunnel with the center of the road entering the tunnel at the origin. Identify the coordinates of the known points. (a)–(b). See margin.

(b) Find an equation of the semielliptical arch.

(c) You are driving a moving truck that has a width of 8 feet and a height of 9 feet. Will the moving truck clear the opening of the arch? Yes

64. **ARCHITECTURE** A fireplace arch is to be constructed in the shape of a semiellipse. The opening is to have a height of 2 feet at the center and a width of 6 feet along the base (see figure). The contractor draws the outline of the ellipse using tacks as described at the beginning of this section. Determine the required positions of the tacks and the length of the string. Positions of tacks: $(\pm\sqrt{5}, 0)$ Length of string: 6 ft

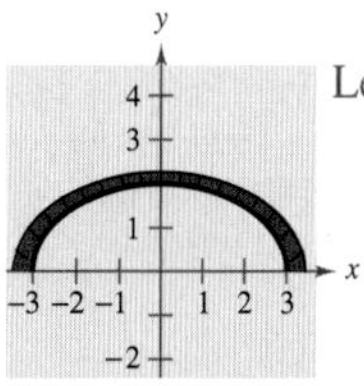

65. **COMET ORBIT** Halley's comet has an elliptical orbit, with the sun at one focus. The eccentricity of the orbit is approximately 0.967. The length of the major axis of the orbit is approximately 35.88 astronomical units. (An astronomical unit is about 93 million miles.)

(a) Find an equation of the orbit. Place the center of the orbit at the origin, and place the major axis on the *x*-axis.

(b) Use a graphing utility to graph the equation of the orbit. (a)–(b). See margin.

(c) Find the greatest (aphelion) and smallest (perihelion) distances from the sun's center to the comet's center.

Aphelion: 35.29 astronomical units
Perihelion: 0.59 astronomical unit

27. $\frac{(x-2)^2}{4} + \frac{(y-2)^2}{1} = 1$

28. $\frac{(x-5)^2}{16} + \frac{(y-6)^2}{36} = 1$

29. Ellipse
Center: (0, 0)
Vertices: $(\pm 5, 0)$
Foci: $(\pm 3, 0)$
Eccentricity: $\frac{3}{5}$

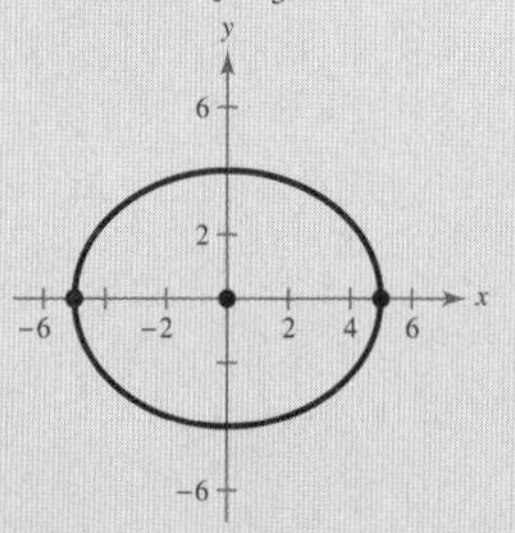

30. Ellipse
Center: (0, 0)
Vertices: $(0, \pm 9)$
Foci: $(0, \pm\sqrt{65})$
Eccentricity: $\frac{\sqrt{65}}{9}$

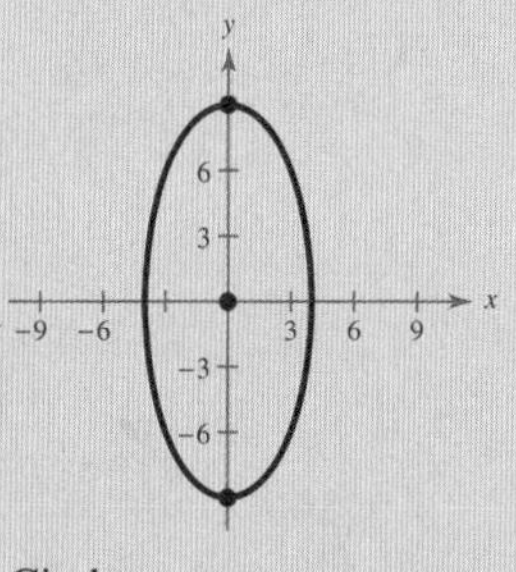

31. Circle
Center: (0, 0)
Radius: 5

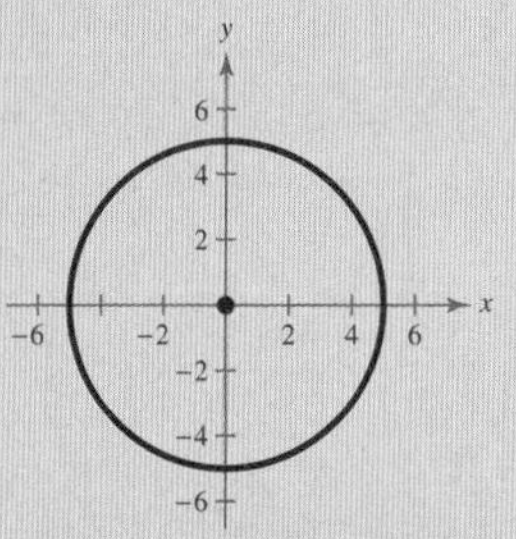

32. Circle
Center: (0, 0)
Radius: 3

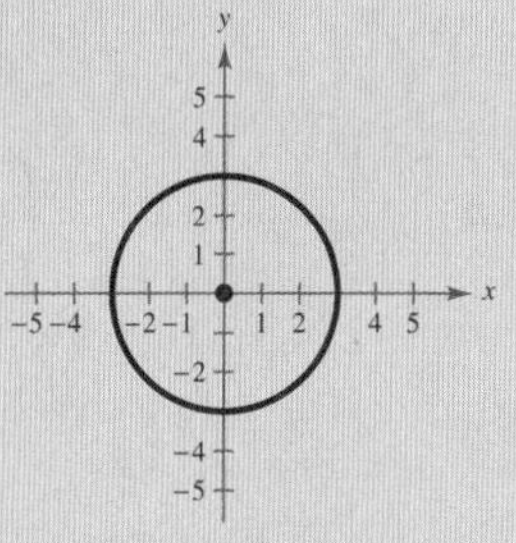

33. Ellipse
Center: (0, 0)
Vertices: $(0, \pm 3)$
Foci: $(0, \pm 2)$
Eccentricity: $\frac{2}{3}$

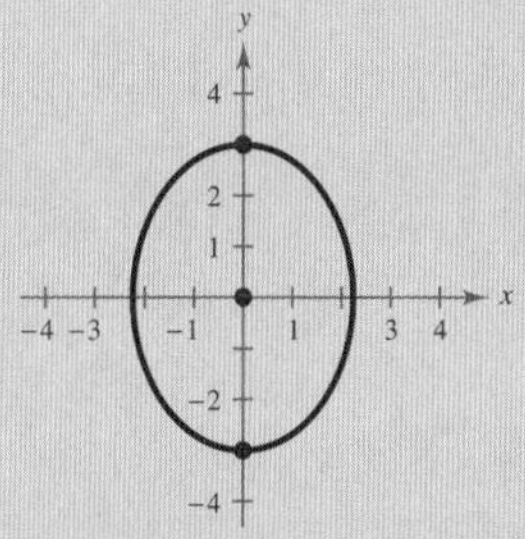

34. Ellipse
Center: (0, 0)
Vertices: $(\pm 8, 0)$
Foci: $(\pm 6, 0)$
Eccentricity: $\frac{3}{4}$

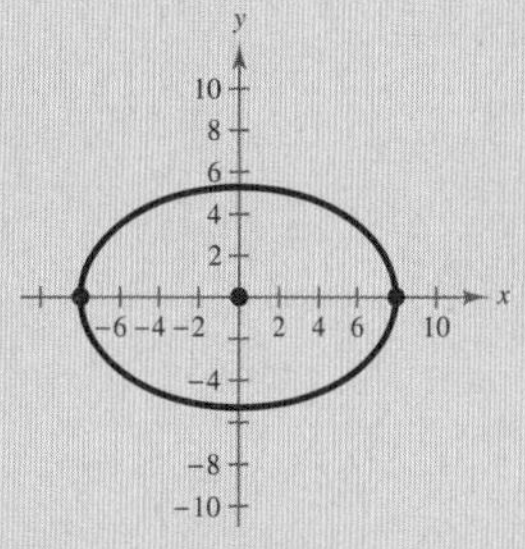

35–56, 61–62, 63(a)–(b), 65(a)–(b). See Additional Answers beginning on page AA1.

66. SATELLITE ORBIT The first artificial satellite to orbit Earth was Sputnik I (launched by the former Soviet Union in 1957). Its highest point above Earth's surface was 947 kilometers, and its lowest point was 228 kilometers (see figure). The center of Earth was at one focus of the elliptical orbit, and the radius of Earth is 6378 kilometers. Find the eccentricity of the orbit. $e \approx 0.052$

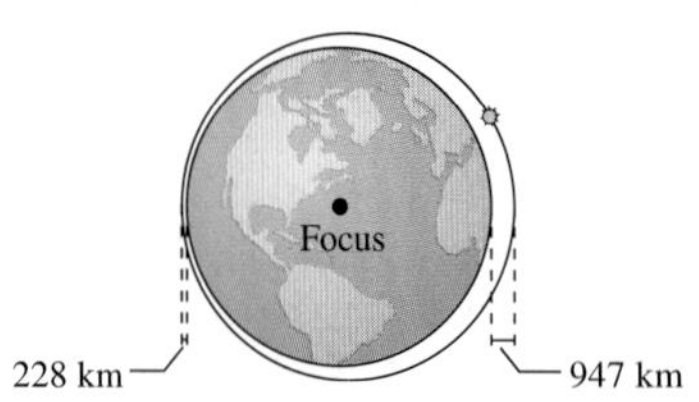

67. MOTION OF A PENDULUM The relation between the velocity y (in radians per second) of a pendulum and its angular displacement θ from the vertical can be modeled by a semiellipse. A 12-centimeter pendulum crests ($y = 0$) when the angular displacement is -0.2 radian and 0.2 radian. When the pendulum is at equilibrium ($\theta = 0$), the velocity is -1.6 radians per second.

(a) Find an equation that models the motion of the pendulum. Place the center at the origin. (a)–(b).

(b) Graph the equation from part (a). See margin.

(c) Which half of the ellipse models the motion of the pendulum? The bottom half

68. GEOMETRY A line segment through a focus of an ellipse with endpoints on the ellipse and perpendicular to the major axis is called a **latus rectum** of the ellipse. Therefore, an ellipse has two latera recta. Knowing the length of the latera recta is helpful in sketching an ellipse because it yields other points on the curve (see figure). Show that the length of each latus rectum is $2b^2/a$. Answers will vary.

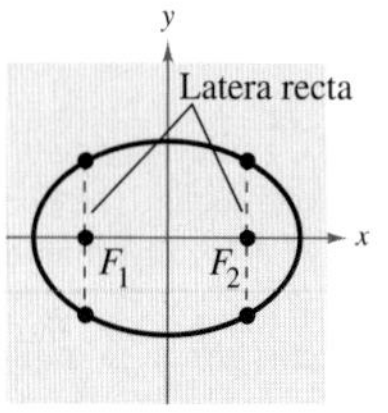

In Exercises 69–72, sketch the graph of the ellipse, using latera recta (see Exercise 68). 69–72. See margin.

69. $\dfrac{x^2}{9} + \dfrac{y^2}{16} = 1$ **70.** $\dfrac{x^2}{4} + \dfrac{y^2}{1} = 1$

71. $5x^2 + 3y^2 = 15$ **72.** $9x^2 + 4y^2 = 36$

EXPLORATION

73–74. See margin.

TRUE OR FALSE? In Exercises 73 and 74, determine whether the statement is true or false. Justify your answer.

73. The graph of $x^2 + 4y^4 - 4 = 0$ is an ellipse.

74. It is easier to distinguish the graph of an ellipse from the graph of a circle if the eccentricity of the ellipse is large (close to 1).

75. Consider the ellipse (a) $A = \pi a(20 - a)$

$\dfrac{x^2}{a^2} + \dfrac{y^2}{b^2} = 1, \quad a + b = 20.$ (b) $\dfrac{x^2}{196} + \dfrac{y^2}{36} = 1$

(a) The area of the ellipse is given by $A = \pi ab$. Write the area of the ellipse as a function of a.

(b) Find the equation of an ellipse with an area of 264 square centimeters.

(c) Complete the table using your equation from part (a), and make a conjecture about the shape of the ellipse with maximum area. (c)–(d). See margin.

a	8	9	10	11	12	13
A						

(d) Use a graphing utility to graph the area function and use the graph to support your conjecture in part (c).

76. THINK ABOUT IT At the beginning of this section it was noted that an ellipse can be drawn using two thumbtacks, a string of fixed length (greater than the distance between the two tacks), and a pencil. If the ends of the string are fastened at the tacks and the string is drawn taut with a pencil, the path traced by the pencil is an ellipse.

(a) What is the length of the string in terms of a? $2a$

(b) Explain why the path is an ellipse. See margin.

77. THINK ABOUT IT Find the equation of an ellipse such that for any point on the ellipse, the sum of the distances from the point (2, 2) and (10, 2) is 36. See margin.

78. CAPSTONE Describe the relationship between circles and ellipses. How are they similar? How do they differ? Answers will vary.

79. PROOF Show that $a^2 = b^2 + c^2$ for the ellipse

$$\frac{x^2}{a^2} + \frac{y^2}{b^2} = 1$$

where $a > 0$, $b > 0$, and the distance from the center of the ellipse (0, 0) to a focus is c. Proof

5 ASSESS AND RETEACH

Daily Homework Quiz

Transparency Available

Available at the Instructor's companion site.

67. (a) $y = -8\sqrt{0.04 - \theta^2}$

(b)

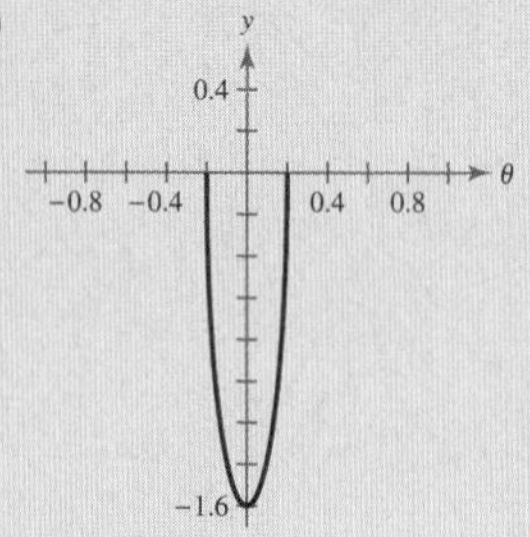

69.

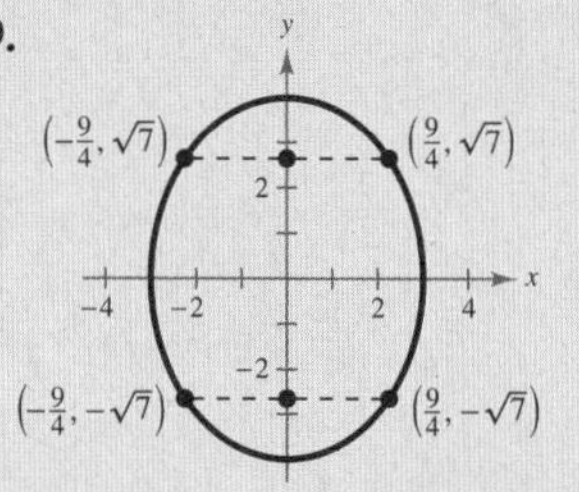

70.

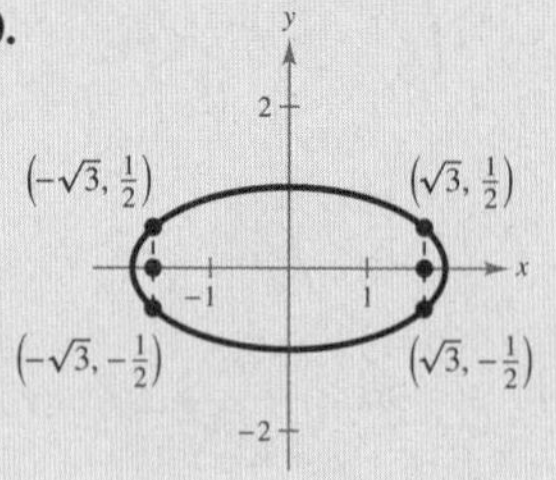

71.

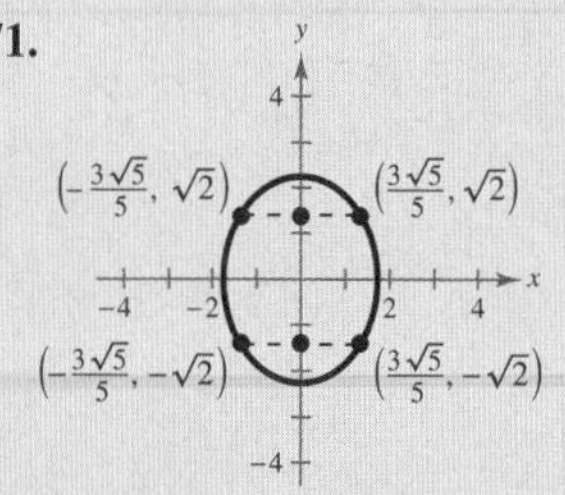

72.

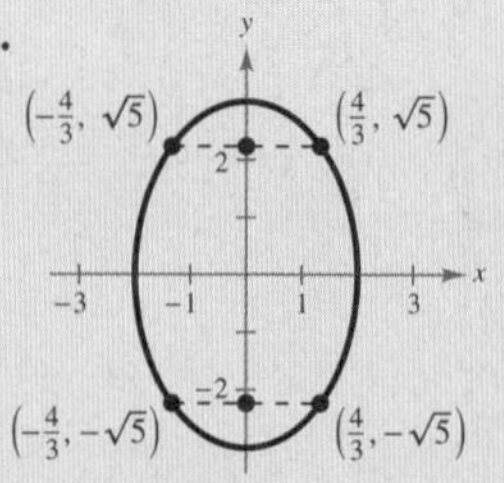

73. False. The graph of $(x^2/4) + y^4 = 1$ is not an ellipse. The degree of y is 4, not 2.

74. True. If e is close to 1, the ellipse is elongated and the foci are close to the vertices.

75. (c)

a	8	9	10	11	12	13
A	301.6	311.0	314.2	311.0	301.6	285.9

$a = 10$, circle

(d)

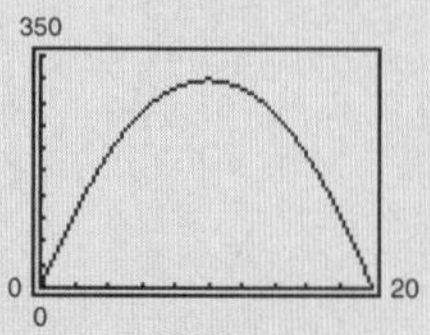

The shape of an ellipse with a maximum area is a circle. The maximum area is found when $a = 10$ (verified in part c) and therefore $b = 10$, so the equation produces a circle.

76. (b) The sum of the distances from the two fixed points is constant.

77. $\dfrac{(x-6)^2}{324} + \dfrac{(y-2)^2}{308} = 1$

10.4 Hyperbolas

What you should learn

- Write equations of hyperbolas in standard form.
- Find asymptotes of and graph hyperbolas.
- Use properties of hyperbolas to solve real-life problems.
- Classify conics from their general equations.

Why you should learn it

Hyperbolas can be used to model and solve many types of real-life problems. For instance, in Exercise 54 on page 759, hyperbolas are used in long distance radio navigation for aircraft and ships.

U.S. Navy, William Lipski/AP Photo

Introduction

The third type of conic is called a **hyperbola.** The definition of a hyperbola is similar to that of an ellipse. The difference is that for an ellipse the *sum* of the distances between the foci and a point on the ellipse is fixed, whereas for a hyperbola the *difference* of the distances between the foci and a point on the hyperbola is fixed.

Definition of Hyperbola

A **hyperbola** is the set of all points (x, y) in a plane, the difference of whose distances from two distinct fixed points **(foci)** is a positive constant. See Figure 10.30.

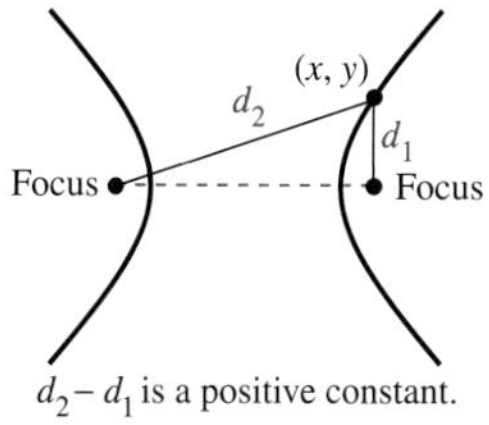

FIGURE 10.30

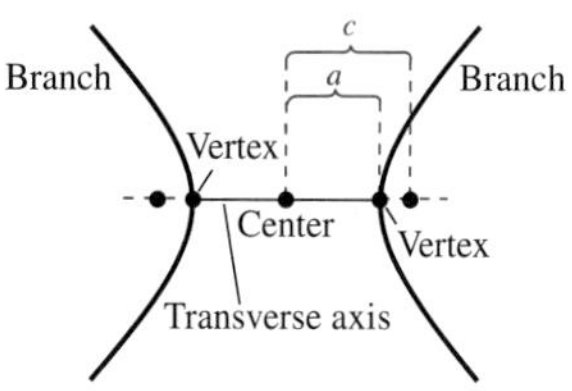

FIGURE 10.31

The graph of a hyperbola has two disconnected **branches.** The line through the two foci intersects the hyperbola at its two **vertices.** The line segment connecting the vertices is the **transverse axis,** and the midpoint of the transverse axis is the **center** of the hyperbola. See Figure 10.31. The development of the standard form of the equation of a hyperbola is similar to that of an ellipse. Note in the definition below that a, b, and c are related differently for hyperbolas than for ellipses.

Standard Equation of a Hyperbola

The **standard form of the equation of a hyperbola** with center (h, k) is

$$\frac{(x-h)^2}{a^2} - \frac{(y-k)^2}{b^2} = 1 \qquad \text{Transverse axis is horizontal.}$$

$$\frac{(y-k)^2}{a^2} - \frac{(x-h)^2}{b^2} = 1. \qquad \text{Transverse axis is vertical.}$$

The vertices are a units from the center, and the foci are c units from the center. Moreover, $c^2 = a^2 + b^2$. If the center of the hyperbola is at the origin $(0, 0)$, the equation takes one of the following forms.

$$\frac{x^2}{a^2} - \frac{y^2}{b^2} = 1 \qquad \text{Transverse axis is horizontal.}$$

$$\frac{y^2}{a^2} - \frac{x^2}{b^2} = 1 \qquad \text{Transverse axis is vertical.}$$

1 Plan and Prepare

Warm-up Exercises

Transparency Available
Available at the Instructor's companion site.

Notetaking Guide

Transparency Available
Promotes interactive learning and notetaking skills.
Available at the Instructor's companion site.

Animated Precalculus

An **Animated Precalculus** tutorial is available at the Student companion site for **Section 10.4.**

Pacing

Average: 2 days
Advanced: 2 days
Block: 0.5 block with 10.3
0.5 block with 10.5

2 Focus and Motivate

Essential Question

How do you solve problems involving hyperbolas and classify a conic section on the basis of its general equation? **Tell students that they will learn how to answer this question by studying the key characteristics of hyperbolas and the coefficients of the general equation.**

Resource Planning Guide

Chapter Resources

- Complete Solutions Guide

Workbooks

- Notetaking Guide
- Student Solutions Guide

Interactive Technology

- Instructor Success Organizer
- Notetaking Guide IAE
- Instructional DVDs
- Animated Precalculus
- PowerLecture with ExamView

3 TEACH

Extra Example 1

Find the standard form of the equation of the hyperbola with foci (0, 0) and (8, 0) and vertices (3, 0) and (5, 0).

$$\frac{(x-4)^2}{1} - \frac{y^2}{15} = 1$$

Avoiding Common Errors

Students often confuse the orientation of the major and transverse axes when given the equation of an ellipse or a hyperbola. With an ellipse, the larger value of a or b determines the major axis because the x- and y-terms are added. With a hyperbola, changing the position of the x- and y-terms changes the equation because subtraction is involved; the leading term shows the orientation of the transverse axis.

Figure 10.32 shows both the horizontal and vertical orientations for a hyperbola.

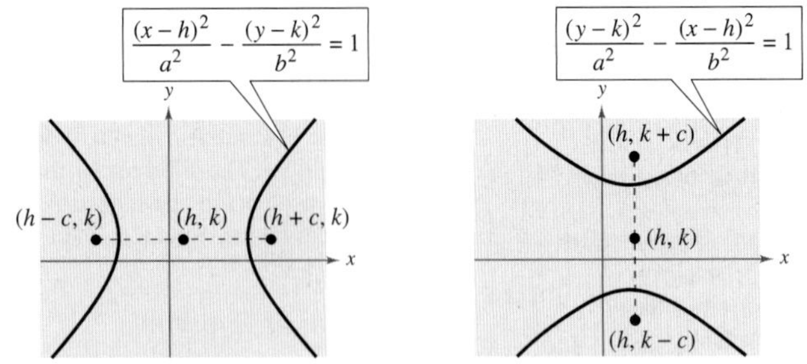

Transverse axis is horizontal. Transverse axis is vertical.

FIGURE 10.32

Example 1 Finding the Standard Equation of a Hyperbola

Find the standard form of the equation of the hyperbola with foci $(-1, 2)$ and $(5, 2)$ and vertices $(0, 2)$ and $(4, 2)$.

Solution

By the Midpoint Formula, the center of the hyperbola occurs at the point $(2, 2)$. Furthermore, $c = 5 - 2 = 3$ and $a = 4 - 2 = 2$, and it follows that

$$b = \sqrt{c^2 - a^2} = \sqrt{3^2 - 2^2} = \sqrt{9 - 4} = \sqrt{5}.$$

So, the hyperbola has a horizontal transverse axis and the standard form of the equation is

$$\frac{(x-2)^2}{2^2} - \frac{(y-2)^2}{(\sqrt{5})^2} = 1.$$ See Figure 10.33.

This equation simplifies to

$$\frac{(x-2)^2}{4} - \frac{(y-2)^2}{5} = 1.$$

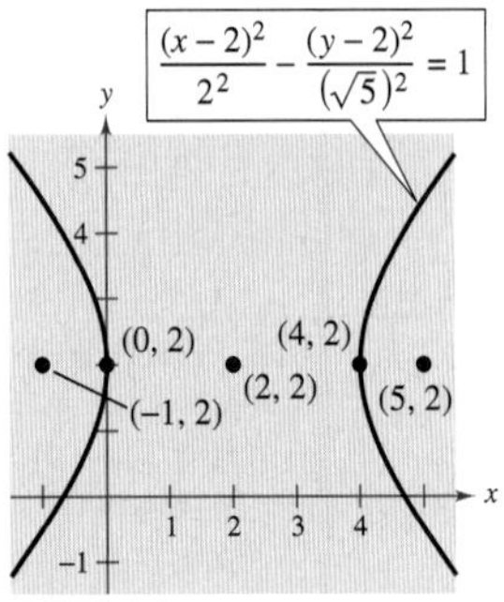

FIGURE 10.33

CHECKPoint Now try Exercise 35.

Study Tip

When finding the standard form of the equation of any conic, it is helpful to sketch a graph of the conic with the given characteristics.

Differentiated Instruction

English Language Learners Students learning English may have difficulty recalling which conic section is a parabola and which is a hyperbola. Tell them that the prefix *hyper-* means "over and above" or "excessive." Help them use this definition to recall that a hyperbola forms two lines on a graph. Two lines are "over and above" the one line of a parabola.

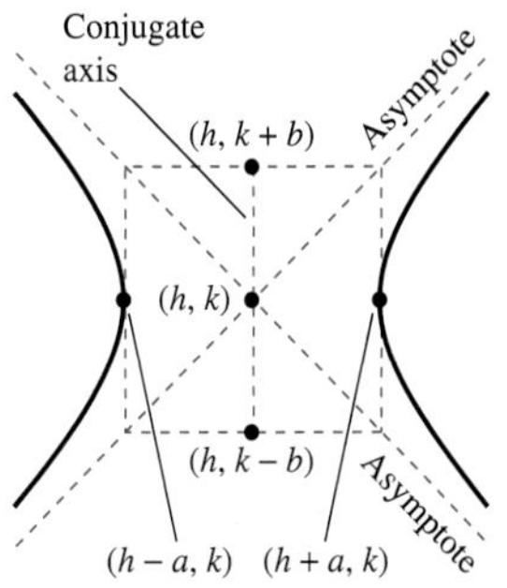

FIGURE 10.34

Asymptotes of a Hyperbola

Each hyperbola has two **asymptotes** that intersect at the center of the hyperbola, as shown in Figure 10.34. The asymptotes pass through the vertices of a rectangle of dimensions $2a$ by $2b$, with its center at (h, k). The line segment of length $2b$ joining $(h, k+b)$ and $(h, k-b)$ [or $(h+b, k)$ and $(h-b, k)$] is the **conjugate axis** of the hyperbola.

Asymptotes of a Hyperbola

The equations of the asymptotes of a hyperbola are

$$y = k \pm \frac{b}{a}(x-h) \qquad \text{Transverse axis is horizontal.}$$

$$y = k \pm \frac{a}{b}(x-h). \qquad \text{Transverse axis is vertical.}$$

Extra Example 2

Sketch the hyperbola whose equation is $4y^2 - 9x^2 = 36$.

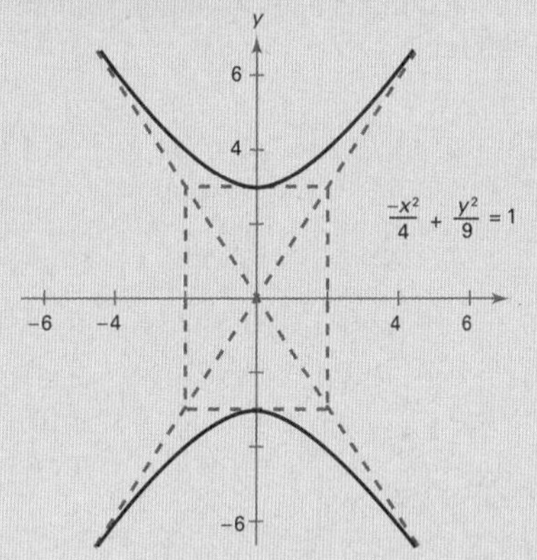

Example 2 Using Asymptotes to Sketch a Hyperbola

Sketch the hyperbola whose equation is $4x^2 - y^2 = 16$.

Algebraic Solution

Divide each side of the original equation by 16, and rewrite the equation in standard form.

$$\frac{x^2}{2^2} - \frac{y^2}{4^2} = 1 \qquad \text{Write in standard form.}$$

From this, you can conclude that $a = 2$, $b = 4$, and the transverse axis is horizontal. So, the vertices occur at $(-2, 0)$ and $(2, 0)$, and the endpoints of the conjugate axis occur at $(0, -4)$ and $(0, 4)$. Using these four points, you are able to sketch the rectangle shown in Figure 10.35. Now, from $c^2 = a^2 + b^2$, you have $c = \sqrt{2^2 + 4^2} = \sqrt{20} = 2\sqrt{5}$. So, the foci of the hyperbola are $(-2\sqrt{5}, 0)$ and $(2\sqrt{5}, 0)$. Finally, by drawing the asymptotes through the corners of this rectangle, you can complete the sketch shown in Figure 10.36. Note that the asymptotes are $y = 2x$ and $y = -2x$.

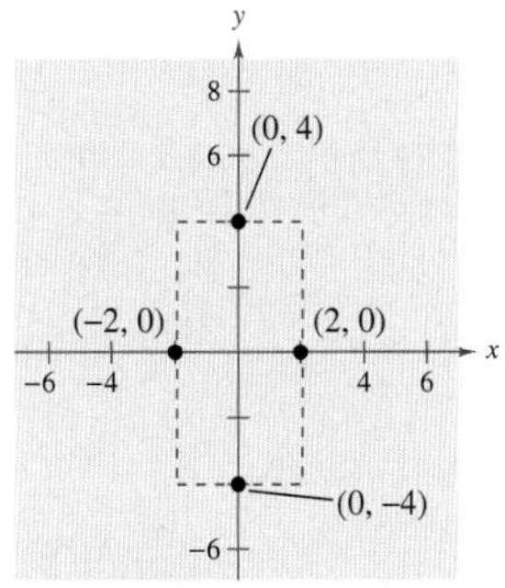

FIGURE 10.35

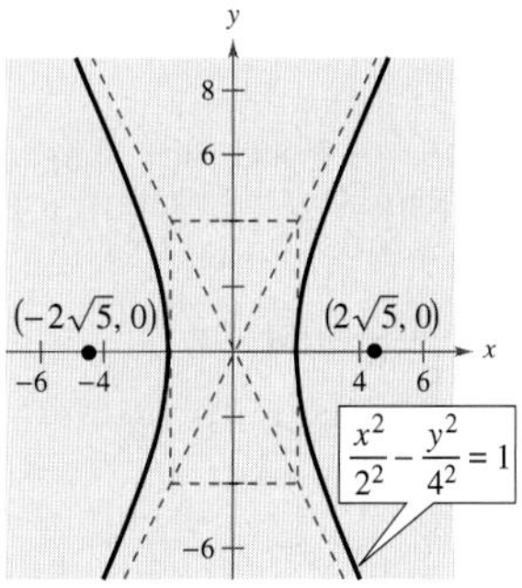

FIGURE 10.36

Graphical Solution

Solve the equation of the hyperbola for y as follows.

$$4x^2 - y^2 = 16$$

$$4x^2 - 16 = y^2$$

$$\pm\sqrt{4x^2 - 16} = y$$

Then use a graphing utility to graph $y_1 = \sqrt{4x^2 - 16}$ and $y_2 = -\sqrt{4x^2 - 16}$ in the same viewing window. Be sure to use a square setting. From the graph in Figure 10.37, you can see that the transverse axis is horizontal. You can use the *zoom* and *trace* features to approximate the vertices to be $(-2, 0)$ and $(2, 0)$.

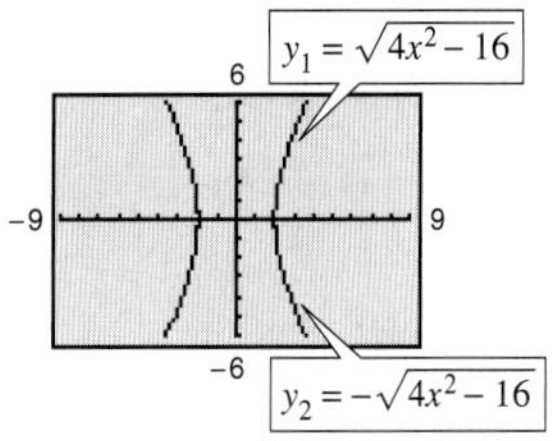

FIGURE 10.37

CHECKPoint Now try Exercise 11.

Extra Example 3

Sketch the hyperbola given by $9x^2 - 4y^2 + 8y - 40 = 0$ and find the equations of its asymptotes and the foci.

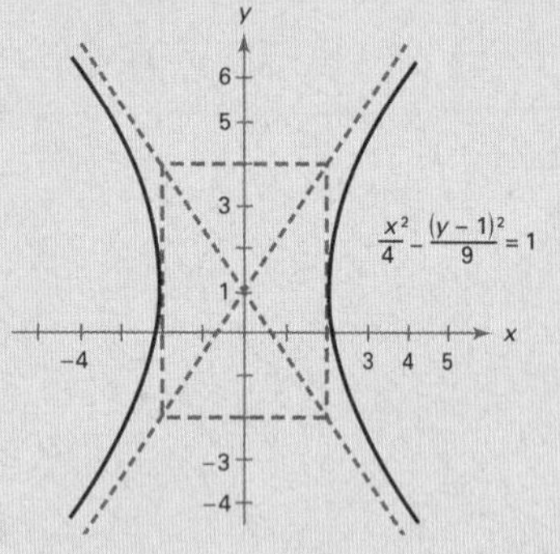

$y = 1 \pm \frac{3}{2}x$; $(-\sqrt{13}, 1)$, $(\sqrt{13}, 1)$

Example 3 Finding the Asymptotes of a Hyperbola

Sketch the hyperbola given by $4x^2 - 3y^2 + 8x + 16 = 0$ and find the equations of its asymptotes and the foci.

Solution

$4x^2 - 3y^2 + 8x + 16 = 0$	Write original equation.
$(4x^2 + 8x) - 3y^2 = -16$	Group terms.
$4(x^2 + 2x) - 3y^2 = -16$	Factor 4 from x-terms.
$4(x^2 + 2x + 1) - 3y^2 = -16 + 4$	Add 4 to each side.
$4(x + 1)^2 - 3y^2 = -12$	Write in completed square form.
$-\frac{(x+1)^2}{3} + \frac{y^2}{4} = 1$	Divide each side by -12.
$\frac{y^2}{2^2} - \frac{(x+1)^2}{(\sqrt{3})^2} = 1$	Write in standard form.

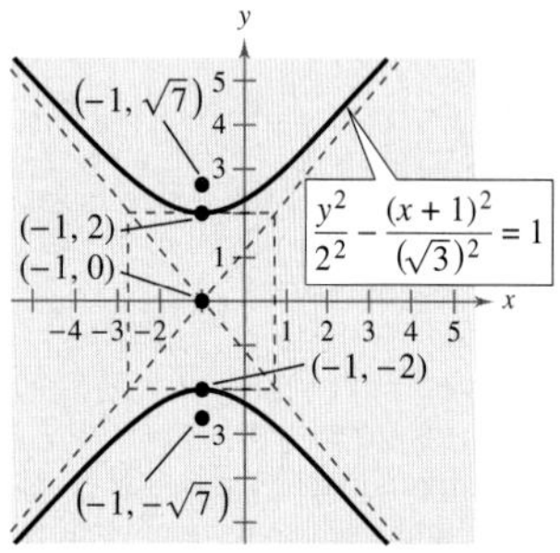

FIGURE 10.38

From this equation you can conclude that the hyperbola has a vertical transverse axis, centered at $(-1, 0)$, has vertices $(-1, 2)$ and $(-1, -2)$, and has a conjugate axis with endpoints $(-1 - \sqrt{3}, 0)$ and $(-1 + \sqrt{3}, 0)$. To sketch the hyperbola, draw a rectangle through these four points. The asymptotes are the lines passing through the corners of the rectangle. Using $a = 2$ and $b = \sqrt{3}$, you can conclude that the equations of the asymptotes are

$$y = \frac{2}{\sqrt{3}}(x + 1) \quad \text{and} \quad y = -\frac{2}{\sqrt{3}}(x + 1).$$

Finally, you can determine the foci by using the equation $c^2 = a^2 + b^2$. So, you have $c = \sqrt{2^2 + (\sqrt{3})^2} = \sqrt{7}$, and the foci are $(-1, \sqrt{7})$ and $(-1, -\sqrt{7})$. The hyperbola is shown in Figure 10.38.

CHECKPoint Now try Exercise 19.

TECHNOLOGY

You can use a graphing utility to graph a hyperbola by graphing the upper and lower portions in the same viewing window. For instance, to graph the hyperbola in Example 3, first solve for y to get

$$y_1 = 2\sqrt{1 + \frac{(x+1)^2}{3}} \quad \text{and} \quad y_2 = -2\sqrt{1 + \frac{(x+1)^2}{3}}.$$

Use a viewing window in which $-9 \le x \le 9$ and $-6 \le y \le 6$. You should obtain the graph shown below. Notice that the graphing utility does not draw the asymptotes. However, if you trace along the branches, you will see that the values of the hyperbola approach the asymptotes.

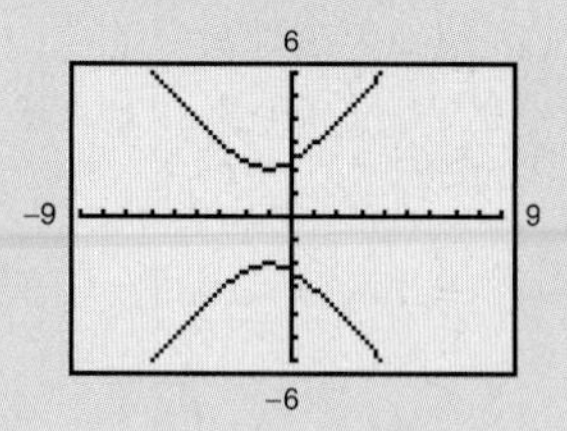

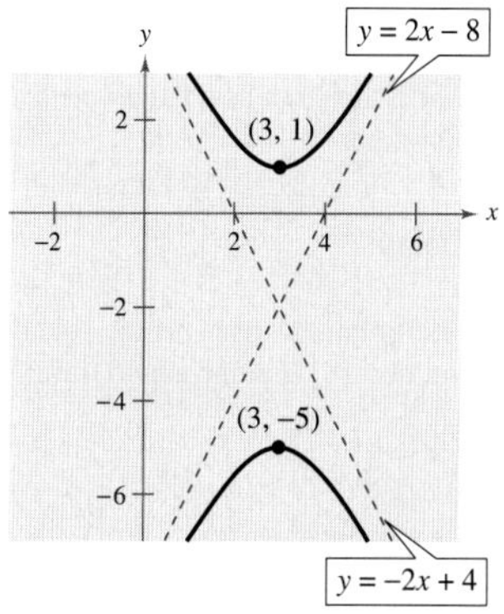

FIGURE 10.39

Example 4 Using Asymptotes to Find the Standard Equation

Find the standard form of the equation of the hyperbola having vertices $(3, -5)$ and $(3, 1)$ and having asymptotes

$$y = 2x - 8 \quad \text{and} \quad y = -2x + 4$$

as shown in Figure 10.39.

Solution

By the Midpoint Formula, the center of the hyperbola is $(3, -2)$. Furthermore, the hyperbola has a vertical transverse axis with $a = 3$. From the original equations, you can determine the slopes of the asymptotes to be

$$m_1 = 2 = \frac{a}{b} \quad \text{and} \quad m_2 = -2 = -\frac{a}{b}$$

and, because $a = 3$, you can conclude

$$2 = \frac{a}{b} \implies 2 = \frac{3}{b} \implies b = \frac{3}{2}.$$

So, the standard form of the equation is

$$\frac{(y+2)^2}{3^2} - \frac{(x-3)^2}{\left(\frac{3}{2}\right)^2} = 1.$$

CHECKPoint Now try Exercise 43.

As with ellipses, the *eccentricity* of a hyperbola is

$$e = \frac{c}{a} \qquad \text{Eccentricity}$$

and because $c > a$, it follows that $e > 1$. If the eccentricity is large, the branches of the hyperbola are nearly flat, as shown in Figure 10.40. If the eccentricity is close to 1, the branches of the hyperbola are more narrow, as shown in Figure 10.41.

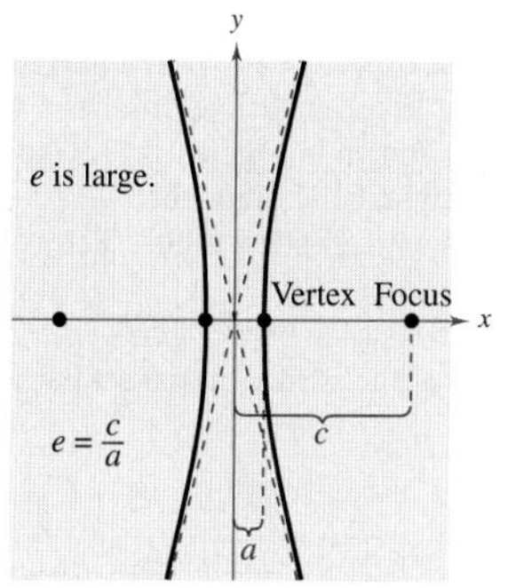

FIGURE 10.40

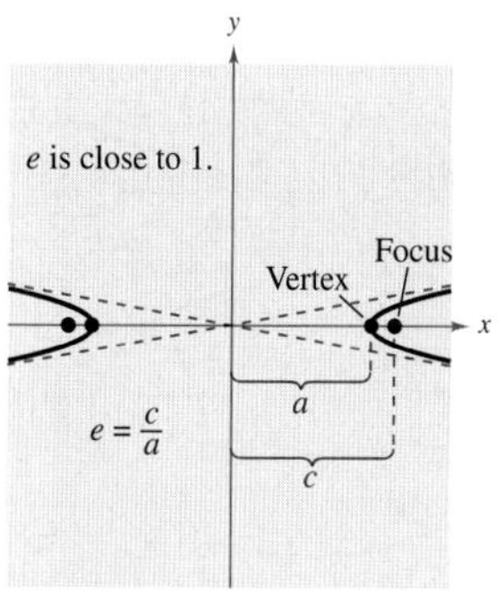

FIGURE 10.41

Extra Example 4

Find the standard form of the equation of the hyperbola having vertices (3, 2) and (9, 2) and having asymptotes $y = -2 + \frac{2}{3}x$ and $y = 6 - \frac{2}{3}x$.

$$\frac{(x-6)^2}{9} - \frac{(y-2)^2}{4} = 1$$

Extra Example 5

Three listening stations located at (4400, 0), (4400, 1100), and (−4400, 0) monitor an explosion. If the last two stations detect the explosion 1 second and 5 seconds after the first, respectively, determine the coordinates of the explosion. (Assume that the coordinate system is measured in feet and that sound travels at 1100 feet per second.)

(4400, −4290)

Applications

The following application was developed during World War II. It shows how the properties of hyperbolas can be used in radar and other detection systems.

Example 5 An Application Involving Hyperbolas

Two microphones, 1 mile apart, record an explosion. Microphone A receives the sound 2 seconds before microphone B. Where did the explosion occur? (Assume sound travels at 1100 feet per second.)

Solution

Assuming sound travels at 1100 feet per second, you know that the explosion took place 2200 feet farther from B than from A, as shown in Figure 10.42. The locus of all points that are 2200 feet closer to A than to B is one branch of the hyperbola

$$\frac{x^2}{a^2} - \frac{y^2}{b^2} = 1$$

where

$$c = \frac{5280}{2} = 2640$$

and

$$a = \frac{2200}{2} = 1100.$$

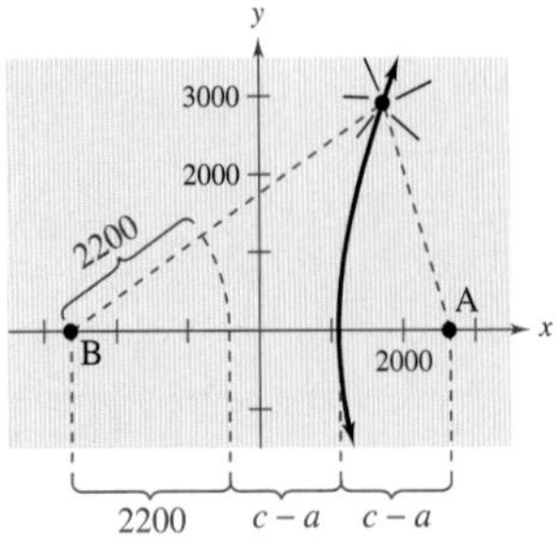

FIGURE 10.42

So, $b^2 = c^2 - a^2 = 2640^2 - 1100^2 = 5{,}759{,}600$, and you can conclude that the explosion occurred somewhere on the right branch of the hyperbola

$$\frac{x^2}{1{,}210{,}000} - \frac{y^2}{5{,}759{,}600} = 1.$$

CHECKPoint Now try Exercise 53.

Another interesting application of conic sections involves the orbits of comets in our solar system. Of the 610 comets identified prior to 1970, 245 have elliptical orbits, 295 have parabolic orbits, and 70 have hyperbolic orbits. The center of the sun is a focus of each of these orbits, and each orbit has a vertex at the point where the comet is closest to the sun, as shown in Figure 10.43. Undoubtedly, there have been many comets with parabolic or hyperbolic orbits that were not identified. We only get to see such comets *once*. Comets with elliptical orbits, such as Halley's comet, are the only ones that remain in our solar system.

If p is the distance between the vertex and the focus (in meters), and v is the velocity of the comet at the vertex (in meters per second), then the type of orbit is determined as follows.

1. Ellipse: $v < \sqrt{2GM/p}$

2. Parabola: $v = \sqrt{2GM/p}$

3. Hyperbola: $v > \sqrt{2GM/p}$

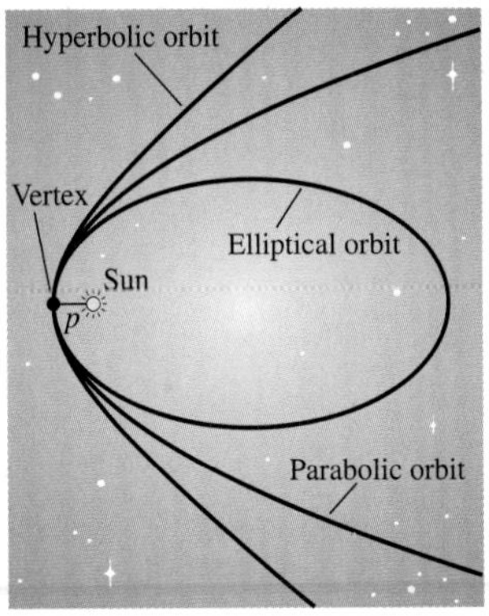

FIGURE 10.43

In each of these relations, $M = 1.989 \times 10^{30}$ kilograms (the mass of the sun) and $G \approx 6.67 \times 10^{-11}$ cubic meter per kilogram-second squared (the universal gravitational constant).

General Equations of Conics

Classifying a Conic from Its General Equation

The graph of $Ax^2 + Cy^2 + Dx + Ey + F = 0$ is one of the following.

1. *Circle:* $A = C$
2. *Parabola:* $AC = 0$ — $A = 0$ or $C = 0$, but not both.
3. *Ellipse:* $AC > 0$ — A and C have like signs.
4. *Hyperbola:* $AC < 0$ — A and C have unlike signs.

The test above is valid *if* the graph is a conic. The test does not apply to equations such as $x^2 + y^2 = -1$, whose graph is not a conic.

Example 6 Classifying Conics from General Equations

Classify the graph of each equation.

a. $4x^2 - 9x + y - 5 = 0$

b. $4x^2 - y^2 + 8x - 6y + 4 = 0$

c. $2x^2 + 4y^2 - 4x + 12y = 0$

d. $2x^2 + 2y^2 - 8x + 12y + 2 = 0$

Solution

a. For the equation $4x^2 - 9x + y - 5 = 0$, you have

$AC = 4(0) = 0.$ Parabola

So, the graph is a parabola.

b. For the equation $4x^2 - y^2 + 8x - 6y + 4 = 0$, you have

$AC = 4(-1) < 0.$ Hyperbola

So, the graph is a hyperbola.

c. For the equation $2x^2 + 4y^2 - 4x + 12y = 0$, you have

$AC = 2(4) > 0.$ Ellipse

So, the graph is an ellipse.

d. For the equation $2x^2 + 2y^2 - 8x + 12y + 2 = 0$, you have

$A = C = 2.$ Circle

So, the graph is a circle.

CHECKPoint Now try Exercise 61.

Classroom Discussion

Sketching Conics Sketch each of the conics described in Example 6. Write a paragraph describing the procedures that allow you to sketch the conics efficiently.

See margin.

HISTORICAL NOTE

Caroline Herschel (1750–1848) was the first woman to be credited with detecting a new comet. During her long life, this English astronomer discovered a total of eight new comets.

Extra Example 6

Classify the graph of each equation.

a. $x^2 - 3y^2 - 4x + 1 = 0$
hyperbola

b. $x^2 + y^2 - 10x + 2y + 22 = 0$
circle

c. $x^2 - 4x - 24y - 4 = 0$
parabola

d. $2x^2 + 3y^2 - 28x - 12y + 104 = 0$
ellipse

Closing the Lesson

Have students summarize the major points of the lesson and answer the Essential Question: How do you solve problems involving hyperbolas and classify a conic section on the basis of its general equation?

- **Describe a hyperbola as the locus of points, the difference of whose distances from two distinct fixed points is constant.**
- **Write the standard form of the equation of a hyperbola, using its center, vertices, transverse axis, and foci.**
- **Find the asymptotes of a hyperbola by using its center and transverse and conjugate axes, and sketch the hyperbola by graphing its asymptotes.**
- **Use the coefficients of the general equation $Ax^2 + Cy^2 + Dx + Ey + F = 0$ to classify a conic as a circle, a parabola, an ellipse, or a hyperbola.**

Classroom Discussion

a.

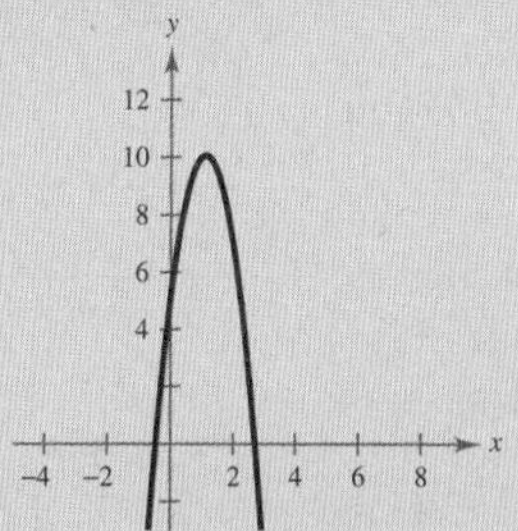

b.

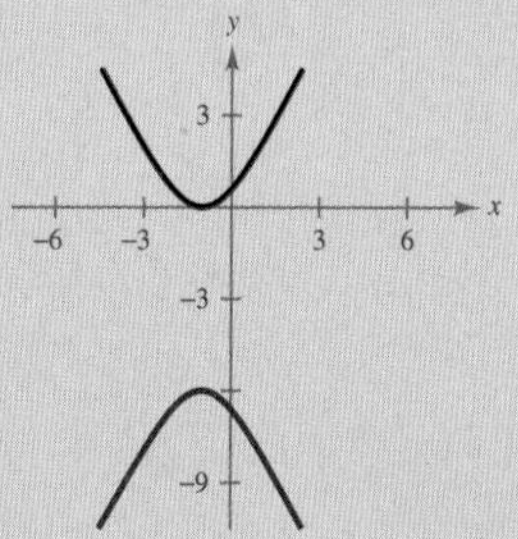

c.

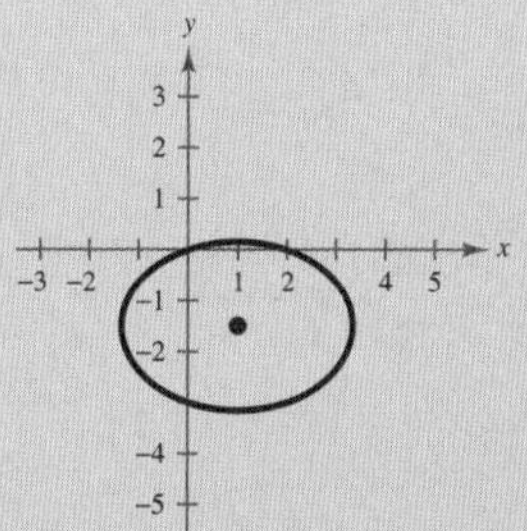

d.

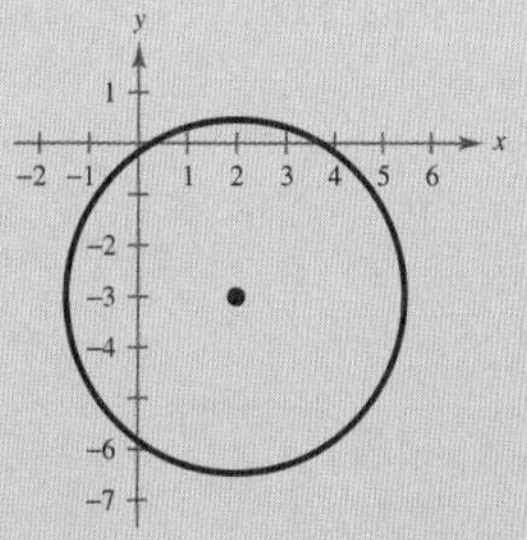

Discussions will vary.

4 PRACTICE AND APPLY

Assignment Guide

Transparencies Available
Available at the Instructor's companion site.

Average:
Day 1: pp. 758–759
Exs. 1–10, 15–18, 21–33 odd, 37–41 odd
Day 2: pp. 759–760
Exs. 45–51 odd, 54, 55–59 odd, 63–71 odd, 73–79

Advanced:
Day 1: pp. 758–759
Exs. 1–8, 12–28 even, 34–42 even
Day 2: pp. 759–760
Exs. 44–56 even, 60–72 even, 73–76, 78–80

Block:
pp. 758–759
Exs. 1–10, 15–18, 21–33 odd, 37–41 odd (with 10.3)
pp. 759–760
Exs. 45–51 odd, 54, 55–59 odd, 63–71 odd, 73–79 (with 10.5)

9. Center: $(0, 0)$
Vertices: $(\pm 1, 0)$
Foci: $(\pm\sqrt{2}, 0)$
Asymptotes: $y = \pm x$

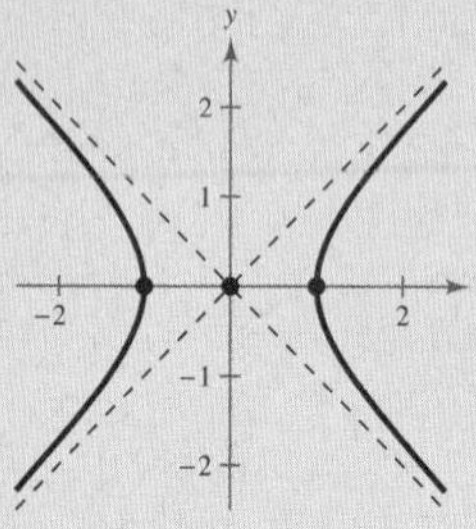

10. Center: $(0, 0)$
Vertices: $(\pm 3, 0)$
Foci: $(\pm\sqrt{34}, 0)$
Asymptotes: $y = \pm\frac{5}{3}x$

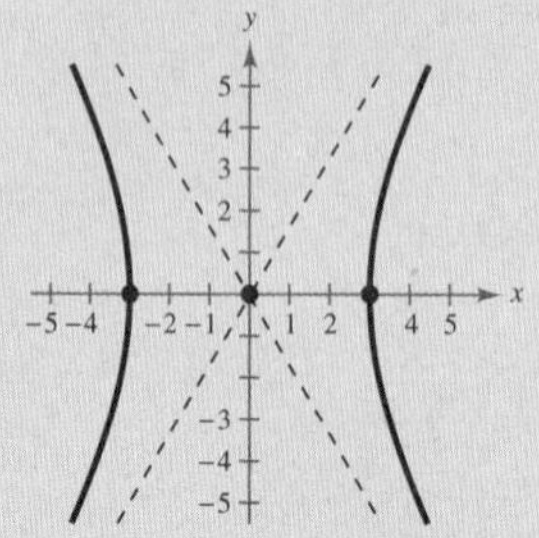

10.4 EXERCISES

See www.CalcChat.com for worked-out solutions to odd-numbered exercises.

VOCABULARY: Fill in the blanks.

1. A hyperbola is the set of all points (x, y) in a plane, the difference of whose distances from two distinct fixed points, called foci, is a positive constant.
2. The graph of a hyperbola has two disconnected parts called branches.
3. The line segment connecting the vertices of a hyperbola is called the transverse axis, and the midpoint of the line segment is the center of the hyperbola.
4. Each hyperbola has two ________ that intersect at the center of the hyperbola. asymptotes

SKILLS AND APPLICATIONS

In Exercises 5–8, match the equation with its graph. [The graphs are labeled (a), (b), (c), and (d).]

(a)

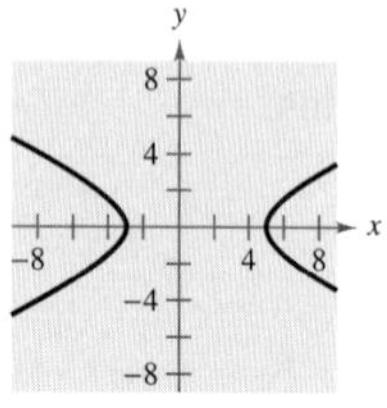

(b)

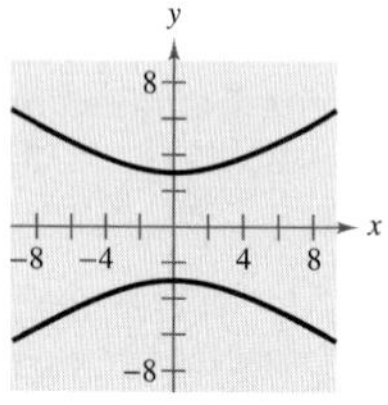

(c)

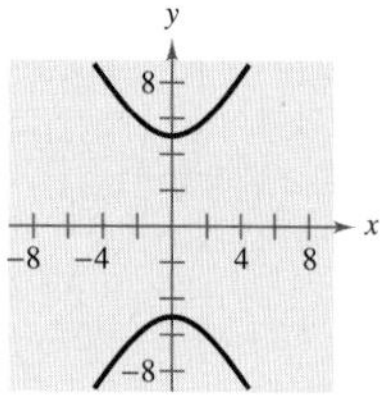

(d)

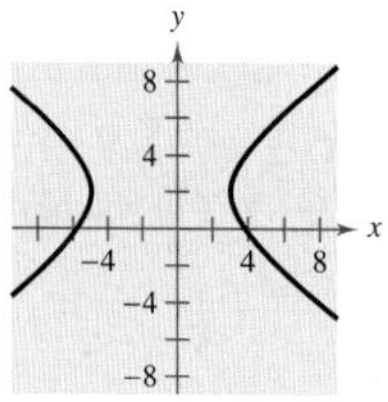

5. $\frac{y^2}{9} - \frac{x^2}{25} = 1$ b
6. $\frac{y^2}{25} - \frac{x^2}{9} = 1$ c
7. $\frac{(x-1)^2}{16} - \frac{y^2}{4} = 1$ a
8. $\frac{(x+1)^2}{16} - \frac{(y-2)^2}{9} = 1$ d

In Exercises 9–22, find the center, vertices, foci, and the equations of the asymptotes of the hyperbola, and sketch its graph using the asymptotes as an aid. 9–22. See margin.

9. $x^2 - y^2 = 1$
10. $\frac{x^2}{9} - \frac{y^2}{25} = 1$
11. $\frac{y^2}{25} - \frac{x^2}{81} = 1$
12. $\frac{x^2}{36} - \frac{y^2}{4} = 1$
13. $\frac{y^2}{1} - \frac{x^2}{4} = 1$
14. $\frac{y^2}{9} - \frac{x^2}{1} = 1$
15. $\frac{(x-1)^2}{4} - \frac{(y+2)^2}{1} = 1$
16. $\frac{(x+3)^2}{144} - \frac{(y-2)^2}{25} = 1$
17. $\frac{(y+6)^2}{1/9} - \frac{(x-2)^2}{1/4} = 1$
18. $\frac{(y-1)^2}{1/4} - \frac{(x+3)^2}{1/16} = 1$
19. $9x^2 - y^2 - 36x - 6y + 18 = 0$
20. $x^2 - 9y^2 + 36y - 72 = 0$
21. $x^2 - 9y^2 + 2x - 54y - 80 = 0$
22. $16y^2 - x^2 + 2x + 64y + 63 = 0$

In Exercises 23–28, find the center, vertices, foci, and the equations of the asymptotes of the hyperbola. Use a graphing utility to graph the hyperbola and its asymptotes. 23–28. See margin.

23. $2x^2 - 3y^2 = 6$
24. $6y^2 - 3x^2 = 18$
25. $4x^2 - 9y^2 = 36$
26. $25x^2 - 4y^2 = 100$
27. $9y^2 - x^2 + 2x + 54y + 62 = 0$
28. $9x^2 - y^2 + 54x + 10y + 55 = 0$

In Exercises 29–34, find the standard form of the equation of the hyperbola with the given characteristics and center at the origin. 29–34. See margin.

29. Vertices: $(0, \pm 2)$; foci: $(0, \pm 4)$
30. Vertices: $(\pm 4, 0)$; foci: $(\pm 6, 0)$
31. Vertices: $(\pm 1, 0)$; asymptotes: $y = \pm 5x$
32. Vertices: $(0, \pm 3)$; asymptotes: $y = \pm 3x$
33. Foci: $(0, \pm 8)$; asymptotes: $y = \pm 4x$
34. Foci: $(\pm 10, 0)$; asymptotes: $y = \pm\frac{3}{4}x$

In Exercises 35–46, find the standard form of the equation of the hyperbola with the given characteristics. 35–38. See margin.

35. Vertices: $(2, 0), (6, 0)$; foci: $(0, 0), (8, 0)$
36. Vertices: $(2, 3), (2, -3)$; foci: $(2, 6), (2, -6)$
37. Vertices: $(4, 1), (4, 9)$; foci: $(4, 0), (4, 10)$
38. Vertices: $(-2, 1), (2, 1)$; foci: $(-3, 1), (3, 1)$

11. Center: $(0, 0)$
Vertices: $(0, \pm 5)$
Foci: $(0, \pm\sqrt{106})$
Asymptotes:
$y = \pm\frac{5}{9}x$

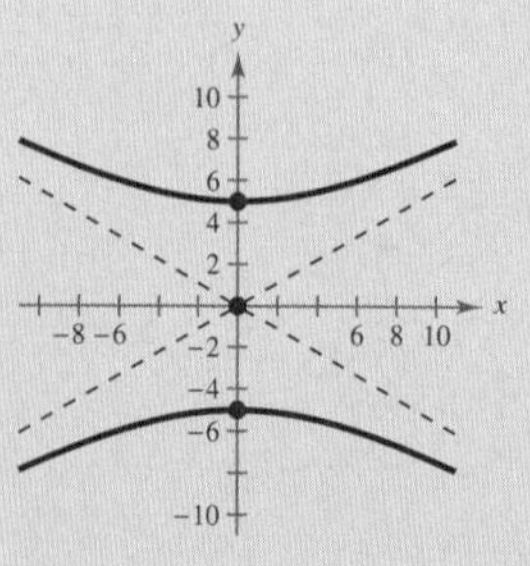

12. Center: $(0, 0)$
Vertices: $(\pm 6, 0)$
Foci: $(\pm 2\sqrt{10}, 0)$
Asymptotes:
$y = \pm\frac{1}{3}x$

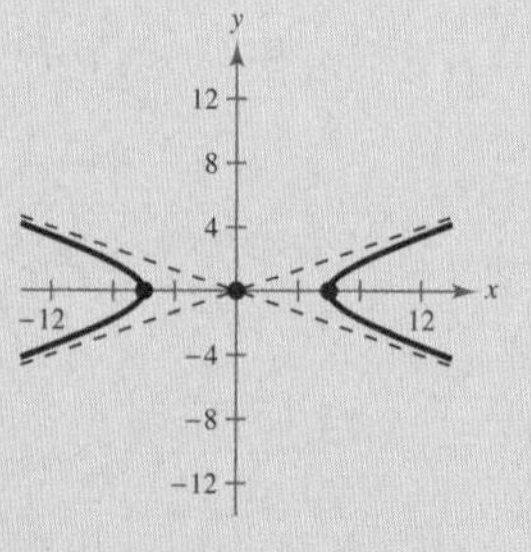

13–15, 29–38. See page 759.
16–28. See Additional Answers beginning on page AA1.

39. Vertices: (2, 3), (2, −3); passes through the point (0, 5)

39–46. See margin.

40. Vertices: (−2, 1), (2, 1); passes through the point (5, 4)

41. Vertices: (0, 4), (0, 0); passes through the point $(\sqrt{5}, -1)$

42. Vertices: (1, 2), (1, −2); passes through the point $(0, \sqrt{5})$

43. Vertices: (1, 2), (3, 2); asymptotes: $y = x$, $y = 4 - x$

44. Vertices: (3, 0), (3, 6); asymptotes: $y = 6 - x$, $y = x$

45. Vertices: (0, 2), (6, 2); asymptotes: $y = \frac{2}{3}x$, $y = 4 - \frac{2}{3}x$

46. Vertices: (3, 0), (3, 4); asymptotes: $y = \frac{2}{3}x$, $y = 4 - \frac{2}{3}x$

In Exercises 47–50, write the standard form of the equation of the hyperbola. 47–50. See margin.

47.

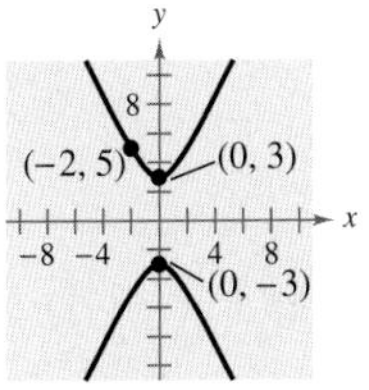

48.

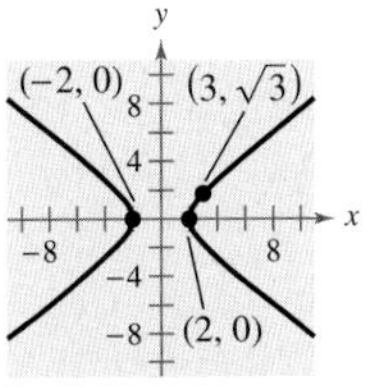

49.

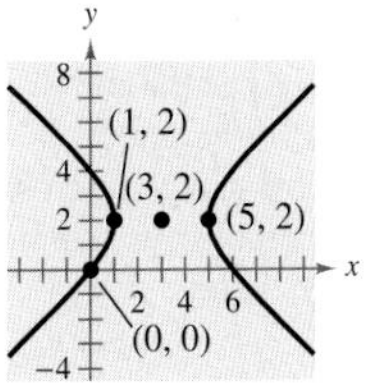

50.

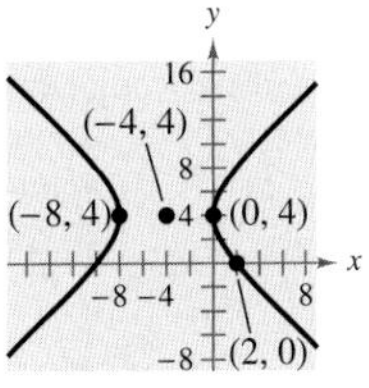

51. ART A sculpture has a hyperbolic cross section (see figure).

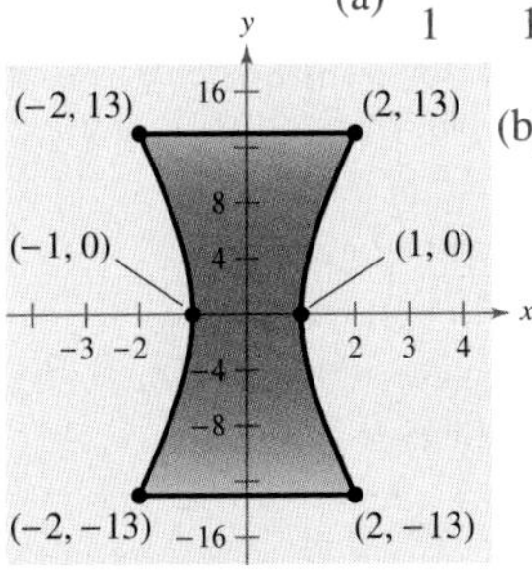

(a) Write an equation that models the curved sides of the sculpture.

(b) Each unit in the coordinate plane represents 1 foot. Find the width of the sculpture at a height of 5 feet.

(a) $\dfrac{x^2}{1} - \dfrac{y^2}{169/3} = 1$

(b) About 2.403 ft

52. SOUND LOCATION You and a friend live 4 miles apart (on the same "east-west" street) and are talking on the phone. You hear a clap of thunder from lightning in a storm, and 18 seconds later your friend hears the thunder. Find an equation that gives the possible places where the lightning could have occurred. (Assume that the coordinate system is measured in feet and that sound travels at 1100 feet per second.) See margin.

53. SOUND LOCATION Three listening stations located at (3300, 0), (3300, 1100), and (−3300, 0) monitor an explosion. The last two stations detect the explosion 1 second and 4 seconds after the first, respectively. Determine the coordinates of the explosion. (Assume that the coordinate system is measured in feet and that sound travels at 1100 feet per second.) (3300, −2750)

54. LORAN Long distance radio navigation for aircraft and ships uses synchronized pulses transmitted by widely separated transmitting stations. These pulses travel at the speed of light (186,000 miles per second). The difference in the times of arrival of these pulses at an aircraft or ship is constant on a hyperbola having the transmitting stations as foci. Assume that two stations, 300 miles apart, are positioned on the rectangular coordinate system at points with coordinates (−150, 0) and (150, 0), and that a ship is traveling on a hyperbolic path with coordinates $(x, 75)$ (see figure).

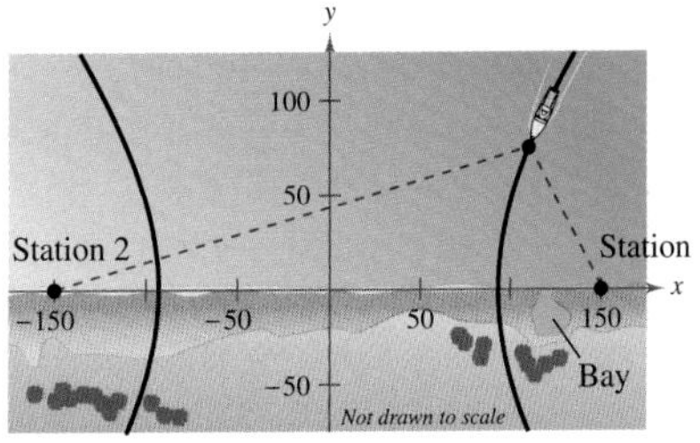

(a) Find the x-coordinate of the position of the ship if the time difference between the pulses from the transmitting stations is 1000 microseconds (0.001 second). $x \approx 110.3$ mi

(b) Determine the distance between the ship and station 1 when the ship reaches the shore. 57.0 mi

(c) The ship wants to enter a bay located between the two stations. The bay is 30 miles from station 1. What should be the time difference between the pulses?

(d) The ship is 60 miles offshore when the time difference in part (c) is obtained. What is the position of the ship?

(c) 0.00129 sec

(d) The ship is at the position (144.2, 60).

13. Center: (0, 0)
Vertices: $(0, \pm 1)$
Foci: $(0, \pm\sqrt{5})$
Asymptotes: $y = \pm\frac{1}{2}x$

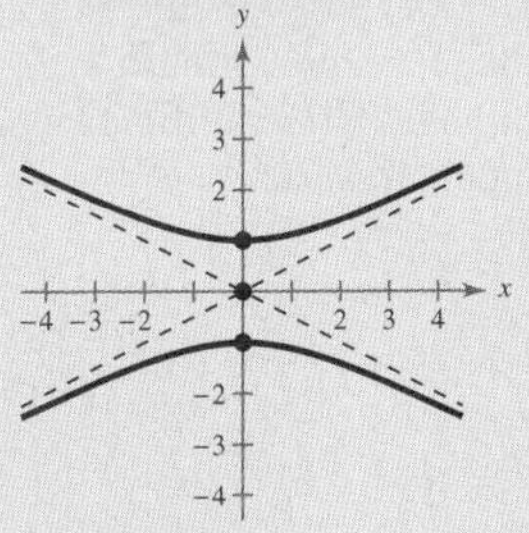

14. Center: (0, 0)
Vertices: $(0, \pm 3)$
Foci: $(0, \pm\sqrt{10})$
Asymptotes: $y = \pm 3x$

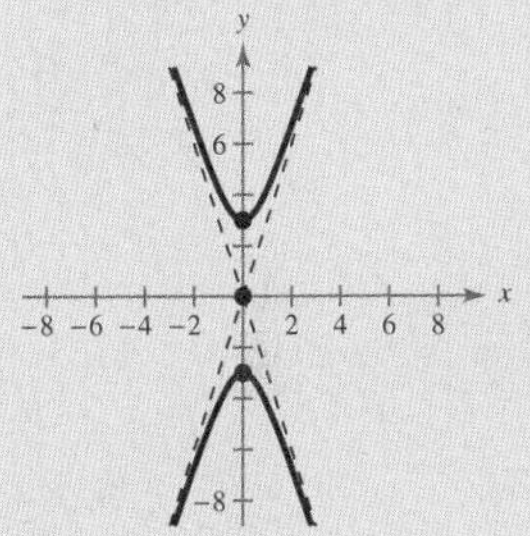

15. Center: (1, −2)
Vertices: (3, −2), (−1, −2)
Foci: $(1 \pm \sqrt{5}, -2)$
Asymptotes: $y = -2 \pm \frac{1}{2}(x - 1)$

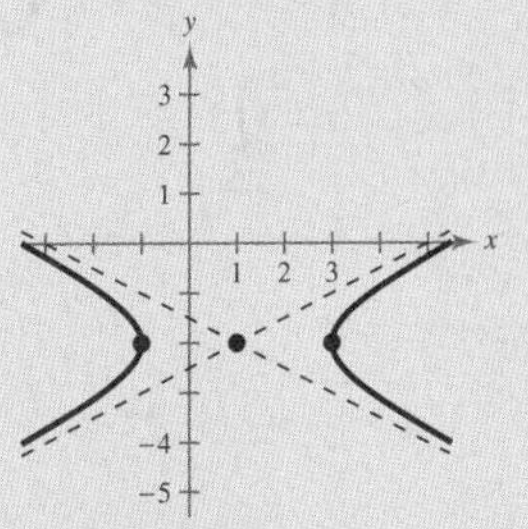

29. $\dfrac{y^2}{4} - \dfrac{x^2}{12} = 1$

30. $\dfrac{x^2}{16} - \dfrac{y^2}{20} = 1$

31. $\dfrac{x^2}{1} - \dfrac{y^2}{25} = 1$

32. $\dfrac{y^2}{9} - \dfrac{x^2}{1} = 1$

33. $\dfrac{17y^2}{1024} - \dfrac{17x^2}{64} = 1$

34. $\dfrac{x^2}{64} - \dfrac{y^2}{36} = 1$

35. $\dfrac{(x-4)^2}{4} - \dfrac{y^2}{12} = 1$

36. $\dfrac{y^2}{9} - \dfrac{(x-2)^2}{27} = 1$

37. $\dfrac{(y-5)^2}{16} - \dfrac{(x-4)^2}{9} = 1$

38. $\dfrac{x^2}{4} - \dfrac{(y-1)^2}{5} = 1$

39. $\dfrac{y^2}{9} - \dfrac{4(x-2)^2}{9} = 1$

40. $\dfrac{x^2}{4} - \dfrac{7(y-1)^2}{12} = 1$

41. $\dfrac{(y-2)^2}{4} - \dfrac{x^2}{4} = 1$

42. $\dfrac{y^2}{4} - \dfrac{(x-1)^2}{4} = 1$

43. $\dfrac{(x-2)^2}{1} - \dfrac{(y-2)^2}{1} = 1$

44. $\dfrac{(y-3)^2}{9} - \dfrac{(x-3)^2}{9} = 1$

45. $\dfrac{(x-3)^2}{9} - \dfrac{(y-2)^2}{4} = 1$

46. $\dfrac{(y-2)^2}{4} - \dfrac{(x-3)^2}{9} = 1$

47. $\dfrac{y^2}{9} - \dfrac{x^2}{9/4} = 1$

48. $\dfrac{x^2}{4} - \dfrac{y^2}{12/5} = 1$

49. $\dfrac{(x-3)^2}{4} - \dfrac{(y-2)^2}{16/5} = 1$

50. $\dfrac{(x+4)^2}{16} - \dfrac{(y-4)^2}{64/5} = 1$

52. $\dfrac{x^2}{98{,}010{,}000} - \dfrac{y^2}{13{,}503{,}600} = 1$

5 ASSESS AND RETEACH

Daily Homework Quiz

Transparency Available

Available at the Instructor's companion site.

73. True. For a hyperbola, $c^2 = a^2 + b^2$. The larger the ratio of b to a, the larger the eccentricity of the hyperbola, $e = c/a$.

74. False. For the trivial solution of two intersecting lines to occur, the standard form of the equation of the hyperbola would be equal to zero,

$$\frac{(x-h)^2}{a^2} - \frac{(y-k)^2}{b^2} = 0 \text{ or}$$
$$\frac{(y-k)^2}{a^2} - \frac{(x-h)^2}{b^2} = 0.$$

75. False. When $D = -E$, the graph is two intersecting lines.

76. True. The asymptotes are $y = \pm(b/a)x$. If they intersect at right angles, then

$$\frac{b}{a} = \frac{-1}{-b/a} = \frac{a}{b}$$

which implies $a = b$.

78. The extended diagonals of the central rectangle are the asymptotes of the hyperbola.

79. $y = 1 - 3\sqrt{\dfrac{(x-3)^2}{4} - 1}$

81.

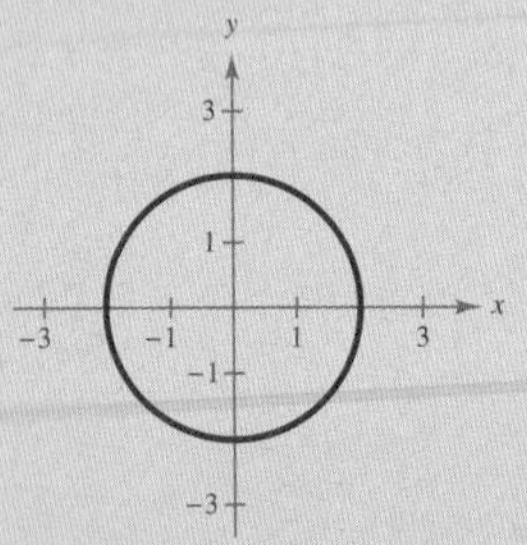

The equation $y = x^2 + C$ is a parabola that could intersect the circle in zero, one, two, three, or four places depending on its location on the y-axis.

(a) $C > 2$ and $C < -\frac{17}{4}$

(b) $C = 2$

(c) $-2 < C < 2,\ C = -\frac{17}{4}$

(d) $C = -2$

(e) $-\frac{17}{4} < C < -2$

55. PENDULUM The base for a pendulum of a clock has the shape of a hyperbola (see figure).

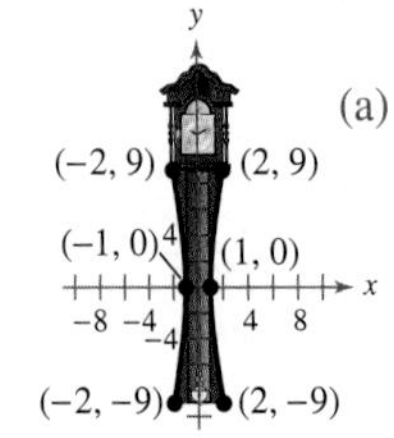

(a) $\dfrac{x^2}{1} - \dfrac{y^2}{27} = 1;\quad -9 \le y \le 9$

(a) Write an equation of the cross section of the base.

(b) Each unit in the coordinate plane represents $\frac{1}{2}$ foot. Find the width of the base of the pendulum 4 inches from the bottom. 1.89 ft

56. HYPERBOLIC MIRROR A hyperbolic mirror (used in some telescopes) has the property that a light ray directed at a focus will be reflected to the other focus. The focus of a hyperbolic mirror (see figure) has coordinates (24, 0). Find the vertex of the mirror if the mount at the top edge of the mirror has coordinates (24, 24).

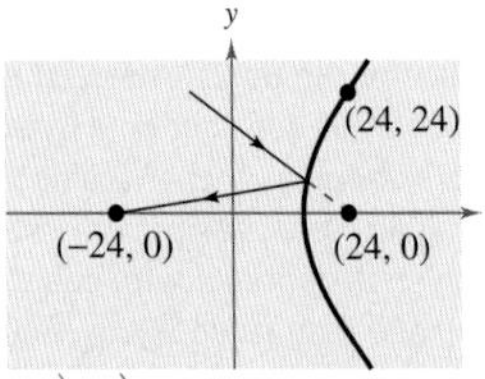

$(12(\sqrt{5} - 1), 0) \approx (14.83, 0)$

In Exercises 57–72, classify the graph of the equation as a circle, a parabola, an ellipse, or a hyperbola.

57. $9x^2 + 4y^2 - 18x + 16y - 119 = 0$ Ellipse

58. $x^2 + y^2 - 4x - 6y - 23 = 0$ Circle

59. $4x^2 - y^2 - 4x - 3 = 0$ Hyperbola

60. $y^2 - 6y - 4x + 21 = 0$ Parabola

61. $y^2 - 4x^2 + 4x - 2y - 4 = 0$ Hyperbola

62. $x^2 + y^2 - 4x + 6y - 3 = 0$ Circle

63. $y^2 + 12x + 4y + 28 = 0$ Parabola

64. $4x^2 + 25y^2 + 16x + 250y + 541 = 0$ Ellipse

65. $4x^2 + 3y^2 + 8x - 24y + 51 = 0$ Ellipse

66. $4y^2 - 2x^2 - 4y - 8x - 15 = 0$ Hyperbola

67. $25x^2 - 10x - 200y - 119 = 0$ Parabola

68. $4y^2 + 4x^2 - 24x + 35 = 0$ Circle

69. $x^2 - 6x - 2y + 7 = 0$ Parabola

70. $9x^2 + 4y^2 - 90x + 8y + 228 = 0$ Ellipse

71. $100x^2 + 100y^2 - 100x + 400y + 409 = 0$ Circle

72. $4x^2 - y^2 + 4x + 2y - 1 = 0$ Hyperbola

EXPLORATION

73–76. See margin.

TRUE OR FALSE? In Exercises 73–76, determine whether the statement is true or false. Justify your answer.

73. In the standard form of the equation of a hyperbola, the larger the ratio of b to a, the larger the eccentricity of the hyperbola.

74. In the standard form of the equation of a hyperbola, the trivial solution of two intersecting lines occurs when $b = 0$.

75. If $D \ne 0$ and $E \ne 0$, then the graph of $x^2 - y^2 + Dx + Ey = 0$ is a hyperbola.

76. If the asymptotes of the hyperbola $\dfrac{x^2}{a^2} - \dfrac{y^2}{b^2} = 1$, where $a, b > 0$, intersect at right angles, then $a = b$.

77. Answers will vary.

77. Consider a hyperbola centered at the origin with a horizontal transverse axis. Use the definition of a hyperbola to derive its standard form.

78. WRITING Explain how the central rectangle of a hyperbola can be used to sketch its asymptotes.

79. THINK ABOUT IT Change the equation of the hyperbola so that its graph is the bottom half of the hyperbola.

$9x^2 - 54x - 4y^2 + 8y + 41 = 0$

78–79. See margin.

80. CAPSTONE Given the hyperbolas

$$\frac{x^2}{16} - \frac{y^2}{9} = 1 \quad \text{and} \quad \frac{y^2}{9} - \frac{x^2}{16} = 1$$

describe any common characteristics that the hyperbolas share, as well as any differences in the graphs of the hyperbolas. Verify your results by using a graphing utility to graph each of the hyperbolas in the same viewing window. Answers will vary.

81. A circle and a parabola can have 0, 1, 2, 3, or 4 points of intersection. Sketch the circle given by $x^2 + y^2 = 4$. Discuss how this circle could intersect a parabola with an equation of the form $y = x^2 + C$. Then find the values of C for each of the five cases described below. Use a graphing utility to verify your results.

(a) No points of intersection See margin.

(b) One point of intersection

(c) Two points of intersection

(d) Three points of intersection

(e) Four points of intersection

10.5 Rotation of Conics

What you should learn

- Rotate the coordinate axes to eliminate the *xy*-term in equations of conics.
- Use the discriminant to classify conics.

Why you should learn it

As illustrated in Exercises 13–26 on page 767, rotation of the coordinate axes can help you identify the graph of a general second-degree equation.

Rotation

In the preceding section, you learned that the equation of a conic with axes parallel to one of the coordinate axes has a standard form that can be written in the general form

$$Ax^2 + Cy^2 + Dx + Ey + F = 0. \qquad \text{Horizontal or vertical axis}$$

In this section, you will study the equations of conics whose axes are rotated so that they are not parallel to either the x-axis or the y-axis. The general equation for such conics contains an xy-term.

$$Ax^2 + Bxy + Cy^2 + Dx + Ey + F = 0 \qquad \text{Equation in } xy\text{-plane}$$

To eliminate this xy-term, you can use a procedure called **rotation of axes.** The objective is to rotate the x- and y-axes until they are parallel to the axes of the conic. The rotated axes are denoted as the x'-axis and the y'-axis, as shown in Figure 10.44.

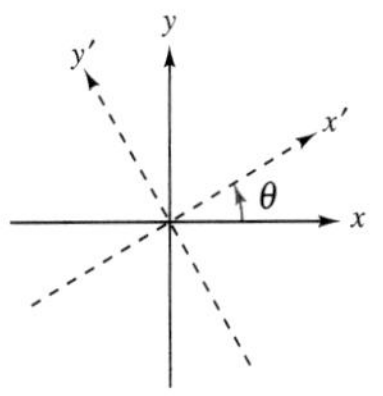

FIGURE 10.44

After the rotation, the equation of the conic in the new $x'y'$-plane will have the form

$$A'(x')^2 + C'(y')^2 + D'x' + E'y' + F' = 0. \qquad \text{Equation in } x'y'\text{-plane}$$

Because this equation has no xy-term, you can obtain a standard form by completing the square. The following theorem identifies how much to rotate the axes to eliminate the xy-term and also the equations for determining the new coefficients A', C', D', E', and F'.

Rotation of Axes to Eliminate an *xy*-Term

The general second-degree equation

$$Ax^2 + Bxy + Cy^2 + Dx + Ey + F = 0$$

can be rewritten as

$$A'(x')^2 + C'(y')^2 + D'x' + E'y' + F' = 0$$

by rotating the coordinate axes through an angle θ, where

$$\cot 2\theta = \frac{A - C}{B}.$$

The coefficients of the new equation are obtained by making the substitutions $x = x'\cos\theta - y'\sin\theta$ and $y = x'\sin\theta + y'\cos\theta$.

1 PLAN AND PREPARE

Warm-up Exercises

Transparency Available
Available at the Instructor's companion site.

Notetaking Guide

Transparency Available
Promotes interactive learning and notetaking skills.
Available at the Instructor's companion site.

Animated Precalculus

An **Animated Precalculus** tutorial is available at the Student companion site for **Section 10.5.**

Pacing

Average: 2 days
Advanced: 2 days
Block: 0.5 block with 10.4
0.5 block with 10.6

2 FOCUS AND MOTIVATE

Essential Question

How do you eliminate the *xy*-term from the general equation for conic sections and classify a conic on the basis of its general equation if $B \neq 0$? **Tell students that they will learn how to answer this question by rotating the axes to eliminate the *xy*-term and studying the features of the equation that do not change during the rotation.**

Resource Planning Guide

Chapter Resources
- Complete Solutions Guide

Workbooks
- Notetaking Guide
- Student Solutions Guide

Interactive Technology
- Instructor Success Organizer
- Notetaking Guide IAE
- Instructional DVDs
- Animated Precalculus
- PowerLecture with ExamView

3 TEACH

Extra Example 1

Write the equation $xy + 2 = 0$ in standard form.

$$\frac{(y')^2}{4} - \frac{(x')^2}{4} = 1$$

WARNING/CAUTION

Remember that the substitutions

$$x = x'\cos\theta - y'\sin\theta$$

and

$$y = x'\sin\theta + y'\cos\theta$$

were developed to eliminate the $x'y'$-term in the rotated system. You can use this as a check on your work. In other words, if your final equation contains an $x'y'$-term, you know that you have made a mistake.

Example 1 Rotation of Axes for a Hyperbola

Write the equation $xy - 1 = 0$ in standard form.

Solution

Because $A = 0$, $B = 1$, and $C = 0$, you have

$$\cot 2\theta = \frac{A - C}{B} = 0 \quad \Longrightarrow \quad 2\theta = \frac{\pi}{2} \quad \Longrightarrow \quad \theta = \frac{\pi}{4}$$

which implies that

$$\begin{aligned} x &= x'\cos\frac{\pi}{4} - y'\sin\frac{\pi}{4} \\ &= x'\left(\frac{1}{\sqrt{2}}\right) - y'\left(\frac{1}{\sqrt{2}}\right) \\ &= \frac{x' - y'}{\sqrt{2}} \end{aligned}$$

and

$$\begin{aligned} y &= x'\sin\frac{\pi}{4} + y'\cos\frac{\pi}{4} \\ &= x'\left(\frac{1}{\sqrt{2}}\right) + y'\left(\frac{1}{\sqrt{2}}\right) \\ &= \frac{x' + y'}{\sqrt{2}}. \end{aligned}$$

The equation in the $x'y'$-system is obtained by substituting these expressions in the equation $xy - 1 = 0$.

$$\left(\frac{x' - y'}{\sqrt{2}}\right)\left(\frac{x' + y'}{\sqrt{2}}\right) - 1 = 0$$

$$\frac{(x')^2 - (y')^2}{2} - 1 = 0$$

$$\frac{(x')^2}{(\sqrt{2})^2} - \frac{(y')^2}{(\sqrt{2})^2} = 1 \qquad \text{Write in standard form.}$$

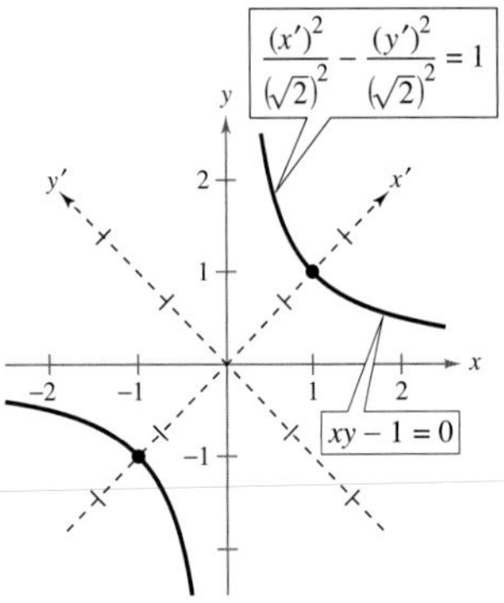

Vertices:
In $x'y'$-system: $(\sqrt{2}, 0), (-\sqrt{2}, 0)$
In xy-system: $(1, 1), (-1, -1)$
FIGURE 10.45

In the $x'y'$-system, this is a hyperbola centered at the origin with vertices at $(\pm\sqrt{2}, 0)$, as shown in Figure 10.45. To find the coordinates of the vertices in the xy-system, substitute the coordinates $(\pm\sqrt{2}, 0)$ in the equations

$$x = \frac{x' - y'}{\sqrt{2}} \quad \text{and} \quad y = \frac{x' + y'}{\sqrt{2}}.$$

This substitution yields the vertices $(1, 1)$ and $(-1, -1)$ in the xy-system. Note also that the asymptotes of the hyperbola have equations $y' = \pm x'$, which correspond to the original x- and y-axes.

CHECKPoint Now try Exercise 13.

Example 2 Rotation of Axes for an Ellipse

Sketch the graph of $7x^2 - 6\sqrt{3}xy + 13y^2 - 16 = 0$.

Solution

Because $A = 7$, $B = -6\sqrt{3}$, and $C = 13$, you have

$$\cot 2\theta = \frac{A - C}{B} = \frac{7 - 13}{-6\sqrt{3}} = \frac{1}{\sqrt{3}}$$

which implies that $\theta = \pi/6$. The equation in the $x'y'$-system is obtained by making the substitutions

$$x = x'\cos\frac{\pi}{6} - y'\sin\frac{\pi}{6}$$
$$= x'\left(\frac{\sqrt{3}}{2}\right) - y'\left(\frac{1}{2}\right)$$
$$= \frac{\sqrt{3}x' - y'}{2}$$

and

$$y = x'\sin\frac{\pi}{6} + y'\cos\frac{\pi}{6}$$
$$= x'\left(\frac{1}{2}\right) + y'\left(\frac{\sqrt{3}}{2}\right)$$
$$= \frac{x' + \sqrt{3}y'}{2}$$

in the original equation. So, you have

$$7x^2 - 6\sqrt{3}xy + 13y^2 - 16 = 0$$
$$7\left(\frac{\sqrt{3}x' - y'}{2}\right)^2 - 6\sqrt{3}\left(\frac{\sqrt{3}x' - y'}{2}\right)\left(\frac{x' + \sqrt{3}y'}{2}\right)$$
$$+ 13\left(\frac{x' + \sqrt{3}y'}{2}\right)^2 - 16 = 0$$

which simplifies to

$$4(x')^2 + 16(y')^2 - 16 = 0$$
$$4(x')^2 + 16(y')^2 = 16$$
$$\frac{(x')^2}{4} + \frac{(y')^2}{1} = 1$$
$$\frac{(x')^2}{2^2} + \frac{(y')^2}{1^2} = 1. \quad \text{Write in standard form.}$$

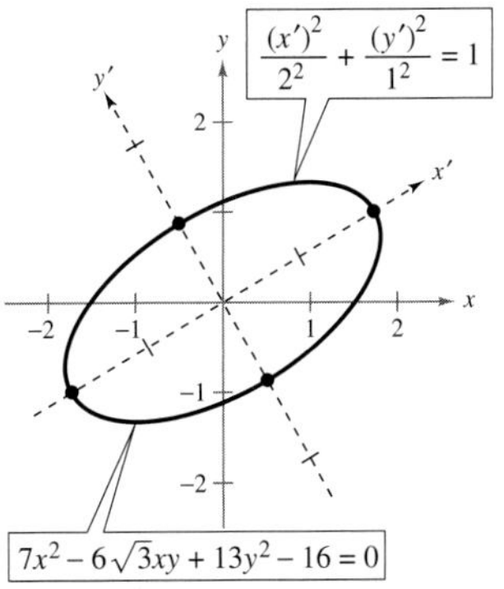

Vertices:
In $x'y'$-system: $(\pm 2, 0)$
In xy-system: $(\sqrt{3}, 1), (-\sqrt{3}, -1)$
FIGURE 10.46

This is the equation of an ellipse centered at the origin with vertices $(\pm 2, 0)$ in the $x'y'$-system, as shown in Figure 10.46.

CHECKPoint Now try Exercise 19.

Extra Example 2

Sketch the graph of $5x^2 - 2xy + 5y^2 - 12 = 0$.

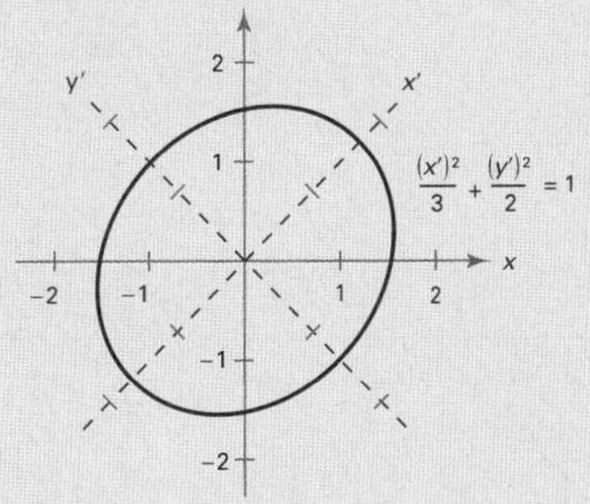

Extra Example 3

Sketch the graph of $4x^2 + 4xy + y^2 - 2\sqrt{5}x + 4\sqrt{5}y - 30 = 0$.

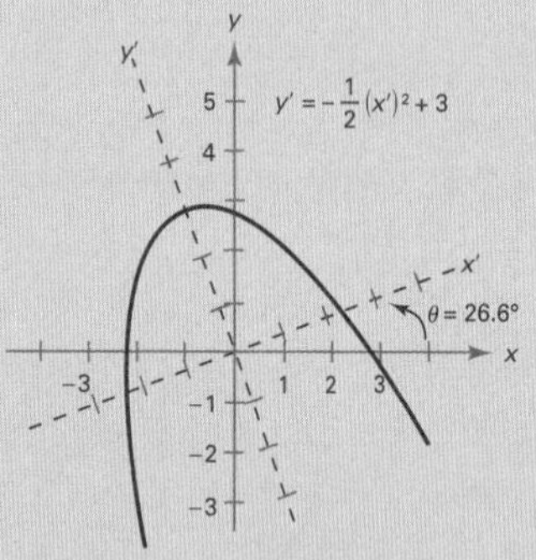

Example 3 Rotation of Axes for a Parabola

Sketch the graph of $x^2 - 4xy + 4y^2 + 5\sqrt{5}y + 1 = 0$.

Solution

Because $A = 1$, $B = -4$, and $C = 4$, you have

$$\cot 2\theta = \frac{A - C}{B} = \frac{1 - 4}{-4} = \frac{3}{4}.$$

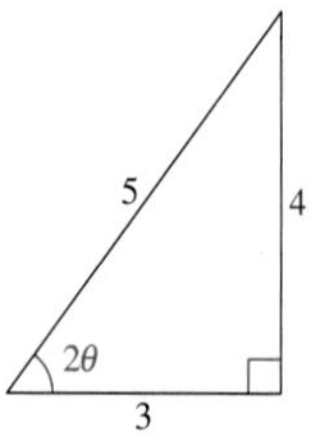

FIGURE 10.47

Using this information, draw a right triangle as shown in Figure 10.47. From the figure, you can see that $\cos 2\theta = \frac{3}{5}$. To find the values of $\sin\theta$ and $\cos\theta$, you can use the half-angle formulas in the forms

$$\sin\theta = \sqrt{\frac{1 - \cos 2\theta}{2}} \quad \text{and} \quad \cos\theta = \sqrt{\frac{1 + \cos 2\theta}{2}}.$$

So,

$$\sin\theta = \sqrt{\frac{1 - \cos 2\theta}{2}} = \sqrt{\frac{1 - \frac{3}{5}}{2}} = \sqrt{\frac{1}{5}} = \frac{1}{\sqrt{5}}$$

$$\cos\theta = \sqrt{\frac{1 + \cos 2\theta}{2}} = \sqrt{\frac{1 + \frac{3}{5}}{2}} = \sqrt{\frac{4}{5}} = \frac{2}{\sqrt{5}}.$$

Consequently, you use the substitutions

$$x = x'\cos\theta - y'\sin\theta$$
$$= x'\left(\frac{2}{\sqrt{5}}\right) - y'\left(\frac{1}{\sqrt{5}}\right) = \frac{2x' - y'}{\sqrt{5}}$$

$$y = x'\sin\theta + y'\cos\theta$$
$$= x'\left(\frac{1}{\sqrt{5}}\right) + y'\left(\frac{2}{\sqrt{5}}\right) = \frac{x' + 2y'}{\sqrt{5}}.$$

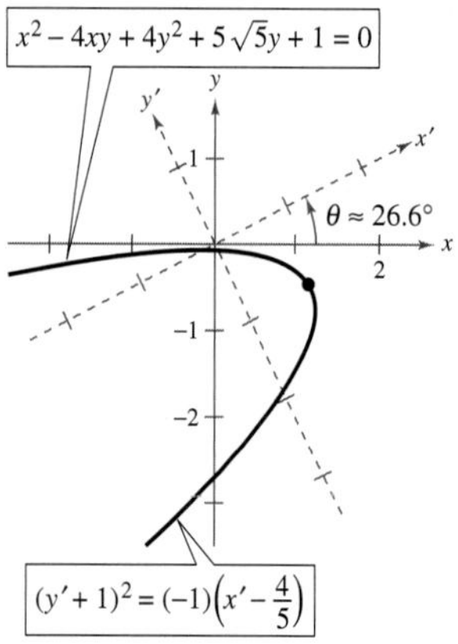

Vertex:
In $x'y'$-system: $\left(\frac{4}{5}, -1\right)$
In xy-system: $\left(\frac{13}{5\sqrt{5}}, -\frac{6}{5\sqrt{5}}\right)$

FIGURE 10.48

Substituting these expressions in the original equation, you have

$$x^2 - 4xy + 4y^2 + 5\sqrt{5}y + 1 = 0$$

$$\left(\frac{2x' - y'}{\sqrt{5}}\right)^2 - 4\left(\frac{2x' - y'}{\sqrt{5}}\right)\left(\frac{x' + 2y'}{\sqrt{5}}\right) + 4\left(\frac{x' + 2y'}{\sqrt{5}}\right)^2 + 5\sqrt{5}\left(\frac{x' + 2y'}{\sqrt{5}}\right) + 1 = 0$$

which simplifies as follows.

$$5(y')^2 + 5x' + 10y' + 1 = 0$$

$$5[(y')^2 + 2y'] = -5x' - 1 \qquad \text{Group terms.}$$

$$5(y' + 1)^2 = -5x' + 4 \qquad \text{Write in completed square form.}$$

$$(y' + 1)^2 = (-1)\left(x' - \frac{4}{5}\right) \qquad \text{Write in standard form.}$$

The graph of this equation is a parabola with vertex $\left(\frac{4}{5}, -1\right)$. Its axis is parallel to the x'-axis in the $x'y'$-system, and because $\sin\theta = 1/\sqrt{5}$, $\theta \approx 26.6°$, as shown in Figure 10.48.

CHECKPoint Now try Exercise 25.

Invariants Under Rotation

In the rotation of axes theorem listed at the beginning of this section, note that the constant term is the same in both equations, $F' = F$. Such quantities are **invariant under rotation.** The next theorem lists some other rotation invariants.

Rotation Invariants

The rotation of the coordinate axes through an angle θ that transforms the equation $Ax^2 + Bxy + Cy^2 + Dx + Ey + F = 0$ into the form

$$A'(x')^2 + C'(y')^2 + D'x' + E'y' + F' = 0$$

has the following rotation invariants.

1. $F = F'$
2. $A + C = A' + C'$
3. $B^2 - 4AC = (B')^2 - 4A'C'$

WARNING / CAUTION

If there is an xy-term in the equation of a conic, you should realize then that the conic is rotated. Before rotating the axes, you should use the discriminant to classify the conic.

You can use the results of this theorem to classify the graph of a second-degree equation *with* an xy-term in much the same way you do for a second-degree equation *without* an xy-term. Note that because $B' = 0$, the invariant $B^2 - 4AC$ reduces to

$$B^2 - 4AC = -4A'C'. \qquad \text{Discriminant}$$

This quantity is called the **discriminant** of the equation

$$Ax^2 + Bxy + Cy^2 + Dx + Ey + F = 0.$$

Now, from the classification procedure given in Section 10.4, you know that the sign of $A'C'$ determines the type of graph for the equation

$$A'(x')^2 + C'(y')^2 + D'x' + E'y' + F' = 0.$$

Consequently, the sign of $B^2 - 4AC$ will determine the type of graph for the original equation, as given in the following classification.

Classification of Conics by the Discriminant

The graph of the equation $Ax^2 + Bxy + Cy^2 + Dx + Ey + F = 0$ is, except in degenerate cases, determined by its discriminant as follows.

1. *Ellipse or circle:* $B^2 - 4AC < 0$
2. *Parabola:* $B^2 - 4AC = 0$
3. *Hyperbola:* $B^2 - 4AC > 0$

For example, in the general equation

$$3x^2 + 7xy + 5y^2 - 6x - 7y + 15 = 0$$

you have $A = 3$, $B = 7$, and $C = 5$. So the discriminant is

$$B^2 - 4AC = 7^2 - 4(3)(5) = 49 - 60 = -11.$$

Because $-11 < 0$, the graph of the equation is an ellipse or a circle.

Avoiding Common Errors

Students can easily make algebraic errors when writing the equation for a rotated conic section. In order to check that the equation in the $x'y'$-system is correct, suggest that students compare the rotation invariants for the equation in each system.

Example 4 **Rotation and Graphing Utilities**

For each equation, classify the graph of the equation, use the Quadratic Formula to solve for y, and then use a graphing utility to graph the equation.

a. $2x^2 - 3xy + 2y^2 - 2x = 0$

b. $x^2 - 6xy + 9y^2 - 2y + 1 = 0$

c. $3x^2 + 8xy + 4y^2 - 7 = 0$

Solution

a. Because $B^2 - 4AC = 9 - 16 < 0$, the graph is a circle or an ellipse. Solve for y as follows.

$$2x^2 - 3xy + 2y^2 - 2x = 0 \qquad \text{Write original equation.}$$

$$2y^2 - 3xy + (2x^2 - 2x) = 0 \qquad \text{Quadratic form } ay^2 + by + c = 0$$

$$y = \frac{-(-3x) \pm \sqrt{(-3x)^2 - 4(2)(2x^2 - 2x)}}{2(2)}$$

$$y = \frac{3x \pm \sqrt{x(16 - 7x)}}{4}$$

Graph both of the equations to obtain the ellipse shown in Figure 10.49.

$$y_1 = \frac{3x + \sqrt{x(16 - 7x)}}{4} \qquad \text{Top half of ellipse}$$

$$y_2 = \frac{3x - \sqrt{x(16 - 7x)}}{4} \qquad \text{Bottom half of ellipse}$$

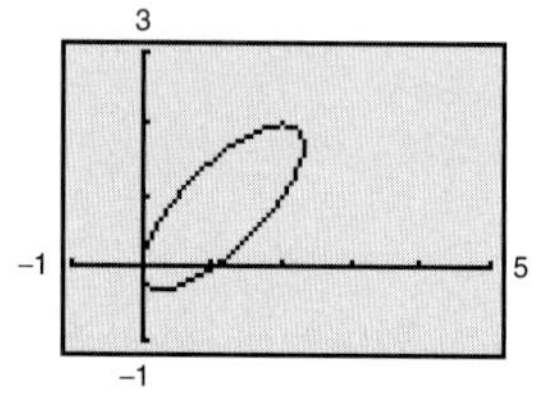

FIGURE 10.49

b. Because $B^2 - 4AC = 36 - 36 = 0$, the graph is a parabola.

$$x^2 - 6xy + 9y^2 - 2y + 1 = 0 \qquad \text{Write original equation.}$$

$$9y^2 - (6x + 2)y + (x^2 + 1) = 0 \qquad \text{Quadratic form } ay^2 + by + c = 0$$

$$y = \frac{(6x + 2) \pm \sqrt{(6x + 2)^2 - 4(9)(x^2 + 1)}}{2(9)}$$

Graphing both of the equations to obtain the parabola shown in Figure 10.50.

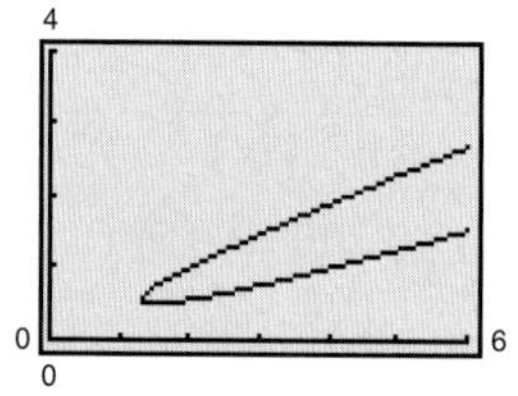

FIGURE 10.50

c. Because $B^2 - 4AC = 64 - 48 > 0$, the graph is a hyperbola.

$$3x^2 + 8xy + 4y^2 - 7 = 0 \qquad \text{Write original equation.}$$

$$4y^2 + 8xy + (3x^2 - 7) = 0 \qquad \text{Quadratic form } ay^2 + by + c = 0$$

$$y = \frac{-8x \pm \sqrt{(8x)^2 - 4(4)(3x^2 - 7)}}{2(4)}$$

The graphs of these two equations yield the hyperbola shown in Figure 10.51.

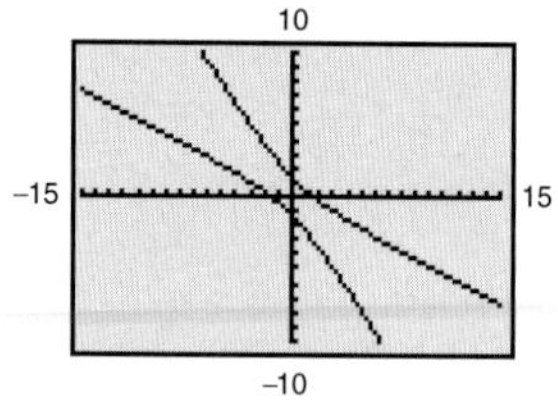

FIGURE 10.51

CHECKPoint Now try Exercise 43.

Classroom Discussion

Classifying a Graph as a Hyperbola In Section 2.6, it was mentioned that the graph of $f(x) = 1/x$ is a hyperbola. Use the techniques in this section to verify this, and justify each step. Compare your results with those of another student.
See margin.

Extra Example 4

For each equation, classify the graph of the equation, use the Quadratic Formula to solve for y, and then use a graphing utility to graph the equation.

a. $16x^2 - 24xy + 9y^2 - 30x - 40y = 0$

Parabola; $y = \dfrac{12x + 20 \pm \sqrt{480x + 670}}{9}$

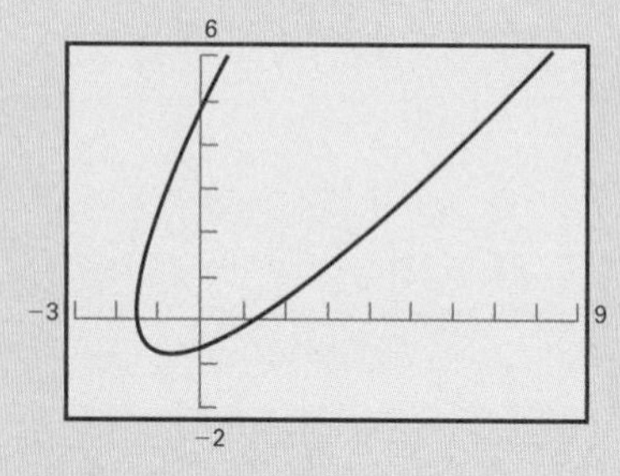

b. $2x^2 - 4xy + 3y^2 - 3x = 0$

Ellipse; $y = \dfrac{2x \pm \sqrt{x(9 - 2x)}}{3}$

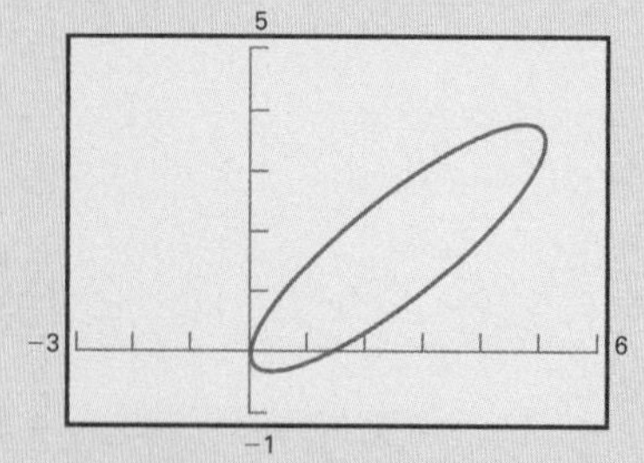

c. $x^2 + 5xy + 2y^2 - 1 = 0$

Hyperbola; $y = \dfrac{-5x \pm \sqrt{17x^2 + 4}}{4}$

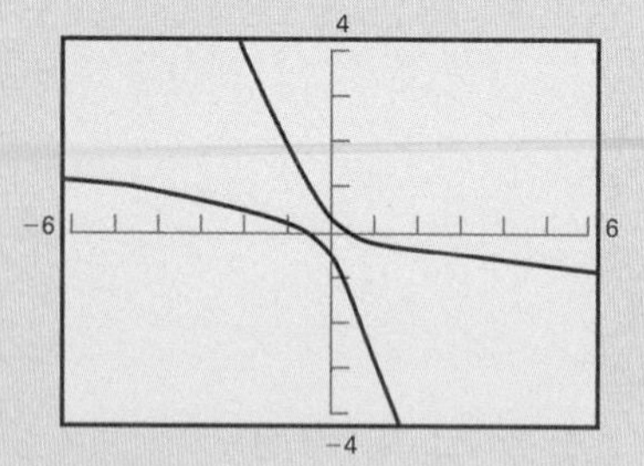

Closing the Lesson

Have students summarize the major points of the lesson and answer the Essential Question: How do you eliminate the xy-term from the general equation for conic sections and classify a conic based on its general equation if $B \neq 0$?

- **In order to eliminate the xy-term, rotate the coordinate axes through an angle θ such that $\cot 2\theta = \dfrac{A - C}{B}$, and rewrite the general equation in terms of x' and y' by substituting $x = x'\cos\theta - y'\sin\theta$ and $y = x'\sin\theta + y'\cos\theta$.**
- **Classify conic sections by calculating the discriminant $B^2 - 4AC$ of the general equation.**
- **Graph the general equation $Ax^2 + Bxy + Cy^2 + Dx + Ey + F = 0$ by solving the equation for y with the Quadratic Formula and graphing both of the resulting equations using a graphing utility.**

Classroom Discussion

$f(x) = 1/x$

$y = 1/x$

$xy = 1$

$xy - 1 = 0 \Rightarrow B = 1$ and $F = -1$

So, $B^2 - 4AC = (1)^2 - 4(0)(0) = 1 > 0.$

Therefore, the graph of $f(x) = 1/x$ is a hyperbola.

10.5 EXERCISES

See www.CalcChat.com for worked-out solutions to odd-numbered exercises.

VOCABULARY: Fill in the blanks.

1. The procedure used to eliminate the xy-term in a general second-degree equation is called rotation of axes.
2. After rotating the coordinate axes through an angle θ, the general second-degree equation in the new $x'y'$-plane will have the form $A'(x')^2 + C'(y')^2 + D'x' + E'y' + F' = 0$
3. Quantities that are equal in both the original equation of a conic and the equation of the rotated conic are invariant under rotation.
4. The quantity $B^2 - 4AC$ is called the ________ of the equation $Ax^2 + Bxy + Cy^2 + Dx + Ey + F = 0$. discriminant

SKILLS AND APPLICATIONS

In Exercises 5–12, the $x'y'$-coordinate system has been rotated θ degrees from the xy-coordinate system. The coordinates of a point in the xy-coordinate system are given. Find the coordinates of the point in the rotated coordinate system.

5. $\theta = 90°, (0, 3)$ $(3, 0)$
6. $\theta = 90°, (2, 2)$ $(2, -2)$
7. $\theta = 30°, (1, 3)$
8. $\theta = 30°, (2, 4)$ 7–12.
9. $\theta = 45°, (2, 1)$
10. $\theta = 45°, (4, 4)$ See margin.
11. $\theta = 60°, (1, 2)$
12. $\theta = 60°, (3, 1)$

In Exercises 13–26, rotate the axes to eliminate the xy-term in the equation. Then write the equation in standard form. Sketch the graph of the resulting equation, showing both sets of axes. 13–26. See margin.

13. $xy + 1 = 0$
14. $xy - 4 = 0$
15. $x^2 - 2xy + y^2 - 1 = 0$
16. $xy + 2x - y + 4 = 0$
17. $xy - 8x - 4y = 0$
18. $2x^2 - 3xy - 2y^2 + 10 = 0$
19. $5x^2 - 6xy + 5y^2 - 12 = 0$
20. $2x^2 + xy + 2y^2 - 8 = 0$
21. $x^2 + 2xy + y^2 - 4x + 4y = 0$
22. $13x^2 + 6\sqrt{3}xy + 7y^2 - 16 = 0$
23. $3x^2 - 2\sqrt{3}xy + y^2 + 2x + 2\sqrt{3}y = 0$
24. $16x^2 - 24xy + 9y^2 - 60x - 80y + 100 = 0$
25. $9x^2 + 24xy + 16y^2 + 90x - 130y = 0$
26. $9x^2 + 24xy + 16y^2 + 80x - 60y = 0$

In Exercises 27–36, use a graphing utility to graph the conic. Determine the angle θ through which the axes are rotated. Explain how you used the graphing utility to obtain the graph. 27–36. See margin.

27. $x^2 + 2xy + y^2 = 20$
28. $x^2 - 4xy + 2y^2 = 6$
29. $17x^2 + 32xy - 7y^2 = 75$
30. $40x^2 + 36xy + 25y^2 = 52$
31. $32x^2 + 48xy + 8y^2 = 50$
32. $24x^2 + 18xy + 12y^2 = 34$
33. $2x^2 + 4xy + 2y^2 + \sqrt{26}x + 3y = -15$
34. $7x^2 - 2\sqrt{3}xy + 5y^2 = 16$
35. $4x^2 - 12xy + 9y^2 + (4\sqrt{13} - 12)x - (6\sqrt{13} + 8)y = 91$
36. $6x^2 - 4xy + 8y^2 + (5\sqrt{5} - 10)x - (7\sqrt{5} + 5)y = 80$

In Exercises 37–42, match the graph with its equation. [The graphs are labeled (a), (b), (c), (d), (e), and (f).]

(a)

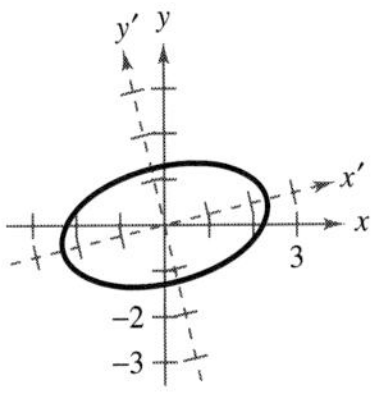

(b)

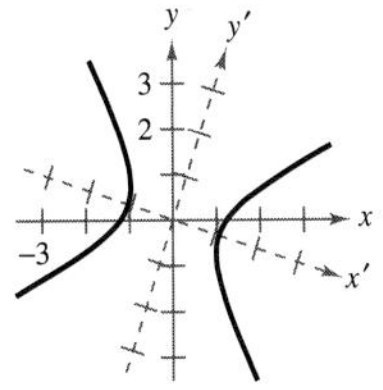

(c)

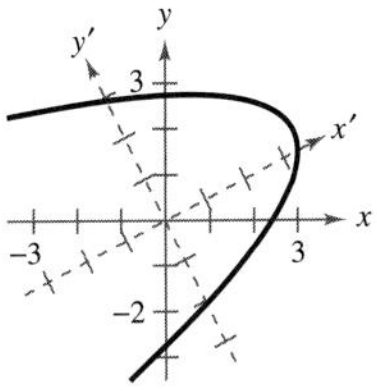

(d)

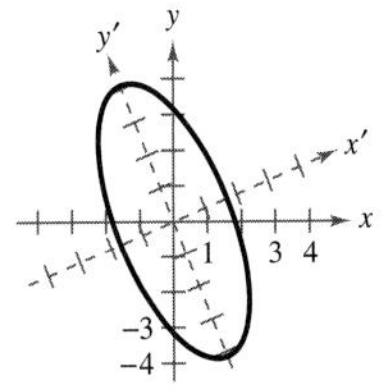

(e)

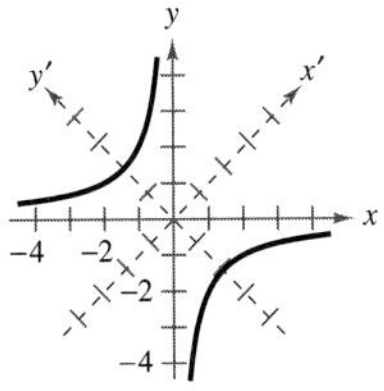

(f)

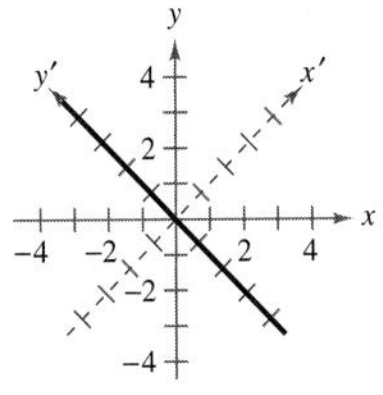

4 PRACTICE AND APPLY

Assignment Guide

Transparencies Available
Available at the Instructor's companion site.

Average:
Day 1: pp. 767–768
Exs. 1, 2, 5–9 odd, 14, 15, 17, 18, 23, 24, 37–40, 51, 55
Day 2: pp. 767–768
Exs. 3, 4, 27–31 odd, 45–49 odd, 57–67 odd, 71–73

Advanced:
Day 1: pp. 767–768
Exs. 1, 2, 6–14 even, 15, 16–26 even, 37–42, 52, 56
Day 2: pp. 767–768
Exs. 3, 4, 28, 32–36 even, 44–50 even, 58–70 even, 71, 72, 74, 75

Block:
pp. 767–768
Exs. 1, 2, 5–9 odd, 14, 15, 17, 18, 23, 24, 37–40, 51, 55 (with 10.4)
pp. 767–768
Exs. 3, 4, 27–31 odd, 45–49 odd, 57–67 odd, 71–73 (with 10.6)

7. $\left(\dfrac{3 + \sqrt{3}}{2}, \dfrac{3\sqrt{3} - 1}{2}\right)$
8. $(\sqrt{3} + 2, 2\sqrt{3} - 1)$
9. $\left(\dfrac{3\sqrt{2}}{2}, -\dfrac{\sqrt{2}}{2}\right)$
10. $(4\sqrt{2}, 0)$
11. $\left(\dfrac{2\sqrt{3} + 1}{2}, \dfrac{2 - \sqrt{3}}{2}\right)$
12. $\left(\dfrac{3 + \sqrt{3}}{2}, \dfrac{1 - 3\sqrt{3}}{2}\right)$
13. $\dfrac{(y')^2}{2} - \dfrac{(x')^2}{2} = 1$

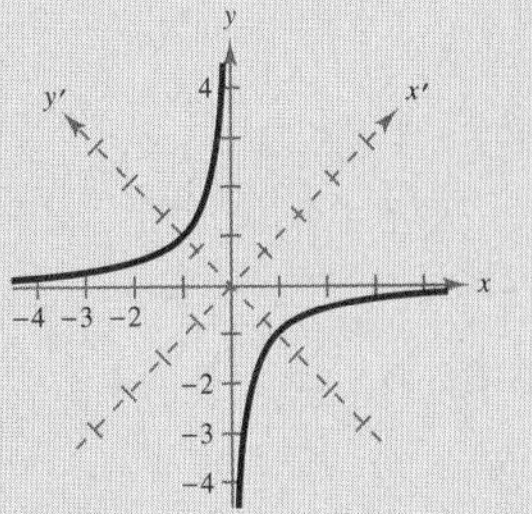

14. $\dfrac{(x')^2}{8} - \dfrac{(y')^2}{8} = 1$

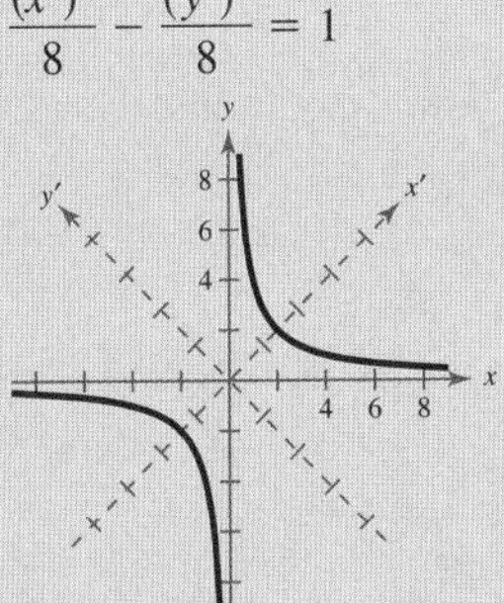

15. $y' = \pm\dfrac{\sqrt{2}}{2}$

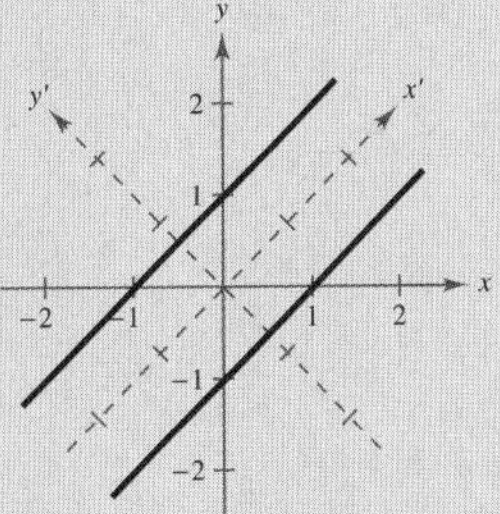

16–36. See Additional Answers beginning on page AA1.

5 ASSESS AND RETEACH

Daily Homework Quiz

Transparency Available

Available at the Instructor's companion site.

51.

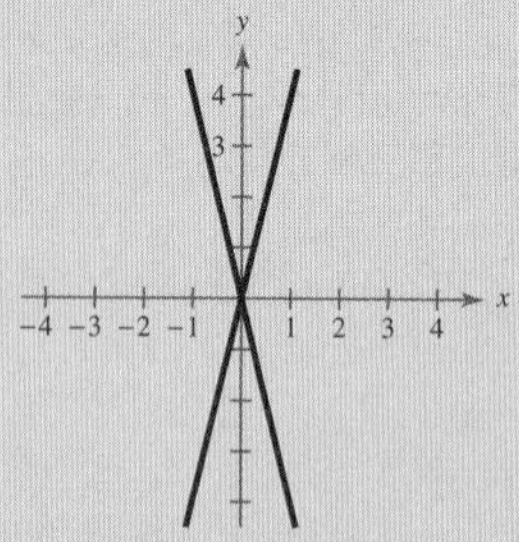

52.

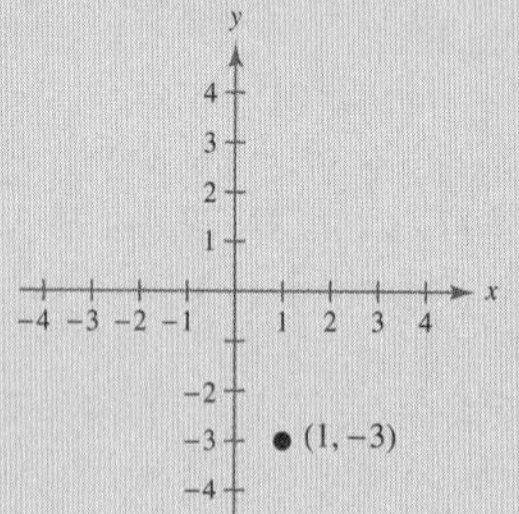

53.

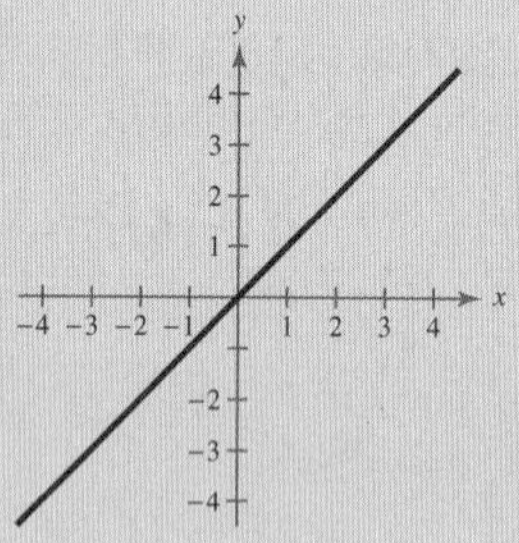

54.

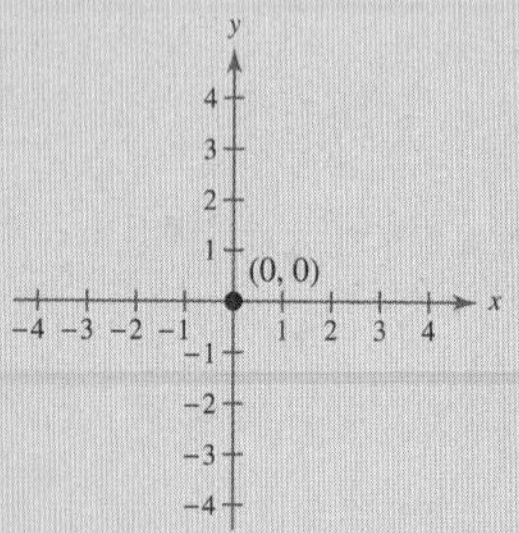

55.

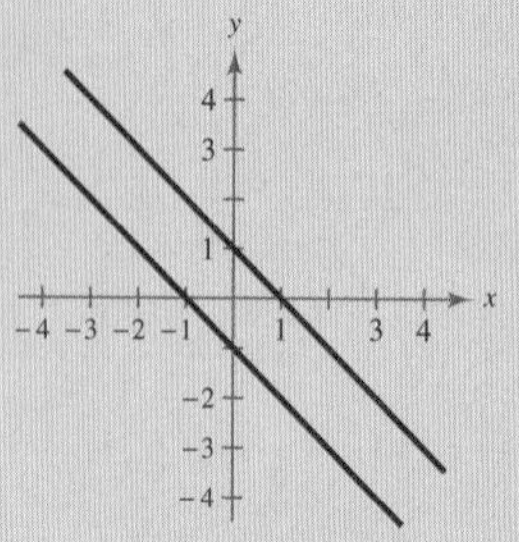

37. $xy + 2 = 0$ e

38. $x^2 + 2xy + y^2 = 0$ f

39. $-2x^2 + 3xy + 2y^2 + 3 = 0$ b

40. $x^2 - xy + 3y^2 - 5 = 0$ a

41. $3x^2 + 2xy + y^2 - 10 = 0$ d

42. $x^2 - 4xy + 4y^2 + 10x - 30 = 0$ c

In Exercises 43–50, (a) use the discriminant to classify the graph, (b) use the Quadratic Formula to solve for y, and (c) use a graphing utility to graph the equation. 43–50. See margin.

43. $16x^2 - 8xy + y^2 - 10x + 5y = 0$

44. $x^2 - 4xy - 2y^2 - 6 = 0$

45. $12x^2 - 6xy + 7y^2 - 45 = 0$

46. $2x^2 + 4xy + 5y^2 + 3x - 4y - 20 = 0$

47. $x^2 - 6xy - 5y^2 + 4x - 22 = 0$

48. $36x^2 - 60xy + 25y^2 + 9y = 0$

49. $x^2 + 4xy + 4y^2 - 5x - y - 3 = 0$

50. $x^2 + xy + 4y^2 + x + y - 4 = 0$

In Exercises 51–56, sketch (if possible) the graph of the degenerate conic. 51–56. See margin.

51. $y^2 - 16x^2 = 0$

52. $x^2 + y^2 - 2x + 6y + 10 = 0$

53. $x^2 - 2xy + y^2 = 0$

54. $5x^2 - 2xy + 5y^2 = 0$

55. $x^2 + 2xy + y^2 - 1 = 0$

56. $x^2 - 10xy + y^2 = 0$

In Exercises 57–70, find any points of intersection of the graphs algebraically and then verify using a graphing utility.

57. $-x^2 + y^2 + 4x - 6y + 4 = 0$
$x^2 + y^2 - 4x - 6y + 12 = 0$ $(2, 2), (2, 4)$

58. $-x^2 - y^2 - 8x + 20y - 7 = 0$
$x^2 + 9y^2 + 8x + 4y + 7 = 0$ $(-7, 0), (-1, 0)$

59. $-4x^2 - y^2 - 16x + 24y - 16 = 0$
$4x^2 + y^2 + 40x - 24y + 208 = 0$ $(-8, 12)$

60. $x^2 - 4y^2 - 20x - 64y - 172 = 0$
$16x^2 + 4y^2 - 320x + 64y + 1600 = 0$ $(14, -8), (6, -8)$

61. $x^2 - y^2 - 12x + 16y - 64 = 0$
$x^2 + y^2 - 12x - 16y + 64 = 0$ $(0, 8), (12, 8)$

62. $x^2 + 4y^2 - 2x - 8y + 1 = 0$
$-x^2 + 2x - 4y - 1 = 0$ $(1, 0)$

63. $-16x^2 - y^2 + 24y - 80 = 0$
$16x^2 + 25y^2 - 400 = 0$ $(0, 4)$

64. $16x^2 - y^2 + 16y - 128 = 0$
$y^2 - 48x - 16y - 32 = 0$ $(-2, 8), \left(5, 8 \pm 4\sqrt{21}\right)$

65. $x^2 + y^2 - 4 = 0$
$3x - y^2 = 0$ $\left(1, \sqrt{3}\right), \left(1, -\sqrt{3}\right)$

66. $4x^2 + 9y^2 - 36y = 0$
$x^2 + 9y - 27 = 0$ $(\pm 3, 2)$

67. $x^2 + 2y^2 - 4x + 6y - 5 = 0$
$-x + y - 4 = 0$ No solution

68. $x^2 + 2y^2 - 4x + 6y - 5 = 0$
$x^2 - 4x - y + 4 = 0$ $(1, 1), (3, 1)$

69. $xy + x - 2y + 3 = 0$
$x^2 + 4y^2 - 9 = 0$ $\left(0, \frac{3}{2}\right), (-3, 0)$

70. $5x^2 - 2xy + 5y^2 - 12 = 0$
$x + y - 1 = 0$
$\left(\frac{1}{6}\left(3 + \sqrt{30}\right), \frac{1}{6}\left(3 - \sqrt{30}\right)\right), \left(\frac{1}{6}\left(3 - \sqrt{30}\right), \frac{1}{6}\left(3 + \sqrt{30}\right)\right)$

EXPLORATION

71–72. See margin.

TRUE OR FALSE? In Exercises 71 and 72, determine whether the statement is true or false. Justify your answer.

71. The graph of the equation

$$x^2 + xy + ky^2 + 6x + 10 = 0$$

where k is any constant less than $\frac{1}{4}$, is a hyperbola.

72. After a rotation of axes is used to eliminate the xy-term from an equation of the form

$$Ax^2 + Bxy + Cy^2 + Dx + Ey + F = 0$$

the coefficients of the x^2- and y^2-terms remain A and C, respectively.

73. Show that the equation

$$x^2 + y^2 = r^2$$ Answers will vary.

is invariant under rotation of axes.

74. CAPSTONE Consider the equation

$$6x^2 - 3xy + 6y^2 - 25 = 0.$$ See margin.

(a) Without calculating, explain how to rewrite the equation so that it does not have an xy-term.

(b) Explain how to identify the graph of the equation.

75. Find the lengths of the major and minor axes of the ellipse graphed in Exercise 22.

Major axis: 4; Minor axis: 2

56.

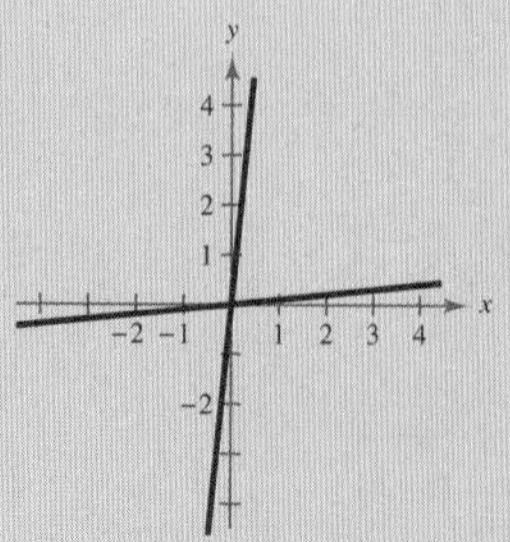

71. True. The graph of the equation can be classified by finding the discriminant. For a graph to be a hyperbola, the discriminant must be greater than zero. If $k \geq \frac{1}{4}$, then the discriminant would be less than or equal to zero.

72. False. The coefficients of the new equation after it has been rotated are obtained by making the substitutions $x = x' \cos \theta - y' \sin \theta$ and $y = x' \sin \theta + y' \cos \theta$.

43–50, 74. See Additional Answers beginning on page AA1.

10.6 Parametric Equations

What you should learn

- Evaluate sets of parametric equations for given values of the parameter.
- Sketch curves that are represented by sets of parametric equations.
- Rewrite sets of parametric equations as single rectangular equations by eliminating the parameter.
- Find sets of parametric equations for graphs.

Why you should learn it

Parametric equations are useful for modeling the path of an object. For instance, in Exercise 63 on page 775, you will use a set of parametric equations to model the path of a baseball.

Jed Jacobsohn/Getty Images

Plane Curves

Up to this point you have been representing a graph by a single equation involving the *two* variables x and y. In this section, you will study situations in which it is useful to introduce a *third* variable to represent a curve in the plane.

To see the usefulness of this procedure, consider the path followed by an object that is propelled into the air at an angle of 45°. If the initial velocity of the object is 48 feet per second, it can be shown that the object follows the parabolic path

$$y = -\frac{x^2}{72} + x \qquad \text{Rectangular equation}$$

as shown in Figure 10.52. However, this equation does not tell the whole story. Although it does tell you *where* the object has been, it does not tell you *when* the object was at a given point (x, y) on the path. To determine this time, you can introduce a third variable t, called a **parameter.** It is possible to write both x and y as functions of t to obtain the **parametric equations**

$$x = 24\sqrt{2}t \qquad \text{Parametric equation for } x$$

$$y = -16t^2 + 24\sqrt{2}t. \qquad \text{Parametric equation for } y$$

From this set of equations you can determine that at time $t = 0$, the object is at the point $(0, 0)$. Similarly, at time $t = 1$, the object is at the point $(24\sqrt{2}, 24\sqrt{2} - 16)$, and so on, as shown in Figure 10.52.

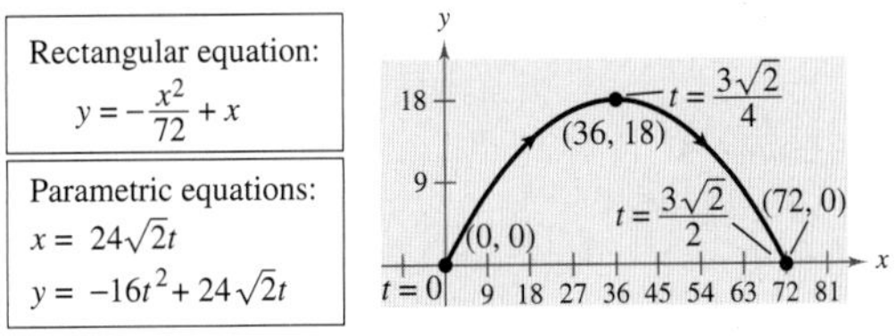

Curvilinear Motion: Two Variables for Position, One Variable for Time

FIGURE 10.52

For this particular motion problem, x and y are continuous functions of t, and the resulting path is a **plane curve.** (Recall that a *continuous function* is one whose graph can be traced without lifting the pencil from the paper.)

> **Definition of Plane Curve**
>
> If f and g are continuous functions of t on an interval I, the set of ordered pairs $(f(t), g(t))$ is a **plane curve** C. The equations
>
> $x = f(t)$ and $y = g(t)$
>
> are **parametric equations** for C, and t is the **parameter.**

1 Plan and Prepare

Warm-up Exercises

Transparency Available
Available at the Instructor's companion site.

Notetaking Guide

Transparency Available
Promotes interactive learning and notetaking skills. Available at the Instructor's companion site.

Animated Precalculus

An **Animated Precalculus** tutorial is available at the Student companion site for **Section 10.6.**

Pacing

Average: 2 days
Advanced: 2 days
Block: 0.5 block with 10.5
0.5 block with 10.7

2 Focus and Motivate

Essential Question

How do you write equations to describe the motion of a point in a plane? **Tell students that they will learn how to answer this question by introducing a third variable, or parameter, and comparing parametric equations with those involving only x and y.**

Resource Planning Guide

Chapter Resources

- Complete Solutions Guide

Workbooks

- Notetaking Guide
- Student Solutions Guide

Interactive Technology

- Instructor Success Organizer
- Notetaking Guide IAE
- Instructional DVDs
- Animated Precalculus
- PowerLecture with ExamView

Sketching a Plane Curve

When sketching a curve represented by a pair of parametric equations, you still plot points in the xy-plane. Each set of coordinates (x, y) is determined from a value chosen for the parameter t. Plotting the resulting points in the order of *increasing* values of t traces the curve in a specific direction. This is called the **orientation** of the curve.

Example 1 Sketching a Curve

Sketch the curve given by the parametric equations

$$x = t^2 - 4 \quad \text{and} \quad y = \frac{t}{2}, \quad -2 \le t \le 3.$$

Solution

Using values of t in the specified interval, the parametric equations yield the points (x, y) shown in the table.

t	x	y
-2	0	-1
-1	-3	$-\frac{1}{2}$
0	-4	0
1	-3	$\frac{1}{2}$
2	0	1
3	5	$\frac{3}{2}$

By plotting these points in the order of increasing t, you obtain the curve C shown in Figure 10.53. Note that the arrows on the curve indicate its orientation as t increases from -2 to 3. So, if a particle were moving on this curve, it would start at $(0, -1)$ and then move along the curve to the point $\left(5, \frac{3}{2}\right)$.

CHECKPoint Now try Exercises 5(a) and (b).

Note that the graph shown in Figure 10.53 does not define y as a function of x. This points out one benefit of parametric equations—they can be used to represent graphs that are more general than graphs of functions.

It often happens that two different sets of parametric equations have the same graph. For example, the set of parametric equations

$$x = 4t^2 - 4 \quad \text{and} \quad y = t, \quad -1 \le t \le \frac{3}{2}$$

has the same graph as the set given in Example 1. However, by comparing the values of t in Figures 10.53 and 10.54, you can see that this second graph is traced out more *rapidly* (considering t as time) than the first graph. So, in applications, different parametric representations can be used to represent various *speeds* at which objects travel along a given path.

WARNING/CAUTION

When using a value of t to find x, be sure to use the same value of t to find the corresponding value of y. Organizing your results in a table, as shown in Example 1, can be helpful.

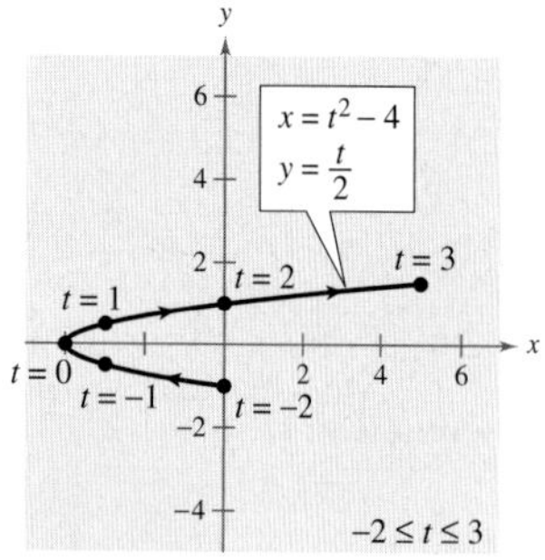

FIGURE 10.53

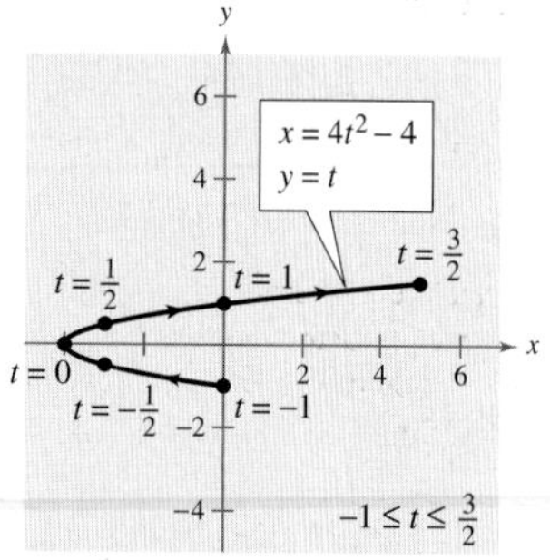

FIGURE 10.54

3 TEACH

Extra Example 1

Sketch the curve represented by the parametric equations $x = t$ and $y = -2t$, $-2 \le t \le 2$.

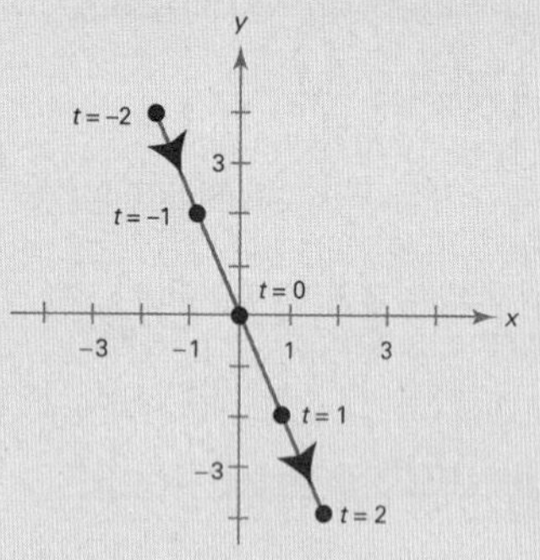

Eliminating the Parameter

Example 1 uses simple point plotting to sketch the curve. This tedious process can sometimes be simplified by finding a rectangular equation (in x and y) that has the same graph. This process is called **eliminating the parameter.**

Parametric equations	→	Solve for t in one equation.	→	Substitute in other equation.	→	Rectangular equation
$x = t^2 - 4$, $y = \dfrac{t}{2}$		$t = 2y$		$x = (2y)^2 - 4$		$x = 4y^2 - 4$

Now you can recognize that the equation $x = 4y^2 - 4$ represents a parabola with a horizontal axis and vertex at $(-4, 0)$.

When converting equations from parametric to rectangular form, you may need to alter the domain of the rectangular equation so that its graph matches the graph of the parametric equations. Such a situation is demonstrated in Example 2.

Example 2 Eliminating the Parameter

Sketch the curve represented by the equations

$$x = \frac{1}{\sqrt{t+1}} \quad \text{and} \quad y = \frac{t}{t+1}$$

by eliminating the parameter and adjusting the domain of the resulting rectangular equation.

Solution

Solving for t in the equation for x produces

$$x = \frac{1}{\sqrt{t+1}} \quad \Longrightarrow \quad x^2 = \frac{1}{t+1}$$

which implies that

$$t = \frac{1 - x^2}{x^2}.$$

Now, substituting in the equation for y, you obtain the rectangular equation

$$y = \frac{t}{t+1} = \frac{\dfrac{(1-x^2)}{x^2}}{\left[\dfrac{(1-x^2)}{x^2}\right] + 1} = \frac{\dfrac{1-x^2}{x^2}}{\dfrac{1-x^2}{x^2} + 1} \cdot \frac{x^2}{x^2} = 1 - x^2.$$

From this rectangular equation, you can recognize that the curve is a parabola that opens downward and has its vertex at $(0, 1)$. Also, this rectangular equation is defined for all values of x, but from the parametric equation for x you can see that the curve is defined only when $t > -1$. This implies that you should restrict the domain of x to positive values, as shown in Figure 10.55.

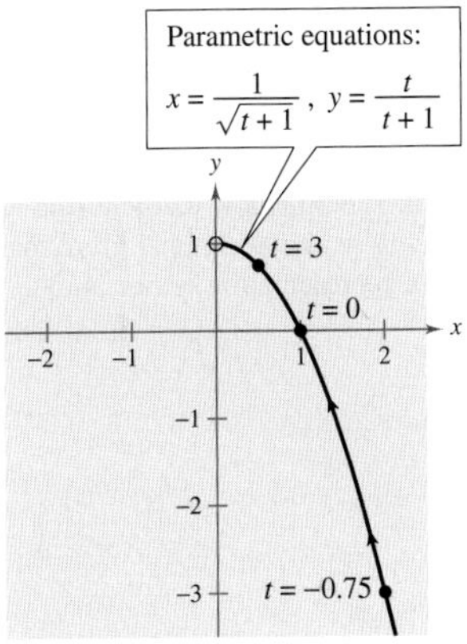

FIGURE 10.55

CHECKPoint Now try Exercise 5(c).

Extra Example 2

Sketch the curve represented by the equations $x = \dfrac{1}{\sqrt{t}}$ and $y = 2t^2$ by eliminating the parameter and adjusting the domain of the resulting rectangular equation.

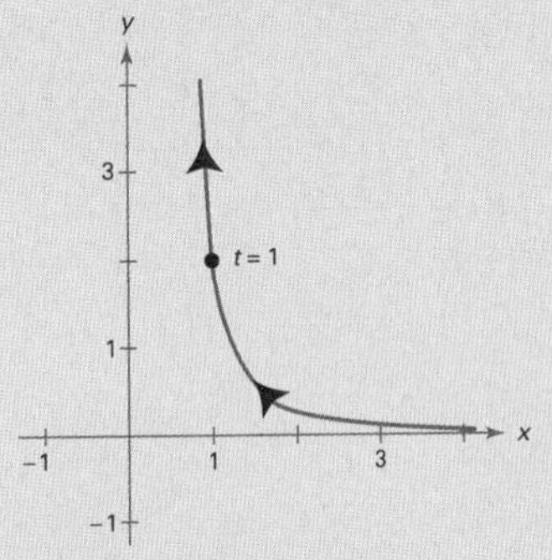

Avoiding Common Errors

When eliminating the parameter in order to sketch a graph, students often neglect to note the domain of the parametric equations. Remind students to sketch only the section of the graph that is valid for the given interval of t.

Extra Example 3

Sketch the curve represented by $x = 2\cos\theta$ and $y = 2\sin\theta$, $0 \le \theta \le 2\pi$, by eliminating the parameter.

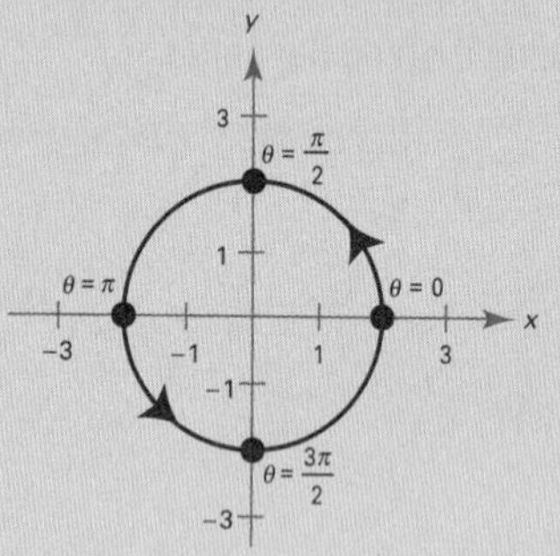

Study Tip

To eliminate the parameter in equations involving trigonometric functions, try using identities such as

$$\sin^2\theta + \cos^2\theta = 1$$

or

$$\sec^2\theta - \tan^2\theta = 1$$

as shown in Example 3.

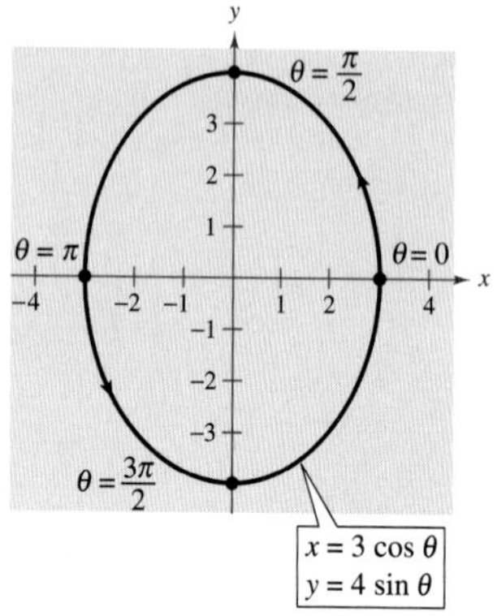

FIGURE 10.56

It is not necessary for the parameter in a set of parametric equations to represent time. The next example uses an *angle* as the parameter.

Example 3 Eliminating an Angle Parameter

Sketch the curve represented by

$$x = 3\cos\theta \quad \text{and} \quad y = 4\sin\theta, \quad 0 \le \theta \le 2\pi$$

by eliminating the parameter.

Solution

Begin by solving for $\cos\theta$ and $\sin\theta$ in the equations.

$$\cos\theta = \frac{x}{3} \quad \text{and} \quad \sin\theta = \frac{y}{4} \qquad \text{Solve for } \cos\theta \text{ and } \sin\theta.$$

Use the identity $\sin^2\theta + \cos^2\theta = 1$ to form an equation involving only x and y.

$$\cos^2\theta + \sin^2\theta = 1 \qquad \text{Pythagorean identity}$$

$$\left(\frac{x}{3}\right)^2 + \left(\frac{y}{4}\right)^2 = 1 \qquad \text{Substitute } \frac{x}{3} \text{ for } \cos\theta \text{ and } \frac{y}{4} \text{ for } \sin\theta.$$

$$\frac{x^2}{9} + \frac{y^2}{16} = 1 \qquad \text{Rectangular equation}$$

From this rectangular equation, you can see that the graph is an ellipse centered at $(0, 0)$, with vertices $(0, 4)$ and $(0, -4)$ and minor axis of length $2b = 6$, as shown in Figure 10.56. Note that the elliptic curve is traced out *counterclockwise* as θ varies from 0 to 2π.

CHECKPoint Now try Exercise 17.

In Examples 2 and 3, it is important to realize that eliminating the parameter is primarily an *aid to curve sketching*. If the parametric equations represent the path of a moving object, the graph alone is not sufficient to describe the object's motion. You still need the parametric equations to tell you the *position*, *direction*, and *speed* at a given time.

Finding Parametric Equations for a Graph

You have been studying techniques for sketching the graph represented by a set of parametric equations. Now consider the *reverse* problem—that is, how can you find a set of parametric equations for a given graph or a given physical description? From the discussion following Example 1, you know that such a representation is not unique. That is, the equations

$$x = 4t^2 - 4 \quad \text{and} \quad y = t, \; -1 \le t \le \frac{3}{2}$$

produced the same graph as the equations

$$x = t^2 - 4 \quad \text{and} \quad y = \frac{t}{2}, \; -2 \le t \le 3.$$

This is further demonstrated in Example 4.

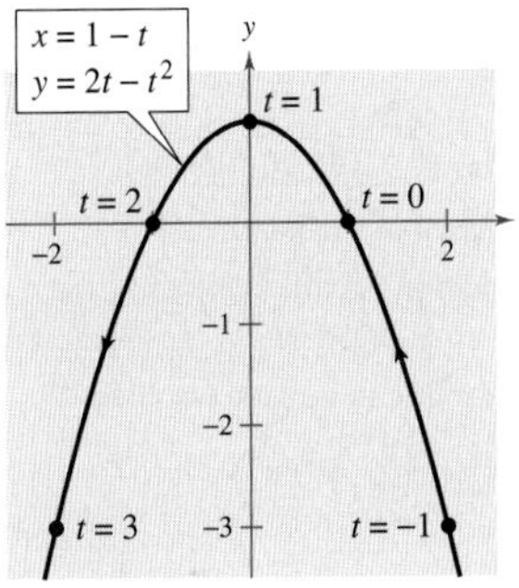

FIGURE 10.57

Example 4 Finding Parametric Equations for a Graph

Find a set of parametric equations to represent the graph of $y = 1 - x^2$, using the following parameters.

a. $t = x$ **b.** $t = 1 - x$

Solution

a. Letting $t = x$, you obtain the parametric equations

$$x = t \quad \text{and} \quad y = 1 - x^2 = 1 - t^2.$$

b. Letting $t = 1 - x$, you obtain the parametric equations

$$x = 1 - t \quad \text{and} \quad y = 1 - x^2 = 1 - (1 - t)^2 = 2t - t^2.$$

In Figure 10.57, note how the resulting curve is oriented by the increasing values of t. For part (a), the curve would have the opposite orientation.

CHECK Point Now try Exercise 45.

Example 5 Parametric Equations for a Cycloid

Describe the **cycloid** traced out by a point P on the circumference of a circle of radius a as the circle rolls along a straight line in a plane.

Solution

As the parameter, let θ be the measure of the circle's rotation, and let the point $P = (x, y)$ begin at the origin. When $\theta = 0$, P is at the origin; when $\theta = \pi$, P is at a maximum point $(\pi a, 2a)$; and when $\theta = 2\pi$, P is back on the x-axis at $(2\pi a, 0)$. From Figure 10.58, you can see that $\angle APC = 180° - \theta$. So, you have

$$\sin\theta = \sin(180° - \theta) = \sin(\angle APC) = \frac{AC}{a} = \frac{BD}{a}$$

$$\cos\theta = -\cos(180° - \theta) = -\cos(\angle APC) = -\frac{AP}{a}$$

which implies that $BD = a\sin\theta$ and $AP = -a\cos\theta$. Because the circle rolls along the x-axis, you know that $OD = \widehat{PD} = a\theta$. Furthermore, because $BA = DC = a$, you have

$$x = OD - BD = a\theta - a\sin\theta \quad \text{and} \quad y = BA + AP = a - a\cos\theta.$$

So, the parametric equations are $x = a(\theta - \sin\theta)$ and $y = a(1 - \cos\theta)$.

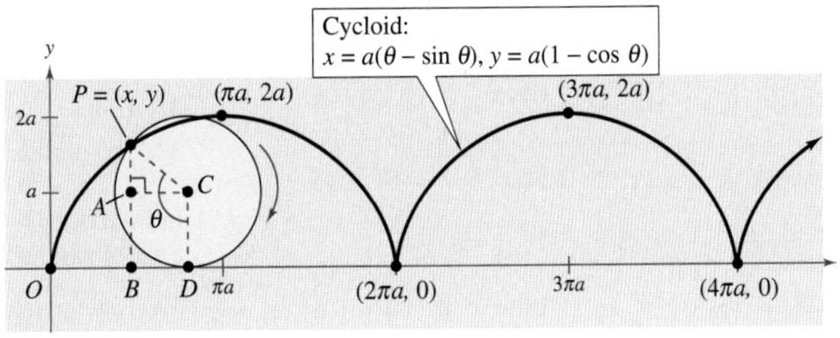

FIGURE 10.58

CHECK Point Now try Exercise 67.

Study Tip

In Example 5, $\widehat{PD}$ represents the arc of the circle between points P and D.

TECHNOLOGY

You can use a graphing utility in *parametric* mode to obtain a graph similar to Figure 10.58 by graphing the following equations.

$X_{1T} = T - \sin T$

$Y_{1T} = 1 - \cos T$

See margin.

Extra Example 4

Find a set of parametric equations to represent the graph of $y = 4x - 3$, using the following parameters.

a. $t = x$

$x = t, y = 4t - 3$

b. $t = 2 - x$

$x = 2 - t, y = 5 - 4t$

Extra Example 5

Describe the cycloid traced out by a point P on the circumference of a circle of radius a rolling along the x-axis, given that P is at a maximum when $x = 0$.

$x = a(\theta + \sin\theta)$ and $y = a(1 + \cos\theta)$

Closing the Lesson

Have students summarize the major points of the lesson and answer the Essential Question: How do you write equations to describe the motion of a point in a plane?

- **Sketch the graph of parametric equations by generating a table for values of t in the given interval.**
- **Find an equation in only x and y by solving one parametric equation for t and substituting into the other equation, thus eliminating the parameter.**
- **Find parametric equations to represent the graph of an equation in x and y by substituting some function of t for x and writing x and y in terms of t.**

Technology

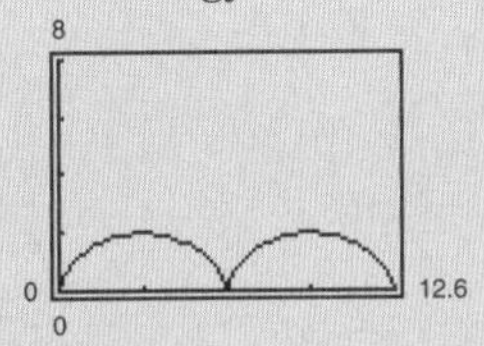

4 PRACTICE AND APPLY

Assignment Guide

Transparencies Available
Available at the Instructor's companion site.

Average:
Day 1: pp. 774–775
Exs. 1–4, 6, 7–15 odd, 19–27 odd, 29–32, 33–39 odd
Day 2: pp. 775–776
Exs. 43, 45, 49–55 odd, 57–61, 63, 65, 68–71

Advanced:
Day 1: pp. 774–775
Exs. 1–4, 6–16 even, 20–28 even, 29–32, 36–40 even
Day 2: pp. 775–776
Exs. 44, 46, 50–56 even, 57–60, 62, 63, 64–68 even, 69, 70, 72, 74

Block:
pp. 774–775
Exs. 1–4, 6, 7–15 odd, 19–27 odd, 29–32, 33–39 odd (with 10.5)
pp. 775–776
Exs. 43, 45, 49–55 odd, 57–61, 63, 65, 68–71 (with 10.7)

5. (a)

t	0	1	2	3	4
x	0	1	$\sqrt{2}$	$\sqrt{3}$	2
y	3	2	1	0	-1

(b)

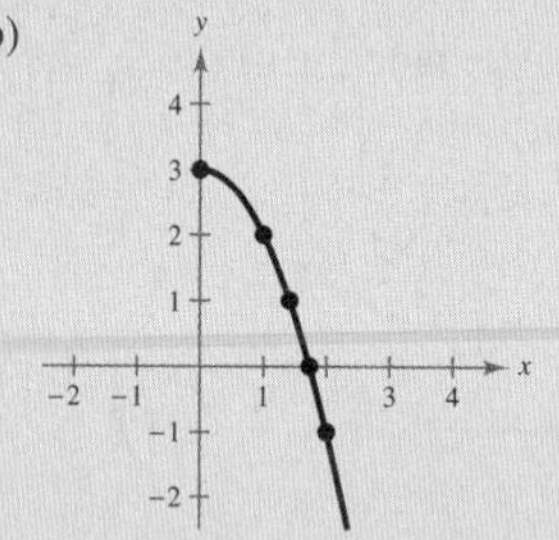

(c) $y = 3 - x^2$

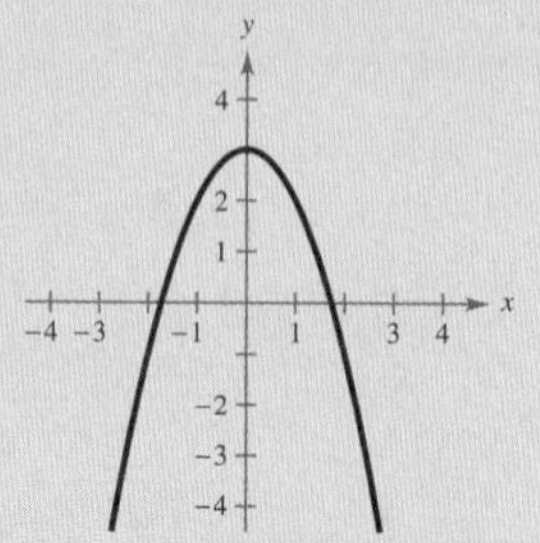

The graph of the rectangular equation shows the entire parabola rather than just the right half.

10.6 EXERCISES

See www.CalcChat.com for worked-out solutions to odd-numbered exercises.

VOCABULARY: Fill in the blanks.

1. If f and g are continuous functions of t on an interval I, the set of ordered pairs $(f(t), g(t))$ is a plane curve C.
2. The orientation of a curve is the direction in which the curve is traced out for increasing values of the parameter.
3. The process of converting a set of parametric equations to a corresponding rectangular equation is called eliminating the parameter
4. A curve traced by a point on the circumference of a circle as the circle rolls along a straight line in a plane is called a cycloid.

SKILLS AND APPLICATIONS

5. Consider the parametric equations $x = \sqrt{t}$ and $y = 3 - t$. See margin.
   (a) Create a table of x- and y-values using $t = 0, 1, 2, 3$, and 4.
   (b) Plot the points (x, y) generated in part (a), and sketch a graph of the parametric equations.
   (c) Find the rectangular equation by eliminating the parameter. Sketch its graph. How do the graphs differ?
6. Consider the parametric equations $x = 4\cos^2\theta$ and $y = 2\sin\theta$. See margin.
   (a) Create a table of x- and y-values using $\theta = -\pi/2, -\pi/4, 0, \pi/4$, and $\pi/2$.
   (b) Plot the points (x, y) generated in part (a), and sketch a graph of the parametric equations.
   (c) Find the rectangular equation by eliminating the parameter. Sketch its graph. How do the graphs differ?

In Exercises 7–26, (a) sketch the curve represented by the parametric equations (indicate the orientation of the curve) and (b) eliminate the parameter and write the corresponding rectangular equation whose graph represents the curve. Adjust the domain of the resulting rectangular equation if necessary. 7–26. See margin.

7. $x = t - 1$, $y = 3t + 1$
8. $x = 3 - 2t$, $y = 2 + 3t$
9. $x = \frac{1}{4}t$, $y = t^2$
10. $x = t$, $y = t^3$
11. $x = t + 2$, $y = t^2$
12. $x = \sqrt{t}$, $y = 1 - t$
13. $x = t + 1$, $y = \dfrac{t}{t + 1}$
14. $x = t - 1$, $y = \dfrac{t}{t - 1}$
15. $x = 2(t + 1)$, $y = |t - 2|$
16. $x = |t - 1|$, $y = t + 2$
17. $x = 4\cos\theta$, $y = 2\sin\theta$
18. $x = 2\cos\theta$, $y = 3\sin\theta$
19. $x = 6\sin 2\theta$, $y = 6\cos 2\theta$
20. $x = \cos\theta$, $y = 2\sin 2\theta$
21. $x = 1 + \cos\theta$, $y = 1 + 2\sin\theta$
22. $x = 2 + 5\cos\theta$, $y = -6 + 4\sin\theta$
23. $x = e^{-t}$, $y = e^{3t}$
24. $x = e^{2t}$, $y = e^t$
25. $x = t^3$, $y = 3\ln t$
26. $x = \ln 2t$, $y = 2t^2$

In Exercises 27 and 28, determine how the plane curves differ from each other. 27–28. See margin.

27. (a) $x = t$, $y = 2t + 1$
    (b) $x = \cos\theta$, $y = 2\cos\theta + 1$
    (c) $x = e^{-t}$, $y = 2e^{-t} + 1$
    (d) $x = e^t$, $y = 2e^t + 1$
28. (a) $x = t$, $y = t^2 - 1$
    (b) $x = t^2$, $y = t^4 - 1$
    (c) $x = \sin t$, $y = \sin^2 t - 1$
    (d) $x = e^t$, $y = e^{2t} - 1$

In Exercises 29–32, eliminate the parameter and obtain the standard form of the rectangular equation. 29–32. See margin.

29. Line through (x_1, y_1) and (x_2, y_2):
    $x = x_1 + t(x_2 - x_1)$, $y = y_1 + t(y_2 - y_1)$
30. Circle: $x = h + r\cos\theta$, $y = k + r\sin\theta$
31. Ellipse: $x = h + a\cos\theta$, $y = k + b\sin\theta$
32. Hyperbola: $x = h + a\sec\theta$, $y = k + b\tan\theta$

In Exercises 33–40, use the results of Exercises 29–32 to find a set of parametric equations for the line or conic.

33. Line: passes through (0, 0) and (3, 6) $x = 3t$, $y = 6t$
34. Line: passes through (3, 2) and $(-6, 3)$
35. Circle: center: (3, 2); radius: 4
36. Circle: center: $(5, -3)$; radius: 4

34. $x = 3 - 9t$, $y = 2 + t$
35. $x = 3 + 4\cos\theta$, $y = 2 + 4\sin\theta$
36. $x = 5 + 4\cos\theta$, $y = -3 + 4\sin\theta$

27. Each curve represents a portion of the line $y = 2x + 1$.

	Domain	Orientation
(a)	$(-\infty, \infty)$	Left to right
(b)	$[-1, 1]$	Depends on θ
(c)	$(0, \infty)$	Right to left
(d)	$(0, \infty)$	Left to right

28. Each curve represents a portion of the parabola $y = x^2 - 1$.

	Domain	Orientation
(a)	$(-\infty, \infty)$	Left to right
(b)	$[0, \infty)$	Depends on t
(c)	$[-1, 1]$	Depends on t
(d)	$(0, \infty)$	Left to right

29. $y - y_1 = m(x - x_1)$
30. $(x - h)^2 + (y - k)^2 = r^2$
31. $\dfrac{(x - h)^2}{a^2} + \dfrac{(y - k)^2}{b^2} = 1$
32. $\dfrac{(x - h)^2}{a^2} - \dfrac{(y - k)^2}{b^2} = 1$

6–26. See Additional Answers beginning on page AA1.

37. Ellipse: vertices: $(\pm 5, 0)$; foci: $(\pm 4, 0)$ $x = 5\cos\theta$, $y = 3\sin\theta$

38. Ellipse: vertices: $(3, 7), (3, -1)$; foci: $(3, 5), (3, 1)$ $x = 3 + 2\sqrt{3}\cos\theta$, $y = 3 + 4\sin\theta$

39. Hyperbola: vertices: $(\pm 4, 0)$; foci: $(\pm 5, 0)$ See margin.

40. Hyperbola: vertices: $(\pm 2, 0)$; foci: $(\pm 4, 0)$ See margin.

In Exercises 41–48, find a set of parametric equations for the rectangular equation using (a) $t = x$ and (b) $t = 2 - x$. 41–48. See margin.

41. $y = 3x - 2$ 42. $x = 3y - 2$

43. $y = 2 - x$ 44. $y = x^2 + 1$

45. $y = x^2 - 3$ 46. $y = 1 - 2x^2$

47. $y = \dfrac{1}{x}$ 48. $y = \dfrac{1}{2x}$

In Exercises 49–56, use a graphing utility to graph the curve represented by the parametric equations. 49–56. See margin.

49. Cycloid: $x = 4(\theta - \sin\theta)$, $y = 4(1 - \cos\theta)$

50. Cycloid: $x = \theta + \sin\theta$, $y = 1 - \cos\theta$

51. Prolate cycloid: $x = \theta - \frac{3}{2}\sin\theta$, $y = 1 - \frac{3}{2}\cos\theta$

52. Prolate cycloid: $x = 2\theta - 4\sin\theta$, $y = 2 - 4\cos\theta$

53. Hypocycloid: $x = 3\cos^3\theta$, $y = 3\sin^3\theta$

54. Curtate cycloid: $x = 8\theta - 4\sin\theta$, $y = 8 - 4\cos\theta$

55. Witch of Agnesi: $x = 2\cot\theta$, $y = 2\sin^2\theta$

56. Folium of Descartes: $x = \dfrac{3t}{1 + t^3}$, $y = \dfrac{3t^2}{1 + t^3}$

In Exercises 57–60, match the parametric equations with the correct graph and describe the domain and range. [The graphs are labeled (a), (b), (c), and (d).] 57–60. See margin.

(a)

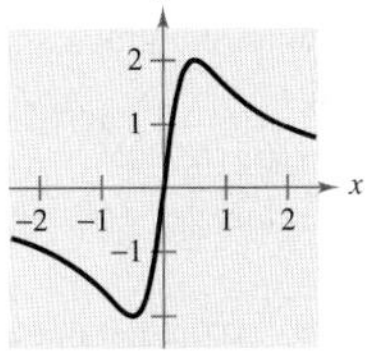

(b)

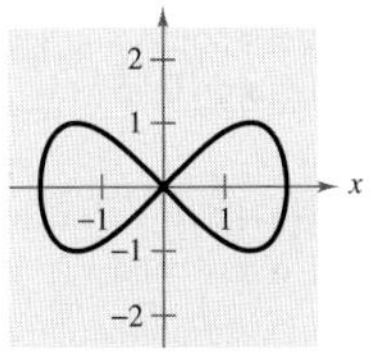

(c)

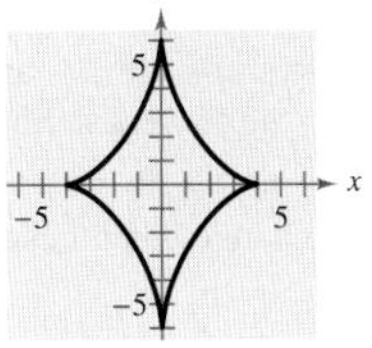

(d)

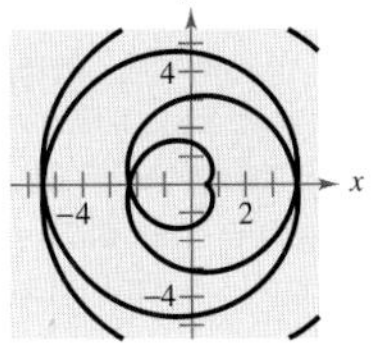

57. Lissajous curve: $x = 2\cos\theta$, $y = \sin 2\theta$

58. Evolute of ellipse: $x = 4\cos^3\theta$, $y = 6\sin^3\theta$

59. Involute of circle: $x = \frac{1}{2}(\cos\theta + \theta\sin\theta)$, $y = \frac{1}{2}(\sin\theta - \theta\cos\theta)$

60. Serpentine curve: $x = \frac{1}{2}\cot\theta$, $y = 4\sin\theta\cos\theta$

PROJECTILE MOTION A projectile is launched at a height of h feet above the ground at an angle of θ with the horizontal. The initial velocity is v_0 feet per second, and the path of the projectile is modeled by the parametric equations

$$x = (v_0 \cos\theta)t \quad \text{and} \quad y = h + (v_0 \sin\theta)t - 16t^2.$$

In Exercises 61 and 62, use a graphing utility to graph the paths of a projectile launched from ground level at each value of θ and v_0. For each case, use the graph to approximate the maximum height and the range of the projectile. 61–62. See margin.

61. (a) $\theta = 60°$, $v_0 = 88$ feet per second
(b) $\theta = 60°$, $v_0 = 132$ feet per second
(c) $\theta = 45°$, $v_0 = 88$ feet per second
(d) $\theta = 45°$, $v_0 = 132$ feet per second

62. (a) $\theta = 15°$, $v_0 = 50$ feet per second
(b) $\theta = 15°$, $v_0 = 120$ feet per second
(c) $\theta = 10°$, $v_0 = 50$ feet per second
(d) $\theta = 10°$, $v_0 = 120$ feet per second

63. **SPORTS** The center field fence in Yankee Stadium is 7 feet high and 408 feet from home plate. A baseball is hit at a point 3 feet above the ground. It leaves the bat at an angle of θ degrees with the horizontal at a speed of 100 miles per hour (see figure).

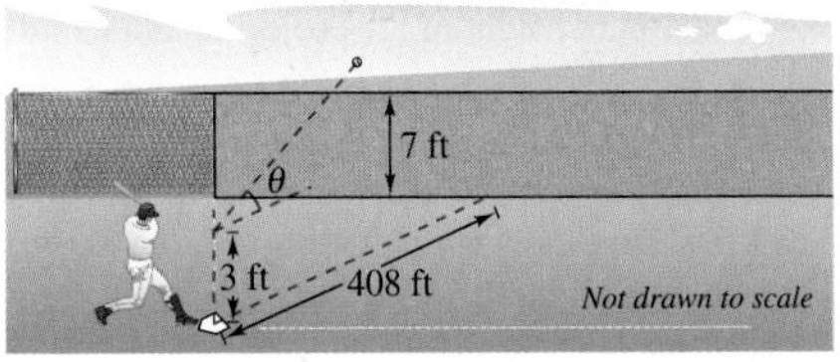

(a) Write a set of parametric equations that model the path of the baseball. (a)–(c). See margin.

(b) Use a graphing utility to graph the path of the baseball when $\theta = 15°$. Is the hit a home run?

(c) Use the graphing utility to graph the path of the baseball when $\theta = 23°$. Is the hit a home run?

(d) Find the minimum angle required for the hit to be a home run. 19.3°

39. $x = 4\sec\theta$
$y = 3\tan\theta$

40. $x = 2\sec\theta$
$y = 2\sqrt{3}\tan\theta$

41. (a) $x = t$, $y = 3t - 2$
(b) $x = -t + 2$, $y = -3t + 4$

42. (a) $x = t$, $y = \frac{1}{3}(t + 2)$
(b) $x = -t + 2$, $y = -\frac{1}{3}(t - 4)$

43. (a) $x = t$, $y = 2 - t$
(b) $x = -t + 2$, $y = t$

44. (a) $x = t$, $y = t^2 + 1$
(b) $x = -t + 2$, $y = t^2 - 4t + 5$

45. (a) $x = t$
$y = t^2 - 3$
(b) $x = 2 - t$
$y = t^2 - 4t + 1$

46. (a) $x = t$
$y = 1 - 2t^2$
(b) $x = 2 - t$
$y = -2t^2 + 8t - 7$

47. (a) $x = t$, $y = \dfrac{1}{t}$
(b) $x = -t + 2$, $y = -\dfrac{1}{t - 2}$

48. (a) $x = t$, $y = \dfrac{1}{2t}$
(b) $x = -t + 2$, $y = \dfrac{1}{-2t + 4}$

49.

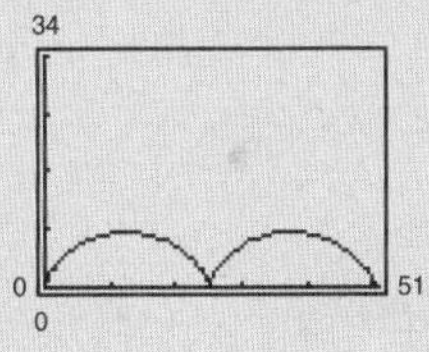

50.

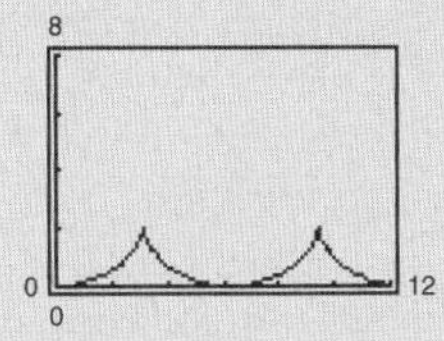

51.

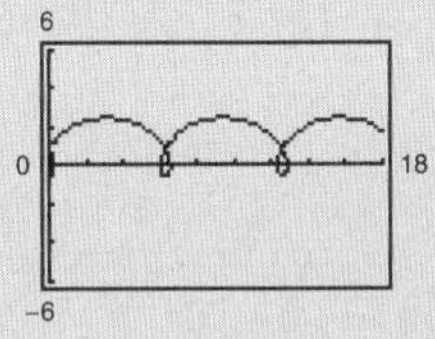

52.

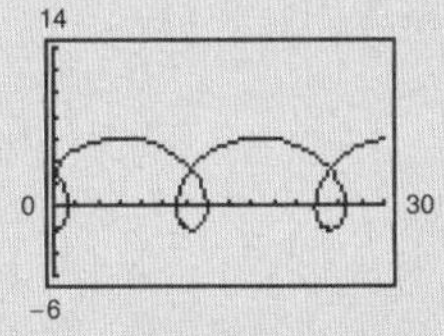

53.

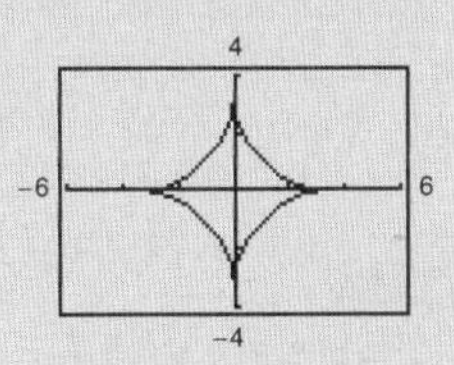

54.

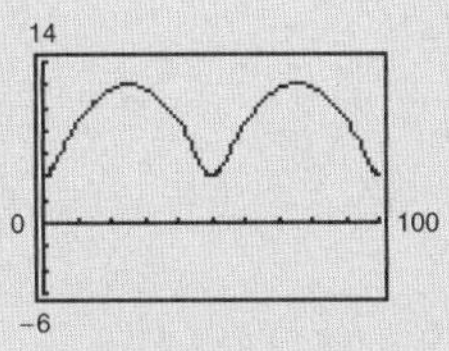

55.

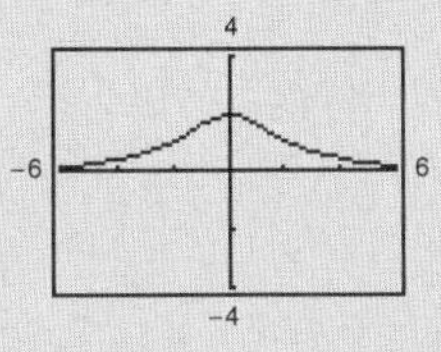

56.

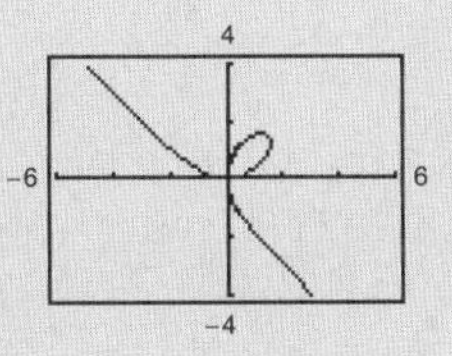

57. b
Domain: $[-2, 2]$
Range: $[-1, 1]$

58. c
Domain: $[-4, 4]$
Range: $[-6, 6]$

59. d
Domain: $(-\infty, \infty)$
Range: $(-\infty, \infty)$

60. a
Domain: $(-\infty, \infty)$
Range: $[-2, 2]$

61–62, 63(a)–(c). See Additional Answers beginning on page AA1.

5 ASSESS AND RETEACH

Daily Homework Quiz

Transparency Available
Available at the Instructor's companion site.

64.
(a) $x = (225 \cos 15°)t$
$y = 5 + (225 \sin 15°)t - 16t^2$

(c)
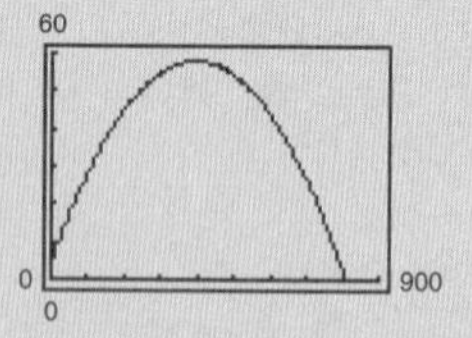

58.0 ft

66. (a) $h = 7, v_0 = 40, \theta = 45°$
$x = (40 \cos 45°)t$
$y = 7 + (40 \sin 45°)t - 16t^2$

(b)
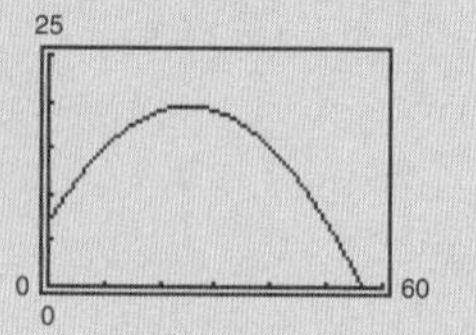

(c) Maximum height: 19.5 ft
Range: 56.2 ft

69. True
$x = t$
$y = t^2 + 1 \Rightarrow y = x^2 + 1$
$x = 3t$
$y = 9t^2 + 1 \Rightarrow y = x^2 + 1$

70. False. The parametric equations $x = t^2$ and $y = t$ give the rectangular equation $x = y^2$, so y is not a function of x.

71. Parametric equations are useful when graphing two functions simultaneously on the same coordinate system. For example, they are useful when tracking the path of an object so that the position and the time associated with that position can be determined.

72. Sketching a plane curve starts by choosing a numeric value for the parameter. Then, the coordinates can be determined from the value chosen for the parameter. Finally, plotting the resulting points in the order of increasing parameter values shows the direction, or orientation, of the curve.

64. SPORTS An archer releases an arrow from a bow at a point 5 feet above the ground. The arrow leaves the bow at an angle of 15° with the horizontal and at an initial speed of 225 feet per second.

(a) Write a set of parametric equations that model the path of the arrow. See margin.

(b) Assuming the ground is level, find the distance the arrow travels before it hits the ground. (Ignore air resistance.) 809 ft

(c) Use a graphing utility to graph the path of the arrow and approximate its maximum height. See margin.

(d) Find the total time the arrow is in the air. 3.72 sec

65. PROJECTILE MOTION Eliminate the parameter t from the parametric equations

$$x = (v_0 \cos \theta)t \quad \text{and} \quad y = h + (v_0 \sin \theta)t - 16t^2$$

for the motion of a projectile to show that the rectangular equation is

$$y = -\frac{16 \sec^2 \theta}{v_0^2}x^2 + (\tan \theta)x + h.$$ Answers will vary.

66. PATH OF A PROJECTILE The path of a projectile is given by the rectangular equation

$$y = 7 + x - 0.02x^2.$$ See margin.

(a) Use the result of Exercise 65 to find h, v_0, and θ. Find the parametric equations of the path.

(b) Use a graphing utility to graph the rectangular equation for the path of the projectile. Confirm your answer in part (a) by sketching the curve represented by the parametric equations.

(c) Use the graphing utility to approximate the maximum height of the projectile and its range.

67. CURTATE CYCLOID A wheel of radius a units rolls along a straight line without slipping. The curve traced by a point P that is b units from the center ($b < a$) is called a **curtate cycloid** (see figure). Use the angle θ shown in the figure to find a set of parametric equations for the curve.

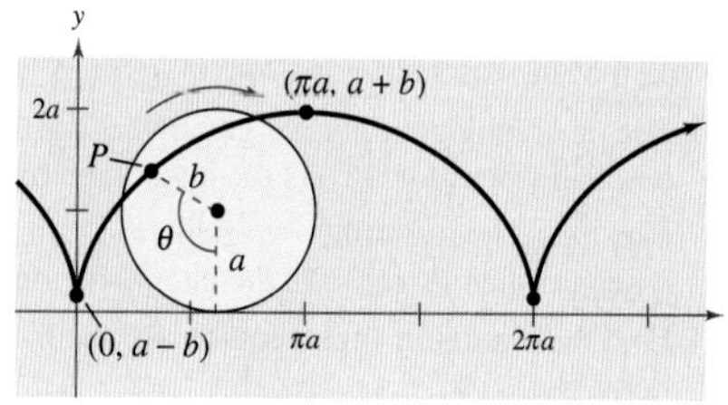

$x = a\theta - b \sin \theta$
$y = a - b \cos \theta$

68. EPICYCLOID A circle of radius one unit rolls around the outside of a circle of radius two units without slipping. The curve traced by a point on the circumference of the smaller circle is called an **epicycloid** (see figure). Use the angle θ shown in the figure to find a set of parametric equations for the curve. $x = 3 \cos \theta - \cos 3\theta$
$y = 3 \sin \theta - \sin 3\theta$

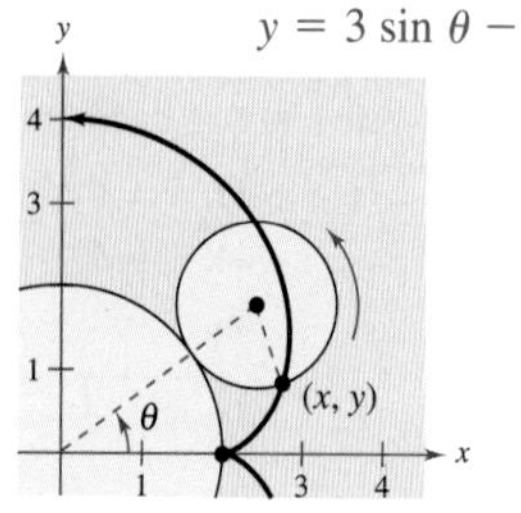

EXPLORATION

69–70. See margin.

TRUE OR FALSE? In Exercises 69 and 70, determine whether the statement is true or false. Justify your answer.

69. The two sets of parametric equations $x = t$, $y = t^2 + 1$ and $x = 3t$, $y = 9t^2 + 1$ have the same rectangular equation.

70. If y is a function of t, and x is a function of t, then y must be a function of x.

71. WRITING Write a short paragraph explaining why parametric equations are useful. See margin.

72. WRITING Explain the process of sketching a plane curve given by parametric equations. What is meant by the orientation of the curve? See margin.

73. Use a graphing utility set in *parametric* mode to enter the parametric equations from Example 2. Over what values should you let t vary to obtain the graph shown in Figure 10.55? $-1 < t < \infty$

74. CAPSTONE Consider the parametric equations $x = 8 \cos t$ and $y = 8 \sin t$.

(a) Describe the curve represented by the parametric equations.

(b) How does the curve represented by the parametric equations $x = 8 \cos t + 3$ and $y = 8 \sin t + 6$ compare with the curve described in part (a)?

(c) How does the original curve change when cosine and sine are interchanged?

(a) The parametric equations represent a circle.
(b) The center of the circle is shifted to (3, 6).
(c) The orientation changes.

10.7 Polar Coordinates

What you should learn

- Plot points on the polar coordinate system.
- Convert points from rectangular to polar form and vice versa.
- Convert equations from rectangular to polar form and vice versa.

Why you should learn it

Polar coordinates offer a different mathematical perspective on graphing. For instance, in Exercises 5–18 on page 781, you are asked to find multiple representations of polar coordinates.

Introduction

So far, you have been representing graphs of equations as collections of points (x, y) on the rectangular coordinate system, where x and y represent the directed distances from the coordinate axes to the point (x, y). In this section, you will study a different system called the **polar coordinate system.**

To form the polar coordinate system in the plane, fix a point O, called the **pole** (or **origin**), and construct from O an initial ray called the **polar axis,** as shown in Figure 10.59. Then each point P in the plane can be assigned **polar coordinates** (r, θ) as follows.

1. r = *directed distance* from O to P
2. θ = *directed angle*, counterclockwise from polar axis to segment $\overline{OP}$

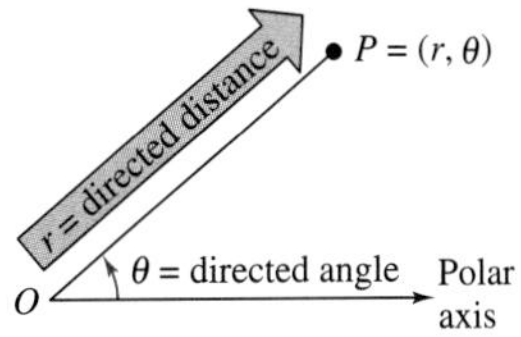

FIGURE 10.59

Example 1 Plotting Points on the Polar Coordinate System

a. The point $(r, \theta) = (2, \pi/3)$ lies two units from the pole on the terminal side of the angle $\theta = \pi/3$, as shown in Figure 10.60.

b. The point $(r, \theta) = (3, -\pi/6)$ lies three units from the pole on the terminal side of the angle $\theta = -\pi/6$, as shown in Figure 10.61.

c. The point $(r, \theta) = (3, 11\pi/6)$ coincides with the point $(3, -\pi/6)$, as shown in Figure 10.62.

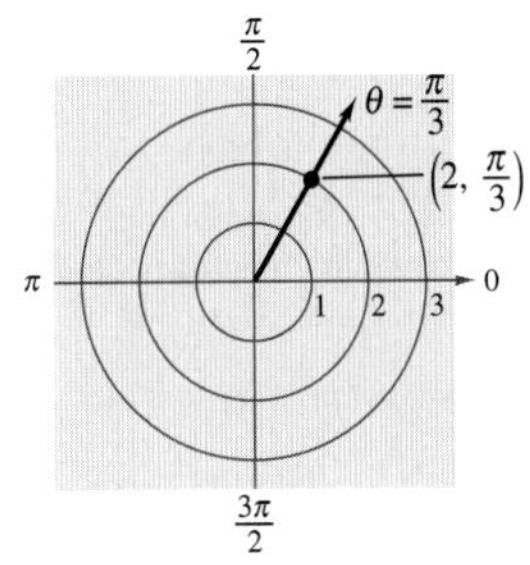

FIGURE 10.60

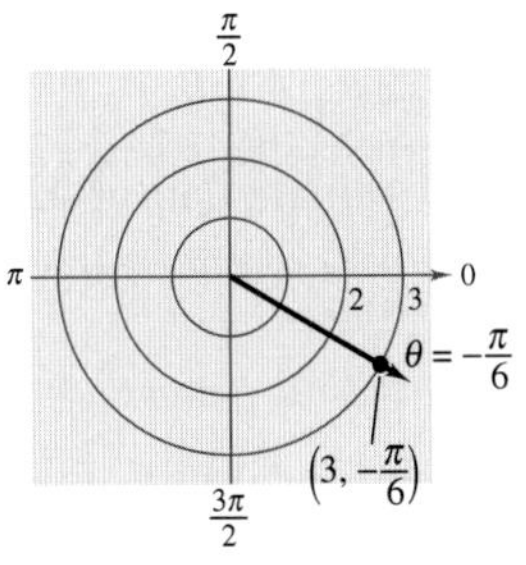

FIGURE 10.61

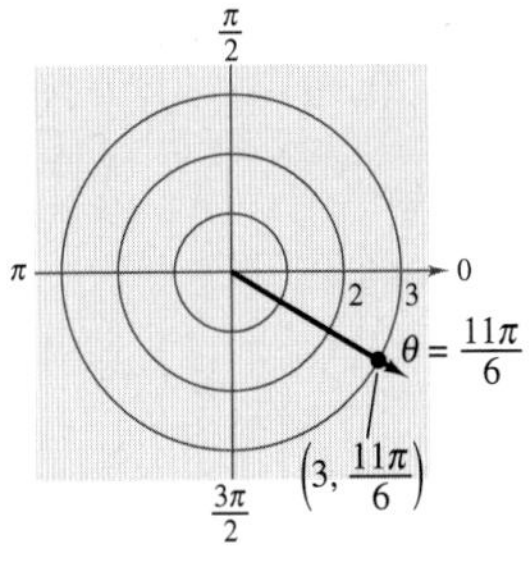

FIGURE 10.62

CHECKPoint Now try Exercise 7.

1 PLAN AND PREPARE

Warm-up Exercises

Transparency Available
Available at the Instructor's companion site.

Notetaking Guide

Transparency Available
Promotes interactive learning and notetaking skills. Available at the Instructor's companion site.

Animated Precalculus

An **Animated Precalculus** tutorial is available at the Student companion site for **Section 10.7.**

Pacing

Average: 2 days
Advanced: 2 days
Block: 0.5 block with 10.6
0.5 block with 10.8

2 FOCUS AND MOTIVATE

Essential Question

How do you describe the position of a point in a plane using distance and angle rather than x- and y-coordinates? **Tell students that they will learn how to answer this question by studying polar coordinates and the conversion of points and equations from rectangular to polar form and vice versa.**

Resource Planning Guide

Chapter Resources
- Complete Solutions Guide

Workbooks
- Notetaking Guide
- Student Solutions Guide

Interactive Technology
- Instructor Success Organizer
- Notetaking Guide IAE
- Instructional DVDs
- Animated Precalculus
- PowerLecture with ExamView

3 TEACH

Extra Example 1

Plot the given point in the polar coordinate system.

a. $\left(3, -\frac{\pi}{3}\right)$

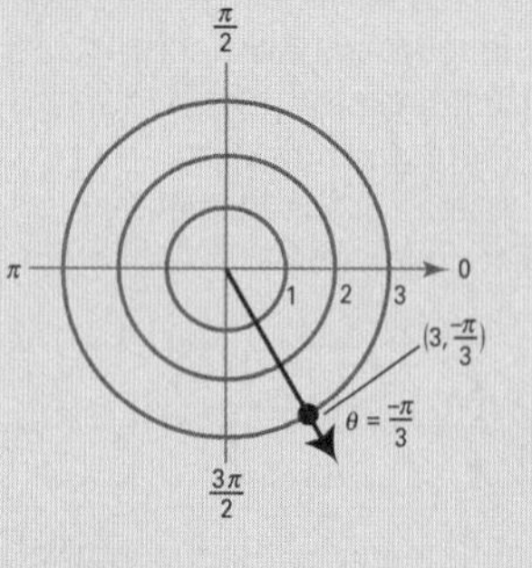

b. $\left(2, \frac{\pi}{6}\right)$

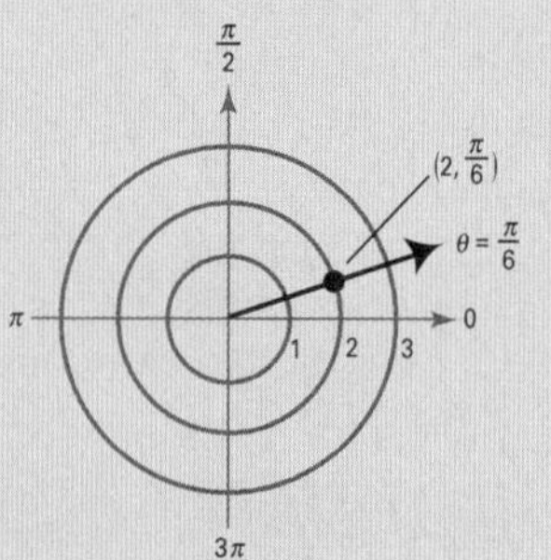

c. $\left(2, -\frac{\pi}{6}\right)$

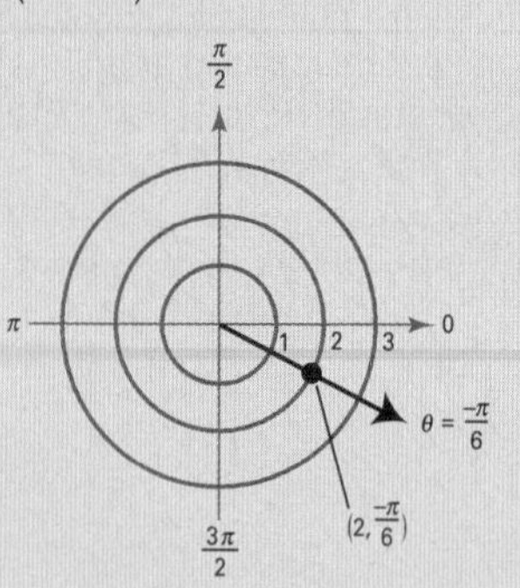

In rectangular coordinates, each point (x, y) has a unique representation. This is not true for polar coordinates. For instance, the coordinates (r, θ) and $(r, \theta + 2\pi)$ represent the same point, as illustrated in Example 1. Another way to obtain multiple representations of a point is to use negative values for r. Because r is a *directed distance*, the coordinates (r, θ) and $(-r, \theta + \pi)$ represent the same point. In general, the point (r, θ) can be represented as

$$(r, \theta) = (r, \theta \pm 2n\pi) \quad \text{or} \quad (r, \theta) = (-r, \theta \pm (2n + 1)\pi)$$

where n is any integer. Moreover, the pole is represented by $(0, \theta)$, where θ is any angle.

Example 2 Multiple Representations of Points

Plot the point $(3, -3\pi/4)$ and find three additional polar representations of this point, using $-2\pi < \theta < 2\pi$.

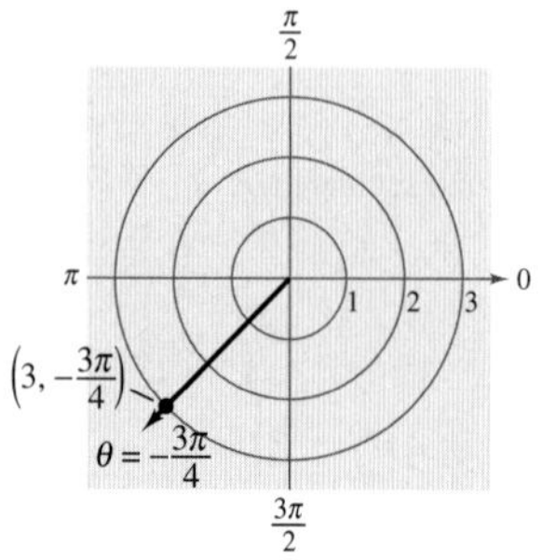

$\left(3, -\frac{3\pi}{4}\right) = \left(3, \frac{5\pi}{4}\right) = \left(-3, -\frac{7\pi}{4}\right) = \left(-3, \frac{\pi}{4}\right) = \ldots$

FIGURE 10.63

Solution

The point is shown in Figure 10.63. Three other representations are as follows.

$\left(3, -\frac{3\pi}{4} + 2\pi\right) = \left(3, \frac{5\pi}{4}\right)$ Add 2π to θ.

$\left(-3, -\frac{3\pi}{4} - \pi\right) = \left(-3, -\frac{7\pi}{4}\right)$ Replace r by $-r$; subtract π from θ.

$\left(-3, -\frac{3\pi}{4} + \pi\right) = \left(-3, \frac{\pi}{4}\right)$ Replace r by $-r$; add π to θ.

CHECKPoint Now try Exercise 13.

Coordinate Conversion

To establish the relationship between polar and rectangular coordinates, let the polar axis coincide with the positive x-axis and the pole with the origin, as shown in Figure 10.64. Because (x, y) lies on a circle of radius r, it follows that $r^2 = x^2 + y^2$. Moreover, for $r > 0$, the definitions of the trigonometric functions imply that

$$\tan\theta = \frac{y}{x}, \quad \cos\theta = \frac{x}{r}, \quad \text{and} \quad \sin\theta = \frac{y}{r}.$$

If $r < 0$, you can show that the same relationships hold.

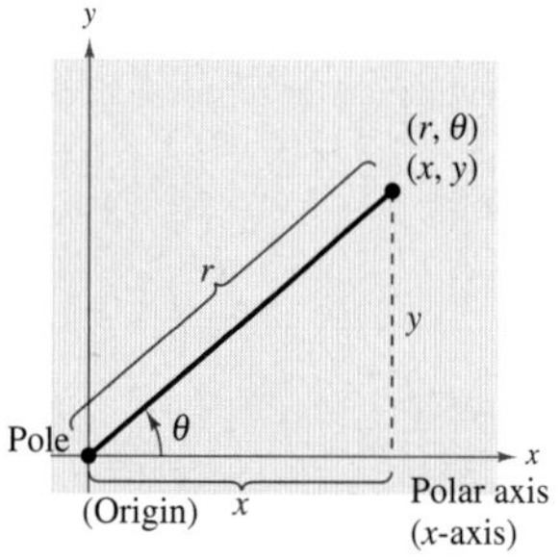

FIGURE 10.64

Coordinate Conversion

The polar coordinates (r, θ) are related to the rectangular coordinates (x, y) as follows.

Polar-to-Rectangular	*Rectangular-to-Polar*
$x = r\cos\theta$	$\tan\theta = \frac{y}{x}$
$y = r\sin\theta$	$r^2 = x^2 + y^2$

Extra Example 2

Plot the point $\left(2, \frac{3\pi}{4}\right)$ and find three additional polar representations of this point, using $-2\pi < \theta < 2\pi$.

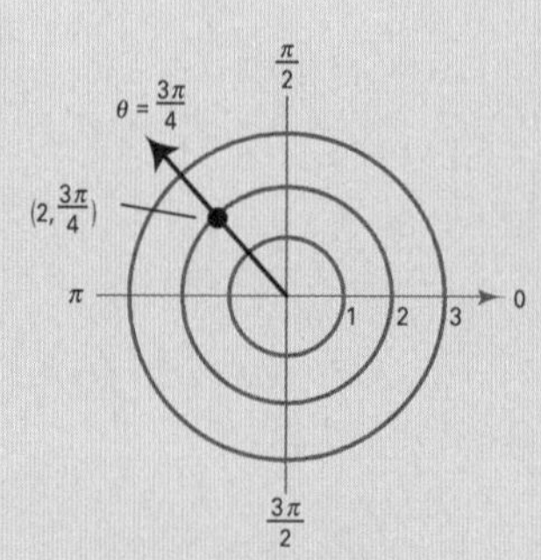

Answers may vary.

$\left(2, -\frac{5\pi}{4}\right), \left(-2, -\frac{\pi}{4}\right), \left(-2, \frac{7\pi}{4}\right)$

Example 3 Polar-to-Rectangular Conversion

Convert each point to rectangular coordinates.

a. $(2, \pi)$ **b.** $\left(\sqrt{3}, \dfrac{\pi}{6}\right)$

Solution

a. For the point $(r, \theta) = (2, \pi)$, you have the following.

$$x = r\cos\theta = 2\cos\pi = -2$$

$$y = r\sin\theta = 2\sin\pi = 0$$

The rectangular coordinates are $(x, y) = (-2, 0)$. (See Figure 10.65.)

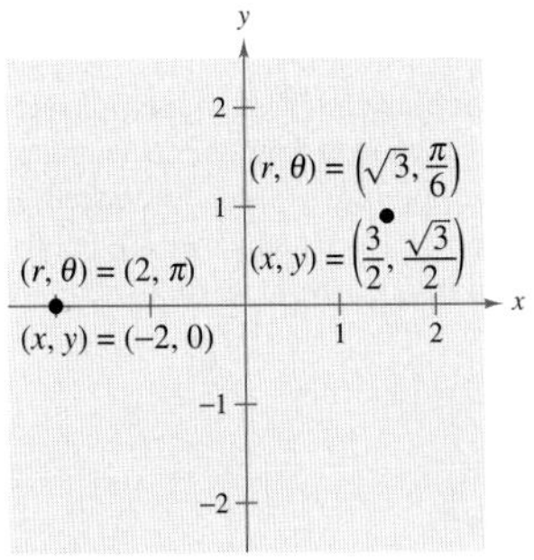

FIGURE 10.65

b. For the point $(r, \theta) = \left(\sqrt{3}, \dfrac{\pi}{6}\right)$, you have the following.

$$x = \sqrt{3}\cos\frac{\pi}{6} = \sqrt{3}\left(\frac{\sqrt{3}}{2}\right) = \frac{3}{2}$$

$$y = \sqrt{3}\sin\frac{\pi}{6} = \sqrt{3}\left(\frac{1}{2}\right) = \frac{\sqrt{3}}{2}$$

The rectangular coordinates are $(x, y) = \left(\dfrac{3}{2}, \dfrac{\sqrt{3}}{2}\right)$.

CHECKPoint Now try Exercise 23.

Example 4 Rectangular-to-Polar Conversion

Convert each point to polar coordinates.

a. $(-1, 1)$ **b.** $(0, 2)$

Solution

a. For the second-quadrant point $(x, y) = (-1, 1)$, you have

$$\tan\theta = \frac{y}{x} = -1$$

$$\theta = \frac{3\pi}{4}.$$

Because θ lies in the same quadrant as (x, y), use positive r.

$$r = \sqrt{x^2 + y^2} = \sqrt{(-1)^2 + (1)^2} = \sqrt{2}$$

So, *one* set of polar coordinates is $(r, \theta) = \left(\sqrt{2}, 3\pi/4\right)$, as shown in Figure 10.66.

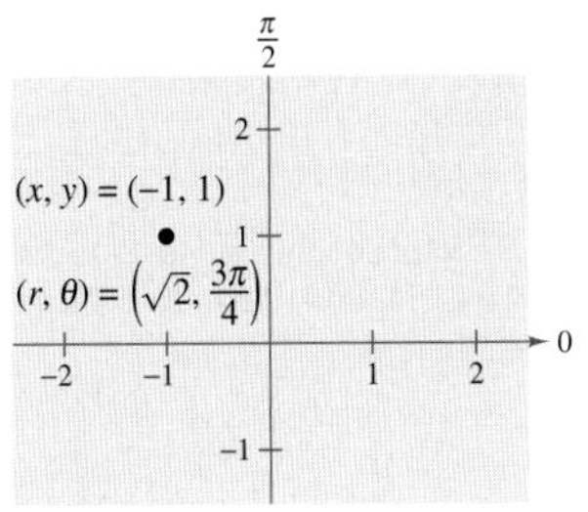

FIGURE 10.66

b. Because the point $(x, y) = (0, 2)$ lies on the positive y-axis, choose

$$\theta = \frac{\pi}{2} \quad \text{and} \quad r = 2.$$

This implies that *one* set of polar coordinates is $(r, \theta) = (2, \pi/2)$, as shown in Figure 10.67.

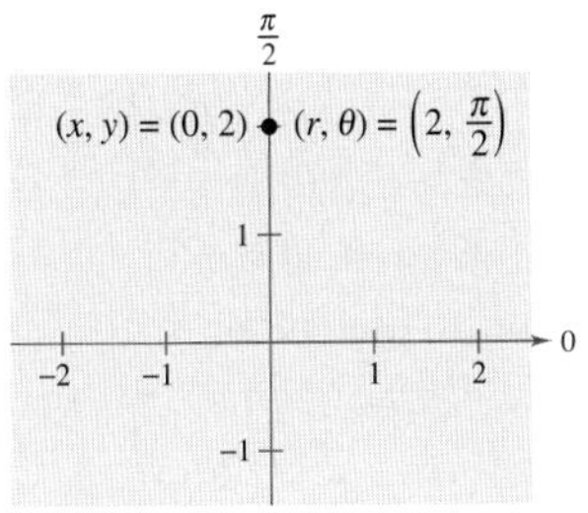

FIGURE 10.67

CHECKPoint Now try Exercise 41.

Extra Example 3

Convert each point to rectangular coordinates.

a. $\left(4, \dfrac{3\pi}{6}\right)$
$(0, 4)$

b. $\left(2, \dfrac{\pi}{6}\right)$
$\left(\sqrt{3}, 1\right)$

Extra Example 4

Convert each point to polar coordinates.

a. $(2, 2)$
$\left(2\sqrt{2}, \dfrac{\pi}{4}\right)$

b. $(-1, 0)$
$(1, \pi)$

Extra Example 5

Describe the graph of each polar equation and find the corresponding rectangular equation.

a. $r = 1$

The graph is a circle of radius 1; $x^2 + y^2 = 1$.

b. $\theta = \dfrac{\pi}{4}$

The graph is the line that makes an angle of $\pi/4$ with the positive polar axis; $y = x$.

c. $r = \csc\theta$

The graph is the line formed by all points that are one unit above the polar axis; $y = 1$.

Closing the Lesson

Have students summarize the major points of the lesson and answer the Essential Question: How do you describe the position of a point in a plane using distance and angle rather than x- and y-coordinates?

- **Describe the location of a point in a plane by its distance from the pole and its angular position from the polar axis.**
- **Convert the coordinates of a point from polar coordinates to rectangular coordinates and vice versa, using coordinate conversion equations.**
- **Convert polar equations to rectangular equations and vice versa by replacing variables according to the coordinate conversion equations.**

Equation Conversion

By comparing Examples 3 and 4, you can see that point conversion from the polar to the rectangular system is straightforward, whereas point conversion from the rectangular to the polar system is more involved. For equations, the opposite is true. To convert a rectangular equation to polar form, you simply replace x by $r\cos\theta$ and y by $r\sin\theta$. For instance, the rectangular equation $y = x^2$ can be written in polar form as follows.

$$y = x^2 \qquad \text{Rectangular equation}$$

$$r\sin\theta = (r\cos\theta)^2 \qquad \text{Polar equation}$$

$$r = \sec\theta\tan\theta \qquad \text{Simplest form}$$

On the other hand, converting a polar equation to rectangular form requires considerable ingenuity.

Example 5 demonstrates several polar-to-rectangular conversions that enable you to sketch the graphs of some polar equations.

Example 5 Converting Polar Equations to Rectangular Form

Describe the graph of each polar equation and find the corresponding rectangular equation.

a. $r = 2$ **b.** $\theta = \dfrac{\pi}{3}$ **c.** $r = \sec\theta$

Solution

a. The graph of the polar equation $r = 2$ consists of all points that are two units from the pole. In other words, this graph is a circle centered at the origin with a radius of 2, as shown in Figure 10.68. You can confirm this by converting to rectangular form, using the relationship $r^2 = x^2 + y^2$.

$$\underbrace{r = 2}_{\text{Polar equation}} \quad \Longrightarrow \quad r^2 = 2^2 \quad \Longrightarrow \quad \underbrace{x^2 + y^2 = 2^2}_{\text{Rectangular equation}}$$

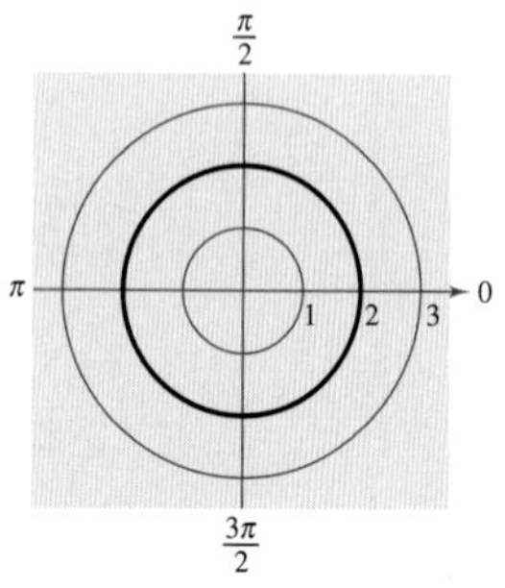

FIGURE 10.68

b. The graph of the polar equation $\theta = \pi/3$ consists of all points on the line that makes an angle of $\pi/3$ with the positive polar axis, as shown in Figure 10.69. To convert to rectangular form, make use of the relationship $\tan\theta = y/x$.

$$\underbrace{\theta = \frac{\pi}{3}}_{\text{Polar equation}} \quad \Longrightarrow \quad \tan\theta = \sqrt{3} \quad \Longrightarrow \quad \underbrace{y = \sqrt{3}x}_{\text{Rectangular equation}}$$

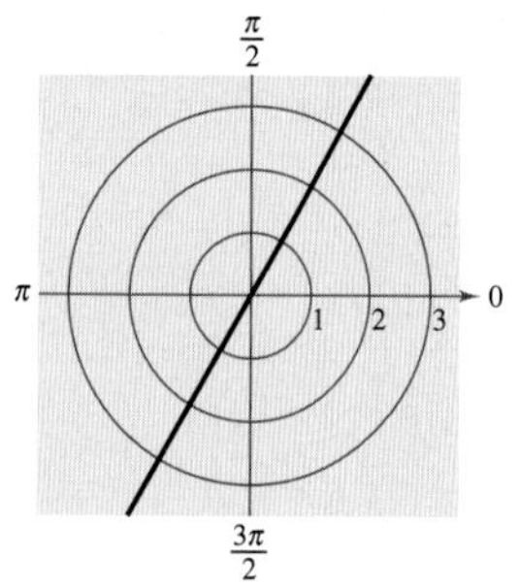

FIGURE 10.69

c. The graph of the polar equation $r = \sec\theta$ is not evident by simple inspection, so convert to rectangular form by using the relationship $r\cos\theta = x$.

$$\underbrace{r = \sec\theta}_{\text{Polar equation}} \quad \Longrightarrow \quad r\cos\theta = 1 \quad \Longrightarrow \quad \underbrace{x = 1}_{\text{Rectangular equation}}$$

Now you see that the graph is a vertical line, as shown in Figure 10.70.

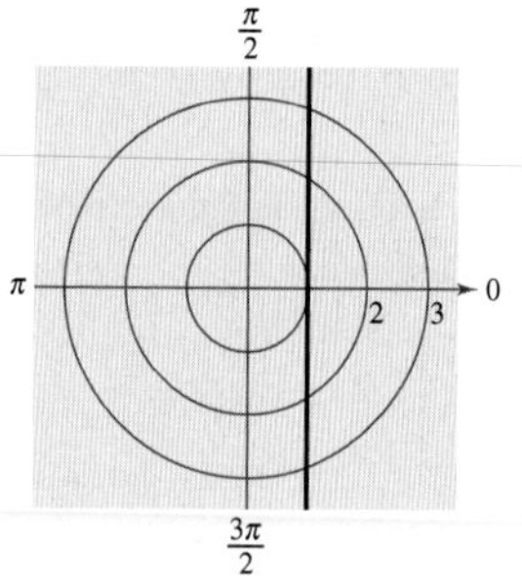

FIGURE 10.70

CHECKPoint Now try Exercise 109.

10.7 EXERCISES

See www.CalcChat.com for worked-out solutions to odd-numbered exercises.

VOCABULARY: Fill in the blanks.

1. The origin of the polar coordinate system is called the pole.
2. For the point (r, θ), r is the directed distance from O to P and θ is the directed angle, counterclockwise from the polar axis to the line segment $\overline{OP}$.
3. To plot the point (r, θ), use the polar coordinate system.
4. The polar coordinates (r, θ) are related to the rectangular coordinates (x, y) as follows:
$x = r\cos\theta$ $\quad y = r\sin\theta$ $\quad \tan\theta = y/x$ $\quad r^2 = x^2 + y^2$

SKILLS AND APPLICATIONS

In Exercises 5–18, plot the point given in polar coordinates and find two additional polar representations of the point, using $-2\pi < \theta < 2\pi$. 5–18. See margin.

5. $\left(2, \dfrac{5\pi}{6}\right)$
6. $\left(3, \dfrac{5\pi}{4}\right)$
7. $\left(4, -\dfrac{\pi}{3}\right)$
8. $\left(-1, -\dfrac{3\pi}{4}\right)$
9. $(2, 3\pi)$
10. $\left(4, \dfrac{5\pi}{2}\right)$
11. $\left(-2, \dfrac{2\pi}{3}\right)$
12. $\left(-3, \dfrac{11\pi}{6}\right)$
13. $\left(0, -\dfrac{7\pi}{6}\right)$
14. $\left(0, -\dfrac{7\pi}{2}\right)$
15. $(\sqrt{2}, 2.36)$
16. $(2\sqrt{2}, 4.71)$
17. $(-3, -1.57)$
18. $(-5, -2.36)$

In Exercises 19–28, a point in polar coordinates is given. Convert the point to rectangular coordinates.

19. $(3, \pi/2)$ $\quad(0, 3)$

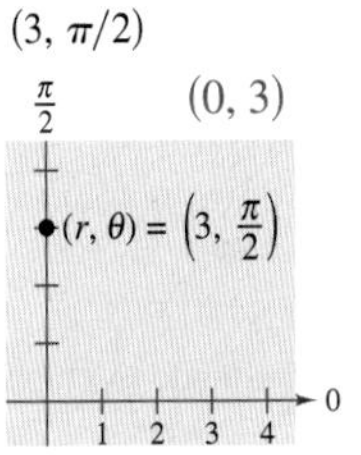

20. $(3, 3\pi/2)$ $\quad(0, -3)$

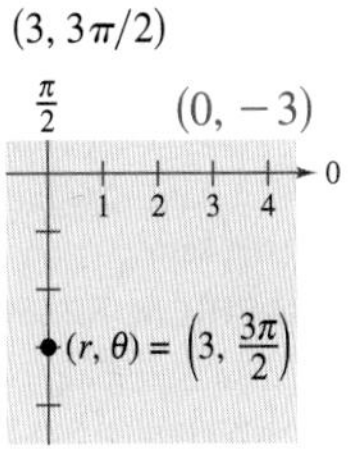

21. $(-1, 5\pi/4)$ $\quad\left(\dfrac{\sqrt{2}}{2}, \dfrac{\sqrt{2}}{2}\right)$

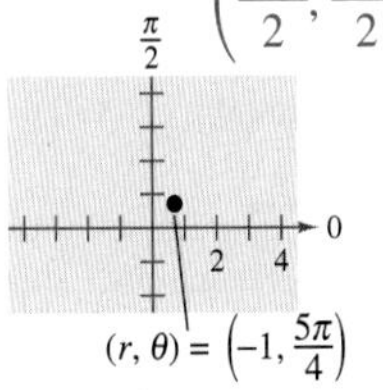

22. $(0, -\pi)$ $\quad(0, 0)$

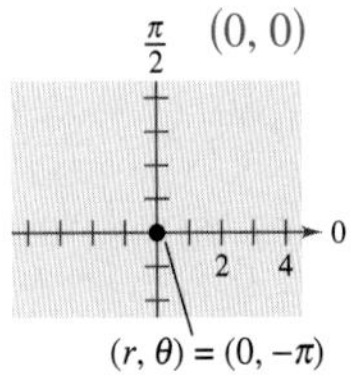

23. $(2, 3\pi/4)$ $\quad(-\sqrt{2}, \sqrt{2})$
24. $(1, 5\pi/4)$ $\quad\left(-\dfrac{\sqrt{2}}{2}, -\dfrac{\sqrt{2}}{2}\right)$
25. $(-2, 7\pi/6)$ $\quad(\sqrt{3}, 1)$
26. $(-3, 5\pi/6)$ $\quad\left(\dfrac{3\sqrt{3}}{2}, -\dfrac{3}{2}\right)$
27. $(-2.5, 1.1)$ $\quad(-1.1, -2.2)$
28. $(-2, 5.76)$ $\quad(-1.7, 1.0)$

In Exercises 29–36, use a graphing utility to find the rectangular coordinates of the point given in polar coordinates. Round your results to two decimal places.

29. $(2, 2\pi/9)$ $\quad(1.53, 1.29)$
30. $(4, 11\pi/9)$ $\quad(-3.06, -2.57)$
31. $(-4.5, 1.3)$ See margin.
32. $(8.25, 3.5)$ $\quad(-7.72, -2.89)$
33. $(2.5, 1.58)$ See margin.
34. $(5.4, 2.85)$ $\quad(-5.17, 1.55)$
35. $(-4.1, -0.5)$ $\quad(-3.60, 1.97)$
36. $(8.2, -3.2)$ $\quad(-8.19, 0.48)$

In Exercises 37–54, a point in rectangular coordinates is given. Convert the point to polar coordinates. 37–50. See margin.

37. $(1, 1)$
38. $(2, 2)$
39. $(-3, -3)$
40. $(-4, -4)$
41. $(-6, 0)$
42. $(3, 0)$
43. $(0, -5)$
44. $(0, 5)$
45. $(-3, 4)$
46. $(-4, -3)$
47. $(-\sqrt{3}, -\sqrt{3})$
48. $(-\sqrt{3}, \sqrt{3})$
49. $(\sqrt{3}, -1)$
50. $(-1, \sqrt{3})$
51. $(6, 9)$ $\quad(3\sqrt{13}, 0.98)$
52. $(6, 2)$ $\quad(2\sqrt{10}, 0.32)$
53. $(5, 12)$ $\quad(13, 1.18)$
54. $(7, 15)$ $\quad(\sqrt{274}, 1.13)$

In Exercises 55–64, use a graphing utility to find one set of polar coordinates for the point given in rectangular coordinates.

55. $(3, -2)$ $\quad(\sqrt{13}, 5.70)$
56. $(-4, -2)$ $\quad(2\sqrt{5}, 3.61)$
57. $(-5, 2)$ $\quad(\sqrt{29}, 2.76)$
58. $(7, -2)$ $\quad(\sqrt{53}, 6.00)$
59. $(\sqrt{3}, 2)$ $\quad(\sqrt{7}, 0.86)$
60. $(5, -\sqrt{2})$ $\quad(3\sqrt{3}, 6.01)$
61. $\left(\frac{5}{2}, \frac{4}{3}\right)$
62. $\left(\frac{9}{5}, \frac{11}{2}\right)$
63. $\left(\frac{7}{4}, \frac{3}{2}\right)$
64. $\left(-\frac{7}{9}, -\frac{3}{4}\right)$

61–64. See margin.

In Exercises 65–84, convert the rectangular equation to polar form. Assume $a > 0$.

65. $x^2 + y^2 = 9$ $\quad r = 3$
66. $x^2 + y^2 = 16$ $\quad r = 4$

4 PRACTICE AND APPLY

Assignment Guide

Transparencies Available
Available at the Instructor's companion site.

Average:
Day 1: p. 781
Exs. 1–4, 8, 10, 15–17, 19–21, 26, 27–31 odd, 37, 39, 42–47, 51, 57–61
Day 2: pp. 781–782
Exs. 65–79 odd, 85–105 odd, 119–122, 124

Advanced:
Day 1: p. 781
Exs. 1–4, 8, 10, 16–18, 20–22, 26–28, 30, 32, 41, 44–52 even, 53, 58–62
Day 2: p. 782
Exs. 68–82 even, 90–100 even, 104–108 even, 119–124, 126

Block:
p. 781
Exs. 1–4, 8, 10, 15–17, 19–21, 26, 27–31 odd, 37, 39, 42–47, 51, 57–61 (with 10.6)
pp. 781–782
Exs. 65–79 odd, 85–105 odd, 119–122, 124 (with 10.8)

5.

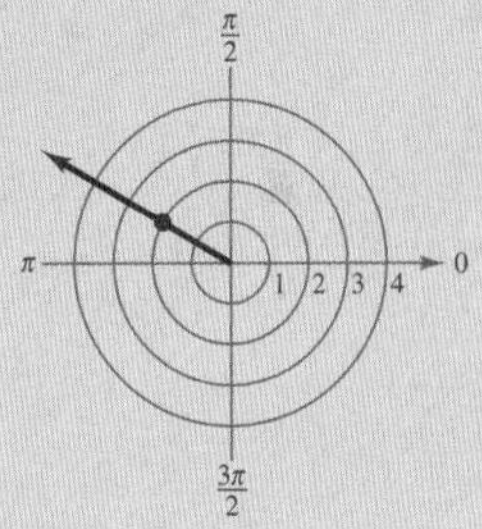

$\left(2, -\dfrac{7\pi}{6}\right), \left(-2, -\dfrac{\pi}{6}\right)$

6.

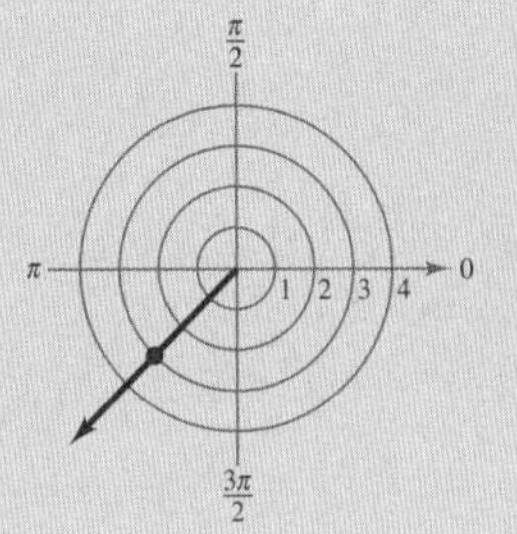

$\left(3, -\dfrac{3\pi}{4}\right), \left(-3, \dfrac{\pi}{4}\right)$

7.

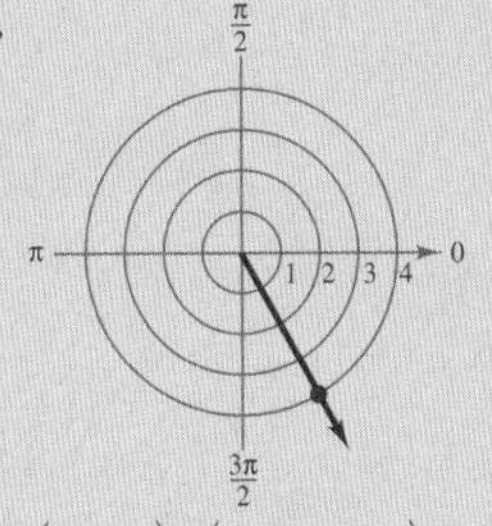

$\left(4, \dfrac{5\pi}{3}\right), \left(-4, -\dfrac{4\pi}{3}\right)$

8.

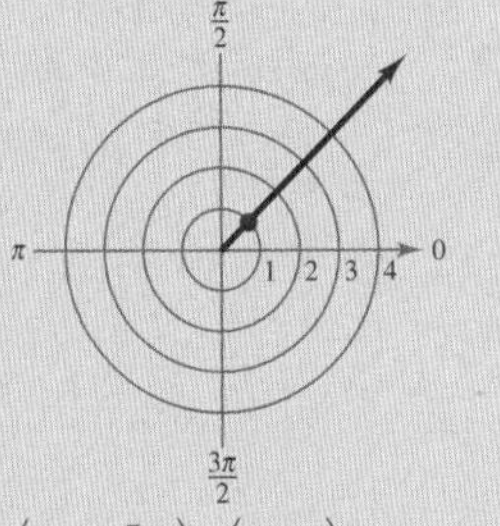

$\left(-1, \dfrac{5\pi}{4}\right), \left(1, \dfrac{\pi}{4}\right)$

31. $(-1.20, -4.34)$
33. $(-0.02, 2.50)$
37. $\left(\sqrt{2}, \dfrac{\pi}{4}\right)$
38. $\left(2\sqrt{2}, \dfrac{\pi}{4}\right)$
39. $\left(3\sqrt{2}, \dfrac{5\pi}{4}\right)$
40. $\left(4\sqrt{2}, \dfrac{5\pi}{4}\right)$
41. $(6, \pi)$
42. $(3, 0)$
43. $\left(5, \dfrac{3\pi}{2}\right)$
44. $\left(5, \dfrac{\pi}{2}\right)$
45. $(5, 2.21)$
46. $(5, 3.78)$
47. $\left(\sqrt{6}, \dfrac{5\pi}{4}\right)$
48. $\left(\sqrt{6}, \dfrac{3\pi}{4}\right)$

9–18, 49–50, 61–64. See Additional Answers beginning on page AA1.

67. $y = 4$ $r = 4 \csc \theta$ **68.** $y = x$ $\theta = \dfrac{\pi}{4}$

69. $x = 10$ $r = 10 \sec \theta$ **70.** $x = 4a$ $r = 4a \sec \theta$

71. $y = -2$ $r = -2 \csc \theta$ **72.** $y = 1$ $r = \csc \theta$

73. $3x - y + 2 = 0$ **74.** $3x + 5y - 2 = 0$

73–82. See margin.

75. $xy = 16$ **76.** $2xy = 1$

77. $y^2 - 8x - 16 = 0$ **78.** $(x^2 + y^2)^2 = 9(x^2 - y^2)$

79. $x^2 + y^2 = a^2$ **80.** $x^2 + y^2 = 9a^2$

81. $x^2 + y^2 - 2ax = 0$ **82.** $x^2 + y^2 - 2ay = 0$

83. $y^3 = x^2$ $r = \cot^2 \theta \csc \theta$ **84.** $y^2 = x^3$ $r = \tan^2 \theta \sec \theta$

In Exercises 85–108, convert the polar equation to rectangular form. 85–108. See margin.

85. $r = 4 \sin \theta$	**86.** $r = 2 \cos \theta$
87. $r = -2 \cos \theta$	**88.** $r = -5 \sin \theta$
89. $\theta = 2\pi/3$	**90.** $\theta = 5\pi/3$
91. $\theta = 11\pi/6$	**92.** $\theta = 5\pi/6$
93. $r = 4$	**94.** $r = 10$
95. $r = 4 \csc \theta$	**96.** $r = 2 \csc \theta$
97. $r = -3 \sec \theta$	**98.** $r = -\sec \theta$
99. $r^2 = \cos \theta$	**100.** $r^2 = 2 \sin \theta$
101. $r^2 = \sin 2\theta$	**102.** $r^2 = \cos 2\theta$
103. $r = 2 \sin 3\theta$	**104.** $r = 3 \cos 2\theta$
105. $r = \dfrac{2}{1 + \sin \theta}$	**106.** $r = \dfrac{1}{1 - \cos \theta}$
107. $r = \dfrac{6}{2 - 3 \sin \theta}$	**108.** $r = \dfrac{6}{2 \cos \theta - 3 \sin \theta}$

In Exercises 109–118, describe the graph of the polar equation and find the corresponding rectangular equation. Sketch its graph. 109–118. See margin.

109. $r = 6$	**110.** $r = 8$
111. $\theta = \pi/6$	**112.** $\theta = 3\pi/4$
113. $r = 2 \sin \theta$	**114.** $r = 4 \cos \theta$
115. $r = -6 \cos \theta$	**116.** $r = -3 \sin \theta$
117. $r = 3 \sec \theta$	**118.** $r = 2 \csc \theta$

EXPLORATION

TRUE OR FALSE? In Exercises 119 and 120, determine whether the statement is true or false. Justify your answer.

119. If $\theta_1 = \theta_2 + 2\pi n$ for some integer n, then (r, θ_1) and (r, θ_2) represent the same point on the polar coordinate system. See below.

120. If $|r_1| = |r_2|$, then (r_1, θ) and (r_2, θ) represent the same point on the polar coordinate system.

119. True. Because r is a directed distance, the point (r, θ) can be represented as $(r, \theta \pm 2\pi n)$.

120. False. If $r_1 = -r_2$, then (r_1, θ) and (r_2, θ) are different points.

121. Convert the polar equation $r = 2(h \cos \theta + k \sin \theta)$ to rectangular form and verify that it is the equation of a circle. Find the radius of the circle and the rectangular coordinates of the center of the circle. See margin.

122. Convert the polar equation $r = \cos \theta + 3 \sin \theta$ to rectangular form and identify the graph. See margin.

123. THINK ABOUT IT See margin.

(a) Show that the distance between the points (r_1, θ_1) and (r_2, θ_2) is $\sqrt{r_1^2 + r_2^2 - 2r_1r_2 \cos(\theta_1 - \theta_2)}$.

(b) Describe the positions of the points relative to each other for $\theta_1 = \theta_2$. Simplify the Distance Formula for this case. Is the simplification what you expected? Explain.

(c) Simplify the Distance Formula for $\theta_1 - \theta_2 = 90°$. Is the simplification what you expected? Explain.

(d) Choose two points on the polar coordinate system and find the distance between them. Then choose different polar representations of the same two points and apply the Distance Formula again. Discuss the result.

124. GRAPHICAL REASONING See margin.

(a) Set the window format of your graphing utility on rectangular coordinates and locate the cursor at any position off the coordinate axes. Move the cursor horizontally and observe any changes in the displayed coordinates of the points. Explain the changes in the coordinates. Now repeat the process moving the cursor vertically.

(b) Set the window format of your graphing utility on polar coordinates and locate the cursor at any position off the coordinate axes. Move the cursor horizontally and observe any changes in the displayed coordinates of the points. Explain the changes in the coordinates. Now repeat the process moving the cursor vertically.

(c) Explain why the results of parts (a) and (b) are not the same.

125. GRAPHICAL REASONING See margin.

(a) Use a graphing utility in *polar* mode to graph the equation $r = 3$.

(b) Use the *trace* feature to move the cursor around the circle. Can you locate the point $(3, 5\pi/4)$?

(c) Can you find other polar representations of the point $(3, 5\pi/4)$? If so, explain how you did it.

126. CAPSTONE In the rectangular coordinate system, each point (x, y) has a unique representation. Explain why this is not true for a point (r, θ) in the polar coordinate system. Answers will vary.

5 ASSESS AND RETEACH

Daily Homework Quiz

Transparency Available

Available at the Instructor's companion site.

73. $r = \dfrac{-2}{3 \cos \theta - \sin \theta}$

74. $r = \dfrac{2}{3 \cos \theta + 5 \sin \theta}$

75. $r^2 = 16 \sec \theta \csc \theta = 32 \csc 2\theta$

76. $r^2 = \frac{1}{2} \sec \theta \csc \theta = \csc 2\theta$

77. $r = \dfrac{4}{1 - \cos \theta}$ or $-\dfrac{4}{1 + \cos \theta}$

78. $r^2 = 9 \cos 2\theta$ **79.** $r = a$

80. $r = 3a$ **81.** $r = 2a \cos \theta$

82. $r = 2a \sin \theta$

85. $x^2 + y^2 - 4y = 0$

86. $x^2 + y^2 - 2x = 0$

87. $x^2 + y^2 + 2x = 0$

88. $x^2 + y^2 + 5y = 0$

89. $\sqrt{3}x + y = 0$

90. $\sqrt{3}x + y = 0$

91. $\dfrac{\sqrt{3}}{3}x + y = 0$

92. $\dfrac{\sqrt{3}}{3}x + y = 0$

93. $x^2 + y^2 = 16$

94. $x^2 + y^2 = 100$ **95.** $y = 4$

96. $y = 2$ **97.** $x = -3$

98. $x = -1$

99. $x^2 + y^2 - x^{2/3} = 0$

100. $x^2 + y^2 - \sqrt[3]{4}y^{2/3} = 0$

101. $(x^2 + y^2)^2 = 2xy$

102. $(x^2 + y^2)^2 = x^2 - y^2$

103. $(x^2 + y^2)^2 = 6x^2y - 2y^3$

104. $(x^2 + y^2)^3 = 9(x^2 - y^2)^2$

105. $x^2 + 4y - 4 = 0$

106. $y^2 = 2x + 1$

107. $4x^2 - 5y^2 - 36y - 36 = 0$

108. $2x - 3y = 6$

109. The graph of the polar equation consists of all points that are six units from the pole.
$x^2 + y^2 = 36$

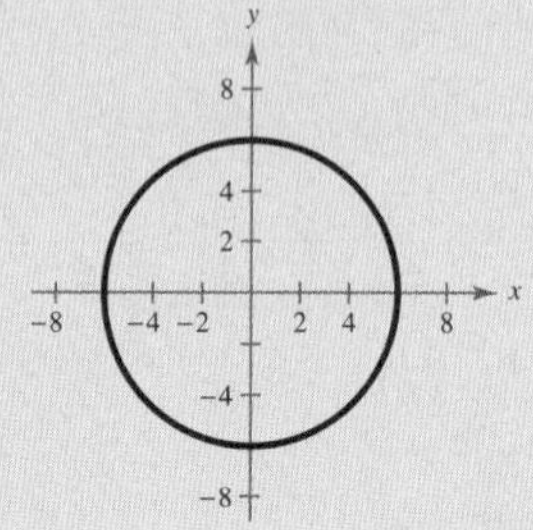

110. The graph of the polar equation consists of all points that are eight units from the pole.
$x^2 + y^2 = 64$

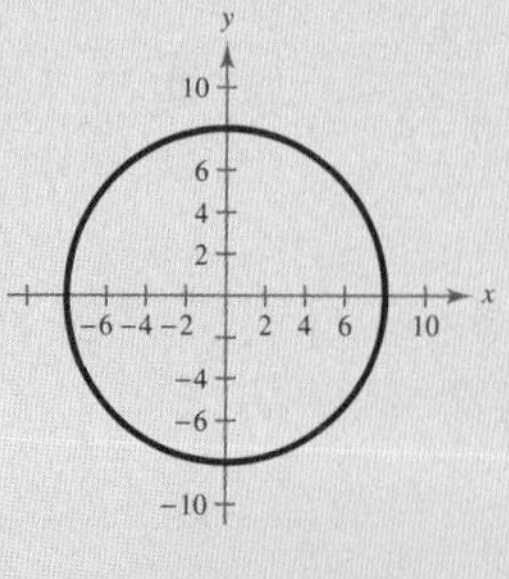

111. The graph of the polar equation consists of all points on the line that makes an angle of $\pi/6$ with the positive polar axis.
$-\sqrt{3}x + 3y = 0$

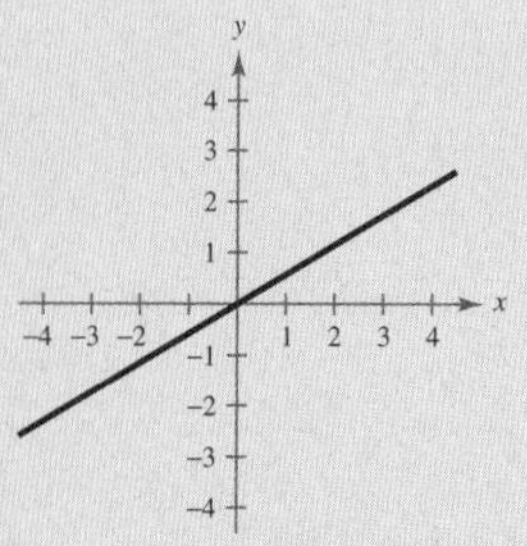

112–118, 121–125. See Additional Answers beginning on page AA1.

10.8 Graphs of Polar Equations

What you should learn

- Graph polar equations by point plotting.
- Use symmetry to sketch graphs of polar equations.
- Use zeros and maximum r-values to sketch graphs of polar equations.
- Recognize special polar graphs.

Why you should learn it

Equations of several common figures are simpler in polar form than in rectangular form. For instance, Exercise 12 on page 789 shows the graph of a circle and its polar equation.

Introduction

In previous chapters, you learned how to sketch graphs on rectangular coordinate systems. You began with the basic point-plotting method. Then you used sketching aids such as symmetry, intercepts, asymptotes, periods, and shifts to further investigate the natures of graphs. This section approaches curve sketching on the polar coordinate system similarly, beginning with a demonstration of point plotting.

Example 1 Graphing a Polar Equation by Point Plotting

Sketch the graph of the polar equation $r = 4 \sin \theta$.

Solution

The sine function is periodic, so you can get a full range of r-values by considering values of θ in the interval $0 \le \theta \le 2\pi$, as shown in the following table.

θ	0	$\frac{\pi}{6}$	$\frac{\pi}{3}$	$\frac{\pi}{2}$	$\frac{2\pi}{3}$	$\frac{5\pi}{6}$	π	$\frac{7\pi}{6}$	$\frac{3\pi}{2}$	$\frac{11\pi}{6}$	2π
r	0	2	$2\sqrt{3}$	4	$2\sqrt{3}$	2	0	-2	-4	-2	0

If you plot these points as shown in Figure 10.71, it appears that the graph is a circle of radius 2 whose center is at the point $(x, y) = (0, 2)$.

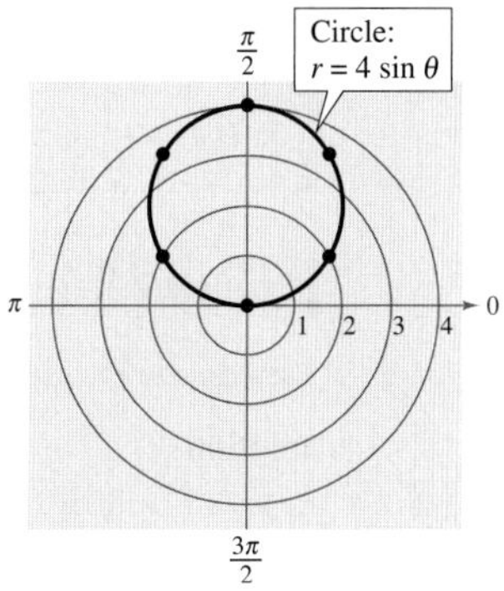

FIGURE 10.71

CHECKPoint Now try Exercise 27.

You can confirm the graph in Figure 10.71 by converting the polar equation to rectangular form and then sketching the graph of the rectangular equation. You can also use a graphing utility set to *polar* mode and graph the polar equation or set the graphing utility to *parametric* mode and graph a parametric representation.

1 PLAN AND PREPARE

Warm-up Exercises

Transparency Available
Available at the Instructor's companion site.

Notetaking Guide

Transparency Available
Promotes interactive learning and notetaking skills.
Available at the Instructor's companion site.

Animated Precalculus

An **Animated Precalculus** tutorial is available at the Student companion site for **Section 10.8.**

Pacing

Average: 2 days
Advanced: 2 days
Block: 0.5 block with 10.7
0.5 block with 10.9

2 FOCUS AND MOTIVATE

Essential Question

How do you sketch graphs of polar equations? **Tell students that they will learn how to answer this question by creating and plotting a table of points, identifying symmetry, and finding intercepts and maximum points.**

Resource Planning Guide

Chapter Resources

- Complete Solutions Guide

Workbooks

- Notetaking Guide
- Student Solutions Guide

Interactive Technology

- Instructor Success Organizer
- Notetaking Guide IAE
- Instructional DVDs
- Animated Precalculus
- PowerLecture with ExamView

3 TEACH

Extra Example 1

Sketch the graph of the polar equation $r = -4\sin\theta$.

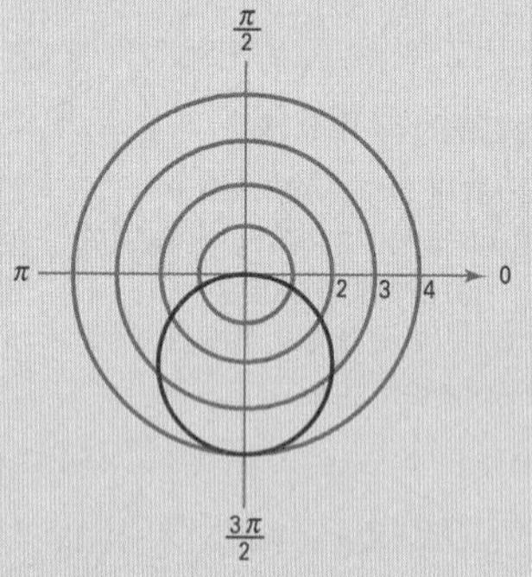

Extra Example 2

Use symmetry to sketch the graph of $r = 2 + 4\sin\theta$.

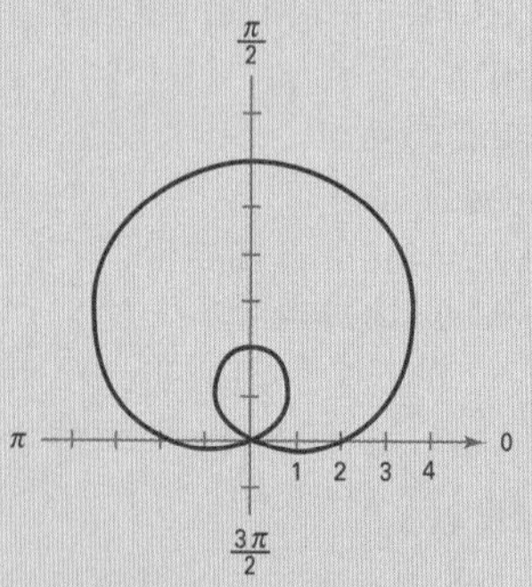

Avoiding Common Errors

When graphing a polar equation, students should be careful of the domain of θ. If graphing by hand or using a graphing calculator, more than one rotation of 2π may be necessary to complete the graph.

Symmetry

In Figure 10.71 on the preceding page, note that as θ increases from 0 to 2π the graph is traced out twice. Moreover, note that the graph is *symmetric with respect to the line* $\theta = \pi/2$. Had you known about this symmetry and retracing ahead of time, you could have used fewer points.

Symmetry with respect to the line $\theta = \pi/2$ is one of three important types of symmetry to consider in polar curve sketching. (See Figure 10.72.)

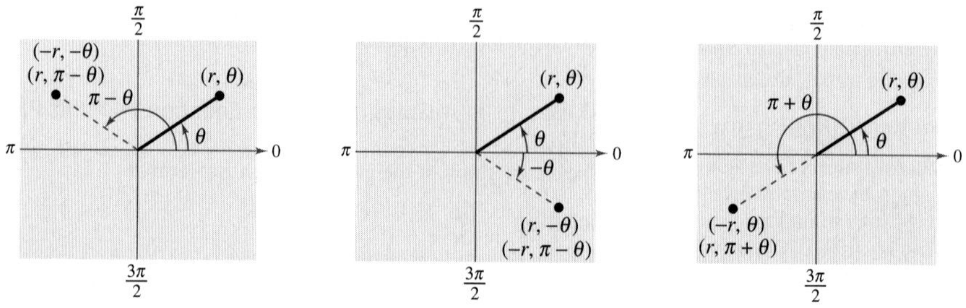

Symmetry with Respect to the Line $\theta = \dfrac{\pi}{2}$ Symmetry with Respect to the Polar Axis Symmetry with Respect to the Pole

FIGURE 10.72

Study Tip

Note in Example 2 that $\cos(-\theta) = \cos\theta$. This is because the cosine function is *even*. Recall from Section 4.2 that the cosine function is even and the sine function is odd. That is, $\sin(-\theta) = -\sin\theta$.

Tests for Symmetry in Polar Coordinates

The graph of a polar equation is symmetric with respect to the following if the given substitution yields an equivalent equation.

1. *The line* $\theta = \pi/2$: Replace (r, θ) by $(r, \pi - \theta)$ or $(-r, -\theta)$.
2. *The polar axis:* Replace (r, θ) by $(r, -\theta)$ or $(-r, \pi - \theta)$.
3. *The pole:* Replace (r, θ) by $(r, \pi + \theta)$ or $(-r, \theta)$.

Example 2 Using Symmetry to Sketch a Polar Graph

Use symmetry to sketch the graph of $r = 3 + 2\cos\theta$.

Solution

Replacing (r, θ) by $(r, -\theta)$ produces

$$r = 3 + 2\cos(-\theta) = 3 + 2\cos\theta. \qquad \cos(-\theta) = \cos\theta$$

So, you can conclude that the curve is symmetric with respect to the polar axis. Plotting the points in the table and using polar axis symmetry, you obtain the graph shown in Figure 10.73. This graph is called a **limaçon.**

θ	0	$\frac{\pi}{3}$	$\frac{\pi}{2}$	$\frac{2\pi}{3}$	π
r	5	4	3	2	1

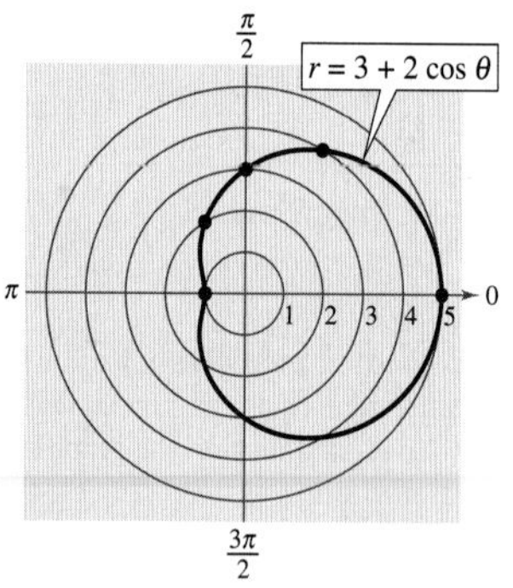

FIGURE 10.73

CHECKPoint Now try Exercise 33.

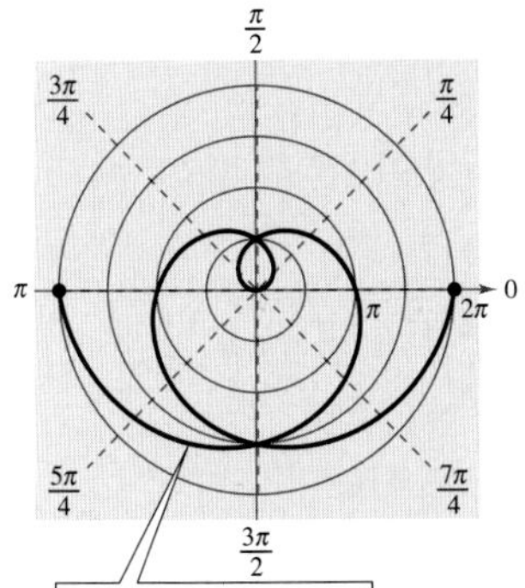

FIGURE 10.74

The three tests for symmetry in polar coordinates listed on page 784 are sufficient to guarantee symmetry, but they are not necessary. For instance, Figure 10.74 shows the graph of $r = \theta + 2\pi$ to be symmetric with respect to the line $\theta = \pi/2$, and yet the tests on page 784 fail to indicate symmetry because neither of the following replacements yields an equivalent equation.

Original Equation	*Replacement*	*New Equation*
$r = \theta + 2\pi$	(r, θ) by $(-r, -\theta)$	$-r = -\theta + 2\pi$
$r = \theta + 2\pi$	(r, θ) by $(r, \pi - \theta)$	$r = -\theta + 3\pi$

The equations discussed in Examples 1 and 2 are of the form

$r = 4 \sin \theta = f(\sin \theta)$ and $r = 3 + 2 \cos \theta = g(\cos \theta)$.

The graph of the first equation is symmetric with respect to the line $\theta = \pi/2$, and the graph of the second equation is symmetric with respect to the polar axis. This observation can be generalized to yield the following tests.

Quick Tests for Symmetry in Polar Coordinates

1. The graph of $r = f(\sin \theta)$ is symmetric with respect to the line $\theta = \dfrac{\pi}{2}$.

2. The graph of $r = g(\cos \theta)$ is symmetric with respect to the polar axis.

Zeros and Maximum *r*-Values

Two additional aids to graphing of polar equations involve knowing the θ-values for which $|r|$ is maximum and knowing the θ-values for which $r = 0$. For instance, in Example 1, the maximum value of $|r|$ for $r = 4 \sin \theta$ is $|r| = 4$, and this occurs when $\theta = \pi/2$, as shown in Figure 10.71. Moreover, $r = 0$ when $\theta = 0$.

Example 3 Sketching a Polar Graph

Sketch the graph of $r = 1 - 2 \cos \theta$.

Solution

From the equation $r = 1 - 2 \cos \theta$, you can obtain the following.

Symmetry: With respect to the polar axis

Maximum value of $|r|$*:* $r = 3$ when $\theta = \pi$

Zero of r: $r = 0$ when $\theta = \pi/3$

The table shows several θ-values in the interval $[0, \pi]$. By plotting the corresponding points, you can sketch the graph shown in Figure 10.75.

θ	0	$\frac{\pi}{6}$	$\frac{\pi}{3}$	$\frac{\pi}{2}$	$\frac{2\pi}{3}$	$\frac{5\pi}{6}$	π
r	-1	-0.73	0	1	2	2.73	3

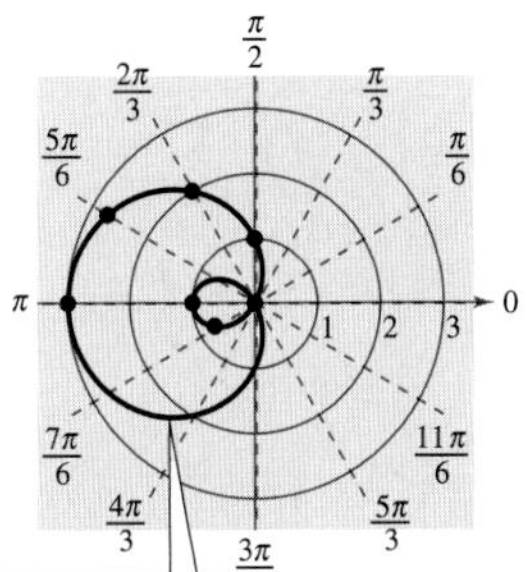

FIGURE 10.75

Note how the negative r-values determine the *inner loop* of the graph in Figure 10.75. This graph, like the one in Figure 10.73, is a limaçon.

CHECKPoint Now try Exercise 35.

Extra Example 3

Sketch the graph of $r = 3 - 2 \cos \theta$.

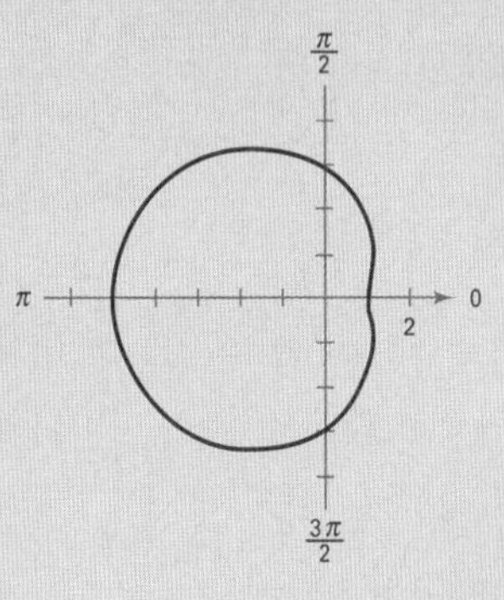

Extra Example 4

Sketch the graph of $r = 4\cos 2\theta$.

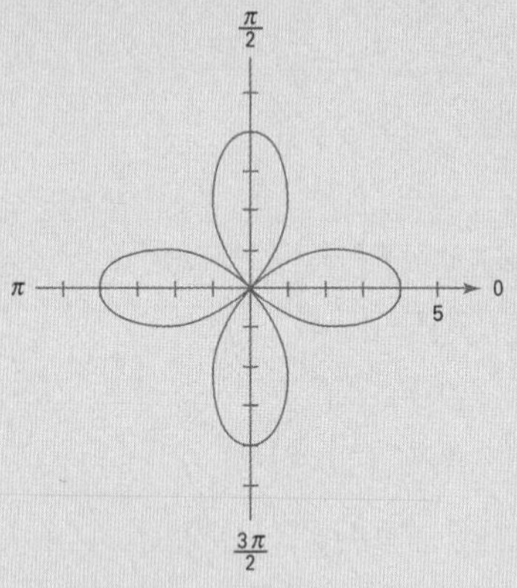

Some curves reach their zeros and maximum r-values at more than one point, as shown in Example 4.

Example 4 Sketching a Polar Graph

Sketch the graph of $r = 2\cos 3\theta$.

Solution

Symmetry: With respect to the polar axis

Maximum value of $|r|$: $|r| = 2$ when $3\theta = 0, \pi, 2\pi, 3\pi$ or $\theta = 0, \frac{\pi}{3}, \frac{2\pi}{3}, \pi$

Zeros of r: $r = 0$ when $3\theta = \frac{\pi}{2}, \frac{3\pi}{2}, \frac{5\pi}{2}$ or $\theta = \frac{\pi}{6}, \frac{\pi}{2}, \frac{5\pi}{6}$

θ	0	$\frac{\pi}{12}$	$\frac{\pi}{6}$	$\frac{\pi}{4}$	$\frac{\pi}{3}$	$\frac{5\pi}{12}$	$\frac{\pi}{2}$
r	2	$\sqrt{2}$	0	$-\sqrt{2}$	-2	$-\sqrt{2}$	0

By plotting these points and using the specified symmetry, zeros, and maximum values, you can obtain the graph shown in Figure 10.76. This graph is called a **rose curve,** and each of the loops on the graph is called a *petal* of the rose curve. Note how the entire curve is generated as θ increases from 0 to π.

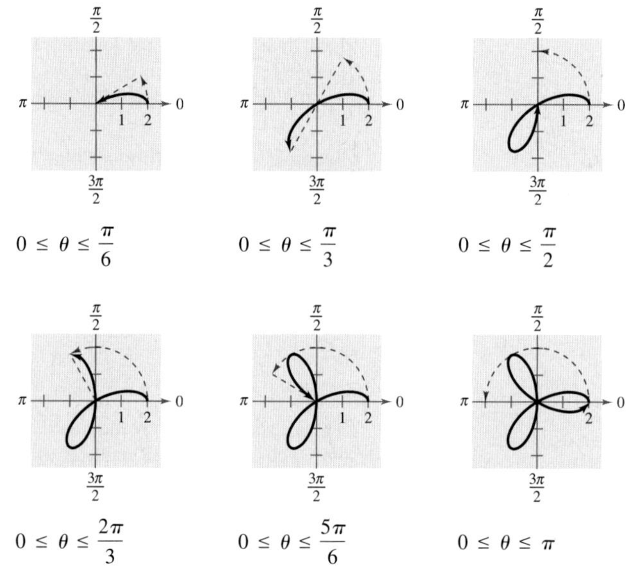

FIGURE 10.76

TECHNOLOGY

Use a graphing utility in *polar* mode to verify the graph of $r = 2\cos 3\theta$ shown in Figure 10.76.

CHECKPoint Now try Exercise 39.

Special Polar Graphs

Several important types of graphs have equations that are simpler in polar form than in rectangular form. For example, the circle

$$r = 4 \sin \theta$$

in Example 1 has the more complicated rectangular equation

$$x^2 + (y - 2)^2 = 4.$$

Several other types of graphs that have simple polar equations are shown below.

Limaçons
$r = a \pm b \cos \theta$
$r = a \pm b \sin \theta$
$(a > 0, b > 0)$

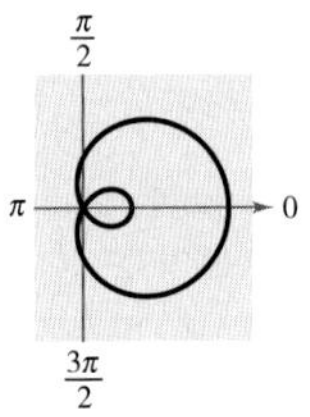

$\frac{a}{b} < 1$
Limaçon with inner loop

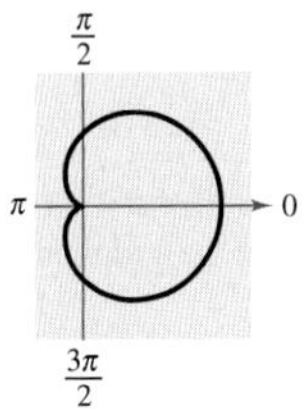

$\frac{a}{b} = 1$
Cardioid (heart-shaped)

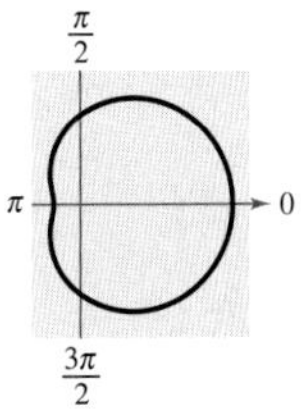

$1 < \frac{a}{b} < 2$
Dimpled limaçon

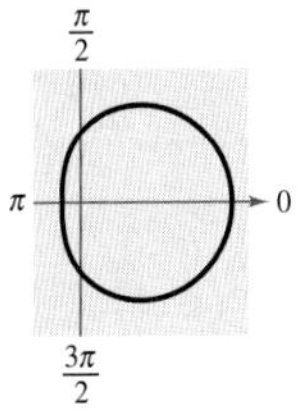

$\frac{a}{b} \geq 2$
Convex limaçon

Rose Curves
n petals if n is odd,
$2n$ petals if n is even
$(n \geq 2)$.

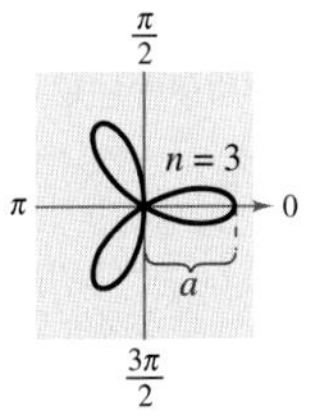

$r = a \cos n\theta$
Rose curve

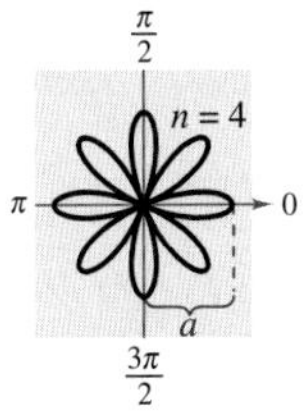

$r = a \cos n\theta$
Rose curve

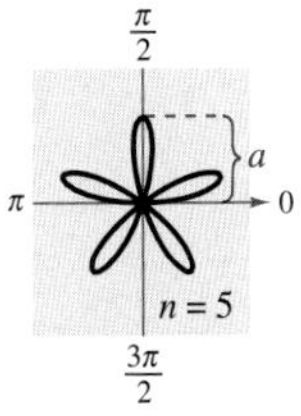

$r = a \sin n\theta$
Rose curve

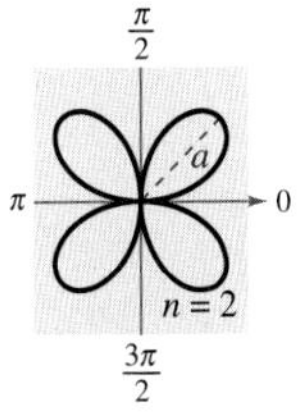

$r = a \sin n\theta$
Rose curve

Circles and Lemniscates

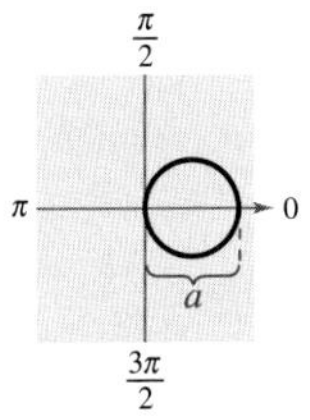

$r = a \cos \theta$
Circle

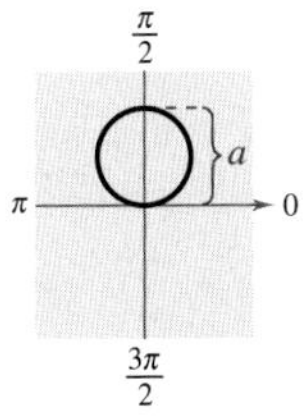

$r = a \sin \theta$
Circle

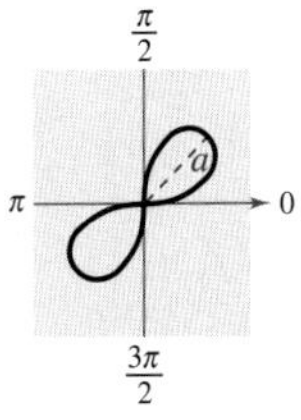

$r^2 = a^2 \sin 2\theta$
Lemniscate

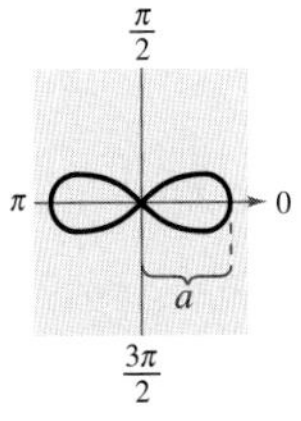

$r^2 = a^2 \cos 2\theta$
Lemniscate

Extra Example 5

Sketch the graph of $r = 3\cos 3\theta$.

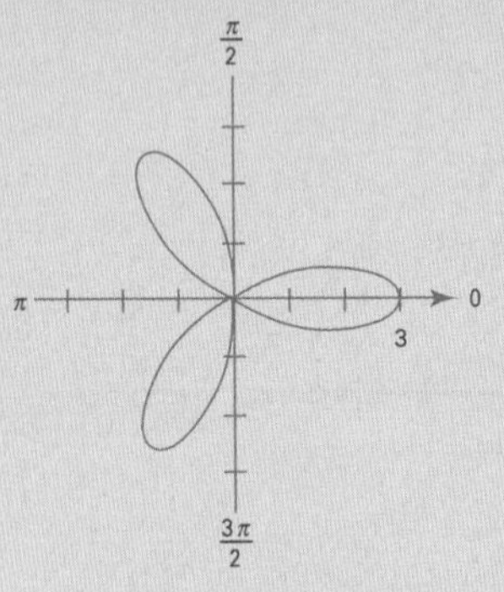

Extra Example 6

Sketch the graph of $r^2 = 4\cos 2\theta$.

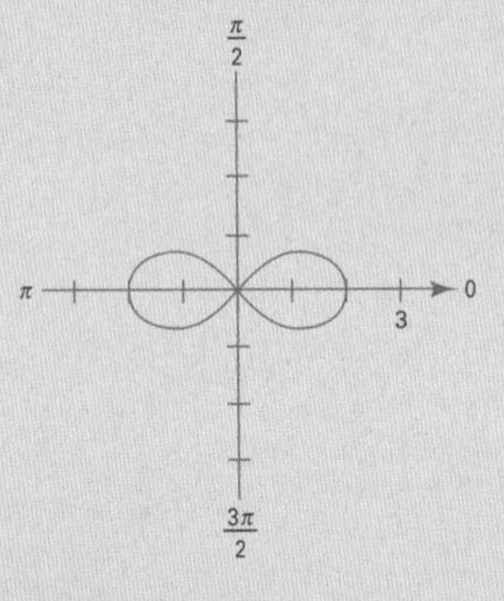

Closing the Lesson

Have students summarize the major points of the lesson and answer the Essential Question: How do you sketch graphs of polar equations?

- **Create a table of points by choosing an interval of θ that will generate a complete set of r-values.**
- **Identify symmetry by replacing either r or θ with its opposite or by adding π to θ and solving to see whether the new equation is equivalent to the original.**
- **Recognize symmetry in polar functions of sine and cosine.**
- **Recognize special polar graphs including limaçons, rose curves, and lemniscates.**

Example 5 Sketching a Rose Curve

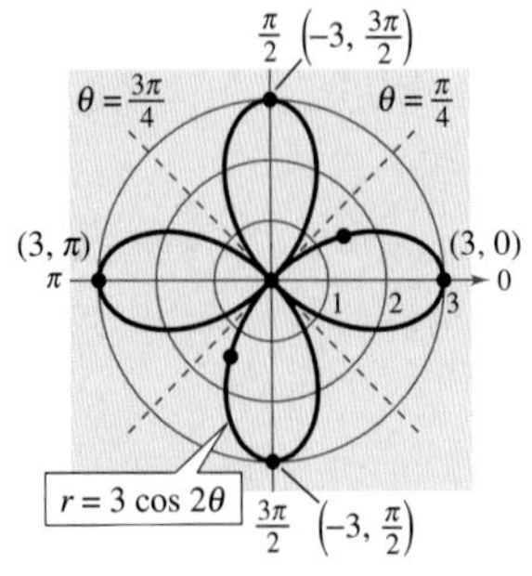

FIGURE 10.77

Sketch the graph of $r = 3\cos 2\theta$.

Solution

Type of curve: Rose curve with $2n = 4$ petals

Symmetry: With respect to polar axis, the line $\theta = \frac{\pi}{2}$, and the pole

Maximum value of $|r|$: $|r| = 3$ when $\theta = 0, \frac{\pi}{2}, \pi, \frac{3\pi}{2}$

Zeros of r: $r = 0$ when $\theta = \frac{\pi}{4}, \frac{3\pi}{4}$

Using this information together with the additional points shown in the following table, you obtain the graph shown in Figure 10.77.

θ	0	$\frac{\pi}{6}$	$\frac{\pi}{4}$	$\frac{\pi}{3}$
r	3	$\frac{3}{2}$	0	$-\frac{3}{2}$

CHECK *Point* Now try Exercise 41.

Example 6 Sketching a Lemniscate

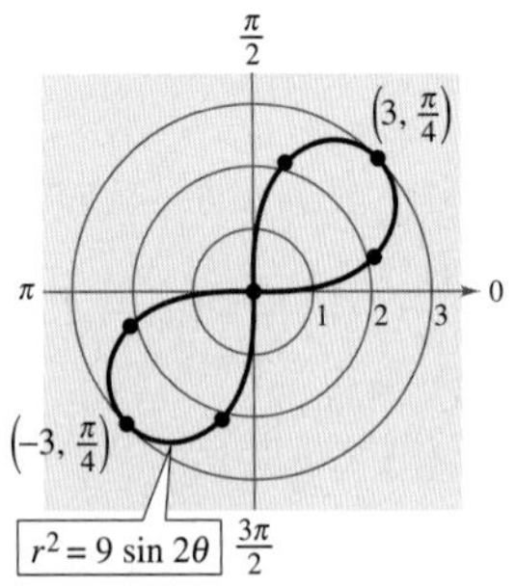

FIGURE 10.78

Sketch the graph of $r^2 = 9\sin 2\theta$.

Solution

Type of curve: Lemniscate

Symmetry: With respect to the pole

Maximum value of $|r|$: $|r| = 3$ when $\theta = \frac{\pi}{4}$

Zeros of r: $r = 0$ when $\theta = 0, \frac{\pi}{2}$

If $\sin 2\theta < 0$, this equation has no solution points. So, you restrict the values of θ to those for which $\sin 2\theta \geq 0$.

$$0 \leq \theta \leq \frac{\pi}{2} \quad \text{or} \quad \pi \leq \theta \leq \frac{3\pi}{2}$$

Moreover, using symmetry, you need to consider only the first of these two intervals. By finding a few additional points (see table below), you can obtain the graph shown in Figure 10.78.

θ	0	$\frac{\pi}{12}$	$\frac{\pi}{4}$	$\frac{5\pi}{12}$	$\frac{\pi}{2}$
$r = \pm 3\sqrt{\sin 2\theta}$	0	$\frac{\pm 3}{\sqrt{2}}$	± 3	$\frac{\pm 3}{\sqrt{2}}$	0

CHECK *Point* Now try Exercise 47.

Differentiated Instruction

Kinesthetic Learners Challenge students to sketch the graphs in Examples 5 and 6 without looking at Figures 10.77 and 10.78. Have them cover the figures as they sketch the graphs. Direct them to refer to the special polar graphs on page 787 to help them with their sketches.

10.8 EXERCISES

See www.CalcChat.com for worked-out solutions to odd-numbered exercises.

VOCABULARY: Fill in the blanks.

1. The graph of $r = f(\sin\theta)$ is symmetric with respect to the line $\theta = \frac{\pi}{2}$.
2. The graph of $r = g(\cos\theta)$ is symmetric with respect to the polar axis.
3. The equation $r = 2 + \cos\theta$ represents a convex limaçon.
4. The equation $r = 2\cos\theta$ represents a circle.
5. The equation $r^2 = 4\sin 2\theta$ represents a lemniscate
6. The equation $r = 1 + \sin\theta$ represents a cardioid.

SKILLS AND APPLICATIONS

In Exercises 7–12, identify the type of polar graph.

7. Rose curve with 4 petals

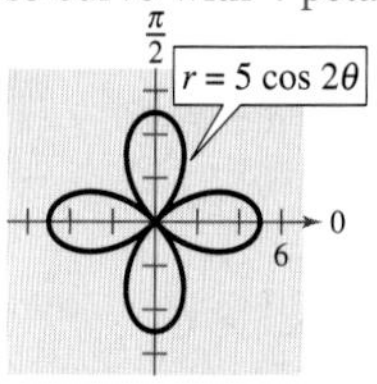

8. Cardioid

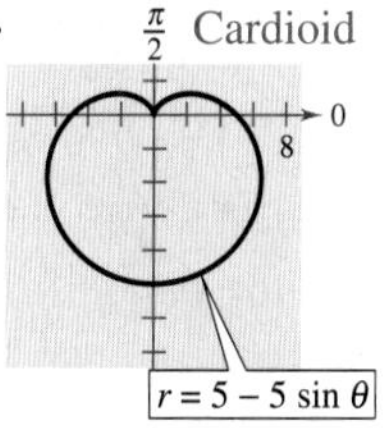

9. Limaçon with inner loop

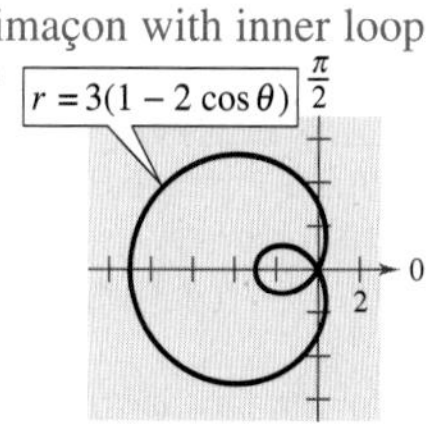

10. Lemniscate

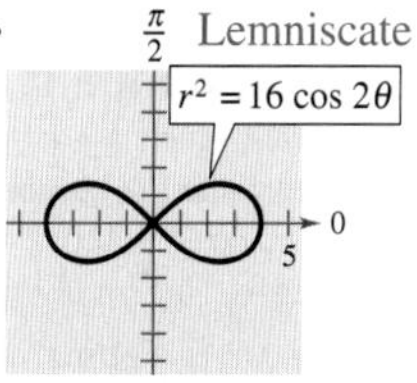

11. Rose curve with 3 petals

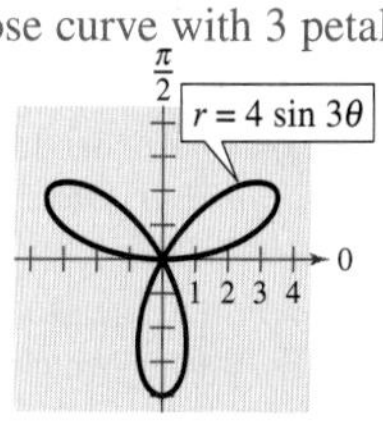

12. Circle

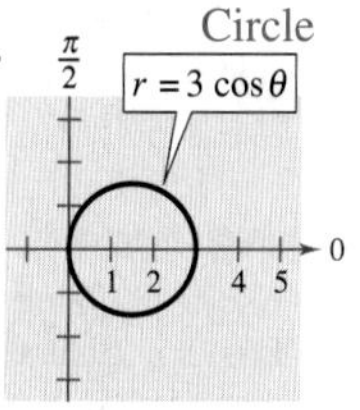

In Exercises 13–18, test for symmetry with respect to $\theta = \pi/2$, the polar axis, and the pole.

13. $r = 4 + 3\cos\theta$ Polar axis
14. $r = 9\cos 3\theta$ Polar axis
15. $r = \dfrac{2}{1 + \sin\theta}$ $\theta = \frac{\pi}{2}$
16. $r = \dfrac{3}{2 + \cos\theta}$ Polar axis
17. $r^2 = 36\cos 2\theta$ See margin.
18. $r^2 = 25\sin 2\theta$ Pole

In Exercises 19–22, find the maximum value of $|r|$ and any zeros of r. 19–22. See margin.

19. $r = 10 - 10\sin\theta$
20. $r = 6 + 12\cos\theta$
21. $r = 4\cos 3\theta$
22. $r = 3\sin 2\theta$

In Exercises 23–48, sketch the graph of the polar equation using symmetry, zeros, maximum r-values, and any other additional points. 23–48. See margin.

23. $r = 4$
24. $r = -7$
25. $r = \dfrac{\pi}{3}$
26. $r = -\dfrac{3\pi}{4}$
27. $r = \sin\theta$
28. $r = 4\cos\theta$
29. $r = 3(1 - \cos\theta)$
30. $r = 4(1 - \sin\theta)$
31. $r = 4(1 + \sin\theta)$
32. $r = 2(1 + \cos\theta)$
33. $r = 3 + 6\sin\theta$
34. $r = 4 - 3\sin\theta$
35. $r = 1 - 2\sin\theta$
36. $r = 2 - 4\cos\theta$
37. $r = 3 - 4\cos\theta$
38. $r = 4 + 3\cos\theta$
39. $r = 5\sin 2\theta$
40. $r = 2\cos 2\theta$
41. $r = 6\cos 3\theta$
42. $r = 3\sin 3\theta$
43. $r = 2\sec\theta$
44. $r = 5\csc\theta$
45. $r = \dfrac{3}{\sin\theta - 2\cos\theta}$
46. $r = \dfrac{6}{2\sin\theta - 3\cos\theta}$
47. $r^2 = 9\cos 2\theta$
48. $r^2 = 4\sin\theta$

In Exercises 49–58, use a graphing utility to graph the polar equation. Describe your viewing window. 49–58. See margin.

49. $r = \dfrac{9}{4}$
50. $r = -\dfrac{5}{2}$
51. $r = \dfrac{5\pi}{8}$
52. $r = -\dfrac{\pi}{10}$
53. $r = 8\cos\theta$
54. $r = \cos 2\theta$
55. $r = 3(2 - \sin\theta)$
56. $r = 2\cos(3\theta - 2)$
57. $r = 8\sin\theta\cos^2\theta$
58. $r = 2\csc\theta + 5$

In Exercises 59–64, use a graphing utility to graph the polar equation. Find an interval for θ for which the graph is traced *only once*. 59–62. See margin.

59. $r = 3 - 8\cos\theta$
60. $r = 5 + 4\cos\theta$
61. $r = 2\cos\left(\dfrac{3\theta}{2}\right)$
62. $r = 3\sin\left(\dfrac{5\theta}{2}\right)$

4 PRACTICE AND APPLY

Assignment Guide

Transparencies Available
Available at the Instructor's companion site.

Average:
Day 1: p. 789
Exs. 1–12, 13–17 odd, 19–21, 23, 25, 28, 29, 31, 36–38, 40, 44–46
Day 2: pp. 789–790
Exs. 49–67 odd, 69–71, 73–75, 77, 80

Advanced:
Day 1: p. 789
Exs. 1–12, 14–18, 20–22, 24–30 even, 31, 32, 34, 36–38, 40–48 even
Day 2: pp. 789–790
Exs. 50–68 even, 69, 70, 72–74, 76–78, 81, 82

Block:
p. 789
Exs. 1–12, 13–17 odd, 19–21, 23, 25, 28, 29, 31, 36–38, 40, 44–46 (with 10.7)
pp. 789–790
Exs. 49–67 odd, 69–71, 73–75, 77, 80 (with 10.9)

17. $\theta = \frac{\pi}{2}$, polar axis, pole

19. Maximum: $|r| = 20$ when $\theta = \frac{3\pi}{2}$
Zero: $r = 0$ when $\theta = \frac{\pi}{2}$

20. Maximum: $|r| = 18$ when $\theta = 0$
Zeros: $r = 0$ when $\theta = \frac{2\pi}{3}, \frac{4\pi}{3}$

21. Maximum: $|r| = 4$ when $\theta = 0, \frac{\pi}{3}, \frac{2\pi}{3}$
Zeros: $r = 0$ when $\theta = \frac{\pi}{6}, \frac{\pi}{2}, \frac{5\pi}{6}$

22. Maximum: $|r| = 3$ when $\theta = \frac{\pi}{4}, \frac{3\pi}{4}, \frac{5\pi}{4}, \frac{7\pi}{4}$
Zeros: $r = 0$ when $\theta = 0, \frac{\pi}{2}, \pi, \frac{3\pi}{2}$

23.

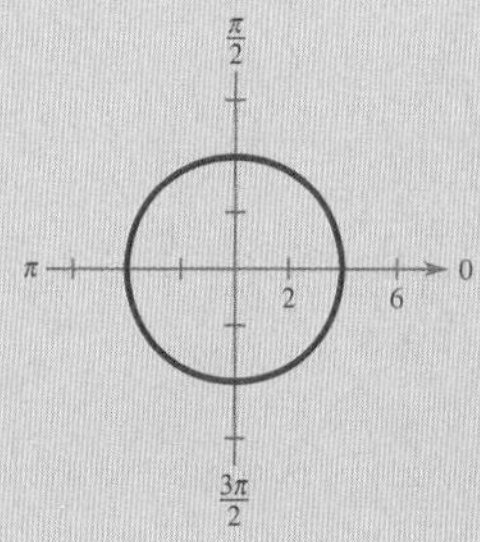

24.

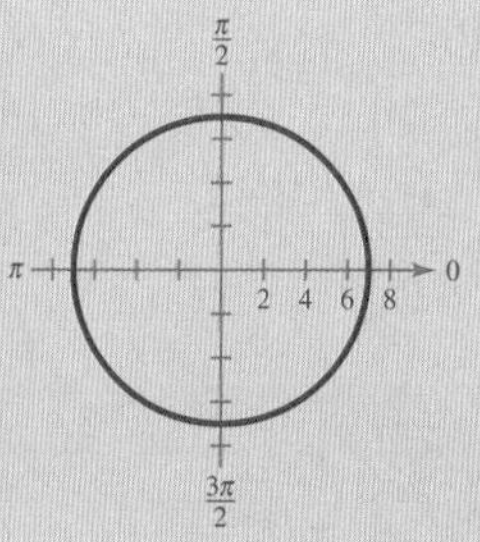

25.

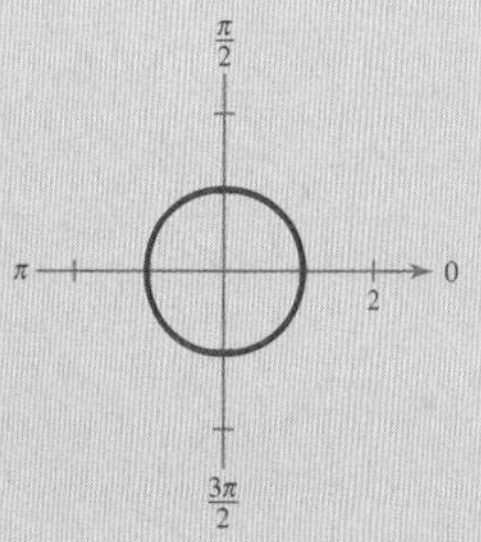

26–62. See Additional Answers beginning on page AA1.

5 ASSESS AND RETEACH

Daily Homework Quiz

Transparency Available

Available at the Instructor's companion site.

63.

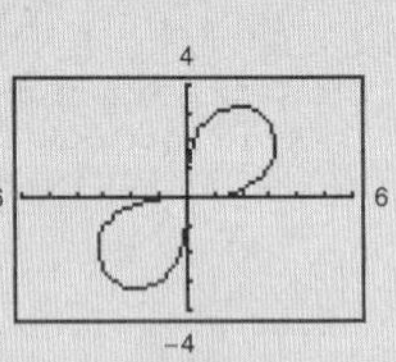

$0 \le \theta < \pi/2$

64.

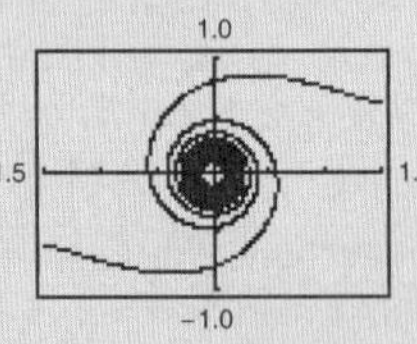

$0 \le \theta < \infty$

65.

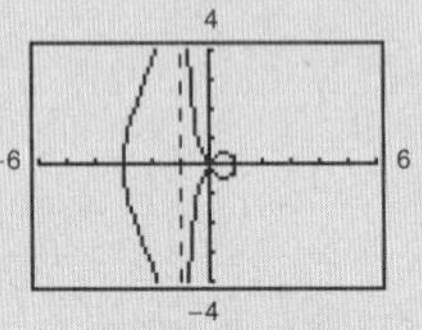

66.

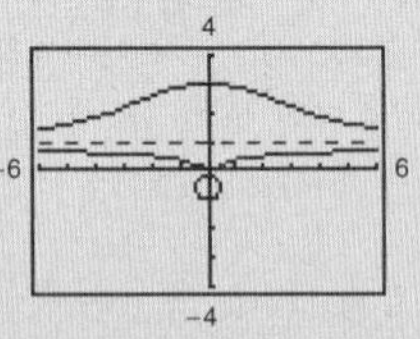

67.

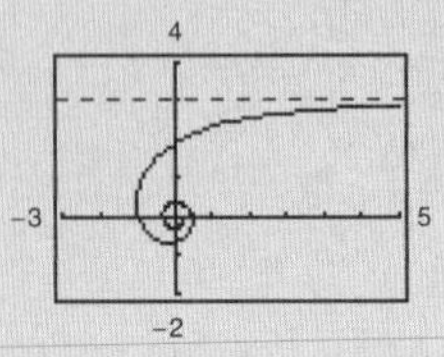

68.

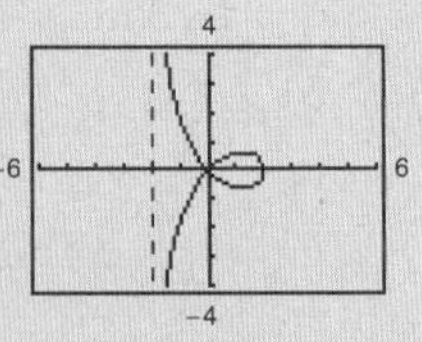

69. True. For a graph to have polar axis symmetry, replace (r, θ) by $(r, -\theta)$ or $(-r, \pi - \theta)$.

70. False. For a graph symmetric with respect to the pole, one portion of the graph coincides with the other portion when rotated π radians about the pole.

63–64. See margin.

63. $r^2 = 16 \sin 2\theta$ **64.** $r^2 = \dfrac{1}{\theta}$

In Exercises 65–68, use a graphing utility to graph the polar equation and show that the indicated line is an asymptote of the graph. 65–68. See margin.

Name of Graph	*Polar Equation*	*Asymptote*
65. Conchoid	$r = 2 - \sec \theta$	$x = -1$
66. Conchoid	$r = 2 + \csc \theta$	$y = 1$
67. Hyperbolic spiral	$r = \dfrac{3}{\theta}$	$y = 3$
68. Strophoid	$r = 2 \cos 2\theta \sec \theta$	$x = -2$

EXPLORATION

69–70. See margin.

TRUE OR FALSE? In Exercises 69 and 70, determine whether the statement is true or false. Justify your answer.

69. In the polar coordinate system, if a graph that has symmetry with respect to the polar axis were folded on the line $\theta = 0$, the portion of the graph above the polar axis would coincide with the portion of the graph below the polar axis.

70. In the polar coordinate system, if a graph that has symmetry with respect to the pole were folded on the line $\theta = 3\pi/4$, the portion of the graph on one side of the fold would coincide with the portion of the graph on the other side of the fold.

71. Sketch the graph of $r = 6 \cos \theta$ over each interval. Describe the part of the graph obtained in each case. See margin.

(a) $0 \le \theta \le \dfrac{\pi}{2}$ (b) $\dfrac{\pi}{2} \le \theta \le \pi$

(c) $-\dfrac{\pi}{2} \le \theta \le \dfrac{\pi}{2}$ (d) $\dfrac{\pi}{4} \le \theta \le \dfrac{3\pi}{4}$

72. GRAPHICAL REASONING Use a graphing utility to graph the polar equation $r = 6[1 + \cos(\theta - \phi)]$ for (a) $\phi = 0$, (b) $\phi = \pi/4$, and (c) $\phi = \pi/2$. Use the graphs to describe the effect of the angle ϕ. Write the equation as a function of $\sin \theta$ for part (c). See margin.

73. The graph of $r = f(\theta)$ is rotated about the pole through an angle ϕ. Show that the equation of the rotated graph is $r = f(\theta - \phi)$. Answers will vary.

74. Consider the graph of $r = f(\sin \theta)$. Answers will vary.

(a) Show that if the graph is rotated counterclockwise $\pi/2$ radians about the pole, the equation of the rotated graph is $r = f(-\cos \theta)$.

(b) Show that if the graph is rotated counterclockwise π radians about the pole, the equation of the rotated graph is $r = f(-\sin \theta)$.

(c) Show that if the graph is rotated counterclockwise $3\pi/2$ radians about the pole, the equation of the rotated graph is $r = f(\cos \theta)$.

In Exercises 75–78, use the results of Exercises 73 and 74.

75. Write an equation for the limaçon $r = 2 - \sin \theta$ after it has been rotated through the given angle. 75–78. See margin.

(a) $\dfrac{\pi}{4}$ (b) $\dfrac{\pi}{2}$ (c) π (d) $\dfrac{3\pi}{2}$

76. Write an equation for the rose curve $r = 2 \sin 2\theta$ after it has been rotated through the given angle.

(a) $\dfrac{\pi}{6}$ (b) $\dfrac{\pi}{2}$ (c) $\dfrac{2\pi}{3}$ (d) π

77. Sketch the graph of each equation.

(a) $r = 1 - \sin \theta$ (b) $r = 1 - \sin\left(\theta - \dfrac{\pi}{4}\right)$

78. Sketch the graph of each equation.

(a) $r = 3 \sec \theta$ (b) $r = 3 \sec\left(\theta - \dfrac{\pi}{4}\right)$

(c) $r = 3 \sec\left(\theta + \dfrac{\pi}{3}\right)$ (d) $r = 3 \sec\left(\theta - \dfrac{\pi}{2}\right)$

79. THINK ABOUT IT How many petals do the rose curves given by $r = 2 \cos 4\theta$ and $r = 2 \sin 3\theta$ have? Determine the numbers of petals for the curves given by $r = 2 \cos n\theta$ and $r = 2 \sin n\theta$, where n is a positive integer. See margin.

80. Use a graphing utility to graph and identify $r = 2 + k \sin \theta$ for $k = 0, 1, 2,$ and 3. See margin.

81. Consider the equation $r = 3 \sin k\theta$.

(a) Use a graphing utility to graph the equation for $k = 1.5$. Find the interval for θ over which the graph is traced only once. (a)–(b). See margin.

(b) Use a graphing utility to graph the equation for $k = 2.5$. Find the interval for θ over which the graph is traced only once.

(c) Is it possible to find an interval for θ over which the graph is traced only once for any rational number k? Explain. Yes. Explanations will vary.

82. CAPSTONE Write a brief paragraph that describes why some polar curves have equations that are simpler in polar form than in rectangular form. Besides a circle, give an example of a curve that is simpler in polar form than in rectangular form. Give an example of a curve that is simpler in rectangular form than in polar form. Answers will vary.

71. (a)

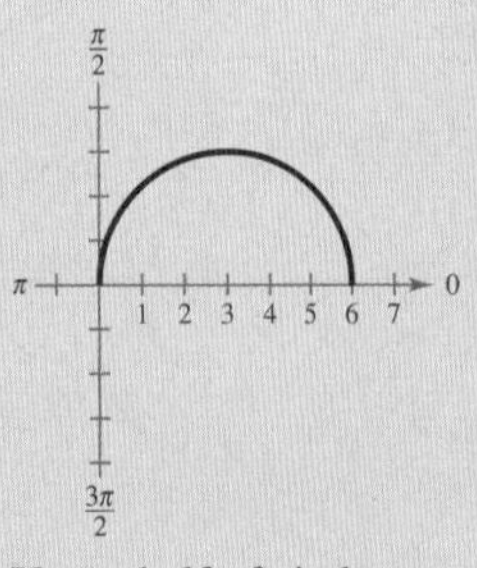

Upper half of circle

(b)

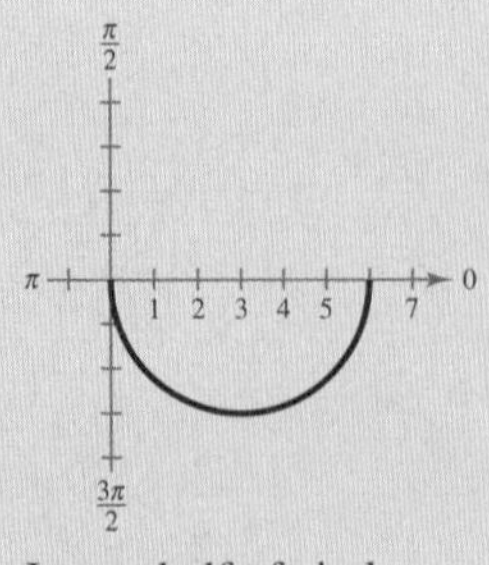

Lower half of circle

(c)

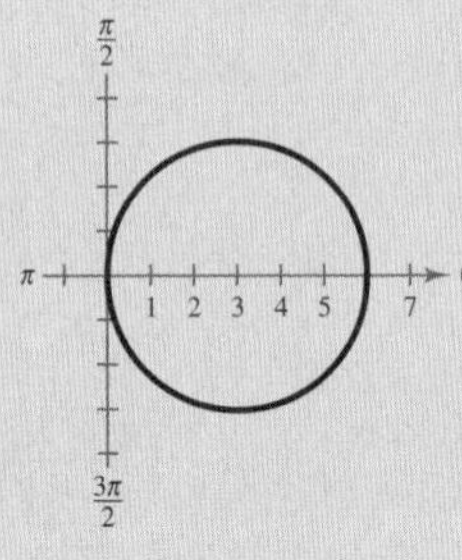

Full circle

71(d), 72, 75–80, 81(a)–(b). See Additional Answers beginning on page AA1.

10.9 POLAR EQUATIONS OF CONICS

What you should learn

- Define conics in terms of eccentricity.
- Write and graph equations of conics in polar form.
- Use equations of conics in polar form to model real-life problems.

Why you should learn it

The orbits of planets and satellites can be modeled with polar equations. For instance, in Exercise 65 on page 796, a polar equation is used to model the orbit of a satellite.

Corbis

Alternative Definition of Conic

In Sections 10.3 and 10.4, you learned that the rectangular equations of ellipses and hyperbolas take simple forms when the origin lies at their *centers*. As it happens, there are many important applications of conics in which it is more convenient to use one of the *foci* as the origin. In this section, you will learn that polar equations of conics take simple forms if one of the foci lies at the pole.

To begin, consider the following alternative definition of conic that uses the concept of eccentricity.

> **Alternative Definition of Conic**
>
> The locus of a point in the plane that moves so that its distance from a fixed point (focus) is in a constant ratio to its distance from a fixed line (directrix) is a **conic.** The constant ratio is the eccentricity of the conic and is denoted by e. Moreover, the conic is an **ellipse** if $e < 1$, a **parabola** if $e = 1$, and a **hyperbola** if $e > 1$. (See Figure 10.79.)

In Figure 10.79, note that for each type of conic, the focus is at the pole.

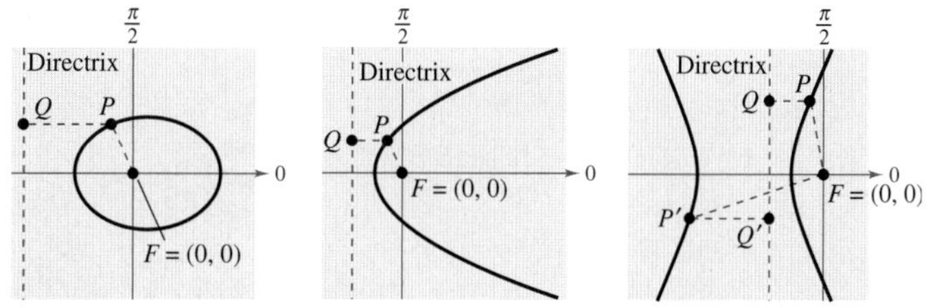

Ellipse: $0 < e < 1$ $\frac{PF}{PQ} < 1$

Parabola: $e = 1$ $\frac{PF}{PQ} = 1$

Hyperbola $e > 1$ $\frac{PF}{PQ} = \frac{P'F}{P'Q'} > 1$

FIGURE 10.79

Polar Equations of Conics

The benefit of locating a focus of a conic at the pole is that the equation of the conic takes on a simpler form. For a proof of the polar equations of conics, see Proofs in Mathematics on page 806.

> **Polar Equations of Conics**
>
> The graph of a polar equation of the form
>
> **1.** $r = \dfrac{ep}{1 \pm e \cos \theta}$ or **2.** $r = \dfrac{ep}{1 \pm e \sin \theta}$
>
> is a conic, where $e > 0$ is the eccentricity and $|p|$ is the distance between the focus (pole) and the directrix.

1 PLAN AND PREPARE

Warm-up Exercises

Transparency Available
Available at the Instructor's companion site.

Notetaking Guide

Transparency Available
Promotes interactive learning and notetaking skills. Available at the Instructor's companion site.

Animated Precalculus

An **Animated Precalculus** tutorial is available at the Student companion site for **Section 10.9.**

Pacing

Average: 2 days
Advanced: 2 days
Block: 0.5 block with 10.8
0.5 block with Review

2 FOCUS AND MOTIVATE

Essential Question

How do you represent conic sections in polar coordinates?
Tell students that they will learn how to answer this question by studying the eccentricity definition of a conic and the resulting polar conic equations.

Resource Planning Guide

Chapter Resources

- Complete Solutions Guide

Workbooks

- Notetaking Guide
- Student Solutions Guide

Interactive Technology

- Instructor Success Organizer
- Notetaking Guide IAE
- Instructional DVDs
- Animated Precalculus
- PowerLecture with ExamView

3 TEACH

Extra Example 1

Identify the type of conic represented by the equation

$$r = \frac{2}{2 + \cos \theta}.$$

ellipse

Equations of the form

$$r = \frac{ep}{1 \pm e \cos \theta} = g(\cos \theta) \qquad \text{Vertical directrix}$$

correspond to conics with a vertical directrix and symmetry with respect to the polar axis. Equations of the form

$$r = \frac{ep}{1 \pm e \sin \theta} = g(\sin \theta) \qquad \text{Horizontal directrix}$$

correspond to conics with a horizontal directrix and symmetry with respect to the line $\theta = \pi/2$. Moreover, the converse is also true—that is, any conic with a focus at the pole and having a horizontal or vertical directrix can be represented by one of these equations.

Example 1 Identifying a Conic from Its Equation

Identify the type of conic represented by the equation $r = \dfrac{15}{3 - 2 \cos \theta}$.

Algebraic Solution

To identify the type of conic, rewrite the equation in the form $r = (ep)/(1 \pm e \cos \theta)$.

$$r = \frac{15}{3 - 2\cos \theta} \qquad \text{Write original equation.}$$

$$= \frac{5}{1 - (2/3)\cos \theta} \qquad \text{Divide numerator and denominator by 3.}$$

Because $e = \frac{2}{3} < 1$, you can conclude that the graph is an ellipse.

CHECKPoint Now try Exercise 15.

Graphical Solution

You can start sketching the graph by plotting points from $\theta = 0$ to $\theta = \pi$. Because the equation is of the form $r = g(\cos \theta)$, the graph of r is symmetric with respect to the polar axis. So, you can complete the sketch, as shown in Figure 10.80. From this, you can conclude that the graph is an ellipse.

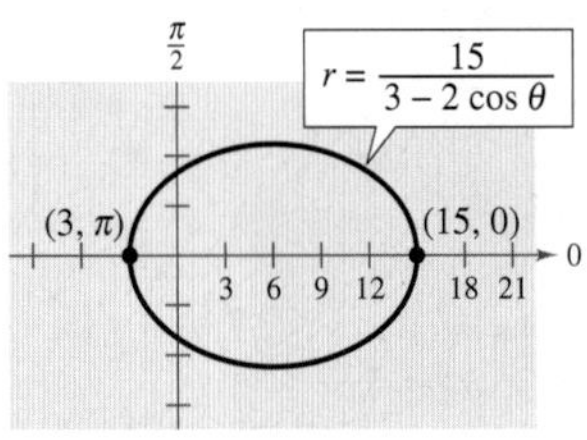

FIGURE 10.80

For the ellipse in Figure 10.80, the major axis is horizontal and the vertices lie at $(15, 0)$ and $(3, \pi)$. So, the length of the *major* axis is $2a = 18$. To find the length of the *minor* axis, you can use the equations $e = c/a$ and $b^2 = a^2 - c^2$ to conclude that

$$\begin{aligned} b^2 &= a^2 - c^2 \\ &= a^2 - (ea)^2 \\ &= a^2(1 - e^2). \qquad \text{Ellipse} \end{aligned}$$

Because $e = \frac{2}{3}$, you have $b^2 = 9^2\left[1 - \left(\frac{2}{3}\right)^2\right] = 45$, which implies that $b = \sqrt{45} = 3\sqrt{5}$. So, the length of the minor axis is $2b = 6\sqrt{5}$. A similar analysis for hyperbolas yields

$$\begin{aligned} b^2 &= c^2 - a^2 \\ &= (ea)^2 - a^2 \\ &= a^2(e^2 - 1). \qquad \text{Hyperbola} \end{aligned}$$

Example 2 Sketching a Conic from Its Polar Equation

Identify the conic $r = \dfrac{32}{3 + 5 \sin \theta}$ and sketch its graph.

Solution

Dividing the numerator and denominator by 3, you have

$$r = \frac{32/3}{1 + (5/3) \sin \theta}.$$

Because $e = \frac{5}{3} > 1$, the graph is a hyperbola. The transverse axis of the hyperbola lies on the line $\theta = \pi/2$, and the vertices occur at $(4, \pi/2)$ and $(-16, 3\pi/2)$. Because the length of the transverse axis is 12, you can see that $a = 6$. To find b, write

$$b^2 = a^2(e^2 - 1) = 6^2\left[\left(\frac{5}{3}\right)^2 - 1\right] = 64.$$

So, $b = 8$. Finally, you can use a and b to determine that the asymptotes of the hyperbola are $y = 10 \pm \frac{3}{4}x$. The graph is shown in Figure 10.81.

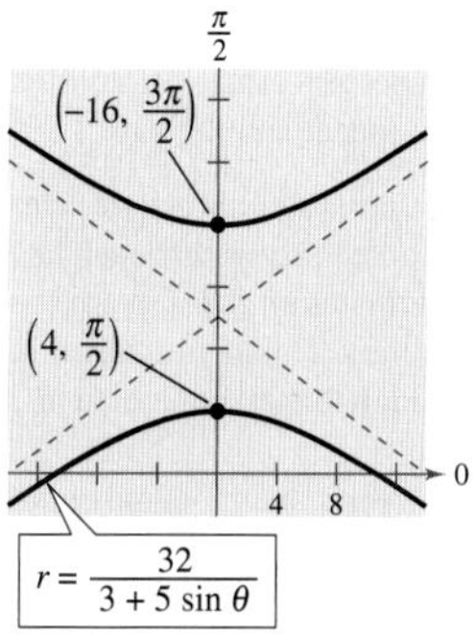

FIGURE 10.81

CHECKPoint Now try Exercise 23.

In the next example, you are asked to find a polar equation of a specified conic. To do this, let p be the distance between the pole and the directrix.

1. *Horizontal directrix above the pole:* $r = \dfrac{ep}{1 + e \sin \theta}$
2. *Horizontal directrix below the pole:* $r = \dfrac{ep}{1 - e \sin \theta}$
3. *Vertical directrix to the right of the pole:* $r = \dfrac{ep}{1 + e \cos \theta}$
4. *Vertical directrix to the left of the pole:* $r = \dfrac{ep}{1 - e \cos \theta}$

TECHNOLOGY

Use a graphing utility set in *polar* mode to verify the four orientations shown at the right. Remember that e must be positive, but p can be positive or negative.

Example 3 Finding the Polar Equation of a Conic

Find the polar equation of the parabola whose focus is the pole and whose directrix is the line $y = 3$.

Solution

From Figure 10.82, you can see that the directrix is horizontal and above the pole, so you can choose an equation of the form

$$r = \frac{ep}{1 + e \sin \theta}.$$

Moreover, because the eccentricity of a parabola is $e = 1$ and the distance between the pole and the directrix is $p = 3$, you have the equation

$$r = \frac{3}{1 + \sin \theta}.$$

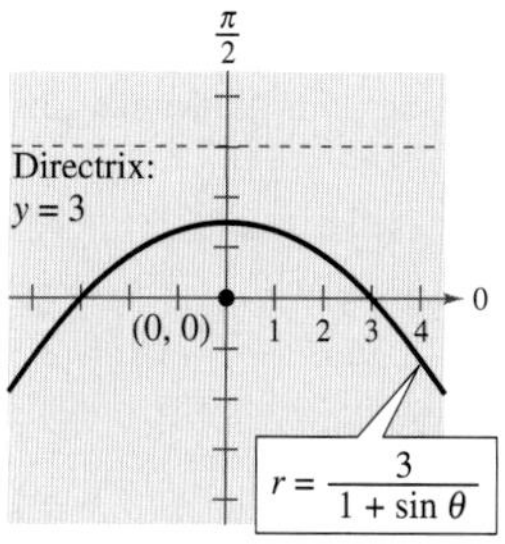

FIGURE 10.82

CHECKPoint Now try Exercise 39.

Extra Example 2

Identify the conic

$$r = \frac{3}{2 - 4 \sin \theta}$$

and sketch its graph.

hyperbola

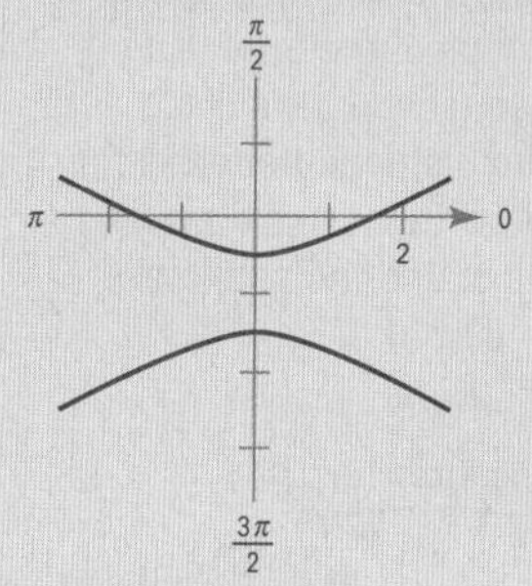

Extra Example 3

Find the polar equation of the parabola whose focus is the pole and whose directrix is the line $x = -2$.

$$r = \frac{2}{1 - \cos \theta}$$

Extra Example 4

On November 26, 1963, the United States launched *Explorer 18.* Its low and high points above the surface of Earth were 119 miles and 122,000 miles, respectively (see figure). The center of Earth is at one focus of the orbit. Find the polar equation of the orbit, and find the distance between the surface of Earth (assume a radius of 4000 miles) and the satellite when $\theta = 60°$.

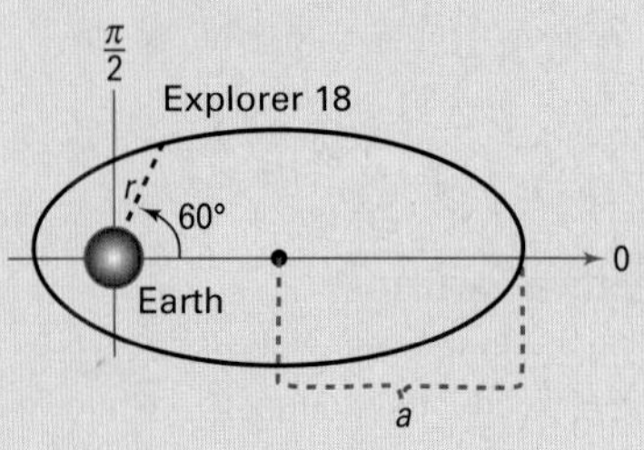

$r \approx \dfrac{7977.22}{1 - 0.937\cos\theta}$; $\approx$ **11,004 miles**

Closing the Lesson

Have students summarize the major points of the lesson and answer the Essential Question: How do you represent conic sections in polar coordinates?

- **Define a conic section as a set of points for which the distance to a set point is in constant ratio *e* to the distance to a set line.**
- **Classify the conic as an ellipse if *e* < 1, a parabola if *e* = 1, and a hyperbola if *e* > 1.**
- **Use equations of the form**

$$r = \frac{ep}{1 \pm e\cos\theta} \text{ or}$$

$$r = \frac{ep}{1 \pm e\sin\theta}$$

to represent a conic with a vertical or horizontal directrix, respectively.

Applications

Kepler's Laws (listed below), named after the German astronomer Johannes Kepler (1571–1630), can be used to describe the orbits of the planets about the sun.

1. Each planet moves in an elliptical orbit with the sun at one focus.
2. A ray from the sun to the planet sweeps out equal areas of the ellipse in equal times.
3. The square of the period (the time it takes for a planet to orbit the sun) is proportional to the cube of the mean distance between the planet and the sun.

Although Kepler simply stated these laws on the basis of observation, they were later validated by Isaac Newton (1642–1727). In fact, Newton was able to show that each law can be deduced from a set of universal laws of motion and gravitation that govern the movement of all heavenly bodies, including comets and satellites. This is illustrated in the next example, which involves the comet named after the English mathematician and physicist Edmund Halley (1656–1742).

If you use Earth as a reference with a period of 1 year and a distance of 1 astronomical unit (an *astronomical unit* is defined as the mean distance between Earth and the sun, or about 93 million miles), the proportionality constant in Kepler's third law is 1. For example, because Mars has a mean distance to the sun of $d = 1.524$ astronomical units, its period P is given by $d^3 = P^2$. So, the period of Mars is $P \approx 1.88$ years.

Example 4 Halley's Comet

Halley's comet has an elliptical orbit with an eccentricity of $e \approx 0.967$. The length of the major axis of the orbit is approximately 35.88 astronomical units. Find a polar equation for the orbit. How close does Halley's comet come to the sun?

Solution

Using a vertical axis, as shown in Figure 10.83, choose an equation of the form $r = ep/(1 + e\sin\theta)$. Because the vertices of the ellipse occur when $\theta = \pi/2$ and $\theta = 3\pi/2$, you can determine the length of the major axis to be the sum of the r-values of the vertices. That is,

$$2a = \frac{0.967p}{1 + 0.967} + \frac{0.967p}{1 - 0.967} \approx 29.79p \approx 35.88.$$

So, $p \approx 1.204$ and $ep \approx (0.967)(1.204) \approx 1.164$. Using this value of ep in the equation, you have

$$r = \frac{1.164}{1 + 0.967\sin\theta}$$

where r is measured in astronomical units. To find the closest point to the sun (the focus), substitute $\theta = \pi/2$ in this equation to obtain

$$r = \frac{1.164}{1 + 0.967\sin(\pi/2)}$$

$$\approx 0.59 \text{ astronomical unit}$$

$$\approx 55{,}000{,}000 \text{ miles.}$$

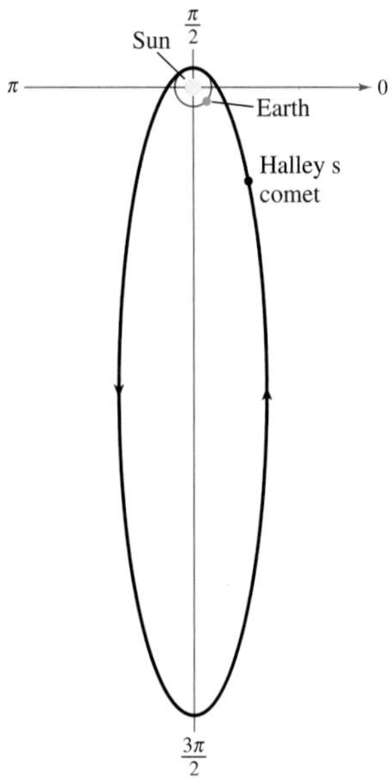

FIGURE 10.83

CHECKPoint Now try Exercise 63.

10.9 EXERCISES

See www.CalcChat.com for worked-out solutions to odd-numbered exercises.

VOCABULARY

In Exercises 1–3, fill in the blanks.

1. The locus of a point in the plane that moves so that its distance from a fixed point (focus) is in a constant ratio to its distance from a fixed line (directrix) is a __conic__.
2. The constant ratio is the ________ of the conic and is denoted by ________. eccentricity; e
3. An equation of the form $r = \dfrac{ep}{1 + e\cos\theta}$ has a __vertical__ directrix to the __right__ of the pole.
4. Match the conic with its eccentricity.

   (a) $e < 1$ iii (b) $e = 1$ i (c) $e > 1$ ii

   (i) parabola (ii) hyperbola (iii) ellipse

SKILLS AND APPLICATIONS

In Exercises 5–8, write the polar equation of the conic for $e = 1$, $e = 0.5$, and $e = 1.5$. Identify the conic for each equation. Verify your answers with a graphing utility. 5–8. See margin.

5. $r = \dfrac{2e}{1 + e\cos\theta}$
6. $r = \dfrac{2e}{1 - e\cos\theta}$
7. $r = \dfrac{2e}{1 - e\sin\theta}$
8. $r = \dfrac{2e}{1 + e\sin\theta}$

In Exercises 9–14, match the polar equation with its graph. [The graphs are labeled (a), (b), (c), (d), (e), and (f).]

(a)

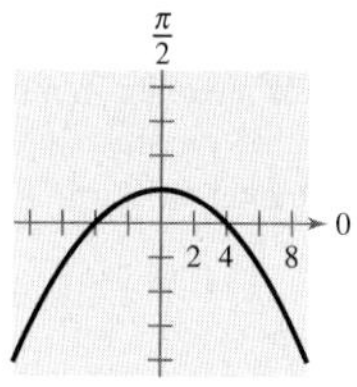

(b)

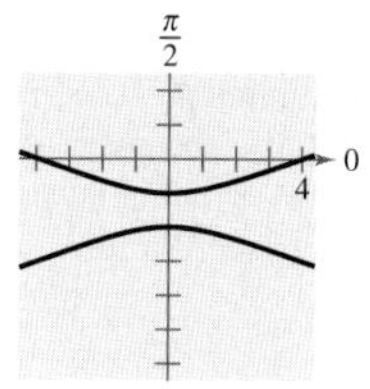

(c)

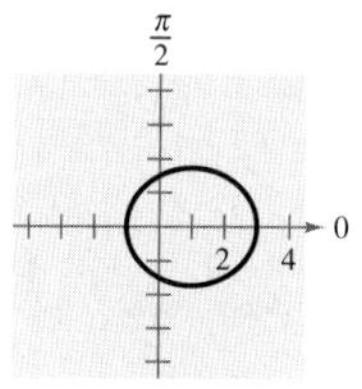

(d)

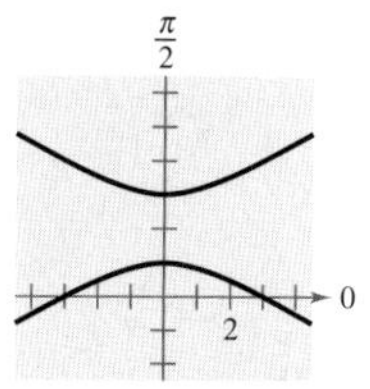

(e)

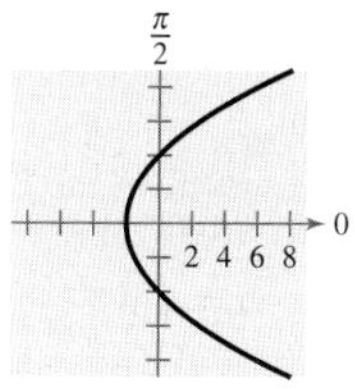

(f)

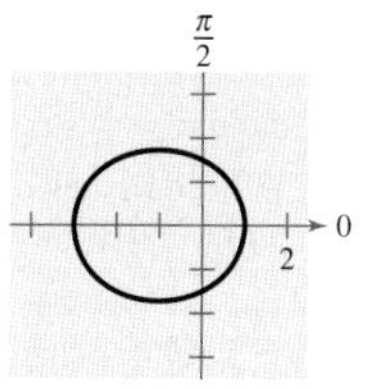

9. $r = \dfrac{4}{1 - \cos\theta}$ e
10. $r = \dfrac{3}{2 - \cos\theta}$ c
11. $r = \dfrac{3}{1 + 2\sin\theta}$ d
12. $r = \dfrac{3}{2 + \cos\theta}$ f
13. $r = \dfrac{4}{1 + \sin\theta}$ a
14. $r = \dfrac{4}{1 - 3\sin\theta}$ b

In Exercises 15–28, identify the conic and sketch its graph. 15–28. See margin.

15. $r = \dfrac{3}{1 - \cos\theta}$
16. $r = \dfrac{7}{1 + \sin\theta}$
17. $r = \dfrac{5}{1 + \sin\theta}$
18. $r = \dfrac{6}{1 + \cos\theta}$
19. $r = \dfrac{2}{2 - \cos\theta}$
20. $r = \dfrac{4}{4 + \sin\theta}$
21. $r = \dfrac{6}{2 + \sin\theta}$
22. $r = \dfrac{9}{3 - 2\cos\theta}$
23. $r = \dfrac{3}{2 + 4\sin\theta}$
24. $r = \dfrac{5}{-1 + 2\cos\theta}$
25. $r = \dfrac{3}{2 - 6\cos\theta}$
26. $r = \dfrac{3}{2 + 6\sin\theta}$
27. $r = \dfrac{4}{2 - \cos\theta}$
28. $r = \dfrac{2}{2 + 3\sin\theta}$

In Exercises 29–34, use a graphing utility to graph the polar equation. Identify the graph. 29–34. See margin.

29. $r = \dfrac{-1}{1 - \sin\theta}$
30. $r = \dfrac{-5}{2 + 4\sin\theta}$
31. $r = \dfrac{3}{-4 + 2\cos\theta}$
32. $r = \dfrac{4}{1 - 2\cos\theta}$
33. $r = \dfrac{14}{14 + 17\sin\theta}$
34. $r = \dfrac{12}{2 - \cos\theta}$

4 PRACTICE AND APPLY

Assignment Guide

Transparencies Available
Available at the Instructor's companion site.

Average:
Day 1: pp. 795–796
Exs. 1–5, 7, 9–14, 17–21 odd, 25–35 odd, 41–51 odd
Day 2: pp. 796–797
Exs. 55, 56, 57–65 odd, 67–70, 72, 73–81 odd

Advanced:
Day 1: pp. 795–796
Exs. 1–4, 6, 8–14, 18–26 even, 30–54 even
Day 2: pp. 796–797
Exs. 55, 56–64 even, 66–70, 72–82 even

Block:
pp. 795–796
Exs. 1–5, 7, 9–14, 17–21 odd, 25–35 odd, 41–51 odd (with 10.8)
pp. 796–797
Exs. 55, 56, 57–65 odd, 67–70, 72, 73–81 odd (with Review)

5. $e = 1$: $r = \dfrac{2}{1 + \cos\theta}$, parabola
$e = 0.5$: $r = \dfrac{1}{1 + 0.5\cos\theta}$, ellipse
$e = 1.5$: $r = \dfrac{3}{1 + 1.5\cos\theta}$, hyperbola

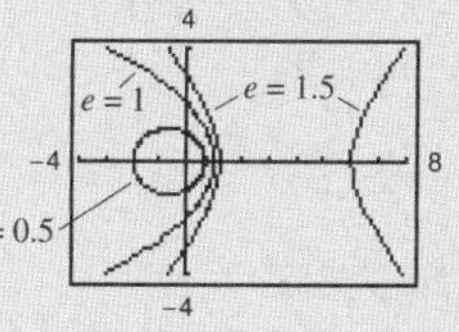

6. $e = 1$: $r = \dfrac{2}{1 - \cos\theta}$, parabola
$e = 0.5$: $r = \dfrac{1}{1 - 0.5\cos\theta}$, ellipse
$e = 1.5$: $r = \dfrac{3}{1 - 1.5\cos\theta}$, hyperbola

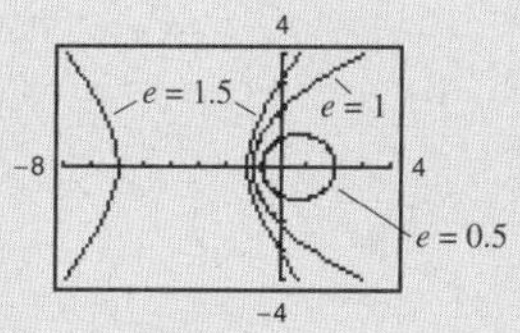

7. $e = 1$: $r = \dfrac{2}{1 - \sin\theta}$, parabola
$e = 0.5$: $r = \dfrac{1}{1 - 0.5\sin\theta}$, ellipse
$e = 1.5$: $r = \dfrac{3}{1 - 1.5\sin\theta}$, hyperbola

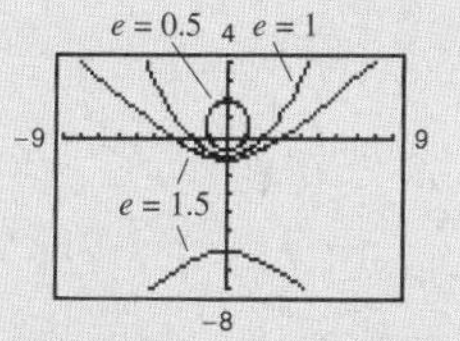

8. $e = 1$: $r = \dfrac{2}{1 + \sin\theta}$, parabola
$e = 0.5$: $r = \dfrac{1}{1 + 0.5\sin\theta}$, ellipse
$e = 1.5$: $r = \dfrac{3}{1 + 1.5\sin\theta}$, hyperbola

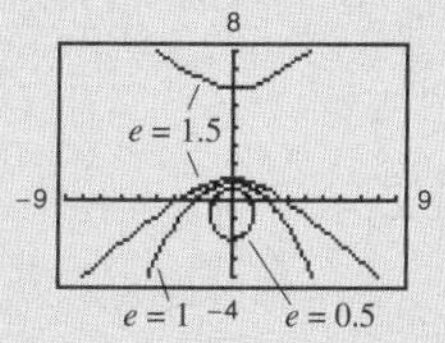

15–34. See Additional Answers beginning on page AA1.

In Exercises 35–38, use a graphing utility to graph the rotated conic. 35–38. See margin.

35. $r = \dfrac{3}{1 - \cos(\theta - \pi/4)}$ (See Exercise 15.)

36. $r = \dfrac{4}{4 + \sin(\theta - \pi/3)}$ (See Exercise 20.)

37. $r = \dfrac{6}{2 + \sin(\theta + \pi/6)}$ (See Exercise 21.)

38. $r = \dfrac{5}{-1 + 2\cos(\theta + 2\pi/3)}$ (See Exercise 24.)

In Exercises 39–54, find a polar equation of the conic with its focus at the pole. 39–54. See margin.

	Conic	*Eccentricity*	*Directrix*
39.	Parabola	$e = 1$	$x = -1$
40.	Parabola	$e = 1$	$y = -4$
41.	Ellipse	$e = \frac{1}{2}$	$y = 1$
42.	Ellipse	$e = \frac{3}{4}$	$y = -2$
43.	Hyperbola	$e = 2$	$x = 1$
44.	Hyperbola	$e = \frac{3}{2}$	$x = -1$

	Conic	*Vertex or Vertices*
45.	Parabola	$(1, -\pi/2)$
46.	Parabola	$(8, 0)$
47.	Parabola	$(5, \pi)$
48.	Parabola	$(10, \pi/2)$
49.	Ellipse	$(2, 0), (10, \pi)$
50.	Ellipse	$(2, \pi/2), (4, 3\pi/2)$
51.	Ellipse	$(20, 0), (4, \pi)$
52.	Hyperbola	$(2, 0), (8, 0)$
53.	Hyperbola	$(1, 3\pi/2), (9, 3\pi/2)$
54.	Hyperbola	$(4, \pi/2), (1, \pi/2)$

55. PLANETARY MOTION The planets travel in elliptical orbits with the sun at one focus. Assume that the focus is at the pole, the major axis lies on the polar axis, and the length of the major axis is $2a$ (see figure). Show that the polar equation of the orbit is $r = a(1 - e^2)/(1 - e\cos\theta)$, where e is the eccentricity. Answers will vary.

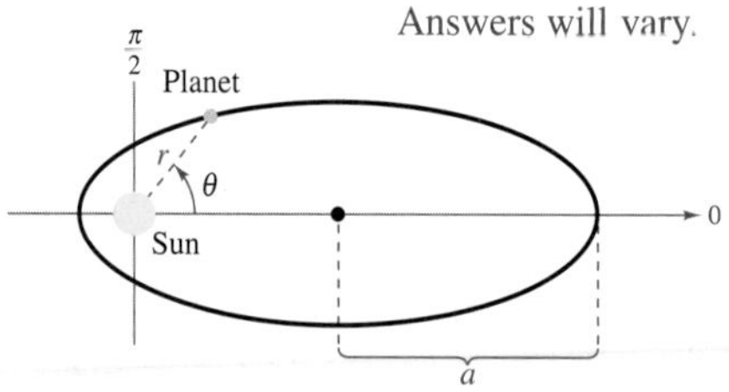

Answers will vary.

56. PLANETARY MOTION Use the result of Exercise 55 to show that the minimum distance (*perihelion distance*) from the sun to the planet is $r = a(1 - e)$ and the maximum distance (*aphelion distance*) is $r = a(1 + e)$.

57–62. See margin.

PLANETARY MOTION In Exercises 57–62, use the results of Exercises 55 and 56 to find the polar equation of the planet's orbit and the perihelion and aphelion distances.

57. Earth $a = 95.956 \times 10^6$ miles, $e = 0.0167$

58. Saturn $a = 1.427 \times 10^9$ kilometers, $e = 0.0542$

59. Venus $a = 108.209 \times 10^6$ kilometers, $e = 0.0068$

60. Mercury $a = 35.98 \times 10^6$ miles, $e = 0.2056$

61. Mars $a = 141.63 \times 10^6$ miles, $e = 0.0934$

62. Jupiter $a = 778.41 \times 10^6$ kilometers, $e = 0.0484$

63. ASTRONOMY The comet Encke has an elliptical orbit with an eccentricity of $e \approx 0.847$. The length of the major axis of the orbit is approximately 4.42 astronomical units. Find a polar equation for the orbit. How close does the comet come to the sun? See margin.

64. ASTRONOMY The comet Hale-Bopp has an elliptical orbit with an eccentricity of $e \approx 0.995$. The length of the major axis of the orbit is approximately 500 astronomical units. Find a polar equation for the orbit. How close does the comet come to the sun? See margin.

65. SATELLITE TRACKING A satellite in a 100-mile-high circular orbit around Earth has a velocity of approximately 17,500 miles per hour. If this velocity is multiplied by $\sqrt{2}$, the satellite will have the minimum velocity necessary to escape Earth's gravity and will follow a parabolic path with the center of Earth as the focus (see figure).

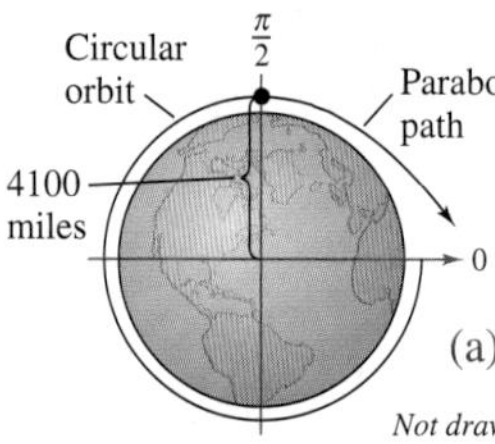

(a) $r = \dfrac{8200}{1 + \sin\theta}$

Not drawn to scale

(a) Find a polar equation of the parabolic path of the satellite (assume the radius of Earth is 4000 miles).

(b) Use a graphing utility to graph the equation you found in part (a). See margin.

(c) Find the distance between the surface of the Earth and the satellite when $\theta = 30°$. 1467 mi

(d) Find the distance between the surface of Earth and the satellite when $\theta = 60°$. 394 mi

35.

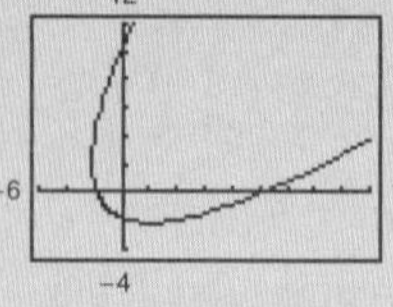

36.

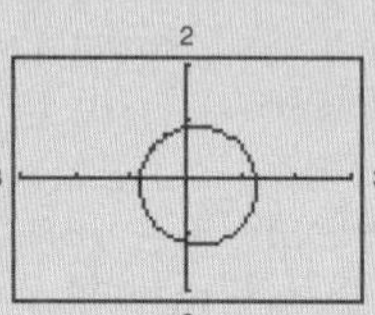

37.

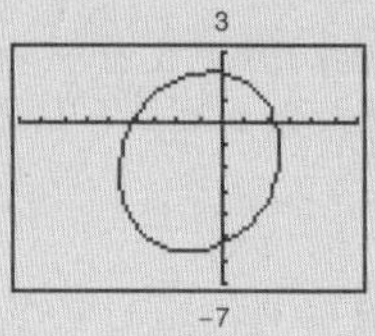

38.

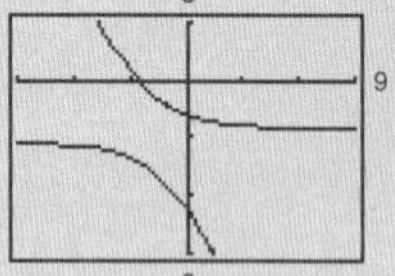

39. $r = \dfrac{1}{1 - \cos\theta}$

40. $r = \dfrac{4}{1 - \sin\theta}$

41. $r = \dfrac{1}{2 + \sin\theta}$

42. $r = \dfrac{6}{4 - 3\sin\theta}$

43. $r = \dfrac{2}{1 + 2\cos\theta}$

44. $r = \dfrac{3}{2 - 3\cos\theta}$

45. $r = \dfrac{2}{1 - \sin\theta}$

46. $r = \dfrac{16}{1 + \cos\theta}$

47. $r = \dfrac{10}{1 - \cos\theta}$

48. $r = \dfrac{20}{1 + \sin\theta}$

49. $r = \dfrac{10}{3 + 2\cos\theta}$

50. $r = \dfrac{8}{3 + \sin\theta}$

51. $r = \dfrac{20}{3 - 2\cos\theta}$

52. $r = \dfrac{16}{3 + 5\cos\theta}$

53. $r = \dfrac{9}{4 - 5\sin\theta}$

54. $r = \dfrac{8}{3 + 5\sin\theta}$

57. $r = \dfrac{9.5929 \times 10^7}{1 - 0.0167\cos\theta}$
Perihelion: 9.4354×10^7 mi
Aphelion: 9.7558×10^7 mi

58. $r = \dfrac{1.4228 \times 10^9}{1 - 0.0542\cos\theta}$
Perihelion: 1.3497×10^9 km
Aphelion: 1.5043×10^9 km

59. $r = \dfrac{1.0820 \times 10^8}{1 - 0.0068\cos\theta}$
Perihelion: 1.0747×10^8 km
Aphelion: 1.0894×10^8 km

60. $r = \dfrac{3.4459 \times 10^7}{1 - 0.2056\cos\theta}$
Perihelion: 2.8583×10^7 mi
Aphelion: 4.3377×10^7 mi

61. $r = \dfrac{1.4039 \times 10^8}{1 - 0.0934\cos\theta}$
Perihelion: 1.2840×10^8 mi
Aphelion: 1.5486×10^8 mi

62. $r = \dfrac{7.7659 \times 10^8}{1 - 0.0484\cos\theta}$
Perihelion: 7.4073×10^8 km
Aphelion: 8.1609×10^8 km

63. $r = \dfrac{0.624}{1 + 0.847\sin\theta}$;
$r \approx 0.338$ astronomical unit

64. $r = \dfrac{2.494}{1 + 0.995\sin\theta}$;
$r \approx 1.25$ astronomical units

65(b). See Additional Answers beginning on page AA1.

66. ROMAN COLISEUM The Roman Coliseum is an elliptical amphitheater measuring approximately 188 meters long and 156 meters wide. See margin.

(a) Find an equation to model the coliseum that is of the form

$$\frac{x^2}{a^2} + \frac{y^2}{b^2} = 1.$$

(b) Find a polar equation to model the coliseum. (Assume $e \approx 0.5581$ and $p \approx 115.98$.)

(c) Use a graphing utility to graph the equations you found in parts (a) and (b). Are the graphs the same? Why or why not?

(d) In part (c), did you prefer graphing the rectangular equation or the polar equation? Explain.

EXPLORATION

TRUE OR FALSE? In Exercises 67–70, determine whether the statement is true or false. Justify your answer.

67. For a given value of $e > 1$ over the interval $\theta = 0$ to $\theta = 2\pi$, the graph of

$$r = \frac{ex}{1 - e\cos\theta}$$

True. The graphs represent the same hyperbola.

is the same as the graph of

$$r = \frac{e(-x)}{1 + e\cos\theta}.$$

68. The graph of

$$r = \frac{4}{-3 - 3\sin\theta}$$

False. The graph has a horizontal directrix below the pole.

has a horizontal directrix above the pole.

69. The conic represented by the following equation is an ellipse.

$$r^2 = \frac{16}{9 - 4\cos\left(\theta + \frac{\pi}{4}\right)}$$

True. The conic is an ellipse because the eccentricity is less than 1.

70. The conic represented by the following equation is a parabola. See margin.

$$r = \frac{6}{3 - 2\cos\theta}$$

71. WRITING Explain how the graph of each conic differs from the graph of $r = \dfrac{5}{1 + \sin\theta}$. (See Exercise 17.) See margin.

(a) $r = \dfrac{5}{1 - \cos\theta}$ (b) $r = \dfrac{5}{1 - \sin\theta}$

(c) $r = \dfrac{5}{1 + \cos\theta}$ (d) $r = \dfrac{5}{1 - \sin[\theta - (\pi/4)]}$

72. CAPSTONE In your own words, define the term *eccentricity* and explain how it can be used to classify conics. Answers will vary.

73. Show that the polar equation of the ellipse

$$\frac{x^2}{a^2} + \frac{y^2}{b^2} = 1 \quad \text{is} \quad r^2 = \frac{b^2}{1 - e^2\cos^2\theta}.$$

Answers will vary.

74. Show that the polar equation of the hyperbola

$$\frac{x^2}{a^2} - \frac{y^2}{b^2} = 1 \quad \text{is} \quad r^2 = \frac{-b^2}{1 - e^2\cos^2\theta}.$$

Answers will vary.

In Exercises 75–80, use the results of Exercises 73 and 74 to write the polar form of the equation of the conic. 75–78. See margin.

75. $\dfrac{x^2}{169} + \dfrac{y^2}{144} = 1$ **76.** $\dfrac{x^2}{25} + \dfrac{y^2}{16} = 1$

77. $\dfrac{x^2}{9} - \dfrac{y^2}{16} = 1$ **78.** $\dfrac{x^2}{36} - \dfrac{y^2}{4} = 1$

79. Hyperbola One focus: $\left(5, \frac{\pi}{2}\right)$ $r^2 = \dfrac{144}{25\cos^2\theta - 16}$

Vertices: $\left(4, \frac{\pi}{2}\right), \left(4, -\frac{\pi}{2}\right)$

80. Ellipse One focus: $(4, 0)$ $r^2 = \dfrac{225}{25 - 16\cos^2\theta}$

Vertices: $(5, 0), (5, \pi)$

81. Consider the polar equation

$$r = \frac{4}{1 - 0.4\cos\theta}.$$

See margin.

(a) Identify the conic without graphing the equation.

(b) Without graphing the following polar equations, describe how each differs from the given polar equation.

$$r_1 = \frac{4}{1 + 0.4\cos\theta} \qquad r_2 = \frac{4}{1 - 0.4\sin\theta}$$

(c) Use a graphing utility to verify your results in part (b).

82. The equation

$$r = \frac{ep}{1 \pm e\sin\theta}$$

See margin.

is the equation of an ellipse with $e < 1$. What happens to the lengths of both the major axis and the minor axis when the value of e remains fixed and the value of p changes? Use an example to explain your reasoning.

81. (c)

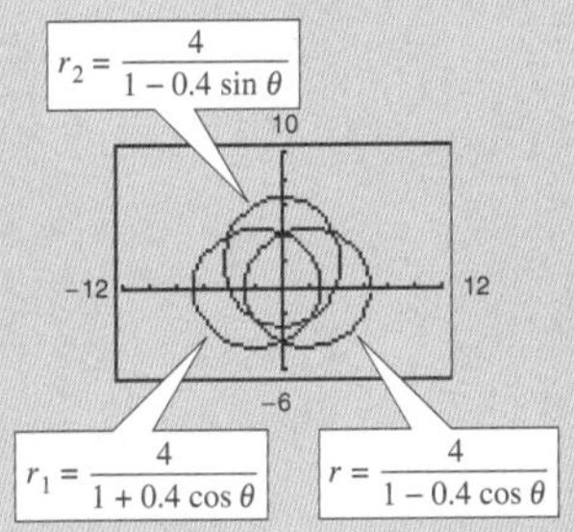

82. If e remains fixed and p changes, then the lengths of both the major axis and the minor axis change. For example, graph

$$r = \frac{5}{1 - \frac{2}{3}\sin\theta},$$

with $e = \frac{2}{3}$ and $p = \frac{15}{2}$, and graph

$$r = \frac{6}{1 - \frac{2}{3}\sin\theta},$$

with $e = \frac{2}{3}$ and $p = 9$, on the same set of coordinate axes.

5 ASSESS AND RETEACH

Daily Homework Quiz

Transparency Available
Available at the Instructor's companion site.

66. (a) $\dfrac{x^2}{8836} + \dfrac{y^2}{6084} = 1$

(b) $r = \dfrac{64.7284}{1 - 0.5581(\cos\theta)}$

(c)

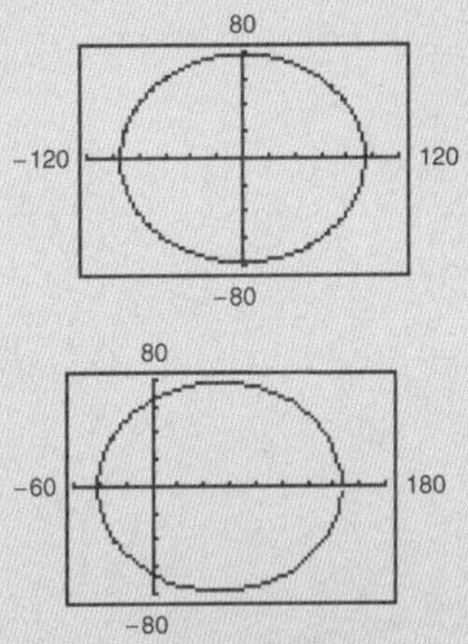

No, because the graphs have different centers.

(d) Answers will vary.

70. False. Every term in the fraction needs to be divided by 3. This yields

$$r = \frac{2}{1 - \frac{2}{3}\cos\theta}.$$

The eccentricity is $\frac{2}{3}$, so the graph is an ellipse.

71. The original equation graphs as a parabola that opens downward.

(a) The parabola opens to the right.

(b) The parabola opens up.

(c) The parabola opens to the left.

(d) The parabola has been rotated.

75. $r^2 = \dfrac{24{,}336}{169 - 25\cos^2\theta}$

76. $r^2 = \dfrac{400}{25 - 9\cos^2\theta}$

77. $r^2 = \dfrac{144}{25\cos^2\theta - 9}$

78. $r^2 = \dfrac{36}{10\cos^2\theta - 9}$

81. (a) Ellipse

(b) The given polar equation, r, has a vertical directrix to the left of the pole. The equation r_1 has a vertical directrix to the right of the pole, and the equation r_2 has a horizontal directrix below the pole.

10 Chapter Summary

	What Did You Learn?	Explanation/Examples	Review Exercises
Section 10.1	Find the inclination of a line *(p. 726).*	If a nonvertical line has inclination θ and slope m, then $m = \tan\theta$.	1–4
	Find the angle between two lines *(p. 727).*	If two nonperpendicular lines have slopes m_1 and m_2, the angle between the lines is $\tan\theta = \lvert(m_2 - m_1)/(1 + m_1m_2)\rvert$.	5–8
	Find the distance between a point and a line *(p. 728).*	The distance between the point (x_1, y_1) and the line $Ax + By + C = 0$ is $d = \lvert Ax_1 + By_1 + C\rvert/\sqrt{A^2 + B^2}$.	9, 10
Section 10.2	Recognize a conic as the intersection of a plane and a double-napped cone *(p. 733).*	In the formation of the four basic conics, the intersecting plane does not pass through the vertex of the cone. (See Figure 10.9.)	11, 12
	Write equations of parabolas in standard form and graph parabolas *(p. 734).*	The standard form of the equation of a parabola with vertex at (h, k) is $(x - h)^2 = 4p(y - k)$, $p \neq 0$ (vertical axis), or $(y - k)^2 = 4p(x - h)$, $p \neq 0$ (horizontal axis).	13–16
	Use the reflective property of parabolas to solve real-life problems *(p. 736).*	The tangent line to a parabola at a point P makes equal angles with (1) the line passing through P and the focus and (2) the axis of the parabola.	17–20
Section 10.3	Write equations of ellipses in standard form and graph ellipses *(p. 742).*	**Horizontal Major Axis** $\frac{(x-h)^2}{a^2} + \frac{(y-k)^2}{b^2} = 1$ **Vertical Major Axis** $\frac{(x-h)^2}{b^2} + \frac{(y-k)^2}{a^2} = 1$	21–24
	Use properties of ellipses to model and solve real-life problems *(p. 746).*	The properties of ellipses can be used to find distances from Earth's center to the moon's center in its orbit. (See Example 4.)	25, 26
	Find eccentricities *(p. 746).*	The eccentricity e of an ellipse is given by $e = c/a$.	27–30
Section 10.4	Write equations of hyperbolas in standard form *(p. 751)* and find asymptotes of and graph hyperbolas *(p. 753).*	**Horizontal Transverse Axis** $\frac{(x-h)^2}{a^2} - \frac{(y-k)^2}{b^2} = 1$ **Asymptotes** $y = k \pm (b/a)(x - h)$ **Vertical Transverse Axis** $\frac{(y-k)^2}{a^2} - \frac{(x-h)^2}{b^2} = 1$ **Asymptotes** $y = k \pm (a/b)(x - h)$	31–38
	Use properties of hyperbolas to solve real-life problems *(p. 756).*	The properties of hyperbolas can be used in radar and other detection systems. (See Example 5.)	39, 40
	Classify conics from their general equations *(p. 757).*	The graph of $Ax^2 + Cy^2 + Dx + Ey + F = 0$ is a circle if $A = C$, a parabola if $AC = 0$, an ellipse if $AC > 0$, and a hyperbola if $AC < 0$.	41–44
Section 10.5	Rotate the coordinate axes to eliminate the xy-term in equations of conics *(p. 761).*	The equation $Ax^2 + Bxy + Cy^2 + Dx + Ey + F = 0$ can be rewritten as $A'(x')^2 + C'(y')^2 + D'x' + E'y' + F' = 0$ by rotating the coordinate axes through an angle θ, where $\cot 2\theta = (A - C)/B$.	45–48
	Use the discriminant to classify conics *(p. 765).*	The graph of $Ax^2 + Bxy + Cy^2 + Dx + Ey + F = 0$ is, except in degenerate cases, an ellipse or a circle if $B^2 - 4AC < 0$, a parabola if $B^2 - 4AC = 0$, and a hyperbola if $B^2 - 4AC > 0$.	49–52

	What Did You Learn?	Explanation/Examples	Review Exercises
Section 10.6	Evaluate sets of parametric equations for given values of the parameter *(p. 769)*.	If f and g are continuous functions of t on an interval I, the set of ordered pairs $(f(t), g(t))$ is a plane curve C. The equations $x = f(t)$ and $y = g(t)$ are parametric equations for C, and t is the parameter.	53, 54
	Sketch curves that are represented by sets of parametric equations *(p. 770)*.	Sketching a curve represented by parametric equations requires plotting points in the xy-plane. Each set of coordinates (x, y) is determined from a value chosen for t.	55–60
	Rewrite sets of parametric equations as single rectangular equations by eliminating the parameter *(p. 771)*.	To eliminate the parameter in a pair of parametric equations, solve for t in one equation and substitute that value of t into the other equation. The result is the corresponding rectangular equation.	55–60
	Find sets of parametric equations for graphs *(p. 772)*.	When finding a set of parametric equations for a given graph, remember that the parametric equations are not unique.	61–64
Section 10.7	Plot points on the polar coordinate system *(p. 777)*.	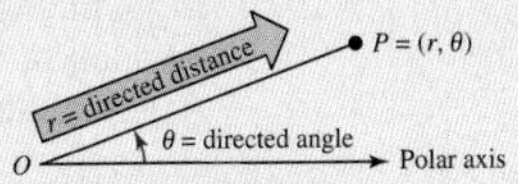	65–68
	Convert points *(p. 778)* and equations *(p. 780)* from rectangular to polar form and vice versa.	**Polar Coordinates (r, θ) and Rectangular Coordinates (x, y)** Polar-to-Rectangular: $x = r\cos\theta$, $y = r\sin\theta$ Rectangular-to-Polar: $\tan\theta = y/x$, $r^2 = x^2 + y^2$ To convert a rectangular equation to polar form, replace x by $r\cos\theta$ and y by $r\sin\theta$. Converting from a polar equation to rectangular form is more complex.	69–88
Section 10.8	Use point plotting *(p. 783)* and symmetry *(p. 784)* to sketch graphs of polar equations.	Graphing a polar equation by point plotting is similar to graphing a rectangular equation. A polar graph is symmetric with respect to the following if the given substitution yields an equivalent equation. **1.** Line $\theta = \pi/2$: Replace (r, θ) by $(r, \pi - \theta)$ or $(-r, -\theta)$. **2.** Polar axis: Replace (r, θ) by $(r, -\theta)$ or $(-r, \pi - \theta)$. **3.** Pole: Replace (r, θ) by $(r, \pi + \theta)$ or $(-r, \theta)$.	89–98
	Use zeros and maximum r-values to sketch graphs of polar equations *(p. 785)*.	Two additional aids to graphing polar equations involve knowing the θ-values for which $\lvert r\rvert$ is maximum and knowing the θ-values for which $r = 0$.	89–98
	Recognize special polar graphs *(p. 787)*.	Several types of graphs, such as limaçons, rose curves, circles, and lemniscates, have equations that are simpler in polar form than in rectangular form. (See page 787.)	99–102
Section 10.9	Define conics in terms of eccentricity *(p. 791)*.	The eccentricity of a conic is denoted by e. **ellipse:** $e < 1$ **parabola:** $e = 1$ **hyperbola:** $e > 1$	103–110
	Write and graph equations of conics in polar form *(p. 791)*.	The graph of a polar equation of the form (1) $r = (ep)/(1 \pm e\cos\theta)$ or (2) $r = (ep)/(1 \pm e\sin\theta)$ is a conic, where $e > 0$ is the eccentricity and $\lvert p\rvert$ is the distance between the focus (pole) and the directrix.	103–110
	Use equations of conics in polar form to model real-life problems *(p. 794)*.	Equations of conics in polar form can be used to model the orbit of Halley's comet. (See Example 4.)	111, 112

10 REVIEW EXERCISES

See www.CalcChat.com for worked-out solutions to odd-numbered exercises.

10.1 **In Exercises 1–4, find the inclination θ (in radians and degrees) of the line with the given characteristics.**

1. Passes through the points $(-1, 2)$ and $(2, 5)$ $\frac{\pi}{4}$ rad, 45°
2. Passes through the points $(3, 4)$ and $(-2, 7)$ 2.6012 rad, 149.04°
3. Equation: $y = 2x + 4$ 1.1071 rad, 63.43°
4. Equation: $x - 5y = 7$ 0.1974 rad, 11.31°

In Exercises 5–8, find the angle θ (in radians and degrees) between the lines.

5. $4x + y = 2$, $-5x + y = -1$ 0.4424 rad, 25.35°
6. $-5x + 3y = 3$, $-2x + 3y = 1$ 0.4424 rad, 25.35°
7. $2x - 7y = 8$, $0.4x + y = 0$ 0.6588 rad, 37.75°
8. $0.02x + 0.07y = 0.18$, $0.09x - 0.04y = 0.17$ 1.4309 rad, 81.98°

In Exercises 9 and 10, find the distance between the point and the line.

	Point	*Line*
9.	$(5, 3)$ $4\sqrt{2}$	$x - y - 10 = 0$
10.	$(0, 4)$ $\frac{6\sqrt{5}}{5}$	$x + 2y - 2 = 0$

10.2 **In Exercises 11 and 12, state what type of conic is formed by the intersection of the plane and the double-napped cone.**

11. Hyperbola

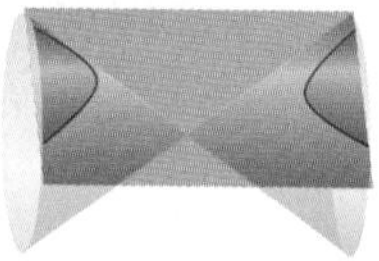

12. Parabola

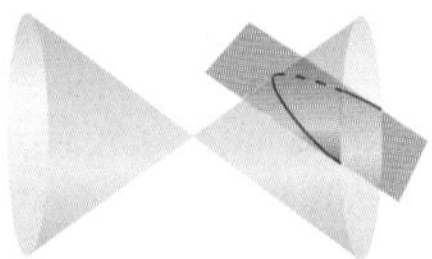

In Exercises 13–16, find the standard form of the equation of the parabola with the given characteristics. Then graph the parabola. 13–16. See margin.

13. Vertex: $(0, 0)$; Focus: $(4, 0)$
14. Vertex: $(2, 0)$; Focus: $(0, 0)$
15. Vertex: $(0, 2)$; Directrix: $x = -3$
16. Vertex: $(-3, -3)$; Directrix: $y = 0$

In Exercises 17 and 18, find an equation of the tangent line to the parabola at the given point, and find the x-intercept of the line.

17. $y = 2x^2$, $(-1, 2)$ $y = -4x - 2$; $\left(-\frac{1}{2}, 0\right)$
18. $x^2 = -2y$, $(-4, -8)$ $y = 4x + 8$; $(-2, 0)$
19. **ARCHITECTURE** A parabolic archway is 12 meters high at the vertex. At a height of 10 meters, the width of the archway is 8 meters (see figure). How wide is the archway at ground level? $8\sqrt{6}$ m

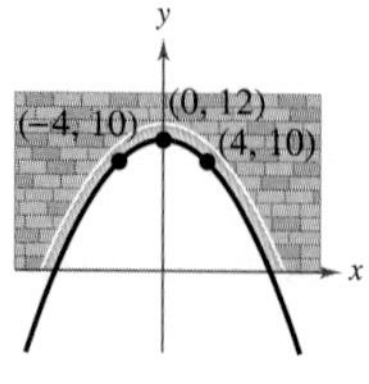

FIGURE FOR 19

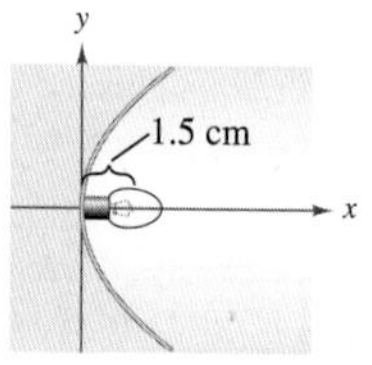

FIGURE FOR 20

20. **FLASHLIGHT** The light bulb in a flashlight is at the focus of its parabolic reflector, 1.5 centimeters from the vertex of the reflector (see figure). Write an equation of a cross section of the flashlight's reflector with its focus on the positive x-axis and its vertex at the origin. $y^2 = 6x$

10.3 **In Exercises 21–24, find the standard form of the equation of the ellipse with the given characteristics. Then graph the ellipse.** 21–24. See margin.

21. Vertices: $(-2, 0), (8, 0)$; foci: $(0, 0), (6, 0)$
22. Vertices: $(4, 3), (4, 7)$; foci: $(4, 4), (4, 6)$
23. Vertices: $(0, 1), (4, 1)$; endpoints of the minor axis: $(2, 0), (2, 2)$
24. Vertices: $(-4, -1), (-4, 11)$; endpoints of the minor axis: $(-6, 5), (-2, 5)$
25. **ARCHITECTURE** A semielliptical archway is to be formed over the entrance to an estate. The arch is to be set on pillars that are 10 feet apart and is to have a height (atop the pillars) of 4 feet. Where should the foci be placed in order to sketch the arch? See below.
26. **WADING POOL** You are building a wading pool that is in the shape of an ellipse. Your plans give an equation for the elliptical shape of the pool measured in feet as
$$\frac{x^2}{324} + \frac{y^2}{196} = 1.$$
Find the longest distance across the pool, the shortest distance, and the distance between the foci.
Longest distance: 36 ft
Shortest distance: 28 ft
Distance between foci: $16\sqrt{2}$ ft

In Exercises 27–30, find the center, vertices, foci, and eccentricity of the ellipse. 27–30. See margin.

27. $\dfrac{(x + 1)^2}{25} + \dfrac{(y - 2)^2}{49} = 1$
28. $\dfrac{(x - 5)^2}{1} + \dfrac{(y + 3)^2}{36} = 1$
29. $16x^2 + 9y^2 - 32x + 72y + 16 = 0$
30. $4x^2 + 25y^2 + 16x - 150y + 141 = 0$

25. The foci occur 3 feet from the center of the arch on a line connecting the tops of the pillars.

13. $y^2 = 16x$

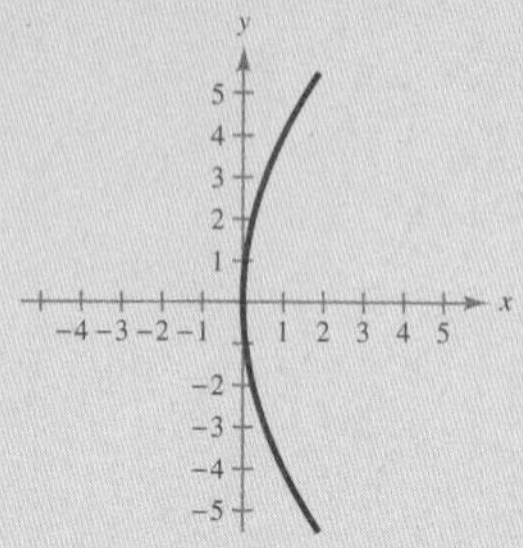

14. $y^2 = -8(x - 2)$

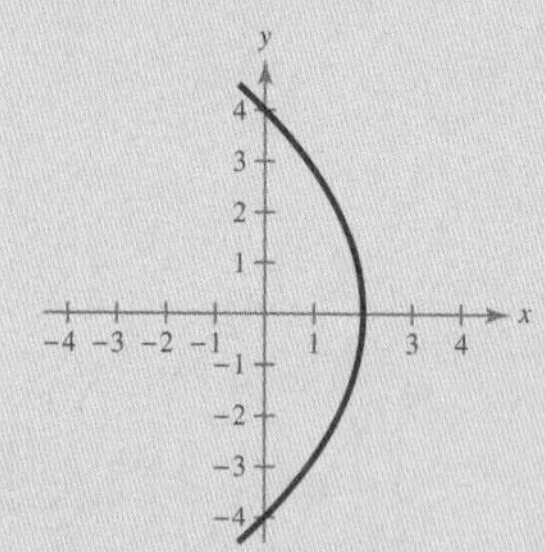

15. $(y - 2)^2 = 12x$

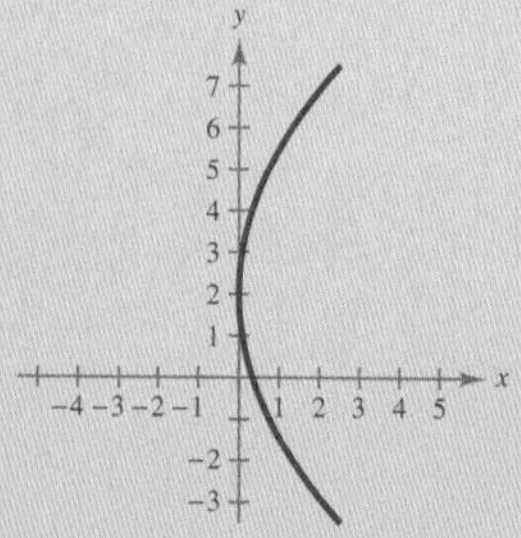

16. $(x + 3)^2 = -12(y + 3)$

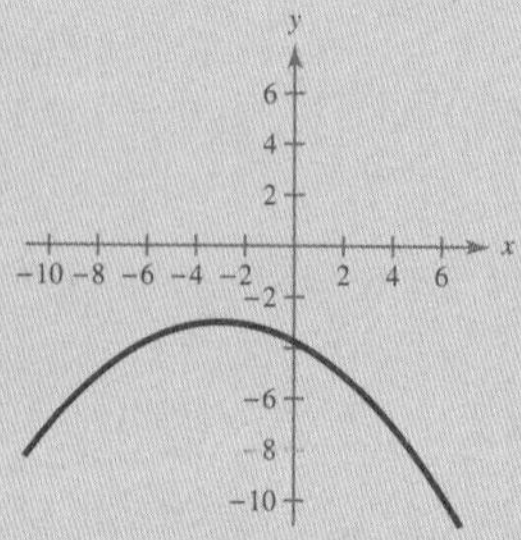

21. $\dfrac{(x - 3)^2}{25} + \dfrac{y^2}{16} = 1$

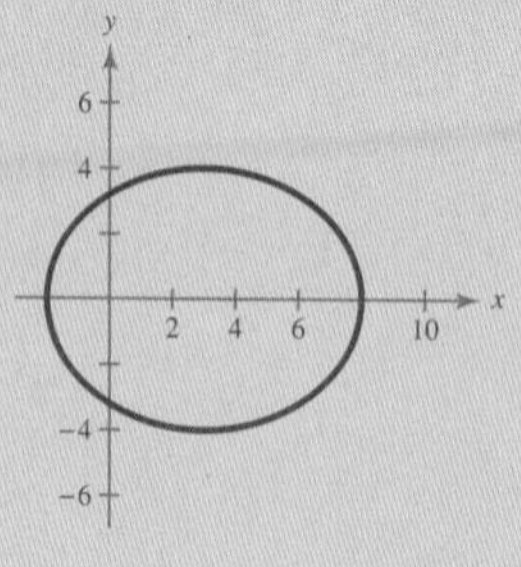

22. $\dfrac{(x - 4)^2}{3} + \dfrac{(y - 5)^2}{4} = 1$

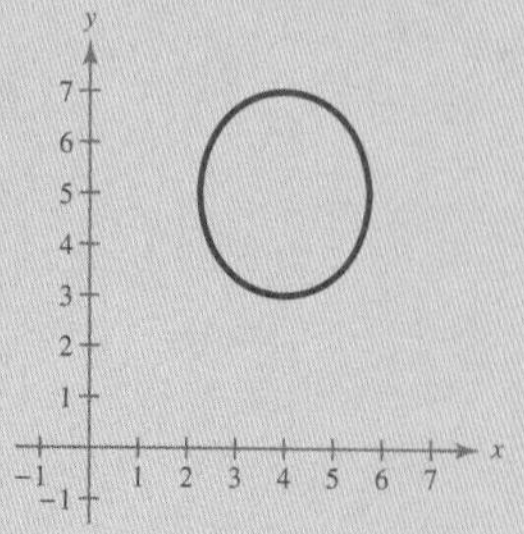

23. $\dfrac{(x - 2)^2}{4} + \dfrac{(y - 1)^2}{1} = 1$

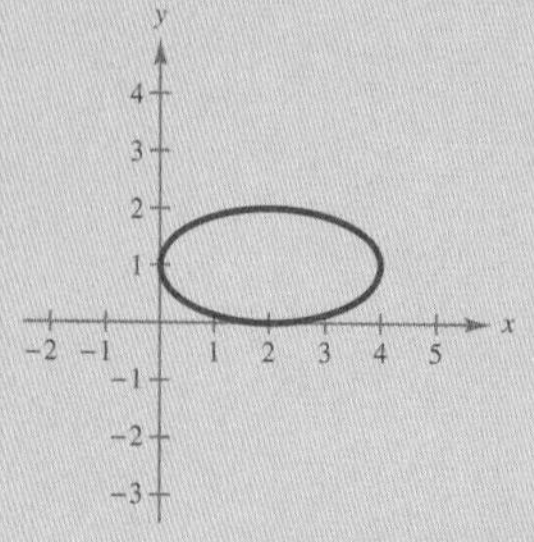

24. $\dfrac{(x + 4)^2}{4} + \dfrac{(y - 5)^2}{36} = 1$

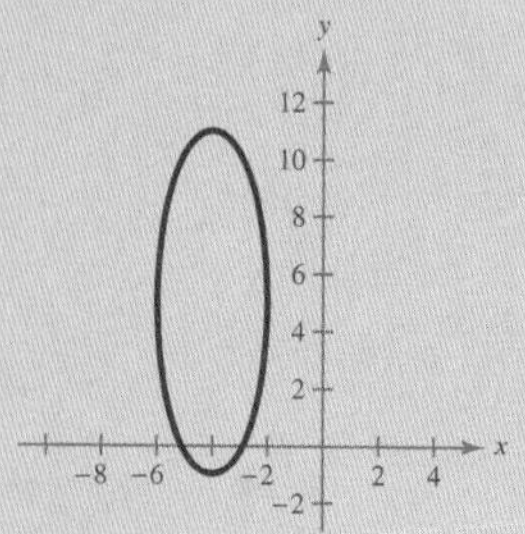

27–30. See Additional Answers beginning on page AA1.

10.4 In Exercises 31–34, find the standard form of the equation of the hyperbola with the given characteristics.

31. Vertices: $(0, \pm 1)$; foci: $(0, \pm 2)$ $\frac{y^2}{1} - \frac{x^2}{3} = 1$

32. Vertices: $(3, 3), (-3, 3)$; foci: $(4, 3), (-4, 3)$

33. Foci: $(0, 0), (8, 0)$; asymptotes: $y = \pm 2(x - 4)$

34. Foci: $(3, \pm 2)$; asymptotes: $y = \pm 2(x - 3)$ 32–34. See margin.

In Exercises 35–38, find the center, vertices, foci, and the equations of the asymptotes of the hyperbola, and sketch its graph using the asymptotes as an aid. 35–38. See margin.

35. $\frac{(x-5)^2}{36} - \frac{(y+3)^2}{16} = 1$

36. $\frac{(y-1)^2}{4} - x^2 = 1$

37. $9x^2 - 16y^2 - 18x - 32y - 151 = 0$

38. $-4x^2 + 25y^2 - 8x + 150y + 121 = 0$

39. LORAN Radio transmitting station A is located 200 miles east of transmitting station B. A ship is in an area to the north and 40 miles west of station A. Synchronized radio pulses transmitted at 186,000 miles per second by the two stations are received 0.0005 second sooner from station A than from station B. How far north is the ship? 72 mi

40. LOCATING AN EXPLOSION Two of your friends live 4 miles apart and on the same "east-west" street, and you live halfway between them. You are having a three-way phone conversation when you hear an explosion. Six seconds later, your friend to the east hears the explosion, and your friend to the west hears it 8 seconds after you do. Find equations of two hyperbolas that would locate the explosion. (Assume that the coordinate system is measured in feet and that sound travels at 1100 feet per second.) See margin.

In Exercises 41–44, classify the graph of the equation as a circle, a parabola, an ellipse, or a hyperbola.

41. $5x^2 - 2y^2 + 10x - 4y + 17 = 0$ Hyperbola

42. $-4y^2 + 5x + 3y + 7 = 0$ Parabola

43. $3x^2 + 2y^2 - 12x + 12y + 29 = 0$ Ellipse

44. $4x^2 + 4y^2 - 4x + 8y - 11 = 0$ Circle

10.5 In Exercises 45–48, rotate the axes to eliminate the xy-term in the equation. Then write the equation in standard form. Sketch the graph of the resulting equation, showing both sets of axes. 45–48. See margin.

45. $xy + 3 = 0$

46. $x^2 - 4xy + y^2 + 9 = 0$

47. $5x^2 - 2xy + 5y^2 - 12 = 0$

48. $4x^2 + 8xy + 4y^2 + 7\sqrt{2}x + 9\sqrt{2}y = 0$

In Exercises 49–52, (a) use the discriminant to classify the graph, (b) use the Quadratic Formula to solve for y, and (c) use a graphing utility to graph the equation. 49–52. See margin.

49. $16x^2 - 24xy + 9y^2 - 30x - 40y = 0$

50. $13x^2 - 8xy + 7y^2 - 45 = 0$

51. $x^2 + y^2 + 2xy + 2\sqrt{2}x - 2\sqrt{2}y + 2 = 0$

52. $x^2 - 10xy + y^2 + 1 = 0$

10.6 In Exercises 53 and 54, (a) create a table of x- and y-values for the parametric equations using $t = -2, -1, 0, 1$, and 2, and (b) plot the points (x, y) generated in part (a) and sketch a graph of the parametric equations. 53–54. See margin.

53. $x = 3t - 2$ and $y = 7 - 4t$

54. $x = \frac{1}{4}t$ and $y = \frac{6}{t+3}$

In Exercises 55–60, (a) sketch the curve represented by the parametric equations (indicate the orientation of the curve) and (b) eliminate the parameter and write the corresponding rectangular equation whose graph represents the curve. Adjust the domain of the resulting rectangular equation, if necessary. (c) Verify your result with a graphing utility. 55–60. See margin.

55. $x = 2t$, $y = 4t$

56. $x = 1 + 4t$, $y = 2 - 3t$

57. $x = t^2$, $y = \sqrt{t}$

58. $x = t + 4$, $y = t^2$

59. $x = 3\cos\theta$, $y = 3\sin\theta$

60. $x = 3 + 3\cos\theta$, $y = 2 + 5\sin\theta$

61. Find a parametric representation of the line that passes through the points $(-4, 4)$ and $(9, -10)$. See margin.

62. Find a parametric representation of the circle with center $(5, 4)$ and radius 6. See margin.

63. Find a parametric representation of the ellipse with center $(-3, 4)$, major axis horizontal and eight units in length, and minor axis six units in length. See margin.

64. Find a parametric representation of the hyperbola with vertices $(0, \pm 4)$ and foci $(0, \pm 5)$. $x = 3\tan\theta$, $y = 4\sec\theta$

10.7 In Exercises 65–68, plot the point given in polar coordinates and find two additional polar representations of the point, using $-2\pi < \theta < 2\pi$. 65–68. See margin.

65. $\left(2, \frac{\pi}{4}\right)$

66. $\left(-5, -\frac{\pi}{3}\right)$

67. $(-7, 4.19)$

68. $(\sqrt{3}, 2.62)$

32. $\frac{x^2}{9} - \frac{(y-3)^2}{7} = 1$

33. $\frac{5(x-4)^2}{16} - \frac{5y^2}{64} = 1$

34. $\frac{5y^2}{16} - \frac{5(x-3)^2}{4} = 1$

35. Center: $(5, -3)$
Vertices: $(11, -3), (-1, -3)$
Foci: $(5 \pm 2\sqrt{13}, -3)$
Asymptotes: $y = -3 \pm \frac{2}{3}(x - 5)$

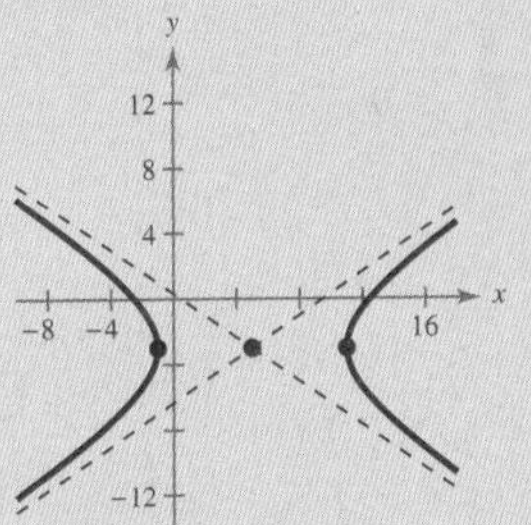

36. Center: $(0, 1)$
Vertices: $(0, 3), (0, -1)$
Foci: $(0, 1 \pm \sqrt{5})$
Asymptotes: $y = 1 \pm 2x$

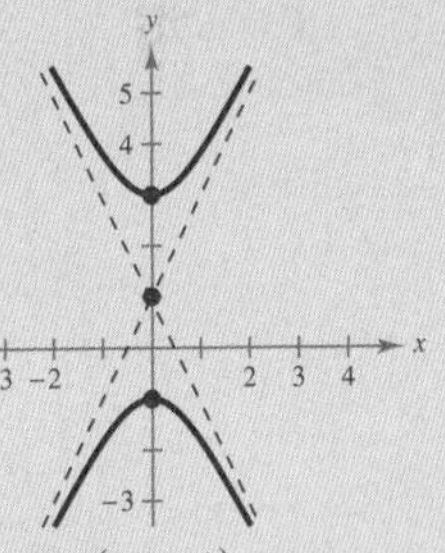

37. Center: $(1, -1)$
Vertices: $(5, -1), (-3, -1)$
Foci: $(6, -1), (-4, -1)$
Asymptotes: $y = -1 \pm \frac{3}{4}(x - 1)$

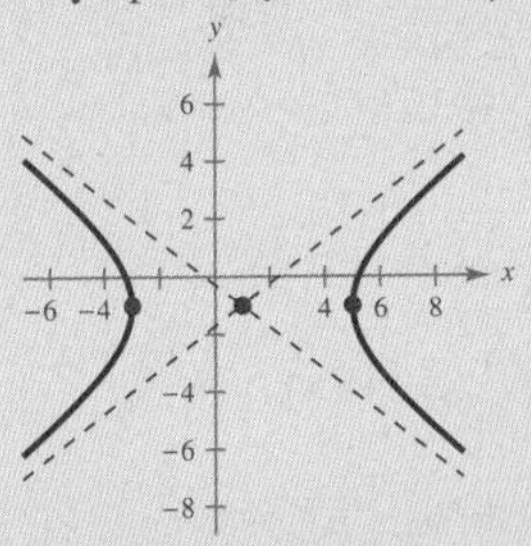

38. Center: $(-1, -3)$
Vertices: $(-1, -1), (-1, -5)$
Foci: $(-1, -3 \pm \sqrt{29})$
Asymptotes: $y = -3 \pm \frac{2}{5}(x + 1)$

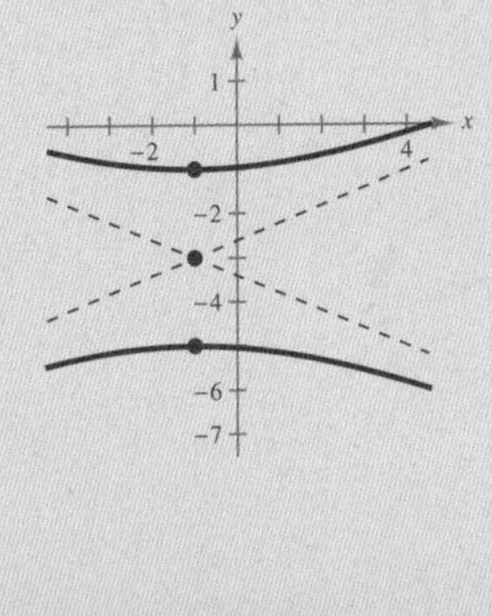

40. $\frac{576x^2}{25} - \frac{576y^2}{2279} = 1$
$\frac{64(x-1)^2}{25} - \frac{64y^2}{39} = 1$

45. $\frac{(y')^2}{6} - \frac{(x')^2}{6} = 1$

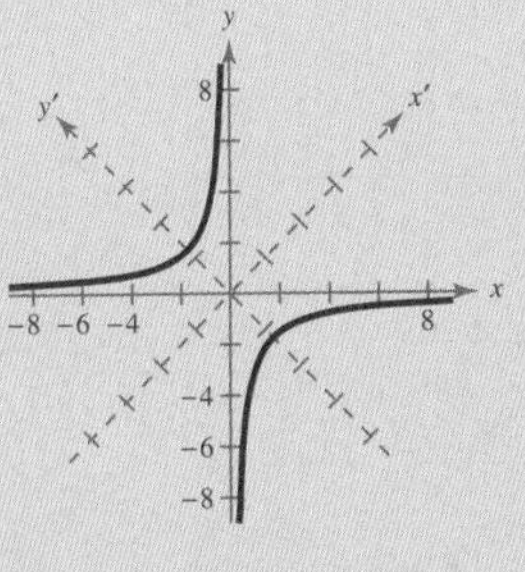

46. $\frac{(x')^2}{9} - \frac{(y')^2}{3} = 1$

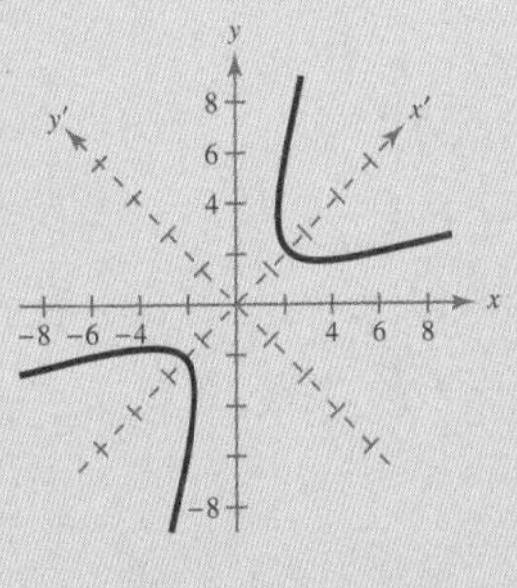

47–63, 65–68. See Additional Answers beginning on page AA1.

In Exercises 69–72, a point in polar coordinates is given. Convert the point to rectangular coordinates.

69. $\left(-1, \frac{\pi}{3}\right)$ $\left(-\frac{1}{2}, -\frac{\sqrt{3}}{2}\right)$ **70.** $\left(2, \frac{5\pi}{4}\right)$ $\left(-\sqrt{2}, -\sqrt{2}\right)$

71. $\left(3, \frac{3\pi}{4}\right)$ $\left(-\frac{3\sqrt{2}}{2}, \frac{3\sqrt{2}}{2}\right)$ **72.** $\left(0, \frac{\pi}{2}\right)$ $(0, 0)$

In Exercises 73–76, a point in rectangular coordinates is given. Convert the point to polar coordinates.

73. $(0, 1)$ $\left(1, \frac{\pi}{2}\right)$ **74.** $(-\sqrt{5}, \sqrt{5})$ $\left(\sqrt{10}, \frac{3\pi}{4}\right)$

75. $(4, 6)$ $(2\sqrt{13}, 0.9828)$ **76.** $(3, -4)$ $(5, 5.3559)$

In Exercises 77–82, convert the rectangular equation to polar form. 79. $r = 6 \sin \theta$

77. $x^2 + y^2 = 81$ $r = 9$ **78.** $x^2 + y^2 = 48$ $r = 4\sqrt{3}$

79. $x^2 + y^2 - 6y = 0$ **80.** $x^2 + y^2 - 4x = 0$ $r = 4 \cos \theta$

81. $xy = 5$ $r^2 = 10 \csc 2\theta$ **82.** $xy = -2$ $r^2 = -4 \csc 2\theta$

In Exercises 83–88, convert the polar equation to rectangular form. 85. $x^2 + y^2 = 3x$

83. $r = 5$ $x^2 + y^2 = 25$ **84.** $r = 12$ $x^2 + y^2 = 144$

85. $r = 3 \cos \theta$ **86.** $r = 8 \sin \theta$ $x^2 + y^2 = 8y$

87. $r^2 = \sin \theta$ $x^2 + y^2 = y^{2/3}$ **88.** $r^2 = 4 \cos 2\theta$ $(x^2 + y^2)^2 = 4(x^2 - y^2)$

10.8 In Exercises 89–98, determine the symmetry of r, the maximum value of $|r|$, and any zeros of r. Then sketch the graph of the polar equation (plot additional points if necessary). 89–98. See margin.

89. $r = 6$ **90.** $r = 11$

91. $r = 4 \sin 2\theta$ **92.** $r = \cos 5\theta$

93. $r = -2(1 + \cos \theta)$ **94.** $r = 1 - 4 \cos \theta$

95. $r = 2 + 6 \sin \theta$ **96.** $r = 5 - 5 \cos \theta$

97. $r = -3 \cos 2\theta$ **98.** $r^2 = \cos 2\theta$

In Exercises 99–102, identify the type of polar graph and use a graphing utility to graph the equation. 99–102. See margin.

99. $r = 3(2 - \cos \theta)$ **100.** $r = 5(1 - 2 \cos \theta)$

101. $r = 8 \cos 3\theta$ **102.** $r^2 = 2 \sin 2\theta$

10.9 In Exercises 103–106, identify the conic and sketch its graph. 103–106. See margin.

103. $r = \dfrac{1}{1 + 2 \sin \theta}$ **104.** $r = \dfrac{6}{1 + \sin \theta}$

105. $r = \dfrac{4}{5 - 3 \cos \theta}$ **106.** $r = \dfrac{16}{4 + 5 \cos \theta}$

In Exercises 107–110, find a polar equation of the conic with its focus at the pole. 108–110. See margin.

107. Parabola Vertex: $(2, \pi)$ 107. $r = \dfrac{4}{1 - \cos \theta}$

108. Parabola Vertex: $(2, \pi/2)$

109. Ellipse Vertices: $(5, 0), (1, \pi)$

110. Hyperbola Vertices: $(1, 0), (7, 0)$

111. EXPLORER 18 On November 27, 1963, the United States launched Explorer 18. Its low and high points above the surface of Earth were 119 miles and 122,800 miles, respectively. The center of Earth was at one focus of the orbit (see figure). Find the polar equation of the orbit and find the distance between the surface of Earth (assume Earth has a radius of 4000 miles) and the satellite when $\theta = \pi/3$.

$r = \dfrac{7978.81}{1 - 0.937 \cos \theta}$; 11,011.87 mi

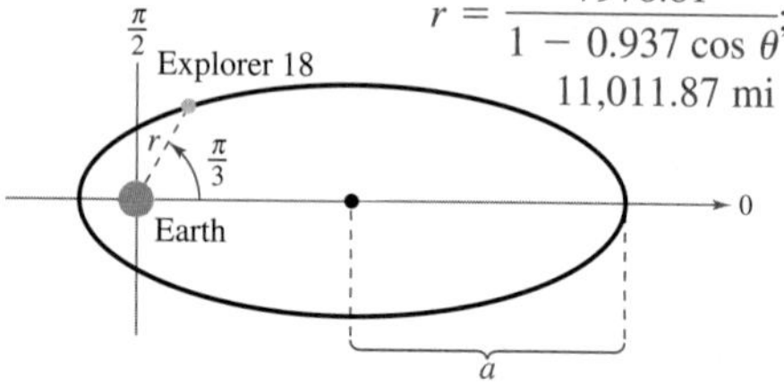

112. ASTEROID An asteroid takes a parabolic path with Earth as its focus. It is about 6,000,000 miles from Earth at its closest approach. Write the polar equation of the path of the asteroid with its vertex at $\theta = \pi/2$. Find the distance between the asteroid and Earth when $\theta = -\pi/3$. $r = \dfrac{12{,}000{,}000}{1 + \sin \theta}$; 89,600,000 mi

EXPLORATION

113–115. See margin.

TRUE OR FALSE? In Exercises 113–115, determine whether the statement is true or false. Justify your answer.

113. The graph of $\frac{1}{4}x^2 - y^4 = 1$ is a hyperbola.

114. Only one set of parametric equations can represent the line $y = 3 - 2x$.

115. There is a unique polar coordinate representation of each point in the plane.

116. Consider an ellipse with the major axis horizontal and 10 units in length. The number b in the standard form of the equation of the ellipse must be less than what real number? Explain the change in the shape of the ellipse as b approaches this number. See below.

117. What is the relationship between the graphs of the rectangular and polar equations? (a) The graphs are the same. (b) The graphs are the same.

(a) $x^2 + y^2 = 25,\ r = 5$

(b) $x - y = 0,\ \theta = \dfrac{\pi}{4}$

116. 5. The ellipse becomes more circular and approaches a circle of radius 5.

99. Limaçon

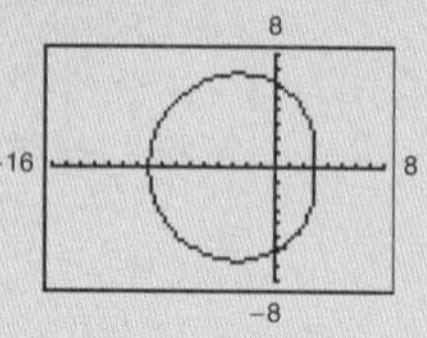

100. Limaçon

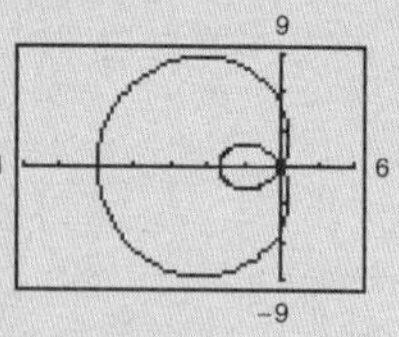

101. Rose curve

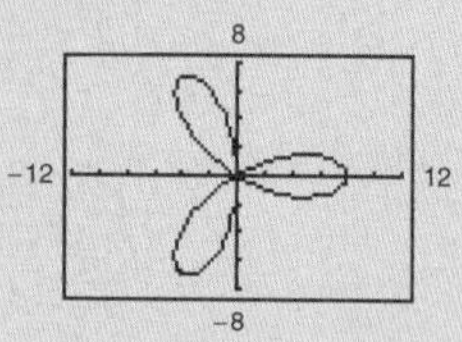

102. Lemniscate

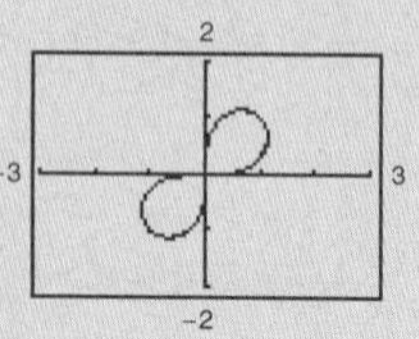

103. Hyperbola

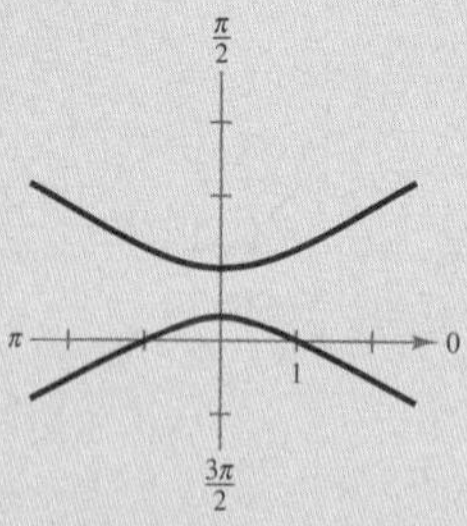

104. Parabola

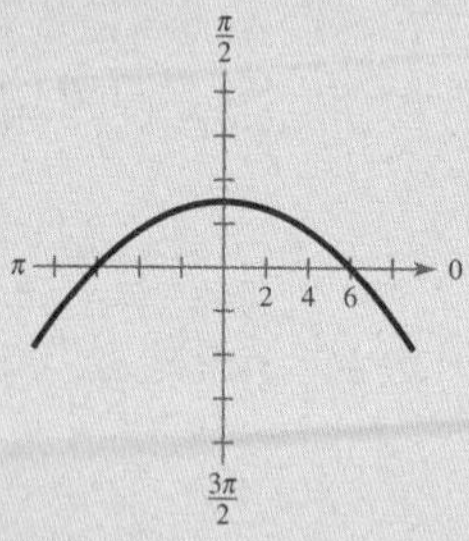

105. Ellipse

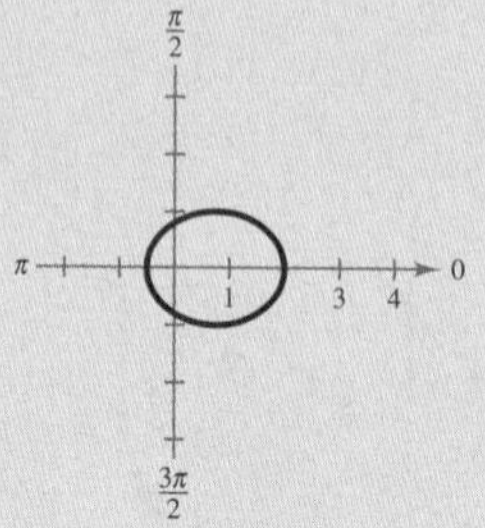

106. Hyperbola

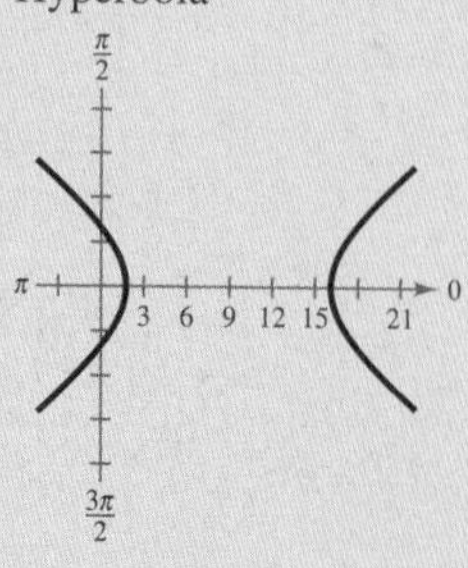

108. $r = \dfrac{4}{1 + \sin \theta}$

109. $r = \dfrac{5}{3 - 2 \cos \theta}$

110. $r = \dfrac{7}{3 + 4 \cos \theta}$

113. False. The equation of a hyperbola is a second-degree equation.

114. False. The following are two sets of parametric equations for the line.

$x = t,\ y = 3 - 2t$

$x = 3t,\ y = 3 - 6t$

115. False. $(2, \pi/4)$, $(-2, 5\pi/4)$, and $(2, 9\pi/4)$ all represent the same point.

89–98. See Additional Answers beginning on page AA1.

10 Chapter Test

See www.CalcChat.com for worked-out solutions to odd-numbered exercises.

Take this test as you would take a test in class. When you are finished, check your work against the answers given in the back of the book.

1. Find the inclination of the line $2x - 5y + 5 = 0$. 1. 0.3805 rad, 21.8°

2. Find the angle between the lines $3x + 2y - 4 = 0$ and $4x - y + 6 = 0$. 2. 0.8330 rad, 47.7°

3. Find the distance between the point $(7, 5)$ and the line $y = 5 - x$. $\frac{7\sqrt{2}}{2}$

In Exercises 4–7, classify the conic and write the equation in standard form. Identify the center, vertices, foci, and asymptotes (if applicable). Then sketch the graph of the conic. 4–7. See margin.

4. $y^2 - 2x + 2 = 0$

5. $x^2 - 4y^2 - 4x = 0$

6. $9x^2 + 16y^2 + 54x - 32y - 47 = 0$

7. $2x^2 + 2y^2 - 8x - 4y + 9 = 0$

8. Find the standard form of the equation of the parabola with vertex $(2, -3)$, with a vertical axis, and passing through the point $(4, 0)$. $(x - 2)^2 = \frac{4}{3}(y + 3)$

9. Find the standard form of the equation of the hyperbola with foci $(0, 0)$ and $(0, 4)$ and asymptotes $y = \pm\frac{1}{2}x + 2$.

9. $\frac{5(y - 2)^2}{4} - \frac{5x^2}{16} = 1$

10. (a) Determine the number of degrees the axis must be rotated to eliminate the xy-term of the conic $x^2 + 6xy + y^2 - 6 = 0$. (a) 45° (b) See margin.

(b) Graph the conic from part (a) and use a graphing utility to confirm your result.

11. Sketch the curve represented by the parametric equations $x = 2 + 3\cos\theta$ and $y = 2\sin\theta$. Eliminate the parameter and write the corresponding rectangular equation. See margin.

12. Find a set of parametric equations of the line passing through the points $(2, -3)$ and $(6, 4)$. (There are many correct answers.) $x = 6 + 4t,\ y = 4 + 7t$

13. Convert the polar coordinate $\left(-2, \frac{5\pi}{6}\right)$ to rectangular form. $\left(\sqrt{3}, -1\right)$

14. Convert the rectangular coordinate $(2, -2)$ to polar form and find two additional polar representations of this point.

14. $\left(2\sqrt{2}, \frac{7\pi}{4}\right)$, $\left(-2\sqrt{2}, \frac{3\pi}{4}\right)$, $\left(2\sqrt{2}, -\frac{\pi}{4}\right)$

15. Convert the rectangular equation $x^2 + y^2 - 3x = 0$ to polar form. $r = 3\cos\theta$

In Exercises 16–19, sketch the graph of the polar equation. Identify the type of graph. 16–19. See margin.

16. $r = \frac{4}{1 + \cos\theta}$

17. $r = \frac{4}{2 + \sin\theta}$

18. $r = 2 + 3\sin\theta$

19. $r = 2\sin 4\theta$

20. Find a polar equation of the ellipse with focus at the pole, eccentricity $e = \frac{1}{4}$, and directrix $y = 4$.

20. Answers will vary. For example: $r = \frac{1}{1 + 0.25\sin\theta}$

21. A straight road rises with an inclination of 0.15 radian from the horizontal. Find the slope of the road and the change in elevation over a one-mile stretch of the road.

21. Slope: 0.1511; Change in elevation: 789 ft

22. A baseball is hit at a point 3 feet above the ground toward the left field fence. The fence is 10 feet high and 375 feet from home plate. The path of the baseball can be modeled by the parametric equations $x = (115\cos\theta)t$ and $y = 3 + (115\sin\theta)t - 16t^2$. Will the baseball go over the fence if it is hit at an angle of $\theta = 30°$? Will the baseball go over the fence if $\theta = 35°$? No; Yes

4. Parabola: $y^2 = 2(x - 1)$
Vertex: $(1, 0)$
Focus: $\left(\frac{3}{2}, 0\right)$

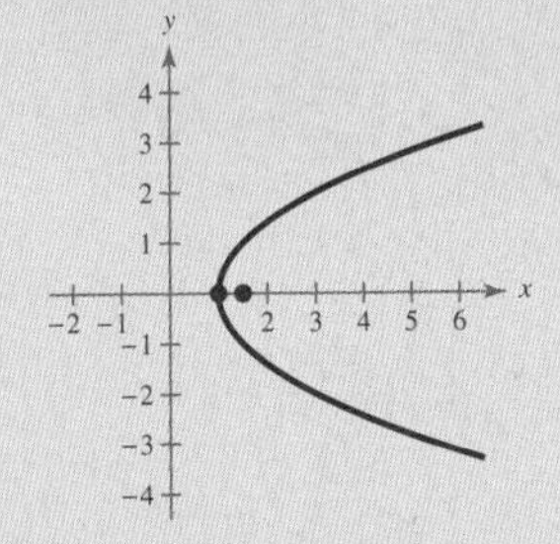

5. Hyperbola: $\frac{(x - 2)^2}{4} - y^2 = 1$
Center: $(2, 0)$
Vertices: $(0, 0), (4, 0)$
Foci: $\left(2 \pm \sqrt{5}, 0\right)$
Asymptotes: $y = \pm\frac{1}{2}(x - 2)$

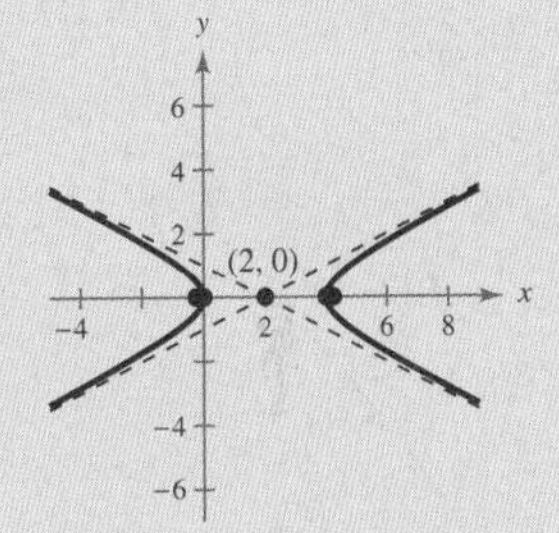

6. Ellipse: $\frac{(x + 3)^2}{16} + \frac{(y - 1)^2}{9} = 1$
Center: $(-3, 1)$
Vertices: $(1, 1), (-7, 1)$
Foci: $\left(-3 \pm \sqrt{7}, 1\right)$

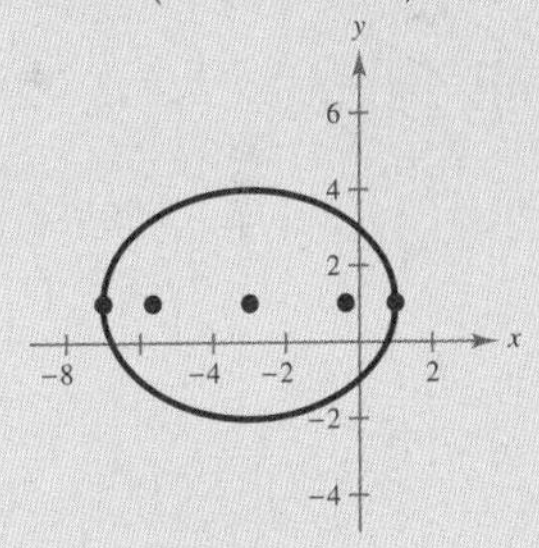

7. Circle: $(x - 2)^2 + (y - 1)^2 = \frac{1}{2}$
Center: $(2, 1)$

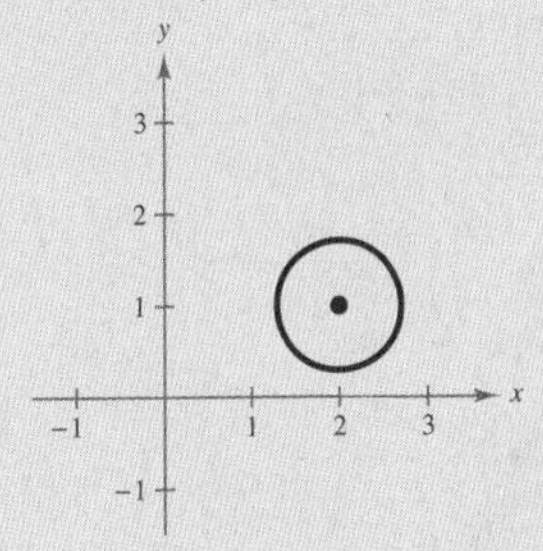

10. (b)

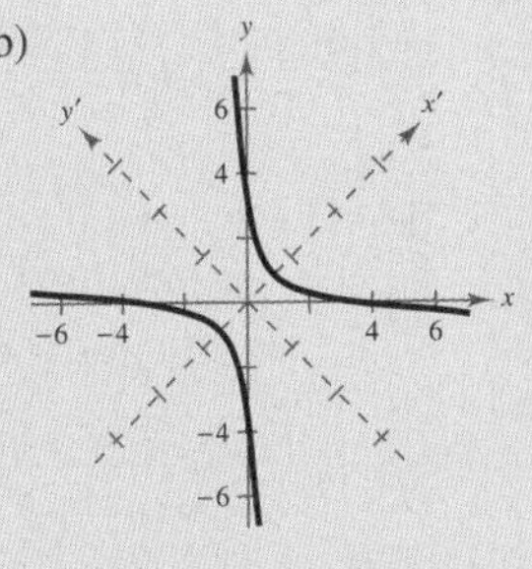

11.

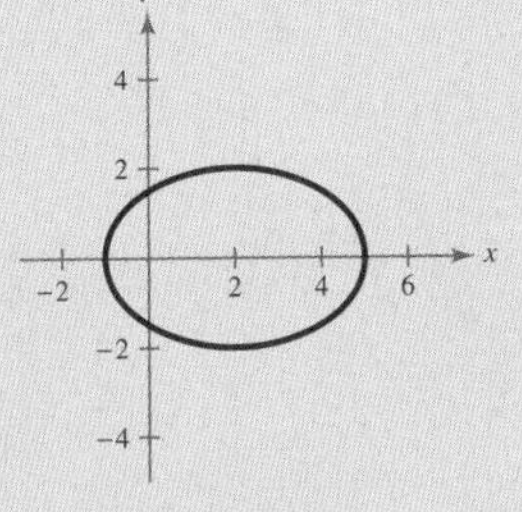

$\frac{(x - 2)^2}{9} + \frac{y^2}{4} = 1$

16.

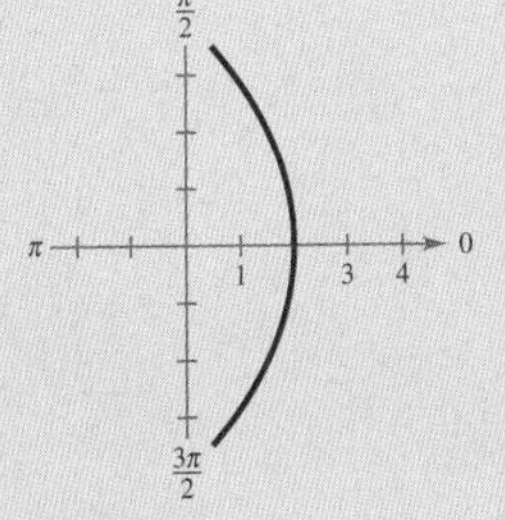

Parabola

17–19. See Additional Answers beginning on page AA1.

PROOFS IN MATHEMATICS

Inclination and Slope *(p. 726)*

If a nonvertical line has inclination θ and slope m, then $m = \tan \theta$.

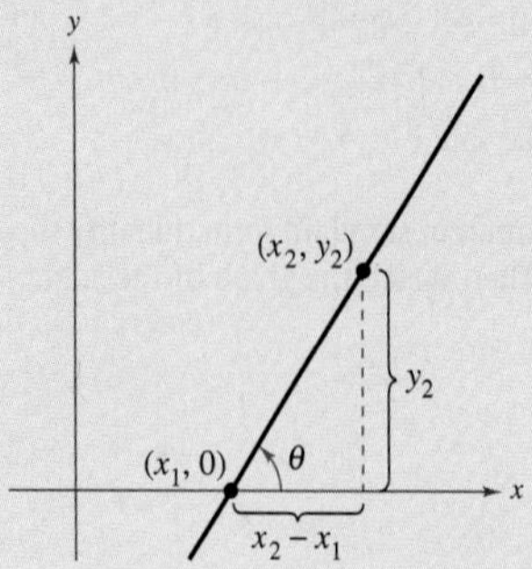

Proof

If $m = 0$, the line is horizontal and $\theta = 0$. So, the result is true for horizontal lines because $m = 0 = \tan 0$.

If the line has a positive slope, it will intersect the x-axis. Label this point $(x_1, 0)$, as shown in the figure. If (x_2, y_2) is a second point on the line, the slope is

$$m = \frac{y_2 - 0}{x_2 - x_1} = \frac{y_2}{x_2 - x_1} = \tan \theta.$$

The case in which the line has a negative slope can be proved in a similar manner.

Distance Between a Point and a Line *(p. 728)*

The distance between the point (x_1, y_1) and the line $Ax + By + C = 0$ is

$$d = \frac{|Ax_1 + By_1 + C|}{\sqrt{A^2 + B^2}}.$$

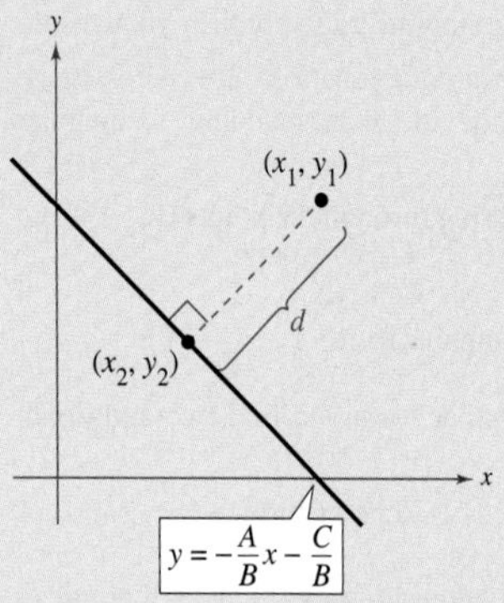

Proof

For simplicity, assume that the given line is neither horizontal nor vertical (see figure). By writing the equation $Ax + By + C = 0$ in slope-intercept form

$$y = -\frac{A}{B}x - \frac{C}{B}$$

you can see that the line has a slope of $m = -A/B$. So, the slope of the line passing through (x_1, y_1) and perpendicular to the given line is B/A, and its equation is $y - y_1 = (B/A)(x - x_1)$. These two lines intersect at the point (x_2, y_2), where

$$x_2 = \frac{B(Bx_1 - Ay_1) - AC}{A^2 + B^2} \quad \text{and} \quad y_2 = \frac{A(-Bx_1 + Ay_1) - BC}{A^2 + B^2}.$$

Finally, the distance between (x_1, y_1) and (x_2, y_2) is

$$\begin{aligned} d &= \sqrt{(x_2 - x_1)^2 + (y_2 - y_1)^2} \\ &= \sqrt{\left(\frac{B^2x_1 - ABy_1 - AC}{A^2 + B^2} - x_1\right)^2 + \left(\frac{-ABx_1 + A^2y_1 - BC}{A^2 + B^2} - y_1\right)^2} \\ &= \sqrt{\frac{A^2(Ax_1 + By_1 + C)^2 + B^2(Ax_1 + By_1 + C)^2}{(A^2 + B^2)^2}} \\ &= \frac{|Ax_1 + By_1 + C|}{\sqrt{A^2 + B^2}}. \end{aligned}$$

804

Parabolic Paths

There are many natural occurrences of parabolas in real life. For instance, the famous astronomer Galileo discovered in the 17th century that an object that is projected upward and obliquely to the pull of gravity travels in a parabolic path. Examples of this are the center of gravity of a jumping dolphin and the path of water molecules in a drinking fountain.

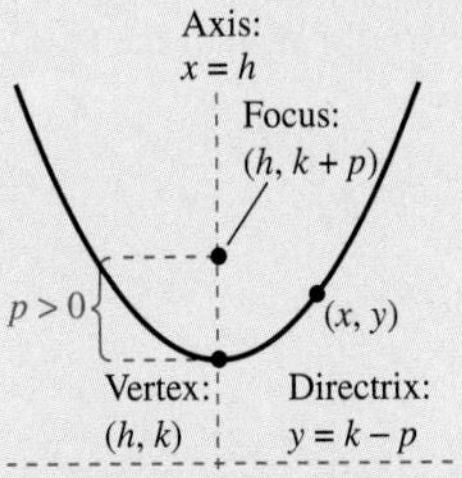

Parabola with vertical axis

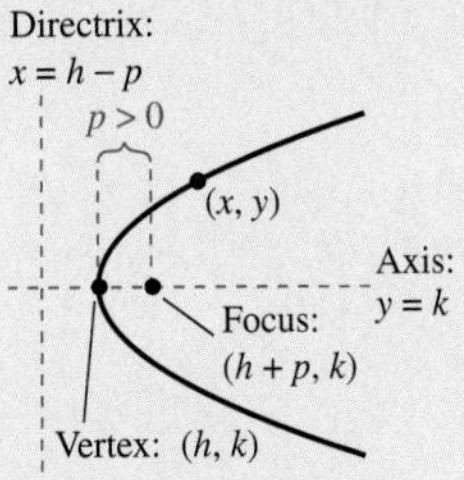

Parabola with horizontal axis

Standard Equation of a Parabola *(p. 734)*

The standard form of the equation of a parabola with vertex at (h, k) is as follows.

$(x - h)^2 = 4p(y - k), \quad p \neq 0$ — Vertical axis, directrix: $y = k - p$

$(y - k)^2 = 4p(x - h), \quad p \neq 0$ — Horizontal axis, directrix: $x = h - p$

The focus lies on the axis p units (*directed distance*) from the vertex. If the vertex is at the origin $(0, 0)$, the equation takes one of the following forms.

$x^2 = 4py$ — Vertical axis

$y^2 = 4px$ — Horizontal axis

Proof

For the case in which the directrix is parallel to the x-axis and the focus lies above the vertex, as shown in the top figure, if (x, y) is any point on the parabola, then, by definition, it is equidistant from the focus $(h, k + p)$ and the directrix $y = k - p$. So, you have

$$\sqrt{(x - h)^2 + [y - (k + p)]^2} = y - (k - p)$$
$$(x - h)^2 + [y - (k + p)]^2 = [y - (k - p)]^2$$
$$(x - h)^2 + y^2 - 2y(k + p) + (k + p)^2 = y^2 - 2y(k - p) + (k - p)^2$$
$$(x - h)^2 + y^2 - 2ky - 2py + k^2 + 2pk + p^2 = y^2 - 2ky + 2py + k^2 - 2pk + p^2$$
$$(x - h)^2 - 2py + 2pk = 2py - 2pk$$
$$(x - h)^2 = 4p(y - k).$$

For the case in which the directrix is parallel to the y-axis and the focus lies to the right of the vertex, as shown in the bottom figure, if (x, y) is any point on the parabola, then, by definition, it is equidistant from the focus $(h + p, k)$ and the directrix $x = h - p$. So, you have

$$\sqrt{[x - (h + p)]^2 + (y - k)^2} = x - (h - p)$$
$$[x - (h + p)]^2 + (y - k)^2 = [x - (h - p)]^2$$
$$x^2 - 2x(h + p) + (h + p)^2 + (y - k)^2 = x^2 - 2x(h - p) + (h - p)^2$$
$$x^2 - 2hx - 2px + h^2 + 2ph + p^2 + (y - k)^2 = x^2 - 2hx + 2px + h^2 - 2ph + p^2$$
$$-2px + 2ph + (y - k)^2 = 2px - 2ph$$
$$(y - k)^2 = 4p(x - h).$$

Note that if a parabola is centered at the origin, then the two equations above would simplify to $x^2 = 4py$ and $y^2 = 4px$, respectively.

805

Polar Equations of Conics *(p. 791)*

The graph of a polar equation of the form

1. $r = \dfrac{ep}{1 \pm e \cos \theta}$

or

2. $r = \dfrac{ep}{1 \pm e \sin \theta}$

is a conic, where $e > 0$ is the eccentricity and $|p|$ is the distance between the focus (pole) and the directrix.

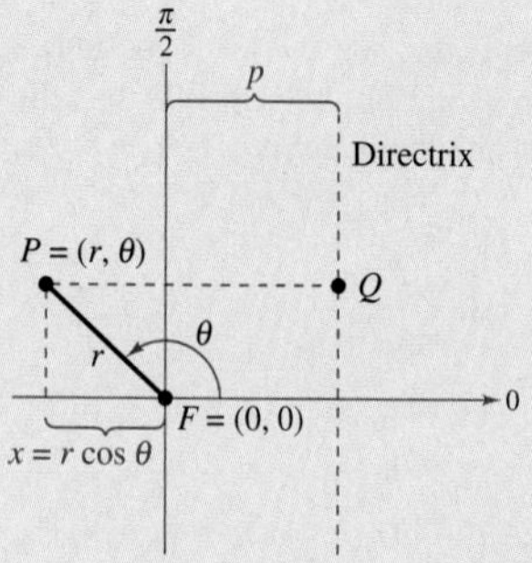

Proof

A proof for $r = \dfrac{ep}{1 + e \cos \theta}$ with $p > 0$ is shown here. The proofs of the other cases are similar. In the figure, consider a vertical directrix, p units to the right of the focus $F = (0, 0)$. If $P = (r, \theta)$ is a point on the graph of

$$r = \frac{ep}{1 + e \cos \theta}$$

the distance between P and the directrix is

$$\begin{aligned} PQ &= |p - x| \\ &= |p - r \cos \theta| \\ &= \left| p - \left(\frac{ep}{1 + e \cos \theta} \right) \cos \theta \right| \\ &= \left| p \left(1 - \frac{e \cos \theta}{1 + e \cos \theta} \right) \right| \\ &= \left| \frac{p}{1 + e \cos \theta} \right| \\ &= \left| \frac{r}{e} \right|. \end{aligned}$$

Moreover, because the distance between P and the pole is simply $PF = |r|$, the ratio of PF to PQ is

$$\begin{aligned} \frac{PF}{PQ} &= \frac{|r|}{\left| \dfrac{r}{e} \right|} \\ &= |e| \\ &= e \end{aligned}$$

and, by definition, the graph of the equation must be a conic.

806

PROBLEM SOLVING

This collection of thought-provoking and challenging exercises further explores and expands upon concepts learned in this chapter.

1. Several mountain climbers are located in a mountain pass between two peaks. The angles of elevation to the two peaks are 0.84 radian and 1.10 radians. A range finder shows that the distances to the peaks are 3250 feet and 6700 feet, respectively (see figure).

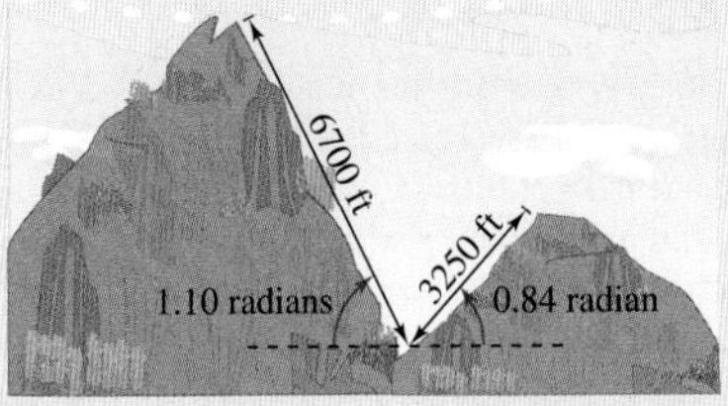

(a) Find the angle between the two lines of sight to the peaks. (a) 1.2016 rad (b) 2420 ft, 5971 ft

(b) Approximate the amount of vertical climb that is necessary to reach the summit of each peak.

2. Statuary Hall is an elliptical room in the United States Capitol in Washington D.C. The room is also called the Whispering Gallery because a person standing at one focus of the room can hear even a whisper spoken by a person standing at the other focus. This occurs because any sound that is emitted from one focus of an ellipse will reflect off the side of the ellipse to the other focus. Statuary Hall is 46 feet wide and 97 feet long. (a) See margin.

(a) Find an equation that models the shape of the room.

(b) How far apart are the two foci? About 85.4 ft

(c) What is the area of the floor of the room? (The area of an ellipse is $A = \pi ab$.) $1115.5\pi \text{ ft}^2 \approx 3504.45 \text{ ft}^2$

3. Find the equation(s) of all parabolas that have the x-axis as the axis of symmetry and focus at the origin.

4. Find the area of the square inscribed in the ellipse below.

3–4. See margin.

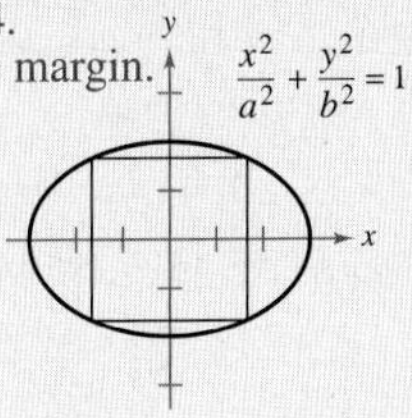

FIGURE FOR 4

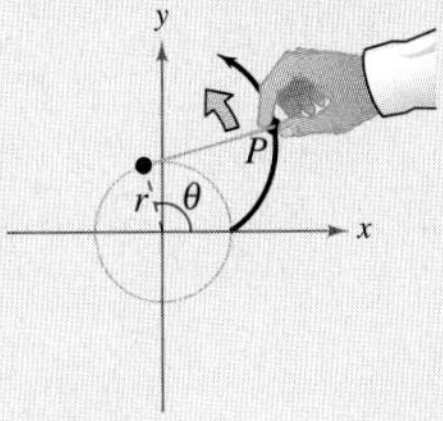

FIGURE FOR 5

5. The *involute* of a circle is described by the endpoint P of a string that is held taut as it is unwound from a spool (see figure). The spool does not rotate. Show that

$$x = r(\cos\theta + \theta\sin\theta) \qquad y = r(\sin\theta - \theta\cos\theta)$$

is a parametric representation of the involute of a circle. Answers will vary.

6. A tour boat travels between two islands that are 12 miles apart (see figure). For a trip between the islands, there is enough fuel for a 20-mile trip.

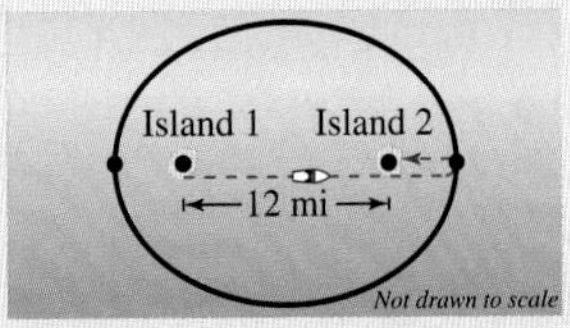

(a) Explain why the region in which the boat can travel is bounded by an ellipse. See margin.

(b) Let $(0, 0)$ represent the center of the ellipse. Find the coordinates of each island. See margin.

(c) The boat travels from one island, straight past the other island to the vertex of the ellipse, and back to the second island. How many miles does the boat travel? Use your answer to find the coordinates of the vertex. 20 mi; Vertex: $(10, 0)$

(d) Use the results from parts (b) and (c) to write an equation of the ellipse that bounds the region in which the boat can travel. See margin.

7. Find an equation of the hyperbola such that for any point on the hyperbola, the difference between its distances from the points $(2, 2)$ and $(10, 2)$ is 6. See margin.

8. Prove that the graph of the equation

$$Ax^2 + Cy^2 + Dx + Ey + F = 0 \qquad \text{Proof}$$

is one of the following (except in degenerate cases).

Conic	*Condition*
(a) Circle	$A = C$
(b) Parabola	$A = 0$ or $C = 0$ (but not both)
(c) Ellipse	$AC > 0$
(d) Hyperbola	$AC < 0$

9. The following sets of parametric equations model projectile motion. See margin.

$$x = (v_0\cos\theta)t \qquad x = (v_0\cos\theta)t$$

$$y = (v_0\sin\theta)t \qquad y = h + (v_0\sin\theta)t - 16t^2$$

(a) Under what circumstances would you use each model?

(b) Eliminate the parameter for each set of equations.

(c) In which case is the path of the moving object not affected by a change in the velocity v? Explain.

2. (a) $\frac{x^2}{2352.25} + \frac{y^2}{529} = 1$

3. $y^2 = 4p(x + p)$

4. $A = \frac{4a^2b^2}{a^2 + b^2}$

6. (a) Because $d_1 + d_2 \le 20$, by definition, the outer bound that the boat can travel is an ellipse. The islands are the foci.

(b) Island 1: $(-6, 0)$; Island 2: $(6, 0)$

(d) $\frac{x^2}{100} + \frac{y^2}{64} = 1$

7. $\frac{(x - 6)^2}{9} - \frac{(y - 2)^2}{7} = 1$

9. (a) The first set of parametric equations models projectile motion along a straight line. The second set of parametric equations models projectile motion of an object launched at a height of h units above the ground that will eventually fall back to the ground.

(b) $y = (\tan\theta)x$;

$y = h + x\tan\theta - \frac{16x^2\sec^2\theta}{v_0^2}$

(c) In the first case, the path of the moving object is not affected by a change in the velocity because eliminating the parameter removes v_0.

10. Answers will vary. For example: $x = \cos(-t),\ y = 2\sin(-t)$

11. (a)

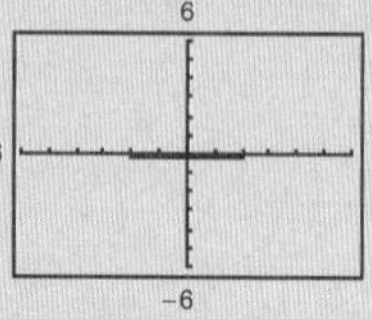

The graph is a line between -2 and 2 on the x-axis.

(b)

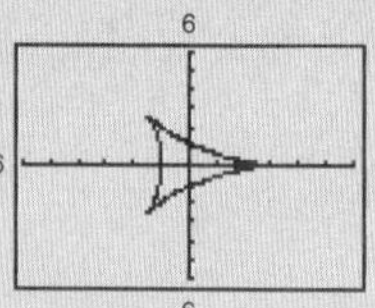

The graph is a three-sided figure with counterclockwise orientation.

(c)

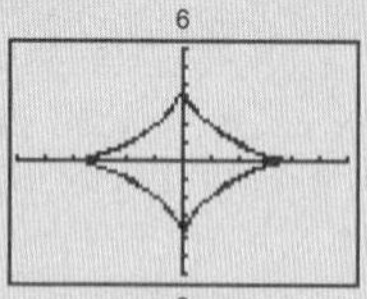

The graph is a four-sided figure with counterclockwise orientation.

(d)

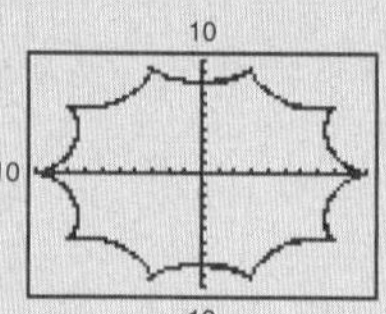

The graph is a 10-sided figure with counterclockwise orientation.

(e)

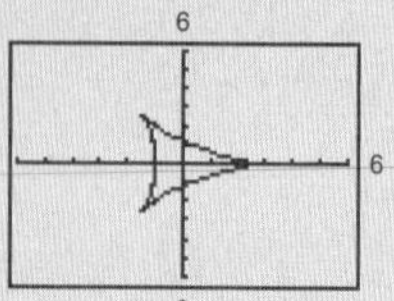

The graph is a three-sided figure with clockwise orientation.

(f)

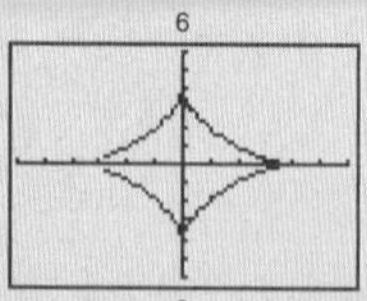

The graph is a four-sided figure with clockwise orientation.

12. (c)

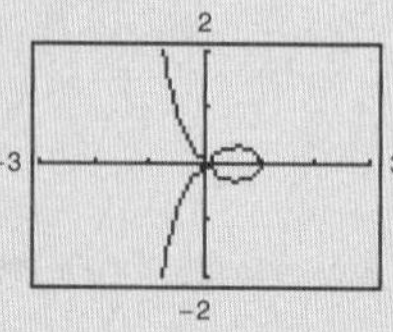

10. As t increases, the ellipse given by the parametric equations $x = \cos t$ and $y = 2\sin t$ is traced out *counterclockwise*. Find a parametric representation for which the same ellipse is traced out *clockwise*. See margin.

11. A **hypocycloid** has the parametric equations

$$x = (a - b)\cos t + b\cos\left(\frac{a-b}{b}t\right)$$

and

$$y = (a - b)\sin t - b\sin\left(\frac{a-b}{b}t\right).$$

Use a graphing utility to graph the hypocycloid for each value of a and b. Describe each graph. See margin.

(a) $a = 2, b = 1$ (b) $a = 3, b = 1$

(c) $a = 4, b = 1$ (d) $a = 10, b = 1$

(e) $a = 3, b = 2$ (f) $a = 4, b = 3$

12. The curve given by the parametric equations

$$x = \frac{1 - t^2}{1 + t^2} \quad \text{and} \quad y = \frac{t(1 - t^2)}{1 + t^2}$$

is called a **strophoid.**

(a) Find a rectangular equation of the strophoid.

(b) Find a polar equation of the strophoid.

(c) Use a graphing utility to graph the strophoid.

(a) $y^2 = x^2\left(\frac{1-x}{1+x}\right)$ (b) $r = \cos 2\theta \sec\theta$ (c) See margin.

13. The rose curves described in this chapter are of the form

$$r = a\cos n\theta \quad \text{or} \quad r = a\sin n\theta$$

where n is a positive integer that is greater than or equal to 2. Use a graphing utility to graph $r = a\cos n\theta$ and $r = a\sin n\theta$ for some noninteger values of n. Describe the graphs. See margin.

14. What conic section is represented by the polar equation

$r = a\sin\theta + b\cos\theta$? Circle

15. The graph of the polar equation

$$r = e^{\cos\theta} - 2\cos 4\theta + \sin^5\left(\frac{\theta}{12}\right)$$

is called the *butterfly curve*, as shown in the figure.

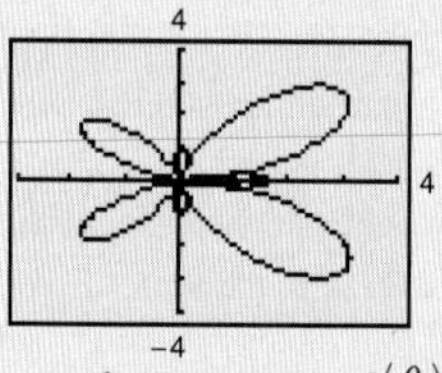

$r = e^{\cos\theta} - 2\cos 4\theta + \sin^5\left(\frac{\theta}{12}\right)$

(a) The graph shown was produced using $0 \le \theta \le 2\pi$. Does this show the entire graph? Explain your reasoning.

(b) Approximate the maximum r-value of the graph. Does this value change if you use $0 \le \theta \le 4\pi$ instead of $0 \le \theta \le 2\pi$? Explain.

16. Use a graphing utility to graph the polar equation

$$r = \cos 5\theta + n\cos\theta$$

for $0 \le \theta \le \pi$ for the integers $n = -5$ to $n = 5$. As you graph these equations, you should see the graph change shape from a heart to a bell. Write a short paragraph explaining what values of n produce the heart portion of the curve and what values of n produce the bell portion. See margin.

17. The planets travel in elliptical orbits with the sun at one focus. The polar equation of the orbit of a planet with one focus at the pole and major axis of length $2a$ (see figure) is

$$r = \frac{(1 - e^2)a}{1 - e\cos\theta}$$

where e is the eccentricity. The minimum distance (perihelion) from the sun to a planet is $r = a(1 - e)$ and the maximum distance (aphelion) is $r = a(1 + e)$. For the planet Neptune, $a = 4.495 \times 10^9$ kilometers and $e = 0.0086$. For the dwarf planet Pluto, $a = 5.906 \times 10^9$ kilometers and $e = 0.2488$. See margin.

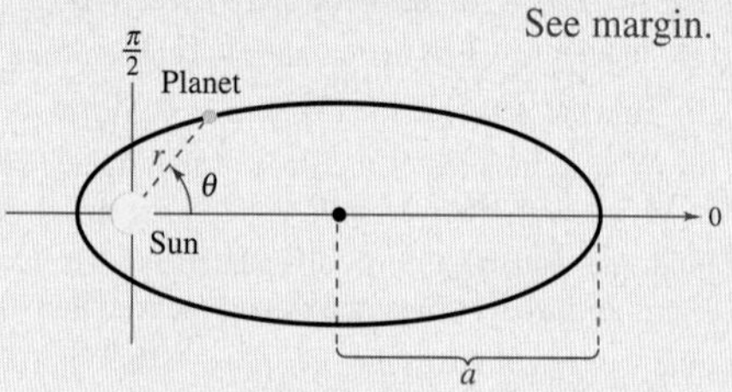

(a) Find the polar equation of the orbit of each planet.

(b) Find the perihelion and aphelion distances for each planet.

(c) Use a graphing utility to graph the equations of the orbits of Neptune and Pluto in the same viewing window.

(d) Is Pluto ever closer to the sun than Neptune? Until recently, Pluto was considered the ninth planet. Why was Pluto called the ninth planet and Neptune the eighth planet?

(e) Do the orbits of Neptune and Pluto intersect? Will Neptune and Pluto ever collide? Why or why not?

15. (a) No. Because of the exponential, the graph will continue to trace the butterfly curve at larger values of r.

(b) $r \approx 4.1$. This value will increase if θ is increased.

13.

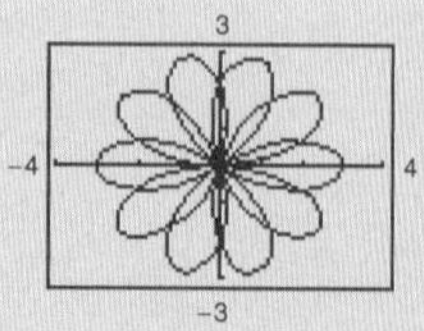

$r = 3\sin\left(\frac{5\theta}{2}\right)$

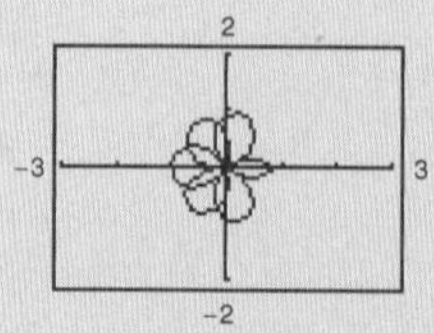

$r = -\cos(\sqrt{2}\theta),\ -2\pi \le \theta \le 2\pi$

Sample answer: If n is a rational number, then the curve has a finite number of petals. If n is an irrational number, then the curve has an infinite number of petals.

16–17. See Additional Answers beginning on page AA1.

REGULAR SCHEDULE

Lesson	Day	AVERAGE	ADVANCED
11.1	Day 1	p. 815 Exs. 1–5, 9–13, 17–20, 21–25 odd, 28–35, 37–43 odd	p. 815 Exs. 1–5, 10–20, 22–26 even, 29–36, 38–44 even
	Day 2	pp. 815–816 Exs. 6–8, 47–51 odd, 54, 55–61 odd, 65–69, 72, 73	pp. 815–816 Exs. 6–8, 48–54 even, 56–60, 64–70, 73, 74
	Day 3	p. 816 Exs. 75, 77–81, 83–85	p. 816 Exs. 76–78, 81–86
11.2	Day 1	pp. 822–823 Exs. 1–8, 10, 11–29 odd, 32, 33, 36, 37	pp. 822–823 Exs. 1–8, 10–14, 16–34 even, 36–38
	Day 2	p. 823 Exs. 40–43, 48, 49, 52, 53–57 odd, 60–64	p. 823 Exs. 40–44, 48–56 even, 57, 58, 60–64
11.3	Day 1	p. 829 Exs. 1–3, 5–11, 15, 17, 21, 23, 27–29, 32–35, 37–41 odd	p. 829 Exs. 1–3, 5–10, 12–30 even, 33–36, 38–42 even
	Day 2	pp. 829–830 Exs. 4, 44, 45, 47–49, 53, 55, 56, 59, 61–64, 66	pp. 829–830 Exs. 4, 44, 46, 48–50, 52–58 even, 60–65, 68, 69
11.4	Day 1	p. 838 Exs. 1–4, 6–9, 12–16, 19, 21–23, 25, 27, 28	p. 838 Exs. 1–4, 6–10, 14–18, 20, 22–24, 26–30 even
	Day 2	pp. 838–839 Exs. 31–35 odd, 37–39, 41, 48, 49, 51, 53–55, 57, 58, 60, 61, 63–65	pp. 838–839 Exs. 32–36 even, 37–40, 42–46 even, 49, 50–60 even, 61–65, 67, 68
Review	Day 1	pp. 842–843 Exs. 1–7 odd, 15, 19–27 odd, 31, 35–55 odd, 59–71 odd, 75–77	pp. 842–843 Exs. 2–8 even, 18–28 even, 32–44 even, 45, 46–62 even, 64–66, 68, 72, 75, 76, 78
Assess	Day 1	Chapter 11 Test	Chapter 11 Test

Yearly Pacing Chapter 11 Total – 11 days Remaining – 13 days

BLOCK SCHEDULE

DAY 1	DAY 2	DAY 3	DAY 4	DAY 5	DAY 6
11.1	**11.1 (CONT.)**	**11.2 (CONT.)**	**11.3 (CONT.)**	**11.4 (CONT.)**	**ASSESS**
pp. 815–816 Exs. 1–13, 17–20, 21–25 odd, 28–35, 37–43 odd, 47–51 odd, 54, 55–61 odd, 65–69, 72, 73	p. 816 Exs. 75, 77–81, 83–85	p. 823 Exs. 40–43, 48, 49, 52, 53–57 odd, 60–64	pp. 829–830 Exs. 4, 44, 45, 47–49, 53, 55, 56, 59, 61–64, 66	pp. 838–839 Exs. 31–35 odd, 37–39, 41, 48, 49, 51, 53–55, 57, 58, 60, 61, 63–65	Chapter 11 Test
	11.2	**11.3**	**11.4**	**REVIEW**	**12.1**
	pp. 822–823 Exs. 1–8, 10, 11–29 odd, 32, 33, 36, 37	p. 829 Exs. 1–3, 5–11, 15, 17, 21, 23, 27–29, 32–35, 37–41 odd	p. 838 Exs. 1–4, 6–9, 12–16, 19, 21–23, 25, 27, 28	pp. 842–843 Exs. 1–7 odd, 15, 19–27 odd, 31, 35–55 odd, 59–71 odd, 75–77	Begin Chapter 12

Yearly Pacing Chapter 11 Total – 5.5 days Remaining – 6.5 days

Analytic Geometry in Three Dimensions

11

In Mathematics

A three-dimensional coordinate system is formed by passing a z-axis perpendicular to both the x- and y-axes at the origin. When the concept of vectors is extended to three-dimensional space, they are denoted by ordered triples $\mathbf{v} = \langle v_1, v_2, v_3 \rangle$.

In Real Life

The concepts discussed in this chapter have many applications in physics and engineering. For instance, vectors can be used to find the angle between two adjacent sides of a grain elevator chute. (See Exercise 62, page 839.)

George Ostertag/PhotoLibrary

IN CAREERS

There are many careers that use topics in analytic geometry in three dimensions. Several are listed below.

- Architect
  Exercise 77, page 816
- Geographer
  Exercise 78, page 816
- Cyclist
  Exercises 61 and 62, page 830
- Consumer Research Analyst
  Exercise 61, page 839

PLAN AND PREPARE

Main Ideas

In Chapter 11, students describe and analyze points, vectors, lines, and planes in three-dimensional space. The chapter begins by introducing the three-dimensional coordinate system and methods for describing three-dimensional vectors. Students then use this system to analyze the relationship between two or three vectors in space by calculating quantities such as the dot or cross products. Finally, students study parametric and symmetric equations and compare lines and planes in space.

Chapter Planning Guide

Chapter Resources
- Complete Solutions Guide

Interactive Technology
- Instructor Success Organizer
- Notetaking Guide IAE
- Instructional DVDs
- Animated Precalculus
- PowerLecture with ExamView

1 PLAN AND PREPARE

Warm-up Exercises

Transparency Available
Available at the Instructor's companion site.

Notetaking Guide

Transparency Available
Promotes interactive learning and notetaking skills.
Available at the Instructor's companion site.

Animated Precalculus

An **Animated Precalculus** tutorial is available at the Student companion site for **Section 11.1.**

Pacing

Average: 3 days
Advanced: 3 days
Block: 1 block
0.5 block with 11.2

2 FOCUS AND MOTIVATE

Essential Question

How do you locate points, find distances, and graph equations in three dimensions? **Tell students that they will learn how to answer this question by studying solid analytic geometry, where a third coordinate axis is used in addition to the x- and y-axes of the two-dimensional plane.**

11.1 THE THREE-DIMENSIONAL COORDINATE SYSTEM

What you should learn

- Plot points in the three-dimensional coordinate system.
- Find distances between points in space and find midpoints of line segments joining points in space.
- Write equations of spheres in standard form and find traces of surfaces in space.

Why you should learn it

The three-dimensional coordinate system can be used to graph equations that model surfaces in space, such as the spherical shape of Earth, as shown in Exercise 78 on page 816.

NASA

The Three-Dimensional Coordinate System

Recall that the Cartesian plane is determined by two perpendicular number lines called the x-axis and the y-axis. These axes, together with their point of intersection (the origin), allow you to develop a two-dimensional coordinate system for identifying points in a plane. To identify a point in space, you must introduce a third dimension to the model. The geometry of this three-dimensional model is called **solid analytic geometry.**

You can construct a **three-dimensional coordinate system** by passing a z-axis perpendicular to both the x- and y-axes at the origin. Figure 11.1 shows the positive portion of each coordinate axis. Taken as pairs, the axes determine three **coordinate planes:** the ***xy*-plane,** the ***xz*-plane,** and the ***yz*-plane.** These three coordinate planes separate the three-dimensional coordinate system into eight **octants.** The first octant is the one in which all three coordinates are positive. In this three-dimensional system, a point P in space is determined by an ordered triple (x, y, z), where x, y, and z are as follows.

$x =$ directed distance from yz-plane to P

$y =$ directed distance from xz-plane to P

$z =$ directed distance from xy-plane to P

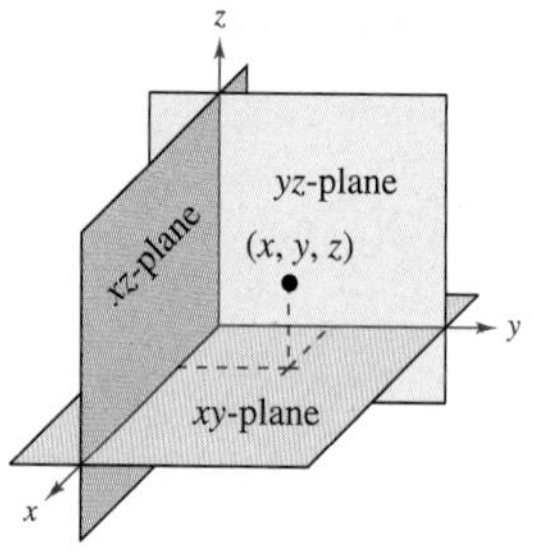

FIGURE 11.1

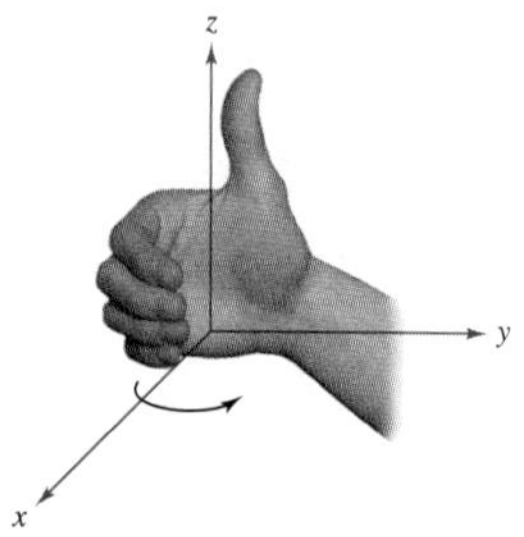

FIGURE 11.2

A three-dimensional coordinate system can have either a **left-handed** or a **right-handed** orientation. In this text, you will work exclusively with right-handed systems, as illustrated in Figure 11.2. In a right-handed system, Octants II, III, and IV are found by rotating counterclockwise around the positive z-axis. Octant V is vertically below Octant I. Octants VI, VII, and VIII are then found by rotating counterclockwise around the negative z-axis. See Figure 11.3.

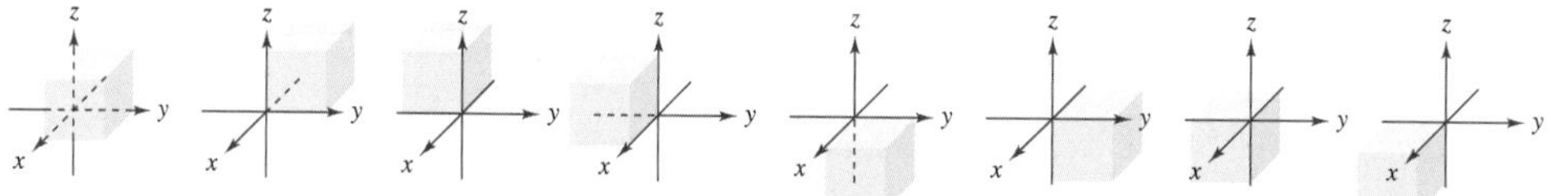

Octant I Octant II Octant III Octant IV Octant V Octant VI Octant VII Octant VIII

FIGURE 11.3

Resource Planning Guide

Chapter Resources
- Complete Solutions Guide

Workbooks
- Notetaking Guide
- Student Solutions Guide

Interactive Technology
- Instructor Success Organizer
- Notetaking Guide IAE
- Instructional DVDs
- Animated Precalculus
- PowerLecture with ExamView

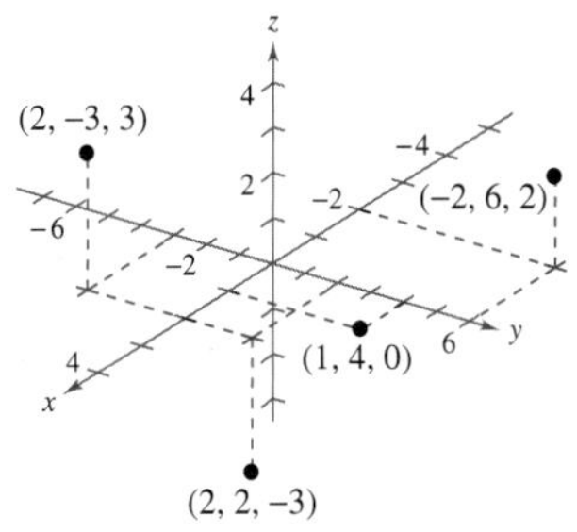

FIGURE 11.4

Example 1 Plotting Points in Space

Plot each point in space.

a. $(2, -3, 3)$ **b.** $(-2, 6, 2)$ **c.** $(1, 4, 0)$ **d.** $(2, 2, -3)$

Solution

To plot the point $(2, -3, 3)$, notice that $x = 2, y = -3$, and $z = 3$. To help visualize the point, locate the point $(2, -3)$ in the xy-plane (denoted by a cross in Figure 11.4). The point $(2, -3, 3)$ lies three units above the cross. The other three points are also shown in Figure 11.4.

CHECKPoint Now try Exercise 13.

The Distance and Midpoint Formulas

Many of the formulas established for the two-dimensional coordinate system can be extended to three dimensions. For example, to find the distance between two points in space, you can use the Pythagorean Theorem twice, as shown in Figure 11.5. Note that $a = x_2 - x_1$, $b = y_2 - y_1$, and $c = z_2 - z_1$.

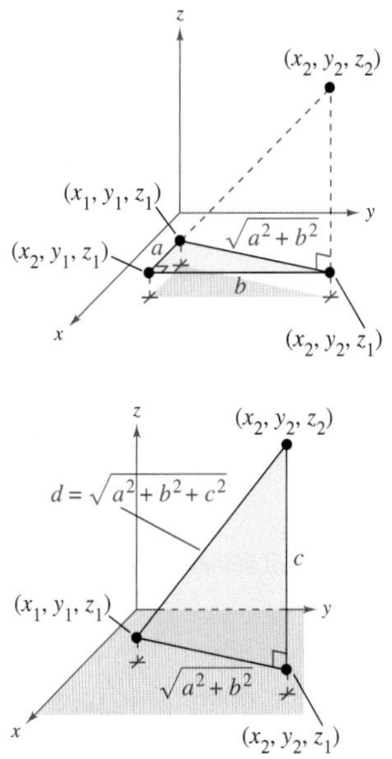

FIGURE 11.5

Distance Formula in Space

The distance between the points (x_1, y_1, z_1) and (x_2, y_2, z_2) given by the Distance Formula in Space is

$$d = \sqrt{(x_2 - x_1)^2 + (y_2 - y_1)^2 + (z_2 - z_1)^2}.$$

Example 2 Finding the Distance Between Two Points in Space

Find the distance between $(1, 0, 2)$ and $(2, 4, -3)$.

Solution

$$d = \sqrt{(x_2 - x_1)^2 + (y_2 - y_1)^2 + (z_2 - z_1)^2} \quad \text{Distance Formula in Space}$$

$$= \sqrt{(2-1)^2 + (4-0)^2 + (-3-2)^2} \quad \text{Substitute.}$$

$$= \sqrt{1 + 16 + 25} \quad \text{Simplify.}$$

$$= \sqrt{42} \quad \text{Simplify.}$$

CHECKPoint Now try Exercise 27.

Notice the similarity between the Distance Formulas in the plane and in space. The Midpoint Formulas in the plane and in space are also similar.

Midpoint Formula in Space

The midpoint of the line segment joining the points (x_1, y_1, z_1) and (x_2, y_2, z_2) given by the Midpoint Formula in Space is

$$\left(\frac{x_1 + x_2}{2}, \frac{y_1 + y_2}{2}, \frac{z_1 + z_2}{2}\right).$$

3 TEACH

Extra Example 1

Plot each point in space.

a. $(-1, 3, 4)$
b. $(2, 5, 0)$
c. $(1, 3, 6)$
d. $(2, -1, 4)$

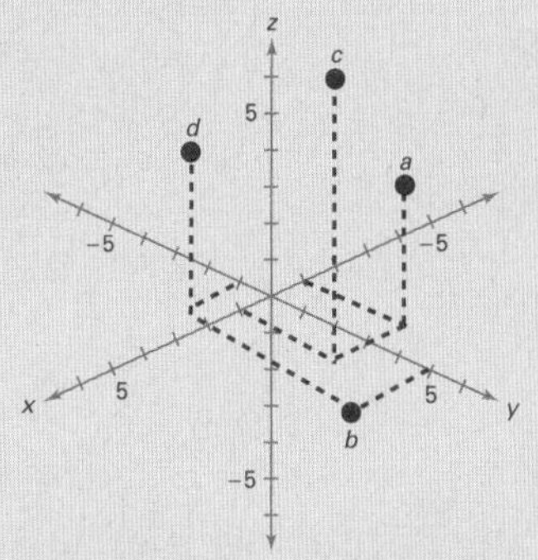

Avoiding Common Errors

Students should be consistent when orienting axes in a three-dimensional graph. The most common representation is the right-handed orientation, drawn so that the xy-plane is horizontal and the positive values of each axis are closest to the viewer.

Extra Example 2

Find the distance between $(3, 1, 4)$ and $(0, -1, 2)$.

$\sqrt{17}$

Differentiated Instruction

Visual and Kinesthetic Learners Students who learn better with visual representations may wish to construct a three-dimensional coordinate system; then they can refer to it as they work through examples in this section. Refer students to Figure 11.1 on page 810, and encourage them to use lightweight paperboard in a light color so that they can draw gridlines on each piece.

Extra Example 3

Find the midpoint of the line segment joining (2, −2, 4) and (1, 3, 6).

$\left(\frac{3}{2}, \frac{1}{2}, 5\right)$

Example 3 Using the Midpoint Formula in Space

Find the midpoint of the line segment joining (5, −2, 3) and (0, 4, 4).

Solution

Using the Midpoint Formula in Space, the midpoint is

$$\left(\frac{5+0}{2}, \frac{-2+4}{2}, \frac{3+4}{2}\right) = \left(\frac{5}{2}, 1, \frac{7}{2}\right)$$

as shown in Figure 11.6.

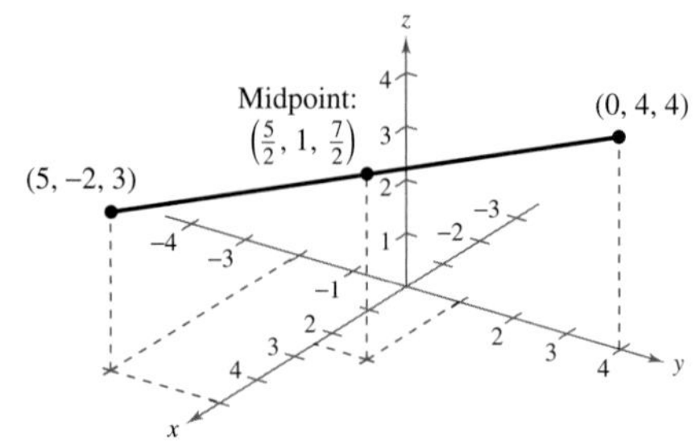

FIGURE 11.6

CHECKPoint Now try Exercise 45.

The Equation of a Sphere

A **sphere** with center (h, k, j) and radius r is defined as the set of all points (x, y, z) such that the distance between (x, y, z) and (h, k, j) is r, as shown in Figure 11.7. Using the Distance Formula, this condition can be written as

$$\sqrt{(x-h)^2 + (y-k)^2 + (z-j)^2} = r.$$

By squaring each side of this equation, you obtain the standard equation of a sphere.

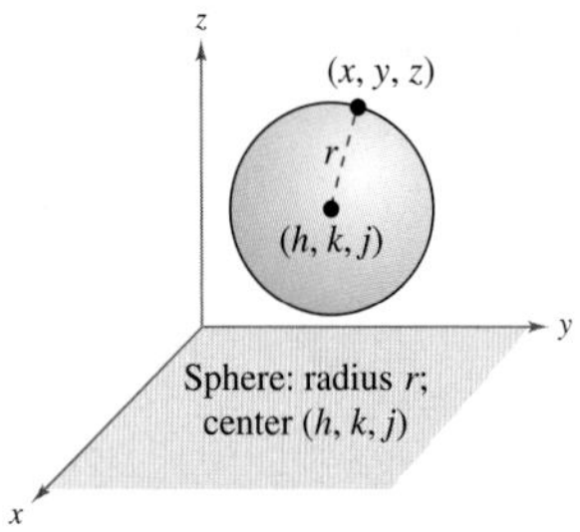

FIGURE 11.7

Standard Equation of a Sphere

The **standard equation of a sphere** with center (h, k, j) and radius r is given by

$$(x-h)^2 + (y-k)^2 + (z-j)^2 = r^2.$$

Notice the similarity of this formula to the equation of a circle in the plane.

$(x-h)^2 + (y-k)^2 + (z-j)^2 = r^2$ Equation of sphere in space

$(x-h)^2 + (y-k)^2 = r^2$ Equation of circle in the plane

As is true with the equation of a circle, the equation of a sphere is simplified when the center lies at the origin. In this case, the equation is

$x^2 + y^2 + z^2 = r^2.$ Sphere with center at origin

Example 4 Finding the Equation of a Sphere

Find the standard equation of the sphere with center (2, 4, 3) and radius 3. Does this sphere intersect the xy-plane?

Solution

$$(x-h)^2+(y-k)^2+(z-j)^2=r^2 \quad \text{Standard equation}$$

$$(x-2)^2+(y-4)^2+(z-3)^2=3^2 \quad \text{Substitute.}$$

From the graph shown in Figure 11.8, you can see that the center of the sphere lies three units above the xy-plane. Because the sphere has a radius of 3, you can conclude that it does intersect the xy-plane—at the point (2, 4, 0).

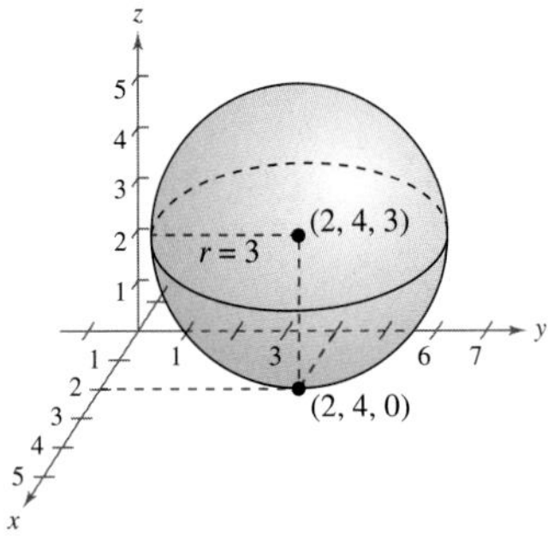

FIGURE 11.8

CHECKPoint Now try Exercise 53.

Example 5 Finding the Center and Radius of a Sphere

Find the center and radius of the sphere given by

$$x^2+y^2+z^2-2x+4y-6z+8=0.$$

Solution

To obtain the standard equation of this sphere, complete the square as follows.

$$x^2+y^2+z^2-2x+4y-6z+8=0$$

$$(x^2-2x+\quad)+(y^2+4y+\quad)+(z^2-6z+\quad)=-8$$

$$(x^2-2x+1)+(y^2+4y+4)+(z^2-6z+9)=-8+1+4+9$$

$$(x-1)^2+(y+2)^2+(z-3)^2=(\sqrt{6})^2$$

So, the center of the sphere is $(1, -2, 3)$, and its radius is $\sqrt{6}$. See Figure 11.9.

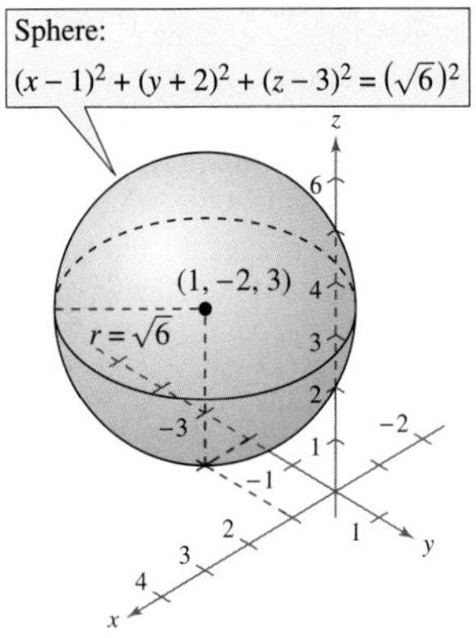

FIGURE 11.9

CHECKPoint Now try Exercise 63.

Note in Example 5 that the points satisfying the equation of the sphere are "surface points," not "interior points." In general, the collection of points satisfying an equation involving x, y, and z is called a **surface in space.**

Extra Example 4

Find the standard equation of the sphere with center $(1, 5, -2)$ and radius 4. Does this sphere intersect the xy-plane?

$(x-1)^2+(y-5)^2+(z+2)^2=16$; This sphere does intersect the xy-plane.

Extra Example 5

Find the center and radius of the sphere given by $x^2+y^2+z^2+4x-2y+8z+10=0$.

Center: $(-2, 1, -4)$

Radius: $\sqrt{11}$

Extra Example 6

Sketch the xy-trace of the sphere given by $(x-2)^2+(y-3)^2+(z+6)^2=7^2$.

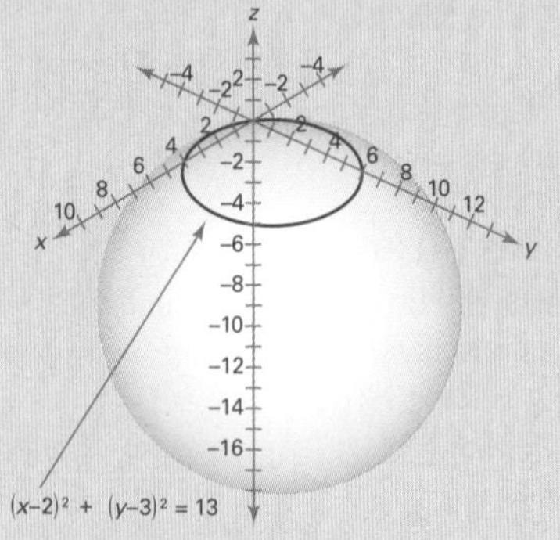

Closing the Lesson

Have students summarize the major points of the lesson and answer the Essential Question: How do you locate points, find distances, and graph equations in three dimensions?

- **Locate points in the three-dimensional coordinate system, given coordinates (x, y, z).**
- **Find the distance between two points by applying the Pythagorean Theorem in three dimensions.**
- **Find the midpoint between two points by finding the average of the x-, y-, and z-coordinates of the two points.**
- **Solve problems involving the equation for a sphere.**

Finding the intersection of a surface with one of the three coordinate planes (or with a plane parallel to one of the three coordinate planes) helps one visualize the surface. Such an intersection is called a **trace** of the surface. For example, the xy-trace of a surface consists of all points that are common to both the surface *and* the xy-plane. Similarly, the xz-trace of a surface consists of all points that are common to both the surface and the xz-plane.

Example 6 Finding a Trace of a Surface

Sketch the xy-trace of the sphere given by $(x-3)^2+(y-2)^2+(z+4)^2=5^2$.

Solution

To find the xy-trace of this surface, use the fact that every point in the xy-plane has a z-coordinate of zero. By substituting $z=0$ into the original equation, the resulting equation will represent the intersection of the surface with the xy-plane.

$$(x-3)^2+(y-2)^2+(z+4)^2=5^2 \quad \text{Write original equation.}$$
$$(x-3)^2+(y-2)^2+(0+4)^2=5^2 \quad \text{Substitute 0 for } z.$$
$$(x-3)^2+(y-2)^2+16=25 \quad \text{Simplify.}$$
$$(x-3)^2+(y-2)^2=9 \quad \text{Subtract 16 from each side.}$$
$$(x-3)^2+(y-2)^2=3^2 \quad \text{Equation of circle}$$

You can see that the xy-trace is a circle of radius 3, as shown in Figure 11.10.

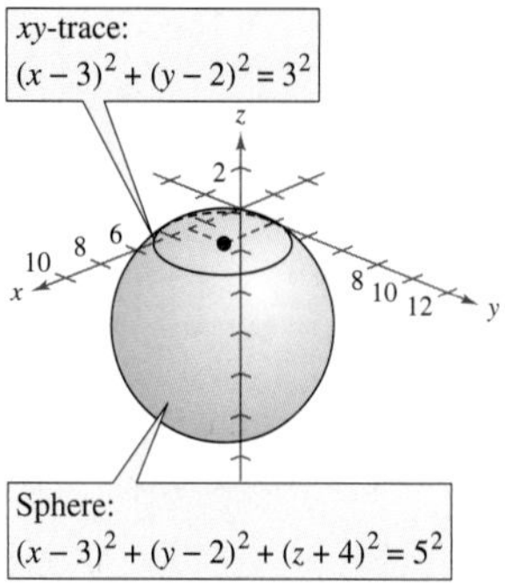

FIGURE 11.10

CHECKPoint Now try Exercise 71.

TECHNOLOGY

Most three-dimensional graphing utilities and computer algebra systems represent *surfaces* by sketching several traces of the surface. The traces are usually taken in equally spaced parallel planes. To graph an equation involving x, y, and z with a three-dimensional "function grapher," you must first set the graphing mode to *three-dimensional* and solve the equation for z. After entering the equation, you need to specify a rectangular viewing cube (the three-dimensional analog of a viewing window). For instance, to graph the top half of the sphere from Example 6, solve the equation for z to obtain the solutions $z=-4 \pm \sqrt{25-(x-3)^2-(y-2)^2}$. The equation $z=-4+\sqrt{25-(x-3)^2-(y-2)^2}$ represents the top half of the sphere. Enter this equation, as shown in Figure 11.11. Next, use the viewing cube shown in Figure 11.12. Finally, you can display the graph, as shown in Figure 11.13.

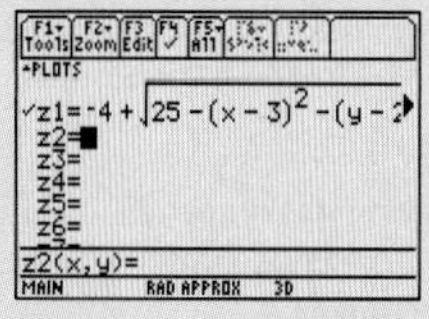

FIGURE 11.11

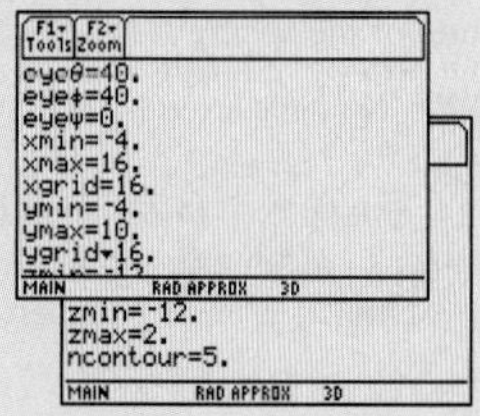

FIGURE 11.12

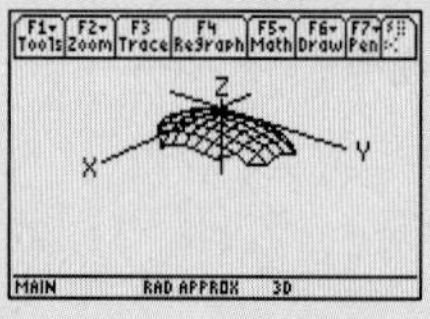

FIGURE 11.13

11.1 EXERCISES

See www.CalcChat.com for worked-out solutions to odd-numbered exercises.

VOCABULARY: Fill in the blanks.

1. A _______ coordinate system can be formed by passing a z-axis perpendicular to both the x-axis and the y-axis at the origin. three-dimensional
2. The three coordinate planes of a three-dimensional coordinate system are the xy-plane, the xz-plane, and the yz-plane.
3. The coordinate planes of a three-dimensional coordinate system separate the coordinate system into eight octants.
4. The distance between the points (x_1, y_1, z_1) and (x_2, y_2, z_2) can be found using the Distance Formula in Space.
5. The midpoint of the line segment joining the points (x_1, y_1, z_1) and (x_2, y_2, z_2) given by the Midpoint Formula in Space is See margin.
6. A sphere is the set of all points (x, y, z) such that the distance between (x, y, z) and a fixed point (h, k, j) is r.
7. A surface in space is the collection of points satisfying an equation involving x, y, and z.
8. The intersection of a surface with one of the three coordinate planes is called a trace of the surface.

SKILLS AND APPLICATIONS

In Exercises 9 and 10, approximate the coordinates of the points. 9–10. See margin.

9.

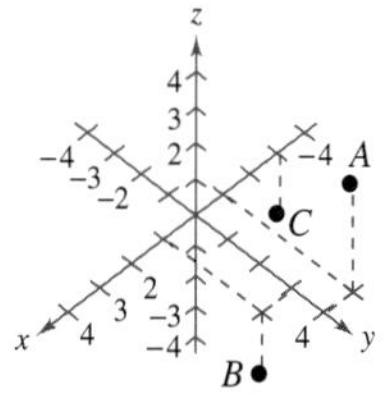

10.

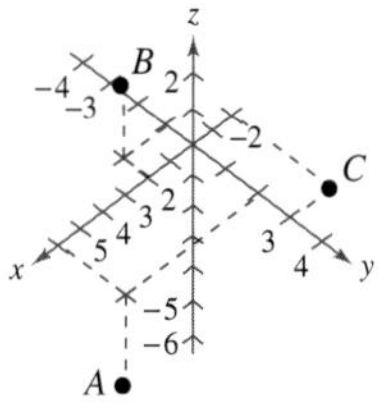

In Exercises 11–16, plot each point in the same three-dimensional coordinate system. 11–16. See margin.

11. (a) $(2, 1, 3)$ (b) $(1, -1, -2)$

12. (a) $(3, 0, 0)$ (b) $(-3, -2, -1)$

13. (a) $(3, -1, 0)$ (b) $(-4, 2, 2)$

14. (a) $(0, 4, -3)$ (b) $(4, 0, 4)$

15. (a) $(3, -2, 5)$ (b) $(\frac{3}{2}, 4, -2)$

16. (a) $(5, -2, 2)$ (b) $(5, -2, -2)$

In Exercises 17–20, find the coordinates of the point.

17. The point is located three units behind the yz-plane, four units to the right of the xz-plane, and five units above the xy-plane. $(-3, 4, 5)$
18. The point is located seven units in front of the yz-plane, two units to the left of the xz-plane, and one unit below the xy-plane. $(7, -2, -1)$
19. The point is located on the x-axis, eight units in front of the yz-plane. $(8, 0, 0)$
20. The point is located in the yz-plane, one unit to the right of the xz-plane, and six units above the xy-plane. $(0, 1, 6)$

In Exercises 21–26, determine the octant(s) in which (x, y, z) is located so that the condition(s) is (are) satisfied.

21. $x > 0, y < 0, z > 0$ IV

22. $x < 0, y > 0, z < 0$ VI

23. $z > 0$ I, II, III, IV

24. $y < 0$ III, IV, VII, VIII

25. $xy < 0$ II, IV, VI, VIII

26. $yz > 0$ I, II, VII, VIII

In Exercises 27–36, find the distance between the points. 27–30. See margin.

27. $(0, 0, 0), (5, 2, 6)$

28. $(1, 0, 0), (7, 0, 4)$

29. $(3, 2, 5), (7, 4, 8)$

30. $(4, 1, 5), (8, 2, 6)$

31. $(-1, 4, -2), (6, 0, -9)$ $\sqrt{114}$ units

32. $(1, 1, -7), (-2, -3, -7)$ 5 units

33. $(0, -3, 0), (1, 0, -10)$ 33. $\sqrt{110}$ units

34. $(2, -4, 0), (0, 6, -3)$ 34. $\sqrt{113}$ units

35. $(6, -9, 1), (-2, -1, 5)$ 12 units

36. $(4, 0, -6), (8, 8, 20)$ $6\sqrt{21}$ units

In Exercises 37–40, find the lengths of the sides of the right triangle with the indicated vertices. Show that these lengths satisfy the Pythagorean Theorem.

37. $(0, 0, 2), (-2, 5, 2), (0, 4, 0)$ $(2\sqrt{5})^2 + 3^2 = (\sqrt{29})^2$

38. $(2, -1, 2), (-4, 4, 1), (-2, 5, 0)$ See margin.

39. $(0, 0, 0), (2, 2, 1), (2, -4, 4)$ $3^2 + 6^2 = (3\sqrt{5})^2$

40. $(1, 0, 1), (1, 3, 1), (1, 0, 3)$ $3^2 + 2^2 = (\sqrt{13})^2$

In Exercises 41–44, find the lengths of the sides of the triangle with the indicated vertices, and determine whether the triangle is a right triangle, an isosceles triangle, or neither.

41. $(1, -3, -2), (5, -1, 2), (-1, 1, 2)$

42. $(5, 3, 4), (7, 1, 3), (3, 5, 3)$

43. $(4, -1, -2), (8, 1, 2), (2, 3, 2)$

44. $(1, -2, -1), (3, 0, 0), (3, -6, 3)$

41. $6, 6, 2\sqrt{10}$; isosceles triangle
42. $3, 3, 4\sqrt{2}$; isosceles triangle
43. $6, 6, 2\sqrt{10}$; isosceles triangle
44. $3, 6, 3\sqrt{5}$; right triangle

4 PRACTICE AND APPLY

Assignment Guide

Transparencies Available
Available at the Instructor's companion site.

Average:
Day 1: p. 815
Exs. 1–5, 9–13, 17–20, 21–25 odd, 28–35, 37–43 odd
Day 2: pp. 815–816
Exs. 6–8, 47–51 odd, 54, 55–61 odd, 65–69, 72, 73
Day 3: p. 816
Exs. 75, 77–81, 83–85

Advanced:
Day 1: p. 815
Exs. 1–5, 10–20, 22–26 even, 29–36, 38–44 even
Day 2: pp. 815–816
Exs. 6–8, 48–54 even, 56–60, 64–70, 73, 74
Day 3: p. 816
Exs. 76–78, 81–86

Block:
pp. 815–816
Exs. 1–13, 17–20, 21–25 odd, 28–35, 37–43 odd, 47–51 odd, 54, 55–61 odd, 65–69, 72, 73
p. 816
Exs. 75, 77–81, 83–85 (with 11.2)

5. $\left(\frac{x_1 + x_2}{2}, \frac{y_1 + y_2}{2}, \frac{z_1 + z_2}{2}\right)$

9. A: $(-1, 4, 4)$, B: $(1, 3, -2)$, C: $(-3, 0, -2)$

10. A: $(6, 2, -3)$, B: $(2, -1, 2)$, C: $(-2, 3, 0)$

11.

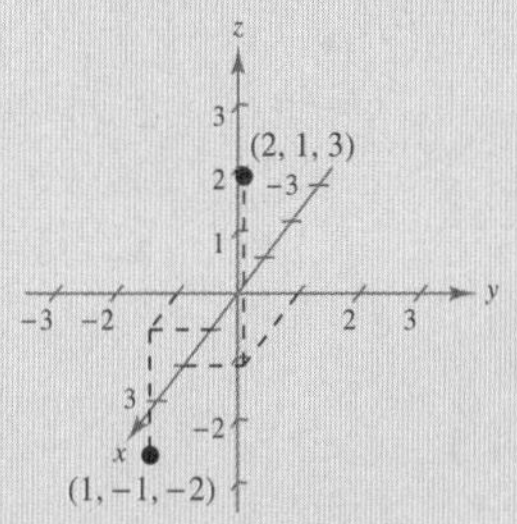

12.

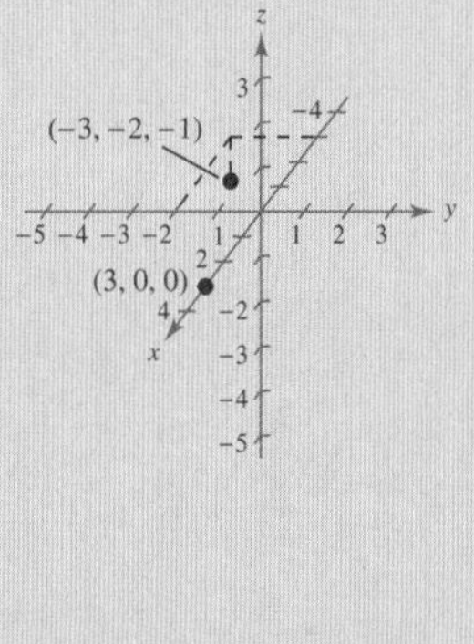

13.

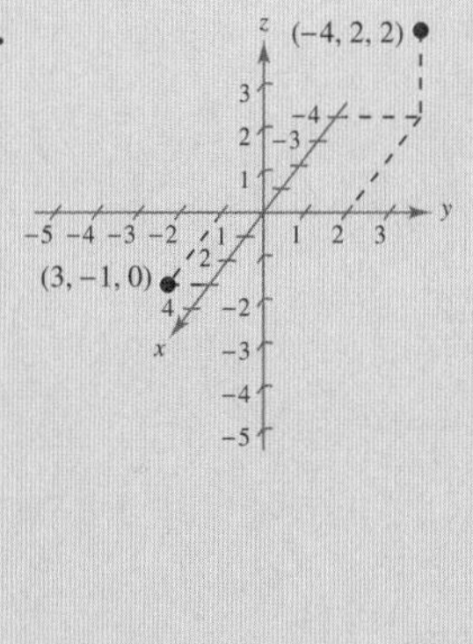

14.

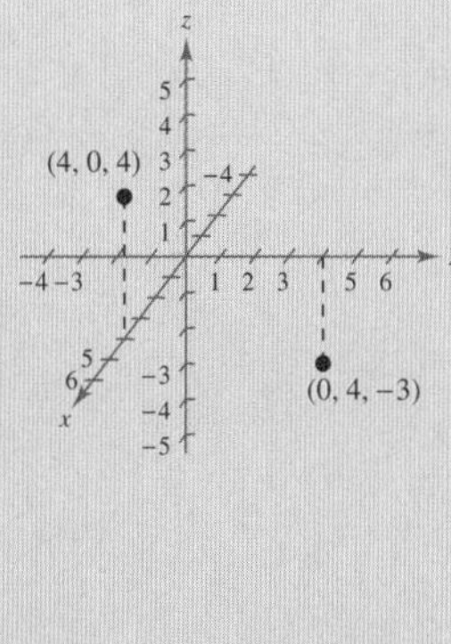

15.

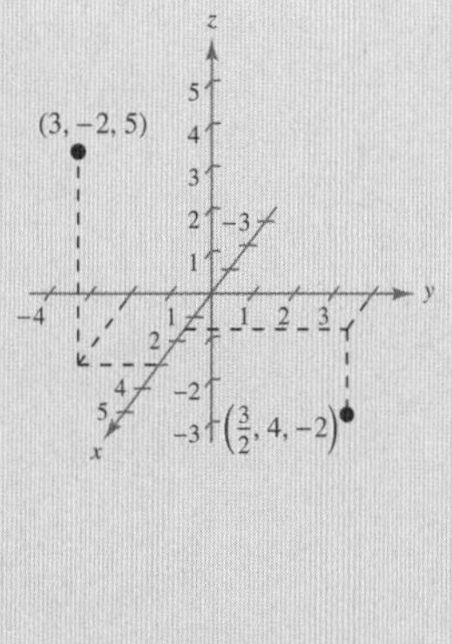

16, 27–30, 38. See Additional Answers beginning on page AA1.

5 ASSESS AND RETEACH

Daily Homework Quiz

Transparency Available
Available at the Instructor's companion site.

53–57. See below.

58. $x^2 + (y - 5)^2 + (z + 9)^2 = 16$

59. $\left(x - \frac{3}{2}\right)^2 + y^2 + (z - 3)^2 = \frac{45}{4}$

64. Center: $(3, -2, 0)$; radius: 2

65. Center: $(-2, 0, 4)$; radius: 1

66. Center: $(0, 4, 3)$; radius: $2\sqrt{3}$

67. Center: $\left(1, \frac{1}{3}, 4\right)$; radius: 3

68. Center: $\left(\frac{1}{2}, \frac{3}{2}, 1\right)$; radius: 1

69. Center: $\left(\frac{1}{3}, -1, 0\right)$; radius: 1

71.

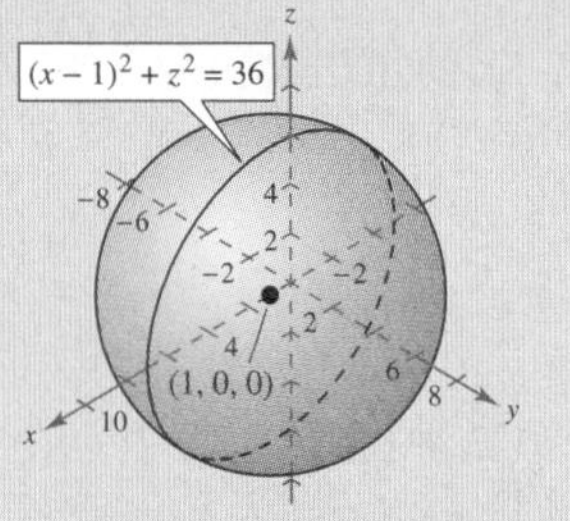

72.

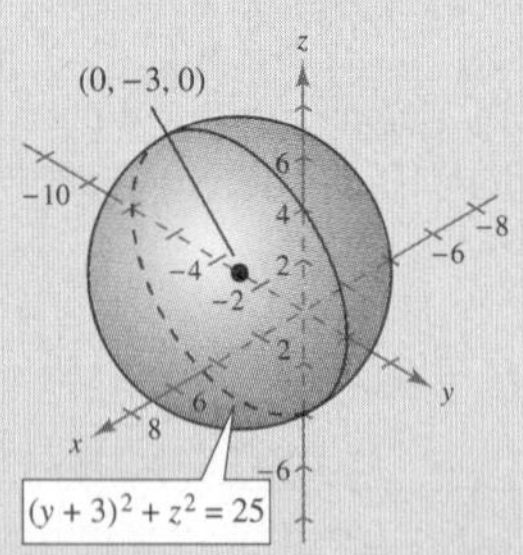

73.

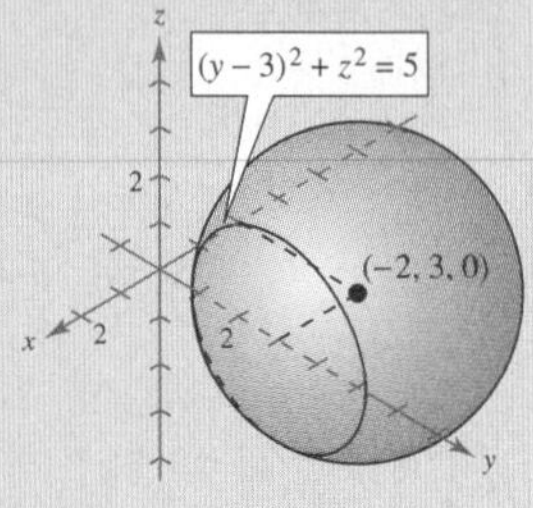

74.

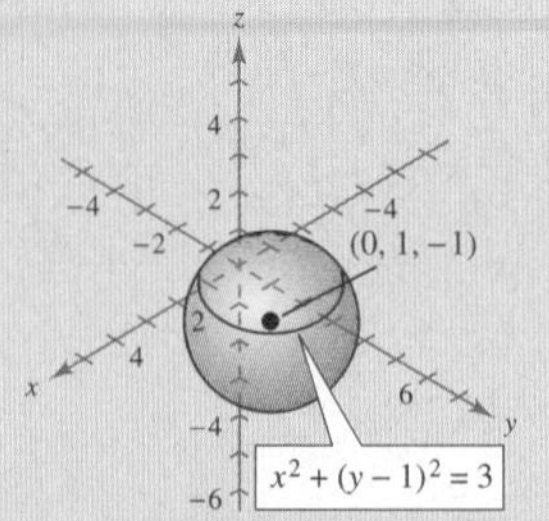

77. $x^2 + y^2 + z^2 = \frac{205^2}{4}$

78. (a) $x^2 + y^2 + z^2 = 4000^2$
(b) xz-trace: $x^2 + z^2 = 4000^2$;
yz-trace: $y^2 + z^2 = 4000^2$
These traces would form circles.

In Exercises 45–52, find the midpoint of the line segment joining the points.

45. $(0, 0, 0), (3, -2, 4)$ $\left(\frac{3}{2}, -1, 2\right)$

46. $(1, 5, -1), (2, 2, 2)$ $\left(\frac{3}{2}, \frac{7}{2}, \frac{1}{2}\right)$

47. $(3, -6, 10), (-3, 4, 4)$ $(0, -1, 7)$

48. $(-1, 5, -3), (3, 7, -1)$ $(1, 6, -2)$

49. $(-5, -2, 5), (6, 3, -7)$ $\left(\frac{1}{2}, \frac{1}{2}, -1\right)$

50. $(0, -2, 5), (4, 2, 7)$ $(2, 0, 6)$

51. $(-2, 8, 10), (7, -4, 2)$ $\left(\frac{5}{2}, 2, 6\right)$

52. $(9, -5, 1), (9, -2, -4)$ $\left(9, -\frac{7}{2}, -\frac{3}{2}\right)$

In Exercises 53–60, find the standard form of the equation of the sphere with the given characteristics. 53–59. See margin.

53. Center: $(3, 2, 4)$; radius: 4

54. Center: $(-3, 4, 3)$; radius: 2

55. Center: $(5, 0, -2)$; radius: 6

56. Center: $(4, -1, 1)$; radius: 5

57. Center: $(-3, 7, 5)$; diameter: 10

58. Center: $(0, 5, -9)$; diameter: 8

59. Endpoints of a diameter: $(3, 0, 0), (0, 0, 6)$

60. Endpoints of a diameter: $(1, 0, 0), (0, 5, 0)$
$\left(x - \frac{1}{2}\right)^2 + \left(y - \frac{5}{2}\right)^2 + z^2 = \frac{13}{2}$

In Exercises 61–70, find the center and radius of the sphere.

61. $x^2 + y^2 + z^2 - 6x = 0$ Center: $(3, 0, 0)$; radius: 3

62. $x^2 + y^2 + z^2 - 9x = 0$ Center: $\left(\frac{9}{2}, 0, 0\right)$; radius: $\frac{9}{2}$

63. $x^2 + y^2 + z^2 - 4x + 2y - 6z + 10 = 0$ Center: $(2, -1, 3)$; radius: 2

64. $x^2 + y^2 + z^2 - 6x + 4y + 9 = 0$

65. $x^2 + y^2 + z^2 + 4x - 8z + 19 = 0$ 64–69. See margin.

66. $x^2 + y^2 + z^2 - 8y - 6z + 13 = 0$

67. $9x^2 + 9y^2 + 9z^2 - 18x - 6y - 72z + 73 = 0$

68. $2x^2 + 2y^2 + 2z^2 - 2x - 6y - 4z + 5 = 0$

69. $9x^2 + 9y^2 + 9z^2 - 6x + 18y + 1 = 0$

70. $4x^2 + 4y^2 + 4z^2 - 4x - 32y + 8z + 33 = 0$
Center: $\left(\frac{1}{2}, 4, -1\right)$; radius: 3

In Exercises 71–74, sketch the graph of the equation and sketch the specified trace. 71–74. See margin.

71. $(x - 1)^2 + y^2 + z^2 = 36$; xz-trace

72. $x^2 + (y + 3)^2 + z^2 = 25$; yz-trace

73. $(x + 2)^2 + (y - 3)^2 + z^2 = 9$; yz-trace

74. $x^2 + (y - 1)^2 + (z + 1)^2 = 4$; xy-trace

In Exercises 75 and 76, use a three-dimensional graphing utility to graph the sphere. 75–76. See margin.

75. $x^2 + y^2 + z^2 - 6x - 8y - 10z + 46 = 0$

76. $x^2 + y^2 + z^2 + 6y - 8z + 21 = 0$

77. ARCHITECTURE A spherical building has a diameter of 205 feet. The center of the building is placed at the origin of a three-dimensional coordinate system. What is the equation of the sphere? See margin.

78. GEOGRAPHY Assume that Earth is a sphere with a radius of 4000 miles. The center of Earth is placed at the origin of a three-dimensional coordinate system. See margin.

(a) What is the equation of the sphere?

(b) Lines of longitude that run north-south could be represented by what trace(s)? What shape would each of these traces form?

(c) Lines of latitude that run east-west could be represented by what trace(s)? What shape would each of these traces form?

EXPLORATION 79. False. z is the directed distance from the xy-plane to P.

TRUE OR FALSE? In Exercises 79 and 80, determine whether the statement is true or false. Justify your answer.

79. In the ordered triple (x, y, z) that represents point P in space, x is the directed distance from the xy-plane to P.

80. The surface consisting of all points (x, y, z) in space that are the same distance r from the point (h, j, k) has a circle as its xy-trace. False. The xy-trace could also be a point or may not exist.

81. THINK ABOUT IT What is the z-coordinate of any point in the xy-plane? What is the y-coordinate of any point in the xz-plane? What is the x-coordinate of any point in the yz-plane? 0; 0; 0

82. CAPSTONE Find the equation of the sphere that has the points $(3, -2, 6)$ and $(-1, 4, 2)$ as endpoints of a diameter. Explain how this problem gives you a chance to use these formulas: the Distance Formula in Space, the Midpoint Formula in Space, and the standard equation of a sphere. See margin.

83. See margin.

83. A sphere intersects the yz-plane. Describe the trace.

84. A plane intersects the xy-plane. Describe the trace.

85. A line segment has (x_1, y_1, z_1) as one endpoint and (x_m, y_m, z_m) as its midpoint. Find the other endpoint (x_2, y_2, z_2) of the line segment in terms of x_1, y_1, z_1, x_m, y_m, and z_m. 84–85. See below.

86. Use the result of Exercise 85 to find the coordinates of the endpoint of a line segment if the coordinates of the other endpoint and the midpoint are $(3, 0, 2)$ and $(5, 8, 7)$, respectively. $(7, 16, 12)$

84. A straight line in the xy-plane

85. $(x_2, y_2, z_2) = (2x_m - x_1, 2y_m - y_1, 2z_m - z_1)$

(c) Latitudes are traces of planes parallel to the xy-plane, and the xy-trace is $x^2 + y^2 = 4000^2$. These traces would form circles, except at the poles, where the traces would be points.

82. $(x - 1)^2 + (y - 1)^2 + (z - 4)^2 = 17$
Midpoint Formula locates center; Distance Formula finds radius; standard equation finds equation.

83. A point or a circle (where the sphere and the yz-plane meet)

53. $(x - 3)^2 + (y - 2)^2 + (z - 4)^2 = 16$

54. $(x + 3)^2 + (y - 4)^2 + (z - 3)^2 = 4$

55. $(x - 5)^2 + y^2 + (z + 2)^2 = 36$

56. $(x - 4)^2 + (y + 1)^2 + (z - 1)^2 = 25$

57. $(x + 3)^2 + (y - 7)^2 + (z - 5)^2 = 25$

75–76. See Additional Answers beginning on page AA1.

11.2 Vectors in Space

What you should learn

- Find the component forms of the unit vectors in the same direction of, the magnitudes of, the dot products of, and the angles between vectors in space.
- Determine whether vectors in space are parallel or orthogonal.
- Use vectors in space to solve real-life problems.

Why you should learn it

Vectors in space can be used to represent many physical forces, such as tension in the cables used to support auditorium lights, as shown in Exercise 60 on page 823.

Vectors in Space

Physical forces and velocities are not confined to the plane, so it is natural to extend the concept of vectors from two-dimensional space to three-dimensional space. In space, vectors are denoted by ordered triples

$\mathbf{v} = \langle v_1, v_2, v_3 \rangle.$ Component form

The **zero vector** is denoted by $\mathbf{0} = \langle 0, 0, 0 \rangle$. Using the unit vectors $\mathbf{i} = \langle 1, 0, 0 \rangle$, $\mathbf{j} = \langle 0, 1, 0 \rangle$, and $\mathbf{k} = \langle 0, 0, 1 \rangle$ in the direction of the positive z-axis, the **standard unit vector notation** for $\mathbf{v}$ is

$\mathbf{v} = v_1\mathbf{i} + v_2\mathbf{j} + v_3\mathbf{k}$ Unit vector form

as shown in Figure 11.14. If $\mathbf{v}$ is represented by the directed line segment from $P(p_1, p_2, p_3)$ to $Q(q_1, q_2, q_3)$, as shown in Figure 11.15, the **component form** of $\mathbf{v}$ is produced by subtracting the coordinates of the initial point from the corresponding coordinates of the terminal point

$\mathbf{v} = \langle v_1, v_2, v_3 \rangle = \langle q_1 - p_1, q_2 - p_2, q_3 - p_3 \rangle.$

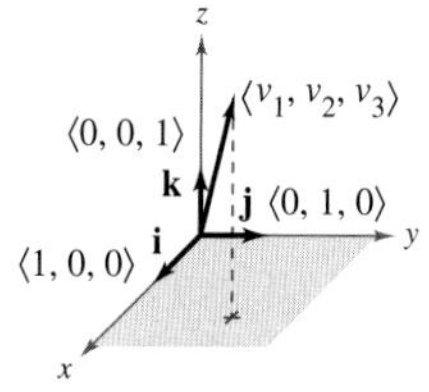

FIGURE 11.14

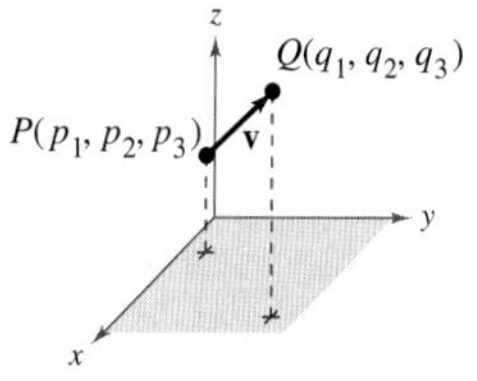

FIGURE 11.15

Vectors in Space

1. Two vectors are **equal** if and only if their corresponding components are equal.
2. The **magnitude** (or **length**) of $\mathbf{u} = \langle u_1, u_2, u_3 \rangle$ is $\|\mathbf{u}\| = \sqrt{u_1^2 + u_2^2 + u_3^2}$.
3. A **unit vector u** in the direction of **v** is $\mathbf{u} = \dfrac{\mathbf{v}}{\|\mathbf{v}\|}$, $\mathbf{v} \neq \mathbf{0}$.
4. The **sum** of $\mathbf{u} = \langle u_1, u_2, u_3 \rangle$ and $\mathbf{v} = \langle v_1, v_2, v_3 \rangle$ is

   $\mathbf{u} + \mathbf{v} = \langle u_1 + v_1, u_2 + v_2, u_3 + v_3 \rangle.$ Vector addition
5. The **scalar multiple** of the real number c and $\mathbf{u} = \langle u_1, u_2, u_3 \rangle$ is

   $c\mathbf{u} = \langle cu_1, cu_2, cu_3 \rangle.$ Scalar multiplication
6. The **dot product** of $\mathbf{u} = \langle u_1, u_2, u_3 \rangle$ and $\mathbf{v} = \langle v_1, v_2, v_3 \rangle$ is

   $\mathbf{u} \cdot \mathbf{v} = u_1v_1 + u_2v_2 + u_3v_3.$ Dot product

1 PLAN AND PREPARE

Warm-up Exercises

Transparency Available
Available at the Instructor's companion site.

Notetaking Guide

Transparency Available
Promotes interactive learning and notetaking skills.
Available at the Instructor's companion site.

Animated Precalculus

An **Animated Precalculus** tutorial is available at the Student companion site for **Section 11.2.**

Pacing

Average: 2 days
Advanced: 2 days
Block: 0.5 block with 11.1
0.5 block with 11.3

2 FOCUS AND MOTIVATE

Essential Question

How do you describe, compare, and solve problems involving vectors in three dimensions? **Tell students that they will learn how to answer this question by finding the component forms of, calculating the dot products of, finding the angle between, and identifying parallel vectors.**

Resource Planning Guide

Chapter Resources
- Complete Solutions Guide

Workbooks
- Notetaking Guide
- Student Solutions Guide

Interactive Technology
- Instructor Success Organizer
- Notetaking Guide IAE
- Instructional DVDs
- Animated Precalculus
- PowerLecture with ExamView

3 TEACH

Extra Example 1

Find the component form and length of the vector **v** having the initial point (2, 4, 1) and terminal point (3, 5, 2). Then find a unit vector in the direction of **v**.

Component form: $\langle -1, -1, -1\rangle$;
Magnitude: $\sqrt{3}$;
Unit vector in the direction of v:

$$\left\langle -\frac{\sqrt{3}}{3}, -\frac{\sqrt{3}}{3}, -\frac{\sqrt{3}}{3}\right\rangle$$

Avoiding Common Errors

Students should consider vectors in space as extensions of the vectors studied in Chapter 6. Reviewing the definitions and properties will help in understanding this section.

Extra Example 2

Find the dot product of $\langle -1, 3, 5\rangle$ and $\langle 0, 4, -2\rangle$.

2

TECHNOLOGY

Some graphing utilities have the capability to perform vector operations, such as the dot product. Consult the user's guide for your graphing utility for specific instructions.

Example 1 Finding the Component Form of a Vector

Find the component form and magnitude of the vector **v** having initial point (3, 4, 2) and terminal point (3, 6, 4). Then find a unit vector in the direction of **v**.

Solution

The component form of **v** is

$$\mathbf{v} = \langle 3-3, 6-4, 4-2\rangle = \langle 0, 2, 2\rangle$$

which implies that its magnitude is

$$\|\mathbf{v}\| = \sqrt{0^2+2^2+2^2} = \sqrt{8} = 2\sqrt{2}.$$

The unit vector in the direction of **v** is

$$\mathbf{u} = \frac{\mathbf{v}}{\|\mathbf{v}\|} = \frac{1}{2\sqrt{2}}\langle 0, 2, 2\rangle = \left\langle 0, \frac{1}{\sqrt{2}}, \frac{1}{\sqrt{2}}\right\rangle = \left\langle 0, \frac{\sqrt{2}}{2}, \frac{\sqrt{2}}{2}\right\rangle.$$

CHECKPoint Now try Exercise 9.

Example 2 Finding the Dot Product of Two Vectors

Find the dot product of $\langle 0, 3, -2\rangle$ and $\langle 4, -2, 3\rangle$.

Solution

$$\langle 0, 3, -2\rangle \cdot \langle 4, -2, 3\rangle = 0(4) + 3(-2) + (-2)(3)$$
$$= 0 - 6 - 6 = -12$$

Note that the dot product of two vectors is a real number, not a vector.

CHECKPoint Now try Exercise 31.

As was discussed in Section 6.4, the **angle between two nonzero vectors** is the angle θ, $0 \le \theta \le \pi$, between their respective standard position vectors, as shown in Figure 11.16. This angle can be found using the dot product. (Note that the angle between the zero vector and another vector is not defined.)

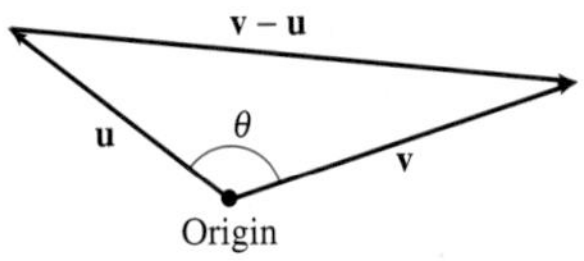

FIGURE 11.16

Angle Between Two Vectors

If θ is the angle between two nonzero vectors **u** and **v**, then $\cos\theta = \dfrac{\mathbf{u}\cdot\mathbf{v}}{\|\mathbf{u}\|\,\|\mathbf{v}\|}$.

If the dot product of two nonzero vectors is zero, the angle between the vectors is 90° (recall that $\cos 90° = 0$). Such vectors are called **orthogonal.** For instance, the standard unit vectors **i**, **j**, and **k** are orthogonal to each other.

Example 3 Finding the Angle Between Two Vectors

Find the angle between $\mathbf{u} = \langle 1, 0, 2 \rangle$ and $\mathbf{v} = \langle 3, 1, 0 \rangle$.

Solution

$$\cos\theta = \frac{\mathbf{u} \cdot \mathbf{v}}{\|\mathbf{u}\|\,\|\mathbf{v}\|} = \frac{\langle 1, 0, 2 \rangle \cdot \langle 3, 1, 0 \rangle}{\|\langle 1, 0, 2 \rangle\|\,\|\langle 3, 1, 0 \rangle\|} = \frac{3}{\sqrt{50}}$$

This implies that the angle between the two vectors is

$$\theta = \arccos \frac{3}{\sqrt{50}}$$

$$\approx 64.9^\circ$$

as shown in Figure 11.17.

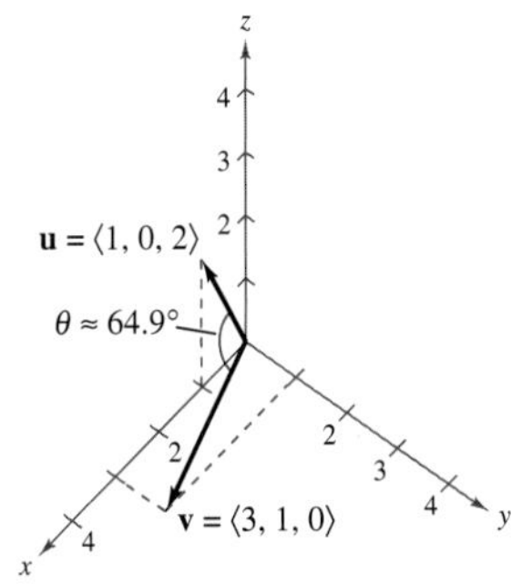

FIGURE 11.17

CHECK Point Now try Exercise 35.

Parallel Vectors

Recall from the definition of scalar multiplication that positive scalar multiples of a nonzero vector **v** have the same direction as **v**, whereas negative multiples have the direction opposite that of **v**. In general, two nonzero vectors **u** and **v** are **parallel** if there is some scalar c such that $\mathbf{u} = c\mathbf{v}$. For example, in Figure 11.18, the vectors **u**, **v**, and **w** are parallel because $\mathbf{u} = 2\mathbf{v}$ and $\mathbf{w} = -\mathbf{v}$.

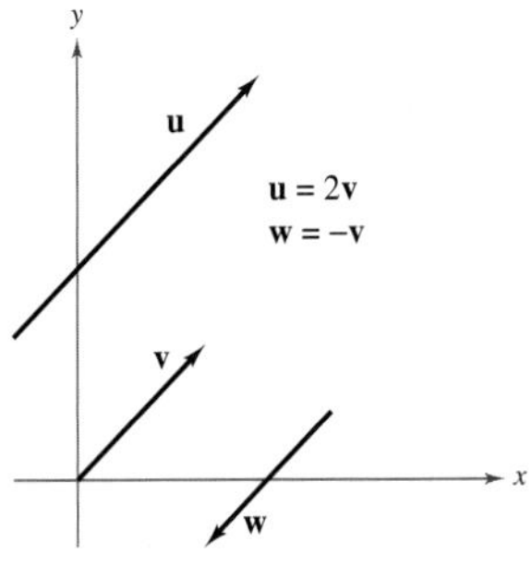

FIGURE 11.18

Example 4 Parallel Vectors

Vector **w** has initial point $(1, -2, 0)$ and terminal point $(3, 2, 1)$. Which of the following vectors is parallel to **w**?

a. $\mathbf{u} = \langle 4, 8, 2 \rangle$

b. $\mathbf{v} = \langle 4, 8, 4 \rangle$

Solution

Begin by writing **w** in component form.

$$\mathbf{w} = \langle 3 - 1, 2 - (-2), 1 - 0 \rangle = \langle 2, 4, 1 \rangle$$

a. Because

$$\mathbf{u} = \langle 4, 8, 2 \rangle$$
$$= 2\langle 2, 4, 1 \rangle$$
$$= 2\mathbf{w}$$

you can conclude that **u** *is* parallel to **w**.

b. In this case, you need to find a scalar c such that

$$\langle 4, 8, 4 \rangle = c\langle 2, 4, 1 \rangle.$$

However, equating corresponding components produces $c = 2$ for the first two components and $c = 4$ for the third. So, the equation has no solution, and the vectors **v** and **w** are *not* parallel.

CHECK Point Now try Exercise 39.

Extra Example 3

Find the angle between $\mathbf{u} = \langle 4, -1, 3 \rangle$ and $\mathbf{v} = \langle 0, 1, 5 \rangle$.

≈ 57.4°

Extra Example 4

Vector **w** has initial point (3, 0, −1) and terminal point (2, 1, 4). Which of the following vectors is parallel to **w**?

a. $\mathbf{u} = \langle 0, 1, 5 \rangle$

Not parallel

b. $\mathbf{v} = \langle 6, -6, -30 \rangle$

v is parallel to w because $\mathbf{v} = -6\mathbf{w}$.

Extra Example 5

Determine whether the points $P(1, -1, 3)$, $Q(0, 4, -2)$, and $R(6, 13, -5)$ are collinear.

Because $\overrightarrow{PQ}$ and $\overrightarrow{QR}$ are not parallel, the points P, Q, and R are not collinear.

Extra Example 6

The initial point of the vector $\mathbf{v} = \langle 6, -1, 4 \rangle$ is $P(0, 2, -3)$. What is the terminal point of this vector?

(6, 1, 1)

You can use vectors to determine whether three points are collinear (lie on the same line). The points P, Q, and R are **collinear** if and only if the vectors $\overrightarrow{PQ}$ and $\overrightarrow{PR}$ are parallel.

Example 5 Using Vectors to Determine Collinear Points

Determine whether the points $P(2, -1, 4)$, $Q(5, 4, 6)$, and $R(-4, -11, 0)$ are collinear.

Solution

The component forms of $\overrightarrow{PQ}$ and $\overrightarrow{PR}$ are

$$\overrightarrow{PQ} = \langle 5 - 2, 4 - (-1), 6 - 4 \rangle = \langle 3, 5, 2 \rangle$$

and

$$\overrightarrow{PR} = \langle -4 - 2, -11 - (-1), 0 - 4 \rangle = \langle -6, -10, -4 \rangle.$$

Because $\overrightarrow{PR} = -2\overrightarrow{PQ}$, you can conclude that they are parallel. Therefore, the points P, Q, and R lie on the same line, as shown in Figure 11.19.

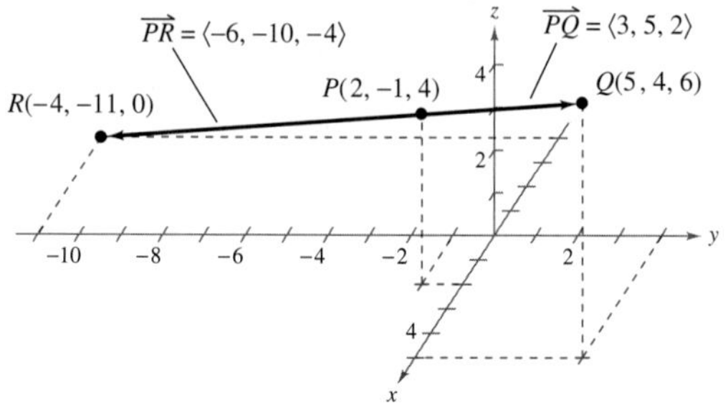

FIGURE 11.19

CHECKPoint Now try Exercise 47.

Example 6 Finding the Terminal Point of a Vector

The initial point of the vector $\mathbf{v} = \langle 4, 2, -1 \rangle$ is $P(3, -1, 6)$. What is the terminal point of this vector?

Solution

Using the component form of the vector whose initial point is $P(3, -1, 6)$ and whose terminal point is $Q(q_1, q_2, q_3)$, you can write

$$\overrightarrow{PQ} = \langle q_1 - p_1, q_2 - p_2, q_3 - p_3 \rangle$$
$$= \langle q_1 - 3, q_2 + 1, q_3 - 6 \rangle = \langle 4, 2, -1 \rangle.$$

This implies that $q_1 - 3 = 4$, $q_2 + 1 = 2$, and $q_3 - 6 = -1$. The solutions of these three equations are $q_1 = 7$, $q_2 = 1$, and $q_3 = 5$. So, the terminal point is $Q(7, 1, 5)$.

CHECKPoint Now try Exercise 51.

Application

In Section 6.3, you saw how to use vectors to solve an equilibrium problem in a plane. The next example shows how to use vectors to solve an equilibrium problem in space.

Example 7 Solving an Equilibrium Problem

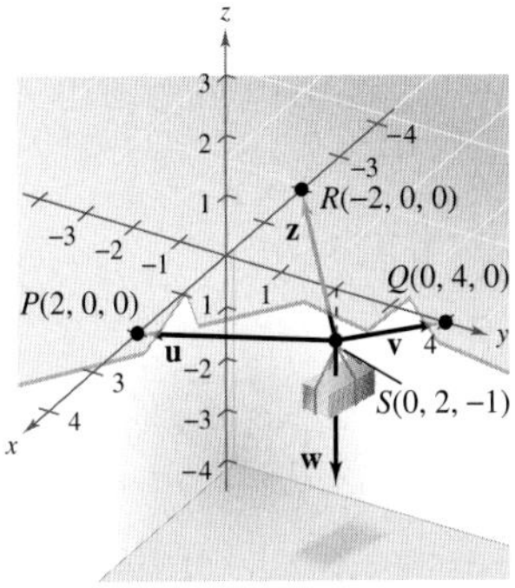

FIGURE 11.20

A weight of 480 pounds is supported by three ropes. As shown in Figure 11.20, the weight is located at $S(0, 2, -1)$. The ropes are tied to the points $P(2, 0, 0)$, $Q(0, 4, 0)$, and $R(-2, 0, 0)$. Find the force (or tension) on each rope.

Solution

The (downward) force of the weight is represented by the vector

$$\mathbf{w} = \langle 0, 0, -480 \rangle.$$

The force vectors corresponding to the ropes are as follows.

$$\mathbf{u} = \|\mathbf{u}\|\frac{\overrightarrow{SP}}{\|\overrightarrow{SP}\|} = \|\mathbf{u}\|\frac{\langle 2-0, 0-2, 0-(-1)\rangle}{3} = \|\mathbf{u}\|\left\langle \frac{2}{3}, -\frac{2}{3}, \frac{1}{3}\right\rangle$$

$$\mathbf{v} = \|\mathbf{v}\|\frac{\overrightarrow{SQ}}{\|\overrightarrow{SQ}\|} = \|\mathbf{v}\|\frac{\langle 0-0, 4-2, 0-(-1)\rangle}{\sqrt{5}} = \|\mathbf{v}\|\left\langle 0, \frac{2}{\sqrt{5}}, \frac{1}{\sqrt{5}}\right\rangle$$

$$\mathbf{z} = \|\mathbf{z}\|\frac{\overrightarrow{SR}}{\|\overrightarrow{SR}\|} = \|\mathbf{z}\|\frac{\langle -2-0, 0-2, 0-(-1)\rangle}{3} = \|\mathbf{z}\|\left\langle -\frac{2}{3}, -\frac{2}{3}, \frac{1}{3}\right\rangle$$

For the system to be in equilibrium, it must be true that

$$\mathbf{u} + \mathbf{v} + \mathbf{z} + \mathbf{w} = \mathbf{0} \quad \text{or} \quad \mathbf{u} + \mathbf{v} + \mathbf{z} = -\mathbf{w}.$$

This yields the following system of linear equations.

$$\begin{aligned} \frac{2}{3}\|\mathbf{u}\| \qquad\qquad\quad - \frac{2}{3}\|\mathbf{z}\| &= 0 \\ -\frac{2}{3}\|\mathbf{u}\| + \frac{2}{\sqrt{5}}\|\mathbf{v}\| - \frac{2}{3}\|\mathbf{z}\| &= 0 \\ \frac{1}{3}\|\mathbf{u}\| + \frac{1}{\sqrt{5}}\|\mathbf{v}\| + \frac{1}{3}\|\mathbf{z}\| &= 480 \end{aligned}$$

Using the techniques demonstrated in Chapter 7, you can find the solution of the system to be

$$\|\mathbf{u}\| = 360.0$$

$$\|\mathbf{v}\| \approx 536.7$$

$$\|\mathbf{z}\| = 360.0.$$

So, the rope attached at point P has 360 pounds of tension, the rope attached at point Q has about 536.7 pounds of tension, and the rope attached at point R has 360 pounds of tension.

CHECKPoint Now try Exercise 59.

Extra Example 7

A weight of 510 pounds is supported by three ropes. The weight is located at $S(0, 3, -1)$. The ropes are tied at the points $P(3, 0, 0)$, $Q(0, 5, 0)$, and $R(-1, 0, 0)$. Find the force (or tension) on each rope.

The rope attached at point P has about 222.3 pounds of tension, the rope attached at point Q has about 684.2 pounds of tension, and the rope attached at point R has about 507.4 pounds of tension.

Closing the Lesson

Have students summarize the major points of the lesson and answer the Essential Question: How do you describe, compare, and solve problems involving vectors in three dimensions?

- **Find the component form of a vector by subtracting the coordinates of the initial point from the coordinates of the terminal point.**
- **Find the dot product of two vectors by calculating the sum of the products of corresponding coordinates.**
- **Find the angle between two vectors by using the formula**

  $\cos\theta = \dfrac{\mathbf{u}\cdot\mathbf{v}}{\|\mathbf{u}\|\,\|\mathbf{v}\|}.$
- **Conclude that two vectors written in component form are parallel if a scalar multiple of one vector is equivalent to the other vector.**

4 PRACTICE AND APPLY

Assignment Guide

Transparencies Available
Available at the Instructor's companion site.

Average:
Day 1: pp. 822–823
Exs. 1–8, 10, 11–29 odd, 32, 33, 36, 37
Day 2: p. 823
Exs. 40–43, 48, 49, 52, 53–57 odd, 60–64

Advanced:
Day 1: pp. 822–823
Exs. 1–8, 10–14, 16–34 even, 36–38
Day 2: p. 823
Exs. 40–44, 48–56 even, 57, 58, 60–64

Block:
pp. 822–823
Exs. 1–8, 10, 11–29 odd, 32, 33, 36, 37 (with 11.1)
p. 823
Exs. 40–43, 48, 49, 52, 53–57 odd, 60–64 (with 11.3)

11.2 EXERCISES

See www.CalcChat.com for worked-out solutions to odd-numbered exercises.

VOCABULARY: Fill in the blanks.

1. The zero vector is denoted by $\mathbf{0} = \langle 0, 0, 0\rangle$.
2. The standard unit vector notation for a vector $\mathbf{v}$ is given by ______ . $\mathbf{v} = v_1\mathbf{i} + v_2\mathbf{j} + v_3\mathbf{k}$
3. The component form of a vector $\mathbf{v}$ is produced by subtracting the coordinates of the initial point from the corresponding coordinates of the terminal point.
4. If the dot product of two nonzero vectors is zero, the angle between the vectors is 90° and the vectors are called orthogonal
5. Two nonzero vectors $\mathbf{u}$ and $\mathbf{v}$ are parallel if there is some scalar c such that $\mathbf{u} = c\mathbf{v}$.
6. The points P, Q, and R are ______ if and only if the vectors $\overrightarrow{PQ}$ and $\overrightarrow{PR}$ are parallel. collinear

SKILLS AND APPLICATIONS

In Exercises 7 and 8, (a) find the component form of the vector v and (b) sketch the vector with its initial point at the origin. 7–8. See margin.

7.

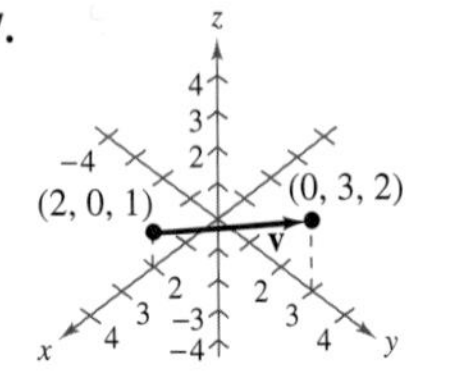

8.

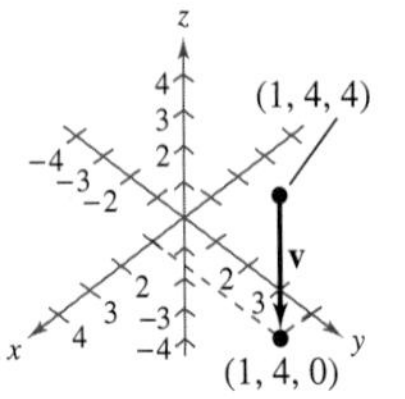

In Exercises 9 and 10, (a) write the component form of the vector v, (b) find the magnitude of v, and (c) find a unit vector in the direction of v.

9. Initial point: $(-6, 4, -2)$
Terminal point: $(1, -1, 3)$
(a) $\langle 7, -5, 5\rangle$ (b) $3\sqrt{11}$ (c) $\frac{\sqrt{11}}{33}\langle 7, -5, 5\rangle$

10. Initial point: $(-7, 3, 5)$
Terminal point: $(0, 0, 2)$
(a) $\langle 7, -3, -3\rangle$ (b) $\sqrt{67}$ (c) $\frac{\sqrt{67}}{67}\langle 7, -3, -3\rangle$

In Exercises 11–14, sketch each scalar multiple of v. 11–14. See margin.

11. $\mathbf{v} = \langle 1, 1, 3\rangle$
(a) $2\mathbf{v}$ (b) $-\mathbf{v}$ (c) $\frac{3}{2}\mathbf{v}$ (d) $0\mathbf{v}$

12. $\mathbf{v} = \langle -1, 2, 2\rangle$
(a) $-\mathbf{v}$ (b) $2\mathbf{v}$ (c) $\frac{1}{2}\mathbf{v}$ (d) $\frac{5}{2}\mathbf{v}$

13. $\mathbf{v} = 2\mathbf{i} + 2\mathbf{j} - \mathbf{k}$
(a) $2\mathbf{v}$ (b) $-\mathbf{v}$ (c) $\frac{5}{2}\mathbf{v}$ (d) $0\mathbf{v}$

14. $\mathbf{v} = \mathbf{i} - 2\mathbf{j} + \mathbf{k}$
(a) $4\mathbf{v}$ (b) $-2\mathbf{v}$ (c) $\frac{1}{2}\mathbf{v}$ (d) $0\mathbf{v}$

In Exercises 15–18, find the vector z, given $\mathbf{u} = \langle -1, 3, 2\rangle$, $\mathbf{v} = \langle 1, -2, -2\rangle$, and $\mathbf{w} = \langle 5, 0, -5\rangle$.

15. $\mathbf{z} = \mathbf{u} - 2\mathbf{v}$
16. $\mathbf{z} = 7\mathbf{u} + \mathbf{v} - \frac{1}{5}\mathbf{w}$
17. $2\mathbf{z} - 4\mathbf{u} = \mathbf{w}$
18. $\mathbf{u} + \mathbf{v} + \mathbf{z} = \mathbf{0}$

15. $\mathbf{z} = \langle -3, 7, 6\rangle$
16. $\mathbf{z} = \langle -7, 19, 13\rangle$
17. $\mathbf{z} = \langle \frac{1}{2}, 6, \frac{3}{2}\rangle$
18. $\mathbf{z} = \langle 0, -1, 0\rangle$

In Exercises 19–28, find the magnitude of v.

19. $\mathbf{v} = \langle 7, 8, 7\rangle$ $9\sqrt{2}$
20. $\mathbf{v} = \langle -2, 0, -5\rangle$ $\sqrt{29}$
21. $\mathbf{v} = \langle 1, -2, 4\rangle$ $\sqrt{21}$
22. $\mathbf{v} = \langle -1, 0, 3\rangle$ $\sqrt{10}$
23. $\mathbf{v} = \mathbf{i} + 3\mathbf{j} - \mathbf{k}$ $\sqrt{11}$
24. $\mathbf{v} = -\mathbf{i} - 4\mathbf{j} + 3\mathbf{k}$ $\sqrt{26}$
25. $\mathbf{v} = 4\mathbf{i} - 3\mathbf{j} - 7\mathbf{k}$ $\sqrt{74}$
26. $\mathbf{v} = 2\mathbf{i} - \mathbf{j} + 6\mathbf{k}$ $\sqrt{41}$
27. Initial point: $(1, -3, 4)$
Terminal point: $(1, 0, -1)$ $\sqrt{34}$
28. Initial point: $(0, -1, 0)$
Terminal point: $(1, 2, -2)$ $\sqrt{14}$

In Exercises 29 and 30, find a unit vector (a) in the direction of u and (b) in the direction opposite of u. 29–30. See margin.

29. $\mathbf{u} = 8\mathbf{i} + 3\mathbf{j} - \mathbf{k}$
30. $\mathbf{u} = -3\mathbf{i} + 5\mathbf{j} + 10\mathbf{k}$

In Exercises 31–34, find the dot product of u and v.

31. $\mathbf{u} = \langle 4, 4, -1\rangle$ -4
$\mathbf{v} = \langle 2, -5, -8\rangle$
32. $\mathbf{u} = \langle 3, -1, 6\rangle$ 28
$\mathbf{v} = \langle 4, -10, 1\rangle$
33. $\mathbf{u} = 2\mathbf{i} - 5\mathbf{j} + 3\mathbf{k}$ 0
$\mathbf{v} = 9\mathbf{i} + 3\mathbf{j} - \mathbf{k}$
34. $\mathbf{u} = 3\mathbf{j} - 6\mathbf{k}$ 0
$\mathbf{v} = 6\mathbf{i} - 4\mathbf{j} - 2\mathbf{k}$

7. (a) $\langle -2, 3, 1\rangle$
(b)

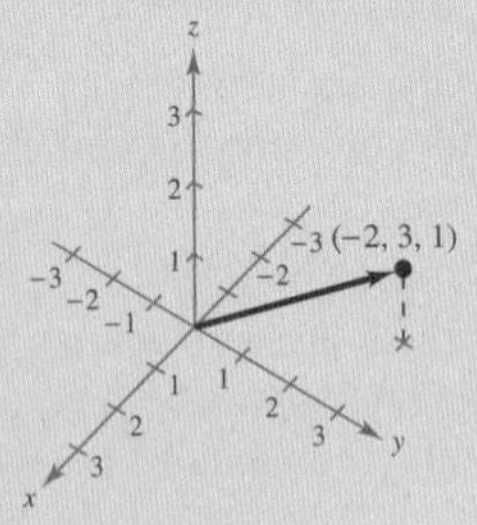

8. (a) $\langle 0, 0, -4\rangle$
(b)

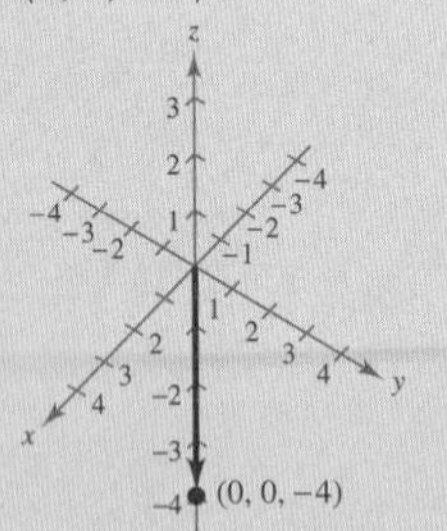

11. (a)

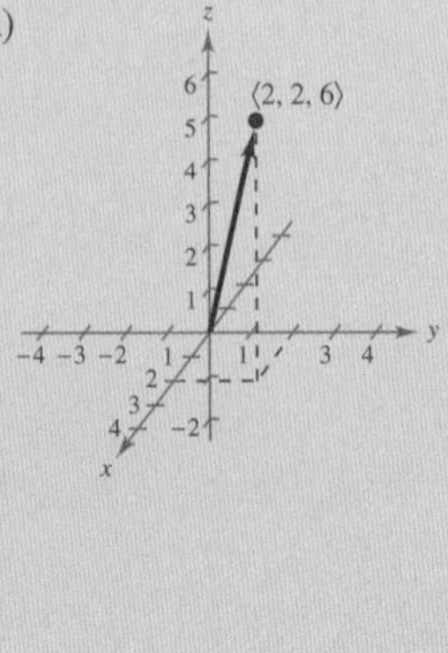

(b)

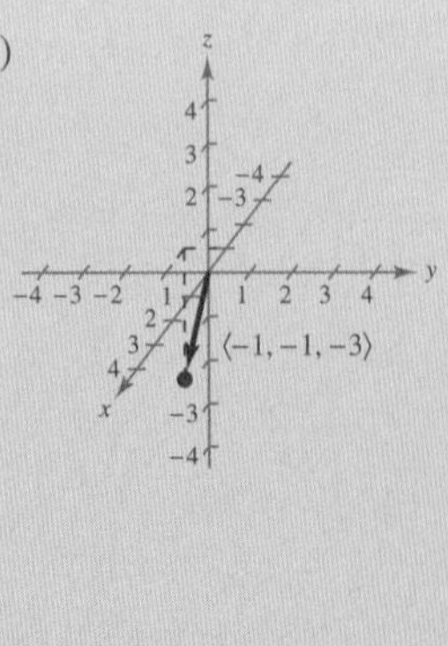

(c)

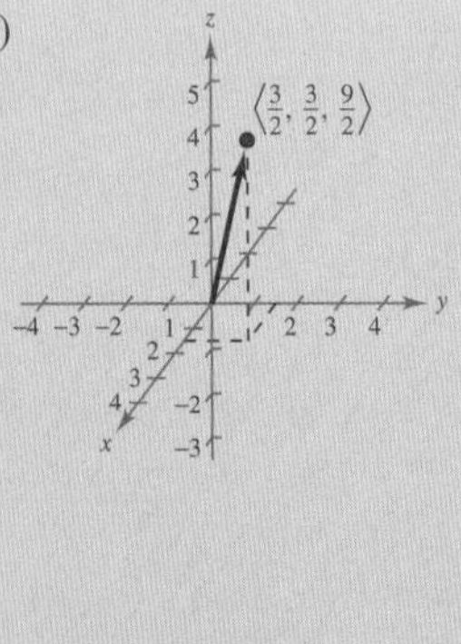

(d)

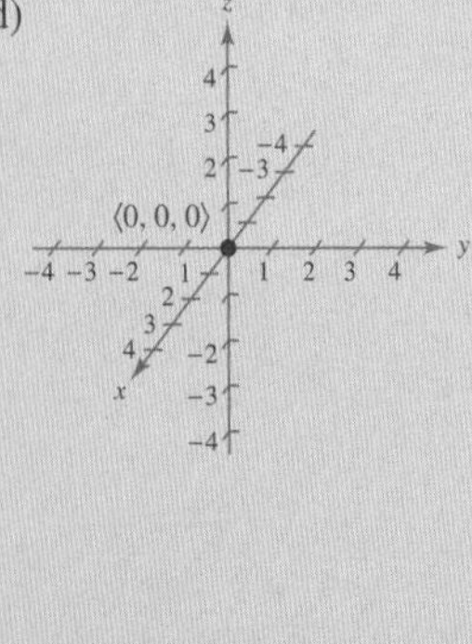

12–14, 29–30. See Additional Answers beginning on page AA1.

In Exercises 35–38, find the angle θ between the vectors.

35. $\mathbf{u} = \langle 0, 2, 2 \rangle$ About
$\mathbf{v} = \langle 3, 0, -4 \rangle$ 124.45°

36. $\mathbf{u} = \langle -1, 3, 0 \rangle$ About
$\mathbf{v} = \langle 1, 2, -1 \rangle$ 49.80°

37. $\mathbf{u} = 10\mathbf{i} + 40\mathbf{j}$ About
$\mathbf{v} = -3\mathbf{j} + 8\mathbf{k}$ 109.92°

38. $\mathbf{u} = 8\mathbf{j} - 20\mathbf{k}$ About
$\mathbf{v} = 10\mathbf{i} - 5\mathbf{k}$ 65.47°

In Exercises 39–46, determine whether **u** and **v** are orthogonal, parallel, or neither. 43. Orthogonal

39. $\mathbf{u} = \langle -12, 6, 15 \rangle$
$\mathbf{v} = \langle 8, -4, -10 \rangle$ Parallel

40. $\mathbf{u} = \langle -1, 3, -1 \rangle$
$\mathbf{v} = \langle 2, -1, 5 \rangle$ Neither

41. $\mathbf{u} = \langle 0, 1, 6 \rangle$
$\mathbf{v} = \langle 1, -2, -1 \rangle$ Neither

42. $\mathbf{u} = \langle 0, 4, -1 \rangle$
$\mathbf{v} = \langle 1, 0, 0 \rangle$ Orthogonal

43. $\mathbf{u} = \frac{3}{4}\mathbf{i} - \frac{1}{2}\mathbf{j} + 2\mathbf{k}$
$\mathbf{v} = 4\mathbf{i} + 10\mathbf{j} + \mathbf{k}$

44. $\mathbf{u} = -\mathbf{i} + \frac{1}{2}\mathbf{j} - \mathbf{k}$
$\mathbf{v} = 8\mathbf{i} - 4\mathbf{j} + 8\mathbf{k}$ Parallel

45. $\mathbf{u} = -2\mathbf{i} + 3\mathbf{j} - \mathbf{k}$
$\mathbf{v} = 2\mathbf{i} + \mathbf{j} - \mathbf{k}$
Orthogonal

46. $\mathbf{u} = 2\mathbf{i} - 3\mathbf{j} + \mathbf{k}$
$\mathbf{v} = -\mathbf{i} - \mathbf{j} - \mathbf{k}$
Orthogonal

In Exercises 47–50, use vectors to determine whether the points are collinear.

47. $(5, 4, 1), (7, 3, -1), (4, 5, 3)$ Not collinear

48. $(-2, 7, 4), (-4, 8, 1), (0, 6, 7)$ Collinear

49. $(1, 3, 2), (-1, 2, 5), (3, 4, -1)$ Collinear

50. $(0, 4, 4), (-1, 5, 6), (-2, 6, 7)$ Not collinear

In Exercises 51–54, the vector **v** and its initial point are given. Find the terminal point.

51. $\mathbf{v} = \langle 2, -4, 7 \rangle$
Initial point: $(1, 5, 0)$ $(3, 1, 7)$

52. $\mathbf{v} = \langle 4, -1, -1 \rangle$
Initial point: $(6, -4, 3)$ $(10, -5, 2)$

53. $\mathbf{v} = \left\langle 4, \frac{3}{2}, -\frac{1}{4} \right\rangle$
Initial point: $\left(2, 1, -\frac{3}{2}\right)$ $\left(6, \frac{5}{2}, -\frac{7}{4}\right)$

54. $\mathbf{v} = \left\langle \frac{5}{2}, -\frac{1}{2}, 4 \right\rangle$
Initial point: $\left(3, 2, -\frac{1}{2}\right)$ $\left(\frac{11}{2}, \frac{3}{2}, \frac{7}{2}\right)$

55. $\pm\frac{3\sqrt{14}}{14}$

55. Determine the values of c such that $\|c\mathbf{u}\| = 3$, where $\mathbf{u} = \mathbf{i} + 2\mathbf{j} + 3\mathbf{k}$.

56. Determine the values of c such that $\|c\mathbf{u}\| = 12$, where $\mathbf{u} = -2\mathbf{i} + 2\mathbf{j} - 4\mathbf{k}$. $\pm\sqrt{6}$

In Exercises 57 and 58, write the component form of **v**.

57. **v** lies in the yz-plane, has magnitude 4, and makes an angle of 45° with the positive y-axis.

58. **v** lies in the xz-plane, has magnitude 10, and makes an angle of 60° with the positive z-axis.

57. $\left\langle 0, 2\sqrt{2}, 2\sqrt{2} \right\rangle$ or $\left\langle 0, 2\sqrt{2}, -2\sqrt{2} \right\rangle$
58. $\left\langle 5\sqrt{3}, 0, 5 \right\rangle$ or $\left\langle -5\sqrt{3}, 0, 5 \right\rangle$

59. TENSION The weight of a crate is 500 newtons. Find the tension in each of the supporting cables shown in the figure. B: 226.52 N, C: 202.92 N, D: 157.91 N

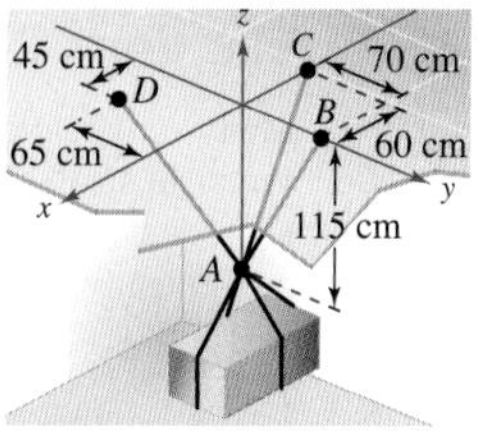

FIGURE FOR 59

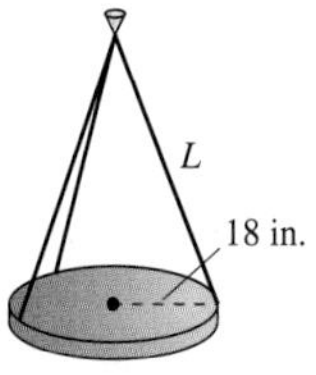

FIGURE FOR 60

60. TENSION The lights in an auditorium are 24-pound disks of radius 18 inches. Each disk is supported by three equally spaced cables that are L inches long (see figure). See margin.

(a) Write the tension T in each cable as a function of L. Determine the domain of the function.

(b) Use the function from part (a) to complete the table.

L	20	25	30	35	40	45	50
T							

(c) Use a graphing utility to graph the function in part (a). What are the asymptotes of the graph? Interpret their meaning in the context of the problem.

(d) Determine the minimum length of each cable if a cable can carry a maximum load of 10 pounds.

EXPLORATION

TRUE OR FALSE? In Exercises 61 and 62, determine whether the statement is true or false. Justify your answer.

61. If the dot product of two nonzero vectors is zero, then the angle between the vectors is a right angle. True

62. If AB and AC are parallel vectors, then points A, B, and C are collinear. True

63. What is known about the nonzero vectors **u** and **v** if $\mathbf{u} \cdot \mathbf{v} < 0$? Explain.
The angle between **u** and **v** is an obtuse angle.

64. CAPSTONE Consider the two nonzero vectors **u** and **v**. Describe the geometric figure generated by the terminal points of the vectors

$t\mathbf{v}$, $\mathbf{u} + t\mathbf{v}$, and $s\mathbf{u} + t\mathbf{v}$

where s and t represent real numbers. A line

5 ASSESS AND RETEACH

Daily Homework Quiz
Transparency Available
Available at the Instructor's companion site.

60. (a) $T = \dfrac{8L}{\sqrt{L^2 - 18^2}}$, $L > 18$

(b) See below.

(c)

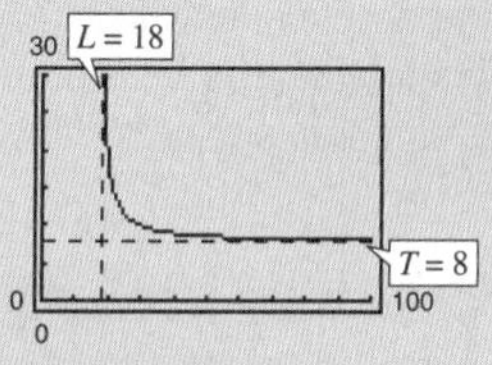

Horizontal asymptote: $T = 8$
Vertical asymptote: $L = 18$
The minimum tension in each cable is 8; the minimum cable length is 18.

(d) 30 in.

60. (b)

L	20	25	30	35	40	45	50
T	18.4	11.5	10	9.3	9.0	8.7	8.6

1 PLAN AND PREPARE

Warm-up Exercises

Transparency Available
Available at the Instructor's companion site.

Notetaking Guide

Transparency Available
Promotes interactive learning and notetaking skills.
Available at the Instructor's companion site.

Animated Precalculus

An **Animated Precalculus** tutorial is available at the Student companion site for **Section 11.3.**

Pacing

Average: 2 days
Advanced: 2 days
Block: 0.5 block with 11.2
0.5 block with 11.4

2 FOCUS AND MOTIVATE

Essential Question

How do you find orthogonal vectors, the areas of parallelograms, and the volumes of geometric solids given two or more vectors? **Tell students that they will learn how to answer this question by calculating the cross product and the triple scalar product of two or three vectors, respectively.**

11.3 The Cross Product of Two Vectors

What you should learn

- Find cross products of vectors in space.
- Use geometric properties of cross products of vectors in space.
- Use triple scalar products to find volumes of parallelepipeds.

Why you should learn it

The cross product of two vectors in space has many applications in physics and engineering. For instance, in Exercise 61 on page 830, the cross product is used to find the torque on the crank of a bicycle's brake.

David L. Moore/Alsport/Alamy

The Cross Product

Many applications in physics, engineering, and geometry involve finding a vector in space that is orthogonal to two given vectors. In this section, you will study a product that will yield such a vector. It is called the **cross product,** and it is conveniently defined and calculated using the standard unit vector form.

Definition of Cross Product of Two Vectors in Space

Let

$$\mathbf{u} = u_1\mathbf{i} + u_2\mathbf{j} + u_3\mathbf{k} \quad \text{and} \quad \mathbf{v} = v_1\mathbf{i} + v_2\mathbf{j} + v_3\mathbf{k}$$

be vectors in space. The cross product of **u** and **v** is the vector

$$\mathbf{u} \times \mathbf{v} = (u_2v_3 - u_3v_2)\mathbf{i} - (u_1v_3 - u_3v_1)\mathbf{j} + (u_1v_2 - u_2v_1)\mathbf{k}.$$

It is important to note that this definition applies only to three-dimensional vectors. The cross product is not defined for two-dimensional vectors.

A convenient way to calculate $\mathbf{u} \times \mathbf{v}$ is to use the following *determinant form* with cofactor expansion. (This 3×3 determinant form is used simply to help remember the formula for the cross product—it is technically not a determinant because the entries of the corresponding matrix are not all real numbers.)

$$\mathbf{u} \times \mathbf{v} = \begin{vmatrix} \mathbf{i} & \mathbf{j} & \mathbf{k} \\ u_1 & u_2 & u_3 \\ v_1 & v_2 & v_3 \end{vmatrix} \quad \begin{matrix} \\ \text{Put } \mathbf{u} \text{ in Row 2.} \\ \text{Put } \mathbf{v} \text{ in Row 3.} \end{matrix}$$

$$= \begin{vmatrix} \mathbf{i} & \mathbf{j} & \mathbf{k} \\ u_1 & u_2 & u_3 \\ v_1 & v_2 & v_3 \end{vmatrix}\mathbf{i} - \begin{vmatrix} \mathbf{i} & \mathbf{j} & \mathbf{k} \\ u_1 & u_2 & u_3 \\ v_1 & v_2 & v_3 \end{vmatrix}\mathbf{j} + \begin{vmatrix} \mathbf{i} & \mathbf{j} & \mathbf{k} \\ u_1 & u_2 & u_3 \\ v_1 & v_2 & v_3 \end{vmatrix}\mathbf{k}$$

$$= \begin{vmatrix} u_2 & u_3 \\ v_2 & v_3 \end{vmatrix}\mathbf{i} - \begin{vmatrix} u_1 & u_3 \\ v_1 & v_3 \end{vmatrix}\mathbf{j} + \begin{vmatrix} u_1 & u_2 \\ v_1 & v_2 \end{vmatrix}\mathbf{k}$$

$$= (u_2v_3 - u_3v_2)\mathbf{i} - (u_1v_3 - u_3v_1)\mathbf{j} + (u_1v_2 - u_2v_1)\mathbf{k}$$

Note the minus sign in front of the **j**-component. Recall from Section 8.4 that each of the three 2×2 determinants can be evaluated by using the following pattern.

$$\begin{vmatrix} a_1 & b_1 \\ a_2 & b_2 \end{vmatrix} = a_1b_2 - a_2b_1$$

TECHNOLOGY

Some graphing utilities have the capability to perform vector operations, such as the cross product. Consult the user's guide for your graphing utility for specific instructions.

Resource Planning Guide

Chapter Resources
- Complete Solutions Guide

Workbooks
- Notetaking Guide
- Student Solutions Guide

Interactive Technology
- Instructor Success Organizer
- Notetaking Guide IAE
- Instructional DVDs
- Animated Precalculus
- PowerLecture with ExamView

Example 1 **Finding Cross Products**

Given $\mathbf{u} = \mathbf{i} + 2\mathbf{j} + \mathbf{k}$ and $\mathbf{v} = 3\mathbf{i} + \mathbf{j} + 2\mathbf{k}$, find each cross product.

a. $\mathbf{u} \times \mathbf{v}$ **b.** $\mathbf{v} \times \mathbf{u}$ **c.** $\mathbf{v} \times \mathbf{v}$

Solution

$$\textbf{a. } \mathbf{u} \times \mathbf{v} = \begin{vmatrix} \mathbf{i} & \mathbf{j} & \mathbf{k} \\ 1 & 2 & 1 \\ 3 & 1 & 2 \end{vmatrix}$$

$$= \begin{vmatrix} 2 & 1 \\ 1 & 2 \end{vmatrix}\mathbf{i} - \begin{vmatrix} 1 & 1 \\ 3 & 2 \end{vmatrix}\mathbf{j} + \begin{vmatrix} 1 & 2 \\ 3 & 1 \end{vmatrix}\mathbf{k}$$

$$= (4 - 1)\mathbf{i} - (2 - 3)\mathbf{j} + (1 - 6)\mathbf{k}$$

$$= 3\mathbf{i} + \mathbf{j} - 5\mathbf{k}$$

$$\textbf{b. } \mathbf{v} \times \mathbf{u} = \begin{vmatrix} \mathbf{i} & \mathbf{j} & \mathbf{k} \\ 3 & 1 & 2 \\ 1 & 2 & 1 \end{vmatrix}$$

$$= \begin{vmatrix} 1 & 2 \\ 2 & 1 \end{vmatrix}\mathbf{i} - \begin{vmatrix} 3 & 2 \\ 1 & 1 \end{vmatrix}\mathbf{j} + \begin{vmatrix} 3 & 1 \\ 1 & 2 \end{vmatrix}\mathbf{k}$$

$$= (1 - 4)\mathbf{i} - (3 - 2)\mathbf{j} + (6 - 1)\mathbf{k}$$

$$= -3\mathbf{i} - \mathbf{j} + 5\mathbf{k}$$

$$\textbf{c. } \mathbf{v} \times \mathbf{v} = \begin{vmatrix} \mathbf{i} & \mathbf{j} & \mathbf{k} \\ 3 & 1 & 2 \\ 3 & 1 & 2 \end{vmatrix} = \mathbf{0}$$

CHECK*Point* Now try Exercise 25.

The results obtained in Example 1 suggest some interesting algebraic properties of the cross product. For instance,

$$\mathbf{u} \times \mathbf{v} = -(\mathbf{v} \times \mathbf{u}) \quad \text{and} \quad \mathbf{v} \times \mathbf{v} = \mathbf{0}.$$

These properties, and several others, are summarized in the following list.

Algebraic Properties of the Cross Product

Let $\mathbf{u}$, $\mathbf{v}$, and $\mathbf{w}$ be vectors in space and let c be a scalar.

1. $\mathbf{u} \times \mathbf{v} = -(\mathbf{v} \times \mathbf{u})$
2. $\mathbf{u} \times (\mathbf{v} + \mathbf{w}) = (\mathbf{u} \times \mathbf{v}) + (\mathbf{u} \times \mathbf{w})$
3. $c(\mathbf{u} \times \mathbf{v}) = (c\mathbf{u}) \times \mathbf{v} = \mathbf{u} \times (c\mathbf{v})$
4. $\mathbf{u} \times \mathbf{0} = \mathbf{0} \times \mathbf{u} = \mathbf{0}$
5. $\mathbf{u} \times \mathbf{u} = \mathbf{0}$
6. $\mathbf{u} \cdot (\mathbf{v} \times \mathbf{w}) = (\mathbf{u} \times \mathbf{v}) \cdot \mathbf{w}$

For proofs of the Algebraic Properties of the Cross Product, see Proofs in Mathematics on page 845.

3 TEACH

Extra Example 1

Given $\mathbf{u} = 2\mathbf{i} + \mathbf{j} + 3\mathbf{k}$ and $\mathbf{v} = \mathbf{i} + 3\mathbf{j} + 2\mathbf{k}$, find each cross product.

a. $\mathbf{u} \times \mathbf{v}$
$-7\mathbf{i} - \mathbf{j} + 5\mathbf{k}$

b. $\mathbf{v} \times \mathbf{u}$
$7\mathbf{i} + \mathbf{j} - 5\mathbf{k}$

c. $\mathbf{v} \times \mathbf{v}$
$\mathbf{0}$

Avoiding Common Errors

Students often misinterpret the results of vector operations. Remind them that the cross product of two three-dimensional vectors is another three-dimensional vector and that the magnitude and the triple scalar product are always scalar values.

Extra Example 2

Find a unit vector that is orthogonal to both $\mathbf{u} = 2\mathbf{i} + 3\mathbf{j} - 4\mathbf{k}$ and $\mathbf{v} = -\mathbf{i} + 2\mathbf{j}$.

A unit vector orthogonal to both u and v is

$$\frac{8}{\sqrt{129}}\mathbf{i} + \frac{4}{\sqrt{129}}\mathbf{j} + \frac{7}{\sqrt{129}}\mathbf{k}.$$

Geometric Properties of the Cross Product

The first property listed on the preceding page indicates that the cross product is *not commutative*. In particular, this property indicates that the vectors $\mathbf{u} \times \mathbf{v}$ and $\mathbf{v} \times \mathbf{u}$ have equal lengths but opposite directions. The following list gives some other *geometric* properties of the cross product of two vectors.

Geometric Properties of the Cross Product

Let $\mathbf{u}$ and $\mathbf{v}$ be nonzero vectors in space, and let θ be the angle between $\mathbf{u}$ and $\mathbf{v}$.

1. $\mathbf{u} \times \mathbf{v}$ is orthogonal to both $\mathbf{u}$ and $\mathbf{v}$.
2. $\|\mathbf{u} \times \mathbf{v}\| = \|\mathbf{u}\|\,\|\mathbf{v}\| \sin \theta$
3. $\mathbf{u} \times \mathbf{v} = \mathbf{0}$ if and only if $\mathbf{u}$ and $\mathbf{v}$ are scalar multiples of each other.
4. $\|\mathbf{u} \times \mathbf{v}\| =$ area of parallelogram having $\mathbf{u}$ and $\mathbf{v}$ as adjacent sides.

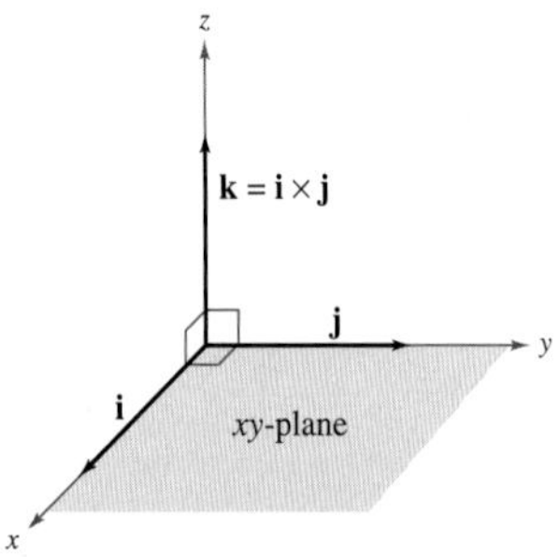

FIGURE 11.21

For proofs of the Geometric Properties of the Cross Product, see Proofs in Mathematics on page 846.

Both $\mathbf{u} \times \mathbf{v}$ and $\mathbf{v} \times \mathbf{u}$ are perpendicular to the plane determined by $\mathbf{u}$ and $\mathbf{v}$. One way to remember the orientations of the vectors $\mathbf{u}$, $\mathbf{v}$, and $\mathbf{u} \times \mathbf{v}$ is to compare them with the unit vectors $\mathbf{i}$, $\mathbf{j}$, and $\mathbf{k} = \mathbf{i} \times \mathbf{j}$, as shown in Figure 11.21. The three vectors $\mathbf{u}$, $\mathbf{v}$, and $\mathbf{u} \times \mathbf{v}$ form a *right-handed system.*

Example 2 Using the Cross Product

Find a unit vector that is orthogonal to both

$$\mathbf{u} = 3\mathbf{i} - 4\mathbf{j} + \mathbf{k} \quad \text{and} \quad \mathbf{v} = -3\mathbf{i} + 6\mathbf{j}.$$

Solution

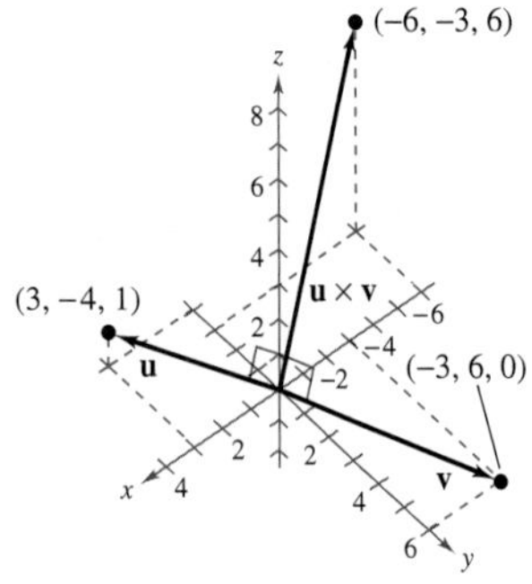

FIGURE 11.22

The cross product $\mathbf{u} \times \mathbf{v}$, as shown in Figure 11.22, is orthogonal to both $\mathbf{u}$ and $\mathbf{v}$.

$$\mathbf{u} \times \mathbf{v} = \begin{vmatrix} \mathbf{i} & \mathbf{j} & \mathbf{k} \\ 3 & -4 & 1 \\ -3 & 6 & 0 \end{vmatrix}$$

$$= -6\mathbf{i} - 3\mathbf{j} + 6\mathbf{k}$$

Because

$$\|\mathbf{u} \times \mathbf{v}\| = \sqrt{(-6)^2 + (-3)^2 + 6^2}$$

$$= \sqrt{81}$$

$$= 9$$

a unit vector orthogonal to both $\mathbf{u}$ and $\mathbf{v}$ is

$$\frac{\mathbf{u} \times \mathbf{v}}{\|\mathbf{u} \times \mathbf{v}\|} = -\frac{2}{3}\mathbf{i} - \frac{1}{3}\mathbf{j} + \frac{2}{3}\mathbf{k}.$$

CHECKPoint Now try Exercise 31.

In Example 2, note that you could have used the cross product $\mathbf{v} \times \mathbf{u}$ to form a unit vector that is orthogonal to both $\mathbf{u}$ and $\mathbf{v}$. With that choice, you would have obtained the *negative* of the unit vector found in the example.

The fourth geometric property of the cross product states that $\|\mathbf{u} \times \mathbf{v}\|$ is the area of the parallelogram that has $\mathbf{u}$ and $\mathbf{v}$ as adjacent sides. A simple example of this is given by the unit square with adjacent sides of $\mathbf{i}$ and $\mathbf{j}$. Because

$$\mathbf{i} \times \mathbf{j} = \mathbf{k}$$

and $\|\mathbf{k}\| = 1$, it follows that the square has an area of 1. This geometric property of the cross product is illustrated further in the next example.

Example 3 Geometric Application of the Cross Product

Show that the quadrilateral with vertices at the following points is a parallelogram. Then find the area of the parallelogram. Is the parallelogram a rectangle?

$$A(5, 2, 0), \quad B(2, 6, 1), \quad C(2, 4, 7), \quad D(5, 0, 6)$$

Solution

From Figure 11.23 you can see that the sides of the quadrilateral correspond to the following four vectors.

$$\overrightarrow{AB} = -3\mathbf{i} + 4\mathbf{j} + \mathbf{k}$$

$$\overrightarrow{CD} = 3\mathbf{i} - 4\mathbf{j} - \mathbf{k} = -\overrightarrow{AB}$$

$$\overrightarrow{AD} = 0\mathbf{i} - 2\mathbf{j} + 6\mathbf{k}$$

$$\overrightarrow{CB} = 0\mathbf{i} + 2\mathbf{j} - 6\mathbf{k} = -\overrightarrow{AD}$$

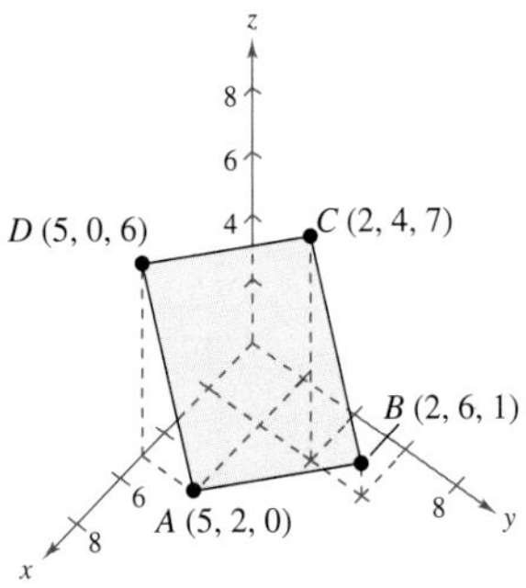

FIGURE 11.23

Because $\overrightarrow{CD} = -\overrightarrow{AB}$ and $\overrightarrow{CB} = -\overrightarrow{AD}$, you can conclude that $\overrightarrow{AB}$ is parallel to $\overrightarrow{CD}$ and $\overrightarrow{AD}$ is parallel to $\overrightarrow{CB}$. It follows that the quadrilateral is a parallelogram with $\overrightarrow{AB}$ and $\overrightarrow{AD}$ as adjacent sides. Moreover, because

$$\overrightarrow{AB} \times \overrightarrow{AD} = \begin{vmatrix} \mathbf{i} & \mathbf{j} & \mathbf{k} \\ -3 & 4 & 1 \\ 0 & -2 & 6 \end{vmatrix} = 26\mathbf{i} + 18\mathbf{j} + 6\mathbf{k}$$

the area of the parallelogram is

$$\|\overrightarrow{AB} \times \overrightarrow{AD}\| = \sqrt{26^2 + 18^2 + 6^2} = \sqrt{1036} \approx 32.19.$$

You can tell whether the parallelogram is a rectangle by finding the angle between the vectors $\overrightarrow{AB}$ and $\overrightarrow{AD}$.

$$\sin \theta = \frac{\|\overrightarrow{AB} \times \overrightarrow{AD}\|}{\|\overrightarrow{AB}\| \, \|\overrightarrow{AD}\|}$$

$$\sin \theta = \frac{\sqrt{1036}}{\sqrt{26}\sqrt{40}}$$

$$\sin \theta \approx 0.998$$

$$\theta \approx \arcsin 0.998$$

$$\theta \approx 86.4^\circ$$

Because $\theta \neq 90^\circ$, the parallelogram is not a rectangle.

CHECKPoint Now try Exercise 43.

Extra Example 3

Show that the quadrilateral with vertices $A(3, 5, 0)$, $B(1, 2, 4)$, $C(1, 3, 4)$, and $D(3, 6, 0)$ is a parallelogram. Then, find the area of the parallelogram. Is the parallelogram a rectangle?

$\overrightarrow{CD}$ is parallel to $\overrightarrow{AB}$, and $\overrightarrow{CB}$ is parallel to $\overrightarrow{AD}$, so it follows that the quadrilateral is a parallelogram. The area of the parallelogram is about 4.5 square units. The parallelogram is not a rectangle.

Extra Example 4

Find the volume of the parallelepiped having $\mathbf{u} = \mathbf{i} + 2\mathbf{j} - \mathbf{k}$, $\mathbf{v} = -\mathbf{i} + 2\mathbf{j} + 2\mathbf{k}$, and $\mathbf{w} = 2\mathbf{i} + \mathbf{k}$ as adjacent edges.

16

Closing the Lesson

Have students summarize the major points of the lesson and answer the Essential Question: How do you find orthogonal vectors, the areas of parallelograms, and the volumes of geometric solids, given two or more vectors?

- **Use the definition of or determinant form for cross product to calculate the cross product for two vectors.**
- **Find a vector orthogonal to and the area of a parallelogram defined by two vectors by calculating the cross product of the two vectors.**
- **Find the triple scalar product of three vectors by finding the dot product of one vector with the cross product of the other two.**
- **Find the volume of a parallelepiped formed by three vectors by calculating the triple scalar product of the vectors.**

The Triple Scalar Product

For the vectors **u**, **v**, and **w** in space, the dot product of **u** and $\mathbf{v} \times \mathbf{w}$ is called the triple scalar product of **u**, **v**, and **w**.

The Triple Scalar Product

For $\mathbf{u} = u_1\mathbf{i} + u_2\mathbf{j} + u_3\mathbf{k}$, $\mathbf{v} = v_1\mathbf{i} + v_2\mathbf{j} + v_3\mathbf{k}$, and $\mathbf{w} = w_1\mathbf{i} + w_2\mathbf{j} + w_3\mathbf{k}$, the **triple scalar product** is given by

$$\mathbf{u} \cdot (\mathbf{v} \times \mathbf{w}) = \begin{vmatrix} u_1 & u_2 & u_3 \\ v_1 & v_2 & v_3 \\ w_1 & w_2 & w_3 \end{vmatrix}.$$

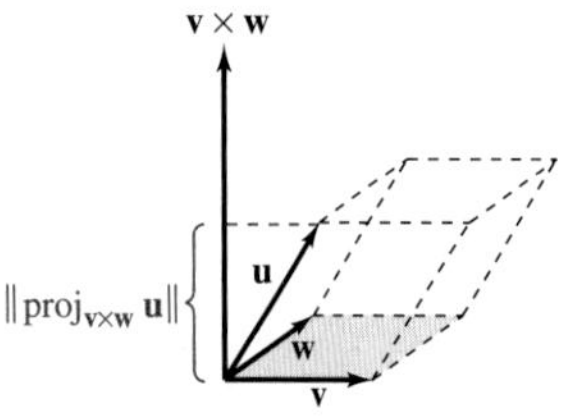

Area of base $= \|\mathbf{v} \times \mathbf{w}\|$
Volume of parallelepiped $= |\mathbf{u} \cdot (\mathbf{v} \times \mathbf{w})|$
FIGURE 11.24

If the vectors **u**, **v**, and **w** do not lie in the same plane, the triple scalar product $\mathbf{u} \cdot (\mathbf{v} \times \mathbf{w})$ can be used to determine the volume of the parallelepiped (a polyhedron, all of whose faces are parallelograms) with **u**, **v**, and **w** as adjacent edges, as shown in Figure 11.24.

Geometric Property of the Triple Scalar Product

The volume V of a parallelepiped with vectors **u**, **v**, and **w** as adjacent edges is given by

$$V = |\mathbf{u} \cdot (\mathbf{v} \times \mathbf{w})|.$$

Example 4 Volume by the Triple Scalar Product

Find the volume of the parallelepiped having

$\mathbf{u} = 3\mathbf{i} - 5\mathbf{j} + \mathbf{k}$, $\mathbf{v} = 2\mathbf{j} - 2\mathbf{k}$, and $\mathbf{w} = 3\mathbf{i} + \mathbf{j} + \mathbf{k}$

as adjacent edges, as shown in Figure 11.25.

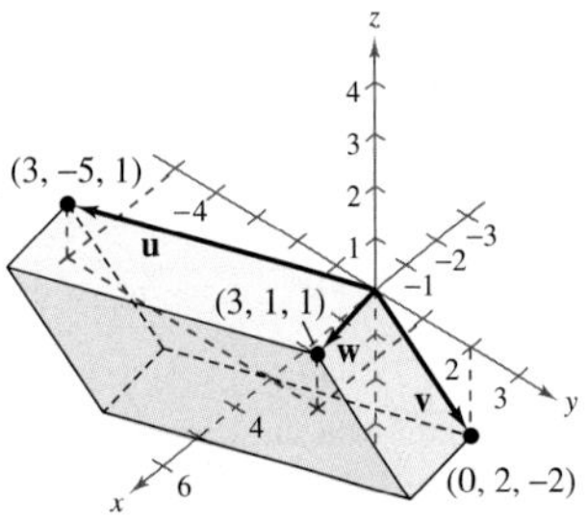

FIGURE 11.25

Solution

The value of the triple scalar product is

$$\begin{aligned}
\mathbf{u} \cdot (\mathbf{v} \times \mathbf{w}) &= \begin{vmatrix} 3 & -5 & 1 \\ 0 & 2 & -2 \\ 3 & 1 & 1 \end{vmatrix} \\
&= 3\begin{vmatrix} 2 & -2 \\ 1 & 1 \end{vmatrix} - (-5)\begin{vmatrix} 0 & -2 \\ 3 & 1 \end{vmatrix} + 1\begin{vmatrix} 0 & 2 \\ 3 & 1 \end{vmatrix} \\
&= 3(4) + 5(6) + 1(-6) \\
&= 36.
\end{aligned}$$

So, the volume of the parallelepiped is

$$|\mathbf{u} \cdot (\mathbf{v} \times \mathbf{w})| = |36| = 36.$$

CHECKPoint Now try Exercise 57.

11.3 EXERCISES

See www.CalcChat.com for worked-out solutions to odd-numbered exercises.

VOCABULARY: Fill in the blanks.

1. To find a vector in space that is orthogonal to two given vectors, find the cross product of the two vectors.
2. $\mathbf{u} \times \mathbf{u} =$ 0
3. $\|\mathbf{u} \times \mathbf{v}\| =$ $\|\mathbf{u}\|\,\|\mathbf{v}\| \sin \theta$
4. The dot product of **u** and $\mathbf{v} \times \mathbf{w}$ is called the triple scalar product of **u**, **v**, and **w**.

SKILLS AND APPLICATIONS

In Exercises 5–10, find the cross product of the unit vectors and sketch the result. 5–10. See margin.

5. $\mathbf{j} \times \mathbf{i}$
6. $\mathbf{i} \times \mathbf{j}$
7. $\mathbf{i} \times \mathbf{k}$
8. $\mathbf{k} \times \mathbf{i}$
9. $\mathbf{j} \times \mathbf{k}$
10. $\mathbf{k} \times \mathbf{j}$

In Exercises 11–20, use the vectors **u** and **v** to find each expression.

$\mathbf{u} = 3\mathbf{i} - \mathbf{j} + 4\mathbf{k}$ $\quad$ $\mathbf{v} = 2\mathbf{i} + 2\mathbf{j} - \mathbf{k}$

11. $\mathbf{u} \times \mathbf{v}$ $\;-7\mathbf{i} + 11\mathbf{j} + 8\mathbf{k}$
12. $\mathbf{v} \times \mathbf{u}$ $\;7\mathbf{i} - 11\mathbf{j} - 8\mathbf{k}$
13. $\mathbf{v} \times \mathbf{v}$ $\;\mathbf{0}$
14. $\mathbf{v} \times (\mathbf{u} \times \mathbf{u})$ $\;\mathbf{0}$
15. $(3\mathbf{u}) \times \mathbf{v}$
16. $\mathbf{u} \times (2\mathbf{v})$ $\;$ 15–18. See margin.
17. $\mathbf{u} \times (-\mathbf{v})$
18. $(-2\mathbf{u}) \times \mathbf{v}$
19. $\mathbf{u} \cdot (\mathbf{u} \times \mathbf{v})$ $\;0$
20. $\mathbf{v} \cdot (\mathbf{v} \times \mathbf{u})$ $\;0$

In Exercises 21–30, find $\mathbf{u} \times \mathbf{v}$ and show that it is orthogonal to both **u** and **v**. 21–26. See margin.

21. $\mathbf{u} = \langle 2, -3, 4 \rangle$, $\mathbf{v} = \langle 0, -1, 1 \rangle$
22. $\mathbf{u} = \langle 6, 8, 3 \rangle$, $\mathbf{v} = \langle 5, -2, -5 \rangle$
23. $\mathbf{u} = \langle -10, 0, 6 \rangle$, $\mathbf{v} = \langle 7, 0, 0 \rangle$
24. $\mathbf{u} = \langle -7, 1, 12 \rangle$, $\mathbf{v} = \langle 2, 2, 3 \rangle$
25. $\mathbf{u} = 6\mathbf{i} + 2\mathbf{j} + \mathbf{k}$, $\mathbf{v} = \mathbf{i} + 3\mathbf{j} - 2\mathbf{k}$
26. $\mathbf{u} = \mathbf{i} + \frac{3}{2}\mathbf{j} - \frac{5}{2}\mathbf{k}$, $\mathbf{v} = \frac{1}{2}\mathbf{i} - \frac{3}{4}\mathbf{j} + \frac{1}{4}\mathbf{k}$
27. $\mathbf{u} = 6\mathbf{k}$, $\mathbf{v} = -\mathbf{i} + 3\mathbf{j} + \mathbf{k}$ $\;-18\mathbf{i} - 6\mathbf{j}$
28. $\mathbf{u} = \frac{1}{3}\mathbf{i}$, $\mathbf{v} = \frac{2}{3}\mathbf{j} - 9\mathbf{k}$ $\;3\mathbf{j} + \frac{2}{9}\mathbf{k}$
29. $\mathbf{u} = -\mathbf{i} + \mathbf{k}$, $\mathbf{v} = \mathbf{j} - 2\mathbf{k}$ $\;-\mathbf{i} - 2\mathbf{j} - \mathbf{k}$
30. $\mathbf{u} = \mathbf{i} - 2\mathbf{k}$, $\mathbf{v} = -\mathbf{j} + \mathbf{k}$ $\;-2\mathbf{i} - \mathbf{j} - \mathbf{k}$

In Exercises 31–36, find a unit vector orthogonal to **u** and **v**. 31–34. See margin.

31. $\mathbf{u} = 3\mathbf{i} + \mathbf{j}$, $\mathbf{v} = \mathbf{j} + \mathbf{k}$
32. $\mathbf{u} = \mathbf{i} + 2\mathbf{j}$, $\mathbf{v} = \mathbf{i} - 3\mathbf{k}$
33. $\mathbf{u} = -3\mathbf{i} + 2\mathbf{j} - 5\mathbf{k}$, $\mathbf{v} = \frac{1}{2}\mathbf{i} - \frac{3}{4}\mathbf{j} + \frac{1}{10}\mathbf{k}$
34. $\mathbf{u} = 7\mathbf{i} - 14\mathbf{j} + 5\mathbf{k}$, $\mathbf{v} = 14\mathbf{i} + 28\mathbf{j} - 15\mathbf{k}$
35. $\mathbf{u} = \mathbf{i} + \mathbf{j} - \mathbf{k}$, $\mathbf{v} = \mathbf{i} + \mathbf{j} + \mathbf{k}$ $\;\frac{\sqrt{2}}{2}(\mathbf{i} - \mathbf{j})$
36. $\mathbf{u} = \mathbf{i} - 2\mathbf{j} + 2\mathbf{k}$, $\mathbf{v} = 2\mathbf{i} - \mathbf{j} - 2\mathbf{k}$ $\;\frac{2}{3}\mathbf{i} + \frac{2}{3}\mathbf{j} + \frac{1}{3}\mathbf{k}$

In Exercises 37–42, find the area of the parallelogram that has the vectors as adjacent sides.

37. $\mathbf{u} = \mathbf{k}$, $\mathbf{v} = \mathbf{i} + \mathbf{k}$ $\;1$
38. $\mathbf{u} = \mathbf{i} + 2\mathbf{j} + 2\mathbf{k}$, $\mathbf{v} = \mathbf{i} + \mathbf{k}$ $\;3$
39. $\mathbf{u} = 4\mathbf{i} + 3\mathbf{j} + 7\mathbf{k}$, $\mathbf{v} = 2\mathbf{i} - 4\mathbf{j} + 6\mathbf{k}$ $\;30\sqrt{3}$
40. $\mathbf{u} = -2\mathbf{i} + 3\mathbf{j} + 2\mathbf{k}$, $\mathbf{v} = \mathbf{i} + 2\mathbf{j} + 4\mathbf{k}$ $\;\sqrt{213}$
41. $\mathbf{u} = \langle 4, 4, -6 \rangle$, $\mathbf{v} = \langle 0, 4, 6 \rangle$ $\;56$
42. $\mathbf{u} = \langle 4, -3, 2 \rangle$, $\mathbf{v} = \langle 5, 0, 1 \rangle$ $\;3\sqrt{30}$

In Exercises 43–46, (a) verify that the points are the vertices of a parallelogram, (b) find its area, and (c) determine whether the parallelogram is a rectangle. 43–46. See margin.

43. $A(2, -1, 4)$, $B(3, 1, 2)$, $C(0, 5, 6)$, $D(-1, 3, 8)$
44. $A(1, 1, 1)$, $B(2, 3, 4)$, $C(6, 5, 2)$, $D(7, 7, 5)$
45. $A(3, 2, -1)$, $B(-2, 2, -3)$, $C(3, 5, -2)$, $D(-2, 5, -4)$
46. $A(2, 1, 1)$, $B(2, 3, 1)$, $C(-2, 4, 1)$, $D(-2, 6, 1)$

In Exercises 47–50, find the area of the triangle with the given vertices. (The area A of the triangle having **u** and **v** as adjacent sides is given by $A = \frac{1}{2}\|\mathbf{u} \times \mathbf{v}\|$.)

47. $(0, 0, 0)$, $(1, 2, 3)$, $(-3, 0, 0)$ $\;\frac{3\sqrt{13}}{2}$
48. $(1, -4, 3)$, $(2, 0, 2)$, $(-2, 2, 0)$ $\;3\sqrt{11}$
49. $(2, 3, -5)$, $(-2, -2, 0)$, $(3, 0, 6)$ $\;\frac{1}{2}\sqrt{4290}$
50. $(2, 4, 0)$, $(-2, -4, 0)$, $(0, 0, 4)$ $\;8\sqrt{5}$

In Exercises 51–54, find the triple scalar product.

51. $\mathbf{u} = \langle 3, 4, 4 \rangle$, $\mathbf{v} = \langle 2, 3, 0 \rangle$, $\mathbf{w} = \langle 0, 0, 6 \rangle$ $\;6$
52. $\mathbf{u} = \langle 4, 0, 1 \rangle$, $\mathbf{v} = \langle 0, 5, 0 \rangle$, $\mathbf{w} = \langle 0, 0, 1 \rangle$ $\;20$
53. $\mathbf{u} = 2\mathbf{i} + 3\mathbf{j} + \mathbf{k}$, $\mathbf{v} = \mathbf{i} - \mathbf{j}$, $\mathbf{w} = 4\mathbf{i} + 3\mathbf{j} + \mathbf{k}$ $\;2$
54. $\mathbf{u} = \mathbf{i} + 4\mathbf{j} - 7\mathbf{k}$, $\mathbf{v} = 2\mathbf{i} + 4\mathbf{k}$, $\mathbf{w} = -3\mathbf{j} + 6\mathbf{k}$ $\;6$

4 PRACTICE AND APPLY

Assignment Guide

Transparencies Available
Available at the Instructor's companion site.

Average:
Day 1: p. 829
Exs. 1–3, 5–11, 15, 17, 21, 23, 27–29, 32–35, 37–41 odd
Day 2: pp. 829–830
Exs. 4, 44, 45, 47–49, 53, 55, 56, 59, 61–64, 66

Advanced:
Day 1: p. 829
Exs. 1–3, 5–10, 12–30 even, 33–36, 38–42 even
Day 2: pp. 829–830
Exs. 4, 44, 46, 48–50, 52–58 even, 60–65, 68, 69

Block:
p. 829
Exs. 1–3, 5–11, 15, 17, 21, 23, 27–29, 32–35, 37–41 odd (with 11.2)
pp. 829–830
Exs. 4, 44, 45, 47–49, 53, 55, 56, 59, 61–64, 66 (with 11.4)

15. $-21\mathbf{i} + 33\mathbf{j} + 24\mathbf{k}$
16. $-14\mathbf{i} + 22\mathbf{j} + 16\mathbf{k}$
17. $7\mathbf{i} - 11\mathbf{j} - 8\mathbf{k}$
18. $14\mathbf{i} - 22\mathbf{j} - 16\mathbf{k}$
21. $\langle 1, -2, -2 \rangle$
22. $\langle -34, 45, -52 \rangle$
23. $\langle 0, 42, 0 \rangle$
24. $\langle -21, 45, -16 \rangle$
25. $-7\mathbf{i} + 13\mathbf{j} + 16\mathbf{k}$
26. $-\frac{3}{2}\mathbf{i} - \frac{3}{2}\mathbf{j} - \frac{3}{2}\mathbf{k}$
31. $\frac{\sqrt{19}}{19}(\mathbf{i} - 3\mathbf{j} + 3\mathbf{k})$
32. $\frac{1}{7}(-6\mathbf{i} + 3\mathbf{j} - 2\mathbf{k})$
33. $\frac{\sqrt{7602}}{7602}(-71\mathbf{i} - 44\mathbf{j} + 25\mathbf{k})$
34. $\frac{\sqrt{429}}{1287}(10\mathbf{i} + 25\mathbf{j} + 56\mathbf{k})$
43. (a) $\overrightarrow{AB} = \langle 1, 2, -2 \rangle$ and is parallel to $\overrightarrow{DC} = \langle 1, 2, -2 \rangle$. $\overrightarrow{AD} = \langle -3, 4, 4 \rangle$ and is parallel to $\overrightarrow{BC} = \langle -3, 4, 4 \rangle$.
 (b) Area is $\|\overrightarrow{AB} \times \overrightarrow{AD}\| = 6\sqrt{10}$.
 (c) The dot product is not 0 and therefore the parallelogram is not a rectangle.

44. (a) $\overrightarrow{AB} = \langle 1, 2, 3 \rangle$ and is parallel to $\overrightarrow{CD} = \langle 1, 2, 3 \rangle$. $\overrightarrow{BD} = \langle 5, 4, 1 \rangle$ and is parallel to $\overrightarrow{AC} = \langle 5, 4, 1 \rangle$.
 (b) Area is $\|\overrightarrow{AB} \times \overrightarrow{AC}\| = 2\sqrt{83}$.
 (c) The dot product is not 0 and therefore the parallelogram is not a rectangle.

45. (a) $\overrightarrow{AB} = \langle -5, 0, -2 \rangle$ and is parallel to $\overrightarrow{CD} = \langle -5, 0, -2 \rangle$. $\overrightarrow{AC} = \langle 0, 3, -1 \rangle$ and is parallel to $\overrightarrow{BD} = \langle 0, 3, -1 \rangle$.
 (b) Area is $\|\overrightarrow{AB} \times \overrightarrow{DB}\| = \sqrt{286}$.
 (c) The dot product is not 0 and therefore the parallelogram is not a rectangle.

46. (a) $\overrightarrow{AB} = \langle 0, 2, 0 \rangle$ and is parallel to $\overrightarrow{CD} = \langle 0, 2, 0 \rangle$. $\overrightarrow{AC} = \langle -4, 3, 0 \rangle$ and is parallel to $\overrightarrow{BD} = \langle -4, 3, 0 \rangle$.
 (b) Area is $\|\overrightarrow{AB} \times \overrightarrow{DB}\| = 8$.
 (c) The dot product is not 0 and therefore the parallelogram is not a rectangle.

5–10. See Additional Answers beginning on page AA1.

5 ASSESS AND RETEACH

Daily Homework Quiz

Transparency Available
Available at the Instructor's companion site.

61. (a) $T = \frac{p}{2}\cos 40°$

(b) See below.

63. True. The cross product is not defined for two-dimensional vectors.

64. False. The cross product is not commutative.

65. $\mathbf{u} \times \mathbf{v} = -(\mathbf{v} \times \mathbf{u})$; Answers will vary.

66. The magnitude of the cross product will be four times as large.

67. Yes. The area of the triangle is $\frac{1}{2}\|\mathbf{u} \times \mathbf{v}\|$.

In Exercises 55–58, use the triple scalar product to find the volume of the parallelepiped having adjacent edges **u**, **v**, and **w**.

55. $\mathbf{u} = \mathbf{i} + \mathbf{j}$ 2
$\mathbf{v} = \mathbf{j} + \mathbf{k}$
$\mathbf{w} = \mathbf{i} + \mathbf{k}$

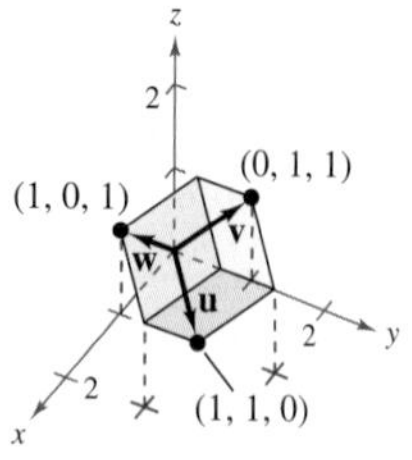

56. $\mathbf{u} = \mathbf{i} + \mathbf{j} + 3\mathbf{k}$ 9
$\mathbf{v} = 3\mathbf{j} + 3\mathbf{k}$
$\mathbf{w} = 3\mathbf{i} + 3\mathbf{k}$

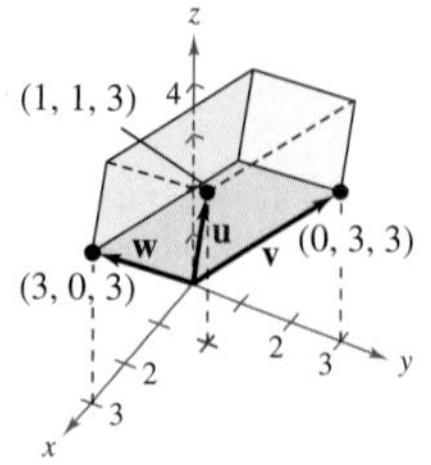

57. $\mathbf{u} = \langle 0, 2, 2\rangle$ 12
$\mathbf{v} = \langle 0, 0, -2\rangle$
$\mathbf{w} = \langle 3, 0, 2\rangle$

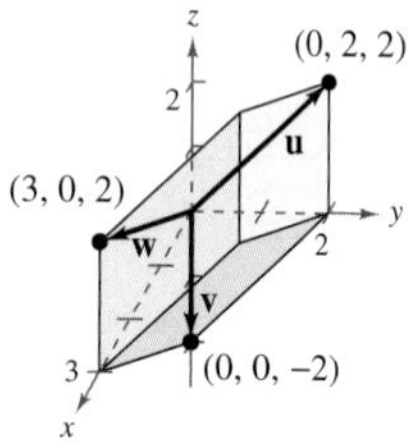

58. $\mathbf{u} = \langle 1, 2, -1\rangle$ 16
$\mathbf{v} = \langle -1, 2, 2\rangle$
$\mathbf{w} = \langle 2, 0, 1\rangle$

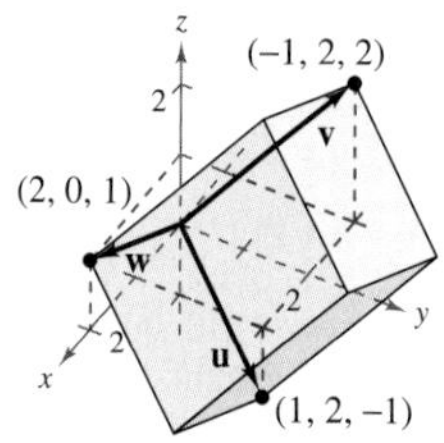

In Exercises 59 and 60, find the volume of the parallelepiped with the given vertices.

59. $A(0, 0, 0)$, $B(4, 0, 0)$, $C(4, -2, 3)$, $D(0, -2, 3)$, 84
$E(4, 5, 3)$, $F(0, 5, 3)$, $G(0, 3, 6)$, $H(4, 3, 6)$

60. $A(0, 0, 0)$, $B(1, 1, 0)$, $C(1, 0, 2)$, $D(0, 1, 1)$, 3
$E(2, 1, 2)$, $F(1, 1, 3)$, $G(1, 2, 1)$, $H(2, 2, 3)$

61. TORQUE The brakes on a bicycle are applied by using a downward force of p pounds on the pedal when the six-inch crank makes a 40° angle with the horizontal (see figure). Vectors representing the position of the crank and the force are $\mathbf{V} = \frac{1}{2}(-\cos 40°\mathbf{j} - \sin 40°\mathbf{k})$ and $\mathbf{F} = -p\mathbf{k}$, respectively. See margin.

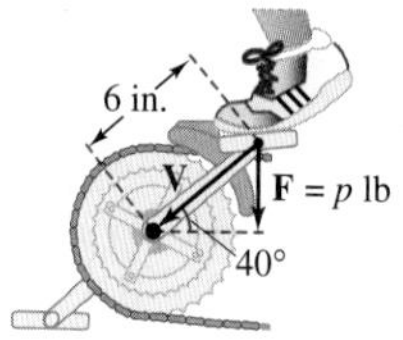

(a) The magnitude of the torque on the crank is given by $\|\mathbf{V} \times \mathbf{F}\|$. Using the given information, write the torque T on the crank as a function of p.

(b) Use the function from part (a) to complete the table.

p	15	20	25	30	35	40	45
T							

62. TORQUE Both the magnitude and direction of the force on a crankshaft change as the crankshaft rotates. Use the technique given in Exercise 61 to find the magnitude of the torque on the crankshaft using the position and data shown in the figure. $160\sqrt{3}$ ft-lb

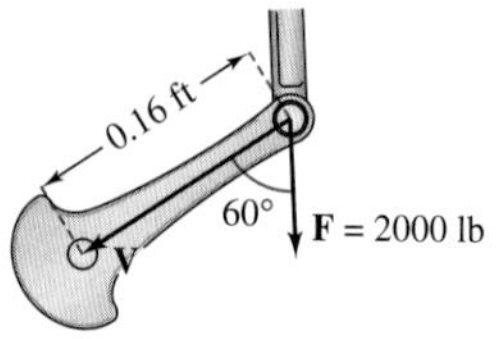

EXPLORATION

63–64. See margin.

TRUE OR FALSE? In Exercises 63 and 64, determine whether the statement is true or false. Justify your answer.

63. The cross product is not defined for vectors in the plane.

64. If **u** and **v** are vectors in space that are nonzero and nonparallel, then $\mathbf{u} \times \mathbf{v} = \mathbf{v} \times \mathbf{u}$.

65. THINK ABOUT IT Calculate $\mathbf{u} \times \mathbf{v}$ and $-(\mathbf{v} \times \mathbf{u})$ for several values of **u** and **v**. What do your results imply? Interpret your results geometrically. See margin.

66. THINK ABOUT IT If the magnitudes of two vectors are doubled, how will the magnitude of the cross product of the vectors change? See margin.

67. THINK ABOUT IT If you connect the terminal points of two vectors **u** and **v** that have the same initial points, a triangle is formed. Is it possible to use the cross product $\mathbf{u} \times \mathbf{v}$ to determine the area of the triangle? Explain. Verify your conclusion using two vectors from Example 3. See margin.

68. CAPSTONE Define the cross product of two vectors in space, **u** and **v**, where $\mathbf{u} = u_1\mathbf{i} + u_2\mathbf{j} + u_3\mathbf{k}$ and $\mathbf{v} = v_1\mathbf{i} + v_2\mathbf{j} + v_3\mathbf{k}$. Explain, in your own words, what the cross product $\mathbf{u} \times \mathbf{v}$ represents. What does it mean when $\mathbf{u} \times \mathbf{v} = 0$? Answers will vary.

69. PROOF Consider the vectors $\mathbf{u} = \langle \cos\alpha, \sin\alpha, 0\rangle$ and $\mathbf{v} = \langle \cos\beta, \sin\beta, 0\rangle$, where $\alpha > \beta$. Find the cross product of the vectors and use the result to prove the identity $\sin(\alpha - \beta) = \sin\alpha\cos\beta - \cos\alpha\sin\beta$. Proof

61. (b)

p	15	20	25	30	35	40	45
T	5.75	7.66	9.58	11.49	13.41	15.32	17.24

11.4 LINES AND PLANES IN SPACE

What you should learn

- Find parametric and symmetric equations of lines in space.
- Find equations of planes in space.
- Sketch planes in space.
- Find distances between points and planes in space.

Why you should learn it

Equations in three variables can be used to model real-life data. For instance, in Exercise 61 on page 839, you will determine how changes in the consumption of two types of beverages affect the consumption of a third type of beverage.

Lines in Space

In the plane, *slope* is used to determine an equation of a line. In space, it is more convenient to use *vectors* to determine the equation of a line.

In Figure 11.26, consider the line L through the point $P(x_1, y_1, z_1)$ and parallel to the vector

$$\mathbf{v} = \langle a, b, c \rangle. \qquad \text{Direction vector for } L$$

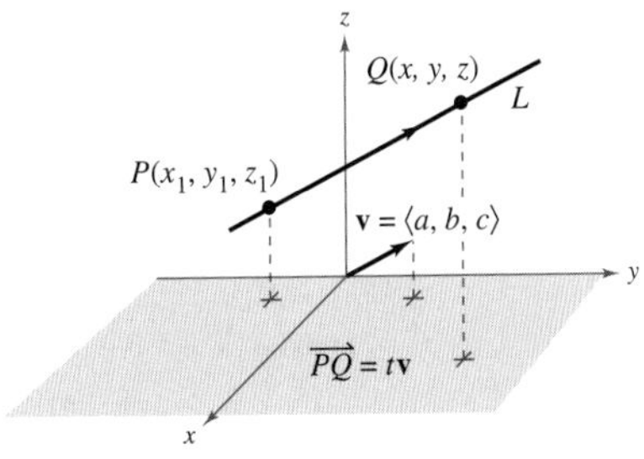

FIGURE 11.26

The vector **v** is the **direction vector** for the line L, and a, b, and c are the **direction numbers.** One way of describing the line L is to say that it consists of all points $Q(x, y, z)$ for which the vector $\overrightarrow{PQ}$ is parallel to **v**. This means that $\overrightarrow{PQ}$ is a scalar multiple of **v**, and you can write $\overrightarrow{PQ} = t\mathbf{v}$, where t is a scalar.

$$\begin{aligned}\overrightarrow{PQ} &= \langle x - x_1, y - y_1, z - z_1 \rangle \\ &= \langle at, bt, ct \rangle \\ &= t\mathbf{v}\end{aligned}$$

By equating corresponding components, you can obtain the **parametric equations of a line in space.**

Parametric Equations of a Line in Space

A line L parallel to the vector $\mathbf{v} = \langle a, b, c \rangle$ and passing through the point $P(x_1, y_1, z_1)$ is represented by the parametric equations

$$x = x_1 + at, \qquad y = y_1 + bt, \qquad \text{and} \qquad z = z_1 + ct.$$

If the direction numbers a, b, and c are all nonzero, you can eliminate the parameter t to obtain the **symmetric equations** of a line.

$$\frac{x - x_1}{a} = \frac{y - y_1}{b} = \frac{z - z_1}{c} \qquad \text{Symmetric equations}$$

1 PLAN AND PREPARE

Warm-up Exercises

Transparency Available
Available at the Instructor's companion site.

Notetaking Guide

Transparency Available
Promotes interactive learning and notetaking skills. Available at the Instructor's companion site.

Animated Precalculus

An **Animated Precalculus** tutorial is available at the Student companion site for **Section 11.4.**

Pacing

Average: 2 days
Advanced: 2 days
Block: 0.5 block with 11.3
0.5 block with Review

2 FOCUS AND MOTIVATE

Essential Question

How do you describe and compare lines and planes in space? **Tell students that they will learn how to answer this question by writing equations for lines and planes, finding the intersection line of two planes, sketching planes, and finding the distance between a point and a plane.**

Resource Planning Guide

Chapter Resources

- Complete Solutions Guide

Workbooks

- Notetaking Guide
- Student Solutions Guide

Interactive Technology

- Instructor Success Organizer
- Notetaking Guide IAE
- Instructional DVDs
- Animated Precalculus
- PowerLecture with ExamView

3 TEACH

Extra Example 1

Find parametric and symmetric equations of the line L that passes through the point (3, 2, 1) and is parallel to $\mathbf{v} = \langle -1, 3, 5\rangle$.

Parametric equations:
$x = 3 - t, y = 2 + 3t, z = 1 + 5t$;
Symmetric equations:

$$\frac{x-3}{-1} = \frac{y-2}{3} = \frac{z-1}{5}$$

Extra Example 2

Find a set of parametric and symmetric equations of the line that passes through the points (1, 3, −2) and (4, 0, 1).

Parametric equations:
$x = 1 + 3t, y = 3 - 3t, z = -2 + 3t$;
Symmetric equations:

$$\frac{x-1}{3} = \frac{y-3}{-3} = \frac{z+2}{3}$$

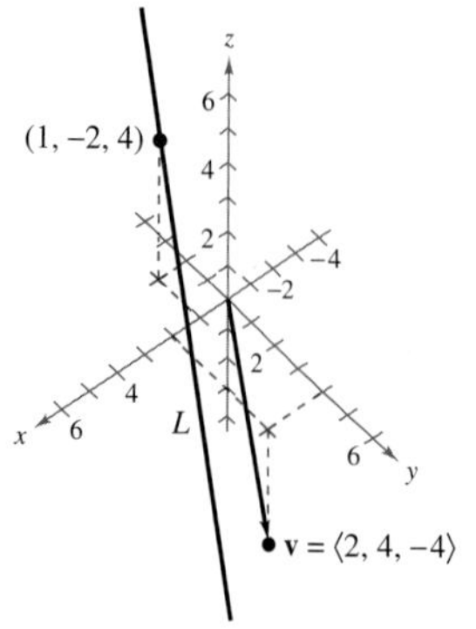

FIGURE 11.27

Example 1 Finding Parametric and Symmetric Equations

Find parametric and symmetric equations of the line L that passes through the point $(1, -2, 4)$ and is parallel to $\mathbf{v} = \langle 2, 4, -4\rangle$.

Solution

To find a set of parametric equations of the line, use the coordinates $x_1 = 1$, $y_1 = -2$, and $z_1 = 4$ and direction numbers $a = 2$, $b = 4$, and $c = -4$ (see Figure 11.27).

$$x = 1 + 2t, \quad y = -2 + 4t, \quad z = 4 - 4t \qquad \text{Parametric equations}$$

Because a, b, and c are all nonzero, a set of symmetric equations is

$$\frac{x-1}{2} = \frac{y+2}{4} = \frac{z-4}{-4}. \qquad \text{Symmetric equations}$$

CHECKPoint Now try Exercise 5.

Neither the parametric equations nor the symmetric equations of a given line are unique. For instance, in Example 1, by letting $t = 1$ in the parametric equations you would obtain the point $(3, 2, 0)$. Using this point with the direction numbers $a = 2$, $b = 4$, and $c = -4$ produces the parametric equations

$$x = 3 + 2t, \quad y = 2 + 4t, \quad \text{and} \quad z = -4t.$$

Example 2 Parametric and Symmetric Equations of a Line Through Two Points

Find a set of parametric and symmetric equations of the line that passes through the points $(-2, 1, 0)$ and $(1, 3, 5)$.

Solution

Begin by letting $P = (-2, 1, 0)$ and $Q = (1, 3, 5)$. Then a direction vector for the line passing through P and Q is

$$\begin{aligned}\mathbf{v} &= \overrightarrow{PQ}\\ &= \langle 1-(-2), 3-1, 5-0\rangle\\ &= \langle 3, 2, 5\rangle\\ &= \langle a, b, c\rangle.\end{aligned}$$

Using the direction numbers $a = 3$, $b = 2$, and $c = 5$ with the initial point $P(-2, 1, 0)$, you can obtain the parametric equations

$$x = -2 + 3t, \quad y = 1 + 2t, \quad \text{and} \quad z = 5t. \qquad \text{Parametric equations}$$

Because a, b, and c are all nonzero, a set of symmetric equations is

$$\frac{x+2}{3} = \frac{y-1}{2} = \frac{z}{5}. \qquad \text{Symmetric equations}$$

CHECKPoint Now try Exercise 11.

Study Tip

To check the answer to Example 2, verify that the two original points lie on the line. For the point $(-2, 1, 0)$, you can substitute in the parametric equations.

$$x = -2 + 3t \qquad y = 1 + 2t \qquad z = 5t$$

$$-2 = -2 + 3t \qquad 1 = 1 + 2t \qquad 0 = 5t$$

$$0 = t \qquad 0 = t \qquad 0 = t$$

Try checking the point $(1, 3, 5)$ on your own. Note that you can also check the answer using the symmetric equations.

Planes in Space

You have seen how an equation of a line in space can be obtained from a point on the line and a vector *parallel* to it. You will now see that an equation of a plane in space can be obtained from a point in the plane and a vector *normal* (perpendicular) to the plane.

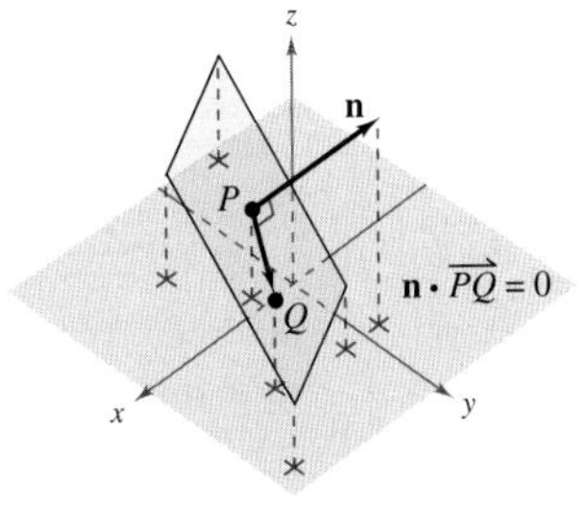

FIGURE 11.28

Consider the plane containing the point $P(x_1, y_1, z_1)$ having a nonzero normal vector $\mathbf{n} = \langle a, b, c \rangle$, as shown in Figure 11.28. This plane consists of all points $Q(x, y, z)$ for which the vector $\overrightarrow{PQ}$ is orthogonal to $\mathbf{n}$. Using the dot product, you can write

$$\mathbf{n} \cdot \overrightarrow{PQ} = 0 \qquad \overrightarrow{PQ} \text{ is orthogonal to } \mathbf{n}.$$

$$\langle a, b, c \rangle \cdot \langle x - x_1, y - y_1, z - z_1 \rangle = 0$$

$$a(x - x_1) + b(y - y_1) + c(z - z_1) = 0.$$

The third equation of the plane is said to be in standard form.

Standard Equation of a Plane in Space

The plane containing the point (x_1, y_1, z_1) and having normal vector $\mathbf{n} = \langle a, b, c \rangle$ can be represented by the **standard form of the equation of a plane**

$$a(x - x_1) + b(y - y_1) + c(z - z_1) = 0.$$

Regrouping terms yields the **general form of the equation of a plane** in space

$$ax + by + cz + d = 0. \qquad \text{General form of equation of plane}$$

Given the general form of the equation of a plane, it is easy to find a normal vector to the plane. Use the coefficients of x, y, and z to write $\mathbf{n} = \langle a, b, c \rangle$.

Extra Example 3

Find the general equation of the plane passing through the points $(3, 2, 2)$, $(1, 5, 0)$, and $(1, -3, 1)$.

$-13x + 2y + 16z + 3 = 0$

Example 3 Finding an Equation of a Plane in Three-Space

Find the general form of the equation of the plane passing through the points $(2, 1, 1)$, $(0, 4, 1)$, and $(-2, 1, 4)$.

Solution

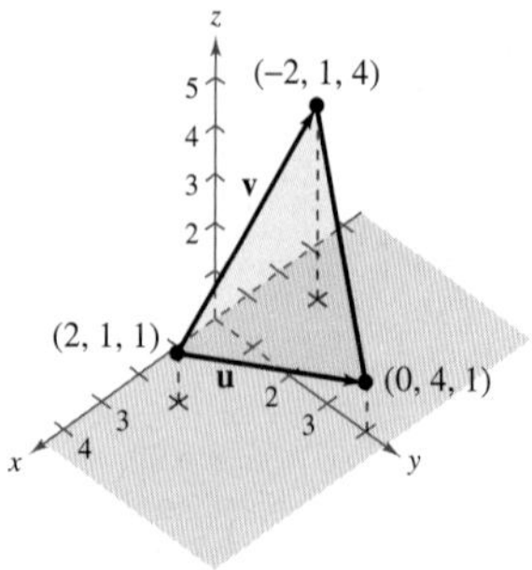

FIGURE 11.29

To find the equation of the plane, you need a point in the plane and a vector that is normal to the plane. There are three choices for the point, but no normal vector is given. To obtain a normal vector, use the cross product of vectors **u** and **v** extending from the point $(2, 1, 1)$ to the points $(0, 4, 1)$ and $(-2, 1, 4)$, as shown in Figure 11.29. The component forms of **u** and **v** are

$$\mathbf{u} = \langle 0 - 2, 4 - 1, 1 - 1 \rangle = \langle -2, 3, 0 \rangle$$

$$\mathbf{v} = \langle -2 - 2, 1 - 1, 4 - 1 \rangle = \langle -4, 0, 3 \rangle$$

and it follows that

$$\mathbf{n} = \mathbf{u} \times \mathbf{v} = \begin{vmatrix} \mathbf{i} & \mathbf{j} & \mathbf{k} \\ -2 & 3 & 0 \\ -4 & 0 & 3 \end{vmatrix}$$

$$= 9\mathbf{i} + 6\mathbf{j} + 12\mathbf{k}$$

$$= \langle a, b, c \rangle$$

is normal to the given plane. Using the direction numbers for **n** and the initial point $(x_1, y_1, z_1) = (2, 1, 1)$, you can determine an equation of the plane to be

$$a(x - x_1) + b(y - y_1) + c(z - z_1) = 0$$

$$9(x - 2) + 6(y - 1) + 12(z - 1) = 0 \qquad \text{Standard form}$$

$$9x + 6y + 12z - 36 = 0$$

$$3x + 2y + 4z - 12 = 0. \qquad \text{General form}$$

Check that each of the three points satisfies the equation $3x + 2y + 4z - 12 = 0$.

CHECKPoint Now try Exercise 29.

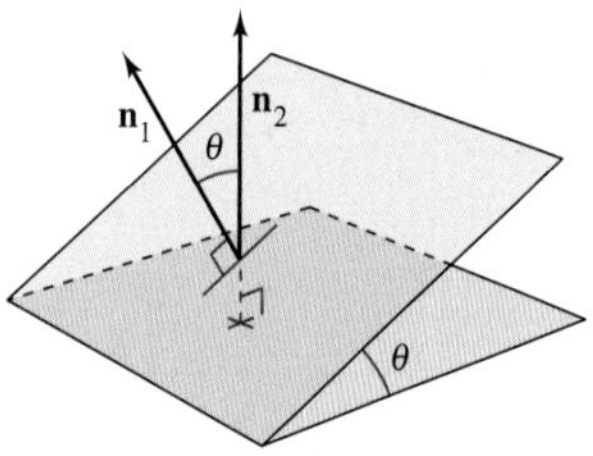

FIGURE 11.30

Two distinct planes in three-space either are parallel or intersect in a line. If they intersect, you can determine the angle θ $(0 \le \theta \le 90°)$ between them from the angle between their normal vectors, as shown in Figure 11.30. Specifically, if vectors $\mathbf{n}_1$ and $\mathbf{n}_2$ are normal to two intersecting planes, the angle θ between the normal vectors is equal to the **angle between the two planes** and is given by

$$\cos\theta = \frac{|\mathbf{n}_1 \cdot \mathbf{n}_2|}{\|\mathbf{n}_1\| \, \|\mathbf{n}_2\|}. \qquad \text{Angle between two planes}$$

Consequently, two planes with normal vectors $\mathbf{n}_1$ and $\mathbf{n}_2$ are

1. *perpendicular* if $\mathbf{n}_1 \cdot \mathbf{n}_2 = 0$.
2. *parallel* if $\mathbf{n}_1$ is a scalar multiple of $\mathbf{n}_2$.

Example 4 Finding the Line of Intersection of Two Planes

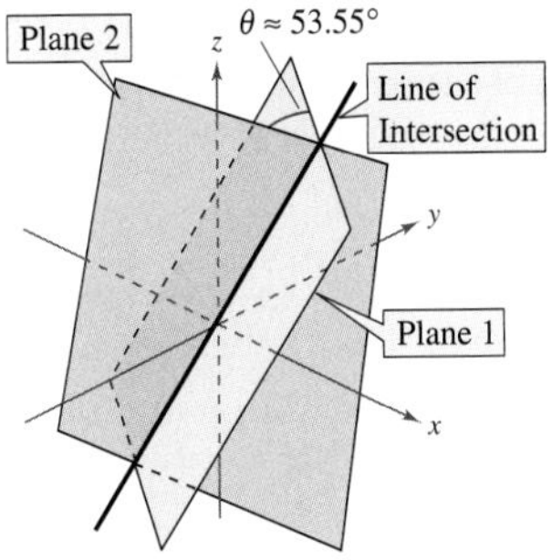

FIGURE 11.31

Find the angle between the two planes given by

$$x - 2y + z = 0 \quad \text{Equation for plane 1}$$
$$2x + 3y - 2z = 0 \quad \text{Equation for plane 2}$$

and find parametric equations of their line of intersection (see Figure 11.31).

Solution

The normal vectors for the planes are $\mathbf{n}_1 = \langle 1, -2, 1\rangle$ and $\mathbf{n}_2 = \langle 2, 3, -2\rangle$. Consequently, the angle between the two planes is determined as follows.

$$\cos\theta = \frac{|\mathbf{n}_1 \cdot \mathbf{n}_2|}{\|\mathbf{n}_1\|\,\|\mathbf{n}_2\|} = \frac{|-6|}{\sqrt{6}\sqrt{17}} = \frac{6}{\sqrt{102}} \approx 0.59409.$$

This implies that the angle between the two planes is $\theta \approx 53.55°$. You can find the line of intersection of the two planes by simultaneously solving the two linear equations representing the planes. One way to do this is to multiply the first equation by -2 and add the result to the second equation.

$$\begin{array}{r} x - 2y + z = 0 \\ 2x + 3y - 2z = 0 \end{array} \Longrightarrow \begin{array}{r} -2x + 4y - 2z = 0 \\ \underline{2x + 3y - 2z = 0} \\ 7y - 4z = 0 \end{array} \Longrightarrow y = \frac{4z}{7}$$

Substituting $y = 4z/7$ back into one of the original equations, you can determine that $x = z/7$. Finally, by letting $t = z/7$, you obtain the parametric equations

$$x = t = x_1 + at \quad \text{Parametric equation for } x$$
$$y = 4t = y_1 + bt \quad \text{Parametric equation for } y$$
$$z = 7t = z_1 + ct. \quad \text{Parametric equation for } z$$

Because $(x_1, y_1, z_1) = (0, 0, 0)$ lies in both planes, you can substitute for x_1, y_1, and z_1 in these parametric equations, which indicates that $a = 1$, $b = 4$, and $c = 7$ are direction numbers for the line of intersection.

CHECKPoint Now try Exercise 47.

Note that the direction numbers in Example 4 can also be obtained from the cross product of the two normal vectors as follows.

$$\mathbf{n}_1 \times \mathbf{n}_2 = \begin{vmatrix} \mathbf{i} & \mathbf{j} & \mathbf{k} \\ 1 & -2 & 1 \\ 2 & 3 & -2 \end{vmatrix}$$
$$= \begin{vmatrix} -2 & 1 \\ 3 & -2 \end{vmatrix}\mathbf{i} - \begin{vmatrix} 1 & 1 \\ 2 & -2 \end{vmatrix}\mathbf{j} + \begin{vmatrix} 1 & -2 \\ 2 & 3 \end{vmatrix}\mathbf{k}$$
$$= \mathbf{i} + 4\mathbf{j} + 7\mathbf{k}$$

This means that the *line of intersection of the two planes is parallel to the cross product of their normal vectors.*

Extra Example 4

Find the angle between the two planes given by $2x - y + 3z = 0$ and $-x + 2y + z = 0$, and find parametric equations of their line of intersection.

Angle between the two planes: $\approx 96.26°$; Parametric equations: $x = -7t$, $y = -5t$, $z = 3t$

Sketching Planes in Space

> **TECHNOLOGY**
>
> Most three-dimensional graphing utilities and computer algebra systems can graph a plane in space. Consult the user's guide for your utility for specific instructions.

As discussed in Section 11.1, if a plane in space intersects one of the coordinate planes, the line of intersection is called the *trace* of the given plane in the coordinate plane. To sketch a plane in space, it is helpful to find its points of intersection with the coordinate axes and its traces in the coordinate planes. For example, consider the plane

$$3x + 2y + 4z = 12. \qquad \text{Equation of plane}$$

You can find the xy-trace by letting $z = 0$ and sketching the line

$$3x + 2y = 12 \qquad xy\text{-trace}$$

in the xy-plane. This line intersects the x-axis at $(4, 0, 0)$ and the y-axis at $(0, 6, 0)$. In Figure 11.32, this process is continued by finding the yz-trace and the xz-trace and then shading the triangular region lying in the first octant.

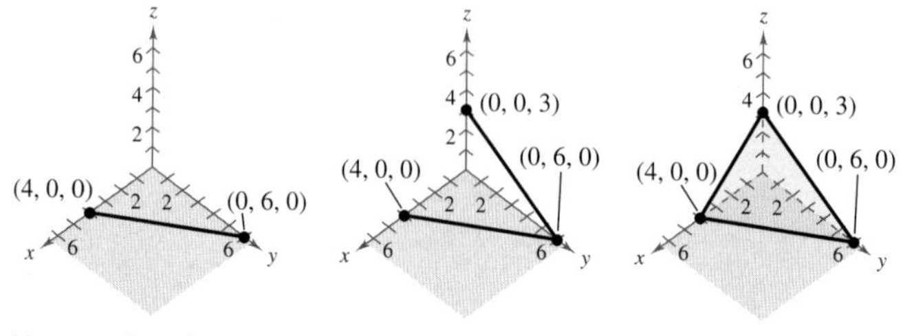

(a) ***xy*-trace ($z = 0$):** $3x + 2y = 12$ **(b)** ***yz*-trace ($x = 0$):** $2y + 4z = 12$ **(c)** ***xz*-trace ($y = 0$):** $3x + 4z = 12$

FIGURE 11.32

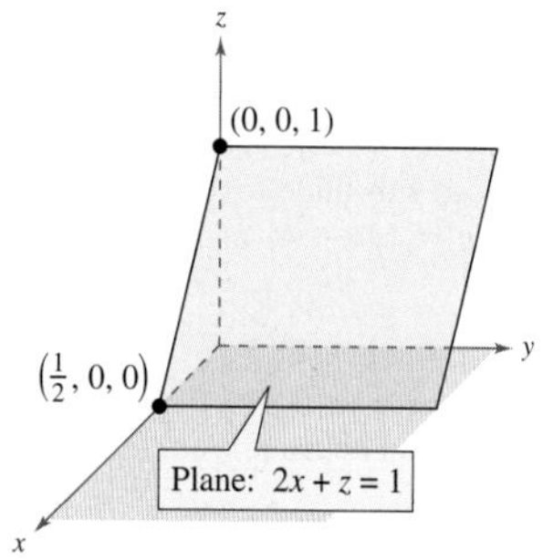

Plane is parallel to y-axis

FIGURE 11.33

If the equation of a plane has a missing variable, such as $2x + z = 1$, the plane must be *parallel to the axis* represented by the missing variable, as shown in Figure 11.33. If two variables are missing from the equation of a plane, then it is *parallel to the coordinate* plane represented by the missing variables, as shown in Figure 11.34.

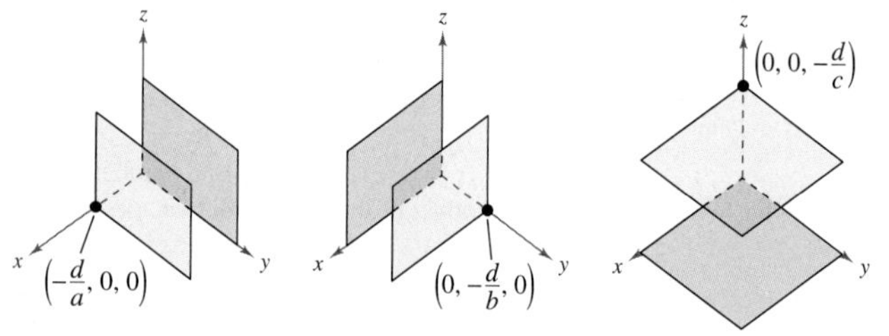

(a) Plane $ax + d = 0$ is parallel to yz-plane. **(b) Plane $by + d = 0$ is parallel to xz-plane.** **(c) Plane $cz + d = 0$ is parallel to xy-plane.**

FIGURE 11.34

> ***Differentiated Instruction***
>
> **Auditory Learners** Once students have studied how to sketch planes in space, have them find a partner. Have them explain to each other how to sketch the plane in space without referring to Figure 11.34. Then have students do the same using an equation of a plane from Exercises 51–56.

Distance Between a Point and a Plane

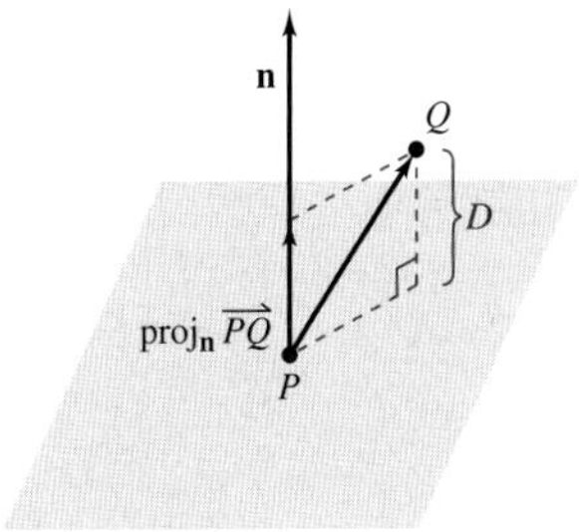

$D = \|\text{proj}_{\mathbf{n}}\overrightarrow{PQ}\|$

FIGURE 11.35

The distance D between a point Q and a plane is the length of the shortest line segment connecting Q to the plane, as shown in Figure 11.35. If P is *any* point in the plane, you can find this distance by projecting the vector $\overrightarrow{PQ}$ onto the normal vector $\mathbf{n}$. The length of this projection is the desired distance.

Distance Between a Point and a Plane

The **distance between a plane and a point** Q (not in the plane) is

$$D = \|\text{proj}_{\mathbf{n}}\overrightarrow{PQ}\|$$

$$= \frac{|\overrightarrow{PQ} \cdot \mathbf{n}|}{\|\mathbf{n}\|}$$

where P is a point in the plane and $\mathbf{n}$ is normal to the plane.

To find a point in the plane given by $ax + by + cz + d = 0$, where $a \neq 0$, let $y = 0$ and $z = 0$. Then, from the equation $ax + d = 0$, you can conclude that the point $(-d/a, 0, 0)$ lies in the plane.

Example 5 Finding the Distance Between a Point and a Plane

Find the distance between the point $Q(1, 5, -4)$ and the plane $3x - y + 2z = 6$.

Solution

You know that $\mathbf{n} = \langle 3, -1, 2\rangle$ is normal to the given plane. To find a point in the plane, let $y = 0$ and $z = 0$, and obtain the point $P(2, 0, 0)$. The vector from P to Q is

$$\overrightarrow{PQ} = \langle 1 - 2, 5 - 0, -4 - 0\rangle$$

$$= \langle -1, 5, -4\rangle.$$

The formula for the distance between a point and a plane produces

$$D = \frac{|\overrightarrow{PQ} \cdot \mathbf{n}|}{\|\mathbf{n}\|}$$

$$= \frac{|\langle -1, 5, -4\rangle \cdot \langle 3, -1, 2\rangle|}{\sqrt{9 + 1 + 4}}$$

$$= \frac{|-3 - 5 - 8|}{\sqrt{14}}$$

$$= \frac{16}{\sqrt{14}}.$$

CHECKPoint Now try Exercise 59.

The choice of the point P in Example 5 is arbitrary. Try choosing a different point to verify that you obtain the same distance.

Extra Example 5

Find the distance between the point $Q(2, 3, -1)$ and the plane $2x - 3y + 4z = 8$.

$$\frac{17}{\sqrt{29}}$$

Closing the Lesson

Have students summarize the major points of the lesson and answer the Essential Question: How do you describe and compare lines and planes in space?

- **Write the parametric and symmetric equations for a line through space.**
- **Write the equation for a plane in space, given three points or a normal vector and a point in the plane.**
- **Find the equation for the line of intersection between two planes by simultaneously solving the equations for the planes.**
- **Find the distance from a point P to a plane by choosing a point Q on the plane and calculating the length of the projection of $\overrightarrow{PQ}$ onto the normal vector.**

11.4 EXERCISES

See www.CalcChat.com for worked-out solutions to odd-numbered exercises.

VOCABULARY: Fill in the blanks.

1. The ______ vector for a line L is given by $\mathbf{v} =$ ______. direction; $\dfrac{\overrightarrow{PQ}}{t}$
2. The ______ ______ of a line in space are given by $x = x_1 + at$, $y = y_1 + bt$, and $z = z_1 + ct$. parametric equations
3. If the direction numbers a, b, and c of the vector $\mathbf{v} = \langle a, b, c\rangle$ are all nonzero, you can eliminate the parameter to obtain the ______ ______ of a line. symmetric equations
4. A vector that is perpendicular to a plane is called normal.

SKILLS AND APPLICATIONS

In Exercises 5–10, find a set of (a) parametric equations and (b) symmetric equations for the line through the point and parallel to the specified vector or line. (For each line, write the direction numbers as integers.) 5–10. See margin.

	Point	*Parallel to*
5.	$(0, 0, 0)$	$\mathbf{v} = \langle 1, 2, 3\rangle$
6.	$(3, -5, 1)$	$\mathbf{v} = \langle 3, -7, -10\rangle$
7.	$(-4, 1, 0)$	$\mathbf{v} = \frac{1}{2}\mathbf{i} + \frac{4}{3}\mathbf{j} - \mathbf{k}$
8.	$(-2, 0, 3)$	$\mathbf{v} = 2\mathbf{i} + 4\mathbf{j} - 2\mathbf{k}$
9.	$(2, -3, 5)$	$x = 5 + 2t, y = 7 - 3t, z = -2 + t$
10.	$(1, 0, 1)$	$x = 3 + 3t, y = 5 - 2t, z = -7 + t$

In Exercises 11–18, find (a) a set of parametric equations and (b) if possible, a set of symmetric equations of the line that passes through the given points. (For each line, write the direction numbers as integers.) 11–18. See margin.

11. $(2, 0, 2), (1, 4, -3)$
12. $(2, 3, 0), (10, 8, 12)$
13. $(-3, 8, 15), (1, -2, 16)$
14. $(2, 3, -1), (1, -5, 3)$
15. $(3, 1, 2), (-1, 1, 5)$
16. $(2, -1, 5), (2, 1, -3)$
17. $\left(-\frac{1}{2}, 2, \frac{1}{2}\right), \left(1, -\frac{1}{2}, 0\right)$
18. $\left(-\frac{3}{2}, \frac{3}{2}, 2\right), (3, -5, -4)$

In Exercises 19 and 20, sketch a graph of the line. 19–20. See margin.

19. $x = 2t, y = 2 + t, z = 1 + \frac{1}{2}t$
20. $x = 5 - 2t, y = 1 + t, z = 5 - \frac{1}{2}t$

In Exercises 21–26, find the general form of the equation of the plane passing through the point and perpendicular to the specified vector or line.

	Point	*Perpendicular to*	
21.	$(2, 1, 2)$	$\mathbf{n} = \mathbf{i}$	$x - 2 = 0$
22.	$(1, 0, -3)$	$\mathbf{n} = \mathbf{k}$	$z + 3 = 0$
23.	$(5, 6, 3)$	$\mathbf{n} = -2\mathbf{i} + \mathbf{j} - 2\mathbf{k}$	See below.
24.	$(0, 0, 0)$	$\mathbf{n} = -3\mathbf{j} + 5\mathbf{k}$	$-3y + 5z = 0$
25.	$(2, 0, 0)$	$x = 3 - t, y = 2 - 2t, z = 4 + t$	See below.
26.	$(0, 0, 6)$	$x = 1 - t, y = 2 + t, z = 4 - 2t$	See below.

23. $-2x + y - 2z + 10 = 0$
25. $-x - 2y + z + 2 = 0$
26. $-x + y - 2z + 12 = 0$

In Exercises 27–30, find the general form of the equation of the plane passing through the three points.

27. $(0, 0, 0), (1, 2, 3), (-2, 3, 3)$ $-3x - 9y + 7z = 0$
28. $(4, -1, 3), (2, 5, 1), (-1, 2, 1)$ See margin.
29. $(2, 3, -2), (3, 4, 2), (1, -1, 0)$ $6x - 2y - z - 8 = 0$
30. $(5, -1, 4), (1, -1, 2), (2, 1, -3)$ $2x - 11y - 4z - 5 = 0$

In Exercises 31–36, find the general form of the equation of the plane with the given characteristics. 31–36. See margin.

31. Passes through $(2, 5, 3)$ and is parallel to the xz-plane
32. Passes through $(1, 2, 3)$ and is parallel to the yz-plane
33. Passes through $(0, 2, 4)$ and $(-1, -2, 0)$ and is perpendicular to the yz-plane
34. Passes through $(1, -2, 4)$ and $(4, 0, -1)$ and is perpendicular to the xz-plane
35. Passes through $(2, 2, 1)$ and $(-1, 1, -1)$ and is perpendicular to $2x - 3y + z = 3$
36. Passes through $(1, 2, 0)$ and $(-1, -1, 2)$ and is perpendicular to $2x - 3y + z = 6$

In Exercises 37–40, determine whether the planes are parallel, orthogonal, or neither. If they are neither parallel nor orthogonal, find the angle of intersection.

37. $5x - 3y + z = 4$, $x + 4y + 7z = 1$ Orthogonal
38. $3x + y - 4z = 3$, $-9x - 3y + 12z = 4$ Parallel
39. $2x - z = 1$, $4x + y + 8z = 10$ Orthogonal
40. $x - 5y - z = 1$, $5x - 25y - 5z = -3$ Parallel

In Exercises 41–46, find a set of parametric equations of the line. (There are many correct answers.) 41–43. See below.

41. Passes through $(2, 3, 4)$ and is parallel to the xz-plane and the yz-plane
42. Passes through $(-4, 5, 2)$ and is parallel to the xy-plane and the yz-plane
43. Passes through $(2, 3, 4)$ and is perpendicular to $3x + 2y - z = 6$

41. $x = 2$, $y = 3$, $z = 4 + t$
42. $x = -4$, $y = 5 + t$, $z = 2$
43. $x = 2 + 3t$, $y = 3 + 2t$, $z = 4 - t$

4 PRACTICE AND APPLY

Assignment Guide

Transparencies Available
Available at the Instructor's companion site.

Average:
Day 1: p. 838
Exs. 1–4, 6–9, 12–16, 19, 21–23, 25, 27, 28
Day 2: pp. 838–839
Exs. 31–35 odd, 37–39, 41, 48, 49, 51, 53–55, 57, 58, 60, 61, 63–65

Advanced:
Day 1: p. 838
Exs. 1–4, 6–10, 14–18, 20, 22–24, 26–30 even
Day 2: pp. 838–839
Exs. 32–36 even, 37–40, 42–46 even, 49, 50–60 even, 61–65, 67, 68

Block:
p. 838
Exs. 1–4, 6–9, 12–16, 19, 21–23, 25, 27, 28 (with 11.3)
pp. 838–839
Exs. 31–35 odd, 37–39, 41, 48, 49, 51, 53–55, 57, 58, 60, 61, 63–65 (with Review)

5. (a) $x = t, y = 2t, z = 3t$
(b) $x = \dfrac{y}{2} = \dfrac{z}{3}$

6. (a) $x = 3 + 3t, y = -5 - 7t, z = 1 - 10t$
(b) $\dfrac{x-3}{3} = \dfrac{y+5}{-7} = \dfrac{z-1}{-10}$

7. (a) $x = -4 + 3t, y = 1 + 8t, z = -6t$
(b) $\dfrac{x+4}{3} = \dfrac{y-1}{8} = \dfrac{z}{-6}$

8. (a) $x = -2 + 2t, y = 4t, z = 3 - 2t$
(b) $\dfrac{x+2}{2} = \dfrac{y}{4} = \dfrac{z-3}{-2}$

9. (a) $x = 2 + 2t, y = -3 - 3t, z = 5 + t$
(b) $\dfrac{x-2}{2} = \dfrac{y+3}{-3} = z - 5$

10. (a) $x = 1 + 3t, y = -2t, z = 1 + t$
(b) $\dfrac{x-1}{3} = \dfrac{y}{-2} = z - 1$

11. (a) $x = 2 - t, y = 4t, z = 2 - 5t$
(b) $\dfrac{x-2}{-1} = \dfrac{y}{4} = \dfrac{z-2}{-5}$

12. (a) $x = 2 + 8t, y = 3 + 5t, z = 12t$
(b) $\dfrac{x-2}{8} = \dfrac{y-3}{5} = \dfrac{z}{12}$

13. (a) $x = -3 + 4t, y = 8 - 10t, z = 15 + t$
(b) $\dfrac{x+3}{4} = \dfrac{y-8}{-10} = z - 15$

14. (a) $x = 2 - t, y = 3 - 8t, z = -1 + 4t$
(b) $\dfrac{x-2}{-1} = \dfrac{y-3}{-8} = \dfrac{z+1}{4}$

15. (a) $x = 3 - 4t, y = 1, z = 2 + 3t$
(b) No symmetric equations

16. (a) $x = 2, y = -1 + 2t, z = 5 - 8t$
(b) No symmetric equations

17. (a) $x = -\dfrac{1}{2} + 3t, y = 2 - 5t, z = \dfrac{1}{2} - t$
(b) $\dfrac{2x+1}{6} = \dfrac{y-2}{-5} = \dfrac{2z-1}{-2}$

18. (a) $x = 3 + 9t, y = -5 - 13t, z = -4 - 12t$
(b) $\dfrac{x-3}{9} = \dfrac{y+5}{-13} = \dfrac{2z-4}{-12}$

28. $-x + y + 4z - 7 = 0$

19–20, 31–36. See Additional Answers beginning on page AA1.

44. Passes through $(-4, 5, 2)$ and is perpendicular to $-x + 2y + z = 5$ $x = -4 - t, y = 5 + 2t, z = 2 + t$

45. Passes through $(5, -3, -4)$ and is parallel to $\mathbf{v} = \langle 2, -1, 3 \rangle$ $x = 5 + 2t, y = -3 - t, z = -4 + 3t$

46. Passes through $(-1, 4, -3)$ and is parallel to $\mathbf{v} = 5\mathbf{i} - \mathbf{j}$ $x = -1 + 5t, y = 4 - t, z = -3$

In Exercises 47–50, (a) find the angle between the two planes and (b) find parametric equations of their line of intersection. 47–50. See margin.

47. $3x - 4y + 5z = 6$, $x + y - z = 2$

48. $x - 3y + z = -2$, $2x + 5z + 3 = 0$

49. $x + y - z = 0$, $2x - 5y - z = 1$

50. $2x + 4y - 2z = 1$, $-3x - 6y + 3z = 10$

In Exercises 51–56, plot the intercepts and sketch a graph of the plane. 51–56. See margin.

51. $x + 2y + 3z = 6$

52. $2x - y + 4z = 4$

53. $x + 2y = 4$

54. $y + z = 5$

55. $3x + 2y - z = 6$

56. $x - 3z = 6$

In Exercises 57–60, find the distance between the point and the plane.

57. $(0, 0, 0)$, $8x - 4y + z = 8$ $\frac{8}{9}$

58. $(3, 2, 1)$, $x - y + 2z = 4$ $\frac{\sqrt{6}}{6}$

59. $(4, -2, -2)$, $2x - y + z = 4$

60. $(-1, 2, 5)$, $2x + 3y + z = 12$

59–60. See margin.

61. DATA ANALYSIS: BEVERAGE CONSUMPTION The table shows the per capita consumption (in gallons) of different types of beverages sold by a company from 2006 through 2010. Consumption of energy drinks, soft drinks, and bottled water are represented by the variables x, y, and z, respectively.

Year	x	y	z
2006	2.3	3.4	3.9
2007	2.2	3.2	3.8
2008	2.0	3.1	3.5
2009	1.9	3.0	3.4
2010	1.8	2.9	3.3

A model for the data is given by

$$1.54x - 0.32y - z = -1.45.$$

(a). See margin.

(a) Complete a fifth column in the table using the model to approximate z for the given values of x and y.

(b) Compare the approximations from part (a) with the actual values of z.
The approximations are very similar to the actual values of z.

(c) According to this model, any increases or decreases in consumption of two types of beverages will have what effect on the consumption of the third type of beverage? Answers will vary.

62. MECHANICAL DESIGN A chute at the top of a grain elevator of a combine funnels the grain into a bin, as shown in the figure. Find the angle between two adjacent sides. 89.1°

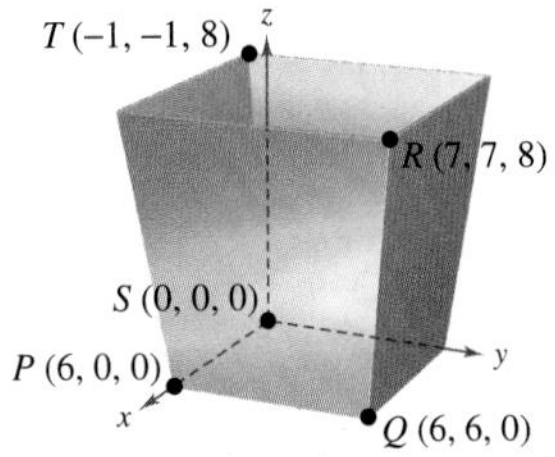

63. False. Lines that do not intersect and are not in the same plane may not be parallel.

EXPLORATION

TRUE OR FALSE? **In Exercises 63 and 64, determine whether the statement is true or false. Justify your answer.**

63. Every two lines in space are either intersecting or parallel.

64. Two nonparallel planes in space will always intersect. True

65. The direction numbers of two distinct lines in space are 10, −18, 20, and −15, 27, −30. What is the relationship between the lines? Explain. See below.

66. Consider the following four planes.

$2x + 3y - z = 2$ $\mathbf{n} = \langle 2, 3, -1 \rangle$;

$4x + 6y - 2z = 5$ $\mathbf{n} = \langle 4, 6, -2 \rangle$;

$-2x - 3y + z = -2$ $\mathbf{n} = \langle -2, -3, 1 \rangle$;

$-6x - 9y + 3z = 11$ $\mathbf{n} = \langle -6, -9, 3 \rangle$;

The planes are parallel to each other.

What are the normal vectors for each plane? What can you say about the relative positions of these planes in space?

67. (a) Describe and find an equation for the surface generated by all points (x, y, z) that are two units from the point $(4, -1, 1)$. See below.

(b) Describe and find an equation for the surface generated by all points (x, y, z) that are two units from the plane $4x - 3y + z = 10$. See below.

68. CAPSTONE Give the parametric equations and the symmetric equations of a line in space. Describe what is required to find these equations. Answers will vary.

65. Parallel. $\langle 10, -18, 20 \rangle$ is a scalar multiple of $\langle -15, 27, -30 \rangle$.

67. (a) Sphere: $(x - 4)^2 + (y + 1)^2 + (z - 1)^2 = 4$
(b) Two planes: $4x - 3y + z = 10 \pm 2\sqrt{26}$

5 ASSESS AND RETEACH

Daily Homework Quiz

Transparency Available
Available at the Instructor's companion site.

47. (a) 60.7°
(b) $x = -t + 2, y = 8t, z = 7t$

48. (a) 66.9°
(b) $x = -5t - \frac{3}{2}, y = -t + \frac{1}{6}, z = 2t$

49. (a) 77.8°
(b) $x = 6t + 1, y = t, z = 7t + 1$

50. (a) and (b). The two planes are parallel because the normal vector $\mathbf{n}_1 = \langle 2, 4, -2 \rangle$ is a scalar multiple of the normal vector $\mathbf{n}_2 = \langle -3, -6, 3 \rangle$, and the planes do not intersect.

51.

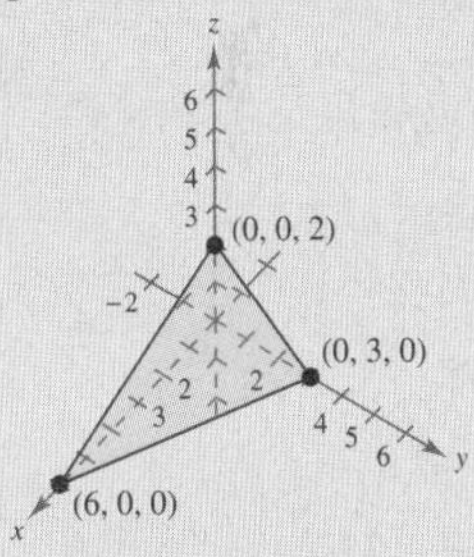

52.

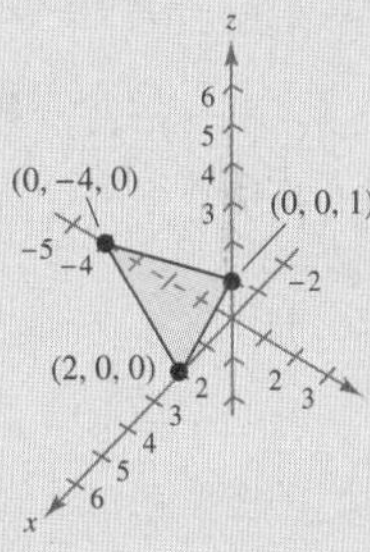

53.

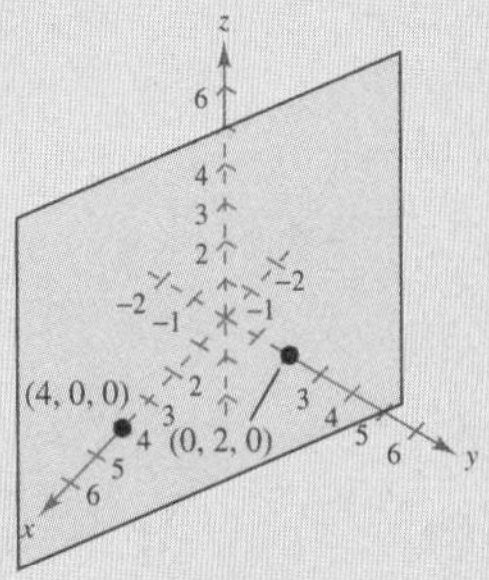

54.

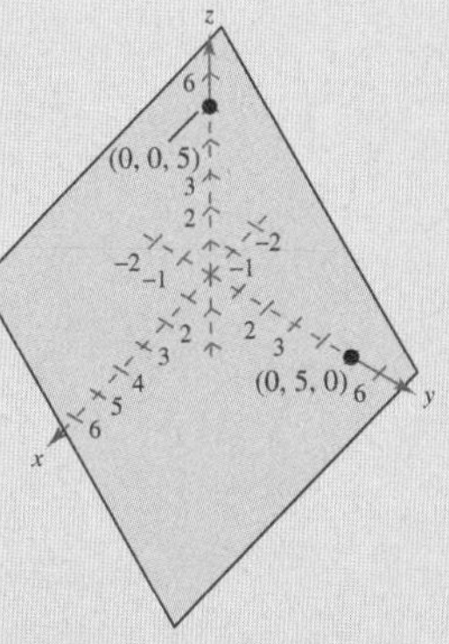

55.

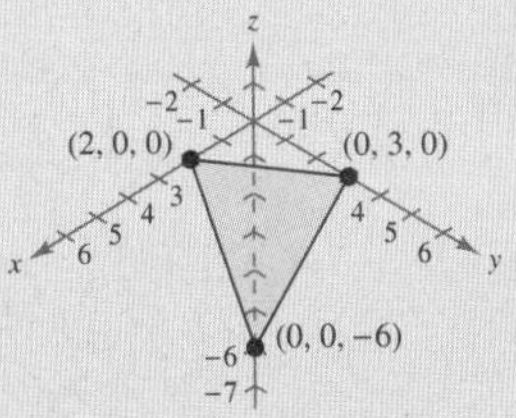

56.

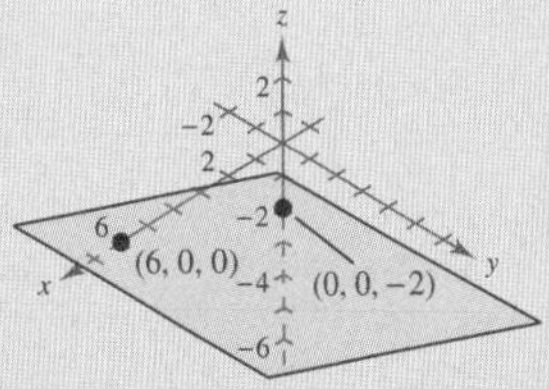

59. $\frac{4}{\sqrt{6}} = \frac{2\sqrt{6}}{3}$

60. $\frac{3}{\sqrt{14}} = \frac{3\sqrt{14}}{14}$

61(a). See Additional Answers beginning on page AA1.

11 Chapter Summary

	What Did You Learn?	Explanation/Examples	Review Exercises
Section 11.1	Plot points in the three-dimensional coordinate system *(p. 810)*.	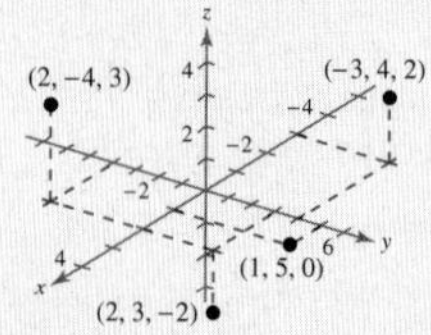	1–4
	Find distances between points in space and find midpoints of line segments joining points in space *(p. 811)*.	The distance between the points (x_1, y_1, z_1) and (x_2, y_2, z_2) given by the Distance Formula in Space is $d = \sqrt{(x_2 - x_1)^2 + (y_2 - y_1)^2 + (z_2 - z_1)^2}$. The midpoint of the line segment joining the points (x_1, y_1, z_1) and (x_2, y_2, z_2) given by the Midpoint Formula in Space is $\left(\frac{x_1 + x_2}{2}, \frac{y_1 + y_2}{2}, \frac{z_1 + z_2}{2}\right)$.	5–14
	Write equations of spheres in standard form and find traces of surfaces in space *(p. 812)*.	**Standard Equation of a Sphere** The standard equation of a sphere with center (h, k, j) and radius r is given by $(x - h)^2 + (y - k)^2 + (z - j)^2 = r^2$.	15–26
Section 11.2	Find the component forms of the unit vectors in the same direction of, the magnitudes of, the dot products of, and the angles between vectors in space *(p. 817)*.	**Vectors in Space** **1.** Two vectors are equal if and only if their corresponding components are equal. **2.** Magnitude of $\mathbf{u} = \langle u_1, u_2, u_3 \rangle$: $\lVert\mathbf{u}\rVert = \sqrt{u_1^2 + u_2^2 + u_3^2}$ **3.** A unit vector $\mathbf{u}$ in the direction of $\mathbf{v}$ is $\mathbf{u} = \frac{\mathbf{v}}{\lVert\mathbf{v}\rVert}$, $\mathbf{v} \neq 0$. **4.** The sum of $\mathbf{u} = \langle u_1, u_2, u_3 \rangle$ and $\mathbf{v} = \langle v_1, v_2, v_3 \rangle$ is $\mathbf{u} + \mathbf{v} = \langle u_1 + v_1, u_2 + v_2, u_3 + v_3 \rangle$. **5.** The scalar multiple of the real number c and $\mathbf{u} = \langle u_1, u_2, u_3 \rangle$ is $c\mathbf{u} = \langle cu_1, cu_2, cu_3 \rangle$. **6.** The dot product of $\mathbf{u} = \langle u_1, u_2, u_3 \rangle$ and $\mathbf{v} = \langle v_1, v_2, v_3 \rangle$ is $\mathbf{u} \cdot \mathbf{v} = u_1v_1 + u_2v_2 + u_3v_3$. **Angle Between Two Vectors** If θ is the angle between two nonzero vectors $\mathbf{u}$ and $\mathbf{v}$, then $\cos\theta = \frac{\mathbf{u} \cdot \mathbf{v}}{\lVert\mathbf{u}\rVert\,\lVert\mathbf{v}\rVert}$.	27–36
	Determine whether vectors in space are parallel or orthogonal *(p. 819)*.	Two nonzero vectors $\mathbf{u}$ and $\mathbf{v}$ are parallel if there is some scalar c such that $\mathbf{u} = c\mathbf{v}$.	37–44
	Use vectors in space to solve real-life problems *(p. 821)*.	Vectors can be used to solve equilibrium problems in space. (See Example 7.)	45, 46

	What Did You Learn?	Explanation/Examples	Review Exercises
Section 11.3	Find cross products of vectors in space *(p. 824)*.	**Definition of Cross Product of Two Vectors in Space** Let $\mathbf{u} = u_1\mathbf{i} + u_2\mathbf{j} + u_3\mathbf{k}$ and $\mathbf{v} = v_1\mathbf{i} + v_2\mathbf{j} + v_3\mathbf{k}$ be vectors in space. The cross product of **u** and **v**, $\mathbf{u} \times \mathbf{v}$, is the vector $(u_2v_3 - u_3v_2)\mathbf{i} - (u_1v_3 - u_3v_1)\mathbf{j} + (u_1v_2 - u_2v_1)\mathbf{k}$.	47–50
	Use geometric properties of cross products of vectors in space *(p. 826)*.	**Geometric Properties of the Cross Product** Let **u** and **v** be nonzero vectors in space, and let θ be the angle between **u** and **v**. **1.** $\mathbf{u} \times \mathbf{v}$ is orthogonal to both **u** and **v**. **2.** $\\|\mathbf{u} \times \mathbf{v}\\| = \\|\mathbf{u}\\|\,\\|\mathbf{v}\\| \sin \theta$ **3.** $\mathbf{u} \times \mathbf{v} = \mathbf{0}$ if and only if **u** and **v** are scalar multiples of each other. **4.** $\\|\mathbf{u} \times \mathbf{v}\\|$ = area of parallelogram having **u** and **v** as adjacent sides	51–56
	Use triple scalar products to find volumes of parallelepipeds *(p. 828)*.	**The Triple Scalar Product** For $\mathbf{u} = u_1\mathbf{i} + u_2\mathbf{j} + u_3\mathbf{k}$, $\mathbf{v} = v_1\mathbf{i} + v_2\mathbf{j} + v_3\mathbf{k}$, and $\mathbf{w} = w_1\mathbf{i} + w_2\mathbf{j} + w_3\mathbf{k}$, the triple scalar product is given by $\mathbf{u} \cdot (\mathbf{v} \times \mathbf{w}) = \begin{vmatrix} u_1 & u_2 & u_3 \\ v_1 & v_2 & v_3 \\ w_1 & w_2 & w_3 \end{vmatrix}.$ **Geometric Property of the Triple Scalar Product** The volume V of a parallelepiped with vectors **u**, **v**, and **w** as adjacent edges is given by $V = \|\mathbf{u} \cdot (\mathbf{v} \times \mathbf{w})\|$.	57, 58
Section 11.4	Find parametric and symmetric equations of lines in space *(p. 831)*.	**Parametric Equations of a Line in Space** A line L parallel to the vector $\mathbf{v} = \langle a, b, c \rangle$ and passing through the point $P(x_1, y_1, z_1)$ is represented by the parametric equations $x = x_1 + at$, $y = y_1 + bt$, and $z = z_1 + ct$.	59–62
	Find equations of planes in space *(p. 833)*.	**Standard Equation of a Plane in Space** The plane containing the point (x_1, y_1, z_1) and having normal vector $\mathbf{n} = \langle a, b, c \rangle$ can be represented by the standard form of the equation of a plane $a(x - x_1) + b(y - y_1) + c(z - z_1) = 0.$	63–66
	Sketch planes in space *(p. 836)*.	See Figure 11.32, which shows how to sketch the plane $3x + 2y + 4z = 12$.	67–70
	Find distances between points and planes in space *(p. 837)*.	**Distance Between a Point and a Plane** The distance between a plane and a point Q (not in the plane) is $D = \\|\text{proj}_{\mathbf{n}}\overrightarrow{PQ}\\| = \dfrac{\|\overrightarrow{PQ} \cdot \mathbf{n}\|}{\\|\mathbf{n}\\|}$ where P is a point in the plane and **n** is normal to the plane.	71–74

11 Review Exercises

See www.CalcChat.com for worked-out solutions to odd-numbered exercises.

11.1 In Exercises 1 and 2, plot each point in the same three-dimensional coordinate system. 1–2. See margin.

1. (a) $(5, -1, 2)$ (b) $(-3, 3, 0)$

2. (a) $(2, 4, -3)$ (b) $(0, 0, 5)$

3. Find the coordinates of the point in the xy-plane four units to the right of the xz-plane and five units behind the yz-plane. $(-5, 4, 0)$

4. Find the coordinates of the point located on the y-axis and seven units to the left of the xz-plane. $(0, -7, 0)$

In Exercises 5–8, find the distance between the points.

5. $(4, 0, 7), (5, 2, 1)$ $\sqrt{41}$

6. $(2, 3, -4), (-1, -3, 0)$ $\sqrt{61}$

7. $(-7, -5, 6), (1, 1, 6)$ 10

8. $(0, 0, 0), (4, 4, 4)$ $4\sqrt{3}$

In Exercises 9 and 10, find the lengths of the sides of the right triangle. Show that these lengths satisfy the Pythagorean Theorem. 9–10. See margin.

9.

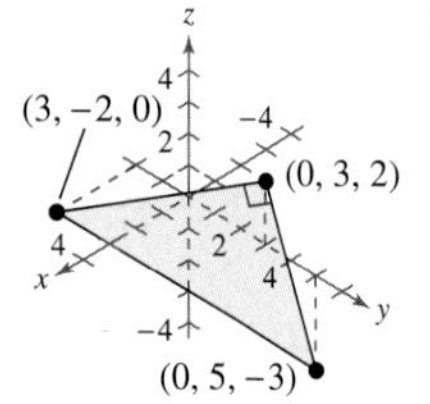

10.

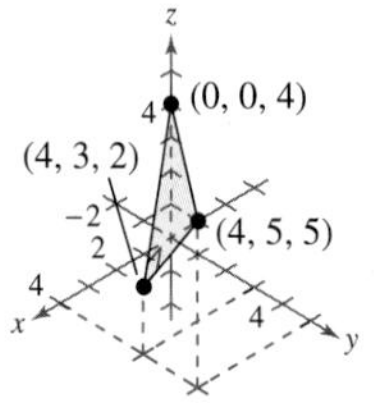

In Exercises 11–14, find the midpoint of the line segment joining the points.

11. $(8, -2, 3), (5, 6, 7)$ $\left(\frac{13}{2}, 2, 5\right)$

12. $(7, 1, -4), (1, -1, 2)$ $(4, 0, -1)$

13. $(10, 6, -12), (-8, -2, -6)$ $(1, 2, -9)$

14. $(-5, -3, 1), (-7, -9, -5)$ $(-6, -6, -2)$

In Exercises 15–20, find the standard form of the equation of the sphere with the given characteristics. 15–20. See below.

15. Center: $(2, 3, 5)$; radius: 1

16. Center: $(3, -2, 4)$; radius: 4

17. Center: $(1, 5, 2)$; diameter: 12

18. Center: $(0, 4, -1)$; diameter: 15

19. Endpoints of a diameter: $(-2, -2, -2), (2, 2, 2)$

20. Endpoints of a diameter: $(4, -1, -3), (-2, 5, 3)$

15. $(x-2)^2 + (y-3)^2 + (z-5)^2 = 1$
16. $(x-3)^2 + (y+2)^2 + (z-4)^2 = 16$
17. $(x-1)^2 + (y-5)^2 + (z-2)^2 = 36$
18. $x^2 + (y-4)^2 + (z+1)^2 = \frac{225}{4}$
19. $x^2 + y^2 + z^2 = 12$
20. $(x-1)^2 + (y-2)^2 + z^2 = 27$

In Exercises 21–24, find the center and radius of the sphere.

21. $x^2 + y^2 + z^2 - 8z = 0$ Center: $(0, 0, 4)$; radius: 4

22. $x^2 + y^2 + z^2 - 4x - 6y + 4 = 0$ 22–24. See margin.

23. $x^2 + y^2 + z^2 - 10x + 6y - 4z + 34 = 0$

24. $2x^2 + 2y^2 + 2z^2 + 2x + 2y + 2z + 1 = 0$

In Exercises 25 and 26, sketch the graph of the equation and sketch the specified trace. 25–26. See margin.

25. $x^2 + (y-3)^2 + z^2 = 16$

(a) xz-trace (b) yz-trace

26. $(x+2)^2 + (y-1)^2 + z^2 = 9$

(a) xy-trace (b) yz-trace

11.2 In Exercises 27–30, (a) write the component form of the vector **v**, (b) find the magnitude of **v**, and (c) find a unit vector in the direction of **v**. 27–30. See margin.

27. Initial point: $(3, -2, 1)$
Terminal point: $(4, 4, 0)$

28. Initial point: $(2, -1, 2)$
Terminal point: $(-3, 2, 3)$

29. Initial point: $(7, -4, 3)$
Terminal point: $(-3, 2, 10)$

30. Initial point: $(0, 3, -1)$
Terminal point: $(5, -8, 6)$

In Exercises 31–34, find the dot product of **u** and **v**.

31. $\mathbf{u} = \langle -1, 4, 3\rangle$, $\mathbf{v} = \langle 0, -6, 5\rangle$ -9

32. $\mathbf{u} = \langle 8, -4, 2\rangle$, $\mathbf{v} = \langle 2, 5, 2\rangle$ 0

33. $\mathbf{u} = 2\mathbf{i} - \mathbf{j} + \mathbf{k}$, $\mathbf{v} = \mathbf{i} - \mathbf{k}$ 1

34. $\mathbf{u} = 2\mathbf{i} + \mathbf{j} - 2\mathbf{k}$, $\mathbf{v} = \mathbf{i} - 3\mathbf{j} + 2\mathbf{k}$ -5

In Exercises 35 and 36, find the angle θ between the vectors.

35. $\mathbf{u} = \langle 2, -1, 0\rangle$, $\mathbf{v} = \langle 1, 2, 1\rangle$ $90°$

36. $\mathbf{u} = \langle 3, 1, -1\rangle$, $\mathbf{v} = \langle 4, 5, 2\rangle$ $47.61°$

In Exercises 37–40, determine whether **u** and **v** are orthogonal, parallel, or neither. 37–40. See below.

37. $\mathbf{u} = \langle 39, -12, 21\rangle$, $\mathbf{v} = \langle -26, 8, -14\rangle$

38. $\mathbf{u} = \langle 8, 5, -8\rangle$, $\mathbf{v} = \left\langle -2, 4, \frac{1}{2}\right\rangle$

39. $\mathbf{u} = 6\mathbf{i} + 5\mathbf{j} + 9\mathbf{k}$, $\mathbf{v} = 5\mathbf{i} + 3\mathbf{j} - 5\mathbf{k}$

40. $\mathbf{u} = 3\mathbf{j} + 2\mathbf{k}$, $\mathbf{v} = 12\mathbf{i} - 18\mathbf{k}$

37. Parallel
38. Orthogonal
39. Orthogonal
40. Neither

1.

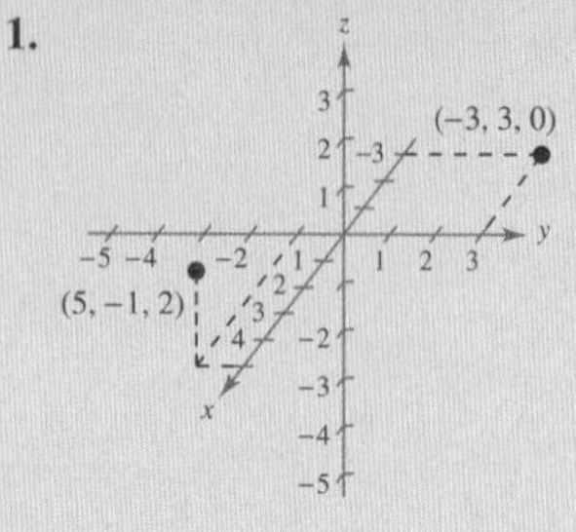

2.

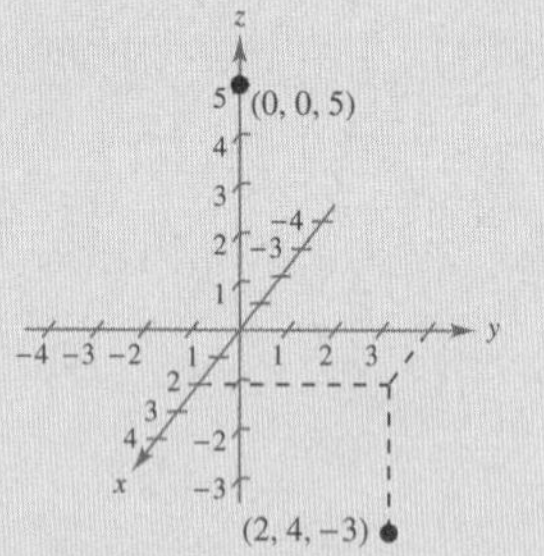

9. $\sqrt{29}, \sqrt{38}, \sqrt{67}$
$(\sqrt{29})^2 + (\sqrt{38})^2 = (\sqrt{67})^2$

10. $\sqrt{29}, \sqrt{13}, \sqrt{42}$
$(\sqrt{29})^2 + (\sqrt{13})^2 = (\sqrt{42})^2$

22. Center: $(2, 3, 0)$; radius: 3

23. Center: $(5, -3, 2)$; radius: 2

24. Center: $\left(-\frac{1}{2}, -\frac{1}{2}, -\frac{1}{2}\right)$; radius: $\frac{1}{2}$

25. (a)

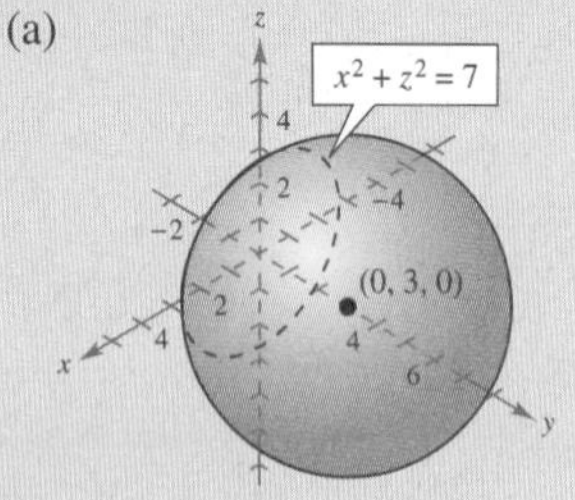

(b)

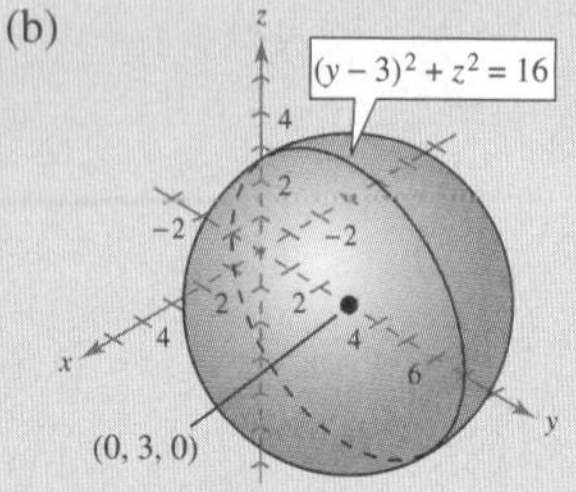

26. (a)

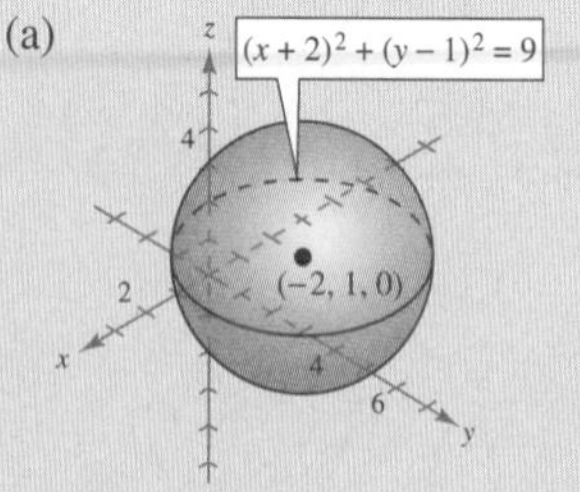

(b)

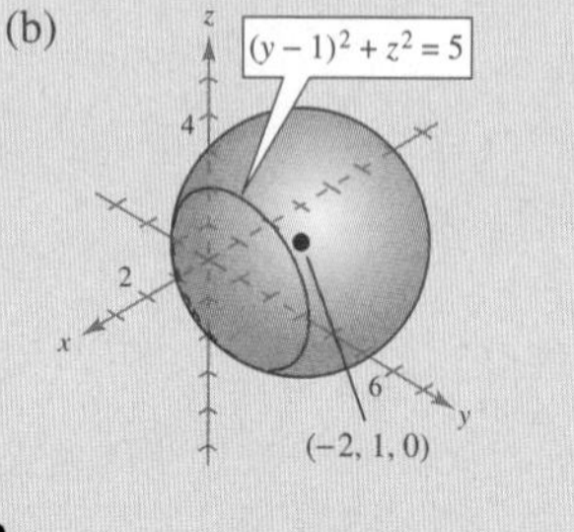

27. (a) $\langle 1, 6, -1\rangle$ (b) $\sqrt{38}$
(c) $\left\langle \frac{\sqrt{38}}{38}, \frac{3\sqrt{38}}{19}, -\frac{\sqrt{38}}{38}\right\rangle$

28. (a) $\langle -5, 3, 1\rangle$ (b) $\sqrt{35}$
(c) $\left\langle -\frac{\sqrt{35}}{7}, \frac{3\sqrt{35}}{35}, \frac{\sqrt{35}}{35}\right\rangle$

29. (a) $\langle -10, 6, 7\rangle$ (b) $\sqrt{185}$
(c) $\left\langle \frac{-2\sqrt{185}}{37}, \frac{6\sqrt{185}}{185}, \frac{7\sqrt{185}}{185}\right\rangle$

30. (a) $\langle 5, -11, 7\rangle$ (b) $\sqrt{195}$
(c) $\left\langle \frac{\sqrt{195}}{39}, \frac{-11\sqrt{195}}{195}, \frac{7\sqrt{195}}{195}\right\rangle$

In Exercises 41–44, use vectors to determine whether the points are collinear.

41. $(6, 3, -1), (5, 8, 3), (7, -2, -5)$ Collinear

42. $(5, 2, 0), (2, 6, 1), (2, 4, 7)$ Not collinear

43. $(5, -4, 7), (8, -5, 5), (11, 6, 3)$ Not collinear

44. $(3, 4, -1), (-1, 6, 9), (5, 3, -6)$ Collinear

45. TENSION A load of 300 pounds is supported by three cables, as shown in the figure. Find the tension in each of the supporting cables. A: 159.1 lb B: 115.6 lb C: 115.6 lb

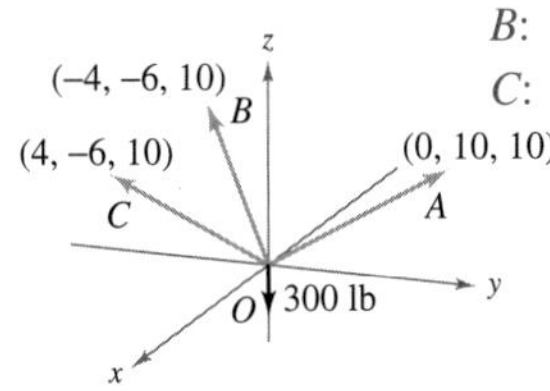

46. TENSION Determine the tension in each of the supporting cables in Exercise 45 if the load is 200 pounds. A: 106.1 lb, B: 77.1 lb, C: 77.1 lb

11.3 In Exercises 47–50, find $\mathbf{u} \times \mathbf{v}$.

47. $\mathbf{u} = \langle -2, 8, 2 \rangle$, $\mathbf{v} = \langle 1, 1, -1 \rangle$ $\langle -10, 0, -10 \rangle$

48. $\mathbf{u} = \langle 10, 15, 5 \rangle$, $\mathbf{v} = \langle 5, -3, 0 \rangle$ $\langle 15, 25, -105 \rangle$

49. $\mathbf{u} = 2\mathbf{i} + 3\mathbf{j} + 2\mathbf{k}$, $\mathbf{v} = 3\mathbf{i} + \mathbf{j} + 2\mathbf{k}$ $4\mathbf{i} + 2\mathbf{j} - 7\mathbf{k}$

50. $\mathbf{u} = -\mathbf{i} + 2\mathbf{j} - 2\mathbf{k}$, $\mathbf{v} = \mathbf{i}$ $-2\mathbf{j} - 2\mathbf{k}$

In Exercises 51–54, find a unit vector orthogonal to u and v. 51–53. See margin.

51. $\mathbf{u} = 2\mathbf{i} - \mathbf{j} + \mathbf{k}$, $\mathbf{v} = -\mathbf{i} + \mathbf{j} - 2\mathbf{k}$

52. $\mathbf{u} = \mathbf{j} + 4\mathbf{k}$, $\mathbf{v} = -\mathbf{i} + 3\mathbf{j}$

53. $\mathbf{u} = -3\mathbf{i} + 2\mathbf{j} - 5\mathbf{k}$, $\mathbf{v} = 10\mathbf{i} - 15\mathbf{j} + 2\mathbf{k}$

54. $\mathbf{u} = 4\mathbf{k}$, $\mathbf{v} = \mathbf{i} + 12\mathbf{k}$ $\mathbf{j}$

In Exercises 55 and 56, verify that the points are the vertices of a parallelogram and find its area. 55–56. See below.

55. $(2, -1, 1), (5, 1, 4), (0, 1, 1), (3, 3, 4)$

56. $(0, 4, 0), (1, 4, 1), (0, 6, 0), (1, 6, 1)$

In Exercises 57 and 58, find the volume of the parallelepiped with the given vertices.

57. $A(0, 0, 0), B(3, 0, 0), C(0, 5, 1), D(3, 5, 1), E(2, 0, 5), F(5, 0, 5), G(2, 5, 6), H(5, 5, 6)$ 75

58. $A(0, 0, 0), B(2, 0, 0), C(2, 4, 0), D(0, 4, 0), E(0, 0, 6), F(2, 0, 6), G(2, 4, 6), H(0, 4, 6)$ 48

55. Area $= \sqrt{172} = 2\sqrt{43} \approx 13.11$

56. Area $= \sqrt{8} = 2\sqrt{2} \approx 2.83$

11.4 In Exercises 59–62, find a set of (a) parametric equations and (b) symmetric equations for the specified line. 59–62. See margin.

59. Passes through $(-1, 3, 5)$ and $(3, 6, -1)$

60. Passes through $(0, -10, 3)$ and $(5, 10, 0)$

61. Passes through $(0, 0, 0)$ and is parallel to $\mathbf{v} = \langle -2, \frac{5}{2}, 1 \rangle$

62. Passes through $(3, 2, 1)$ and is parallel to the line given by $x = y = z$

In Exercises 63–66, find the general form of the equation of the specified plane. 63–66. See margin.

63. Passes through $(0, 0, 0)$, $(5, 0, 2)$, and $(2, 3, 8)$

64. Passes through $(-1, 3, 4)$, $(4, -2, 2)$, and $(2, 8, 6)$

65. Passes through $(5, 3, 2)$ and is parallel to the xy-plane

66. Passes through $(0, 0, 6)$ and is perpendicular to the line given by $x = 1 - t$, $y = 2 + t$, and $z = 4 - 2t$

In Exercises 67–70, plot the intercepts and sketch a graph of the plane. 67–70. See margin.

67. $3x - 2y + 3z = 6$

68. $5x - y - 5z = 5$

69. $2x - 3z = 6$

70. $4y - 3z = 12$

In Exercises 71–74, find the distance between the point and the plane.

71. $(1, 2, 3)$, $2x - y + z = 4$ $\dfrac{\sqrt{6}}{6}$

72. $(2, 3, 10)$, $x - 10y + 3z = 3$ $\dfrac{\sqrt{110}}{110}$

73. $(0, 0, 0)$, $2x + 3y + z = 12$ $\dfrac{6\sqrt{14}}{7}$

74. $(0, 0, 0)$, $x - 10y + 3z = 2$ $\dfrac{\sqrt{110}}{55}$

EXPLORATION

TRUE OR FALSE? In Exercises 75 and 76, determine whether the statement is true or false. Justify your answer.

75. The cross product is commutative. False. $\mathbf{u} \times \mathbf{v} = -(\mathbf{v} \times \mathbf{u})$

76. The triple scalar product of three vectors in space is a scalar. True. See page 828.

In Exercises 77 and 78, let $\mathbf{u} = \langle u_1, u_2, u_3 \rangle$, $\mathbf{v} = \langle v_1, v_2, v_3 \rangle$, and $\mathbf{w} = \langle w_1, w_2, w_3 \rangle$. 77–78. Answers will vary.

77. Show that $\mathbf{u} \cdot (\mathbf{v} + \mathbf{w}) = \mathbf{u} \cdot \mathbf{v} + \mathbf{u} \cdot \mathbf{w}$.

78. Show that $\mathbf{u} \times (\mathbf{v} + \mathbf{w}) = (\mathbf{u} \times \mathbf{v}) + (\mathbf{u} \times \mathbf{w})$.

52. $-\dfrac{12\sqrt{161}}{161}\mathbf{i} - \dfrac{4\sqrt{161}}{161}\mathbf{j} + \dfrac{\sqrt{161}}{161}\mathbf{k}$

53. $-\dfrac{71\sqrt{7602}}{7602}\mathbf{i} - \dfrac{22\sqrt{7602}}{3801}\mathbf{j} + \dfrac{25\sqrt{7602}}{7602}\mathbf{k}$

51. $\dfrac{\sqrt{11}}{11}\mathbf{i} + \dfrac{3\sqrt{11}}{11}\mathbf{j} + \dfrac{\sqrt{11}}{11}\mathbf{k}$

52. See below.

53. See below.

59. (a) $x = -1 + 4t, y = 3 + 3t, z = 5 - 6t$
(b) $\dfrac{x+1}{4} = \dfrac{y-3}{3} = \dfrac{z-5}{-6}$

60. (a) $x = 5t, y = -10 + 20t, z = 3 - 3t$
(b) $\dfrac{x}{5} = \dfrac{y+10}{20} = \dfrac{z-3}{-3}$

61. (a) $x = -4t, y = 5t, z = 2t$
(b) $\dfrac{x}{-4} = \dfrac{y}{5} = \dfrac{z}{2}$

62. (a) $x = 3 + t, y = 2 + t, z = 1 + t$
(b) $x - 3 = y - 2 = z - 1$

63. $-2x - 12y + 5z = 0$

64. $-2y + 5z - 14 = 0$

65. $z - 2 = 0$

66. $-x + y - 2z + 12 = 0$

67.

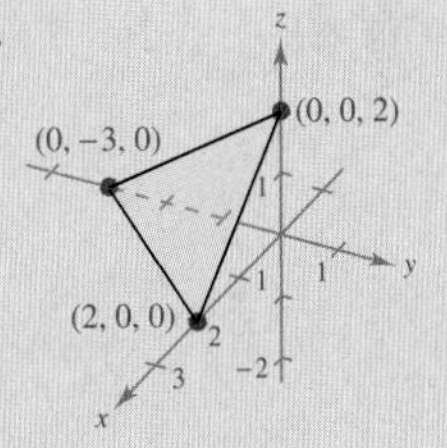

68.

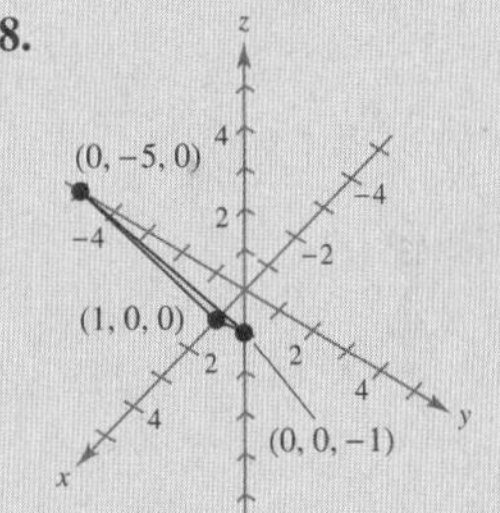

69.

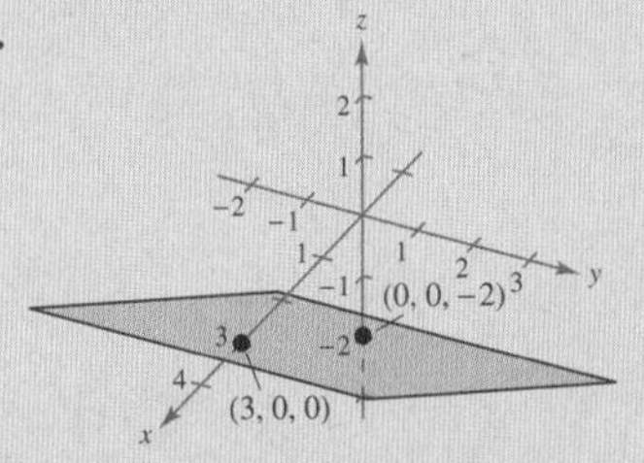

70.

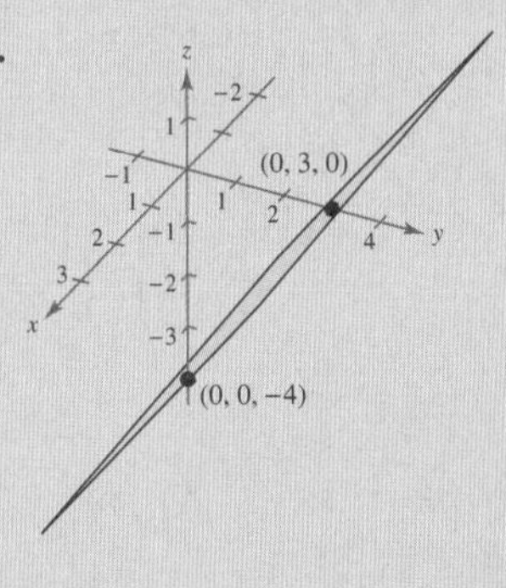

11 Chapter Test

See www.CalcChat.com for worked-out solutions to odd-numbered exercises.

Take this test as you would take a test in class. When you are finished, check your work against the answers given in the back of the book.

1. Plot each point in the same three-dimensional coordinate system.

(a) $(3, -7, 2)$

(b) $(2, 2, -1)$

See margin.

In Exercises 2–4, use the points $A(8, -2, 5)$, $B(6, 4, -1)$, and $C(-4, 3, 0)$, to solve the problem. 2. No. $(\sqrt{76})^2 + (\sqrt{102})^2 \neq (\sqrt{194})^2$ 3. $(7, 1, 2)$

2. Consider the triangle with vertices A, B, and C. Is it a right triangle? Explain.

3. Find the coordinates of the midpoint of the line segment joining points A and B.

4. Find the standard form of the equation of the sphere for which A and B are the endpoints of a diameter. Sketch the sphere and its xz-trace. See margin.

In Exercises 5–9, let u and v be the vectors from $A(8, -2, 5)$ to $B(6, 4, -1)$ and from A to $C(-4, 3, 0)$, respectively.

5. Write **u** and **v** in component form. $\mathbf{u} = \langle -2, 6, -6 \rangle$, $\mathbf{v} = \langle -12, 5, -5 \rangle$

6. Find (a) $\mathbf{u} \cdot \mathbf{v}$ and (b) $\mathbf{u} \times \mathbf{v}$. (a) 84 (b) $\langle 0, 62, 62 \rangle$

7. Find (a) a unit vector in the direction of **u** and (b) a unit vector in the direction of **v**. 7. See margin.

8. Find the angle between **u** and **v**. $46.23°$

9. Find a set of (a) parametric equations and (b) symmetric equations for the line through points A and B. See margin.

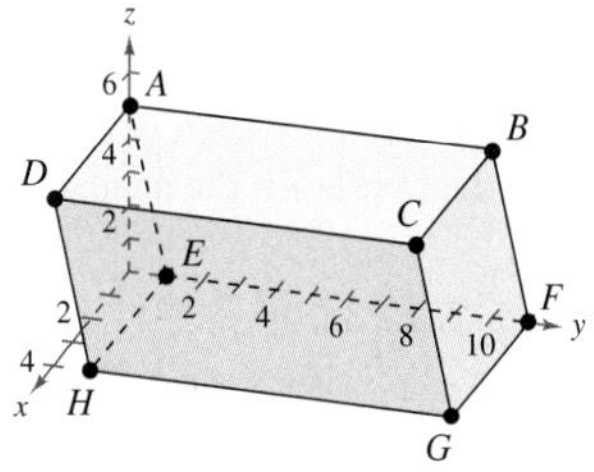

FIGURE FOR 14

In Exercises 10–12, determine whether u and v are orthogonal, parallel, or neither.

10. $\mathbf{u} = \mathbf{i} - 2\mathbf{j} - \mathbf{k}$, $\mathbf{v} = \mathbf{j} + 6\mathbf{k}$ Neither

11. $\mathbf{u} = -3\mathbf{i} + 2\mathbf{j} - \mathbf{k}$, $\mathbf{v} = \mathbf{i} + \mathbf{j} - \mathbf{k}$ Orthogonal

12. $\mathbf{u} = \langle 4, -1, 6 \rangle$, $\mathbf{v} = \langle -2, \frac{1}{2}, -3 \rangle$ Parallel

13. Verify that the points $A(2, -3, 1)$, $B(6, 5, -1)$, $C(3, -6, 4)$, and $D(7, 2, 2)$ are the vertices of a parallelogram, and find its area. See margin.

14. Find the volume of the parallelepiped at the left with the given vertices.

$A(0, 0, 5)$, $B(0, 10, 5)$, $C(4, 10, 5)$, $D(4, 0, 5)$,

$E(0, 1, 0)$, $F(0, 11, 0)$, $G(4, 11, 0)$, $H(4, 1, 0)$ 200

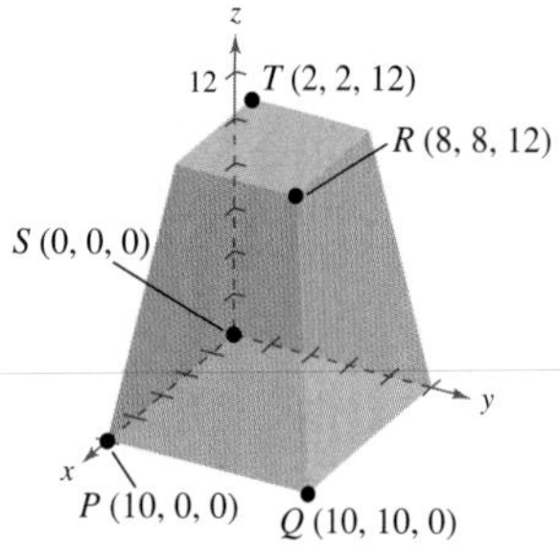

FIGURE FOR 19

In Exercises 15 and 16, plot the intercepts and sketch a graph of the plane. 15–16. See margin.

15. $3x + 6y + 2z = 18$

16. $5x - y - 2z = 10$

17. Find the general form of the equation of the plane passing through the points $(-3, -4, 2)$, $(-3, 4, 1)$, and $(1, 1, -2)$. $27x + 4y + 32z + 33 = 0$

18. Find the distance between the point $(2, -1, 6)$ and the plane $3x - 2y + z = 6$.

19. A tractor fuel tank has the shape and dimensions shown in the figure. In fabricating the tank, it is necessary to know the angle between two adjacent sides. Find this angle. $88.5°$

18. $\dfrac{8}{\sqrt{14}} = \dfrac{4\sqrt{14}}{7}$

1.

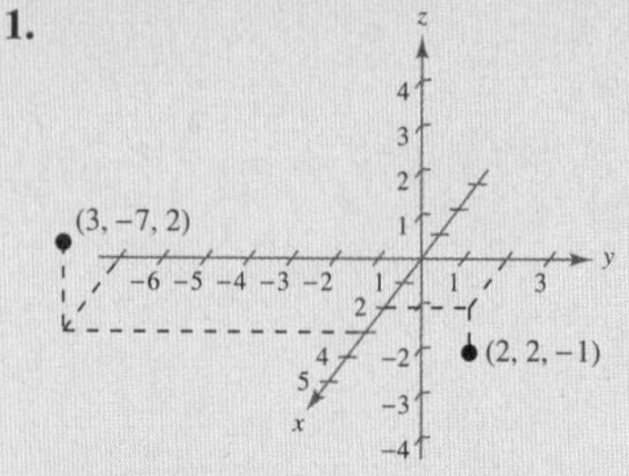

4. See below.

7. (a) $\left\langle -\frac{\sqrt{19}}{19}, \frac{3\sqrt{19}}{19}, -\frac{3\sqrt{19}}{19} \right\rangle$

(b) $\left\langle -\frac{6\sqrt{194}}{97}, \frac{5\sqrt{194}}{194}, -\frac{5\sqrt{194}}{194} \right\rangle$

9. (a) $x = 8 - 2t$, $y = -2 + 6t$, $z = 5 - 6t$

(b) $\dfrac{x - 8}{-2} = \dfrac{y + 2}{6} = \dfrac{z - 5}{-6}$

13. $\overrightarrow{AB}$ is parallel to $\overrightarrow{CD} = \langle 4, 8, -2 \rangle$. $\overrightarrow{AC}$ is parallel to $\overrightarrow{BD} = \langle 1, -3, 3 \rangle$. Area $= 2\sqrt{230}$

15.

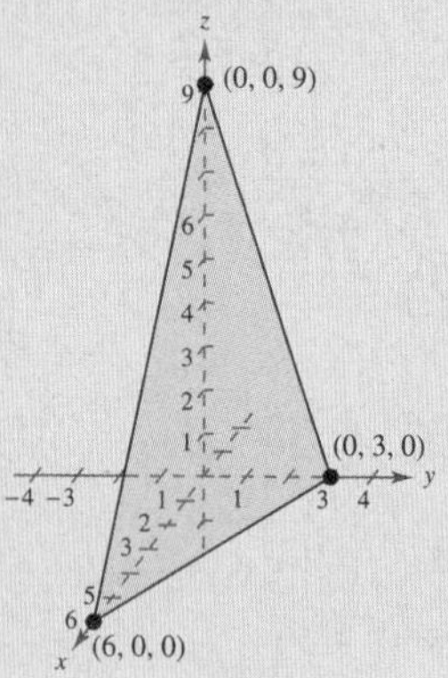

16.

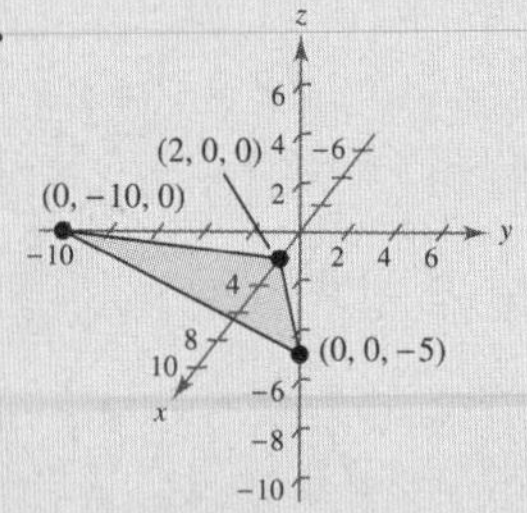

4. $(x - 7)^2 + (y - 1)^2 + (z - 2)^2 = 19$

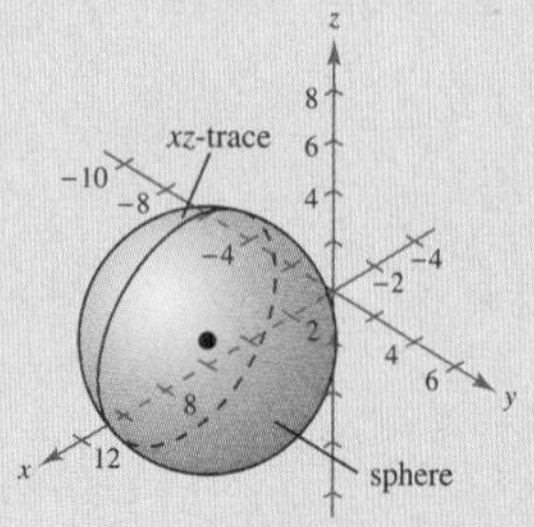

Notation for Dot and Cross Products

The notation for the dot product and the cross product of vectors was first introduced by the American physicist Josiah Willard Gibbs (1839–1903). In the early 1880s, Gibbs built a system to represent physical quantities called *vector analysis*. The system was a departure from William Hamilton's theory of quaternions.

Algebraic Properties of the Cross Product *(p. 825)*

Let $\mathbf{u}$, $\mathbf{v}$, and $\mathbf{w}$ be vectors in space and let c be a scalar.

1. $\mathbf{u} \times \mathbf{v} = -(\mathbf{v} \times \mathbf{u})$
2. $\mathbf{u} \times (\mathbf{v} + \mathbf{w}) = (\mathbf{u} \times \mathbf{v}) + (\mathbf{u} \times \mathbf{w})$
3. $c(\mathbf{u} \times \mathbf{v}) = (c\mathbf{u}) \times \mathbf{v} = \mathbf{u} \times (c\mathbf{v})$
4. $\mathbf{u} \times \mathbf{0} = \mathbf{0} \times \mathbf{u} = \mathbf{0}$
5. $\mathbf{u} \times \mathbf{u} = \mathbf{0}$
6. $\mathbf{u} \cdot (\mathbf{v} \times \mathbf{w}) = (\mathbf{u} \times \mathbf{v}) \cdot \mathbf{w}$

Proof

Let $\mathbf{u} = u_1\mathbf{i} + u_2\mathbf{j} + u_3\mathbf{k}$, $\mathbf{v} = v_1\mathbf{i} + v_2\mathbf{j} + v_3\mathbf{k}$, $\mathbf{w} = w_1\mathbf{i} + w_2\mathbf{j} + w_3\mathbf{k}$, $\mathbf{0} = 0\mathbf{i} + 0\mathbf{j} + 0\mathbf{k}$, and let c be a scalar.

1. $$\mathbf{u} \times \mathbf{v} = (u_2v_3 - u_3v_2)\mathbf{i} - (u_1v_3 - u_3v_1)\mathbf{j} + (u_1v_2 - u_2v_1)\mathbf{k}$$
$$\mathbf{v} \times \mathbf{u} = (v_2u_3 - v_3u_2)\mathbf{i} - (v_1u_3 - v_3u_1)\mathbf{j} + (v_1u_2 - v_2u_1)\mathbf{k}$$

So, this implies $\mathbf{u} \times \mathbf{v} = -(\mathbf{v} \times \mathbf{u})$.

2. $$\begin{aligned}\mathbf{u} \times (\mathbf{v} + \mathbf{w}) &= [u_2(v_3 + w_3) - u_3(v_2 + w_2)]\mathbf{i} - [u_1(v_3 + w_3) - u_3(v_1 + w_1)]\mathbf{j} + [u_1(v_2 + w_2) - u_2(v_1 + w_1)]\mathbf{k}\\ &= (u_2v_3 - u_3v_2)\mathbf{i} - (u_1v_3 - u_3v_1)\mathbf{j} + (u_1v_2 - u_2v_1)\mathbf{k} + (u_2w_3 - u_3w_2)\mathbf{i} - (u_1w_3 - u_3w_1)\mathbf{j} + (u_1w_2 - u_2w_1)\mathbf{k}\\ &= (\mathbf{u} \times \mathbf{v}) + (\mathbf{u} \times \mathbf{w})\end{aligned}$$

3. $$\begin{aligned}(c\mathbf{u}) \times \mathbf{v} &= (cu_2v_3 - cu_3v_2)\mathbf{i} - (cu_1v_3 - cu_3v_1)\mathbf{j} + (cu_1v_2 - cu_2v_1)\mathbf{k}\\ &= c[(u_2v_3 - u_3v_2)\mathbf{i} - (u_1v_3 - u_3v_1)\mathbf{j} + (u_1v_2 - u_2v_1)\mathbf{k}]\\ &= c(\mathbf{u} \times \mathbf{v})\end{aligned}$$

4. $$\begin{aligned}\mathbf{u} \times \mathbf{0} &= (u_2 \cdot 0 - u_3 \cdot 0)\mathbf{i} - (u_1 \cdot 0 - u_3 \cdot 0)\mathbf{j} + (u_1 \cdot 0 - u_2 \cdot 0)\mathbf{k}\\ &= 0\mathbf{i} + 0\mathbf{j} + 0\mathbf{k} = \mathbf{0}\end{aligned}$$
$$\begin{aligned}\mathbf{0} \times \mathbf{u} &= (0 \cdot u_3 - 0 \cdot u_2)\mathbf{i} - (0 \cdot u_3 - 0 \cdot u_1)\mathbf{j} + (0 \cdot u_2 - 0 \cdot u_1)\mathbf{k}\\ &= 0\mathbf{i} + 0\mathbf{j} + 0\mathbf{k} = \mathbf{0}\end{aligned}$$

So, this implies $\mathbf{u} \times \mathbf{0} = \mathbf{0} \times \mathbf{u} = \mathbf{0}$.

5. $$\mathbf{u} \times \mathbf{u} = (u_2u_3 - u_3u_2)\mathbf{i} - (u_1u_3 - u_3u_1)\mathbf{j} + (u_1u_2 - u_2u_1)\mathbf{k} = \mathbf{0}$$

6. $$\mathbf{u} \cdot (\mathbf{v} \times \mathbf{w}) = \begin{vmatrix} u_1 & u_2 & u_3 \\ v_1 & v_2 & v_3 \\ w_1 & w_2 & w_3 \end{vmatrix}$$ and

$$(\mathbf{u} \times \mathbf{v}) \cdot \mathbf{w} = \mathbf{w} \cdot (\mathbf{u} \times \mathbf{v}) = \begin{vmatrix} w_1 & w_2 & w_3 \\ u_1 & u_2 & u_3 \\ v_1 & v_2 & v_3 \end{vmatrix}$$

$$\begin{aligned}\mathbf{u} \cdot (\mathbf{v} \times \mathbf{w}) &= u_1(v_2w_3 - w_2v_3) - u_2(v_1w_3 - w_1v_3) + u_3(v_1w_2 - w_1v_2)\\ &= u_1v_2w_3 - u_1w_2v_3 - u_2v_1w_3 + u_2w_1v_3 + u_3v_1w_2 - u_3w_1v_2\\ &= u_2w_1v_3 - u_3w_1v_2 - u_1w_2v_3 + u_3v_1w_2 + u_1v_2w_3 - u_2v_1w_3\\ &= w_1(u_2v_3 - u_3v_2) - w_2(u_1v_3 - u_3v_1) + w_3(u_1v_2 - u_2v_1)\\ &= (\mathbf{u} \times \mathbf{v}) \cdot \mathbf{w}\end{aligned}$$

845

Geometric Properties of the Cross Product (p. 826)

Let $\mathbf{u}$ and $\mathbf{v}$ be nonzero vectors in space, and let θ be the angle between $\mathbf{u}$ and $\mathbf{v}$.

1. $\mathbf{u} \times \mathbf{v}$ is orthogonal to both $\mathbf{u}$ and $\mathbf{v}$.
2. $\|\mathbf{u} \times \mathbf{v}\| = \|\mathbf{u}\|\,\|\mathbf{v}\| \sin \theta$
3. $\mathbf{u} \times \mathbf{v} = \mathbf{0}$ if and only if $\mathbf{u}$ and $\mathbf{v}$ are scalar multiples of each other.
4. $\|\mathbf{u} \times \mathbf{v}\| =$ area of parallelogram having $\mathbf{u}$ and $\mathbf{v}$ as adjacent sides.

Proof

Let $\mathbf{u} = u_1\mathbf{i} + u_2\mathbf{j} + u_3\mathbf{k}$, $\mathbf{v} = v_1\mathbf{i} + v_2\mathbf{j} + v_3\mathbf{k}$, and $\mathbf{0} = 0\mathbf{i} + 0\mathbf{j} + 0\mathbf{k}$.

1.

$$\begin{aligned}
\mathbf{u} \times \mathbf{v} &= (u_2v_3 - u_3v_2)\mathbf{i} - (u_1v_3 - u_3v_1)\mathbf{j} + (u_1v_2 - u_2v_1)\mathbf{k} \\
(\mathbf{u} \times \mathbf{v}) \cdot \mathbf{u} &= (u_2v_3 - u_3v_2)u_1 - (u_1v_3 - u_3v_1)u_2 + (u_1v_2 - u_2v_1)u_3 \\
&= u_1u_2v_3 - u_1u_3v_2 - u_1u_2v_3 + u_2u_3v_1 + u_1u_3v_2 - u_2u_3v_1 = 0 \\
(\mathbf{u} \times \mathbf{v}) \cdot \mathbf{v} &= (u_2v_3 - u_3v_2)v_1 - (u_1v_3 - u_3v_1)v_2 + (u_1v_2 - u_2v_1)v_3 \\
&= u_2v_1v_3 - u_3v_1v_2 - u_1v_2v_3 + u_3v_1v_2 + u_1v_2v_3 - u_2v_1v_3 = 0
\end{aligned}$$

Because two vectors are orthogonal if their dot product is zero, it follows that $\mathbf{u} \times \mathbf{v}$ is orthogonal to both $\mathbf{u}$ and $\mathbf{v}$.

2. Note that $\cos \theta = \dfrac{\mathbf{u} \cdot \mathbf{v}}{\|\mathbf{u}\|\,\|\mathbf{v}\|}$. So,

$$\begin{aligned}
\|\mathbf{u}\|\,\|\mathbf{v}\| \sin \theta &= \|\mathbf{u}\|\,\|\mathbf{v}\| \sqrt{1 - \cos^2 \theta} \\
&= \|\mathbf{u}\|\,\|\mathbf{v}\| \sqrt{1 - \frac{(\mathbf{u} \cdot \mathbf{v})^2}{\|\mathbf{u}\|^2\,\|\mathbf{v}\|^2}} \\
&= \sqrt{\|\mathbf{u}\|^2\|\mathbf{v}\|^2 - (\mathbf{u} \cdot \mathbf{v})^2} \\
&= \sqrt{(u_1^2 + u_2^2 + u_3^2)(v_1^2 + v_2^2 + v_3^2) - (u_1v_1 + u_2v_2 + u_3v_3)^2} \\
&= \sqrt{(u_2v_3 - u_3v_2)^2 + (u_1v_3 - u_3v_1)^2 + (u_1v_2 - u_2v_1)^2} = \|\mathbf{u} \times \mathbf{v}\|.
\end{aligned}$$

3. If $\mathbf{u}$ and $\mathbf{v}$ are scalar multiples of each other, then $\mathbf{u} = c\mathbf{v}$ for some scalar c.

$$\mathbf{u} \times \mathbf{v} = (c\mathbf{v}) \times \mathbf{v} = c(\mathbf{v} \times \mathbf{v}) = c(\mathbf{0}) = \mathbf{0}$$

If $\mathbf{u} \times \mathbf{v} = \mathbf{0}$, then $\|\mathbf{u}\|\,\|\mathbf{v}\| \sin \theta = 0$. (Assume $\mathbf{u} \neq \mathbf{0}$ and $\mathbf{v} \neq \mathbf{0}$.) So, $\sin \theta = 0$, and $\theta = 0$ or $\theta = \pi$. In either case, because θ is the angle between the vectors, $\mathbf{u}$ and $\mathbf{v}$ are parallel. So, $\mathbf{u} = c\mathbf{v}$ for some scalar c.

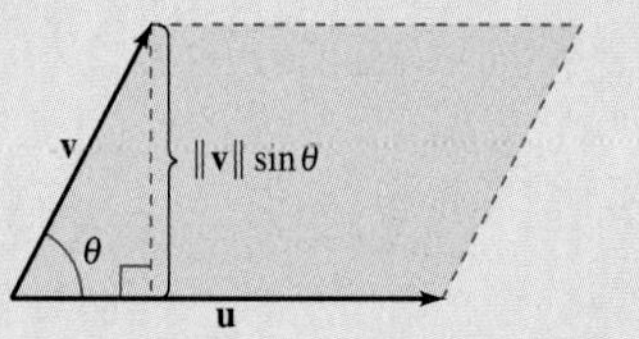

4. The figure at the left is a parallelogram having $\mathbf{v}$ and $\mathbf{u}$ as adjacent sides. Because the height of the parallelogram is $\|\mathbf{v}\| \sin \theta$, the area is

$$\begin{aligned}
\text{Area} &= (\text{base})(\text{height}) \\
&= \|\mathbf{u}\|\,\|\mathbf{v}\| \sin \theta \\
&= \|\mathbf{u} \times \mathbf{v}\|.
\end{aligned}$$

846

PROBLEM SOLVING

This collection of thought-provoking and challenging exercises further explores and expands upon concepts learned in this chapter.

1. Let $\mathbf{u} = \mathbf{i} + \mathbf{j}$, $\mathbf{v} = \mathbf{j} + \mathbf{k}$, and $\mathbf{w} = a\mathbf{u} + b\mathbf{v}$.
   (a) Sketch **u** and **v**. See margin.
   (b) If $\mathbf{w} = \mathbf{0}$, show that a and b must both be zero. Answers will vary.
   (c) Find a and b such that $\mathbf{w} = \mathbf{i} + 2\mathbf{j} + \mathbf{k}$. $a = b = 1$
   (d) Show that no choice of a and b yields $\mathbf{w} = \mathbf{i} + 2\mathbf{j} + 3\mathbf{k}$. Answers will vary.
2. The initial and terminal points of **v** are (x_1, y_1, z_1) and (x, y, z), respectively. Describe the set of all points (x, y, z) such that $\|\mathbf{v}\| = 4$. See margin.
3. You are given the component forms of the vectors **u** and **v**. Write a program for a graphing utility in which the output is (a) the component form of $\mathbf{u} + \mathbf{v}$, (b) $\|\mathbf{u} + \mathbf{v}\|$, (c) $\|\mathbf{u}\|$, and (d) $\|\mathbf{v}\|$. Answers will vary.
4. Run the program you wrote in Exercise 3 for the vectors $\mathbf{u} = \langle -1, 3, 4\rangle$ and $\mathbf{v} = \langle 5, 4.5, -6\rangle$. Answers will vary.
5. The vertices of a triangle are given. Determine whether the triangle is an acute triangle, an obtuse triangle, or a right triangle. Explain your reasoning.
   (a) $(1, 2, 0), (0, 0, 0), (-2, 1, 0)$ Right triangle
   (b) $(-3, 0, 0), (0, 0, 0), (1, 2, 3)$ Obtuse triangle
   (c) $(2, -3, 4), (0, 1, 2), (-1, 2, 0)$ Obtuse triangle
   (d) $(2, -7, 3), (-1, 5, 8), (4, 6, -1)$ Acute triangle
6. A television camera weighing 120 pounds is supported by a tripod (see figure). Represent the force exerted on each leg of the tripod as a vector. See margin.

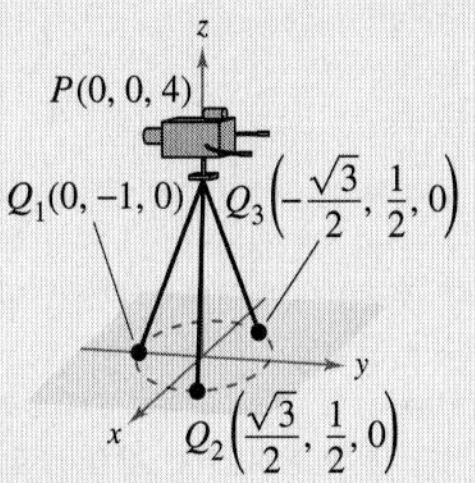

7. A precast concrete wall is temporarily kept in its vertical position by ropes (see figure). Find the total force exerted on the pin at position A. The tensions in AB and AC are 420 pounds and 650 pounds, respectively. About 860.0 lb

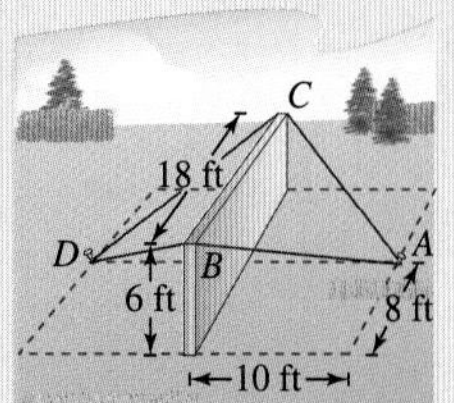

FIGURE FOR 7

8–11. Proofs

8. Prove $\|\mathbf{u} \times \mathbf{v}\| = \|\mathbf{u}\|\,\|\mathbf{v}\|$ if **u** and **v** are orthogonal.
9. Prove $\mathbf{u} \times (\mathbf{v} \times \mathbf{w}) = (\mathbf{u} \cdot \mathbf{w})\mathbf{v} - (\mathbf{u} \cdot \mathbf{v})\mathbf{w}$.
10. Prove that the triple scalar product of **u**, **v**, and **w** is given by

$$\mathbf{u} \cdot (\mathbf{v} \times \mathbf{w}) = \begin{vmatrix} u_1 & u_2 & u_3 \\ v_1 & v_2 & v_3 \\ w_1 & w_2 & w_3 \end{vmatrix}.$$

11. Prove that the volume V of a parallelepiped with vectors **u**, **v**, and **w** as adjacent edges is given by

$$V = |\mathbf{u} \cdot (\mathbf{v} \times \mathbf{w})|.$$

12. In physics, the cross product can be used to measure **torque,** or the **moment M** of a force **F** about a point P. If the point of application of the force is Q, the moment of **F** about P is given by $\mathbf{M} = \overrightarrow{PQ} \times \mathbf{F}$. A force of 60 pounds acts on the pipe wrench shown in the figure.

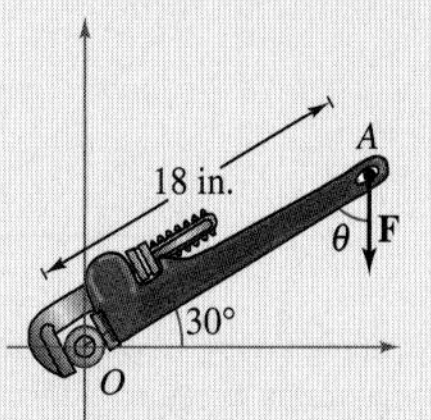

(a). See margin.
   (a) Find the magnitude of the moment about O. Use a graphing utility to graph the resulting function of θ.
   (b) Use the result of part (a) to determine the magnitude of the moment when $\theta = 45°$. $540\sqrt{2} \approx 763.68$
   (c) Use the result of part (a) to determine the angle θ when the magnitude of the moment is maximum. Is the answer what you expected? Why or why not?
   $\theta = 90°$. This is what should be expected. When $\theta = 90°$, the pipe wrench is horizontal.

1. (a)

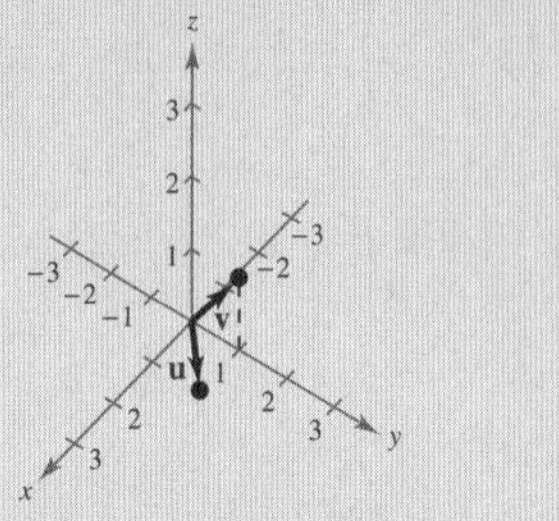

2. Sphere of radius 4 centered at (x_1, y_1, z_1)
6. $\mathbf{F}_1 = \langle 0, -10, -40\rangle$, $\mathbf{F}_2 = \langle 5\sqrt{3}, 5, -40\rangle$, $\mathbf{F}_3 = \langle -5\sqrt{3}, 5, -40\rangle$
12. (a) $1080 \sin \theta$

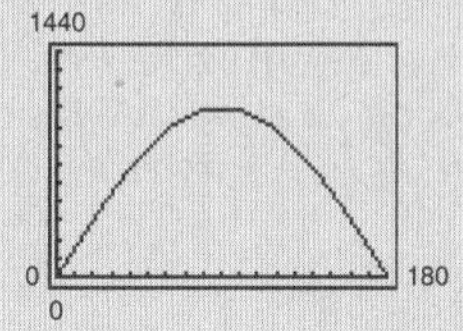

847

13. (a) $\overrightarrow{AB} = -\frac{5}{4}\mathbf{j} + \mathbf{k}$,
$\mathbf{F} = -200(\cos\theta\mathbf{j} + \sin\theta\mathbf{k})$
(b) See below.
(c) $\|\overrightarrow{AB} \times \mathbf{F}\| \approx 298.2$ when $\theta = 30°$.
(d) $\theta \approx 51.34°$
(e) The zero is $\theta \approx 141.34°$; the angle making $\overrightarrow{AB}$ parallel to $\mathbf{F}$.

15. (b)

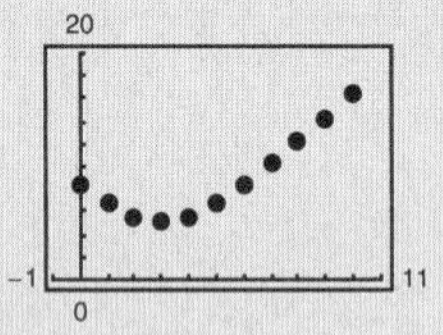

(c) The distance between the two insects appears to lessen in the first 3 seconds but then begins to increase with time.
(d) The insects get within 5 inches of each other.

17. (a) $D = \dfrac{3\sqrt{2}}{2}$

18. (b)

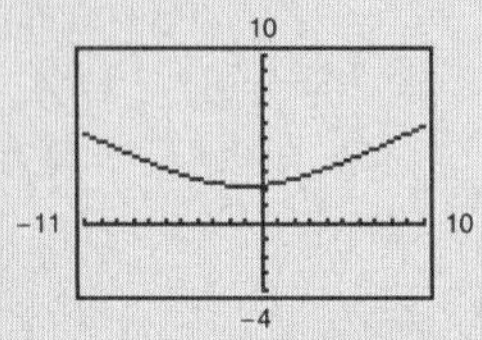

The minimum is $D \approx 2.2361$ at $s = -1$.

13. A force of 200 pounds acts on the bracket shown in the figure. See margin.

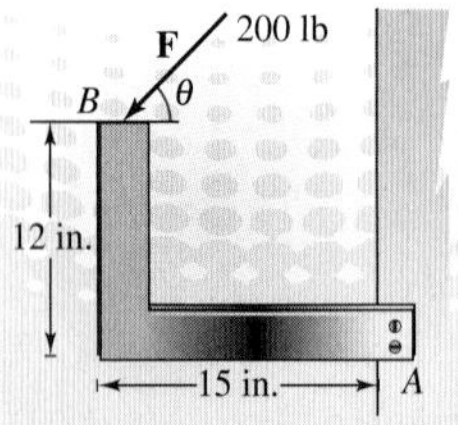

(a) Determine the vector $\overrightarrow{AB}$ and the vector $\mathbf{F}$ representing the force. ($\mathbf{F}$ will be in terms of θ.)

(b) Find the magnitude of the moment (torque) about A by evaluating $\|\overrightarrow{AB} \times \mathbf{F}\|$. Use a graphing utility to graph the resulting function of θ for $0° \le \theta \le 180°$.

(c) Use the result of part (b) to determine the magnitude of the moment when $\theta = 30°$.

(d) Use the result of part (b) to determine the angle θ when the magnitude of the moment is maximum.

(e) Use the graph in part (b) to approximate the zero of the function. Interpret the meaning of the zero in the context of the problem.

14. Using vectors, prove the Law of Sines: If $\mathbf{a}$, $\mathbf{b}$, and $\mathbf{c}$ are three sides of the triangle shown in the figure, then

$$\frac{\sin A}{\|\mathbf{a}\|} = \frac{\sin B}{\|\mathbf{b}\|} = \frac{\sin C}{\|\mathbf{c}\|}.$$ Proof

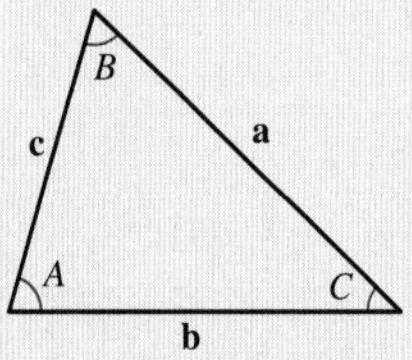

15. Two insects are crawling along different lines in three-space. At time t (in minutes), the first insect is at the point (x, y, z) on the line given by

$$x = 6 + t,\ y = 8 - t,\ z = 3 + t.$$

Also, at time t, the second insect is at the point (x, y, z) on the line given by

$$x = 1 + t,\ y = 2 + t,\ z = 2t.$$

Assume distances are given in inches.

(a) Find the distance between the two insects at time $t = 0$. $d = \sqrt{70}$ when $t = 0$.

(b) Use a graphing utility to graph the distance between the insects from $t = 0$ to $t = 10$.

(b)–(d). See margin.

(c) Using the graph from part (b), what can you conclude about the distance between the insects?

(d) Using the graph from part (b), determine how close the insects get to each other.

16. The distance between a point Q and a line in space is given by

$$D = \frac{\|\overrightarrow{PQ} \times \mathbf{u}\|}{\|\mathbf{u}\|}$$

where $\mathbf{u}$ is a direction vector for the line and P is a point on the line. Find the distance between the point and the line given by each set of parametric equations.

(a) $(1, 5, -2)$

$x = -2 + 4t,\ y = 3,\ z = 1 - t$

(a) $D = \dfrac{\sqrt{149}}{\sqrt{17}} = \dfrac{\sqrt{2533}}{17}$

(b) $(1, -2, 4)$

$x = 2t,\ y = -3 + t,\ z = 2 + 2t$ $\quad D = \dfrac{\sqrt{5}}{3}$

17. Use the formula given in Exercise 16.

(a) Find the shortest distance between the point $Q(2, 0, 0)$ and the line determined by the points $P_1(0, 0, 1)$ and $P_2(0, 1, 2)$. See margin.

(b) Find the shortest distance between the point $Q(2, 0, 0)$ and the line segment joining the points $P_1(0, 0, 1)$ and $P_2(0, 1, 2)$. $D = \sqrt{5}$

18. Consider the line given by the parametric equations

$$x = -t + 3,\ y = \frac{1}{2}t + 1,\ z = 2t - 1$$

and the point $(4, 3, s)$ for any real number s.

(a) Write the distance between the point and the line as a function of s. (*Hint:* Use the formula given in Exercise 16.) See below.

(b) Use a graphing utility to graph the function from part (a). Use the graph to find the value of s such that the distance between the point and the line is a minimum. See margin.

(c) Use the *zoom* feature of the graphing utility to zoom out several times on the graph in part (b). Does it appear that the graph has slant asymptotes? Explain. If it appears to have slant asymptotes, find them.

Yes, there are slant asymptotes. Using $s = x$, we have the slant asymptotes

$$y = \pm\frac{\sqrt{105}}{21}(s + 1).$$

18. (a) $D = \dfrac{\|\overrightarrow{PQ} \times \mathbf{u}\|}{\|\mathbf{u}\|} = \dfrac{\sqrt{105s^2 + 210s + 2310}}{21}$

13. (b) $\|\overrightarrow{AB} \times \mathbf{F}\| = 25|10\sin\theta + 8\cos\theta|$

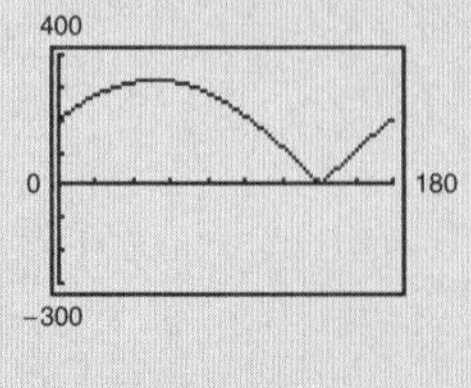

REGULAR SCHEDULE

Lesson	Day	AVERAGE	ADVANCED
12.1	Day 1	pp. 858–859 Exs. 6–10 even, 13–19, 23, 25, 28–30, 37–43 odd	pp. 858–859 Exs. 6–14 even, 16–20, 24, 25, 28–30, 36–44 even
	Day 2	p. 860 Exs. 45, 48, 49, 53–67 odd, 69–72, 74, 77	p. 860 Exs. 46–50 even, 54–68 even, 69–74, 76, 77
12.2	Day 1	pp. 868–869 Exs. 1, 2, 5–9 odd, 12, 17–23 odd, 27–39 odd, 43–47 odd	pp. 868–869 Exs. 1, 2, 6–12 even, 18–24 even, 28–40 even, 44–48 even
	Day 2	pp. 868–870 Exs. 3, 4, 49, 53, 56, 57, 60, 63–73 odd, 77, 79, 82, 84–88	pp. 868–870 Exs. 3, 4, 50–56 even, 60–72 even, 76, 80, 82–84, 86–89
12.3	Day 1	p. 878 Exs. 1–3, 6, 8, 10–15, 18–21, 23–27	p. 878 Exs. 1–3, 6–10 even, 12–16, 19–22, 24–28
	Day 2	pp. 878–880 Exs. 4, 29, 31, 35, 39, 41, 46, 47–65 odd, 71, 73, 75–81, 83	pp. 878–880 Exs. 4, 32–42 even, 47, 48–62 even, 71–73, 75–80, 82–86 even
12.4	Day 1	pp. 887–888 Exs. 5–8, 10–15, 18, 19–37 odd, 53, 56	pp. 887–888 Exs. 5–8, 12–16, 18–38 even, 54, 56
	Day 2	pp. 888–890 Exs. 40, 41–49 odd, 57, 59–63, 65–67, 70	pp. 888–890 Exs. 42–50 even, 58–61, 63, 64, 66–68, 70, 71
12.5	Day 1	p. 896 Exs. 1–3, 6–14, 16, 18, 19, 21–25, 27	p. 896 Exs. 1–3, 6–14, 16, 18–24, 26–28
	Day 2	pp. 896–897 Exs. 4, 29–41 odd, 44–47, 49–53	pp. 896–897 Exs. 4, 30–44 even, 46–54
Review	Day 1	pp. 900–901 Exs. 1, 3, 5–9, 13–25 odd, 26, 31–55 odd	pp. 900–901 Exs. 2, 4–8, 10, 16–24 even, 28–40 even, 41–44, 50–56 even
	Day 2	pp. 901–902 Exs. 57–67 odd, 71–75 odd, 81–89, 93–111 odd, 114, 115	pp. 901–902 Exs. 58–68 even, 74–82 even, 88–92, 94–112 even, 113, 116
Assess	Day 1	Chapter 12 Test	Chapter 12 Test

Yearly Pacing Chapter 12 Total – 13 days Remaining – 0 days

BLOCK SCHEDULE

DAY 1	DAY 2	DAY 3	DAY 4	DAY 5	DAY 6	DAY 7
ASSESS	**12.1 (CONT.)**	**12.2 (CONT.)**	**12.3 (CONT.)**	**12.4 (CONT.)**	**12.5 (CONT.)**	**REVIEW (CONT.)**
Chapter 11 Test	p. 860 Exs. 45, 48, 49, 53–67 odd, 69–72, 74, 77	pp. 868–870 Exs. 3, 4, 49, 53, 56, 57, 60, 63–73 odd, 77, 79, 82, 84–88	pp. 878–880 Exs. 4, 29, 31, 35, 39, 41, 46, 47–65 odd, 71, 73, 75–81, 83	pp. 888–890 Exs. 40, 41–49 odd, 57, 59–63, 65–67, 70	pp. 896–897 Exs. 4, 29–41 odd, 44–47, 49–53	pp. 901–902 Exs. 57–67 odd, 71–75 odd, 81–89, 93–111 odd, 114, 115
12.1	**12.2**	**12.3**	**12.4**	**12.5**	**REVIEW**	**ASSESS**
pp. 858–859 Exs. 6–10 even, 13–19, 23, 25, 28–30, 37–43 odd	pp. 868–869 Exs. 1, 2, 5–9 odd, 12, 17–23 odd, 27–39 odd, 43–47 odd	p. 878 Exs. 1–3, 6, 8, 10–15, 18–21, 23–27	pp. 887–888 Exs. 5–8, 10–15, 18, 19–37 odd, 53, 56	p. 896 Exs. 1–3, 6–14, 16, 18, 19, 21–25, 27	pp. 900–901 Exs. 1, 3, 5–9, 13–25 odd, 26, 31–55 odd	Chapter 12 Test

Yearly Pacing Chapter 12 Total – 6.5 days Remaining – 0 days

Limits and an Introduction to Calculus

12

In Mathematics

If a function becomes arbitrarily close to a unique number *L* as *x* approaches *c* from either side, the limit of the function as *x* approaches *c* is *L*.

In Real Life

The fundamental concept of integral calculus is the calculation of the area of a plane region bounded by the graph of a function. For instance, in surveying, a civil engineer uses integration to estimate the areas of irregular plots of real estate. (See Exercises 49 and 50, page 897.)

David Frazier/PhotoEdit

IN CAREERS

There are many careers that use limit concepts. Several are listed below.

- Market Researcher
  Exercise 74, page 880
- Aquatic Biologist
  Exercise 53, page 888
- Business Economist
  Exercises 55 and 56, page 888
- Data Analyst
  Exercises 57 and 58, pages 888 and 889

PLAN AND PREPARE

Main Ideas

In Chapter 12, students find tangent lines of a function and the area of a region, two basic problems in calculus. The chapter begins with an introduction to limits, including techniques for calculating the limit of a graph at a given value of *x*. Students then find the slope of a graph at a given point and calculate the derivative of a function. They then find the limit of functions at infinity and the limits of sequences. Finally, students apply these techniques to find the area of a region bounded by a function.

Chapter Planning Guide

Chapter Resources

- Complete Solutions Guide

Interactive Technology

- Instructor Success Organizer
- Notetaking Guide IAE
- Instructional DVDs
- Animated Precalculus
- PowerLecture with ExamView

1 PLAN AND PREPARE

Warm-up Exercises

Transparency Available
Available at the Instructor's companion site.

Notetaking Guide

Transparency Available
Promotes interactive learning and notetaking skills.
Available at the Instructor's companion site.

Animated Precalculus

An **Animated Precalculus** tutorial is available at the Student companion site for **Section 12.1.**

Pacing

Average: 2 days
Advanced: 2 days
Block: 0.5 block with Chapter 11 Test
0.5 block with 12.2

2 FOCUS AND MOTIVATE

Essential Question

How do you find and interpret the limit of a function for a certain value of x? **Tell students that they will learn how to answer this question by calculating the value of a function for x-values that are very close to a given x-value.**

12.1 INTRODUCTION TO LIMITS

What you should learn

- Use the definition of limit to estimate limits.
- Determine whether limits of functions exist.
- Use properties of limits and direct substitution to evaluate limits.

Why you should learn it

The concept of a limit is useful in applications involving maximization. For instance, in Exercise 5 on page 858, the concept of a limit is used to verify the maximum volume of an open box.

Dick Luria/FPG/Getty Images

The Limit Concept

The notion of a limit is a *fundamental* concept of calculus. In this chapter, you will learn how to evaluate limits and how they are used in the two basic problems of calculus: the tangent line problem and the area problem.

Example 1 Finding a Rectangle of Maximum Area

You are given 24 inches of wire and are asked to form a rectangle whose area is as large as possible. Determine the dimensions of the rectangle that will produce a maximum area.

Solution

Let w represent the width of the rectangle and let l represent the length of the rectangle. Because

$$2w + 2l = 24 \quad \text{Perimeter is 24.}$$

it follows that $l = 12 - w$, as shown in Figure 12.1. So, the area of the rectangle is

$$A = lw \quad \text{Formula for area}$$
$$= (12 - w)w \quad \text{Substitute } 12 - w \text{ for } l.$$
$$= 12w - w^2. \quad \text{Simplify.}$$

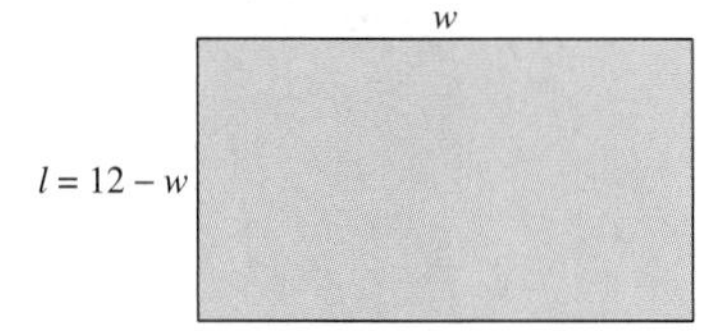

FIGURE 12.1

Using this model for area, you can experiment with different values of w to see how to obtain the maximum area. After trying several values, it appears that the maximum area occurs when $w = 6$, as shown in the table.

Width, w	5.0	5.5	5.9	6.0	6.1	6.5	7.0
Area, A	35.00	35.75	35.99	36.00	35.99	35.75	35.00

In limit terminology, you can say that "the limit of A as w approaches 6 is 36." This is written as

$$\lim_{w \to 6} A = \lim_{w \to 6} (12w - w^2) = 36.$$

CHECKPoint Now try Exercise 5.

Resource Planning Guide

Chapter Resources
- Complete Solutions Guide

Workbooks
- Notetaking Guide
- Student Solutions Guide

Interactive Technology
- Instructor Success Organizer
- Notetaking Guide IAE
- Instructional DVDs
- Animated Precalculus
- PowerLecture with ExamView

Definition of Limit

Definition of Limit

If $f(x)$ becomes arbitrarily close to a unique number L as x approaches c from either side, the limit of $f(x)$ as x approaches c is L. This is written as

$$\lim_{x \to c} f(x) = L.$$

Study Tip

An alternative notation for $\lim_{x \to c} f(x) = L$ is

$$f(x) \to L \text{ as } x \to c$$

which is read as "$f(x)$ approaches L as x approaches c."

Example 2 Estimating a Limit Numerically

Use a table to estimate numerically the limit: $\lim_{x \to 2} (3x - 2)$.

Solution

Let $f(x) = 3x - 2$. Then construct a table that shows values of $f(x)$ for two sets of x-values—one set that approaches 2 from the left and one that approaches 2 from the right.

x	1.9	1.99	1.999	2.0	2.001	2.01	2.1
$f(x)$	3.700	3.970	3.997	?	4.003	4.030	4.300

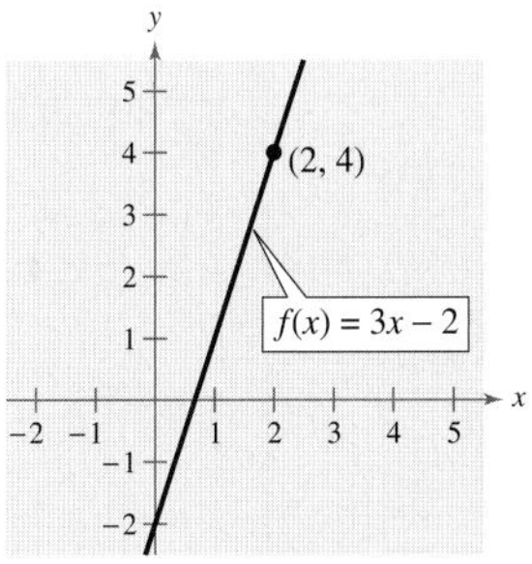

FIGURE 12.2

From the table, it appears that the closer x gets to 2, the closer $f(x)$ gets to 4. So, you can estimate the limit to be 4. Figure 12.2 adds further support for this conclusion.

CHECKPoint Now try Exercise 7.

In Figure 12.2, note that the graph of $f(x) = 3x - 2$ is continuous. For graphs that are not continuous, finding a limit can be more difficult.

Example 3 Estimating a Limit Numerically

Use a table to estimate numerically the limit: $\lim_{x \to 0} \dfrac{x}{\sqrt{x+1} - 1}$.

Solution

Let $f(x) = x/(\sqrt{x+1} - 1)$. Then construct a table that shows values of $f(x)$ for two sets of x-values—one set that approaches 0 from the left and one that approaches 0 from the right.

x	−0.01	−0.001	−0.0001	0	0.0001	0.001	0.01
$f(x)$	1.99499	1.99949	1.99995	?	2.00005	2.00050	2.00499

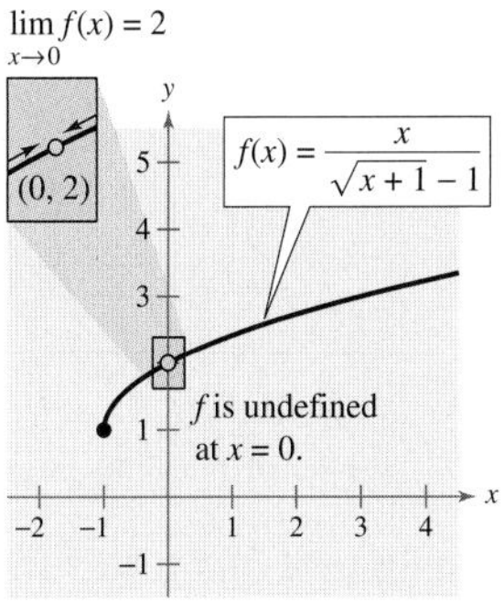

FIGURE 12.3

From the table, it appears that the limit is 2. The graph shown in Figure 12.3 verifies that the limit is 2.

CHECKPoint Now try Exercise 9.

3 TEACH

Extra Example 1

You are given 32 inches of wire and are asked to form a rectangle whose area is as large as possible. Determine the dimensions of the rectangle that will produce a maximum area.

8 inches by 8 inches

Extra Example 2

Use a table to estimate numerically the limit: $\lim_{x \to 3} (5x - 3)$.

x	$f(x)$
2.9	11.500
2.99	11.950
2.999	11.995
3.0	?
3.001	12.005
3.01	12.05
3.1	12.5

The limit appears to be 12.

Extra Example 3

Use a table to estimate numerically the limit: $\lim_{x \to 0} \dfrac{x}{\sqrt{x+9} - 3}$.

x	$f(x)$
−0.01	5.998
−0.001	5.9998
−0.0001	5.99998
0	?
0.0001	6.00002
0.001	6.0002
0.01	6.002

The limit appears to be 6.

Extra Example 4

Estimate the limit:

$$\lim_{x \to 2} \frac{x^3 - 2x^2 + 2x - 4}{x - 2}.$$

x	$f(x)$
1.9	5.61
1.99	5.9601
1.999	5.996
2.0	?
2.001	6.004
2.01	6.0401
2.1	6.41

The limit appears to be 6.

Avoiding Common Errors

Students often think of a limit as a quantity that can be approached but not reached. Remind them that some limits are like that, but that many limits are quantities that do exist on the function. For example, the limits shown in Examples 1 and 2 are defined and attained at simple function values.

Extra Example 5

Find the limit of $f(x)$ as x approaches 5, where f is defined as

$$f(x) = \begin{cases} 1, & x \neq 5 \\ -2, & x = 5 \end{cases}.$$

The limit of $f(x)$ as x approaches 5 is 1, as shown on the graph.

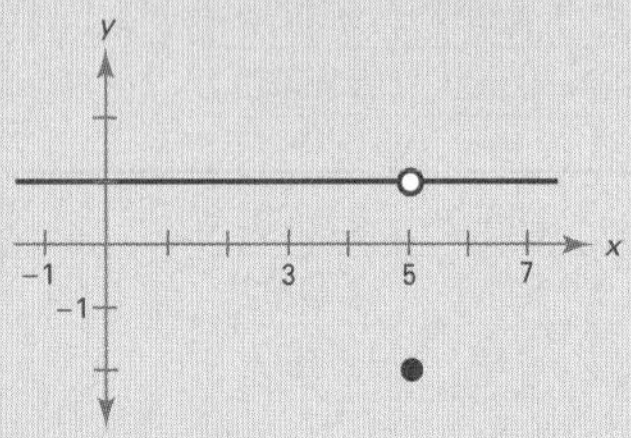

In Example 3, note that $f(x)$ has a limit when $x \to 0$ even though the function is not defined when $x = 0$. This often happens, and it is important to realize that *the existence or nonexistence of $f(x)$ at $x = c$ has no bearing on the existence of the limit of $f(x)$ as x approaches c.*

Example 4 Estimating a Limit

Estimate the limit: $\lim_{x \to 1} \dfrac{x^3 - x^2 + x - 1}{x - 1}.$

Numerical Solution

Let $f(x) = (x^3 - x^2 + x - 1)/(x - 1)$. Then construct a table that shows values of $f(x)$ for two sets of x-values—one set that approaches 1 from the left and one that approaches 1 from the right.

x	0.9	0.99	0.999	1.0
$f(x)$	1.8100	1.9801	1.9980	?

x	1.0	1.001	1.01	1.1
$f(x)$	?	2.0020	2.0201	2.2100

From the tables, it appears that the limit is 2.

Graphical Solution

Let $f(x) = (x^3 - x^2 + x - 1)/(x - 1)$. Then sketch a graph of the function, as shown in Figure 12.4. From the graph, it appears that as x approaches 1 from either side, $f(x)$ approaches 2. So, you can estimate the limit to be 2.

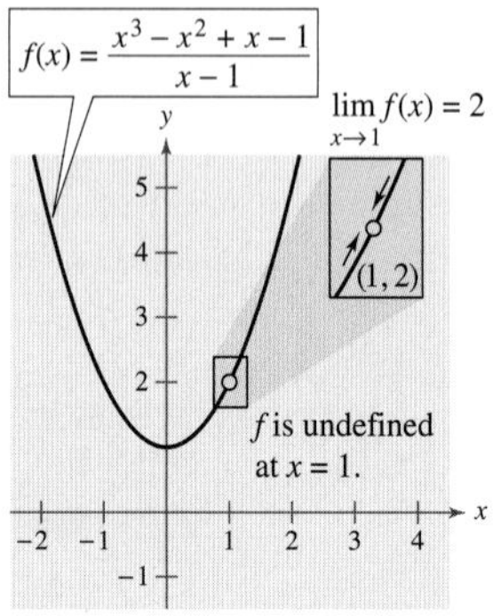

FIGURE 12.4

CHECKPoint Now try Exercise 13.

Example 5 Using a Graph to Find a Limit

Find the limit of $f(x)$ as x approaches 3, where f is defined as

$$f(x) = \begin{cases} 2, & x \neq 3 \\ 0, & x = 3 \end{cases}.$$

Solution

Because $f(x) = 2$ for all x other than $x = 3$ and because the value of $f(3)$ is immaterial, it follows that the limit is 2 (see Figure 12.5). So, you can write

$$\lim_{x \to 3} f(x) = 2.$$

The fact that $f(3) = 0$ has no bearing on the existence or value of the limit as x approaches 3. For instance, if the function were defined as

$$f(x) = \begin{cases} 2, & x \neq 3 \\ 4, & x = 3 \end{cases}$$

the limit as x approaches 3 would be the same.

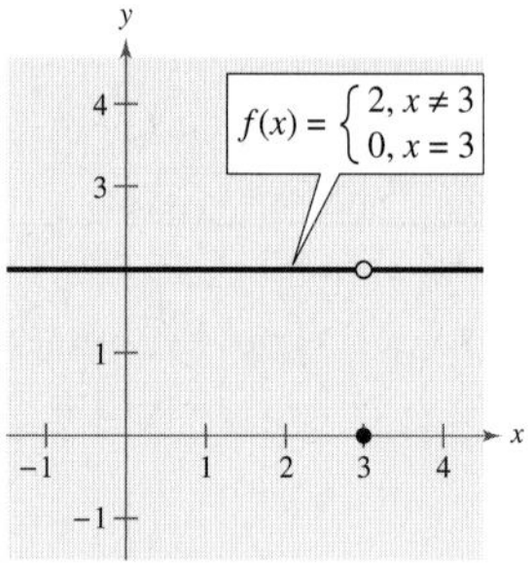

FIGURE 12.5

CHECKPoint Now try Exercise 27.

Differentiated Instruction

Inclusion Many students will benefit from additional practice in using a graph to find limits. Present different graphs to students and ask them to identify the limit graphically. Have students check their answers by finding the limit numerically through the use of a table.

Limits That Fail to Exist

Next, you will examine some functions for which limits do not exist.

Example 6 Comparing Left and Right Behavior

Show that the limit does not exist.

$$\lim_{x \to 0} \frac{|x|}{x}$$

Solution

Consider the graph of the function given by $f(x) = |x|/x$. From Figure 12.6, you can see that for positive x-values

$$\frac{|x|}{x} = 1, \quad x > 0$$

and for negative x-values

$$\frac{|x|}{x} = -1, \quad x < 0.$$

This means that no matter how close x gets to 0, there will be both positive and negative x-values that yield $f(x) = 1$ and $f(x) = -1$. This implies that the limit does not exist.

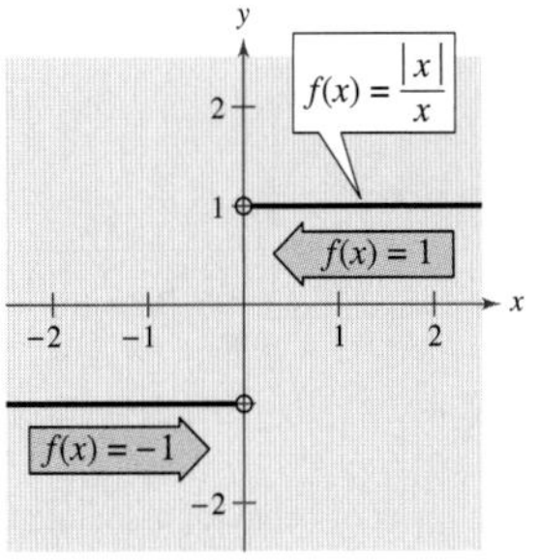

FIGURE 12.6

CHECKPoint Now try Exercise 31.

Example 7 Unbounded Behavior

Discuss the existence of the limit.

$$\lim_{x \to 0} \frac{1}{x^2}$$

Solution

Let $f(x) = 1/x^2$. In Figure 12.7, note that as x approaches 0 from either the right or the left, $f(x)$ increases without bound. This means that by choosing x close enough to 0, you can force $f(x)$ to be as large as you want. For instance, $f(x)$ will be larger than 100 if you choose x that is within $\frac{1}{10}$ of 0. That is,

$$0 < |x| < \frac{1}{10} \quad \Longrightarrow \quad f(x) = \frac{1}{x^2} > 100.$$

Similarly, you can force $f(x)$ to be larger than 1,000,000, as follows.

$$0 < |x| < \frac{1}{1000} \quad \Longrightarrow \quad f(x) = \frac{1}{x^2} > 1{,}000{,}000$$

Because $f(x)$ is not approaching a unique real number L as x approaches 0, you can conclude that the limit does not exist.

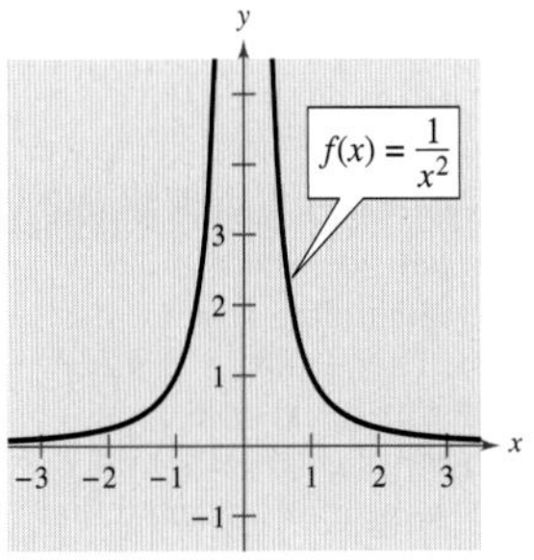

FIGURE 12.7

CHECKPoint Now try Exercise 33.

Extra Example 6

Show that the limit does not exist.

$$\lim_{x \to 0} \frac{x}{|x|}$$

As shown on the graph, $f(x) = \frac{x}{|x|} = 1$ for $x > 0$ and $f(x) = \frac{x}{|x|} = -1$ for $x < 0$. This implies that the limit does not exist.

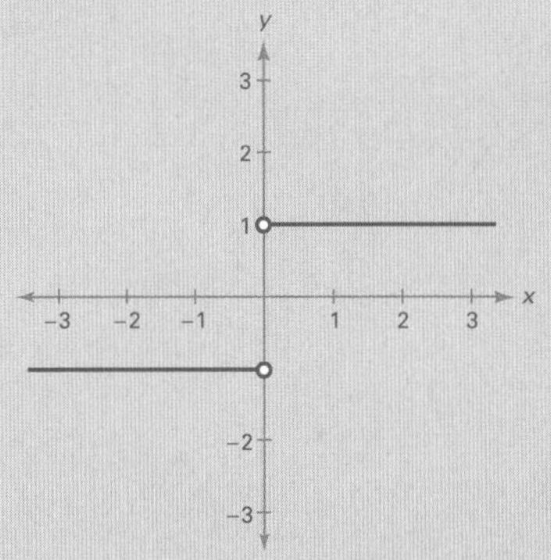

Extra Example 7

Discuss the existence of the limit.

$$\lim_{x \to 0} \frac{1}{x^4}$$

As x approaches 0 from either the left or the right, $f(x) = \frac{1}{x^4}$ increases without bound as shown. Because $f(x)$ is not approaching a unique real number L as x approaches 0, you can conclude that the limit does not exist.

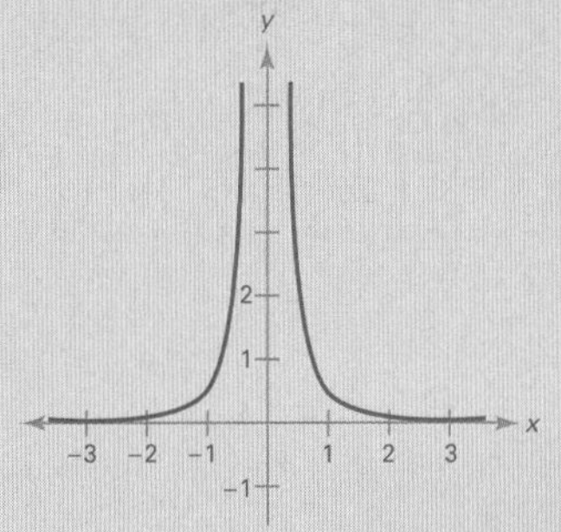

Extra Example 8

Discuss the existence of the limit:

$\lim_{x\to 0} \cos\left(\frac{1}{x}\right)$.

Let $f(x) = \cos\left(\frac{1}{x}\right)$. In the figure, note that as x approaches 0, $f(x)$ oscillates between -1 and 1. Therefore, the limit does not exist.

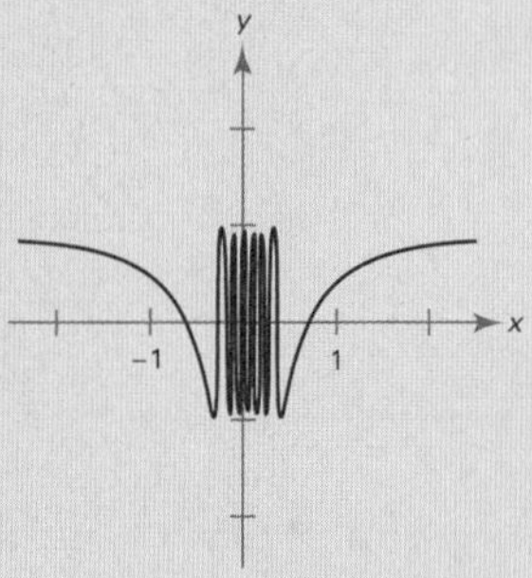

Example 8 Oscillating Behavior

Discuss the existence of the limit.

$$\lim_{x\to 0} \sin \frac{1}{x}$$

Solution

Let $f(x) = \sin(1/x)$. In Figure 12.8, you can see that as x approaches 0, $f(x)$ oscillates between -1 and 1. Therefore, the limit does not exist because no matter how close you are to 0, it is possible to choose values of x_1 and x_2 such that $\sin(1/x_1) = 1$ and $\sin(1/x_2) = -1$, as indicated in the table.

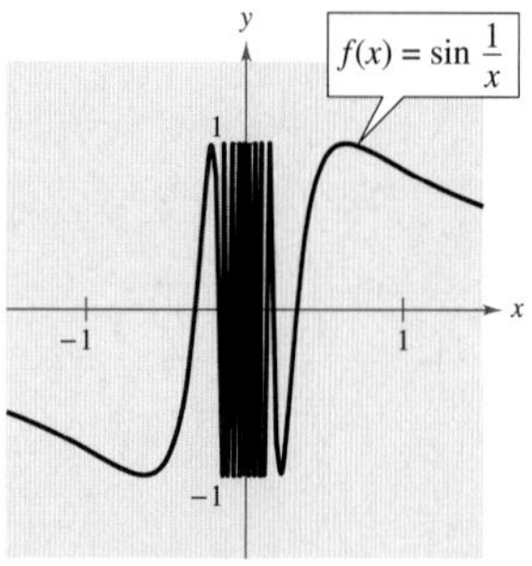

FIGURE 12.8

x	$-\frac{2}{\pi}$	$-\frac{2}{3\pi}$	$-\frac{2}{5\pi}$	0	$\frac{2}{5\pi}$	$\frac{2}{3\pi}$	$\frac{2}{\pi}$
$\sin \frac{1}{x}$	-1	1	-1	?	1	-1	1

CHECK *Point* Now try Exercise 35.

Examples 6, 7, and 8 show three of the most common types of behavior associated with the *nonexistence* of a limit.

Conditions Under Which Limits Do Not Exist

The limit of $f(x)$ as $x \to c$ does not exist if any of the following conditions are true.

1. $f(x)$ approaches a different number from the right side of c than it approaches from the left side of c. — Example 6
2. $f(x)$ increases or decreases without bound as x approaches c. — Example 7
3. $f(x)$ oscillates between two fixed values as x approaches c. — Example 8

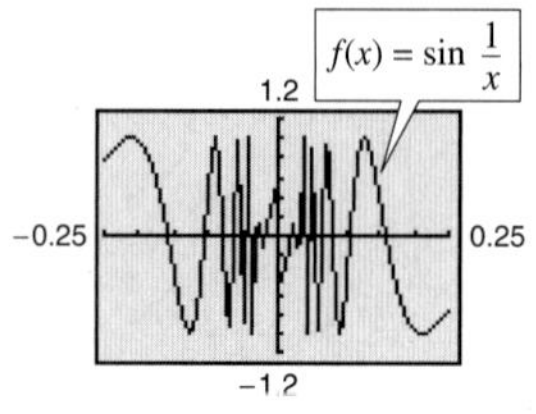

FIGURE 12.9

TECHNOLOGY

A graphing utility can help you discover the behavior of a function near the x-value at which you are trying to evaluate a limit. When you do this, however, you should realize that you can't always trust the graphs that graphing utilities display. For instance, if you use a graphing utility to graph the function in Example 8 over an interval containing 0, you will most likely obtain an incorrect graph, as shown in Figure 12.9. The reason that a graphing utility can't show the correct graph is that the graph has infinitely many oscillations over any interval that contains 0.

Properties of Limits and Direct Substitution

You have seen that sometimes the limit of $f(x)$ as $x \to c$ is simply $f(c)$, as shown in Example 2. In such cases, it is said that the limit can be evaluated by **direct substitution.** That is,

$$\lim_{x \to c} f(x) = f(c). \qquad \text{Substitute } c \text{ for } x.$$

There are many "well-behaved" functions, such as polynomial functions and rational functions with nonzero denominators, that have this property. Some of the basic ones are included in the following list.

Basic Limits

Let b and c be real numbers and let n be a positive integer.

1. $\lim_{x \to c} b = b$ — Limit of a constant function
2. $\lim_{x \to c} x = c$ — Limit of the identity function
3. $\lim_{x \to c} x^n = c^n$ — Limit of a power function
4. $\lim_{x \to c} \sqrt[n]{x} = \sqrt[n]{c}$, for n even and $c > 0$ — Limit of a radical function

For a proof of the limit of a power function, see Proofs in Mathematics on page 906.

Trigonometric functions can also be included in this list. For instance,

$$\lim_{x \to \pi} \sin x = \sin \pi = 0$$

and

$$\lim_{x \to 0} \cos x = \cos 0 = 1.$$

By combining the basic limits with the following operations, you can find limits for a wide variety of functions.

Properties of Limits

Let b and c be real numbers, let n be a positive integer, and let f and g be functions with the following limits.

$$\lim_{x \to c} f(x) = L \quad \text{and} \quad \lim_{x \to c} g(x) = K$$

1. Scalar multiple: $\lim_{x \to c} [b f(x)] = bL$
2. Sum or difference: $\lim_{x \to c} [f(x) \pm g(x)] = L \pm K$
3. Product: $\lim_{x \to c} [f(x)g(x)] = LK$
4. Quotient: $\lim_{x \to c} \dfrac{f(x)}{g(x)} = \dfrac{L}{K}$, provided $K \neq 0$
5. Power: $\lim_{x \to c} [f(x)]^n = L^n$

Extra Example 9

Find each limit.

a. $\lim_{x\to 2} x^3$

8

b. $\lim_{x\to 4} 8x$

32

c. $\lim_{x\to 16} \sqrt[4]{x}$

2

d. $\lim_{x\to 3\pi/4} \tan x$

-1

Example 9 Direct Substitution and Properties of Limits

Find each limit.

a. $\lim_{x\to 4} x^2$ **b.** $\lim_{x\to 4} 5x$ **c.** $\lim_{x\to \pi} \dfrac{\tan x}{x}$

d. $\lim_{x\to 9} \sqrt{x}$ **e.** $\lim_{x\to \pi} (x \cos x)$ **f.** $\lim_{x\to 3} (x + 4)^2$

Solution

You can use the properties of limits and direct substitution to evaluate each limit.

a. $\lim_{x\to 4} x^2 = (4)^2$
$= 16$

b. $\lim_{x\to 4} 5x = 5 \lim_{x\to 4} x$ Property 1
$= 5(4)$
$= 20$

c. $\lim_{x\to \pi} \dfrac{\tan x}{x} = \dfrac{\lim_{x\to \pi} \tan x}{\lim_{x\to \pi} x}$ Property 4
$= \dfrac{0}{\pi} = 0$

d. $\lim_{x\to 9} \sqrt{x} = \sqrt{9} = 3$

e. $\lim_{x\to \pi} (x \cos x) = \left(\lim_{x\to \pi} x\right)\left(\lim_{x\to \pi} \cos x\right)$ Property 3
$= \pi(\cos \pi)$
$= -\pi$

f. $\lim_{x\to 3} (x + 4)^2 = \left[\left(\lim_{x\to 3} x\right) + \left(\lim_{x\to 3} 4\right)\right]^2$ Properties 2 and 5
$= (3 + 4)^2$
$= 7^2 = 49$

CHECKPoint Now try Exercise 47.

When evaluating limits, remember that there are several ways to solve most problems. Often, a problem can be solved *numerically*, *graphically*, or *algebraically*. The limits in Example 9 were found algebraically. You can verify the solutions numerically and/or graphically. For instance, to verify the limit in Example 9(a) numerically, create a table that shows values of x^2 for two sets of x-values—one set that approaches 4 from the left and one that approaches 4 from the right, as shown below. From the table, you can see that the limit as x approaches 4 is 16. Now, to verify the limit graphically, sketch the graph of $y = x^2$. From the graph shown in Figure 12.10, you can determine that the limit as x approaches 4 is 16.

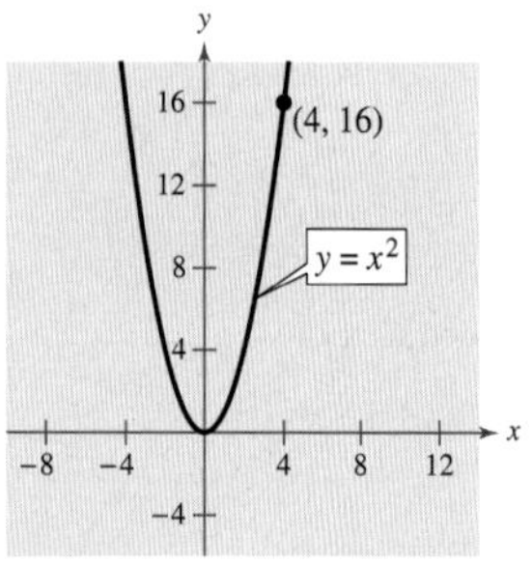

FIGURE 12.10

x	3.9	3.99	3.999	4.0	4.001	4.01	4.1
x^2	15.2100	15.9201	15.9920	?	16.0080	16.0801	16.8100

The results of using direct substitution to evaluate limits of polynomial and rational functions are summarized as follows.

Limits of Polynomial and Rational Functions

1. If p is a polynomial function and c is a real number, then

$$\lim_{x\to c} p(x) = p(c).$$

2. If r is a rational function given by $r(x) = p(x)/q(x)$, and c is a real number such that $q(c) \neq 0$, then

$$\lim_{x\to c} r(x) = r(c) = \frac{p(c)}{q(c)}.$$

For a proof of the limit of a polynomial function, see Proofs in Mathematics on page 906.

Example 10 Evaluating Limits by Direct Substitution

Find each limit.

a. $\lim_{x\to -1} (x^2 + x - 6)$ **b.** $\lim_{x\to -1} \frac{x^2 + x - 6}{x + 3}$

Solution

The first function is a polynomial function and the second is a rational function (with a nonzero denominator at $x = -1$). So, you can evaluate the limits by direct substitution.

a. $\lim_{x\to -1} (x^2 + x - 6) = (-1)^2 + (-1) - 6$

$= -6$

b. $\lim_{x\to -1} \frac{x^2 + x - 6}{x + 3} = \frac{(-1)^2 + (-1) - 6}{-1 + 3}$

$= -\frac{6}{2}$

$= -3$

CHECKPoint Now try Exercise 51.

Classroom Discussion

Graphs with Holes Sketch the graph of each function. Then find the limits of each function as x approaches 1 and as x approaches 2. What conclusions can you make?

a. $f(x) = x + 1$ b. $g(x) = \dfrac{x^2 - 1}{x - 1}$ c. $h(x) = \dfrac{x^3 - 2x^2 - x + 2}{x^2 - 3x + 2}$

Use a graphing utility to graph each function above. Does the graphing utility distinguish among the three graphs? Write a short explanation of your findings.
See margin.

Extra Example 10

Find each limit.

a. $\lim_{x\to 2} (x^2 + 5x + 4)$

18

b. $\lim_{x\to 2} \frac{x^2 + 5x + 4}{x + 4}$

3

Closing the Lesson

Have students summarize the major points of the lesson and answer the Essential Question: How do you find and interpret the limit of a function for a certain value of x?

- **Estimate the limit of a function as x approaches a certain value c by calculating $f(x)$ for several x-values that approach c from the left and several that approach c from the right.**
- **Identify limits that do not exist because the function approaches two different values or because the function increases without bound as x approaches c from the left and right.**
- **Recognize basic limits that can be evaluated by direct substitution, including rational functions with a nonzero denominator.**

Classroom Discussion

(a)

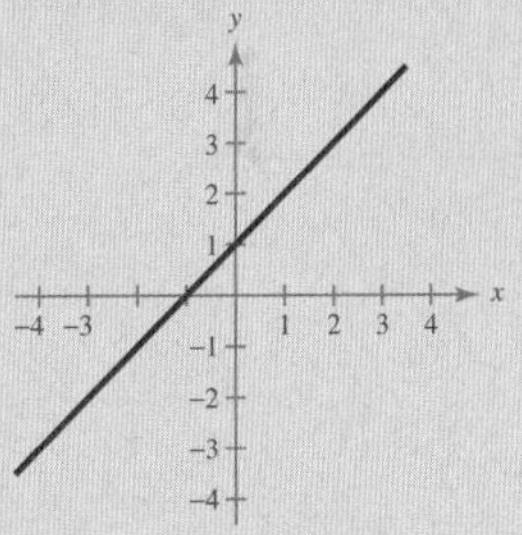

$\lim_{x\to 1} f(x) = 2$, $\lim_{x\to 2} f(x) = 3$

Both $f(1)$ and $f(2)$ exist and so do $\lim_{x\to 1} f(x)$ and $\lim_{x\to 2} f(x)$.

(b)

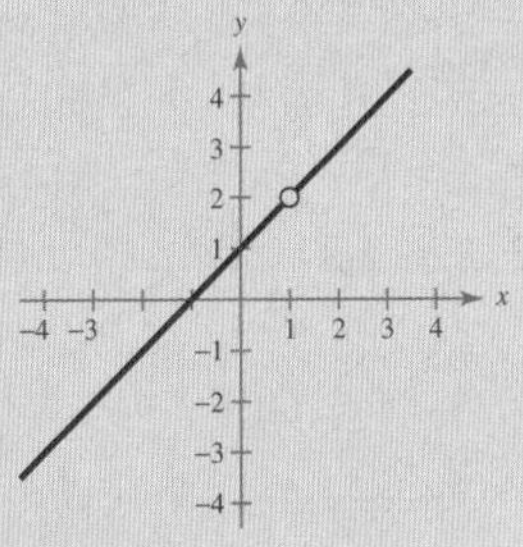

$\lim_{x\to 1} g(x) = 2$, $\lim_{x\to 2} g(x) = 3$

$g(1)$ does not exist, but $\lim_{x\to 1} g(x)$ does exist.

(c)

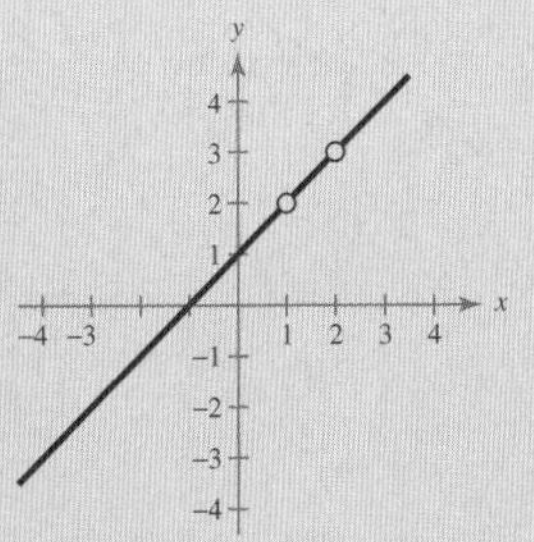

$\lim_{x\to 1} h(x) = 2$, $\lim_{x\to 2} h(x) = 3$

$h(1)$ does not exist, but $\lim_{x\to 1} h(x)$ does exist.

$h(2)$ does not exist, but $\lim_{x\to 2} h(x)$ does exist.

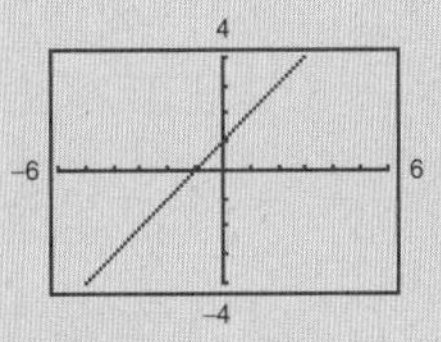

A graphing utility does not distinguish among the graphs. Explanations will vary.

4 PRACTICE AND APPLY

Assignment Guide

Transparencies Available
Available at the Instructor's companion site.

Average:
Day 1: pp. 858–859
Exs. 6–10 even, 13–19, 23, 25, 28–30, 37–43 odd
Day 2: p. 860
Exs. 45, 48, 49, 53–67 odd, 69–72, 74, 77

Advanced:
Day 1: pp. 858–859
Exs. 6–14 even, 16–20, 24, 25, 28–30, 36–44 even
Day 2: p. 860
Exs. 46–50 even, 54–68 even, 69–74, 76, 77

Block:
pp. 858–859
Exs. 6–10 even, 13–19, 23, 25, 28–30, 37–43 odd (with Chapter 11 Test)
p. 860
Exs. 45, 48, 49, 53–67 odd, 69–72, 74, 77 (with 12.2)

12.1 EXERCISES

See www.CalcChat.com for worked-out solutions to odd-numbered exercises.

VOCABULARY: Fill in the blanks.

1. If $f(x)$ becomes arbitrarily close to a unique number L as x approaches c from either side, the limit of $f(x)$ as x approaches c is L.
2. An alternative notation for $\lim_{x \to c} f(x) = L$ is $f(x) \to L$ as $x \to c$, which is read as "$f(x)$ _______ L as x _______ c." approaches; approaches
3. The limit of $f(x)$ as $x \to c$ does not exist if $f(x)$ oscillates between two fixed values.
4. To evaluate the limit of a polynomial function, use direct substitution

SKILLS AND APPLICATIONS

5. **GEOMETRY** You create an open box from a square piece of material 24 centimeters on a side. You cut equal squares from the corners and turn up the sides. See margin.
   (a) Draw and label a diagram that represents the box.
   (b) Verify that the volume V of the box is given by
   $$V = 4x(12 - x)^2.$$
   (c) The box has a maximum volume when $x = 4$. Use a graphing utility to complete the table and observe the behavior of the function as x approaches 4. Use the table to find $\lim_{x \to 4} V$.

x	3	3.5	3.9	4	4.1	4.5	5
V							

   (d) Use a graphing utility to graph the volume function. Verify that the volume is maximum when $x = 4$.

6. **GEOMETRY** You are given wire and are asked to form a right triangle with a hypotenuse of $\sqrt{18}$ inches whose area is as large as possible. See margin.
   (a) Draw and label a diagram that shows the base x and height y of the triangle.
   (b) Verify that the area A of the triangle is given by
   $$A = \tfrac{1}{2}x\sqrt{18 - x^2}.$$
   (c) The triangle has a maximum area when $x = 3$ inches. Use a graphing utility to complete the table and observe the behavior of the function as x approaches 3. Use the table to find $\lim_{x \to 3} A$.

x	2	2.5	2.9	3	3.1	3.5	4
A							

   (d) Use a graphing utility to graph the area function. Verify that the area is maximum when $x = 3$ inches.

In Exercises 7–12, complete the table and use the result to estimate the limit numerically. Determine whether or not the limit can be reached. 7–11. See margin.

7. $\lim_{x \to 2} (5x + 4)$

x	1.9	1.99	1.999	2	2.001	2.01	2.1
$f(x)$				?			

8. $\lim_{x \to 1} (2x^2 + x - 4)$

x	0.9	0.99	0.999	1	1.001	1.01	1.1
$f(x)$				?			

9. $\lim_{x \to 3} \dfrac{x - 3}{x^2 - 9}$

x	2.9	2.99	2.999	3	3.001	3.01	3.1
$f(x)$				?			

10. $\lim_{x \to -1} \dfrac{x + 1}{x^2 - x - 2}$

x	−1.1	−1.01	−1.001	−1	−0.999	−0.99	−0.9
$f(x)$				?			

11. $\lim_{x \to 0} \dfrac{\sin 2x}{x}$

x	−0.1	−0.01	−0.001	0	0.001	0.01	0.1
$f(x)$				?			

5. (a)

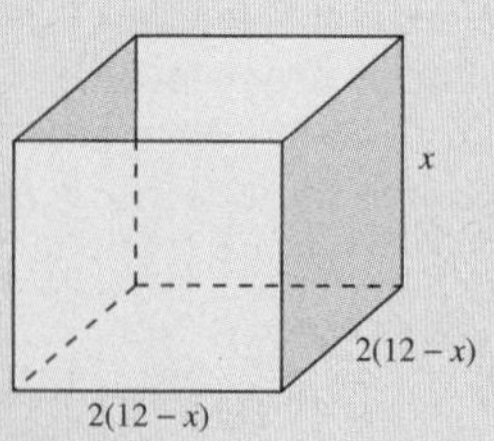

(b)
$V = lwh$
$= 2(12 - x) \cdot 2(12 - x) \cdot x$
$= 4x(12 - x)^2$

(c)

x	3	3.5	3.9	4	4.1	4.5	5
V	972	1011.5	1023.5	1024	1023.5	1012.5	980

$\lim_{x \to 4} V = 1024$

(d)

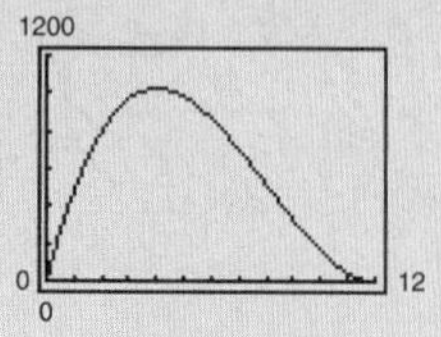

6. (a)

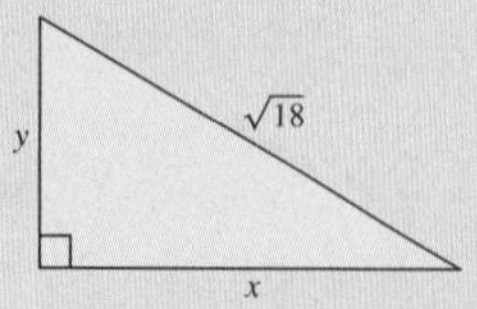

(b) $A = \frac{1}{2}bh$
$= \frac{1}{2}xy$
$= \frac{1}{2}x\sqrt{18 - x^2}$

(c)

x	2	2.5	2.9	3	3.1	3.5	4
A	3.7417	4.2848	4.4903	4.5	4.4897	4.1964	2.8284

$\lim_{x \to 3} A = 4.5$

(d)

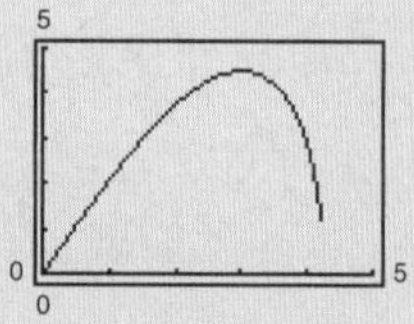

7–11. See Additional Answers beginning on page AA1.

12. $\lim\limits_{x \to 0} \dfrac{\tan x}{2x}$ See margin.

x	-0.1	-0.01	-0.001	0	0.001
$f(x)$				?	

x	0.01	0.1
$f(x)$		

In Exercises 13–26, create a table of values for the function and use the result to estimate the limit numerically. Use a graphing utility to graph the corresponding function to confirm your result graphically. 13–26. See margin.

13. $\lim\limits_{x \to 1} \dfrac{x - 1}{x^2 + 2x - 3}$

14. $\lim\limits_{x \to -2} \dfrac{x + 2}{x^2 + 5x + 6}$

15. $\lim\limits_{x \to 0} \dfrac{\sqrt{x + 5} - \sqrt{5}}{x}$

16. $\lim\limits_{x \to -3} \dfrac{\sqrt{1 - x} - 2}{x + 3}$

17. $\lim\limits_{x \to -4} \dfrac{\dfrac{x}{x + 2} - 2}{x + 4}$

18. $\lim\limits_{x \to 2} \dfrac{\dfrac{1}{x + 2} - \dfrac{1}{4}}{x - 2}$

19. $\lim\limits_{x \to 0} \dfrac{\sin x}{x}$

20. $\lim\limits_{x \to 0} \dfrac{\cos x - 1}{x}$

21. $\lim\limits_{x \to 0} \dfrac{\sin^2 x}{x}$

22. $\lim\limits_{x \to 0} \dfrac{2x}{\tan 4x}$

23. $\lim\limits_{x \to 0} \dfrac{e^{2x} - 1}{2x}$

24. $\lim\limits_{x \to 0} \dfrac{1 - e^{-4x}}{x}$

25. $\lim\limits_{x \to 1} \dfrac{\ln(2x - 1)}{x - 1}$

26. $\lim\limits_{x \to 1} \dfrac{\ln(x^2)}{x - 1}$

In Exercises 27 and 28, graph the function and find the limit (if it exists) as *x* approaches 2. 27–28. See margin.

27. $f(x) = \begin{cases} 2x + 1, & x < 2 \\ x + 3, & x \geq 2 \end{cases}$

28. $f(x) = \begin{cases} -2x, & x \leq 2 \\ x^2 - 4x + 1, & x > 2 \end{cases}$

In Exercises 29–36, use the graph to find the limit (if it exists). If the limit does not exist, explain why.

29. $\lim\limits_{x \to -4} (x^2 - 3)$ 13

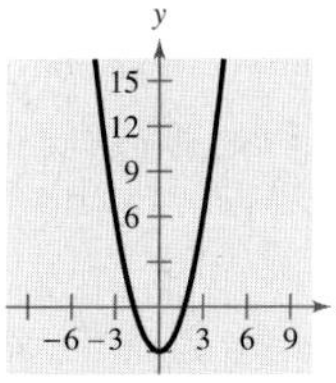

30. $\lim\limits_{x \to 2} \dfrac{3x^2 - 12}{x - 2}$ 12

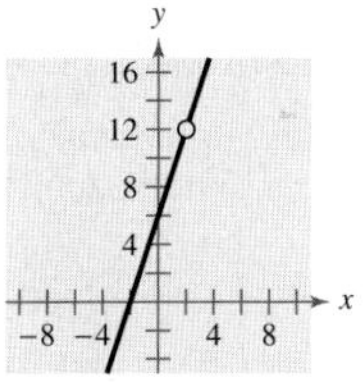

31. $\lim\limits_{x \to -2} \dfrac{|x + 2|}{x + 2}$

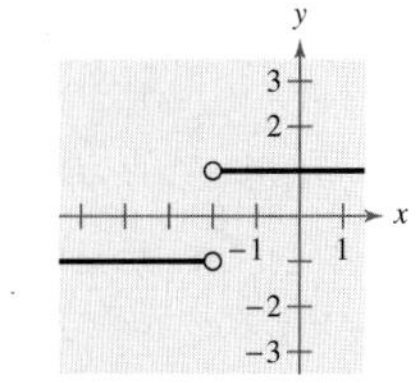

32. $\lim\limits_{x \to 1} \dfrac{|x - 1|}{x - 1}$ 31–35. Limit does not exist. Answers will vary.

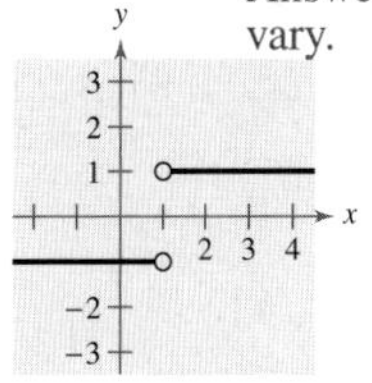

33. $\lim\limits_{x \to -2} \dfrac{x - 2}{x^2 - 4}$

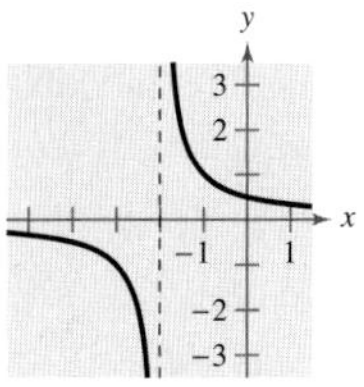

34. $\lim\limits_{x \to 1} \dfrac{1}{x - 1}$

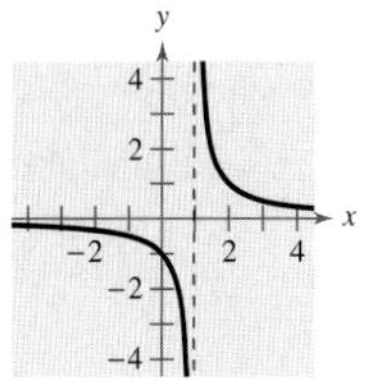

35. $\lim\limits_{x \to 0} 2 \cos \dfrac{\pi}{x}$

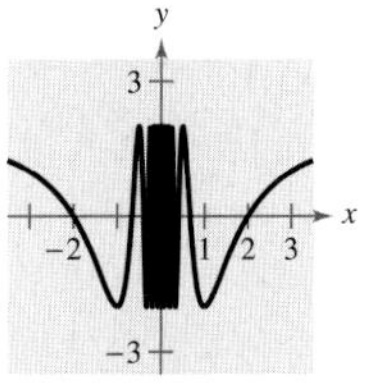

36. $\lim\limits_{x \to -1} \sin \dfrac{\pi x}{2}$ -1

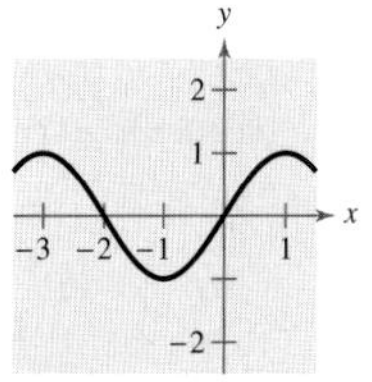

In Exercises 37–44, use a graphing utility to graph the function and use the graph to determine whether the limit exists. If the limit does not exist, explain why. 37–44. See margin.

37. $f(x) = \dfrac{5}{2 + e^{1/x}}, \quad \lim\limits_{x \to 0} f(x)$

38. $f(x) = \ln(7 - x), \quad \lim\limits_{x \to -1} f(x)$

39. $f(x) = \cos \dfrac{1}{x}, \quad \lim\limits_{x \to 0} f(x)$

40. $f(x) = \sin \pi x, \quad \lim\limits_{x \to 1} f(x)$

41. $f(x) = \dfrac{\sqrt{x + 3} - 1}{x - 4}, \quad \lim\limits_{x \to 4} f(x)$

42. $f(x) = \dfrac{\sqrt{x + 5} - 4}{x - 2}, \quad \lim\limits_{x \to 2} f(x)$

43. $f(x) = \dfrac{x - 1}{x^2 - 4x + 3}, \quad \lim\limits_{x \to 1} f(x)$

44. $f(x) = \dfrac{7}{x - 3}, \quad \lim\limits_{x \to 3} f(x)$

27.

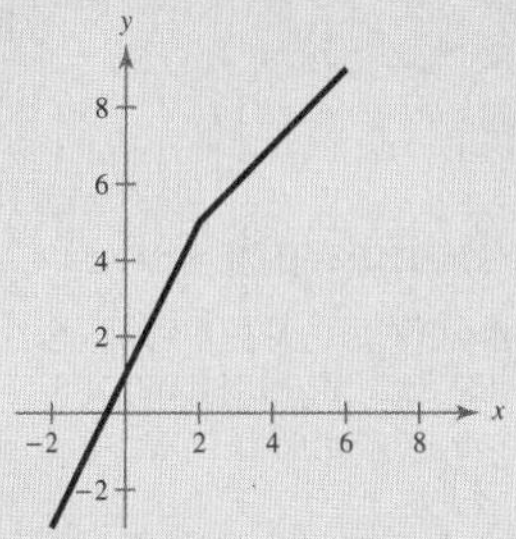

5

28.

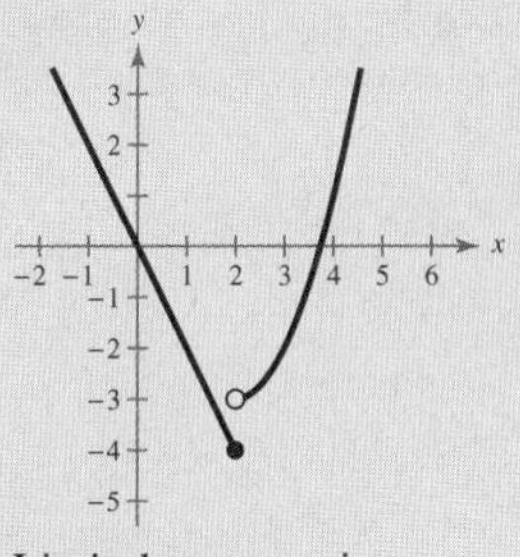

Limit does not exist.

37.

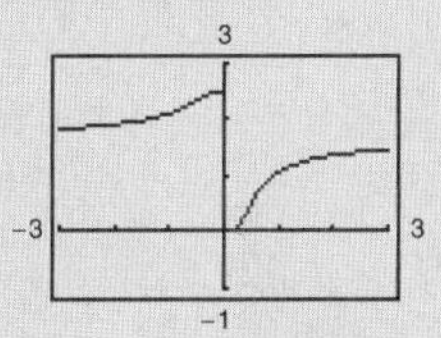

Limit does not exist. Answers will vary.

38.

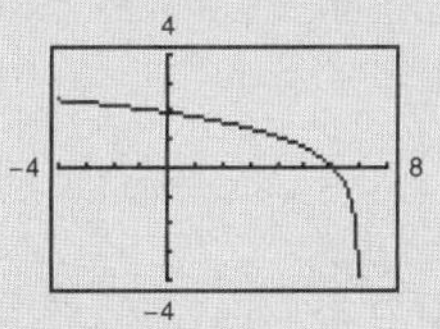

Limit exists.

39.

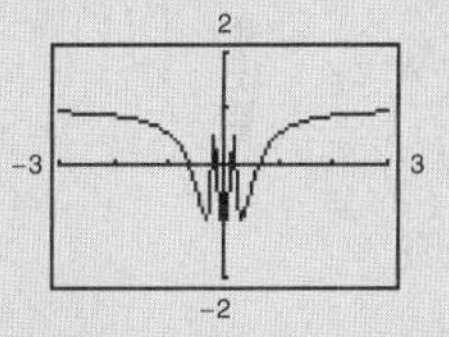

Limit does not exist. Answers will vary.

40.

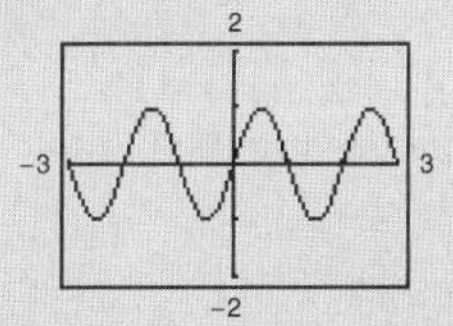

Limit exists.

41.

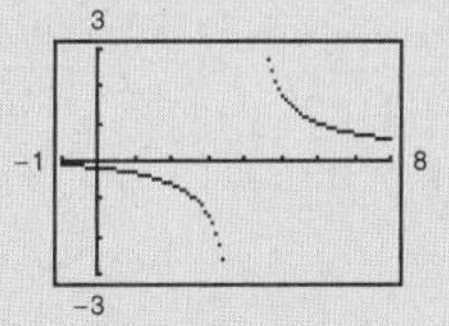

Limit does not exist. Answers will vary.

42.

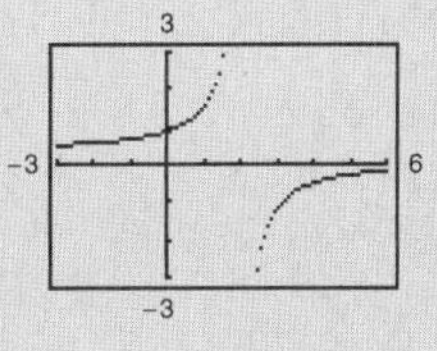

Limit does not exist. Answers will vary.

43.

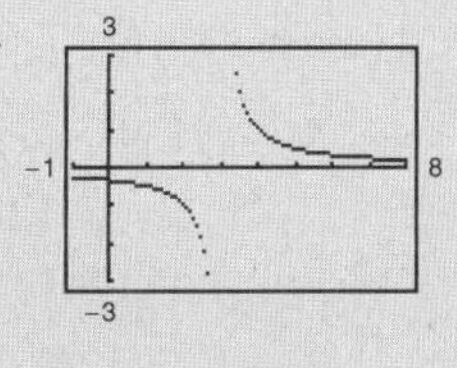

Limit exists.

44.

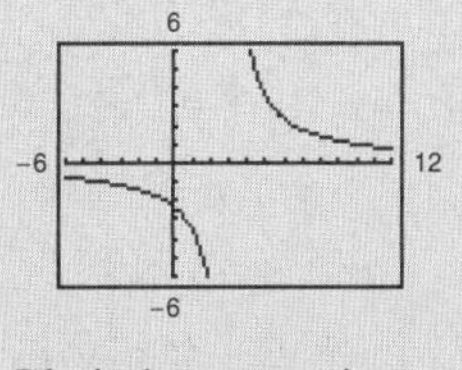

Limit does not exist. Answers will vary.

12–26. See Additional Answers beginning on page AA1.

5 ASSESS AND RETEACH

Daily Homework Quiz

Transparency Available
Available at the Instructor's companion site.

73. (a) No. The function may approach different values from the right and left of 2. For example,
$$f(x) = \begin{cases} 0, & x < 2 \\ 4, & x = 2 \\ 6, & x > 2 \end{cases}$$
implies $f(2) = 4$, but $\lim_{x\to 2} f(x) \neq 4$.
(b) No. The function may approach 4 as x approaches 2, but the function could be undefined at $x = 2$. For example, in the function
$$f(x) = \frac{4\sin(x-2)}{x-2},$$
the limit is 4 as x approaches 2, but $f(2)$ is not defined.

74. As the function's x-value approaches 5 from both the right and left sides, its corresponding output values approach 12.

75.

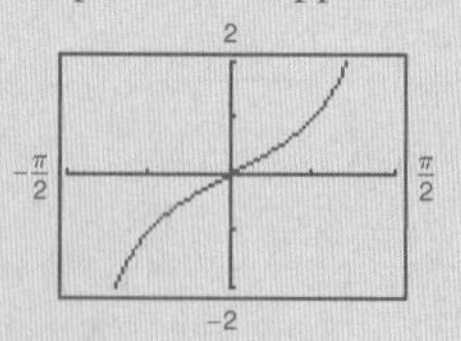

$\lim_{x\to 0} \tan x = 0$

$\lim_{x\to \pi/4} \tan x = 1$

$\lim_{x\to \pi/2} \tan x$ does not exist.

76. (a) 1
(b) Does not exist. Answers will vary.
(c) Undefined. Answers will vary.
(d) 3

77.

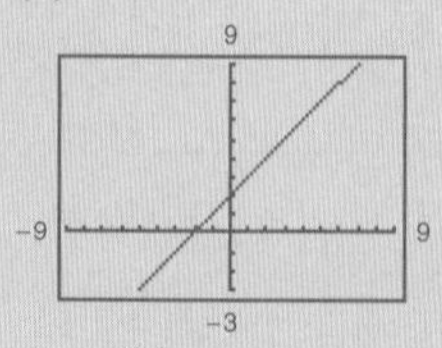

$\lim_{x\to 4} f(x) = 6$

$\lim_{x\to 5} f(x) = 7$

No; No

In Exercises 45 and 46, use the given information to evaluate each limit.

45. $\lim_{x\to c} f(x) = 3, \quad \lim_{x\to c} g(x) = 6$

(a) $\lim_{x\to c} [-2g(x)]$ -12 (b) $\lim_{x\to c} [f(x) + g(x)]$ 9

(c) $\lim_{x\to c} \frac{f(x)}{g(x)}$ $\frac{1}{2}$ (d) $\lim_{x\to c} \sqrt{f(x)}$ $\sqrt{3}$

46. $\lim_{x\to c} f(x) = 5, \quad \lim_{x\to c} g(x) = -2$ (a) 9

(a) $\lim_{x\to c} [f(x) + g(x)]^2$ (b) $\lim_{x\to c} [6f(x)g(x)]$ -60

(c) $\lim_{x\to c} \frac{5g(x)}{4f(x)}$ $-\frac{1}{2}$ (d) $\lim_{x\to c} \frac{1}{\sqrt{f(x)}}$ $\frac{\sqrt{5}}{5}$

In Exercises 47 and 48, find (a) $\lim_{x\to 2} f(x)$, (b) $\lim_{x\to 2} g(x)$, (c) $\lim_{x\to 2} [f(x)g(x)]$, and (d) $\lim_{x\to 2} [g(x) - f(x)]$.

47. $f(x) = x^3, \quad g(x) = \frac{\sqrt{x^2+5}}{2x^2}$ (a) 8 (b) $\frac{3}{8}$ (c) 3 (d) $-\frac{61}{8}$

48. $f(x) = \frac{x}{3-x}, \quad g(x) = \sin \pi x$ (a) 2 (b) 0 (c) 0 (d) -2

In Exercises 49–68, find the limit by direct substitution.

49. $\lim_{x\to 5} (10 - x^2)$ -15

50. $\lim_{x\to -2} \left(\frac{1}{2}x^3 - 5x\right)$ 6

51. $\lim_{x\to -3} (2x^2 + 4x + 1)$ 7

52. $\lim_{x\to -2} (x^3 - 6x + 5)$ 9

53. $\lim_{x\to 3} \left(-\frac{9}{x}\right)$ -3

54. $\lim_{x\to -5} \frac{6}{x+2}$ -2

55. $\lim_{x\to -3} \frac{3x}{x^2+1}$ $-\frac{9}{10}$

56. $\lim_{x\to 4} \frac{x-1}{x^2+2x+3}$ $\frac{1}{9}$

57. $\lim_{x\to -2} \frac{5x+3}{2x-9}$ $\frac{7}{13}$

58. $\lim_{x\to 3} \frac{x^2+1}{x}$ $\frac{10}{3}$

59. $\lim_{x\to -1} \sqrt{x+2}$ 1

60. $\lim_{x\to 3} \sqrt[3]{x^2-1}$ 2

61. $\lim_{x\to 7} \frac{5x}{\sqrt{x+2}}$ $\frac{35}{3}$

62. $\lim_{x\to 8} \frac{\sqrt{x+1}}{x-4}$ $\frac{3}{4}$

63. $\lim_{x\to 3} e^x$ $e^3 \approx 20.09$

64. $\lim_{x\to e} \ln x$ 1

65. $\lim_{x\to \pi} \sin 2x$ 0

66. $\lim_{x\to \pi} \tan x$ 0

67. $\lim_{x\to 1/2} \arcsin x$ $\frac{\pi}{6}$

68. $\lim_{x\to 1} \arccos \frac{x}{2}$ $\frac{\pi}{3}$

EXPLORATION

TRUE OR FALSE? In Exercises 69 and 70, determine whether the statement is true or false. Justify your answer.

69. The limit of a function as x approaches c does not exist if the function approaches -3 from the left of c and 3 from the right of c. True

70. The limit of the product of two functions is equal to the product of the limits of the two functions. See below.

71. THINK ABOUT IT From Exercises 7–12, select a limit that can be reached and one that cannot be reached.

(a) Use a graphing utility to graph the corresponding functions using a standard viewing window. Do the graphs reveal whether or not the limit can be reached? Explain. (a)–(b). Answers will vary.

(b) Use a graphing utility to graph the corresponding functions using a *decimal* setting. Do the graphs reveal whether or not the limit can be reached? Explain.

72. THINK ABOUT IT Use the results of Exercise 71 to draw a conclusion as to whether or not you can use the graph generated by a graphing utility to determine reliably if a limit can be reached. Answers will vary.

73. THINK ABOUT IT See margin.

(a) If $f(2) = 4$, can you conclude anything about $\lim_{x\to 2} f(x)$? Explain your reasoning.

(b) If $\lim_{x\to 2} f(x) = 4$, can you conclude anything about $f(2)$? Explain your reasoning.

74. WRITING Write a brief description of the meaning of the notation $\lim_{x\to 5} f(x) = 12$. See margin.

75. THINK ABOUT IT Use a graphing utility to graph the tangent function. What are $\lim_{x\to 0} \tan x$ and $\lim_{x\to \pi/4} \tan x$? What can you say about the existence of the limit $\lim_{x\to \pi/2} \tan x$? See margin.

76. CAPSTONE Use the graph of the function f to decide whether the value of the given quantity exists. If it does, find it. If not, explain why. See margin.

(a) $f(0)$

(b) $\lim_{x\to 0} f(x)$

(c) $f(2)$

(d) $\lim_{x\to 2} f(x)$

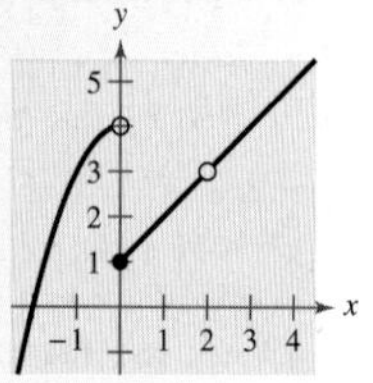

77. WRITING Use a graphing utility to graph the function given by $f(x) = \frac{x^2 - 3x - 10}{x - 5}$. Use the *trace* feature to approximate $\lim_{x\to 4} f(x)$. What do you think $\lim_{x\to 5} f(x)$ equals? Is f defined at $x = 5$? Does this affect the existence of the limit as x approaches 5? See margin.

70. True, provided the individual limits exist.

12.2 TECHNIQUES FOR EVALUATING LIMITS

What you should learn

- Use the dividing out technique to evaluate limits of functions.
- Use the rationalizing technique to evaluate limits of functions.
- Approximate limits of functions graphically and numerically.
- Evaluate one-sided limits of functions.
- Evaluate limits of difference quotients from calculus.

Why you should learn it

Limits can be applied in real-life situations. For instance, in Exercise 84 on page 870, you will determine limits involving the costs of making photocopies.

Michael Krasowitz/TAXI/Getty Images

Dividing Out Technique

In Section 12.1, you studied several types of functions whose limits can be evaluated by direct substitution. In this section, you will study several techniques for evaluating limits of functions for which direct substitution fails.

Suppose you were asked to find the following limit.

$$\lim_{x \to -3} \frac{x^2 + x - 6}{x + 3}$$

Direct substitution produces 0 in both the numerator and denominator.

$$(-3)^2 + (-3) - 6 = 0 \qquad \text{Numerator is 0 when } x = -3.$$

$$-3 + 3 = 0 \qquad \text{Denominator is 0 when } x = -3.$$

The resulting fraction, $\frac{0}{0}$, has no meaning as a real number. It is called an **indeterminate form** because you cannot, from the form alone, determine the limit. By using a table, however, it appears that the limit of the function as $x \to -3$ is -5.

x	-3.01	-3.001	-3.0001	-3	-2.9999	-2.999	-2.99
$\frac{x^2 + x - 6}{x + 3}$	-5.01	-5.001	-5.0001	?	-4.9999	-4.999	-4.99

When you try to evaluate a limit of a rational function by direct substitution and encounter the indeterminate form $\frac{0}{0}$, you can conclude that the numerator and denominator must have a common factor. After factoring and dividing out, you should try direct substitution again. Example 1 shows how you can use the **dividing out technique** to evaluate limits of these types of functions.

Example 1 Dividing Out Technique

Find the limit: $\lim_{x \to -3} \frac{x^2 + x - 6}{x + 3}$.

Solution

From the discussion above, you know that direct substitution fails. So, begin by factoring the numerator and dividing out any common factors.

$$\lim_{x \to -3} \frac{x^2 + x - 6}{x + 3} = \lim_{x \to -3} \frac{(x - 2)(x + 3)}{x + 3} \qquad \text{Factor numerator.}$$

$$= \lim_{x \to -3} \frac{(x - 2)\cancel{(x + 3)}}{\cancel{x + 3}} \qquad \text{Divide out common factor.}$$

$$= \lim_{x \to -3} (x - 2) \qquad \text{Simplify.}$$

$$= -3 - 2 = -5 \qquad \text{Direct substitution and simplify.}$$

CHECKPoint Now try Exercise 11.

1 PLAN AND PREPARE

Warm-up Exercises

Transparency Available
Available at the Instructor's companion site.

Notetaking Guide

Transparency Available
Promotes interactive learning and notetaking skills.
Available at the Instructor's companion site.

Animated Precalculus

An **Animated Precalculus** tutorial is available at the Student companion site for **Section 12.2.**

Pacing

Average: 2 days
Advanced: 2 days
Block: 0.5 block with 12.1
0.5 block with 12.3

2 FOCUS AND MOTIVATE

Essential Question

How do you evaluate limits that cannot be solved through use of direct substitution? **Tell students that they will learn how to answer this question by studying dividing out, rationalizing, and graphical techniques to evaluate or approximate limits.**

Resource Planning Guide

Chapter Resources

- Complete Solutions Guide

Workbooks

- Notetaking Guide
- Student Solutions Guide

Interactive Technology

- Instructor Success Organizer
- Notetaking Guide IAE
- Instructional DVDs
- Animated Precalculus
- PowerLecture with ExamView

3 TEACH

Extra Example 1

Find the limit: $\lim_{x \to 2} \frac{x^2 + 2x - 8}{x - 2}$.

6

Extra Example 2

Find the limit:

$\lim_{x \to 2} \frac{x - 2}{x^3 - 2x^2 + 2x - 4}$.

$\frac{1}{6}$

The validity of the dividing out technique stems from the fact that if two functions agree at all but a single number c, they must have identical limit behavior at $x = c$. In Example 1, the functions given by

$$f(x) = \frac{x^2 + x - 6}{x + 3} \quad \text{and} \quad g(x) = x - 2$$

agree at all values of x other than $x = -3$. So, you can use $g(x)$ to find the limit of $f(x)$.

Example 2 Dividing Out Technique

Find the limit.

$$\lim_{x \to 1} \frac{x - 1}{x^3 - x^2 + x - 1}$$

Solution

Begin by substituting $x = 1$ into the numerator and denominator.

$$1 - 1 = 0 \qquad \text{Numerator is 0 when } x = 1.$$

$$1^3 - 1^2 + 1 - 1 = 0 \qquad \text{Denominator is 0 when } x = 1.$$

Because both the numerator and denominator are zero when $x = 1$, direct substitution will not yield the limit. To find the limit, you should factor the numerator and denominator, divide out any common factors, and then try direct substitution again.

$$\lim_{x \to 1} \frac{x - 1}{x^3 - x^2 + x - 1} = \lim_{x \to 1} \frac{x - 1}{(x - 1)(x^2 + 1)} \qquad \text{Factor denominator.}$$

$$= \lim_{x \to 1} \frac{\cancel{x - 1}}{\cancel{(x - 1)}(x^2 + 1)} \qquad \text{Divide out common factor.}$$

$$= \lim_{x \to 1} \frac{1}{x^2 + 1} \qquad \text{Simplify.}$$

$$= \frac{1}{1^2 + 1} \qquad \text{Direct substitution}$$

$$= \frac{1}{2} \qquad \text{Simplify.}$$

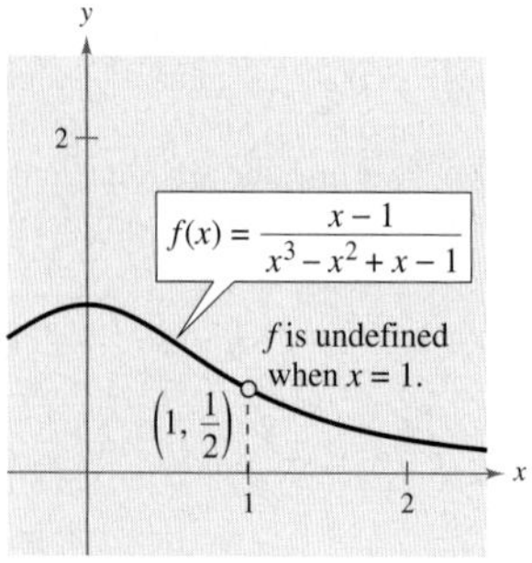

FIGURE 12.11

This result is shown graphically in Figure 12.11.

CHECK Point Now try Exercise 15.

In Example 2, the factorization of the denominator can be obtained by dividing by $(x - 1)$ or by grouping as follows.

$$x^3 - x^2 + x - 1 = x^2(x - 1) + (x - 1)$$

$$= (x - 1)(x^2 + 1)$$

Differentiated Instruction

Auditory Learners Have students work in pairs. One partner will be an auditory learner and the other will not. Instruct partners to work through Example 2 in the following way: the partner who is not an auditory learner will describe the process of dividing out to find the limit. The auditory learner will follow his or her partner's instructions to find the limit. Students may switch roles for Example 3 on page 863.

Rationalizing Technique

Another way to find the limits of some functions is first to rationalize the numerator of the function. This is called the **rationalizing technique.** Recall that rationalizing the numerator means multiplying the numerator and denominator by the conjugate of the numerator. For instance, the conjugate of $\sqrt{x} + 4$ is $\sqrt{x} - 4$.

Algebra Help

You can review the techniques for rationalizing numerators and denominators in Appendix A.2.

Example 3 Rationalizing Technique

Find the limit: $\lim_{x \to 0} \dfrac{\sqrt{x+1} - 1}{x}$.

Solution

By direct substitution, you obtain the indeterminate form $\frac{0}{0}$.

$$\lim_{x \to 0} \frac{\sqrt{x+1} - 1}{x} = \frac{\sqrt{0+1} - 1}{0} = \frac{0}{0} \qquad \text{Indeterminate form}$$

In this case, you can rewrite the fraction by rationalizing the numerator.

$$\frac{\sqrt{x+1} - 1}{x} = \left(\frac{\sqrt{x+1} - 1}{x}\right)\left(\frac{\sqrt{x+1} + 1}{\sqrt{x+1} + 1}\right)$$

$$= \frac{(x+1) - 1}{x(\sqrt{x+1} + 1)} \qquad \text{Multiply.}$$

$$= \frac{x}{x(\sqrt{x+1} + 1)} \qquad \text{Simplify.}$$

$$= \frac{\cancel{x}}{\cancel{x}(\sqrt{x+1} + 1)} \qquad \text{Divide out common factor.}$$

$$= \frac{1}{\sqrt{x+1} + 1}, \quad x \neq 0 \qquad \text{Simplify.}$$

Now you can evaluate the limit by direct substitution.

$$\lim_{x \to 0} \frac{\sqrt{x+1} - 1}{x} = \lim_{x \to 0} \frac{1}{\sqrt{x+1} + 1} = \frac{1}{\sqrt{0+1} + 1} = \frac{1}{1+1} = \frac{1}{2}$$

You can reinforce your conclusion that the limit is $\frac{1}{2}$ by constructing a table, as shown below, or by sketching a graph, as shown in Figure 12.12.

x	-0.1	-0.01	-0.001	0	0.001	0.01	0.1
$f(x)$	0.5132	0.5013	0.5001	?	0.4999	0.4988	0.4881

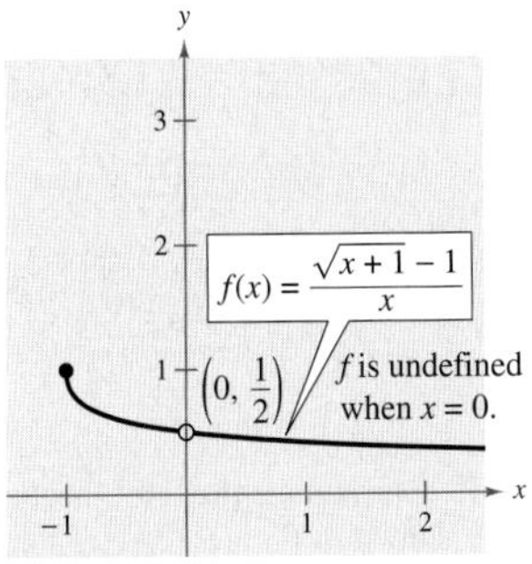

FIGURE 12.12

CHECKPoint Now try Exercise 25.

The rationalizing technique for evaluating limits is based on multiplication by a convenient form of 1. In Example 3, the convenient form is

$$1 = \frac{\sqrt{x+1} + 1}{\sqrt{x+1} + 1}.$$

Extra Example 3

Find the limit: $\lim_{x \to 0} \dfrac{\sqrt{x+9} - 3}{x}$.

$\frac{1}{6}$

Extra Example 4

Approximate the limit:

$$\lim_{x \to -1} \frac{x^2 - 4x - 5}{x + 1}.$$

X	Y_1	
−1.003	−6.003	
−1.002	−6.002	
−1.001	−6.001	
−1	ERROR	
−.999	−5.999	
−.998	−5.998	
−.997	−5.997	
X = −1		

The table indicates that the limit as x approaches −1 is −6.

Extra Example 5

Approximate the limit:

$$\lim_{x \to 0} \frac{1 - \cos x}{x}.$$

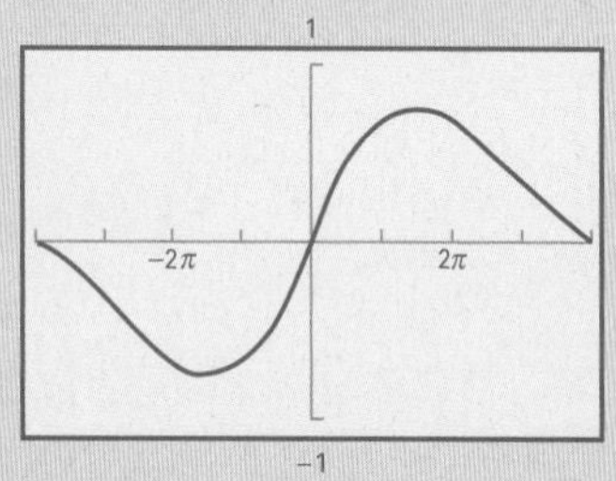

The graph indicates that the limit as x approaches 0 is 0.

Using Technology

The dividing out and rationalizing techniques may not work well for finding limits of nonalgebraic functions. You often need to use more sophisticated analytic techniques to find limits of these types of functions.

Example 4 Approximating a Limit

Approximate the limit: $\lim\limits_{x \to 0} (1 + x)^{1/x}$.

Numerical Solution

Let $f(x) = (1 + x)^{1/x}$. Because you are finding the limit when $x = 0$, use the *table* feature of a graphing utility to create a table that shows the values of f for x starting at $x = -0.01$ and has a step of 0.001, as shown in Figure 12.13. Because 0 is halfway between −0.001 and 0.001, use the average of the values of f at these two x-coordinates to estimate the limit, as follows.

$$\lim_{x \to 0} (1 + x)^{1/x} \approx \frac{2.7196 + 2.7169}{2} = 2.71825$$

The actual limit can be found algebraically to be $e \approx 2.71828$.

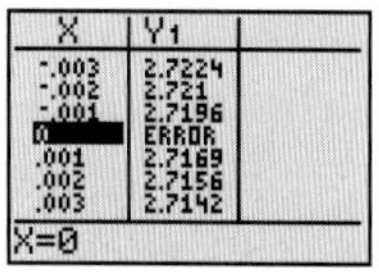

FIGURE 12.13

CHECK Point Now try Exercise 37.

Graphical Solution

To approximate the limit graphically, graph the function $f(x) = (1 + x)^{1/x}$, as shown in Figure 12.14. Using the *zoom* and *trace* features of the graphing utility, choose two points on the graph of f, such as

$$(-0.00017, 2.7185) \quad \text{and} \quad (0.00017, 2.7181)$$

as shown in Figure 12.15. Because the x-coordinates of these two points are equidistant from 0, you can approximate the limit to be the average of the y-coordinates. That is,

$$\lim_{x \to 0} (1 + x)^{1/x} \approx \frac{2.7185 + 2.7181}{2} = 2.7183.$$

The actual limit can be found algebraically to be $e \approx 2.71828$.

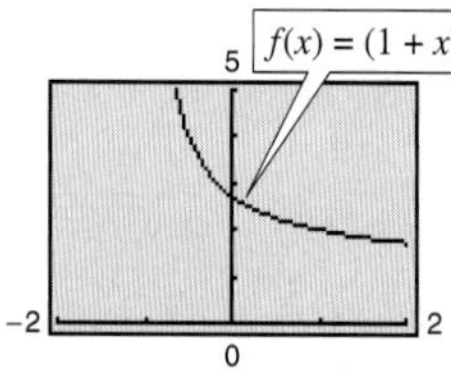

FIGURE 12.14

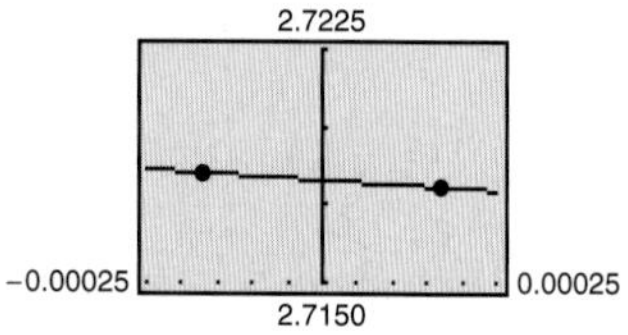

FIGURE 12.15

Example 5 Approximating a Limit Graphically

Approximate the limit: $\lim\limits_{x \to 0} \dfrac{\sin x}{x}$.

Solution

Direct substitution produces the indeterminate form $\frac{0}{0}$. To approximate the limit, begin by using a graphing utility to graph $f(x) = (\sin x)/x$, as shown in Figure 12.16. Then use the *zoom* and *trace* features of the graphing utility to choose a point on each side of 0, such as $(-0.0012467, 0.9999997)$ and $(0.0012467, 0.9999997)$. Finally, approximate the limit as the average of the y-coordinates of these two points, $\lim\limits_{x \to 0} (\sin x)/x \approx 0.9999997$. It can be shown algebraically that this limit is exactly 1.

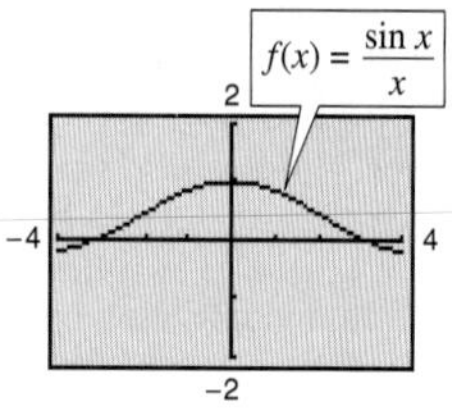

FIGURE 12.16

CHECK Point Now try Exercise 41.

TECHNOLOGY

The graphs shown in Figures 12.14 and 12.16 appear to be continuous at $x = 0$. However, when you try to use the *trace* or the *value* feature of a graphing utility to determine the value of y when $x = 0$, no value is given. Some graphing utilities can show breaks or holes in a graph when an appropriate viewing window is used. Because the holes in the graphs in Figures 12.14 and 12.16 occur on the y-axis, the holes are not visible.

One-Sided Limits

In Section 12.1, you saw that one way in which a limit can fail to exist is when a function approaches a different value from the left side of c than it approaches from the right side of c. This type of behavior can be described more concisely with the concept of a **one-sided limit.**

$$\lim_{x \to c^-} f(x) = L_1 \text{ or } f(x) \to L_1 \text{ as } x \to c^- \qquad \text{Limit from the left}$$

$$\lim_{x \to c^+} f(x) = L_2 \text{ or } f(x) \to L_2 \text{ as } x \to c^+ \qquad \text{Limit from the right}$$

Example 6 Evaluating One-Sided Limits

Find the limit as $x \to 0$ from the left and the limit as $x \to 0$ from the right for

$$f(x) = \frac{|2x|}{x}.$$

Solution

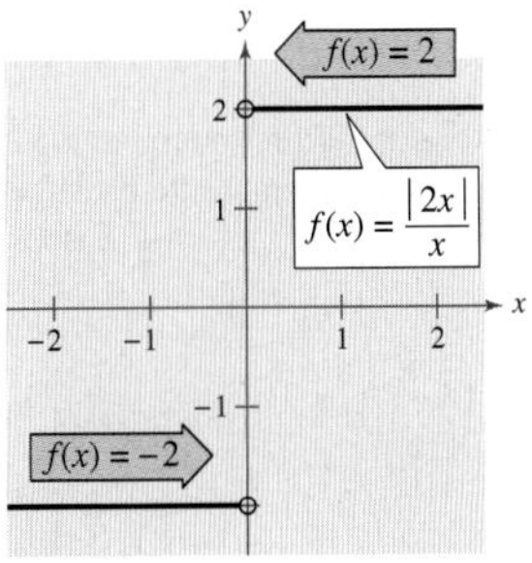

FIGURE 12.17

From the graph of f, shown in Figure 12.17, you can see that $f(x) = -2$ for all $x < 0$. Therefore, the limit from the left is

$$\lim_{x \to 0^-} \frac{|2x|}{x} = -2. \qquad \text{Limit from the left: } f(x) \to -2 \text{ as } x \to 0^-$$

Because $f(x) = 2$ for all $x > 0$, the limit from the right is

$$\lim_{x \to 0^+} \frac{|2x|}{x} = 2. \qquad \text{Limit from the right: } f(x) \to 2 \text{ as } x \to 0^+$$

CHECKPoint Now try Exercise 55.

In Example 6, note that the function approaches different limits from the left and from the right. In such cases, the limit of $f(x)$ as $x \to c$ does not exist. For the limit of a function to exist as $x \to c$, it must be true that both one-sided limits exist and are equal.

Existence of a Limit

If f is a function and c and L are real numbers, then

$$\lim_{x \to c} f(x) = L$$

if and only if both the left and right limits *exist* and are *equal* to L.

Extra Example 6

Find the limit as $x \to 0$ from the left and the limit as $x \to 0$ from the right for $f(x) = \dfrac{|x|}{4x}$.

$$\lim_{x \to 0^-} \frac{|x|}{4x} = -\frac{1}{4}; \quad \lim_{x \to 0^+} \frac{|x|}{4x} = \frac{1}{4}$$

Example 7 Finding One-Sided Limits

Find the limit of $f(x)$ as x approaches 1.

$$f(x) = \begin{cases} 4 - x, & x < 1 \\ 4x - x^2, & x > 1 \end{cases}$$

Solution

Remember that you are concerned about the value of f *near* $x = 1$ rather than *at* $x = 1$. So, for $x < 1$, $f(x)$ is given by $4 - x$, and you can use direct substitution to obtain

$$\lim_{x \to 1^-} f(x) = \lim_{x \to 1^-} (4 - x) = 4 - 1 = 3.$$

For $x > 1$, $f(x)$ is given by $4x - x^2$, and you can use direct substitution to obtain

$$\lim_{x \to 1^+} f(x) = \lim_{x \to 1^+} (4x - x^2) = 4(1) - 1^2 = 3.$$

Because the one-sided limits both exist and are equal to 3, it follows that

$$\lim_{x \to 1} f(x) = 3.$$

The graph in Figure 12.18 confirms this conclusion.

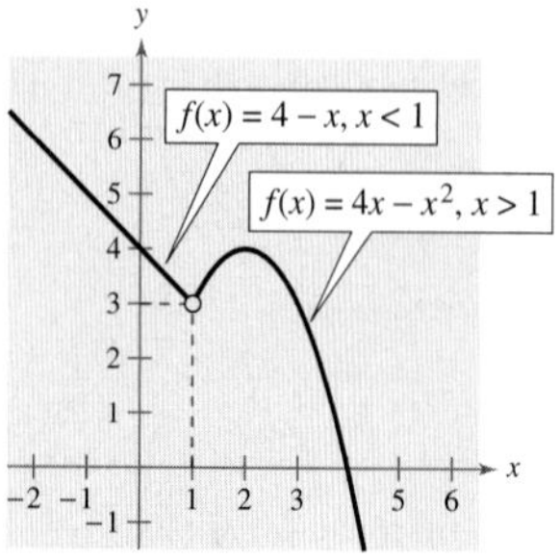

FIGURE 12.18

CHECKPoint Now try Exercise 59.

Example 8 Comparing Limits from the Left and Right

To ship a package overnight, a delivery service charges \$18 for the first pound and \$2 for each additional pound or portion of a pound. Let x represent the weight of a package and let $f(x)$ represent the shipping cost. Show that the limit of $f(x)$ as $x \to 2$ does not exist.

$$f(x) = \begin{cases} \$18, & 0 < x \le 1 \\ \$20, & 1 < x \le 2 \\ \$22, & 2 < x \le 3 \end{cases}$$

Solution

The graph of f is shown in Figure 12.19. The limit of $f(x)$ as x approaches 2 from the left is

$$\lim_{x \to 2^-} f(x) = 20$$

whereas the limit of $f(x)$ as x approaches 2 from the right is

$$\lim_{x \to 2^+} f(x) = 22.$$

Because these one-sided limits are not equal, the limit of $f(x)$ as $x \to 2$ does not exist.

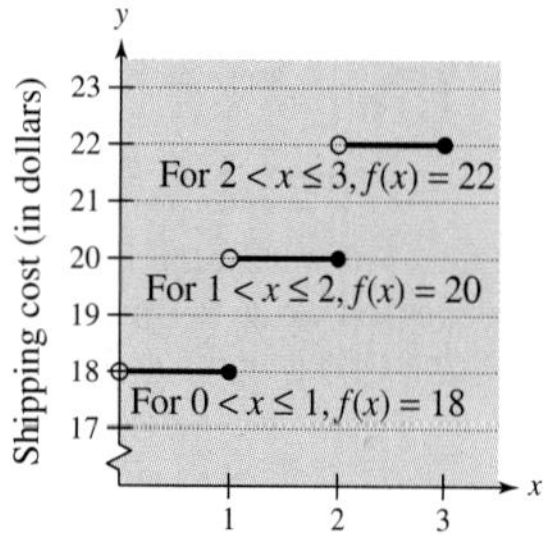

FIGURE 12.19

CHECKPoint Now try Exercise 81.

Extra Example 7

Find the limit of $f(x)$ as x approaches 2.

$$f(x) = \begin{cases} x^2 + 1, & x < 2 \\ -\frac{1}{2}x + 6, & x > 2 \end{cases}$$

$$\lim_{x \to 2} f(x) = 5$$

Extra Example 8

To ship a package overnight, a delivery service charges \$9 for the first pound and \$1 for each additional pound or portion of a pound. Let x represent the weight of the package and let $f(x)$ represent the shipping cost. Show that the limit of $f(x)$ as x approaches 3 does not exist.

$$f(x) = \begin{cases} 9, & 0 < x \le 1 \\ 10, & 1 < x \le 2 \\ 11, & 2 < x \le 3 \\ 12, & 3 < x \le 4 \end{cases}$$

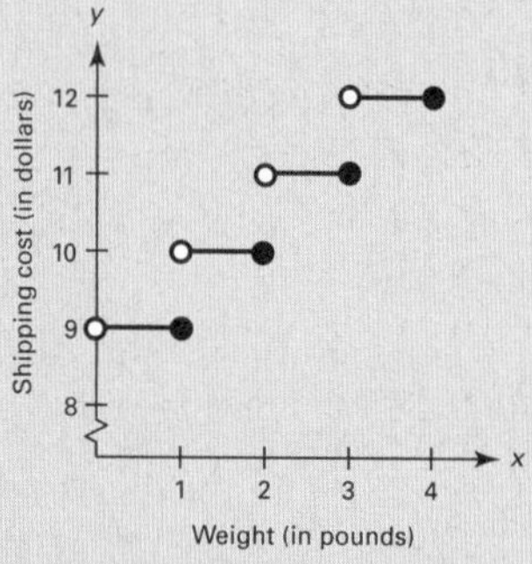

Because $\lim_{x \to 3^-} f(x) = 11$ and $\lim_{x \to 3^+} f(x) = 12$ are not equal, the limit of $f(x)$ as x approaches 3 does not exist.

A Limit from Calculus

In the next section, you will study an important type of limit from calculus—the limit of a **difference quotient.**

Example 9 Evaluating a Limit from Calculus

For the function given by $f(x) = x^2 - 1$, find

$$\lim_{h \to 0} \frac{f(3 + h) - f(3)}{h}.$$

Solution

Direct substitution produces an indeterminate form.

$$\lim_{h \to 0} \frac{f(3 + h) - f(3)}{h} = \lim_{h \to 0} \frac{[(3 + h)^2 - 1] - [(3)^2 - 1]}{h}$$
$$= \lim_{h \to 0} \frac{9 + 6h + h^2 - 1 - 9 + 1}{h}$$
$$= \lim_{h \to 0} \frac{6h + h^2}{h}$$
$$= \frac{0}{0}$$

By factoring and dividing out, you obtain the following.

$$\lim_{h \to 0} \frac{f(3 + h) - f(3)}{h} = \lim_{h \to 0} \frac{6h + h^2}{h} = \lim_{h \to 0} \frac{\cancel{h}(6 + h)}{\cancel{h}}$$
$$= \lim_{h \to 0} (6 + h)$$
$$= 6 + 0$$
$$= 6$$

So, the limit is 6.

CHECKPoint Now try Exercise 75.

Note that for any x-value, the limit of a difference quotient is an expression of the form

$$\lim_{h \to 0} \frac{f(x + h) - f(x)}{h}.$$

Direct substitution into the difference quotient always produces the indeterminate form $\frac{0}{0}$. For instance,

$$\lim_{h \to 0} \frac{f(x + h) - f(x)}{h} = \frac{f(x + 0) - f(x)}{0}$$
$$= \frac{f(x) - f(x)}{0}$$
$$= \frac{0}{0}.$$

Algebra Help

For a review of evaluating difference quotients, refer to Section 1.4.

Extra Example 9

For the function given by $f(x) = 2x^2 + 1$, find

$$\lim_{h \to 0} \frac{f(2 + h) - f(2)}{h}.$$

8

Closing the Lesson

Have students summarize the major points of the lesson and answer the Essential Question: How do you evaluate limits that cannot be solved through use of direct substitution?

- **Find the limit as x approaches c of a rational function by factoring its numerator and denominator, dividing out the common factors, and evaluating the resulting function at $x = c$.**
- **Find the limit as x approaches c of a function containing an irrational number in its numerator by multiplying its numerator and denominator by the conjugate of the numerator and evaluating the result at $x = c$.**
- **Use a graphing utility to find the limit as x approaches c of a function by zooming and tracing the graph to find the value of the function to the left and right of $x = c$.**
- **Find the one-sided limit of a function by evaluating the limit as x approaches c from either the left or the right.**

4 PRACTICE AND APPLY

Assignment Guide

Transparencies Available
Available at the Instructor's companion site.

Average:
Day 1: pp. 868–869
Exs. 1, 2, 5–9 odd, 12, 17–23 odd, 27–39 odd, 43–47 odd
Day 2: pp. 868–870
Exs. 3, 4, 49, 53, 56, 57, 60, 63–73 odd, 77, 79, 82, 84–88

Advanced:
Day 1: pp. 868–869
Exs. 1, 2, 6–12 even, 18–24 even, 28–40 even, 44–48 even
Day 2: pp. 868–870
Exs. 3, 4, 50–56 even, 60–72 even, 76, 80, 82–84, 86–89

Block:
pp. 868–869
Exs. 1, 2, 5–9 odd, 12, 17–23 odd, 27–39 odd, 43–47 odd (with 12.1)
pp. 868–870
Exs. 3, 4, 49, 53, 56, 57, 60, 63–73 odd, 77, 79, 82, 84–88 (with 12.3)

21. $\frac{\sqrt{5}}{10}$

22. $-\frac{\sqrt{7}}{14}$

23. $\frac{\sqrt{3}}{6}$

12.2 EXERCISES

See www.CalcChat.com for worked-out solutions to odd-numbered exercises.

VOCABULARY: Fill in the blanks.

1. To evaluate the limit of a rational function that has common factors in its numerator and denominator, use the dividing out technique.
2. The fraction $\frac{0}{0}$ has no meaning as a real number and therefore is called an indeterminate form.
3. The limit $\lim_{x\to c^-} f(x) = L_1$ is an example of a one-sided limit.
4. The limit of a difference quotient is an expression of the form $\lim_{h\to 0} \frac{f(x+h)-f(x)}{h}$.

SKILLS AND APPLICATIONS

In Exercises 5–8, use the graph to determine each limit visually (if it exists). Then identify another function that agrees with the given function at all but one point.

5. $g(x) = \dfrac{-2x^2 + x}{x}$

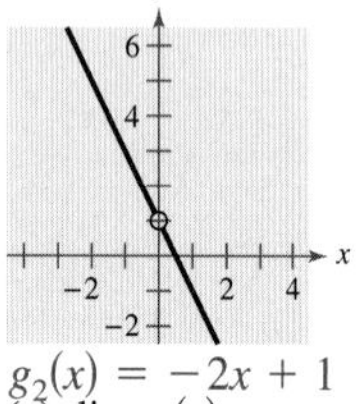

$g_2(x) = -2x + 1$

(a) $\lim_{x\to 0} g(x)$ 1
(b) $\lim_{x\to -1} g(x)$ 3
(c) $\lim_{x\to -2} g(x)$ 5

6. $h(x) = \dfrac{x^2 - 3x}{x}$

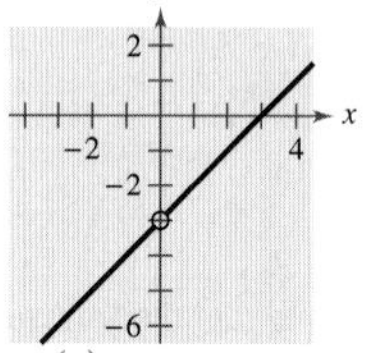

$h_2(x) = x - 3$

(a) $\lim_{x\to -2} h(x)$ -5
(b) $\lim_{x\to 0} h(x)$ -3
(c) $\lim_{x\to 3} h(x)$ 0

7. $g(x) = \dfrac{x^3 - x}{x - 1}$

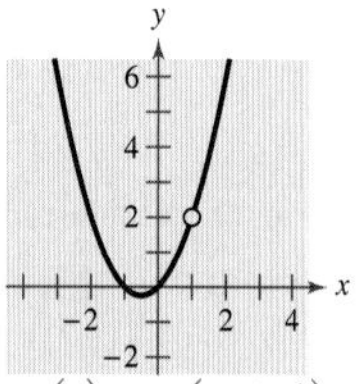

$g_2(x) = x(x + 1)$

(a) $\lim_{x\to 1} g(x)$ 2
(b) $\lim_{x\to -1} g(x)$ 0
(c) $\lim_{x\to 0} g(x)$ 0

8. $f(x) = \dfrac{x^2 - 1}{x + 1}$

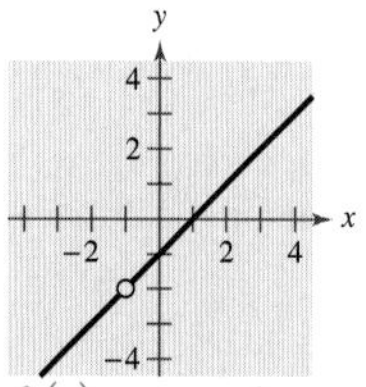

$f_2(x) = x - 1$

(a) $\lim_{x\to 1} f(x)$ 0
(b) $\lim_{x\to 2} f(x)$ 1
(c) $\lim_{x\to -1} f(x)$ -2

In Exercises 9–36, find the limit (if it exists). Use a graphing utility to verify your result graphically.

9. $\lim_{x\to 6} \dfrac{x - 6}{x^2 - 36}$ $\frac{1}{12}$
10. $\lim_{x\to 7} \dfrac{7 - x}{x^2 - 49}$ $-\frac{1}{14}$
11. $\lim_{x\to 1} \dfrac{x^2 + 2x - 3}{x - 1}$ 4
12. $\lim_{x\to -2} \dfrac{x^2 + 6x + 8}{x + 2}$ 2
13. $\lim_{x\to -1} \dfrac{1 - 2x - 3x^2}{1 + x}$ 4
14. $\lim_{x\to -3} \dfrac{2x^2 + 5x - 3}{x + 3}$ -7
15. $\lim_{t\to 2} \dfrac{t^3 - 8}{t - 2}$ 12
16. $\lim_{a\to -4} \dfrac{a^3 + 64}{a + 4}$ 48
17. $\lim_{x\to 2} \dfrac{x^5 - 32}{x - 2}$ 80
18. $\lim_{x\to 1} \dfrac{x^4 - 1}{x - 1}$ 4
19. $\lim_{x\to 1} \dfrac{x^2 + x - 2}{x^2 - 3x + 2}$ -3
20. $\lim_{x\to 4} \dfrac{x^2 - 2x - 8}{x^2 - 3x - 4}$ $\frac{6}{5}$

21–23. See margin.

21. $\lim_{y\to 0} \dfrac{\sqrt{5 + y} - \sqrt{5}}{y}$
22. $\lim_{z\to 0} \dfrac{\sqrt{7 - z} - \sqrt{7}}{z}$
23. $\lim_{x\to 0} \dfrac{\sqrt{x + 3} - \sqrt{3}}{x}$
24. $\lim_{x\to 0} \dfrac{\sqrt{x + 4} - 2}{x}$ $\frac{1}{4}$
25. $\lim_{x\to 0} \dfrac{\sqrt{2x + 1} - 1}{x}$ 1
26. $\lim_{x\to 9} \dfrac{3 - \sqrt{x}}{x - 9}$ $-\frac{1}{6}$
27. $\lim_{x\to -3} \dfrac{\sqrt{x + 7} - 2}{x + 3}$ $\frac{1}{4}$
28. $\lim_{x\to 2} \dfrac{4 - \sqrt{18 - x}}{x - 2}$ $\frac{1}{8}$
29. $\lim_{x\to 0} \dfrac{\frac{1}{x + 1} - 1}{x}$ -1
30. $\lim_{x\to 0} \dfrac{\frac{1}{x - 8} + \frac{1}{8}}{x}$ $-\frac{1}{64}$
31. $\lim_{x\to 0} \dfrac{\frac{1}{x + 4} - \frac{1}{4}}{x}$ $-\frac{1}{16}$
32. $\lim_{x\to 0} \dfrac{\frac{1}{2 + x} - \frac{1}{2}}{x}$ $-\frac{1}{4}$
33. $\lim_{x\to 0} \dfrac{\sec x}{\tan x}$ Does not exist
34. $\lim_{x\to \pi} \dfrac{\csc x}{\cot x}$ -1
35. $\lim_{x\to \pi/2} \dfrac{1 - \sin x}{\cos x}$ 0
36. $\lim_{x\to \pi/2} \dfrac{\cos x - 1}{\sin x}$ -1

In Exercises 37–48, use a graphing utility to graph the function and approximate the limit accurate to three decimal places. 37–48. See margin.

37. $\lim\limits_{x \to 0} \dfrac{e^{2x} - 1}{x}$

38. $\lim\limits_{x \to 0} \dfrac{1 - e^{-x}}{x}$

39. $\lim\limits_{x \to 0^+} (x \ln x)$

40. $\lim\limits_{x \to 0^+} (x^2 \ln x)$

41. $\lim\limits_{x \to 0} \dfrac{\sin 2x}{x}$

42. $\lim\limits_{x \to 0} \dfrac{\sin 3x}{x}$

43. $\lim\limits_{x \to 0} \dfrac{\tan x}{x}$

44. $\lim\limits_{x \to 0} \dfrac{1 - \cos 2x}{x}$

45. $\lim\limits_{x \to 1} \dfrac{1 - \sqrt[3]{x}}{1 - x}$

46. $\lim\limits_{x \to 1} \dfrac{\sqrt[3]{x} - x}{x - 1}$

47. $\lim\limits_{x \to 0} (1 - x)^{2/x}$

48. $\lim\limits_{x \to 0} (1 + 2x)^{1/x}$

GRAPHICAL, NUMERICAL, AND ALGEBRAIC ANALYSIS In Exercises 49–54, (a) graphically approximate the limit (if it exists) by using a graphing utility to graph the function, (b) numerically approximate the limit (if it exists) by using the *table* feature of a graphing utility to create a table, and (c) algebraically evaluate the limit (if it exists) by the appropriate technique(s). 49–54. See margin.

49. $\lim\limits_{x \to 1^-} \dfrac{x - 1}{x^2 - 1}$

50. $\lim\limits_{x \to 5^+} \dfrac{5 - x}{25 - x^2}$

51. $\lim\limits_{x \to 2} \dfrac{x^4 - 1}{x^4 - 3x^2 - 4}$

52. $\lim\limits_{x \to 2} \dfrac{x^4 - 2x^2 - 8}{x^4 - 6x^2 + 8}$

53. $\lim\limits_{x \to 16^+} \dfrac{4 - \sqrt{x}}{x - 16}$

54. $\lim\limits_{x \to 0^-} \dfrac{\sqrt{x + 2} - \sqrt{2}}{x}$

In Exercises 55–62, graph the function. Determine the limit (if it exists) by evaluating the corresponding one-sided limits. 55–62. See margin.

55. $\lim\limits_{x \to 6} \dfrac{|x - 6|}{x - 6}$

56. $\lim\limits_{x \to 2} \dfrac{|x - 2|}{x - 2}$

57. $\lim\limits_{x \to 1} \dfrac{1}{x^2 + 1}$

58. $\lim\limits_{x \to 1} \dfrac{1}{x^2 - 1}$

59. $\lim\limits_{x \to 2} f(x)$ where $f(x) = \begin{cases} x - 1, & x \le 2 \\ 2x - 3, & x > 2 \end{cases}$

60. $\lim\limits_{x \to 1} f(x)$ where $f(x) = \begin{cases} 2x + 1, & x < 1 \\ 4 - x^2, & x \ge 1 \end{cases}$

61. $\lim\limits_{x \to 1} f(x)$ where $f(x) = \begin{cases} 4 - x^2, & x \le 1 \\ 3 - x, & x > 1 \end{cases}$

62. $\lim\limits_{x \to 0} f(x)$ where $f(x) = \begin{cases} 4 - x^2, & x \le 0 \\ x + 4, & x > 0 \end{cases}$

In Exercises 63–68, use a graphing utility to graph the function and the equations $y = x$ and $y = -x$ in the same viewing window. Use the graph to find $\lim\limits_{x \to 0} f(x)$. 63–68. See margin.

63. $f(x) = x \cos x$

64. $f(x) = |x \sin x|$

65. $f(x) = |x| \sin x$

66. $f(x) = |x| \cos x$

67. $f(x) = x \sin \dfrac{1}{x}$

68. $f(x) = x \cos \dfrac{1}{x}$

In Exercises 69 and 70, state which limit can be evaluated by using direct substitution. Then evaluate or approximate each limit.

69. (a) $\lim\limits_{x \to 0} x^2 \sin x^2$ (b) $\lim\limits_{x \to 0} \dfrac{\sin x^2}{x^2}$ Limit (a) can be evaluated by direct substitution. (a) 0 (b) 1

70. (a) $\lim\limits_{x \to 0} \dfrac{x}{\cos x}$ (b) $\lim\limits_{x \to 0} \dfrac{1 - \cos x}{x}$ Limit (a) can be evaluated by direct substitution. (a) 0 (b) 0

In Exercises 71–78, find $\lim\limits_{h \to 0} \dfrac{f(x + h) - f(x)}{h}$.

71. $f(x) = 2x + 1$ 2

72. $f(x) = 3 - 4x$ -4

73. $f(x) = \sqrt{x}$

74. $f(x) = \sqrt{x - 2}$

73. $\dfrac{1}{2\sqrt{x}}$ 74. $\dfrac{1}{2\sqrt{x - 2}}$

75. $f(x) = x^2 - 3x$ $2x - 3$

76. $f(x) = 4 - 2x - x^2$ $-2x - 2$

77. $f(x) = \dfrac{1}{x + 2}$ $-\dfrac{1}{(x + 2)^2}$

78. $f(x) = \dfrac{1}{x - 1}$ $-\dfrac{1}{(x - 1)^2}$

FREE-FALLING OBJECT In Exercises 79 and 80, use the position function

$s(t) = -16t^2 + 256$

which gives the height (in feet) of a free-falling object. The velocity at time $t = a$ seconds is given by $\lim\limits_{t \to a} [s(a) - s(t)]/(a - t)$.

79. Find the velocity when $t = 1$ second. -32 ft/sec

80. Find the velocity when $t = 2$ seconds. -64 ft/sec

37. 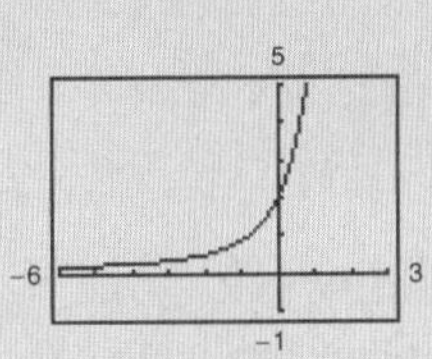

2.000

38. 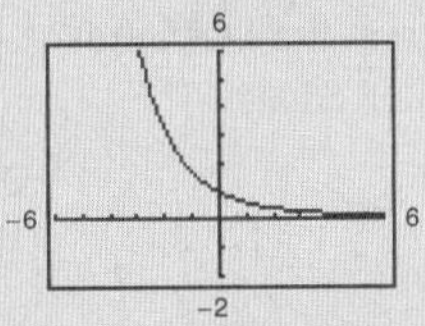

1.000

39. 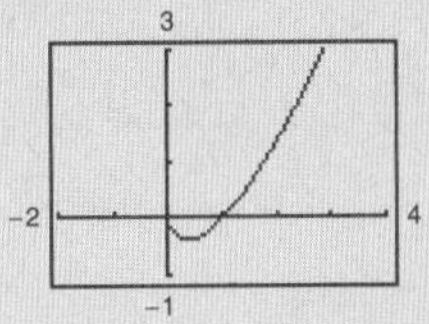

0

40. 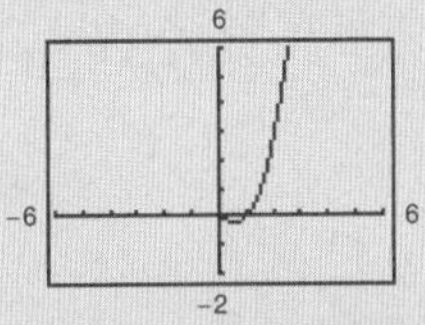

0

41. 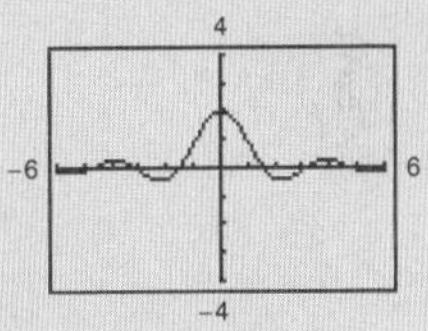

2.000

42. 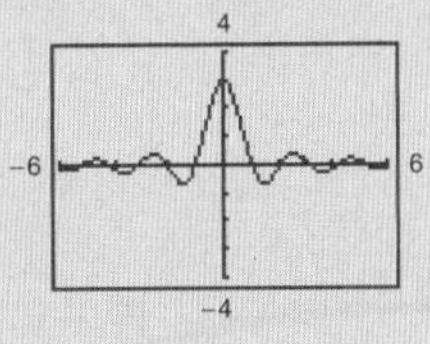

3.000

43. 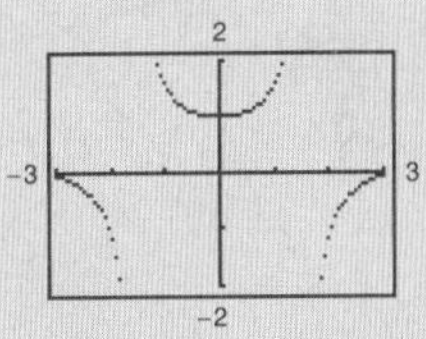

1.000

44. 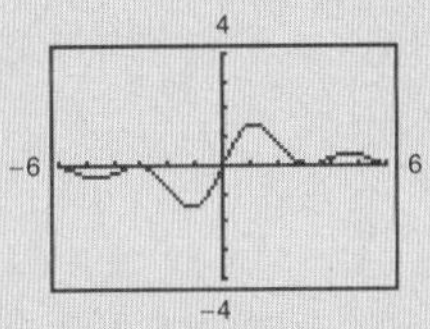

0

45. 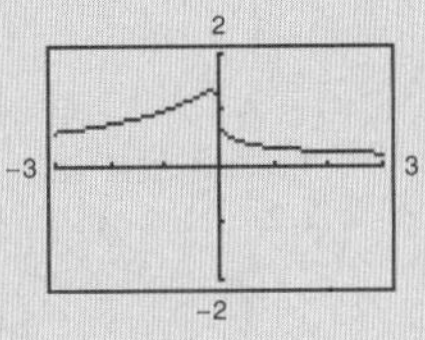

0.333

46. 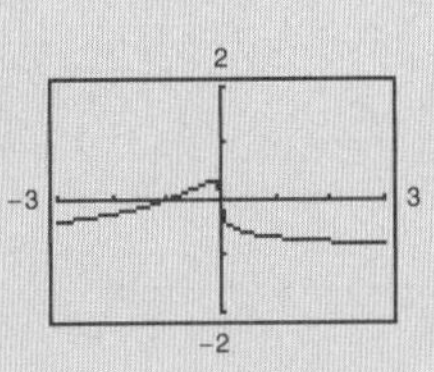

-0.667

47. 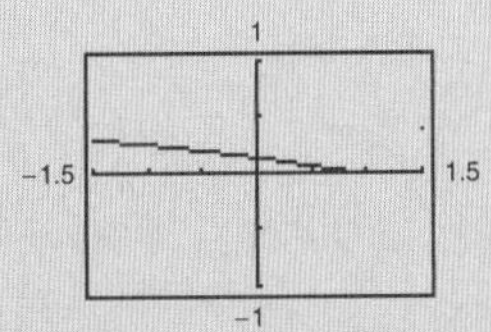

0.135

48. 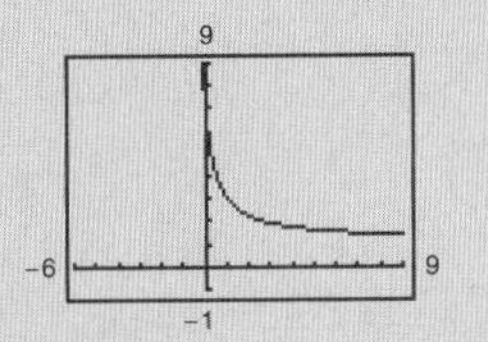

7.389

49. (a) 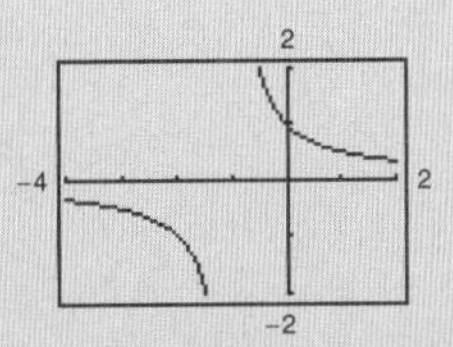

(b)

x	0.9	0.99	0.999	0.9999
$f(x)$	0.5263	0.5025	0.5003	0.50003

(c) $\lim\limits_{x \to 1^-} \dfrac{x - 1}{x^2 - 1} = 0.5$

50–68. See Additional Answers beginning on page AA1.

5 ASSESS AND RETEACH

Daily Homework Quiz

Transparency Available
Available at the Instructor's companion site.

83. (a)

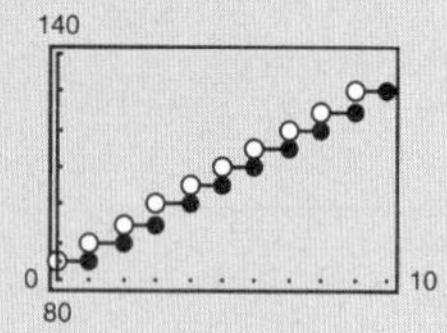

(b)–(c). See below.

84. (a)

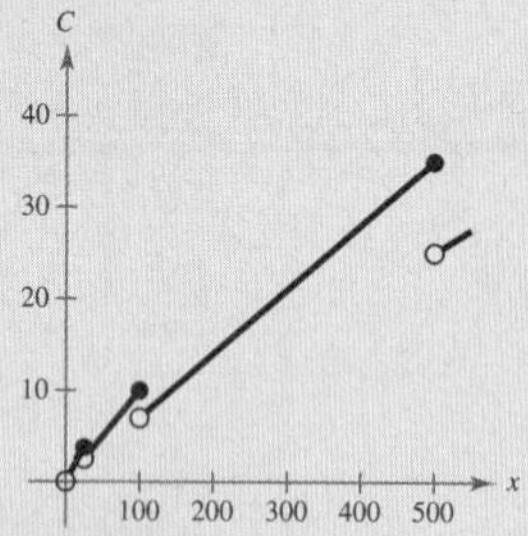

(b) (i) 2.25 (ii) 9.9 (iii) 21.35
(c) See below.
(d) The graph shows that the one-sided limits are not equal, which can be seen when the graph "jumps" at $x = 25$, 100, and 500.

86. False. Exercise 61 is a counterexample.

81. SALARY CONTRACT A union contract guarantees an 8% salary increase yearly for 3 years. For a current salary of \$30,000, the salaries $f(t)$ (in thousands of dollars) for the next 3 years are given by

$$f(t) = \begin{cases} 30.000, & 0 < t \le 1 \\ 32.400, & 1 < t \le 2 \\ 34.992, & 2 < t \le 3 \end{cases}$$

where t represents the time in years. Show that the limit of f as $t \to 2$ does not exist. Answers will vary.

82. CONSUMER AWARENESS The cost of sending a package overnight is \$15 for the first pound and \$1.30 for each additional pound or portion of a pound. A plastic mailing bag can hold up to 3 pounds. The cost $f(x)$ of sending a package in a plastic mailing bag is given by

$$f(x) = \begin{cases} 15.00, & 0 < x \le 1 \\ 16.30, & 1 < x \le 2 \\ 17.60, & 2 < x \le 3 \end{cases}$$

Answers will vary.

where x represents the weight of the package (in pounds). Show that the limit of f as $x \to 1$ does not exist.

83. CONSUMER AWARENESS The cost of hooking up and towing a car is \$85 for the first mile and \$5 for each additional mile or portion of a mile. A model for the cost C (in dollars) is $C(x) = 85 - 5[\![-(x - 1)]\!]$, where x is the distance in miles. (Recall from Section 1.6 that $f(x) = [\![x]\!]$ = the greatest integer less than or equal to x.)

(a) Use a graphing utility to graph C for $0 < x \le 10$.

(b) Complete the table and observe the behavior of C as x approaches 5.5. Use the graph from part (a) and the table to find $\lim_{x \to 5.5} C(x)$. (a)–(c). See margin.

x	5	5.3	5.4	5.5	5.6	5.7	6
C				?			

(c) Complete the table and observe the behavior of C as x approaches 5. Does the limit of $C(x)$ as x approaches 5 exist? Explain.

x	4	4.5	4.9	5	5.1	5.5	6
C				?			

84. CONSUMER AWARENESS The cost C (in dollars) of making x photocopies at a copy shop is given by the function

$$C(x) = \begin{cases} 0.15x, & 0 < x \le 25 \\ 0.10x, & 25 < x \le 100 \\ 0.07x, & 100 < x \le 500 \\ 0.05x, & x > 500 \end{cases}$$

See margin.

(a) Sketch a graph of the function.

(b) Find each limit and interpret your result in the context of the situation.

(i) $\lim_{x \to 15} C(x)$ (ii) $\lim_{x \to 99} C(x)$ (iii) $\lim_{x \to 305} C(x)$

(c) Create a table of values to show numerically that each limit does not exist.

(i) $\lim_{x \to 25} C(x)$ (ii) $\lim_{x \to 100} C(x)$ (iii) $\lim_{x \to 500} C(x)$

(d) Explain how you can use the graph in part (a) to verify that the limits in part (c) do not exist.

EXPLORATION

TRUE OR FALSE? In Exercises 85 and 86, determine whether the statement is true or false. Justify your answer.

85. When your attempt to find the limit of a rational function yields the indeterminate form $\frac{0}{0}$, the rational function's numerator and denominator have a common factor. True

86. If $f(c) = L$, then $\lim_{x \to c} f(x) = L$. See margin.

87. THINK ABOUT IT (a)–(b). Graphs will vary.

(a) Sketch the graph of a function for which $f(2)$ is defined but for which the limit of $f(x)$ as x approaches 2 does not exist.

(b) Sketch the graph of a function for which the limit of $f(x)$ as x approaches 1 is 4 but for which $f(1) \neq 4$.

88. CAPSTONE Given

$$f(x) = \begin{cases} 2x, & x \le 0 \\ x^2 + 1, & x > 0 \end{cases}$$

(c) Does not exist. Answers will vary.

find each of the following limits. If the limit does not exist, explain why.

(a) $\lim_{x \to 0^-} f(x)$ 0 (b) $\lim_{x \to 0^+} f(x)$ 1 (c) $\lim_{x \to 0} f(x)$

89. WRITING Consider the limit of the rational function given by $p(x)/q(x)$. What conclusion can you make if direct substitution produces each expression? Write a short paragraph explaining your reasoning. Answers will vary.

(a) $\lim_{x \to c} \frac{p(x)}{q(x)} = \frac{0}{1}$

(b) $\lim_{x \to c} \frac{p(x)}{q(x)} = \frac{1}{1}$

(c) $\lim_{x \to c} \frac{p(x)}{q(x)} = \frac{1}{0}$

(d) $\lim_{x \to c} \frac{p(x)}{q(x)} = \frac{0}{0}$

83. (b)

x	5	5.3	5.4	5.5	5.6	5.7	6
$C(x)$	105	110	110	110	110	110	110

$\lim_{x \to 5.5} C(x) = 110$

(c)

x	4	4.5	4.9	5	5.1	5.5	6
$C(x)$	100	105	105	105	110	110	110

The limit does not exist.

84. (c) Answers will vary.

x	24.99	24.999	25	25.001	25.01
$C(x)$	3.7485	3.74985	DNE	2.5001	2.501

x	99.99	99.999	100	100.001	100.01
$C(x)$	9.999	9.9999	DNE	7.00007	7.0007

x	499.99	499.999	500	500.001	500.01
$C(x)$	34.9993	34.99993	DNE	25.00005	25.0005

12.3 THE TANGENT LINE PROBLEM

What you should learn

- Use a tangent line to approximate the slope of a graph at a point.
- Use the limit definition of slope to find exact slopes of graphs.
- Find derivatives of functions and use derivatives to find slopes of graphs.

Why you should learn it

The slope of the graph of a function can be used to analyze rates of change at particular points on the graph. For instance, in Exercise 74 on page 880, the slope of the graph is used to analyze the rate of change in book sales for particular selling prices.

Bob Rowan, Progressive Image/Corbis

Tangent Line to a Graph

Calculus is a branch of mathematics that studies rates of change of functions. If you go on to take a course in calculus, you will learn that rates of change have many applications in real life.

Earlier in the text, you learned how the slope of a line indicates the rate at which a line rises or falls. For a line, this rate (or slope) is the same at every point on the line. For graphs other than lines, the rate at which the graph rises or falls changes from point to point. For instance, in Figure 12.20, the parabola is rising more quickly at the point (x_1, y_1) than it is at the point (x_2, y_2). At the vertex (x_3, y_3), the graph levels off, and at the point (x_4, y_4), the graph is falling.

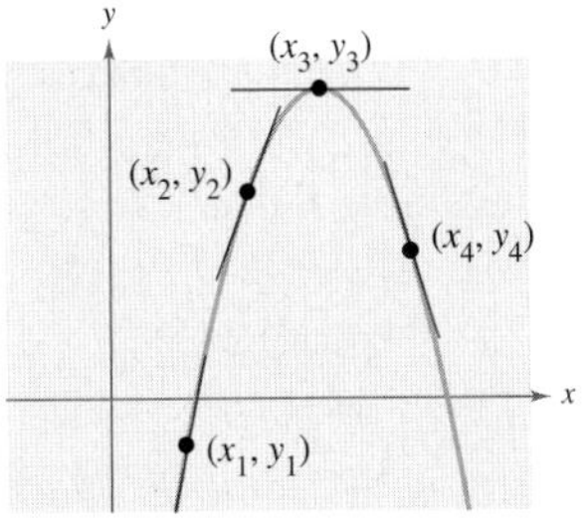

FIGURE 12.20

To determine the rate at which a graph rises or falls at a *single point*, you can find the slope of the tangent line at that point. In simple terms, the **tangent line** to the graph of a function f at a point $P(x_1, y_1)$ is the line that best approximates the slope of the graph at the point. Figure 12.21 shows other examples of tangent lines.

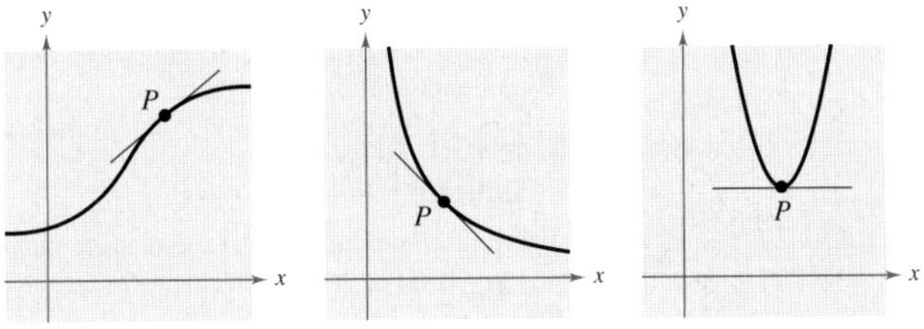

FIGURE 12.21

From geometry, you know that a line is tangent to a circle if the line intersects the circle at only one point. Tangent lines to noncircular graphs, however, can intersect the graph at more than one point. For instance, in the first graph in Figure 12.21, if the tangent line were extended, it would intersect the graph at a point other than the point of tangency.

1 PLAN AND PREPARE

Warm-up Exercises

Transparency Available
Available at the Instructor's companion site.

Notetaking Guide

Transparency Available
Promotes interactive learning and notetaking skills. Available at the Instructor's companion site.

Animated Precalculus

An **Animated Precalculus** tutorial is available at the Student companion site for **Section 12.3.**

Pacing

Average: 2 days
Advanced: 2 days
Block: 0.5 block with 12.2
0.5 block with 12.4

2 FOCUS AND MOTIVATE

Essential Question

How do you find the slope of a graph at any single point?
Tell students that they will learn how to answer this question by finding the slope of a tangent line that intersects the graph at a given point.

Resource Planning Guide

Chapter Resources

- Complete Solutions Guide

Workbooks

- Notetaking Guide
- Student Solutions Guide

Interactive Technology

- Instructor Success Organizer
- Notetaking Guide IAE
- Instructional DVDs
- Animated Precalculus
- PowerLecture with ExamView

3 TEACH

Extra Example 1

Use the figure to approximate the slope of the graph of $f(x) = x^3$ at the point (1, 1).

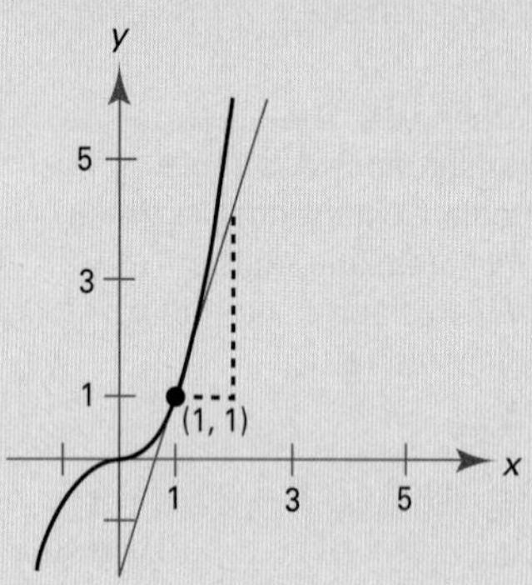

The graph of *f* has a slope of about 3 at (1, 1).

Extra Example 2

The graph below depicts the monthly normal temperature in a local city. Approximate the slope of the graph at the indicated point, and give a physical interpretation of the result.

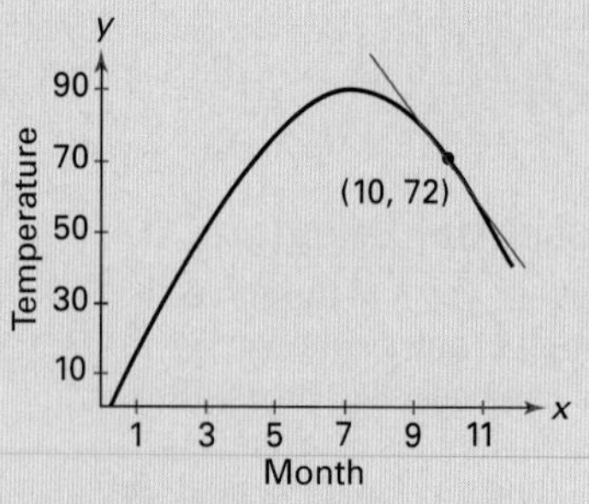

The graph indicates that the tangent line at the point has a slope of about −10 degrees per month. This means that you can expect the monthly normal temperature in November to be about 10 degrees lower than the normal temperature in October.

Slope of a Graph

Because a tangent line approximates the slope of the graph at a point, the problem of finding the slope of a graph at a point is the same as finding the slope of the tangent line at the point.

Example 1 Visually Approximating the Slope of a Graph

Use the graph in Figure 12.22 to approximate the slope of the graph of $f(x) = x^2$ at the point $(1, 1)$.

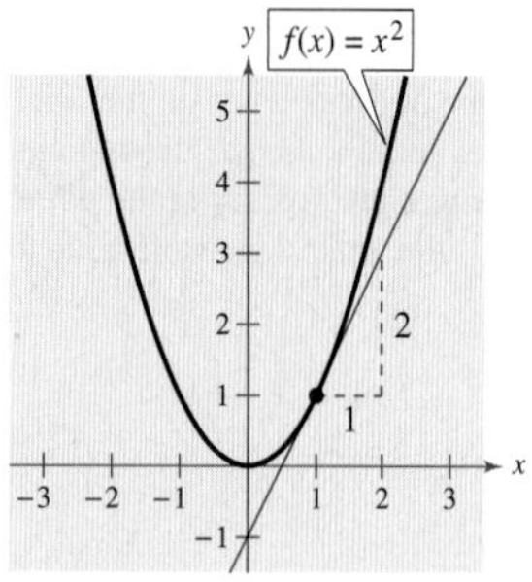

FIGURE 12.22

Solution

From the graph of $f(x) = x^2$, you can see that the tangent line at $(1, 1)$ rises approximately two units for each unit change in x. So, you can estimate the slope of the tangent line at $(1, 1)$ to be

$$\text{Slope} = \frac{\text{change in } y}{\text{change in } x} \approx \frac{2}{1} = 2.$$

Because the tangent line at the point $(1, 1)$ has a slope of about 2, you can conclude that the graph of f has a slope of about 2 at the point $(1, 1)$.

CHECKPoint Now try Exercise 5.

When you are visually approximating the slope of a graph, remember that the scales on the horizontal and vertical axes may differ. When this happens (as it frequently does in applications), the slope of the tangent line is distorted, and you must be careful to account for the difference in scales.

Example 2 Approximating the Slope of a Graph

Figure 12.23 graphically depicts the monthly normal temperatures (in degrees Fahrenheit) for Dallas, Texas. Approximate the slope of this graph at the indicated point and give a physical interpretation of the result. (Source: National Climatic Data Center)

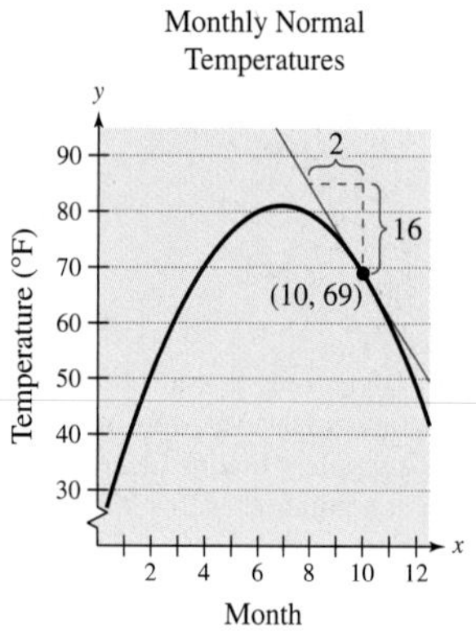

FIGURE 12.23

Solution

From the graph, you can see that the tangent line at the given point falls approximately 16 units for each two-unit change in x. So, you can estimate the slope at the given point to be

$$\text{Slope} = \frac{\text{change in } y}{\text{change in } x} \approx \frac{-16}{2} = -8 \text{ degrees per month.}$$

This means that you can expect the monthly normal temperature in November to be about 8 degrees lower than the normal temperature in October.

CHECKPoint Now try Exercise 7.

Slope and the Limit Process

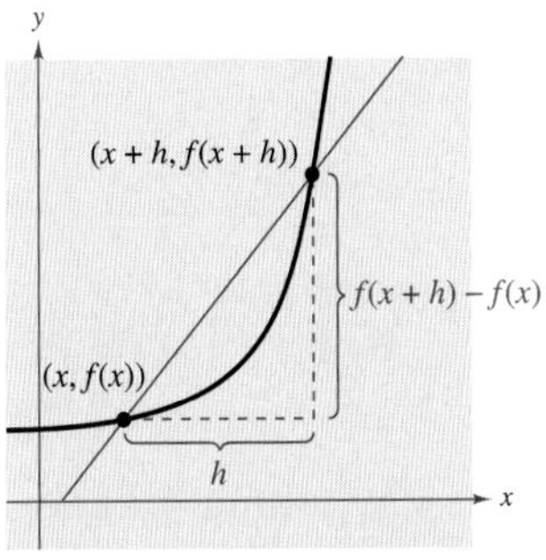

FIGURE 12.24

In Examples 1 and 2, you approximated the slope of a graph at a point by creating a graph and then "eyeballing" the tangent line at the point of tangency. A more precise method of approximating tangent lines makes use of a **secant line** through the point of tangency and a second point on the graph, as shown in Figure 12.24. If $(x, f(x))$ is the point of tangency and $(x + h, f(x + h))$ is a second point on the graph of f, the slope of the secant line through the two points is given by

$$m_{\text{sec}} = \frac{\text{change in } y}{\text{change in } x} = \frac{f(x + h) - f(x)}{h}.$$ Slope of secant line

The right side of this equation is called the **difference quotient.** The denominator h is the *change in x*, and the numerator is the *change in y*. The beauty of this procedure is that you obtain more and more accurate approximations of the slope of the tangent line by choosing points closer and closer to the point of tangency, as shown in Figure 12.25.

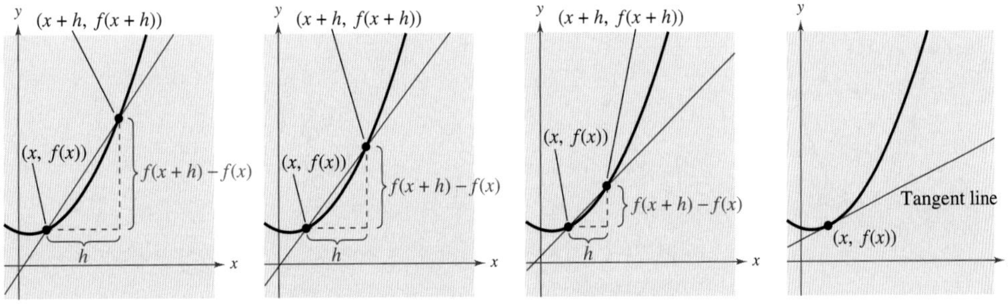

As h approaches 0, the secant line approaches the tangent line.
FIGURE 12.25

Using the limit process, you can find the *exact* slope of the tangent line at $(x, f(x))$.

Definition of the Slope of a Graph

The **slope** m of the graph of f at the point $(x, f(x))$ is equal to the slope of its tangent line at $(x, f(x))$, and is given by

$$\begin{aligned} m &= \lim_{h \to 0} m_{\text{sec}} \\ &= \lim_{h \to 0} \frac{f(x + h) - f(x)}{h} \end{aligned}$$

provided this limit exists.

From the definition above and from Section 12.2, you can see that the difference quotient is used frequently in calculus. Using the difference quotient to find the slope of a tangent line to a graph is a major concept of calculus.

Extra Example 3

Find the slope of the graph of $f(x) = x^3$ at the point (2, 8).

12

Avoiding Common Errors

Remind students to be careful when substituting values in the definition of slope of a tangent line. They are not finding a limit of x, but the limit of the expression as $h \to 0$. When finding the slope at a given point, students should substitute the value of x, leaving a limit that can be evaluated at $h = 0$.

Extra Example 4

Find the slope of $f(x) = -3x + 5$.

−3

Example 3 Finding the Slope of a Graph

Find the slope of the graph of $f(x) = x^2$ at the point $(-2, 4)$.

Solution

Find an expression that represents the slope of a secant line at $(-2, 4)$.

$$m_{sec} = \frac{f(-2+h) - f(-2)}{h} \qquad \text{Set up difference quotient.}$$

$$= \frac{(-2+h)^2 - (-2)^2}{h} \qquad \text{Substitute in } f(x) = x^2.$$

$$= \frac{4 - 4h + h^2 - 4}{h} \qquad \text{Expand terms.}$$

$$= \frac{-4h + h^2}{h} \qquad \text{Simplify.}$$

$$= \frac{h(-4+h)}{h} \qquad \text{Factor and divide out.}$$

$$= -4 + h, \quad h \neq 0 \qquad \text{Simplify.}$$

Next, take the limit of m_{sec} as h approaches 0.

$$m = \lim_{h \to 0} m_{sec} = \lim_{h \to 0} (-4 + h) = -4$$

The graph has a slope of -4 at the point $(-2, 4)$, as shown in Figure 12.26.

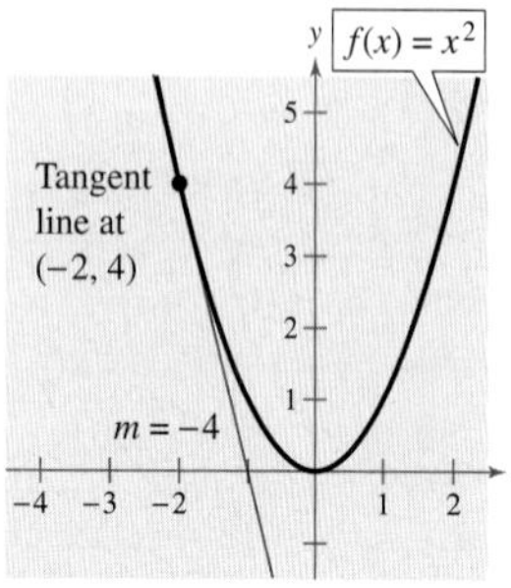

FIGURE 12.26

CHECKPoint Now try Exercise 9.

Example 4 Finding the Slope of a Graph

Find the slope of $f(x) = -2x + 4$.

Solution

$$m = \lim_{h \to 0} \frac{f(x+h) - f(x)}{h} \qquad \text{Set up difference quotient.}$$

$$= \lim_{h \to 0} \frac{[-2(x+h) + 4] - (-2x + 4)}{h} \qquad \text{Substitute in } f(x) = -2x + 4.$$

$$= \lim_{h \to 0} \frac{-2x - 2h + 4 + 2x - 4}{h} \qquad \text{Expand terms.}$$

$$= \lim_{h \to 0} \frac{-2h}{h} \qquad \text{Divide out.}$$

$$= -2 \qquad \text{Simplify.}$$

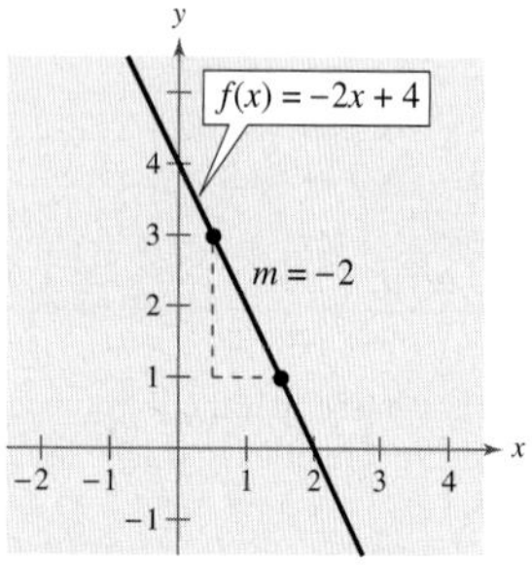

FIGURE 12.27

You know from your study of linear functions that the line given by $f(x) = -2x + 4$ has a slope of -2, as shown in Figure 12.27. This conclusion is consistent with that obtained by the limit definition of slope, as shown above.

CHECKPoint Now try Exercise 11.

It is important that you see the difference between the ways the difference quotients were set up in Examples 3 and 4. In Example 3, you were finding the slope of a graph at a specific point $(c, f(c))$. To find the slope in such a case, you can use the following form of the difference quotient.

$$m = \lim_{h \to 0} \frac{f(c+h) - f(c)}{h} \qquad \text{Slope at specific point}$$

In Example 4, however, you were finding a *formula* for the slope at *any* point on the graph. In such cases, you should use x, rather than c, in the difference quotient.

$$m = \lim_{h \to 0} \frac{f(x+h) - f(x)}{h} \qquad \text{Formula for slope}$$

Except for linear functions, this form will always produce a function of x, which can then be evaluated to find the slope at any desired point.

TECHNOLOGY

Try verifying the result in Example 5 by using a graphing utility to graph the function and the tangent lines at $(-1, 2)$ and $(2, 5)$ as

$y_1 = x^2 + 1$

$y_2 = -2x$

$y_3 = 4x - 3$

in the same viewing window. Some graphing utilities even have a *tangent* feature that automatically graphs the tangent line to a curve at a given point. If you have such a graphing utility, try verifying Example 5 using this feature.

Example 5 Finding a Formula for the Slope of a Graph

Find a formula for the slope of the graph of $f(x) = x^2 + 1$. What are the slopes at the points $(-1, 2)$ and $(2, 5)$?

Solution

$$m_{\text{sec}} = \frac{f(x+h) - f(x)}{h} \qquad \text{Set up difference quotient.}$$

$$= \frac{[(x+h)^2 + 1] - (x^2 + 1)}{h} \qquad \text{Substitute in } f(x) = x^2 + 1.$$

$$= \frac{x^2 + 2xh + h^2 + 1 - x^2 - 1}{h} \qquad \text{Expand terms.}$$

$$= \frac{2xh + h^2}{h} \qquad \text{Simplify.}$$

$$= \frac{\cancel{h}(2x + h)}{\cancel{h}} \qquad \text{Factor and divide out.}$$

$$= 2x + h, \quad h \neq 0 \qquad \text{Simplify.}$$

Next, take the limit of m_{sec} as h approaches 0.

$$m = \lim_{h \to 0} m_{\text{sec}} = \lim_{h \to 0} (2x + h) = 2x \qquad \text{Formula for finding slope}$$

Using the formula $m = 2x$ for the slope at $(x, f(x))$, you can find the slope at the specified points. At $(-1, 2)$, the slope is

$$m = 2(-1) = -2$$

and at $(2, 5)$, the slope is

$$m = 2(2) = 4.$$

The graph of f is shown in Figure 12.28.

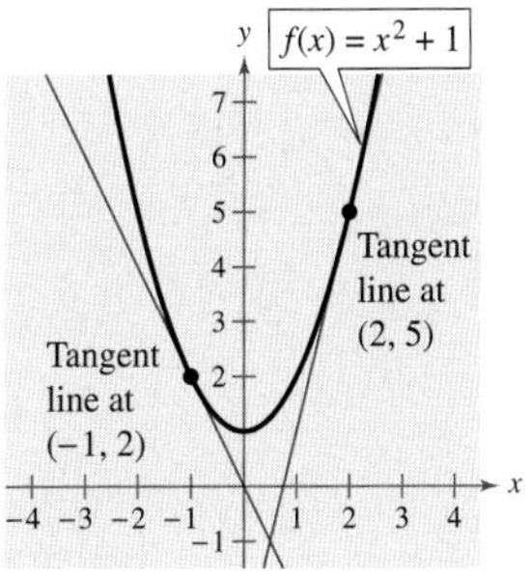

FIGURE 12.28

CHECKPoint Now try Exercise 17.

Extra Example 5

Find the formula for the slope of the graph of $f(x) = x^2 - 2$. What are the slopes at $(-3, 7)$ and $(1, -1)$?

$m = 2x$; $(-3, 7)$: $m = -6$; $(1, -1)$: $m = 2$

Extra Example 6

Find the derivative of $f(x) = 4x^2 - 5x$.

$f'(x) = 8x - 5$

The Derivative of a Function

In Example 5, you started with the function $f(x) = x^2 + 1$ and used the limit process to derive another function, $m = 2x$, that represents the slope of the graph of f at the point $(x, f(x))$. This derived function is called the **derivative** of f at x. It is denoted by $f'(x)$, which is read as "f prime of x."

Study Tip

In Section 1.5, you studied the slope of a line, which represents the *average rate of change* over an interval. The derivative of a function is a formula which represents the *instantaneous rate of change* at a point.

Definition of Derivative

The **derivative** of f at x is given by

$$f'(x) = \lim_{h \to 0} \frac{f(x+h) - f(x)}{h}$$

provided this limit exists.

Remember that the derivative $f'(x)$ is a formula for the slope of the tangent line to the graph of f at the point $(x, f(x))$.

Example 6 Finding a Derivative

Find the derivative of $f(x) = 3x^2 - 2x$.

Solution

$$\begin{aligned} f'(x) &= \lim_{h \to 0} \frac{f(x+h) - f(x)}{h} \\ &= \lim_{h \to 0} \frac{[3(x+h)^2 - 2(x+h)] - (3x^2 - 2x)}{h} \\ &= \lim_{h \to 0} \frac{3x^2 + 6xh + 3h^2 - 2x - 2h - 3x^2 + 2x}{h} \\ &= \lim_{h \to 0} \frac{6xh + 3h^2 - 2h}{h} \\ &= \lim_{h \to 0} \frac{\cancel{h}(6x + 3h - 2)}{\cancel{h}} \\ &= \lim_{h \to 0} (6x + 3h - 2) \\ &= 6x - 2 \end{aligned}$$

So, the derivative of $f(x) = 3x^2 - 2x$ is

$$f'(x) = 6x - 2.$$

CHECKPoint Now try Exercise 33.

Note that in addition to $f'(x)$, other notations can be used to denote the derivative of $y = f(x)$. The most common are

$$\frac{dy}{dx}, \quad y', \quad \frac{d}{dx}[f(x)], \quad \text{and} \quad D_x[y].$$

Example 7 Using the Derivative

Find $f'(x)$ for $f(x) = \sqrt{x}$. Then find the slopes of the graph of f at the points (1, 1) and (4, 2).

Solution

$$f'(x) = \lim_{h \to 0} \frac{f(x+h) - f(x)}{h}$$

$$= \lim_{h \to 0} \frac{\sqrt{x+h} - \sqrt{x}}{h}$$

Because direct substitution yields the indeterminate form $\frac{0}{0}$, you should use the rationalizing technique discussed in Section 12.2 to find the limit.

$$= \lim_{h \to 0} \left(\frac{\sqrt{x+h} - \sqrt{x}}{h}\right)\left(\frac{\sqrt{x+h} + \sqrt{x}}{\sqrt{x+h} + \sqrt{x}}\right)$$

$$= \lim_{h \to 0} \frac{(x+h) - x}{h(\sqrt{x+h} + \sqrt{x})}$$

$$= \lim_{h \to 0} \frac{\cancel{h}}{\cancel{h}(\sqrt{x+h} + \sqrt{x})}$$

$$= \lim_{h \to 0} \frac{1}{\sqrt{x+h} + \sqrt{x}} = \frac{1}{2\sqrt{x}}$$

At the point (1, 1), the slope is

$$f'(1) = \frac{1}{2\sqrt{1}} = \frac{1}{2}.$$

At the point (4, 2), the slope is

$$f'(4) = \frac{1}{2\sqrt{4}} = \frac{1}{4}.$$

The graph of f is shown in Figure 12.29.

CHECKPoint Now try Exercise 43.

Study Tip

Remember that in order to rationalize the numerator of an expression, you must multiply the numerator and denominator by the conjugate of the numerator.

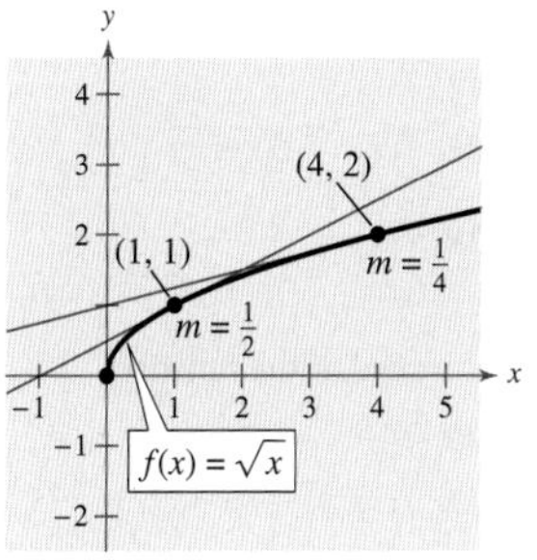

FIGURE 12.29

Classroom Discussion

Using a Derivative to Find Slope In many applications, it is convenient to use a variable other than x as the independent variable. Complete the following limit process to find the derivative of $f(t) = 3/t$. Then use the result to find the slope of the graph of $f(t) = 3/t$ at the point (3, 1).

$$f'(t) = \lim_{h \to 0} \frac{f(t+h) - f(t)}{h} = \lim_{h \to 0} \frac{\frac{3}{t+h} - \frac{3}{t}}{h} = \ldots f'(t) = -\frac{1}{t^2};\ f'(3) = -\frac{1}{9}$$

Write a short paragraph summarizing your findings. Summaries will vary.

Extra Example 7

Find $f'(x)$ for $f(x) = \sqrt{x} + 1$. Then find the slopes of the graph of f at the points (4, 3) and (9, 4).

$f'(x) = \frac{1}{2\sqrt{x}}$, $f'(4) = \frac{1}{4}$, $f'(9) = \frac{1}{6}$

Closing the Lesson

Have students summarize the major points of the lesson and answer the Essential Question: How do you find the slope of a graph at any single point?

- **Identify the slope of a graph at a given point by finding the slope of a line that is tangent to the graph at the point.**
- **Calculate the slope of a graph at a given point, and find a formula for the derivative of a function by finding $\lim_{h \to 0} \frac{f(x+h) - f(x)}{h}$.**

4 PRACTICE AND APPLY

Assignment Guide

Transparencies Available
Available at the Instructor's companion site.

Average:
Day 1: p. 878
Exs. 1–3, 6, 8, 10–15, 18–21, 23–27
Day 2: pp. 878–880
Exs. 4, 29, 31, 35, 39, 41, 46, 47–65 odd, 71, 73, 75–81, 83

Advanced:
Day 1: p. 878
Exs. 1–3, 6–10 even, 12–16, 19–22, 24–28
Day 2: pp. 878–880
Exs. 4, 32–42 even, 47, 48–62 even, 71–73, 75–80, 82–86 even

Block:
p. 878
Exs. 1–3, 6, 8, 10–15, 18–21, 23–27 (with 12.2)
pp. 878–880
Exs. 4, 29, 31, 35, 39, 41, 46, 47–65 odd, 71, 73, 75–81, 83 (with 12.4)

12.3 EXERCISES

See www.CalcChat.com for worked-out solutions to odd-numbered exercises.

VOCABULARY: Fill in the blanks.

1. Calculus is the study of the rates of change of functions.
2. The tangent line to the graph of a function at a point is the line that best approximates the slope of the graph at the point.
3. A secant line is a line through the point of tangency and a second point on the graph.
4. The slope of the tangent line to a graph at $(x, f(x))$ is given by the limit of a difference quotient

SKILLS AND APPLICATIONS

In Exercises 5–8, use the figure to approximate the slope of the curve at the point (x, y).

5. 0

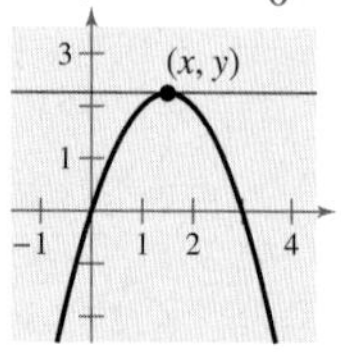

6. -1

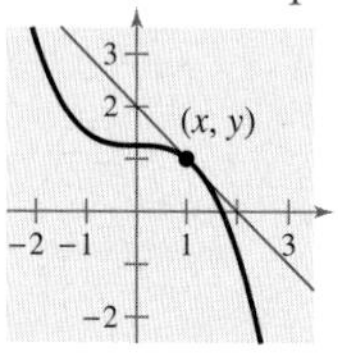

7. $\frac{1}{2}$

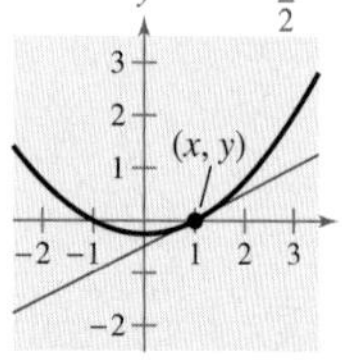

8. -2

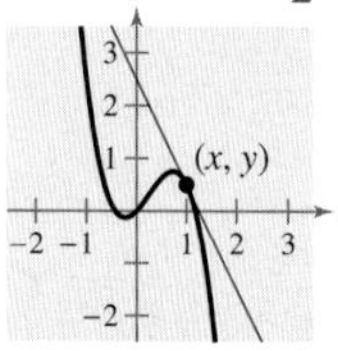

In Exercises 9–16, use the limit process to find the slope of the graph of the function at the specified point. Use a graphing utility to confirm your result.

9. $g(x) = x^2 - 4x$, $(3, -3)$ 2
10. $f(x) = 10x - 2x^2$, $(3, 12)$ -2
11. $g(x) = 5 - 2x$, $(1, 3)$ -2
12. $h(x) = 2x + 5$, $(-1, 3)$ 2
13. $g(x) = \frac{4}{x}$, $(2, 2)$ -1
14. $g(x) = \frac{1}{x - 2}$, $\left(4, \frac{1}{2}\right)$ $-\frac{1}{4}$
15. $h(x) = \sqrt{x}$, $(9, 3)$ $\frac{1}{6}$
16. $h(x) = \sqrt{x + 10}$, $(-1, 3)$ $\frac{1}{6}$

In Exercises 17–22, find a formula for the slope of the graph of f at the point $(x, f(x))$. Then use it to find the slope at the two given points.

17. $f(x) = 4 - x^2$
(a) $(0, 4)$
(b) $(-1, 3)$
$m = -2x$; (a) 0 (b) 2

18. $f(x) = x^3$
(a) $(1, 1)$
(b) $(-2, -8)$
$m = 3x^2$; (a) 3 (b) 12

19–22. See margin.

19. $f(x) = \frac{1}{x + 4}$
(a) $\left(0, \frac{1}{4}\right)$
(b) $\left(-2, \frac{1}{2}\right)$

20. $f(x) = \frac{1}{x + 2}$
(a) $\left(0, \frac{1}{2}\right)$
(b) $(-1, 1)$

21. $f(x) = \sqrt{x - 1}$
(a) $(5, 2)$
(b) $(10, 3)$

22. $f(x) = \sqrt{x - 4}$
(a) $(5, 1)$
(b) $(8, 2)$

In Exercises 23–28, sketch a graph of the function and the tangent line at the point $(1, f(1))$. Use the graph to approximate the slope of the tangent line. 23–28. See margin.

23. $f(x) = x^2 - 2$
24. $f(x) = x^2 - 2x + 1$
25. $f(x) = \sqrt{2 - x}$
26. $f(x) = \sqrt{x + 3}$
27. $f(x) = \frac{4}{x + 1}$
28. $f(x) = \frac{3}{2 - x}$

In Exercises 29–42, find the derivative of the function.

29. $f(x) = 5$ 0
30. $f(x) = -1$ 0
31. $g(x) = 9 - \frac{1}{3}x$ $-\frac{1}{3}$
32. $f(x) = -5x + 2$ -5
33. $f(x) = 4 - 3x^2$ $-6x$
34. $f(x) = x^2 - 3x + 4$
35. $f(x) = \frac{1}{x^2}$
36. $f(x) = \frac{1}{x^3}$
34–42. See margin.
37. $f(x) = \sqrt{x - 11}$
38. $f(x) = \sqrt{x + 8}$
39. $f(x) = \frac{1}{x + 6}$
40. $f(x) = \frac{1}{x - 5}$
41. $f(x) = \frac{1}{\sqrt{x - 9}}$
42. $h(s) = \frac{1}{\sqrt{s + 1}}$

In Exercises 43–50, (a) find the slope of the graph of f at the given point, (b) use the result of part (a) to find an equation of the tangent line to the graph at the point, and (c) graph the function and the tangent line. 43–46. See margin.

43. $f(x) = x^2 - 1$, $(2, 3)$
44. $f(x) = 4 - x^2$, $(1, 3)$
45. $f(x) = x^3 - 2x$, $(1, -1)$
46. $f(x) = x^3 - x$, $(2, 6)$

---

19. $m = -\frac{1}{(x + 4)^2}$;
(a) $-\frac{1}{16}$ (b) $-\frac{1}{4}$

20. $m = -\frac{1}{(x + 2)^2}$;
(a) $-\frac{1}{4}$ (b) -1

21. $m = \frac{1}{2\sqrt{x - 1}}$; (a) $\frac{1}{4}$ (b) $\frac{1}{6}$

22. $m = \frac{1}{2\sqrt{x - 4}}$; (a) $\frac{1}{2}$ (b) $\frac{1}{4}$

23. 2

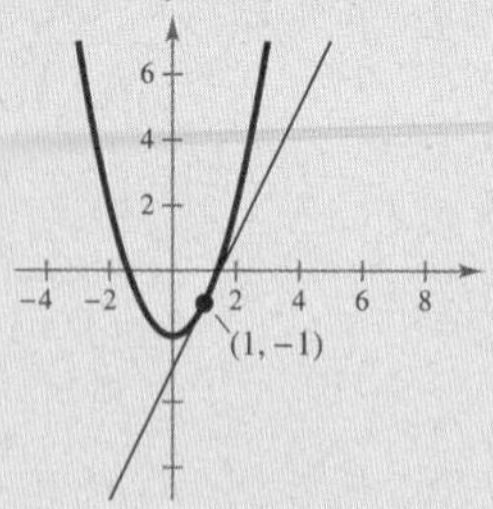

24. 0

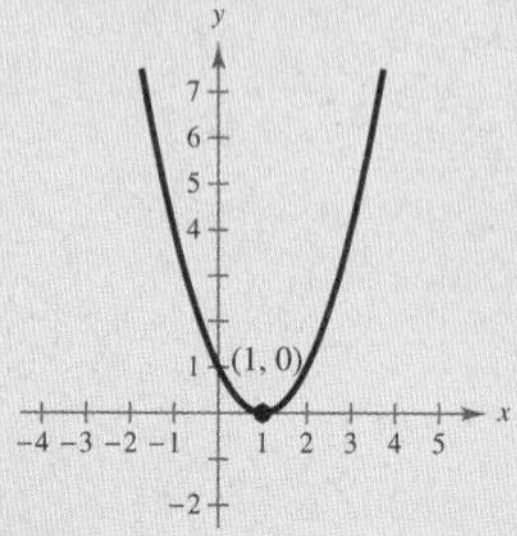

25. $-\frac{1}{2}$

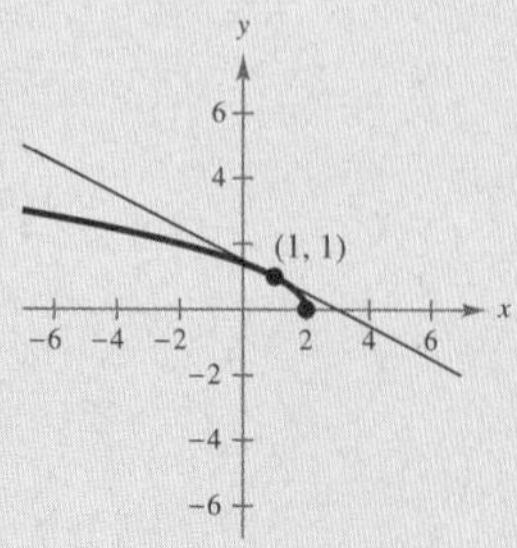

26. $\frac{1}{4}$

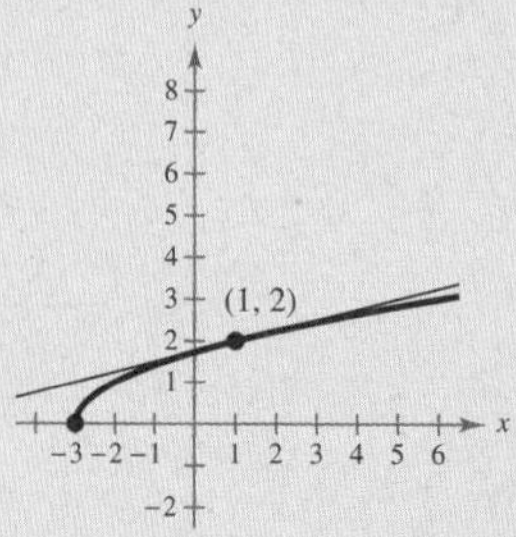

27. -1

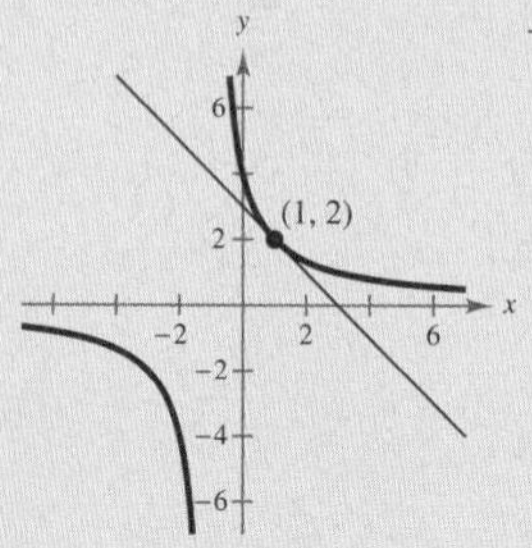

28, 34–46. See Additional Answers beginning on page AA1.

47. $f(x) = \sqrt{x+1}$, $(3, 2)$ 47–50. See margin.

48. $f(x) = \sqrt{x-2}$, $(3, 1)$

49. $f(x) = \dfrac{1}{x+5}$, $(-4, 1)$

50. $f(x) = \dfrac{1}{x-3}$, $(4, 1)$

In Exercises 51–54, use a graphing utility to graph f over the interval $[-2, 2]$ and complete the table. Compare the value of the first derivative with a visual approximation of the slope of the graph. 51–54. See margin.

x	-2	-1.5	-1	-0.5	0	0.5	1	1.5	2
$f(x)$									
$f'(x)$									

51. $f(x) = \frac{1}{2}x^2$

52. $f(x) = \frac{1}{4}x^3$

53. $f(x) = \sqrt{x+3}$

54. $f(x) = \dfrac{x^2-4}{x+4}$

In Exercises 55–58, find an equation of the line that is tangent to the graph of f and parallel to the given line.

Function	*Line*
55. $f(x) = -\frac{1}{4}x^2$	$x + y = 0$ $y = -x + 1$
56. $f(x) = x^2 + 1$	$2x + y = 0$ $y = -2x$
57. $f(x) = -\frac{1}{2}x^3$	$6x + y + 4 = 0$ $y = -6x \pm 8$
58. $f(x) = x^2 - x$	$x + 2y - 6 = 0$ $y = -\frac{1}{2}x - \frac{1}{16}$

In Exercises 59–62, find the derivative of f. Use the derivative to determine any points on the graph of f at which the tangent line is horizontal. Use a graphing utility to verify your results. 59–62. See margin.

59. $f(x) = x^2 - 4x + 3$

60. $f(x) = x^2 - 6x + 4$

61. $f(x) = 3x^3 - 9x$

62. $f(x) = x^3 + 3x$

In Exercises 63–70, use the function and its derivative to determine any points on the graph of f at which the tangent line is horizontal. Use a graphing utility to verify your results.

63. $f(x) = x^4 - 2x^2$, $f'(x) = 4x^3 - 4x$ $(-1, -1), (0, 0), (1, -1)$

64. $f(x) = 3x^4 + 4x^3$, $f'(x) = 12x^3 + 12x^2$ $(0, 0), (-1, -1)$

65. $f(x) = 2\cos x + x$, $f'(x) = -2\sin x + 1$, over the interval $(0, 2\pi)$ See below.

66. $f(x) = x - 2\sin x$, $f'(x) = 1 - 2\cos x$, over the interval $(0, 2\pi)$ See below.

67. $f(x) = x^2e^x$, $f'(x) = x^2e^x + 2xe^x$ $(0, 0), (-2, 4e^{-2})$

68. $f(x) = xe^{-x}$, $f'(x) = e^{-x} - xe^{-x}$ $(1, e^{-1})$

69. $f(x) = x\ln x$, $f'(x) = \ln x + 1$ $(e^{-1}, -e^{-1})$

70. $f(x) = \dfrac{\ln x}{x}$, $f'(x) = \dfrac{1-\ln x}{x^2}$ (e, e^{-1})

71. PATH OF A BALL The path of a ball thrown by a child is modeled by

$$y = -x^2 + 5x + 2$$

where y is the height of the ball (in feet) and x is the horizontal distance (in feet) from the point from which the ball was thrown. Using your knowledge of the slopes of tangent lines, show that the height of the ball is increasing on the interval $[0, 2]$ and decreasing on the interval $[3, 5]$. Explain your reasoning. Answers will vary.

72. PROFIT The profit P (in hundreds of dollars) that a company makes depends on the amount x (in hundreds of dollars) the company spends on advertising. The profit function is given by

$$P(x) = 200 + 30x - 0.5x^2.$$

Using your knowledge of the slopes of tangent lines, show that the profit is increasing on the interval $[0, 20]$ and decreasing on the interval $[40, 60]$. Answers will vary.

73. The table shows the revenues y (in millions of dollars) for eBay, Inc. from 2000 through 2007. (Source: eBay, Inc.)

Year	Revenue, y
2000	431.4
2001	748.8
2002	1214.1
2003	2165.1
2004	3271.3
2005	4552.4
2006	5969.7
2007	7672.3

(a) Use the *regression* feature of a graphing utility to find a quadratic model for the data. Let x represent the time in years, with $x = 0$ corresponding to 2000. $y = 112.87x^2 + 256.45x + 380.3$

(b) Use a graphing utility to graph the model found in part (a). Estimate the slope of the graph when $x = 5$ and give an interpretation of the result. See margin.

(c) Use a graphing utility to graph the tangent line to the model when $x = 5$. Compare the slope given by the graphing utility with the estimate in part (b). See margin.

65. $\left(\dfrac{\pi}{6}, \sqrt{3} + \dfrac{\pi}{6}\right), \left(\dfrac{5\pi}{6}, \dfrac{5\pi}{6} - \sqrt{3}\right)$ 66. $\left(\dfrac{\pi}{3}, \dfrac{\pi}{3} - \sqrt{3}\right), \left(\dfrac{5\pi}{3}, \dfrac{5\pi}{3} + \sqrt{3}\right)$

73. (b)

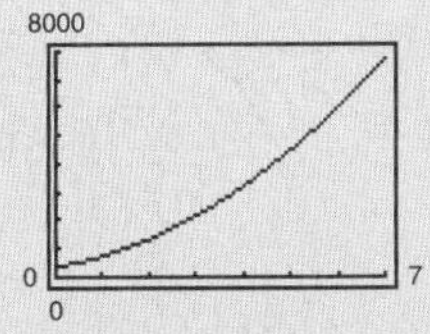

Slope when $x = 5$ is about 1385.2. This represents \$1385.2 million and the rate of change of revenue in 2005.

(c)

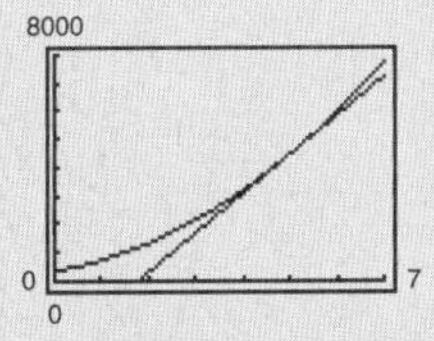

The slopes are the same.

47. (a) $\frac{1}{4}$ (b) $y = \frac{1}{4}x + \frac{5}{4}$

(c)

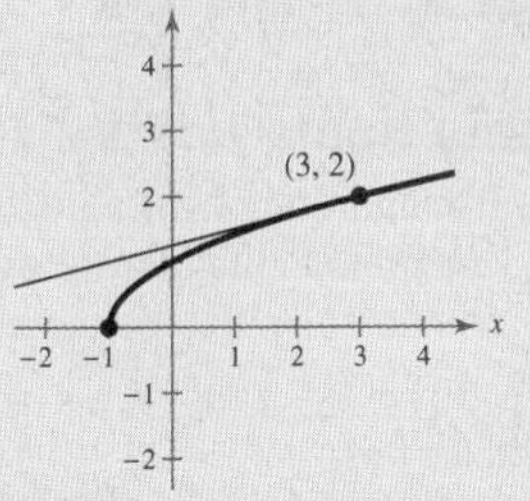

48. (a) $\frac{1}{2}$ (b) $y = \frac{1}{2}x - \frac{1}{2}$

(c)

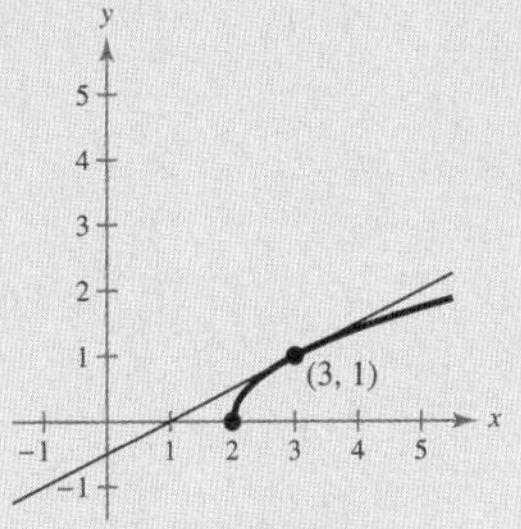

49. (a) -1 (b) $y = -x - 3$

(c)

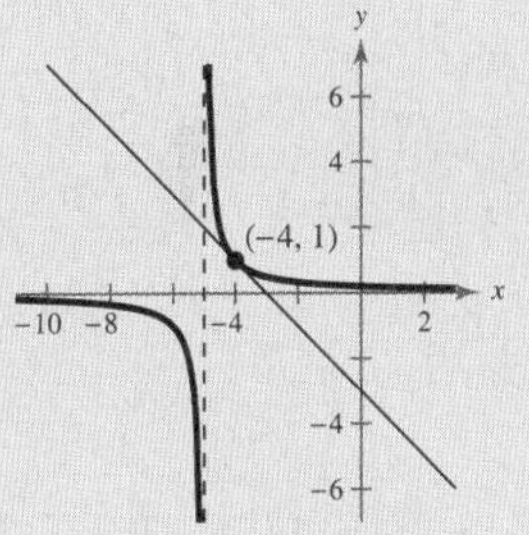

50. (a) -1 (b) $y = -x + 5$

(c)

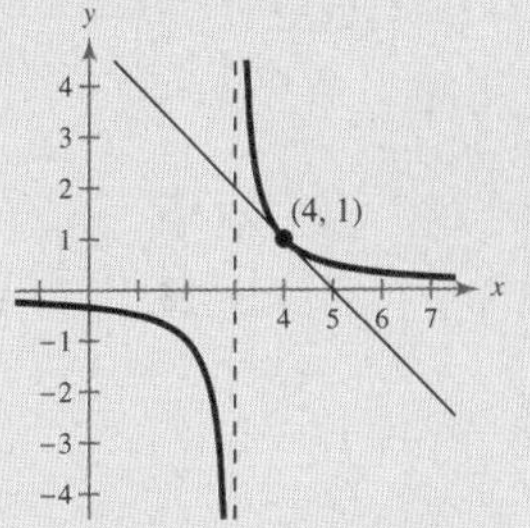

59. $f'(x) = 2x - 4$; horizontal tangent at $(2, -1)$

60. $f'(x) = 2x - 6$; horizontal tangent at $(3, -5)$

61. $f'(x) = 9x^2 - 9$; horizontal tangents at $(-1, 6)$ and $(1, -6)$

62. $f'(x) = 3x^2 + 3$; no horizontal tangents

51–54. See Additional Answers beginning on page AA1.

74. MARKET RESEARCH The data in the table show the number N (in thousands) of books sold when the price per book is p (in dollars). See margin.

Price, p	Number of books, N
\$10	900
\$15	630
\$20	396
\$25	227
\$30	102
\$35	36

(a) Use the *regression* feature of a graphing utility to find a quadratic model for the data.

(b) Use a graphing utility to graph the model found in part (a). Estimate the slopes of the graph when $p = \$15$ and $p = \$30$.

(c) Use a graphing utility to graph the tangent lines to the model when $p = \$15$ and $p = \$30$. Compare the slopes given by the graphing utility with your estimates in part (b).

(d) The slopes of the tangent lines at $p = \$15$ and $p = \$30$ are not the same. Explain what this means to the company selling the books.

EXPLORATION

75–76. See margin.

TRUE OR FALSE? In Exercises 75 and 76, determine whether the statement is true or false. Justify your answer.

75. The slope of the graph of $y = x^2$ is different at every point on the graph of f.

76. A tangent line to a graph can intersect the graph only at the point of tangency.

In Exercises 77–80, match the function with the graph of its *derivative*. It is not necessary to find the derivative of the function. [The graphs are labeled (a), (b), (c), and (d).]

(a)

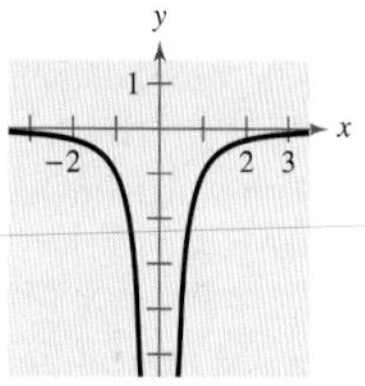

(b)

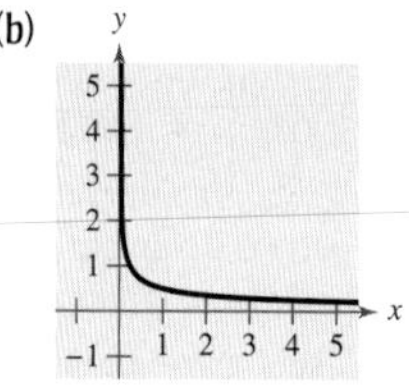

(c)

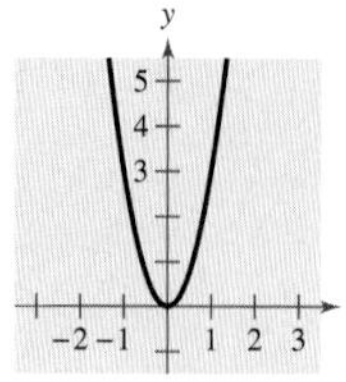

(d)

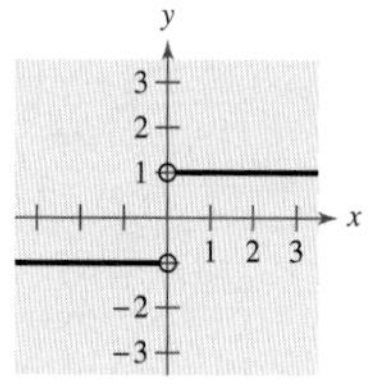

77. $f(x) = \sqrt{x}$ b

78. $f(x) = \dfrac{1}{x}$ a

79. $f(x) = |x|$ d

80. $f(x) = x^3$ c

81. THINK ABOUT IT Sketch the graph of a function whose derivative is always positive. See margin.

82. THINK ABOUT IT Sketch the graph of a function whose derivative is always negative. See margin.

83. THINK ABOUT IT Sketch the graph of a function for which $f'(x) < 0$ for $x < 1$, $f'(x) \geq 0$ for $x > 1$, and $f'(1) = 0$. See margin.

84. CONJECTURE Consider the functions $f(x) = x^2$ and $g(x) = x^3$. See margin.

(a) Sketch the graphs of f and f' on the same set of coordinate axes.

(b) Sketch the graphs of g and g' on the same set of coordinate axes.

(c) Identify any pattern between the functions f and g and their respective derivatives. Use the pattern to make a conjecture about $h'(x)$ if $h(x) = x^n$, where n is an integer and $n \geq 2$.

85. Consider the function $f(x) = 3x^2 - 2x$. See margin.

(a) Use a graphing utility to graph the function.

(b) Use the *trace* feature to approximate the coordinates of the vertex of this parabola.

(c) Use the derivative of $f(x) = 3x^2 - 2x$ to find the slope of the tangent line at the vertex.

(d) Make a conjecture about the slope of the tangent line at the vertex of an arbitrary parabola.

86. CAPSTONE Explain how the slope of the secant line is used to derive the slope of the tangent line and the definition of the derivative of a function f at a point $(x, f(x))$. Include diagrams or sketches as necessary. Answers will vary.

PROJECT: ADVERTISING To work an extended application analyzing the amount spent on advertising in the United States, visit this text's website at *academic.cengage.com*. (Data Source: Universal McCann)

5 ASSESS AND RETEACH

Daily Homework Quiz

Transparency Available

Available at the Instructor's companion site.

74. (a) $N(p) = 1.04p^2 - 81.5p + 1613$

(b)

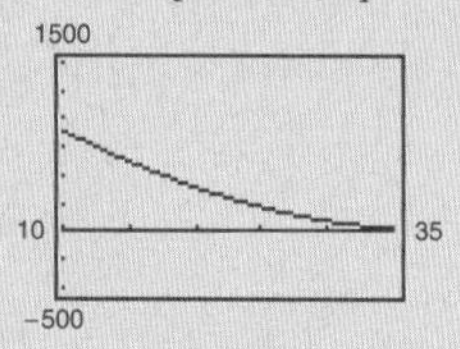

$p = \$15$: -50

$p = \$30$: -19

(c) $p = \$15$

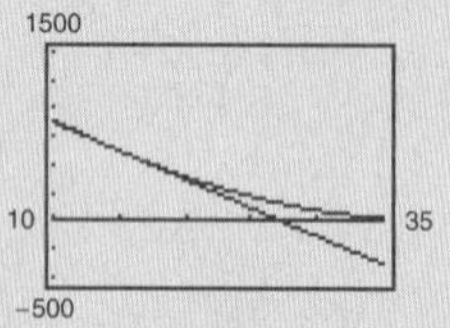

$p = \$30$

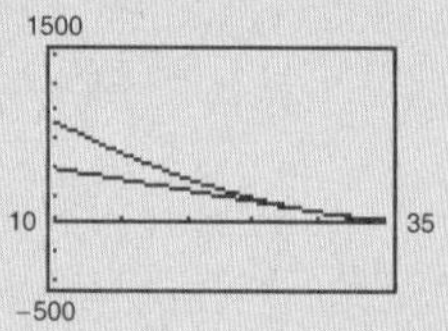

The slopes (-50.3 and -19.1) given by the graphing utility are close to the estimates (-50 and -19).

(d) The rate of decrease in sales decreases as the price increases.

75. True. The slope is dependent on x.

76. False. Tangent lines to noncircular graphs can intersect the graph at more than one point.

81. Answers will vary. Example: a sketch of any linear function with positive slope

82. Answers will vary. Example: a sketch of any linear function with negative slope

83. Answers will vary. Example: a sketch of any quadratic function of the form $y = a(x - 1)^2 + k$, where $a > 0$

84. (a)

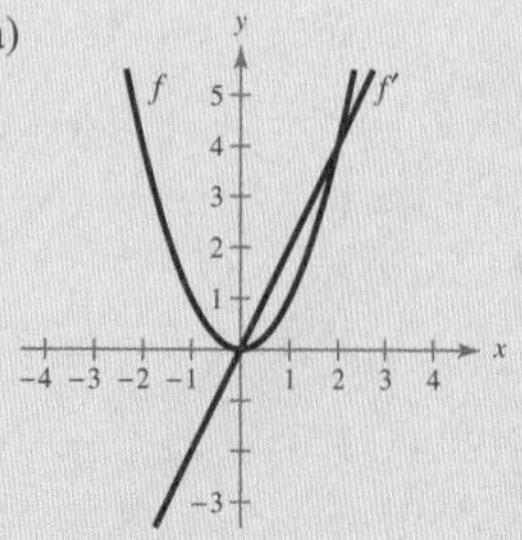

(b)

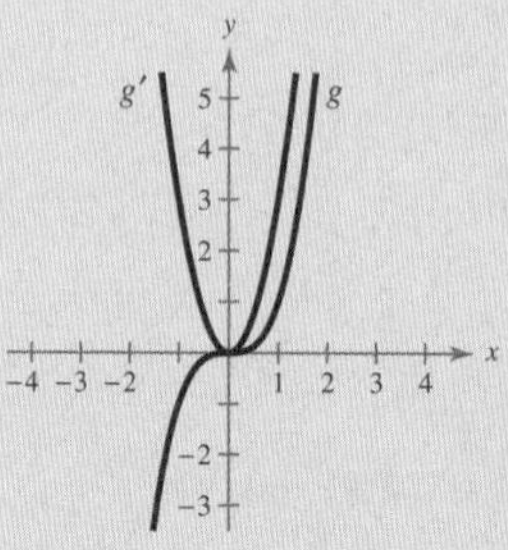

(c) Answers will vary. $h'(x) = nx^{n-1}$

85. (a)

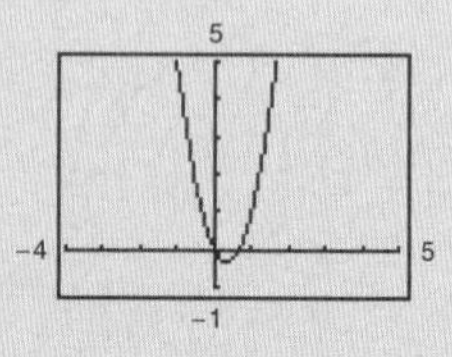

(b) About $(0.33, -0.33)$

(c) Slope at vertex is 0.

(d) Slope of tangent line at vertex is 0.

12.4 LIMITS AT INFINITY AND LIMITS OF SEQUENCES

What you should learn

- Evaluate limits of functions at infinity.
- Find limits of sequences.

Why you should learn it

Finding limits at infinity is useful in many types of real-life applications. For instance, in Exercise 58 on page 889, you are asked to find a limit at infinity to determine the number of military reserve personnel in the future.

Algebra Help

The function $f(x) = \dfrac{x+1}{2x}$ is a rational function. You can review rational functions in Section 2.6.

Limits at Infinity and Horizontal Asymptotes

As pointed out at the beginning of this chapter, there are two basic problems in calculus: finding **tangent lines** and finding the area of a region. In Section 12.3, you saw how limits can be used to solve the tangent line problem. In this section and the next, you will see how a different type of limit, a *limit at infinity*, can be used to solve the area problem. To get an idea of what is meant by a limit at infinity, consider the function given by

$$f(x) = \frac{x+1}{2x}.$$

The graph of f is shown in Figure 12.30. From earlier work, you know that $y = \frac{1}{2}$ is a horizontal asymptote of the graph of this function. Using limit notation, this can be written as follows.

$$\lim_{x\to-\infty} f(x) = \frac{1}{2}$$ Horizontal asymptote to the left

$$\lim_{x\to\infty} f(x) = \frac{1}{2}$$ Horizontal asymptote to the right

These limits mean that the value of $f(x)$ gets arbitrarily close to $\frac{1}{2}$ as x decreases or increases without bound.

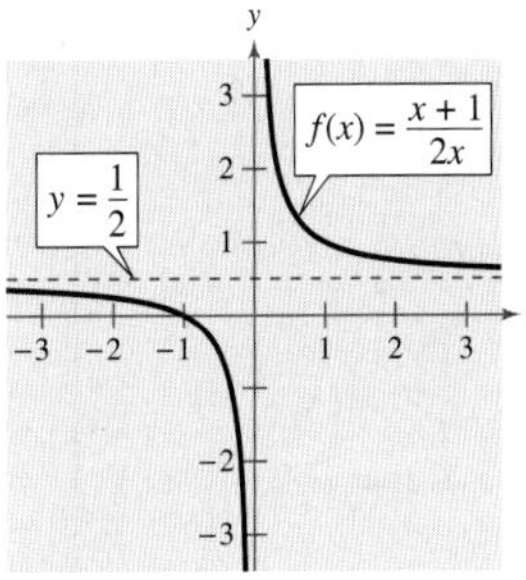

FIGURE 12.30

Definition of Limits at Infinity

If f is a function and L_1 and L_2 are real numbers, the statements

$$\lim_{x\to-\infty} f(x) = L_1$$ Limit as x approaches $-\infty$

and

$$\lim_{x\to\infty} f(x) = L_2$$ Limit as x approaches ∞

denote the **limits at infinity.** The first statement is read "*the limit of $f(x)$ as x approaches $-\infty$ is L_1*," and the second is read "*the limit of $f(x)$ as x approaches ∞ is L_2*."

1 PLAN AND PREPARE

Warm-up Exercises

Transparency Available
Available at the Instructor's companion site.

Notetaking Guide

Transparency Available
Promotes interactive learning and notetaking skills. Available at the Instructor's companion site.

Animated **Precalculus**

An **Animated Precalculus** tutorial is available at the Student companion site for **Section 12.4.**

Pacing

Average: 2 days
Advanced: 2 days
Block: 0.5 block with 12.3
0.5 block with 12.5

2 FOCUS AND MOTIVATE

Essential Question

How do you find the limits of functions at infinity and the limits of sequences? **Tell students that they will learn how to answer this question by studying the behavior of different parts of a function as *x* increases or decreases without bound.**

Resource Planning Guide

Chapter Resources
- Complete Solutions Guide

Workbooks
- Notetaking Guide
- Student Solutions Guide

Interactive Technology
- Instructor Success Organizer
- Notetaking Guide IAE
- Instructional DVDs
- Animated Precalculus
- PowerLecture with ExamView

3 TEACH

Extra Example 1

Find the limit: $\lim_{x\to\infty}\left(7 - \frac{1}{x^2}\right)$.

$\lim_{x\to\infty}\left(7 - \frac{1}{x^2}\right) = 7$

To help evaluate limits at infinity, you can use the following definition.

> **Limits at Infinity**
>
> If r is a positive real number, then
>
> $$\lim_{x\to\infty}\frac{1}{x^r} = 0. \qquad \text{Limit toward the right}$$
>
> Furthermore, if x^r is defined when $x < 0$, then
>
> $$\lim_{x\to-\infty}\frac{1}{x^r} = 0. \qquad \text{Limit toward the left}$$

Limits at infinity share many of the properties of limits listed in Section 12.1. Some of these properties are demonstrated in the next example.

Example 1 Evaluating a Limit at Infinity

Find the limit.

$$\lim_{x\to\infty}\left(4 - \frac{3}{x^2}\right)$$

Algebraic Solution

Use the properties of limits listed in Section 12.1.

$$\begin{aligned}\lim_{x\to\infty}\left(4 - \frac{3}{x^2}\right) &= \lim_{x\to\infty} 4 - \lim_{x\to\infty}\frac{3}{x^2}\\ &= \lim_{x\to\infty} 4 - 3\left(\lim_{x\to\infty}\frac{1}{x^2}\right)\\ &= 4 - 3(0)\\ &= 4\end{aligned}$$

So, the limit of $f(x) = 4 - \dfrac{3}{x^2}$ as x approaches ∞ is 4.

Graphical Solution

Use a graphing utility to graph $y = 4 - 3/x^2$. Then use the *trace* feature to determine that as x gets larger and larger, y gets closer and closer to 4, as shown in Figure 12.31. Note that the line $y = 4$ is a horizontal asymptote to the right.

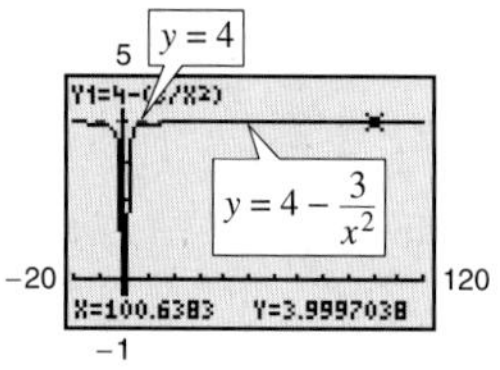

FIGURE 12.31

CHECKPoint Now try Exercise 9.

In Figure 12.31, it appears that the line $y = 4$ is also a horizontal asymptote *to the left*. You can verify this by showing that

$$\lim_{x\to-\infty}\left(4 - \frac{3}{x^2}\right) = 4.$$

The graph of a rational function need not have a horizontal asymptote. If it does, however, its left and right horizontal asymptotes must be the same.

When evaluating limits at infinity for more complicated rational functions, divide the numerator and denominator by the *highest-powered term* in the denominator. This enables you to evaluate each limit using the limits at infinity at the top of this page.

Example 2 Comparing Limits at Infinity

Find the limit as x approaches ∞ for each function.

a. $f(x) = \dfrac{-2x + 3}{3x^2 + 1}$ **b.** $f(x) = \dfrac{-2x^2 + 3}{3x^2 + 1}$ **c.** $f(x) = \dfrac{-2x^3 + 3}{3x^2 + 1}$

Solution

In each case, begin by dividing both the numerator and denominator by x^2, the highest-powered term in the denominator.

a.
$$\lim_{x\to\infty} \frac{-2x + 3}{3x^2 + 1} = \lim_{x\to\infty} \frac{-\dfrac{2}{x} + \dfrac{3}{x^2}}{3 + \dfrac{1}{x^2}}$$
$$= \frac{-0 + 0}{3 + 0}$$
$$= 0$$

b.
$$\lim_{x\to\infty} \frac{-2x^2 + 3}{3x^2 + 1} = \lim_{x\to\infty} \frac{-2 + \dfrac{3}{x^2}}{3 + \dfrac{1}{x^2}}$$
$$= \frac{-2 + 0}{3 + 0}$$
$$= -\frac{2}{3}$$

c.
$$\lim_{x\to\infty} \frac{-2x^3 + 3}{3x^2 + 1} = \lim_{x\to\infty} \frac{-2x + \dfrac{3}{x^2}}{3 + \dfrac{1}{x^2}}$$

In this case, you can conclude that the limit does not exist because the numerator decreases without bound as the denominator approaches 3.

CHECK*Point* Now try Exercise 19.

In Example 2, observe that when the degree of the numerator is less than the degree of the denominator, as in part (a), the limit is 0. When the degrees of the numerator and denominator are equal, as in part (b), the limit is the ratio of the coefficients of the highest-powered terms. When the degree of the numerator is greater than the degree of the denominator, as in part (c), the limit does not exist.

This result seems reasonable when you realize that for large values of x, the highest-powered term of a polynomial is the most "influential" term. That is, a polynomial tends to behave as its highest-powered term behaves as x approaches positive or negative infinity.

Extra Example 2

Find the limit as x approaches ∞ for each function.

a. $f(x) = \dfrac{-x + 4}{5x^2 + 2}$

0

b. $f(x) = \dfrac{-x^2 + 4}{5x^2 + 2}$

$-\dfrac{1}{5}$

c. $f(x) = \dfrac{-x^3 + 4}{5x^2 + 2}$

Does not exist

Extra Example 3

You are manufacturing greeting cards that cost \$0.65 per card to produce. Your initial investment is \$4500, which implies that the total cost C of producing x cards is given by $C(x) = 0.65x + 4500$. The average cost $\overline{C}$ per card is given by

$$\overline{C}(x) = \frac{C}{x} = \frac{0.65x + 4500}{x}.$$

Find the average cost per card when (a) $x = 5000$, (b) $x = 50{,}000$, and (c) $x = 500{,}000$. (d) What is the limit of $\overline{C}$ as x approaches infinity?

(a) \$1.55; (b) \$0.74; (c) \$0.66; (d) \$0.65

Limits at Infinity for Rational Functions

Consider the rational function $f(x) = N(x)/D(x)$, where

$$N(x) = a_nx^n + \cdot\cdot\cdot + a_0 \quad \text{and} \quad D(x) = b_mx^m + \cdot\cdot\cdot + b_0.$$

The limit of $f(x)$ as x approaches positive or negative infinity is as follows.

$$\lim_{x\to\pm\infty} f(x) = \begin{cases} 0, & n < m \\ \dfrac{a_n}{b_m}, & n = m \end{cases}$$

If $n > m$, the limit does not exist.

Example 3 Finding the Average Cost

You are manufacturing greeting cards that cost \$0.50 per card to produce. Your initial investment is \$5000, which implies that the total cost C of producing x cards is given by $C = 0.50x + 5000$. The average cost $\overline{C}$ per card is given by

$$\overline{C} = \frac{C}{x} = \frac{0.50x + 5000}{x}.$$

Find the average cost per card when (a) $x = 1000$, (b) $x = 10{,}000$, and (c) $x = 100{,}000$. (d) What is the limit of $\overline{C}$ as x approaches infinity?

Solution

a. When $x = 1000$, the average cost per card is

$$\overline{C} = \frac{0.50(1000) + 5000}{1000} \qquad x = 1000$$

$$= \$5.50.$$

b. When $x = 10{,}000$, the average cost per card is

$$\overline{C} = \frac{0.50(10{,}000) + 5000}{10{,}000} \qquad x = 10{,}000$$

$$= \$1.00.$$

c. When $x = 100{,}000$, the average cost per card is

$$\overline{C} = \frac{0.50(100{,}000) + 5000}{100{,}000} \qquad x = 100{,}000$$

$$= \$0.55.$$

d. As x approaches infinity, the limit of $\overline{C}$ is

$$\lim_{x\to\infty} \frac{0.50x + 5000}{x} = \$0.50. \qquad x \to \infty$$

The graph of $\overline{C}$ is shown in Figure 12.32.

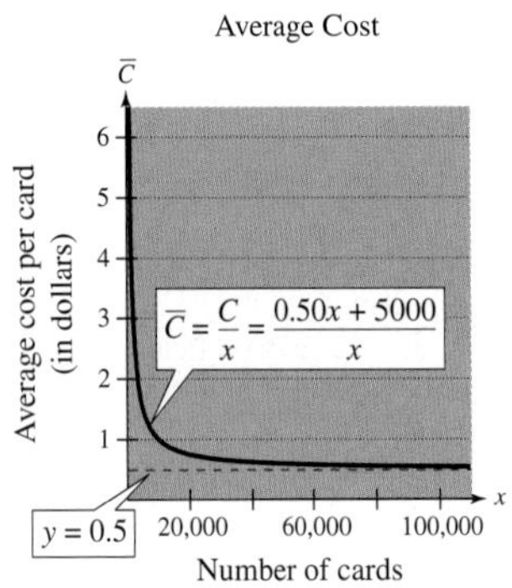

As $x \to \infty$, the average cost per card approaches \$0.50.
FIGURE 12.32

CHECKPoint Now try Exercise 55.

Algebra Help

You can review sequences in Sections 9.1–9.3.

TECHNOLOGY

There are a number of ways to use a graphing utility to generate the terms of a sequence. For instance, you can display the first 10 terms of the sequence

$$a_n = \frac{1}{2^n}$$

using the *sequence* feature or the *table* feature.

Limits of Sequences

Limits of sequences have many of the same properties as limits of functions. For instance, consider the sequence whose nth term is $a_n = 1/2^n$.

$$\frac{1}{2}, \frac{1}{4}, \frac{1}{8}, \frac{1}{16}, \frac{1}{32}, . . .$$

As n increases without bound, the terms of this sequence get closer and closer to 0, and the sequence is said to **converge** to 0. Using limit notation, you can write

$$\lim_{n\to\infty} \frac{1}{2^n} = 0.$$

The following relationship shows how limits of functions of x can be used to evaluate the limit of a sequence.

Limit of a Sequence

Let f be a function of a real variable such that

$$\lim_{x\to\infty} f(x) = L.$$

If $\{a_n\}$ is a sequence such that $f(n) = a_n$ for every positive integer n, then

$$\lim_{n\to\infty} a_n = L.$$

A sequence that does not converge is said to **diverge.** For instance, the terms of the sequence $1, -1, 1, -1, 1, . . .$ oscillate between 1 and -1. Therefore, the sequence diverges because it does not approach a unique number.

Example 4 Finding the Limit of a Sequence

Find the limit of each sequence. (Assume n begins with 1.)

a. $a_n = \dfrac{2n + 1}{n + 4}$

b. $b_n = \dfrac{2n + 1}{n^2 + 4}$

c. $c_n = \dfrac{2n^2 + 1}{4n^2}$

Solution

a. $\displaystyle\lim_{n\to\infty} \frac{2n + 1}{n + 4} = 2$ $\quad \frac{3}{5}, \frac{5}{6}, \frac{7}{7}, \frac{9}{8}, \frac{11}{9}, \frac{13}{10}, . . . \to 2$

b. $\displaystyle\lim_{n\to\infty} \frac{2n + 1}{n^2 + 4} = 0$ $\quad \frac{3}{5}, \frac{5}{8}, \frac{7}{13}, \frac{9}{20}, \frac{11}{29}, \frac{13}{40}, . . . \to 0$

c. $\displaystyle\lim_{n\to\infty} \frac{2n^2 + 1}{4n^2} = \frac{1}{2}$ $\quad \frac{3}{4}, \frac{9}{16}, \frac{19}{36}, \frac{33}{64}, \frac{51}{100}, \frac{73}{144}, . . . \to \frac{1}{2}$

CHECKPoint Now try Exercise 39.

Study Tip

You can use the definition of limits at infinity for rational functions on page 884 to verify the limits of the sequences in Example 4.

Extra Example 4

Find the limit of each sequence. (Assume n begins with 1.)

a. $a_n = \dfrac{4n + 5}{n - 1}$

4

b. $a_n = \dfrac{4n + 5}{n^2 - 1}$

0

c. $a_n = \dfrac{4n^2 + 5}{12n^2}$

$\dfrac{1}{3}$

Avoiding Common Errors

Students sometimes forget that only the highest powers in a rational function dictate the limit at infinity. Remind them of the methods used to find horizontal asymptotes in Chapter 2.

Extra Example 5

Find the limit of the sequence whose nth term is

$$a_n = \frac{5}{n^3}\left[\frac{n(n+1)(2n+1)}{6}\right].$$

$\frac{5}{3}$

Closing the Lesson

Have students summarize the major points of the lesson and answer the Essential Question: How do you find the limits of functions at infinity and the limits of sequences?

- **Evaluate the limits at infinity of rational functions by dividing both the numerator and denominator by the highest-powered term.**
- **Recognize that if the greatest power of a rational function is in its numerator, then the function has no limit at infinity.**
- **Identify that the limit at infinity of a rational function with its greatest power in the denominator is zero.**
- **Find the limit at infinity of a rational function with equal powers in its numerator and denominator by dividing the leading coefficient of the numerator by the leading coefficient of the denominator.**
- **Find the limit of a sequence by finding the limit at infinity of the series' nth term.**

In the next section, you will encounter limits of sequences such as that shown in Example 5. A strategy for evaluating such limits is to begin by writing the nth term in standard rational function form. Then you can determine the limit by comparing the degrees of the numerator and denominator, as shown on page 884.

Example 5 Finding the Limit of a Sequence

Find the limit of the sequence whose nth term is

$$a_n = \frac{8}{n^3}\left[\frac{n(n+1)(2n+1)}{6}\right].$$

Algebraic Solution

Begin by writing the nth term in standard rational function form—as the ratio of two polynomials.

$$a_n = \frac{8}{n^3}\left[\frac{n(n+1)(2n+1)}{6}\right] \quad \text{Write original } n\text{th term.}$$

$$= \frac{8(n)(n+1)(2n+1)}{6n^3} \quad \text{Multiply fractions.}$$

$$= \frac{8n^3 + 12n^2 + 4n}{3n^3} \quad \text{Write in standard rational form.}$$

From this form, you can see that the degree of the numerator is equal to the degree of the denominator. So, the limit of the sequence is the ratio of the coefficients of the highest-powered terms.

$$\lim_{n\to\infty} \frac{8n^3 + 12n^2 + 4n}{3n^3} = \frac{8}{3}$$

CHECK*Point* Now try Exercise 49.

Numerical Solution

Construct a table that shows the value of a_n as n becomes larger and larger, as shown below.

n	a_n
1	8
10	3.08
100	2.707
1000	2.671
10,000	2.667

From the table, you can estimate that as n approaches ∞, a_n gets closer and closer to $2.667 \approx \frac{8}{3}$.

Classroom Discussion

Comparing Rates of Convergence In the table in Example 5 above, the value of a_n approaches its limit of $\frac{8}{3}$ rather slowly. (The first term to be accurate to three decimal places is $a_{4801} \approx 2.667$.) Each of the following sequences converges to 0. Which converges the quickest? Which converges the slowest? Why? Write a short paragraph discussing your conclusions.

a. $a_n = \frac{1}{n}$ b. $b_n = \frac{1}{n^2}$ c. $c_n = \frac{1}{2^n}$

d. $d_n = \frac{1}{n!}$ e. $h_n = \frac{2^n}{n!}$

(d) converges the fastest and (a) converges the slowest. Conclusions will vary.

12.4 EXERCISES

See www.CalcChat.com for worked-out solutions to odd-numbered exercises.

VOCABULARY: Fill in the blanks.

1. A limit at infinity can be used to solve the area problem in calculus.
2. When evaluating limits at infinity for complicated rational functions, you can divide the numerator and denominator by the ________ term in the denominator. highest-powered
3. A sequence that has a limit is said to converge.
4. A sequence that does not have a limit is said to diverge.

SKILLS AND APPLICATIONS

In Exercises 5–8, match the function with its graph, using horizontal asymptotes as aids. [The graphs are labeled (a), (b), (c), and (d).]

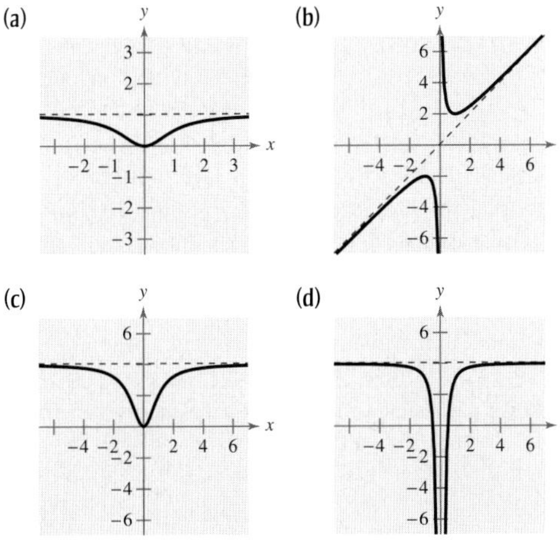

5. $f(x) = \dfrac{4x^2}{x^2 + 1}$ c
6. $f(x) = \dfrac{x^2}{x^2 + 1}$ a
7. $f(x) = 4 - \dfrac{1}{x^2}$ d
8. $f(x) = x + \dfrac{1}{x}$ b

In Exercises 9–28, find the limit (if it exists). If the limit does not exist, explain why. Use a graphing utility to verify your result graphically.

9. $\lim\limits_{x\to\infty}\left(\dfrac{3}{x^2} + 1\right)$ 1
10. $\lim\limits_{x\to\infty}\left(\dfrac{4}{3x} - 5\right)$ -5
11. $\lim\limits_{x\to\infty}\left(\dfrac{1 - x}{1 + x}\right)$ -1
12. $\lim\limits_{x\to\infty}\left(\dfrac{1 + 5x}{1 - 4x}\right)$ $-\frac{5}{4}$
13. $\lim\limits_{x\to-\infty}\dfrac{4x - 3}{2x + 1}$ 2
14. $\lim\limits_{x\to\infty}\dfrac{1 - 2x}{x + 2}$ -2
15. $\lim\limits_{x\to-\infty}\dfrac{3x^2 - 4}{1 - x^2}$ -3
16. $\lim\limits_{x\to-\infty}\dfrac{3x^2 + 1}{4x^2 - 5}$ $\frac{3}{4}$
17. $\lim\limits_{t\to\infty}\dfrac{t^2}{t + 3}$ Does not exist
18. $\lim\limits_{y\to\infty}\dfrac{4y^4}{y^2 + 3}$ Does not exist
19. $\lim\limits_{t\to\infty}\dfrac{4t^2 - 2t + 1}{-3t^2 + 2t + 2}$ $-\frac{4}{3}$
20. $\lim\limits_{x\to-\infty}\dfrac{2x^2 - 5x - 12}{1 - 6x - 8x^2}$ $-\frac{1}{4}$
21. $\lim\limits_{x\to-\infty}\dfrac{-(x^2 + 3)}{(2 - x)^2}$ -1
22. $\lim\limits_{x\to\infty}\dfrac{2x^2 - 6}{(x - 1)^2}$ 2
23. $\lim\limits_{x\to\infty}\dfrac{5x^3 + 1}{10x^3 - 3x^2 + 7}$ $\frac{1}{2}$
24. $\lim\limits_{x\to-\infty}\left(\dfrac{1}{2}x - \dfrac{4}{x^2}\right)$ Does not exist
25. $\lim\limits_{x\to-\infty}\left[\dfrac{x}{(x + 1)^2} - 4\right]$
26. $\lim\limits_{x\to\infty}\left[7 + \dfrac{2x^2}{(x + 3)^2}\right]$ 9
27. $\lim\limits_{t\to\infty}\left(\dfrac{1}{3t^2} - \dfrac{5t}{t + 2}\right)$ -5
28. $\lim\limits_{x\to\infty}\left[\dfrac{x}{2x + 1} + \dfrac{3x^2}{(x - 3)^2}\right]$ $\frac{7}{2}$

25. -4

In Exercises 29–34, use a graphing utility to graph the function and verify that the horizontal asymptote corresponds to the limit at infinity. 29–34. See margin.

29. $y = \dfrac{3x}{1 - x}$
30. $y = \dfrac{x^2}{x^2 + 4}$
31. $y = \dfrac{2x}{1 - x^2}$
32. $y = \dfrac{2x + 1}{x^2 - 1}$
33. $y = 1 - \dfrac{3}{x^2}$
34. $y = 2 + \dfrac{1}{x}$

NUMERICAL AND GRAPHICAL ANALYSIS In Exercises 35–38, (a) complete the table and numerically estimate the limit as x approaches infinity, and (b) use a graphing utility to graph the function and estimate the limit graphically.

x	10^0	10^1	10^2	10^3	10^4	10^5	10^6
$f(x)$							

35–38. See margin.

35. $f(x) = x - \sqrt{x^2 + 2}$
36. $f(x) = 3x - \sqrt{9x^2 + 1}$
37. $f(x) = 3\left(2x - \sqrt{4x^2 + x}\right)$
38. $f(x) = 4\left(4x - \sqrt{16x^2 - x}\right)$

4 PRACTICE AND APPLY

Assignment Guide

Transparencies Available
Available at the Instructor's companion site.

Average:
Day 1: pp. 887–888
Exs. 5–8, 10–15, 18, 19–37 odd, 53, 56
Day 2: pp. 888–890
Exs. 40, 41–49 odd, 57, 59–63, 65–67, 70

Advanced:
Day 1: pp. 887–888
Exs. 5–8, 12–16, 18–38 even, 54, 56
Day 2: pp. 888–890
Exs. 42–50 even, 58–61, 63, 64, 66–68, 70, 71

Block:
pp. 887–888
Exs. 5–8, 10–15, 18, 19–37 odd, 53, 56 (with 12.3)
pp. 888–890
Exs. 40, 41–49 odd, 57, 59–63, 65–67, 70 (with 12.5)

29.

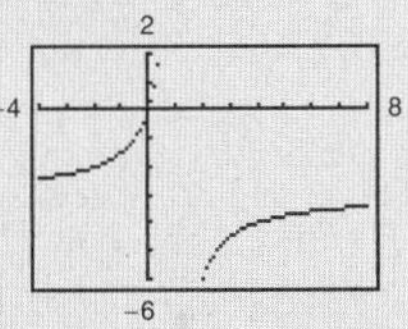

Horizontal asymptote: $y = -3$

30.

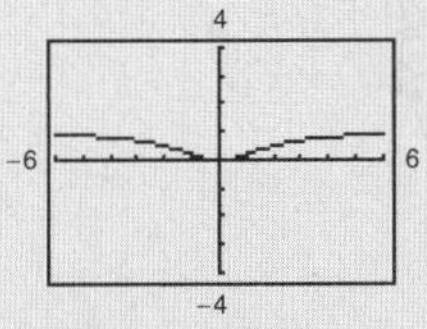

Horizontal asymptote: $y = 1$

31.

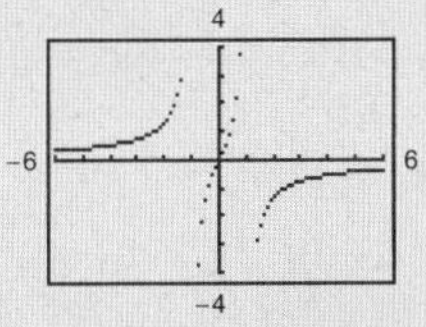

Horizontal asymptote: $y = 0$

32.

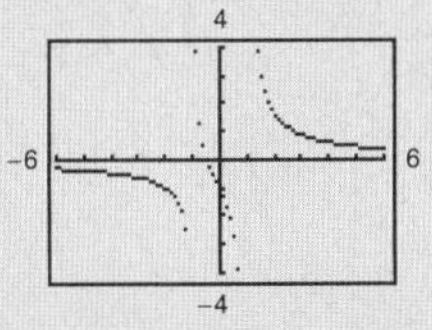

Horizontal asymptote: $y = 0$

33.

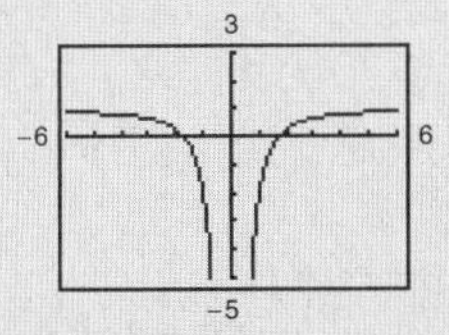

Horizontal asymptote: $y = 1$

34.

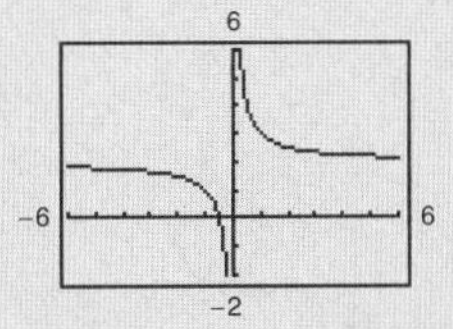

Horizontal asymptote: $y = 2$

35–38. See Additional Answers beginning on page AA1.

In Exercises 39–48, write the first five terms of the sequence and find the limit of the sequence (if it exists). If the limit does not exist, explain why. Assume n begins with 1. 39–48. See margin.

39. $a_n = \dfrac{n+1}{n^2+1}$

40. $a_n = \dfrac{3n}{n^2+2}$

41. $a_n = \dfrac{n}{2n+1}$

42. $a_n = \dfrac{4n-1}{n+3}$

43. $a_n = \dfrac{n^2}{2n+3}$

44. $a_n = \dfrac{4n^2+1}{2n}$

45. $a_n = \dfrac{(n+1)!}{n!}$

46. $a_n = \dfrac{(3n-1)!}{(3n+1)!}$

47. $a_n = \dfrac{(-1)^n}{n}$

48. $a_n = \dfrac{(-1)^{n+1}}{n^2}$

In Exercises 49–52, find the limit of the sequence. Then verify the limit numerically by using a graphing utility to complete the table. 49–52. See margin.

n	10^0	10^1	10^2	10^3	10^4	10^5	10^6
a_n							

49. $a_n = \dfrac{1}{n}\left(n + \dfrac{1}{n}\left[\dfrac{n(n+1)}{2}\right]\right)$

50. $a_n = \dfrac{4}{n}\left(n + \dfrac{4}{n}\left[\dfrac{n(n+1)}{2}\right]\right)$

51. $a_n = \dfrac{16}{n^3}\left[\dfrac{n(n+1)(2n+1)}{6}\right]$

52. $a_n = \dfrac{n(n+1)}{n^2} - \dfrac{1}{n^4}\left[\dfrac{n(n+1)}{2}\right]^2$

53. OXYGEN LEVEL Suppose that $f(t)$ measures the level of oxygen in a pond, where $f(t) = 1$ is the normal (unpolluted) level and the time t is measured in weeks. When $t = 0$, organic waste is dumped into the pond, and as the waste material oxidizes, the level of oxygen in the pond is given by

$$f(t) = \frac{t^2 - t + 1}{t^2 + 1}.$$ See margin.

(a) What is the limit of f as t approaches infinity?

(b) Use a graphing utility to graph the function and verify the result of part (a).

(c) Explain the meaning of the limit in the context of the problem.

54. TYPING SPEED The average typing speed S (in words per minute) for a student after t weeks of lessons is given by

$$S = \frac{100t^2}{65 + t^2}, \quad t > 0.$$ See margin.

(a) What is the limit of S as t approaches infinity?

(b) Use a graphing utility to graph the function and verify the result of part (a).

(c) Explain the meaning of the limit in the context of the problem.

55. AVERAGE COST The cost function for a certain model of personal digital assistant (PDA) is given by $C = 13.50x + 45{,}750$, where C is measured in dollars and x is the number of PDAs produced. See margin.

(a) Write a model for the average cost per unit produced.

(b) Find the average costs per unit when $x = 100$ and $x = 1000$.

(c) Determine the limit of the average cost function as x approaches infinity. Explain the meaning of the limit in the context of the problem.

56. AVERAGE COST The cost function for a company to recycle x tons of material is given by $C = 1.25x + 10{,}500$, where C is measured in dollars.

(a) Write a model for the average cost per ton of material recycled. (a)–(c). See margin.

(b) Find the average costs of recycling 100 tons of material and 1000 tons of material.

(c) Determine the limit of the average cost function as x approaches infinity. Explain the meaning of the limit in the context of the problem.

57. DATA ANALYSIS: SOCIAL SECURITY The table shows the average monthly Social Security benefits B (in dollars) for retired workers aged 62 or over from 2001 through 2007. (Source: U.S. Social Security Administration)

Year	Benefit, B
2001	874
2002	895
2003	922
2004	955
2005	1002
2006	1044
2007	1079

A model for the data is given by

$$B = \frac{867.3 + 707.56t}{1.0 + 0.83t - 0.030t^2}, \quad 1 \le t \le 7$$

where t represents the year, with $t = 1$ corresponding to 2001. See margin.

39. $1, \frac{3}{5}, \frac{2}{5}, \frac{5}{17}, \frac{3}{13}$
Limit: 0

40. $1, 1, \frac{9}{11}, \frac{2}{3}, \frac{5}{9}$
Limit: 0

41. $\frac{1}{3}, \frac{2}{5}, \frac{3}{7}, \frac{4}{9}, \frac{5}{11}$
Limit: $\frac{1}{2}$

42. $\frac{3}{4}, \frac{7}{5}, \frac{11}{6}, \frac{15}{7}, \frac{19}{8}$
Limit: 4

43. $\frac{1}{5}, \frac{4}{7}, 1, \frac{16}{11}, \frac{25}{13}$
Limit does not exist.

44. $\frac{5}{2}, \frac{17}{4}, \frac{37}{6}, \frac{65}{8}, \frac{101}{10}$
Limit does not exist.

45. 2, 3, 4, 5, 6
Limit does not exist.

46. $\frac{1}{12}, \frac{1}{42}, \frac{1}{90}, \frac{1}{156}, \frac{1}{240}$
Limit: 0

47. $-1, \frac{1}{2}, -\frac{1}{3}, \frac{1}{4}, -\frac{1}{5}$
Limit: 0

48. $1, -\frac{1}{4}, \frac{1}{9}, -\frac{1}{16}, \frac{1}{25}$
Limit: 0

53. (a) 1

(b)
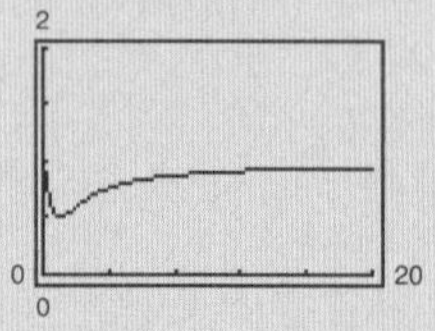

(c) Over a long period of time, the level of the oxygen in the pond returns to the normal level.

54. (a) 100

(b)
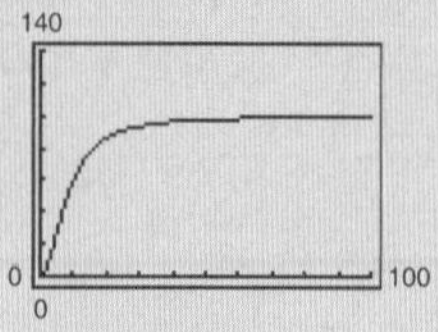

(c) A student's average typing speed approaches 100 words per minute.

55. (a) $\overline{C}(x) = \dfrac{13.50x + 45{,}750}{x}$

(b) \$471; \$59.25

(c) \$13.50. As the number of PDAs gets very large, the average cost approaches \$13.50.

56. (a) $\overline{C}(x) = \dfrac{1.25x + 10{,}500}{x}$

(b) \$106.25, \$11.75

(c) \$1.25; As the number of tons of material gets very large, the average cost to recycle approaches \$1.25 per ton.

57. (a)
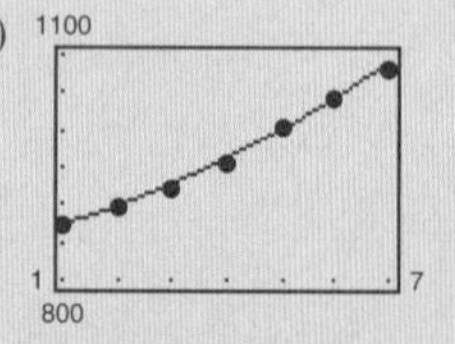

The model is a good fit for the data.

(b) \$1598.39

(c) When t is slightly less than 29, a vertical asymptote is found.

49–52. See Additional Answers beginning on page AA1.

(a) Use a graphing utility to create a scatter plot of the data and graph the model in the same viewing window. How well does the model fit the data?

(b) Use the model to predict the average monthly benefit in 2014.

(c) Discuss why this model should not be used for long-term predictions of average monthly Social Security benefits.

58. DATA ANALYSIS: MILITARY The table shows the numbers N (in thousands) of U.S. military reserve personnel for the years 2001 through 2007. (Source: U.S. Department of Defense)

Year	Number, N
2001	1249
2002	1222
2003	1189
2004	1167
2005	1136
2006	1120
2007	1110

A model for the data is given by

$$N = \frac{1287.9 + 61.53t}{1.0 + 0.08t}, \quad 1 \le t \le 7$$

where t represents the year, with $t = 1$ corresponding to 2001. See margin.

(a) Use a graphing utility to create a scatter plot of the data and graph the model in the same viewing window. How well does the model fit the data?

(b) Use the model to predict the number of military reserve personnel in 2014.

(c) What is the limit of the function as t approaches infinity? Explain the meaning of the limit in the context of the problem. Do you think the limit is realistic? Explain.

EXPLORATION

59–62. See margin.

TRUE OR FALSE? In Exercises 59–62, determine whether the statement is true or false. Justify your answer.

59. Every rational function has a horizontal asymptote.

60. If $f(x)$ increases without bound as x approaches c, then the limit of $f(x)$ exists.

61. If a sequence converges, then it has a limit.

62. When the degrees of the numerator and denominator of a rational function are equal, the limit does not exist.

63. THINK ABOUT IT Find the functions f and g such that both $f(x)$ and $g(x)$ increase without bound as x approaches c, but $\lim_{x\to c}[f(x) - g(x)]$ exists. See margin.

64. THINK ABOUT IT Use a graphing utility to graph the function given by

$$f(x) = \frac{x}{\sqrt{x^2 + 1}}.$$

See margin.

How many horizontal asymptotes does the function appear to have? What are the horizontal asymptotes?

In Exercises 65–68, create a scatter plot of the terms of the sequence. Determine whether the sequence converges or diverges. If it converges, estimate its limit. 65–68. See margin.

65. $a_n = 4\left(\frac{2}{3}\right)^n$ **66.** $a_n = 3\left(\frac{3}{2}\right)^n$

67. $a_n = \dfrac{3[1 - (1.5)^n]}{1 - 1.5}$ **68.** $a_n = \dfrac{3[1 - (0.5)^n]}{1 - 0.5}$

69. Use a graphing utility to graph the two functions given by

$$y_1 = \frac{1}{\sqrt{x}} \quad \text{and} \quad y_2 = \frac{1}{\sqrt[3]{x}}$$

in the same viewing window. Why does y_1 not appear to the left of the y-axis? How does this relate to the statement at the top of page 882 about the infinite limit

$$\lim_{x\to-\infty} \frac{1}{x^r}?$$ See margin.

70. CAPSTONE Use the graph to estimate (a) $\lim_{x\to\infty} f(x)$, (b) $\lim_{x\to-\infty} f(x)$, and (c) the horizontal asymptote of the graph of f.

(a) (i) 0 (ii) 2 (b) (i) 0 (ii) 2
(c) (i) $y = 0$ (ii) $y = 2$

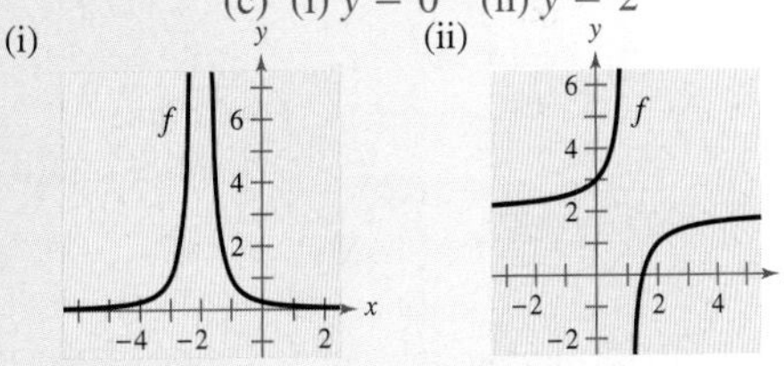

71. Use a graphing utility to complete the table below to verify that $\lim_{x\to\infty} (1/x) = 0$.

x	10^0	10^1	10^2	10^3	10^4	10^5
$\dfrac{1}{x}$						

Make a conjecture about $\lim_{x\to 0} \dfrac{1}{x}$. See margin.

5 ASSESS AND RETEACH

Daily Homework Quiz

Transparency Available
Available at the Instructor's companion site.

58. (a)

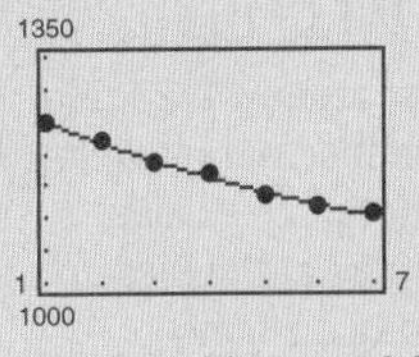

The model is a good fit for the data.

(b) 1014 thousand

(c) 769 thousand; The number of military reserves available will not go below 769 thousand. Answers will vary.

59. False. Graph $y = \dfrac{x^2}{x + 1}$.

60. False. The limit does not exist.

61. True. If the sequence converges, then the limit exists.

62. False. The limit is the ratio of the coefficients of the highest-powered terms.

63. Let $f(x) = \dfrac{1}{x^2}$, $g(x) = \dfrac{1}{x^2}$, and $c = 0$. Now $\dfrac{1}{x^2}$ increases without bound as $x \to 0$ and $\lim_{x\to 0}[f(x) - g(x)] = 0$.

64.

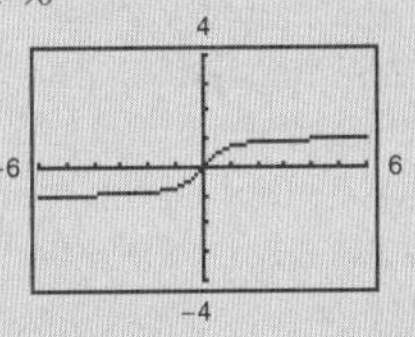

Two horizontal asymptotes: $y = -1$ and $y = 1$

65.

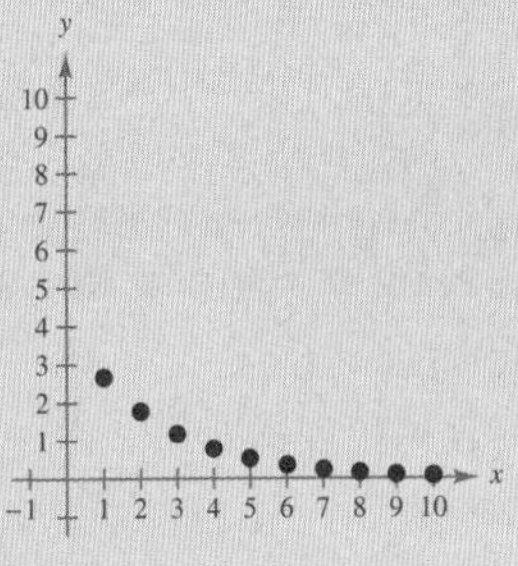

Converges to 0

66.

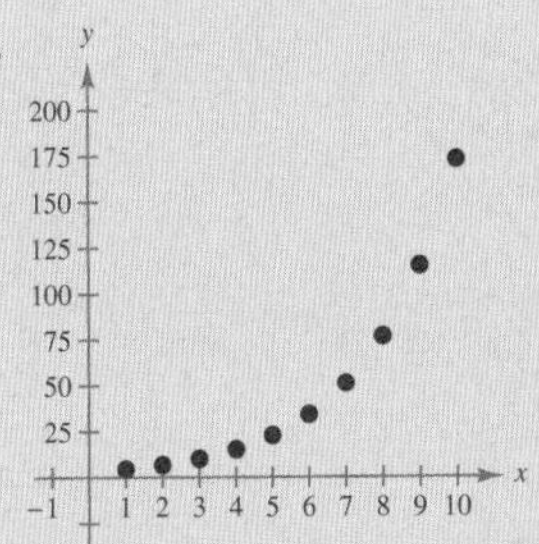

Diverges

67.

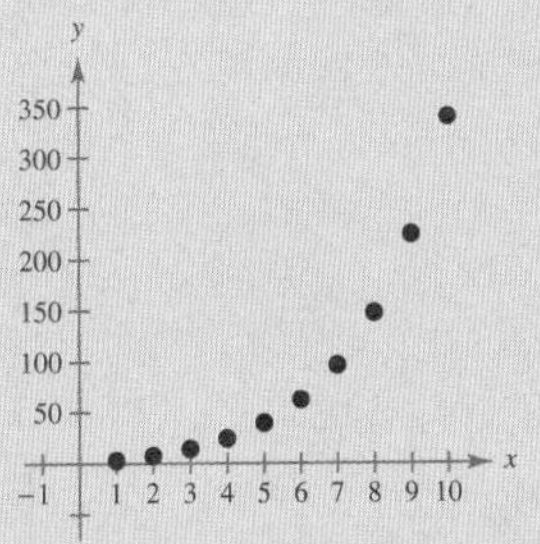

Diverges

68.

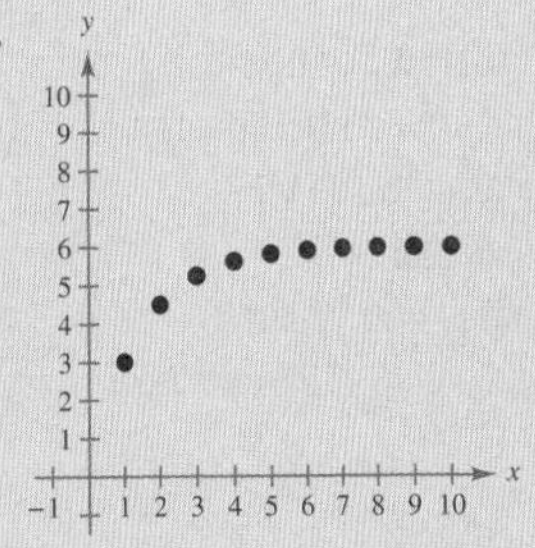

Converges to 6

69, 71. See Additional Answers beginning on page AA1.

12.5 The Area Problem

What you should learn

- Find limits of summations.
- Use rectangles to approximate areas of plane regions.
- Use limits of summations to find areas of plane regions.

Why you should learn it

The limits of summations are useful in determining areas of plane regions. For instance, in Exercise 50 on page 897, you are asked to find the limit of a summation to determine the area of a parcel of land bounded by a stream and two roads.

© Adam Woolfitt/Corbis

Limits of Summations

Earlier in the text, you used the concept of a limit to obtain a formula for the sum S of an infinite geometric series

$$S = a_1 + a_1 r + a_1 r^2 + \cdot \cdot \cdot = \sum_{i=1}^{\infty} a_1 r^{i-1} = \frac{a_1}{1-r}, \quad |r| < 1.$$

Using limit notation, this sum can be written as

$$S = \lim_{n\to\infty} \sum_{i=1}^{n} a_1 r^{i-1} = \lim_{n\to\infty} \frac{a_1(1-r^n)}{1-r} = \frac{a_1}{1-r}. \qquad \lim_{n\to\infty} r^n = 0 \text{ for } |r| < 1$$

The following summation formulas and properties are used to evaluate finite and infinite summations.

Summation Formulas and Properties

1. $\sum_{i=1}^{n} c = cn$, c is a constant.
2. $\sum_{i=1}^{n} i = \frac{n(n+1)}{2}$
3. $\sum_{i=1}^{n} i^2 = \frac{n(n+1)(2n+1)}{6}$
4. $\sum_{i=1}^{n} i^3 = \frac{n^2(n+1)^2}{4}$
5. $\sum_{i=1}^{n} (a_i \pm b_i) = \sum_{i=1}^{n} a_i \pm \sum_{i=1}^{n} b_i$
6. $\sum_{i=1}^{n} ka_i = k\sum_{i=1}^{n} a_i$, k is a constant.

Example 1 Evaluating a Summation

Evaluate the summation.

$$\sum_{i=1}^{200} i = 1 + 2 + 3 + 4 + \cdot \cdot \cdot + 200$$

Solution

Using the second summation formula with $n = 200$, you can write

$$\sum_{i=1}^{n} i = \frac{n(n+1)}{2}$$

$$\sum_{i=1}^{200} i = \frac{200(200+1)}{2}$$

$$= \frac{40{,}200}{2}$$

$$= 20{,}100.$$

CHECKPoint Now try Exercise 5.

Algebra Help

Recall from Section 9.3 that the sum of a finite geometric sequence is given by

$$\sum_{i=1}^{n} a_1 r^{i-1} = a_1\left(\frac{1-r^n}{1-r}\right).$$

Furthermore, if $0 < |r| < 1$, then $r^n \to 0$ as $n \to \infty$.

1 PLAN AND PREPARE

Warm-up Exercises

Transparency Available
Available at the Instructor's companion site.

Notetaking Guide

Transparency Available
Promotes interactive learning and notetaking skills.
Available at the Instructor's companion site.

Animated Precalculus

An **Animated Precalculus** tutorial is available at the Student companion site for **Section 12.5.**

Pacing

Average: 2 days
Advanced: 2 days
Block: 0.5 block with 12.4
0.5 block with Review

2 FOCUS AND MOTIVATE

Essential Question

How do you approximate and find exact areas of plane regions defined by functions? **Tell students that they will learn how to answer this question by finding the limits of summations and by dividing the plane region into smaller and smaller rectangles.**

Resource Planning Guide

Chapter Resources
- Complete Solutions Guide

Workbooks
- Notetaking Guide
- Student Solutions Guide

Interactive Technology
- Instructor Success Organizer
- Notetaking Guide IAE
- Instructional DVDs
- Animated Precalculus
- PowerLecture with ExamView

TECHNOLOGY

Some graphing utilities have a *sum sequence* feature that is useful for computing summations. Consult the user's guide for your graphing utility for the required keystrokes.

Example 2 Evaluating a Summation

Evaluate the summation

$$S = \sum_{i=1}^{n} \frac{i+2}{n^2} = \frac{3}{n^2} + \frac{4}{n^2} + \frac{5}{n^2} + \cdots + \frac{n+2}{n^2}$$

for $n = 10, 100, 1000$, and 10,000.

Solution

Begin by applying summation formulas and properties to simplify S. In the second line of the solution, note that $1/n^2$ can be factored out of the sum because n is considered to be constant. You could not factor i out of the summation because i is the (variable) index of summation.

$$S = \sum_{i=1}^{n} \frac{i+2}{n^2}$$ Write original form of summation.

$$= \frac{1}{n^2}\sum_{i=1}^{n}(i+2)$$ Factor constant $1/n^2$ out of sum.

$$= \frac{1}{n^2}\left(\sum_{i=1}^{n} i + \sum_{i=1}^{n} 2\right)$$ Write as two sums.

$$= \frac{1}{n^2}\left[\frac{n(n+1)}{2} + 2n\right]$$ Apply Formulas 1 and 2.

$$= \frac{1}{n^2}\left(\frac{n^2+5n}{2}\right)$$ Add fractions.

$$= \frac{n+5}{2n}$$ Simplify.

Now you can evaluate the sum by substituting the appropriate values of n, as shown in the following table.

n	10	100	1000	10,000
$\sum_{i=1}^{n} \frac{i+2}{n^2} = \frac{n+5}{2n}$	0.75	0.525	0.5025	0.50025

CHECKPoint Now try Exercise 15.

In Example 2, note that the sum appears to approach a limit as n increases. To find the limit of

$$\frac{n+5}{2n}$$

as n approaches infinity, you can use the techniques from Section 12.4 to write

$$\lim_{n\to\infty} \frac{n+5}{2n} = \frac{1}{2}.$$

3 TEACH

Extra Example 1

Evaluate the summation.

$$\sum_{i=1}^{50} i^2 = 1^2 + 2^2 + 3^2 + 4^2 + \cdots + 50^2$$

42,925

Extra Example 2

Simplify the summation.

$$S = \sum_{i=1}^{n} \frac{i+3}{n^2} = \frac{4}{n^2} + \frac{5}{n^2} + \frac{6}{n^2} + \cdots + \frac{n+3}{n^2}$$

$$\mathbf{\frac{n+7}{2n}}$$

Extra Example 3

Find the limit of $S(n)$ as $n \to \infty$.

$$S(n) = \sum_{i=1}^{n} \left(2 + \frac{i}{n}\right)^2 \left(\frac{1}{n}\right)$$

$\frac{19}{3}$

Be sure you notice the strategy used in Example 2. Rather than separately evaluating the sums

$$\sum_{i=1}^{10} \frac{i+2}{n^2}, \quad \sum_{i=1}^{100} \frac{i+2}{n^2}, \quad \sum_{i=1}^{1000} \frac{i+2}{n^2}, \quad \sum_{i=1}^{10,000} \frac{i+2}{n^2}$$

it was more efficient first to convert to rational form using the summation formulas and properties listed on page 890.

$$S = \underbrace{\sum_{i=1}^{n} \frac{i+2}{n^2}}_{\text{Summation form}} = \underbrace{\frac{n+5}{2n}}_{\text{Rational form}}$$

With this rational form, each sum can be evaluated by simply substituting appropriate values of n.

Example 3 Finding the Limit of a Summation

Find the limit of $S(n)$ as $n \to \infty$.

$$S(n) = \sum_{i=1}^{n} \left(1 + \frac{i}{n}\right)^2 \left(\frac{1}{n}\right)$$

Solution

Begin by rewriting the summation in rational form.

$$S(n) = \sum_{i=1}^{n} \left(1 + \frac{i}{n}\right)^2 \left(\frac{1}{n}\right) \qquad \text{Write original form of summation.}$$

$$= \sum_{i=1}^{n} \left(\frac{n^2 + 2ni + i^2}{n^2}\right)\left(\frac{1}{n}\right) \qquad \text{Square } (1 + i/n) \text{ and write as a single fraction.}$$

$$= \frac{1}{n^3} \sum_{i=1}^{n} (n^2 + 2ni + i^2) \qquad \text{Factor constant } 1/n^3 \text{ out of the sum.}$$

$$= \frac{1}{n^3}\left(\sum_{i=1}^{n} n^2 + \sum_{i=1}^{n} 2ni + \sum_{i=1}^{n} i^2\right) \qquad \text{Write as three sums.}$$

$$= \frac{1}{n^3}\left\{n^3 + 2n\left[\frac{n(n+1)}{2}\right] + \frac{n(n+1)(2n+1)}{6}\right\} \qquad \text{Use summation formulas.}$$

$$= \frac{14n^3 + 9n^2 + n}{6n^3} \qquad \text{Simplify.}$$

In this rational form, you can now find the limit as $n \to \infty$.

$$\lim_{n \to \infty} S(n) = \lim_{n \to \infty} \frac{14n^3 + 9n^2 + n}{6n^3}$$

$$= \frac{14}{6}$$

$$= \frac{7}{3}$$

CHECKPoint Now try Exercise 17.

Algebra Help

As you can see from Example 3, there is a lot of algebra involved in rewriting a summation in rational form. You may want to review simplifying rational expressions if you are having difficulty with this procedure. (See Appendix A.4.)

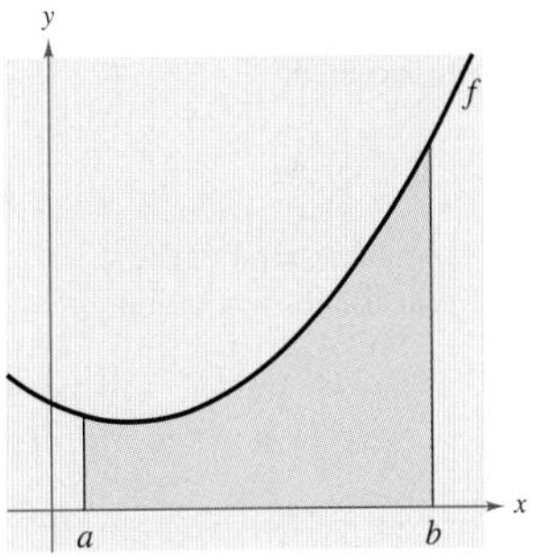

FIGURE 12.33

The Area Problem

You now have the tools needed to solve the second basic problem of calculus: the area problem. The problem is to find the *area* of the region R bounded by the graph of a nonnegative, continuous function f, the x-axis, and the vertical lines $x = a$ and $x = b$, as shown in Figure 12.33.

If the region R is a square, a triangle, a trapezoid, or a semicircle, you can find its area by using a geometric formula. For more general regions, however, you must use a different approach—one that involves the limit of a summation. The basic strategy is to use a collection of rectangles of equal width that approximates the region R, as illustrated in Example 4.

Example 4 Approximating the Area of a Region

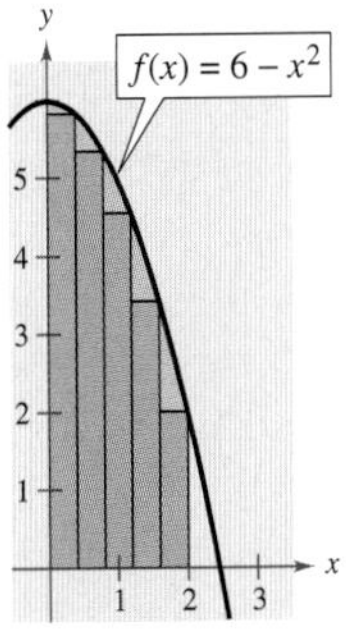

FIGURE 12.34

Use the five rectangles in Figure 12.34 to approximate the area of the region bounded by the graph of $f(x) = 6 - x^2$, the x-axis, and the lines $x = 0$ and $x = 2$.

Solution

Because the length of the interval along the x-axis is 2 and there are five rectangles, the width of each rectangle is $\frac{2}{5}$. The height of each rectangle can be obtained by evaluating f at the right endpoint of each interval. The five intervals are as follows.

$$\left[0, \frac{2}{5}\right], \quad \left[\frac{2}{5}, \frac{4}{5}\right], \quad \left[\frac{4}{5}, \frac{6}{5}\right], \quad \left[\frac{6}{5}, \frac{8}{5}\right], \quad \left[\frac{8}{5}, \frac{10}{5}\right]$$

Notice that the right endpoint of each interval is $\frac{2}{5}i$ for $i = 1, 2, 3, 4, 5$. The sum of the areas of the five rectangles is

$$\sum_{i=1}^{5} \overbrace{f\left(\frac{2i}{5}\right)}^{\text{Height}}\overbrace{\left(\frac{2}{5}\right)}^{\text{Width}} = \sum_{i=1}^{5}\left[6 - \left(\frac{2i}{5}\right)^2\right]\left(\frac{2}{5}\right)$$

$$= \frac{2}{5}\left(\sum_{i=1}^{5} 6 - \frac{4}{25}\sum_{i=1}^{5} i^2\right)$$

$$= \frac{2}{5}\left[6(5) - \frac{4}{25} \cdot \frac{5(5 + 1)(10 + 1)}{6}\right]$$

$$= \frac{2}{5}\left(30 - \frac{44}{5}\right)$$

$$= \frac{212}{25} = 8.48.$$

So, you can approximate the area of R as 8.48 square units.

CHECK *Point* Now try Exercise 23.

By increasing the number of rectangles used in Example 4, you can obtain closer and closer approximations of the area of the region. For instance, using 25 rectangles of width $\frac{2}{25}$ each, you can approximate the area to be $A \approx 9.17$ square units. The following table shows even better approximations.

n	5	25	100	1000	5000
Approximate area	8.48	9.17	9.29	9.33	9.33

Extra Example 4

Use the five rectangles in the figure below to approximate the area of the region bounded by $f(x) = 8 - x^2$, the x-axis, and the lines $x = 0$ and $x = 2$.

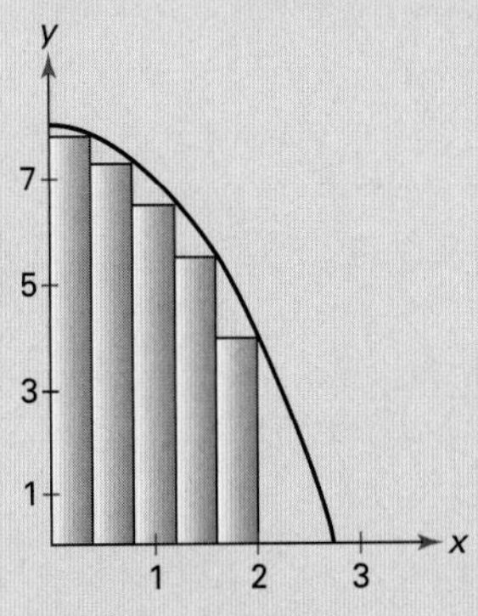

12.48 square units

Extra Example 5

Find the area of the region bounded by the graph of $f(x) = 2x^2$ and the x-axis between $x = 0$ and $x = 1$.

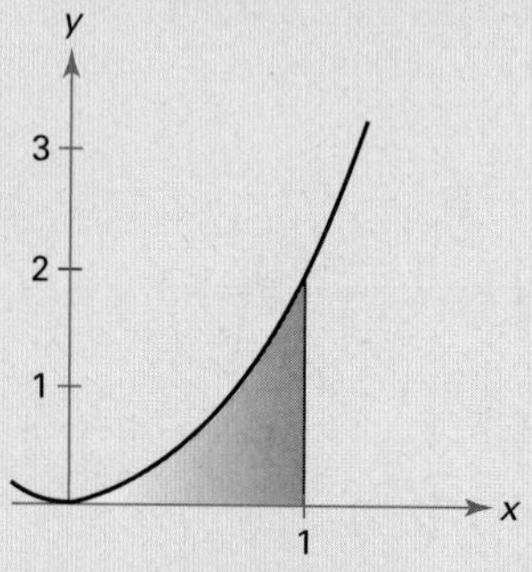

$\frac{2}{3}$

Avoiding Common Errors

When solving problems that involve a large number of steps, students often make mistakes in basic algebra. Remind students to be especially careful with signs, coefficients, and powers when they are factoring and distributing over expressions.

Based on the procedure illustrated in Example 4, the *exact* **area of a plane region** R is given by the limit of the sum of n rectangles as n approaches ∞.

Area of a Plane Region

Let f be continuous and nonnegative on the interval $[a, b]$. The area A of the region bounded by the graph of f, the x-axis, and the vertical lines $x = a$ and $x = b$ is given by

$$A = \lim_{n\to\infty} \sum_{i=1}^{n} \underbrace{f\left(a + \frac{(b-a)i}{n}\right)}_{\text{Height}} \underbrace{\left(\frac{b-a}{n}\right)}_{\text{Width}}.$$

Example 5 Finding the Area of a Region

Find the area of the region bounded by the graph of $f(x) = x^2$ and the x-axis between $x = 0$ and $x = 1$, as shown in Figure 12.35.

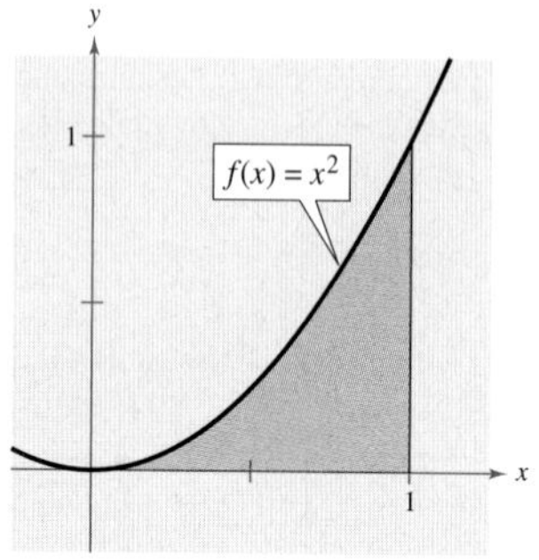

FIGURE 12.35

Solution

Begin by finding the dimensions of the rectangles.

$$\textit{Width: } \frac{b-a}{n} = \frac{1-0}{n} = \frac{1}{n}$$

$$\textit{Height: } f\left(a + \frac{(b-a)i}{n}\right) = f\left(0 + \frac{(1-0)i}{n}\right) = f\left(\frac{i}{n}\right) = \frac{i^2}{n^2}$$

Next, approximate the area as the sum of the areas of n rectangles.

$$A \approx \sum_{i=1}^{n} f\left(a + \frac{(b-a)i}{n}\right)\left(\frac{b-a}{n}\right)$$

$$= \sum_{i=1}^{n} \left(\frac{i^2}{n^2}\right)\left(\frac{1}{n}\right) \qquad \text{Summation form}$$

$$= \sum_{i=1}^{n} \frac{i^2}{n^3}$$

$$= \frac{1}{n^3}\sum_{i=1}^{n} i^2$$

$$= \frac{1}{n^3}\left[\frac{n(n+1)(2n+1)}{6}\right]$$

$$= \frac{2n^3 + 3n^2 + n}{6n^3} \qquad \text{Rational form}$$

Finally, find the exact area by taking the limit as n approaches ∞.

$$A = \lim_{n\to\infty} \frac{2n^3 + 3n^2 + n}{6n^3} = \frac{1}{3}$$

CHECKPoint Now try Exercise 37.

Example 6 Finding the Area of a Region

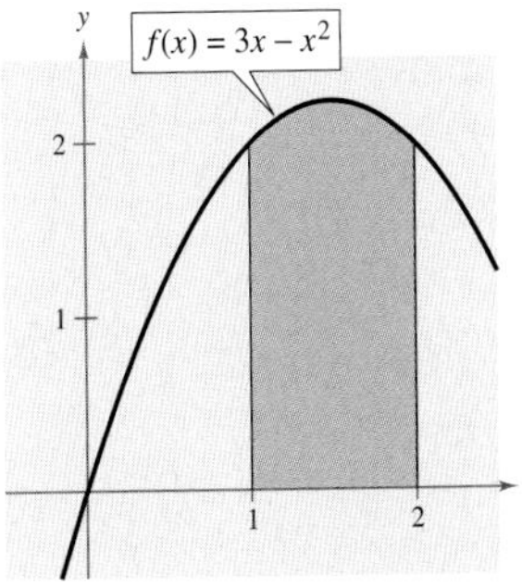

FIGURE 12.36

Find the area of the region bounded by the graph of $f(x) = 3x - x^2$ and the x-axis between $x = 1$ and $x = 2$, as shown in Figure 12.36.

Solution

Begin by finding the dimensions of the rectangles.

$$\textit{Width: } \frac{b-a}{n} = \frac{2-1}{n} = \frac{1}{n}$$

$$\begin{aligned}\textit{Height: } f\left(a + \frac{(b-a)i}{n}\right) &= f\left(1 + \frac{i}{n}\right)\\ &= 3\left(1 + \frac{i}{n}\right) - \left(1 + \frac{i}{n}\right)^2\\ &= 3 + \frac{3i}{n} - \left(1 + \frac{2i}{n} + \frac{i^2}{n^2}\right)\\ &= 2 + \frac{i}{n} - \frac{i^2}{n^2}\end{aligned}$$

Next, approximate the area as the sum of the areas of n rectangles.

$$\begin{aligned}A &\approx \sum_{i=1}^{n} f\left(a + \frac{(b-a)i}{n}\right)\left(\frac{b-a}{n}\right)\\ &= \sum_{i=1}^{n}\left(2 + \frac{i}{n} - \frac{i^2}{n^2}\right)\left(\frac{1}{n}\right)\\ &= \frac{1}{n}\sum_{i=1}^{n} 2 + \frac{1}{n^2}\sum_{i=1}^{n} i - \frac{1}{n^3}\sum_{i=1}^{n} i^2\\ &= \frac{1}{n}(2n) + \frac{1}{n^2}\left[\frac{n(n+1)}{2}\right] - \frac{1}{n^3}\left[\frac{n(n+1)(2n+1)}{6}\right]\\ &= 2 + \frac{n^2+n}{2n^2} - \frac{2n^3+3n^2+n}{6n^3}\\ &= 2 + \frac{1}{2} + \frac{1}{2n} - \frac{1}{3} - \frac{1}{2n} - \frac{1}{6n^2}\\ &= \frac{13}{6} - \frac{1}{6n^2}\end{aligned}$$

Finally, find the exact area by taking the limit as n approaches ∞.

$$\begin{aligned}A &= \lim_{n\to\infty}\left(\frac{13}{6} - \frac{1}{6n^2}\right)\\ &= \frac{13}{6}\end{aligned}$$

CHECKPoint Now try Exercise 43.

Extra Example 6

Find the area of the region bounded by the graph of $f(x) = 4x - x^2$ and the x-axis between $x = 1$ and $x = 3$.

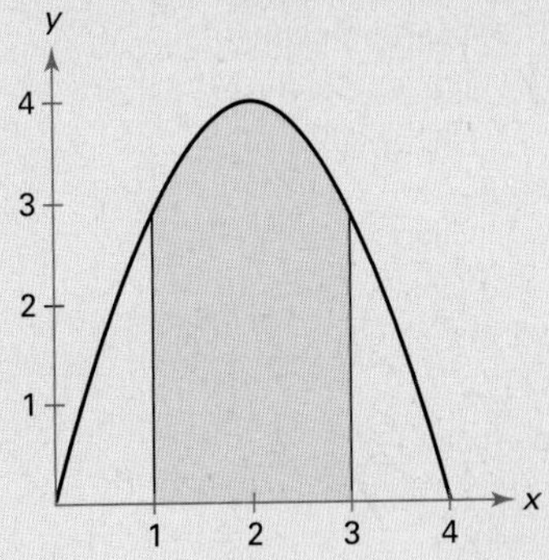

$\frac{22}{3}$

Closing the Lesson

Have students summarize the major points of the lesson and answer the Essential Question: How do you approximate and find exact areas of plane regions defined by functions?

- **Find the limit of a summation by writing the summation in rational form and then finding the limit as n approaches infinity.**
- **Find the area of a plane region by dividing the region into smaller and smaller rectangles and finding the sum of their areas by using the formula**

$$A = \lim_{n\to\infty} \sum_{i=1}^{n} f\left(a + \frac{(b-a)i}{n}\right)\left(\frac{b-a}{n}\right).$$

4 PRACTICE AND APPLY

Assignment Guide

Transparencies Available
Available at the Instructor's companion site.

Average:
Day 1: p. 896
Exs. 1–3, 6–14, 16, 18, 19, 21–25, 27
Day 2: pp. 896–897
Exs. 4, 29–41 odd, 44–47, 49–53

Advanced:
Day 1: p. 896
Exs. 1–3, 6–14, 16, 18–24, 26–28
Day 2: pp. 896–897
Exs. 4, 30–44 even, 46–54

Block:
p. 896
Exs. 1–3, 6–14, 16, 18, 19, 21–25, 27 (with 12.4)
pp. 896–897
Exs. 4, 29–41 odd, 44–47, 49–53 (with Review)

12.5 EXERCISES

See www.CalcChat.com for worked-out solutions to odd-numbered exercises.

VOCABULARY: Fill in the blanks.

1. $\sum_{i=1}^{n} c =$ ___cn___, c is a constant.
2. $\sum_{i=1}^{n} i =$ ___$\dfrac{n(n+1)}{2}$___
3. $\sum_{i=1}^{n} i^3 =$ ___$\dfrac{n^2(n+1)^2}{4}$___
4. The exact ___area___ of a plane region R is given by the limit of the sum of n rectangles as n approaches ∞.

SKILLS AND APPLICATIONS

In Exercises 5–12, evaluate the sum using the summation formulas and properties.

5. $\sum_{i=1}^{60} 7$ 420
6. $\sum_{i=1}^{45} 3$ 135
7. $\sum_{i=1}^{20} i^3$ 44,100
8. $\sum_{i=1}^{30} i^2$ 9455
9. $\sum_{k=1}^{20} (k^3 + 2)$ 44,140
10. $\sum_{k=1}^{50} (2k + 1)$ 2600
11. $\sum_{j=1}^{25} (j^2 + j)$ 5850
12. $\sum_{j=1}^{10} (j^3 - 3j^2)$ 1870

In Exercises 13–20, (a) rewrite the sum as a rational function $S(n)$, (b) use $S(n)$ to complete the table, and (c) find $\lim_{n\to\infty} S(n)$.

n	10^0	10^1	10^2	10^3	10^4
$S(n)$					

13–20. See margin.

13. $\sum_{i=1}^{n} \dfrac{i^3}{n^4}$
14. $\sum_{i=1}^{n} \dfrac{i}{n^2}$
15. $\sum_{i=1}^{n} \dfrac{3}{n^3}(1 + i^2)$
16. $\sum_{i=1}^{n} \dfrac{2i + 3}{n^2}$
17. $\sum_{i=1}^{n} \left(\dfrac{i^2}{n^3} + \dfrac{2}{n}\right)\left(\dfrac{1}{n}\right)$
18. $\sum_{i=1}^{n} \left[3 - 2\left(\dfrac{i}{n}\right)\right]\left(\dfrac{1}{n}\right)$
19. $\sum_{i=1}^{n} \left[1 - \left(\dfrac{i}{n}\right)^2\right]\left(\dfrac{1}{n}\right)$
20. $\sum_{i=1}^{n} \left[\dfrac{4}{n} + \left(\dfrac{2i}{n^2}\right)\right]\left(\dfrac{2i}{n}\right)$

In Exercises 21–24, approximate the area of the region using the indicated number of rectangles of equal width.

21. $f(x) = x + 4$

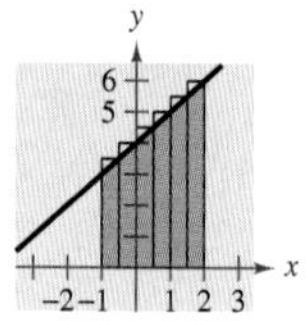

14.25 square units

22. $f(x) = 2 - x^2$

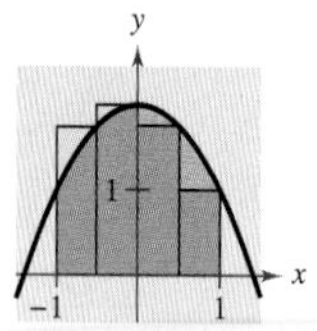

3.25 square units

23. $f(x) = \frac{1}{4}x^3$

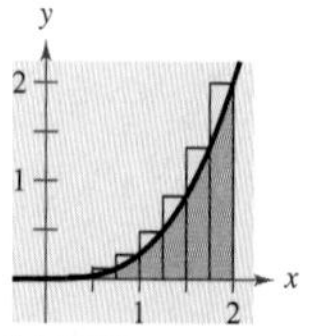

1.2656 square units

24. $f(x) = \frac{1}{2}(x - 1)^3$

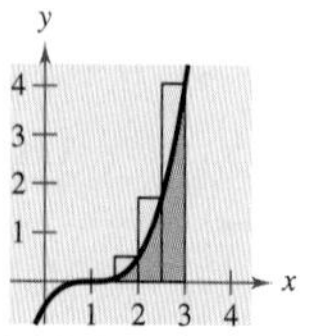

3.125 square units

In Exercises 25–28, complete the table showing the approximate area of the region in the graph using n rectangles of equal width. 25–28. See margin.

n	4	8	20	50
Approximate area				

25. $f(x) = -\frac{1}{3}x + 4$

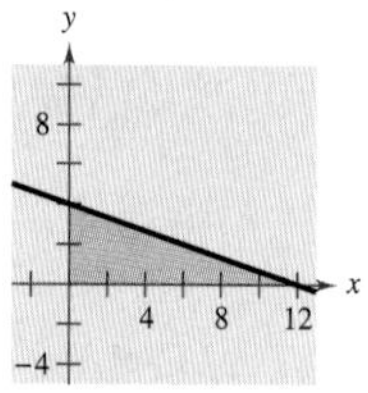

26. $f(x) = 9 - x^2$

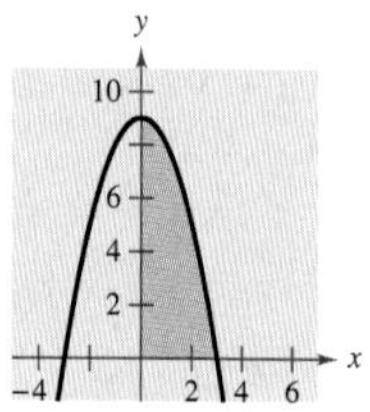

27. $f(x) = \frac{1}{9}x^3$

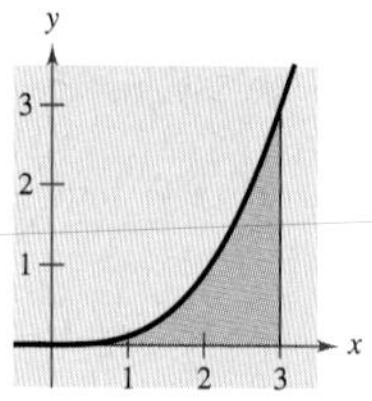

28. $f(x) = 3 - \frac{1}{4}x^3$

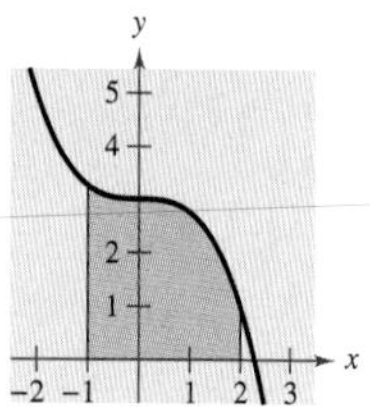

13. (a) $S(n) = \dfrac{n^2 + 2n + 1}{4n^2}$
 (b) See below.
 (c) Limit: $\frac{1}{4}$

14. (a) $S(n) = \dfrac{n + 1}{2n}$
 (b) See below.
 (c) Limit: $\frac{1}{2}$

15. (a) $S(n) = \dfrac{2n^2 + 3n + 7}{2n^2}$
 (b) See below.
 (c) Limit: 1

16. (a) $S(n) = \dfrac{n + 4}{n}$
 (b) See below.
 (c) Limit: 1

17. (a) $S(n) = \dfrac{14n^2 + 3n + 1}{6n^3}$
 (b) See below.
 (c) Limit: 0

18. (a) $S(n) = \dfrac{2n - 1}{n}$
 (b) See right.
 (c) Limit: 2

19. (a) $S(n) = \dfrac{4n^2 - 3n - 1}{6n^2}$
 (b) See right.
 (c) Limit: $\frac{2}{3}$

20. (a) $S(n) = \dfrac{16n^2 + 18n + 2}{3n^2}$
 (b) See right.
 (c) Limit: $\frac{16}{3}$

13. (b)

n	10^0	10^1	10^2	10^3	10^4
$S(n)$	1	0.3025	0.25503	0.25050	0.25005

14. (b)

n	10^0	10^1	10^2	10^3	10^4
$S(n)$	1	0.55	0.505	0.5005	0.50005

15. (b)

n	10^0	10^1	10^2	10^3	10^4
$S(n)$	6	1.185	1.0154	1.0015	1.00015

16. (b)

n	10^0	10^1	10^2	10^3	10^4
$S(n)$	5	1.4	1.04	1.004	1.0004

17. (b)

n	10^0	10^1	10^2	10^3	10^4
$S(n)$	3	0.2385	0.02338	0.002334	0.000233

18. (b)

n	10^0	10^1	10^2	10^3	10^4
$S(n)$	1	1.9	1.99	1.999	1.9999

19(b), 20(b), 25–28. See Additional Answers beginning on page AA1.

In Exercises 29–36, complete the table using the function $f(x)$, over the specified interval $[a, b]$, to approximate the area of the region bounded by the graph of $y = f(x)$, the x-axis, and the vertical lines $x = a$ and $x = b$ using the indicated number of rectangles. Then find the exact area as $n \to \infty$.

n	4	8	20	50	100	∞
Approximate area						

29–36. See margin.

Function	*Interval*
29. $f(x) = 2x + 5$	$[0, 4]$
30. $f(x) = 3x + 1$	$[0, 4]$
31. $f(x) = 16 - 2x$	$[1, 5]$
32. $f(x) = 20 - 2x$	$[2, 6]$
33. $f(x) = 9 - x^2$	$[0, 2]$
34. $f(x) = x^2 + 1$	$[4, 6]$
35. $f(x) = \frac{1}{2}x + 4$	$[-1, 3]$
36. $f(x) = \frac{1}{2}x + 1$	$[-2, 2]$

In Exercises 37–48, use the limit process to find the area of the region between the graph of the function and the x-axis over the specified interval.

Function	*Interval*	
37. $f(x) = 4x + 1$	$[0, 1]$	3 square units
38. $f(x) = 3x + 2$	$[0, 2]$	10 square units
39. $f(x) = -2x + 3$	$[0, 1]$	2 square units
40. $f(x) = 3x - 4$	$[2, 5]$	$\frac{39}{2}$ square units
41. $f(x) = 2 - x^2$	$[-1, 1]$	$\frac{10}{3}$ square units
42. $f(x) = x^2 + 2$	$[0, 1]$	$\frac{7}{3}$ square units
43. $g(x) = 8 - x^3$	$[1, 2]$	$\frac{17}{4}$ square units
44. $g(x) = 64 - x^3$	$[1, 4]$	$\frac{513}{4}$ square units
45. $g(x) = 2x - x^3$	$[0, 1]$	$\frac{3}{4}$ square unit
46. $g(x) = 4x - x^3$	$[0, 2]$	4 square units
47. $f(x) = \frac{1}{4}(x^2 + 4x)$	$[1, 4]$	$\frac{51}{4}$ square units
48. $f(x) = x^2 - x^3$	$[-1, 1]$	$\frac{2}{3}$ square unit

49. CIVIL ENGINEERING The boundaries of a parcel of land are two edges modeled by the coordinate axes and a stream modeled by the equation

$$y = (-3.0 \times 10^{-6})x^3 + 0.002x^2 - 1.05x + 400.$$

Use a graphing utility to graph the equation. Find the area of the property. Assume all distances are measured in feet. See margin.

50. CIVIL ENGINEERING The table shows the measurements (in feet) of a lot bounded by a stream and two straight roads that meet at right angles (see figure).

x	0	50	100	150	200	250	300
y	450	362	305	268	245	156	0

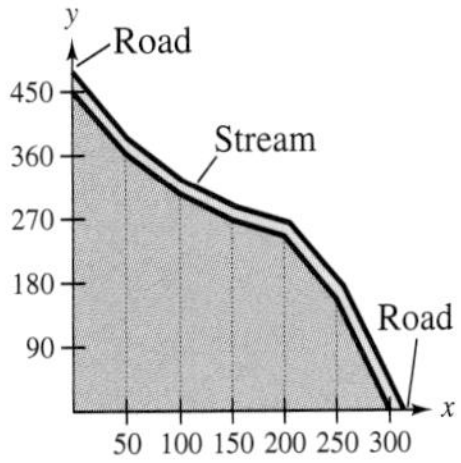

See margin.

(a) Use the *regression* feature of a graphing utility to find a model of the form $y = ax^3 + bx^2 + cx + d$.

(b) Use a graphing utility to plot the data and graph the model in the same viewing window.

(c) Use the model in part (a) to estimate the area of the lot.

EXPLORATION

TRUE OR FALSE? In Exercises 51 and 52, determine whether the statement is true or false. Justify your answer.

51. The sum of the first n positive integers is $n(n + 1)/2$. True

52. The exact area of a region is given by the limit of the sum of n rectangles as n approaches 0. See margin.

53. THINK ABOUT IT Determine which value best approximates the area of the region shown in the graph. (Make your selection on the basis of the sketch of the region and not by performing any calculations.)

(a) -2 (b) 1 (c) 4 (d) 6 (e) 9 c

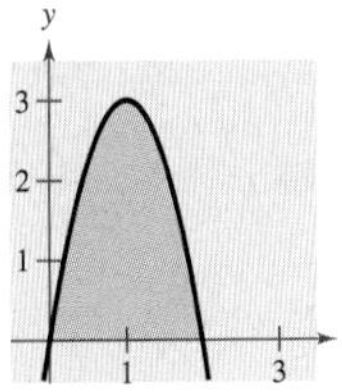

54. CAPSTONE Describe the process of finding the area of a region bounded by the graph of a nonnegative, continuous function f, the x-axis, and the vertical lines $x = a$ and $x = b$. Answers will vary.

5 ASSESS AND RETEACH

Daily Homework Quiz

Transparency Available

Available at the Instructor's companion site.

49.

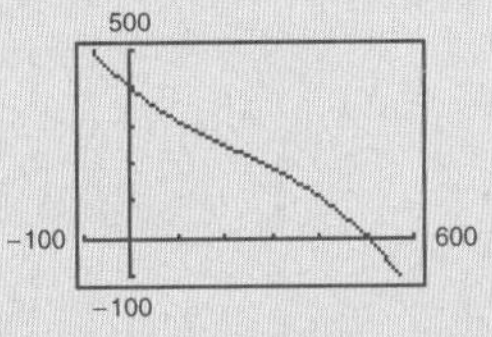

Area is $105{,}208.33 \text{ ft}^2 \approx 2.4153$ acres

50. (a) $y = (-4.088889 \times 10^{-5})x^3 + 0.0162x^2 - 2.67x + 453$

(b)

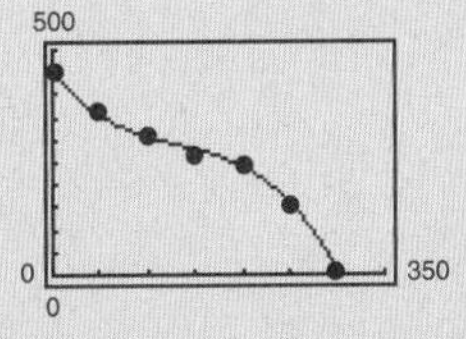

(c) $78{,}750 \text{ ft}^2$ (Answers will vary.)

52. False. The exact area of a region is given by the limit of the sum of n rectangles as n approaches infinity.

29–36. See Additional Answers beginning on page AA1.

12 Chapter Summary

	What Did You Learn?	Explanation/Examples	Review Exercises
Section 12.1	Use the definition of limit to estimate limits *(p. 851)*.	If $f(x)$ becomes arbitrarily close to a unique number L as x approaches c from either side, the limit of $f(x)$ as x approaches c is L. This is written as $\lim_{x \to c} f(x) = L$.	1–4
	Determine whether limits of functions exist *(p. 853)*.	**Conditions Under Which Limits Do Not Exist** The limit of $f(x)$ as $x \to c$ does not exist if any of the following conditions are true. **1.** $f(x)$ approaches a different number from the right side of c than it approaches from the left side of c. **2.** $f(x)$ increases or decreases without bound as x approaches c. **3.** $f(x)$ oscillates between two fixed values as x approaches c.	5–8
	Use properties of limits and direct substitution to evaluate limits *(p. 855)*.	Let b and c be real numbers and let n be a positive integer. **1.** $\lim_{x \to c} b = b$ **2.** $\lim_{x \to c} x = c$ **3.** $\lim_{x \to c} x^n = c^n$ **4.** $\lim_{x \to c} \sqrt[n]{x} = \sqrt[n]{c}$, for n even and $c > 0$ **Properties of Limits** Let b and c be real numbers, let n be a positive integer, and let f and g be functions where $\lim_{x \to c} f(x) = L$ and $\lim_{x \to c} g(x) = K$. **1.** $\lim_{x \to c} [bf(x)] = bL$ **2.** $\lim_{x \to c} [f(x) \pm g(x)] = L \pm K$ **3.** $\lim_{x \to c} [f(x)g(x)] = LK$ **4.** $\lim_{x \to c} \frac{f(x)}{g(x)} = \frac{L}{K}$, $K \neq 0$ **5.** $\lim_{x \to c} [f(x)]^n = L^n$	9–24
Section 12.2	Use the dividing out technique to evaluate limits of functions *(p. 861)*.	When evaluating a limit of a rational function by direct substitution, you may encounter the indeterminate form $0/0$. In this case, factor and divide out any common factors, then try direct substitution again. (See Examples 1 and 2.)	25–32
	Use the rationalizing technique to evaluate limits of functions *(p. 863)*.	The rationalizing technique involves rationalizing the numerator of the function when finding a limit. (See Example 3.)	33–36
	Approximate limits of functions *(p. 864)*.	The *table* feature or *zoom* and *trace* features of a graphing utility can be used to approximate limits. (See Examples 4 and 5.)	37–44
	Evaluate one-sided limits of functions *(p. 865)*.	**Limit from left:** $\lim_{x \to c^-} f(x) = L_1$ or $f(x) \to L_1$ as $x \to c^-$ **Limit from right:** $\lim_{x \to c^+} f(x) = L_2$ or $f(x) \to L_2$ as $x \to c^+$	45–52
	Evaluate limits of difference quotients from calculus *(p. 867)*.	For any x-value, the limit of a difference quotient is an expression of the form $\lim_{h \to 0} \frac{f(x+h) - f(x)}{h}$.	53–56

	What Did You Learn?	Explanation/Examples	Review Exercises
Section 12.3	Use a tangent line to approximate the slope of a graph at a point *(p. 871)*.	The tangent line to the graph of a function f at a point $P(x_1, y_1)$ is the line that best approximates the slope of the graph at the point. 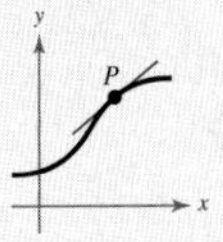	57–64
	Use the limit definition of slope to find exact slopes of graphs *(p. 873)*.	**Definition of the Slope of a Graph** The slope m of the graph of f at the point $(x, f(x))$ is equal to the slope of its tangent line at $(x, f(x))$ and is given by $m = \lim_{h \to 0} m_{sec} = \lim_{h \to 0} \frac{f(x+h) - f(x)}{h}$ provided this limit exists.	65–68
	Find derivatives of functions and use derivatives to find slopes of graphs *(p. 876)*.	The derivative of f at x is given by $f'(x) = \lim_{h \to 0} \frac{f(x+h) - f(x)}{h}$ provided this limit exists. The derivative $f'(x)$ is a formula for the slope of the tangent line to the graph of f at the point $(x, f(x))$.	69–82
Section 12.4	Evaluate limits of functions at infinity *(p. 881)*.	If f is a function and L_1 and L_2 are real numbers, the statements $\lim_{x \to -\infty} f(x) = L_1$ and $\lim_{x \to \infty} f(x) = L_2$ denote the limits at infinity.	83–92
	Find limits of sequences *(p. 885)*.	**Limit of a Sequence** Let f be a function of a real variable such that $\lim_{x \to \infty} f(x) = L$. If $\{a_n\}$ is a sequence such that $f(n) = a_n$ for every positive integer n, then $\lim_{n \to \infty} a_n = L$.	93–98
Section 12.5	Find limits of summations *(p. 890)*.	**Summation Formulas and Properties** **1.** $\sum_{i=1}^{n} c = cn$, c is a constant. **2.** $\sum_{i=1}^{n} i = \frac{n(n+1)}{2}$ **3.** $\sum_{i=1}^{n} i^2 = \frac{n(n+1)(2n+1)}{6}$ **4.** $\sum_{i=1}^{n} i^3 = \frac{n^2(n+1)^2}{4}$ **5.** $\sum_{i=1}^{n} (a_i \pm b_i) = \sum_{i=1}^{n} a_i \pm \sum_{i=1}^{n} b_i$ **6.** $\sum_{i=1}^{n} ka_i = k\sum_{i=1}^{n} a_i$, k is a constant.	99, 100
	Use rectangles to approximate areas of plane regions *(p. 893)*.	A collection of rectangles of equal width can be used to approximate the area of a region. Increasing the number of rectangles gives a closer approximation. (See Example 4.)	101–104
	Use limits of summations to find areas of plane regions *(p. 894)*.	**Area of a Plane Region** Let f be continuous and nonnegative on $[a, b]$. The area A of the region bounded by the graph of f, the x-axis, and the vertical lines $x = a$ and $x = b$ is given by $A = \lim_{n \to \infty} \sum_{i=1}^{n} f\left(a + \frac{(b-a)i}{n}\right)\left(\frac{b-a}{n}\right)$.	105–113

1. See table below.
$\lim_{x\to 3}(6x - 1) = 17$;
The limit can be reached.
2. See table below.
$\lim_{x\to 2}(x^2 - 3x + 1) = -1$;
The limit can be reached.
3. See table below.
$\lim_{x\to 0}\frac{1 - e^{-x}}{x} = 1$;
The limit cannot be reached.
4. See table below.
$\lim_{x\to 0}\frac{\ln(1 - x)}{x} = -1$;
The limit cannot be reached.

12 Review Exercises

See www.CalcChat.com for worked-out solutions to odd-numbered exercises.

12.1 In Exercises 1–4, complete the table and use the result to estimate the limit numerically. Determine whether or not the limit can be reached. 1–4. See margin.

1. $\lim_{x\to 3}(6x - 1)$

x	2.9	2.99	2.999	3	3.001	3.01	3.1
$f(x)$				?			

2. $\lim_{x\to 2}(x^2 - 3x + 1)$

x	1.9	1.99	1.999	2	2.001	2.01	2.1
$f(x)$				?			

3. $\lim_{x\to 0}\frac{1 - e^{-x}}{x}$

x	−0.1	−0.01	−0.001	0	0.001	0.01	0.1
$f(x)$				?			

4. $\lim_{x\to 0}\frac{\ln(1 - x)}{x}$

x	−0.1	−0.01	−0.001	0	0.001	0.01	0.1
$f(x)$				?			

In Exercises 5–8, use the graph to find the limit (if it exists). If the limit does not exist, explain why.

5. $\lim_{x\to 1}(3 - x)$ 2

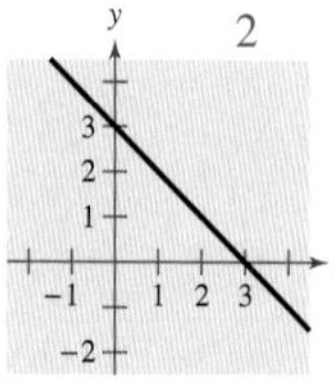

6. $\lim_{x\to 2}\frac{1}{x - 2}$ Limit does not exist.

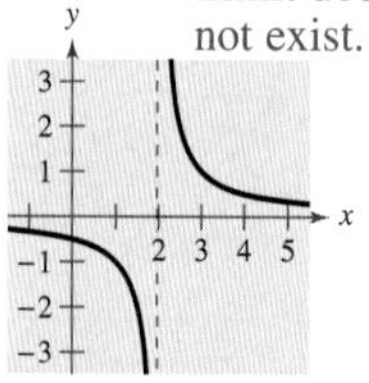

7. $\lim_{x\to 1}\frac{x^2 - 1}{x - 1}$ 2

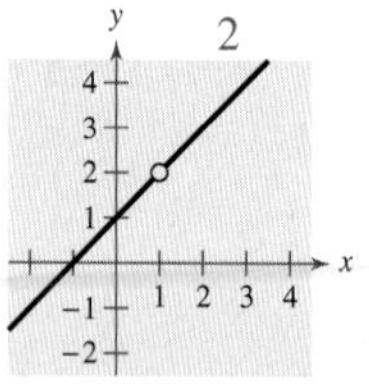

8. $\lim_{x\to -1}(2x^2 + 1)$ 3

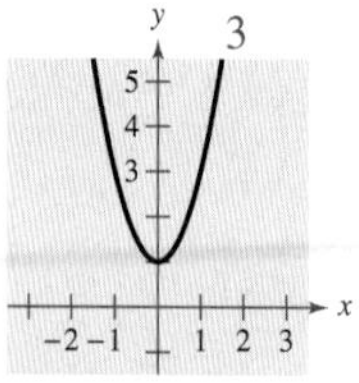

In Exercises 9 and 10, use the given information to evaluate each limit.

9. $\lim_{x\to c} f(x) = 4,\ \lim_{x\to c} g(x) = 5$

(a) $\lim_{x\to c}[f(x)]^3$ 64 (b) $\lim_{x\to c}[3f(x) - g(x)]$ 7

(c) $\lim_{x\to c}[f(x)g(x)]$ 20 (d) $\lim_{x\to c}\frac{f(x)}{g(x)}$ $\frac{4}{5}$

10. $\lim_{x\to c} f(x) = 27,\ \lim_{x\to c} g(x) = 12$

(a) $\lim_{x\to c}\sqrt[3]{f(x)}$ 3 (b) $\lim_{x\to c}\frac{f(x)}{18}$ $\frac{3}{2}$

(c) $\lim_{x\to c}[f(x)g(x)]$ 324 (d) $\lim_{x\to c}[f(x) - 2g(x)]$ 3

In Exercises 11–24, find the limit by direct substitution.

11. $\lim_{x\to 4}\left(\frac{1}{2}x + 3\right)$ 5 **12.** $\lim_{x\to -1}\sqrt{5 - x}$ $\sqrt{6}$

13. $\lim_{x\to 2}\frac{x^2 - 1}{x^3 + 2}$ $\frac{3}{10}$ **14.** $\lim_{x\to e} 7$ 7

15. $\lim_{x\to \pi}\sin 3x$ 0 **16.** $\lim_{x\to 0}\tan x$ 0

17. $\lim_{x\to 3}(5x - 4)$ 11 **18.** $\lim_{x\to -2}(5 - 2x - x^2)$ 5

19. $\lim_{x\to 2}(5x - 3)(3x + 5)$ 77 **20.** $\lim_{x\to -2}\sqrt[3]{4x}$ −2

21. $\lim_{t\to 3}\frac{t^2 + 1}{t}$ $\frac{10}{3}$ **22.** $\lim_{x\to 2}\frac{3x + 5}{5x - 3}$ $\frac{11}{7}$

23. $\lim_{x\to -1} 2e^x$ $2e^{-1}$ **24.** $\lim_{x\to 0}\arctan x$ 0

12.2 In Exercises 25–36, find the limit (if it exists). Use a graphing utility to verify your result graphically.

25. $\lim_{t\to -2}\frac{t + 2}{t^2 - 4}$ $-\frac{1}{4}$ **26.** $\lim_{x\to 5}\frac{5 - x}{x^2 - 25}$ $-\frac{1}{10}$

27. $\lim_{x\to 5}\frac{x - 5}{x^2 + 5x - 50}$ $\frac{1}{15}$ **28.** $\lim_{x\to -1}\frac{x + 1}{x^2 - 5x - 6}$ $-\frac{1}{7}$

29. $\lim_{x\to -2}\frac{x^2 - 4}{x^3 + 8}$ $-\frac{1}{3}$ **30.** $\lim_{t\to -3}\frac{t^3 + 27}{t + 3}$ 27

31. $\lim_{x\to -1}\frac{\frac{1}{x + 2} - 1}{x + 1}$ −1 **32.** $\lim_{x\to 0}\frac{\frac{1}{x + 1} - 1}{x}$ −1

33. $\lim_{u\to 0}\frac{\sqrt{4 + u} - 2}{u}$ $\frac{1}{4}$ **34.** $\lim_{v\to 0}\frac{\sqrt{v + 9} - 3}{v}$ $\frac{1}{6}$

35. $\lim_{x\to 5}\frac{\sqrt{x - 1} - 2}{x - 5}$ $\frac{1}{4}$

36. $\lim_{x\to 1}\frac{\sqrt{3} - \sqrt{x + 2}}{1 - x}$ $\frac{\sqrt{3}}{6}$

1.

x	2.9	2.99	2.999	3	3.001	3.01	3.1
$f(x)$	16.4	16.94	16.994	17	17.006	17.06	17.6

2.

x	1.9	1.99	1.999	2	2.001	2.01	2.1
$f(x)$	−1.09	−1.0099	−1.001	−1	−0.99	−0.9899	−0.89

3.

x	−0.1	−0.01	−0.001	0	0.001	0.01	0.1
$f(x)$	1.0517	1.005	1.0005	Error	0.9995	0.995	0.9516

4.

x	−0.1	−0.01	−0.001	0
$f(x)$	−0.9531	−0.995	−0.9995	Error

x	0.001	0.01	0.1
$f(x)$	−1.0005	−1.005	−1.0536

GRAPHICAL AND NUMERICAL ANALYSIS In Exercises 37–44, (a) graphically approximate the limit (if it exists) by using a graphing utility to graph the function, and (b) numerically approximate the limit (if it exists) by using the *table* feature of a graphing utility to create a table. 37–44. See margin.

37. $\lim_{x \to 3} \frac{x-3}{x^2-9}$ **38.** $\lim_{x \to 4} \frac{4-x}{16-x^2}$

39. $\lim_{x \to 0} e^{-2/x}$ **40.** $\lim_{x \to 0} e^{-4/x^2}$

41. $\lim_{x \to 0} \frac{\sin 4x}{2x}$ **42.** $\lim_{x \to 0} \frac{\tan 2x}{x}$

43. $\lim_{x \to 1^+} \frac{\sqrt{2x+1}-\sqrt{3}}{x-1}$ **44.** $\lim_{x \to 1^+} \frac{1-\sqrt{x}}{x-1}$

In Exercises 45–52, graph the function. Determine the limit (if it exists) by evaluating the corresponding one-sided limits. 45–52. See margin.

45. $\lim_{x \to 3} \frac{|x-3|}{x-3}$ **46.** $\lim_{x \to 8} \frac{|8-x|}{8-x}$

47. $\lim_{x \to 2} \frac{2}{x^2-4}$ **48.** $\lim_{x \to -3} \frac{1}{x^2+9}$

49. $\lim_{x \to 5} \frac{|x-5|}{x-5}$ **50.** $\lim_{x \to -2} \frac{|x+2|}{x+2}$

51. $\lim_{x \to 2} f(x)$ where $f(x) = \begin{cases} 5-x, & x \le 2 \\ x^2-3, & x > 2 \end{cases}$

52. $\lim_{x \to 0} f(x)$ where $f(x) = \begin{cases} x-6, & x \ge 0 \\ x^2-4, & x < 0 \end{cases}$

In Exercises 53–56, find $\lim_{h \to 0} \frac{f(x+h)-f(x)}{h}$.

53. $f(x) = 4x + 3$ 4 **54.** $f(x) = 11 - 2x$ -2

55. $f(x) = 3x - x^2$ $3 - 2x$ **56.** $f(x) = x^2 - 5x - 2$ $2x - 5$

12.3 In Exercises 57 and 58, approximate the slope of the tangent line to the graph at the point (x, y).

57. 2

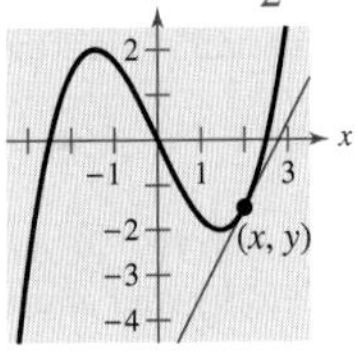

58. 0

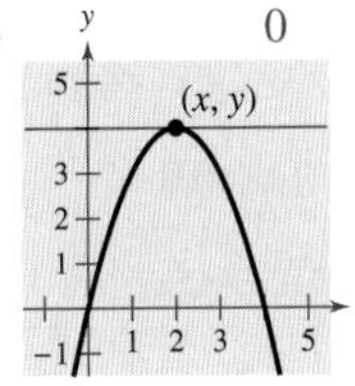

In Exercises 59–64, sketch a graph of the function and the tangent line at the point $(2, f(2))$. Use the graph to approximate the slope of the tangent line. 59–64. See margin.

59. $f(x) = x^2 - 2x$ **60.** $f(x) = 6 - x^2$

61. $f(x) = \sqrt{x+2}$ **62.** $f(x) = \sqrt{x^2+5}$

63. $f(x) = \frac{6}{x-4}$ **64.** $f(x) = \frac{1}{3-x}$

In Exercises 65–68, find a formula for the slope of the graph of f at the point $(x, f(x))$. Then use it to find the slope at the two given points.

65. $f(x) = x^2 - 4x$ $m = 2x - 4$;
(a) $(0, 0)$ (b) $(5, 5)$ (a) -4 (b) 6

66. $f(x) = \frac{1}{4}x^4$ $m = x^3$;
(a) $(-2, 4)$ (b) $\left(1, \frac{1}{4}\right)$ (a) -8 (b) 1

67. $f(x) = \frac{4}{x-6}$ $m = -\frac{4}{(x-6)^2}$;
(a) $(7, 4)$ (b) $(8, 2)$ (a) -4 (b) -1

68. $f(x) = \sqrt{x}$ $m = \frac{1}{2\sqrt{x}}$; (a) $\frac{1}{2}$ (b) $\frac{1}{4}$
(a) $(1, 1)$ (b) $(4, 2)$

In Exercises 69–80, find the derivative of the function. 69–80. See margin.

69. $f(x) = 5$ **70.** $g(x) = -3$

71. $h(x) = 5 - \frac{1}{2}x$ **72.** $f(x) = 3x$

73. $g(x) = 2x^2 - 1$ **74.** $f(x) = -x^3 + 4x$

75. $f(t) = \sqrt{t+5}$ **76.** $g(t) = \sqrt{t-3}$

77. $g(s) = \frac{4}{s+5}$ **78.** $g(t) = \frac{6}{5-t}$

79. $g(x) = \frac{1}{\sqrt{x+4}}$ **80.** $f(x) = \frac{1}{\sqrt{12-x}}$

In Exercises 81 and 82, (a) find the slope of the graph of f at the given point, (b) use the result of part (a) to find an equation of the tangent line to the graph at the point, and (c) graph the function and the tangent line. 81–82. See margin.

81. $f(x) = 2x^2 - 1$, $(0, -1)$

82. $f(x) = x^2 + 10$, $(2, 14)$

12.4 In Exercises 83–92, find the limit (if it exists). If the limit does not exist, explain why. Use a graphing utility to verify your result graphically.

83. $\lim_{x \to \infty} \frac{4x}{2x-3}$ 2 **84.** $\lim_{x \to \infty} \frac{7x}{14x+2}$ $\frac{1}{2}$

85. $\lim_{x \to \infty} \frac{3+x}{3-x}$ -1 **86.** $\lim_{x \to \infty} \frac{1-2x}{x+2}$ -2

87. $\lim_{x \to -\infty} \frac{2x}{x^2-25}$ 0 **88.** $\lim_{x \to -\infty} \frac{3x}{(1-x)^3}$ 0

89. $\lim_{x \to \infty} \frac{x^2}{2x+3}$ Limit does not exist. **90.** $\lim_{y \to \infty} \frac{3y^4}{y^2+1}$ Limit does not exist.

91. $\lim_{x \to \infty} \left[\frac{x}{(x-2)^2} + 3\right]$ 3 **92.** $\lim_{x \to \infty} \left[2 - \frac{2x^2}{(x+1)^2}\right]$ 0

37. (a) $\frac{1}{6}$

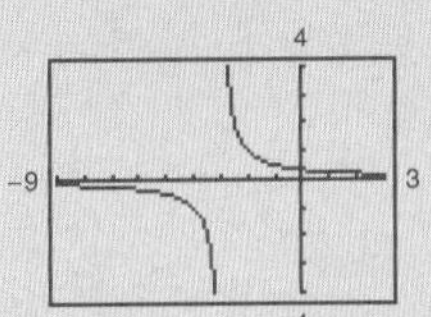

(b)

x	2.9	2.99	3
$f(x)$	0.1695	0.1669	Error

x	3.01	3.1
$f(x)$	0.1664	0.1639

0.1667

38. (a) $\frac{1}{8}$

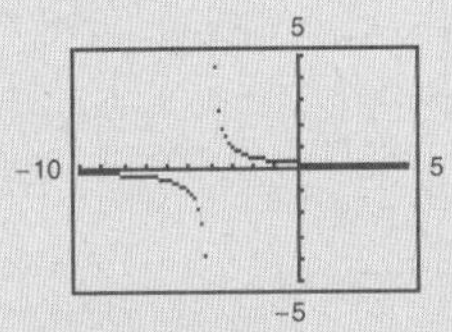

(b) See table below; 0.1250.

39. (a)

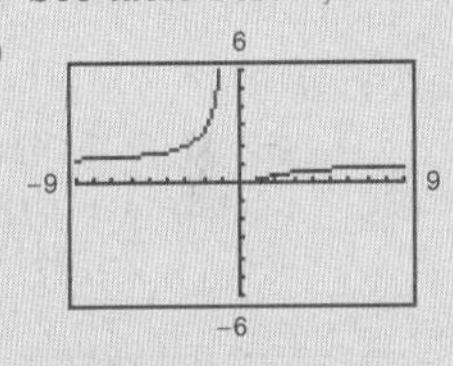

Limit does not exist.
(b) See table below.
Limit does not exist.

40. (a) 0

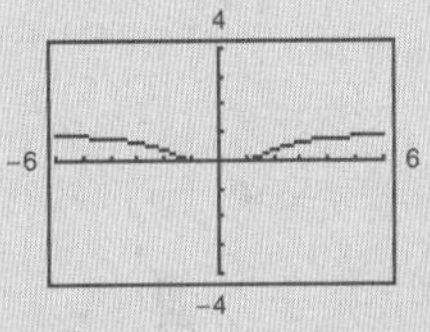

(b) See table below; 0.

41. (a) 2

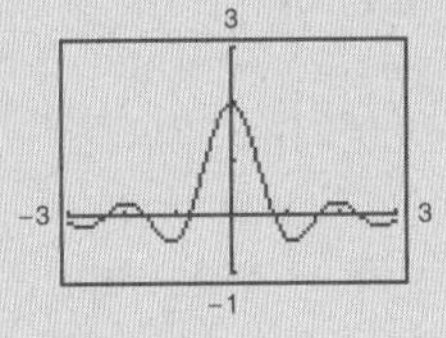

(b) See below; 2.

38. (b)

x	3.9	3.99	3.999	4	4.001	4.01	4.1
$f(x)$	0.12658	0.12516	0.12502	Error	0.12498	0.12484	0.12346

39. (b)

x	-0.1	-0.01	-0.001	0	0.001	0.01	0.1
$f(x)$	4.85E8	7.2E86	Error	Error	0	1E–87	2.1E–9

40. (b)

x	-0.1	-0.01	-0.001	0	0.001	0.01	0.1
$f(x)$	0	0	0	Error	0	0	0

41(b), 42–52, 59–64, 69–82. See Additional Answers beginning on page AA1.

In Exercises 93–98, write the first five terms of the sequence and find the limit of the sequence (if it exists). If the limit does not exist, explain why. Assume n begins with 1. 93–98. See margin.

93. $a_n = \dfrac{4n-1}{3n+1}$ **94.** $a_n = \dfrac{n}{n^2+1}$

95. $a_n = \dfrac{(-1)^n}{n^3}$ **96.** $a_n = \dfrac{(-1)^{n+1}}{n}$

97. $a_n = \dfrac{n^2}{3n+2}$ **98.** $a_n = \dfrac{1}{2n^2}[3 - 2n(n+1)]$

12.5 In Exercises 99 and 100, (a) use the summation formulas and properties to rewrite the sum as a rational function $S(n)$, (b) use $S(n)$ to complete the table, and (c) find $\lim_{n\to\infty} S(n)$.

n	10^0	10^1	10^2	10^3	10^4
$S(n)$					

99–100. See margin.

99. $\displaystyle\sum_{i=1}^{n}\left(\frac{4i^2}{n^2} - \frac{i}{n}\right)\left(\frac{1}{n}\right)$ **100.** $\displaystyle\sum_{i=1}^{n}\left[4 - \left(\frac{3i}{n}\right)^2\right]\left(\frac{3i}{n^2}\right)$

In Exercises 101 and 102, approximate the area of the region using the indicated number of rectangles of equal width.

101. $f(x) = 4 - x$ **102.** $f(x) = 4 - x^2$

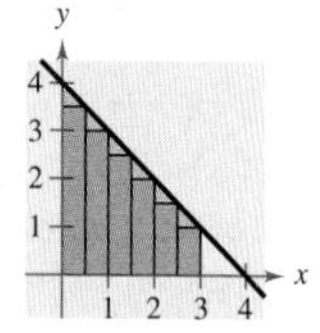

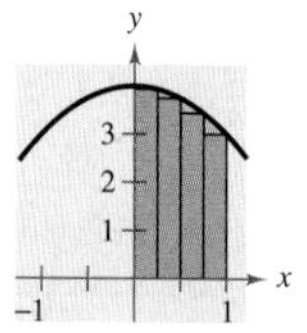

$\frac{27}{4} = 6.75$ square units $\frac{113}{32} \approx 3.5313$ square units

In Exercises 103 and 104, complete the table to show the approximate area of the region in the graph using n rectangles of equal width. 103–104. See margin.

n	4	8	20	50
Approximate area				

103. $f(x) = \frac{1}{4}x^2$ **104.** $f(x) = 4x - x^2$

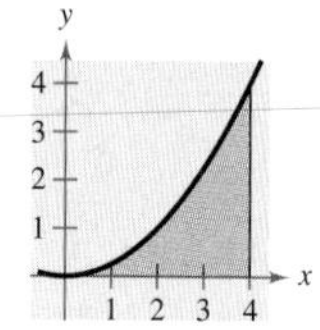

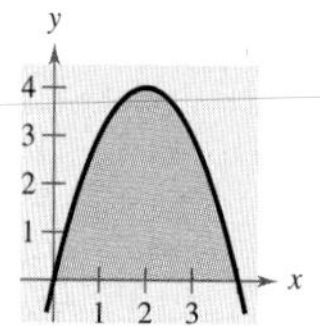

In Exercises 105–112, use the limit process to find the area of the region between the graph of the function and the x-axis over the specified interval.

	Function	*Interval*	
105.	$f(x) = 10 - x$	$[0, 10]$	50 square units
106.	$f(x) = 2x - 6$	$[3, 6]$	9 square units
107.	$f(x) = x^2 + 4$	$[-1, 2]$	15 square units
108.	$f(x) = 8(x - x^2)$	$[0, 1]$	$\frac{4}{3}$ square units
109.	$f(x) = x^3 + 1$	$[0, 2]$	6 square units
110.	$f(x) = 1 - x^3$	$[-3, -1]$	22 square units
111.	$f(x) = 2(x^2 - x^3)$	$[-1, 1]$	$\frac{4}{3}$ square units
112.	$f(x) = 4 - (x - 2)^2$	$[0, 4]$	$\frac{32}{3}$ square units

113. CIVIL ENGINEERING The table shows the measurements (in feet) of a lot bounded by a stream and two straight roads that meet at right angles (see figure).

x	0	100	200	300	400	500
y	125	125	120	112	90	90

x	600	700	800	900	1000
y	95	88	75	35	0

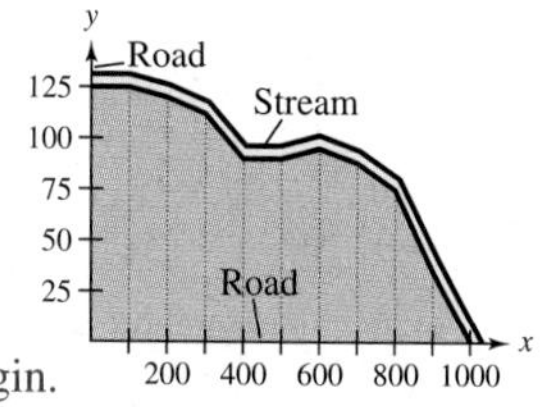

See margin.

(a) Use the *regression* feature of a graphing utility to find a model of the form $y = ax^3 + bx^2 + cx + d$.

(b) Use a graphing utility to plot the data and graph the model in the same viewing window.

(c) Use the model in part (a) to estimate the area of the lot.

EXPLORATION

114–115. See margin.

TRUE OR FALSE? In Exercises 114 and 115, determine whether the statement is true or false. Justify your answer.

114. The limit of the sum of two functions is the sum of the limits of the two functions.

115. If the degree of the numerator $N(x)$ of a rational function $f(x) = N(x)/D(x)$ is greater than the degree of its denominator $D(x)$, then the limit of the rational function as x approaches ∞ is 0.

116. WRITING Write a paragraph explaining several reasons why the limit of a function may not exist. Answers will vary.

93. $\frac{3}{4}, 1, \frac{11}{10}, \frac{15}{13}, \frac{19}{16}$
Limit: $\frac{4}{3}$

94. $\frac{1}{2}, \frac{2}{5}, \frac{3}{10}, \frac{4}{17}, \frac{5}{26}$
Limit: 0

95. $-1, \frac{1}{8}, -\frac{1}{27}, \frac{1}{64}, -\frac{1}{125}$
Limit: 0

96. $1, -\frac{1}{2}, \frac{1}{3}, -\frac{1}{4}, \frac{1}{5}$
Limit: 0

97. $\frac{1}{5}, \frac{1}{2}, \frac{9}{11}, \frac{8}{7}, \frac{25}{17}$
Limit does not exist.

98. $-\frac{1}{2}, -\frac{9}{8}, -\frac{7}{6}, -\frac{37}{32}, -\frac{57}{50}$
Limit: -1

99. (a) $S(n) = \dfrac{(n+1)(5n+4)}{6n^2}$
(b) See below.
(c) Limit: $\frac{5}{6}$

100. (a) $S(n) = -\dfrac{3(n+1)(n+9)}{4n^2}$
(b) See below.
(c) Limit: $-\frac{3}{4}$

103. See below.

104. See below.

113. (a) $y = (-3.376068 \times 10^{-7})x^3 + (3.7529 \times 10^{-4})x^2 - 0.17x + 132$

(b)

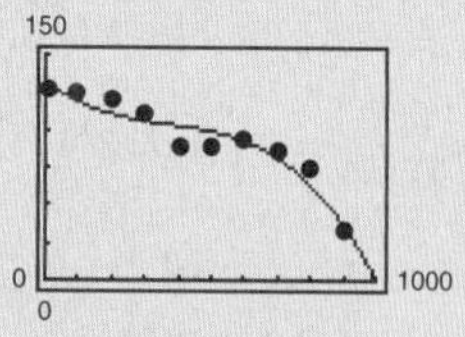

(c) About 87,695.0 ft^2 (Answers will vary.)

114. True. $\lim_{x\to c}[f(x) + g(x)] = \lim_{x\to c} f(x) + \lim_{x\to c} g(x)$, if both limits exist.

115. False. The limit of the rational function as x approaches ∞ does not exist.

99. (b)

n	10^0	10^1	10^2	10^3	10^4
$S(n)$	3	0.99	0.8484	0.8348	0.8335

100. (b)

n	10^0	10^1	10^2	10^3	10^4
$S(n)$	-15	-1.5675	-0.8257	-0.7575	-0.7508

103.

n	4	8	20	50
Approximate area	7.5	6.375	5.74	5.4944

104.

n	4	8	20	50
Approximate area	10	10.5	10.64	10.6624

12 Chapter Test

See www.CalcChat.com for worked-out solutions to odd-numbered exercises.

Take this test as you would take a test in class. When you are finished, check your work against the answers given in the back of the book.

In Exercises 1–3, sketch a graph of the function and approximate the limit (if it exists). Then find the limit (if it exists) algebraically by using appropriate techniques. 1–3. See margin.

1. $\lim_{x \to -2} \dfrac{x^2 - 1}{2x}$ **2.** $\lim_{x \to 1} \dfrac{-x^2 + 5x - 3}{1 - x}$ **3.** $\lim_{x \to 5} \dfrac{\sqrt{x} - 2}{x - 5}$

In Exercises 4 and 5, use a graphing utility to graph the function and approximate the limit. Write an approximation that is accurate to four decimal places. Then create a table to verify your limit numerically. 4–5. See margin.

4. $\lim_{x \to 0} \dfrac{\sin 3x}{x}$ **5.** $\lim_{x \to 0} \dfrac{e^{2x} - 1}{x}$

6. Find a formula for the slope of the graph of f at the point $(x, f(x))$. Then use the formula to find the slope at the given point.

(a) $f(x) = 3x^2 - 5x - 2,\ (2, 0)$ $m = 6x - 5;\ 7$

(b) $f(x) = 2x^3 + 6x,\ (-1, -8)$ $m = 6x^2 + 6;\ 12$

In Exercises 7–9, find the derivative of the function.

7. $f(x) = 5 - \frac{2}{5}x$ $f'(x) = -\frac{2}{5}$ **8.** $f(x) = 2x^2 + 4x - 1$ $f'(x) = 4x + 4$ **9.** $f(x) = \dfrac{1}{x + 3}$ See margin.

In Exercises 10–12, find the limit (if it exists). If the limit does not exist, explain why. Use a graphing utility to verify your result graphically.

10. $\lim_{x \to \infty} \dfrac{6}{5x - 1}$ 0 **11.** $\lim_{x \to \infty} \dfrac{1 - 3x^2}{x^2 - 5}$ -3 **12.** $\lim_{x \to -\infty} \dfrac{x^2}{3x + 2}$ Limit does not exist.

In Exercises 13 and 14, write the first five terms of the sequence and find the limit of the sequence (if it exists). If the limit does not exist, explain why. Assume n begins with 1.

13. $a_n = \dfrac{n^2 + 3n - 4}{2n^2 + n - 2}$ $0, \frac{3}{4}, \frac{14}{19}, \frac{12}{17}, \frac{36}{53}$ Limit: $\frac{1}{2}$ **14.** $a_n = \dfrac{1 + (-1)^n}{n}$ $0, 1, 0, \frac{1}{2}, 0$ Limit: 0

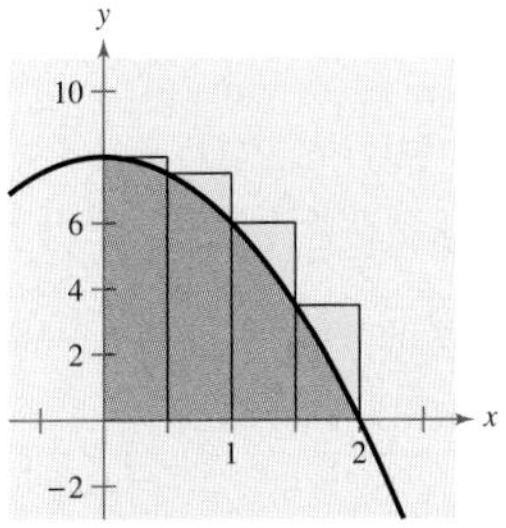

FIGURE FOR 15

15. Approximate the area of the region bounded by the graph of $f(x) = 8 - 2x^2$ shown at the left using the indicated number of rectangles of equal width. $\frac{25}{2}$ square units

In Exercises 16 and 17, use the limit process to find the area of the region between the graph of the function and the x-axis over the specified interval.

16. $f(x) = x + 2$; interval: $[-2, 2]$ 8 square units **17.** $f(x) = 3 - x^2$; interval: $[-1, 1]$ $\frac{16}{3}$ square units

Time (seconds), x	Altitude (feet), y
0	0
1	1
2	23
3	60
4	115
5	188

TABLE FOR 18

18. The table shows the altitude of a space shuttle during its first 5 seconds of motion.

(a) Use the *regression* feature of a graphing utility to find a quadratic model $y = ax^2 + bx + c$ for the data. $y = 8.786x^2 - 6.25x - 0.4$

(b) The value of the derivative of the model is the rate of change of altitude with respect to time, or the velocity, at that instant. Find the velocity of the shuttle after 5 seconds. 81.6 ft/sec

1.

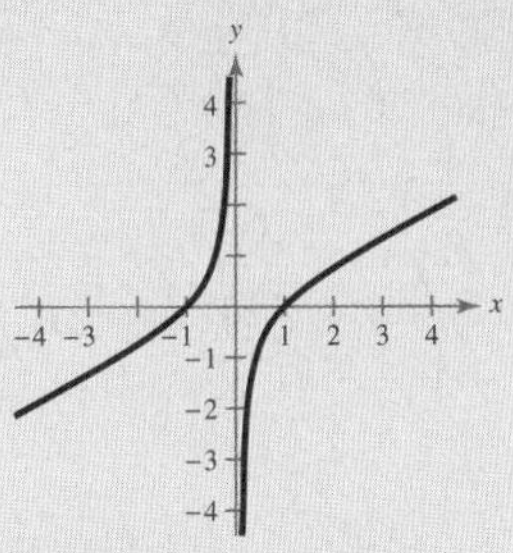

$\lim_{x \to -2} \dfrac{x^2 - 1}{2x} = -\dfrac{3}{4}$

2.

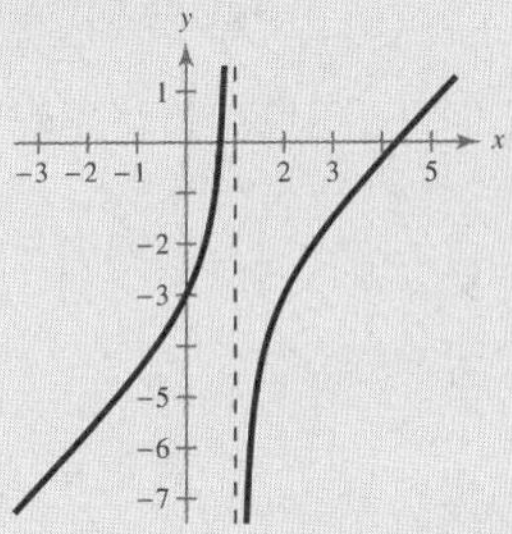

The limit does not exist.

3.

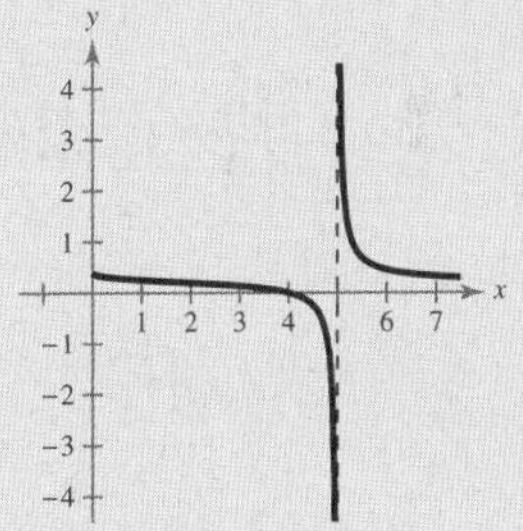

The limit does not exist.

4.

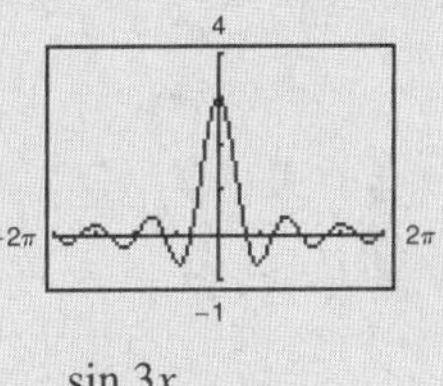

$\lim_{x \to 0} \dfrac{\sin 3x}{x} = 3$

See table below.

5.

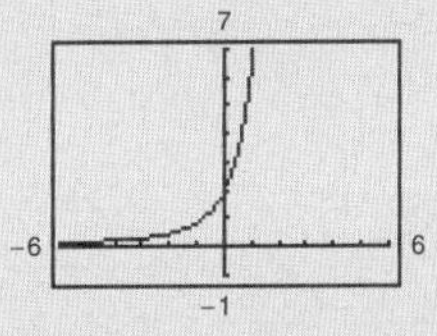

$\lim_{x \to 0} \dfrac{e^{2x} - 1}{x} = 2$

See table below.

9. $f'(x) = -\dfrac{1}{(x + 3)^2}$

4.

x	-0.02	-0.01	0	0.01	0.02
$f(x)$	2.9982	2.9996	Error	2.9996	2.9982

5.

x	-0.004	-0.003	-0.002	-0.001	0
$f(x)$	1.9920	1.9940	1.9960	1.9980	Error

1. Ellipse

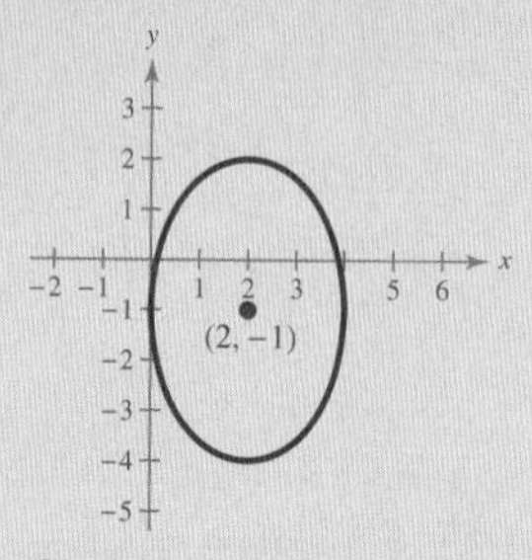

2. Circle

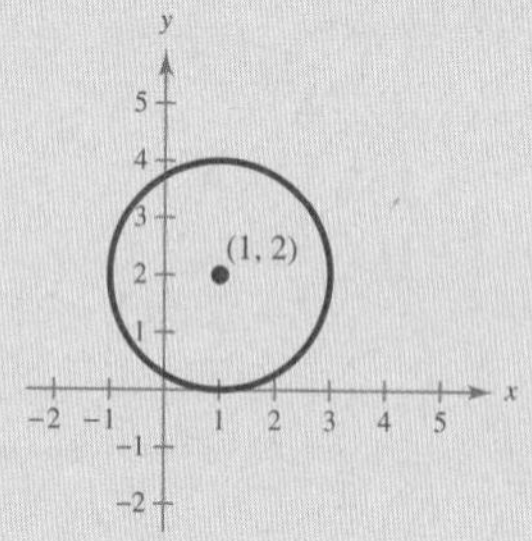

4. $\theta \approx 37.98°$

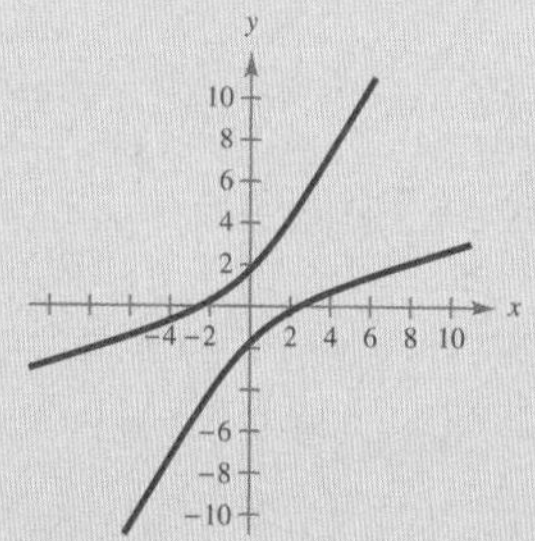

5.

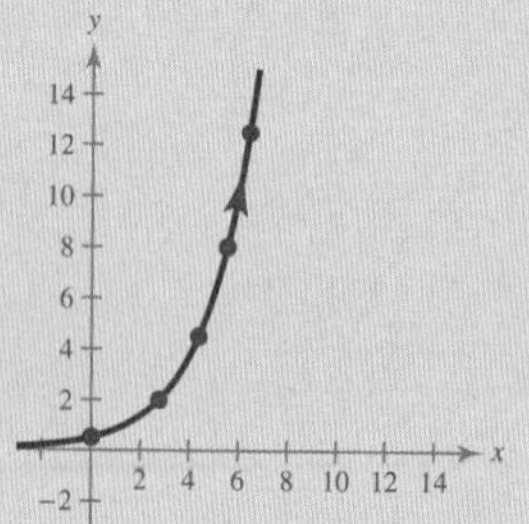

The corresponding rectangular equation is $y = \sqrt{e^x}/2$.

6.

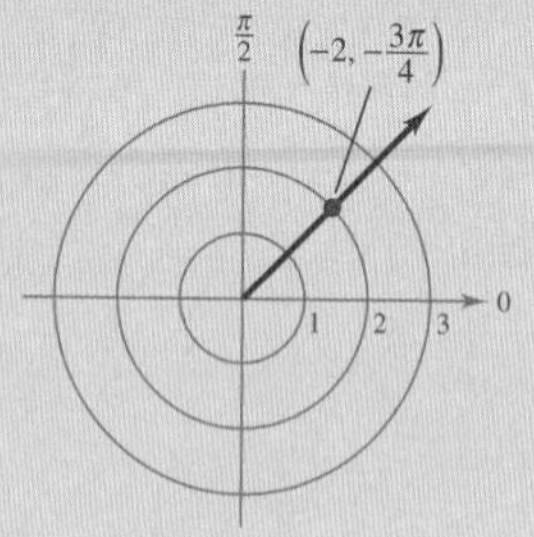

$\left(-2, \frac{5\pi}{4}\right), \left(2, -\frac{7\pi}{4}\right), \left(2, \frac{\pi}{4}\right)$

12 CUMULATIVE TEST FOR CHAPTERS 10–12

See www.CalcChat.com for worked-out solutions to odd-numbered exercises.

Take this test as you would take a test in class. When you are finished, check your work against the answers given in the back of the book.

In Exercises 1 and 2, identify the conic and sketch its graph. 1–2. See margin.

1. $\dfrac{(x-2)^2}{4} + \dfrac{(y+1)^2}{9} = 1$ **2.** $x^2 + y^2 - 2x - 4y + 1 = 0$

3. Find the standard form of the equation of the ellipse with vertices $(0, 0)$ and $(0, 4)$ and endpoints of the minor axis $(1, 2)$ and $(-1, 2)$.

3. $\dfrac{x^2}{1} + \dfrac{(y-2)^2}{4} = 1$

4. Determine the number of degrees through which the axis must be rotated to eliminate the xy-term of the conic $x^2 - 4xy + 2y^2 = 6$. Then graph the conic.

4. See margin.

5. Sketch the curve represented by the parametric equations $x = 4 \ln t$ and $y = \frac{1}{2}t^2$. Then eliminate the parameter and write the corresponding rectangular equation whose graph represents the curve. See margin.

6. Plot the point $(-2, -3\pi/4)$ and find three additional polar representations for $-2\pi < \theta < 2\pi$. See margin.

7. Convert the rectangular equation $-8x - 3y + 5 = 0$ to polar form.

7. $-8r\cos\theta - 3r\sin\theta + 5 = 0$ or $r = \dfrac{5}{8\cos\theta + 3\sin\theta}$

8. Convert the polar equation $r = \dfrac{2}{4 - 5\cos\theta}$ to rectangular form. $9x^2 + 20x - 16y^2 + 4 = 0$

In Exercises 9–11, sketch the graph of the polar equation. Identify the type of graph. 9–11. See margin.

9. $r = -\dfrac{\pi}{6}$ **10.** $r = 3 - 2\sin\theta$ **11.** $r = 2 + 5\cos\theta$

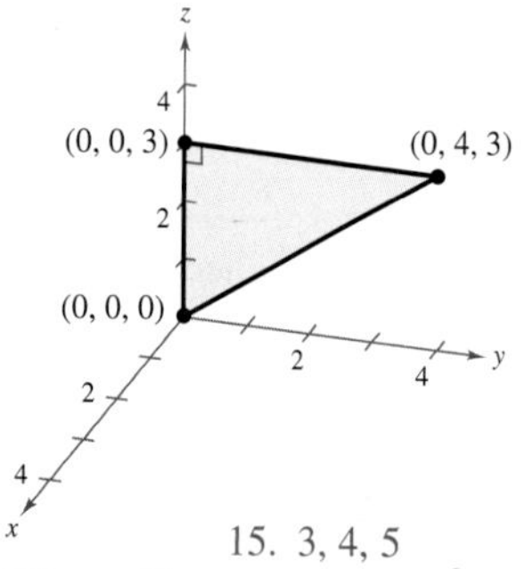

FIGURE FOR 15

In Exercises 12 and 13, find the coordinates of the point.

12. The point is located six units behind the yz-plane, one unit to the right of the xz-plane, and three units above the xy-plane. $(-6, 1, 3)$

13. The point is located on the y-axis, four units to the left of the xz-plane. $(0, -4, 0)$

14. Find the distance between the points $(-2, 3, -6)$ and $(4, -5, 1)$. $\sqrt{149}$

15. Find the lengths of the sides of the right triangle at the left. Show that these lengths satisfy the Pythagorean Theorem.

15. 3, 4, 5
$3^2 + 4^2 \stackrel{?}{=} 5^2$
$9 + 16 \stackrel{?}{=} 25$
$25 = 25$

16. Find the coordinates of the midpoint of the line segment joining $(3, 4, -1)$ and $(-5, 0, 2)$. $\left(-1, 2, \frac{1}{2}\right)$

17. Find an equation of the sphere for which the endpoints of a diameter are $(0, 0, 0)$ and $(4, 4, 8)$. $(x-2)^2 + (y-2)^2 + (z-4)^2 = 24$

18. Sketch the graph of the equation $(x-2)^2 + (y+1)^2 + z^2 = 4$, and sketch the xy-trace and the yz-trace. See margin.

19. For the vectors $\mathbf{u} = \langle 2, -6, 0\rangle$ and $\mathbf{v} = \langle -4, 5, 3\rangle$, find $\mathbf{u} \cdot \mathbf{v}$ and $\mathbf{u} \times \mathbf{v}$.
$\mathbf{u} \cdot \mathbf{v} = -38$, $\mathbf{u} \times \mathbf{v} = \langle -18, -6, -14\rangle$

In Exercises 20–22, determine whether u and v are orthogonal, parallel, or neither.

20. $\mathbf{u} = \langle 4, 4, 0\rangle$, $\mathbf{v} = \langle 0, -8, 6\rangle$ Neither

21. $\mathbf{u} = \langle 4, -2, 10\rangle$, $\mathbf{v} = \langle -2, 6, 2\rangle$ Orthogonal

22. $\mathbf{u} = \langle -1, 6, -3\rangle$, $\mathbf{v} = \langle 3, -18, 9\rangle$ Parallel

23. Find sets of (a) parametric equations and (b) symmetric equations for the line passing through the points $(-2, 3, 0)$ and $(5, 8, 25)$. See margin.

24. Find the parametric form of the equation of the line passing through the point $(-1, 2, 0)$ and perpendicular to $2x - 4y + z = 8$.
$x = -1 + 2t$, $y = 2 - 4t$, $z = t$

9.

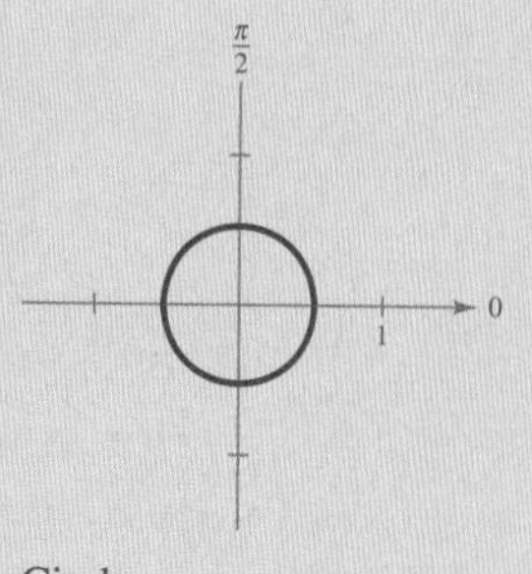

Circle

10.

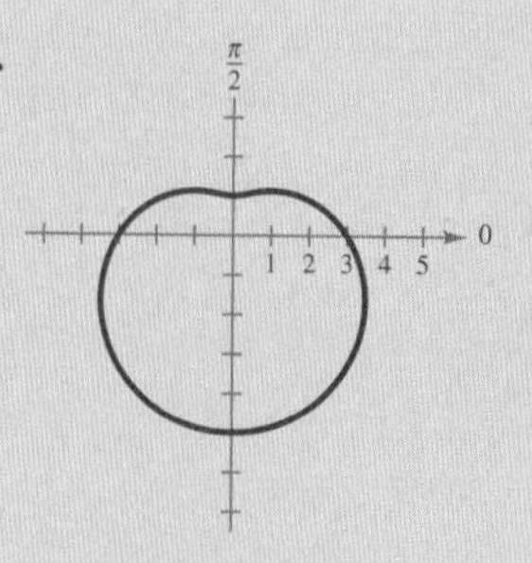

Dimpled limaçon

11.

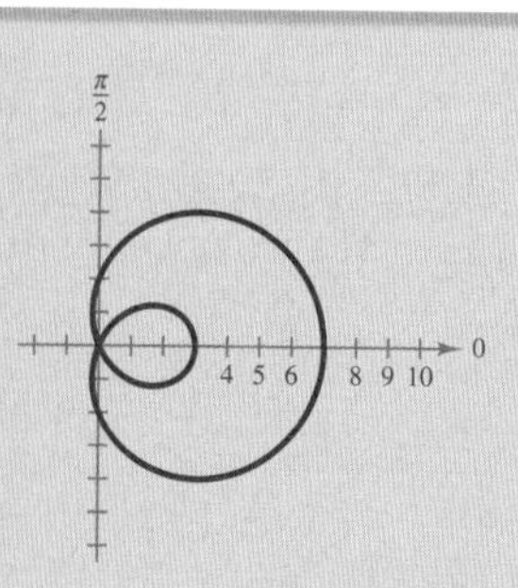

Limaçon with inner loop

18, 23. See Additional Answers beginning on page AA1.

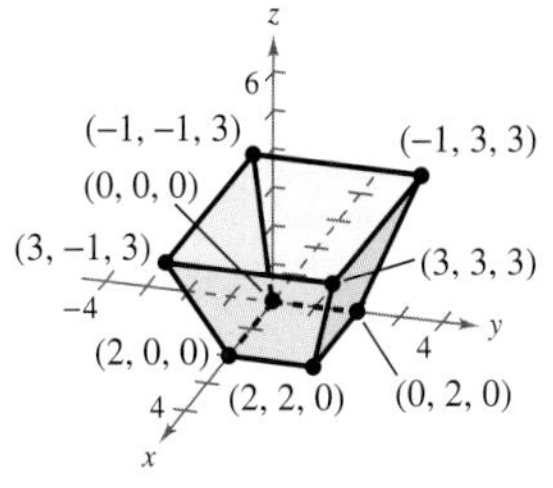

FIGURE FOR 28

25. Find an equation of the plane passing through the points $(0, 0, 0)$, $(-2, 3, 0)$, and $(5, 8, 25)$. $75x + 50y - 31z = 0$

26–27. See margin.

26. Sketch the graph and label the intercepts of the plane given by $3x - 6y - 12z = 24$.

27. Find the distance between the point $(0, 0, 25)$ and the plane $2x - 5y + z = 10$.

28. A plastic wastebasket has the shape and dimensions shown in the figure. In fabricating a mold for making the wastebasket, it is necessary to know the angle between two adjacent sides. Find the angle. $84.26°$

26.

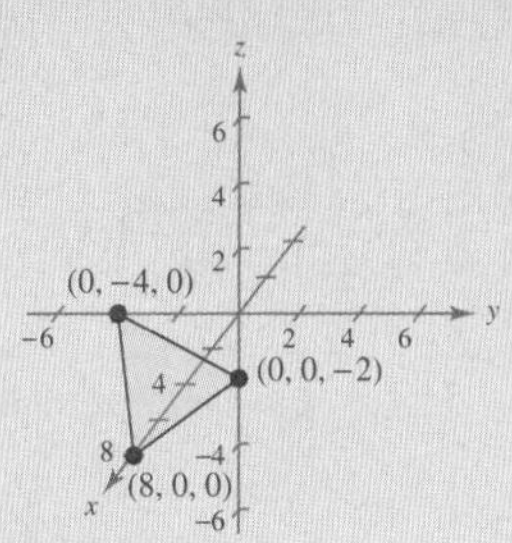

27. $\dfrac{\sqrt{30}}{2} \approx 2.74$

In Exercises 29–34, find the limit (if it exists). If the limit does not exist, explain why. Use a graphing utility to verify your result graphically.

29. $\displaystyle\lim_{x\to 0} \frac{\sqrt{x+4}-2}{x}$ $\frac{1}{4}$ **30.** $\displaystyle\lim_{x\to 4^-} \frac{|x-4|}{x-4}$ -1 **31.** $\displaystyle\lim_{x\to 0} \sin\left(\frac{\pi}{x}\right)$ Limit does not exist.

32. $\displaystyle\lim_{x\to 0} \frac{\frac{1}{x-3}+\frac{1}{3}}{x}$ $-\frac{1}{9}$ **33.** $\displaystyle\lim_{x\to 0} \frac{\sqrt{x+16}-4}{x}$ $\frac{1}{8}$ **34.** $\displaystyle\lim_{x\to 2^-} \frac{x-2}{x^2-4}$ $\frac{1}{4}$

In Exercises 35–38, find a formula for the slope of the graph of f at the point $(x, f(x))$. Then use the formula to find the slope at the given point.

35. $f(x) = 4 - x^2$, $(-2, 0)$ $m = -2x; 4$ **36.** $f(x) = \sqrt{x+3}$, $(-2, 1)$ $m = \frac{1}{2}(x+3)^{-1/2}; \frac{1}{2}$

37. $f(x) = \dfrac{1}{x+3}$, $\left(1, \dfrac{1}{4}\right)$ $m = -(x+3)^{-2}; -\frac{1}{16}$ **38.** $f(x) = x^2 - x$, $(1, 0)$ $m = 2x - 1; 1$

In Exercises 39–44, find the limit (if it exists). If the limit does not exist, explain why. Use a graphing utility to verify your result graphically.

39–40. Limit does not exist.

39. $\displaystyle\lim_{x\to\infty} \frac{2x^4 - x^3 + 4}{x^2 - 9}$ **40.** $\displaystyle\lim_{x\to\infty} \frac{x^3}{x^2-9}$ **41.** $\displaystyle\lim_{x\to\infty} \frac{3-7x}{x+4}$ -7

42. $\displaystyle\lim_{x\to\infty} \frac{3x^2+1}{x^2+4}$ 3 **43.** $\displaystyle\lim_{x\to\infty} \frac{2x}{x^2+3x-2}$ 0 **44.** $\displaystyle\lim_{x\to\infty} \frac{3-x}{x^2+1}$ 0

In Exercises 45–47, evaluate the sum using the summation formulas and properties.

45. $\displaystyle\sum_{i=1}^{50} (1 - i^2)$ $-42{,}875$ **46.** $\displaystyle\sum_{k=1}^{20} (3k^2 - 2k)$ 8190 **47.** $\displaystyle\sum_{i=1}^{40} (12 + i^3)$ $672{,}880$

In Exercises 48 and 49, approximate the area of the region using the indicated number of rectangles of equal width.

48.

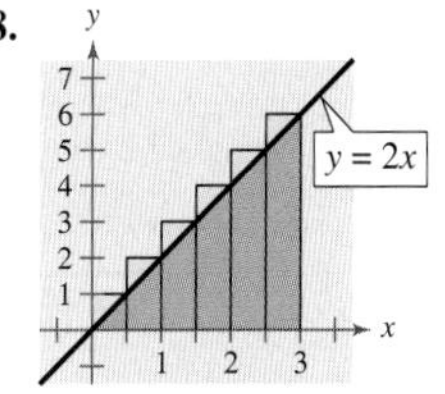

$A = 10.5$ square units

49.

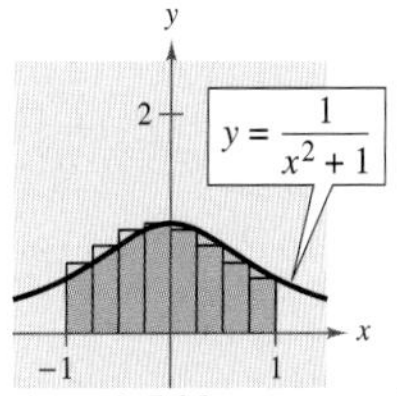

$A \approx 1.566$ square units

In Exercises 50–52, use the limit process to find the area of the region between the graph of the function and the x-axis over the specified interval.

50. $f(x) = 1 - x^3$
Interval: $[0, 1]$
$\frac{3}{4}$ square unit

51. $f(x) = x + 2$
Interval: $[0, 1]$
$\frac{5}{2}$ square units

52. $f(x) = 4 - x^2$
Interval: $[0, 2]$
$\frac{16}{3}$ square units

PROOFS IN MATHEMATICS

Many of the proofs of the definitions and properties presented in this chapter are beyond the scope of this text. Included below are simple proofs for the limit of a power function and the limit of a polynomial function.

Proving Limits

To prove most of the definitions and properties in this chapter, you must use the *formal* definition of limit. This definition is called the epsilon-delta definition and was first introduced by Karl Weierstrass (1815–1897). If you go on to take a course in calculus, you will use this definition of limit extensively.

Limit of a Power Function *(p. 855)*

$\lim\limits_{x \to c} x^n = c^n$, c is a real number and n is a positive integer.

Proof

$$\lim_{x \to c} x^n = \lim_{x \to c}(\underbrace{x \cdot x \cdot x \cdot \cdot \cdot \cdot \cdot x}_{n \text{ factors}})$$

$$= \underbrace{\lim_{x \to c} x \cdot \lim_{x \to c} x \cdot \lim_{x \to c} x \cdot \cdot \cdot \cdot \cdot \lim_{x \to c} x}_{n \text{ factors}} \qquad \text{Product Property of Limits}$$

$$= \underbrace{c \cdot c \cdot c \cdot \cdot \cdot \cdot \cdot c}_{n \text{ factors}} \qquad \text{Limit of the identity function}$$

$$= c^n \qquad \text{Exponential form}$$

Limit of a Polynomial Function *(p. 857)*

If p is a polynomial function and c is a real number, then

$$\lim_{x \to c} p(x) = p(c).$$

Proof

Let p be a polynomial function such that

$$p(x) = a_n x^n + a_{n-1}x^{n-1} + \cdot \cdot \cdot + a_2 x^2 + a_1 x + a_0.$$

Because a polynomial function is the sum of monomial functions, you can write the following.

$$\lim_{x \to c} p(x) = \lim_{x \to c} (a_n x^n + a_{n-1}x^{n-1} + \cdot \cdot \cdot + a_2 x^2 + a_1 x + a_0)$$

$$= \lim_{x \to c} a_n x^n + \lim_{x \to c} a_{n-1}x^{n-1} + \cdot \cdot \cdot + \lim_{x \to c} a_2 x^2 + \lim_{x \to c} a_1 x + \lim_{x \to c} a_0$$

$$= a_n c^n + a_{n-1}c^{n-1} + \cdot \cdot \cdot + a_2 c^2 + a_1 c + a_0 \qquad \text{Scalar Multiple Property of Limits and limit of a power function}$$

$$= p(c) \qquad p \text{ evaluated at } c$$

906

PROBLEM SOLVING

This collection of thought-provoking and challenging exercises further explores and expands upon concepts learned in this chapter.

1. Consider the graphs of the four functions g_1, g_2, g_3, and g_4.

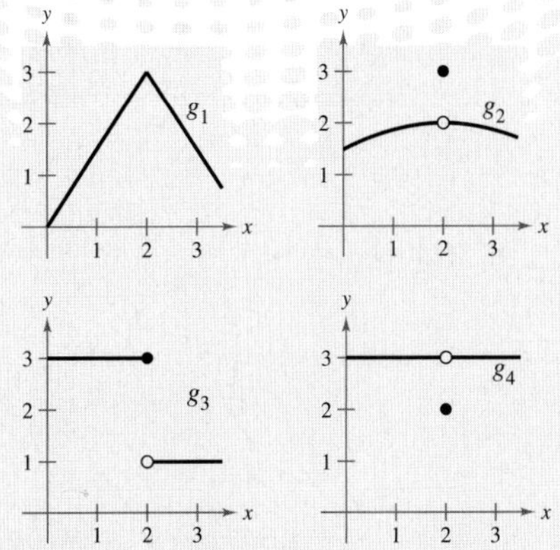

For each given condition of the function f, which of the graphs could be the graph of f?

(a) $\lim_{x\to 2} f(x) = 3$ g_1, g_4 (b) $\lim_{x\to 2^-} f(x) = 3$ g_1, g_3, g_4

(c) $\lim_{x\to 2^+} f(x) = 3$ g_1, g_4

2. Sketch the graph of the function given by $f(x) = [\![x]\!] + [\![-x]\!]$. See margin.

(a) Evaluate $f(1), f(0), f\left(\frac{1}{2}\right)$, and $f(-2.7)$.

(b) Evaluate the following limits.

$$\lim_{x\to 1^-} f(x),\ \lim_{x\to 1^+} f(x),\ \lim_{x\to 1/2} f(x)$$

3. Sketch the graph of the function given by $f(x) = \left[\!\!\left[\frac{1}{x}\right]\!\!\right]$. See margin.

(a) Evaluate $f\left(\frac{1}{4}\right), f(3)$, and $f(1)$.

(b) Evaluate the following limits.

$$\lim_{x\to 1^-} f(x),\ \lim_{x\to 1^+} f(x),\ \lim_{x\to (1/2)^-} f(x),\ \lim_{x\to (1/2)^+} f(x)$$

4. Let $P(3, 4)$ be a point on the circle $x^2 + y^2 = 25$ (see figure).

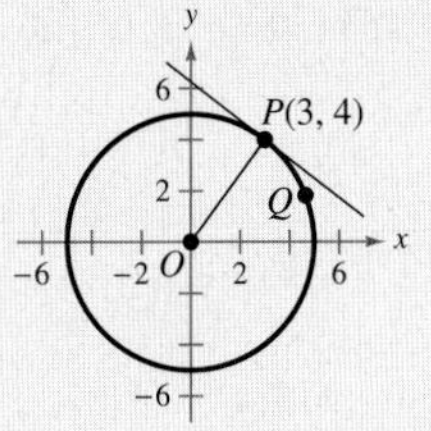

(a) What is the slope of the line joining P and $O(0, 0)$? $\frac{4}{3}$

(b) Find an equation of the tangent line to the circle at P.

(b) $y = -\frac{3}{4}x + \frac{25}{4}$ (c) $m_x = \dfrac{\sqrt{25 - x^2} - 4}{x - 3}$

(c) Let $Q(x, y)$ be another point on the circle in the first quadrant. Find the slope m_x of the line joining P and Q in terms of x. See below.

(d) Evaluate $\lim_{x\to 3} m_x$. How does this number relate to your answer in part (b)? $-\frac{3}{4}$; the slopes are the same.

5. Find the values of the constants a and b such that

$$\lim_{x\to 0} \frac{\sqrt{a + bx} - \sqrt{3}}{x} = \sqrt{3}.\quad a = 3, b = 6$$

6. Consider the function given by

$$f(x) = \frac{\sqrt{3 + x^{1/3}} - 2}{x - 1}.$$

(a) Find the domain of f. Domain: $x \geq -27,\ x \neq 1$

(b) Use a graphing utility to graph the function. See margin.

(c) Evaluate $\lim_{x\to -27^+} f(x)$. Verify your result using the graph in part (b). $\frac{1}{14}$

(d) Evaluate $\lim_{x\to 1} f(x)$. Verify your result using the graph in part (b). $\frac{1}{12}$

7. Let

$$f(x) = \begin{cases} 0, & \text{if } x \text{ is rational} \\ 1, & \text{if } x \text{ is irrational} \end{cases}$$

and

$$g(x) = \begin{cases} 0, & \text{if } x \text{ is rational} \\ x, & \text{if } x \text{ is irrational}. \end{cases}$$

Find (if possible) $\lim_{x\to 0} f(x)$ and $\lim_{x\to 0} g(x)$. Explain your reasoning. 7–9. See margin.

8. Graph the two parabolas $y = x^2$ and $y = -x^2 + 2x - 5$ in the same coordinate plane. Find equations of the two lines that are simultaneously tangent to both parabolas.

9. Find a function of the form $f(x) = a + b\sqrt{x}$ that is tangent to the line $2y - 3x = 5$ at the point $(1, 4)$.

10. (a) Find an equation of the tangent line to the parabola $y = x^2$ at the point $(2, 4)$.

(b) Find an equation of the normal line to $y = x^2$ at the point $(2, 4)$. (The **normal line** is perpendicular to the tangent line.) Where does this line intersect the parabola a second time?

(c) Find equations of the tangent line and normal line to $y = x^2$ at the point $(0, 0)$.

(a) Tangent line: $y = 4x - 4$

(b) Normal line: $y = -\frac{1}{4}x + \frac{9}{2}$

Intersection point: $\left(-\frac{9}{4}, \frac{81}{16}\right)$

(c) Tangent line: $y = 0$; normal line: $x = 0$

2.

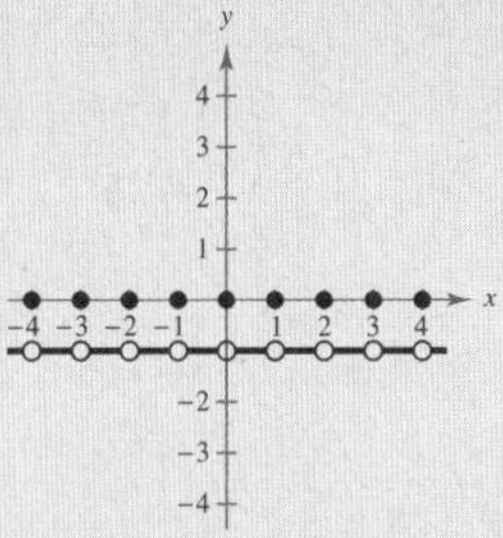

The graph jumps at every integer.

(a) $f(1) = 0, f(0) = 0,$

$f\left(\frac{1}{2}\right) = -1, f(-2.7) = -1$

(b) $\lim_{x\to 1^-} f(x) = -1,$

$\lim_{x\to 1^+} f(x) = -1,$

$\lim_{x\to 1/2} f(x) = -1$

3.

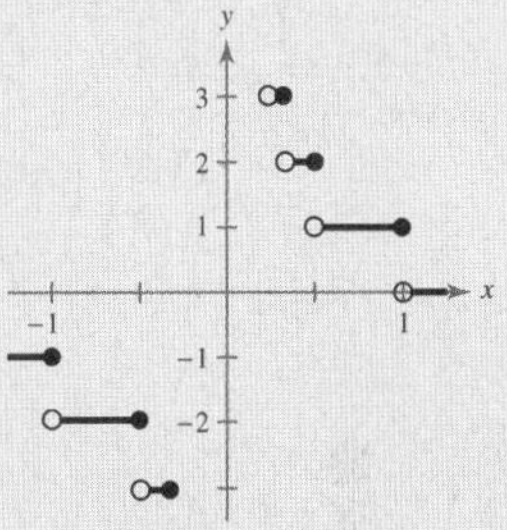

(a) $f\left(\frac{1}{4}\right) = [\![4]\!] = 4$

$f(3) = \left[\!\!\left[\frac{1}{3}\right]\!\!\right] = 0$

$f(1) = [\![1]\!] = 1$

(b) $\lim_{x\to 1^-} f(x) = 1$

$\lim_{x\to 1^+} f(x) = 0$

$\lim_{x\to (1/2)^-} f(x) = 2$

$\lim_{x\to (1/2)^+} f(x) = 1$

6. (b)

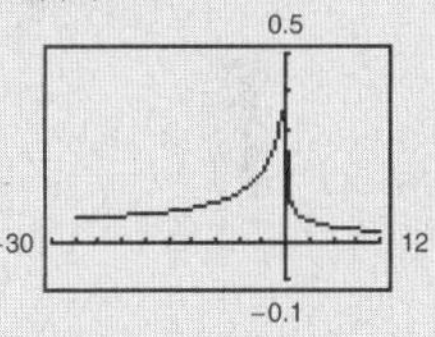

7. $\lim_{x\to 0} f(x)$ does not exist. No matter how close x is to 0, there are still an infinite number of rational and irrational numbers, so $\lim_{x\to 0} f(x)$ does not exist.

$\lim_{x\to 0} g(x) = 0$. When x is close to 0, both parts of the function are close to 0.

8.

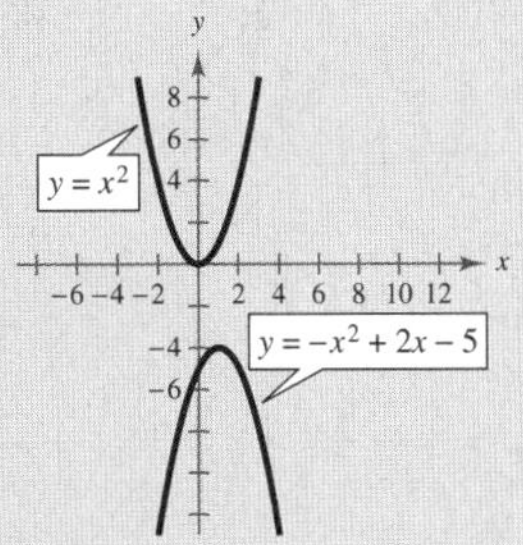

Tangent lines: $y = -2x - 1$ and $y = 4x - 4$

9. $y = 1 + 3\sqrt{x}$

11. A line with slope m passes through the point $(0, 4)$.

(a) Recall that the distance d between a point (x_1, y_1) and the line $Ax + By + C = 0$ is given by

$$d = \frac{|Ax_1 + By_1 + C|}{\sqrt{A^2 + B^2}}. \quad d(m) = \frac{|3m + 3|}{\sqrt{m^2 + 1}}$$

Write the distance d between the line and the point $(3, 1)$ as a function of m.

(b) Use a graphing utility to graph the function from part (a). See margin.

(c) Find $\lim_{m\to\infty} d(m)$ and $\lim_{m\to-\infty} d(m)$. Give a geometric interpretation of the results. See margin.

12. A heat probe is attached to the heat exchanger of a heating system. The temperature T (in degrees Celsius) is recorded t seconds after the furnace is started. The results for the first 2 minutes are recorded in the table.

t	T
0	25.2°
15	36.9°
30	45.5°
45	51.4°
60	56.0°
75	59.6°
90	62.0°
105	64.0°
120	65.2°

(a) Use the *regression* feature of a graphing utility to find a model of the form $T_1 = at^2 + bt + c$ for the data. $T_1 = -0.00303t^2 + 0.677t + 26.56$

(b) Use a graphing utility to graph T_1 with the original data. How well does the model fit the data? See margin.

(c) A rational model for the data is given by

$$T_2 = \frac{86t + 1451}{t + 58}.$$

Use a graphing utility to graph T_2 with the original data. How well does the model fit the data? See margin.

(d) Evaluate $T_1(0)$ and $T_2(0)$. $T_1(0) = 26.56$, $T_2(0) = 25.02$

(e) Find $\lim_{t\to\infty} T_2$. Verify your result using the graph in part (c). $\lim_{x\to\infty} T_2 = 86$

(f) Interpret the result of part (e) in the context of the problem. Is it possible to do this type of analysis using T_1? Explain your reasoning.
The heat exchanger reaches a maximum temperature of 86°C. No, this type of analysis is not possible using T_1 because as t gets larger, T_1 approaches negative infinity.

13. When using a graphing utility to generate a table to approximate

$$\lim_{x\to0} \frac{\tan 2x}{x}$$

The error was probably due to the calculator being in degree mode rather than radian mode.

a student concluded that the limit was 0.03491 rather than 2. Determine the probable cause of the error.

14. Let $P(x, y)$ be a point on the parabola $y = x^2$ in the first quadrant. Consider the triangle PAO formed by P, $A(0, 1)$, and the origin $O(0, 0)$, and the triangle PBO formed by P, $B(1, 0)$, and the origin (see figure).

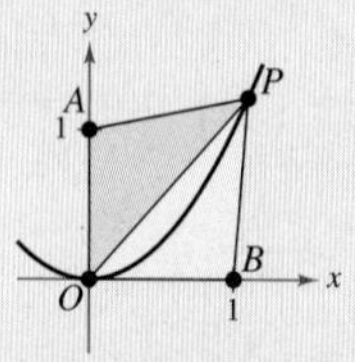

See margin.

(a) Write the perimeter of each triangle in terms of x.

(b) Complete the table. Let $r(x)$ be the ratio of the perimeters of the two triangles.

$$r(x) = \frac{\text{Perimeter } \triangle PAO}{\text{Perimeter } \triangle PBO}$$

x	4	2	1	0.1	0.01
Perimeter $\triangle PAO$					
Perimeter $\triangle PBO$					
$r(x)$					

(c) Find $\lim_{x\to0^+} r(x)$.

15. Archimedes showed that the area of a parabolic arch is equal to $\frac{2}{3}$ the product of the base and the height (see figure). See margin.

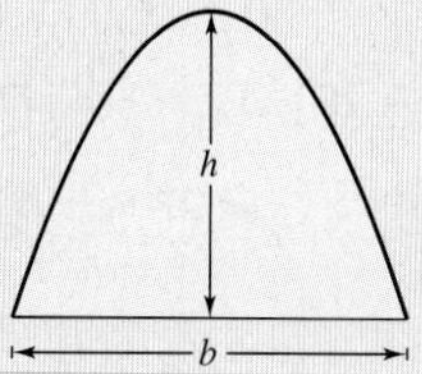

(a) Graph the parabolic arch bounded by $y = 9 - x^2$ and the x-axis.

(b) Use the limit process to find the area of the parabolic arch.

(c) Find the base and height of the arch and verify Archimedes' formula.

11. (b)

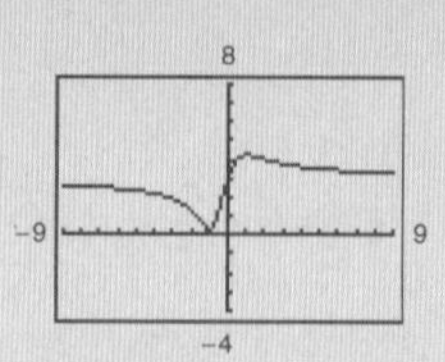

(c) $\lim_{m\to\infty} d(m) = 3$, $\lim_{m\to-\infty} d(m) = 3$. This indicates that the distance between the point and the line approaches 3 as the slope approaches positive or negative infinity.

12. (b)

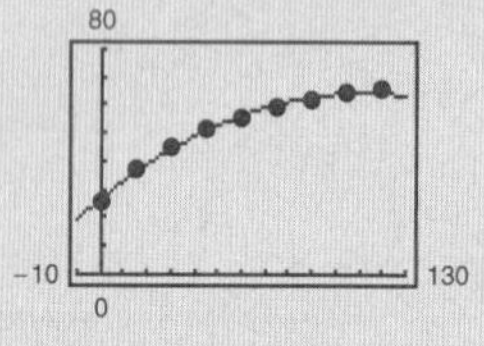

The model is a good fit for the data.

(c)

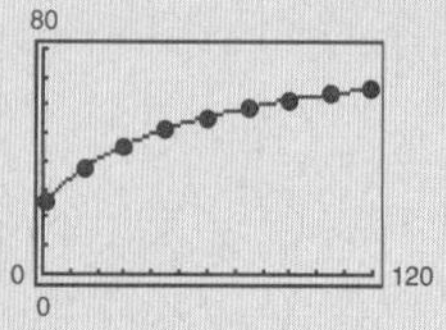

The model is a good fit for the data.

14. See below.

15. (a)

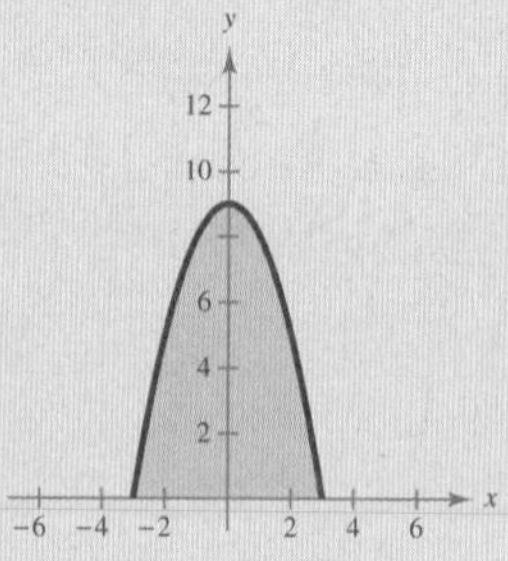

(b) $A = 36$

(c) Base $= 6$, height $= 9$; Area $= \frac{2}{3}bh = 36$

14. (a) Perimeter $\triangle PAO = 1 + \sqrt{(x^2 - 1)^2 + x^2} + \sqrt{x^4 + x^2}$
Perimeter $\triangle PBO = 1 + \sqrt{x^4 + (x - 1)^2} + \sqrt{x^4 + x^2}$

(b)

x	4	2	1	0.1	0.01
Perimeter $\triangle PAO$	33.0166	9.0777	3.4142	2.0955	2.0100
Perimeter $\triangle PBO$	33.7712	9.5952	3.4142	2.0006	2.0000
$r(x)$	0.9777	0.9461	1.0000	1.0474	1.005

(c) 1

Appendix A Review of Fundamental Concepts of Algebra

A.1 Real Numbers and Their Properties

What you should learn

- Represent and classify real numbers.
- Order real numbers and use inequalities.
- Find the absolute values of real numbers and find the distance between two real numbers.
- Evaluate algebraic expressions.
- Use the basic rules and properties of algebra.

Why you should learn it

Real numbers are used to represent many real-life quantities. For example, in Exercises 83–88 on page A12, you will use real numbers to represent the federal deficit.

Real Numbers

Real numbers are used in everyday life to describe quantities such as age, miles per gallon, and population. Real numbers are represented by symbols such as

$$-5, 9, 0, \frac{4}{3}, 0.666\ldots, 28.21, \sqrt{2}, \pi, \text{ and } \sqrt[3]{-32}.$$

Here are some important **subsets** (each member of subset B is also a member of set A) of the real numbers. The three dots, called *ellipsis points*, indicate that the pattern continues indefinitely.

$\{1, 2, 3, 4, \ldots\}$ Set of natural numbers

$\{0, 1, 2, 3, 4, \ldots\}$ Set of whole numbers

$\{\ldots, -3, -2, -1, 0, 1, 2, 3, \ldots\}$ Set of integers

A real number is **rational** if it can be written as the ratio p/q of two integers, where $q \neq 0$. For instance, the numbers

$$\frac{1}{3} = 0.3333\ldots = 0.\overline{3}, \frac{1}{8} = 0.125, \text{ and } \frac{125}{111} = 1.126126\ldots = 1.\overline{126}$$

are rational. The decimal representation of a rational number either repeats $\left(\text{as in } \frac{173}{55} = 3.1\overline{45}\right)$ or terminates $\left(\text{as in } \frac{1}{2} = 0.5\right)$. A real number that cannot be written as the ratio of two integers is called **irrational.** Irrational numbers have infinite nonrepeating decimal representations. For instance, the numbers

$$\sqrt{2} = 1.4142135\ldots \approx 1.41 \quad \text{and} \quad \pi = 3.1415926\ldots \approx 3.14$$

are irrational. (The symbol $\approx$ means "is approximately equal to.") Figure A.1 shows subsets of real numbers and their relationships to each other.

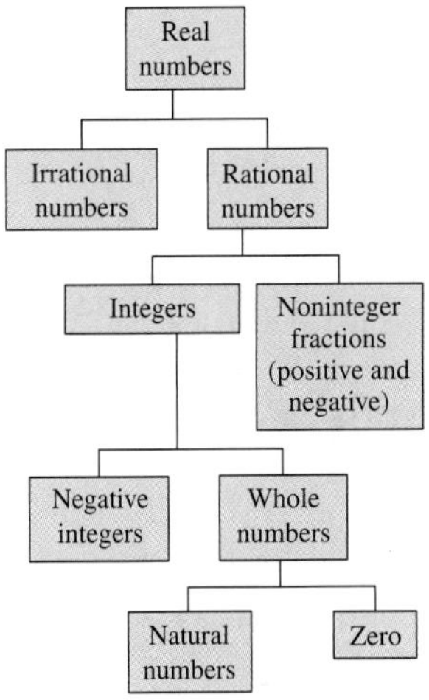

FIGURE A.1 Subsets of real numbers

Example 1 Classifying Real Numbers

Determine which numbers in the set

$$\left\{-13, -\sqrt{5}, -1, -\frac{1}{3}, 0, \frac{5}{8}, \sqrt{2}, \pi, 7\right\}$$

are (a) natural numbers, (b) whole numbers, (c) integers, (d) rational numbers, and (e) irrational numbers.

Solution

a. Natural numbers: $\{7\}$

b. Whole numbers: $\{0, 7\}$

c. Integers: $\{-13, -1, 0, 7\}$

d. Rational numbers: $\left\{-13, -1, -\frac{1}{3}, 0, \frac{5}{8}, 7\right\}$

e. Irrational numbers: $\left\{-\sqrt{5}, \sqrt{2}, \pi\right\}$

CHECK*Point* Now try Exercise 11.

A1

Real numbers are represented graphically on the **real number line.** When you draw a point on the real number line that corresponds to a real number, you are **plotting** the real number. The point 0 on the real number line is the **origin.** Numbers to the right of 0 are positive, and numbers to the left of 0 are negative, as shown in Figure A.2. The term **nonnegative** describes a number that is either positive or zero.

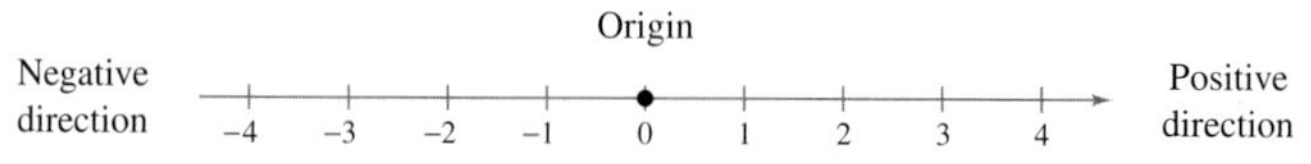

FIGURE A.2 The real number line

As illustrated in Figure A.3, there is a *one-to-one correspondence* between real numbers and points on the real number line.

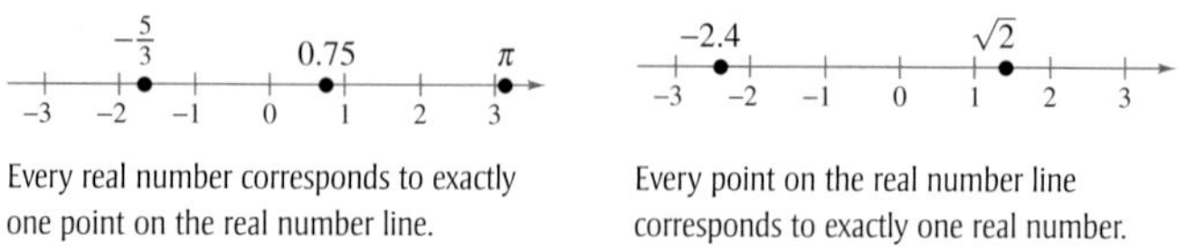

FIGURE A.3 One-to-one correspondence

Example 2 Plotting Points on the Real Number Line

Plot the real numbers on the real number line.

a. $-\dfrac{7}{4}$

b. 2.3

c. $\dfrac{2}{3}$

d. -1.8

Solution

All four points are shown in Figure A.4.

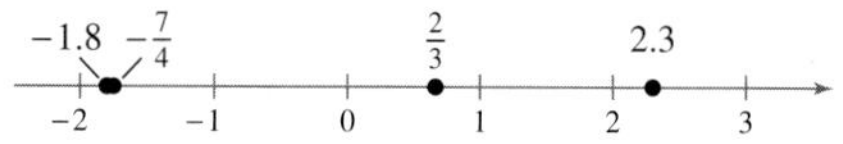

FIGURE A.4

a. The point representing the real number $-\frac{7}{4} = -1.75$ lies between -2 and -1, but closer to -2, on the real number line.

b. The point representing the real number 2.3 lies between 2 and 3, but closer to 2, on the real number line.

c. The point representing the real number $\frac{2}{3} = 0.666\ldots$ lies between 0 and 1, but closer to 1, on the real number line.

d. The point representing the real number -1.8 lies between -2 and -1, but closer to -2, on the real number line. Note that the point representing -1.8 lies slightly to the left of the point representing $-\frac{7}{4}$.

CHECK*Point* Now try Exercise 17.

Ordering Real Numbers

One important property of real numbers is that they are *ordered*.

> **Definition of Order on the Real Number Line**
>
> If a and b are real numbers, a is less than b if $b - a$ is positive. The **order** of a and b is denoted by the **inequality** $a < b$. This relationship can also be described by saying that b is *greater than* a and writing $b > a$. The inequality $a \le b$ means that a is *less than or equal to* b, and the inequality $b \ge a$ means that b is *greater than or equal to* a. The symbols $<$, $>$, $\le$, and $\ge$ are *inequality symbols*.

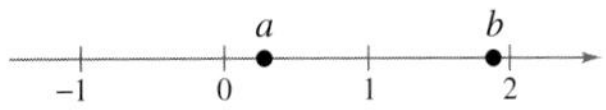

FIGURE A.5 $a < b$ if and only if a lies to the left of b.

Geometrically, this definition implies that $a < b$ if and only if a lies to the *left* of b on the real number line, as shown in Figure A.5.

Example 3 Ordering Real Numbers

Place the appropriate inequality symbol ($<$ or $>$) between the pair of real numbers.

a. $-3, 0$ **b.** $-2, -4$ **c.** $\frac{1}{4}, \frac{1}{3}$ **d.** $-\frac{1}{5}, -\frac{1}{2}$

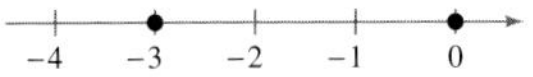

FIGURE A.6

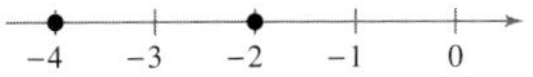

FIGURE A.7

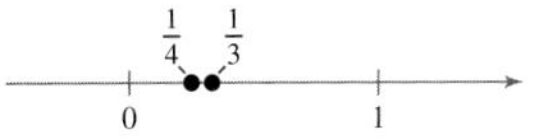

FIGURE A.8

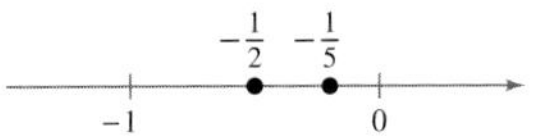

FIGURE A.9

Solution

a. Because -3 lies to the left of 0 on the real number line, as shown in Figure A.6, you can say that -3 is *less than* 0, and write $-3 < 0$.

b. Because -2 lies to the right of -4 on the real number line, as shown in Figure A.7, you can say that -2 is *greater than* -4, and write $-2 > -4$.

c. Because $\frac{1}{4}$ lies to the left of $\frac{1}{3}$ on the real number line, as shown in Figure A.8, you can say that $\frac{1}{4}$ is *less than* $\frac{1}{3}$, and write $\frac{1}{4} < \frac{1}{3}$.

d. Because $-\frac{1}{5}$ lies to the right of $-\frac{1}{2}$ on the real number line, as shown in Figure A.9, you can say that $-\frac{1}{5}$ is *greater than* $-\frac{1}{2}$, and write $-\frac{1}{5} > -\frac{1}{2}$.

CHECK*Point* Now try Exercise 25.

Example 4 Interpreting Inequalities

Describe the subset of real numbers represented by each inequality.

a. $x \le 2$ **b.** $-2 \le x < 3$

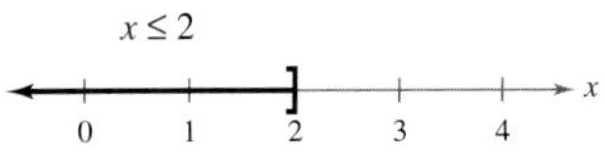

FIGURE A.10

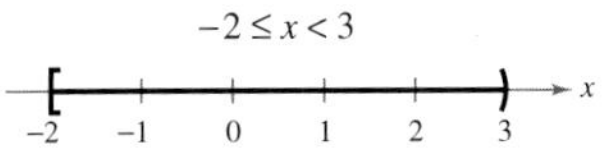

FIGURE A.11

Solution

a. The inequality $x \le 2$ denotes all real numbers less than or equal to 2, as shown in Figure A.10.

b. The inequality $-2 \le x < 3$ means that $x \ge -2$ *and* $x < 3$. This "double inequality" denotes all real numbers between -2 and 3, including -2 but not including 3, as shown in Figure A.11.

CHECK*Point* Now try Exercise 31.

Inequalities can be used to describe subsets of real numbers called **intervals.** In the bounded intervals below, the real numbers a and b are the **endpoints** of each interval. The endpoints of a closed interval are included in the interval, whereas the endpoints of an open interval are not included in the interval.

Bounded Intervals on the Real Number Line

Notation	*Interval Type*	*Inequality*	*Graph*
$[a, b]$	Closed	$a \le x \le b$	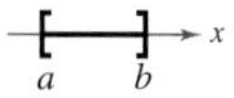
(a, b)	Open	$a < x < b$	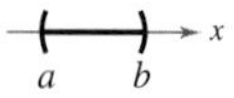
$[a, b)$		$a \le x < b$	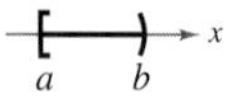
$(a, b]$		$a < x \le b$	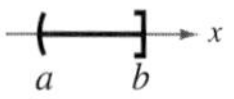

Study Tip

The reason that the four types of intervals at the right are called *bounded* is that each has a finite length. An interval that does not have a finite length is *unbounded* (see below).

WARNING/CAUTION

Whenever you write an interval containing ∞ or $-\infty$, always use a parenthesis and never a bracket. This is because ∞ and $-\infty$ are never an endpoint of an interval and therefore are not included in the interval.

The symbols ∞, **positive infinity,** and $-\infty$, **negative infinity,** do not represent real numbers. They are simply convenient symbols used to describe the unboundedness of an interval such as $(1, \infty)$ or $(-\infty, 3]$.

Unbounded Intervals on the Real Number Line

Notation	*Interval Type*	*Inequality*	*Graph*
$[a, \infty)$		$x \ge a$	
(a, ∞)	Open	$x > a$	
$(-\infty, b]$		$x \le b$	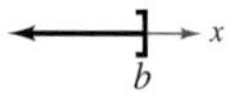
$(-\infty, b)$	Open	$x < b$	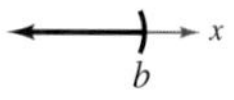
$(-\infty, \infty)$	Entire real line	$-\infty < x < \infty$	

Example 5 **Using Inequalities to Represent Intervals**

Use inequality notation to describe each of the following.

a. c is at most 2. **b.** m is at least -3. **c.** All x in the interval $(-3, 5]$

Solution

a. The statement "c is at most 2" can be represented by $c \le 2$.

b. The statement "m is at least -3" can be represented by $m \ge -3$.

c. "All x in the interval $(-3, 5]$" can be represented by $-3 < x \le 5$.

CHECKPoint Now try Exercise 45.

Example 6 Interpreting Intervals

Give a verbal description of each interval.

a. $(-1, 0)$ **b.** $[2, \infty)$ **c.** $(-\infty, 0)$

Solution

a. This interval consists of all real numbers that are greater than -1 and less than 0.

b. This interval consists of all real numbers that are greater than or equal to 2.

c. This interval consists of all negative real numbers.

CHECKPoint Now try Exercise 41.

Absolute Value and Distance

The **absolute value** of a real number is its *magnitude*, or the distance between the origin and the point representing the real number on the real number line.

> **Definition of Absolute Value**
>
> If a is a real number, then the absolute value of a is
>
> $$|a| = \begin{cases} a, & \text{if } a \geq 0 \\ -a, & \text{if } a < 0 \end{cases}.$$

Notice in this definition that the absolute value of a real number is never negative. For instance, if $a = -5$, then $|-5| = -(-5) = 5$. The absolute value of a real number is either positive or zero. Moreover, 0 is the only real number whose absolute value is 0. So, $|0| = 0$.

Example 7 Finding Absolute Values

a. $|-15| = 15$ **b.** $\left|\dfrac{2}{3}\right| = \dfrac{2}{3}$

c. $|-4.3| = 4.3$ **d.** $-|-6| = -(6) = -6$

CHECKPoint Now try Exercise 51.

Example 8 Evaluating the Absolute Value of a Number

Evaluate $\dfrac{|x|}{x}$ for (a) $x > 0$ and (b) $x < 0$.

Solution

a. If $x > 0$, then $|x| = x$ and $\dfrac{|x|}{x} = \dfrac{x}{x} = 1$.

b. If $x < 0$, then $|x| = -x$ and $\dfrac{|x|}{x} = \dfrac{-x}{x} = -1$.

CHECKPoint Now try Exercise 59.

The **Law of Trichotomy** states that for any two real numbers a and b, *precisely* one of three relationships is possible:

$a = b, \quad a < b, \quad \text{or} \quad a > b.$ Law of Trichotomy

Example 9 Comparing Real Numbers

Place the appropriate symbol (<, >, or =) between the pair of real numbers.

a. $|-4| \quad\square\quad |3|$ **b.** $|-10| \quad\square\quad |10|$ **c.** $-|-7| \quad\square\quad |-7|$

Solution

a. $|-4| > |3|$ because $|-4| = 4$ and $|3| = 3$, and 4 is greater than 3.

b. $|-10| = |10|$ because $|-10| = 10$ and $|10| = 10$.

c. $-|-7| < |-7|$ because $-|-7| = -7$ and $|-7| = 7$, and -7 is less than 7.

CHECK *Point* Now try Exercise 61.

Properties of Absolute Values

1. $|a| \geq 0$ **2.** $|-a| = |a|$

3. $|ab| = |a||b|$ **4.** $\left|\dfrac{a}{b}\right| = \dfrac{|a|}{|b|}, \quad b \neq 0$

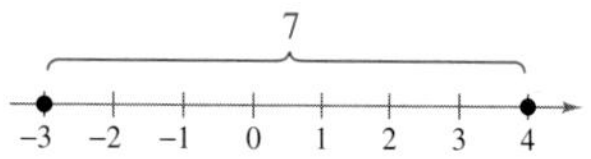

FIGURE A.12 The distance between -3 and 4 is 7.

Absolute value can be used to define the distance between two points on the real number line. For instance, the distance between -3 and 4 is

$$|-3 - 4| = |-7|$$
$$= 7$$

as shown in Figure A.12.

Distance Between Two Points on the Real Number Line

Let a and b be real numbers. The **distance between a and b** is

$$d(a, b) = |b - a| = |a - b|.$$

Example 10 Finding a Distance

Find the distance between -25 and 13.

Solution

The distance between -25 and 13 is given by

$|-25 - 13| = |-38| = 38.$ Distance between -25 and 13

The distance can also be found as follows.

$|13 - (-25)| = |38| = 38$ Distance between -25 and 13

CHECK *Point* Now try Exercise 67.

Algebraic Expressions

One characteristic of algebra is the use of letters to represent numbers. The letters are **variables,** and combinations of letters and numbers are **algebraic expressions.** Here are a few examples of algebraic expressions.

$$5x, \qquad 2x - 3, \qquad \frac{4}{x^2 + 2}, \qquad 7x + y$$

Definition of an Algebraic Expression

An **algebraic expression** is a collection of letters **(variables)** and real numbers **(constants)** combined using the operations of addition, subtraction, multiplication, division, and exponentiation.

The **terms** of an algebraic expression are those parts that are separated by *addition.* For example,

$$x^2 - 5x + 8 = x^2 + (-5x) + 8$$

has three terms: x^2 and $-5x$ are the **variable terms** and 8 is the **constant term.** The numerical factor of a term is called the **coefficient.** For instance, the coefficient of $-5x$ is -5, and the coefficient of x^2 is 1.

Example 11 Identifying Terms and Coefficients

Algebraic Expression	*Terms*	*Coefficients*
a. $5x - \frac{1}{7}$	$5x, -\frac{1}{7}$	$5, -\frac{1}{7}$
b. $2x^2 - 6x + 9$	$2x^2, -6x, 9$	$2, -6, 9$
c. $\frac{3}{x} + \frac{1}{2}x^4 - y$	$\frac{3}{x}, \frac{1}{2}x^4, -y$	$3, \frac{1}{2}, -1$

CHECK *Point* Now try Exercise 89.

To **evaluate** an algebraic expression, substitute numerical values for each of the variables in the expression, as shown in the next example.

Example 12 Evaluating Algebraic Expressions

Expression	*Value of Variable*	*Substitute*	*Value of Expression*
a. $-3x + 5$	$x = 3$	$-3(3) + 5$	$-9 + 5 = -4$
b. $3x^2 + 2x - 1$	$x = -1$	$3(-1)^2 + 2(-1) - 1$	$3 - 2 - 1 = 0$
c. $\frac{2x}{x + 1}$	$x = -3$	$\frac{2(-3)}{-3 + 1}$	$\frac{-6}{-2} = 3$

Note that you must substitute the value for *each* occurrence of the variable.

CHECK *Point* Now try Exercise 95.

When an algebraic expression is evaluated, the **Substitution Principle** is used. It states that "If $a = b$, then a can be replaced by b in any expression involving a." In Example 12(a), for instance, 3 is *substituted* for x in the expression $-3x + 5$.

Basic Rules of Algebra

There are four arithmetic operations with real numbers: *addition*, *multiplication*, *subtraction*, and *division*, denoted by the symbols $+$, $\times$ or $\cdot$, $-$, and $\div$ or $/$. Of these, addition and multiplication are the two primary operations. Subtraction and division are the inverse operations of addition and multiplication, respectively.

Definitions of Subtraction and Division

Subtraction: Add the opposite. **Division:** Multiply by the reciprocal.

$a - b = a + (-b)$ If $b \neq 0$, then $a/b = a\left(\frac{1}{b}\right) = \frac{a}{b}$.

In these definitions, $-b$ is the **additive inverse** (or opposite) of b, and $1/b$ is the **multiplicative inverse** (or reciprocal) of b. In the fractional form a/b, a is the **numerator** of the fraction and b is the **denominator.**

Because the properties of real numbers below are true for variables and algebraic expressions as well as for real numbers, they are often called the **Basic Rules of Algebra.** Try to formulate a verbal description of each property. For instance, the first property states that *the order in which two real numbers are added does not affect their sum.*

Basic Rules of Algebra

Let a, b, and c be real numbers, variables, or algebraic expressions.

Property		*Example*
Commutative Property of Addition:	$a + b = b + a$	$4x + x^2 = x^2 + 4x$
Commutative Property of Multiplication:	$ab = ba$	$(4 - x)x^2 = x^2(4 - x)$
Associative Property of Addition:	$(a + b) + c = a + (b + c)$	$(x + 5) + x^2 = x + (5 + x^2)$
Associative Property of Multiplication:	$(ab)c = a(bc)$	$(2x \cdot 3y)(8) = (2x)(3y \cdot 8)$
Distributive Properties:	$a(b + c) = ab + ac$	$3x(5 + 2x) = 3x \cdot 5 + 3x \cdot 2x$
	$(a + b)c = ac + bc$	$(y + 8)y = y \cdot y + 8 \cdot y$
Additive Identity Property:	$a + 0 = a$	$5y^2 + 0 = 5y^2$
Multiplicative Identity Property:	$a \cdot 1 = a$	$(4x^2)(1) = 4x^2$
Additive Inverse Property:	$a + (-a) = 0$	$5x^3 + (-5x^3) = 0$
Multiplicative Inverse Property:	$a \cdot \frac{1}{a} = 1, \quad a \neq 0$	$(x^2 + 4)\left(\frac{1}{x^2 + 4}\right) = 1$

Because subtraction is defined as "adding the opposite," the Distributive Properties are also true for subtraction. For instance, the "subtraction form" of $a(b + c) = ab + ac$ is $a(b - c) = ab - ac$. Note that the operations of subtraction and division are neither commutative nor associative. The examples

$$7 - 3 \neq 3 - 7 \quad \text{and} \quad 20 \div 4 \neq 4 \div 20$$

show that subtraction and division are not commutative. Similarly

$$5 - (3 - 2) \neq (5 - 3) - 2 \quad \text{and} \quad 16 \div (4 \div 2) \neq (16 \div 4) \div 2$$

demonstrate that subtraction and division are not associative.

Example 13 Identifying Rules of Algebra

Identify the rule of algebra illustrated by the statement.

a. $(5x^3)2 = 2(5x^3)$

b. $\left(4x + \frac{1}{3}\right) - \left(4x + \frac{1}{3}\right) = 0$

c. $7x \cdot \frac{1}{7x} = 1, \quad x \neq 0$

d. $(2 + 5x^2) + x^2 = 2 + (5x^2 + x^2)$

Solution

a. This statement illustrates the Commutative Property of Multiplication. In other words, you obtain the same result whether you multiply $5x^3$ by 2, or 2 by $5x^3$.

b. This statement illustrates the Additive Inverse Property. In terms of subtraction, this property simply states that when any expression is subtracted from itself the result is 0.

c. This statement illustrates the Multiplicative Inverse Property. Note that it is important that x be a nonzero number. If x were 0, the reciprocal of x would be undefined.

d. This statement illustrates the Associative Property of Addition. In other words, to form the sum

$$2 + 5x^2 + x^2$$

it does not matter whether 2 and $5x^2$, or $5x^2$ and x^2 are added first.

CHECK *Point* Now try Exercise 101.

Study Tip

Notice the difference between the *opposite of a number* and a *negative number*. If a is already negative, then its opposite, $-a$, is positive. For instance, if $a = -5$, then

$$-a = -(-5) = 5.$$

Properties of Negation and Equality

Let a, b, and c be real numbers, variables, or algebraic expressions.

Property	*Example*
1. $(-1)a = -a$	$(-1)7 = -7$
2. $-(-a) = a$	$-(-6) = 6$
3. $(-a)b = -(ab) = a(-b)$	$(-5)3 = -(5 \cdot 3) = 5(-3)$
4. $(-a)(-b) = ab$	$(-2)(-x) = 2x$
5. $-(a + b) = (-a) + (-b)$	$-(x + 8) = (-x) + (-8)$ $= -x - 8$
6. If $a = b$, then $a \pm c = b \pm c$.	$\frac{1}{2} + 3 = 0.5 + 3$
7. If $a = b$, then $ac = bc$.	$4^2 \cdot 2 = 16 \cdot 2$
8. If $a \pm c = b \pm c$, then $a = b$.	$1.4 - 1 = \frac{7}{5} - 1 \Rightarrow 1.4 = \frac{7}{5}$
9. If $ac = bc$ and $c \neq 0$, then $a = b$.	$3x = 3 \cdot 4 \Rightarrow x = 4$

Study Tip

The "or" in the Zero-Factor Property includes the possibility that either or both factors may be zero. This is an **inclusive or,** and it is the way the word "or" is generally used in mathematics.

Properties of Zero

Let a and b be real numbers, variables, or algebraic expressions.

1. $a + 0 = a$ and $a - 0 = a$ **2.** $a \cdot 0 = 0$

3. $\frac{0}{a} = 0, \quad a \neq 0$ **4.** $\frac{a}{0}$ is undefined.

5. Zero-Factor Property: If $ab = 0$, then $a = 0$ or $b = 0$.

Properties and Operations of Fractions

Let a, b, c, and d be real numbers, variables, or algebraic expressions such that $b \neq 0$ and $d \neq 0$.

1. Equivalent Fractions: $\frac{a}{b} = \frac{c}{d}$ if and only if $ad = bc$.

2. Rules of Signs: $-\frac{a}{b} = \frac{-a}{b} = \frac{a}{-b}$ and $\frac{-a}{-b} = \frac{a}{b}$

3. Generate Equivalent Fractions: $\frac{a}{b} = \frac{ac}{bc}, \quad c \neq 0$

4. Add or Subtract with Like Denominators: $\frac{a}{b} \pm \frac{c}{b} = \frac{a \pm c}{b}$

5. Add or Subtract with Unlike Denominators: $\frac{a}{b} \pm \frac{c}{d} = \frac{ad \pm bc}{bd}$

6. Multiply Fractions: $\frac{a}{b} \cdot \frac{c}{d} = \frac{ac}{bd}$

7. Divide Fractions: $\frac{a}{b} \div \frac{c}{d} = \frac{a}{b} \cdot \frac{d}{c} = \frac{ad}{bc}, \quad c \neq 0$

Study Tip

In Property 1 of fractions, the phrase "if and only if" implies two statements. One statement is: If $a/b = c/d$, then $ad = bc$. The other statement is: If $ad = bc$, where $b \neq 0$ and $d \neq 0$, then $a/b = c/d$.

Example 14 Properties and Operations of Fractions

a. Equivalent fractions: $\frac{x}{5} = \frac{3 \cdot x}{3 \cdot 5} = \frac{3x}{15}$ **b.** Divide fractions: $\frac{7}{x} \div \frac{3}{2} = \frac{7}{x} \cdot \frac{2}{3} = \frac{14}{3x}$

c. Add fractions with unlike denominators: $\frac{x}{3} + \frac{2x}{5} = \frac{5 \cdot x + 3 \cdot 2x}{3 \cdot 5} = \frac{11x}{15}$

CHECK*Point* Now try Exercise 119.

If a, b, and c are integers such that $ab = c$, then a and b are **factors** or **divisors** of c. A **prime number** is an integer that has exactly two positive factors—itself and 1—such as 2, 3, 5, 7, and 11. The numbers 4, 6, 8, 9, and 10 are **composite** because each can be written as the product of two or more prime numbers. The number 1 is neither prime nor composite. The **Fundamental Theorem of Arithmetic** states that every positive integer greater than 1 can be written as the product of prime numbers in precisely one way (disregarding order). For instance, the *prime factorization* of 24 is $24 = 2 \cdot 2 \cdot 2 \cdot 3$.

A.1 EXERCISES

See www.CalcChat.com for worked-out solutions to odd-numbered exercises.

VOCABULARY: Fill in the blanks.

1. A real number is rational if it can be written as the ratio $\frac{p}{q}$ of two integers, where $q \neq 0$.
2. Irrational numbers have infinite nonrepeating decimal representations.
3. The point 0 on the real number line is called the origin.
4. The distance between the origin and a point representing a real number on the real number line is the absolute value of the real number.
5. A number that can be written as the product of two or more prime numbers is called a composite number.
6. An integer that has exactly two positive factors, the integer itself and 1, is called a prime number.
7. An algebraic expression is a collection of letters called variables and real numbers called constants.
8. The terms of an algebraic expression are those parts separated by addition.
9. The numerical factor of a variable term is the ________ of the variable term. coefficient
10. The ________ ________ states that if $ab = 0$, then $a = 0$ or $b = 0$. Zero-Factor Property

SKILLS AND APPLICATIONS

In Exercises 11–16, determine which numbers in the set are (a) natural numbers, (b) whole numbers, (c) integers, (d) rational numbers, and (e) irrational numbers. 11–16. See margin.

11. $\left\{-9, -\frac{7}{2}, 5, \frac{2}{3}, \sqrt{2}, 0, 1, -4, 2, -11\right\}$
12. $\left\{\sqrt{5}, -7, -\frac{7}{3}, 0, 3.12, \frac{5}{4}, -3, 12, 5\right\}$
13. $\{2.01, 0.666\ldots, -13, 0.010110111\ldots, 1, -6\}$
14. $\{2.3030030003\ldots, 0.7575, -4.63, \sqrt{10}, -75, 4\}$
15. $\left\{-\pi, -\frac{1}{3}, \frac{6}{3}, \frac{1}{2}\sqrt{2}, -7.5, -1, 8, -22\right\}$
16. $\left\{25, -17, -\frac{12}{5}, \sqrt{9}, 3.12, \frac{1}{2}\pi, 7, -11.1, 13\right\}$

In Exercises 17 and 18, plot the real numbers on the real number line. 17–18. See margin.

17. (a) 3 (b) $\frac{7}{2}$ (c) $-\frac{5}{2}$ (d) -5.2
18. (a) 8.5 (b) $\frac{4}{3}$ (c) -4.75 (d) $-\frac{8}{3}$

In Exercises 19–22, use a calculator to find the decimal form of the rational number. If it is a nonterminating decimal, write the repeating pattern.

19. $\frac{5}{8}$ 0.625
20. $\frac{1}{3}$ $0.\overline{3}$
21. $\frac{41}{333}$ $0.\overline{123}$
22. $\frac{6}{11}$ $0.\overline{54}$

In Exercises 23 and 24, approximate the numbers and place the correct symbol (< or >) between them.

$-2.5 < 2$

23. 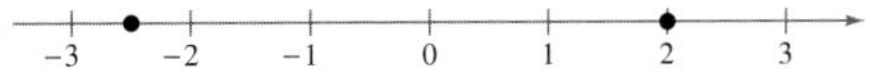

24. 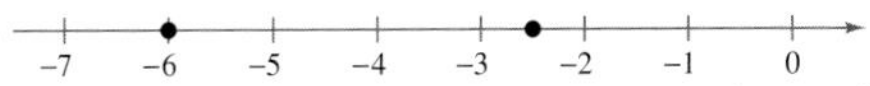

$-6 < -2.5$

In Exercises 25–30, plot the two real numbers on the real number line. Then place the appropriate inequality symbol (< or >) between them. 25–30. See margin.

25. $-4, -8$
26. $-3.5, 1$
27. $\frac{3}{2}, 7$
28. $1, \frac{16}{3}$
29. $\frac{5}{6}, \frac{2}{3}$
30. $-\frac{8}{7}, -\frac{3}{7}$

In Exercises 31–42, (a) give a verbal description of the subset of real numbers represented by the inequality or the interval, (b) sketch the subset on the real number line, and (c) state whether the interval is bounded or unbounded. 31–42. See margin.

31. $x \leq 5$
32. $x \geq -2$
33. $x < 0$
34. $x > 3$
35. $[4, \infty)$
36. $(-\infty, 2)$
37. $-2 < x < 2$
38. $0 \leq x \leq 5$
39. $-1 \leq x < 0$
40. $0 < x \leq 6$
41. $[-2, 5)$
42. $(-1, 2]$

In Exercises 43–50, use inequality notation and interval notation to describe the set. 43–50. See margin.

43. y is nonnegative.
44. y is no more than 25.
45. x is greater than -2 and at most 4.
46. y is at least -6 and less than 0.
47. t is at least 10 and at most 22.
48. k is less than 5 but no less than -3.
49. The dog's weight W is more than 65 pounds.
50. The annual rate of inflation r is expected to be at least 2.5% but no more than 5%.

11. (a) 5, 1, 2 (b) 0, 5, 1, 2
 (c) $-9, 5, 0, 1, -4, 2, -11$
 (d) $-\frac{7}{2}, \frac{2}{3}, -9, 5, 0, 1, -4, 2, -11$
 (e) $\sqrt{2}$
12. (a) 12, 5 (b) 12, 5, 0
 (c) $-7, 12, 5, 0, -3$
 (d) $-7, -\frac{7}{3}, 0, 3.12, \frac{5}{4}, -3, 12, 5$
 (e) $\sqrt{5}$
13. (a) 1 (b) 1
 (c) $-13, 1, -6$
 (d) $2.01, -13, 1, -6, 0.666\ldots$
 (e) $0.010110111\ldots$
14. (a) 4 (b) 4 (c) $-75, 4$
 (d) $-75, 4, -4.63, 0.7575$
 (e) $2.3030030003\ldots, \sqrt{10}$
15. (a) $\frac{6}{3}, 8$ (b) $\frac{6}{3}, 8$
 (c) $\frac{6}{3}, -1, 8, -22$
 (d) $-\frac{1}{3}, \frac{6}{3}, -7.5, -1, 8, -22$
 (e) $-\pi, \frac{1}{2}\sqrt{2}$
16. (a) $25, \sqrt{9}, 7, 13$
 (b) $25, \sqrt{9}, 7, 13$
 (c) $25, -17, \sqrt{9}, 7, 13$
 (d) $-\frac{12}{5}, \sqrt{9}, 3.12, 25, -17, -11.1, 7, 13$
 (e) $\frac{\pi}{2}$
17. (a) 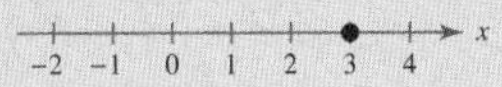
 (b) 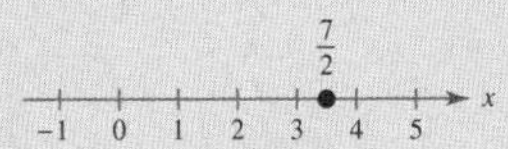
 (c) 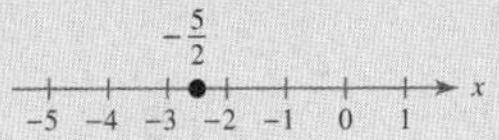
 (d) 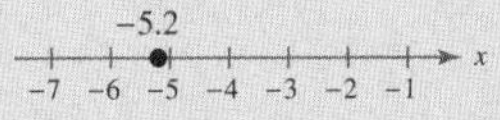
18. (a) 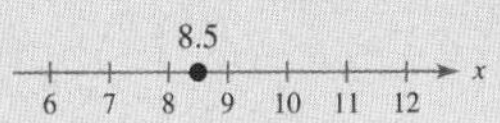
 (b) 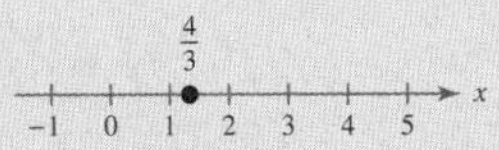
 (c) 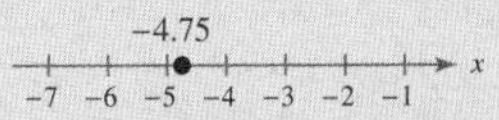
 (d) 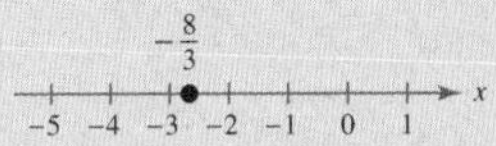
25. 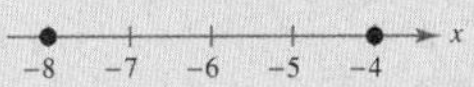

 $-4 > -8$
26. 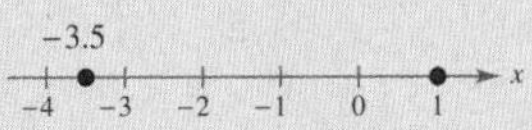

 $-3.5 < 1$
27. 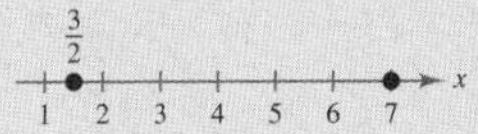

 $\frac{3}{2} < 7$
28. 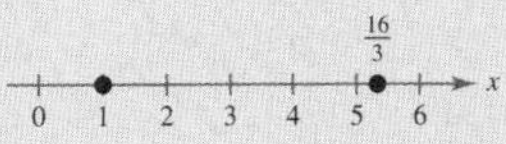

 $1 < \frac{16}{3}$
29. 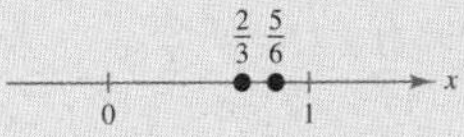

 $\frac{5}{6} > \frac{2}{3}$
30. 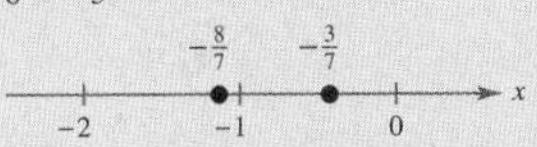

 $-\frac{8}{7} < -\frac{3}{7}$

31. (a) $x \leq 5$ denotes the set of all real numbers less than or equal to 5.
 (b) 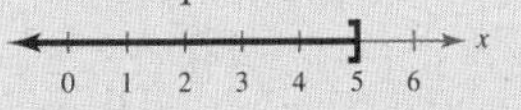 (c) Unbounded
32. (a) $x \geq -2$ denotes the set of all real numbers greater than or equal to -2.
 (b) 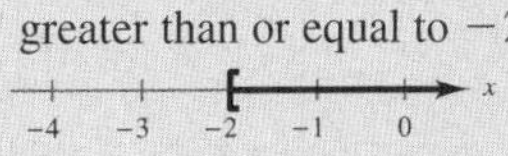 (c) Unbounded
33. (a) $x < 0$ denotes the set of all real numbers less than 0.
 (b) 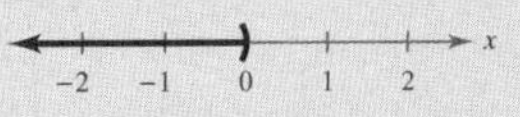 (c) Unbounded

34–50. See Additional Answers beginning on page AA1.

In Exercises 51–60, evaluate the expression.

51. $|-10|$ 10

52. $|0|$ 0

53. $|3-8|$ 5

54. $|4-1|$ 3

55. $|-1|-|-2|$ -1

56. $-3-|-3|$ -6

57. $\dfrac{-5}{|-5|}$ -1

58. $-3|-3|$ -9

59. $\dfrac{|x+2|}{x+2},\ x<-2$ -1

60. $\dfrac{|x-1|}{x-1},\ x>1$ 1

In Exercises 61–66, place the correct symbol ($<$, $>$, or $=$) between the two real numbers.

61. $|-3|$ ☐ $-|-3|$ $|-3| > -|-3|$

62. $|-4|$ ☐ $|4|$ $|-4| = |4|$

63. -5 ☐ $-|5|$ $-5 = -|5|$

64. $-|-6|$ ☐ $|-6|$ $-|-6| < |-6|$

65. $-|-2|$ ☐ $-|2|$ $-|-2| = -|2|$

66. $-(-2)$ ☐ -2 $-(-2) > -2$

In Exercises 67–72, find the distance between a and b.

67. $a=126,\ b=75$ 51

68. $a=-126,\ b=-75$ 51

69. $a=-\frac{5}{2},\ b=0$ $\frac{5}{2}$

70. $a=\frac{1}{4},\ b=\frac{11}{4}$ $\frac{5}{2}$

71. $a=\frac{16}{5},\ b=\frac{112}{75}$ $\frac{128}{75}$

72. $a=9.34,\ b=-5.65$ 14.99

In Exercises 73–78, use absolute value notation to describe the situation.

73. The distance between x and 5 is no more than 3. $|x-5| \le 3$

74. The distance between x and -10 is at least 6. $|x+10| \ge 6$

75. y is at least six units from 0. $|y| \ge 6$

76. y is at most two units from a. $|y-a| \le 2$

77. While traveling on the Pennsylvania Turnpike, you pass milepost 57 near Pittsburgh, then milepost 236 near Gettysburg. How many miles do you travel during that time period? $|57-236| = 179$ mi

78. The temperature in Bismarck, North Dakota was 60°F at noon, then 23°F at midnight. What was the change in temperature over the 12-hour period? $|60-23| = 37$°F

BUDGET VARIANCE In Exercises 79–82, the accounting department of a sports drink bottling company is checking to see whether the actual expenses of a department differ from the budgeted expenses by more than \$500 or by more than 5%. Fill in the missing parts of the table, and determine whether each actual expense passes the "budget variance test." 79–82. See margin.

	Budgeted Expense, b	*Actual Expense, a*	$\lvert a-b\rvert$	$0.05b$
79. Wages	\$112,700	\$113,356		
80. Utilities	\$9,400	\$9,772		
81. Taxes	\$37,640	\$37,335		
82. Insurance	\$2,575	\$2,613		

FEDERAL DEFICIT In Exercises 83–88, use the bar graph, which shows the receipts of the federal government (in billions of dollars) for selected years from 1996 through 2006. In each exercise you are given the expenditures of the federal government. Find the magnitude of the surplus or deficit for the year. (Source: U.S. Office of Management and Budget) 83–88. See margin.

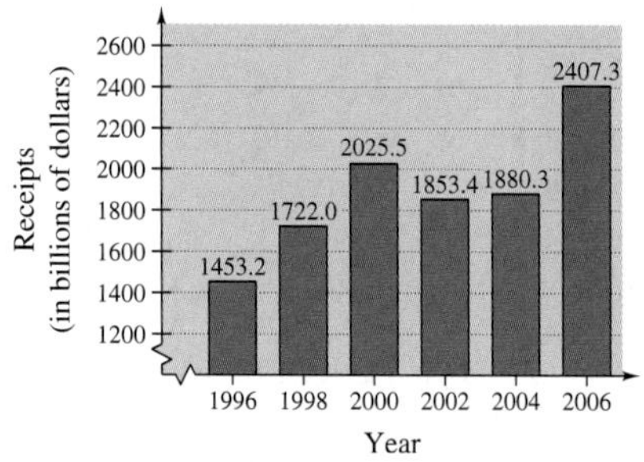

Year	*Receipts*	*Expenditures*	*|Receipts − Expenditures|*
83. 1996		\$1560.6 billion	
84. 1998		\$1652.7 billion	
85. 2000		\$1789.2 billion	
86. 2002		\$2011.2 billion	
87. 2004		\$2293.0 billion	
88. 2006		\$2655.4 billion	

In Exercises 89–94, identify the terms. Then identify the coefficients of the variable terms of the expression.

89. $7x+4$

90. $6x^3-5x$

91. $\sqrt{3}x^2-8x-11$

92. $3\sqrt{3}x^2+1$

93. $4x^3+\dfrac{x}{2}-5$

94. $3x^4-\dfrac{x^2}{4}$

89–94. See margin.

79. See below.

80. See below.

81. See below.

82. $|\$2613-\$2575| = \$38 < \$500$
$0.05(\$2575) = \$128.75$
Because the difference between the actual expense and the budget is less than \$500 and less than 5% of the budgeted amount, there is compliance with the "budget variance test."

83. \$1453.2 billion; \$107.4 billion

84. \$1722.0 billion; \$69.3 billion

85. \$2025.5 billion; \$236.3 billion

86. \$1853.4 billion; \$157.8 billion

87. \$1880.3 billion; \$412.7 billion

88. \$2407.3 billion; \$248.1 billion

89. $7x$ and 4 are the terms; 7 is the coefficient.

90. $6x^3$ and $-5x$ are the terms; 6 and -5 are the coefficients.

91. $\sqrt{3}x^2$, $-8x$, and -11 are the terms; $\sqrt{3}$ and -8 are the coefficients.

92. $3\sqrt{3}x^2$ and 1 are the terms; $3\sqrt{3}$ is the coefficient.

93. $4x^3$, $x/2$, and -5 are the terms; 4 and $\frac{1}{2}$ are the coefficients.

94. $3x^4$ and $-x^2/4$ are the terms; 3 and $-\frac{1}{4}$ are the coefficients.

79. $|\$113{,}356-\$112{,}700| = \$656 > \$500$
$0.05(\$112{,}700) = \$5635$
Because the actual expense differs from the budget by more than \$500, there is failure to meet the "budget variance test."

80. $|\$9772-\$9400| = \$372 < \$500$
$0.05(\$9400) = \$470$
Because the difference between the actual expense and the budget is less than \$500 and less than 5% of the budgeted amount, there is compliance with the "budget variance test."

81. $|\$37{,}335-\$37{,}640| = \$305 < \$500$
$0.05(\$37{,}640) = \$1882$
Because the difference between the actual expense and the budget is less than \$500 and less than 5% of the budgeted amount, there is compliance with the "budget variance test."

In Exercises 95–100, evaluate the expression for each value of x. (If not possible, state the reason.)

	Expression	*Values*	
95.	$4x - 6$	(a) $x = -1$ -10	(b) $x = 0$ -6
96.	$9 - 7x$	(a) $x = -3$ 30	(b) $x = 3$ -12
97.	$x^2 - 3x + 4$	(a) $x = -2$ 14	(b) $x = 2$ 2
98.	$-x^2 + 5x - 4$	(a) $x = -1$ -10	(b) $x = 1$ 0
99.	$\frac{x+1}{x-1}$	(a) $x = 1$ Division by 0 is undefined.	(b) $x = -1$ 0
100.	$\frac{x}{x+2}$	(a) $x = 2$ $\frac{1}{2}$	(b) $x = -2$ Division by 0 is undefined.

In Exercises 101–112, identify the rule(s) of algebra illustrated by the statement.

101. $x + 9 = 9 + x$ Commutative Property of Addition

102. $2\left(\frac{1}{2}\right) = 1$ Multiplicative Inverse Property

103. $\frac{1}{h+6}(h + 6) = 1, \quad h \neq -6$ Multiplicative Inverse Property

104. $(x + 3) - (x + 3) = 0$ Additive Inverse Property

105. $2(x + 3) = 2 \cdot x + 2 \cdot 3$ Distributive Property

106. $(z - 2) + 0 = z - 2$ Additive Identity Property

107. $1 \cdot (1 + x) = 1 + x$ Multiplicative Identity Property

108. $(z + 5)x = z \cdot x + 5 \cdot x$ Distributive Property

109. $x + (y + 10) = (x + y) + 10$ See margin.

110. $x(3y) = (x \cdot 3)y = (3x)y$ See margin.

111. $3(t - 4) = 3 \cdot t - 3 \cdot 4$ Distributive Property

112. $\frac{1}{7}(7 \cdot 12) = \left(\frac{1}{7} \cdot 7\right)12 = 1 \cdot 12 = 12$ See margin.

In Exercises 113–120, perform the operation(s). (Write fractional answers in simplest form.)

113. $\frac{3}{16} + \frac{5}{16}$ $\frac{1}{2}$

114. $\frac{6}{7} - \frac{4}{7}$ $\frac{2}{7}$

115. $\frac{5}{8} - \frac{5}{12} + \frac{1}{6}$ $\frac{3}{8}$

116. $\frac{10}{11} + \frac{6}{33} - \frac{13}{66}$ $\frac{59}{66}$

117. $12 \div \frac{1}{4}$ 48

118. $-\left(6 \cdot \frac{4}{8}\right)$ -3

119. $\frac{2x}{3} - \frac{x}{4}$ $\frac{5x}{12}$

120. $\frac{5x}{6} \cdot \frac{2}{9}$ $\frac{5x}{27}$

EXPLORATION

In Exercises 121 and 122, use the real numbers A, B, and C shown on the number line. Determine the sign of each expression.

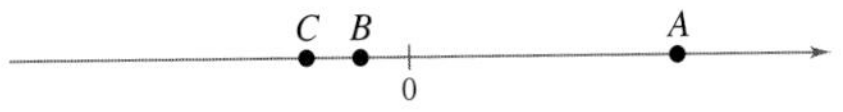

121. (a) $-A$ Negative (b) $B - A$ Negative

122. (a) $-C$ Positive (b) $A - C$ Positive

123. CONJECTURE See margin.

(a) Use a calculator to complete the table.

n	1	0.5	0.01	0.0001	0.000001
$5/n$					

(b) Use the result from part (a) to make a conjecture about the value of $5/n$ as n approaches 0.

124. CONJECTURE See margin.

(a) Use a calculator to complete the table.

n	1	10	100	10,000	100,000
$5/n$					

(b) Use the result from part (a) to make a conjecture about the value of $5/n$ as n increases without bound.

125–128. See margin.

TRUE OR FALSE? In Exercises 125–128, determine whether the statement is true or false. Justify your answer.

125. If $a > 0$ and $b < 0$, then $a - b > 0$.

126. If $a > 0$ and $b < 0$, then $ab > 0$.

127. If $a < b$, then $\frac{1}{a} < \frac{1}{b}$, where $a \neq 0$ and $b \neq 0$.

128. Because $\frac{a+b}{c} = \frac{a}{c} + \frac{b}{c}$, then $\frac{c}{a+b} = \frac{c}{a} + \frac{c}{b}$.

129. THINK ABOUT IT Consider $|u + v|$ and $|u| + |v|$, where $u \neq 0$ and $v \neq 0$. See margin.

(a) Are the values of the expressions always equal? If not, under what conditions are they unequal?

(b) If the two expressions are not equal for certain values of u and v, is one of the expressions always greater than the other? Explain.

130. THINK ABOUT IT Is there a difference between saying that a real number is positive and saying that a real number is nonnegative? Explain. See margin.

131. THINK ABOUT IT Because every even number is divisible by 2, is it possible that there exist any even prime numbers? Explain. See margin.

132. THINK ABOUT IT Is it possible for a real number to be both rational and irrational? Explain. See margin.

133. WRITING Can it ever be true that $|a| = -a$ for a real number a? Explain. Yes. $|a| = -a$ if $a < 0$.

134. CAPSTONE Describe the differences among the sets of natural numbers, whole numbers, integers, rational numbers, and irrational numbers. See margin.

109. Associative Property of Addition

110. Associative and Commutative Properties of Multiplication

112. See below.

123. See below.

124. See below.

125. True. Because $b < 0$, $a - b$ subtracts a negative number from (or adds a positive number to) a positive number. The sum of two positive numbers is positive.

126. False. Two numbers with different signs will always have a product less than 0.

127. False. If $a < b$, then $\frac{1}{a} > \frac{1}{b}$, where $a \neq 0$ and $b \neq 0$.

128. False. The denominators cannot be added when adding fractions.

129. (a) No. If one variable is negative and the other is positive, the expressions are unequal.

(b) No. $|u + v| \leq |u| + |v|$ The expressions are equal when u and v have the same sign. If u and v differ in sign, $|u + v|$ is less than $|u| + |v|$.

130. Yes. y is nonnegative if $y \geq 0$. y is positive if $y > 0$.

131. The only even prime number is 2, because its only factors are itself and 1.

132. No. A real number can be either rational or irrational but not both, because an irrational number is any real number that is not rational.

112. $\frac{1}{7}(7 \cdot 12) = \left(\frac{1}{7} \cdot 7\right)12$ Associative Property of Multiplication

$= 1 \cdot 12$ Multiplicative Inverse Property

$= 12$ Multiplicative Identity Property

123. (a)

n	1	0.5	0.01	0.0001	0.000001
$5/n$	5	10	500	50,000	5,000,000

(b) The value of $5/n$ approaches infinity as n approaches 0.

124. (a)

n	1	10	100	10,000	100,000
$5/n$	5	0.5	0.05	0.0005	0.00005

(b) The value of $5/n$ approaches 0 as n increases without bound.

134. See Additional Answers beginning on page AA1.

A.2 EXPONENTS AND RADICALS

What you should learn

- Use properties of exponents.
- Use scientific notation to represent real numbers.
- Use properties of radicals.
- Simplify and combine radicals.
- Rationalize denominators and numerators.
- Use properties of rational exponents.

Why you should learn it

Real numbers and algebraic expressions are often written with exponents and radicals. For instance, in Exercise 121 on page A26, you will use an expression involving rational exponents to find the times required for a funnel to empty for different water heights.

Integer Exponents

Repeated *multiplication* can be written in **exponential form.**

Repeated Multiplication	*Exponential Form*
$a \cdot a \cdot a \cdot a \cdot a$	a^5
$(-4)(-4)(-4)$	$(-4)^3$
$(2x)(2x)(2x)(2x)$	$(2x)^4$

Exponential Notation

If a is a real number and n is a positive integer, then

$$a^n = \underbrace{a \cdot a \cdot a \cdot \cdot \cdot a}_{n \text{ factors}}$$

where n is the **exponent** and a is the **base.** The expression a^n is read "a to the nth **power.**"

An exponent can also be negative. In Property 3 below, be sure you see how to use a negative exponent.

Properties of Exponents

Let a and b be real numbers, variables, or algebraic expressions, and let m and n be integers. (All denominators and bases are nonzero.)

Property	*Example*
1. $a^m a^n = a^{m+n}$	$3^2 \cdot 3^4 = 3^{2+4} = 3^6 = 729$
2. $\dfrac{a^m}{a^n} = a^{m-n}$	$\dfrac{x^7}{x^4} = x^{7-4} = x^3$
3. $a^{-n} = \dfrac{1}{a^n} = \left(\dfrac{1}{a}\right)^n$	$y^{-4} = \dfrac{1}{y^4} = \left(\dfrac{1}{y}\right)^4$
4. $a^0 = 1, \quad a \neq 0$	$(x^2 + 1)^0 = 1$
5. $(ab)^m = a^m b^m$	$(5x)^3 = 5^3x^3 = 125x^3$
6. $(a^m)^n = a^{mn}$	$(y^3)^{-4} = y^{3(-4)} = y^{-12} = \dfrac{1}{y^{12}}$
7. $\left(\dfrac{a}{b}\right)^m = \dfrac{a^m}{b^m}$	$\left(\dfrac{2}{x}\right)^3 = \dfrac{2^3}{x^3} = \dfrac{8}{x^3}$
8. $\lvert a^2 \rvert = \lvert a \rvert^2 = a^2$	$\lvert(-2)^2\rvert = \lvert -2 \rvert^2 = (2)^2 = 4$

TECHNOLOGY

You can use a calculator to evaluate exponential expressions. When doing so, it is important to know when to use parentheses because the calculator follows the order of operations. For instance, evaluate $(-2)^4$ as follows.

Scientific:

(2 +/−) y^x 4 =

Graphing:

((−) 2) ^ 4 ENTER

The display will be 16. If you omit the parentheses, the display will be −16.

It is important to recognize the difference between expressions such as $(-2)^4$ and -2^4. In $(-2)^4$, the parentheses indicate that the exponent applies to the negative sign as well as to the 2, but in $-2^4 = -(2^4)$, the exponent applies only to the 2. So, $(-2)^4 = 16$ and $-2^4 = -16$.

The properties of exponents listed on the preceding page apply to *all* integers m and n, not just to positive integers, as shown in the examples in this section.

Example 1 Evaluating Exponential Expressions

a. $(-5)^2 = (-5)(-5) = 25$ — Negative sign is part of the base.

b. $-5^2 = -(5)(5) = -25$ — Negative sign is *not* part of the base.

c. $2 \cdot 2^4 = 2^{1+4} = 2^5 = 32$ — Property 1

d. $\dfrac{4^4}{4^6} = 4^{4-6} = 4^{-2} = \dfrac{1}{4^2} = \dfrac{1}{16}$ — Properties 2 and 3

CHECK**Point** Now try Exercise 11.

Example 2 Evaluating Algebraic Expressions

Evaluate each algebraic expression when $x = 3$.

a. $5x^{-2}$ **b.** $\frac{1}{3}(-x)^3$

Solution

a. When $x = 3$, the expression $5x^{-2}$ has a value of

$$5x^{-2} = 5(3)^{-2} = \frac{5}{3^2} = \frac{5}{9}.$$

b. When $x = 3$, the expression $\frac{1}{3}(-x)^3$ has a value of

$$\frac{1}{3}(-x)^3 = \frac{1}{3}(-3)^3 = \frac{1}{3}(-27) = -9.$$

CHECK**Point** Now try Exercise 23.

Example 3 Using Properties of Exponents

Use the properties of exponents to simplify each expression.

a. $(-3ab^4)(4ab^{-3})$ **b.** $(2xy^2)^3$ **c.** $3a(-4a^2)^0$ **d.** $\left(\dfrac{5x^3}{y}\right)^2$

Solution

a. $(-3ab^4)(4ab^{-3}) = (-3)(4)(a)(a)(b^4)(b^{-3}) = -12a^2b$

b. $(2xy^2)^3 = 2^3(x)^3(y^2)^3 = 8x^3y^6$

c. $3a(-4a^2)^0 = 3a(1) = 3a, \quad a \neq 0$

d. $\left(\dfrac{5x^3}{y}\right)^2 = \dfrac{5^2(x^3)^2}{y^2} = \dfrac{25x^6}{y^2}$

CHECK**Point** Now try Exercise 31.

Study Tip

Rarely in algebra is there only one way to solve a problem. Don't be concerned if the steps you use to solve a problem are not exactly the same as the steps presented in this text. The important thing is to use steps that you understand and, of course, steps that are justified by the rules of algebra. For instance, you might prefer the following steps for Example 4(d).

$$\left(\frac{3x^2}{y}\right)^{-2} = \left(\frac{y}{3x^2}\right)^2 = \frac{y^2}{9x^4}$$

Note how Property 3 is used in the first step of this solution. The fractional form of this property is

$$\left(\frac{a}{b}\right)^{-m} = \left(\frac{b}{a}\right)^m.$$

Example 4 Rewriting with Positive Exponents

Rewrite each expression with positive exponents.

a. x^{-1} **b.** $\dfrac{1}{3x^{-2}}$ **c.** $\dfrac{12a^3b^{-4}}{4a^{-2}b}$ **d.** $\left(\dfrac{3x^2}{y}\right)^{-2}$

Solution

a. $x^{-1} = \dfrac{1}{x}$ Property 3

b. $\dfrac{1}{3x^{-2}} = \dfrac{1(x^2)}{3} = \dfrac{x^2}{3}$ The exponent -2 does not apply to 3.

c. $\dfrac{12a^3b^{-4}}{4a^{-2}b} = \dfrac{12a^3 \cdot a^2}{4b \cdot b^4}$ Property 3

$= \dfrac{3a^5}{b^5}$ Property 1

d. $\left(\dfrac{3x^2}{y}\right)^{-2} = \dfrac{3^{-2}(x^2)^{-2}}{y^{-2}}$ Properties 5 and 7

$= \dfrac{3^{-2}x^{-4}}{y^{-2}}$ Property 6

$= \dfrac{y^2}{3^2x^4}$ Property 3

$= \dfrac{y^2}{9x^4}$ Simplify.

CHECKPoint Now try Exercise 41.

Scientific Notation

Exponents provide an efficient way of writing and computing with very large (or very small) numbers. For instance, there are about 359 billion billion gallons of water on Earth—that is, 359 followed by 18 zeros.

359,000,000,000,000,000,000

It is convenient to write such numbers in **scientific notation.** This notation has the form $\pm c \times 10^n$, where $1 \le c < 10$ and n is an integer. So, the number of gallons of water on Earth can be written in scientific notation as

$$3.59 \times 100{,}000{,}000{,}000{,}000{,}000{,}000 = 3.59 \times 10^{20}.$$

The *positive* exponent 20 indicates that the number is *large* (10 or more) and that the decimal point has been moved 20 places. A *negative* exponent indicates that the number is *small* (less than 1). For instance, the mass (in grams) of one electron is approximately

$$9.0 \times 10^{-28} = 0.0000000000000000000000000009.$$

28 decimal places

Example 5 **Scientific Notation**

Write each number in scientific notation.

a. 0.0000782 **b.** 836,100,000

Solution

a. $0.0000782 = 7.82 \times 10^{-5}$

b. $836{,}100{,}000 = 8.361 \times 10^{8}$

CHECK*Point* Now try Exercise 45.

Example 6 **Decimal Notation**

Write each number in decimal notation.

a. -9.36×10^{-6}

b. 1.345×10^{2}

Solution

a. $-9.36 \times 10^{-6} = -0.00000936$

b. $1.345 \times 10^{2} = 134.5$

CHECK*Point* Now try Exercise 55.

TECHNOLOGY

Most calculators automatically switch to scientific notation when they are showing large (or small) numbers that exceed the display range.

To *enter* numbers in scientific notation, your calculator should have an exponential entry key labeled

EE or EXP.

Consult the user's guide for your calculator for instructions on keystrokes and how numbers in scientific notation are displayed.

Example 7 **Using Scientific Notation**

Evaluate $\dfrac{(2{,}400{,}000{,}000)(0.0000045)}{(0.00003)(1500)}$.

Solution

Begin by rewriting each number in scientific notation and simplifying.

$$\begin{aligned}
\frac{(2{,}400{,}000{,}000)(0.0000045)}{(0.00003)(1500)} &= \frac{(2.4 \times 10^{9})(4.5 \times 10^{-6})}{(3.0 \times 10^{-5})(1.5 \times 10^{3})} \\
&= \frac{(2.4)(4.5)(10^{3})}{(4.5)(10^{-2})} \\
&= (2.4)(10^{5}) \\
&= 240{,}000
\end{aligned}$$

CHECK*Point* Now try Exercise 63(b).

Radicals and Their Properties

A **square root** of a number is one of its two equal factors. For example, 5 is a square root of 25 because 5 is one of the two equal factors of 25. In a similar way, a **cube root** of a number is one of its three equal factors, as in $125 = 5^3$.

> **Definition of *n*th Root of a Number**
>
> Let a and b be real numbers and let $n \geq 2$ be a positive integer. If
>
> $$a = b^n$$
>
> then b is an ***n*th root of *a*.** If $n = 2$, the root is a **square root.** If $n = 3$, the root is a **cube root.**

Some numbers have more than one nth root. For example, both 5 and -5 are square roots of 25. The *principal square root* of 25, written as $\sqrt{25}$, is the positive root, 5. The **principal *n*th root** of a number is defined as follows.

> **Principal *n*th Root of a Number**
>
> Let a be a real number that has at least one nth root. The **principal *n*th root of *a*** is the nth root that has the same sign as a. It is denoted by a **radical symbol**
>
> $\sqrt[n]{a}$. Principal nth root
>
> The positive integer n is the **index** of the radical, and the number a is the **radicand.** If $n = 2$, omit the index and write $\sqrt{a}$ rather than $\sqrt[2]{a}$. (The plural of index is *indices.*)

A common misunderstanding is that the square root sign implies both negative and positive roots. This is not correct. The square root sign implies only a positive root. When a negative root is needed, you must use the negative sign with the square root sign.

Incorrect: ~~$\sqrt{4} = \pm 2$~~ *Correct:* $-\sqrt{4} = -2$ *and* $\sqrt{4} = 2$

Example 8 **Evaluating Expressions Involving Radicals**

a. $\sqrt{36} = 6$ because $6^2 = 36$.

b. $-\sqrt{36} = -6$ because $-(\sqrt{36}) = -(\sqrt{6^2}) = -(6) = -6$.

c. $\sqrt[3]{\dfrac{125}{64}} = \dfrac{5}{4}$ because $\left(\dfrac{5}{4}\right)^3 = \dfrac{5^3}{4^3} = \dfrac{125}{64}$.

d. $\sqrt[5]{-32} = -2$ because $(-2)^5 = -32$.

e. $\sqrt[4]{-81}$ is not a real number because there is no real number that can be raised to the fourth power to produce -81.

CHECK*Point* Now try Exercise 65.

Here are some generalizations about the nth roots of real numbers.

Generalizations About nth Roots of Real Numbers

Real Number a	Integer n	Root(s) of a	Example
$a > 0$	$n > 0$, n is even.	$\sqrt[n]{a}$, $-\sqrt[n]{a}$	$\sqrt[4]{81} = 3$, $-\sqrt[4]{81} = -3$
$a > 0$ or $a < 0$	n is odd.	$\sqrt[n]{a}$	$\sqrt[3]{-8} = -2$
$a < 0$	n is even.	No real roots	$\sqrt{-4}$ is not a real number.
$a = 0$	n is even or odd.	$\sqrt[n]{0} = 0$	$\sqrt[5]{0} = 0$

Integers such as 1, 4, 9, 16, 25, and 36 are called **perfect squares** because they have integer square roots. Similarly, integers such as 1, 8, 27, 64, and 125 are called **perfect cubes** because they have integer cube roots.

Properties of Radicals

Let a and b be real numbers, variables, or algebraic expressions such that the indicated roots are real numbers, and let m and n be positive integers.

Property	*Example*
1. $\sqrt[n]{a^m} = \left(\sqrt[n]{a}\right)^m$	$\sqrt[3]{8^2} = \left(\sqrt[3]{8}\right)^2 = (2)^2 = 4$
2. $\sqrt[n]{a} \cdot \sqrt[n]{b} = \sqrt[n]{ab}$	$\sqrt{5} \cdot \sqrt{7} = \sqrt{5 \cdot 7} = \sqrt{35}$
3. $\dfrac{\sqrt[n]{a}}{\sqrt[n]{b}} = \sqrt[n]{\dfrac{a}{b}}, \quad b \neq 0$	$\dfrac{\sqrt[4]{27}}{\sqrt[4]{9}} = \sqrt[4]{\dfrac{27}{9}} = \sqrt[4]{3}$
4. $\sqrt[m]{\sqrt[n]{a}} = \sqrt[mn]{a}$	$\sqrt[3]{\sqrt{10}} = \sqrt[6]{10}$
5. $\left(\sqrt[n]{a}\right)^n = a$	$\left(\sqrt{3}\right)^2 = 3$
6. For n even, $\sqrt[n]{a^n} = \lvert a \rvert$.	$\sqrt{(-12)^2} = \lvert -12 \rvert = 12$
For n odd, $\sqrt[n]{a^n} = a$.	$\sqrt[3]{(-12)^3} = -12$

A common special case of Property 6 is $\sqrt{a^2} = \lvert a \rvert$.

Example 9 Using Properties of Radicals

Use the properties of radicals to simplify each expression.

a. $\sqrt{8} \cdot \sqrt{2}$ **b.** $\left(\sqrt[3]{5}\right)^3$ **c.** $\sqrt[3]{x^3}$ **d.** $\sqrt[6]{y^6}$

Solution

a. $\sqrt{8} \cdot \sqrt{2} = \sqrt{8 \cdot 2} = \sqrt{16} = 4$

b. $\left(\sqrt[3]{5}\right)^3 = 5$

c. $\sqrt[3]{x^3} = x$

d. $\sqrt[6]{y^6} = \lvert y \rvert$

CHECK*Point* Now try Exercise 77.

Simplifying Radicals

An expression involving radicals is in **simplest form** when the following conditions are satisfied.

1. All possible factors have been removed from the radical.
2. All fractions have radical-free denominators (accomplished by a process called *rationalizing the denominator*).
3. The index of the radical is reduced.

To simplify a radical, factor the radicand into factors whose exponents are multiples of the index. The roots of these factors are written outside the radical, and the "leftover" factors make up the new radicand.

WARNING/CAUTION

When you simplify a radical, it is important that both expressions are defined for the same values of the variable. For instance, in Example 10(b), $\sqrt{75x^3}$ and $5x\sqrt{3x}$ are both defined only for nonnegative values of x. Similarly, in Example 10(c), $\sqrt[4]{(5x)^4}$ and $5|x|$ are both defined for all real values of x.

Example 10 Simplifying Even Roots

a. $\sqrt[4]{48} = \sqrt[4]{16 \cdot 3} = \sqrt[4]{2^4 \cdot 3} = 2\sqrt[4]{3}$ (16: Perfect 4th power; 3: Leftover factor)

b. $\sqrt{75x^3} = \sqrt{25x^2 \cdot 3x}$ (25x²: Perfect square; 3x: Leftover factor) Find largest square factor.

$= \sqrt{(5x)^2 \cdot 3x}$

$= 5x\sqrt{3x}$ Find root of perfect square.

c. $\sqrt[4]{(5x)^4} = |5x| = 5|x|$

CHECKPoint Now try Exercise 79(a).

Example 11 Simplifying Odd Roots

a. $\sqrt[3]{24} = \sqrt[3]{8 \cdot 3} = \sqrt[3]{2^3 \cdot 3} = 2\sqrt[3]{3}$ (8: Perfect cube; 3: Leftover factor)

b. $\sqrt[3]{24a^4} = \sqrt[3]{8a^3 \cdot 3a}$ (8a³: Perfect cube; 3a: Leftover factor) Find largest cube factor.

$= \sqrt[3]{(2a)^3 \cdot 3a}$

$= 2a\sqrt[3]{3a}$ Find root of perfect cube.

c. $\sqrt[3]{-40x^6} = \sqrt[3]{(-8x^6) \cdot 5}$ Find largest cube factor.

$= \sqrt[3]{(-2x^2)^3 \cdot 5}$

$= -2x^2\sqrt[3]{5}$ Find root of perfect cube.

CHECKPoint Now try Exercise 79(b).

Radical expressions can be combined (added or subtracted) if they are **like radicals**—that is, if they have the same index and radicand. For instance, $\sqrt{2}$, $3\sqrt{2}$, and $\frac{1}{2}\sqrt{2}$ are like radicals, but $\sqrt{3}$ and $\sqrt{2}$ are unlike radicals. To determine whether two radicals can be combined, you should first simplify each radical.

Example 12 Combining Radicals

a. $2\sqrt{48} - 3\sqrt{27} = 2\sqrt{16 \cdot 3} - 3\sqrt{9 \cdot 3}$ — Find square factors.

$= 8\sqrt{3} - 9\sqrt{3}$ — Find square roots and multiply by coefficients.

$= (8 - 9)\sqrt{3}$ — Combine like terms.

$= -\sqrt{3}$ — Simplify.

b. $\sqrt[3]{16x} - \sqrt[3]{54x^4} = \sqrt[3]{8 \cdot 2x} - \sqrt[3]{27 \cdot x^3 \cdot 2x}$ — Find cube factors.

$= 2\sqrt[3]{2x} - 3x\sqrt[3]{2x}$ — Find cube roots.

$= (2 - 3x)\sqrt[3]{2x}$ — Combine like terms.

CHECK*Point* Now try Exercise 87.

Rationalizing Denominators and Numerators

To rationalize a denominator or numerator of the form $a - b\sqrt{m}$ or $a + b\sqrt{m}$, multiply both numerator and denominator by a **conjugate:** $a + b\sqrt{m}$ and $a - b\sqrt{m}$ are conjugates of each other. If $a = 0$, then the rationalizing factor for $\sqrt{m}$ is itself, $\sqrt{m}$. For cube roots, choose a rationalizing factor that generates a perfect cube.

Example 13 Rationalizing Single-Term Denominators

Rationalize the denominator of each expression.

a. $\dfrac{5}{2\sqrt{3}}$ **b.** $\dfrac{2}{\sqrt[3]{5}}$

Solution

a. $\dfrac{5}{2\sqrt{3}} = \dfrac{5}{2\sqrt{3}} \cdot \dfrac{\sqrt{3}}{\sqrt{3}}$ — $\sqrt{3}$ is rationalizing factor.

$= \dfrac{5\sqrt{3}}{2(3)}$ — Multiply.

$= \dfrac{5\sqrt{3}}{6}$ — Simplify.

b. $\dfrac{2}{\sqrt[3]{5}} = \dfrac{2}{\sqrt[3]{5}} \cdot \dfrac{\sqrt[3]{5^2}}{\sqrt[3]{5^2}}$ — $\sqrt[3]{5^2}$ is rationalizing factor.

$= \dfrac{2\sqrt[3]{5^2}}{\sqrt[3]{5^3}}$ — Multiply.

$= \dfrac{2\sqrt[3]{25}}{5}$ — Simplify.

CHECK*Point* Now try Exercise 95.

Example 14 Rationalizing a Denominator with Two Terms

$$\frac{2}{3+\sqrt{7}} = \frac{2}{3+\sqrt{7}} \cdot \frac{3-\sqrt{7}}{3-\sqrt{7}}$$ Multiply numerator and denominator by conjugate of denominator.

$$= \frac{2(3-\sqrt{7})}{3(3)+3(-\sqrt{7})+\sqrt{7}(3)-(\sqrt{7})(\sqrt{7})}$$ Use Distributive Property.

$$= \frac{2(3-\sqrt{7})}{(3)^2-(\sqrt{7})^2}$$ Simplify.

$$= \frac{2(3-\sqrt{7})}{9-7}$$ Square terms of denominator.

$$= \frac{2(3-\sqrt{7})}{2} = 3-\sqrt{7}$$ Simplify.

CHECKPoint Now try Exercise 97.

Sometimes it is necessary to rationalize the numerator of an expression. For instance, in Appendix A.4 you will use the technique shown in the next example to rationalize the numerator of an expression from calculus.

WARNING/CAUTION

Do not confuse the expression $\sqrt{5}+\sqrt{7}$ with the expression $\sqrt{5+7}$. In general, $\sqrt{x+y}$ does not equal $\sqrt{x}+\sqrt{y}$. Similarly, $\sqrt{x^2+y^2}$ does not equal $x+y$.

Example 15 Rationalizing a Numerator

$$\frac{\sqrt{5}-\sqrt{7}}{2} = \frac{\sqrt{5}-\sqrt{7}}{2} \cdot \frac{\sqrt{5}+\sqrt{7}}{\sqrt{5}+\sqrt{7}}$$ Multiply numerator and denominator by conjugate of numerator.

$$= \frac{(\sqrt{5})^2-(\sqrt{7})^2}{2(\sqrt{5}+\sqrt{7})}$$ Simplify.

$$= \frac{5-7}{2(\sqrt{5}+\sqrt{7})}$$ Square terms of numerator.

$$= \frac{-2}{2(\sqrt{5}+\sqrt{7})} = \frac{-1}{\sqrt{5}+\sqrt{7}}$$ Simplify.

CHECKPoint Now try Exercise 101.

Rational Exponents

Definition of Rational Exponents

If a is a real number and n is a positive integer such that the principal nth root of a exists, then $a^{1/n}$ is defined as

$$a^{1/n} = \sqrt[n]{a}, \text{ where } 1/n \text{ is the \textbf{rational exponent} of } a.$$

Moreover, if m is a positive integer that has no common factor with n, then

$$a^{m/n} = (a^{1/n})^m = (\sqrt[n]{a})^m \quad \text{and} \quad a^{m/n} = (a^m)^{1/n} = \sqrt[n]{a^m}.$$

The symbol ∫ indicates an example or exercise that highlights algebraic techniques specifically used in calculus.

WARNING / CAUTION

Rational exponents can be tricky, and you must remember that the expression $b^{m/n}$ is not defined unless $\sqrt[n]{b}$ is a real number. This restriction produces some unusual-looking results. For instance, the number $(-8)^{1/3}$ is defined because $\sqrt[3]{-8} = -2$, but the number $(-8)^{2/6}$ is undefined because $\sqrt[6]{-8}$ is not a real number.

The numerator of a rational exponent denotes the *power* to which the base is raised, and the denominator denotes the *index* or the *root* to be taken.

Power, Index

$$b^{m/n} = \left(\sqrt[n]{b}\right)^m = \sqrt[n]{b^m}$$

When you are working with rational exponents, the properties of integer exponents still apply. For instance, $2^{1/2}2^{1/3} = 2^{(1/2)+(1/3)} = 2^{5/6}$.

Example 16 Changing From Radical to Exponential Form

a. $\sqrt{3} = 3^{1/2}$

b. $\sqrt{(3xy)^5} = \sqrt[2]{(3xy)^5} = (3xy)^{5/2}$

c. $2x\sqrt[4]{x^3} = (2x)(x^{3/4}) = 2x^{1+(3/4)} = 2x^{7/4}$

CHECKPoint Now try Exercise 103.

TECHNOLOGY

There are four methods of evaluating radicals on most graphing calculators. For square roots, you can use the *square root key* ($\sqrt{\ }$). For cube roots, you can use the *cube root key* ($\sqrt[3]{\ }$). For other roots, you can first convert the radical to exponential form and then use the *exponential key* (^), or you can use the *x*th root key ($\sqrt[x]{\ }$) (or menu choice). Consult the user's guide for your calculator for specific keystrokes.

Example 17 Changing From Exponential to Radical Form

a. $(x^2 + y^2)^{3/2} = \left(\sqrt{x^2 + y^2}\right)^3 = \sqrt{(x^2 + y^2)^3}$

b. $2y^{3/4}z^{1/4} = 2(y^3z)^{1/4} = 2\sqrt[4]{y^3z}$

c. $a^{-3/2} = \dfrac{1}{a^{3/2}} = \dfrac{1}{\sqrt{a^3}}$

d. $x^{0.2} = x^{1/5} = \sqrt[5]{x}$

CHECKPoint Now try Exercise 105.

Rational exponents are useful for evaluating roots of numbers on a calculator, for reducing the index of a radical, and for simplifying expressions in calculus.

Example 18 Simplifying with Rational Exponents

a. $(-32)^{-4/5} = \left(\sqrt[5]{-32}\right)^{-4} = (-2)^{-4} = \dfrac{1}{(-2)^4} = \dfrac{1}{16}$

b. $(-5x^{5/3})(3x^{-3/4}) = -15x^{(5/3)-(3/4)} = -15x^{11/12}, \quad x \neq 0$

c. $\sqrt[9]{a^3} = a^{3/9} = a^{1/3} = \sqrt[3]{a}$ Reduce index.

d. $\sqrt[3]{\sqrt{125}} = \sqrt[6]{125} = \sqrt[6]{(5)^3} = 5^{3/6} = 5^{1/2} = \sqrt{5}$

e. $(2x - 1)^{4/3}(2x - 1)^{-1/3} = (2x - 1)^{(4/3)-(1/3)}$

$= 2x - 1, \quad x \neq \dfrac{1}{2}$

CHECKPoint Now try Exercise 115.

The expression in Example 18(e) is not defined when $x = \frac{1}{2}$ because

$$\left(2 \cdot \frac{1}{2} - 1\right)^{-1/3} = (0)^{-1/3}$$

is not a real number.

A.2 EXERCISES

See www.CalcChat.com for worked-out solutions to odd-numbered exercises.

VOCABULARY: Fill in the blanks.

1. In the exponential form a^n, n is the exponent and a is the base.
2. A convenient way of writing very large or very small numbers is called scientific notation.
3. One of the two equal factors of a number is called a square root of the number.
4. The principal nth root of a number a is the nth root that has the same sign as a, and is denoted by $\sqrt[n]{a}$.
5. In the radical form $\sqrt[n]{a}$, the positive integer n is called the index of the radical and the number a is called the radicand.
6. When an expression involving radicals has all possible factors removed, radical-free denominators, and a reduced index, it is in simplest form.
7. Radical expressions can be combined (added or subtracted) if they are like radicals.
8. The expressions $a + b\sqrt{m}$ and $a - b\sqrt{m}$ are _______ of each other. conjugates
9. The process used to create a radical-free denominator is known as _______ the denominator. rationalizing
10. In the expression $b^{m/n}$, m denotes the power to which the base is raised and n denotes the index or root to be taken.

SKILLS AND APPLICATIONS

In Exercises 11–18, evaluate each expression.

11. (a) $3^2 \cdot 3$ 27 (b) $3 \cdot 3^3$ 81
12. (a) $\dfrac{5^5}{5^2}$ 125 (b) $\dfrac{3^2}{3^4}$ $\frac{1}{9}$
13. (a) $(3^3)^0$ 1 (b) -3^2 -9
14. (a) $(2^3 \cdot 3^2)^2$ 5184 (b) $\left(-\frac{3}{5}\right)^3\left(\frac{5}{3}\right)^2$ $-\frac{3}{5}$
15. (a) $\dfrac{3}{3^{-4}}$ 243 (b) $48(-4)^{-3}$ $-\frac{3}{4}$
16. (a) $\dfrac{4 \cdot 3^{-2}}{2^{-2} \cdot 3^{-1}}$ $\frac{16}{3}$ (b) $(-2)^0$ 1
17. (a) $2^{-1} + 3^{-1}$ $\frac{5}{6}$ (b) $(2^{-1})^{-2}$ 4
18. (a) $3^{-1} + 2^{-2}$ $\frac{7}{12}$ (b) $(3^{-2})^2$ $\frac{1}{81}$

In Exercises 19–22, use a calculator to evaluate the expression. (If necessary, round your answer to three decimal places.)

19. $(-4)^3(5^2)$ -1600
20. $(8^{-4})(10^3)$ 0.244
21. $\dfrac{3^6}{7^3}$ 2.125
22. $\dfrac{4^3}{3^{-4}}$ 5184

In Exercises 23–30, evaluate the expression for the given value of x.

23. $-3x^3$, $x = 2$ -24
24. $7x^{-2}$, $x = 4$ $\frac{7}{16}$
25. $6x^0$, $x = 10$ 6
26. $5(-x)^3$, $x = 3$ -135
27. $2x^3$, $x = -3$ -54
28. $-3x^4$, $x = -2$ -48
29. $-20x^2$, $x = -\frac{1}{2}$ -5
30. $12(-x)^3$, $x = -\frac{1}{3}$ $\frac{4}{9}$

In Exercises 31–38, simplify each expression.

31. (a) $(-5z)^3$ $-125z^3$ (b) $5x^4(x^2)$ $5x^6$
32. (a) $(3x)^2$ $9x^2$ (b) $(4x^3)^0$, $x \neq 0$ 1
33. (a) $6y^2(2y^0)^2$ $24y^2$ (b) $\dfrac{3x^5}{x^3}$ $3x^2$
34. (a) $(-z)^3(3z^4)$ $-3z^7$ (b) $\dfrac{25y^8}{10y^4}$ $\frac{5}{2}y^4$
35. (a) $\dfrac{7x^2}{x^3}$ See below. (b) $\dfrac{12(x+y)^3}{9(x+y)}$
36. (a) $\dfrac{r^4}{r^6}$ $\frac{1}{r^2}$ (b) $\left(\frac{4}{y}\right)^3\left(\frac{3}{y}\right)^4$ $\frac{5184}{y^7}$
37. (a) $[(x^2y^{-2})^{-1}]^{-1}$ $\frac{x^2}{y^2}$ (b) $\left(\frac{a^{-2}}{b^{-2}}\right)\left(\frac{b}{a}\right)^3$ $\frac{b^5}{a^5}$
38. (a) $(6x^7)^0$, $x \neq 0$ 1 (b) $(5x^2z^6)^3(5x^2z^6)^{-3}$ 1

In Exercises 39–44, rewrite each expression with positive exponents and simplify.

39. (a) $(x+5)^0$, $x \neq -5$ 1 (b) $(2x^2)^{-2}$ $\frac{1}{4x^4}$
40. (a) $(2x^5)^0$, $x \neq 0$ See below. (b) $(z+2)^{-3}(z+2)^{-1}$
41. (a) $(-2x^2)^3(4x^3)^{-1}$ $-2x^3$ (b) $\left(\frac{x}{10}\right)^{-1}$ $\frac{10}{x}$
42. (a) $(4y^{-2})(8y^4)$ $32y^2$ (b) $\left(\frac{x^{-3}y^4}{5}\right)^{-3}$ $\frac{125x^9}{y^{12}}$
43. (a) $3^n \cdot 3^{2n}$ 3^{3n} (b) $\left(\frac{a^{-2}}{b^{-2}}\right)\left(\frac{b}{a}\right)^3$ $\frac{b^5}{a^5}$
44. (a) $\dfrac{x^2 \cdot x^n}{x^3 \cdot x^n}$ $\frac{1}{x}$ (b) $\left(\frac{a^{-3}}{b^{-3}}\right)\left(\frac{a}{b}\right)^3$ 1

35. (a) $\dfrac{7}{x}$ (b) $\dfrac{4}{3}(x+y)^2$ 40. (a) 1 (b) $\dfrac{1}{(z+2)^4}$

In Exercises 45–52, write the number in scientific notation.

45. 10,250.4 1.02504×10^4 **46.** $-7{,}280{,}000$ -7.28×10^6

47. -0.000125 -1.25×10^{-4} **48.** 0.00052 5.2×10^{-4}

49. Land area of Earth: 57,300,000 square miles See margin.

50. Light year: 9,460,000,000,000 kilometers 9.46×10^{12} km

51. Relative density of hydrogen: 0.0000899 gram per cubic centimeter $8.99 \times 10^{-5}\ \text{g/cm}^3$

52. One micron (millionth of a meter): 0.00003937 inch 3.937×10^{-5} in.

In Exercises 53–60, write the number in decimal notation.

53. 1.25×10^5 125,000 **54.** -1.801×10^5 $-180{,}100$

55. -2.718×10^{-3} -0.002718 **56.** 3.14×10^{-4} 0.000314

57. Interior temperature of the sun: 1.5×10^7 degrees Celsius 15,000,000°C

58. Charge of an electron: 1.6022×10^{-19} coulomb See margin.

59. Width of a human hair: 9.0×10^{-5} meter 0.00009 m

60. Gross domestic product of the United States in 2007: 1.3743021×10^{13} dollars (Source: U.S. Department of Commerce) \$13,743,021,000,000

In Exercises 61 and 62, evaluate each expression without using a calculator.

61. (a) $(2.0 \times 10^9)(3.4 \times 10^{-4})$ 6.8×10^5

(b) $(1.2 \times 10^7)(5.0 \times 10^{-3})$ 6.0×10^4

62. (a) $\dfrac{6.0 \times 10^8}{3.0 \times 10^{-3}}$ 2.0×10^{11} (b) $\dfrac{2.5 \times 10^{-3}}{5.0 \times 10^2}$ 5.0×10^{-6}

In Exercises 63 and 64, use a calculator to evaluate each expression. (Round your answer to three decimal places.)

63. (a) $750\left(1 + \dfrac{0.11}{365}\right)^{800}$ 954.448

(b) $\dfrac{67{,}000{,}000 + 93{,}000{,}000}{0.0052}$ 3.077×10^{10}

64. (a) $(9.3 \times 10^6)^3(6.1 \times 10^{-4})$ 4.907×10^{17} (b) $\dfrac{(2.414 \times 10^4)^6}{(1.68 \times 10^5)^5}$ 1.479

In Exercises 65–70, evaluate each expression without using a calculator.

65. (a) $\sqrt{9}$ 3 (b) $\sqrt[3]{\frac{27}{8}}$ $\frac{3}{2}$

66. (a) $27^{1/3}$ 3 (b) $36^{3/2}$ 216

67. (a) $32^{-3/5}$ $\frac{1}{8}$ (b) $\left(\frac{16}{81}\right)^{-3/4}$ $\frac{27}{8}$

68. (a) $100^{-3/2}$ $\frac{1}{1000}$ (b) $\left(\frac{9}{4}\right)^{-1/2}$ $\frac{2}{3}$

69. (a) $\left(-\dfrac{1}{64}\right)^{-1/3}$ -4 (b) $\left(\dfrac{1}{\sqrt{32}}\right)^{-2/5}$ 2

70. (a) $\left(-\dfrac{125}{27}\right)^{-1/3}$ $-\frac{3}{5}$ (b) $-\left(\dfrac{1}{125}\right)^{-4/3}$ -625

In Exercises 71–76, use a calculator to approximate the number. (Round your answer to three decimal places.)

71. (a) $\sqrt{57}$ 7.550 (b) $\sqrt[5]{-27^3}$ -7.225

72. (a) $\sqrt[3]{45^2}$ 12.651 (b) $\sqrt[6]{125}$ 2.236

73. (a) $(-12.4)^{-1.8}$ -0.011 (b) $(5\sqrt{3})^{-2.5}$ 0.005

74. (a) $\dfrac{7 - (4.1)^{-3.2}}{2}$ 3.495 (b) $\left(\dfrac{13}{3}\right)^{-3/2} - \left(-\dfrac{3}{2}\right)^{13/3}$ 5.906

75. (a) $\sqrt{4.5 \times 10^9}$ 67,082.039 (b) $\sqrt[3]{6.3 \times 10^4}$ 39.791

76. (a) $(2.65 \times 10^{-4})^{1/3}$ 0.064 (b) $\sqrt{9 \times 10^{-4}}$ 0.03

In Exercises 77 and 78, use the properties of radicals to simplify each expression.

77. (a) $(\sqrt[5]{2})^5$ 2 (b) $\sqrt[5]{96x^5}$ $2\sqrt[5]{3}x$

78. (a) $\sqrt{12} \cdot \sqrt{3}$ 6 (b) $\sqrt[4]{(3x^2)^4}$ $3x^2$

In Exercises 79–90, simplify each radical expression.

79. (a) $\sqrt{20}$ $2\sqrt{5}$ (b) $\sqrt[3]{128}$ $4\sqrt[3]{2}$

80. (a) $\sqrt[3]{\frac{16}{27}}$ See margin. (b) $\sqrt{\frac{75}{4}}$

81. (a) $\sqrt{72x^3}$ $6x\sqrt{2x}$ (b) $\sqrt{\dfrac{18^2}{z^3}}$ $\dfrac{18\sqrt{z}}{z^2}$

82. (a) $\sqrt{54xy^4}$ $3y^2\sqrt{6x}$ (b) $\sqrt{\dfrac{32a^4}{b^2}}$ $\dfrac{4a^2}{|b|}\sqrt{2}$

83. (a) $\sqrt[3]{16x^5}$ $2x\sqrt[3]{2x^2}$ (b) $\sqrt{75x^2y^{-4}}$ See margin.

84. (a) $\sqrt[4]{3x^4y^2}$ $\sqrt[4]{3}|x|\sqrt{y}$ (b) $\sqrt[5]{160x^8z^4}$ $2x\sqrt[5]{5x^3z^4}$

85. (a) $2\sqrt{50} + 12\sqrt{8}$ $34\sqrt{2}$ (b) $10\sqrt{32} - 6\sqrt{18}$ $22\sqrt{2}$

86. (a) $4\sqrt{27} - \sqrt{75}$ $7\sqrt{3}$ (b) $\sqrt[3]{16} + 3\sqrt[3]{54}$ $11\sqrt[3]{2}$

87. (a) $5\sqrt{x} - 3\sqrt{x}$ $2\sqrt{x}$ (b) $-2\sqrt{9y} + 10\sqrt{y}$ $4\sqrt{y}$

88. (a) $8\sqrt{49x} - 14\sqrt{100x}$ $-84\sqrt{x}$

(b) $-3\sqrt{48x^2} + 7\sqrt{75x^2}$ $23|x|\sqrt{3}$

89. (a) $3\sqrt{x+1} + 10\sqrt{x+1}$ $13\sqrt{x+1}$

(b) $7\sqrt{80x} - 2\sqrt{125x}$ $18\sqrt{5x}$

90. (a) $-\sqrt{x^3 - 7} + 5\sqrt{x^3 - 7}$ $4\sqrt{x^3 - 7}$

(b) $11\sqrt{245x^3} - 9\sqrt{45x^3}$ $50x\sqrt{5x}$

In Exercises 91–94, complete the statement with <, =, or >. 91–94. See margin.

91. $\sqrt{5} + \sqrt{3}$ ▢ $\sqrt{5 + 3}$ **92.** $\sqrt{\dfrac{3}{11}}$ ▢ $\dfrac{\sqrt{3}}{\sqrt{11}}$

93. 5 ▢ $\sqrt{3^2 + 2^2}$ **94.** 5 ▢ $\sqrt{3^2 + 4^2}$

In Exercises 95–98, rationalize the denominator of the expression. Then simplify your answer.

95. $\dfrac{1}{\sqrt{3}}$ $\dfrac{\sqrt{3}}{3}$ **96.** $\dfrac{8}{\sqrt[3]{2}}$ $4\sqrt[3]{4}$

97. $\dfrac{5}{\sqrt{14} - 2}$ $\dfrac{\sqrt{14} + 2}{2}$ **98.** $\dfrac{3}{\sqrt{5} + \sqrt{6}}$ $3(\sqrt{6} - \sqrt{5})$

49. $5.73 \times 10^7\ \text{mi}^2$

58. 0.00000000000000000016022 coulomb

80. (a) $\dfrac{2\sqrt[3]{2}}{3}$ (b) $\dfrac{5\sqrt{3}}{2}$

83. (b) $\dfrac{5|x|\sqrt{3}}{y^2}$

91. $\sqrt{5} + \sqrt{3} > \sqrt{5 + 3}$

92. $\sqrt{\dfrac{3}{11}} = \dfrac{\sqrt{3}}{\sqrt{11}}$

93. $5 > \sqrt{3^2 + 2^2}$

94. $5 = \sqrt{3^2 + 4^2}$

In Exercises 99–102, rationalize the numerator of the expression. Then simplify your answer.

99. $\frac{\sqrt{8}}{2}$ $\frac{2}{\sqrt{2}}$

100. $\frac{\sqrt{2}}{3}$ $\frac{2}{3\sqrt{2}}$

101. $\frac{\sqrt{5}+\sqrt{3}}{3}$ $\frac{2}{3(\sqrt{5}-\sqrt{3})}$

102. $\frac{\sqrt{7}-3}{4}$ $-\frac{1}{2(\sqrt{7}+3)}$

In Exercises 103–110, fill in the missing form of the expression.

	Radical Form	Rational Exponent Form
103.	$\sqrt{2.5}$	$2.5^{1/2}$
104.	$\sqrt[3]{64}$	$64^{1/3}$
105.	$\sqrt[4]{81}$	$81^{1/4}$
106.	$-\sqrt{144}$	$-(144^{1/2})$
107.	$\sqrt[3]{-216}$	$(-216)^{1/3}$
108.	$\sqrt[5]{-243}$	$(-243)^{1/5}$
109.	$(\sqrt[4]{81})^3$	$81^{3/4}$
110.	$\sqrt[4]{16^5}$	$16^{5/4}$

In Exercises 111–114, perform the operations and simplify.

111. $\frac{(2x^2)^{3/2}}{2^{1/2}x^4}$ $\frac{2}{|x|}$

112. $\frac{x^{4/3}y^{2/3}}{(xy)^{1/3}}$ $xy^{1/3}$

113. $\frac{x^{-3}\cdot x^{1/2}}{x^{3/2}\cdot x^{-1}}$, $x > 0$ $\frac{1}{x^3}$

114. $\frac{5^{-1/2}\cdot 5x^{5/2}}{(5x)^{3/2}}$, $x > 0$ $\frac{x}{5}$

In Exercises 115 and 116, reduce the index of each radical.

115. (a) $\sqrt[4]{3^2}$ $\sqrt{3}$ (b) $\sqrt[6]{(x+1)^4}$ $\sqrt[3]{(x+1)^2}$

116. (a) $\sqrt[6]{x^3}$ $\sqrt{x}$ (b) $\sqrt[4]{(3x^2)^4}$ $3x^2$

In Exercises 117 and 118, write each expression as a single radical. Then simplify your answer.

117. (a) $\sqrt{\sqrt{32}}$ $2\sqrt[4]{2}$ (b) $\sqrt{\sqrt[4]{2x}}$ $\sqrt[8]{2x}$

118. (a) $\sqrt{\sqrt{243(x+1)}}$ $3\sqrt[4]{3(x+1)}$ (b) $\sqrt{\sqrt[3]{10a^7b}}$ $|a|\sqrt[6]{10ab}$

119. **PERIOD OF A PENDULUM** The period T (in seconds) of a pendulum is $T = 2\pi\sqrt{L/32}$, where L is the length of the pendulum (in feet). Find the period of a pendulum whose length is 2 feet. See below.

120. **EROSION** A stream of water moving at the rate of v feet per second can carry particles of size $0.03\sqrt{v}$ inches. Find the size of the largest particle that can be carried by a stream flowing at the rate of $\frac{3}{4}$ foot per second. 0.026 in.

121. **MATHEMATICAL MODELING** A funnel is filled with water to a height of h centimeters. The formula

$$t = 0.03[12^{5/2} - (12-h)^{5/2}],\quad 0 \le h \le 12$$

represents the amount of time t (in seconds) that it will take for the funnel to empty.

(a) Use the table feature of a graphing utility to find the times required for the funnel to empty for water heights of $h = 0, h = 1, h = 2, \ldots h = 12$ centimeters. See margin.

(b) What value does t appear to be approaching as the height of the water becomes closer and closer to 12 centimeters? $t \to 8.64\sqrt{3} \approx 14.96$

122. **SPEED OF LIGHT** The speed of light is approximately 11,180,000 miles per minute. The distance from the sun to Earth is approximately 93,000,000 miles. Find the time for light to travel from the sun to Earth. 8.32 min

EXPLORATION

123–124. See margin.

TRUE OR FALSE? In Exercises 123 and 124, determine whether the statement is true or false. Justify your answer.

123. $\frac{x^{k+1}}{x} = x^k$

124. $(a^n)^k = a^{n^k}$

125. Verify that $a^0 = 1, a \neq 0$. (*Hint:* Use the property of exponents $a^m/a^n = a^{m-n}$.) See margin.

126. Explain why each of the following pairs is not equal. See margin.

(a) $(3x)^{-1} \neq \frac{3}{x}$ (b) $y^3\cdot y^2 \neq y^6$

(c) $(a^2b^3)^4 \neq a^6b^7$ (d) $(a+b)^2 \neq a^2+b^2$

(e) $\sqrt{4x^2} \neq 2x$ (f) $\sqrt{2}+\sqrt{3} \neq \sqrt{5}$

127. **THINK ABOUT IT** Is 52.7×10^5 written in scientific notation? Why or why not? See margin.

128. List all possible digits that occur in the units place of the square of a positive integer. Use that list to determine whether $\sqrt{5233}$ is an integer. See margin.

129. **THINK ABOUT IT** Square the real number $5/\sqrt{3}$ and note that the radical is eliminated from the denominator. Is this equivalent to rationalizing the denominator? Why or why not? See margin.

130. **CAPSTONE** See margin.

(a) Explain how to simplify the expression $(3x^3y^{-2})^{-2}$.

(b) Is the expression $\sqrt{\frac{4}{x^3}}$ in simplest form? Why or why not?

The symbol ∫ indicates an example or exercise that highlights algebraic techniques specifically used in calculus.

The symbol [graphing utility icon] indicates an exercise or a part of an exercise in which you are instructed to use a graphing utility.

119. $\frac{\pi}{2} \approx 1.57$ sec

(b) No. Four is a perfect square, and there is still a radical in the denominator.

$$\sqrt{\frac{4}{x^3}} = \frac{2}{\sqrt{x^3}} = \frac{2}{\sqrt{x^3}}\cdot\frac{\sqrt{x^3}}{\sqrt{x^3}} = \frac{2\sqrt{x^3}}{x^3} = \frac{2x\sqrt{x}}{x^3} = \frac{2\sqrt{x}}{x^2}$$

121. (a)

h	0	1	2	3	4	5	6
t	0	2.93	5.48	7.67	9.53	11.08	12.32

h	7	8	9	10	11	12
t	13.29	14.00	14.50	14.80	14.93	14.96

121. (a) See below.

123. True. When dividing variables, you subtract exponents.

124. False. When a power is raised to a power, you multiply the exponents: $(a^n)^k = a^{nk}$.

125. $a^0 = 1, a \neq 0$, using the property

$\frac{a^m}{a^n} = a^{m-n}$:

$\frac{a^m}{a^m} = a^{m-m} = a^0 = 1.$

126. (a) 3 is also raised to the -1 power, so $(3x)^{-1} = \frac{1}{3x}$.

(b) When two powers with the same base are multiplied, the exponents are added: $y^3\cdot y^2 = y^5$.

(c) When a power is raised to a power, the exponents are multiplied: $(a^2b^3)^4 = a^8b^{12}$.

(d) The square of a binomial contains a cross-product term: $(a+b)^2 = a^2+2ab+b^2$.

(e) If $x < 0$, then $\sqrt{4x^2} > 0$ but $2x < 0$: $\sqrt{4x^2} = 2|x|$.

(f) Radicals can be added together only if they have the same radicand and index: $\sqrt{2}+\sqrt{2} = 2\sqrt{2}$.

127. No. A number is in scientific notation when there is only one nonzero digit to the left of the decimal point.

128. When any positive integer is squared, the units digit is 0, 1, 4, 5, 6, or 9. Therefore, $\sqrt{5233}$ is not an integer.

129. No. Rationalizing the denominator produces a number equivalent to the original fraction; squaring does not.

130. (a) Multiply the exponent of each factor in the parentheses by -2. Then, put the factors with positive exponents in the numerator and the factors with negative exponents in the denominator. Finally, simplify the factor 3^2 in the denominator.

$$(3x^3y^{-2})^{-2} = 3^{-2}x^{-6}y^4 = \frac{y^4}{3^2x^6} = \frac{y^4}{9x^6}$$

A.3 Polynomials and Factoring

What you should learn

- Write polynomials in standard form.
- Add, subtract, and multiply polynomials.
- Use special products to multiply polynomials.
- Remove common factors from polynomials.
- Factor special polynomial forms.
- Factor trinomials as the product of two binomials.
- Factor polynomials by grouping.

Why you should learn it

Polynomials can be used to model and solve real-life problems. For instance, in Exercise 224 on page A37, a polynomial is used to model the volume of a shipping box.

Polynomials

The most common type of algebraic expression is the **polynomial.** Some examples are $2x + 5$, $3x^4 - 7x^2 + 2x + 4$, and $5x^2y^2 - xy + 3$. The first two are *polynomials in x* and the third is a *polynomial in x and y*. The terms of a polynomial in x have the form ax^k, where a is the **coefficient** and k is the **degree** of the term. For instance, the polynomial

$$2x^3 - 5x^2 + 1 = 2x^3 + (-5)x^2 + (0)x + 1$$

has coefficients 2, -5, 0, and 1.

Definition of a Polynomial in x

Let $a_0, a_1, a_2, \ldots, a_n$ be real numbers and let n be a nonnegative integer. A polynomial in x is an expression of the form

$$a_nx^n + a_{n-1}x^{n-1} + \cdot \cdot \cdot + a_1x + a_0$$

where $a_n \neq 0$. The polynomial is of **degree** n, a_n is the **leading coefficient,** and a_0 is the **constant term.**

Polynomials with one, two, and three terms are called **monomials, binomials,** and **trinomials,** respectively. In **standard form,** a polynomial is written with descending powers of x.

Example 1 Writing Polynomials in Standard Form

Polynomial	*Standard Form*	*Degree*	*Leading Coefficient*
a. $4x^2 - 5x^7 - 2 + 3x$	$-5x^7 + 4x^2 + 3x - 2$	7	-5
b. $4 - 9x^2$	$-9x^2 + 4$	2	-9
c. 8	$8 \; (8 = 8x^0)$	0	8

CHECK *Point* Now try Exercise 19.

A polynomial that has all zero coefficients is called the **zero polynomial,** denoted by 0. No degree is assigned to this particular polynomial. For polynomials in more than one variable, the degree of a *term* is the sum of the exponents of the variables in the term. The degree of the *polynomial* is the highest degree of its terms. For instance, the degree of the polynomial $-2x^3y^6 + 4xy - x^7y^4$ is 11 because the sum of the exponents in the last term is the greatest. The leading coefficient of the polynomial is the coefficient of the highest-degree term. Expressions are not polynomials if a variable is underneath a radical or if a polynomial expression (with degree greater than 0) is in the denominator of a term. The following expressions are not polynomials.

$$x^3 - \sqrt{3x} = x^3 - (3x)^{1/2}$$ The exponent "1/2" is not an integer.

$$x^2 + \frac{5}{x} = x^2 + 5x^{-1}$$ The exponent "-1" is not a nonnegative integer.

Operations with Polynomials

You can add and subtract polynomials in much the same way you add and subtract real numbers. Simply add or subtract the *like terms* (terms having the same variables to the same powers) by adding their coefficients. For instance, $-3xy^2$ and $5xy^2$ are like terms and their sum is

$$-3xy^2 + 5xy^2 = (-3 + 5)xy^2$$
$$= 2xy^2.$$

WARNING/CAUTION

When an expression inside parentheses is preceded by a negative sign, remember to distribute the negative sign to each term inside the parentheses, as shown.

$$-(x^2 - x + 3)$$
$$= -x^2 + x - 3$$

Example 2 Sums and Differences of Polynomials

a. $(5x^3 - 7x^2 - 3) + (x^3 + 2x^2 - x + 8)$

$= (5x^3 + x^3) + (-7x^2 + 2x^2) - x + (-3 + 8)$ Group like terms.

$= 6x^3 - 5x^2 - x + 5$ Combine like terms.

b. $(7x^4 - x^2 - 4x + 2) - (3x^4 - 4x^2 + 3x)$

$= 7x^4 - x^2 - 4x + 2 - 3x^4 + 4x^2 - 3x$ Distributive Property

$= (7x^4 - 3x^4) + (-x^2 + 4x^2) + (-4x - 3x) + 2$ Group like terms.

$= 4x^4 + 3x^2 - 7x + 2$ Combine like terms.

CHECKPoint Now try Exercise 41.

To find the *product* of two polynomials, use the left and right Distributive Properties. For example, if you treat $5x + 7$ as a single quantity, you can multiply $3x - 2$ by $5x + 7$ as follows.

$$(3x - 2)(5x + 7) = 3x(5x + 7) - 2(5x + 7)$$
$$= (3x)(5x) + (3x)(7) - (2)(5x) - (2)(7)$$
$$= 15x^2 + 21x - 10x - 14$$

Product of First terms; Product of Outer terms; Product of Inner terms; Product of Last terms

$$= 15x^2 + 11x - 14$$

Note in this **FOIL Method** (which can only be used to multiply two binomials) that the outer (O) and inner (I) terms are like terms and can be combined.

Example 3 Finding a Product by the FOIL Method

Use the FOIL Method to find the product of $2x - 4$ and $x + 5$.

Solution

F O I L

$$(2x - 4)(x + 5) = 2x^2 + 10x - 4x - 20$$
$$= 2x^2 + 6x - 20$$

CHECKPoint Now try Exercise 55.

Special Products

Some binomial products have special forms that occur frequently in algebra. You do not need to memorize these formulas because you can use the Distributive Property to multiply. However, becoming familiar with these formulas will enable you to manipulate the algebra more quickly.

Special Products

Let u and v be real numbers, variables, or algebraic expressions.

Special Product	*Example*
Sum and Difference of Same Terms	
$(u + v)(u - v) = u^2 - v^2$	$(x + 4)(x - 4) = x^2 - 4^2$ $= x^2 - 16$
Square of a Binomial	
$(u + v)^2 = u^2 + 2uv + v^2$	$(x + 3)^2 = x^2 + 2(x)(3) + 3^2$ $= x^2 + 6x + 9$
$(u - v)^2 = u^2 - 2uv + v^2$	$(3x - 2)^2 = (3x)^2 - 2(3x)(2) + 2^2$ $= 9x^2 - 12x + 4$
Cube of a Binomial	
$(u + v)^3 = u^3 + 3u^2v + 3uv^2 + v^3$	$(x + 2)^3 = x^3 + 3x^2(2) + 3x(2^2) + 2^3$ $= x^3 + 6x^2 + 12x + 8$
$(u - v)^3 = u^3 - 3u^2v + 3uv^2 - v^3$	$(x - 1)^3 = x^3 - 3x^2(1) + 3x(1^2) - 1^3$ $= x^3 - 3x^2 + 3x - 1$

Example 4 Special Products

Find each product.

a. $(5x + 9)(5x - 9)$ **b.** $(x + y - 2)(x + y + 2)$

Solution

a. The product of a sum and a difference of the *same* two terms has no middle term and takes the form $(u + v)(u - v) = u^2 - v^2$.

$$(5x + 9)(5x - 9) = (5x)^2 - 9^2 = 25x^2 - 81$$

b. By grouping $x + y$ in parentheses, you can write the product of the trinomials as a special product.

$$(x + y - 2)(x + y + 2) = [\underset{\text{Difference}}{(x + y) - 2}][\underset{\text{Sum}}{(x + y) + 2}]$$

$$= (x + y)^2 - 2^2 \qquad \text{Sum and difference of same terms}$$

$$= x^2 + 2xy + y^2 - 4$$

CHECK*Point* Now try Exercise 75.

Polynomials with Common Factors

The process of writing a polynomial as a product is called **factoring.** It is an important tool for solving equations and for simplifying rational expressions.

Unless noted otherwise, when you are asked to factor a polynomial, you can assume that you are looking for factors with integer coefficients. If a polynomial cannot be factored using integer coefficients, then it is **prime** or **irreducible over the integers.** For instance, the polynomial $x^2 - 3$ is irreducible over the integers. Over the *real numbers*, this polynomial can be factored as

$$x^2 - 3 = \left(x + \sqrt{3}\right)\left(x - \sqrt{3}\right).$$

A polynomial is **completely factored** when each of its factors is prime. For instance

$$x^3 - x^2 + 4x - 4 = (x - 1)(x^2 + 4) \qquad \text{Completely factored}$$

is completely factored, but

$$x^3 - x^2 - 4x + 4 = (x - 1)(x^2 - 4) \qquad \text{Not completely factored}$$

is not completely factored. Its complete factorization is

$$x^3 - x^2 - 4x + 4 = (x - 1)(x + 2)(x - 2).$$

The simplest type of factoring involves a polynomial that can be written as the product of a monomial and another polynomial. The technique used here is the Distributive Property, $a(b + c) = ab + ac$, in the *reverse* direction.

$$ab + ac = a(b + c) \qquad a \text{ is a common factor.}$$

Removing (factoring out) any common factors is the first step in completely factoring a polynomial.

Example 5 Removing Common Factors

Factor each expression.

a. $6x^3 - 4x$

b. $-4x^2 + 12x - 16$

c. $(x - 2)(2x) + (x - 2)(3)$

Solution

a. $6x^3 - 4x = 2x(3x^2) - 2x(2)$ — $2x$ is a common factor.

$= 2x(3x^2 - 2)$

b. $-4x^2 + 12x - 16 = -4(x^2) + (-4)(-3x) + (-4)4$ — -4 is a common factor.

$= -4(x^2 - 3x + 4)$

c. $(x - 2)(2x) + (x - 2)(3) = (x - 2)(2x + 3)$ — $(x - 2)$ is a common factor.

CHECKPoint Now try Exercise 99.

Factoring Special Polynomial Forms

Some polynomials have special forms that arise from the special product forms on page A29. You should learn to recognize these forms so that you can factor such polynomials easily.

Factoring Special Polynomial Forms

Factored Form	*Example*
Difference of Two Squares	
$u^2 - v^2 = (u + v)(u - v)$	$9x^2 - 4 = (3x)^2 - 2^2 = (3x + 2)(3x - 2)$
Perfect Square Trinomial	
$u^2 + 2uv + v^2 = (u + v)^2$	$x^2 + 6x + 9 = x^2 + 2(x)(3) + 3^2 = (x + 3)^2$
$u^2 - 2uv + v^2 = (u - v)^2$	$x^2 - 6x + 9 = x^2 - 2(x)(3) + 3^2 = (x - 3)^2$
Sum or Difference of Two Cubes	
$u^3 + v^3 = (u + v)(u^2 - uv + v^2)$	$x^3 + 8 = x^3 + 2^3 = (x + 2)(x^2 - 2x + 4)$
$u^3 - v^3 = (u - v)(u^2 + uv + v^2)$	$27x^3 - 1 = (3x)^3 - 1^3 = (3x - 1)(9x^2 + 3x + 1)$

One of the easiest special polynomial forms to factor is the difference of two squares. The factored form is always a set of *conjugate pairs*.

$$u^2 - v^2 = (u + v)(u - v)$$ Conjugate pairs

Difference (pointing to the minus in $u^2 - v^2$); Opposite signs (pointing to the signs in $(u + v)(u - v)$)

To recognize perfect square terms, look for coefficients that are squares of integers and variables raised to *even powers*.

> **Study Tip**
>
> In Example 6, note that the first step in factoring a polynomial is to check for any common factors. Once the common factors are removed, it is often possible to recognize patterns that were not immediately obvious.

Example 6 Removing a Common Factor First

$3 - 12x^2 = 3(1 - 4x^2)$ 3 is a common factor.

$= 3[1^2 - (2x)^2]$

$= 3(1 + 2x)(1 - 2x)$ Difference of two squares

CHECK*Point* Now try Exercise 113.

Example 7 Factoring the Difference of Two Squares

a. $(x + 2)^2 - y^2 = [(x + 2) + y][(x + 2) - y]$

$= (x + 2 + y)(x + 2 - y)$

b. $16x^4 - 81 = (4x^2)^2 - 9^2$

$= (4x^2 + 9)(4x^2 - 9)$ Difference of two squares

$= (4x^2 + 9)[(2x)^2 - 3^2]$

$= (4x^2 + 9)(2x + 3)(2x - 3)$ Difference of two squares

CHECK*Point* Now try Exercise 117.

A **perfect square trinomial** is the square of a binomial, and it has the following form.

$$u^2 + 2uv + v^2 = (u + v)^2 \quad \text{or} \quad u^2 - 2uv + v^2 = (u - v)^2$$

Like signs   Like signs

Note that the first and last terms are squares and the middle term is twice the product of u and v.

Example 8 Factoring Perfect Square Trinomials

Factor each trinomial.

a. $x^2 - 10x + 25$

b. $16x^2 + 24x + 9$

Solution

a. $x^2 - 10x + 25 = x^2 - 2(x)(5) + 5^2 = (x - 5)^2$

b. $16x^2 + 24x + 9 = (4x)^2 + 2(4x)(3) + 3^2 = (4x + 3)^2$

CHECK*Point* Now try Exercise 123.

The next two formulas show the sums and differences of cubes. Pay special attention to the signs of the terms.

Like signs   Like signs

$$u^3 + v^3 = (u + v)(u^2 - uv + v^2) \qquad u^3 - v^3 = (u - v)(u^2 + uv + v^2)$$

Unlike signs   Unlike signs

Example 9 Factoring the Difference of Cubes

Factor $x^3 - 27$.

Solution

$x^3 - 27 = x^3 - 3^3$ Rewrite 27 as 3^3.

$= (x - 3)(x^2 + 3x + 9)$ Factor.

CHECK*Point* Now try Exercise 133.

Example 10 Factoring the Sum of Cubes

a. $y^3 + 8 = y^3 + 2^3$ Rewrite 8 as 2^3.

$= (y + 2)(y^2 - 2y + 4)$ Factor.

b. $3(x^3 + 64) = 3(x^3 + 4^3)$ Rewrite 64 as 4^3.

$= 3(x + 4)(x^2 - 4x + 16)$ Factor.

CHECK*Point* Now try Exercise 135.

Trinomials with Binomial Factors

To factor a trinomial of the form $ax^2 + bx + c$, use the following pattern.

Factors of a

$$ax^2 + bx + c = (\square x + \square)(\square x + \square)$$

Factors of c

The goal is to find a combination of factors of a and c such that the outer and inner products add up to the middle term bx. For instance, in the trinomial $6x^2 + 17x + 5$, you can write all possible factorizations and determine which one has outer and inner products that add up to $17x$.

$$(6x + 5)(x + 1),\ (6x + 1)(x + 5),\ (2x + 1)(3x + 5),\ (2x + 5)(3x + 1)$$

You can see that $(2x + 5)(3x + 1)$ is the correct factorization because the outer (O) and inner (I) products add up to $17x$.

F O I L O + I

$$(2x + 5)(3x + 1) = 6x^2 + 2x + 15x + 5 = 6x^2 + 17x + 5$$

Example 11 Factoring a Trinomial: Leading Coefficient Is 1

Factor $x^2 - 7x + 12$.

Solution

The possible factorizations are

$$(x - 2)(x - 6),\quad (x - 1)(x - 12),\quad \text{and}\quad (x - 3)(x - 4).$$

Testing the middle term, you will find the correct factorization to be

$$x^2 - 7x + 12 = (x - 3)(x - 4).$$

CHECK *Point* Now try Exercise 145.

Example 12 Factoring a Trinomial: Leading Coefficient Is Not 1

Factor $2x^2 + x - 15$.

Solution

The eight possible factorizations are as follows.

$(2x - 1)(x + 15)$ $(2x + 1)(x - 15)$

$(2x - 3)(x + 5)$ $(2x + 3)(x - 5)$

$(2x - 5)(x + 3)$ $(2x + 5)(x - 3)$

$(2x - 15)(x + 1)$ $(2x + 15)(x - 1)$

Testing the middle term, you will find the correct factorization to be

$$2x^2 + x - 15 = (2x - 5)(x + 3). \qquad O + I = 6x - 5x = x$$

CHECK *Point* Now try Exercise 153.

Study Tip

Factoring a trinomial can involve trial and error. However, once you have produced the factored form, it is an easy matter to check your answer. For instance, you can verify the factorization in Example 11 by multiplying out the expression $(x - 3)(x - 4)$ to see that you obtain the original trinomial, $x^2 - 7x + 12$.

Factoring by Grouping

Sometimes polynomials with more than three terms can be factored by a method called **factoring by grouping.** It is not always obvious which terms to group, and sometimes several different groupings will work.

Example 13 Factoring by Grouping

Use factoring by grouping to factor $x^3 - 2x^2 - 3x + 6$.

Solution

$$x^3 - 2x^2 - 3x + 6 = (x^3 - 2x^2) - (3x - 6) \qquad \text{Group terms.}$$
$$= x^2(x - 2) - 3(x - 2) \qquad \text{Factor each group.}$$
$$= (x - 2)(x^2 - 3) \qquad \text{Distributive Property}$$

CHECK*Point* Now try Exercise 161.

Study Tip

Another way to factor the polynomial in Example 13 is to group the terms as follows.

$$x^3 - 2x^2 - 3x + 6$$
$$= (x^3 - 3x) - (2x^2 - 6)$$
$$= x(x^2 - 3) - 2(x^2 - 3)$$
$$= (x^2 - 3)(x - 2)$$

As you can see, you obtain the same result as in Example 13.

Factoring a trinomial can involve quite a bit of trial and error. Some of this trial and error can be lessened by using factoring by grouping. The key to this method of factoring is knowing how to rewrite the middle term. In general, to factor a trinomial $ax^2 + bx + c$ by grouping, choose factors of the product ac that add up to b and use these factors to rewrite the middle term. This technique is illustrated in Example 14.

Example 14 Factoring a Trinomial by Grouping

Use factoring by grouping to factor $2x^2 + 5x - 3$.

Solution

In the trinomial $2x^2 + 5x - 3$, $a = 2$ and $c = -3$, which implies that the product ac is -6. Now, -6 factors as $(6)(-1)$ and $6 - 1 = 5 = b$. So, you can rewrite the middle term as $5x = 6x - x$. This produces the following.

$$2x^2 + 5x - 3 = 2x^2 + 6x - x - 3 \qquad \text{Rewrite middle term.}$$
$$= (2x^2 + 6x) - (x + 3) \qquad \text{Group terms.}$$
$$= 2x(x + 3) - (x + 3) \qquad \text{Factor groups.}$$
$$= (x + 3)(2x - 1) \qquad \text{Distributive Property}$$

So, the trinomial factors as $2x^2 + 5x - 3 = (x + 3)(2x - 1)$.

CHECK*Point* Now try Exercise 167.

Guidelines for Factoring Polynomials

1. Factor out any common factors using the Distributive Property.
2. Factor according to one of the special polynomial forms.
3. Factor as $ax^2 + bx + c = (mx + r)(nx + s)$.
4. Factor by grouping.

A.3 EXERCISES

See www.CalcChat.com for worked-out solutions to odd-numbered exercises.

VOCABULARY: Fill in the blanks.

1. For the polynomial $a_nx^n + a_{n-1}x^{n-1} + \cdot \cdot \cdot + a_1x + a_0$, $a_n \neq 0$, the degree is n, the leading coefficient is a_n, and the constant term is a_0.
2. A polynomial in x in standard form is written with descending powers of x.
3. A polynomial with one term is called a monomial, while a polynomial with two terms is called a binomial, and a polynomial with three terms is called a trinomial.
4. To add or subtract polynomials, add or subtract the like terms by adding their coefficients.
5. The letters in "FOIL" stand for the following. F First terms O Outer terms I Inner terms L Last terms
6. The process of writing a polynomial as a product is called factoring.
7. A polynomial is completely factored when each of its factors is prime.
8. A polynomial $u^2 + 2uv + v^2$ is called a perfect square trinomial.

SKILLS AND APPLICATIONS

In Exercises 9–14, match the polynomial with its description. [The polynomials are labeled (a), (b), (c), (d), (e), and (f).]

(a) $3x^2$ (b) $1 - 2x^3$
(c) $x^3 + 3x^2 + 3x + 1$ (d) 12
(e) $-3x^5 + 2x^3 + x$ (f) $\frac{2}{3}x^4 + x^2 + 10$

9. A polynomial of degree 0 d
10. A trinomial of degree 5 e
11. A binomial with leading coefficient -2 b
12. A monomial of positive degree a
13. A trinomial with leading coefficient $\frac{2}{3}$ f
14. A third-degree polynomial with leading coefficient 1 c

In Exercises 15–18, write a polynomial that fits the description. (There are many correct answers.) 15–16. See margin.

15. A third-degree polynomial with leading coefficient -2
16. A fifth-degree polynomial with leading coefficient 6
17. A fourth-degree binomial with a negative leading coefficient $-15x^4 + 1$
18. A third-degree binomial with an even leading coefficient $20x^3 + 5$

In Exercises 19–30, (a) write the polynomial in standard form, (b) identify the degree and leading coefficient of the polynomial, and (c) state whether the polynomial is a monomial, a binomial, or a trinomial. 19–30. See margin.

19. $14x - \frac{1}{2}x^5$
20. $2x^2 - x + 1$
21. $x^2 - 4 - 3x^4$
22. $7x$
23. $3 - x^6$
24. $-y + 25y^2 + 1$
25. 3
26. $-8 + t^2$
27. $1 + 6x^4 - 4x^5$
28. $3 + 2x$
29. $4x^3y$
30. $-x^5y + 2x^2y^2 + xy^4$

In Exercises 31–36, determine whether the expression is a polynomial. If so, write the polynomial in standard form. 31–35. See margin.

31. $2x - 3x^3 + 8$
32. $5x^4 - 2x^2 + x^{-2}$
33. $\frac{3x + 4}{x}$
34. $\frac{x^2 + 2x - 3}{2}$
35. $y^2 - y^4 + y^3$
36. $y^4 - \sqrt{y}$ Not a polynomial because of the square root

In Exercises 37–54, perform the operation and write the result in standard form.

37. $(6x + 5) - (8x + 15)$ $-2x - 10$
38. $(2x^2 + 1) - (x^2 - 2x + 1)$ $x^2 + 2x$
39. $-(t^3 - 1) + (6t^3 - 5t)$ $5t^3 - 5t + 1$
40. $-(5x^2 - 1) - (-3x^2 + 5)$ $-2x^2 - 4$
41. $(15x^2 - 6) - (-8.3x^3 - 14.7x^2 - 17)$ 41–42. See margin.
42. $(15.6w^4 - 14w - 17.4) - (16.9w^4 - 9.2w + 13)$
43. $5z - [3z - (10z + 8)]$ $12z + 8$
44. $(y^3 + 1) - [(y^2 + 1) + (3y - 7)]$ $y^3 - y^2 - 3y + 7$
45. $3x(x^2 - 2x + 1)$
46. $y^2(4y^2 + 2y - 3)$
47. $-5z(3z - 1)$
48. $(-3x)(5x + 2)$ 45–54. See margin.
49. $(1 - x^3)(4x)$
50. $-4x(3 - x^3)$
51. $(1.5t^2 + 5)(-3t)$
52. $(2 - 3.5y)(2y^3)$
53. $-2x(0.1x + 17)$
54. $6y(5 - \frac{3}{8}y)$

In Exercises 55–92, multiply or find the special product.

55. $(x + 3)(x + 4)$
56. $(x - 5)(x + 10)$ 55–64. See margin.
57. $(3x - 5)(2x + 1)$
58. $(7x - 2)(4x - 3)$
59. $(x + 10)(x - 10)$
60. $(2x + 3)(2x - 3)$
61. $(x + 2y)(x - 2y)$
62. $(4a + 5b)(4a - 5b)$
63. $(2x + 3)^2$
64. $(5 - 8x)^2$

34. Polynomial: $\frac{1}{2}x^2 + x - \frac{3}{2}$
35. Polynomial: $-y^4 + y^3 + y^2$
41. $8.3x^3 + 29.7x^2 + 11$
42. $-1.3w^4 - 4.8w - 30.4$
45. $3x^3 - 6x^2 + 3x$
46. $4y^4 + 2y^3 - 3y^2$
47. $-15z^2 + 5z$
48. $-15x^2 - 6x$
49. $-4x^4 + 4x$
50. $4x^4 - 12x$
51. $-4.5t^3 - 15t$
52. $-7y^4 + 4y^3$
53. $-0.2x^2 - 34x$
54. $-\frac{9}{4}y^2 + 30y$
55. $x^2 + 7x + 12$
56. $x^2 + 5x - 50$
57. $6x^2 - 7x - 5$
58. $28x^2 - 29x + 6$
59. $x^2 - 100$
60. $4x^2 - 9$
61. $x^2 - 4y^2$
62. $16a^2 - 25b^2$
63. $4x^2 + 12x + 9$
64. $64x^2 - 80x + 25$

15. $-2x^3 + 4x^2 - 3x + 20$
16. $6x^5 + 3x + 1$
19. (a) $-\frac{1}{2}x^5 + 14x$
(b) Degree: 5; Leading coefficient: $-\frac{1}{2}$
(c) Binomial
20. (a) $2x^2 - x + 1$
(b) Degree: 2; Leading coefficient: 2
(c) Trinomial
21. (a) $-3x^4 + x^2 - 4$
(b) Degree: 4; Leading coefficient: -3
(c) Trinomial
22. (a) $7x$
(b) Degree: 1; Leading coefficient: 7
(c) Monomial
23. (a) $-x^6 + 3$
(b) Degree: 6; Leading coefficient: -1
(c) Binomial
24. (a) $25y^2 - y + 1$
(b) Degree: 2; Leading coefficient: 25
(c) Trinomial
25. (a) 3
(b) Degree: 0; Leading coefficient: 3
(c) Monomial
26. (a) $t^2 - 8$
(b) Degree: 2; Leading coefficient: 1
(c) Binomial
27. (a) $-4x^5 + 6x^4 + 1$
(b) Degree: 5; Leading coefficient: -4
(c) Trinomial
28. (a) $2x + 3$
(b) Degree: 1; Leading coefficient: 2
(c) Binomial
29. (a) $4x^3y$
(b) Degree: 4; Leading coefficient: 4
(c) Monomial
30. (a) $-x^5y + 2x^2y^2 + xy^4$
(b) Degree: 6; Leading coefficient: -1
(c) Trinomial
31. Polynomial: $-3x^3 + 2x + 8$
32. Not a polynomial because of the negative exponent
33. Not a polynomial because it includes a term with a negative exponent

65. $(x + 1)^3$ 65–69. **66.** $(x - 2)^3$

67. $(2x - y)^3$ See margin. **68.** $(3x + 2y)^3$

69. $(4x^3 - 3)^2$ **70.** $(8x + 3)^2$ $64x^2 + 48x + 9$

71. $(x^2 - x + 1)(x^2 + x + 1)$ $x^4 + x^2 + 1$

72. $(x^2 + 3x - 2)(x^2 - 3x - 2)$ $x^4 - 13x^2 + 4$

73. $(-x^2 + x - 5)(3x^2 + 4x + 1)$ See margin.

74. $(2x^2 - x + 4)(x^2 + 3x + 2)$ See margin.

75. $[(m - 3) + n][(m - 3) - n]$ $m^2 - n^2 - 6m + 9$

76. $[(x - 3y) + z][(x - 3y) - z]$ $x^2 - 6xy + 9y^2 - z^2$

77. $[(x - 3) + y]^2$ **78.** $[(x + 1) - y]^2$

79. $(2r^2 - 5)(2r^2 + 5)$ **80.** $(3a^3 - 4b^2)(3a^3 + 4b^2)$

81. $\left(\frac{1}{4}x - 5\right)^2$ **82.** $\left(\frac{3}{5}t + 4\right)^2$

83. $\left(\frac{1}{5}x - 3\right)\left(\frac{1}{5}x + 3\right)$ **84.** $\left(3x + \frac{1}{6}\right)\left(3x - \frac{1}{6}\right)$ 77–88.

85. $(2.4x + 3)^2$ **86.** $(1.8y - 5)^2$ See margin.

87. $(1.5x - 4)(1.5x + 4)$ **88.** $(2.5y + 3)(2.5y - 3)$

89. $5x(x + 1) - 3x(x + 1)$ $2x^2 + 2x$

90. $(2x - 1)(x + 3) + 3(x + 3)$ $2x^2 + 8x + 6$

91. $(u + 2)(u - 2)(u^2 + 4)$ $u^4 - 16$

92. $(x + y)(x - y)(x^2 + y^2)$ $x^4 - y^4$

In Exercises 93–96, find the product. (The expressions are not polynomials, but the formulas can still be used.)

93. $\left(\sqrt{x} + \sqrt{y}\right)\left(\sqrt{x} - \sqrt{y}\right)$ $x - y$

94. $\left(5 + \sqrt{x}\right)\left(5 - \sqrt{x}\right)$ $25 - x$

95. $\left(x - \sqrt{5}\right)^2$ $x^2 - 2\sqrt{5}x + 5$ **96.** $\left(x + \sqrt{3}\right)^2$ $x^2 + 2x\sqrt{3} + 3$

In Exercises 97–104, factor out the common factor.
97–104. See margin.

97. $4x + 16$ **98.** $5y - 30$

99. $2x^3 - 6x$ **100.** $3z^3 - 6z^2 + 9z$

101. $3x(x - 5) + 8(x - 5)$ **102.** $3x(x + 2) - 4(x + 2)$

103. $(x + 3)^2 - 4(x + 3)$ **104.** $(5x - 4)^2 + (5x - 4)$

In Exercises 105–110, find the greatest common factor such that the remaining factors have only integer coefficients.

105. $\frac{1}{2}x + 4$ $\frac{1}{2}(x + 8)$ **106.** $\frac{1}{3}y + 5$ $\frac{1}{3}(y + 15)$

107. $\frac{1}{2}x^3 + 2x^2 - 5x$ **108.** $\frac{1}{3}y^4 - 5y^2 + 2y$ 107–108. See margin.

109. $\frac{2}{3}x(x - 3) - 4(x - 3)$ $\frac{2}{3}(x - 6)(x - 3)$ **110.** $\frac{4}{5}y(y + 1) - 2(y + 1)$ $\frac{2}{5}(y + 1)(2y - 5)$

In Exercises 111–120, completely factor the difference of two squares. 111–117. See margin.

111. $x^2 - 81$ **112.** $x^2 - 64$

113. $48y^2 - 27$ **114.** $50 - 98z^2$

115. $16x^2 - \frac{1}{9}$ **116.** $\frac{4}{25}y^2 - 64$

117. $(x - 1)^2 - 4$ **118.** $25 - (z + 5)^2$ $-z(z + 10)$

119. $9u^2 - 4v^2$ $(3u + 2v)(3u - 2v)$ **120.** $25x^2 - 16y^2$ $(5x + 4y)(5x - 4y)$

121–132. See margin.
In Exercises 121–132, factor the perfect square trinomial.

121. $x^2 - 4x + 4$ **122.** $x^2 + 10x + 25$

123. $4t^2 + 4t + 1$ **124.** $9x^2 - 12x + 4$

125. $25y^2 - 10y + 1$ **126.** $36y^2 - 108y + 81$

127. $9u^2 + 24uv + 16v^2$ **128.** $4x^2 - 4xy + y^2$

129. $x^2 - \frac{4}{3}x + \frac{4}{9}$ **130.** $z^2 + z + \frac{1}{4}$

131. $4x^2 - \frac{4}{3}x + \frac{1}{9}$ **132.** $9y^2 - \frac{3}{2}y + \frac{1}{16}$

133–144. See margin.
In Exercises 133–144, factor the sum or difference of cubes.

133. $x^3 - 8$ **134.** $x^3 - 27$

135. $y^3 + 64$ **136.** $z^3 + 216$

137. $x^3 - \frac{8}{27}$ **138.** $y^3 + \frac{8}{125}$

139. $8t^3 - 1$ **140.** $27x^3 + 8$

141. $u^3 + 27v^3$ **142.** $64x^3 - y^3$

143. $(x + 2)^3 - y^3$ **144.** $(x - 3y)^3 - 8z^3$

145–158. See margin.
In Exercises 145–158, factor the trinomial.

145. $x^2 + x - 2$ **146.** $x^2 + 5x + 6$

147. $s^2 - 5s + 6$ **148.** $t^2 - t - 6$

149. $20 - y - y^2$ **150.** $24 + 5z - z^2$

151. $x^2 - 30x + 200$ **152.** $x^2 - 13x + 42$

153. $3x^2 - 5x + 2$ **154.** $2x^2 - x - 1$

155. $5x^2 + 26x + 5$ **156.** $12x^2 + 7x + 1$

157. $-9z^2 + 3z + 2$ **158.** $-5u^2 - 13u + 6$

159–166. See margin.
In Exercises 159–166, factor by grouping.

159. $x^3 - x^2 + 2x - 2$ **160.** $x^3 + 5x^2 - 5x - 25$

161. $2x^3 - x^2 - 6x + 3$ **162.** $5x^3 - 10x^2 + 3x - 6$

163. $6 + 2x - 3x^3 - x^4$ **164.** $x^5 + 2x^3 + x^2 + 2$

165. $6x^3 - 2x + 3x^2 - 1$ **166.** $8x^5 - 6x^2 + 12x^3 - 9$

167–172. See margin.
In Exercises 167–172, factor the trinomial by grouping.

167. $3x^2 + 10x + 8$ **168.** $2x^2 + 9x + 9$

169. $6x^2 + x - 2$ **170.** $6x^2 - x - 15$

171. $15x^2 - 11x + 2$ **172.** $12x^2 - 13x + 1$

173–182. See margin.
In Exercises 173–206, completely factor the expression.

173. $6x^2 - 54$ **174.** $12x^2 - 48$

175. $x^3 - x^2$ **176.** $x^3 - 4x^2$

177. $x^3 - 16x$ **178.** $x^3 - 9x$

179. $x^2 - 2x + 1$ **180.** $16 + 6x - x^2$

181. $1 - 4x + 4x^2$ **182.** $-9x^2 + 6x - 1$

183. $2x^2 + 4x - 2x^3$ **184.** $13x + 6 + 5x^2$

185. $\frac{1}{81}x^2 + \frac{2}{9}x - 8$ **186.** $\frac{1}{8}x^2 - \frac{1}{96}x - \frac{1}{16}$

183. $-2x(x + 1)(x - 2)$ 184. $(5x + 3)(x + 2)$

185. $\frac{1}{81}(x + 36)(x - 18)$ 186. $\frac{1}{96}(4x - 3)(3x + 2)$

65. $x^3 + 3x^2 + 3x + 1$
66. $x^3 - 6x^2 + 12x - 8$
67. $8x^3 - 12x^2y + 6xy^2 - y^3$
68. $27x^3 + 54x^2y + 36xy^2 + 8y^3$
69. $16x^6 - 24x^3 + 9$
73. $-3x^4 - x^3 - 12x^2 - 19x - 5$
74. $2x^4 + 5x^3 + 5x^2 + 10x + 8$
77. $x^2 + 2xy + y^2 - 6x - 6y + 9$
78. $x^2 - 2xy + y^2 + 2x - 2y + 1$
79. $4r^4 - 25$ **80.** $9a^6 - 16b^4$
81. $\frac{1}{16}x^2 - \frac{5}{2}x + 25$
82. $\frac{9}{25}t^2 + \frac{24}{5}t + 16$
83. $\frac{1}{25}x^2 - 9$ **84.** $9x^2 - \frac{1}{36}$
85. $5.76x^2 + 14.4x + 9$
86. $3.24y^2 - 18y + 25$
87. $2.25x^2 - 16$
88. $6.25y^2 - 9$ **97.** $4(x + 4)$
98. $5(y - 6)$ **99.** $2x(x^2 - 3)$
100. $3z(z^2 - 2z + 3)$
101. $(x - 5)(3x + 8)$
102. $(x + 2)(3x - 4)$
103. $(x + 3)(x - 1)$
104. $(5x - 4)(5x - 3)$
107. $\frac{1}{2}x(x^2 + 4x - 10)$
108. $\frac{1}{3}y(y^3 - 15y + 6)$
111. $(x + 9)(x - 9)$
112. $(x - 8)(x + 8)$
113. $3(4y - 3)(4y + 3)$
114. $-2(7z - 5)(7z + 5)$
115. $\left(4x + \frac{1}{3}\right)\left(4x - \frac{1}{3}\right)$
116. $\left(\frac{2}{5}y + 8\right)\left(\frac{2}{5}y - 8\right)$
117. $(x + 1)(x - 3)$
121. $(x - 2)^2$ **122.** $(x + 5)^2$
123. $(2t + 1)^2$ **124.** $(3x - 2)^2$
125. $(5y - 1)^2$ **126.** $(6y - 9)^2$
127. $(3u + 4v)^2$ **128.** $(2x - y)^2$
129. $\left(x - \frac{2}{3}\right)^2$ **130.** $\left(z + \frac{1}{2}\right)^2$
131. $\frac{1}{9}(6x - 1)^2$
132. $\frac{1}{16}(12y - 1)^2$
133. $(x - 2)(x^2 + 2x + 4)$
134. $(x - 3)(x^2 + 3x + 9)$
135. $(y + 4)(y^2 - 4y + 16)$
136. $(z + 6)(z^2 - 6z + 36)$
137. $\frac{1}{27}(3x - 2)(9x^2 + 6x + 4)$
138. $\frac{1}{125}(5y + 2)(25y^2 - 10y + 4)$
139. $(2t - 1)(4t^2 + 2t + 1)$
140. $(3x + 2)(9x^2 - 6x + 4)$
141. $(u + 3v)(u^2 - 3uv + 9v^2)$
142. $(4x - y)(16x^2 + 4xy + y^2)$
143–144. See right.
145. $(x + 2)(x - 1)$
146. $(x + 2)(x + 3)$
147. $(s - 3)(s - 2)$
148. $(t + 2)(t - 3)$
149. $-(y + 5)(y - 4)$

150. $-(z - 8)(z + 3)$ **151.** $(x - 20)(x - 10)$ **171.** $(3x - 1)(5x - 2)$ **172.** $(x - 1)(12x - 1)$
152. $(x - 6)(x - 7)$ **153.** $(3x - 2)(x - 1)$ **173.** $6(x + 3)(x - 3)$ **174.** $12(x + 2)(x - 2)$
154. $(2x + 1)(x - 1)$ **155.** $(5x + 1)(x + 5)$ **175.** $x^2(x - 1)$ **176.** $x^2(x - 4)$
156. $(3x + 1)(4x + 1)$ **157.** $-(3z - 2)(3z + 1)$ **177.** $x(x - 4)(x + 4)$ **178.** $x(x + 3)(x - 3)$
158. $-(5u - 2)(u + 3)$ **159.** $(x - 1)(x^2 + 2)$ **179.** $(x - 1)^2$ **180.** $(8 - x)(2 + x)$
160. $(x + 5)(x^2 - 5)$ **161.** $(2x - 1)(x^2 - 3)$ **181.** $(1 - 2x)^2$ **182.** $(-3x + 1)(3x - 1)$
162. $(x - 2)(5x^2 + 3)$ **163.** $(3 + x)(2 - x^3)$
164. $(x^2 + 2)(x + 1)(x^2 - x + 1)$
165. $(3x^2 - 1)(2x + 1)$ **166.** $(4x^3 - 3)(2x^2 + 3)$
167. $(x + 2)(3x + 4)$ **168.** $(x + 3)(2x + 3)$
169. $(2x - 1)(3x + 2)$ **170.** $(2x + 3)(3x - 5)$

143. $(x - y + 2)(x^2 + xy + 4x + y^2 + 2y + 4)$
144. $(x - 3y - 2z)(x^2 + 2xz - 6xy + 9y^2 - 6yz + 4z^2)$

187–205. See margin.

187. $3x^3 + x^2 + 15x + 5$ **188.** $5 - x + 5x^2 - x^3$

189. $x^4 - 4x^3 + x^2 - 4x$ **190.** $3x^3 + x^2 - 27x - 9$

191. $\frac{1}{4}x^3 + 3x^2 + \frac{3}{4}x + 9$ **192.** $\frac{1}{5}x^3 + x^2 - x - 5$

193. $(t - 1)^2 - 49$ **194.** $(x^2 + 1)^2 - 4x^2$

195. $(x^2 + 8)^2 - 36x^2$ **196.** $2t^3 - 16$

197. $5x^3 + 40$ **198.** $4x(2x - 1) + (2x - 1)^2$

199. $5(3 - 4x)^2 - 8(3 - 4x)(5x - 1)$

200. $2(x + 1)(x - 3)^2 - 3(x + 1)^2(x - 3)$

201. $7(3x + 2)^2(1 - x)^2 + (3x + 2)(1 - x)^3$

202. $7x(2)(x^2 + 1)(2x) - (x^2 + 1)^2(7)$

203. $3(x - 2)^2(x + 1)^4 + (x - 2)^3(4)(x + 1)^3$

204. $2x(x - 5)^4 - x^2(4)(x - 5)^3$

205. $5(x^6 + 1)^4(6x^5)(3x + 2)^3 + 3(3x + 2)^2(3)(x^6 + 1)^5$

206. $\frac{x^2}{2}(x^2 + 1)^4 - (x^2 + 1)^5$ $-(x^2 + 1)^4\left(\frac{x^2}{2} + 1\right)$

In Exercises 207–212, completely factor the expression.

207. $x^4(4)(2x + 1)^3(2x) + (2x + 1)^4(4x^3)$ 207–210. See margin.

208. $x^3(3)(x^2 + 1)^2(2x) + (x^2 + 1)^3(3x^2)$

209. $(2x - 5)^4(3)(5x - 4)^2(5) + (5x - 4)^3(4)(2x - 5)^3(2)$

210. $(x^2 - 5)^3(2)(4x + 3)(4) + (4x + 3)^2(3)(x^2 - 5)^2(x^2)$

211. $\dfrac{(5x - 1)(3) - (3x + 1)(5)}{(5x - 1)^2}$ $-\dfrac{8}{(5x - 1)^2}$

212. $\dfrac{(2x + 3)(4) - (4x - 1)(2)}{(2x + 3)^2}$ $\dfrac{14}{(2x + 3)^2}$

In Exercises 213–216, find all values of b for which the trinomial can be factored. 213–216. See margin.

213. $x^2 + bx - 15$ **214.** $x^2 + bx - 12$

215. $x^2 + bx + 50$ **216.** $x^2 + bx + 24$

In Exercises 217–220, find two integer values of c such that the trinomial can be factored. (There are many correct answers.) 217–219. See below.

217. $2x^2 + 5x + c$ **218.** $3x^2 - 10x + c$

219. $3x^2 - x + c$ **220.** $2x^2 + 9x + c$

Two possible answers: 9, 7

221. COST, REVENUE, AND PROFIT An electronics manufacturer can produce and sell x MP3 players per week. The total cost C (in dollars) of producing x MP3 players is $C = 73x + 25{,}000$, and the total revenue R (in dollars) is $R = 95x$.

(a) Find the profit P in terms of x. $P = 22x - 25{,}000$

(b) Find the profit obtained by selling 5000 MP3 players per week. \$85,000

217. Two possible answers: 2, −12
218. Two possible answers: 3, −8
219. Two possible answers: −2, −4

222. COMPOUND INTEREST After 3 years, an investment of \$1200 compounded annually at an interest rate r will yield an amount of $1200(1 + r)^3$. See margin.

(a) Write this polynomial in standard form.

(b) Use a calculator to evaluate the polynomial for the values of r shown in the table.

r	2%	3%	$3\frac{1}{2}$%	4%	$4\frac{1}{2}$%
$1200(1 + r)^3$					

(c) What conclusion can you make from the table?

223. VOLUME OF A BOX A take-out fast-food restaurant is constructing an open box by cutting squares from the corners of a piece of cardboard that is 18 centimeters by 26 centimeters (see figure). The edge of each cut-out square is x centimeters. See margin.

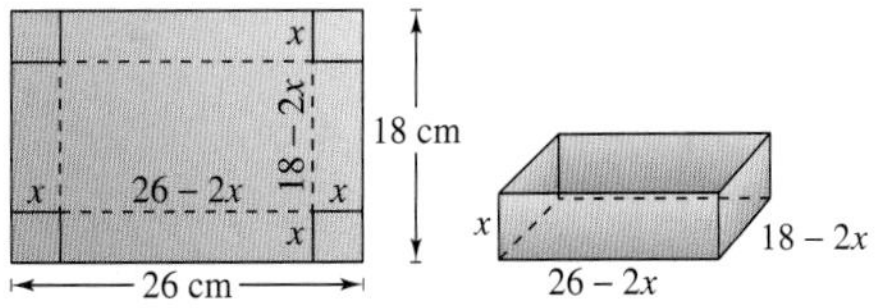

(a) Find the volume of the box in terms of x.

(b) Find the volume when $x = 1$, $x = 2$, and $x = 3$.

224. VOLUME OF A BOX An overnight shipping company is designing a closed box by cutting along the solid lines and folding along the broken lines on the rectangular piece of corrugated cardboard shown in the figure. The length and width of the rectangle are 45 centimeters and 15 centimeters, respectively. See margin.

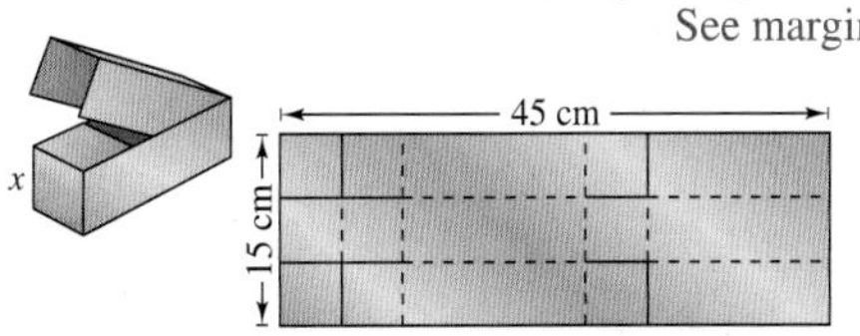

(a) Find the volume of the shipping box in terms of x.

(b) Find the volume when $x = 3$, $x = 5$, and $x = 7$.

225. GEOMETRY Find a polynomial that represents the total number of square feet for the floor plan shown in the figure. $44x + 308$

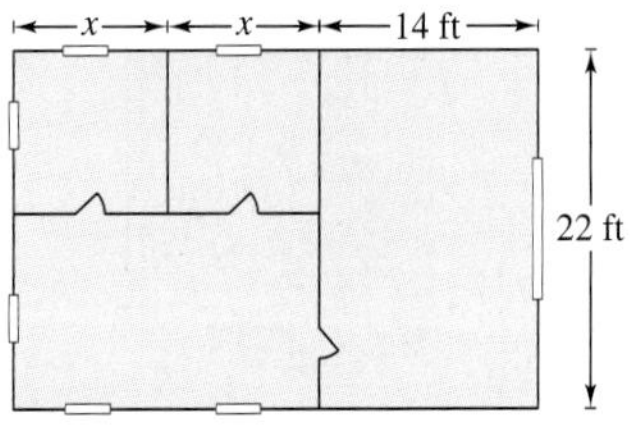

187. $(3x + 1)(x^2 + 5)$
188. $(5 - x)(1 + x^2)$
189. $x(x - 4)(x^2 + 1)$
190. $(x - 3)(x + 3)(3x + 1)$
191. $\frac{1}{4}(x^2 + 3)(x + 12)$
192. $\frac{1}{5}(x^2 - 5)(x + 5)$
193. $(t + 6)(t - 8)$
194. $(x + 1)^2(x - 1)^2$
195. $(x + 2)(x + 4)(x - 2)(x - 4)$
196. $2(t - 2)(t^2 + 2t + 4)$
197. $5(x + 2)(x^2 - 2x + 4)$
198. $(2x - 1)(6x - 1)$
199. $(3 - 4x)(23 - 60x)$
200. $-(x + 1)(x - 3)(x + 9)$
201. $5(1 - x)^2(3x + 2)(4x + 3)$
202. $7(x^2 + 1)(3x^2 - 1)$
203. $(x - 2)^2(x + 1)^3(7x - 5)$
204. $-2x(x - 5)^3(x + 5)$
205. See below.
207. $4x^3(2x + 1)^3(2x^2 + 2x + 1)$
208. $3x^2(x^2 + 1)^2(3x^2 + 1)$
209. $(2x - 5)^3(5x - 4)^2(70x - 107)$
210. See below.
213. −14, 14, −2, 2
214. −1, 1, −4, 4, −11, 11
215. −51, 51, −15, 15, −27, 27
216. −25, 25, −14, 14, −11, 11, −10, 10
222. See below.
223. (a) $V = 4x^3 - 88x^2 + 468x$
(b)

x (cm)	1	2	3
V (cm³)	384	616	720

224. (a) $V = \frac{1}{2}(6x^3 - 135x^2 + 675x)$
(b)

x (cm)	3	5	7
V (cm³)	486	375	84

205. $3(x^2 + 1)^4(x^4 - x^2 + 1)^4(3x + 2)^2(33x^6 + 20x^5 + 3)$
210. $(4x + 3)(x^2 - 5)^2(12x^3 + 17x^2 - 40)$
222. (a) $1200r^3 + 3600r^2 + 3600r + 1200$
(b)

r	2%	3%	$3\frac{1}{2}$%	4%	$4\frac{1}{2}$%
$1200(1 + r)^3$	\$1273.45	\$1311.27	\$1330.46	\$1349.84	\$1369.40

(c) The amount increases with increasing r.

228.

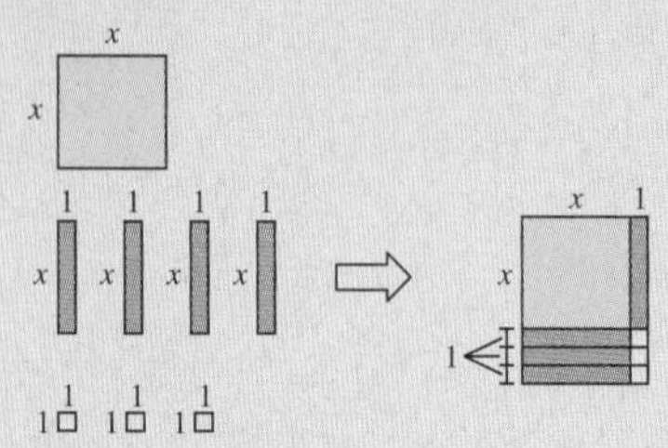

230.

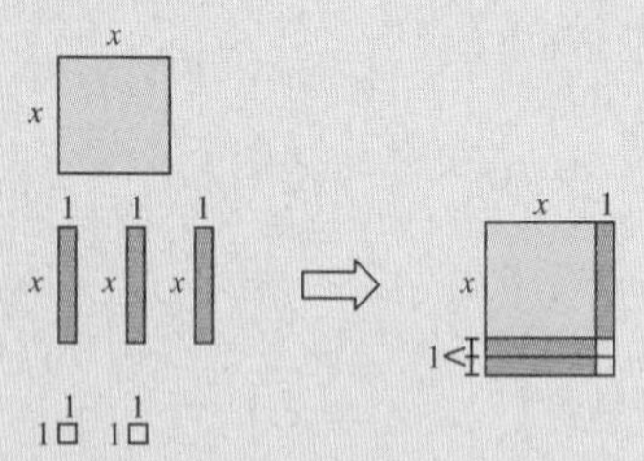

233. (a) $V = \pi h(R + r)(R - r)$

(b)

$$V = \pi h(R + r)(R - r)$$
$$= \frac{2}{2}\pi h(R + r)(R - r)$$
$$= 2\pi\left(\frac{R + r}{2}\right)(R - r)h$$

235. False.

$$(4x^2 + 1)(3x + 1) = 12x^3 + 4x^2 + 3x + 1$$

236. See below.

237. True.

$$a^2 - b^2 = (a + b)(a - b)$$

238. False. A perfect square trinomial can be factored as the binomial sum squared.

241. $-x^3 + 8x^2 + 2x + 7$

242. $(3 + 4)^2 = 49 \neq 25 = 3^2 + 4^2$

If either x or y is zero, then $(x + y)^2 = x^2 + y^2$.

243. $(x^n + y^n)(x^n - y^n)$

244. $(x^n + y^n)(x^{2n} - x^ny^n + y^{2n})$

226. GEOMETRY Find the area of the shaded region in each figure. Write your result as a polynomial in standard form.

(a)

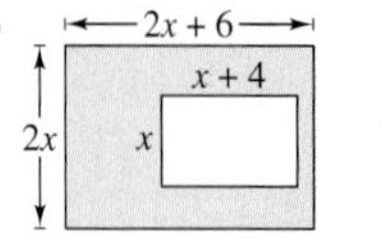

$3x^2 + 8x$

(b)

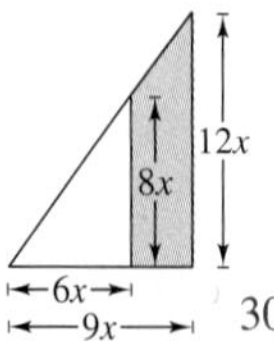

$30x^2$

GEOMETRIC MODELING In Exercises 227–230, draw a "geometric factoring model" to represent the factorization. For instance, a factoring model for

$2x^2 + 3x + 1 = (2x + 1)(x + 1)$

is shown in the figure. 227–230. See margin.

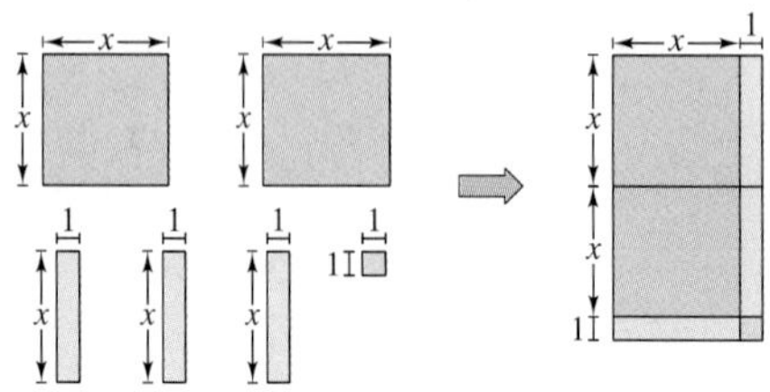

227. $3x^2 + 7x + 2 = (3x + 1)(x + 2)$

228. $x^2 + 4x + 3 = (x + 3)(x + 1)$

229. $2x^2 + 7x + 3 = (2x + 1)(x + 3)$

230. $x^2 + 3x + 2 = (x + 2)(x + 1)$

GEOMETRY In Exercises 231 and 232, write an expression in factored form for the area of the shaded portion of the figure.

231.

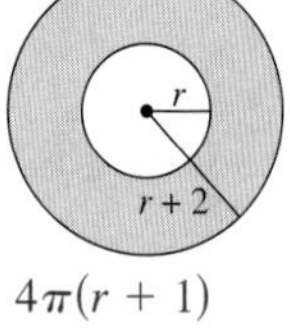

$4\pi(r + 1)$

232. $\frac{5}{8}(x + 7)(x - 1)$

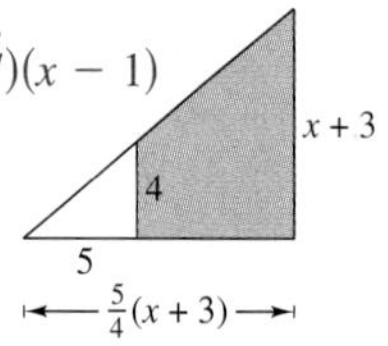

233. GEOMETRY The cylindrical shell shown in the figure has a volume of $V = \pi R^2h - \pi r^2h$. See margin.

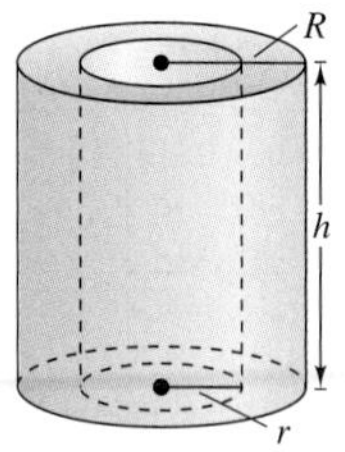

(a) Factor the expression for the volume.

(b) From the result of part (a), show that the volume is 2π (average radius)(thickness of the shell)h.

234. CHEMISTRY The rate of change of an autocatalytic chemical reaction is $kQx - kx^2$, where Q is the amount of the original substance, x is the amount of substance formed, and k is a constant of proportionality. Factor the expression. $kx(Q - x)$

EXPLORATION

235–238. See margin.

TRUE OR FALSE? In Exercises 235–238, determine whether the statement is true or false. Justify your answer.

235. The product of two binomials is always a second-degree polynomial.

236. The sum of two binomials is always a binomial.

237. The difference of two perfect squares can be factored as the product of conjugate pairs.

238. The sum of two perfect squares can be factored as the binomial sum squared.

239. Find the degree of the product of two polynomials of degrees m and n. $m + n$

240. Find the degree of the sum of two polynomials of degrees m and n if $m < n$. n

241. THINK ABOUT IT When the polynomial $-x^3 + 3x^2 + 2x - 1$ is subtracted from an unknown polynomial, the difference is $5x^2 + 8$. If it is possible, find the unknown polynomial. See margin.

242. LOGICAL REASONING Verify that $(x + y)^2$ is not equal to $x^2 + y^2$ by letting $x = 3$ and $y = 4$ and evaluating both expressions. Are there any values of x and y for which $(x + y)^2 = x^2 + y^2$? Explain.

243. Factor $x^{2n} - y^{2n}$ as completely as possible.

244. Factor $x^{3n} + y^{3n}$ as completely as possible.

242–244. See margin.

245. Give an example of a polynomial that is prime with respect to the integers.

Answers will vary. Sample answer: $x^2 - 3$

246. CAPSTONE A third-degree polynomial and a fourth-degree polynomial are added. See margin.

(a) Can the sum be a fourth-degree polynomial? Explain or give an example.

(b) Can the sum be a second-degree polynomial? Explain or give an example.

(c) Can the sum be a seventh-degree polynomial? Explain or give an example.

(d) After adding the two polynomials and factoring the sum, you obtain a polynomial that is in factored form. Explain what is meant by saying that a polynomial is in factored form.

236. False.

$$(4x + 3) + (-4x + 6) = 4x + 3 - 4x + 6 = 3 + 6 = 9$$

246. (a) Yes. Sample answer:

$$(4x^3 + 2x + 1) + (5x^4 - 6) = 5x^4 + 4x^3 + 2x - 5$$

(b) No. Sample answer:

$$(4x^3 + 1) + (5x^4 - 6) = 5x^4 + 4x^3 - 5$$

(c) No. Sample answer:

$$(4x^3 + 1) + (5x^4 - 6) = 5x^4 + 4x^3 - 5$$

(d) Sample answer: A polynomial is in factored form when each of its factors is prime.

227, 229. See Additional Answers beginning on page AA1.

A.4 RATIONAL EXPRESSIONS

What you should learn

- Find domains of algebraic expressions.
- Simplify rational expressions.
- Add, subtract, multiply, and divide rational expressions.
- Simplify complex fractions and rewrite difference quotients.

Why you should learn it

Rational expressions can be used to solve real-life problems. For instance, in Exercise 102 on page A48, a rational expression is used to model the projected numbers of U.S. households banking and paying bills online from 2002 through 2007.

Domain of an Algebraic Expression

The set of real numbers for which an algebraic expression is defined is the **domain** of the expression. Two algebraic expressions are **equivalent** if they have the same domain and yield the same values for all numbers in their domain. For instance, $(x + 1) + (x + 2)$ and $2x + 3$ are equivalent because

$$\begin{aligned}(x + 1) + (x + 2) &= x + 1 + x + 2\\ &= x + x + 1 + 2\\ &= 2x + 3.\end{aligned}$$

Example 1 Finding the Domain of an Algebraic Expression

a. The domain of the polynomial

$$2x^3 + 3x + 4$$

is the set of all real numbers. In fact, the domain of any polynomial is the set of all real numbers, unless the domain is specifically restricted.

b. The domain of the radical expression

$$\sqrt{x - 2}$$

is the set of real numbers greater than or equal to 2, because the square root of a negative number is not a real number.

c. The domain of the expression

$$\frac{x + 2}{x - 3}$$

is the set of all real numbers except $x = 3$, which would result in division by zero, which is undefined.

CHECK*Point* Now try Exercise 7.

The quotient of two algebraic expressions is a *fractional expression*. Moreover, the quotient of two *polynomials* such as

$$\frac{1}{x}, \quad \frac{2x - 1}{x + 1}, \quad \text{or} \quad \frac{x^2 - 1}{x^2 + 1}$$

is a **rational expression.**

Simplifying Rational Expressions

Recall that a fraction is in simplest form if its numerator and denominator have no factors in common aside from ± 1. To write a fraction in simplest form, divide out common factors.

$$\frac{a \cdot \cancel{c}}{b \cdot \cancel{c}} = \frac{a}{b}, \quad c \neq 0$$

The key to success in simplifying rational expressions lies in your ability to *factor* polynomials. When simplifying rational expressions, be sure to factor each polynomial completely before concluding that the numerator and denominator have no factors in common.

Example 2 Simplifying a Rational Expression

Write $\dfrac{x^2 + 4x - 12}{3x - 6}$ in simplest form.

Solution

$$\frac{x^2 + 4x - 12}{3x - 6} = \frac{(x + 6)\cancel{(x - 2)}}{3\cancel{(x - 2)}} \qquad \text{Factor completely.}$$

$$= \frac{x + 6}{3}, \quad x \neq 2 \qquad \text{Divide out common factors.}$$

Note that the original expression is undefined when $x = 2$ (because division by zero is undefined). To make sure that the simplified expression is *equivalent* to the original expression, you must restrict the domain of the simplified expression by excluding the value $x = 2$.

WARNING/CAUTION

In Example 2, do not make the mistake of trying to simplify further by dividing out terms.

$$\frac{\cancel{x + 6}}{\cancel{3}} = \frac{x + \cancel{6}}{\cancel{3}} = x + 2$$

Remember that to simplify fractions, divide out common *factors*, not terms.

CHECKPoint Now try Exercise 33.

Sometimes it may be necessary to change the sign of a factor by factoring out (-1) to simplify a rational expression, as shown in Example 3.

Example 3 Simplifying Rational Expressions

Write $\dfrac{12 + x - x^2}{2x^2 - 9x + 4}$ in simplest form.

Solution

$$\frac{12 + x - x^2}{2x^2 - 9x + 4} = \frac{(4 - x)(3 + x)}{(2x - 1)(x - 4)} \qquad \text{Factor completely.}$$

$$= \frac{-\cancel{(x - 4)}(3 + x)}{(2x - 1)\cancel{(x - 4)}} \qquad (4 - x) = -(x - 4)$$

$$= -\frac{3 + x}{2x - 1}, \quad x \neq 4 \qquad \text{Divide out common factors.}$$

CHECKPoint Now try Exercise 39.

In this text, when a rational expression is written, the domain is usually not listed with the expression. It is *implied* that the real numbers that make the denominator zero are excluded from the expression. Also, when performing operations with rational expressions, this text follows the convention of listing *by the simplified expression* all values of x that must be specifically excluded from the domain in order to make the domains of the simplified and original expressions agree. In Example 3, for instance, the restriction $x \neq 4$ is listed with the simplified expression to make the two domains agree. Note that the value $x = \frac{1}{2}$ is excluded from *both* domains, so it is not necessary to list this value.

Operations with Rational Expressions

To multiply or divide rational expressions, use the properties of fractions discussed in Appendix A.1. Recall that to divide fractions, you invert the divisor and multiply.

Example 4 Multiplying Rational Expressions

$$\frac{2x^2+x-6}{x^2+4x-5} \cdot \frac{x^3-3x^2+2x}{4x^2-6x} = \frac{(2x-3)(x+2)}{(x+5)(x-1)} \cdot \frac{x(x-2)(x-1)}{2x(2x-3)}$$

$$= \frac{(x+2)(x-2)}{2(x+5)}, \quad x \neq 0, x \neq 1, x \neq \tfrac{3}{2}$$

CHECK Point Now try Exercise 53.

In Example 4, the restrictions $x \neq 0$, $x \neq 1$, and $x \neq \frac{3}{2}$ are listed with the simplified expression in order to make the two domains agree. Note that the value $x = -5$ is excluded from both domains, so it is not necessary to list this value.

Example 5 Dividing Rational Expressions

$$\frac{x^3-8}{x^2-4} \div \frac{x^2+2x+4}{x^3+8} = \frac{x^3-8}{x^2-4} \cdot \frac{x^3+8}{x^2+2x+4} \qquad \text{Invert and multiply.}$$

$$= \frac{(x-2)(x^2+2x+4)}{(x+2)(x-2)} \cdot \frac{(x+2)(x^2-2x+4)}{(x^2+2x+4)}$$

$$= x^2-2x+4, \quad x \neq \pm 2 \qquad \text{Divide out common factors.}$$

CHECK Point Now try Exercise 55.

To add or subtract rational expressions, you can use the LCD (least common denominator) method or the *basic definition*

$$\frac{a}{b} \pm \frac{c}{d} = \frac{ad \pm bc}{bd}, \quad b \neq 0, d \neq 0. \qquad \text{Basic definition}$$

This definition provides an efficient way of adding or subtracting *two* fractions that have no common factors in their denominators.

Example 6 Subtracting Rational Expressions

$$\frac{x}{x-3} - \frac{2}{3x+4} = \frac{x(3x+4)-2(x-3)}{(x-3)(3x+4)} \qquad \text{Basic definition}$$

$$= \frac{3x^2+4x-2x+6}{(x-3)(3x+4)} \qquad \text{Distributive Property}$$

$$= \frac{3x^2+2x+6}{(x-3)(3x+4)} \qquad \text{Combine like terms.}$$

CHECK Point Now try Exercise 65.

WARNING / CAUTION

When subtracting rational expressions, remember to distribute the negative sign to all the terms in the quantity that is being subtracted.

For three or more fractions, or for fractions with a repeated factor in the denominators, the LCD method works well. Recall that the least common denominator of several fractions consists of the product of all prime factors in the denominators, with each factor given the highest power of its occurrence in any denominator. Here is a numerical example.

$$\begin{aligned}\frac{1}{6}+\frac{3}{4}-\frac{2}{3}&=\frac{1\cdot 2}{6\cdot 2}+\frac{3\cdot 3}{4\cdot 3}-\frac{2\cdot 4}{3\cdot 4} && \text{The LCD is 12.}\\ &=\frac{2}{12}+\frac{9}{12}-\frac{8}{12}\\ &=\frac{3}{12}\\ &=\frac{1}{4}\end{aligned}$$

Sometimes the numerator of the answer has a factor in common with the denominator. In such cases the answer should be simplified. For instance, in the example above, $\frac{3}{12}$ was simplified to $\frac{1}{4}$.

Example 7 Combining Rational Expressions: The LCD Method

Perform the operations and simplify.

$$\frac{3}{x-1}-\frac{2}{x}+\frac{x+3}{x^2-1}$$

Solution

Using the factored denominators $(x-1)$, x, and $(x+1)(x-1)$, you can see that the LCD is $x(x+1)(x-1)$.

$$\begin{aligned}\frac{3}{x-1}-\frac{2}{x}+\frac{x+3}{(x+1)(x-1)}&=\frac{3(x)(x+1)}{x(x+1)(x-1)}-\frac{2(x+1)(x-1)}{x(x+1)(x-1)}+\frac{(x+3)(x)}{x(x+1)(x-1)}\\ &=\frac{3(x)(x+1)-2(x+1)(x-1)+(x+3)(x)}{x(x+1)(x-1)}\\ &=\frac{3x^2+3x-2x^2+2+x^2+3x}{x(x+1)(x-1)} && \text{Distributive Property}\\ &=\frac{3x^2-2x^2+x^2+3x+3x+2}{x(x+1)(x-1)} && \text{Group like terms.}\\ &=\frac{2x^2+6x+2}{x(x+1)(x-1)} && \text{Combine like terms.}\\ &=\frac{2(x^2+3x+1)}{x(x+1)(x-1)} && \text{Factor.}\end{aligned}$$

CHECKPoint Now try Exercise 67.

Complex Fractions and the Difference Quotient

Fractional expressions with separate fractions in the numerator, denominator, or both are called **complex fractions.** Here are two examples.

$$\frac{\left(\frac{1}{x}\right)}{x^2+1} \quad \text{and} \quad \frac{\left(\frac{1}{x}\right)}{\left(\frac{1}{x^2+1}\right)}$$

To simplify a complex fraction, combine the fractions in the numerator into a single fraction and then combine the fractions in the denominator into a single fraction. Then invert the denominator and multiply.

Example 8 **Simplifying a Complex Fraction**

$$\frac{\left(\frac{2}{x}-3\right)}{\left(1-\frac{1}{x-1}\right)} = \frac{\left[\frac{2-3(x)}{x}\right]}{\left[\frac{1(x-1)-1}{x-1}\right]} \qquad \text{Combine fractions.}$$

$$= \frac{\left(\frac{2-3x}{x}\right)}{\left(\frac{x-2}{x-1}\right)} \qquad \text{Simplify.}$$

$$= \frac{2-3x}{x}\cdot\frac{x-1}{x-2} \qquad \text{Invert and multiply.}$$

$$= \frac{(2-3x)(x-1)}{x(x-2)}, \quad x \neq 1$$

CHECK*Point* Now try Exercise 73.

Another way to simplify a complex fraction is to multiply its numerator and denominator by the LCD of all fractions in its numerator and denominator. This method is applied to the fraction in Example 8 as follows.

$$\frac{\left(\frac{2}{x}-3\right)}{\left(1-\frac{1}{x-1}\right)} = \frac{\left(\frac{2}{x}-3\right)}{\left(1-\frac{1}{x-1}\right)}\cdot\frac{x(x-1)}{x(x-1)} \qquad \text{LCD is } x(x-1).$$

$$= \frac{\left(\frac{2-3x}{\cancel{x}}\right)\cdot \cancel{x}(x-1)}{\left(\frac{x-2}{\cancel{x-1}}\right)\cdot x\cancel{(x-1)}}$$

$$= \frac{(2-3x)(x-1)}{x(x-2)}, \quad x \neq 1$$

The next three examples illustrate some methods for simplifying rational expressions involving negative exponents and radicals. These types of expressions occur frequently in calculus.

To simplify an expression with negative exponents, one method is to begin by factoring out the common factor with the *smaller* exponent. Remember that when factoring, you *subtract* exponents. For instance, in $3x^{-5/2} + 2x^{-3/2}$ the smaller exponent is $-\frac{5}{2}$ and the common factor is $x^{-5/2}$.

$$\begin{aligned}3x^{-5/2} + 2x^{-3/2} &= x^{-5/2}[3(1) + 2x^{-3/2-(-5/2)}]\\ &= x^{-5/2}(3 + 2x^{1})\\ &= \frac{3 + 2x}{x^{5/2}}\end{aligned}$$

Example 9 Simplifying an Expression

Simplify the following expression containing negative exponents.

$$x(1 - 2x)^{-3/2} + (1 - 2x)^{-1/2}$$

Solution

Begin by factoring out the common factor with the *smaller exponent.*

$$\begin{aligned}x(1 - 2x)^{-3/2} + (1 - 2x)^{-1/2} &= (1 - 2x)^{-3/2}[x + (1 - 2x)^{(-1/2)-(-3/2)}]\\ &= (1 - 2x)^{-3/2}[x + (1 - 2x)^{1}]\\ &= \frac{1 - x}{(1 - 2x)^{3/2}}\end{aligned}$$

CHECKPoint Now try Exercise 81.

A second method for simplifying an expression with negative exponents is shown in the next example.

Example 10 Simplifying an Expression with Negative Exponents

$$\begin{aligned}&\frac{(4 - x^2)^{1/2} + x^2(4 - x^2)^{-1/2}}{4 - x^2}\\ &= \frac{(4 - x^2)^{1/2} + x^2(4 - x^2)^{-1/2}}{4 - x^2} \cdot \frac{(4 - x^2)^{1/2}}{(4 - x^2)^{1/2}}\\ &= \frac{(4 - x^2)^{1} + x^2(4 - x^2)^{0}}{(4 - x^2)^{3/2}}\\ &= \frac{4 - x^2 + x^2}{(4 - x^2)^{3/2}}\\ &= \frac{4}{(4 - x^2)^{3/2}}\end{aligned}$$

CHECKPoint Now try Exercise 83.

Example 11 Rewriting a Difference Quotient

The following expression from calculus is an example of a *difference quotient*.

$$\frac{\sqrt{x+h}-\sqrt{x}}{h}$$

Rewrite this expression by rationalizing its numerator.

Solution

$$\frac{\sqrt{x+h}-\sqrt{x}}{h} = \frac{\sqrt{x+h}-\sqrt{x}}{h} \cdot \frac{\sqrt{x+h}+\sqrt{x}}{\sqrt{x+h}+\sqrt{x}}$$

$$= \frac{(\sqrt{x+h})^2-(\sqrt{x})^2}{h(\sqrt{x+h}+\sqrt{x})}$$

$$= \frac{h}{h(\sqrt{x+h}+\sqrt{x})}$$

$$= \frac{1}{\sqrt{x+h}+\sqrt{x}}, \quad h \neq 0$$

Algebra Help

You can review the techniques for rationalizing a numerator in Appendix A.2.

Notice that the original expression is undefined when $h = 0$. So, you must exclude $h = 0$ from the domain of the simplified expression so that the expressions are equivalent.

CHECKPoint Now try Exercise 89.

Difference quotients, such as that in Example 11, occur frequently in calculus. Often, they need to be rewritten in an equivalent form that can be evaluated when $h = 0$. Note that the equivalent form is not simpler than the original form, but it has the advantage that it is defined when $h = 0$.

A.4 EXERCISES

See www.CalcChat.com for worked-out solutions to odd-numbered exercises.

VOCABULARY: Fill in the blanks.

1. The set of real numbers for which an algebraic expression is defined is the domain of the expression.
2. The quotient of two algebraic expressions is a fractional expression and the quotient of two polynomials is a rational expression.
3. Fractional expressions with separate fractions in the numerator, denominator, or both are called complex fractions.
4. To simplify an expression with negative exponents, it is possible to begin by factoring out the common factor with the smaller exponent.
5. Two algebraic expressions that have the same domain and yield the same values for all numbers in their domains are called equivalent.
6. An important rational expression, such as $\frac{(x+h)^2 - x^2}{h}$, that occurs in calculus is called a difference quotient.

SKILLS AND APPLICATIONS

7–22. See margin.

In Exercises 7–22, find the domain of the expression.

7. $3x^2 - 4x + 7$
8. $2x^2 + 5x - 2$
9. $4x^3 + 3, \quad x \geq 0$
10. $6x^2 - 9, \quad x > 0$
11. $\dfrac{1}{3 - x}$
12. $\dfrac{x + 6}{3x + 2}$
13. $\dfrac{x^2 - 1}{x^2 - 2x + 1}$
14. $\dfrac{x^2 - 5x + 6}{x^2 - 4}$
15. $\dfrac{x^2 - 2x - 3}{x^2 - 6x + 9}$
16. $\dfrac{x^2 - x - 12}{x^2 - 8x + 16}$
17. $\sqrt{x + 7}$
18. $\sqrt{4 - x}$
19. $\sqrt{2x - 5}$
20. $\sqrt{4x + 5}$
21. $\dfrac{1}{\sqrt{x - 3}}$
22. $\dfrac{1}{\sqrt{x + 2}}$

In Exercises 23 and 24, find the missing factor in the numerator such that the two fractions are equivalent.

23. $\dfrac{5}{2x} = \dfrac{5(\quad)}{6x^2}$ $3x, \ x \neq 0$
24. $\dfrac{3}{4} = \dfrac{3(\quad)}{4(x + 1)}$ $(x + 1), \ x \neq -1$

In Exercises 25–42, write the rational expression in simplest form.

25. $\dfrac{15x^2}{10x}$ $\dfrac{3x}{2}, \ x \neq 0$
26. $\dfrac{18y^2}{60y^5}$ $\dfrac{3}{10y^3}$
27. $\dfrac{3xy}{xy + x}$ $\dfrac{3y}{y + 1}, \ x \neq 0$
28. $\dfrac{2x^2y}{xy - y}$ $\dfrac{2x^2}{x - 1}$
29. $\dfrac{4y - 8y^2}{10y - 5}$ $\dfrac{-4y}{5}, \ y \neq \dfrac{1}{2}$
30. $\dfrac{9x^2 + 9x}{2x + 2}$ $\dfrac{9x}{2}, \ x \neq -1$
31. $\dfrac{x - 5}{10 - 2x}$ $-\frac{1}{2}, \ x \neq 5$
32. $\dfrac{12 - 4x}{x - 3}$ $-4, \ x \neq 3$
33. $\dfrac{y^2 - 16}{y + 4}$ $y - 4, \ y \neq -4$
34. $\dfrac{x^2 - 25}{5 - x}$ $-(x + 5), \ x \neq 5$
35. $\dfrac{x^3 + 5x^2 + 6x}{x^2 - 4}$
36. $\dfrac{x^2 + 8x - 20}{x^2 + 11x + 10}$ 35–40. See margin.
37. $\dfrac{y^2 - 7y + 12}{y^2 + 3y - 18}$
38. $\dfrac{x^2 - 7x + 6}{x^2 + 11x + 10}$
39. $\dfrac{2 - x + 2x^2 - x^3}{x^2 - 4}$
40. $\dfrac{x^2 - 9}{x^3 + x^2 - 9x - 9}$
41. $\dfrac{z^3 - 8}{z^2 + 2z + 4}$ $z - 2$
42. $\dfrac{y^3 - 2y^2 - 3y}{y^3 + 1}$ $\dfrac{y(y - 3)}{y^2 - y + 1}, \ y \neq -1$

43. *Error Analysis* Describe the error.

$$\frac{5x^3}{2x^3 + 4} = \frac{5x^3}{2x^3 + 4} = \frac{5}{2 + 4} = \frac{5}{6}$$ (crossed out)

When simplifying fractions, you can only divide out common factors, not terms.

44. *Error Analysis* Describe the error.

$$\frac{x^3 + 25x}{x^2 - 2x - 15} = \frac{x(x^2 + 25)}{(x - 5)(x + 3)} = \frac{x(x + 5)(x - 5)}{(x - 5)(x + 3)} = \frac{x(x + 5)}{x + 3}$$ (crossed out)

The polynomial $x^2 + 25$ cannot be factored.

In Exercises 45 and 46, complete the table. What can you conclude? 45–46. See margin.

45.

x	0	1	2	3	4	5	6
$\dfrac{x^2 - 2x - 3}{x - 3}$							
$x + 1$							

46.

x	0	1	2	3	4	5	6
$\dfrac{x - 3}{x^2 - x - 6}$							
$\dfrac{1}{x + 2}$							

GEOMETRY In Exercises 47 and 48, find the ratio of the area of the shaded portion of the figure to the total area of the figure.

47.

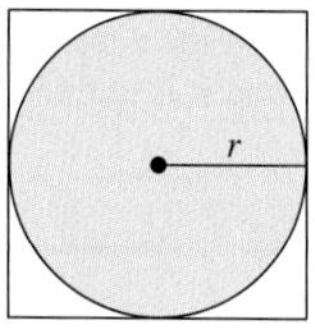

$\dfrac{\pi}{4}, \ r \neq 0$

48.

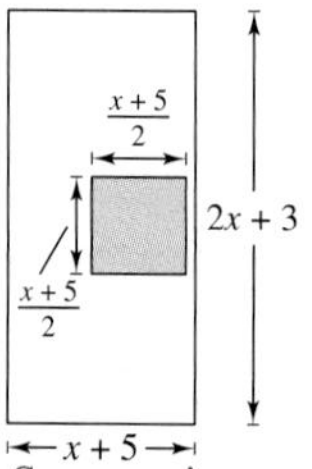

See margin.

In Exercises 49–56, perform the multiplication or division and simplify. 49–52. See margin.

49. $\dfrac{5}{x - 1} \cdot \dfrac{x - 1}{25(x - 2)}$
50. $\dfrac{x + 13}{x^3(3 - x)} \cdot \dfrac{x(x - 3)}{5}$
51. $\dfrac{r}{r - 1} \div \dfrac{r^2}{r^2 - 1}$
52. $\dfrac{4y - 16}{5y + 15} \div \dfrac{4 - y}{2y + 6}$
53. $\dfrac{t^2 - t - 6}{t^2 + 6t + 9} \cdot \dfrac{t + 3}{t^2 - 4}$ $\dfrac{t - 3}{(t + 3)(t - 2)}, \ t \neq -2$
54. $\dfrac{x^2 + xy - 2y^2}{x^3 + x^2y} \cdot \dfrac{x}{x^2 + 3xy + 2y^2}$ See below.
55. $\dfrac{x^2 - 36}{x} \div \dfrac{x^3 - 6x^2}{x^2 + x}$ $\dfrac{(x + 6)(x + 1)}{x^2}, \ x \neq 6, -1$
56. $\dfrac{x^2 - 14x + 49}{x^2 - 49} \div \dfrac{3x - 21}{x + 7}$ $\dfrac{1}{3}, \ x \neq \pm 7$

54. $\dfrac{x - y}{x(x + y)^2}, \ x \neq -2y$

7. All real numbers
8. All real numbers
9. All nonnegative real numbers
10. All positive real numbers
11. All real numbers x such that $x \neq 3$
12. All real numbers x such that $x \neq -\frac{2}{3}$
13. All real numbers x such that $x \neq 1$
14. All real numbers x such that $x \neq \pm 2$
15. All real numbers x such that $x \neq 3$
16. All real numbers x such that $x \neq 4$
17. All real numbers x such that $x \geq -7$
18. All real numbers x such that $x \leq 4$
19. All real numbers x such that $x \geq \frac{5}{2}$
20. All real numbers x such that $x \geq -\frac{5}{4}$
21. All real numbers x such that $x > 3$
22. All real numbers x such that $x > -2$

35. $\dfrac{x(x + 3)}{x - 2}, \ x \neq -2$
36. $\dfrac{x - 2}{x + 1}, \ x \neq -10$
37. $\dfrac{y - 4}{y + 6}, \ y \neq 3$
38. $\dfrac{(x - 6)(x - 1)}{(x + 10)(x + 1)}$
39. $\dfrac{-(x^2 + 1)}{(x + 2)}, \ x \neq 2$
40. $\dfrac{1}{x + 1}, \ x \neq \pm 3$

45–46. See below.

48. $\dfrac{x + 5}{4(2x + 3)}, \ x \neq -5$
49. $\dfrac{1}{5(x - 2)}, \ x \neq 1$
50. $-\dfrac{x + 13}{5x^2}, \ x \neq 3$
51. $\dfrac{r + 1}{r}, \ r \neq 1$
52. $-\dfrac{8}{5}, \ y \neq -3, 4$

45.

x	0	1	2	3	4	5	6
$\dfrac{x^2 - 2x - 3}{x - 3}$	1	2	3	Undef.	5	6	7
$x + 1$	1	2	3	4	5	6	7

The expressions are equivalent except at $x = 3$.

46.

x	0	1	2	3	4	5	6
$\dfrac{x - 3}{x^2 - x - 6}$	$\dfrac{1}{2}$	$\dfrac{1}{3}$	$\dfrac{1}{4}$	Undef.	$\dfrac{1}{6}$	$\dfrac{1}{7}$	$\dfrac{1}{8}$
$\dfrac{1}{x + 2}$	$\dfrac{1}{2}$	$\dfrac{1}{3}$	$\dfrac{1}{4}$	$\dfrac{1}{5}$	$\dfrac{1}{6}$	$\dfrac{1}{7}$	$\dfrac{1}{8}$

The expressions are equivalent except at $x = 3$.

In Exercises 57–68, perform the addition or subtraction and simplify. 57–64. See margin.

57. $6 - \dfrac{5}{x+3}$ **58.** $\dfrac{3}{x-1} - 5$

59. $\dfrac{5}{x-1} + \dfrac{x}{x-1}$ **60.** $\dfrac{2x-1}{x+3} + \dfrac{1-x}{x+3}$

61. $\dfrac{3}{x-2} + \dfrac{5}{2-x}$ **62.** $\dfrac{2x}{x-5} - \dfrac{5}{5-x}$

63. $\dfrac{4}{2x+1} - \dfrac{x}{x+2}$ **64.** $\dfrac{2}{x-3} + \dfrac{5x}{3x+4}$

65. $\dfrac{1}{x^2-x-2} - \dfrac{x}{x^2-5x+6}$ $\dfrac{x^2+3}{(x+1)(x-2)(x-3)}$

66. $\dfrac{2}{x^2-x-2} + \dfrac{10}{x^2+2x-8}$ $\dfrac{6(2x+3)}{(x-2)(x+1)(x+4)}$

67. $-\dfrac{1}{x} + \dfrac{2}{x^2+1} + \dfrac{1}{x^3+x}$ $\dfrac{2-x}{x^2+1},\ x \neq 0$

68. $\dfrac{2}{x+1} + \dfrac{2}{x-1} + \dfrac{1}{x^2-1}$ $\dfrac{4x+1}{(x-1)(x+1)}$

ERROR ANALYSIS In Exercises 69 and 70, describe the error. 69. Incorrect subtraction in the numerator

69. $\dfrac{x+4}{x+2} - \dfrac{3x-8}{x+2} = \dfrac{x+4-3x-8}{x+2} = \dfrac{-2x-4}{x+2} = \dfrac{-2(x+2)}{x+2} = -2$

70. $\dfrac{6-x}{x(x+2)} + \dfrac{x+2}{x^2} + \dfrac{8}{x^2(x+2)}$
$= \dfrac{x(6-x)+(x+2)^2+8}{x^2(x+2)}$
$= \dfrac{6x-x^2+x^2+4+8}{x^2(x+2)}$
$= \dfrac{6(x+2)}{x^2(x+2)} = \dfrac{6}{x^2}$

Incorrect expansion of $(x+2)^2$ in the numerator

In Exercises 71–76, simplify the complex fraction.

71. $\dfrac{\left(\dfrac{x}{2}-1\right)}{(x-2)}$ $\dfrac{1}{2},\ x \neq 2$ **72.** $\dfrac{(x-4)}{\left(\dfrac{x}{4}-\dfrac{4}{x}\right)}$ $\dfrac{4x}{x+4},\ x \neq 0, 4$

73. $\dfrac{\left[\dfrac{x^2}{(x+1)^2}\right]}{\left[\dfrac{x}{(x+1)^3}\right]}$ $x(x+1),\ x \neq -1, 0$ **74.** $\dfrac{\left(\dfrac{x^2-1}{x}\right)}{\left[\dfrac{(x-1)^2}{x}\right]}$ $\dfrac{x+1}{x-1},\ x \neq 0$

75. $\dfrac{\left(\sqrt{x}-\dfrac{1}{2\sqrt{x}}\right)}{\sqrt{x}}$ $\dfrac{2x-1}{2x},\ x > 0$ **76.** $\dfrac{\left(\dfrac{t^2}{\sqrt{t^2+1}}-\sqrt{t^2+1}\right)}{t^2}$ $\dfrac{-1}{t^2\sqrt{t^2+1}}$

In Exercises 77–82, factor the expression by removing the common factor with the smaller exponent. 77–82. See margin.

77. $x^5 - 2x^{-2}$ **78.** $x^5 - 5x^{-3}$

79. $x^2(x^2+1)^{-5} - (x^2+1)^{-4}$

80. $2x(x-5)^{-3} - 4x^2(x-5)^{-4}$

81. $2x^2(x-1)^{1/2} - 5(x-1)^{-1/2}$

82. $4x^3(2x-1)^{3/2} - 2x(2x-1)^{-1/2}$

In Exercises 83 and 84, simplify the expression.

83. $\dfrac{3x^{1/3}-x^{-2/3}}{3x^{-2/3}}$ $\dfrac{3x-1}{3},\ x \neq 0$

84. $\dfrac{-x^3(1-x^2)^{-1/2}-2x(1-x^2)^{1/2}}{x^4}$ $\dfrac{x^2-2}{x^3(1-x^2)^{1/2}}$

In Exercises 85–88, simplify the difference quotient. 85–88. See margin.

85. $\dfrac{\left(\dfrac{1}{x+h}-\dfrac{1}{x}\right)}{h}$ **86.** $\dfrac{\left[\dfrac{1}{(x+h)^2}-\dfrac{1}{x^2}\right]}{h}$

87. $\dfrac{\left(\dfrac{1}{x+h-4}-\dfrac{1}{x-4}\right)}{h}$ **88.** $\dfrac{\left(\dfrac{x+h}{x+h+1}-\dfrac{x}{x+1}\right)}{h}$

In Exercises 89–94, simplify the difference quotient by rationalizing the numerator. 89–94. See margin.

89. $\dfrac{\sqrt{x+2}-\sqrt{x}}{2}$ **90.** $\dfrac{\sqrt{z-3}-\sqrt{z}}{3}$

91. $\dfrac{\sqrt{t+3}-\sqrt{3}}{t}$ **92.** $\dfrac{\sqrt{x+5}-\sqrt{5}}{x}$

93. $\dfrac{\sqrt{x+h+1}-\sqrt{x+1}}{h}$

94. $\dfrac{\sqrt{x+h-2}-\sqrt{x-2}}{h}$

PROBABILITY In Exercises 95 and 96, consider an experiment in which a marble is tossed into a box whose base is shown in the figure. The probability that the marble will come to rest in the shaded portion of the box is equal to the ratio of the shaded area to the total area of the figure. Find the probability. 95–96. See margin.

95.

96.

97. RATE A digital copier copies in color at a rate of 50 pages per minute.

(a) Find the time required to copy one page. $\frac{1}{50}$ min

57. $\dfrac{6x+13}{x+3}$

58. $\dfrac{8-5x}{x-1}$

59. $\dfrac{x+5}{x-1}$

60. $\dfrac{x}{x+3}$

61. $-\dfrac{2}{x-2}$

62. $\dfrac{2x+5}{x-5}$

63. $\dfrac{-2x^2+3x+8}{(2x+1)(x+2)}$

64. $\dfrac{5x^2-9x+8}{(x-3)(3x+4)}$

77. $\dfrac{x^7-2}{x^2}$

78. $\dfrac{x^8-5}{x^3}$

79. $\dfrac{-1}{(x^2+1)^5}$

80. $\dfrac{-2x(x+5)}{(x-5)^4}$

81. $\dfrac{2x^3-2x^2-5}{(x-1)^{1/2}}$

82. $\dfrac{4x^3(2x-1)^2-2x}{(2x-1)^{1/2}}$

85. $\dfrac{-1}{x(x+h)},\ h \neq 0$

86. $-\dfrac{2x+h}{x^2(x+h)^2},\ h \neq 0$

87. $\dfrac{-1}{(x-4)(x+h-4)},\ h \neq 0$

88. $\dfrac{1}{(x+h+1)(x+1)},\ h \neq 0$

89. $\dfrac{1}{\sqrt{x+2}+\sqrt{x}}$

90. $\dfrac{-1}{\sqrt{z-3}+\sqrt{z}}$

91. $\dfrac{1}{\sqrt{t+3}+\sqrt{3}},\ t \neq 0$

92. $\dfrac{1}{\sqrt{x+5}+\sqrt{5}},\ x \neq 0$

93. $\dfrac{1}{\sqrt{x+h+1}+\sqrt{x+1}},\ h \neq 0$

94. $\dfrac{1}{\sqrt{x+h-2}+\sqrt{x-2}},$ $h \neq 0$

95. $\dfrac{x}{2(2x+1)},\ x \neq 0$

96. $\dfrac{8(x+2)}{(x+4)^2},\ x \neq 0$

(b) Find the time required to copy x pages. $(x/50)$ min

(c) Find the time required to copy 120 pages. $\frac{120}{50} = 2.4$ min

98. RATE After working together for t hours on a common task, two workers have done fractional parts of the job equal to $t/3$ and $t/5$, respectively. What fractional part of the task has been completed? $\frac{8t}{15}$

FINANCE In Exercises 99 and 100, the formula that approximates the annual interest rate r of a monthly installment loan is given by

$$r = \frac{\left[\dfrac{24(NM - P)}{N}\right]}{\left(P + \dfrac{NM}{12}\right)}$$

where N is the total number of payments, M is the monthly payment, and P is the amount financed.

99. (a) Approximate the annual interest rate for a four-year car loan of \$20,000 that has monthly payments of \$475. 6.39%

(b) Simplify the expression for the annual interest rate r, and then rework part (a). See margin.

100. (a) Approximate the annual interest rate for a five-year car loan of \$28,000 that has monthly payments of \$525. 4.57%

(b) Simplify the expression for the annual interest rate r, and then rework part (a). See margin.

101. REFRIGERATION When food (at room temperature) is placed in a refrigerator, the time required for the food to cool depends on the amount of food, the air circulation in the refrigerator, the original temperature of the food, and the temperature of the refrigerator. The model that gives the temperature of food that has an original temperature of 75°F and is placed in a 40°F refrigerator is

$$T = 10\left(\frac{4t^2 + 16t + 75}{t^2 + 4t + 10}\right)$$

where T is the temperature (in degrees Fahrenheit) and t is the time (in hours).

(a) Complete the table. See margin.

t	0	2	4	6	8	10	12
T							

t	14	16	18	20	22
T					

(b) What value of T does the mathematical model appear to be approaching?
The model is approaching a T-value of 40.

102. INTERACTIVE MONEY MANAGEMENT The table shows the projected numbers of U.S. households (in millions) banking online and paying bills online from 2002 through 2007. (Source: eMarketer; Forrester Research)

Year	Banking	Paying Bills
2002	21.9	13.7
2003	26.8	17.4
2004	31.5	20.9
2005	35.0	23.9
2006	40.0	26.7
2007	45.0	29.1

Mathematical models for these data are

$$\text{Number banking online} = \frac{-0.728t^2 + 23.81t - 0.3}{-0.049t^2 + 0.61t + 1.0}$$

and

$$\text{Number paying bills online} = \frac{4.39t + 5.5}{0.002t^2 + 0.01t + 1.0}$$

where t represents the year, with $t = 2$ corresponding to 2002. See margin.

(a) Using the models, create a table to estimate the projected numbers of households banking online and the projected numbers of households paying bills online for the given years.

(b) Compare the values given by the models with the actual data.

(c) Determine a model for the ratio of the projected number of households paying bills online to the projected number of households banking online.

(d) Use the model from part (c) to find the ratios for the given years. Interpret your results.

EXPLORATION

103–104. See margin.

TRUE OR FALSE? In Exercises 103 and 104, determine whether the statement is true or false. Justify your answer.

103. $\dfrac{x^{2n} - 1^{2n}}{x^n - 1^n} = x^n + 1^n$

104. $\dfrac{x^2 - 3x + 2}{x - 1} = x - 2$, for all values of x

105. THINK ABOUT IT How do you determine whether a rational expression is in simplest form? See margin.

106. CAPSTONE In your own words, explain how to divide rational expressions. Invert the divisor and multiply the rational expressions. Then divide out the common factors.

99. (b) $\dfrac{288(MN - P)}{N(MN + 12P)}$; 6.39%

100. (b) $\dfrac{288(MN - P)}{N(MN + 12P)}$; 4.57%

101. (a) See below.

102. (a)

Year, t	Banking (millions)	Paying bills (millions)
2002	21.9	13.9
2003	27.0	17.8
2004	31.4	21.5
2005	35.6	25.0
2006	40.2	28.1
2007	45.6	31.0

(b) The estimates are fairly close to the actual numbers of households.

(c) See below.

(d)

Year	2002	2003	2004
Ratio	0.6333	0.6592	0.6861

Year	2005	2006	2007
Ratio	0.7013	0.7003	0.6812

Interpretations will vary.

103. False. In order for the simplified expression to be equivalent to the original expression, the domain of the simplified expression needs to be restricted. If n is even, $x \neq -1, 1$. If n is odd, $x \neq 1$.

104. False. The two expressions are equivalent for all values of x such that $x \neq 1$.

105. Completely factor each polynomial in the numerator and in the denominator. Then conclude that there are no common factors.

101. (a)

t	0	2	4	6	8	10	12	14	16	18	20	22
T	75	55.9	48.3	45	43.3	42.3	41.7	41.3	41.1	40.9	40.7	40.6

102. (c) $\text{Ratio} = \dfrac{-0.2151t^3 + 2.408t^2 + 7.75t + 5.5}{-0.00146t^4 + 0.0403t^3 - 0.491t^2 + 23.81t - 0.3}$

A.5 SOLVING EQUATIONS

What you should learn

- Identify different types of equations.
- Solve linear equations in one variable and equations that lead to linear equations.
- Solve quadratic equations by factoring, extracting square roots, completing the square, and using the Quadratic Formula.
- Solve polynomial equations of degree three or greater.
- Solve equations involving radicals.
- Solve equations with absolute values.
- Use common formulas to solve real-life problems.

Why you should learn it

Linear equations are used in many real-life applications. For example, in Exercises 155 and 156 on pages A61 and A62, linear equations can be used to model the relationship between the length of a thigh bone and the height of a person, helping researchers learn about ancient cultures.

Equations and Solutions of Equations

An **equation** in x is a statement that two algebraic expressions are equal. For example

$$3x - 5 = 7,\ x^2 - x - 6 = 0,\ \text{and}\ \sqrt{2x} = 4$$

are equations. To **solve** an equation in x means to find all values of x for which the equation is true. Such values are **solutions.** For instance, $x = 4$ is a solution of the equation

$$3x - 5 = 7$$

because $3(4) - 5 = 7$ is a true statement.

The solutions of an equation depend on the kinds of numbers being considered. For instance, in the set of rational numbers, $x^2 = 10$ has no solution because there is no rational number whose square is 10. However, in the set of real numbers, the equation has the two solutions $x = \sqrt{10}$ and $x = -\sqrt{10}$.

An equation that is true for *every* real number in the *domain* of the variable is called an **identity.** The domain is the set of all real numbers for which the equation is defined. For example

$$x^2 - 9 = (x + 3)(x - 3) \qquad \text{Identity}$$

is an identity because it is a true statement for any real value of x. The equation

$$\frac{x}{3x^2} = \frac{1}{3x} \qquad \text{Identity}$$

where $x \neq 0$, is an identity because it is true for any nonzero real value of x.

An equation that is true for just *some* (or even none) of the real numbers in the domain of the variable is called a **conditional equation.** For example, the equation

$$x^2 - 9 = 0 \qquad \text{Conditional equation}$$

is conditional because $x = 3$ and $x = -3$ are the only values in the domain that satisfy the equation. The equation $2x - 4 = 2x + 1$ is conditional because there are no real values of x for which the equation is true.

Linear Equations in One Variable

Definition of a Linear Equation

A **linear equation in one variable** x is an equation that can be written in the standard form

$$ax + b = 0$$

where a and b are real numbers with $a \neq 0$.

Study Tip

Note that some linear equations in nonstandard form have *no solution* or *infinitely many solutions*. For instance,

$$x = x + 1$$

has no solution because it is not true for any value of x. Because

$$5x + 10 = 5(x + 2)$$

is true for any value of x, the equation has infinitely many solutions.

A linear equation in one variable, written in standard form, always has *exactly one* solution. To see this, consider the following steps.

$ax + b = 0$	Original equation, with $a \neq 0$
$ax = -b$	Subtract b from each side.
$x = -\dfrac{b}{a}$	Divide each side by a.

To solve a conditional equation in x, isolate x on one side of the equation by a sequence of **equivalent** (and usually simpler) **equations,** each having the same solution(s) as the original equation. The operations that yield equivalent equations come from the Substitution Principle (see Appendix A.1) and simplification techniques.

Generating Equivalent Equations

An equation can be transformed into an *equivalent equation* by one or more of the following steps.

	Given Equation	*Equivalent Equation*
1. Remove symbols of grouping, combine like terms, or simplify fractions on one or both sides of the equation.	$2x - x = 4$	$x = 4$
2. Add (or subtract) the same quantity to (from) *each* side of the equation.	$x + 1 = 6$	$x = 5$
3. Multiply (or divide) *each* side of the equation by the same *nonzero* quantity.	$2x = 6$	$x = 3$
4. Interchange the two sides of the equation.	$2 = x$	$x = 2$

Study Tip

After solving an equation, you should check each solution in the original equation. For instance, you can check the solution of Example 1(a) as follows.

$3x - 6 = 0$	Write original equation.
$3(2) - 6 \stackrel{?}{=} 0$	Substitute 2 for x.
$0 = 0$	Solution checks. ✓

Try checking the solution of Example 1(b).

Example 1 Solving a Linear Equation

a. $3x - 6 = 0$	Original equation
$3x = 6$	Add 6 to each side.
$x = 2$	Divide each side by 3.
b. $5x + 4 = 3x - 8$	Original equation
$2x + 4 = -8$	Subtract $3x$ from each side.
$2x = -12$	Subtract 4 from each side.
$x = -6$	Divide each side by 2.

CHECKPoint Now try Exercise 15.

> ### *Study Tip*
> An equation with a *single fraction* on each side can be cleared of denominators by **cross multiplying.** To do this, multiply the left numerator by the right denominator and the right numerator by the left denominator as follows.
>
> $\frac{a}{b} = \frac{c}{d}$ Original equation
>
> $ad = cb$ Cross multiply.

To solve an equation involving fractional expressions, find the least common denominator (LCD) of all terms and multiply every term by the LCD. This process will clear the original equation of fractions and produce a simpler equation.

Example 2 An Equation Involving Fractional Expressions

Solve $\frac{x}{3} + \frac{3x}{4} = 2.$

Solution

$\frac{x}{3} + \frac{3x}{4} = 2$	Write original equation.
$(12)\frac{x}{3} + (12)\frac{3x}{4} = (12)2$	Multiply each term by the LCD of 12.
$4x + 9x = 24$	Divide out and multiply.
$13x = 24$	Combine like terms.
$x = \frac{24}{13}$	Divide each side by 13.

The solution is $x = \frac{24}{13}$. Check this in the original equation.

CHECK*Point* Now try Exercise 23.

When multiplying or dividing an equation by a *variable* quantity, it is possible to introduce an extraneous solution. An **extraneous solution** is one that does not satisfy the original equation. Therefore, it is essential that you check your solutions.

Example 3 An Equation with an Extraneous Solution

Solve $\frac{1}{x-2} = \frac{3}{x+2} - \frac{6x}{x^2-4}.$

Solution

The LCD is $x^2 - 4$, or $(x + 2)(x - 2)$. Multiply each term by this LCD.

$$\frac{1}{x-2}(x+2)(x-2) = \frac{3}{x+2}(x+2)(x-2) - \frac{6x}{x^2-4}(x+2)(x-2)$$

$$x + 2 = 3(x - 2) - 6x, \quad x \neq \pm 2$$

$$x + 2 = 3x - 6 - 6x$$

$$x + 2 = -3x - 6$$

$4x = -8$ ⇨ $x = -2$ Extraneous solution

In the original equation, $x = -2$ yields a denominator of zero. So, $x = -2$ is an extraneous solution, and the original equation has *no solution*.

CHECK*Point* Now try Exercise 35.

> ### *Study Tip*
> Recall that the least common denominator of two or more fractions consists of the product of all prime factors in the denominators, with each factor given the highest power of its occurrence in any denominator. For instance, in Example 3, by factoring each denominator you can determine that the LCD is $(x + 2)(x - 2)$.

Quadratic Equations

A **quadratic equation** in x is an equation that can be written in the general form

$$ax^2 + bx + c = 0$$

where a, b, and c are real numbers, with $a \neq 0$. A quadratic equation in x is also known as a **second-degree polynomial equation** in x.

You should be familiar with the following four methods of solving quadratic equations.

Solving a Quadratic Equation

Factoring: If $ab = 0$, then $a = 0$ or $b = 0$.

Example:

$$x^2 - x - 6 = 0$$
$$(x - 3)(x + 2) = 0$$
$$x - 3 = 0 \quad \Rightarrow \quad x = 3$$
$$x + 2 = 0 \quad \Rightarrow \quad x = -2$$

Square Root Principle: If $u^2 = c$, where $c > 0$, then $u = \pm\sqrt{c}$.

Example:

$$(x + 3)^2 = 16$$
$$x + 3 = \pm 4$$
$$x = -3 \pm 4$$
$$x = 1 \quad \text{or} \quad x = -7$$

Completing the Square: If $x^2 + bx = c$, then

$$x^2 + bx + \left(\frac{b}{2}\right)^2 = c + \left(\frac{b}{2}\right)^2 \qquad \text{Add } \left(\frac{b}{2}\right)^2 \text{ to each side.}$$
$$\left(x + \frac{b}{2}\right)^2 = c + \frac{b^2}{4}.$$

Example:

$$x^2 + 6x = 5$$
$$x^2 + 6x + 3^2 = 5 + 3^2 \qquad \text{Add } \left(\frac{6}{2}\right)^2 \text{ to each side.}$$
$$(x + 3)^2 = 14$$
$$x + 3 = \pm\sqrt{14}$$
$$x = -3 \pm \sqrt{14}$$

Quadratic Formula: If $ax^2 + bx + c = 0$, then $x = \dfrac{-b \pm \sqrt{b^2 - 4ac}}{2a}$.

Example:

$$2x^2 + 3x - 1 = 0$$
$$x = \frac{-3 \pm \sqrt{3^2 - 4(2)(-1)}}{2(2)}$$
$$= \frac{-3 \pm \sqrt{17}}{4}$$

Study Tip

The Square Root Principle is also referred to as *extracting square roots*.

Study Tip

You can solve every quadratic equation by completing the square or using the Quadratic Formula.

Example 4 Solving a Quadratic Equation by Factoring

a. $2x^2 + 9x + 7 = 3$ Original equation

$2x^2 + 9x + 4 = 0$ Write in general form.

$(2x + 1)(x + 4) = 0$ Factor.

$2x + 1 = 0 \Rightarrow x = -\frac{1}{2}$ Set 1st factor equal to 0.

$x + 4 = 0 \Rightarrow x = -4$ Set 2nd factor equal to 0.

The solutions are $x = -\frac{1}{2}$ and $x = -4$. Check these in the original equation.

b. $6x^2 - 3x = 0$ Original equation

$3x(2x - 1) = 0$ Factor.

$3x = 0 \Rightarrow x = 0$ Set 1st factor equal to 0.

$2x - 1 = 0 \Rightarrow x = \frac{1}{2}$ Set 2nd factor equal to 0.

The solutions are $x = 0$ and $x = \frac{1}{2}$. Check these in the original equation.

CHECK*Point* Now try Exercise 49.

Note that the method of solution in Example 4 is based on the Zero-Factor Property from Appendix A.1. Be sure you see that this property works *only* for equations written in general form (in which the right side of the equation is zero). So, all terms must be collected on one side *before* factoring. For instance, in the equation $(x - 5)(x + 2) = 8$, it is *incorrect* to set each factor equal to 8. Try to solve this equation correctly.

Example 5 Extracting Square Roots

Solve each equation by extracting square roots.

a. $4x^2 = 12$ **b.** $(x - 3)^2 = 7$

Solution

a. $4x^2 = 12$ Write original equation.

$x^2 = 3$ Divide each side by 4.

$x = \pm\sqrt{3}$ Extract square roots.

When you take the square root of a variable expression, you must account for both positive and negative solutions. So, the solutions are $x = \sqrt{3}$ and $x = -\sqrt{3}$. Check these in the original equation.

b. $(x - 3)^2 = 7$ Write original equation.

$x - 3 = \pm\sqrt{7}$ Extract square roots.

$x = 3 \pm \sqrt{7}$ Add 3 to each side.

The solutions are $x = 3 \pm \sqrt{7}$. Check these in the original equation.

CHECK*Point* Now try Exercise 65.

When solving quadratic equations by completing the square, you must add $(b/2)^2$ to *each side* in order to maintain equality. If the leading coefficient is *not* 1, you must divide each side of the equation by the leading coefficient *before* completing the square, as shown in Example 7.

Example 6 Completing the Square: Leading Coefficient Is 1

Solve $x^2 + 2x - 6 = 0$ by completing the square.

Solution

$$x^2 + 2x - 6 = 0 \qquad \text{Write original equation.}$$

$$x^2 + 2x = 6 \qquad \text{Add 6 to each side.}$$

$$x^2 + 2x + 1^2 = 6 + 1^2 \qquad \text{Add } 1^2 \text{ to each side.}$$

(half of 2)^2

$$(x + 1)^2 = 7 \qquad \text{Simplify.}$$

$$x + 1 = \pm\sqrt{7} \qquad \text{Take square root of each side.}$$

$$x = -1 \pm \sqrt{7} \qquad \text{Subtract 1 from each side.}$$

The solutions are $x = -1 \pm \sqrt{7}$. Check these in the original equation.

CHECKPoint Now try Exercise 73.

Example 7 Completing the Square: Leading Coefficient Is Not 1

$$3x^2 - 4x - 5 = 0 \qquad \text{Original equation}$$

$$3x^2 - 4x = 5 \qquad \text{Add 5 to each side.}$$

$$x^2 - \frac{4}{3}x = \frac{5}{3} \qquad \text{Divide each side by 3.}$$

$$x^2 - \frac{4}{3}x + \left(-\frac{2}{3}\right)^2 = \frac{5}{3} + \left(-\frac{2}{3}\right)^2 \qquad \text{Add } \left(-\tfrac{2}{3}\right)^2 \text{ to each side.}$$

(half of $-\frac{4}{3}$)^2

$$x^2 - \frac{4}{3}x + \frac{4}{9} = \frac{19}{9} \qquad \text{Simplify.}$$

$$\left(x - \frac{2}{3}\right)^2 = \frac{19}{9} \qquad \text{Perfect square trinomial}$$

$$x - \frac{2}{3} = \pm\frac{\sqrt{19}}{3} \qquad \text{Extract square roots.}$$

$$x = \frac{2}{3} \pm \frac{\sqrt{19}}{3} \qquad \text{Solutions}$$

CHECKPoint Now try Exercise 77.

WARNING / CAUTION

When using the Quadratic Formula, remember that *before* the formula can be applied, you must first write the quadratic equation in general form.

Example 8 The Quadratic Formula: Two Distinct Solutions

Use the Quadratic Formula to solve $x^2 + 3x = 9$.

Solution

$$x^2 + 3x = 9$$ Write original equation.

$$x^2 + 3x - 9 = 0$$ Write in general form.

$$x = \frac{-b \pm \sqrt{b^2 - 4ac}}{2a}$$ Quadratic Formula

$$x = \frac{-3 \pm \sqrt{(3)^2 - 4(1)(-9)}}{2(1)}$$ Substitute $a = 1$, $b = 3$, and $c = -9$.

$$x = \frac{-3 \pm \sqrt{45}}{2}$$ Simplify.

$$x = \frac{-3 \pm 3\sqrt{5}}{2}$$ Simplify.

The equation has two solutions:

$$x = \frac{-3 + 3\sqrt{5}}{2} \quad \text{and} \quad x = \frac{-3 - 3\sqrt{5}}{2}.$$

Check these in the original equation.

CHECK*Point* Now try Exercise 87.

Example 9 The Quadratic Formula: One Solution

Use the Quadratic Formula to solve $8x^2 - 24x + 18 = 0$.

Solution

$$8x^2 - 24x + 18 = 0$$ Write original equation.

$$4x^2 - 12x + 9 = 0$$ Divide out common factor of 2.

$$x = \frac{-b \pm \sqrt{b^2 - 4ac}}{2a}$$ Quadratic Formula

$$x = \frac{-(-12) \pm \sqrt{(-12)^2 - 4(4)(9)}}{2(4)}$$ Substitute $a = 4$, $b = -12$, and $c = 9$.

$$x = \frac{12 \pm \sqrt{0}}{8} = \frac{3}{2}$$ Simplify.

This quadratic equation has only one solution: $x = \frac{3}{2}$. Check this in the original equation.

CHECK*Point* Now try Exercise 91.

Note that Example 9 could have been solved without first dividing out a common factor of 2. Substituting $a = 8$, $b = -24$, and $c = 18$ into the Quadratic Formula produces the same result.

Polynomial Equations of Higher Degree

The methods used to solve quadratic equations can sometimes be extended to solve polynomial equations of higher degree.

WARNING/CAUTION

A common mistake that is made in solving equations such as the equation in Example 10 is to divide each side of the equation by the variable factor x^2. This loses the solution $x = 0$. When solving an equation, always write the equation in general form, then factor the equation and set each factor equal to zero. Do not divide each side of an equation by a variable factor in an attempt to simplify the equation.

Example 10 Solving a Polynomial Equation by Factoring

Solve $3x^4 = 48x^2$.

Solution

First write the polynomial equation in general form with zero on one side, factor the other side, and then set each factor equal to zero and solve.

$3x^4 = 48x^2$ Write original equation.

$3x^4 - 48x^2 = 0$ Write in general form.

$3x^2(x^2 - 16) = 0$ Factor out common factor.

$3x^2(x + 4)(x - 4) = 0$ Write in factored form.

$3x^2 = 0 \Rightarrow x = 0$ Set 1st factor equal to 0.

$x + 4 = 0 \Rightarrow x = -4$ Set 2nd factor equal to 0.

$x - 4 = 0 \Rightarrow x = 4$ Set 3rd factor equal to 0.

You can check these solutions by substituting in the original equation, as follows.

Check

$3(0)^4 = 48(0)^2$ 0 checks. ✓

$3(-4)^4 = 48(-4)^2$ −4 checks. ✓

$3(4)^4 = 48(4)^2$ 4 checks. ✓

So, you can conclude that the solutions are $x = 0$, $x = -4$, and $x = 4$.

CHECK*Point* Now try Exercise 113.

Example 11 Solving a Polynomial Equation by Factoring

Solve $x^3 - 3x^2 - 3x + 9 = 0$.

Solution

$x^3 - 3x^2 - 3x + 9 = 0$ Write original equation.

$x^2(x - 3) - 3(x - 3) = 0$ Factor by grouping.

$(x - 3)(x^2 - 3) = 0$ Distributive Property

$x - 3 = 0 \Rightarrow x = 3$ Set 1st factor equal to 0.

$x^2 - 3 = 0 \Rightarrow x = \pm\sqrt{3}$ Set 2nd factor equal to 0.

The solutions are $x = 3$, $x = \sqrt{3}$, and $x = -\sqrt{3}$. Check these in the original equation.

CHECK*Point* Now try Exercise 119.

Equations Involving Radicals

Operations such as squaring each side of an equation, raising each side of an equation to a rational power, and multiplying each side of an equation by a variable quantity all can introduce extraneous solutions. So, when you use any of these operations, checking your solutions is crucial.

Example 12 Solving Equations Involving Radicals

a.

$\sqrt{2x+7} - x = 2$	Original equation
$\sqrt{2x+7} = x + 2$	Isolate radical.
$2x + 7 = x^2 + 4x + 4$	Square each side.
$0 = x^2 + 2x - 3$	Write in general form.
$0 = (x+3)(x-1)$	Factor.
$x + 3 = 0 \quad \Rightarrow \quad x = -3$	Set 1st factor equal to 0.
$x - 1 = 0 \quad \Rightarrow \quad x = 1$	Set 2nd factor equal to 0.

By checking these values, you can determine that the only solution is $x = 1$.

b.

$\sqrt{2x-5} - \sqrt{x-3} = 1$	Original equation
$\sqrt{2x-5} = \sqrt{x-3} + 1$	Isolate $\sqrt{2x-5}$.
$2x - 5 = x - 3 + 2\sqrt{x-3} + 1$	Square each side.
$2x - 5 = x - 2 + 2\sqrt{x-3}$	Combine like terms.
$x - 3 = 2\sqrt{x-3}$	Isolate $2\sqrt{x-3}$.
$x^2 - 6x + 9 = 4(x-3)$	Square each side.
$x^2 - 10x + 21 = 0$	Write in general form.
$(x-3)(x-7) = 0$	Factor.
$x - 3 = 0 \quad \Rightarrow \quad x = 3$	Set 1st factor equal to 0.
$x - 7 = 0 \quad \Rightarrow \quad x = 7$	Set 2nd factor equal to 0.

The solutions are $x = 3$ and $x = 7$. Check these in the original equation.

CHECK Point Now try Exercise 129.

Study Tip

When an equation contains two radicals, it may not be possible to isolate both. In such cases, you may have to raise each side of the equation to a power at *two* different stages in the solution, as shown in Example 12(b).

Example 13 Solving an Equation Involving a Rational Exponent

$(x-4)^{2/3} = 25$	Original equation
$\sqrt[3]{(x-4)^2} = 25$	Rewrite in radical form.
$(x-4)^2 = 15{,}625$	Cube each side.
$x - 4 = \pm 125$	Take square root of each side.
$x = 129, \quad x = -121$	Add 4 to each side.

CHECK Point Now try Exercise 137.

Equations with Absolute Values

To solve an equation involving an absolute value, remember that the expression inside the absolute value signs can be positive or negative. This results in *two* separate equations, each of which must be solved. For instance, the equation

$$|x - 2| = 3$$

results in the two equations $x - 2 = 3$ and $-(x - 2) = 3$, which implies that the equation has two solutions: $x = 5$ and $x = -1$.

Example 14 Solving an Equation Involving Absolute Value

Solve $|x^2 - 3x| = -4x + 6$.

Solution

Because the variable expression inside the absolute value signs can be positive or negative, you must solve the following two equations.

First Equation

$x^2 - 3x = -4x + 6$ Use positive expression.

$x^2 + x - 6 = 0$ Write in general form.

$(x + 3)(x - 2) = 0$ Factor.

$x + 3 = 0 \Rightarrow x = -3$ Set 1st factor equal to 0.

$x - 2 = 0 \Rightarrow x = 2$ Set 2nd factor equal to 0.

Second Equation

$-(x^2 - 3x) = -4x + 6$ Use negative expression.

$x^2 - 7x + 6 = 0$ Write in general form.

$(x - 1)(x - 6) = 0$ Factor.

$x - 1 = 0 \Rightarrow x = 1$ Set 1st factor equal to 0.

$x - 6 = 0 \Rightarrow x = 6$ Set 2nd factor equal to 0.

Check

$|(-3)^2 - 3(-3)| \stackrel{?}{=} -4(-3) + 6$ Substitute -3 for x.

$18 = 18$ -3 checks. ✓

$|(2)^2 - 3(2)| \stackrel{?}{=} -4(2) + 6$ Substitute 2 for x.

$2 \neq -2$ 2 does not check.

$|(1)^2 - 3(1)| \stackrel{?}{=} -4(1) + 6$ Substitute 1 for x.

$2 = 2$ 1 checks. ✓

$|(6)^2 - 3(6)| \stackrel{?}{=} -4(6) + 6$ Substitute 6 for x.

$18 \neq -18$ 6 does not check.

The solutions are $x = -3$ and $x = 1$.

CHECKPoint Now try Exercise 151.

Common Formulas

The following geometric formulas are used at various times throughout this course. For your convenience, some of these formulas along with several others are also provided on the inside cover of this text.

Common Formulas for Area A, Perimeter P, Circumference C, and Volume V

Rectangle	*Circle*	*Triangle*	*Rectangular Solid*	*Circular Cylinder*	*Sphere*
$A = lw$	$A = \pi r^2$	$A = \frac{1}{2}bh$	$V = lwh$	$V = \pi r^2 h$	$V = \frac{4}{3}\pi r^3$
$P = 2l + 2w$	$C = 2\pi r$	$P = a + b + c$			

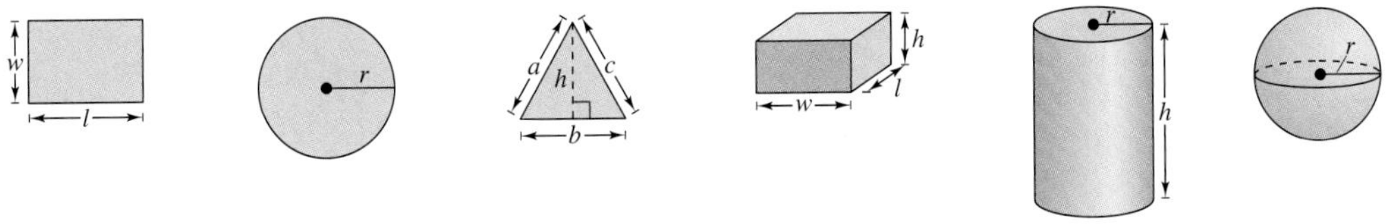

Example 15 Using a Geometric Formula

FIGURE A.13

A cylindrical can has a volume of 200 cubic centimeters (cm^3) and a radius of 4 centimeters (cm), as shown in Figure A.13. Find the height of the can.

Solution

The formula for the *volume of a cylinder* is $V = \pi r^2 h$. To find the height of the can, solve for h.

$$h = \frac{V}{\pi r^2}$$

Then, using $V = 200$ and $r = 4$, find the height.

$$h = \frac{200}{\pi(4)^2}$$ Substitute 200 for V and 4 for r.

$$= \frac{200}{16\pi}$$ Simplify denominator.

$$\approx 3.98$$ Use a calculator.

Because the value of h was rounded in the solution, a check of the solution will not result in an equality. If the solution is valid, the expressions on each side of the equal sign will be approximately equal to each other.

$$V = \pi r^2 h$$ Write original equation.

$$200 \stackrel{?}{\approx} \pi(4)^2(3.98)$$ Substitute 200 for V, 4 for r, and 3.98 for h.

$$200 \approx 200.06$$ Solution checks. ✓

You can also use unit analysis to check that your answer is reasonable.

$$\frac{200\text{ cm}^3}{16\pi\text{ cm}^2} \approx 3.98\text{ cm}$$

CHECK*Point* Now try Exercise 157.

35. No solution. The solution is extraneous.
37. No solution. The solution is extraneous.
39. No solution. The solution is extraneous.
40. No solution. The solution is extraneous.
42. No solution. The x-terms sum to zero, but the constant terms do not.
43. $2x^2 + 8x - 3 = 0$
44. $-3x^2 - 42x - 134 = 0$
45. $3x^2 - 90x - 10 = 0$
46. $4x^2 - 2x + 1 = 0$
47. $0, -\frac{1}{2}$
48. $-\frac{2}{3}, \frac{2}{3}$
49. $4, -2$
50. $9, 1$
51. $5, 7$
52. $-\frac{3}{2}$
53. $3, -\frac{1}{2}$
54. $-\frac{3}{2}, 11$
55. $2, -6$
56. $-8, 16$
64. $-18, -8$
65. $-2 \pm \sqrt{14}$
66. $5 \pm \sqrt{30}$
67. $\dfrac{1 \pm 3\sqrt{2}}{2}$
68. $\dfrac{-3 \pm 3\sqrt{3}}{2}$
69. 2
70. $-\dfrac{9}{2}$

A.5 EXERCISES

See www.CalcChat.com for worked-out solutions to odd-numbered exercises.

VOCABULARY: Fill in the blanks.

1. A(n) equation is a statement that equates two algebraic expressions.
2. A linear equation in one variable is an equation that can be written in the standard form $ax + b = 0$
3. When solving an equation, it is possible to introduce an ________ solution, which is a value that does not satisfy the original equation. extraneous
4. The four methods that can be used to solve a quadratic equation are ________, ________, ________, and the ________. factoring; extracting square roots; completing the square; Quadratic Formula

SKILLS AND APPLICATIONS

In Exercises 5–12, determine whether the equation is an identity or a conditional equation.

5. $4(x + 1) = 4x + 4$ Identity
6. $2(x - 3) = 7x - 1$ Conditional equation
7. $-6(x - 3) + 5 = -2x + 10$ Conditional equation
8. $3(x + 2) - 5 = 3x + 1$ Identity
9. $4(x + 1) - 2x = 2(x + 2)$ Identity
10. $x^2 + 2(3x - 2) = x^2 + 6x - 4$ Identity
11. $3 + \dfrac{1}{x + 1} = \dfrac{4x}{x + 1}$ Conditional equation
12. $\dfrac{5}{x} + \dfrac{3}{x} = 24$ Conditional equation

In Exercises 13–26, solve the equation and check your solution.

13. $x + 11 = 15$ 4
14. $7 - x = 19$ -12
15. $7 - 2x = 25$ -9
16. $7x + 2 = 23$ 3
17. $8x - 5 = 3x + 20$ 5
18. $7x + 3 = 3x - 17$ -5
19. $4y + 2 - 5y = 7 - 6y$ 1
20. $3(x + 3) = 5(1 - x) - 1$ $-\frac{5}{8}$
21. $x - 3(2x + 3) = 8 - 5x$ No solution
22. $9x - 10 = 5x + 2(2x - 5)$ All real numbers x
23. $\dfrac{3x}{8} - \dfrac{4x}{3} = 4$ $-\frac{96}{23}$
24. $\dfrac{x}{5} - \dfrac{x}{2} = 3 + \dfrac{3x}{10}$ -5
25. $\frac{3}{2}(z + 5) - \frac{1}{4}(z + 24) = 0$ $-\frac{6}{5}$
26. $0.60x + 0.40(100 - x) = 50$ 50

In Exercises 27–42, solve the equation and check your solution. (If not possible, explain why.)

27. $x + 8 = 2(x - 2) - x$ 27–28. See below.
28. $8(x + 2) - 3(2x + 1) = 2(x + 5)$
29. $\dfrac{100 - 4x}{3} = \dfrac{5x + 6}{4} + 6$ 10
30. $\dfrac{17 + y}{y} + \dfrac{32 + y}{y} = 100$ $\frac{1}{2}$
31. $\dfrac{5x - 4}{5x + 4} = \dfrac{2}{3}$ 4
32. $\dfrac{15}{x} - 4 = \dfrac{6}{x} + 3$ $\frac{9}{7}$

27–28. No solution. The x-terms sum to zero, but the constant terms do not.

33. $3 = 2 + \dfrac{2}{z + 2}$ 0
34. $\dfrac{1}{x} + \dfrac{2}{x - 5} = 0$ $\frac{5}{3}$
35. $\dfrac{x}{x + 4} + \dfrac{4}{x + 4} + 2 = 0$ See margin.
36. $\dfrac{7}{2x + 1} - \dfrac{8x}{2x - 1} = -4$ $\frac{11}{6}$
37. $\dfrac{2}{(x - 4)(x - 2)} = \dfrac{1}{x - 4} + \dfrac{2}{x - 2}$ See margin.
38. $\dfrac{1}{x - 2} + \dfrac{3}{x + 3} = \dfrac{4}{x^2 + x - 6}$ $\frac{7}{4}$
39. $\dfrac{3}{x^2 - 3x} + \dfrac{4}{x} = \dfrac{1}{x - 3}$
40. $\dfrac{6}{x} - \dfrac{2}{x + 3} = \dfrac{3(x + 5)}{x^2 + 3x}$
41. $(x + 2)^2 + 5 = (x + 3)^2$ 0
42. $(2x + 1)^2 = 4(x^2 + x + 1)$

39, 40, 42. See margin.

In Exercises 43–46, write the quadratic equation in general form. 43–46. See margin.

43. $2x^2 = 3 - 8x$
44. $13 - 3(x + 7)^2 = 0$
45. $\frac{1}{5}(3x^2 - 10) = 18x$
46. $x(x + 2) = 5x^2 + 1$

47–56. See margin.

In Exercises 47–58, solve the quadratic equation by factoring.

47. $6x^2 + 3x = 0$
48. $9x^2 - 4 = 0$
49. $x^2 - 2x - 8 = 0$
50. $x^2 - 10x + 9 = 0$
51. $x^2 - 12x + 35 = 0$
52. $4x^2 + 12x + 9 = 0$
53. $3 + 5x - 2x^2 = 0$
54. $2x^2 = 19x + 33$
55. $x^2 + 4x = 12$
56. $\frac{1}{8}x^2 - x - 16 = 0$
57. $x^2 + 2ax + a^2 = 0$, a is a real number $-a$
58. $(x + a)^2 - b^2 = 0$, a and b are real numbers $-a - b, -a + b$

In Exercises 59–70, solve the equation by extracting square roots.

59. $x^2 = 49$ ± 7
60. $x^2 = 32$ $\pm 4\sqrt{2}$
61. $3x^2 = 81$ $\pm 3\sqrt{3}$
62. $9x^2 = 36$ ± 2
63. $(x - 12)^2 = 16$ 8, 16
64. $(x + 13)^2 = 25$
65. $(x + 2)^2 = 14$
66. $(x - 5)^2 = 30$
67. $(2x - 1)^2 = 18$
68. $(2x + 3)^2 - 27 = 0$
69. $(x - 7)^2 = (x + 3)^2$
70. $(x + 5)^2 = (x + 4)^2$

64–70. See margin.

In Exercises 71–80, solve the quadratic equation by completing the square. 71–80. See margin.

71. $x^2 + 4x - 32 = 0$ **72.** $x^2 + 6x + 2 = 0$

73. $x^2 + 12x + 25 = 0$ **74.** $x^2 + 8x + 14 = 0$

75. $8 + 4x - x^2 = 0$ **76.** $9x^2 - 12x = 14$

77. $2x^2 + 5x - 8 = 0$ **78.** $4x^2 - 4x - 99 = 0$

79. $5x^2 - 15x + 7 = 0$ **80.** $3x^2 + 9x + 5 = 0$

In Exercises 81–98, use the Quadratic Formula to solve the equation. 81–98. See margin.

81. $2x^2 + x - 1 = 0$ **82.** $25x^2 - 20x + 3 = 0$

83. $2 + 2x - x^2 = 0$ **84.** $x^2 - 10x + 22 = 0$

85. $x^2 + 14x + 44 = 0$ **86.** $6x = 4 - x^2$

87. $x^2 + 8x - 4 = 0$ **88.** $4x^2 - 4x - 4 = 0$

89. $12x - 9x^2 = -3$ **90.** $16x^2 + 22 = 40x$

91. $9x^2 + 24x + 16 = 0$ **92.** $16x^2 - 40x + 5 = 0$

93. $28x - 49x^2 = 4$ **94.** $3x + x^2 - 1 = 0$

95. $8t = 5 + 2t^2$ **96.** $25h^2 + 80h + 61 = 0$

97. $(y - 5)^2 = 2y$ **98.** $(\frac{5}{7}x - 14)^2 = 8x$

In Exercises 99–104, use the Quadratic Formula to solve the equation. (Round your answer to three decimal places.)

99. $0.1x^2 + 0.2x - 0.5 = 0$ $-3.449, 1.449$

100. $2x^2 - 2.50x - 0.42 = 0$ $1.400, -0.150$

101. $-0.067x^2 - 0.852x + 1.277 = 0$ $1.355, -14.071$

102. $-0.005x^2 + 0.101x - 0.193 = 0$ $2.137, 18.063$

103. $422x^2 - 506x - 347 = 0$ $1.687, -0.488$

104. $-3.22x^2 - 0.08x + 28.651 = 0$ $-2.995, 2.971$

In Exercises 105–112, solve the equation using any convenient method. 105–112. See margin.

105. $x^2 - 2x - 1 = 0$ **106.** $11x^2 + 33x = 0$

107. $(x + 3)^2 = 81$ **108.** $x^2 - 14x + 49 = 0$

109. $x^2 - x - \frac{11}{4} = 0$ **110.** $3x + 4 = 2x^2 - 7$

111. $4x^2 + 2x + 4 = 2x + 8$

112. $a^2x^2 - b^2 = 0$, a and b are real numbers, $a \neq 0$

In Exercises 113–126, find all real solutions of the equation. Check your solutions in the original equation.

113. $2x^4 - 50x^2 = 0$ $0, \pm 5$ **114.** $20x^3 - 125x = 0$ $0, \pm\frac{5}{2}$

115. $x^4 - 81 = 0$ ± 3 **116.** $x^6 - 64 = 0$ ± 2

117. $x^3 + 216 = 0$ -6

118. $9x^4 - 24x^3 + 16x^2 = 0$ $0, \frac{4}{3}$

119. $x^3 - 3x^2 - x + 3 = 0$ $3, 1, -1$

120. $x^3 + 2x^2 + 3x + 6 = 0$ -2

121. $x^4 + x = x^3 + 1$ ± 1

122. $x^4 - 2x^3 = 16 + 8x - 4x^3$ ± 2

123–124. See margin.

123. $x^4 - 4x^2 + 3 = 0$ **124.** $36t^4 + 29t^2 - 7 = 0$

125. $x^6 + 7x^3 - 8 = 0$ $1, -2$ **126.** $x^6 + 3x^3 + 2 = 0$ $-\sqrt[3]{2}, -1$

In Exercises 127–154, find all solutions of the equation. Check your solutions in the original equation. 127–154. See margin.

127. $\sqrt{2x} - 10 = 0$ **128.** $7\sqrt{x} - 6 = 0$

129. $\sqrt{x - 10} - 4 = 0$ **130.** $\sqrt{5 - x} - 3 = 0$

131. $\sqrt{2x + 5} + 3 = 0$ **132.** $\sqrt{3 - 2x} - 2 = 0$

133. $\sqrt[3]{2x + 1} + 8 = 0$ **134.** $\sqrt[3]{4x - 3} + 2 = 0$

135. $\sqrt{5x - 26} + 4 = x$ **136.** $\sqrt{x + 5} = \sqrt{2x - 5}$

137. $(x - 6)^{3/2} = 8$ **138.** $(x + 3)^{3/2} = 8$

139. $(x + 3)^{2/3} = 5$ **140.** $(x^2 - x - 22)^{4/3} = 16$

141. $3x(x - 1)^{1/2} + 2(x - 1)^{3/2} = 0$

142. $4x^2(x - 1)^{1/3} + 6x(x - 1)^{4/3} = 0$

143. $x = \frac{3}{x} + \frac{1}{2}$ **144.** $\frac{4}{x + 1} - \frac{3}{x + 2} = 1$

145. $\frac{20 - x}{x} = x$ **146.** $4x + 1 = \frac{3}{x}$

147. $\frac{x}{x^2 - 4} + \frac{1}{x + 2} = 3$ **148.** $\frac{x + 1}{3} - \frac{x + 1}{x + 2} = 0$

149. $|2x - 1| = 5$ **150.** $|13x + 1| = 12$

151. $|x| = x^2 + x - 3$ **152.** $|x^2 + 6x| = 3x + 18$

153. $|x + 1| = x^2 - 5$ **154.** $|x - 10| = x^2 - 10x$

ANTHROPOLOGY In Exercises 155 and 156, use the following information. The relationship between the length of an adult's femur (thigh bone) and the height of the adult can be approximated by the linear equations

$y = 0.432x - 10.44$ Female

$y = 0.449x - 12.15$ Male

where y is the length of the femur in inches and x is the height of the adult in inches (see figure).

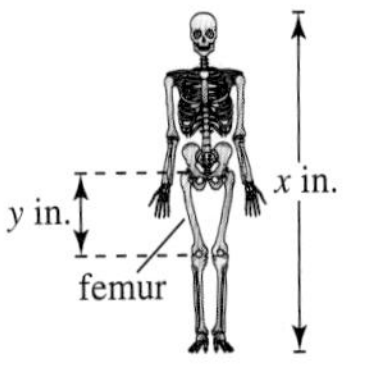

155. An anthropologist discovers a femur belonging to an adult human female. The bone is 16 inches long. Estimate the height of the female. 61.2 in.

71. $4, -8$ **72.** $-3 \pm \sqrt{7}$

73. $\sqrt{11} - 6, -\sqrt{11} - 6$

74. $-4 \pm \sqrt{2}$ **75.** $2 \pm 2\sqrt{3}$

76. $\frac{2}{3} \pm \sqrt{2}$ **77.** $\frac{-5 \pm \sqrt{89}}{4}$

78. $\frac{11}{2}, -\frac{9}{2}$ **79.** $\frac{15 \pm \sqrt{85}}{10}$

80. $\frac{-9 \pm \sqrt{21}}{6}$ **81.** $\frac{1}{2}, -1$

82. $\frac{3}{5}, \frac{1}{5}$ **83.** $1 \pm \sqrt{3}$

84. $5 \pm \sqrt{3}$ **85.** $-7 \pm \sqrt{5}$

86. $-3 \pm \sqrt{13}$ **87.** $-4 \pm 2\sqrt{5}$

88. $\frac{1}{2} \pm \frac{\sqrt{5}}{2}$ **89.** $\frac{2}{3} \pm \frac{\sqrt{7}}{3}$

90. $\frac{5}{4} \pm \frac{\sqrt{3}}{4}$ **91.** $-\frac{4}{3}$

92. $\frac{5}{4} \pm \frac{\sqrt{5}}{2}$ **93.** $\frac{2}{7}$

94. $-\frac{3}{2} \pm \frac{\sqrt{13}}{2}$ **95.** $2 \pm \frac{\sqrt{6}}{2}$

96. $-\frac{8}{5} \pm \frac{\sqrt{3}}{5}$ **97.** $6 \pm \sqrt{11}$

98. $\frac{686 \pm 196\sqrt{6}}{25}$

105. $1 \pm \sqrt{2}$ **106.** $0, -3$

107. $6, -12$ **108.** 7

109. $\frac{1}{2} \pm \sqrt{3}$ **110.** $\frac{3}{4} \pm \frac{\sqrt{97}}{4}$

111. ± 1 **112.** $-\frac{b}{a}, \frac{b}{a}$

123. $\pm\sqrt{3}, \pm 1$ **124.** $\pm\frac{\sqrt{7}}{6}$

127. 50 **128.** $\frac{36}{49}$

129. 26 **130.** -4

131. No solution **132.** $-\frac{1}{2}$

133. $-\frac{513}{2}$ **134.** $-\frac{5}{4}$

135. $6, 7$ **136.** 10

137. 10 **138.** 1

139. $-3 \pm 5\sqrt{5}$

140. $-5, \frac{1 \pm \sqrt{57}}{2}, 6$

141. 1 **142.** $0, 1, \frac{3}{5}$

143. $2, -\frac{3}{2}$ **144.** $-3, 1$

145. $4, -5$ **146.** $\frac{3}{4}, -1$

147. $\frac{1 \pm \sqrt{31}}{3}$ **148.** ± 1

149. $3, -2$ **150.** $-1, \frac{11}{13}$

151. $\sqrt{3}, -3$ **152.** $-6, -3, 3$

153. $3, \frac{-1 - \sqrt{17}}{2}$

154. $10, -1$

156. Yes. The estimated height of a male with a 19-inch femur is 69.4 inches.

159. 43 cm; $\frac{1849\sqrt{3}}{4} \approx 800.6\text{ cm}^2$

160. About 34 cm

161. (a) 1998
(b) 2011; Answers will vary.

165. Equivalent equations have the same solution set, and one is derived from the other by steps for generating equivalent equations.
$2x = 5,\ 2x + 3 = 8$

166. (a) and (b) $x = -5, -\frac{10}{3}$
(c) The method used in part (a) requires fewer algebraic steps.

171. Sample answer: $a = 9, b = 9$

172. Isolate the absolute value by subtracting x from both sides of the equation. The expression inside the absolute value signs can be positive or negative, so two separate equations must be solved. Each solution must be checked because extraneous solutions may be included.

173. Sample answer: $a = 20, b = 20$

174. Isolate the radical by subtracting x from both sides of the equation. Then square both sides to eliminate the radical, and rewrite the equation in standard form. The solutions can now be found by using the Quadratic Formula. Each solution must be checked because extraneous solutions may be included.

176. (a) An identity is true for all real numbers, whereas a conditional equation is true for just some (or none) of the real numbers in the domain.
(b) Sample answer: $|x - 4| = 0$
(c) The opposite of b plus or minus the square root of the quantity b squared minus the product of 4, a, and c, all divided by the product of 2 and a.
(d) No. For instance, $x = 2$ is not equivalent to $x^2 = 4$ because for $x^2 = 4$, the solutions are $x = 2$ and $x = -2$.

156. From the foot bones of an adult human male, an anthropologist estimates that the person's height was 69 inches. A few feet away from the site where the foot bones were discovered, the anthropologist discovers a male adult femur that is 19 inches long. Is it likely that both the foot bones and the thigh bone came from the same person? See margin.

157. VOLUME OF A BILLIARD BALL A billiard ball has a volume of 5.96 cubic inches. Find the radius of a billiard ball. About 1.12 in.

158. LENGTH OF A TANK The diameter of a cylindrical propane gas tank is 4 feet. The total volume of the tank is 603.2 cubic feet. Find the length of the tank. 158. About 48 ft

159. GEOMETRY A "Slow Moving Vehicle" sign has the shape of an equilateral triangle. The sign has a perimeter of 129 centimeters. Find the length of each side of the sign. Find the area of the sign. See margin.

160. GEOMETRY The radius of a traffic cone is 14 centimeters and the lateral surface area of the cone is 1617 square centimeters. Find the height of the cone. See margin.

161. VOTING POPULATION The total voting-age population P (in millions) in the United States from 1990 through 2006 can be modeled by

$$P = \frac{182.17 - 1.542t}{1 - 0.018t}, \quad 0 \le t \le 16$$

where t represents the year, with $t = 0$ corresponding to 1990. (Source: U.S. Census Bureau) See margin.

(a) In which year did the total voting-age population reach 200 million?

(b) Use the model to predict the year in which the total voting-age population will reach 241 million. Is this prediction reasonable? Explain.

162. AIRLINE PASSENGERS An airline offers daily flights between Chicago and Denver. The total monthly cost C (in millions of dollars) of these flights is $C = \sqrt{0.2x + 1}$, where x is the number of passengers (in thousands). The total cost of the flights for June is 2.5 million dollars. How many passengers flew in June? 26,250 passengers

EXPLORATION

TRUE OR FALSE? In Exercises 163 and 164, determine whether the statement is true or false. Justify your answer.

163. An equation can never have more than one extraneous solution. False. See Example 14 on page A58.

164. When solving an absolute value equation, you will always have to check more than one solution.
False. $|x| = 0$ has only one solution to check, 0.

165. THINK ABOUT IT What is meant by *equivalent equations*? Give an example of two equivalent equations. See margin.

166. Solve $3(x + 4)^2 + (x + 4) - 2 = 0$ in two ways.

(a) Let $u = x + 4$, and solve the resulting equation for u. Then solve the u-solution for x.

(b) Expand and collect like terms in the equation, and solve the resulting equation for x. (a)–(c).

(c) Which method is easier? Explain. See margin.

THINK ABOUT IT In Exercises 167–170, write a quadratic equation that has the given solutions. (There are many correct answers.)

167. -3 and 6 $\quad x^2 - 3x - 18 = 0$

168. -4 and -11 $\quad x^2 + 15x + 44 = 0$

169. $1 + \sqrt{2}$ and $1 - \sqrt{2}$ $\quad x^2 - 2x - 1 = 0$

170. $-3 + \sqrt{5}$ and $-3 - \sqrt{5}$ $\quad x^2 + 6x + 4 = 0$

In Exercises 171 and 172, consider an equation of the form $x + |x - a| = b$, where a and b are constants. 171–172. See margin.

171. Find a and b when the solution of the equation is $x = 9$. (There are many correct answers.)

172. WRITING Write a short paragraph listing the steps required to solve this equation involving absolute values, and explain why it is important to check your solutions.

In Exercises 173 and 174, consider an equation of the form $x + \sqrt{x - a} = b$, where a and b are constants. 173–174. See margin.

173. Find a and b when the solution of the equation is $x = 20$. (There are many correct answers.)

174. WRITING Write a short paragraph listing the steps required to solve this equation involving radicals, and explain why it is important to check your solutions.

175. Solve each equation, given that a and b are not zero.

(a) $ax^2 + bx = 0$ $\quad$ (a) $x = 0, -\frac{b}{a}$

(b) $ax^2 - ax = 0$ $\quad$ (b) $x = 0, 1$

176. CAPSTONE See margin.

(a) Explain the difference between a conditional equation and an identity.

(b) Give an example of an absolute value equation that has only one solution.

(c) State the Quadratic Formula in words.

(d) Does raising each side of an equation to the nth power always yield an equivalent equation? Explain.

A.6 LINEAR INEQUALITIES IN ONE VARIABLE

What you should learn

- Represent solutions of linear inequalities in one variable.
- Use properties of inequalities to create equivalent inequalities.
- Solve linear inequalities in one variable.
- Solve inequalities involving absolute values.
- Use inequalities to model and solve real-life problems.

Why you should learn it

Inequalities can be used to model and solve real-life problems. For instance, in Exercise 121 on page A71, you will use a linear inequality to analyze the average salary for elementary school teachers.

Introduction

Simple inequalities were discussed in Appendix A.1. There, you used the inequality symbols $<$, $\leq$, $>$, and $\geq$ to compare two numbers and to denote subsets of real numbers. For instance, the simple inequality

$$x \geq 3$$

denotes all real numbers x that are greater than or equal to 3.

Now, you will expand your work with inequalities to include more involved statements such as

$$5x - 7 < 3x + 9$$

and

$$-3 \leq 6x - 1 < 3.$$

As with an equation, you **solve an inequality** in the variable x by finding all values of x for which the inequality is true. Such values are **solutions** and are said to **satisfy** the inequality. The set of all real numbers that are solutions of an inequality is the **solution set** of the inequality. For instance, the solution set of

$$x + 1 < 4$$

is all real numbers that are less than 3.

The set of all points on the real number line that represents the solution set is the **graph of the inequality.** Graphs of many types of inequalities consist of intervals on the real number line. See Appendix A.1 to review the nine basic types of intervals on the real number line. Note that each type of interval can be classified as *bounded* or *unbounded.*

Example 1 Intervals and Inequalities

Write an inequality to represent each interval, and state whether the interval is bounded or unbounded.

a. $(-3, 5]$

b. $(-3, \infty)$

c. $[0, 2]$

d. $(-\infty, \infty)$

Solution

a. $(-3, 5]$ corresponds to $-3 < x \leq 5$. Bounded

b. $(-3, \infty)$ corresponds to $-3 < x$. Unbounded

c. $[0, 2]$ corresponds to $0 \leq x \leq 2$. Bounded

d. $(-\infty, \infty)$ corresponds to $-\infty < x < \infty$. Unbounded

CHECKPoint Now try Exercise 9.

Properties of Inequalities

The procedures for solving linear inequalities in one variable are much like those for solving linear equations. To isolate the variable, you can make use of the **Properties of Inequalities.** These properties are similar to the properties of equality, but there are two important exceptions. When each side of an inequality is multiplied or divided by a negative number, the direction of the inequality symbol must be reversed. Here is an example.

$$-2 < 5$$ Original inequality

$$(-3)(-2) > (-3)(5)$$ Multiply each side by -3 and reverse inequality.

$$6 > -15$$ Simplify.

Notice that if the inequality was not reversed, you would obtain the false statement $6 < -15$.

Two inequalities that have the same solution set are **equivalent.** For instance, the inequalities

$$x + 2 < 5$$

and

$$x < 3$$

are equivalent. To obtain the second inequality from the first, you can subtract 2 from each side of the inequality. The following list describes the operations that can be used to create equivalent inequalities.

Properties of Inequalities

Let a, b, c, and d be real numbers.

1. Transitive Property

$a < b$ and $b < c \implies a < c$

2. Addition of Inequalities

$a < b$ and $c < d \implies a + c < b + d$

3. Addition of a Constant

$a < b \implies a + c < b + c$

4. Multiplication by a Constant

For $c > 0$, $a < b \implies ac < bc$

For $c < 0$, $a < b \implies ac > bc$ Reverse the inequality.

Each of the properties above is true if the symbol $<$ is replaced by $\le$ and the symbol $>$ is replaced by $\ge$. For instance, another form of the multiplication property would be as follows.

For $c > 0$, $a \le b \implies ac \le bc$

For $c < 0$, $a \le b \implies ac \ge bc$

Solving a Linear Inequality in One Variable

The simplest type of inequality is a **linear inequality** in one variable. For instance, $2x + 3 > 4$ is a linear inequality in x.

In the following examples, pay special attention to the steps in which the inequality symbol is reversed. Remember that when you multiply or divide by a negative number, you must reverse the inequality symbol.

Example 2 Solving a Linear Inequality

Solve $5x - 7 > 3x + 9$.

Solution

$5x - 7 > 3x + 9$	Write original inequality.
$2x - 7 > 9$	Subtract $3x$ from each side.
$2x > 16$	Add 7 to each side.
$x > 8$	Divide each side by 2.

The solution set is all real numbers that are greater than 8, which is denoted by $(8, \infty)$. The graph of this solution set is shown in Figure A.14. Note that a parenthesis at 8 on the real number line indicates that 8 *is not* part of the solution set.

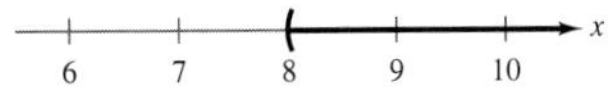

Solution interval: $(8, \infty)$

FIGURE A.14

CHECKPoint Now try Exercise 35.

Study Tip

Checking the solution set of an inequality is not as simple as checking the solutions of an equation. You can, however, get an indication of the validity of a solution set by substituting a few convenient values of x. For instance, in Example 2, try substituting $x = 5$ and $x = 10$ into the original inequality.

Example 3 Solving a Linear Inequality

Solve $1 - \frac{3}{2}x \ge x - 4$.

Algebraic Solution

$1 - \dfrac{3x}{2} \ge x - 4$	Write original inequality.
$2 - 3x \ge 2x - 8$	Multiply each side by 2.
$2 - 5x \ge -8$	Subtract $2x$ from each side.
$-5x \ge -10$	Subtract 2 from each side.
$x \le 2$	Divide each side by -5 and reverse the inequality.

The solution set is all real numbers that are less than or equal to 2, which is denoted by $(-\infty, 2]$. The graph of this solution set is shown in Figure A.15. Note that a bracket at 2 on the real number line indicates that 2 *is* part of the solution set.

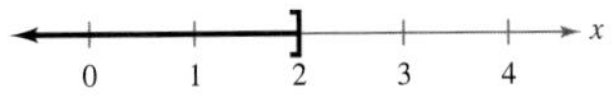

Solution interval: $(-\infty, 2]$

FIGURE A.15

CHECKPoint Now try Exercise 37.

Graphical Solution

Use a graphing utility to graph $y_1 = 1 - \frac{3}{2}x$ and $y_2 = x - 4$ in the same viewing window. In Figure A.16, you can see that the graphs appear to intersect at the point $(2, -2)$. Use the *intersect* feature of the graphing utility to confirm this. The graph of y_1 lies above the graph of y_2 to the left of their point of intersection, which implies that $y_1 \ge y_2$ for all $x \le 2$.

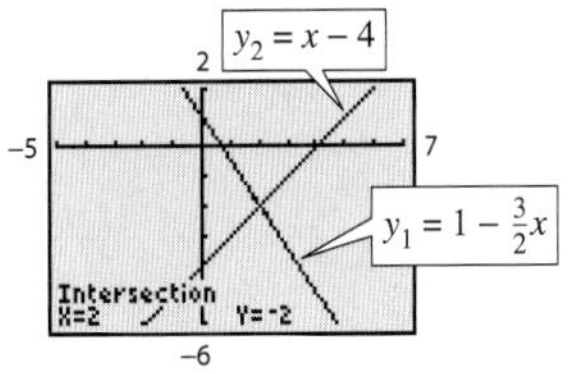

FIGURE A.16

Sometimes it is possible to write two inequalities as a **double inequality.** For instance, you can write the two inequalities $-4 \le 5x - 2$ and $5x - 2 < 7$ more simply as

$$-4 \le 5x - 2 < 7. \qquad \text{Double inequality}$$

This form allows you to solve the two inequalities together, as demonstrated in Example 4.

Example 4 Solving a Double Inequality

To solve a double inequality, you can isolate x as the middle term.

$$-3 \le 6x - 1 < 3 \qquad \text{Original inequality}$$

$$-3 + 1 \le 6x - 1 + 1 < 3 + 1 \qquad \text{Add 1 to each part.}$$

$$-2 \le 6x < 4 \qquad \text{Simplify.}$$

$$\frac{-2}{6} \le \frac{6x}{6} < \frac{4}{6} \qquad \text{Divide each part by 6.}$$

$$-\frac{1}{3} \le x < \frac{2}{3} \qquad \text{Simplify.}$$

The solution set is all real numbers that are greater than or equal to $-\frac{1}{3}$ and less than $\frac{2}{3}$, which is denoted by $\left[-\frac{1}{3}, \frac{2}{3}\right)$. The graph of this solution set is shown in Figure A.17.

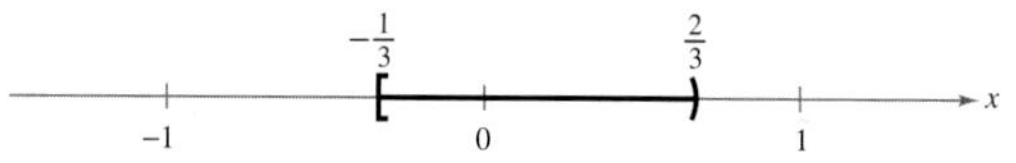

Solution interval: $\left[-\frac{1}{3}, \frac{2}{3}\right)$

FIGURE A.17

CHECK Point Now try Exercise 47.

The double inequality in Example 4 could have been solved in two parts, as follows.

$$-3 \le 6x - 1 \quad \text{and} \quad 6x - 1 < 3$$

$$-2 \le 6x \qquad\qquad 6x < 4$$

$$-\frac{1}{3} \le x \qquad\qquad x < \frac{2}{3}$$

The solution set consists of all real numbers that satisfy *both* inequalities. In other words, the solution set is the set of all values of x for which

$$-\frac{1}{3} \le x < \frac{2}{3}.$$

When combining two inequalities to form a double inequality, be sure that the inequalities satisfy the Transitive Property. For instance, it is *incorrect* to combine the inequalities $3 < x$ and $x \le -1$ as $3 < x \le -1$. This "inequality" is wrong because 3 is not less than -1.

Inequalities Involving Absolute Values

TECHNOLOGY

A graphing utility can be used to identify the solution set of the graph of an inequality. For instance, to find the solution set of $|x - 5| < 2$ (see Example 5a), rewrite the inequality as $|x - 5| - 2 < 0$, enter

Y1 = abs (X − 5) − 2

and press the *graph* key. The graph should look like the one shown below.

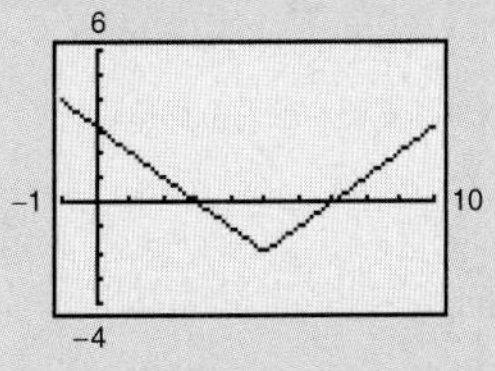

Notice that the graph is below the x-axis on the interval $(3, 7)$.

Solving an Absolute Value Inequality

Let x be a variable or an algebraic expression and let a be a real number such that $a \geq 0$.

1. The solutions of $|x| < a$ are all values of x that lie between $-a$ and a.

   $|x| < a$ if and only if $-a < x < a$. Double inequality

2. The solutions of $|x| > a$ are all values of x that are less than $-a$ or greater than a.

   $|x| > a$ if and only if $x < -a$ or $x > a$. Compound inequality

These rules are also valid if $<$ is replaced by $\leq$ and $>$ is replaced by $\geq$.

Example 5 Solving an Absolute Value Inequality

Solve each inequality.

a. $|x - 5| < 2$ **b.** $|x + 3| \geq 7$

Solution

a.

$\|x - 5\| < 2$	Write original inequality.
$-2 < x - 5 < 2$	Write equivalent inequalities.
$-2 + 5 < x - 5 + 5 < 2 + 5$	Add 5 to each part.
$3 < x < 7$	Simplify.

The solution set is all real numbers that are greater than 3 and less than 7, which is denoted by $(3, 7)$. The graph of this solution set is shown in Figure A.18.

b.

$\|x + 3\| \geq 7$			Write original inequality.
$x + 3 \leq -7$	or	$x + 3 \geq 7$	Write equivalent inequalities.
$x + 3 - 3 \leq -7 - 3$		$x + 3 - 3 \geq 7 - 3$	Subtract 3 from each side.
$x \leq -10$		$x \geq 4$	Simplify.

The solution set is all real numbers that are less than or equal to -10 *or* greater than or equal to 4. The interval notation for this solution set is $(-\infty, -10] \cup [4, \infty)$. The symbol $\cup$ is called a *union* symbol and is used to denote the combining of two sets. The graph of this solution set is shown in Figure A.19.

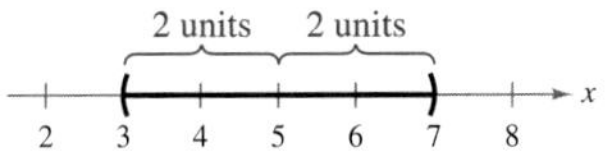

$|x - 5| < 2$: Solutions lie inside $(3, 7)$.
FIGURE A.18

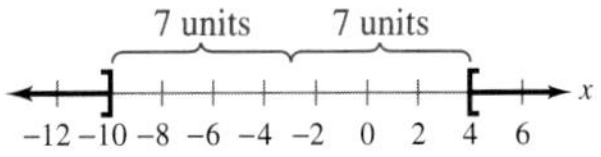

$|x + 3| \geq 7$: Solutions lie outside $(-10, 4)$.
FIGURE A.19

CHECKPoint Now try Exercise 61.

Study Tip

Note that the graph of the inequality $|x - 5| < 2$ can be described as all real numbers *within* two units of 5, as shown in Figure A.18.

Applications

A problem-solving plan can be used to model and solve real-life problems that involve inequalities, as illustrated in Example 6.

Example 6 Comparative Shopping

You are choosing between two different cell phone plans. Plan A costs \$49.99 per month for 500 minutes plus \$0.40 for each additional minute. Plan B costs \$45.99 per month for 500 minutes plus \$0.45 for each additional minute. How many *additional* minutes must you use in one month for plan B to cost more than plan A?

Solution

Verbal Model: Monthly cost for plan B > Monthly cost for plan A

Labels: Minutes used (over 500) in one month $= m$ (minutes)
Monthly cost for plan A $= 0.40m + 49.99$ (dollars)
Monthly cost for plan B $= 0.45m + 45.99$ (dollars)

Inequality: $0.45m + 45.99 > 0.40m + 49.99$

$$0.05m > 4$$

$$m > 80 \text{ minutes}$$

Plan B costs more if you use more than 80 additional minutes in one month.

CHECK *Point* Now try Exercise 111.

Example 7 Accuracy of a Measurement

You go to a candy store to buy chocolates that cost \$9.89 per pound. The scale that is used in the store has a state seal of approval that indicates the scale is accurate to within half an ounce (or $\frac{1}{32}$ of a pound). According to the scale, your purchase weighs one-half pound and costs \$4.95. How much might you have been undercharged or overcharged as a result of inaccuracy in the scale?

Solution

Let x represent the *true* weight of the candy. Because the scale is accurate to within half an ounce (or $\frac{1}{32}$ of a pound), the difference between the exact weight (x) and the scale weight $\left(\frac{1}{2}\right)$ is less than or equal to $\frac{1}{32}$ of a pound. That is, $\left|x - \frac{1}{2}\right| \le \frac{1}{32}$. You can solve this inequality as follows.

$$-\frac{1}{32} \le x - \frac{1}{2} \le \frac{1}{32}$$

$$\frac{15}{32} \le x \le \frac{17}{32}$$

$$0.46875 \le x \le 0.53125$$

In other words, your "one-half pound" of candy could have weighed as little as 0.46875 pound (which would have cost \$4.64) or as much as 0.53125 pound (which would have cost \$5.25). So, you could have been overcharged by as much as \$0.31 or undercharged by as much as \$0.30.

CHECK *Point* Now try Exercise 125.

A.6 EXERCISES

See www.CalcChat.com for worked-out solutions to odd-numbered exercises.

VOCABULARY: Fill in the blanks.

1. The set of all real numbers that are solutions of an inequality is the <u>solution set</u> of the inequality.
2. The set of all points on the real number line that represents the solution set of an inequality is the <u>graph</u> of the inequality.
3. To solve a linear inequality in one variable, you can use the properties of inequalities, which are identical to those used to solve equations, with the exception of multiplying or dividing each side by a <u>negative</u> number.
4. Two inequalities that have the same solution set are <u>equivalent</u>.
5. It is sometimes possible to write two inequalities as one inequality, called a <u>double</u> inequality.
6. The symbol $\cup$ is called a <u>union</u> symbol and is used to denote the combining of two sets.

SKILLS AND APPLICATIONS

In Exercises 7–14, (a) write an inequality that represents the interval and (b) state whether the interval is bounded or unbounded. 7–14. See margin.

7. $[0, 9)$ **8.** $(-7, 4)$

9. $[-1, 5]$ **10.** $(2, 10]$

11. $(11, \infty)$ **12.** $[-5, \infty)$

13. $(-\infty, -2)$ **14.** $(-\infty, 7]$

In Exercises 15–22, match the inequality with its graph. [The graphs are labeled (a)–(h).]

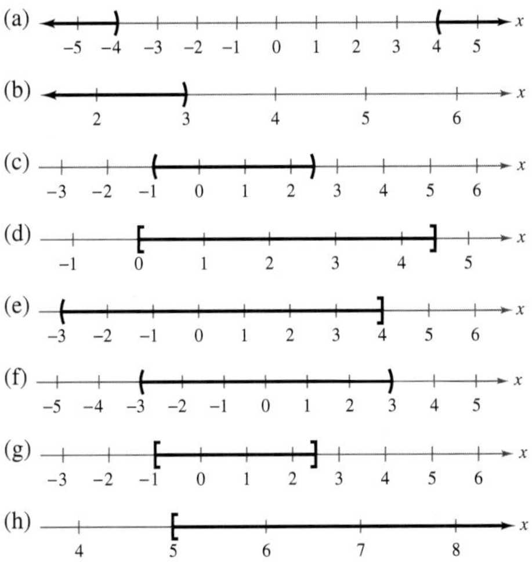

15. $x < 3$ b **16.** $x \geq 5$ h

17. $-3 < x \leq 4$ e **18.** $0 \leq x \leq \frac{9}{2}$ d

19. $|x| < 3$ f **20.** $|x| > 4$ a

21. $-1 \leq x \leq \frac{5}{2}$ g **22.** $-1 < x < \frac{5}{2}$ c

In Exercises 23–28, determine whether each value of x is a solution of the inequality.

Inequality	*Values*	
23. $5x - 12 > 0$	Yes (a) $x = 3$	(b) $x = -3$ No
	Yes (c) $x = \frac{5}{2}$	(d) $x = \frac{3}{2}$ No
24. $2x + 1 < -3$	No (a) $x = 0$	(b) $x = -\frac{1}{4}$ No
	Yes (c) $x = -4$	(d) $x = -\frac{3}{2}$ No
25. $0 < \frac{x-2}{4} < 2$	Yes (a) $x = 4$	(b) $x = 10$ No
	No (c) $x = 0$	(d) $x = \frac{7}{2}$ Yes
26. $-5 < 2x - 1 \leq 1$	Yes (a) $x = -\frac{1}{2}$	(b) $x = -\frac{5}{2}$ No
	No (c) $x = \frac{4}{3}$	(d) $x = 0$ Yes
27. $\lvert x - 10\rvert \geq 3$	Yes (a) $x = 13$	(b) $x = -1$ Yes
	Yes (c) $x = 14$	(d) $x = 9$ No
28. $\lvert 2x - 3\rvert < 15$	No (a) $x = -6$	(b) $x = 0$ Yes
	No (c) $x = 12$	(d) $x = 7$ Yes

In Exercises 29–56, solve the inequality and sketch the solution on the real number line. (Some inequalities have no solutions.) 29–50. See margin.

29. $4x < 12$ **30.** $10x < -40$

31. $-2x > -3$ **32.** $-6x > 15$

33. $x - 5 \geq 7$ **34.** $x + 7 \leq 12$

35. $2x + 7 < 3 + 4x$ **36.** $3x + 1 \geq 2 + x$

37. $2x - 1 \geq 1 - 5x$ **38.** $6x - 4 \leq 2 + 8x$

39. $4 - 2x < 3(3 - x)$ **40.** $4(x + 1) < 2x + 3$

41. $\frac{3}{4}x - 6 \leq x - 7$ **42.** $3 + \frac{2}{7}x > x - 2$

43. $\frac{1}{2}(8x + 1) \geq 3x + \frac{5}{2}$ **44.** $9x - 1 < \frac{3}{4}(16x - 2)$

45. $3.6x + 11 \geq -3.4$ **46.** $15.6 - 1.3x < -5.2$

47. $1 < 2x + 3 < 9$

48. $-8 \leq -(3x + 5) < 13$

49. $-8 \leq 1 - 3(x - 2) < 13$

50. $0 \leq 2 - 3(x + 1) < 20$

7. (a) $0 \leq x < 9$ (b) Bounded

8. (a) $-7 < x < 4$ (b) Bounded

9. (a) $-1 \leq x \leq 5$ (b) Bounded

10. (a) $2 < x \leq 10$ (b) Bounded

11. (a) $x > 11$ (b) Unbounded

12. (a) $x \geq -5$ (b) Unbounded

13. (a) $x < -2$ (b) Unbounded

14. (a) $x \leq 7$ (b) Unbounded

29. $x < 3$

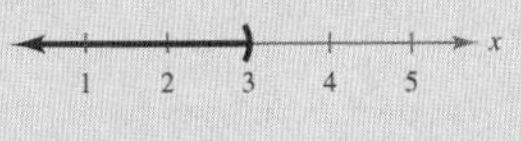

30. $x < -4$

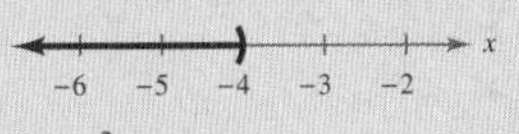

31. $x < \frac{3}{2}$

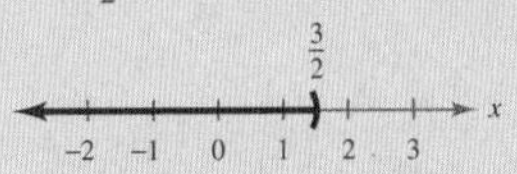

32. $x < -\frac{5}{2}$

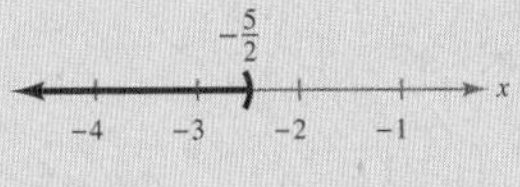

33. $x \geq 12$

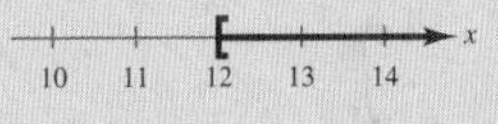

34. $x \leq 5$

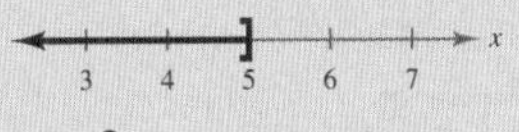

35. $x > 2$

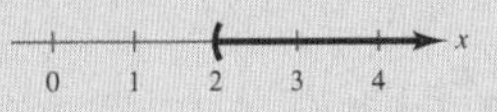

36. $x \geq \frac{1}{2}$

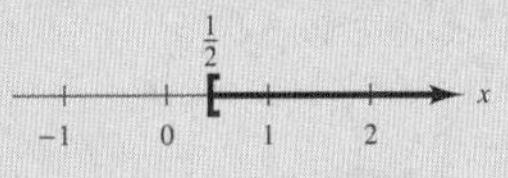

37. $x \geq \frac{2}{7}$

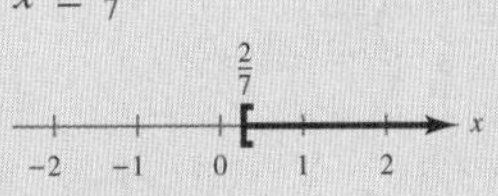

38. $x \geq -3$

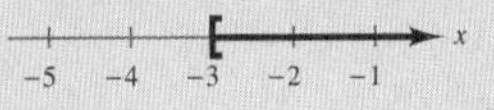

39. $x < 5$

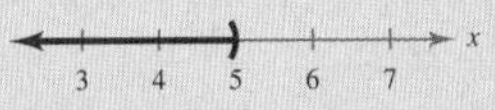

40. $x < -\frac{1}{2}$

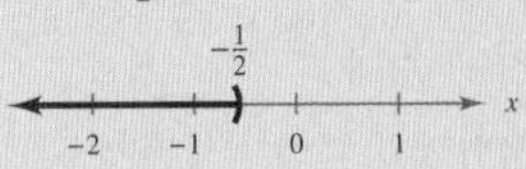

41. $x \geq 4$

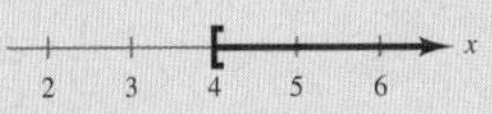

42. $x < 7$

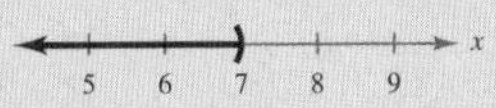

43. $x \geq 2$

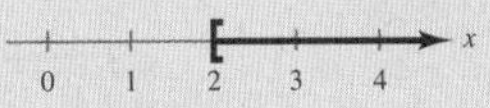

44. $x > \frac{1}{6}$

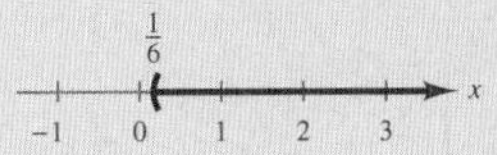

45. $x \geq -4$

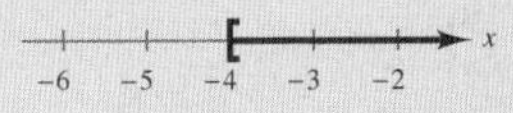

46. $x > 16$

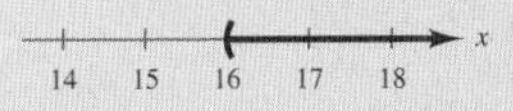

47. $-1 < x < 3$

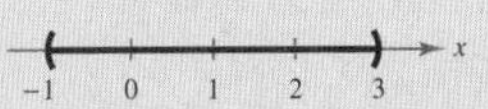

48. $-6 < x \leq 1$

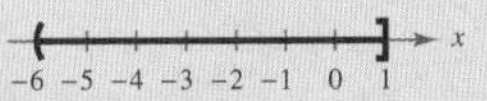

49. $-2 < x \leq 5$

50. $-7 < x \leq -\frac{1}{3}$

51. $-4 < \dfrac{2x-3}{3} < 4$ **52.** $0 \le \dfrac{x+3}{2} < 5$ 51–56. See margin.

53. $\dfrac{3}{4} > x + 1 > \dfrac{1}{4}$ **54.** $-1 < 2 - \dfrac{x}{3} < 1$

55. $3.2 \le 0.4x - 1 \le 4.4$ **56.** $4.5 > \dfrac{1.5x + 6}{2} > 10.5$

In Exercises 57–72, solve the inequality and sketch the solution on the real number line. (Some inequalities have no solution.) 57–72. See margin.

57. $|x| < 5$ **58.** $|x| \ge 8$

59. $\left|\dfrac{x}{2}\right| > 1$ **60.** $\left|\dfrac{x}{5}\right| > 3$

61. $|x - 5| < -1$ **62.** $|x - 7| < -5$

63. $|x - 20| \le 6$ **64.** $|x - 8| \ge 0$

65. $|3 - 4x| \ge 9$ **66.** $|1 - 2x| < 5$

67. $\left|\dfrac{x-3}{2}\right| \ge 4$ **68.** $\left|1 - \dfrac{2x}{3}\right| < 1$

69. $|9 - 2x| - 2 < -1$ **70.** $|x + 14| + 3 > 17$

71. $2|x + 10| \ge 9$ **72.** $3|4 - 5x| \le 9$

GRAPHICAL ANALYSIS In Exercises 73–82, use a graphing utility to graph the inequality and identify the solution set. 73–82. See margin.

73. $6x > 12$ **74.** $3x - 1 \le 5$

75. $5 - 2x \ge 1$ **76.** $20 < 6x - 1$

77. $4(x - 3) \le 8 - x$ **78.** $3(x + 1) < x + 7$

79. $|x - 8| \le 14$ **80.** $|2x + 9| > 13$

81. $2|x + 7| \ge 13$ **82.** $\frac{1}{2}|x + 1| \le 3$

GRAPHICAL ANALYSIS In Exercises 83–88, use a graphing utility to graph the equation. Use the graph to approximate the values of x that satisfy each inequality. 83–88. See margin.

	Equation	Inequalities	
83.	$y = 2x - 3$	(a) $y \ge 1$	(b) $y \le 0$
84.	$y = \frac{2}{3}x + 1$	(a) $y \le 5$	(b) $y \ge 0$
85.	$y = -\frac{1}{2}x + 2$	(a) $0 \le y \le 3$	(b) $y \ge 0$
86.	$y = -3x + 8$	(a) $-1 \le y \le 3$	(b) $y \le 0$
87.	$y = \|x - 3\|$	(a) $y \le 2$	(b) $y \ge 4$
88.	$y = \left\|\frac{1}{2}x + 1\right\|$	(a) $y \le 4$	(b) $y \ge 1$

In Exercises 89–94, find the interval(s) on the real number line for which the radicand is nonnegative.

89. $\sqrt{x - 5}$ $[5, \infty)$ **90.** $\sqrt{x - 10}$ $[10, \infty)$

91. $\sqrt{x + 3}$ $[-3, \infty)$ **92.** $\sqrt{3 - x}$ $(-\infty, 3]$

93. $\sqrt[4]{7 - 2x}$ $\left(-\infty, \frac{7}{2}\right]$ **94.** $\sqrt[4]{6x + 15}$ $\left[-\frac{5}{2}, \infty\right)$

See margin.

95. THINK ABOUT IT The graph of $|x - 5| < 3$ can be described as all real numbers within three units of 5. Give a similar description of $|x - 10| < 8$.

96. THINK ABOUT IT The graph of $|x - 2| > 5$ can be described as all real numbers more than five units from 2. Give a similar description of $|x - 8| > 4$. See margin.

In Exercises 97–104, use absolute value notation to define the interval (or pair of intervals) on the real number line.

97. $|x| \le 3$

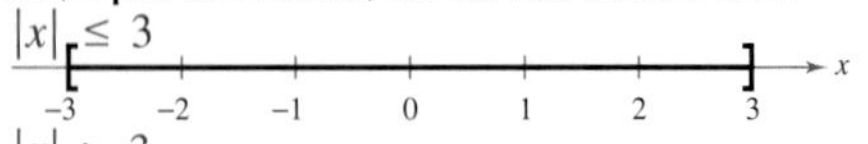

98. $|x| > 3$

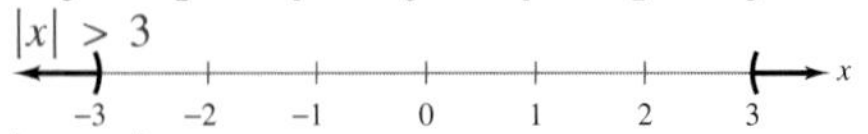

99. $|x - 7| \ge 3$

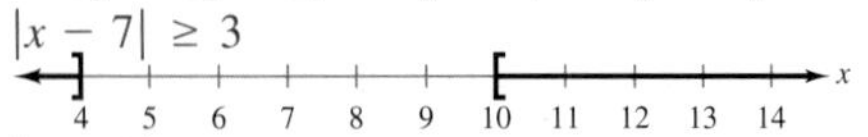

100. $|x + 1| \le 4$

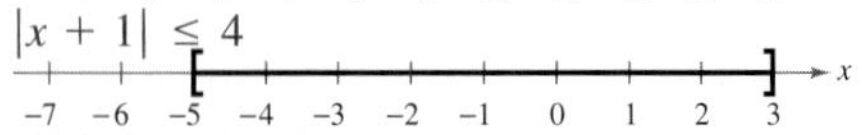

101–104. See margin.

101. All real numbers within 10 units of 12

102. All real numbers at least five units from 8

103. All real numbers more than four units from -3

104. All real numbers no more than seven units from -6

In Exercises 105–108, use inequality notation to describe the subset of real numbers. 105. See margin.

105. A company expects its earnings per share E for the next quarter to be no less than \$4.10 and no more than \$4.25.

106. The estimated daily oil production p at a refinery is greater than 2 million barrels but less than 2.4 million barrels. $2{,}000{,}000 < p < 2{,}400{,}000$

107. According to a survey, the percent p of U.S. citizens that now conduct most of their banking transactions online is no more than 45%. $p \le 0.45$

108. The net income I of a company is expected to be no less than \$239 million. $I \ge 239{,}000{,}000$

PHYSIOLOGY In Exercises 109 and 110, use the following information. The maximum heart rate of a person in normal health is related to the person's age by the equation $r = 220 - A$, where r is the maximum heart rate in beats per minute and A is the person's age in years. Some physiologists recommend that during physical activity a sedentary person should strive to increase his or her heart rate to at least 50% of the maximum heart rate, and a highly fit person should strive to increase his or her heart rate to at most 85% of the maximum heart rate. (Source: American Heart Association)

109. Express as an interval the range of the target heart rate for a 20-year-old. $100 \le r \le 170$

110. Express as an interval the range of the target heart rate for a 40-year-old. $90 \le r \le 153$

51. $-\frac{9}{2} < x < \frac{15}{2}$

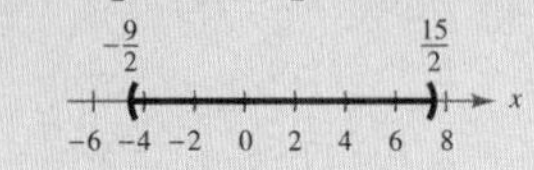

52. $-3 \le x < 7$

53. $-\frac{3}{4} < x < -\frac{1}{4}$

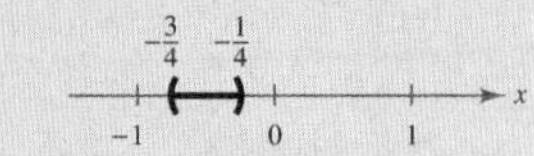

54. $3 < x < 9$

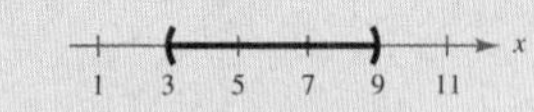

55. $10.5 \le x \le 13.5$

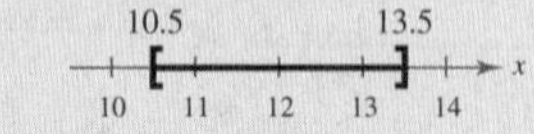

56. No solution

57. $-5 < x < 5$

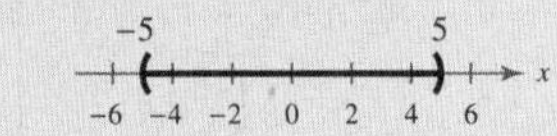

58. $x \le -8, x \ge 8$

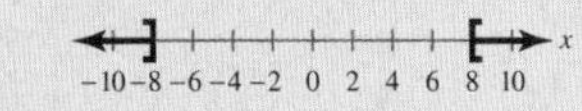

59. $x < -2, x > 2$

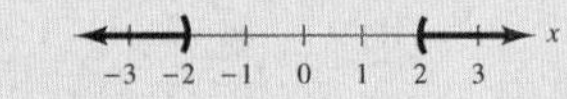

60. $x < -15,\ x > 15$

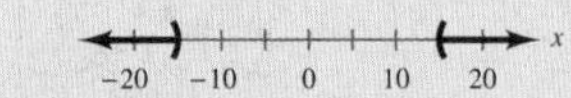

61. No solution **62.** No solution

63. $14 \le x \le 26$

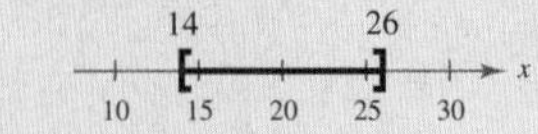

64. All real numbers x

65. $x \le -\frac{3}{2}, x \ge 3$

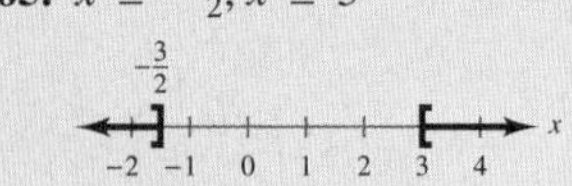

66. $-2 < x < 3$

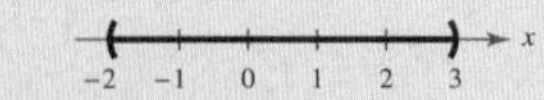

67. $x \le -5,\ x \ge 11$

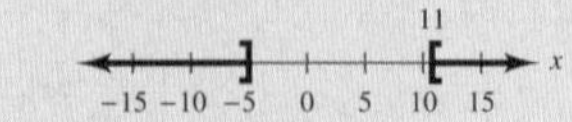

68. $0 < x < 3$

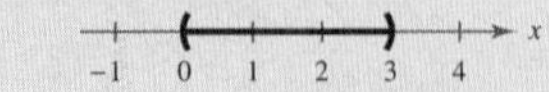

69. $4 < x < 5$

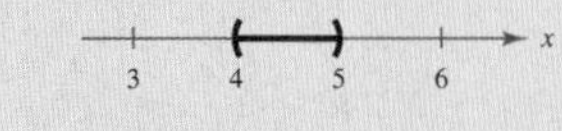

70. $x < -28,\ x > 0$

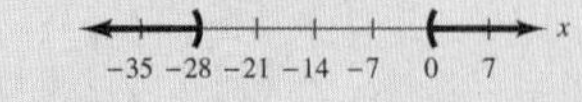

71. $x \le -\frac{29}{2},\ x \ge -\frac{11}{2}$

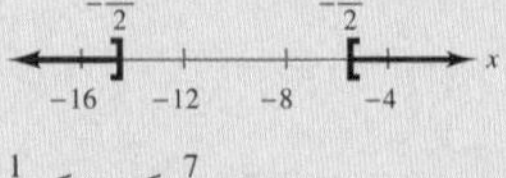

72. $\frac{1}{5} \le x \le \frac{7}{5}$

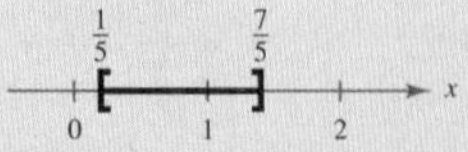

73.

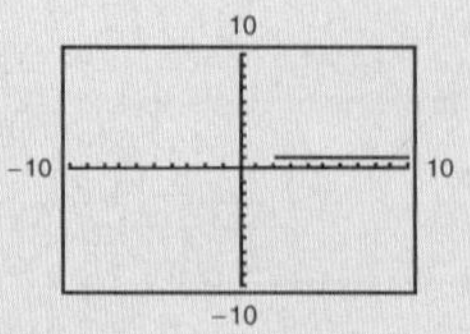

$x > 2$

74.

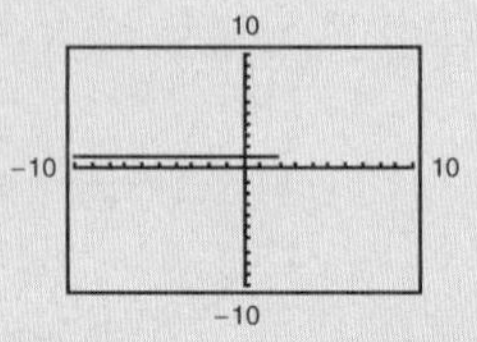

$x \le 2$

75–88, 95, 96, 101–105. See Additional Answers beginning on page AA1.

111. JOB OFFERS You are considering two job offers. The first job pays \$13.50 per hour. The second job pays \$9.00 per hour plus \$0.75 per unit produced per hour. Write an inequality yielding the number of units x that must be produced per hour to make the second job pay the greater hourly wage. Solve the inequality. See margin.

112. JOB OFFERS You are considering two job offers. The first job pays \$3000 per month. The second job pays \$1000 per month plus a commission of 4% of your gross sales. Write an inequality yielding the gross sales x per month for which the second job will pay the greater monthly wage. Solve the inequality. See margin.

113. INVESTMENT In order for an investment of \$1000 to grow to more than \$1062.50 in 2 years, what must the annual interest rate be? $[A = P(1 + rt)]$ $r > 3.125\%$

114. INVESTMENT In order for an investment of \$750 to grow to more than \$825 in 2 years, what must the annual interest rate be? $[A = P(1 + rt)]$ $r > 5\%$

115. COST, REVENUE, AND PROFIT The revenue from selling x units of a product is $R = 115.95x$. The cost of producing x units is $C = 95x + 750$. To obtain a profit, the revenue must be greater than the cost. For what values of x will this product return a profit? $x \geq 36$

116. COST, REVENUE, AND PROFIT The revenue from selling x units of a product is $R = 24.55x$. The cost of producing x units is $C = 15.4x + 150{,}000$. To obtain a profit, the revenue must be greater than the cost. For what values of x will this product return a profit? $x \geq 16{,}394$

117. DAILY SALES A doughnut shop sells a dozen doughnuts for \$4.50. Beyond the fixed costs (rent, utilities, and insurance) of \$220 per day, it costs \$2.75 for enough materials (flour, sugar, and so on) and labor to produce a dozen doughnuts. The daily profit from doughnut sales varies from \$60 to \$270. Between what levels (in dozens) do the daily sales vary? $160 \leq x \leq 280$

118. WEIGHT LOSS PROGRAM A person enrolls in a diet and exercise program that guarantees a loss of at least $1\frac{1}{2}$ pounds per week. The person's weight at the beginning of the program is 164 pounds. Find the maximum number of weeks before the person attains a goal weight of 128 pounds. 24 wk

119. DATA ANALYSIS: IQ SCORES AND GPA The admissions office of a college wants to determine whether there is a relationship between IQ scores x and grade-point averages y after the first year of school. An equation that models the data the admissions office obtained is $y = 0.067x - 5.638$.

(a) Use a graphing utility to graph the model. See margin.

(b) Use the graph to estimate the values of x that predict a grade-point average of at least 3.0.
$x \geq 129$

120. DATA ANALYSIS: WEIGHTLIFTING You want to determine whether there is a relationship between an athlete's weight x (in pounds) and the athlete's maximum bench-press weight y (in pounds). The table shows a sample of data from 12 athletes. See margin.

Athlete's weight, x	Bench-press weight, y
165	170
184	185
150	200
210	255
196	205
240	295
202	190
170	175
185	195
190	185
230	250
160	155

(a) Use a graphing utility to plot the data.

(b) A model for the data is $y = 1.3x - 36$. Use a graphing utility to graph the model in the same viewing window used in part (a).

(c) Use the graph to estimate the values of x that predict a maximum bench-press weight of at least 200 pounds.

(d) Verify your estimate from part (c) algebraically.

(e) Use the graph to write a statement about the accuracy of the model. If you think the graph indicates that an athlete's weight is not a particularly good indicator of the athlete's maximum bench-press weight, list other factors that might influence an individual's maximum bench-press weight.

121. TEACHERS' SALARIES The average salaries S (in thousands of dollars) for elementary school teachers in the United States from 1990 through 2005 are approximated by the model

$$S = 1.09t + 30.9, \quad 0 \leq t \leq 15$$

where t represents the year, with $t = 0$ corresponding to 1990. (Source: National Education Association)

(a) According to this model, when was the average salary at least \$32,500, but not more than \$42,000?

(b) According to this model, when will the average salary exceed \$54,000?

(a) $1.47 \leq t \leq 10.18$ (Between 1991 and 2000)
(b) $t > 21.19$ (2011)

111. $9.00 + 0.75x > 13.50$; $x > 6$

112. $1000 + 0.04x > 3000$;
$x > 50{,}000$

119. (a)

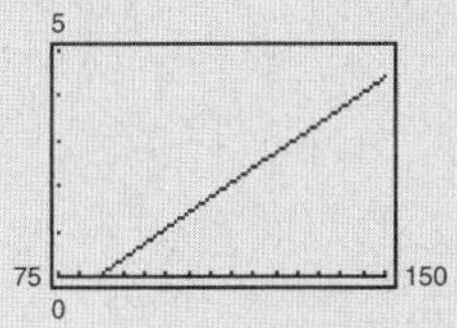

120. (a) and (b)

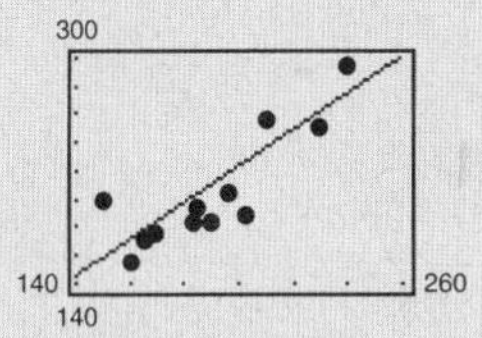

(c) $x \geq 182$ (d) $x \geq 181.54$

(e) An athlete's weight is not a particularly good indicator of the athlete's maximum bench-press weight. Other factors, such as muscle tone and exercise habits, influence maximum bench-press weight.

122. (a) $1.32 \le t \le 7.89$ (Between 1991 and 1997)
(b) $t > 21.05$ (2011)
123. See below.
124. See below.
125. You might be undercharged or overcharged by \$0.21.
126. \$0.47
131. False. c has to be greater than zero.
132. False. If $-10 \le x \le 8$, then $10 \ge -x$ and $-x \ge -8$.
134. One set (the solution is not unique): $a = 1, b = 5, c = 5$
136. When each side of an inequality is multiplied or divided by a negative number, the direction of the inequality symbol must be reversed.

122. EGG PRODUCTION The numbers of eggs E (in billions) produced in the United States from 1990 through 2006 can be modeled by

$$E = 1.52t + 68.0, \quad 0 \le t \le 16$$ See margin.

where t represents the year, with $t = 0$ corresponding to 1990. (Source: U.S. Department of Agriculture)

(a) According to this model, when was the annual egg production 70 billion, but no more than 80 billion?

(b) According to this model, when will the annual egg production exceed 100 billion?

123. GEOMETRY The side of a square is measured as 10.4 inches with a possible error of $\frac{1}{16}$ inch. Using these measurements, determine the interval containing the possible areas of the square. See margin.

124. GEOMETRY The side of a square is measured as 24.2 centimeters with a possible error of 0.25 centimeter. Using these measurements, determine the interval containing the possible areas of the square. See margin.

125. ACCURACY OF MEASUREMENT You stop at a self-service gas station to buy 15 gallons of 87-octane gasoline at \$2.09 a gallon. The gas pump is accurate to within $\frac{1}{10}$ of a gallon. How much might you be undercharged or overcharged? See margin.

126. ACCURACY OF MEASUREMENT You buy six T-bone steaks that cost \$14.99 per pound. The weight that is listed on the package is 5.72 pounds. The scale that weighed the package is accurate to within $\frac{1}{2}$ ounce. How much might you be undercharged or overcharged? See margin.

127. TIME STUDY A time study was conducted to determine the length of time required to perform a particular task in a manufacturing process. The times required by approximately two-thirds of the workers in the study satisfied the inequality $13.7 < t < 17.5$

$$\left|\frac{t - 15.6}{1.9}\right| < 1$$

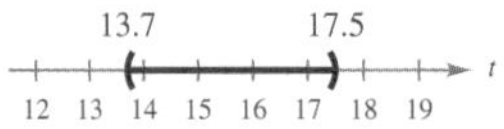

where t is time in minutes. Determine the interval on the real number line in which these times lie.

128. HEIGHT The heights h of two-thirds of the members of a population satisfy the inequality $65.8 \le h \le 71.2$

$$\left|\frac{h - 68.5}{2.7}\right| \le 1$$

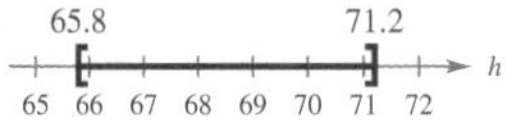

where h is measured in inches. Determine the interval on the real number line in which these heights lie.

129. METEOROLOGY An electronic device is to be operated in an environment with relative humidity h in the interval defined by $|h - 50| \le 30$. What are the minimum and maximum relative humidities for the operation of this device? $20 \le h \le 80$

130. MUSIC Michael Kasha of Florida State University used physics and mathematics to design a new classical guitar. The model he used for the frequency of the vibrations on a circular plate was $v = (2.6t/d^2)\sqrt{E/\rho}$, where v is the frequency (in vibrations per second), t is the plate thickness (in millimeters), d is the diameter of the plate, E is the elasticity of the plate material, and ρ is the density of the plate material. For fixed values of d, E, and ρ, the graph of the equation is a line (see figure).

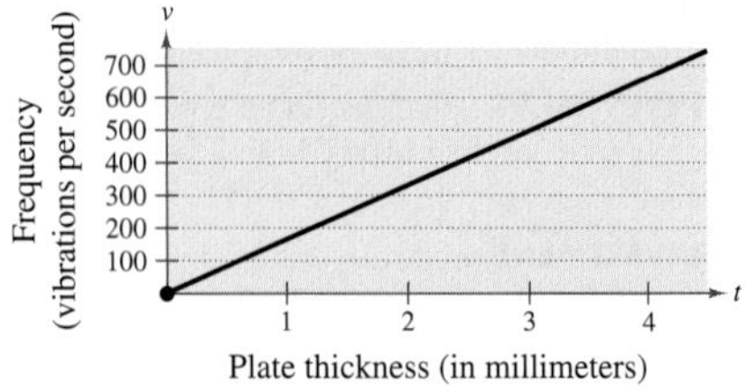

(a) Estimate the frequency when the plate thickness is 2 millimeters. About 330 vibrations/sec

(b) Estimate the plate thickness when the frequency is 600 vibrations per second. About 3.6 mm

(c) Approximate the interval for the plate thickness when the frequency is between 200 and 400 vibrations per second. $1.2 \text{ mm} \le t \le 2.4 \text{ mm}$

(d) Approximate the interval for the frequency when the plate thickness is less than 3 millimeters. $v < 500$ vibrations/sec

EXPLORATION

131–132. See margin.

TRUE OR FALSE? In Exercises 131 and 132, determine whether the statement is true or false. Justify your answer.

131. If a, b, and c are real numbers, and $a \le b$, then $ac \le bc$.

132. If $-10 \le x \le 8$, then $-10 \ge -x$ and $-x \ge -8$.

133. Identify the graph of the inequality $|x - a| \ge 2$. b

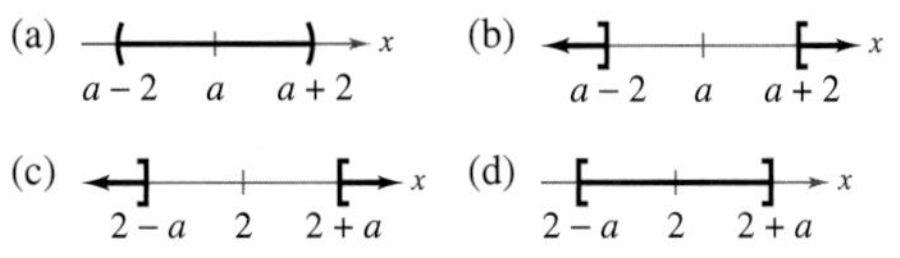

134. Find sets of values of a, b, and c such that $0 \le x \le 10$ is a solution of the inequality $|ax - b| \le c$. See margin.

135. Give an example of an inequality with an unbounded solution set. Sample answer: $x > 5$

136. CAPSTONE Describe any differences between properties of equalities and properties of inequalities. See margin.

123. $106.864 \text{ in.}^2 \le \text{area} \le 109.464 \text{ in.}^2$
124. $573.6025 \text{ cm}^2 \le \text{area} \le 597.8025 \text{ cm}^2$

A.7 Errors and the Algebra of Calculus

What you should learn

- Avoid common algebraic errors.
- Recognize and use algebraic techniques that are common in calculus.

Why you should learn it

An efficient command of algebra is critical in mastering this course and in the study of calculus.

Algebraic Errors to Avoid

This section contains five lists of common algebraic errors: errors involving parentheses, errors involving fractions, errors involving exponents, errors involving radicals, and errors involving dividing out. Many of these errors are made because they seem to be the *easiest* things to do. For instance, the operations of subtraction and division are often believed to be commutative and associative. The following examples illustrate the fact that subtraction and division are neither commutative nor associative.

Not commutative	*Not associative*
$4 - 3 \neq 3 - 4$	$8 - (6 - 2) \neq (8 - 6) - 2$
$15 \div 5 \neq 5 \div 15$	$20 \div (4 \div 2) \neq (20 \div 4) \div 2$

Errors Involving Parentheses

Potential Error	*Correct Form*	*Comment*
~~$a - (x - b) = a - x - b$~~	$a - (x - b) = a - x + b$	Change all signs when distributing minus sign.
~~$(a + b)^2 = a^2 + b^2$~~	$(a + b)^2 = a^2 + 2ab + b^2$	Remember the middle term when squaring binomials.
~~$\left(\frac{1}{2}a\right)\left(\frac{1}{2}b\right) = \frac{1}{2}(ab)$~~	$\left(\frac{1}{2}a\right)\left(\frac{1}{2}b\right) = \frac{1}{4}(ab) = \frac{ab}{4}$	$\frac{1}{2}$ occurs twice as a factor.
~~$(3x + 6)^2 = 3(x + 2)^2$~~	$(3x + 6)^2 = [3(x + 2)]^2$ $= 3^2(x + 2)^2$	When factoring, apply exponents to all factors.

Errors Involving Fractions

Potential Error	*Correct Form*	*Comment*
~~$\frac{a}{x + b} = \frac{a}{x} + \frac{a}{b}$~~	Leave as $\frac{a}{x + b}$.	Do not add denominators when adding fractions.
~~$\frac{\left(\frac{x}{a}\right)}{b} = \frac{bx}{a}$~~	$\frac{\left(\frac{x}{a}\right)}{b} = \left(\frac{x}{a}\right)\left(\frac{1}{b}\right) = \frac{x}{ab}$	Multiply by the reciprocal when dividing fractions.
~~$\frac{1}{a} + \frac{1}{b} = \frac{1}{a + b}$~~	$\frac{1}{a} + \frac{1}{b} = \frac{b + a}{ab}$	Use the property for adding fractions.
~~$\frac{1}{3x} = \frac{1}{3}x$~~	$\frac{1}{3x} = \frac{1}{3} \cdot \frac{1}{x}$	Use the property for multiplying fractions.
~~$(1/3)x = \frac{1}{3x}$~~	$(1/3)x = \frac{1}{3} \cdot x = \frac{x}{3}$	Be careful when using a slash to denote division.
~~$(1/x) + 2 = \frac{1}{x + 2}$~~	$(1/x) + 2 = \frac{1}{x} + 2 = \frac{1 + 2x}{x}$	Be careful when using a slash to denote division and be sure to find a common denominator before you add fractions.

Errors Involving Exponents

Potential Error	*Correct Form*	*Comment*
~~$(x^2)^3 = x^5$~~	$(x^2)^3 = x^{2 \cdot 3} = x^6$	Multiply exponents when raising a power to a power.
~~$x^2 \cdot x^3 = x^6$~~	$x^2 \cdot x^3 = x^{2+3} = x^5$	Add exponents when multiplying powers with like bases.
~~$2x^3 = (2x)^3$~~	$2x^3 = 2(x^3)$	Exponents have priority over coefficients.
~~$\dfrac{1}{x^2 - x^3} = x^{-2} - x^{-3}$~~	Leave as $\dfrac{1}{x^2 - x^3}$.	Do not move term-by-term from denominator to numerator.

Errors Involving Radicals

Potential Error	*Correct Form*	*Comment*
~~$\sqrt{5x} = 5\sqrt{x}$~~	$\sqrt{5x} = \sqrt{5}\sqrt{x}$	Radicals apply to every factor inside the radical.
~~$\sqrt{x^2 + a^2} = x + a$~~	Leave as $\sqrt{x^2 + a^2}$.	Do not apply radicals term-by-term when adding or subtracting terms.
~~$\sqrt{-x + a} = -\sqrt{x - a}$~~	Leave as $\sqrt{-x + a}$.	Do not factor minus signs out of square roots.

Errors Involving Dividing Out

Potential Error	*Correct Form*	*Comment*
~~$\dfrac{a + bx}{a} = 1 + bx$~~	$\dfrac{a + bx}{a} = \dfrac{a}{a} + \dfrac{bx}{a} = 1 + \dfrac{b}{a}x$	Divide out common factors, not common terms.
~~$\dfrac{a + ax}{a} = a + x$~~	$\dfrac{a + ax}{a} = \dfrac{a(1 + x)}{a} = 1 + x$	Factor before dividing out.
~~$1 + \dfrac{x}{2x} = 1 + \dfrac{1}{x}$~~	$1 + \dfrac{x}{2x} = 1 + \dfrac{1}{2} = \dfrac{3}{2}$	Divide out common factors.

A good way to avoid errors is to *work slowly*, *write neatly*, and *talk to yourself*. Each time you write a step, ask yourself why the step is algebraically legitimate. You can justify the step below because *dividing the numerator and denominator by the same nonzero number produces an equivalent fraction.*

$$\frac{2x}{6} = \frac{\cancel{2} \cdot x}{\cancel{2} \cdot 3} = \frac{x}{3}$$

Example 1 Using the Property for Adding Fractions

Describe and correct the error. ~~$\dfrac{1}{2x} + \dfrac{1}{3x} = \dfrac{1}{5x}$~~

Solution

When adding fractions, use the property for adding fractions: $\dfrac{1}{a} + \dfrac{1}{b} = \dfrac{b + a}{ab}$.

$$\frac{1}{2x} + \frac{1}{3x} = \frac{3x + 2x}{6x^2} = \frac{5x}{6x^2} = \frac{5}{6x}$$

CHECK*Point* Now try Exercise 19.

Some Algebra of Calculus

In calculus it is often necessary to take a simplified algebraic expression and rewrite it. See the following lists, taken from a standard calculus text.

Unusual Factoring

Expression	*Useful Calculus Form*	*Comment*
$\frac{5x^4}{8}$	$\frac{5}{8}x^4$	Write with fractional coefficient.
$\frac{x^2 + 3x}{-6}$	$-\frac{1}{6}(x^2 + 3x)$	Write with fractional coefficient.
$2x^2 - x - 3$	$2\left(x^2 - \frac{x}{2} - \frac{3}{2}\right)$	Factor out the leading coefficient.
$\frac{x}{2}(x + 1)^{-1/2} + (x + 1)^{1/2}$	$\frac{(x + 1)^{-1/2}}{2}[x + 2(x + 1)]$	Factor out factor with lowest power.

Writing with Negative Exponents

Expression	*Useful Calculus Form*	*Comment*
$\frac{9}{5x^3}$	$\frac{9}{5}x^{-3}$	Move the factor to the numerator and change the sign of the exponent.
$\frac{7}{\sqrt{2x - 3}}$	$7(2x - 3)^{-1/2}$	Move the factor to the numerator and change the sign of the exponent.

Writing a Fraction as a Sum

Expression	*Useful Calculus Form*	*Comment*
$\frac{x + 2x^2 + 1}{\sqrt{x}}$	$x^{1/2} + 2x^{3/2} + x^{-1/2}$	Divide each term by $x^{1/2}$.
$\frac{1 + x}{x^2 + 1}$	$\frac{1}{x^2 + 1} + \frac{x}{x^2 + 1}$	Rewrite the fraction as a sum of fractions.
$\frac{2x}{x^2 + 2x + 1}$	$\frac{2x + 2 - 2}{x^2 + 2x + 1}$	Add and subtract the same term.
	$= \frac{2x + 2}{x^2 + 2x + 1} - \frac{2}{(x + 1)^2}$	Rewrite the fraction as a difference of fractions.
$\frac{x^2 - 2}{x + 1}$	$x - 1 - \frac{1}{x + 1}$	Use long division. (See Section 2.3.)
$\frac{x + 7}{x^2 - x - 6}$	$\frac{2}{x - 3} - \frac{1}{x + 2}$	Use the method of partial fractions. (See Section 7.4.)

Inserting Factors and Terms

Expression	*Useful Calculus Form*	*Comment*
$(2x - 1)^3$	$\frac{1}{2}(2x - 1)^3(2)$	Multiply and divide by 2.
$7x^2(4x^3 - 5)^{1/2}$	$\frac{7}{12}(4x^3 - 5)^{1/2}(12x^2)$	Multiply and divide by 12.
$\frac{4x^2}{9} - 4y^2 = 1$	$\frac{x^2}{9/4} - \frac{y^2}{1/4} = 1$	Write with fractional denominators.
$\frac{x}{x+1}$	$\frac{x+1-1}{x+1} = 1 - \frac{1}{x+1}$	Add and subtract the same term.

The next five examples demonstrate many of the steps in the preceding lists.

Example 2 Factors Involving Negative Exponents

Factor $x(x + 1)^{-1/2} + (x + 1)^{1/2}$.

Solution

When multiplying factors with like bases, you add exponents. When factoring, you are undoing multiplication, and so you *subtract* exponents.

$$\begin{aligned} x(x + 1)^{-1/2} + (x + 1)^{1/2} &= (x + 1)^{-1/2}[x(x + 1)^0 + (x + 1)^1] \\ &= (x + 1)^{-1/2}[x + (x + 1)] \\ &= (x + 1)^{-1/2}(2x + 1) \end{aligned}$$

CHECK*Point* Now try Exercise 29.

Another way to simplify the expression in Example 2 is to multiply the expression by a fractional form of 1 and then use the Distributive Property.

$$\begin{aligned} x(x + 1)^{-1/2} + (x + 1)^{1/2} &= [x(x + 1)^{-1/2} + (x + 1)^{1/2}] \cdot \frac{(x + 1)^{1/2}}{(x + 1)^{1/2}} \\ &= \frac{x(x + 1)^0 + (x + 1)^1}{(x + 1)^{1/2}} = \frac{2x + 1}{\sqrt{x + 1}} \end{aligned}$$

Example 3 Inserting Factors in an Expression

Insert the required factor: $\dfrac{x + 2}{(x^2 + 4x - 3)^2} = (\quad)\dfrac{1}{(x^2 + 4x - 3)^2}(2x + 4)$.

Solution

The expression on the right side of the equation is twice the expression on the left side. To make both sides equal, insert a factor of $\frac{1}{2}$.

$$\frac{x + 2}{(x^2 + 4x - 3)^2} = \left(\frac{1}{2}\right)\frac{1}{(x^2 + 4x - 3)^2}(2x + 4)$$ Right side is multiplied and divided by 2.

CHECK*Point* Now try Exercise 31.

Example 4 Rewriting Fractions

Explain why the two expressions are equivalent.

$$\frac{4x^2}{9} - 4y^2 = \frac{x^2}{\frac{9}{4}} - \frac{y^2}{\frac{1}{4}}$$

Solution

To write the expression on the left side of the equation in the form given on the right side, multiply the numerators and denominators of both terms by $\frac{1}{4}$.

$$\frac{4x^2}{9} - 4y^2 = \frac{4x^2}{9}\left(\frac{\frac{1}{4}}{\frac{1}{4}}\right) - 4y^2\left(\frac{\frac{1}{4}}{\frac{1}{4}}\right) = \frac{x^2}{\frac{9}{4}} - \frac{y^2}{\frac{1}{4}}$$

CHECKPoint Now try Exercise 35.

Example 5 Rewriting with Negative Exponents

Rewrite each expression using negative exponents.

a. $\dfrac{-4x}{(1 - 2x^2)^2}$ **b.** $\dfrac{2}{5x^3} - \dfrac{1}{\sqrt{x}} + \dfrac{3}{5(4x)^2}$

Solution

a. $\dfrac{-4x}{(1 - 2x^2)^2} = -4x(1 - 2x^2)^{-2}$

b. Begin by writing the second term in exponential form.

$$\frac{2}{5x^3} - \frac{1}{\sqrt{x}} + \frac{3}{5(4x)^2} = \frac{2}{5x^3} - \frac{1}{x^{1/2}} + \frac{3}{5(4x)^2}$$

$$= \frac{2}{5}x^{-3} - x^{-1/2} + \frac{3}{5}(4x)^{-2}$$

CHECKPoint Now try Exercise 47.

Example 6 Writing a Fraction as a Sum of Terms

Rewrite each fraction as the sum of three terms.

a. $\dfrac{x^2 - 4x + 8}{2x}$ **b.** $\dfrac{x + 2x^2 + 1}{\sqrt{x}}$

Solution

a. $\dfrac{x^2 - 4x + 8}{2x} = \dfrac{x^2}{2x} - \dfrac{4x}{2x} + \dfrac{8}{2x}$

$$= \frac{x}{2} - 2 + \frac{4}{x}$$

b. $\dfrac{x + 2x^2 + 1}{\sqrt{x}} = \dfrac{x}{x^{1/2}} + \dfrac{2x^2}{x^{1/2}} + \dfrac{1}{x^{1/2}}$

$$= x^{1/2} + 2x^{3/2} + x^{-1/2}$$

CHECKPoint Now try Exercise 51.

A.7 EXERCISES

See www.CalcChat.com for worked-out solutions to odd-numbered exercises.

VOCABULARY: Fill in the blanks.

1. To write the expression $\frac{3}{x^5}$ with negative exponents, move x^5 to the numerator and change the sign of the exponent.
2. When dividing fractions, multiply by the reciprocal.

SKILLS AND APPLICATIONS

In Exercises 3–22, describe and correct the error. 3–22. See margin.

3. $2x - (3y + 4) = 2x - 3y + 4$
4. $5z + 3(x - 2) = 5z + 3x - 2$
5. $\dfrac{4}{16x - (2x + 1)} = \dfrac{4}{14x + 1}$
6. $\dfrac{1 - x}{(5 - x)(-x)} = \dfrac{x - 1}{x(x - 5)}$
7. $(5z)(6z) = 30z$
8. $x(yz) = (xy)(xz)$
9. $a\left(\dfrac{x}{y}\right) = \dfrac{ax}{ay}$
10. $(4x)^2 = 4x^2$
11. $\sqrt{x + 9} = \sqrt{x} + 3$
12. $\sqrt{25 - x^2} = 5 - x$
13. $\dfrac{2x^2 + 1}{5x} = \dfrac{2x + 1}{5}$
14. $\dfrac{6x + y}{6x - y} = \dfrac{x + y}{x - y}$
15. $\dfrac{1}{a^{-1} + b^{-1}} = \left(\dfrac{1}{a + b}\right)^{-1}$
16. $\dfrac{1}{x + y^{-1}} = \dfrac{y}{x + 1}$
17. $(x^2 + 5x)^{1/2} = x(x + 5)^{1/2}$
18. $x(2x - 1)^2 = (2x^2 - x)^2$
19. $\dfrac{3}{x} + \dfrac{4}{y} = \dfrac{7}{x + y}$
20. $\dfrac{1}{2y} = (1/2)y$
21. $\dfrac{x}{2y} + \dfrac{y}{3} = \dfrac{x + y}{2y + 3}$
22. $5 + (1/y) = \dfrac{1}{5 + y}$

In Exercises 23–44, insert the required factor in the parentheses. 23–44. See margin.

23. $\dfrac{5x + 3}{4} = \dfrac{1}{4}(\quad)$
24. $\dfrac{7x^2}{10} = \dfrac{7}{10}(\quad)$
25. $\frac{2}{3}x^2 + \frac{1}{3}x + 5 = \frac{1}{3}(\quad)$
26. $\frac{3}{4}x + \frac{1}{2} = \frac{1}{4}(\quad)$
27. $x^2(x^3 - 1)^4 = (\quad)(x^3 - 1)^4(3x^2)$
28. $x(1 - 2x^2)^3 = (\quad)(1 - 2x^2)^3(-4x)$
29. $2(y - 5)^{1/2} + y(y - 5)^{-1/2} = (y - 5)^{-1/2}(\quad)$
30. $3t(6t + 1)^{-1/2} + (6t + 1)^{1/2} = (6t + 1)^{-1/2}(\quad)$
31. $\dfrac{4x + 6}{(x^2 + 3x + 7)^3} = (\quad)\dfrac{1}{(x^2 + 3x + 7)^3}(2x + 3)$
32. $\dfrac{x + 1}{(x^2 + 2x - 3)^2} = (\quad)\dfrac{1}{(x^2 + 2x - 3)^2}(2x + 2)$
33. $\dfrac{3}{x} + \dfrac{5}{2x^2} - \dfrac{3}{2}x = (\quad)(6x + 5 - 3x^3)$
34. $\dfrac{(x - 1)^2}{169} + (y + 5)^2 = \dfrac{(x - 1)^2}{169(\quad)} + (y + 5)^2$
35. $\dfrac{25x^2}{36} + \dfrac{4y^2}{9} = \dfrac{x^2}{(\quad)} + \dfrac{y^2}{(\quad)}$
36. $\dfrac{5x^2}{9} - \dfrac{16y^2}{49} = \dfrac{x^2}{(\quad)} - \dfrac{y^2}{(\quad)}$
37. $\dfrac{x^2}{3/10} - \dfrac{y^2}{4/5} = \dfrac{10x^2}{(\quad)} - \dfrac{5y^2}{(\quad)}$
38. $\dfrac{x^2}{5/8} + \dfrac{y^2}{6/11} = \dfrac{8x^2}{(\quad)} + \dfrac{11y^2}{(\quad)}$
39. $x^{1/3} - 5x^{4/3} = x^{1/3}(\quad)$
40. $3(2x + 1)x^{1/2} + 4x^{3/2} = x^{1/2}(\quad)$
41. $(1 - 3x)^{4/3} - 4x(1 - 3x)^{1/3} = (1 - 3x)^{1/3}(\quad)$
42. $\dfrac{1}{2\sqrt{x}} + 5x^{3/2} - 10x^{5/2} = \dfrac{1}{2\sqrt{x}}(\quad)$
43. $\dfrac{1}{10}(2x + 1)^{5/2} - \dfrac{1}{6}(2x + 1)^{3/2} = \dfrac{(2x + 1)^{3/2}}{15}(\quad)$
44. $\dfrac{3}{7}(t + 1)^{7/3} - \dfrac{3}{4}(t + 1)^{4/3} = \dfrac{3(t + 1)^{4/3}}{28}(\quad)$

In Exercises 45–50, write the expression using negative exponents. 45–50. See margin.

45. $\dfrac{7}{(x + 3)^5}$
46. $\dfrac{2 - x}{(x + 1)^{3/2}}$
47. $\dfrac{2x^5}{(3x + 5)^4}$
48. $\dfrac{x + 1}{x(6 - x)^{1/2}}$
49. $\dfrac{4}{3x} + \dfrac{4}{x^4} - \dfrac{7x}{\sqrt[3]{2x}}$
50. $\dfrac{x}{x - 2} + \dfrac{1}{x^2} + \dfrac{8}{3(9x)^3}$

In Exercises 51–56, write the fraction as a sum of two or more terms. 51–56. See margin.

51. $\dfrac{x^2 + 6x + 12}{3x}$
52. $\dfrac{x^3 - 5x^2 + 4}{x^2}$
53. $\dfrac{4x^3 - 7x^2 + 1}{x^{1/3}}$
54. $\dfrac{2x^5 - 3x^3 + 5x - 1}{x^{3/2}}$
55. $\dfrac{3 - 5x^2 - x^4}{\sqrt{x}}$
56. $\dfrac{x^3 - 5x^4}{3x^2}$

3. Change all signs when distributing the minus sign.
$2x - (3y + 4) = 2x - 3y - 4$
4. The 3 is distributed to both terms.
$5z + 3(x - 2) = 5z + 3x - 6$
5. Change all signs when distributing the minus sign.
$\dfrac{4}{16x - (2x + 1)} = \dfrac{4}{14x - 1}$
6. The expression on the right should be negated.
$\dfrac{1 - x}{(5 - x)(-x)} = -\dfrac{x - 1}{x(x - 5)}$
7. z occurs twice as a factor.
$(5z)(6z) = 30z^2$
8. yz is one term, not two.
$x(yz) = xyz$
9. The fraction as a whole is multiplied by a, not the numerator and denominator separately.
$a\left(\dfrac{x}{y}\right) = \dfrac{ax}{y}$
10. The exponent also applies to the coefficient.
$(4x)^2 = 16x^2$
11. $\sqrt{x + 9}$ cannot be simplified.
12. Do not apply radicals term-by-term.
$\sqrt{25 - x^2} = \sqrt{(5 + x)(5 - x)}$
13. Divide out common factors, not common terms.
$\dfrac{2x^2 + 1}{5x}$ cannot be simplified.
14. $\dfrac{6x + y}{6x - y}$ cannot be simplified.
15. See below.
16. The negative exponent is on a term of the denominator, not a factor.
$\dfrac{1}{x + y^{-1}} = \dfrac{y}{xy + 1}, \ y \neq 0$
17. See below.
18. See below.
19. To add fractions, first find a common denominator.
$\dfrac{3}{x} + \dfrac{4}{y} = \dfrac{3y + 4x}{xy}$
20. Be careful when using a slash to denote division.
$(1/2)y = \dfrac{1}{2} \cdot y = \dfrac{y}{2}$
21. To add fractions, first find a common denominator.
$\dfrac{x}{2y} + \dfrac{y}{3} = \dfrac{3x + 2y^2}{6y}$
22. To add fractions, first find a common denominator.
$5 + \left(\dfrac{1}{y}\right) = \dfrac{5y + 1}{y}$

23. $5x + 3$ 24. x^2 25. $2x^2 + x + 15$
26. $3x + 2$ 27. $\frac{1}{3}$ 28. $-\frac{1}{4}$ 29. $3y - 10$
30. $9t + 1$ 31. 2 32. $\dfrac{1}{2}$ 33. $\dfrac{1}{2x^2}$
34. $x - 1$ 35. $\frac{36}{25}, \frac{9}{4}$ 36. $\frac{9}{5}, \frac{49}{16}$ 37. 3, 4
38. 5, 6 39. $1 - 5x$ 40. $10x + 3$
41. $1 - 7x$ 42. $1 + 10x^2 - 20x^3$ 43. $3x - 1$
44. $4t - 3$ 45. $7(x + 3)^{-5}$

46. $(2 - x)(x + 1)^{-3/2}$ 47. $2x^5(3x + 5)^{-4}$
48. $(x + 1)x^{-1}(6 - x)^{-1/2}$

15. To get rid of negative exponents:
$\dfrac{1}{a^{-1} + b^{-1}} = \dfrac{1}{a^{-1} + b^{-1}} \cdot \dfrac{ab}{ab} = \dfrac{ab}{b + a}.$
17. Factor within grouping symbols before applying exponent to each factor.
$(x^2 + 5x)^{1/2} = [x(x + 5)]^{1/2} = x^{1/2}(x + 5)^{1/2}$
18. Exponents are applied before multiplying.
$x(2x - 1)^2 = x(4x^2 - 4x + 1) = 4x^3 - 4x^2 + x$

49–56. See Additional Answers beginning on page AA1.

In Exercises 57–68, simplify the expression. 57–64. See margin.

57. $\dfrac{-2(x^2-3)^{-3}(2x)(x+1)^3-3(x+1)^2(x^2-3)^{-2}}{[(x+1)^3]^2}$

58. $\dfrac{x^5(-3)(x^2+1)^{-4}(2x)-(x^2+1)^{-3}(5)x^4}{(x^5)^2}$

59. $\dfrac{(6x+1)^3(27x^2+2)-(9x^3+2x)(3)(6x+1)^2(6)}{[(6x+1)^3]^2}$

60. $\dfrac{(4x^2+9)^{1/2}(2)-(2x+3)\left(\frac{1}{2}\right)(4x^2+9)^{-1/2}(8x)}{[(4x^2+9)^{1/2}]^2}$

61. $\dfrac{(x+2)^{3/4}(x+3)^{-2/3}-(x+3)^{1/3}(x+2)^{-1/4}}{[(x+2)^{3/4}]^2}$

62. $(2x-1)^{1/2}-(x+2)(2x-1)^{-1/2}$

63. $\dfrac{2(3x-1)^{1/3}-(2x+1)\left(\frac{1}{3}\right)(3x-1)^{-2/3}(3)}{(3x-1)^{2/3}}$

64. $\dfrac{(x+1)\left(\frac{1}{2}\right)(2x-3x^2)^{-1/2}(2-6x)-(2x-3x^2)^{1/2}}{(x+1)^2}$

65. $\dfrac{1}{(x^2+4)^{1/2}}\cdot\dfrac{1}{2}(x^2+4)^{-1/2}(2x)$ $\quad\dfrac{x}{x^2+4}$

66. $\dfrac{1}{x^2-6}(2x)+\dfrac{1}{2x+5}(2)$ $\quad\dfrac{2(3x^2+5x-6)}{(x^2-6)(2x+5)}$

67. $(x^2+5)^{1/2}\left(\frac{3}{2}\right)(3x-2)^{1/2}(3)$
$+(3x-2)^{3/2}\left(\frac{1}{2}\right)(x^2+5)^{-1/2}(2x)$ See margin.

68. $(3x+2)^{-1/2}(3)(x-6)^{1/2}(1)$
$+(x-6)^3\left(-\frac{1}{2}\right)(3x+2)^{-3/2}(3)$ See margin.

69. **ATHLETICS** An athlete has set up a course for training as part of her regimen in preparation for an upcoming triathlon. She is dropped off by a boat 2 miles from the nearest point on shore. The finish line is 4 miles down the coast and 2 miles inland (see figure). She can swim 2 miles per hour and run 6 miles per hour. The time t (in hours) required for her to reach the finish line can be approximated by the model

$$t=\frac{\sqrt{x^2+4}}{2}+\frac{\sqrt{(4-x)^2+4}}{6}$$

where x is the distance down the coast (in miles) to the point at which she swims and then leaves the water to start her run. See margin.

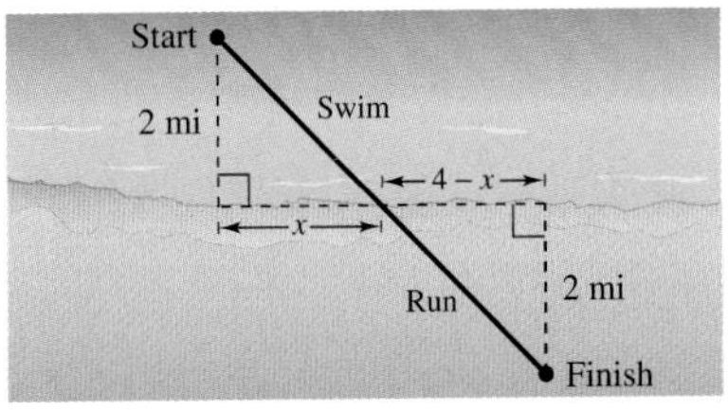

(a) Find the times required for the triathlete to finish when she swims to the points $x = 0.5$, $x = 1.0, \ldots, x = 3.5$, and $x = 4.0$ miles down the coast.

(b) Use your results from part (a) to determine the distance down the coast that will yield the minimum amount of time required for the triathlete to reach the finish line.

(c) The expression below was obtained using calculus. It can be used to find the minimum amount of time required for the triathlete to reach the finish line. Simplify the expression.

$$\frac{1}{2}x(x^2+4)^{-1/2}+\frac{1}{6}(x-4)(x^2-8x+20)^{-1/2}$$

70. (a) Verify that $y_1 = y_2$ analytically. See margin.

$$y_1=x^2\left(\frac{1}{3}\right)(x^2+1)^{-2/3}(2x)+(x^2+1)^{1/3}(2x)$$

$$y_2=\frac{2x(4x^2+3)}{3(x^2+1)^{2/3}}$$

(b) Complete the table and demonstrate the equality in part (a) numerically. See margin.

x	-2	-1	$-\frac{1}{2}$	0	1	2	$\frac{5}{2}$
y_1							
y_2							

EXPLORATION

71. **WRITING** Write a paragraph explaining to a classmate why $\dfrac{1}{(x-2)^{1/2}+x^4}\neq(x-2)^{-1/2}+x^{-4}$. See margin.

72. **CAPSTONE** You are taking a course in calculus, and for one of the homework problems you obtain the following answer.

$$\frac{1}{10}(2x-1)^{5/2}+\frac{1}{6}(2x-1)^{3/2}$$

The answer in the back of the book is $\frac{1}{15}(2x-1)^{3/2}(3x+1)$. Show how the second answer can be obtained from the first. Then use the same technique to simplify each of the following expressions. See margin.

(a) $\dfrac{2}{3}x(2x-3)^{3/2}-\dfrac{2}{15}(2x-3)^{5/2}$

(b) $\dfrac{2}{3}x(4+x)^{3/2}-\dfrac{2}{15}(4+x)^{5/2}$

57. $\dfrac{-7x^2-4x+9}{(x^2-3)^3(x+1)^4}$

58. $\dfrac{-11x^2-5}{x^6(x^2+1)^4}$

59. $\dfrac{27x^2-24x+2}{(6x+1)^4}$

60. $\dfrac{-6(2x-3)}{(4x^2+9)^{3/2}}$

61. $\dfrac{-1}{(x+3)^{2/3}(x+2)^{7/4}}$

62. $\dfrac{x-3}{(2x-1)^{1/2}}$

63. $\dfrac{4x-3}{(3x-1)^{4/3}}$

64. $\dfrac{1-4x}{(x+1)^2(2x-3x^2)^{1/2}}$

67. $\dfrac{(3x-2)^{1/2}(15x^2-4x+45)}{2(x^2+5)^{1/2}}$

68. $\dfrac{3(x-6)^{1/2}[6x+4-(x-6)^{5/2}]}{2(3x+2)^{3/2}}$

69. (a)

x	0.50	1.0	1.5	2.0
t	1.70	1.72	1.78	1.89

x	2.5	3.0	3.5	4.0
t	2.02	2.18	2.36	2.57

(b) $x = 0.5$ mi
(c) See below.

70. (a) Answers will vary.
(b) See below.

71. You cannot move term-by-term from the denominator to the numerator.

69. (c) $\dfrac{3x\sqrt{x^2-8x+20}+(x-4)\sqrt{x^2+4}}{6\sqrt{x^2+4}\sqrt{x^2-8x+20}}$

72. The two answers are equivalent and can be obtained by factoring.

$$\frac{1}{10}(2x-1)^{5/2}+\frac{1}{6}(2x-1)^{3/2}=\frac{1}{60}(2x-1)^{3/2}[6(2x-1)+10]$$
$$=\frac{1}{60}(2x-1)^{3/2}(12x+4)$$
$$=\frac{4}{60}(2x-1)^{3/2}(3x+1)$$
$$=\frac{1}{15}(2x-1)^{3/2}(3x+1)$$

(a) $\frac{2}{5}(2x-3)^{3/2}(x+1)$
(b) $\frac{8}{15}(4+x)^{3/2}(x-1)$

70(b). See Additional Answers beginning on page AA1.

Answers to Odd-Numbered Exercises and Tests

Chapter 1

Section 1.1 *(page 8)*

1. (a) v (b) vi (c) i (d) iv (e) iii (f) ii

3. Distance Formula

5. A: (2, 6), B: (−6, −2), C: (4, −4), D: (−3, 2)

7.

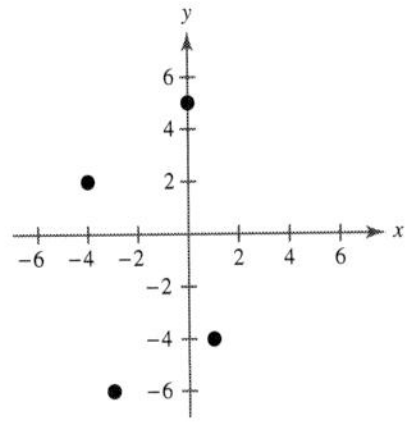

9.

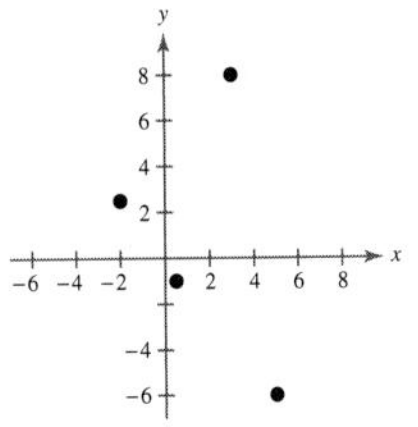

11. (−3, 4) **13.** (−5, −5) **15.** Quadrant IV

17. Quadrant II **19.** Quadrant III or IV **21.** Quadrant III

23. Quadrant I or III

25.

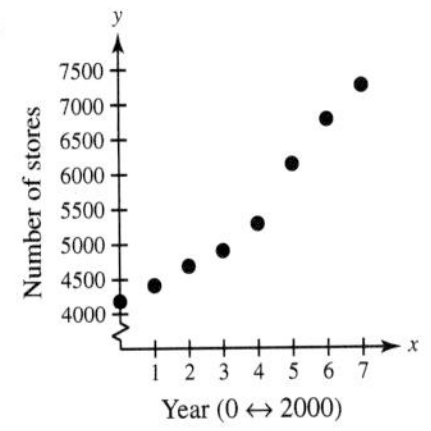

27. 8 **29.** 5 **31.** 13 **33.** $\sqrt{61}$ **35.** $\dfrac{\sqrt{277}}{6}$

37. 8.47 **39.** (a) 4, 3, 5 (b) $4^2 + 3^2 = 5^2$

41. (a) 10, 3, $\sqrt{109}$ (b) $10^2 + 3^2 = \left(\sqrt{109}\right)^2$

43. $\left(\sqrt{5}\right)^2 + \left(\sqrt{45}\right)^2 = \left(\sqrt{50}\right)^2$

45. Distances between the points: $\sqrt{29}$, $\sqrt{58}$, $\sqrt{29}$

47. (a)

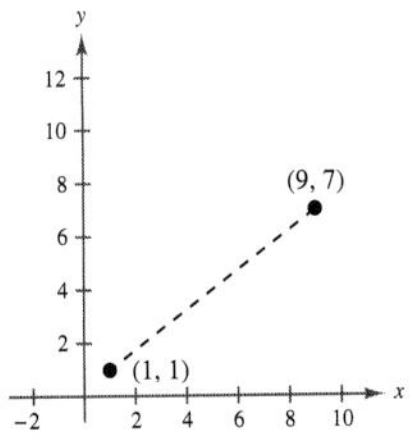

(b) 10
(c) (5, 4)

49. (a)

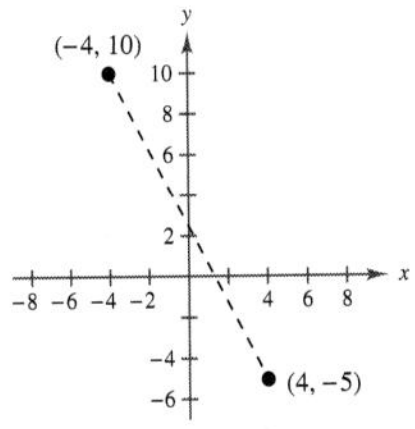

(b) 17
(c) $\left(0, \frac{5}{2}\right)$

51. (a)

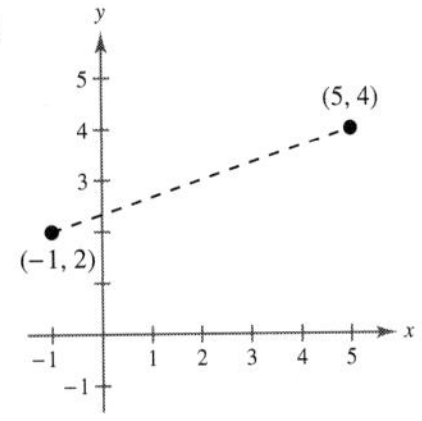

(b) $2\sqrt{10}$
(c) (2, 3)

53. (a)

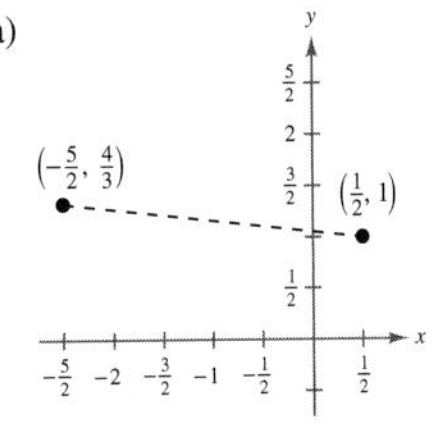

(b) $\dfrac{\sqrt{82}}{3}$
(c) $\left(-1, \dfrac{7}{6}\right)$

55. (a)

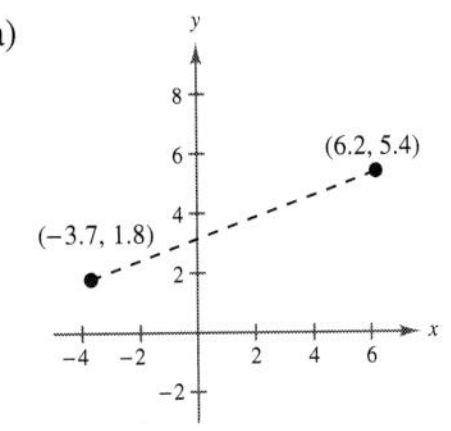

(b) $\sqrt{110.97}$
(c) (1.25, 3.6)

57. $30\sqrt{41} \approx 192$ km **59.** \$4415 million

61. (0, 1), (4, 2), (1, 4) **63.** (−3, 6), (2, 10), (2, 4), (−3, 4)

65. \$3.87/gal; 2007

67. (a) About 9.6% (b) About 28.6%

69. The number of performers elected each year seems to be nearly steady except for the middle years. Five performers will be elected in 2010.

71. \$24,331 million

73. (a)

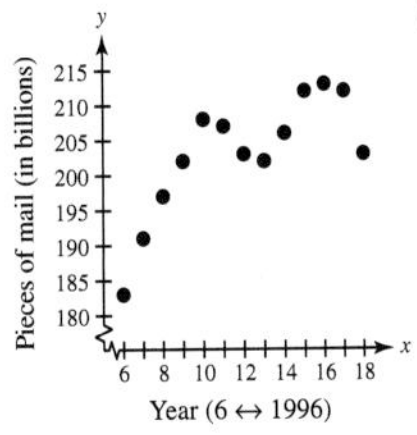

(b) 2008

(c) Answers will vary. Sample answer: Technology now enables us to transport information in many ways other than by mail. The Internet is one example.

75. $(2x_m - x_1, 2y_m - y_1)$

77. $\left(\dfrac{3x_1 + x_2}{4}, \dfrac{3y_1 + y_2}{4}\right), \left(\dfrac{x_1 + x_2}{2}, \dfrac{y_1 + y_2}{2}\right),$
$\left(\dfrac{x_1 + 3x_2}{4}, \dfrac{y_1 + 3y_2}{4}\right)$

CHAPTER 1

79.

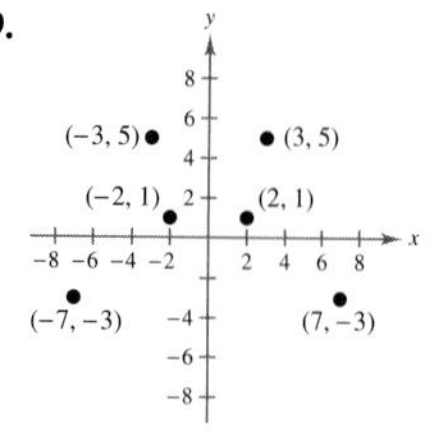

(a) The point is reflected through the y-axis.
(b) The point is reflected through the x-axis.
(c) The point is reflected through the origin.

81. False. The Midpoint Formula would be used 15 times.

83. No. It depends on the magnitudes of the quantities measured.

85. Use the Midpoint Formula to prove that the diagonals of the parallelogram bisect each other.

$$\left(\frac{b+a}{2}, \frac{c+0}{2}\right) = \left(\frac{a+b}{2}, \frac{c}{2}\right)$$

$$\left(\frac{a+b+0}{2}, \frac{c+0}{2}\right) = \left(\frac{a+b}{2}, \frac{c}{2}\right)$$

Section 1.2 *(page 21)*

1. solution or solution point **3.** intercepts

5. circle; (h, k); r

7. (a) Yes (b) Yes **9.** (a) Yes (b) No

11. (a) Yes (b) No **13.** (a) No (b) Yes

15.

x	-1	0	1	2	$\frac{5}{2}$
y	7	5	3	1	0
(x, y)	$(-1, 7)$	$(0, 5)$	$(1, 3)$	$(2, 1)$	$\left(\frac{5}{2}, 0\right)$

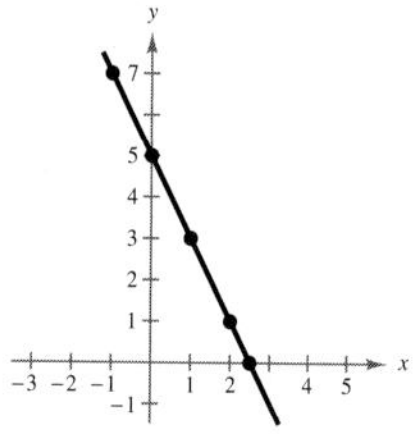

17.

x	-1	0	1	2	3
y	4	0	-2	-2	0
(x, y)	$(-1, 4)$	$(0, 0)$	$(1, -2)$	$(2, -2)$	$(3, 0)$

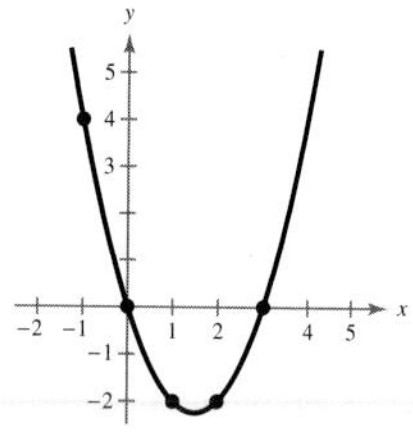

19. x-intercept: $(3, 0)$
y-intercept: $(0, 9)$

21. x-intercept: $(-2, 0)$
y-intercept: $(0, 2)$

23. x-intercept: $\left(\frac{6}{5}, 0\right)$
y-intercept: $(0, -6)$

25. x-intercept: $(-4, 0)$
y-intercept: $(0, 2)$

27. x-intercept: $\left(\frac{7}{3}, 0\right)$
y-intercept: $(0, 7)$

29. x-intercepts: $(0, 0)$, $(2, 0)$
y-intercept: $(0, 0)$

31. x-intercept: $(6, 0)$
y-intercepts: $\left(0, \pm\sqrt{6}\right)$

33. y-axis symmetry

35. Origin symmetry

37. Origin symmetry

39. x-axis symmetry

41.

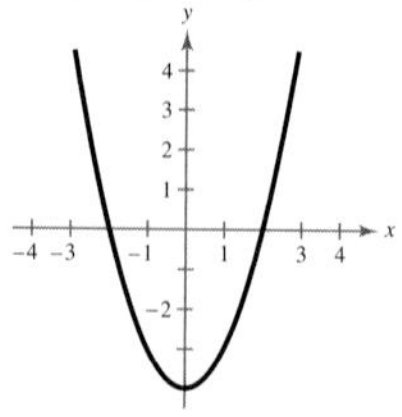

43.

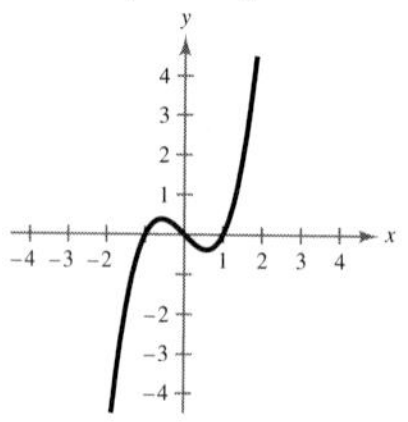

45. x-intercept: $\left(\frac{1}{3}, 0\right)$
y-intercept: $(0, 1)$
No symmetry

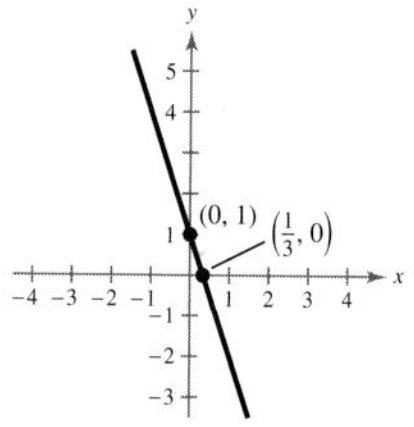

47. x-intercepts: $(0, 0)$, $(2, 0)$
y-intercept: $(0, 0)$
No symmetry

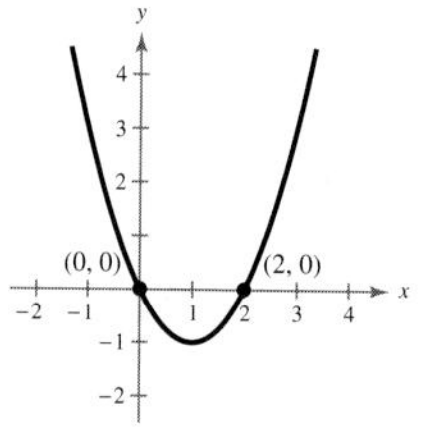

49. x-intercept: $\left(\sqrt[3]{-3}, 0\right)$
y-intercept: $(0, 3)$
No symmetry

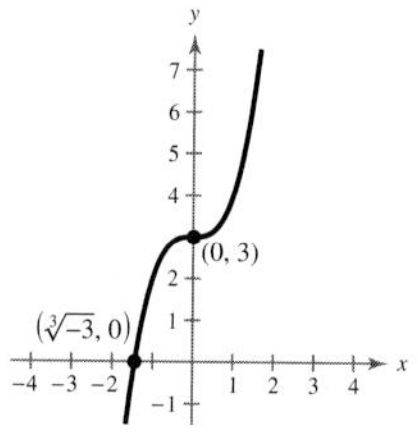

51. x-intercept: $(3, 0)$
y-intercept: None
No symmetry

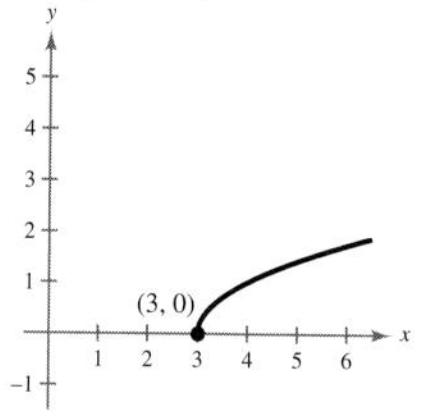

53. x-intercept: $(6, 0)$
y-intercept: $(0, 6)$
No symmetry

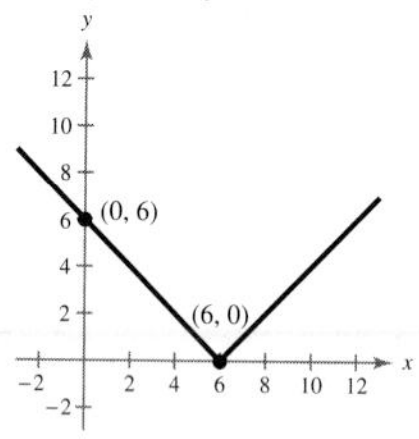

55. x-intercept: $(-1, 0)$
y-intercepts: $(0, \pm 1)$
x-axis symmetry

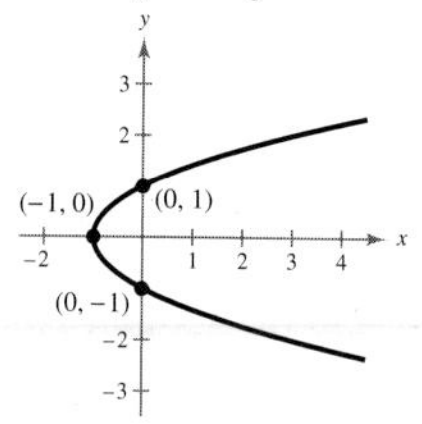

57.

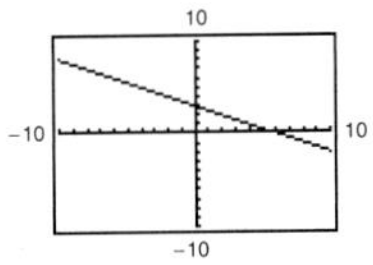

Intercepts: $(6, 0), (0, 3)$

59.

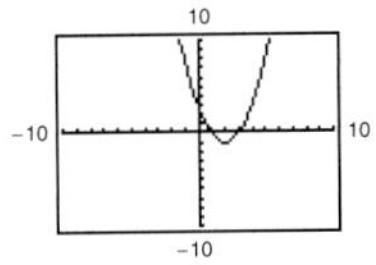

Intercepts: $(3, 0), (1, 0), (0, 3)$

61.

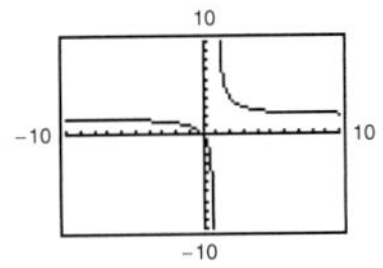

Intercept: $(0, 0)$

63.

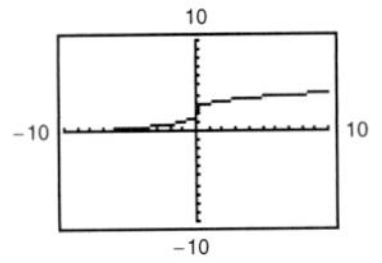

Intercepts: $(-8, 0), (0, 2)$

65.

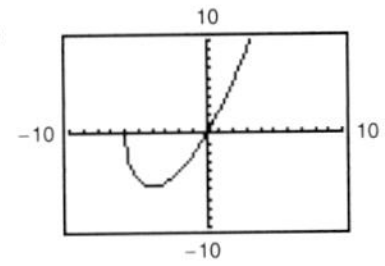

Intercepts: $(0, 0), (-6, 0)$

67.

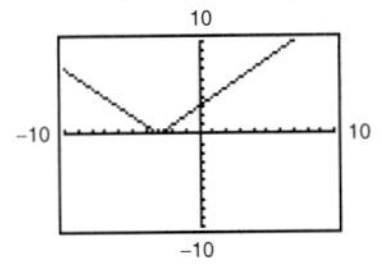

Intercepts: $(-3, 0), (0, 3)$

69. $x^2 + y^2 = 16$ **71.** $(x - 2)^2 + (y + 1)^2 = 16$

73. $(x + 1)^2 + (y - 2)^2 = 5$

75. $(x - 3)^2 + (y - 4)^2 = 25$

77. Center: $(0, 0)$; Radius: 5

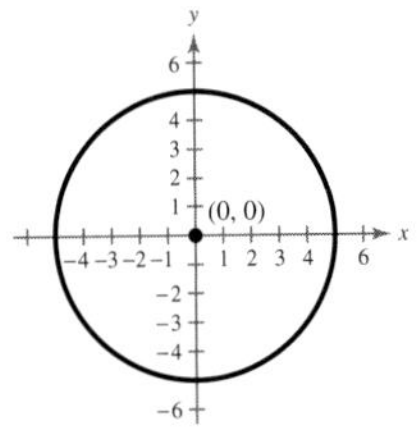

79. Center: $(1, -3)$; Radius: 3

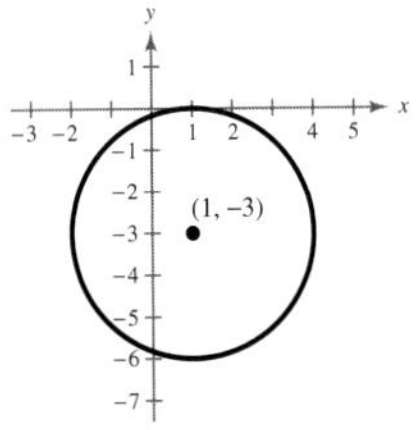

81. Center: $\left(\frac{1}{2}, \frac{1}{2}\right)$; Radius: $\frac{3}{2}$

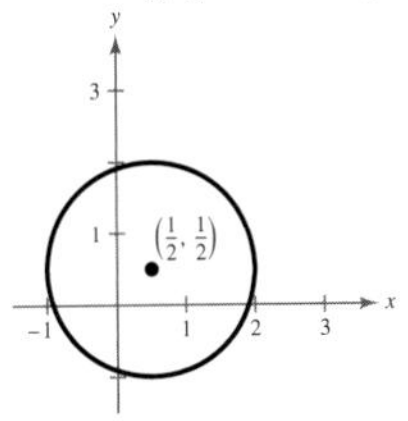

83.

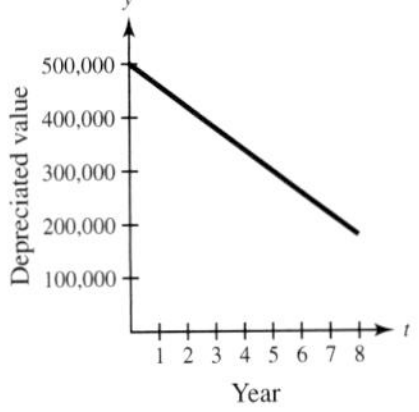

85. (a)

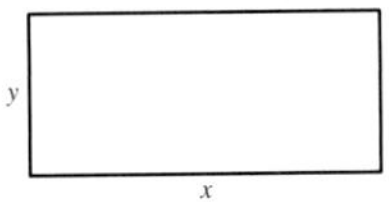

(b) Answers will vary.

(c)

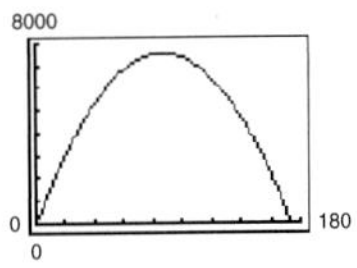

(d) $x = 86\frac{2}{3}, y = 86\frac{2}{3}$

(e) A regulation NFL playing field is 120 yards long and $53\frac{1}{3}$ yards wide. The actual area is 6400 square yards.

87. (a)

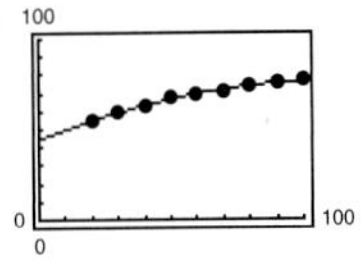

(b) 75.66 yr
(c) 1993

The model fits the data very well.

(d) The projection given by the model, 77.2 years, is less.

(e) Answers will vary.

89. (a) $a = 1, b = 0$ (b) $a = 0, b = 1$

Section 1.3 *(page 33)*

1. linear **3.** parallel **5.** rate or rate of change

7. general **9.** (a) L_2 (b) L_3 (c) L_1

11.

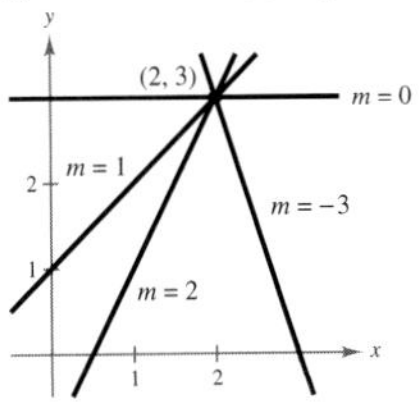

13. $\frac{3}{2}$ **15.** -4

17. $m = 5$
y-intercept: $(0, 3)$

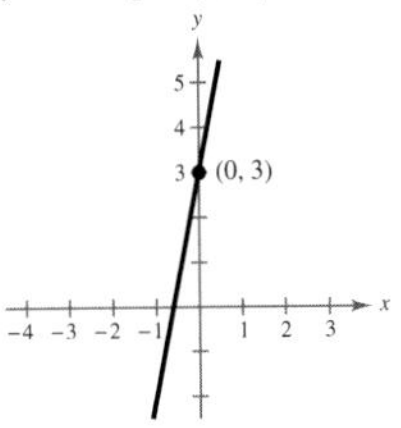

19. $m = -\frac{1}{2}$
y-intercept: $(0, 4)$

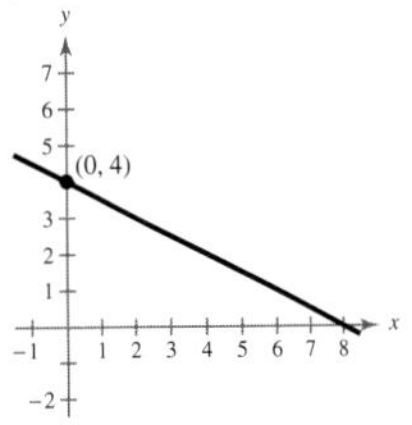

21. m is undefined.
There is no y-intercept.

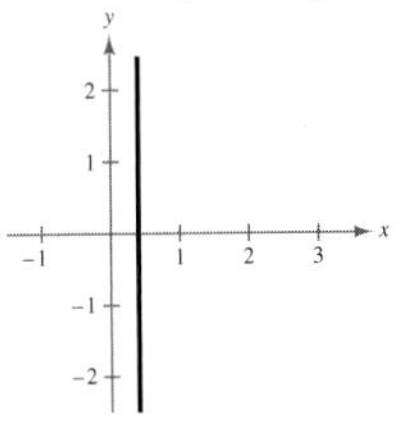

23. $m = -\frac{7}{6}$
y-intercept: $(0, 5)$

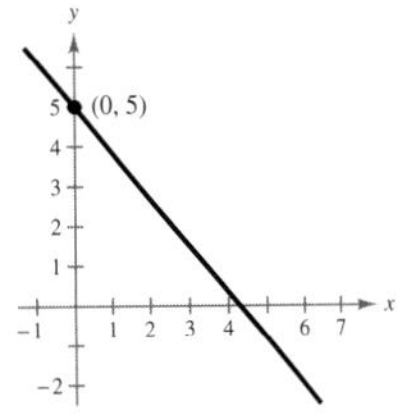

25. $m = 0$
y-intercept: $(0, 3)$

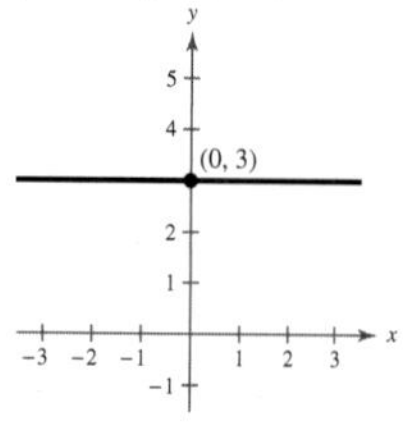

27. m is undefined.
There is no y-intercept.

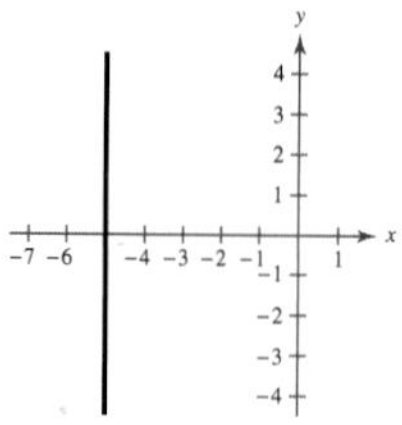

29.

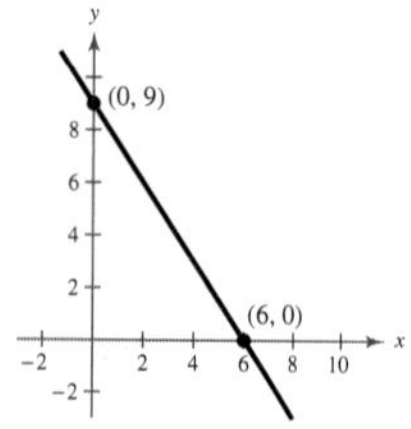

$m = -\frac{3}{2}$

31.

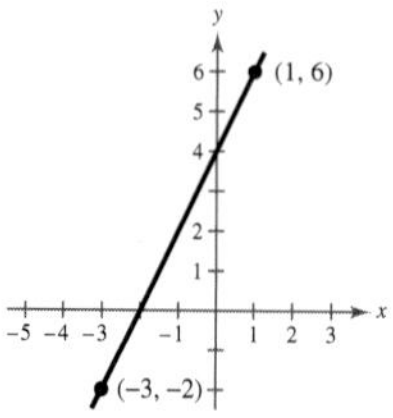

$m = 2$

33.

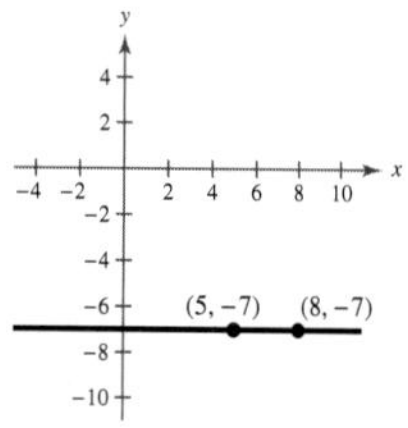

$m = 0$

35.

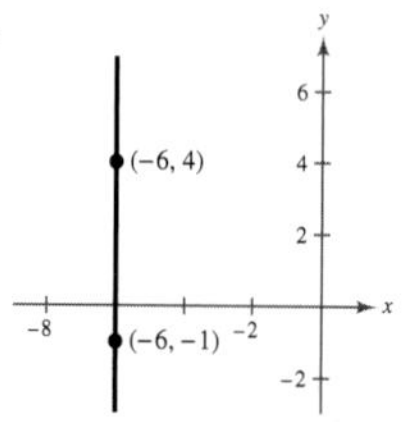

m is undefined.

37.

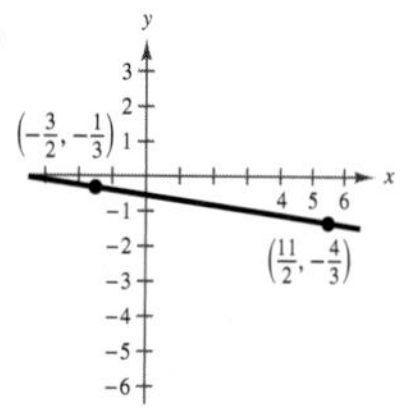

$m = -\frac{1}{7}$

39.

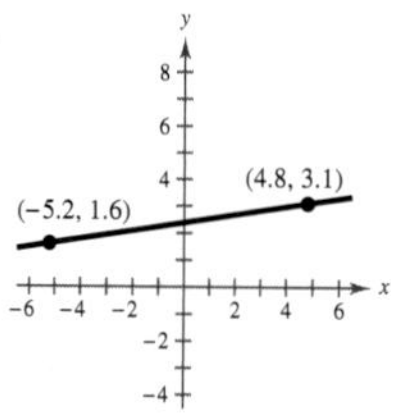

$m = 0.15$

41. $(0, 1), (3, 1), (-1, 1)$ **43.** $(6, -5), (7, -4), (8, -3)$

45. $(-8, 0), (-8, 2), (-8, 3)$ **47.** $(-4, 6), (-3, 8), (-2, 10)$

49. $(9, -1), (11, 0), (13, 1)$

51. $y = 3x - 2$

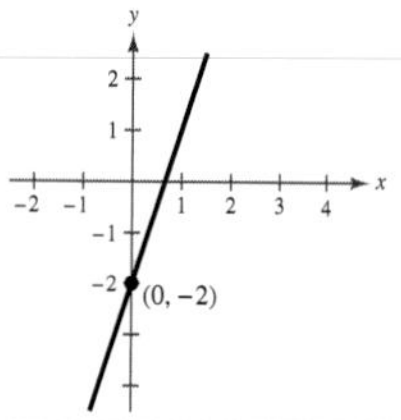

53. $y = -2x$

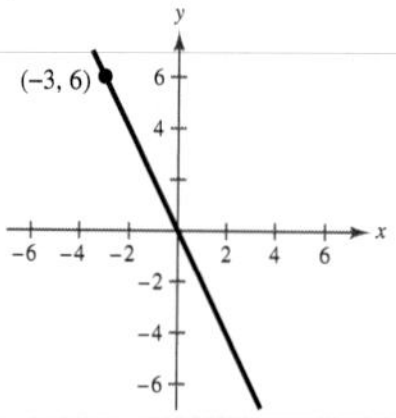

55. $y = -\frac{1}{3}x + \frac{4}{3}$

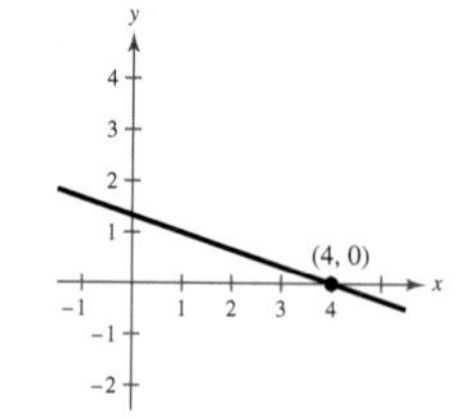

57. $y = -\frac{1}{2}x - 2$

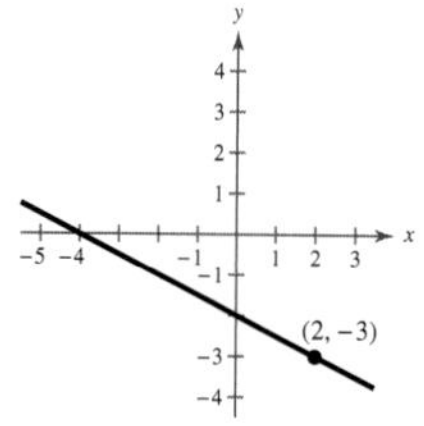

59. $x = 6$

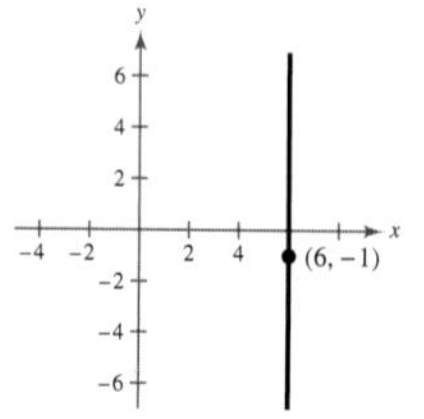

61. $y = \frac{5}{2}$

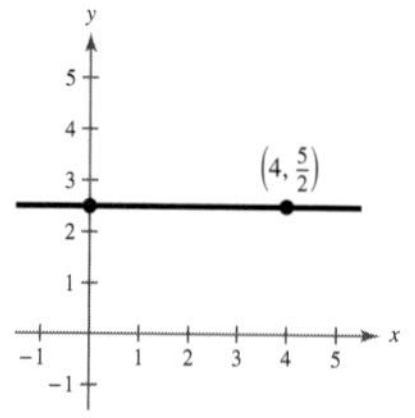

63. $y = 5x + 27.3$

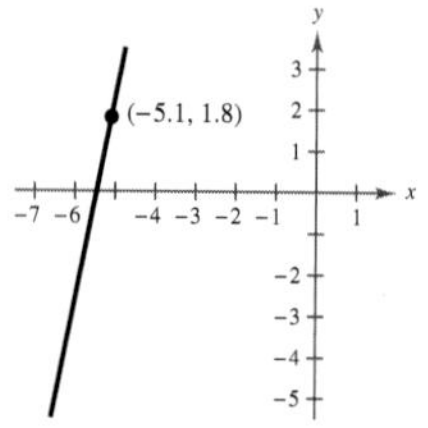

65. $y = -\frac{3}{5}x + 2$

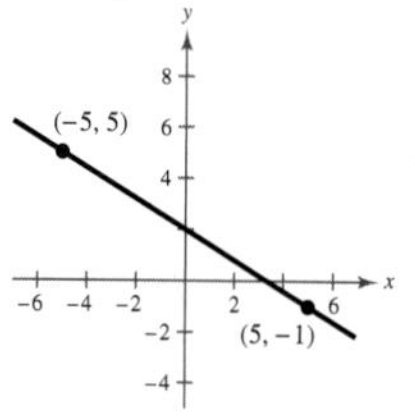

67. $x = -8$

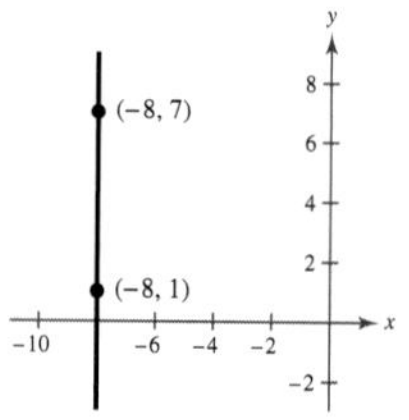

69. $y = -\frac{1}{2}x + \frac{3}{2}$

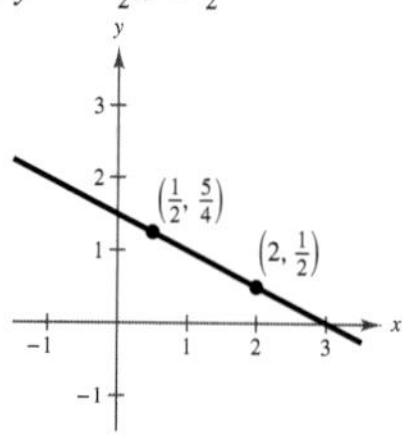

71. $y = -\frac{6}{5}x - \frac{18}{25}$

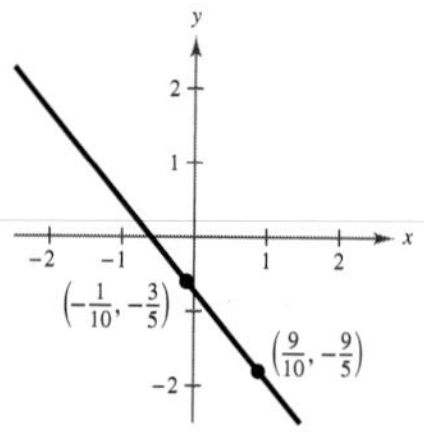

73. $y = 0.4x + 0.2$

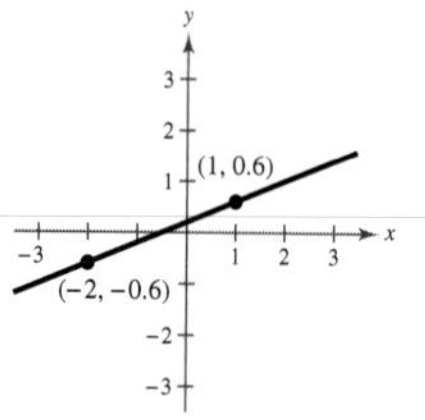

75. $y = -1$

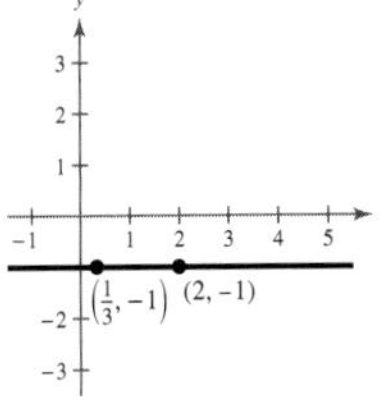

77. $x = \frac{7}{3}$

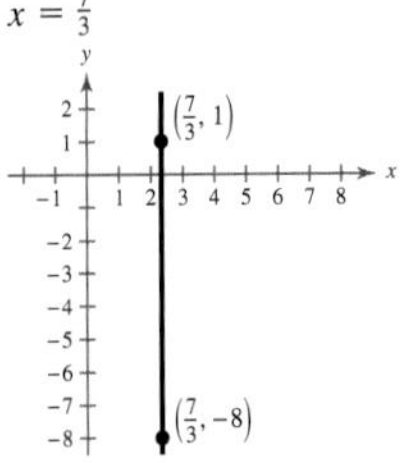

79. Parallel **81.** Neither **83.** Perpendicular
85. Parallel **87.** (a) $y = 2x - 3$ (b) $y = -\frac{1}{2}x + 2$
89. (a) $y = -\frac{3}{4}x + \frac{3}{8}$ (b) $y = \frac{4}{3}x + \frac{127}{72}$
91. (a) $y = 0$ (b) $x = -1$
93. (a) $x = 3$ (b) $y = -2$
95. (a) $y = x + 4.3$ (b) $y = -x + 9.3$
97. $3x + 2y - 6 = 0$ **99.** $12x + 3y + 2 = 0$
101. $x + y - 3 = 0$
103. Line (b) is perpendicular to line (c).

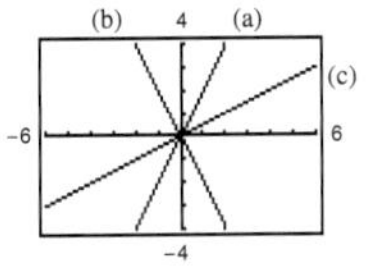

105. Line (a) is parallel to line (b).
Line (c) is perpendicular to line (a) and line (b).

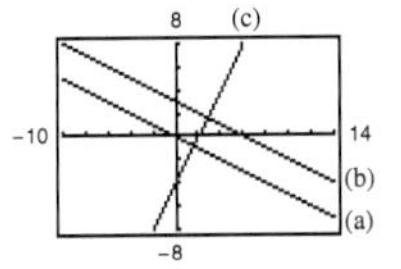

107. $3x - 2y - 1 = 0$ **109.** $80x + 12y + 139 = 0$
111. (a) Sales increasing 135 units/yr
(b) No change in sales
(c) Sales decreasing 40 units/yr
113. (a) The average salary increased the greatest from 2006 to 2008 and increased the least from 2002 to 2004.
(b) $m = 2350.75$
(c) The average salary increased \$2350.75 per year over the 12 years between 1996 and 2008.
115. 12 ft **117.** $V(t) = 3790 - 125t$
119. V-intercept: initial cost; Slope: annual depreciation
121. $V = -175t + 875$ **123.** $S = 0.8L$
125. $W = 0.07S + 2500$
127. $y = 0.03125t + 0.92875$; $y(22) \approx \$1.62$; $y(24) \approx \$1.68$
129. (a) $y(t) = 442.625t + 40{,}571$
(b) $y(10) = 44{,}997$; $y(15) = 47{,}210$
(c) $m = 442.625$; Each year, enrollment increases by about 443 students.
131. (a) $C = 18t + 42{,}000$ (b) $R = 30t$
(c) $P = 12t - 42{,}000$ (d) $t = 3500$ h
133. (a)

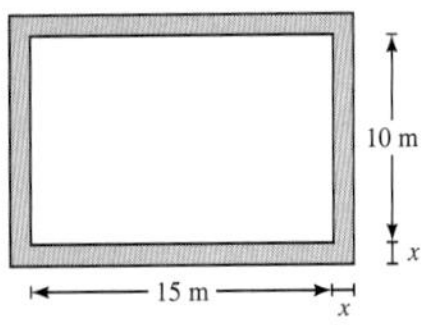

(b) $y = 8x + 50$

(c)

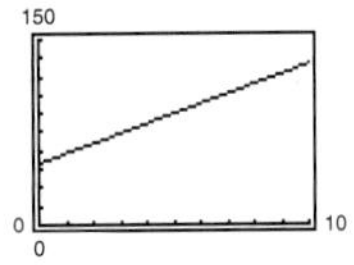

(d) $m = 8$, 8 m

135. (a) and (b)

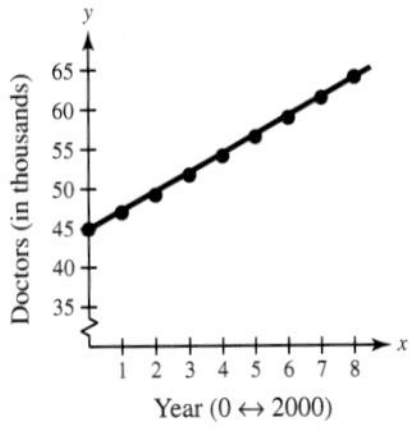

(c) Answers will vary. Sample answer: $y = 2.39x + 44.9$
(d) Answers will vary. Sample answer: The y-intercept indicates that in 2000 there were 44.9 thousand doctors of osteopathic medicine. The slope means that the number of doctors increases by 2.39 thousand each year.
(e) The model is accurate.
(f) Answers will vary. Sample answer: 73.6 thousand
137. False. The slope with the greatest magnitude corresponds to the steepest line.
139. Find the distance between each two points and use the Pythagorean Theorem.
141. No. The slope cannot be determined without knowing the scale on the y-axis. The slopes could be the same.
143. The line $y = 4x$ rises most quickly, and the line $y = -4x$ falls most quickly. The greater the magnitude of the slope (the absolute value of the slope), the faster the line rises or falls.
145. No. The slopes of two perpendicular lines have opposite signs (assume that neither line is vertical or horizontal).

Section 1.4 *(page 48)*

1. domain; range; function **3.** independent; dependent
5. implied domain **7.** Yes **9.** No
11. Yes, each input value has exactly one output value.
13. No, the input values 7 and 10 each have two different output values.
15. (a) Function
(b) Not a function, because the element 1 in A corresponds to two elements, -2 and 1, in B.
(c) Function
(d) Not a function, because not every element in A is matched with an element in B.
17. Each is a function. For each year there corresponds one and only one circulation.
19. Not a function **21.** Function **23.** Function

25. Not a function **27.** Not a function **29.** Function
31. Function **33.** Not a function **35.** Function
37. (a) -1 (b) -9 (c) $2x - 5$
39. (a) 36π (b) $\frac{9}{2}\pi$ (c) $\frac{32}{3}\pi r^3$
41. (a) 15 (b) $4t^2 - 19t + 27$ (c) $4t^2 - 3t - 10$
43. (a) 1 (b) 2.5 (c) $3 - 2|x|$
45. (a) $-\dfrac{1}{9}$ (b) Undefined (c) $\dfrac{1}{y^2 + 6y}$
47. (a) 1 (b) -1 (c) $\dfrac{|x - 1|}{x - 1}$
49. (a) -1 (b) 2 (c) 6 **51.** (a) -7 (b) 4 (c) 9

53.

x	-2	-1	0	1	2
$f(x)$	1	-2	-3	-2	1

55.

t	-5	-4	-3	-2	-1
$h(t)$	1	$\frac{1}{2}$	0	$\frac{1}{2}$	1

57.

x	-2	-1	0	1	2
$f(x)$	5	$\frac{9}{2}$	4	1	0

59. 5 **61.** $\frac{4}{3}$ **63.** ± 3 **65.** $0, \pm 1$ **67.** $-1, 2$
69. $0, \pm 2$ **71.** All real numbers x
73. All real numbers t except $t = 0$
75. All real numbers y such that $y \geq 10$
77. All real numbers x except $x = 0, -2$
79. All real numbers s such that $s \geq 1$ except $s = 4$
81. All real numbers x such that $x > 0$
83. $\{(-2, 4), (-1, 1), (0, 0), (1, 1), (2, 4)\}$
85. $\{(-2, 4), (-1, 3), (0, 2), (1, 3), (2, 4)\}$
87. $A = \dfrac{P^2}{16}$
89. (a) The maximum volume is 1024 cubic centimeters.
(b)

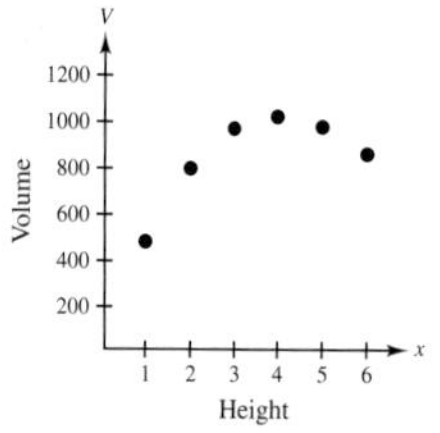

Yes, V is a function of x.
(c) $V = x(24 - 2x)^2, \quad 0 < x < 12$
91. $A = \dfrac{x^2}{2(x - 2)}, \quad x > 2$
93. Yes, the ball will be at a height of 6 feet.
95. 1998: \$136,164 2003: \$180,419
1999: \$140,971 2004: \$195,900
2000: \$147,800 2005: \$216,900
2001: \$156,651 2006: \$224,000
2002: \$167,524 2007: \$217,200

97. (a) $C = 12.30x + 98{,}000$ (b) $R = 17.98x$
(c) $P = 5.68x - 98{,}000$
99. (a) $R = \dfrac{240n - n^2}{20}, \quad n \geq 80$
(b)

n	90	100	110	120	130	140	150
$R(n)$	\$675	\$700	\$715	\$720	\$715	\$700	\$675

The revenue is maximum when 120 people take the trip.
101. (a)

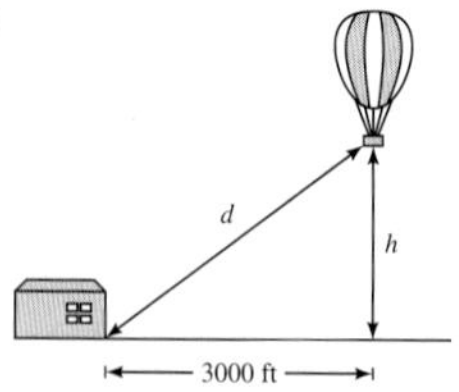

(b) $h = \sqrt{d^2 - 3000^2}, \quad d \geq 3000$
103. $3 + h, \ h \neq 0$ **105.** $3x^2 + 3xh + h^2 + 3, \ h \neq 0$
107. $-\dfrac{x + 3}{9x^2}, \ x \neq 3$ **109.** $\dfrac{\sqrt{5x} - 5}{x - 5}$
111. $g(x) = cx^2; \ c = -2$ **113.** $r(x) = \dfrac{c}{x}; \ c = 32$
115. False. A function is a special type of relation.
117. False. The range is $[-1, \infty)$.
119. Domain of $f(x)$: all real numbers $x \geq 1$
Domain of $g(x)$: all real numbers $x > 1$
Notice that the domain of $f(x)$ includes $x = 1$ and the domain of $g(x)$ does not because you cannot divide by 0.
121. No; x is the independent variable, f is the name of the function.
123. (a) Yes. The amount you pay in sales tax will increase as the price of the item purchased increases.
(b) No. The length of time that you study will not necessarily determine how well you do on an exam.

Section 1.5 *(page 61)*

1. ordered pairs **3.** zeros **5.** maximum **7.** odd
9. Domain: $(-\infty, -1] \cup [1, \infty)$; Range: $[0, \infty)$
11. Domain: $[-4, 4]$; Range: $[0, 4]$
13. Domain: $(-\infty, \infty)$; Range: $[-4, \infty)$
(a) 0 (b) -1 (c) 0 (d) -2
15. Domain: $(-\infty, \infty)$; Range: $(-2, \infty)$
(a) 0 (b) 1 (c) 2 (d) 3
17. Function **19.** Not a function **21.** Function
23. $-\frac{5}{2}, 6$ **25.** 0 **27.** $0, \pm\sqrt{2}$ **29.** $\pm\frac{1}{2}, 6$ **31.** $\frac{1}{2}$
33.

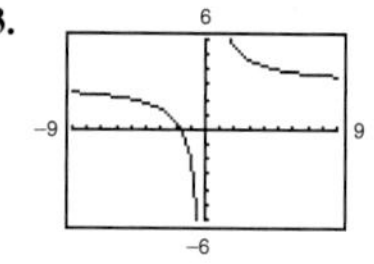

$-\frac{5}{3}$

35.

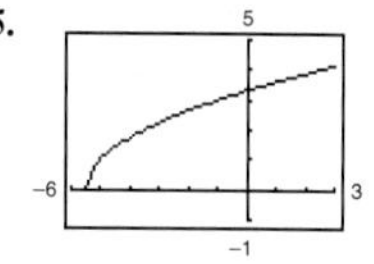

$-\frac{11}{2}$

37. 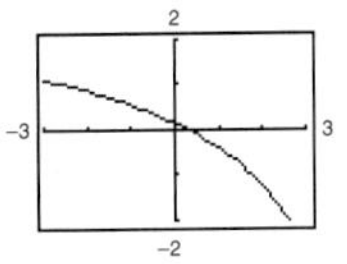

$\frac{1}{3}$

39. Increasing on $(-\infty, \infty)$

41. Increasing on $(-\infty, 0)$ and $(2, \infty)$
Decreasing on $(0, 2)$

43. Increasing on $(1, \infty)$; Decreasing on $(-\infty, -1)$
Constant on $(-1, 1)$

45. Increasing on $(-\infty, 0)$ and $(2, \infty)$; Constant on $(0, 2)$

47. 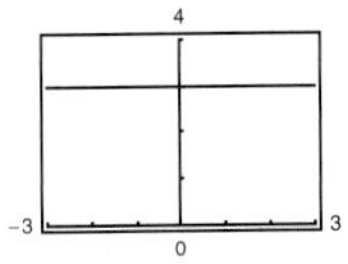

Constant on $(-\infty, \infty)$

49. 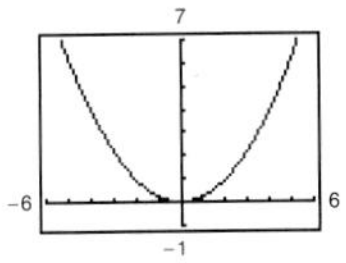

Decreasing on $(-\infty, 0)$
Increasing on $(0, \infty)$

51. 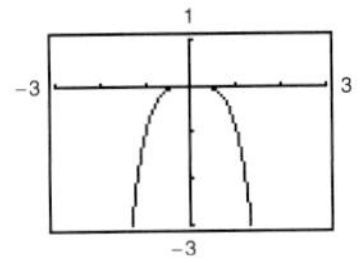

Increasing on $(-\infty, 0)$
Decreasing on $(0, \infty)$

53. 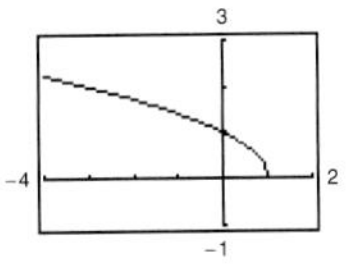

Decreasing on $(-\infty, 1)$

55. 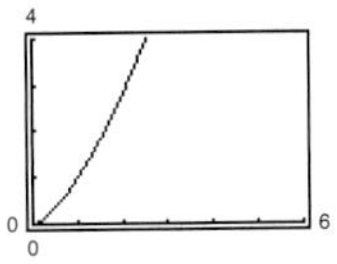

Increasing on $(0, \infty)$

57. 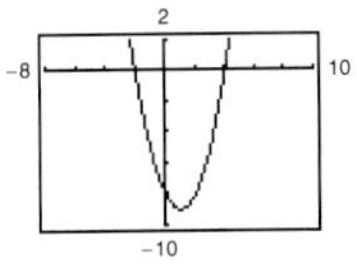

Relative minimum: $(1, -9)$

59. 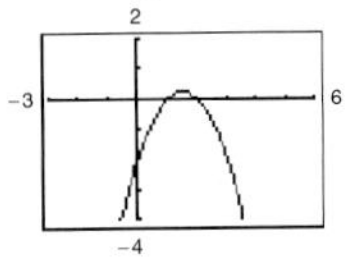

Relative maximum: $(1.5, 0.25)$

61. 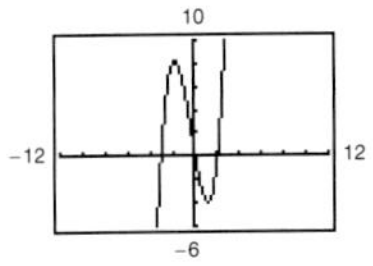

Relative maximum: $(-1.79, 8.21)$
Relative minimum: $(1.12, -4.06)$

63. 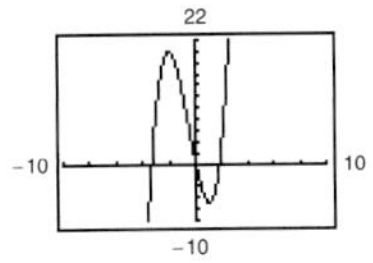

Relative maximum: $(-2, 20)$
Relative minimum: $(1, -7)$

65. 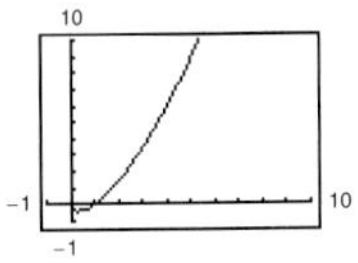

Relative minimum: $(0.33, -0.38)$

67. 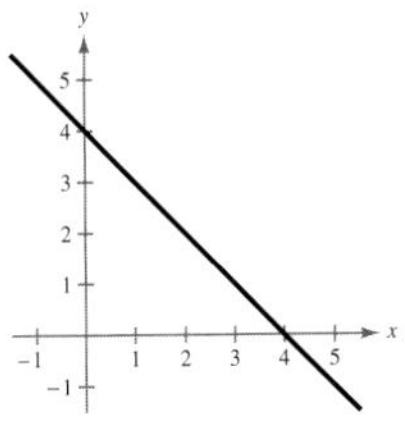

$(-\infty, 4]$

69. 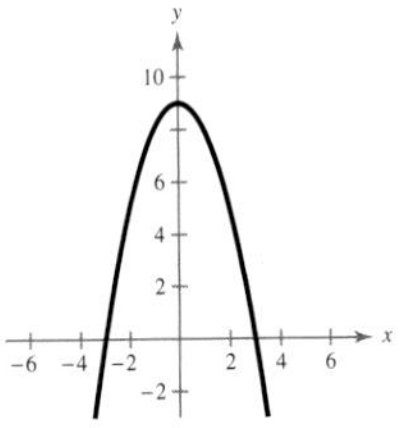

$[-3, 3]$

71. 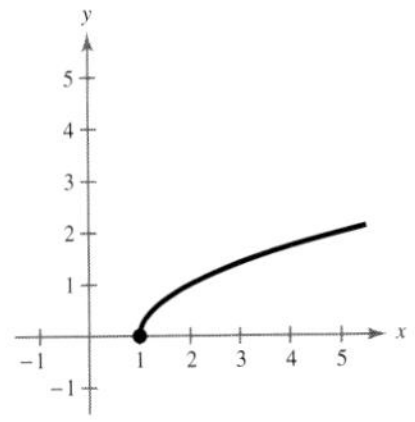

$[1, \infty)$

73. 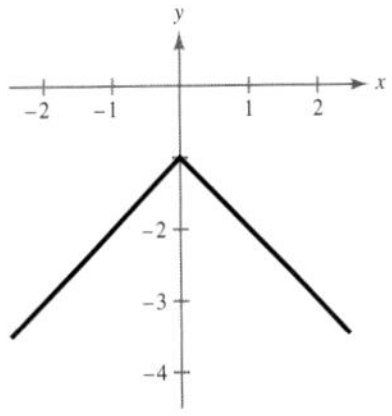

$f(x) < 0$ for all x

75. The average rate of change from $x_1 = 0$ to $x_2 = 3$ is -2.

77. The average rate of change from $x_1 = 1$ to $x_2 = 5$ is 18.

79. The average rate of change from $x_1 = 1$ to $x_2 = 3$ is 0.

81. The average rate of change from $x_1 = 3$ to $x_2 = 11$ is $-\frac{1}{4}$.

83. Even; y-axis symmetry

85. Odd; origin symmetry

87. Neither; no symmetry

89. Neither; no symmetry

91. 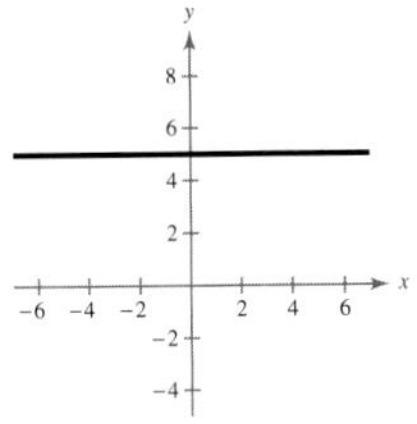

Even

93. 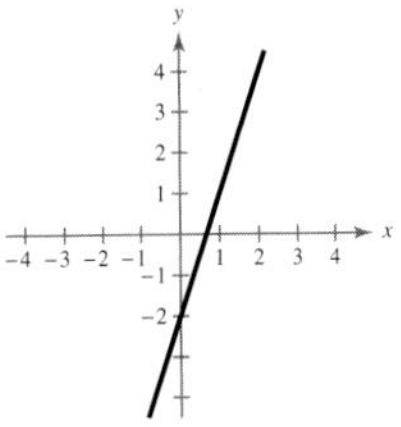

Neither

95. 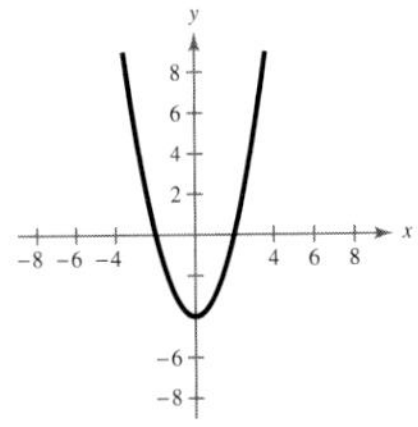

Even

97. 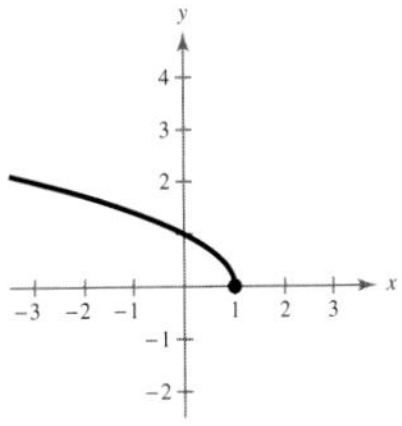

Neither

99.

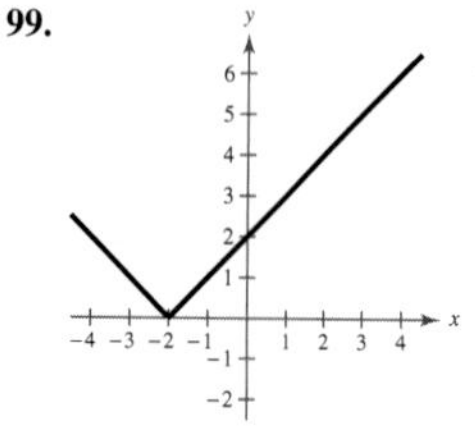

Neither

101. $h = -x^2 + 4x - 3$ **103.** $h = 2x - x^2$

105. $L = \frac{1}{2}y^2$ **107.** $L = 4 - y^2$

109. (a)

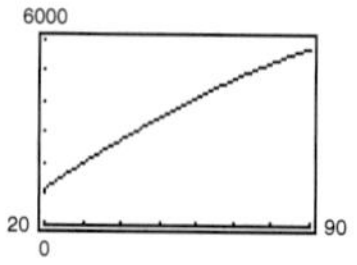

(b) 30 W

111. (a) Ten thousands (b) Ten millions (c) Percents

113. (a)

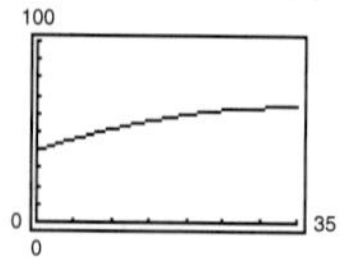

(b) The average rate of change from 1970 to 2005 is 0.705. The enrollment rate of children in preschool has slowly been increasing each year.

115. (a) $s = -16t^2 + 64t + 6$

(b)

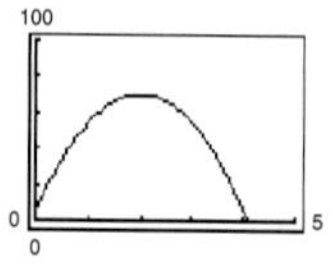

(c) Average rate of change = 16

(d) The slope of the secant line is positive.

(e) Secant line: $16t + 6$

(f)

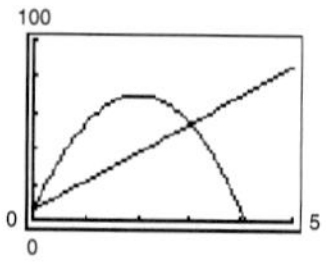

117. (a) $s = -16t^2 + 120t$

(b)

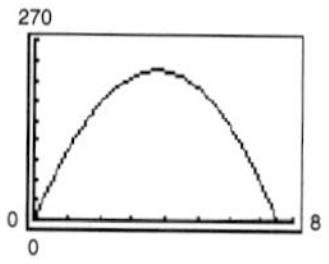

(c) Average rate of change = −8

(d) The slope of the secant line is negative.

(e) Secant line: $-8t + 240$

(f)

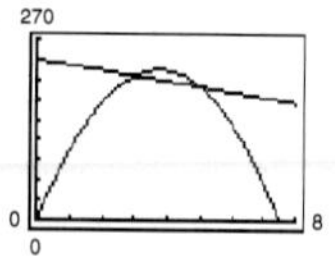

119. (a) $s = -16t^2 + 120$

(b)

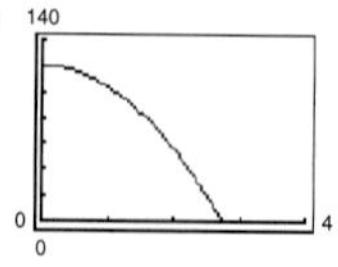

(c) Average rate of change = −32

(d) The slope of the secant line is negative.

(e) Secant line: $-32t + 120$

(f)

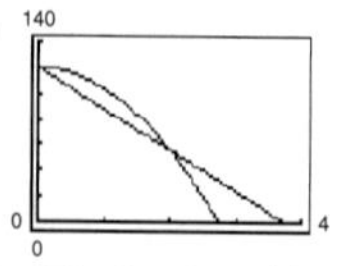

121. False. The function $f(x) = \sqrt{x^2 + 1}$ has a domain of all real numbers.

123. (a) Even. The graph is a reflection in the x-axis.

(b) Even. The graph is a reflection in the y-axis.

(c) Even. The graph is a vertical translation of f.

(d) Neither. The graph is a horizontal translation of f.

125. (a) $\left(\frac{3}{2}, 4\right)$ (b) $\left(\frac{3}{2}, -4\right)$

127. (a) $(-4, 9)$ (b) $(-4, -9)$

129. (a) $(-x, -y)$ (b) $(-x, y)$

131. (a)

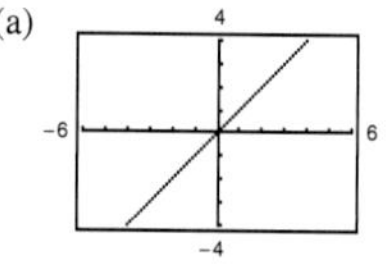

(b)

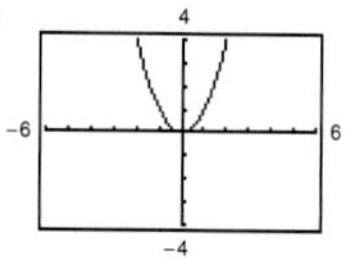

(c)

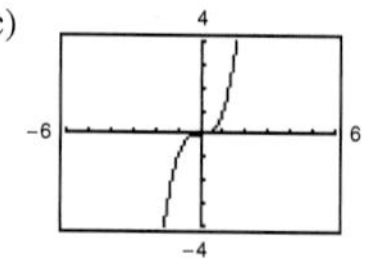

(d)

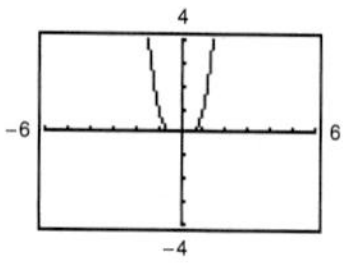

(e)

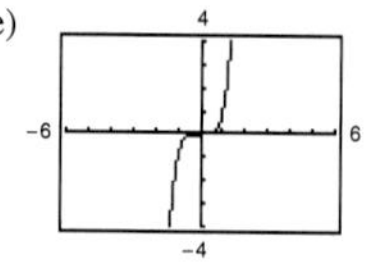

(f)

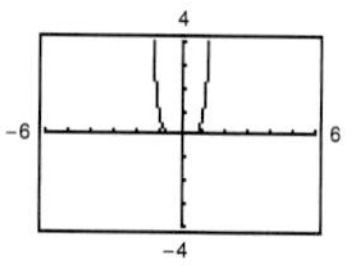

All the graphs pass through the origin. The graphs of the odd powers of x are symmetric with respect to the origin, and the graphs of the even powers are symmetric with respect to the y-axis. As the powers increase, the graphs become flatter in the interval $-1 < x < 1$.

133. 60 ft/sec; As the time traveled increases, the distance increases rapidly, causing the average speed to increase with each time increment. From $t = 0$ to $t = 4$, the average speed is less than from $t = 4$ to $t = 9$. Therefore, the overall average from $t = 0$ to $t = 9$ falls below the average found in part (b).

135. Answers will vary.

Section 1.6 *(page 71)*

1. g **2.** i **3.** h **4.** a **5.** b **6.** e **7.** f
8. c **9.** d

11. (a) $f(x) = -2x + 6$
(b)
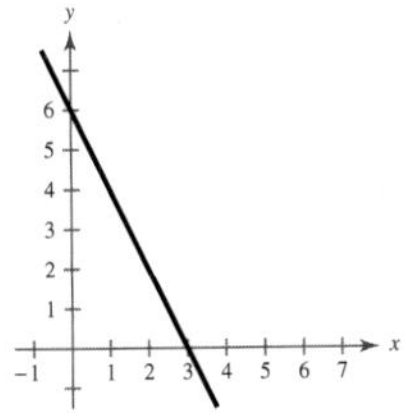

13. (a) $f(x) = -3x + 11$
(b)
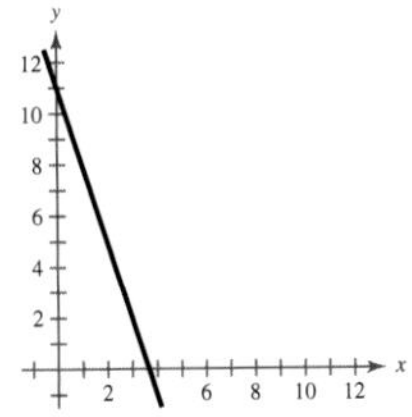

15. (a) $f(x) = -1$
(b)
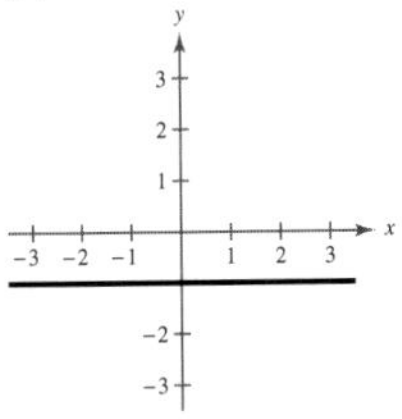

17. (a) $f(x) = \frac{6}{7}x - \frac{45}{7}$
(b)
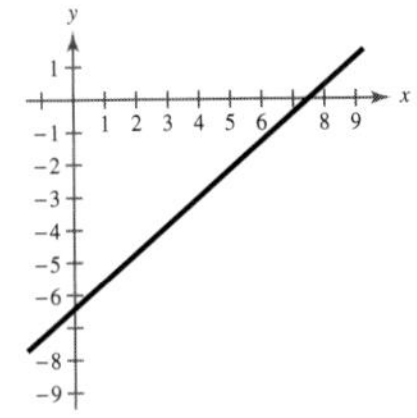

19.
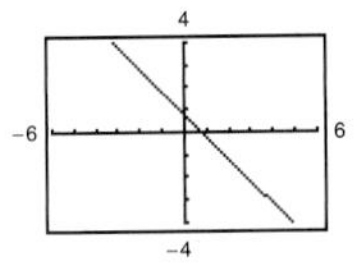

21.
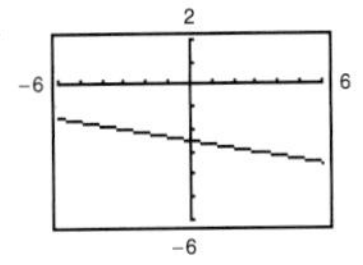

23.
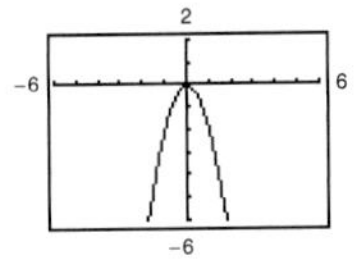

25.
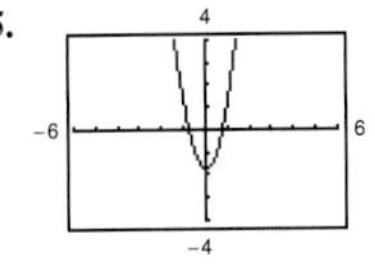

27.
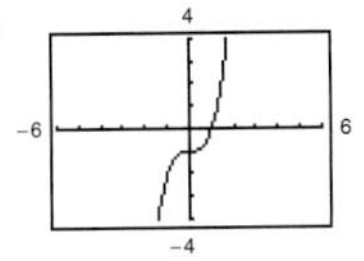

29.
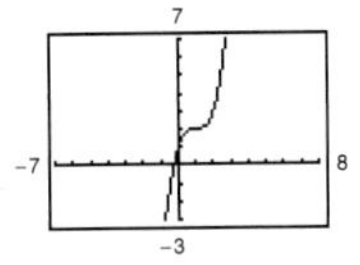

31.
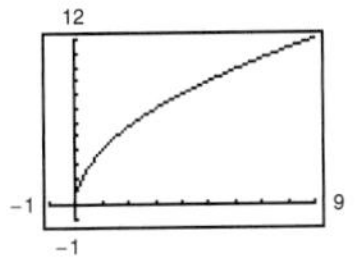

33.
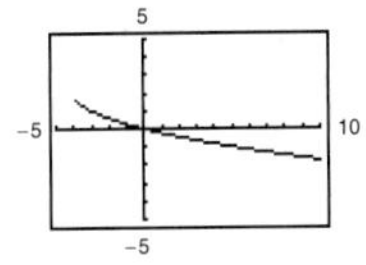

35.
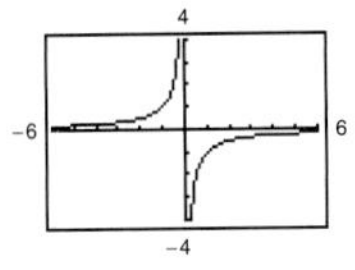

37.
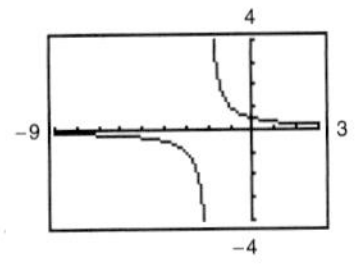

39.
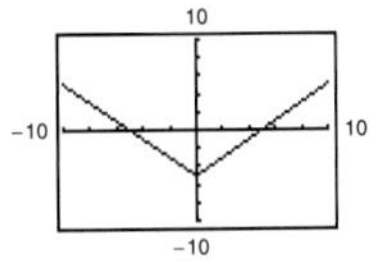

41.
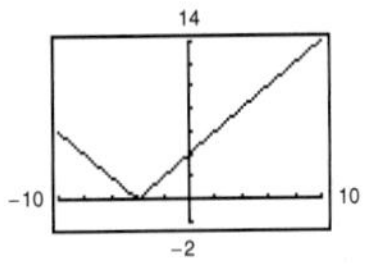

43. (a) 2 (b) 2 (c) -4 (d) 3
45. (a) 1 (b) 3 (c) 7 (d) -19
47. (a) 6 (b) -11 (c) 6 (d) -22
49. (a) -10 (b) -4 (c) -1 (d) 41

51.
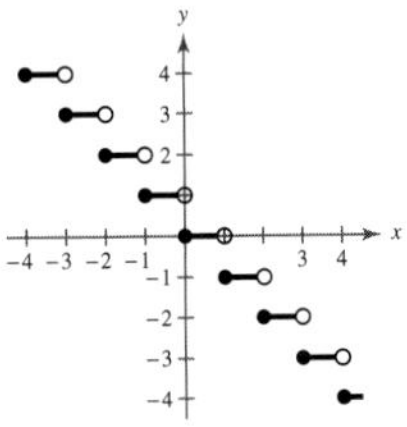

53.
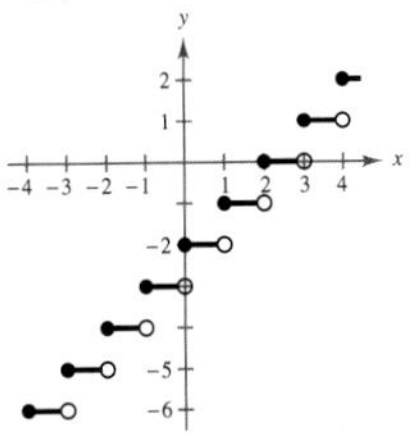

55.
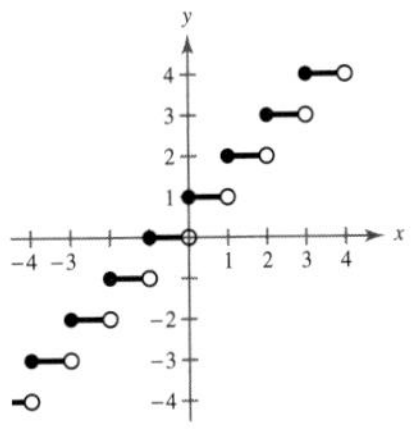

57.
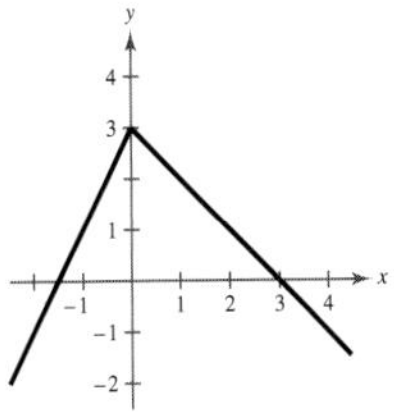

59.
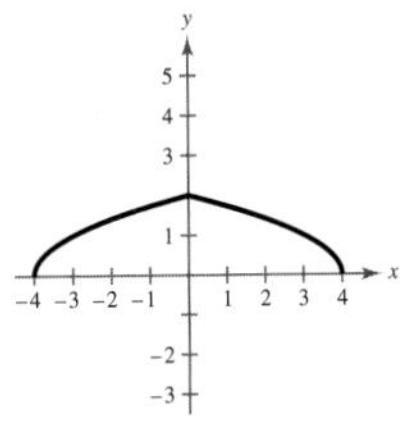

61.
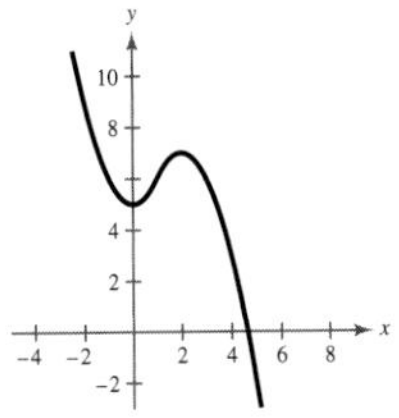

63.
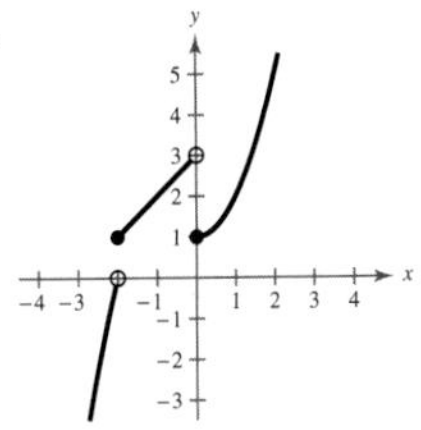

65. (a)
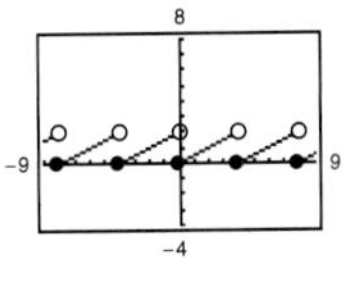

(b) Domain: $(-\infty, \infty)$
Range: $[0, 2)$
(c) Sawtooth pattern

67. (a)

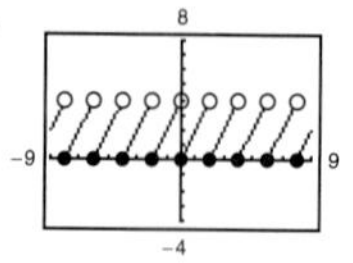

(b) Domain: $(-\infty, \infty)$
Range: $[0, 4)$
(c) Sawtooth pattern

69. (a)

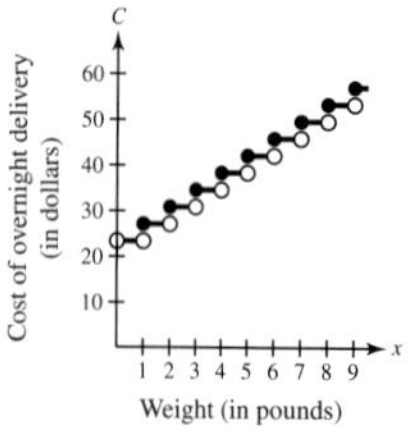

(b) \$57.15

71. (a) $W(30) = 420$; $W(40) = 560$; $W(45) = 665$; $W(50) = 770$

(b) $W(h) = \begin{cases} 14h, & 0 < h \le 45 \\ 21(h - 45) + 630, & h > 45 \end{cases}$

73. (a)

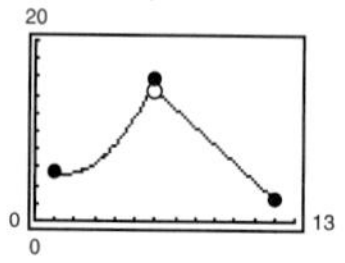

$f(x) = \begin{cases} 0.505x^2 - 1.47x + 6.3, & 1 \le x \le 6 \\ -1.97x + 26.3, & 6 < x \le 12 \end{cases}$

Answers will vary. Sample answer: The domain is determined by inspection of a graph of the data with the two models.

(b) $f(5) = 11.575$, $f(11) = 4.63$; These values represent the revenue for the months of May and November, respectively.

(c) These values are quite close to the actual data values.

75. False. A linear equation could be a horizontal or vertical line.

Section 1.7 *(page 78)*

1. rigid **3.** nonrigid **5.** vertical stretch; vertical shrink

7. (a)

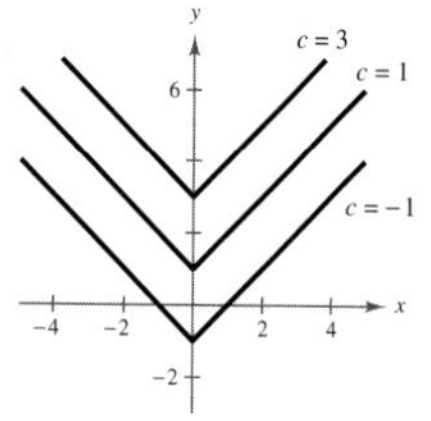

(b)

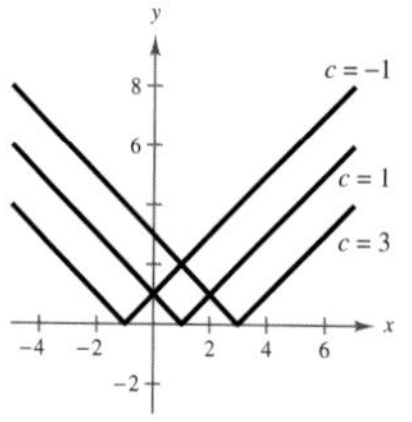

(c)

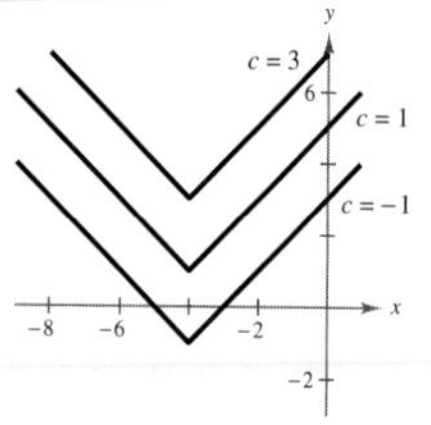

9. (a)

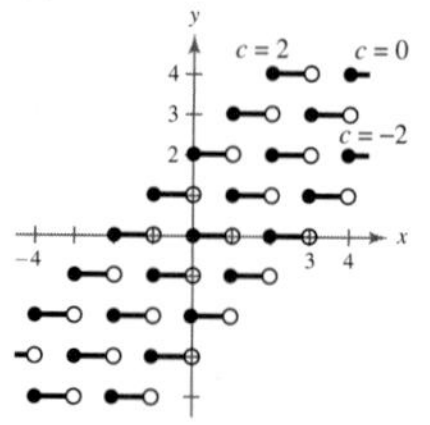

(b)

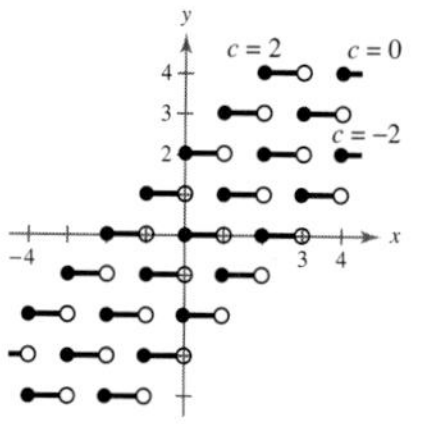

(c)

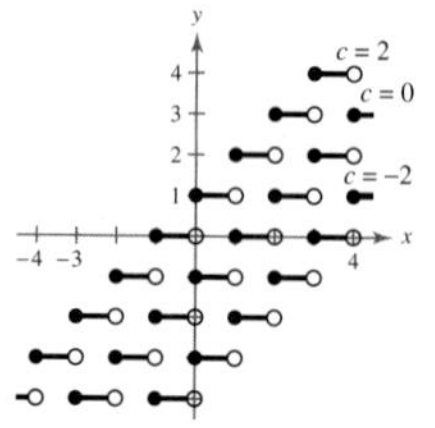

11. (a)

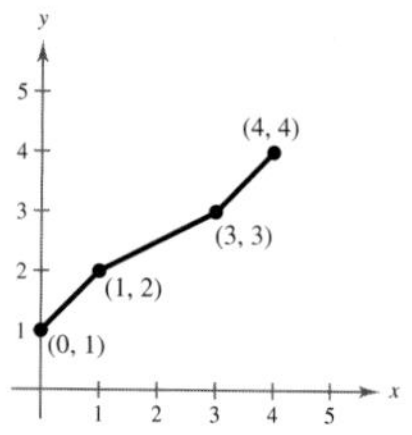

(b)

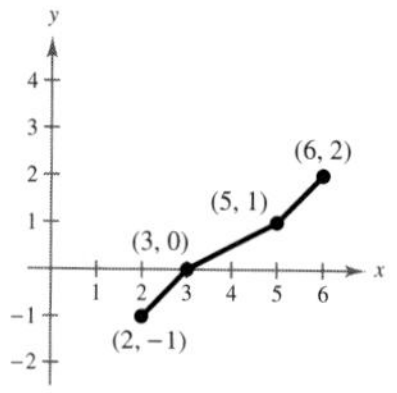

(c)

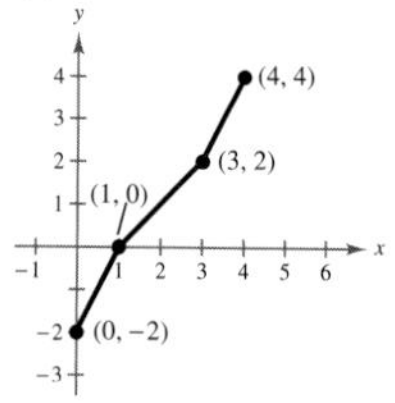

(d)

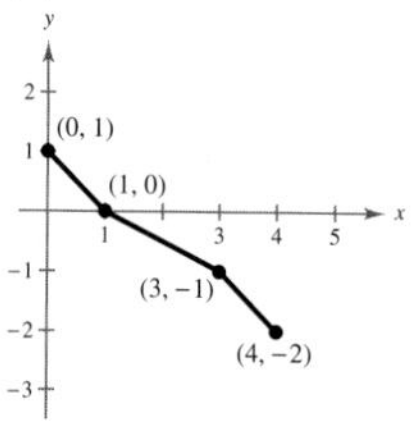

(e)

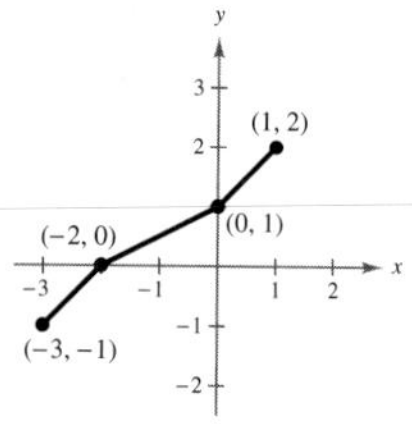

(f)

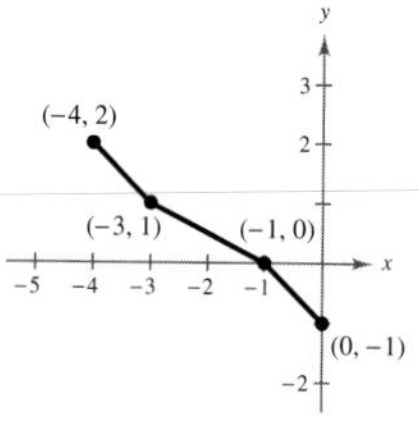

(g)

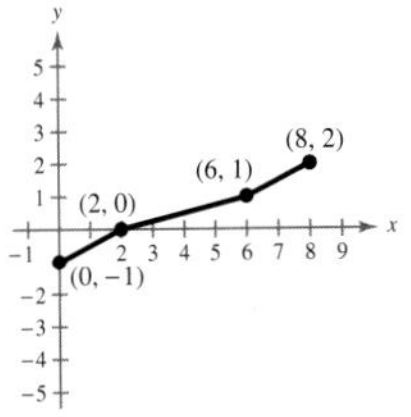

13. (a)

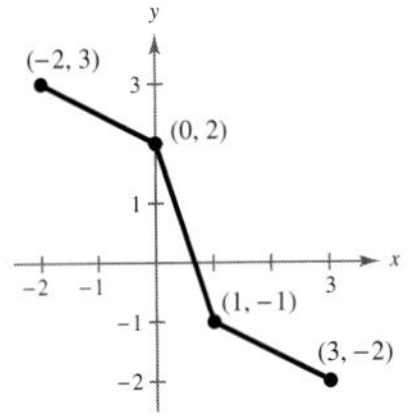

(b)

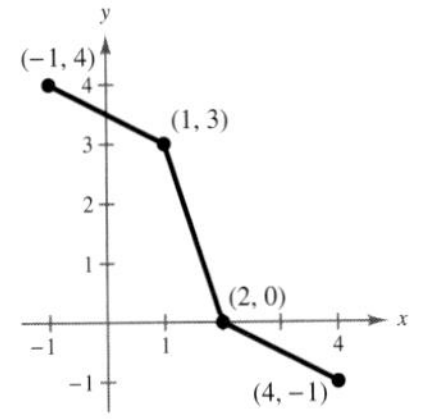

(c)

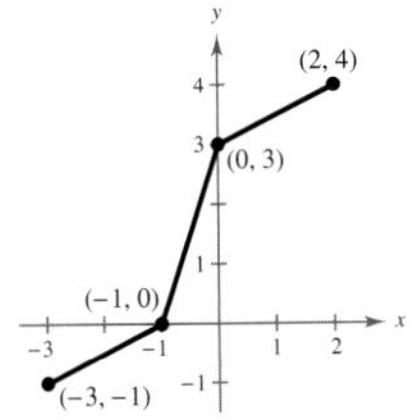

(d)

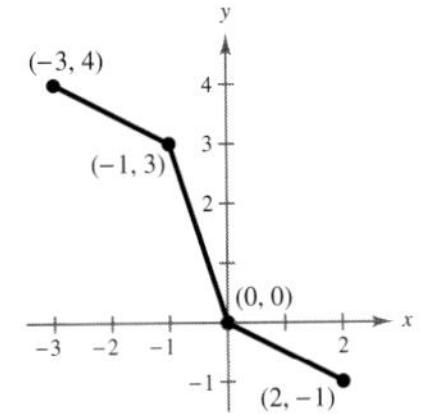

(e)

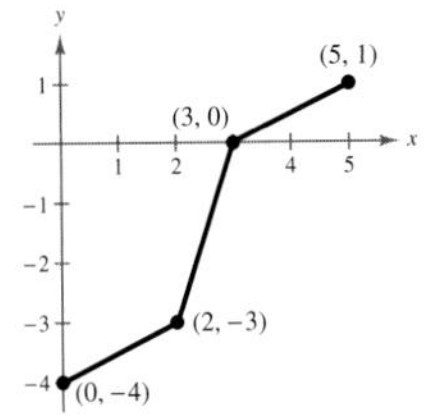

(f)

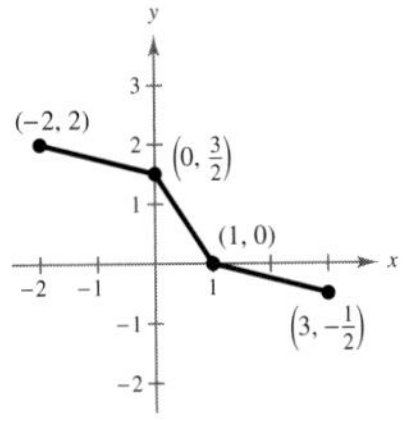

(g)

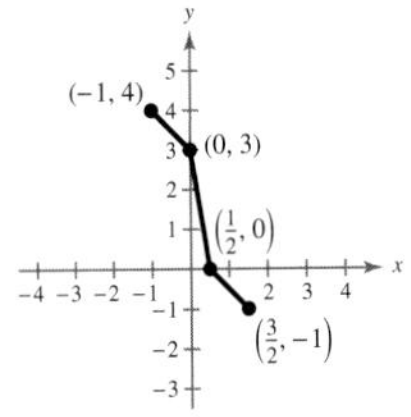

15. (a) $y = x^2 - 1$ (b) $y = 1 - (x + 1)^2$
(c) $y = -(x - 2)^2 + 6$ (d) $y = (x - 5)^2 - 3$

17. (a) $y = |x| + 5$ (b) $y = -|x + 3|$
(c) $y = |x - 2| - 4$ (d) $y = -|x - 6| - 1$

19. Horizontal shift of $y = x^3$; $y = (x - 2)^3$

21. Reflection in the x-axis of $y = x^2$; $y = -x^2$

23. Reflection in the x-axis and vertical shift of $y = \sqrt{x}$; $y = 1 - \sqrt{x}$

25. (a) $f(x) = x^2$
(b) Reflection in the x-axis and vertical shift 12 units upward
(c)

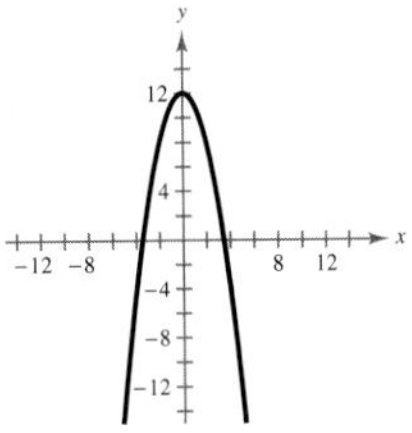

(d) $g(x) = 12 - f(x)$

27. (a) $f(x) = x^3$
(b) Vertical shift seven units upward
(c)

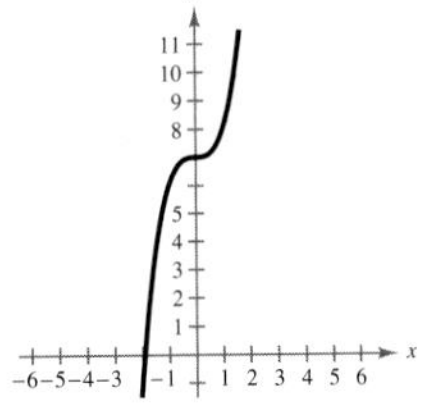

(d) $g(x) = f(x) + 7$

29. (a) $f(x) = x^2$
(b) Vertical shrink of two-thirds and vertical shift four units upward
(c)

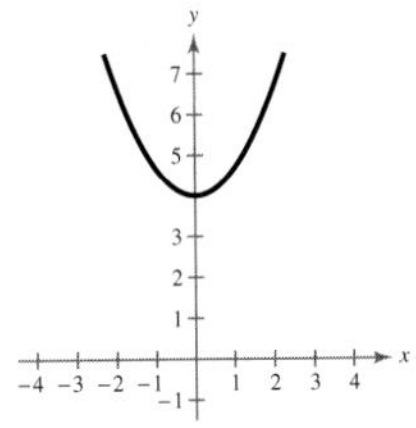

(d) $g(x) = \frac{2}{3}f(x) + 4$

31. (a) $f(x) = x^2$
(b) Reflection in the x-axis, horizontal shift five units to the left, and vertical shift two units upward
(c)

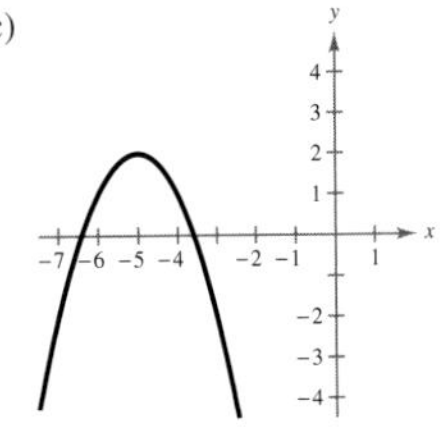

(d) $g(x) = 2 - f(x + 5)$

33. (a) $f(x) = x^2$
(b) Vertical stretch of two, horizontal shift four units to the right, and vertical shift three units upward

(c)

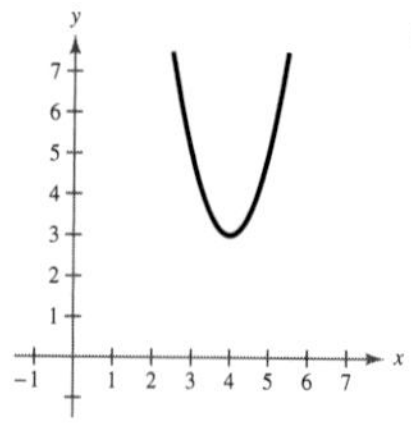

(d) $g(x) = 3 + 2f(x - 4)$

35. (a) $f(x) = \sqrt{x}$

(b) Horizontal shrink of one-third

(c)

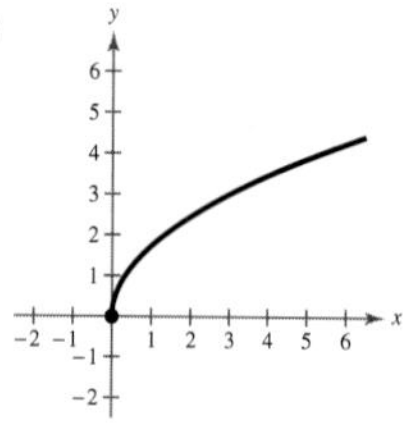

(d) $g(x) = f(3x)$

37. (a) $f(x) = x^3$

(b) Vertical shift two units upward and horizontal shift one unit to the right

(c)

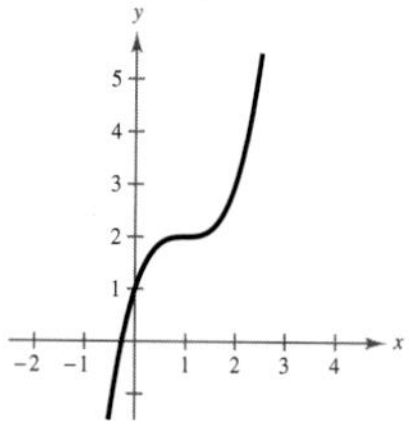

(d) $g(x) = f(x - 1) + 2$

39. (a) $f(x) = x^3$

(b) Vertical stretch of three and horizontal shift two units to the right

(c)

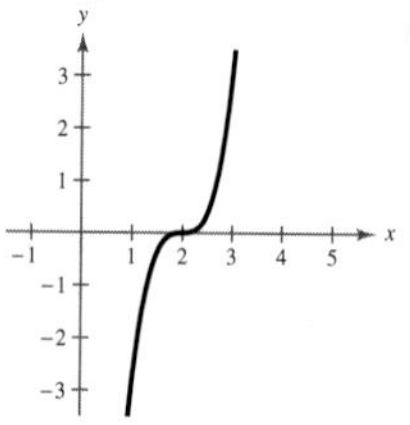

(d) $g(x) = 3f(x - 2)$

41. (a) $f(x) = |x|$

(b) Reflection in the x-axis and vertical shift two units downward

(c)

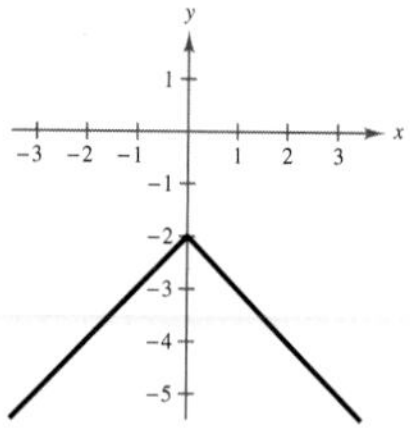

(d) $g(x) = -f(x) - 2$

43. (a) $f(x) = |x|$

(b) Reflection in the x-axis, horizontal shift four units to the left, and vertical shift eight units upward

(c)

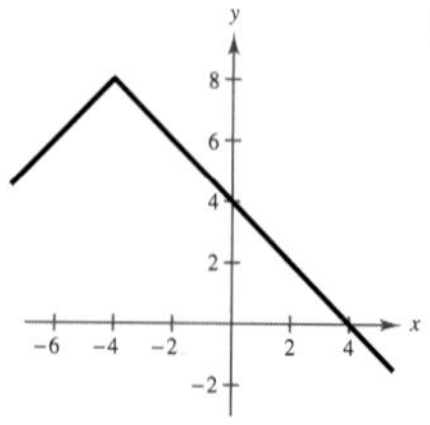

(d) $g(x) = -f(x + 4) + 8$

45. (a) $f(x) = |x|$

(b) Reflection in the x-axis, vertical stretch of two, horizontal shift one unit to the right, and vertical shift four units downward

(c)

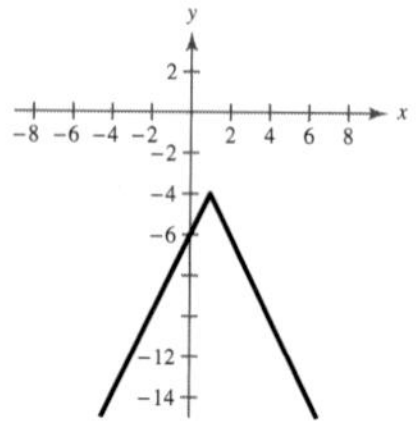

(d) $g(x) = -2f(x - 1) - 4$

47. (a) $f(x) = [\![x]\!]$

(b) Reflection in the x-axis and vertical shift three units upward

(c)

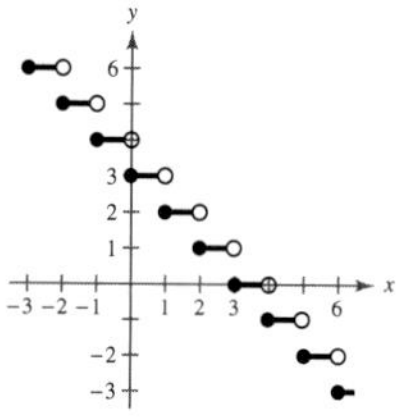

(d) $g(x) = 3 - f(x)$

49. (a) $f(x) = \sqrt{x}$

(b) Horizontal shift nine units to the right

(c)

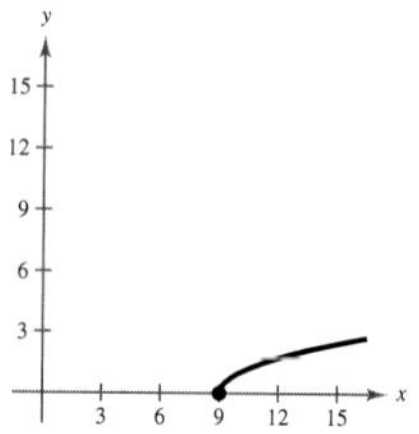

(d) $g(x) = f(x - 9)$

51. (a) $f(x) = \sqrt{x}$

(b) Reflection in the y-axis, horizontal shift seven units to the right, and vertical shift two units downward

(c)

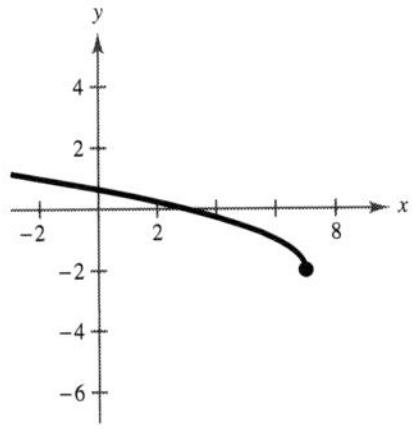

(d) $g(x) = f(7 - x) - 2$

(e)

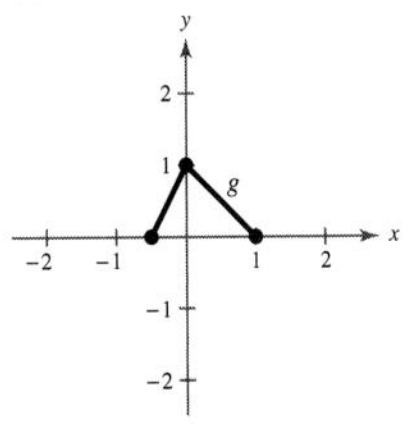

(f)

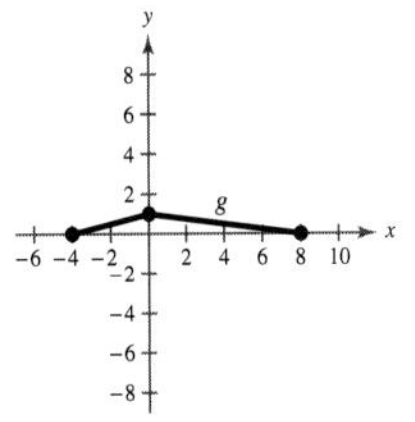

53. (a) $f(x) = \sqrt{x}$
(b) Horizontal stretch and vertical shift four units downward
(c)

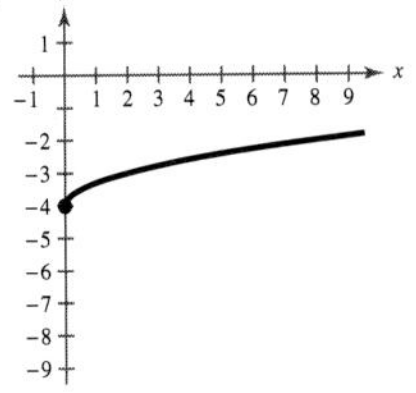

(d) $g(x) = f\left(\frac{1}{2}x\right) - 4$

55. $g(x) = (x - 3)^2 - 7$ **57.** $g(x) = (x - 13)^3$
59. $g(x) = -|x| + 12$ **61.** $g(x) = -\sqrt{-x + 6}$
63. (a) $y = -3x^2$ (b) $y = 4x^2 + 3$
65. (a) $y = -\frac{1}{2}|x|$ (b) $y = 3|x| - 3$
67. Vertical stretch of $y = x^3$; $y = 2x^3$
69. Reflection in the x-axis and vertical shrink of $y = x^2$; $y = -\frac{1}{2}x^2$
71. Reflection in the y-axis and vertical shrink of $y = \sqrt{x}$; $y = \frac{1}{2}\sqrt{-x}$
73. $y = -(x - 2)^3 + 2$ **75.** $y = -\sqrt{x} - 3$
77. (a)

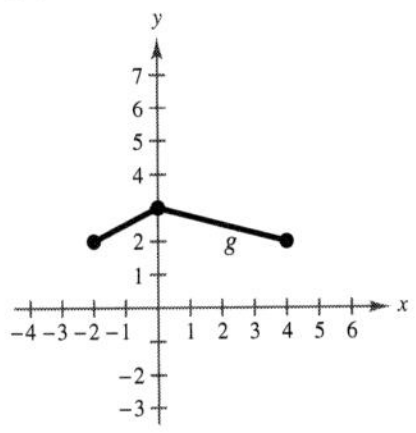

(b)

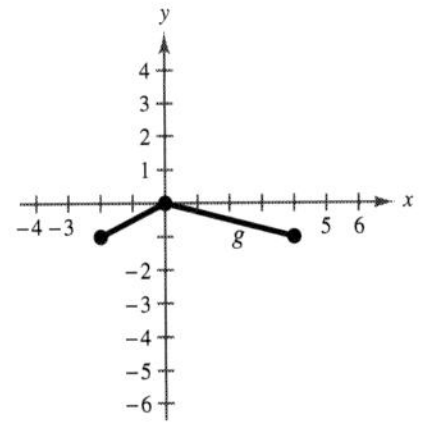

(c)

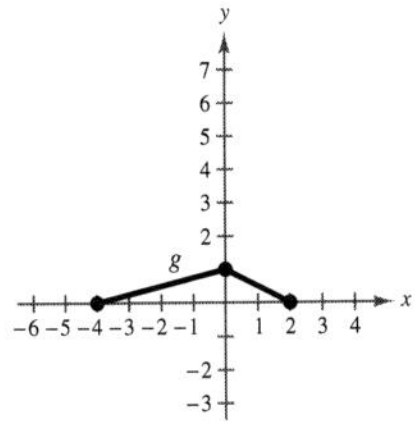

(d)

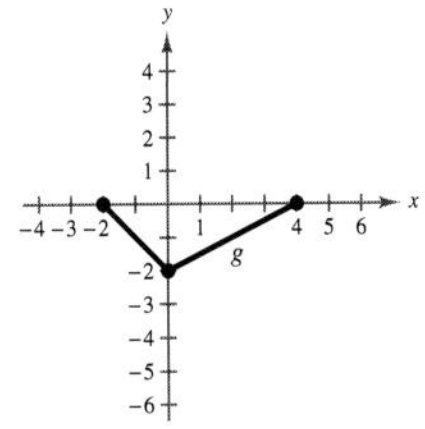

79. (a) Vertical stretch of 128.0 and a vertical shift of 527 units upward

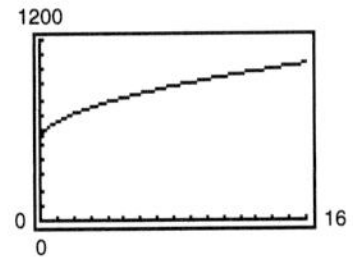

(b) 32; Each year, the total number of miles driven by vans, pickups, and SUVs increases by an average of 32 billion miles.
(c) $f(t) = 527 + 128\sqrt{t + 10}$; The graph is shifted 10 units to the left.
(d) 1127 billion miles; Answers will vary. Sample answer: Yes, because the number of miles driven has been steadily increasing.
81. False. The graph of $y = f(-x)$ is a reflection of the graph of $f(x)$ in the y-axis.
83. True. $|-x| = |x|$
85. (a) $g(t) = \frac{3}{4}f(t)$ (b) $g(t) = f(t) + 10{,}000$
(c) $g(t) = f(t - 2)$
87. $(-2, 0), (-1, 1), (0, 2)$
89. No. $g(x) = -x^4 - 2$. Yes. $h(x) = -(x - 3)^4$.

Section 1.8 *(page 88)*

1. addition; subtraction; multiplication; division **3.** $g(x)$
5.

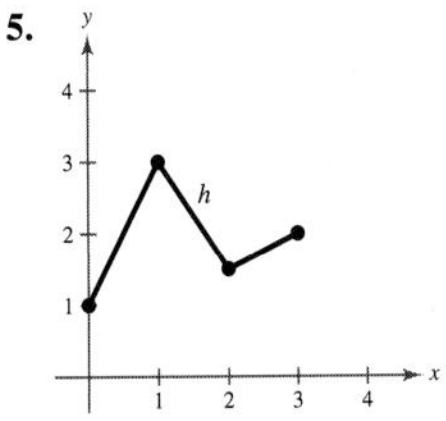

7.

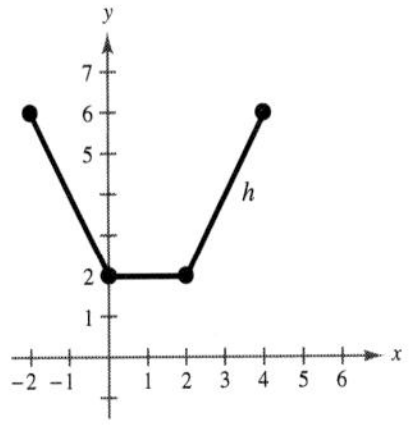

9. (a) $2x$ (b) 4 (c) $x^2 - 4$
(d) $\dfrac{x + 2}{x - 2}$; all real numbers x except $x = 2$
11. (a) $x^2 + 4x - 5$ (b) $x^2 - 4x + 5$ (c) $4x^3 - 5x^2$
(d) $\dfrac{x^2}{4x - 5}$; all real numbers x except $x = \dfrac{5}{4}$
13. (a) $x^2 + 6 + \sqrt{1 - x}$ (b) $x^2 + 6 - \sqrt{1 - x}$
(c) $(x^2 + 6)\sqrt{1 - x}$
(d) $\dfrac{(x^2 + 6)\sqrt{1 - x}}{1 - x}$; all real numbers x such that $x < 1$

15. (a) $\dfrac{x+1}{x^2}$ (b) $\dfrac{x-1}{x^2}$ (c) $\dfrac{1}{x^3}$
(d) x; all real numbers x except $x = 0$

17. 3 **19.** 5 **21.** $9t^2 - 3t + 5$ **23.** 74

25. 26 **27.** $\frac{3}{5}$

29.

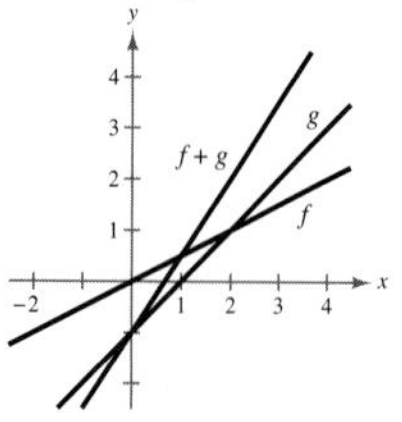

31.

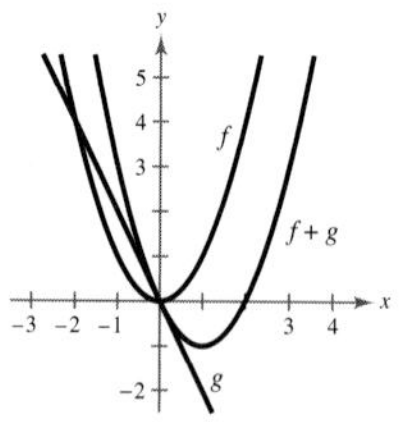

33.

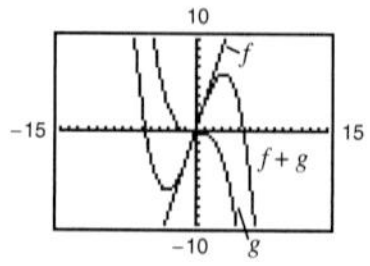

$f(x), g(x)$

35.

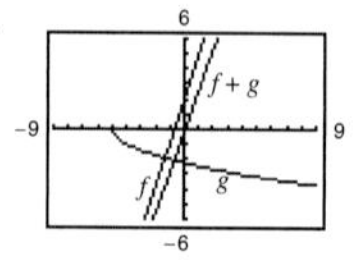

$f(x), f(x)$

37. (a) $(x-1)^2$ (b) $x^2 - 1$ (c) $x - 2$

39. (a) x (b) x (c) $x^9 + 3x^6 + 3x^3 + 2$

41. (a) $\sqrt{x^2+4}$ (b) $x + 4$
Domains of f and $g \circ f$: all real numbers x such that $x \geq -4$
Domains of g and $f \circ g$: all real numbers x

43. (a) $x + 1$ (b) $\sqrt{x^2+1}$
Domains of f and $g \circ f$: all real numbers x
Domains of g and $f \circ g$: all real numbers x such that $x \geq 0$

45. (a) $|x + 6|$ (b) $|x| + 6$
Domains of f, g, $f \circ g$, and $g \circ f$: all real numbers x

47. (a) $\dfrac{1}{x+3}$ (b) $\dfrac{1}{x} + 3$
Domains of f and $g \circ f$: all real numbers x except $x = 0$
Domain of g: all real numbers x
Domain of $f \circ g$: all real numbers x except $x = -3$

49. (a) 3 (b) 0 **51.** (a) 0 (b) 4

53. $f(x) = x^2$, $g(x) = 2x + 1$

55. $f(x) = \sqrt[3]{x}$, $g(x) = x^2 - 4$

57. $f(x) = \dfrac{1}{x}$, $g(x) = x + 2$ **59.** $f(x) = \dfrac{x+3}{4+x}$, $g(x) = -x^2$

61. (a) $T = \frac{3}{4}x + \frac{1}{15}x^2$
(b)

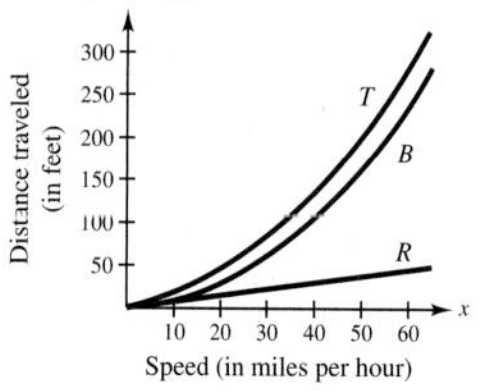

(c) The braking function $B(x)$. As x increases, $B(x)$ increases at a faster rate than $R(x)$.

63. (a) $c(t) = \dfrac{b(t) - d(t)}{p(t)} \times 100$
(b) $c(5)$ is the percent change in the population due to births and deaths in the year 2005.

65. (a) $(N + M)(t) = 0.227t^3 - 4.11t^2 + 14.6t + 544$, which represents the total number of Navy and Marines personnel combined.
$(N + M)(0) = 544$
$(N + M)(6) \approx 533$
$(N + M)(12) \approx 520$
(b) $(N - M)(t) = 0.157t^3 - 3.65t^2 + 11.2t + 200$, which represents the difference between the number of Navy personnel and the number of Marines personnel.
$(N - M)(0) = 200$
$(N - M)(6) \approx 170$
$(N - M)(12) \approx 80$

67. $(B - D)(t) = -0.197t^3 + 10.17t^2 - 128.0t + 2043$, which represents the change in the United States population.

69. (a) For each time t there corresponds one and only one temperature T.
(b) 60°, 72°
(c) All the temperature changes occur 1 hour later.
(d) The temperature is decreased by 1 degree.
(e) $T(t) = \begin{cases} 60, & 0 \leq t \leq 6 \\ 12t - 12, & 6 < t < 7 \\ 72, & 7 \leq t \leq 20 \\ -12t + 312, & 20 < t < 21 \\ 60, & 21 \leq t \leq 24 \end{cases}$

71. $(A \circ r)(t) = 0.36\pi t^2$; $(A \circ r)(t)$ represents the area of the circle at time t.

73. (a) $N(T(t)) = 30(3t^2 + 2t + 20)$; This represents the number of bacteria in the food as a function of time.
(b) About 653 bacteria (c) 2.846 h

75. $g(f(x))$ represents 3 percent of an amount over $500,000.

77. False. $(f \circ g)(x) = 6x + 1$ and $(g \circ f)(x) = 6x + 6$

79. (a) $O(M(Y)) = 2\left(6 + \frac{1}{2}Y\right) = 12 + Y$
(b) Middle child is 8 years old; youngest child is 4 years old.

81. Proof

83. (a) Proof
(b) $\frac{1}{2}[f(x) + f(-x)] + \frac{1}{2}[f(x) - f(-x)]$
$= \frac{1}{2}[f(x) + f(-x) + f(x) - f(-x)]$
$= \frac{1}{2}[2f(x)]$
$= f(x)$
(c) $f(x) = (x^2 + 1) + (-2x)$
$k(x) = \dfrac{-1}{(x+1)(x-1)} + \dfrac{x}{(x+1)(x-1)}$

Section 1.9 *(page 98)*

1. inverse **3.** range; domain **5.** one-to-one

7. $f^{-1}(x) = \frac{1}{6}x$ **9.** $f^{-1}(x) = x - 9$ **11.** $f^{-1}(x) = \dfrac{x-1}{3}$

13. $f^{-1}(x) = x^3$ **15.** c **16.** b **17.** a **18.** d

19. $f(g(x)) = f\left(-\dfrac{2x+6}{7}\right) = -\dfrac{7}{2}\left(-\dfrac{2x+6}{7}\right) - 3 = x$

$g(f(x)) = g\left(-\dfrac{7}{2}x - 3\right) = -\dfrac{2\left(-\frac{7}{2}x - 3\right) + 6}{7} = x$

21. $f(g(x)) = f(\sqrt[3]{x-5}) = (\sqrt[3]{x-5})^3 + 5 = x$
$g(f(x)) = g(x^3 + 5) = \sqrt[3]{(x^3+5) - 5} = x$

23. (a) $f(g(x)) = f\left(\frac{x}{2}\right) = 2\left(\frac{x}{2}\right) = x$

$g(f(x)) = g(2x) = \frac{(2x)}{2} = x$

(b)

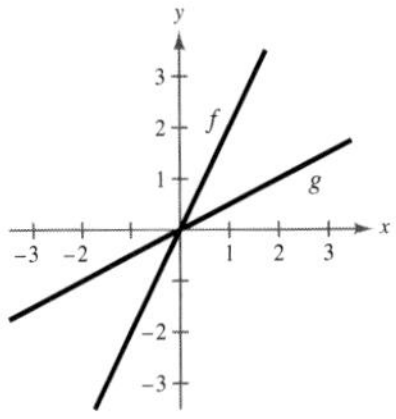

25. (a) $f(g(x)) = f\left(\frac{x-1}{7}\right) = 7\left(\frac{x-1}{7}\right) + 1 = x$

$g(f(x)) = g(7x+1) = \frac{(7x+1) - 1}{7} = x$

(b)

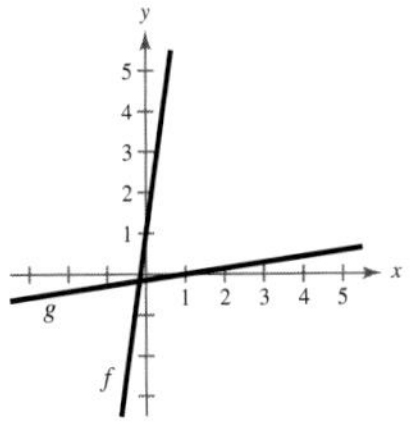

27. (a) $f(g(x)) = f(\sqrt[3]{8x}) = \frac{(\sqrt[3]{8x})^3}{8} = x$

$g(f(x)) = g\left(\frac{x^3}{8}\right) = \sqrt[3]{8\left(\frac{x^3}{8}\right)} = x$

(b)

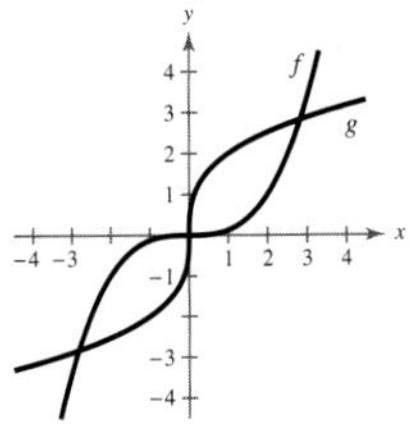

29. (a) $f(g(x)) = f(x^2 + 4),\ x \ge 0$
$= \sqrt{(x^2+4) - 4} = x$
$g(f(x)) = g(\sqrt{x-4})$
$= (\sqrt{x-4})^2 + 4 = x$

(b)

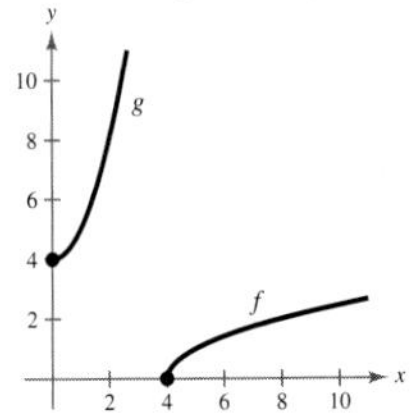

31. (a) $f(g(x)) = f(\sqrt{9-x}),\ x \le 9$
$= 9 - (\sqrt{9-x})^2 = x$
$g(f(x)) = g(9 - x^2),\ x \ge 0$
$= \sqrt{9 - (9 - x^2)} = x$

(b)

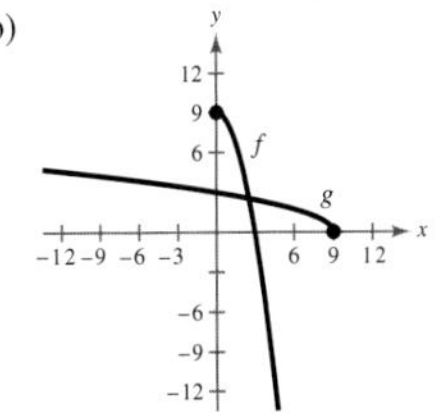

33. (a) $f(g(x)) = f\left(-\frac{5x+1}{x-1}\right) = \dfrac{-\left(\frac{5x+1}{x-1}\right) - 1}{-\left(\frac{5x+1}{x-1}\right) + 5}$

$= \frac{-5x - 1 - x + 1}{-5x - 1 + 5x - 5} = x$

$g(f(x)) = g\left(\frac{x-1}{x+5}\right) = \dfrac{-5\left(\frac{x-1}{x+5}\right) - 1}{\frac{x-1}{x+5} - 1}$

$= \frac{-5x + 5 - x - 5}{x - 1 - x - 5} = x$

(b)

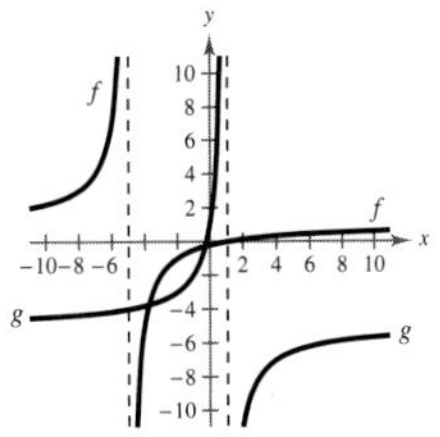

35. No

37.

x	-2	0	2	4	6	8
$f^{-1}(x)$	-2	-1	0	1	2	3

39. Yes **41.** No

43.

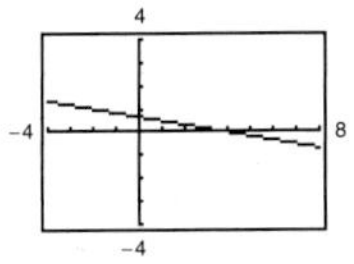

The function has an inverse.

45.

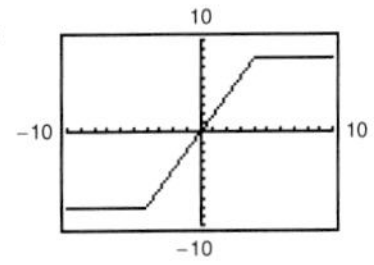

The function does not have an inverse.

47.

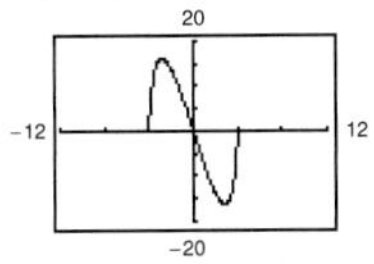

The function does not have an inverse.

CHAPTER 1

49. (a) $f^{-1}(x) = \dfrac{x+3}{2}$

(b)

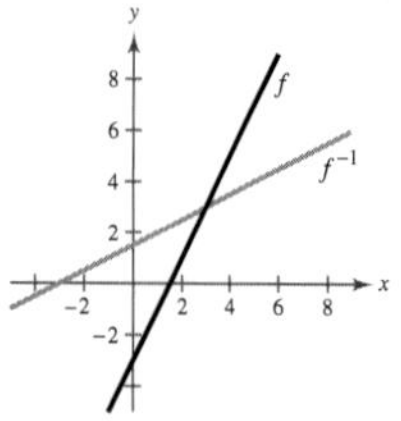

(c) The graph of f^{-1} is the reflection of the graph of f in the line $y = x$.

(d) The domains and ranges of f and f^{-1} are all real numbers.

51. (a) $f^{-1}(x) = \sqrt[5]{x+2}$

(b)

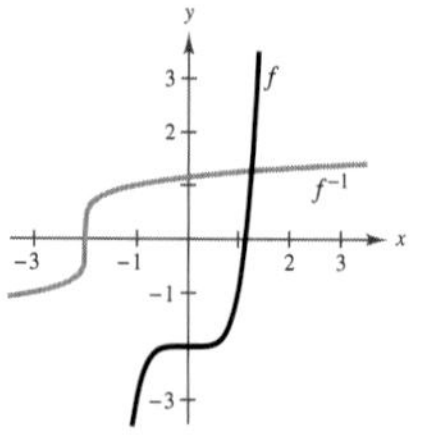

(c) The graph of f^{-1} is the reflection of the graph of f in the line $y = x$.

(d) The domains and ranges of f and f^{-1} are all real numbers.

53. (a) $f^{-1}(x) = \sqrt{4 - x^2},\ 0 \le x \le 2$

(b)

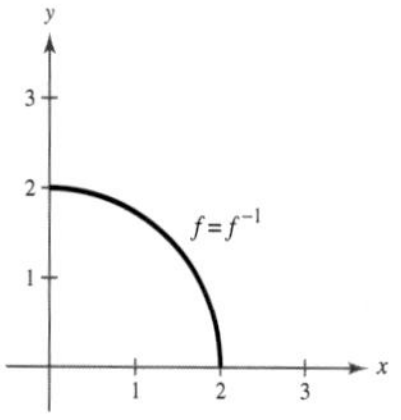

(c) The graph of f^{-1} is the same as the graph of f.

(d) The domains and ranges of f and f^{-1} are all real numbers x such that $0 \le x \le 2$.

55. (a) $f^{-1}(x) = \dfrac{4}{x}$

(b)

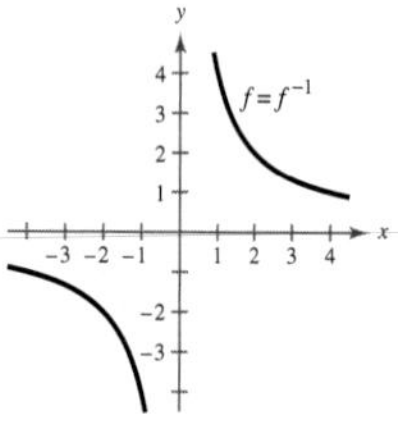

(c) The graph of f^{-1} is the same as the graph of f.

(d) The domains and ranges of f and f^{-1} are all real numbers x except $x = 0$.

57. (a) $f^{-1}(x) = \dfrac{2x+1}{x-1}$

(b)

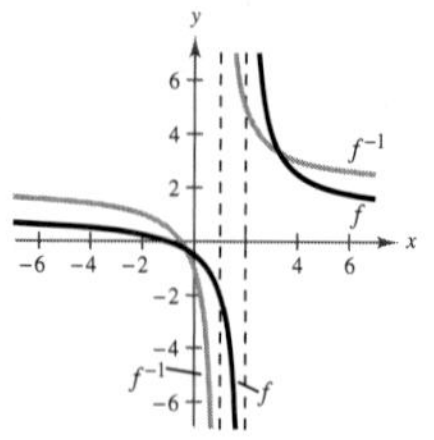

(c) The graph of f^{-1} is the reflection of the graph of f in the line $y = x$.

(d) The domain of f and the range of f^{-1} are all real numbers x except $x = 2$. The domain of f^{-1} and the range of f are all real numbers x except $x = 1$.

59. (a) $f^{-1}(x) = x^3 + 1$

(b)

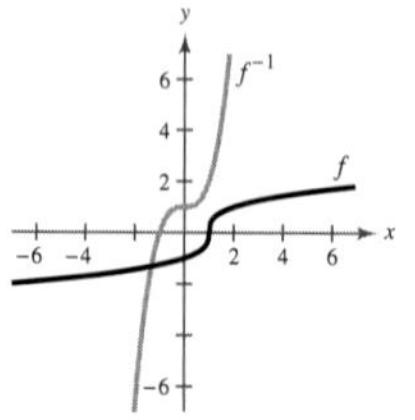

(c) The graph of f^{-1} is the reflection of the graph of f in the line $y = x$.

(d) The domains and ranges of f and f^{-1} are all real numbers.

61. (a) $f^{-1}(x) = \dfrac{5x-4}{6-4x}$

(b)

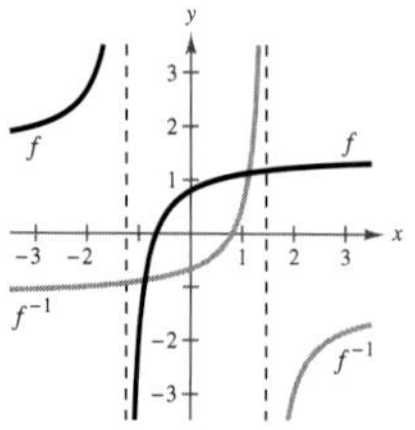

(c) The graph of f^{-1} is the reflection of the graph of f in the line $y = x$.

(d) The domain of f and the range of f^{-1} are all real numbers x except $x = -\frac{5}{4}$. The domain of f^{-1} and the range of f are all real numbers x except $x = \frac{3}{2}$.

63. No inverse **65.** $g^{-1}(x) = 8x$ **67.** No inverse

69. $f^{-1}(x) = \sqrt{x} - 3$ **71.** No inverse **73.** No inverse

75. $f^{-1}(x) = \dfrac{x^2 - 3}{2},\quad x \ge 0$

77. $f^{-1}(x) = \sqrt{x} + 2$

The domain of f and the range of f^{-1} are all real numbers x such that $x \ge 2$. The domain of f^{-1} and the range of f are all real numbers x such that $x \ge 0$.

79. $f^{-1}(x) = x - 2$

The domain of f and the range of f^{-1} are all real numbers x such that $x \ge -2$. The domain of f^{-1} and the range of f are all real numbers x such that $x \ge 0$.

81. $f^{-1}(x) = \sqrt{x} - 6$
The domain of f and the range of f^{-1} are all real numbers x such that $x \geq -6$. The domain of f^{-1} and the range of f are all real numbers x such that $x \geq 0$.

83. $f^{-1}(x) = \dfrac{\sqrt{-2(x-5)}}{2}$
The domain of f and the range of f^{-1} are all real numbers x such that $x \geq 0$. The domain of f^{-1} and the range of f are all real numbers x such that $x \leq 5$.

85. $f^{-1}(x) = x + 3$
The domain of f and the range of f^{-1} are all real numbers x such that $x \geq 4$. The domain of f^{-1} and the range of f are all real numbers x such that $x \geq 1$.

87. 32 **89.** 600 **91.** $2\sqrt[3]{x+3}$

93. $\dfrac{x+1}{2}$ **95.** $\dfrac{x+1}{2}$

97. (a) Yes; each European shoe size corresponds to exactly one U.S. shoe size.
(b) 45 (c) 10 (d) 41 (e) 13

99. (a) Yes
(b) S^{-1} represents the time in years for a given sales level.
(c) $S^{-1}(8430) = 6$
(d) No, because then the sales for 2007 and 2009 would be the same, so the function would no longer be one-to-one.

101. (a) $y = \dfrac{x - 10}{0.75}$
x = hourly wage; y = number of units produced
(b) 19 units

103. False. $f(x) = x^2$ has no inverse. **105.** Proof

107.

x	1	3	4	6
y	1	2	6	7

x	1	2	6	7
$f^{-1}(x)$	1	3	4	6

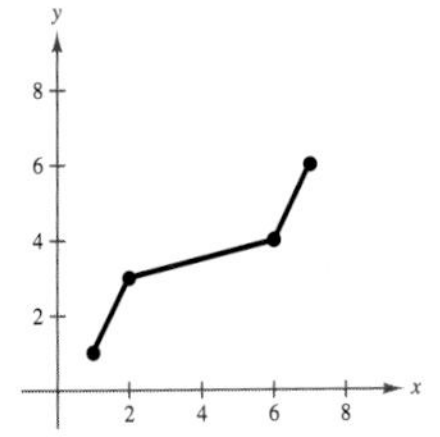

109. This situation could be represented by a one-to-one function if the runner does not stop to rest. The inverse function would represent the time in hours for a given number of miles completed.

111. This function could not be represented by a one-to-one function because it oscillates.

113. $k = \frac{1}{4}$

115.

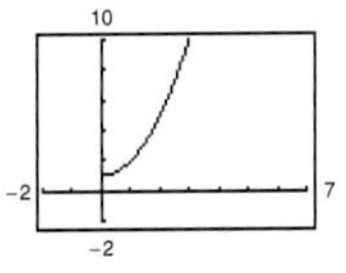

There is an inverse function $f^{-1}(x) = \sqrt{x-1}$ because the domain of f is equal to the range of f^{-1} and the range of f is equal to the domain of f^{-1}.

Section 1.10 *(page 108)*

1. variation; regression **3.** least squares regression
5. directly proportional **7.** directly proportional
9. combined

11.

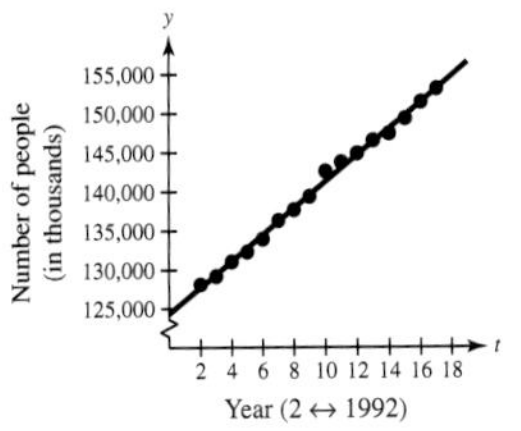

The model is a good fit for the actual data.

13.

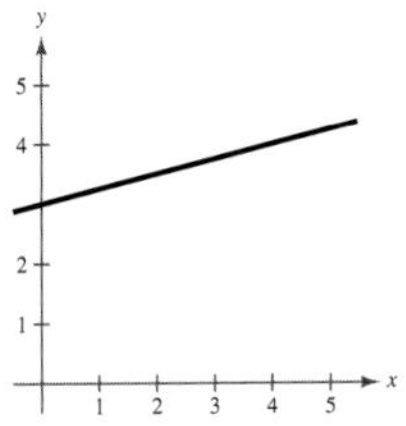

$y = \frac{1}{4}x + 3$

15.

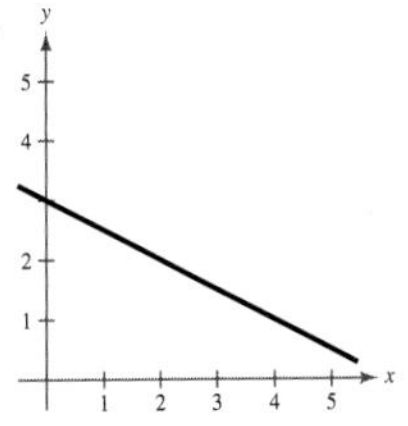

$y = -\frac{1}{2}x + 3$

17. (a) and (b)

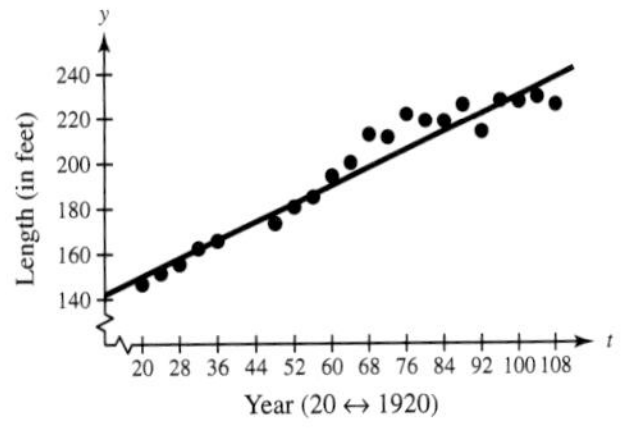

$y \approx t + 130$
(c) $y = 1.01t + 130.82$ (d) The models are similar.
(e) Part (b): 242 ft; Part (c): 243.94 ft
(f) Answers will vary.

19. (a)

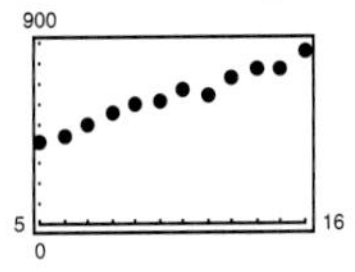

(b) $S = 38.3t + 224$

(c) 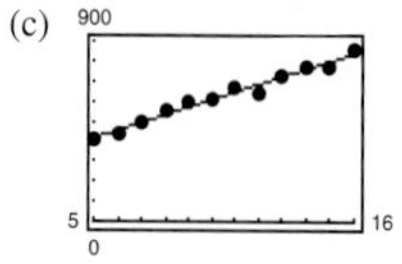

The model is a good fit.

(d) 2007: \$875.1 million; 2009: \$951.7 million

(e) Each year the annual gross ticket sales for Broadway shows in New York City increase by \$38.3 million.

21. Inversely

23.

x	2	4	6	8	10
$y = kx^2$	4	16	36	64	100

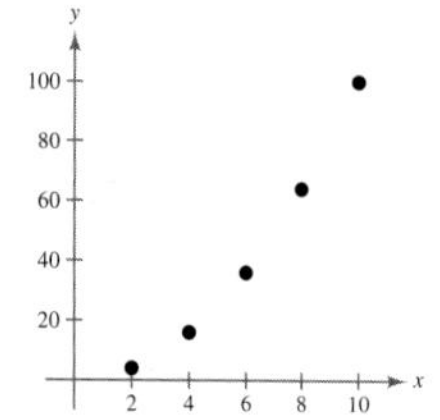

25.

x	2	4	6	8	10
$y = kx^2$	2	8	18	32	50

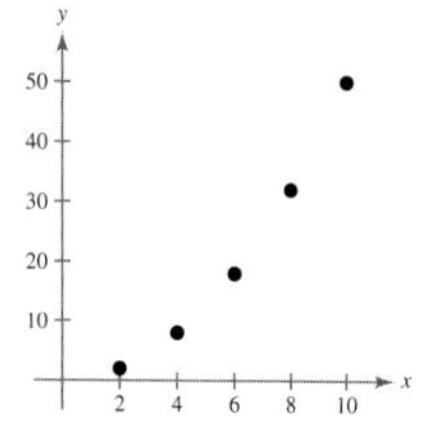

27.

x	2	4	6	8	10
$y = k/x^2$	$\frac{1}{2}$	$\frac{1}{8}$	$\frac{1}{18}$	$\frac{1}{32}$	$\frac{1}{50}$

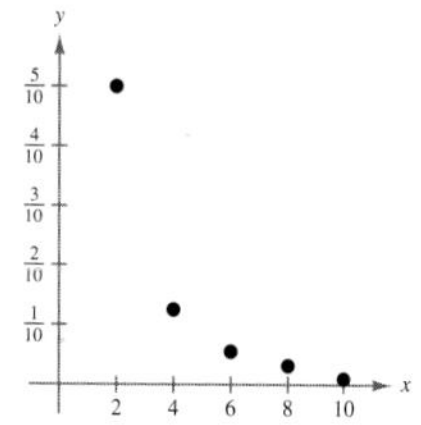

29.

x	2	4	6	8	10
$y = k/x^2$	$\frac{5}{2}$	$\frac{5}{8}$	$\frac{5}{18}$	$\frac{5}{32}$	$\frac{1}{10}$

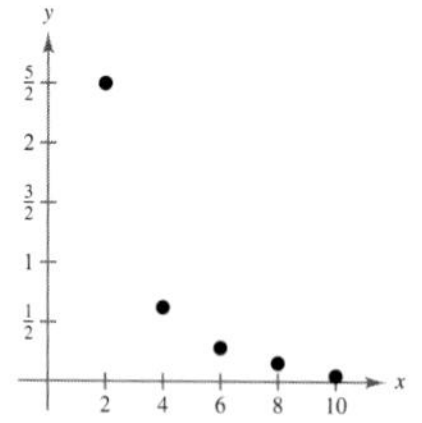

31. $y = \frac{5}{x}$ **33.** $y = -\frac{7}{10}x$ **35.** $y = \frac{12}{5}x$

37. $y = 205x$ **39.** $I = 0.035P$

41. Model: $y = \frac{33}{13}x$; 25.4 cm, 50.8 cm

43. $y = 0.0368x$; \$8280

45. (a) 0.05 m (b) $176\frac{2}{3}$ N **47.** 39.47 lb

49. $A = kr^2$ **51.** $y = \frac{k}{x^2}$ **53.** $F = \frac{kg}{r^2}$ **55.** $P = \frac{k}{V}$

57. $F = \frac{km_1m_2}{r^2}$

59. The area of a triangle is jointly proportional to its base and height.

61. The area of an equilateral triangle varies directly as the square of one of its sides.

63. The volume of a sphere varies directly as the cube of its radius.

65. Average speed is directly proportional to the distance and inversely proportional to the time.

67. $A = \pi r^2$ **69.** $y = \frac{28}{x}$ **71.** $F = 14rs^3$

73. $z = \frac{2x^2}{3y}$ **75.** About 0.61 mi/h **77.** 506 ft

79. 1470 J **81.** The velocity is increased by one-third.

83. (a) 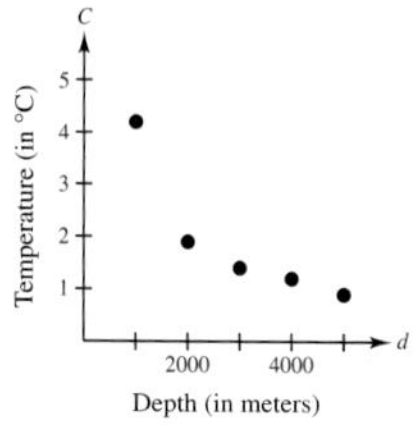

(b) Yes. $k_1 = 4200, k_2 = 3800, k_3 = 4200,$ $k_4 = 4800, k_5 = 4500$

(c) $C = \frac{4300}{d}$

(d) 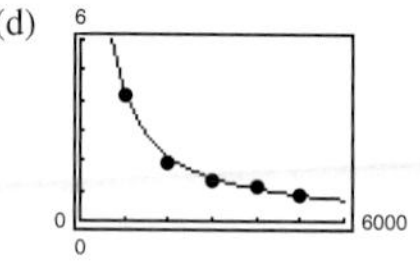

(e) About 1433 m

85. (a)

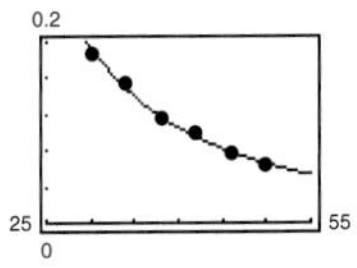

(b) 0.2857 $\mu W/\text{cm}^2$

87. False. E is jointly proportional to the mass of an object and the square of its velocity.

89. (a) Good approximation (b) Poor approximation
(c) Poor approximation (d) Good approximation

91. As one variable increases, the other variable will also increase.

93. (a) y will change by a factor of one-fourth.
(b) y will change by a factor of four.

Review Exercises *(page 116)*

1.

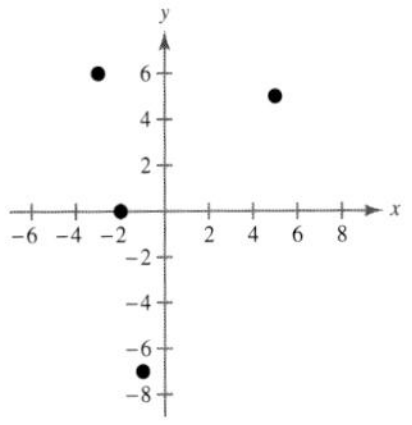

3. Quadrant IV

5. (a)

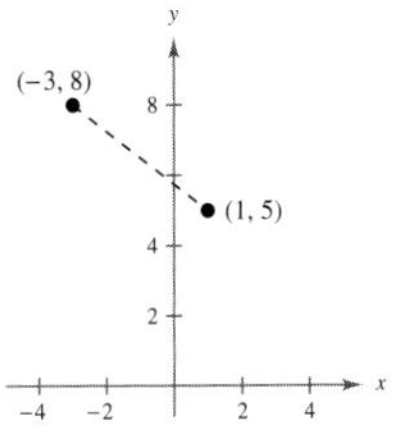

(b) 5
(c) $\left(-1, \frac{13}{2}\right)$

7. (a)

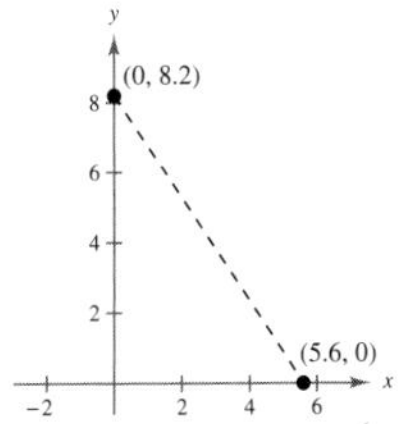

(b) $\sqrt{98.6}$
(c) (2.8, 4.1)

9. (0, 0), (2, 0), (0, −5), (2, −5)

11. \$6.275 billion

13.

x	−2	−1	0	1	2
y	−11	−8	−5	−2	1

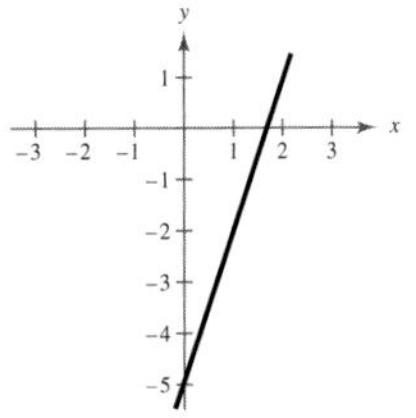

15.

x	−1	0	1	2	3	4
y	4	0	−2	−2	0	4

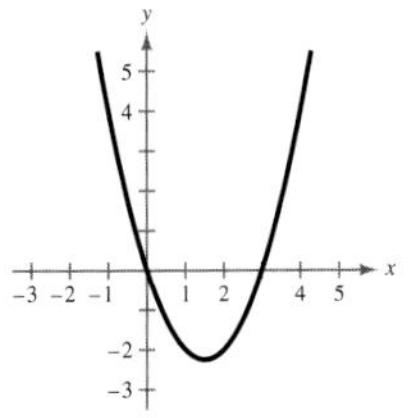

17.

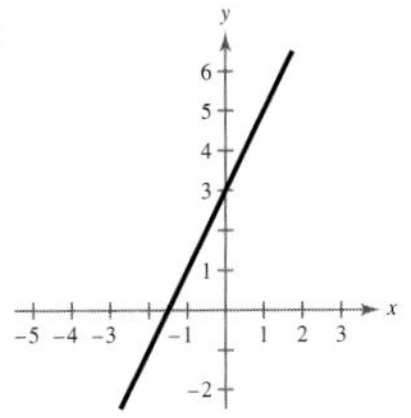

19.

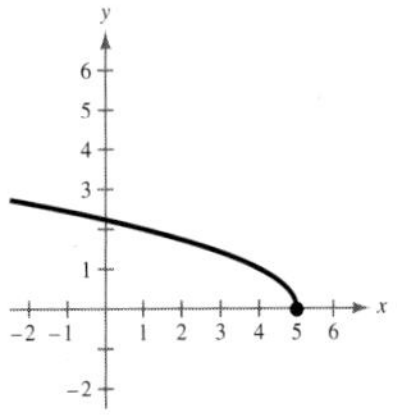

21.

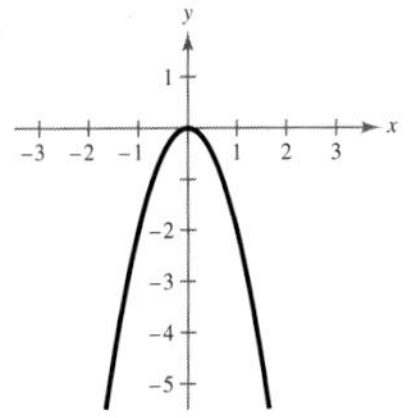

23. x-intercept: $\left(-\frac{7}{2}, 0\right)$
y-intercept: (0, 7)

25. x-intercepts: (1, 0), (5, 0)
y-intercept: (0, 5)

CHAPTER 1

27. x-intercept: $\left(\frac{1}{4}, 0\right)$
y-intercept: $(0, 1)$
No symmetry

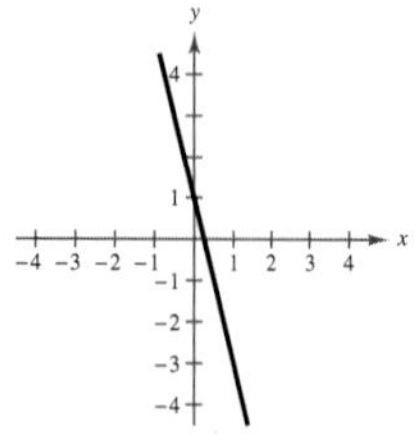

29. x-intercepts: $\left(\pm\sqrt{5}, 0\right)$
y-intercept: $(0, 5)$
y-axis symmetry

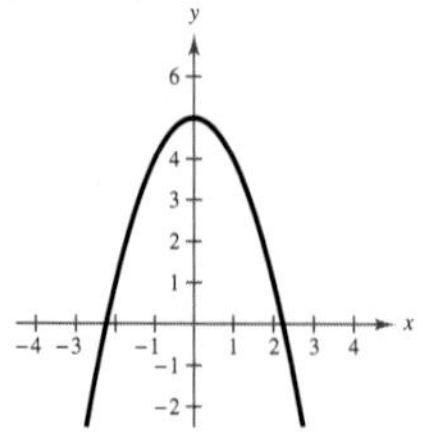

31. x-intercept: $\left(\sqrt[3]{-3}, 0\right)$
y-intercept: $(0, 3)$
No symmetry

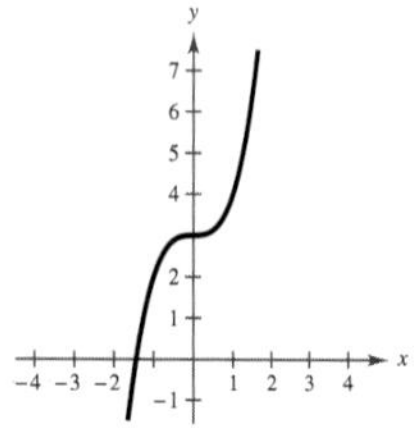

33. x-intercept: $(-5, 0)$
y-intercept: $\left(0, \sqrt{5}\right)$
No symmetry

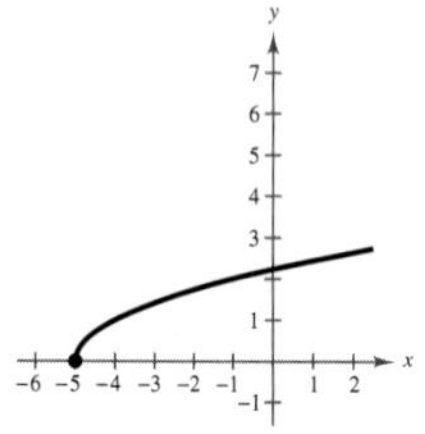

35. Center: $(0, 0)$
Radius: 3

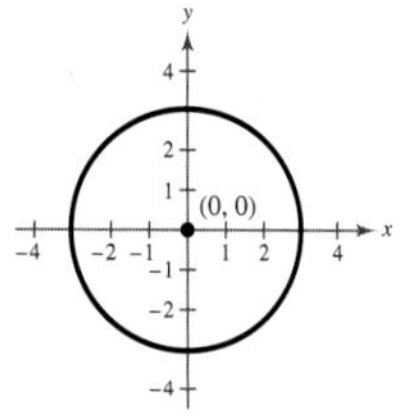

37. Center: $(-2, 0)$
Radius: 4

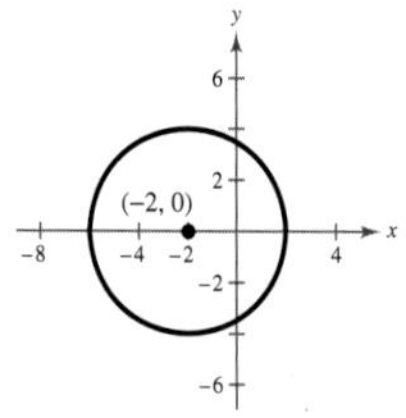

39. Center: $\left(\frac{1}{2}, -1\right)$
Radius: 6

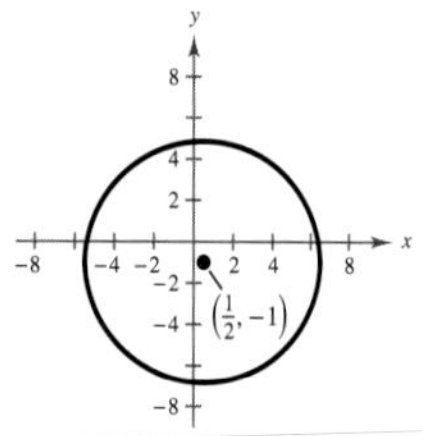

41. $(x - 2)^2 + (y + 3)^2 = 13$

43. (a)

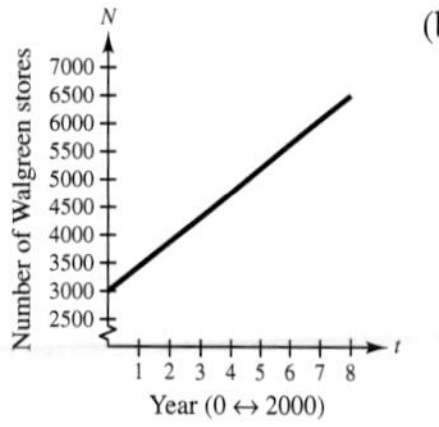

(b) 2008

45. Slope: 0
y-intercept: 6

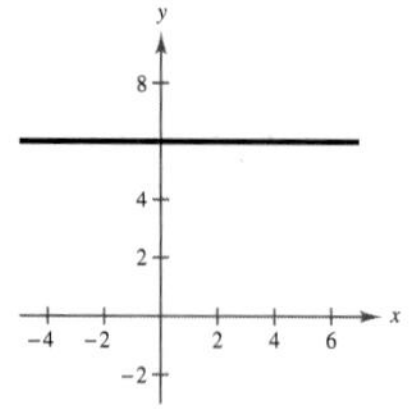

47. Slope: 3
y-intercept: 13

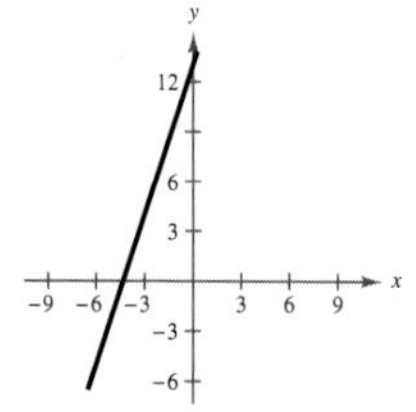

49.

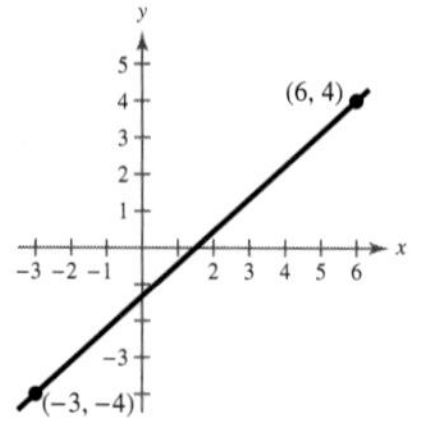

$m = \frac{8}{9}$

51.

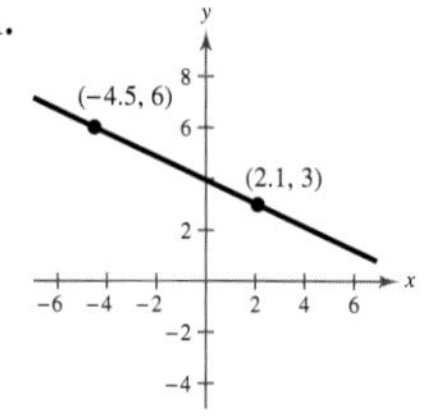

$m = -\frac{5}{11}$

53. $y = \frac{2}{3}x - 2$

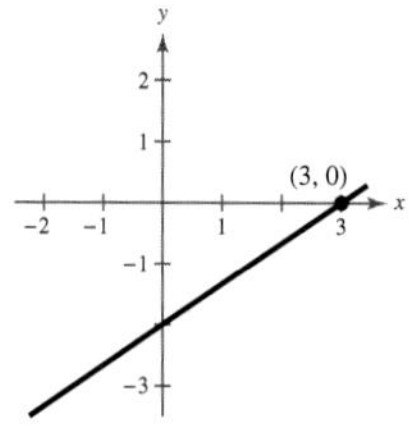

55. $y = -\frac{1}{2}x + 2$

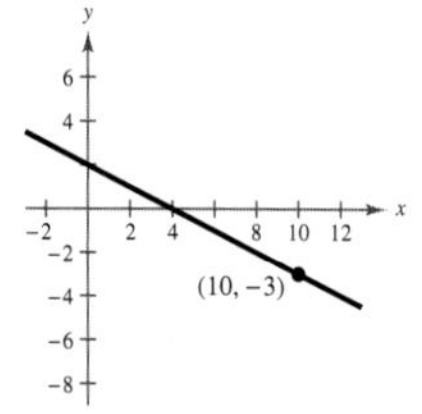

57. $x = 0$ **59.** $y = \frac{2}{7}x + \frac{2}{7}$

61. (a) $y = \frac{5}{4}x - \frac{23}{4}$ (b) $y = -\frac{4}{5}x + \frac{2}{5}$

63. $V = -850t + 21{,}000,\ \ 10 \le t \le 15$

65. No **67.** Yes

69. (a) 5 (b) 17 (c) $t^4 + 1$ (d) $t^2 + 2t + 2$

71. All real numbers x such that $-5 \le x \le 5$

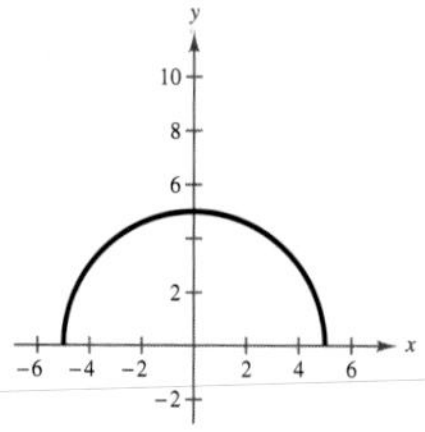

73. All real numbers x except $x = 3, -2$

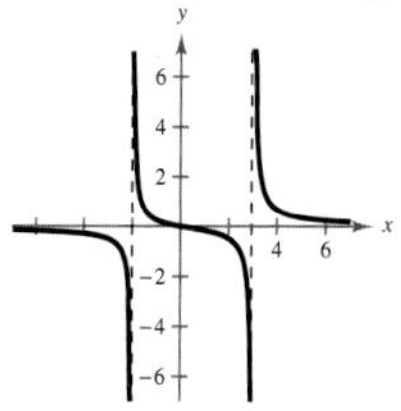

75. (a) 16 ft/sec (b) 1.5 sec (c) -16 ft/sec

77. $4x + 2h + 3, \quad h \neq 0$ **79.** Function

81. Not a function **83.** $\frac{7}{3}, 3$ **85.** $-\frac{3}{8}$

87.

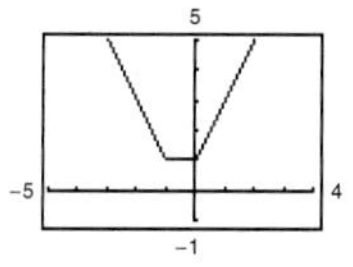

Increasing on $(0, \infty)$
Decreasing on $(-\infty, -1)$
Constant on $(-1, 0)$

89.

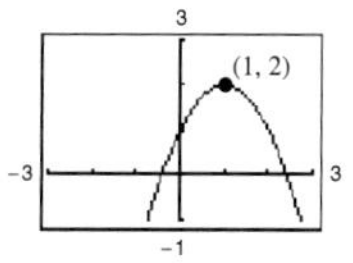

91.

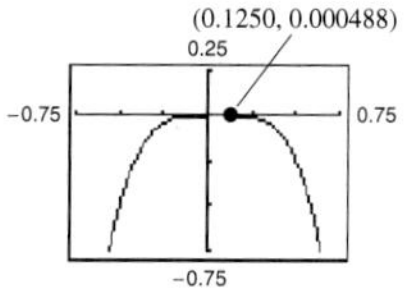

93. 4 **95.** $\frac{1 - \sqrt{2}}{2}$ **97.** Neither **99.** Odd

101. $f(x) = -3x$

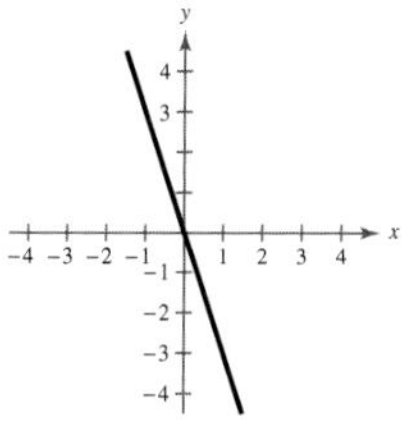

103.

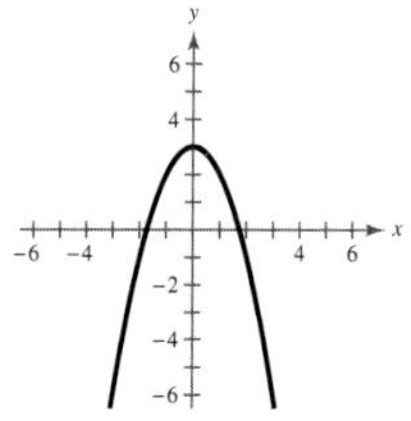

105.

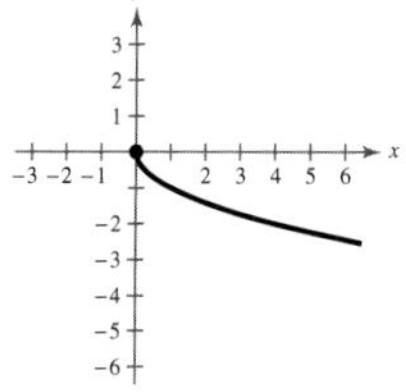

107.

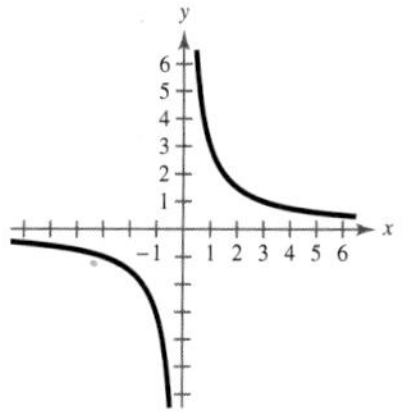

109.

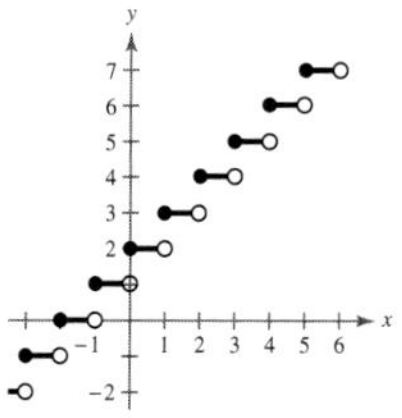

111.

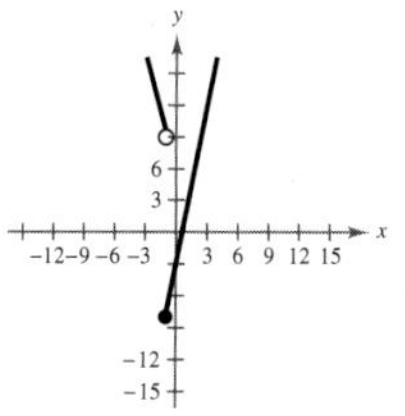

113. $y = x^3$

115. (a) $f(x) = x^2$

(b) Vertical shift nine units downward

(c)

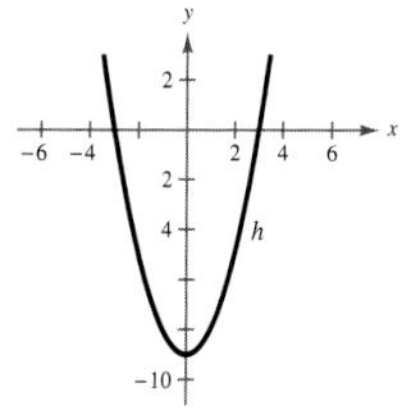

(d) $h(x) = f(x) - 9$

117. (a) $f(x) = \sqrt{x}$

(b) Reflection in the x-axis and vertical shift four units upward

(c)

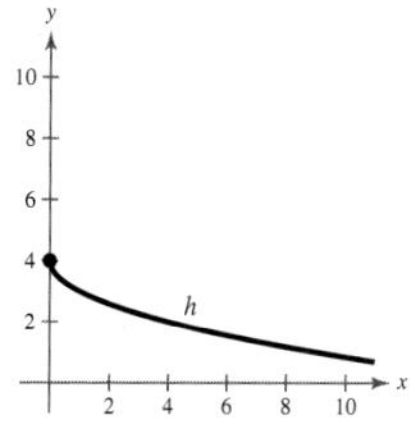

(d) $h(x) = -f(x) + 4$

119. (a) $f(x) = x^2$

(b) Reflection in the x-axis, horizontal shift two units to the left, and vertical shift three units upward

(c)

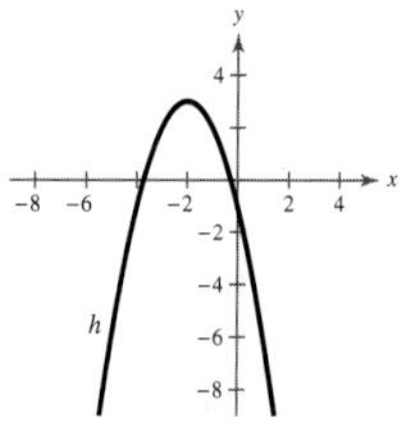

(d) $h(x) = -f(x + 2) + 3$

121. (a) $f(x) = [\![x]\!]$

(b) Reflection in the x-axis and vertical shift six units upward

(c)

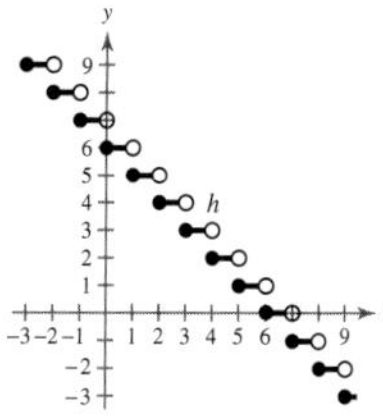

(d) $h(x) = -f(x) + 6$

123. (a) $f(x) = |x|$

(b) Reflections in the x-axis and the y-axis, horizontal shift four units to the right, and vertical shift six units upward

CHAPTER 1

(c)

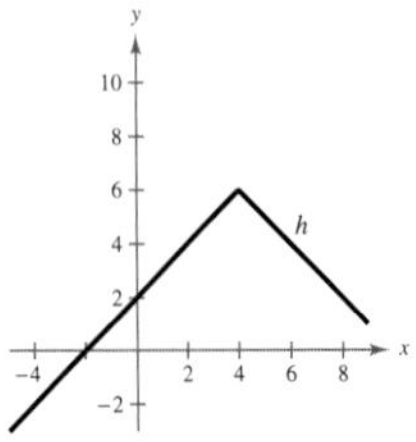

(d) $h(x) = -f(-x + 4) + 6$

125. (a) $f(x) = [\![x]\!]$

(b) Horizontal shift nine units to the right and vertical stretch

(c)

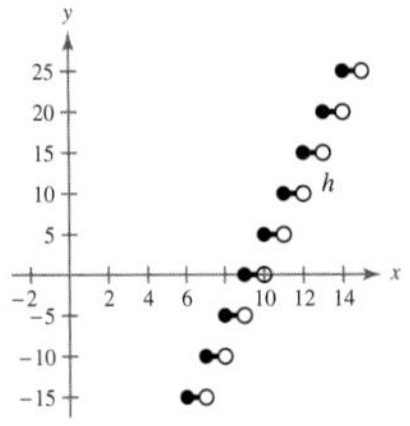

(d) $h(x) = 5f(x - 9)$

127. (a) $f(x) = \sqrt{x}$

(b) Reflection in the x-axis, vertical stretch, and horizontal shift four units to the right

(c)

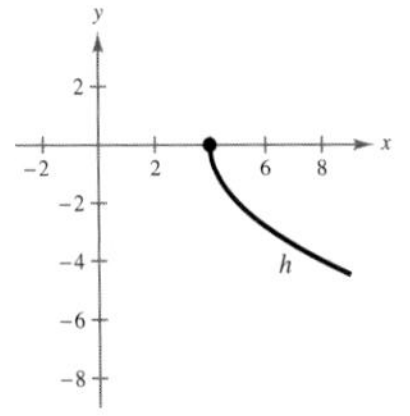

(d) $h(x) = -2f(x - 4)$

129. (a) $x^2 + 2x + 2$ (b) $x^2 - 2x + 4$

(c) $2x^3 - x^2 + 6x - 3$

(d) $\dfrac{x^2 + 3}{2x - 1}$; all real numbers x except $x = \dfrac{1}{2}$

131. (a) $x - \frac{8}{3}$ (b) $x - 8$

Domains of f, g, $f \circ g$, and $g \circ f$: all real numbers

133. $f(x) = x^3$, $g(x) = 1 - 2x$

135. (a) $(r + c)(t) = 178.8t + 856$; This represents the average annual expenditures for both residential and cellular phone services.

(b)

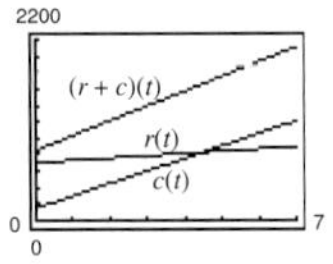

(c) $(r + c)(13) = 3180.4$

137. $f^{-1}(x) = \frac{1}{3}(x - 8)$ **139.** The function has an inverse.

141.

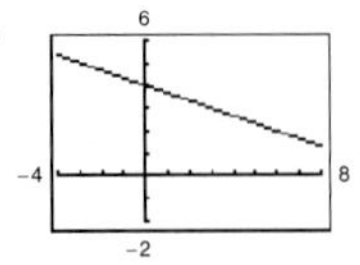

The function has an inverse.

143.

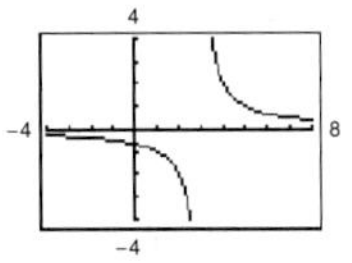

The function has an inverse.

145. (a) $f^{-1}(x) = 2x + 6$

(b)

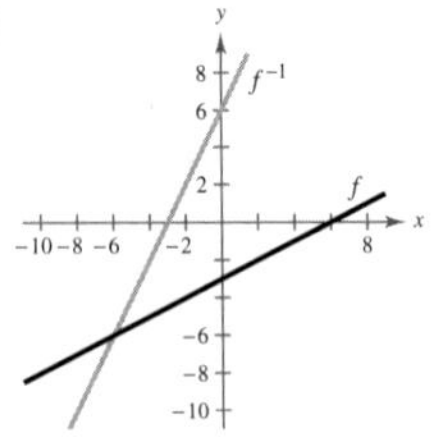

(c) The graph of f^{-1} is the reflection of the graph of f in the line $y = x$.

(d) Both f and f^{-1} have domains and ranges that are all real numbers.

147. (a) $f^{-1}(x) = x^2 - 1,\ x \ge 0$

(b)

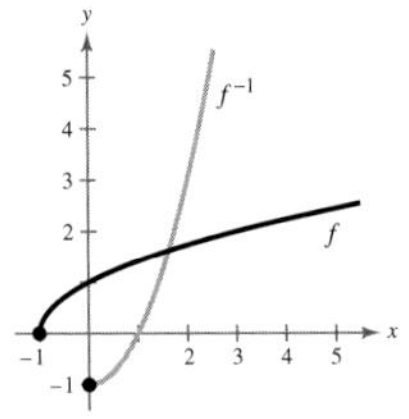

(c) The graph of f^{-1} is the reflection of the graph of f in the line $y = x$.

(d) f has a domain of $[-1, \infty)$ and a range of $[0, \infty)$; f^{-1} has a domain of $[0, \infty)$ and a range of $[-1, \infty)$.

149. $x > 4$; $f^{-1}(x) = \sqrt{\dfrac{x}{2}} + 4, x \neq 0$

151. (a)

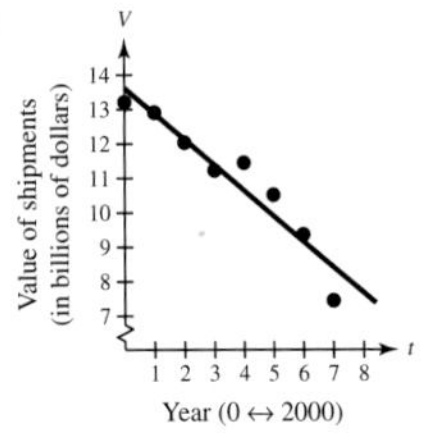

(b) The model is a good fit for the actual data.

153. Model: $k = \frac{8}{5}m$; 3.2 km, 16 km

155. A factor of 4 **157.** About 2 h, 26 min

159. False. The graph is reflected in the x-axis, shifted 9 units to the left, and then shifted 13 units downward.

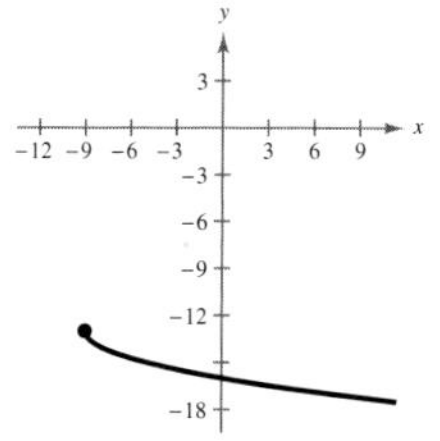

161. The Vertical Line Test is used to determine if the graph of y is a function of x. The Horizontal Line Test is used to determine if a function has an inverse function.

Chapter Test *(page 121)*

1.

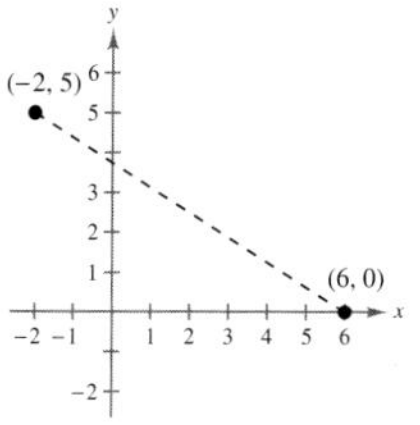

Midpoint: $\left(2, \frac{5}{2}\right)$; Distance: $\sqrt{89}$

2. About 11.937 cm

3. No symmetry

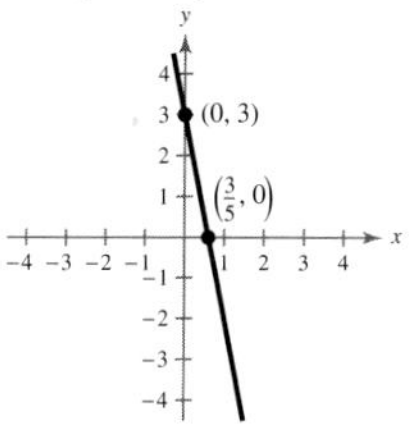

4. y-axis symmetry

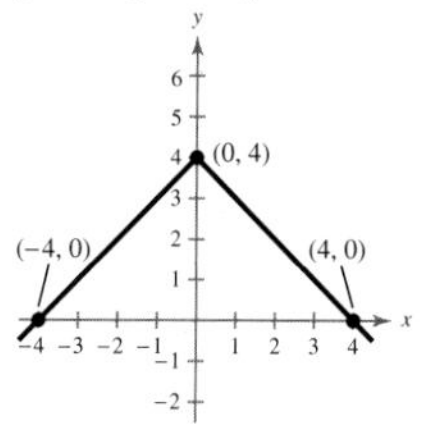

5. y-axis symmetry

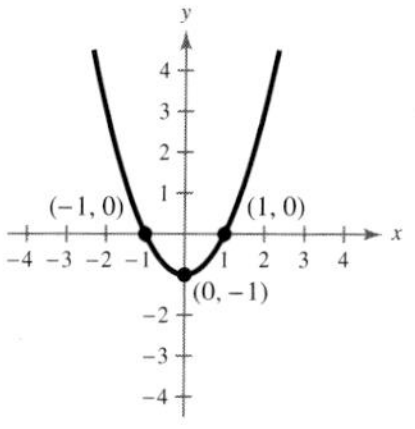

6. $(x - 1)^2 + (y - 3)^2 = 16$

7. $y = -2x + 1$ **8.** $y = -1.7x + 5.9$

9. (a) $5x + 2y - 8 = 0$ (b) $-2x + 5y - 20 = 0$

10. (a) $-\dfrac{1}{8}$ (b) $-\dfrac{1}{28}$ (c) $\dfrac{\sqrt{x}}{x^2 - 18x}$ **11.** $x \leq 3$

12. (a) $0, \pm 0.4314$

(b)

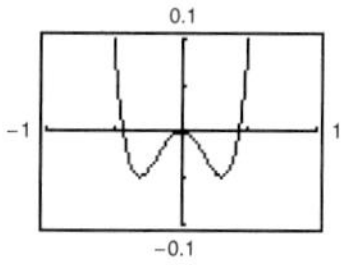

(c) Increasing on $(-0.31, 0), (0.31, \infty)$
Decreasing on $(-\infty, -0.31), (0, 0.31)$

(d) Even

13. (a) $0, 3$

(b)

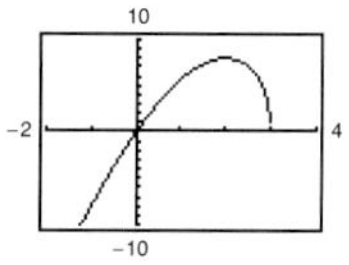

(c) Increasing on $(-\infty, 2)$
Decreasing on $(2, 3)$

(d) Neither

14. (a) -5

(b)

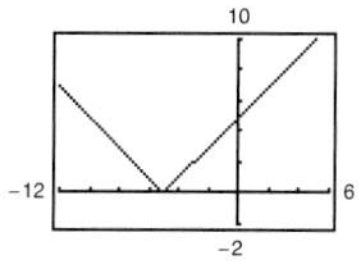

(c) Increasing on $(-5, \infty)$
Decreasing on $(-\infty, -5)$

(d) Neither

15.

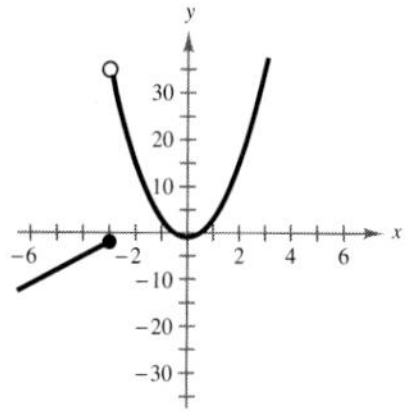

16. Reflection in the x-axis of $y = [\![x]\!]$

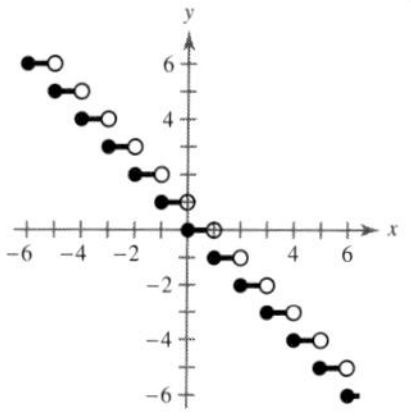

17. Reflection in the x-axis, horizontal shift, and vertical shift of $y = \sqrt{x}$

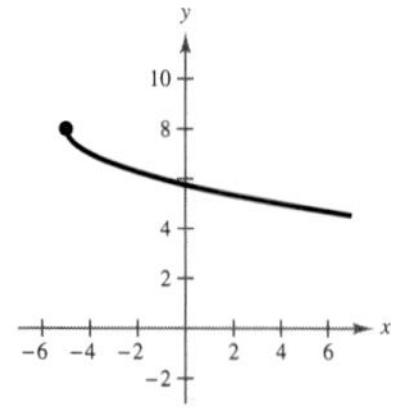

18. Reflection in the x-axis, vertical stretch, horizontal shift, and vertical shift of $y = x^3$

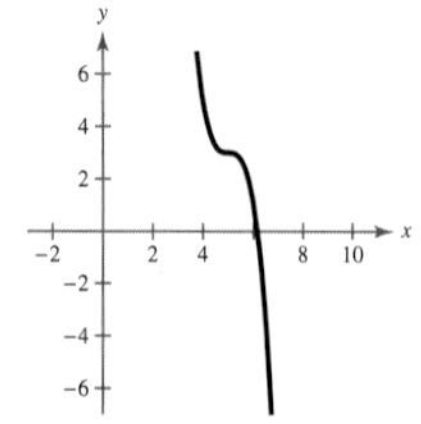

19. (a) $2x^2 - 4x - 2$ (b) $4x^2 + 4x - 12$
(c) $-3x^4 - 12x^3 + 22x^2 + 28x - 35$
(d) $\dfrac{3x^2 - 7}{-x^2 - 4x + 5}$, $x \neq -5, 1$
(e) $3x^4 + 24x^3 + 18x^2 - 120x + 68$
(f) $-9x^4 + 30x^2 - 16$

20. (a) $\dfrac{1 + 2x^{3/2}}{x}$, $x > 0$ (b) $\dfrac{1 - 2x^{3/2}}{x}$, $x > 0$
(c) $\dfrac{2\sqrt{x}}{x}$, $x > 0$ (d) $\dfrac{1}{2x^{3/2}}$, $x > 0$
(e) $\dfrac{\sqrt{x}}{2x}$, $x > 0$ (f) $\dfrac{2\sqrt{x}}{x}$, $x > 0$

21. $f^{-1}(x) = \sqrt[3]{x - 8}$ **22.** No inverse

23. $f^{-1}(x) = \left(\frac{1}{3}x\right)^{2/3}$, $x \geq 0$ **24.** $v = 6\sqrt{s}$

25. $A = \dfrac{25}{6}xy$ **26.** $b = \dfrac{48}{a}$

Problem Solving *(page 123)*

1. (a) $W_1 = 2000 + 0.07S$ (b) $W_2 = 2300 + 0.05S$
(c)

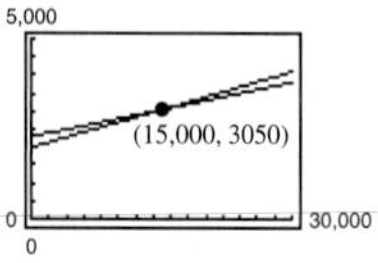

Both jobs pay the same monthly salary if sales equal \$15,000.

(d) No. Job 1 would pay \$3400 and job 2 would pay \$3300.

3. (a) The function will be even.
(b) The function will be odd.
(c) The function will be neither even nor odd.

5. $f(x) = a_{2n}x^{2n} + a_{2n-2}x^{2n-2} + \cdots + a_2x^2 + a_0$
$f(-x) = a_{2n}(-x)^{2n} + a_{2n-2}(-x)^{2n-2} + \cdots + a_2(-x)^2 + a_0$
$= f(x)$

7. (a) $81\frac{2}{3}$ h (b) $25\frac{5}{7}$ mi/h
(c) $y = -\frac{180}{7}x + 3400$
Domain: $0 \leq x \leq \frac{1190}{9}$
Range: $0 \leq y \leq 3400$
(d)

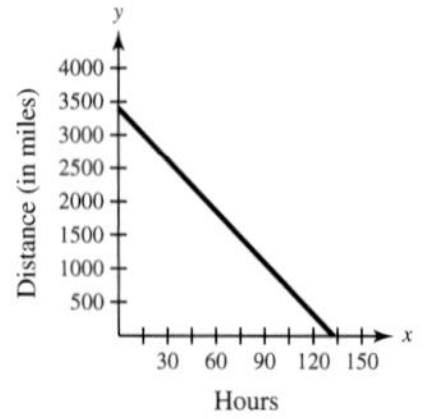

9. (a) $(f \circ g)(x) = 4x + 24$ (b) $(f \circ g)^{-1}(x) = \frac{1}{4}x - 6$
(c) $f^{-1}(x) = \frac{1}{4}x$; $g^{-1}(x) = x - 6$
(d) $(g^{-1} \circ f^{-1})(x) = \frac{1}{4}x - 6$; They are the same.
(e) $(f \circ g)(x) = 8x^3 + 1$; $(f \circ g)^{-1}(x) = \frac{1}{2}\sqrt[3]{x - 1}$;
$f^{-1}(x) = \sqrt[3]{x - 1}$; $g^{-1}(x) = \frac{1}{2}x$;
$(g^{-1} \circ f^{-1})(x) = \frac{1}{2}\sqrt[3]{x - 1}$
(f) Answers will vary.
(g) $(f \circ g)^{-1}(x) = (g^{-1} \circ f^{-1})(x)$

11. (a)

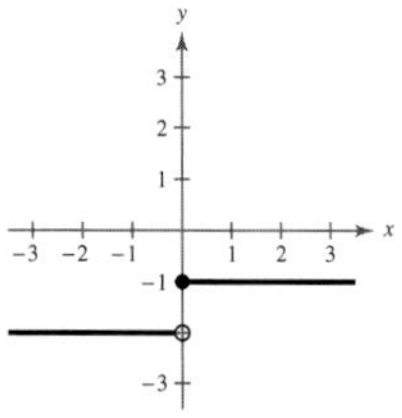

(b)

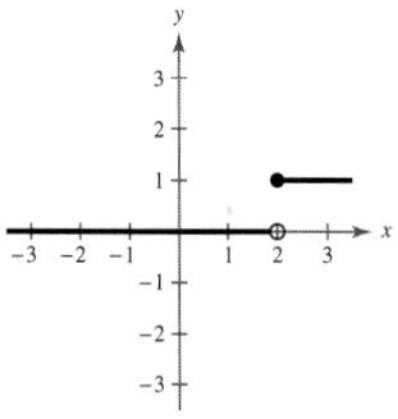

(c)

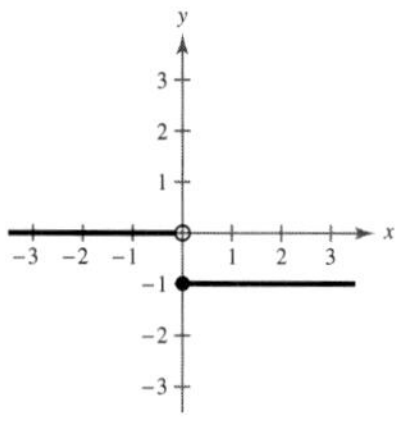

(d)

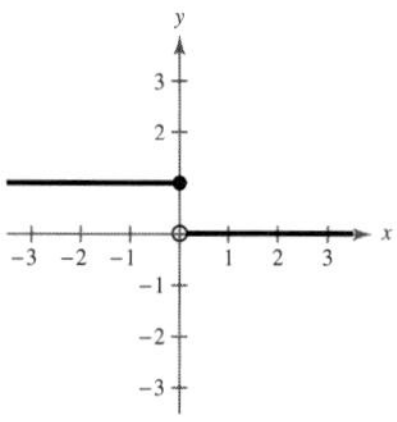

(e)

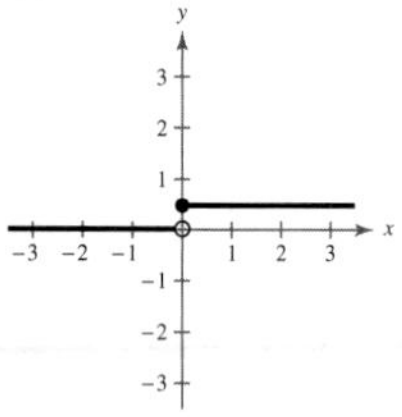

(f)

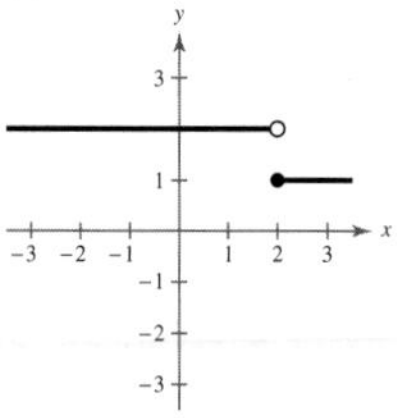

13. Proof

15. (a)

x	-4	-2	0	4
$f(f^{-1}(x))$	-4	-2	0	4

(b)

x	-3	-2	0	1
$(f + f^{-1})(x)$	5	1	-3	-5

(c)

x	-3	-2	0	1
$(f \cdot f^{-1})(x)$	4	0	2	6

(d)

x	-4	-3	0	4
$\lvert f^{-1}(x) \rvert$	2	1	1	3

Chapter 2

Section 2.1 *(page 132)*

1. polynomial **3.** quadratic; parabola

5. positive; minimum

7. e **8.** c **9.** b **10.** a **11.** f **12.** d

13. (a)

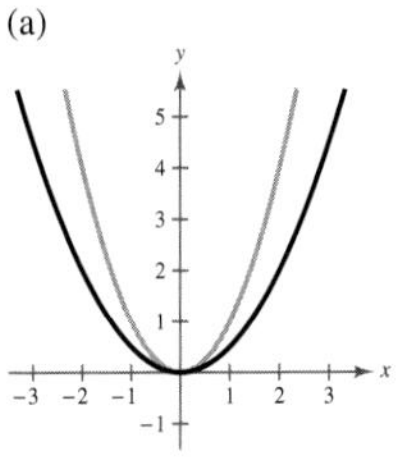

Vertical shrink

(b)

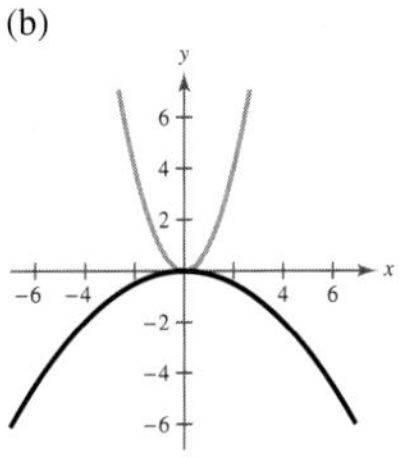

Vertical shrink and reflection in the x-axis

(c)

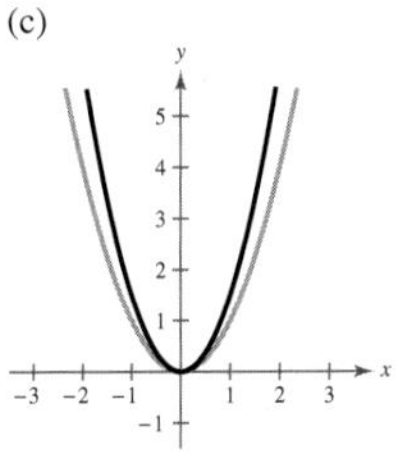

Vertical stretch

(d)

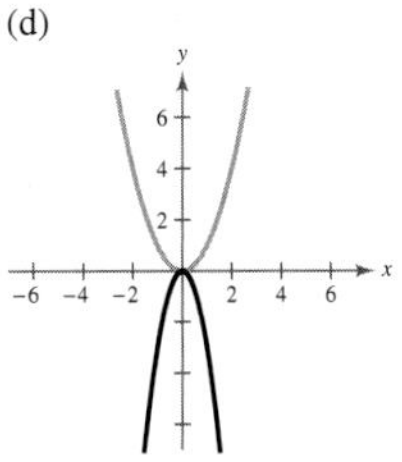

Vertical stretch and reflection in the x-axis

15. (a)

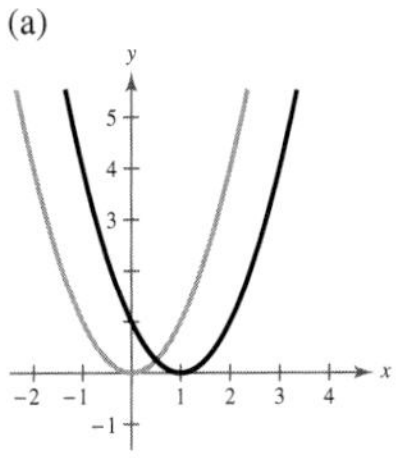

Horizontal shift one unit to the right

(b)

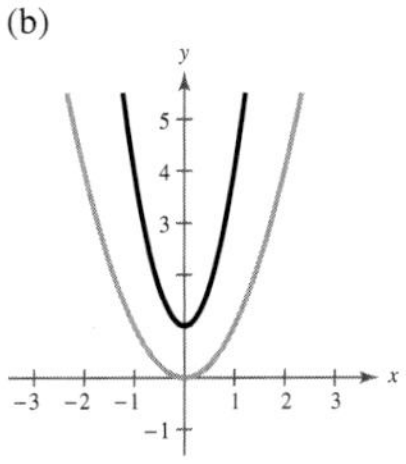

Horizontal shrink and vertical shift one unit upward

(c)

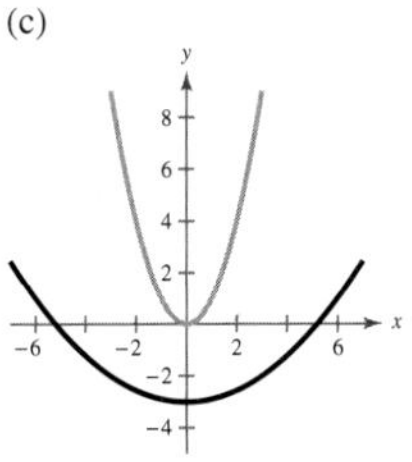

Horizontal stretch and vertical shift three units downward

(d)

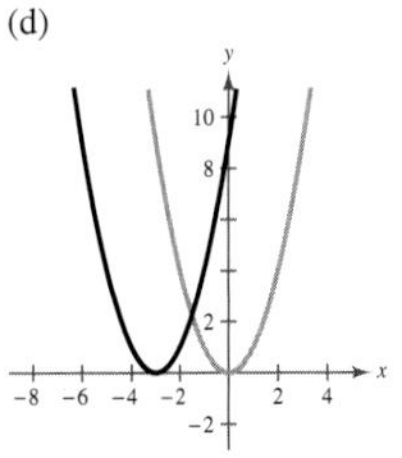

Horizontal shift three units to the left

17.

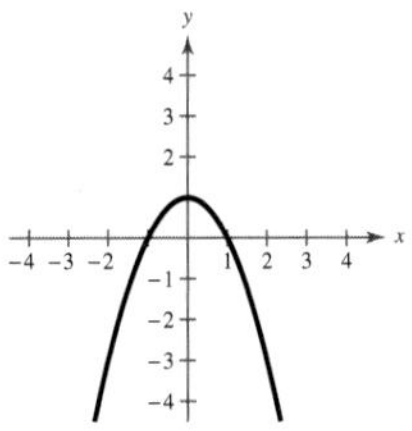

Vertex: $(0, 1)$
Axis of symmetry: y-axis
x-intercepts: $(-1, 0)$ $(1, 0)$

19.

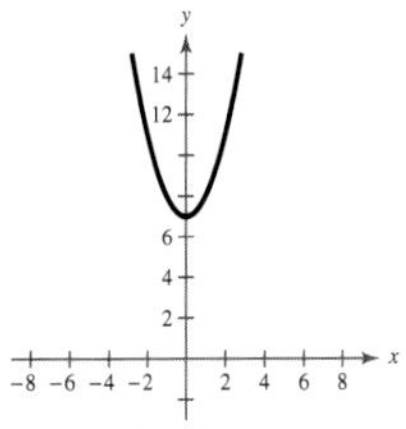

Vertex: $(0, 7)$
Axis of symmetry: y-axis
No x-intercept

21.

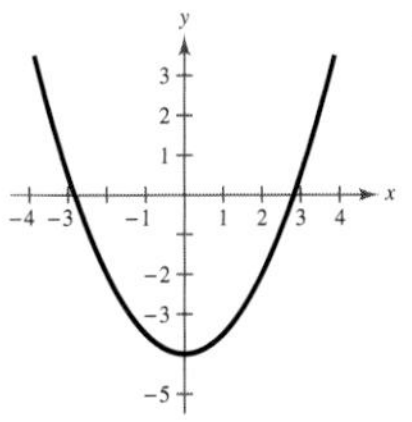

Vertex: $(0, -4)$
Axis of symmetry: y-axis
x-intercepts: $(\pm 2\sqrt{2}, 0)$

23.

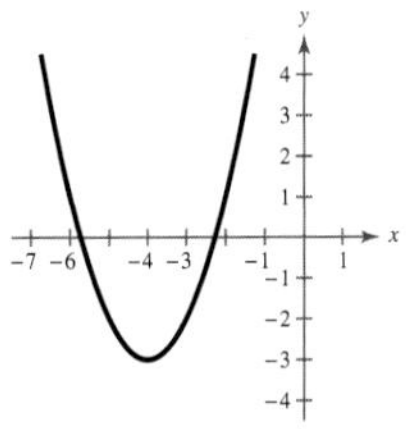

Vertex: $(-4, -3)$
Axis of symmetry: $x = -4$
x-intercepts: $(-4 \pm \sqrt{3}, 0)$

25.

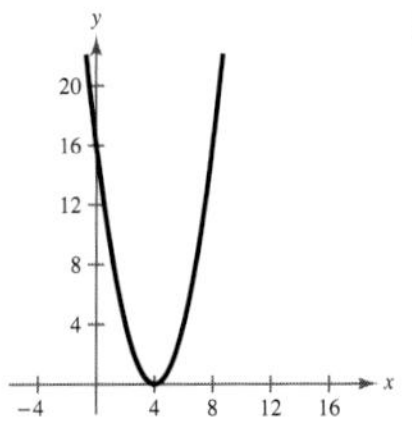

Vertex: $(4, 0)$
Axis of symmetry: $x = 4$
x-intercept: $(4, 0)$

27.

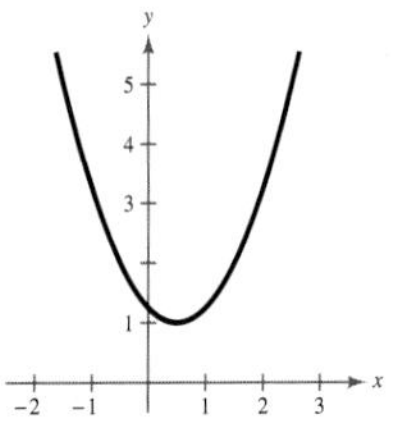

Vertex: $(\frac{1}{2}, 1)$
Axis of symmetry: $x = \frac{1}{2}$
No x-intercept

29.

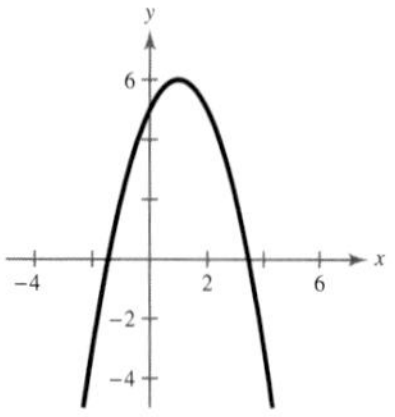

Vertex: (1, 6)
Axis of symmetry: $x = 1$
x-intercepts: $(1 \pm \sqrt{6}, 0)$

31.

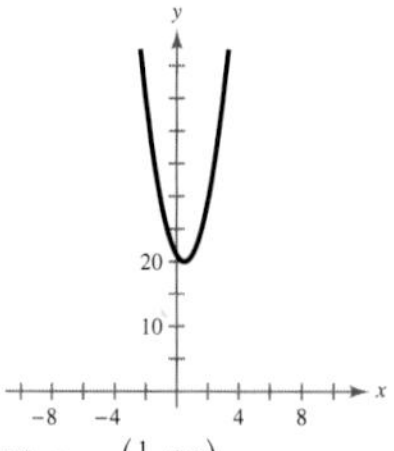

Vertex: $\left(\frac{1}{2}, 20\right)$
Axis of symmetry: $x = \frac{1}{2}$
No x-intercept

33.

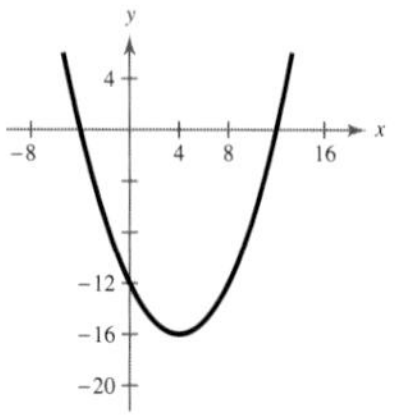

Vertex: $(4, -16)$
Axis of symmetry: $x = 4$
x-intercepts: $(-4, 0), (12, 0)$

35.

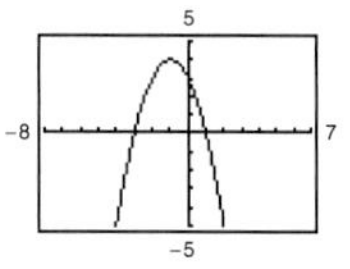

Vertex: $(-1, 4)$
Axis of symmetry: $x = -1$
x-intercepts: $(1, 0), (-3, 0)$

37.

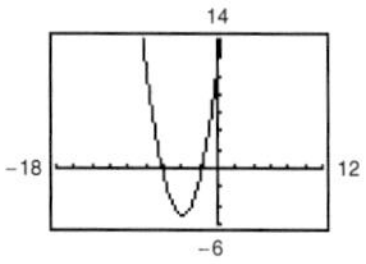

Vertex: $(-4, -5)$
Axis of symmetry: $x = -4$
x-intercepts: $(-4 \pm \sqrt{5}, 0)$

39.

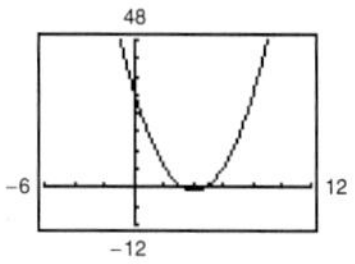

Vertex: $(4, -1)$
Axis of symmetry: $x = 4$
x-intercepts: $\left(4 \pm \frac{1}{2}\sqrt{2}, 0\right)$

41.

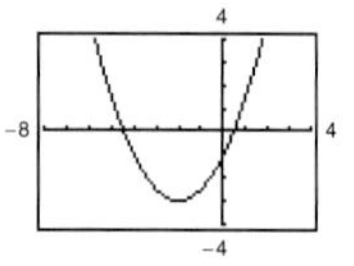

Vertex: $(-2, -3)$
Axis of symmetry: $x = -2$
x-intercepts: $(-2 \pm \sqrt{6}, 0)$

43. $y = -(x + 1)^2 + 4$ **45.** $y = -2(x + 2)^2 + 2$
47. $f(x) = (x + 2)^2 + 5$ **49.** $f(x) = 4(x - 1)^2 - 2$
51. $f(x) = \frac{3}{4}(x - 5)^2 + 12$ **53.** $f(x) = -\frac{24}{49}\left(x + \frac{1}{4}\right)^2 + \frac{3}{2}$
55. $f(x) = -\frac{16}{3}\left(x + \frac{5}{2}\right)^2$ **57.** $(5, 0), (-1, 0)$

59.

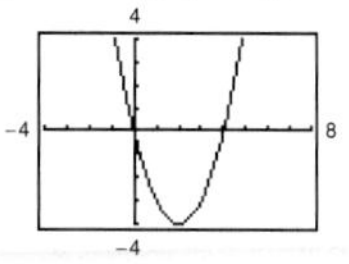

$(0, 0), (4, 0)$

61.

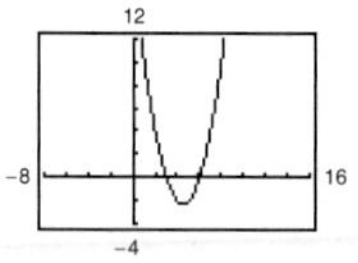

$(3, 0), (6, 0)$

63.

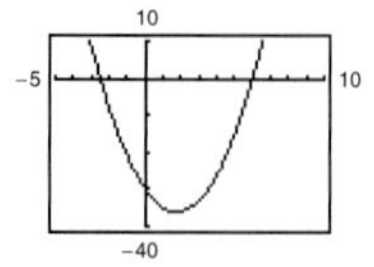

$\left(-\frac{5}{2}, 0\right), (6, 0)$

65. $f(x) = x^2 - 2x - 3$
$g(x) = -x^2 + 2x + 3$

67. $f(x) = x^2 - 10x$
$g(x) = -x^2 + 10x$

69. $f(x) = 2x^2 + 7x + 3$
$g(x) = -2x^2 - 7x - 3$

71. 55, 55 **73.** 12, 6 **75.** 16 ft **77.** 20 fixtures

79. (a) \$14,000,000; \$14,375,000; \$13,500,000
(b) \$24; \$14,400,000
Answers will vary.

81. (a) $A = \dfrac{8x(50 - x)}{3}$

(b)

x	5	10	15	20	25	30
a	600	$1066\frac{2}{3}$	1400	1600	$1666\frac{2}{3}$	1600

$x = 25$ ft, $y = 33\frac{1}{3}$ ft

(c)

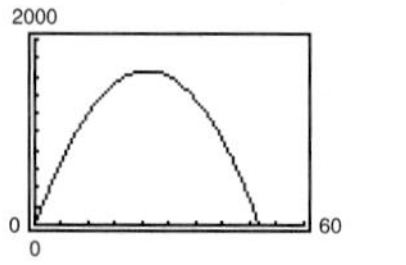

$x = 25$ ft, $y = 33\frac{1}{3}$ ft

(d) $A = -\frac{8}{3}(x - 25)^2 + \frac{5000}{3}$ (e) They are identical.

83. (a) $R = -100x^2 + 3500x, \quad 15 \le x \le 20$
(b) \$17.50; \$30,625

85. (a)

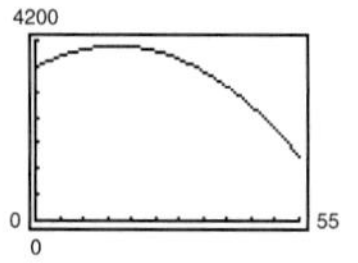

(b) 4075 cigarettes; Yes, the warning had an effect because the maximum consumption occurred in 1966.
(c) 7366 cigarettes per year; 20 cigarettes per day

87. True. The equation has no real solutions, so the graph has no x-intercepts.

89. True. The graph of a quadratic function with a negative leading coefficient will be a downward-opening parabola.

91. $b = \pm 20$ **93.** $b = \pm 8$

95. $f(x) = a\left(x + \dfrac{b}{2a}\right)^2 + \dfrac{4ac - b^2}{4a}$

97. (a)

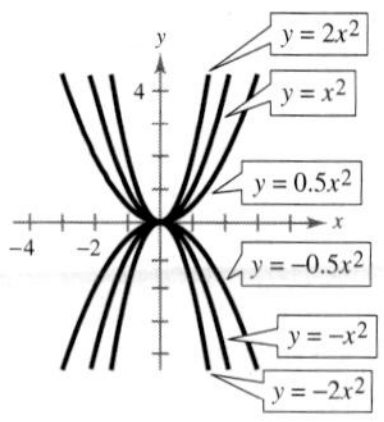

As $|a|$ increases, the parabola becomes narrower. For $a > 0$, the parabola opens upward. For $a < 0$, the parabola opens downward.

(b)

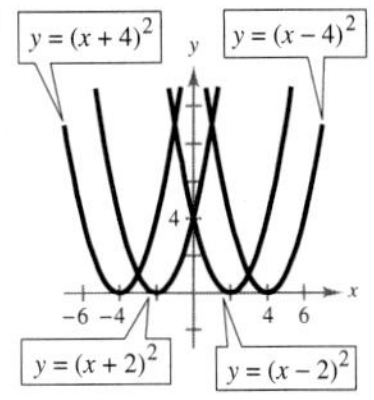

For $h < 0$, the vertex will be on the negative x-axis. For $h > 0$, the vertex will be on the positive x-axis. As $|h|$ increases, the parabola moves away from the origin.

(c)

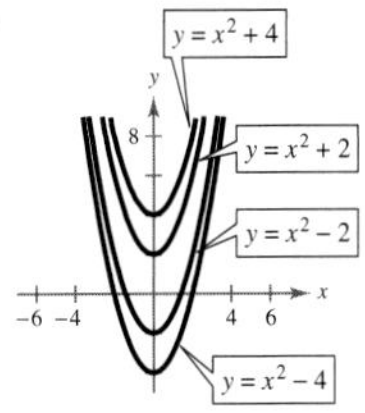

As $|k|$ increases, the vertex moves upward (for $k > 0$) or downward (for $k < 0$), away from the origin.

99. Yes. A graph of a quadratic equation whose vertex is on the x-axis has only one x-intercept.

Section 2.2 *(page 145)*

1. continuous **3.** x^n

5. (a) solution; (b) $(x - a)$; (c) x-intercept **7.** standard

9. c **10.** g **11.** h **12.** f

13. a **14.** e **15.** d **16.** b

17. (a)

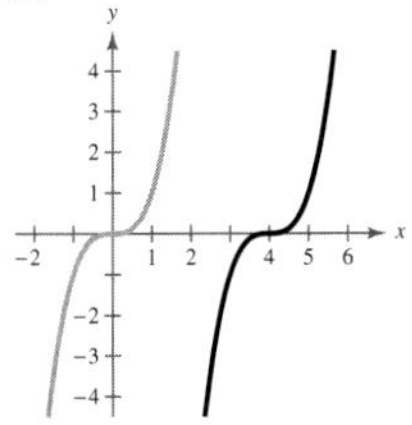

(b)

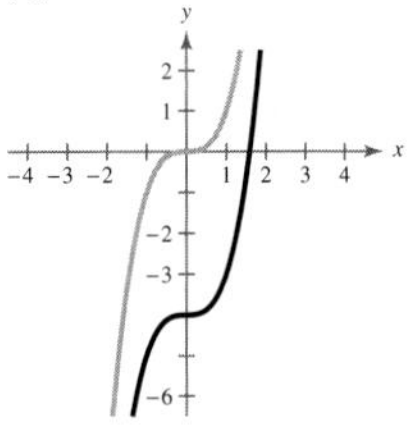

(c)

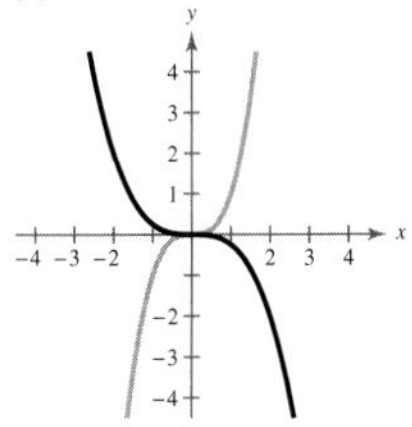

(d)

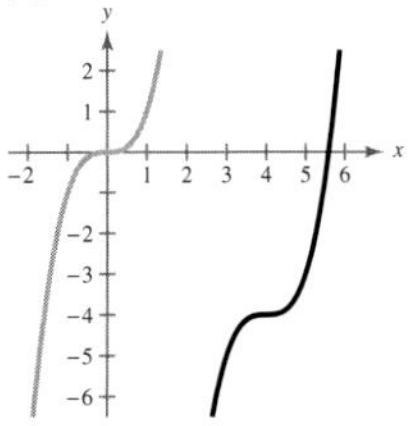

19. (a)

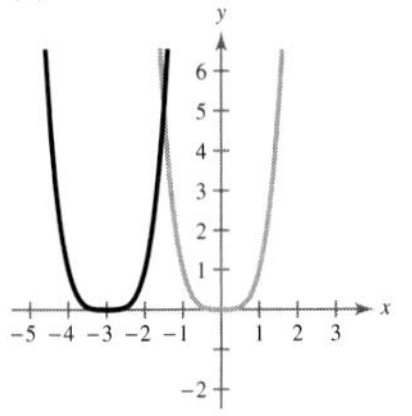

(b)

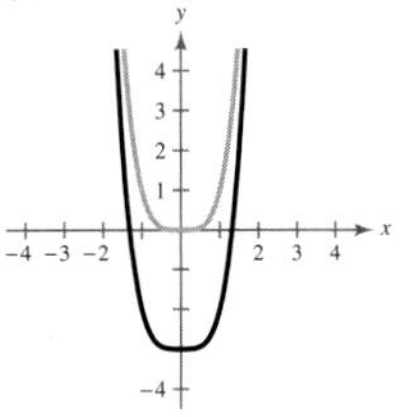

(c)

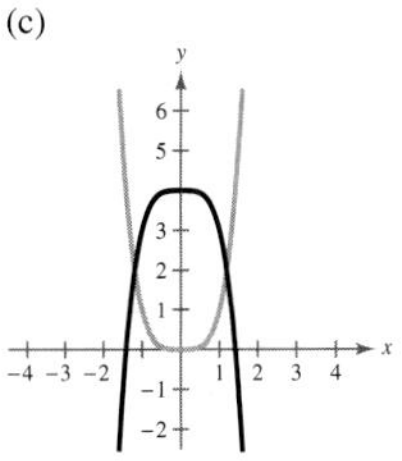

(d)

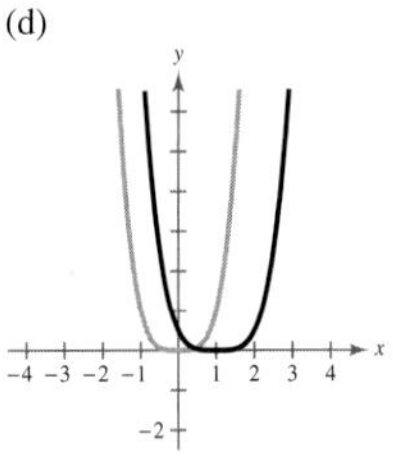

(e)

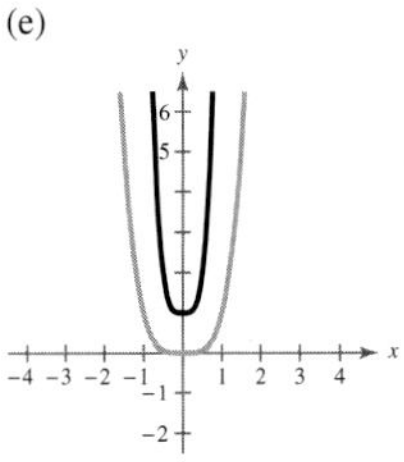

(f)

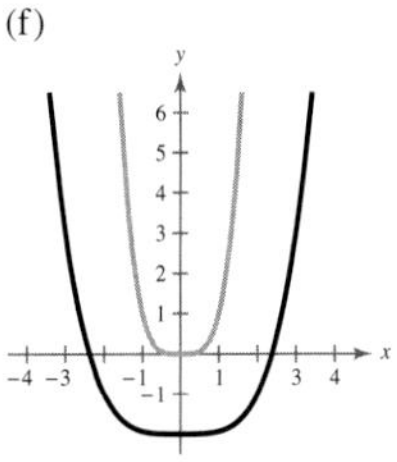

21. Falls to the left, rises to the right

23. Falls to the left, falls to the right

25. Rises to the left, falls to the right

27. Rises to the left, falls to the right

29. Falls to the left, falls to the right

31.

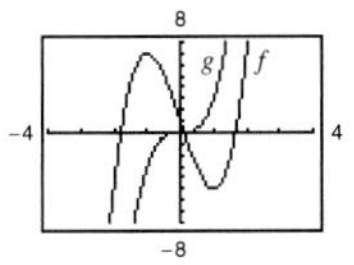

33.

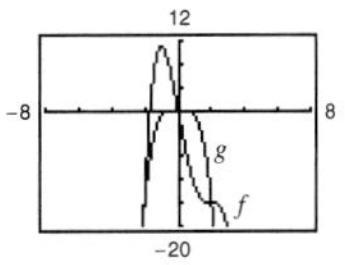

35. (a) ± 6

(b) Odd multiplicity; number of turning points: 1

(c)

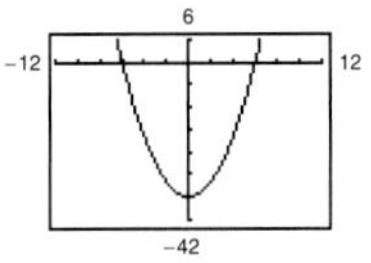

37. (a) 3

(b) Even multiplicity; number of turning points: 1

(c)

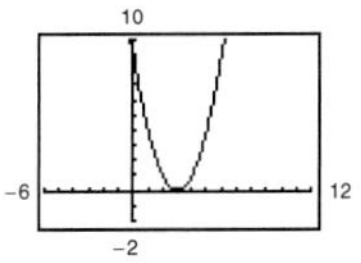

39. (a) $-2, 1$

(b) Odd multiplicity; number of turning points: 1

(c)

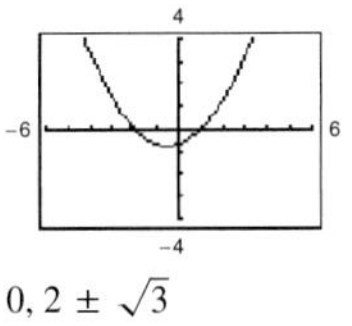

41. (a) $0, 2 \pm \sqrt{3}$

(b) Odd multiplicity; number of turning points: 2

(c) 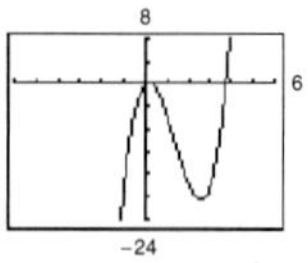

43. (a) 0, 4
(b) 0, odd multiplicity; 4, even multiplicity; number of turning points: 2
(c) 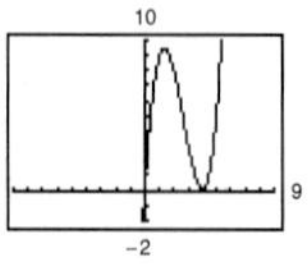

45. (a) $0, \pm\sqrt{3}$
(b) 0, odd multiplicity; $\pm\sqrt{3}$, even multiplicity; number of turning points: 4
(c) 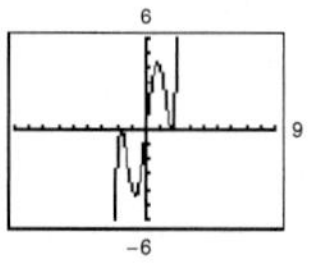

47. (a) No real zeros
(b) Number of turning points: 1
(c) 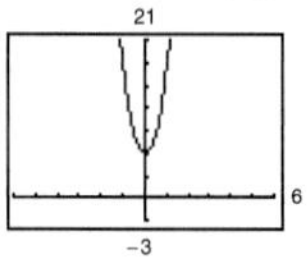

49. (a) $\pm 2, -3$
(b) Odd multiplicity; number of turning points: 2
(c) 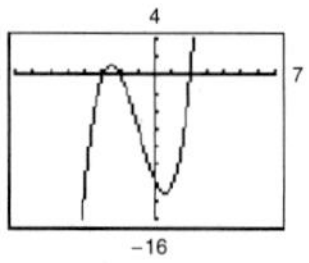

51. (a) 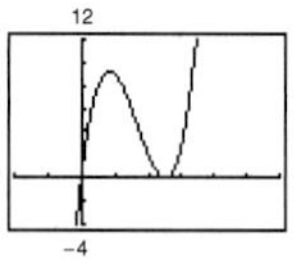

(b) x-intercepts: $(0, 0), \left(\frac{5}{2}, 0\right)$ (c) $x = 0, \frac{5}{2}$
(d) The answers in part (c) match the x-intercepts.

53. (a) 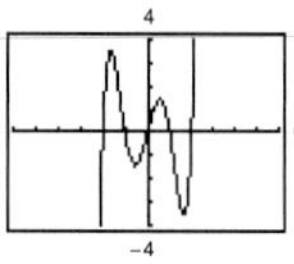

(b) x-intercepts: $(0, 0), (\pm 1, 0), (\pm 2, 0)$
(c) $x = 0, 1, -1, 2, -2$
(d) The answers in part (c) match the x-intercepts.

55. $f(x) = x^2 - 8x$ **57.** $f(x) = x^2 + 4x - 12$
59. $f(x) = x^3 + 9x^2 + 20x$
61. $f(x) = x^4 - 4x^3 - 9x^2 + 36x$ **63.** $f(x) = x^2 - 2x - 2$
65. $f(x) = x^2 + 6x + 9$ **67.** $f(x) = x^3 + 4x^2 - 5x$
69. $f(x) = x^3 - 3x$ **71.** $f(x) = x^4 + x^3 - 15x^2 + 23x - 10$
73. $f(x) = x^5 + 16x^4 + 96x^3 + 256x^2 + 256x$

75. (a) Falls to the left, rises to the right
(b) 0, 5, −5 (c) Answers will vary.
(d) 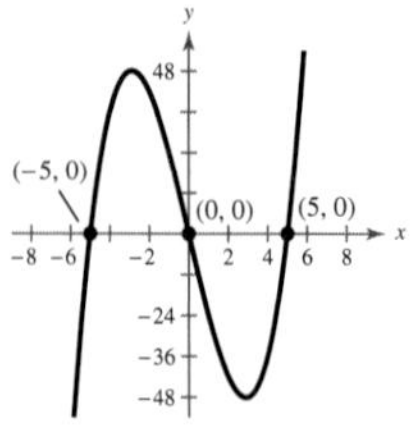

77. (a) Rises to the left, rises to the right
(b) No zeros (c) Answers will vary.
(d) 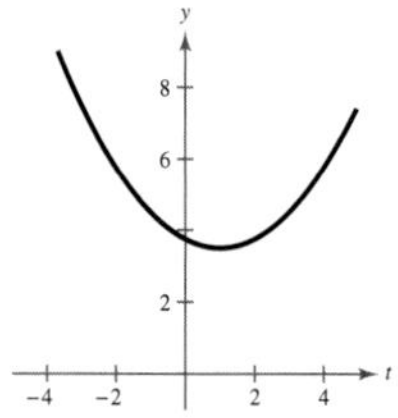

79. (a) Falls to the left, rises to the right
(b) 0, 2 (c) Answers will vary.
(d) 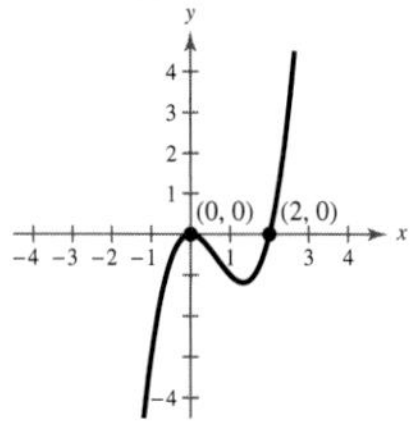

81. (a) Falls to the left, rises to the right
(b) 0, 2, 3 (c) Answers will vary.
(d) 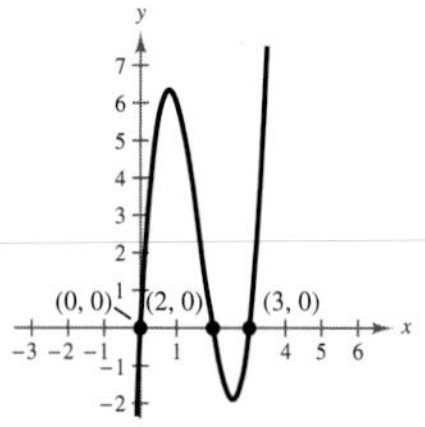

83. (a) Rises to the left, falls to the right
(b) −5, 0 (c) Answers will vary.

(d)

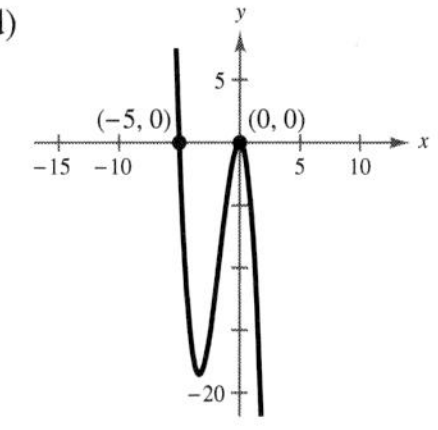

85. (a) Falls to the left, rises to the right
(b) 0, 4 (c) Answers will vary.
(d)

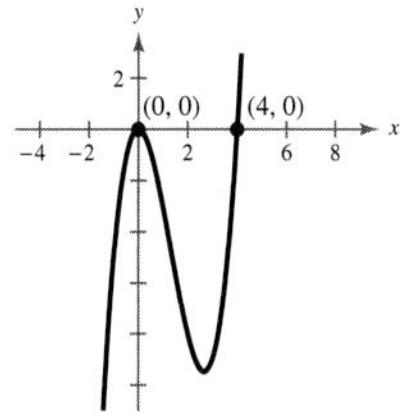

87. (a) Falls to the left, falls to the right
(b) ± 2 (c) Answers will vary.
(d)

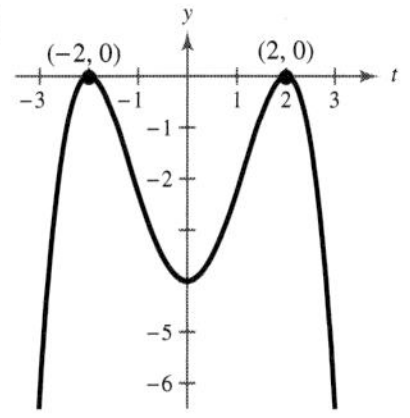

89.

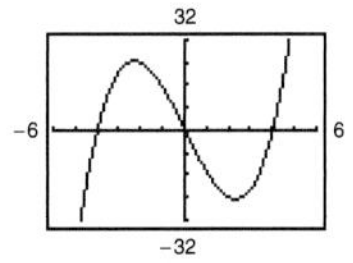

Zeros: $0, \pm 4$, odd multiplicity

91.

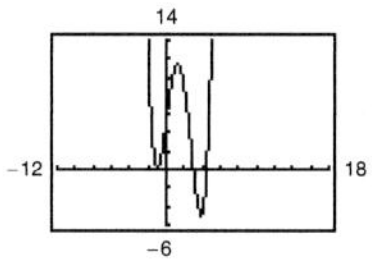

Zeros: -1, even multiplicity; $3, \frac{9}{2}$, odd multiplicity

93. $[-1, 0], [1, 2], [2, 3]$; about $-0.879, 1.347, 2.532$

95. $[-2, -1], [0, 1]$; about $-1.585, 0.779$

97. (a) $V(x) = x(36 - 2x)^2$ (b) Domain: $0 < x < 18$
(c)

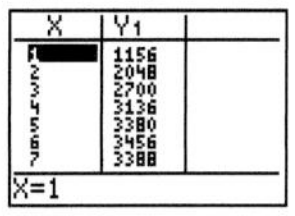

6 in. × 24 in. × 24 in.
(d)

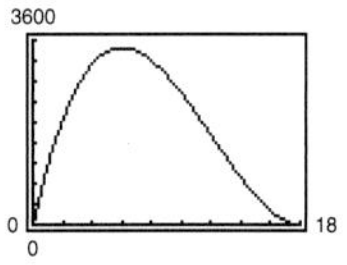

$x = 6$; The results are the same.

99. (a) $A = -2x^2 + 12x$ (b) $V = -384x^2 + 2304x$
(c) 0 in. $< x <$ 6 in.
(d)

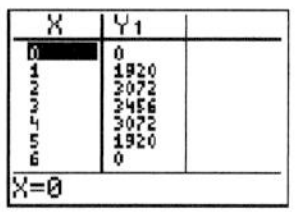

When $x = 3$, the volume is maximum at $V = 3456$; dimensions of gutter are 3 in. × 6 in. × 3 in.
(e)

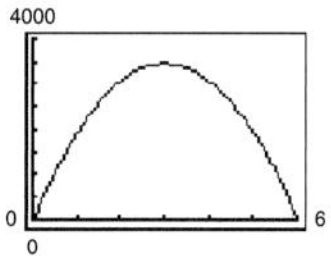

The maximum value is the same.
(f) No. Answers will vary.

101. (a)

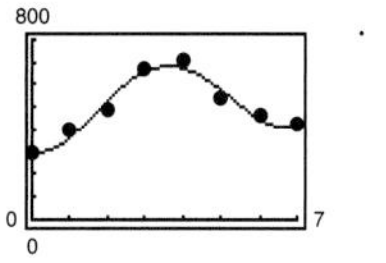

(b) The model fits the data well.
(c) Relative minima: (0.21, 300.54), (6.62, 410.74)
Relative maximum: (3.62, 681.72)
(d) Increasing: (0.21, 3.62), (6.62, 7)
Decreasing: (0, 0.21), (3.62, 6.62)
(e) Answers will vary.

103. (a)

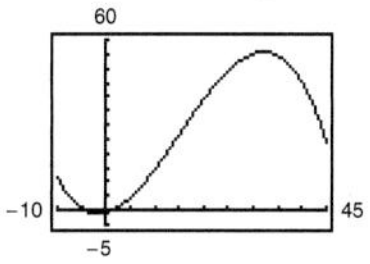

(b) $t \approx 15$
(c) Vertex: (15.22, 2.54)
(d) The results are approximately equal.

105. False. A fifth-degree polynomial can have at most four turning points.

107. True. The degree of the function is odd and its leading coefficient is negative, so the graph rises to the left and falls to the right.

109.

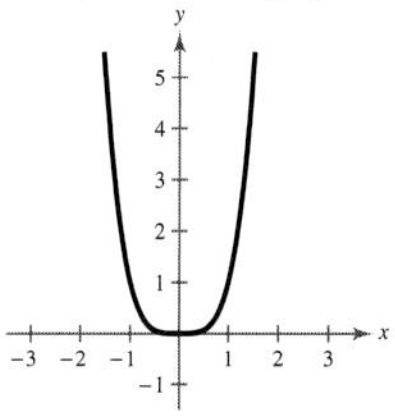

(a) Vertical shift two units upward; Even
(b) Horizontal shift two units to the left; Neither
(c) Reflection in the y-axis; Even
(d) Reflection in the x-axis; Even
(e) Horizontal stretch; Even
(f) Vertical shrink; Even
(g) $g(x) = x^3, x \geq 0$; Neither
(h) $g(x) = x^{16}$; Even

CHAPTER 2

111. (a)

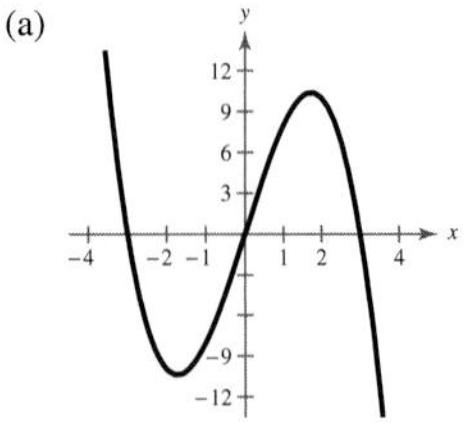

Zeros: 3
Relative minimum: 1
Relative maximum: 1
The number of zeros is the same as the degree, and the number of extrema is one less than the degree.

(b)

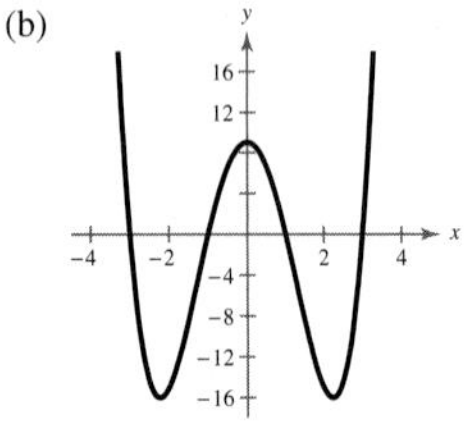

Zeros: 4
Relative minima: 2
Relative maximum: 1
The number of zeros is the same as the degree, and the number of extrema is one less than the degree.

(c)

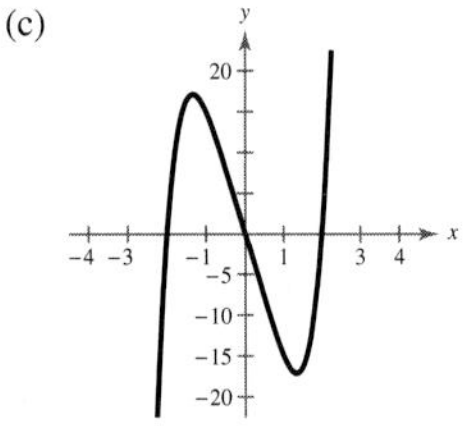

Zeros: 3
Relative minimum: 1
Relative maximum: 1
The number of zeros and the number of extrema are both less than the degree.

Section 2.3 *(page 156)*

1. $f(x)$: dividend; $d(x)$: divisor; $q(x)$: quotient; $r(x)$: remainder

3. improper **5.** Factor **7.** Answers will vary.

9. (a) and (b)

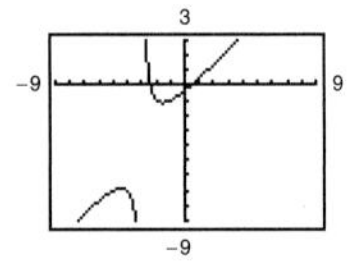

(c) Answers will vary.

11. $2x + 4,\ x \neq -3$ **13.** $x^2 - 3x + 1,\ x \neq -\frac{5}{4}$

15. $x^3 + 3x^2 - 1,\ x \neq -2$ **17.** $x^2 + 3x + 9,\ x \neq 3$

19. $7 - \dfrac{11}{x + 2}$ **21.** $x - \dfrac{x + 9}{x^2 + 1}$ **23.** $2x - 8 + \dfrac{x - 1}{x^2 + 1}$

25. $x + 3 + \dfrac{6x^2 - 8x + 3}{(x - 1)^3}$ **27.** $3x^2 - 2x + 5,\ x \neq 5$

29. $6x^2 + 25x + 74 + \dfrac{248}{x - 3}$ **31.** $4x^2 - 9,\ x \neq -2$

33. $-x^2 + 10x - 25,\ x \neq -10$

35. $5x^2 + 14x + 56 + \dfrac{232}{x - 4}$

37. $10x^3 + 10x^2 + 60x + 360 + \dfrac{1360}{x - 6}$

39. $x^2 - 8x + 64,\ x \neq -8$

41. $-3x^3 - 6x^2 - 12x - 24 - \dfrac{48}{x - 2}$

43. $-x^3 - 6x^2 - 36x - 36 - \dfrac{216}{x - 6}$

45. $4x^2 + 14x - 30,\ x \neq -\frac{1}{2}$

47. $f(x) = (x - 4)(x^2 + 3x - 2) + 3,\ f(4) = 3$

49. $f(x) = \left(x + \frac{2}{3}\right)(15x^3 - 6x + 4) + \frac{34}{3},\ f\left(-\frac{2}{3}\right) = \frac{34}{3}$

51. $f(x) = \left(x - \sqrt{2}\right)\left[x^2 + \left(3 + \sqrt{2}\right)x + 3\sqrt{2}\right] - 8,$ $f\left(\sqrt{2}\right) = -8$

53. $f(x) = \left(x - 1 + \sqrt{3}\right)\left[-4x^2 + \left(2 + 4\sqrt{3}\right)x + \left(2 + 2\sqrt{3}\right)\right],$ $f\left(1 - \sqrt{3}\right) = 0$

55. (a) -2 (b) 1 (c) $-\frac{1}{4}$ (d) 5

57. (a) -35 (b) -22 (c) -10 (d) -211

59. $(x - 2)(x + 3)(x - 1)$; Solutions: $2, -3, 1$

61. $(2x - 1)(x - 5)(x - 2)$; Solutions: $\frac{1}{2}, 5, 2$

63. $\left(x + \sqrt{3}\right)\left(x - \sqrt{3}\right)(x + 2)$; Solutions: $-\sqrt{3}, \sqrt{3}, -2$

65. $(x - 1)\left(x - 1 - \sqrt{3}\right)\left(x - 1 + \sqrt{3}\right)$; Solutions: $1,\ 1 + \sqrt{3},\ 1 - \sqrt{3}$

67. (a) Answers will vary. (b) $2x - 1$
(c) $f(x) = (2x - 1)(x + 2)(x - 1)$
(d) $\frac{1}{2}, -2, 1$ (e)

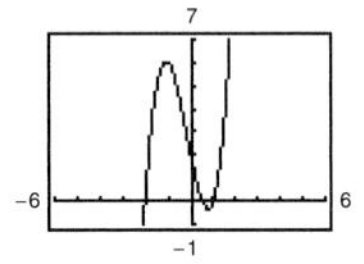

69. (a) Answers will vary. (b) $(x - 1), (x - 2)$
(c) $f(x) = (x - 1)(x - 2)(x - 5)(x + 4)$
(d) $1, 2, 5, -4$ (e)

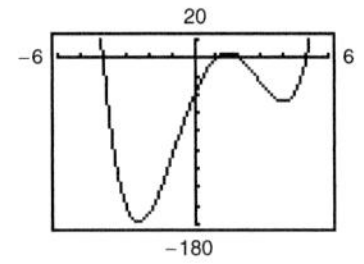

71. (a) Answers will vary. (b) $x + 7$
(c) $f(x) = (x + 7)(2x + 1)(3x - 2)$
(d) $-7, -\frac{1}{2}, \frac{2}{3}$ (e)

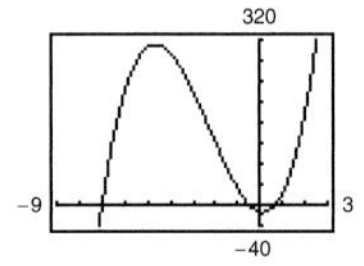

73. (a) Answers will vary. (b) $x - \sqrt{5}$
(c) $f(x) = \left(x - \sqrt{5}\right)\left(x + \sqrt{5}\right)(2x - 1)$
(d) $\pm\sqrt{5}, \frac{1}{2}$ (e)

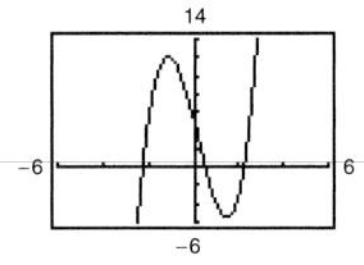

75. (a) Zeros are 2 and about ± 2.236.
(b) $x = 2$ (c) $f(x) = (x - 2)\left(x - \sqrt{5}\right)\left(x + \sqrt{5}\right)$

77. (a) Zeros are -2, about 0.268, and about 3.732.
(b) $t = -2$
(c) $h(t) = (t + 2)\left[t - \left(2 + \sqrt{3}\right)\right]\left[t - \left(2 - \sqrt{3}\right)\right]$

79. (a) Zeros are 0, 3, 4, and about ± 1.414.
(b) $x = 0$
(c) $h(x) = x(x - 4)(x - 3)(x + \sqrt{2})(x - \sqrt{2})$

81. $2x^2 - x - 1,\ x \neq \frac{3}{2}$ **83.** $x^2 + 3x,\ x \neq -2, -1$

85. (a) and (b)

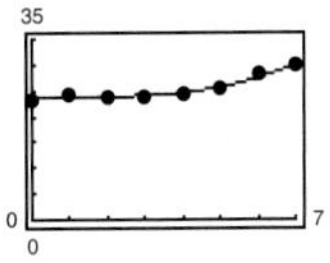

$A = 0.0349t^3 - 0.168t^2 + 0.42t + 23.4$

(c)

t	0	1	2	3
$A(t)$	23.4	23.7	23.8	24.1

t	4	5	6	7
$A(t)$	24.6	25.7	27.4	30.1

(d) \$45.7 billion; No, because the model will approach infinity quickly.

87. False. $-\frac{4}{7}$ is a zero of f.

89. True. The degree of the numerator is greater than the degree of the denominator.

91. $x^{2n} + 6x^n + 9,\ x^n \neq -3$ **93.** The remainder is 0.

95. $c = -210$ **97.** $k = 7$

99. (a) $x + 1,\ x \neq 1$ (b) $x^2 + x + 1,\ x \neq 1$
(c) $x^3 + x^2 + x + 1,\ x \neq 1$
In general, $\frac{x^n - 1}{x - 1} = x^{n-1} + x^{n-2} + \cdots + x + 1,\ x \neq 1$

Section 2.4 *(page 164)*

1. (a) iii (b) i (c) ii **3.** principal square
5. $a = -12,\ b = 7$ **7.** $a = 6,\ b = 5$ **9.** $8 + 5i$
11. $2 - 3\sqrt{3}i$ **13.** $4\sqrt{5}i$ **15.** 14 **17.** $-1 - 10i$
19. $0.3i$ **21.** $10 - 3i$ **23.** 1 **25.** $3 - 3\sqrt{2}i$
27. $-14 + 20i$ **29.** $\frac{1}{6} + \frac{7}{6}i$ **31.** $5 + i$ **33.** $108 + 12i$
35. 24 **37.** $-13 + 84i$ **39.** -10 **41.** $9 - 2i$, 85
43. $-1 + \sqrt{5}i$, 6 **45.** $-2\sqrt{5}i$, 20 **47.** $\sqrt{6}$, 6
49. $-3i$ **51.** $\frac{8}{41} + \frac{10}{41}i$ **53.** $\frac{12}{13} + \frac{5}{13}i$ **55.** $-4 - 9i$
57. $-\frac{120}{1681} - \frac{27}{1681}i$ **59.** $-\frac{1}{2} - \frac{5}{2}i$ **61.** $\frac{62}{949} + \frac{297}{949}i$
63. $-2\sqrt{3}$ **65.** -15
67. $(21 + 5\sqrt{2}) + (7\sqrt{5} - 3\sqrt{10})i$ **69.** $1 \pm i$
71. $-2 \pm \frac{1}{2}i$ **73.** $-\frac{5}{2}, -\frac{3}{2}$ **75.** $2 \pm \sqrt{2}i$
77. $\frac{5}{7} \pm \frac{5\sqrt{15}}{7}$ **79.** $-1 + 6i$ **81.** $-14i$
83. $-432\sqrt{2}i$ **85.** i **87.** 81
89. (a) $z_1 = 9 + 16i,\ z_2 = 20 - 10i$
(b) $z = \frac{11{,}240}{877} + \frac{4630}{877}i$
91. (a) 16 (b) 16 (c) 16 (d) 16
93. False. If the complex number is real, the number equals its conjugate.
95. False.
$i^{44} + i^{150} - i^{74} - i^{109} + i^{61} = 1 - 1 + 1 - i + i = 1$

97. $i, -1, -i, 1, i, -1, -i, 1$; The pattern repeats the first four results. Divide the exponent by 4.
If the remainder is 1, the result is i.
If the remainder is 2, the result is -1.
If the remainder is 3, the result is $-i$.
If the remainder is 0, the result is 1.

99. $\sqrt{-6}\sqrt{-6} = \sqrt{6}i\sqrt{6}i = 6i^2 = -6$ **101.** Proof

Section 2.5 *(page 176)*

1. Fundamental Theorem of Algebra **3.** Rational Zero
5. linear; quadratic; quadratic **7.** Descartes's Rule of Signs
9. 0, 6 **11.** 2, -4 **13.** $-6, \pm i$ **15.** $\pm 1, \pm 2$
17. $\pm 1, \pm 3, \pm 5, \pm 9, \pm 15, \pm 45, \pm\frac{1}{2}, \pm\frac{3}{2}, \pm\frac{5}{2}, \pm\frac{9}{2}, \pm\frac{15}{2}, \pm\frac{45}{2}$
19. 1, 2, 3 **21.** 1, -1, 4 **23.** $-6, -1$ **25.** $\frac{1}{2}, -1$
27. $-2, 3, \pm\frac{2}{3}$ **29.** -2, 1 **31.** $-4, \frac{1}{2}, 1, 1$
33. (a) $\pm 1, \pm 2, \pm 4$
(b)

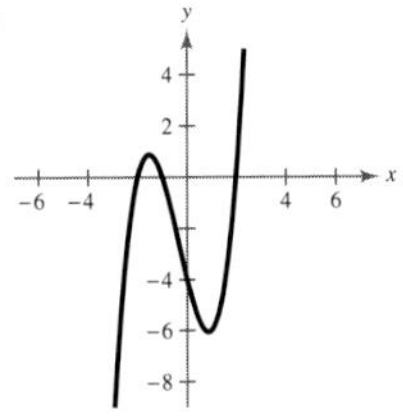

(c) $-2, -1, 2$

35. (a) $\pm 1, \pm 3, \pm\frac{1}{2}, \pm\frac{3}{2}, \pm\frac{1}{4}, \pm\frac{3}{4}$
(b)

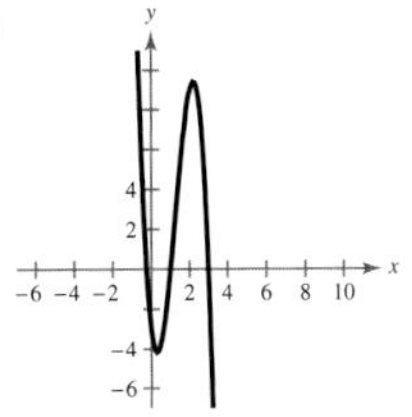

(c) $-\frac{1}{4}, 1, 3$

37. (a) $\pm 1, \pm 2, \pm 4, \pm 8, \pm\frac{1}{2}$
(b)

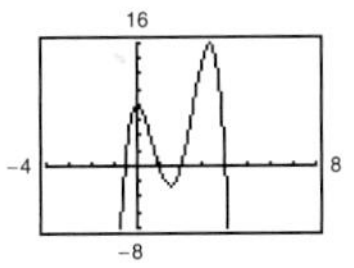

(c) $-\frac{1}{2}, 1, 2, 4$

39. (a) $\pm 1, \pm 3, \pm\frac{1}{2}, \pm\frac{3}{2}, \pm\frac{1}{4}, \pm\frac{3}{4}, \pm\frac{1}{8}, \pm\frac{3}{8}, \pm\frac{1}{16}, \pm\frac{3}{16}, \pm\frac{1}{32}, \pm\frac{3}{32}$
(b)

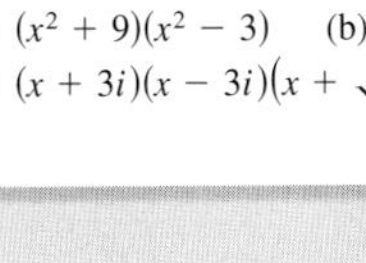

(c) $1, \frac{3}{4}, -\frac{1}{8}$

41. (a) ± 1, about ± 1.414 (b) $\pm 1, \pm\sqrt{2}$
(c) $f(x) = (x + 1)(x - 1)(x + \sqrt{2})(x - \sqrt{2})$

43. (a) 0, 3, 4, about ± 1.414 (b) 0, 3, 4, $\pm\sqrt{2}$
(c) $h(x) = x(x - 3)(x - 4)(x + \sqrt{2})(x - \sqrt{2})$

45. $x^3 - x^2 + 25x - 25$ **47.** $x^3 - 12x^2 + 46x - 52$

49. $3x^4 - 17x^3 + 25x^2 + 23x - 22$

51. (a) $(x^2 + 9)(x^2 - 3)$ (b) $(x^2 + 9)(x + \sqrt{3})(x - \sqrt{3})$
(c) $(x + 3i)(x - 3i)(x + \sqrt{3})(x - \sqrt{3})$

53. (a) $(x^2 - 2x - 2)(x^2 - 2x + 3)$
(b) $(x - 1 + \sqrt{3})(x - 1 - \sqrt{3})(x^2 - 2x + 3)$
(c) $(x - 1 + \sqrt{3})(x - 1 - \sqrt{3})(x - 1 + \sqrt{2}i)$
$(x - 1 - \sqrt{2}i)$

55. $\pm 2i, 1$ **57.** $\pm 5i, -\frac{1}{2}, 1$ **59.** $-3 \pm i, \frac{1}{4}$

61. $2, -3 \pm \sqrt{2}i, 1$ **63.** $\pm 6i$; $(x + 6i)(x - 6i)$

65. $1 \pm 4i$; $(x - 1 - 4i)(x - 1 + 4i)$

67. $\pm 2, \pm 2i$; $(x - 2)(x + 2)(x - 2i)(x + 2i)$

69. $1 \pm i$; $(z - 1 + i)(z - 1 - i)$

71. $-1, 2 \pm i$; $(x + 1)(x - 2 + i)(x - 2 - i)$

73. $-2, 1 \pm \sqrt{2}i$; $(x + 2)(x - 1 + \sqrt{2}i)(x - 1 - \sqrt{2}i)$

75. $-\frac{1}{5}, 1 \pm \sqrt{5}i$; $(5x + 1)(x - 1 + \sqrt{5}i)(x - 1 - \sqrt{5}i)$

77. $2, \pm 2i$; $(x - 2)^2(x + 2i)(x - 2i)$

79. $\pm i, \pm 3i$; $(x + i)(x - i)(x + 3i)(x - 3i)$

81. $-10, -7 \pm 5i$ **83.** $-\frac{3}{4}, 1 \pm \frac{1}{2}i$ **85.** $-2, -\frac{1}{2}, \pm i$

87. One positive zero **89.** One negative zero

91. One positive zero, one negative zero

93. One or three positive zeros **95–97.** Answers will vary.

99. $1, -\frac{1}{2}$ **101.** $-\frac{3}{4}$ **103.** $\pm 2, \pm\frac{3}{2}$ **105.** $\pm 1, \frac{1}{4}$

107. d **108.** a **109.** b **110.** c

111. (a)

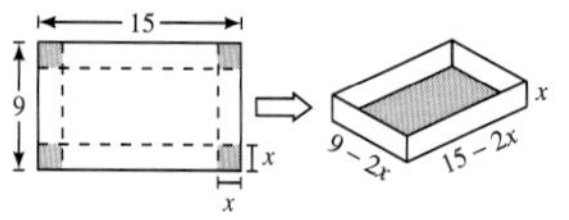

(b) $V(x) = x(9 - 2x)(15 - 2x)$
Domain: $0 < x < \frac{9}{2}$

(c)

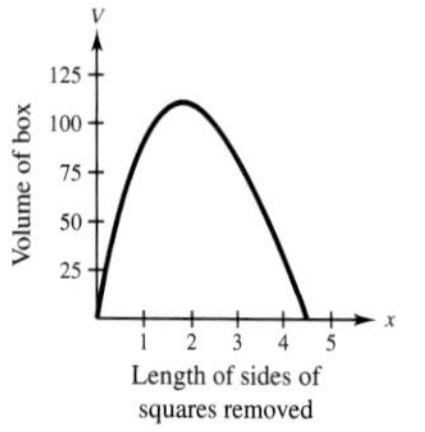

1.82 cm × 5.36 cm × 11.36 cm

(d) $\frac{1}{2}, \frac{7}{2}, 8$; 8 is not in the domain of V.

113. $x \approx 38.4$, or \$384,000

115. (a) $V(x) = x^3 + 9x^2 + 26x + 24 = 120$
(b) 4 ft × 5 ft × 6 ft

117. $x \approx 40$, or 4000 units

119. No. Setting $p = 9{,}000{,}000$ and solving the resulting equation yields imaginary roots.

121. False. The most complex zeros it can have is two, and the Linear Factorization Theorem guarantees that there are three linear factors, so one zero must be real.

123. r_1, r_2, r_3 **125.** $5 + r_1, 5 + r_2, 5 + r_3$

127. The zeros cannot be determined.

129. Answers will vary. There are infinitely many possible functions for f. Sample equation and graph:
$f(x) = -2x^3 + 3x^2 + 11x - 6$

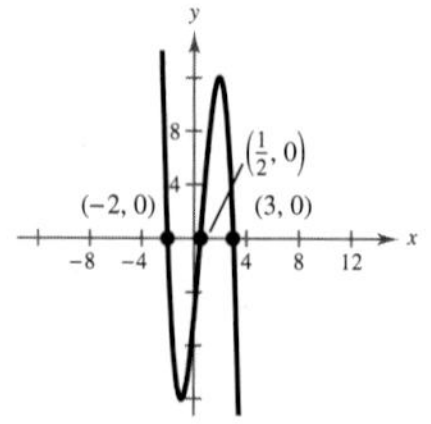

131. Answers will vary. Sample graph:

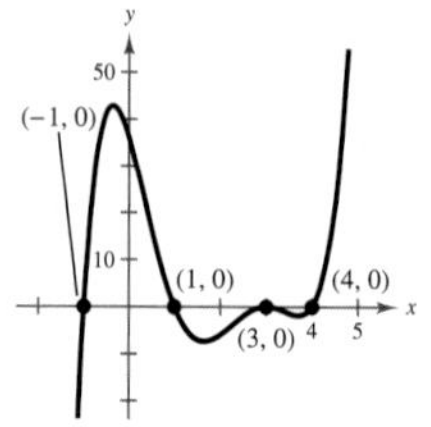

133. $f(x) = x^4 + 5x^2 + 4$ **135.** $f(x) = x^3 - 3x^2 + 4x - 2$

137. (a) $-2, 1, 4$
(b) The graph touches the x-axis at $x = 1$.
(c) The least possible degree of the function is 4, because there are at least four real zeros (1 is repeated) and a function can have at most the number of real zeros equal to the degree of the function. The degree cannot be odd by the definition of multiplicity.
(d) Positive. From the information in the table, it can be concluded that the graph will eventually rise to the left and rise to the right.
(e) $f(x) = x^4 - 4x^3 - 3x^2 + 14x - 8$
(f)

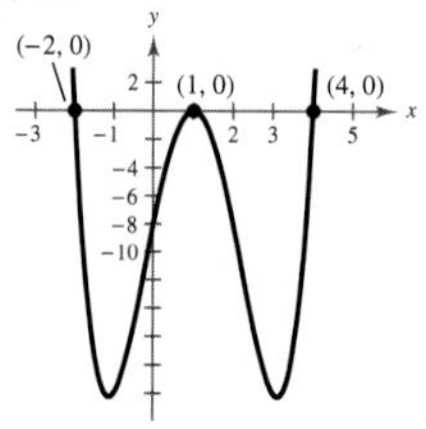

139. (a) Not correct because f has $(0, 0)$ as an intercept.
(b) Not correct because the function must be at least a fourth-degree polynomial.
(c) Correct function
(d) Not correct because k has $(-1, 0)$ as an intercept.

Section 2.6 *(page 190)*

1. rational functions **3.** horizontal asymptote

5. (a)

x	$f(x)$	x	$f(x)$	x	$f(x)$
0.5	-2	1.5	2	5	0.25
0.9	-10	1.1	10	10	$0.\overline{1}$
0.99	-100	1.01	100	100	$0.\overline{01}$
0.999	-1000	1.001	1000	1000	$0.\overline{001}$

(b) Vertical asymptote: $x = 1$
Horizontal asymptote: $y = 0$
(c) Domain: all real numbers x except $x = 1$

7. (a)

x	$f(x)$	x	$f(x)$	x	$f(x)$
0.5	-1	1.5	5.4	5	3.125
0.9	-12.79	1.1	17.29	10	$3.\overline{03}$
0.99	-147.8	1.01	152.3	100	$3.\overline{0003}$
0.999	-1498	1.001	1502	1000	3

(b) Vertical asymptotes: $x = \pm 1$
Horizontal asymptote: $y = 3$
(c) Domain: all real numbers x except $x = \pm 1$

9. Domain: all real numbers x except $x = 0$
Vertical asymptote: $x = 0$
Horizontal asymptote: $y = 0$

11. Domain: all real numbers x except $x = 5$
Vertical asymptote: $x = 5$
Horizontal asymptote: $y = -1$

13. Domain: all real numbers x except $x = \pm 1$
Vertical asymptotes: $x = \pm 1$

15. Domain: all real numbers x
Horizontal asymptote: $y = 3$

17. d **18.** a **19.** c **20.** b **21.** 3 **23.** 9

25. Domain: all real numbers x except $x = \pm 4$;
Vertical asymptote: $x = -4$; horizontal asymptote: $y = 0$

27. Domain: all real numbers x except $x = -1, 5$;
Vertical asymptote: $x = -1$; horizontal asymptote: $y = 1$

29. Domain: all real numbers x except $x = -1, \frac{1}{2}$;
Vertical asymptote: $x = \frac{1}{2}$; horizontal asymptote: $y = \frac{1}{2}$

31. (a) Domain: all real numbers x except $x = -2$
(b) y-intercept: $\left(0, \frac{1}{2}\right)$
(c) Vertical asymptote: $x = -2$
Horizontal asymptote: $y = 0$
(d)

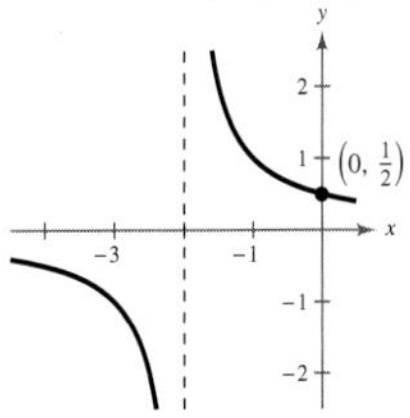

33. (a) Domain: all real numbers x except $x = -4$
(b) y-intercept: $\left(0, -\frac{1}{4}\right)$
(c) Vertical asymptote: $x = -4$
Horizontal asymptote: $y = 0$
(d)

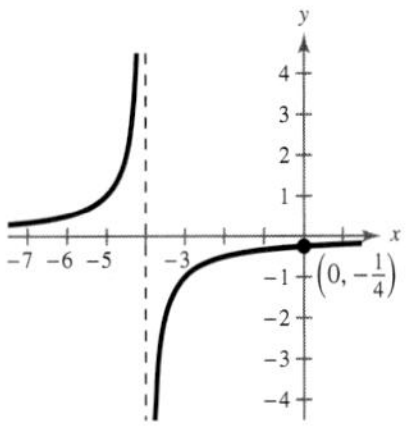

35. (a) Domain: all real numbers x except $x = -2$
(b) x-intercept: $\left(-\frac{7}{2}, 0\right)$
y-intercept: $\left(0, \frac{7}{2}\right)$
(c) Vertical asymptote: $x = -2$
Horizontal asymptote: $y = 2$
(d)

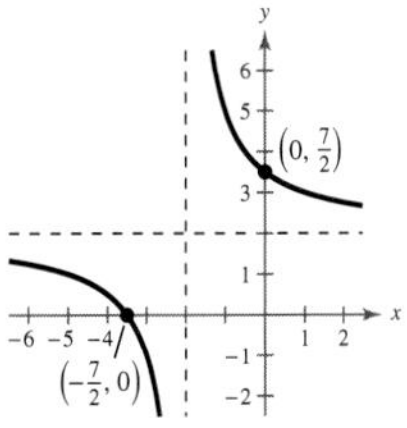

37. (a) Domain: all real numbers x
(b) Intercept: $(0, 0)$
(c) Horizontal asymptote: $y = 1$
(d)

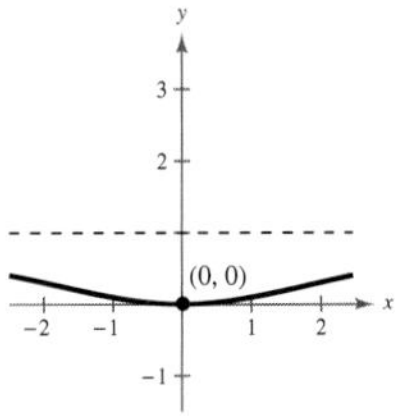

39. (a) Domain: all real numbers s
(b) Intercept: $(0, 0)$ (c) Horizontal asymptote: $y = 0$
(d)

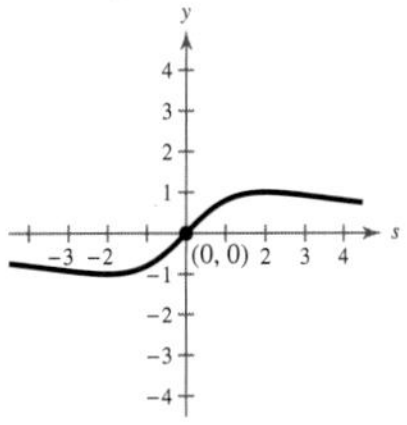

41. (a) Domain: all real numbers x except $x = \pm 2$
(b) x-intercepts: $(1, 0)$ and $(4, 0)$
y-intercept: $(0, -1)$
(c) Vertical asymptotes: $x = \pm 2$
Horizontal asymptote: $y = 1$

(d)

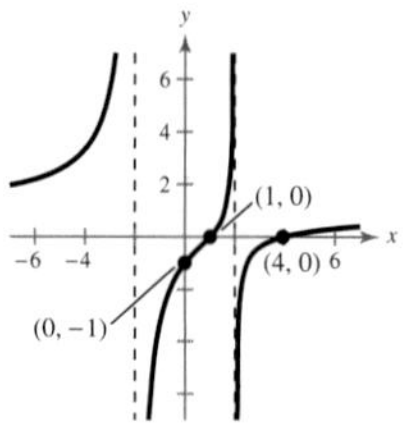

43. (a) Domain: all real numbers x except $x = \pm 1, 2$
(b) x-intercepts: $(3, 0), \left(-\frac{1}{2}, 0\right)$
y-intercept: $\left(0, -\frac{3}{2}\right)$
(c) Vertical asymptotes: $x = 2, x = \pm 1$
Horizontal asymptote: $y = 0$
(d)

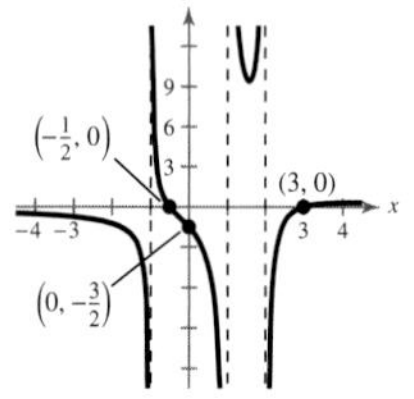

45. (a) Domain: all real numbers x except $x = 2, -3$
(b) Intercept: $(0, 0)$
(c) Vertical asymptote: $x = 2$
Horizontal asymptote: $y = 1$
(d)

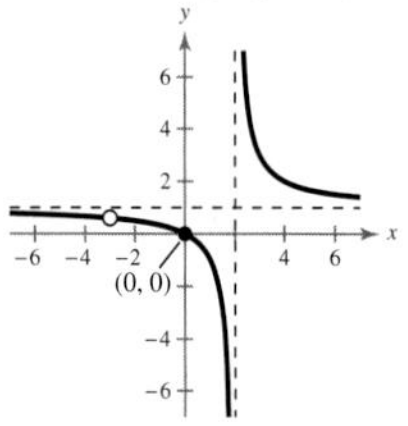

47. (a) Domain: all real numbers x except $x = -\frac{3}{2}, 2$
(b) x-intercept: $\left(\frac{1}{2}, 0\right)$
y-intercept: $\left(0, -\frac{1}{3}\right)$
(c) Vertical asymptote: $x = -\frac{3}{2}$
Horizontal asymptote: $y = 1$
(d)

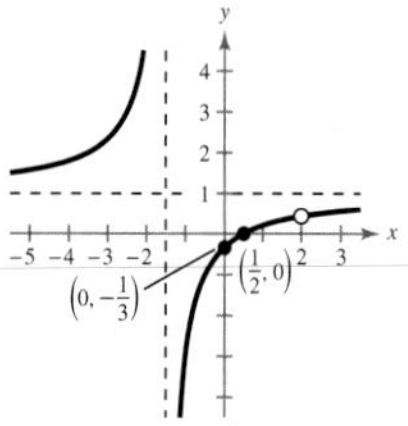

49. (a) Domain: all real numbers t except $t = 1$
(b) t-intercept: $(-1, 0)$
y-intercept: $(0, 1)$
(c) Vertical asymptote: None
Horizontal asymptote: None

(d)

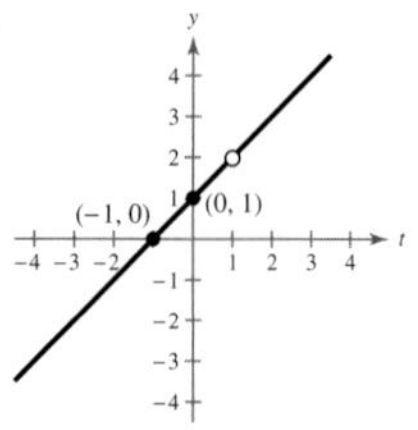

51. (a) Domain of f: all real numbers x except $x = -1$
Domain of g: all real numbers x
(b) $x - 1$; Vertical asymptotes: None
(c)

x	-3	-2	-1.5	-1	-0.5	0	1
$f(x)$	-4	-3	-2.5	Undef.	-1.5	-1	0
$g(x)$	-4	-3	-2.5	-2	-1.5	-1	0

(d)

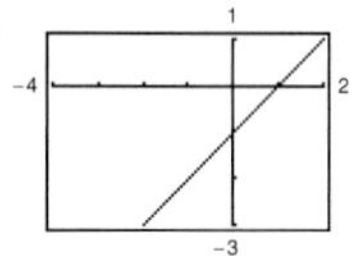

(e) Because there are only a finite number of pixels, the graphing utility may not attempt to evaluate the function where it does not exist.

53. (a) Domain of f: all real numbers x except $x = 0, 2$
Domain of g: all real numbers x except $x = 0$
(b) $\frac{1}{x}$; Vertical asymptote: $x = 0$
(c)

x	-0.5	0	0.5	1	1.5	2	3
$f(x)$	-2	Undef.	2	1	$\frac{2}{3}$	Undef.	$\frac{1}{3}$
$g(x)$	-2	Undef.	2	1	$\frac{2}{3}$	$\frac{1}{2}$	$\frac{1}{3}$

(d)

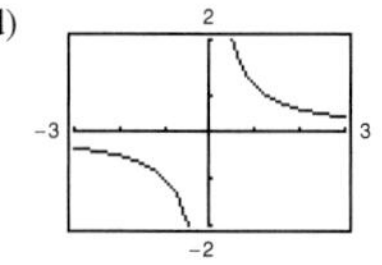

(e) Because there are only a finite number of pixels, the graphing utility may not attempt to evaluate the function where it does not exist.

55. (a) Domain: all real numbers x except $x = 0$
(b) x-intercepts: $(-3, 0), (3, 0)$
(c) Vertical asymptote: $x = 0$
Slant asymptote: $y = x$
(d)

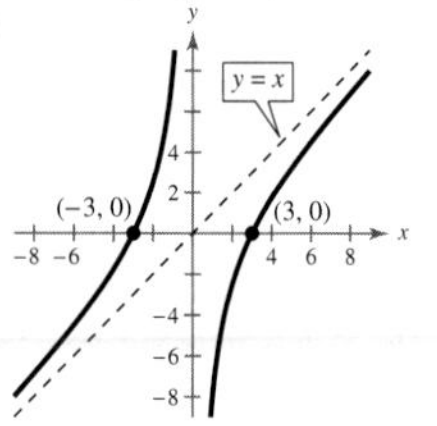

57. (a) Domain: all real numbers x except $x = 0$
(b) No intercepts
(c) Vertical asymptote: $x = 0$
Slant asymptote: $y = 2x$
(d)

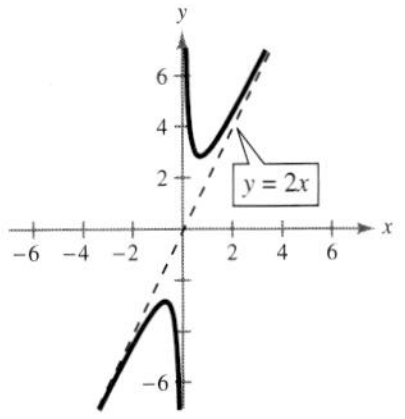

59. (a) Domain: all real numbers x except $x = 0$
(b) No intercepts
(c) Vertical asymptote: $x = 0$
Slant asymptote: $y = x$
(d)

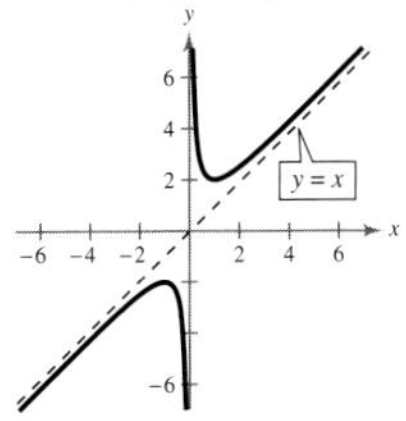

61. (a) Domain: all real numbers t except $t = -5$
(b) y-intercept: $\left(0, -\frac{1}{5}\right)$
(c) Vertical asymptote: $t = -5$
Slant asymptote: $y = -t + 5$
(d)

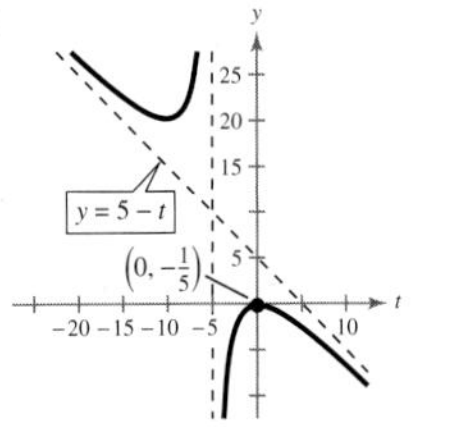

63. (a) Domain: all real numbers x except $x = \pm 2$
(b) Intercept: $(0, 0)$
(c) Vertical asymptotes: $x = \pm 2$
Slant asymptote: $y = x$
(d)

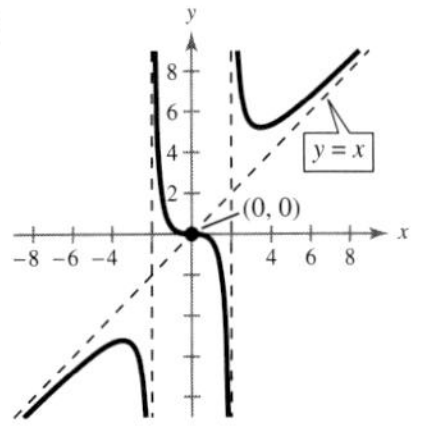

65. (a) Domain: all real numbers x except $x = 1$
(b) y-intercept: $(0, -1)$
(c) Vertical asymptote: $x = 1$
Slant asymptote: $y = x$
(d)

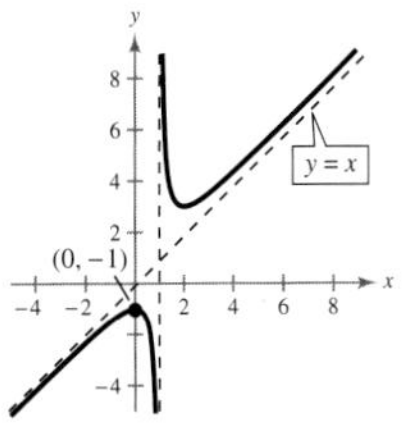

67. (a) Domain: all real numbers x except $x = -1, -2$
(b) y-intercept: $\left(0, \frac{1}{2}\right)$
x-intercepts: $\left(\frac{1}{2}, 0\right)$, $(1, 0)$
(c) Vertical asymptote: $x = -2$
Slant asymptote: $y = 2x - 7$
(d)

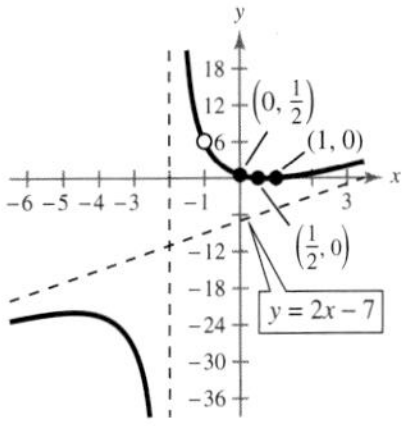

69.

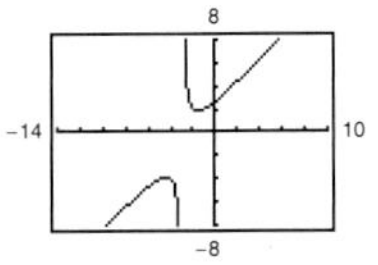

Domain: all real numbers x except $x = -3$
Vertical asymptote: $x = -3$
Slant asymptote: $y = x + 2$
$y = x + 2$

71.

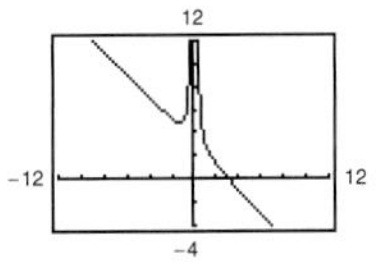

Domain: all real numbers x except $x = 0$
Vertical asymptote: $x = 0$
Slant asymptote: $y = -x + 3$
$y = -x + 3$

73. (a) $(-1, 0)$ (b) -1

75. (a) $(1, 0)$, $(-1, 0)$ (b) ± 1

77. (a)

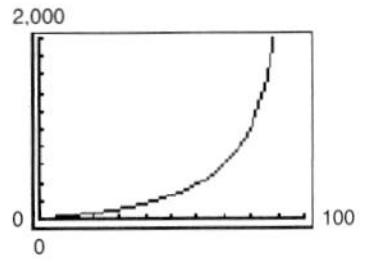

(b) \$28.33 million; \$170 million; \$765 million
(c) No. The function is undefined at $p = 100$.

79. (a) 333 deer, 500 deer, 800 deer (b) 1500 deer

81. (a) $A = \dfrac{2x(x + 11)}{x - 4}$ (b) $(4, \infty)$

(c) 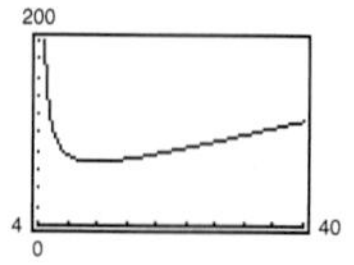

11.75 in. × 5.87 in.

83. (a) Answers will vary.

(b) Vertical asymptote: $x = 25$

Horizontal asymptote: $y = 25$

(c) 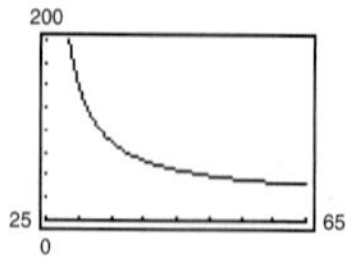

(d)

x	30	35	40	45	50	55	60
y	150	87.5	66.7	56.3	50	45.8	42.9

(e) Sample answer: No. You might expect the average speed for the round trip to be the average of the average speeds for the two parts of the trip.

(f) No. At 20 miles per hour you would use more time in one direction than is required for the round trip at an average speed of 50 miles per hour.

85. False. Polynomials do not have vertical asymptotes.

87. False. If the degree of the numerator is greater than the degree of the denominator, no horizontal asymptote exists. However, a slant asymptote exists only if the degree of the numerator is one greater than the degree of the denominator.

89. c

Section 2.7 *(page 201)*

1. positive; negative **3.** zeros; undefined values

5. (a) No (b) Yes (c) Yes (d) No

7. (a) Yes (b) No (c) No (d) Yes

9. $-\frac{2}{3}, 1$ **11.** 4, 5

13. $(-3, 3)$

15. $[-7, 3]$

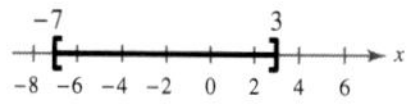

17. $(-\infty, -5] \cup [1, \infty)$

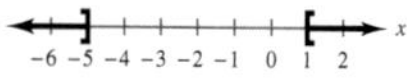

19. $(-3, 2)$

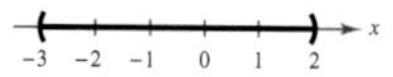

21. $(-3, 1)$

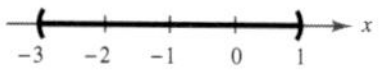

23. $\left(-\infty, -\frac{4}{3}\right) \cup (5, \infty)$

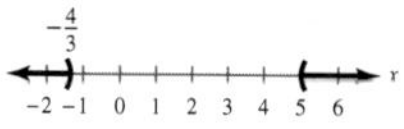

25. $(-\infty, -3) \cup (6, \infty)$

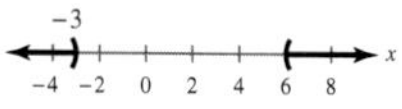

27. $(-1, 1) \cup (3, \infty)$

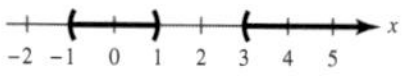

29. $x = \frac{1}{2}$

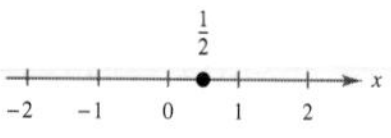

31. $(-\infty, 0) \cup \left(0, \frac{3}{2}\right)$ **33.** $[-2, 0] \cup [2, \infty)$ **35.** $[-2, \infty)$

37. 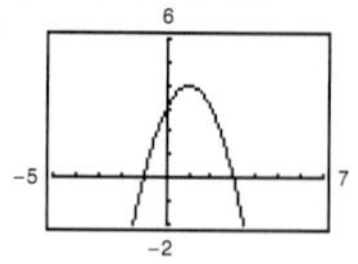

(a) $x \le -1, x \ge 3$

(b) $0 \le x \le 2$

39. 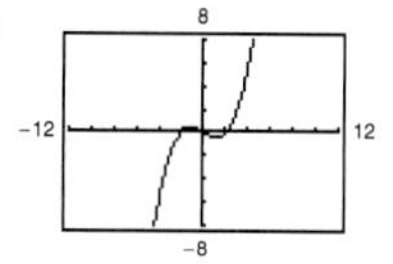

(a) $-2 \le x \le 0,$

$2 \le x < \infty$

(b) $x \le 4$

41. $(-\infty, 0) \cup \left(\frac{1}{4}, \infty\right)$

43. $\left(-\infty, \frac{5}{3}\right] \cup (5, \infty)$

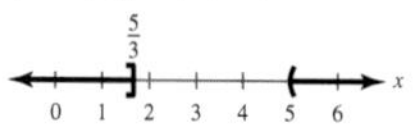

45. $(-\infty, -1) \cup (4, \infty)$

47. $(-5, 3) \cup (11, \infty)$

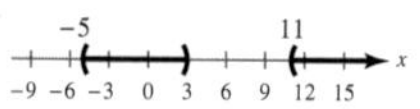

49. $\left(-\frac{3}{4}, 3\right) \cup [6, \infty)$

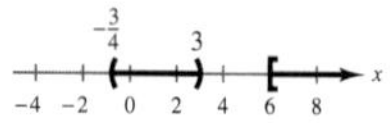

51. $(-3, -2] \cup [0, 3)$

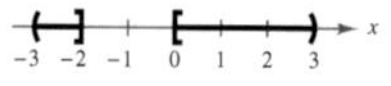

53. $(-\infty, -1) \cup (1, \infty)$

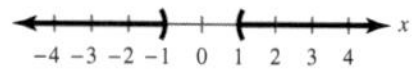

55. 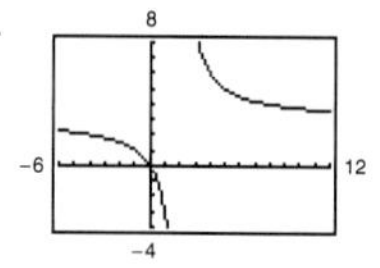

(a) $0 \le x < 2$

(b) $2 < x \le 4$

57. 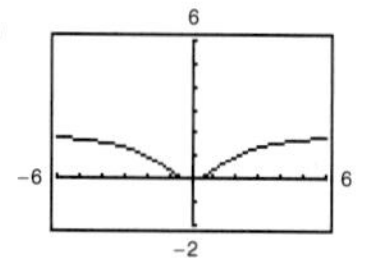

(a) $|x| \ge 2$

(b) $-\infty < x < \infty$

59. $[-2, 2]$ **61.** $(-\infty, 4] \cup [5, \infty)$

63. $(-5, 0] \cup (7, \infty)$ **65.** $(-3.51, 3.51)$

67. $(-0.13, 25.13)$ **69.** $(2.26, 2.39)$

71. (a) $t = 10$ sec (b) 4 sec $< t <$ 6 sec

73. 13.8 m $\le L \le$ 36.2 m

75. $40{,}000 \le x \le 50{,}000$; $\$50.00 \le p \le \$55.00$

77. (a) and (c) 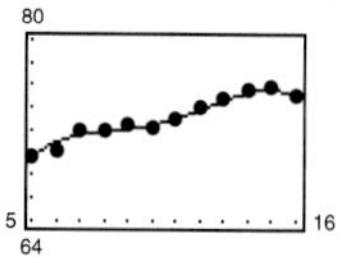

The model fits the data well.

(b) $N = -0.00412t^4 + 0.1705t^3 - 2.538t^2 + 16.55t + 31.5$

(d) 2003 to 2006

(e) No; The model decreases sharply after 2006.

79. $R_1 \ge 2$ ohms

81. True. The test intervals are $(-\infty, -3)$, $(-3, 1)$, $(1, 4)$, and $(4, \infty)$.

83. (a) $(-\infty, -4] \cup [4, \infty)$

(b) If $a > 0$ and $c > 0$, $b \le -2\sqrt{ac}$ or $b \ge 2\sqrt{ac}$.

85. (a) $\left(-\infty, -2\sqrt{30}\right] \cup \left[2\sqrt{30}, \infty\right)$
(b) If $a > 0$ and $c > 0$, $b \le -2\sqrt{ac}$ or $b \ge 2\sqrt{ac}$.

87.

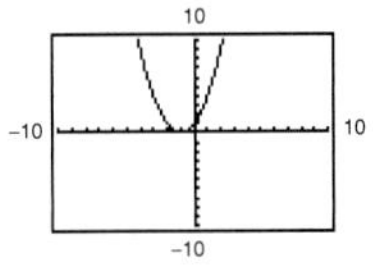

For part (b), the y-values that are less than or equal to 0 occur only at $x = -1$.

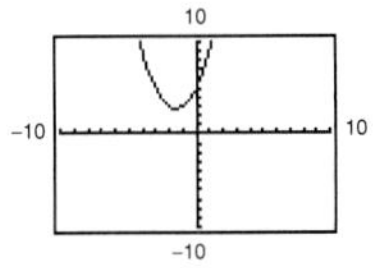

For part (c), there are no y-values that are less than 0.

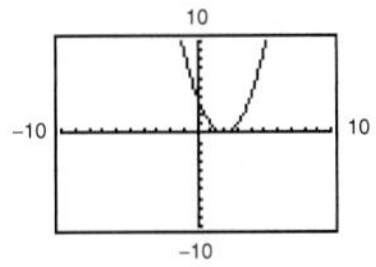

For part (d), the y-values that are greater than 0 occur for all values of x except 2.

Review Exercises *(page 206)*

1. (a)

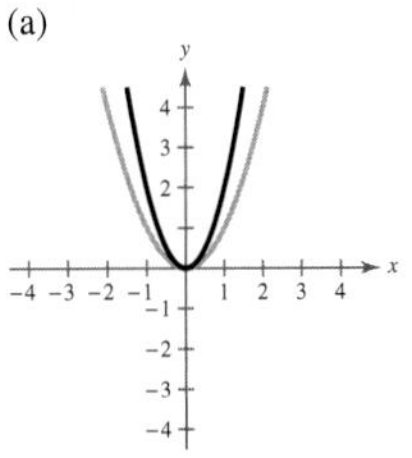

Vertical stretch

(b)

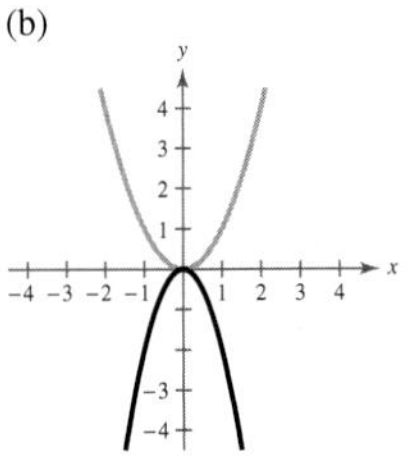

Vertical stretch and reflection in the x-axis

(c)

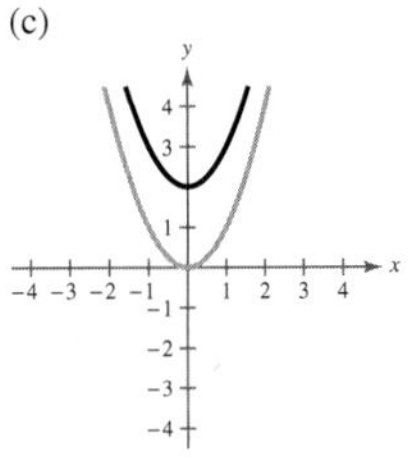

Vertical shift two units upward

(d)

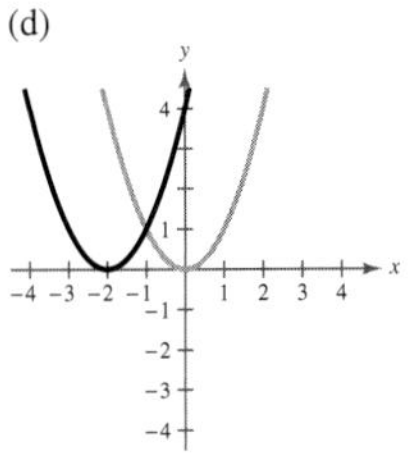

Horizontal shift two units to the left

3. $g(x) = (x - 1)^2 - 1$

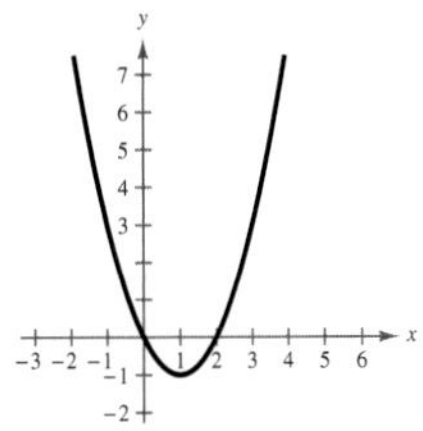

Vertex: $(1, -1)$
Axis of symmetry: $x = 1$
x-intercepts: $(0, 0)$, $(2, 0)$

5. $f(x) = (x + 4)^2 - 6$

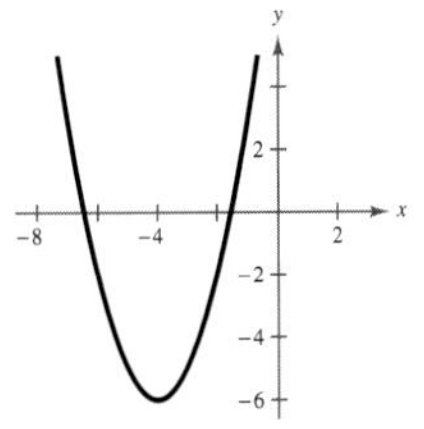

Vertex: $(-4, -6)$
Axis of symmetry: $x = -4$
x-intercepts: $\left(-4 \pm \sqrt{6}, 0\right)$

7. $f(t) = -2(t - 1)^2 + 3$

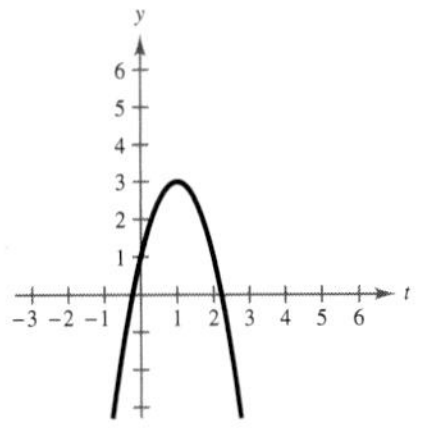

Vertex: $(1, 3)$
Axis of symmetry: $t = 1$
t-intercepts: $\left(1 \pm \dfrac{\sqrt{6}}{2}, 0\right)$

9. $h(x) = 4\left(x + \frac{1}{2}\right)^2 + 12$

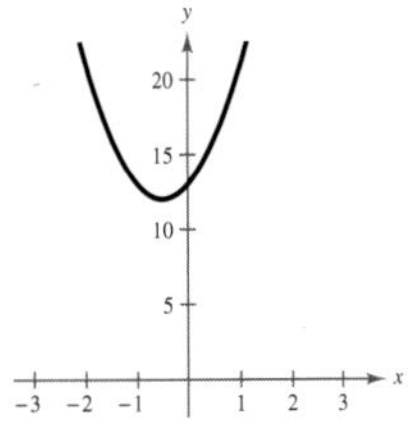

Vertex: $\left(-\frac{1}{2}, 12\right)$
Axis of symmetry: $x = -\frac{1}{2}$
No x-intercept

11. $h(x) = \left(x + \frac{5}{2}\right)^2 - \frac{41}{4}$

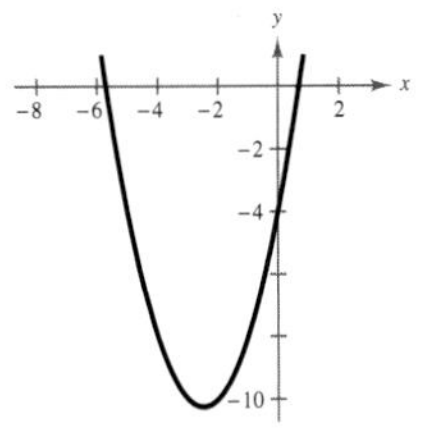

Vertex: $\left(-\frac{5}{2}, -\frac{41}{4}\right)$
Axis of symmetry: $x = -\frac{5}{2}$
x-intercepts: $\left(\dfrac{\pm\sqrt{41} - 5}{2}, 0\right)$

13. $f(x) = \frac{1}{3}\left(x + \frac{5}{2}\right)^2 - \frac{41}{12}$

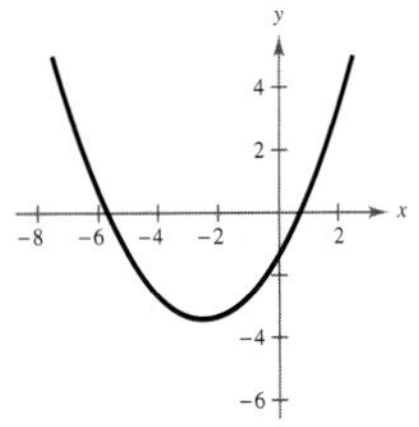

Vertex: $\left(-\frac{5}{2}, -\frac{41}{12}\right)$
Axis of symmetry: $x = -\frac{5}{2}$
x-intercepts: $\left(\dfrac{\pm\sqrt{41} - 5}{2}, 0\right)$

15. $f(x) = -\frac{1}{2}(x - 4)^2 + 1$

17. $f(x) = (x - 1)^2 - 4$

19. $y = -\frac{11}{36}\left(x + \frac{3}{2}\right)^2$

21. (a)

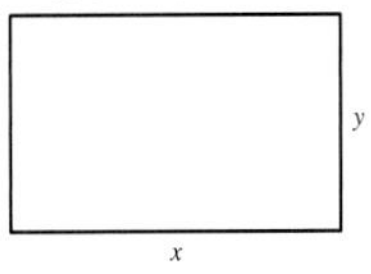

(b) $y = 500 - x$
$A(x) = 500x - x^2$
(c) $x = 250$, $y = 250$

23. 1091 units

CHAPTER 2

25.
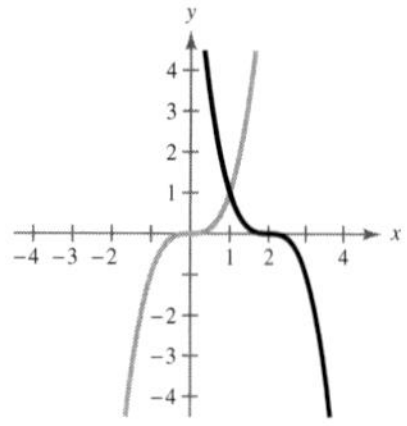

27.
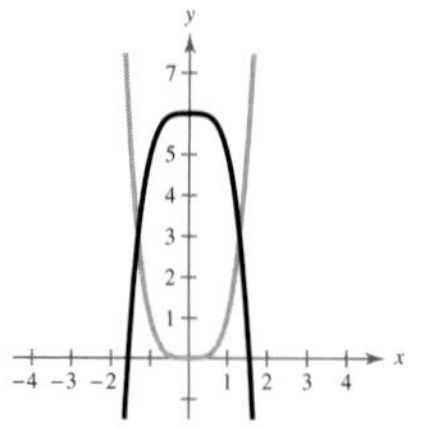

29.
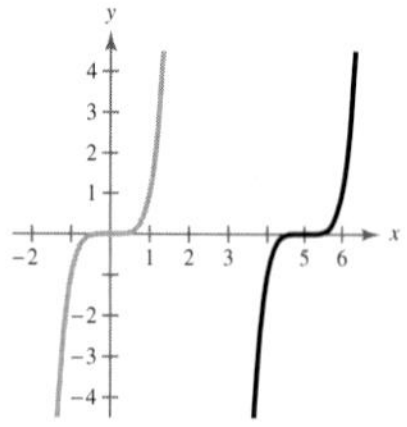

31. Falls to the left, falls to the right

33. Rises to the left, rises to the right

35. $-8, \frac{4}{3}$, odd multiplicity; turning points: 1

37. $0, \pm\sqrt{3}$, odd multiplicity; turning points: 2

39. 0, even multiplicity; $\frac{2}{3}$, odd multiplicity; turning points: 2

41. (a) Rises to the left, falls to the right (b) -1
(c) Answers will vary.
(d)
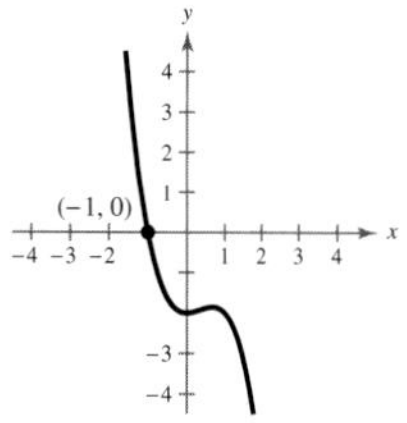

43. (a) Rises to the left, rises to the right (b) $-3, 0, 1$
(c) Answers will vary.
(d)
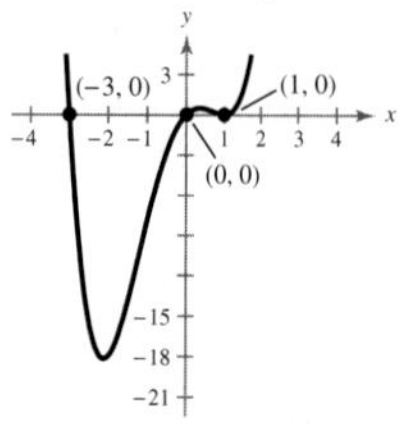

45. (a) $[-1, 0]$ (b) About -0.900

47. (a) $[-1, 0], [1, 2]$ (b) About -0.200, about 1.772

49. $6x + 3 + \dfrac{17}{5x - 3}$ 51. $5x + 4, \quad x \neq \dfrac{5}{2} \pm \dfrac{\sqrt{29}}{2}$

53. $x^2 - 3x + 2 - \dfrac{1}{x^2 + 2}$

55. $6x^3 + 8x^2 - 11x - 4 - \dfrac{8}{x - 2}$

57. $2x^2 - 9x - 6, \quad x \neq 8$

59. (a) Yes (b) Yes (c) Yes (d) No

61. (a) -421 (b) -9

63. (a) Answers will vary.
(b) $(x + 7), (x + 1)$
(c) $f(x) = (x + 7)(x + 1)(x - 4)$
(d) $-7, -1, 4$
(e)
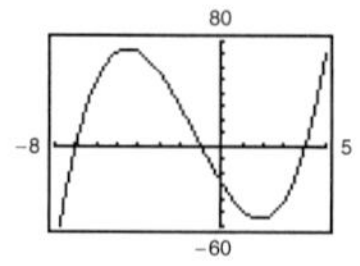

65. (a) Answers will vary. (b) $(x + 1), (x - 4)$
(c) $f(x) = (x + 1)(x - 4)(x + 2)(x - 3)$
(d) $-2, -1, 3, 4$
(e)
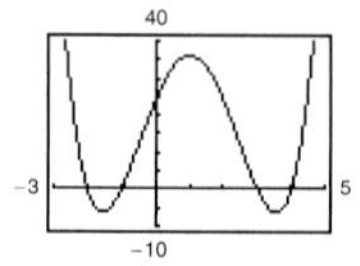

67. $8 + 10i$ 69. $-1 + 3i$ 71. $3 + 7i$

73. $63 + 77i$ 75. $-4 - 46i$ 77. $39 - 80i$

79. $\dfrac{23}{17} + \dfrac{10}{17}i$ 81. $\dfrac{21}{13} - \dfrac{1}{13}i$ 83. $\pm\dfrac{\sqrt{10}}{5}i$ 85. $1 \pm 3i$

87. 0, 3 89. 2, 9 91. $-4, 6, \pm 2i$

93. $\pm 1, \pm 3, \pm 5, \pm 15, \pm\frac{1}{2}, \pm\frac{3}{2}, \pm\frac{5}{2}, \pm\frac{15}{2}, \pm\frac{1}{4}, \pm\frac{3}{4}, \pm\frac{5}{4}, \pm\frac{15}{4}$

95. $-6, -2, 5$ 97. 1, 8 99. $-4, 3$

101. $f(x) = 3x^4 - 14x^3 + 17x^2 - 42x + 24$

103. $4, \pm i$ 105. $-3, \frac{1}{2}, 2 \pm i$

107. $0, 1, -5; f(x) = x(x - 1)(x + 5)$

109. $-4, 2 \pm 3i; g(x) = (x + 4)^2(x - 2 - 3i)(x - 2 + 3i)$

111. Two or no positive zeros, one negative zero

113. Answers will vary.

115. Domain: all real numbers x except $x = -10$

117. Domain: all real numbers x except $x = 6, 4$

119. Vertical asymptote: $x = -3$
Horizontal asymptote: $y = 0$

121. Vertical asymptote: $x = 6$
Horizontal asymptote: $y = 0$

123. (a) Domain: all real numbers x except $x = 0$
(b) No intercepts
(c) Vertical asymptote: $x = 0$
Horizontal asymptote: $y = 0$
(d)
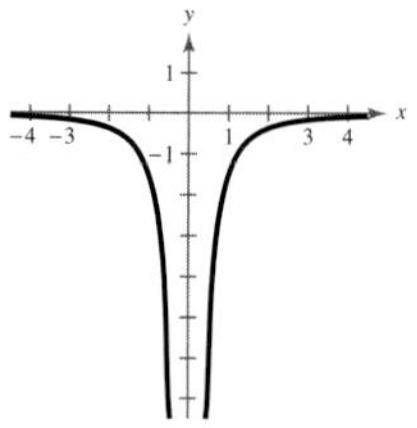

125. (a) Domain: all real numbers x except $x = 1$
(b) x-intercept: $(-2, 0)$
y-intercept: $(0, 2)$

(c) Vertical asymptote: $x = 1$
Horizontal asymptote: $y = -1$

(d)

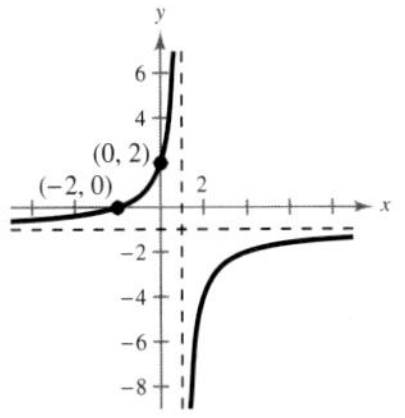

127. (a) Domain: all real numbers x
(b) Intercept: $(0, 0)$
(c) Horizontal asymptote: $y = \frac{5}{4}$
(d)

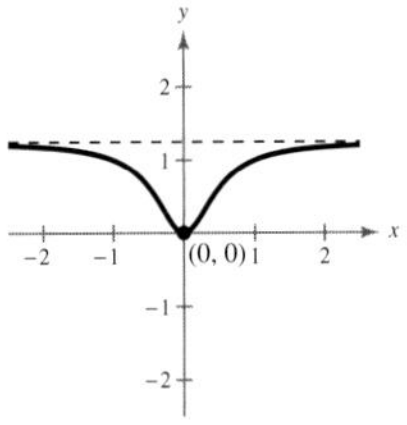

129. (a) Domain: all real numbers x
(b) Intercept: $(0, 0)$
(c) Horizontal asymptote: $y = 0$
(d)

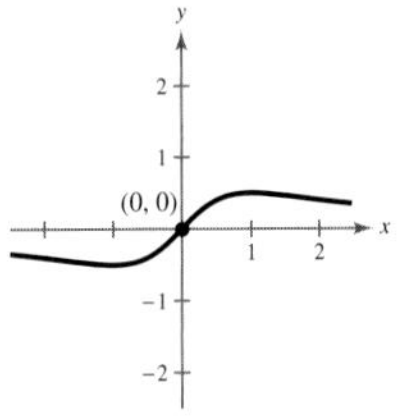

131. (a) Domain: all real numbers x
(b) Intercept: $(0, 0)$
(c) Horizontal asymptote: $y = -6$
(d)

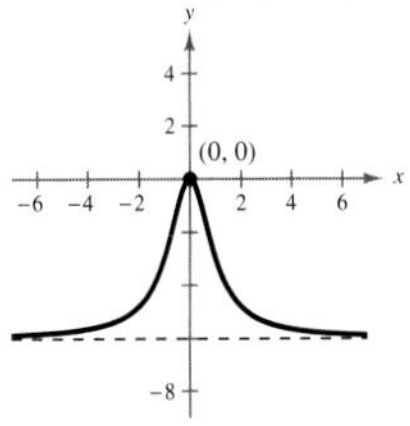

133. (a) Domain: all real numbers x except $x = 0, \frac{1}{3}$
(b) x-intercept: $\left(\frac{3}{2}, 0\right)$
(c) Vertical asymptote: $x = 0$
Horizontal asymptote: $y = 2$

(d)

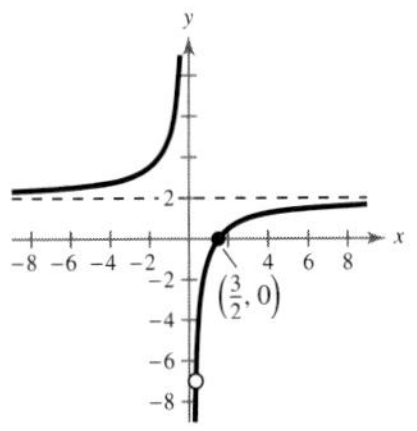

135. (a) Domain: all real numbers x
(b) Intercept: $(0, 0)$ (c) Slant asymptote: $y = 2x$
(d)

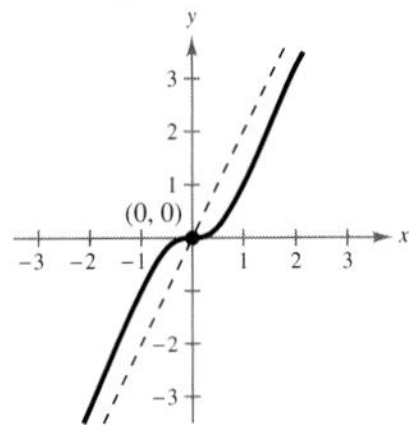

137. (a) Domain: all real numbers x except $x = \frac{4}{3}, -1$
(b) y-intercept: $\left(0, -\frac{1}{2}\right)$
x-intercepts: $\left(\frac{2}{3}, 0\right), (1, 0)$
(c) Vertical asymptote: $x = \frac{4}{3}$
Slant asymptote: $y = x - \frac{1}{3}$
(d)

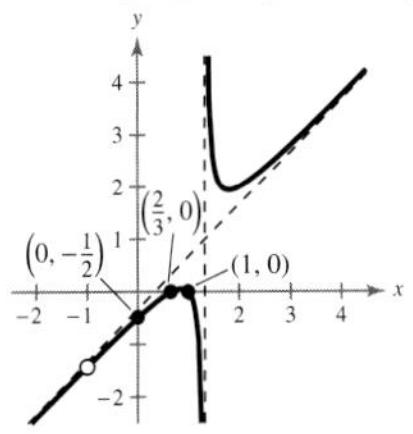

139. $\overline{C} = 0.5 = \$0.50$

141. (a)

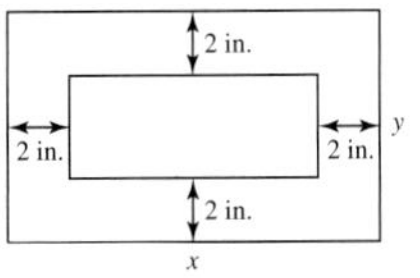

(b) $A = \dfrac{2x(2x + 7)}{x - 4}$ (c) $4 < x < \infty$

(d)

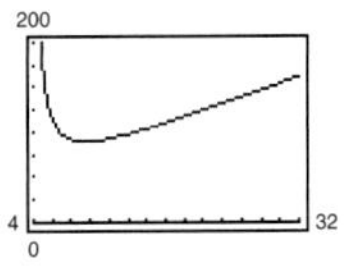

9.48 in. × 9.48 in.

143. $\left(-\frac{2}{3}, \frac{1}{4}\right)$ **145.** $[-4, 0] \cup [4, \infty)$
147. $[-5, -1) \cup (1, \infty)$ **149.** $(-\infty, 0) \cup [4, 5]$
151. 4.9%
153. False. A fourth-degree polynomial can have at most four zeros, and complex zeros occur in conjugate pairs.

155. Find the vertex of the quadratic function and write the function in standard form. If the leading coefficient is positive, the vertex is a minimum. If the leading coefficient is negative, the vertex is a maximum.

157. An asymptote of a graph is a line to which the graph becomes arbitrarily close as x increases or decreases without bound.

Chapter Test *(page 210)*

1. (a) Reflection in the x-axis followed by a vertical shift two units upward
(b) Horizontal shift $\frac{3}{2}$ units to the right

2. $y = (x - 3)^2 - 6$

3. (a) 50 ft
(b) 5. Yes, changing the constant term results in a vertical translation of the graph and therefore changes the maximum height.

4. Rises to the left, falls to the right

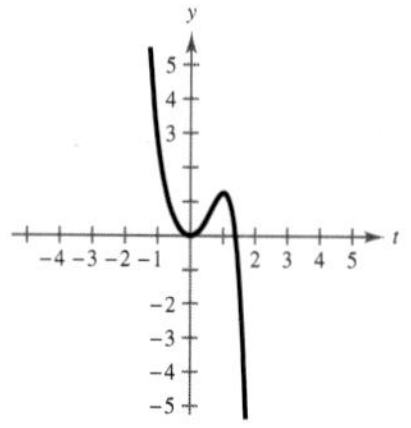

5. $3x + \dfrac{x - 1}{x^2 + 1}$ **6.** $2x^3 + 4x^2 + 3x + 6 + \dfrac{9}{x - 2}$

7. $(2x - 5)(x + \sqrt{3})(x - \sqrt{3})$;
Zeros: $\frac{5}{2}, \pm\sqrt{3}$

8. (a) $-3 + 5i$ (b) 7 **9.** $2 - i$

10. $f(x) = x^4 - 7x^3 + 17x^2 - 15x$

11. $f(x) = 4x^2 - 16x + 16$

12. $-5, -\frac{2}{3}, 1$ **13.** $-2, 4, -1 \pm \sqrt{2}i$

14. x-intercepts: $(-2, 0), (2, 0)$
Vertical asymptote: $x = 0$
Horizontal asymptote: $y = -1$

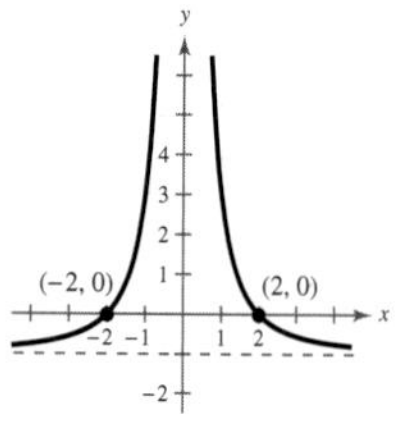

15. x-intercept: $\left(-\frac{3}{2}, 0\right)$
y-intercept: $\left(0, \frac{3}{4}\right)$
Vertical asymptote: $x = -4$
Horizontal asymptote: $y = 2$

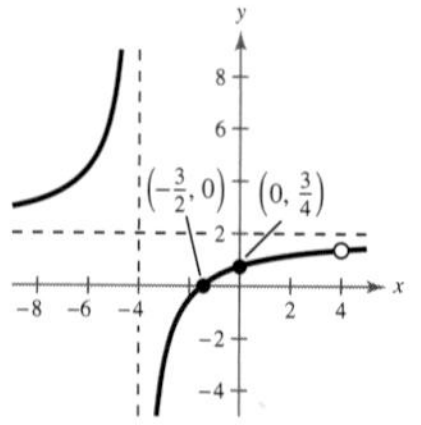

16. y-intercept: $(0, -2)$
Vertical asymptote: $x = 1$
Slant asymptote: $y = x + 1$

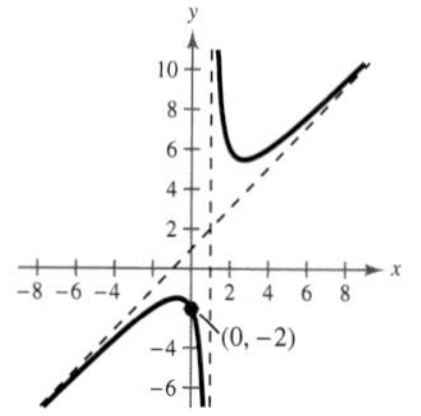

17. $x < -4$ or $x > \frac{3}{2}$

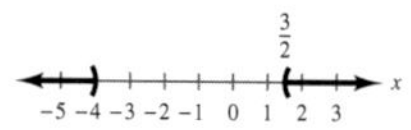

18. $x \le -12$ or $-6 < x < 0$

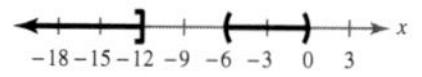

Problem Solving *(page 213)*

1. Answers will vary. **3.** 2 in. × 2 in. × 5 in.

5. (a) and (b) $y = -x^2 + 5x - 4$

7. (a) $f(x) = (x - 2)x^2 + 5 = x^3 - 2x^2 + 5$
(b) $f(x) = -(x + 3)x^2 + 1 = -x^3 - 3x^2 + 1$

9. $(a + bi)(a - bi) = a^2 + abi - abi - b^2i^2$
$= a^2 + b^2$

11. (a) As $|a|$ increases, the graph stretches vertically. For $a < 0$, the graph is reflected in the x-axis.
(b) As $|b|$ increases, the vertical asymptote is translated. For $b > 0$, the graph is translated to the right. For $b < 0$, the graph is reflected in the x-axis and is translated to the left.

Chapter 3

Section 3.1 *(page 224)*

1. algebraic **3.** One-to-One **5.** $A = P\left(1 + \dfrac{r}{n}\right)^{nt}$

7. 0.863 **9.** 0.006 **11.** 1767.767

13. d **14.** c **15.** a **16.** b

17.

x	-2	-1	0	1	2
$f(x)$	4	2	1	0.5	0.25

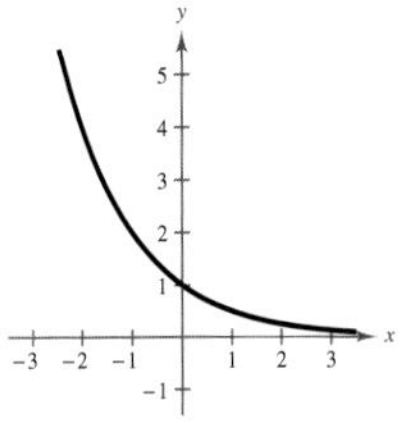

19.

x	-2	-1	0	1	2
$f(x)$	36	6	1	0.167	0.028

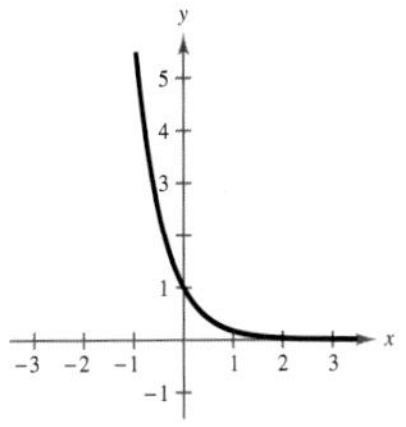

21.

x	-2	-1	0	1	2
$f(x)$	0.125	0.25	0.5	1	2

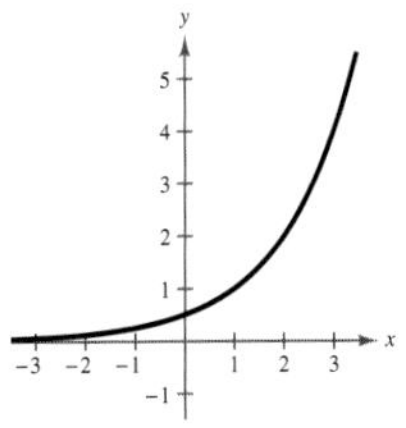

23. Shift the graph of f one unit upward.

25. Reflect the graph of f in the x-axis and shift three units upward.

27. Reflect the graph of f in the origin.

29.

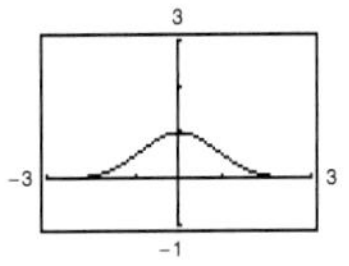

31.

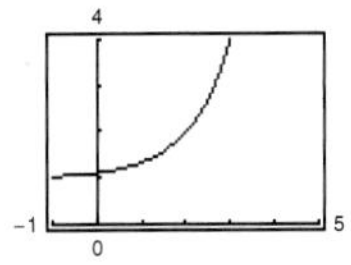

33. 0.472 **35.** 3.857×10^{-22} **37.** 7166.647

39.

x	-2	-1	0	1	2
$f(x)$	0.135	0.368	1	2.718	7.389

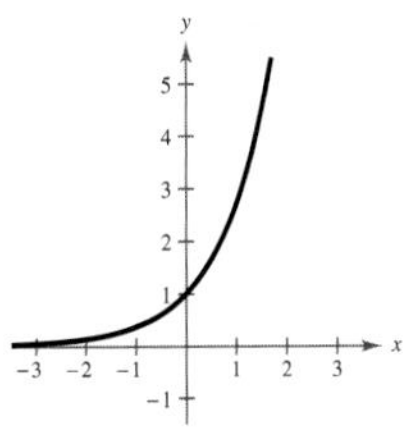

41.

x	-8	-7	-6	-5	-4
$f(x)$	0.055	0.149	0.406	1.104	3

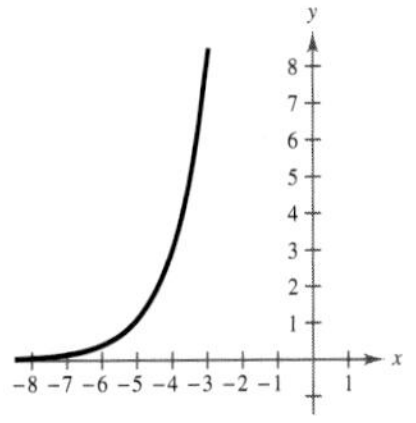

43.

x	-2	-1	0	1	2
$f(x)$	4.037	4.100	4.271	4.736	6

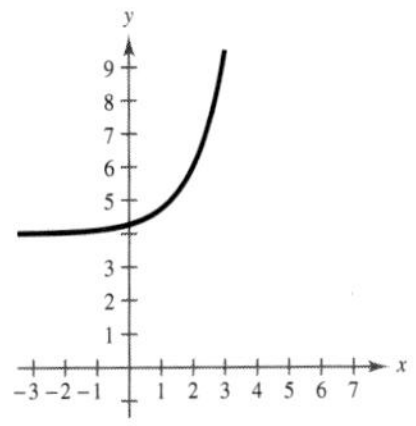

45.

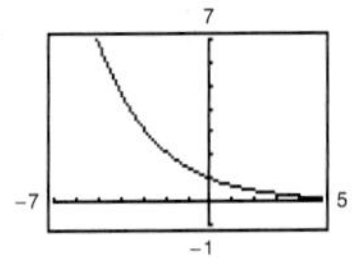

47.

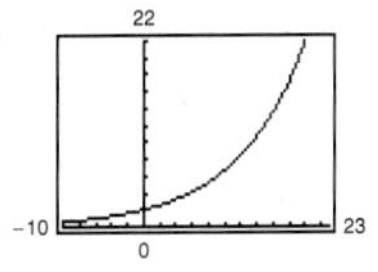

49.

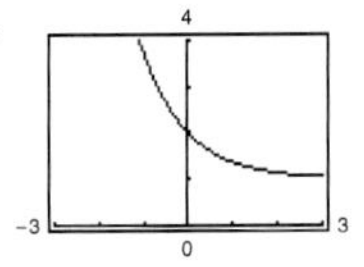

51. $x = 2$ **53.** $x = -5$ **55.** $x = \frac{1}{3}$ **57.** $x = 3, -1$

59.

n	1	2	4	12
A	\$1828.49	\$1830.29	\$1831.19	\$1831.80

n	365	Continuous
A	\$1832.09	\$1832.10

61.

n	1	2	4	12
A	\$5477.81	\$5520.10	\$5541.79	\$5556.46

n	365	Continuous
A	\$5563.61	\$5563.85

63.

t	10	20	30
A	\$17,901.90	\$26,706.49	\$39,841.40

t	40	50
A	\$59,436.39	\$88,668.67

65.

t	10	20	30
A	\$22,986.49	\$44,031.56	\$84,344.25

t	40	50
A	\$161,564.86	\$309,484.08

67. \$104,710.29 **69.** \$35.45

71. (a)

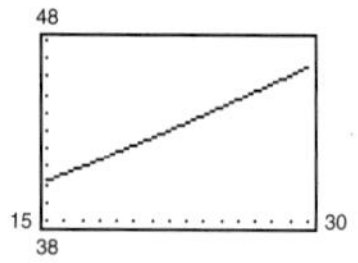

(b)

t	15	16	17	18	19	20
P (in millions)	40.19	40.59	40.99	41.39	41.80	42.21

t	21	22	23	24	25	26
P (in millions)	42.62	43.04	43.47	43.90	44.33	44.77

t	27	28	29	30
P (in millions)	45.21	45.65	46.10	46.56

(c) 2038

73. (a) 16 g (b) 1.85 g

(c)

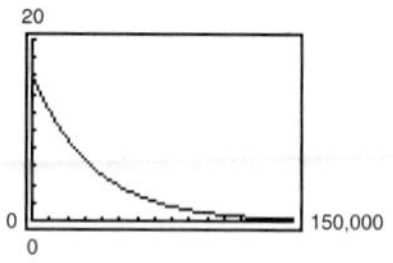

75. (a) $V(t) = 30{,}500\left(\frac{7}{8}\right)^t$ (b) \$17,878.54

77. True. As $x \to -\infty$, $f(x) \to -2$ but never reaches -2.

79. $f(x) = h(x)$ **81.** $f(x) = g(x) = h(x)$

83. (a) $x < 0$ (b) $x > 0$

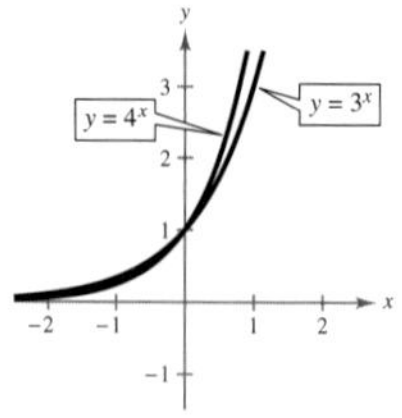

85.

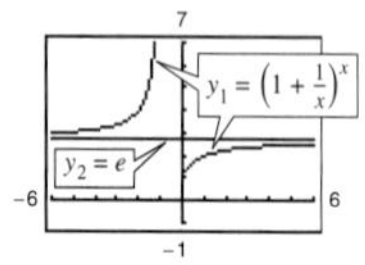

As the x-value increases, y_1 approaches the value of e.

87. (a)

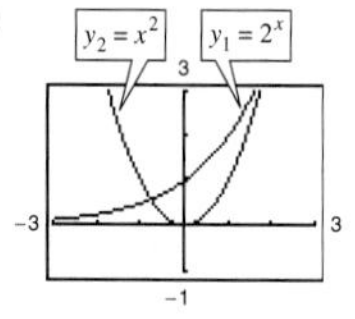

(b)

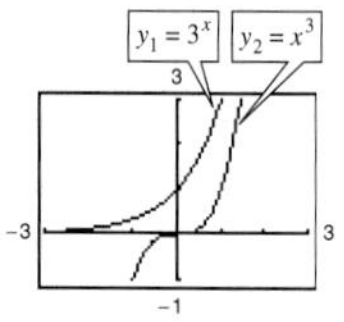

In both viewing windows, the constant raised to a variable power increases more rapidly than the variable raised to a constant power.

89. (a) $A = \$5466.09$ (b) $A = \$5466.35$
(c) $A = \$5466.36$ (d) $A = \$5466.38$
No. Answers will vary.

Section 3.2 *(page 234)*

1. logarithmic **3.** natural; e **5.** $x = y$ **7.** $4^2 = 16$
9. $9^{-2} = \frac{1}{81}$ **11.** $32^{2/5} = 4$ **13.** $64^{1/2} = 8$
15. $\log_5 125 = 3$ **17.** $\log_{81} 3 = \frac{1}{4}$ **19.** $\log_6 \frac{1}{36} = -2$
21. $\log_{24} 1 = 0$ **23.** 6 **25.** 0 **27.** 2
29. -0.058 **31.** 1.097 **33.** 7 **35.** 1

37.

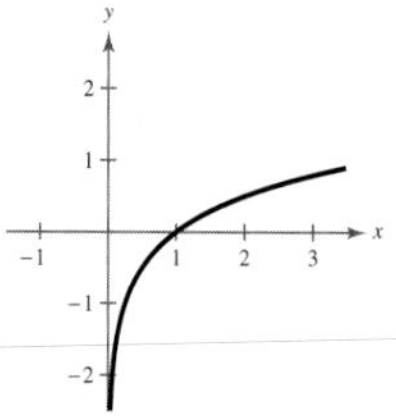

Domain: $(0, \infty)$
x-intercept: $(1, 0)$
Vertical asymptote: $x = 0$

39.

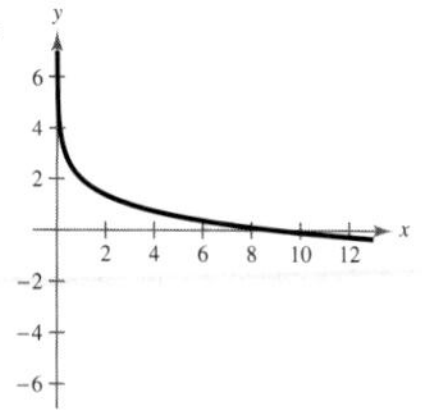

Domain: $(0, \infty)$
x-intercept: $(9, 0)$
Vertical asymptote: $x = 0$

41.

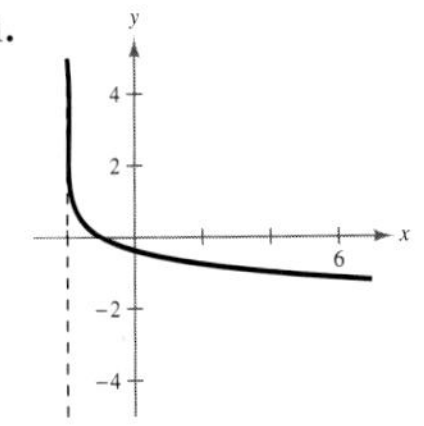

Domain: $(-2, \infty)$
x-intercept: $(-1, 0)$
Vertical asymptote: $x = -2$

43.

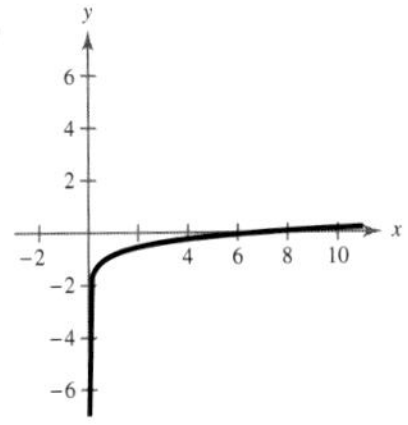

Domain: $(0, \infty)$
x-intercept: $(7, 0)$
Vertical asymptote: $x = 0$

45. c **46.** f **47.** d **48.** e **49.** b **50.** a
51. $e^{-0.693\ldots} = \frac{1}{2}$ **53.** $e^{1.945\ldots} = 7$ **55.** $e^{5.521\ldots} = 250$
57. $e^0 = 1$ **59.** $\ln 54.598\ldots = 4$
61. $\ln 1.6487\ldots = \frac{1}{2}$ **63.** $\ln 0.406\ldots = -0.9$
65. $\ln 4 = x$ **67.** 2.913 **69.** -23.966
71. 5 **73.** $-\frac{5}{6}$

75.

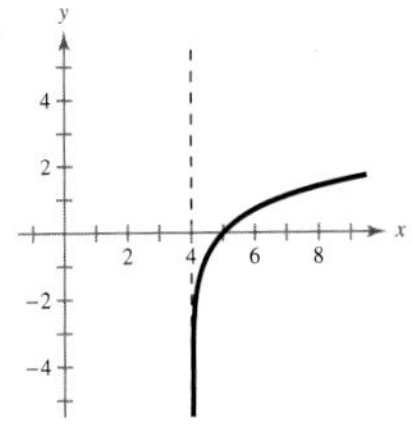

Domain: $(4, \infty)$
x-intercept: $(5, 0)$
Vertical asymptote: $x = 4$

77.

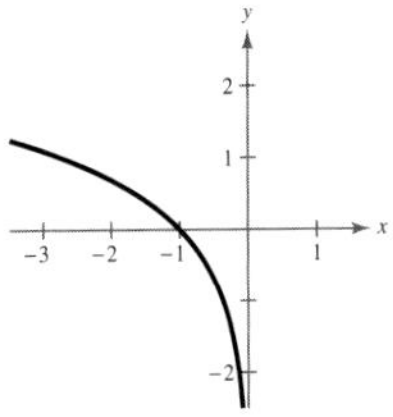

Domain: $(-\infty, 0)$
x-intercept: $(-1, 0)$
Vertical asymptote: $x = 0$

79.

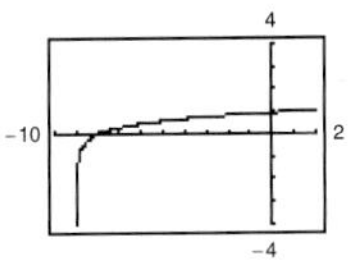

81.

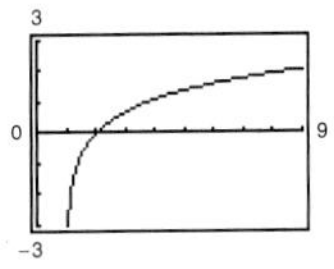

83.

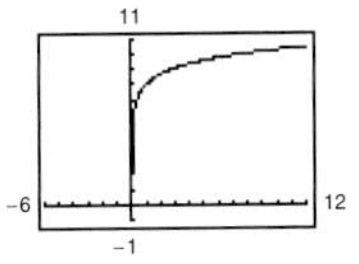

85. $x = 5$ **87.** $x = 7$ **89.** $x = 8$ **91.** $x = -5, 5$
93. (a) 30 yr; 10 yr (b) \$323,179; \$199,109
(c) \$173,179; \$49,109
(d) $x = 750$; The monthly payment must be greater than \$750.

95. (a)

t	1	2	3	4	5	6
C	10.36	9.94	9.37	8.70	7.96	7.15

(b)

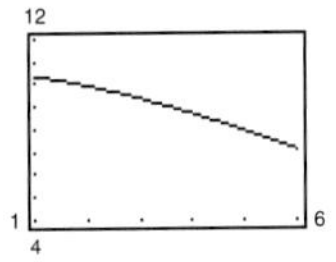

(c) No, the model begins to decrease rapidly, eventually producing negative values.

97. (a)

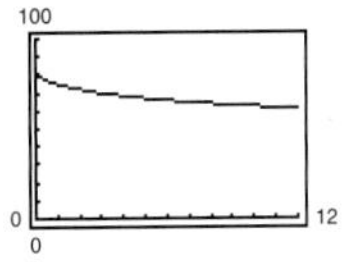

(b) 80 (c) 68.1 (d) 62.3

99. False. Reflecting $g(x)$ about the line $y = x$ will determine the graph of $f(x)$.

101.

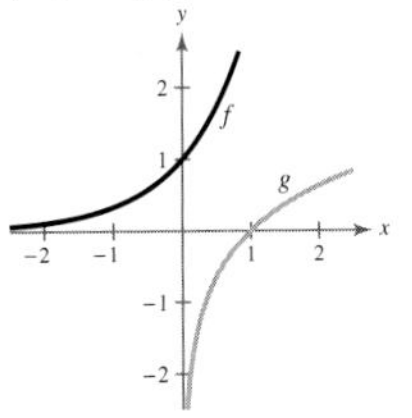

The functions f and g are inverses.

103.

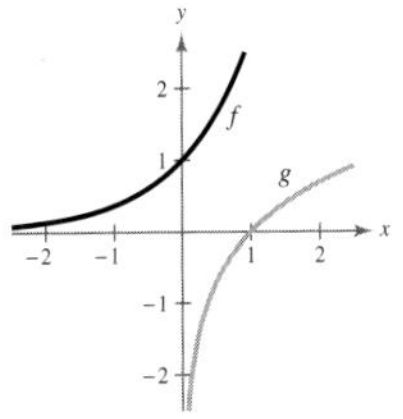

The functions f and g are inverses.

105.

x	-2	-1	0	1	2
$f(x) = 10^x$	$\frac{1}{100}$	$\frac{1}{10}$	1	10	100

x	$\frac{1}{100}$	$\frac{1}{10}$	1	10	100
$f(x) = \log x$	-2	-1	0	1	2

The domain of $f(x) = 10^x$ is equal to the range of $f(x) = \log x$ and vice versa. $f(x) = 10^x$ and $f(x) = \log x$ are inverses of each other.

107. (a)

x	1	5	10	10^2
$f(x)$	0	0.322	0.230	0.046

x	10^4	10^6
$f(x)$	0.00092	0.0000138

(b) 0

(c)

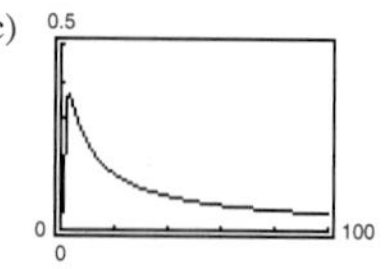

109. Answers will vary.

111. (a)

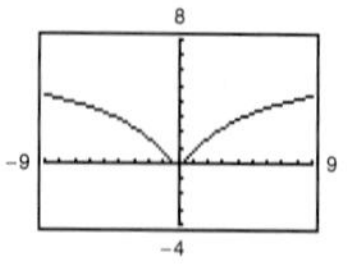

(b) Increasing: $(0, \infty)$
Decreasing: $(-\infty, 0)$

(c) Relative minimum: $(0, 0)$

Section 3.3 *(page 241)*

1. change-of-base **3.** $\dfrac{1}{\log_b a}$ **4.** c **5.** a **6.** b

7. (a) $\dfrac{\log 16}{\log 5}$ (b) $\dfrac{\ln 16}{\ln 5}$ **9.** (a) $\dfrac{\log x}{\log \frac{1}{5}}$ (b) $\dfrac{\ln x}{\ln \frac{1}{5}}$

11. (a) $\dfrac{\log \frac{3}{10}}{\log x}$ (b) $\dfrac{\ln \frac{3}{10}}{\ln x}$ **13.** (a) $\dfrac{\log x}{\log 2.6}$ (b) $\dfrac{\ln x}{\ln 2.6}$

15. 1.771 **17.** -2.000 **19.** -1.048 **21.** 2.633

23. $\frac{3}{2}$ **25.** $-3 - \log_5 2$ **27.** $6 + \ln 5$ **29.** 2

31. $\frac{3}{4}$ **33.** 4 **35.** -2 is not in the domain of $\log_2 x$.

37. 4.5 **39.** $-\frac{1}{2}$ **41.** 7 **43.** 2 **45.** $\ln 4 + \ln x$

47. $4 \log_8 x$ **49.** $1 - \log_5 x$ **51.** $\frac{1}{2} \ln z$

53. $\ln x + \ln y + 2 \ln z$ **55.** $\ln z + 2 \ln(z - 1)$

57. $\frac{1}{2} \log_2(a - 1) - 2 \log_2 3$ **59.** $\frac{1}{3} \ln x - \frac{1}{3} \ln y$

61. $2 \ln x + \frac{1}{2} \ln y - \frac{1}{2} \ln z$

63. $2 \log_5 x - 2 \log_5 y - 3 \log_5 z$

65. $\dfrac{3}{4} \ln x + \dfrac{1}{4} \ln(x^2 + 3)$ **67.** $\ln 2x$ **69.** $\log_4 \dfrac{z}{y}$

71. $\log_2 x^2 y^4$ **73.** $\log_3 \sqrt[4]{5x}$ **75.** $\log \dfrac{x}{(x + 1)^2}$

77. $\log \dfrac{xz^3}{y^2}$ **79.** $\ln \dfrac{x}{(x + 1)(x - 1)}$

81. $\ln \sqrt[3]{\dfrac{x(x + 3)^2}{x^2 - 1}}$ **83.** $\log_8 \dfrac{\sqrt[3]{y}(y + 4)^2}{y - 1}$

85. $\log_2 \frac{32}{4} = \log_2 32 - \log_2 4$; Property 2

87. $\beta = 10(\log I + 12)$; 60 dB **89.** 70 dB

91. $\ln y = \frac{1}{4} \ln x$ **93.** $\ln y = -\frac{1}{4} \ln x + \ln \frac{5}{2}$

95. $y = 256.24 - 20.8 \ln x$

97. (a) and (b)

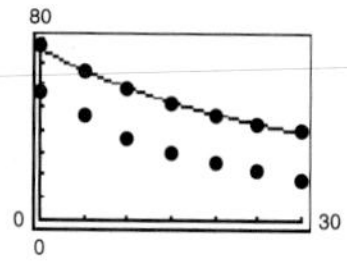

(c)

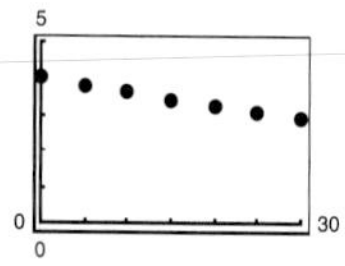

$T = 21 + e^{-0.037t + 3.997}$

The results are similar.

(d)

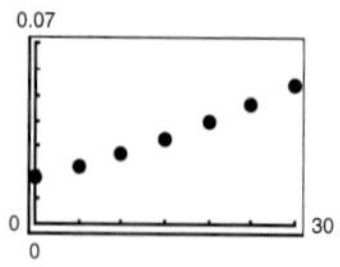

$T = 21 + \dfrac{1}{0.001t + 0.016}$

(e) Answers will vary.

99. Proof

101. False; $\ln 1 = 0$ **103.** False; $\ln(x - 2) \neq \ln x - \ln 2$

105. False; $u = v^2$

107. $f(x) = \dfrac{\log x}{\log 2} = \dfrac{\ln x}{\ln 2}$

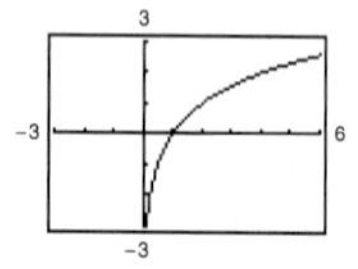

109. $f(x) = \dfrac{\log x}{\log \frac{1}{2}} = \dfrac{\ln x}{\ln \frac{1}{2}}$

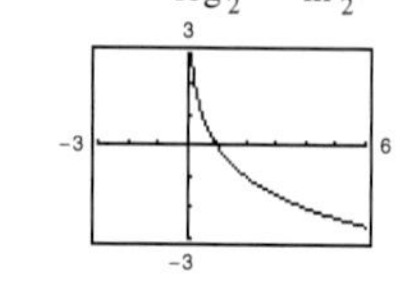

111. $f(x) = \dfrac{\log x}{\log 11.8} = \dfrac{\ln x}{\ln 11.8}$

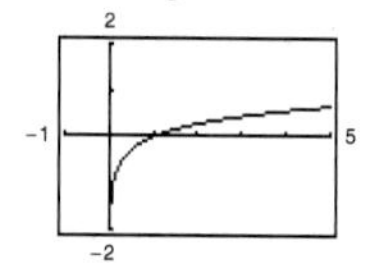

113. $f(x) = h(x)$; Property 2

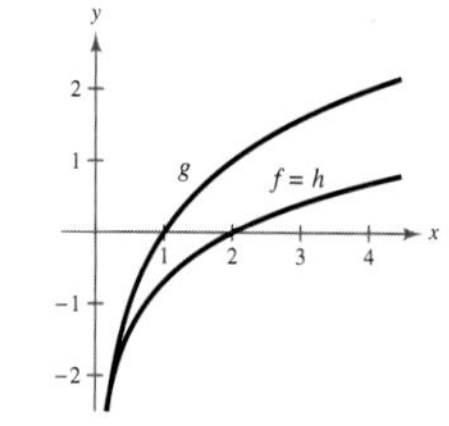

115.

$\ln 1 = 0$	$\ln 9 \approx 2.1972$
$\ln 2 \approx 0.6931$	$\ln 10 \approx 2.3025$
$\ln 3 \approx 1.0986$	$\ln 12 \approx 2.4848$
$\ln 4 \approx 1.3862$	$\ln 15 \approx 2.7080$
$\ln 5 \approx 1.6094$	$\ln 16 \approx 2.7724$
$\ln 6 \approx 1.7917$	$\ln 18 \approx 2.8903$
$\ln 8 \approx 2.0793$	$\ln 20 \approx 2.9956$

Section 3.4 *(page 251)*

1. solve

3. (a) One-to-One (b) logarithmic; logarithmic
(c) exponential; exponential

5. (a) Yes (b) No

7. (a) No (b) Yes (c) Yes, approximate

9. (a) Yes, approximate (b) No (c) Yes

11. (a) No (b) Yes (c) Yes, approximate

13. 2 **15.** -5 **17.** 2 **19.** $\ln 2 \approx 0.693$

21. $e^{-1} \approx 0.368$ **23.** 64 **25.** (3, 8) **27.** (9, 2)

29. 2, −1 **31.** About 1.618, about −0.618

33. $\frac{\ln 5}{\ln 3} \approx 1.465$ **35.** $\ln 5 \approx 1.609$ **37.** $\ln 28 \approx 3.332$

39. $\frac{\ln 80}{2 \ln 3} \approx 1.994$ **41.** 2 **43.** 4

45. $3 - \frac{\ln 565}{\ln 2} \approx -6.142$ **47.** $\frac{1}{3}\log\left(\frac{3}{2}\right) \approx 0.059$

49. $1 + \frac{\ln 7}{\ln 5} \approx 2.209$ **51.** $\frac{\ln 12}{3} \approx 0.828$

53. $-\ln \frac{3}{5} \approx 0.511$ **55.** 0 **57.** $\frac{\ln \frac{8}{3}}{3 \ln 2} + \frac{1}{3} \approx 0.805$

59. $\ln 5 \approx 1.609$ **61.** $\ln 4 \approx 1.386$

63. $2 \ln 75 \approx 8.635$ **65.** $\frac{1}{2} \ln 1498 \approx 3.656$

67. $\frac{\ln 4}{365 \ln\left(1 + \frac{0.065}{365}\right)} \approx 21.330$ **69.** $\frac{\ln 2}{12 \ln\left(1 + \frac{0.10}{12}\right)} \approx 6.960$

71.

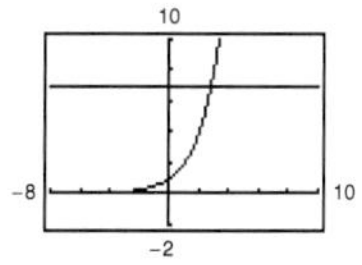

2.807

73.

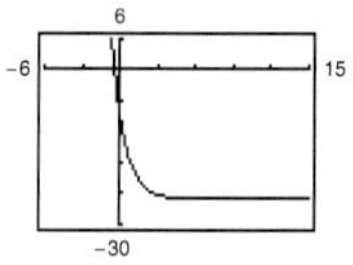

−0.427

75.

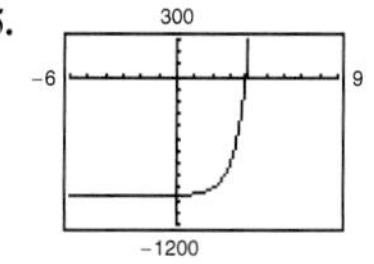

3.847

77.

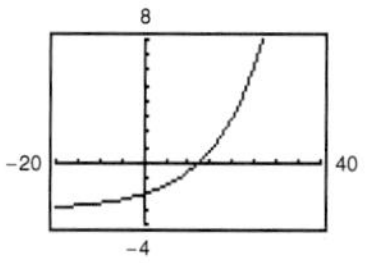

12.207

79.

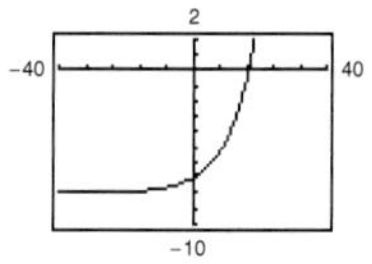

16.636

81. $e^{-3} \approx 0.050$ **83.** $e^{7} \approx 1096.633$ **85.** $\frac{e^{2.4}}{2} \approx 5.512$

87. 1,000,000 **89.** $\frac{e^{10/3}}{5} \approx 5.606$

91. $e^2 - 2 \approx 5.389$ **93.** $e^{-2/3} \approx 0.513$

95. $\frac{e^{19/2}}{3} \approx 4453.242$ **97.** $2(3^{11/6}) \approx 14.988$

99. No solution **101.** $1 + \sqrt{1 + e} \approx 2.928$

103. No solution **105.** 7 **107.** $\frac{-1 + \sqrt{17}}{2} \approx 1.562$

109. 2 **111.** $\frac{725 + 125\sqrt{33}}{8} \approx 180.384$

113.

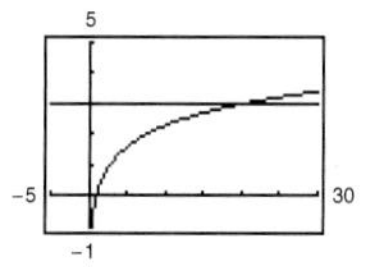

20.086

115.

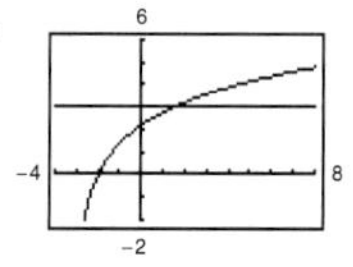

1.482

117. (a) 13.86 yr (b) 21.97 yr

119. (a) 27.73 yr (b) 43.94 yr

121. −1, 0 **123.** 1 **125.** $e^{-1/2} \approx 0.607$

127. $e^{-1} \approx 0.368$ **129.** (a) 210 coins (b) 588 coins

131. (a)

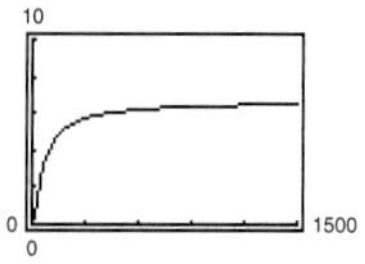

(b) $V = 6.7$; The yield will approach 6.7 million cubic feet per acre.

(c) 29.3 yr

133. 2003

135. (a) $y = 100$ and $y = 0$; The range falls between 0% and 100%.

(b) Males: 69.71 in. Females: 64.51 in.

137. (a)

x	0.2	0.4	0.6	0.8	1.0
y	162.6	78.5	52.5	40.5	33.9

(b)

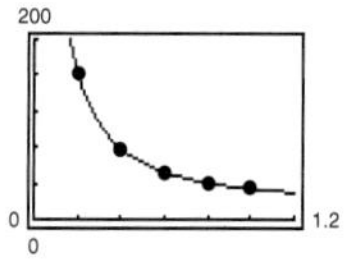

The model appears to fit the data well.

(c) 1.2 m

(d) No. According to the model, when the number of g's is less than 23, x is between 2.276 meters and 4.404 meters, which isn't realistic in most vehicles.

139. $\log_b uv = \log_b u + \log_b v$

True by Property 1 in Section 3.3.

141. $\log_b(u - v) = \log_b u - \log_b v$

False

$1.95 \approx \log(100 - 10) \neq \log 100 - \log 10 = 1$

143. Yes. See Exercise 103.

145. Yes. Time to double: $t = \frac{\ln 2}{r}$;

Time to quadruple: $t = \frac{\ln 4}{r} = 2\left(\frac{\ln 2}{r}\right)$

147. (a)

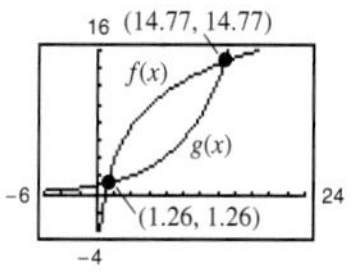

(b) $a = e^{1/e}$

(c) $1 < a < e^{1/e}$

Section 3.5 *(page 262)*

1. $y = ae^{bx}$; $y = ae^{-bx}$ **3.** normally distributed

5. $y = \frac{a}{1 + be^{-rx}}$ **7.** c **8.** e **9.** b

10. a **11.** d **12.** f

CHAPTER 3

13. (a) $P = \dfrac{A}{e^{rt}}$ (b) $t = \dfrac{\ln\left(\dfrac{A}{P}\right)}{r}$

	Initial Investment	*Annual % Rate*	*Time to Double*	*Amount After 10 years*
15.	\$1000	3.5%	19.8 yr	\$1419.07
17.	\$750	8.9438%	7.75 yr	\$1834.37
19.	\$500	11.0%	6.3 yr	\$1505.00
21.	\$6376.28	4.5%	15.4 yr	\$10,000.00

23. \$303,580.52

25. (a) 7.27 yr (b) 6.96 yr (c) 6.93 yr (d) 6.93 yr

27.

r	2%	4%	6%	8%	10%	12%
t	54.93	27.47	18.31	13.73	10.99	9.16

29.

r	2%	4%	6%	8%	10%	12%
t	55.48	28.01	18.85	14.27	11.53	9.69

31.

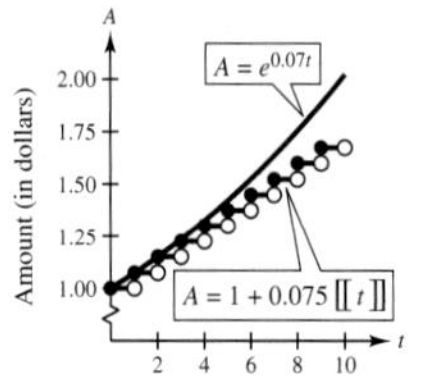

Continuous compounding

	Half-life (years)	*Initial Quantity*	*Amount After 1000 Years*
33.	1599	10 g	6.48 g
35.	24,100	2.1 g	2.04 g
37.	5715	2.26 g	2 g

39. $y = e^{0.7675x}$ **41.** $y = 5e^{-0.4024x}$

43. (a)

Year	1970	1980	1990	2000	2007
Population	73.7	103.74	143.56	196.35	243.24

(b) 2014

(c) No; The population will not continue to grow at such a quick rate.

45. $k = 0.2988$; About 5,309,734 hits

47. (a) $k = 0.02603$; The population is increasing because $k > 0$.
(b) 449,910; 512,447 (c) 2014

49. About 800 bacteria

51. (a) About 12,180 yr old (b) About 4797 yr old

53. (a) $V = -5400t + 23,300$ (b) $V = 23,300e^{-0.311t}$

(c)

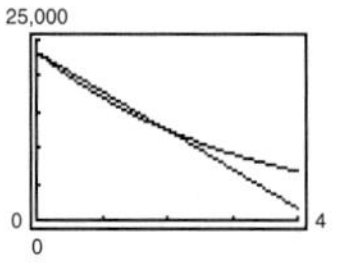

The exponential model depreciates faster.

(d)

t	1 yr	3 yr
$V = -5400t + 23,300$	17,900	7100
$V = 23,300e^{-0.311t}$	17,072	9166

(e) Answers will vary.

55. (a) $S(t) = 100(1 - e^{-0.1625t})$

(b)

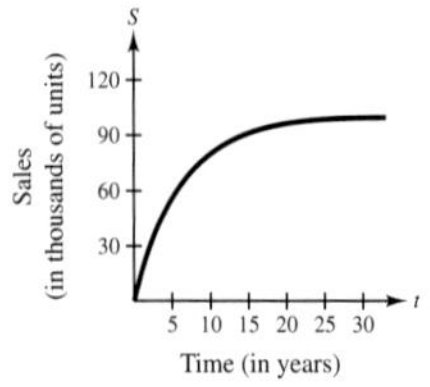

(c) 55,625

57. (a)

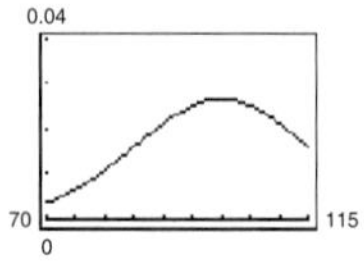

(b) 100

59. (a) 715; 90,880; 199,043

(b)

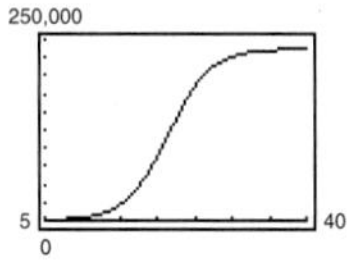

(c) 2014

(d) $235,000 = \dfrac{237,101}{1 + 1950e^{-0.355t}}$

$t \approx 34.63$

61. (a) 203 animals (b) 13 mo

(c)

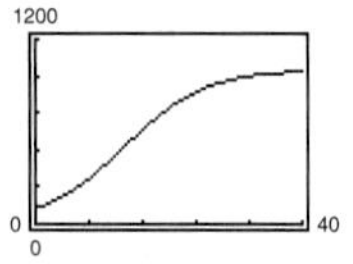

Horizontal asymptotes: $p = 0$, $p = 1000$. The population size will approach 1000 as time increases.

63. (a) $10^{8.5} \approx 316,227,766$ (b) $10^{5.4} \approx 251,189$
(c) $10^{6.1} \approx 1,258,925$

65. (a) 20 dB (b) 70 dB (c) 40 dB (d) 120 dB

67. 95% **69.** 4.64 **71.** 1.58×10^{-6} moles/L

73. $10^{5.1}$ **75.** 3:00 A.M.

77. (a)

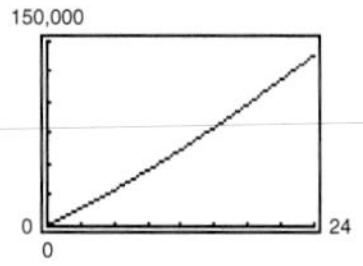

(b) $t \approx 21$ yr; Yes

79. False. The domain can be the set of real numbers for a logistic growth function.

81. False. The graph of $f(x)$ is the graph of $g(x)$ shifted upward five units.

83. Answers will vary.

Review Exercises *(page 270)*

1. 0.164 **3.** 0.337 **5.** 1456.529

7. Shift the graph of f two units downward.

9. Reflect f in the y-axis and shift two units to the right.

11. Reflect f in the x-axis and shift one unit upward.

13. Reflect f in the x-axis and shift two units to the left.

15.

x	-1	0	1	2	3
$f(x)$	8	5	4.25	4.063	4.016

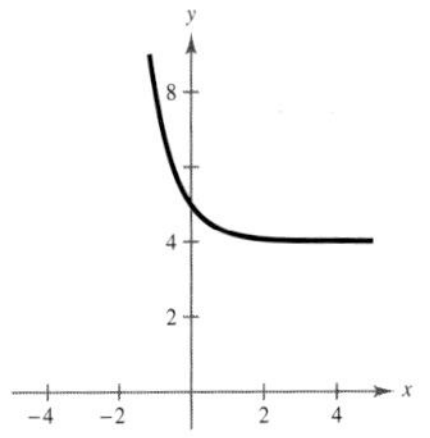

17.

x	-1	0	1	2	3
$f(x)$	4.008	4.04	4.2	5	9

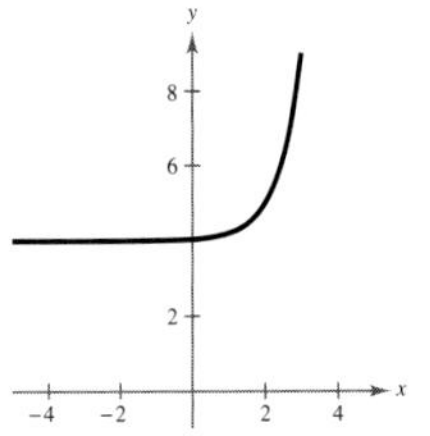

19.

x	-2	-1	0	1	2
$f(x)$	3.25	3.5	4	5	7

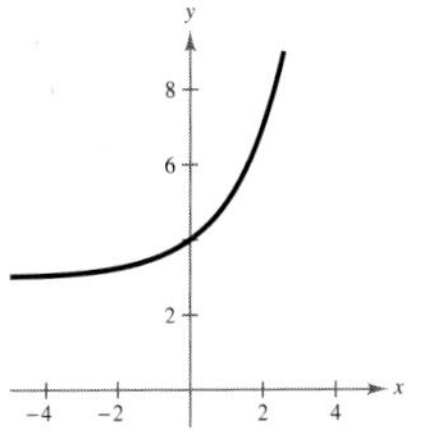

21. $x = 1$ **23.** $x = 4$ **25.** 2980.958 **27.** 0.183

29.

x	-2	-1	0	1	2
$h(x)$	2.72	1.65	1	0.61	0.37

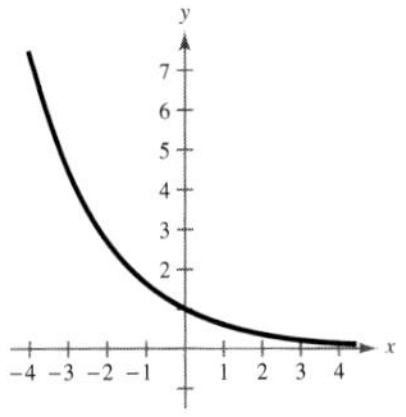

31.

x	-3	-2	-1	0	1
$f(x)$	0.37	1	2.72	7.39	20.09

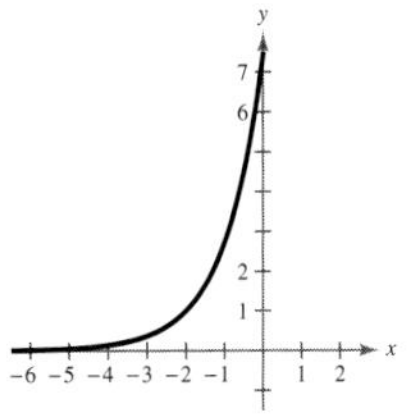

33.

n	1	2	4	12
A	\$6719.58	\$6734.28	\$6741.74	\$6746.77

n	365	Continuous
A	\$6749.21	\$6749.29

35. (a) 0.154 (b) 0.487 (c) 0.811

37. $\log_3 27 = 3$ **39.** $\ln 2.2255 \ldots = 0.8$

41. 3 **43.** -2 **45.** $x = 7$ **47.** $x = -5$

49. Domain: $(0, \infty)$
x-intercept: $(1, 0)$
Vertical asymptote: $x = 0$

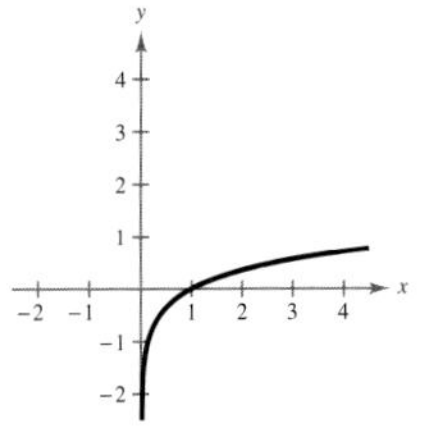

51. Domain: $(-5, \infty)$
x-intercept: $(9995, 0)$
Vertical asymptote: $x = -5$

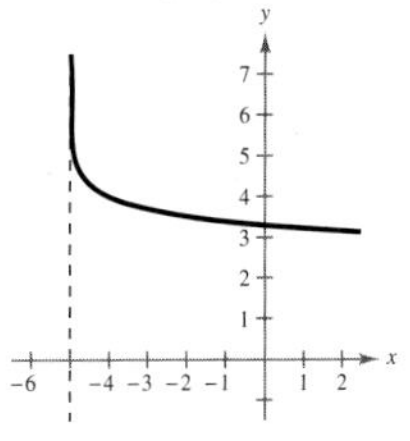

53. (a) 3.118 (b) -0.020

55. Domain: $(0, \infty)$
x-intercept: $(e^{-3}, 0)$
Vertical asymptote: $x = 0$

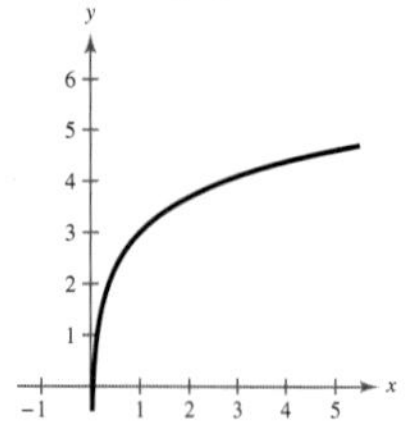

57. Domain: $(-\infty, 0), (0, \infty)$
x-intercept: $(\pm 1, 0)$
Vertical asymptote: $x = 0$

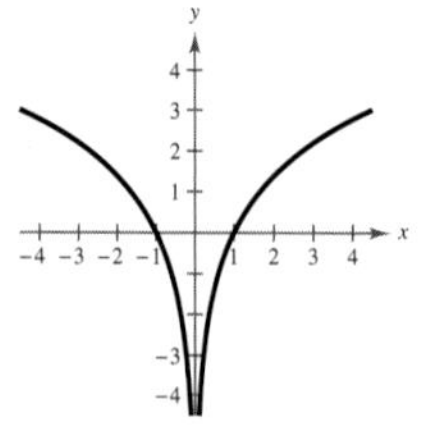

59. 53.4 in. **61.** 2.585 **63.** -2.322
65. $\log 2 + 2 \log 3 \approx 1.255$ **67.** $2 \ln 2 + \ln 5 \approx 2.996$
69. $1 + 2 \log_5 x$ **71.** $2 - \frac{1}{2} \log_3 x$
73. $2 \ln x + 2 \ln y + \ln z$ **75.** $\log_2 5x$ **77.** $\ln \frac{x}{\sqrt[4]{y}}$
79. $\log_3 \frac{\sqrt{x}}{(y + 8)^2}$
81. (a) $0 \le h < 18{,}000$
(b)

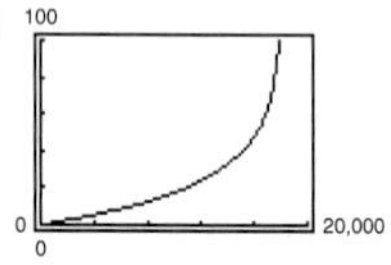

Vertical asymptote: $h = 18{,}000$
(c) The plane is climbing at a slower rate, so the time required increases.
(d) 5.46 min
83. 3 **85.** $\ln 3 \approx 1.099$ **87.** $e^4 \approx 54.598$
89. $x = 1, 3$ **91.** $\frac{\ln 32}{\ln 2} = 5$
93.

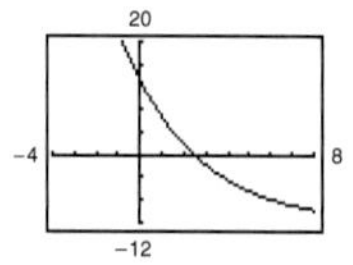

2.447

95. $\frac{1}{3}e^{8.2} \approx 1213.650$ **97.** $3e^2 \approx 22.167$
99. $e^8 \approx 2980.958$ **101.** No solution **103.** 0.900
105.

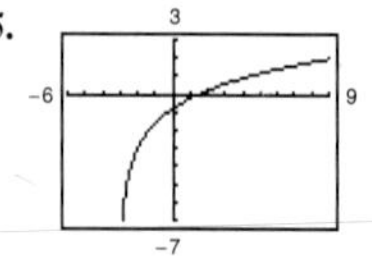

1.482

107.

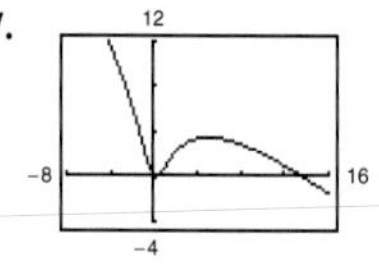

0, 0.416, 13.627

109. 31.4 yr **111.** e **112.** b **113.** f **114.** d
115. a **116.** c **117.** $y = 2e^{0.1014x}$
119. (a)

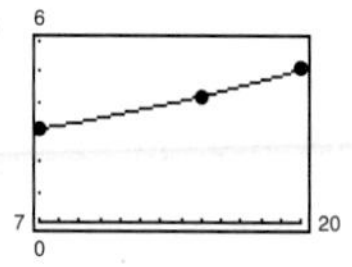

The model fits the data well.
(b) 2022; Answers will vary.
121. (a)

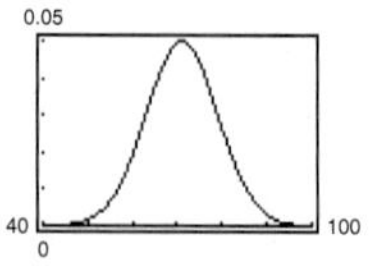

(b) 71
123. (a) $10^{-6}\ \text{W/m}^2$ (b) $10\sqrt{10}\ \text{W/m}^2$
(c) $1.259 \times 10^{-12}\ \text{W/m}^2$
125. True by the inverse properties

Chapter Test *(page 273)*

1. 2.366 **2.** 687.291 **3.** 0.497 **4.** 22.198
5.

x	-1	$-\frac{1}{2}$	0	$\frac{1}{2}$	1
$f(x)$	10	3.162	1	0.316	0.1

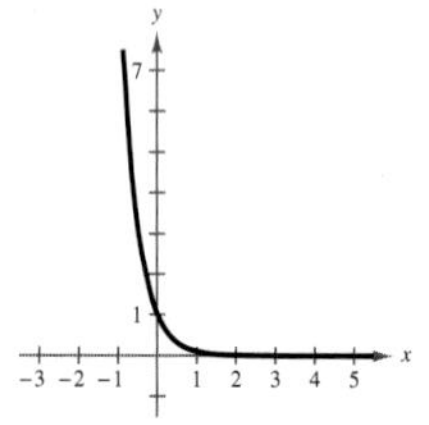

6.

x	-1	0	1	2	3
$f(x)$	-0.005	-0.028	-0.167	-1	-6

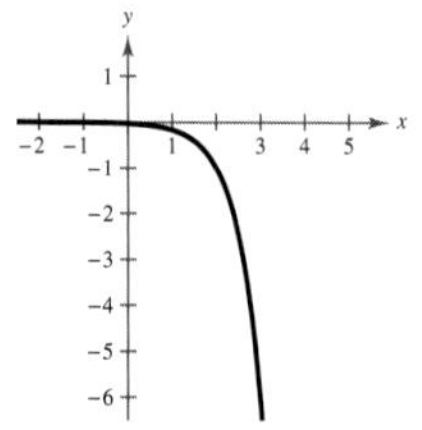

7.

x	-1	$-\frac{1}{2}$	0	$\frac{1}{2}$	1
$f(x)$	0.865	0.632	0	-1.718	-6.389

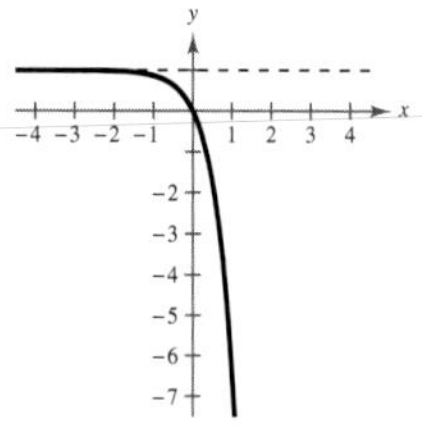

8. (a) -0.89 (b) 9.2

9.

x	$\frac{1}{2}$	1	$\frac{3}{2}$	2	4
$f(x)$	-5.699	-6	-6.176	-6.301	-6.602

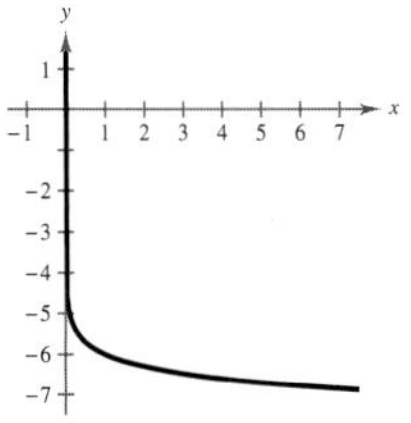

Vertical asymptote: $x = 0$

10.

x	5	7	9	11	13
$f(x)$	0	1.099	1.609	1.946	2.197

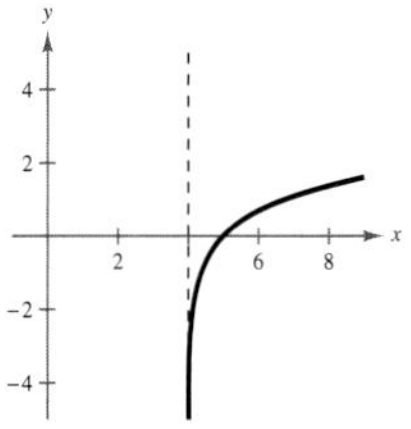

Vertical asymptote: $x = 4$

11.

x	-5	-3	-1	0	1
$f(x)$	1	2.099	2.609	2.792	2.946

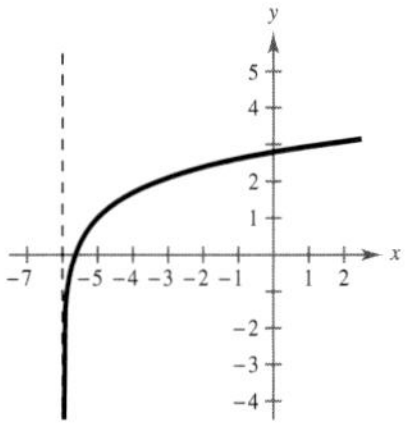

Vertical asymptote: $x = -6$

12. 1.945 **13.** -0.167 **14.** -11.047

15. $\log_2 3 + 4 \log_2 |a|$ **16.** $\ln 5 + \frac{1}{2}\ln x - \ln 6$

17. $3 \log(x - 1) - 2 \log y - \log z$ **18.** $\log_3 13y$

19. $\ln \dfrac{x^4}{y^4}$ **20.** $\ln\left(\dfrac{x^3y^2}{x + 3}\right)$ **21.** $x = -2$

22. $x = \dfrac{\ln 44}{-5} \approx -0.757$ **23.** $\dfrac{\ln 197}{4} \approx 1.321$

24. $e^{1/2} \approx 1.649$ **25.** $e^{-11/4} \approx 0.0639$ **26.** 20

27. $y = 2745e^{0.1570t}$ **28.** 55%

29. (a)

x	$\frac{1}{4}$	1	2	4	5	6
H	58.720	75.332	86.828	103.43	110.59	117.38

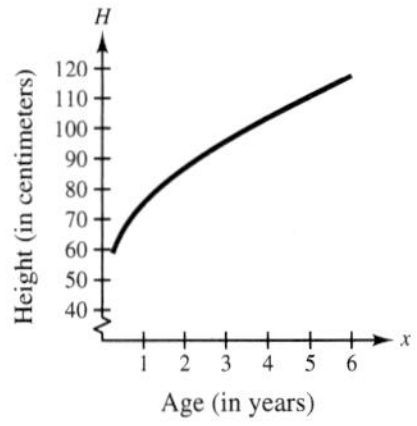

(b) 103 cm; 103.43 cm

Cumulative Test for Chapters 1–3 *(page 274)*

1.

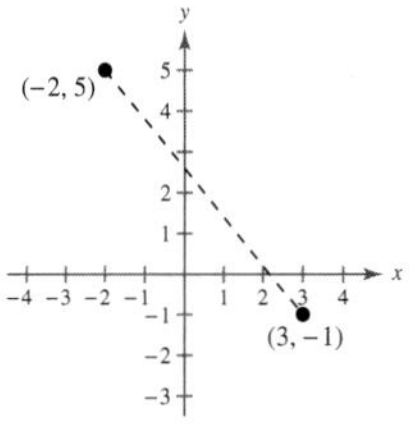

Midpoint: $\left(\frac{1}{2}, 2\right)$; Distance: $\sqrt{61}$

2.

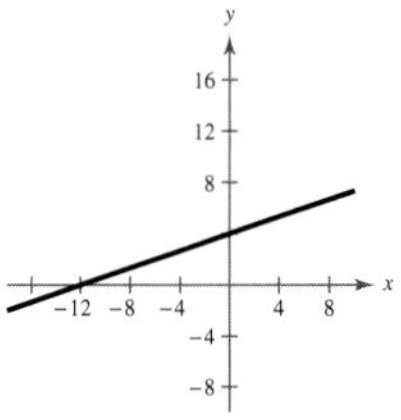

3.

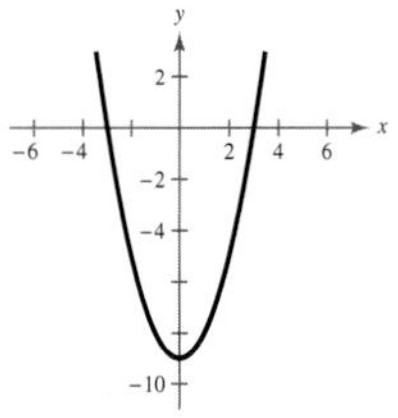

4.

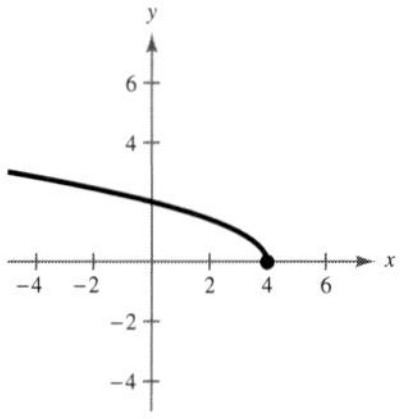

5. $y = 2x + 2$

6. For some values of x there correspond two values of y.

7. (a) $\dfrac{3}{2}$ (b) Division by 0 is undefined. (c) $\dfrac{s + 2}{s}$

8. (a) Vertical shrink by $\frac{1}{2}$
(b) Vertical shift two units upward
(c) Horizontal shift two units to the left

9. (a) $5x - 2$ (b) $-3x - 4$ (c) $4x^2 - 11x - 3$
(d) $\dfrac{x - 3}{4x + 1}$; Domain: all real numbers x except $x = -\dfrac{1}{4}$

10. (a) $\sqrt{x-1} + x^2 + 1$ (b) $\sqrt{x-1} - x^2 - 1$
(c) $x^2\sqrt{x-1} + \sqrt{x-1}$
(d) $\dfrac{\sqrt{x-1}}{x^2+1}$; Domain: all real numbers x such that $x \geq 1$

11. (a) $2x + 12$ (b) $\sqrt{2x^2 + 6}$
Domain of $f \circ g$: all real numbers x such that $x \geq -6$
Domain of $g \circ f$: all real numbers

12. (a) $|x| - 2$ (b) $|x - 2|$
Domain of $f \circ g$ and $g \circ f$: all real numbers

13. Yes; $h^{-1}(x) = -\frac{1}{5}(x - 3)$ **14.** 2438.65 kW

15. $y = -\frac{3}{4}(x + 8)^2 + 5$

16.

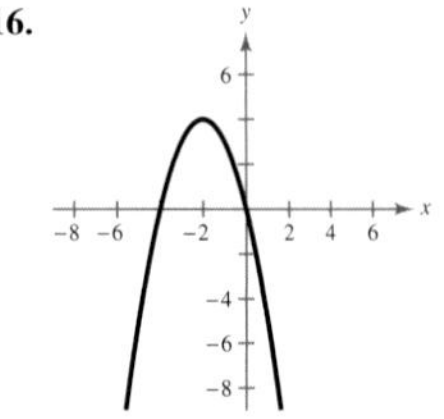

17.

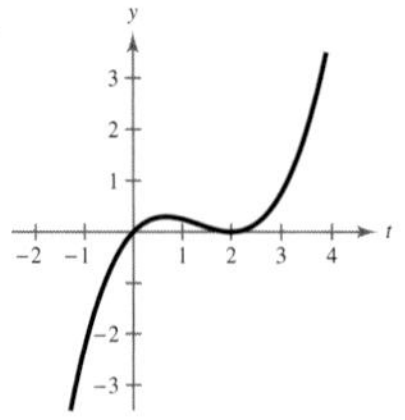

18.

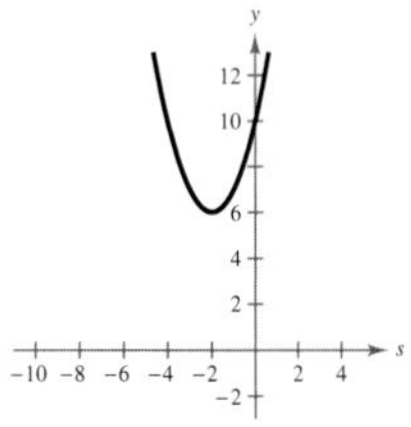

19. $-2, \pm 2i$; $(x + 2)(x + 2i)(x - 2i)$

20. $-7, 0, 3$; $x(x)(x - 3)(x + 7)$

21. $4, -\frac{1}{2}, 1 \pm 3i$; $(x - 4)(2x + 1)(x - 1 + 3i)(x - 1 - 3i)$

22. $3x - 2 - \dfrac{3x - 2}{2x^2 + 1}$ **23.** $3x^3 + 6x^2 + 14x + 23 + \dfrac{49}{x - 2}$

24.

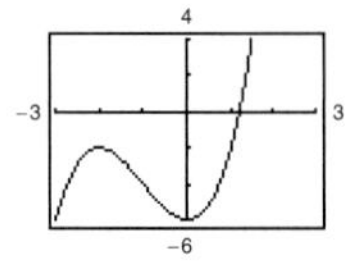

Interval: $[1, 2]$; 1.20

25. Intercept: $(0, 0)$
Vertical asymptotes: $x = -3, x = 1$
Horizontal asymptote: $y = 0$

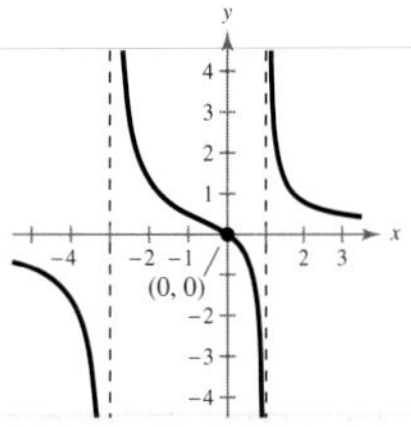

26. y-intercept: $(0, 2)$
x-intercept: $(2, 0)$
Vertical asymptote: $x = 1$
Horizontal asymptote: $y = 1$

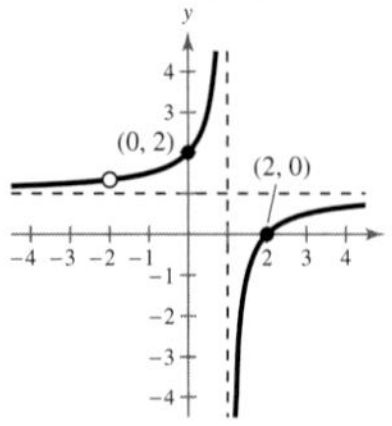

27. y-intercept: $(0, 6)$
x-intercepts: $(2, 0), (3, 0)$
Vertical asymptote: $x = -1$
Slant asymptote: $y = x - 6$

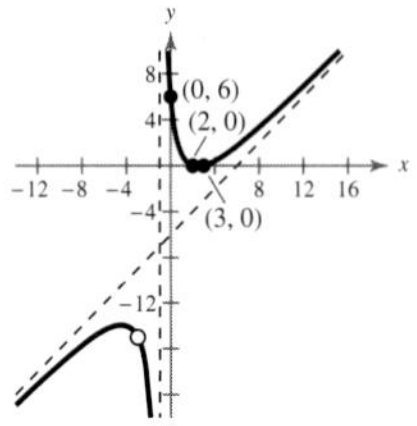

28. $x \leq -3$ or $0 \leq x \leq 3$

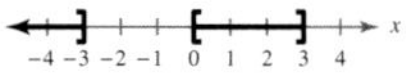

29. All real numbers x such that $x < -5$ or $x > -1$

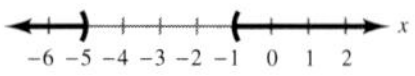

30. Reflect f in the x-axis and y-axis, and shift three units to the right.

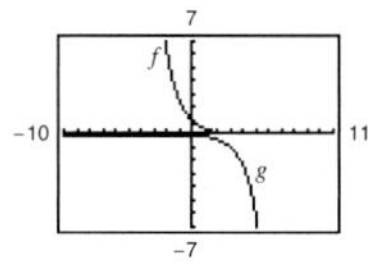

31. Reflect f in the x-axis, and shift four units upward.

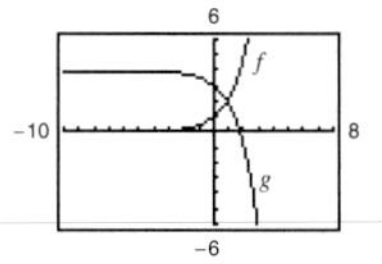

32. 1.991 **33.** -0.067 **34.** 1.717 **35.** 0.281

36. $\ln(x + 4) + \ln(x - 4) - 4 \ln x, x > 4$

37. $\ln \dfrac{x^2}{\sqrt{x + 5}}, x > 0$ **38.** $x = \dfrac{\ln 12}{2} \approx 1.242$

39. $\ln 6 \approx 1.792$ or $\ln 7 \approx 1.946$ **40.** $e^6 - 2 \approx 401.429$

41. (a)
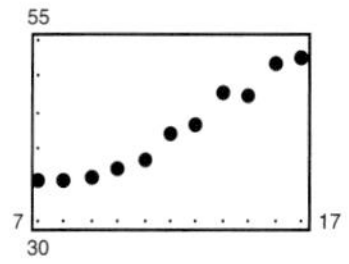

(b) $S = -0.0297t^3 + 1.175t^2 - 12.96t + 79.0$

(c)
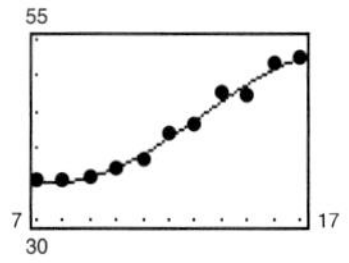

The model is a good fit for the data.

(d) \$25.3 billion; Answers will vary. Sample answer: No, this is not reasonable because the model decreases sharply after 2009.

42. 6.3 h

Problem Solving *(page 277)*

1.
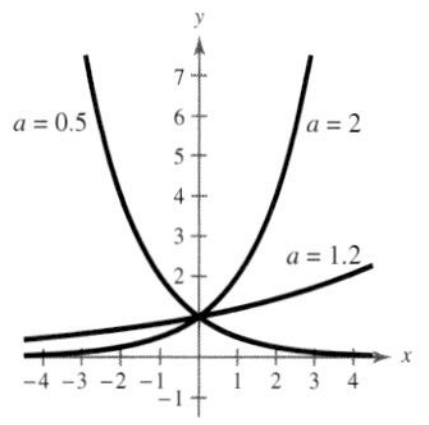

$y = 0.5^x$ and $y = 1.2^x$

$0 < a \le e^{1/e}$

3. As $x \to \infty$, the graph of e^x increases at a greater rate than the graph of x^n.

5. Answers will vary.

7. (a)
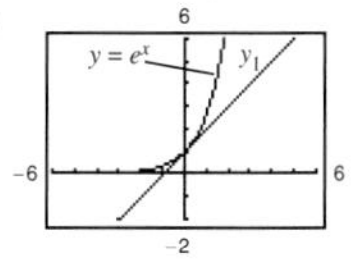

(b)
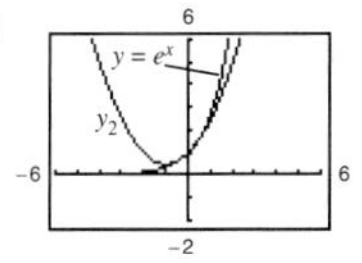

(c)
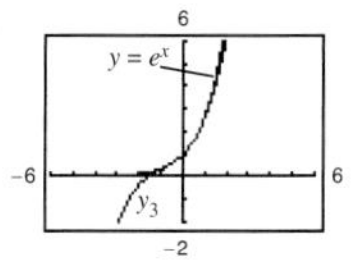

9.
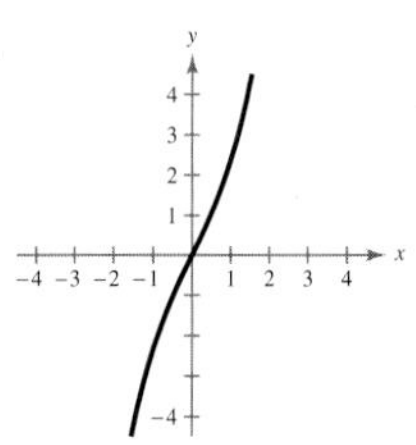

$f^{-1}(x) = \ln\left(\dfrac{x + \sqrt{x^2 + 4}}{2}\right)$

11. c **13.** $t = \dfrac{\ln c_1 - \ln c_2}{\left(\dfrac{1}{k_2} - \dfrac{1}{k_1}\right)\ln\dfrac{1}{2}}$

15. (a) $y_1 = 252{,}606(1.0310)^t$

(b) $y_2 = 400.88t^2 - 1464.6t + 291{,}782$

(c)
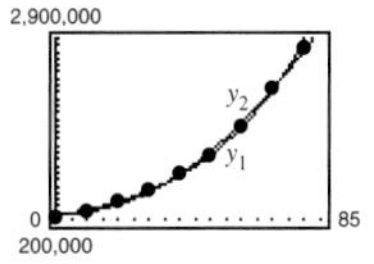

(d) The exponential model is a better fit. No, because the model is rapidly approaching infinity.

17. $1, e^2$

19. $y_4 = (x - 1) - \frac{1}{2}(x - 1)^2 + \frac{1}{3}(x - 1)^3 - \frac{1}{4}(x - 1)^4$

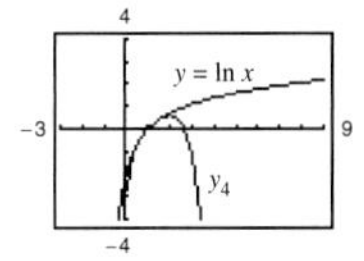

The pattern implies that

$\ln x = (x - 1) - \frac{1}{2}(x - 1)^2 + \frac{1}{3}(x - 1)^3 - \cdots.$

21.
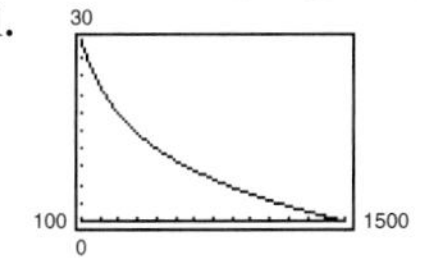

$17.7 \text{ ft}^3/\text{min}$

23. (a)
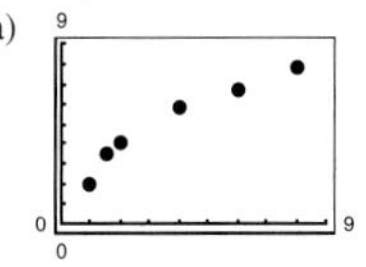

(b)–(e) Answers will vary.

25. (a)
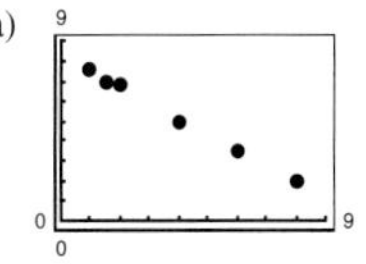

(b)–(e) Answers will vary.

Chapter 4

Section 4.1 *(page 288)*

1. Trigonometry **3.** coterminal **5.** acute; obtuse
7. degree **9.** linear; angular **11.** 1 rad **13.** 5.5 rad
15. -3 rad
17. (a) Quadrant I (b) Quadrant III
19. (a) Quadrant IV (b) Quadrant IV
21. (a) Quadrant III (b) Quadrant II

23. (a)
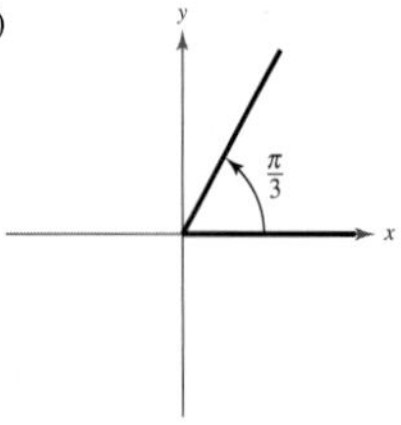

(b)
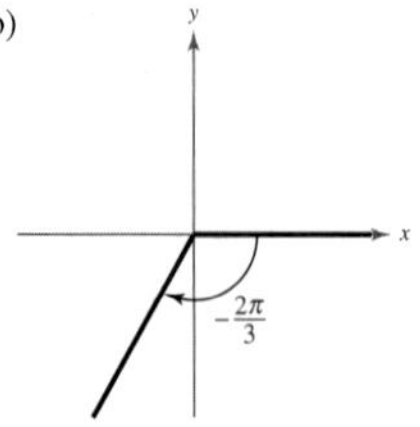

25. (a)
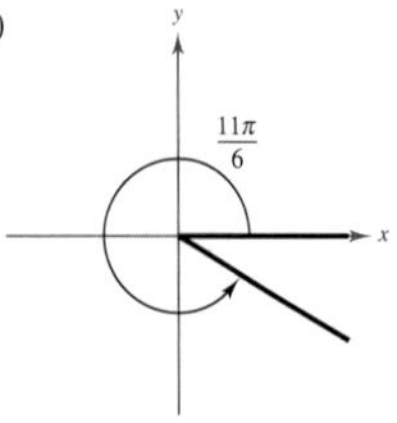

(b)
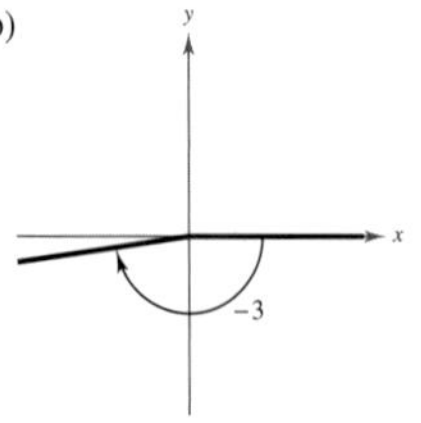

27. Sample answers: (a) $\frac{13\pi}{6}, -\frac{11\pi}{6}$ (b) $\frac{17\pi}{6}, -\frac{7\pi}{6}$

29. Sample answers: (a) $\frac{8\pi}{3}, -\frac{4\pi}{3}$ (b) $\frac{25\pi}{12}, -\frac{23\pi}{12}$

31. (a) Complement: $\frac{\pi}{6}$; Supplement: $\frac{2\pi}{3}$
(b) Complement: $\frac{\pi}{4}$; Supplement: $\frac{3\pi}{4}$

33. (a) Complement: $\frac{\pi}{2} - 1 \approx 0.57$;
Supplement: $\pi - 1 \approx 2.14$
(b) Complement: none; Supplement: $\pi - 2 \approx 1.14$

35. $210°$ **37.** $-60°$ **39.** $165°$

41. (a) Quadrant II (b) Quadrant IV

43. (a) Quadrant III (b) Quadrant I

45. (a)
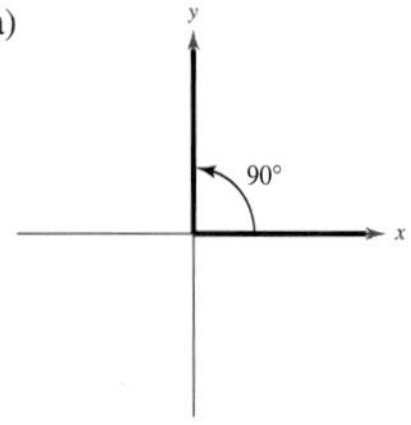

(b)
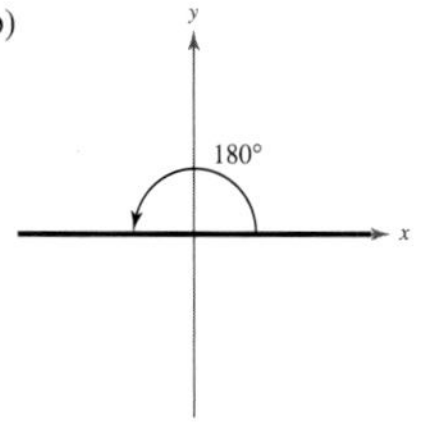

47. (a)
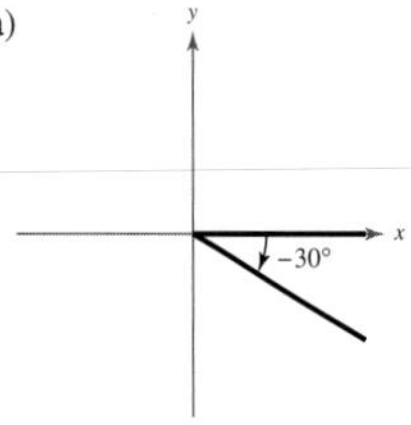

(b)
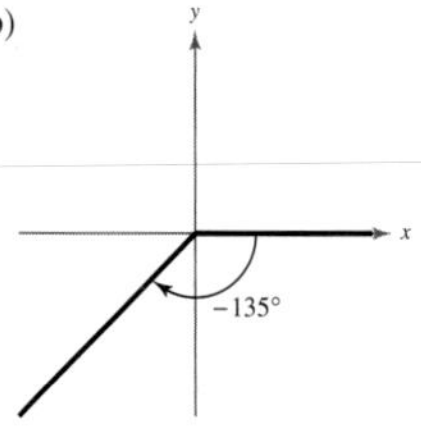

49. Sample answers: (a) $405°, -315°$ (b) $324°, -396°$

51. Sample answers: (a) $600°, -120°$ (b) $180°, -540°$

53. (a) Complement: 72°; Supplement: 162°
(b) Complement: 5°; Supplement: 95°

55. (a) Complement: none; Supplement: 30°
(b) Complement: 11°; Supplement: 101°

57. (a) $\frac{\pi}{6}$ (b) $\frac{\pi}{4}$ **59.** (a) $-\frac{\pi}{9}$ (b) $-\frac{\pi}{3}$

61. (a) 270° (b) 210° **63.** (a) 225° (b) $-420°$

65. 0.785 **67.** -3.776 **69.** 9.285 **71.** -0.014

73. 25.714° **75.** 337.500° **77.** $-756.000°$

79. $-114.592°$ **81.** (a) 54.75° (b) $-128.5°$

83. (a) 85.308° (b) 330.007°

85. (a) $240° 36'$ (b) $-145° 48'$

87. (a) $2° 30'$ (b) $-3° 34' 48''$ **89.** 10π in. ≈ 31.42 in.

91. 2.5π m ≈ 7.85 m **93.** $\frac{9}{2}$ rad **95.** $\frac{21}{50}$ rad **97.** $\frac{1}{2}$ rad

99. 4 rad **101.** 6π in.$^2 \approx 18.85$ in.^{2} **103.** 12.27 ft^2

105. 591.3 mi **107.** 0.071 rad $\approx 4.04°$ **109.** $\frac{5}{12}$ rad

111. (a) $10{,}000\pi$ rad/min $\approx 31{,}415.93$ rad/min
(b) 9490.23 ft/min

113. (a) $[400\pi, 1000\pi]$ rad/min (b) $[2400\pi, 6000\pi]$ cm/min

115. (a) 910.37 revolutions/min (b) 5720 rad/min

117.
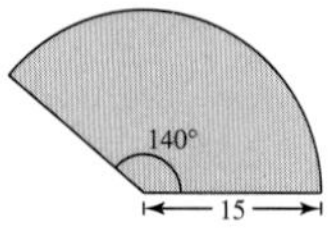

$A = 87.5\pi$ m$^2 \approx 274.89$ m^2

119. (a) $\frac{14\pi}{3}$ ft/sec ≈ 10 mi/h (b) $d = \frac{7\pi}{7920}n$
(c) $d = \frac{7\pi}{7920}t$ (d) The functions are both linear.

121. False. A measurement of 4π radians corresponds to two complete revolutions from the initial side to the terminal side of an angle.

123. False. The terminal side of the angle lies on the *x*-axis.

125. Radian. 1 rad $\approx 57.3°$

127. Proof

Section 4.2 *(page 297)*

1. unit circle **3.** period

5. $\sin t = \frac{5}{13}$ $\csc t = \frac{13}{5}$
$\cos t = \frac{12}{13}$ $\sec t = \frac{13}{12}$
$\tan t = \frac{5}{12}$ $\cot t = \frac{12}{5}$

7. $\sin t = -\frac{3}{5}$ $\csc t = -\frac{5}{3}$
$\cos t = -\frac{4}{5}$ $\sec t = -\frac{5}{4}$
$\tan t = \frac{3}{4}$ $\cot t = \frac{4}{3}$

9. $(0, 1)$ **11.** $\left(\frac{\sqrt{2}}{2}, \frac{\sqrt{2}}{2}\right)$ **13.** $\left(-\frac{\sqrt{3}}{2}, \frac{1}{2}\right)$

15. $\left(-\frac{1}{2}, -\frac{\sqrt{3}}{2}\right)$

17. $\sin\frac{\pi}{4} = \frac{\sqrt{2}}{2}$
$\cos\frac{\pi}{4} = \frac{\sqrt{2}}{2}$
$\tan\frac{\pi}{4} = 1$

19. $\sin\left(-\frac{\pi}{6}\right) = -\frac{1}{2}$
$\cos\left(-\frac{\pi}{6}\right) = \frac{\sqrt{3}}{2}$
$\tan\left(-\frac{\pi}{6}\right) = -\frac{\sqrt{3}}{3}$

21. $\sin\left(-\frac{7\pi}{4}\right) = \frac{\sqrt{2}}{2}$
$\cos\left(-\frac{7\pi}{4}\right) = \frac{\sqrt{2}}{2}$
$\tan\left(-\frac{7\pi}{4}\right) = 1$

23. $\sin\frac{11\pi}{6} = -\frac{1}{2}$
$\cos\frac{11\pi}{6} = \frac{\sqrt{3}}{2}$
$\tan\frac{11\pi}{6} = -\frac{\sqrt{3}}{3}$

25. $\sin\left(-\frac{3\pi}{2}\right) = 1$
$\cos\left(-\frac{3\pi}{2}\right) = 0$
$\tan\left(-\frac{3\pi}{2}\right)$ is undefined.

27. $\sin\frac{2\pi}{3} = \frac{\sqrt{3}}{2}$ $\quad\csc\frac{2\pi}{3} = \frac{2\sqrt{3}}{3}$
$\cos\frac{2\pi}{3} = -\frac{1}{2}$ $\quad\sec\frac{2\pi}{3} = -2$
$\tan\frac{2\pi}{3} = -\sqrt{3}$ $\quad\cot\frac{2\pi}{3} = -\frac{\sqrt{3}}{3}$

29. $\sin\frac{4\pi}{3} = -\frac{\sqrt{3}}{2}$ $\quad\csc\frac{4\pi}{3} = -\frac{2\sqrt{3}}{3}$
$\cos\frac{4\pi}{3} = -\frac{1}{2}$ $\quad\sec\frac{4\pi}{3} = -2$
$\tan\frac{4\pi}{3} = \sqrt{3}$ $\quad\cot\frac{4\pi}{3} = \frac{\sqrt{3}}{3}$

31. $\sin\frac{3\pi}{4} = \frac{\sqrt{2}}{2}$ $\quad\csc\frac{3\pi}{4} = \sqrt{2}$
$\cos\frac{3\pi}{4} = -\frac{\sqrt{2}}{2}$ $\quad\sec\frac{3\pi}{4} = -\sqrt{2}$
$\tan\frac{3\pi}{4} = -1$ $\quad\cot\frac{3\pi}{4} = -1$

33. $\sin\left(-\frac{\pi}{2}\right) = -1$ $\quad\csc\left(-\frac{\pi}{2}\right) = -1$
$\cos\left(-\frac{\pi}{2}\right) = 0$ $\quad\sec\left(-\frac{\pi}{2}\right)$ is undefined.
$\tan\left(-\frac{\pi}{2}\right)$ is undefined. $\quad\cot\left(-\frac{\pi}{2}\right) = 0$

35. $\sin 4\pi = \sin 0 = 0$ **37.** $\cos\frac{7\pi}{3} = \cos\frac{\pi}{3} = \frac{1}{2}$

39. $\cos\frac{17\pi}{4} = \cos\frac{\pi}{4} = \frac{\sqrt{2}}{2}$

41. $\sin\left(-\frac{8\pi}{3}\right) = \sin\frac{4\pi}{3} = -\frac{\sqrt{3}}{2}$

43. (a) $-\frac{1}{2}$ (b) -2 **45.** (a) $-\frac{1}{5}$ (b) -5

47. (a) $\frac{4}{5}$ (b) $-\frac{4}{5}$ **49.** 0.7071 **51.** 1.0000

53. -0.1288 **55.** 1.3940 **57.** -1.4486

59. (a) 0.25 ft (b) 0.02 ft (c) -0.25 ft

61. False. $\sin(-t) = -\sin(t)$ means that the function is odd, not that the sine of a negative angle is a negative number.

63. False. The real number 0 corresponds to the point $(1, 0)$.

65. (a) y-axis symmetry (b) $\sin t_1 = \sin(\pi - t_1)$
(c) $\cos(\pi - t_1) = -\cos t_1$

67. Answers will vary. **69.** It is an odd function.

71. (a)

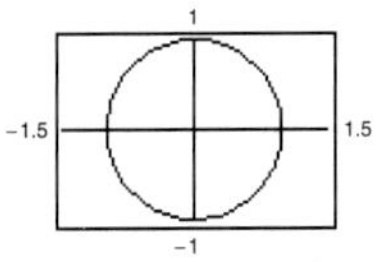

Circle of radius 1 centered at (0, 0)

(b) The t-values represent the central angle in radians. The x- and y-values represent the location in the coordinate plane.

(c) $-1 \le x \le 1, -1 \le y \le 1$

Section 4.3 *(page 306)*

1. (a) v (b) iv (c) vi (d) iii (e) i (f) ii

3. complementary

5. $\sin\theta = \frac{3}{5}$ $\quad\csc\theta = \frac{5}{3}$
$\cos\theta = \frac{4}{5}$ $\quad\sec\theta = \frac{5}{4}$
$\tan\theta = \frac{3}{4}$ $\quad\cot\theta = \frac{4}{3}$

7. $\sin\theta = \frac{9}{41}$ $\quad\csc\theta = \frac{41}{9}$
$\cos\theta = \frac{40}{41}$ $\quad\sec\theta = \frac{41}{40}$
$\tan\theta = \frac{9}{40}$ $\quad\cot\theta = \frac{40}{9}$

9. $\sin\theta = \frac{8}{17}$ $\quad\csc\theta = \frac{17}{8}$
$\cos\theta = \frac{15}{17}$ $\quad\sec\theta = \frac{17}{15}$
$\tan\theta = \frac{8}{15}$ $\quad\cot\theta = \frac{15}{8}$
The triangles are similar, and corresponding sides are proportional.

11. $\sin\theta = \frac{1}{3}$ $\quad\csc\theta = 3$
$\cos\theta = \frac{2\sqrt{2}}{3}$ $\quad\sec\theta = \frac{3\sqrt{2}}{4}$
$\tan\theta = \frac{\sqrt{2}}{4}$ $\quad\cot\theta = 2\sqrt{2}$
The triangles are similar, and corresponding sides are proportional.

13.

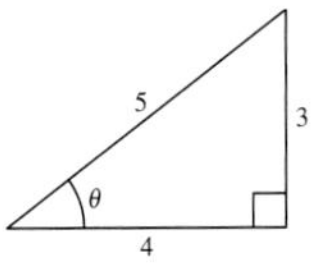

$\sin\theta = \frac{3}{5}$ $\quad\csc\theta = \frac{5}{3}$
$\cos\theta = \frac{4}{5}$ $\quad\sec\theta = \frac{5}{4}$
$\cot\theta = \frac{4}{3}$

15.

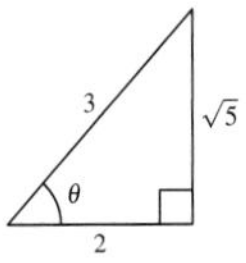

$\sin\theta = \frac{\sqrt{5}}{3}$ $\quad\csc\theta = \frac{3\sqrt{5}}{5}$
$\cos\theta = \frac{2}{3}$
$\tan\theta = \frac{\sqrt{5}}{2}$ $\quad\cot\theta = \frac{2\sqrt{5}}{5}$

17.

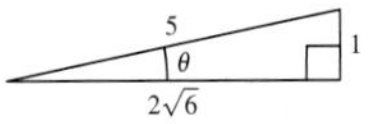

$\csc\theta = 5$
$\cos\theta = \frac{2\sqrt{6}}{5}$ $\quad\sec\theta = \frac{5\sqrt{6}}{12}$
$\tan\theta = \frac{\sqrt{6}}{12}$ $\quad\cot\theta = 2\sqrt{6}$

19.

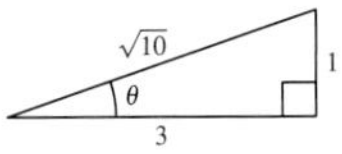

$\sin\theta = \frac{\sqrt{10}}{10}$ $\quad\csc\theta = \sqrt{10}$
$\cos\theta = \frac{3\sqrt{10}}{10}$ $\quad\sec\theta = \frac{\sqrt{10}}{3}$
$\tan\theta = \frac{1}{3}$

21. $\frac{\pi}{6}; \frac{1}{2}$ **23.** $45°; \sqrt{2}$ **25.** $60°; \frac{\pi}{3}$ **27.** $30°; 2$

29. $45°; \frac{\pi}{4}$ **31.** (a) $\frac{1}{2}$ (b) $\frac{\sqrt{3}}{2}$ (c) $\sqrt{3}$ (d) $\frac{\sqrt{3}}{3}$

33. (a) $\frac{2\sqrt{2}}{3}$ (b) $2\sqrt{2}$ (c) 3 (d) 3

35. (a) $\frac{1}{5}$ (b) $\sqrt{26}$ (c) $\frac{1}{5}$ (d) $\frac{5\sqrt{26}}{26}$

37–45. Answers will vary. **47.** (a) 0.1736 (b) 0.1736

49. (a) 0.2815 (b) 3.5523 **51.** (a) 0.9964 (b) 1.0036

53. (a) 5.0273 (b) 0.1989 **55.** (a) 1.8527 (b) 0.9817

57. (a) $30° = \frac{\pi}{6}$ (b) $30° = \frac{\pi}{6}$

59. (a) $60° = \frac{\pi}{3}$ (b) $45° = \frac{\pi}{4}$

61. (a) $60° = \frac{\pi}{3}$ (b) $45° = \frac{\pi}{4}$

63. $9\sqrt{3}$ **65.** $\frac{32\sqrt{3}}{3}$

67. 443.2 m; 323.3 m **69.** $30° = \pi/6$

71. (a) 219.9 ft (b) 160.9 ft

73. $(x_1, y_1) = (28\sqrt{3}, 28)$
$(x_2, y_2) = (28, 28\sqrt{3})$

75. $\sin 20° \approx 0.34$, $\cos 20° \approx 0.94$, $\tan 20° \approx 0.36$, $\csc 20° \approx 2.92$, $\sec 20° \approx 1.06$, $\cot 20° \approx 2.75$

77. True, $\csc x = \frac{1}{\sin x}$. **79.** False, $\frac{\sqrt{2}}{2} + \frac{\sqrt{2}}{2} \neq 1$.

81. False, $1.7321 \neq 0.0349$.

83. (a)

θ	0.1	0.2	0.3	0.4	0.5
$\sin\theta$	0.0998	0.1987	0.2955	0.3894	0.4794

(b) θ (c) As $\theta \to 0$, $\sin\theta \to 0$ and $\frac{\theta}{\sin\theta} \to 1$.

85. Corresponding sides of similar triangles are proportional.

87. Yes, $\tan\theta$ is equal to opp/adj. You can find the value of the hypotenuse by the Pythagorean Theorem, then you can find $\sec\theta$, which is equal to hyp/adj.

Section 4.4 *(page 316)*

1. $\frac{y}{r}$ **3.** $\frac{y}{x}$ **5.** $\cos\theta$ **7.** zero; defined

9. (a) $\sin\theta = \frac{3}{5}$ $\csc\theta = \frac{5}{3}$
$\cos\theta = \frac{4}{5}$ $\sec\theta = \frac{5}{4}$
$\tan\theta = \frac{3}{4}$ $\cot\theta = \frac{4}{3}$
(b) $\sin\theta = \frac{15}{17}$ $\csc\theta = \frac{17}{15}$
$\cos\theta = -\frac{8}{17}$ $\sec\theta = -\frac{17}{8}$
$\tan\theta = -\frac{15}{8}$ $\cot\theta = -\frac{8}{15}$

11. (a) $\sin\theta = -\frac{1}{2}$ $\csc\theta = -2$
$\cos\theta = -\frac{\sqrt{3}}{2}$ $\sec\theta = -\frac{2\sqrt{3}}{3}$
$\tan\theta = \frac{\sqrt{3}}{3}$ $\cot\theta = \sqrt{3}$
(b) $\sin\theta = -\frac{\sqrt{17}}{17}$ $\csc\theta = -\sqrt{17}$
$\cos\theta = \frac{4\sqrt{17}}{17}$ $\sec\theta = \frac{\sqrt{17}}{4}$
$\tan\theta = -\frac{1}{4}$ $\cot\theta = -4$

13. $\sin\theta = \frac{12}{13}$ $\csc\theta = \frac{13}{12}$
$\cos\theta = \frac{5}{13}$ $\sec\theta = \frac{13}{5}$
$\tan\theta = \frac{12}{5}$ $\cot\theta = \frac{5}{12}$

15. $\sin\theta = -\frac{2\sqrt{29}}{29}$ $\csc\theta = -\frac{\sqrt{29}}{2}$
$\cos\theta = -\frac{5\sqrt{29}}{29}$ $\sec\theta = -\frac{\sqrt{29}}{5}$
$\tan\theta = \frac{2}{5}$ $\cot\theta = \frac{5}{2}$

17. $\sin\theta = \frac{4}{5}$ $\csc\theta = \frac{5}{4}$
$\cos\theta = -\frac{3}{5}$ $\sec\theta = -\frac{5}{3}$
$\tan\theta = -\frac{4}{3}$ $\cot\theta = -\frac{3}{4}$

19. Quadrant I **21.** Quadrant II

23. $\sin\theta = \frac{15}{17}$ $\csc\theta = \frac{17}{15}$
$\cos\theta = -\frac{8}{17}$ $\sec\theta = -\frac{17}{8}$
$\tan\theta = -\frac{15}{8}$ $\cot\theta = -\frac{8}{15}$

25. $\sin\theta = \frac{3}{5}$ $\csc\theta = \frac{5}{3}$
$\cos\theta = -\frac{4}{5}$ $\sec\theta = -\frac{5}{4}$
$\tan\theta = -\frac{3}{4}$ $\cot\theta = -\frac{4}{3}$

27. $\sin\theta = -\frac{\sqrt{10}}{10}$ $\csc\theta = -\sqrt{10}$
$\cos\theta = \frac{3\sqrt{10}}{10}$ $\sec\theta = \frac{\sqrt{10}}{3}$
$\tan\theta = -\frac{1}{3}$ $\cot\theta = -3$

29. $\sin\theta = -\frac{\sqrt{3}}{2}$ $\csc\theta = -\frac{2\sqrt{3}}{3}$
$\cos\theta = -\frac{1}{2}$ $\sec\theta = -2$
$\tan\theta = \sqrt{3}$ $\cot\theta = \frac{\sqrt{3}}{3}$

31. $\sin\theta = 0$ $\csc\theta$ is undefined.
$\cos\theta = -1$ $\sec\theta = -1$
$\tan\theta = 0$ $\cot\theta$ is undefined.

33. $\sin\theta = \frac{\sqrt{2}}{2}$ $\csc\theta = \sqrt{2}$
$\cos\theta = -\frac{\sqrt{2}}{2}$ $\sec\theta = -\sqrt{2}$
$\tan\theta = -1$ $\cot\theta = -1$

35. $\sin\theta = -\frac{2\sqrt{5}}{5}$ $\csc\theta = -\frac{\sqrt{5}}{2}$
$\cos\theta = -\frac{\sqrt{5}}{5}$ $\sec\theta = -\sqrt{5}$
$\tan\theta = 2$ $\cot\theta = \frac{1}{2}$

37. 0 **39.** Undefined **41.** 1 **43.** Undefined

45. $\theta' = 20°$

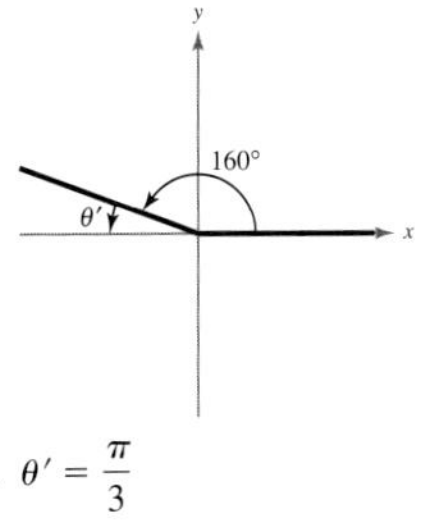

47. $\theta' = 55°$

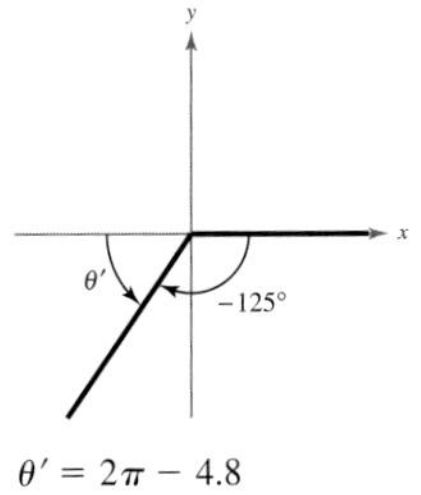

49. $\theta' = \frac{\pi}{3}$

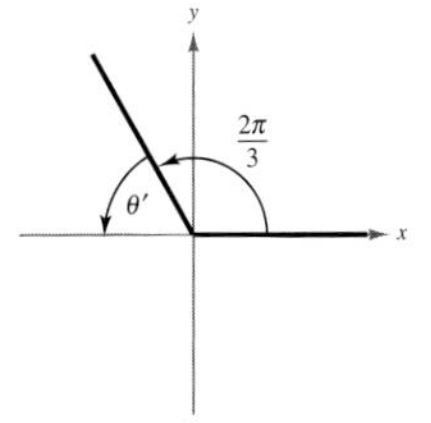

51. $\theta' = 2\pi - 4.8$

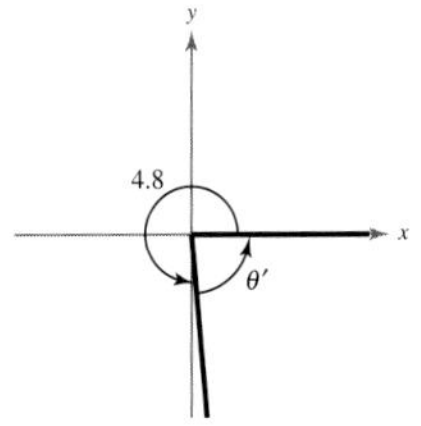

53. $\sin 225° = -\frac{\sqrt{2}}{2}$
$\cos 225° = -\frac{\sqrt{2}}{2}$
$\tan 225° = 1$

55. $\sin 750° = \frac{1}{2}$
$\cos 750° = \frac{\sqrt{3}}{2}$
$\tan 750° = \frac{\sqrt{3}}{3}$

57. $\sin(-150°) = -\frac{1}{2}$
$\cos(-150°) = -\frac{\sqrt{3}}{2}$
$\tan(-150°) = \frac{\sqrt{3}}{3}$

59. $\sin\frac{2\pi}{3} = \frac{\sqrt{3}}{2}$
$\cos\frac{2\pi}{3} = -\frac{1}{2}$
$\tan\frac{2\pi}{3} = -\sqrt{3}$

61. $\sin\frac{5\pi}{4} = -\frac{\sqrt{2}}{2}$
$\cos\frac{5\pi}{4} = -\frac{\sqrt{2}}{2}$
$\tan\frac{5\pi}{4} = 1$

63. $\sin\left(-\frac{\pi}{6}\right) = -\frac{1}{2}$
$\cos\left(-\frac{\pi}{6}\right) = \frac{\sqrt{3}}{2}$
$\tan\left(-\frac{\pi}{6}\right) = -\frac{\sqrt{3}}{3}$

65. $\sin\frac{9\pi}{4} = \frac{\sqrt{2}}{2}$
$\cos\frac{9\pi}{4} = \frac{\sqrt{2}}{2}$
$\tan\frac{9\pi}{4} = 1$

67. $\sin\left(-\frac{3\pi}{2}\right) = 1$
$\cos\left(-\frac{3\pi}{2}\right) = 0$
$\tan\left(-\frac{3\pi}{2}\right)$ is undefined.

69. $\frac{4}{5}$ **71.** $-\frac{\sqrt{13}}{2}$ **73.** $\frac{8}{5}$

75. 0.1736 **77.** −0.3420 **79.** −1.4826 **81.** 3.2361
83. 4.6373 **85.** 0.3640 **87.** −0.6052 **89.** −0.4142

91. (a) $30° = \frac{\pi}{6}$, $150° = \frac{5\pi}{6}$ (b) $210° = \frac{7\pi}{6}$, $330° = \frac{11\pi}{6}$

93. (a) $60° = \frac{\pi}{3}$, $120° = \frac{2\pi}{3}$ (b) $135° = \frac{3\pi}{4}$, $315° = \frac{7\pi}{4}$

95. (a) $45° = \frac{\pi}{4}$, $225° = \frac{5\pi}{4}$ (b) $150° = \frac{5\pi}{6}$, $330° = \frac{11\pi}{6}$

97. (a) 12 mi (b) 6 mi (c) 6.9 mi

99. (a) $N = 22.099 \sin(0.522t - 2.219) + 55.008$
$F = 36.641 \sin(0.502t - 1.831) + 25.610$
(b) February: $N = 34.6°$, $F = -1.4°$
March: $N = 41.6°$, $F = 13.9°$
May: $N = 63.4°$, $F = 48.6°$
June: $N = 72.5°$, $F = 59.5°$
August: $N = 75.5°$, $F = 55.6°$
September: $N = 68.6°$, $F = 41.7°$
November: $N = 46.8°$, $F = 6.5°$
(c) Answers will vary.

101. (a) 2 cm (b) 0.11 cm (c) −1.2 cm

103. False. In each of the four quadrants, the signs of the secant function and the cosine function will be the same, because these functions are reciprocals of each other.

105. As θ increases from 0° to 90°, x decreases from 12 cm to 0 cm and y increases from 0 cm to 12 cm. Therefore, $\sin\theta = y/12$ increases from 0 to 1 and $\cos\theta = x/12$ decreases from 1 to 0. Thus, $\tan\theta = y/x$ increases without bound. When $\theta = 90°$, the tangent is undefined.

107. (a) $\sin t = y$ (b) $r = 1$ because it is a unit circle.
$\cos t = x$
(c) $\sin\theta = y$ (d) $\sin t = \sin\theta$, and $\cos t = \cos\theta$.
$\cos\theta = x$

Section 4.5 *(page 326)*

1. cycle **3.** phase shift **5.** Period: $\frac{2\pi}{5}$; Amplitude: 2

7. Period: 4π; Amplitude: $\frac{3}{4}$ **9.** Period: 6; Amplitude: $\frac{1}{2}$

11. Period: 2π; Amplitude: 4

13. Period: $\frac{\pi}{5}$; Amplitude: 3

15. Period: $\frac{5\pi}{2}$; Amplitude: $\frac{5}{3}$

17. Period: 1; Amplitude: $\frac{1}{4}$

19. g is a shift of f π units to the right.

21. g is a reflection of f in the x-axis.

23. The period of f is twice the period of g.

25. g is a shift of f three units upward.

27. The graph of g has twice the amplitude of the graph of f.

29. The graph of g is a horizontal shift of the graph of f π units to the right.

31.

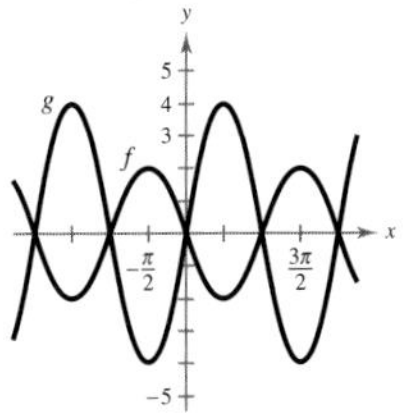

33.

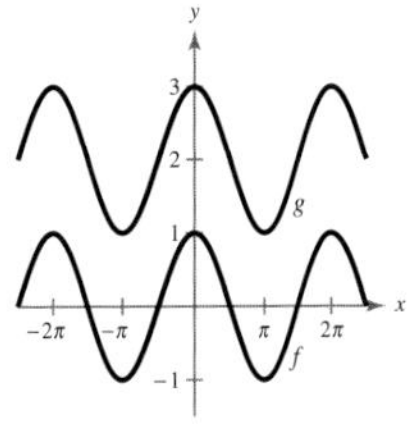

CHAPTER 4

35.
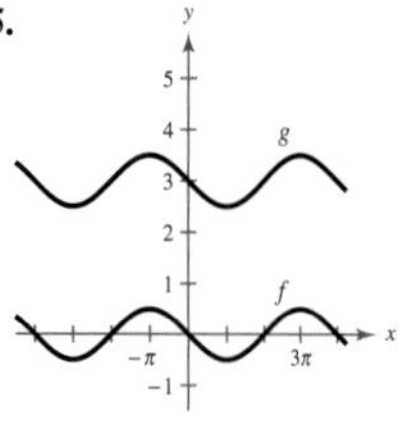

37.
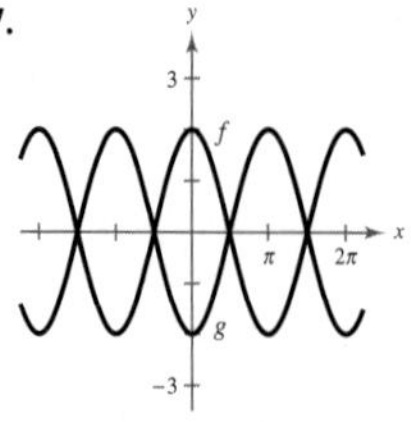

39.
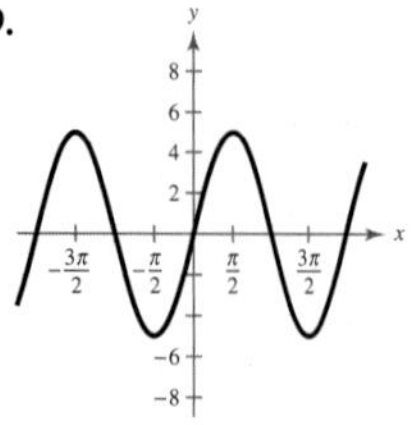

41.
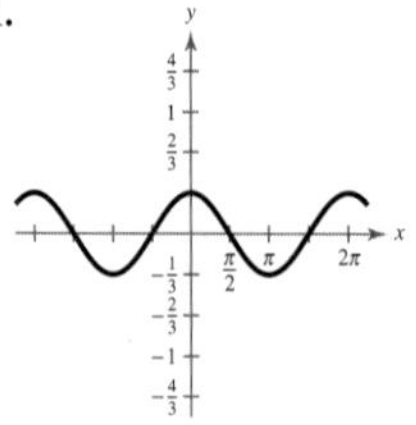

43.
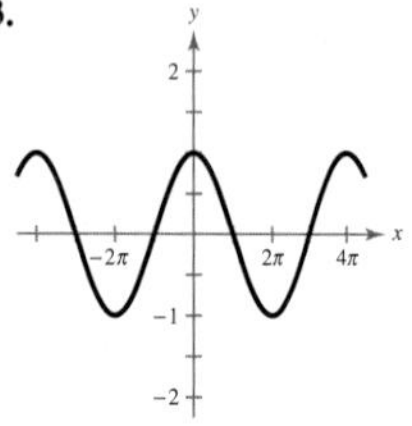

45.
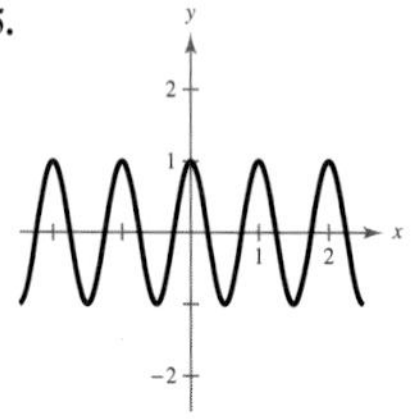

47.
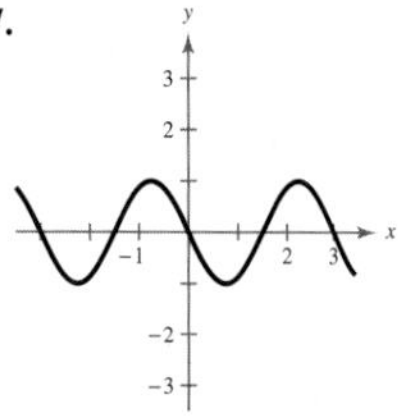

49.
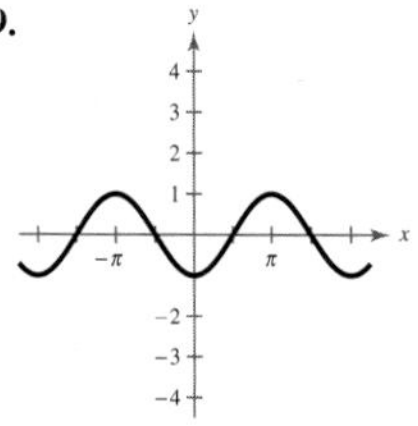

51.
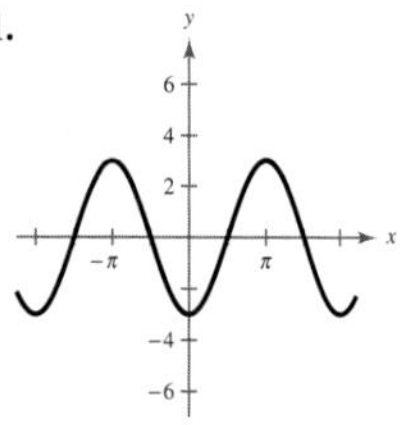

53.
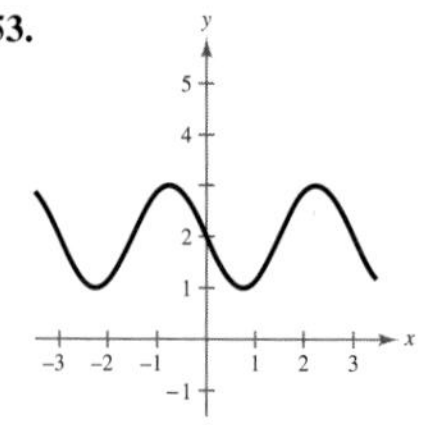

55.
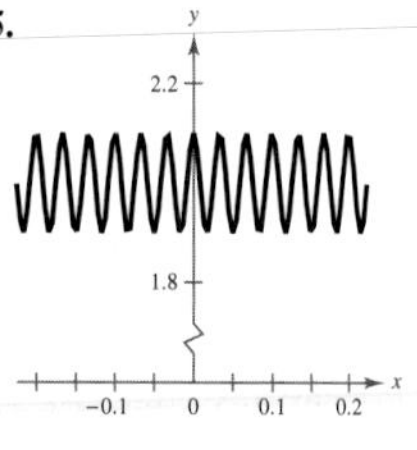

57.
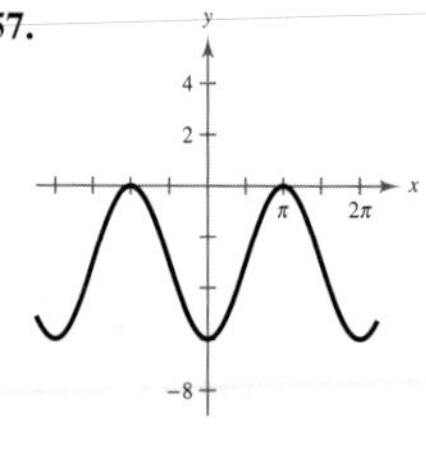

59.
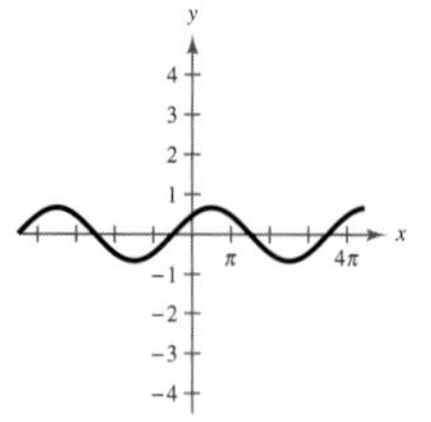

61. (a) $g(x)$ is obtained by a horizontal shrink of four, and one cycle of $g(x)$ corresponds to the interval $[\pi/4, 3\pi/4]$.

(b)
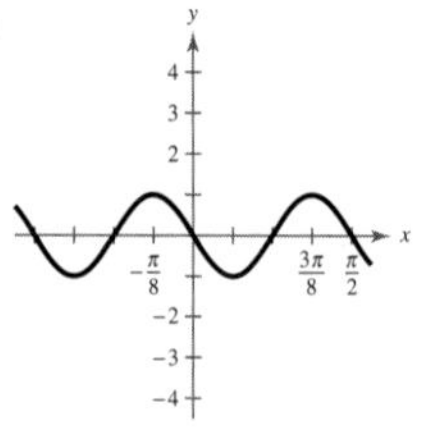

(c) $g(x) = f(4x - \pi)$

63. (a) One cycle of $g(x)$ corresponds to the interval $[\pi, 3\pi]$, and $g(x)$ is obtained by shifting $f(x)$ upward two units.

(b)
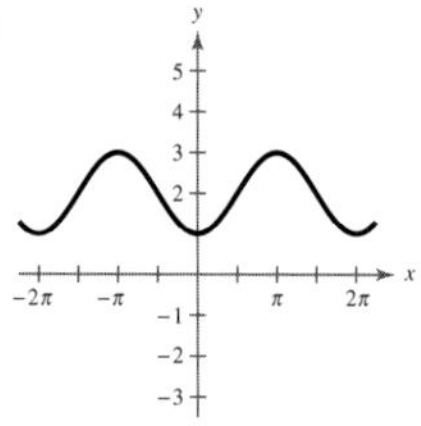

(c) $g(x) = f(x - \pi) + 2$

65. (a) One cycle of $g(x)$ is $[\pi/4, 3\pi/4]$. $g(x)$ is also shifted down three units and has an amplitude of two.

(b)
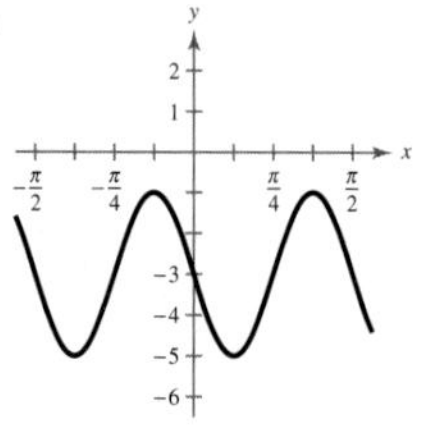

(c) $g(x) = 2f(4x - \pi) - 3$

67.
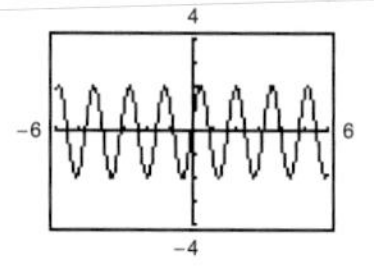

69.
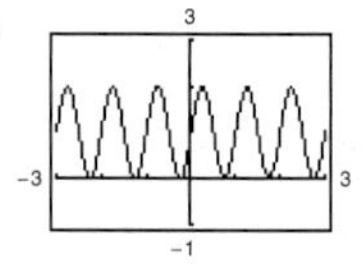

71.

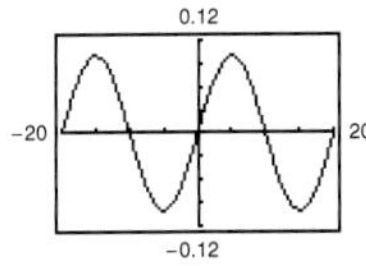

73. $a = 2, d = 1$ **75.** $a = -4, d = 4$

77. $a = -3, b = 2, c = 0$ **79.** $a = 2, b = 1, c = -\frac{\pi}{4}$

81.

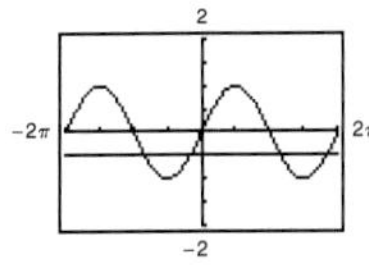

$x = -\frac{\pi}{6}, -\frac{5\pi}{6}, \frac{7\pi}{6}, \frac{11\pi}{6}$

83. $y = 1 + 2\sin(2x - \pi)$ **85.** $y = \cos(2x + 2\pi) - \frac{3}{2}$

87. (a) 6 sec (b) 10 cycles/min

(c)

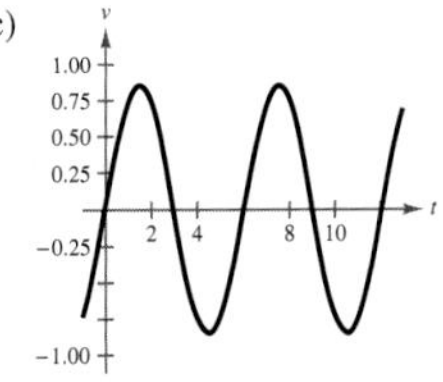

89. (a) $I(t) = 46.2 + 32.4\cos\left(\frac{\pi t}{6} - 3.67\right)$

(b)

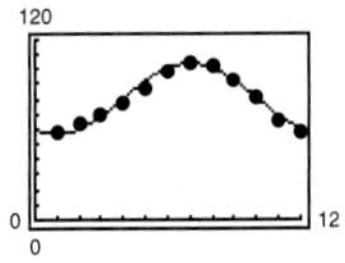

The model fits the data well.

(c)

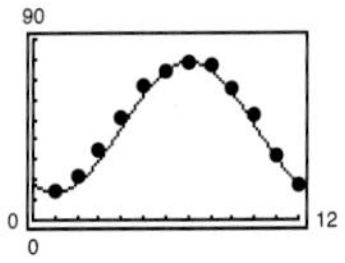

The model fits the data well.

(d) Las Vegas: 80.6°; International Falls: 46.2°
The constant term gives the annual average temperature.

(e) 12; yes; One full period is one year.

(f) International Falls; amplitude; The greater the amplitude, the greater the variability in temperature.

91. (a) $\frac{1}{440}$ sec (b) 440 cycles/sec

93. (a) 365; Yes, because there are 365 days in a year.

(b) 30.3 gal; the constant term

(c)

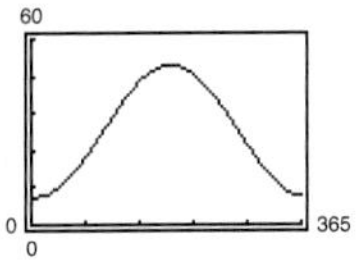

$124 < t < 252$

95. False. The graph of $f(x) = \sin(x + 2\pi)$ translates the graph of $f(x) = \sin x$ exactly one period to the left so that the two graphs look identical.

97. True. Because $\cos x = \sin\left(x + \frac{\pi}{2}\right)$, $y = -\cos x$ is a reflection in the x-axis of $y = \sin\left(x + \frac{\pi}{2}\right)$.

99.

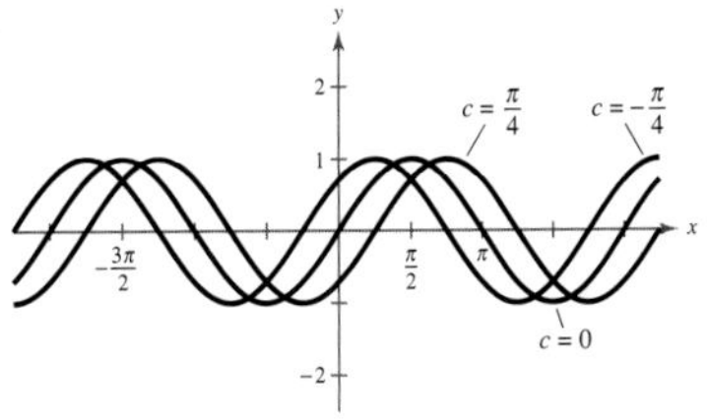

The value of c is a horizontal translation of the graph.

101.

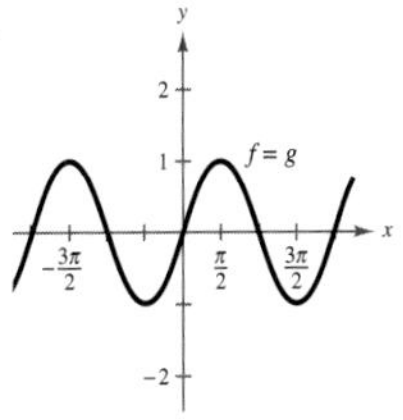

Conjecture:
$\sin x = \cos\left(x - \frac{\pi}{2}\right)$

103. (a)

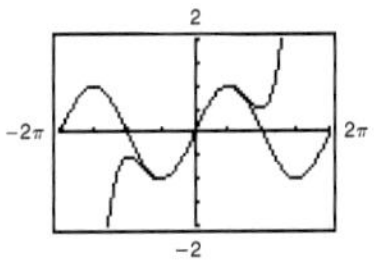

The graphs appear to coincide from $-\frac{\pi}{2}$ to $\frac{\pi}{2}$.

(b)

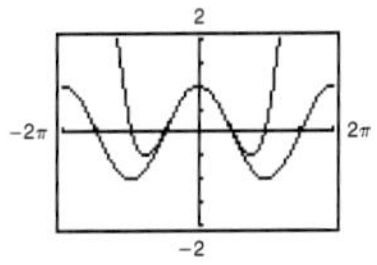

The graphs appear to coincide from $-\frac{\pi}{2}$ to $\frac{\pi}{2}$.

(c) $-\frac{x^7}{7!}, -\frac{x^6}{6!}$

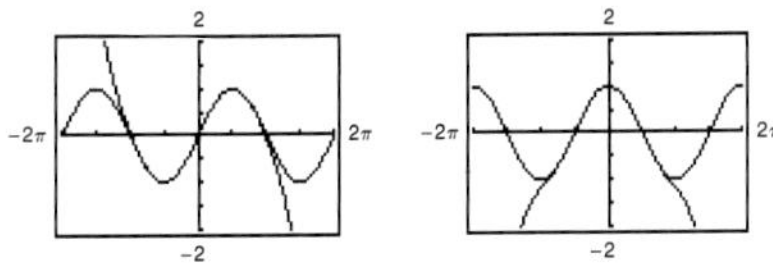

The interval of accuracy increased.

CHAPTER 4

Section 4.6 *(page 337)*

1. odd; origin **3.** reciprocal **5.** π

7. $(-\infty, -1] \cup [1, \infty)$ **9.** e, π **10.** c, 2π

11. a, 1 **12.** d, 2π **13.** f, 4 **14.** b, 4

15.

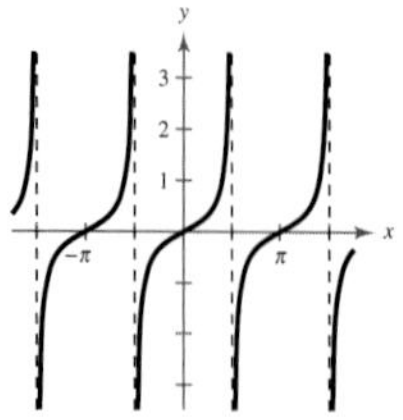

17.

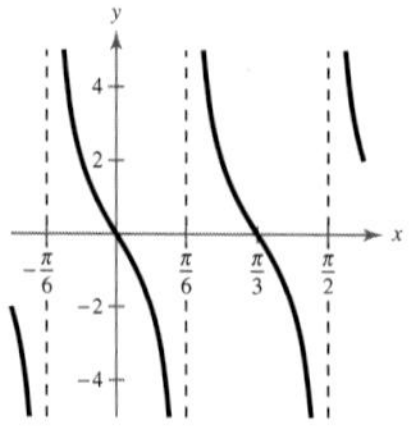

19.

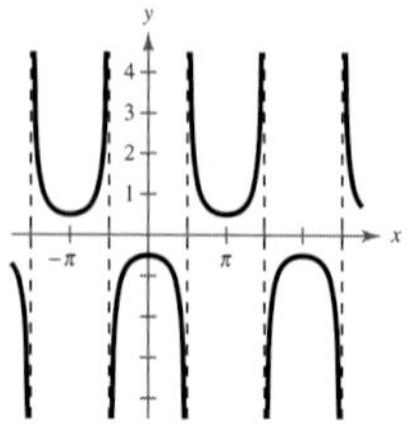

21.

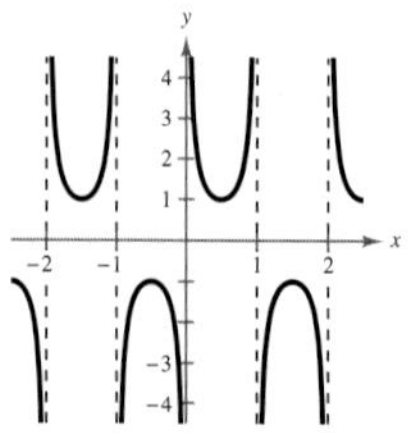

23.

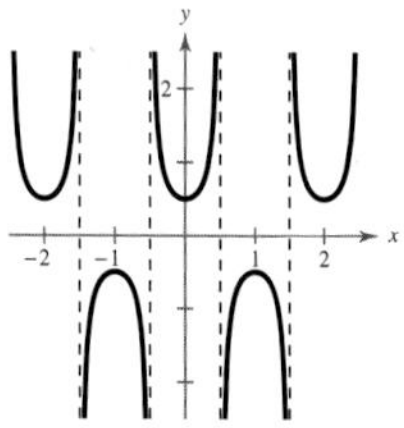

25.

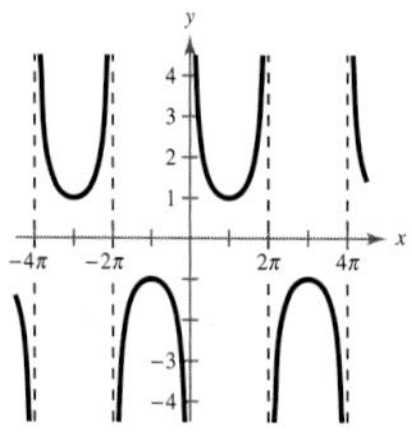

27.

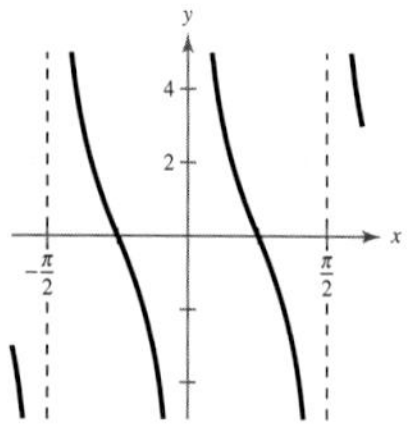

29.

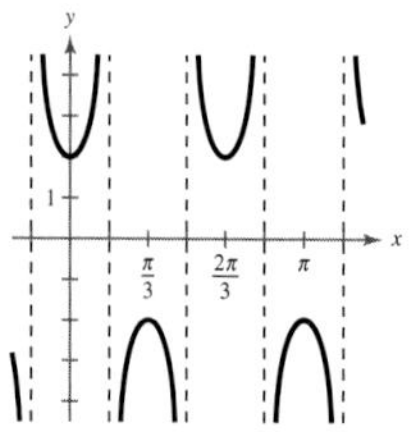

31.

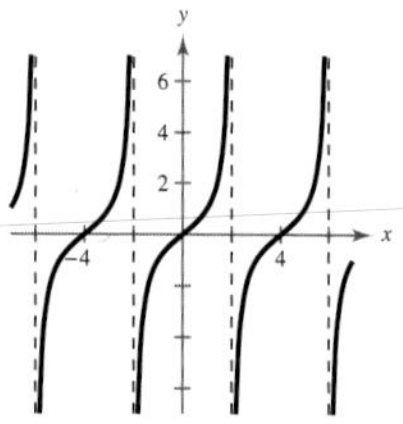

33.

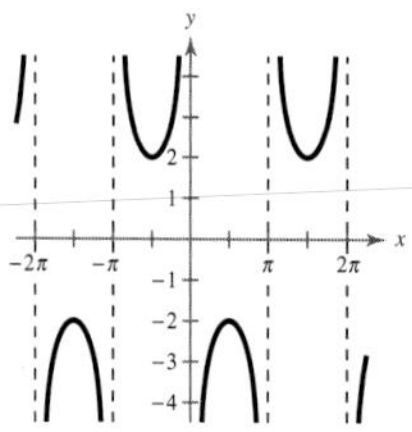

35.

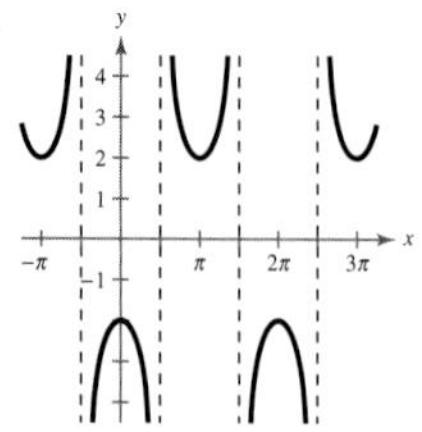

37.

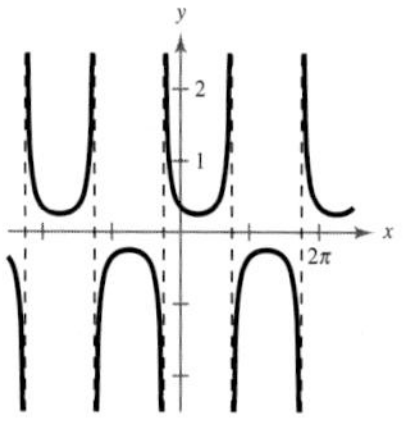

39.

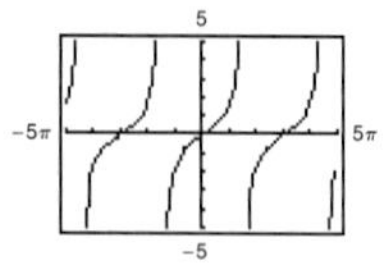

41.

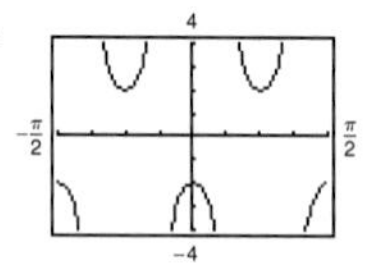

43.

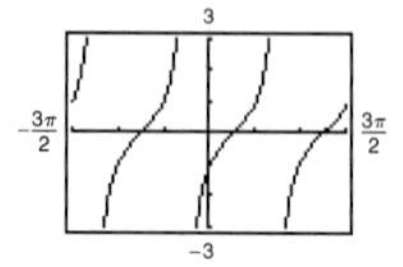

45.

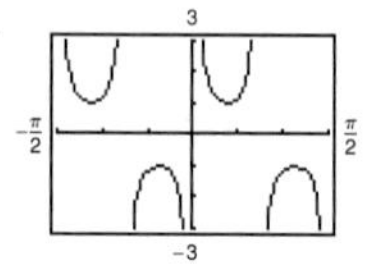

47.

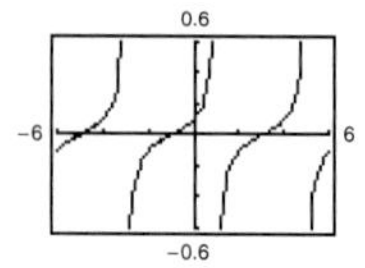

49. $-\frac{7\pi}{4}, -\frac{3\pi}{4}, \frac{\pi}{4}, \frac{5\pi}{4}$ **51.** $-\frac{4\pi}{3}, -\frac{\pi}{3}, \frac{2\pi}{3}, \frac{5\pi}{3}$

53. $-\frac{4\pi}{3}, -\frac{2\pi}{3}, \frac{2\pi}{3}, \frac{4\pi}{3}$ **55.** $-\frac{7\pi}{4}, -\frac{5\pi}{4}, \frac{\pi}{4}, \frac{3\pi}{4}$

57. Even **59.** Odd **61.** Odd **63.** Even

65. (a)

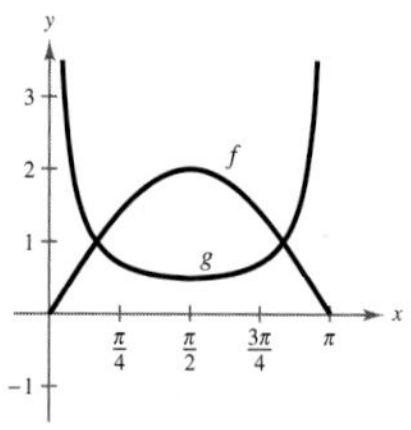

(b) $\frac{\pi}{6} < x < \frac{5\pi}{6}$

(c) f approaches 0 and g approaches $+\infty$ because the cosecant is the reciprocal of the sine.

67.

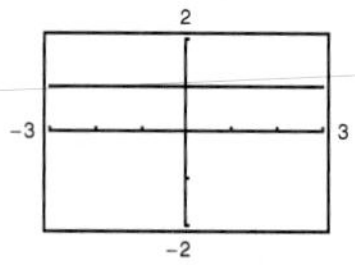

The expressions are equivalent except when $\sin x = 0$, y_1 is undefined.

69.

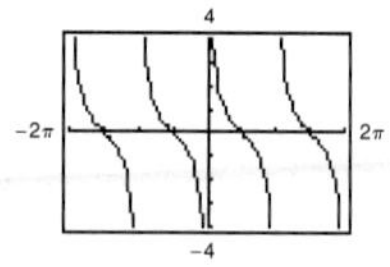

The expressions are equivalent.

71.

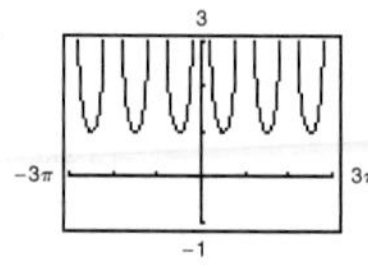

The expressions are equivalent.

73. d, $f \to 0$ as $x \to 0$. **74.** a, $f \to 0$ as $x \to 0$.
75. b, $g \to 0$ as $x \to 0$. **76.** c, $g \to 0$ as $x \to 0$.

77.

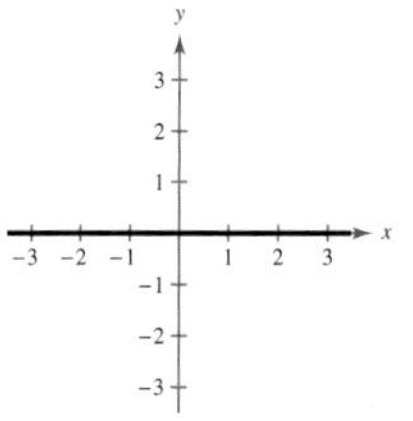

The functions are equal.

79.

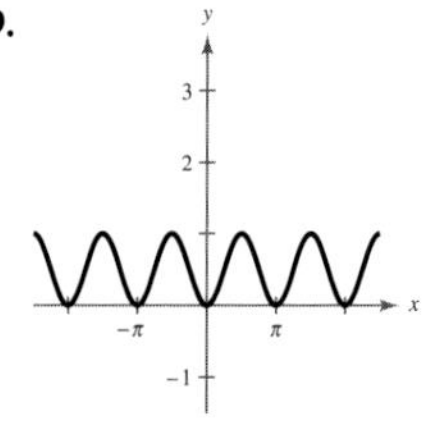

The functions are equal.

81.

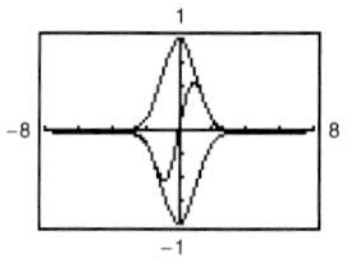

As $x \to \infty$, $g(x) \to 0$.

83.

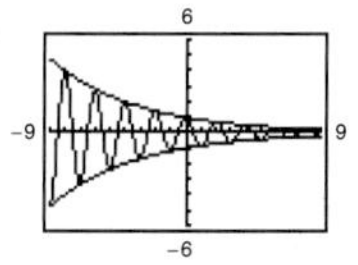

As $x \to \infty$, $f(x) \to 0$.

85.

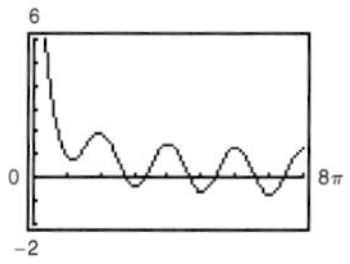

As $x \to 0$, $y \to \infty$.

87.

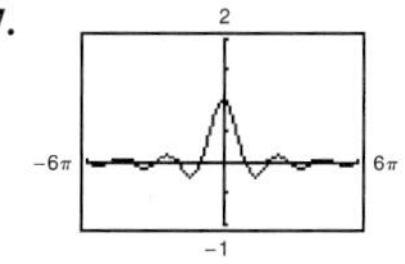

As $x \to 0$, $g(x) \to 1$.

89.

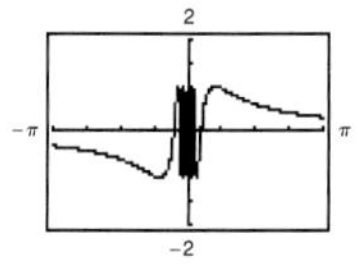

As $x \to 0$, $f(x)$ oscillates between 1 and -1.

91. $d = 7 \cot x$

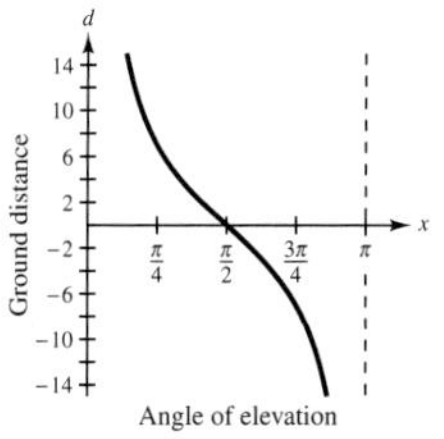

93. (a) Period of $H(t)$: 12 mo
Period of $L(t)$: 12 mo
(b) Summer; winter
(c) About 0.5 mo

95. (a)

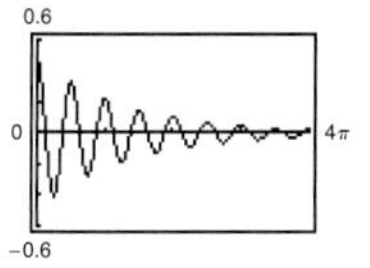

(b) y approaches 0 as t increases.

97. True. $y = \sec x$ is equal to $y = 1/\cos x$, and if the reciprocal of $y = \sin x$ is translated $\pi/2$ units to the left, then

$$\frac{1}{\sin\left(x + \frac{\pi}{2}\right)} = \frac{1}{\cos x} = \sec x.$$

99. (a) As $x \to \frac{\pi}{2}^{+}$, $f(x) \to -\infty$.
(b) As $x \to \frac{\pi}{2}^{-}$, $f(x) \to \infty$.
(c) As $x \to -\frac{\pi}{2}^{+}$, $f(x) \to -\infty$.
(d) As $x \to -\frac{\pi}{2}^{-}$, $f(x) \to \infty$.

101. (a) As $x \to 0^{+}$, $f(x) \to \infty$.
(b) As $x \to 0^{-}$, $f(x) \to -\infty$.
(c) As $x \to \pi^{+}$, $f(x) \to \infty$.
(d) As $x \to \pi^{-}$, $f(x) \to -\infty$.

103. (a)

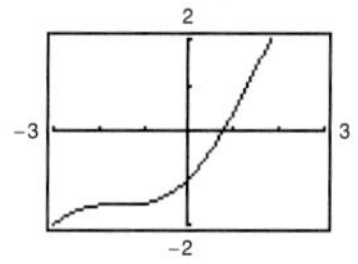

0.7391
(b) 1, 0.5403, 0.8576, 0.6543, 0.7935, 0.7014, 0.7640, 0.7221, 0.7504, 0.7314, . . . ; 0.7391

105.

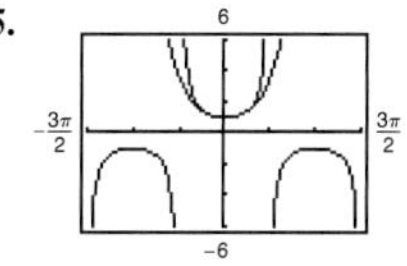

The graphs appear to coincide on the interval $-1.1 \le x \le 1.1$.

Section 4.7 *(page 347)*

1. $y = \sin^{-1} x$; $-1 \le x \le 1$

3. $y = \tan^{-1} x$; $-\infty < x < \infty$; $-\frac{\pi}{2} < y < \frac{\pi}{2}$

5. $\frac{\pi}{6}$ **7.** $\frac{\pi}{3}$ **9.** $\frac{\pi}{6}$ **11.** $\frac{5\pi}{6}$ **13.** $-\frac{\pi}{3}$

15. $\frac{2\pi}{3}$ **17.** $-\frac{\pi}{3}$ **19.** 0

21.

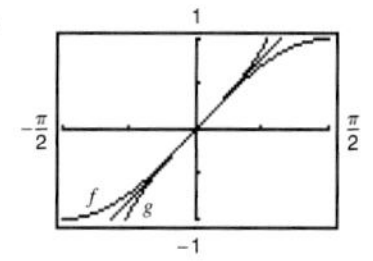

23. 1.19 **25.** -0.85 **27.** -1.25 **29.** 0.32
31. 1.99 **33.** 0.74 **35.** 1.07 **37.** 1.36
39. -1.52 **41.** $-\frac{\pi}{3}$, $-\frac{\sqrt{3}}{3}$, 1 **43.** $\theta = \arctan \frac{x}{4}$
45. $\theta = \arcsin \frac{x+2}{5}$ **47.** $\theta = \arccos \frac{x+3}{2x}$
49. 0.3 **51.** -0.1 **53.** 0 **55.** $\frac{3}{5}$ **57.** $\frac{\sqrt{5}}{5}$
59. $\frac{12}{13}$ **61.** $\frac{\sqrt{34}}{5}$ **63.** $\frac{\sqrt{5}}{3}$ **65.** 2 **67.** $\frac{1}{x}$
69. $\sqrt{1-4x^2}$ **71.** $\sqrt{1-x^2}$ **73.** $\frac{\sqrt{9-x^2}}{x}$
75. $\frac{\sqrt{x^2+2}}{x}$

77.

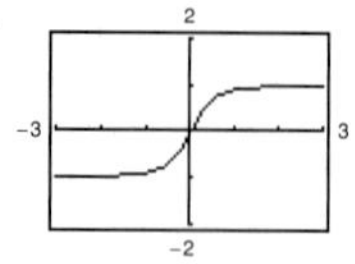

Asymptotes: $y = \pm 1$

79. $\dfrac{9}{\sqrt{x^2 + 81}}$, $x > 0$; $\dfrac{-9}{\sqrt{x^2 + 81}}$, $x < 0$

81. $\dfrac{|x - 1|}{\sqrt{x^2 - 2x + 10}}$

83.

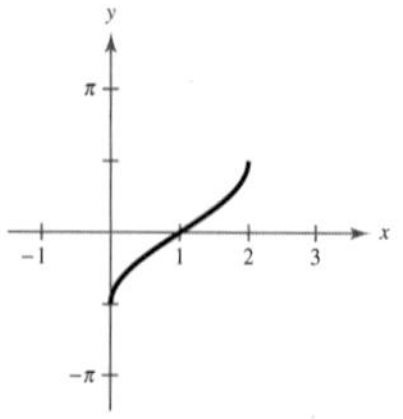

The graph of g is a horizontal shift one unit to the right of f.

85.

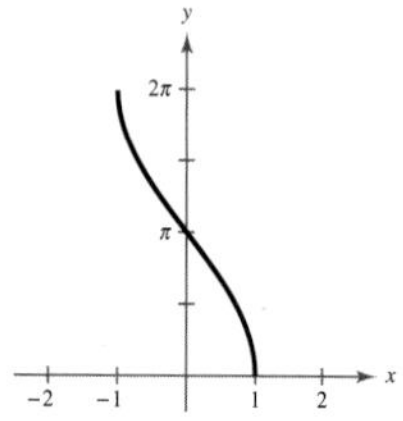

87.

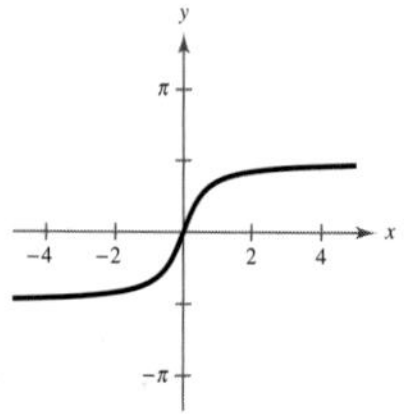

89.

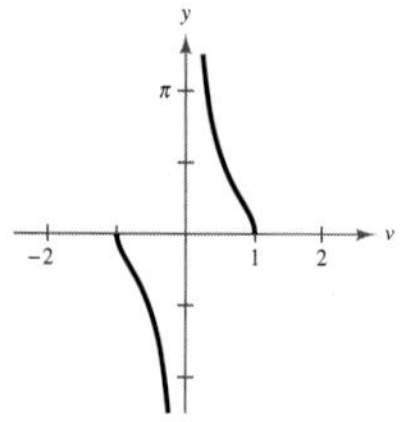

91.

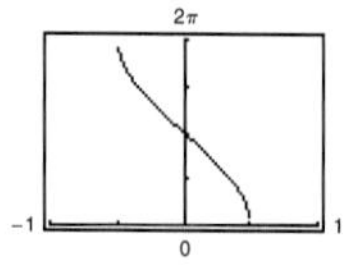

93.

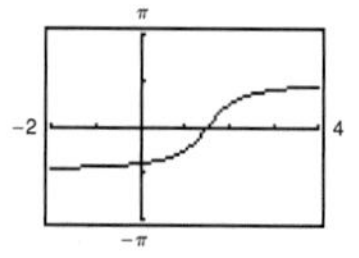

95.

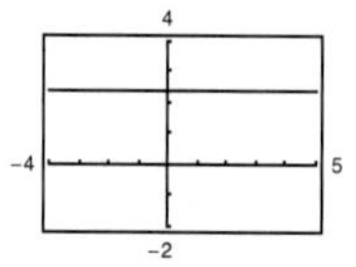

97. $3\sqrt{2}\sin\left(2t + \dfrac{\pi}{4}\right)$

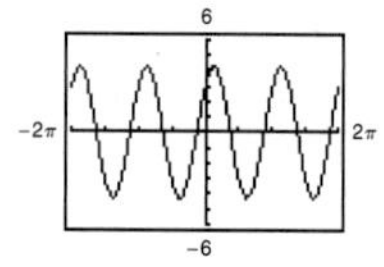

The graph implies that the identity is true.

99. $\dfrac{\pi}{2}$ **101.** $\dfrac{\pi}{2}$ **103.** π

105. (a) $\theta = \arcsin \dfrac{5}{s}$ (b) 0.13, 0.25

107. (a)

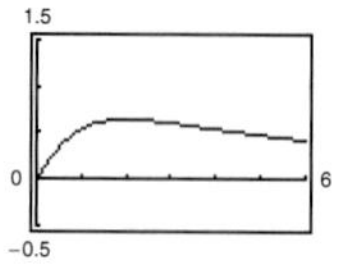

(b) 2 ft (c) $\beta = 0$; As x increases, β approaches 0.

109. (a) $\theta \approx 26.0°$ (b) 24.4 ft

111. (a) $\theta = \arctan \dfrac{x}{20}$ (b) 14.0°, 31.0°

113. False. $\dfrac{5\pi}{4}$ is not in the range of the arctangent.

115. Domain: $(-\infty, \infty)$
Range: $(0, \pi)$

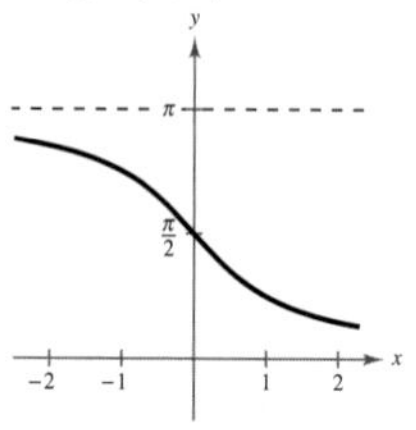

117. Domain: $(-\infty, -1] \cup [1, \infty)$
Range: $[-\pi/2, 0) \cup (0, \pi/2]$

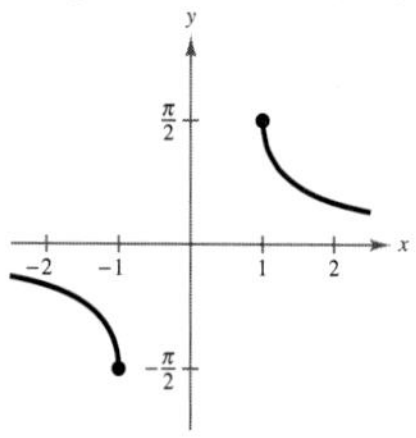

119. $\dfrac{\pi}{4}$ **121.** $\dfrac{3\pi}{4}$ **123.** $\dfrac{\pi}{6}$ **125.** $\dfrac{\pi}{3}$ **127.** 1.17

129. 0.19 **131.** 0.54 **133.** -0.12

135. (a) $\dfrac{\pi}{4}$ (b) $\dfrac{\pi}{2}$ (c) 1.25 (d) 2.03

137. (a) $f \circ f^{-1}$

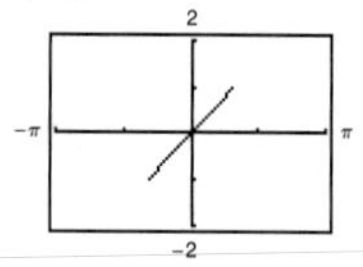

$f^{-1} \circ f$

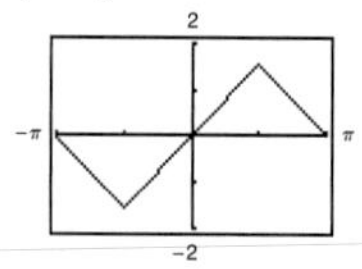

(b) The domains and ranges of the functions are restricted. The graphs of $f \circ f^{-1}$ and $f^{-1} \circ f$ differ because of the domains and ranges of f and f^{-1}.

Section 4.8 *(page 357)*

1. bearing **3.** period

5. $a \approx 1.73$
$c \approx 3.46$
$B = 60°$

7. $a \approx 8.26$
$c \approx 25.38$
$A = 19°$

9. $c = 5$
$A \approx 36.87°$
$B \approx 53.13°$

11. $a \approx 49.48$ $A \approx 72.08°$ $B \approx 17.92°$
13. $a \approx 91.34$ $b \approx 420.70$ $B = 77°45'$

15. 3.00 **17.** 2.50 **19.** 214.45 ft **21.** 19.7 ft

23. 19.9 ft **25.** 11.8 km **27.** 56.3° **29.** 2.06°

31. (a) $\sqrt{h^2 + 34h + 10{,}289}$ (b) $\theta = \arccos\left(\frac{100}{l}\right)$
(c) 53.02 ft

33. (a) $l = 250$ ft, $A \approx 36.87°$, $B \approx 53.13°$
(b) 4.87 sec

35. 554 mi north; 709 mi east

37. (a) 104.95 nautical mi south; 58.18 nautical mi west
(b) S 36.7° W; distance = 130.9 nautical mi

39. N 56.31° W **41.** (a) N 58° E (b) 68.82 m

43. 78.7° **45.** 35.3° **47.** 29.4 in. **49.** $y = \sqrt{3}r$

51. $a \approx 12.2, b \approx 7$ **53.** $d = 4\sin(\pi t)$

55. $d = 3\cos\left(\frac{4\pi t}{3}\right)$

57. (a) 9 (b) $\frac{3}{5}$ (c) 9 (d) $\frac{5}{12}$

59. (a) $\frac{1}{4}$ (b) 3 (c) 0 (d) $\frac{1}{6}$ **61.** $\omega = 528\pi$

63. (a)

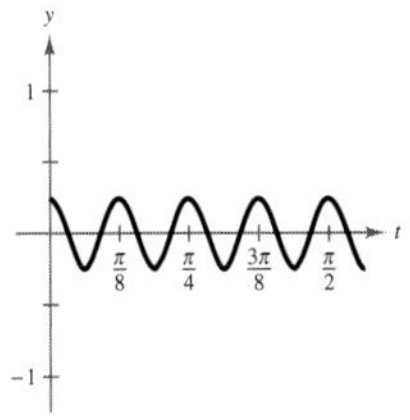

(b) $\frac{\pi}{8}$ (c) $\frac{\pi}{32}$

65. (a)

θ	L_1	L_2	$L_1 + L_2$
0.1	$\frac{2}{\sin 0.1}$	$\frac{3}{\cos 0.1}$	23.0
0.2	$\frac{2}{\sin 0.2}$	$\frac{3}{\cos 0.2}$	13.1
0.3	$\frac{2}{\sin 0.3}$	$\frac{3}{\cos 0.3}$	9.9
0.4	$\frac{2}{\sin 0.4}$	$\frac{3}{\cos 0.4}$	8.4

(b)

θ	L_1	L_2	$L_1 + L_2$
0.5	$\frac{2}{\sin 0.5}$	$\frac{3}{\cos 0.5}$	7.6
0.6	$\frac{2}{\sin 0.6}$	$\frac{3}{\cos 0.6}$	7.2
0.7	$\frac{2}{\sin 0.7}$	$\frac{3}{\cos 0.7}$	7.0
0.8	$\frac{2}{\sin 0.8}$	$\frac{3}{\cos 0.8}$	7.1

7.0 m

(c) $L = L_1 + L_2 = \frac{2}{\sin\theta} + \frac{3}{\cos\theta}$

(d)

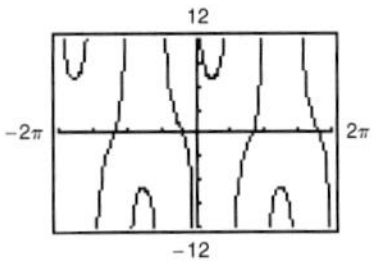

7.0 m; The answers are the same.

67. (a)

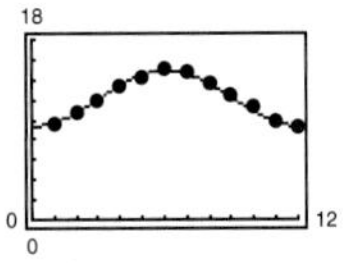

(b) 12; Yes, there are 12 months in a year.
(c) 2.77; The maximum change in the number of hours of daylight

69. False. The scenario does not create a right triangle because the tower is not vertical.

Review Exercises *(page 364)*

1. (a)

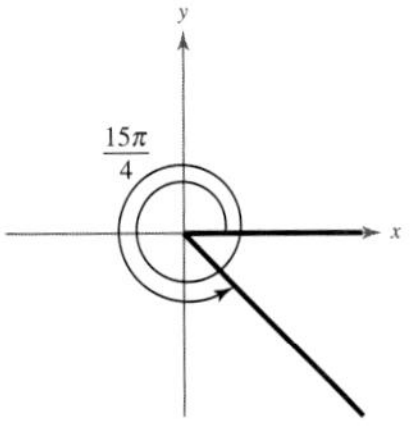

(b) Quadrant IV
(c) $\frac{23\pi}{4}, -\frac{\pi}{4}$

3. (a)

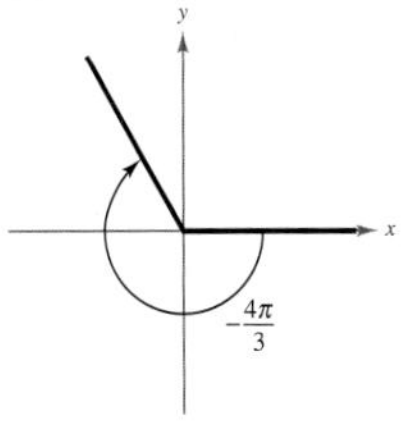

(b) Quadrant II
(c) $\frac{2\pi}{3}, -\frac{10\pi}{3}$

5. (a)

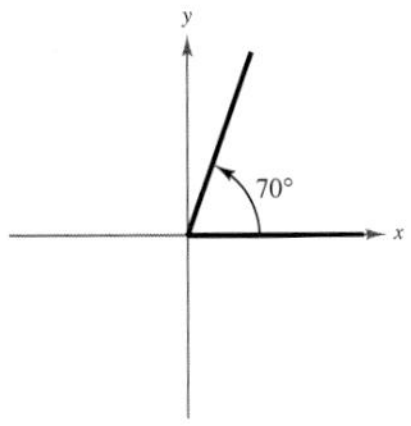

(b) Quadrant I
(c) 430°, −290°

7. (a)

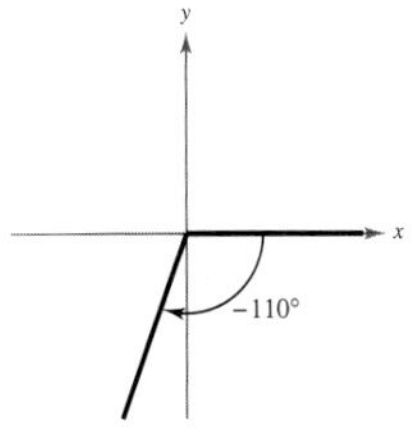

(b) Quadrant III
(c) 250°, −470°

9. 7.854 **11.** −0.589 **13.** 54.000° **15.** −200.535°

17. 198° 24′ **19.** 0° 39′ **21.** 48.17 in.

23. Area ≈ 339.29 in.^{2} **25.** $\left(-\frac{1}{2}, \frac{\sqrt{3}}{2}\right)$

27. $\left(-\frac{\sqrt{3}}{2}, -\frac{1}{2}\right)$

29. $\sin\frac{7\pi}{6} = -\frac{1}{2}$ $\quad \csc\frac{7\pi}{6} = -2$

$\cos\frac{7\pi}{6} = -\frac{\sqrt{3}}{2}$ $\quad \sec\frac{7\pi}{6} = -\frac{2\sqrt{3}}{3}$

$\tan\frac{7\pi}{6} = \frac{\sqrt{3}}{3}$ $\quad \cot\frac{7\pi}{6} = \sqrt{3}$

31. $\sin\left(-\frac{2\pi}{3}\right) = -\frac{\sqrt{3}}{2}$ $\quad \csc\left(-\frac{2\pi}{3}\right) = -\frac{2\sqrt{3}}{3}$

$\cos\left(-\frac{2\pi}{3}\right) = -\frac{1}{2}$ $\quad \sec\left(-\frac{2\pi}{3}\right) = -2$

$\tan\left(-\frac{2\pi}{3}\right) = \sqrt{3}$ $\quad \cot\left(-\frac{2\pi}{3}\right) = \frac{\sqrt{3}}{3}$

33. $\sin\frac{11\pi}{4} = \sin\frac{3\pi}{4} = \frac{\sqrt{2}}{2}$

35. $\sin\left(-\frac{17\pi}{6}\right) = \sin\frac{7\pi}{6} = -\frac{1}{2}$

37. -75.3130 **39.** 3.2361

41. $\sin\theta = \frac{4\sqrt{41}}{41}$ $\quad \csc\theta = \frac{\sqrt{41}}{4}$

$\cos\theta = \frac{5\sqrt{41}}{41}$ $\quad \sec\theta = \frac{\sqrt{41}}{5}$

$\tan\theta = \frac{4}{5}$ $\quad \cot\theta = \frac{5}{4}$

43. (a) 3 (b) $\frac{2\sqrt{2}}{3}$ (c) $\frac{3\sqrt{2}}{4}$ (d) $\frac{\sqrt{2}}{4}$

45. (a) $\frac{1}{4}$ (b) $\frac{\sqrt{15}}{4}$ (c) $\frac{4\sqrt{15}}{15}$ (d) $\frac{\sqrt{15}}{15}$

47. 0.6494 **49.** 0.5621 **51.** 3.6722

53. 0.6104 **55.** 71.3 m

57. $\sin\theta = \frac{4}{5}$ $\quad \csc\theta = \frac{5}{4}$

$\cos\theta = \frac{3}{5}$ $\quad \sec\theta = \frac{5}{3}$

$\tan\theta = \frac{4}{3}$ $\quad \cot\theta = \frac{3}{4}$

59. $\sin\theta = \frac{15\sqrt{241}}{241}$ $\quad \csc\theta = \frac{\sqrt{241}}{15}$

$\cos\theta = \frac{4\sqrt{241}}{241}$ $\quad \sec\theta = \frac{\sqrt{241}}{4}$

$\tan\theta = \frac{15}{4}$ $\quad \cot\theta = \frac{4}{15}$

61. $\sin\theta = \frac{9\sqrt{82}}{82}$ $\quad \csc\theta = \frac{\sqrt{82}}{9}$

$\cos\theta = \frac{-\sqrt{82}}{82}$ $\quad \sec\theta = -\sqrt{82}$

$\tan\theta = -9$ $\quad \cot\theta = -\frac{1}{9}$

63. $\sin\theta = \frac{4\sqrt{17}}{17}$ $\quad \csc\theta = \frac{\sqrt{17}}{4}$

$\cos\theta = \frac{\sqrt{17}}{17}$ $\quad \sec\theta = \sqrt{17}$

$\tan\theta = 4$ $\quad \cot\theta = \frac{1}{4}$

65. $\sin\theta = -\frac{\sqrt{11}}{6}$ $\quad \csc\theta = -\frac{6\sqrt{11}}{11}$

$\cos\theta = \frac{5}{6}$ $\quad \cot\theta = -\frac{5\sqrt{11}}{11}$

$\tan\theta = -\frac{\sqrt{11}}{5}$

67. $\cos\theta = -\frac{\sqrt{55}}{8}$ $\quad \sec\theta = -\frac{8\sqrt{55}}{55}$

$\tan\theta = -\frac{3\sqrt{55}}{55}$ $\quad \cot\theta = -\frac{\sqrt{55}}{3}$

$\csc\theta = \frac{8}{3}$

69. $\sin\theta = \frac{\sqrt{21}}{5}$ $\quad \sec\theta = -\frac{5}{2}$

$\tan\theta = -\frac{\sqrt{21}}{2}$ $\quad \cot\theta = -\frac{2\sqrt{21}}{21}$

$\csc\theta = \frac{5\sqrt{21}}{21}$

71. $\theta' = 84°$

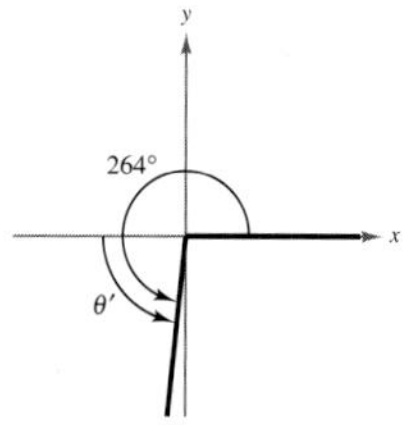

73. $\theta' = \frac{\pi}{5}$

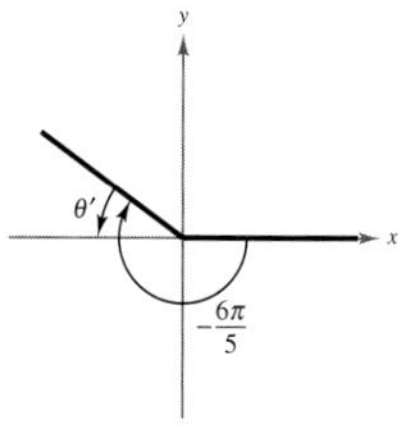

75. $\sin\frac{\pi}{3} = \frac{\sqrt{3}}{2}$; $\cos\frac{\pi}{3} = \frac{1}{2}$; $\tan\frac{\pi}{3} = \sqrt{3}$

77. $\sin\left(-\frac{7\pi}{3}\right) = -\frac{\sqrt{3}}{2}$; $\cos\left(-\frac{7\pi}{3}\right) = \frac{1}{2}$;

$\tan\left(-\frac{7\pi}{3}\right) = -\sqrt{3}$

79. $\sin 495° = \frac{\sqrt{2}}{2}$; $\cos 495° = -\frac{\sqrt{2}}{2}$; $\tan 495° = -1$

81. -0.7568 **83.** 0.9511

85.

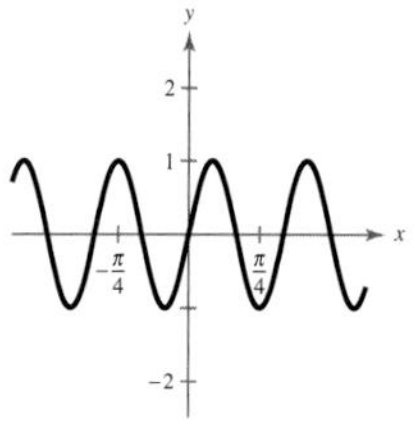

87.

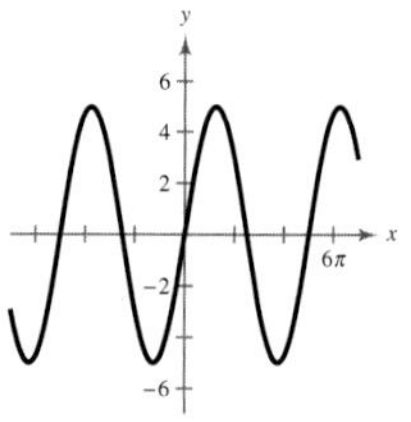

89.

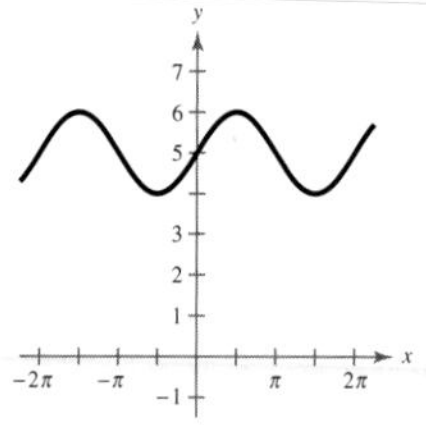

91.

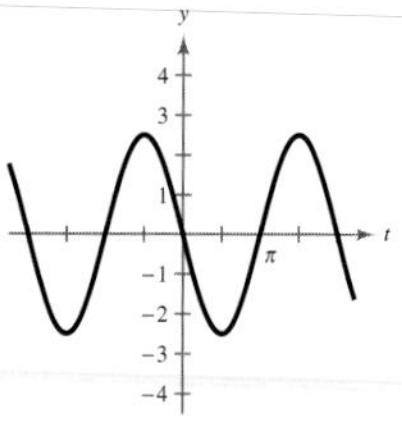

93. (a) $y = 2 \sin 528\pi x$ (b) 264 cycles/sec

95.

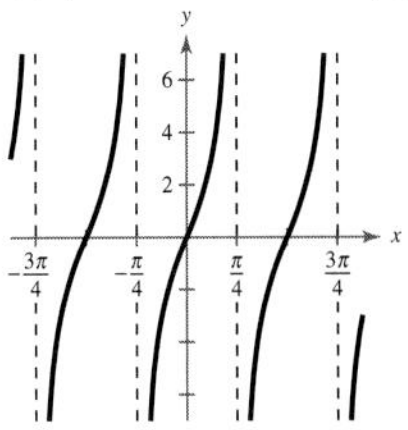

97.

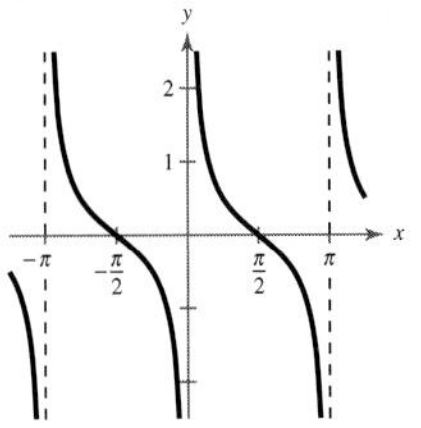

99.

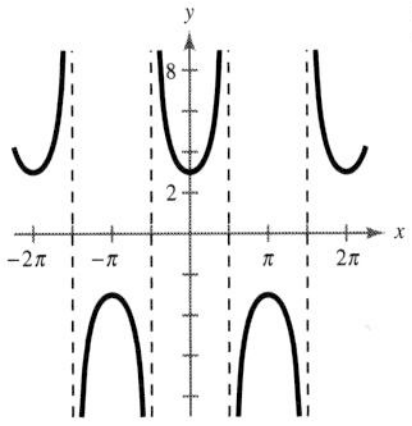

101.

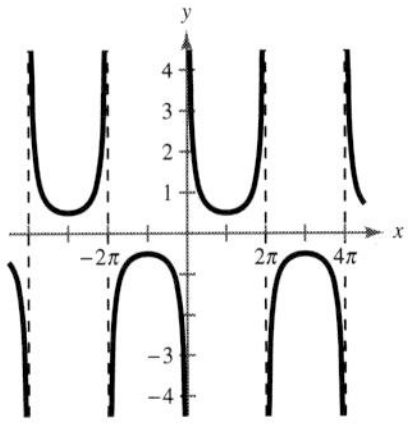

103.

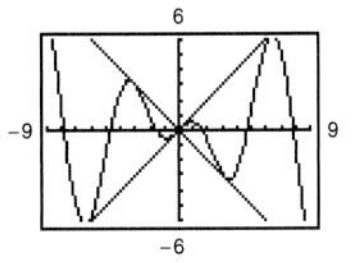

As $x \to +\infty$, $f(x)$ oscillates.

105. $-\frac{\pi}{6}$ **107.** 0.41 **109.** -0.46 **111.** $\frac{3\pi}{4}$

113. π **115.** 1.24 **117.** -0.98

119.

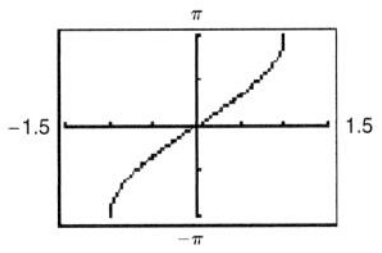

121.

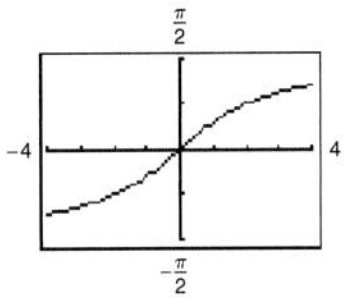

123. $\frac{4}{5}$ **125.** $\frac{13}{5}$ **127.** $\frac{10}{7}$ **129.** $\frac{\sqrt{4 - x^2}}{x}$

131. $\frac{\pi}{6}$ **133.** $\frac{3\pi}{4}$ **135.** 0.09 **137.** 1.98

139.

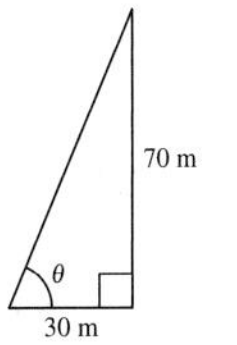

$\theta \approx 66.8°$

141. 1221 mi, 85.6°

143. False. For each θ there corresponds exactly one value of y.

145. The function is undefined because $\sec \theta = 1/\cos \theta$.

147. The ranges of the other four trigonometric functions are $(-\infty, \infty)$ or $(-\infty, -1] \cup [1, \infty)$.

Chapter Test *(page 367)*

1. (a)

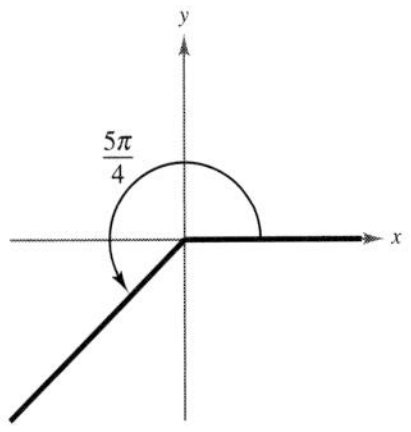

(b) $\frac{13\pi}{4}, -\frac{3\pi}{4}$

(c) 225°

2. 3500 rad/min **3.** About 709.04 ft^2

4. $\sin \theta = \frac{3\sqrt{10}}{10}$ $\csc \theta = \frac{\sqrt{10}}{3}$

$\cos \theta = -\frac{\sqrt{10}}{10}$ $\sec \theta = -\sqrt{10}$

$\tan \theta = -3$ $\cot \theta = -\frac{1}{3}$

5. For $0 \le \theta < \frac{\pi}{2}$:

$\sin \theta = \frac{3\sqrt{13}}{13}$

$\cos \theta = \frac{2\sqrt{13}}{13}$

$\csc \theta = \frac{\sqrt{13}}{3}$

$\sec \theta = \frac{\sqrt{13}}{2}$

$\cot \theta = \frac{2}{3}$

For $\pi \le \theta < \frac{3\pi}{2}$:

$\sin \theta = -\frac{3\sqrt{13}}{13}$

$\cos \theta = -\frac{2\sqrt{13}}{13}$

$\csc \theta = -\frac{\sqrt{13}}{3}$

$\sec \theta = -\frac{\sqrt{13}}{2}$

$\cot \theta = \frac{2}{3}$

6. $\theta' = 25°$

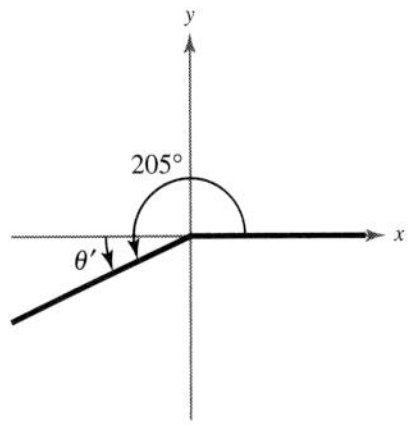

7. Quadrant III **8.** 150°, 210° **9.** 1.33, 1.81

10. $\sin \theta = -\frac{4}{5}$
$\tan \theta = -\frac{4}{3}$
$\csc \theta = -\frac{5}{4}$
$\sec \theta = \frac{5}{3}$
$\cot \theta = -\frac{3}{4}$

11. $\sin \theta = \frac{21}{29}$
$\cos \theta = -\frac{20}{29}$
$\tan \theta = -\frac{21}{20}$
$\csc \theta = \frac{29}{21}$
$\cot \theta = -\frac{20}{21}$

12.

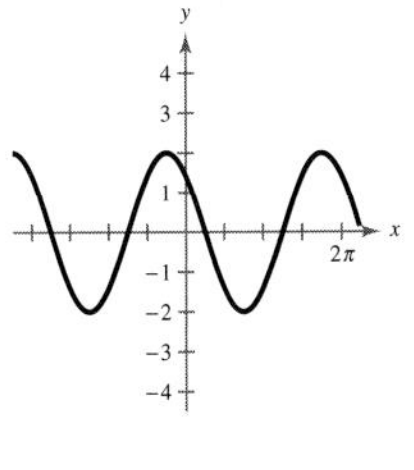

13.

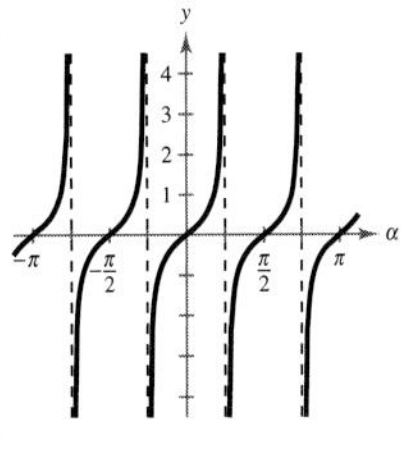

CHAPTER 4

14.

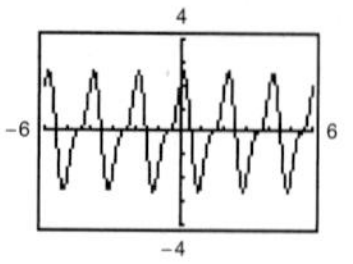

Period: 2

15.

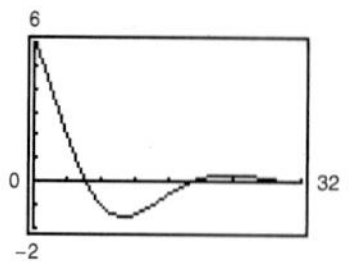

Not periodic

16. $a = -2, b = \frac{1}{2}, c = -\frac{\pi}{4}$

17. $\frac{\sqrt{55}}{3}$

18.

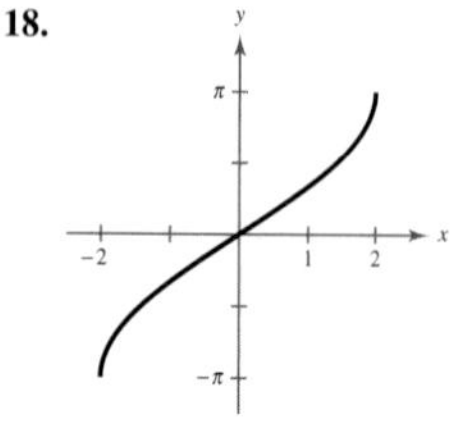

19. $309.3°$

20. $d = -6 \cos \pi t$

Problem Solving (page 369)

1. (a) $\frac{11\pi}{2}$ rad or $990°$ (b) About 816.42 ft

3. (a) 4767 ft (b) 3705 ft

(c) $w = 2183$ ft, $\tan 63° = \frac{w + 3705}{3000}$

5. (a)

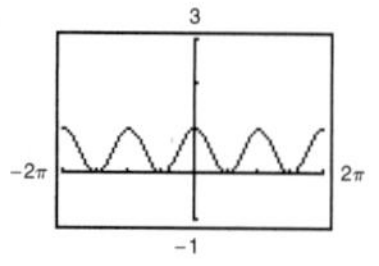

Even

(b)

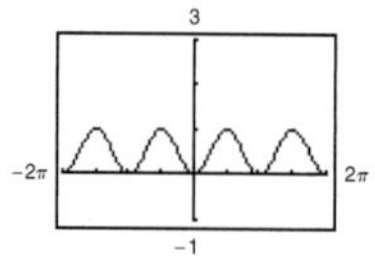

Even

7. $h = 51 - 50 \sin\left(8\pi t + \frac{\pi}{2}\right)$

9. (a)

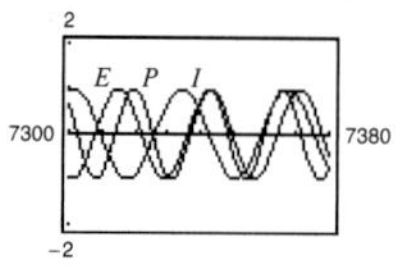

(b)

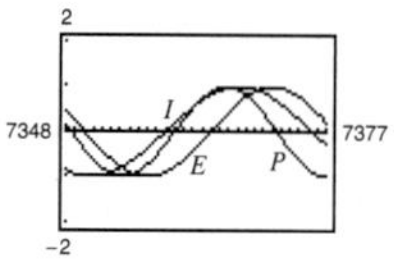

(c) $P(7369) = 0.631$
$E(7369) = 0.901$
$I(7369) = 0.945$

All three drop earlier in the month, then peak toward the middle of the month, and drop again toward the latter part of the month.

11. (a) 3.35, 7.35 (b) -0.65

(c) Yes. There is a difference of nine periods between the values.

13. (a) $40.5°$ (b) $x \approx 1.71$ ft; $y \approx 3.46$ ft

(c) About 1.75 ft

(d) As you move closer to the rock, d must get smaller and smaller. The angles θ_1 and θ_2 will decrease along with the distance y, so d will decrease.

Chapter 5

Section 5.1 (page 377)

1. $\tan u$ **3.** $\cot u$ **5.** $\cot^2 u$ **7.** $\cos u$ **9.** $\cos u$

11. $\sin x = \frac{1}{2}$
$\cos x = \frac{\sqrt{3}}{2}$
$\tan x = \frac{\sqrt{3}}{3}$
$\csc x = 2$
$\sec x = \frac{2\sqrt{3}}{3}$
$\cot x = \sqrt{3}$

13. $\sin \theta = -\frac{\sqrt{2}}{2}$
$\cos \theta = \frac{\sqrt{2}}{2}$
$\tan \theta = -1$
$\csc \theta = -\sqrt{2}$
$\sec \theta = \sqrt{2}$
$\cot \theta = -1$

15. $\sin x = -\frac{8}{17}$
$\cos x = -\frac{15}{17}$
$\tan x = \frac{8}{15}$
$\csc x = -\frac{17}{8}$
$\sec x = -\frac{17}{15}$
$\cot x = \frac{15}{8}$

17. $\sin \phi = -\frac{\sqrt{5}}{3}$
$\cos \phi = \frac{2}{3}$
$\tan \phi = -\frac{\sqrt{5}}{2}$
$\csc \phi = -\frac{3\sqrt{5}}{5}$
$\sec \phi = \frac{3}{2}$
$\cot \phi = -\frac{2\sqrt{5}}{5}$

19. $\sin x = \frac{1}{3}$
$\cos x = -\frac{2\sqrt{2}}{3}$
$\tan x = -\frac{\sqrt{2}}{4}$
$\csc x = 3$
$\sec x = -\frac{3\sqrt{2}}{4}$
$\cot x = -2\sqrt{2}$

21. $\sin \theta = -\frac{2\sqrt{5}}{5}$
$\cos \theta = -\frac{\sqrt{5}}{5}$
$\tan \theta = 2$
$\csc \theta = -\frac{\sqrt{5}}{2}$
$\sec \theta = -\sqrt{5}$
$\cot \theta = \frac{1}{2}$

23. $\sin \theta = -1$ $\csc \theta = -1$
$\cos \theta = 0$ $\sec \theta$ is undefined.
$\tan \theta$ is undefined. $\cot \theta = 0$

25. d **26.** a **27.** b **28.** f **29.** e **30.** c
31. b **32.** c **33.** f **34.** a **35.** e **36.** d
37. $\csc \theta$ **39.** $-\sin x$ **41.** $\cos^2 \phi$ **43.** $\cos x$
45. $\sin^2 x$ **47.** $\cos \theta$ **49.** 1 **51.** $\tan x$
53. $1 + \sin y$ **55.** $\sec \beta$ **57.** $\cos u + \sin u$ **59.** $\sin^2 x$
61. $\sin^2 x \tan^2 x$ **63.** $\sec x + 1$ **65.** $\sec^4 x$
67. $\sin^2 x - \cos^2 x$ **69.** $\cot^2 x(\csc x - 1)$
71. $1 + 2 \sin x \cos x$ **73.** $4 \cot^2 x$ **75.** $2 \csc^2 x$
77. $2 \sec x$ **79.** $\sec x$ **81.** $1 + \cos y$
83. $3(\sec x + \tan x)$

85.

x	0.2	0.4	0.6	0.8	1.0
y_1	0.1987	0.3894	0.5646	0.7174	0.8415
y_2	0.1987	0.3894	0.5646	0.7174	0.8415

x	1.2	1.4
y_1	0.9320	0.9854
y_2	0.9320	0.9854

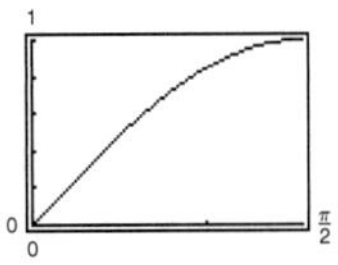

$y_1 = y_2$

87.

x	0.2	0.4	0.6	0.8	1.0
y_1	1.2230	1.5085	1.8958	2.4650	3.4082
y_2	1.2230	1.5085	1.8958	2.4650	3.4082

x	1.2	1.4
y_1	5.3319	11.6814
y_2	5.3319	11.6814

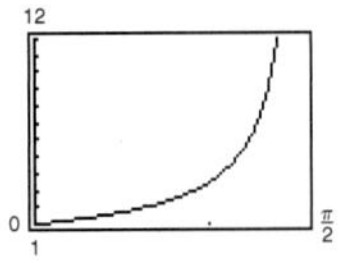

$y_1 = y_2$

89. $\csc x$ **91.** $\tan x$ **93.** $3 \sin \theta$ **95.** $4 \cos \theta$
97. $3 \tan \theta$ **99.** $5 \sec \theta$ **101.** $3 \sec \theta$ **103.** $\sqrt{2} \cos \theta$
105. $3 \cos \theta = 3$; $\sin \theta = 0$; $\cos \theta = 1$
107. $4 \sin \theta = 2\sqrt{2}$; $\sin \theta = \frac{\sqrt{2}}{2}$; $\cos \theta = \frac{\sqrt{2}}{2}$
109. $0 \leq \theta \leq \pi$ **111.** $0 \leq \theta < \frac{\pi}{2}, \frac{3\pi}{2} < \theta < 2\pi$
113. $\ln|\cot x|$ **115.** $\ln|\cos x|$ **117.** $\ln|\csc t \sec t|$
119. (a) $\csc^2 132° - \cot^2 132° \approx 1.8107 - 0.8107 = 1$
(b) $\csc^2 \frac{2\pi}{7} - \cot^2 \frac{2\pi}{7} \approx 1.6360 - 0.6360 = 1$
121. (a) $\cos(90° - 80°) = \sin 80° \approx 0.9848$
(b) $\cos\left(\frac{\pi}{2} - 0.8\right) = \sin 0.8 \approx 0.7174$
123. $\mu = \tan \theta$ **125.** Answers will vary.
127. True. For example, $\sin(-x) = -\sin x$.
129. 1, 1 **131.** ∞, 0
133. Not an identity because $\cos \theta = \pm\sqrt{1 - \sin^2 \theta}$
135. Not an identity because $\frac{\sin k\theta}{\cos k\theta} = \tan k\theta$
137. An identity because $\sin \theta \cdot \frac{1}{\sin \theta} = 1$
139. $a \cos \theta$ **141.** $a \tan \theta$

Section 5.2 *(page 385)*

1. identity **3.** $\tan u$ **5.** $\cos^2 u$ **7.** $-\csc u$
9–49. Answers will vary.
51. In the first line, $\cot(x)$ is substituted for $\cot(-x)$, which is incorrect; $\cot(-x) = -\cot(x)$.

53. (a)

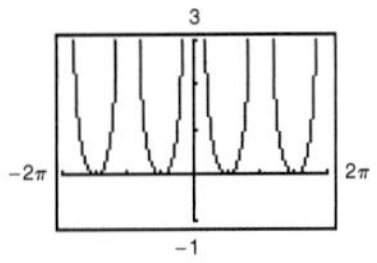

(b)

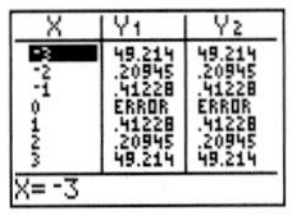

Identity

(c) Answers will vary.

55. (a)

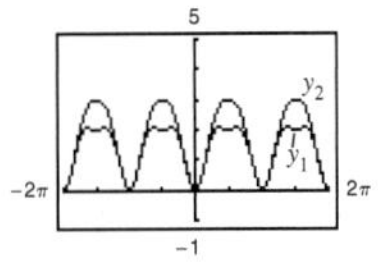

(b)

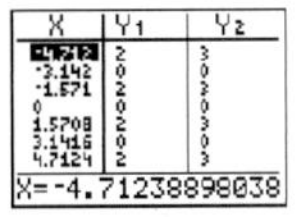

Not an identity

(c) Answers will vary.

57. (a)

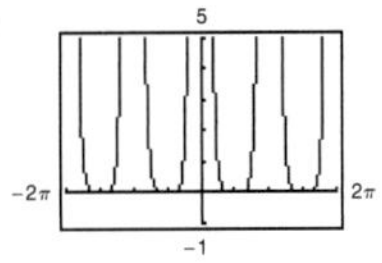

(b)

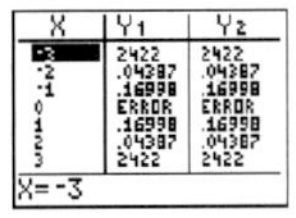

Identity

(c) Answers will vary.

59. (a)

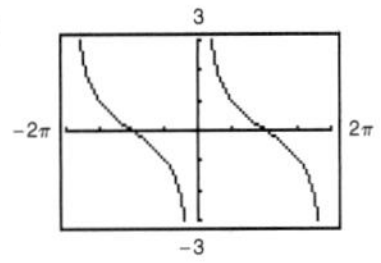

(b)

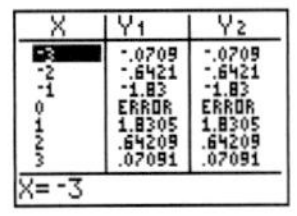

Identity

(c) Answers will vary.

61–63. Answers will vary. **65.** 1 **67.** 2
69. Answers will vary.
71. True. Many different techniques can be used to verify identities.
73. The equation is not an identity because $\sin \theta = \pm\sqrt{1 - \cos^2 \theta}$.
Possible answer: $\frac{7\pi}{4}$
75. The equation is not an identity because $1 - \cos^2 \theta = \sin^2 \theta$.
Possible answer: $-\frac{\pi}{2}$
77. The equation is not an identity because $1 + \tan^2 \theta = \sec^2 \theta$.
Possible answer: $\frac{\pi}{6}$

Section 5.3 *(page 394)*

1. isolate **3.** quadratic **5–9.** Answers will vary.
11. $\frac{2\pi}{3} + 2n\pi, \frac{4\pi}{3} + 2n\pi$ **13.** $\frac{\pi}{3} + 2n\pi, \frac{2\pi}{3} + 2n\pi$
15. $\frac{\pi}{6} + n\pi, \frac{5\pi}{6} + n\pi$ **17.** $n\pi, \frac{3\pi}{2} + 2n\pi$
19. $\frac{\pi}{3} + n\pi, \frac{2\pi}{3} + n\pi$ **21.** $\frac{\pi}{8} + \frac{n\pi}{2}, \frac{3\pi}{8} + \frac{n\pi}{2}$
23. $\frac{n\pi}{3}, \frac{\pi}{4} + n\pi$ **25.** $0, \frac{\pi}{2}, \pi, \frac{3\pi}{2}$
27. $0, \pi, \frac{\pi}{6}, \frac{5\pi}{6}, \frac{7\pi}{6}, \frac{11\pi}{6}$ **29.** $\frac{\pi}{3}, \frac{5\pi}{3}, \pi$
31. No solution **33.** $\pi, \frac{\pi}{3}, \frac{5\pi}{3}$
35. $\frac{\pi}{6}, \frac{5\pi}{6}, \frac{7\pi}{6}, \frac{11\pi}{6}$ **37.** $\frac{\pi}{2}$ **39.** $\frac{\pi}{6} + n\pi, \frac{5\pi}{6} + n\pi$

CHAPTER 5

41. $\frac{\pi}{12} + \frac{n\pi}{3}$ **43.** $\frac{\pi}{2} + 4n\pi, \frac{7\pi}{2} + 4n\pi$ **45.** $3 + 4n$

47. $-2 + 6n, 2 + 6n$ **49.** 2.678, 5.820

51. 1.047, 5.236 **53.** 0.860, 3.426

55. 0, 2.678, 3.142, 5.820 **57.** 0.983, 1.768, 4.124, 4.910

59. 0.3398, 0.8481, 2.2935, 2.8018

61. 1.9357, 2.7767, 5.0773, 5.9183

63. $\arctan(-4) + \pi, \arctan(-4) + 2\pi, \arctan 3, \arctan 3 + \pi$

65. $\frac{\pi}{4}, \frac{5\pi}{4}$, arctan 5, arctan 5 + π **67.** $\frac{\pi}{3}, \frac{5\pi}{3}$

69. $\arctan(\frac{1}{3}), \arctan(\frac{1}{3}) + \pi, \arctan(-\frac{1}{3}) + \pi, \arctan(-\frac{1}{3}) + 2\pi$

71. $\arccos(\frac{1}{4}), 2\pi - \arccos(\frac{1}{4})$

73. $\frac{\pi}{2}, \arcsin\left(-\frac{1}{4}\right) + 2\pi, \arcsin\left(\frac{1}{4}\right) + \pi$

75. $-1.154, 0.534$ **77.** 1.110

79. (a)

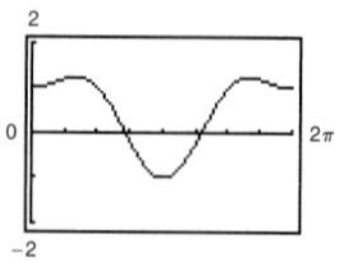

Maximum: (1.0472, 1.25)
Maximum: (5.2360, 1.25)
Minimum: (0, 1)
Minimum: (3.1416, −1)

(b) $\frac{\pi}{3} \approx 1.0472$
$\frac{5\pi}{3} \approx 5.2360$
0
$\pi \approx 3.1416$

81. (a)

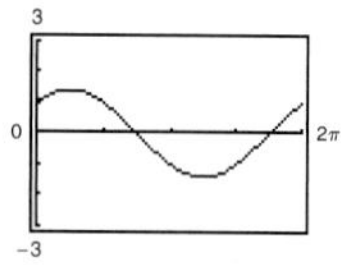

Maximum: (0.7854, 1.4142)
Minimum: (3.9270, −1.4142)

(b) $\frac{\pi}{4} \approx 0.7854$
$\frac{5\pi}{4} \approx 3.9270$

83. (a)

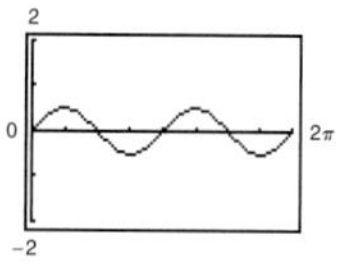

Maximum: (0.7854, 0.5)
Maximum: (3.9270, 0.5)
Minimum: (2.3562, −0.5)
Minimum: (5.4978, −0.5)

(b) $\frac{\pi}{4} \approx 0.7854$
$\frac{5\pi}{4} \approx 3.9270$
$\frac{3\pi}{4} \approx 2.3562$
$\frac{7\pi}{4} \approx 5.4978$

85. 1

87. (a) All real numbers x except $x = 0$
(b) y-axis symmetry; Horizontal asymptote: $y = 1$
(c) Oscillates (d) Infinitely many solutions; $\frac{2}{2n\pi + \pi}$
(e) Yes, 0.6366

89. 0.04 sec, 0.43 sec, 0.83 sec

91. February, March, and April **93.** 36.9°, 53.1°

95. (a) $t = 8$ sec and $t = 24$ sec
(b) 5 times: $t = 16, 48, 80, 112, 144$ sec

97. (a)

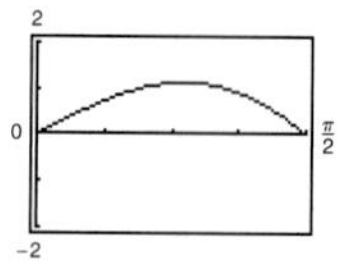

$A \approx 1.12$

(b) $0.6 < x < 1.1$

99. True. The first equation has a smaller period than the second equation, so it will have more solutions in the interval $[0, 2\pi)$.

101. The equation would become $\cos^2 x = 2$; this is not the correct method to use when solving equations.

103. Answers will vary.

Section 5.4 *(page 402)*

1. $\sin u \cos v - \cos u \sin v$ **3.** $\frac{\tan u + \tan v}{1 - \tan u \tan v}$

5. $\cos u \cos v + \sin u \sin v$

7. (a) $\frac{\sqrt{2} - \sqrt{6}}{4}$ (b) $\frac{\sqrt{2} + 1}{2}$

9. (a) $\frac{1}{2}$ (b) $\frac{-\sqrt{3} - 1}{2}$

11. (a) $\frac{\sqrt{6} + \sqrt{2}}{4}$ (b) $\frac{\sqrt{2} - \sqrt{3}}{2}$

13. $\sin \frac{11\pi}{12} = \frac{\sqrt{2}}{4}(\sqrt{3} - 1)$
$\cos \frac{11\pi}{12} = -\frac{\sqrt{2}}{4}(\sqrt{3} + 1)$
$\tan \frac{11\pi}{12} = -2 + \sqrt{3}$

15. $\sin \frac{17\pi}{12} = -\frac{\sqrt{2}}{4}(\sqrt{3} + 1)$
$\cos \frac{17\pi}{12} = \frac{\sqrt{2}}{4}(1 - \sqrt{3})$
$\tan \frac{17\pi}{12} = 2 + \sqrt{3}$

17. $\sin 105° = \frac{\sqrt{2}}{4}(\sqrt{3} + 1)$
$\cos 105° = \frac{\sqrt{2}}{4}(1 - \sqrt{3})$
$\tan 105° = -2 - \sqrt{3}$

19. $\sin 195° = \frac{\sqrt{2}}{4}(1 - \sqrt{3})$
$\cos 195° = -\frac{\sqrt{2}}{4}(\sqrt{3} + 1)$
$\tan 195° = 2 - \sqrt{3}$

21. $\sin \frac{13\pi}{12} = \frac{\sqrt{2}}{4}(1 - \sqrt{3})$
$\cos \frac{13\pi}{12} = -\frac{\sqrt{2}}{4}(1 + \sqrt{3})$
$\tan \frac{13\pi}{12} = 2 - \sqrt{3}$

23. $\sin\left(-\frac{13\pi}{12}\right) = \frac{\sqrt{2}}{4}(\sqrt{3} - 1)$
$\cos\left(-\frac{13\pi}{12}\right) = -\frac{\sqrt{2}}{4}(\sqrt{3} + 1)$
$\tan\left(-\frac{13\pi}{12}\right) = -2 + \sqrt{3}$

25. $\sin 285° = -\frac{\sqrt{2}}{4}(\sqrt{3} + 1)$

$\cos 285° = \frac{\sqrt{2}}{4}(\sqrt{3} - 1)$

$\tan 285° = -(2 + \sqrt{3})$

27. $\sin(-165°) = -\frac{\sqrt{2}}{4}(\sqrt{3} - 1)$

$\cos(-165°) = -\frac{\sqrt{2}}{4}(1 + \sqrt{3})$

$\tan(-165°) = 2 - \sqrt{3}$

29. $\sin 1.8$ **31.** $\sin 75°$ **33.** $\tan 15°$ **35.** $\tan 3x$

37. $\frac{\sqrt{3}}{2}$ **39.** $\frac{\sqrt{3}}{2}$ **41.** $-\sqrt{3}$ **43.** $-\frac{63}{65}$ **45.** $\frac{16}{65}$

47. $-\frac{63}{16}$ **49.** $\frac{65}{56}$ **51.** $\frac{3}{5}$ **53.** $-\frac{44}{117}$ **55.** $-\frac{125}{44}$

57. 1 **59.** 0 **61–69.** Proofs **71.** $-\sin x$

73. $-\cos\theta$ **75.** $\frac{\pi}{6}, \frac{5\pi}{6}$ **77.** $\frac{2\pi}{3}, \frac{4\pi}{3}$ **79.** $\frac{\pi}{3}, \frac{5\pi}{3}$

81. $\frac{5\pi}{4}, \frac{7\pi}{4}$ **83.** $0, \frac{\pi}{2}, \frac{3\pi}{2}$ **85.** $\frac{\pi}{4}, \frac{7\pi}{4}$ **87.** $\frac{\pi}{2}, \pi, \frac{3\pi}{2}$

89. (a) $y = \frac{5}{12}\sin(2t + 0.6435)$ (b) $\frac{5}{12}$ ft (c) $\frac{1}{\pi}$ cycle/sec

91. True. $\sin(u \pm v) = \sin u \cos v \pm \cos u \sin v$

93. False. $\tan\left(x - \frac{\pi}{4}\right) = \frac{\tan x - 1}{1 + \tan x}$

95–97. Answers will vary.

99. (a) $\sqrt{2}\sin\left(\theta + \frac{\pi}{4}\right)$ (b) $\sqrt{2}\cos\left(\theta - \frac{\pi}{4}\right)$

101. (a) $13\sin(3\theta + 0.3948)$ (b) $13\cos(3\theta - 1.1760)$

103. $\sqrt{2}\sin\theta + \sqrt{2}\cos\theta$ **105.** Answers will vary.

107. 15°

109.

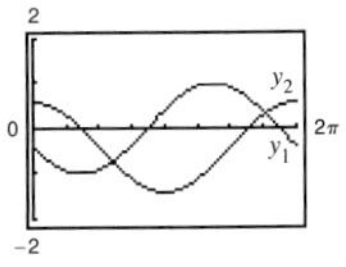

No, $y_1 \neq y_2$ because their graphs are different.

111. (a) and (b) Proofs

Section 5.5 *(page 413)*

1. $2\sin u\cos u$

3. $\cos^2 u - \sin^2 u = 2\cos^2 u - 1 = 1 - 2\sin^2 u$

5. $\pm\sqrt{\frac{1 - \cos u}{2}}$ **7.** $\frac{1}{2}[\cos(u - v) + \cos(u + v)]$

9. $2\sin\left(\frac{u + v}{2}\right)\cos\left(\frac{u - v}{2}\right)$ **11.** $\frac{15}{17}$ **13.** $\frac{8}{15}$

15. $\frac{17}{8}$ **17.** $\frac{240}{289}$ **19.** $0, \frac{\pi}{3}, \pi, \frac{5\pi}{3}$

21. $\frac{\pi}{12}, \frac{5\pi}{12}, \frac{13\pi}{12}, \frac{17\pi}{12}$ **23.** $0, \frac{2\pi}{3}, \frac{4\pi}{3}$ **25.** $0, \frac{\pi}{2}, \pi, \frac{3\pi}{2}$

27. $\frac{\pi}{2}, \frac{\pi}{6}, \frac{5\pi}{6}, \frac{7\pi}{6}, \frac{3\pi}{2}, \frac{11\pi}{6}$ **29.** $3\sin 2x$ **31.** $3\cos 2x$

33. $4\cos 2x$ **35.** $\cos 2x$

37. $\sin 2u = -\frac{24}{25}$, $\cos 2u = \frac{7}{25}$, $\tan 2u = -\frac{24}{7}$

39. $\sin 2u = \frac{15}{17}$, $\cos 2u = \frac{8}{17}$, $\tan 2u = \frac{15}{8}$

41. $\sin 2u = -\frac{\sqrt{3}}{2}$, $\cos 2u = -\frac{1}{2}$, $\tan 2u = \sqrt{3}$

43. $\frac{1}{8}(3 + 4\cos 2x + \cos 4x)$ **45.** $\frac{1}{8}(3 + 4\cos 4x + \cos 8x)$

47. $\frac{(3 - 4\cos 4x + \cos 8x)}{(3 + 4\cos 4x + \cos 8x)}$ **49.** $\frac{1}{8}(1 - \cos 8x)$

51. $\frac{1}{16}(1 - \cos 2x - \cos 4x + \cos 2x\cos 4x)$

53. $\frac{4\sqrt{17}}{17}$ **55.** $\frac{1}{4}$ **57.** $\sqrt{17}$

59. $\sin 75° = \frac{1}{2}\sqrt{2 + \sqrt{3}}$

$\cos 75° = \frac{1}{2}\sqrt{2 - \sqrt{3}}$

$\tan 75° = 2 + \sqrt{3}$

61. $\sin 112° 30' = \frac{1}{2}\sqrt{2 + \sqrt{2}}$

$\cos 112° 30' = -\frac{1}{2}\sqrt{2 - \sqrt{2}}$

$\tan 112° 30' = -1 - \sqrt{2}$

63. $\sin\frac{\pi}{8} = \frac{1}{2}\sqrt{2 - \sqrt{2}}$

$\cos\frac{\pi}{8} = \frac{1}{2}\sqrt{2 + \sqrt{2}}$

$\tan\frac{\pi}{8} = \sqrt{2} - 1$

65. $\sin\frac{3\pi}{8} = \frac{1}{2}\sqrt{2 + \sqrt{2}}$

$\cos\frac{3\pi}{8} = \frac{1}{2}\sqrt{2 - \sqrt{2}}$

$\tan\frac{3\pi}{8} = \sqrt{2} + 1$

67. (a) Quadrant I

(b) $\sin\frac{u}{2} = \frac{3}{5}$, $\cos\frac{u}{2} = \frac{4}{5}$, $\tan\frac{u}{2} = \frac{3}{4}$

69. (a) Quadrant II

(b) $\sin\frac{u}{2} = \frac{\sqrt{26}}{26}$, $\cos\frac{u}{2} = -\frac{5\sqrt{26}}{26}$, $\tan\frac{u}{2} = -\frac{1}{5}$

71. (a) Quadrant II

(b) $\sin\frac{u}{2} = \frac{3\sqrt{10}}{10}$, $\cos\frac{u}{2} = -\frac{\sqrt{10}}{10}$, $\tan\frac{u}{2} = -3$

73. $|\sin 3x|$ **75.** $-|\tan 4x|$

77. π

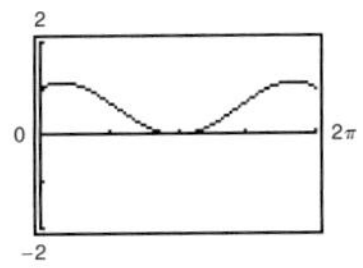

79. $\frac{\pi}{3}, \pi, \frac{5\pi}{3}$

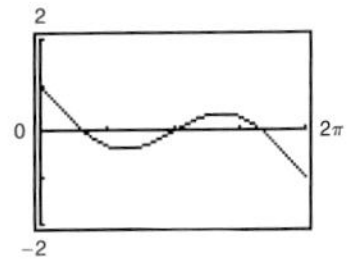

81. $\frac{1}{2}\left(\sin\frac{\pi}{2} + \sin\frac{\pi}{6}\right)$ **83.** $5(\cos 60° + \cos 90°)$

85. $\frac{1}{2}(\cos 2\theta - \cos 8\theta)$ **87.** $\frac{7}{2}(\sin(-2\beta) - \sin(-8\beta))$

89. $\frac{1}{2}(\cos 2y - \cos 2x)$ **91.** $2\sin 2\theta\cos\theta$

93. $2\cos 4x\cos 2x$ **95.** $2\cos\alpha\sin\beta$

97. $-2\sin\theta\sin\frac{\pi}{2} = -2\sin\theta$ **99.** $\frac{\sqrt{6}}{2}$ **101.** $-\sqrt{2}$

CHAPTER 5

103. $0, \frac{\pi}{4}, \frac{\pi}{2}, \frac{3\pi}{4}, \pi, \frac{5\pi}{4}, \frac{3\pi}{2}, \frac{7\pi}{4}$

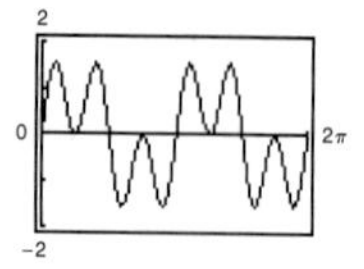

105. $\frac{\pi}{6}, \frac{5\pi}{6}$

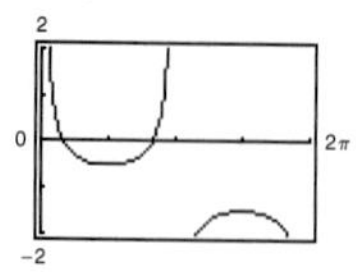

107. $\frac{120}{169}$ **109.** $\frac{3\sqrt{10}}{10}$ **111–123.** Answers will vary.

125.

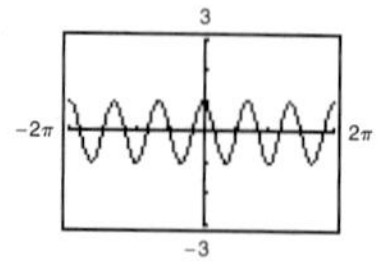

127.

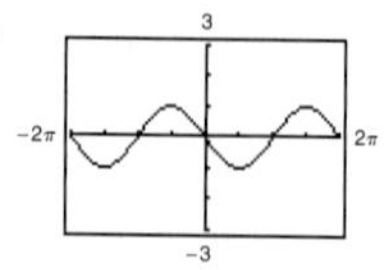

129.

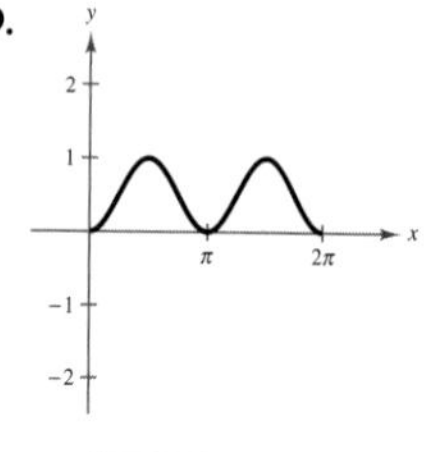

131. $2x\sqrt{1-x^2}$ **133.** $1 - 2x^2$ **135.** 23.85°

137. (a) π (b) 0.4482 (c) 760 mi/h; 3420 mi/h

(d) $\theta = 2\sin^{-1}\left(\frac{1}{M}\right)$

139. False. For $u < 0$,

$$\begin{aligned}\sin 2u &= -\sin(-2u)\\ &= -2\sin(-u)\cos(-u)\\ &= -2(-\sin u)\cos u\\ &= 2\sin u\cos u.\end{aligned}$$

Review Exercises *(page 418)*

1. $\tan x$ **3.** $\cos x$ **5.** $|\csc x|$

7. $\tan x = \frac{5}{12}$, $\csc x = \frac{13}{5}$, $\sec x = \frac{13}{12}$, $\cot x = \frac{12}{5}$

9. $\cos x = \frac{\sqrt{2}}{2}$, $\tan x = -1$, $\csc x = -\sqrt{2}$, $\sec x = \sqrt{2}$, $\cot x = -1$

11. $\sin^2 x$ **13.** 1 **15.** $\cot\theta$ **17.** $\csc\theta$ **19.** $\cot^2 x$

21. $\sec x + 2\sin x$ **23.** $-2\tan^2\theta$ **25.** $5\cos\theta$

27–35. Answers will vary.

37. $\frac{\pi}{3} + 2n\pi, \frac{2\pi}{3} + 2n\pi$ **39.** $\frac{\pi}{6} + n\pi$

41. $\frac{\pi}{3} + n\pi, \frac{2\pi}{3} + n\pi$ **43.** $0, \frac{2\pi}{3}, \frac{4\pi}{3}$ **45.** $0, \frac{\pi}{2}, \pi$

47. $\frac{\pi}{8}, \frac{3\pi}{8}, \frac{9\pi}{8}, \frac{11\pi}{8}$ **49.** $\frac{\pi}{2}$

51. $0, \frac{\pi}{8}, \frac{3\pi}{8}, \frac{5\pi}{8}, \frac{7\pi}{8}, \frac{9\pi}{8}, \frac{11\pi}{8}, \frac{13\pi}{8}, \frac{15\pi}{8}$

53. $0, \pi$

55. $\arctan(-3) + \pi, \arctan(-3) + 2\pi, \arctan 2, \arctan 2 + \pi$

57. $\sin 285° = -\frac{\sqrt{2}}{4}(\sqrt{3}+1)$

$\cos 285° = \frac{\sqrt{2}}{4}(\sqrt{3}-1)$

$\tan 285° = -2 - \sqrt{3}$

59. $\sin\frac{25\pi}{12} = \frac{\sqrt{2}}{4}(\sqrt{3}-1)$

$\cos\frac{25\pi}{12} = \frac{\sqrt{2}}{4}(\sqrt{3}+1)$

$\tan\frac{25\pi}{12} = 2 - \sqrt{3}$

61. $\sin 15°$ **63.** $\tan 35°$ **65.** $-\frac{24}{25}$ **67.** -1

69. $-\frac{7}{25}$ **71–75.** Answers will vary.

77. $\frac{\pi}{4}, \frac{7\pi}{4}$ **79.** $\frac{\pi}{6}, \frac{11\pi}{6}$

81. $\sin 2u = \frac{24}{25}$

$\cos 2u = -\frac{7}{25}$

$\tan 2u = -\frac{24}{7}$

83. $\sin 2u = -\frac{4\sqrt{2}}{9}, \cos 2u = -\frac{7}{9}, \tan 2u = \frac{4\sqrt{2}}{7}$

85.

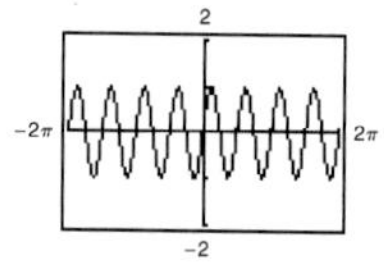

87. $\frac{1-\cos 4x}{1+\cos 4x}$ **89.** $\frac{3 - 4\cos 2x + \cos 4x}{4(1+\cos 2x)}$

91. $\sin(-75°) = -\frac{1}{2}\sqrt{2+\sqrt{3}}$

$\cos(-75°) = \frac{1}{2}\sqrt{2-\sqrt{3}}$

$\tan(-75°) = -2 - \sqrt{3}$

93. $\sin\frac{19\pi}{12} = -\frac{1}{2}\sqrt{2+\sqrt{3}}$

$\cos\frac{19\pi}{12} = \frac{1}{2}\sqrt{2-\sqrt{3}}$

$\tan\frac{19\pi}{12} = -2 - \sqrt{3}$

95. (a) Quadrant I

(b) $\sin\frac{u}{2} = \frac{\sqrt{2}}{10}, \cos\frac{u}{2} = \frac{7\sqrt{2}}{10}, \tan\frac{u}{2} = \frac{1}{7}$

97. (a) Quadrant I

(b) $\sin\frac{u}{2} = \frac{3\sqrt{14}}{14}, \cos\frac{u}{2} = \frac{\sqrt{70}}{14}, \tan\frac{u}{2} = \frac{3\sqrt{5}}{5}$

99. $-|\cos 5x|$ **101.** $\frac{1}{2}\left(\sin\frac{\pi}{3} - \sin 0\right) = \frac{1}{2}\sin\frac{\pi}{3}$

103. $\frac{1}{2}[\sin 10\theta - \sin(-2\theta)]$ **105.** $2\cos 6\theta\sin(-2\theta)$

107. $-2\sin x\sin\frac{\pi}{6}$ **109.** $\theta = 15°$ or $\frac{\pi}{12}$

111.

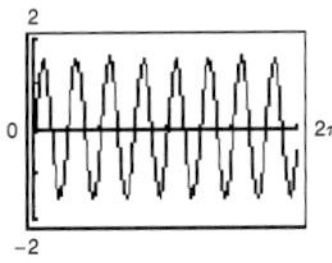

113. $\frac{1}{2}\sqrt{10}$ ft

115. False. If $(\pi/2) < \theta < \pi$, then $\cos(\theta/2) > 0$. The sign of $\cos(\theta/2)$ depends on the quadrant in which $\theta/2$ lies.

117. True. $4 \sin(-x)\cos(-x) = 4(-\sin x)\cos x$
$= -4 \sin x \cos x$
$= -2(2 \sin x \cos x)$
$= -2 \sin 2x$

119. Reciprocal identities:

$\sin\theta = \frac{1}{\csc\theta}$, $\cos\theta = \frac{1}{\sec\theta}$, $\tan\theta = \frac{1}{\cot\theta}$,

$\csc\theta = \frac{1}{\sin\theta}$, $\sec\theta = \frac{1}{\cos\theta}$, $\cot\theta = \frac{1}{\tan\theta}$

Quotient identities: $\tan\theta = \frac{\sin\theta}{\cos\theta}$, $\cot\theta = \frac{\cos\theta}{\sin\theta}$

Pythagorean identities: $\sin^2\theta + \cos^2\theta = 1$,
$1 + \tan^2\theta = \sec^2\theta$, $1 + \cot^2\theta = \csc^2\theta$

121. $-1 \le \sin x \le 1$ for all x **123.** $y_1 = y_2 + 1$

125. $-1.8431, 2.1758, 3.9903, 8.8935, 9.8820$

Chapter Test *(page 421)*

1. $\sin\theta = -\frac{6\sqrt{61}}{61}$ $\csc\theta = -\frac{\sqrt{61}}{6}$

$\cos\theta = -\frac{5\sqrt{61}}{61}$ $\sec\theta = -\frac{\sqrt{61}}{5}$

$\tan\theta = \frac{6}{5}$ $\cot\theta = \frac{5}{6}$

2. 1 **3.** 1 **4.** $\csc\theta \sec\theta$

5. $\theta = 0, \frac{\pi}{2} < \theta \le \pi, \frac{3\pi}{2} < \theta < 2\pi$

6.

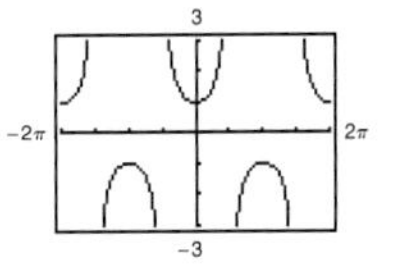

$y_1 = y_2$

7–12. Answers will vary. **13.** $\frac{1}{8}(3 - 4\cos x + \cos 2x)$

14. $\tan 2\theta$ **15.** $2(\sin 5\theta + \sin\theta)$

16. $-2\sin 2\theta \sin\theta$ **17.** $0, \frac{3\pi}{4}, \pi, \frac{7\pi}{4}$

18. $\frac{\pi}{6}, \frac{\pi}{2}, \frac{5\pi}{6}, \frac{3\pi}{2}$ **19.** $\frac{\pi}{6}, \frac{5\pi}{6}, \frac{7\pi}{6}, \frac{11\pi}{6}$

20. $\frac{\pi}{6}, \frac{5\pi}{6}, \frac{3\pi}{2}$ **21.** $-2.596, 0, 2.596$ **22.** $\frac{\sqrt{2} - \sqrt{6}}{4}$

23. $\sin 2u = -\frac{20}{29}$, $\cos 2u = -\frac{21}{29}$, $\tan 2u = \frac{20}{21}$

24. Day 123 to day 223

25. $t = 0.26$ min
0.58 min
0.89 min
1.20 min
1.52 min
1.83 min

Problem Solving *(page 425)*

1. (a) $\cos\theta = \pm\sqrt{1 - \sin^2\theta}$

$\tan\theta = \pm\frac{\sin\theta}{\sqrt{1 - \sin^2\theta}}$

$\cot\theta = \pm\frac{\sqrt{1 - \sin^2\theta}}{\sin\theta}$

$\sec\theta = \pm\frac{1}{\sqrt{1 - \sin^2\theta}}$

$\csc\theta = \frac{1}{\sin\theta}$

(b) $\sin\theta = \pm\sqrt{1 - \cos^2\theta}$

$\tan\theta = \pm\frac{\sqrt{1 - \cos^2\theta}}{\cos\theta}$

$\csc\theta = \pm\frac{1}{\sqrt{1 - \cos^2\theta}}$

$\sec\theta = \frac{1}{\cos\theta}$

$\cot\theta = \pm\frac{\cos\theta}{\sqrt{1 - \cos^2\theta}}$

3. Answers will vary. **5.** $u + v = w$

7. $\sin\frac{\theta}{2} = \sqrt{\frac{1 - \cos\theta}{2}}$

$\cos\frac{\theta}{2} = \sqrt{\frac{1 + \cos\theta}{2}}$

$\tan\frac{\theta}{2} = \frac{\sin\theta}{1 + \cos\theta}$

9. (a)

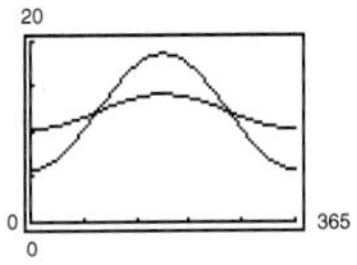

(b) $t \approx 91$ (April 1), $t \approx 274$ (October 1)
(c) Seward; The amplitudes: 6.4 and 1.9
(d) 365.2 days

11. (a) $\frac{\pi}{6} \le x \le \frac{5\pi}{6}$ (b) $\frac{2\pi}{3} \le x \le \frac{4\pi}{3}$

(c) $\frac{\pi}{2} < x < \pi, \frac{3\pi}{2} < x < 2\pi$

(d) $0 \le x \le \frac{\pi}{4}, \frac{5\pi}{4} \le x \le 2\pi$

13. (a) $\sin(u + v + w)$
$= \sin u \cos v \cos w - \sin u \sin v \sin w$
$+ \cos u \sin v \cos w + \cos u \cos v \sin w$

(b) $\tan(u + v + w)$
$= \frac{\tan u + \tan v + \tan w - \tan u \tan v \tan w}{1 - \tan u \tan v - \tan u \tan w - \tan v \tan w}$

15. (a)

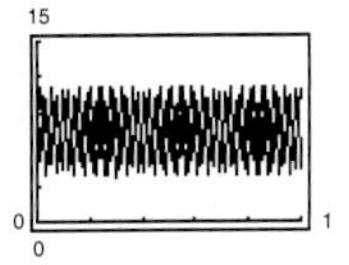

(b) 233.3 times/sec

Chapter 6

Section 6.1 (page 434)

1. oblique **3.** angles; side
5. $A = 30°, a \approx 14.14, c \approx 27.32$
7. $C = 120°, b \approx 4.75, c \approx 7.17$
9. $B = 60.9°, b \approx 19.32, c \approx 6.36$
11. $B = 42°4', a \approx 22.05, b \approx 14.88$
13. $C = 80°, a \approx 5.82, b \approx 9.20$
15. $C = 83°, a \approx 0.62, b \approx 0.51$
17. $B \approx 21.55°, C \approx 122.45°, c \approx 11.49$
19. $A \approx 10°11', C \approx 154°19', c \approx 11.03$
21. $B \approx 9.43°, C = 25.57°, c \approx 10.53$
23. $B \approx 18°13', C \approx 51°32', c \approx 40.06$
25. $B \approx 48.74°, C \approx 21.26°, c \approx 48.23$
27. No solution
29. Two solutions:
$B \approx 72.21°, C \approx 49.79°, c \approx 10.27$
$B \approx 107.79°, C \approx 14.21°, c \approx 3.30$
31. No solution **33.** $B = 45°, C = 90°, c \approx 1.41$
35. (a) $b \le 5, b = \frac{5}{\sin 36°}$ (b) $5 < b < \frac{5}{\sin 36°}$
(c) $b > \frac{5}{\sin 36°}$
37. (a) $b \le 10.8, b = \frac{10.8}{\sin 10°}$ (b) $10.8 < b < \frac{10.8}{\sin 10°}$
(c) $b > \frac{10.8}{\sin 10°}$
39. 10.4 **41.** 1675.2 **43.** 3204.5 **45.** 24.1 m
47. 16.1° **49.** 77 m
51. (a)

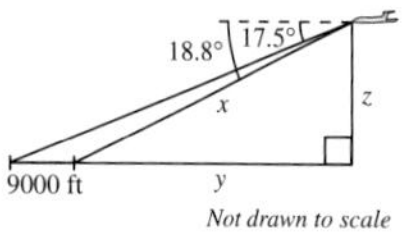

(b) 22.6 mi
(c) 21.4 mi
(d) 7.3 mi

53. 3.2 mi **55.** 5.86 mi
57. True. If an angle of a triangle is obtuse (greater than 90°), then the other two angles must be acute and therefore less than 90°. The triangle is oblique.
59. False. If just three angles are known, the triangle cannot be solved.
61. (a) $A = 20\left(15 \sin \frac{3\theta}{2} - 4 \sin \frac{\theta}{2} - 6 \sin \theta\right)$
(b)

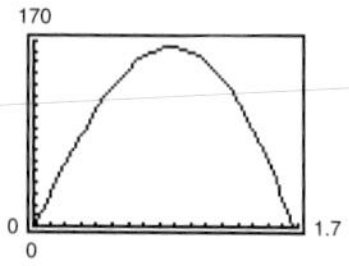

(c) Domain: $0 \le \theta \le 1.6690$
The domain would increase in length and the area would have a greater maximum value.

Section 6.2 (page 441)

1. Cosines **3.** $b^2 = a^2 + c^2 - 2ac \cos B$
5. $A \approx 38.62°, B \approx 48.51°, C \approx 92.87°$
7. $B \approx 23.79°, C \approx 126.21°, a \approx 18.59$
9. $A \approx 30.11°, B \approx 43.16°, C \approx 106.73°$
11. $A \approx 92.94°, B \approx 43.53°, C \approx 43.53°$
13. $B \approx 27.46°, C \approx 32.54°, a \approx 11.27$
15. $A \approx 141°45', C \approx 27°40', b \approx 11.87$
17. $A = 27°10', C = 27°10', b \approx 65.84$
19. $A \approx 33.80°, B \approx 103.20°, c \approx 0.54$

	a	b	c	d	θ	ϕ
21.	5	8	12.07	5.69	45°	135°
23.	10	14	20	13.86	68.2°	111.8°
25.	15	16.96	25	20	77.2°	102.8°

27. Law of Cosines; $A \approx 102.44°, C \approx 37.56°, b \approx 5.26$
29. Law of Sines; No solution
31. Law of Sines; $C = 103°, a \approx 0.82, b \approx 0.71$
33. 43.52 **35.** 10.4 **37.** 52.11 **39.** 0.18
41.

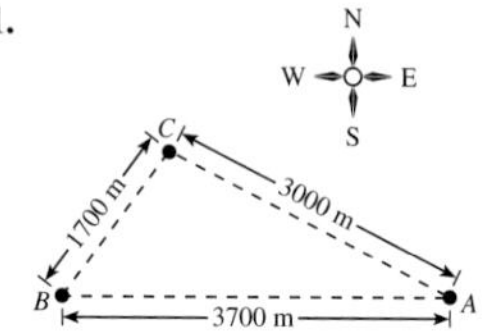

N 37.1° E, S 63.1° E

43. 373.3 m **45.** 72.3° **47.** 43.3 mi
49. (a) N 58.4° W (b) S 81.5° W **51.** 63.7 ft
53. 24.2 mi **55.** $\overline{PQ} \approx 9.4, \overline{QS} = 5, \overline{RS} \approx 12.8$
57.

d (inches)	9	10	12	13	14
θ (degrees)	60.9°	69.5°	88.0°	98.2°	109.6°
s (inches)	20.88	20.28	18.99	18.28	17.48

d (inches)	15	16
θ (degrees)	122.9°	139.8°
s (inches)	16.55	15.37

59. 46,837.5 ft² **61.** \$83,336.37
63. False. For s to be the average of the lengths of the three sides of the triangle, s would be equal to $(a + b + c)/3$.
65. No. The three side lengths do not form a triangle.
67. (a) and (b) Proofs **69.** 405.2 ft
71. Either; Because A is obtuse, there is only one solution for B or C.
73. The Law of Cosines can be used to solve the single-solution case of SSA. There is no method that can solve the no-solution case of SSA.
75. Proof

Section 6.3 (page 454)

1. directed line segment **3.** magnitude
5. magnitude; direction **7.** unit vector **9.** resultant
11. $\|\mathbf{u}\| = \|\mathbf{v}\| = \sqrt{17}$, $\text{slope}_\mathbf{u} = \text{slope}_\mathbf{v} = \frac{1}{4}$
u and **v** have the same magnitude and direction, so they are equal.

13. $\mathbf{v} = \langle 1, 3\rangle$, $\|\mathbf{v}\| = \sqrt{10}$ **15.** $\mathbf{v} = \langle 4, 6\rangle$; $\|\mathbf{v}\| = 2\sqrt{13}$
17. $\mathbf{v} = \langle 0, 5\rangle$; $\|\mathbf{v}\| = 5$ **19.** $\mathbf{v} = \langle 8, 6\rangle$; $\|\mathbf{v}\| = 10$
21. $\mathbf{v} = \langle -9, -12\rangle$; $\|\mathbf{v}\| = 15$ **23.** $\mathbf{v} = \langle 16, 7\rangle$; $\|\mathbf{v}\| = \sqrt{305}$

25.

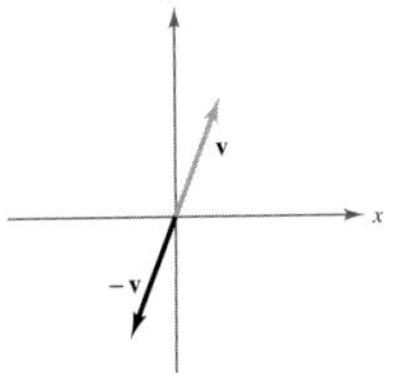

27.

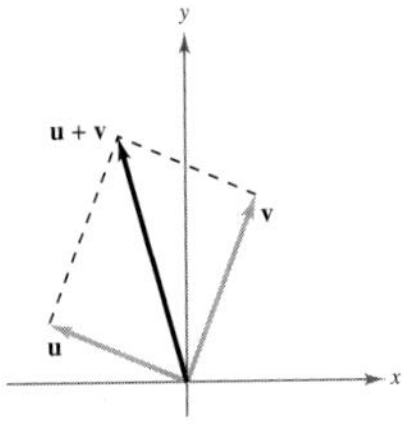

29.

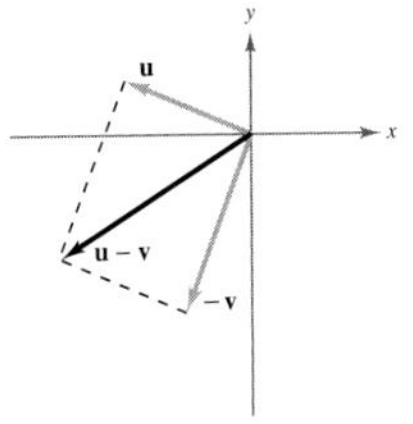

31. (a) $\langle 3, 4\rangle$

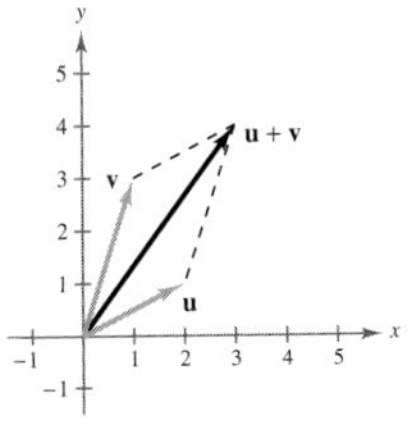

(b) $\langle 1, -2\rangle$

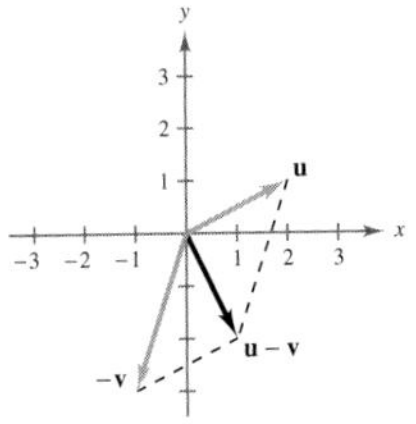

(c) $\langle 1, -7\rangle$

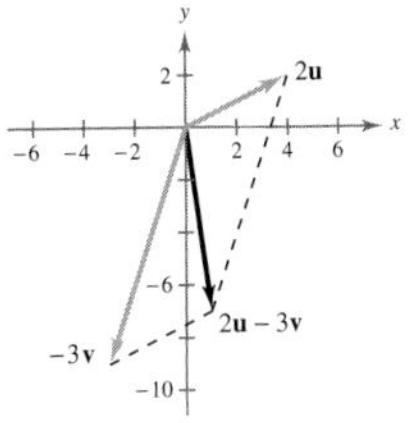

33. (a) $\langle -5, 3\rangle$

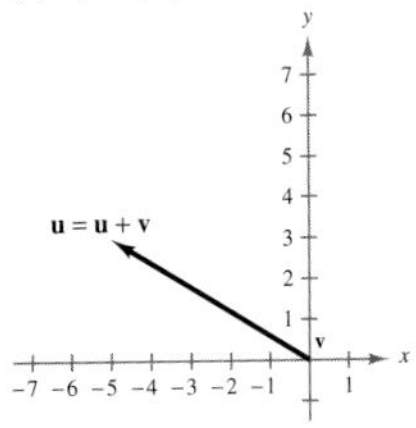

(b) $\langle -5, 3\rangle$

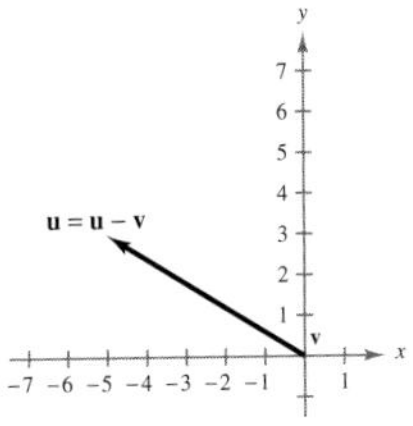

(c) $\langle -10, 6\rangle$

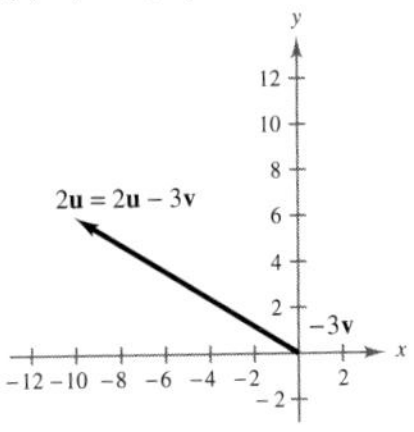

35. (a) $3\mathbf{i} - 2\mathbf{j}$

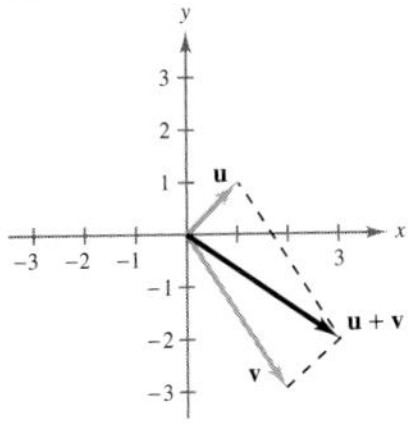

(b) $-\mathbf{i} + 4\mathbf{j}$

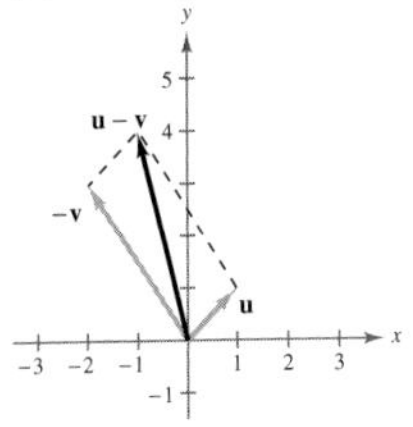

(c) $-4\mathbf{i} + 11\mathbf{j}$

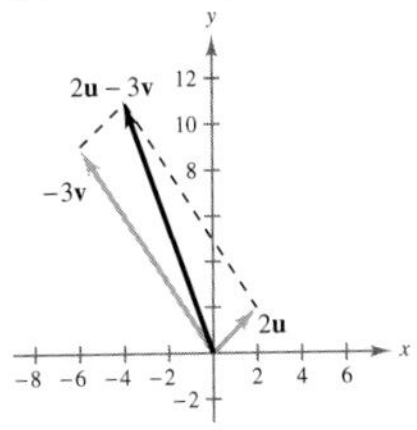

37. (a) $2\mathbf{i} + \mathbf{j}$

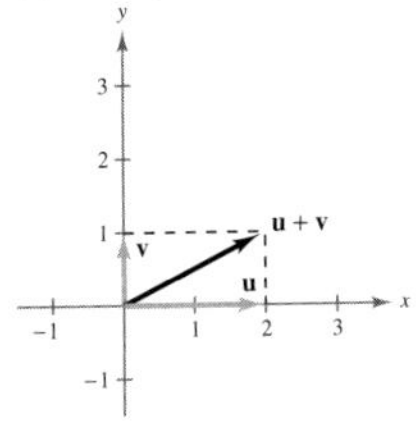

(b) $2\mathbf{i} - \mathbf{j}$

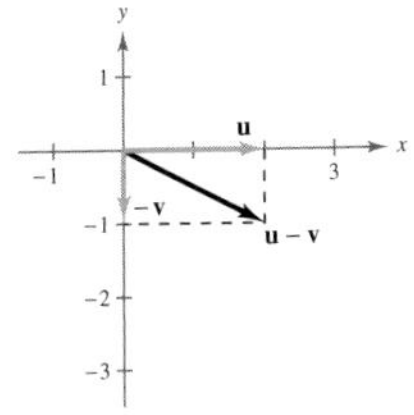

(c) $4\mathbf{i} - 3\mathbf{j}$

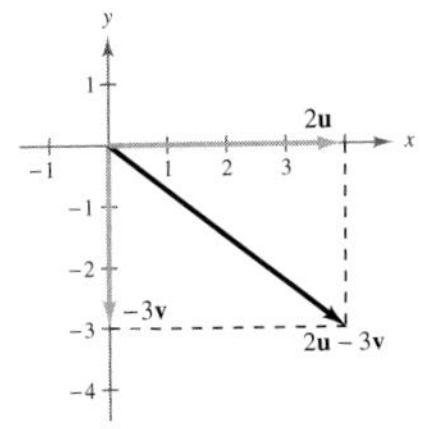

39. $\langle 1, 0\rangle$ **41.** $\left\langle -\frac{\sqrt{2}}{2}, \frac{\sqrt{2}}{2}\right\rangle$ **43.** $\frac{\sqrt{2}}{2}\mathbf{i} + \frac{\sqrt{2}}{2}\mathbf{j}$

45. $\mathbf{j}$ **47.** $\frac{\sqrt{5}}{5}\mathbf{i} - \frac{2\sqrt{5}}{5}\mathbf{j}$ **49.** $\mathbf{v} = \langle -6, 8\rangle$

CHAPTER 6

51. $\mathbf{v} = \left\langle \frac{18\sqrt{29}}{29}, \frac{45\sqrt{29}}{29} \right\rangle$ **53.** $5\mathbf{i} - 3\mathbf{j}$ **55.** $6\mathbf{i} - 3\mathbf{j}$

57. $\mathbf{v} = \langle 3, -\frac{3}{2} \rangle$

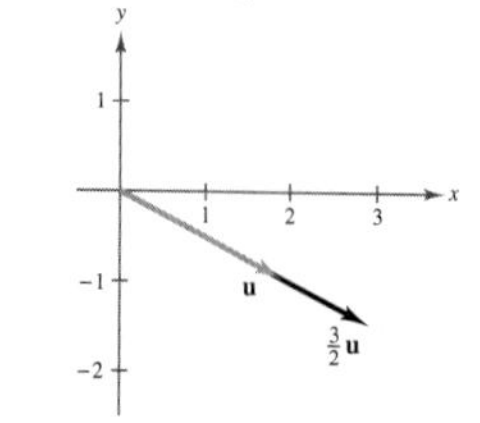

59. $\mathbf{v} = \langle 4, 3 \rangle$

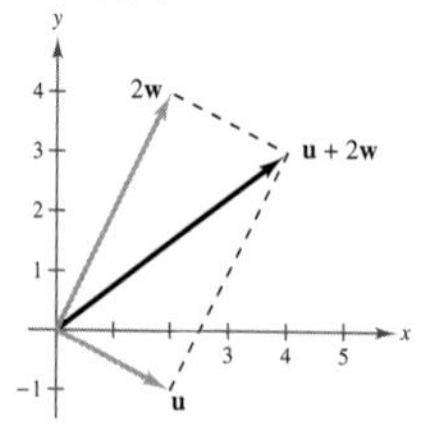

61. $\mathbf{v} = \langle \frac{7}{2}, -\frac{1}{2} \rangle$

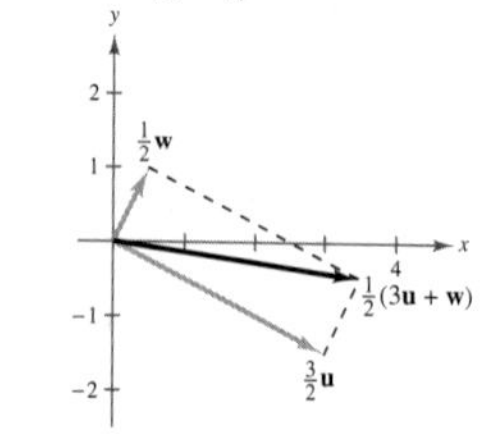

63. $\|\mathbf{v}\| = 6\sqrt{2}$; $\theta = 315°$ **65.** $\|\mathbf{v}\| = 3$; $\theta = 60°$

67. $\mathbf{v} = \langle 3, 0 \rangle$

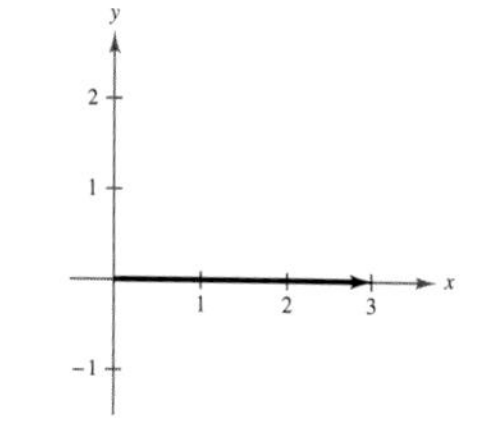

69. $\mathbf{v} = \left\langle -\frac{7\sqrt{3}}{4}, \frac{7}{4} \right\rangle$

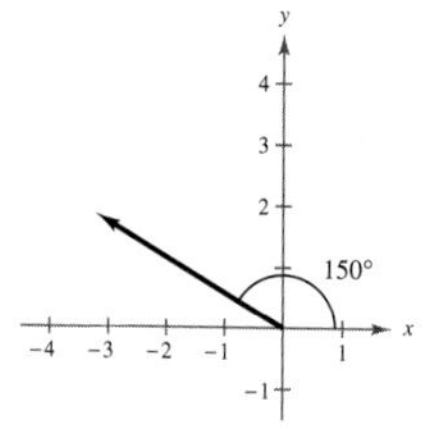

71. $\mathbf{v} = \langle \sqrt{6}, \sqrt{6} \rangle$

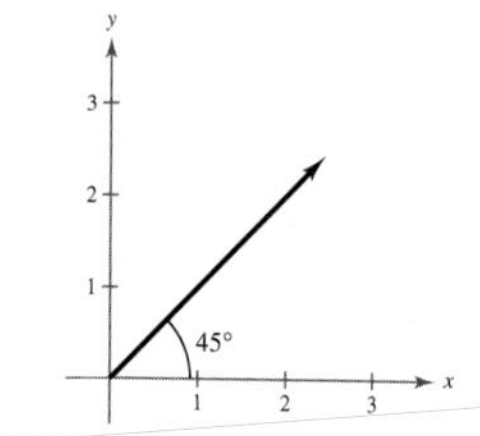

73. $\mathbf{v} = \left\langle \frac{9}{5}, \frac{12}{5} \right\rangle$

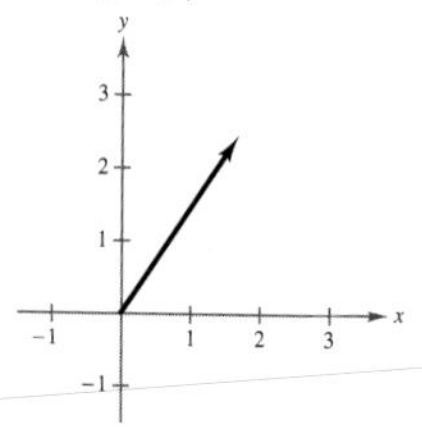

75. $\langle 5, 5 \rangle$ **77.** $\langle 10\sqrt{2} - 50, 10\sqrt{2} \rangle$

79. 90° **81.** 62.7°

83. Vertical ≈ 125.4 ft/sec, Horizontal ≈ 1193.4 ft/sec

85. 12.8°; 398.32 N **87.** 71.3°; 228.5 lb **89.** 17.5 lb

91. $T_{AC} \approx 1758.8$ lb; $T_{BC} \approx 1305.4$ lb

93. 3154.4 lb **95.** 20.8 lb **97.** 19.5°

99. 1928.4 ft-lb **101.** N 21.4° E; 138.7 km/h

103. True. The magnitudes are equal and the directions are opposite.

105. True. $\mathbf{a} - \mathbf{b} = \mathbf{c}$ and $\mathbf{u} = -\mathbf{b}$

107. True. $\mathbf{a} = -\mathbf{d}$, $\mathbf{w} = -\mathbf{d}$ **109.** False. $\mathbf{u} - \mathbf{v} = -(\mathbf{b} + \mathbf{t})$

111. Proof

113. (a) $5\sqrt{5 + 4\cos\theta}$

(b)

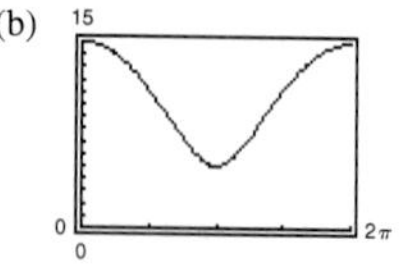

(c) Range: $[5, 15]$
Maximum is 15 when $\theta = 0$.
Minimum is 5 when $\theta = \pi$.

(d) The magnitudes of $\mathbf{F}_1$ and $\mathbf{F}_2$ are not the same.

115. $\langle 1, 3 \rangle$ or $\langle -1, -3 \rangle$ **117.** Answers will vary.

119. (a) Vector. Velocity has both magnitude and direction.
(b) Scalar. Price has only magnitude.
(c) Scalar. Temperature has only magnitude.
(d) Vector. Weight has both magnitude and direction.

Section 6.4 *(page 465)*

1. dot product **3.** $\frac{\mathbf{u} \cdot \mathbf{v}}{\|\mathbf{u}\|\|\mathbf{v}\|}$ **5.** $\left(\frac{\mathbf{u} \cdot \mathbf{v}}{\|\mathbf{v}\|^2}\right)\mathbf{v}$

7. -19 **9.** -11 **11.** 6 **13.** -12 **15.** 18; scalar

17. $\langle 24, -12 \rangle$; vector **19.** $\langle -126, -126 \rangle$; vector

21. $\sqrt{10} - 1$; scalar **23.** -12; scalar

25. 17 **27.** $5\sqrt{41}$ **29.** 6 **31.** 90° **33.** 143.13°

35. 60.26° **37.** 90° **39.** $\frac{5\pi}{12}$

41.

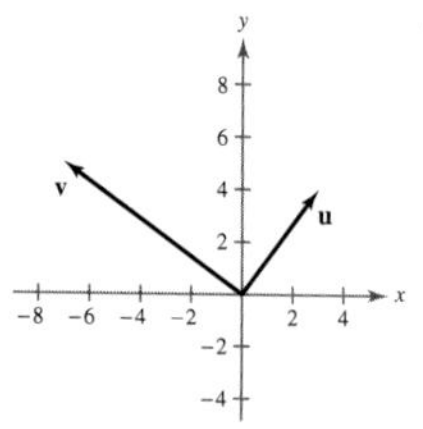

About 91.33°

43.

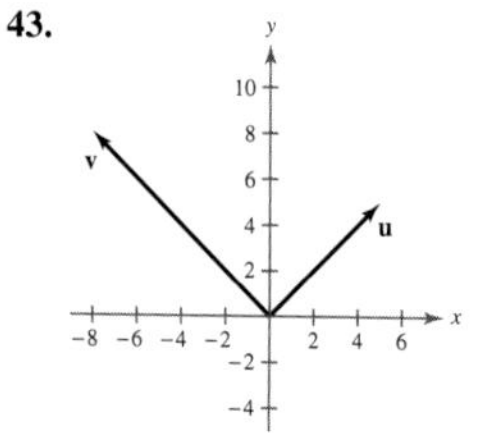

90°

45. 26.57°, 63.43°, 90° **47.** 41.63°, 53.13°, 85.24°

49. -20 **51.** -229.1 **53.** Parallel **55.** Neither

57. Orthogonal **59.** $\frac{1}{37}\langle 84, 14 \rangle, \frac{1}{37}\langle -10, 60 \rangle$

61. $\frac{45}{229}\langle 2, 15 \rangle, \frac{6}{229}\langle -15, 2 \rangle$ **63.** $\langle 3, 2 \rangle$ **65.** $\langle 0, 0 \rangle$

67. $\langle -5, 3 \rangle, \langle 5, -3 \rangle$ **69.** $\frac{2}{3}\mathbf{i} + \frac{1}{2}\mathbf{j}, -\frac{2}{3}\mathbf{i} - \frac{1}{2}\mathbf{j}$ **71.** 32

73. (a) $892,901.50
This value gives the total revenue that can be earned by selling all of the cellular phones.

(b) $1.05\mathbf{v}$

75. (a) Force = 30,000 sin d

(b)

d	0°	1°	2°	3°	4°	5°
Force	0	523.6	1047.0	1570.1	2092.7	2614.7

d	6°	7°	8°	9°	10°
Force	3135.9	3656.1	4175.2	4693.0	5209.4

(c) 29,885.8 lb

77. 735 N-m **79.** 779.4 ft-lb **81.** 21,650.64 ft-lb

83. Answers will vary. **85.** Answers will vary.
87. False. Work is represented by a scalar. **89.** Proof
91. (a) **u** and **v** are parallel. (b) **u** and **v** are orthogonal.
93. Proof

Section 6.5 *(page 476)*

1. absolute value **3.** DeMoivre's

5.

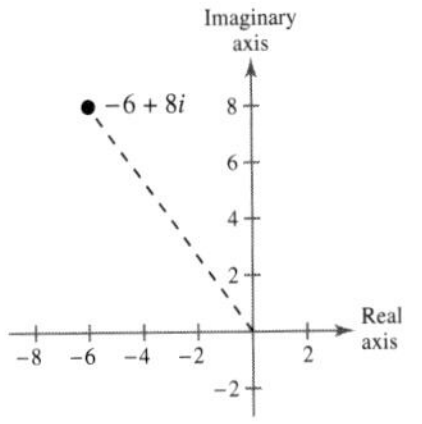

10

7.

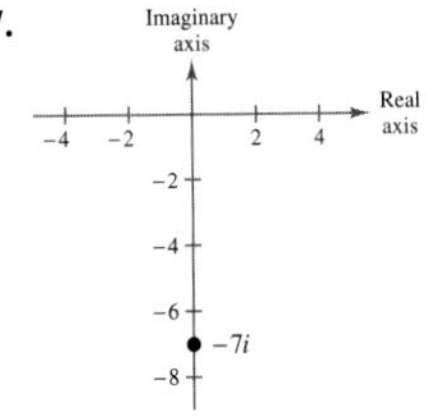

7

9.

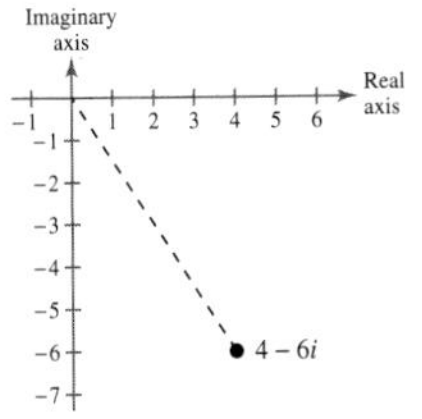

$2\sqrt{13}$

11. $3\left(\cos\frac{\pi}{2} + i\sin\frac{\pi}{2}\right)$ **13.** $3\sqrt{2}\left(\cos\frac{5\pi}{4} + i\sin\frac{5\pi}{4}\right)$

15.

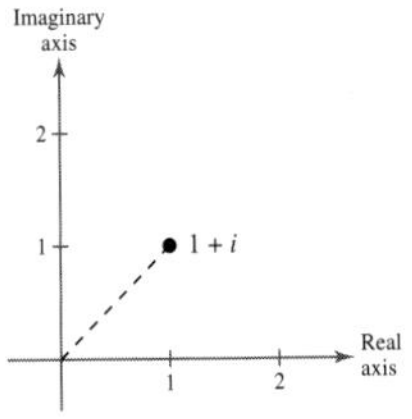

$\sqrt{2}\left(\cos\frac{\pi}{4} + i\sin\frac{\pi}{4}\right)$

17.

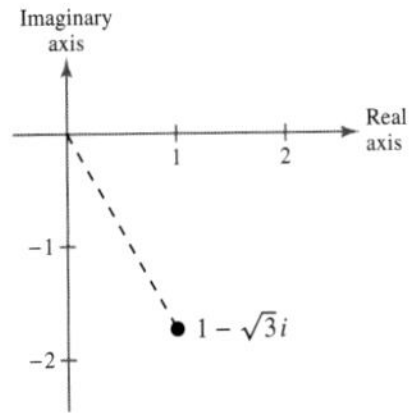

$2\left(\cos\frac{5\pi}{3} + i\sin\frac{5\pi}{3}\right)$

19.

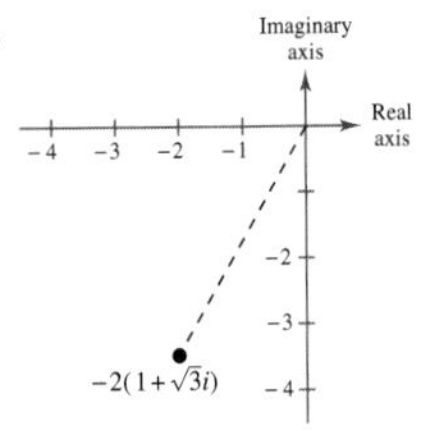

$4\left(\cos\frac{4\pi}{3} + i\sin\frac{4\pi}{3}\right)$

21.

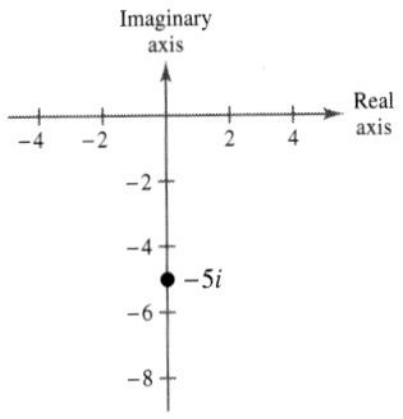

$5\left(\cos\frac{3\pi}{2} + i\sin\frac{3\pi}{2}\right)$

23.

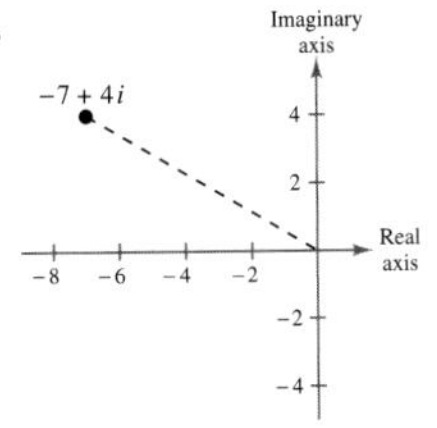

$\sqrt{65}\,(\cos 2.62 + i\sin 2.62)$

25.

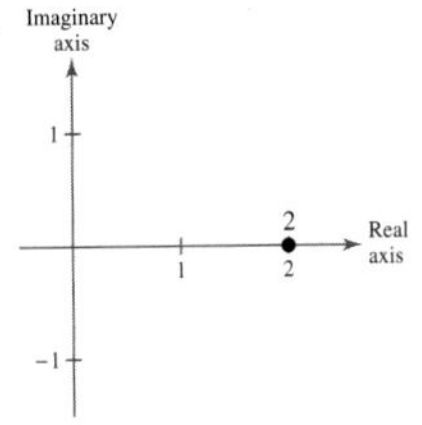

$2(\cos 0 + i\sin 0)$

27.

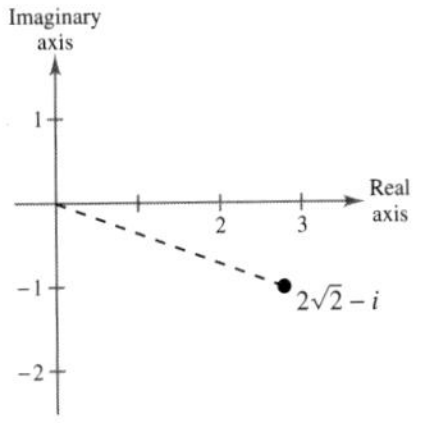

$3(\cos 5.94 + i\sin 5.94)$

29.

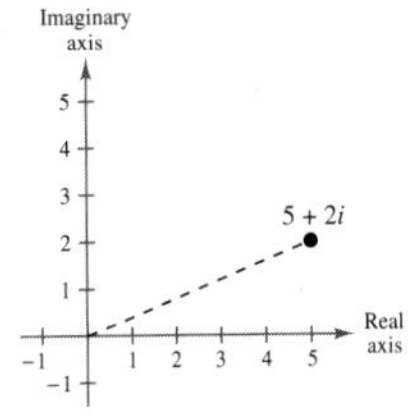

$\sqrt{29}(\cos 0.38 + i\sin 0.38)$

31.

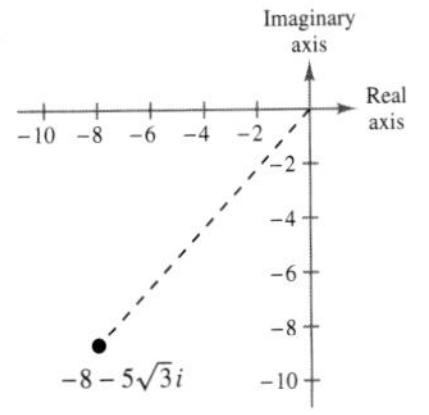

$\sqrt{139}(\cos 3.97 + i\sin 3.97)$

33.

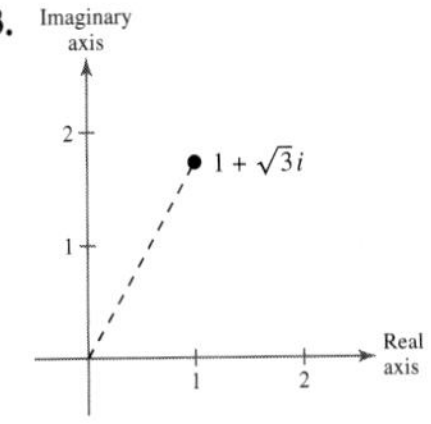

$1 + \sqrt{3}i$

35.

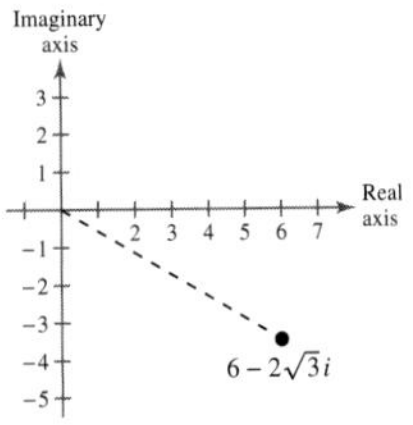

$6 - 2\sqrt{3}i$

37.

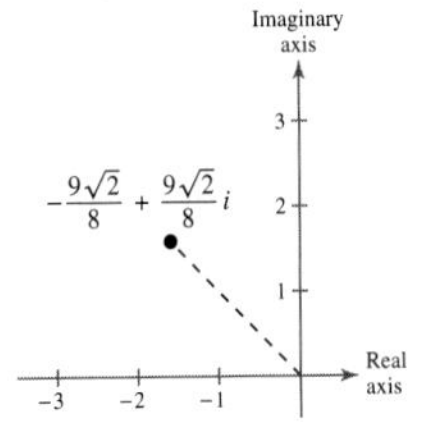

$-\frac{9\sqrt{2}}{8} + \frac{9\sqrt{2}}{8}i$

39.

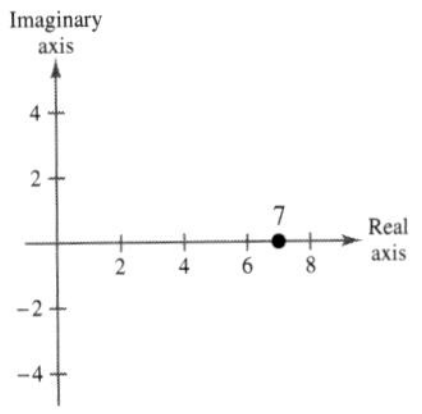

7

41.

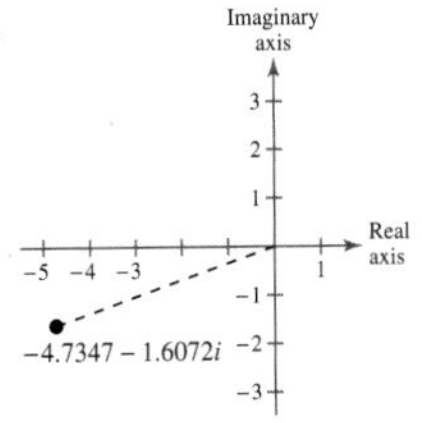

$-4.7347 - 1.6072i$

43. $4.6985 + 1.7101i$ **45.** $-1.8126 + 0.8452i$

47. $12\left(\cos\frac{\pi}{3} + i\sin\frac{\pi}{3}\right)$ **49.** $\frac{10}{9}(\cos 150° + i\sin 150°)$

51. $\cos 50° + i \sin 50°$ **53.** $\frac{1}{3}(\cos 30° + i \sin 30°)$

55. $\cos \frac{2\pi}{3} + i \sin \frac{2\pi}{3}$ **57.** $6(\cos 330° + i \sin 330°)$

59. (a) $\left[2\sqrt{2}\left(\cos \frac{\pi}{4} + i \sin \frac{\pi}{4}\right)\right]\left[\sqrt{2}\left(\cos \frac{7\pi}{4} + i \sin \frac{7\pi}{4}\right)\right]$

(b) $4(\cos 0 + i \sin 0) = 4$ (c) 4

61. (a) $\left[2\left(\cos \frac{3\pi}{2} + i \sin \frac{3\pi}{2}\right)\right]\left[\sqrt{2}\left(\cos \frac{\pi}{4} + i \sin \frac{\pi}{4}\right)\right]$

(b) $2\sqrt{2}\left(\cos \frac{7\pi}{4} + i \sin \frac{7\pi}{4}\right) = 2 - 2i$

(c) $-2i - 2i^2 = -2i + 2 = 2 - 2i$

63. (a) $[5(\cos 0.93 + i \sin 0.93)] \div \left[2\left(\cos \frac{5\pi}{3} + i \sin \frac{5\pi}{3}\right)\right]$

(b) $\frac{5}{2}(\cos 1.97 + i \sin 1.97) \approx -0.982 + 2.299i$

(c) About $-0.982 + 2.299i$

65.

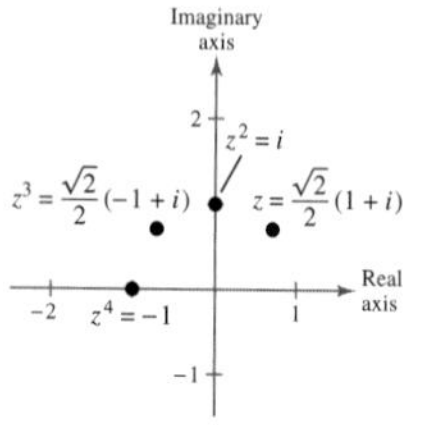

The absolute value of each is 1, and the consecutive powers of z are each 45° apart.

67. $-4 - 4i$ **69.** $8i$ **71.** $1024 - 1024\sqrt{3}i$

73. $\frac{125}{2} + \frac{125\sqrt{3}}{2}i$ **75.** -1 **77.** $608.0 + 144.7i$

79. $-597 - 122i$ **81.** $\frac{81}{2} + \frac{81\sqrt{3}}{2}i$

83. (a) $\sqrt{5}(\cos 60° + i \sin 60°)$

$\sqrt{5}(\cos 240° + i \sin 240°)$

(b)

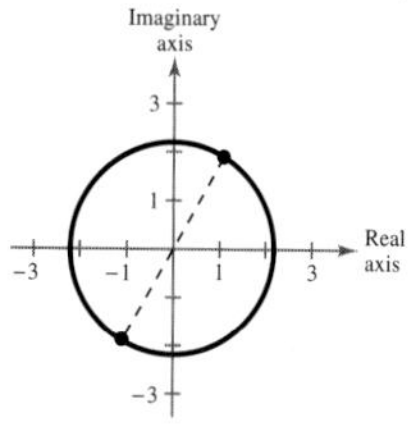

(c) $\frac{\sqrt{5}}{2} + \frac{\sqrt{15}}{2}i,\ -\frac{\sqrt{5}}{2} - \frac{\sqrt{15}}{2}i$

85. (a) $2\left(\cos \frac{2\pi}{9} + i \sin \frac{2\pi}{9}\right)$

$2\left(\cos \frac{8\pi}{9} + i \sin \frac{8\pi}{9}\right)$

$2\left(\cos \frac{14\pi}{9} + i \sin \frac{14\pi}{9}\right)$

(b)

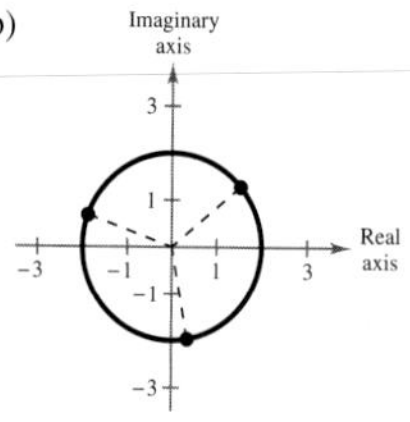

(c) $1.5321 + 1.2856i$,

$-1.8794 + 0.6840i$,

$0.3473 - 1.9696i$

87. (a) $5\left(\cos \frac{4\pi}{9} + i \sin \frac{4\pi}{9}\right)$

$5\left(\cos \frac{10\pi}{9} + i \sin \frac{10\pi}{9}\right)$

$5\left(\cos \frac{16\pi}{9} + i \sin \frac{16\pi}{9}\right)$

(b)

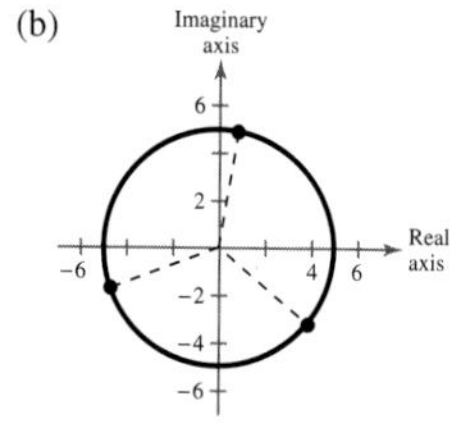

(c) $0.8682 + 4.9240i$,

$-4.6985 - 1.7101i$,

$3.8302 - 3.2140i$

89. (a) $5\left(\cos \frac{3\pi}{4} + i \sin \frac{3\pi}{4}\right)$

$5\left(\cos \frac{7\pi}{4} + i \sin \frac{7\pi}{4}\right)$

(b)

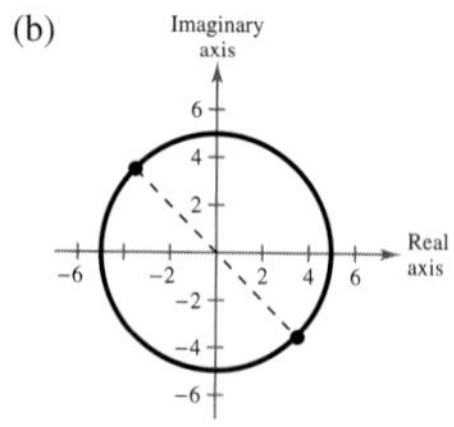

(c) $-\frac{5\sqrt{2}}{2} + \frac{5\sqrt{2}}{2}i$

$\frac{5\sqrt{2}}{2} - \frac{5\sqrt{2}}{2}i$

91. (a) $2(\cos 0 + i \sin 0)$

$2\left(\cos \frac{\pi}{2} + i \sin \frac{\pi}{2}\right)$

$2(\cos \pi + i \sin \pi)$

$2\left(\cos \frac{3\pi}{2} + i \sin \frac{3\pi}{2}\right)$

(b)

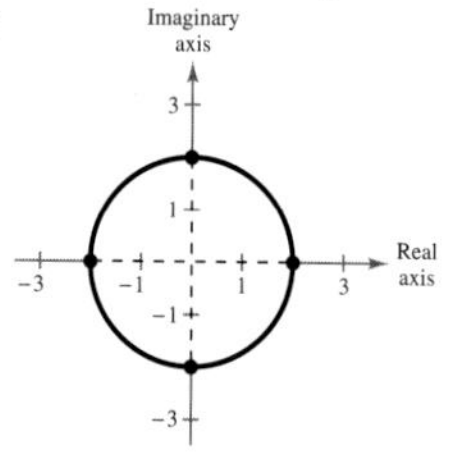

(c) $2, 2i, -2, -2i$

93. (a) $\cos 0 + i \sin 0$

$\cos \frac{2\pi}{5} + i \sin \frac{2\pi}{5}$

$\cos \frac{4\pi}{5} + i \sin \frac{4\pi}{5}$

$\cos \frac{6\pi}{5} + i \sin \frac{6\pi}{5}$

$\cos \frac{8\pi}{5} + i \sin \frac{8\pi}{5}$

(b)

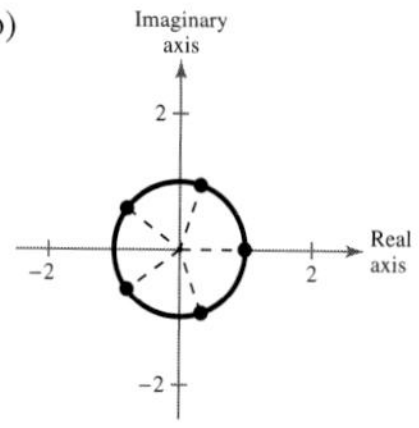

(c) $1, 0.3090 + 0.9511i$,

$-0.8090 + 0.5878i, -0.8090 - 0.5878i$,

$0.3090 - 0.9511i$

95. (a) $5\left(\cos \frac{\pi}{3} + i \sin \frac{\pi}{3}\right)$

$5(\cos \pi + i \sin \pi)$

$5\left(\cos \frac{5\pi}{3} + i \sin \frac{5\pi}{3}\right)$

(b)

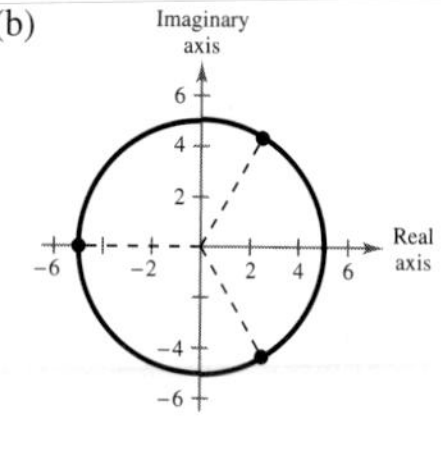

(c) $\frac{5}{2} + \frac{5\sqrt{3}}{2}i, -5$,

$\frac{5}{2} - \frac{5\sqrt{3}}{2}i$

97. (a) $\sqrt{2}\left(\cos\frac{7\pi}{20} + i\sin\frac{7\pi}{20}\right)$

$\sqrt{2}\left(\cos\frac{3\pi}{4} + i\sin\frac{3\pi}{4}\right)$

$\sqrt{2}\left(\cos\frac{23\pi}{20} + i\sin\frac{23\pi}{20}\right)$

$\sqrt{2}\left(\cos\frac{31\pi}{20} + i\sin\frac{31\pi}{20}\right)$

$\sqrt{2}\left(\cos\frac{39\pi}{20} + i\sin\frac{39\pi}{20}\right)$

(b)

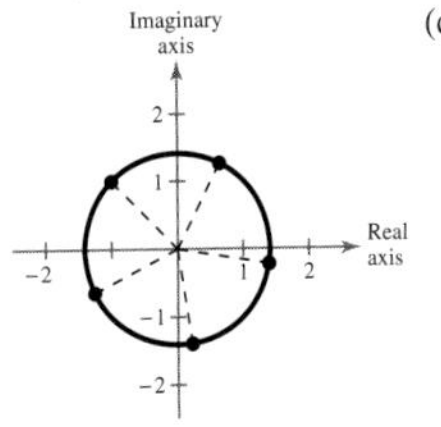

(c) $0.6420 + 1.2601i$,
$-1 + i$,
$-1.2601 - 0.6420i$,
$0.2212 - 1.3968i$,
$1.3968 - 0.2212i$

99. $\cos\frac{3\pi}{8} + i\sin\frac{3\pi}{8}$

$\cos\frac{7\pi}{8} + i\sin\frac{7\pi}{8}$

$\cos\frac{11\pi}{8} + i\sin\frac{11\pi}{8}$

$\cos\frac{15\pi}{8} + i\sin\frac{15\pi}{8}$

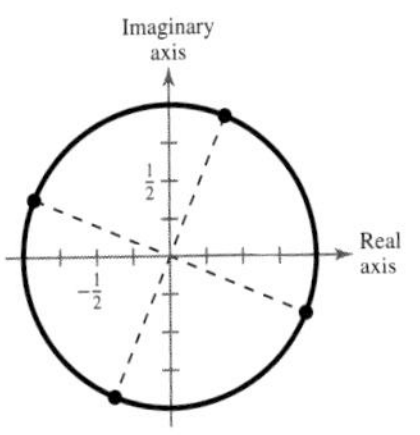

101. $3\left(\cos\frac{\pi}{5} + i\sin\frac{\pi}{5}\right)$

$3\left(\cos\frac{3\pi}{5} + i\sin\frac{3\pi}{5}\right)$

$3(\cos\pi + i\sin\pi)$

$3\left(\cos\frac{7\pi}{5} + i\sin\frac{7\pi}{5}\right)$

$3\left(\cos\frac{9\pi}{5} + i\sin\frac{9\pi}{5}\right)$

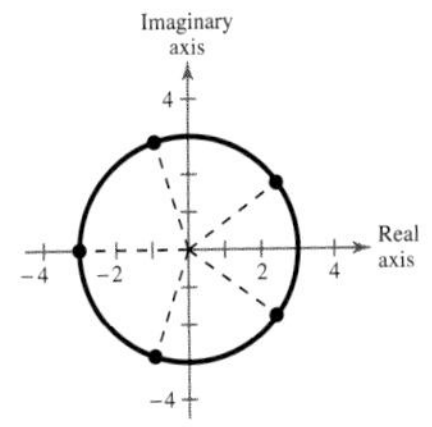

103. $2\left(\cos\frac{3\pi}{8} + i\sin\frac{3\pi}{8}\right)$

$2\left(\cos\frac{7\pi}{8} + i\sin\frac{7\pi}{8}\right)$

$2\left(\cos\frac{11\pi}{8} + i\sin\frac{11\pi}{8}\right)$

$2\left(\cos\frac{15\pi}{8} + i\sin\frac{15\pi}{8}\right)$

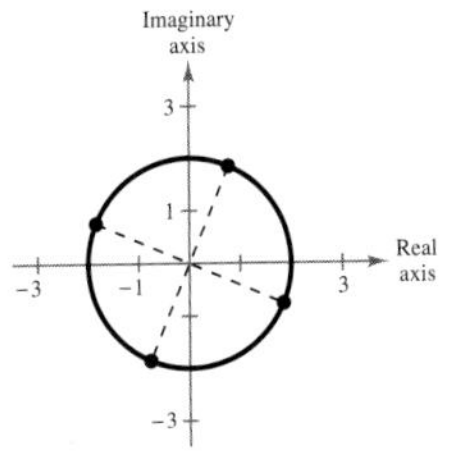

105. $\sqrt[6]{2}\left(\cos\frac{7\pi}{12} + i\sin\frac{7\pi}{12}\right)$

$\sqrt[6]{2}\left(\cos\frac{5\pi}{4} + i\sin\frac{5\pi}{4}\right)$

$\sqrt[6]{2}\left(\cos\frac{23\pi}{12} + i\sin\frac{23\pi}{12}\right)$

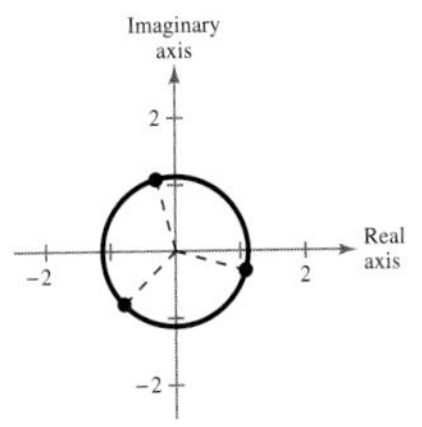

107. False. They are equally spaced around the circle centered at the origin with radius $\sqrt[n]{r}$.

109. Answers will vary. **111.** (a) r^2 (b) $\cos 2\theta + i\sin 2\theta$

113. Answers will vary.

115. The given equation can be written as
$x^4 = -16 = 16(\cos\pi + i\sin\pi)$
which means that you can solve the equation by finding the four fourth roots of -16. Each of these roots has the form

$$\sqrt[4]{16}\left(\cos\frac{\pi + 2\pi k}{4} + i\sin\frac{\pi + 2\pi k}{4}\right).$$

Review Exercises *(page 480)*

1. $C = 72°, b \approx 12.21, c \approx 12.36$
3. $A = 26°, a \approx 24.89, c \approx 56.23$
5. $C = 66°, a \approx 2.53, b \approx 9.11$
7. $B = 108°, a \approx 11.76, c \approx 21.49$
9. $A \approx 20.41°, C \approx 9.59°, a \approx 20.92$
11. $B \approx 39.48°, C \approx 65.52°, c \approx 48.24$
13. 19.06 **15.** 47.23 **17.** 31.1 m **19.** 31.01 ft
21. $A \approx 27.81°, B \approx 54.75°, C \approx 97.44°$
23. $A \approx 16.99°, B \approx 26.00°, C \approx 137.01°$
25. $A \approx 29.92°, B \approx 86.18°, C \approx 63.90°$
27. $A = 36°, C = 36°, b \approx 17.80$
29. $A \approx 45.76°, B \approx 91.24°, c \approx 21.42$
31. Law of Sines; $A \approx 77.52°, B \approx 38.48°, a \approx 14.12$
33. Law of Cosines; $A \approx 28.62°, B \approx 33.56°, C \approx 117.82°$
35. About 4.3 ft, about 12.6 ft
37. 615.1 m **39.** 7.64 **41.** 8.36
43. $\|\mathbf{u}\| = \|\mathbf{v}\| = \sqrt{61}$, $\text{slope}_{\mathbf{u}} = \text{slope}_{\mathbf{v}} = \frac{5}{6}$
45. $\langle 7, -5\rangle$ **47.** $\langle 7, -7\rangle$ **49.** $\langle -4, 4\sqrt{3}\rangle$
51. (a) $\langle -4, 3\rangle$ (b) $\langle 2, -9\rangle$
(c) $\langle -4, -12\rangle$ (d) $\langle -14, 3\rangle$
53. (a) $\langle -1, 6\rangle$ (b) $\langle -9, -2\rangle$
(c) $\langle -20, 8\rangle$ (d) $\langle -13, 22\rangle$
55. (a) $7\mathbf{i} + 2\mathbf{j}$ (b) $-3\mathbf{i} - 4\mathbf{j}$ (c) $8\mathbf{i} - 4\mathbf{j}$ (d) $25\mathbf{i} + 4\mathbf{j}$
57. (a) $3\mathbf{i} + 6\mathbf{j}$ (b) $5\mathbf{i} - 6\mathbf{j}$ (c) $16\mathbf{i}$ (d) $17\mathbf{i} + 18\mathbf{j}$
59. $\langle 22, -7\rangle$

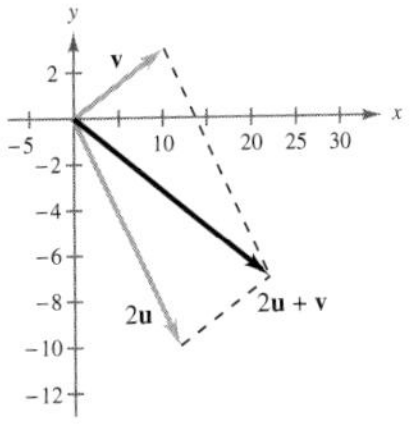

61. $\langle 30, 9\rangle$

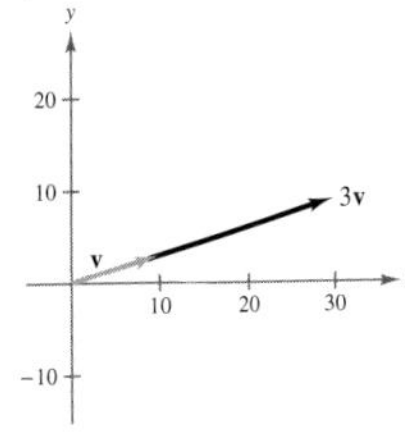

63. $-\mathbf{i} + 5\mathbf{j}$ **65.** $6\mathbf{i} + 4\mathbf{j}$
67. $10\sqrt{2}(\cos 135°\mathbf{i} + \sin 135°\mathbf{j})$
69. $\|\mathbf{v}\| = 7;\ \theta = 60°$ **71.** $\|\mathbf{v}\| = \sqrt{41};\ \theta = 38.7°$
73. $\|\mathbf{v}\| = 3\sqrt{2};\ \theta = 225°$
75. The resultant force is 133.92 pounds and 5.6° from the 85-pound force.
77. 422.30 mi/h; 130.4° **79.** 45 **81.** -2
83. 40; scalar **85.** $4 - 2\sqrt{5}$; scalar

87. $\langle 72, -36\rangle$; vector **89.** 38; scalar **91.** $\dfrac{11\pi}{12}$

93. 160.5° **95.** Orthogonal **97.** Neither

99. $-\frac{13}{17}\langle 4, 1\rangle, \frac{16}{17}\langle -1, 4\rangle$ **101.** $\frac{5}{2}\langle -1, 1\rangle, \frac{9}{2}\langle 1, 1\rangle$ **103.** 48

105. 72,000 ft-lb

107.

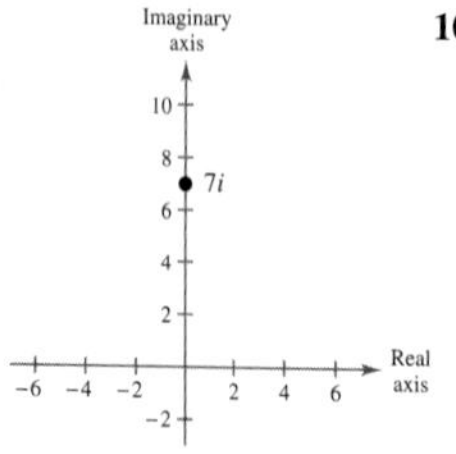

7

109.

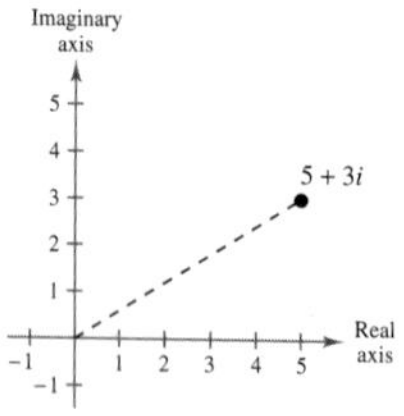

$\sqrt{34}$

111.

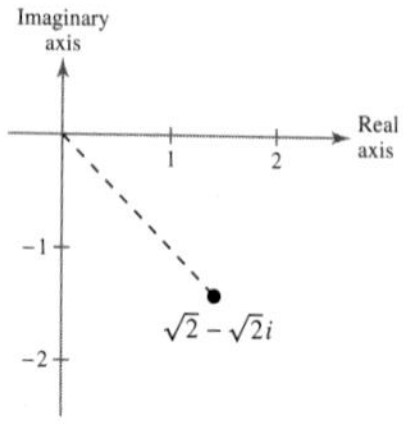

2

113. $4\left(\cos\dfrac{\pi}{2} + i\sin\dfrac{\pi}{2}\right)$ **115.** $5\sqrt{2}\left(\cos\dfrac{7\pi}{4} + i\sin\dfrac{7\pi}{4}\right)$

117. $13(\cos 4.32 + i\sin 4.32)$

119. (a) $z_1 = 4\left(\cos\dfrac{11\pi}{6} + i\sin\dfrac{11\pi}{6}\right)$

$z_2 = 10\left(\cos\dfrac{3\pi}{2} + i\sin\dfrac{3\pi}{2}\right)$

(b) $z_1z_2 = 40\left(\cos\dfrac{10\pi}{3} + i\sin\dfrac{10\pi}{3}\right)$

$\dfrac{z_1}{z_2} = \dfrac{2}{5}\left(\cos\dfrac{\pi}{3} + i\sin\dfrac{\pi}{3}\right)$

121. $\dfrac{625}{2} + \dfrac{625\sqrt{3}}{2}i$ **123.** $2035 - 828i$

125. (a) $3\left(\cos\dfrac{\pi}{4} + i\sin\dfrac{\pi}{4}\right)$

$3\left(\cos\dfrac{7\pi}{12} + i\sin\dfrac{7\pi}{12}\right)$

$3\left(\cos\dfrac{11\pi}{12} + i\sin\dfrac{11\pi}{12}\right)$

$3\left(\cos\dfrac{5\pi}{4} + i\sin\dfrac{5\pi}{4}\right)$

$3\left(\cos\dfrac{19\pi}{12} + i\sin\dfrac{19\pi}{12}\right)$

$3\left(\cos\dfrac{23\pi}{12} + i\sin\dfrac{23\pi}{12}\right)$

(b)

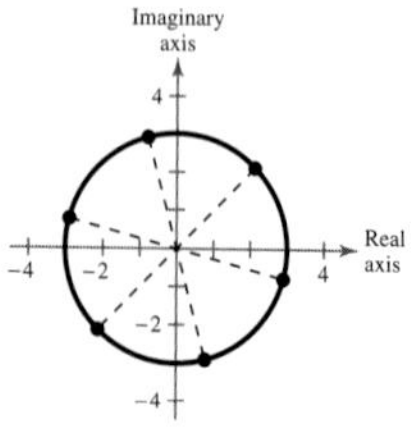

(c) $\dfrac{3\sqrt{2}}{2} + \dfrac{3\sqrt{2}}{2}i, -0.776 + 2.898i,$

$-2.898 + 0.776i, -\dfrac{3\sqrt{2}}{2} - \dfrac{3\sqrt{2}}{2}i,$

$0.776 - 2.898i, 2.898 - 0.776i$

127. (a) $2(\cos 0 + i\sin 0)$

$2\left(\cos\dfrac{2\pi}{3} + i\sin\dfrac{2\pi}{3}\right)$

$2\left(\cos\dfrac{4\pi}{3} + i\sin\dfrac{4\pi}{3}\right)$

(b)

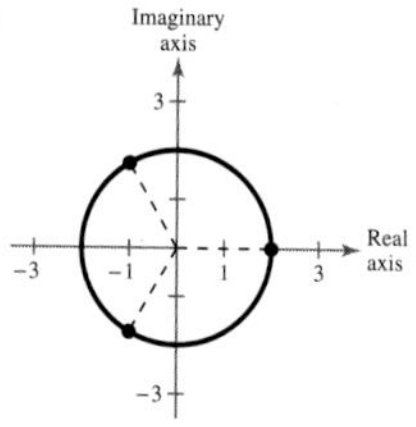

(c) $2, -1 + \sqrt{3}i, -1 - \sqrt{3}i$

129. $3\left(\cos\dfrac{\pi}{4} + i\sin\dfrac{\pi}{4}\right) = \dfrac{3\sqrt{2}}{2} + \dfrac{3\sqrt{2}}{2}i$

$3\left(\cos\dfrac{3\pi}{4} + i\sin\dfrac{3\pi}{4}\right) = -\dfrac{3\sqrt{2}}{2} + \dfrac{3\sqrt{2}}{2}i$

$3\left(\cos\dfrac{5\pi}{4} + i\sin\dfrac{5\pi}{4}\right) = -\dfrac{3\sqrt{2}}{2} - \dfrac{3\sqrt{2}}{2}i$

$3\left(\cos\dfrac{7\pi}{4} + i\sin\dfrac{7\pi}{4}\right) = \dfrac{3\sqrt{2}}{2} - \dfrac{3\sqrt{2}}{2}i$

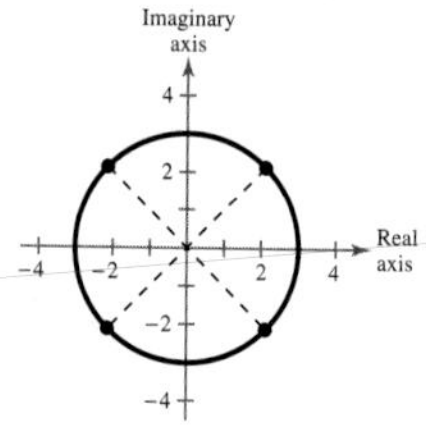

131. $2\left(\cos\frac{\pi}{2} + i\sin\frac{\pi}{2}\right) = 2i$

$2\left(\cos\frac{7\pi}{6} + i\sin\frac{7\pi}{6}\right) = -\sqrt{3} - i$

$2\left(\cos\frac{11\pi}{6} + i\sin\frac{11\pi}{6}\right) = \sqrt{3} - i$

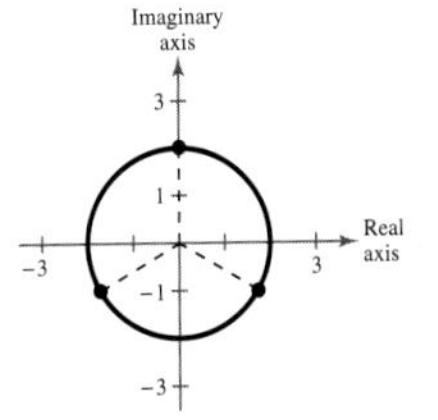

133. $\cos 0 + i\sin 0 = 1$

$\cos\frac{\pi}{2} + i\sin\frac{\pi}{2} = i$

$\cos\frac{2\pi}{3} + i\sin\frac{2\pi}{3} = -\frac{1}{2} + \frac{\sqrt{3}}{2}i$

$\cos\frac{4\pi}{3} + i\sin\frac{4\pi}{3} = -\frac{1}{2} - \frac{\sqrt{3}}{2}i$

$\cos\frac{3\pi}{2} + i\sin\frac{3\pi}{2} = -i$

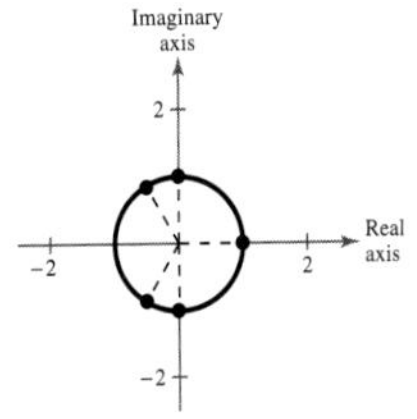

135. True. Sin 90° is defined in the Law of Sines.

137. True. By definition, $\mathbf{u} = \frac{\mathbf{v}}{\|\mathbf{v}\|}$, so $\mathbf{v} = \|\mathbf{v}\|\mathbf{u}$.

139. False. The solutions to $x^2 - 8i = 0$ are $x = 2 + 2i$ and $x = -2 - 2i$.

141. $a^2 = b^2 + c^2 - 2bc\cos A$, $b^2 = a^2 + c^2 - 2ac\cos B$, $c^2 = a^2 + b^2 - 2ab\cos C$

143. A and C

145. If $k > 0$, the direction is the same and the magnitude is k times as great.
If $k < 0$, the result is a vector in the opposite direction and the magnitude is $|k|$ times as great.

147. (a) $4(\cos 60° + i\sin 60°)$ (b) -64
$4(\cos 180° + i\sin 180°)$
$4(\cos 300° + i\sin 300°)$

149. $z_1z_2 = -4;\ \frac{z_1}{z_2} = \cos(2\theta - \pi) + i\sin(2\theta - \pi)$
$= -\cos 2\theta - i\sin 2\theta$

Chapter Test *(page 484)*

1. $C = 88°, b \approx 27.81, c \approx 29.98$

2. $A = 42°, b \approx 21.91, c \approx 10.95$

3. Two solutions:
$B \approx 29.12°, C \approx 126.88°, c \approx 22.03$
$B \approx 150.88°, C \approx 5.12°, c \approx 2.46$

4. No solution

5. $A \approx 39.96°, C \approx 40.04°, c \approx 15.02$

6. $A \approx 21.90°, B \approx 37.10°, c \approx 78.15$ **7.** 2052.5 m^2

8. 606.3 mi; 29.1° **9.** $\langle 14, -23\rangle$

10. $\left\langle \frac{18\sqrt{34}}{17}, -\frac{30\sqrt{34}}{17}\right\rangle$

11. $\langle -4, 12\rangle$

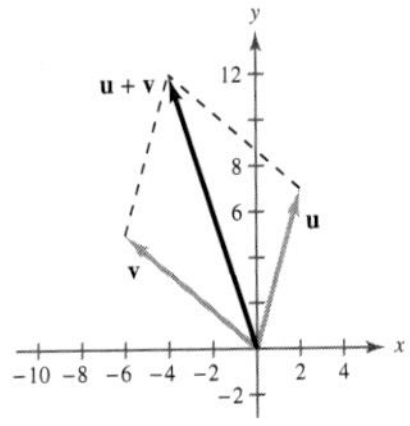

12. $\langle 8, 2\rangle$

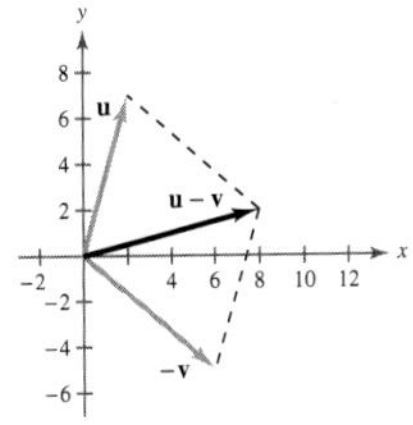

13. $\langle 28, 20\rangle$

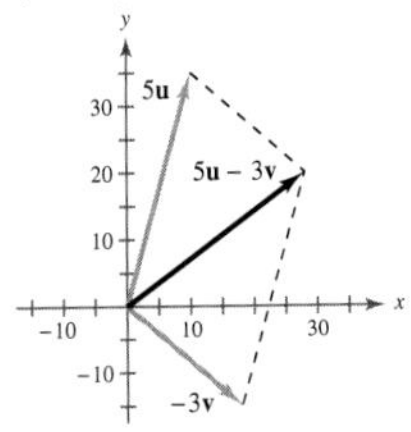

14. $\langle -4, 38\rangle$

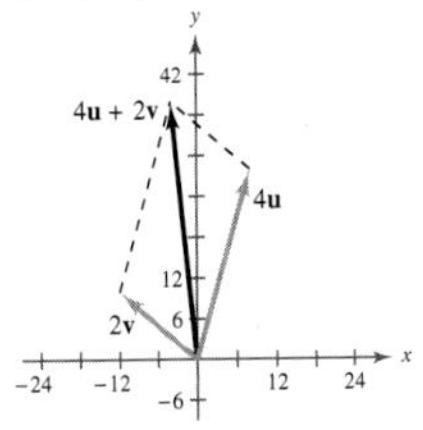

15. $\left\langle \frac{24}{25}, -\frac{7}{25}\right\rangle$ **16.** 14.9°; 250.15 lb **17.** 135° **18.** Yes

19. $\frac{37}{26}\langle 5, 1\rangle$; $\frac{29}{26}\langle -1, 5\rangle$ **20.** About 104 lb

21. $5\sqrt{2}\left(\cos\frac{7\pi}{4} + i\sin\frac{7\pi}{4}\right)$ **22.** $-3 + 3\sqrt{3}i$

23. $-\frac{6561}{2} - \frac{6561\sqrt{3}}{2}i$ **24.** $5832i$

25. $4\sqrt[4]{2}\left(\cos\frac{\pi}{12} + i\sin\frac{\pi}{12}\right)$

$4\sqrt[4]{2}\left(\cos\frac{7\pi}{12} + i\sin\frac{7\pi}{12}\right)$

$4\sqrt[4]{2}\left(\cos\frac{13\pi}{12} + i\sin\frac{13\pi}{12}\right)$

$4\sqrt[4]{2}\left(\cos\frac{19\pi}{12} + i\sin\frac{19\pi}{12}\right)$

26. $3\left(\cos\frac{\pi}{6} + i\sin\frac{\pi}{6}\right)$

$3\left(\cos\frac{5\pi}{6} + i\sin\frac{5\pi}{6}\right)$

$3\left(\cos\frac{3\pi}{2} + i\sin\frac{3\pi}{2}\right)$

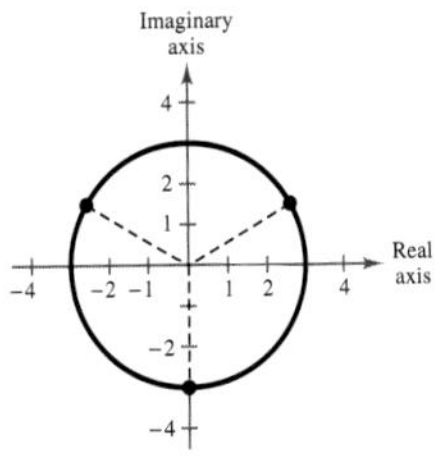

Cumulative Test for Chapters 4–6 *(page 485)*

1. (a)

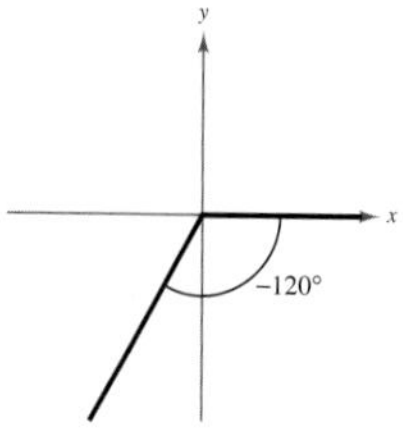

(b) $240°$

(c) $-\frac{2\pi}{3}$

(d) $60°$

(e) $\sin(-120°) = -\frac{\sqrt{3}}{2}$ $\quad \csc(-120°) = -\frac{2\sqrt{3}}{3}$

$\cos(-120°) = -\frac{1}{2}$ $\quad \sec(-120°) = -2$

$\tan(-120°) = \sqrt{3}$ $\quad \cot(-120°) = \frac{\sqrt{3}}{3}$

2. $-83.1°$ **3.** $\frac{20}{29}$

4.

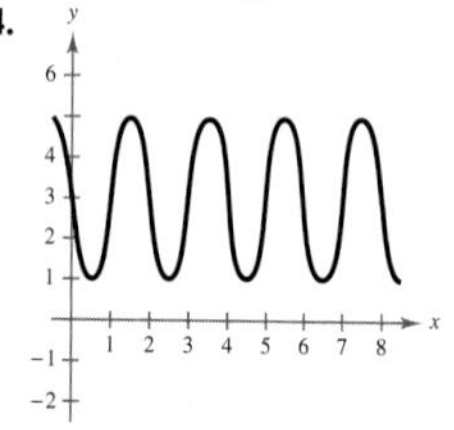

5.

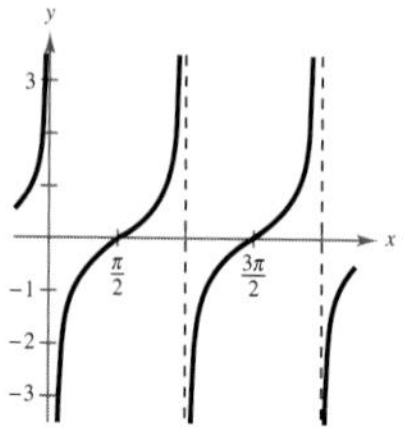

6.

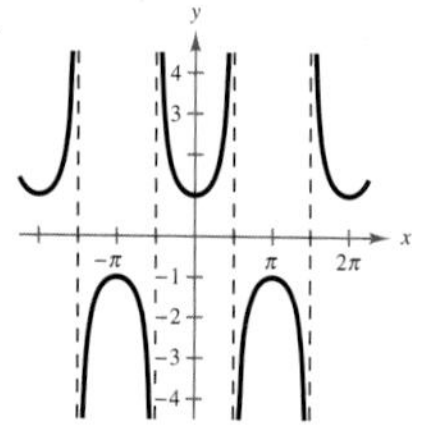

7. $a = -3, b = \pi, c = 0$

8.

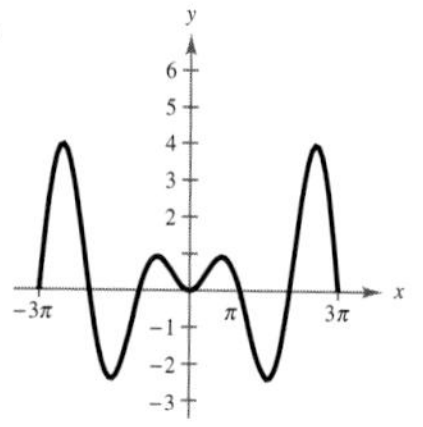

9. 4.9 **10.** $\frac{3}{4}$

11. $\sqrt{1 - 4x^2}$ **12.** 1 **13.** $2 \tan \theta$

14–16. Answers will vary. **17.** $\frac{\pi}{3}, \frac{\pi}{2}, \frac{3\pi}{2}, \frac{5\pi}{3}$

18. $\frac{\pi}{6}, \frac{5\pi}{6}, \frac{7\pi}{6}, \frac{11\pi}{6}$ **19.** $\frac{3\pi}{2}$ **20.** $\frac{16}{63}$ **21.** $\frac{4}{3}$

22. $\frac{\sqrt{5}}{5}, \frac{2\sqrt{5}}{5}$ **23.** $\frac{5}{2}\left(\sin \frac{5\pi}{2} - \sin \pi\right)$

24. $-2 \sin 8x \sin x$ **25.** $B \approx 26.39°, C \approx 123.61°, c \approx 14.99$

26. $B \approx 52.48°, C \approx 97.52°, a \approx 5.04$

27. $B = 60°, a \approx 5.77, c \approx 11.55$

28. $A \approx 26.28°, B \approx 49.74°, C \approx 103.98°$

29. Law of Sines; $C = 109°, a \approx 14.96, b \approx 9.27$

30. Law of Cosines; $A \approx 6.75°, B \approx 93.25°, c \approx 9.86$

31. 41.48 in.^{2} **32.** 599.09 m^2 **33.** $7\mathbf{i} + 8\mathbf{j}$

34. $\left\langle \frac{\sqrt{2}}{2}, \frac{\sqrt{2}}{2} \right\rangle$ **35.** -5 **36.** $-\frac{1}{13}\langle 1, 5\rangle; \frac{21}{13}\langle 5, -1\rangle$

37. $2\sqrt{2}\left(\cos \frac{3\pi}{4} + i \sin \frac{3\pi}{4}\right)$ **38.** $-12\sqrt{3} + 12i$

39. $\cos 0 + i \sin 0 = 1$

$\cos \frac{2\pi}{3} + i \sin \frac{2\pi}{3} = -\frac{1}{2} + \frac{\sqrt{3}}{2}i$

$\cos \frac{4\pi}{3} + i \sin \frac{4\pi}{3} = -\frac{1}{2} - \frac{\sqrt{3}}{2}i$

40. $3\left(\cos \frac{\pi}{5} + i \sin \frac{\pi}{5}\right)$

$3\left(\cos \frac{3\pi}{5} + i \sin \frac{3\pi}{5}\right)$

$3(\cos \pi + i \sin \pi)$

$3\left(\cos \frac{7\pi}{5} + i \sin \frac{7\pi}{5}\right)$

$3\left(\cos \frac{9\pi}{5} + i \sin \frac{9\pi}{5}\right)$

41. About 395.8 rad/min; about 8312.7 in./min

42. 42π yd$^2 \approx 131.95$ yd^2 **43.** 5 ft **44.** 22.6°

45. $d = 4 \cos \frac{\pi}{4}t$ **46.** 32.6°; 543.9 km/h

47. 425 ft-lb

Problem Solving *(page 491)*

1. 2.01 ft

3. (a)

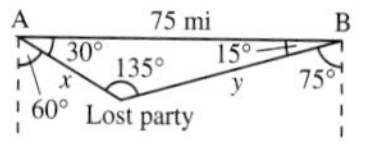

(b) Station A: 27.45 mi; Station B: 53.03 mi

(c) 11.03 mi; S 21.7° E

5. (a) (i) $\sqrt{2}$ (ii) $\sqrt{5}$ (iii) 1

(iv) 1 (v) 1 (vi) 1

(b) (i) 1 (ii) $3\sqrt{2}$ (iii) $\sqrt{13}$

(iv) 1 (v) 1 (vi) 1

(c) (i) $\frac{\sqrt{5}}{2}$ (ii) $\sqrt{13}$ (iii) $\frac{\sqrt{85}}{2}$

(iv) 1 (v) 1 (vi) 1

(d) (i) $2\sqrt{5}$ (ii) $5\sqrt{2}$ (iii) $5\sqrt{2}$

(iv) 1 (v) 1 (vi) 1

7. $\mathbf{w} = \frac{1}{2}(\mathbf{u} + \mathbf{v}); \mathbf{w} = \frac{1}{2}(\mathbf{v} - \mathbf{u})$

9. (a)

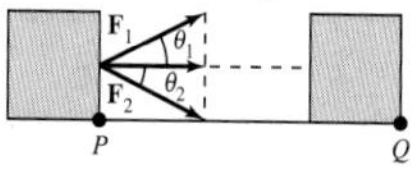

The amount of work done by $\mathbf{F}_1$ is equal to the amount of work done by $\mathbf{F}_2$.

(b)

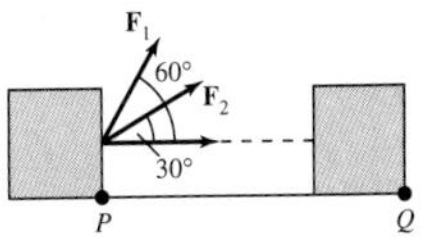

The amount of work done by $\mathbf{F}_2$ is $\sqrt{3}$ times as great as the amount of work done by $\mathbf{F}_1$.

Chapter 7

Section 7.1 *(page 501)*

1. system; equations **3.** solving **5.** point; intersection
7. (a) No (b) No (c) No (d) Yes
9. (a) No (b) Yes (c) No (d) No
11. $(2, 2)$ **13.** $(2, 6), (-1, 3)$ **15.** $(-3, -4), (5, 0)$
17. $(0, 0), (2, -4)$ **19.** $(0, 1), (1, -1), (3, 1)$ **21.** $(6, 4)$
23. $\left(\frac{1}{2}, 3\right)$ **25.** $(1, 1)$ **27.** $\left(\frac{20}{3}, \frac{40}{3}\right)$ **29.** No solution
31. $(-2, 4), (0, 0)$ **33.** No solution **35.** $(6, 2)$
37. $\left(-\frac{3}{2}, \frac{1}{2}\right)$ **39.** $(2, 2), (4, 0)$ **41.** $(1, 4), (4, 7)$
43. $\left(4, -\frac{1}{2}\right)$ **45.** No solution **47.** $(4, 3), (-4, 3)$

49.

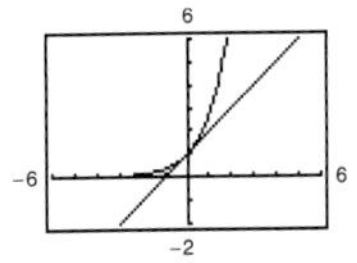

$(0, 1)$

51.

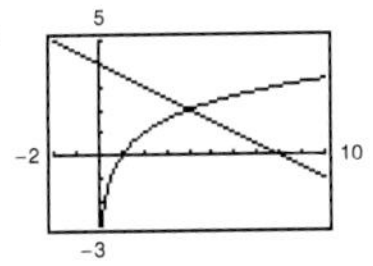

$(4, 2)$

53.

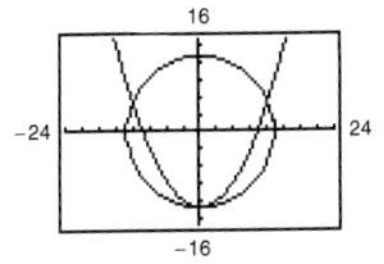

$(0, -13), (\pm 12, 5)$

55. $(1, 2)$ **57.** No solution **59.** $(0.287, 1.751)$
61. $(-1, 0), (0, 1), (1, 0)$ **63.** $\left(\frac{1}{2}, 2\right), \left(-4, -\frac{1}{4}\right)$
65. 192 units **67.** (a) 1013 units (b) 5061 units
69. (a) 8 weeks
(b)

	1	2	3	4
$360 - 24x$	336	312	288	264
$24 + 18x$	42	60	78	96

	5	6	7	8
$360 - 24x$	240	216	192	168
$24 + 18x$	114	132	150	168

71. More than \$16,666.67
73. (a) $\begin{cases} x + y = 25{,}000 \\ 0.06x + 0.085y = 2{,}000 \end{cases}$

(b)

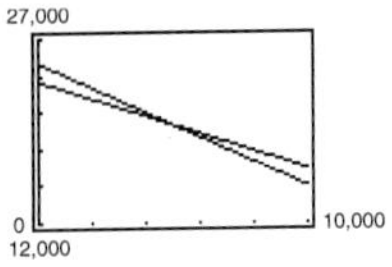

(c) \$5000

Decreases; Interest is fixed.

75. (a) Solar: $0.0598t^3 - 1.719t^2 + 14.66t + 32.2$
Wind: $3.237t^2 - 51.97t + 247.9$
(b)

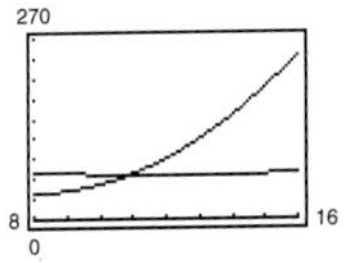

(c) Point of intersection: (10.9, 65.26); Consumption of solar and wind energy are equal at this point in time in the year 2000.
(d) Answers will vary
(e) Answers will vary.

77. (a) $T_1 = 26.560t^2 + 85.54t + 2468.5$
$T_2 = 794.14t + 14{,}124.6$
(b)

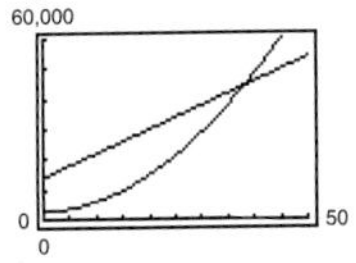

(c) 2038 (d) 2038

79. 60 cm × 80 cm **81.** 44 ft × 198 ft
83. 10 km × 12 km
85. False. To solve a system of equations by substitution, you can solve for either variable in one of the two equations and then back-substitute.

87.

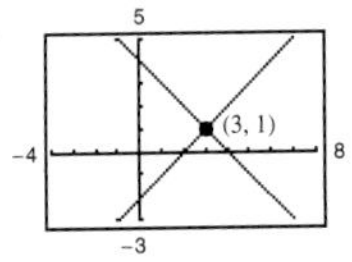

(3, 1); The point of intersection is equal to the solution found in Example 1.

89. For a linear system, the result will be a contradictory equation such as $0 = N$, where N is a nonzero real number. For a nonlinear system, there may be an equation with imaginary solutions.
91. (a) $y = 2x$ (b) $y = 0$ (c) $y = x - 2$

Section 7.2 *(page 513)*

1. elimination **3.** consistent; inconsistent
5. $(2, 1)$

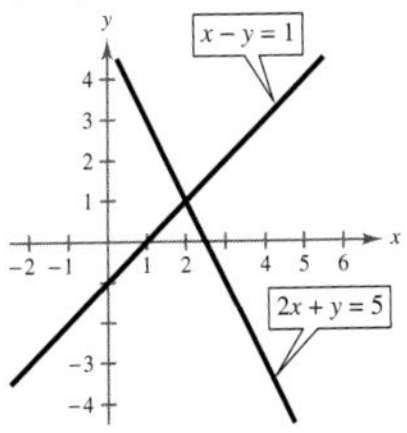

7. $(1, -1)$

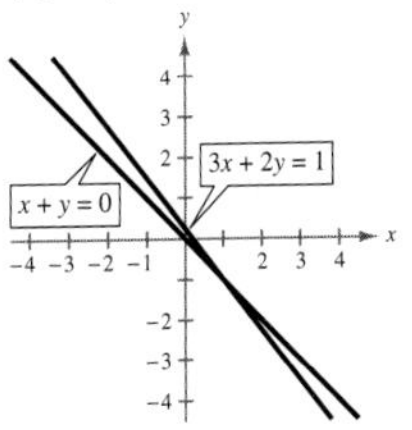

9. No solution

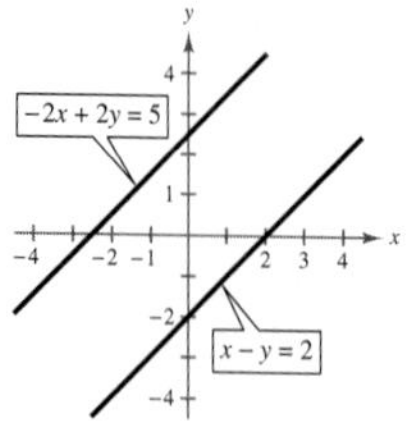

11. $\left(a, \frac{3}{2}a - \frac{5}{2}\right)$

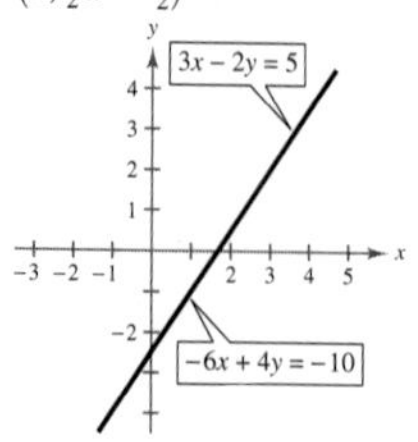

13. $(4, 1)$ **15.** $\left(\frac{3}{2}, -\frac{1}{2}\right)$ **17.** $(4, -1)$ **19.** $\left(\frac{12}{7}, \frac{18}{7}\right)$

21. No solution **23.** Infinitely many solutions: $\left(a, -\frac{1}{2} + \frac{5}{6}a\right)$

25. $(101, 96)$ **27.** $\left(-\frac{6}{35}, \frac{43}{35}\right)$ **29.** $(5, -2)$

31. b; one solution; consistent

33. a; infinitely many solutions; consistent

35. $(4, 1)$ **37.** $(2, -1)$ **39.** $(6, -3)$ **41.** $\left(\frac{49}{4}, \frac{33}{4}\right)$

43. 550 mi/h, 50 mi/h **45.** $(240, 404)$

47. $(2{,}000{,}000, 100)$

49. Cheeseburger: 300 calories; French fries: 230 calories

51. (a) $\begin{cases} x + y = 30 \\ 0.25x + 0.5y = 12 \end{cases}$

(b)

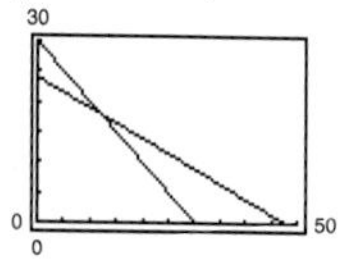

Decreases

(c) 25% solution: 12 L; 50% solution: 18 L

53. \$18,000

55. (a)

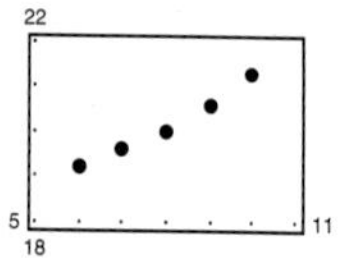

Pharmacy A: $P = 0.52t + 16.0$

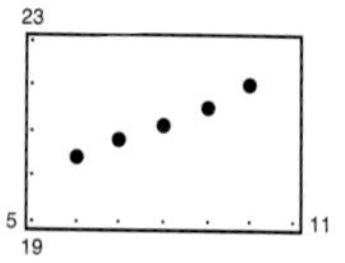

Pharmacy B: $P = 0.39t + 18.0$

(b) Yes, in the year 2015

57. $y = 0.97x + 2.1$ **59.** $y = -2x + 8$

61. (a) $y = 14x + 19$ (b) 41.4 bushels/acre

63. False. Two lines that coincide have infinitely many points of intersection.

65. No. Two lines will intersect only once or will coincide, and if they coincide the system will have infinitely many solutions.

67. The method of elimination is much easier.

69. (39,600, 398). It is necessary to change the scale on the axes to see the point of intersection.

71. $k = -4$ **73.** $u = 1, v = -\tan x$

Section 7.3 *(page 525)*

1. row-echelon **3.** Gaussian **5.** nonsquare

7. (a) No (b) No (c) No (d) Yes

9. (a) No (b) No (c) Yes (d) No

11. $(-13, -10, 8)$ **13.** $(3, 10, 2)$ **15.** $\left(\frac{11}{4}, 7, 11\right)$

17. $\begin{cases} x - 2y + 3z = 5 \\ y - 2z = 9 \\ 2x - 3z = 0 \end{cases}$ First step in putting the system in row-echelon form.

19. $(4, 1, 2)$ **21.** $(-4, 8, 5)$ **23.** $(5, -2, 0)$

25. No solution **27.** $\left(-\frac{1}{2}, 1, \frac{3}{2}\right)$

29. $(-3a + 10, 5a - 7, a)$ **31.** $(-a + 3, a + 1, a)$

33. $(2a, 21a - 1, 8a)$ **35.** $\left(-\frac{3}{2}a + \frac{1}{2}, -\frac{2}{3}a + 1, a\right)$

37. $(1, 1, 1, 1)$ **39.** No solution **41.** $(0, 0, 0)$

43. $(9a, -35a, 67a)$ **45.** $s = -16t^2 + 144$

47. $s = -16t^2 - 32t + 400$

49. $y = \frac{1}{2}x^2 - 2x$

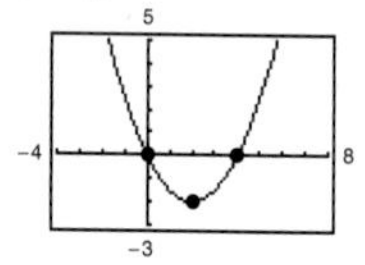

51. $y = x^2 - 6x + 8$

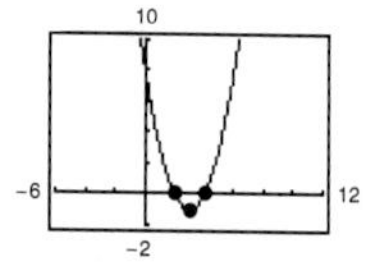

53. $y = 4x^2 - 2x + 1$

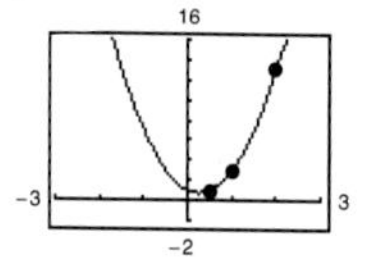

55. $x^2 + y^2 - 10x = 0$

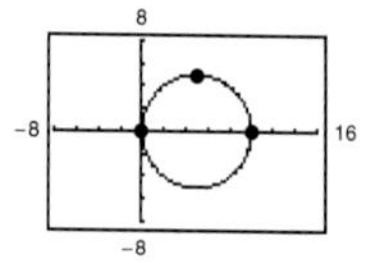

57. $x^2 + y^2 + 6x - 8y = 0$

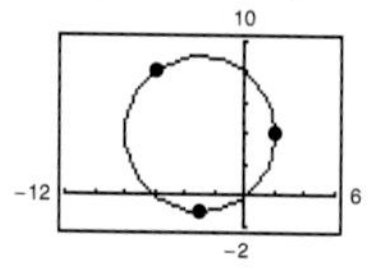

59. 6 touchdowns, 6 extra-point kicks, 1 field goal

61. \$300,000 at 8%
\$400,000 at 9%
\$75,000 at 10%

63. $187{,}500 + s$ in certificates of deposit
$187{,}500 - s$ in municipal bonds
$125{,}000 - s$ in blue-chip stocks
s in growth stocks

65. Brand X = 4 lb
Brand Y = 9 lb
Brand Z = 9 lb

67. 48 ft, 35 ft, 27 ft **69.** $x = 60°, y = 67°, z = 53°$

71. Television = 30 ads
Radio = 10 ads
Newspaper = 20 ads

73. (a) 1 L of 10%, 7 L of 20%, 2 L of 50%
(b) 0 L of 10%, $8\frac{1}{3}$ L of 20%, $1\frac{2}{3}$ L of 50%
(c) $6\frac{1}{4}$ L of 10%, 0 L of 20%, $3\frac{3}{4}$ L of 50%

75. $I_1 = 1, I_2 = 2, I_3 = 1$ **77.** $y = -\frac{5}{24}x^2 - \frac{3}{10}x + \frac{41}{6}$

79. $y = x^2 - x$

81. (a) $y = -0.0075x^2 + 1.3x + 20$

(b)

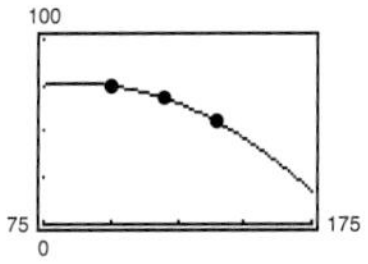

(c)

x	100	120	140
y	75	68	55

The values are the same.

(d) 24.25% (e) 156 females

83. 6 touchdowns, 6 extra-point kicks, 2 field goals, 1 safety

85. $x = 5, y = 5, \lambda = -5$

87. $x = \pm\frac{\sqrt{2}}{2}, \; y = \frac{1}{2}, \; \lambda = 1$ or $x = 0, y = 0, \lambda = 0$

89. False. Equation 2 does not have a leading coefficient of 1.

91. No. Answers will vary.

93. Sample answers:

$$\begin{cases} 2x + y - z = 0 \\ y + 2z = 0 \\ -x + 2y + z = -9 \end{cases} \qquad \begin{cases} x + y + z = 1 \\ 2x \quad - z = 4 \\ 4y + 8z = 0 \end{cases}$$

95. Sample answers:

$$\begin{cases} x + 2y + 4z = -14 \\ x - 12y \quad = 0 \\ x \quad - 8z = 8 \end{cases} \qquad \begin{cases} 4x - 2y - 8z = -9 \\ -x \quad + 4z = -1 \\ -7y + 2z = 0 \end{cases}$$

Section 7.4 *(page 536)*

1. partial fraction decomposition **3.** partial fraction

5. b **6.** c **7.** d **8.** a

9. $\frac{A}{x} + \frac{B}{x-2}$ **11.** $\frac{A}{x} + \frac{B}{x^2} + \frac{C}{x-7}$

13. $\frac{A}{x-5} + \frac{B}{(x-5)^2} + \frac{C}{(x-5)^3}$ **15.** $\frac{A}{x} + \frac{Bx+C}{x^2+10}$

17. $\frac{A}{x} + \frac{Bx+C}{x^2+1} + \frac{Dx+E}{(x^2+1)^2}$ **19.** $\frac{1}{x} - \frac{1}{x+1}$

21. $\frac{1}{x} - \frac{2}{2x+1}$ **23.** $\frac{1}{x-1} - \frac{1}{x+2}$

25. $\frac{1}{2}\left(\frac{1}{x-1} - \frac{1}{x+1}\right)$ **27.** $-\frac{3}{x} - \frac{1}{x+2} + \frac{5}{x-2}$

29. $\frac{3}{x-3} + \frac{9}{(x-3)^2}$ **31.** $\frac{3}{x} - \frac{1}{x^2} + \frac{1}{x+1}$

33. $\frac{3}{x} - \frac{2x-2}{x^2+1}$ **35.** $-\frac{1}{x-1} + \frac{x+2}{x^2-2}$

37. $\frac{2}{x^2+4} + \frac{x}{(x^2+4)^2}$

39. $\frac{1}{8}\left(\frac{1}{2x+1} + \frac{1}{2x-1} - \frac{4x}{4x^2+1}\right)$

41. $\frac{1}{x+1} + \frac{2}{x^2-2x+3}$ **43.** $1 - \frac{2x+1}{x^2+x+1}$

45. $2x - 7 + \frac{17}{x+2} + \frac{1}{x+1}$

47. $x + 3 + \frac{6}{x-1} + \frac{4}{(x-1)^2} + \frac{1}{(x-1)^3}$

49. $x + \frac{2}{x} + \frac{1}{x+1} + \frac{3}{(x+1)^2}$ **51.** $\frac{3}{2x-1} - \frac{2}{x+1}$

53. $\frac{1}{2}\left[-\frac{1}{x} + \frac{5}{x+1} - \frac{3}{(x+1)^2}\right]$ **55.** $\frac{1}{x^2+2} + \frac{x}{(x^2+2)^2}$

57. $2x + \frac{1}{2}\left(\frac{3}{x-4} - \frac{1}{x+2}\right)$

59. (a) $\frac{3}{x} - \frac{2}{x-4}$

(b) $y = \frac{x-12}{x(x-4)}$ $\qquad y = \frac{3}{x}, \; y = -\frac{2}{x-4}$

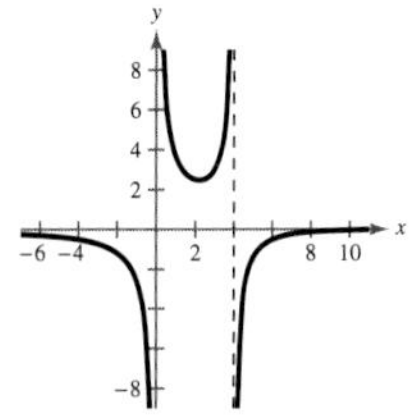

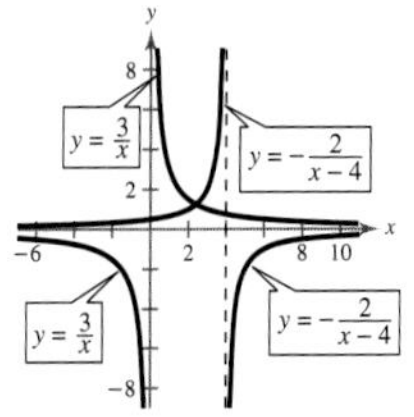

(c) The vertical asymptotes are the same.

61. $\frac{60}{100-p} - \frac{60}{100+p}$

63. False. The partial fraction decomposition is

$\frac{A}{x+10} + \frac{B}{x-10} + \frac{C}{(x-10)^2}$.

65. True. The expression is an improper rational expression.

67. $\frac{1}{2a}\left(\frac{1}{a+x} + \frac{1}{a-x}\right)$ **69.** $\frac{1}{a}\left(\frac{1}{y} + \frac{1}{a-y}\right)$

71. Answers will vary. Sample answer: You can substitute any convenient values of x that will help determine the constants. You can also find the basic equation, expand it, then equate coefficients of like terms.

Section 7.5 *(page 545)*

1. solution **3.** linear **5.** solution set

7.

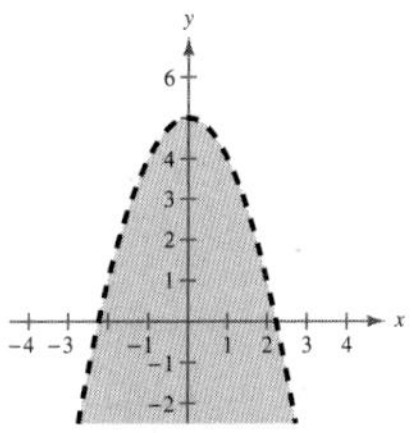

9.

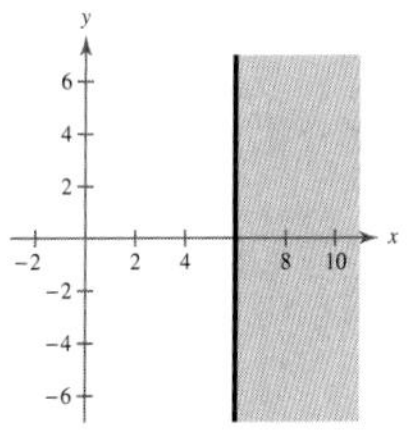

11.

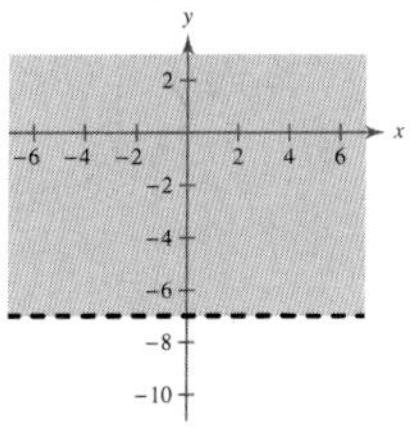

13.

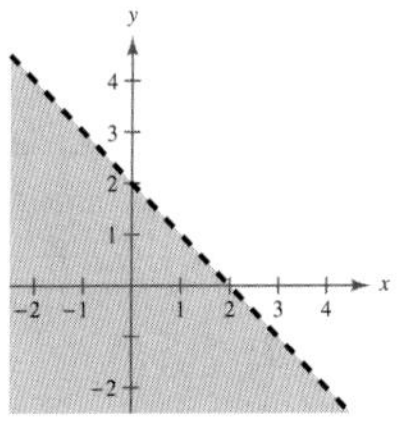

15.

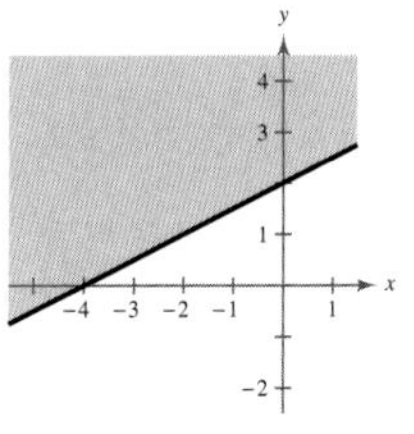

17.

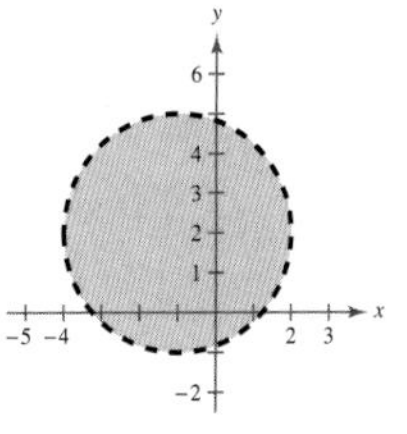

CHAPTER 7

19.

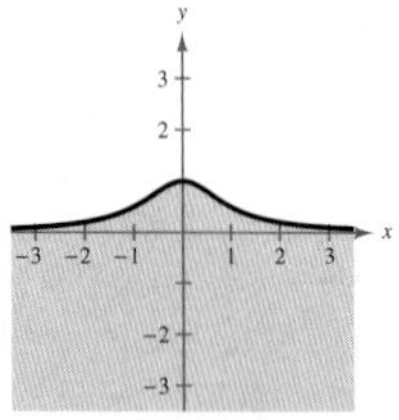

21.

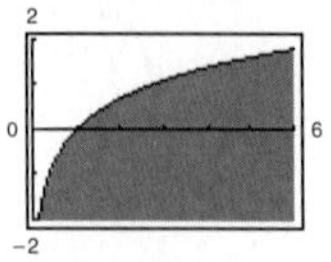

23.

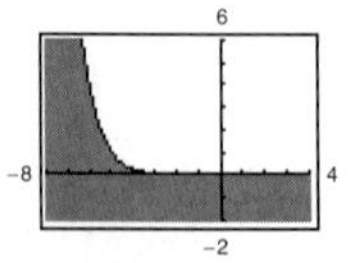

25.

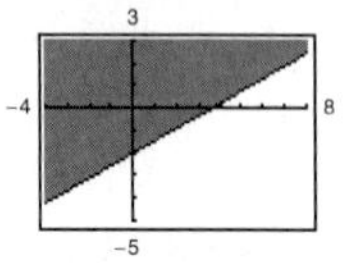

27.

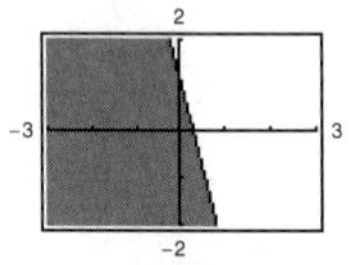

29.

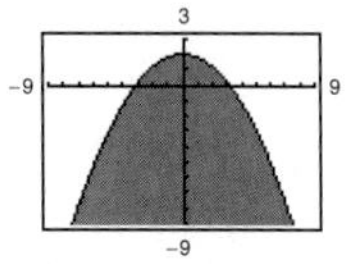

31.

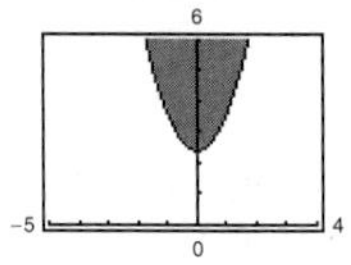

33. $y < 5x + 5$ **35.** $y \geq -\frac{2}{3}x + 2$

37. (a) No (b) No (c) Yes (d) Yes

39. (a) Yes (b) No (c) Yes (d) Yes

41.

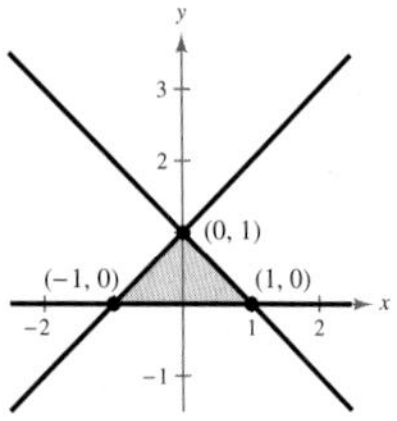

43.

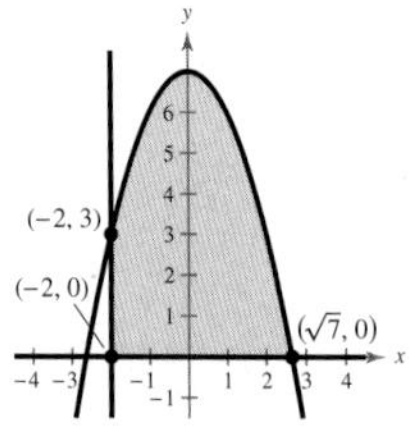

45.

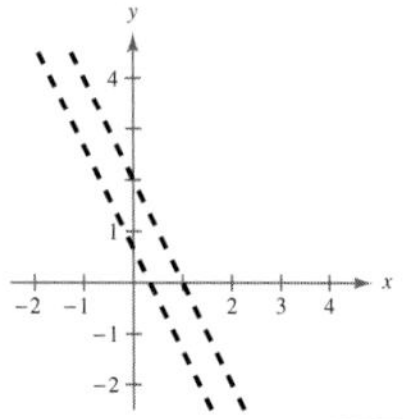

No solution

47.

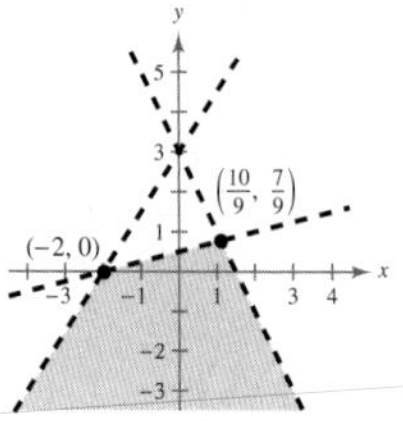

49.

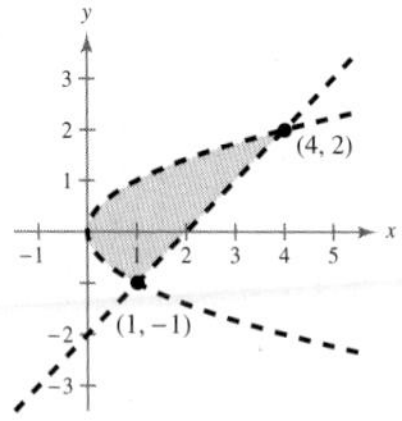

51.

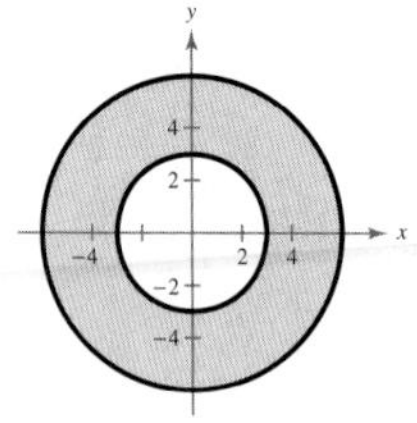

53.

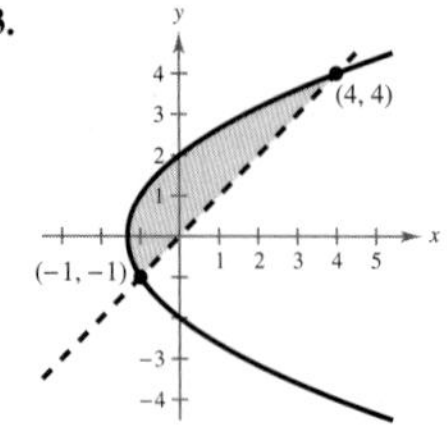

55.

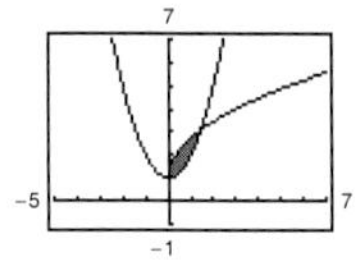

57.

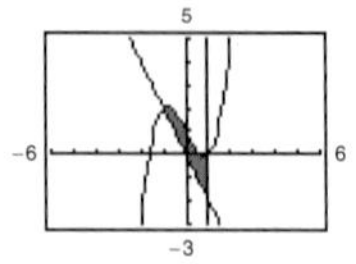

59.

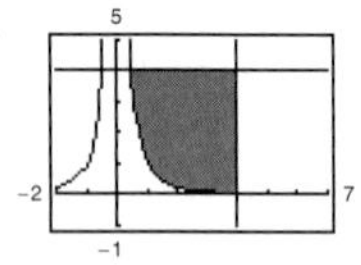

61. $\begin{cases} x \geq 0 \\ y \geq 0 \\ y \leq 6 - x \end{cases}$

63. $\begin{cases} y \geq 4 - x \\ y \geq 2 - \frac{1}{4}x \\ x \geq 0, \ y \geq 0 \end{cases}$

65. $\begin{cases} x \geq 0 \\ y \geq 0 \\ x^2 + y^2 < 64 \end{cases}$

67. $\begin{cases} x \geq 4 \\ x \leq 9 \\ y \geq 3 \\ y \leq 9 \end{cases}$

69. $\begin{cases} y \geq 0 \\ y \leq 5x \\ y \leq -x + 6 \end{cases}$

71. (a)

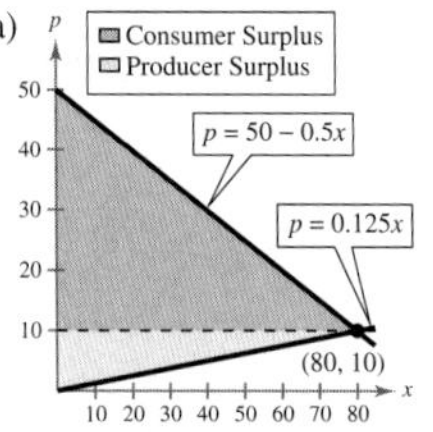

(b) Consumer surplus: \$1600
Producer surplus: \$400

73. (a)

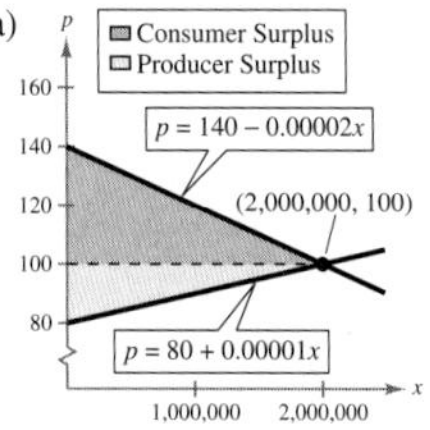

(b) Consumer surplus: \$40,000,000
Producer surplus: \$20,000,000

75. $\begin{cases} x + \frac{3}{2}y \leq 12 \\ \frac{4}{3}x + \frac{3}{2}y \leq 15 \\ x \geq 0 \\ y \geq 0 \end{cases}$

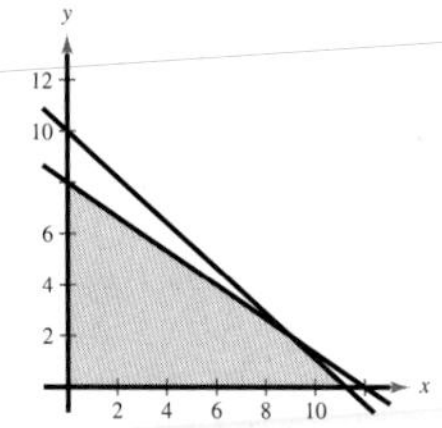

77. $\begin{cases} x + y \le 20{,}000 \\ y \ge 2x \\ x \ge 5{,}000 \\ y \ge 5{,}000 \end{cases}$

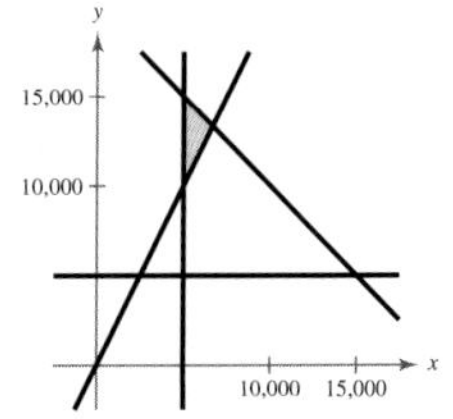

79. $\begin{cases} 55x + 70y \le 7500 \\ x \ge 50 \\ y \ge 40 \end{cases}$

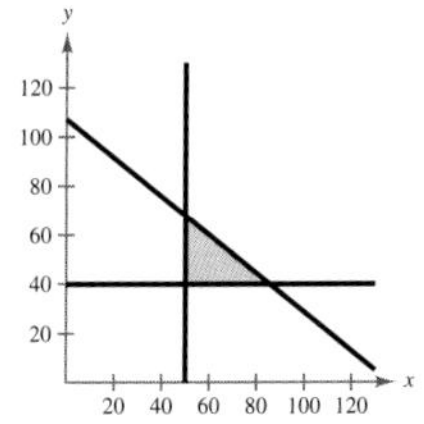

81. (a) $\begin{cases} 20x + 10y \ge 300 \\ 15x + 10y \ge 150 \\ 10x + 20y \ge 200 \\ x \ge 0 \\ y \ge 0 \end{cases}$ (b)

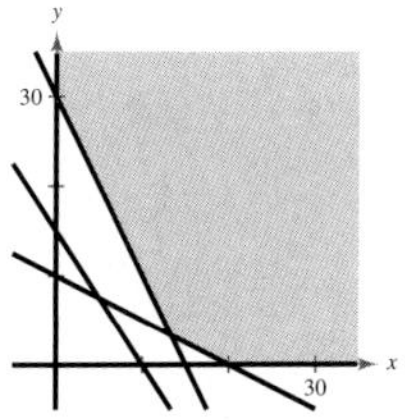

(c) Answers will vary.

83. (a) $y = 16.75t + 148.4$

(b)

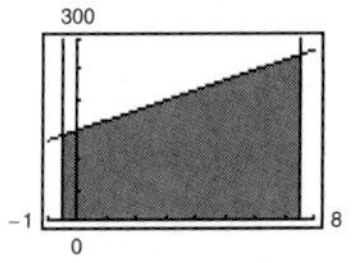

(c) \$1656.2 billion

85. (a) $\begin{cases} xy \ge 500 \\ 2x + \pi y \ge 125 \\ x \ge 0 \\ y \ge 0 \end{cases}$ (b)

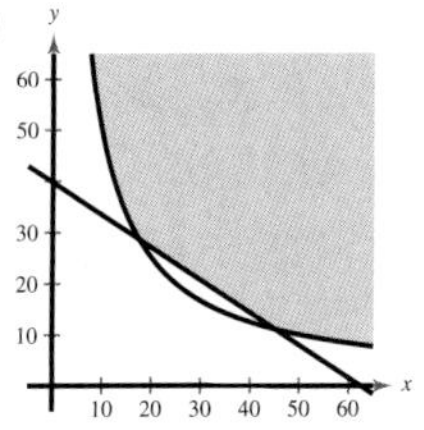

87. False. The graph shows the solution of the system

$\begin{cases} y < 6 \\ -4x - 9y < 6. \\ 3x + y^2 \ge 2 \end{cases}$

89. (a) $\begin{cases} \pi y^2 - \pi x^2 \ge 10 \\ y > x \\ x > 0 \end{cases}$ (b)

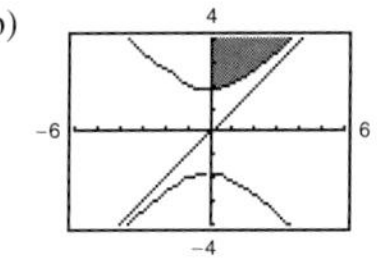

(c) The line is an asymptote to the boundary. The larger the circles, the closer the radii can be while still satisfying the constraint.

91. d **92.** b **93.** c **94.** a

Section 7.6 *(page 555)*

1. optimization **3.** objective **5.** inside; on

7. Minimum at (0, 0): 0
Maximum at (5, 0): 20

9. Minimum at (0, 0): 0
Maximum at (3, 4): 26

11. Minimum at (0, 0): 0
Maximum at (60, 20): 740

13.

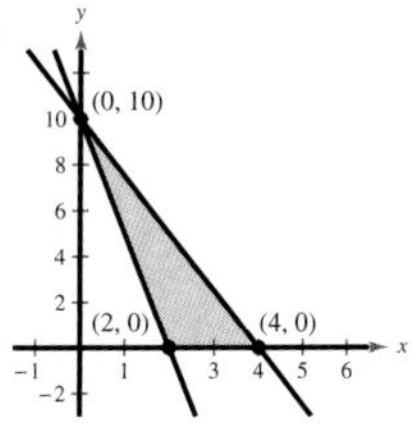

Minimum at (2, 0): 6
Maximum at (0, 10): 20

15.

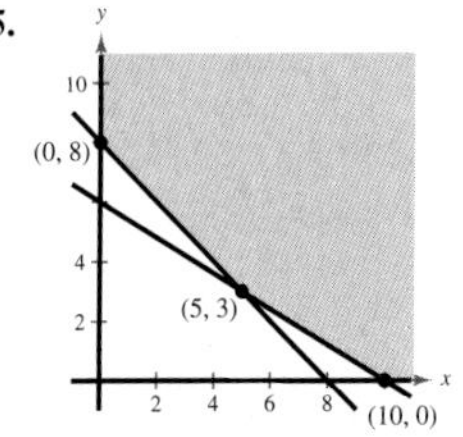

Minimum at (5, 3): 35
No maximum

17.

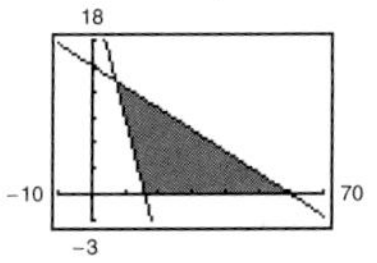

Minimum at (7.2, 13.2): 34.8
Maximum at (60, 0): 180

19.

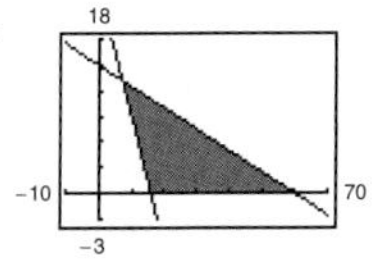

Minimum at (16, 0): 16
Maximum at any point on the line segment connecting (7.2, 13.2) and (60, 0): 60

21. Minimum at (0, 0): 0
Maximum at (3, 6): 12

23. Minimum at (0, 0): 0
Maximum at (0, 10): 10

25. Minimum at (0, 0): 0
Maximum at (0, 5): 25

27. Minimum at (0, 0): 0
Maximum at $\left(\frac{22}{3}, \frac{19}{6}\right)$: $\frac{271}{6}$

29.

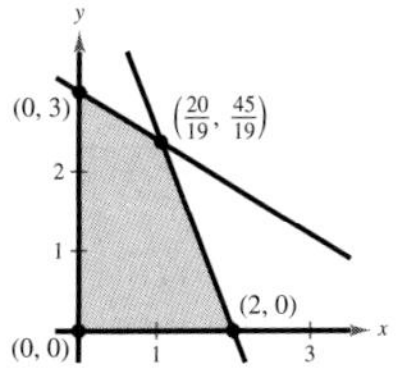

The maximum, 5, occurs at any point on the line segment connecting (2, 0) and $\left(\frac{20}{19}, \frac{45}{19}\right)$. Minimum at (0, 0): 0

31.

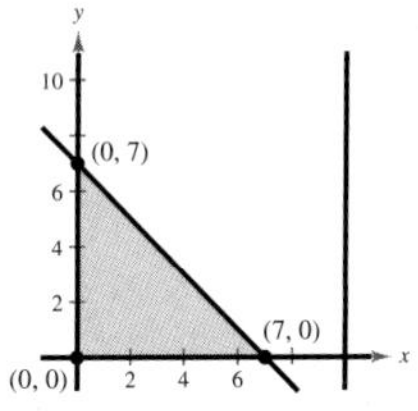

The constraint $x \le 10$ is extraneous. Minimum at (7, 0): -7; maximum at (0, 7): 14

CHAPTER 7

33.

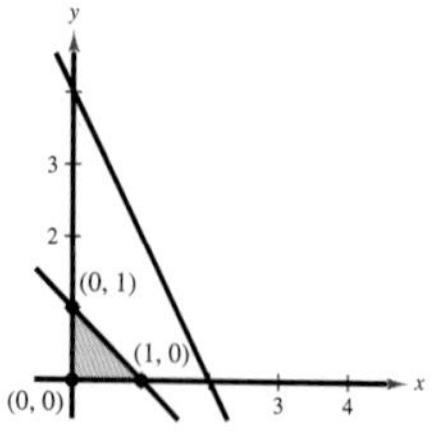

The constraint $2x + y \le 4$ is extraneous. Minimum at $(0, 0)$: 0; maximum at $(0, 1)$: 4

35. 230 units of the \$225 model; 45 units of the \$250 model
Optimal profit: \$8295

37. 3 bags of brand X; 6 bags of brand Y
Optimal cost: \$195

39. 13 audits; 0 tax returns
Optimal revenue: \$20,800

41. \$0 on TV ads; \$1,000,000 on newspaper ads
Optimal audience: 250 million people

43. \$62,500 to type A; \$187,500 to type B
Optimal return: \$23,750

45. True. The objective function has a maximum value at any point on the line segment connecting the two vertices.

47. True. If an objective function has a maximum value at more than one vertex, then any point on the line segment connecting the points will produce the maximum value.

Review Exercises *(page 560)*

1. $(1, 1)$ **3.** $\left(\frac{3}{2}, 5\right)$ **5.** $(0.25, 0.625)$ **7.** $(5, 4)$
9. $(0, 0), (2, 8), (-2, 8)$ **11.** $(4, -2)$
13. $(1.41, -0.66), (-1.41, 10.66)$

15.

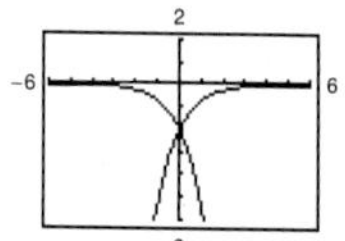

$(0, -2)$

17.

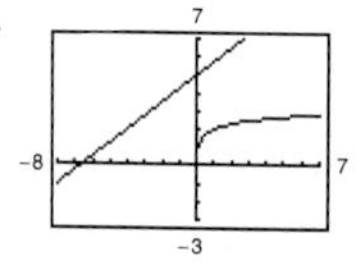

No solution

19. 3847 units **21.** 96 m × 144 m **23.** 8 in. × 12 in.
25. $\left(\frac{5}{2}, 3\right)$ **27.** $(-0.5, 0.8)$ **29.** $(0, 0)$ **31.** $\left(\frac{8}{5}a + \frac{14}{5}, a\right)$
33. d, one solution, consistent
34. c, infinitely many solutions, consistent
35. b, no solution, inconsistent **36.** a, one solution, consistent
37. $\left(\frac{500{,}000}{7}, \frac{159}{7}\right)$ **39.** $(2, -4, -5)$ **41.** $(-6, 7, 10)$
43. $\left(\frac{24}{5}, \frac{22}{5}, -\frac{8}{5}\right)$ **45.** $(3a + 4, 2a + 5, a)$ **47.** $(1, 1, 1, 0)$
49. $(a - 4, a - 3, a)$ **51.** $y = 2x^2 + x - 5$
53. $x^2 + y^2 - 4x + 4y - 1 = 0$
55. (a) $y = 0.25x^2 + 27.95x - 36.7$
(b)

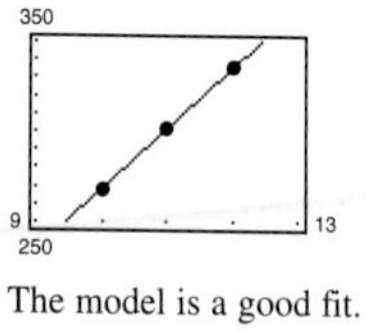

The model is a good fit.
(c) \$438.8 billion; yes

57. \$16,000 at 7%; \$13,000 at 9%; \$11,000 at 11%
59. 4 par-3 holes, 10 par-4 holes, 4 par-5 holes
61. $\frac{A}{x} + \frac{B}{x + 20}$ **63.** $\frac{A}{x} + \frac{B}{x^2} + \frac{C}{x - 5}$
65. $\frac{3}{x + 2} - \frac{4}{x + 4}$ **67.** $1 - \frac{25}{8(x + 5)} + \frac{9}{8(x - 3)}$
69. $\frac{1}{2}\left(\frac{3}{x - 1} - \frac{x - 3}{x^2 + 1}\right)$ **71.** $\frac{3}{x^2 + 1} + \frac{4x - 3}{(x^2 + 1)^2}$

73.

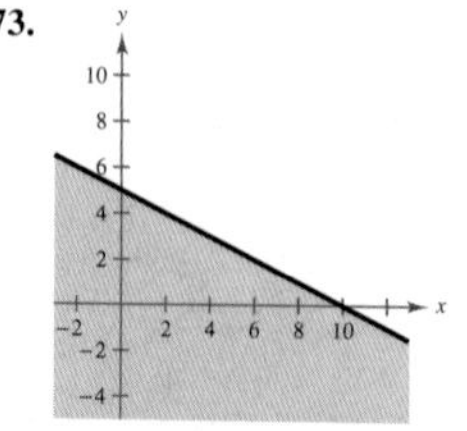

75.

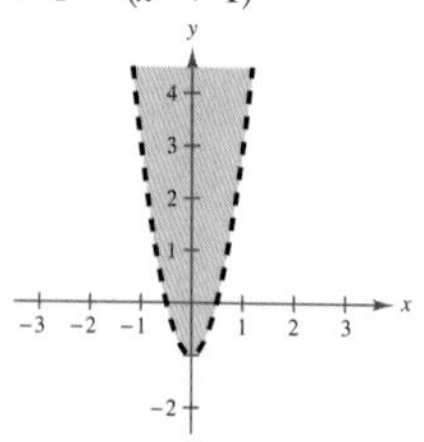

77.

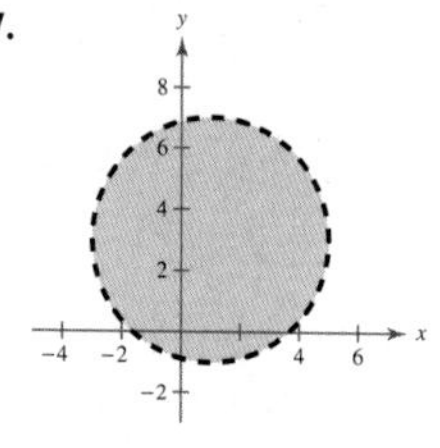

79.

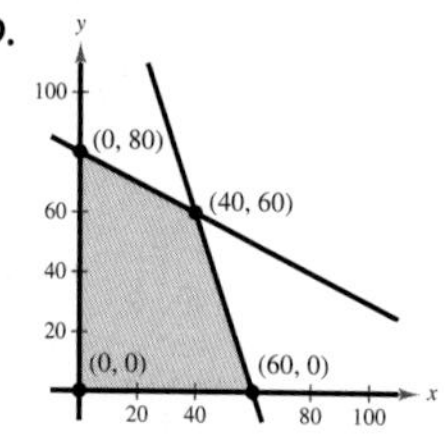

81.

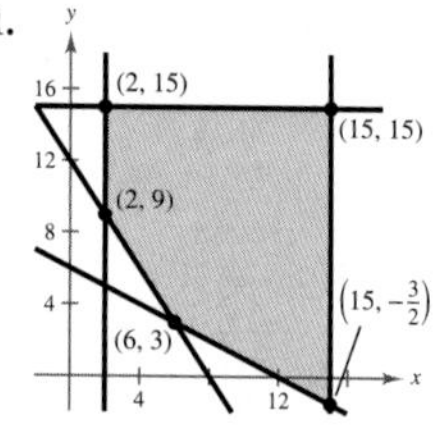

83.

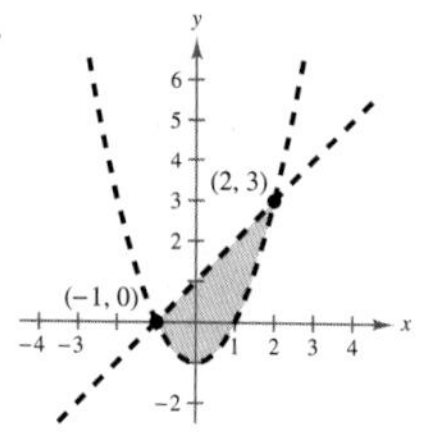

85.

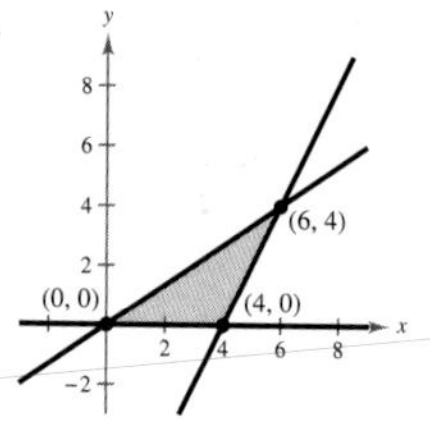

87. $\begin{cases} 20x + 30y \le 24{,}000 \\ 12x + 8y \le 12{,}400 \\ x \ge 0 \\ y \ge 0 \end{cases}$

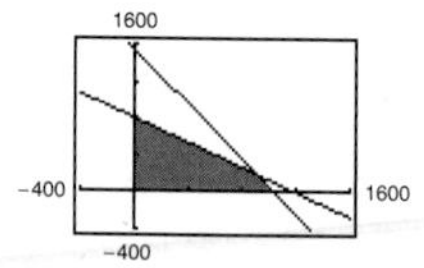

89. (a)
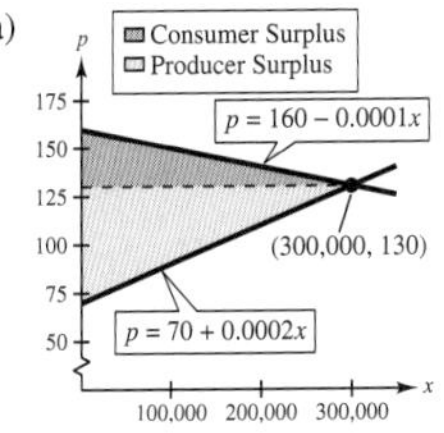

(b) Consumer surplus: \$4,500,000
Producer surplus: \$9,000,000

91. $\begin{cases} x \ge 3 \\ x \le 7 \\ y \ge 1 \\ y \le 10 \end{cases}$

93.
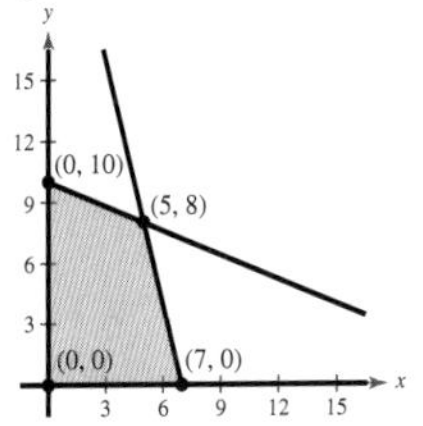

Minimum at $(0, 0)$: 0
Maximum at $(5, 8)$: 47

95.
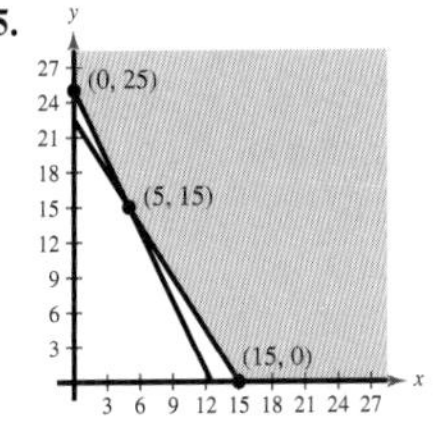

Minimum at $(15, 0)$: 26.25
No maximum

97.
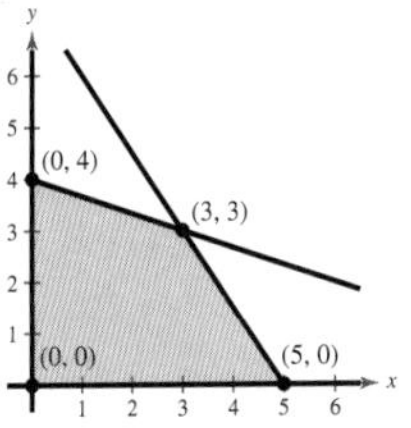

Minimum at $(0, 0)$: 0
Maximum at $(3, 3)$: 48

99. 72 haircuts, 0 permanents; Optimal revenue: \$1800

101. 750 units of model A
1000 units of model B
Optimal profit: \$83,750

103. $\frac{2}{3}$ regular unleaded
$\frac{1}{3}$ premium unleaded
Optimal cost: \$1.93

105. False. To represent a region covered by an isosceles trapezoid, the last two inequality signs should be $\le$.

107. $\begin{cases} 4x + y = -22 \\ \frac{1}{2}x + y = 6 \end{cases}$

109. $\begin{cases} 3x + y = 7 \\ -6x + 3y = 1 \end{cases}$

111. $\begin{cases} x + y + z = 6 \\ x + y - z = 0 \\ x - y - z = 2 \end{cases}$

113. $\begin{cases} 2x + 2y - 3z = 7 \\ x - 2y + z = 4 \\ -x + 4y - z = -1 \end{cases}$

115. An inconsistent system of linear equations has no solution.

Chapter Test *(page 565)*

1. $(-4, -5)$ **2.** $(0, -1), (1, 0), (2, 1)$

3. $(8, 4), (2, -2)$

4.
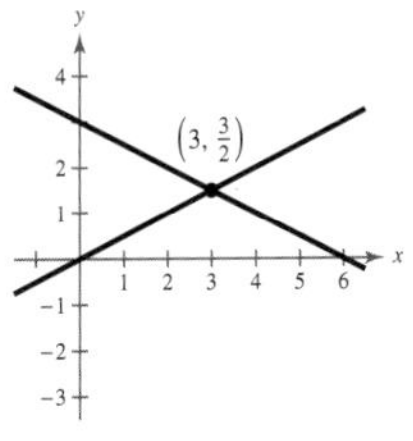

$\left(3, \frac{3}{2}\right)$

5.
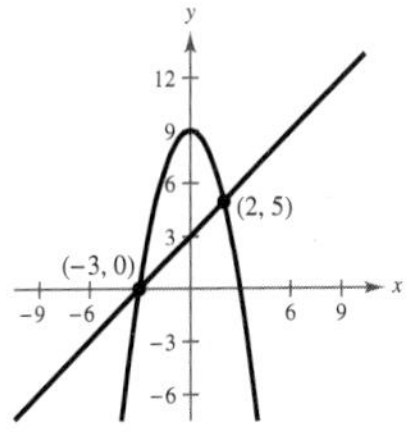

$(-3, 0), (2, 5)$

6.
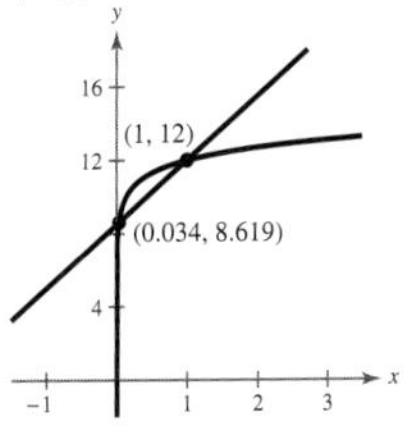

$(1, 12), (0.034, 8.619)$

7. $(-2, -5)$ **8.** $(10, -3)$ **9.** $(2, -3, 1)$

10. No solution

11. $-\dfrac{1}{x+1} + \dfrac{3}{x-2}$ **12.** $\dfrac{2}{x^2} + \dfrac{3}{2-x}$

13. $-\dfrac{5}{x} + \dfrac{3}{x+1} + \dfrac{3}{x-1}$ **14.** $-\dfrac{2}{x} + \dfrac{3x}{x^2+2}$

15.
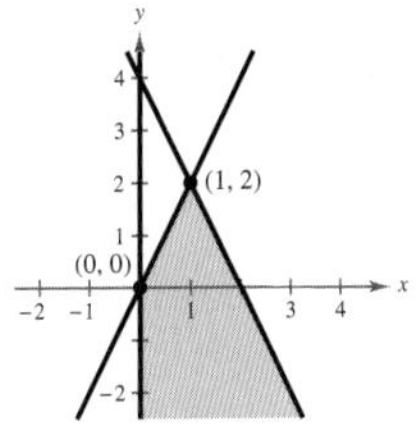

16.
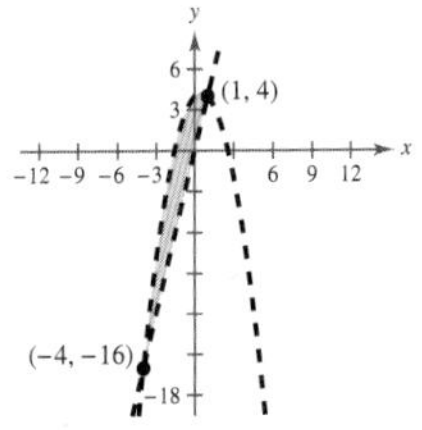

17.
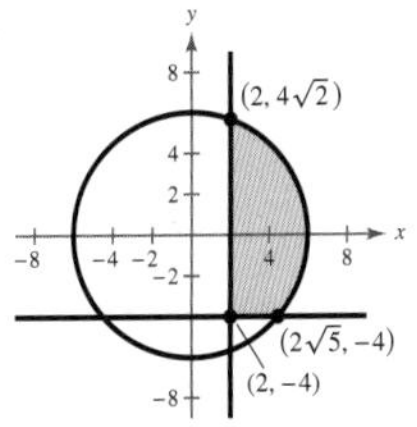

18. Maximum at $(12, 0)$: 240; Minimum at $(0, 0)$: 0

19. \$24,000 in 4% fund
\$26,000 in 5.5% fund

20. $y = -\frac{1}{2}x^2 + x + 6$

21. 0 units of model I
5300 units of model II
Optimal profit: \$212,000

CHAPTER 7

Problem Solving *(page 567)*

1.

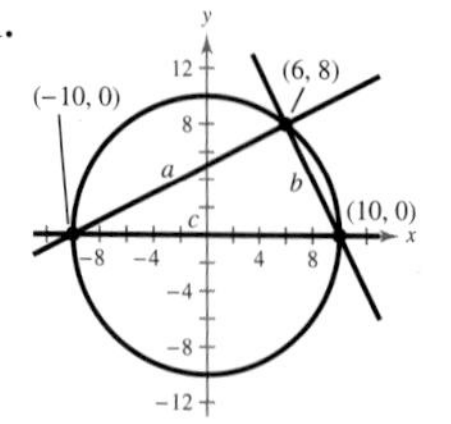

$a = 8\sqrt{5},\ b = 4\sqrt{5},\ c = 20$

$(8\sqrt{5})^2 + (4\sqrt{5})^2 = 20^2$

Therefore, the triangle is a right triangle.

3. $ad \neq bc$ **5.** (a) One (b) Two (c) Four

7. 10.1 ft; About 252.7 ft **9.** $12.00

11. (a) $(3, -4)$ (b) $\left(\dfrac{2}{-a+5}, \dfrac{1}{4a-1}, \dfrac{1}{a}\right)$

13. (a) $\left(\dfrac{-5a+16}{6}, \dfrac{5a-16}{6}, a\right)$

(b) $\left(\dfrac{-11a+36}{14}, \dfrac{13a-40}{14}, a\right)$

(c) $(-a+3, a-3, a)$ (d) Infinitely many

15. $\begin{cases} a + t \le 32 \\ 0.15a \ge 1.9 \\ 193a + 772t \ge 11{,}000 \end{cases}$

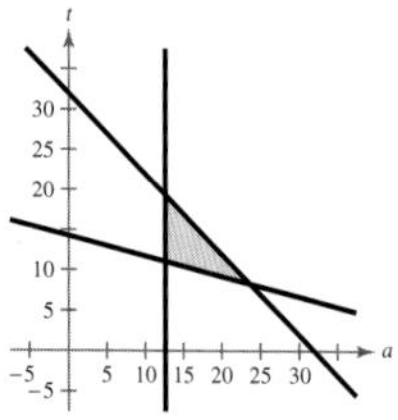

17. (a) $\begin{cases} x + y \le 200 \\ x \ge 60 \\ 0 < y \le 130 \end{cases}$ (b)

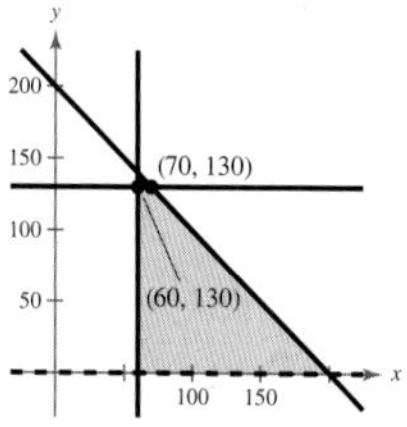

(c) No, because the total cholesterol is greater than 200 milligrams per deciliter.

(d) LDL: 135 mg/dL, HDL: 65 mg/dL, LDL + HDL: 200 mg/dL

(e) (75, 105); $\frac{180}{75} = 2.4 < 5$; Answers will vary.

Chapter 8

Section 8.1 *(page 579)*

1. matrix **3.** main diagonal **5.** augmented

7. row-equivalent **9.** 1×2 **11.** 3×1 **13.** 2×2

15. $\left[\begin{array}{cc:c} 4 & -3 & -5 \\ -1 & 3 & 12 \end{array}\right]$ **17.** $\left[\begin{array}{ccc:c} 1 & 10 & -2 & 2 \\ 5 & -3 & 4 & 0 \\ 2 & 1 & 0 & 6 \end{array}\right]$

19. $\left[\begin{array}{ccc:c} 7 & -5 & 1 & 13 \\ 19 & 0 & -8 & 10 \end{array}\right]$ **21.** $\begin{cases} x + 2y = 7 \\ 2x - 3y = 4 \end{cases}$

23. $\begin{cases} 2x + 5z = -12 \\ y - 2z = 7 \\ 6x + 3y = 2 \end{cases}$

25. $\begin{cases} 9x + 12y + 3z = 0 \\ -2x + 18y + 5z + 2w = 10 \\ x + 7y - 8z = -4 \\ 3x + 2z = -10 \end{cases}$

27. $\begin{bmatrix} 1 & 4 & 3 \\ 0 & 2 & -1 \end{bmatrix}$ **29.** $\begin{bmatrix} 1 & 1 & 1 \\ 0 & -7 & -1 \end{bmatrix}$

31. $\begin{bmatrix} 1 & 0 & 14 & -11 \\ 0 & 1 & -2 & 2 \\ 0 & 0 & 1 & -7 \end{bmatrix}$

33. $\begin{bmatrix} 1 & 1 & 4 & -1 \\ 0 & 5 & -2 & 6 \\ 0 & 3 & 20 & 4 \end{bmatrix}\begin{bmatrix} 1 & 1 & 4 & -1 \\ 0 & 1 & -\frac{2}{5} & \frac{6}{5} \\ 0 & 3 & 20 & 4 \end{bmatrix}$

35. Add 5 times Row 2 to Row 1.

37. Interchange Row 1 and Row 2.
Add 4 times new Row 1 to Row 3.

39. (a) $\begin{bmatrix} 1 & 2 & 3 \\ 0 & -5 & -10 \\ 3 & 1 & -1 \end{bmatrix}$ (b) $\begin{bmatrix} 1 & 2 & 3 \\ 0 & -5 & -10 \\ 0 & -5 & -10 \end{bmatrix}$

(c) $\begin{bmatrix} 1 & 2 & 3 \\ 0 & -5 & -10 \\ 0 & 0 & 0 \end{bmatrix}$ (d) $\begin{bmatrix} 1 & 2 & 3 \\ 0 & 1 & 2 \\ 0 & 0 & 0 \end{bmatrix}$

(e) $\begin{bmatrix} 1 & 0 & -1 \\ 0 & 1 & 2 \\ 0 & 0 & 0 \end{bmatrix}$

The matrix is in reduced row-echelon form.

41. Reduced row-echelon form

43. Not in row-echelon form

45. $\begin{bmatrix} 1 & 1 & 0 & 5 \\ 0 & 1 & 2 & 0 \\ 0 & 0 & 1 & -1 \end{bmatrix}$ **47.** $\begin{bmatrix} 1 & -1 & -1 & 1 \\ 0 & 1 & 6 & 3 \\ 0 & 0 & 0 & 0 \end{bmatrix}$

49. $\begin{bmatrix} 1 & 0 & 0 \\ 0 & 1 & 0 \\ 0 & 0 & 1 \end{bmatrix}$ **51.** $\begin{bmatrix} 1 & 2 & 0 & 0 \\ 0 & 0 & 1 & 0 \\ 0 & 0 & 0 & 1 \\ 0 & 0 & 0 & 0 \end{bmatrix}$ **53.** $\begin{bmatrix} 1 & 0 & 3 & 16 \\ 0 & 1 & 2 & 12 \end{bmatrix}$

55. $\begin{cases} x - 2y = 4 \\ y = -3 \end{cases}$ $(-2, -3)$

57. $\begin{cases} x - y + 2z = 4 \\ y - z = 2 \\ z = -2 \end{cases}$ $(8, 0, -2)$

59. $(3, -4)$ **61.** $(-4, -10, 4)$ **63.** $(3, 2)$

65. $(-5, 6)$ **67.** $(-1, -4)$ **69.** $\left(\frac{1}{2}, -\frac{3}{4}\right)$

71. $(4, -3, 2)$ **73.** $(7, -3, 4)$ **75.** $(-4, -3, 6)$

77. $(0, 0)$ **79.** $(5a + 4, -3a + 2, a)$ **81.** Inconsistent

83. $(3, -2, 5, 0)$ **85.** $(0, 2 - 4a, a)$ **87.** $(1, 0, 4, -2)$

89. $(-2a, a, a, 0)$ **91.** Yes; $(-1, 1, -3)$

93. No **95.** $f(x) = -x^2 + x + 1$

97. $f(x) = -9x^2 - 5x + 11$ **99.** $f(x) = x^3 - 2x^2 + x - 1$

101. $f(x) = x^3 - 2x^2 - 4x + 1$

103. $\begin{bmatrix} 1 & 3 & \frac{3}{2} & \vdots & 4 \\ 0 & 1 & \frac{7}{4} & \vdots & -\frac{3}{2} \\ 0 & 0 & 1 & \vdots & 2 \end{bmatrix}, \begin{bmatrix} 1 & 3 & 1 & \vdots & 3 \\ 0 & 1 & 2 & \vdots & -1 \\ 0 & 0 & 1 & \vdots & 2 \end{bmatrix}$

105. $\dfrac{4x^2}{(x+1)^2(x-1)} = \dfrac{1}{x-1} + \dfrac{3}{x+1} - \dfrac{2}{(x+1)^2}$

107. \$150,000 at 7%
\$750,000 at 8%
\$600,000 at 10%

109. $\begin{cases} x + 5y + 10z + 20w = 95 \\ x + y + z + w = 26 \\ y - 4z = 0 \\ x - 2y = -1 \end{cases}$ \$1 bills: 15; \$5 bills: 8; \$10 bills: 2; \$20 bills: 1

111. $y = x^2 + 2x + 5$

113. (a) $y = -0.004x^2 + 0.367x + 5$
(b)

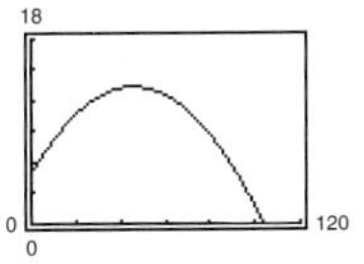

(c) 13 ft, 104 ft (d) 13.418 ft, 103.793 ft
(e) The results are similar.

115. (a) $x_1 = s, x_2 = t, x_3 = 600 - s, x_4 = s - t, x_5 = 500 - t, x_6 = s, x_7 = t$
(b) $x_1 = 0, x_2 = 0, x_3 = 600, x_4 = 0, x_5 = 500, x_6 = 0, x_7 = 0$
(c) $x_1 = 500, x_2 = 100, x_3 = 100, x_4 = 400, x_5 = 400, x_6 = 500, x_7 = 100$

117. False. It is a 2×4 matrix.

119. Answers will vary. For example:
$\begin{cases} x + y + 7z = -1 \\ x + 2y + 11z = 0 \\ 2x + y + 10z = -3 \end{cases}$

121. Interchange two rows.
Multiply a row by a nonzero constant.
Add a multiple of a row to another row.

123. They are the same.

Section 8.2 *(page 594)*

1. equal **3.** zero; O

5. (a) iii (b) iv (c) i (d) v (e) ii

7. $x = -4, y = 22$ **9.** $x = 2, y = 3$

11. (a) $\begin{bmatrix} 3 & -2 \\ 1 & 7 \end{bmatrix}$ (b) $\begin{bmatrix} -1 & 0 \\ 3 & -9 \end{bmatrix}$ (c) $\begin{bmatrix} 3 & -3 \\ 6 & -3 \end{bmatrix}$
(d) $\begin{bmatrix} -1 & -1 \\ 8 & -19 \end{bmatrix}$

13. (a) $\begin{bmatrix} 9 & 5 \\ 1 & -2 \\ -3 & 15 \end{bmatrix}$ (b) $\begin{bmatrix} 7 & -7 \\ 3 & 8 \\ -5 & -5 \end{bmatrix}$ (c) $\begin{bmatrix} 24 & -3 \\ 6 & 9 \\ -12 & 15 \end{bmatrix}$
(d) $\begin{bmatrix} 22 & -15 \\ 8 & 19 \\ -14 & -5 \end{bmatrix}$

15. (a) $\begin{bmatrix} 5 & 5 & -2 & 4 & 4 \\ -5 & 10 & 0 & -4 & -7 \end{bmatrix}$
(b) $\begin{bmatrix} 3 & 5 & 0 & 2 & 4 \\ 7 & -6 & -4 & 2 & 7 \end{bmatrix}$
(c) $\begin{bmatrix} 12 & 15 & -3 & 9 & 12 \\ 3 & 6 & -6 & -3 & 0 \end{bmatrix}$
(d) $\begin{bmatrix} 10 & 15 & -1 & 7 & 12 \\ 15 & -10 & -10 & 3 & 14 \end{bmatrix}$

17. (a), (b), and (d) not possible (c) $\begin{bmatrix} 18 & 0 & 9 \\ -3 & -12 & 0 \end{bmatrix}$

19. $\begin{bmatrix} -8 & -7 \\ 15 & -1 \end{bmatrix}$ **21.** $\begin{bmatrix} -24 & -4 & 12 \\ -12 & 32 & 12 \end{bmatrix}$

23. $\begin{bmatrix} 10 & 8 \\ -59 & 9 \end{bmatrix}$ **25.** $\begin{bmatrix} -17.143 & 2.143 \\ 11.571 & 10.286 \end{bmatrix}$

27. $\begin{bmatrix} -1.581 & -3.739 \\ -4.252 & -13.249 \\ 9.713 & -0.362 \end{bmatrix}$ **29.** $\begin{bmatrix} -6 & -9 \\ -1 & 0 \\ 17 & -10 \end{bmatrix}$

31. $\begin{bmatrix} 3 & 3 \\ -\frac{1}{2} & 0 \\ -\frac{13}{2} & \frac{11}{2} \end{bmatrix}$ **33.** Not possible

35. $\begin{bmatrix} -2 & 51 \\ -8 & 33 \\ 0 & 27 \end{bmatrix}$ Order: 3×2 **37.** $\begin{bmatrix} 1 & 0 & 0 \\ 0 & 1 & 0 \\ 0 & 0 & \frac{7}{2} \end{bmatrix}$ Order: 3×3

39. $\begin{bmatrix} 60 & -20 & 10 & 60 \\ 72 & -24 & 12 & 72 \end{bmatrix}$ Order: 2×4

41. $\begin{bmatrix} 70 & -17 & 73 \\ 32 & 11 & 6 \\ 16 & -38 & 70 \end{bmatrix}$ **43.** $\begin{bmatrix} 151 & 25 & 48 \\ 516 & 279 & 387 \\ 47 & -20 & 87 \end{bmatrix}$

45. Not possible

47. (a) $\begin{bmatrix} 0 & 15 \\ 6 & 12 \end{bmatrix}$ (b) $\begin{bmatrix} -2 & 2 \\ 31 & 14 \end{bmatrix}$ (c) $\begin{bmatrix} 9 & 6 \\ 12 & 12 \end{bmatrix}$

49. (a) $\begin{bmatrix} 0 & -10 \\ 10 & 0 \end{bmatrix}$ (b) $\begin{bmatrix} 0 & -10 \\ 10 & 0 \end{bmatrix}$ (c) $\begin{bmatrix} 8 & -6 \\ 6 & 8 \end{bmatrix}$

51. (a) $\begin{bmatrix} 7 & 7 & 14 \\ 8 & 8 & 16 \\ -1 & -1 & -2 \end{bmatrix}$ (b) $[13]$ (c) Not possible

53. $\begin{bmatrix} 5 & 8 \\ -4 & -16 \end{bmatrix}$ **55.** $\begin{bmatrix} -4 & 10 \\ 3 & 14 \end{bmatrix}$

57. (a) $\begin{bmatrix} -1 & 1 \\ -2 & 1 \end{bmatrix} \begin{bmatrix} x_1 \\ x_2 \end{bmatrix} = \begin{bmatrix} 4 \\ 0 \end{bmatrix}$ (b) $\begin{bmatrix} 4 \\ 8 \end{bmatrix}$

59. (a) $\begin{bmatrix} -2 & -3 \\ 6 & 1 \end{bmatrix} \begin{bmatrix} x_1 \\ x_2 \end{bmatrix} = \begin{bmatrix} -4 \\ -36 \end{bmatrix}$ (b) $\begin{bmatrix} -7 \\ 6 \end{bmatrix}$

61. (a) $\begin{bmatrix} 1 & -2 & 3 \\ -1 & 3 & -1 \\ 2 & -5 & 5 \end{bmatrix} \begin{bmatrix} x_1 \\ x_2 \\ x_3 \end{bmatrix} = \begin{bmatrix} 9 \\ -6 \\ 17 \end{bmatrix}$ (b) $\begin{bmatrix} 1 \\ -1 \\ 2 \end{bmatrix}$

63. (a) $\begin{bmatrix} 1 & -5 & 2 \\ -3 & 1 & -1 \\ 0 & -2 & 5 \end{bmatrix} \begin{bmatrix} x_1 \\ x_2 \\ x_3 \end{bmatrix} = \begin{bmatrix} -20 \\ 8 \\ -16 \end{bmatrix}$ (b) $\begin{bmatrix} -1 \\ 3 \\ -2 \end{bmatrix}$

65. $\begin{bmatrix} 84 & 60 & 30 \\ 42 & 120 & 84 \end{bmatrix}$

67. (a) $A = \begin{bmatrix} 125 & 100 & 75 \\ 100 & 175 & 125 \end{bmatrix}$

The entries represent the numbers of bushels of each crop that are shipped to each outlet.

(b) $B = [\$3.50 \quad \$6.00]$

The entries represent the profits per bushel of each crop.

(c) $BA = [\$1037.50 \quad \$1400 \quad \$1012.50]$

The entries represent the profits from both crops at each of the three outlets.

69. $\begin{bmatrix} \$15{,}770 & \$18{,}300 \\ \$26{,}500 & \$29{,}250 \\ \$21{,}260 & \$24{,}150 \end{bmatrix}$

The entries represent the wholesale and retail values of the inventories at the three outlets.

71. $P^3 = \begin{bmatrix} 0.300 & 0.175 & 0.175 \\ 0.308 & 0.433 & 0.217 \\ 0.392 & 0.392 & 0.608 \end{bmatrix}$

$P^4 = \begin{bmatrix} 0.250 & 0.188 & 0.188 \\ 0.315 & 0.377 & 0.248 \\ 0.435 & 0.435 & 0.565 \end{bmatrix}$

$P^5 = \begin{bmatrix} 0.225 & 0.194 & 0.194 \\ 0.314 & 0.345 & 0.267 \\ 0.461 & 0.461 & 0.539 \end{bmatrix}$

$P^6 = \begin{bmatrix} 0.213 & 0.197 & 0.197 \\ 0.311 & 0.326 & 0.280 \\ 0.477 & 0.477 & 0.523 \end{bmatrix}$

$P^7 = \begin{bmatrix} 0.206 & 0.198 & 0.198 \\ 0.308 & 0.316 & 0.288 \\ 0.486 & 0.486 & 0.514 \end{bmatrix}$

$P^8 = \begin{bmatrix} 0.203 & 0.199 & 0.199 \\ 0.305 & 0.309 & 0.292 \\ 0.492 & 0.492 & 0.508 \end{bmatrix}$

Approaches the matrix $\begin{bmatrix} 0.2 & 0.2 & 0.2 \\ 0.3 & 0.3 & 0.3 \\ 0.5 & 0.5 & 0.5 \end{bmatrix}$

73. (a)

Sales \$	Profit
571.8	206.6
798.9	288.8
936	337.8

The entries represent the total sales and profits for milk on Friday, Saturday, and Sunday.

(b) \$833.20

75. (a) $[2 \quad 0.5 \quad 3]$

(b) 120 lb 150 lb

$[473.5 \quad 588.5]$

The entries represent the total calories burned.

77. True. The sum of two matrices of different orders is undefined.

79. Not possible **81.** Not possible

83. 2×2 **85.** 2×3

87. (a) $A + B = \begin{bmatrix} 1 & -1 \\ 12 & 8 \end{bmatrix}$, $B + A = \begin{bmatrix} 1 & -1 \\ 12 & 8 \end{bmatrix}$

(b) $(A + B) + C = \begin{bmatrix} 6 & 1 \\ 14 & 2 \end{bmatrix}$, $(B + C) + A = \begin{bmatrix} 6 & 1 \\ 14 & 2 \end{bmatrix}$

(c) $2A + 2B = \begin{bmatrix} 2 & -2 \\ 24 & 16 \end{bmatrix}$, $2(A + B) = \begin{bmatrix} 2 & -2 \\ 24 & 16 \end{bmatrix}$

89. $AC = BC = \begin{bmatrix} 2 & 3 \\ 2 & 3 \end{bmatrix}$

91. AB is a diagonal matrix whose entries are the products of the corresponding entries of A and B.

93. Answers will vary.

Section 8.3 *(page 605)*

1. square **3.** nonsingular; singular

5–11. $AB = I$ and $BA = I$

13. $\begin{bmatrix} \frac{1}{2} & 0 \\ 0 & \frac{1}{3} \end{bmatrix}$ **15.** $\begin{bmatrix} -3 & 2 \\ -2 & 1 \end{bmatrix}$ **17.** $\begin{bmatrix} 1 & -\frac{1}{2} \\ -2 & \frac{3}{2} \end{bmatrix}$

19. $\begin{bmatrix} 1 & 1 & -1 \\ -3 & 2 & -1 \\ 3 & -3 & 2 \end{bmatrix}$ **21.** Does not exist

23. $\begin{bmatrix} -\frac{1}{8} & 0 & 0 & 0 \\ 0 & 1 & 0 & 0 \\ 0 & 0 & \frac{1}{4} & 0 \\ 0 & 0 & 0 & -\frac{1}{5} \end{bmatrix}$ **25.** $\begin{bmatrix} -175 & 37 & -13 \\ 95 & -20 & 7 \\ 14 & -3 & 1 \end{bmatrix}$

27. $\begin{bmatrix} -1.5 & 1.5 & 1 \\ 4.5 & -3.5 & -3 \\ -1 & 1 & 1 \end{bmatrix}$ **29.** $\begin{bmatrix} -12 & -5 & -9 \\ -4 & -2 & -4 \\ -8 & -4 & -6 \end{bmatrix}$

31. $\begin{bmatrix} 0 & -1.\overline{81} & 0.\overline{90} \\ -10 & 5 & 5 \\ 10 & -2.\overline{72} & -3.\overline{63} \end{bmatrix}$ **33.** $\begin{bmatrix} 1 & 0 & 1 & 0 \\ 0 & 1 & 0 & 1 \\ 2 & 0 & 1 & 0 \\ 0 & 1 & 0 & 2 \end{bmatrix}$

35. $\begin{bmatrix} \frac{5}{13} & -\frac{3}{13} \\ \frac{1}{13} & \frac{2}{13} \end{bmatrix}$ **37.** Does not exist **39.** $\begin{bmatrix} \frac{16}{59} & \frac{15}{59} \\ -\frac{4}{59} & \frac{70}{59} \end{bmatrix}$

41. $(5, 0)$ **43.** $(-8, -6)$ **45.** $(3, 8, -11)$

47. $(2, 1, 0, 0)$ **49.** $(0, 1, 2, -1, 0)$ **51.** $(2, -2)$

53. No solution **55.** $(-4, -8)$ **57.** $(-1, 3, 2)$

59. $\left(\frac{5}{16}a + \frac{13}{16}, \frac{19}{16}a + \frac{11}{16}, a\right)$ **61.** $(-7, 3, -2)$

63. $A^{-1} = \begin{bmatrix} \sin\theta & -\cos\theta \\ \cos\theta & \sin\theta \end{bmatrix}$

65. \$7000 in AAA-rated bonds
\$1000 in A-rated bonds
\$2000 in B-rated bonds

67. \$9000 in AAA-rated bonds
\$1000 in A-rated bonds
\$2000 in B-rated bonds

69. 0 muffins, 300 bones, 200 cookies

71. 100 muffins, 300 bones, 150 cookies

73. (a) $\begin{cases} 2f + 2.5h + 3s = 26 \\ f + h + s = 10 \\ h - s = 0 \end{cases}$

(b) $\begin{bmatrix} 2 & 2.5 & 3 \\ 1 & 1 & 1 \\ 0 & 1 & -1 \end{bmatrix} \begin{bmatrix} f \\ h \\ s \end{bmatrix} = \begin{bmatrix} 26 \\ 10 \\ 0 \end{bmatrix}$

(c) 2 pounds of French vanilla, 4 pounds of hazelnut, 4 pounds of Swiss chocolate

75. (a) $\begin{cases} 100a + 10b + c = 13.89 \\ 121a + 11b + c = 14.04 \\ 144a + 12b + c = 14.20 \end{cases}$

(b) $y = 0.005t^2 + 0.045t + 12.94$

(c)

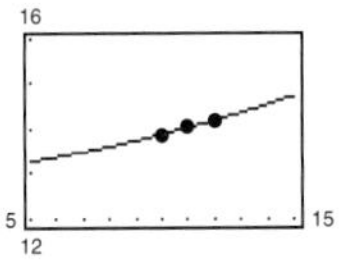

(d) For the immediate future it is, but not for long-term predictions.

77. True. If B is the inverse of A, then $AB = I = BA$.

79. Answers will vary.

81. (a) Answers will vary.

(b) $A^{-1} = \begin{bmatrix} \frac{1}{a_{11}} & 0 & 0 & \cdots & 0 \\ 0 & \frac{1}{a_{22}} & 0 & \cdots & 0 \\ 0 & 0 & \frac{1}{a_{33}} & \cdots & 0 \\ \vdots & \vdots & \vdots & \cdots & \vdots \\ 0 & 0 & 0 & \cdots & \frac{1}{a_{nn}} \end{bmatrix}$

Section 8.4 *(page 613)*

1. determinant **3.** cofactor **5.** 4 **7.** 16 **9.** 28

11. 0 **13.** 6 **15.** -9 **17.** -24 **19.** $\frac{11}{6}$

21. -0.002 **23.** -4.842

25. (a) $M_{11} = -6, M_{12} = 3, M_{21} = 5, M_{22} = 4$

(b) $C_{11} = -6, C_{12} = -3, C_{21} = -5, C_{22} = 4$

27. (a) $M_{11} = -4, M_{12} = -2, M_{21} = 1, M_{22} = 3$

(b) $C_{11} = -4, C_{12} = 2, C_{21} = -1, C_{22} = 3$

29. (a) $M_{11} = 3, M_{12} = -4, M_{13} = 1, M_{21} = 2, M_{22} = 2, M_{23} = -4, M_{31} = -4, M_{32} = 10, M_{33} = 8$

(b) $C_{11} = 3, C_{12} = 4, C_{13} = 1, C_{21} = -2, C_{22} = 2, C_{23} = 4, C_{31} = -4, C_{32} = -10, C_{33} = 8$

31. (a) $M_{11} = 10, M_{12} = -43, M_{13} = 2, M_{21} = -30, M_{22} = 17, M_{23} = -6, M_{31} = 54, M_{32} = -53, M_{33} = -34$

(b) $C_{11} = 10, C_{12} = 43, C_{13} = 2, C_{21} = 30, C_{22} = 17, C_{23} = 6, C_{31} = 54, C_{32} = 53, C_{33} = -34$

33. (a) -75 (b) -75 **35.** (a) 96 (b) 96

37. (a) 170 (b) 170 **39.** 0 **41.** 0 **43.** -9

45. -58 **47.** -30 **49.** -168 **51.** 0 **53.** 412

55. -126 **57.** 0 **59.** -336 **61.** 410

63. (a) -3 (b) -2 (c) $\begin{bmatrix} -2 & 0 \\ 0 & -3 \end{bmatrix}$ (d) 6

65. (a) -8 (b) 0 (c) $\begin{bmatrix} -4 & 4 \\ 1 & -1 \end{bmatrix}$ (d) 0

67. (a) -21 (b) -19 (c) $\begin{bmatrix} 7 & 1 & 4 \\ -8 & 9 & -3 \\ 7 & -3 & 9 \end{bmatrix}$ (d) 399

69. (a) 2 (b) -6 (c) $\begin{bmatrix} 1 & 4 & 3 \\ -1 & 0 & 3 \\ 0 & 2 & 0 \end{bmatrix}$ (d) -12

71–75. Answers will vary. **77.** $x = \pm 2$

79. $x = 1 \pm \sqrt{2}$ **81.** $-1, 4$ **83.** $-1, -4$

85. $8uv - 1$ **87.** e^{5x} **89.** $1 - \ln x$

91. True. If an entire row is zero, then each cofactor in the expansion is multiplied by zero.

93. Answers will vary.

95. A square matrix is a square array of numbers. The determinant of a square matrix is a real number.

97. (a) Columns 2 and 3 of A were interchanged.
$|A| = -115 = -|B|$

(b) Rows 1 and 3 of A were interchanged.
$|A| = -40 = -|B|$

99. (a) Multiply Row 1 by 5.

(b) Multiply Column 2 by 4 and Column 3 by 3.

101. 10 **103.** -9

105. The determinant of a triangular matrix is the product of the terms in the diagonal.

Section 8.5 *(page 625)*

1. Cramer's Rule

3. $A = \pm\frac{1}{2}\begin{vmatrix} x_1 & y_1 & 1 \\ x_2 & y_2 & 1 \\ x_3 & y_3 & 1 \end{vmatrix}$

5. uncoded; coded **7.** $(-3, -2)$ **9.** Not possible

11. $\left(\frac{32}{7}, \frac{30}{7}\right)$ **13.** $(-1, 3, 2)$ **15.** $(-2, 1, -1)$

17. $\left(0, -\frac{1}{2}, \frac{1}{2}\right)$ **19.** $(1, -1, 2)$ **21.** 7 **23.** 14

25. $\frac{33}{8}$ **27.** $\frac{5}{2}$ **29.** 28 **31.** $\frac{41}{4}$ **33.** $y = \frac{16}{5}$ or $y = 0$

35. $y = -3$ or $y = -11$ **37.** 250 mi^2

39. Collinear **41.** Not collinear **43.** Collinear

45. $y = -3$ **47.** $3x - 5y = 0$ **49.** $x + 3y - 5 = 0$

51. $2x + 3y - 8 = 0$

53. (a) Uncoded: [3 15], [13 5], [0 8], [15 13], [5 0], [19 15], [15 14]

(b) Encoded: 48 81 28 51 24 40 54 95 5 10 64 113 57 100

55. (a) Uncoded: [3 1 12], [12 0 13], [5 0 20], [15 13 15], [18 18 15], [23 0 0]

(b) Encoded: -68 21 35 -66 14 39 -115 35 60 -62 15 32 -54 12 27 23 -23 0

57. 1 -25 -65 17 15 -9 -12 -62 -119 27 51 48 43 67 48 57 111 117

59. -5 -41 -87 91 207 257 11 -5 -41 40 80 84 76 177 227

61. HAPPY NEW YEAR **63.** CLASS IS CANCELED

65. SEND PLANES **67.** MEET ME TONIGHT RON

69. (a) $\begin{cases} 8c + 28b + 140a = 182.1 \\ 28c + 140b + 784a = 713.4 \\ 140c + 784b + 4676a = 3724.8 \end{cases}$

(b) $y = 0.034t^2 + 1.57t + 16.66$

(c)

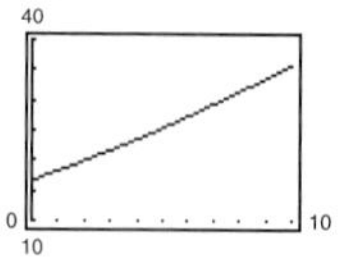

(d) 2009

71. False. The denominator is the determinant of the coefficient matrix.

73. False. If the determinant of the coefficient matrix is zero, the system has either no solution or infinitely many solutions.

75. Answers will vary. **77.** 12

Review Exercises *(page 630)*

1. 3×1 **3.** 1×1 **5.** $\left[\begin{array}{cc:c} 3 & -10 & 15 \\ 5 & 4 & 22 \end{array}\right]$

7. $\begin{cases} 5x + y + 7z = -9 \\ 4x + 2y = 10 \\ 9x + 4y + 2z = 3 \end{cases}$ **9.** $\begin{bmatrix} 1 & 2 & 3 \\ 0 & 1 & 1 \\ 0 & 0 & 1 \end{bmatrix}$

11. $\begin{cases} x + 2y + 3z = 9 \\ y - 2z = 2 \\ z = 0 \end{cases}$ **13.** $\begin{cases} x - 5y + 4z = 1 \\ y + 2z = 3 \\ z = 4 \end{cases}$

$(5, 2, 0)$ $(-40, -5, 4)$

15. $(10, -12)$ **17.** $\left(-\frac{1}{5}, \frac{7}{10}\right)$ **19.** Inconsistent

21. $(1, -2, 2)$ **23.** $\left(-2a + \frac{3}{2}, 2a + 1, a\right)$

25. $(5, 2, -6)$ **27.** $(1, 0, 4, 3)$ **29.** $(1, 2, 2)$

31. $(2, -3, 3)$ **33.** $(2, 3, -1)$ **35.** $(2, 6, -10, -3)$

37. $x = 12, y = -7$ **39.** $x = 1, y = 11$

41. (a) $\begin{bmatrix} -1 & 8 \\ 15 & 13 \end{bmatrix}$ (b) $\begin{bmatrix} 5 & -12 \\ -9 & -3 \end{bmatrix}$

(c) $\begin{bmatrix} 8 & -8 \\ 12 & 20 \end{bmatrix}$ (d) $\begin{bmatrix} -7 & 28 \\ 39 & 29 \end{bmatrix}$

43. (a) $\begin{bmatrix} 5 & 7 \\ -3 & 14 \\ 31 & 42 \end{bmatrix}$ (b) $\begin{bmatrix} 5 & 1 \\ -11 & -10 \\ -9 & -38 \end{bmatrix}$

(c) $\begin{bmatrix} 20 & 16 \\ -28 & 8 \\ 44 & 8 \end{bmatrix}$ (d) $\begin{bmatrix} 5 & 13 \\ 5 & 38 \\ 71 & 122 \end{bmatrix}$

45. $\begin{bmatrix} 17 & -17 \\ 13 & 2 \end{bmatrix}$ **47.** $\begin{bmatrix} 54 & 4 \\ -2 & 24 \\ -4 & 32 \end{bmatrix}$ **49.** $\begin{bmatrix} 48 & -18 & -3 \\ 15 & 51 & 33 \end{bmatrix}$

51. $\begin{bmatrix} -11 & -6 \\ 8 & -13 \\ -18 & -8 \end{bmatrix}$ **53.** $\begin{bmatrix} 3 & \frac{2}{3} \\ -\frac{4}{3} & \frac{11}{3} \\ \frac{10}{3} & 0 \end{bmatrix}$ **55.** $\begin{bmatrix} -30 & 4 \\ 51 & 70 \end{bmatrix}$

57. $\begin{bmatrix} 100 & 220 \\ 12 & -4 \\ 84 & 212 \end{bmatrix}$ **59.** $\begin{bmatrix} 14 & -2 & 8 \\ 14 & -10 & 40 \\ 36 & -12 & 48 \end{bmatrix}$ **61.** $\begin{bmatrix} 44 & 4 \\ 20 & 8 \end{bmatrix}$

63. Not possible. The number of columns of the first matrix does not equal the number of rows of the second matrix.

65. $\begin{bmatrix} 1 & 17 \\ 12 & 36 \end{bmatrix}$

67. $\begin{bmatrix} 14 & -22 & 22 \\ 19 & -41 & 80 \\ 42 & -66 & 66 \end{bmatrix}$ **69.** $\begin{bmatrix} 76 & 114 & 133 \\ 38 & 95 & 76 \end{bmatrix}$

71. [\$2,396,539 \$2,581,388]
The merchandise shipped to warehouse 1 is worth \$2,396,539 and the merchandise shipped to warehouse 2 is worth \$2,581,388.

73–75. $AB = I$ and $BA = I$

77. $\begin{bmatrix} 4 & -5 \\ 5 & -6 \end{bmatrix}$ **79.** $\begin{bmatrix} \frac{1}{2} & -1 & -\frac{1}{2} \\ \frac{1}{2} & -\frac{2}{3} & -\frac{5}{6} \\ 0 & \frac{2}{3} & \frac{1}{3} \end{bmatrix}$

81. $\begin{bmatrix} 13 & 6 & -4 \\ -12 & -5 & 3 \\ 5 & 2 & -1 \end{bmatrix}$ **83.** $\begin{bmatrix} -3 & 6 & -5.5 & 3.5 \\ 1 & -2 & 2 & -1 \\ 7 & -15 & 14.5 & -9.5 \\ -1 & 2.5 & -2.5 & 1.5 \end{bmatrix}$

85. $\begin{bmatrix} 1 & -1 \\ 4 & -\frac{7}{2} \end{bmatrix}$ **87.** Does not exist

89. $\begin{bmatrix} 2 & \frac{20}{3} \\ \frac{1}{10} & \frac{1}{6} \end{bmatrix}$ **91.** $\begin{bmatrix} \frac{20}{9} & \frac{5}{9} \\ -\frac{10}{9} & -\frac{25}{9} \end{bmatrix}$ **93.** $(36, 11)$

95. $(-6, -1)$ **97.** $(2, 3)$ **99.** $(-8, 18)$

101. $(2, -1, -2)$ **103.** $(6, 1, -1)$ **105.** $(-3, 1)$

107. $\left(\frac{1}{6}, -\frac{7}{4}\right)$ **109.** $(1, 1, -2)$ **111.** -42 **113.** 550

115. (a) $M_{11} = 4, M_{12} = 7, M_{21} = -1, M_{22} = 2$
(b) $C_{11} = 4, C_{12} = -7, C_{21} = 1, C_{22} = 2$

117. (a) $M_{11} = 30, M_{12} = -12, M_{13} = -21,$
$M_{21} = 20, M_{22} = 19, M_{23} = 22, M_{31} = 5,$
$M_{32} = -2, M_{33} = 19$
(b) $C_{11} = 30, C_{12} = 12, C_{13} = -21,$
$C_{21} = -20, C_{22} = 19, C_{23} = -22,$
$C_{31} = 5, C_{32} = 2, C_{33} = 19$

119. -6 **121.** 15 **123.** 130 **125.** -8 **127.** 279

129. $(4, 7)$ **131.** $(-1, 4, 5)$ **133.** 16 **135.** 10

137. Collinear **139.** $x - 2y + 4 = 0$

141. $2x + 6y - 13 = 0$

143. (a) Uncoded: [12 15 15], [11 0 15], [21 20 0], [2 5 12], [15 23 0]
(b) Encoded: -21 6 0 -68 8 45 102 -42 -60 -53 20 21 99 -30 -69

145. SEE YOU FRIDAY

147. False. The matrix must be square.

149. An error message appears because $1(6) - (-2)(-3) = 0$.

151. If A is a square matrix, the cofactor C_{ij} of the entry a_{ij} is $(-1)^{i+j}M_{ij}$, where M_{ij} is the determinant obtained by deleting the ith row and jth column of A. The determinant of A is the sum of the entries of any row or column of A multiplied by their respective cofactors.

153. The part of the matrix corresponding to the coefficients of the system reduces to a matrix in which the number of rows with nonzero entries is the same as the number of variables.

Chapter Test *(page 635)*

1. $\begin{bmatrix} 1 & 0 & 0 \\ 0 & 1 & 0 \\ 0 & 0 & 1 \end{bmatrix}$ **2.** $\begin{bmatrix} 1 & 0 & -1 & 2 \\ 0 & 1 & 0 & -1 \\ 0 & 0 & 0 & 0 \\ 0 & 0 & 0 & 0 \end{bmatrix}$

3. $\begin{bmatrix} 4 & 3 & -2 & \vdots & 14 \\ -1 & -1 & 2 & \vdots & -5 \\ 3 & 1 & -4 & \vdots & 8 \end{bmatrix}, \left(1, 3, -\frac{1}{2}\right)$

4. (a) $\begin{bmatrix} 1 & 5 \\ 0 & -4 \end{bmatrix}$ (b) $\begin{bmatrix} 18 & 15 \\ -15 & -15 \end{bmatrix}$

(c) $\begin{bmatrix} 8 & 15 \\ -5 & -13 \end{bmatrix}$ (d) $\begin{bmatrix} 5 & -5 \\ 0 & 5 \end{bmatrix}$

5. $\begin{bmatrix} \frac{2}{7} & \frac{3}{7} \\ \frac{5}{7} & \frac{4}{7} \end{bmatrix}$ **6.** $\begin{bmatrix} -\frac{5}{2} & 4 & -3 \\ 5 & -7 & 6 \\ 4 & -6 & 5 \end{bmatrix}$

7. (12, 18) **8.** -112 **9.** 29 **10.** 43

11. $(-3, 5)$ **12.** $(-2, 4, 6)$ **13.** 7

14. Uncoded: [11 14 15], [3 11 0], [15 14 0], [23 15 15], [4 0 0]

Encoded: 115 −41 −59 14 −3 −11 29 −15 −14 128 −53 −60 4 −4 0

15. 75 L of 60% solution, 25 L of 20% solution

Problem Solving *(page 637)*

1. (a) $AT = \begin{bmatrix} -1 & -4 & -2 \\ 1 & 2 & 3 \end{bmatrix}$

$AAT = \begin{bmatrix} -1 & -2 & -3 \\ -1 & -4 & -2 \end{bmatrix}$

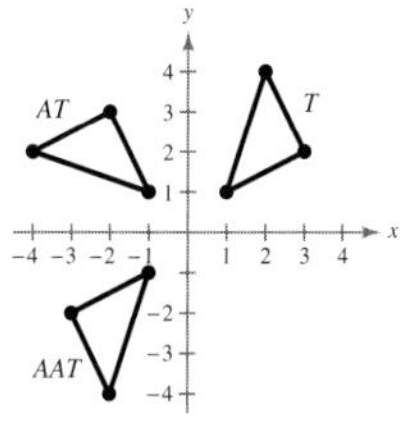

A represents a counterclockwise rotation.

(b) *AAT* is rotated clockwise 90° to obtain *AT*. *AT* is then rotated clockwise 90° to obtain *T*.

3. (a) Yes (b) No (c) No (d) No

5. (a) Gold Satellite System: 28,750 subscribers
Galaxy Satellite Network: 35,750 subscribers
Nonsubscribers: 35,500
Answers will vary.

(b) Gold Satellite System: 30,813 subscribers
Galaxy Satellite Network: 39,675 subscribers
Nonsubscribers: 29,513
Answers will vary.

(c) Gold Satellite System: 31,947 subscribers
Galaxy Satellite Network: 42,329 subscribers
Nonsubscribers: 25,724
Answers will vary.

(d) Satellite companies are increasing the number of subscribers, while the nonsubscribers are decreasing.

7. $x = 6$ **9–11.** Answers will vary.

13. Sulfur: 32 atomic mass units
Nitrogen: 14 atomic mass units
Fluorine: 19 atomic mass units

15. $A^T = \begin{bmatrix} -1 & 2 \\ 1 & 0 \\ -2 & 1 \end{bmatrix}$ $B^T = \begin{bmatrix} -3 & 1 & 1 \\ 0 & 2 & -1 \end{bmatrix}$

$(AB)^T = \begin{bmatrix} 2 & -5 \\ 4 & -1 \end{bmatrix} = B^TA^T$

17. (a) $A^{-1} = \begin{bmatrix} 1 & -2 \\ 1 & -3 \end{bmatrix}$ (b) JOHN RETURN TO BASE

19. $|A| = 0$

Chapter 9

Section 9.1 *(page 647)*

1. infinite sequence **3.** finite **5.** factorial

7. index; upper; lower **9.** 7, 9, 11, 13, 15

11. 2, 4, 8, 16, 32 **13.** −2, 4, −8, 16, −32

15. $3, 2, \frac{5}{3}, \frac{3}{2}, \frac{7}{5}$ **17.** $3, \frac{12}{11}, \frac{9}{13}, \frac{24}{47}, \frac{15}{37}$ **19.** $0, 1, 0, \frac{1}{2}, 0$

21. $\frac{5}{3}, \frac{17}{9}, \frac{53}{27}, \frac{161}{81}, \frac{485}{243}$ **23.** $1, \frac{1}{2^{3/2}}, \frac{1}{3^{3/2}}, \frac{1}{8}, \frac{1}{5^{3/2}}$

25. $-1, \frac{1}{4}, -\frac{1}{9}, \frac{1}{16}, -\frac{1}{25}$ **27.** $\frac{2}{3}, \frac{2}{3}, \frac{2}{3}, \frac{2}{3}, \frac{2}{3}$ **29.** 0, 0, 6, 24, 60

31. $\frac{1}{2}, -\frac{1}{5}, \frac{1}{10}, -\frac{1}{17}, \frac{1}{26}$ **33.** -73 **35.** $\frac{44}{239}$

37.

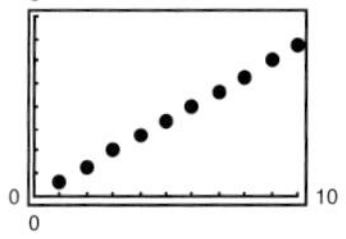

39.

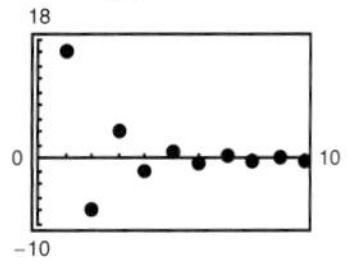

41.

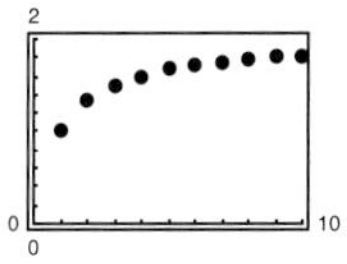

43. c **44.** b **45.** d **46.** a

47. $a_n = 3n - 2$ **49.** $a_n = n^2 - 1$

51. $a_n = \frac{(-1)^n(n + 1)}{n + 2}$ **53.** $a_n = \frac{n + 1}{2n - 1}$ **55.** $a_n = \frac{1}{n^2}$

57. $a_n = (-1)^{n+1}$ **59.** $a_n = (-1)^n + 2$ **61.** $a_n = 1 + \frac{1}{n}$

63. 28, 24, 20, 16, 12 **65.** 3, 4, 6, 10, 18

67. 6, 8, 10, 12, 14; $a_n = 2n + 4$

69. 81, 27, 9, 3, 1; $a_n = \frac{243}{3^n}$

71. $1, 1, \frac{1}{2}, \frac{1}{6}, \frac{1}{24}$ **73.** $1, \frac{1}{2}, \frac{1}{6}, \frac{1}{24}, \frac{1}{120}$

75. $1, \frac{1}{2}, \frac{1}{24}, \frac{1}{720}, \frac{1}{40{,}320}$ **77.** $\frac{1}{30}$ **79.** 495 **81.** $n + 1$

83. $\frac{1}{2n(2n + 1)}$ **85.** 35 **87.** 40 **89.** 30 **91.** $\frac{9}{5}$

93. 88 **95.** 30 **97.** $\frac{6508}{3465}$ **99.** $\frac{47}{60}$ **101.** 1.33

103. $\sum_{i=1}^{9} \frac{1}{3i}$ **105.** $\sum_{i=1}^{8} \left[2\left(\frac{i}{8}\right) + 3\right]$ **107.** $\sum_{i=1}^{6} (-1)^{i+1} 3^i$

109. $\sum_{i=1}^{20} \frac{(-1)^{i+1}}{i^2}$ **111.** $\sum_{i=1}^{5} \frac{2^i - 1}{2^{i+1}}$ **113.** $\frac{75}{16}$ **115.** $-\frac{3}{2}$

117. $\frac{2}{3}$ **119.** $\frac{7}{9}$

121. (a) $A_1 = \$25{,}145.83$, $A_2 = \$25{,}292.52$, $A_3 = \$25{,}440.06$, $A_4 = \$25{,}588.46$, $A_5 = \$25{,}737.72$, $A_6 = \$25{,}887.86$
(b) \$35,440.63 (c) No; $A_{120} = \$50{,}241.53$

123. (a) $b_n = 76.4n + 380$
(b) $c_n = 2.18n^2 + 56.8n + 418$
(c)

n	2	3	4	5	6	7
a_n	548	595	668	786	822	923
b_n	533	609	686	762	838	915
c_n	540	608	680	757	837	922

The quadratic model fits better.
(d) The quadratic model; 1524

125. (a) $a_5 = \$5057.7$, $a_6 = \$5128.9$, $a_7 = \$5226.6$, $a_8 = \$5357.4$, $a_9 = \$5527.9$, $a_{10} = \$5744.5$, $a_{11} = \$6013.9$, $a_{12} = \$6342.5$, $a_{13} = \$6737.0$, $a_{14} = \$7203.8$, $a_{15} = \$7749.5$, $a_{16} = \$8380.7$, $a_{17} = \$9103.8$

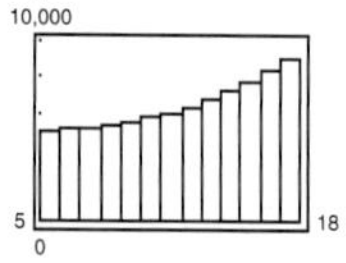

(b) The federal debt is increasing.

127. True by the Properties of Sums

129. 1, 1, 2, 3, 5, 8, 13, 21, 34, 55, 89, 144
1, 2, $\frac{3}{2}$, $\frac{5}{3}$, $\frac{8}{5}$, $\frac{13}{8}$, $\frac{21}{13}$, $\frac{34}{21}$, $\frac{55}{34}$, $\frac{89}{55}$

131. \$500.95 **133.** Proof **135.** $x, \frac{x^2}{2}, \frac{x^3}{6}, \frac{x^4}{24}, \frac{x^5}{120}$

137. $-\frac{x^2}{2}, \frac{x^4}{24}, -\frac{x^6}{720}, \frac{x^8}{40{,}320}, -\frac{x^{10}}{3{,}628{,}800}$

139. $\frac{1}{3}, -\frac{1}{5}, \frac{1}{7}, -\frac{1}{9}, \frac{1}{11}$; No, the signs are opposite.

141. (a)

Number of blue cube faces	0	1	2	3
3 × 3 × 3	1	6	12	8

(b)

Number of blue cube faces	0	1	2	3
4 × 4 × 4	8	24	24	8
5 × 5 × 5	27	54	36	8
6 × 6 × 6	64	96	48	8

(c) The different columns change at different rates.

(d)

Number of blue cube faces	0	1	2	3
$n \times n \times n$	$(n-2)^3$	$6(n-2)^2$	$12(n-2)$	8

Section 9.2 *(page 657)*

1. arithmetic; common **3.** recursion
5. Arithmetic sequence, $d = -2$
7. Not an arithmetic sequence
9. Arithmetic sequence, $d = -\frac{1}{4}$
11. Arithmetic sequence, $d = 0.6$
13. Not an arithmetic sequence
15. 8, 11, 14, 17, 20
Arithmetic sequence, $d = 3$
17. 7, 3, -1, -5, -9
Arithmetic sequence, $d = -4$
19. -1, 1, -1, 1, -1
Not an arithmetic sequence
21. $-3, \frac{3}{2}, -1, \frac{3}{4}, -\frac{3}{5}$
Not an arithmetic sequence
23. $a_n = 3n - 2$ **25.** $a_n = -8n + 108$
27. $a_n = -\frac{5}{2}n + \frac{13}{2}$ **29.** $a_n = \frac{10}{3}n + \frac{5}{3}$
31. $a_n = -3n + 103$ **33.** 5, 11, 17, 23, 29
35. -2.6, -3.0, -3.4, -3.8, -4.2 **37.** 2, 6, 10, 14, 18
39. -2, 2, 6, 10, 14 **41.** 15, 19, 23, 27, 31
43. 200, 190, 180, 170, 160 **45.** $\frac{5}{8}, \frac{1}{2}, \frac{3}{8}, \frac{1}{4}, \frac{1}{8}$ **47.** 59
49. 18.6 **51.** 110 **53.** -25 **55.** 2550
57. -4585 **59.** 620 **61.** 17.4 **63.** 265
65. 4000 **67.** 1275 **69.** 30,030 **71.** 355
73. 129,250 **75.** b **76.** d **77.** c **78.** a

79.

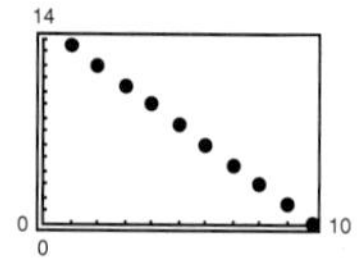

81.

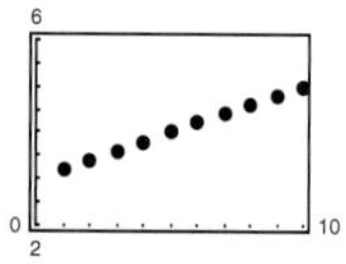

83. 440 **85.** 2575 **87.** 14,268
89. (a) \$40,000 (b) \$217,500
91. 2340 seats **93.** 405 bricks **95.** 490 m
97. (a) $a_n = -25n + 225$ (b) \$900
99. \$70,500; Answers will vary.
101. (a)

Month	1	2	3	4	5	6
Monthly payment	\$220	\$218	\$216	\$214	\$212	\$210
Unpaid balance	\$1800	\$1600	\$1400	\$1200	\$1000	\$800

(b) \$110

103. (a) $a_n = 1594n + 27{,}087$

(b) 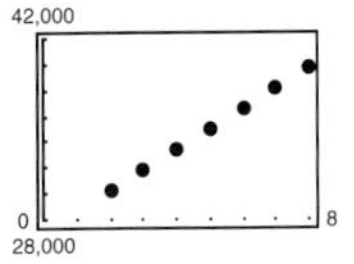

(c) $41,433

(d) Answers will vary.

105. True. Given a_1 and a_2, $d = a_2 - a_1$ and $a_n = a_1 + (n - 1)d$.

107. $x, 3x, 5x, 7x, 9x, 11x, 13x, 15x, 17x, 19x$

109. Add the first term to $(n - 1)$ times the common difference.

111. (a) 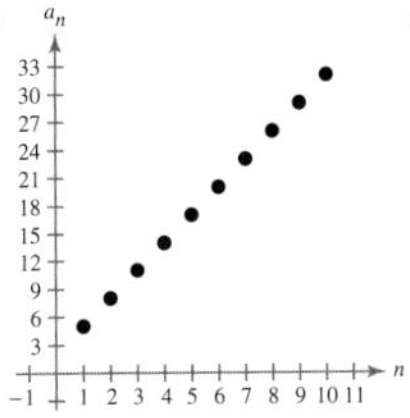

(b) 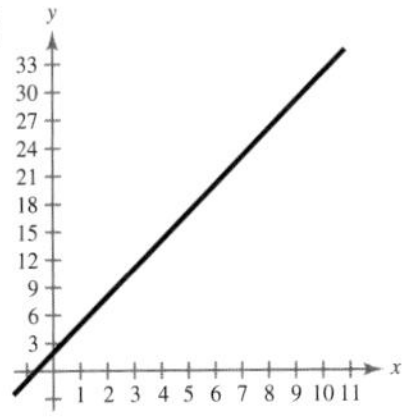

(c) The graph of $y = 3x + 2$ contains all points on the line. The graph of $a_n = 2 + 3n$ contains only points at the positive integers.

(d) The slope of the line and the common difference of the arithmetic sequence are equal.

113. 4

Section 9.3 *(page 667)*

1. geometric; common **3.** $S_n = a_1\left(\frac{1 - r^n}{1 - r}\right)$

5. Geometric sequence, $r = 5$ **7.** Not a geometric sequence

9. Geometric sequence, $r = -\frac{1}{2}$

11. Geometric sequence, $r = 2$

13. Not a geometric sequence

15. Geometric sequence, $r = -\sqrt{7}$

17. 4, 12, 36, 108, 324 **19.** $1, \frac{1}{2}, \frac{1}{4}, \frac{1}{8}, \frac{1}{16}$

21. $5, -\frac{1}{2}, \frac{1}{20}, -\frac{1}{200}, \frac{1}{2000}$ **23.** $1, e, e^2, e^3, e^4$

25. $3, 3\sqrt{5}, 15, 15\sqrt{5}, 75$ **27.** $2, \frac{x}{2}, \frac{x^2}{8}, \frac{x^3}{32}, \frac{x^4}{128}$

29. $64, 32, 16, 8, 4;\ r = \frac{1}{2};\ a_n = 128\left(\frac{1}{2}\right)^n$

31. $9, 18, 36, 72, 144;\ r = 2;\ a_n = \frac{9}{2}(2)^n$

33. $6, -9, \frac{27}{2}, -\frac{81}{4}, \frac{243}{8};\ r = -\frac{3}{2};\ a_n = -4\left(-\frac{3}{2}\right)^n$

35. $a_n = 4\left(\frac{1}{2}\right)^{n-1};\ \frac{1}{128}$ **37.** $a_n = 6\left(-\frac{1}{3}\right)^{n-1};\ -\frac{2}{59,049}$

39. $a_n = 100e^{x(n-1)};\ 100e^{8x}$ **41.** $a_n = \left(\sqrt{2}\right)^{n-1};\ 32\sqrt{2}$

43. $a_n = 500(1.02)^{n-1}$; About 1082.372

45. $a_9 = 72,171$ **47.** $a_{10} = 50,388,480$

49. $a_8 = -\frac{1}{32,768}$ **51.** $a_3 = 9$ **53.** $a_6 = -2$

55. $a_5 = -\frac{1}{\sqrt{2}}$ **57.** a **58.** c **59.** b **60.** d

61. 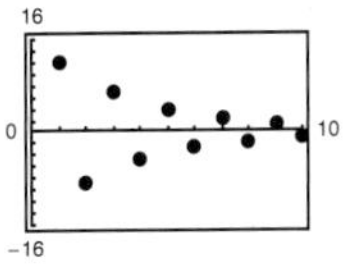

63. 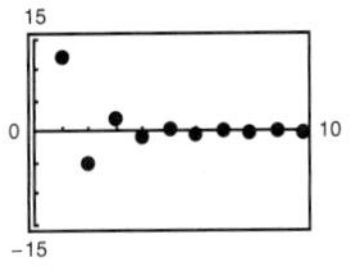

65. 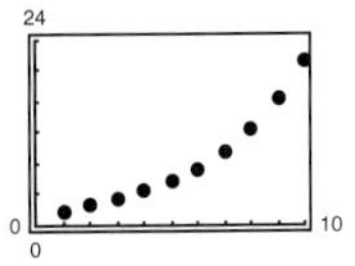

67. 5461 **69.** −14,706 **71.** 43 **73.** $\frac{1365}{32}$

75. 29,921.311 **77.** 592.647 **79.** 2092.596

81. 1.600 **83.** 6.400 **85.** 3.750 **87.** $\sum_{n=1}^{7} 10(3)^{n-1}$

89. $\sum_{n=1}^{7} 2\left(-\frac{1}{4}\right)^{n-1}$ **91.** $\sum_{n=1}^{6} 0.1(4)^{n-1}$ **93.** 2 **95.** $\frac{2}{3}$

97. $\frac{16}{3}$ **99.** $\frac{5}{3}$ **101.** −30 **103.** 32

105. Undefined **107.** $\frac{4}{11}$ **109.** $\frac{7}{22}$

111. 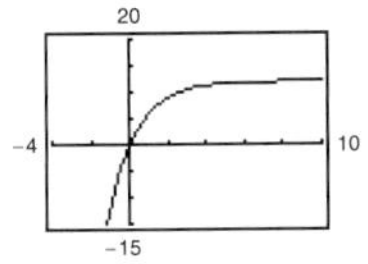

Horizontal asymptote: $y = 12$

Corresponds to the sum of the series

113. (a) $a_n = 1269.10(1.006)^n$

(b) The population is growing at a rate of 0.6% per year.

(c) 1388.2 million. This value is close to the prediction.

(d) 2010

115. (a) $3714.87 (b) $3722.16 (c) $3725.85

(d) $3728.32 (e) $3729.52

117. $7011.89 **119.** Answers will vary.

121. (a) $20,637.32 (b) $20,662.37

123. (a) $73,565.97 (b) $73,593.75

125. Answers will vary. **127.** $1600

129. About $2181.82 **131.** 126 in.^{2} **133.** $5,435,989.84

135. (a) 3208.53 ft; 2406.4 ft; 5614.93 ft (b) 5950 ft

137. False. A sequence is geometric if the ratios of consecutive terms are the same.

139. (a) 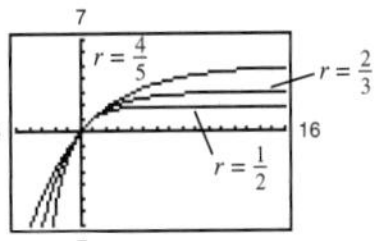

As $x \to \infty$, $y \to \frac{1}{1 - r}$.

(b) 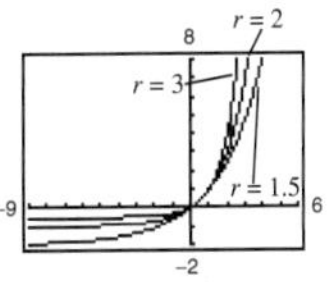

As $x \to \infty$, $y \to \infty$.

141. Given a real number r between −1 and 1, as the exponent n increases, r^n approaches zero.

Section 9.4 *(page 679)*

1. mathematical induction **3.** arithmetic

5. $\frac{5}{(k + 1)(k + 2)}$ **7.** $\frac{(k + 1)^2(k + 4)^2}{6}$

9. $\frac{3}{(k + 3)(k + 4)}$ **11–41.** Proofs

CHAPTER 9

43. $S_n = n(2n-1)$ **45.** $S_n = 10 - 10\left(\frac{9}{10}\right)^n$

47. $S_n = \frac{n}{2(n+1)}$ **49.** 120 **51.** 91 **53.** 979

55. 70 **57.** -3402 **59.** Linear; $a_n = 8n - 3$

61. Quadratic; $a_n = 3n^2 + 3$ **63.** Quadratic; $a_n = n^2 - 3$

65. 0, 3, 6, 9, 12, 15
First differences: 3, 3, 3, 3, 3
Second differences: 0, 0, 0, 0
Linear

67. 3, 1, -2, -6, -11, -17
First differences: -2, -3, -4, -5, -6
Second differences: -1, -1, -1, -1
Quadratic

69. 2, 4, 16, 256, 65,536, 4,294,967,296
First differences: 2, 12, 240, 65,280, 4,294,901,760
Second differences: 10, 228, 65,040, 4,294,836,480
Neither

71. 2, 0, 3, 1, 4, 2
First differences: -2, 3, -2, 3, -2
Second differences: 5, -5, 5, -5
Neither

73. $a_n = n^2 - n + 3$ **75.** $a_n = \frac{1}{2}n^2 + n - 3$

77. $a_n = n^2 + 5n - 6$

79. (a) 8, 11, 7, 8, 6
(b) A linear model can be used.
$a_n = 8n + 627$
(c) $a_n = 8.1n + 628$
(d) Part (b): $a_n = 731$; Part (c): $a_n = 733.3$
The values are very similar.

81. True. P_7 may be false.

83. True. If the second differences are all zero, then the first differences are all the same and the sequence is arithmetic.

85. False. A sequence that is arithmetic has second differences equal to zero.

Section 9.5 *(page 686)*

1. binomial coefficients **3.** $\binom{n}{r}$; ${}_nC_r$

5. 10 **7.** 1 **9.** 15,504 **11.** 210 **13.** 4950

15. 6 **17.** 35 **19.** $x^4 + 4x^3 + 6x^2 + 4x + 1$

21. $a^4 + 24a^3 + 216a^2 + 864a + 1296$

23. $y^3 - 12y^2 + 48y - 64$

25. $x^5 + 5x^4y + 10x^3y^2 + 10x^2y^3 + 5xy^4 + y^5$

27. $8x^3 + 12x^2y + 6xy^2 + y^3$

29. $r^6 + 18r^5s + 135r^4s^2 + 540r^3s^3 + 1215r^2s^4 + 1458rs^5 + 729s^6$

31. $243a^5 - 1620a^4b + 4320a^3b^2 - 5760a^2b^3 + 3840ab^4 - 1024b^5$

33. $x^8 + 4x^6y^2 + 6x^4y^4 + 4x^2y^6 + y^8$

35. $\frac{1}{x^5} + \frac{5y}{x^4} + \frac{10y^2}{x^3} + \frac{10y^3}{x^2} + \frac{5y^4}{x} + y^5$

37. $\frac{16}{x^4} - \frac{32y}{x^3} + \frac{24y^2}{x^2} - \frac{8y^3}{x} + y^4$

39. $2x^4 - 24x^3 + 113x^2 - 246x + 207$

41. $32t^5 - 80t^4s + 80t^3s^2 - 40t^2s^3 + 10ts^4 - s^5$

43. $x^5 + 10x^4y + 40x^3y^2 + 80x^2y^3 + 80xy^4 + 32y^5$

45. $120x^7y^3$ **47.** $360x^3y^2$ **49.** $1{,}259{,}712x^2y^7$

51. $-4{,}330{,}260{,}000y^9x^3$ **53.** 1,732,104 **55.** 720

57. $-6{,}300{,}000$ **59.** 210

61. $x^{3/2} + 15x + 75x^{1/2} + 125$

63. $x^2 - 3x^{4/3}y^{1/3} + 3x^{2/3}y^{2/3} - y$

65. $81t^2 + 108t^{7/4} + 54t^{3/2} + 12t^{5/4} + t$

67. $3x^2 + 3xh + h^2,\ h \neq 0$

69. $6x^5 + 15x^4h + 20x^3h^2 + 15x^2h^3 + 6xh^4 + h^5,\ h \neq 0$

71. $\frac{1}{\sqrt{x+h} + \sqrt{x}},\ h \neq 0$ **73.** -4 **75.** $2035 + 828i$

77. 1 **79.** 1.172 **81.** 510,568.785

83.

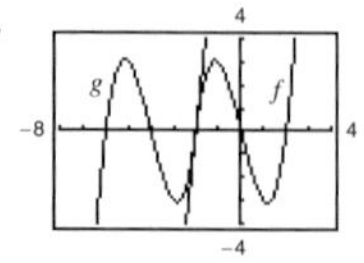

g is shifted four units to the left of f.
$g(x) = x^3 + 12x^2 + 44x + 48$

85. 0.273 **87.** 0.171 **89.** Fibonacci sequence

91. (a) $g(t) = -4.702t^2 + 63.16t + 1460.05$
(b)

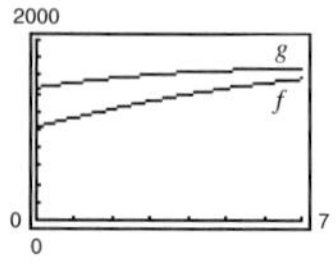

(c) 2007

93. True. The coefficients from the Binomial Theorem can be used to find the numbers in Pascal's Triangle.

95. False. The coefficient of the x^{10}-term is 1,732,104 and the coefficient of the x^{14}-term is 192,456.

97.
1 8 28 56 70 56 28 8 1
1 9 36 84 126 126 84 36 9 1
1 10 45 120 210 252 210 120 45 10 1

99.

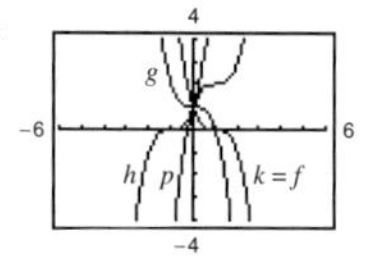

$k(x)$ is the expansion of $f(x)$.

101–103. Proofs

105.

n	r	${}_nC_r$	${}_nC_{n-r}$
9	5	126	126
7	1	7	7
12	4	495	495
6	0	1	1
10	7	120	120

${}_nC_r = {}_nC_{n-r}$
This illustrates the symmetry of Pascal's Triangle.

Section 9.6 *(page 696)*

1. Fundamental Counting Principle **3.** ${}_nP_r = \frac{n!}{(n-r)!}$

5. combinations **7.** 6 **9.** 5 **11.** 3 **13.** 8

15. 30 **17.** 30 **19.** 64 **21.** 175,760,000
23. (a) 900 (b) 648 (c) 180 (d) 600
25. 64,000 **27.** (a) 40,320 (b) 384
29. 24 **31.** 336 **33.** 120 **35.** 1,860,480
37. 970,200 **39.** 120 **41.** 11,880
43. 420 **45.** 2520
47. ABCD, ABDC, ACBD, ACDB, ADBC, ADCB, BACD, BADC, CABD, CADB, DABC, DACB, BCAD, BDAC, CBAD, CDAB, DBAC, DCAB, BCDA, BDCA, CBDA, CDBA, DBCA, DCBA
49. 1,816,214,400 **51.** 10 **53.** 4 **55.** 1
57. 4845 **59.** 850,668
61. AB, AC, AD, AE, AF, BC, BD, BE, BF, CD, CE, CF, DE, DF, EF
63. 5,586,853,480 **65.** 324,632
67. (a) 7315 (b) 693 (c) 12,628
69. (a) 3744 (b) 24 **71.** 292,600 **73.** 5 **75.** 20
77. 36 **79.** $n = 5$ or $n = 6$ **81.** $n = 10$
83. $n = 3$ **85.** $n = 2$
87. False. It is an example of a combination.
89. They are equal. **91–93.** Proofs
95. No. For some calculators the number is too great.
97. The symbol ${}_nP_r$ denotes the number of ways to choose and order r elements out of a collection of n elements.

Section 9.7 *(page 707)*

1. experiment; outcomes **3.** probability
5. mutually exclusive **7.** complement
9. $\{(H, 1), (H, 2), (H, 3), (H, 4), (H, 5), (H, 6), (T, 1), (T, 2), (T, 3), (T, 4), (T, 5), (T, 6)\}$
11. {ABC, ACB, BAC, BCA, CAB, CBA}
13. {AB, AC, AD, AE, BC, BD, BE, CD, CE, DE}
15. $\frac{3}{8}$ **17.** $\frac{1}{2}$ **19.** $\frac{7}{8}$ **21.** $\frac{3}{13}$ **23.** $\frac{3}{26}$ **25.** $\frac{5}{36}$
27. $\frac{11}{12}$ **29.** $\frac{1}{3}$ **31.** $\frac{1}{5}$ **33.** $\frac{2}{5}$ **35.** 0.13 **37.** $\frac{3}{4}$
39. 0.77 **41.** $\frac{18}{35}$
43. (a) 1.25 million (b) $\frac{2}{5}$ (c) $\frac{13}{50}$ (d) $\frac{29}{100}$
45. (a) 243 (b) $\frac{1}{50}$ (c) $\frac{16}{25}$
47. (a) 58% (b) 95.6% (c) 0.4%
49. (a) $\frac{112}{209}$ (b) $\frac{97}{209}$ (c) $\frac{274}{627}$
51. 19% **53.** (a) $\frac{21}{1292}$ (b) $\frac{225}{646}$ (c) $\frac{49}{323}$
55. (a) $\frac{1}{120}$ (b) $\frac{1}{24}$ **57.** (a) $\frac{5}{13}$ (b) $\frac{1}{2}$ (c) $\frac{4}{13}$
59. (a) $\frac{14}{55}$ (b) $\frac{12}{55}$ (c) $\frac{54}{55}$
61. (a) $\frac{1}{4}$ (b) $\frac{1}{2}$ (c) $\frac{841}{1600}$ (d) $\frac{1}{40}$
63. 0.4746 **65.** (a) 0.9702 (b) 0.9998 (c) 0.0002
67. (a) $\frac{1}{38}$ (b) $\frac{9}{19}$ (c) $\frac{10}{19}$ (d) $\frac{1}{1444}$ (e) $\frac{729}{6859}$ **69.** $\frac{7}{16}$
71. True. Two events are independent if the occurrence of one has no effect on the occurrence of the other.
73. (a) As you consider successive people with distinct birthdays, the probabilities must decrease to take into account the birth dates already used. Because the birth dates of people are independent events, multiply the respective probabilities of distinct birthdays.
(b) $\frac{365}{365} \cdot \frac{364}{365} \cdot \frac{363}{365} \cdot \frac{362}{365}$ (c) Answers will vary.
(d) Q_n is the probability that the birthdays are *not* distinct, which is equivalent to at least two people having the same birthday.
(e)

n	10	15	20	23	30	40	50
P_n	0.88	0.75	0.59	0.49	0.29	0.11	0.03
Q_n	0.12	0.25	0.41	0.51	0.71	0.89	0.97

(f) 23; $Q_n > 0.5$ for $n \geq 23$.
75. Meteorological records indicate that over an extended period of time with similar weather conditions it will rain 40% of the time.

Review Exercises *(page 714)*

1. $8, 5, 4, \frac{7}{2}, \frac{16}{5}$ **3.** $72, 36, 12, 3, \frac{3}{5}$ **5.** $a_n = 2(-1)^n$
7. $a_n = \frac{4}{n}$ **9.** 362,880 **11.** 1 **13.** 48
15. $\frac{205}{24}$ **17.** 6050 **19.** $\sum_{k=1}^{20} \frac{1}{2k}$ **21.** $\frac{4}{9}$
23. (a) $A_1 = \$10{,}066.67, A_2 = \$10{,}133.78,$
$A_3 = \$10{,}201.34, A_4 = \$10{,}269.35,$
$A_5 = \$10{,}337.81, A_6 = \$10{,}406.73,$
$A_7 = \$10{,}476.10, A_8 = \$10{,}545.95,$
$A_9 = \$10{,}616.25, A_{10} = \$10{,}687.03$
(b) $A_{120} = \$22{,}196.40$
25. Arithmetic sequence, $d = -7$
27. Arithmetic sequence, $d = \frac{1}{2}$
29. 3, 14, 25, 36, 47 **31.** 25, 28, 31, 34, 37
33. $a_n = 12n - 5$ **35.** $a_n = 3ny - 2y$
37. $a_n = -7n + 107$ **39.** 35,350 **41.** 80 **43.** 88
45. (a) \$51,600 (b) \$238,500
47. Geometric sequence, $r = 2$
49. Geometric sequence, $r = -3$
51. $4, -1, \frac{1}{4}, -\frac{1}{16}, \frac{1}{64}$ **53.** $9, 6, 4, \frac{8}{3}, \frac{16}{9}$ or $9, -6, 4, -\frac{8}{3}, \frac{16}{9}$
55. $a_n = 18\left(-\frac{1}{2}\right)^{n-1}; \frac{9}{512}$
57. $a_n = 100(1.05)^{n-1}$; About 155.133
59. 127 **61.** $\frac{15}{16}$ **63.** 31 **65.** 24.85 **67.** 8
69. 12 **71.** (a) $a_n = 120{,}000(0.7)^n$ (b) \$20,168.40
73–75. Proofs **77.** $S_n = n(2n + 7)$
79. $S_n = \frac{5}{2}\left[1 - \left(\frac{3}{5}\right)^n\right]$ **81.** 1275
83. 5, 10, 15, 20, 25
First differences: 5, 5, 5, 5
Second differences: 0, 0, 0
Linear
85. 16, 15, 14, 13, 12
First differences: $-1, -1, -1, -1$
Second differences: 0, 0, 0
Linear
87. 15 **89.** 28 **91.** $x^4 + 16x^3 + 96x^2 + 256x + 256$
93. $a^5 - 15a^4b + 90a^3b^2 - 270a^2b^3 + 405ab^4 - 243b^5$
95. $41 + 840i$ **97.** 11 **99.** 10,000 **101.** 720
103. 56 **105.** $\frac{1}{9}$ **107.** (a) 43% (b) 82%
109. $\frac{1}{1296}$ **111.** $\frac{3}{4}$
113. True. $\frac{(n+2)!}{n!} = \frac{(n+2)(n+1)n!}{n!} = (n+2)(n+1)$
115. True by Properties of Sums
117. The set of natural numbers
119. Each term of the sequence is defined in terms of preceding terms.

Chapter Test (page 717)

1. $-\frac{1}{5}, \frac{1}{8}, -\frac{1}{11}, \frac{1}{14}, -\frac{1}{17}$ **2.** $a_n = \frac{n+2}{n!}$
3. 60, 73, 86; 243 **4.** $a_n = 0.8n + 1.4$
5. $a_n = 7(4)^{n-1}$ **6.** 5, 10, 20, 40, 80 **7.** 86,100
8. 477 **9.** 4 **10.** Proof
11. (a) $x^4 + 24x^3y + 216x^2y^2 + 864xy^3 + 1296y^4$
(b) $3x^5 - 30x^4 + 124x^3 - 264x^2 + 288x - 128$
12. $-22{,}680$ **13.** (a) 72 (b) 328,440
14. (a) 330 (b) 720,720 **15.** 26,000 **16.** 720
17. $\frac{1}{15}$ **18.** $\frac{1}{27{,}405}$ **19.** 10%

Cumulative Test for Chapters 7–9 (page 718)

1. $(1, 2), \left(-\frac{3}{2}, \frac{3}{4}\right)$ **2.** $(-3, -1)$
3. $(5, -2, -2)$ **4.** $(1, -2, 1)$
5.

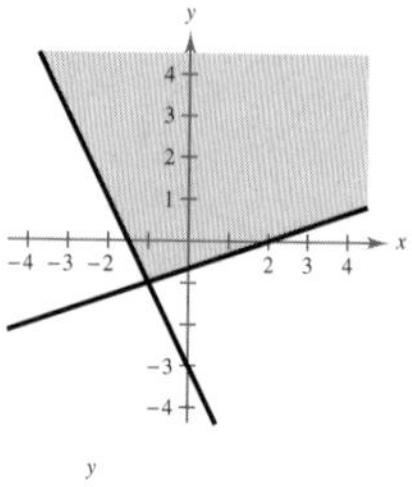

6.

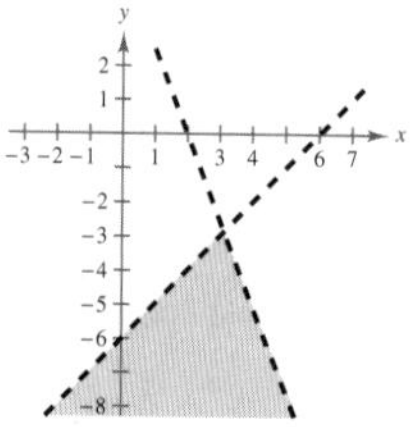

7.

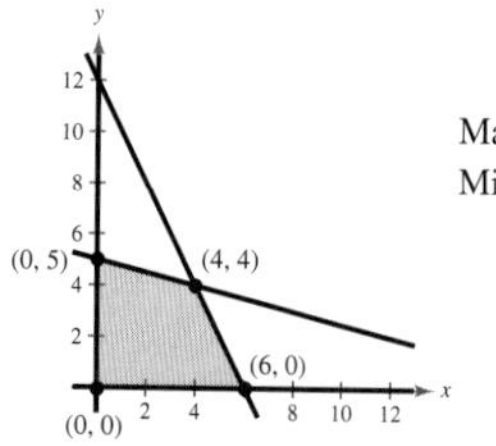

Maximum at (4, 4): $z = 20$
Minimum at (0, 0): $z = 0$

8. \$0.75 mixture: 120 lb; \$1.25 mixture: 80 lb
9. $y = \frac{1}{4}x^2 - 2x + 6$

10. $\begin{bmatrix} -1 & 2 & -1 & \vdots & 9 \\ 2 & -1 & 2 & \vdots & -9 \\ 3 & 3 & -4 & \vdots & 7 \end{bmatrix}$ **11.** $(-2, 3, -1)$

12. $\begin{bmatrix} 1 & 5 \\ -1 & 3 \end{bmatrix}$ **13.** $\begin{bmatrix} 16 & -40 \\ 0 & 8 \end{bmatrix}$ **14.** $\begin{bmatrix} 16 & -25 \\ -2 & 13 \end{bmatrix}$

15. $\begin{bmatrix} -6 & 15 \\ 2 & -9 \end{bmatrix}$ **16.** $\begin{bmatrix} 9 & 0 \\ -7 & 16 \end{bmatrix}$ **17.** $\begin{bmatrix} -15 & 35 \\ 1 & -5 \end{bmatrix}$

18. 203 **19.** $\begin{bmatrix} -175 & 37 & -13 \\ 95 & -20 & 7 \\ 14 & -3 & 1 \end{bmatrix}$

20. Gym shoes: \$2042 million; Jogging shoes: \$1733 million; Walking shoes: \$3415 million
21. $(-5, 4)$ **22.** $(-3, 4, 2)$ **23.** 9
24. $\frac{1}{5}, -\frac{1}{7}, \frac{1}{9}, -\frac{1}{11}, \frac{1}{13}$ **25.** $a_n = \frac{(n+1)!}{n+3}$ **26.** 1536
27. (a) 65.4 (b) $a_n = 3.2n + 1.4$ **28.** 3, 6, 12, 24, 48
29. $\frac{130}{9}$ **30.** Proof
31. $w^4 - 36w^3 + 486w^2 - 2916w + 6561$ **32.** 2184
33. 600 **34.** 70 **35.** 462 **36.** 453,600
37. 151,200 **38.** 720 **39.** $\frac{1}{4}$

Problem Solving (page 723)

1. 1, 1.5, $1.41\overline{6}$, 1.414215686, 1.414213562, 1.414213562, . . .
x_n approaches $\sqrt{2}$.
3. (a)

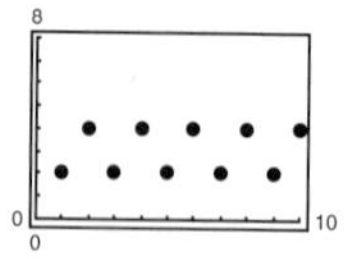

(b) If n is odd, $a_n = 2$, and if n is even, $a_n = 4$.
(c)

n	1	10	101	1000	10,001
a_n	2	4	2	4	2

(d) It is not possible to find the value of a_n as n approaches infinity.
5. (a) 3, 5, 7, 9, 11, 13, 15, 17; $a_n = 2n + 1$
(b) To obtain the arithmetic sequence, find the differences of consecutive terms of the sequence of perfect cubes. Then find the differences of consecutive terms of the resulting sequence.
(c) 12, 18, 24, 30, 36, 42, 48; $a_n = 6n + 6$
(d) To obtain the arithmetic sequence, find the third sequence obtained by taking the differences of consecutive terms in consecutive sequences.
(e) 60, 84, 108, 132, 156, 180; $a_n = 24n + 36$
7. $S_n = \left(\frac{1}{2}\right)^{n-1}$; $A_n = \frac{\sqrt{3}}{4}S_n^{\,2}$
9. Proof **11.** (a) Proof (b) 17,710
13. $\frac{1}{3}$ **15.** (a) $-\$0.71$ (b) 2.53, 24 turns

Chapter 10

Section 10.1 (page 730)

1. inclination **3.** $\left|\frac{m_2 - m_1}{1 + m_1m_2}\right|$ **5.** $\frac{\sqrt{3}}{3}$ **7.** -1
9. $\sqrt{3}$ **11.** 3.2236 **13.** $\frac{3\pi}{4}$ rad, 135°
15. $\frac{\pi}{4}$ rad, 45° **17.** 0.6435 rad, 36.9° **19.** $\frac{\pi}{6}$ rad, 30°
21. $\frac{5\pi}{6}$ rad, 150° **23.** 1.0517 rad, 60.3°
25. 2.1112 rad, 121.0° **27.** $\frac{3\pi}{4}$ rad, 135°
29. $\frac{\pi}{4}$ rad, 45° **31.** $\frac{5\pi}{6}$ rad, 150° **33.** 1.2490 rad, 71.6°
35. 2.1112 rad, 121.0° **37.** 1.1071 rad, 63.4°
39. 0.1974 rad, 11.3° **41.** 1.4289 rad, 81.9°
43. 0.9273 rad, 53.1° **45.** 0.8187 rad, 46.9°
47. $(1, 5) \leftrightarrow (4, 5)$: slope $= 0$
$(4, 5) \leftrightarrow (3, 8)$: slope $= -3$
$(3, 8) \leftrightarrow (1, 5)$: slope $= \frac{3}{2}$
(1, 5); 56.3°; (4, 5): 71.6°; (3, 8): 52.1°

49. $(-4, -1) \leftrightarrow (3, 2)$: slope $= \frac{3}{7}$
$(3, 2) \leftrightarrow (1, 0)$: slope $= 1$
$(1, 0) \leftrightarrow (-4, -1)$: slope $= \frac{1}{5}$
$(-4, -1)$: 11.9°; $(3, 2)$: 21.8°; $(1, 0)$: 146.3°

51. 0 **53.** $\frac{4\sqrt{10}}{5} \approx 2.5298$ **55.** 7

57. $\frac{8\sqrt{37}}{37} \approx 1.3152$

59. (a)

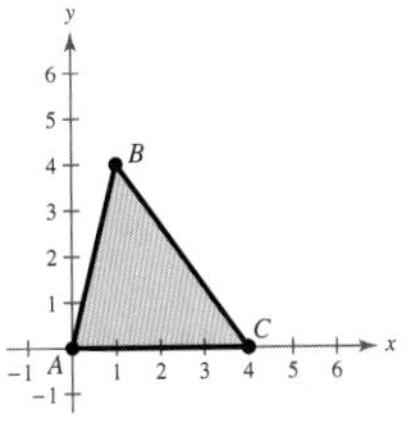

(b) 4 (c) 8

61. (a)

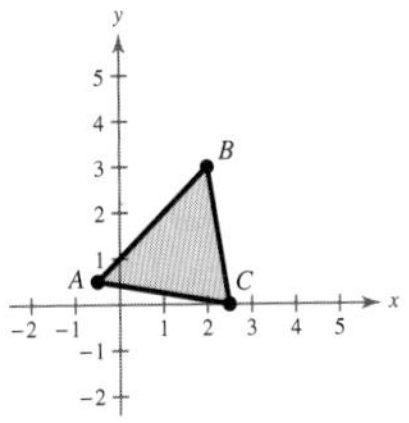

(b) $\frac{35\sqrt{37}}{74}$ (c) $\frac{35}{8}$

63. $2\sqrt{2}$ **65.** 0.1003, 1054 ft **67.** 31.0°

69. $\alpha \approx 33.69°$; $\beta \approx 56.31°$

71. True. The inclination of a line is related to its slope by $m = \tan \theta$. If the angle is greater than $\pi/2$ but less than π, then the angle is in the second quadrant, where the tangent function is negative.

73. (a) $d = \frac{4}{\sqrt{m^2 + 1}}$

(b)

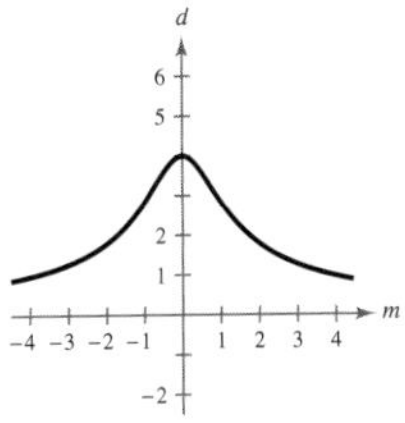

(c) $m = 0$

(d) The graph has a horizontal asymptote of $d = 0$. As the slope becomes larger, the distance between the origin and the line, $y = mx + 4$, becomes smaller and approaches 0.

75. (a) $d = \frac{3|m + 1|}{\sqrt{m^2 + 1}}$

(b)

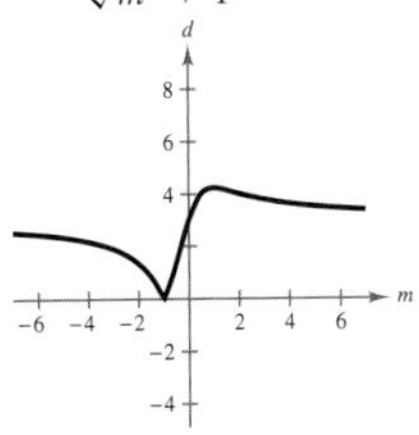

(c) $m = 1$

(d) Yes. $m = -1$

(e) $d = 3$. As the line approaches the vertical, the distance approaches 3.

Section 10.2 *(page 738)*

1. conic **3.** locus **5.** axis **7.** focal chord

9. A circle is formed when a plane intersects the top or bottom half of a double-napped cone and is perpendicular to the axis of the cone.

11. A parabola is formed when a plane intersects the top or bottom half of a double-napped cone, is parallel to the side of the cone, and does not intersect the vertex.

13. e **14.** b **15.** d **16.** f **17.** a **18.** c

19. $x^2 = \frac{3}{2}y$ **21.** $x^2 = 2y$ **23.** $y^2 = -8x$

25. $x^2 = -4y$ **27.** $y^2 = 4x$ **29.** $x^2 = \frac{8}{3}y$

31. $y^2 = -\frac{25}{2}x$

33. Vertex: $(0, 0)$
Focus: $\left(0, \frac{1}{2}\right)$
Directrix: $y = -\frac{1}{2}$

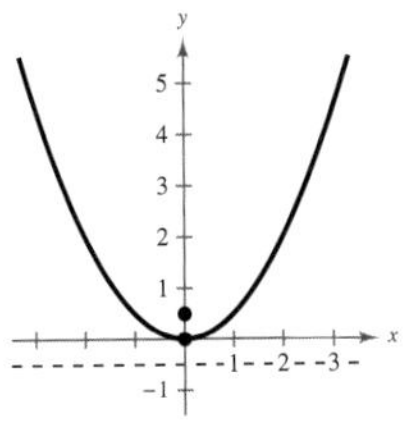

35. Vertex: $(0, 0)$
Focus: $\left(-\frac{3}{2}, 0\right)$
Directrix: $x = \frac{3}{2}$

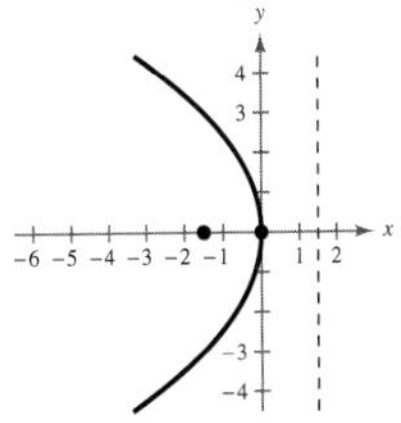

37. Vertex: $(0, 0)$
Focus: $\left(0, -\frac{3}{2}\right)$
Directrix: $y = \frac{3}{2}$

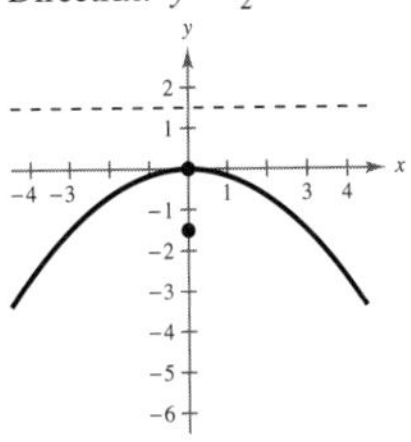

39. Vertex: $(1, -2)$
Focus: $(1, -4)$
Directrix: $y = 0$

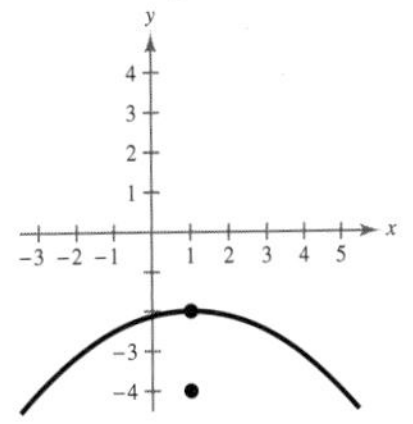

41. Vertex: $\left(-3, \frac{3}{2}\right)$
Focus: $\left(-3, \frac{5}{2}\right)$
Directrix: $y = \frac{1}{2}$

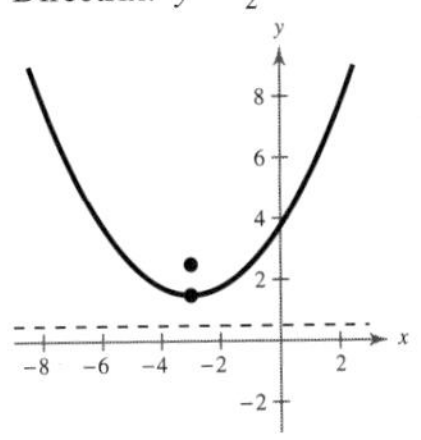

43. Vertex: $(1, 1)$
Focus: $(1, 2)$
Directrix: $y = 0$

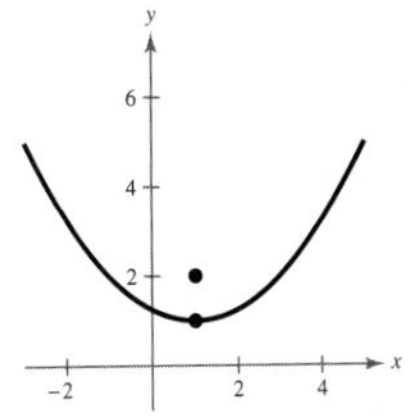

45. Vertex: $(-2, -3)$
Focus: $(-4, -3)$
Directrix: $x = 0$

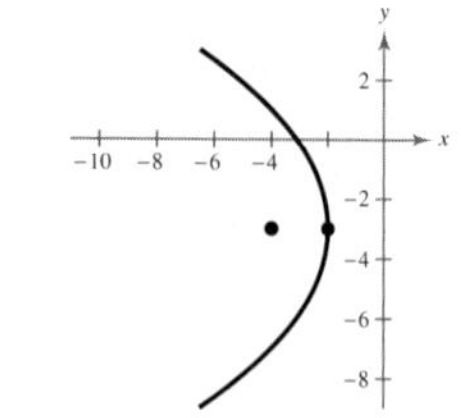

47. Vertex: $(-2, 1)$
Focus: $\left(-2, -\frac{1}{2}\right)$
Directrix: $y = \frac{5}{2}$

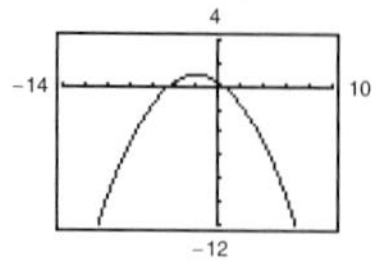

49. Vertex: $\left(\frac{1}{4}, -\frac{1}{2}\right)$
Focus: $\left(0, -\frac{1}{2}\right)$
Directrix: $x = \frac{1}{2}$

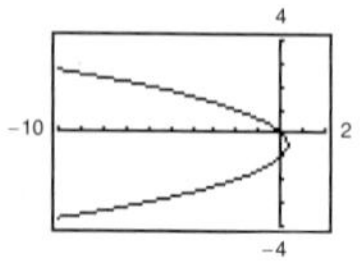

51. $(x - 3)^2 = -(y - 1)$ **53.** $y^2 = 4(x + 4)$
55. $(y - 3)^2 = 8(x - 4)$ **57.** $x^2 = -8(y - 2)$
59. $(y - 2)^2 = 8x$ **61.** $y = \sqrt{6(x + 1)} + 3$
63.

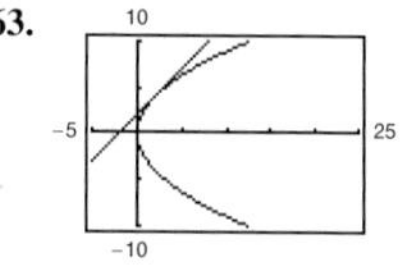

(2, 4)

65. $4x - y - 8 = 0$; $(2, 0)$ **67.** $4x - y + 2 = 0$; $\left(-\frac{1}{2}, 0\right)$
69.

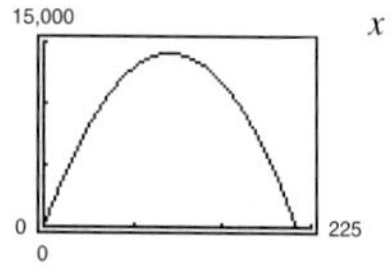

$x = 106$ units

71. (a)

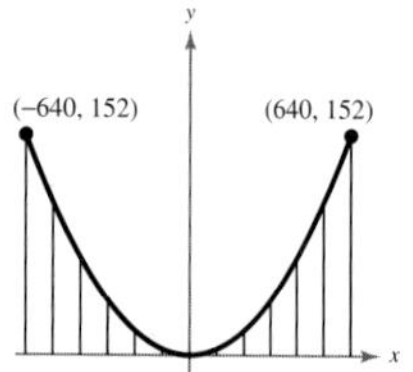

(b) $y = \dfrac{19x^2}{51{,}200}$

(c)

Distance, x	0	100	250	400	500
Height, y	0	3.71	23.19	59.38	92.77

73. (a) $y = -\frac{1}{640}x^2$ (b) 8 ft
75. (a) $x^2 = 180{,}000y$ (b) $300\sqrt{2}$ cm ≈ 424.26 cm
77. $x^2 = -\frac{25}{4}(y - 48)$
79. (a) $17{,}500\sqrt{2}$ mi/h $\approx 24{,}750$ mi/h
(b) $x^2 = -16{,}400(y - 4100)$
81. (a) $x^2 = -49(y - 100)$ (b) 70 ft
83. False. If the graph crossed the directrix, there would exist points closer to the directrix than the focus.
85. $m = \dfrac{x_1}{2p}$
87. (a)

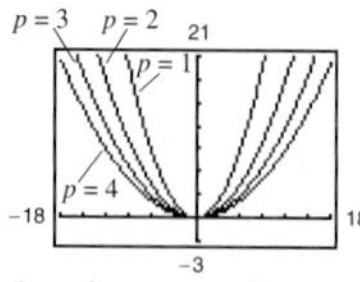

As p increases, the graph becomes wider.
(b) (0, 1), (0, 2), (0, 3), (0, 4) (c) 4, 8, 12, 16; $4|p|$
(d) It is an easy way to determine two additional points on the graph.

Section 10.3 *(page 748)*

1. ellipse; foci **3.** minor axis
5. b **6.** c **7.** d **8.** f **9.** a **10.** e
11. $\dfrac{x^2}{4} + \dfrac{y^2}{16} = 1$ **13.** $\dfrac{x^2}{49} + \dfrac{y^2}{45} = 1$ **15.** $\dfrac{x^2}{49} + \dfrac{y^2}{24} = 1$
17. $\dfrac{21x^2}{400} + \dfrac{y^2}{25} = 1$ **19.** $\dfrac{(x - 2)^2}{1} + \dfrac{(y - 3)^2}{9} = 1$
21. $\dfrac{(x - 4)^2}{16} + \dfrac{(y - 2)^2}{1} = 1$ **23.** $\dfrac{x^2}{48} + \dfrac{(y - 4)^2}{64} = 1$
25. $\dfrac{x^2}{16} + \dfrac{(y - 4)^2}{12} = 1$ **27.** $\dfrac{(x - 2)^2}{4} + \dfrac{(y - 2)^2}{1} = 1$

29. Ellipse
Center: (0, 0)
Vertices: $(\pm 5, 0)$
Foci: $(\pm 3, 0)$
Eccentricity: $\frac{3}{5}$

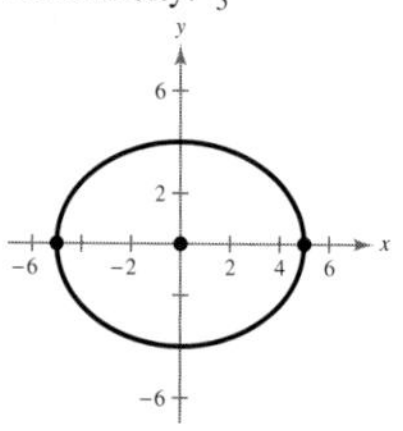

31. Circle
Center: (0, 0)
Radius: 5

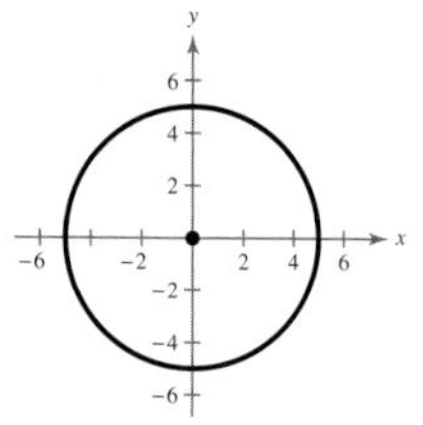

33. Ellipse
Center: (0, 0)
Vertices: $(0, \pm 3)$
Foci: $(0, \pm 2)$
Eccentricity: $\frac{2}{3}$

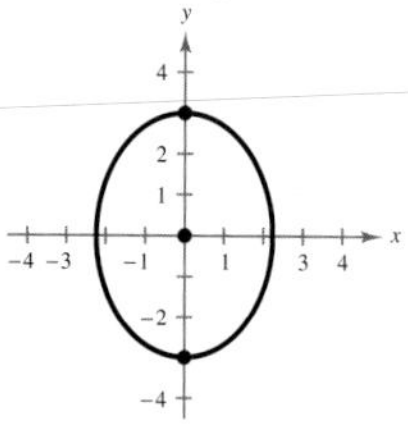

35. Ellipse
Center: $(4, -1)$
Vertices: $(4, -6)$, $(4, 4)$
Foci: $(4, 2)$, $(4, -4)$
Eccentricity: $\frac{3}{5}$

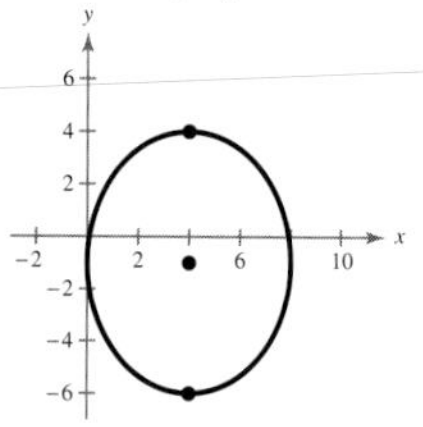

37. Circle
Center: $(0, -1)$
Radius: $\frac{2}{3}$

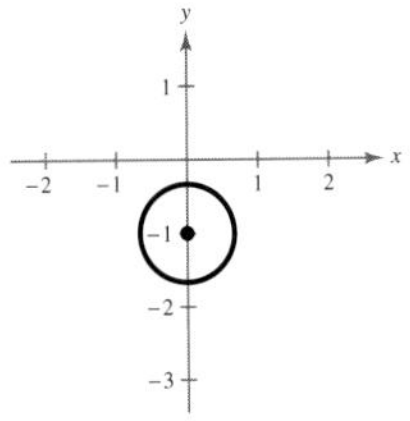

39. Ellipse
Center: $(-2, -4)$
Vertices: $(-3, -4), (-1, -4)$
Foci: $\left(\dfrac{-4 \pm \sqrt{3}}{2}, -4\right)$
Eccentricity: $\dfrac{\sqrt{3}}{2}$

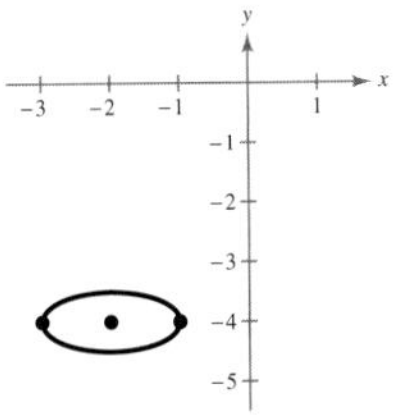

41. Ellipse
Center: $(-2, 3)$
Vertices: $(-2, 6), (-2, 0)$
Foci: $(-2, 3 \pm \sqrt{5})$
Eccentricity: $\dfrac{\sqrt{5}}{3}$

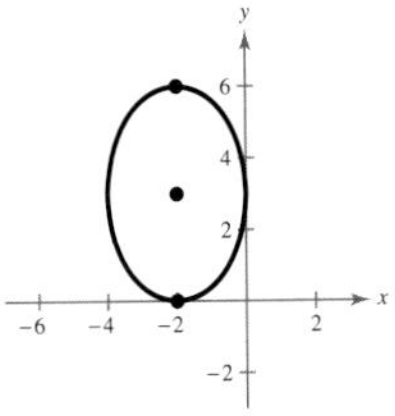

43. Circle
Center: $(1, -2)$
Radius: 6

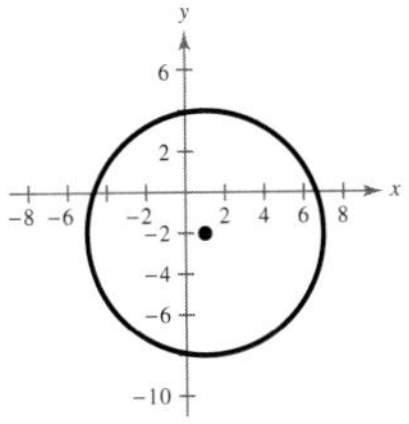

45. Ellipse
Center: $(-3, 1)$
Vertices: $(-3, 7), (-3, -5)$
Foci: $(-3, 1 \pm 2\sqrt{6})$
Eccentricity: $\dfrac{\sqrt{6}}{3}$

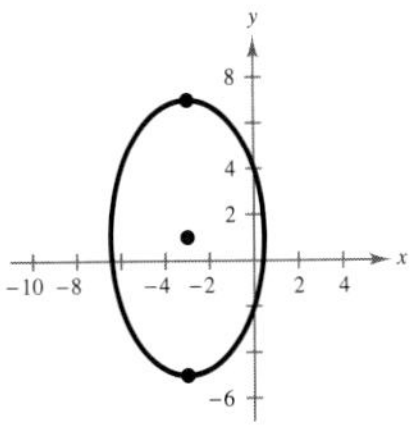

47. Ellipse
Center: $\left(3, -\dfrac{5}{2}\right)$
Vertices: $\left(9, -\dfrac{5}{2}\right), \left(-3, -\dfrac{5}{2}\right)$
Foci: $\left(3 \pm 3\sqrt{3}, -\dfrac{5}{2}\right)$
Eccentricity: $\dfrac{\sqrt{3}}{2}$

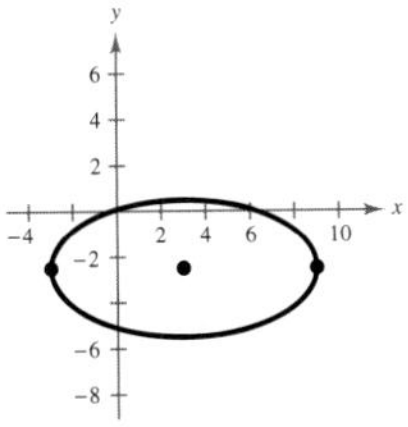

49. Circle
Center: $(-1, 1)$
Radius: $\frac{2}{3}$

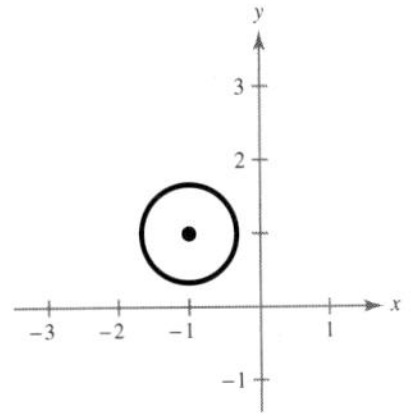

51. Ellipse
Center: $(2, 1)$
Vertices: $\left(\frac{7}{3}, 1\right), \left(\frac{5}{3}, 1\right)$
Foci: $\left(\frac{34}{15}, 1\right), \left(\frac{26}{15}, 1\right)$
Eccentricity: $\frac{4}{5}$

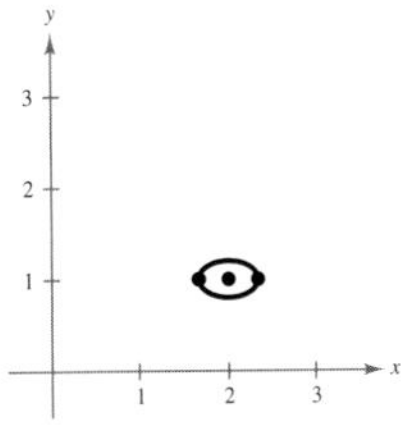

53.

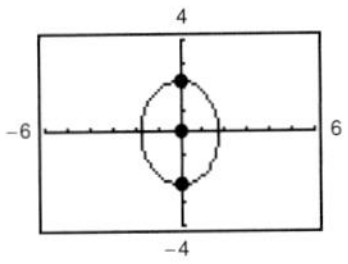

Center: $(0, 0)$
Vertices: $(0, \pm\sqrt{5})$
Foci: $(0, \pm\sqrt{2})$

55.

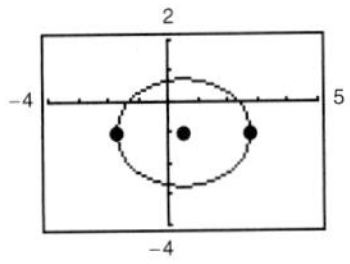

Center: $\left(\frac{1}{2}, -1\right)$
Vertices: $\left(\frac{1}{2} \pm \sqrt{5}, -1\right)$
Foci: $\left(\frac{1}{2} \pm \sqrt{2}, -1\right)$

57. $\dfrac{\sqrt{5}}{3}$ **59.** $\dfrac{2\sqrt{2}}{3}$ **61.** $\dfrac{x^2}{25} + \dfrac{y^2}{16} = 1$

63. (a)

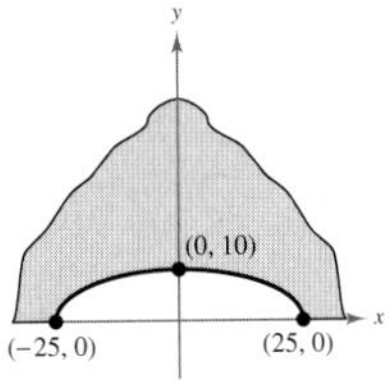

(b) $\dfrac{x^2}{625} + \dfrac{y^2}{100} = 1$
(c) Yes

65. (a) $\dfrac{x^2}{321.84} + \dfrac{y^2}{20.89} = 1$ (b)

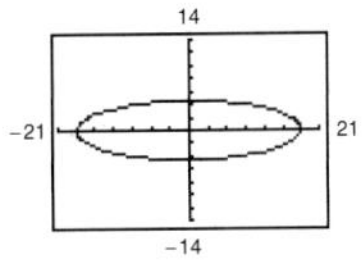

(c) Aphelion:
35.29 astronomical units
Perihelion:
0.59 astronomical unit

67. (a) $y = -8\sqrt{0.04 - \theta^2}$ (b)

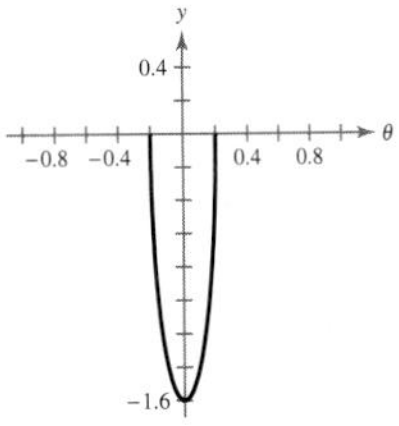

(c) The bottom half

CHAPTER 10

69.

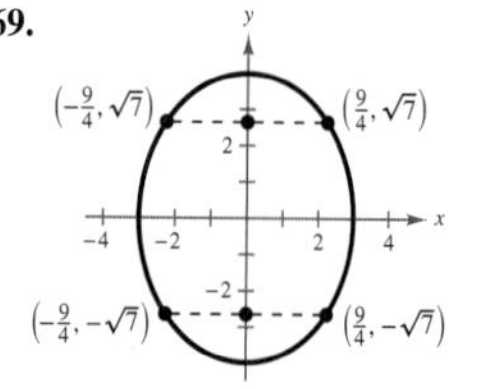

71.

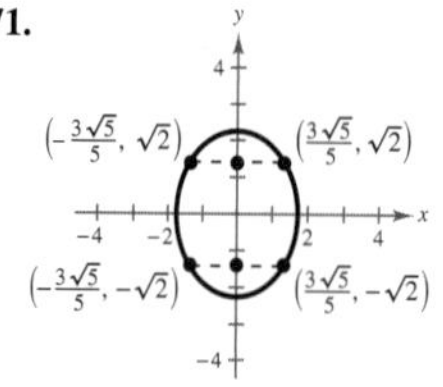

73. False. The graph of $(x^2/4) + y^4 = 1$ is not an ellipse. The degree of y is 4, not 2.

75. (a) $A = \pi a(20 - a)$ (b) $\dfrac{x^2}{196} + \dfrac{y^2}{36} = 1$

(c)

a	8	9	10	11	12	13
A	301.6	311.0	314.2	311.0	301.6	285.9

$a = 10$, circle

(d)

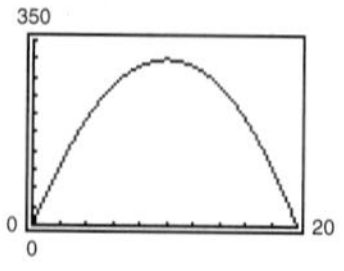

The shape of an ellipse with a maximum area is a circle. The maximum area is found when $a = 10$ (verified in part c) and therefore $b = 10$, so the equation produces a circle.

77. $\dfrac{(x-6)^2}{324} + \dfrac{(y-2)^2}{308} = 1$ **79.** Proof

Section 10.4 *(page 758)*

1. hyperbola; foci **3.** transverse axis; center

5. b **6.** c **7.** a **8.** d

9. Center: $(0, 0)$
Vertices: $(\pm 1, 0)$
Foci: $(\pm\sqrt{2}, 0)$
Asymptotes: $y = \pm x$

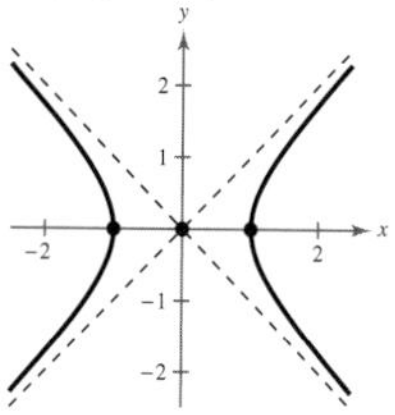

11. Center: $(0, 0)$
Vertices: $(0, \pm 5)$
Foci: $(0, \pm\sqrt{106})$
Asymptotes: $y = \pm\frac{5}{9}x$

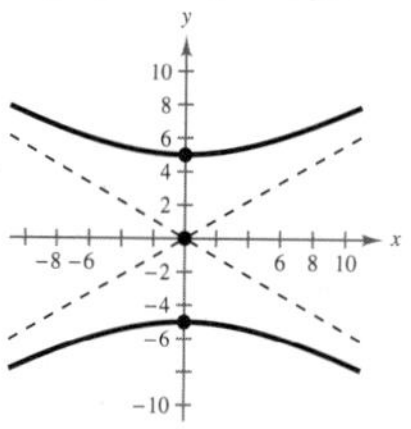

13. Center: $(0, 0)$
Vertices: $(0, \pm 1)$
Foci: $(0, \pm\sqrt{5})$
Asymptotes: $y = \pm\frac{1}{2}x$

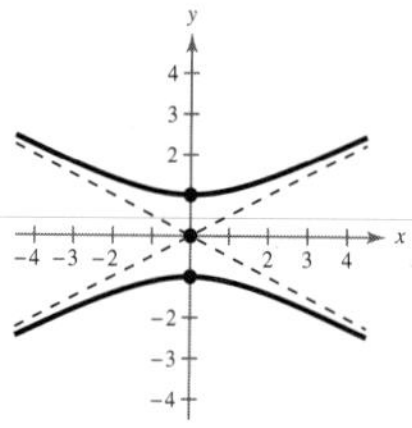

15. Center: $(1, -2)$
Vertices: $(3, -2), (-1, -2)$
Foci: $(1 \pm \sqrt{5}, -2)$
Asymptotes:
$y = -2 \pm \frac{1}{2}(x - 1)$

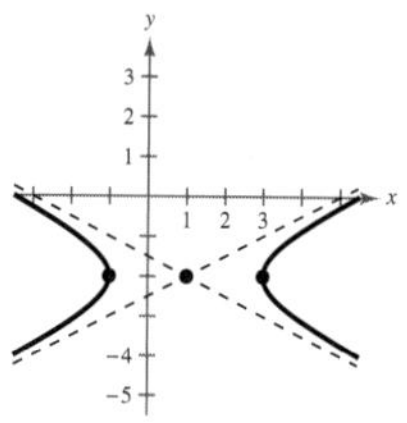

17. Center: $(2, -6)$
Vertices:
$\left(2, -\frac{17}{3}\right), \left(2, -\frac{19}{3}\right)$
Foci: $\left(2, -6 \pm \frac{\sqrt{13}}{6}\right)$
Asymptotes:
$y = -6 \pm \frac{2}{3}(x - 2)$

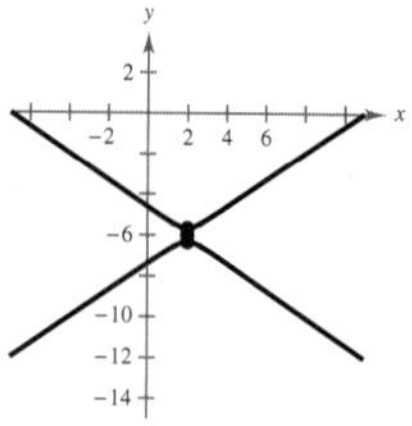

19. Center: $(2, -3)$
Vertices: $(3, -3), (1, -3)$
Foci: $(2 \pm \sqrt{10}, -3)$
Asymptotes:
$y = -3 \pm 3(x - 2)$

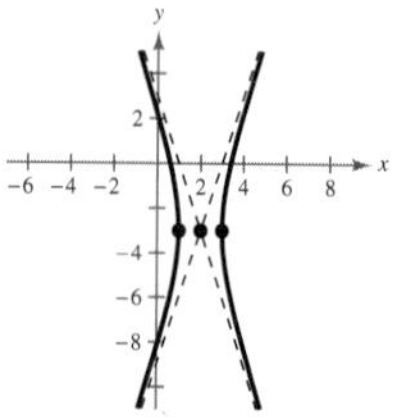

21. The graph of this equation is two lines intersecting at $(-1, -3)$.

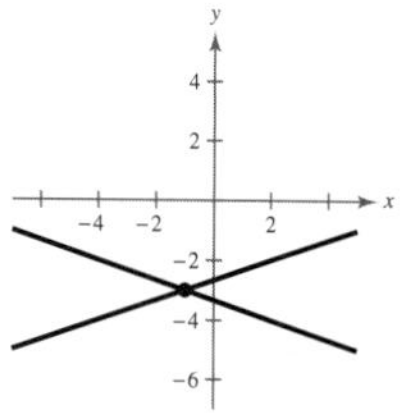

23. Center: $(0, 0)$
Vertices: $(\pm\sqrt{3}, 0)$
Foci: $(\pm\sqrt{5}, 0)$
Asymptotes: $y = \pm\frac{\sqrt{6}}{3}x$

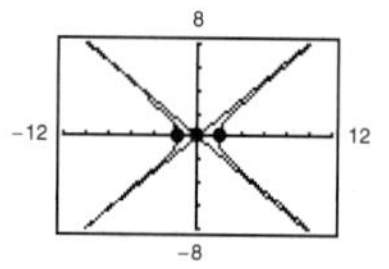

25. Center: $(0, 0)$
Vertices: $(\pm 3, 0)$
Foci: $(\pm\sqrt{13}, 0)$
Asymptotes: $y = \pm\frac{2}{3}x$

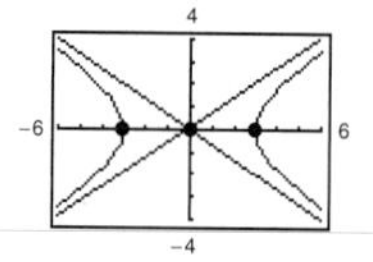

27. Center: $(1, -3)$
Vertices: $(1, -3 \pm \sqrt{2})$
Foci: $(1, -3 \pm 2\sqrt{5})$
Asymptotes:
$y = -3 \pm \frac{1}{3}(x - 1)$

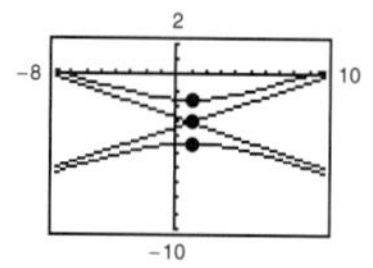

29. $\dfrac{y^2}{4} - \dfrac{x^2}{12} = 1$ **31.** $\dfrac{x^2}{1} - \dfrac{y^2}{25} = 1$

33. $\dfrac{17y^2}{1024} - \dfrac{17x^2}{64} = 1$ **35.** $\dfrac{(x-4)^2}{4} - \dfrac{y^2}{12} = 1$

37. $\dfrac{(y-5)^2}{16} - \dfrac{(x-4)^2}{9} = 1$ **39.** $\dfrac{y^2}{9} - \dfrac{4(x-2)^2}{9} = 1$

41. $\dfrac{(y-2)^2}{4} - \dfrac{x^2}{4} = 1$ **43.** $\dfrac{(x-2)^2}{1} - \dfrac{(y-2)^2}{1} = 1$

45. $\dfrac{(x-3)^2}{9} - \dfrac{(y-2)^2}{4} = 1$ **47.** $\dfrac{y^2}{9} - \dfrac{x^2}{9/4} = 1$

49. $\dfrac{(x-3)^2}{4} - \dfrac{(y-2)^2}{16/5} = 1$

51. (a) $\dfrac{x^2}{1} - \dfrac{y^2}{169/3} = 1$ (b) About 2.403 ft

53. $(3300, -2750)$

55. (a) $\dfrac{x^2}{1} - \dfrac{y^2}{27} = 1;\ -9 \le y \le 9$ (b) 1.89 ft

57. Ellipse **59.** Hyperbola **61.** Hyperbola

63. Parabola **65.** Ellipse **67.** Parabola

69. Parabola **71.** Circle

73. True. For a hyperbola, $c^2 = a^2 + b^2$. The larger the ratio of b to a, the larger the eccentricity of the hyperbola, $e = c/a$.

75. False. When $D = -E$, the graph is two intersecting lines.

77. Answers will vary.

79. $y = 1 - 3\sqrt{\dfrac{(x-3)^2}{4} - 1}$

81.

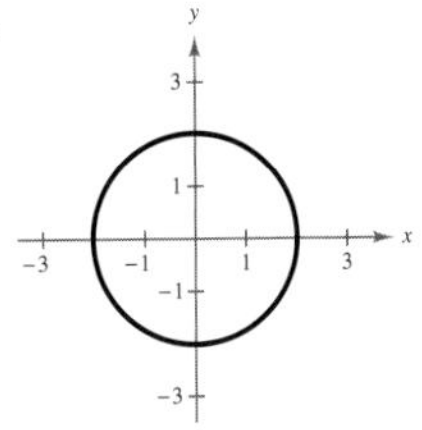

The equation $y = x^2 + C$ is a parabola that could intersect the circle in zero, one, two, three, or four places depending on its location on the y-axis.

(a) $C > 2$ and $C < -\frac{17}{4}$ (b) $C = 2$
(c) $-2 < C < 2,\ C = -\frac{17}{4}$ (d) $C = -2$
(e) $-\frac{17}{4} < C < -2$

Section 10.5 *(page 767)*

1. rotation; axes **3.** invariant under rotation **5.** $(3, 0)$

7. $\left(\dfrac{3+\sqrt{3}}{2}, \dfrac{3\sqrt{3}-1}{2}\right)$ **9.** $\left(\dfrac{3\sqrt{2}}{2}, -\dfrac{\sqrt{2}}{2}\right)$

11. $\left(\dfrac{2\sqrt{3}+1}{2}, \dfrac{2-\sqrt{3}}{2}\right)$

13. $\dfrac{(y')^2}{2} - \dfrac{(x')^2}{2} = 1$ **15.** $y' = \pm\dfrac{\sqrt{2}}{2}$

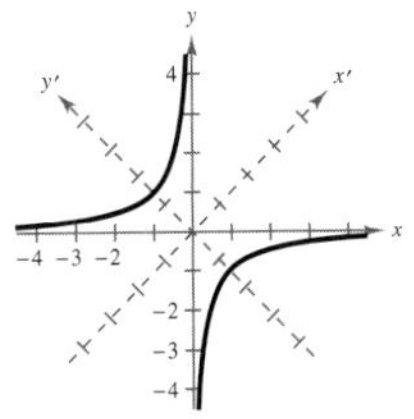

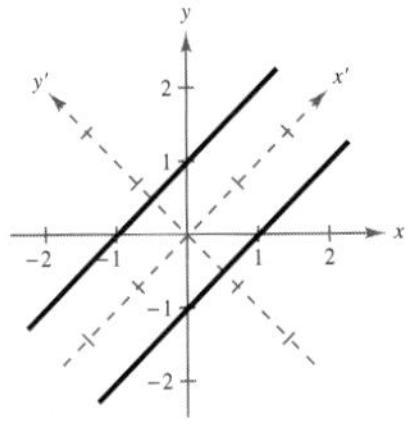

17. $\dfrac{\left(x' - 6\sqrt{2}\right)^2}{64} - \dfrac{\left(y' - 2\sqrt{2}\right)^2}{64} = 1$

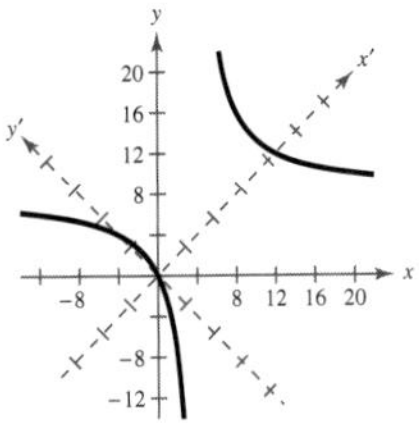

19. $\dfrac{(x')^2}{6} + \dfrac{(y')^2}{3/2} = 1$

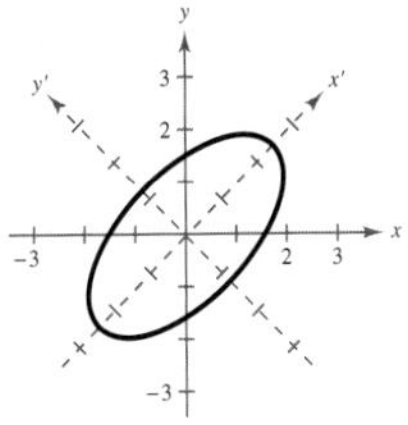

21. $y' = \dfrac{-\sqrt{2}}{4}(x')^2$

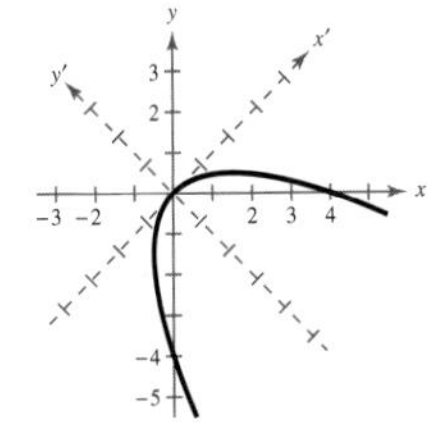

23. $(y')^2 = -x'$

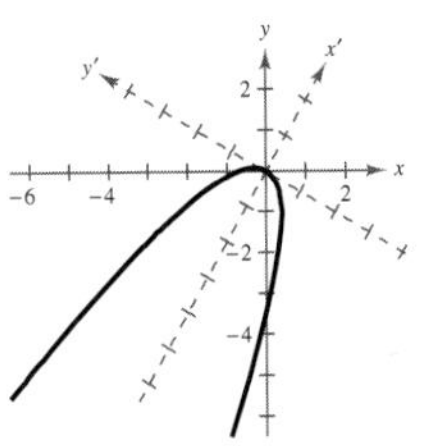

25. $(x'-1)^2 = 6\left(y' + \frac{1}{6}\right)$

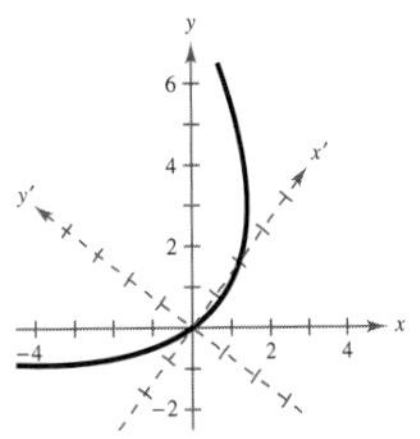

27.

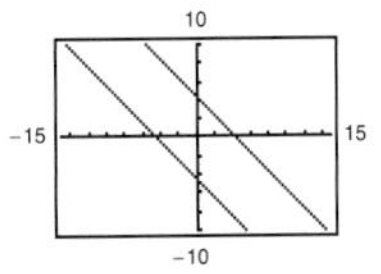

$\theta = 45°$

29.

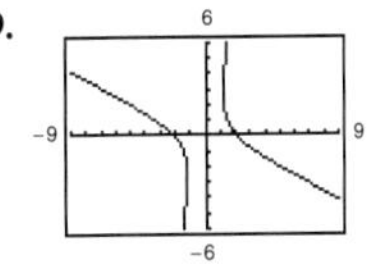

$\theta \approx 26.57°$

31.

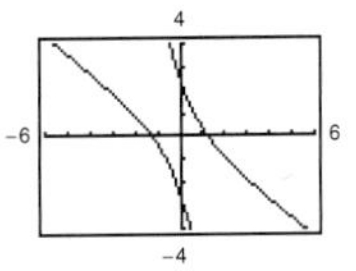

$\theta \approx 31.72°$

33.

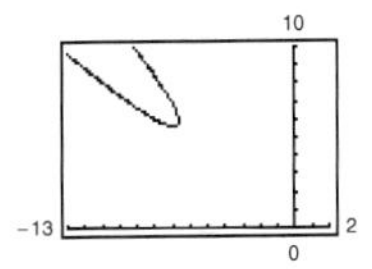

$\theta = 45°$

35.

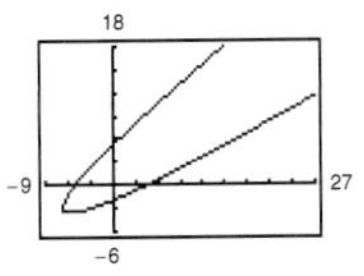

$\theta \approx 33.69°$

37. e **38.** f **39.** b **40.** a **41.** d **42.** c

43. (a) Parabola

(b) $y = \dfrac{(8x - 5) \pm \sqrt{(8x - 5)^2 - 4(16x^2 - 10x)}}{2}$

(c)

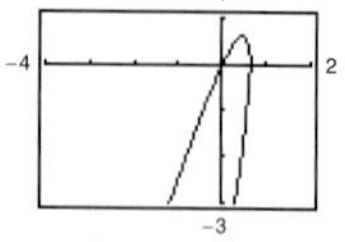

45. (a) Ellipse (b) $y = \dfrac{6x \pm \sqrt{36x^2 - 28(12x^2 - 45)}}{14}$

(c)

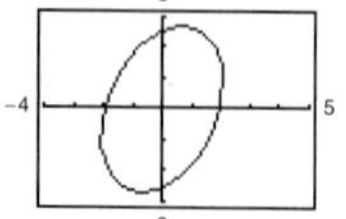

47. (a) Hyperbola (b) $y = \dfrac{6x \pm \sqrt{36x^2 + 20(x^2 + 4x - 22)}}{-10}$

(c)

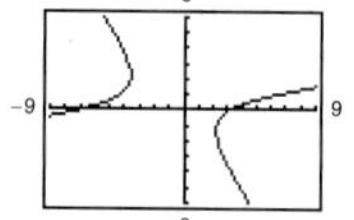

49. (a) Parabola

(b) $y = \dfrac{-(4x - 1) \pm \sqrt{(4x - 1)^2 - 16(x^2 - 5x - 3)}}{8}$

(c)

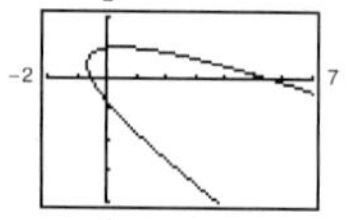

51.

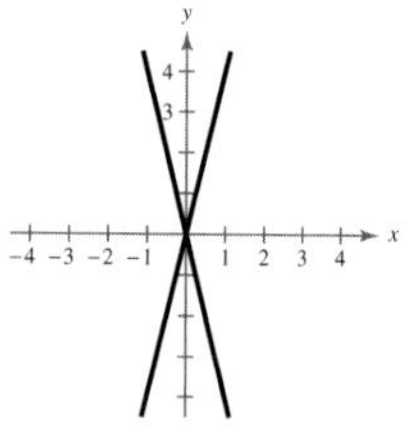

53.

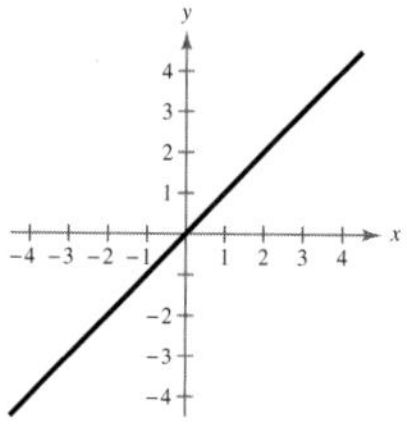

55.

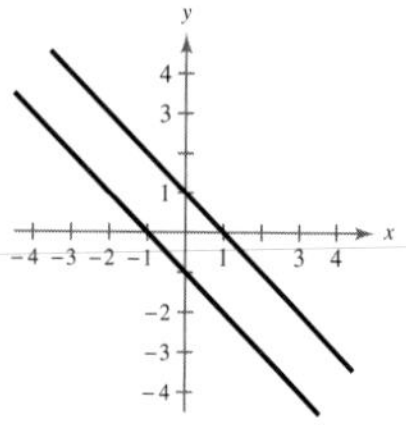

57. (2, 2), (2, 4) **59.** (−8, 12) **61.** (0, 8), (12, 8)
63. (0, 4) **65.** $(1, \sqrt{3}), (1, -\sqrt{3})$ **67.** No solution
69. $(0, \frac{3}{2}), (-3, 0)$

71. True. The graph of the equation can be classified by finding the discriminant. For a graph to be a hyperbola, the discriminant must be greater than zero. If $k \geq \frac{1}{4}$, then the discriminant would be less than or equal to zero.

73. Answers will vary. **75.** Major axis: 4; Minor axis: 2

Section 10.6 *(page 774)*

1. plane curve **3.** eliminating; parameter

5. (a)

t	0	1	2	3	4
x	0	1	$\sqrt{2}$	$\sqrt{3}$	2
y	3	2	1	0	−1

(b)

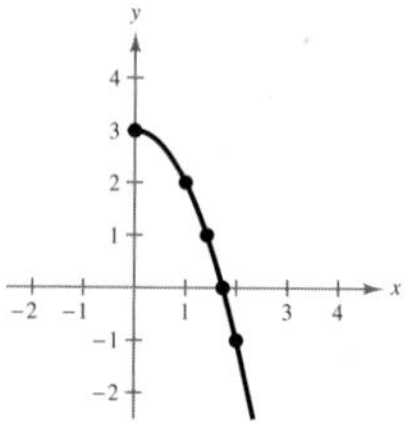

(c) $y = 3 - x^2$

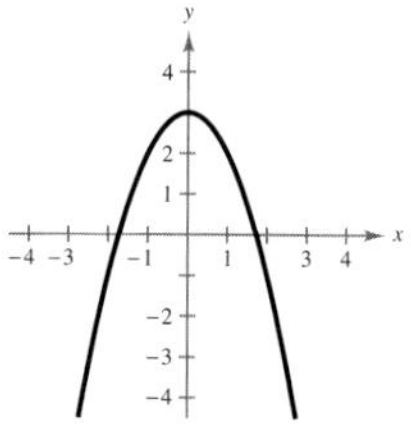

The graph of the rectangular equation shows the entire parabola rather than just the right half.

7. (a)

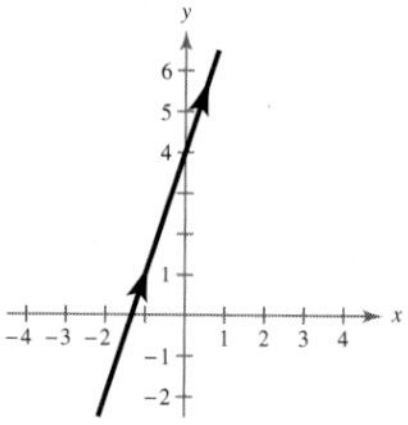

(b) $y = 3x + 4$

9. (a)

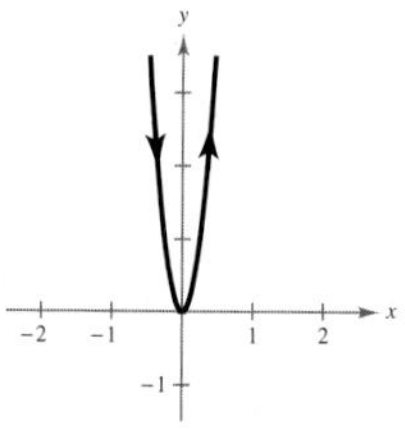

(b) $y = 16x^2$

11. (a)

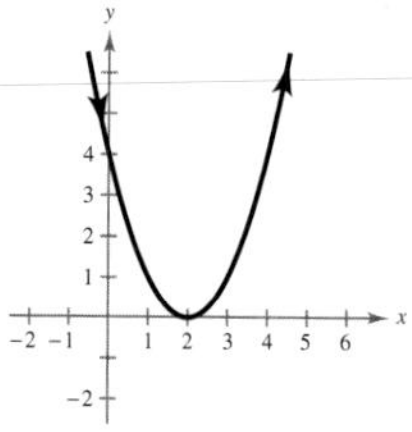

(b) $y = x^2 - 4x + 4$

13. (a)

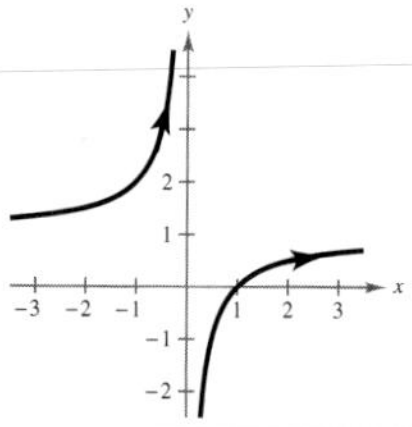

(b) $y = \dfrac{(x - 1)}{x}$

15. (a)

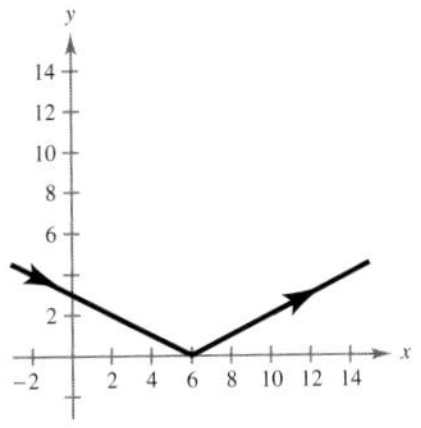

(b) $y = \left|\frac{x}{2} - 3\right|$

17. (a)

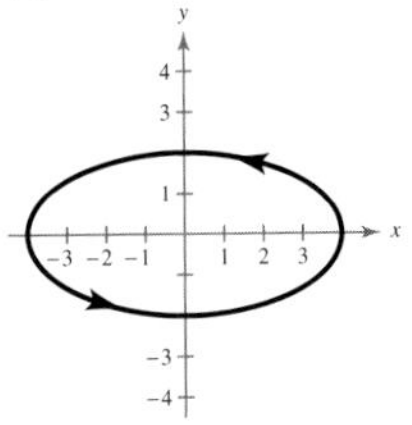

(b) $\frac{x^2}{16} + \frac{y^2}{4} = 1$

19. (a)

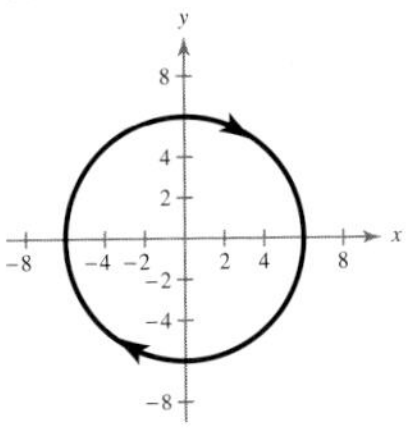

(b) $\frac{x^2}{36} + \frac{y^2}{36} = 1$

21. (a)

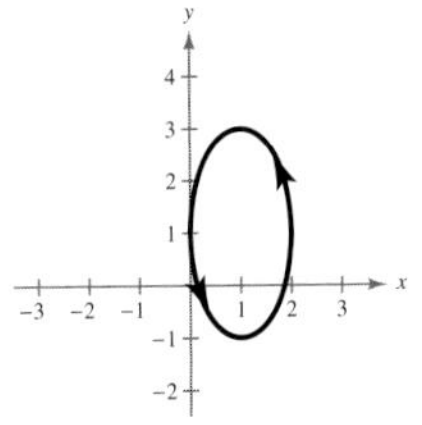

(b) $\frac{(x-1)^2}{1} + \frac{(y-1)^2}{4} = 1$

23. (a)

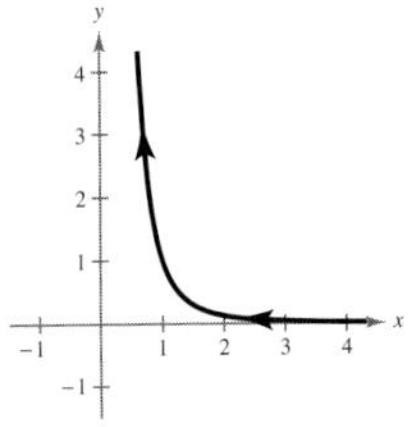

(b) $y = \frac{1}{x^3}, \quad x > 0$

25. (a)

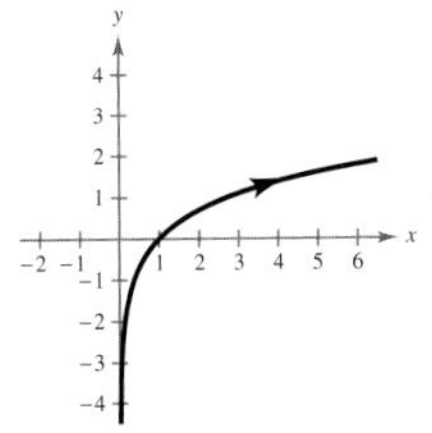

(b) $y = \ln x$

27. Each curve represents a portion of the line $y = 2x + 1$.

	Domain	*Orientation*
(a)	$(-\infty, \infty)$	Left to right
(b)	$[-1, 1]$	Depends on θ
(c)	$(0, \infty)$	Right to left
(d)	$(0, \infty)$	Left to right

29. $y - y_1 = m(x - x_1)$

31. $\frac{(x-h)^2}{a^2} + \frac{(y-k)^2}{b^2} = 1$

33. $x = 3t$
$y = 6t$

35. $x = 3 + 4\cos\theta$
$y = 2 + 4\sin\theta$

37. $x = 5\cos\theta$
$y = 3\sin\theta$

39. $x = 4\sec\theta$
$y = 3\tan\theta$

41. (a) $x = t,\ y = 3t - 2$ (b) $x = -t + 2,\ y = -3t + 4$

43. (a) $x = t, y = 2 - t$ (b) $x = -t + 2, y = t$

45. (a) $x = t, y = t^2 - 3$ (b) $x = 2 - t, y = t^2 - 4t + 1$

47. (a) $x = t, y = \frac{1}{t}$ (b) $x = -t + 2, y = -\frac{1}{t-2}$

49.

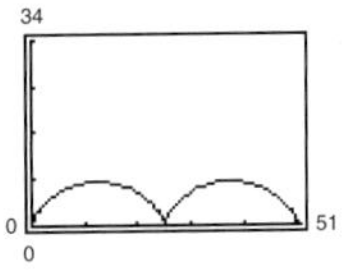

51.

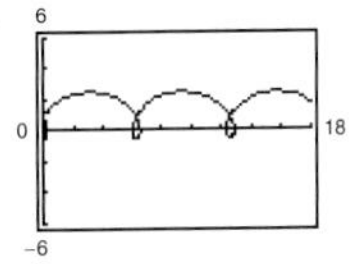

53.

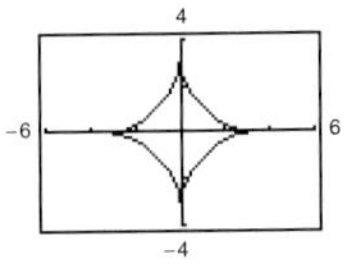

55.

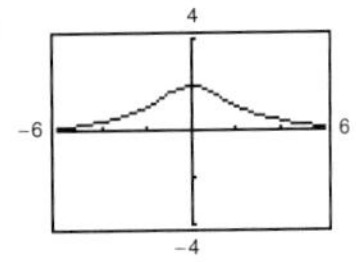

57. b
Domain: $[-2, 2]$
Range: $[-1, 1]$

58. c
Domain: $[-4, 4]$
Range: $[-6, 6]$

59. d
Domain: $(-\infty, \infty)$
Range: $(-\infty, \infty)$

60. a
Domain: $(-\infty, \infty)$
Range: $[-2, 2]$

61. (a)

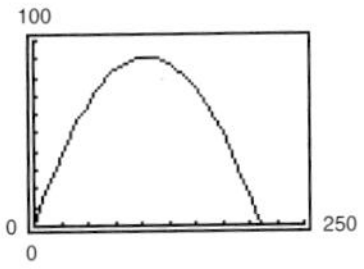

Maximum height: 90.7 ft
Range: 209.6 ft

(b)

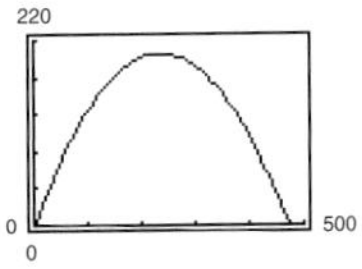

Maximum height: 204.2 ft
Range: 471.6 ft

(c)

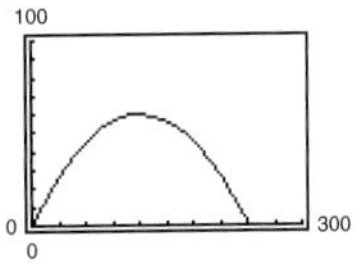

Maximum height: 60.5 ft
Range: 242.0 ft

(d)

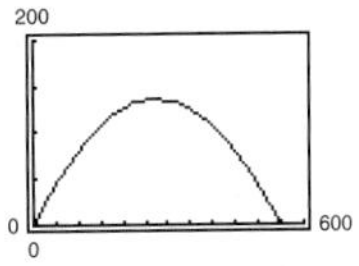

Maximum height: 136.1 ft
Range: 544.5 ft

63. (a) $x = (146.67\cos\theta)t$
$y = 3 + (146.67\sin\theta)t - 16t^2$

(b)

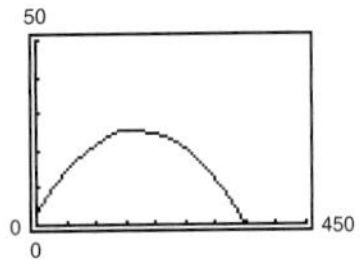

No

(c)

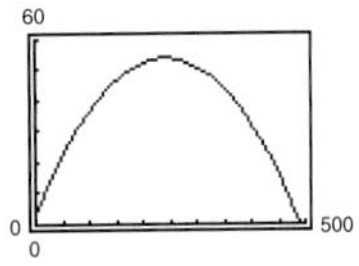

Yes

(d) 19.3°

65. Answers will vary.

CHAPTER 10

67. $x = a\theta - b \sin \theta$
$y = a - b \cos \theta$

69. True
$x = t$
$y = t^2 + 1 \Rightarrow y = x^2 + 1$
$x = 3t$
$y = 9t^2 + 1 \Rightarrow y = x^2 + 1$

71. Parametric equations are useful when graphing two functions simultaneously on the same coordinate system. For example, they are useful when tracking the path of an object so that the position and the time associated with that position can be determined.

73. $-1 < t < \infty$

Section 10.7 *(page 781)*

1. pole **3.** polar

5.

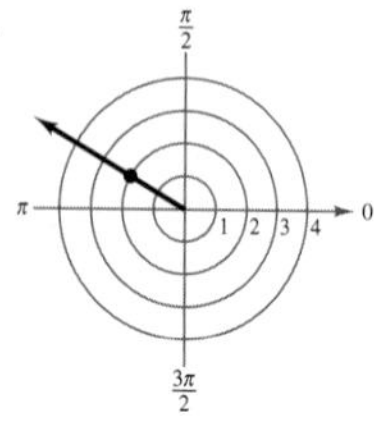

$\left(2, -\frac{7\pi}{6}\right), \left(-2, -\frac{\pi}{6}\right)$

7.

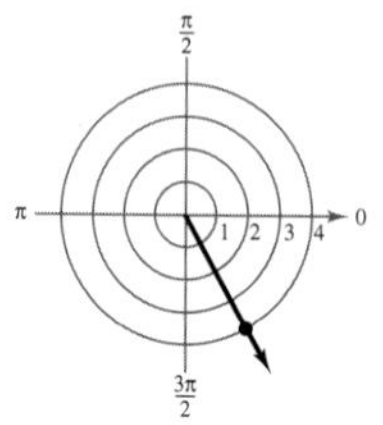

$\left(4, \frac{5\pi}{3}\right), \left(-4, -\frac{4\pi}{3}\right)$

9.

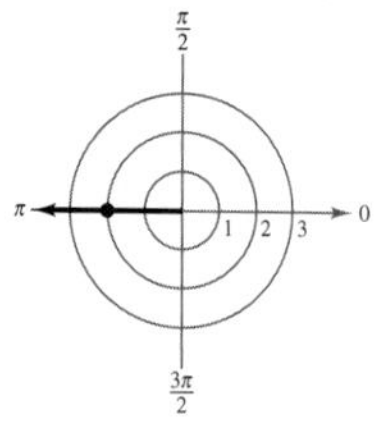

$(2, \pi), (-2, 0)$

11.

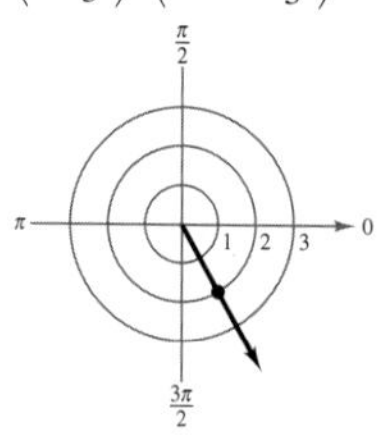

$\left(-2, -\frac{4\pi}{3}\right), \left(2, \frac{5\pi}{3}\right)$

13.

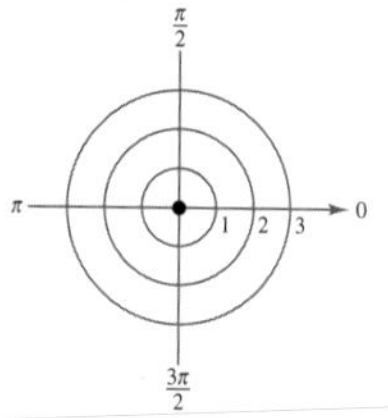

$\left(0, \frac{5\pi}{6}\right), \left(0, -\frac{\pi}{6}\right)$

15.

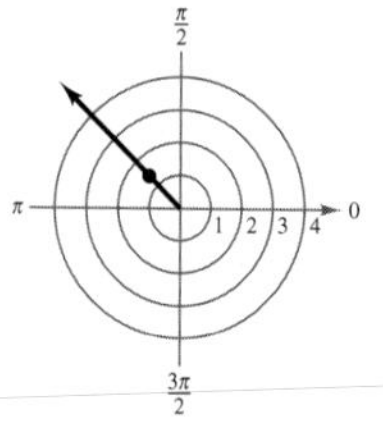

$\left(\sqrt{2}, -3.92\right), \left(-\sqrt{2}, -0.78\right)$

17.

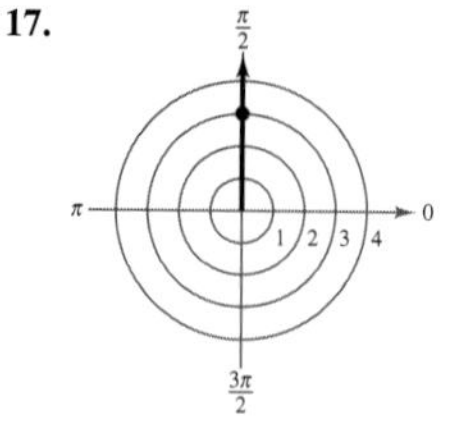

$(-3, 4.71), (3, 1.57)$

19. $(0, 3)$ **21.** $\left(\frac{\sqrt{2}}{2}, \frac{\sqrt{2}}{2}\right)$ **23.** $\left(-\sqrt{2}, \sqrt{2}\right)$

25. $\left(\sqrt{3}, 1\right)$ **27.** $(-1.1, -2.2)$ **29.** $(1.53, 1.29)$

31. $(-1.20, -4.34)$ **33.** $(-0.02, 2.50)$

35. $(-3.60, 1.97)$ **37.** $\left(\sqrt{2}, \frac{\pi}{4}\right)$ **39.** $\left(3\sqrt{2}, \frac{5\pi}{4}\right)$

41. $(6, \pi)$ **43.** $\left(5, \frac{3\pi}{2}\right)$ **45.** $(5, 2.21)$

47. $\left(\sqrt{6}, \frac{5\pi}{4}\right)$ **49.** $\left(2, \frac{11\pi}{6}\right)$ **51.** $\left(3\sqrt{13}, 0.98\right)$

53. $(13, 1.18)$ **55.** $\left(\sqrt{13}, 5.70\right)$ **57.** $\left(\sqrt{29}, 2.76\right)$

59. $\left(\sqrt{7}, 0.86\right)$ **61.** $\left(\frac{17}{6}, 0.49\right)$ **63.** $\left(\frac{\sqrt{85}}{4}, 0.71\right)$

65. $r = 3$ **67.** $r = 4 \csc \theta$ **69.** $r = 10 \sec \theta$

71. $r = -2 \csc \theta$ **73.** $r = \dfrac{-2}{3 \cos \theta - \sin \theta}$

75. $r^2 = 16 \sec \theta \csc \theta = 32 \csc 2\theta$

77. $r = \dfrac{4}{1 - \cos \theta}$ or $-\dfrac{4}{1 + \cos \theta}$ **79.** $r = a$

81. $r = 2a \cos \theta$ **83.** $r = \cot^2 \theta \csc \theta$

85. $x^2 + y^2 - 4y = 0$ **87.** $x^2 + y^2 + 2x = 0$

89. $\sqrt{3}x + y = 0$ **91.** $\frac{\sqrt{3}}{3}x + y = 0$

93. $x^2 + y^2 = 16$ **95.** $y = 4$ **97.** $x = -3$

99. $x^2 + y^2 - x^{2/3} = 0$ **101.** $(x^2 + y^2)^2 = 2xy$

103. $(x^2 + y^2)^2 = 6x^2y - 2y^3$ **105.** $x^2 + 4y - 4 = 0$

107. $4x^2 - 5y^2 - 36y - 36 = 0$

109. The graph of the polar equation consists of all points that are six units from the pole.
$x^2 + y^2 = 36$

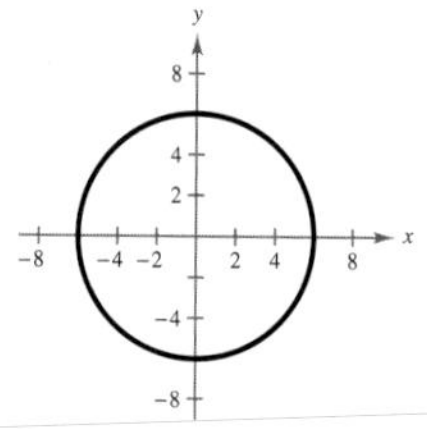

111. The graph of the polar equation consists of all points on the line that makes an angle of $\pi/6$ with the positive polar axis.
$-\sqrt{3}x + 3y = 0$

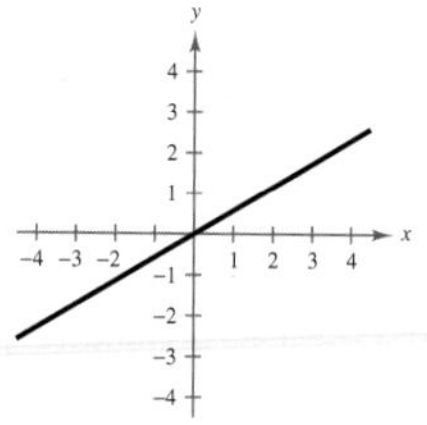

113. The graph of the polar equation is not evident by simple inspection, so convert to rectangular form.
$x^2 + (y - 1)^2 = 1$

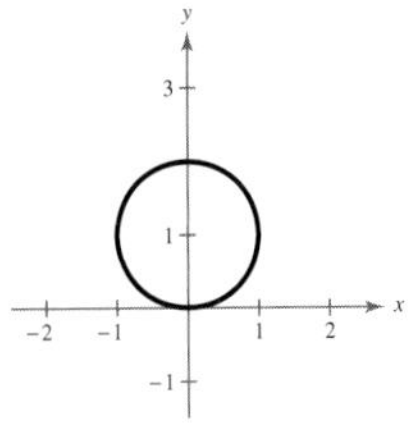

115. The graph of the polar equation is not evident by simple inspection, so convert to rectangular form.
$(x + 3)^2 + y^2 = 9$

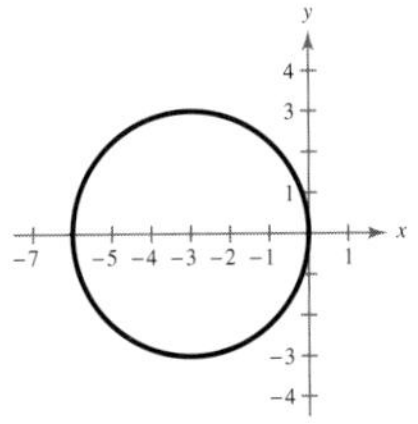

117. The graph of the polar equation is not evident by simple inspection, so convert to rectangular form.
$x - 3 = 0$

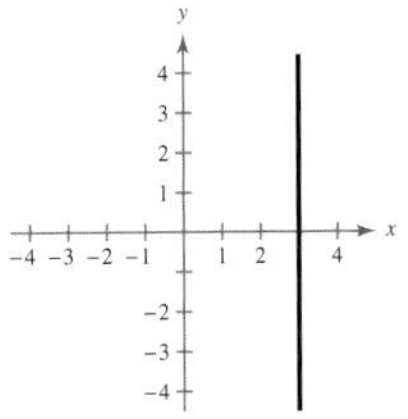

119. True. Because r is a directed distance, the point (r, θ) can be represented as $(r, \theta \pm 2\pi n)$.

121. $(x - h)^2 + (y - k)^2 = h^2 + k^2$
Radius: $\sqrt{h^2 + k^2}$
Center: (h, k)

123. (a) Answers will vary.
(b) (r_1, θ_1), (r_2, θ_2) and the pole are collinear.
$d = \sqrt{r_1^2 + r_2^2 - 2r_1r_2} = |r_1 - r_2|$
This represents the distance between two points on the line $\theta = \theta_1 = \theta_2$.
(c) $d = \sqrt{r_1^2 + r_2^2}$
This is the result of the Pythagorean Theorem.
(d) Answers will vary. For example:
Points: $(3, \pi/6)$, $(4, \pi/3)$
Distance: 2.053
Points: $(-3, 7\pi/6)$, $(-4, 4\pi/3)$
Distance: 2.053

125. (a)

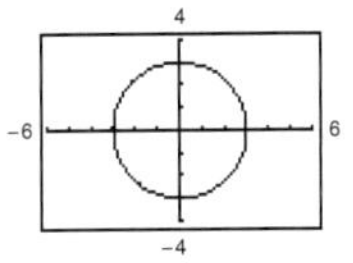

(b) Yes. $\theta \approx 3.927$, $x \approx -2.121$, $y \approx -2.121$
(c) Yes. Answers will vary.

Section 10.8 *(page 789)*

1. $\theta = \dfrac{\pi}{2}$ **3.** convex limaçon **5.** lemniscate

7. Rose curve with 4 petals **9.** Limaçon with inner loop

11. Rose curve with 3 petals **13.** Polar axis

15. $\theta = \dfrac{\pi}{2}$ **17.** $\theta = \dfrac{\pi}{2}$, polar axis, pole

19. Maximum: $|r| = 20$ when $\theta = \dfrac{3\pi}{2}$

Zero: $r = 0$ when $\theta = \dfrac{\pi}{2}$

21. Maximum: $|r| = 4$ when $\theta = 0, \dfrac{\pi}{3}, \dfrac{2\pi}{3}$

Zeros: $r = 0$ when $\theta = \dfrac{\pi}{6}, \dfrac{\pi}{2}, \dfrac{5\pi}{6}$

23.

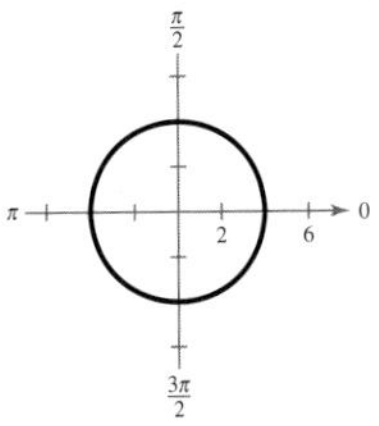

25.

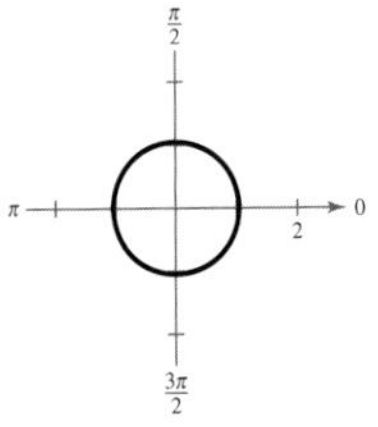

27.

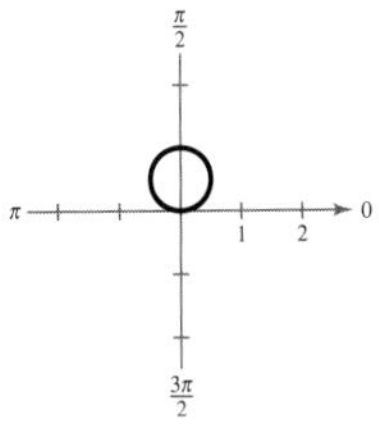

29.

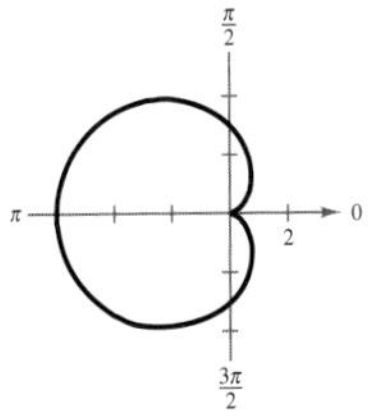

31.

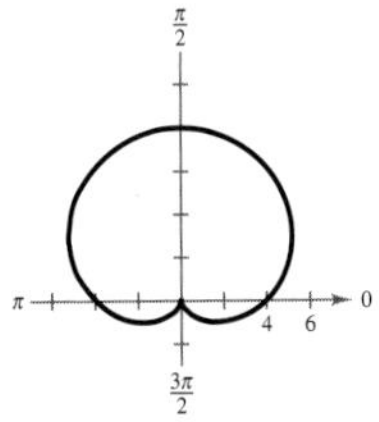

33.

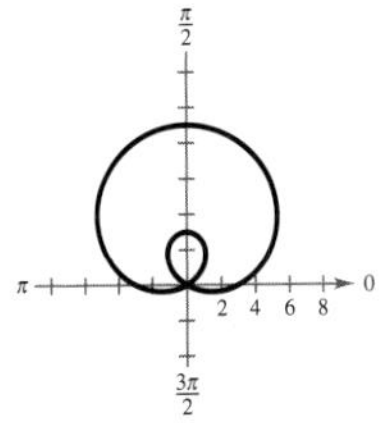

35.

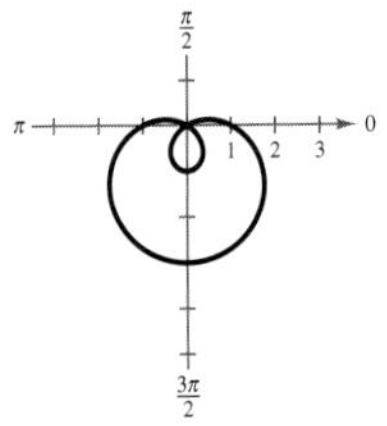

37.

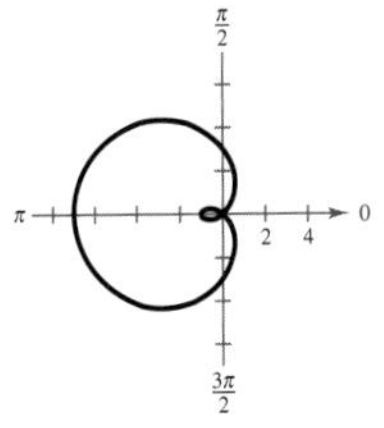

39.
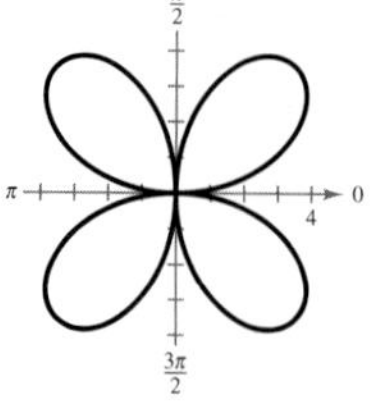

41.
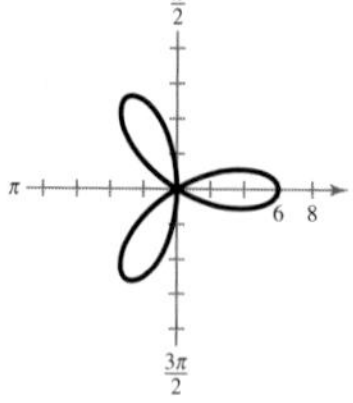

43.
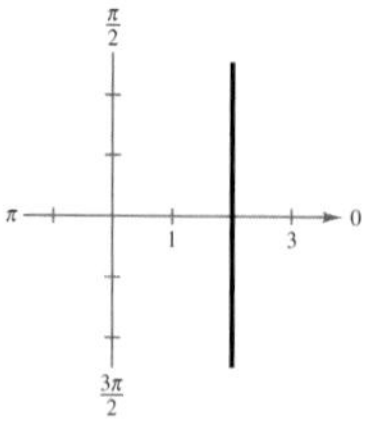

45.
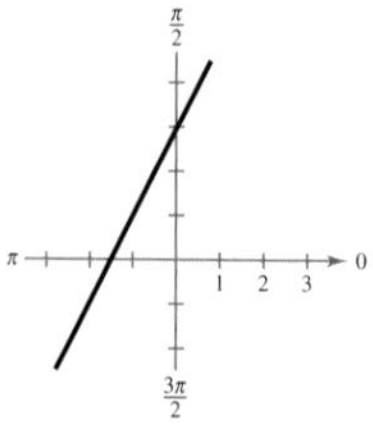

47.
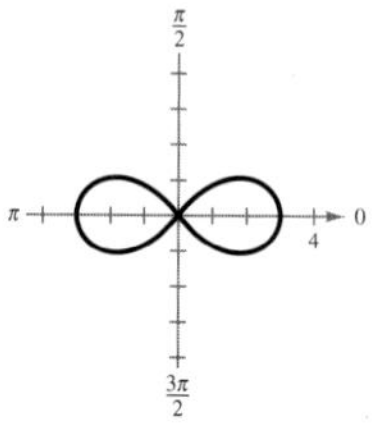

49.
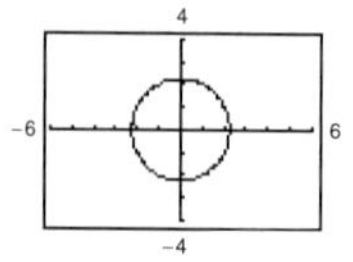

51.
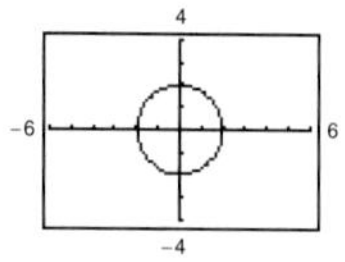

53.
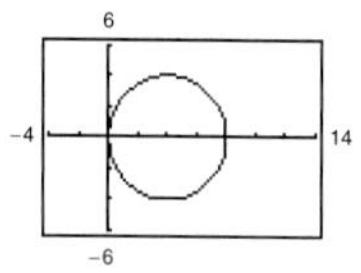

55.
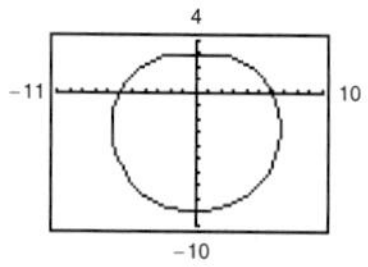

57.
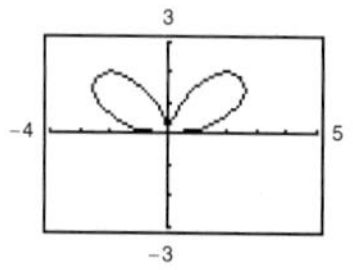

59.
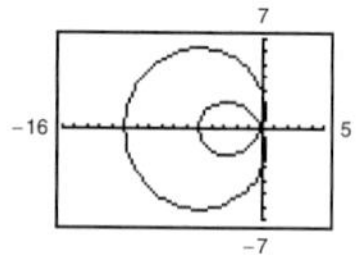

$0 \le \theta < 2\pi$

61.
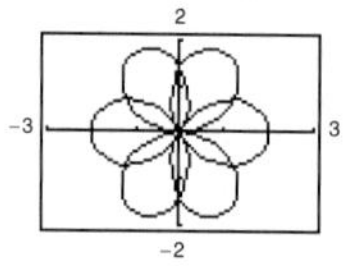

$0 \le \theta < 4\pi$

63.
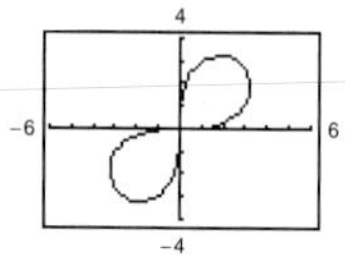

$0 \le \theta < \pi/2$

65.
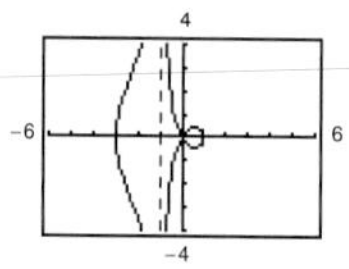

67.
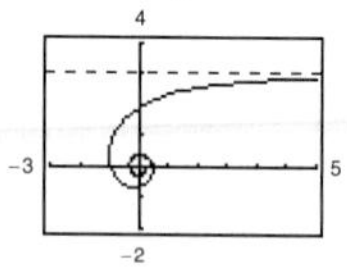

69. True. For a graph to have polar axis symmetry, replace (r, θ) by $(r, -\theta)$ or $(-r, \pi - \theta)$.

71. (a)
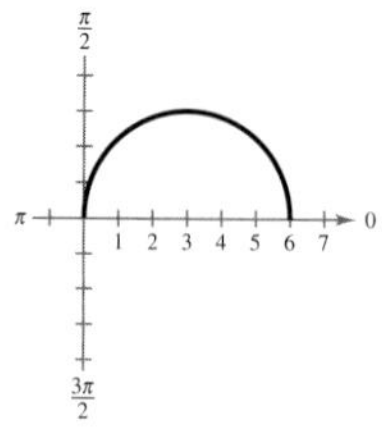

Upper half of circle

(b)
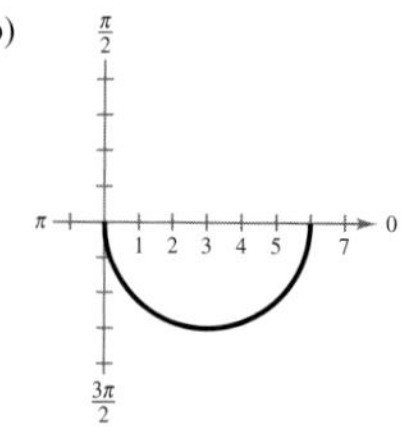

Lower half of circle

(c)
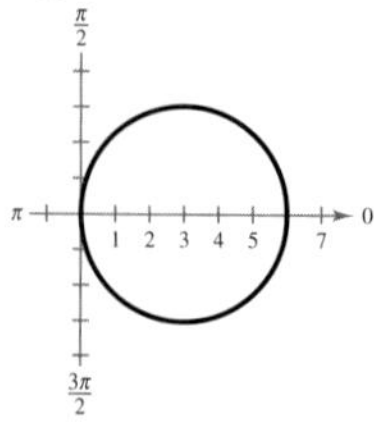

Full circle

(d)
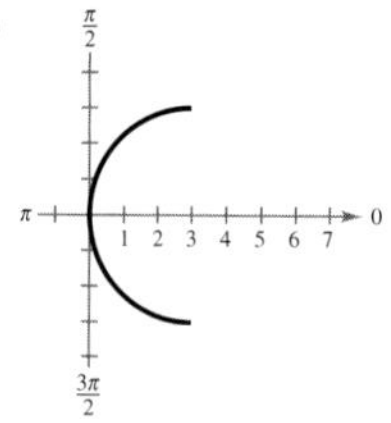

Left half of circle

73. Answers will vary.

75. (a) $r = 2 - \frac{\sqrt{2}}{2}(\sin\theta - \cos\theta)$ (b) $r = 2 + \cos\theta$

(c) $r = 2 + \sin\theta$ (d) $r = 2 - \cos\theta$

77. (a)
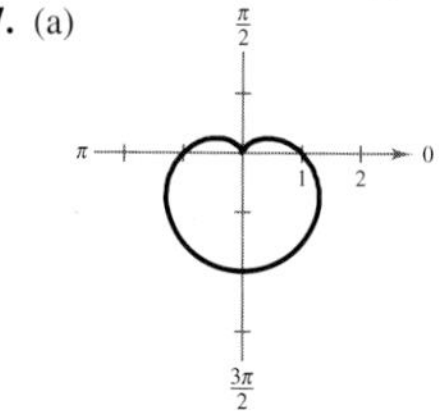

(b)
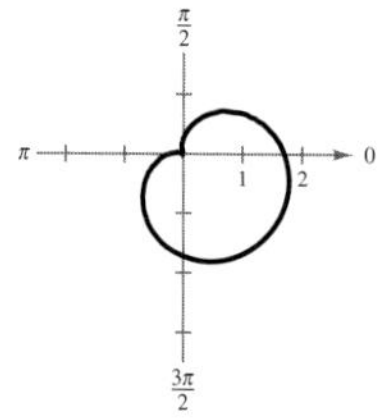

79. 8 petals; 3 petals; For $r = 2\cos n\theta$ and $r = 2\sin n\theta$, there are n petals if n is odd, $2n$ petals if n is even.

81. (a)
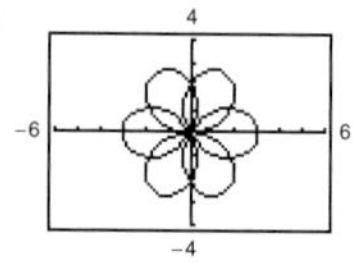

$0 \le \theta < 4\pi$

(b)
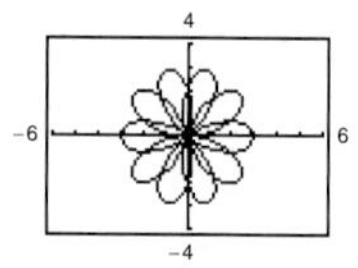

$0 \le \theta < 4\pi$

(c) Yes. Explanations will vary.

Section 10.9 *(page 795)*

1. conic **3.** vertical; right

5. $e = 1$: $r = \dfrac{2}{1 + \cos\theta}$, parabola

$e = 0.5$: $r = \dfrac{1}{1 + 0.5\cos\theta}$, ellipse

$e = 1.5$: $r = \dfrac{3}{1 + 1.5\cos\theta}$, hyperbola

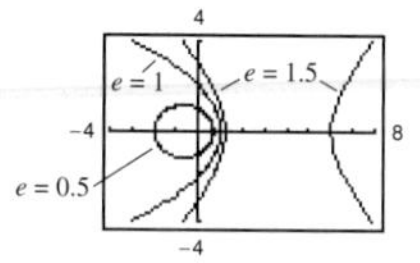

7. $e = 1$: $r = \dfrac{2}{1 - \sin\theta}$, parabola

$e = 0.5$: $r = \dfrac{1}{1 - 0.5\sin\theta}$, ellipse

$e = 1.5$: $r = \dfrac{3}{1 - 1.5\sin\theta}$, hyperbola

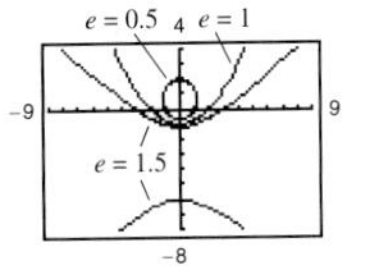

9. e **10.** c **11.** d **12.** f **13.** a **14.** b

15. Parabola

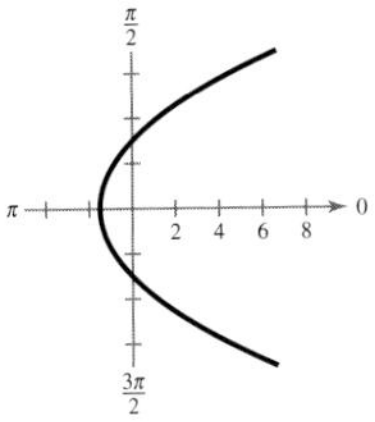

17. Parabola

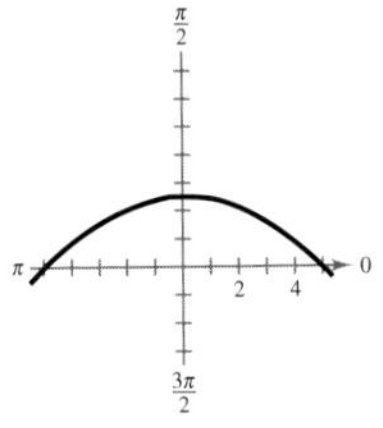

19. Ellipse

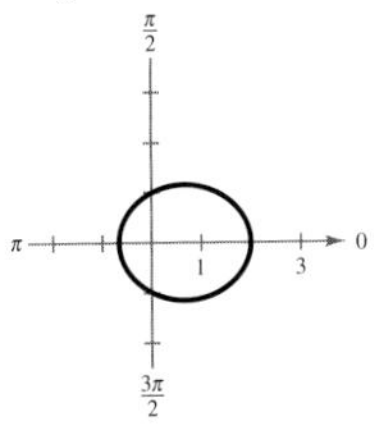

21. Ellipse

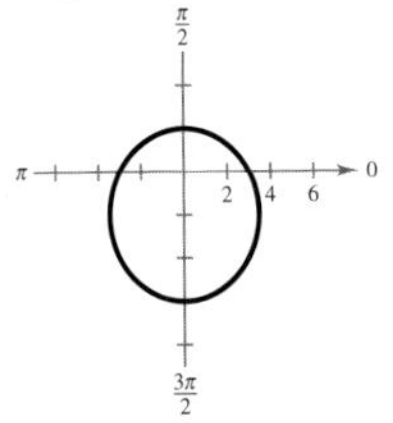

23. Hyperbola

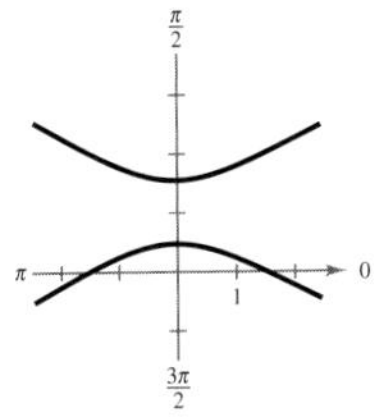

25. Hyperbola

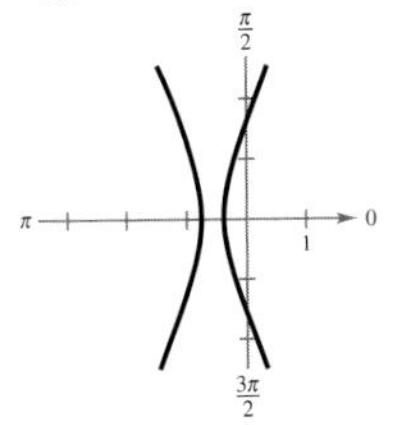

27. Ellipse

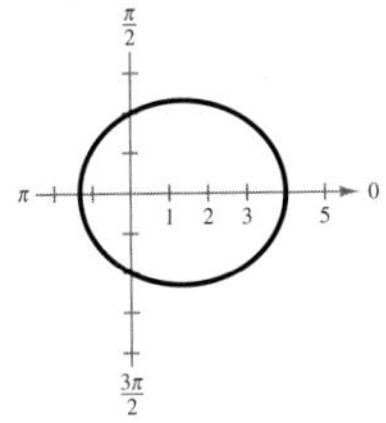

29.

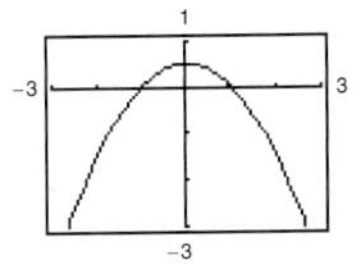

Parabola

31.

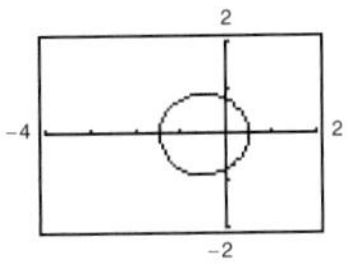

Ellipse

33.

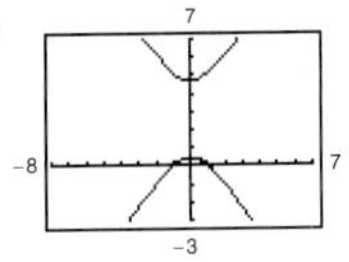

Hyperbola

35.

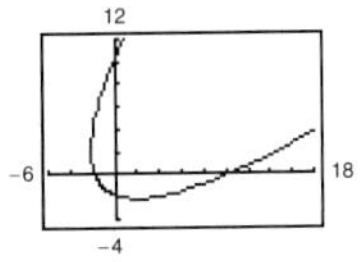

37.

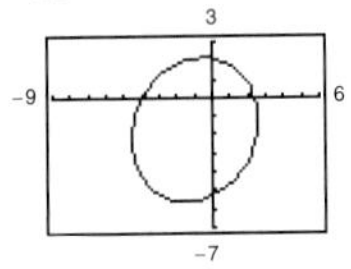

39. $r = \dfrac{1}{1 - \cos\theta}$ **41.** $r = \dfrac{1}{2 + \sin\theta}$

43. $r = \dfrac{2}{1 + 2\cos\theta}$ **45.** $r = \dfrac{2}{1 - \sin\theta}$

47. $r = \dfrac{10}{1 - \cos\theta}$ **49.** $r = \dfrac{10}{3 + 2\cos\theta}$

51. $r = \dfrac{20}{3 - 2\cos\theta}$ **53.** $r = \dfrac{9}{4 - 5\sin\theta}$

55. Answers will vary.

57. $r = \dfrac{9.5929 \times 10^7}{1 - 0.0167\cos\theta}$

Perihelion: 9.4354×10^7 mi

Aphelion: 9.7558×10^7 mi

59. $r = \dfrac{1.0820 \times 10^8}{1 - 0.0068\cos\theta}$

Perihelion: 1.0747×10^8 km

Aphelion: 1.0894×10^8 km

61. $r = \dfrac{1.4039 \times 10^8}{1 - 0.0934\cos\theta}$

Perihelion: 1.2840×10^8 mi

Aphelion: 1.5486×10^8 mi

63. $r = \dfrac{0.624}{1 + 0.847\sin\theta}$; $r \approx 0.338$ astronomical unit

65. (a) $r = \dfrac{8200}{1 + \sin\theta}$

(b)

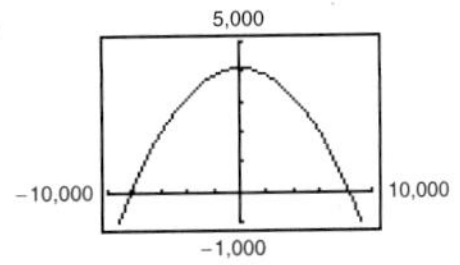

(c) 1467 mi (d) 394 mi

67. True. The graphs represent the same hyperbola.

69. True. The conic is an ellipse because the eccentricity is less than 1.

71. The original equation graphs as a parabola that opens downward.

(a) The parabola opens to the right.

(b) The parabola opens up.

(c) The parabola opens to the left.

(d) The parabola has been rotated.

73. Answers will vary.

75. $r^2 = \dfrac{24{,}336}{169 - 25\cos^2\theta}$ **77.** $r^2 = \dfrac{144}{25\cos^2\theta - 9}$

CHAPTER 10

79. $r^2 = \dfrac{144}{25\cos^2\theta - 16}$

81. (a) Ellipse

(b) The given polar equation, r, has a vertical directrix to the left of the pole. The equation r_1 has a vertical directrix to the right of the pole, and the equation r_2 has a horizontal directrix below the pole.

(c)

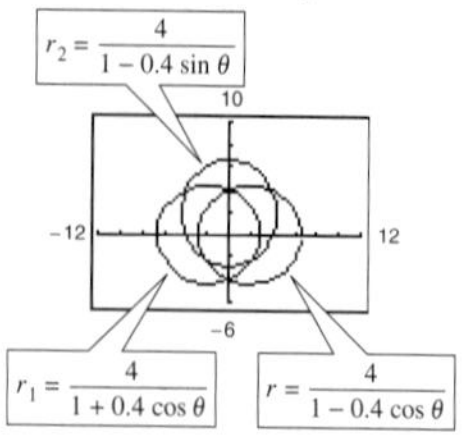

Review Exercises *(page 800)*

1. $\dfrac{\pi}{4}$ rad, 45° **3.** 1.1071 rad, 63.43°

5. 0.4424 rad, 25.35° **7.** 0.6588 rad, 37.75°

9. $4\sqrt{2}$ **11.** Hyperbola

13. $y^2 = 16x$

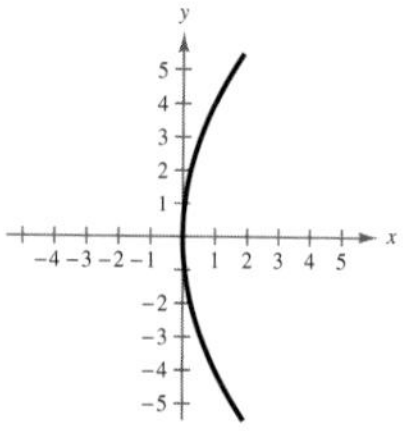

15. $(y - 2)^2 = 12x$

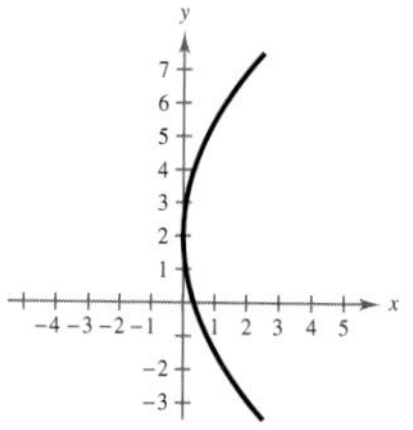

17. $y = -4x - 2;\ \left(-\frac{1}{2}, 0\right)$ **19.** $8\sqrt{6}$ m

21. $\dfrac{(x-3)^2}{25} + \dfrac{y^2}{16} = 1$

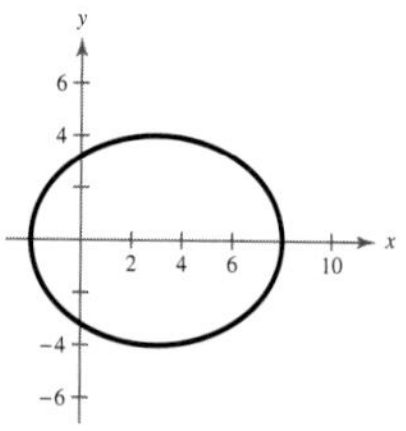

23. $\dfrac{(x-2)^2}{4} + \dfrac{(y-1)^2}{1} = 1$

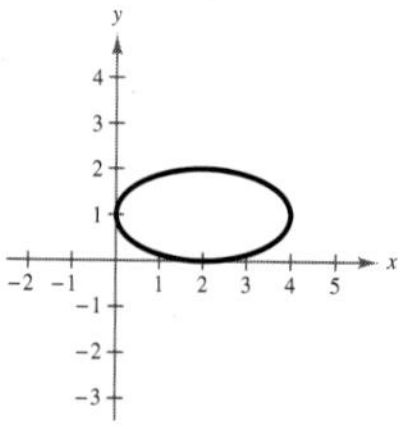

25. The foci occur 3 feet from the center of the arch on a line connecting the tops of the pillars.

27. Center: $(-1, 2)$
Vertices: $(-1, 9), (-1, -5)$
Foci: $\left(-1, 2 \pm 2\sqrt{6}\right)$
Eccentricity: $\dfrac{2\sqrt{6}}{7}$

29. Center: $(1, -4)$
Vertices: $(1, 0), (1, -8)$
Foci: $\left(1, -4 \pm \sqrt{7}\right)$
Eccentricity: $\dfrac{\sqrt{7}}{4}$

31. $\dfrac{y^2}{1} - \dfrac{x^2}{3} = 1$ **33.** $\dfrac{5(x-4)^2}{16} - \dfrac{5y^2}{64} = 1$

35. Center: $(5, -3)$
Vertices: $(11, -3), (-1, -3)$
Foci: $\left(5 \pm 2\sqrt{13}, -3\right)$
Asymptotes:
$y = -3 \pm \frac{2}{3}(x - 5)$

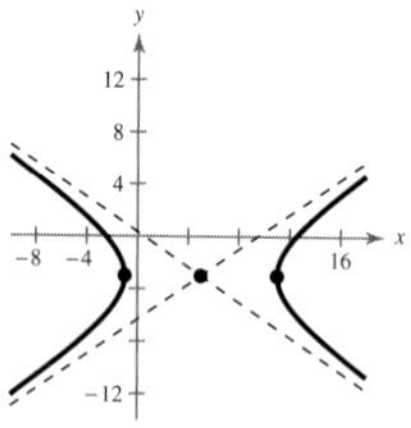

37. Center: $(1, -1)$
Vertices: $(5, -1), (-3, -1)$
Foci: $(6, -1), (-4, -1)$
Asymptotes:
$y = -1 \pm \frac{3}{4}(x - 1)$

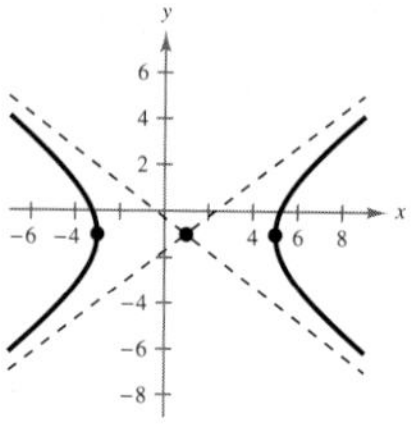

39. 72 mi **41.** Hyperbola **43.** Ellipse

45. $\dfrac{(y')^2}{6} - \dfrac{(x')^2}{6} = 1$

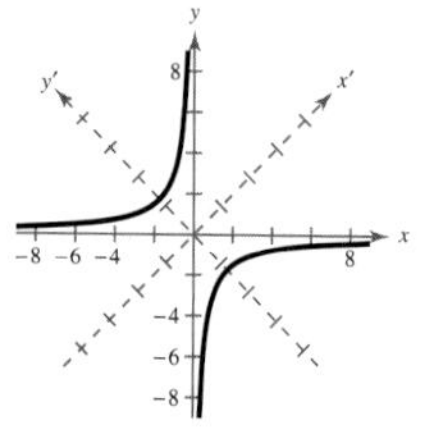

47. $\dfrac{(x')^2}{3} + \dfrac{(y')^2}{2} = 1$

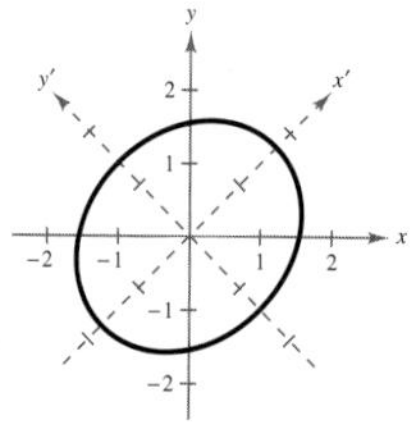

49. (a) Parabola

(b) $y = \dfrac{24x + 40 \pm \sqrt{(24x + 40)^2 - 36(16x^2 - 30x)}}{18}$

(c)

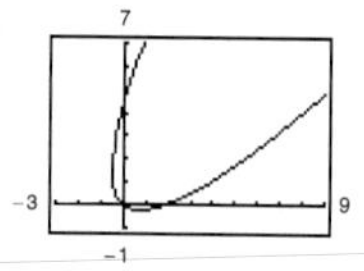

51. (a) Parabola

(b) $y = \dfrac{-\left(2x - 2\sqrt{2}\right) \pm \sqrt{\left(2x - 2\sqrt{2}\right)^2 - 4\left(x^2 + 2\sqrt{2}x + 2\right)}}{2}$

(c)

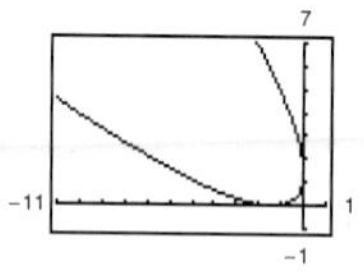

53. (a)

t	-2	-1	0	1	2
x	-8	-5	-2	1	4
y	15	11	7	3	-1

(b)

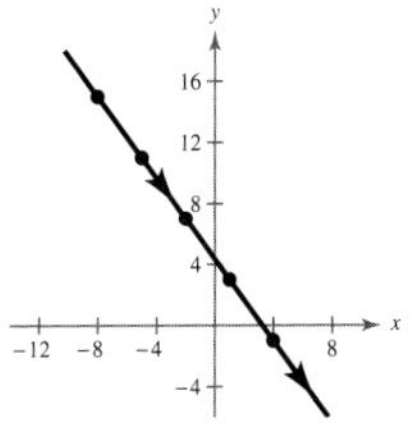

55. (a)

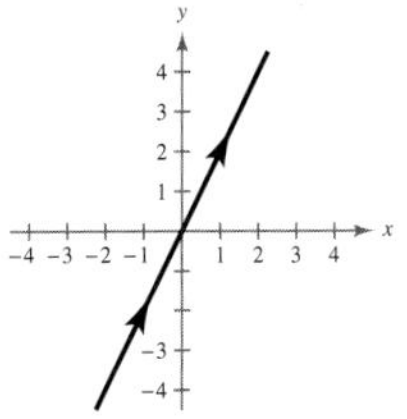

(b) $y = 2x$

57. (a)

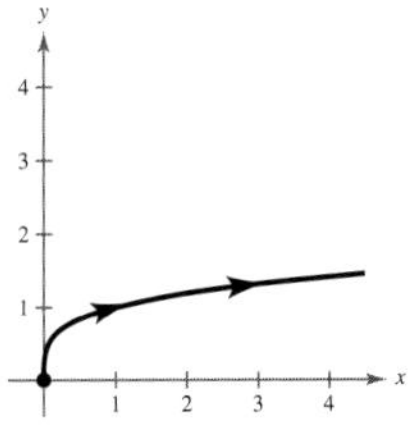

(b) $y = \sqrt[4]{x}$

59. (a)

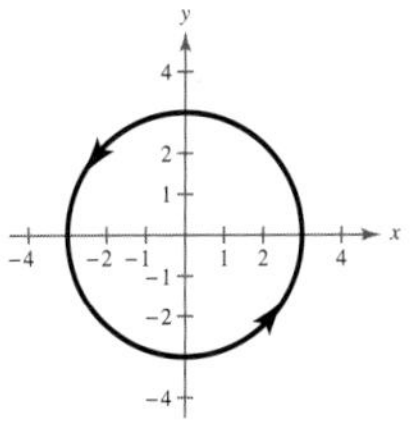

(b) $x^2 + y^2 = 9$

61. $x = -4 + 13t$
$y = 4 - 14t$

63. $x = -3 + 4\cos\theta$
$y = 4 + 3\sin\theta$

65.

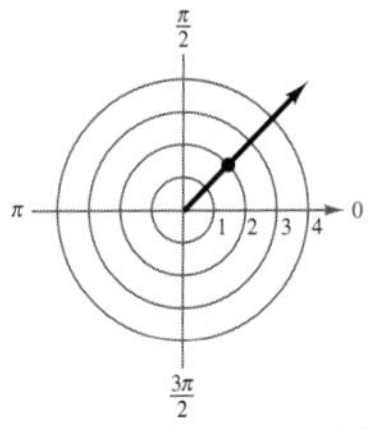

$(2, -7\pi/4), (-2, 5\pi/4)$

67.

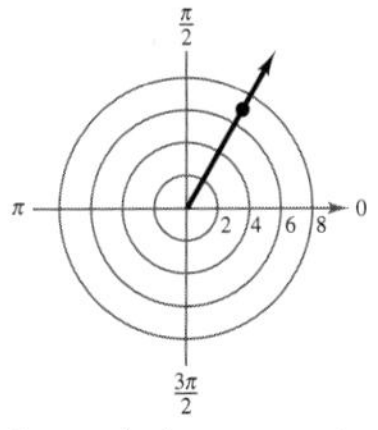

$(7, 1.05), (-7, -2.09)$

69. $\left(-\frac{1}{2}, -\frac{\sqrt{3}}{2}\right)$ **71.** $\left(-\frac{3\sqrt{2}}{2}, \frac{3\sqrt{2}}{2}\right)$ **73.** $\left(1, \frac{\pi}{2}\right)$

75. $\left(2\sqrt{13}, 0.9828\right)$ **77.** $r = 9$ **79.** $r = 6\sin\theta$

81. $r^2 = 10\csc 2\theta$ **83.** $x^2 + y^2 = 25$ **85.** $x^2 + y^2 = 3x$

87. $x^2 + y^2 = y^{2/3}$

89. Symmetry: $\theta = \frac{\pi}{2}$, polar axis, pole
Maximum value of $|r|$:
$|r| = 6$ for all values of θ
No zeros of r

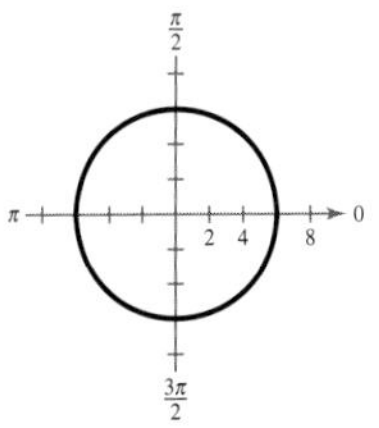

91. Symmetry: $\theta = \frac{\pi}{2}$, polar axis, pole
Maximum value of $|r|$: $|r| = 4$ when $\theta = \frac{\pi}{4}, \frac{3\pi}{4}, \frac{5\pi}{4}, \frac{7\pi}{4}$
Zeros of r: $r = 0$ when
$\theta = 0, \frac{\pi}{2}, \pi, \frac{3\pi}{2}$

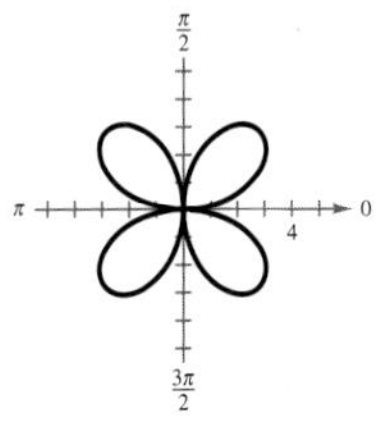

93. Symmetry: polar axis
Maximum value of $|r|$:
$|r| = 4$ when $\theta = 0$
Zeros of r: $r = 0$
when $\theta = \pi$

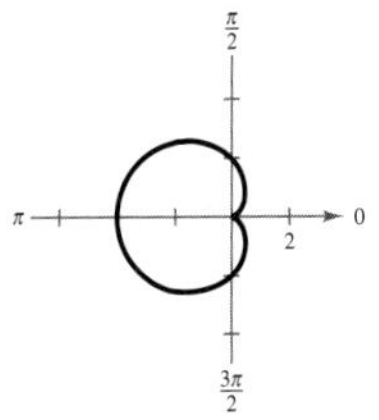

95. Symmetry: $\theta = \frac{\pi}{2}$
Maximum value of $|r|$: $|r| = 8$ when $\theta = \frac{\pi}{2}$
Zeros of r: $r = 0$ when $\theta = 3.4814, 5.9433$

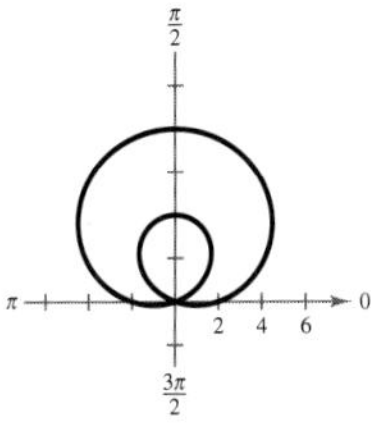

97. Symmetry: $\theta = \frac{\pi}{2}$, polar axis, pole

Maximum value of $|r|$: $|r| = 3$ when $\theta = 0, \frac{\pi}{2}, \pi, \frac{3\pi}{2}$

Zeros of r: $r = 0$ when $\theta = \frac{\pi}{4}, \frac{3\pi}{4}, \frac{5\pi}{4}, \frac{7\pi}{4}$

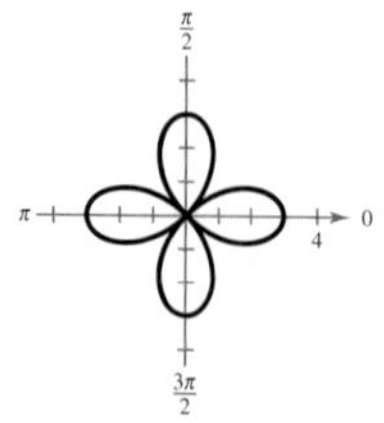

99. Limaçon

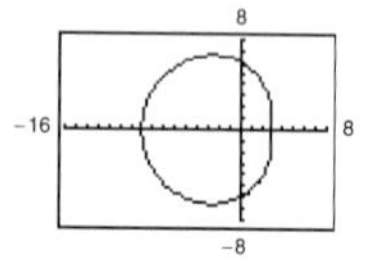

101. Rose curve

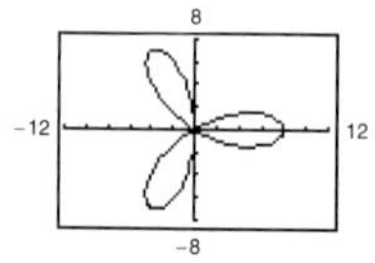

103. Hyperbola

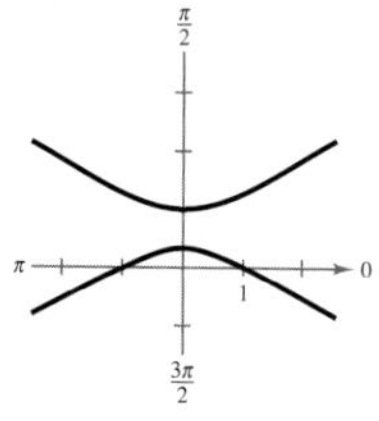

105. Ellipse

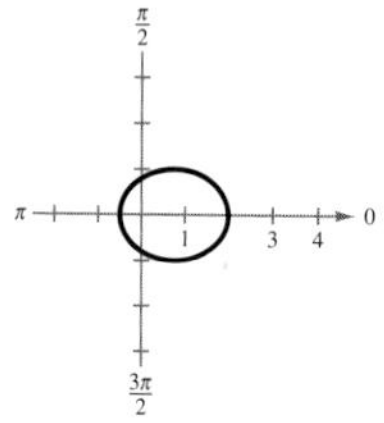

107. $r = \dfrac{4}{1 - \cos\theta}$ **109.** $r = \dfrac{5}{3 - 2\cos\theta}$

111. $r = \dfrac{7978.81}{1 - 0.937\cos\theta}$; 11,011.87 mi

113. False. The equation of a hyperbola is a second-degree equation.

115. False. $(2, \pi/4)$, $(-2, 5\pi/4)$, and $(2, 9\pi/4)$ all represent the same point.

117. (a) The graphs are the same. (b) The graphs are the same.

Chapter Test *(page 803)*

1. 0.3805 rad, 21.8° **2.** 0.8330 rad, 47.7°

3. $\dfrac{7\sqrt{2}}{2}$

4. Parabola: $y^2 = 2(x - 1)$
Vertex: $(1, 0)$
Focus: $\left(\frac{3}{2}, 0\right)$

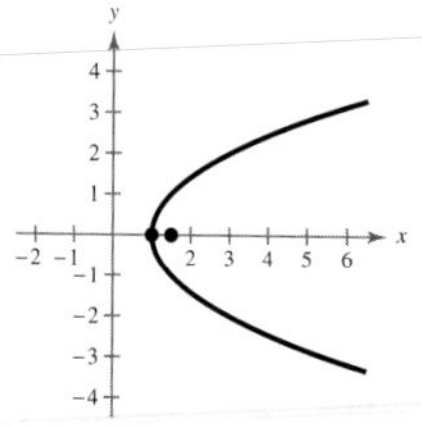

5. Hyperbola: $\dfrac{(x-2)^2}{4} - y^2 = 1$
Center: $(2, 0)$
Vertices: $(0, 0), (4, 0)$
Foci: $\left(2 \pm \sqrt{5}, 0\right)$
Asymptotes: $y = \pm\frac{1}{2}(x - 2)$

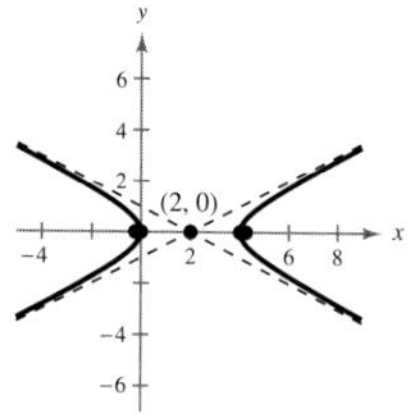

6. Ellipse: $\dfrac{(x+3)^2}{16} + \dfrac{(y-1)^2}{9} = 1$
Center: $(-3, 1)$
Vertices: $(1, 1), (-7, 1)$
Foci: $\left(-3 \pm \sqrt{7}, 1\right)$

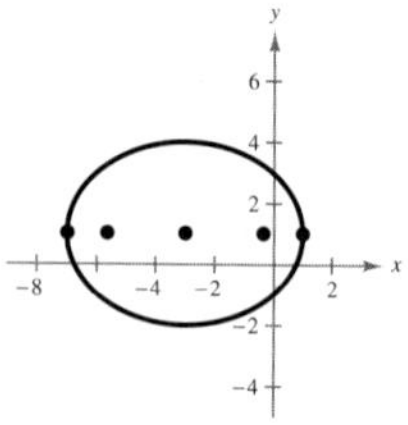

7. Circle: $(x - 2)^2 + (y - 1)^2 = \frac{1}{2}$
Center: $(2, 1)$

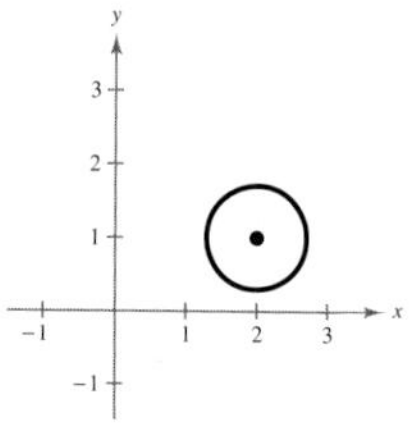

8. $(x - 2)^2 = \frac{4}{3}(y + 3)$ **9.** $\dfrac{5(y-2)^2}{4} - \dfrac{5x^2}{16} = 1$

10. (a) 45°
(b)

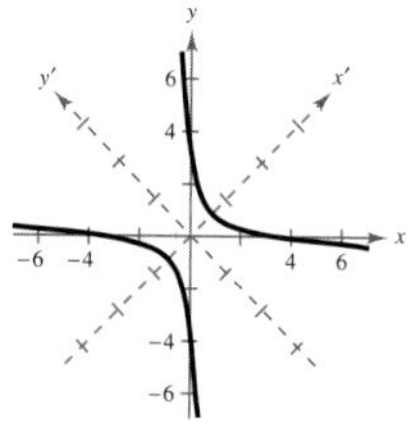

11.

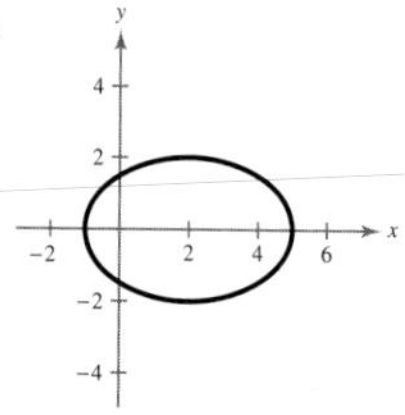

$\dfrac{(x-2)^2}{9} + \dfrac{y^2}{4} = 1$

12. $x = 6 + 4t$
$y = 4 + 7t$

13. $\left(\sqrt{3}, -1\right)$ **14.** $\left(2\sqrt{2}, \frac{7\pi}{4}\right), \left(-2\sqrt{2}, \frac{3\pi}{4}\right), \left(2\sqrt{2}, -\frac{\pi}{4}\right)$

15. $r = 3\cos\theta$

16.

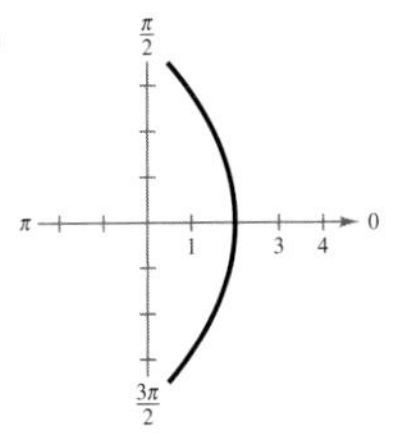

Parabola

17.

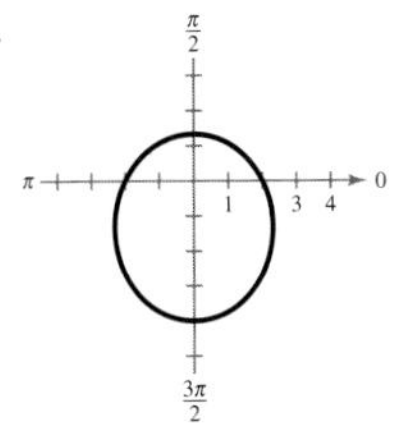

Ellipse

18.

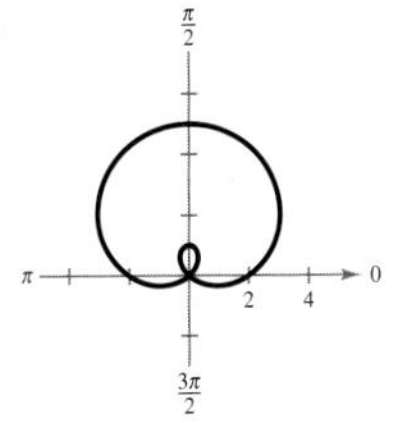

Limaçon with inner loop

19.

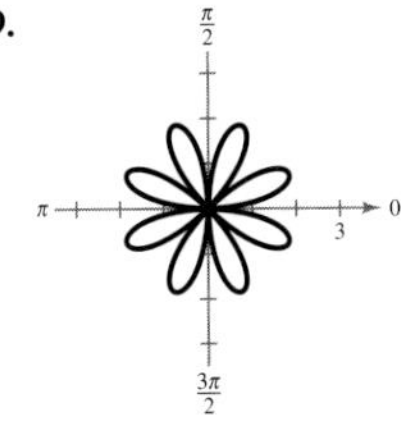

Rose curve

20. Answers will vary. For example: $r = \dfrac{1}{1 + 0.25 \sin \theta}$

21. Slope: 0.1511; Change in elevation: 789 ft

22. No; Yes

Problem Solving *(page 807)*

1. (a) 1.2016 rad (b) 2420 ft, 5971 ft

3. $y^2 = 4p(x + p)$ **5.** Answers will vary.

7. $\dfrac{(x-6)^2}{9} - \dfrac{(y-2)^2}{7} = 1$

9. (a) The first set of parametric equations models projectile motion along a straight line. The second set of parametric equations models projectile motion of an object launched at a height of h units above the ground that will eventually fall back to the ground.

(b) $y = (\tan \theta)x$; $y = h + x \tan \theta - \dfrac{16x^2 \sec^2 \theta}{v_0^2}$

(c) In the first case, the path of the moving object is not affected by a change in the velocity because eliminating the parameter removes v_0.

11. (a)

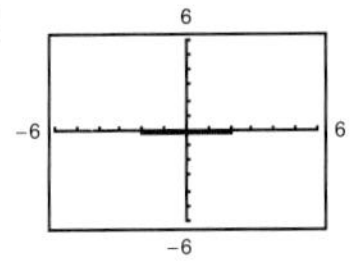

The graph is a line between -2 and 2 on the x-axis.

(b)

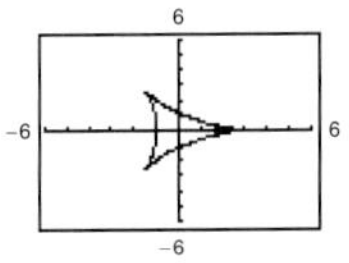

The graph is a three-sided figure with counterclockwise orientation.

(c)

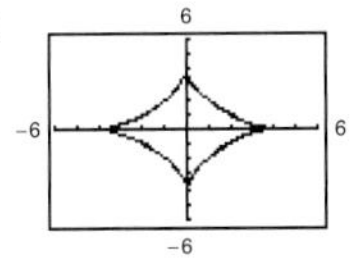

The graph is a four-sided figure with counterclockwise orientation.

(d)

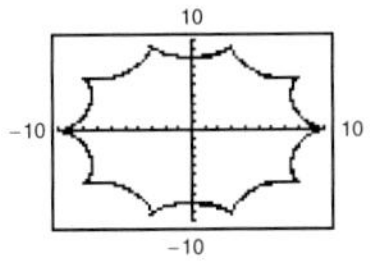

The graph is a 10-sided figure with counterclockwise orientation.

(e)

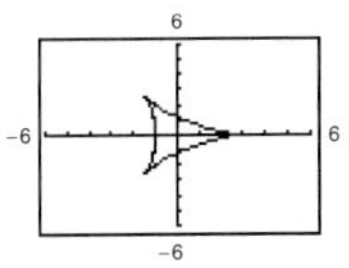

The graph is a three-sided figure with clockwise orientation.

(f)

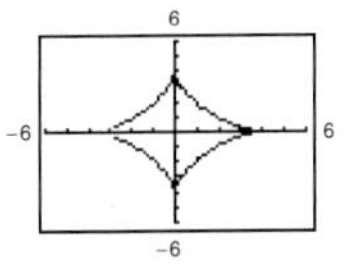

The graph is a four-sided figure with clockwise orientation.

13.

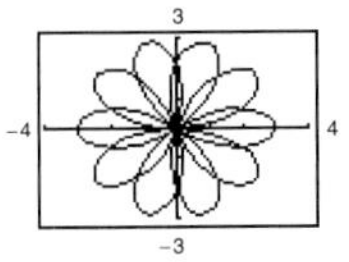

$r = 3 \sin\left(\dfrac{5\theta}{2}\right)$

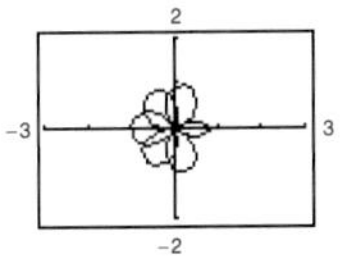

$r = -\cos(\sqrt{2}\theta)$, $-2\pi \le \theta \le 2\pi$

Sample answer: If n is a rational number, then the curve has a finite number of petals. If n is an irrational number, then the curve has an infinite number of petals.

15. (a) No. Because of the exponential, the graph will continue to trace the butterfly curve at larger values of r.

(b) $r \approx 4.1$. This value will increase if θ is increased.

17. (a) $r_{\text{Neptune}} = \dfrac{4.4947 \times 10^9}{1 - 0.0086 \cos \theta}$

$r_{\text{Pluto}} = \dfrac{5.54 \times 10^9}{1 - 0.2488 \cos \theta}$

(b) Neptune: Aphelion $= 4.534 \times 10^9$ km
Perihelion $= 4.456 \times 10^9$ km

Pluto: Aphelion $= 7.375 \times 10^9$ km
Perihelion $= 4.437 \times 10^9$ km

(c)

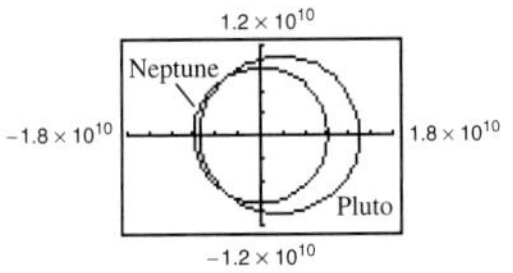

(d) Yes, at times Pluto can be closer to the sun than Neptune. Pluto was called the ninth planet because it has the longest orbit around the sun and therefore also reaches the furthest distance away from the sun.

(e) If the orbits were in the same plane, then they would intersect. Furthermore, since the orbital periods differ (Neptune = 164.79 years, Pluto = 247.68 years), then the two planets would ultimately collide if the orbits intersect. The orbital inclination of Pluto is significantly larger than that of Neptune (17.16° vs. 1.769°), so further analysis is required to determine if the orbits intersect.

CHAPTER 10

Chapter 11

Section 11.1 (page 815)

1. three-dimensional **3.** octants

5. $\left(\frac{x_1 + x_2}{2}, \frac{y_1 + y_2}{2}, \frac{z_1 + z_2}{2}\right)$ **7.** surface; space

9. A: $(-1, 4, 4)$, B: $(1, 3, -2)$, C: $(-3, 0, -2)$

11.

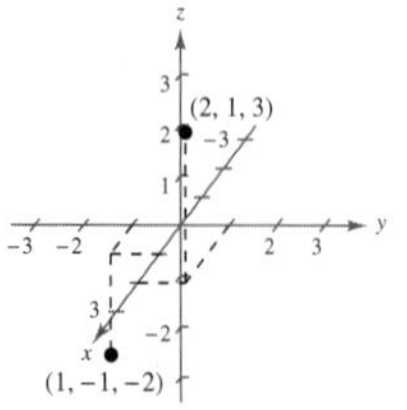

13.

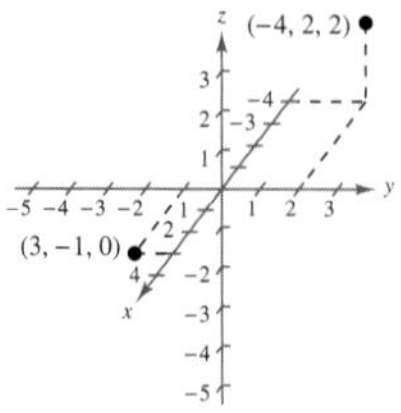

15.

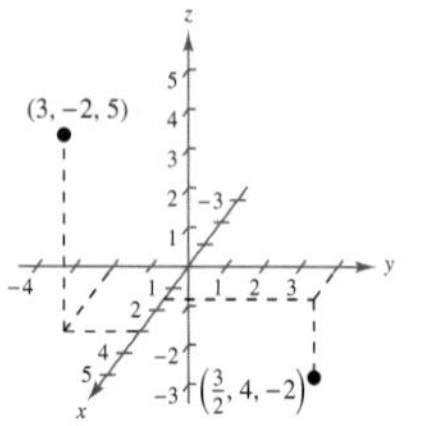

17. $(-3, 4, 5)$ **19.** $(8, 0, 0)$ **21.** Octant IV

23. Octants I, II, III, and IV **25.** Octants II, IV, VI, and VII

27. $\sqrt{65}$ units **29.** $\sqrt{29}$ units **31.** $\sqrt{114}$ units

33. $\sqrt{110}$ units **35.** 12 units

37. $(2\sqrt{5})^2 + 3^2 = (\sqrt{29})^2$ **39.** $3^2 + 6^2 = (3\sqrt{5})^2$

41. $6, 6, 2\sqrt{10}$; isosceles triangle

43. $6, 6, 2\sqrt{10}$; isosceles triangle

45. $\left(\frac{3}{2}, -1, 2\right)$ **47.** $(0, -1, 7)$ **49.** $\left(\frac{1}{2}, \frac{1}{2}, -1\right)$

51. $\left(\frac{5}{2}, 2, 6\right)$ **53.** $(x - 3)^2 + (y - 2)^2 + (z - 4)^2 = 16$

55. $(x - 5)^2 + y^2 + (z + 2)^2 = 36$

57. $(x + 3)^2 + (y - 7)^2 + (z - 5)^2 = 25$

59. $\left(x - \frac{3}{2}\right)^2 + y^2 + (z - 3)^2 = \frac{45}{4}$

61. Center: $(3, 0, 0)$; radius: 3

63. Center: $(2, -1, 3)$; radius: 2

65. Center: $(-2, 0, 4)$; radius: 1

67. Center: $\left(1, \frac{1}{3}, 4\right)$; radius: 3

69. Center: $\left(\frac{1}{3}, -1, 0\right)$; radius: 1

71.

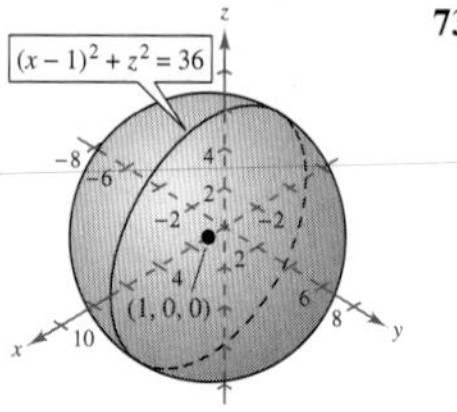

73.

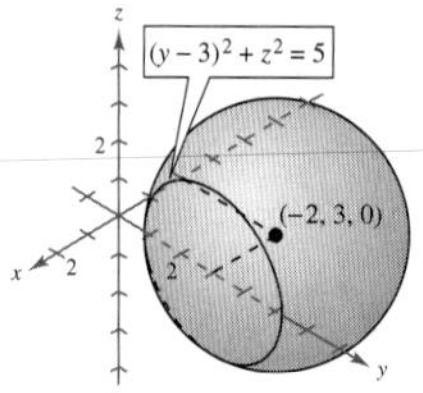

75.

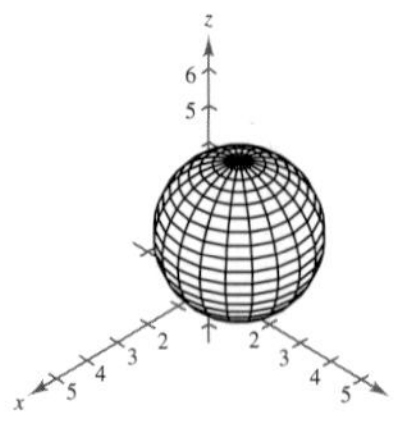

77. $x^2 + y^2 + z^2 = \frac{205^2}{4}$

79. False. z is the directed distance from the xy-plane to P.

81. 0; 0; 0

83. A point or a circle (where the sphere and the yz-plane meet)

85. $(x_2, y_2, z_2) = (2x_m - x_1, 2y_m - y_1, 2z_m - z_1)$

Section 11.2 (page 822)

1. zero **3.** component form **5.** parallel

7. (a) $\langle -2, 3, 1 \rangle$

(b)

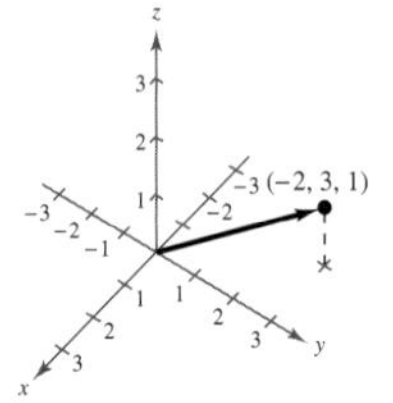

9. (a) $\langle 7, -5, 5 \rangle$ (b) $3\sqrt{11}$ (c) $\frac{\sqrt{11}}{33}\langle 7, -5, 5 \rangle$

11. (a)

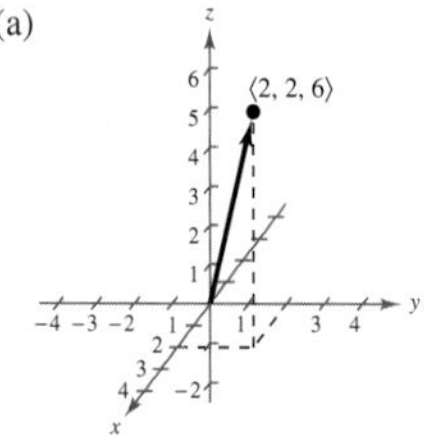

(b)

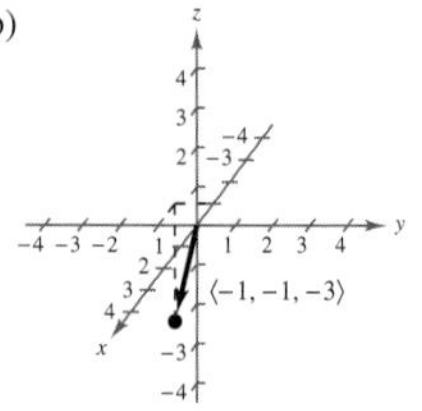

(c)

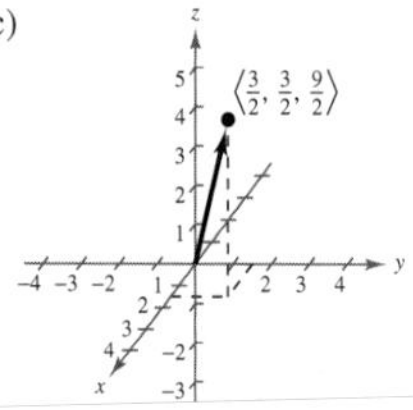

(d)

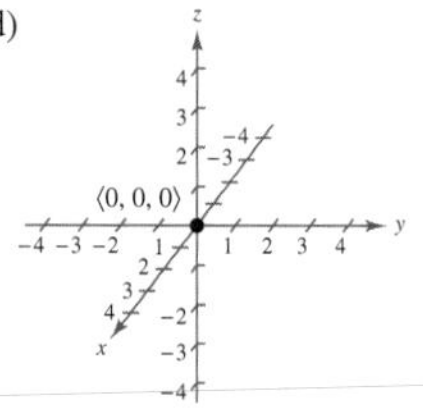

13. (a)

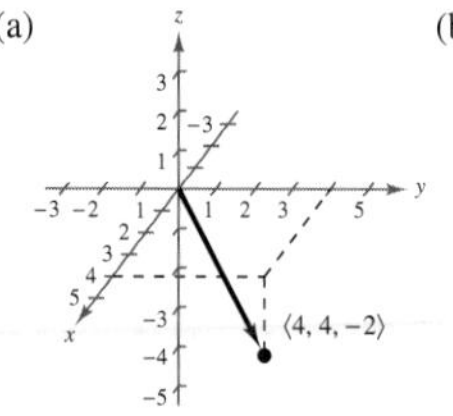

(b)

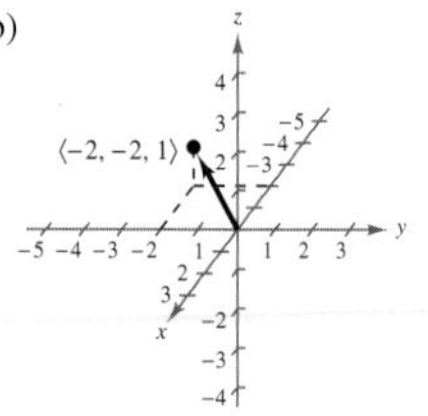

(c)

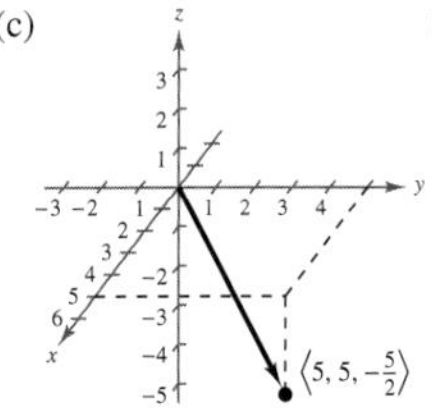

(d)

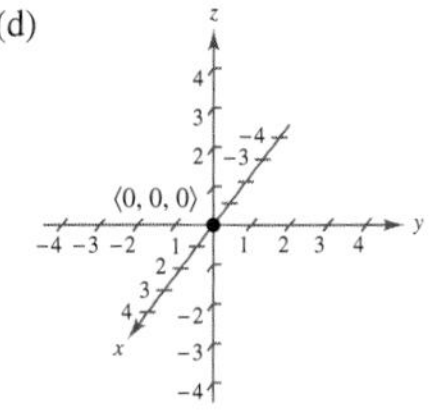

15. $\mathbf{z} = \langle -3, 7, 6\rangle$ **17.** $\mathbf{z} = \left\langle \frac{1}{2}, 6, \frac{3}{2}\right\rangle$ **19.** $9\sqrt{2}$
21. $\sqrt{21}$ **23.** $\sqrt{11}$ **25.** $\sqrt{74}$ **27.** $\sqrt{34}$
29. (a) $\frac{\sqrt{74}}{74}(8\mathbf{i} + 3\mathbf{j} - \mathbf{k})$ (b) $-\frac{\sqrt{74}}{74}(8\mathbf{i} + 3\mathbf{j} - \mathbf{k})$
31. -4 **33.** 0 **35.** About 124.45° **37.** About 109.92°
39. Parallel **41.** Neither **43.** Orthogonal
45. Orthogonal **47.** Not collinear **49.** Collinear
51. (3, 1, 7) **53.** $\left(6, \frac{5}{2}, -\frac{7}{4}\right)$ **55.** $\pm\frac{3\sqrt{14}}{14}$
57. $\langle 0, 2\sqrt{2}, 2\sqrt{2}\rangle$ or $\langle 0, 2\sqrt{2}, -2\sqrt{2}\rangle$
59. *B:* 226.52 N, *C:* 202.92 N, *D:* 157.91 N
61. True **63.** The angle between **u** and **v** is an obtuse angle.

Section 11.3 *(page 829)*

1. cross product **3.** $\|\mathbf{u}\|\,\|\mathbf{v}\|\sin\theta$
5. $-\mathbf{k}$

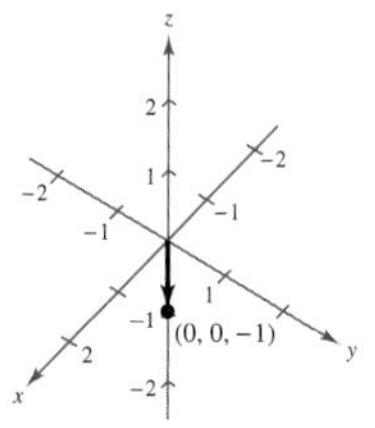

7. $-\mathbf{j}$

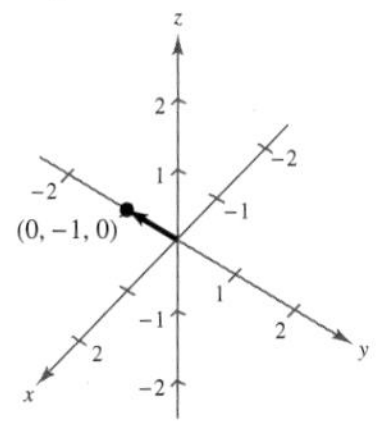

9. $\mathbf{i}$

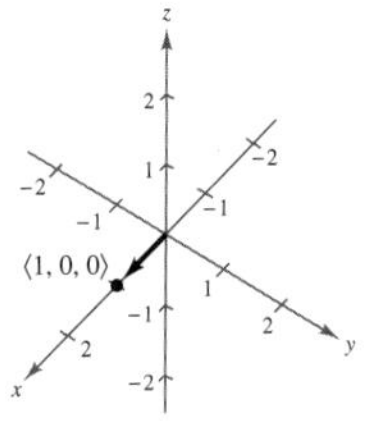

11. $-7\mathbf{i} + 11\mathbf{j} + 8\mathbf{k}$ **13.** $\mathbf{0}$ **15.** $-21\mathbf{i} + 33\mathbf{j} + 24\mathbf{k}$
17. $7\mathbf{i} - 11\mathbf{j} - 8\mathbf{k}$ **19.** 0 **21.** $\langle 1, -2, -2\rangle$
23. $\langle 0, 42, 0\rangle$ **25.** $-7\mathbf{i} + 13\mathbf{j} + 16\mathbf{k}$ **27.** $-18\mathbf{i} - 6\mathbf{j}$
29. $-\mathbf{i} - 2\mathbf{j} - \mathbf{k}$ **31.** $\frac{\sqrt{19}}{19}(\mathbf{i} - 3\mathbf{j} + 3\mathbf{k})$
33. $\frac{\sqrt{7602}}{7602}(-71\mathbf{i} - 44\mathbf{j} + 25\mathbf{k})$ **35.** $\frac{\sqrt{2}}{2}(\mathbf{i} - \mathbf{j})$
37. 1 **39.** $30\sqrt{3}$ **41.** 56
43. (a) $\overrightarrow{AB} = \langle 1, 2, -2\rangle$ and is parallel to $\overrightarrow{DC} = \langle 1, 2, -2\rangle$.
$\overrightarrow{AD} = \langle -3, 4, 4\rangle$ and is parallel to $\overrightarrow{BC} = \langle -3, 4, 4\rangle$.
(b) Area is $\|\overrightarrow{AB} \times \overrightarrow{AD}\| = 6\sqrt{10}$.
(c) The dot product is not 0 and therefore the parallelogram is not a rectangle.
45. (a) $\overrightarrow{AB} = \langle -5, 0, -2\rangle$ and is parallel to $\overrightarrow{CD} = \langle -5, 0, -2\rangle$.
$\overrightarrow{AC} = \langle 0, 3, -1\rangle$ and is parallel to $\overrightarrow{BD} = \langle 0, 3, -1\rangle$.
(b) Area is $\|\overrightarrow{AB} \times \overrightarrow{DB}\| = \sqrt{286}$.
(c) The dot product is not 0 and therefore the parallelogram is not a rectangle.
47. $\frac{3\sqrt{13}}{2}$ **49.** $\frac{1}{2}\sqrt{4290}$
51. 6 **53.** 2 **55.** 2 **57.** 12 **59.** 84
61. (a) $T = \frac{p}{2}\cos 40°$
(b)

p	15	20	25	30	35	40	45
T	5.75	7.66	9.58	11.49	13.41	15.32	17.24

63. True. The cross product is not defined for two-dimensional vectors.
65. $\mathbf{u} \times \mathbf{v} = -(\mathbf{v} \times \mathbf{u})$; Answers will vary.
67. Yes. The area of the triangle is $\frac{1}{2}\|\mathbf{u} \times \mathbf{v}\|$. **69.** Proof

Section 11.4 *(page 838)*

1. direction; $\frac{\overrightarrow{PQ}}{t}$ **3.** symmetric equations
5. (a) $x = t,\ y = 2t,\ z = 3t$ (b) $x = \frac{y}{2} = \frac{z}{3}$
7. (a) $x = -4 + 3t,\ y = 1 + 8t,\ z = -6t$
(b) $\frac{x + 4}{3} = \frac{y - 1}{8} = \frac{z}{-6}$
9. (a) $x = 2 + 2t,\ y = -3 - 3t,\ z = 5 + t$
(b) $\frac{x - 2}{2} = \frac{y + 3}{-3} = z - 5$
11. (a) $x = 2 - t,\ y = 4t,\ z = 2 - 5t$
(b) $\frac{x - 2}{-1} = \frac{y}{4} = \frac{z - 2}{-5}$
13. (a) $x = -3 + 4t,\ y = 8 - 10t,\ z = 15 + t$
(b) $\frac{x + 3}{4} = \frac{y - 8}{-10} = z - 15$
15. (a) $x = 3 - 4t, y = 1, z = 2 + 3t$
(b) No symmetric equations
17. (a) $x = -\frac{1}{2} + 3t, y = 2 - 5t, z = \frac{1}{2} - t$
(b) $\frac{2x + 1}{6} = \frac{y - 2}{-5} = \frac{2z - 1}{-2}$
19.

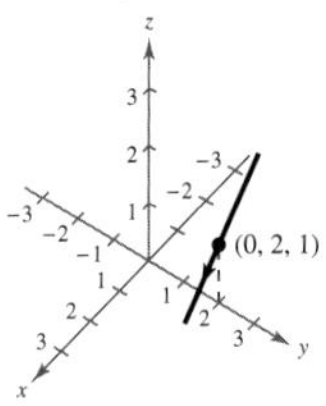

21. $x - 2 = 0$ **23.** $-2x + y - 2z + 10 = 0$

25. $-x - 2y + z + 2 = 0$ **27.** $-3x - 9y + 7z = 0$

29. $6x - 2y - z - 8 = 0$ **31.** $y - 5 = 0$

33. $y - z + 2 = 0$ **35.** $7x + y - 11z - 5 = 0$

37. Orthogonal **39.** Orthogonal

41. $x = 2$, $y = 3$, $z = 4 + t$ **43.** $x = 2 + 3t$, $y = 3 + 2t$, $z = 4 - t$ **45.** $x = 5 + 2t$, $y = -3 - t$, $z = -4 + 3t$

47. (a) 60.7° (b) $x = -t + 2,\ y = 8t,\ z = 7t$

49. (a) 77.8° (b) $x = 6t + 1,\ y = t,\ z = 7t + 1$

51.

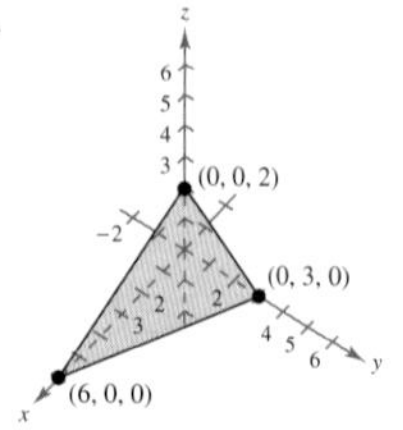

53.

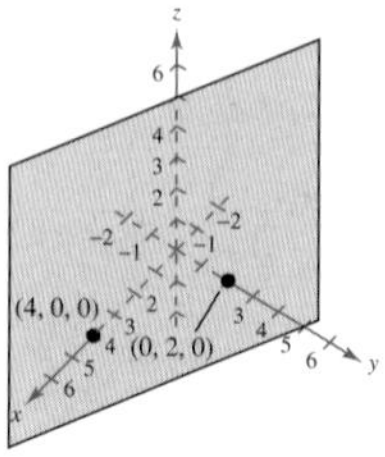

55.

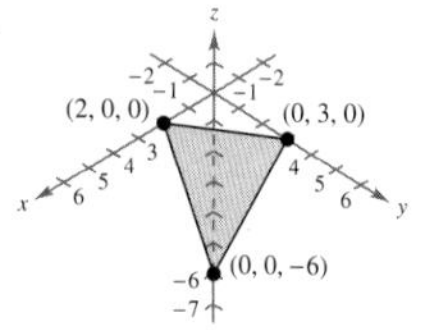

57. $\frac{8}{9}$ **59.** $\frac{4}{\sqrt{6}} = \frac{2\sqrt{6}}{3}$

61. (a)

Year	Model
2006	3.90
2007	3.81
2008	3.54
2009	3.42
2010	3.29

(b) The approximations are very similar to the actual values of z.

(c) Answers will vary.

63. False. Lines that do not intersect and are not in the same plane may not be parallel.

65. Parallel. $\langle 10, -18, 20\rangle$ is a scalar multiple of $\langle -15, 27, -30\rangle$.

67. (a) Sphere: $(x - 4)^2 + (y + 1)^2 + (z - 1)^2 = 4$

(b) Two planes: $4x - 3y + z = 10 \pm 2\sqrt{26}$

Review Exercises *(page 842)*

1.

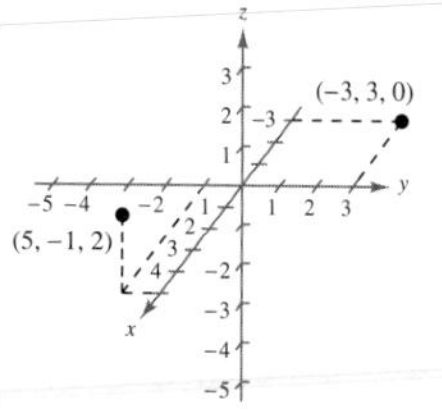

3. $(-5, 4, 0)$ **5.** $\sqrt{41}$ **7.** 10

9. $\sqrt{29}, \sqrt{38}, \sqrt{67}$

$\left(\sqrt{29}\right)^2 + \left(\sqrt{38}\right)^2 = \left(\sqrt{67}\right)^2$

11. $\left(\frac{13}{2}, 2, 5\right)$ **13.** $(1, 2, -9)$

15. $(x - 2)^2 + (y - 3)^2 + (z - 5)^2 = 1$

17. $(x - 1)^2 + (y - 5)^2 + (z - 2)^2 = 36$

19. $x^2 + y^2 + z^2 = 12$

21. Center: $(0, 0, 4)$; radius: 4

23. Center: $(5, -3, 2)$; radius: 2

25. (a)

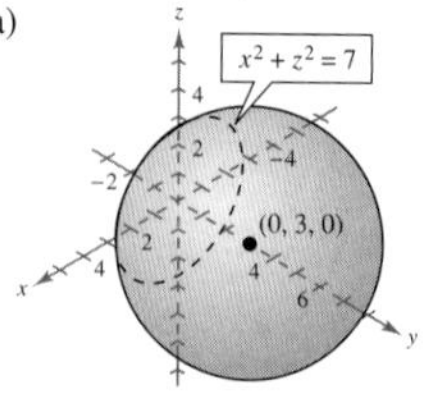

(b)

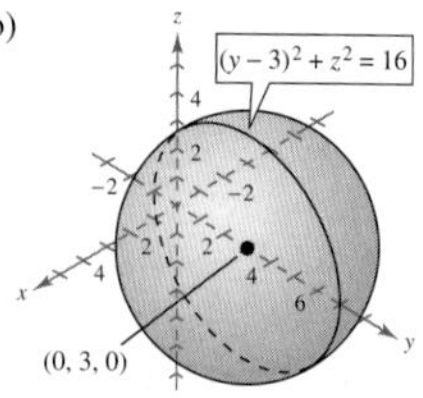

27. (a) $\langle 1, 6, -1\rangle$ (b) $\sqrt{38}$ (c) $\left\langle \frac{\sqrt{38}}{38}, \frac{3\sqrt{38}}{19}, -\frac{\sqrt{38}}{38}\right\rangle$

29. (a) $\langle -10, 6, 7\rangle$ (b) $\sqrt{185}$

(c) $\left\langle \frac{-2\sqrt{185}}{37}, \frac{6\sqrt{185}}{185}, \frac{7\sqrt{185}}{185}\right\rangle$

31. -9 **33.** 1 **35.** 90° **37.** Parallel

39. Orthogonal **41.** Collinear **43.** Not collinear

45. A: 159.1 lb

B: 115.6 lb

C: 115.6 lb

47. $\langle -10, 0, -10\rangle$ **49.** $4\mathbf{i} + 2\mathbf{j} - 7\mathbf{k}$

51. $\frac{\sqrt{11}}{11}\mathbf{i} + \frac{3\sqrt{11}}{11}\mathbf{j} + \frac{\sqrt{11}}{11}\mathbf{k}$

53. $-\frac{71\sqrt{7602}}{7602}\mathbf{i} - \frac{22\sqrt{7602}}{3801}\mathbf{j} + \frac{25\sqrt{7602}}{7602}\mathbf{k}$

55. Area $= \sqrt{172} = 2\sqrt{43} \approx 13.11$ **57.** 75

59. (a) $x = -1 + 4t,\ y = 3 + 3t,\ z = 5 - 6t$

(b) $\frac{x + 1}{4} = \frac{y - 3}{3} = \frac{z - 5}{-6}$

61. (a) $x = -4t,\ y = 5t,\ z = 2t$ (b) $\frac{x}{-4} = \frac{y}{5} = \frac{z}{2}$

63. $-2x - 12y + 5z = 0$ **65.** $z - 2 = 0$

67.

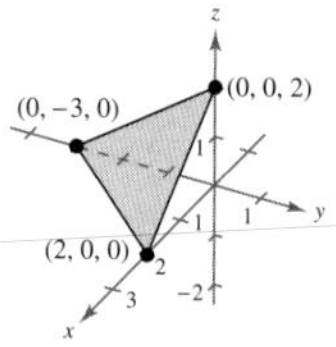

69.

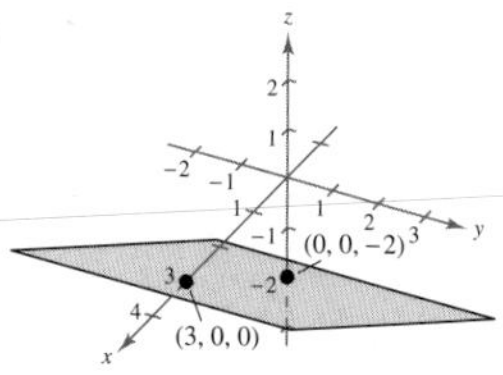

71. $\frac{\sqrt{6}}{6}$ **73.** $\frac{6\sqrt{14}}{7}$ **75.** False. $\mathbf{u} \times \mathbf{v} = -(\mathbf{v} \times \mathbf{u})$

77. Answers will vary.

Chapter Test *(page 844)*

1.

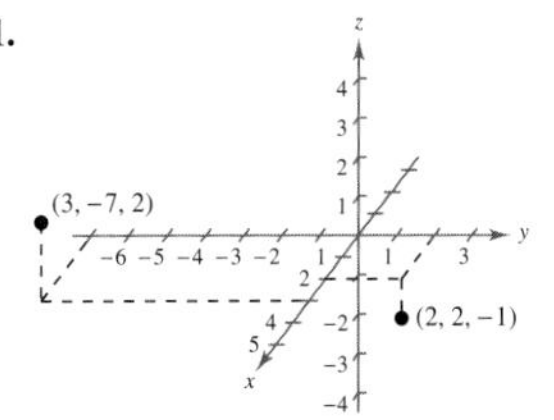

2. No. $(\sqrt{76})^2 + (\sqrt{102})^2 \neq (\sqrt{194})^2$ **3.** (7, 1, 2)

4. $(x - 7)^2 + (y - 1)^2 + (z - 2)^2 = 19$

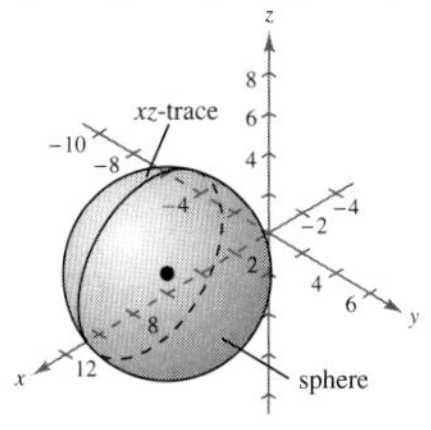

5. $\mathbf{u} = \langle -2, 6, -6 \rangle$, $\mathbf{v} = \langle -12, 5, -5 \rangle$

6. (a) 84 (b) $\langle 0, 62, 62 \rangle$

7. (a) $\left\langle -\dfrac{\sqrt{19}}{19}, \dfrac{3\sqrt{19}}{19}, -\dfrac{3\sqrt{19}}{19} \right\rangle$

(b) $\left\langle -\dfrac{6\sqrt{194}}{97}, \dfrac{5\sqrt{194}}{194}, -\dfrac{5\sqrt{194}}{194} \right\rangle$

8. 46.23°

9. (a) $x = 8 - 2t,\ y = -2 + 6t,\ z = 5 - 6t$

(b) $\dfrac{x - 8}{-2} = \dfrac{y + 2}{6} = \dfrac{z - 5}{-6}$

10. Neither **11.** Orthogonal **12.** Parallel

13. $\overrightarrow{AB}$ is parallel to $\overrightarrow{CD} = \langle 4, 8, -2 \rangle$.
$\overrightarrow{AC}$ is parallel to $\overrightarrow{BD} = \langle 1, -3, 3 \rangle$.
Area $= 2\sqrt{230}$

14. 200

15.

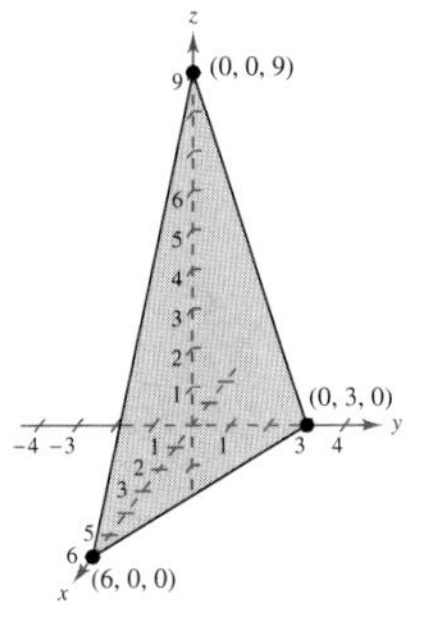

16.

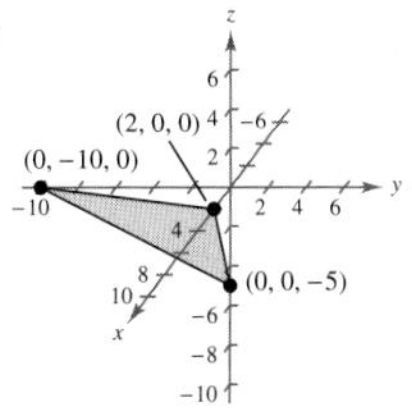

17. $27x + 4y + 32z + 33 = 0$

18. $\dfrac{8}{\sqrt{14}} = \dfrac{4\sqrt{14}}{7}$ **19.** 88.5°

Problem Solving *(page 847)*

1. (a)

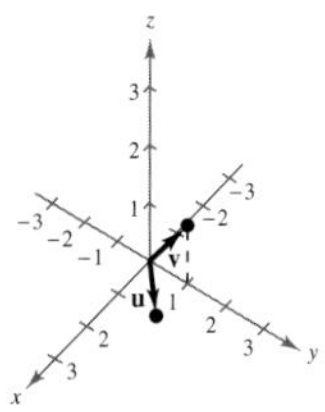

(b) Answers will vary.
(c) $a = b = 1$
(d) Answers will vary.

3. Answers will vary.

5. (a) Right triangle (b) Obtuse triangle
(c) Obtuse triangle (d) Acute triangle

7. About 860.0 lb **9–11.** Proofs

13. (a) $\overrightarrow{AB} = -\frac{5}{4}\mathbf{j} + \mathbf{k}$, $\mathbf{F} = -200(\cos\theta\mathbf{j} + \sin\theta\mathbf{k})$

(b) $\|\overrightarrow{AB} \times \mathbf{F}\| = 25|10\sin\theta + 8\cos\theta|$

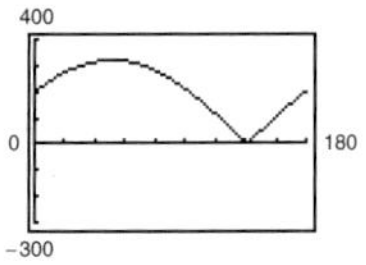

(c) $\|\overrightarrow{AB} \times \mathbf{F}\| \approx 298.2$ when $\theta = 30°$.

(d) $\theta \approx 51.34°$

(e) The zero is $\theta \approx 141.34°$; the angle making $\overrightarrow{AB}$ parallel to $\mathbf{F}$.

15. (a) $d = \sqrt{70}$ when $t = 0$.

(b)

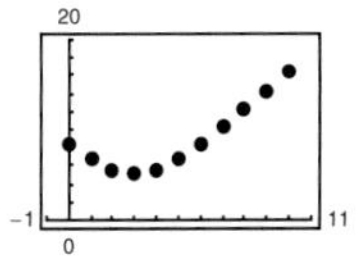

(c) The distance between the two insects appears to lessen in the first 3 seconds but then begins to increase with time.

(d) The insects get within 5 inches of each other.

17. (a) $D = \dfrac{3\sqrt{2}}{2}$ (b) $D = \sqrt{5}$

Chapter 12

Section 12.1 *(page 858)*

1. limit **3.** oscillates

5. (a)

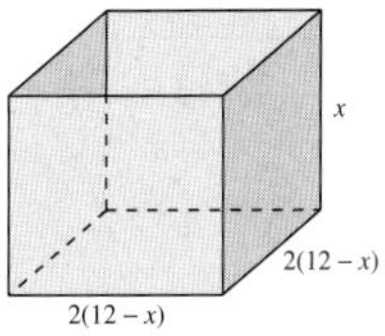

(b) $V = lwh$
$= 2(12 - x) \cdot 2(12 - x) \cdot x$
$= 4x(12 - x)^2$

(c)

x	3	3.5	3.9	4
V	972	1011.5	1023.5	1024

x	4.1	4.5	5
V	1023.5	1012.5	980

$\lim_{x \to 4} V = 1024$

(d)

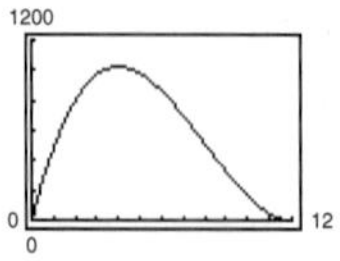

7.

x	1.9	1.99	1.999	2
$f(x)$	13.5	13.95	13.995	14

x	2.001	2.01	2.1
$f(x)$	14.005	14.05	14.5

14; Yes

9.

x	2.9	2.99	2.999	3
$f(x)$	0.1695	0.1669	0.1667	Error

x	3.001	3.01	3.1
$f(x)$	0.1666	0.1664	0.1639

$\frac{1}{6}$; No

11.

x	−0.1	−0.01	−0.001	0
$f(x)$	1.9867	1.9999	1.999999	Error

x	0.001	0.01	0.1
$f(x)$	1.999999	1.9999	1.9867

2; No

13.

x	0.9	0.99	0.999	1
$f(x)$	0.2564	0.2506	0.2501	Error

x	1.001	1.01	1.1
$f(x)$	0.2499	0.2494	0.2439

$\frac{1}{4}$;

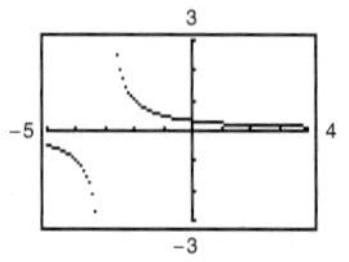

15.

x	−0.1	−0.01	−0.001	0
$f(x)$	0.2247	0.2237	0.2236	Error

x	0.001	0.01	0.1
$f(x)$	0.2236	0.2235	0.2225

$\frac{\sqrt{5}}{10}$;

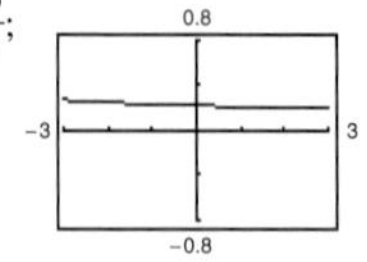

17.

x	−4.1	−4.01	−4.001	−4
$f(x)$	0.4762	0.4975	0.4998	Error

x	−3.999	−3.99	−3.9
$f(x)$	0.5003	0.5025	0.5263

$\frac{1}{2}$;

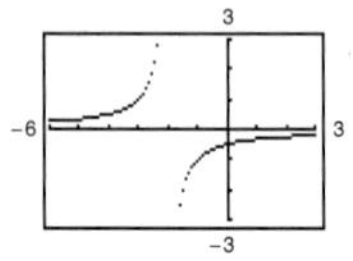

19.

x	−0.1	−0.01	−0.001	0
$f(x)$	0.9983	0.99998	0.9999998	Error

x	0.001	0.01	0.1
$f(x)$	0.9999998	0.99998	0.9983

1;

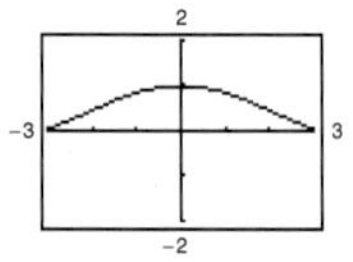

21.

x	−0.1	−0.01	−0.001	0
$f(x)$	−0.1	−0.01	−0.001	Error

x	0.001	0.01	0.1
$f(x)$	0.001	0.01	0.1

0;

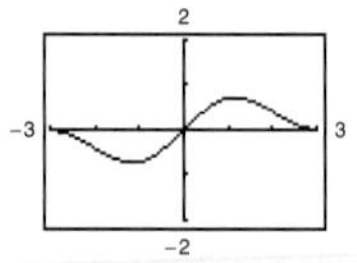

23.

x	-0.1	-0.01	-0.001	0
$f(x)$	0.9063	0.9901	0.9990	Error

x	0.001	0.01	0.1
$f(x)$	1.0010	1.0101	1.1070

1;

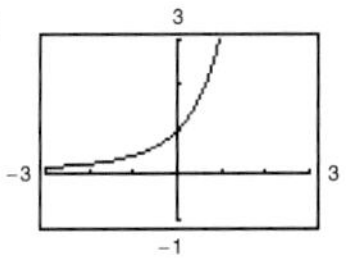

25.

x	0.9	0.99	0.999	1
$f(x)$	2.2314	2.0203	2.0020	Error

x	1.001	1.01	1.1
$f(x)$	1.9980	1.9803	1.8232

2;

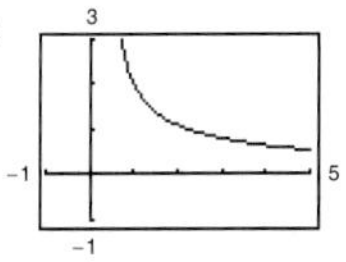

27.

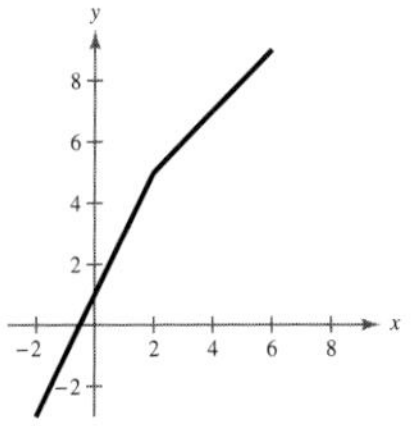

5

29. 13 **31.** Limit does not exist. Answers will vary.
33. Limit does not exist. Answers will vary.
35. Limit does not exist. Answers will vary.

37.

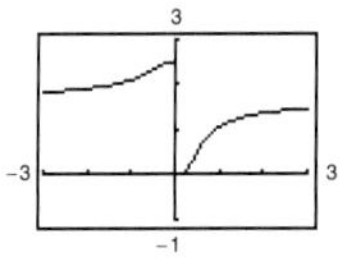

Limit does not exist.
Answers will vary.

39.

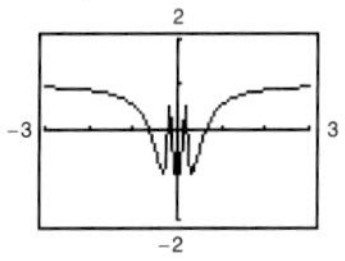

Limit does not exist.
Answers will vary.

41.

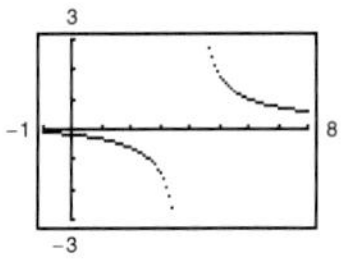

Limit does not exist.
Answers will vary.

43.

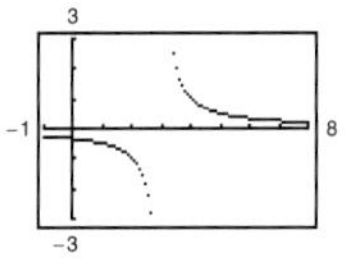

Limit exists.

45. (a) -12 (b) 9 (c) $\frac{1}{2}$ (d) $\sqrt{3}$
47. (a) 8 (b) $\frac{3}{8}$ (c) 3 (d) $-\frac{61}{8}$
49. -15 **51.** 7 **53.** -3 **55.** $-\frac{9}{10}$
57. $\frac{7}{13}$ **59.** 1 **61.** $\frac{35}{3}$ **63.** $e^3 \approx 20.09$
65. 0 **67.** $\dfrac{\pi}{6}$ **69.** True
71. (a) and (b) Answers will vary
73. (a) No. The function may approach different values from the right and left of 2. For example,

$$f(x) = \begin{cases} 0, & x < 2 \\ 4, & x = 2 \\ 6, & x > 2 \end{cases}$$

implies $f(2) = 4$, but $\lim_{x\to 2} f(x) \neq 4$.

(b) No. The function may approach 4 as x approaches 2, but the function could be undefined at $x = 2$. For example, in the function

$$f(x) = \frac{4\sin(x-2)}{x-2},$$

the limit is 4 as x approaches 2, but $f(2)$ is not defined.

75. $\lim_{x\to 0} \tan x = 0$
$\lim_{x\to \pi/4} \tan x = 1$
$\lim_{x\to \pi/2} \tan x$ does not exist.

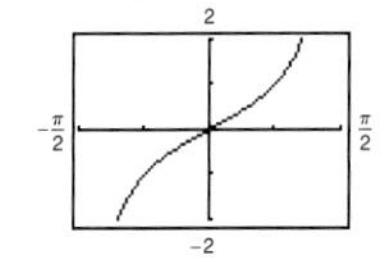

77. $\lim_{x\to 4} f(x) = 6$
$\lim_{x\to 5} f(x) = 7$
No; No

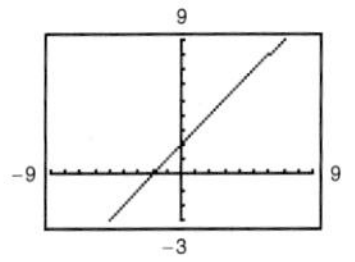

Section 12.2 *(page 868)*

1. dividing out technique **3.** one-sided limit
5. (a) 1 (b) 3 (c) 5
$g_2(x) = -2x + 1$
7. (a) 2 (b) 0 (c) 0
$g_2(x) = x(x + 1)$
9. $\frac{1}{12}$ **11.** 4 **13.** 4 **15.** 12 **17.** 80 **19.** -3
21. $\dfrac{\sqrt{5}}{10}$ **23.** $\dfrac{\sqrt{3}}{6}$ **25.** 1 **27.** $\dfrac{1}{4}$ **29.** -1
31. $-\frac{1}{16}$ **33.** Does not exist **35.** 0

37.

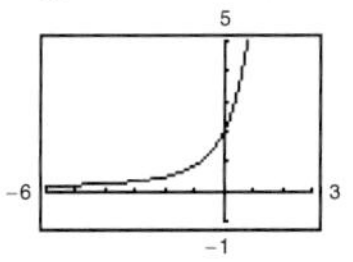

2.000

39.

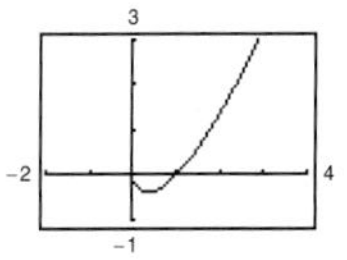

0

41.

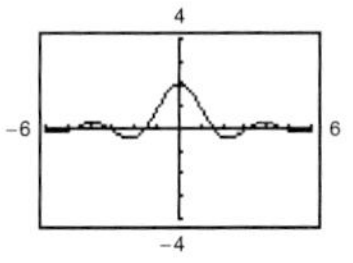

2.000

43.

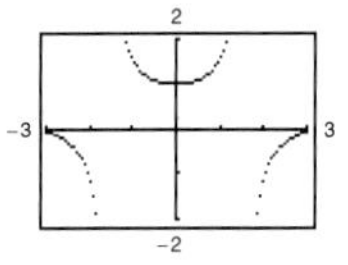

1.000

45. 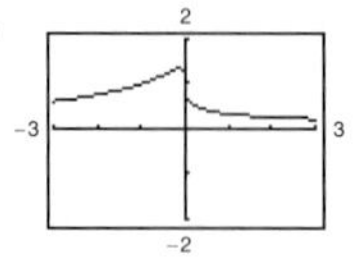

0.333

47. 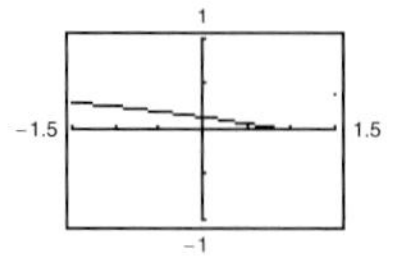

0.135

49. (a) 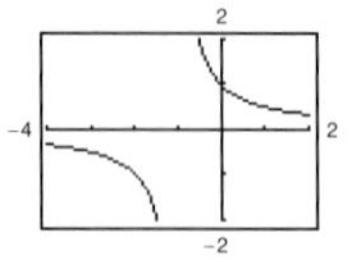

(b)

x	0.9	0.99	0.999	0.9999
$f(x)$	0.5263	0.5025	0.5003	0.50003

(c) $\lim_{x\to 1^-} \dfrac{x-1}{x^2-1} = 0.5$

51. (a) 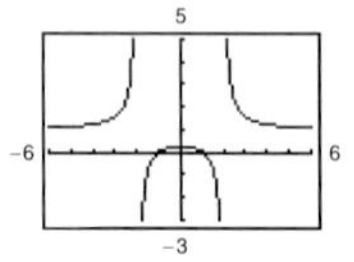

(b)

x	1.9	1.99	1.999	2
$f(x)$	-6.6923	-74.1880	-749.1875	Error

x	2.001	2.01	2.1
$f(x)$	750.8125	75.8130	8.3171

(c) The limit does not exist.

53. (a) 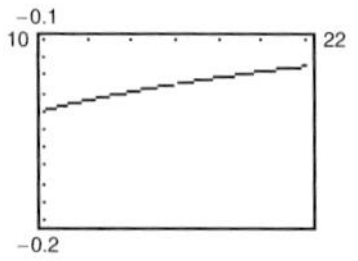

(b)

x	16.1	16.01
$f(x)$	-0.12481	-0.12498

x	16.001	16.0001
$f(x)$	-0.124998	-0.1249998

(c) $\lim_{x\to 16^+} \dfrac{4-\sqrt{x}}{x-16} = -0.125$

55. 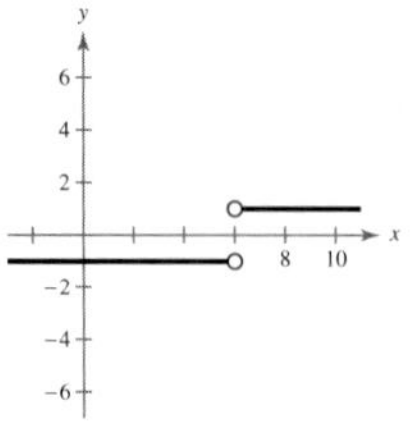

The limit does not exist.

57. 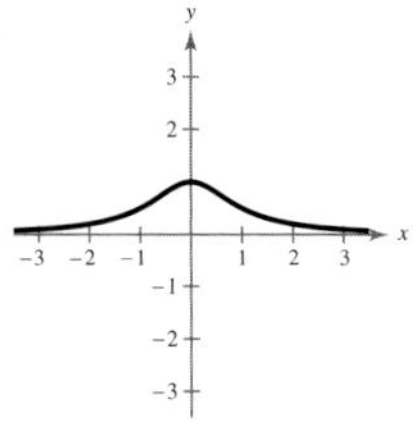

$\lim_{x\to 1} \dfrac{1}{x^2+1} = \dfrac{1}{2}$

59. 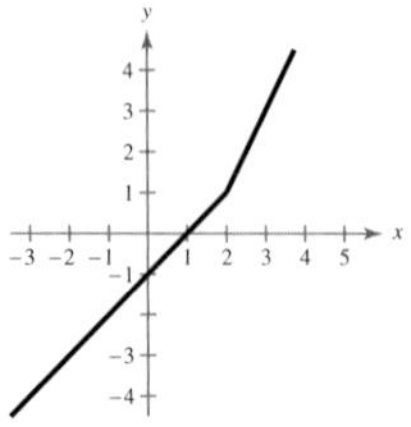

$\lim_{x\to 2} f(x) = 1$

61. 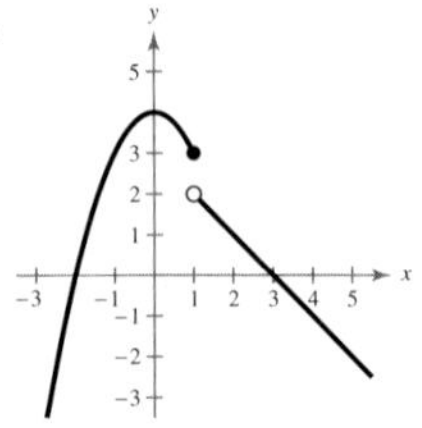

The limit does not exist.

63. 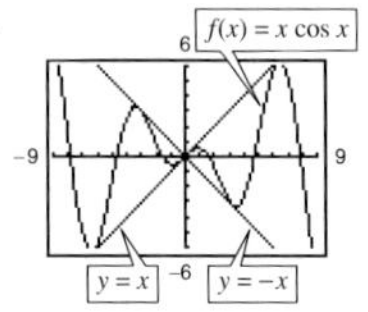

$\lim_{x\to 0} x\cos x = 0$

65. 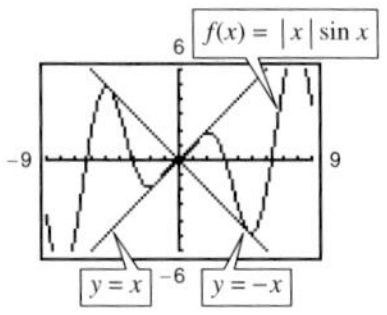

$\lim_{x\to 0} |x|\sin x = 0$

67. 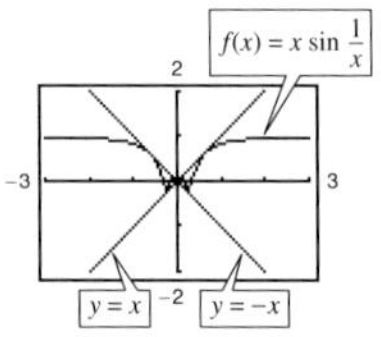

$\lim_{x\to 0} x\sin\dfrac{1}{x} = 0$

69. Limit (a) can be evaluated by direct substitution.
(a) 0 (b) 1

71. 2 **73.** $\dfrac{1}{2\sqrt{x}}$ **75.** $2x-3$ **77.** $-\dfrac{1}{(x+2)^2}$

79. -32 ft/sec **81.** Answers will vary.

83. (a) 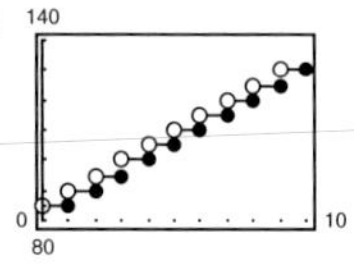

(b)

x	5	5.3	5.4	5.5	5.6	5.7	6
$C(x)$	105	110	110	110	110	110	110

$\lim_{x\to 5.5} C(x) = 110$

(c)

x	4	4.5	4.9	5	5.1	5.5	6
$C(x)$	100	105	105	105	110	110	110

The limit does not exist.

85. True **87.** (a) and (b) Graphs will vary.

89. Answers will vary.

Section 12.3 *(page 878)*

1. Calculus **3.** secant line **5.** 0

7. $\frac{1}{2}$ **9.** 2 **11.** -2 **13.** -1 **15.** $\frac{1}{6}$

17. $m = -2x$; (a) 0 (b) 2

19. $m = -\dfrac{1}{(x+4)^2}$; (a) $-\dfrac{1}{16}$ (b) $-\dfrac{1}{4}$

21. $m = \dfrac{1}{2\sqrt{x-1}}$; (a) $\dfrac{1}{4}$ (b) $\dfrac{1}{6}$

23.

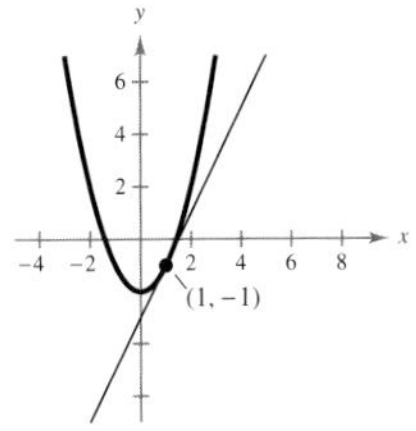

2

25.

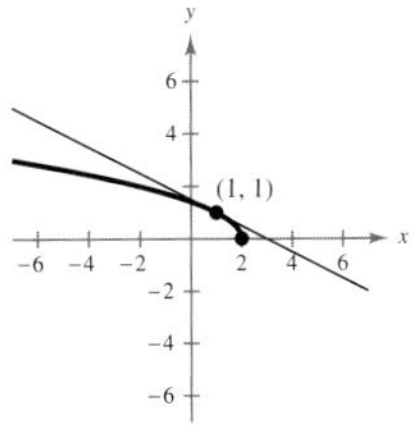

$-\frac{1}{2}$

27.

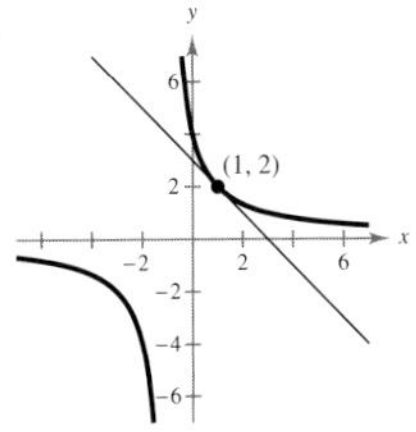

-1

29. 0 **31.** $-\dfrac{1}{3}$ **33.** $-6x$ **35.** $-\dfrac{2}{x^3}$

37. $\dfrac{1}{2\sqrt{x-11}}$ **39.** $\dfrac{-1}{(x+6)^2}$ **41.** $-\dfrac{1}{2(x-9)^{3/2}}$

43. (a) 4 (b) $y = 4x - 5$

(c)

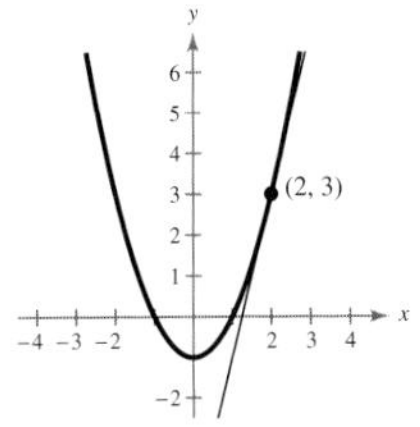

45. (a) 1 (b) $y = x - 2$

(c)

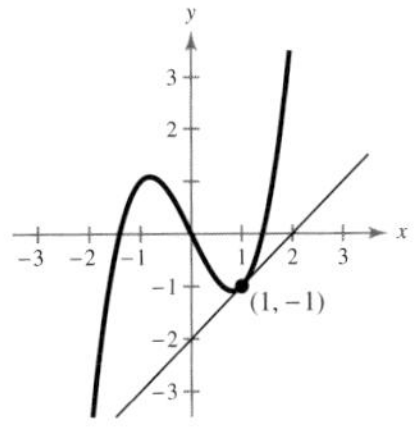

47. (a) $\frac{1}{4}$ (b) $y = \frac{1}{4}x + \frac{5}{4}$

(c)

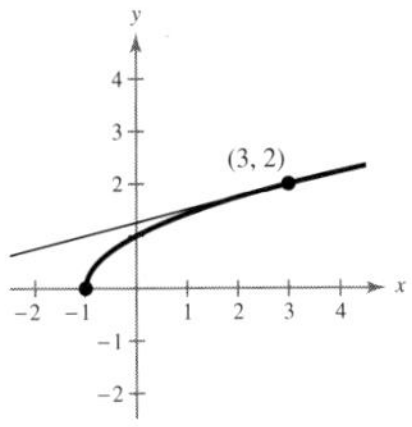

49. (a) -1 (b) $y = -x - 3$

(c)

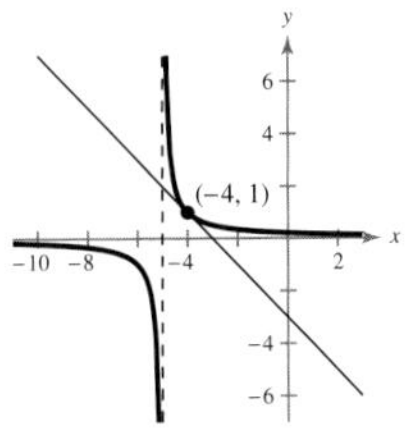

51.

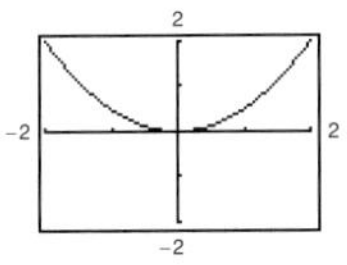

They appear to be the same.

x	-2	-1.5	-1	-0.5	0
$f(x)$	2	1.125	0.5	0.125	0
$f'(x)$	-2	-1.5	-1	-0.5	0

x	0.5	1	1.5	2
$f(x)$	0.125	0.5	1.125	2
$f'(x)$	0.5	1	1.5	2

53.

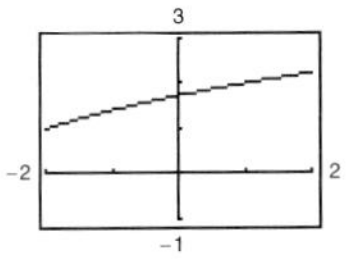

They appear to be the same.

x	-2	-1.5	-1	-0.5	0
$f(x)$	1	1.225	1.414	1.581	1.732
$f'(x)$	0.5	0.408	0.354	0.316	0.289

x	0.5	1	1.5	2
$f(x)$	1.871	2	2.121	2.236
$f'(x)$	0.267	0.25	0.236	0.224

55. $y = -x + 1$ **57.** $y = -6x \pm 8$

59. $f'(x) = 2x - 4$; horizontal tangent at $(2, -1)$

61. $f'(x) = 9x^2 - 9$; horizontal tangents at $(-1, 6)$ and $(1, -6)$

63. $(-1, -1), (0, 0), (1, -1)$

65. $\left(\frac{\pi}{6}, \sqrt{3} + \frac{\pi}{6}\right), \left(\frac{5\pi}{6}, \frac{5\pi}{6} - \sqrt{3}\right)$

67. $(0, 0), (-2, 4e^{-2})$ **69.** $(e^{-1}, -e^{-1})$

71. Answers will vary.

CHAPTER 12

73. (a) $y = 112.87x^2 + 256.45x + 380.3$

(b)

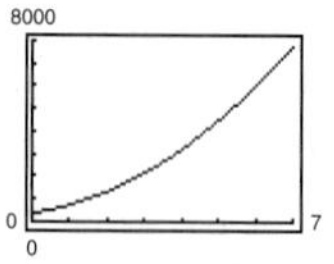

Slope when $x = 5$ is about 1385.2. This represents \$1385.2 million and the rate of change of revenue in 2005.

(c)

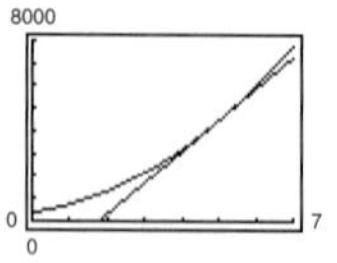

The slopes are the same.

75. True. The slope is dependent on x.

77. b **78.** a **79.** d **80.** c

81. Answers will vary. Example: a sketch of any linear function with positive slope

83. Answers will vary. Example: a sketch of any quadratic function of the form $y = a(x - 1)^2 + k$, where $a > 0$.

85. (a)

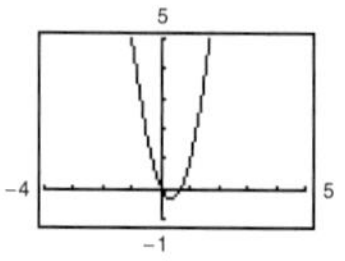

(b) About $(0.33, -0.33)$ (c) Slope at vertex is 0.

(d) Slope of tangent line at vertex is 0.

Section 12.4 *(page 887)*

1. limit; infinity **3.** converge **5.** c **6.** a **7.** d

8. b **9.** 1 **11.** -1 **13.** 2 **15.** -3

17. Does not exist **19.** $-\frac{4}{3}$ **21.** -1 **23.** $\frac{1}{2}$

25. -4 **27.** -5

29.

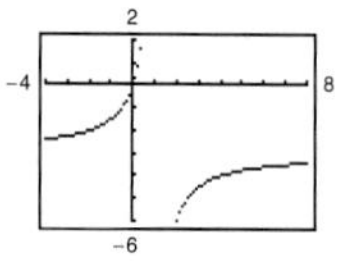

Horizontal asymptote: $y = -3$

31.

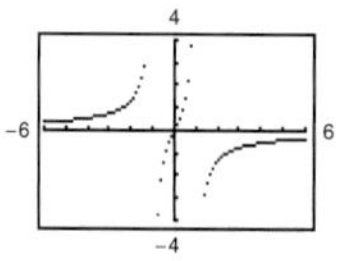

Horizontal asymptote: $y = 0$

33.

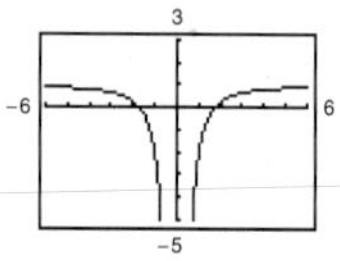

Horizontal asymptote: $y = 1$

35. (a)

x	10^0	10^1	10^2	10^3
$f(x)$	-0.7321	-0.0995	-0.0100	-0.0010

x	10^4	10^5	10^6
$f(x)$	-1.0×10^{-4}	-1.0×10^{-5}	-1.0×10^{-6}

(b)

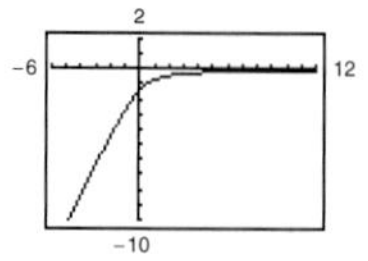

$\lim_{x\to\infty} f(x) = 0$

37. (a)

x	10^0	10^1	10^2	10^3
$f(x)$	-0.7082	-0.7454	-0.7495	-0.74995

x	10^4	10^5	10^6
$f(x)$	-0.749995	-0.7499995	-0.75

(b)

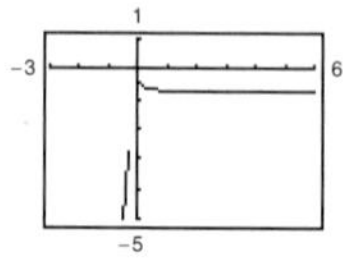

$\lim_{x\to\infty} f(x) = -\frac{3}{4}$

39. $1, \frac{3}{5}, \frac{2}{5}, \frac{5}{17}, \frac{3}{13}$
Limit: 0

41. $\frac{1}{3}, \frac{2}{5}, \frac{3}{7}, \frac{4}{9}, \frac{5}{11}$
Limit: $\frac{1}{2}$

43. $\frac{1}{5}, \frac{4}{7}, 1, \frac{16}{11}, \frac{25}{13}$
Limit does not exist.

45. 2, 3, 4, 5, 6
Limit does not exist.

47. $-1, \frac{1}{2}, -\frac{1}{3}, \frac{1}{4}, -\frac{1}{5}$
Limit: 0

49. $\lim_{n\to\infty} a_n = \frac{3}{2}$

n	10^0	10^1	10^2	10^3
a_n	2	1.55	1.505	1.5005

n	10^4	10^5	10^6
a_n	1.50005	1.500005	1.5000005

51. $\lim_{n\to\infty} a_n = \frac{16}{3}$

n	10^0	10^1	10^2	10^3
a_n	16	6.16	5.4136	5.3413

n	10^4	10^5	10^6
a_n	5.3341	5.33341	5.333341

53. (a) 1

(b)

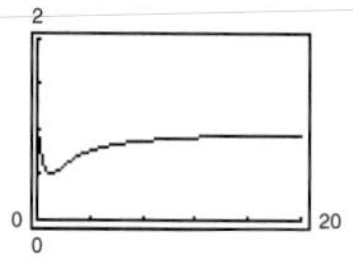

(c) Over a long period of time, the level of the oxygen in the pond returns to the normal level.

55. (a) $\overline{C}(x) = \dfrac{13.50x + 45,750}{x}$

(b) \$471; \$59.25

(c) \$13.50. As the number of PDAs gets very large, the average cost approaches \$13.50.

57. (a)

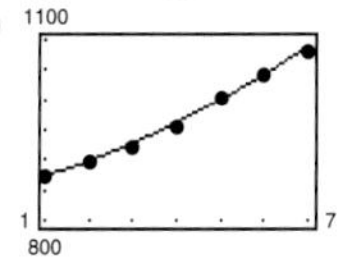

The model is a good fit for the data.

(b) \$1598.39

(c) When t is slightly less than 29, a vertical asymptote is found.

59. False. Graph $y = \dfrac{x^2}{x+1}$.

61. True. If the sequence converges, then the limit exists.

63. Let $f(x) = \dfrac{1}{x^2}$, $g(x) = \dfrac{1}{x^2}$, and $c = 0$. Now $\dfrac{1}{x^2}$ increases without bound as $x \to 0$ and $\lim_{x\to 0}[f(x) - g(x)] = 0$.

65.

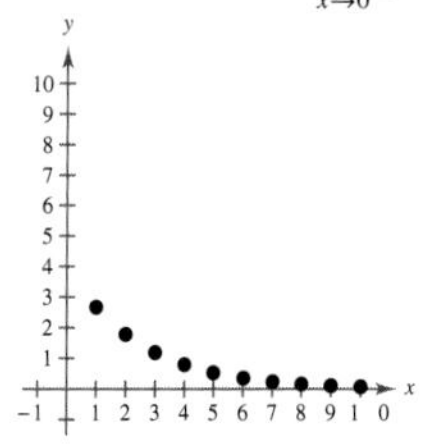

Converges to 0

67.

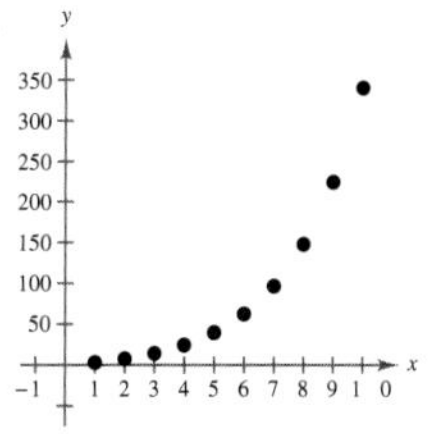

Diverges

69.

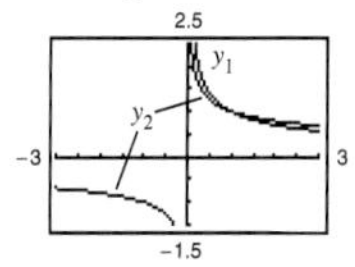

$\sqrt{x}$ is undefined for $x < 0$. Answers will vary.

71.

x	10^0	10^1	10^2	10^3	10^4	10^5
$\dfrac{1}{x}$	1	$\dfrac{1}{10}$	$\dfrac{1}{100}$	$\dfrac{1}{1000}$	$\dfrac{1}{10{,}000}$	$\dfrac{1}{100{,}000}$

$\lim_{x\to 0} \dfrac{1}{x}$ does not exist.

Section 12.5 *(page 896)*

1. cn **3.** $\dfrac{n^2(n+1)^2}{4}$ **5.** 420 **7.** 44,100

9. 44,140 **11.** 5850

13. (a) $S(n) = \dfrac{n^2 + 2n + 1}{4n^2}$

(b)

n	10^0	10^1	10^2	10^3	10^4
$S(n)$	1	0.3025	0.25503	0.25050	0.25005

(c) Limit: $\frac{1}{4}$

15. (a) $S(n) = \dfrac{2n^2 + 3n + 7}{2n^2}$

(b)

n	10^0	10^1	10^2	10^3	10^4
$S(n)$	6	1.185	1.0154	1.0015	1.00015

(c) Limit: 1

17. (a) $S(n) = \dfrac{14n^2 + 3n + 1}{6n^3}$

(b)

n	10^0	10^1	10^2	10^3	10^4
$S(n)$	3	0.2385	0.02338	0.002334	0.000233

(c) Limit: 0

19. (a) $S(n) = \dfrac{4n^2 - 3n - 1}{6n^2}$

(b)

n	10^0	10^1	10^2	10^3	10^4
$S(n)$	0	0.615	0.66165	0.666167	0.666617

(c) Limit: $\frac{2}{3}$

21. 14.25 square units **23.** 1.2656 square units

25.

n	4	8	20	50
Approximate area	18	21	22.8	23.52

27.

n	4	8	20	50
Approximate area	3.52	2.85	2.48	2.34

29.

n	4	8	20	50	100	∞
Approximate area	40	38	36.8	36.32	36.16	36

31.

n	4	8	20	50	100	∞
Approximate area	36	38	39.2	39.68	39.84	40

33.

n	4	8	20
Approximate area	14.25	14.8125	15.13

n	50	100	∞
Approximate area	15.2528	15.2932	$\frac{46}{3}$

35.

n	4	8	20	50	100	∞
Approximate area	19	18.5	18.2	18.08	18.04	18

37. 3 square units **39.** 2 square units

41. $\frac{10}{3}$ square units **43.** $\frac{17}{4}$ square units

45. $\frac{3}{4}$ square unit **47.** $\frac{51}{4}$ square units

49.

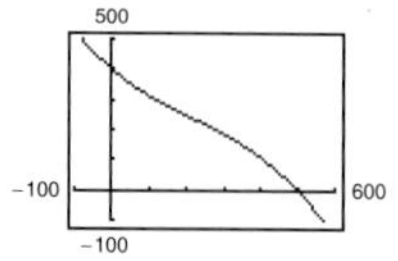

Area is 105,208.33 ft^2 ≈ 2.4153 acres

51. True **53.** c

Review Exercises *(page 900)*

1.

x	2.9	2.99	2.999	3
$f(x)$	16.4	16.94	16.994	17

x	3.001	3.01	3.1
$f(x)$	17.006	17.06	17.6

$\lim_{x\to 3}(6x - 1) = 17$; The limit can be reached.

3.

x	−0.1	−0.01	−0.001	0
$f(x)$	1.0517	1.005	1.0005	Error

x	0.001	0.01	0.1
$f(x)$	0.9995	0.995	0.9516

$\lim_{x\to 0}\dfrac{1 - e^{-x}}{x} = 1$; The limit cannot be reached.

5. 2 **7.** 2 **9.** (a) 64 (b) 7 (c) 20 (d) $\frac{4}{5}$

11. 5 **13.** $\frac{3}{10}$ **15.** 0 **17.** 11 **19.** 77 **21.** $\frac{10}{3}$

23. $2e^{-1}$ **25.** $-\frac{1}{4}$ **27.** $\frac{1}{15}$ **29.** $-\frac{1}{3}$ **31.** −1

33. $\frac{1}{4}$ **35.** $\frac{1}{4}$

37. (a)

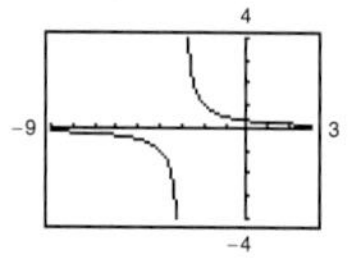

$\frac{1}{6}$

(b)

x	2.9	2.99	3	3.01	3.1
$f(x)$	0.1695	0.1669	Error	0.1664	0.1639

0.1667

39. (a)

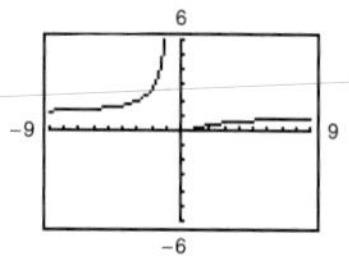

Limit does not exist.

(b)

x	−0.1	−0.01	−0.001	0
$f(x)$	4.85E8	7.2E86	Error	Error

x	0.001	0.01	0.1
$f(x)$	0	1E–87	2.1E–9

Limit does not exist.

41. (a)

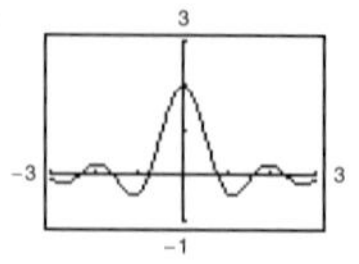

2

(b)

x	−0.1	−0.01	−0.001	0
$f(x)$	1.94709	1.99947	1.999995	Error

x	0.001	0.01	0.1
$f(x)$	1.999995	1.99947	1.94709

2

43. (a)

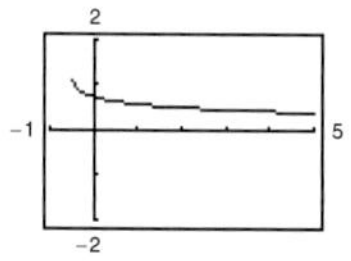

About 0.575

(b)

x	1.1	1.01	1.001	1.0001
$f(x)$	0.5680	0.5764	0.5773	0.5773

About 0.577 $\left(\text{Actual limit is } \dfrac{\sqrt{3}}{3}.\right)$

45.

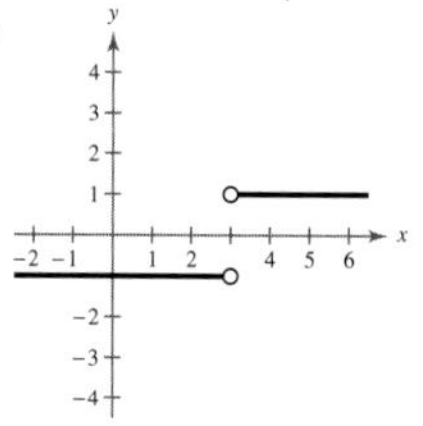

Limit does not exist.

47.

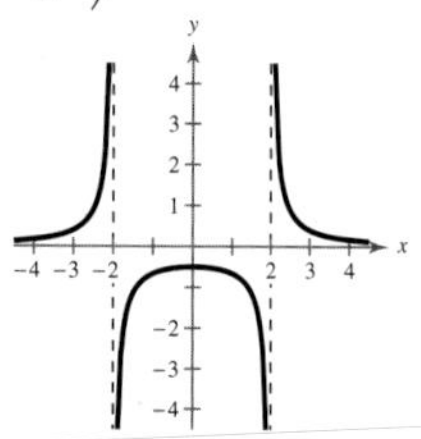

Limit does not exist.

49.

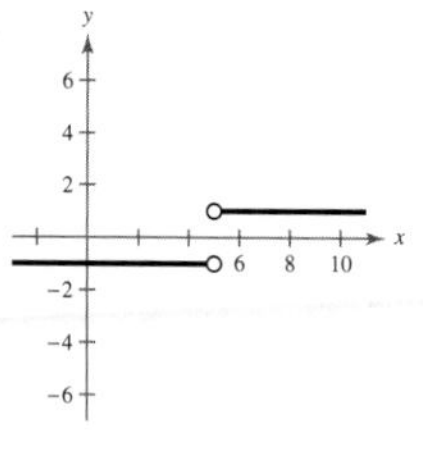

Limit does not exist.

51.

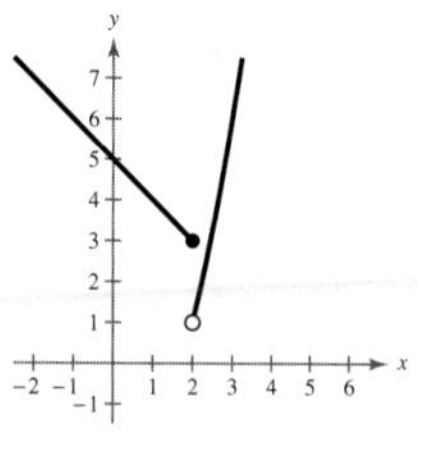

Limit does not exist.

53. 4 **55.** $3 - 2x$ **57.** 2

59.

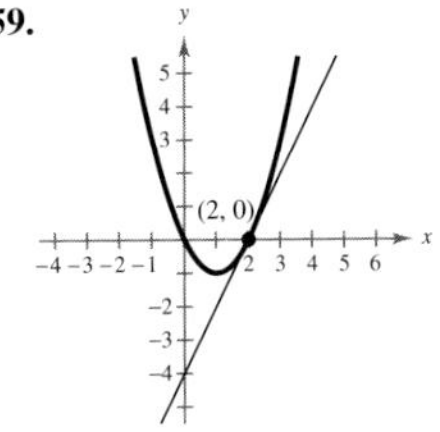

61.

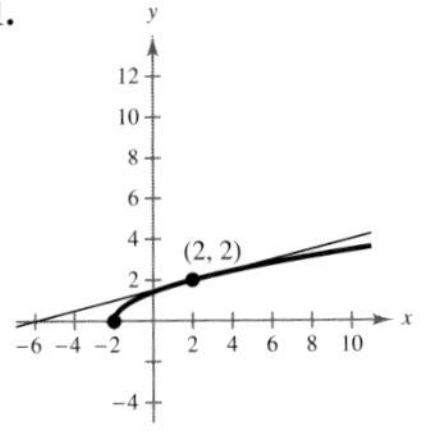

2 $\frac{1}{4}$

63.

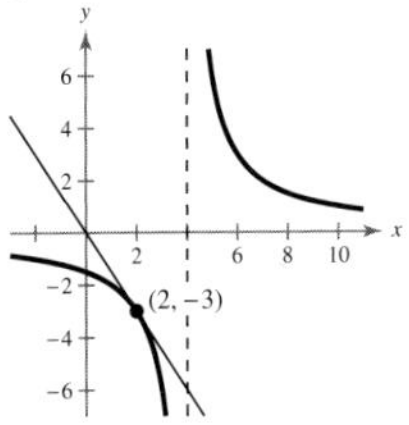

$-\frac{3}{2}$

65. $m = 2x - 4$; (a) -4 (b) 6

67. $m = -\dfrac{4}{(x - 6)^2}$; (a) -4 (b) -1

69. $f'(x) = 0$ **71.** $h'(x) = -\frac{1}{2}$ **73.** $g'(x) = 4x$

75. $f'(t) = \dfrac{1}{2\sqrt{t + 5}}$ **77.** $g'(s) = -\dfrac{4}{(s + 5)^2}$

79. $g'(x) = \dfrac{-1}{2(x + 4)^{3/2}}$

81. (a) 0 (b) $y = -1$

(c)

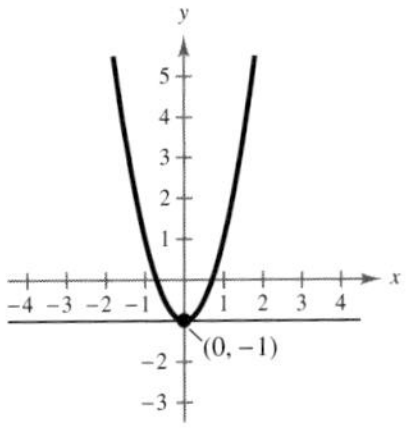

83. 2 **85.** -1 **87.** 0

89. Limit does not exist. **91.** 3

93. $\frac{3}{4}, 1, \frac{11}{10}, \frac{15}{13}, \frac{19}{16}$
Limit: $\frac{4}{3}$

95. $-1, \frac{1}{8}, -\frac{1}{27}, \frac{1}{64}, -\frac{1}{125}$
Limit: 0

97. $\frac{1}{5}, \frac{1}{2}, \frac{9}{11}, \frac{8}{7}, \frac{25}{17}$; Limit does not exist.

99. (a) $S(n) = \dfrac{(n + 1)(5n + 4)}{6n^2}$

(b)

n	10^0	10^1	10^2	10^3	10^4
$S(n)$	3	0.99	0.8484	0.8348	0.8335

(c) Limit: $\frac{5}{6}$

101. $\frac{27}{4} = 6.75$ square units

103.

n	4	8	20	50
Approximate area	7.5	6.375	5.74	5.4944

105. 50 square units **107.** 15 square units

109. 6 square units **111.** $\frac{4}{3}$ square units

113. (a) $y = (-3.376068 \times 10^{-7})x^3 + (3.7529 \times 10^{-4})x^2 - 0.17x + 132$

(b)

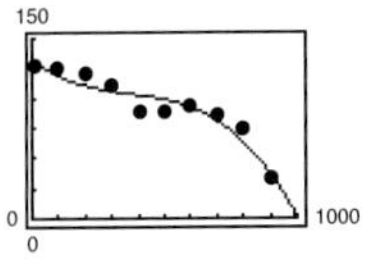

(c) About 87,695.0 ft^2 (Answers will vary.)

115. False. The limit of the rational function as x approaches ∞ does not exist.

Chapter Test *(page 903)*

1.

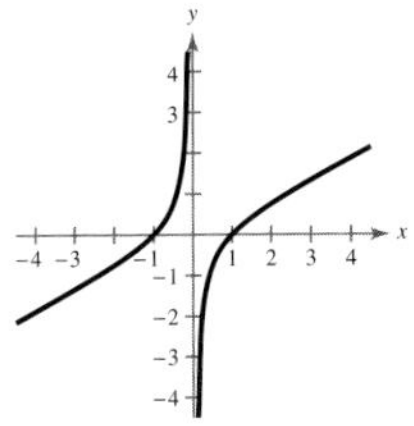

$\lim_{x \to -2} \dfrac{x^2 - 1}{2x} = -\dfrac{3}{4}$

2.

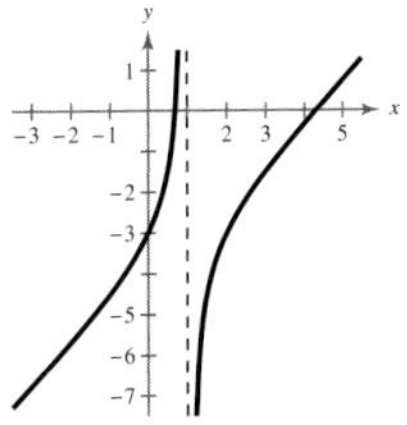

The limit does not exist.

3.

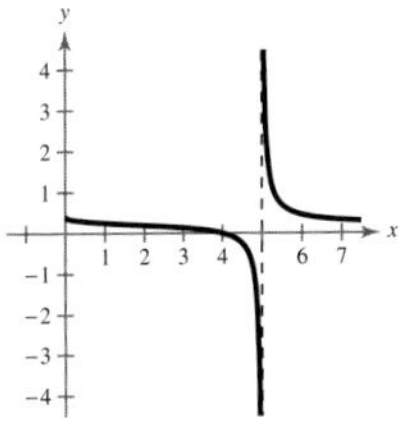

The limit does not exist.

4.

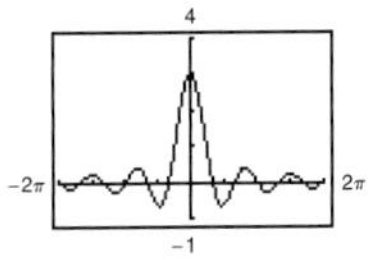

$\lim_{x \to 0} \dfrac{\sin 3x}{x} = 3$

x	-0.02	-0.01	0	0.01	0.02
$f(x)$	2.9982	2.9996	Error	2.9996	2.9982

5.

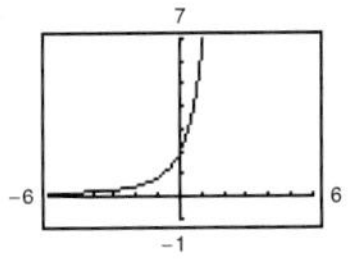

$\lim_{x \to 0} \dfrac{e^{2x} - 1}{x} = 2$

x	-0.004	-0.003	-0.002	-0.001	0
$f(x)$	1.9920	1.9940	1.9960	1.9980	Error

CHAPTER 12

6. (a) $m = 6x - 5;\ 7$ (b) $m = 6x^2 + 6;\ 12$
7. $f'(x) = -\frac{2}{5}$ **8.** $f'(x) = 4x + 4$
9. $f'(x) = -\dfrac{1}{(x+3)^2}$ **10.** 0 **11.** -3
12. The limit does not exist.
13. $0, \frac{3}{4}, \frac{14}{19}, \frac{12}{17}, \frac{36}{53}$
Limit: $\frac{1}{2}$
14. $0, 1, 0, \frac{1}{2}, 0$
Limit: 0
15. $\frac{25}{2}$ square units **16.** 8 square units **17.** $\frac{16}{3}$ square units
18. (a) $y = 8.786x^2 - 6.25x - 0.4$ (b) 81.6 ft/sec

Cumulative Test for Chapters 10–12 *(page 904)*

1. Ellipse

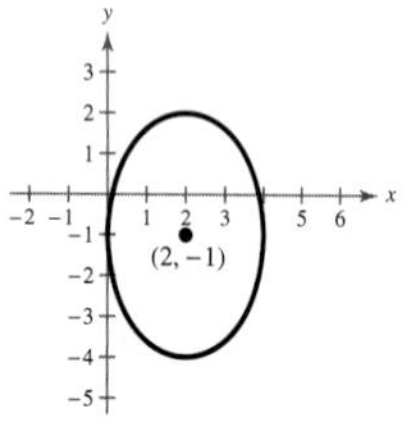

2. Circle

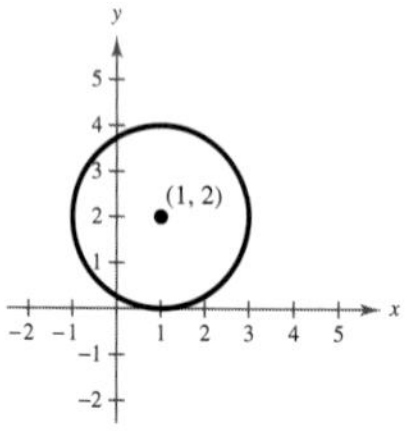

3. $\dfrac{x^2}{1} + \dfrac{(y-2)^2}{4} = 1$

4. $\theta \approx 37.98°$

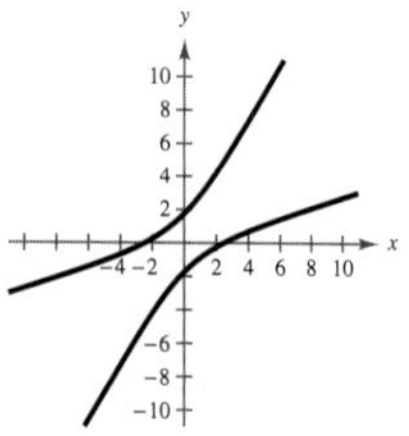

5.

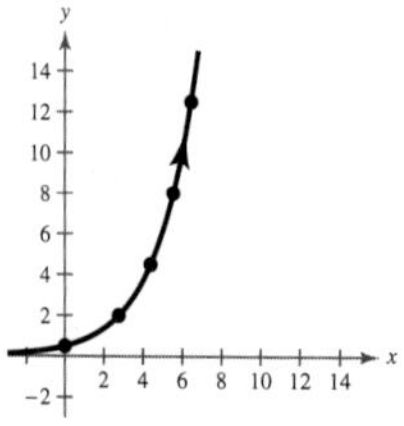

The corresponding rectangular equation is $y = \sqrt{e^x}/2$.

6.

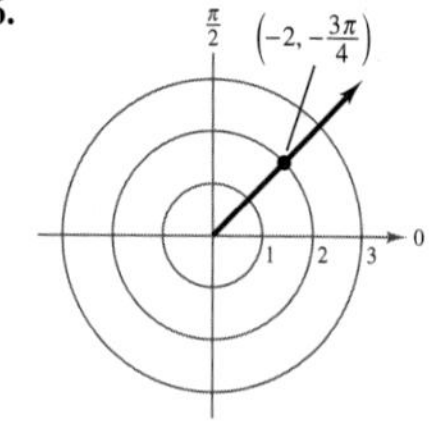

$\left(-2, \dfrac{5\pi}{4}\right), \left(2, -\dfrac{7\pi}{4}\right), \left(2, \dfrac{\pi}{4}\right)$

7. $-8r\cos\theta - 3r\sin\theta + 5 = 0$ or $r = \dfrac{5}{8\cos\theta + 3\sin\theta}$

8. $9x^2 + 20x - 16y^2 + 4 = 0$

9.

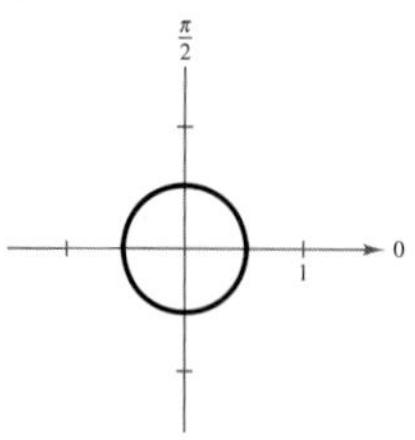

Circle

10.

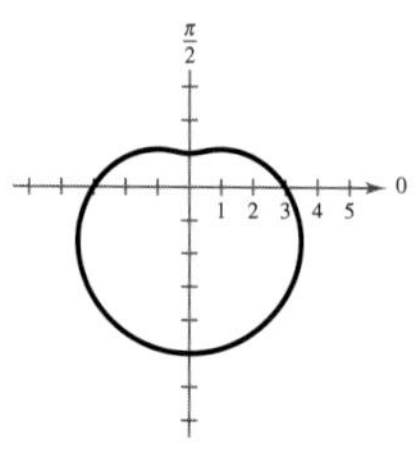

Dimpled limaçon

11.

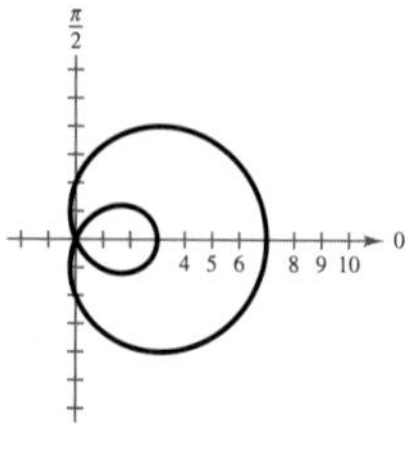

Limaçon with inner loop

12. $(-6, 1, 3)$ **13.** $(0, -4, 0)$ **14.** $\sqrt{149}$

15. 3, 4, 5

$3^2 + 4^2 \stackrel{?}{=} 5^2$

$9 + 16 \stackrel{?}{=} 25$

$25 = 25$

16. $\left(-1, 2, \frac{1}{2}\right)$ **17.** $(x-2)^2 + (y-2)^2 + (z-4)^2 = 24$

18.

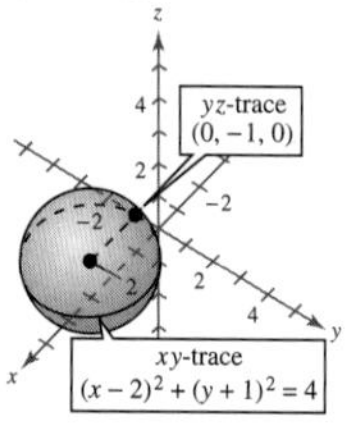

19. $\mathbf{u} \cdot \mathbf{v} = -38$
$\mathbf{u} \times \mathbf{v} = \langle -18, -6, -14 \rangle$

20. Neither **21.** Orthogonal **22.** Parallel

23. (a) $x = -2 + 7t,\ y = 3 + 5t,\ z = 25t$
(b) $\dfrac{x+2}{7} = \dfrac{y-3}{5} = \dfrac{z}{25}$

24. $x = -1 + 2t$
$y = 2 - 4t$
$z = t$

25. $75x + 50y - 31z = 0$

26.

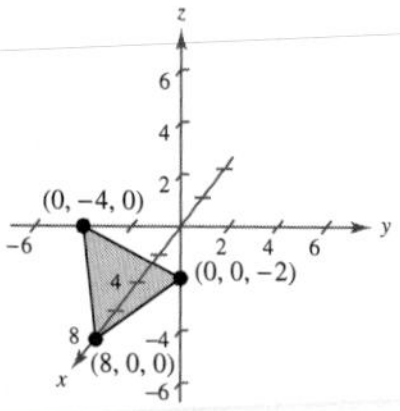

27. $\dfrac{\sqrt{30}}{2} \approx 2.74$

28. $84.26°$ **29.** $\frac{1}{4}$ **30.** -1 **31.** Limit does not exist.
32. $-\frac{1}{9}$ **33.** $\frac{1}{8}$ **34.** $\frac{1}{4}$ **35.** $m = -2x;\ 4$
36. $m = \frac{1}{2}(x+3)^{-1/2};\ \frac{1}{2}$ **37.** $m = -(x+3)^{-2};\ -\frac{1}{16}$

38. $m = 2x - 1$; 1 **39.** Limit does not exist.
40. Limit does not exist. **41.** -7 **42.** 3 **43.** 0
44. 0 **45.** $-42{,}875$ **46.** 8190 **47.** 672,880
48. $A = 10.5$ square units **49.** $A \approx 1.566$ square units
50. $\frac{3}{4}$ square unit **51.** $\frac{5}{2}$ square units **52.** $\frac{16}{3}$ square units

Problem Solving *(page 907)*

1. (a) g_1, g_4 (b) g_1, g_3, g_4 (c) g_1, g_4

3.

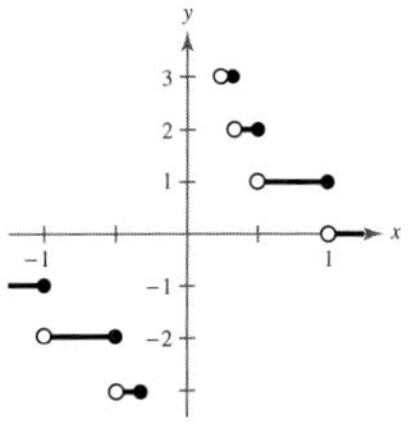

(a) $f\left(\frac{1}{4}\right) = [\![4]\!] = 4$
$f(3) = [\![\frac{1}{3}]\!] = 0$
$f(1) = [\![1]\!] = 1$

(b) $\lim_{x \to 1^-} f(x) = 1$
$\lim_{x \to 1^+} f(x) = 0$
$\lim_{x \to (1/2)^-} f(x) = 2$
$\lim_{x \to (1/2)^+} f(x) = 1$

5. $a = 3, b = 6$

7. $\lim_{x \to 0} f(x)$ does not exist. No matter how close x is to 0, there are still an infinite number of rational and irrational numbers, so $\lim_{x \to 0} f(x)$ does not exist.

$\lim_{x \to 0} g(x) = 0$. When x is close to 0, both parts of the function are close to 0.

9. $y = 1 + 3\sqrt{x}$

11. (a) $d(m) = \dfrac{|3m + 3|}{\sqrt{m^2 + 1}}$

(b)

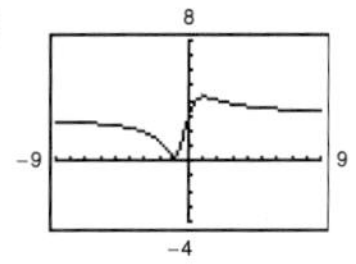

(c) $\lim_{m \to \infty} d(m) = 3$, $\lim_{m \to -\infty} d(m) = 3$. This indicates that the distance between the point and the line approaches 3 as the slope approaches positive or negative infinity.

13. The error was probably due to the calculator being in degree mode rather than radian mode.

15. (a)

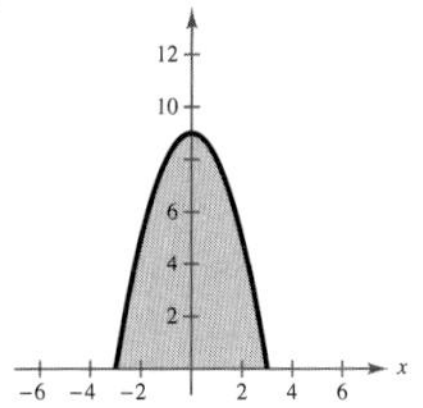

(b) $A = 36$
(c) Base = 6, height = 9; Area $= \frac{2}{3}bh = 36$

Appendix A

Appendix A.1 *(page A11)*

1. rational **3.** origin **5.** composite
7. variables; constants **9.** coefficient
11. (a) 5, 1, 2 (b) 0, 5, 1, 2 (c) $-9, 5, 0, 1, -4, 2, -11$
(d) $-\frac{7}{2}, \frac{2}{3}, -9, 5, 0, 1, -4, 2, -11$ (e) $\sqrt{2}$
13. (a) 1 (b) 1 (c) $-13, 1, -6$
(d) $2.01, -13, 1, -6, 0.666\ldots$ (e) $0.010110111\ldots$
15. (a) $\frac{6}{3}, 8$ (b) $\frac{6}{3}, 8$ (c) $\frac{6}{3}, -1, 8, -22$
(d) $-\frac{1}{3}, \frac{6}{3}, -7.5, -1, 8, -22$ (e) $-\pi, \frac{1}{2}\sqrt{2}$
17. (a)

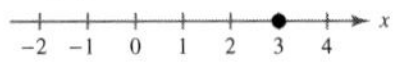

(b)

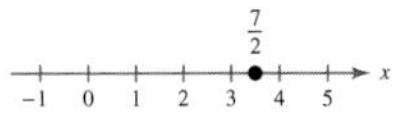

(c)

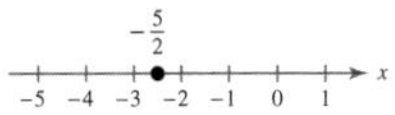

(d)

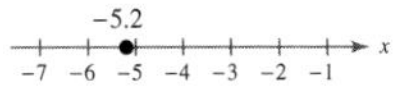

19. 0.625 **21.** $0.\overline{123}$ **23.** $-2.5 < 2$

25.

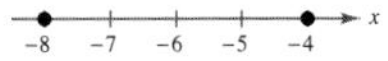

$-4 > -8$

27.

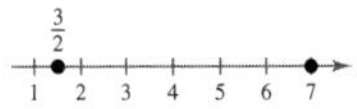

$\frac{3}{2} < 7$

29.

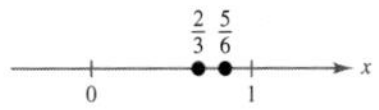

$\frac{5}{6} > \frac{2}{3}$

31. (a) $x \le 5$ denotes the set of all real numbers less than or equal to 5.
(b)

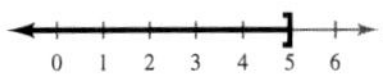

(c) Unbounded

33. (a) $x < 0$ denotes the set of all real numbers less than 0.
(b)

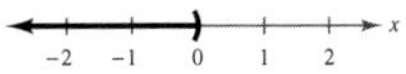

(c) Unbounded

35. (a) $[4, \infty)$ denotes the set of all real numbers greater than or equal to 4.
(b)

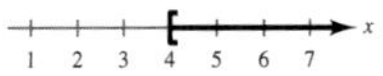

(c) Unbounded

37. (a) $-2 < x < 2$ denotes the set of all real numbers greater than -2 and less than 2.
(b)

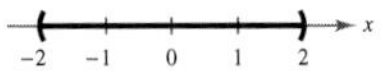

(c) Bounded

39. (a) $-1 \le x < 0$ denotes the set of all real numbers greater than or equal to -1 and less than 0.
(b)

(c) Bounded

41. (a) $[-2, 5)$ denotes the set of all real numbers greater than or equal to -2 and less than 5.
(b)

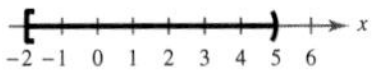

(c) Bounded

APPENDIX A

	Inequality	*Interval*
43.	$y \geq 0$	$[0, \infty)$
45.	$-2 < x \leq 4$	$(-2, 4]$
47.	$10 \leq t \leq 22$	$[10, 22]$
49.	$W > 65$	$(65, \infty)$

51. 10 **53.** 5 **55.** -1 **57.** -1 **59.** -1

61. $|-3| > -|-3|$ **63.** $-5 = -|5|$

65. $-|-2| = -|2|$ **67.** 51 **69.** $\frac{5}{2}$ **71.** $\frac{128}{75}$

73. $|x - 5| \leq 3$ **75.** $|y| \geq 6$

77. $|57 - 236| = 179$ mi

79. $|\$113{,}356 - \$112{,}700| = \$656 > \$500$
$0.05(\$112{,}700) = \$5635$
Because the actual expense differs from the budget by more than \$500, there is failure to meet the "budget variance test."

81. $|\$37{,}335 - \$37{,}640| = \$305 < \$500$
$0.05(\$37{,}640) = \$1882$
Because the difference between the actual expense and the budget is less than \$500 and less than 5% of the budgeted amount, there is compliance with the "budget variance test."

83. \$1453.2 billion; \$107.4 billion

85. \$2025.5 billion; \$236.3 billion

87. \$1880.3 billion; \$412.7 billion

89. $7x$ and 4 are the terms; 7 is the coefficient.

91. $\sqrt{3}x^2$, $-8x$, and -11 are the terms; $\sqrt{3}$ and -8 are the coefficients.

93. $4x^3$, $x/2$, and -5 are the terms; 4 and $\frac{1}{2}$ are the coefficients.

95. (a) -10 (b) -6 **97.** (a) 14 (b) 2

99. (a) Division by 0 is undefined. (b) 0

101. Commutative Property of Addition

103. Multiplicative Inverse Property

105. Distributive Property

107. Multiplicative Identity Property

109. Associative Property of Addition

111. Distributive Property

113. $\frac{1}{2}$ **115.** $\frac{3}{8}$ **117.** 48 **119.** $\frac{5x}{12}$

121. (a) Negative (b) Negative

123. (a)

n	1	0.5	0.01	0.0001	0.000001
$5/n$	5	10	500	50,000	5,000,000

(b) The value of $5/n$ approaches infinity as n approaches 0.

125. True. Because $b < 0$, $a - b$ subtracts a negative number from (or adds a positive number to) a positive number. The sum of two positive numbers is positive.

127. False. If $a < b$, then $\frac{1}{a} > \frac{1}{b}$, where $a \neq 0$ and $b \neq 0$.

129. (a) No. If one variable is negative and the other is positive, the expressions are unequal.
(b) No. $|u + v| \leq |u| + |v|$
The expressions are equal when u and v have the same sign. If u and v differ in sign, $|u + v|$ is less than $|u| + |v|$.

131. The only even prime number is 2, because its only factors are itself and 1.

133. Yes. $|a| = -a$ if $a < 0$.

Appendix A.2 *(page A24)*

1. exponent; base **3.** square root **5.** index; radicand

7. like radicals **9.** rationalizing **11.** (a) 27 (b) 81

13. (a) 1 (b) -9 **15.** (a) 243 (b) $-\frac{3}{4}$

17. (a) $\frac{5}{6}$ (b) 4 **19.** -1600 **21.** 2.125

23. -24 **25.** 6 **27.** -54 **29.** -5

31. (a) $-125z^3$ (b) $5x^6$ **33.** (a) $24y^2$ (b) $3x^2$

35. (a) $\frac{7}{x}$ (b) $\frac{4}{3}(x + y)^2$ **37.** (a) $\frac{x^2}{y^2}$ (b) $\frac{b^5}{a^5}$

39. (a) 1 (b) $\frac{1}{4x^4}$ **41.** (a) $-2x^3$ (b) $\frac{10}{x}$

43. (a) 3^{3n} (b) $\frac{b^5}{a^5}$ **45.** 1.02504×10^4

47. -1.25×10^{-4} **49.** 5.73×10^7 mi^2

51. 8.99×10^{-5} g/cm^3 **53.** 125,000 **55.** -0.002718

57. 15,000,000°C **59.** 0.00009 m

61. (a) 6.8×10^5 (b) 6.0×10^4

63. (a) 954.448 (b) 3.077×10^{10}

65. (a) 3 (b) $\frac{3}{2}$ **67.** (a) $\frac{1}{8}$ (b) $\frac{27}{8}$

69. (a) -4 (b) 2 **71.** (a) 7.550 (b) -7.225

73. (a) -0.011 (b) 0.005

75. (a) 67,082.039 (b) 39.791

77. (a) 2 (b) $2\sqrt[5]{3}x$ **79.** (a) $2\sqrt{5}$ (b) $4\sqrt[3]{2}$

81. (a) $6x\sqrt{2x}$ (b) $\frac{18\sqrt{z}}{z^2}$

83. (a) $2x\sqrt[3]{2x^2}$ (b) $\frac{5|x|\sqrt{3}}{y^2}$

85. (a) $34\sqrt{2}$ (b) $22\sqrt{2}$ **87.** (a) $2\sqrt{x}$ (b) $4\sqrt{y}$

89. (a) $13\sqrt{x + 1}$ (b) $18\sqrt{5x}$

91. $\sqrt{5} + \sqrt{3} > \sqrt{5 + 3}$

93. $5 > \sqrt{3^2 + 2^2}$ **95.** $\frac{\sqrt{3}}{3}$ **97.** $\frac{\sqrt{14} + 2}{2}$

99. $\frac{2}{\sqrt{2}}$ **101.** $\frac{2}{3(\sqrt{5} - \sqrt{3})}$ **103.** $2.5^{1/2}$

105. $\sqrt[4]{81}$ **107.** $(-216)^{1/3}$ **109.** $81^{3/4}$

111. $\frac{2}{|x|}$ **113.** $\frac{1}{x^3}$, $x > 0$

115. (a) $\sqrt{3}$ (b) $\sqrt[3]{(x + 1)^2}$ **117.** (a) $2\sqrt[4]{2}$ (b) $\sqrt[8]{2x}$

119. $\frac{\pi}{2} \approx 1.57$ sec

121. (a)

h	0	1	2	3	4	5	6
t	0	2.93	5.48	7.67	9.53	11.08	12.32

h	7	8	9	10	11	12
t	13.29	14.00	14.50	14.80	14.93	14.96

(b) $t \to 8.64\sqrt{3} \approx 14.96$

123. True. When dividing variables, you subtract exponents.

125. $a^0 = 1, a \neq 0$, using the property $\dfrac{a^m}{a^n} = a^{m-n}$:

$\dfrac{a^m}{a^m} = a^{m-m} = a^0 = 1.$

127. No. A number is in scientific notation when there is only one nonzero digit to the left of the decimal point.

129. No. Rationalizing the denominator produces a number equivalent to the original fraction; squaring does not.

Appendix A.3 *(page A35)*

1. n; a_n; a_0 **3.** monomial; binomial; trinomial
5. First terms; Outer terms; Inner terms; Last terms
7. completely factored **9.** d **10.** e **11.** b
12. a **13.** f **14.** c **15.** $-2x^3 + 4x^2 - 3x + 20$
17. $-15x^4 + 1$
19. (a) $-\frac{1}{2}x^5 + 14x$
(b) Degree: 5; Leading coefficient: $-\frac{1}{2}$
(c) Binomial
21. (a) $-3x^4 + x^2 - 4$
(b) Degree: 4; Leading coefficient: -3
(c) Trinomial
23. (a) $-x^6 + 3$
(b) Degree: 6; Leading coefficient: -1
(c) Binomial
25. (a) 3
(b) Degree: 0; Leading coefficient: 3
(c) Monomial
27. (a) $-4x^5 + 6x^4 + 1$
(b) Degree: 5; Leading coefficient: -4
(c) Trinomial
29. (a) $4x^3y$
(b) Degree: 4; Leading coefficient: 4
(c) Monomial
31. Polynomial: $-3x^3 + 2x + 8$
33. Not a polynomial because it includes a term with a negative exponent
35. Polynomial: $-y^4 + y^3 + y^2$
37. $-2x - 10$ **39.** $5t^3 - 5t + 1$
41. $8.3x^3 + 29.7x^2 + 11$ **43.** $12z + 8$
45. $3x^3 - 6x^2 + 3x$ **47.** $-15z^2 + 5z$ **49.** $-4x^4 + 4x$
51. $-4.5t^3 - 15t$ **53.** $-0.2x^2 - 34x$
55. $x^2 + 7x + 12$ **57.** $6x^2 - 7x - 5$ **59.** $x^2 - 100$
61. $x^2 - 4y^2$ **63.** $4x^2 + 12x + 9$
65. $x^3 + 3x^2 + 3x + 1$ **67.** $8x^3 - 12x^2y + 6xy^2 - y^3$
69. $16x^6 - 24x^3 + 9$ **71.** $x^4 + x^2 + 1$
73. $-3x^4 - x^3 - 12x^2 - 19x - 5$
75. $m^2 - n^2 - 6m + 9$
77. $x^2 + 2xy + y^2 - 6x - 6y + 9$ **79.** $4r^4 - 25$
81. $\frac{1}{16}x^2 - \frac{5}{2}x + 25$ **83.** $\frac{1}{25}x^2 - 9$
85. $5.76x^2 + 14.4x + 9$ **87.** $2.25x^2 - 16$
89. $2x^2 + 2x$ **91.** $u^4 - 16$ **93.** $x - y$
95. $x^2 - 2\sqrt{5}x + 5$ **97.** $4(x + 4)$ **99.** $2x(x^2 - 3)$
101. $(x - 5)(3x + 8)$ **103.** $(x + 3)(x - 1)$
105. $\frac{1}{2}(x + 8)$ **107.** $\frac{1}{2}x(x^2 + 4x - 10)$
109. $\frac{2}{3}(x - 6)(x - 3)$ **111.** $(x + 9)(x - 9)$
113. $3(4y - 3)(4y + 3)$ **115.** $\left(4x + \frac{1}{3}\right)\left(4x - \frac{1}{3}\right)$
117. $(x + 1)(x - 3)$ **119.** $(3u + 2v)(3u - 2v)$
121. $(x - 2)^2$ **123.** $(2t + 1)^2$ **125.** $(5y - 1)^2$
127. $(3u + 4v)^2$ **129.** $\left(x - \frac{2}{3}\right)^2$ **131.** $\frac{1}{9}(6x - 1)^2$
133. $(x - 2)(x^2 + 2x + 4)$ **135.** $(y + 4)(y^2 - 4y + 16)$
137. $\frac{1}{27}(3x - 2)(9x^2 + 6x + 4)$ **139.** $(2t - 1)(4t^2 + 2t + 1)$
141. $(u + 3v)(u^2 - 3uv + 9v^2)$
143. $(x - y + 2)(x^2 + xy + 4x + y^2 + 2y + 4)$
145. $(x + 2)(x - 1)$ **147.** $(s - 3)(s - 2)$
149. $-(y + 5)(y - 4)$ **151.** $(x - 20)(x - 10)$
153. $(3x - 2)(x - 1)$ **155.** $(5x + 1)(x + 5)$
157. $-(3z - 2)(3z + 1)$ **159.** $(x - 1)(x^2 + 2)$
161. $(2x - 1)(x^2 - 3)$ **163.** $(3 + x)(2 - x^3)$
165. $(3x^2 - 1)(2x + 1)$ **167.** $(x + 2)(3x + 4)$
169. $(2x - 1)(3x + 2)$ **171.** $(3x - 1)(5x - 2)$
173. $6(x + 3)(x - 3)$ **175.** $x^2(x - 1)$
177. $x(x - 4)(x + 4)$ **179.** $(x - 1)^2$ **181.** $(1 - 2x)^2$
183. $-2x(x + 1)(x - 2)$ **185.** $\frac{1}{81}(x + 36)(x - 18)$
187. $(3x + 1)(x^2 + 5)$ **189.** $x(x - 4)(x^2 + 1)$
191. $\frac{1}{4}(x^2 + 3)(x + 12)$ **193.** $(t + 6)(t - 8)$
195. $(x + 2)(x + 4)(x - 2)(x - 4)$
197. $5(x + 2)(x^2 - 2x + 4)$ **199.** $(3 - 4x)(23 - 60x)$
201. $5(1 - x)^2(3x + 2)(4x + 3)$
203. $(x - 2)^2(x + 1)^3(7x - 5)$
205. $3(x^2 + 1)^4(x^4 - x^2 + 1)^4(3x + 2)^2(33x^6 + 20x^5 + 3)$
207. $4x^3(2x + 1)^3(2x^2 + 2x + 1)$
209. $(2x - 5)^3(5x - 4)^2(70x - 107)$
211. $-\dfrac{8}{(5x - 1)^2}$ **213.** $-14, 14, -2, 2$
215. $-51, 51, -15, 15, -27, 27$
217. Two possible answers: $2, -12$
219. Two possible answers: $-2, -4$
221. (a) $P = 22x - 25{,}000$ (b) \$85,000
223. (a) $V = 4x^3 - 88x^2 + 468x$
(b)

x (cm)	1	2	3
V (cm³)	384	616	720

225. $44x + 308$
227.

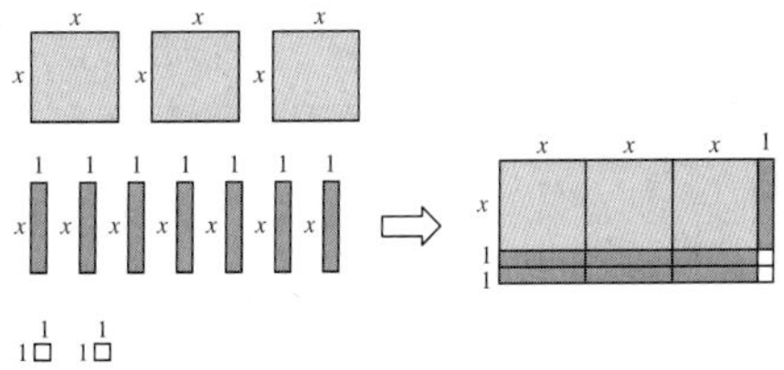

229.

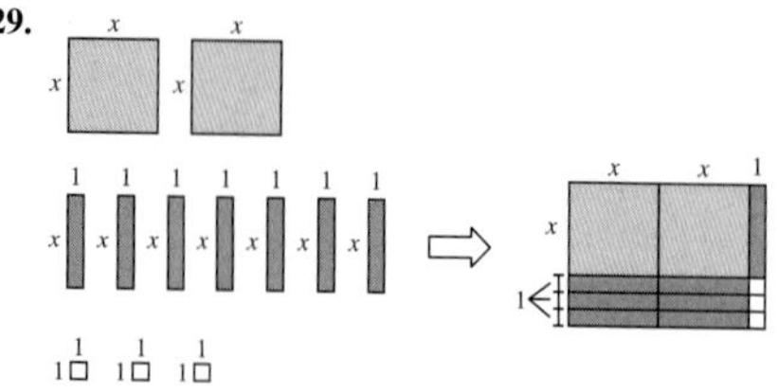

231. $4\pi(r + 1)$

233. (a) $V = \pi h(R + r)(R - r)$
(b) $V = \pi h(R + r)(R - r)$
$= \frac{2}{2}\pi h(R + r)(R - r)$
$= 2\pi\left(\frac{R + r}{2}\right)(R - r)h$

235. False. $(4x^2 + 1)(3x + 1) = 12x^3 + 4x^2 + 3x + 1$

237. True. $a^2 - b^2 = (a + b)(a - b)$

239. $m + n$ **241.** $-x^3 + 8x^2 + 2x + 7$

243. $(x^n + y^n)(x^n - y^n)$

245. Answers will vary. Sample answer: $x^2 - 3$

Appendix A.4 *(page A45)*

1. domain **3.** complex **5.** equivalent

7. All real numbers **9.** All nonnegative real numbers

11. All real numbers x such that $x \neq 3$

13. All real numbers x such that $x \neq 1$

15. All real numbers x such that $x \neq 3$

17. All real numbers x such that $x \geq -7$

19. All real numbers x such that $x \geq \frac{5}{2}$

21. All real numbers x such that $x > 3$

23. $3x,\ x \neq 0$ **25.** $\frac{3x}{2},\ x \neq 0$ **27.** $\frac{3y}{y + 1},\ x \neq 0$

29. $\frac{-4y}{5},\ y \neq \frac{1}{2}$ **31.** $-\frac{1}{2},\ x \neq 5$ **33.** $y - 4,\ y \neq -4$

35. $\frac{x(x + 3)}{x - 2},\ x \neq -2$ **37.** $\frac{y - 4}{y + 6},\ y \neq 3$

39. $\frac{-(x^2 + 1)}{(x + 2)},\ x \neq 2$ **41.** $z - 2$

43. When simplifying fractions, you can only divide out common factors, not terms.

45.

x	0	1	2	3	4	5	6
$\frac{x^2 - 2x - 3}{x - 3}$	1	2	3	Undef.	5	6	7
$x + 1$	1	2	3	4	5	6	7

The expressions are equivalent except at $x = 3$.

47. $\frac{\pi}{4},\ r \neq 0$ **49.** $\frac{1}{5(x - 2)},\ x \neq 1$ **51.** $\frac{r + 1}{r},\ r \neq 1$

53. $\frac{t - 3}{(t + 3)(t - 2)},\ t \neq -2$

55. $\frac{(x + 6)(x + 1)}{x^2},\ x \neq 6, -1$

57. $\frac{6x + 13}{x + 3}$ **59.** $\frac{x + 5}{x - 1}$ **61.** $-\frac{2}{x - 2}$

63. $\frac{-2x^2 + 3x + 8}{(2x + 1)(x + 2)}$ **65.** $-\frac{x^2 + 3}{(x + 1)(x - 2)(x - 3)}$

67. $\frac{2 - x}{x^2 + 1},\ x \neq 0$

69. The error is incorrect subtraction in the numerator.

71. $\frac{1}{2},\ x \neq 2$ **73.** $x(x + 1),\ x \neq -1, 0$

75. $\frac{2x - 1}{2x},\ x > 0$ **77.** $\frac{x^7 - 2}{x^2}$ **79.** $\frac{-1}{(x^2 + 1)^5}$

81. $\frac{2x^3 - 2x^2 - 5}{(x - 1)^{1/2}}$ **83.** $\frac{3x - 1}{3},\ x \neq 0$

85. $\frac{-1}{x(x + h)},\ h \neq 0$ **87.** $\frac{-1}{(x - 4)(x + h - 4)},\ h \neq 0$

89. $\frac{1}{\sqrt{x + 2} + \sqrt{x}}$ **91.** $\frac{1}{\sqrt{t + 3} + \sqrt{3}},\ t \neq 0$

93. $\frac{1}{\sqrt{x + h + 1} + \sqrt{x + 1}},\ h \neq 0$

95. $\frac{x}{2(2x + 1)},\ x \neq 0$

97. (a) $\frac{1}{50}$ min (b) $\frac{x}{50}$ min (c) $\frac{120}{50} = 2.4$ min

99. (a) 6.39% (b) $\frac{288(MN - P)}{N(MN + 12P)}$; 6.39%

101. (a)

t	0	2	4	6	8	10	12	14	16	18	20	22
T	75	55.9	48.3	45	43.3	42.3	41.7	41.3	41.1	40.9	40.7	40.6

(b) The model is approaching a T-value of 40.

103. False. In order for the simplified expression to be equivalent to the original expression, the domain of the simplified expression needs to be restricted. If n is even, $x \neq -1, 1$. If n is odd, $x \neq 1$.

105. Completely factor each polynomial in the numerator and in the denominator. Then conclude that there are no common factors.

Appendix A.5 *(page A60)*

1. equation **3.** extraneous **5.** Identity

7. Conditional equation **9.** Identity

11. Conditional equation **13.** 4 **15.** -9 **17.** 5

19. 1 **21.** No solution **23.** $-\frac{96}{23}$ **25.** $-\frac{6}{5}$

27. No solution. The x-terms sum to zero, but the constant terms do not.

29. 10 **31.** 4 **33.** 0

35. No solution. The solution is extraneous.

37. No solution. The solution is extraneous.

39. No solution. The solution is extraneous.

41. 0 **43.** $2x^2 + 8x - 3 = 0$ **45.** $3x^2 - 90x - 10 = 0$

47. $0, -\frac{1}{2}$ **49.** $4, -2$ **51.** $5, 7$ **53.** $3, -\frac{1}{2}$

55. $2, -6$ **57.** $-a$ **59.** ± 7 **61.** $\pm 3\sqrt{3}$

63. 8, 16 **65.** $-2 \pm \sqrt{14}$ **67.** $\dfrac{1 \pm 3\sqrt{2}}{2}$

69. 2 **71.** 4, -8 **73.** $\sqrt{11} - 6, -\sqrt{11} - 6$

75. $2 \pm 2\sqrt{3}$ **77.** $\dfrac{-5 \pm \sqrt{89}}{4}$ **79.** $\dfrac{15 \pm \sqrt{85}}{10}$

81. $\dfrac{1}{2}, -1$ **83.** $1 \pm \sqrt{3}$ **85.** $-7 \pm \sqrt{5}$

87. $-4 \pm 2\sqrt{5}$ **89.** $\dfrac{2}{3} \pm \dfrac{\sqrt{7}}{3}$ **91.** $-\dfrac{4}{3}$ **93.** $\dfrac{2}{7}$

95. $2 \pm \dfrac{\sqrt{6}}{2}$ **97.** $6 \pm \sqrt{11}$ **99.** $-3.449, 1.449$

101. $1.355, -14.071$ **103.** $1.687, -0.488$ **105.** $1 \pm \sqrt{2}$

107. $6, -12$ **109.** $\dfrac{1}{2} \pm \sqrt{3}$ **111.** ± 1 **113.** $0, \pm 5$

115. ± 3 **117.** -6 **119.** $3, 1, -1$ **121.** ± 1

123. $\pm\sqrt{3}, \pm 1$ **125.** $1, -2$ **127.** 50 **129.** 26

131. No solution **133.** $-\frac{513}{2}$

135. 6, 7 **137.** 10 **139.** $-3 \pm 5\sqrt{5}$ **141.** 1

143. $2, -\frac{3}{2}$ **145.** $4, -5$ **147.** $\dfrac{1 \pm \sqrt{31}}{3}$ **149.** $3, -2$

151. $\sqrt{3}, -3$ **153.** $3, \dfrac{-1 - \sqrt{17}}{2}$ **155.** 61.2 in.

157. About 1.12 in. **159.** 43 cm; $\dfrac{1849\sqrt{3}}{4} \approx 800.6 \text{ cm}^2$

161. (a) 1998 (b) 2011; Answers will vary.

163. False. See Example 14 on page A58.

165. Equivalent equations have the same solution set, and one is derived from the other by steps for generating equivalent equations.
$2x = 5,\ 2x + 3 = 8$

167. $x^2 - 3x - 18 = 0$ **169.** $x^2 - 2x - 1 = 0$

171. Sample answer: $a = 9, b = 9$

173. Sample answer: $a = 20, b = 20$

175. (a) $x = 0, -\dfrac{b}{a}$ (b) $x = 0, 1$

Appendix A.6 *(page A69)*

1. solution set **3.** negative **5.** double

7. (a) $0 \le x < 9$ (b) Bounded

9. (a) $-1 \le x \le 5$ (b) Bounded

11. (a) $x > 11$ (b) Unbounded

13. (a) $x < -2$ (b) Unbounded

15. b **16.** h **17.** e **18.** d

19. f **20.** a **21.** g **22.** c

23. (a) Yes (b) No (c) Yes (d) No

25. (a) Yes (b) No (c) No (d) Yes

27. (a) Yes (b) Yes (c) Yes (d) No

29. $x < 3$

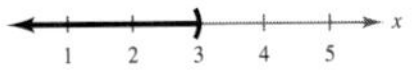

31. $x < \frac{3}{2}$

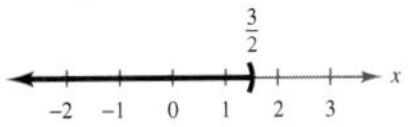

33. $x \ge 12$

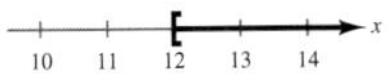

35. $x > 2$

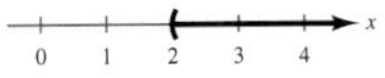

37. $x \ge \frac{2}{7}$

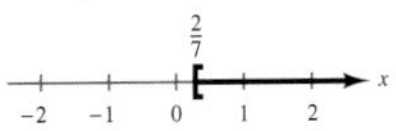

39. $x < 5$

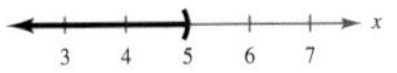

41. $x \ge 4$

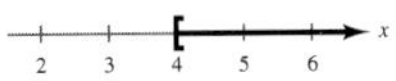

43. $x \ge 2$

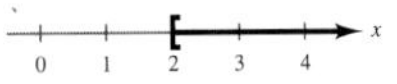

45. $x \ge -4$

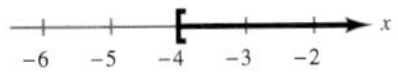

47. $-1 < x < 3$

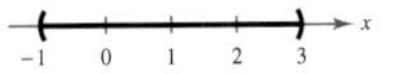

49. $-2 < x \le 5$

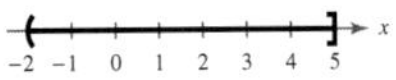

51. $-\frac{9}{2} < x < \frac{15}{2}$

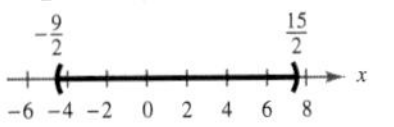

53. $-\frac{3}{4} < x < -\frac{1}{4}$

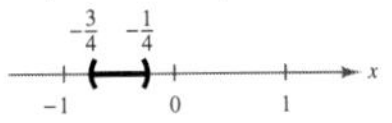

55. $10.5 \le x \le 13.5$

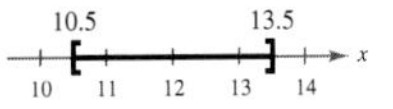

57. $-5 < x < 5$

59. $x < -2, x > 2$

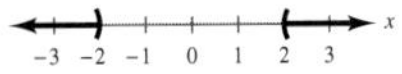

61. No solution

63. $14 \le x \le 26$

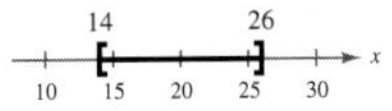

65. $x \le -\frac{3}{2}, x \ge 3$

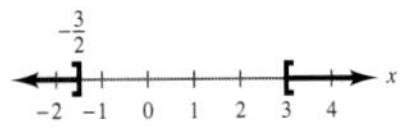

67. $x \le -5,\ x \ge 11$

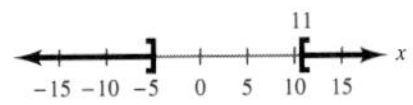

69. $4 < x < 5$

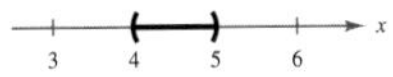

71. $x \le -\frac{29}{2},\ x \ge -\frac{11}{2}$

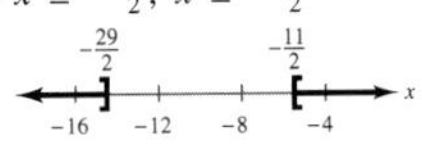

73.

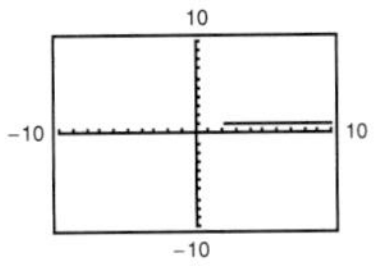

$x > 2$

75.

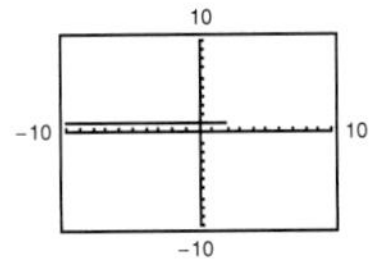

$x \le 2$

77.

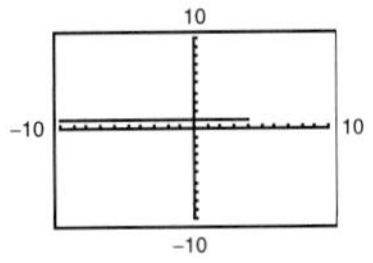

$x \le 4$

79.

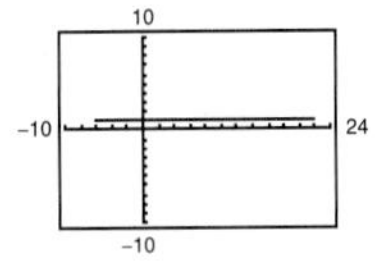

$-6 \le x \le 22$

81.

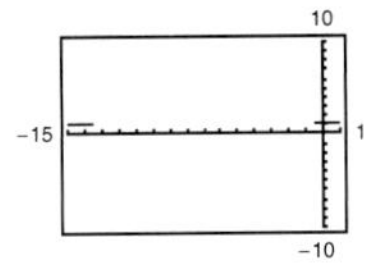

$x \le -\frac{27}{2}, x \ge -\frac{1}{2}$

83.

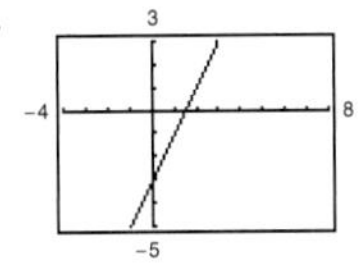

(a) $x \ge 2$
(b) $x \le \frac{3}{2}$

APPENDIX A

85.

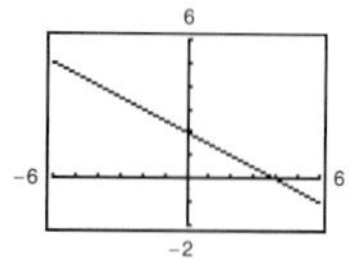

(a) $-2 \le x \le 4$
(b) $x \le 4$

87.

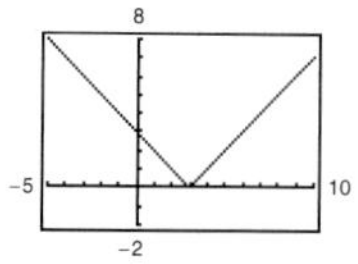

(a) $1 \le x \le 5$
(b) $x \le -1,\ x \ge 7$

89. $[5, \infty)$ **91.** $[-3, \infty)$ **93.** $\left(-\infty, \frac{7}{2}\right]$

95. All real numbers within eight units of 10

97. $|x| \le 3$ **99.** $|x - 7| \ge 3$ **101.** $|x - 12| < 10$

103. $|x + 3| > 4$ **105.** $4.10 \le E \le 4.25$

107. $p \le 0.45$ **109.** $100 \le r \le 170$

111. $9.00 + 0.75x > 13.50;\ x > 6$

113. $r > 3.125\%$ **115.** $x \ge 36$

117. $160 \le x \le 280$

119. (a)

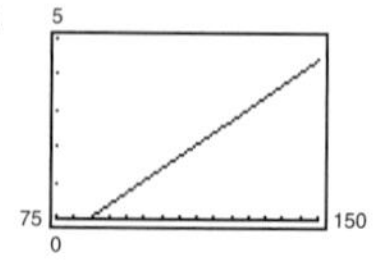

(b) $x \ge 129$

121. (a) $1.47 \le t \le 10.18$ (Between 1991 and 2000)
(b) $t > 21.19$ (2011)

123. 106.864 in.^{2} $\le$ area $\le$ 109.464 in.^{2}

125. You might be undercharged or overcharged by \$0.21.

127. $13.7 < t < 17.5$

129. $20 \le h \le 80$

131. False. c has to be greater than zero. **133.** b

135. Sample answer: $x > 5$

Appendix A.7 *(page A78)*

1. numerator

3. Change all signs when distributing the minus sign.
$2x - (3y + 4) = 2x - 3y - 4$

5. Change all signs when distributing the minus sign.
$$\frac{4}{16x - (2x + 1)} = \frac{4}{14x - 1}$$

7. z occurs twice as a factor. $(5z)(6z) = 30z^2$

9. The fraction as a whole is multiplied by a, not the numerator and denominator separately.
$$a\left(\frac{x}{y}\right) = \frac{ax}{y}$$

11. $\sqrt{x + 9}$ cannot be simplified.

13. Divide out common factors, not common terms.
$\dfrac{2x^2 + 1}{5x}$ cannot be simplified.

15. To get rid of negative exponents:
$$\frac{1}{a^{-1} + b^{-1}} = \frac{1}{a^{-1} + b^{-1}} \cdot \frac{ab}{ab} = \frac{ab}{b + a}.$$

17. Factor within grouping symbols before applying exponent to each factor.
$(x^2 + 5x)^{1/2} = [x(x + 5)]^{1/2} = x^{1/2}(x + 5)^{1/2}$

19. To add fractions, first find a common denominator.
$$\frac{3}{x} + \frac{4}{y} = \frac{3y + 4x}{xy}$$

21. To add fractions, first find a common denominator.
$$\frac{x}{2y} + \frac{y}{3} = \frac{3x + 2y^2}{6y}$$

23. $5x + 3$ **25.** $2x^2 + x + 15$ **27.** $\frac{1}{3}$ **29.** $3y - 10$

31. 2 **33.** $\dfrac{1}{2x^2}$ **35.** $\dfrac{36}{25}, \dfrac{9}{4}$ **37.** 3, 4 **39.** $1 - 5x$

41. $1 - 7x$ **43.** $3x - 1$ **45.** $7(x + 3)^{-5}$

47. $2x^5(3x + 5)^{-4}$ **49.** $\frac{4}{3}x^{-1} + 4x^{-4} - 7x(2x)^{-1/3}$

51. $\dfrac{x}{3} + 2 + \dfrac{4}{x}$ **53.** $4x^{8/3} - 7x^{5/3} + \dfrac{1}{x^{1/3}}$

55. $\dfrac{3}{x^{1/2}} - 5x^{3/2} - x^{7/2}$ **57.** $\dfrac{-7x^2 - 4x + 9}{(x^2 - 3)^3(x + 1)^4}$

59. $\dfrac{27x^2 - 24x + 2}{(6x + 1)^4}$ **61.** $\dfrac{-1}{(x + 3)^{2/3}(x + 2)^{7/4}}$

63. $\dfrac{4x - 3}{(3x - 1)^{4/3}}$ **65.** $\dfrac{x}{x^2 + 4}$

67. $\dfrac{(3x - 2)^{1/2}(15x^2 - 4x + 45)}{2(x^2 + 5)^{1/2}}$

69. (a)

x	0.50	1.0	1.5	2.0
t	1.70	1.72	1.78	1.89

x	2.5	3.0	3.5	4.0
t	2.02	2.18	2.36	2.57

(b) $x = 0.5$ mi

(c) $\dfrac{3x\sqrt{x^2 - 8x + 20} + (x - 4)\sqrt{x^2 + 4}}{6\sqrt{x^2 + 4}\sqrt{x^2 - 8x + 20}}$

71. You cannot move term-by-term from the denominator to the numerator.

D

INDEX

F

G

H

INDEX

I

J

K

L

INDEX

N

O

P

INDEX

Q

R

S

INDEX

T

U

V

W

INDEX

X

Y

Z

INDEX

Additional Answers

Chapter 1

Section 1.1 (page 8)

52. (a)

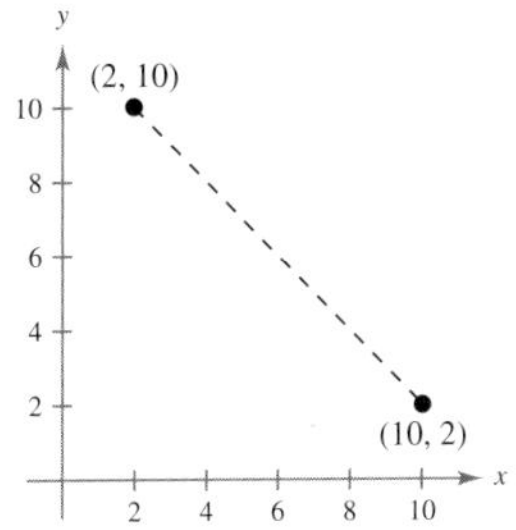

(b) $8\sqrt{2}$
(c) $(6, 6)$

53. (a)

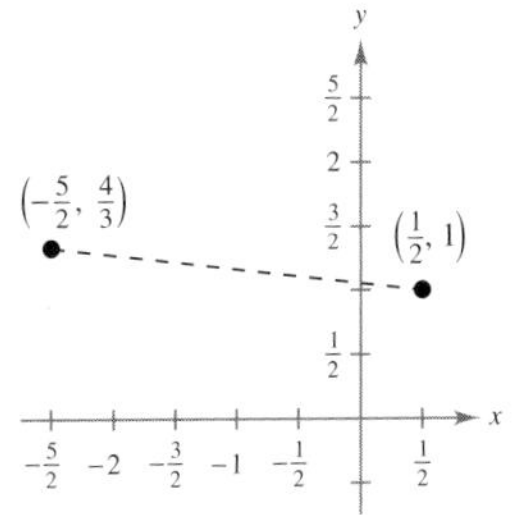

(b) $\dfrac{\sqrt{82}}{3}$
(c) $\left(-1, \dfrac{7}{6}\right)$

54. (a)

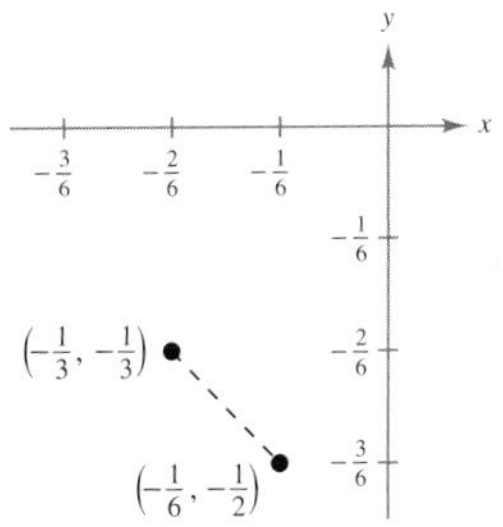

(b) $\dfrac{\sqrt{2}}{6}$
(c) $\left(-\dfrac{1}{4}, -\dfrac{5}{12}\right)$

55. (a)

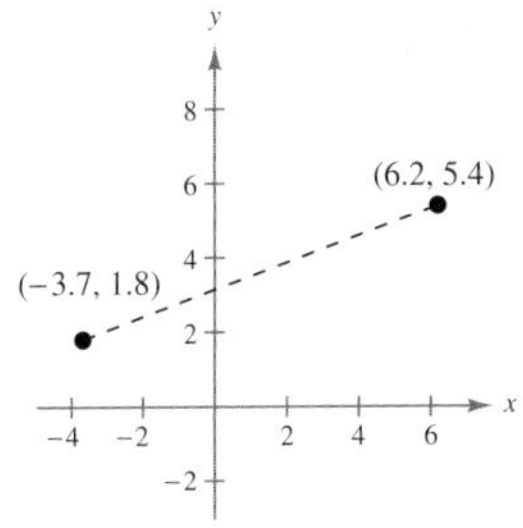

(b) $\sqrt{110.97}$
(c) $(1.25, 3.6)$

56. (a)

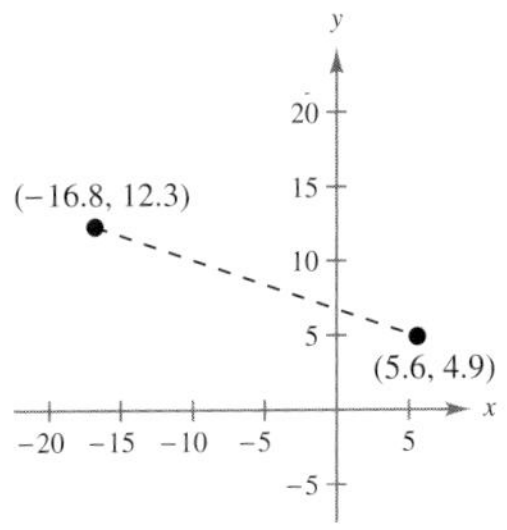

(b) $\sqrt{556.52}$
(c) $(-5.6, 8.6)$

Section 1.2 (page 21)

15.

x	-1	0	1	2	$\frac{5}{2}$
y	7	5	3	1	0
(x, y)	$(-1, 7)$	$(0, 5)$	$(1, 3)$	$(2, 1)$	$\left(\frac{5}{2}, 0\right)$

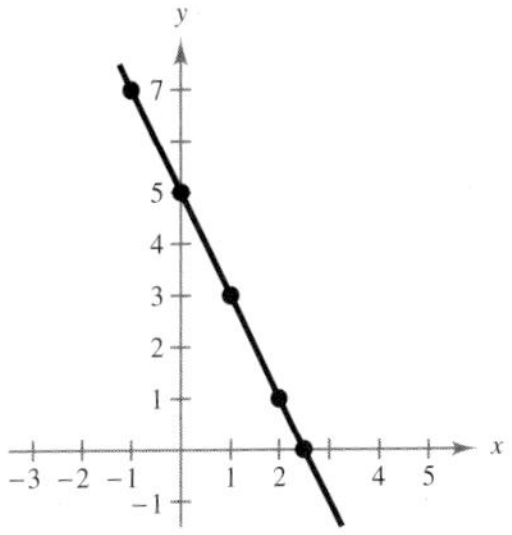

16.

x	-2	0	1	$\frac{4}{3}$	2
y	$-\frac{5}{2}$	-1	$-\frac{1}{4}$	0	$\frac{1}{2}$
(x, y)	$\left(-2, -\frac{5}{2}\right)$	$(0, -1)$	$\left(1, -\frac{1}{4}\right)$	$\left(\frac{4}{3}, 0\right)$	$\left(2, \frac{1}{2}\right)$

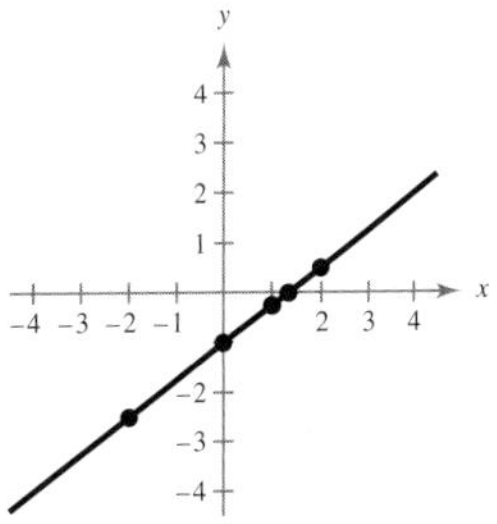

17.

x	-1	0	1	2	3
y	4	0	-2	-2	0
(x, y)	$(-1, 4)$	$(0, 0)$	$(1, -2)$	$(2, -2)$	$(3, 0)$

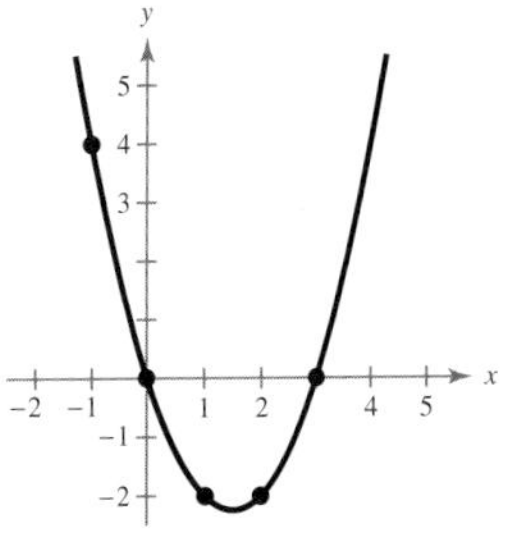

18.

x	-2	-1	0	1	2
y	1	4	5	4	1
(x, y)	$(-2, 1)$	$(-1, 4)$	$(0, 5)$	$(1, 4)$	$(2, 1)$

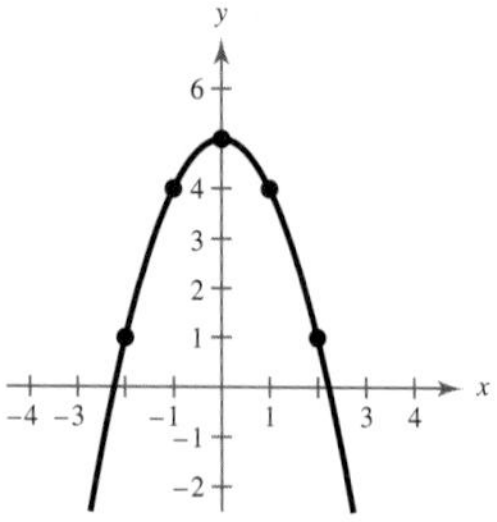

48. x-intercepts: $(-2, 0), (0, 0)$
y-intercept: $(0, 0)$
No symmetry

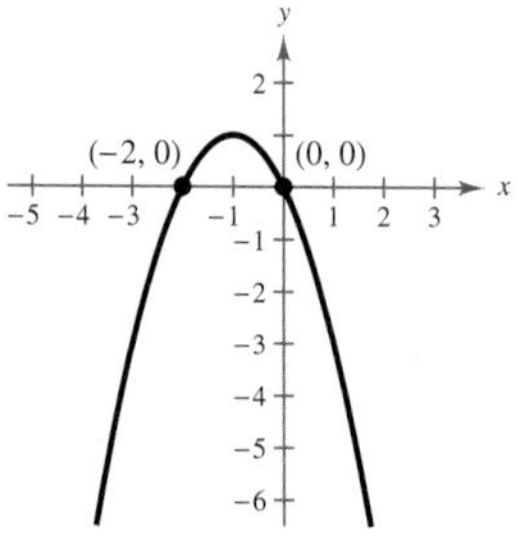

49. x-intercept: $\left(\sqrt[3]{-3}, 0\right)$
y-intercept: $(0, 3)$
No symmetry

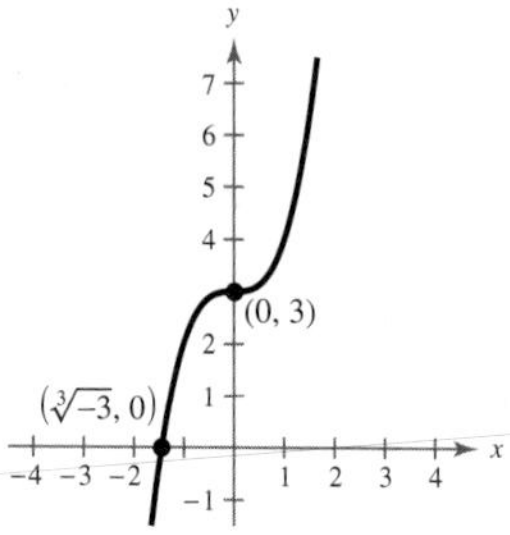

50. x-intercept: $(1, 0)$
y-intercept: $(0, -1)$
No symmetry

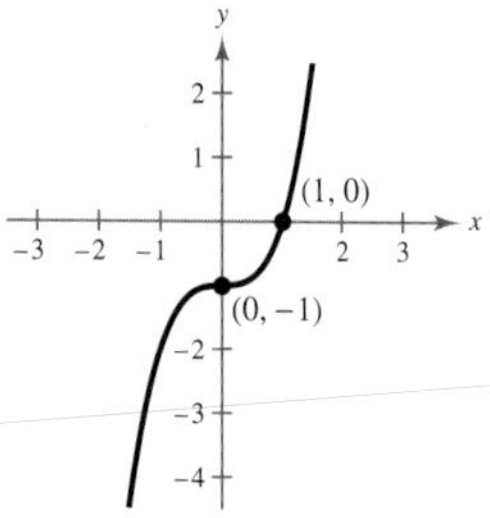

51. x-intercept: $(3, 0)$
y-intercept: None
No symmetry

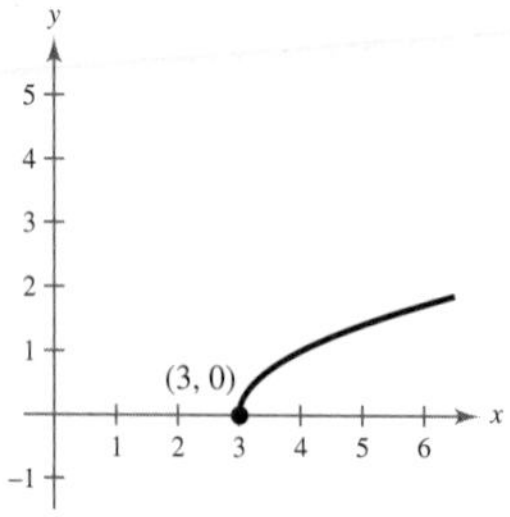

52. x-intercept: $(1, 0)$
y-intercept: $(0, 1)$
No symmetry

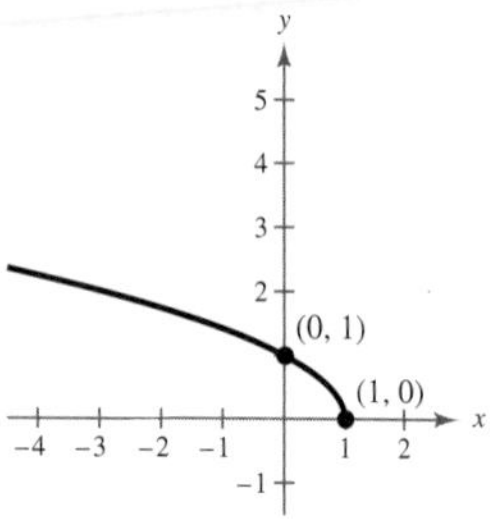

53. x-intercept: $(6, 0)$
y-intercept: $(0, 6)$
No symmetry

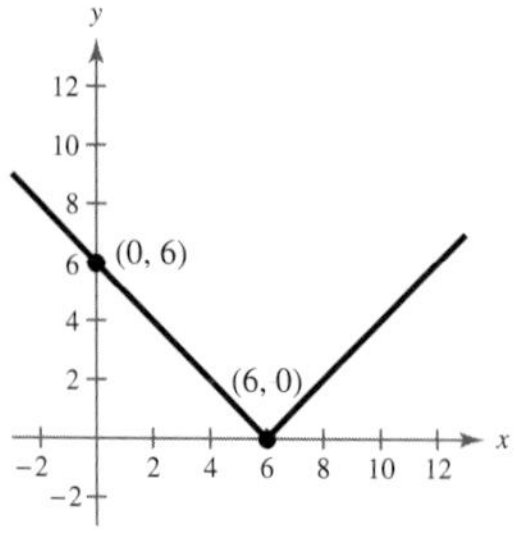

54. x-intercepts: $(\pm 1, 0)$
y-intercept: $(0, 1)$
y-axis symmetry

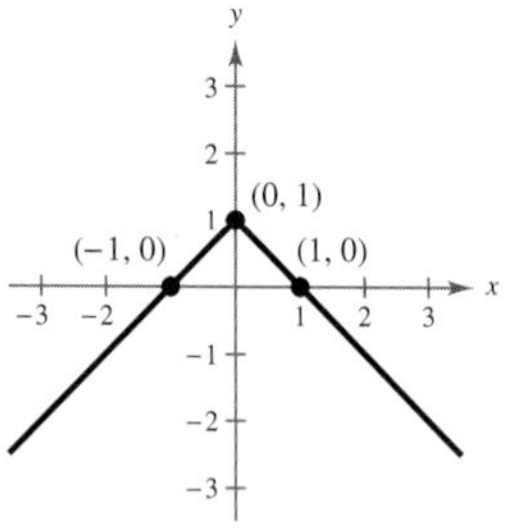

55. x-intercept: $(-1, 0)$
y-intercepts: $(0, \pm 1)$
x-axis symmetry

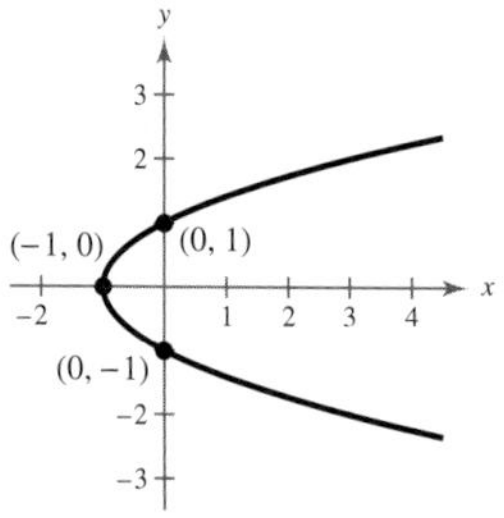

56. x-intercept: $(-5, 0)$
y-intercepts: $\left(0, \pm\sqrt{5}\right)$
x-axis symmetry

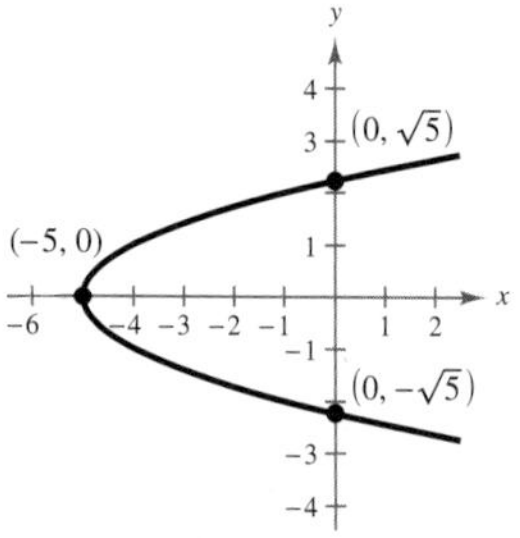

57.

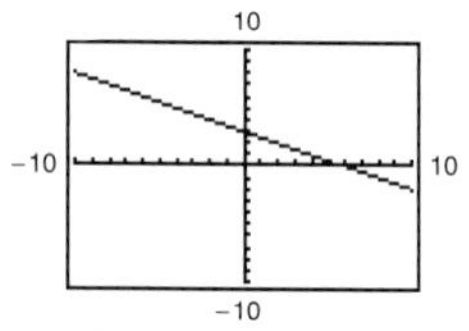

Intercepts: $(6, 0), (0, 3)$

58.

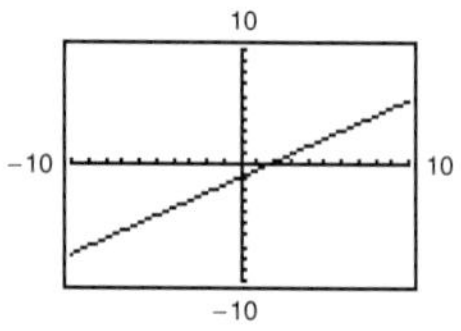

Intercepts: $\left(\frac{3}{2}, 0\right), (0, -1)$

59.

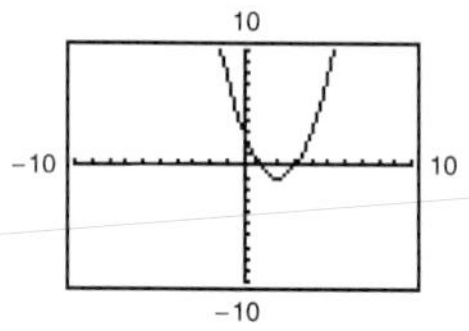

Intercepts: $(3, 0), (1, 0), (0, 3)$

60.

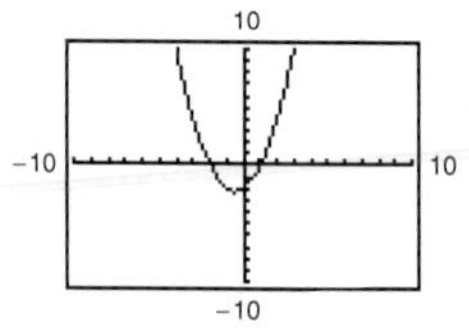

Intercepts: $(-2, 0), (1, 0), (0, -2)$

61.

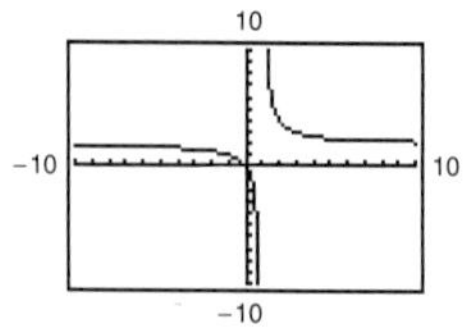

Intercept: $(0, 0)$

62.

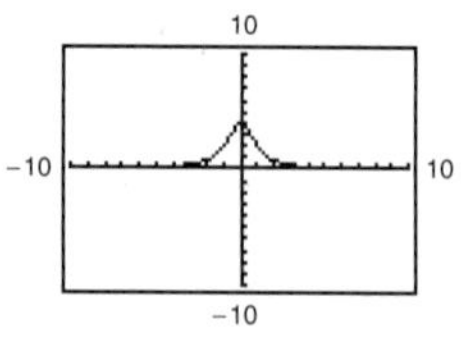

Intercept: $(0, 4)$

ADDITIONAL ANSWERS

63.

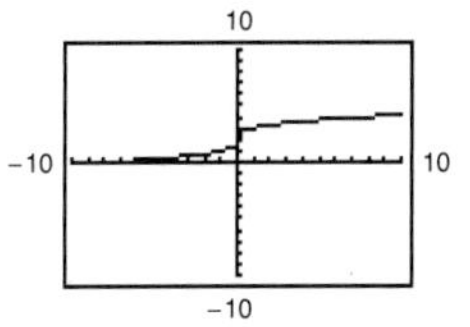

Intercepts: $(-8, 0), (0, 2)$

64.

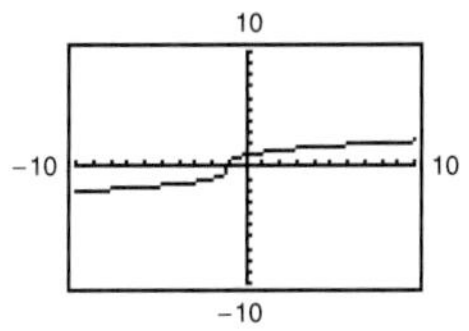

Intercepts: $(-1, 0), (0, 1)$

65.

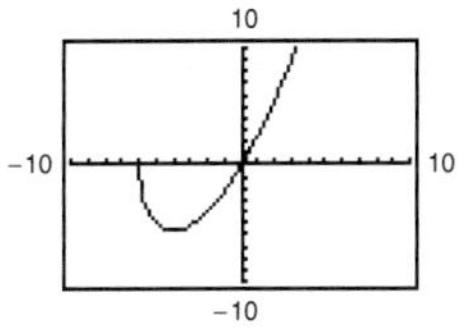

Intercepts: $(0, 0), (-6, 0)$

66.

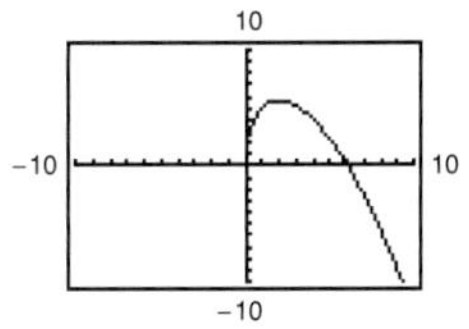

Intercepts: $(0, 0), (6, 0)$

67.

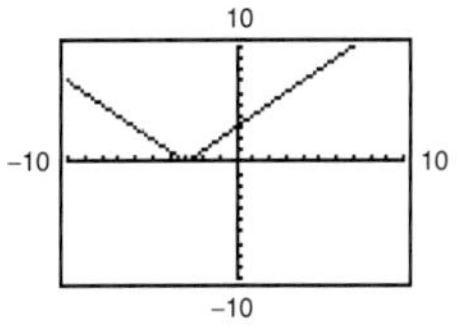

Intercepts: $(-3, 0), (0, 3)$

68.

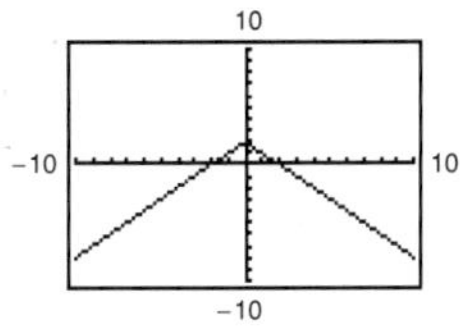

Intercepts: $(\pm 2, 0), (0, 2)$

71. $(x - 2)^2 + (y + 1)^2 = 16$

72. $(x + 7)^2 + (y + 4)^2 = 49$

73. $(x + 1)^2 + (y - 2)^2 = 5$

74. $(x - 3)^2 + (y + 2)^2 = 25$

75. $(x - 3)^2 + (y - 4)^2 = 25$

76. $x^2 + y^2 = 17$

77. Center: $(0, 0)$; Radius: 5

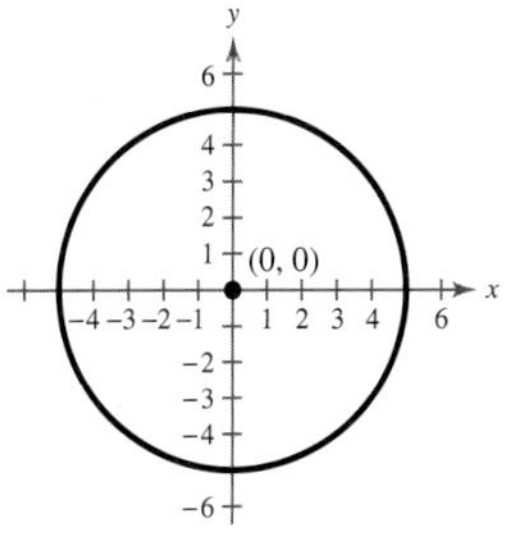

78. Center: $(0, 0)$; Radius: 4

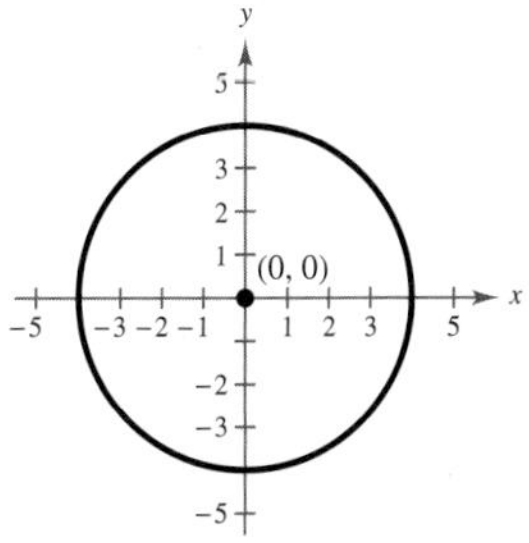

79. Center: $(1, -3)$; Radius: 3

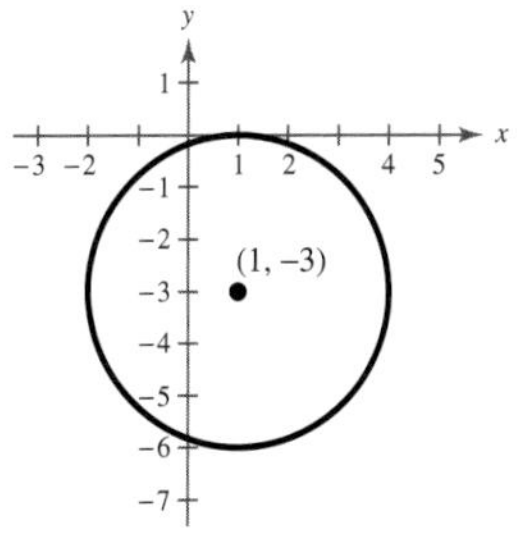

80. Center: $(0, 1)$; Radius: 1

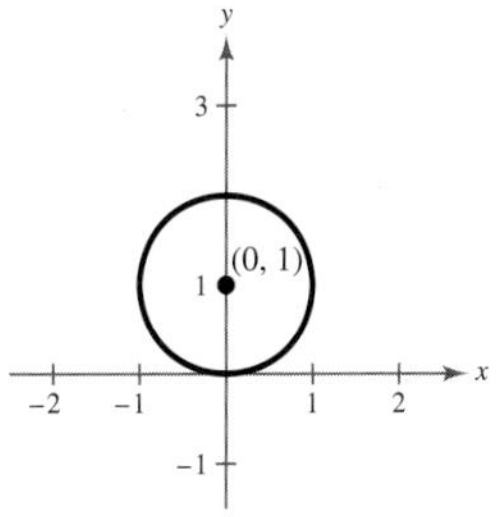

81. Center: $\left(\frac{1}{2}, \frac{1}{2}\right)$; Radius: $\frac{3}{2}$

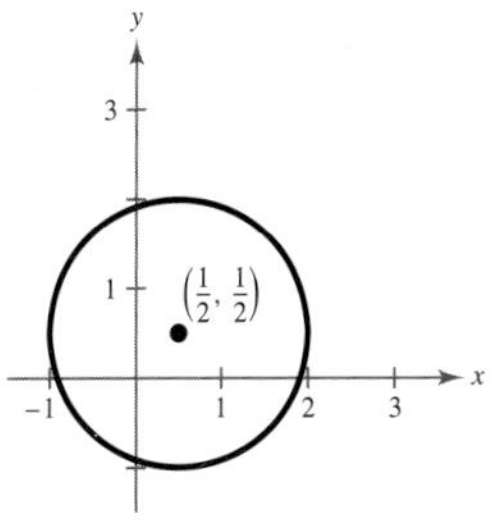

82. Center: $(2, -3)$; Radius: $\frac{4}{3}$

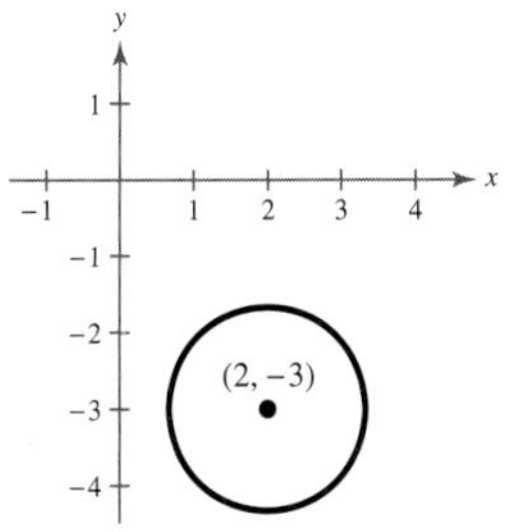

83.

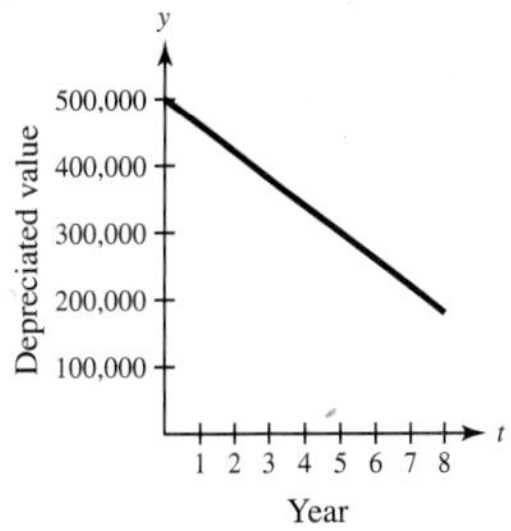

84.

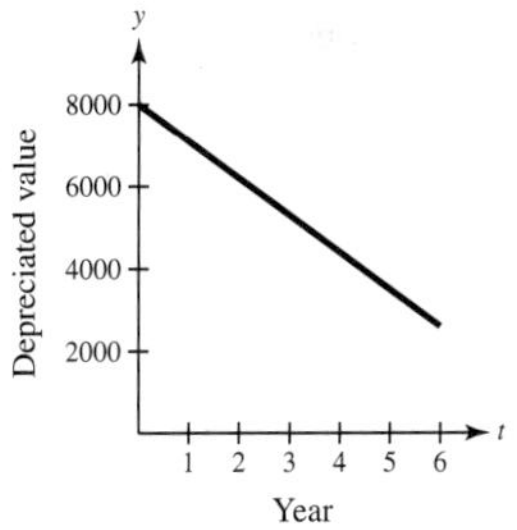

85. (a)

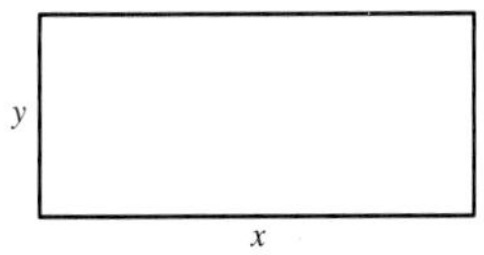

(b) Answers will vary.

(c)

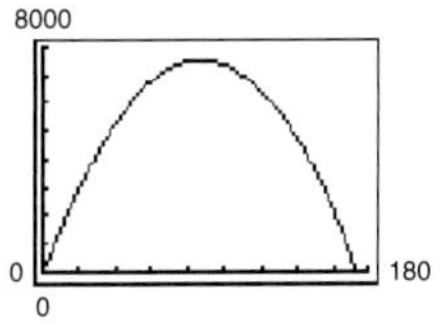

(d) $x = 86\frac{2}{3}, y = 86\frac{2}{3}$

(e) A regulation NFL playing field is 120 yards long and $53\frac{1}{3}$ yards wide. The actual area is 6400 square yards.

88. (a)

x	5	10	20	30	40
y	430.43	107.33	26.56	11.60	6.36

x	50	60	70	80	90	100
y	3.94	2.62	1.83	1.31	0.96	0.71

(b)

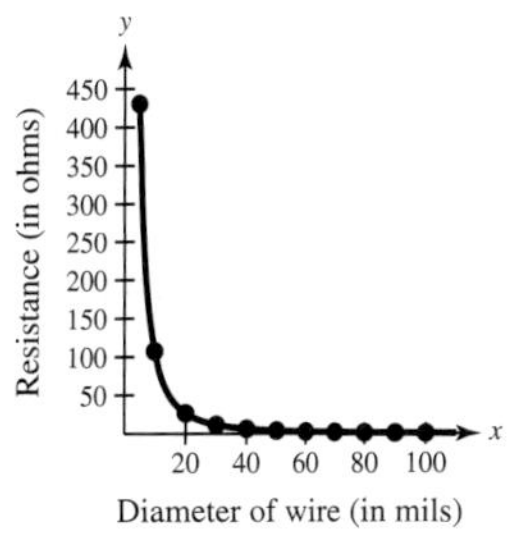

When $x = 85.5$, the resistance is 1.1 ohms.

(c) Answers will vary.

(d) As the diameter of the copper wire increases, the resistance decreases.

Section 1.3 *(page 33)*

20. $m = -\frac{3}{2}$

y-intercept: $(0, 6)$

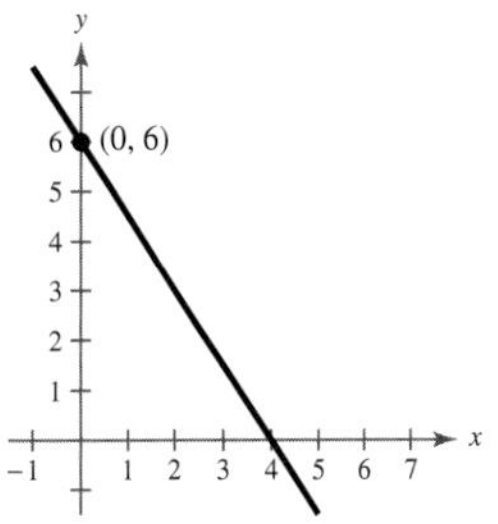

21. m is undefined.
There is no y-intercept.

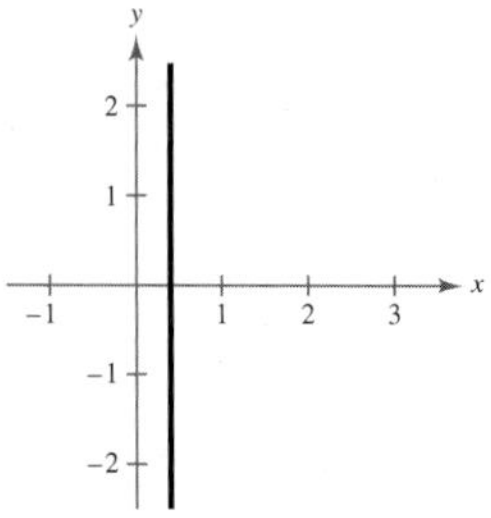

22. $m = 0$
y-intercept: $\left(0, -\frac{5}{3}\right)$

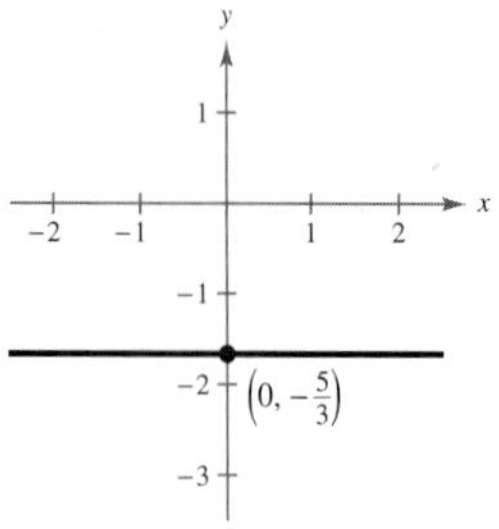

23. $m = -\frac{7}{6}$
y-intercept: $(0, 5)$

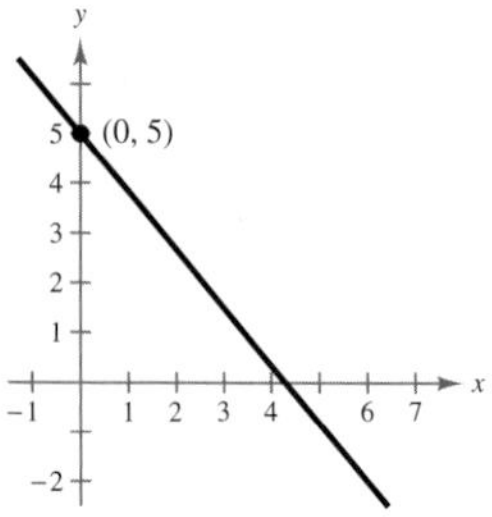

24. $m = -\frac{2}{3}$
y-intercept: $(0, 3)$

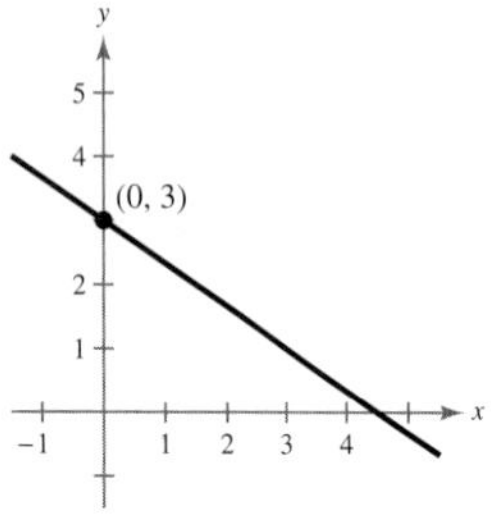

25. $m = 0$
y-intercept: $(0, 3)$

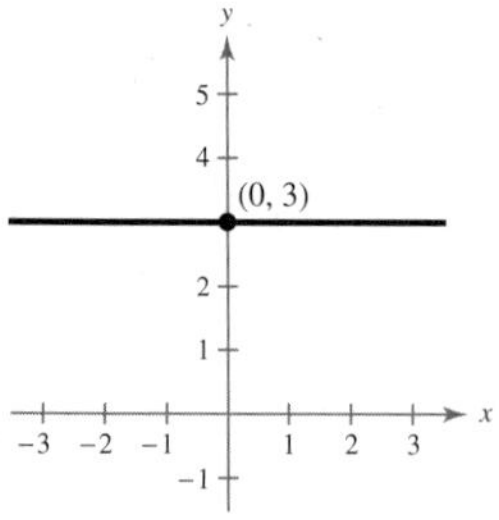

26. $m = 0$
y-intercept: $(0, -4)$

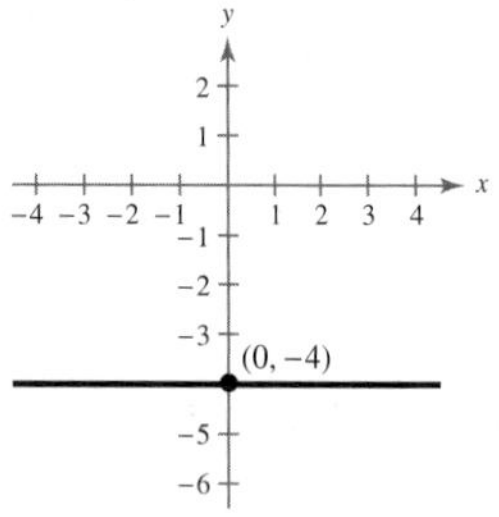

27. m is undefined.
There is no y-intercept.

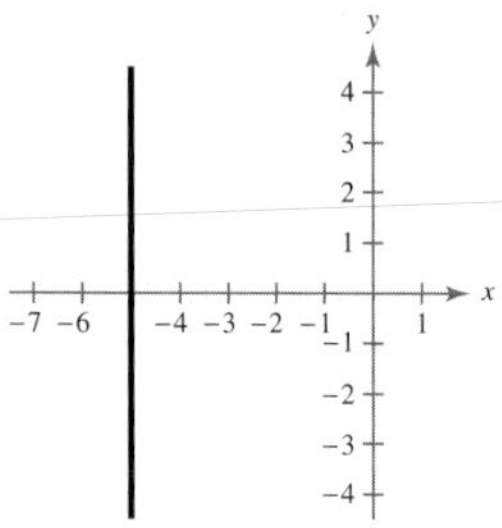

28. m is undefined.
There is no y-intercept.

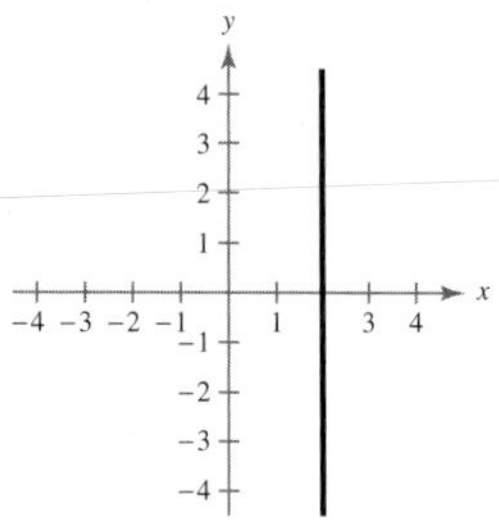

29.

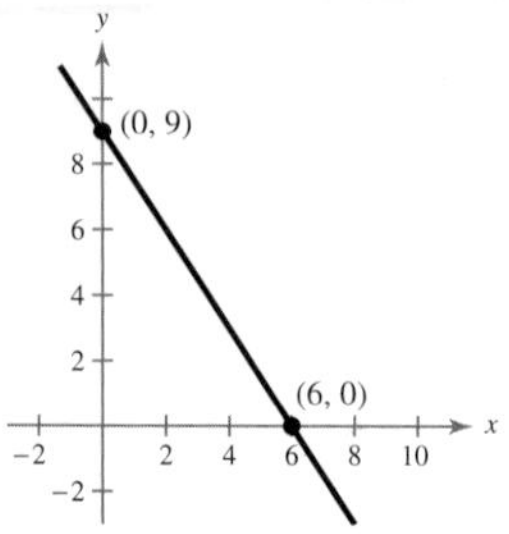

$m = -\frac{3}{2}$

30.

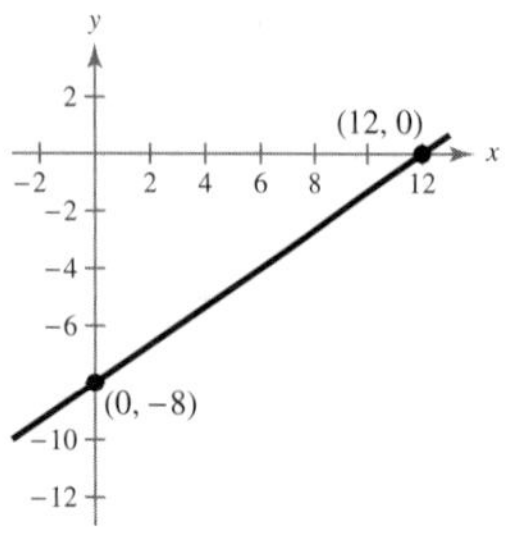

$m = \frac{2}{3}$

31.

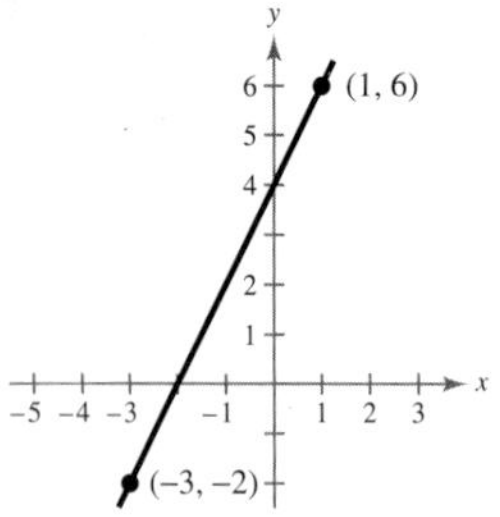

$m = 2$

32.

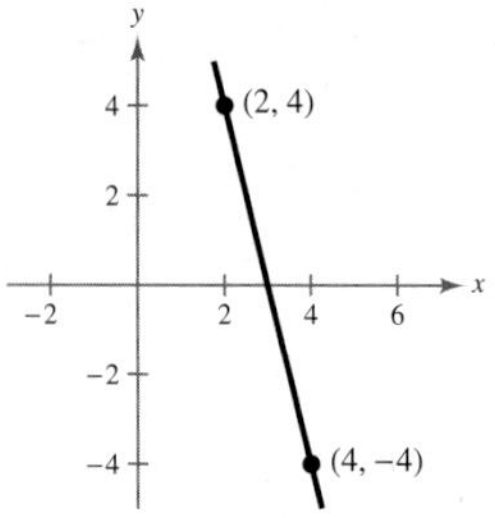

$m = -4$

33.

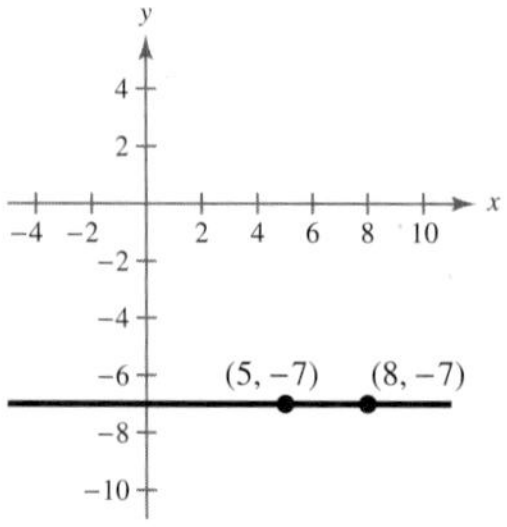

$m = 0$

34.

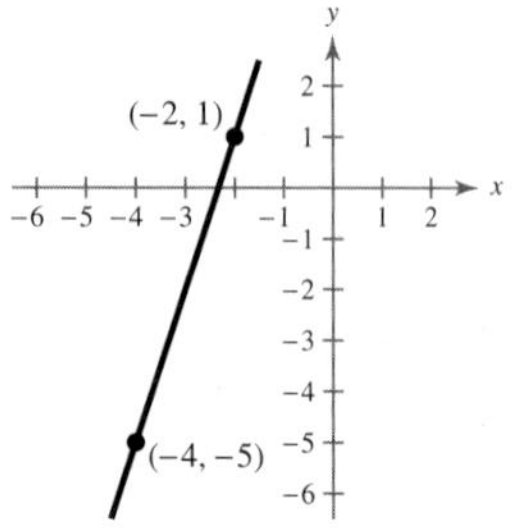

$m = 3$

35.

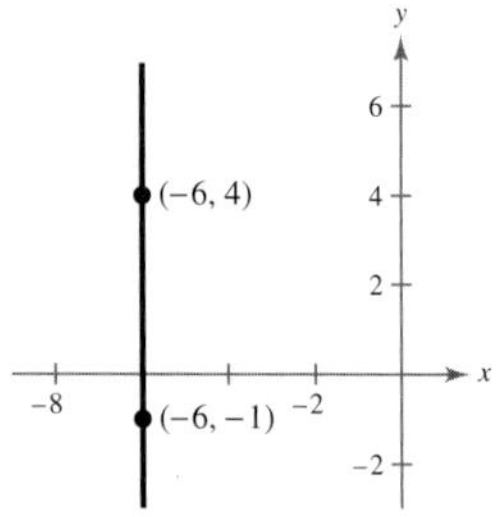

m is undefined.

36.

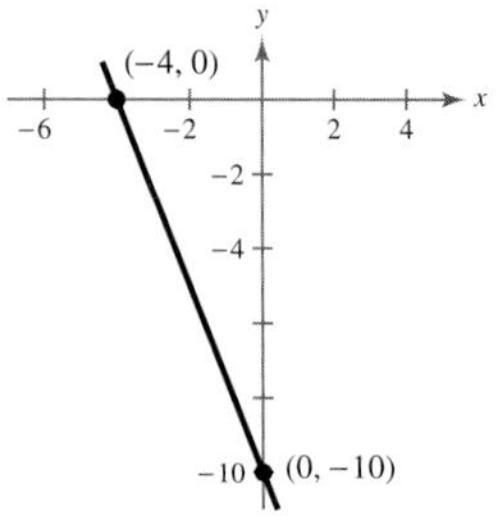

$m = -\frac{5}{2}$

37.

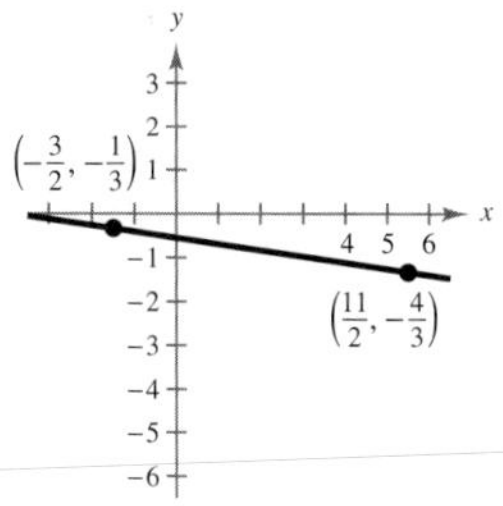

$m = -\frac{1}{7}$

38.

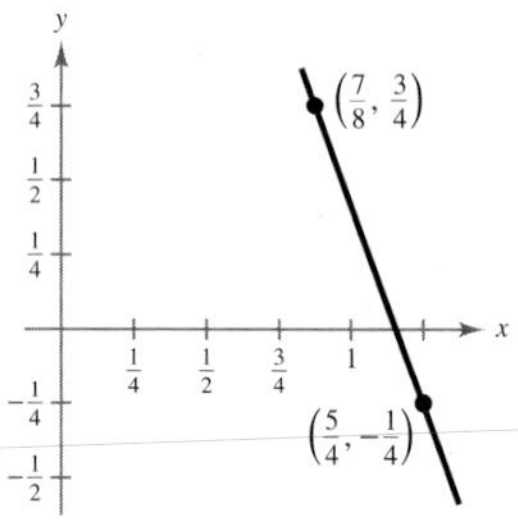

$m = -\frac{8}{3}$

39.

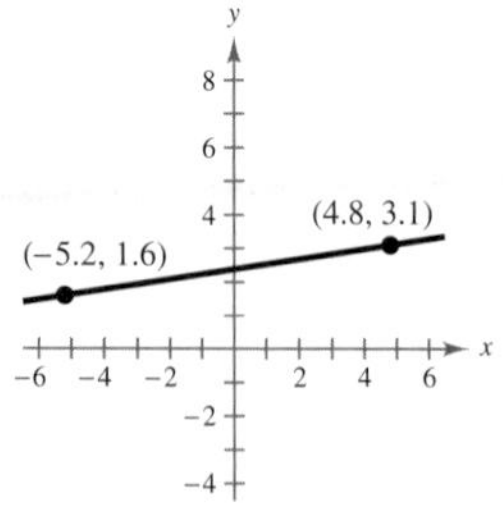

$m = 0.15$

40.

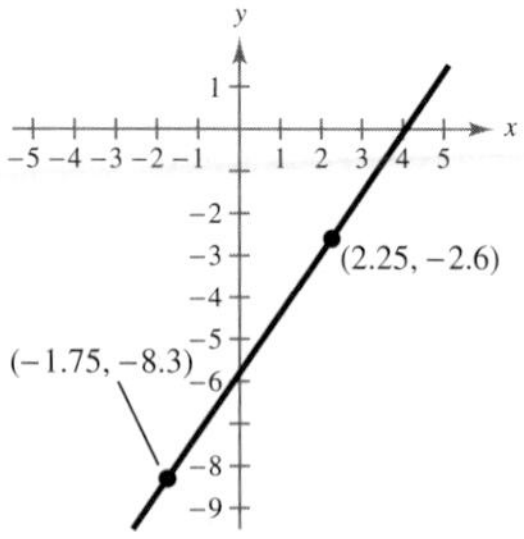

$m = 1.425$

ADDITIONAL ANSWERS

58. $y = \frac{3}{4}x - \frac{7}{2}$

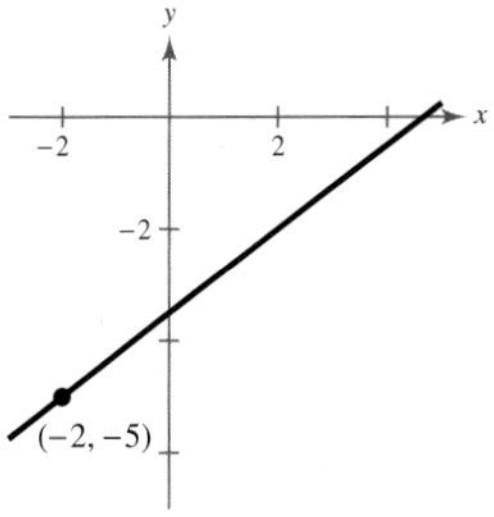

59. $x = 6$

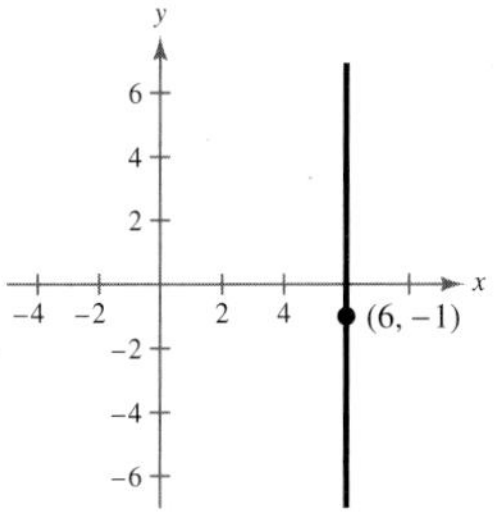

60. $x = -10$

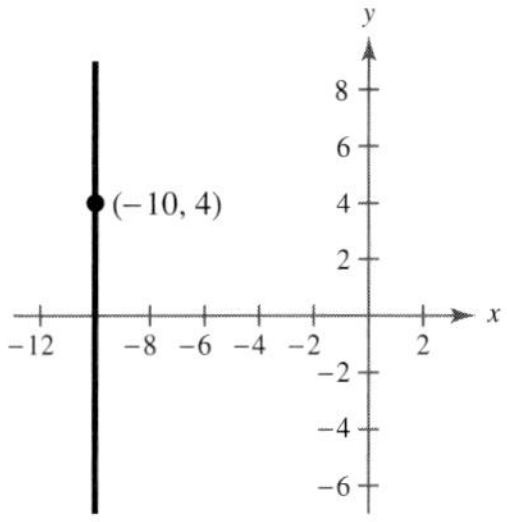

61. $y = \frac{5}{2}$

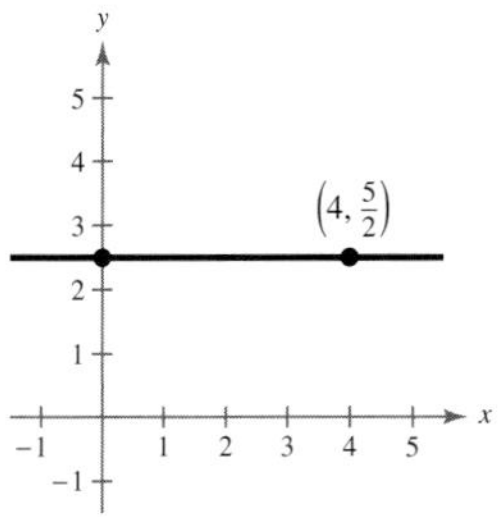

62. $y = \frac{3}{2}$

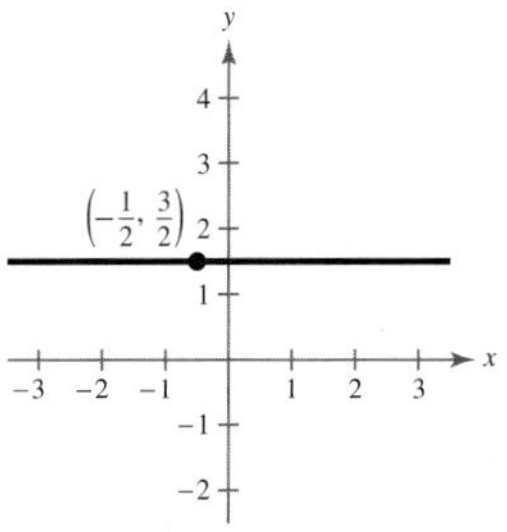

63. $y = 5x + 27.3$

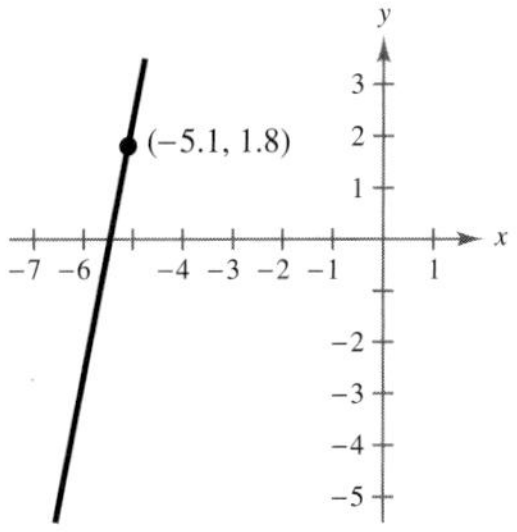

64. $y = -2.5x - 2.75$

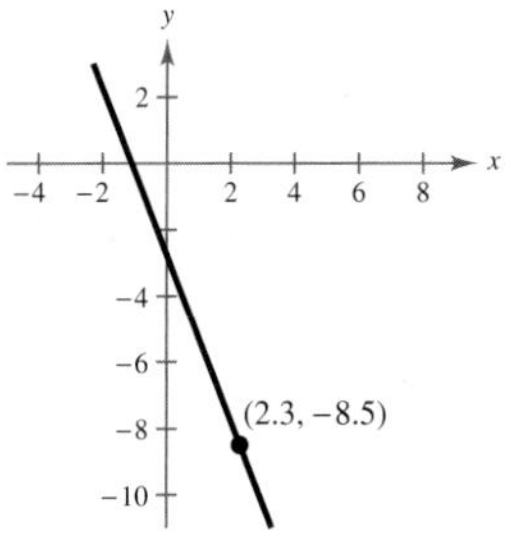

65. $y = -\frac{3}{5}x + 2$

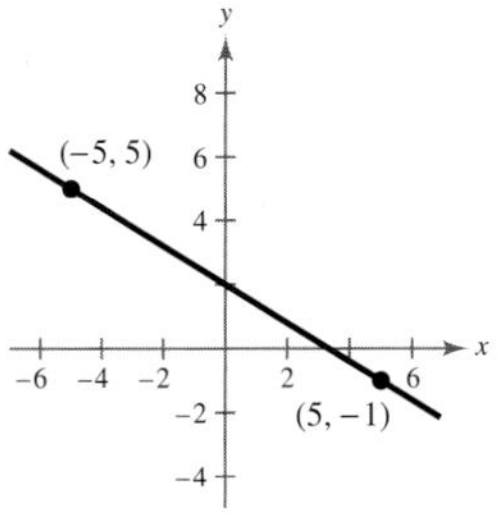

66. $y = \frac{7}{8}x - \frac{1}{2}$

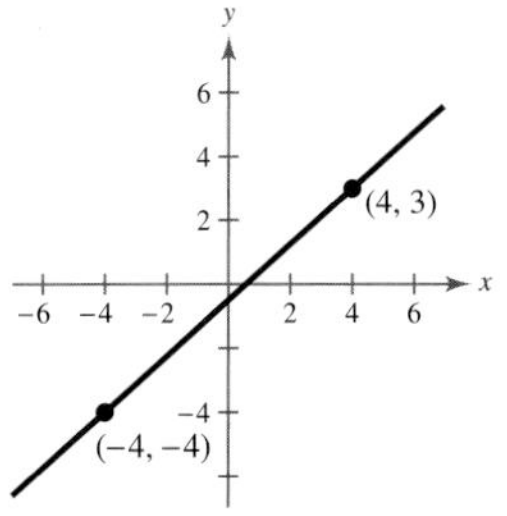

67. $x = -8$

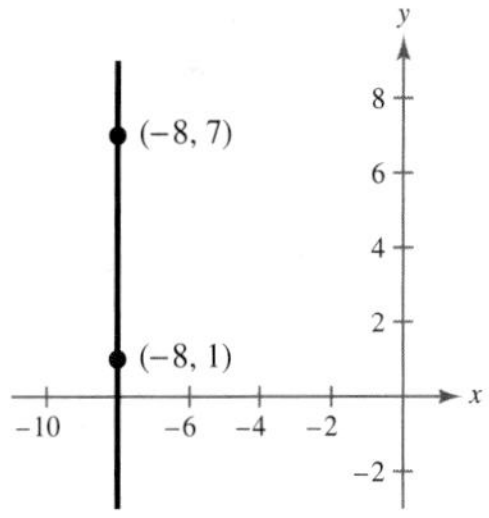

68. $y = 4$

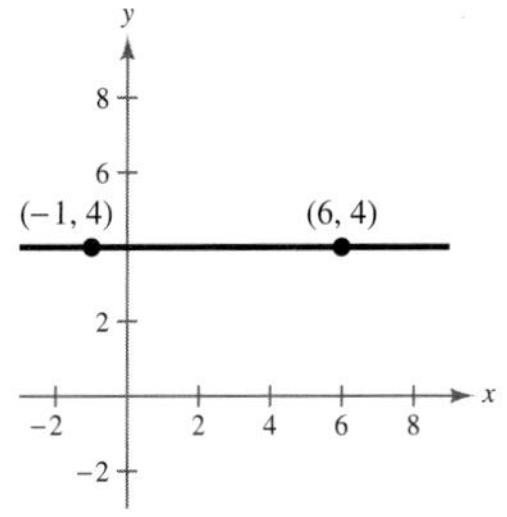

69. $y = -\frac{1}{2}x + \frac{3}{2}$

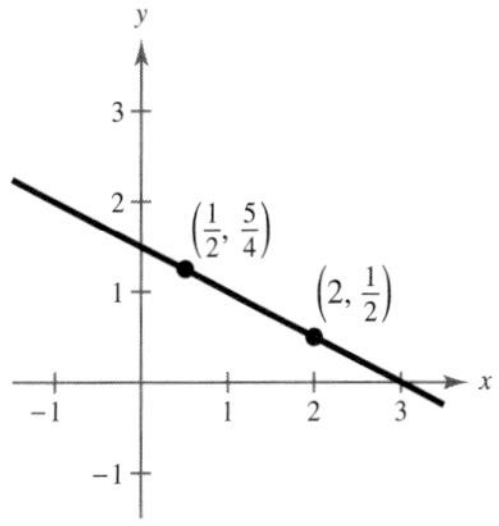

70. $y = -\frac{1}{3}x + \frac{4}{3}$

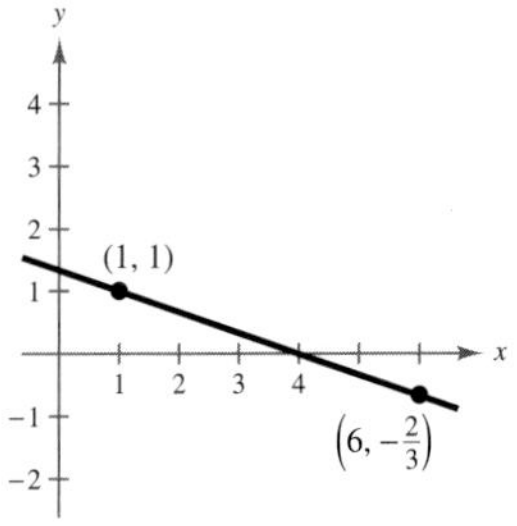

71. $y = -\frac{6}{5}x - \frac{18}{25}$

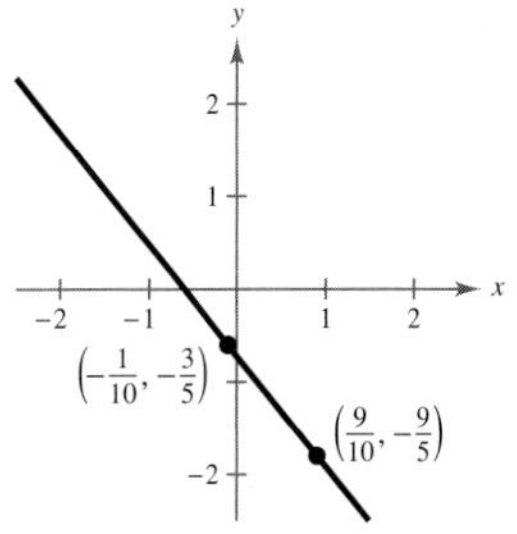

72. $y = -\frac{3}{25}x + \frac{159}{100}$

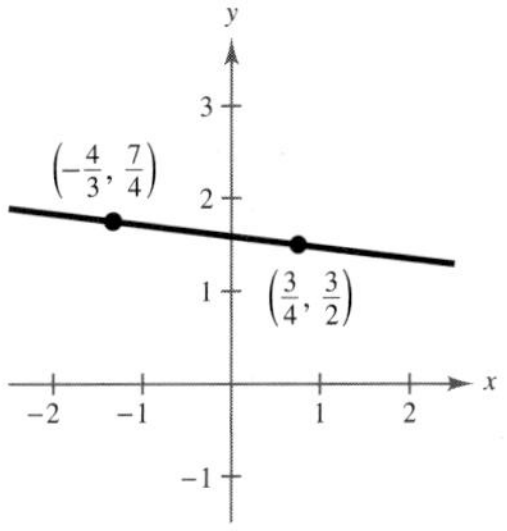

73. $y = 0.4x + 0.2$

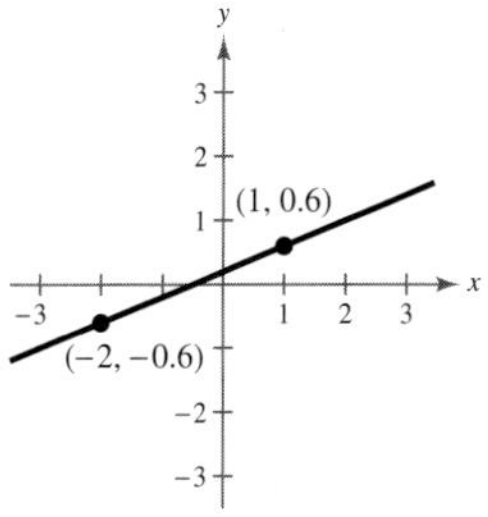

74. $y = -0.3x - 1.8$

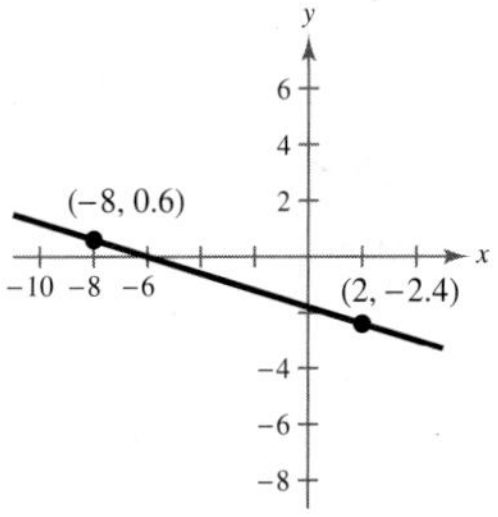

75. $y = -1$

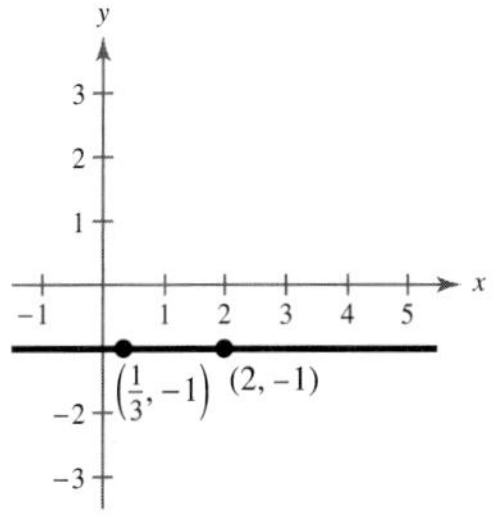

76. $y = -2$

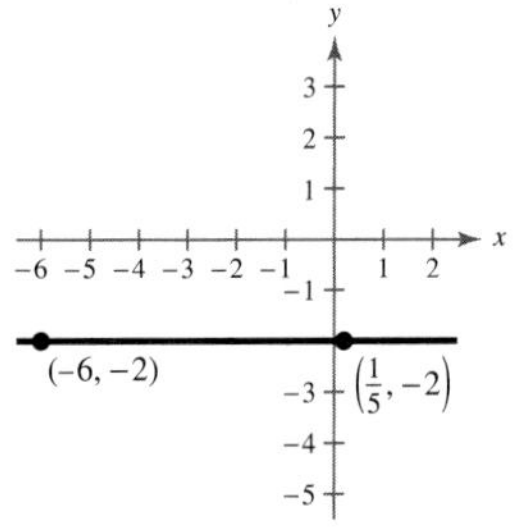

77. $x = \frac{7}{3}$

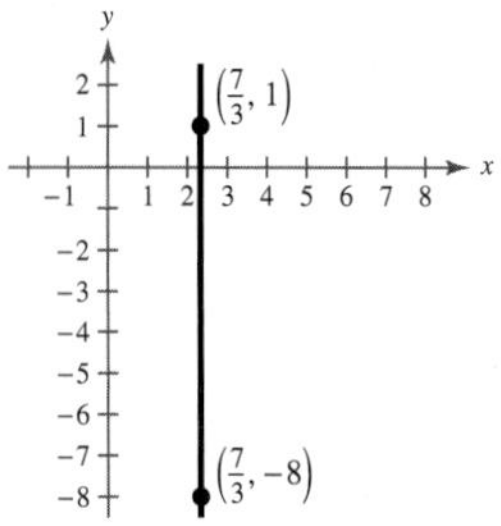

78. $x = 1.5$

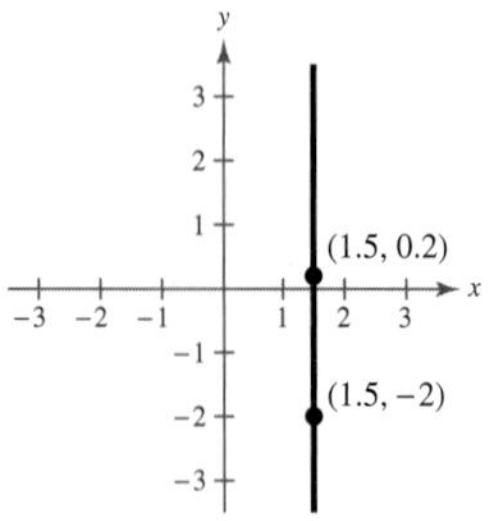

87. (a) $y = 2x - 3$ (b) $y = -\frac{1}{2}x + 2$

88. (a) $y = -x - 1$ (b) $y = x + 5$

89. (a) $y = -\frac{3}{4}x + \frac{3}{8}$ (b) $y = \frac{4}{3}x + \frac{127}{72}$

90. (a) $y = -\frac{5}{3}x + \frac{53}{24}$ (b) $y = \frac{3}{5}x + \frac{9}{40}$

91. (a) $y = 0$ (b) $x = -1$

92. (a) $y = 1$ (b) $x = -4$

93. (a) $x = 3$ (b) $y = -2$

94. (a) $x = -5$ (b) $y = 1$

99. $12x + 3y + 2 = 0$ **100.** $3x - y - 2 = 0$

103. Line (b) is perpendicular to line (c).

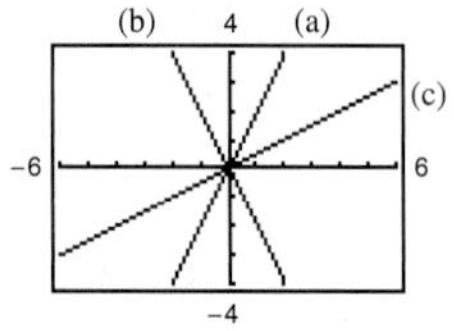

104. Line (a) is parallel to line (c).
Line (b) is perpendicular to line (a) and line (c).

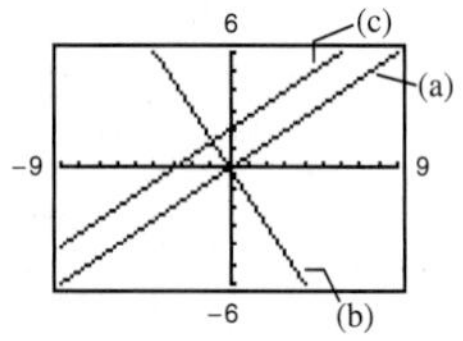

105. Line (a) is parallel to line (b).
Line (c) is perpendicular to line (a) and line (b).

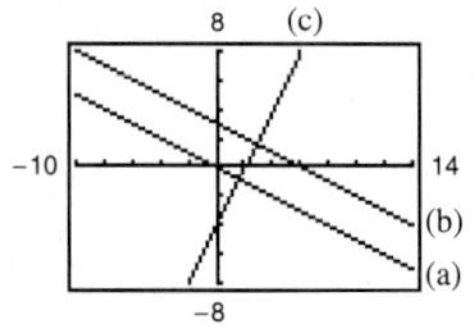

106. Line (a) is parallel to line (b).
Line (c) is perpendicular to line (a) and line (b).

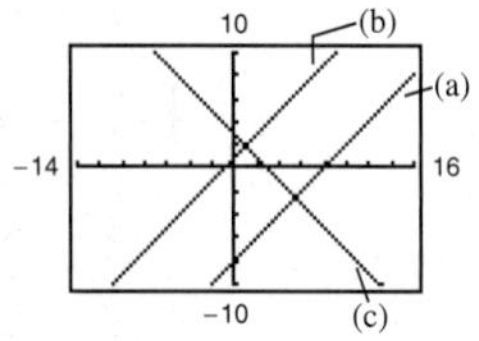

Section 1.4 *(page 48)*

83. $\{(-2, 4), (-1, 1), (0, 0), (1, 1), (2, 4)\}$

84. $\{(-2, 25), (-1, 16), (0, 9), (1, 4), (2, 1)\}$

85. $\{(-2, 4), (-1, 3), (0, 2), (1, 3), (2, 4)\}$

86. $\{(-2, 1), (-1, 0), (0, 1), (1, 2), (2, 3)\}$

100. (a)

y	5	10	20
$F(y)$	26,474.08	149,760.00	847,170.49

y	30	40
$F(y)$	2,334,527.36	4,792,320.00

The deeper the water, the greater the force.

Section 1.5 *(page 61)*

61.

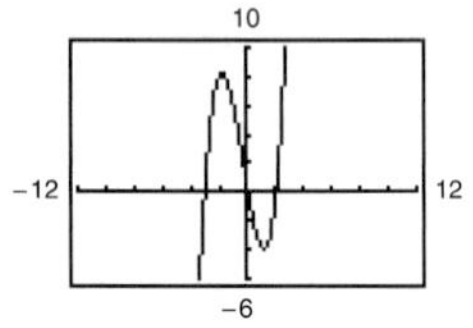

Relative maximum: $(-1.79, 8.21)$
Relative minimum: $(1.12, -4.06)$

62.

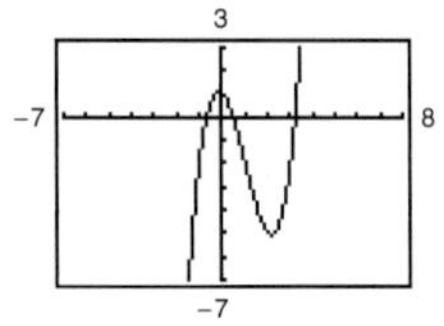

Relative maximum: $(-0.15, 1.08)$
Relative minimum: $(2.15, -5.08)$

63.

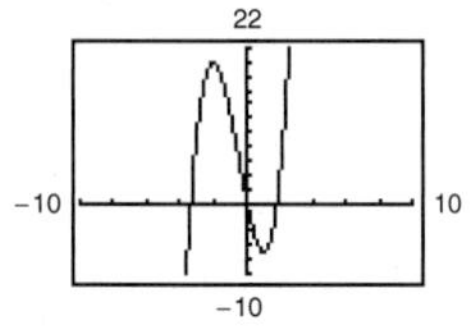

Relative maximum: $(-2, 20)$
Relative minimum: $(1, -7)$

64.

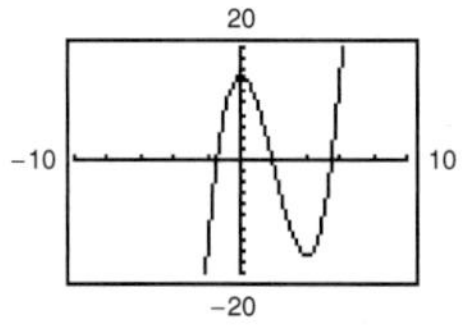

Relative maximum: $(0, 15)$
Relative minimum: $(4, -17)$

65.

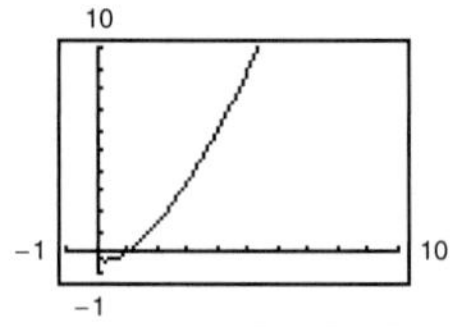

Relative minimum:
$(0.33, -0.38)$

66.

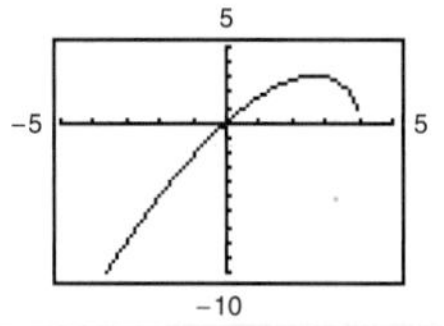

Relative maximum:
$(2.67, 3.08)$

67.

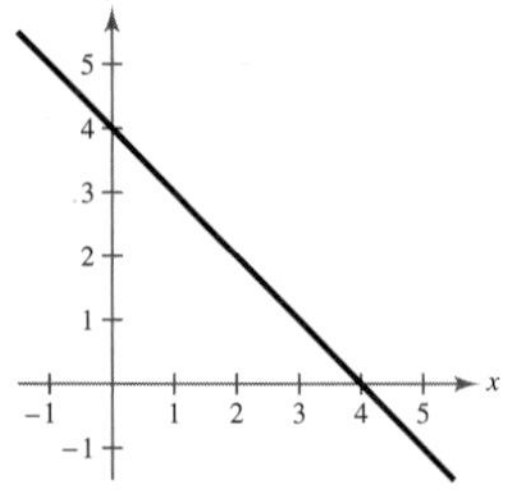

$(-\infty, 4]$

68.

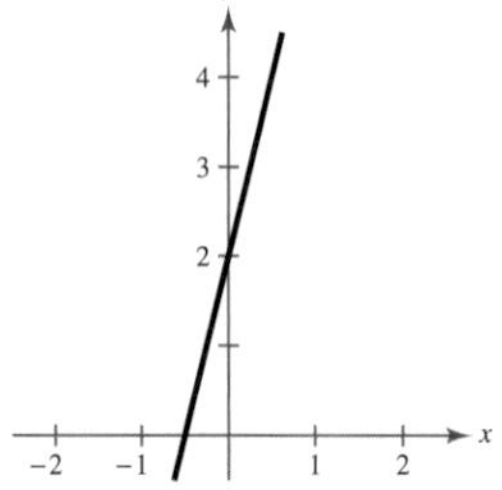

$\left[-\frac{1}{2}, \infty\right)$

69.

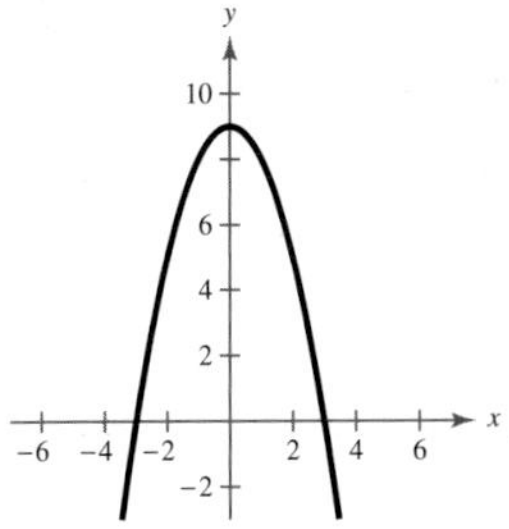

$[-3, 3]$

70.

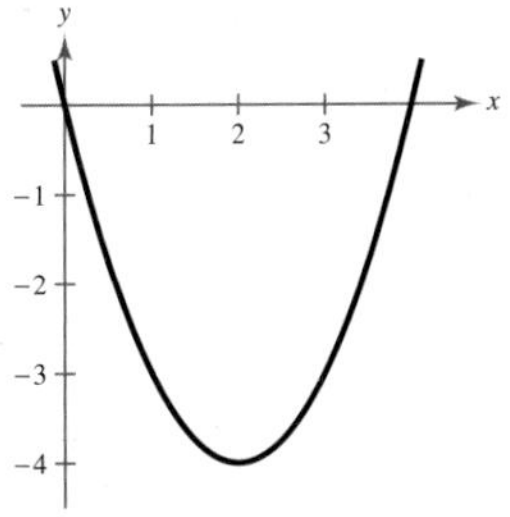

$(-\infty, 0], [4, \infty)$

71.

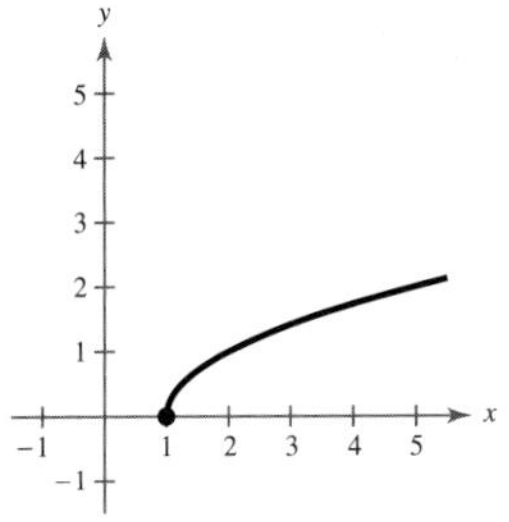

$[1, \infty)$

72.

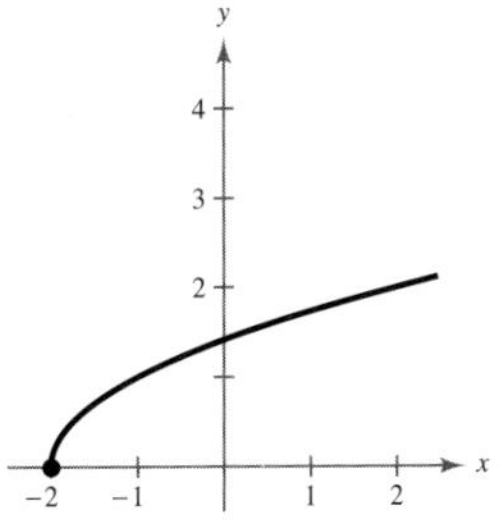

$[-2, \infty)$

73.

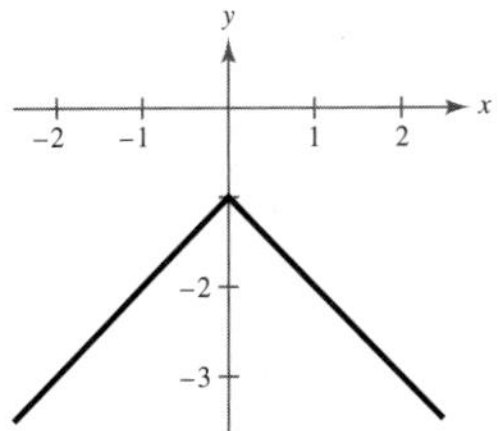

$f(x) < 0$ for all x

74.

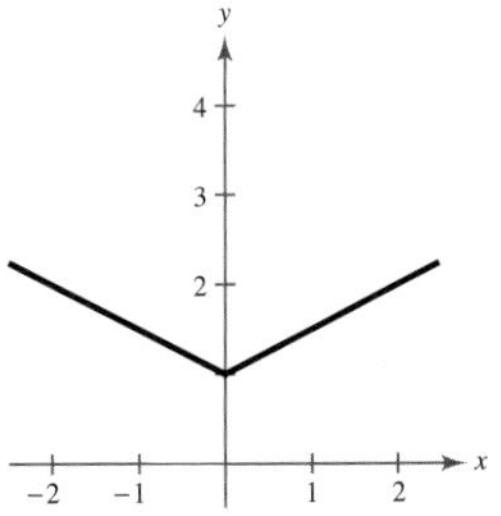

$(-\infty, \infty)$

75. The average rate of change from $x_1 = 0$ to $x_2 = 3$ is -2.
76. The average rate of change from $x_1 = 0$ to $x_2 = 3$ is 3.
77. The average rate of change from $x_1 = 1$ to $x_2 = 5$ is 18.
78. The average rate of change from $x_1 = 1$ to $x_2 = 5$ is 4.
79. The average rate of change from $x_1 = 1$ to $x_2 = 3$ is 0.
80. The average rate of change from $x_1 = 1$ to $x_2 = 6$ is 0.
81. The average rate of change from $x_1 = 3$ to $x_2 = 11$ is $-\frac{1}{4}$.
82. The average rate of change from $x_1 = 3$ to $x_2 = 8$ is $-\frac{1}{5}$.
83. Even; y-axis symmetry **84.** Neither; no symmetry
85. Odd; origin symmetry **86.** Neither; no symmetry
87. Neither; no symmetry **88.** Odd; origin symmetry
89. Neither; no symmetry **90.** Even; y-axis symmetry

91.

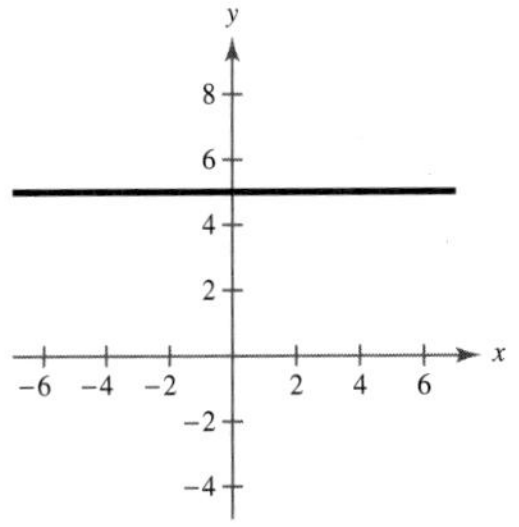

Even

92.

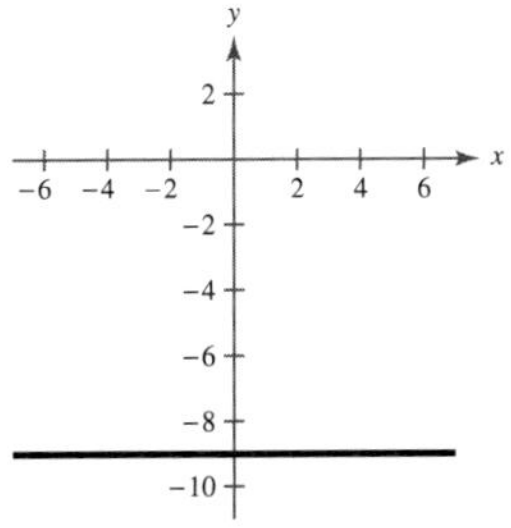

Even

93.

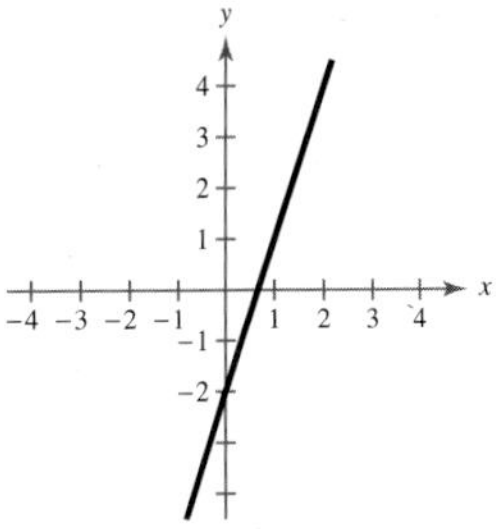

Neither

94.

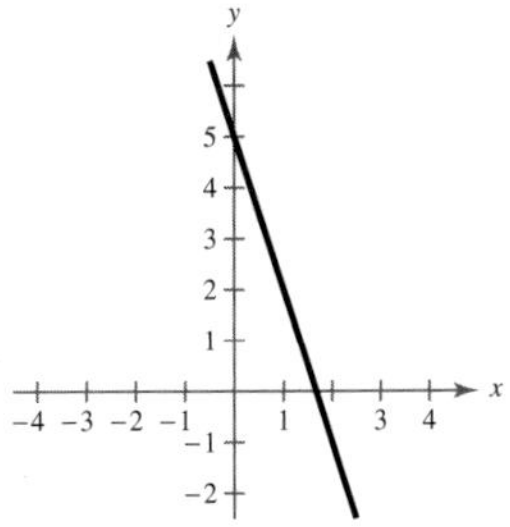

Neither

95.

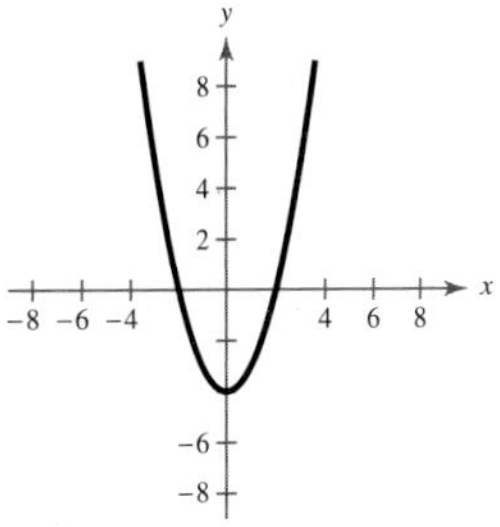

Even

96.

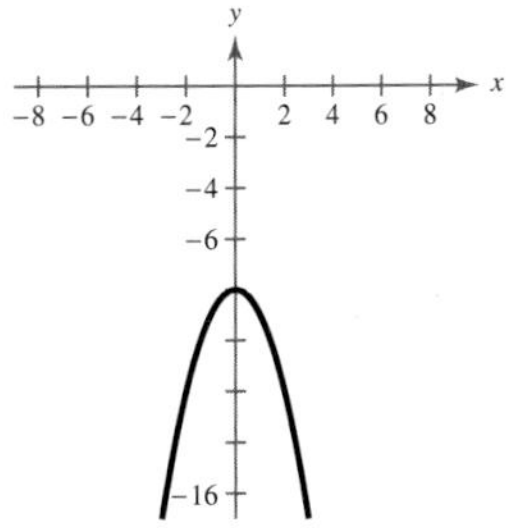

Even

97.

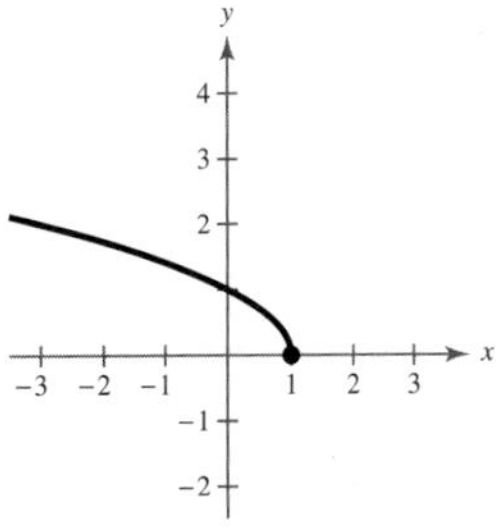

Neither

98.

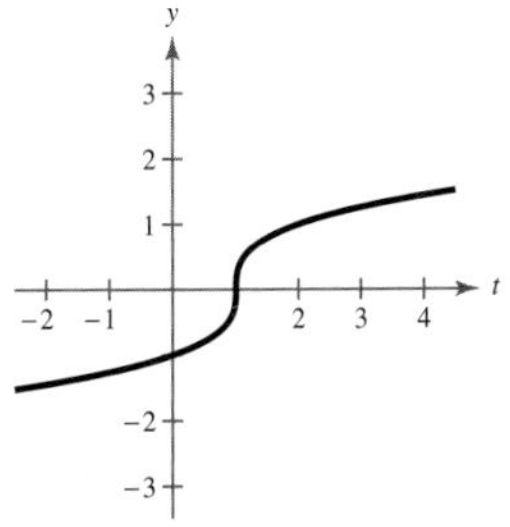

Neither

99.

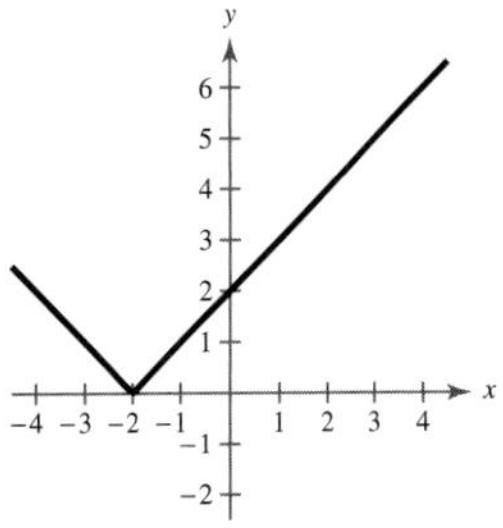

Neither

100.

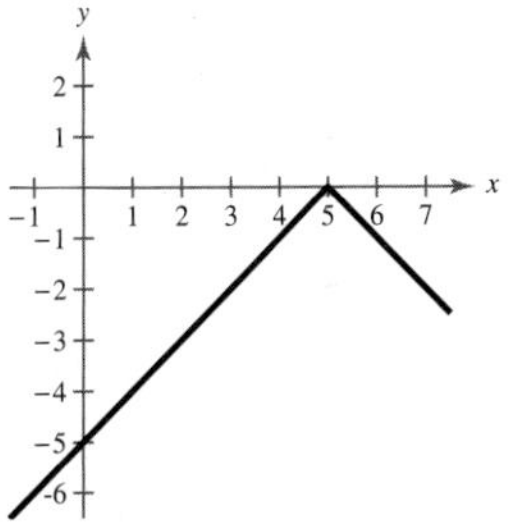

Neither

109. (a)

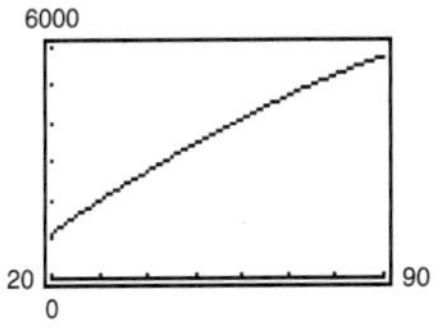

(b) 30 W

120. (a) $s = -16t^2 + 80$

(b)

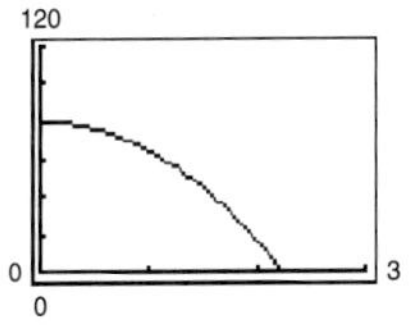

(c) Average rate of change $= -48$
(d) The slope of the secant line is negative.
(e) Secant line: $-48t + 112$

ADDITIONAL ANSWERS

(f)
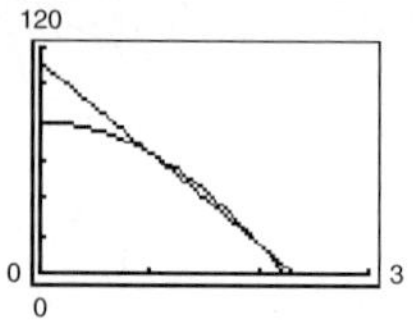

121. False. The function $f(x) = \sqrt{x^2 + 1}$ has a domain of all real numbers.

122. False. An odd function is symmetric with respect to the origin, so its domain must include negative values.

123. (a) Even. The graph is a reflection in the x-axis.
(b) Even. The graph is a reflection in the y-axis.
(c) Even. The graph is a vertical translation of f.
(d) Neither. The graph is a horizontal translation of f.

124. Yes. For each value of y there corresponds one and only one value of x.

125. (a) $\left(\frac{3}{2}, 4\right)$ (b) $\left(\frac{3}{2}, -4\right)$ **126.** (a) $\left(\frac{5}{3}, -7\right)$ (b) $\left(\frac{5}{3}, 7\right)$

127. (a) $(-4, 9)$ (b) $(-4, -9)$

128. (a) $(-5, -1)$ (b) $(-5, 1)$

129. (a) $(-x, -y)$ (b) $(-x, y)$

130. (a) $(-2a, 2c)$ (b) $(-2a, -2c)$

131. (a)
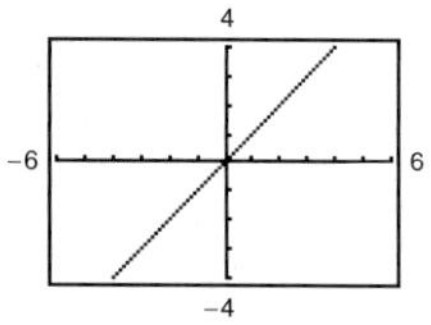
(b)
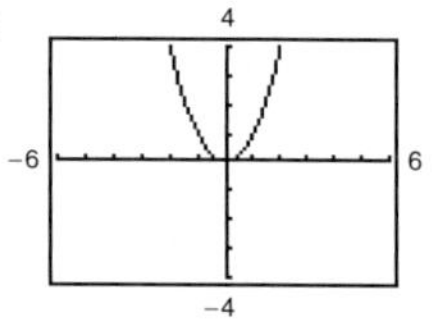
(c)
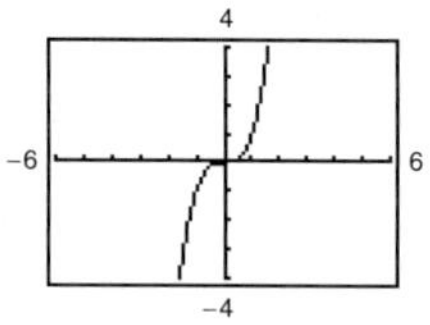
(d)
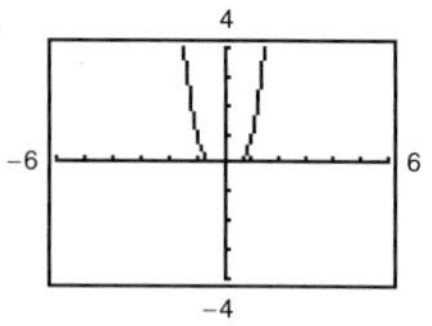
(e)
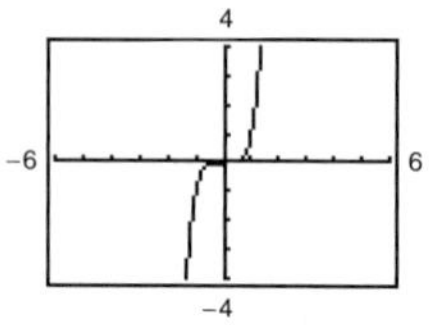
(f)
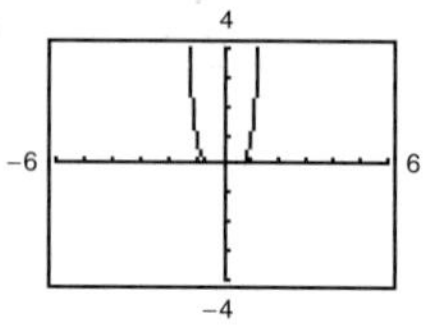

All the graphs pass through the origin. The graphs of the odd powers of x are symmetric with respect to the origin, and the graphs of the even powers are symmetric with respect to the y-axis. As the powers increase, the graphs become flatter in the interval $-1 < x < 1$.

132. Both graphs will pass through the origin. $y = x^7$ will be symmetric with respect to the origin, and $y = x^8$ will be symmetric with respect to the y-axis.

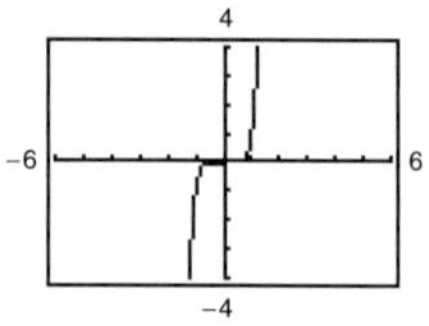
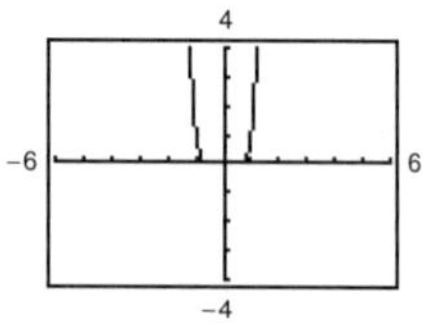

133. 60 ft/sec; As the time traveled increases, the distance increases rapidly, causing the average speed to increase with each time increment. From $t = 0$ to $t = 4$, the average speed is less than from $t = 4$ to $t = 9$. Therefore, the overall average from $t = 0$ to $t = 9$ falls below the average found in part (b).

134.
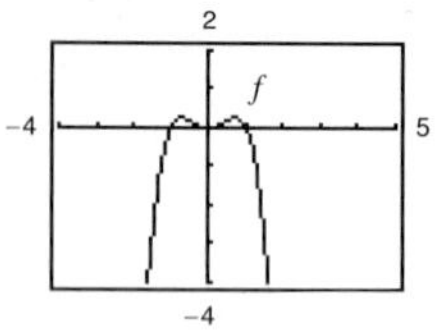
Even

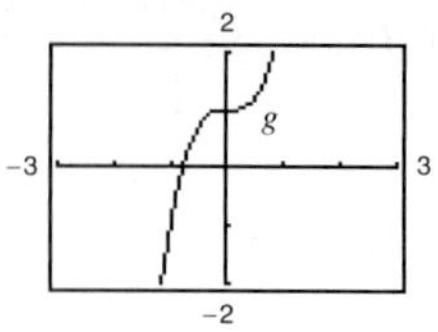
Neither

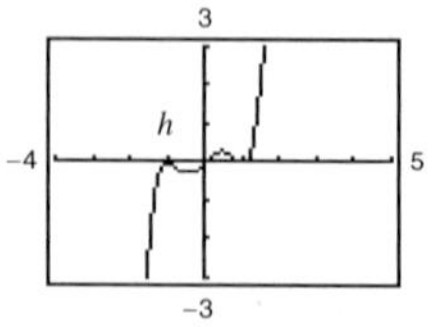
Odd

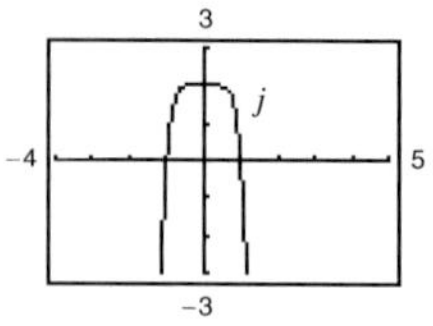
Even

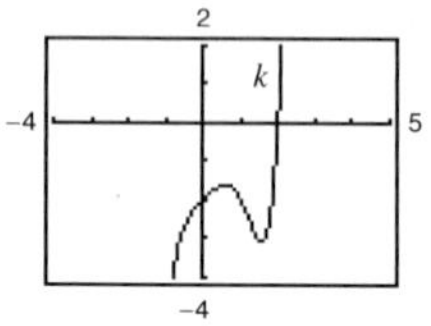
Neither

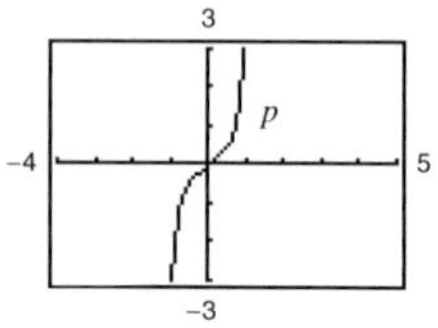
Odd

Equations of odd functions contain only odd powers of x. Equations of even functions contain only even powers of x. Odd functions have all variables raised to odd powers and even functions have all variables raised to even powers. A function that has variables raised to even and odd powers is neither odd nor even.

136. (a) Domain: $[-4, 5)$; Range: $[0, 9]$
(b) $(3, 0)$
(c) Increasing: $(-4, 0) \cup (3, 5)$
Decreasing: $(0, 3)$
(d) Relative maximum: $(0, 9)$
Relative minimum: $(3, 0)$
(e) Neither

Section 1.6 *(page 71)*

18. (a) $f(x) = \frac{3}{4}x - 8$
(b)
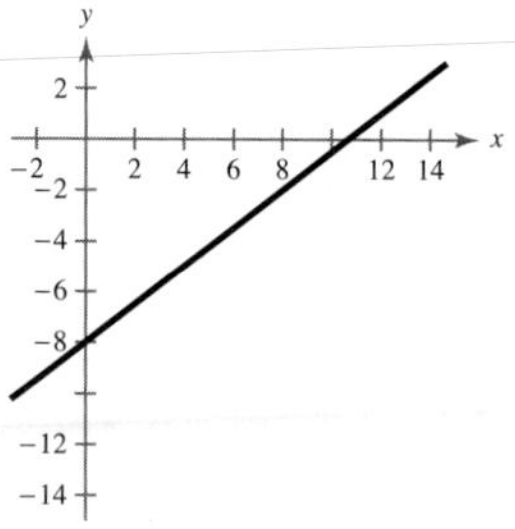

19.
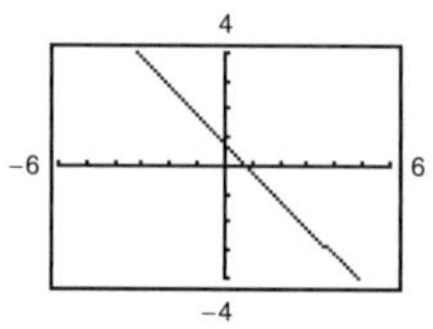

20.
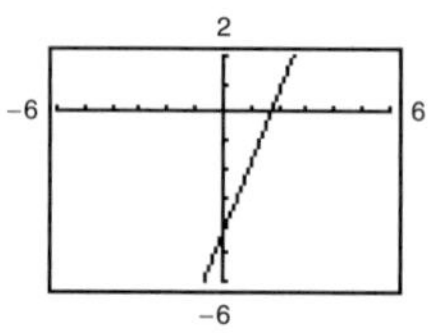

21.
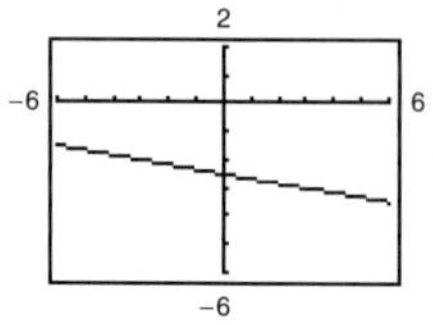

22.
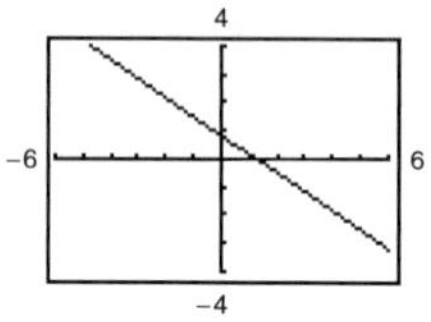

23.
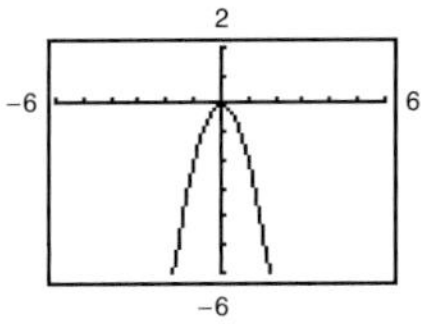

24.
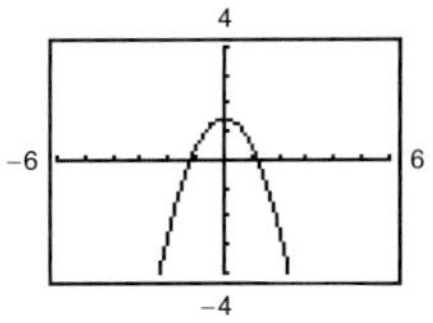

25.
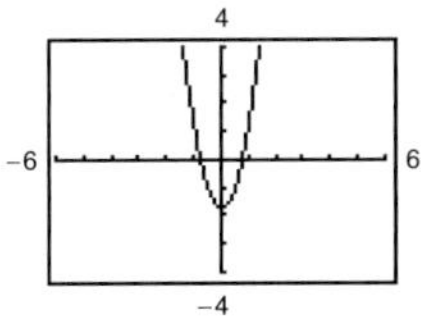

26.
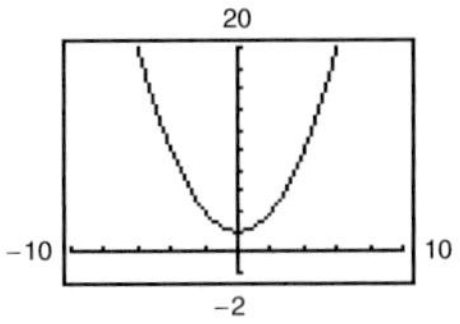

27.
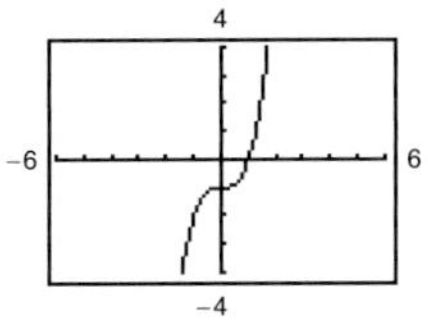

28.
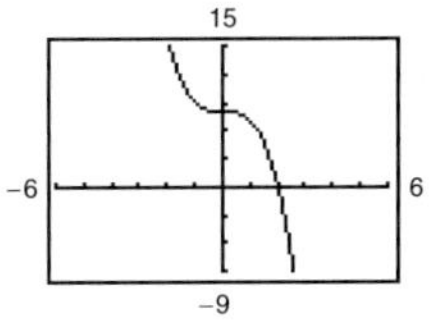

29.
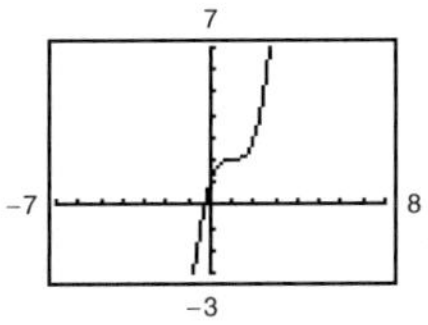

30.
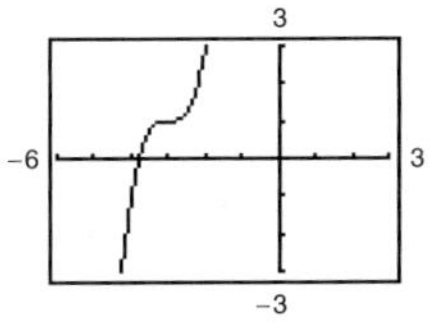

31.
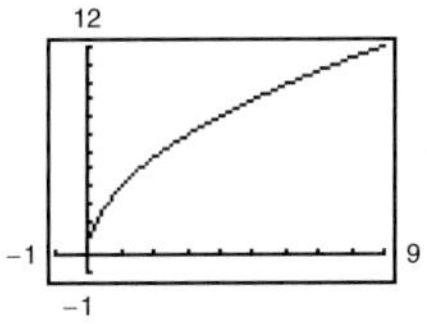

32.
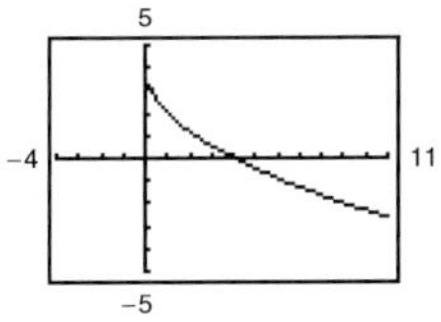

33.
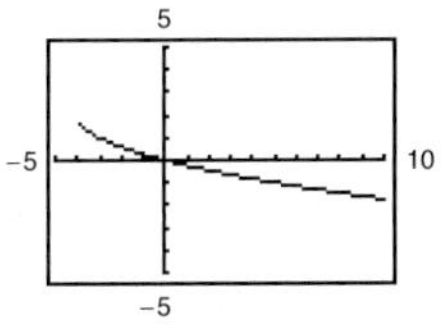

34.
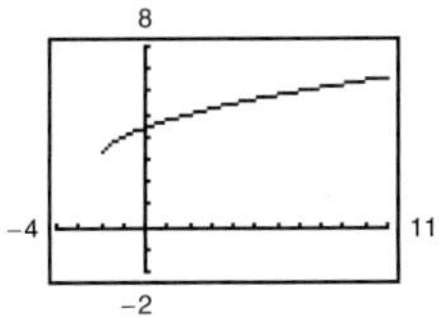

35.
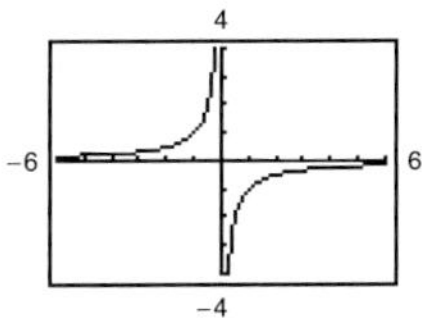

36.
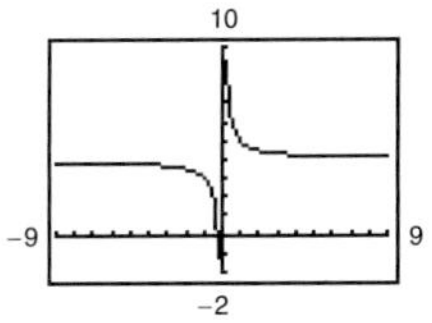

37.
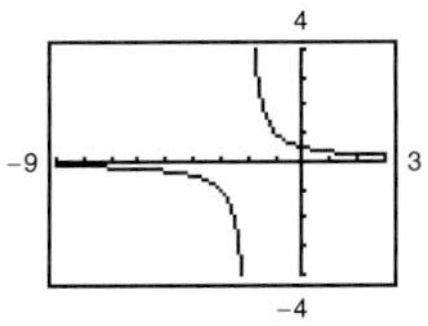

38.
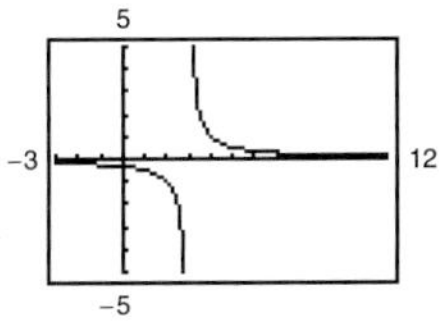

39.
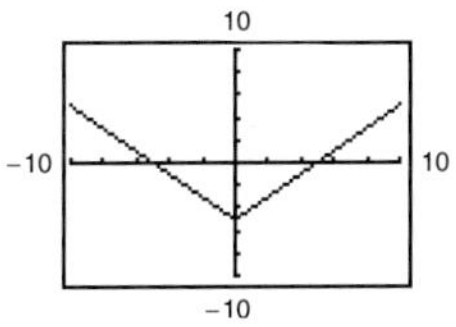

40.
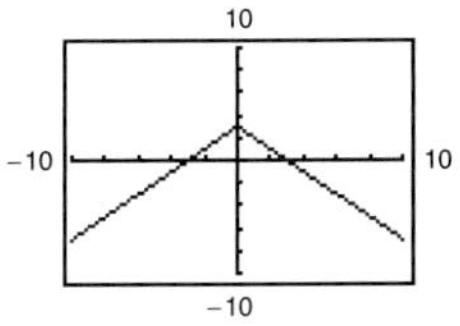

41.
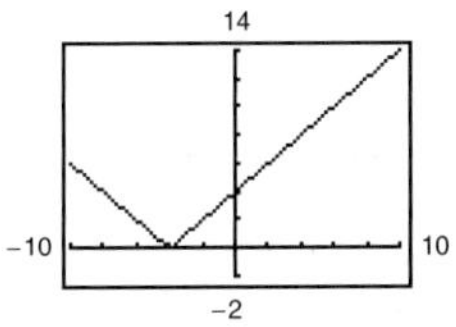

42.
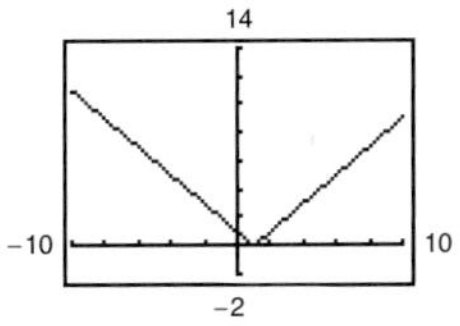

51.
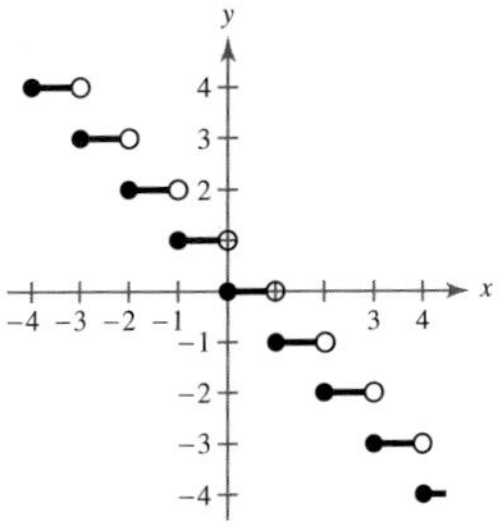

52.
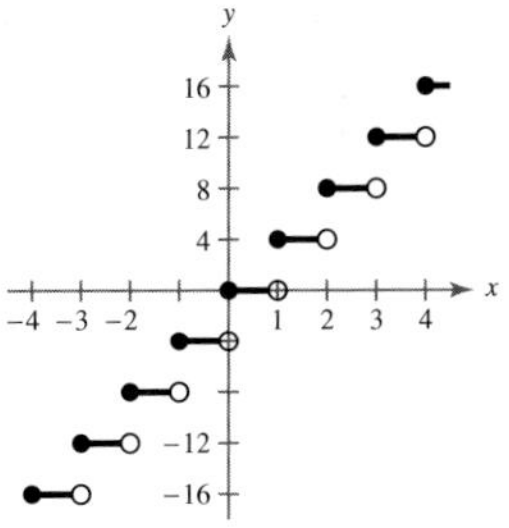

53.
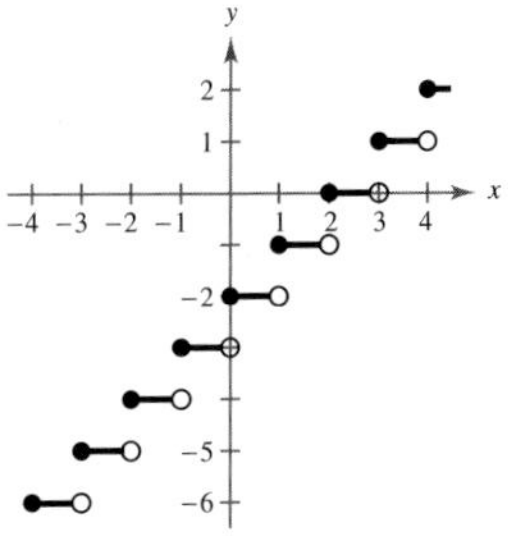

54.
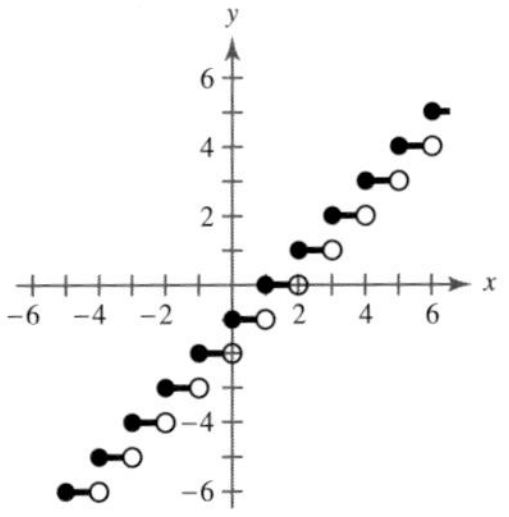

55.
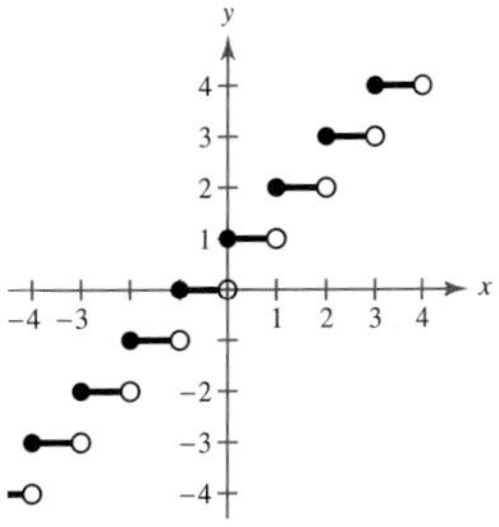

56.
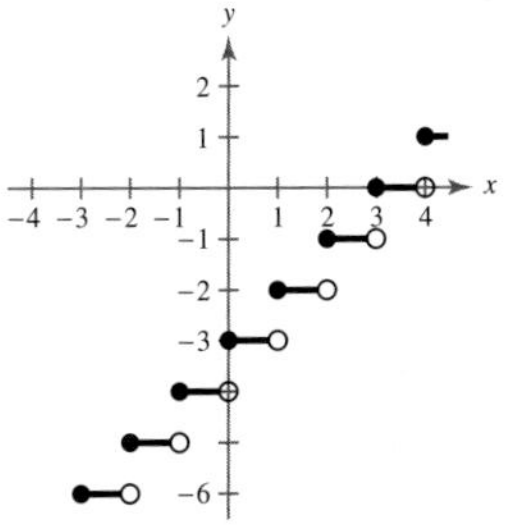

57.
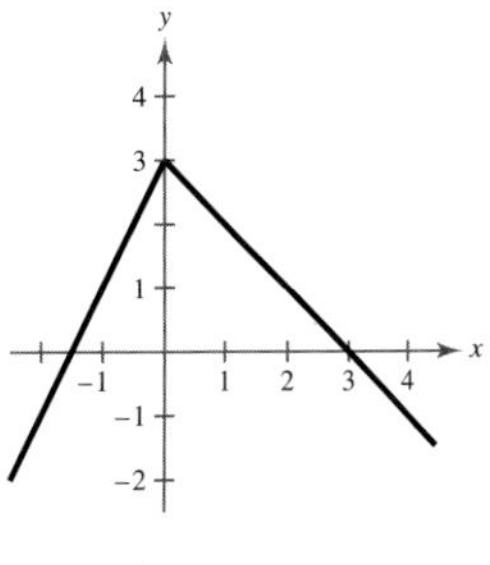

58.
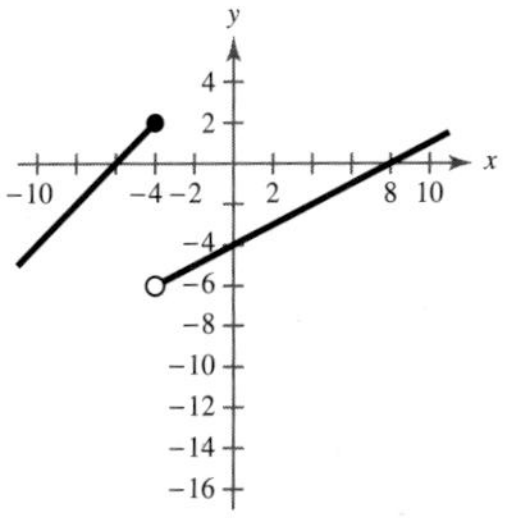

59.
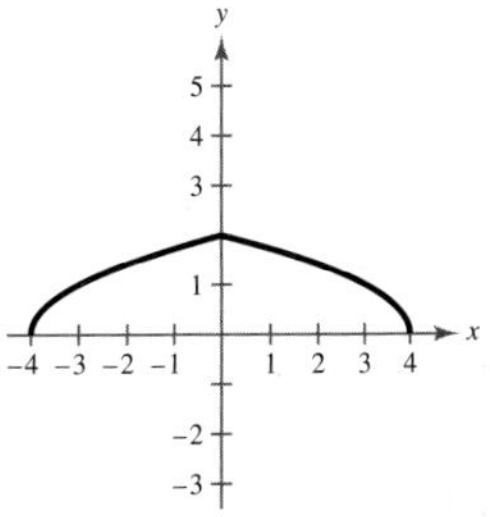

60.
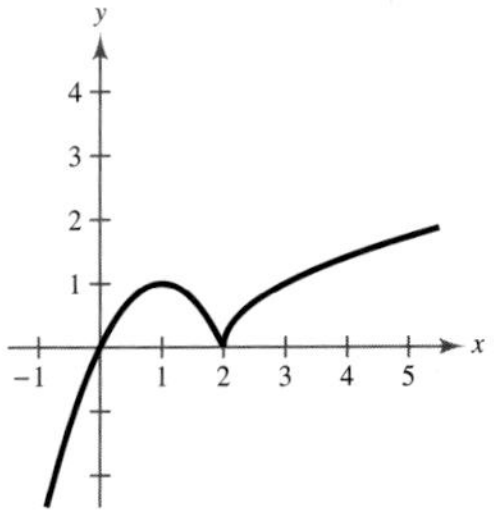

61.
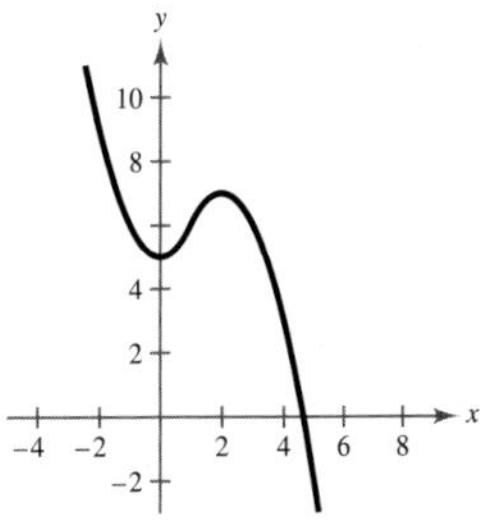

69. (a)

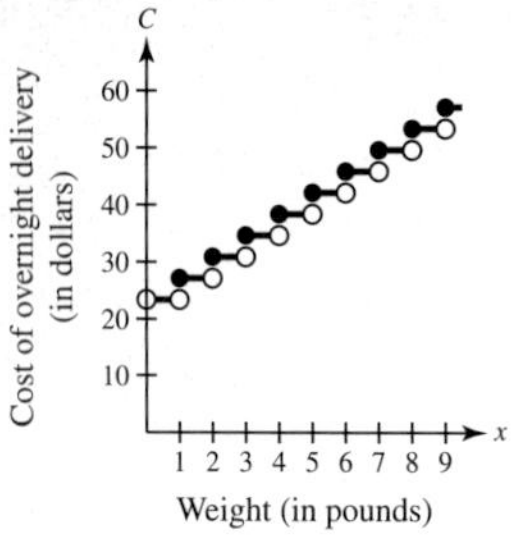

70. (b)

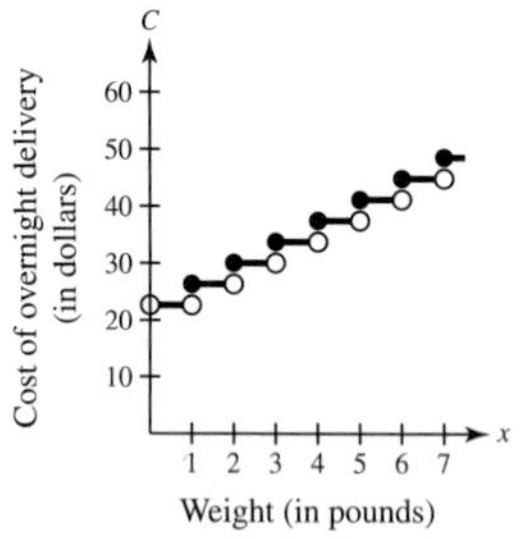

71. (a) $W(30) = 420$; $W(40) = 560$;
$W(45) = 665$; $W(50) = 770$

(b) $W(h) = \begin{cases} 14h, & 0 < h \le 45 \\ 21(h - 45) + 630, & h > 45 \end{cases}$

72. $f(t) = \begin{cases} t, & 0 \le t \le 2 \\ 2t - 2, & 2 < t \le 8 \\ \frac{1}{2}t + 10, & 8 < t \le 9 \end{cases}$

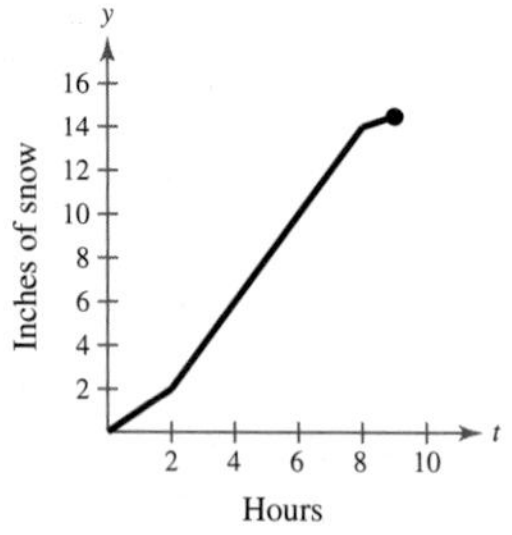

Total accumulation = 14.5 in.

73. (a)

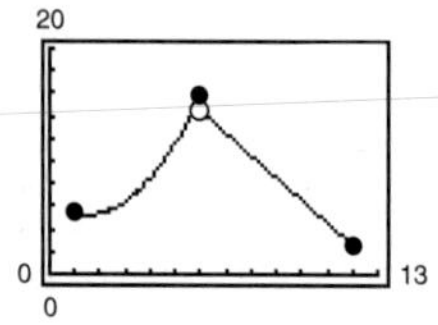

$f(x) = \begin{cases} 0.505x^2 - 1.47x + 6.3, & 1 \le x \le 6 \\ -1.97x + 26.3, & 6 < x \le 12 \end{cases}$

Answers will vary. Sample answer: The domain is determined by inspection of a graph of the data with the two models.

(b) $f(5) = 11.575, f(11) = 4.63$; These values represent the revenue for the months of May and November, respectively.

(c) These values are quite close to the actual data values.

74. False. A piecewise-defined function is a function that is defined by two or more equations over a specified domain. That domain may or may not include x- and y-intercepts.

75. False. A linear equation could be a horizontal or vertical line.

76. $f(x) = c$

(a) Domain: $(-\infty, \infty)$
Range: $y = c$

(b) y-intercept: $(0, c)$

(c) Constant: $(-\infty, \infty)$

(d) Even; y-axis symmetry

$f(x) = x$

(a) Domain: $(-\infty, \infty)$
Range: $(-\infty, \infty)$

(b) x-intercept and y-intercept: $(0, 0)$

(c) Increasing: $(-\infty, \infty)$

(d) Odd; origin symmetry

$f(x) = |x|$

(a) Domain: $(-\infty, \infty)$
Range: $[0, \infty)$

(b) x-intercept and y-intercept: $(0, 0)$

(c) Decreasing: $(-\infty, 0)$
Increasing: $(0, \infty)$

(d) Even; y-axis symmetry

$f(x) = \sqrt{x}$

(a) Domain: $[0, \infty)$
Range: $[0, \infty)$

(b) x-intercept and y-intercept: $(0, 0)$

(c) Increasing: $(0, \infty)$

(d) Neither; no symmetry

$f(x) = x^2$

(a) Domain: $(-\infty, \infty)$
Range: $[0, \infty)$

(b) x-intercept and y-intercept: $(0, 0)$

(c) Decreasing: $(-\infty, 0)$
Increasing: $(0, \infty)$

(d) Even; y-axis symmetry

$f(x) = x^3$

(a) Domain: $(-\infty, \infty)$
Range: $(-\infty, \infty)$

(b) x-intercept and y-intercept: $(0, 0)$

(c) Increasing: $(-\infty, \infty)$

(d) Odd; origin symmetry

$f(x) = \dfrac{1}{x}$

(a) Domain: $(-\infty, 0) \cup (0, \infty)$
Range: $(-\infty, 0) \cup (0, \infty)$

(b) No intercepts

(c) Decreasing: $(-\infty, 0) \cup (0, \infty)$

(d) Odd; origin symmetry

$f(x) = [\![x]\!]$

(a) Domain: $(-\infty, \infty)$
Range: all y such that y is an integer

(b) x-intercept: $(0, 1)$
y-intercept: $(0, 0)$

(c) Constant between pairs of consecutive integers

(d) Neither; no symmetry

Section 1.7 *(page 78)*

9. (a)

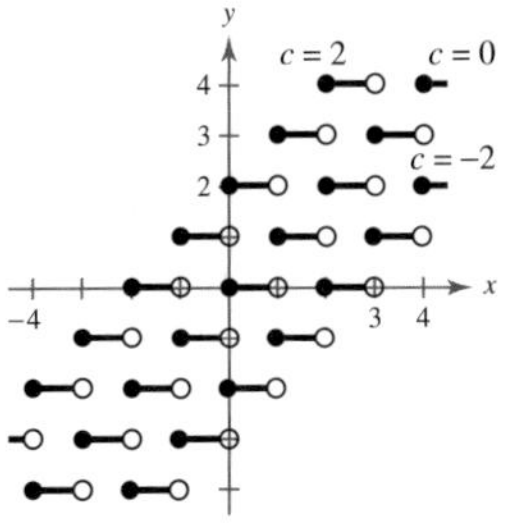

(b)

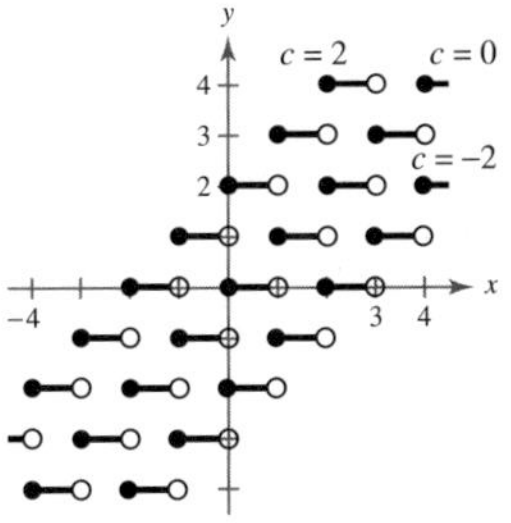

(c)

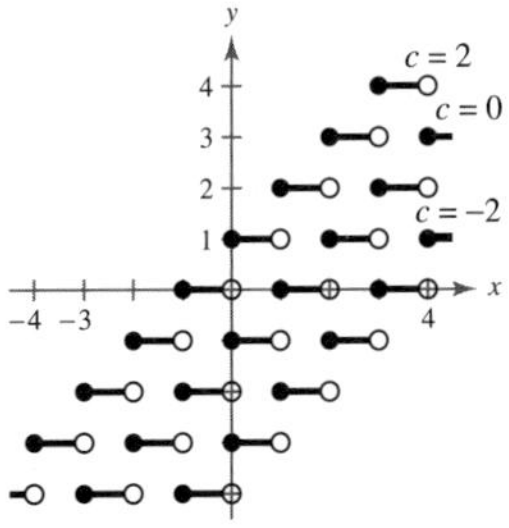

10. (a)

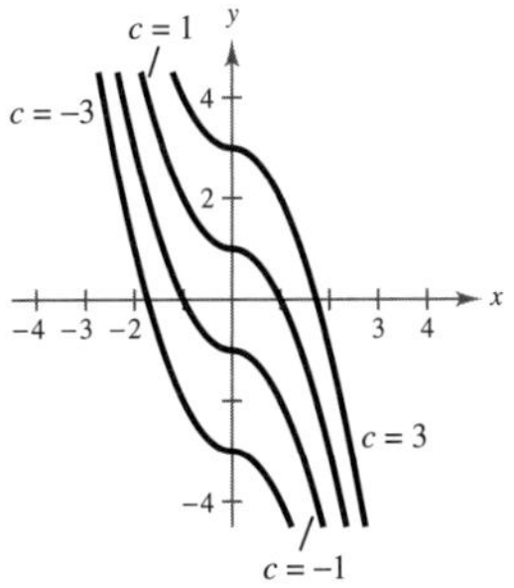

(b)

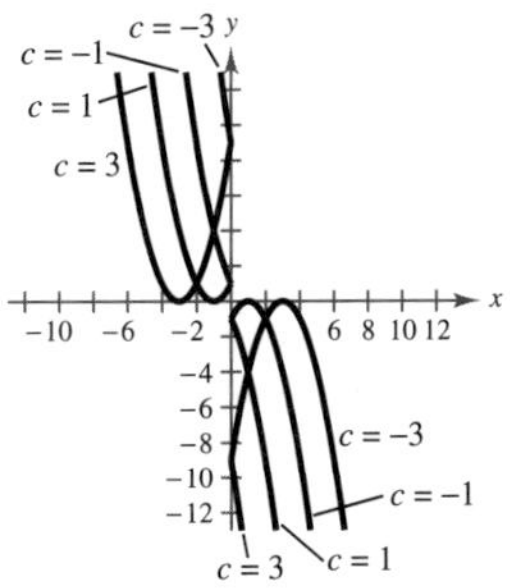

11. (a)

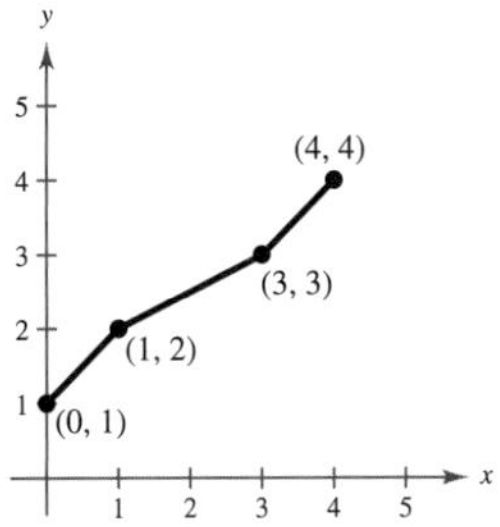

(b)

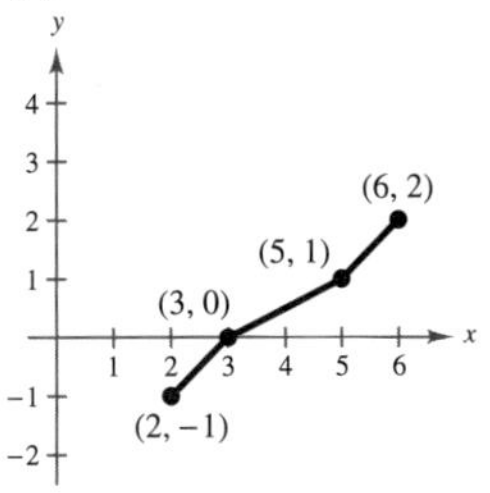

(c)

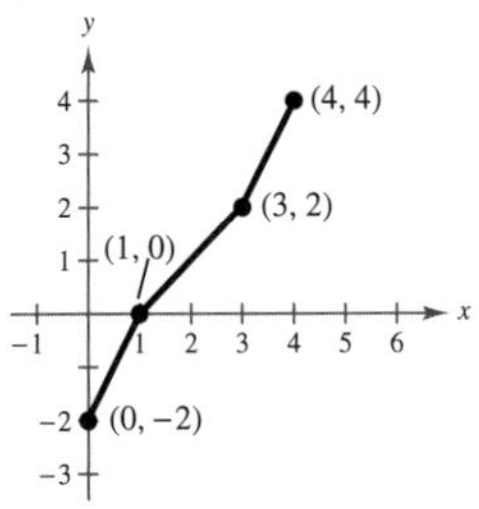

(d)

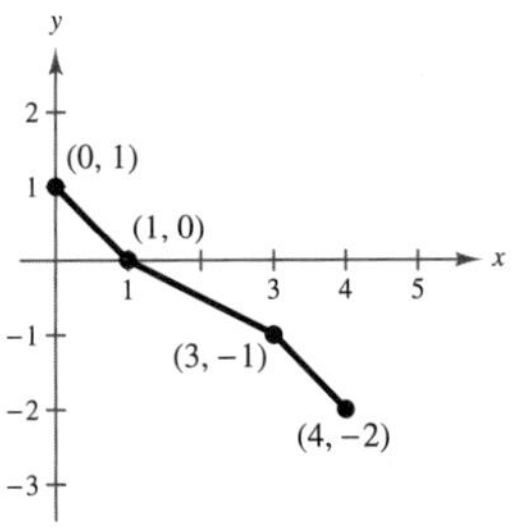

(e)

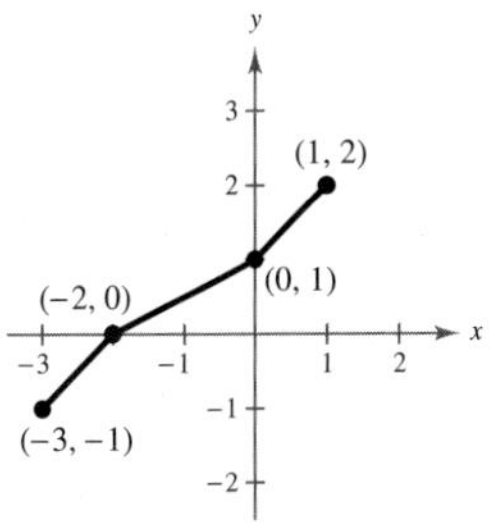

(f)

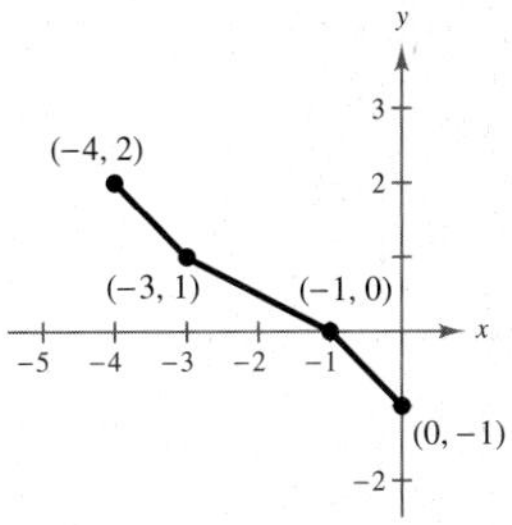

(g)

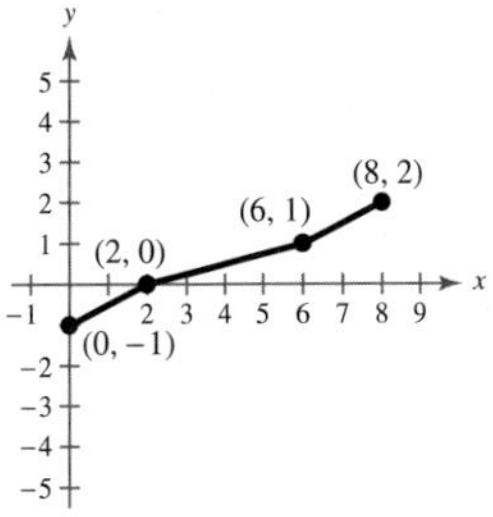

12. (a)

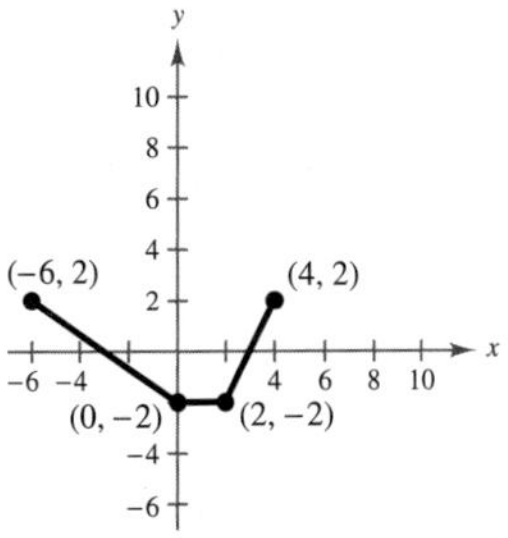

(b)

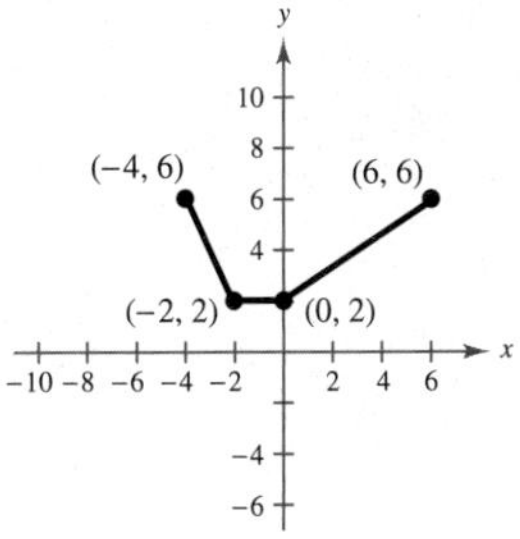

(c)

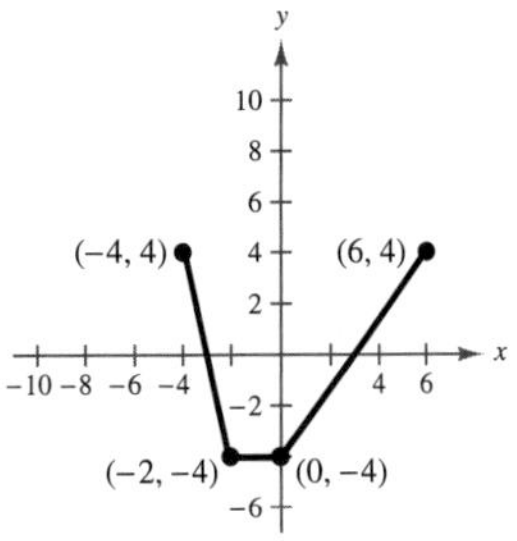

(d)

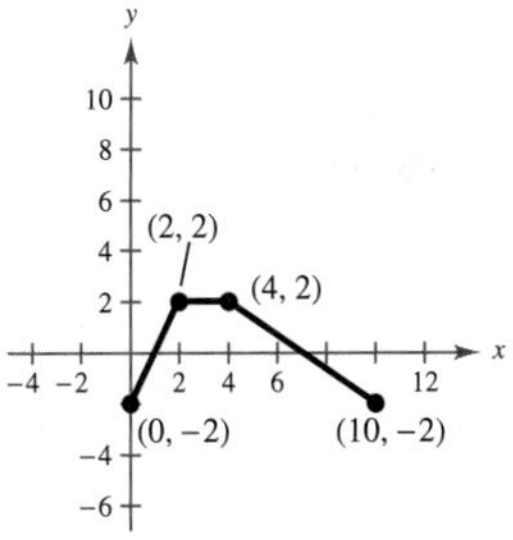

(e)

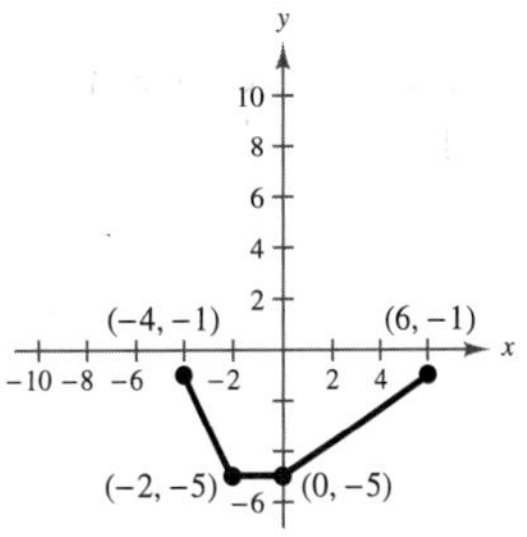

(f)

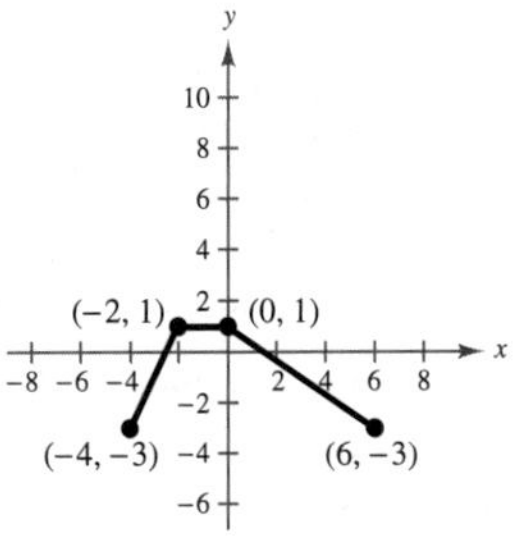

(g)

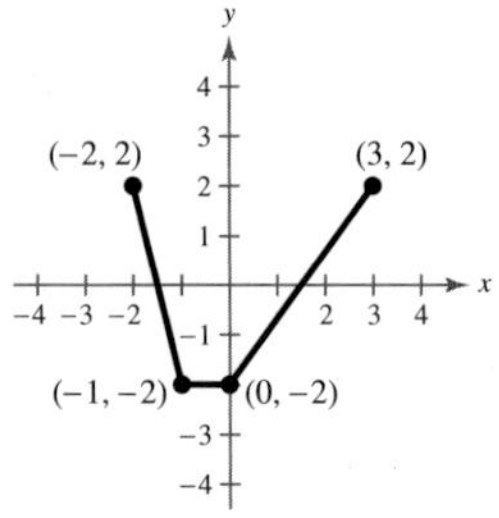

13. (a)

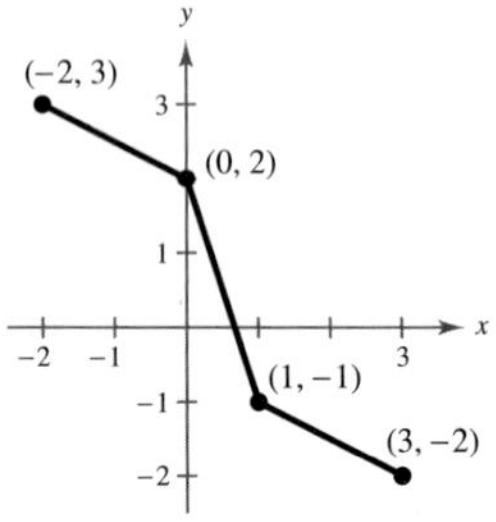

(b)

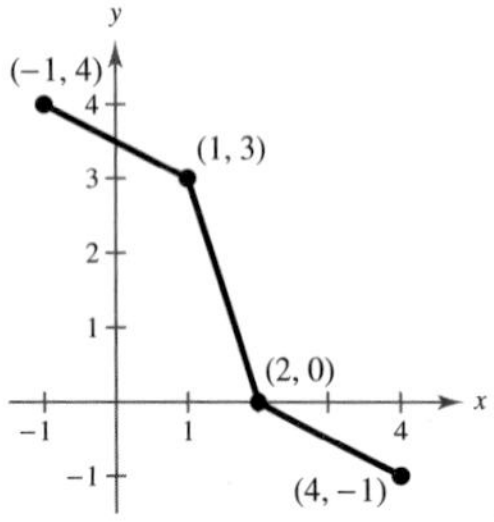

(c)

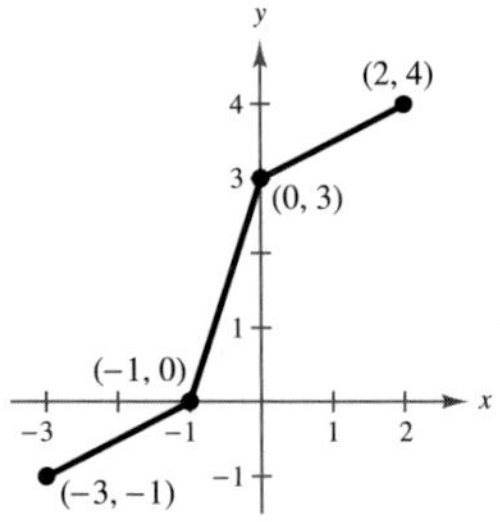

(d)

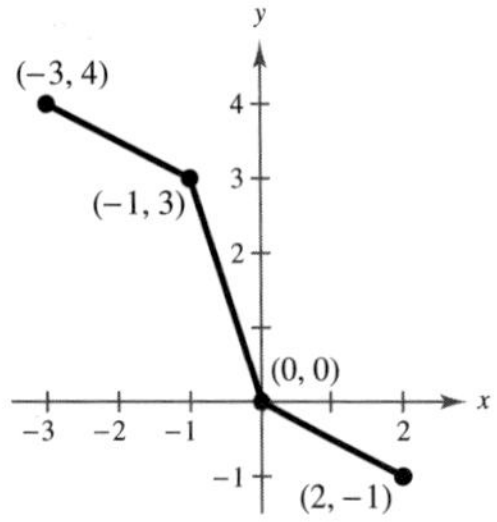

(e)

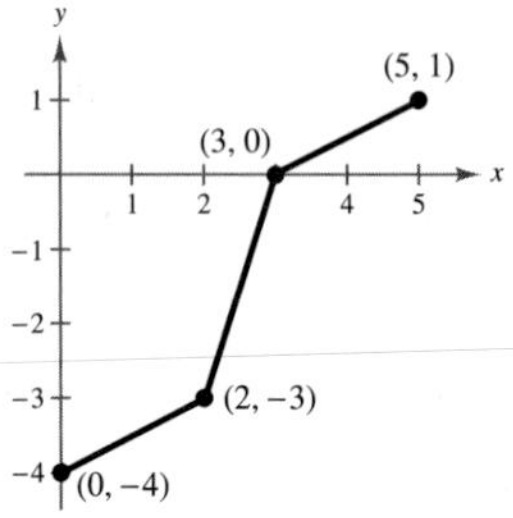

(f)

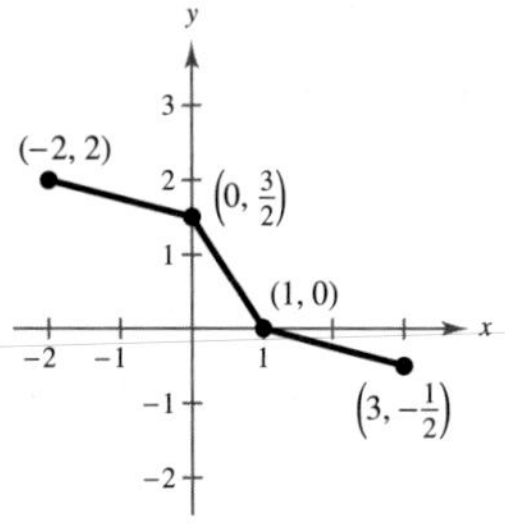

(g)

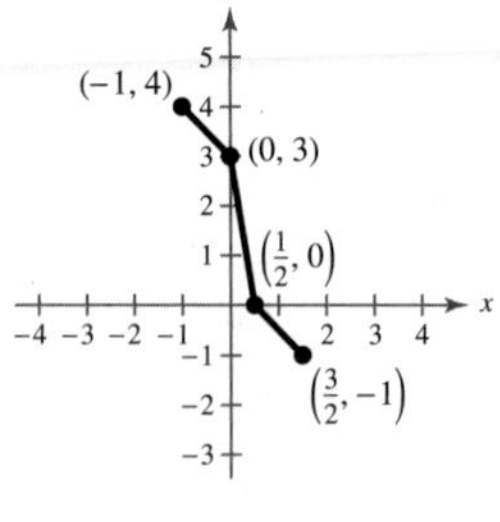

14. (a)

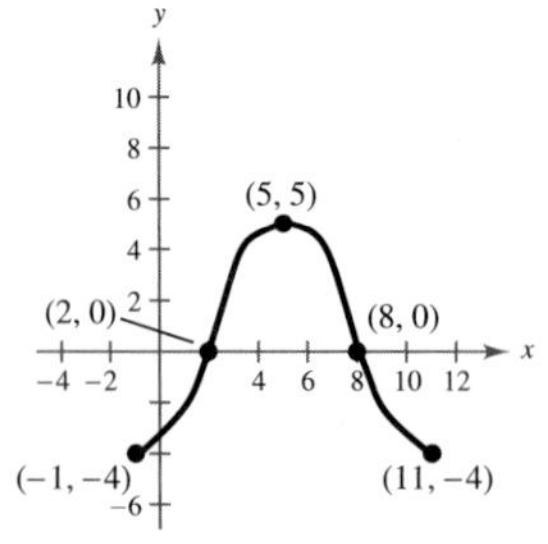

(b)

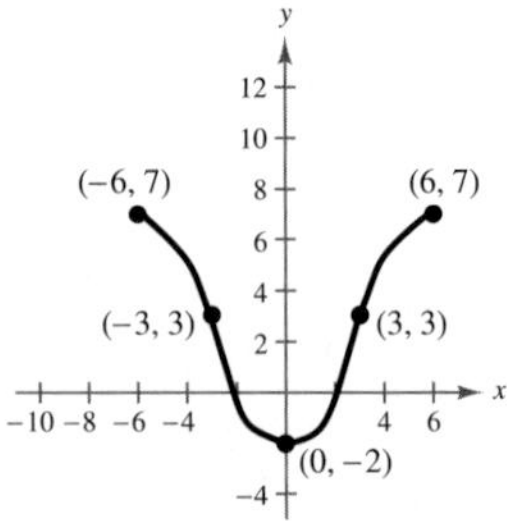

(c)

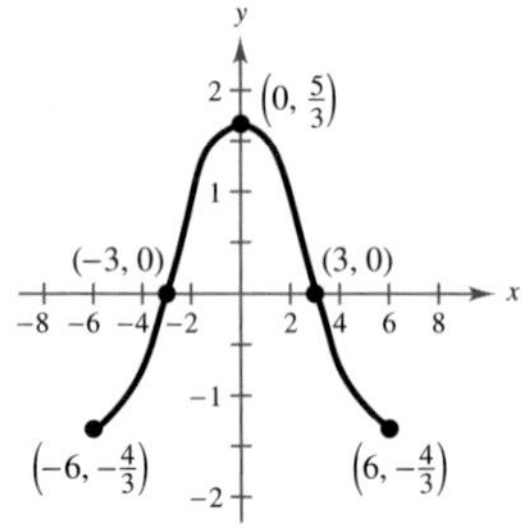

(d)

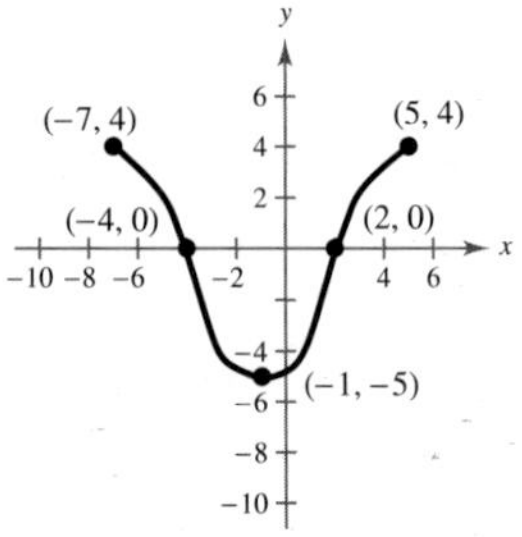

(e)

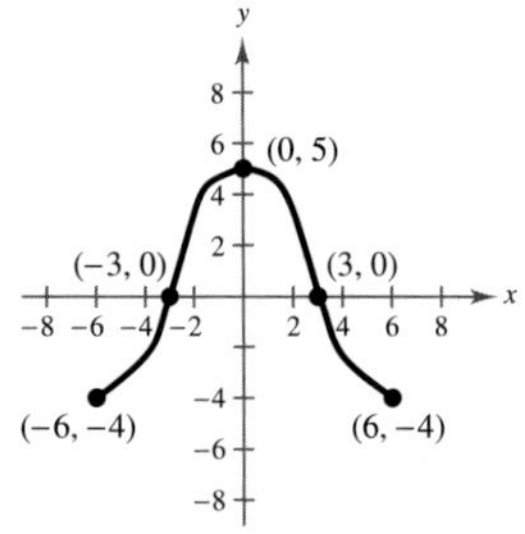

(f)

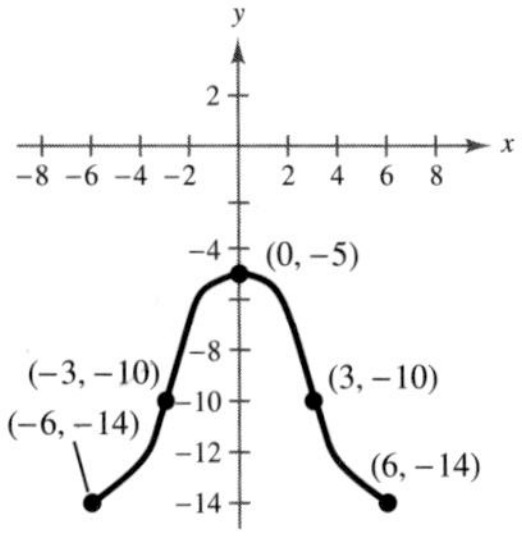

(g)

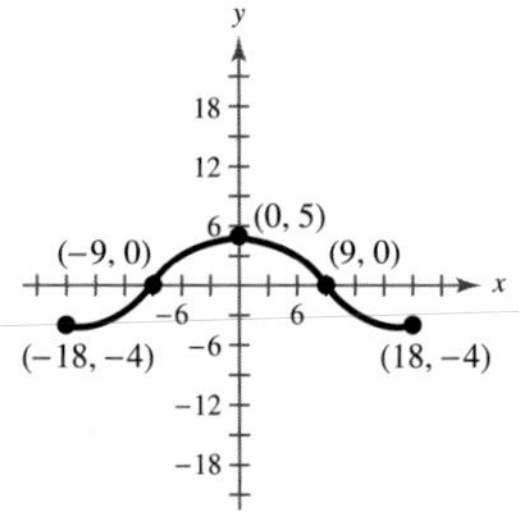

29. (a) $f(x) = x^2$

(b) Vertical shrink of two-thirds and vertical shift four units upward

(c)

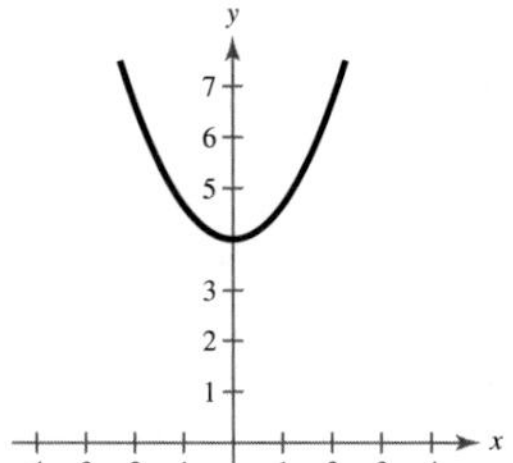

(d) $g(x) = \frac{2}{3}f(x) + 4$

30. (a) $f(x) = x^2$

(b) Vertical stretch of two and horizontal shift seven units to the right

(c) 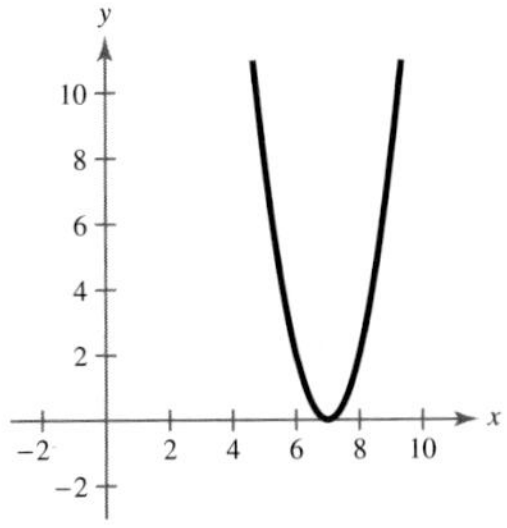

(d) $g(x) = 2f(x - 7)$

31. (a) $f(x) = x^2$

(b) Reflection in the x-axis, horizontal shift five units to the left, and vertical shift two units upward

(c) 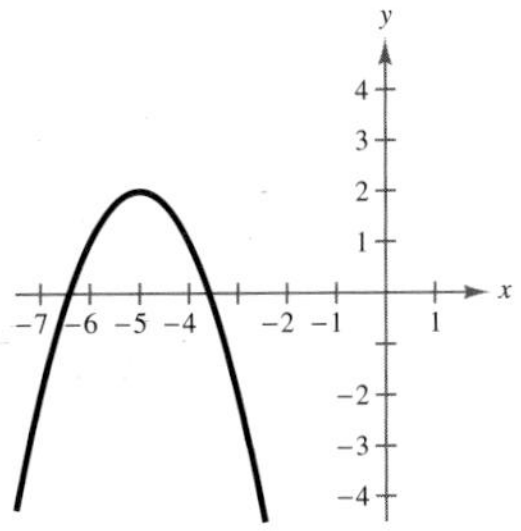

(d) $g(x) = 2 - f(x + 5)$

32. (a) $f(x) = x^2$

(b) Reflection in the x-axis, horizontal shift 10 units to the left, and vertical shift 5 units upward

(c) 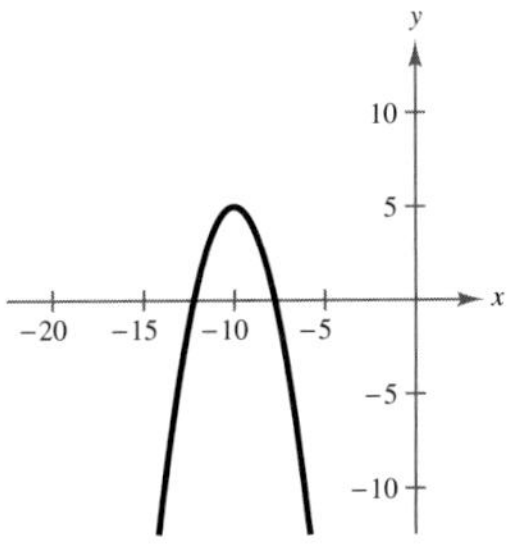

(d) $g(x) = -f(x + 10) + 5$

33. (a) $f(x) = x^2$

(b) Vertical stretch of two, horizontal shift four units to the right, and vertical shift three units upward

(c) 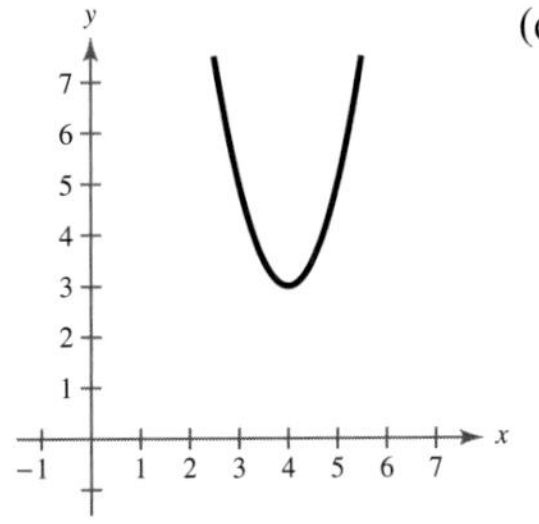

(d) $g(x) = 3 + 2f(x - 4)$

34. (a) $f(x) = x^2$

(b) Reflection in the x-axis, vertical shrink of one-fourth, horizontal shift two units to the left, and vertical shift two units downward

(c) 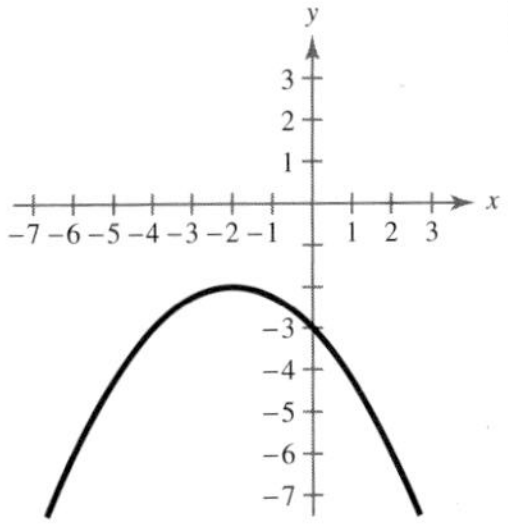

(d) $g(x) = -\frac{1}{4}f(x + 2) - 2$

35. (a) $f(x) = \sqrt{x}$

(b) Horizontal shrink of one-third

(c) 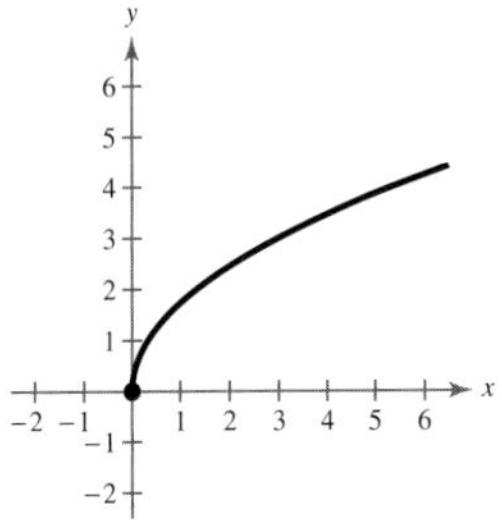

(d) $g(x) = f(3x)$

36. (a) $f(x) = \sqrt{x}$

(b) Horizontal stretch of four

(c) 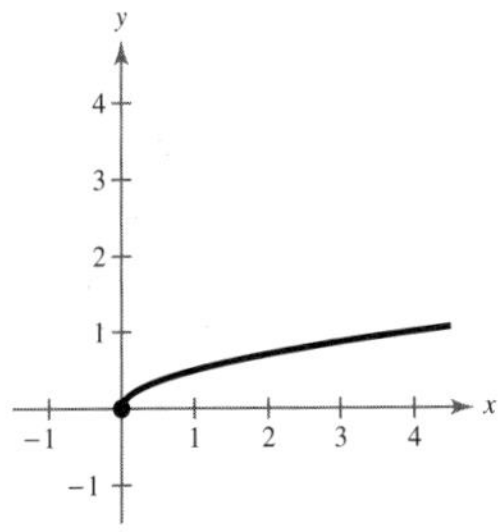

(d) $g(x) = f(\frac{1}{4}x)$

37. (a) $f(x) = x^3$

(b) Vertical shift two units upward and horizontal shift one unit to the right

(c) 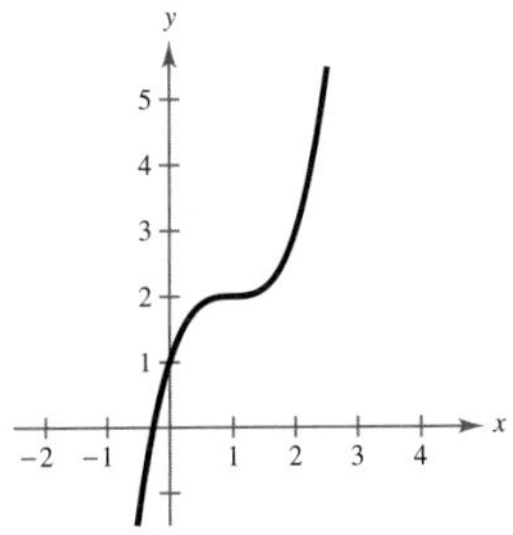

(d) $g(x) = f(x - 1) + 2$

38. (a) $f(x) = x^3$

(b) Vertical shift 10 units downward and horizontal shift 3 units to the left

(c) 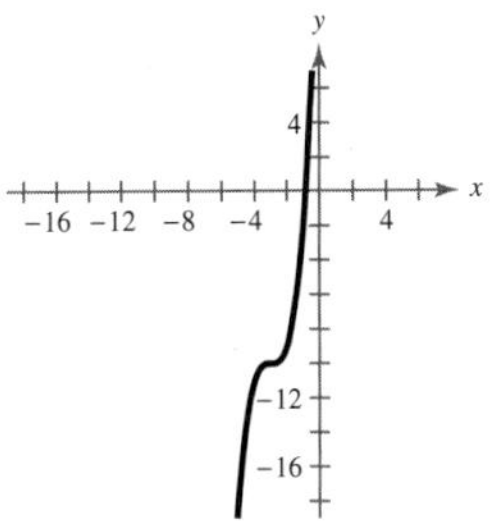

(d) $g(x) = f(x + 3) - 10$

39. (a) $f(x) = x^3$

(b) Vertical stretch of three and horizontal shift two units to the right

(c)

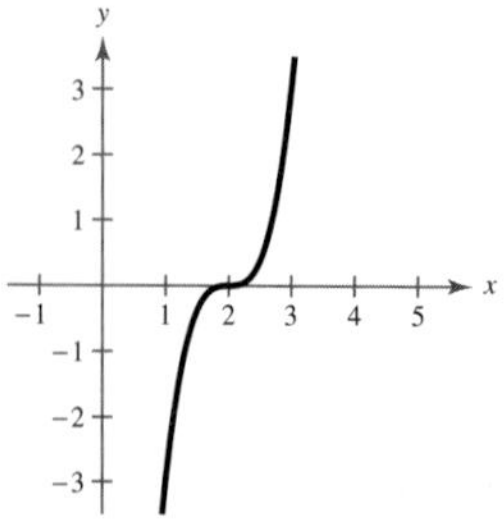

(d) $g(x) = 3f(x - 2)$

40. (a) $f(x) = x^3$

(b) Reflection in the x-axis, vertical shrink of one-half, and horizontal shift one unit to the left

(c)

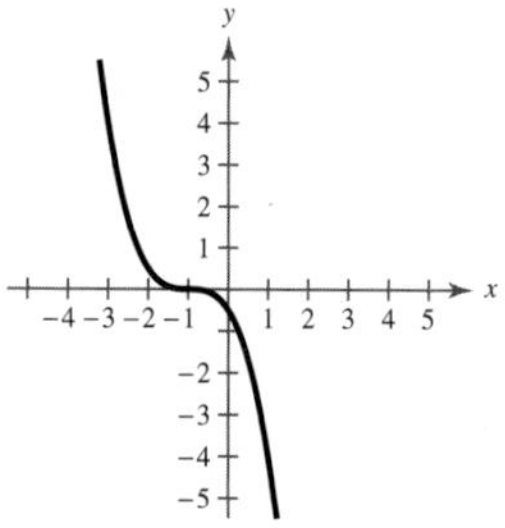

(d) $g(x) = -\frac{1}{2}f(x + 1)$

41. (a) $f(x) = |x|$

(b) Reflection in the x-axis and vertical shift two units downward

(c)

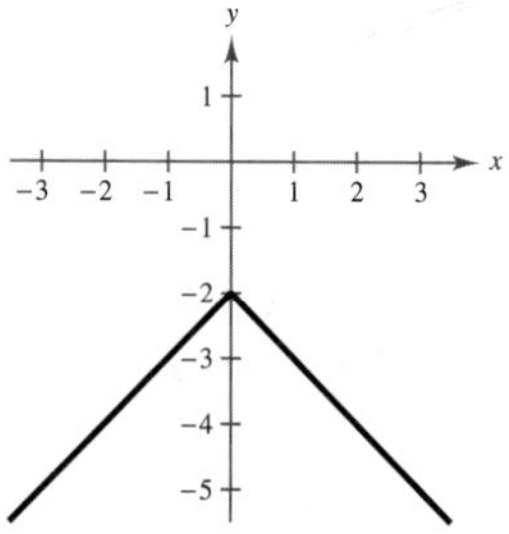

(d) $g(x) = -f(x) - 2$

42. (a) $f(x) = |x|$

(b) Reflection in the x-axis, horizontal shift five units to the left, and vertical shift six units upward

(c)

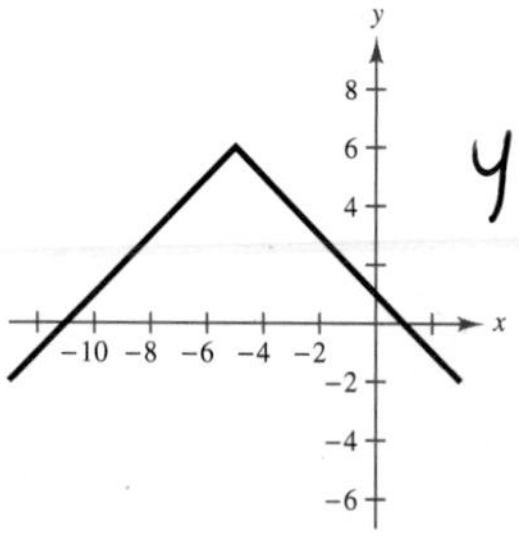

(d) $g(x) = 6 - f(x + 5)$

$y = 6 - |x+5|$

$y = -|x+5| + 6$

43. (a) $f(x) = |x|$

(b) Reflection in the x-axis, horizontal shift four units to the left, and vertical shift eight units upward

(c)

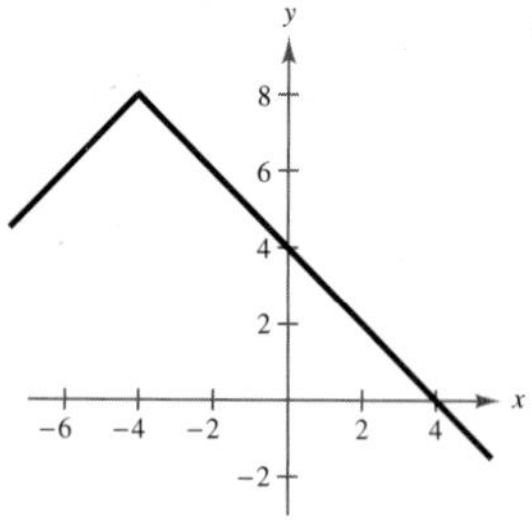

(d) $g(x) = -f(x + 4) + 8$

44. (a) $f(x) = |x|$

(b) Reflection in the y-axis, horizontal shift three units to the right, and vertical shift nine units upward

(c)

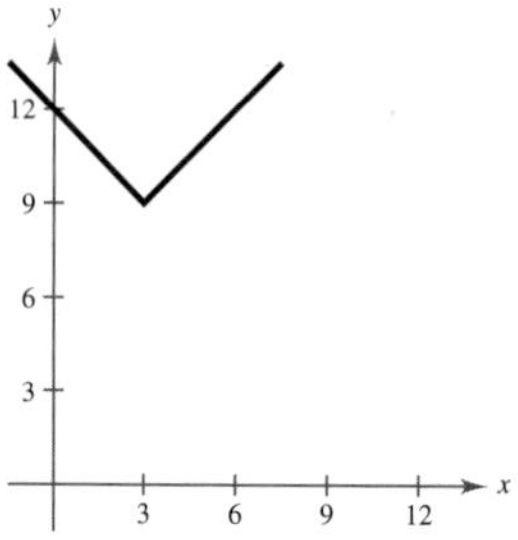

(d) $g(x) = f(-(x - 3)) + 9$

45. (a) $f(x) = |x|$

(b) Reflection in the x-axis, vertical stretch of two, horizontal shift one unit to the right, and vertical shift four units downward

(c)

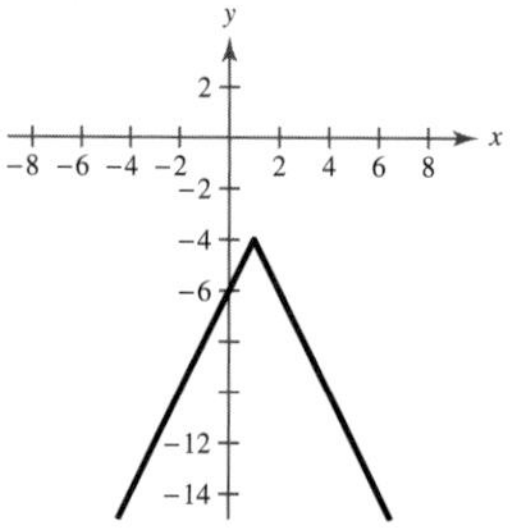

(d) $g(x) = -2f(x - 1) - 4$

46. (a) $f(x) = |x|$

(b) Vertical shrink of one-half, horizontal shift two units to the right, and vertical shift three units downward

(c)

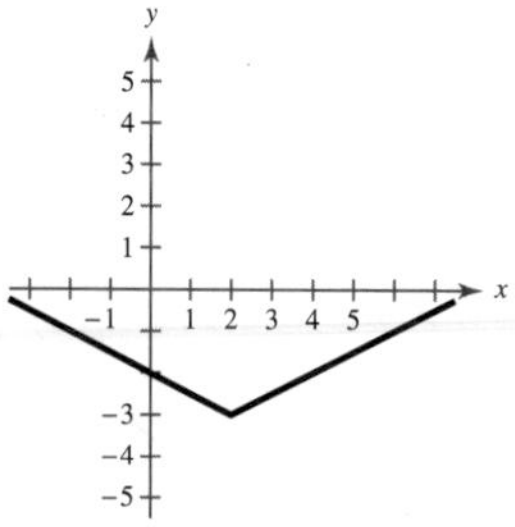

(d) $g(x) = \frac{1}{2}f(x - 2) - 3$

47. (a) $f(x) = [\![x]\!]$

(b) Reflection in the x-axis and vertical shift three units upward

(c)

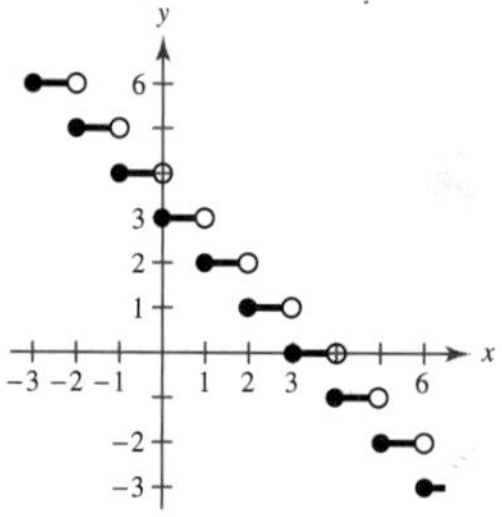

(d) $g(x) = 3 - f(x)$

ADDITIONAL ANSWERS

48. (a) $f(x) = [\![x]\!]$
(b) Horizontal shift five units to the left and vertical stretch of two
(c)
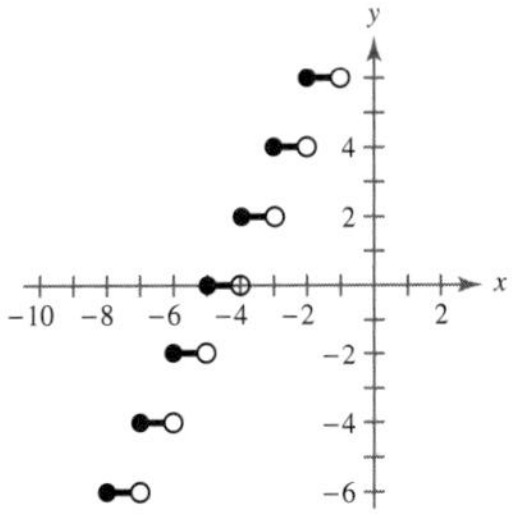
(d) $g(x) = 2f(x + 5)$

49. (a) $f(x) = \sqrt{x}$
(b) Horizontal shift nine units to the right
(c)
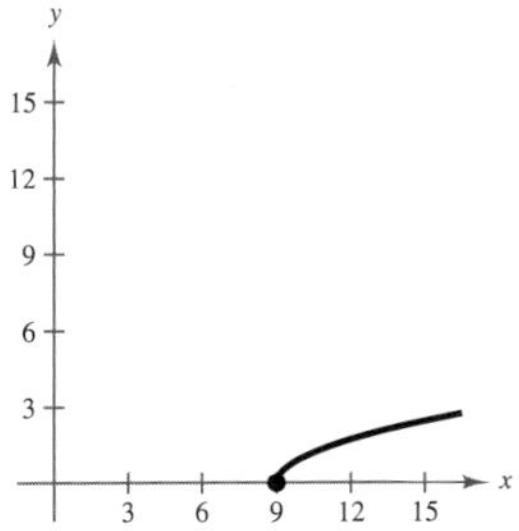
(d) $g(x) = f(x - 9)$

50. (a) $f(x) = \sqrt{x}$
(b) Horizontal shift four units to the left and vertical shift eight units upward
(c)
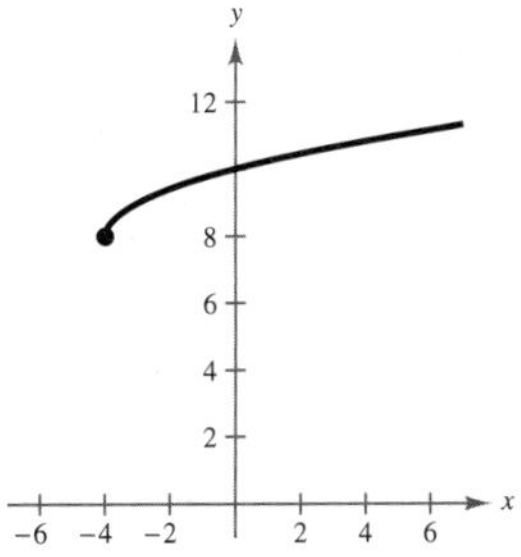
(d) $g(x) = f(x + 4) + 8$

51. (a) $f(x) = \sqrt{x}$
(b) Reflection in the y-axis, horizontal shift seven units to the right, and vertical shift two units downward
(c)
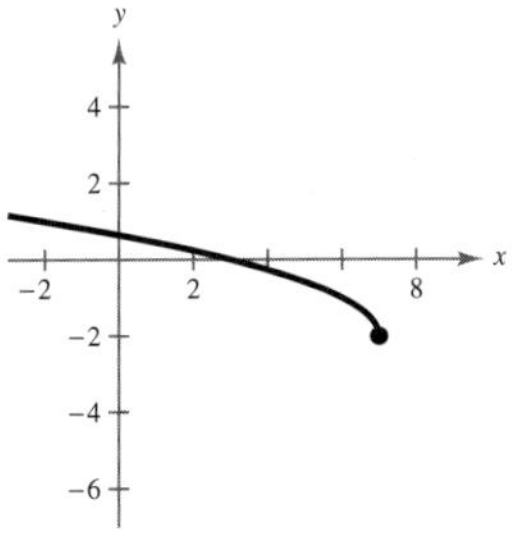
(d) $g(x) = f(7 - x) - 2$

52. (a) $f(x) = \sqrt{x}$
(b) Reflection in the x-axis, vertical shrink of one-half, horizontal shift three units to the left, and vertical shift one unit downward
(c)
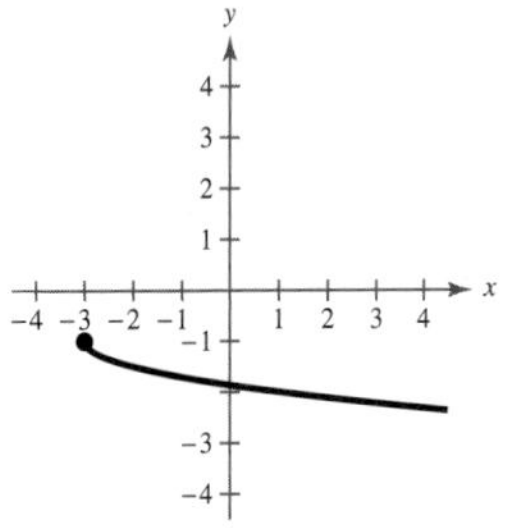
(d) $g(x) = -\frac{1}{2}f(x + 3) - 1$

53. (a) $f(x) = \sqrt{x}$
(b) Horizontal stretch and vertical shift four units downward
(c)
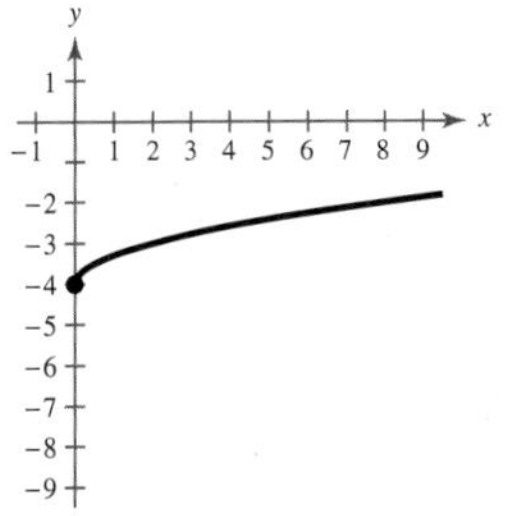
(d) $g(x) = f\left(\frac{1}{2}x\right) - 4$

54. (a) $f(x) = \sqrt{x}$
(b) Horizontal shrink of one-third and vertical shift one unit upward
(c)
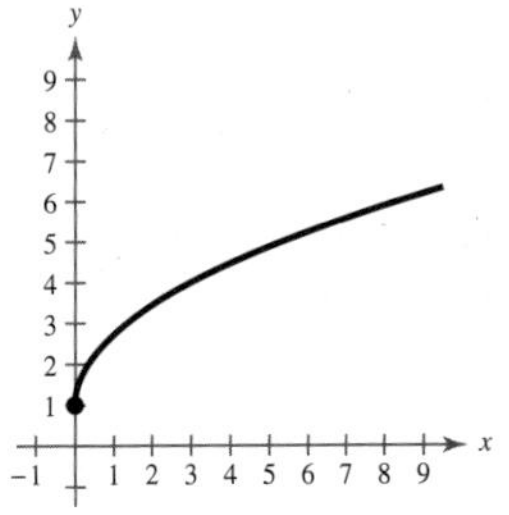
(d) $g(x) = f(3x) + 1$

56. $g(x) = -(x + 2)^2 + 9$ **57.** $g(x) = (x - 13)^3$

61. $g(x) = -\sqrt{-x + 6}$

78. (a)
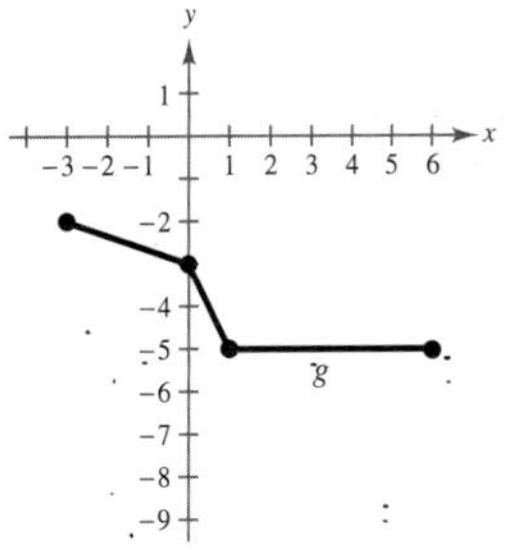

(b)
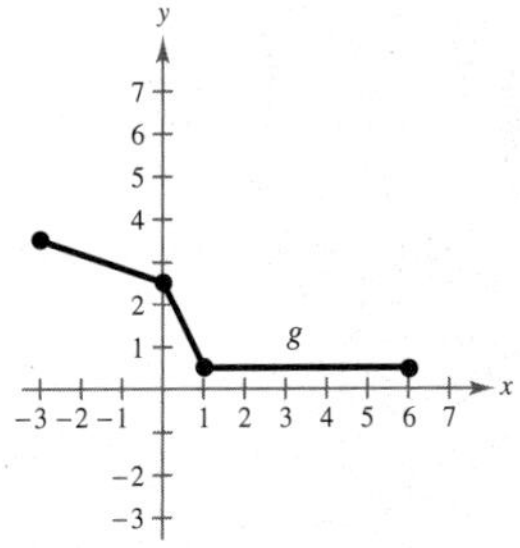

(c)
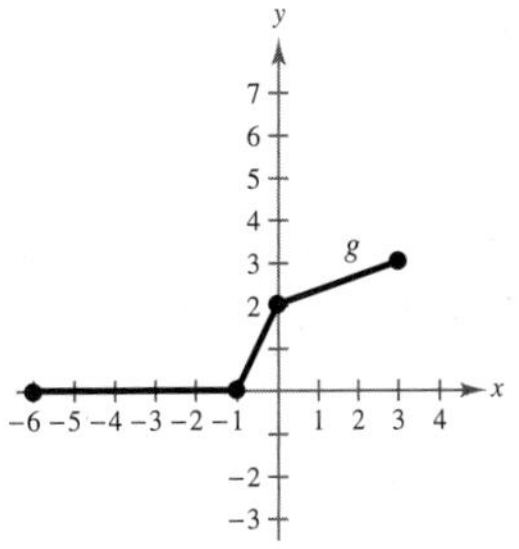

(d)
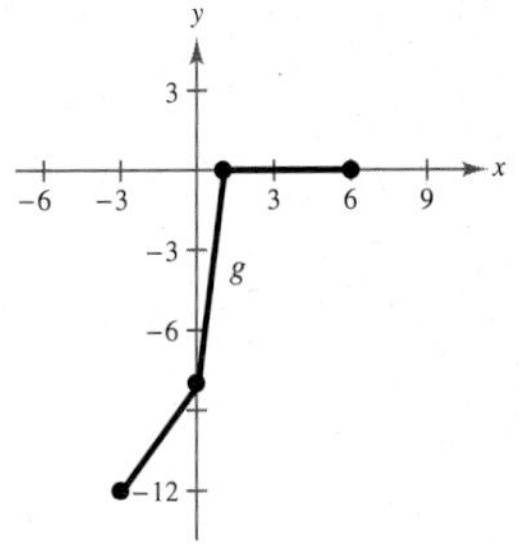

(e)

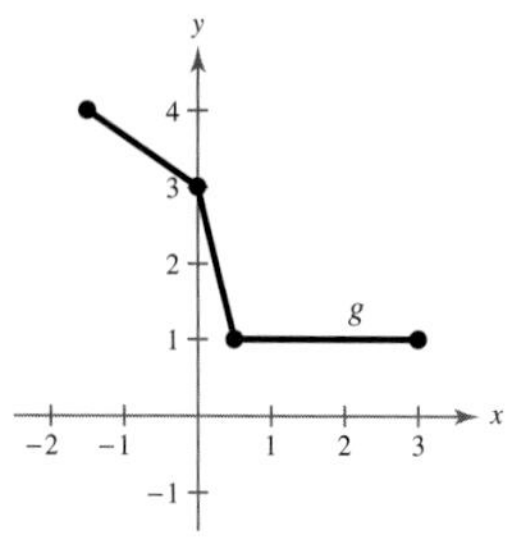

(f)

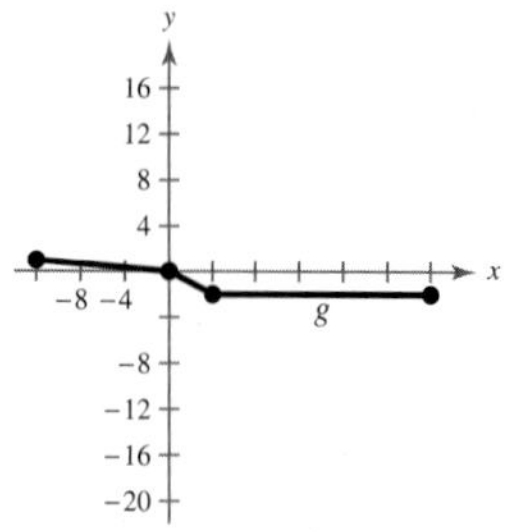

79. (a) Vertical stretch of 128.0 and a vertical shift of 527 units upward

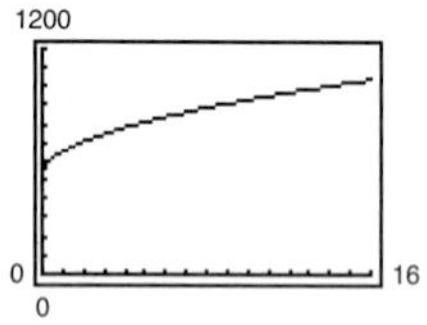

(b) 32; Each year, the total number of miles driven by vans, pickups, and SUVs increases by an average of 32 billion miles.

(c) $f(t) = 527 + 128\sqrt{t + 10}$; The graph is shifted 10 units to the left.

(d) 1127 billion miles; Answers will vary. Sample answer: Yes, because the number of miles driven has been steadily increasing.

Section 1.8 *(page 88)*

14. (a) $\sqrt{x^2 - 4} + \dfrac{x^2}{x^2 + 1}$ (b) $\sqrt{x^2 - 4} - \dfrac{x^2}{x^2 + 1}$

(c) $\dfrac{x^2\sqrt{x^2 - 4}}{x^2 + 1}$

(d) $\dfrac{(x^2 + 1)\sqrt{x^2 - 4}}{x^2}$; all real numbers x such that $|x| \geq 2$

15. (a) $\dfrac{x + 1}{x^2}$ (b) $\dfrac{x - 1}{x^2}$ (c) $\dfrac{1}{x^3}$

(d) x; all real numbers x except $x = 0$

16. (a) $\dfrac{x^4 + x^3 + x}{x + 1}$ (b) $\dfrac{-x^4 - x^3 + x}{x + 1}$ (c) $\dfrac{x^4}{x + 1}$

(d) $\dfrac{1}{x^2(x + 1)}$; all real numbers x except $x = 0, -1$

29.

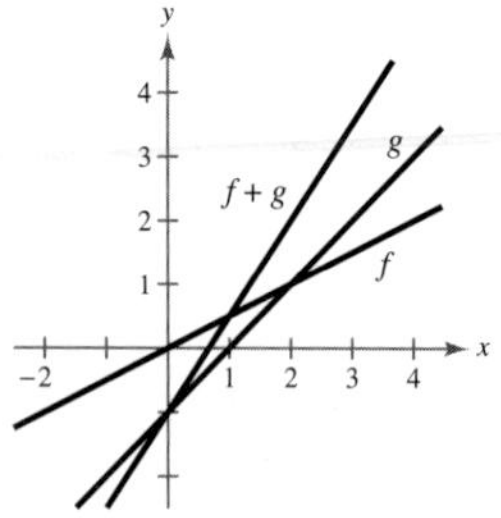

30.

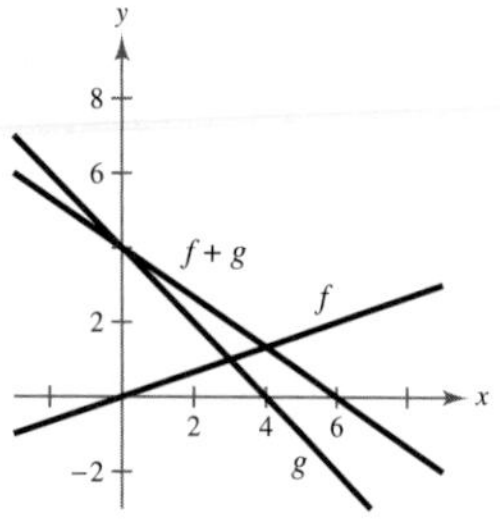

31.

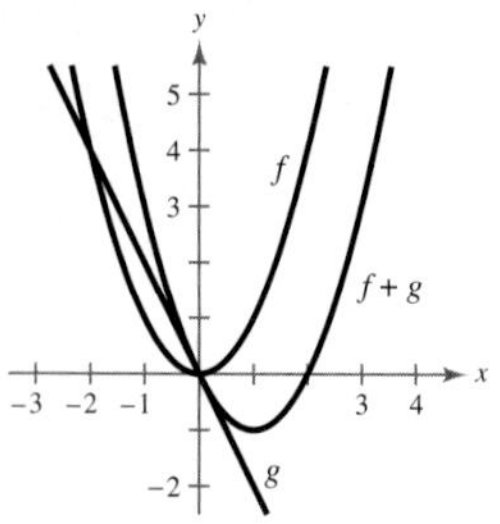

32.

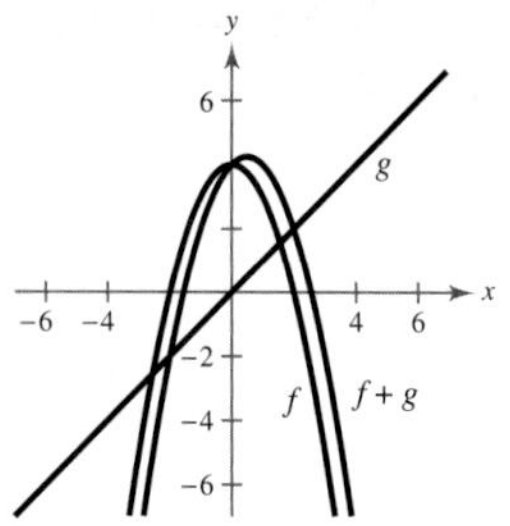

33.

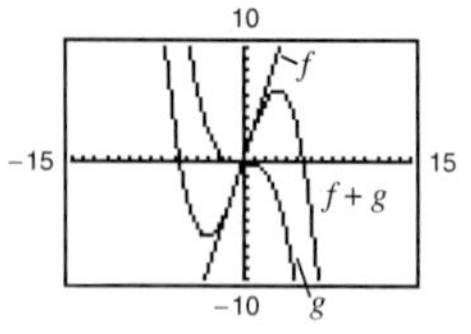

$f(x), g(x)$

34.

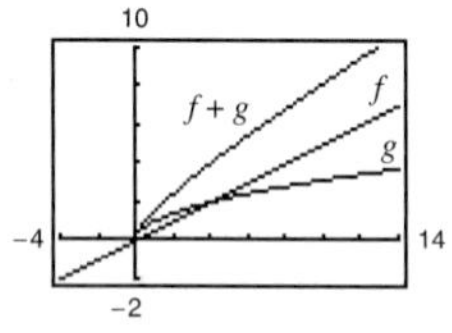

$g(x), f(x)$

35.

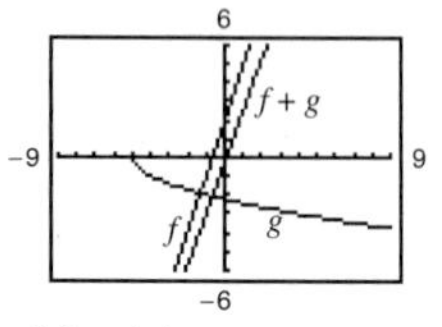

$f(x), f(x)$

36.

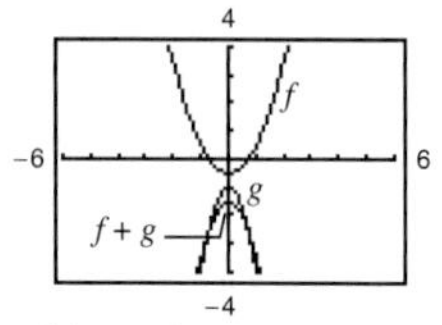

$g(x), g(x)$

37. (a) $(x - 1)^2$ (b) $x^2 - 1$ (c) $x - 2$

38. (a) $20 - 3x$ (b) $-3x$ (c) x

39. (a) x (b) x (c) $x^9 + 3x^6 + 3x^3 + 2$

40. (a) $\dfrac{1}{x^3}$ (b) $\dfrac{1}{x^3}$ (c) x

41. (a) $\sqrt{x^2 + 4}$ (b) $x + 4$

Domains of f and $g \circ f$: all real numbers x such that $x \geq -4$

Domains of g and $f \circ g$: all real numbers x

42. (a) $\sqrt[3]{x^3 - 4}$ (b) $x - 4$

Domains of f, g, $f \circ g$, and $g \circ f$: all real numbers x

66. (a) $h(t) = \dfrac{0.0233t^4 - 0.3408t^3 + 1.556t^2 - 1.86t + 22.8}{2.78t + 282.5}$, which represents the ratio of the number of people playing tennis in the United States to the U.S. population.

(b) $h(0) = 0.0807$; $h(3) = 0.0822$; $h(6) = 0.0810$

67. $(B - D)(t) = -0.197t^3 + 10.17t^2 - 128.0t + 2043$, which represents the change in the United States population.

Section 1.9 *(page 98)*

19. $f(g(x)) = f\left(-\dfrac{2x + 6}{7}\right) = -\dfrac{7}{2}\left(-\dfrac{2x + 6}{7}\right) - 3 = x$

$g(f(x)) = g\left(-\dfrac{7}{2}x - 3\right) = -\dfrac{2\left(-\frac{7}{2}x - 3\right) + 6}{7} = x$

20. $f(g(x)) = f(4x + 9) = \dfrac{(4x + 9) - 9}{4} = x$

$g(f(x)) = g\left(\dfrac{x - 9}{4}\right) = 4\left(\dfrac{x - 9}{4}\right) + 9 = x$

21. $f(g(x)) = f\left(\sqrt[3]{x - 5}\right) = \left(\sqrt[3]{x - 5}\right)^3 + 5 = x$

$g(f(x)) = g(x^3 + 5) = \sqrt[3]{(x^3 + 5) - 5} = x$

22. $f(g(x)) = f\left(\sqrt[3]{2x}\right) = \dfrac{\left(\sqrt[3]{2x}\right)^3}{2} = x$

$g(f(x)) = g\left(\dfrac{x^3}{2}\right) = \sqrt[3]{2\left(\dfrac{x^3}{2}\right)} = x$

ADDITIONAL ANSWERS

24. (a) $f(g(x)) = f(x + 5) = (x + 5) - 5 = x$
$g(f(x)) = g(x - 5) = (x - 5) + 5 = x$

(b)

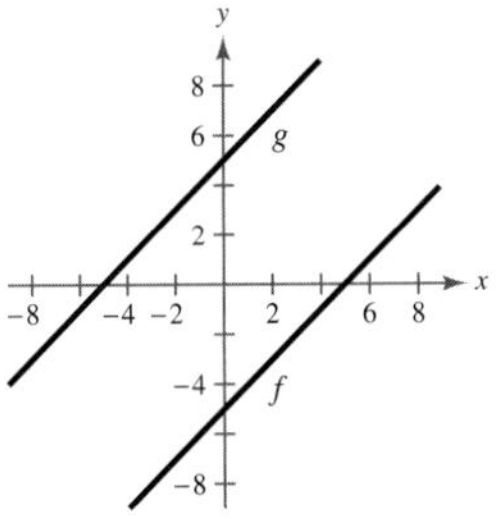

25. (a) $f(g(x)) = f\left(\frac{x - 1}{7}\right) = 7\left(\frac{x - 1}{7}\right) + 1 = x$

$g(f(x)) = g(7x + 1) = \frac{(7x + 1) - 1}{7} = x$

(b)

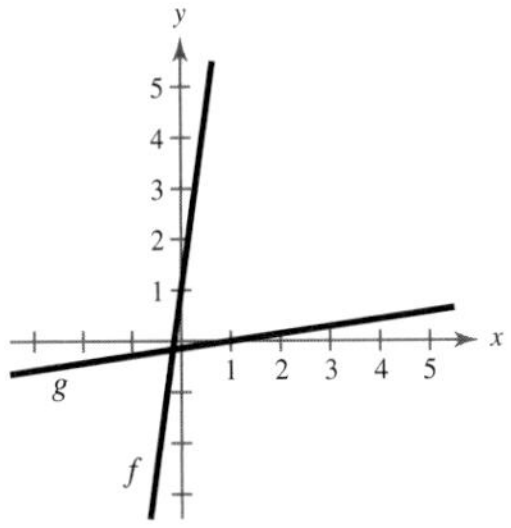

26. (a) $f(g(x)) = f\left(\frac{3 - x}{4}\right) = 3 - 4\left(\frac{3 - x}{4}\right) = x$

$g(f(x)) = g(3 - 4x) = \frac{3 - (3 - 4x)}{4} = x$

(b)

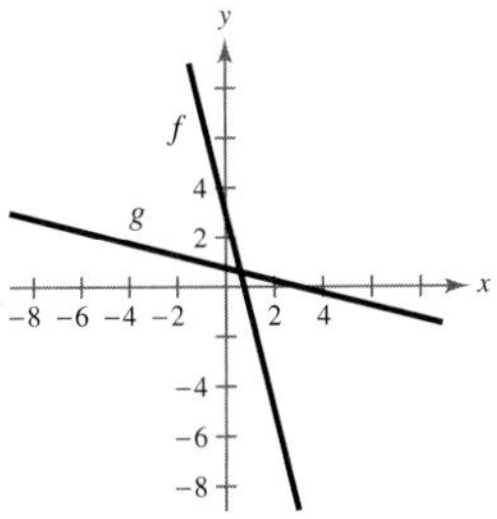

27. (a) $f(g(x)) = f\left(\sqrt[3]{8x}\right) = \frac{\left(\sqrt[3]{8x}\right)^3}{8} = x$

$g(f(x)) = g\left(\frac{x^3}{8}\right) = \sqrt[3]{8\left(\frac{x^3}{8}\right)} = x$

(b)

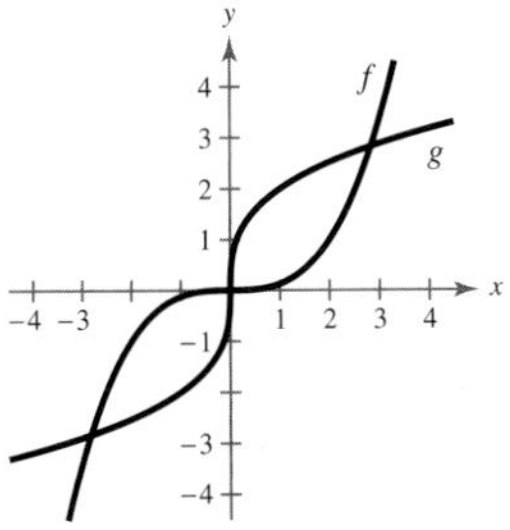

30. (a) $f(g(x)) = f\left(\sqrt[3]{1 - x}\right)$
$= 1 - \left(\sqrt[3]{1 - x}\right)^3 = x$
$g(f(x)) = g(1 - x^3)$
$= \sqrt[3]{1 - (1 - x^3)} = x$

(b)

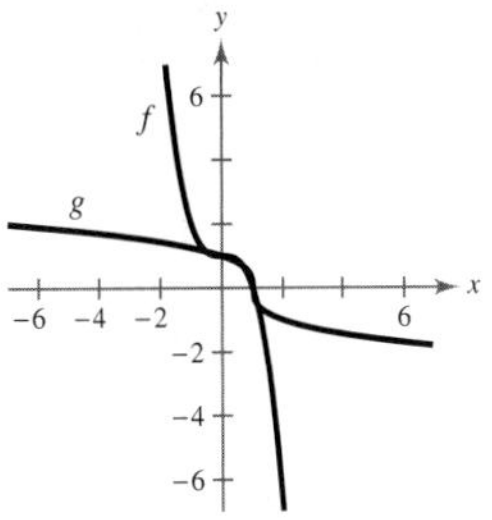

31. (a) $f(g(x)) = f\left(\sqrt{9 - x}\right),\ x \le 9$
$= 9 - \left(\sqrt{9 - x}\right)^2 = x$
$g(f(x)) = g(9 - x^2),\ x \ge 0$
$= \sqrt{9 - (9 - x^2)} = x$

(b)

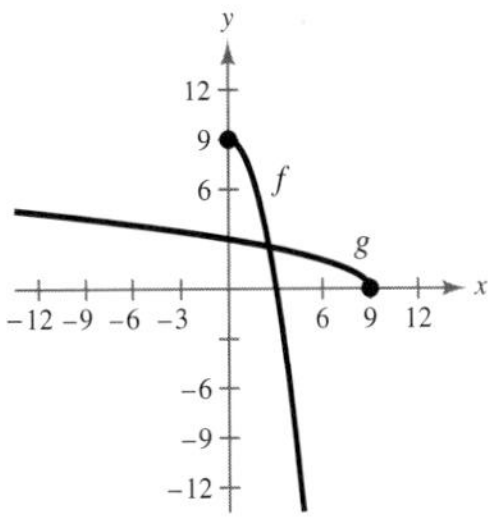

32. (a) $f(g(x)) = f\left(\frac{1 - x}{x}\right),\quad 0 < x \le 1$

$= \frac{1}{1 + (1 - x)/x} = \frac{x}{x + 1 - x} = x$

$g(f(x)) = g\left(\frac{1}{1 + x}\right),\quad x \ge 0$

$= \frac{1 - 1/(1 + x)}{1/(1 + x)} = \frac{1 + x - 1}{1} = x$

(b)

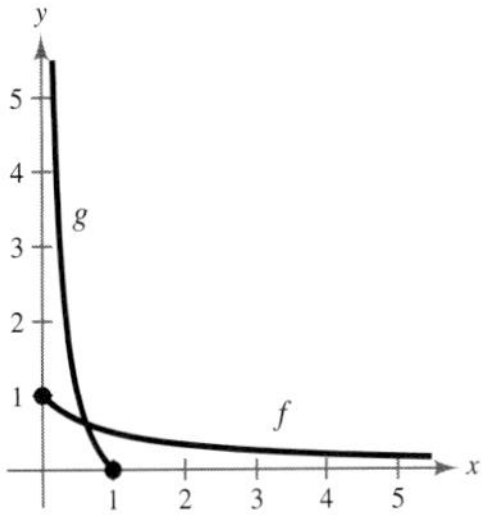

33. (a) $f(g(x)) = f\left(-\frac{5x + 1}{x - 1}\right) = \frac{-\left(\frac{5x + 1}{x - 1}\right) - 1}{-\left(\frac{5x + 1}{x - 1}\right) + 5}$

$= \frac{-5x - 1 - x + 1}{-5x - 1 + 5x - 5} = x$

$g(f(x)) = g\left(\frac{x - 1}{x + 5}\right) = \frac{-5\left(\frac{x - 1}{x + 5}\right) - 1}{\frac{x - 1}{x + 5} - 1}$

$= \frac{-5x + 5 - x - 5}{x - 1 - x - 5} = x$

(b)

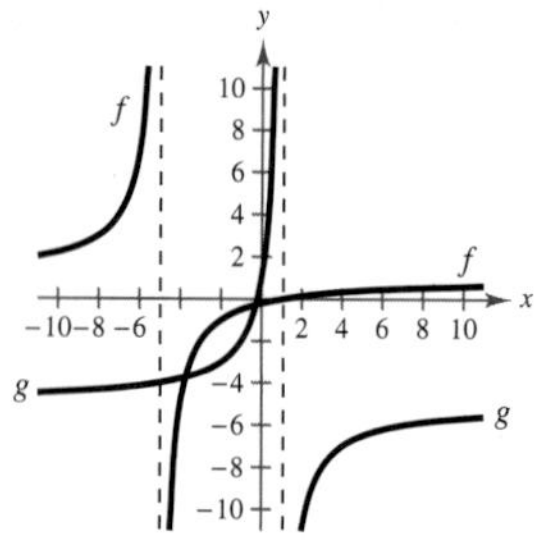

34. (a) $f(g(x)) = f\left(\frac{2x+3}{x-1}\right) = \dfrac{\left(\frac{2x+3}{x-1}\right)+3}{\left(\frac{2x+3}{x-1}\right)-2}$

$= \dfrac{2x+3+3x-3}{2x+3-2x+2} = x$

(b) $g(f(x)) = g\left(\frac{x+3}{x-2}\right) = \dfrac{2\left(\frac{x+3}{x-2}\right)+3}{\left(\frac{x+3}{x-2}\right)-1}$

$= \dfrac{2x+6+3x-6}{x+3-x+2} = x$

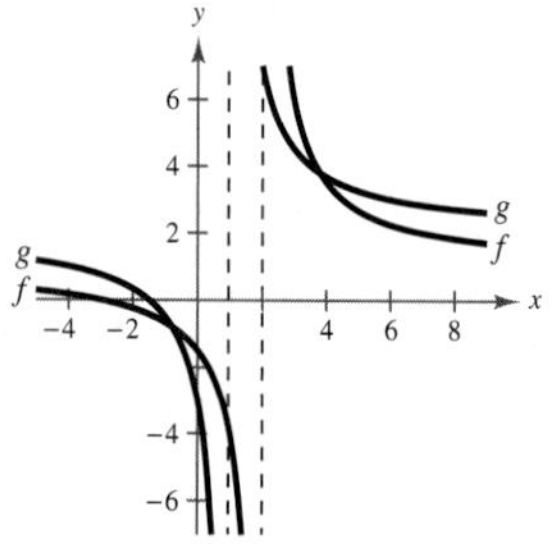

37.

x	-2	0	2	4	6	8
$f^{-1}(x)$	-2	-1	0	1	2	3

38.

x	-10	-7	-4	-1	2	5
$f^{-1}(x)$	-3	-2	-1	0	1	2

51. (a) $f^{-1}(x) = \sqrt[5]{x+2}$

(b)

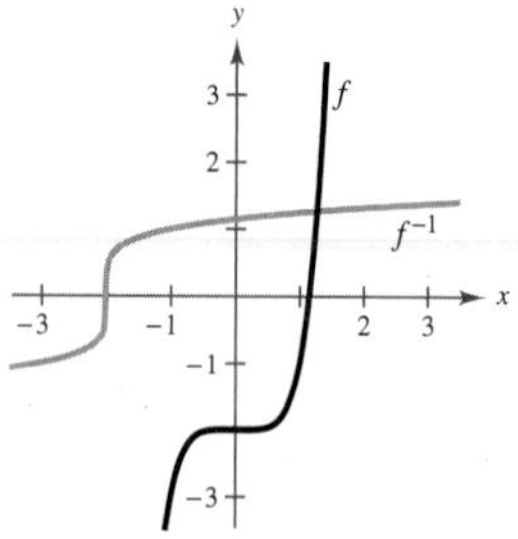

(c) The graph of f^{-1} is the reflection of the graph of f in the line $y = x$.

(d) The domains and ranges of f and f^{-1} are all real numbers.

52. (a) $f^{-1}(x) = \sqrt[3]{x-1}$

(b)

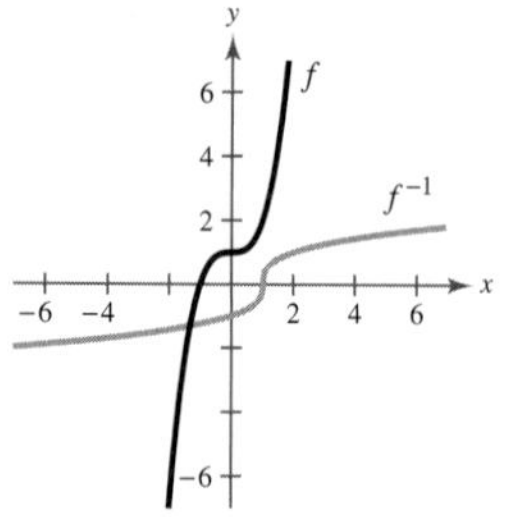

(c) The graph of f^{-1} is the reflection of the graph of f in the line $y = x$.

(d) The domains and ranges of f and f^{-1} are all real numbers.

53. (a) $f^{-1}(x) = \sqrt{4-x^2},\ 0 \le x \le 2$

(b)

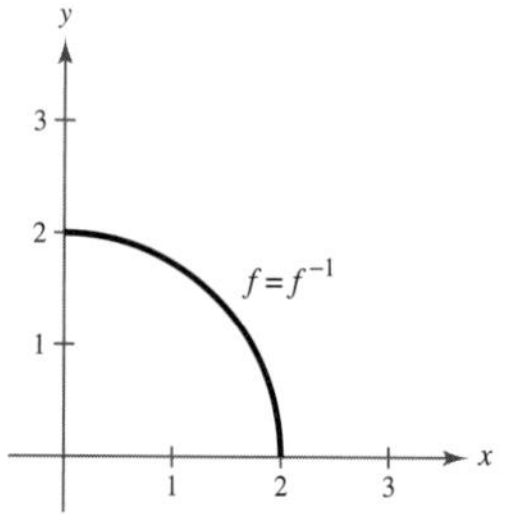

(c) The graph of f^{-1} is the same as the graph of f.

(d) The domains and ranges of f and f^{-1} are all real numbers x such that $0 \le x \le 2$.

54. (a) $f^{-1}(x) = -\sqrt{x+2}$

(b)

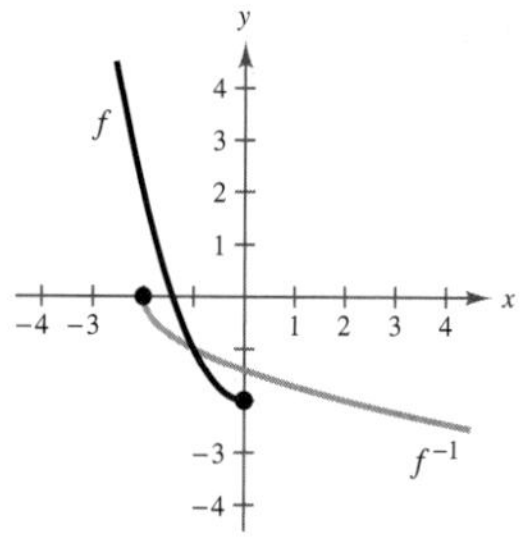

(c) The graph of f^{-1} is the reflection of the graph of f in the line $y = x$.

(d) The domain of f and the range of f^{-1} are all real numbers x such that $x \le 0$. The domain of f^{-1} and the range of f are all real numbers x such that $x \ge -2$.

55. (a) $f^{-1}(x) = \dfrac{4}{x}$

(b)

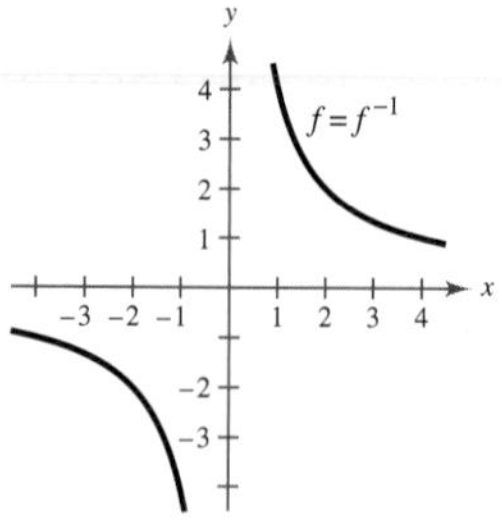

(c) The graph of f^{-1} is the same as the graph of f.

(d) The domains and ranges of f and f^{-1} are all real numbers x except $x = 0$.

56. (a) $f^{-1}(x) = -\dfrac{2}{x}$

(b)

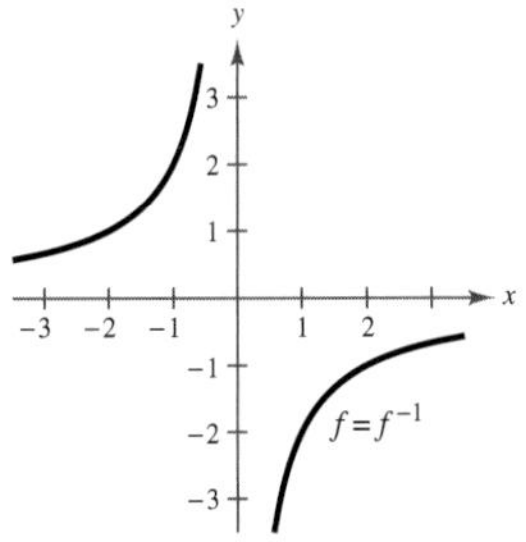

(c) The graph of f^{-1} is the same as the graph of f.

(d) The domains and ranges of f and f^{-1} are all real numbers x except $x = 0$.

57. (a) $f^{-1}(x) = \dfrac{2x + 1}{x - 1}$

(b)

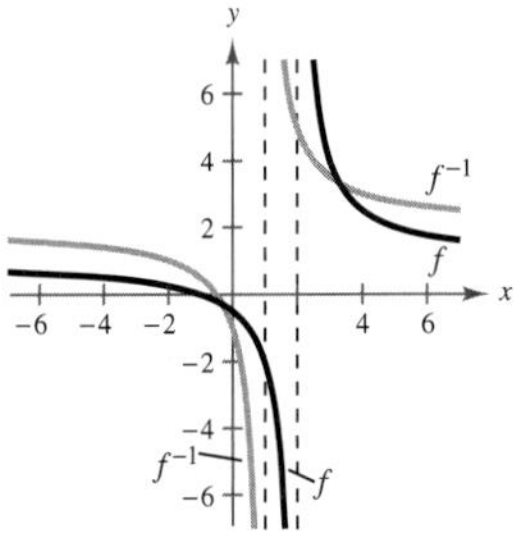

(c) The graph of f^{-1} is the reflection of the graph of f in the line $y = x$.

(d) The domain of f and the range of f^{-1} are all real numbers x except $x = 2$. The domain of f^{-1} and the range of f are all real numbers x except $x = 1$.

58. (a) $f^{-1}(x) = \dfrac{-2x - 3}{x - 1}$

(b)

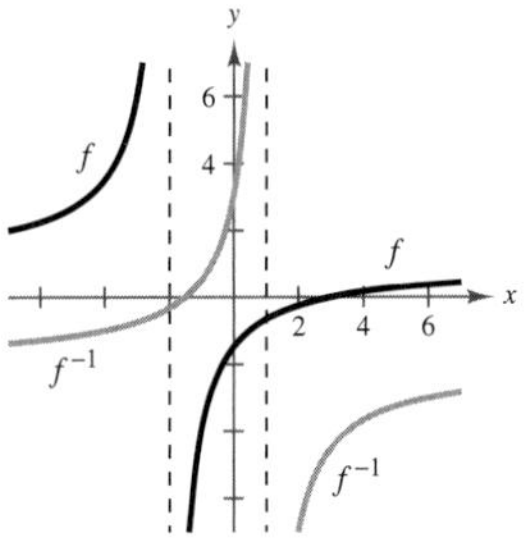

(c) The graph of f^{-1} is the reflection of the graph of f in the line $y = x$.

(d) The domain of f and the range of f^{-1} are all real numbers x except $x = -2$. The domain of f^{-1} and the range of f are all real numbers x except $x = 1$.

59. (a) $f^{-1}(x) = x^3 + 1$

(b)

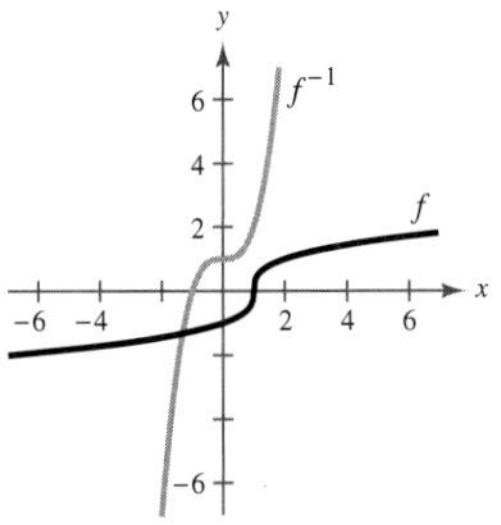

(c) The graph of f^{-1} is the reflection of the graph of f in the line $y = x$.

(d) The domains and ranges of f and f^{-1} are all real numbers.

60. (a) $f^{-1}(x) = x^{5/3}$

(b)

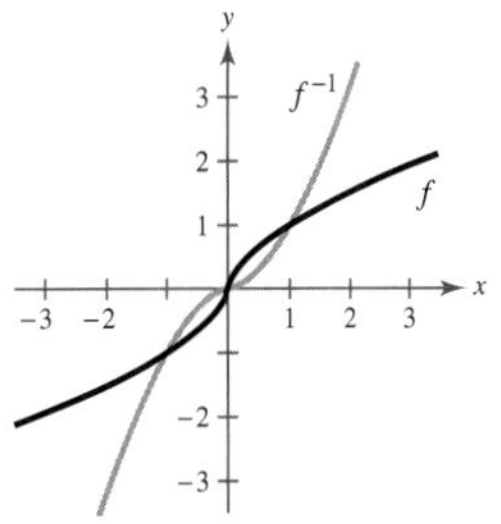

(c) The graph of f^{-1} is the reflection of the graph of f in the line $y = x$.

(d) The domains and ranges of f and f^{-1} are all real numbers.

61. (a) $f^{-1}(x) = \dfrac{5x - 4}{6 - 4x}$

(b)

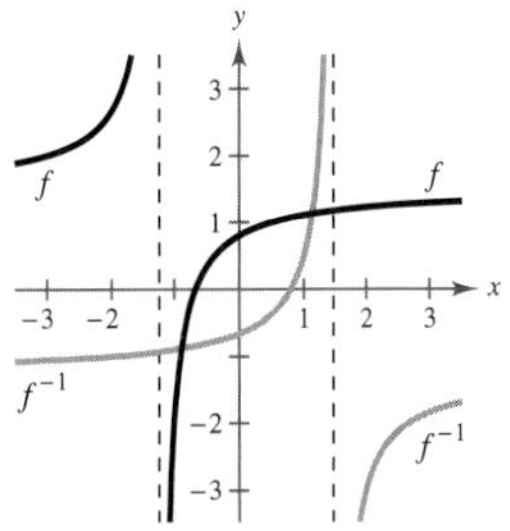

(c) The graph of f^{-1} is the reflection of the graph of f in the line $y = x$.

(d) The domain of f and the range of f^{-1} are all real numbers x except $x = -\frac{5}{4}$. The domain of f^{-1} and the range of f are all real numbers x except $x = \frac{3}{2}$.

62. (a) $f^{-1}(x) = \dfrac{-3x - 2}{x - 4}$

(b)

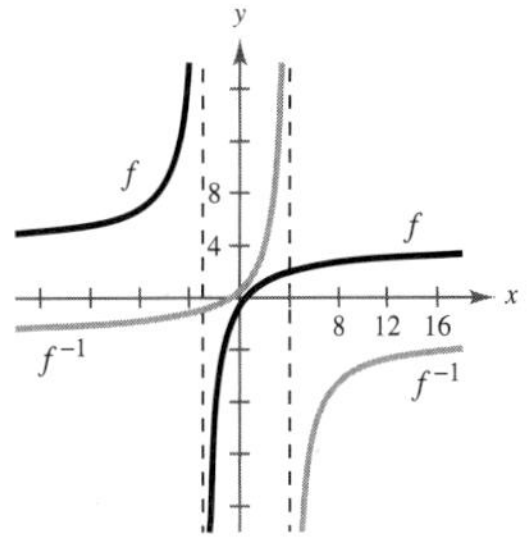

(c) The graph of f^{-1} is the reflection of the graph of f in the line $y = x$.

(d) The domain of f and the range of f^{-1} are all real numbers x except $x = -3$. The domain of f^{-1} and the range of f are all real numbers x except $x = 4$.

115.

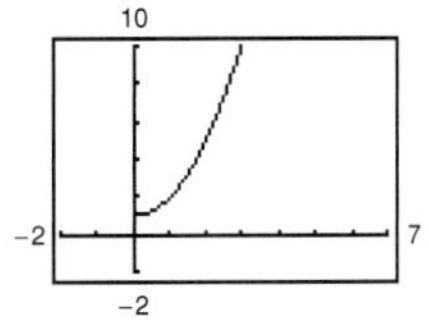

There is an inverse function $f^{-1}(x) = \sqrt{x - 1}$ because the domain of f is equal to the range of f^{-1} and the range of f is equal to the domain of f^{-1}.

Section 1.10 *(page 108)*

17. (a) and (b)

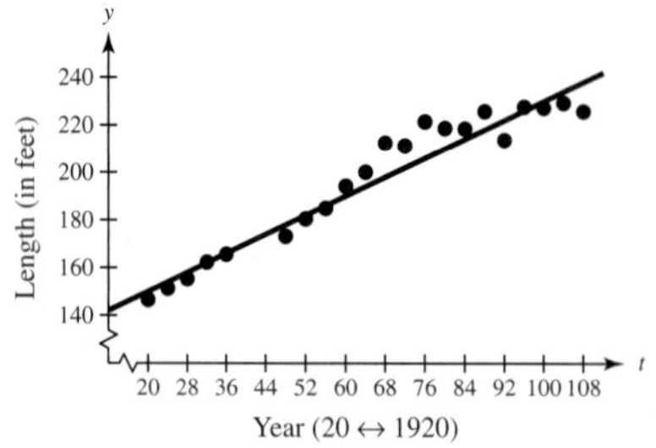

$y \approx t + 130$

(c) $y = 1.01t + 130.82$ (d) The models are similar.

(e) Part (b): 242 ft; Part (c): 243.94 ft

(f) Answers will vary.

27.

x	2	4	6	8	10
$y = k/x^2$	$\frac{1}{2}$	$\frac{1}{8}$	$\frac{1}{18}$	$\frac{1}{32}$	$\frac{1}{50}$

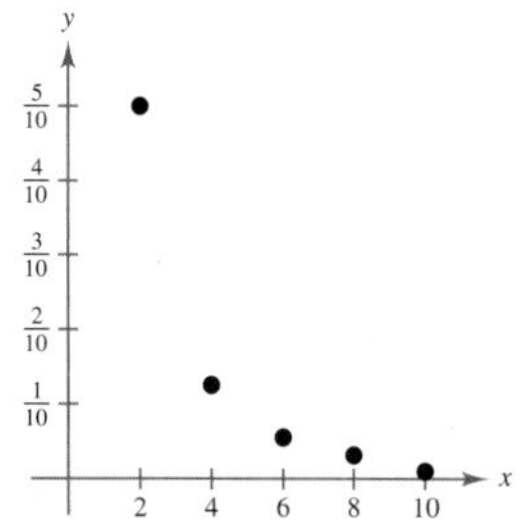

28.

x	2	4	6	8	10
$y = k/x^2$	$\frac{5}{4}$	$\frac{5}{16}$	$\frac{5}{36}$	$\frac{5}{64}$	$\frac{1}{20}$

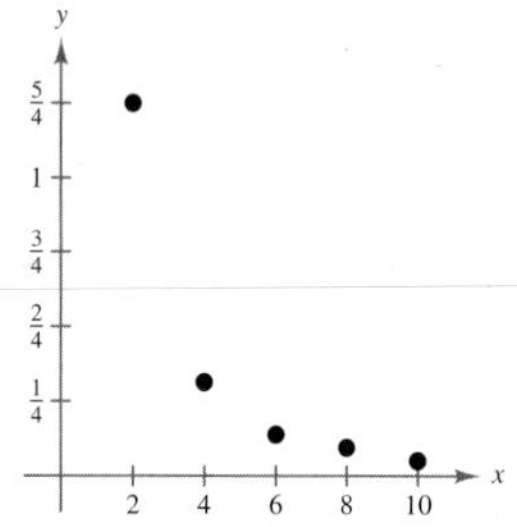

29.

x	2	4	6	8	10
$y = k/x^2$	$\frac{5}{2}$	$\frac{5}{8}$	$\frac{5}{18}$	$\frac{5}{32}$	$\frac{1}{10}$

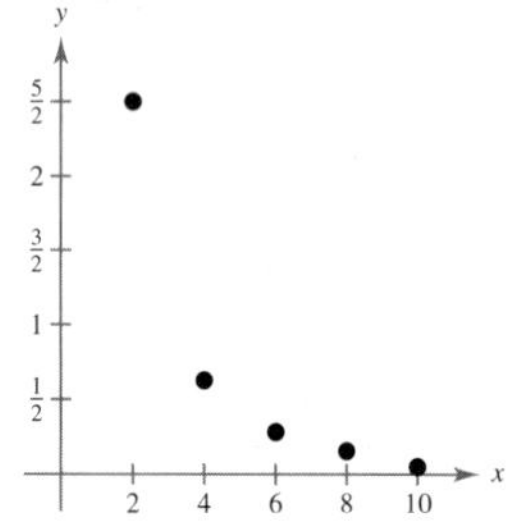

30.

x	2	4	6	8	10
$y = k/x^2$	5	$\frac{5}{4}$	$\frac{5}{9}$	$\frac{5}{16}$	$\frac{1}{5}$

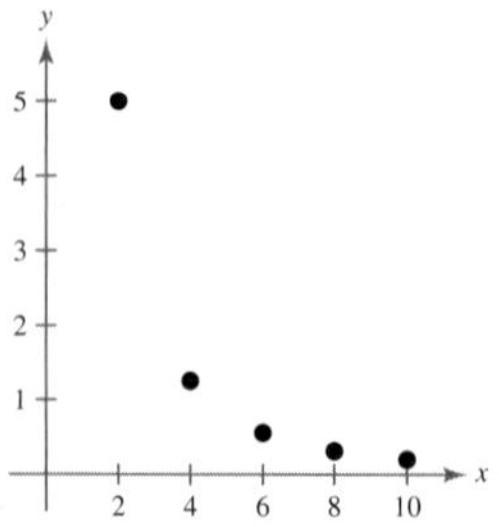

Review Exercises *(page 116)*

13.

x	-2	-1	0	1	2
y	-11	-8	-5	-2	1

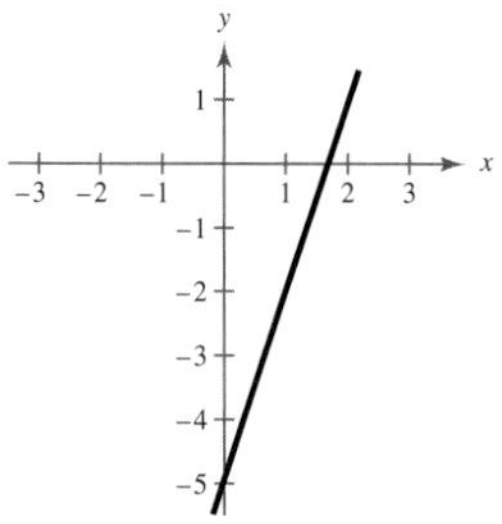

14.

x	-4	-2	0	2	4
y	4	3	2	1	0

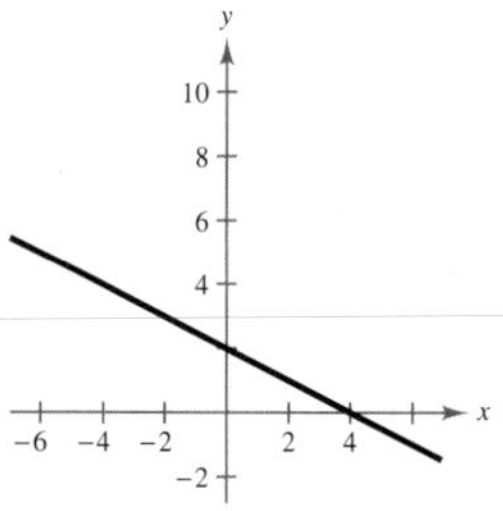

15.

x	-1	0	1	2	3	4
y	4	0	-2	-2	0	4

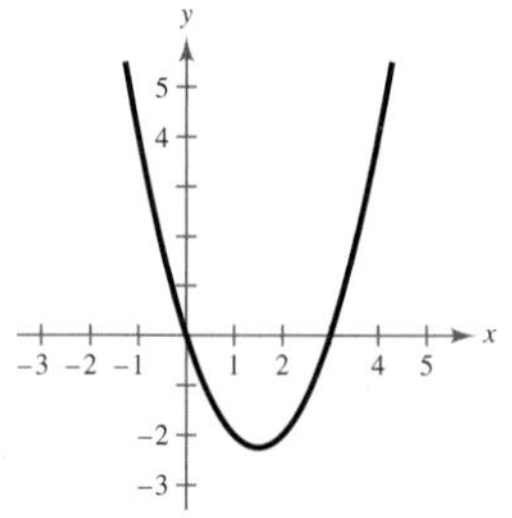

16.

x	-2	-1	0	1	2	3
y	1	-6	-9	-8	-3	6

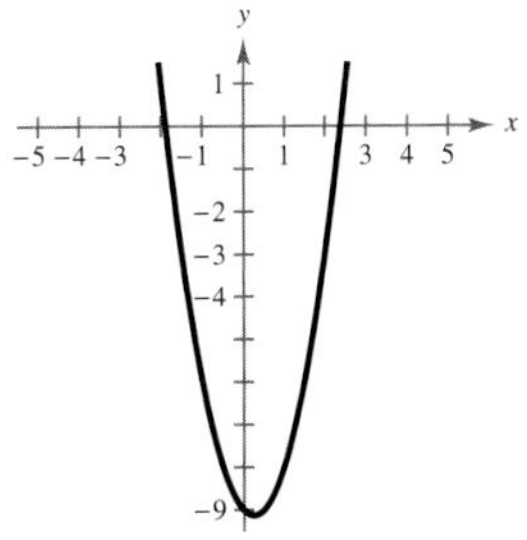

17.

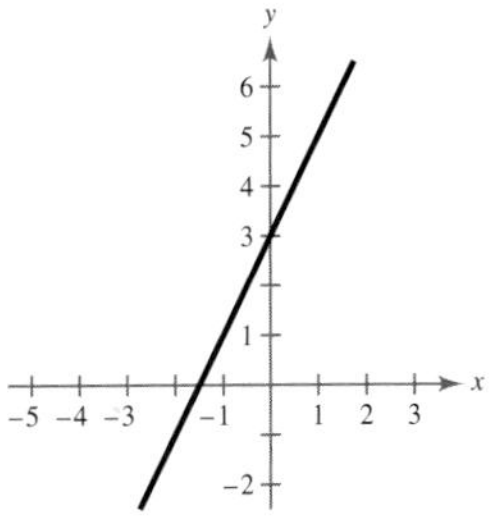

18.

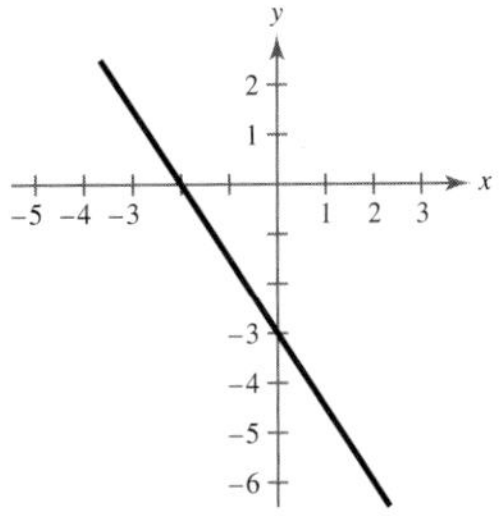

19.

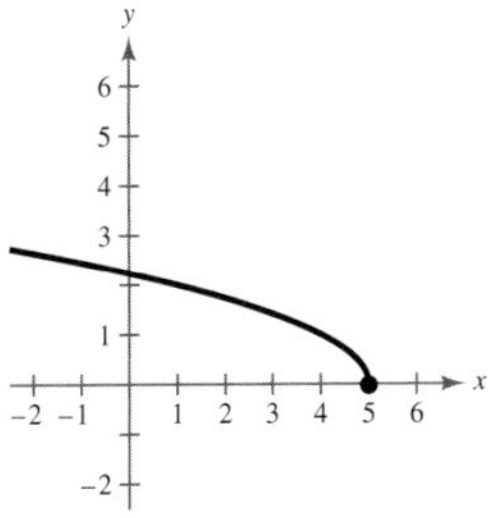

20.

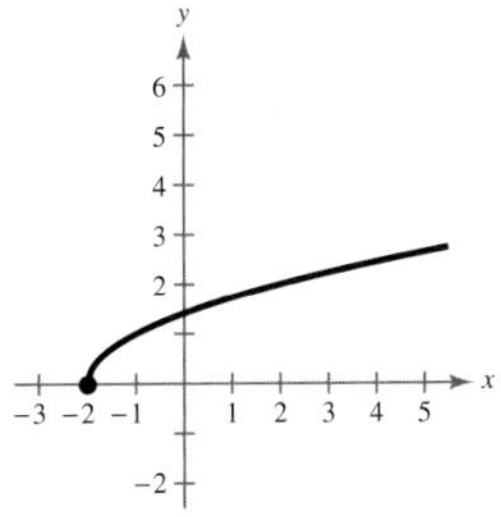

21.

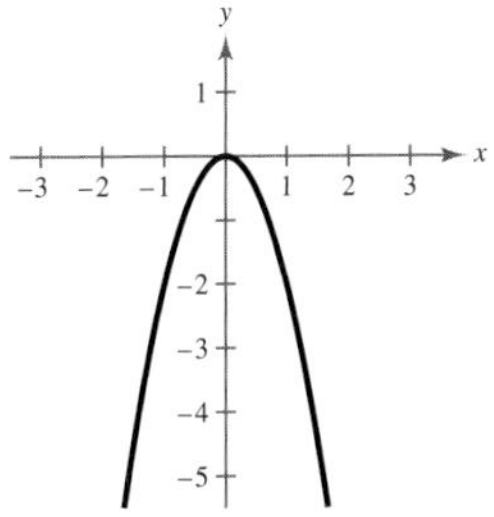

22.

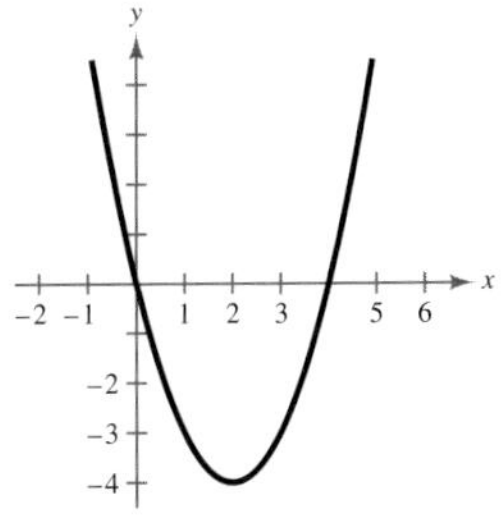

23. x-intercept: $\left(-\frac{7}{2}, 0\right)$
y-intercept: $(0, 7)$

24. x-intercepts: $(2, 0), (-4, 0)$
y-intercept: $(0, -2)$

25. x-intercepts: $(1, 0), (5, 0)$
y-intercept: $(0, 5)$

26. x-intercepts: $(2, 0), (-2, 0), (0, 0)$
y-intercept: $(0, 0)$

27. x-intercept: $\left(\frac{1}{4}, 0\right)$
y-intercept: $(0, 1)$
No symmetry

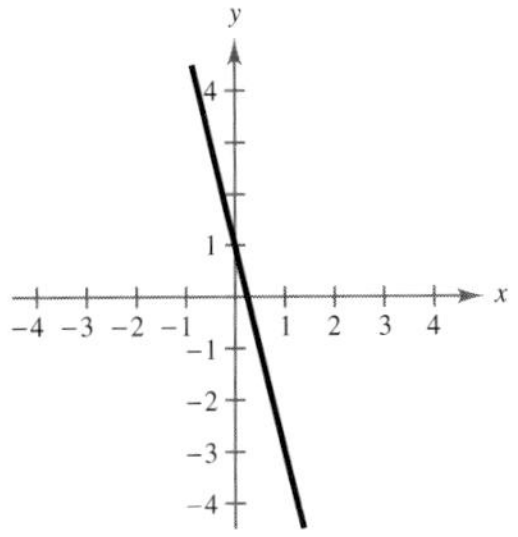

28. x-intercept: $\left(\frac{6}{5}, 0\right)$
y-intercept: $(0, -6)$
No symmetry

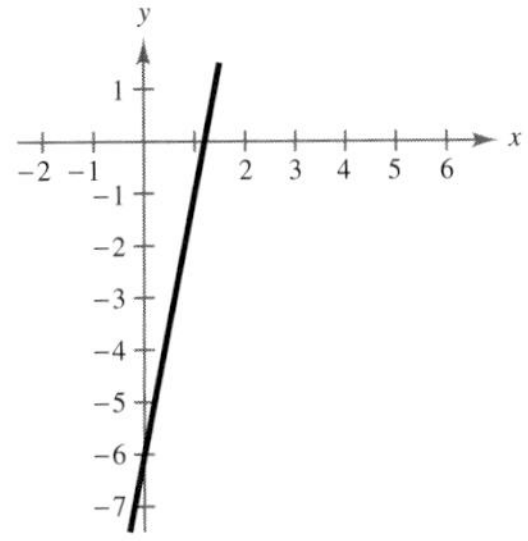

29. x-intercepts: $\left(\pm\sqrt{5}, 0\right)$
y-intercept: $(0, 5)$
y-axis symmetry

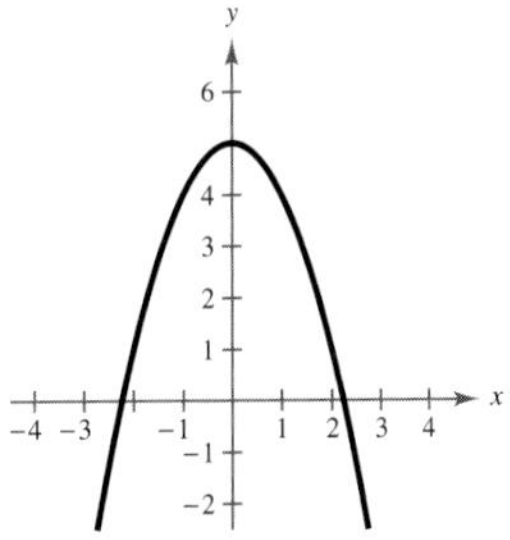

30. x-intercepts: $\left(\pm\sqrt{10}, 0\right)$
y-intercept: $(0, -10)$
y-axis symmetry

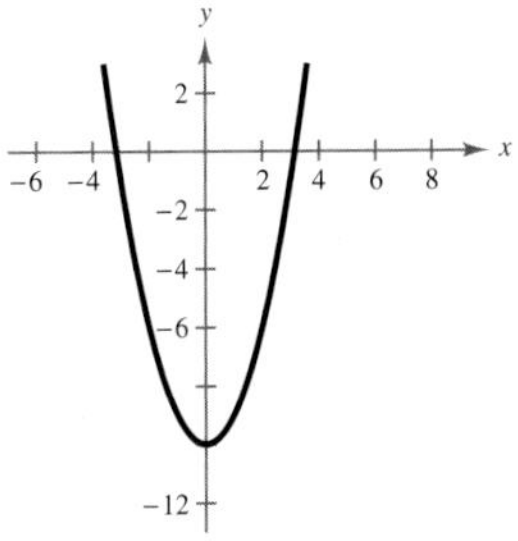

31. x-intercept: $\left(\sqrt[3]{-3}, 0\right)$
y-intercept: $(0, 3)$
No symmetry

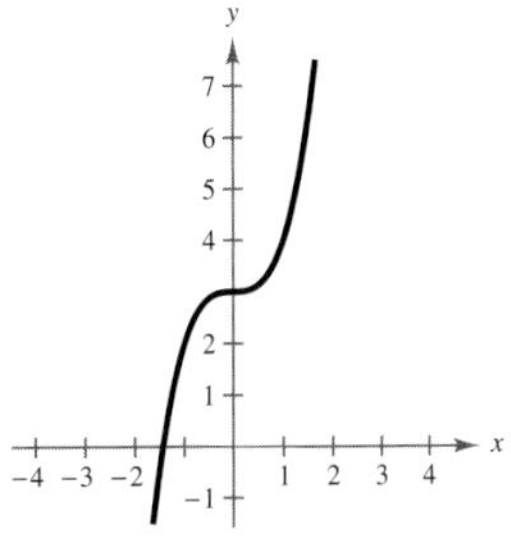

32. x-intercept: $\left(\sqrt[3]{-6}, 0\right)$
y-intercept: $(0, -6)$
No symmetry

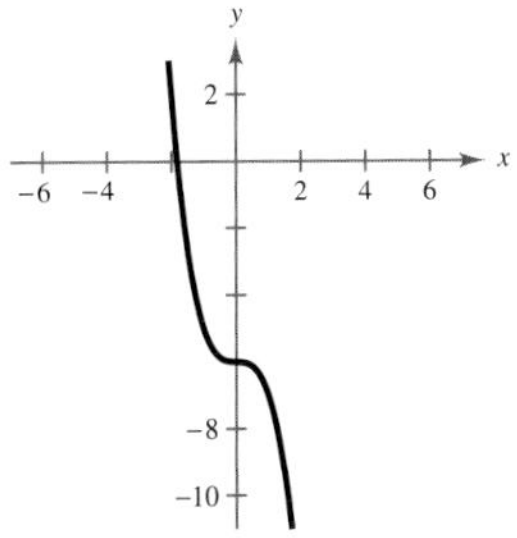

33. x-intercept: $(-5, 0)$
y-intercept: $\left(0, \sqrt{5}\right)$
No symmetry

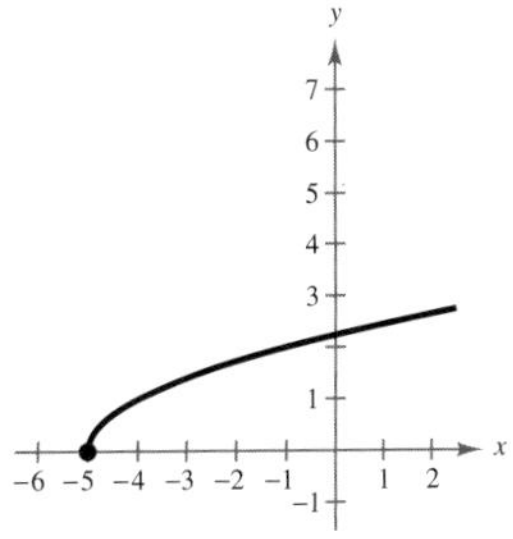

34. y-intercept: $(0, 9)$
y-axis symmetry

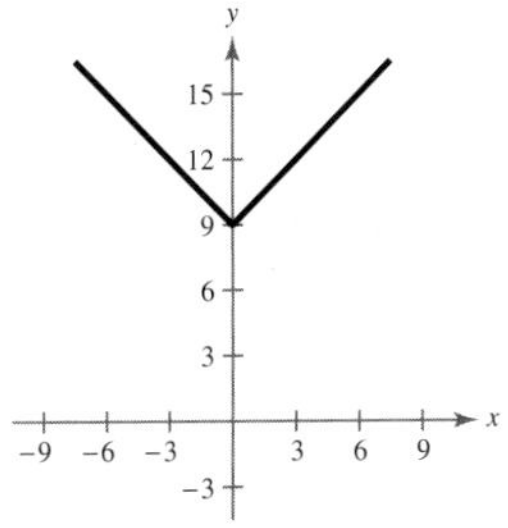

35. Center: $(0, 0)$
Radius: 3

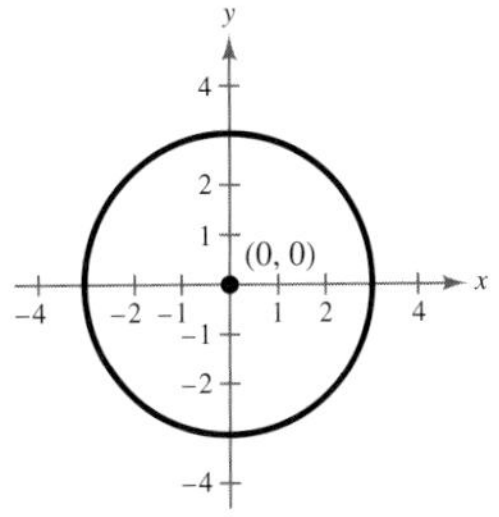

36. Center: $(0, 0)$
Radius: 2

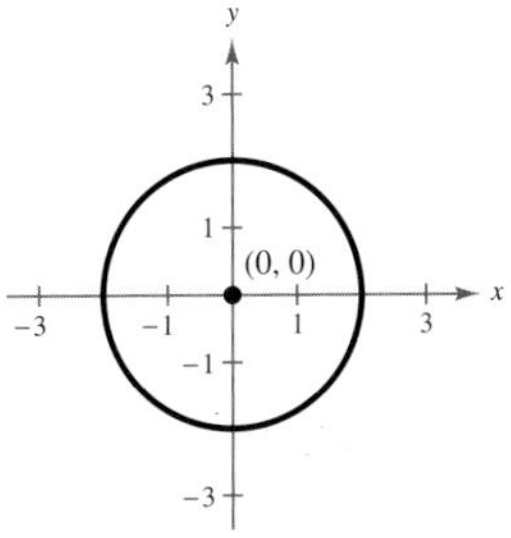

37. Center: $(-2, 0)$
Radius: 4

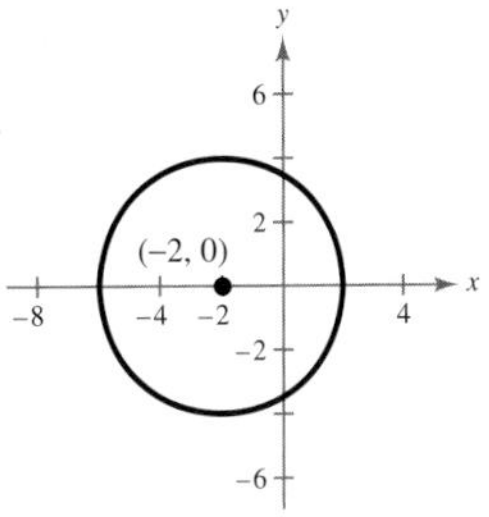

38. Center: $(0, 8)$
Radius: 9

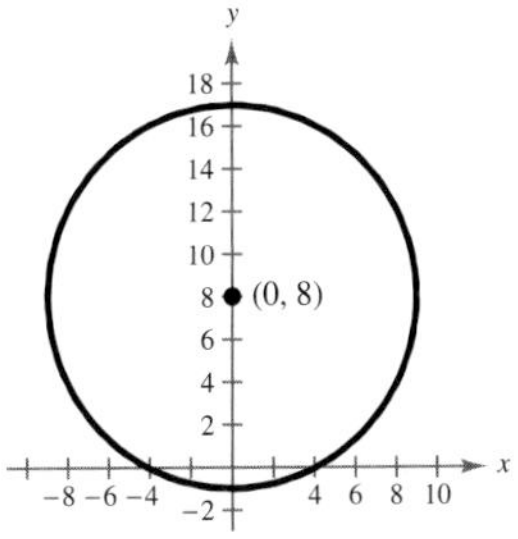

39. Center: $\left(\frac{1}{2}, -1\right)$
Radius: 6

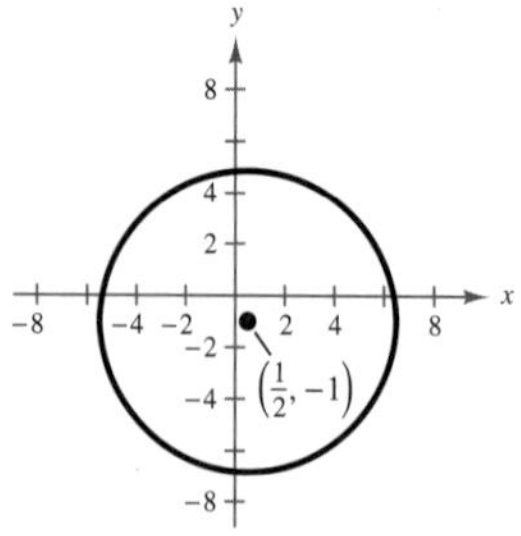

40. Center: $\left(-4, \frac{3}{2}\right)$
Radius: 10

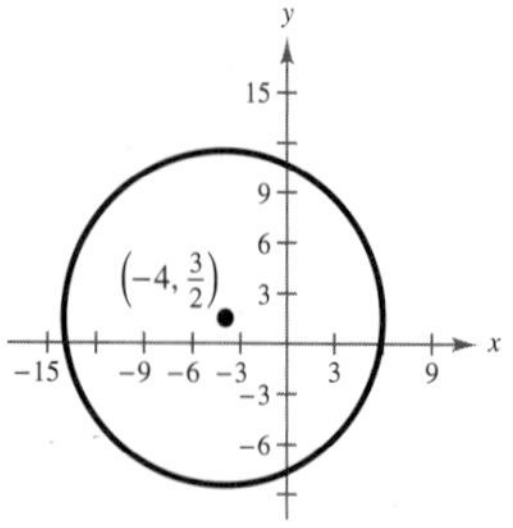

43. (a)

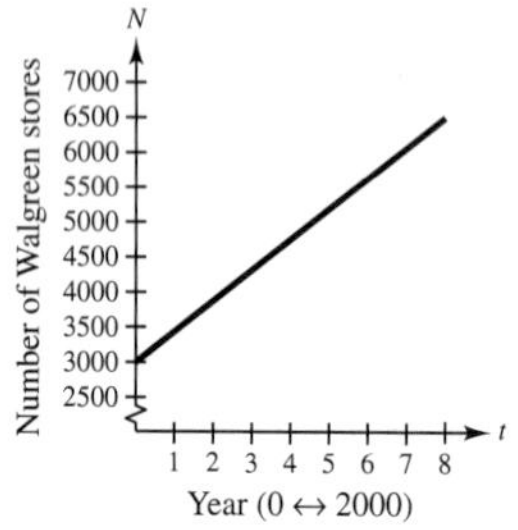

51.

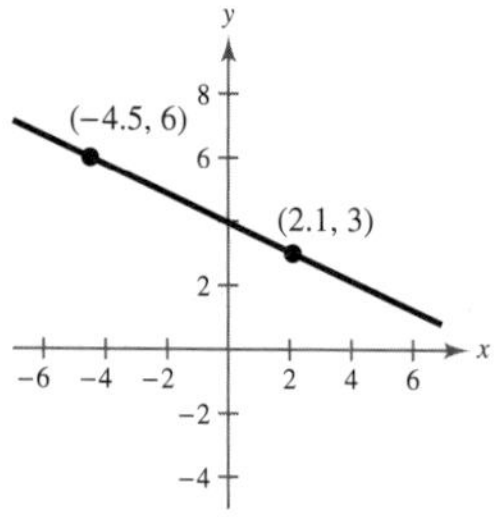

$m = -\frac{5}{11}$

52.

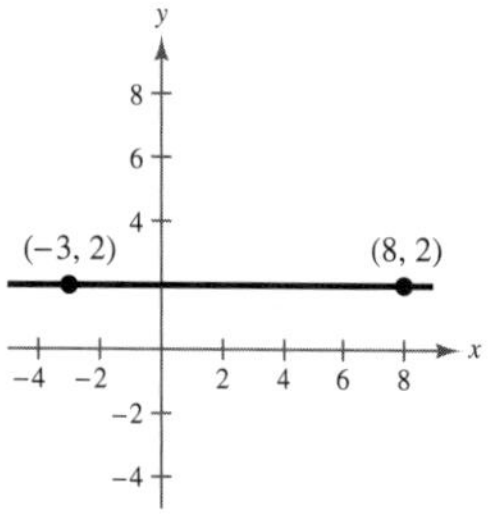

$m = 0$

53. $y = \frac{2}{3}x - 2$

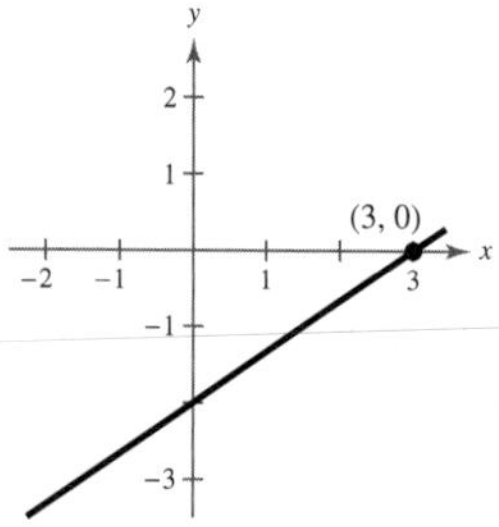

54. $y = 5$

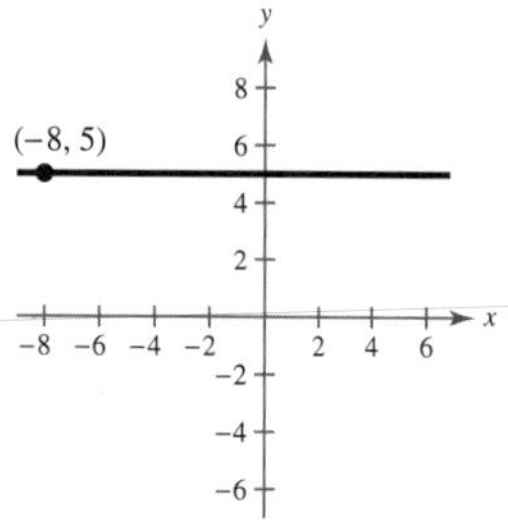

55. $y = -\frac{1}{2}x + 2$

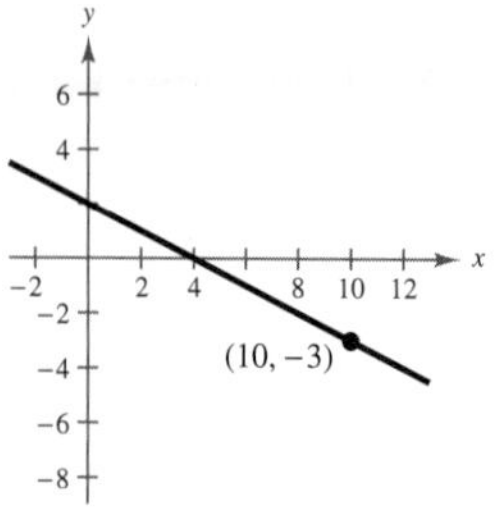

56. $x = 12$

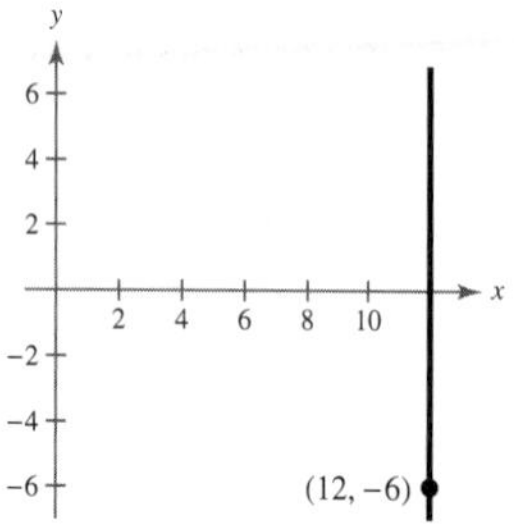

71. All real numbers x such that $-5 \le x \le 5$

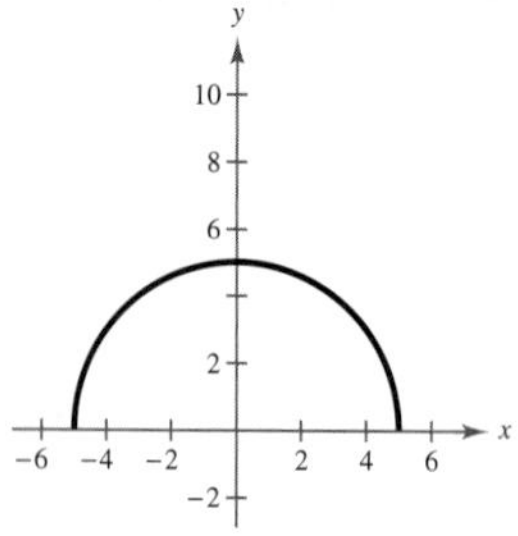

72. All real numbers s except $s = 3$

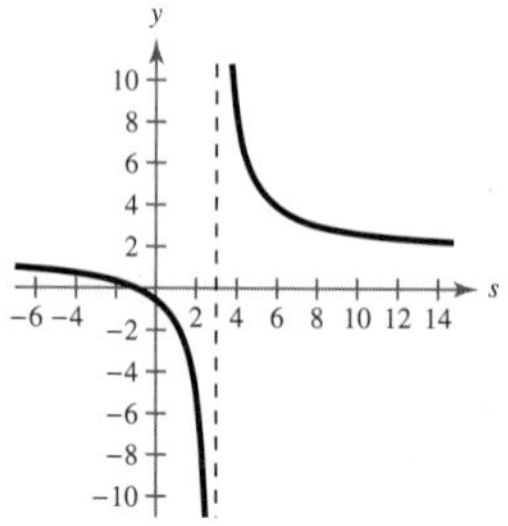

73. All real numbers x except $x = 3, -2$

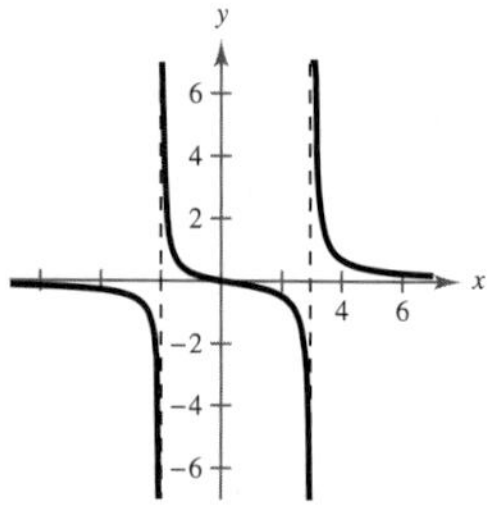

74. All real numbers t

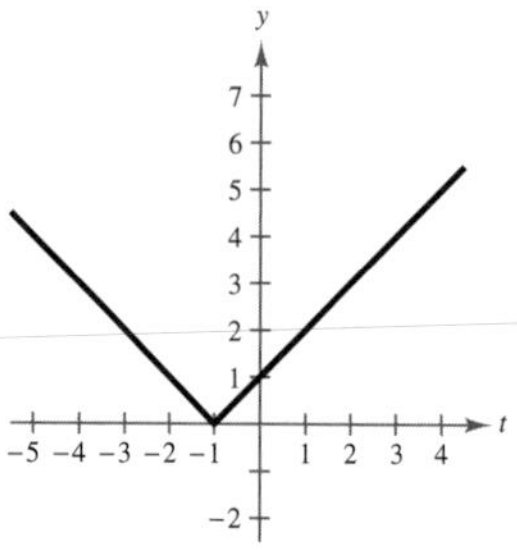

103.

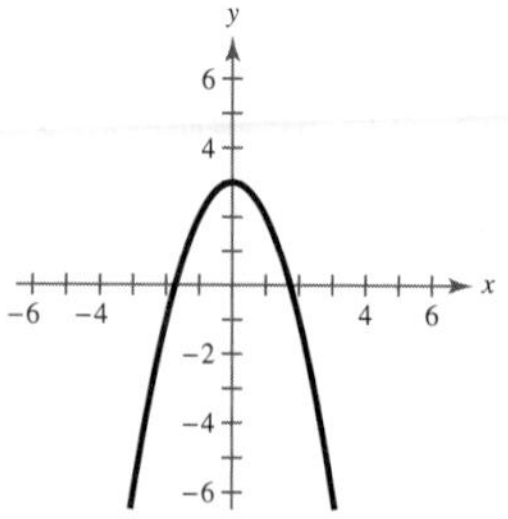

104.

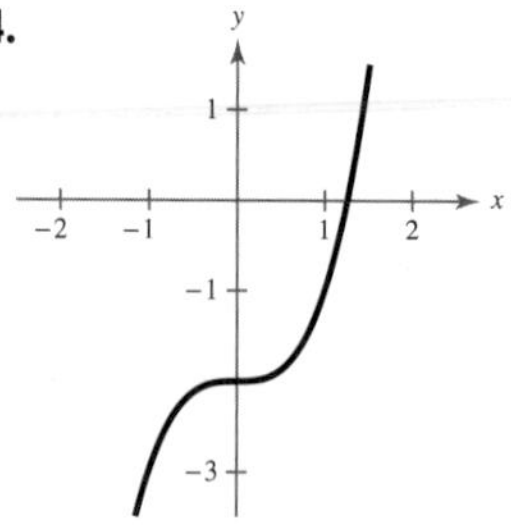

ADDITIONAL ANSWERS

105.

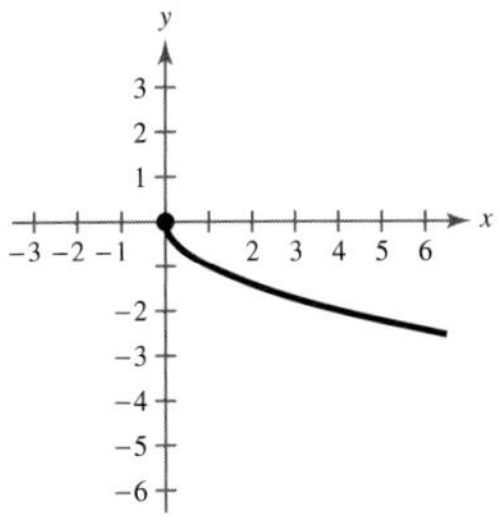

106.

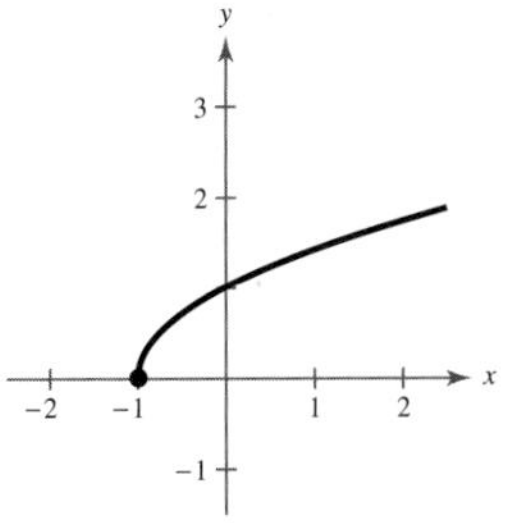

107.

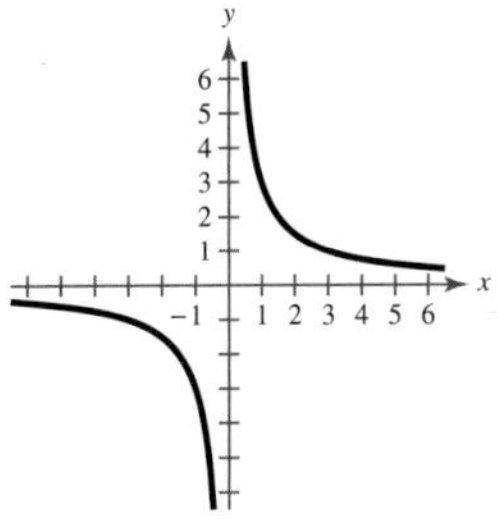

108.

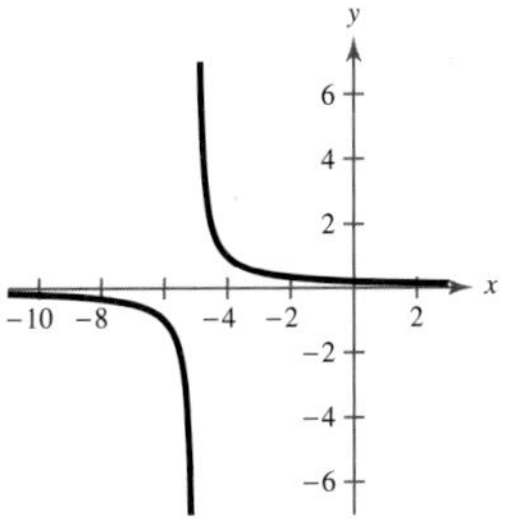

109.

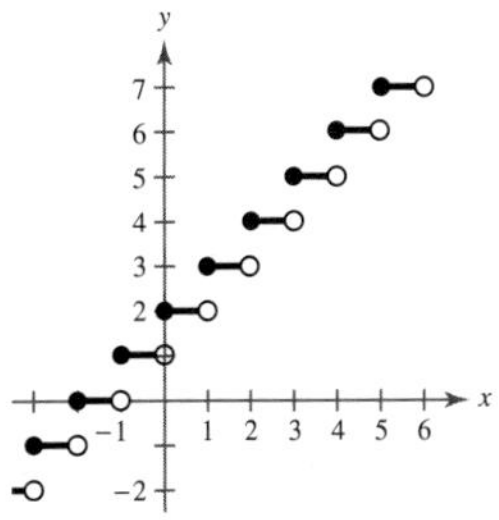

110.

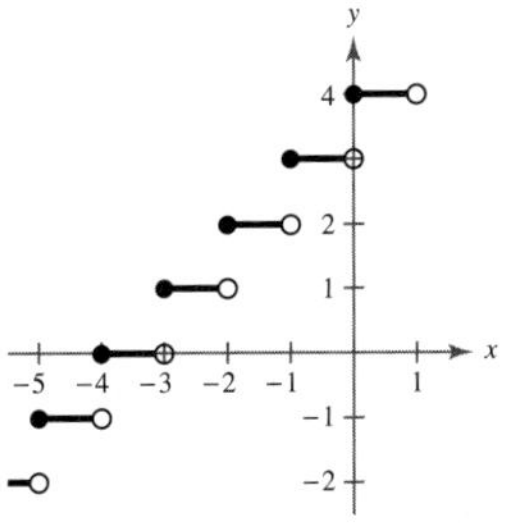

111.

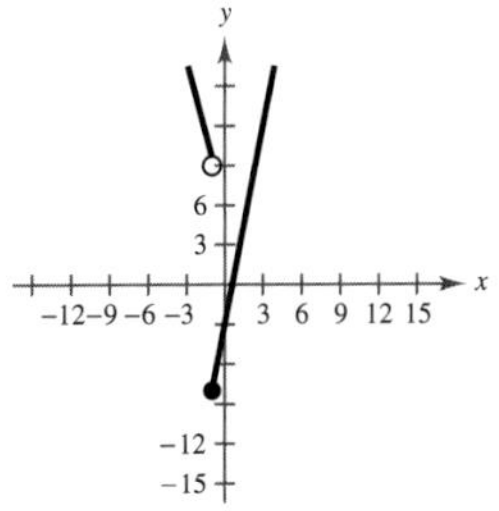

112.

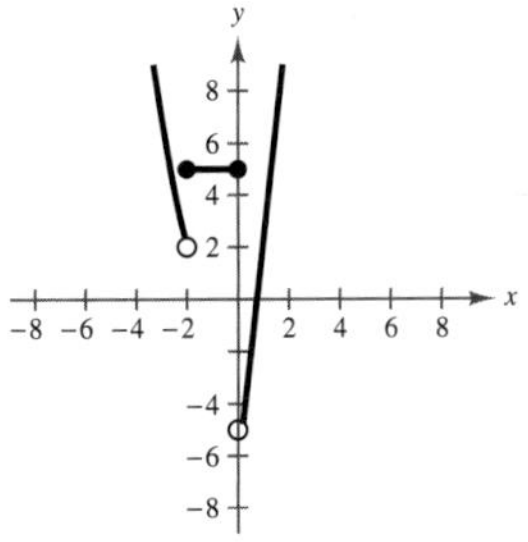

120. (a) $f(x) = x^2$

(b) Vertical shrink of one-half, horizontal shift one unit to the right, and vertical shift two units downward

(c)

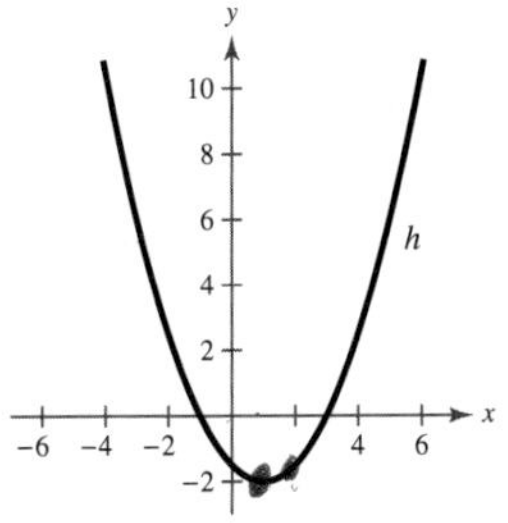

(d) $h(x) = \frac{1}{2}f(x - 1) - 2$

121. (a) $f(x) = [\![x]\!]$

(b) Reflection in the x-axis and vertical shift six units upward

(c)

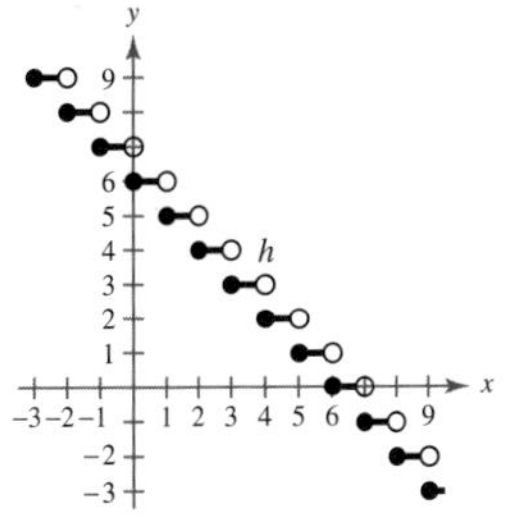

(d) $h(x) = -f(x) + 6$

122. (a) $f(x) = \sqrt{x}$

(b) Reflection in the x-axis, horizontal shift one unit to the left, and vertical shift nine units upward

(c)

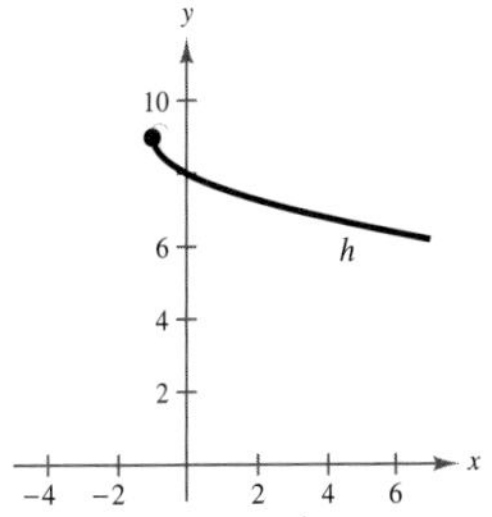

(d) $h(x) = -f(x + 1) + 9$

123. (a) $f(x) = |x|$

(b) Reflections in the x-axis and the y-axis, horizontal shift four units to the right, and vertical shift six units upward

(c)

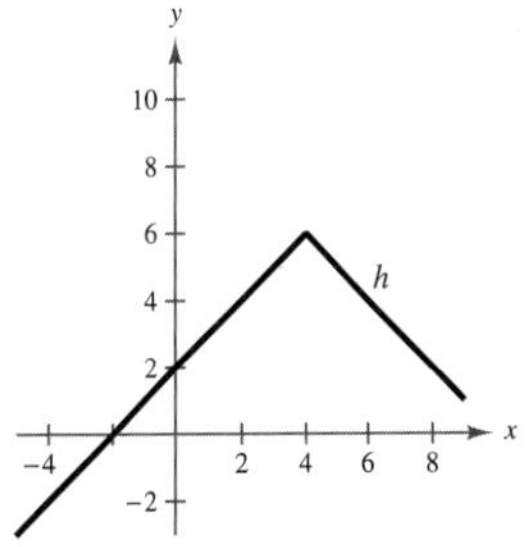

(d) $h(x) = -f(-x + 4) + 6$

124. (a) $f(x) = x^2$

(b) Reflection in the x-axis, horizontal shift one unit to the left, and vertical shift three units downward

(c)

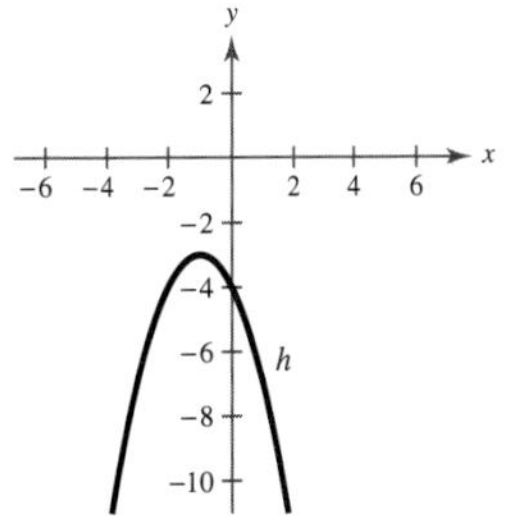

(d) $h(x) = -f(x + 1) - 3$

125. (a) $f(x) = [\![x]\!]$

(b) Horizontal shift nine units to the right and vertical stretch

(c)

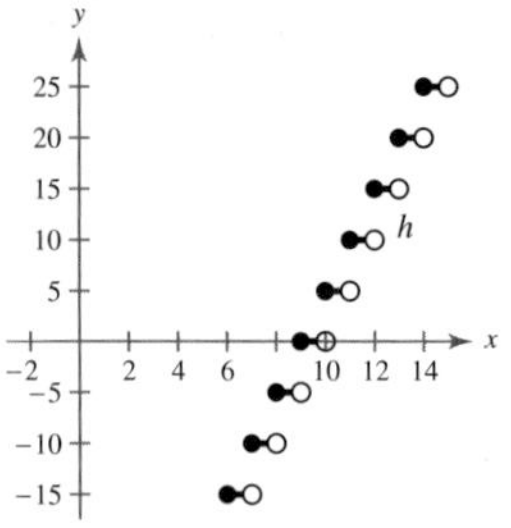

(d) $h(x) = 5f(x - 9)$

126. (a) $f(x) = x^3$

(b) Reflection in the x-axis and vertical shrink

(c)

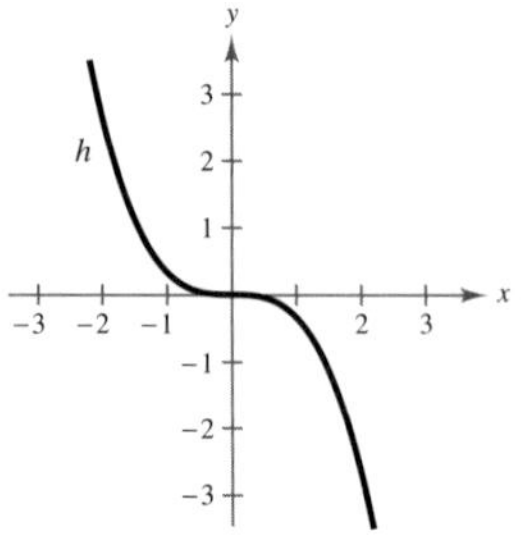

(d) $h(x) = -\frac{1}{3}f(x)$

127. (a) $f(x) = \sqrt{x}$

(b) Reflection in the x-axis, vertical stretch, and horizontal shift four units to the right

(c)

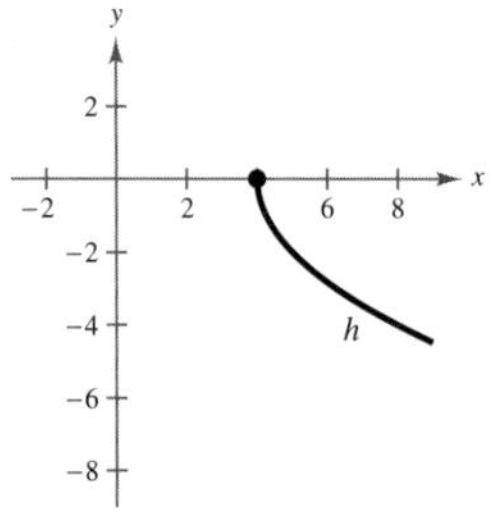

(d) $h(x) = -2f(x - 4)$

128. (a) $f(x) = |x|$

(b) Vertical shrink and vertical shift one unit downward

(c)

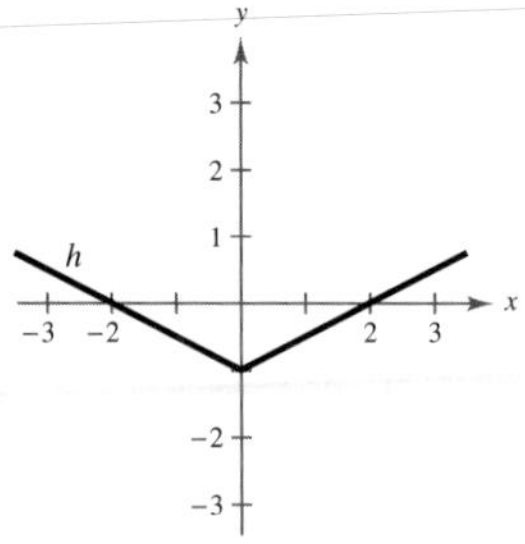

(d) $h(x) = \frac{1}{2}f(x) - 1$

129. (a) $x^2 + 2x + 2$ (b) $x^2 - 2x + 4$

(c) $2x^3 - x^2 + 6x - 3$

(d) $\dfrac{x^2 + 3}{2x - 1}$; all real numbers x except $x = \dfrac{1}{2}$

130. (a) $x^2 - 4 + \sqrt{3 - x}$ (b) $x^2 - 4 - \sqrt{3 - x}$

(c) $(x^2 - 4)\sqrt{3 - x}$

(d) $\dfrac{x^2 - 4}{\sqrt{3 - x}}$; all real numbers x such that $x < 3$

131. (a) $x - \frac{8}{3}$ (b) $x - 8$

Domains of f, g, $f \circ g$, and $g \circ f$: all real numbers

132. (a) $x + 3$ (b) $\sqrt[3]{x^3 + 3}$

Domains of f, g, $f \circ g$, and $g \circ f$: all real numbers

133. $f(x) = x^3$, $g(x) = 1 - 2x$

134. $f(x) = \sqrt[3]{x}$, $g(x) = x + 2$

135. (b)

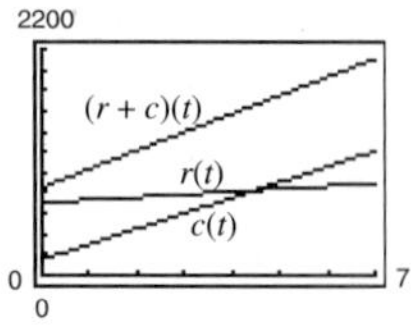

136. (a) $N(T(t)) = 100t^2 + 275$

The composition function $N(T(t))$ represents the number of bacteria in the food as a function of time.

(b) $t = 2.18$

141.

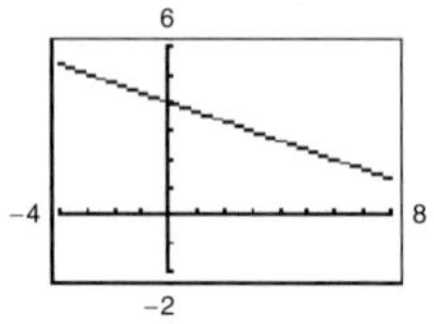

The function has an inverse.

142.

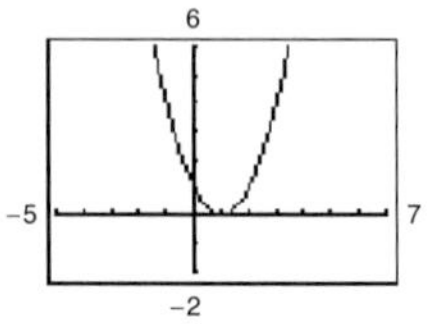

The function does not have an inverse.

143.

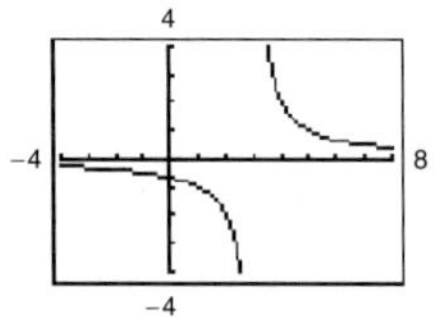

The function has an inverse.

144.

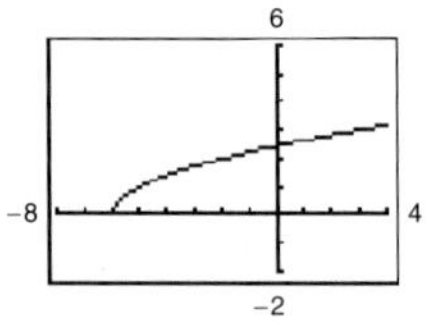

The function has an inverse.

145. (a) $f^{-1}(x) = 2x + 6$

(b)

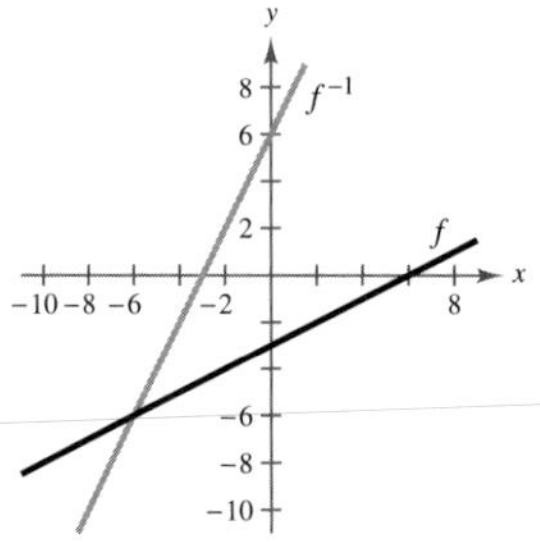

(c) The graph of f^{-1} is the reflection of the graph of f in the line $y = x$.

(d) Both f and f^{-1} have domains and ranges that are all real numbers.

146. (a) $f^{-1}(x) = \dfrac{x + 7}{5}$

(b)

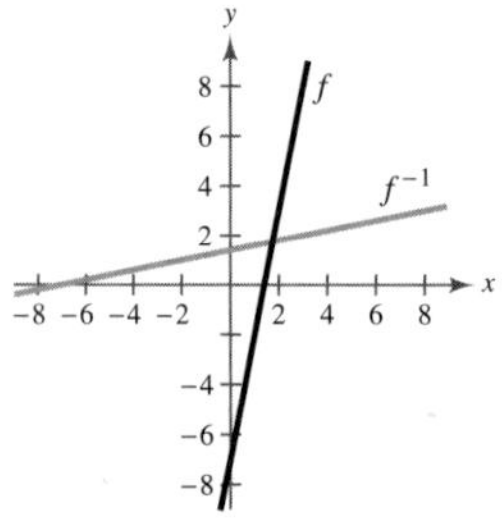

(c) The graphs are reflections of each other in the line $y = x$.

(d) Both f and f^{-1} have domains and ranges that are all real numbers.

147. (a) $f^{-1}(x) = x^2 - 1,\ x \ge 0$

(b)

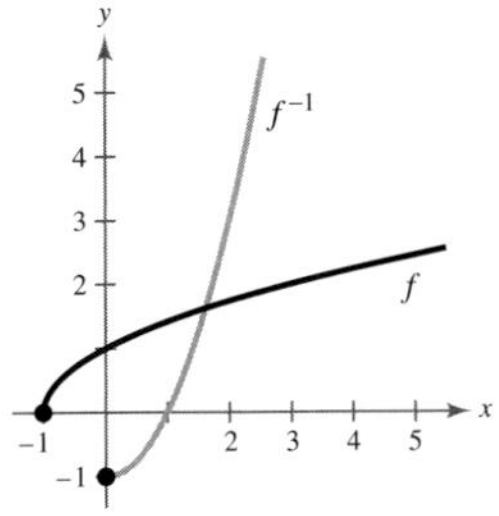

(c) The graph of f^{-1} is the reflection of the graph of f in the line $y = x$.

(d) f has a domain of $[-1, \infty)$ and a range of $[0, \infty)$; f^{-1} has a domain of $[0, \infty)$ and a range of $[-1, \infty)$.

148. (a) $f^{-1}(x) = \sqrt[3]{x - 2}$

(b)

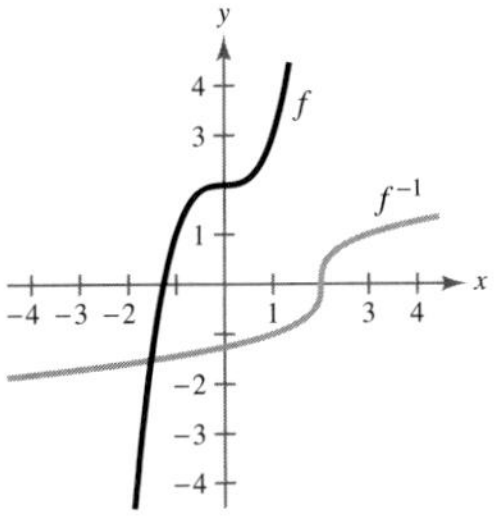

(c) The graphs are reflections of each other in the line $y = x$.

(d) Both f and f^{-1} have domains and ranges that are all real numbers.

149. $x > 4$; $f^{-1}(x) = \sqrt{\dfrac{x}{2}} + 4,\ x \neq 0$

Chapter Test *(page 121)*

15.

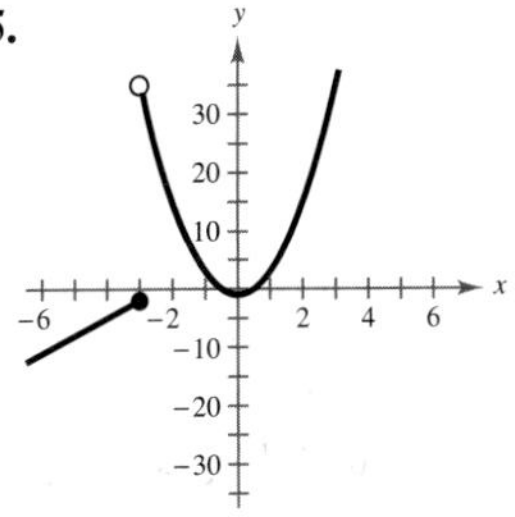

16. Reflection in the x-axis of $y = [\![x]\!]$

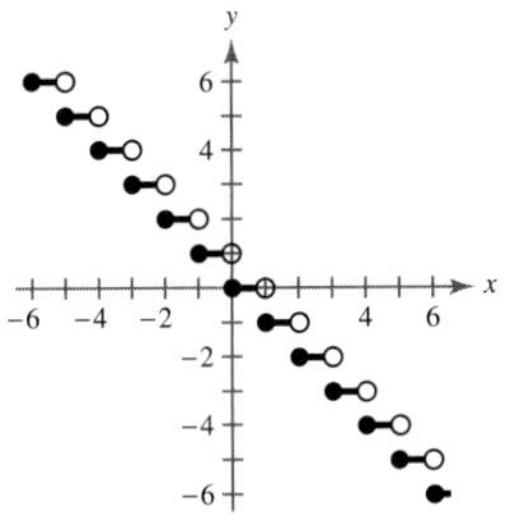

17. Reflection in the x-axis, horizontal shift, and vertical shift of $y = \sqrt{x}$

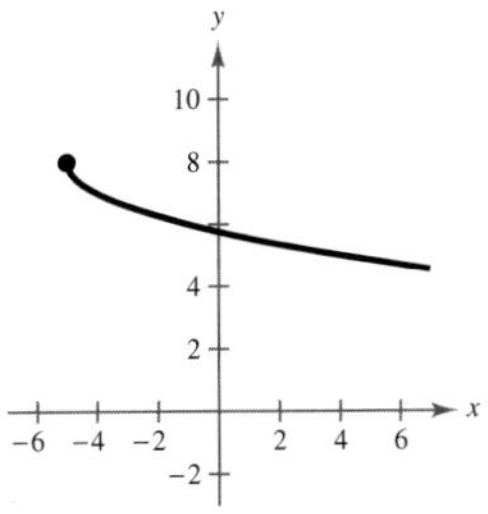

18. Reflection in the x-axis, vertical stretch, horizontal shift, and vertical shift of $y = x^3$

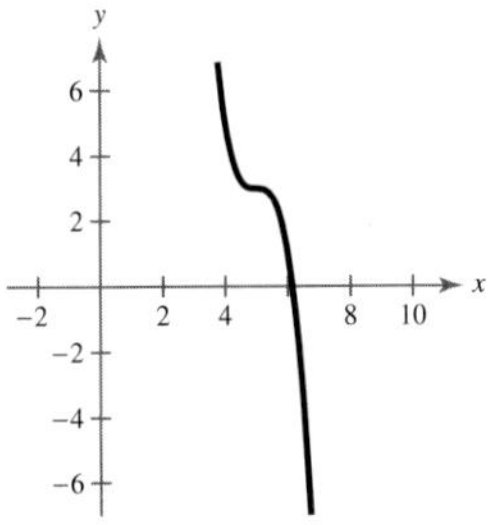

19. (a) $2x^2 - 4x - 2$ (b) $4x^2 + 4x - 12$

(c) $-3x^4 - 12x^3 + 22x^2 + 28x - 35$

(d) $\dfrac{3x^2 - 7}{-x^2 - 4x + 5},\quad x \neq -5, 1$

(e) $3x^4 + 24x^3 + 18x^2 - 120x + 68$

(f) $-9x^4 + 30x^2 - 16$

20. (a) $\dfrac{1 + 2x^{3/2}}{x},\quad x > 0$ (b) $\dfrac{1 - 2x^{3/2}}{x},\quad x > 0$

(c) $\dfrac{2\sqrt{x}}{x},\quad x > 0$ (d) $\dfrac{1}{2x^{3/2}},\quad x > 0$

(e) $\dfrac{\sqrt{x}}{2x},\quad x > 0$ (f) $\dfrac{2\sqrt{x}}{x},\quad x > 0$

Problem Solving *(page 123)*

8. (a) 1 (b) 1.5 (c) 1.75 (d) 1.875 (e) 1.9375

(f) Yes, 2.

(g) a. $y = x - 1$

b. $y = 1.5x - 1.5$

c. $y = 1.75x - 1.75$

d. $y = 1.875x - 1.875$

e. $y = 1.9375x - 1.9375$

(h) $y = 2x - 2$

9. (a) $(f \circ g)(x) = 4x + 24$ (b) $(f \circ g)^{-1}(x) = \frac{1}{4}x - 6$

(c) $f^{-1}(x) = \frac{1}{4}x$; $g^{-1}(x) = x - 6$

(d) $(g^{-1} \circ f^{-1})(x) = \frac{1}{4}x - 6$; They are the same.

(e) $(f \circ g)(x) = 8x^3 + 1$; $(f \circ g)^{-1}(x) = \frac{1}{2}\sqrt[3]{x - 1}$; $f^{-1}(x) = \sqrt[3]{x - 1}$; $g^{-1}(x) = \frac{1}{2}x$; $(g^{-1} \circ f^{-1})(x) = \frac{1}{2}\sqrt[3]{x - 1}$

(f) Answers will vary.

(g) $(f \circ g)^{-1}(x) = (g^{-1} \circ f^{-1})(x)$

14. (a)

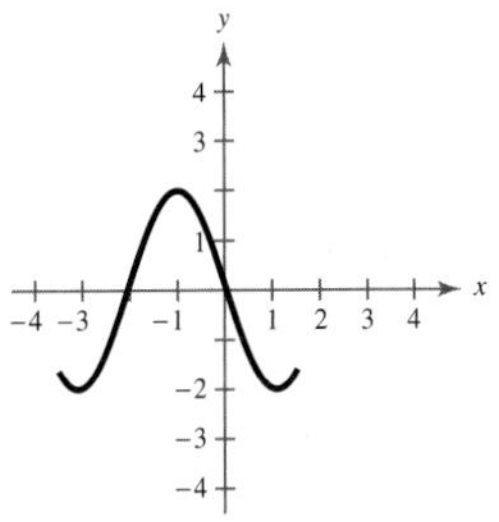

(b)

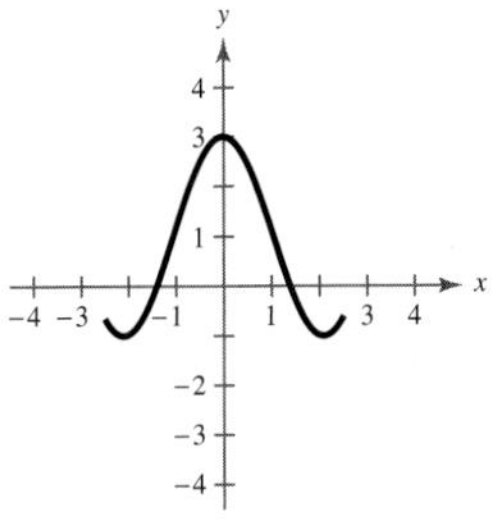

ADDITIONAL ANSWERS

(c)

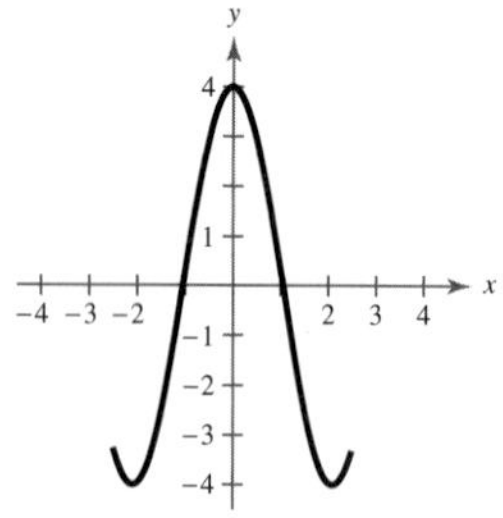

(d)

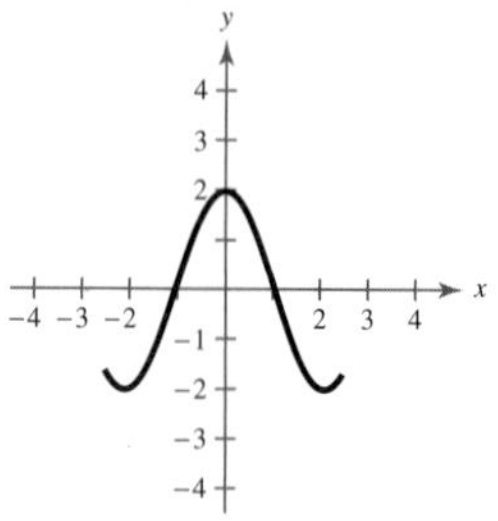

(e)

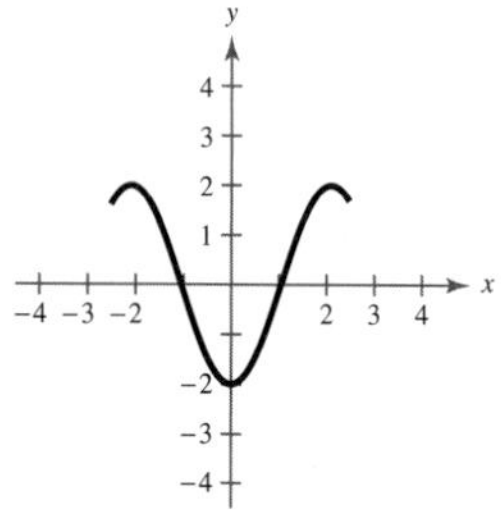

(f)

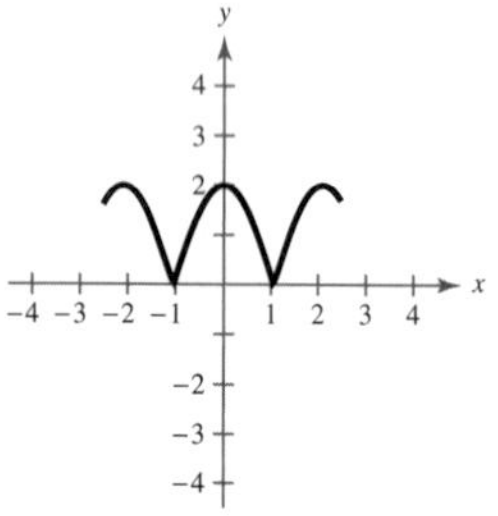

(g)

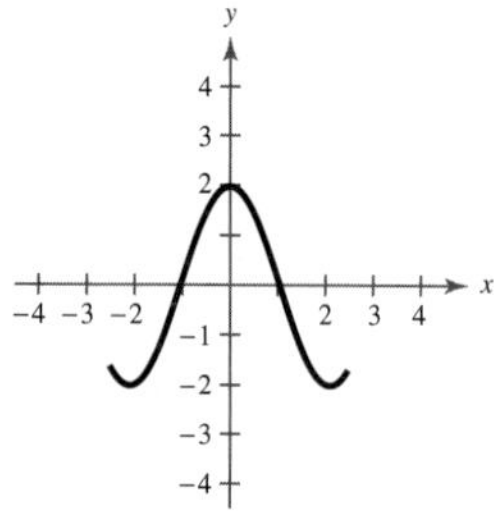

Chapter 2

Section 2.1 *(page 132)*

14. (a)

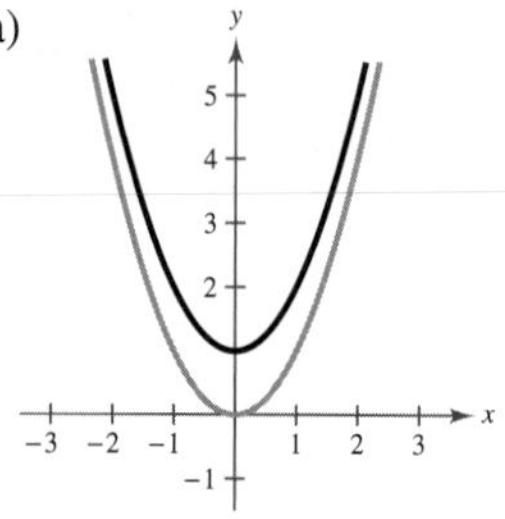

Vertical shift one unit upward

(b)

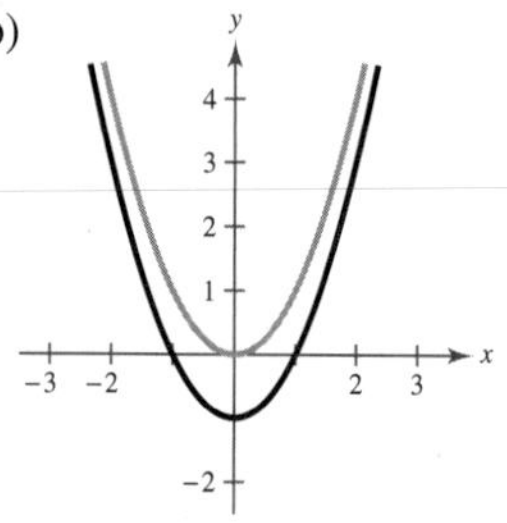

Vertical shift one unit downward

(c)

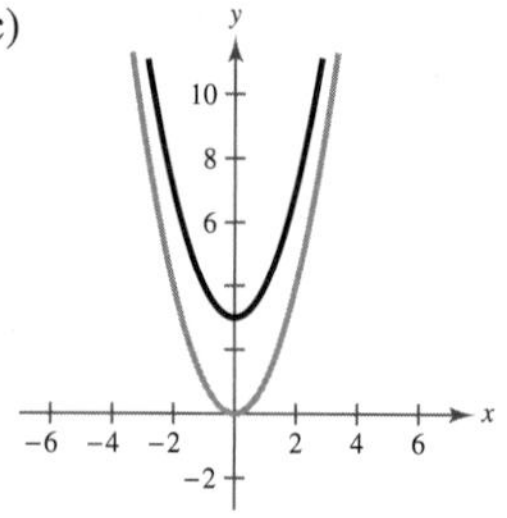

Vertical shift three units upward

(d)

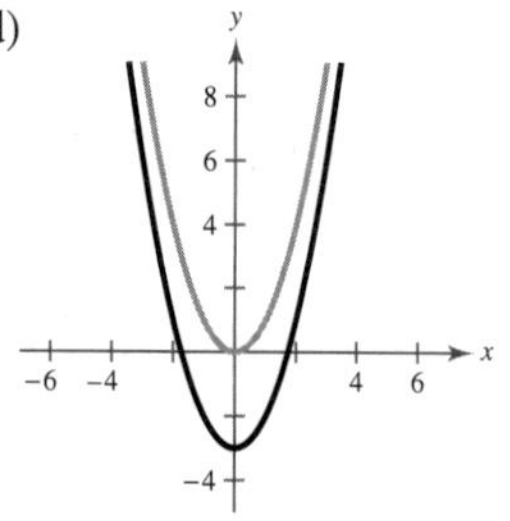

Vertical shift three units downward

15. (a)

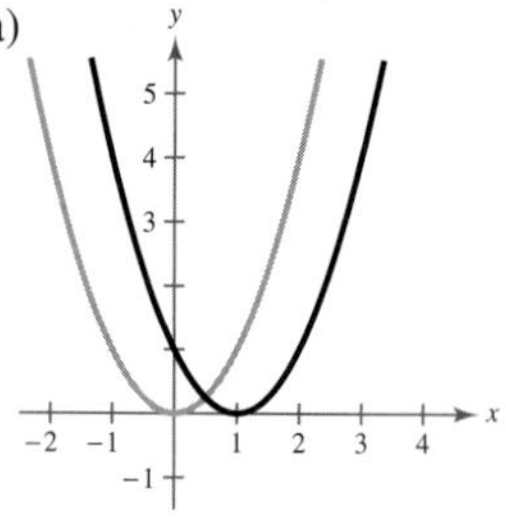

Horizontal shift one unit to the right

(b)

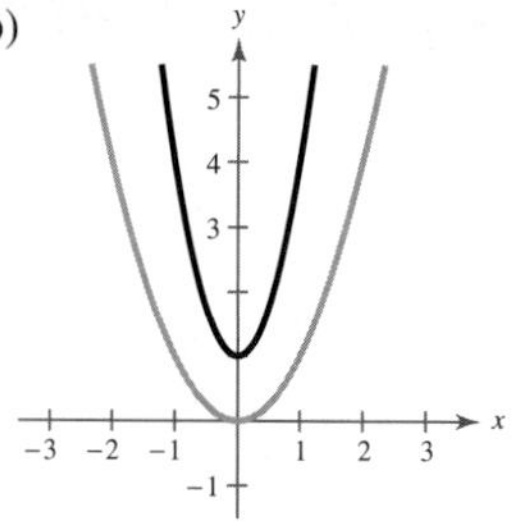

Horizontal shrink and vertical shift one unit upward

(c)

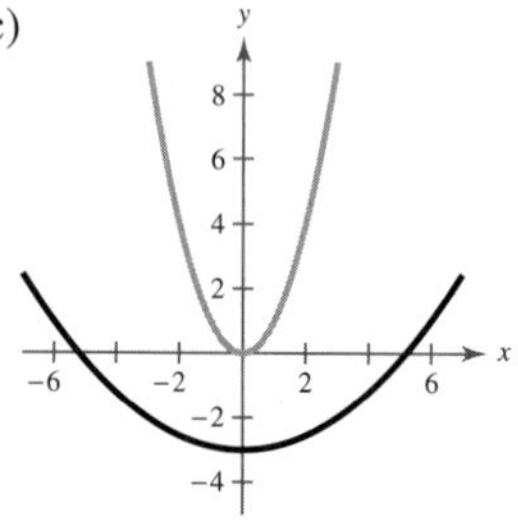

Horizontal stretch and vertical shift three units downward

(d)

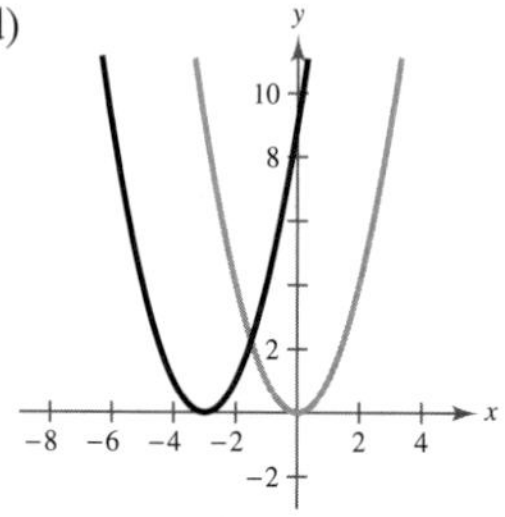

Horizontal shift three units to the left

16. (a)

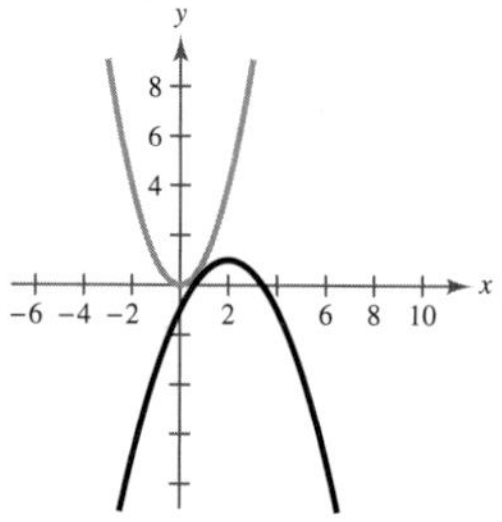

Horizontal shift two units to the right, vertical shrink, reflection in the x-axis, and vertical shift one unit upward

(b)

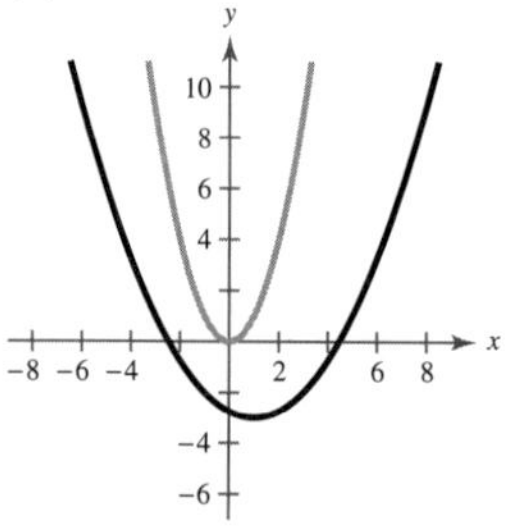

Horizontal shift one unit to the right, horizontal stretch, and vertical shift three units downward

(c)

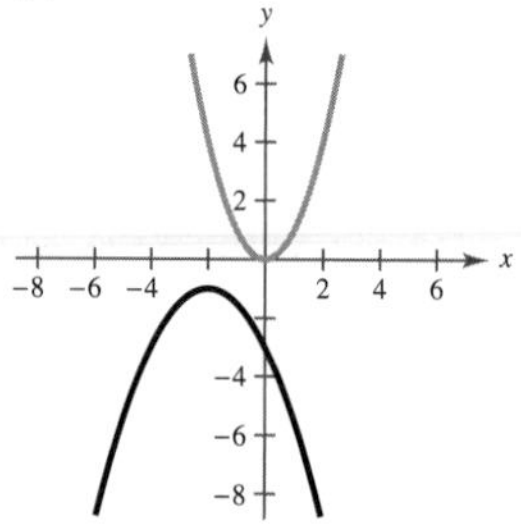

Reflection in the x-axis, vertical shrink, horizontal shift two units to the left, and vertical shift one unit downward

(d)

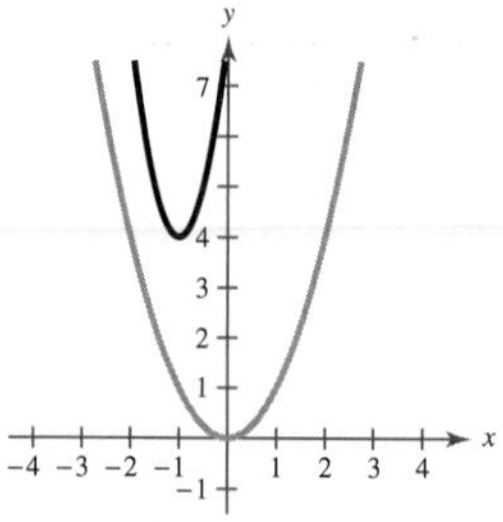

Horizontal shift one unit to the left, horizontal shrink, and vertical shift four units upward

17.

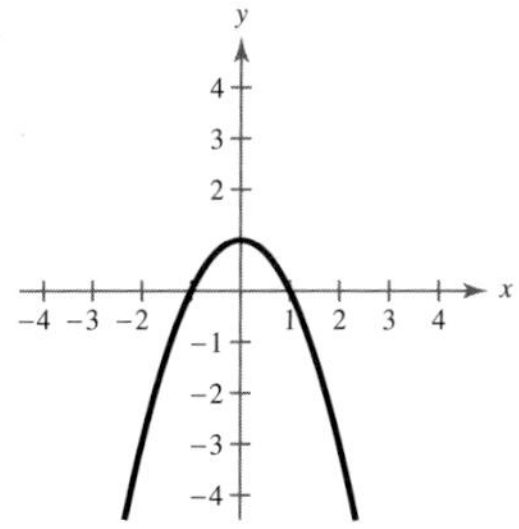

Vertex: $(0, 1)$
Axis of symmetry: y-axis
x-intercepts: $(-1, 0)$ $(1, 0)$

18.

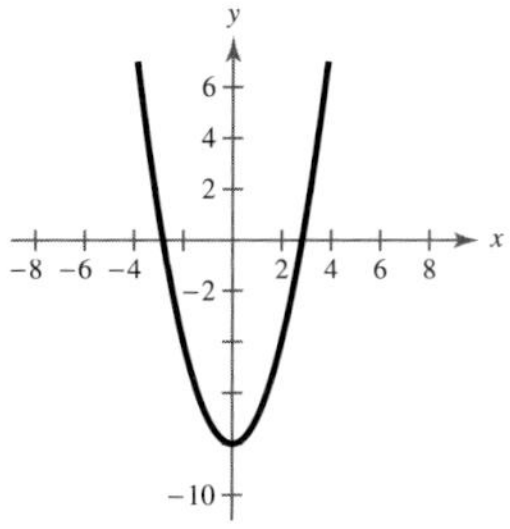

Vertex: $(0, -8)$
Axis of symmetry: y-axis
x-intercepts: $\left(\pm 2\sqrt{2}, 0\right)$

19.

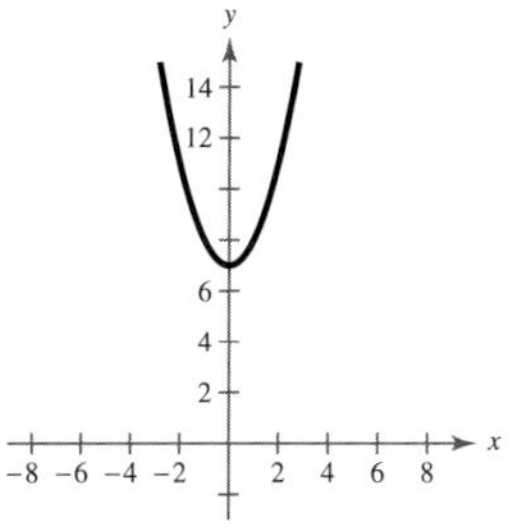

Vertex: $(0, 7)$
Axis of symmetry: y-axis
No x-intercept

20.

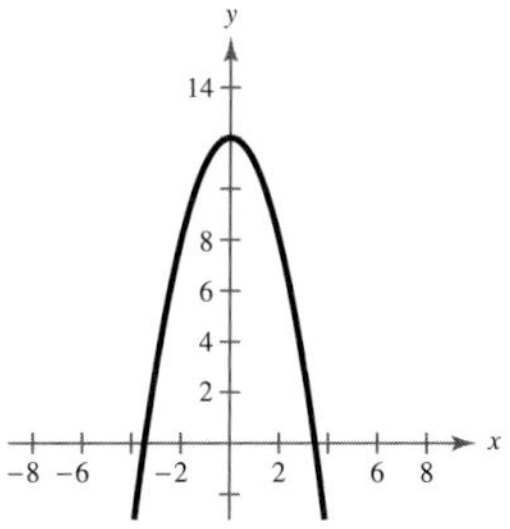

Vertex: $(0, 12)$
Axis of symmetry: y-axis
x-intercepts: $\left(\pm 2\sqrt{3}, 0\right)$

21.

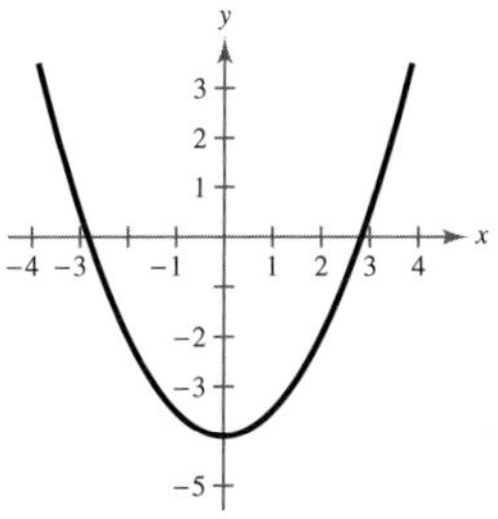

Vertex: $(0, -4)$
Axis of symmetry: y -axis
x-intercepts: $\left(\pm 2\sqrt{2}, 0\right)$

22.

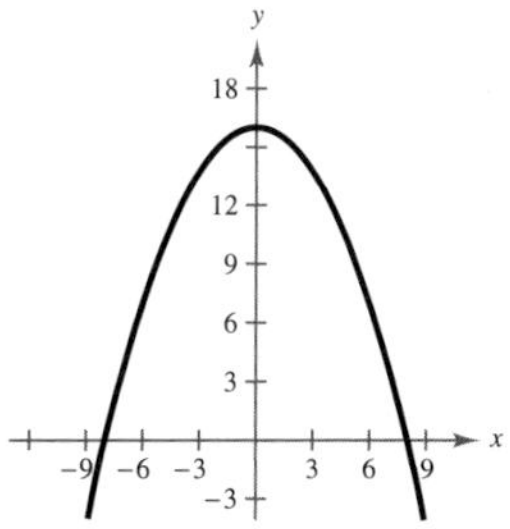

Vertex: $(0, 16)$
Axis of symmetry: y-axis
x-intercepts: $(\pm 8, 0)$

23.

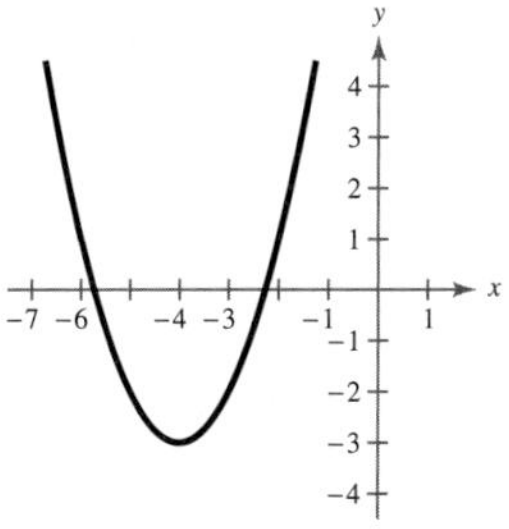

Vertex: $(-4, -3)$
Axis of symmetry: $x = -4$
x-intercepts: $\left(-4 \pm \sqrt{3}, 0\right)$

24.

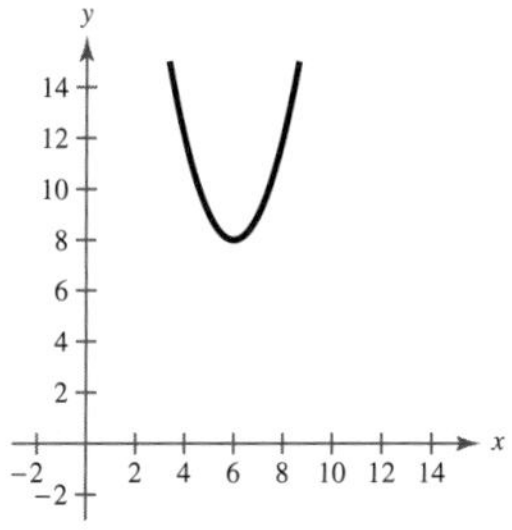

Vertex: $(6, 8)$
Axis of symmetry: $x = 6$
No x-intercept

25.

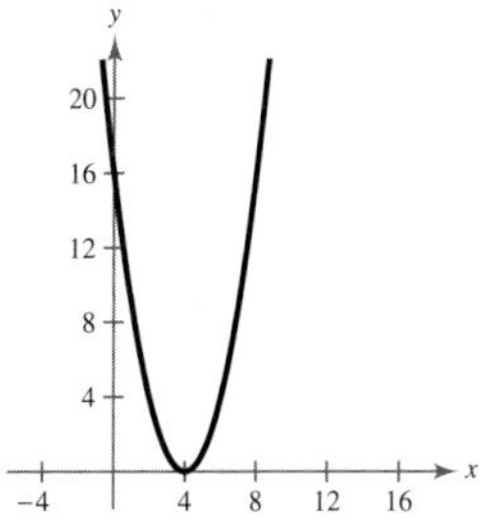

Vertex: $(4, 0)$
Axis of symmetry: $x = 4$
x-intercept: $(4, 0)$

26.

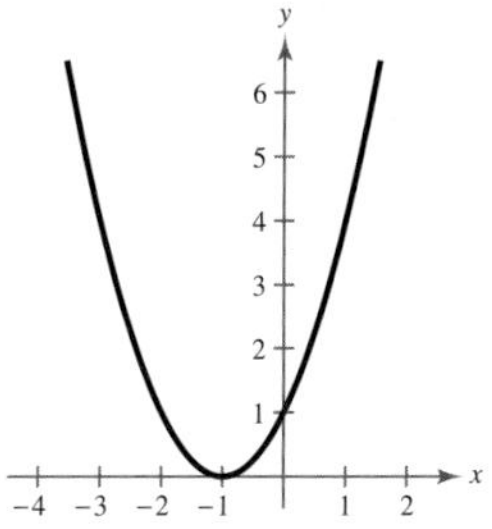

Vertex: $(-1, 0)$
Axis of symmetry: $x = -1$
x-intercept: $(-1, 0)$

27.

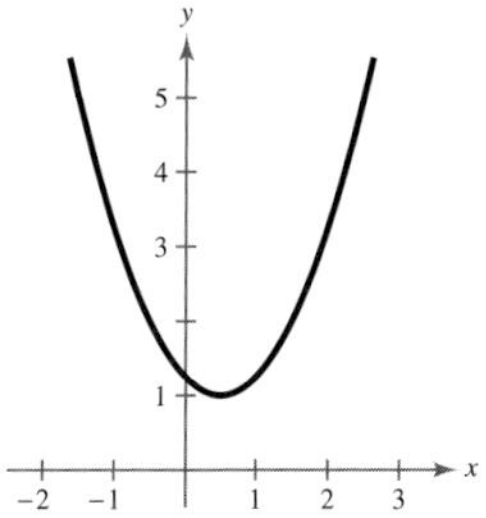

Vertex: $\left(\frac{1}{2}, 1\right)$
Axis of symmetry: $x = \frac{1}{2}$
No x-intercept

28.

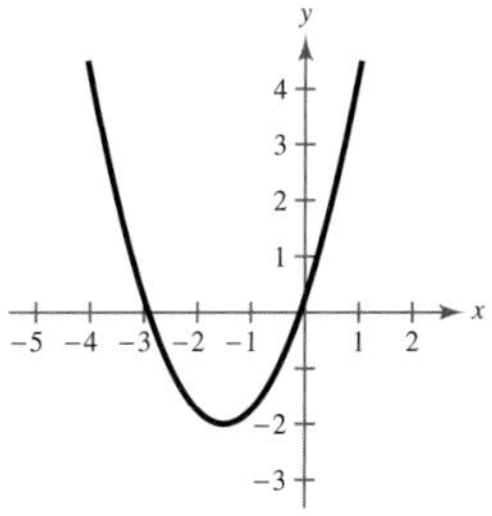

Vertex: $\left(-\frac{3}{2}, -2\right)$
Axis of symmetry: $x = -\frac{3}{2}$
x-intercepts: $\left(-\frac{3}{2} \pm \sqrt{2}, 0\right)$

29.

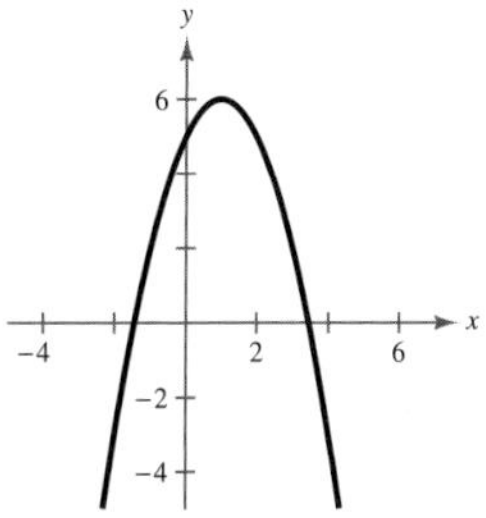

Vertex: $(1, 6)$
Axis of symmetry: $x = 1$
x-intercepts: $\left(1 \pm \sqrt{6}, 0\right)$

30.

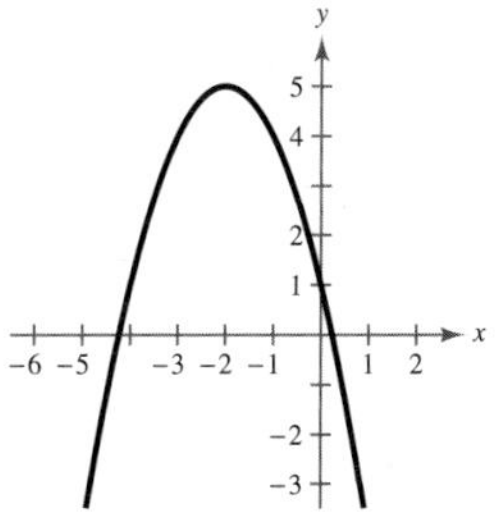

Vertex: $(-2, 5)$
Axis of symmetry: $x = -2$
x-intercepts: $\left(-2 \pm \sqrt{5}, 0\right)$

31.

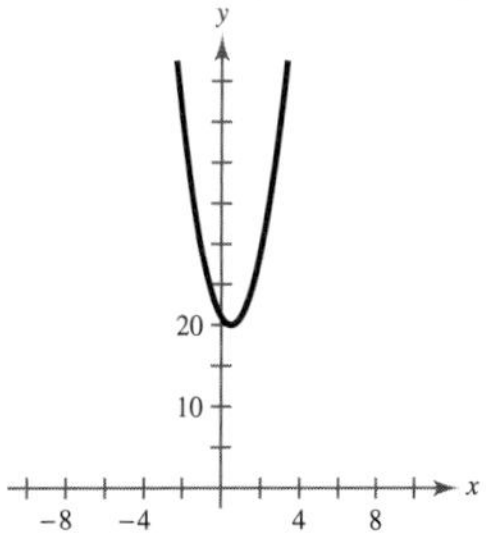

Vertex: $\left(\frac{1}{2}, 20\right)$
Axis of symmetry: $x = \frac{1}{2}$
No x-intercept

32.

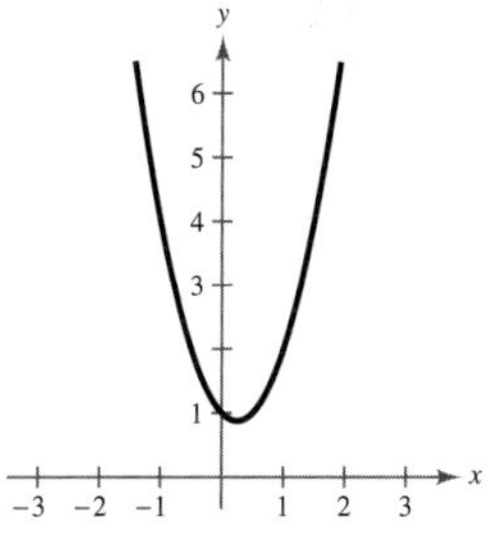

Vertex: $\left(\frac{1}{4}, \frac{7}{8}\right)$
Axis of symmetry: $x = \frac{1}{4}$
No x-intercept

33.

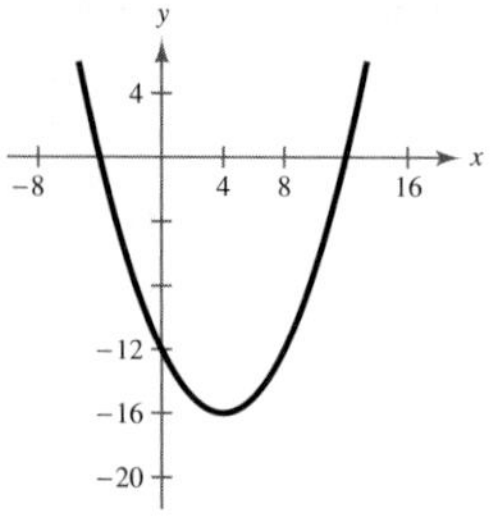

Vertex: $(4, -16)$

Axis of symmetry: $x = 4$

x-intercepts: $(-4, 0)$, $(12, 0)$

34.

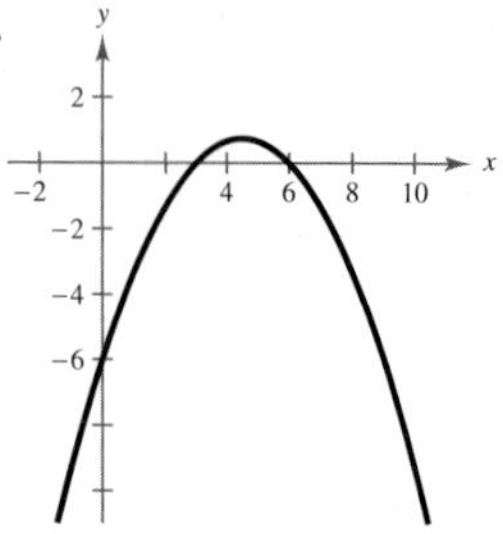

Vertex: $\left(\frac{9}{2}, \frac{3}{4}\right)$

Axis of symmetry: $x = \frac{9}{2}$

x-intercepts: $(3, 0)$, $(6, 0)$

35.

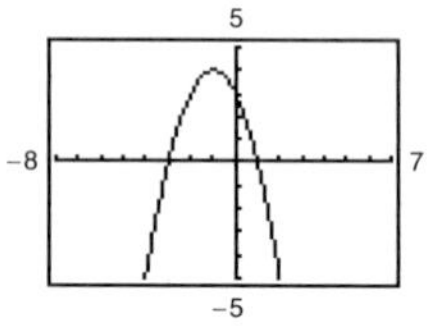

Vertex: $(-1, 4)$

Axis of symmetry: $x = -1$

x-intercepts: $(1, 0)$, $(-3, 0)$

36.

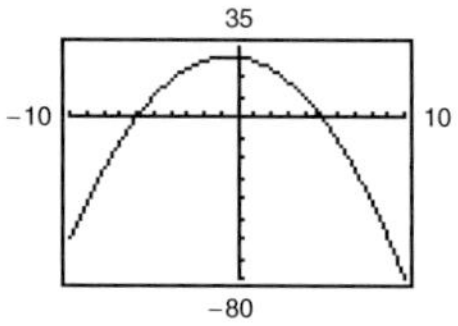

Vertex: $\left(-\frac{1}{2}, \frac{121}{4}\right)$

Axis of symmetry: $x = -\frac{1}{2}$

x-intercepts: $(-6, 0)$, $(5, 0)$

37.

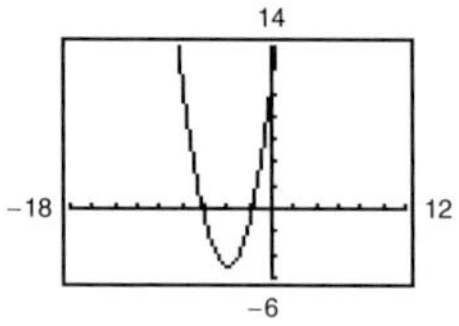

Vertex: $(-4, -5)$

Axis of symmetry: $x = -4$

x-intercepts: $\left(-4 \pm \sqrt{5}, 0\right)$

38.

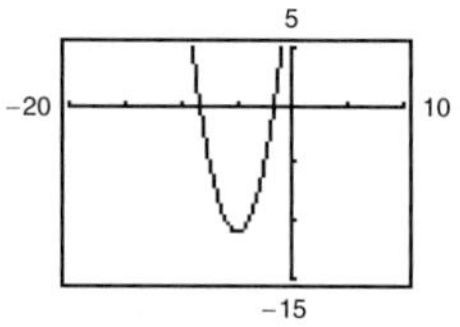

Vertex: $(-5, -11)$

Axis of symmetry: $x = -5$

x-intercepts: $\left(-5 \pm \sqrt{11}, 0\right)$

39.

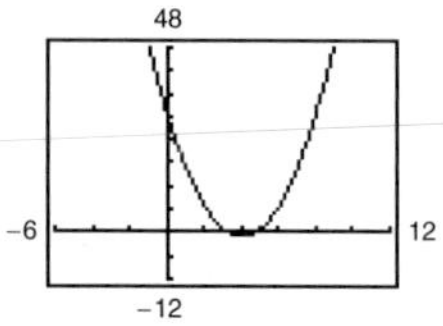

Vertex: $(4, -1)$

Axis of symmetry: $x = 4$

x-intercepts: $\left(4 \pm \frac{1}{2}\sqrt{2}, 0\right)$

40.

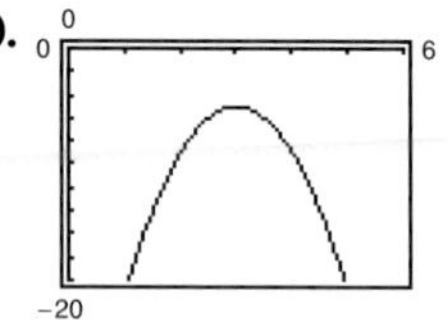

Vertex: $(3, -5)$

Axis of symmetry: $x = 3$

No x-intercept

41.

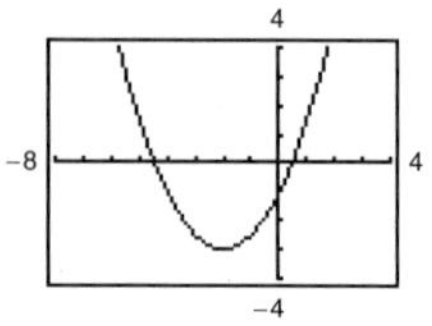

Vertex: $(-2, -3)$

Axis of symmetry: $x = -2$

x-intercepts: $\left(-2 \pm \sqrt{6}, 0\right)$

42.

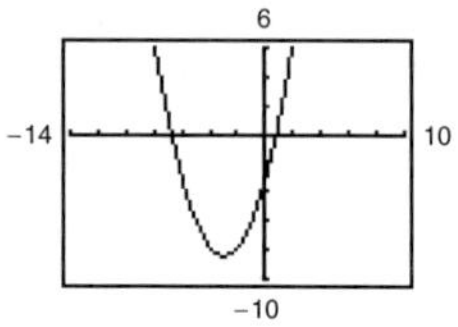

Vertex: $\left(-3, -\frac{42}{5}\right)$

Axis of symmetry: $x = -3$

x-intercepts: $\left(-3 \pm \sqrt{14}, 0\right)$

81. (b)

x	5	10	15	20	25	30
a	600	$1066\frac{2}{3}$	1400	1600	$1666\frac{2}{3}$	1600

$x = 25$ ft, $y = 33\frac{1}{3}$ ft

Section 2.2 *(page 145)*

18. (a)

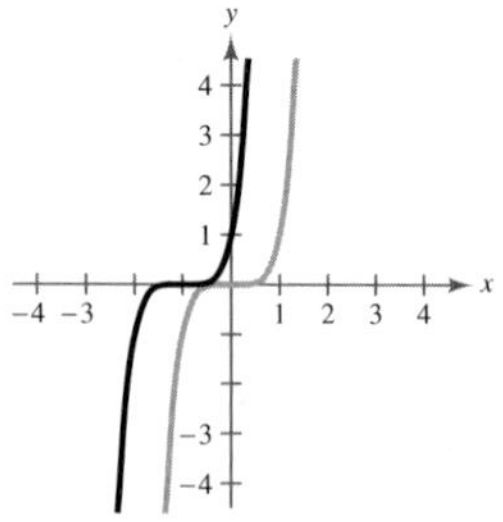

(b)

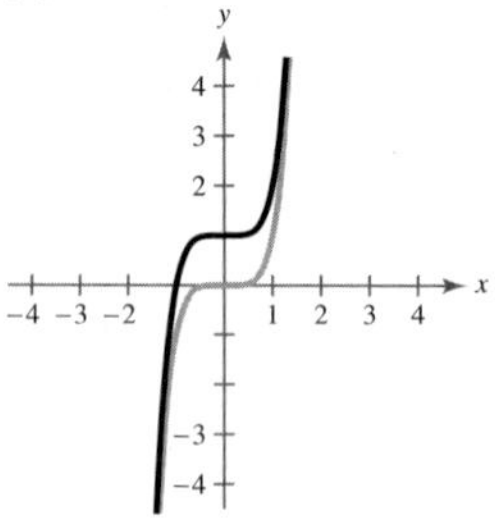

(c)

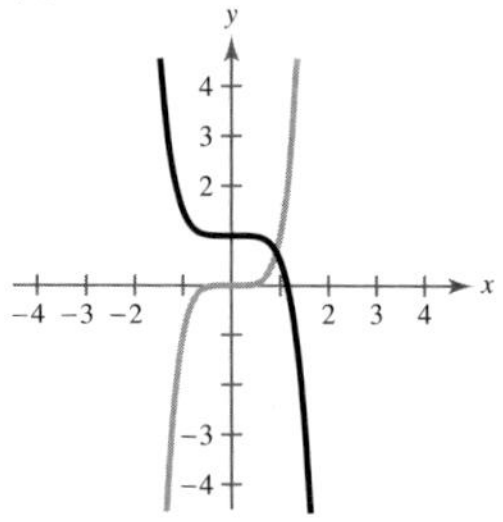

(d)

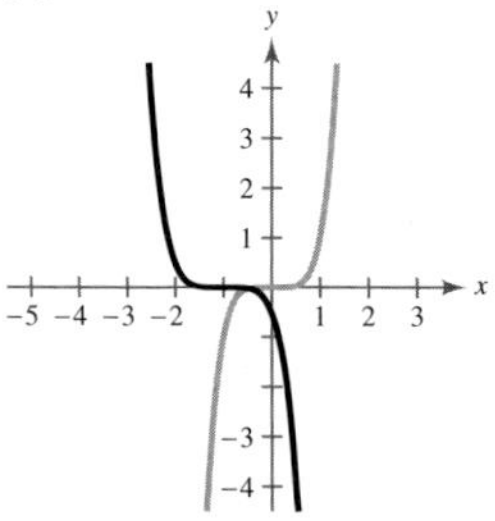

19. (a)

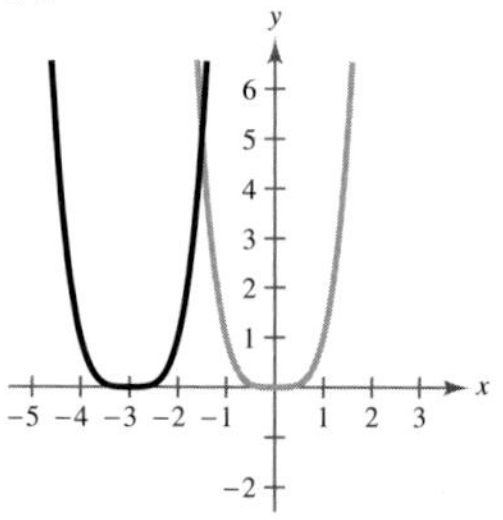

(b)

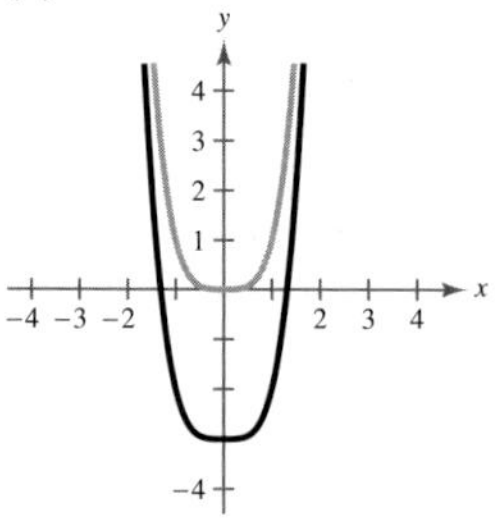

(c)

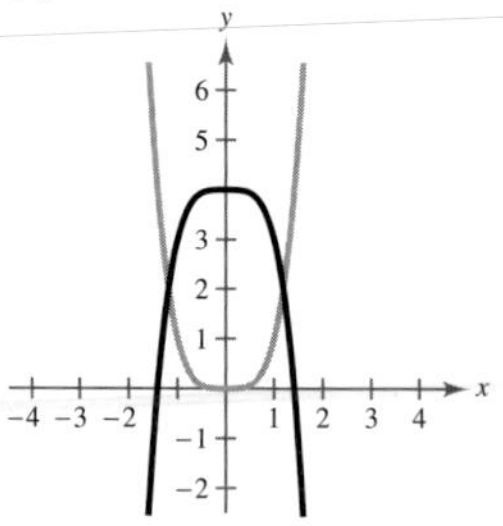

(d)

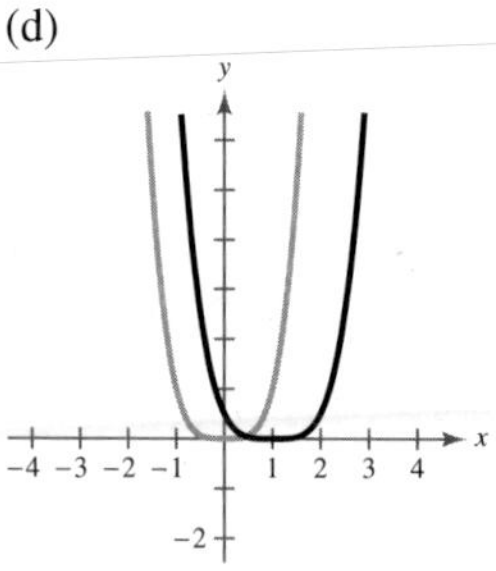

(e)

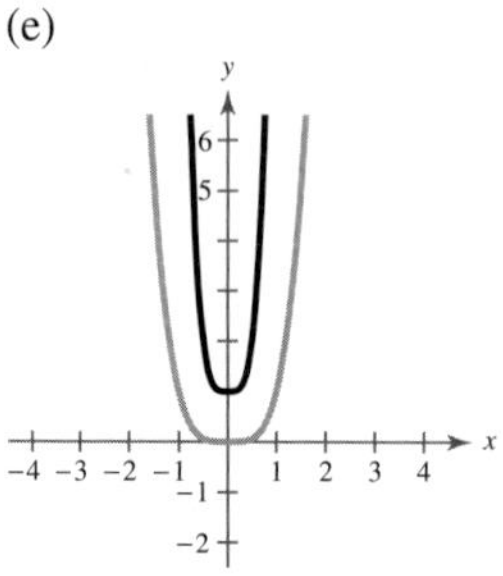

(f)

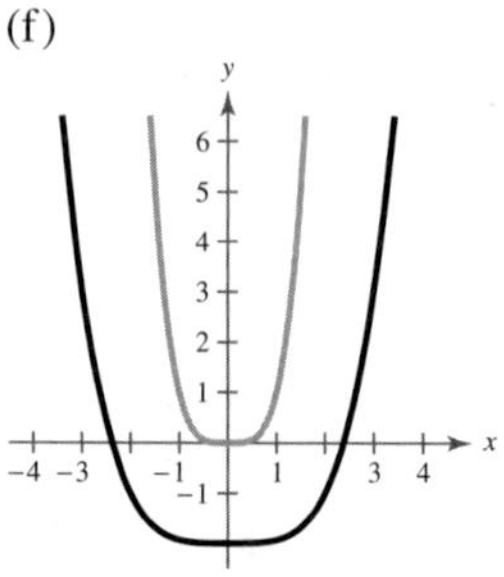

38. (a) -5

(b) Even multiplicity; number of turning points: 1

(c)

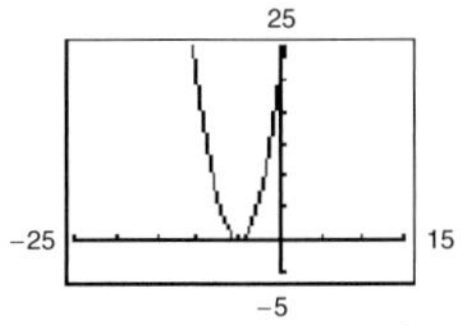

39. (a) $-2, 1$

(b) Odd multiplicity; number of turning points: 1

(c)

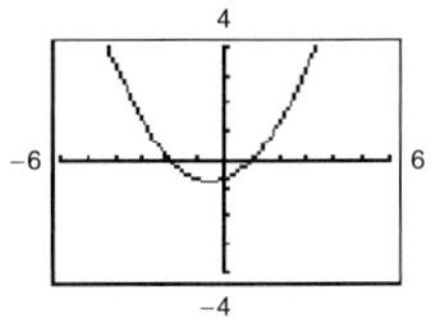

40. (a) $\dfrac{-5 \pm \sqrt{37}}{2}$

(b) Odd multiplicity; number of turning points: 1

(c)

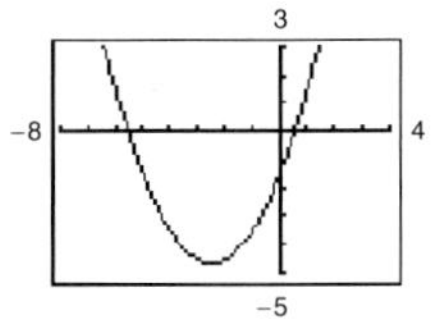

41. (a) $0, 2 \pm \sqrt{3}$

(b) Odd multiplicity; number of turning points: 2

(c)

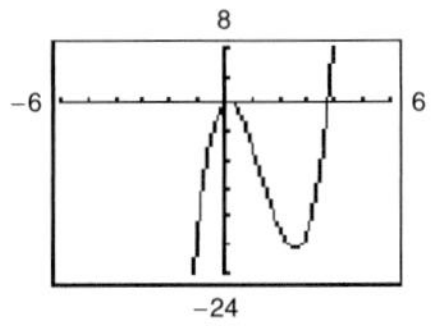

42. (a) $0, 1 \pm \sqrt{2}$

(b) Odd multiplicity; number of turning points: 2

(c)

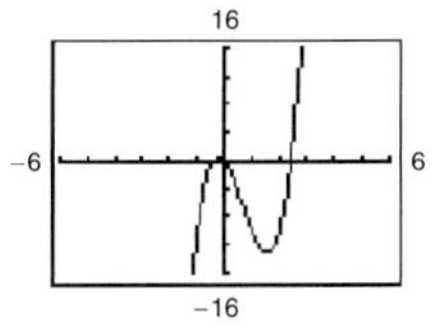

43. (a) $0, 4$

(b) 0, odd multiplicity; 4, even multiplicity; number of turning points: 2

(c)

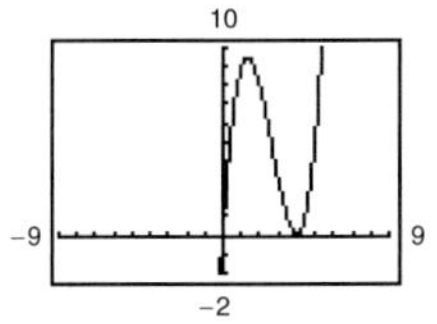

44. (a) $0, 6, -5$

(b) 0, even multiplicity; 6, -5, odd multiplicity; number of turning points: 3

(c)

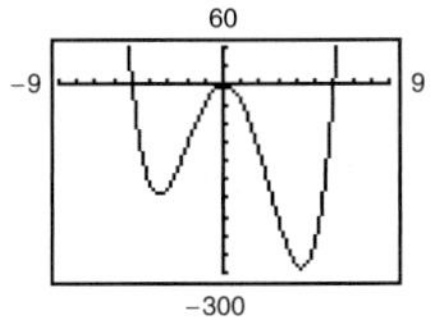

45. (a) $0, \pm\sqrt{3}$

(b) 0, odd multiplicity; $\pm\sqrt{3}$, even multiplicity; number of turning points: 4

(c)

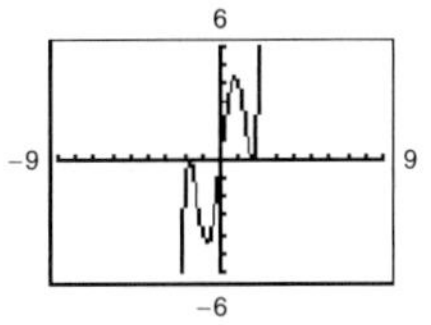

46. (a) $0, \pm\sqrt{2}$

(b) Odd multiplicity; number of turning points: 2

(c)

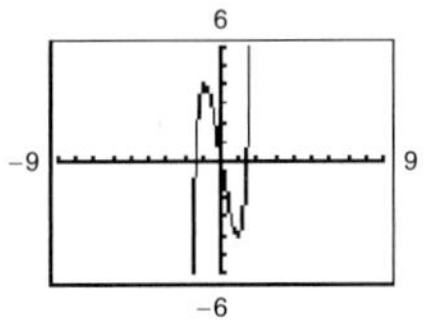

47. (a) No real zeros

(b) Number of turning points: 1

(c)

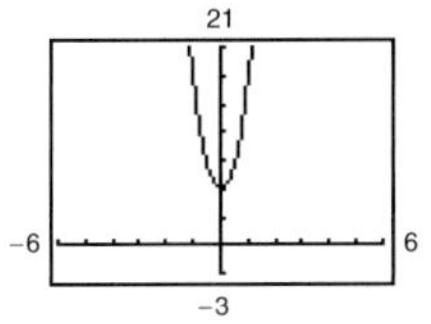

48. (a) $\pm\sqrt{5}$

(b) Odd multiplicity; number of turning points: 3

(c)

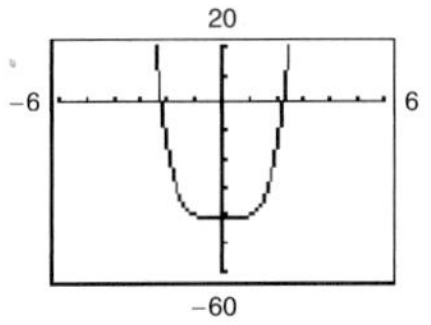

49. (a) $\pm 2, -3$

(b) Odd multiplicity; number of turning points: 2

(c)

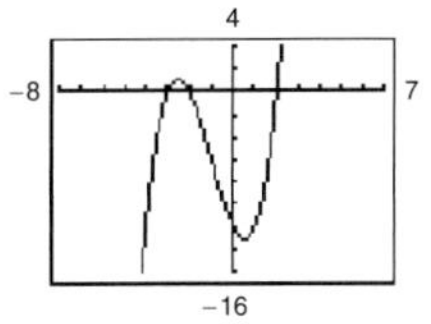

50. (a) $4, \pm 5$

(b) Odd multiplicity; number of turning points: 2

(c)

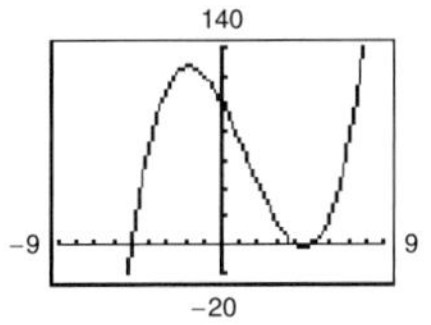

51. (a)

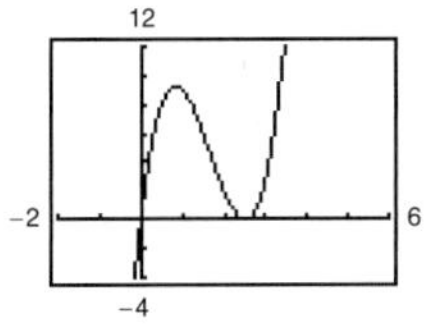

(b) x-intercepts: $(0, 0), \left(\frac{5}{2}, 0\right)$ (c) $x = 0, \frac{5}{2}$

(d) The answers in part (c) match the x-intercepts.

52. (a)
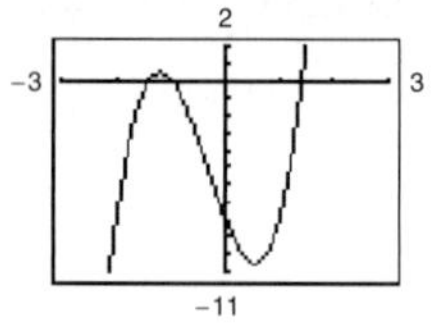

(b) x-intercepts: $(\sqrt{2}, 0), (-\sqrt{2}, 0), (-1, 0)$
(c) $x = \sqrt{2}, -\sqrt{2}, -1$
(d) The answers in part (c) match the x-intercepts.

53. (a)
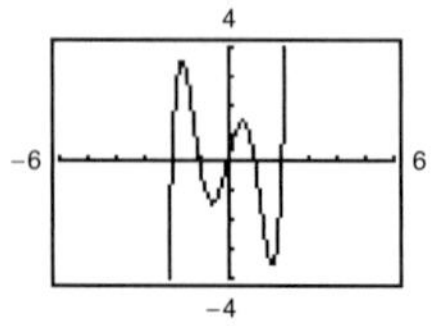

(b) x-intercepts: $(0, 0), (\pm 1, 0), (\pm 2, 0)$
(c) $x = 0, 1, -1, 2, -2$
(d) The answers in part (c) match the x-intercepts.

54. (a)
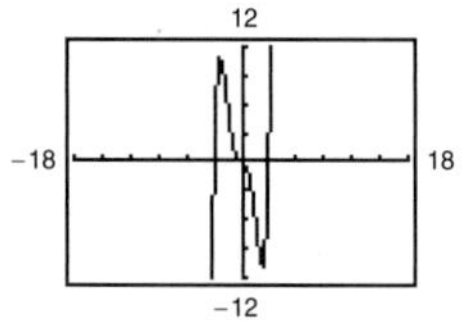

(b) x-intercepts: $(0, 0), (\pm 3, 0)$ (c) $x = 0, 3, -3$
(d) The answers in part (c) match the x-intercepts.

55. $f(x) = x^2 - 8x$ 56. $f(x) = x^2 + 7x$
57. $f(x) = x^2 + 4x - 12$ 58. $f(x) = x^2 - x - 20$
59. $f(x) = x^3 + 9x^2 + 20x$ 60. $f(x) = x^3 - 11x^2 + 10x$
61. $f(x) = x^4 - 4x^3 - 9x^2 + 36x$
62. $f(x) = x^5 - 5x^3 + 4x$ 63. $f(x) = x^2 - 2x - 2$
64. $f(x) = x^3 - 10x^2 + 27x - 22$
65. $f(x) = x^2 + 6x + 9$ 66. $f(x) = x^2 + 18x + 72$
67. $f(x) = x^3 + 4x^2 - 5x$
68. $f(x) = x^3 - 9x^2 + 6x + 56$ 69. $f(x) = x^3 - 3x$
70. $f(x) = x^3 - 27x^2 + 243x - 729$
71. $f(x) = x^4 + x^3 - 15x^2 + 23x - 10$
72. $f(x) = x^4 - 4x^3 - 23x^2 + 54x + 72$
73. $f(x) = x^5 + 16x^4 + 96x^3 + 256x^2 + 256x$
74. $f(x) = x^5 - 17x^4 + 79x^3 - 11x^2 - 332x - 224$

75. (a) Falls to the left, rises to the right
(b) 0, 5, −5 (c) Answers will vary.
(d)
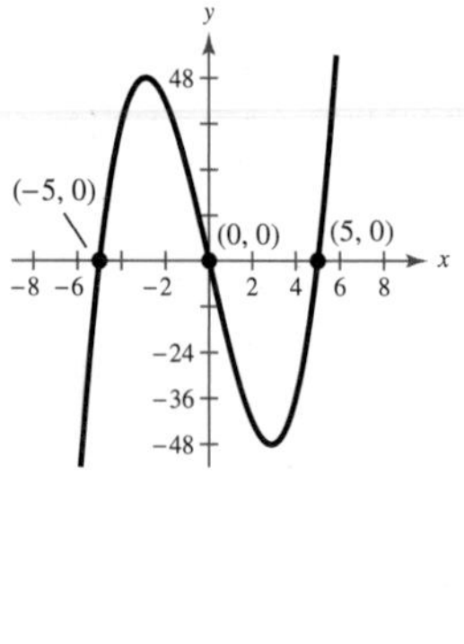

76. (a) Rises to the left, rises to the right
(b) −3, 0, 3 (c) Answers will vary.
(d)
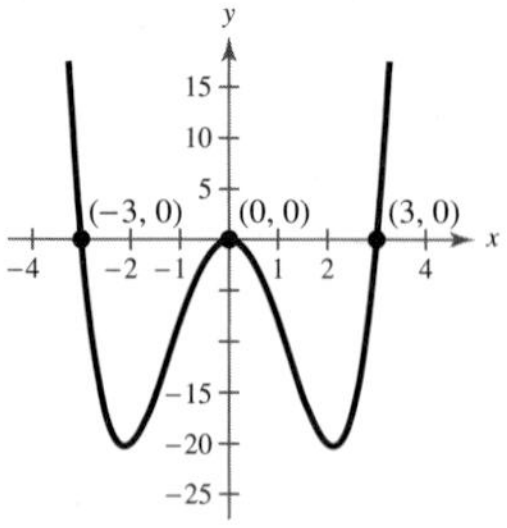

77. (a) Rises to the left, rises to the right
(b) No zeros (c) Answers will vary.
(d)
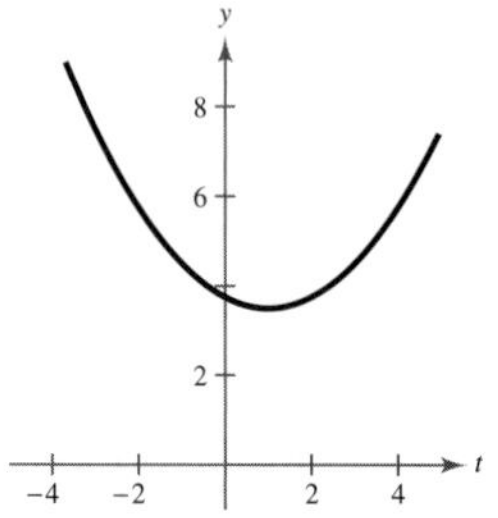

78. (a) Falls to the left, falls to the right
(b) 2, 8 (c) Answers will vary.
(d)
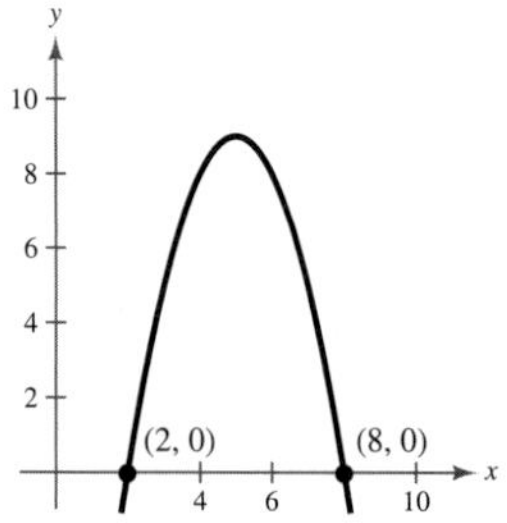

79. (a) Falls to the left, rises to the right
(b) 0, 2 (c) Answers will vary.
(d)
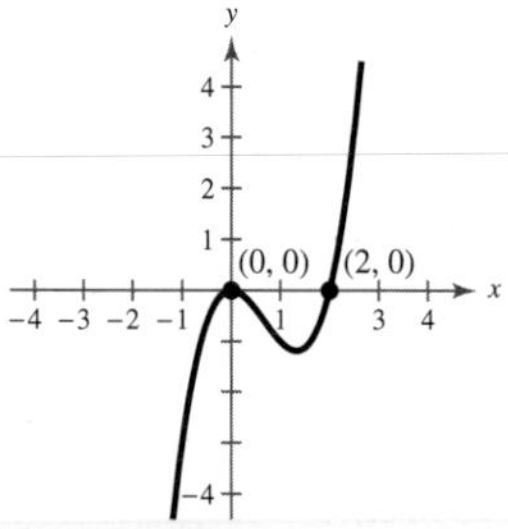

$x^2(x-2)$

80. (a) Rises to the left, falls to the right
(b) 2 (c) Answers will vary.
(d)
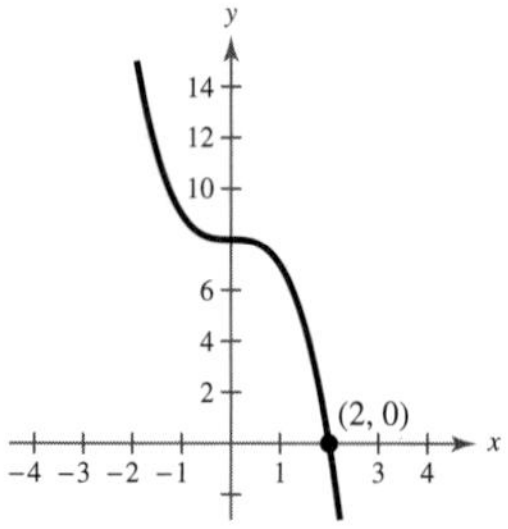

81. (a) Falls to the left, rises to the right
(b) 0, 2, 3 (c) Answers will vary.
(d)
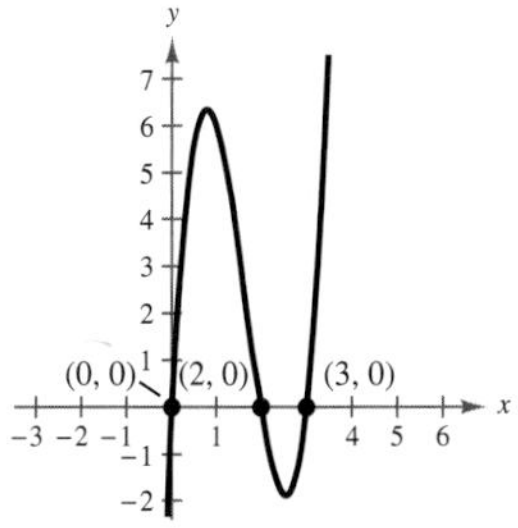

82. (a) Rises to the left, falls to the right
(b) $-\frac{3}{2}, 0, \frac{5}{2}$ (c) Answers will vary.
(d)
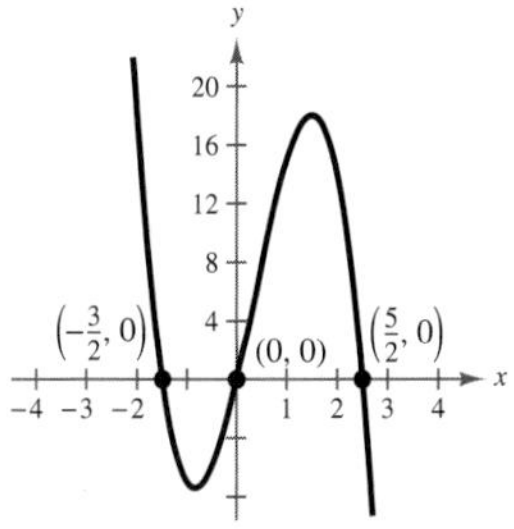

83. (a) Rises to the left, falls to the right
(b) $-5, 0$ (c) Answers will vary.
(d)
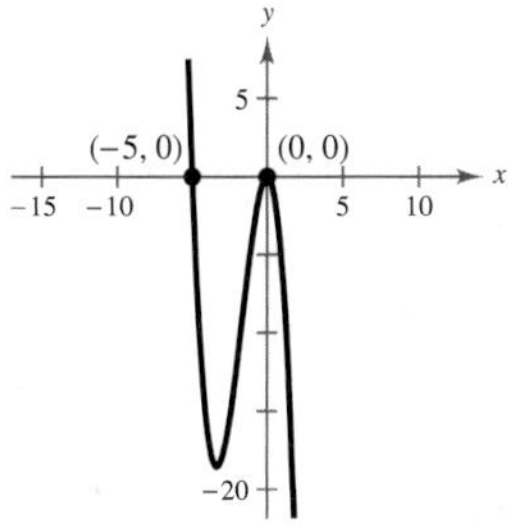

84. (a) Rises to the left, rises to the right
(b) $0, \pm 4$ (c) Answers will vary.
(d)
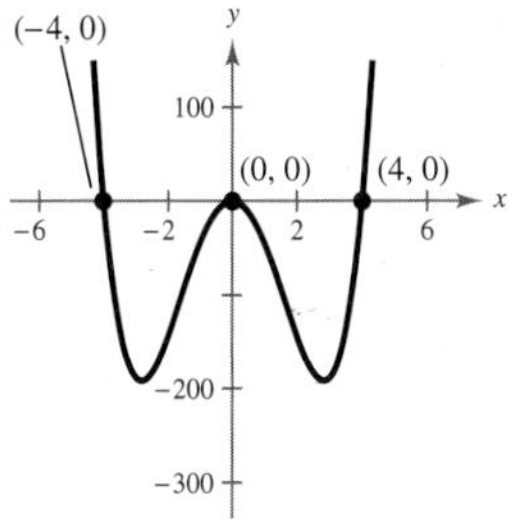

85. (a) Falls to the left, rises to the right
(b) 0, 4 (c) Answers will vary.
(d)
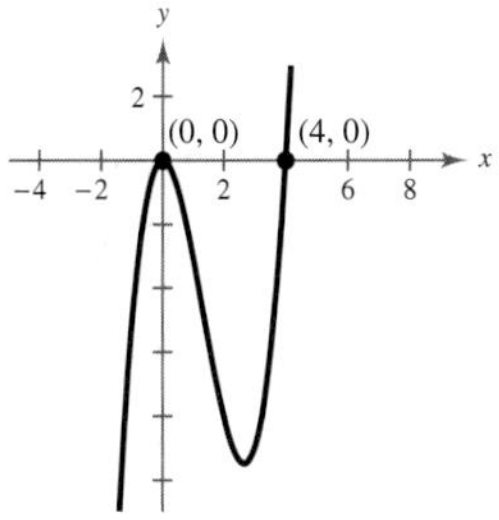

86. (a) Falls to the left, rises to the right
(b) 0, 4 (c) Answers will vary.
(d)
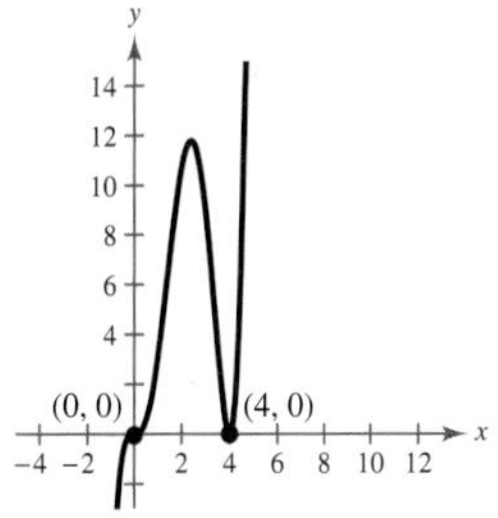

87. (a) Falls to the left, falls to the right
(b) ± 2 (c) Answers will vary.
(d)
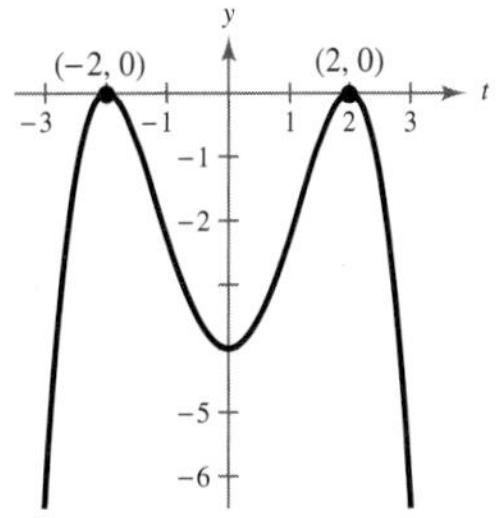

88. (a) Falls to the left, rises to the right
(b) $-1, 3$ (c) Answers will vary.
(d)
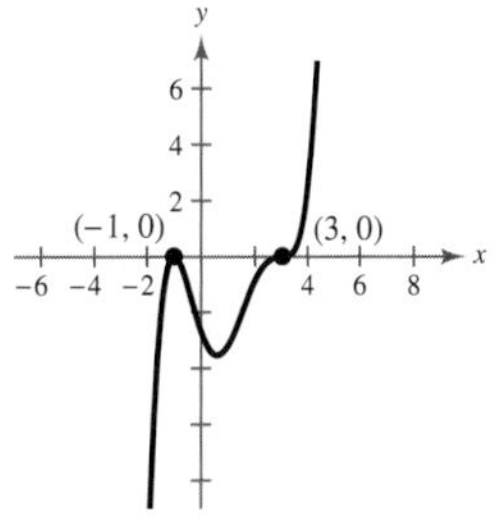

89.
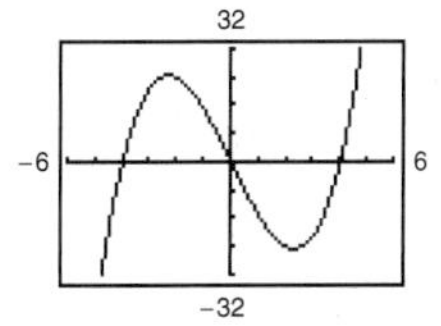

Zeros: $0, \pm 4$,
odd multiplicity

90.
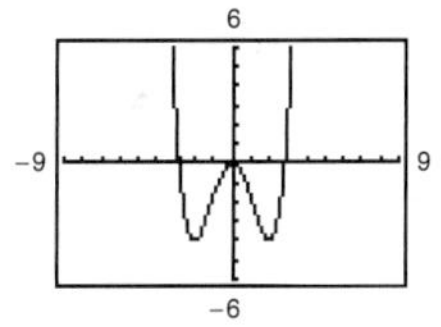

Zeros: $\pm 2\sqrt{2}$,
odd multiplicity; 0,
even multiplicity

91.
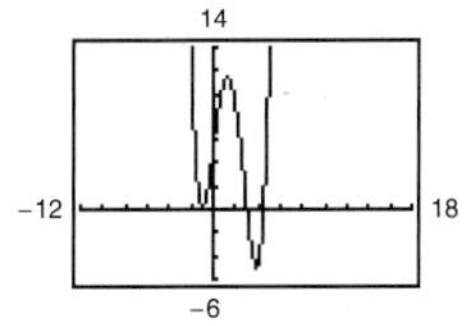

Zeros: -1,
even multiplicity;
$3, \frac{9}{2}$, odd multiplicity

92.
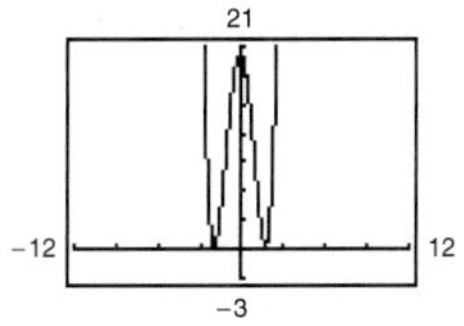

Zeros: $-2, \frac{5}{3}$,
even multiplicity

110. (a) 3, odd; 1, positive
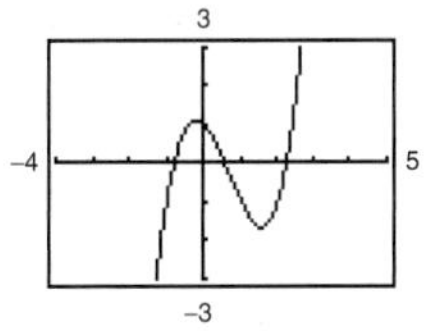

(b) 5, odd; 2, positive
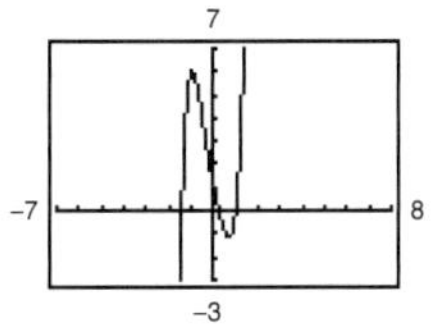

(c) 5, odd; -2, negative

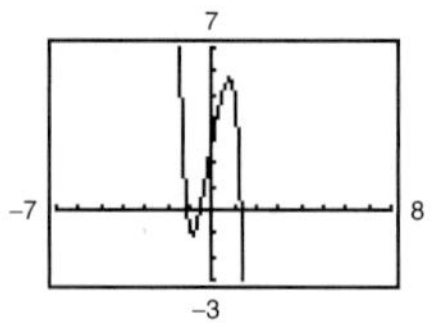

(d) 3, odd; -1, negative

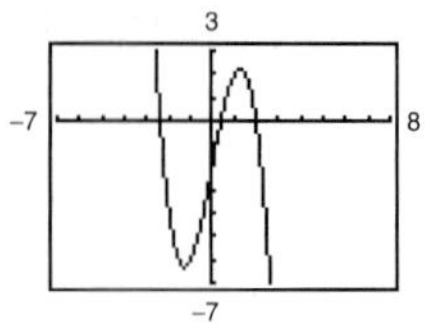

(e) 2, even; 2, positive

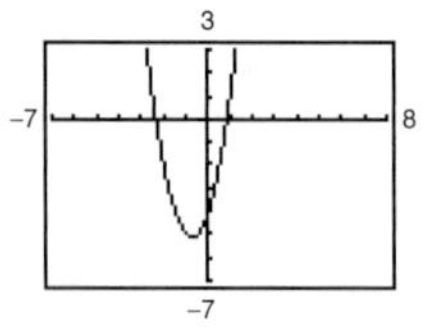

(f) 4, even; 1, positive

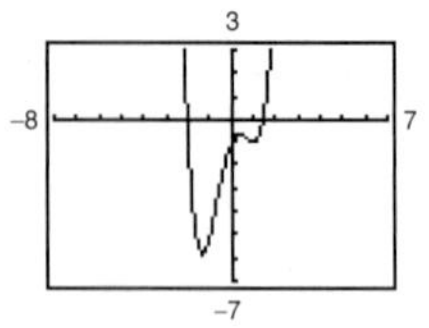

(g) 2, even; 1, positive

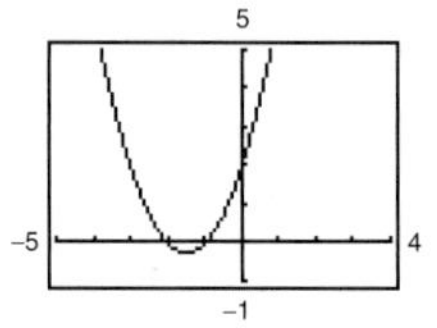

When the degree of the function is odd and the leading coefficient is positive, the graph falls to the left and rises to the right, but if the leading coefficient is negative, the graph falls to the right and rises to the left. When the degree of the function is even and the leading coefficient is positive, the graph rises to the left and right, but if the leading coefficient is negative, the graph falls to the left and right.

111. (a)

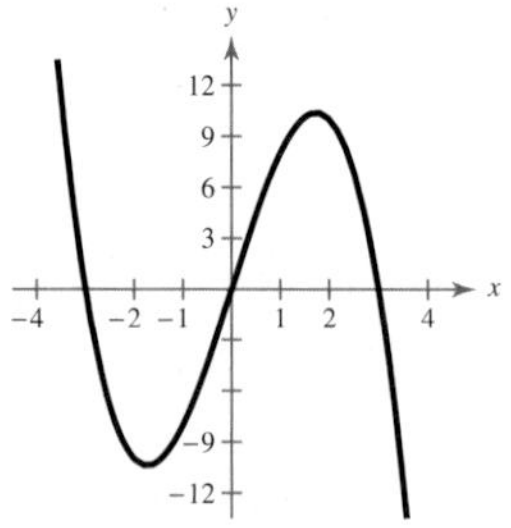

Zeros: 3
Relative minimum: 1
Relative maximum: 1
The number of zeros is the same as the degree, and the number of extrema is one less than the degree.

(b)

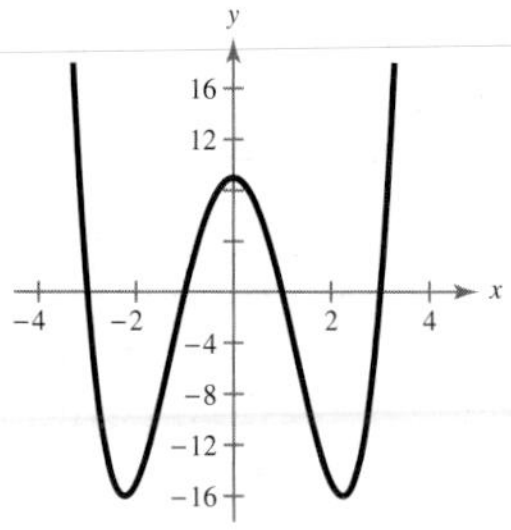

Zeros: 4
Relative minima: 2
Relative maximum: 1
The number of zeros is the same as the degree, and the number of extrema is one less than the degree.

(c)

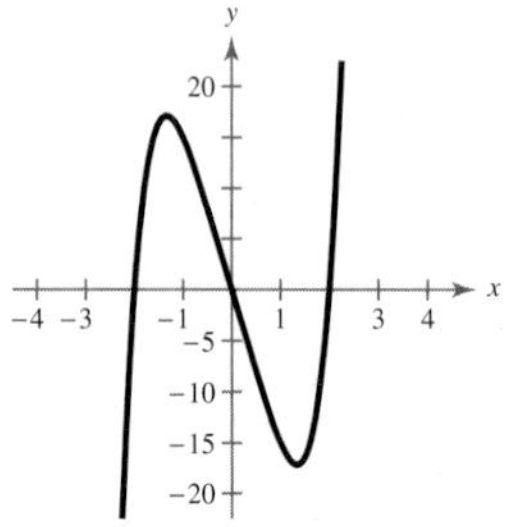

Zeros: 3
Relative minimum: 1
Relative maximum: 1
The number of zeros and the number of extrema are both less than the degree.

Section 2.3 *(page 156)*

42. $-3x^3 + 6x^2 - 12x + 24 - \dfrac{48}{x + 2}$

43. $-x^3 - 6x^2 - 36x - 36 - \dfrac{216}{x - 6}$

44. $-x^2 + 3x - 6 + \dfrac{11}{x + 1}$ **45.** $4x^2 + 14x - 30,\quad x \neq -\dfrac{1}{2}$

46. $3x^2 + \dfrac{1}{2}x + \dfrac{3}{4} + \dfrac{49}{8x - 12}$

47. $f(x) = (x - 4)(x^2 + 3x - 2) + 3,\quad f(4) = 3$

48. $f(x) = (x + 2)(x^2 - 7x + 3) + 2,\quad f(-2) = 2$

49. $f(x) = \left(x + \frac{2}{3}\right)(15x^3 - 6x + 4) + \frac{34}{3},\quad f\left(-\frac{2}{3}\right) = \frac{34}{3}$

50. $f(x) = \left(x - \frac{1}{5}\right)(10x^2 - 20x - 7) + \frac{13}{5},\quad f\left(\frac{1}{5}\right) = \frac{13}{5}$

51. $f(x) = \left(x - \sqrt{2}\right)\left[x^2 + \left(3 + \sqrt{2}\right)x + 3\sqrt{2}\right] - 8,$
$f\left(\sqrt{2}\right) = -8$

52. $f(x) = \left(x + \sqrt{5}\right)\left[x^2 + \left(2 - \sqrt{5}\right)x - 2\sqrt{5}\right] + 6,$
$f\left(-\sqrt{5}\right) = 6$

53. $f(x) = \left(x - 1 + \sqrt{3}\right)\left[-4x^2 + \left(2 + 4\sqrt{3}\right)x + \left(2 + 2\sqrt{3}\right)\right],$
$f\left(1 - \sqrt{3}\right) = 0$

54. $f(x) = \left(x - 2 - \sqrt{2}\right)\left[-3x^2 + \left(2 - 3\sqrt{2}\right)x + 8 - 4\sqrt{2}\right],$
$f\left(2 + \sqrt{2}\right) = 0$

72. (a) Answers will vary. (b) $x - 3$
(c) $f(x) = (x - 3)(2x + 5)(5x - 3)$
(d) $3, -\frac{5}{2}, \frac{3}{5}$ (e)

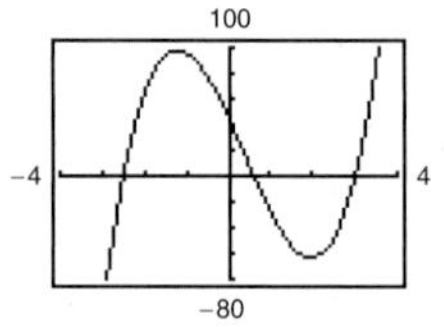

73. (a) Answers will vary. (b) $x - \sqrt{5}$
(c) $f(x) = \left(x - \sqrt{5}\right)\left(x + \sqrt{5}\right)(2x - 1)$
(d) $\pm\sqrt{5}, \frac{1}{2}$ (e)

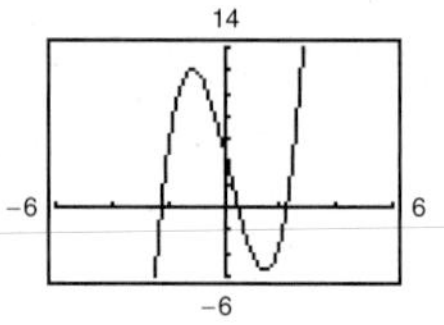

74. (a) Answers will vary. (b) $x - 4\sqrt{3}$
(c) $f(x) = \left(x - 4\sqrt{3}\right)\left(x + 4\sqrt{3}\right)(x + 3)$
(d) $\pm 4\sqrt{3}, -3$ (e)

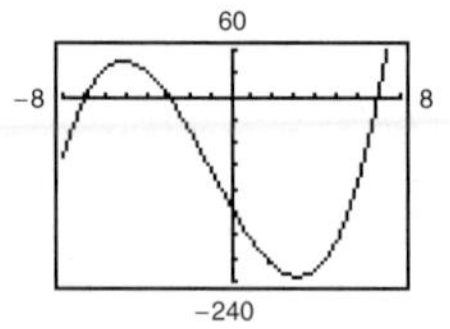

75. (a) Zeros are 2 and about ± 2.236.
(b) $x = 2$ (c) $f(x) = (x - 2)\left(x - \sqrt{5}\right)\left(x + \sqrt{5}\right)$

76. (a) Zeros are 4 and about ± 1.414.
(b) $x = 4$ (c) $g(x) = (x - 4)\left(x - \sqrt{2}\right)\left(x + \sqrt{2}\right)$

77. (a) Zeros are -2, about 0.268, and about 3.732.
(b) $t = -2$
(c) $h(t) = (t + 2)\left[t - \left(2 + \sqrt{3}\right)\right]\left[t - \left(2 - \sqrt{3}\right)\right]$

78. (a) Zeros are 6, about 0.764, and about 5.236.
(b) $s = 6$
(c) $f(s) = (s - 6)\left[s - \left(3 + \sqrt{5}\right)\right]\left[s - \left(3 - \sqrt{5}\right)\right]$

79. (a) Zeros are 0, 3, 4, and about ± 1.414.
(b) $x = 0$
(c) $h(x) = x(x-4)(x-3)(x+\sqrt{2})(x-\sqrt{2})$

80. (a) Zeros are ± 3, about 0.333, and 1.5
(b) $x = -3$
(c) $g(x) = (x-3)(x+3)(2x-3)(3x-1)$

81. $2x^2 - x - 1, \ x \neq \frac{3}{2}$ 82. $x^2 - 7x - 8, \ x \neq -8$

83. $x^2 + 3x, \ x \neq -2, -1$ 84. $x^2 + 9x - 1, \ x \neq \pm 2$

Section 2.5 *(page 176)*

37. (a) $\pm 1, \pm 2, \pm 4, \pm 8, \pm \frac{1}{2}$
(b)
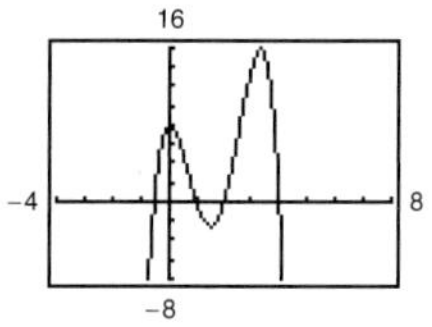

(c) $-\frac{1}{2}, 1, 2, 4$

38. (a) $\pm 1, \pm 2, \pm 4, \pm \frac{1}{2}, \pm \frac{1}{4}$
(b)
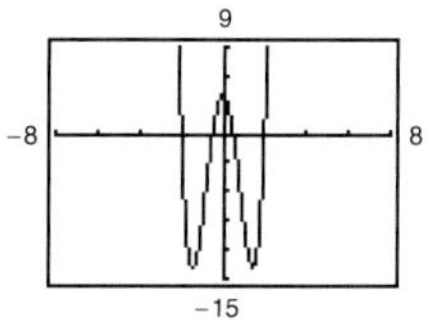

(c) $\pm 2, \pm \frac{1}{2}$

39. (a) $\pm 1, \pm 3, \pm \frac{1}{2}, \pm \frac{3}{2}, \pm \frac{1}{4}, \pm \frac{3}{4}, \pm \frac{1}{8}, \pm \frac{3}{8}, \pm \frac{1}{16}, \pm \frac{3}{16}, \pm \frac{1}{32}, \pm \frac{3}{32}$
(b)
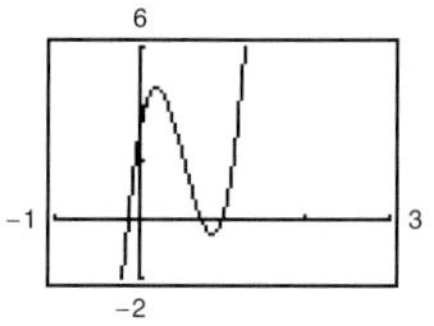

(c) $1, \frac{3}{4}, -\frac{1}{8}$

40. (a) $\pm 1, \pm 2, \pm 3, \pm 6, \pm 9, \pm 18, \pm \frac{1}{2}, \pm \frac{3}{2}, \pm \frac{9}{2}, \pm \frac{1}{4}, \pm \frac{3}{4}, \pm \frac{9}{4}$
(b)
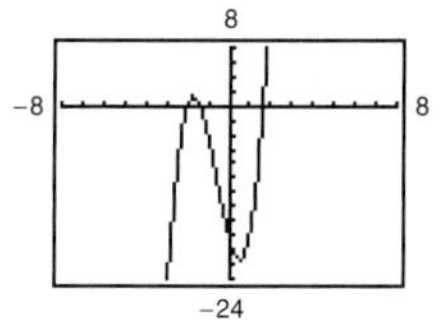

(c) $-2, \frac{1}{8} \pm \frac{\sqrt{145}}{8}$

41. (a) ± 1, about ± 1.414 (b) $\pm 1, \pm \sqrt{2}$
(c) $f(x) = (x+1)(x-1)(x+\sqrt{2})(x-\sqrt{2})$

42. (a) ± 2, about ± 1.732 (b) $\pm 2, \pm \sqrt{3}$
(c) $P(t) = (t+2)(t-2)(t+\sqrt{3})(t-\sqrt{3})$

43. (a) 0, 3, 4, about ± 1.414 (b) $0, 3, 4, \pm \sqrt{2}$
(c) $h(x) = x(x-3)(x-4)(x+\sqrt{2})(x-\sqrt{2})$

44. (a) ± 3, 1.5, 0.333 (b) $\pm 3, \frac{3}{2}, \frac{1}{3}$
(c) $g(x) = (x+3)(x-3)(2x-3)(3x-1)$

63. $\pm 6i$; $(x+6i)(x-6i)$

64. $\frac{1 \pm \sqrt{223}i}{2}$; $\left(x - \frac{1-\sqrt{223}i}{2}\right)\left(x - \frac{1+\sqrt{223}i}{2}\right)$

65. $1 \pm 4i$; $(x-1-4i)(x-1+4i)$

66. $-5 \pm 2\sqrt{2}$; $(x+5-2\sqrt{2})(x+5+2\sqrt{2})$

67. $\pm 2, \pm 2i$; $(x-2)(x+2)(x-2i)(x+2i)$

68. $\pm 4, \pm 4i$; $(y-4)(y+4)(y-4i)(y+4i)$

69. $1 \pm i$; $(z-1+i)(z-1-i)$

70. $1 \pm i, 1$; $(x-1)(x-1+i)(x-1-i)$

71. $-1, 2 \pm i$; $(x+1)(x-2+i)(x-2-i)$

72. $-3, 2 \pm 3i$; $(x+3)(x-2+3i)(x-2-3i)$

73. $-2, 1 \pm \sqrt{2}i$; $(x+2)(x-1+\sqrt{2}i)(x-1-\sqrt{2}i)$

74. $-2 \pm \sqrt{3}i, -5$;
$(x+5)(x+2+\sqrt{3}i)(x+2-\sqrt{3}i)$

75. $-\frac{1}{5}, 1 \pm \sqrt{5}i$; $(5x+1)(x-1+\sqrt{5}i)(x-1-\sqrt{5}i)$

76. $-\frac{3}{2}, 1 \pm \sqrt{6}i$; $(x+\frac{3}{2})(x-1+\sqrt{6}i)(x-1-\sqrt{6}i)$

77. $2, \pm 2i$; $(x-2)^2(x+2i)(x-2i)$

78. $-3, \pm i$; $(x+3)^2(x+i)(x-i)$

79. $\pm i, \pm 3i$; $(x+i)(x-i)(x+3i)(x-3i)$

80. $\pm 2i, \pm 5i$; $(x+2i)(x-2i)(x+5i)(x-5i)$

Section 2.6 *(page 190)*

5. (a)

x	$f(x)$	x	$f(x)$	x	$f(x)$
0.5	-2	1.5	2	5	0.25
0.9	-10	1.1	10	10	$0.\overline{1}$
0.99	-100	1.01	100	100	$0.\overline{01}$
0.999	-1000	1.001	1000	1000	$0.\overline{001}$

(b) Vertical asymptote: $x = 1$
Horizontal asymptote: $y = 0$
(c) Domain: all real numbers x except $x = 1$

6. (a)

x	$f(x)$	x	$f(x)$	x	$f(x)$
0.5	-5	1.5	15	5	6.25
0.9	-45	1.1	55	10	$5.\overline{5}$
0.99	-495	1.01	505	100	$5.\overline{05}$
0.999	-4995	1.001	5005	1000	$5.\overline{005}$

(b) Vertical asymptote: $x = 1$
Horizontal asymptote: $y = 5$
(c) Domain: all real numbers x except $x = 1$

7. (a)

x	$f(x)$	x	$f(x)$	x	$f(x)$
0.5	-1	1.5	5.4	5	3.125
0.9	-12.79	1.1	17.29	10	$3.\overline{03}$
0.99	-147.8	1.01	152.3	100	$3.\overline{0003}$
0.999	-1498	1.001	1502	1000	3

(b) Vertical asymptotes: $x = \pm 1$
Horizontal asymptote: $y = 3$
(c) Domain: all real numbers x except $x = \pm 1$

8. (a)

x	$f(x)$	x	$f(x)$	x	$f(x)$
0.5	$-2.\overline{6}$	1.5	4.8	5	$0.8\overline{3}$
0.9	-18.95	1.1	20.95	10	$0.\overline{40}$
0.99	-199	1.01	201	100	0.04
0.999	-1999	1.001	2001	1000	0.004

(b) Vertical asymptotes: $x = \pm 1$
Horizontal asymptote: $y = 0$
(c) Domain: all real numbers x except $x = \pm 1$

35. (a) Domain: all real numbers x except $x = -2$
(b) x-intercept: $\left(-\frac{7}{2}, 0\right)$
y-intercept: $\left(0, \frac{7}{2}\right)$
(c) Vertical asymptote: $x = -2$
Horizontal asymptote: $y = 2$
(d)

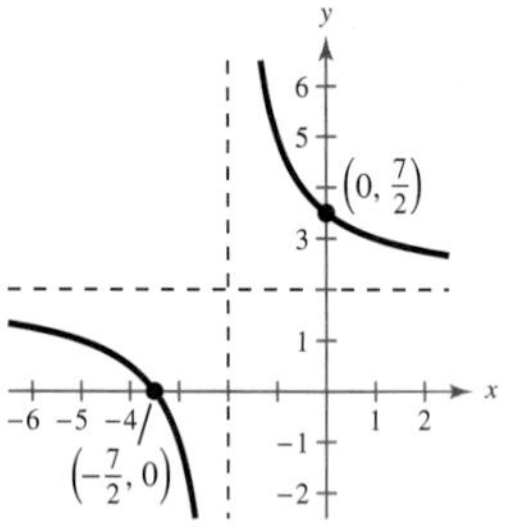

36. (a) Domain: all real numbers x except $x = 1$
(b) x-intercept: $\left(\frac{1}{3}, 0\right)$
y-intercept: $(0, 1)$
(c) Vertical asymptote: $x = 1$
Horizontal asymptote: $y = 3$
(d)

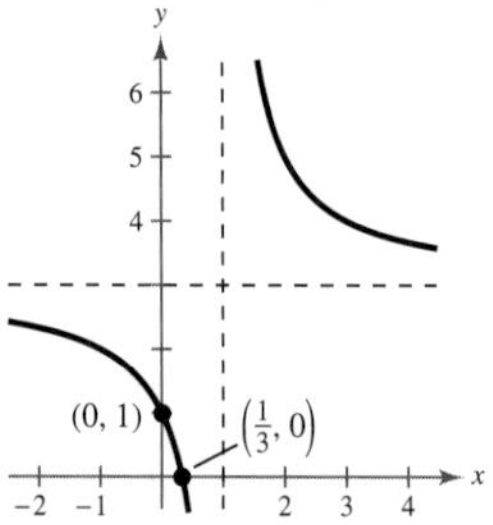

37. (a) Domain: all real numbers x
(b) Intercept: $(0, 0)$
(c) Horizontal asymptote: $y = 1$
(d)

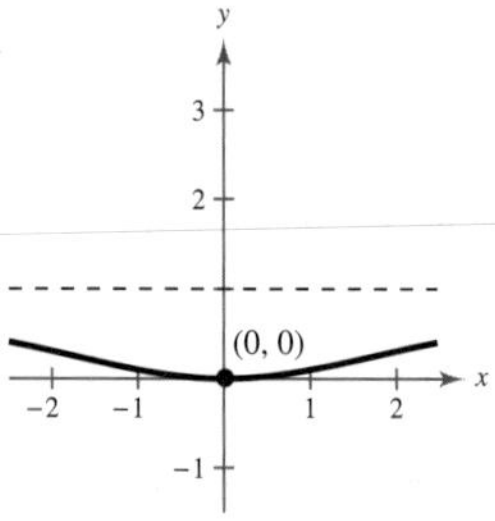

38. (a) Domain: all real numbers t except $t = 0$
(b) t-intercept: $\left(\frac{1}{2}, 0\right)$
(c) Vertical asymptote: $t = 0$
Horizontal asymptote: $y = -2$
(d)

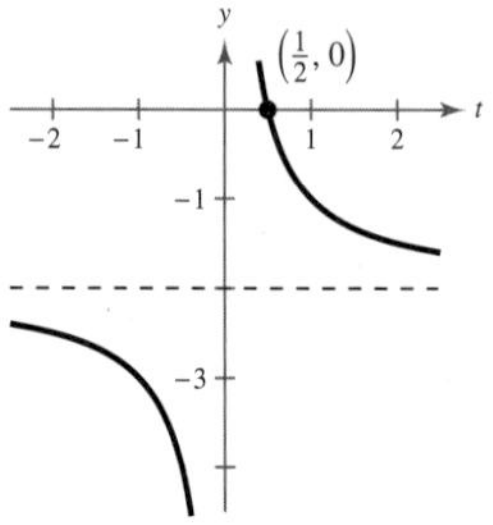

39. (a) Domain: all real numbers s
(b) Intercept: $(0, 0)$ (c) Horizontal asymptote: $y = 0$
(d)

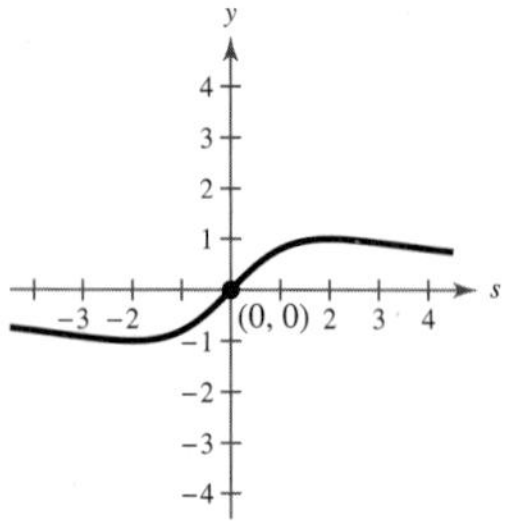

40. (a) Domain: all real numbers x except $x = 2$
(b) y-intercept: $\left(0, -\frac{1}{4}\right)$
(c) Vertical asymptote: $x = 2$
Horizontal asymptote: $y = 0$
(d)

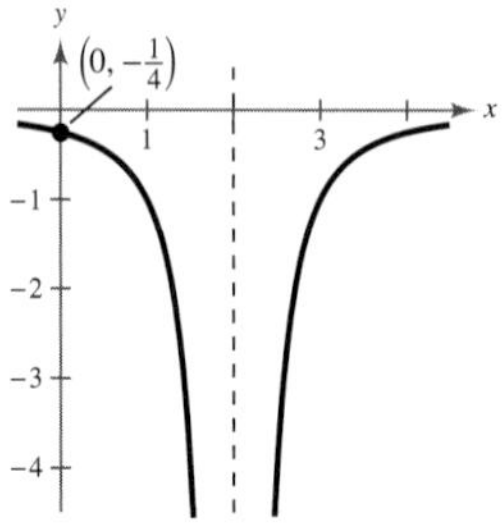

41. (a) Domain: all real numbers x except $x = \pm 2$
(b) x-intercepts: $(1, 0)$ and $(4, 0)$
y-intercept: $(0, -1)$
(c) Vertical asymptotes: $x = \pm 2$
Horizontal asymptote: $y = 1$
(d)

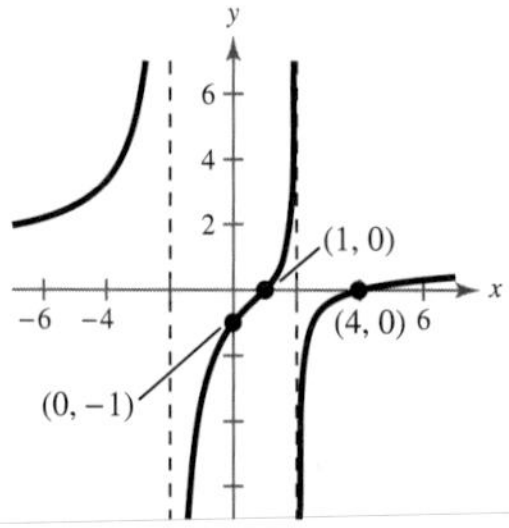

42. (a) Domain: all real numbers x except $x = \pm 3$
(b) x-intercepts: $(-2, 0)$, $(4, 0)$
y-intercept: $\left(0, \frac{8}{9}\right)$
(c) Vertical asymptotes: $x = \pm 3$
Horizontal asymptote: $y = 1$
(d)

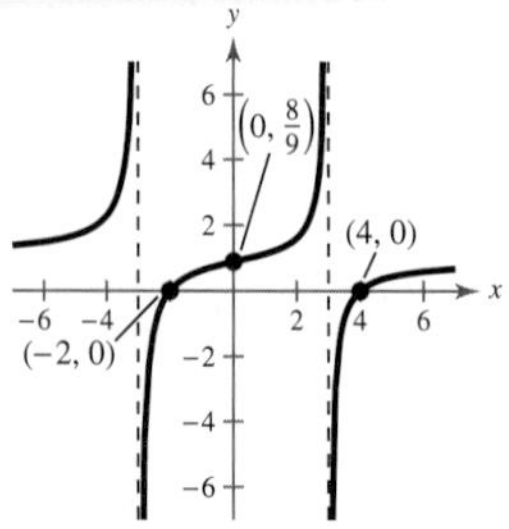

43. (a) Domain: all real numbers x except $x = \pm 1, 2$
(b) x-intercepts: $(3, 0)$, $\left(-\frac{1}{2}, 0\right)$
y-intercept: $\left(0, -\frac{3}{2}\right)$
(c) Vertical asymptotes: $x = 2$, $x = \pm 1$
Horizontal asymptote: $y = 0$

(d)

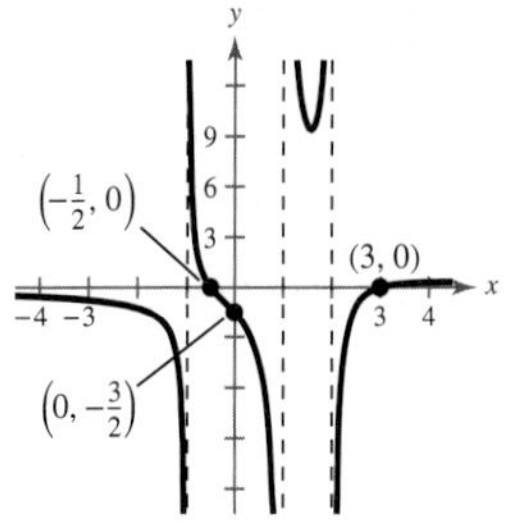

44. (a) Domain: all real numbers x except $x = -2, 1, 3$

(b) x-intercepts: $(-1, 0), (2, 0)$

y-intercept: $\left(0, -\frac{1}{3}\right)$

(c) Vertical asymptotes: $x = -2, x = 1, x = 3$

Horizontal asymptote: $y = 0$

(d)

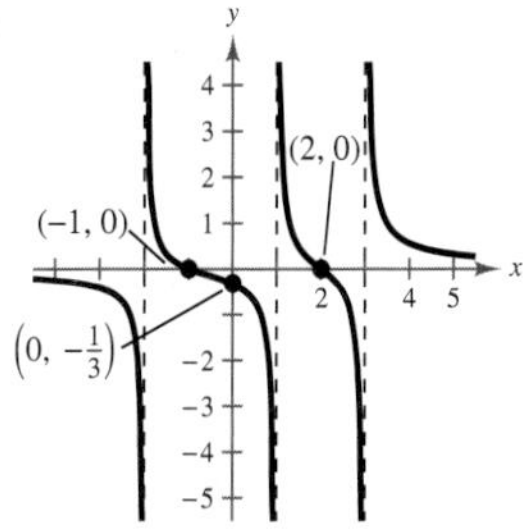

45. (a) Domain: all real numbers x except $x = 2, -3$

(b) Intercept: $(0, 0)$

(c) Vertical asymptote: $x = 2$

Horizontal asymptote: $y = 1$

(d)

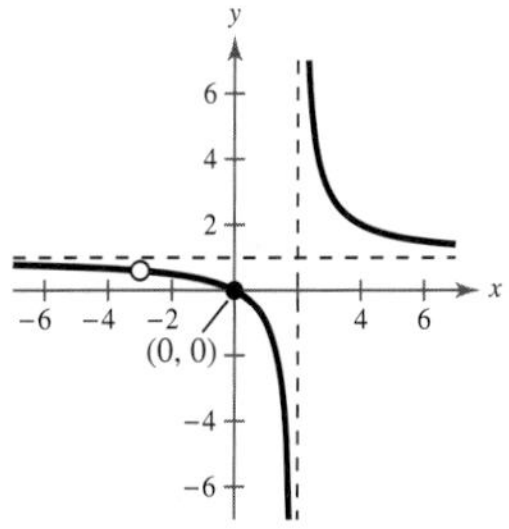

46. (a) Domain: all real numbers x except $x = 3, -4$

(b) y-intercept: $\left(0, -\frac{5}{3}\right)$

(c) Vertical asymptote: $x = 3$

Horizontal asymptote: $y = 0$

(d)

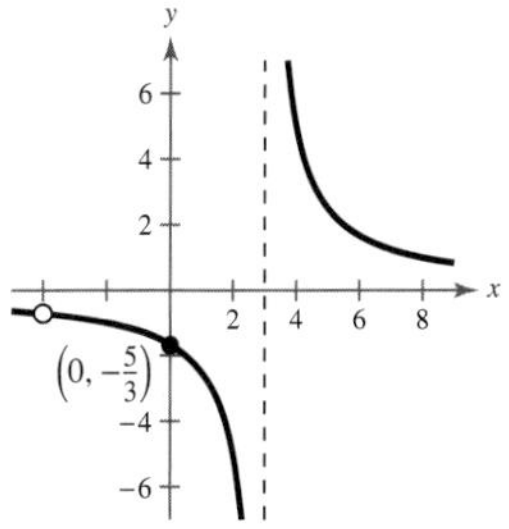

47. (a) Domain: all real numbers x except $x = -\frac{3}{2}, 2$

(b) x-intercept: $\left(\frac{1}{2}, 0\right)$

y-intercept: $\left(0, -\frac{1}{3}\right)$

(c) Vertical asymptote: $x = -\frac{3}{2}$

Horizontal asymptote: $y = 1$

(d)

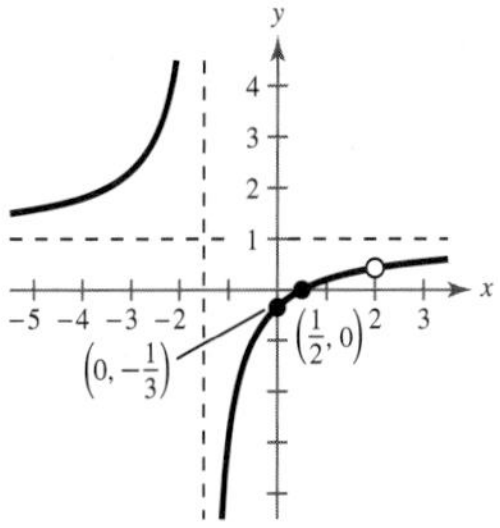

48. (a) Domain: all real numbers x except $x = -\frac{1}{2}, 2$

(b) x-intercept: $\left(\frac{2}{3}, 0\right)$

y-intercept: $(0, -2)$

(c) Vertical asymptote: $x = -\frac{1}{2}$

Horizontal asymptote: $y = \frac{3}{2}$

(d)

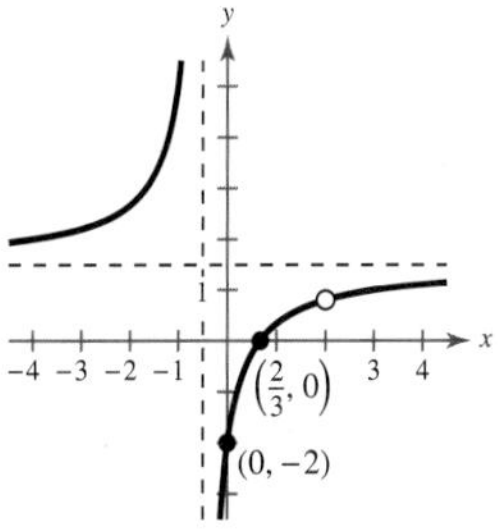

49. (a) Domain: all real numbers t except $t = 1$

(b) t-intercept: $(-1, 0)$

y-intercept: $(0, 1)$

(c) Vertical asymptote: None

Horizontal asymptote: None

(d)

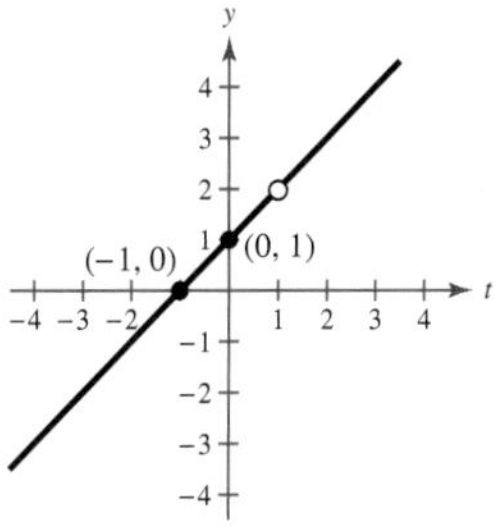

50. (a) Domain: all real numbers x except $x = -6$

(b) x-intercept: $(6, 0)$

y-intercept: $(0, -6)$

(c) Vertical asymptote: None

Horizontal asymptote: None

(d)

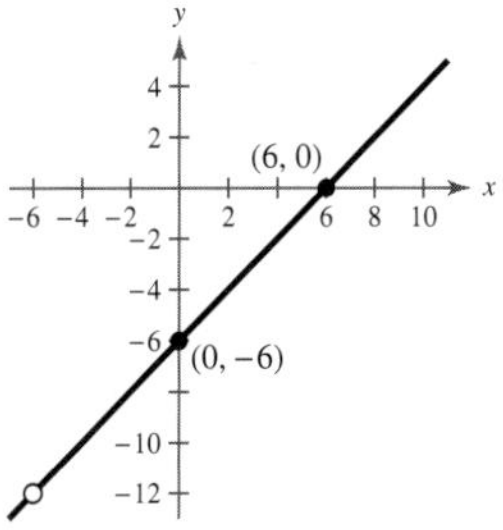

51. (a) Domain of f: all real numbers x except $x = -1$
Domain of g: all real numbers x
(b) $x - 1$; Vertical asymptotes: None
(c)

x	-3	-2	-1.5	-1	-0.5	0	1
$f(x)$	-4	-3	-2.5	Undef.	-1.5	-1	0
$g(x)$	-4	-3	-2.5	-2	-1.5	-1	0

(d)

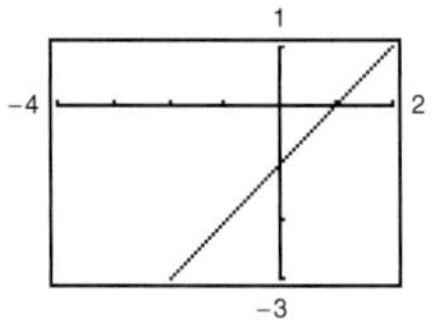

(e) Because there are only a finite number of pixels, the graphing utility may not attempt to evaluate the function where it does not exist.

52. (a) Domain of f: all real numbers x except $x = 0, 2$
Domain of g: all real numbers x
(b) x; Vertical asymptotes: None
(c)

x	-1	0	1	1.5	2	2.5	3
$f(x)$	-1	Undef.	1	1.5	Undef.	2.5	3
$g(x)$	-1	0	1	1.5	2	2.5	3

(d)

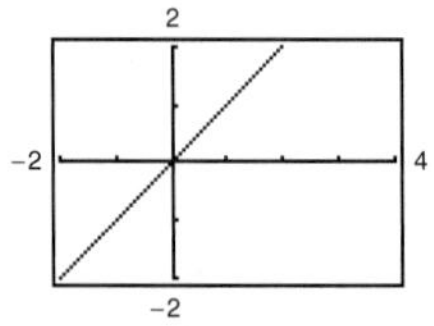

(e) Because there are only a finite number of pixels, the graphing utility may not attempt to evaluate the function where it does not exist.

53. (a) Domain of f: all real numbers x except $x = 0, 2$
Domain of g: all real numbers x except $x = 0$
(b) $\frac{1}{x}$; Vertical asymptote: $x = 0$
(c)

x	-0.5	0	0.5	1	1.5	2	3
$f(x)$	-2	Undef.	2	1	$\frac{2}{3}$	Undef.	$\frac{1}{3}$
$g(x)$	-2	Undef.	2	1	$\frac{2}{3}$	$\frac{1}{2}$	$\frac{1}{3}$

(d)

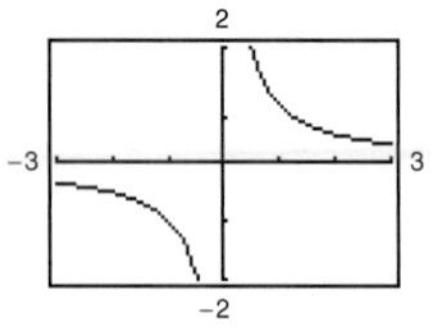

(e) Because there are only a finite number of pixels, the graphing utility may not attempt to evaluate the function where it does not exist.

54. (a) Domain of f: all real numbers x except $x = 3, 4$
Domain of g: all real numbers x except $x = 4$
(b) $\frac{2}{x - 4}$; Vertical asymptote: $x = 4$
(c)

x	0	1	2	3	4	5	6
$f(x)$	$-\frac{1}{2}$	$-\frac{2}{3}$	-1	Undef.	Undef.	2	1
$g(x)$	$-\frac{1}{2}$	$-\frac{2}{3}$	-1	-2	Undef.	2	1

(d)

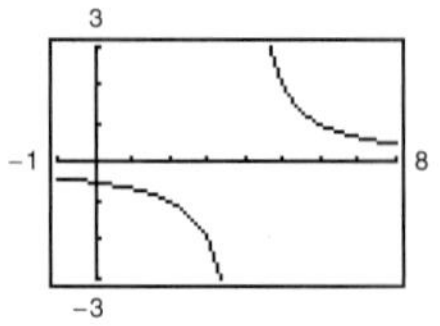

(e) Because there are only a finite number of pixels, the graphing utility may not attempt to evaluate the function where it does not exist.

55. (a) Domain: all real numbers x except $x = 0$
(b) x-intercepts: $(-3, 0)$, $(3, 0)$
(c) Vertical asymptote: $x = 0$
Slant asymptote: $y = x$
(d)

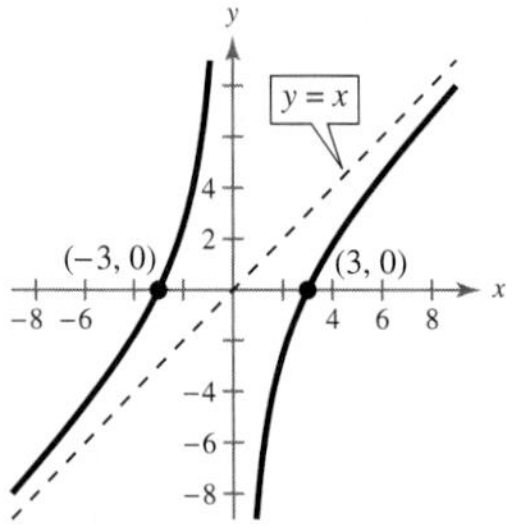

56. (a) Domain: all real numbers x except $x = 0$
(b) No intercepts
(c) Vertical asymptote: $x = 0$
Slant asymptote: $y = x$
(d)

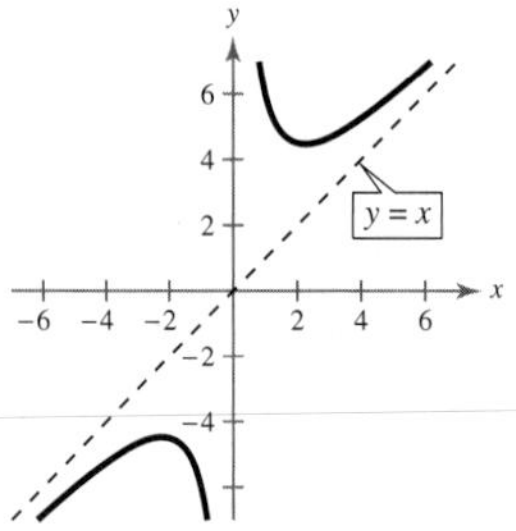

57. (a) Domain: all real numbers x except $x = 0$
(b) No intercepts
(c) Vertical asymptote: $x = 0$
Slant asymptote: $y = 2x$
(d)

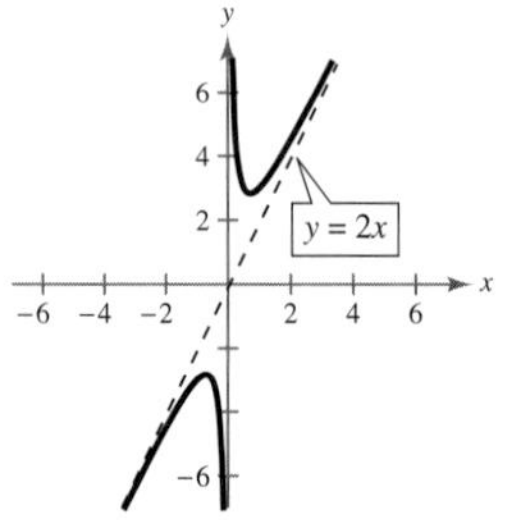

58. (a) Domain: all real numbers x except $x = 0$
(b) x-intercepts: $(-1, 0)$, $(1, 0)$
(c) Vertical asymptote: $x = 0$
Slant asymptote: $y = -x$

ADDITIONAL ANSWERS

(d)

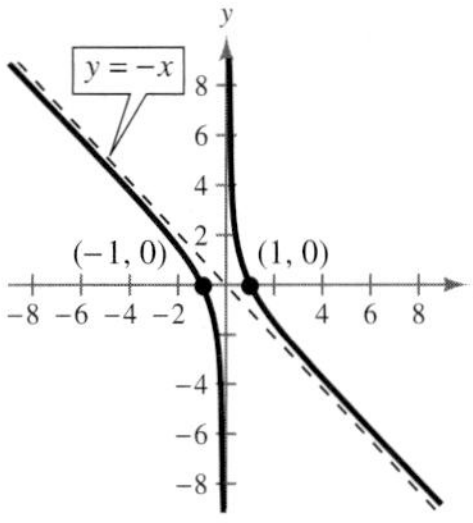

59. (a) Domain: all real numbers x except $x = 0$
(b) No intercepts
(c) Vertical asymptote: $x = 0$
Slant asymptote: $y = x$
(d)

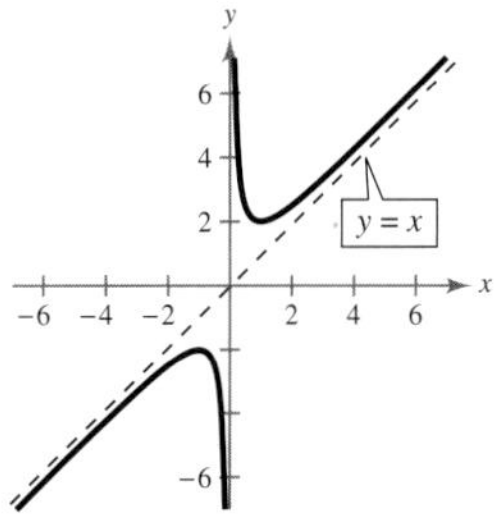

60. (a) Domain: all real numbers x except $x = 1$
(b) Intercept: $(0, 0)$
(c) Vertical asymptote: $x = 1$
Slant asymptote: $y = x + 1$
(d)

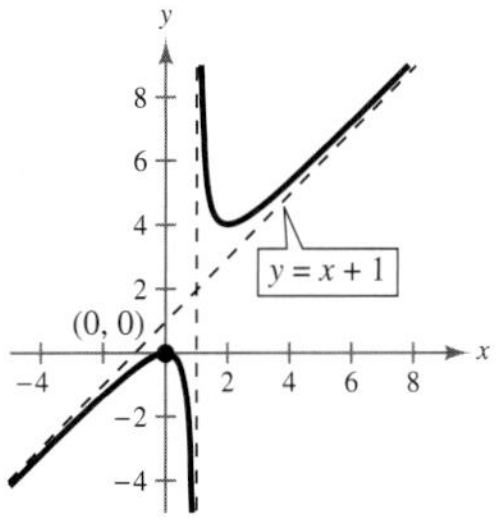

61. (a) Domain: all real numbers t except $t = -5$
(b) y-intercept: $\left(0, -\frac{1}{5}\right)$
(c) Vertical asymptote: $t = -5$
Slant asymptote: $y = -t + 5$
(d)

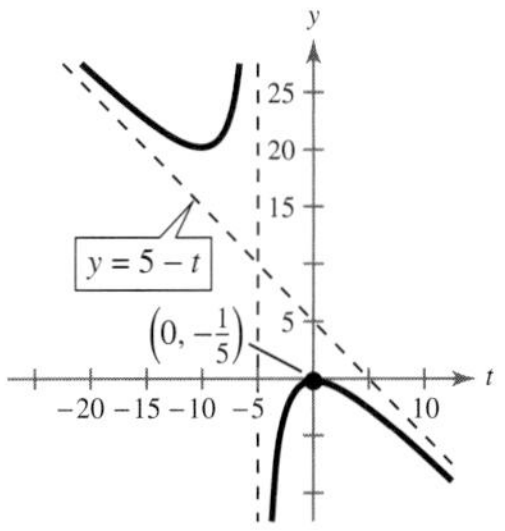

62. (a) Domain: all real numbers x except $x = -\frac{1}{3}$
(b) Intercept: $(0, 0)$
(c) Vertical asymptote: $x = -\frac{1}{3}$
Slant asymptote: $y = \frac{1}{3}x - \frac{1}{9}$

(d)

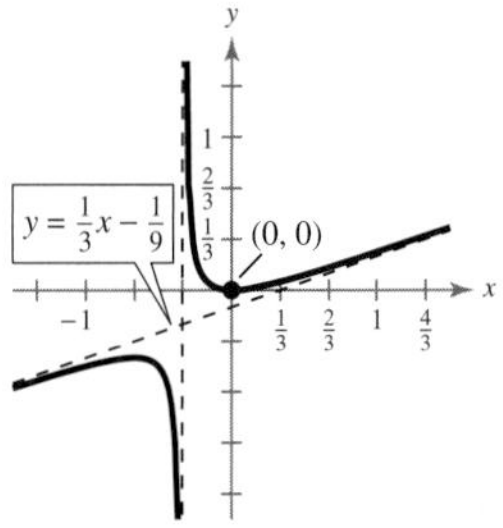

63. (a) Domain: all real numbers x except $x = \pm 2$
(b) Intercept: $(0, 0)$
(c) Vertical asymptotes: $x = \pm 2$
Slant asymptote: $y = x$
(d)

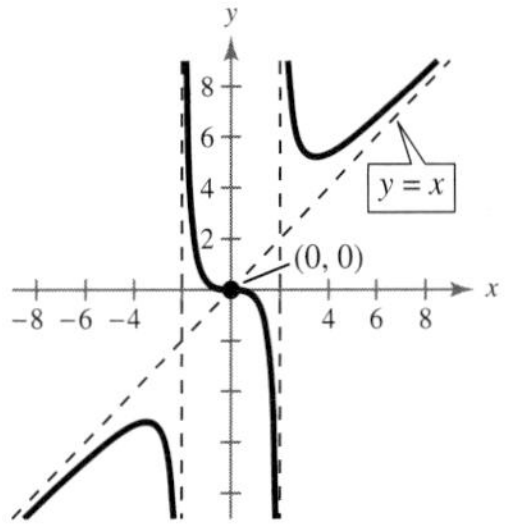

64. (a) Domain: all real numbers x except $x = \pm 2$
(b) Intercept: $(0, 0)$
(c) Vertical asymptotes: $x = \pm 2$
Slant asymptote: $y = \frac{1}{2}x$
(d)

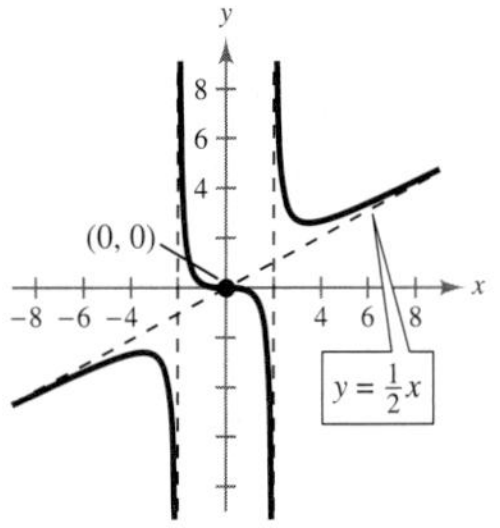

65. (a) Domain: all real numbers x except $x = 1$
(b) y-intercept: $(0, -1)$
(c) Vertical asymptote: $x = 1$
Slant asymptote: $y = x$
(d)

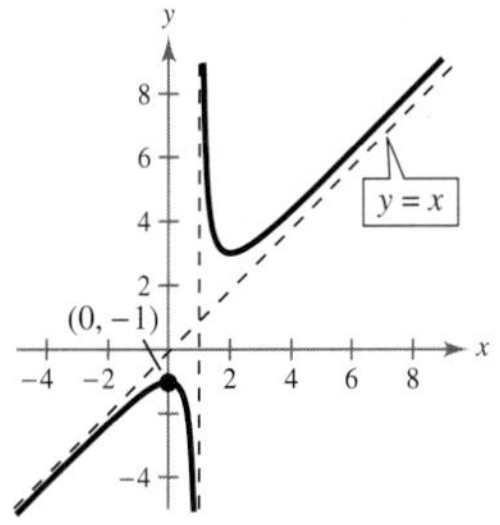

66. (a) Domain: all real numbers x except $x = 2$
(b) y-intercept: $\left(0, -\frac{5}{2}\right)$
(c) Vertical asymptote: $x = 2$
Slant asymptote: $y = 2x - 1$

(d)

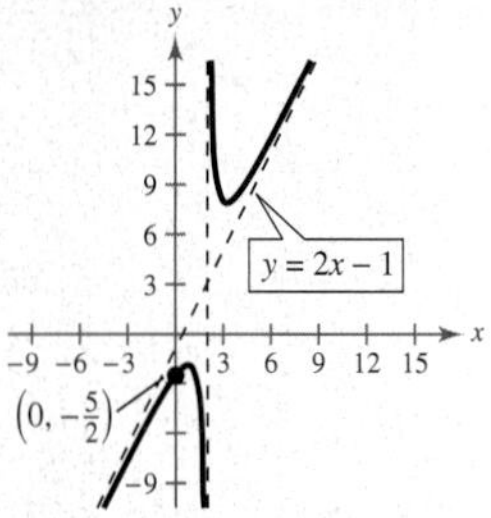

78. (a)

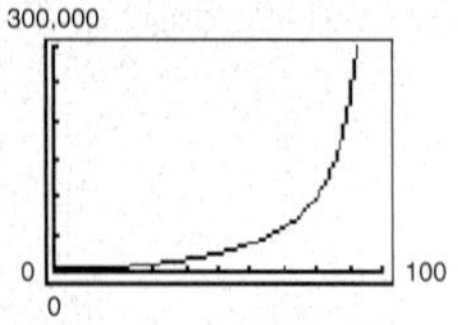

(b) \$4411.76; \$25,000; \$225,000

(c) No. The function is undefined at $p = 100$.

80. (c)

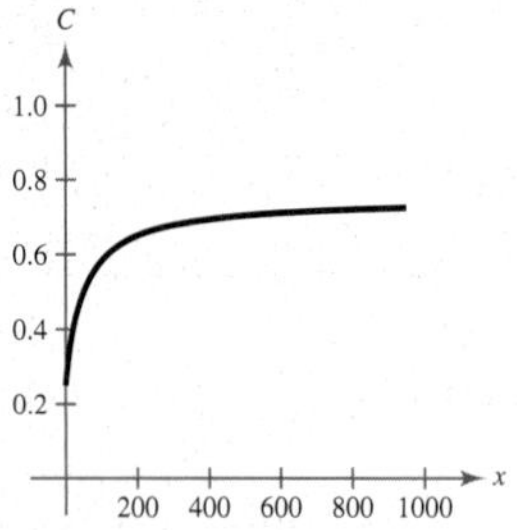

Section 2.7 *(page 201)*

29. $x = \frac{1}{2}$

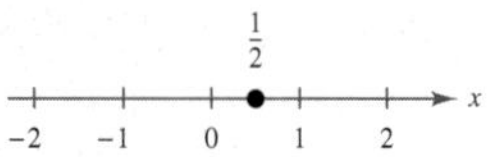

30. All real numbers

31. $(-\infty, 0) \cup \left(0, \frac{3}{2}\right)$ **33.** $[-2, 0] \cup [2, \infty)$

34. $(-\infty, 0] \cup [2, \infty)$

37.

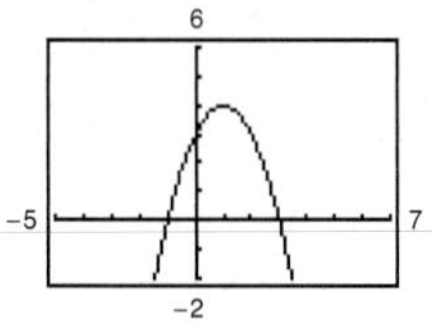

(a) $x \le -1,\ x \ge 3$

(b) $0 \le x \le 2$

38.

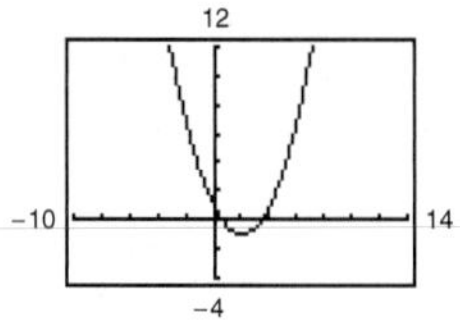

(a) $2 - \sqrt{2} \le x \le 2 + \sqrt{2}$

(b) $x \le -2,\ x \ge 6$

39.

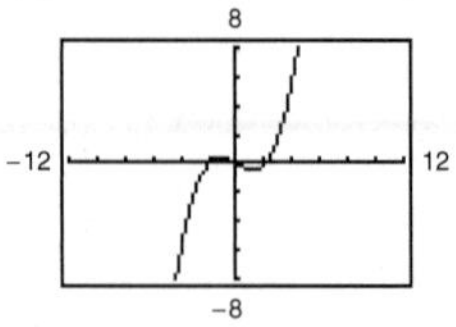

(a) $-2 \le x \le 0,$
$2 \le x < \infty$

(b) $x \le 4$

40.

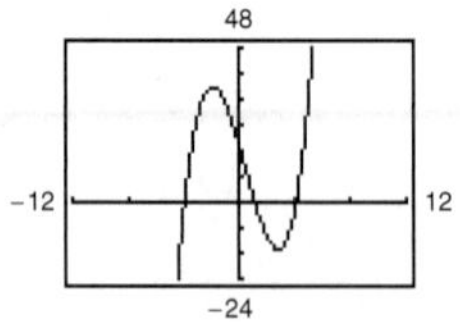

(a) $-\infty < x \le -4,$
$1 \le x \le 4$

(b) $x = -2,\ 5 \le x < \infty$

41. $(-\infty, 0) \cup \left(\frac{1}{4}, \infty\right)$

42. $(-\infty, -1) \cup (0, 1)$

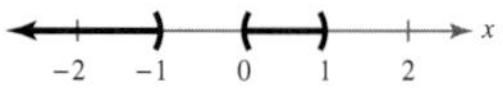

43. $\left(-\infty, \frac{5}{3}\right] \cup (5, \infty)$

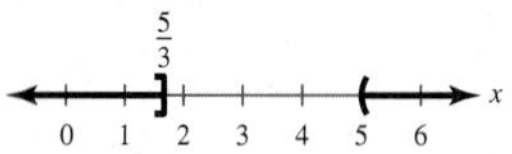

44. $\left(-\infty, -\frac{1}{2}\right) \cup [1, \infty)$

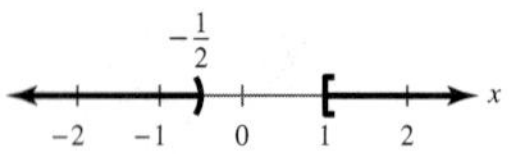

45. $(-\infty, -1) \cup (4, \infty)$

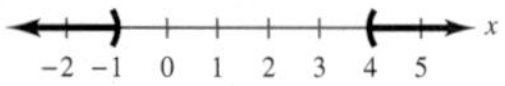

46. $(-2, 3]$

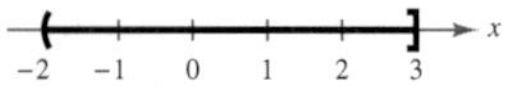

47. $(-5, 3) \cup (11, \infty)$

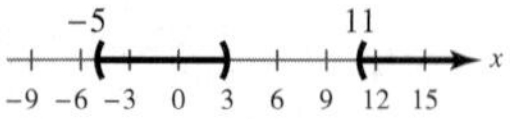

48. $(-14, -2) \cup (6, \infty)$

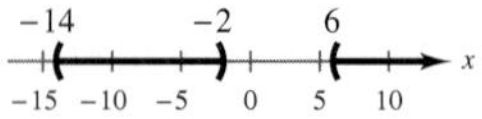

49. $\left(-\frac{3}{4}, 3\right) \cup [6, \infty)$

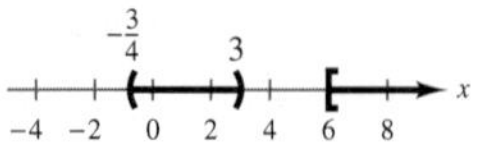

50. $(-\infty, -3) \cup (0, \infty)$

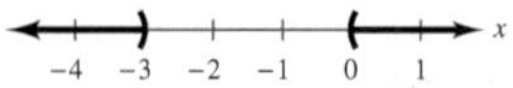

51. $(-3, -2] \cup [0, 3)$

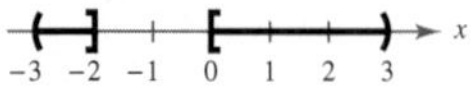

52. $[-3, 0) \cup [2, \infty)$

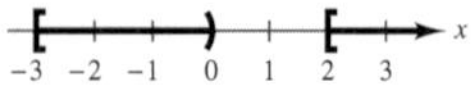

53. $(-\infty, -1) \cup (1, \infty)$

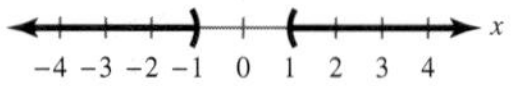

54. $(-\infty, -4) \cup [-2, 1) \cup [6, \infty)$

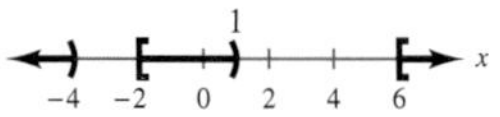

78. (a)

d	4	6	8	10	12
Load	2223.9	5593.9	10,312	16,378	23,792

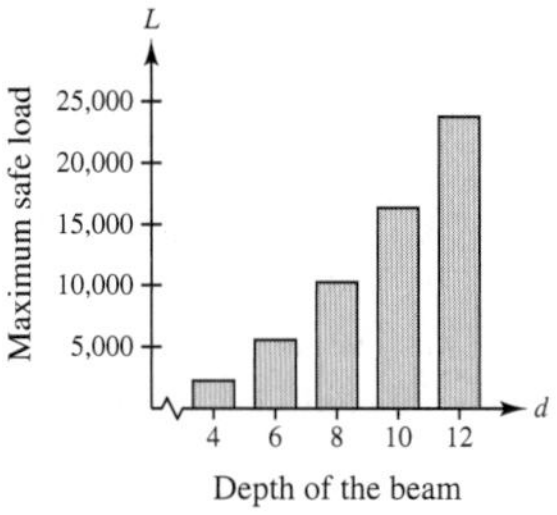

Review Exercises *(page 206)*

3. $g(x) = (x - 1)^2 - 1$

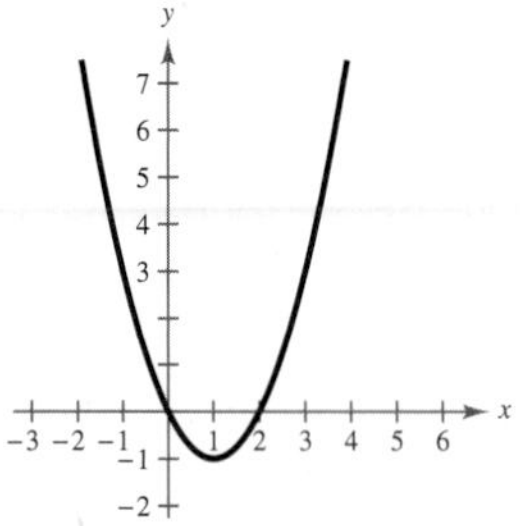

Vertex: $(1, -1)$
Axis of symmetry: $x = 1$
x-intercepts: $(0, 0)$, $(2, 0)$

4. $f(x) = -(x - 3)^2 + 9$

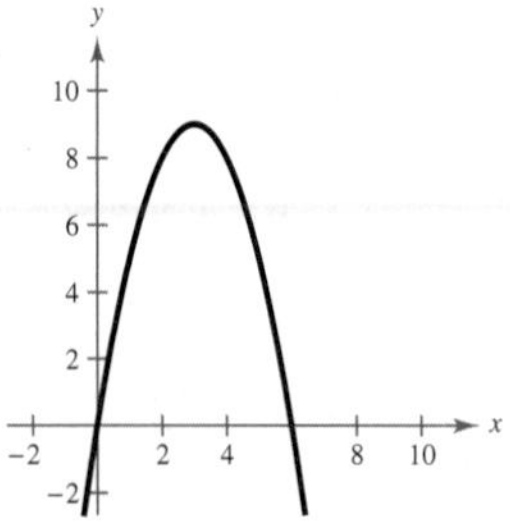

Vertex: $(3, 9)$
Axis of symmetry: $x = 3$
x-intercepts: $(0, 0)$, $(6, 0)$

5. $f(x) = (x + 4)^2 - 6$

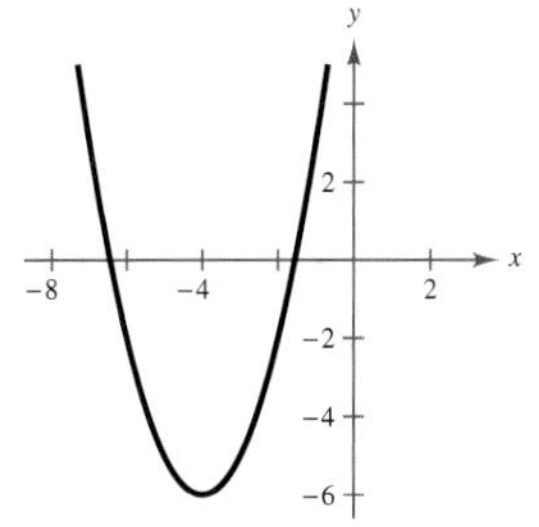

Vertex: $(-4, -6)$
Axis of symmetry: $x = -4$
x-intercepts: $\left(-4 \pm \sqrt{6}, 0\right)$

6. $h(x) = -(x - 2)^2 + 7$

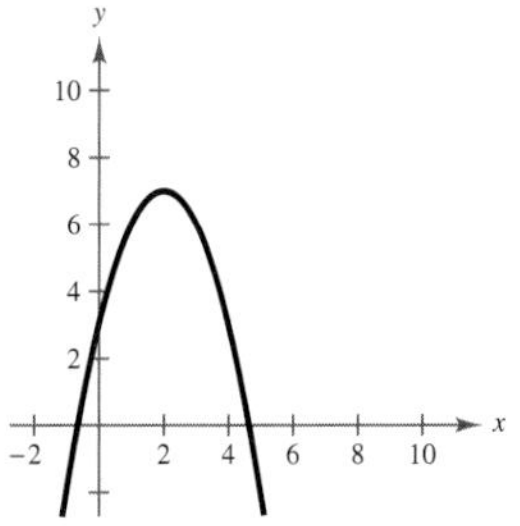

Vertex: $(2, 7)$
Axis of symmetry: $x = 2$
x-intercepts: $\left(2 \pm \sqrt{7}, 0\right)$

7. $f(t) = -2(t - 1)^2 + 3$

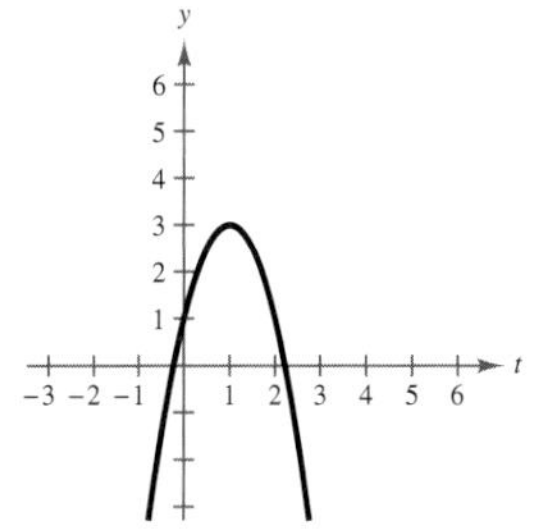

Vertex: $(1, 3)$
Axis of symmetry: $t = 1$
t-intercepts: $\left(1 \pm \dfrac{\sqrt{6}}{2}, 0\right)$

8. $f(x) = (x - 4)^2 - 4$

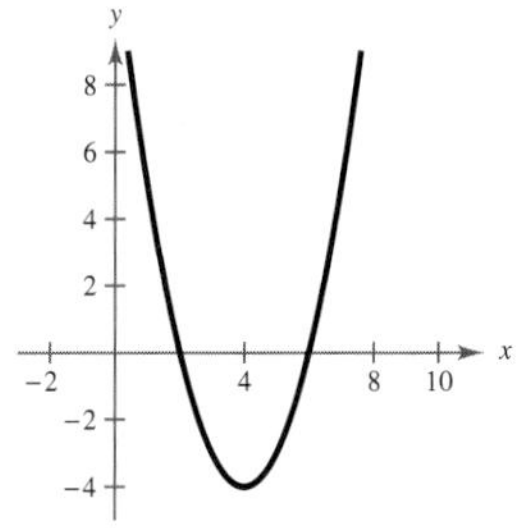

Vertex: $(4, -4)$
Axis of symmetry: $x = 4$
x-intercepts: $(2, 0), (6, 0)$

9. $h(x) = 4\left(x + \frac{1}{2}\right)^2 + 12$

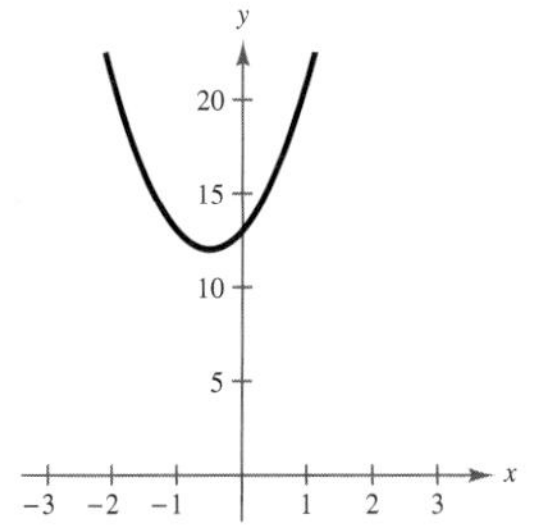

Vertex: $\left(-\frac{1}{2}, 12\right)$
Axis of symmetry: $x = -\frac{1}{2}$
No x-intercept

10. $f(x) = (x - 3)^2 - 8$

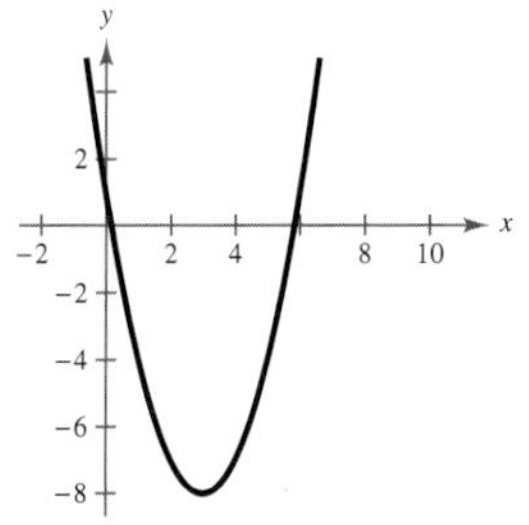

Vertex: $(3, -8)$
Axis of symmetry: $x = 3$
x-intercepts: $\left(3 \pm 2\sqrt{2}, 0\right)$

11. $h(x) = \left(x + \frac{5}{2}\right)^2 - \frac{41}{4}$

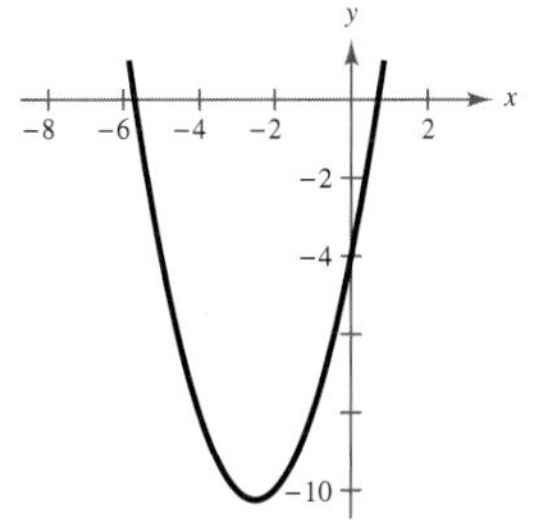

Vertex: $\left(-\frac{5}{2}, -\frac{41}{4}\right)$
Axis of symmetry: $x = -\frac{5}{2}$
x-intercepts: $\left(\dfrac{\pm\sqrt{41} - 5}{2}, 0\right)$

12. $f(x) = 4\left(x + \frac{1}{2}\right)^2 + 4$

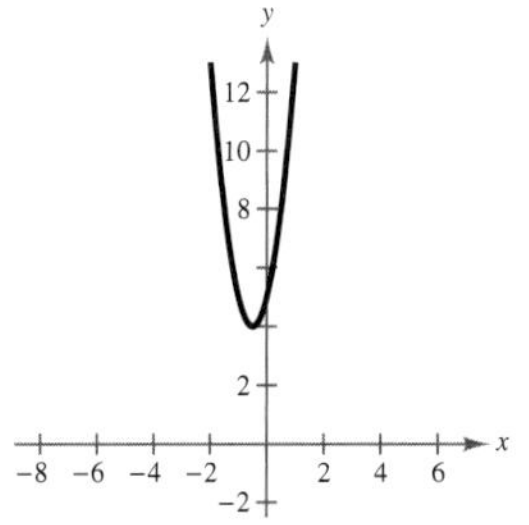

Vertex: $\left(-\frac{1}{2}, 4\right)$
Axis of symmetry: $x = -\frac{1}{2}$
No x-intercept

13. $f(x) = \frac{1}{3}\left(x + \frac{5}{2}\right)^2 - \frac{41}{12}$

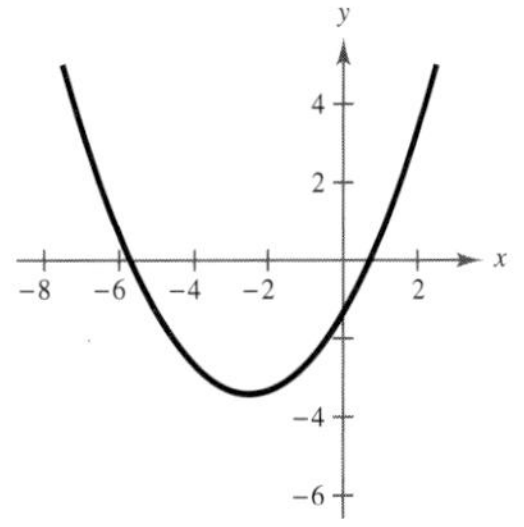

Vertex: $\left(-\frac{5}{2}, -\frac{41}{12}\right)$
Axis of symmetry: $x = -\frac{5}{2}$
x-intercepts: $\left(\dfrac{\pm\sqrt{41} - 5}{2}, 0\right)$

14. $f(x) = 3(x - 2)^2 - 1$

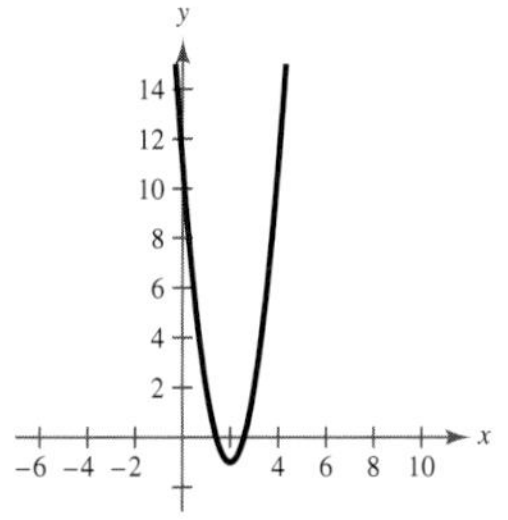

Vertex: $(2, -1)$
Axis of symmetry: $x = 2$
x-intercepts: $\left(2 \pm \dfrac{\sqrt{3}}{3}, 0\right)$

15. $f(x) = -\frac{1}{2}(x - 4)^2 + 1$

21. (a)

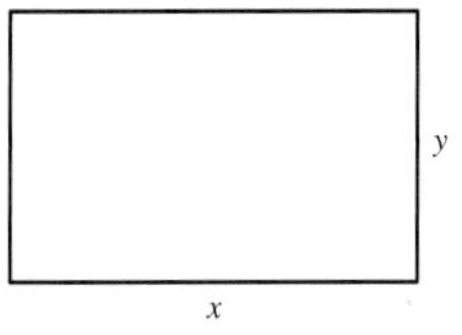

(b) $y = 500 - x$
$A(x) = 500x - x^2$

22. (b) Maximum revenue at \$40; \$16,000; Any price greater or less than \$40 per unit will not yield as much revenue.

24.

About 24 years old

25.

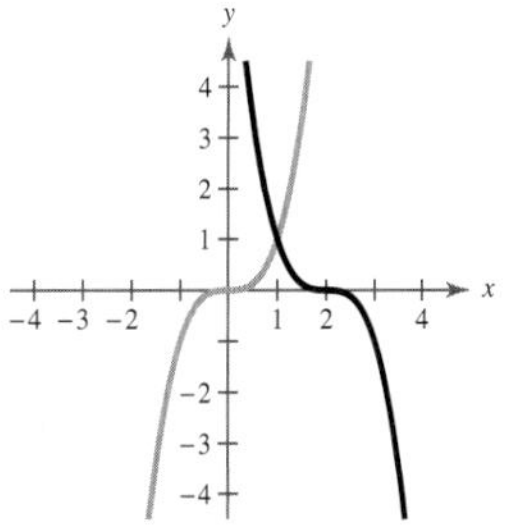

26.

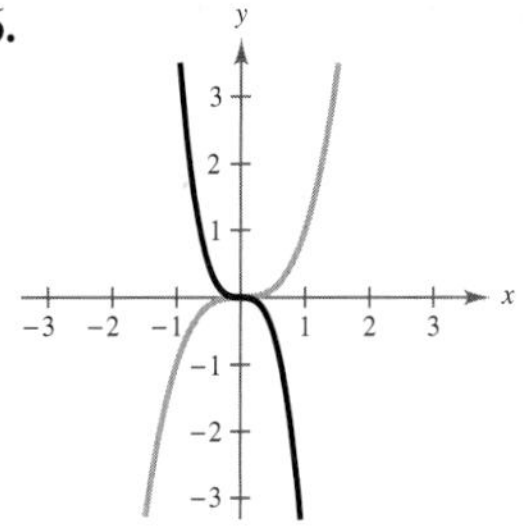

27.

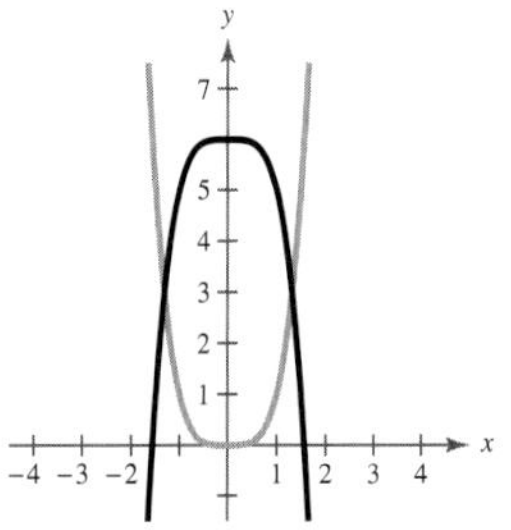

28.

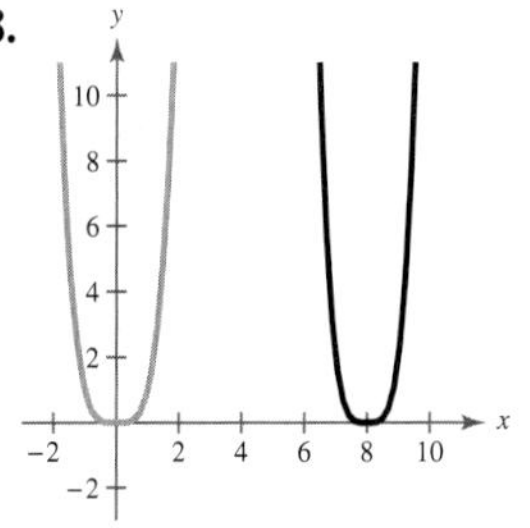

29.

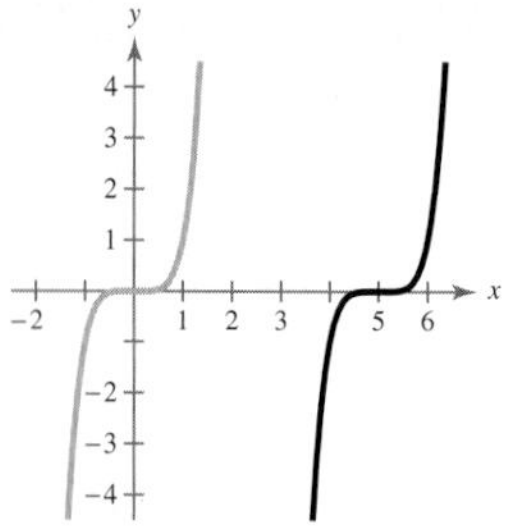

30.

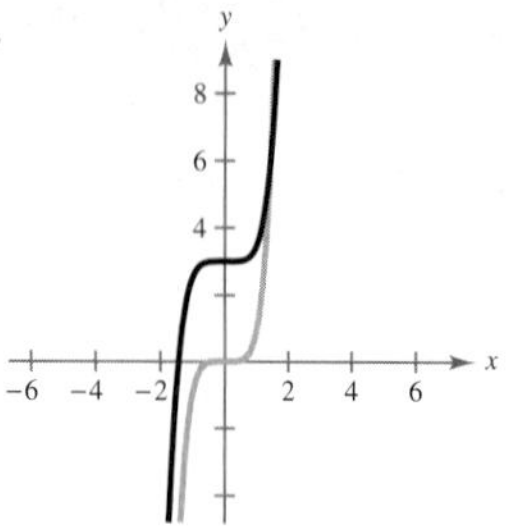

56. $0.1x^2 + 0.8x + 4 + \dfrac{19.5}{x - 5}$

63. (a) Answers will vary.
(b) $(x + 7), (x + 1)$
(c) $f(x) = (x + 7)(x + 1)(x - 4)$
(d) $-7, -1, 4$
(e)

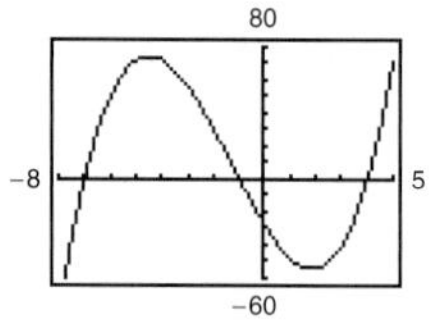

64. (a) Answers will vary. (b) $(2x + 5), (x - 3)$
(c) $f(x) = (2x + 5)(x - 3)(x + 6)$ (d) $-\frac{5}{2}, 3, -6$
(e)

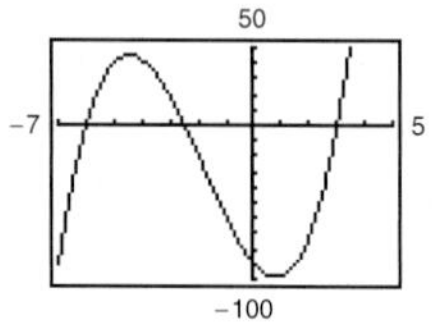

65. (a) Answers will vary. (b) $(x + 1), (x - 4)$
(c) $f(x) = (x + 1)(x - 4)(x + 2)(x - 3)$
(d) $-2, -1, 3, 4$
(e)

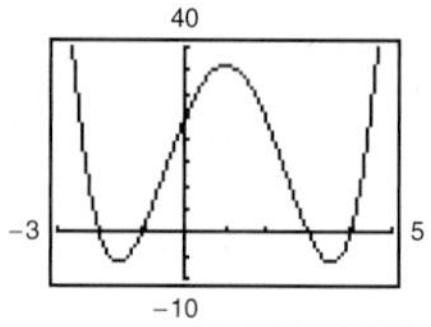

66. (a) Answers will vary. (b) $(x - 1), (x - 3)$
(c) $f(x) = (x - 1)(x - 3)(x - 2)(x - 5)$ (d) 1, 2, 3, 5
(e)

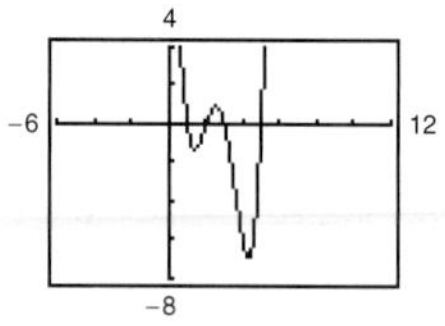

108. $-2, 3, 6$; $g(x) = (x + 2)(x - 3)(x - 6)$

109. $-4, 2 \pm 3i$; $g(x) = (x + 4)^2(x - 2 - 3i)(x - 2 + 3i)$

110. $\pm 3, -4 \pm i$;
$f(x) = (x - 3)(x + 3)(x + 4 - i)(x + 4 + i)$

126. (d)

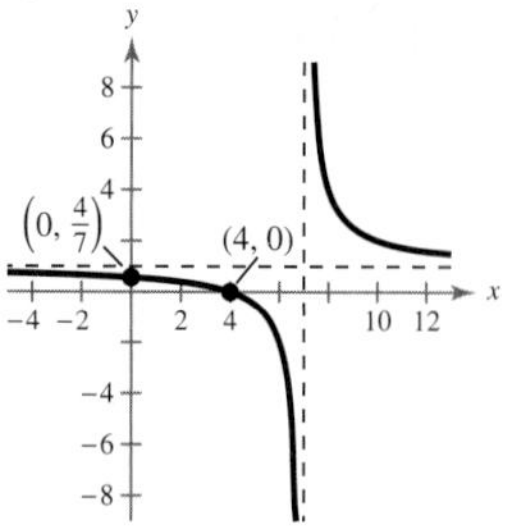

127. (a) Domain: all real numbers x
(b) Intercept: (0, 0)
(c) Horizontal asymptote: $y = \frac{5}{4}$
(d)

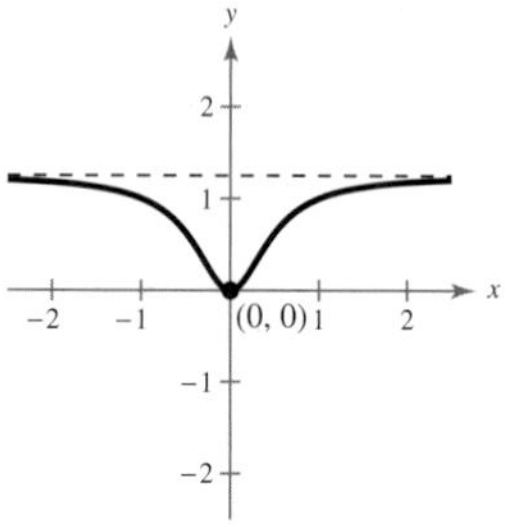

128. (a) Domain: all real numbers x
(b) Intercept: (0, 0)
(c) Horizontal asymptote: $y = 0$
(d)

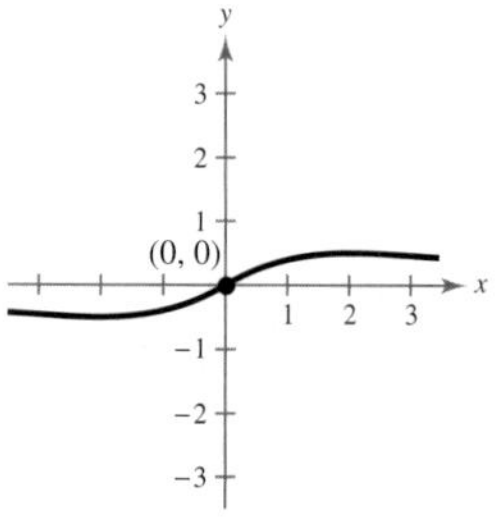

129. (a) Domain: all real numbers x
(b) Intercept: (0, 0)
(c) Horizontal asymptote: $y = 0$
(d)

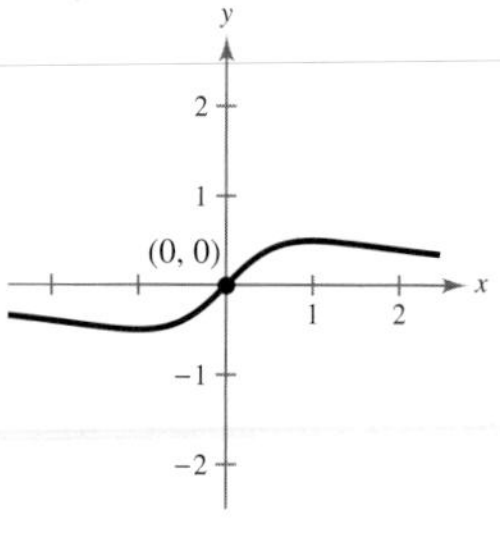

130. (a) Domain: all real numbers x except $x = 3$
(b) y-intercept: (0, 1)
(c) Vertical asymptote: $x = 3$
Horizontal asymptote: $y = 0$
(d)

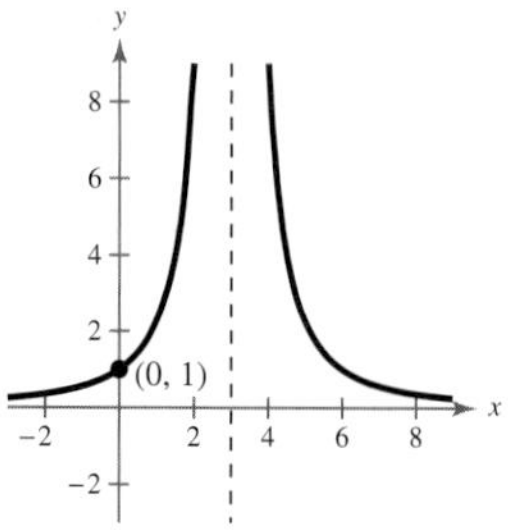

137. (a) Domain: all real numbers x except $x = \frac{4}{3}, -1$
(b) y-intercept: $\left(0, -\frac{1}{2}\right)$
x-intercepts: $\left(\frac{2}{3}, 0\right)$, $(1, 0)$
(c) Vertical asymptote: $x = \frac{4}{3}$
Slant asymptote: $y = x - \frac{1}{3}$
(d)
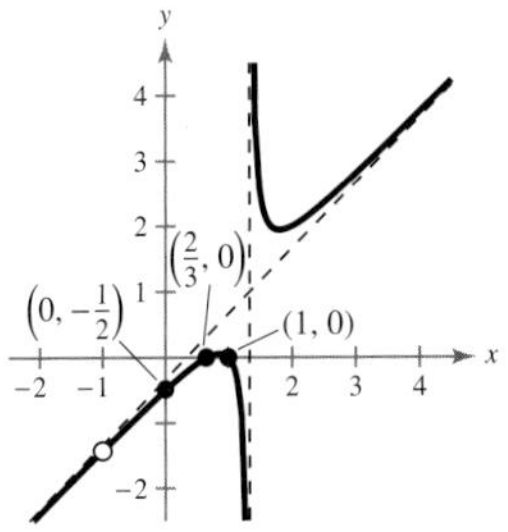

138. (a) Domain: all real numbers x except $x = \frac{1}{3}, -2$
(b) x-intercepts: $(2, 0)$, $\left(\frac{4}{3}, 0\right)$
y-intercept: $(0, -8)$
(c) Vertical asymptote: $x = \frac{1}{3}$
Slant asymptote: $y = x - 3$
(d)
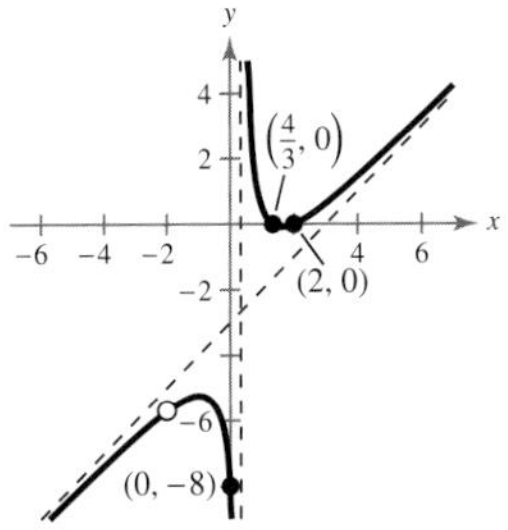

140. (a)
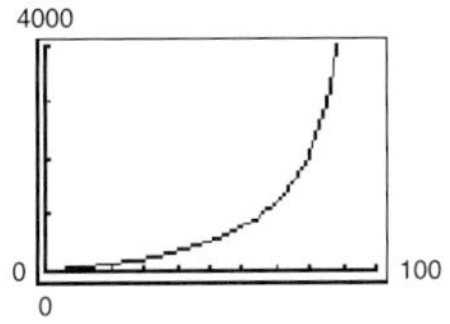

(b) \$176 million; \$528 million; \$1584 million (or \$1.584 billion)
(c) No

141. (a)
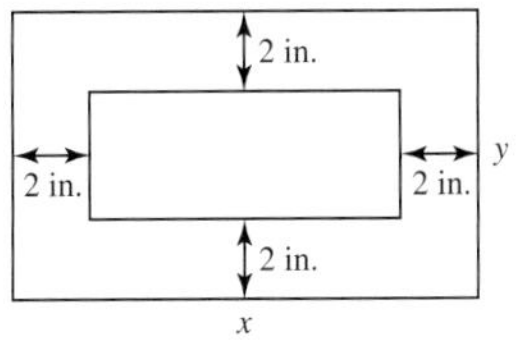

(b) $A = \dfrac{2x(2x + 7)}{x - 4}$ (c) $4 < x < \infty$
(d)
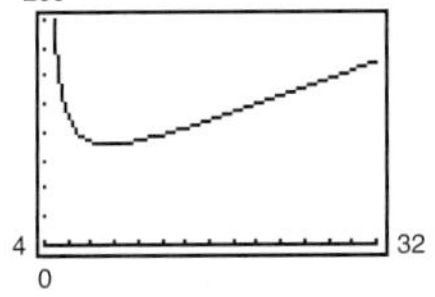

9.48 in. × 9.48 in.

142.
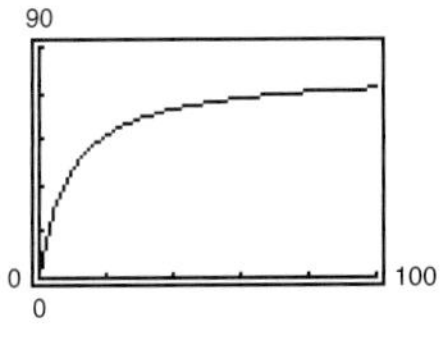

80.3 mg/dm²/h

144. $(-\infty, -3] \cup \left[\frac{8}{3}, \infty\right)$
145. $[-4, 0] \cup [4, \infty)$ **146.** $(-\infty, 0) \cup \left(0, \frac{5}{3}\right)$
147. $[-5, -1) \cup (1, \infty)$ **148.** $(-\infty, 3) \cup (5, \infty)$
153. False. A fourth-degree polynomial can have at most four zeros, and complex zeros occur in conjugate pairs.
154. False. The domain of $f(x) = \dfrac{1}{x^2 + 1}$ is the set of all real numbers.
155. Find the vertex of the quadratic function and write the function in standard form. If the leading coefficient is positive, the vertex is a minimum. If the leading coefficient is negative, the vertex is a maximum.
156. Answers will vary. Sample answer:
A polynomial of degree $n > 0$ with real coefficients can be written as the product of linear and quadratic factors with real coefficients, where the quadratic factors have no real zeros. By setting the factors equal to zero and solving for the variable, you can find the zeros of a polynomial function. To solve an equation is to find all the values of the variable(s) for which the equation is true.
157. An asymptote of a graph is a line to which the graph becomes arbitrarily close as x increases or decreases without bound.

Problem Solving *(page 213)*

9. $(a + bi)(a - bi) = a^2 + abi - abi - b^2i^2$
$= a^2 + b^2$

Chapter 3

Section 3.1 *(page 224)*

17.

x	-2	-1	0	1	2
$f(x)$	4	2	1	0.5	0.25

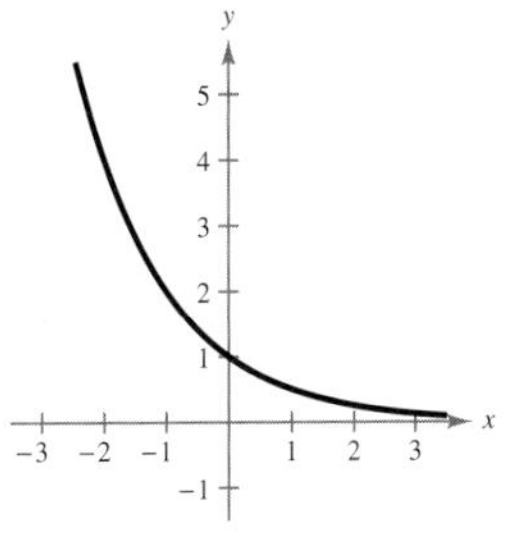

18.

x	-2	-1	0	1	2
$f(x)$	0.25	0.5	1	2	4

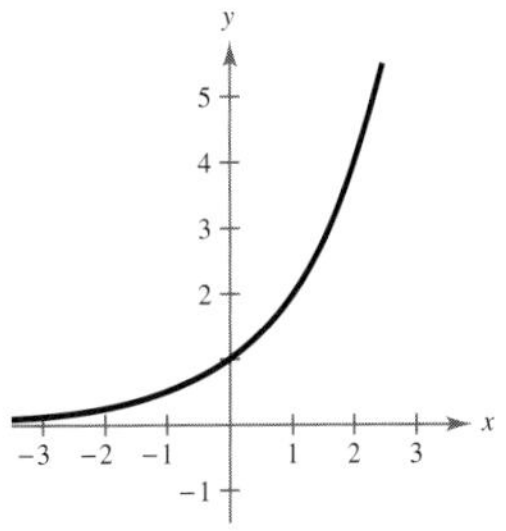

19.

x	-2	-1	0	1	2
$f(x)$	36	6	1	0.167	0.028

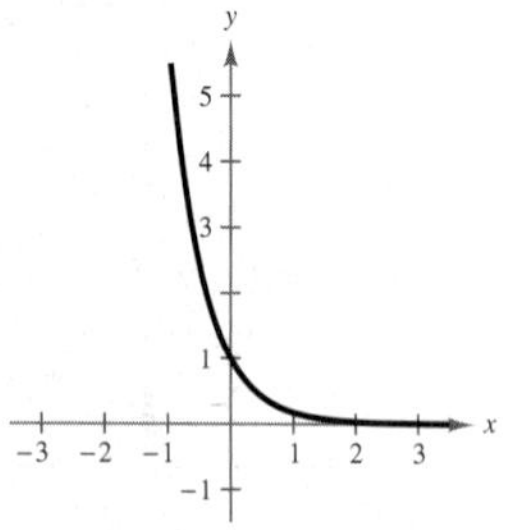

20.

x	-2	-1	0	1	2
$f(x)$	0.028	0.167	1	6	36

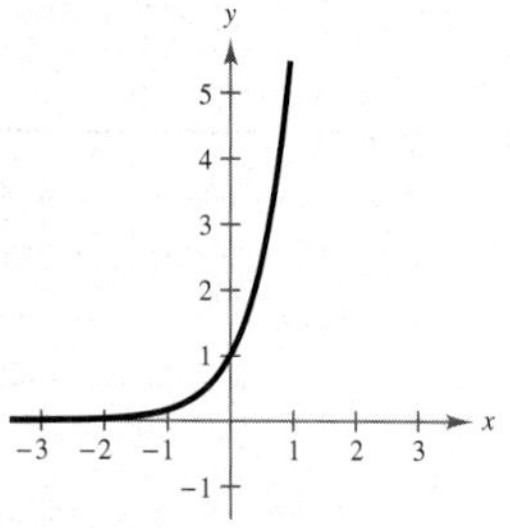

21.

x	-2	-1	0	1	2
$f(x)$	0.125	0.25	0.5	1	2

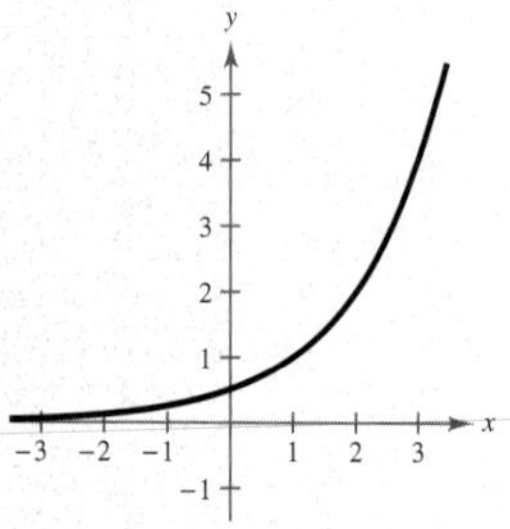

22.

x	-1	0	1	2	3
$f(x)$	3.004	3.016	3.063	3.25	4

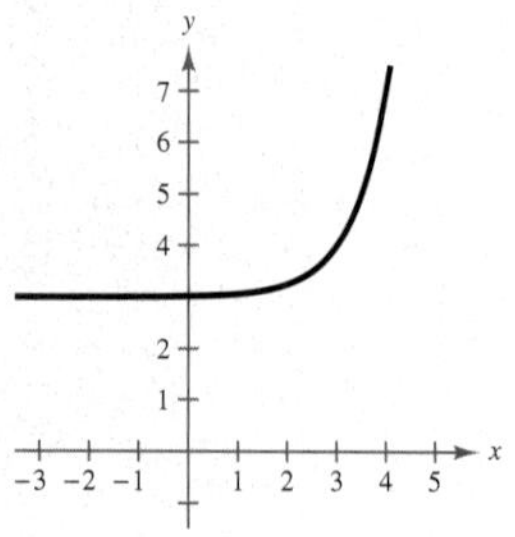

39.

x	-2	-1	0	1	2
$f(x)$	0.135	0.368	1	2.718	7.389

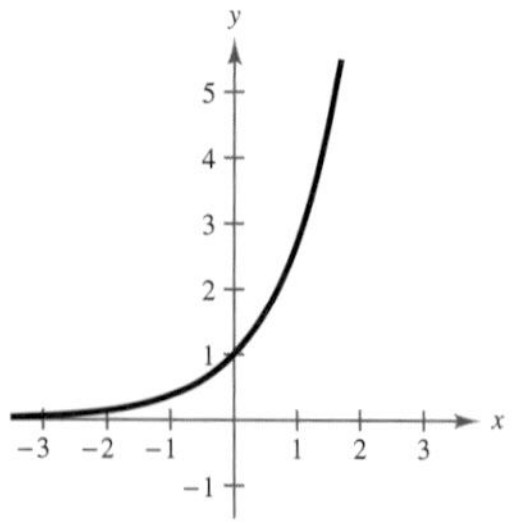

40.

x	-2	-1	0	1	2
$f(x)$	7.389	2.718	1	0.368	0.135

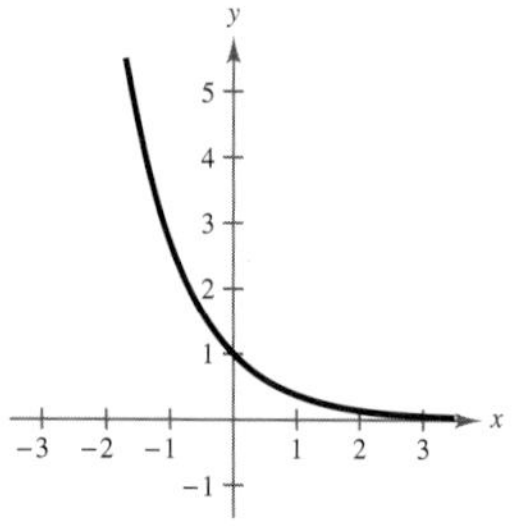

41.

x	-8	-7	-6	-5	-4
$f(x)$	0.055	0.149	0.406	1.104	3

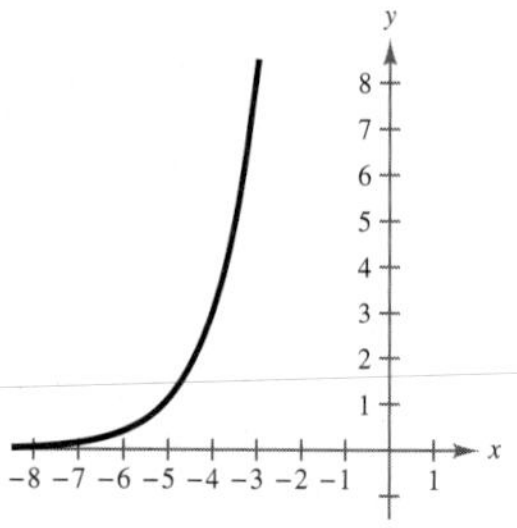

42.

x	-2	-1	0	1	2
$f(x)$	5.437	3.297	2	1.213	0.736

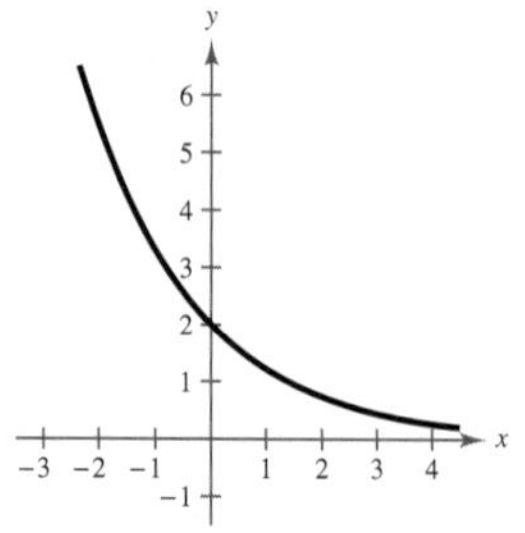

43.

x	-2	-1	0	1	2
$f(x)$	4.037	4.100	4.271	4.736	6

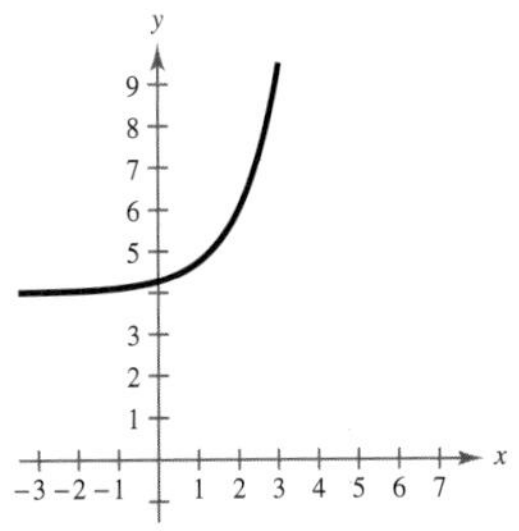

44.

x	0	2	4	5	6
$f(x)$	2.007	2.050	2.368	3	4.718

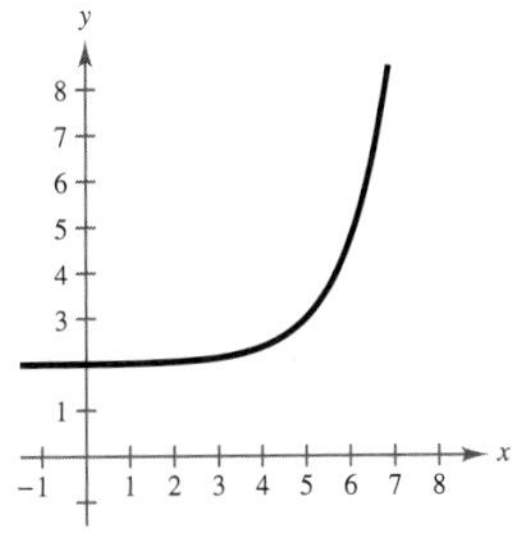

59.

n	1	2	4	12
A	\$1828.49	\$1830.29	\$1831.19	\$1831.80

n	365	Continuous
A	\$1832.09	\$1832.10

60.

n	1	2	4	12
A	\$3526.50	\$3536.95	\$3542.27	\$3545.86

n	365	Continuous
A	\$3547.61	\$3547.67

61.

n	1	2	4	12
A	\$5477.81	\$5520.10	\$5541.79	\$5556.46

n	365	Continuous
A	\$5563.61	\$5563.85

62.

n	1	2	4
A	\$10,285.72	\$10,640.89	\$10,828.46

n	12	365	Continuous
A	\$10,957.45	\$11,021.00	\$11,023.18

63.

t	10	20	30
A	\$17,901.90	\$26,706.49	\$39,841.40

t	40	50
A	\$59,436.39	\$88,668.67

64.

t	10	20	30
A	\$21,865.43	\$39,841.40	\$72,595.77

t	40	50
A	\$132,278.12	\$241,026.44

65.

t	10	20	30
A	\$22,986.49	\$44,031.56	\$84,344.25

t	40	50
A	\$161,564.86	\$309,484.08

66.

t	10	20	30
A	\$17,028.81	\$24,165.03	\$34,291.81

t	40	50
A	\$48,662.40	\$69,055.23

71. (b)

t	15	16	17	18	19	20
P (in millions)	40.19	40.59	40.99	41.39	41.80	42.21

t	21	22	23	24	25	26
P (in millions)	42.62	43.04	43.47	43.90	44.33	44.77

t	27	28	29	30
P (in millions)	45.21	45.65	46.10	46.56

Section 3.2 *(page 234)*

41.

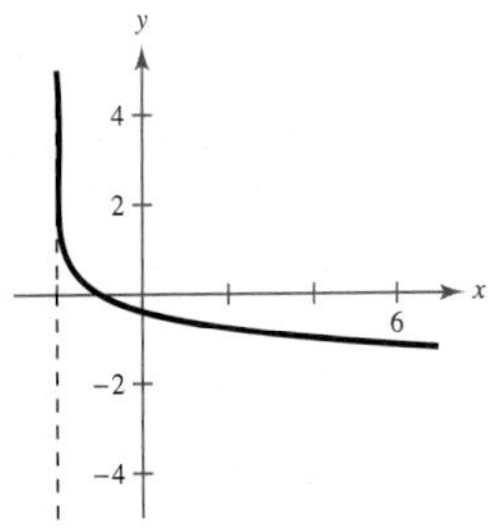

Domain: $(-2, \infty)$
x-intercept: $(-1, 0)$
Vertical asymptote: $x = -2$

42. 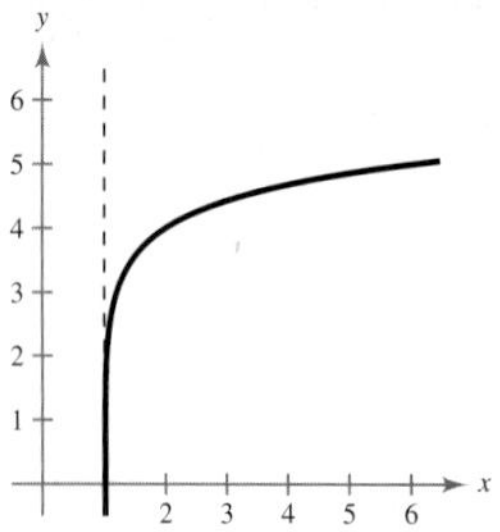

Domain: $(1, \infty)$
x-intercept: $\left(\frac{626}{625}, 0\right)$
Vertical asymptote: $x = 1$

43. 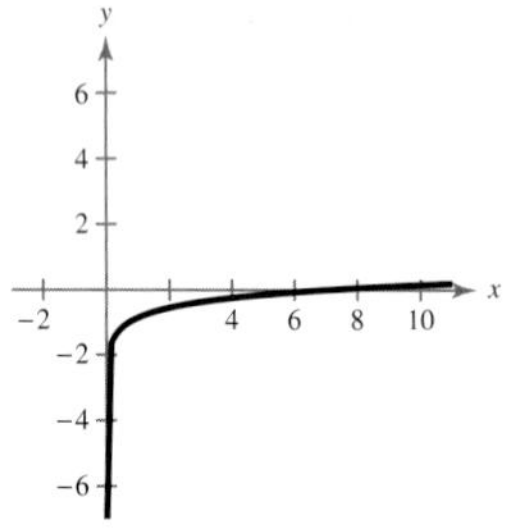

Domain: $(0, \infty)$
x-intercept: $(7, 0)$
Vertical asymptote: $x = 0$

44. 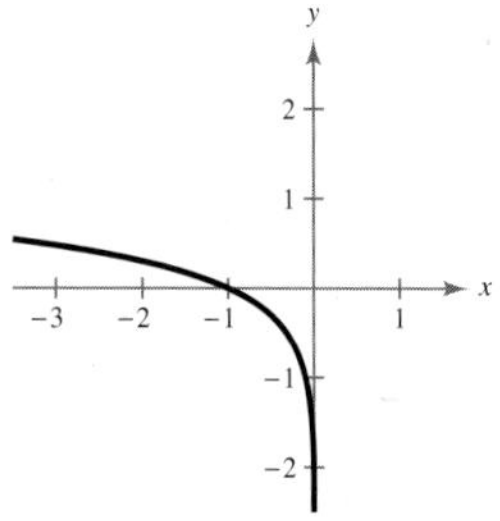

Domain: $(-\infty, 0)$
x-intercept: $(-1, 0)$
Vertical asymptote: $x = 0$

75. 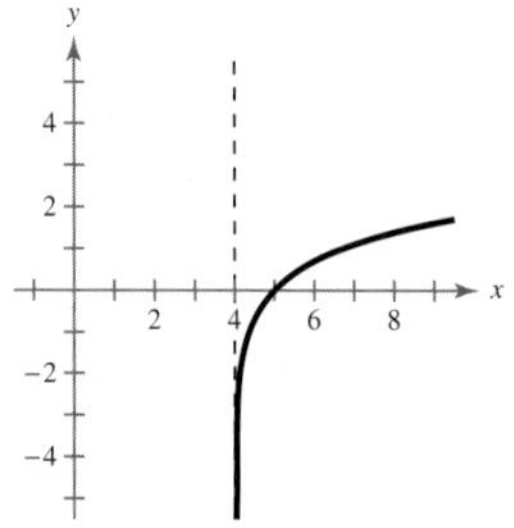

Domain: $(4, \infty)$
x-intercept: $(5, 0)$
Vertical asymptote: $x = 4$

76. 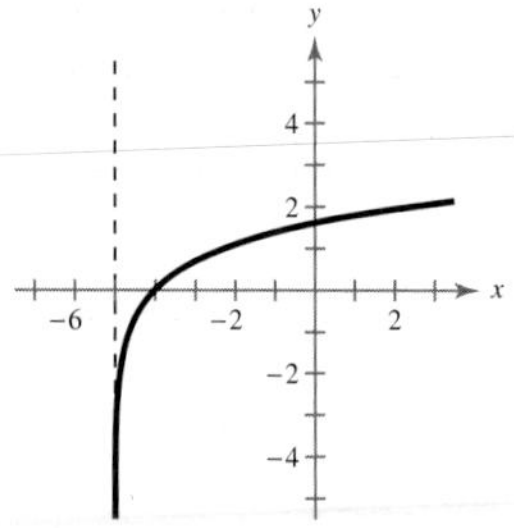

Domain: $(-5, \infty)$
x-intercept: $(-4, 0)$
Vertical asymptote: $x = -5$

77. 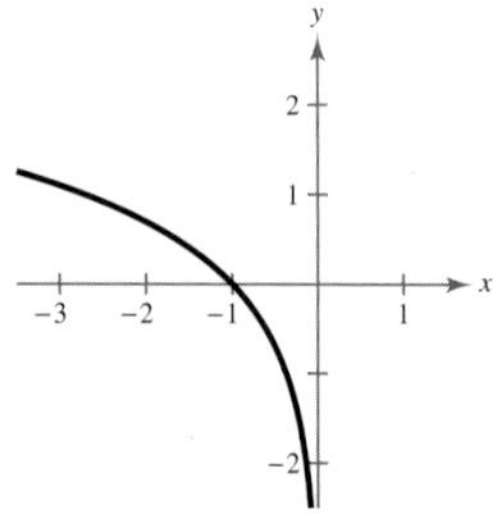

Domain: $(-\infty, 0)$
x-intercept: $(-1, 0)$
Vertical asymptote: $x = 0$

78. 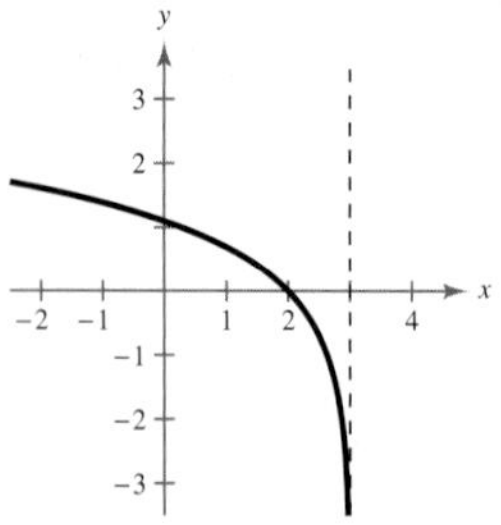

Domain: $(-\infty, 3)$
x-intercept: $(2, 0)$
Vertical asymptote: $x = 3$

95. (a)

t	1	2	3	4	5	6
C	10.36	9.94	9.37	8.70	7.96	7.15

(b) 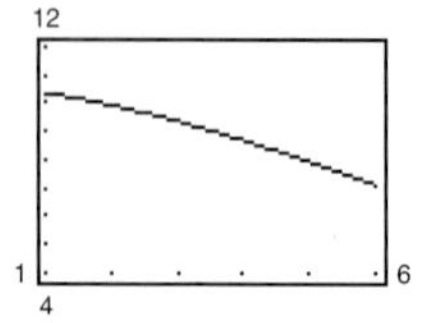

(c) No, the model begins to decrease rapidly, eventually producing negative values.

96. (a)

r	0.005	0.010	0.015	0.020	0.025	0.030
t	138.6	69.3	46.2	34.7	27.7	23.1

As the rate of increase r increases, the time t in years for the population to double decreases.

105.

x	-2	-1	0	1	2
$f(x) = 10^x$	$\frac{1}{100}$	$\frac{1}{10}$	1	10	100

x	$\frac{1}{100}$	$\frac{1}{10}$	1	10	100
$f(x) = \log x$	-2	-1	0	1	2

The domain of $f(x) = 10^x$ is equal to the range of $f(x) = \log x$ and vice versa. $f(x) = 10^x$ and $f(x) = \log x$ are inverses of each other.

106. (a) 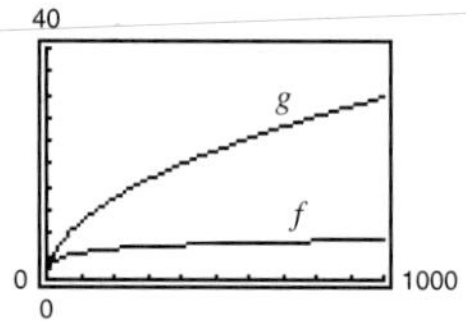

$g(x)$; The natural log function grows at a slower rate than the square root function.

(b) 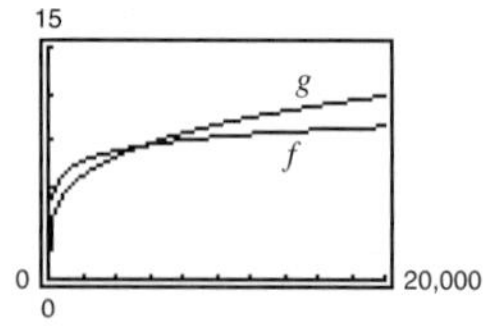

$g(x)$; The natural log function grows at a slower rate than the fourth root function.

107. (a)

x	1	5	10	10^2
$f(x)$	0	0.322	0.230	0.046

x	10^4	10^6
$f(x)$	0.00092	0.0000138

(b) 0

(c)

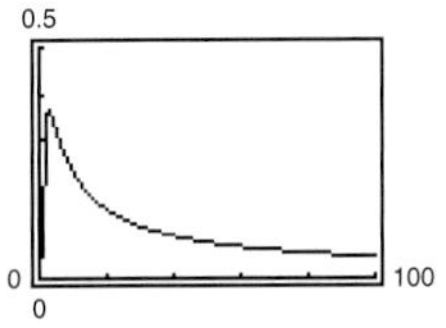

108. (a) False (b) True (c) True (d) False

110. (a)

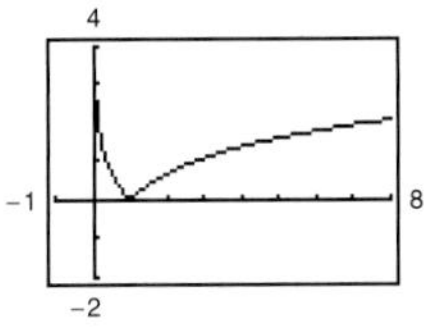

(b) Increasing: $(1, \infty)$
Decreasing: $(0, 1)$
(c) Relative minimum: $(1, 0)$

111. (a)

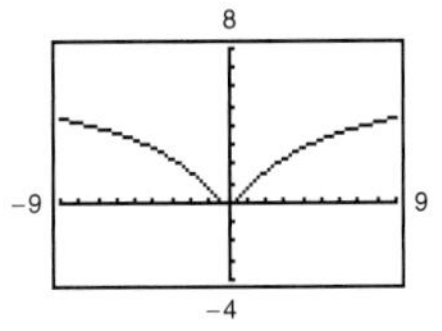

(b) Increasing: $(0, \infty)$
Decreasing: $(-\infty, 0)$
(c) Relative minimum: $(0, 0)$

Section 3.3 *(page 241)*

100. Sample answers:

(a) $\ln(1 + 3) \stackrel{?}{=} \ln(1) + \ln(3)$

$1.39 \neq 0 + 1.10$

$\ln u + \ln v = \ln(uv)$, but $\ln(u + v) \neq \ln u + \ln v$

(b) $\ln(3 - 1) \stackrel{?}{=} \ln(3) - \ln(1)$

$0.69 \neq 1.10 - 0$

$\ln u - \ln v = \ln \frac{u}{v}$, but $\ln(u - v) \neq \ln u - \ln v$

(c) $(\ln 2)^3 \stackrel{?}{=} 3 \ln 2$

$0.33 \neq 2.08$

$n(\ln u) = \ln u^n$, but $(\ln u)^n \neq n(\ln u)$

113. $f(x) = h(x)$; Property 2

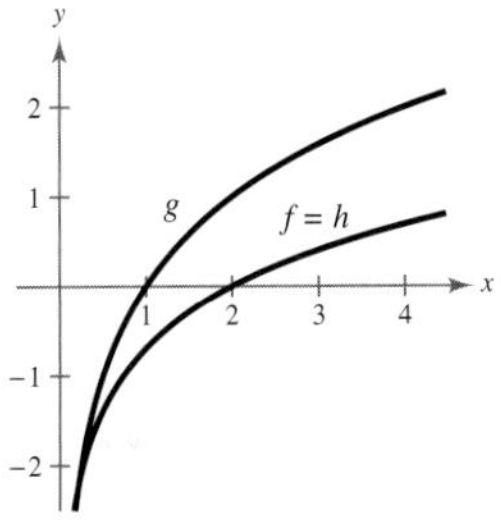

114.

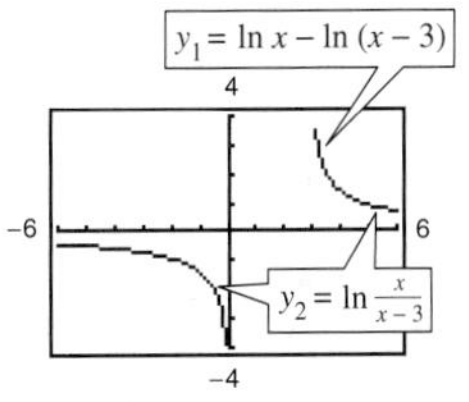

No; the domain of the first graph is $(3, \infty)$ and the domain of the second graph is $(-\infty, 0) \cup (3, \infty)$.

115.

$\ln 1 = 0$	$\ln 9 \approx 2.1972$
$\ln 2 \approx 0.6931$	$\ln 10 \approx 2.3025$
$\ln 3 \approx 1.0986$	$\ln 12 \approx 2.4848$
$\ln 4 \approx 1.3862$	$\ln 15 \approx 2.7080$
$\ln 5 \approx 1.6094$	$\ln 16 \approx 2.7724$
$\ln 6 \approx 1.7917$	$\ln 18 \approx 2.8903$
$\ln 8 \approx 2.0793$	$\ln 20 \approx 2.9956$

Section 3.4 *(page 251)*

77.

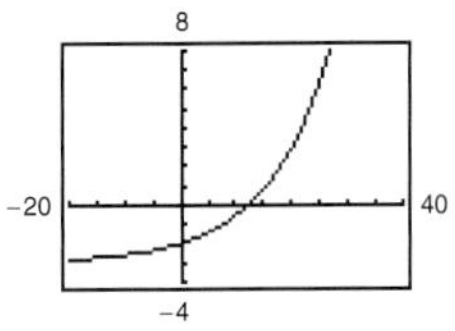

12.207

78.

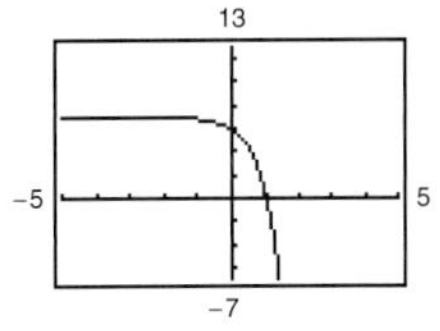

1.081

79.

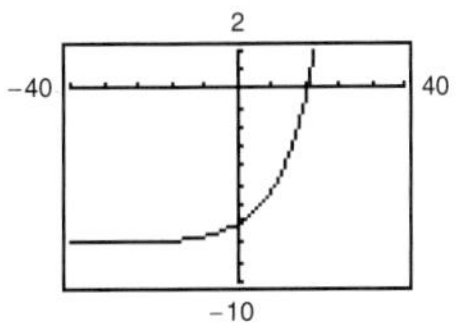

16.636

80.

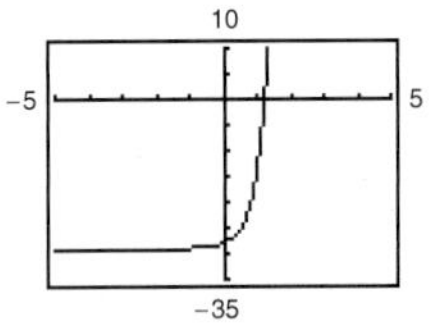

1.236

81. $e^{-3} \approx 0.050$ **82.** $e^{1.6} \approx 4.953$ **83.** $e^7 \approx 1096.633$

84. $e^{-1} \approx 0.368$ **85.** $\frac{e^{2.4}}{2} \approx 5.512$ **86.** $\frac{e^{2.1}}{6} \approx 1.361$

87. 1,000,000 **88.** $\frac{100}{3} \approx 33.333$ **89.** $\frac{e^{10/3}}{5} \approx 5.606$

90. $e^{7/2} \approx 33.115$ **91.** $e^2 - 2 \approx 5.389$

92. $e^{10} + 8 = 22{,}034.466$

95. $\frac{e^{19/2}}{3} \approx 4453.242$ **100.** $\frac{-1 + \sqrt{1 + 4e}}{2} \approx 1.223$

102. $\frac{-3 + \sqrt{9 + 4e}}{2} \approx 0.729$ **104.** $\frac{3 + \sqrt{13}}{2} \approx 3.303$

107. $\frac{-1 + \sqrt{17}}{2} \approx 1.562$ **111.** $\frac{725 + 125\sqrt{33}}{8} \approx 180.384$

112. $\frac{1225 + 125\sqrt{73}}{2} \approx 1146.500$

113.

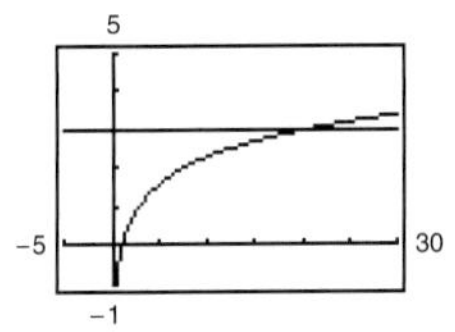

20.086

114.

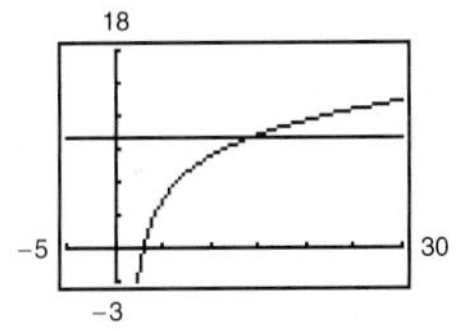

14.182

115.

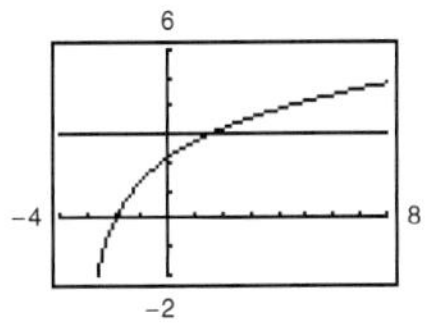

1.482

116.

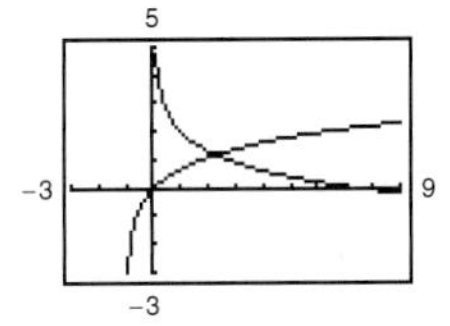

2.264

117. (a) 13.86 yr (b) 21.97 yr

118. (a) 15.40 yr (b) 24.41 yr

Review Exercises (page 270)

15.

x	-1	0	1	2	3
$f(x)$	8	5	4.25	4.063	4.016

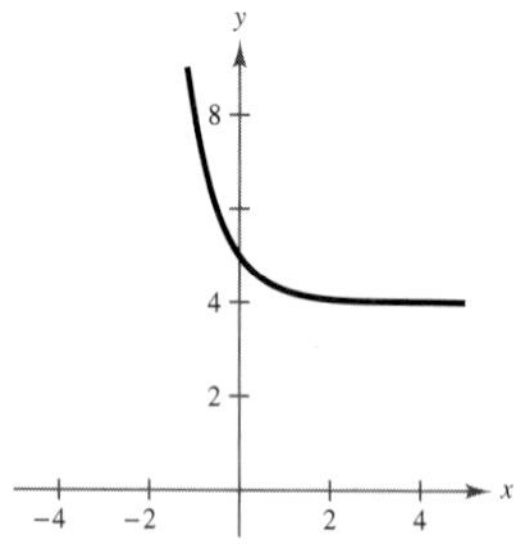

16.

x	-3	-1	0	1	3
$f(x)$	0.020	0.142	0.377	1	7.023

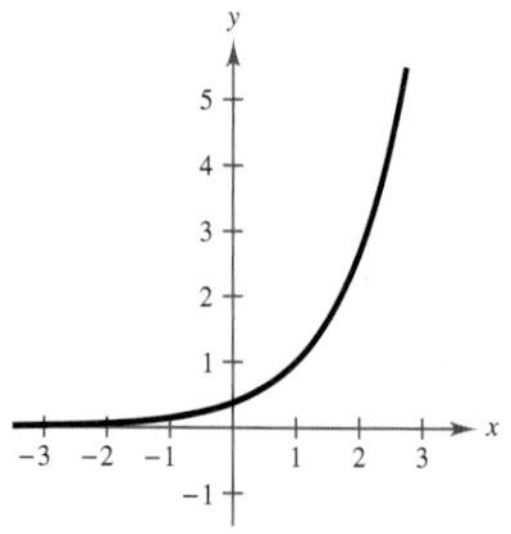

17.

x	-1	0	1	2	3
$f(x)$	4.008	4.04	4.2	5	9

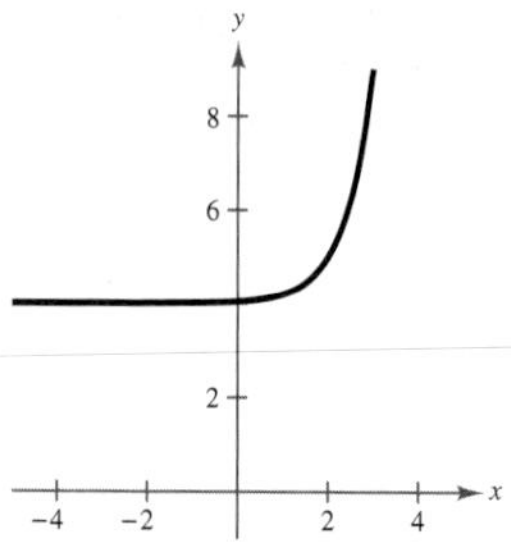

18.

x	0	5	6	7	8	9
$f(x)$	-4.984	-4.5	-4	-3	-1	3

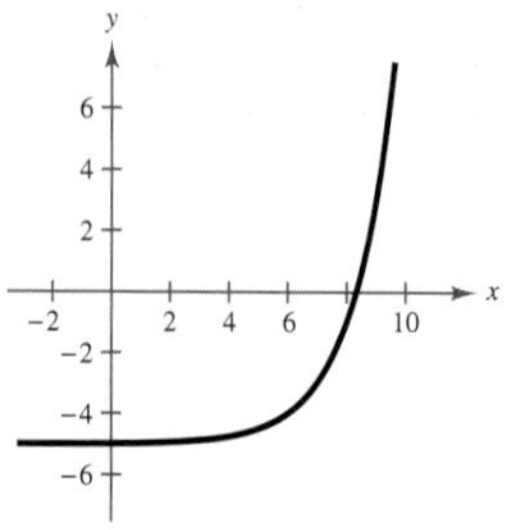

19.

x	-2	-1	0	1	2
$f(x)$	3.25	3.5	4	5	7

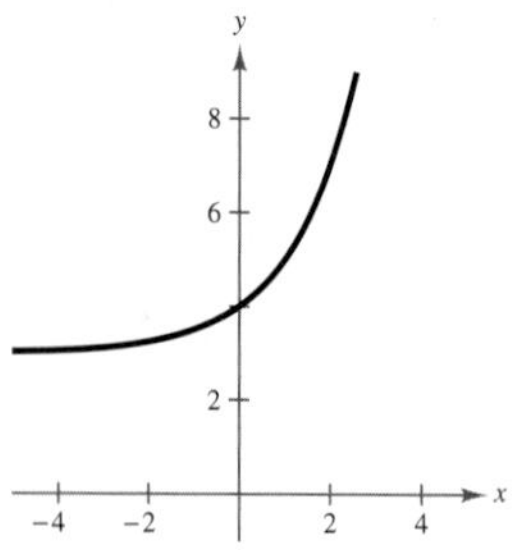

20.

x	-3	-2	-1	0	2
$f(x)$	3	-4	-4.875	-4.984	-5

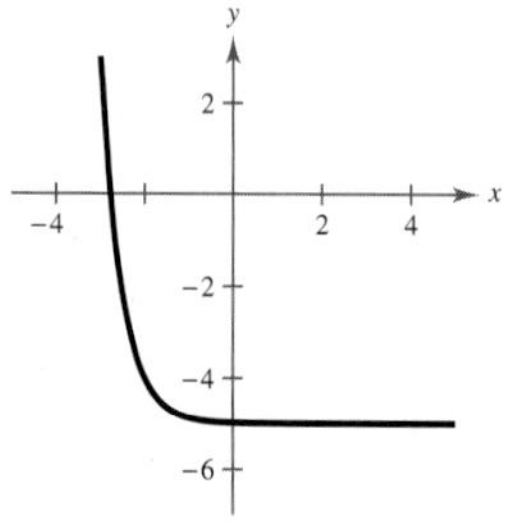

29.

x	-2	-1	0	1	2
$h(x)$	2.72	1.65	1	0.61	0.37

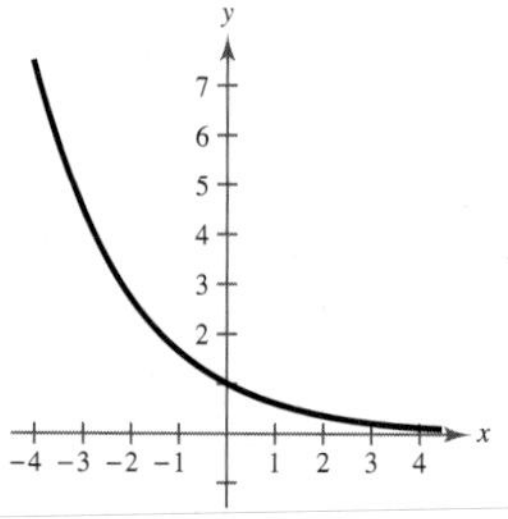

30.

x	-2	-1	0	1	2
$h(x)$	-0.72	0.35	1	1.39	1.63

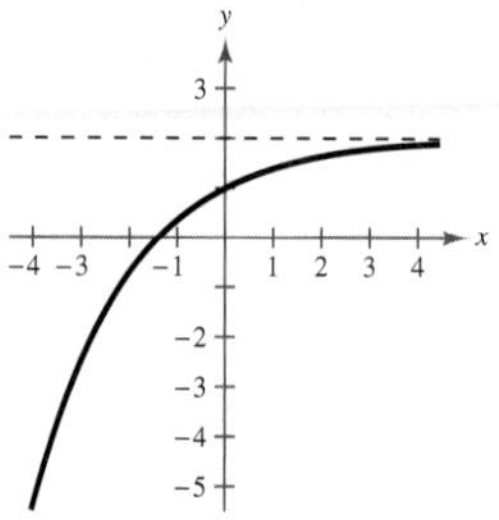

31.

x	-3	-2	-1	0	1
$f(x)$	0.37	1	2.72	7.39	20.09

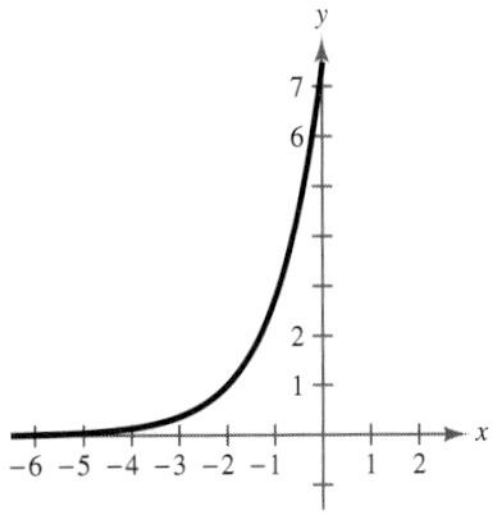

32.

t	$\frac{1}{2}$	1	2	3	4
$s(t)$	0.07	0.54	1.47	2.05	2.43

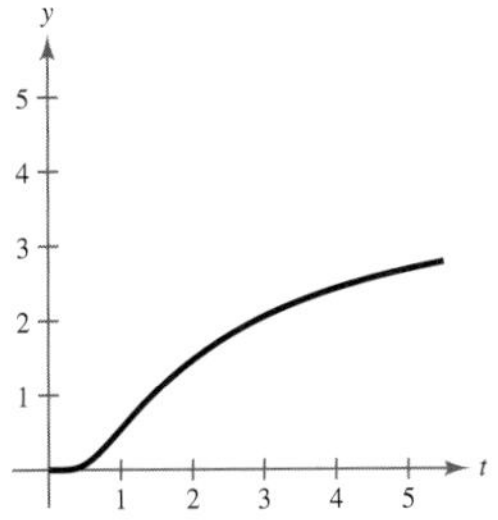

33.

n	1	2	4	12
A	\$6719.58	\$6734.28	\$6741.74	\$6746.77

n	365	Continuous
A	\$6749.21	\$6749.29

34.

n	1	2	4	12
A	\$9439.05	\$9482.32	\$9504.29	\$9519.07

n	365	Continuous
A	\$9526.26	\$9526.50

93.

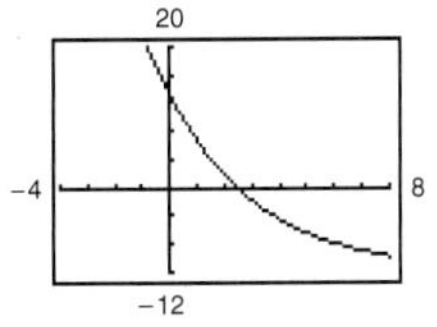

2.447

94.

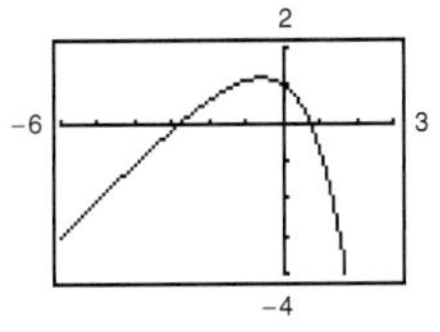

0.728; -2.795

95. $\frac{1}{3}e^{8.2} \approx 1213.650$ **96.** $\frac{1}{3}e^{15/4} \approx 14.174$

97. $3e^2 \approx 22.167$ **98.** $5e^4 \approx 272.991$

99. $e^8 \approx 2980.958$ **100.** $e^6 - 8 \approx 395.429$

Chapter Test *(page 273)*

7.

x	-1	$-\frac{1}{2}$	0	$\frac{1}{2}$	1
$f(x)$	0.865	0.632	0	-1.718	-6.389

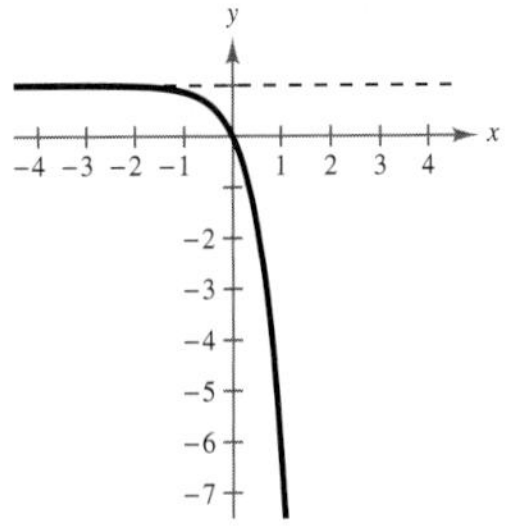

9.

x	$\frac{1}{2}$	1	$\frac{3}{2}$	2	4
$f(x)$	-5.699	-6	-6.176	-6.301	-6.602

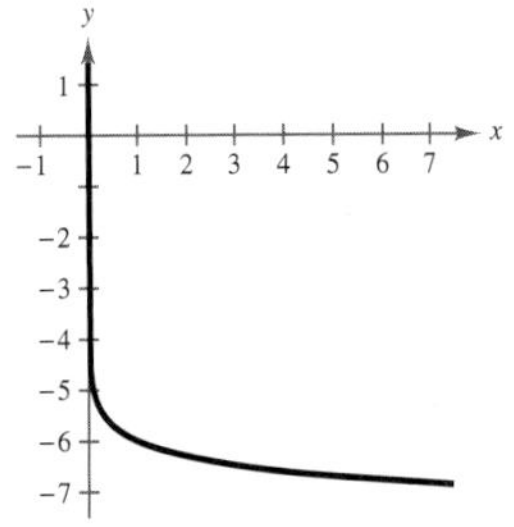

Vertical asymptote: $x = 0$

10.

x	5	7	9	11	13
$f(x)$	0	1.099	1.609	1.946	2.197

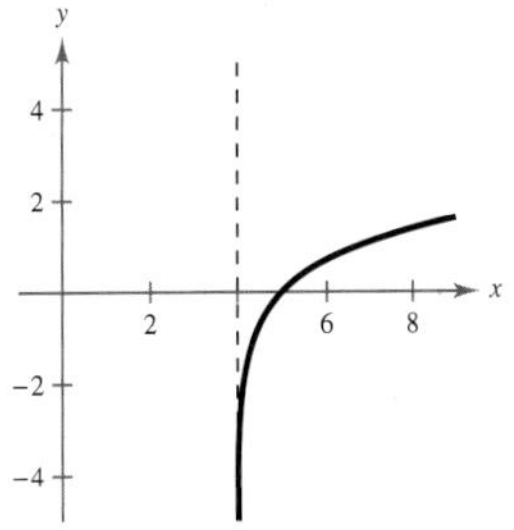

Vertical asymptote: $x = 4$

11.

x	-5	-3	-1	0	1
$f(x)$	1	2.099	2.609	2.792	2.946

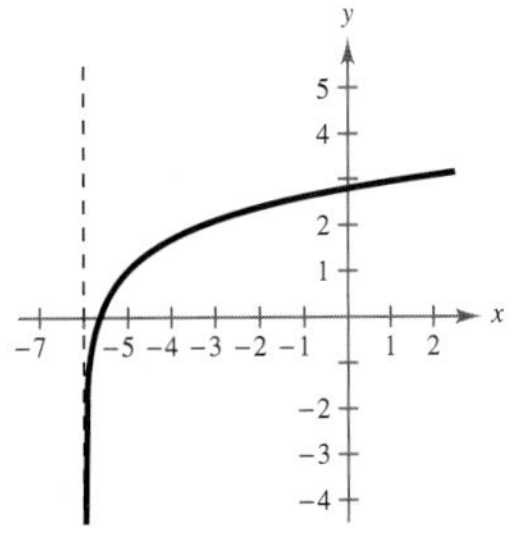

Vertical asymptote: $x = -6$

29. (a)

x	$\frac{1}{4}$	1	2	4	5	6
H	58.720	75.332	86.828	103.43	110.59	117.38

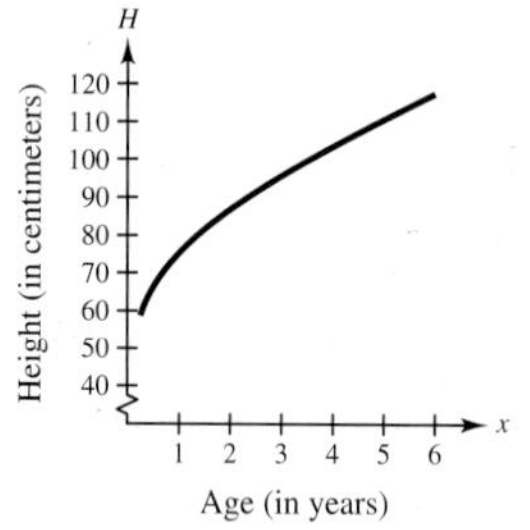

Cumulative Test for Chapters 1–3 *(page 274)*

17.

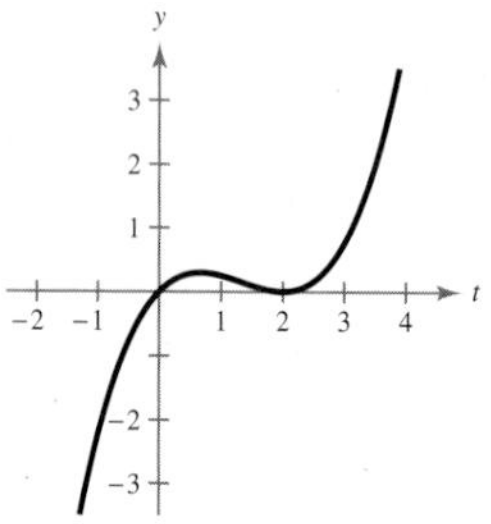

18.

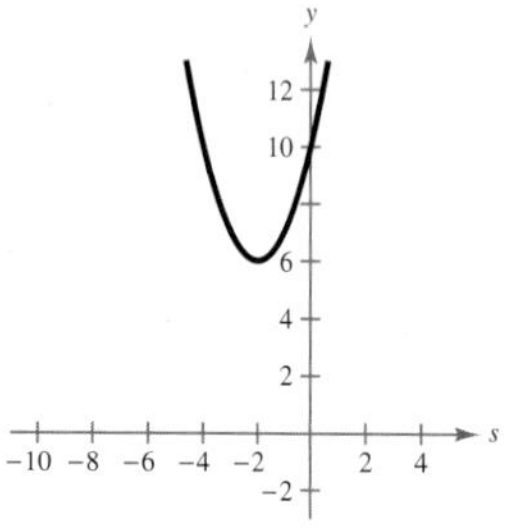

41. (a)

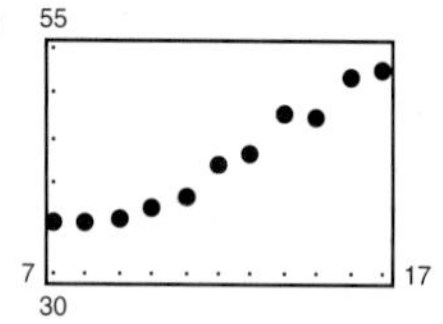

(c)

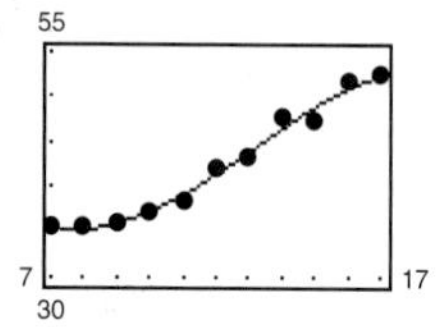

The model is a good fit for the data.

(d) \$25.3 billion; Answers will vary. Sample answer: No, this is not reasonable because the model decreases sharply after 2009.

Problem Solving *(page 277)*

12. (a) The upper graph represents the first investment (compound interest) and the lower graph represents the second investment (simple interest).

(b) $y_1 = 500(1.07)^t$
$y_2 = 35t + 500$

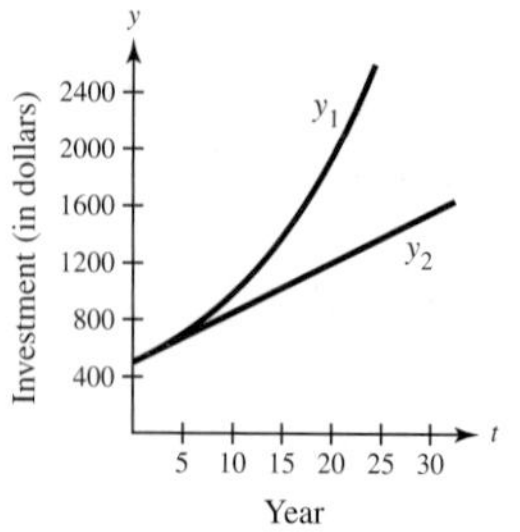

(c) You should choose compound interest because the earnings would be higher.

19. $y_4 = (x - 1) - \frac{1}{2}(x - 1)^2 + \frac{1}{3}(x - 1)^3 - \frac{1}{4}(x - 1)^4$

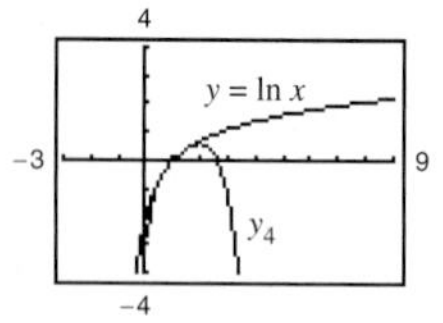

The pattern implies that
$\ln x = (x - 1) - \frac{1}{2}(x - 1)^2 + \frac{1}{3}(x - 1)^3 - \cdots.$

Chapter 4

Section 4.1 *(page 288)*

26. (a)

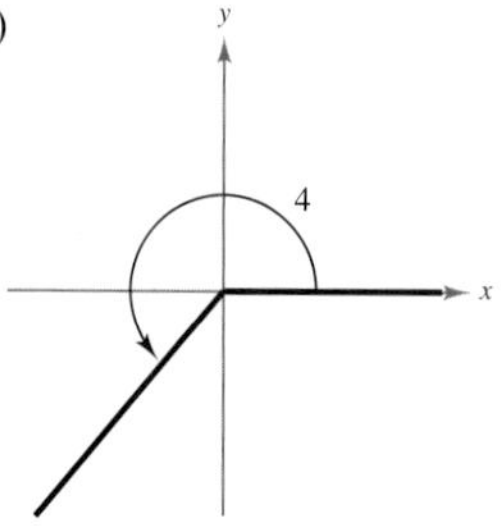

(b)

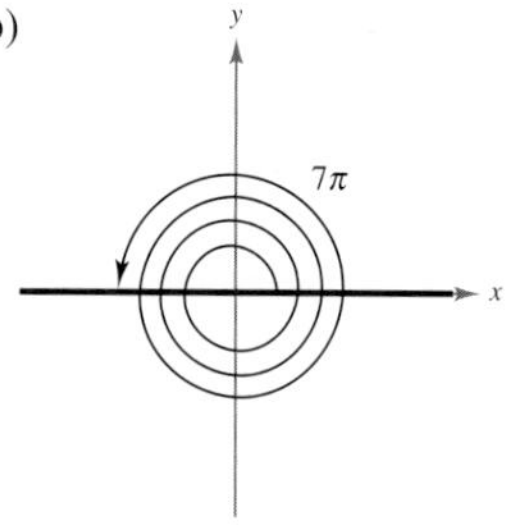

27. Sample answers: (a) $\frac{13\pi}{6}, -\frac{11\pi}{6}$ (b) $\frac{17\pi}{6}, -\frac{7\pi}{6}$

28. Sample answers: (a) $\frac{19\pi}{6}, -\frac{5\pi}{6}$ (b) $\frac{\pi}{6}, -\frac{23\pi}{6}$

29. Sample answers: (a) $\frac{8\pi}{3}, -\frac{4\pi}{3}$ (b) $\frac{25\pi}{12}, -\frac{23\pi}{12}$

30. Sample answers: (a) $\frac{7\pi}{4}, -\frac{\pi}{4}$ (b) $\frac{28\pi}{15}, -\frac{32\pi}{15}$

48. (a)

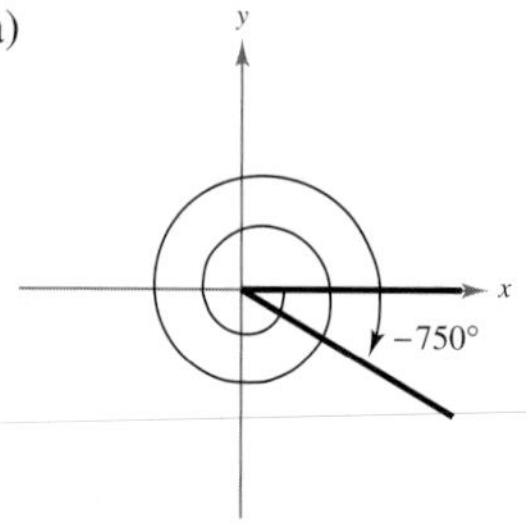

(b)

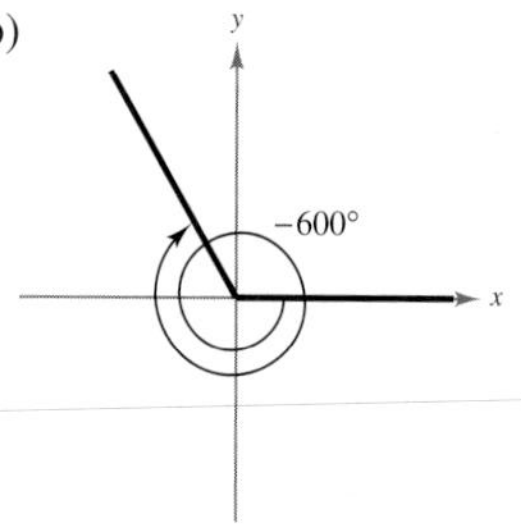

49. Sample answers: (a) 405°, −315° (b) 324°, −396°

50. Sample answers: (a) 480°, −240° (b) 300°, −60°

51. Sample answers: (a) 600°, −120° (b) 180°, −540°

52. Sample answers: (a) 330°, −30° (b) 590°, −130°

53. (a) Complement: 72°; Supplement: 162°
(b) Complement: 5°; Supplement: 95°

54. (a) Complement: 44°; Supplement: 134°
(b) Complement: none; Supplement: 87°

55. (a) Complement: none; Supplement: 30°
(b) Complement: 11°; Supplement: 101°

56. (a) Complement: none; Supplement: 50°
(b) Complement: none; Supplement: 10°

57. (a) $\frac{\pi}{6}$ (b) $\frac{\pi}{4}$ **58.** (a) $\frac{7\pi}{4}$ (b) $\frac{2\pi}{3}$

59. (a) $-\frac{\pi}{9}$ (b) $-\frac{\pi}{3}$ **60.** (a) $-\frac{3\pi}{2}$ (b) $\frac{4\pi}{5}$

Section 4.2 *(page 297)*

25. $\sin\left(-\frac{3\pi}{2}\right) = 1$

$\cos\left(-\frac{3\pi}{2}\right) = 0$

$\tan\left(-\frac{3\pi}{2}\right)$ is undefined.

27. $\sin\frac{2\pi}{3} = \frac{\sqrt{3}}{2}$ $\quad \csc\frac{2\pi}{3} = \frac{2\sqrt{3}}{3}$

$\cos\frac{2\pi}{3} = -\frac{1}{2}$ $\quad \sec\frac{2\pi}{3} = -2$

$\tan\frac{2\pi}{3} = -\sqrt{3}$ $\quad \cot\frac{2\pi}{3} = -\frac{\sqrt{3}}{3}$

28. $\sin\frac{5\pi}{6} = \frac{1}{2}$ $\quad \csc\frac{5\pi}{6} = 2$

$\cos\frac{5\pi}{6} = -\frac{\sqrt{3}}{2}$ $\quad \sec\frac{5\pi}{6} = -\frac{2\sqrt{3}}{3}$

$\tan\frac{5\pi}{6} = -\frac{\sqrt{3}}{3}$ $\quad \cot\frac{5\pi}{6} = -\sqrt{3}$

29. $\sin\frac{4\pi}{3} = -\frac{\sqrt{3}}{2}$ $\quad \csc\frac{4\pi}{3} = -\frac{2\sqrt{3}}{3}$

$\cos\frac{4\pi}{3} = -\frac{1}{2}$ $\quad \sec\frac{4\pi}{3} = -2$

$\tan\frac{4\pi}{3} = \sqrt{3}$ $\quad \cot\frac{4\pi}{3} = \frac{\sqrt{3}}{3}$

30. $\sin\frac{7\pi}{4} = -\frac{\sqrt{2}}{2}$ $\quad \csc\frac{7\pi}{4} = -\sqrt{2}$

$\cos\frac{7\pi}{4} = \frac{\sqrt{2}}{2}$ $\quad \sec\frac{7\pi}{4} = \sqrt{2}$

$\tan\frac{7\pi}{4} = -1$ $\quad \cot\frac{7\pi}{4} = -1$

31. $\sin\frac{3\pi}{4} = \frac{\sqrt{2}}{2}$ $\quad \csc\frac{3\pi}{4} = \sqrt{2}$

$\cos\frac{3\pi}{4} = -\frac{\sqrt{2}}{2}$ $\quad \sec\frac{3\pi}{4} = -\sqrt{2}$

$\tan\frac{3\pi}{4} = -1$ $\quad \cot\frac{3\pi}{4} = -1$

32. $\sin\frac{3\pi}{2} = -1$ $\quad \csc\frac{3\pi}{2} = -1$

$\cos\frac{3\pi}{2} = 0$ $\quad \sec\frac{3\pi}{2}$ is undefined.

$\tan\frac{3\pi}{2}$ is undefined. $\quad \cot\frac{3\pi}{2} = 0$

33. $\sin\left(-\frac{\pi}{2}\right) = -1$ $\quad \csc\left(-\frac{\pi}{2}\right) = -1$

$\cos\left(-\frac{\pi}{2}\right) = 0$ $\quad \sec\left(-\frac{\pi}{2}\right)$ is undefined.

$\tan\left(-\frac{\pi}{2}\right)$ is undefined. $\quad \cot\left(-\frac{\pi}{2}\right) = 0$

34. $\sin(-\pi) = 0$ $\quad \csc(-\pi)$ is undefined.

$\cos(-\pi) = -1$ $\quad \sec(-\pi) = -1$

$\tan(-\pi) = 0$ $\quad \cot(-\pi)$ is undefined.

35. $\sin 4\pi = \sin 0 = 0$ $\quad$ **36.** $\cos 3\pi = \cos \pi = -1$

37. $\cos\frac{7\pi}{3} = \cos\frac{\pi}{3} = \frac{1}{2}$ $\quad$ **38.** $\sin\frac{9\pi}{4} = \sin\frac{\pi}{4} = \frac{\sqrt{2}}{2}$

39. $\cos\frac{17\pi}{4} = \cos\frac{\pi}{4} = \frac{\sqrt{2}}{2}$ $\quad$ **40.** $\sin\frac{19\pi}{6} = \sin\frac{7\pi}{6} = -\frac{1}{2}$

41. $\sin\left(-\frac{8\pi}{3}\right) = \sin\frac{4\pi}{3} = -\frac{\sqrt{3}}{2}$

42. $\cos\left(-\frac{9\pi}{4}\right) = \cos\left(\frac{7\pi}{4}\right) = \frac{\sqrt{2}}{2}$

72.

t	0	$\frac{\pi}{4}$	$\frac{\pi}{2}$	$\frac{3\pi}{4}$	π
x	1	$\frac{\sqrt{2}}{2}$	0	$-\frac{\sqrt{2}}{2}$	-1
y	0	$\frac{\sqrt{2}}{2}$	1	$\frac{\sqrt{2}}{2}$	0
$\sin t$	0	$\frac{\sqrt{2}}{2}$	1	$\frac{\sqrt{2}}{2}$	0
$\cos t$	1	$\frac{\sqrt{2}}{2}$	0	$-\frac{\sqrt{2}}{2}$	-1
$\tan t$	0	1	Undef.	-1	0

The student has used the relationships $\sin t = x$, $\cos t = y$, and $\tan t = x/y$ to complete the table. The correct relationships should be $\sin t = y$, $\cos t = x$, and $\tan t = y/x$.

Section 4.3 *(page 306)*

13.

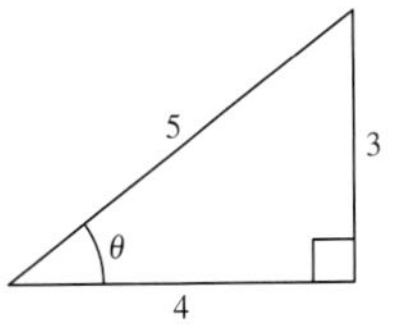

$\sin\theta = \frac{3}{5}$ $\quad \csc\theta = \frac{5}{3}$

$\cos\theta = \frac{4}{5}$ $\quad \sec\theta = \frac{5}{4}$

$\cot\theta = \frac{4}{3}$

14.

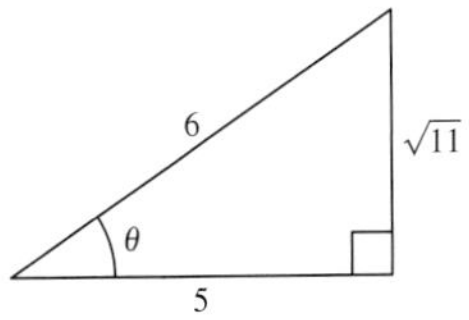

$\sin\theta = \frac{\sqrt{11}}{6}$ $\quad \csc\theta = \frac{6\sqrt{11}}{11}$

$\sec\theta = \frac{6}{5}$

$\tan\theta = \frac{\sqrt{11}}{5}$ $\quad \cot\theta = \frac{5\sqrt{11}}{11}$

15.

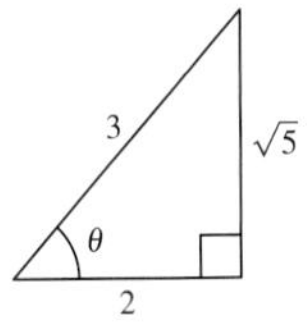

$\sin\theta = \frac{\sqrt{5}}{3}$ $\quad \csc\theta = \frac{3\sqrt{5}}{5}$

$\cos\theta = \frac{2}{3}$

$\tan\theta = \frac{\sqrt{5}}{2}$ $\quad \cot\theta = \frac{2\sqrt{5}}{5}$

16.

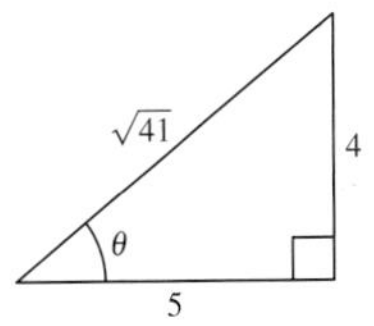

$\sin\theta = \frac{4\sqrt{41}}{41}$ $\quad \csc\theta = \frac{\sqrt{41}}{4}$

$\cos\theta = \frac{5\sqrt{41}}{41}$ $\quad \sec\theta = \frac{\sqrt{41}}{5}$

$\cot\theta = \frac{5}{4}$

17.

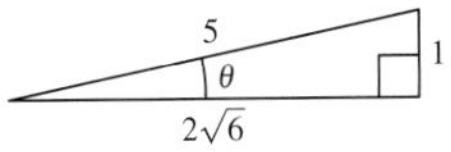

$\csc\theta = 5$

$\cos\theta = \frac{2\sqrt{6}}{5}$ $\quad \sec\theta = \frac{5\sqrt{6}}{12}$

$\tan\theta = \frac{\sqrt{6}}{12}$ $\quad \cot\theta = 2\sqrt{6}$

18.

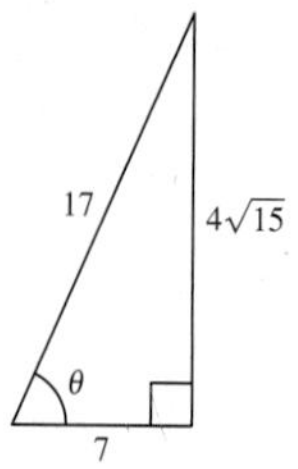

$\sin\theta = \dfrac{4\sqrt{15}}{17}$ $\quad\csc\theta = \dfrac{17\sqrt{15}}{60}$

$\cos\theta = \dfrac{7}{17}$

$\tan\theta = \dfrac{4\sqrt{15}}{7}$ $\quad\cot\theta = \dfrac{7\sqrt{15}}{60}$

19.

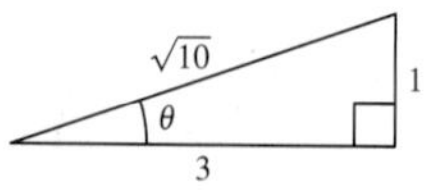

$\sin\theta = \dfrac{\sqrt{10}}{10}$ $\quad\csc\theta = \sqrt{10}$

$\cos\theta = \dfrac{3\sqrt{10}}{10}$ $\quad\sec\theta = \dfrac{\sqrt{10}}{3}$

$\tan\theta = \dfrac{1}{3}$

20.

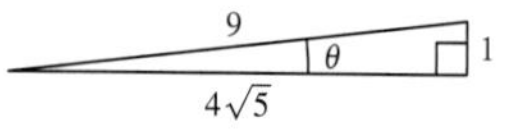

$\sin\theta = \dfrac{1}{9}$

$\cos\theta = \dfrac{4\sqrt{5}}{9}$ $\quad\sec\theta = \dfrac{9\sqrt{5}}{20}$

$\tan\theta = \dfrac{\sqrt{5}}{20}$ $\quad\cot\theta = 4\sqrt{5}$

Section 4.4 *(page 316)*

13. $\sin\theta = \frac{12}{13}$ $\quad\csc\theta = \frac{13}{12}$
$\cos\theta = \frac{5}{13}$ $\quad\sec\theta = \frac{13}{5}$
$\tan\theta = \frac{12}{5}$ $\quad\cot\theta = \frac{5}{12}$

14. $\sin\theta = \frac{15}{17}$ $\quad\csc\theta = \frac{17}{15}$
$\cos\theta = \frac{8}{17}$ $\quad\sec\theta = \frac{17}{8}$
$\tan\theta = \frac{15}{8}$ $\quad\cot\theta = \frac{8}{15}$

15. $\sin\theta = -\dfrac{2\sqrt{29}}{29}$ $\quad\csc\theta = -\dfrac{\sqrt{29}}{2}$

$\cos\theta = -\dfrac{5\sqrt{29}}{29}$ $\quad\sec\theta = -\dfrac{\sqrt{29}}{5}$

$\tan\theta = \dfrac{2}{5}$ $\quad\cot\theta = \dfrac{5}{2}$

16. $\sin\theta = \dfrac{5\sqrt{29}}{29}$ $\quad\csc\theta = \dfrac{\sqrt{29}}{5}$

$\cos\theta = -\dfrac{2\sqrt{29}}{29}$ $\quad\sec\theta = -\dfrac{\sqrt{29}}{2}$

$\tan\theta = -\dfrac{5}{2}$ $\quad\cot\theta = -\dfrac{2}{5}$

17. $\sin\theta = \frac{4}{5}$ $\quad\csc\theta = \frac{5}{4}$
$\cos\theta = -\frac{3}{5}$ $\quad\sec\theta = -\frac{5}{3}$
$\tan\theta = -\frac{4}{3}$ $\quad\cot\theta = -\frac{3}{4}$

18. $\sin\theta = -\dfrac{31\sqrt{1157}}{1157}$ $\quad\csc\theta = -\dfrac{\sqrt{1157}}{31}$

$\cos\theta = \dfrac{14\sqrt{1157}}{1157}$ $\quad\sec\theta = \dfrac{\sqrt{1157}}{14}$

$\tan\theta = -\dfrac{31}{14}$ $\quad\cot\theta = -\dfrac{14}{31}$

23. $\sin\theta = \frac{15}{17}$ $\quad\csc\theta = \frac{17}{15}$
$\cos\theta = -\frac{8}{17}$ $\quad\sec\theta = -\frac{17}{8}$
$\tan\theta = -\frac{15}{8}$ $\quad\cot\theta = -\frac{8}{15}$

24. $\sin\theta = -\frac{15}{17}$ $\quad\csc\theta = -\frac{17}{15}$
$\cos\theta = \frac{8}{17}$ $\quad\sec\theta = \frac{17}{8}$
$\tan\theta = -\frac{15}{8}$ $\quad\cot\theta = -\frac{8}{15}$

25. $\sin\theta = \frac{3}{5}$ $\quad\csc\theta = \frac{5}{3}$
$\cos\theta = -\frac{4}{5}$ $\quad\sec\theta = -\frac{5}{4}$
$\tan\theta = -\frac{3}{4}$ $\quad\cot\theta = -\frac{4}{3}$

26. $\sin\theta = -\frac{3}{5}$ $\quad\csc\theta = -\frac{5}{3}$
$\cos\theta = -\frac{4}{5}$ $\quad\sec\theta = -\frac{5}{4}$
$\tan\theta = \frac{3}{4}$ $\quad\cot\theta = \frac{4}{3}$

27. $\sin\theta = -\dfrac{\sqrt{10}}{10}$ $\quad\csc\theta = -\sqrt{10}$

$\cos\theta = \dfrac{3\sqrt{10}}{10}$ $\quad\sec\theta = \dfrac{\sqrt{10}}{3}$

$\tan\theta = -\dfrac{1}{3}$ $\quad\cot\theta = -3$

28. $\sin\theta = \dfrac{1}{4}$ $\quad\csc\theta = 4$

$\cos\theta = -\dfrac{\sqrt{15}}{4}$ $\quad\sec\theta = -\dfrac{4\sqrt{15}}{15}$

$\tan\theta = -\dfrac{\sqrt{15}}{15}$ $\quad\cot\theta = -\sqrt{15}$

29. $\sin\theta = -\dfrac{\sqrt{3}}{2}$ $\quad\csc\theta = -\dfrac{2\sqrt{3}}{3}$

$\cos\theta = -\dfrac{1}{2}$ $\quad\sec\theta = -2$

$\tan\theta = \sqrt{3}$ $\quad\cot\theta = \dfrac{\sqrt{3}}{3}$

30. $\sin\theta = 0$ $\quad\csc\theta$ is undefined.
$\cos\theta = -1$ $\quad\sec\theta = -1$
$\tan\theta = 0$ $\quad\cot\theta$ is undefined.

31. $\sin\theta = 0$ $\quad\csc\theta$ is undefined.
$\cos\theta = -1$ $\quad\sec\theta = -1$
$\tan\theta = 0$ $\quad\cot\theta$ is undefined.

32. $\sin\theta = -1$ $\quad\csc\theta = -1$
$\cos\theta = 0$ $\quad\sec\theta$ is undefined.
$\tan\theta$ is undefined. $\quad\cot\theta = 0$

33. $\sin\theta = \dfrac{\sqrt{2}}{2}$ $\quad\csc\theta = \sqrt{2}$

$\cos\theta = -\dfrac{\sqrt{2}}{2}$ $\quad\sec\theta = -\sqrt{2}$

$\tan\theta = -1$ $\quad\cot\theta = -1$

34. $\sin\theta = -\dfrac{\sqrt{10}}{10}$ $\quad\csc\theta = -\sqrt{10}$

$\cos\theta = -\dfrac{3\sqrt{10}}{10}$ $\quad\sec\theta = -\dfrac{\sqrt{10}}{3}$

$\tan\theta = \dfrac{1}{3}$ $\quad\cot\theta = 3$

35. $\sin\theta = -\dfrac{2\sqrt{5}}{5}$ $\quad\csc\theta = -\dfrac{\sqrt{5}}{2}$

$\cos\theta = -\dfrac{\sqrt{5}}{5}$ $\quad\sec\theta = -\sqrt{5}$

$\tan\theta = 2$ $\quad\cot\theta = \dfrac{1}{2}$

36. $\sin\theta = -\frac{4}{5}$ $\quad\csc\theta = -\frac{5}{4}$
$\cos\theta = \frac{3}{5}$ $\quad\sec\theta = \frac{5}{3}$
$\tan\theta = -\frac{4}{3}$ $\quad\cot\theta = -\frac{3}{4}$

53. $\sin 225° = -\frac{\sqrt{2}}{2}$

$\cos 225° = -\frac{\sqrt{2}}{2}$

$\tan 225° = 1$

54. $\sin 300° = -\frac{\sqrt{3}}{2}$

$\cos 300° = \frac{1}{2}$

$\tan 300° = -\sqrt{3}$

55. $\sin 750° = \frac{1}{2}$

$\cos 750° = \frac{\sqrt{3}}{2}$

$\tan 750° = \frac{\sqrt{3}}{3}$

56. $\sin(-405°) = -\frac{\sqrt{2}}{2}$

$\cos(-405°) = \frac{\sqrt{2}}{2}$

$\tan(-405°) = -1$

57. $\sin(-150°) = -\frac{1}{2}$

$\cos(-150°) = -\frac{\sqrt{3}}{2}$

$\tan(-150°) = \frac{\sqrt{3}}{3}$

58. $\sin(-840°) = -\frac{\sqrt{3}}{2}$

$\cos(-840°) = -\frac{1}{2}$

$\tan(-840°) = \sqrt{3}$

59. $\sin \frac{2\pi}{3} = \frac{\sqrt{3}}{2}$

$\cos \frac{2\pi}{3} = -\frac{1}{2}$

$\tan \frac{2\pi}{3} = -\sqrt{3}$

60. $\sin \frac{3\pi}{4} = \frac{\sqrt{2}}{2}$

$\cos \frac{3\pi}{4} = -\frac{\sqrt{2}}{2}$

$\tan \frac{3\pi}{4} = -1$

61. $\sin \frac{5\pi}{4} = -\frac{\sqrt{2}}{2}$

$\cos \frac{5\pi}{4} = -\frac{\sqrt{2}}{2}$

$\tan \frac{5\pi}{4} = 1$

62. $\sin \frac{7\pi}{6} = -\frac{1}{2}$

$\cos \frac{7\pi}{6} = -\frac{\sqrt{3}}{2}$

$\tan \frac{7\pi}{6} = \frac{\sqrt{3}}{3}$

63. $\sin\left(-\frac{\pi}{6}\right) = -\frac{1}{2}$

$\cos\left(-\frac{\pi}{6}\right) = \frac{\sqrt{3}}{2}$

$\tan\left(-\frac{\pi}{6}\right) = -\frac{\sqrt{3}}{3}$

64. $\sin\left(-\frac{\pi}{2}\right) = -1$

$\cos\left(-\frac{\pi}{2}\right) = 0$

$\tan\left(-\frac{\pi}{2}\right)$ is undefined.

65. $\sin \frac{9\pi}{4} = \frac{\sqrt{2}}{2}$

$\cos \frac{9\pi}{4} = \frac{\sqrt{2}}{2}$

$\tan \frac{9\pi}{4} = 1$

66. $\sin \frac{10\pi}{3} = -\frac{\sqrt{3}}{2}$

$\cos \frac{10\pi}{3} = -\frac{1}{2}$

$\tan \frac{10\pi}{3} = \sqrt{3}$

67. $\sin\left(-\frac{3\pi}{2}\right) = 1$

$\cos\left(-\frac{3\pi}{2}\right) = 0$

$\tan\left(-\frac{3\pi}{2}\right)$ is undefined.

68. $\sin\left(-\frac{23\pi}{4}\right) = \frac{\sqrt{2}}{2}$

$\cos\left(-\frac{23\pi}{4}\right) = \frac{\sqrt{2}}{2}$

$\tan\left(-\frac{23\pi}{4}\right) = 1$

69. $\frac{4}{5}$ 70. $\frac{\sqrt{10}}{10}$ 71. $-\frac{\sqrt{13}}{2}$

72. $-\sqrt{3}$ 73. $\frac{8}{5}$ 74. $\frac{\sqrt{65}}{4}$

91. (a) $30° = \frac{\pi}{6}$, $150° = \frac{5\pi}{6}$ (b) $210° = \frac{7\pi}{6}$, $330° = \frac{11\pi}{6}$

92. (a) $45° = \frac{\pi}{4}$, $315° = \frac{7\pi}{4}$ (b) $135° = \frac{3\pi}{4}$, $225° = \frac{5\pi}{4}$

93. (a) $60° = \frac{\pi}{3}$, $120° = \frac{2\pi}{3}$ (b) $135° = \frac{3\pi}{4}$, $315° = \frac{7\pi}{4}$

94. (a) $60° = \frac{\pi}{3}$, $300° = \frac{5\pi}{3}$ (b) $120° = \frac{2\pi}{3}$, $240° = \frac{4\pi}{3}$

95. (a) $45° = \frac{\pi}{4}$, $225° = \frac{5\pi}{4}$ (b) $150° = \frac{5\pi}{6}$, $330° = \frac{11\pi}{6}$

96. (a) $60° = \frac{\pi}{3}$, $120° = \frac{2\pi}{3}$ (b) $240° = \frac{4\pi}{3}$, $300° = \frac{5\pi}{3}$

Section 4.5 *(page 326)*

33.

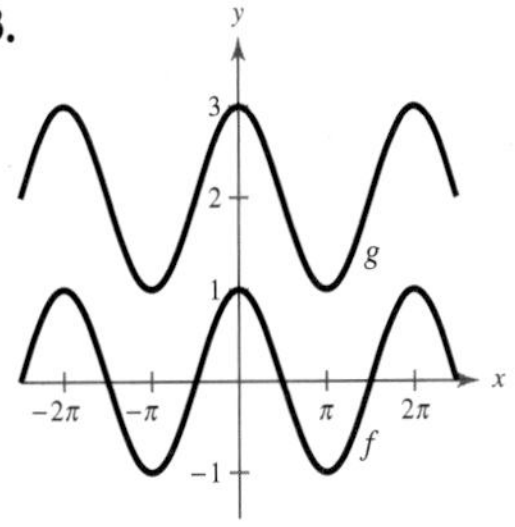

34.

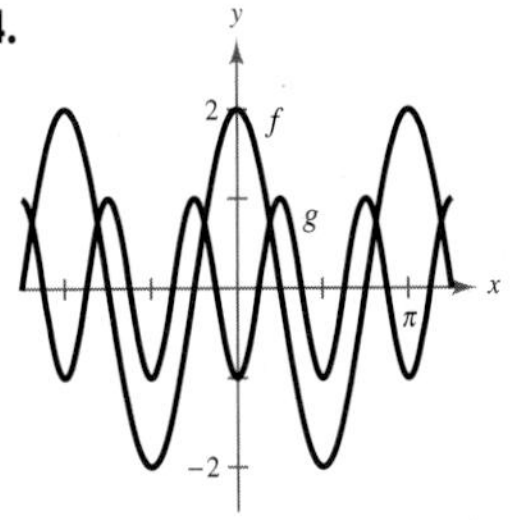

44.

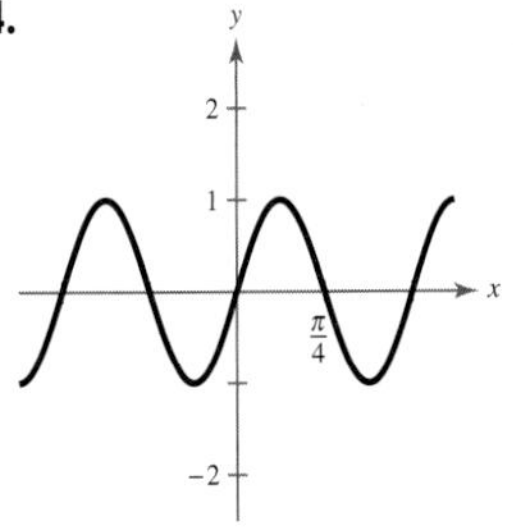

45.

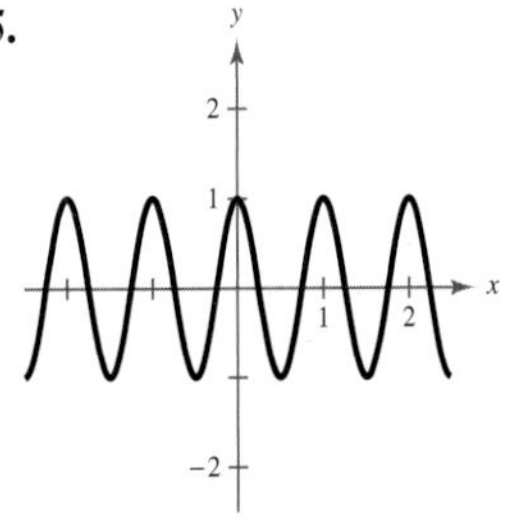

46.

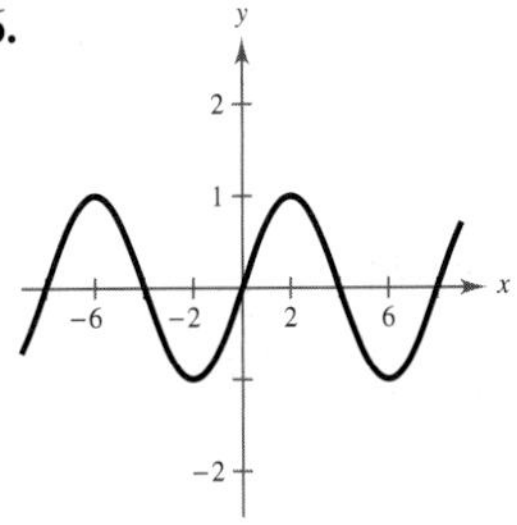

47.

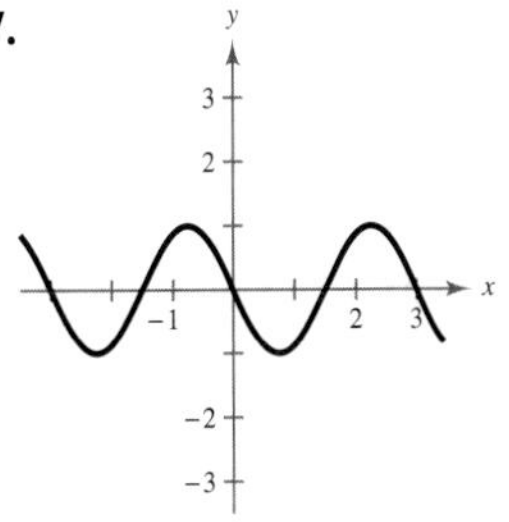

48.

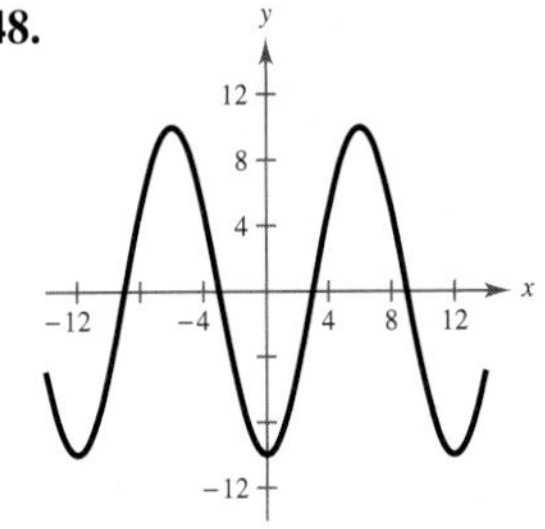

49.

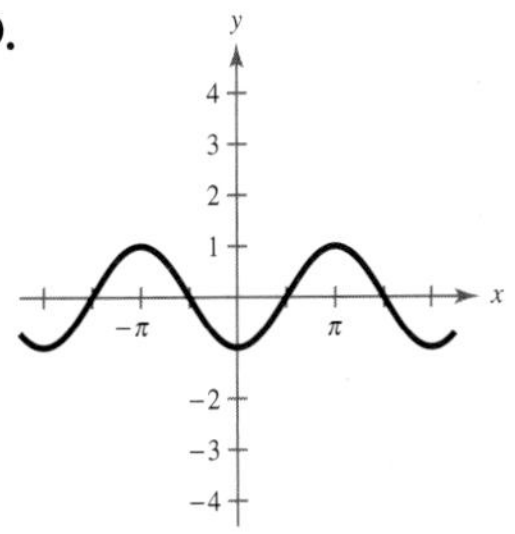

50.

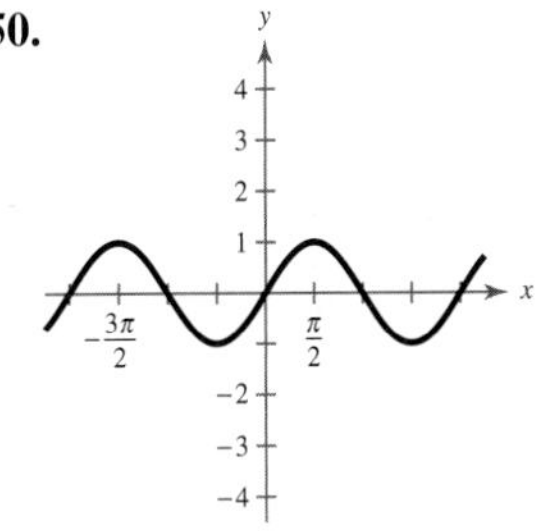

51.

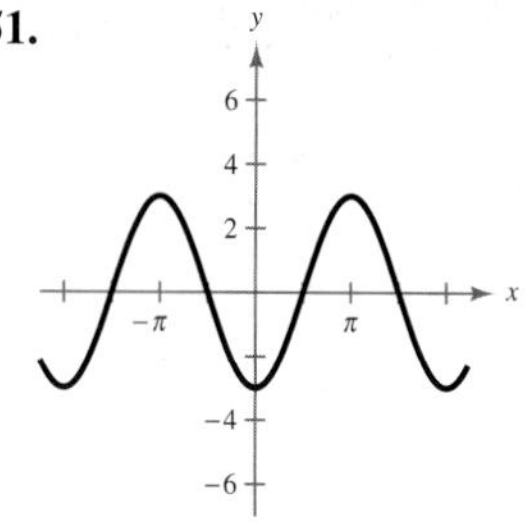

52.

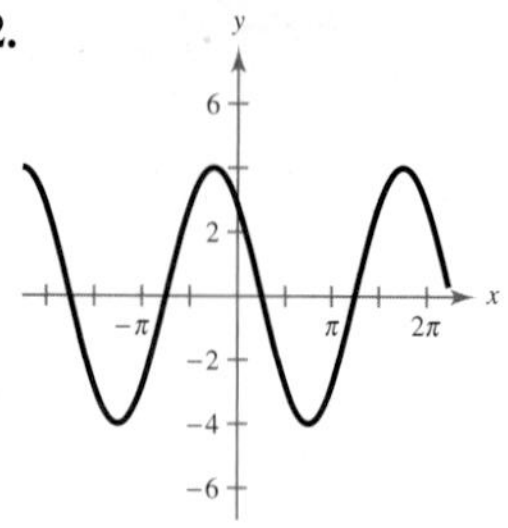

53.

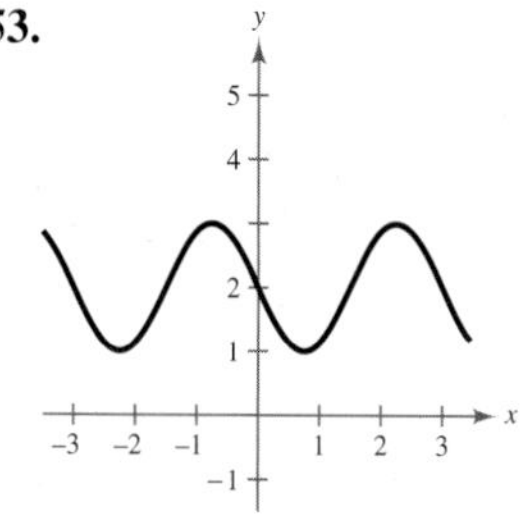

54.

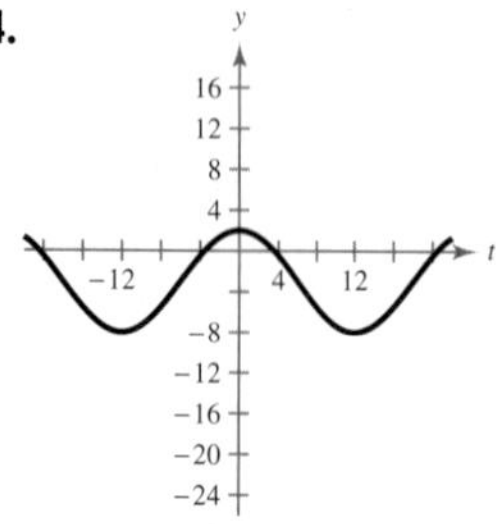

55.

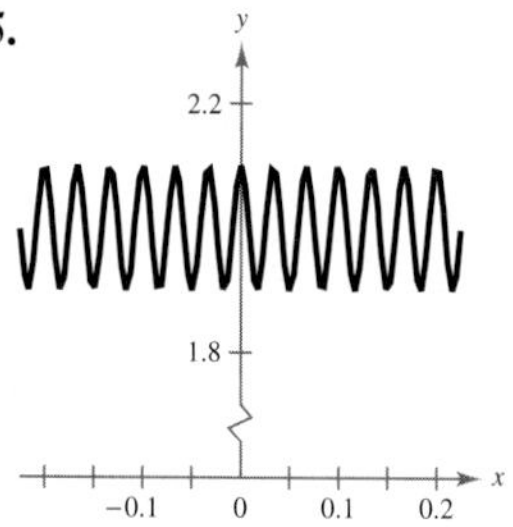

56.

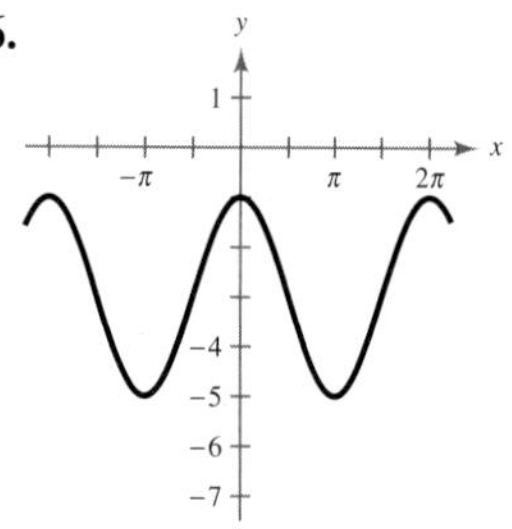

57.

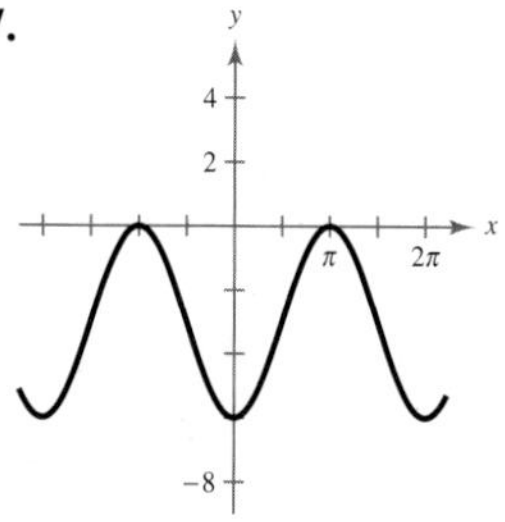

58.

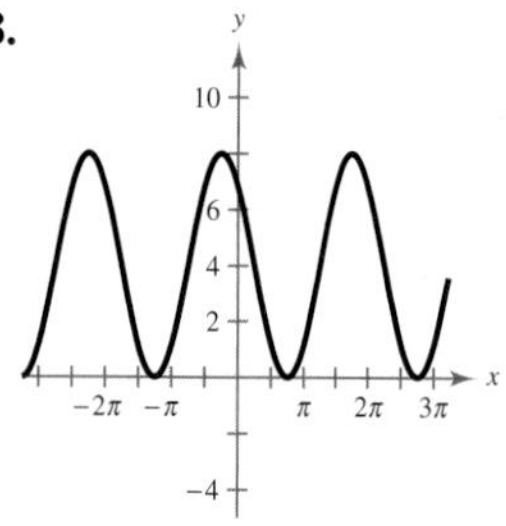

59.

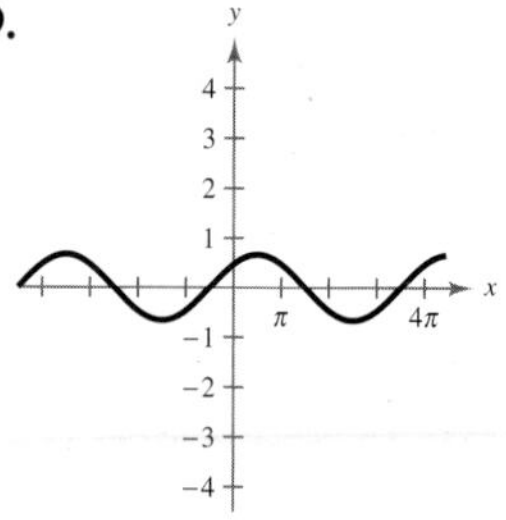

60.

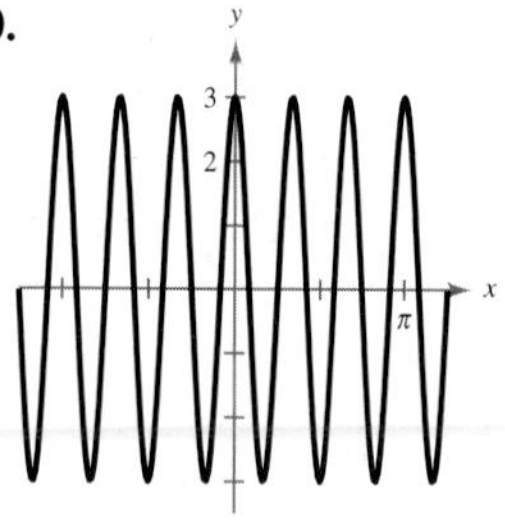

61. (a) $g(x)$ is obtained by a horizontal shrink of four, and one cycle of $g(x)$ corresponds to the interval $[\pi/4, 3\pi/4]$.

(b)

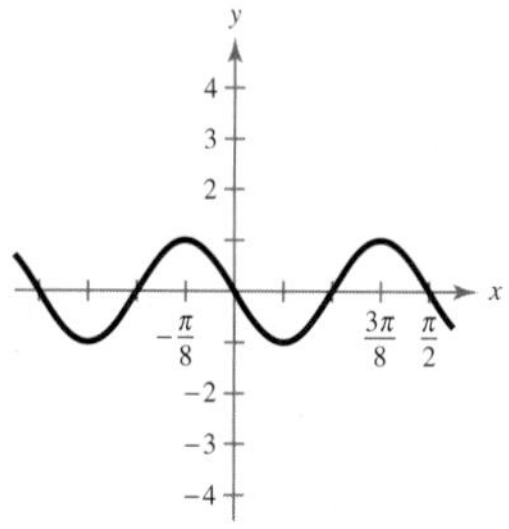

(c) $g(x) = f(4x - \pi)$

62. (a) $g(x)$ is a horizontal shrink of two, and one cycle of $g(x)$ corresponds to the interval $[-\pi/2, \pi/2]$.

(b)

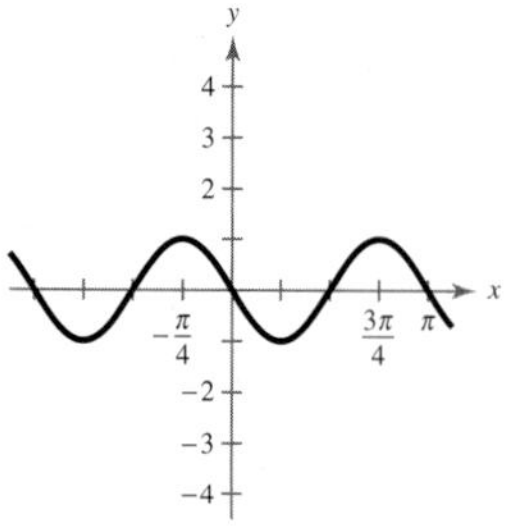

(c) $g(x) = f(2x + \pi)$

63. (a) One cycle of $g(x)$ corresponds to the interval $[\pi, 3\pi]$, and $g(x)$ is obtained by shifting $f(x)$ upward two units.

(b)

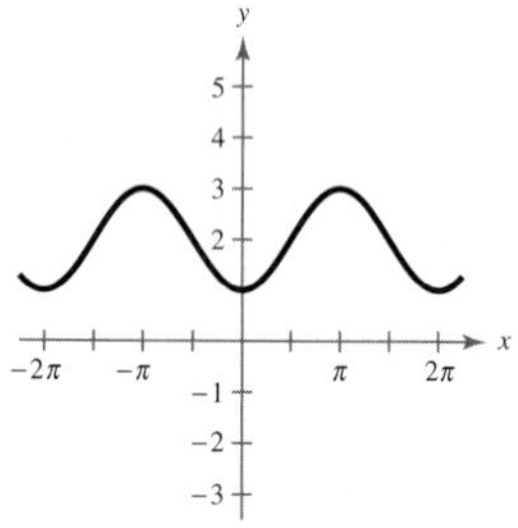

(c) $g(x) = f(x - \pi) + 2$

64. (a) One cycle of $g(x)$ is $[-\pi, \pi]$. $g(x)$ is also shifted up one unit.

(b)

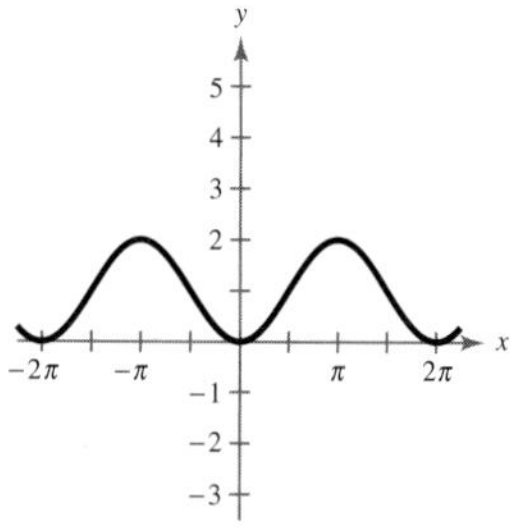

(c) $g(x) = 1 + f(x + \pi)$

65. (a) One cycle of $g(x)$ is $[\pi/4, 3\pi/4]$. $g(x)$ is also shifted down three units and has an amplitude of two.

(b)

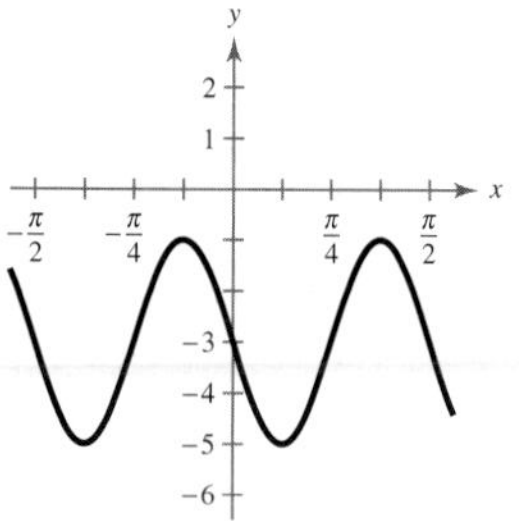

(c) $g(x) = 2f(4x - \pi) - 3$

66. (a) One cycle of $g(x)$ is $[-\pi/2, \pi/2]$. $g(x)$ is also reflected over the x-axis and shifted up four units.

(b)

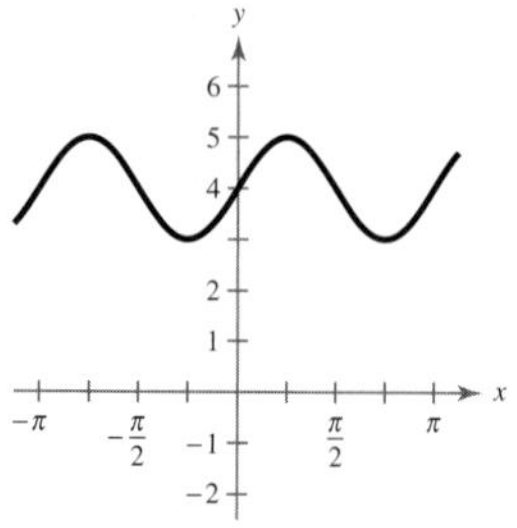

(c) $g(x) = 4 - f(2x + \pi)$

67.

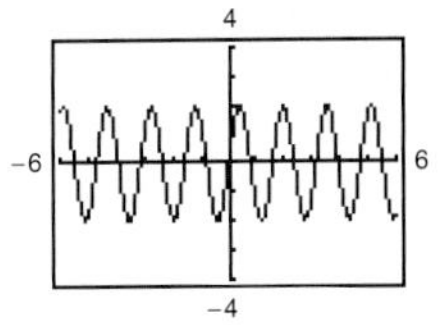

68.

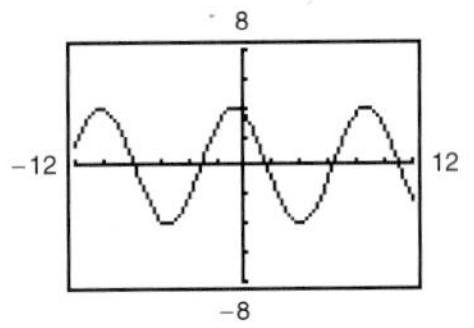

69.

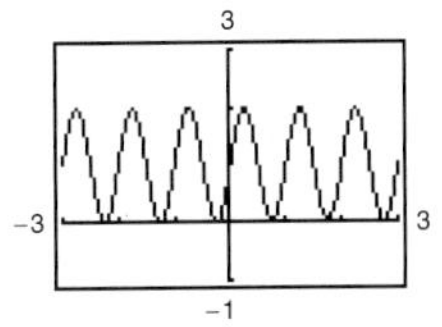

70.

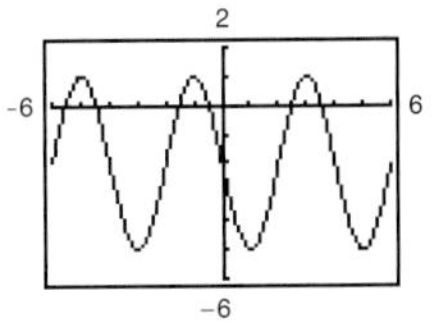

71.

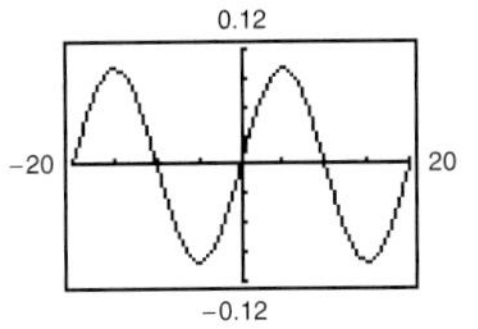

72.

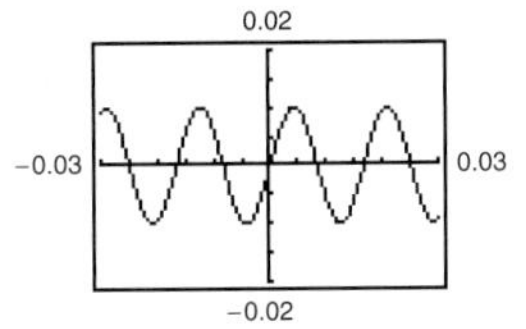

79. $a = 2, b = 1, c = -\frac{\pi}{4}$

80. $a = 2, b = \frac{\pi}{2}, c = -\frac{\pi}{2}$

81.

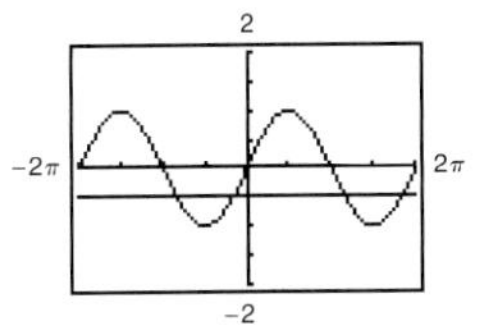

$x = -\frac{\pi}{6}, -\frac{5\pi}{6}, \frac{7\pi}{6}, \frac{11\pi}{6}$

82.

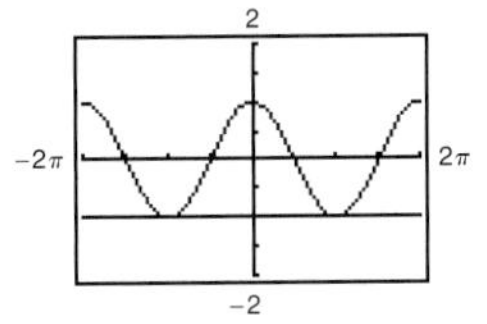

$x = -\pi, \pi$

98.

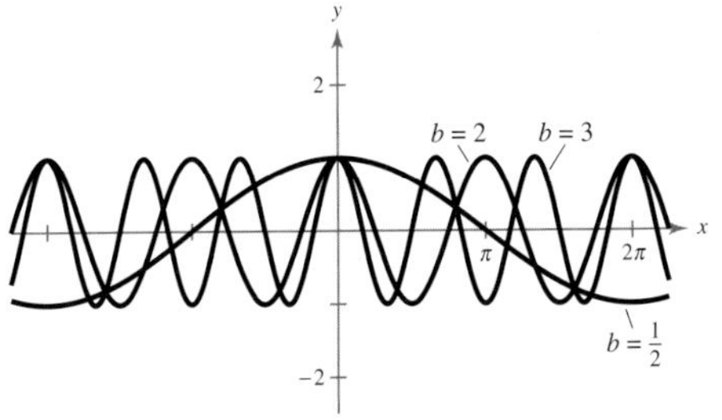

The value of b affects the period of the graph.

$b = \frac{1}{2} \rightarrow \frac{1}{2}$ cycle

$b = 2 \rightarrow 2$ cycles

$b = 3 \rightarrow 3$ cycles

99.

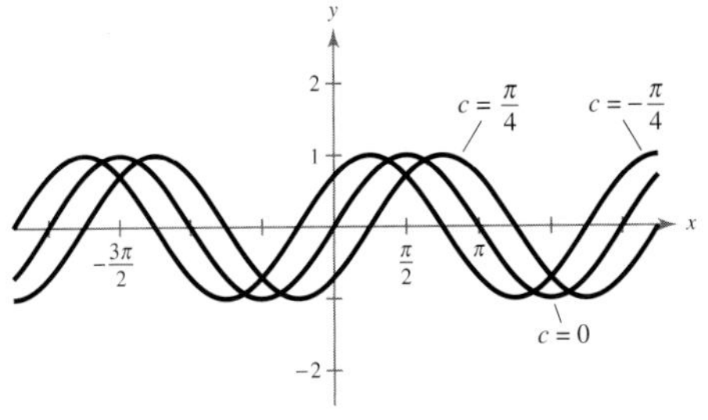

The value of c is a horizontal translation of the graph.

103. (a)

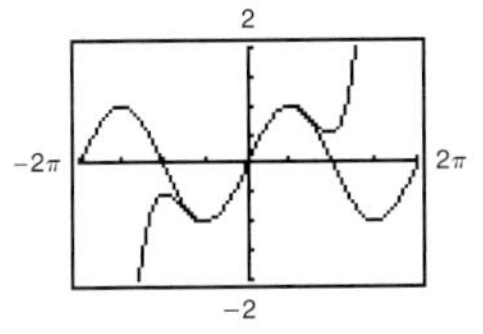

The graphs appear to coincide from $-\frac{\pi}{2}$ to $\frac{\pi}{2}$.

(b)

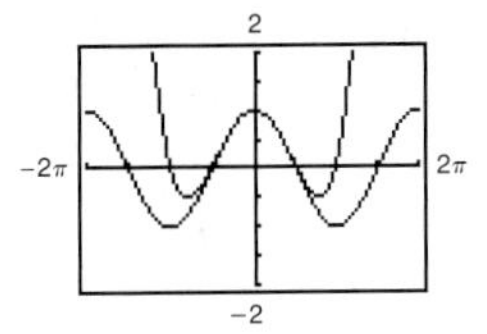

The graphs appear to coincide from $-\frac{\pi}{2}$ to $\frac{\pi}{2}$.

(c) $-\frac{x^7}{7!}, -\frac{x^6}{6!}$

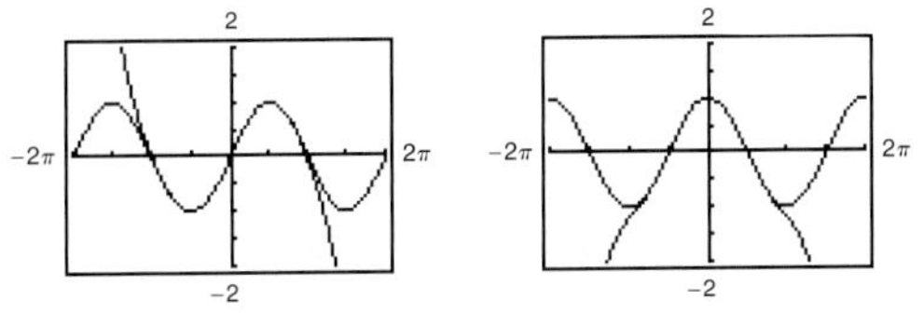

The interval of accuracy increased.

104. (a) 0.4794, 0.4794 (b) 0.8417, 0.8415 (c) 0.5, 0.5
(d) 0.8776, 0.8776 (e) 0.5417, 0.5403
(f) 0.7074, 0.7071
The error increases as x moves farther away from 0.

Section 4.6 *(page 337)*

22.

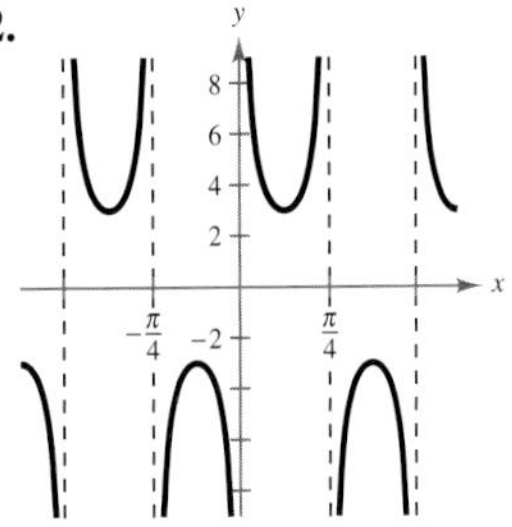

23.

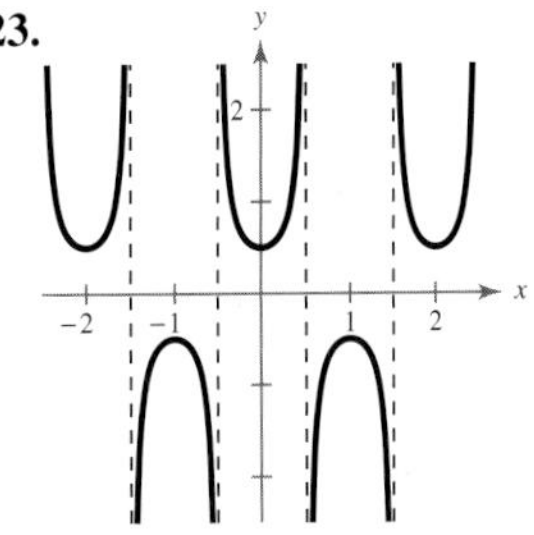

24.

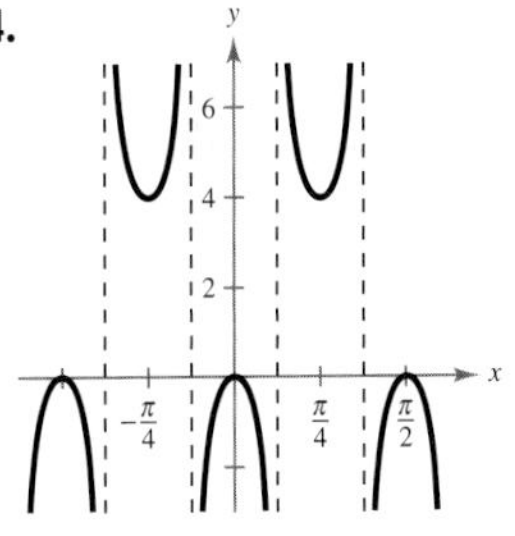

25.

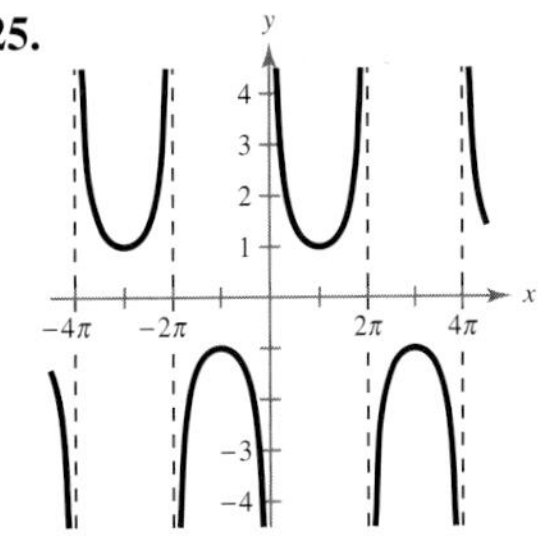

26.

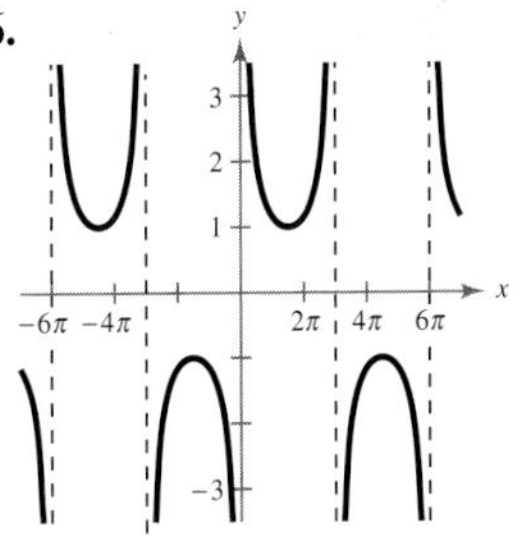

27.

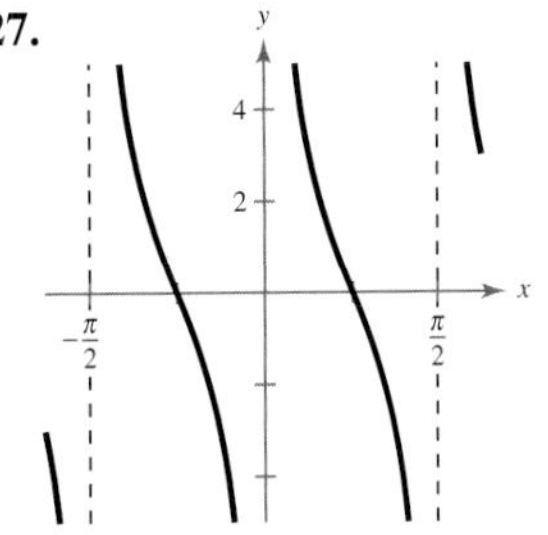

28.

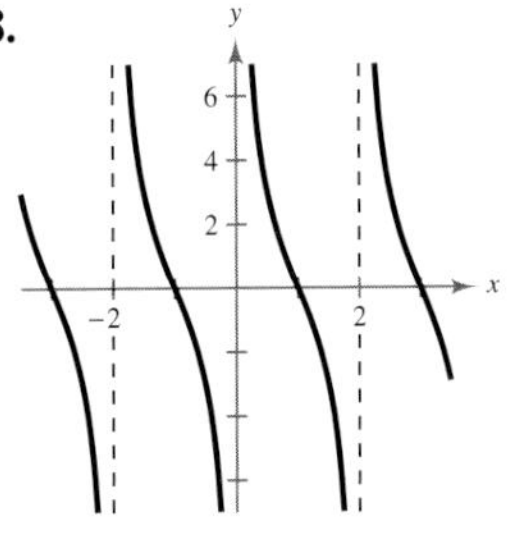

29.

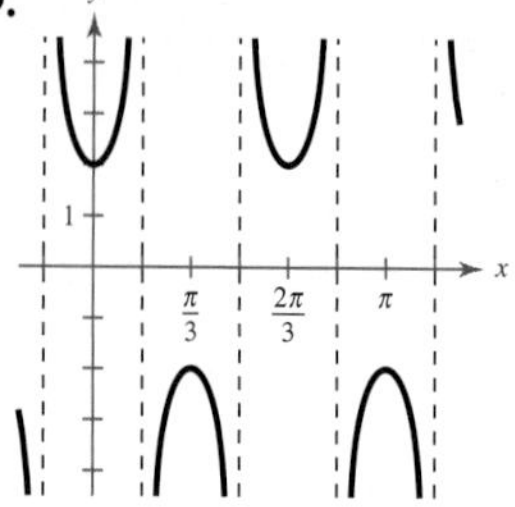

30.

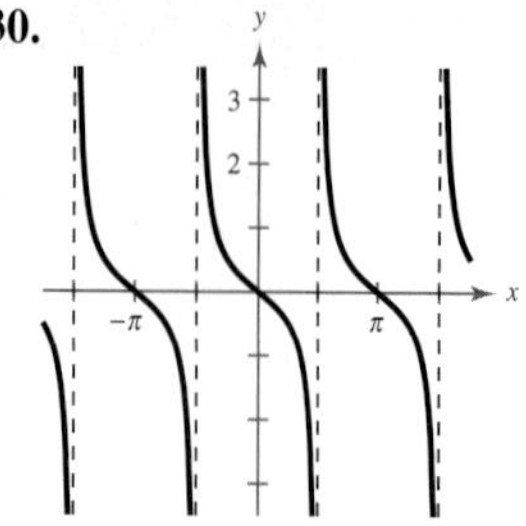

31.

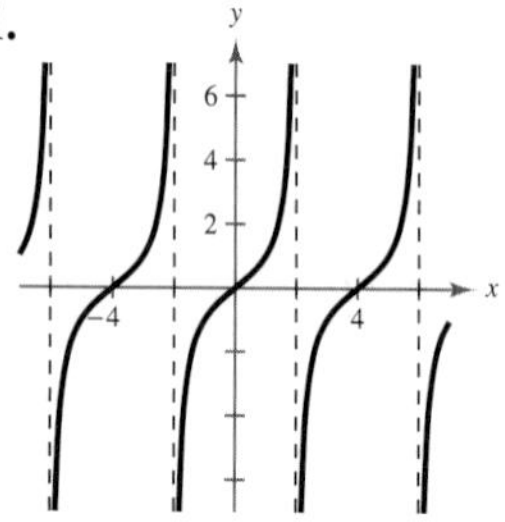

32.

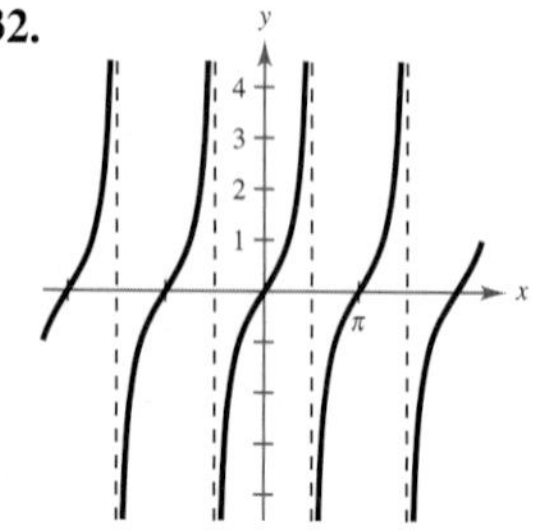

33.

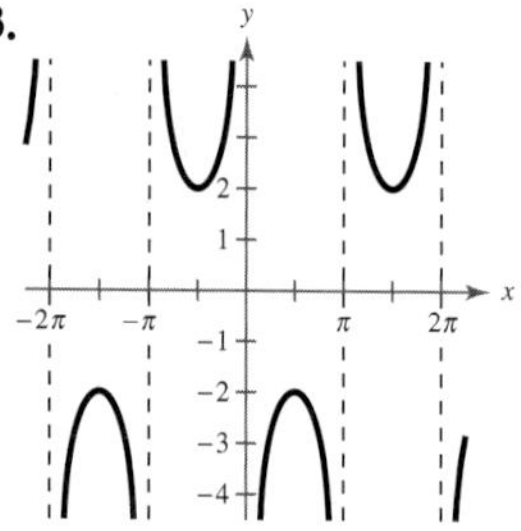

34.

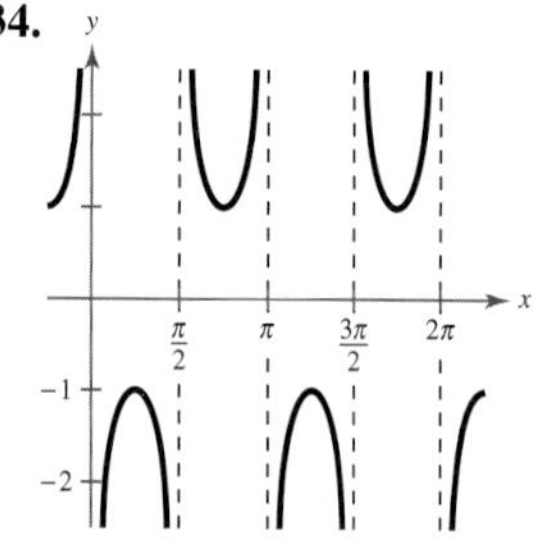

35.

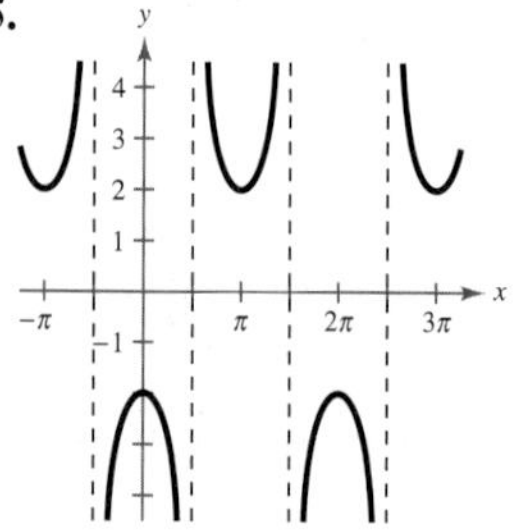

36.

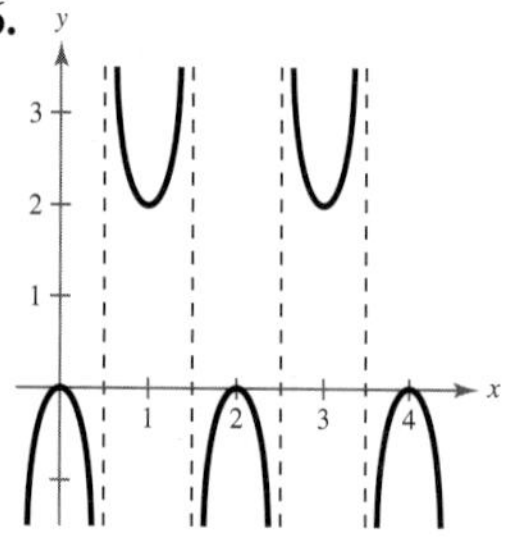

37.

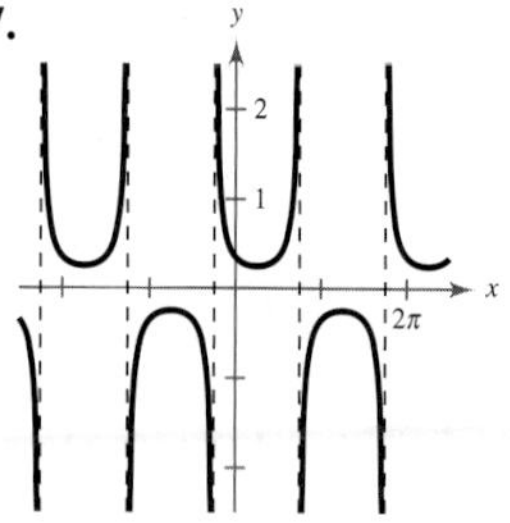

38.

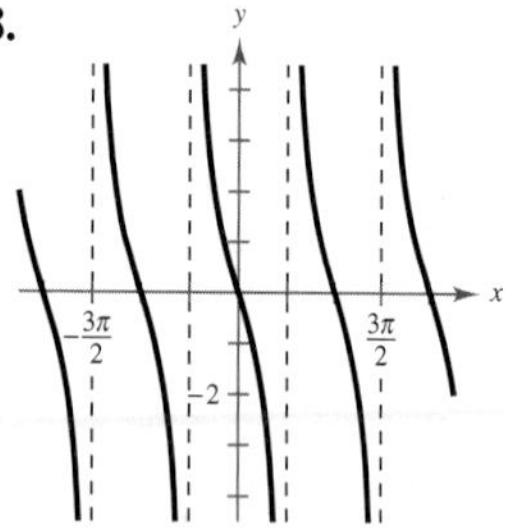

39.

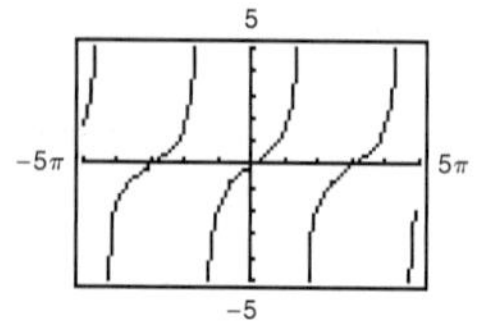

40.

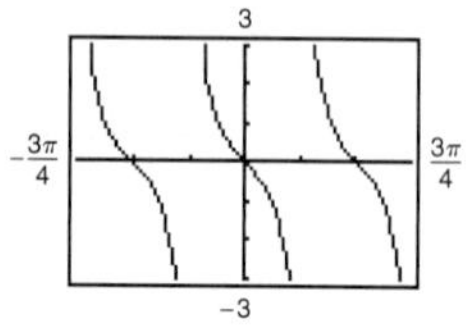

41.

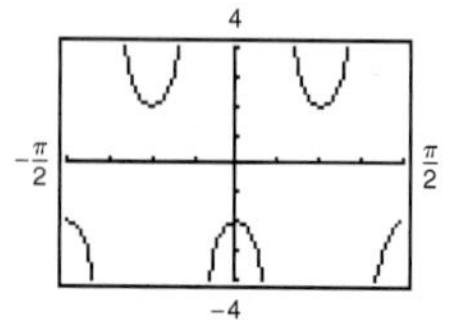

42.

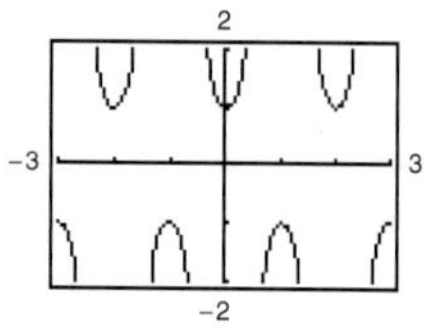

43.

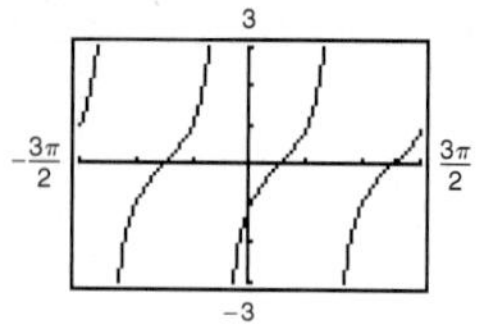

44.

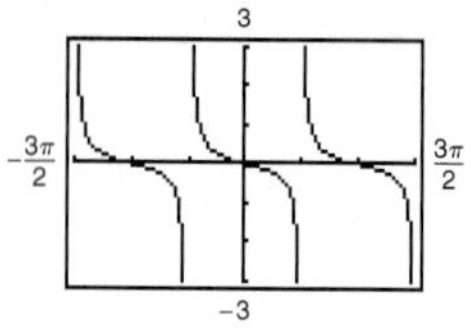

45.

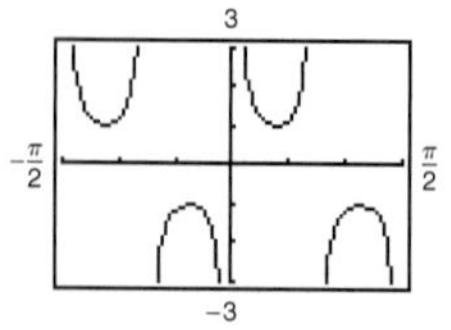

46.

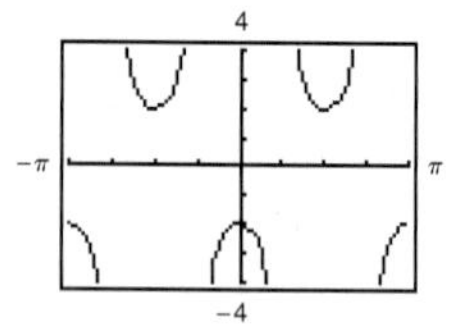

47.

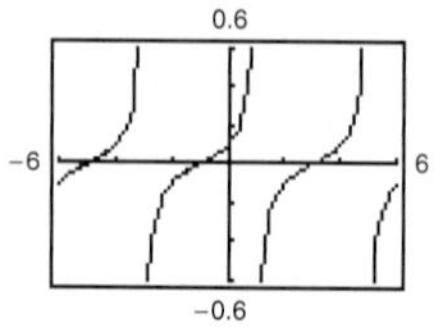

48.

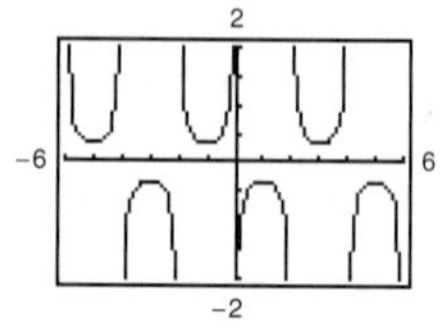

72.

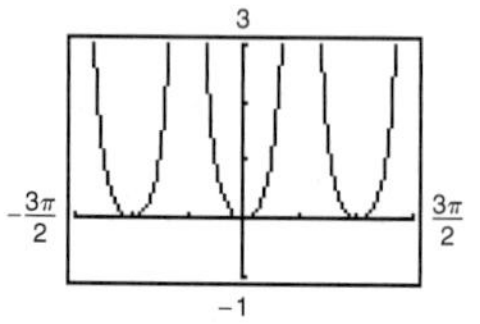

The expressions are equivalent.

77.

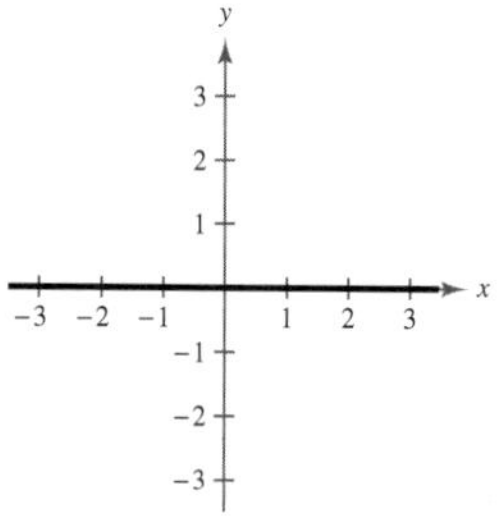

The functions are equal.

78.

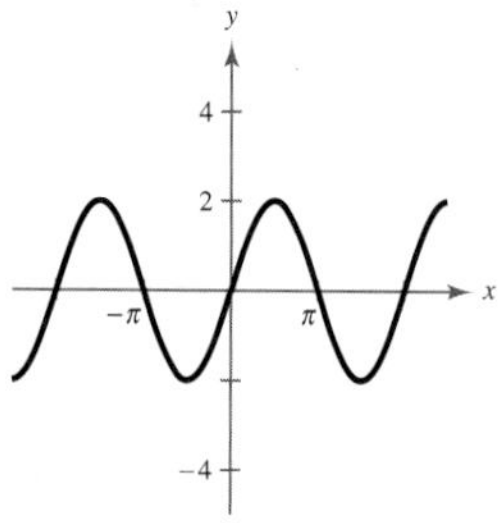

The functions are equal.

79.

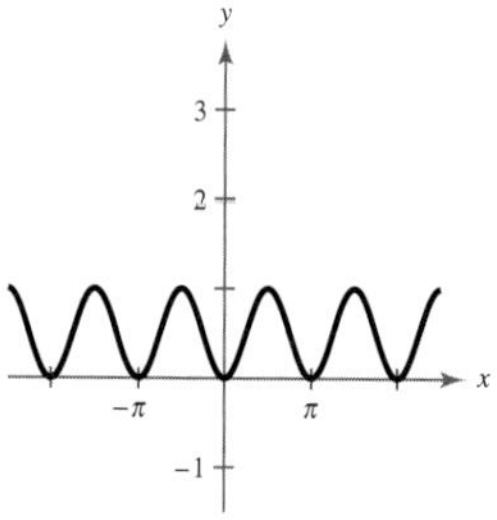

The functions are equal.

80.

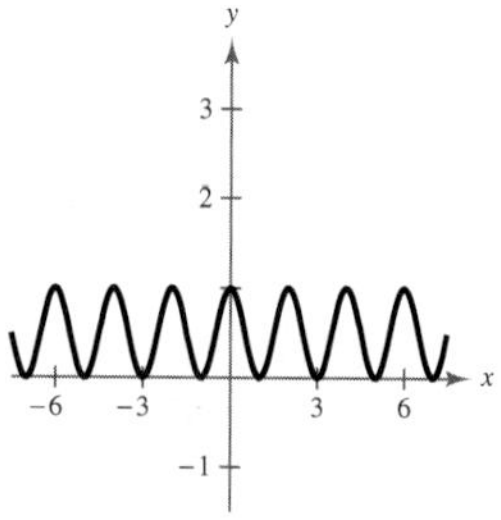

The functions are equal.

81.

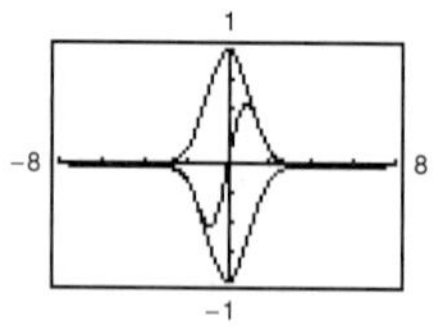

As $x \to \infty$, $g(x) \to 0$.

82.

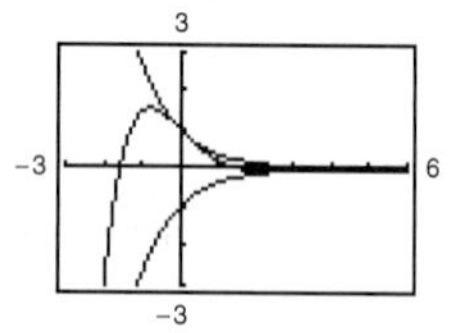

As $x \to \infty$, $f(x) \to 0$.

83.

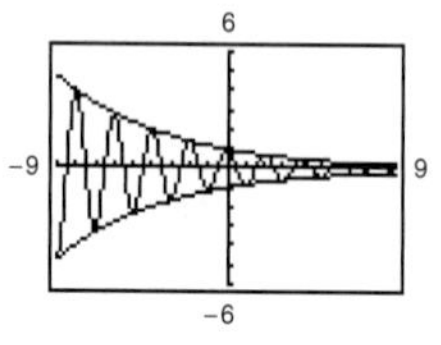

As $x \to \infty$, $f(x) \to 0$.

84.

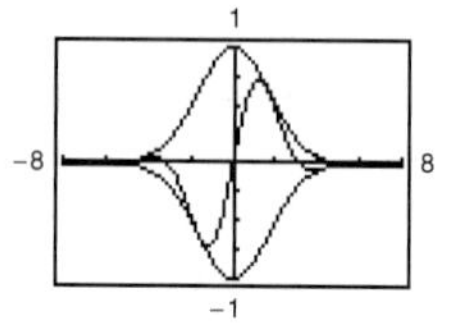

As $x \to \infty$, $h(x) \to 0$.

85.

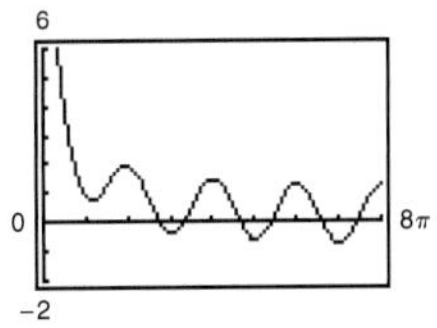

As $x \to 0$, $y \to \infty$.

86.

As $x \to 0$, $y \to \infty$.

106. (a)

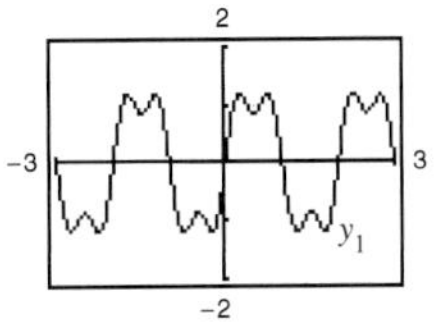

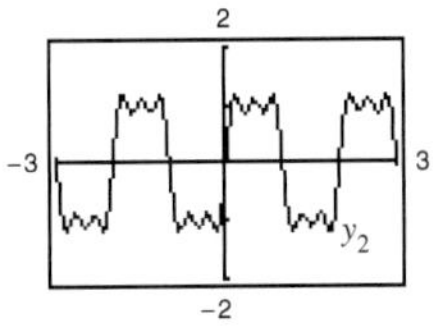

(b) $y_3 = \dfrac{4}{\pi}\left(\sin \pi x + \dfrac{1}{3}\sin 3\pi x + \dfrac{1}{5}\sin 5\pi x + \dfrac{1}{7}\sin 7\pi x\right)$

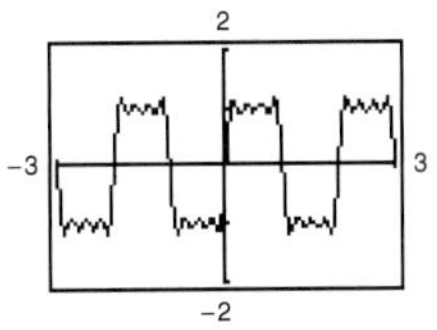

(c) $y_4 = \dfrac{4}{\pi}\left(\sin \pi x + \dfrac{1}{3}\sin 3\pi x + \dfrac{1}{5}\sin 5\pi x + \dfrac{1}{7}\sin 7\pi x + \dfrac{1}{9}\sin 9\pi x\right)$

Section 4.7 *(page 347)*

98. $5\sin\left(\pi t + \arctan \frac{4}{3}\right)$

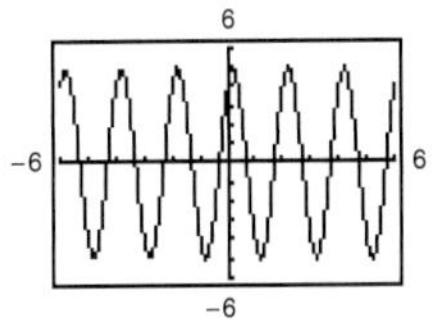

The graph implies that the identity is true.

Section 4.8 *(page 357)*

65. (a)

θ	L_1	L_2	$L_1 + L_2$
0.1	$\dfrac{2}{\sin 0.1}$	$\dfrac{3}{\cos 0.1}$	23.0
0.2	$\dfrac{2}{\sin 0.2}$	$\dfrac{3}{\cos 0.2}$	13.1
0.3	$\dfrac{2}{\sin 0.3}$	$\dfrac{3}{\cos 0.3}$	9.9
0.4	$\dfrac{2}{\sin 0.4}$	$\dfrac{3}{\cos 0.4}$	8.4

(b)

θ	L_1	L_2	$L_1 + L_2$
0.5	$\dfrac{2}{\sin 0.5}$	$\dfrac{3}{\cos 0.5}$	7.6
0.6	$\dfrac{2}{\sin 0.6}$	$\dfrac{3}{\cos 0.6}$	7.2
0.7	$\dfrac{2}{\sin 0.7}$	$\dfrac{3}{\cos 0.7}$	7.0
0.8	$\dfrac{2}{\sin 0.8}$	$\dfrac{3}{\cos 0.8}$	7.1

7.0 m

Review Exercises *(page 364)*

1. (a)

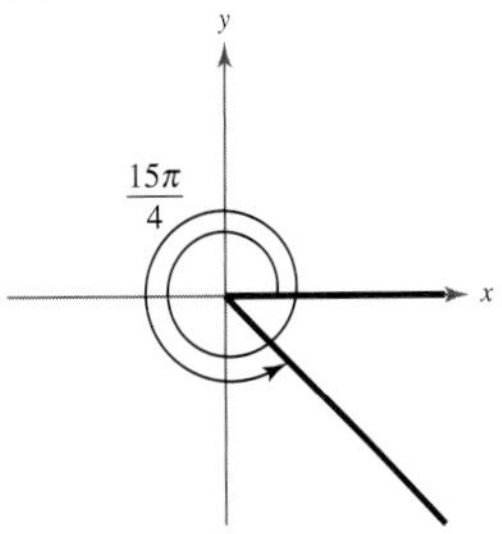

(b) Quadrant IV

(c) $\dfrac{23\pi}{4}, -\dfrac{\pi}{4}$

2. (a)

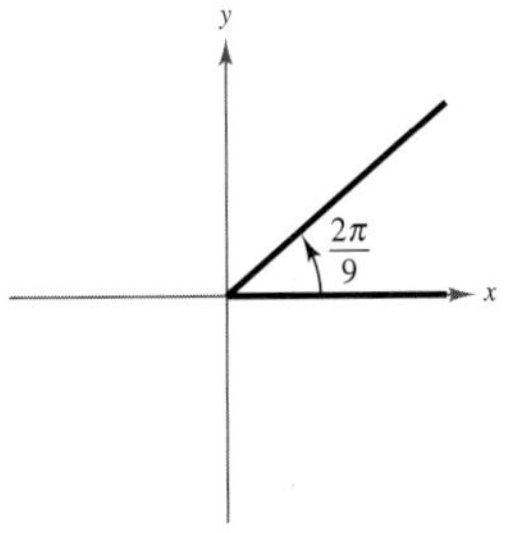

(b) Quadrant I

(c) $\dfrac{20\pi}{9}, -\dfrac{16\pi}{9}$

3. (a)

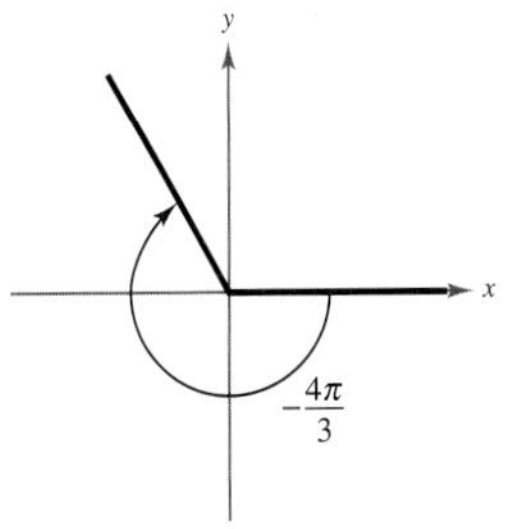

(b) Quadrant II

(c) $\dfrac{2\pi}{3}, -\dfrac{10\pi}{3}$

4. (a)

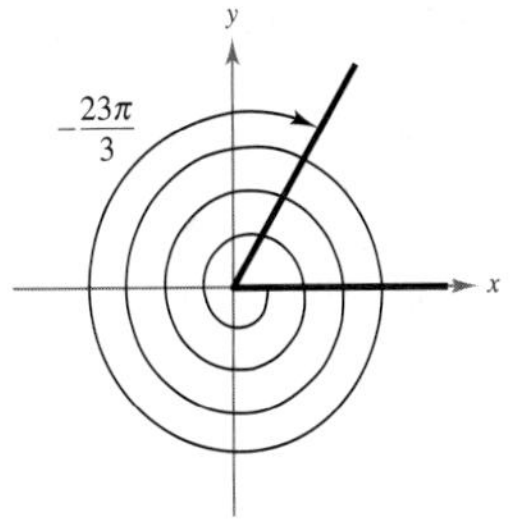

(b) Quadrant I

(c) $\dfrac{\pi}{3}, -\dfrac{17\pi}{3}$

5. (a)

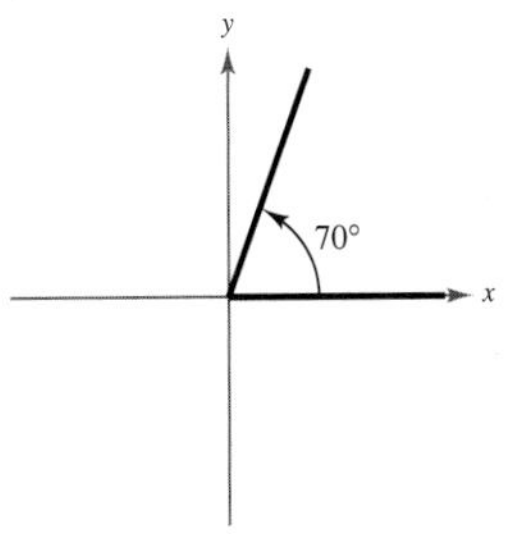

(b) Quadrant I

(c) 430°, −290°

6. (a)

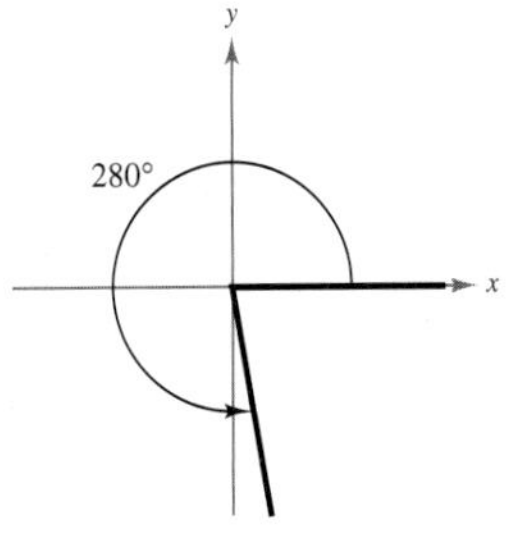

(b) Quadrant IV

(c) 640°, − 80°

7. (a)

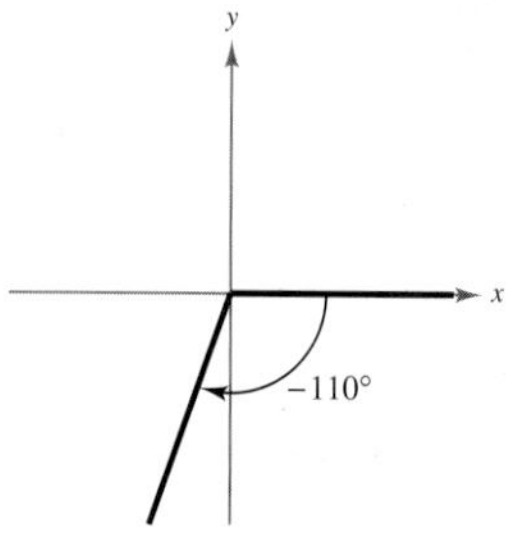

(b) Quadrant III

(c) 250°, −470°

8. (a)

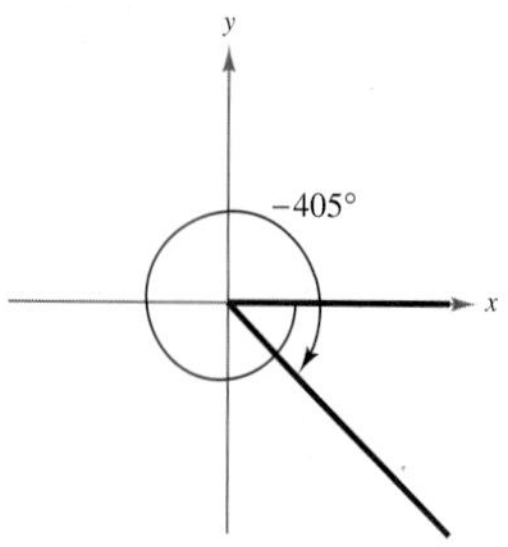

(b) Quadrant IV

(c) 315°, −45°

69. $\sin\theta = \dfrac{\sqrt{21}}{5}$

$\tan\theta = -\dfrac{\sqrt{21}}{2}$

$\csc\theta = \dfrac{5\sqrt{21}}{21}$

$\sec\theta = -\dfrac{5}{2}$

$\cot\theta = -\dfrac{2\sqrt{21}}{21}$

70. $\cos\theta = \dfrac{\sqrt{3}}{2}$

$\tan\theta = -\dfrac{\sqrt{3}}{3}$

$\csc\theta = -2$

$\sec\theta = \dfrac{2\sqrt{3}}{3}$

$\cot\theta = -\sqrt{3}$

71. $\theta' = 84°$

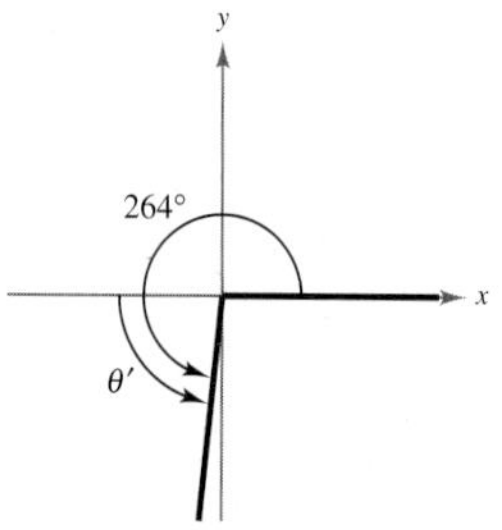

72. $\theta' = 85°$

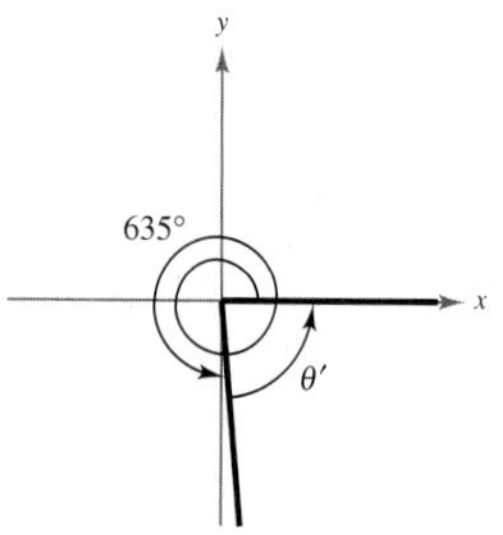

73. $\theta' = \dfrac{\pi}{5}$

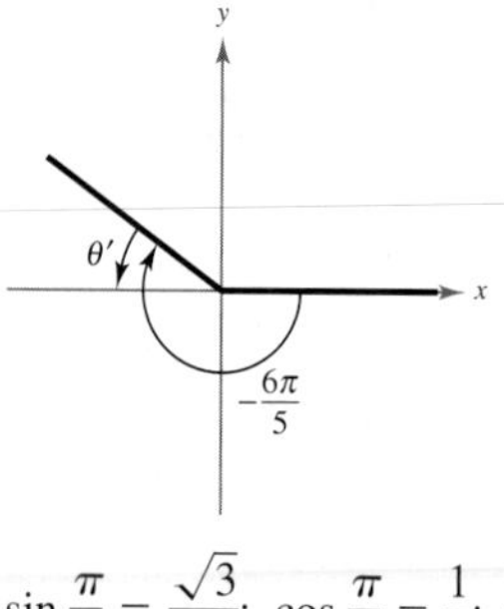

74. $\theta' = \dfrac{\pi}{3}$

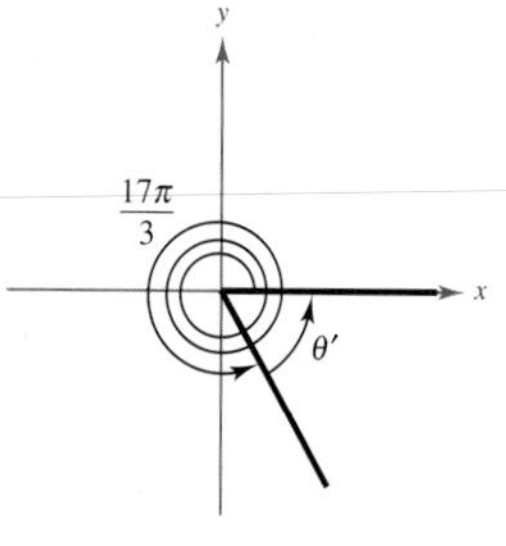

75. $\sin\dfrac{\pi}{3} = \dfrac{\sqrt{3}}{2};\ \cos\dfrac{\pi}{3} = \dfrac{1}{2};\ \tan\dfrac{\pi}{3} = \sqrt{3}$

76. $\sin\dfrac{\pi}{4} = \dfrac{\sqrt{2}}{2};\ \cos\dfrac{\pi}{4} = \dfrac{\sqrt{2}}{2};\ \tan\dfrac{\pi}{4} = 1$

77. $\sin\left(-\dfrac{7\pi}{3}\right) = -\dfrac{\sqrt{3}}{2};\ \cos\left(-\dfrac{7\pi}{3}\right) = \dfrac{1}{2};$

$\tan\left(-\dfrac{7\pi}{3}\right) = -\sqrt{3}$

78. $\sin\left(-\dfrac{5\pi}{4}\right) = \dfrac{\sqrt{2}}{2};\ \cos\left(-\dfrac{5\pi}{4}\right) = -\dfrac{\sqrt{2}}{2};$

$\tan\left(-\dfrac{5\pi}{4}\right) = -1$

79. $\sin 495° = \dfrac{\sqrt{2}}{2};\ \cos 495° = -\dfrac{\sqrt{2}}{2};\ \tan 495° = -1$

80. $\sin(-150°) = -\dfrac{1}{2};\ \cos(-150°) = -\dfrac{\sqrt{3}}{2};$

$\tan(-150°) = \dfrac{\sqrt{3}}{3}$

85.

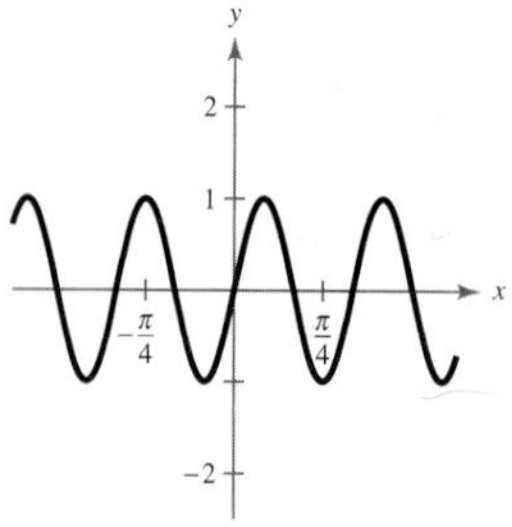

86.

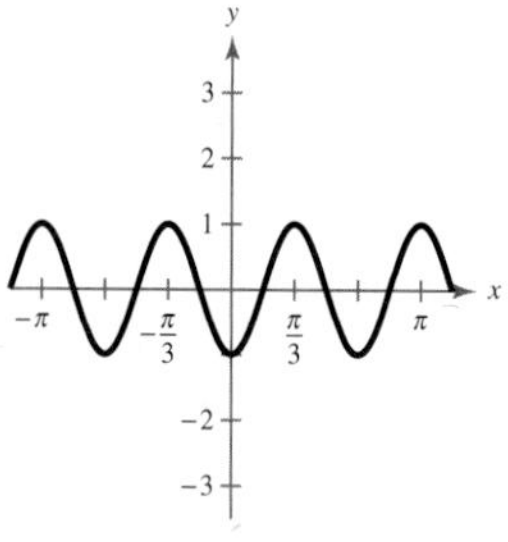

87.

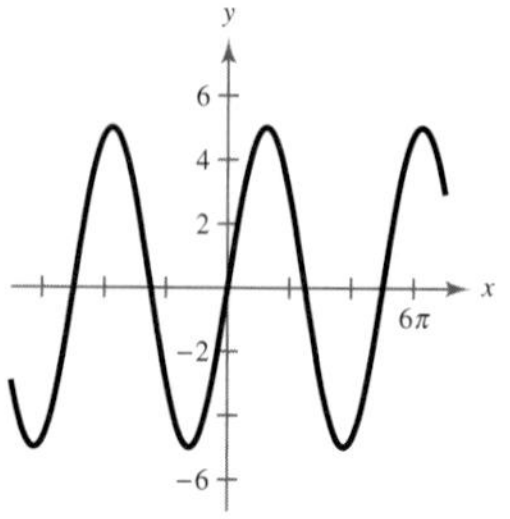

88.

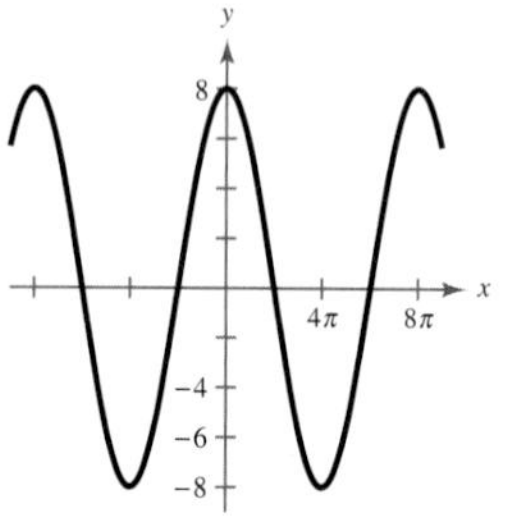

89.

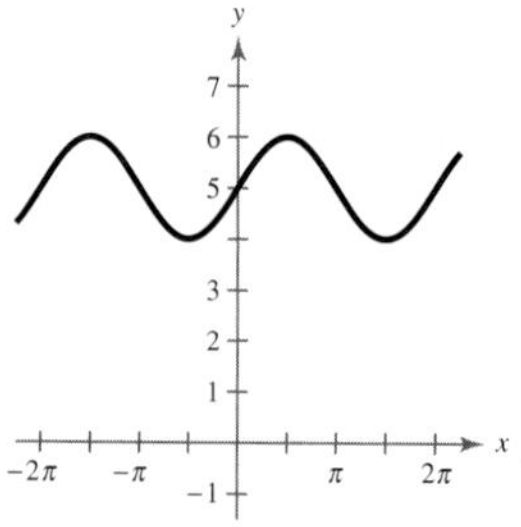

90.

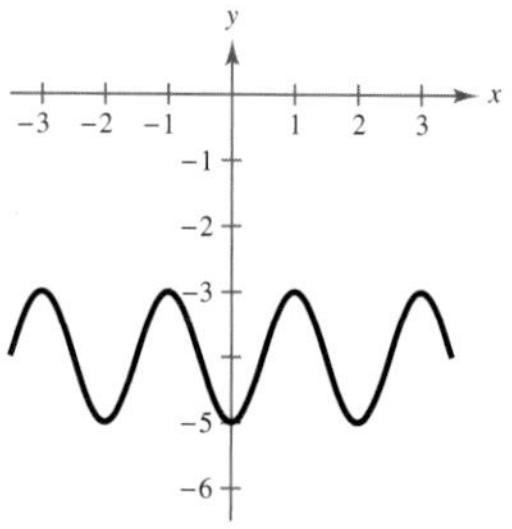

91.

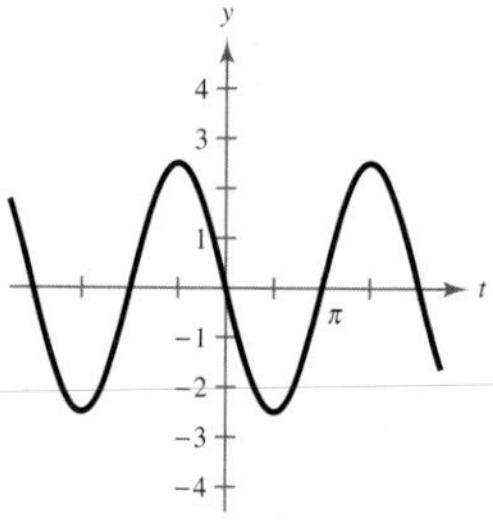

92.

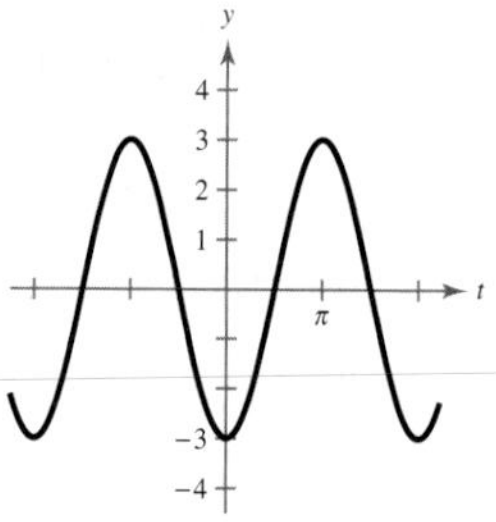

94. (a)

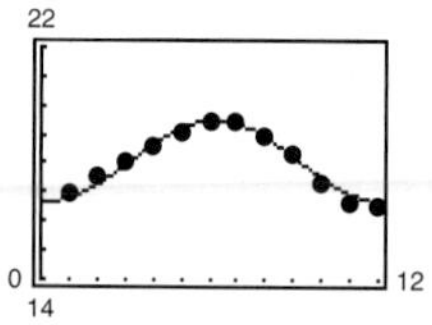

(b) 12. Yes. One period is one year.

(c) 1.41. 1.41 represents the maximum change in time from the average time ($d = 18.09$) of sunset.

95.

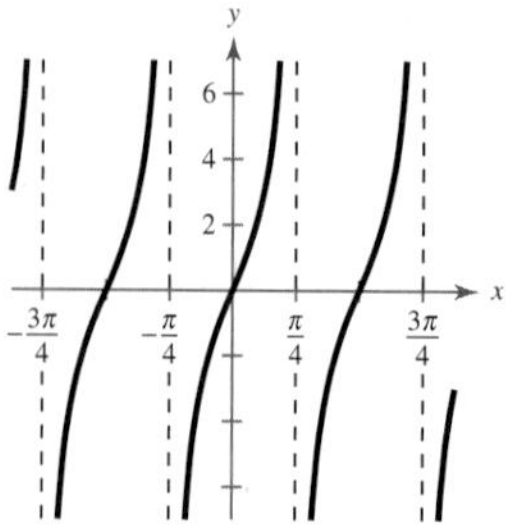

96.

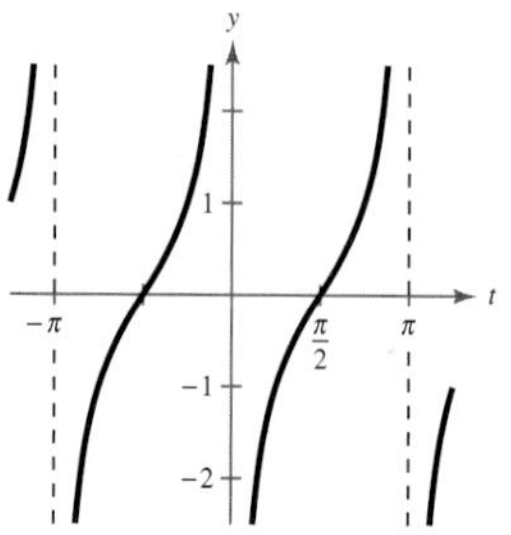

97.

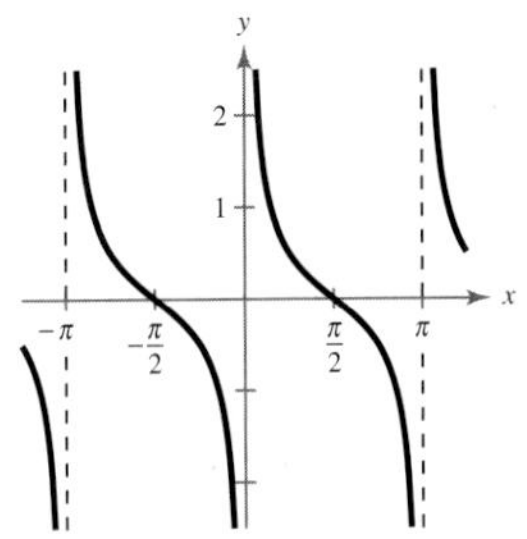

98.

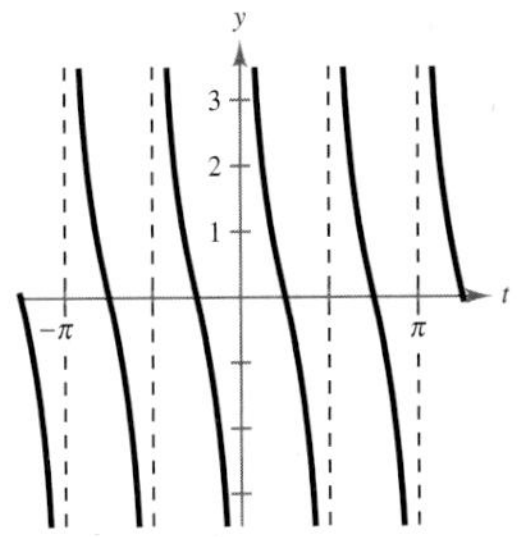

99.

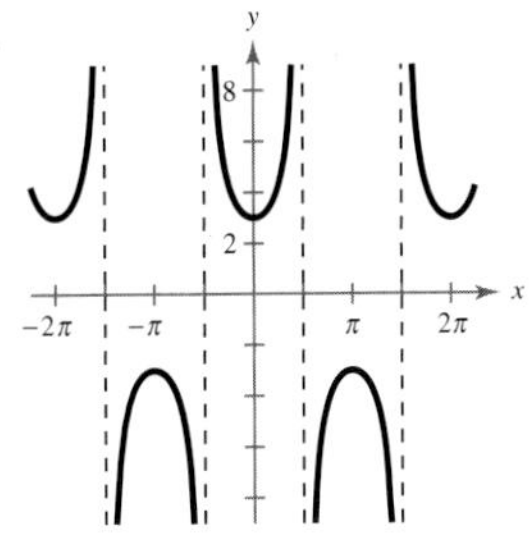

100.

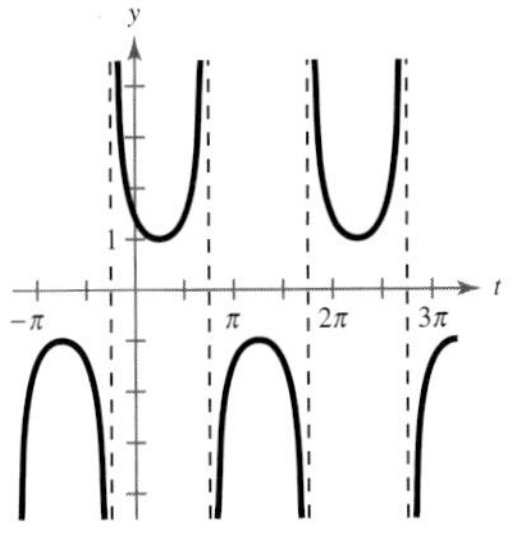

101.

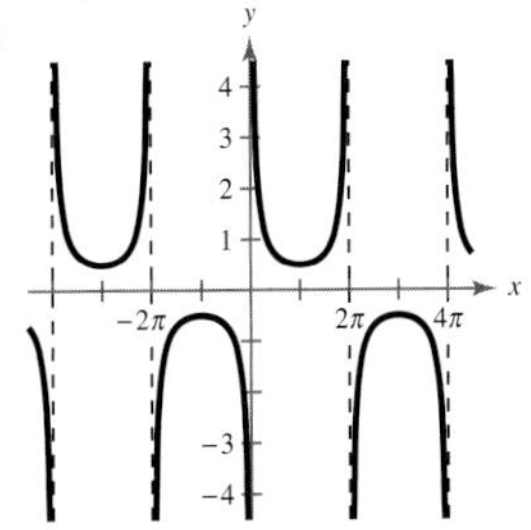

102.

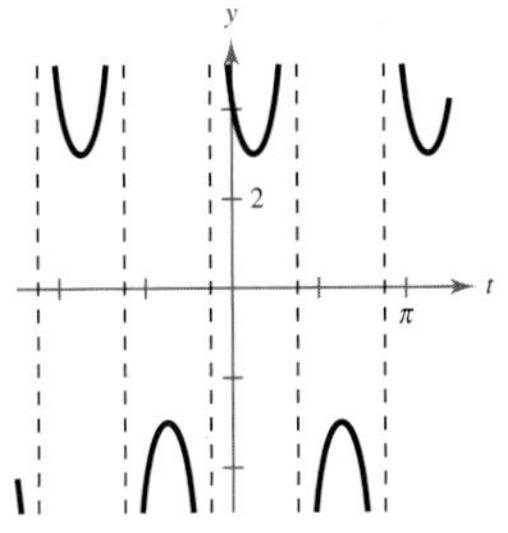

103.

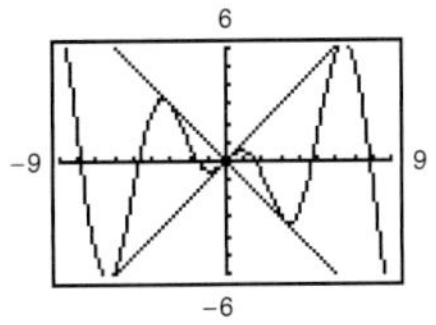

As $x \to +\infty$, $f(x)$ oscillates.

104.

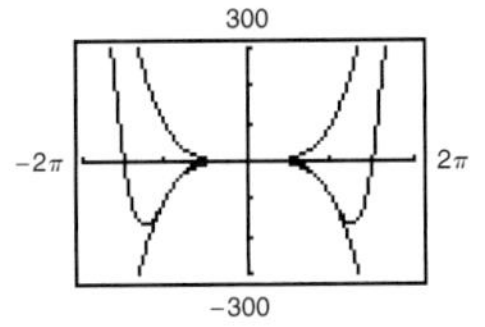

As $x \to +\infty$, $f(x)$ oscillates.

105. $-\dfrac{\pi}{6}$ **106.** $-\dfrac{\pi}{2}$

Chapter Test *(page 367)*

14.

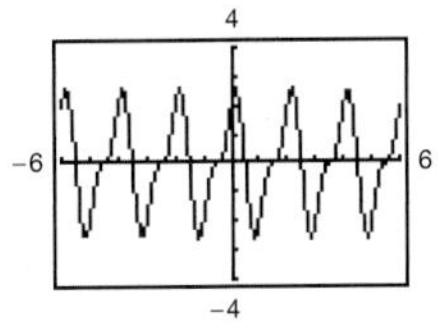

Period: 2

15.

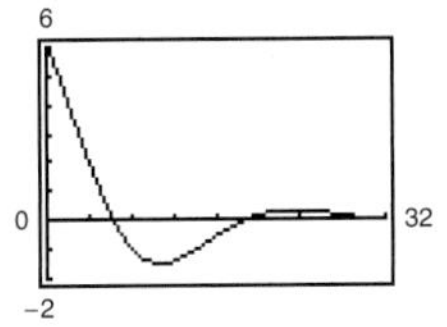

Not periodic

16. $a = -2, b = \dfrac{1}{2}, c = -\dfrac{\pi}{4}$

18.

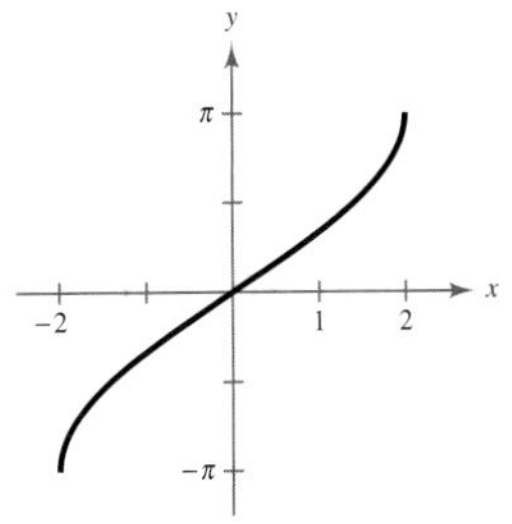

Chapter 5

Section 5.1 *(page 377)*

17. $\sin \phi = -\dfrac{\sqrt{5}}{3}$

$\cos \phi = \dfrac{2}{3}$

$\tan \phi = -\dfrac{\sqrt{5}}{2}$

$\csc \phi = -\dfrac{3\sqrt{5}}{5}$

$\sec \phi = \dfrac{3}{2}$

$\cot \phi = -\dfrac{2\sqrt{5}}{5}$

18. $\sin x = \dfrac{3}{5}$

$\cos x = \dfrac{4}{5}$

$\tan x = \dfrac{3}{4}$

$\csc x = \dfrac{5}{3}$

$\sec x = \dfrac{5}{4}$

$\cot x = \dfrac{4}{3}$

19. $\sin x = \dfrac{1}{3}$

$\cos x = -\dfrac{2\sqrt{2}}{3}$

$\tan x = -\dfrac{\sqrt{2}}{4}$

$\csc x = 3$

$\sec x = -\dfrac{3\sqrt{2}}{4}$

$\cot x = -2\sqrt{2}$

20. $\sin x = \dfrac{\sqrt{15}}{4}$

$\cos x = \dfrac{1}{4}$

$\tan x = \sqrt{15}$

$\csc x = \dfrac{4\sqrt{15}}{15}$

$\sec x = 4$

$\cot x = \dfrac{\sqrt{15}}{15}$

21. $\sin \theta = -\dfrac{2\sqrt{5}}{5}$

$\cos \theta = -\dfrac{\sqrt{5}}{5}$

$\tan \theta = 2$

$\csc \theta = -\dfrac{\sqrt{5}}{2}$

$\sec \theta = -\sqrt{5}$

$\cot \theta = \dfrac{1}{2}$

22. $\sin \theta = -\dfrac{1}{5}$

$\cos \theta = -\dfrac{2\sqrt{6}}{5}$

$\tan \theta = \dfrac{\sqrt{6}}{12}$

$\csc \theta = -5$

$\sec \theta = -\dfrac{5\sqrt{6}}{12}$

$\cot \theta = 2\sqrt{6}$

23. $\sin \theta = -1$
$\cos \theta = 0$
$\tan \theta$ is undefined.
$\csc \theta = -1$
$\sec \theta$ is undefined.
$\cot \theta = 0$

24. $\sin \theta = 1$
$\cos \theta = 0$
$\tan \theta$ is undefined.
$\csc \theta = 1$
$\sec \theta$ is undefined.
$\cot \theta = 0$

87.

x	0.2	0.4	0.6	0.8	1.0
y_1	1.2230	1.5085	1.8958	2.4650	3.4082
y_2	1.2230	1.5085	1.8958	2.4650	3.4082

x	1.2	1.4
y_1	5.3319	11.6814
y_2	5.3319	11.6814

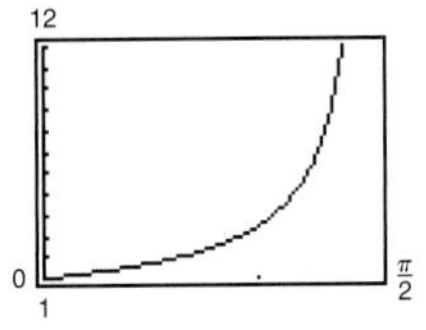

$y_1 = y_2$

88.

x	0.2	0.4	0.6	0.8	1.0
y_1	0.0428	0.2107	0.6871	2.1841	8.3087
y_2	0.0428	0.2107	0.6871	2.1841	8.3087

x	1.2	1.4
y_1	50.3869	1163.6143
y_2	50.3869	1163.6143

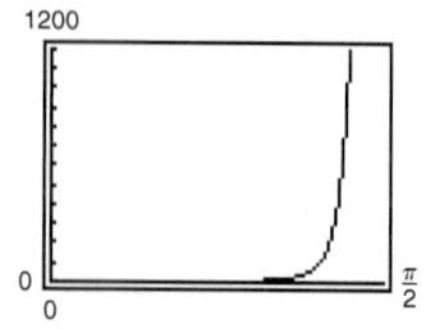

$y_1 = y_2$

Section 5.2 *(page 385)*

58. (a)

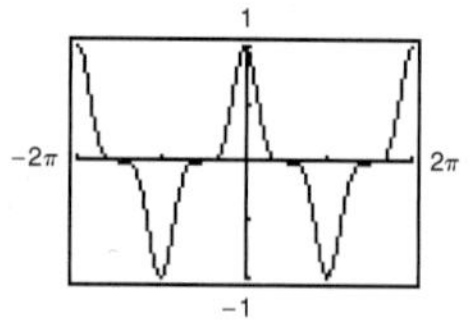

(b)

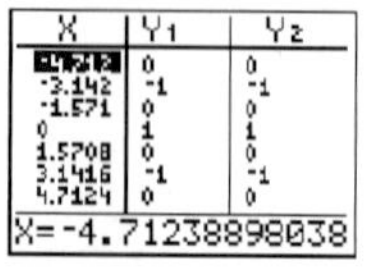

X	Y1	Y2
-4.712	0	0
-3.142	-1	-1
-1.571	0	0
0	1	1
1.5708	0	0
3.1416	-1	-1
4.7124	0	0

X=-4.71238898038

Identity

(c) Answers will vary.

59. (a)

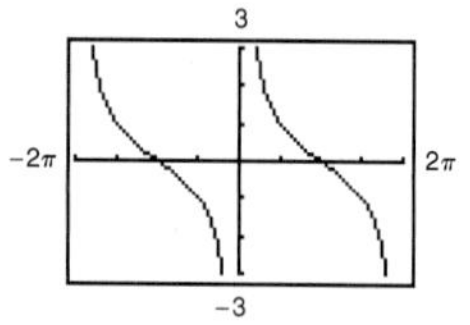

(b)

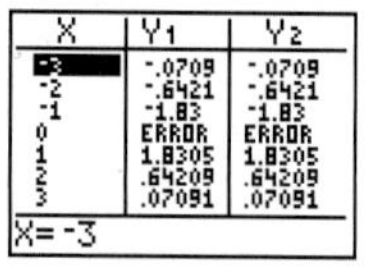

X	Y1	Y2
-3	-.0709	-.0709
-2	-.6421	-.6421
-1	-1.83	-1.83
0	ERROR	ERROR
1	1.8305	1.8305
2	.64209	.64209
3	.07091	.07091

X=-3

Identity

(c) Answers will vary.

60. (a)

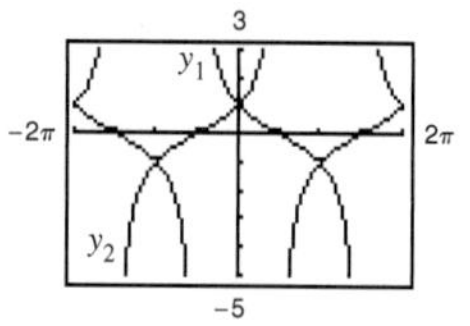

(b)

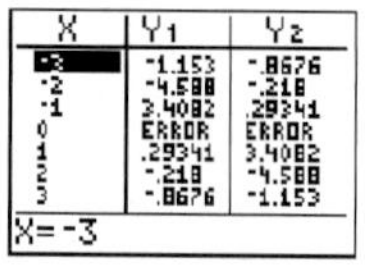

X	Y1	Y2
-3	-1.153	-.8676
-2	-4.588	-.218
-1	3.4082	.29341
0	ERROR	ERROR
1	.29341	3.4082
2	-.218	-4.588
3	-.8676	-1.153

X=-3

Not an identity

(c) Answers will vary.

71. True. Many different techniques can be used to verify identities.

72. False. An identity is an equation that is true for all real values of θ.

73. The equation is not an identity because $\sin\theta = \pm\sqrt{1 - \cos^2\theta}$.

Possible answer: $\dfrac{7\pi}{4}$

74. The equation is not an identity because $\tan\theta = \pm\sqrt{\sec^2\theta - 1}$.

Possible answer: $\dfrac{3\pi}{4}$

75. The equation is not an identity because $1 - \cos^2\theta = \sin^2\theta$.

Possible answer: $-\dfrac{\pi}{2}$

76. The equation is not an identity because $\csc^2\theta - 1 = \cot^2\theta$.

Possible answer: $\dfrac{\pi}{4}$

77. The equation is not an identity because $1 + \tan^2\theta = \sec^2\theta$.

Possible answer: $\dfrac{\pi}{6}$

Section 5.3 *(page 394)*

69. $\arctan\left(\frac{1}{3}\right)$, $\arctan\left(\frac{1}{3}\right) + \pi$, $\arctan\left(-\frac{1}{3}\right) + \pi$, $\arctan\left(-\frac{1}{3}\right) + 2\pi$

82. (a)

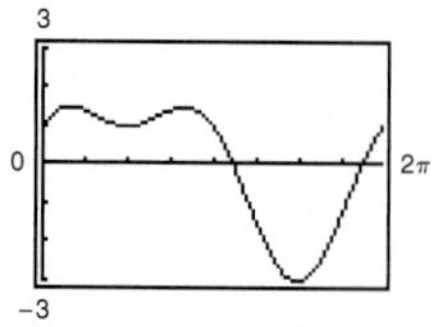

(b) $\dfrac{\pi}{6} \approx 0.5236$

$\dfrac{5\pi}{6} \approx 2.618$

$\dfrac{\pi}{2} \approx 1.5708$

$\dfrac{3\pi}{2} \approx 4.7124$

Maximum: $(0.5236, 1.5)$
Maximum: $(2.6180, 1.5)$
Minimum: $(1.5708, 1)$
Minimum: $(4.7124, -3)$

83. (a)

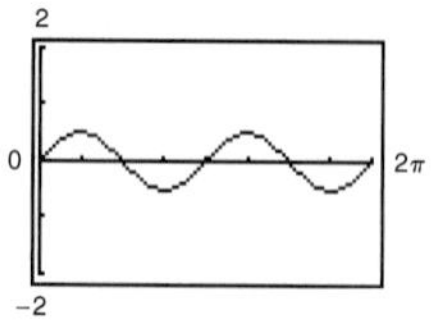

(b) $\dfrac{\pi}{4} \approx 0.7854$

$\dfrac{5\pi}{4} \approx 3.9270$

$\dfrac{3\pi}{4} \approx 2.3562$

$\dfrac{7\pi}{4} \approx 5.4978$

Maximum: $(0.7854, 0.5)$
Maximum: $(3.9270, 0.5)$
Minimum: $(2.3562, -0.5)$
Minimum: $(5.4978, -0.5)$

84. (a)

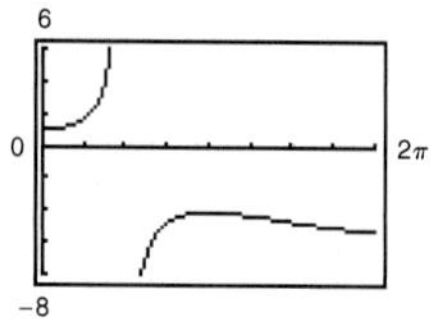

(b) $\pi \approx 3.1416$
0

Maximum: $(3.1416, -4.1416)$
Minimum: $(0, 1)$

87. (a) All real numbers x except $x = 0$
(b) y-axis symmetry; Horizontal asymptote: $y = 1$
(c) Oscillates

104. One solution in $\left[0, \dfrac{\pi}{2}\right)$: $x = \dfrac{\pi}{6}$

Two solutions in $[0, 2\pi)$: $x = \dfrac{\pi}{6}$ and $x = \dfrac{5\pi}{6}$

General solution is all x such that $x = \dfrac{\pi}{6} + 2\pi n$ or $x = \dfrac{5\pi}{6} + 2\pi n$, for integers n.

To find the solutions in the two intervals, you find the angles in each interval for which the sine of the angle is equal to 1/2. To find the general solution, you use the angles you found in the interval $[0, 2\pi)$, which is one cycle of the sine function, and then add or subtract multiples of 2π. The general solution represents all solutions of the equation.

Section 5.4 *(page 402)*

91. True. $\sin(u \pm v) = \sin u \cos v \pm \cos u \sin v$

92. False. $\cos(u \pm v) = \cos u \cos v \mp \sin u \sin v$

94. True.

$$\sin\left(x - \frac{\pi}{2}\right) = \sin x \cos\frac{\pi}{2} - \cos x \sin\frac{\pi}{2} = -\cos x$$

Section 5.5 (page 413)

78. $0, \frac{\pi}{3}, \frac{5\pi}{3}$

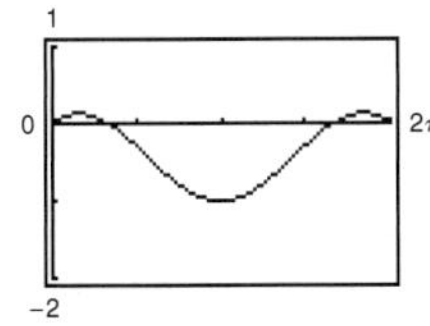

79. $\frac{\pi}{3}, \pi, \frac{5\pi}{3}$

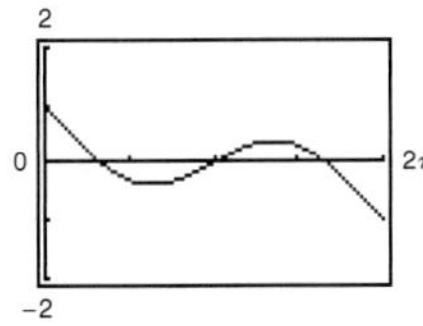

80. $0, \frac{\pi}{2}, \frac{3\pi}{2}$

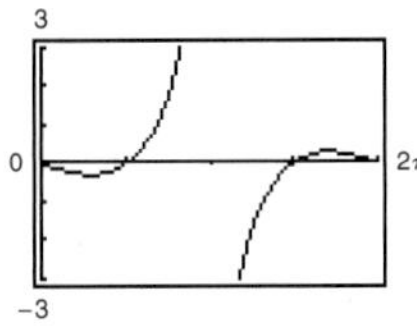

81. $\frac{1}{2}\left(\sin\frac{\pi}{2} + \sin\frac{\pi}{6}\right)$ **82.** $2\left(\sin\frac{7\pi}{6} + \sin\frac{\pi}{2}\right)$

83. $5(\cos 60° + \cos 90°)$ **84.** $3(\sin 60° + \sin 30°)$

85. $\frac{1}{2}(\cos 2\theta - \cos 8\theta)$ **86.** $\frac{3}{2}(\cos(-10\alpha) - \cos 2\alpha)$

87. $\frac{7}{2}(\sin(-2\beta) - \sin(-8\beta))$ **88.** $\frac{1}{2}(\cos(-2\theta) + \cos 6\theta)$

91. $2 \sin 2\theta \cos \theta$ **92.** $2 \cos 4\theta \sin \theta$ **93.** $2 \cos 4x \cos 2x$

94. $2 \cos \frac{5x}{2} \cos\left(-\frac{3x}{2}\right)$ **95.** $2 \cos \alpha \sin \beta$

96. $2 \cos(\phi + \pi) \cos \pi = -2 \cos(\phi + \pi)$

103. $0, \frac{\pi}{4}, \frac{\pi}{2}, \frac{3\pi}{4}, \pi, \frac{5\pi}{4}, \frac{3\pi}{2}, \frac{7\pi}{4}$

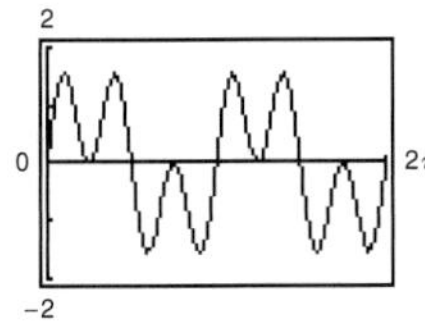

104. $0, \frac{\pi}{4}, \frac{\pi}{2}, \frac{3\pi}{4}, \pi, \frac{5\pi}{4}, \frac{3\pi}{2}, \frac{7\pi}{4}$

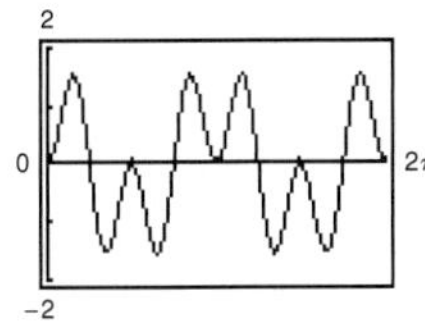

105. $\frac{\pi}{6}, \frac{5\pi}{6}$

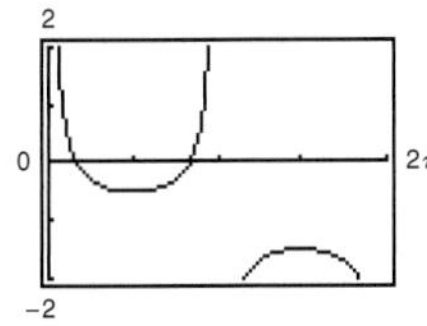

106. $0, \frac{\pi}{2}, \pi, \frac{3\pi}{2}, \frac{\pi}{4}, \frac{3\pi}{4}, \frac{5\pi}{4}, \frac{7\pi}{4}$

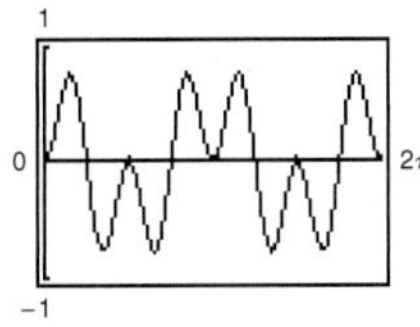

Review Exercises (page 418)

101. $\frac{1}{2}\left(\sin\frac{\pi}{3} - \sin 0\right) = \frac{1}{2}\sin\frac{\pi}{3}$

102. $3[\cos(-30°) - \cos 60°]$

Chapter 6

Section 6.3 (page 454)

29.

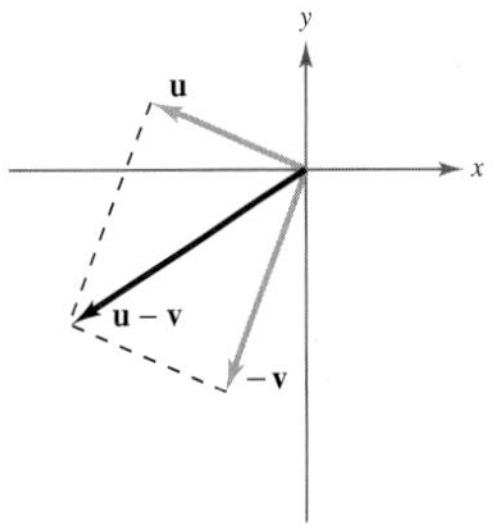

30.

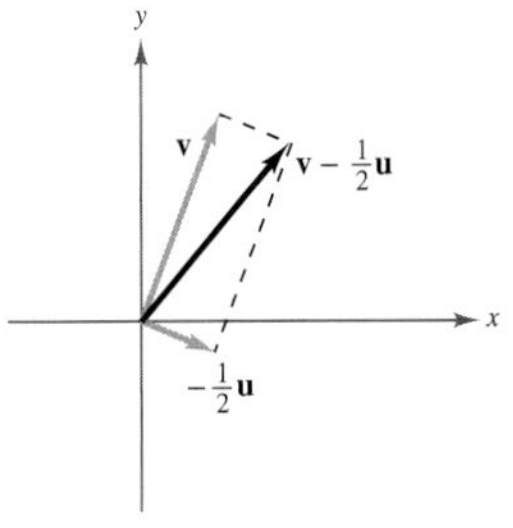

33. (a) $\langle -5, 3\rangle$

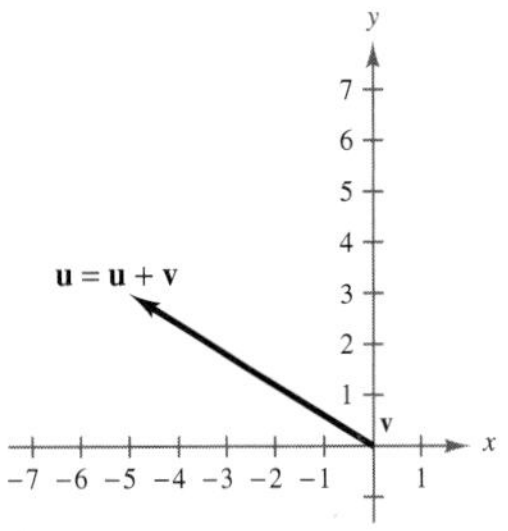

(b) $\langle -5, 3\rangle$

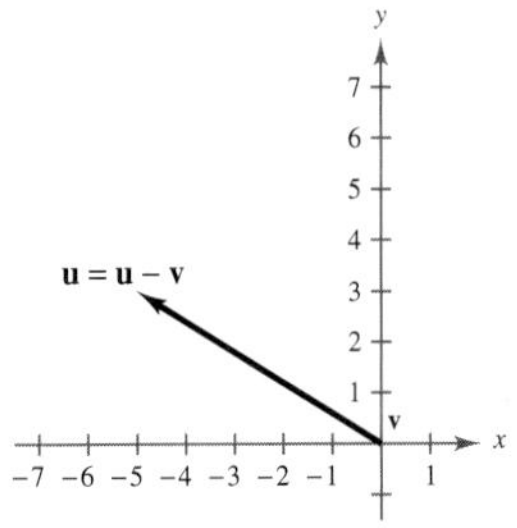

(c) $\langle -10, 6\rangle$

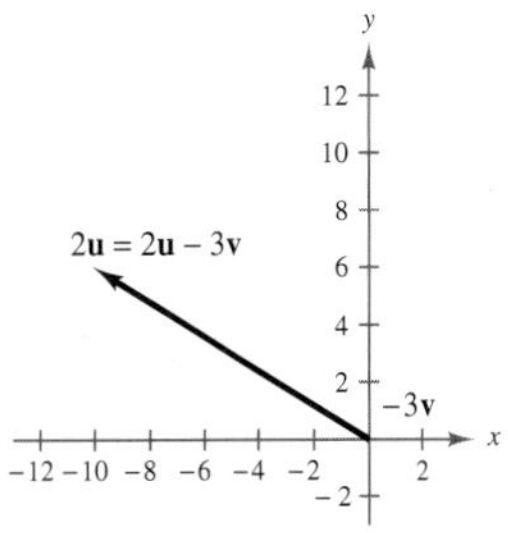

34. (a) $\langle 2, 1\rangle$

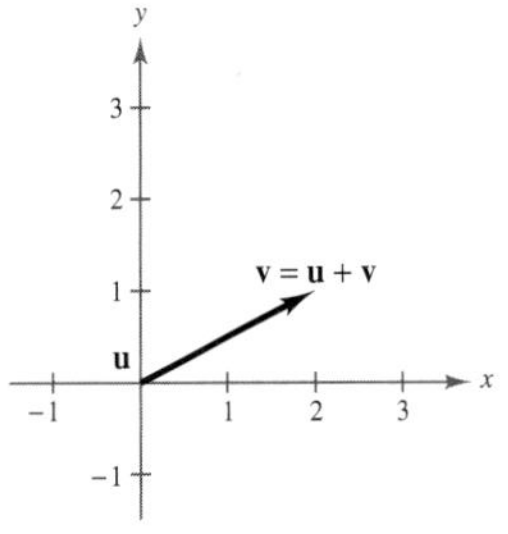

(b) $\langle -2, -1\rangle$

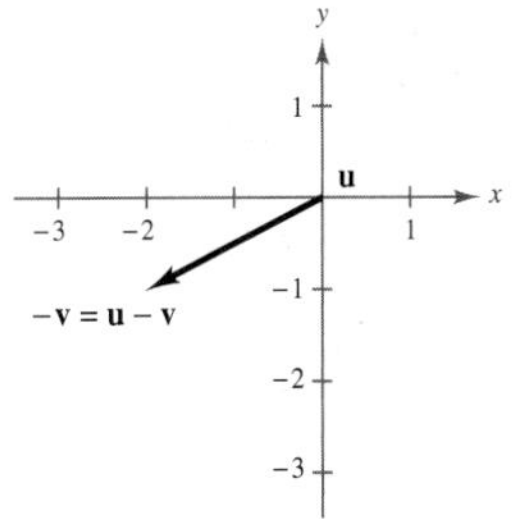

(c) $\langle -6, -3\rangle$

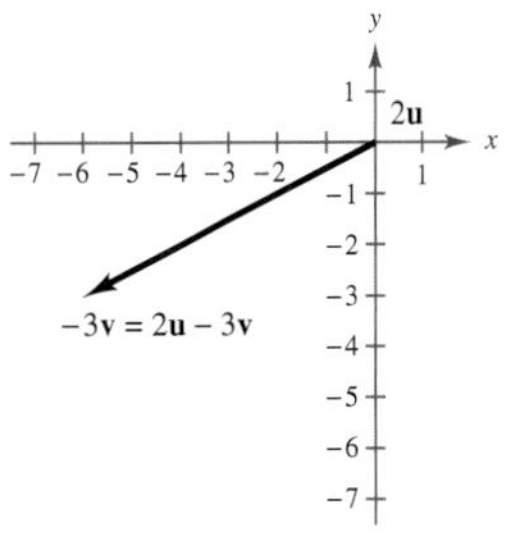

ADDITIONAL ANSWERS

35. (a) $3\mathbf{i} - 2\mathbf{j}$

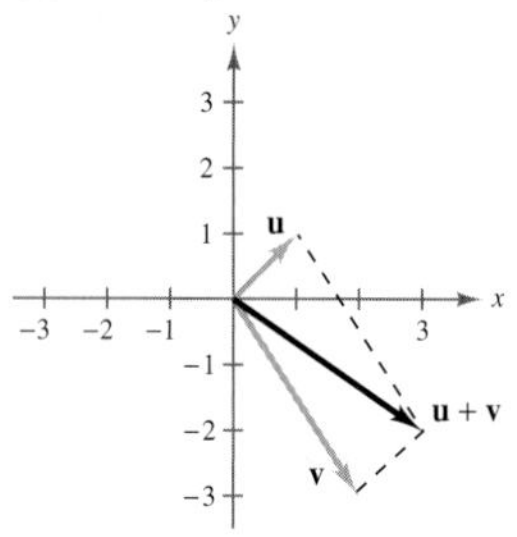

(b) $-\mathbf{i} + 4\mathbf{j}$

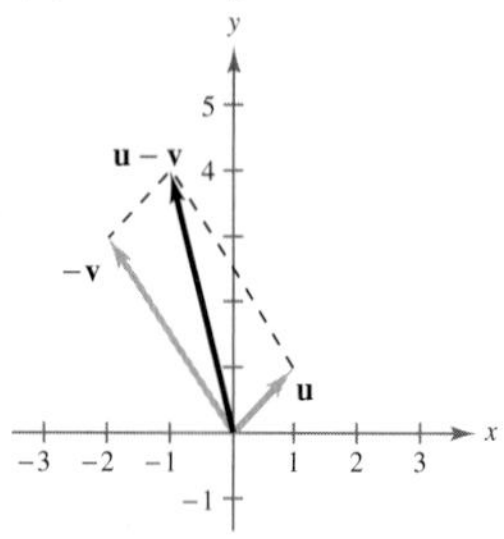

(c) $-4\mathbf{i} + 11\mathbf{j}$

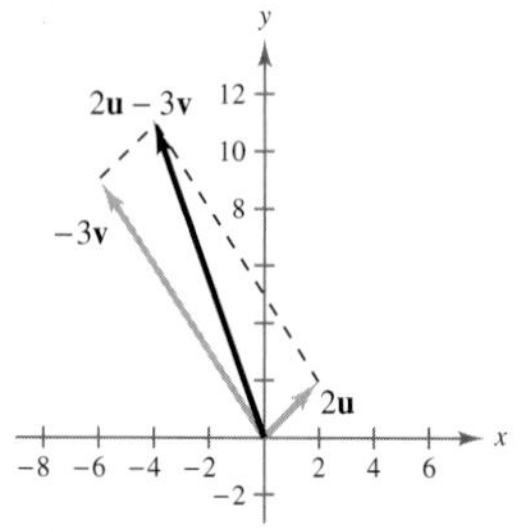

36. (a) $-2\mathbf{i} + 4\mathbf{j}$

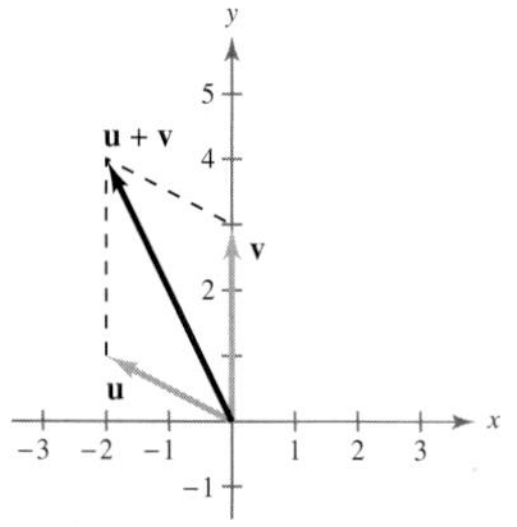

(b) $-2\mathbf{i} - 2\mathbf{j}$

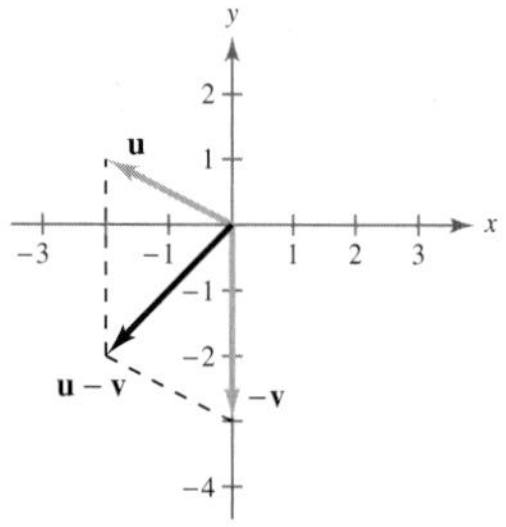

(c) $-4\mathbf{i} - 7\mathbf{j}$

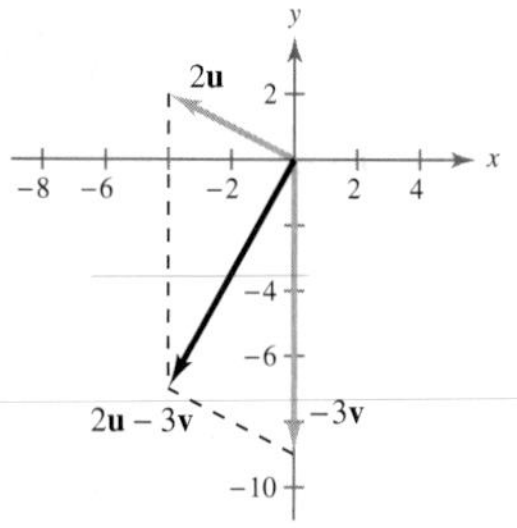

37. (a) $2\mathbf{i} + \mathbf{j}$

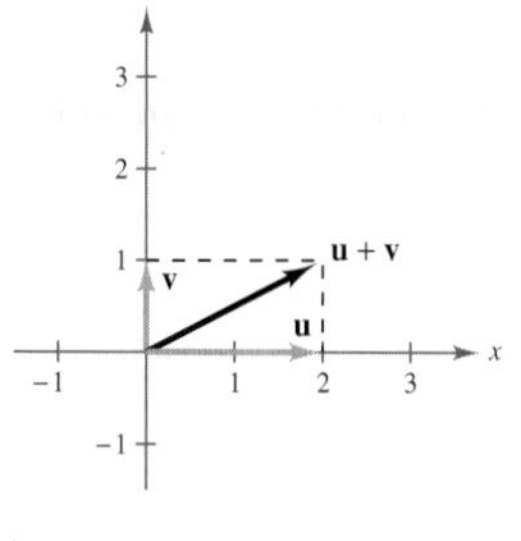

(b) $2\mathbf{i} - \mathbf{j}$

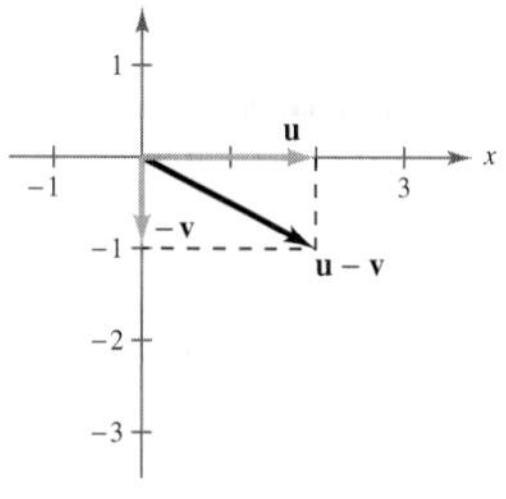

(c) $4\mathbf{i} - 3\mathbf{j}$

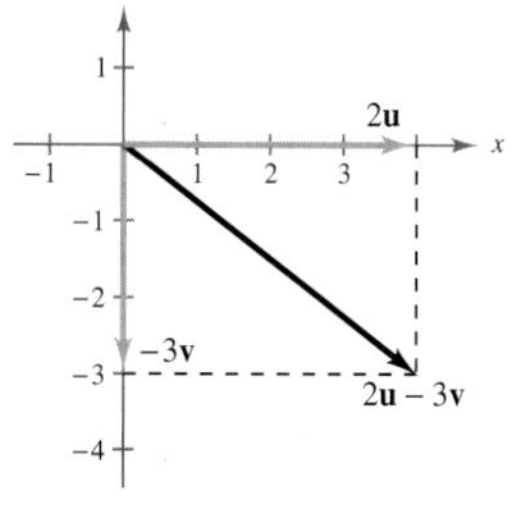

38. (a) $3\mathbf{i} + 2\mathbf{j}$

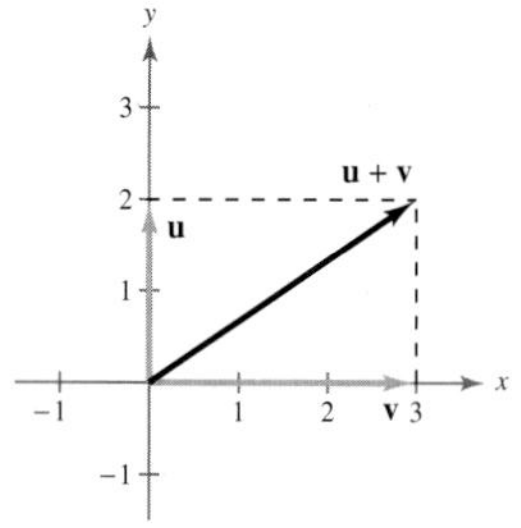

(b) $-3\mathbf{i} + 2\mathbf{j}$

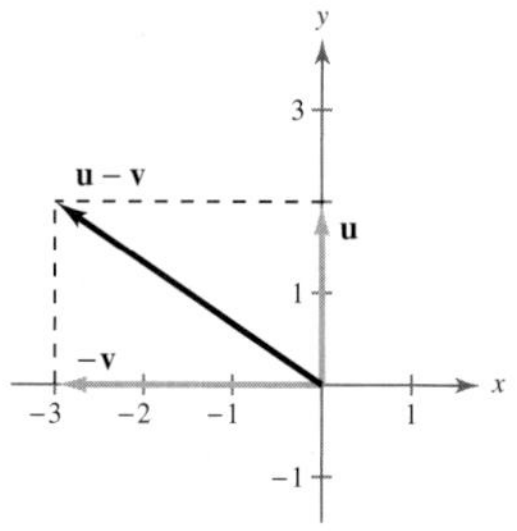

(c) $-9\mathbf{i} + 4\mathbf{j}$

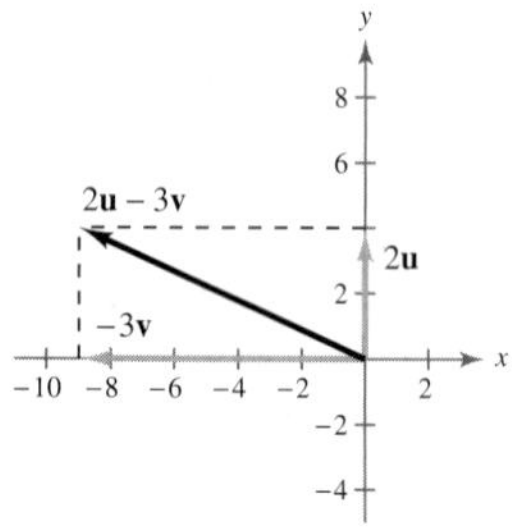

57. $\mathbf{v} = \left\langle 3, -\frac{3}{2} \right\rangle$

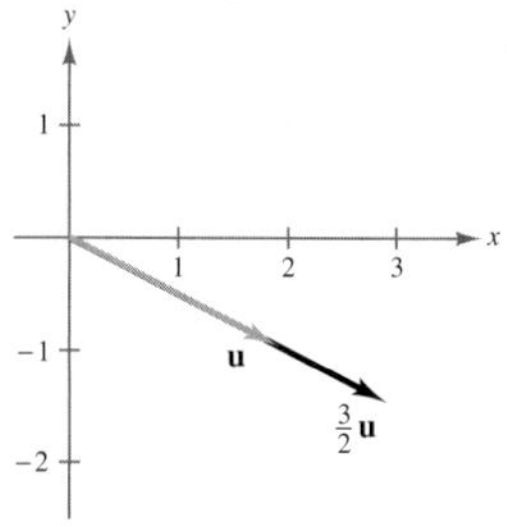

58. $\mathbf{v} = \left\langle \frac{3}{4}, \frac{3}{2} \right\rangle$

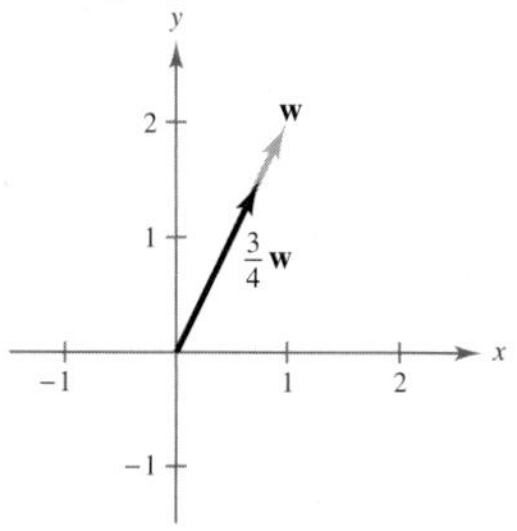

59. $\mathbf{v} = \langle 4, 3 \rangle$

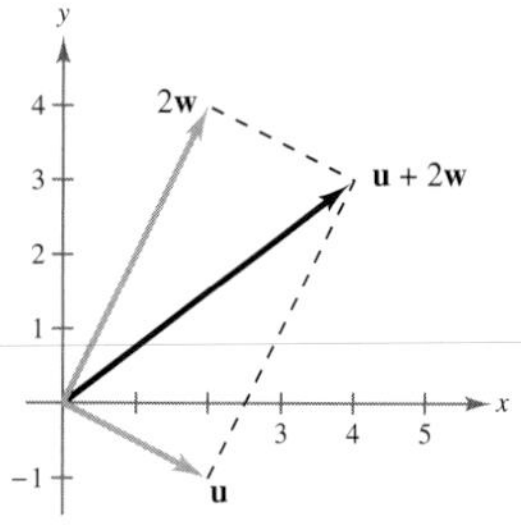

60. $\mathbf{v} = \langle -1, 3 \rangle$

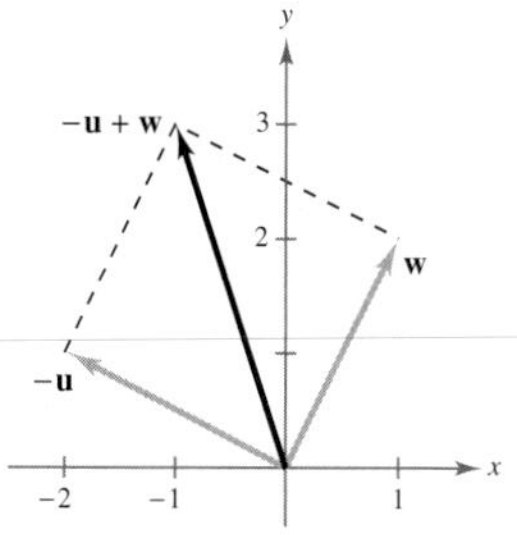

61. $\mathbf{v} = \left\langle \frac{7}{2}, -\frac{1}{2} \right\rangle$

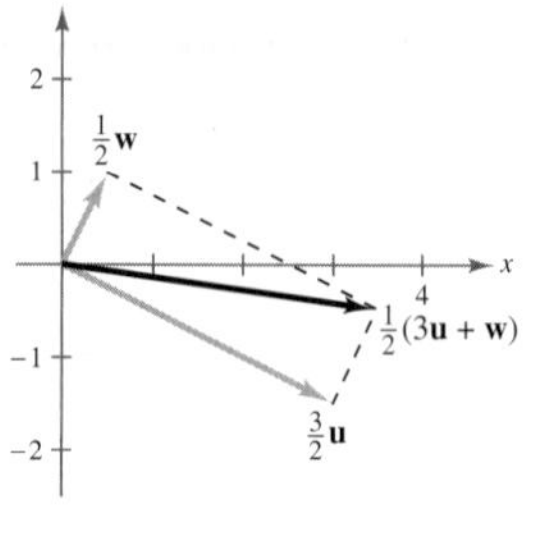

62. $\mathbf{v} = \langle 0, -5 \rangle$

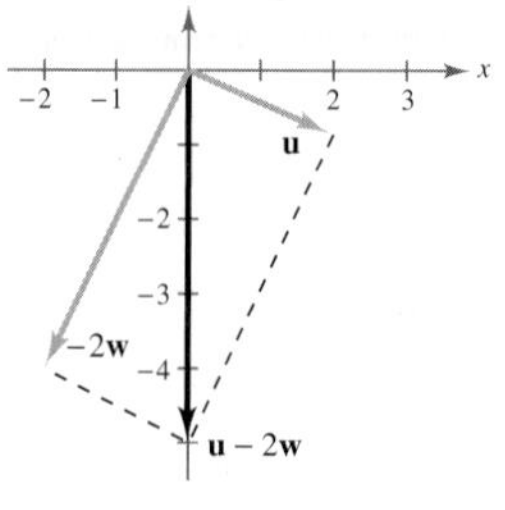

67. $\mathbf{v} = \langle 3, 0 \rangle$

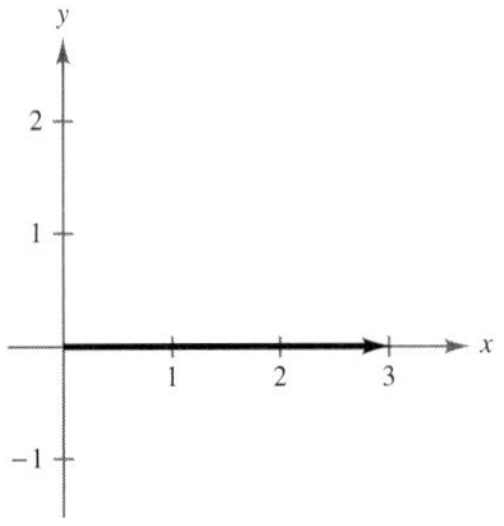

68. $\mathbf{v} = \left\langle \dfrac{\sqrt{2}}{2}, \dfrac{\sqrt{2}}{2} \right\rangle$

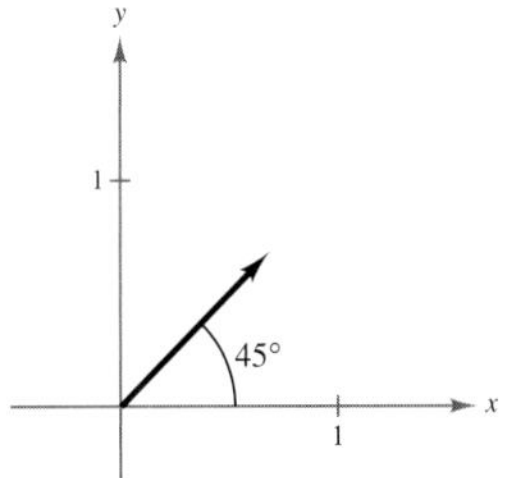

69. $\mathbf{v} = \left\langle -\dfrac{7\sqrt{3}}{4}, \dfrac{7}{4} \right\rangle$

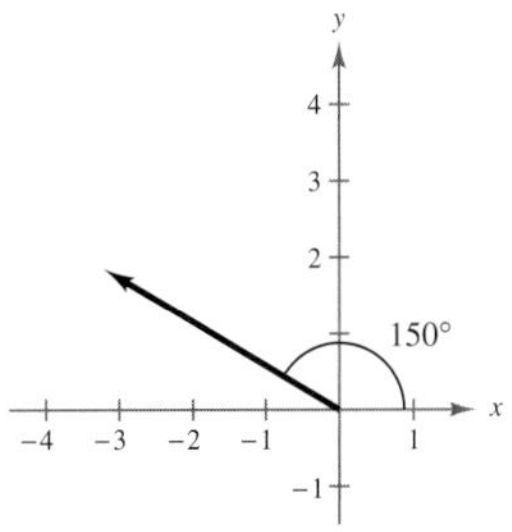

70. $\mathbf{v} = \left\langle -\dfrac{3\sqrt{3}}{8}, \dfrac{3}{8} \right\rangle$

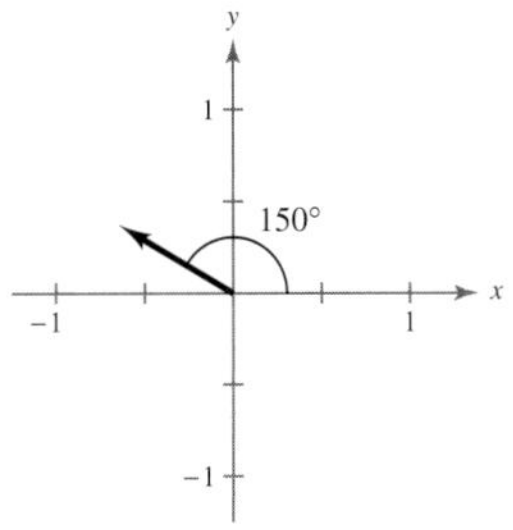

71. $\mathbf{v} = \langle \sqrt{6}, \sqrt{6} \rangle$

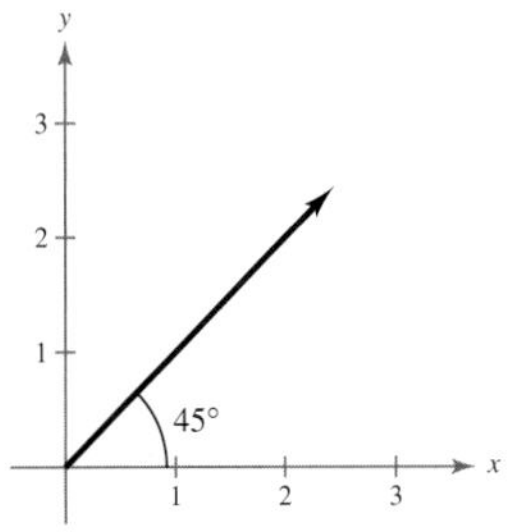

72. $\mathbf{v} = \langle 0, 4\sqrt{3} \rangle$

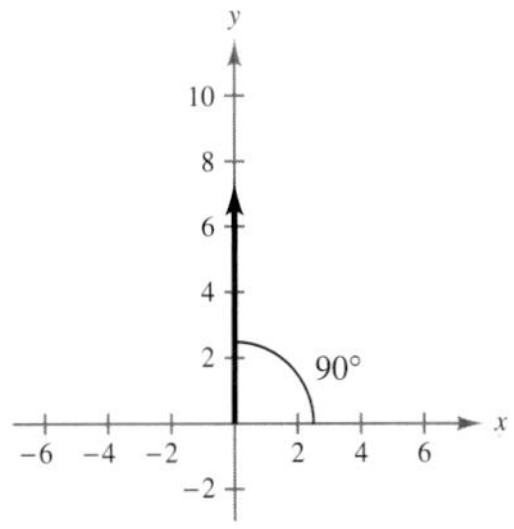

73. $\mathbf{v} = \left\langle \dfrac{9}{5}, \dfrac{12}{5} \right\rangle$

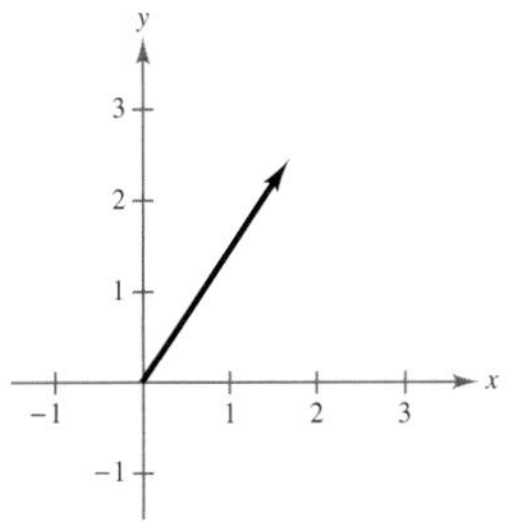

74. $\mathbf{v} = \left\langle \dfrac{\sqrt{10}}{5}, \dfrac{3\sqrt{10}}{5} \right\rangle$

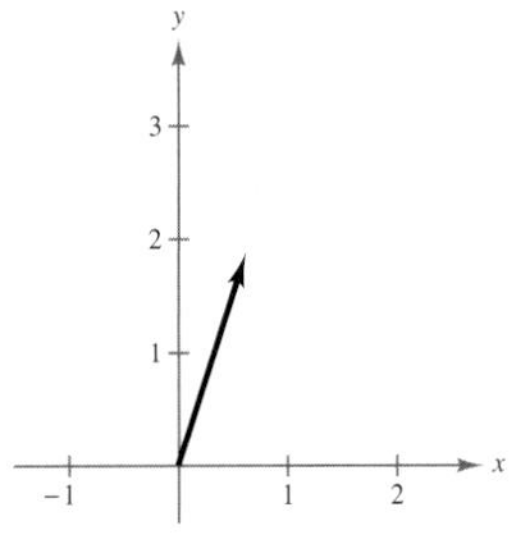

Section 6.5 *(page 476)*

11. $3\left(\cos \dfrac{\pi}{2} + i \sin \dfrac{\pi}{2}\right)$ **12.** $2(\cos \pi + i \sin \pi)$

13. $3\sqrt{2}\left(\cos \dfrac{5\pi}{4} + i \sin \dfrac{5\pi}{4}\right)$ **14.** $2\left(\cos \dfrac{2\pi}{3} + i \sin \dfrac{2\pi}{3}\right)$

15.

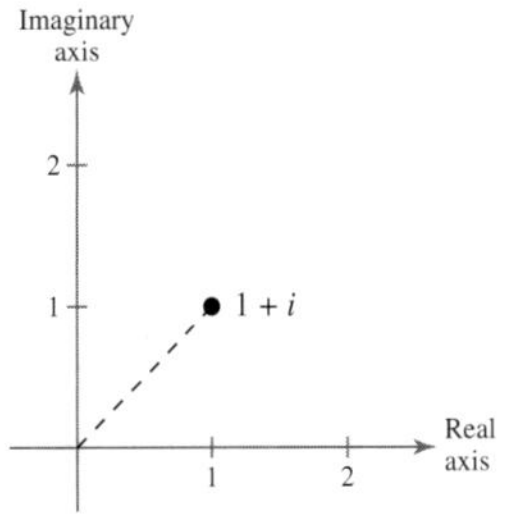

$\sqrt{2}\left(\cos \dfrac{\pi}{4} + i \sin \dfrac{\pi}{4}\right)$

16.

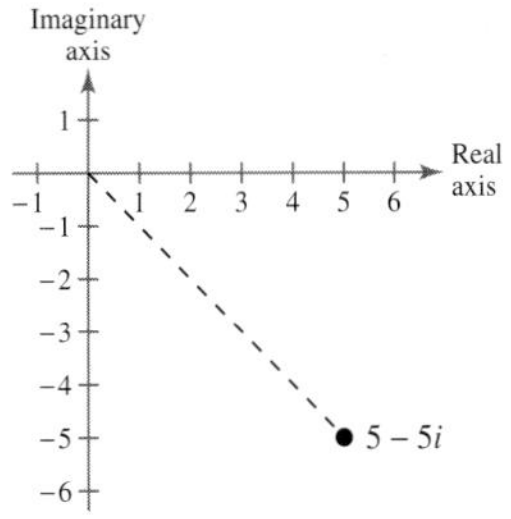

$5\sqrt{2}\left(\cos \dfrac{7\pi}{4} + i \sin \dfrac{7\pi}{4}\right)$

17.

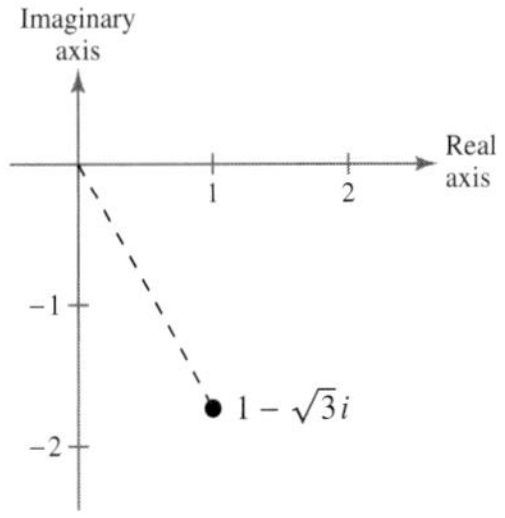

$2\left(\cos \dfrac{5\pi}{3} + i \sin \dfrac{5\pi}{3}\right)$

18.

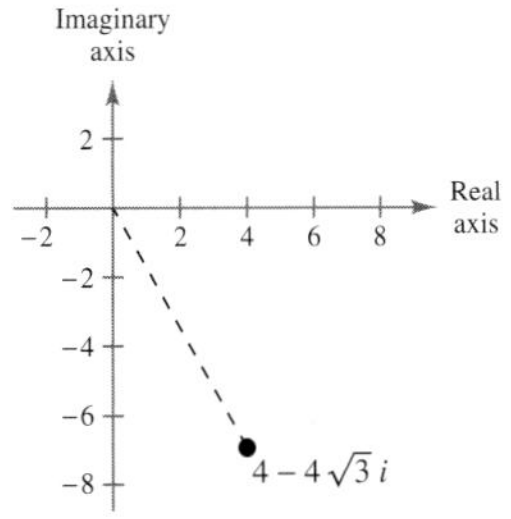

$8\left(\cos \dfrac{5\pi}{3} + i \sin \dfrac{5\pi}{3}\right)$

19.

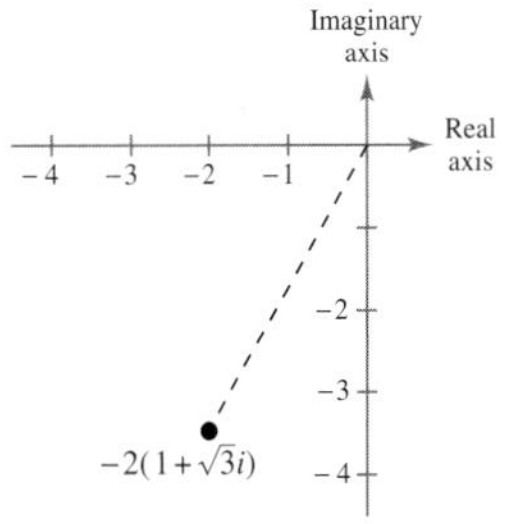

$4\left(\cos \dfrac{4\pi}{3} + i \sin \dfrac{4\pi}{3}\right)$

20.

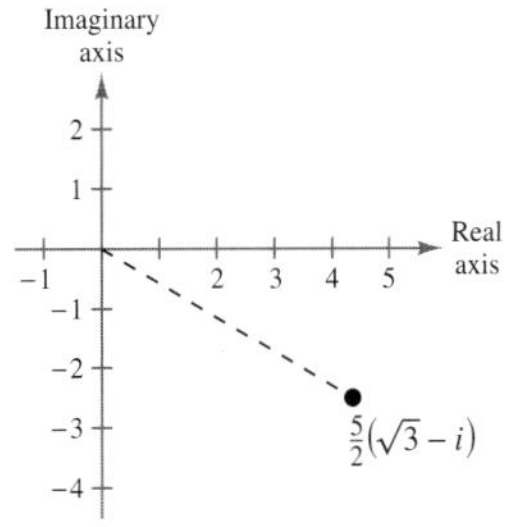

$5\left(\cos \dfrac{11\pi}{6} + i \sin \dfrac{11\pi}{6}\right)$

21.

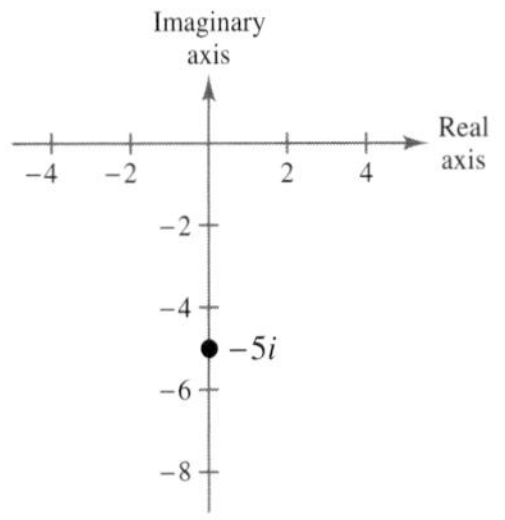

$5\left(\cos \dfrac{3\pi}{2} + i \sin \dfrac{3\pi}{2}\right)$

22.

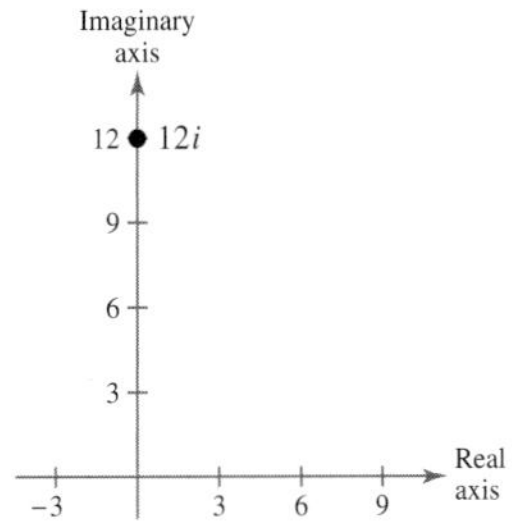

$12\left(\cos \dfrac{\pi}{2} + i \sin \dfrac{\pi}{2}\right)$

23.

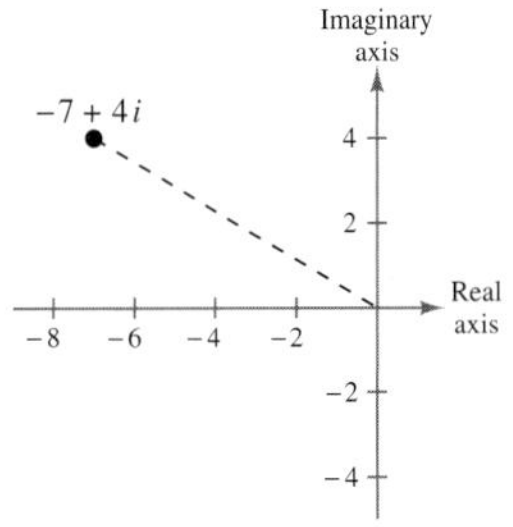

$\sqrt{65}(\cos 2.62 + i \sin 2.62)$

24.

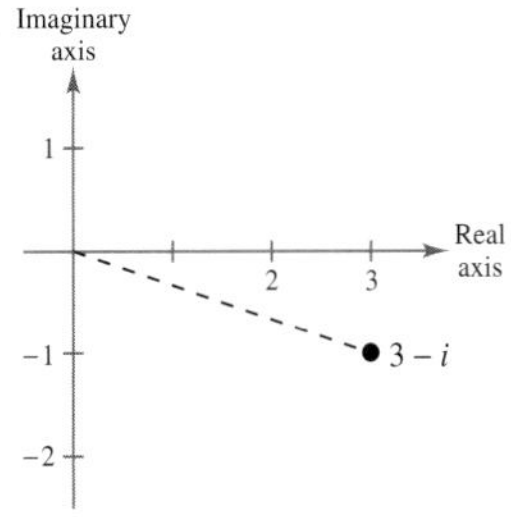

$\sqrt{10}(\cos 5.96 + i \sin 5.96)$

25.

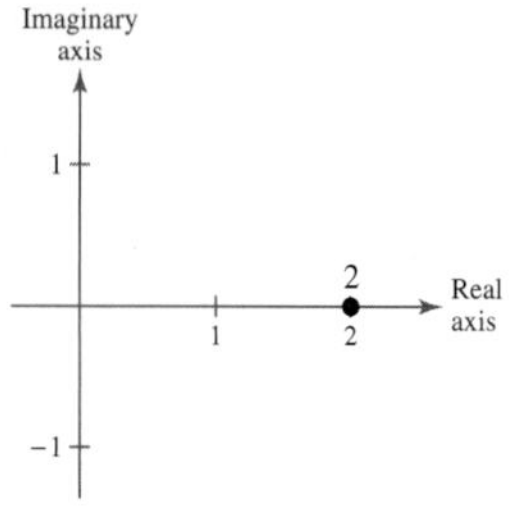

$2(\cos 0 + i \sin 0)$

26.

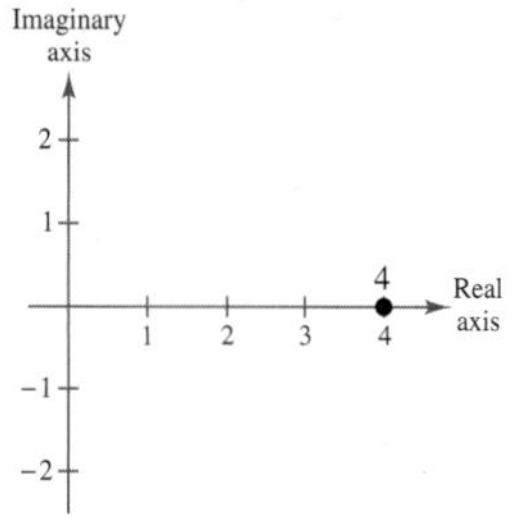

$4(\cos 0 + i \sin 0)$

27.

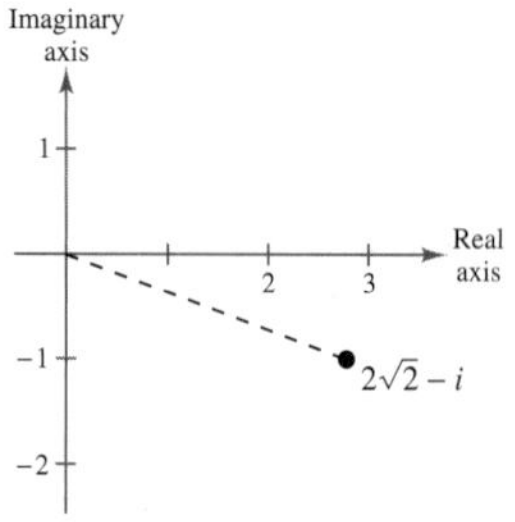

$3(\cos 5.94 + i \sin 5.94)$

28.

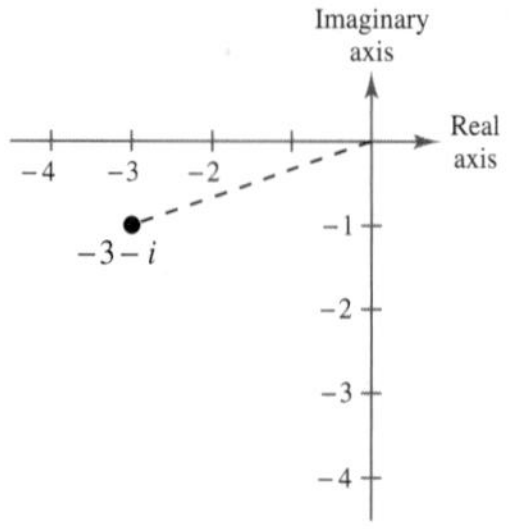

$\sqrt{10}(\cos 3.46 + i \sin 3.46)$

29.

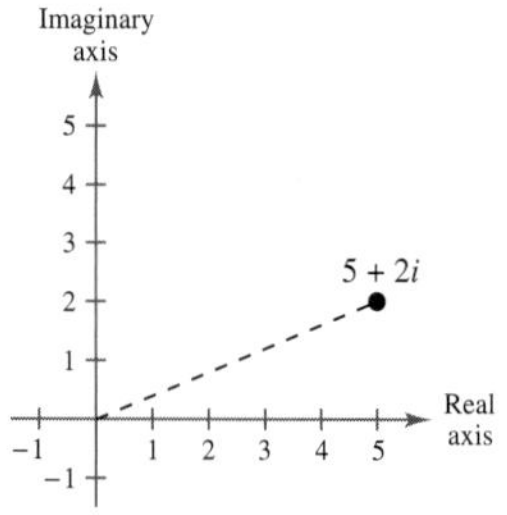

$\sqrt{29}(\cos 0.38 + i \sin 0.38)$

30.

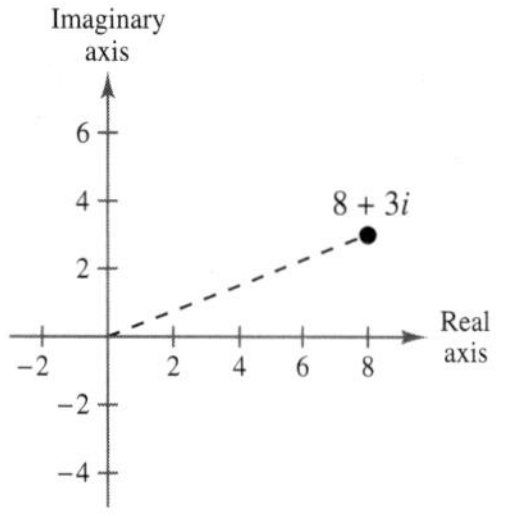

$\sqrt{73}(\cos 0.36 + i \sin 0.36)$

31.

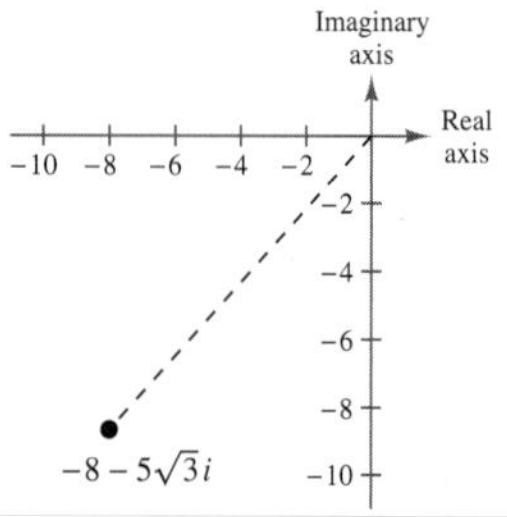

$\sqrt{139}(\cos 3.97 + i \sin 3.97)$

32.

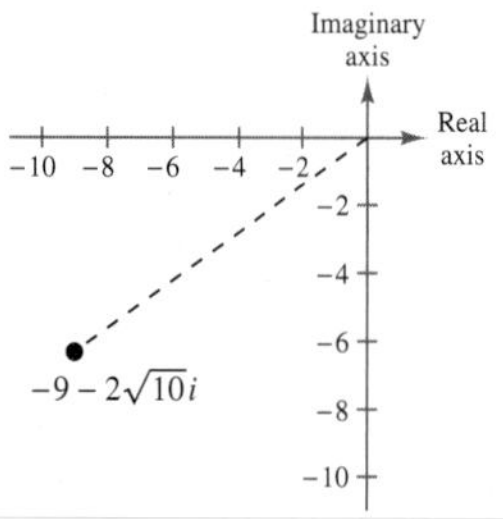

$11(\cos 3.75 + i \sin 3.75)$

33.

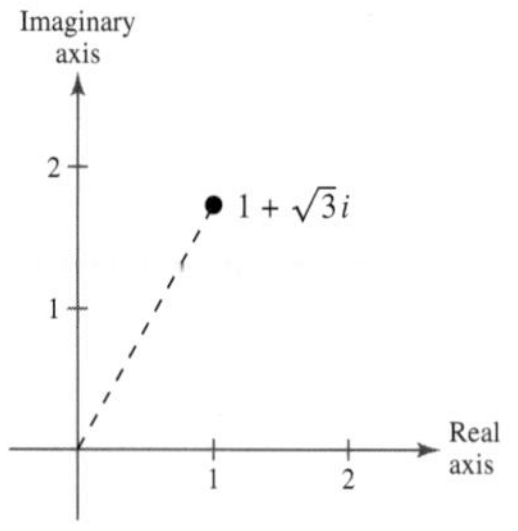

$1 + \sqrt{3}i$

34.

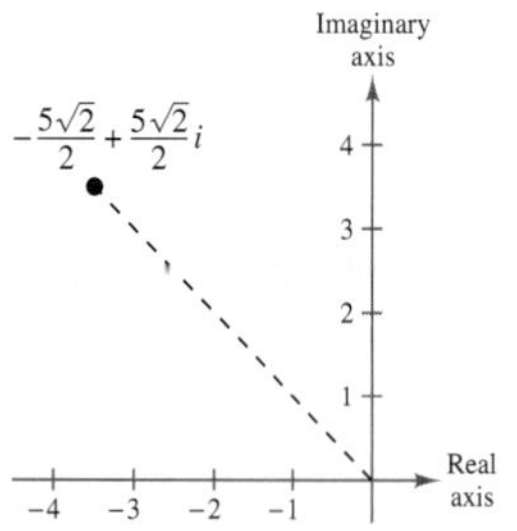

$-\frac{5\sqrt{2}}{2} + \frac{5\sqrt{2}}{2}i$

35.

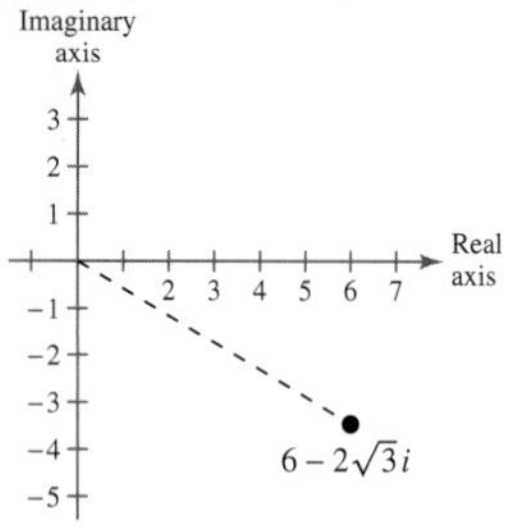

$6 - 2\sqrt{3}i$

36.

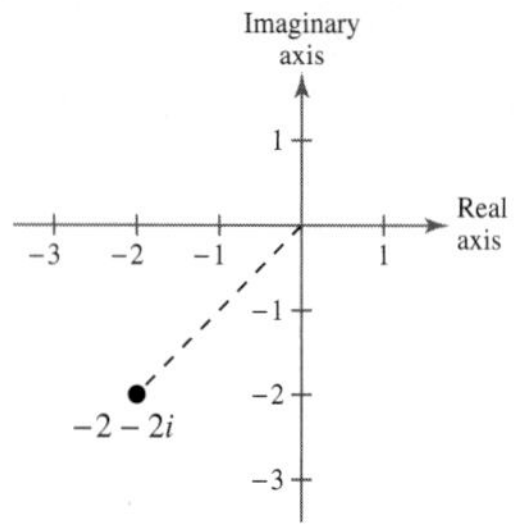

$-2 - 2i$

37.

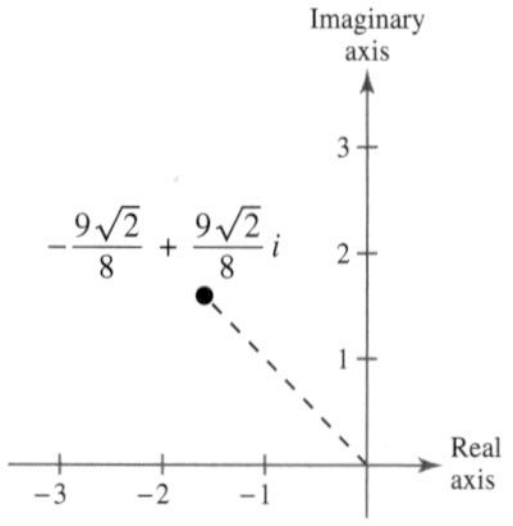

$-\frac{9\sqrt{2}}{8} + \frac{9\sqrt{2}}{8}i$

38.

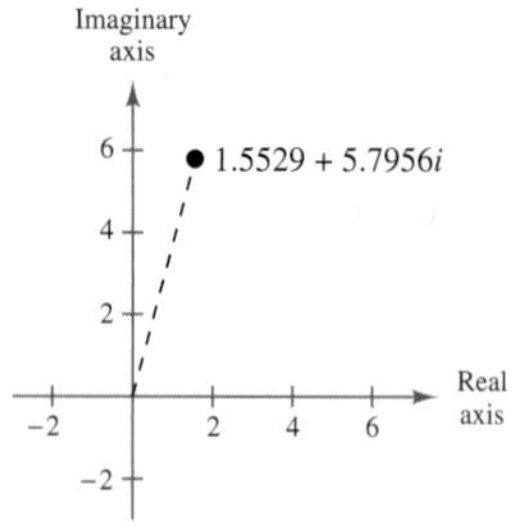

$1.5529 + 5.7956i$

39.

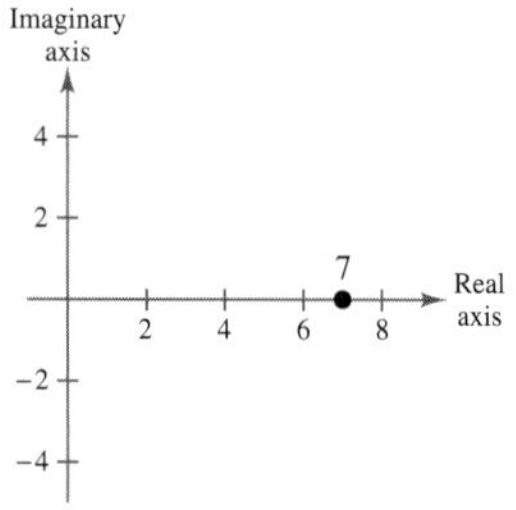

7

40.

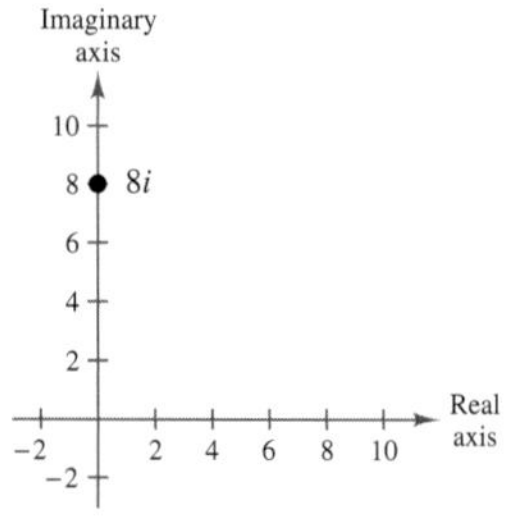

$8i$

41.

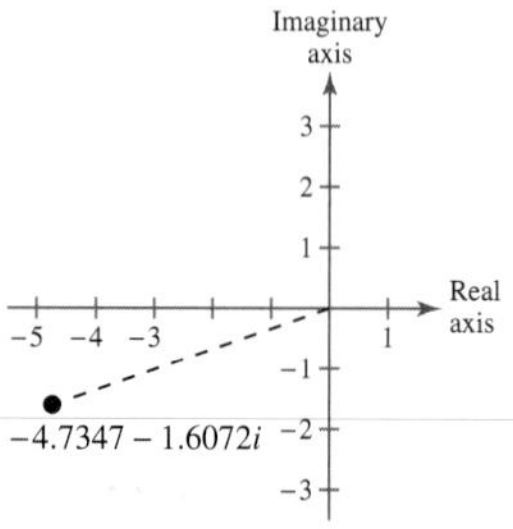

$-4.7347 - 1.6072i$

42.

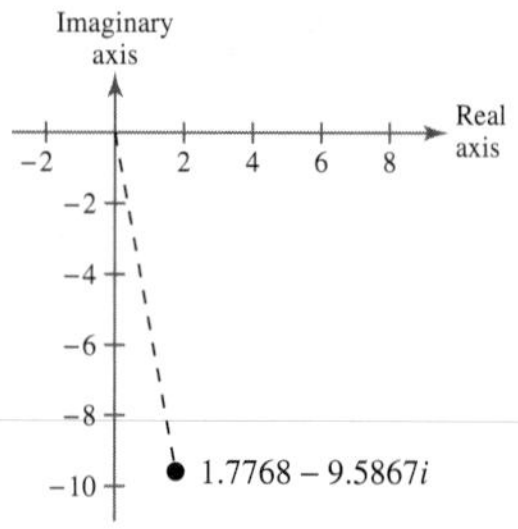

$1.7768 - 9.5867i$

43. $4.6985 + 1.7101i$ **44.** $3.0902 + 9.5106i$

45. $-1.8126 + 0.8452i$ **46.** $4.7693 + 7.6324i$

47. $12\left(\cos \frac{\pi}{3} + i \sin \frac{\pi}{3}\right)$ **48.** $3\left(\cos \frac{13\pi}{12} + i \sin \frac{13\pi}{12}\right)$

49. $\frac{10}{9}(\cos 150° + i \sin 150°)$ **50.** $\frac{2}{5}(\cos 40° + i \sin 40°)$

51. $\cos 50° + i \sin 50°$ **52.** $\cos 25° + i \sin 25°$

53. $\frac{1}{3}(\cos 30° + i \sin 30°)$ **54.** $\frac{1}{2}(\cos 80° + i \sin 80°)$

55. $\cos \frac{2\pi}{3} + i \sin \frac{2\pi}{3}$ **56.** $\frac{5}{4}(\cos 2.2 + i \sin 2.2)$

57. $6(\cos 330° + i \sin 330°)$ **58.** $\frac{6}{7}(\cos 300° + i \sin 300°)$

59. (a) $\left[2\sqrt{2}\left(\cos \frac{\pi}{4} + i \sin \frac{\pi}{4}\right)\right]\left[\sqrt{2}\left(\cos \frac{7\pi}{4} + i \sin \frac{7\pi}{4}\right)\right]$

(b) $4(\cos 0 + i \sin 0) = 4$ (c) 4

60. (a) $\left[2\left(\cos \frac{\pi}{6} + i \sin \frac{\pi}{6}\right)\right]\left[\sqrt{2}\left(\cos \frac{\pi}{4} + i \sin \frac{\pi}{4}\right)\right]$

(b) $2\sqrt{2}\left(\cos \frac{5\pi}{12} + i \sin \frac{5\pi}{12}\right) \approx 0.732 + 2.732i$

(c) $(\sqrt{3} - 1) + (\sqrt{3} + 1)i \approx 0.732 + 2.732i$

61. (a) $\left[2\left(\cos\frac{3\pi}{2} + i\sin\frac{3\pi}{2}\right)\right]\left[\sqrt{2}\left(\cos\frac{\pi}{4} + i\sin\frac{\pi}{4}\right)\right]$

(b) $2\sqrt{2}\left(\cos\frac{7\pi}{4} + i\sin\frac{7\pi}{4}\right) = 2 - 2i$

(c) $-2i - 2i^2 = -2i + 2 = 2 - 2i$

62. (a) $\left[3\left(\cos\frac{\pi}{2} + i\sin\frac{\pi}{2}\right)\right][\sqrt{3}(\cos 5.33 + i\sin 5.33)]$

(b) $3\sqrt{3}(\cos 0.62 + i\sin 0.62) \approx 4.24 + 3i$

(c) $3i - 3\sqrt{2}i^2 = 3i + 3\sqrt{2} \approx 4.24 + 3i$

63. (a) $[5(\cos 0.93 + i\sin 0.93)] \div \left[2\left(\cos\frac{5\pi}{3} + i\sin\frac{5\pi}{3}\right)\right]$

(b) $\frac{5}{2}(\cos 1.97 + i\sin 1.97) \approx -0.982 + 2.299i$

(c) About $-0.982 + 2.299i$

64. (a) $\left[2\left(\cos\frac{\pi}{3} + i\sin\frac{\pi}{3}\right)\right] \div [3\sqrt{5}(\cos 5.82 + i\sin 5.82)]$

(b) $\frac{2\sqrt{5}}{15}(\cos 1.51 + i\sin 1.51) \approx 0.018 + 0.298i$

(c) About $0.018 + 0.298i$

85. (a) $2\left(\cos\frac{2\pi}{9} + i\sin\frac{2\pi}{9}\right)$
$2\left(\cos\frac{8\pi}{9} + i\sin\frac{8\pi}{9}\right)$
$2\left(\cos\frac{14\pi}{9} + i\sin\frac{14\pi}{9}\right)$

(b)

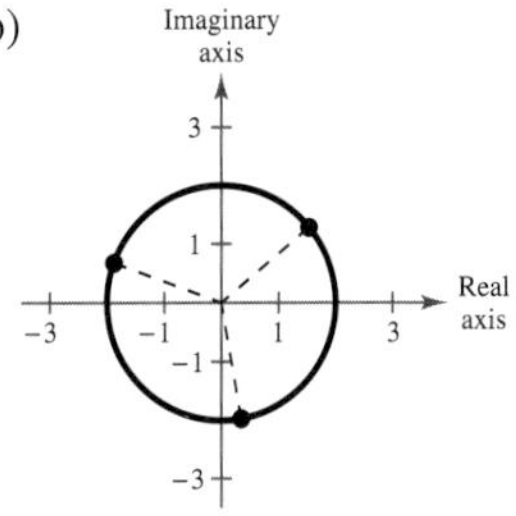

(c) $1.5321 + 1.2856i$,
$-1.8794 + 0.6840i$,
$0.3473 - 1.9696i$

86. (a) $2\left(\cos\frac{\pi}{6} + i\sin\frac{\pi}{6}\right)$
$2\left(\cos\frac{17\pi}{30} + i\sin\frac{17\pi}{30}\right)$
$2\left(\cos\frac{29\pi}{30} + i\sin\frac{29\pi}{30}\right)$
$2\left(\cos\frac{41\pi}{30} + i\sin\frac{41\pi}{30}\right)$
$2\left(\cos\frac{53\pi}{30} + i\sin\frac{53\pi}{30}\right)$

(b)

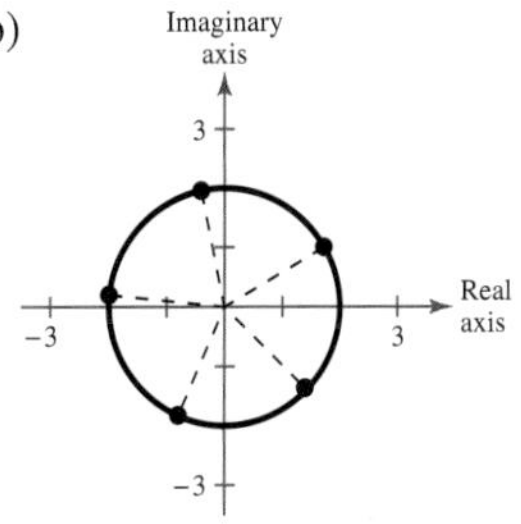

(c) $\sqrt{3} + i, -0.4158 + 1.9563i, -1.9890 + 0.2091i,$
$-0.8135 - 1.8271i, 1.4863 - 1.3383i$

87. (a) $5\left(\cos\frac{4\pi}{9} + i\sin\frac{4\pi}{9}\right)$
$5\left(\cos\frac{10\pi}{9} + i\sin\frac{10\pi}{9}\right)$
$5\left(\cos\frac{16\pi}{9} + i\sin\frac{16\pi}{9}\right)$

(b)

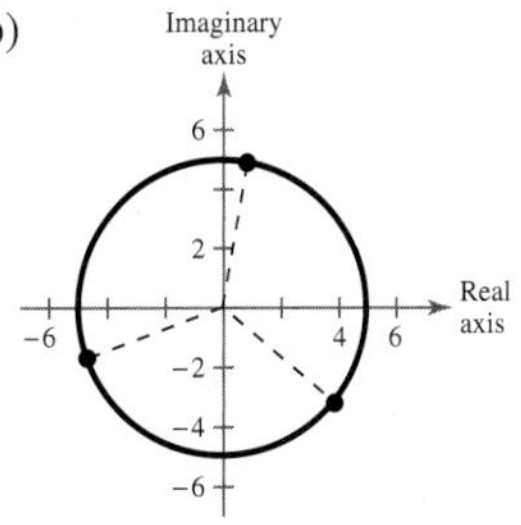

(c) $0.8682 + 4.9240i$,
$-4.6985 - 1.7101i$,
$3.8302 - 3.2140i$

88. (a) $2\left(\cos\frac{7\pi}{12} + i\sin\frac{7\pi}{12}\right)$
$2\left(\cos\frac{5\pi}{4} + i\sin\frac{5\pi}{4}\right)$
$2\left(\cos\frac{23\pi}{12} + i\sin\frac{23\pi}{12}\right)$

(b)

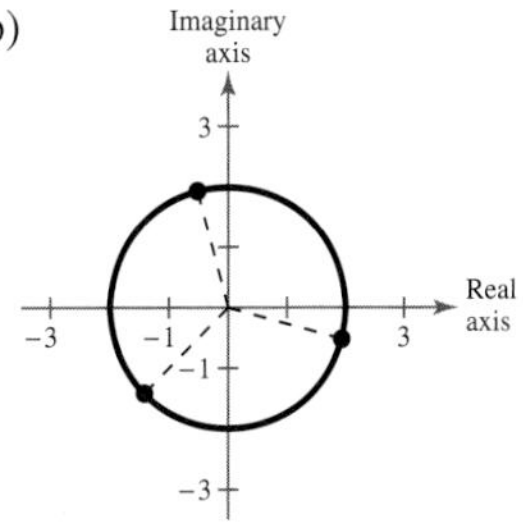

(c) $-0.5176 + 1.9319i$,
$-\sqrt{2} - \sqrt{2}i$,
$1.9319 - 0.5176i$

89. (a) $5\left(\cos\frac{3\pi}{4} + i\sin\frac{3\pi}{4}\right)$
$5\left(\cos\frac{7\pi}{4} + i\sin\frac{7\pi}{4}\right)$

(b)

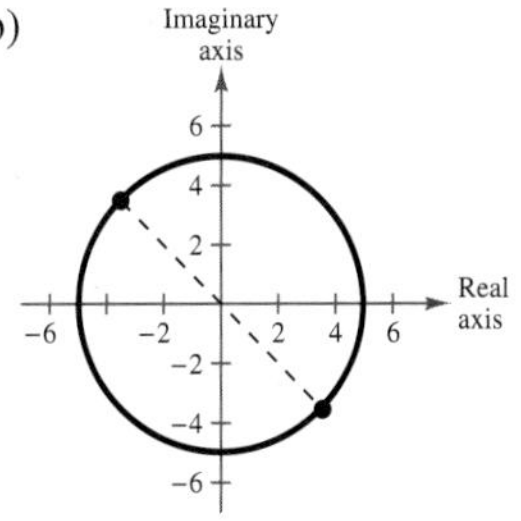

(c) $-\frac{5\sqrt{2}}{2} + \frac{5\sqrt{2}}{2}i$
$\frac{5\sqrt{2}}{2} - \frac{5\sqrt{2}}{2}i$

90. (a) $5\left(\cos\frac{\pi}{8} + i\sin\frac{\pi}{8}\right)$
$5\left(\cos\frac{5\pi}{8} + i\sin\frac{5\pi}{8}\right)$
$5\left(\cos\frac{9\pi}{8} + i\sin\frac{9\pi}{8}\right)$
$5\left(\cos\frac{13\pi}{8} + i\sin\frac{13\pi}{8}\right)$

(b)

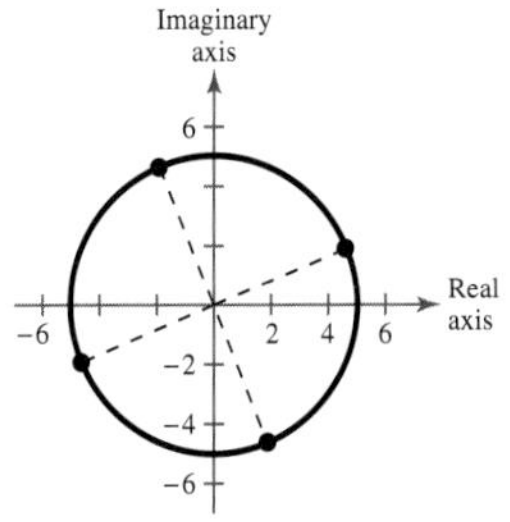

(c) $4.6194 + 1.9134i, -1.9134 + 4.6194i,$
$-4.6194 - 1.9134i, 1.9134 - 4.6194i$

91. (a) $2(\cos 0 + i\sin 0)$
$2\left(\cos\frac{\pi}{2} + i\sin\frac{\pi}{2}\right)$
$2(\cos\pi + i\sin\pi)$
$2\left(\cos\frac{3\pi}{2} + i\sin\frac{3\pi}{2}\right)$

(b)

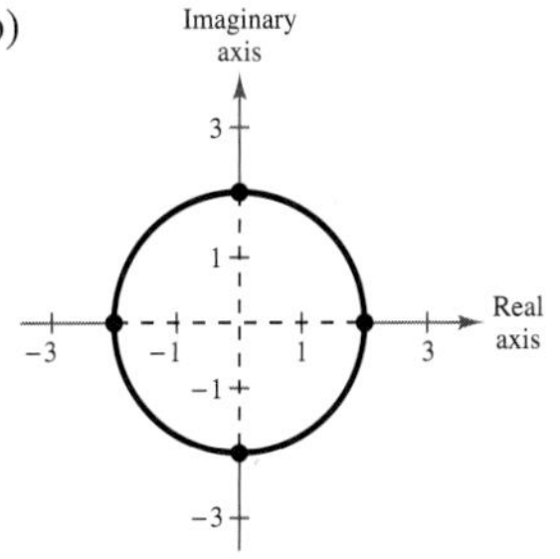

(c) $2, 2i, -2, -2i$

92. (a) $\cos\frac{\pi}{8} + i\sin\frac{\pi}{8}$
$\cos\frac{5\pi}{8} + i\sin\frac{5\pi}{8}$
$\cos\frac{9\pi}{8} + i\sin\frac{9\pi}{8}$
$\cos\frac{13\pi}{8} + i\sin\frac{13\pi}{8}$

(b)

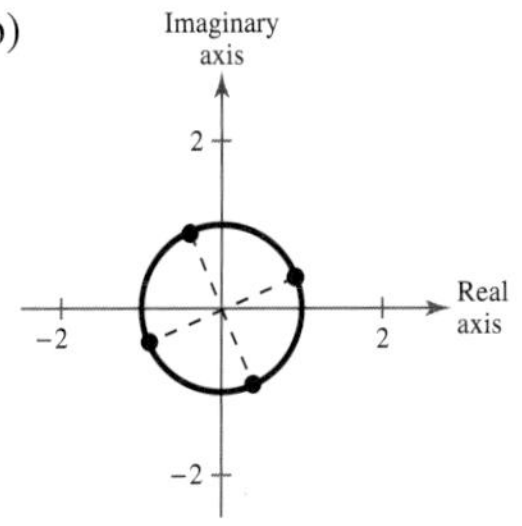

(c) $0.9239 + 0.3827i$,
$-0.3827 + 0.9239i, -0.9239 - 0.3827i,$
$0.3827 - 0.9239i$

93. (a) $\cos 0 + i\sin 0$
$\cos\frac{2\pi}{5} + i\sin\frac{2\pi}{5}$
$\cos\frac{4\pi}{5} + i\sin\frac{4\pi}{5}$
$\cos\frac{6\pi}{5} + i\sin\frac{6\pi}{5}$
$\cos\frac{8\pi}{5} + i\sin\frac{8\pi}{5}$

(b)

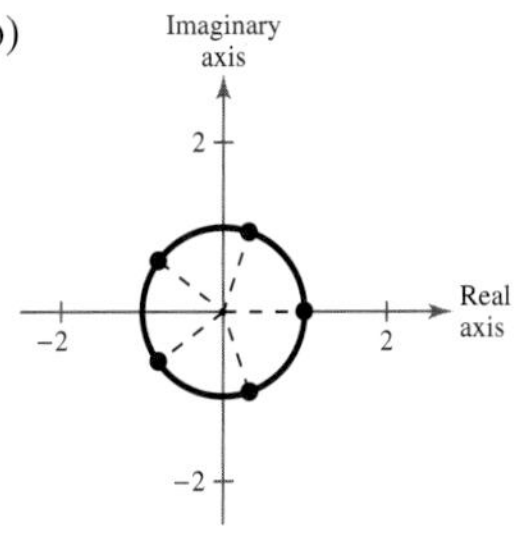

(c) $1, 0.3090 + 0.9511i,$
$-0.8090 + 0.5878i, -0.8090 - 0.5878i,$
$0.3090 - 0.9511i$

94. (a) $10(\cos 0 + i \sin 0)$

$10\left(\cos \frac{2\pi}{3} + i \sin \frac{2\pi}{3}\right)$

$10\left(\cos \frac{4\pi}{3} + i \sin \frac{4\pi}{3}\right)$

(c) $10, -5 + 5\sqrt{3}i, -5 - 5\sqrt{3}i$

(b)

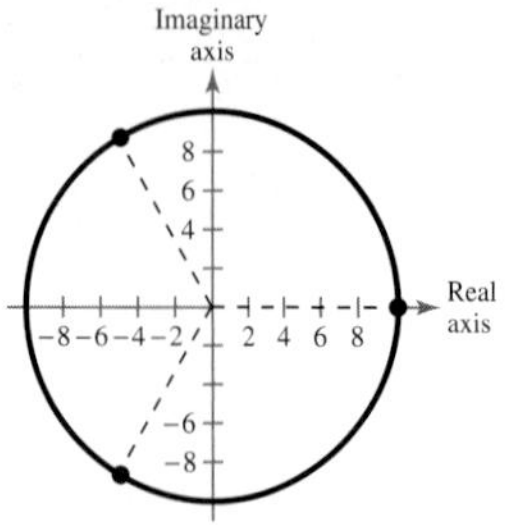

95. (a) $5\left(\cos \frac{\pi}{3} + i \sin \frac{\pi}{3}\right)$

$5(\cos \pi + i \sin \pi)$

$5\left(\cos \frac{5\pi}{3} + i \sin \frac{5\pi}{3}\right)$

(c) $\frac{5}{2} + \frac{5\sqrt{3}}{2}i, -5, \frac{5}{2} - \frac{5\sqrt{3}}{2}i$

(b)

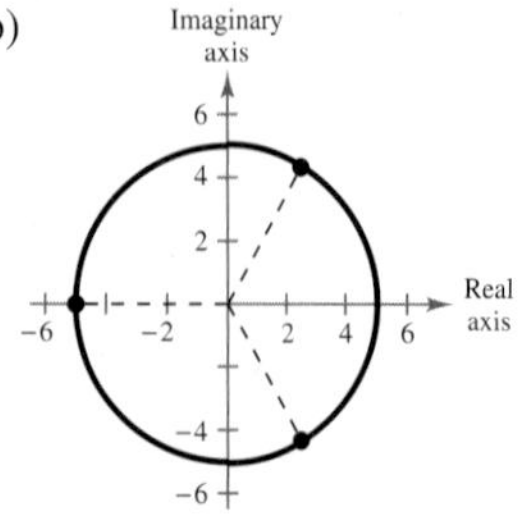

96. (a) $\sqrt{2}\left(\cos \frac{\pi}{4} + i \sin \frac{\pi}{4}\right)$

$\sqrt{2}\left(\cos \frac{3\pi}{4} + i \sin \frac{3\pi}{4}\right)$

$\sqrt{2}\left(\cos \frac{5\pi}{4} + i \sin \frac{5\pi}{4}\right)$

$\sqrt{2}\left(\cos \frac{7\pi}{4} + i \sin \frac{7\pi}{4}\right)$

(c) $1 + i, -1 + i, -1 - i, 1 - i$

(b)

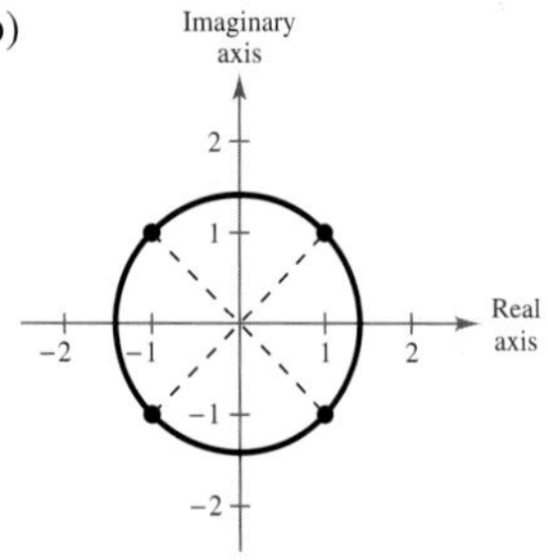

97. (a) $\sqrt{2}\left(\cos \frac{7\pi}{20} + i \sin \frac{7\pi}{20}\right)$

$\sqrt{2}\left(\cos \frac{3\pi}{4} + i \sin \frac{3\pi}{4}\right)$

$\sqrt{2}\left(\cos \frac{23\pi}{20} + i \sin \frac{23\pi}{20}\right)$

$\sqrt{2}\left(\cos \frac{31\pi}{20} + i \sin \frac{31\pi}{20}\right)$

$\sqrt{2}\left(\cos \frac{39\pi}{20} + i \sin \frac{39\pi}{20}\right)$

(c) $0.6420 + 1.2601i$, $-1 + i$, $-1.2601 - 0.6420i$, $0.2212 - 1.3968i$, $1.3968 - 0.2212i$

(b)

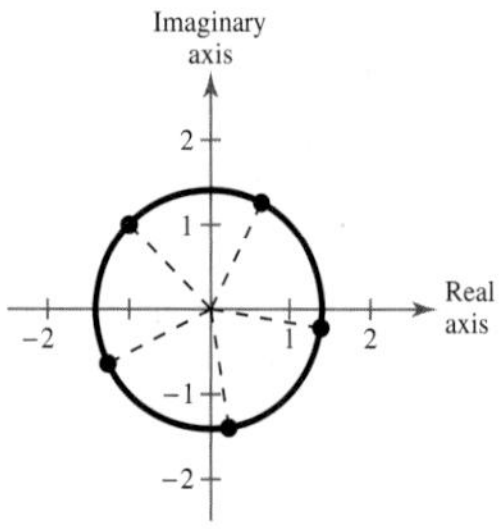

98. (a) $2\left(\cos \frac{\pi}{12} + i \sin \frac{\pi}{12}\right)$

$2\left(\cos \frac{5\pi}{12} + i \sin \frac{5\pi}{12}\right)$

$2\left(\cos \frac{3\pi}{4} + i \sin \frac{3\pi}{4}\right)$

$2\left(\cos \frac{13\pi}{12} + i \sin \frac{13\pi}{12}\right)$

$2\left(\cos \frac{17\pi}{12} + i \sin \frac{17\pi}{12}\right)$

$2\left(\cos \frac{7\pi}{4} + i \sin \frac{7\pi}{4}\right)$

(c) $1.9319 + 0.5176i, 0.5176 + 1.9319i, -\sqrt{2} + \sqrt{2}i, -1.9319 - 0.5176i, -0.5176 - 1.9319i, \sqrt{2} - \sqrt{2}i$

(b)

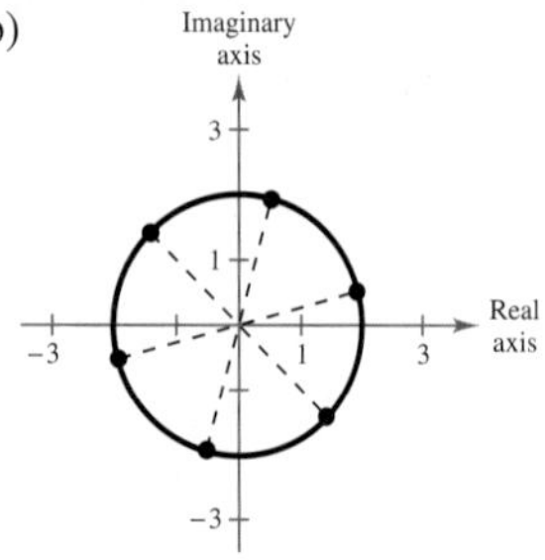

99. $\cos \frac{3\pi}{8} + i \sin \frac{3\pi}{8}$

$\cos \frac{7\pi}{8} + i \sin \frac{7\pi}{8}$

$\cos \frac{11\pi}{8} + i \sin \frac{11\pi}{8}$

$\cos \frac{15\pi}{8} + i \sin \frac{15\pi}{8}$

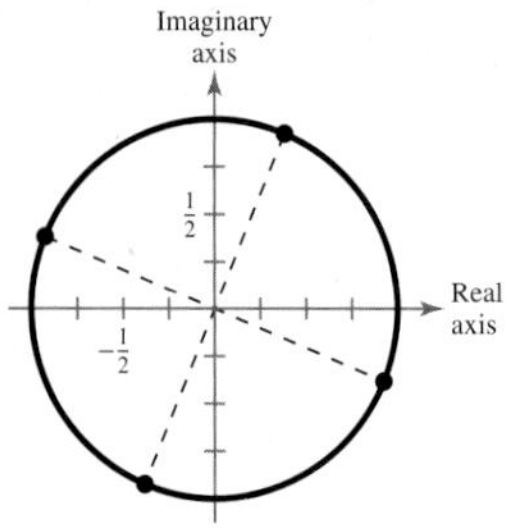

100. $\cos \frac{\pi}{3} + i \sin \frac{\pi}{3}$

$\cos \pi + i \sin \pi$

$\cos \frac{5\pi}{3} + i \sin \frac{5\pi}{3}$

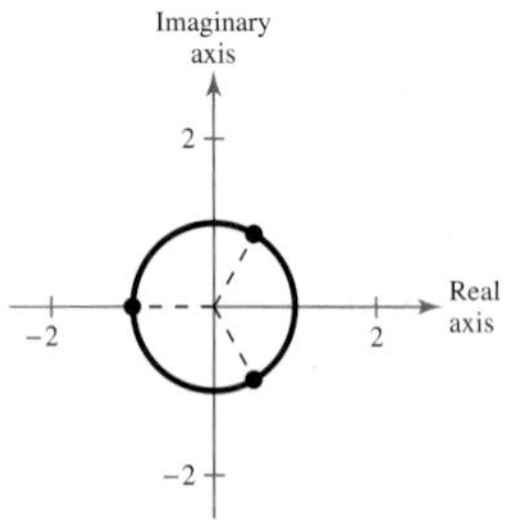

101. $3\left(\cos \frac{\pi}{5} + i \sin \frac{\pi}{5}\right)$

$3\left(\cos \frac{3\pi}{5} + i \sin \frac{3\pi}{5}\right)$

$3(\cos \pi + i \sin \pi)$

$3\left(\cos \frac{7\pi}{5} + i \sin \frac{7\pi}{5}\right)$

$3\left(\cos \frac{9\pi}{5} + i \sin \frac{9\pi}{5}\right)$

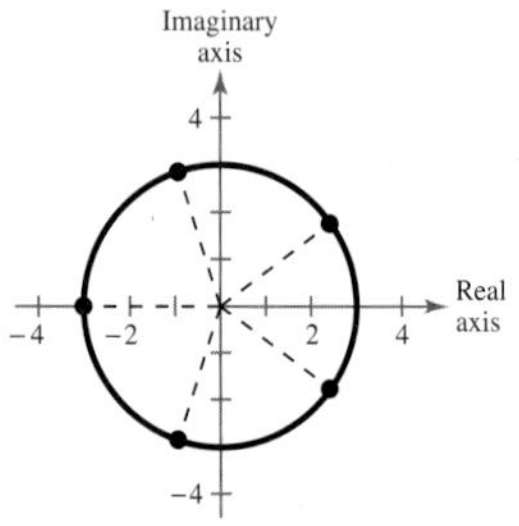

102. $3(\cos 0 + i \sin 0)$

$3\left(\cos \frac{2\pi}{3} + i \sin \frac{2\pi}{3}\right)$

$3\left(\cos \frac{4\pi}{3} + i \sin \frac{4\pi}{3}\right)$

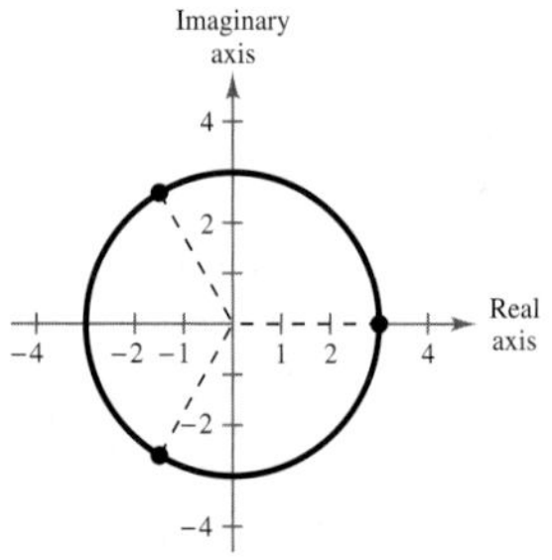

103. $2\left(\cos \frac{3\pi}{8} + i \sin \frac{3\pi}{8}\right)$

$2\left(\cos \frac{7\pi}{8} + i \sin \frac{7\pi}{8}\right)$

$2\left(\cos \frac{11\pi}{8} + i \sin \frac{11\pi}{8}\right)$

$2\left(\cos \frac{15\pi}{8} + i \sin \frac{15\pi}{8}\right)$

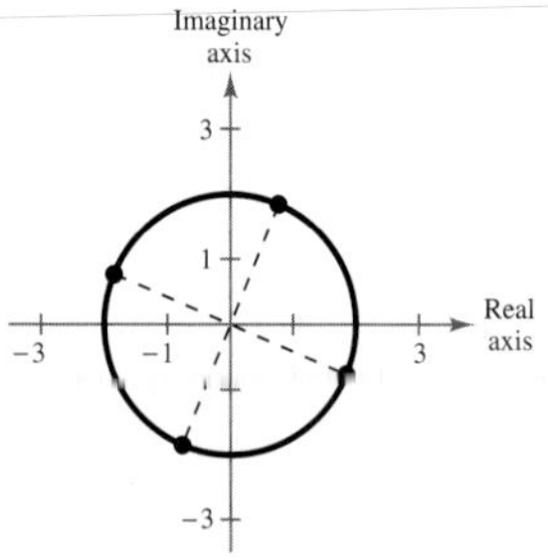

104. $2\left(\cos \frac{\pi}{4} + i \sin \frac{\pi}{4}\right)$

$2\left(\cos \frac{7\pi}{12} + i \sin \frac{7\pi}{12}\right)$

$2\left(\cos \frac{11\pi}{12} + i \sin \frac{11\pi}{12}\right)$

$2\left(\cos \frac{5\pi}{4} + i \sin \frac{5\pi}{4}\right)$

$2\left(\cos \frac{19\pi}{12} + i \sin \frac{19\pi}{12}\right)$

$2\left(\cos \frac{23\pi}{12} + i \sin \frac{23\pi}{12}\right)$

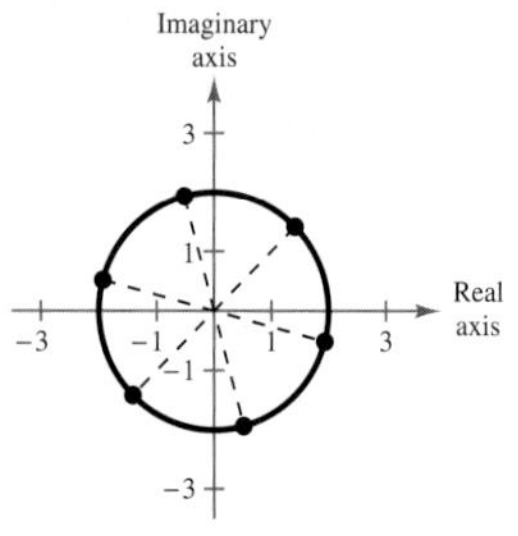

105. $\sqrt[6]{2}\left(\cos\frac{7\pi}{12} + i\sin\frac{7\pi}{12}\right)$

$\sqrt[6]{2}\left(\cos\frac{5\pi}{4} + i\sin\frac{5\pi}{4}\right)$

$\sqrt[6]{2}\left(\cos\frac{23\pi}{12} + i\sin\frac{23\pi}{12}\right)$

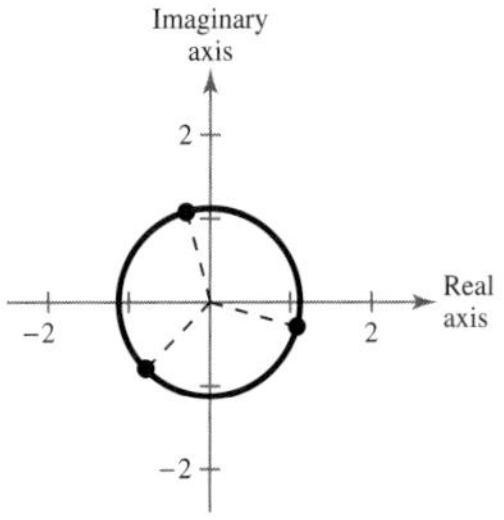

106. $\sqrt[8]{2}\left(\cos\frac{5\pi}{16} + i\sin\frac{5\pi}{16}\right)$

$\sqrt[8]{2}\left(\cos\frac{13\pi}{16} + i\sin\frac{13\pi}{16}\right)$

$\sqrt[8]{2}\left(\cos\frac{21\pi}{16} + i\sin\frac{21\pi}{16}\right)$

$\sqrt[8]{2}\left(\cos\frac{29\pi}{16} + i\sin\frac{29\pi}{16}\right)$

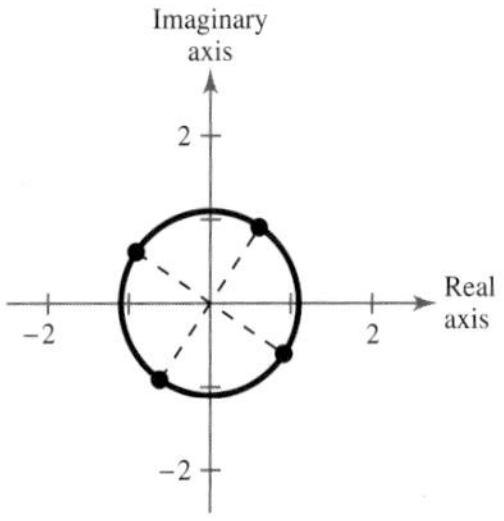

115. The given equation can be written as
$x^4 = -16 = 16(\cos \pi + i \sin \pi)$
which means that you can solve the equation by finding the four fourth roots of -16. Each of these roots has the form

$$\sqrt[4]{16}\left(\cos\frac{\pi + 2\pi k}{4} + i\sin\frac{\pi + 2\pi k}{4}\right).$$

116. (i) (a) $2(\cos 30° + i \sin 30°)$ (b) $8i$
$2(\cos 150° + i \sin 150°)$
$2(\cos 270° + i \sin 270°)$

(ii) (a) $3(\cos 45° + i \sin 45°)$ (b) -81
$3(\cos 135° + i \sin 135°)$
$3(\cos 225° + i \sin 225°)$
$3(\cos 315° + i \sin 315°)$

Review Exercises *(page 480)*

119. (a) $z_1 = 4\left(\cos\frac{11\pi}{6} + i\sin\frac{11\pi}{6}\right)$

$z_2 = 10\left(\cos\frac{3\pi}{2} + i\sin\frac{3\pi}{2}\right)$

(b) $z_1z_2 = 40\left(\cos\frac{10\pi}{3} + i\sin\frac{10\pi}{3}\right)$

$\frac{z_1}{z_2} = \frac{2}{5}\left(\cos\frac{\pi}{3} + i\sin\frac{\pi}{3}\right)$

120. (a) $z_1 = 3\sqrt{2}\left(\cos\frac{5\pi}{4} + i\sin\frac{5\pi}{4}\right)$

$z_2 = 4\left(\cos\frac{\pi}{6} + i\sin\frac{\pi}{6}\right)$

(b) $z_1z_2 = 12\sqrt{2}\left(\cos\frac{17\pi}{12} + i\sin\frac{17\pi}{12}\right)$

$\frac{z_1}{z_2} = \frac{3\sqrt{2}}{4}\left(\cos\frac{13\pi}{12} + i\sin\frac{13\pi}{12}\right)$

125. (a) $3\left(\cos\frac{\pi}{4} + i\sin\frac{\pi}{4}\right)$ (b)

$3\left(\cos\frac{7\pi}{12} + i\sin\frac{7\pi}{12}\right)$

$3\left(\cos\frac{11\pi}{12} + i\sin\frac{11\pi}{12}\right)$

$3\left(\cos\frac{5\pi}{4} + i\sin\frac{5\pi}{4}\right)$

$3\left(\cos\frac{19\pi}{12} + i\sin\frac{19\pi}{12}\right)$

$3\left(\cos\frac{23\pi}{12} + i\sin\frac{23\pi}{12}\right)$

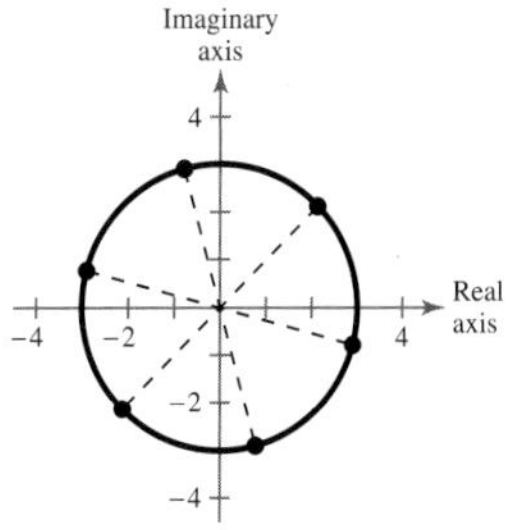

(c) $\frac{3\sqrt{2}}{2} + \frac{3\sqrt{2}}{2}i$, $-0.776 + 2.898i$,
$-2.898 + 0.776i$, $-\frac{3\sqrt{2}}{2} - \frac{3\sqrt{2}}{2}i$,
$0.776 - 2.898i$, $2.898 - 0.776i$

126. (a) $4\left(\cos\frac{\pi}{8} + i\sin\frac{\pi}{8}\right)$ (b)

$4\left(\cos\frac{5\pi}{8} + i\sin\frac{5\pi}{8}\right)$

$4\left(\cos\frac{9\pi}{8} + i\sin\frac{9\pi}{8}\right)$

$4\left(\cos\frac{13\pi}{8} + i\sin\frac{13\pi}{8}\right)$

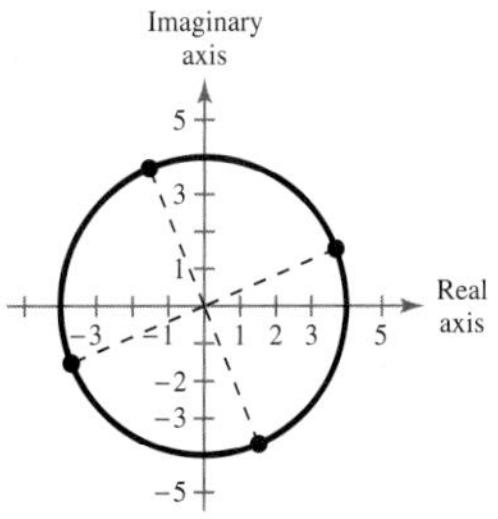

(c) $3.696 + 1.531i$,
$-1.531 + 3.696i$,
$-3.696 - 1.531i$, $1.531 - 3.696i$

127. (a) $2(\cos 0 + i \sin 0)$

$2\left(\cos\frac{2\pi}{3} + i\sin\frac{2\pi}{3}\right)$

$2\left(\cos\frac{4\pi}{3} + i\sin\frac{4\pi}{3}\right)$

(b)

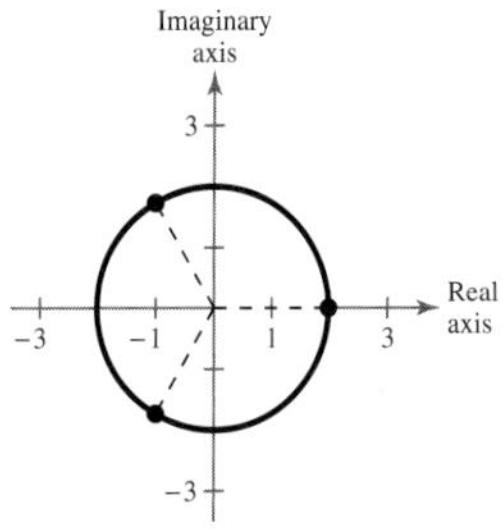

(c) 2, $-1 + \sqrt{3}i$, $-1 - \sqrt{3}i$

128. (a) $4\left(\cos\frac{\pi}{5} + i\sin\frac{\pi}{5}\right)$ (b)

$4\left(\cos\frac{3\pi}{5} + i\sin\frac{3\pi}{5}\right)$

$4(\cos \pi + i \sin \pi)$

$4\left(\cos\frac{7\pi}{5} + i\sin\frac{7\pi}{5}\right)$

$4\left(\cos\frac{9\pi}{5} + i\sin\frac{9\pi}{5}\right)$

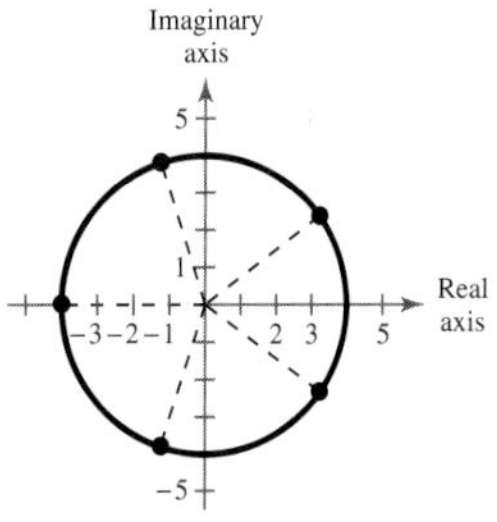

(c) $3.236 + 2.351i$, $-1.236 + 3.804i$,
-4, $-1.236 - 3.804i$, $3.236 - 2.351i$

129. $3\left(\cos\frac{\pi}{4} + i\sin\frac{\pi}{4}\right) = \frac{3\sqrt{2}}{2} + \frac{3\sqrt{2}}{2}i$

$3\left(\cos\frac{3\pi}{4} + i\sin\frac{3\pi}{4}\right) = -\frac{3\sqrt{2}}{2} + \frac{3\sqrt{2}}{2}i$

$3\left(\cos\frac{5\pi}{4} + i\sin\frac{5\pi}{4}\right) = -\frac{3\sqrt{2}}{2} - \frac{3\sqrt{2}}{2}i$

$3\left(\cos\frac{7\pi}{4} + i\sin\frac{7\pi}{4}\right) = \frac{3\sqrt{2}}{2} - \frac{3\sqrt{2}}{2}i$

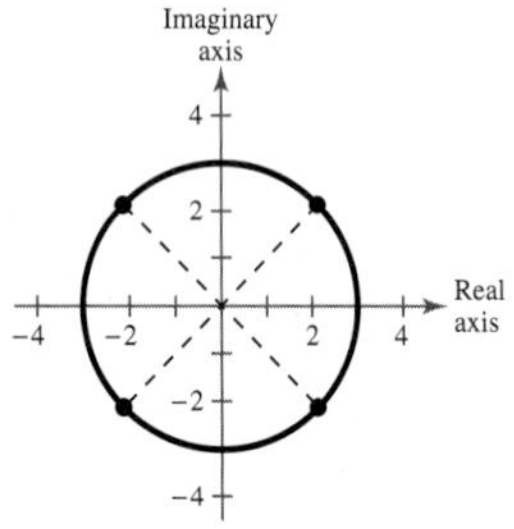

130. $2(\cos 0 + i\sin 0) = 2$

$2\left(\cos\frac{2\pi}{5} + i\sin\frac{2\pi}{5}\right) = 0.6180 + 1.9021i$

$2\left(\cos\frac{4\pi}{5} + i\sin\frac{4\pi}{5}\right) = -1.6180 + 1.1756i$

$2\left(\cos\frac{6\pi}{5} + i\sin\frac{6\pi}{5}\right) = -1.6180 - 1.1756i$

$2\left(\cos\frac{8\pi}{5} + i\sin\frac{8\pi}{5}\right) = 0.6180 - 1.9021i$

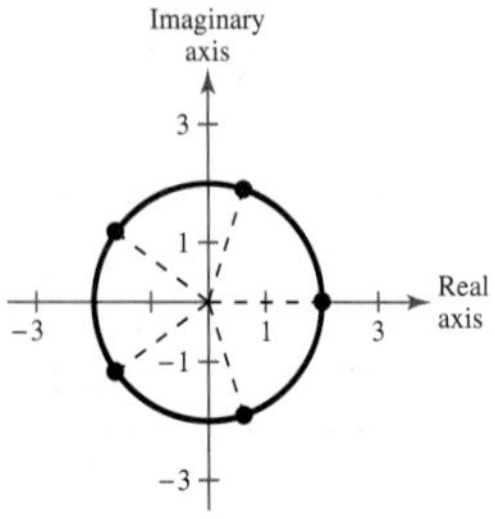

131. $2\left(\cos\frac{\pi}{2} + i\sin\frac{\pi}{2}\right) = 2i$

$2\left(\cos\frac{7\pi}{6} + i\sin\frac{7\pi}{6}\right) = -\sqrt{3} - i$

$2\left(\cos\frac{11\pi}{6} + i\sin\frac{11\pi}{6}\right) = \sqrt{3} - i$

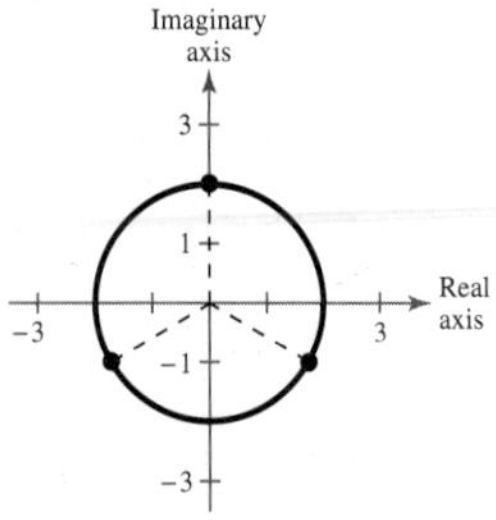

132. $2\sqrt{2}\left(\cos\frac{\pi}{8} + i\sin\frac{\pi}{8}\right) = 2.6131 + 1.0824i$

$2\sqrt{2}\left(\cos\frac{5\pi}{8} + i\sin\frac{5\pi}{8}\right) = -1.0824 + 2.6131i$

$2\sqrt{2}\left(\cos\frac{9\pi}{8} + i\sin\frac{9\pi}{8}\right) = -2.6131 - 1.0824i$

$2\sqrt{2}\left(\cos\frac{13\pi}{8} + i\sin\frac{13\pi}{8}\right) = 1.0824 - 2.6131i$

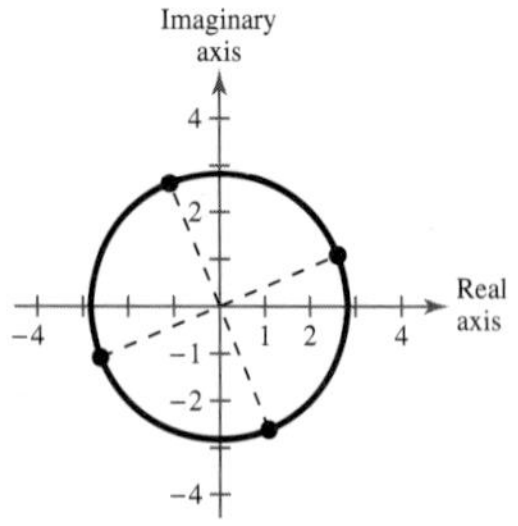

133. $\cos 0 + i\sin 0 = 1$

$\cos\frac{\pi}{2} + i\sin\frac{\pi}{2} = i$

$\cos\frac{2\pi}{3} + i\sin\frac{2\pi}{3} = -\frac{1}{2} + \frac{\sqrt{3}}{2}i$

$\cos\frac{4\pi}{3} + i\sin\frac{4\pi}{3} = -\frac{1}{2} - \frac{\sqrt{3}}{2}i$

$\cos\frac{3\pi}{2} + i\sin\frac{3\pi}{2} = -i$

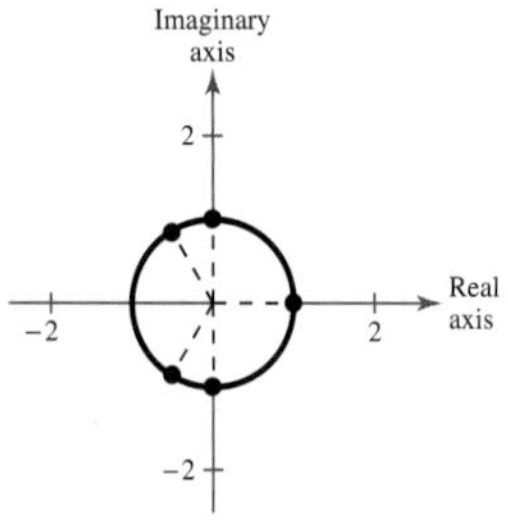

134. $2(\cos 0 + i\sin 0) = 2$

$2\left(\cos\frac{2\pi}{3} + i\sin\frac{2\pi}{3}\right) = -1 + \sqrt{3}i$

$2\left(\cos\frac{4\pi}{3} + i\sin\frac{4\pi}{3}\right) = -1 - \sqrt{3}i$

$2\left(\cos\frac{\pi}{2} + i\sin\frac{\pi}{2}\right) = 2i$

$2\left(\cos\frac{3\pi}{2} + i\sin\frac{3\pi}{2}\right) = -2i$

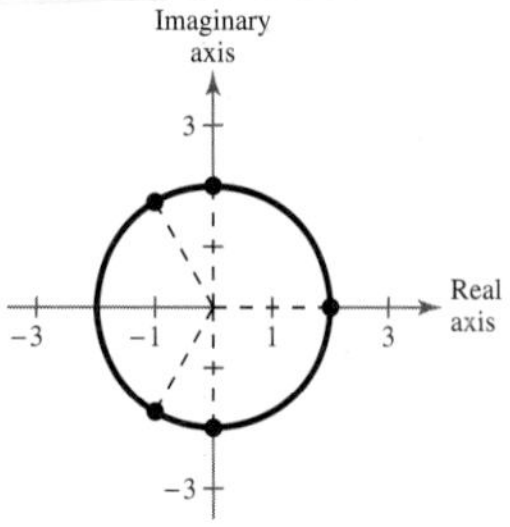

Chapter 7

Section 7.2 (page 513)

11. $\left(a, \frac{3}{2}a - \frac{5}{2}\right)$

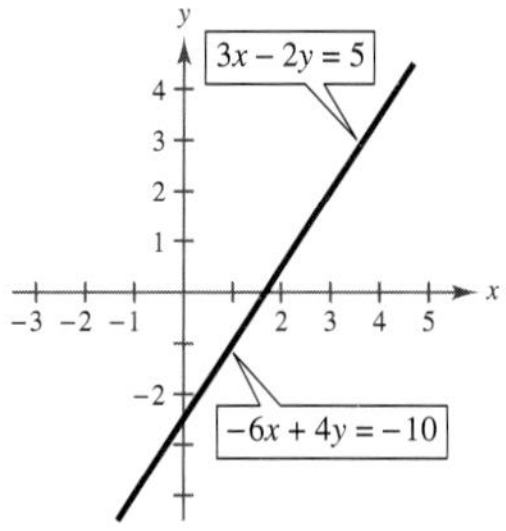

12. $(a, 3a + 5)$

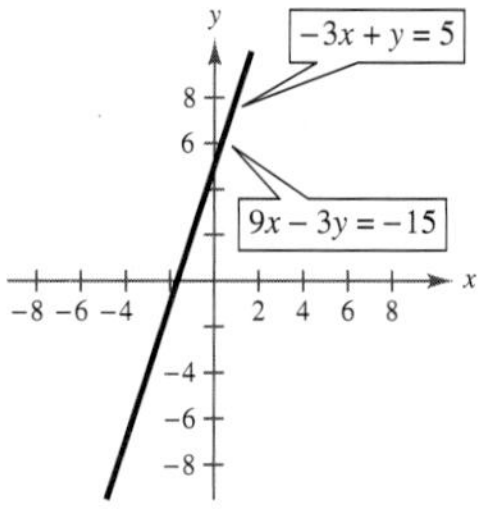

22. Infinitely many solutions: $\left(a, \frac{1}{8} - \frac{3}{4}a\right)$

23. Infinitely many solutions: $\left(a, -\frac{1}{2} + \frac{5}{6}a\right)$

24. Infinitely many solutions: $\left(a, \frac{3}{4} - \frac{7}{8}a\right)$

25. $(101, 96)$ **26.** $\left(\frac{90}{31}, -\frac{67}{31}\right)$

Section 7.4 (page 536)

43. $1 - \dfrac{2x + 1}{x^2 + x + 1}$ **44.** $1 - \dfrac{5x + 6}{x^2 + x + 6}$

45. $2x - 7 + \dfrac{17}{x + 2} + \dfrac{1}{x + 1}$

46. $x - 1 + \dfrac{1}{5}\left(\dfrac{27}{x + 4} + \dfrac{3}{x - 1}\right)$

47. $x + 3 + \dfrac{6}{x - 1} + \dfrac{4}{(x - 1)^2} + \dfrac{1}{(x - 1)^3}$

48. $2x + 3 + \dfrac{6}{2x - 1} + \dfrac{4}{(2x - 1)^2} + \dfrac{1}{(2x - 1)^3}$

56. $\dfrac{1}{2}\left[\dfrac{1}{x + 2} - \dfrac{1}{(x + 2)^2} + \dfrac{1}{x - 2} + \dfrac{1}{(x - 2)^2}\right]$

63. False. The partial fraction decomposition is

$$\frac{A}{x + 10} + \frac{B}{x - 10} + \frac{C}{(x - 10)^2}.$$

64. False. The partial fraction decomposition is

$$\frac{A}{x} + \frac{B}{x^2} + \frac{C}{x + 2} + \frac{D}{(x + 2)^2}.$$

67. $\dfrac{1}{2a}\left(\dfrac{1}{a + x} + \dfrac{1}{a - x}\right)$ **69.** $\dfrac{1}{a}\left(\dfrac{1}{y} + \dfrac{1}{a - y}\right)$

70. $\dfrac{1}{a + 1}\left(\dfrac{1}{x + 1} + \dfrac{1}{a - x}\right)$

Section 7.5 (page 545)

13.

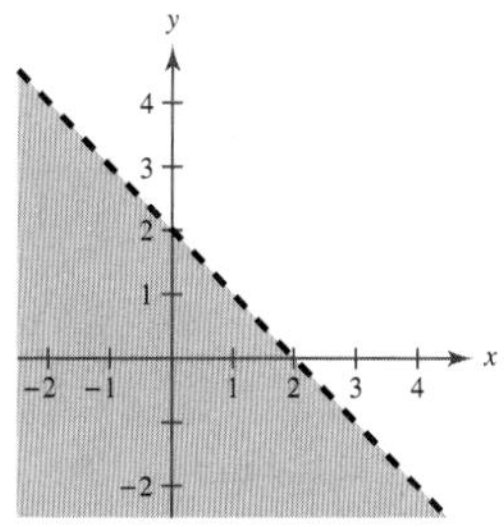

14.

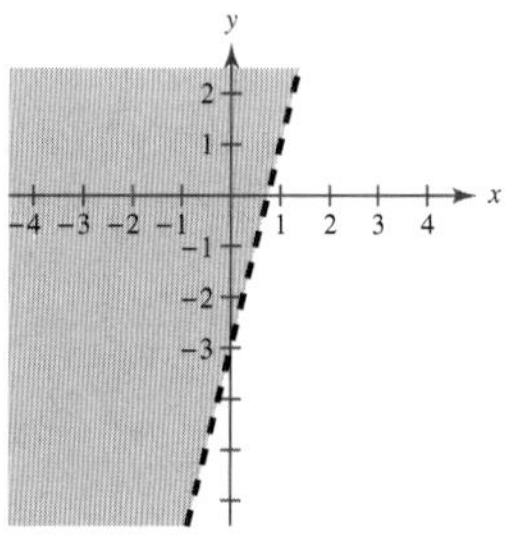

15.

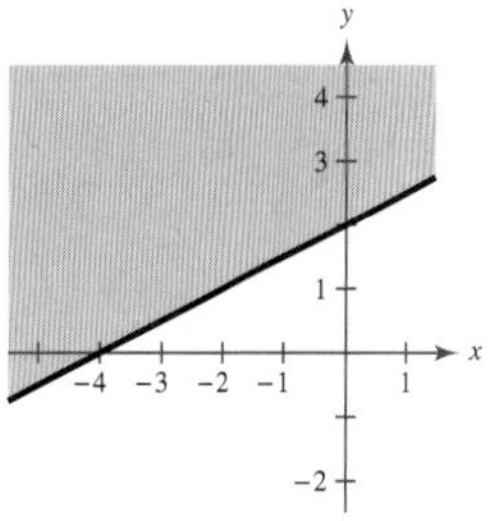

16.

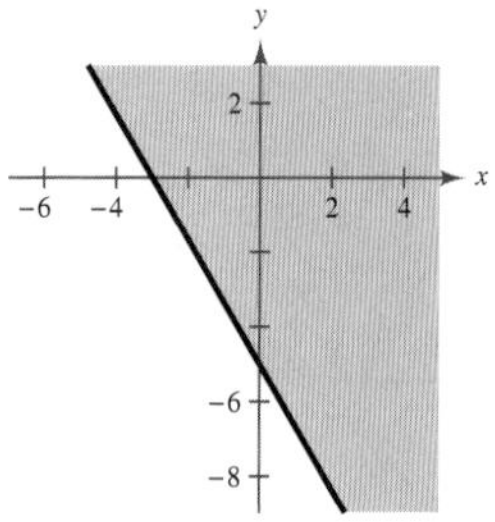

17.

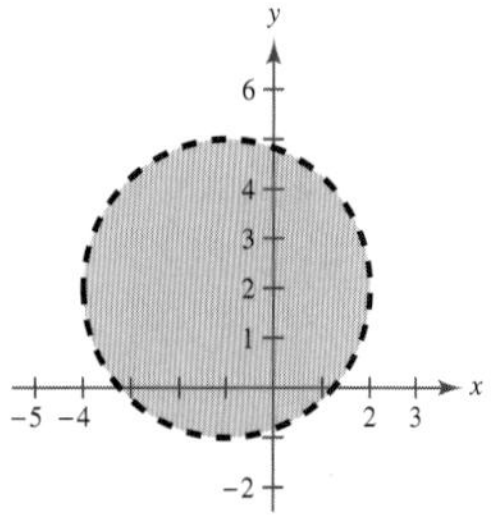

18.

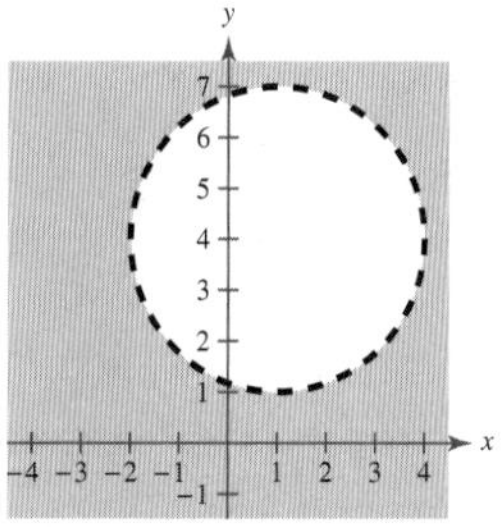

19.

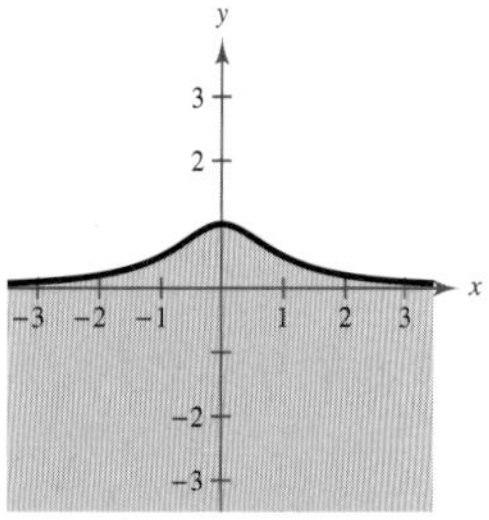

20.

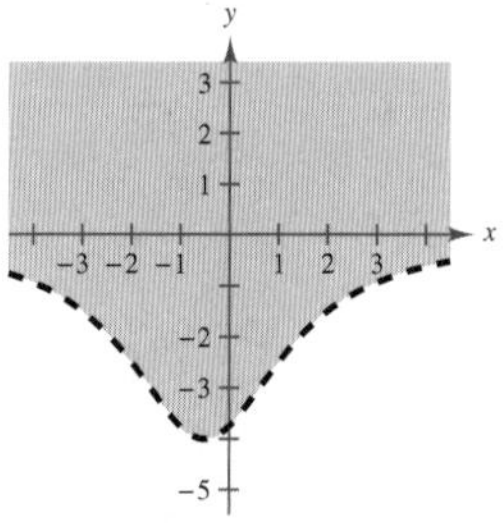

21.

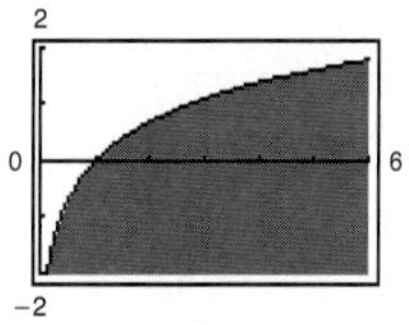

22.

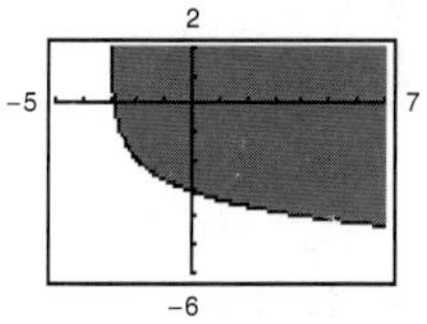

23.

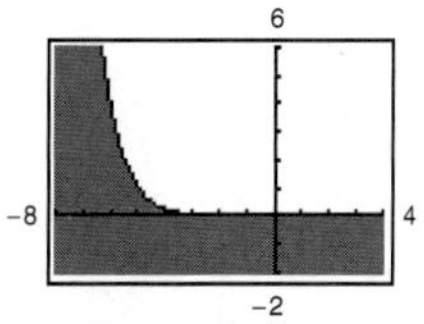

24.

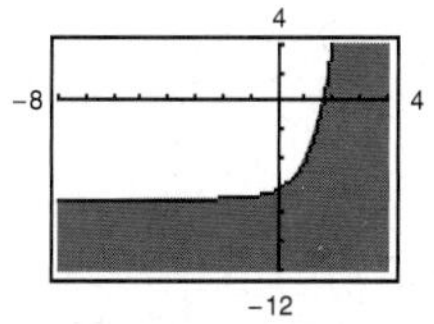

25.

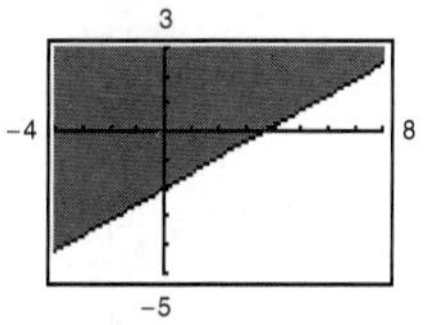

26.

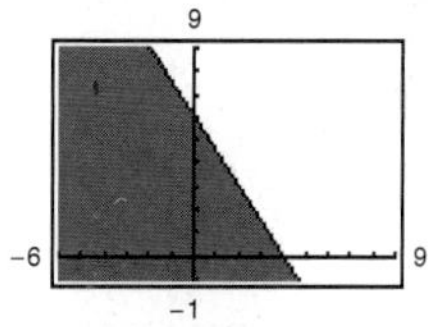

27.

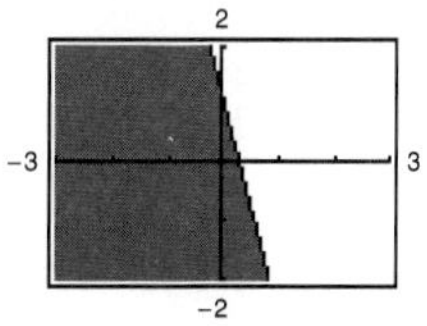

28.

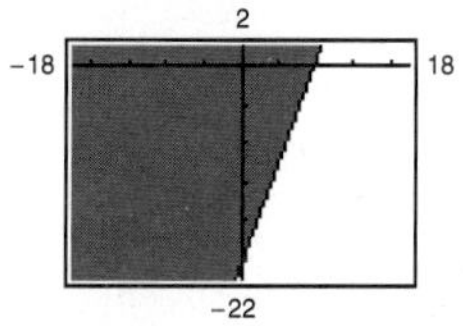

29.

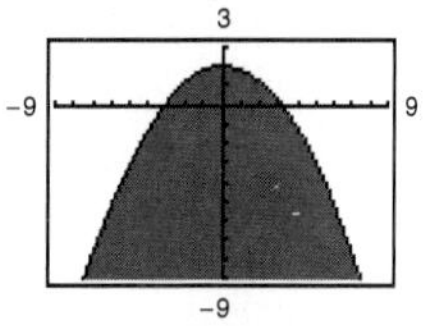

30.

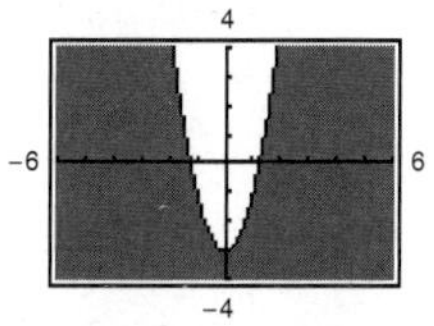

31.

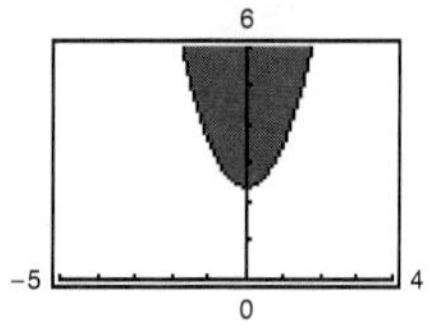

32.

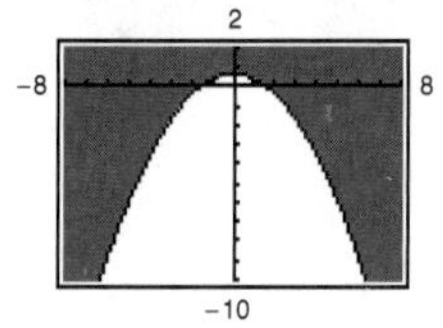

41.

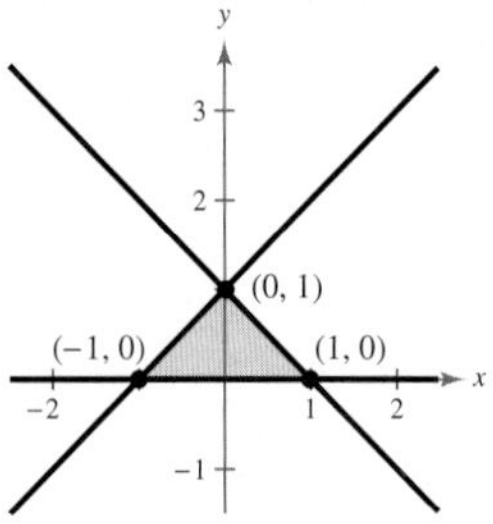

42.

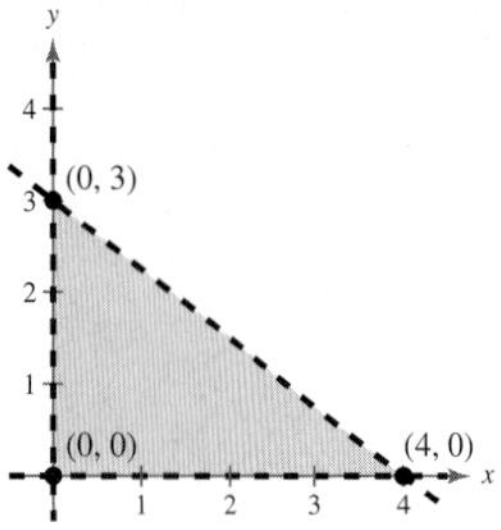

43.

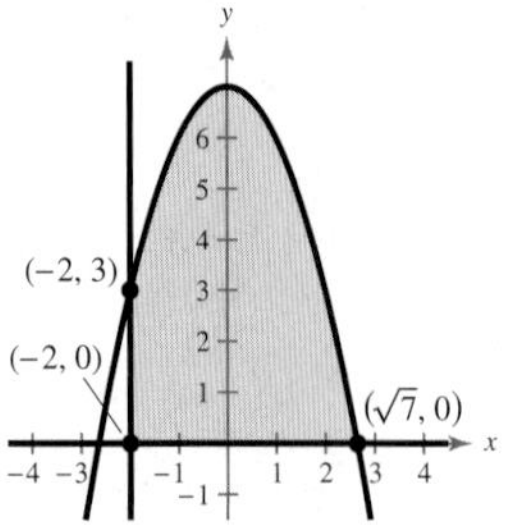

44.

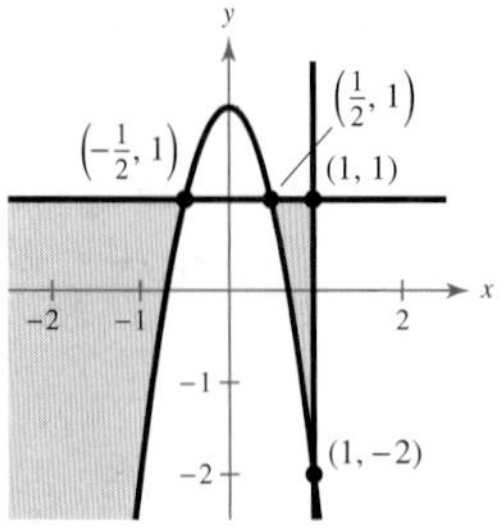

54.

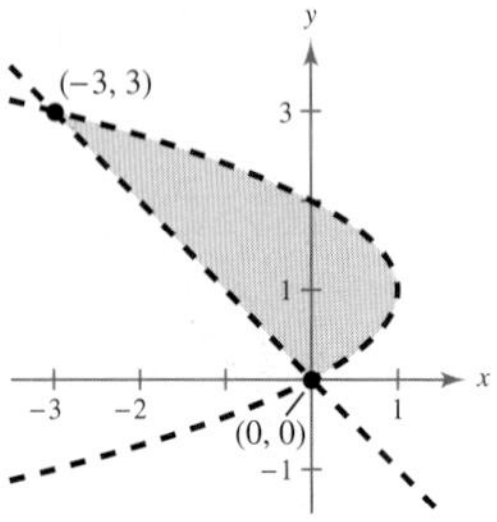

55.

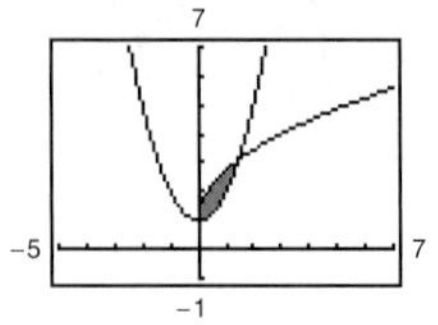

56.

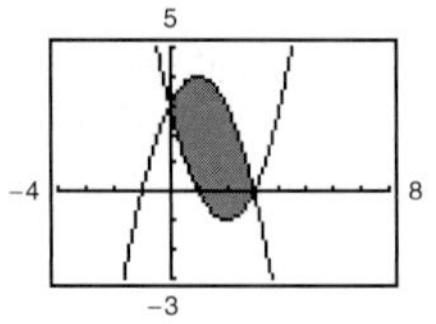

57.

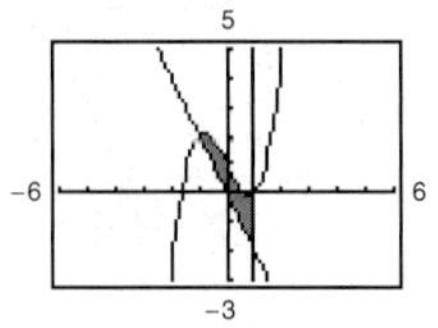

58.

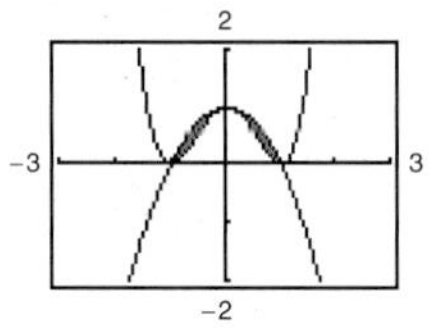

59.

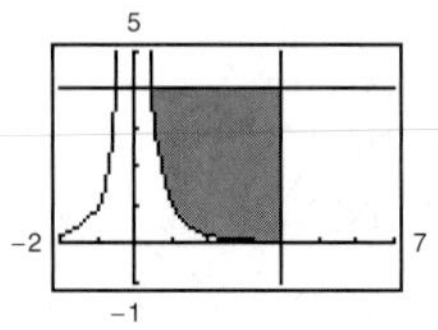

60.

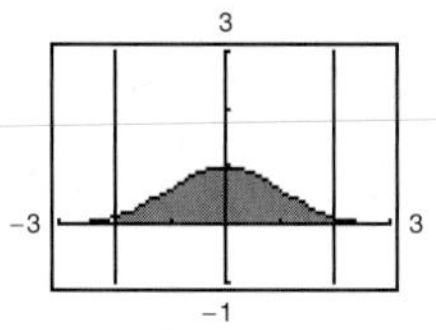

61. $\begin{cases} x \geq 0 \\ y \geq 0 \\ y \leq 6 - x \end{cases}$ **62.** $\begin{cases} y < 6 - 2x \\ y \geq x - 3 \\ x \geq 1 \end{cases}$ **63.** $\begin{cases} y \geq 4 - x \\ y \geq 2 - \frac{1}{4}x \\ x \geq 0,\ y \geq 0 \end{cases}$

64. $x^2 + y^2 \geq 16$

65. $\begin{cases} x \geq 0 \\ y \geq 0 \\ x^2 + y^2 < 64 \end{cases}$ **66.** $\begin{cases} x^2 + y^2 \leq 16 \\ x \leq y \\ x \geq 0 \end{cases}$ **67.** $\begin{cases} x \geq 4 \\ x \leq 9 \\ y \geq 3 \\ y \leq 9 \end{cases}$

68. $\begin{cases} 4x - y \geq 0 \\ 4x - y \leq 16 \\ 0 \leq y \leq 4 \end{cases}$ **69.** $\begin{cases} y \geq 0 \\ y \leq 5x \\ y \leq -x + 6 \end{cases}$ **70.** $\begin{cases} y \leq x + 1 \\ y \leq -x + 1 \\ y \geq 0 \end{cases}$

71. (a)

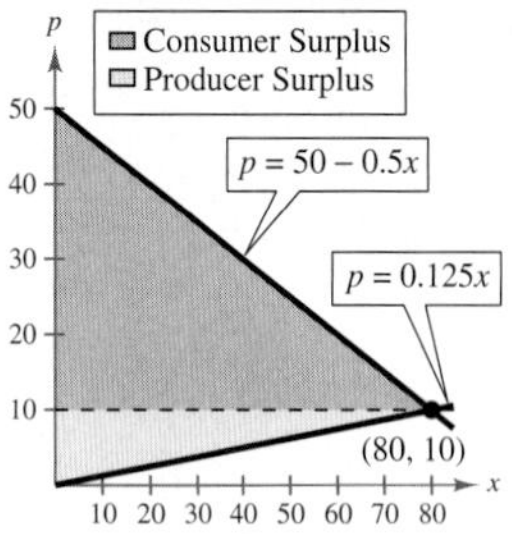

(b) Consumer surplus: \$1600
Producer surplus: \$400

72. (a)

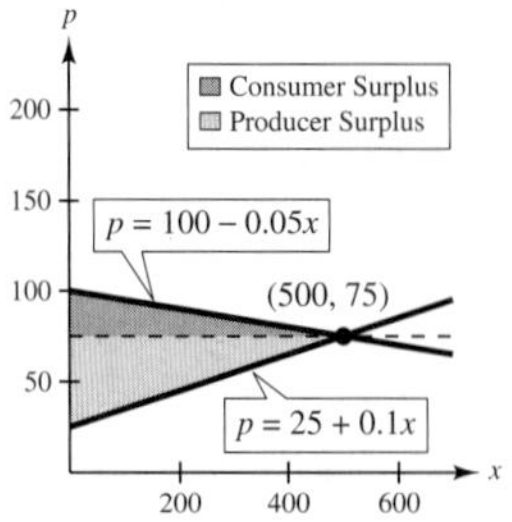

(b) Consumer surplus: \$6250
Producer surplus: \$12,500

73. (a)

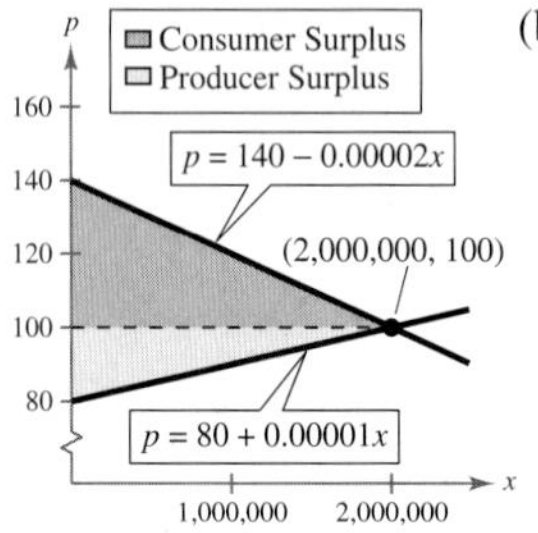

(b) Consumer surplus: \$40,000,000
Producer surplus: \$20,000,000

74. (a)

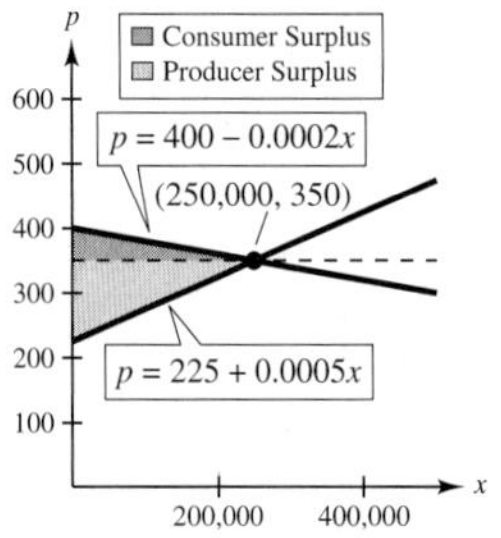

(b) Consumer surplus: \$6,250,000
Producer surplus: \$15,625,000

75. $\begin{cases} x + \frac{3}{2}y \leq 12 \\ \frac{4}{3}x + \frac{3}{2}y \leq 15 \\ x \geq 0 \\ y \geq 0 \end{cases}$

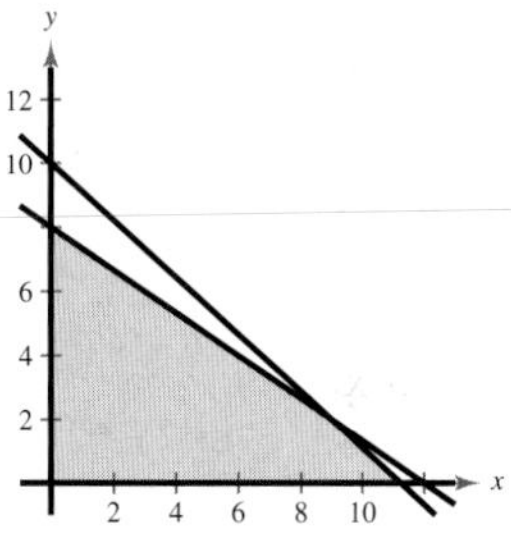

76. $\begin{cases} x \geq 2y \\ 8x + 12y \leq 200 \\ x \geq 4 \\ y \geq 2 \end{cases}$

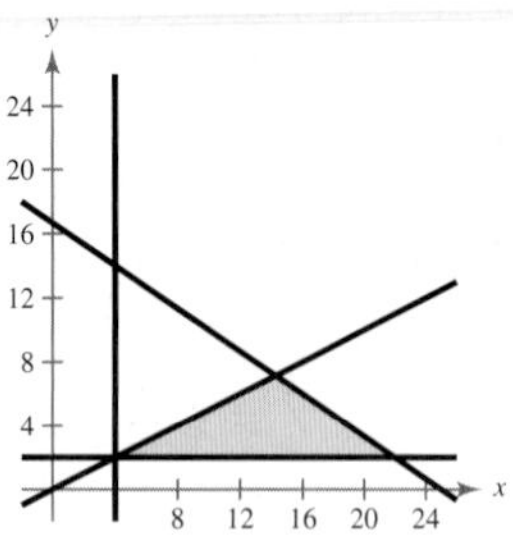

ADDITIONAL ANSWERS

77. $\begin{cases} x + y \le 20{,}000 \\ y \ge 2x \\ x \ge 5{,}000 \\ y \ge 5{,}000 \end{cases}$

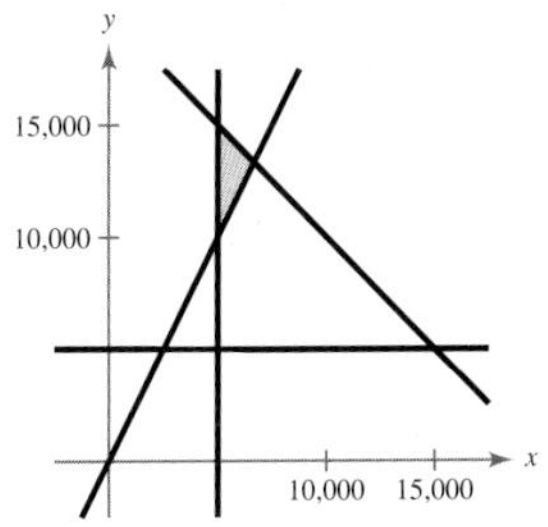

78. $\begin{cases} x + y \le 3{,}000 \\ 30x + 20y \ge 75{,}000 \\ x \le 2{,}000 \\ x \ge 0 \\ y \ge 0 \end{cases}$

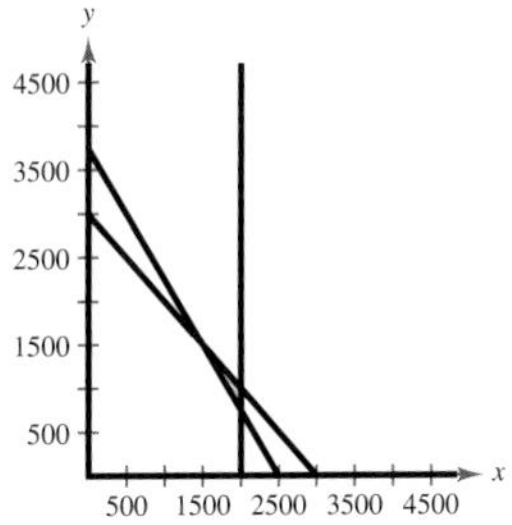

Section 7.6 *(page 555)*

32.

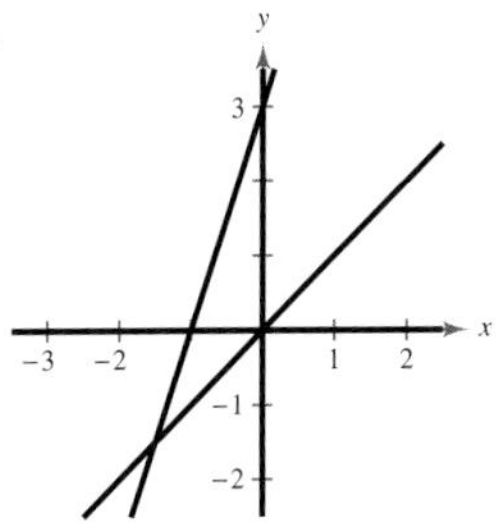

The feasible set is empty.

33.

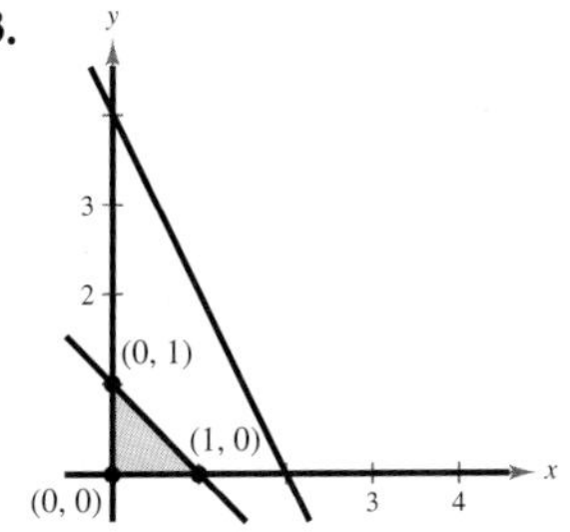

The constraint $2x + y \le 4$ is extraneous. Minimum at $(0, 0)$: 0; maximum at $(0, 1)$: 4

34.

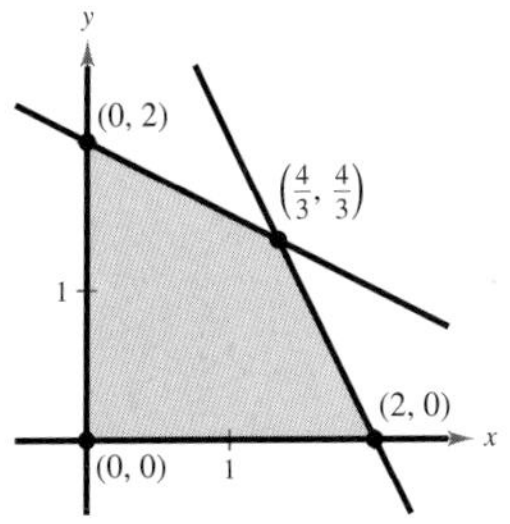

The maximum, 4, occurs at any point on the line segment connecting $(0, 2)$ and $\left(\frac{4}{3}, \frac{4}{3}\right)$. Minimum at $(0, 0)$: 0

35. 230 units of the $225 model
45 units of the $250 model
Optimal profit: $8295

36. 400 units of model X
1200 units of model Y
Optimal profit: $570,000

37. 3 bags of brand X
6 bags of brand Y
Optimal cost: $195

Review Exercises *(page 560)*

79.

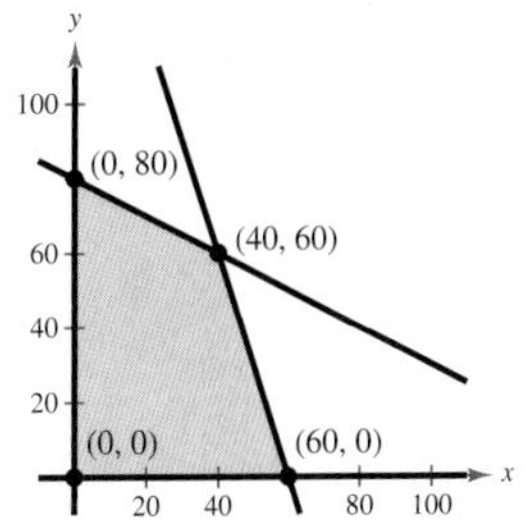

80.

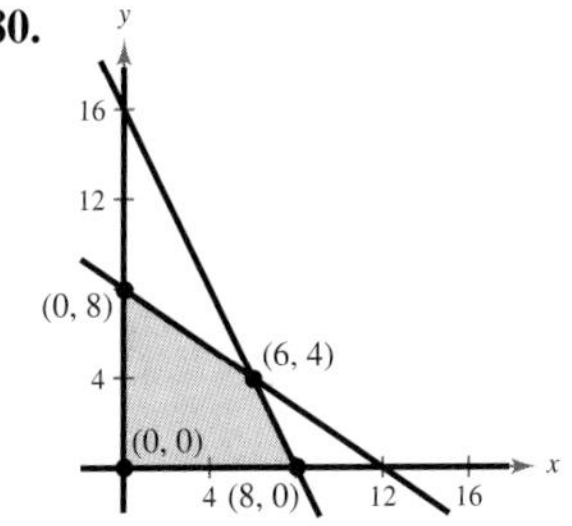

81.

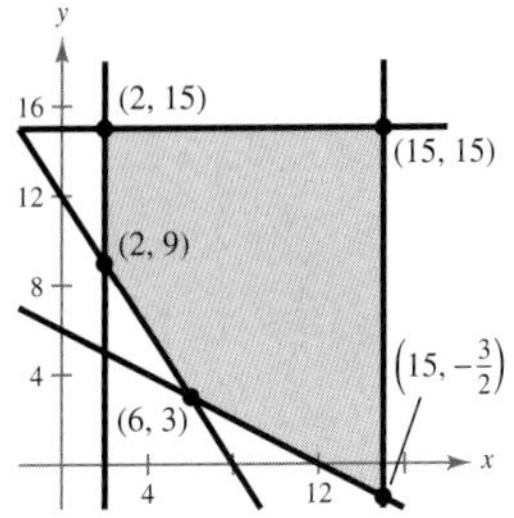

82.

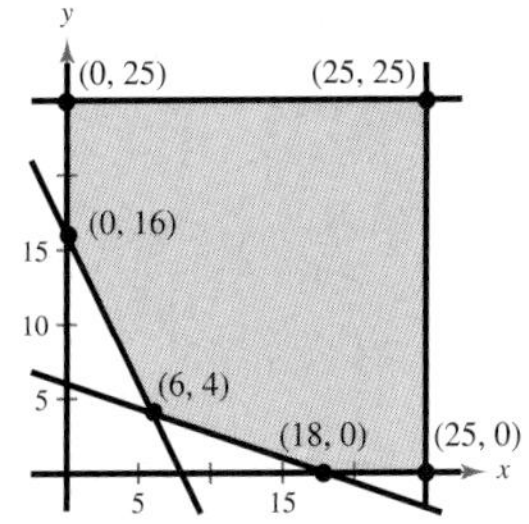

83.

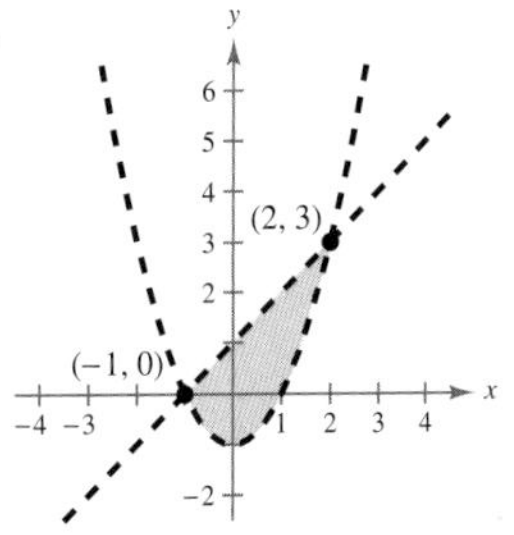

84.

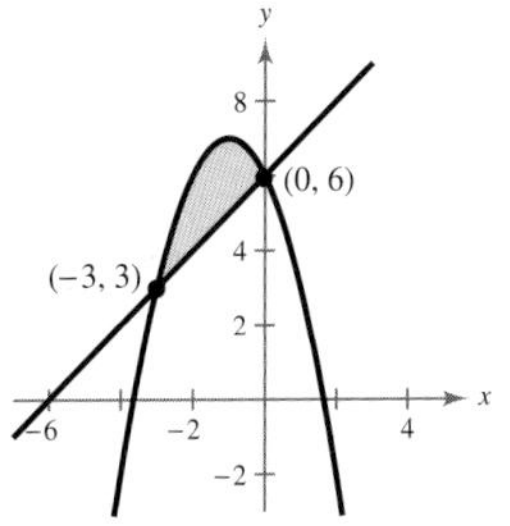

85.

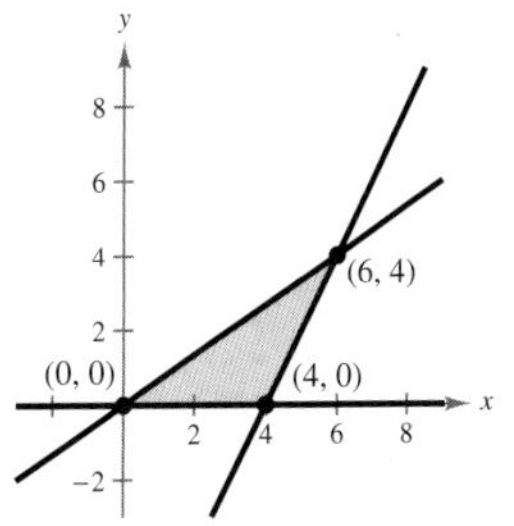

86.

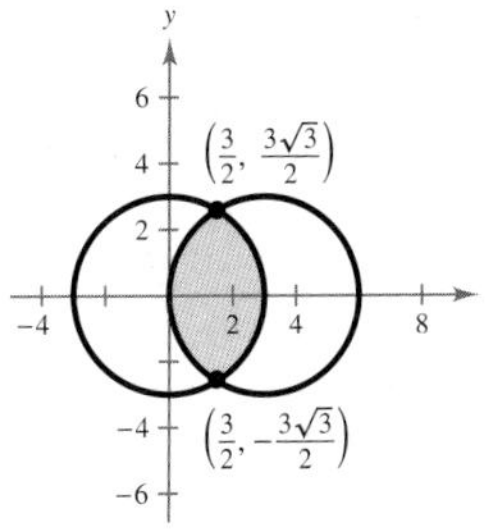

95.

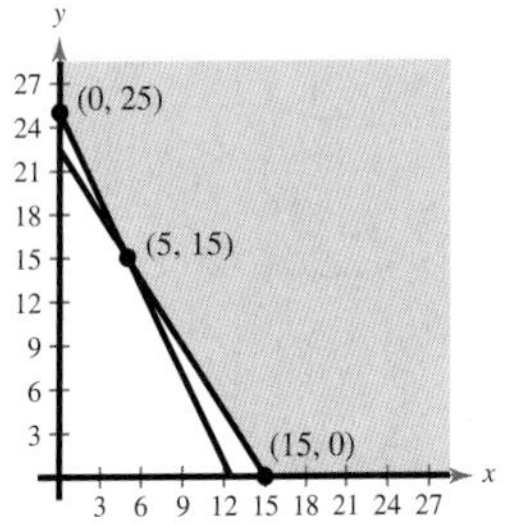

Minimum at $(15, 0)$: 26.25
No maximum

96.

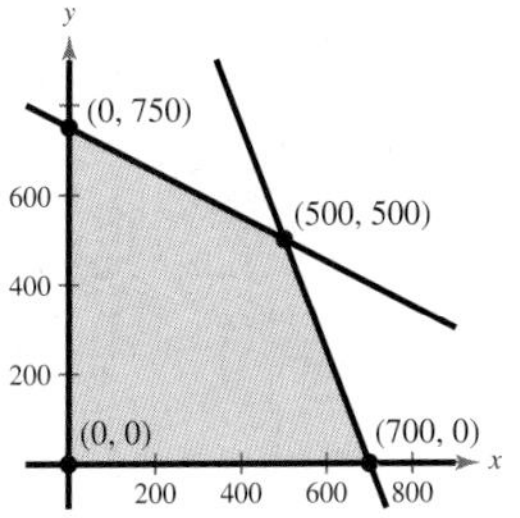

Minimum at $(0, 0)$: 0
Maximum at $(500, 500)$: 60,000

97. 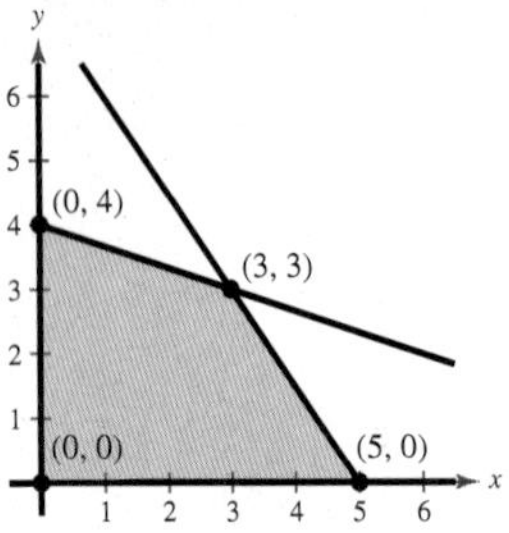

Minimum at (0, 0): 0
Maximum at (3, 3): 48

98. 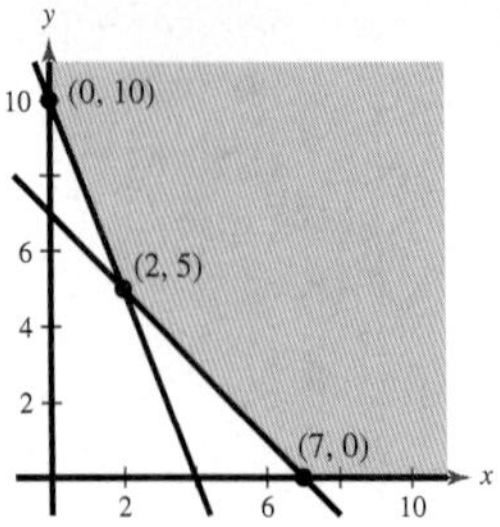

Minimum at (7, 0): −14
No maximum

Chapter 8

Section 8.2 *(page 594)*

16. (a) $\begin{bmatrix} -4 & 9 & 1 \\ 5 & -6 & -5 \\ 15 & -5 & -2 \\ 3 & 10 & -10 \\ -4 & 0 & -2 \end{bmatrix}$ (b) $\begin{bmatrix} 2 & -1 & -1 \\ 1 & 2 & 9 \\ -5 & 13 & 0 \\ -3 & 6 & -2 \\ -4 & -2 & 2 \end{bmatrix}$

(c) $\begin{bmatrix} -3 & 12 & 0 \\ 9 & -6 & 6 \\ 15 & 12 & -3 \\ 0 & 24 & -18 \\ -12 & -3 & 0 \end{bmatrix}$ (d) $\begin{bmatrix} 3 & 2 & -2 \\ 5 & 2 & 20 \\ -5 & 30 & -1 \\ -6 & 20 & -10 \\ -12 & -5 & 4 \end{bmatrix}$

Problem Solving *(page 637)*

4. (a) $A^2 - 2A + 5I$

$$= \begin{bmatrix} 1 & 2 \\ -2 & 1 \end{bmatrix}^2 - 2\begin{bmatrix} 1 & 2 \\ -2 & 1 \end{bmatrix} + 5\begin{bmatrix} 1 & 0 \\ 0 & 1 \end{bmatrix}$$

$$= \begin{bmatrix} -3 & 4 \\ -4 & -3 \end{bmatrix} - \begin{bmatrix} 2 & 4 \\ -4 & 2 \end{bmatrix} + \begin{bmatrix} 5 & 0 \\ 0 & 5 \end{bmatrix}$$

$$= \begin{bmatrix} 0 & 0 \\ 0 & 0 \end{bmatrix}$$

(b) $A^{-1} = \frac{1}{5}(2I - A)$

$$\begin{bmatrix} 1 & 2 \\ -2 & 1 \end{bmatrix}^{-1} = \frac{1}{5}\left(2\begin{bmatrix} 1 & 0 \\ 0 & 1 \end{bmatrix} - \begin{bmatrix} 1 & 2 \\ -2 & 1 \end{bmatrix}\right)$$

$$\begin{bmatrix} \frac{1}{5} & -\frac{2}{5} \\ \frac{2}{5} & \frac{1}{5} \end{bmatrix} = \frac{1}{5}\left(\begin{bmatrix} 2 & 0 \\ 0 & 2 \end{bmatrix} - \begin{bmatrix} 1 & 2 \\ -2 & 1 \end{bmatrix}\right)$$

$$\begin{bmatrix} \frac{1}{5} & -\frac{2}{5} \\ \frac{2}{5} & \frac{1}{5} \end{bmatrix} = \frac{1}{5}\begin{bmatrix} 1 & -2 \\ 2 & 1 \end{bmatrix}$$

$$\begin{bmatrix} \frac{1}{5} & -\frac{2}{5} \\ \frac{2}{5} & \frac{1}{5} \end{bmatrix} = \begin{bmatrix} \frac{1}{5} & -\frac{2}{5} \\ \frac{2}{5} & \frac{1}{5} \end{bmatrix}$$

(c) Answers will vary.

Chapter 9

Section 9.1 *(page 647)*

41. 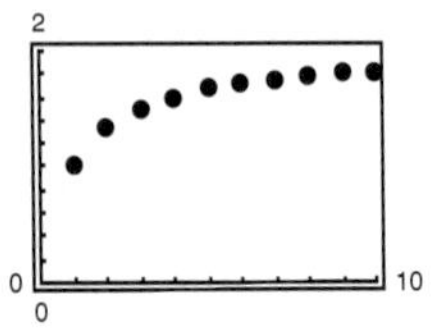

42. 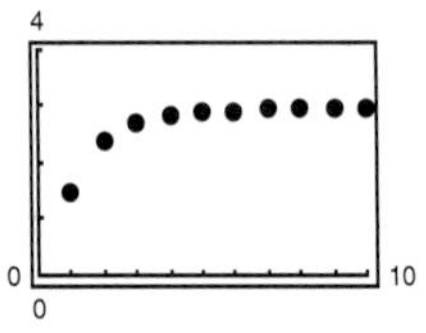

Section 9.5 *(page 686)*

36. $\frac{1}{x^6} + \frac{12y}{x^5} + \frac{60y^2}{x^4} + \frac{160y^3}{x^3} + \frac{240y^4}{x^2} + \frac{192y^5}{x} + 64y^6$

41. $32t^5 - 80t^4s + 80t^3s^2 - 40t^2s^3 + 10ts^4 - s^5$

42. $81 - 216z + 216z^2 - 96z^3 + 16z^4$

43. $x^5 + 10x^4y + 40x^3y^2 + 80x^2y^3 + 80xy^4 + 32y^5$

44. $729v^6 + 2916v^5 + 4860v^4 + 4320v^3$
$+ 2160v^2 + 576v + 64$

64. $u^3 + 10u^{12/5} + 40u^{9/5} + 80u^{6/5} + 80u^{3/5} + 32$

65. $81t^2 + 108t^{7/4} + 54t^{3/2} + 12t^{5/4} + t$

66. $16x^5 - 32x^{9/2} + 24x^4 - 8x^{7/2} + x^3$

69. $6x^5 + 15x^4h + 20x^3h^2 + 15x^2h^3 + 6xh^4 + h^5,\ h \neq 0$

70. $8x^7 + 28x^6h + 56x^5h^2 + 70x^4h^3 + 56x^3h^4$
$+ 28x^2h^5 + 8xh^6 + h^7,\ h \neq 0$

92. (a) $f(t) = -0.00015t^3 + 0.0559t^2 - 0.037t + 8.34$

(b) 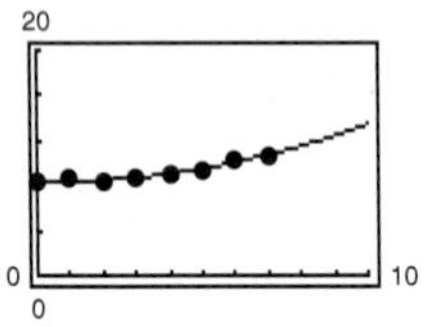

(c) $g(t) = -0.00015t^3 + 0.0537t^2 + 0.511t + 9.53$

(d) 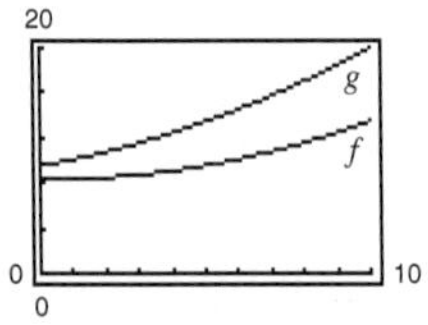

Chapter 10

Section 10.2 *(page 738)*

40. Vertex: $(-5, 1)$
Focus: $\left(-\frac{21}{4}, 1\right)$
Directrix: $x = -\frac{19}{4}$

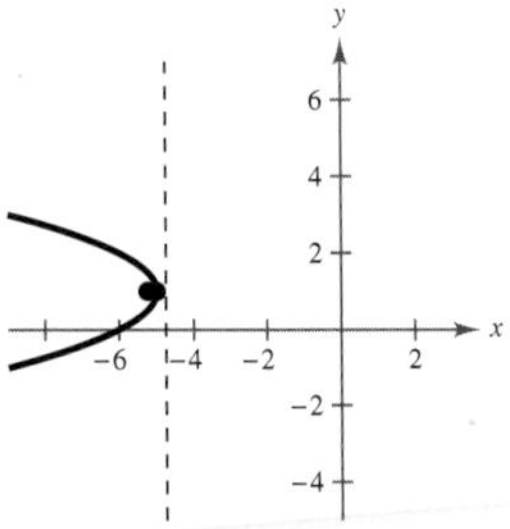

41. Vertex: $\left(-3, \frac{3}{2}\right)$
Focus: $\left(-3, \frac{5}{2}\right)$
Directrix: $y = \frac{1}{2}$

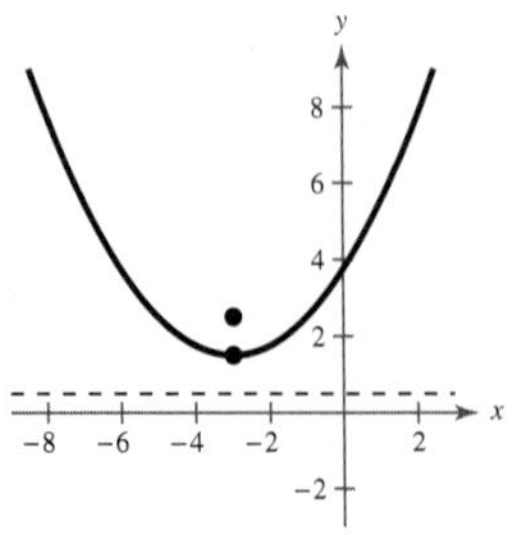

42. Vertex: $\left(-\frac{1}{2}, 1\right)$
Focus: $\left(-\frac{1}{2}, 2\right)$
Directrix: $y = 0$

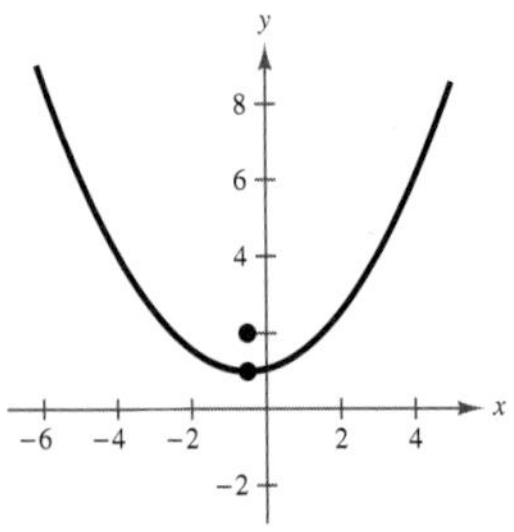

43. Vertex: $(1, 1)$
Focus: $(1, 2)$
Directrix: $y = 0$

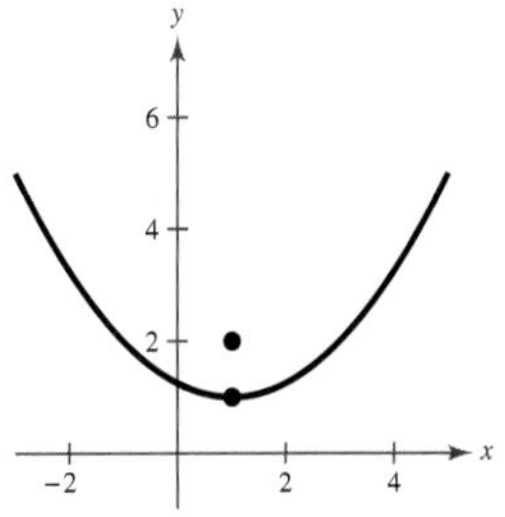

44. Vertex: $(8, -1)$
Focus: $(9, -1)$
Directrix: $x = 7$

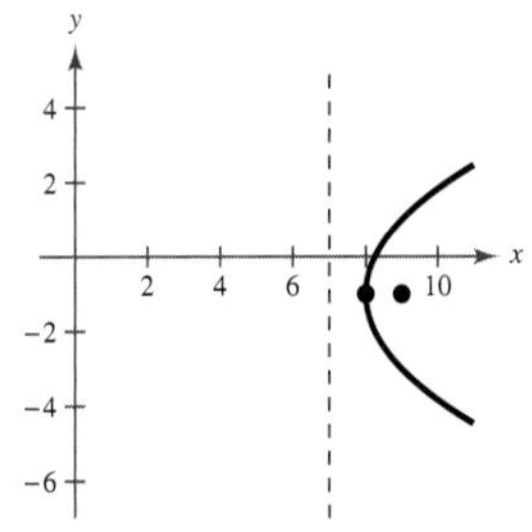

45. Vertex: $(-2, -3)$
Focus: $(-4, -3)$
Directrix: $x = 0$

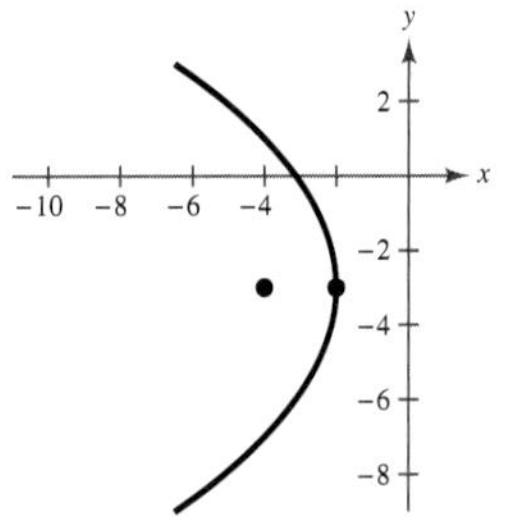

46. Vertex: $(-1, 2)$
Focus: $(0, 2)$
Directrix: $x = -2$

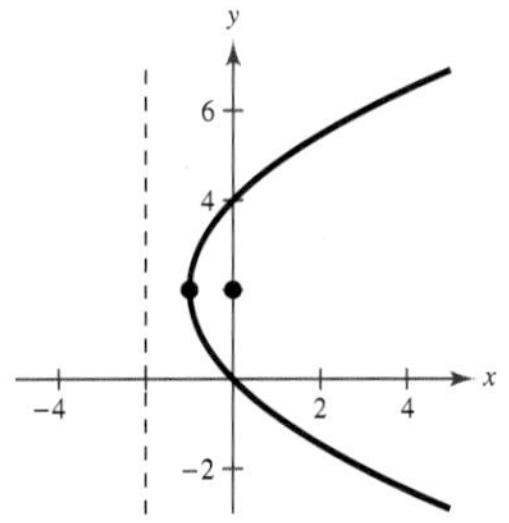

47. Vertex: $(-2, 1)$
Focus: $\left(-2, -\frac{1}{2}\right)$
Directrix: $y = \frac{5}{2}$

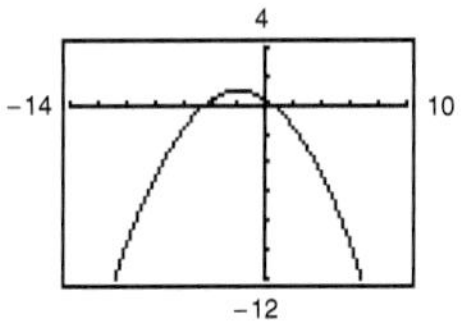

48. Vertex: $(1, -1)$
Focus: $(1, -3)$
Directrix: $y = 1$

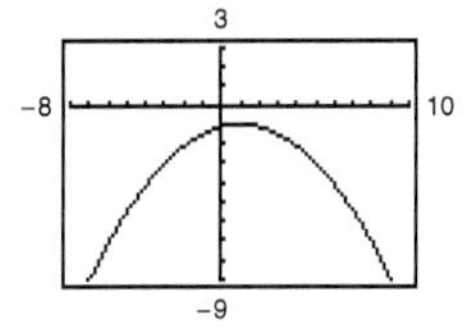

49. Vertex: $\left(\frac{1}{4}, -\frac{1}{2}\right)$
Focus: $\left(0, -\frac{1}{2}\right)$
Directrix: $x = \frac{1}{2}$

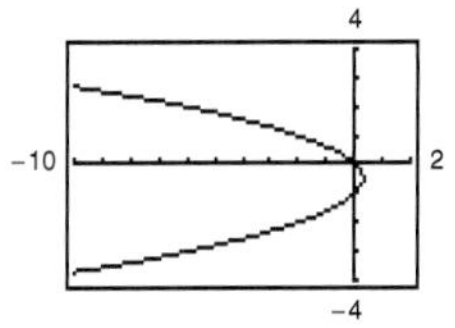

50. Vertex: $(-1, 0)$
Focus: $(0, 0)$
Directrix: $x = -2$

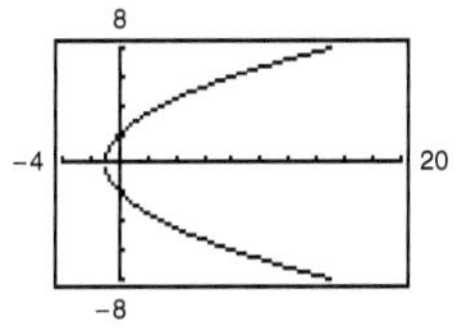

63.

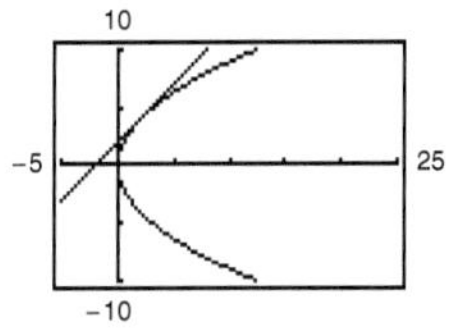

$(2, 4)$

64.

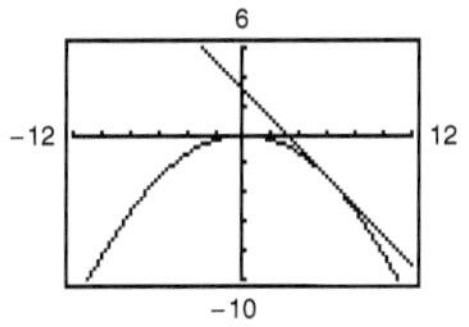

$(6, -3)$

65. $4x - y - 8 = 0$; $(2, 0)$

66. $6x + 2y + 9 = 0$; $\left(-\frac{3}{2}, 0\right)$

67. $4x - y + 2 = 0$; $\left(-\frac{1}{2}, 0\right)$

68. $8x + y - 8 = 0$; $(1, 0)$

69.

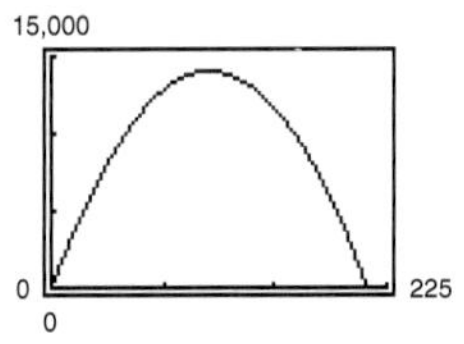

$x = 106$ units

70.

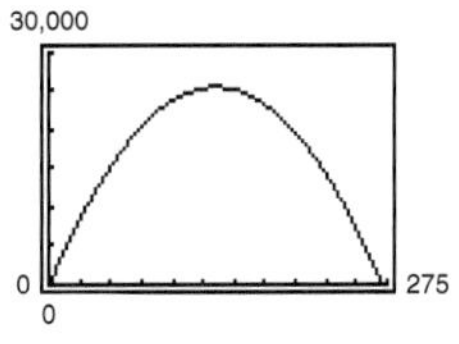

$x = 135$ units

71. (a)

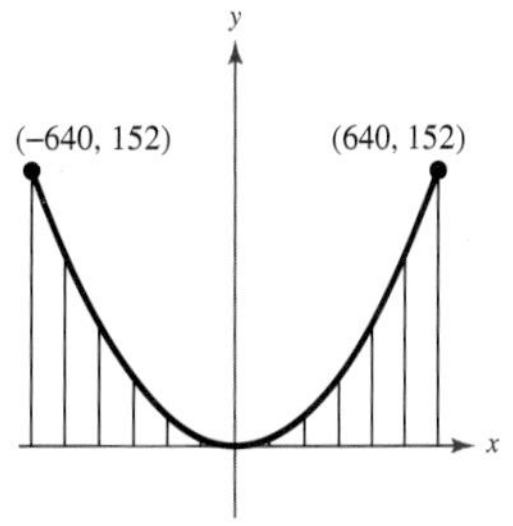

Section 10.3 *(page 748)*

35. Ellipse
Center: $(4, -1)$
Vertices: $(4, -6), (4, 4)$
Foci: $(4, 2), (4, -4)$
Eccentricity: $\frac{3}{5}$

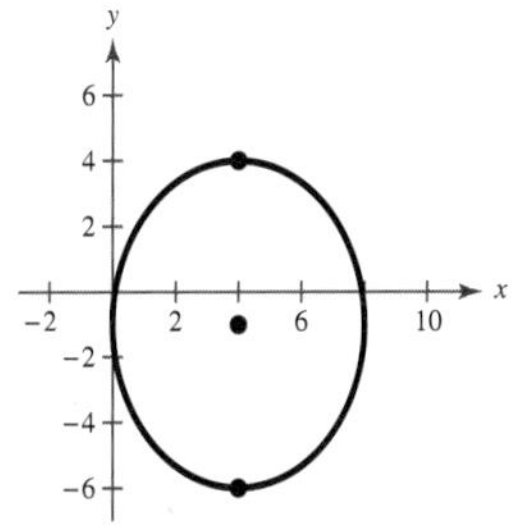

36. Ellipse
Center: $(-3, 2)$
Vertices: $(-3, 6), (-3, -2)$
Foci: $(-3, 4), (-3, 0)$
Eccentricity: $\frac{1}{2}$

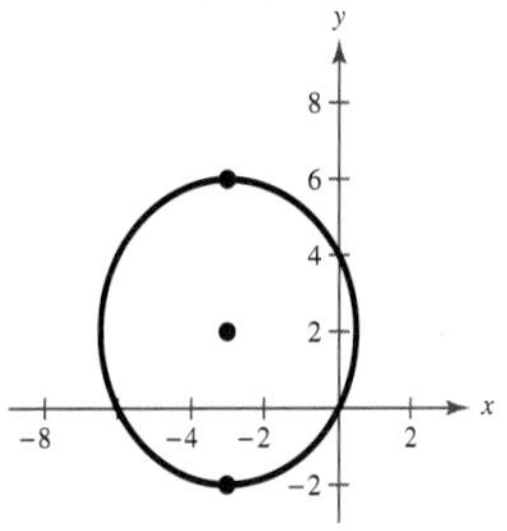

37. Circle
Center: $(0, -1)$
Radius: $\frac{2}{3}$

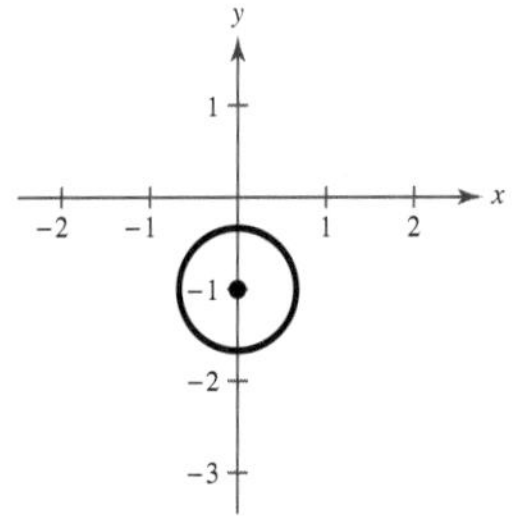

38. Ellipse
Center: $(-5, 1)$
Vertices: $\left(-\dfrac{7}{2}, 1\right), \left(-\dfrac{13}{2}, 1\right)$
Foci: $\left(-5 \pm \dfrac{\sqrt{5}}{2}, 1\right)$
Eccentricity: $\dfrac{\sqrt{5}}{3}$

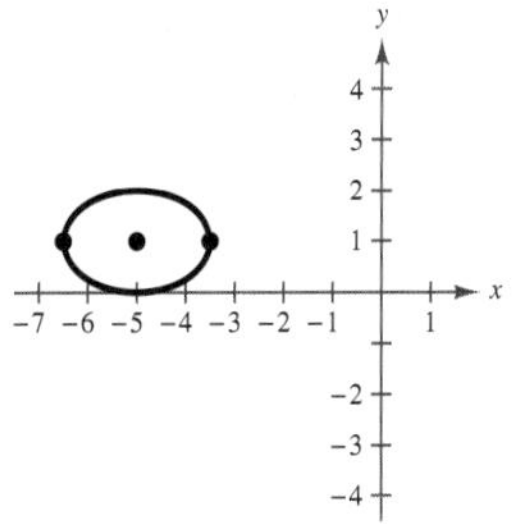

39. Ellipse
Center: $(-2, -4)$
Vertices: $(-3, -4), (-1, -4)$
Foci: $\left(\dfrac{-4 \pm \sqrt{3}}{2}, -4\right)$
Eccentricity: $\dfrac{\sqrt{3}}{2}$

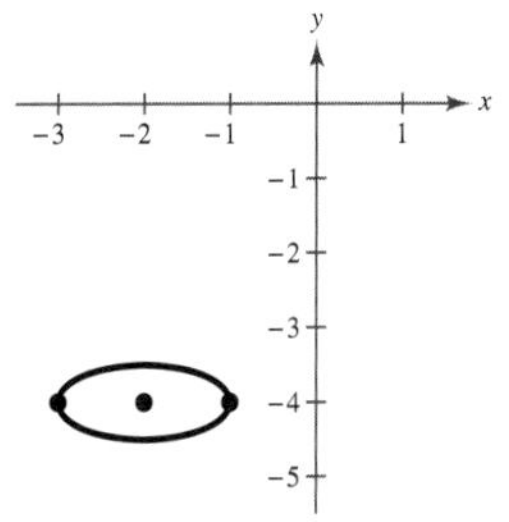

40. Circle
Center: $(3, 1)$
Radius: $\frac{5}{2}$

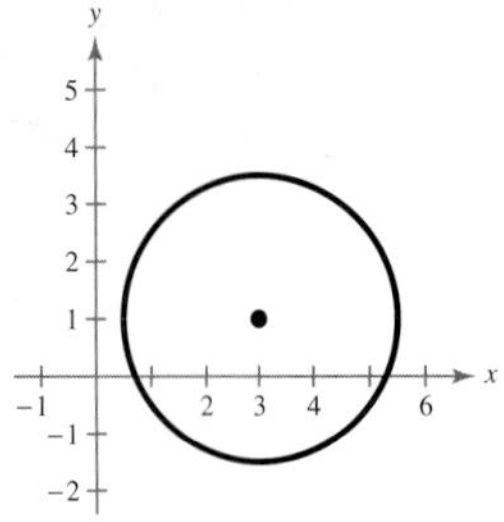

41. Ellipse
Center: $(-2, 3)$
Vertices: $(-2, 6), (-2, 0)$
Foci: $\left(-2, 3 \pm \sqrt{5}\right)$
Eccentricity: $\dfrac{\sqrt{5}}{3}$

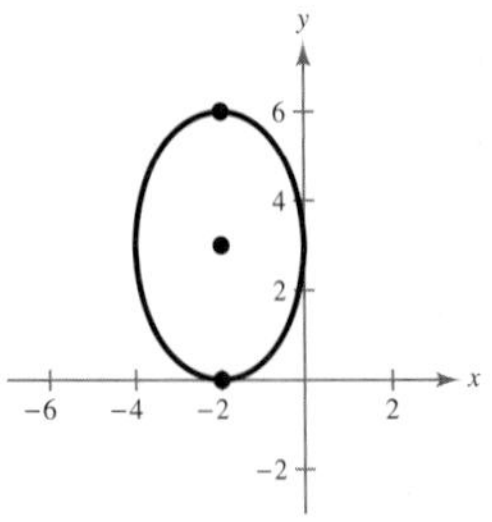

42. Ellipse
Center: $(3, -5)$
Vertices: $(3, 1), (3, -11)$
Foci: $\left(3, -5 \pm 2\sqrt{5}\right)$
Eccentricity: $\dfrac{\sqrt{5}}{3}$

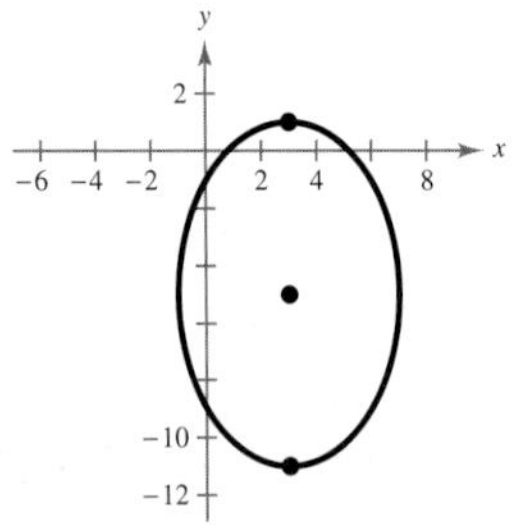

43. Circle
Center: $(1, -2)$
Radius: 6

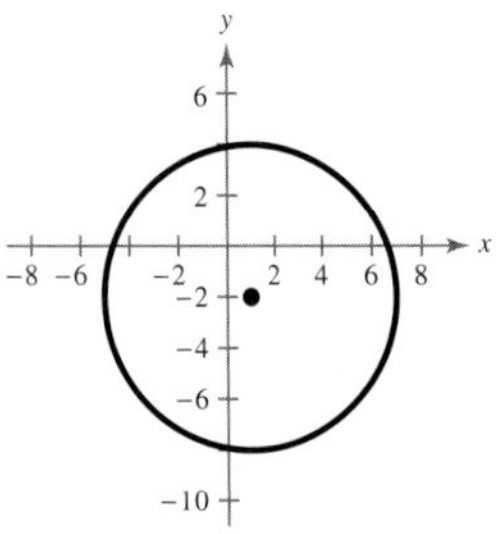

44. Ellipse
Center: $(4, 3)$
Vertices: $(14, 3), (-6, 3)$
Foci: $\left(4 \pm 4\sqrt{5}, 3\right)$
Eccentricity: $\dfrac{2\sqrt{5}}{5}$

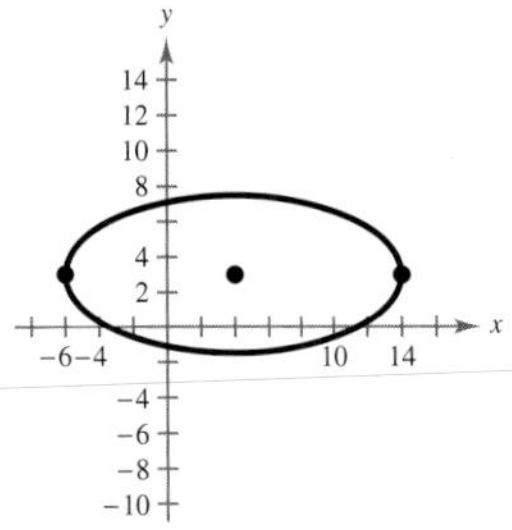

45. Ellipse
Center: $(-3, 1)$
Vertices: $(-3, 7), (-3, -5)$
Foci: $\left(-3, 1 \pm 2\sqrt{6}\right)$
Eccentricity: $\dfrac{\sqrt{6}}{3}$

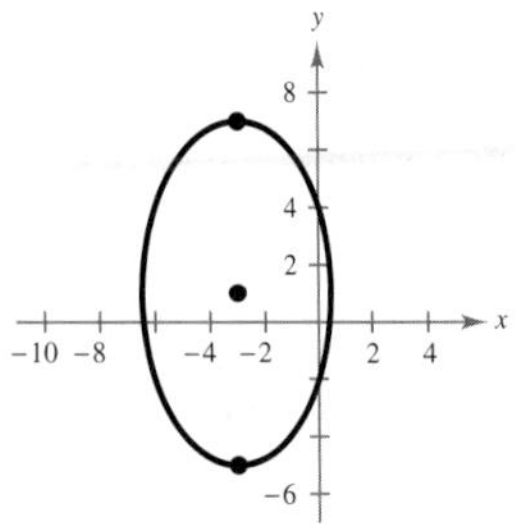

46. Ellipse
Center: $\left(-\dfrac{3}{2}, \dfrac{5}{2}\right)$
Vertices: $\left(-\dfrac{3}{2}, \dfrac{5}{2} \pm 2\sqrt{3}\right)$
Foci: $\left(-\dfrac{3}{2}, \dfrac{5}{2} \pm 2\sqrt{2}\right)$
Eccentricity: $\dfrac{\sqrt{6}}{3}$

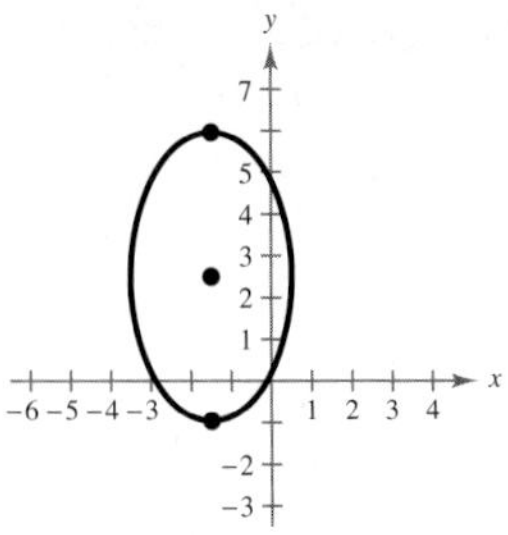

47. Ellipse
Center: $\left(3, -\dfrac{5}{2}\right)$
Vertices: $\left(9, -\dfrac{5}{2}\right), \left(-3, -\dfrac{5}{2}\right)$
Foci: $\left(3 \pm 3\sqrt{3}, -\dfrac{5}{2}\right)$
Eccentricity: $\dfrac{\sqrt{3}}{2}$

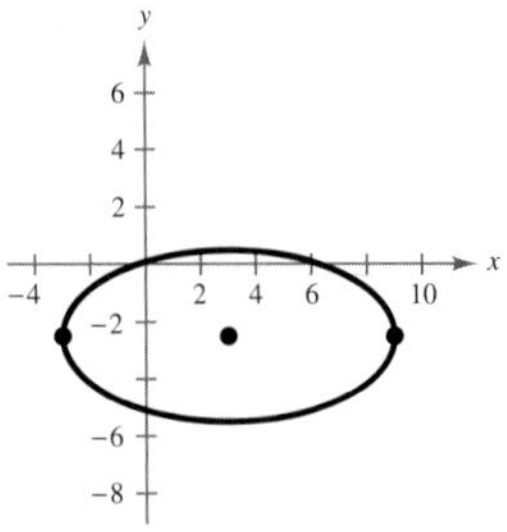

48. Circle
Center: $(2, -3)$
Radius: 4

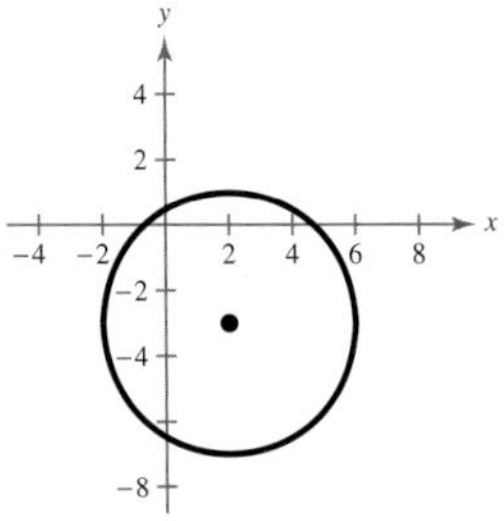

49. Circle
Center: $(-1, 1)$
Radius: $\frac{2}{3}$

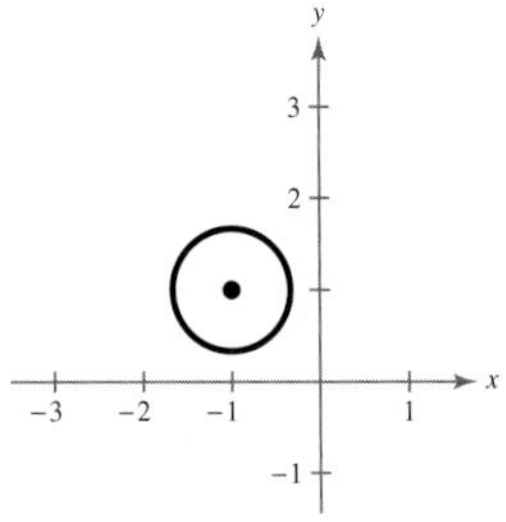

50. Ellipse
Center: $(1, -1)$
Vertices: $\left(\frac{9}{4}, -1\right), \left(-\frac{1}{4}, -1\right)$
Foci: $\left(\frac{7}{4}, -1\right), \left(\frac{1}{4}, -1\right)$
Eccentricity: $\frac{3}{5}$

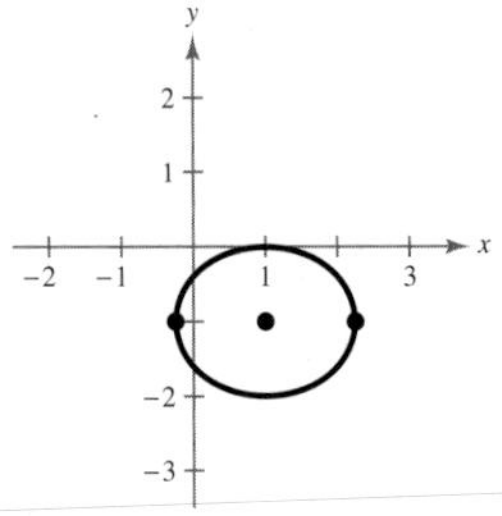

51. Ellipse
Center: $(2, 1)$
Vertices: $\left(\frac{7}{3}, 1\right), \left(\frac{5}{3}, 1\right)$
Foci: $\left(\frac{34}{15}, 1\right), \left(\frac{26}{15}, 1\right)$
Eccentricity: $\frac{4}{5}$

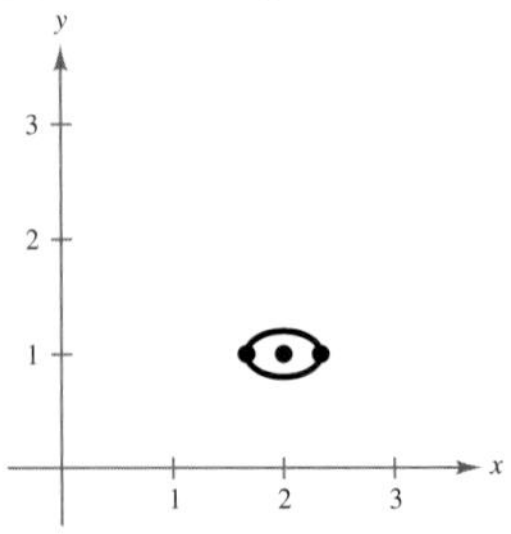

52. Circle
Center: $(2, -1)$
Radius: $\frac{5}{4}$

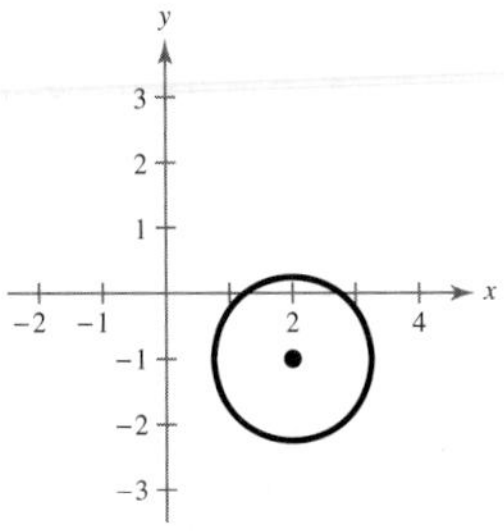

53.

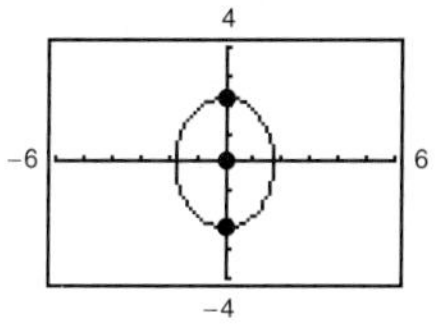

Center: $(0, 0)$
Vertices: $(0, \pm\sqrt{5})$
Foci: $(0, \pm\sqrt{2})$

54.

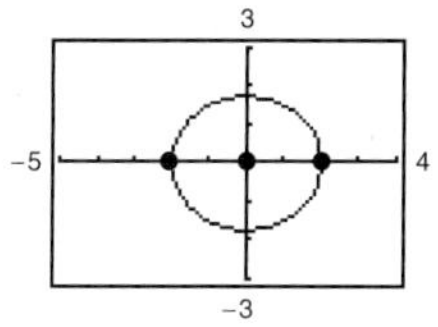

Center: $(0, 0)$
Vertices: $(\pm 2, 0)$
Foci: $(\pm 1, 0)$

55.

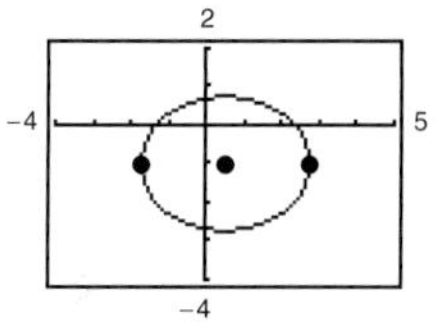

Center: $\left(\frac{1}{2}, -1\right)$
Vertices: $\left(\frac{1}{2} \pm \sqrt{5}, -1\right)$
Foci: $\left(\frac{1}{2} \pm \sqrt{2}, -1\right)$

56.

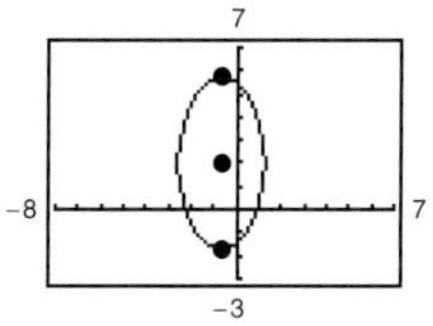

Center: $\left(-\frac{2}{3}, 2\right)$

Vertices: $\left(-\frac{2}{3}, 2 \pm \frac{2\sqrt{31}}{3}\right)$

Foci: $\left(-\frac{2}{3}, 2 \pm \frac{\sqrt{93}}{3}\right)$

61. $\frac{x^2}{25} + \frac{y^2}{16} = 1$ **62.** $\frac{x^2}{48} + \frac{y^2}{64} = 1$

63. (a)

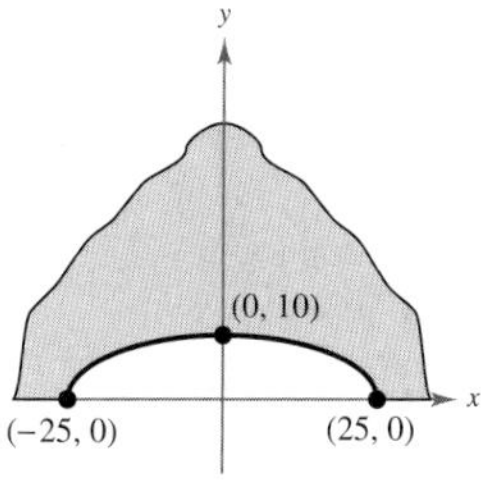

(b) $\frac{x^2}{625} + \frac{y^2}{100} = 1$

65. (a) $\frac{x^2}{321.84} + \frac{y^2}{20.89} = 1$

(b)

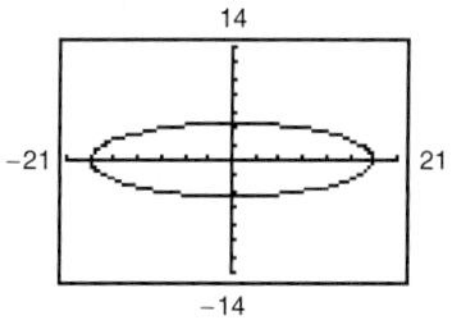

Section 10.4 *(page 758)*

16. Center: $(-3, 2)$
Vertices: $(9, 2), (-15, 2)$
Foci: $(10, 2), (-16, 2)$
Asymptotes:
$y = 2 \pm \frac{5}{12}(x + 3)$

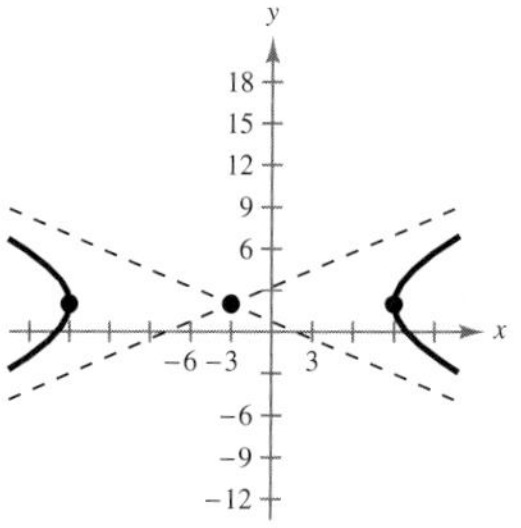

17. Center: $(2, -6)$
Vertices:
$\left(2, -\frac{17}{3}\right), \left(2, -\frac{19}{3}\right)$
Foci: $\left(2, -6 \pm \frac{\sqrt{13}}{6}\right)$
Asymptotes:
$y = -6 \pm \frac{2}{3}(x - 2)$

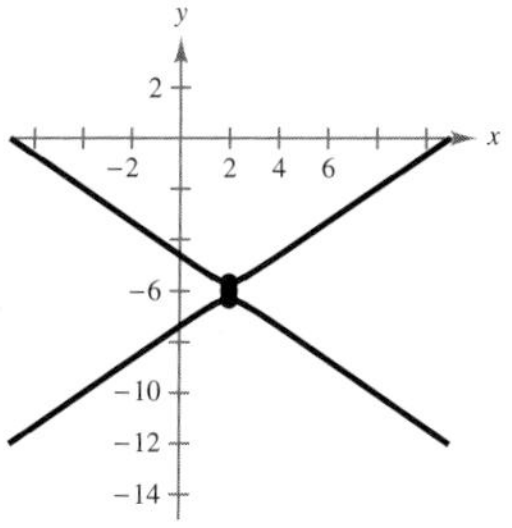

18. Center: $(-3, 1)$
Vertices: $\left(-3, \frac{3}{2}\right), \left(-3, \frac{1}{2}\right)$
Foci: $\left(-3, 1 \pm \frac{\sqrt{5}}{4}\right)$
Asymptotes:
$y = 1 \pm 2(x + 3)$

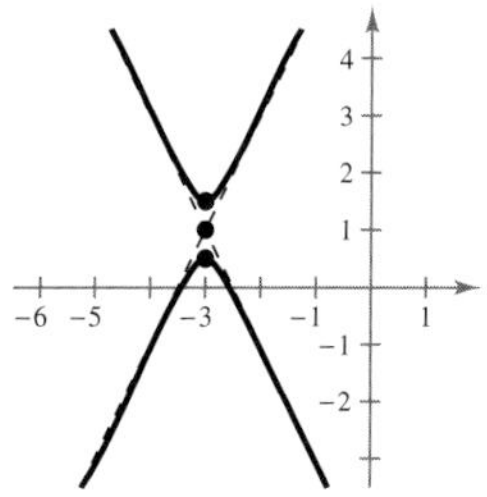

19. Center: $(2, -3)$
Vertices: $(3, -3), (1, -3)$
Foci: $(2 \pm \sqrt{10}, -3)$
Asymptotes:
$y = -3 \pm 3(x - 2)$

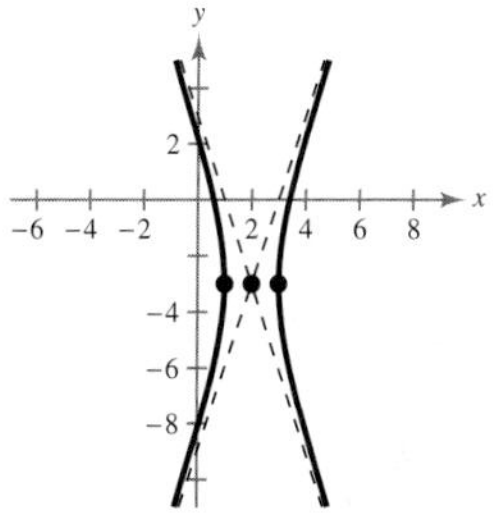

20. Center: $(0, 2)$
Vertices: $(\pm 6, 2)$
Foci: $(\pm 2\sqrt{10}, 2)$
Asymptotes: $y = 2 \pm \frac{1}{3}x$

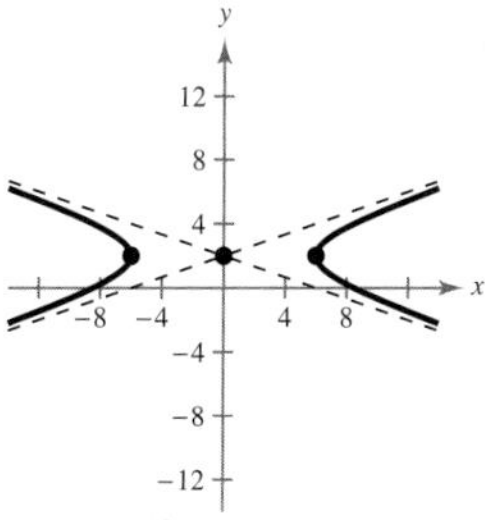

21. The graph of this equation is two lines intersecting at $(-1, -3)$.

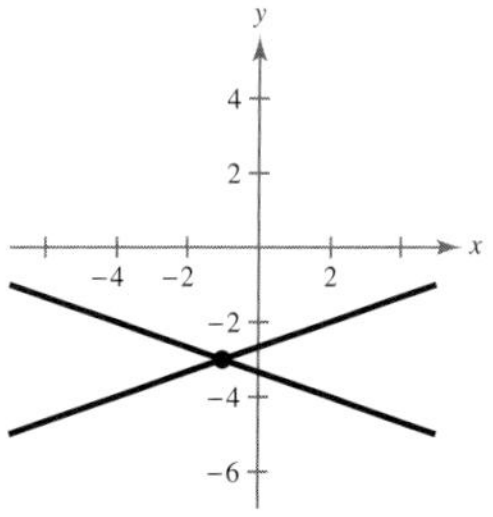

22. The graph of this equation is two lines intersecting at $(1, -2)$.

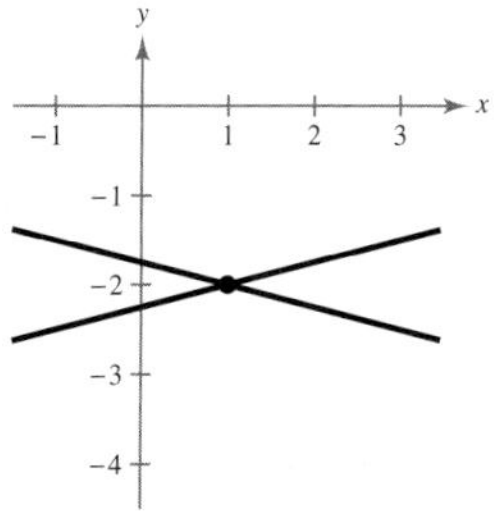

23. Center: $(0, 0)$
Vertices: $(\pm\sqrt{3}, 0)$
Foci: $(\pm\sqrt{5}, 0)$
Asymptotes: $y = \pm\frac{\sqrt{6}}{3}x$

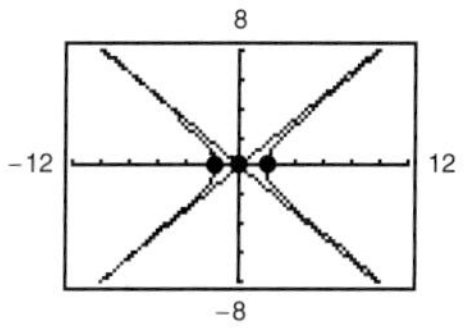

24. Center: $(0, 0)$
Vertices: $(0, \pm\sqrt{3})$
Foci: $(0, \pm 3)$
Asymptotes: $y = \pm\frac{\sqrt{2}}{2}x$

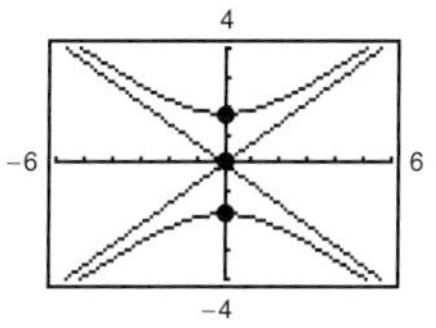

ADDITIONAL ANSWERS

25. Center: $(0, 0)$
Vertices: $(\pm 3, 0)$
Foci: $(\pm\sqrt{13}, 0)$
Asymptotes: $y = \pm\frac{2}{3}x$

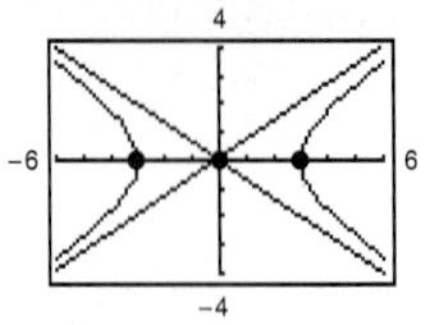

26. Center: $(0, 0)$
Vertices: $(\pm 2, 0)$
Foci: $(\pm\sqrt{29}, 0)$
Asymptotes: $y = \pm\frac{5}{2}x$

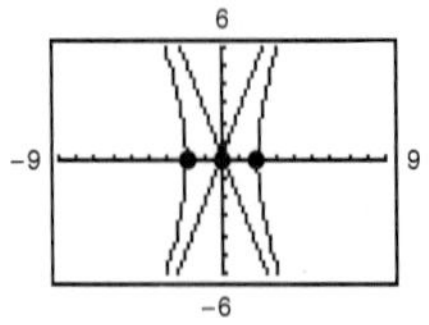

27. Center: $(1, -3)$
Vertices: $(1, -3 \pm \sqrt{2})$
Foci: $(1, -3 \pm 2\sqrt{5})$
Asymptotes:
$y = -3 \pm \frac{1}{3}(x - 1)$

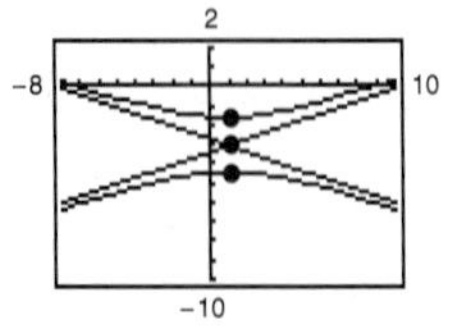

28. Center: $(-3, 5)$
Vertices: $\left(-\dfrac{10}{3}, 5\right), \left(-\dfrac{8}{3}, 5\right)$
Foci: $\left(-3 \pm \dfrac{\sqrt{10}}{3}, 5\right)$
Asymptotes: $y = 5 \pm 3(x + 3)$

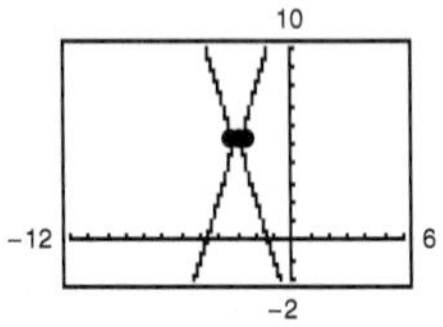

Section 10.5 *(page 767)*

16. $$\frac{\left(y' + \dfrac{3\sqrt{2}}{2}\right)^2}{12} - \frac{\left(x' + \dfrac{\sqrt{2}}{2}\right)^2}{12} = 1$$

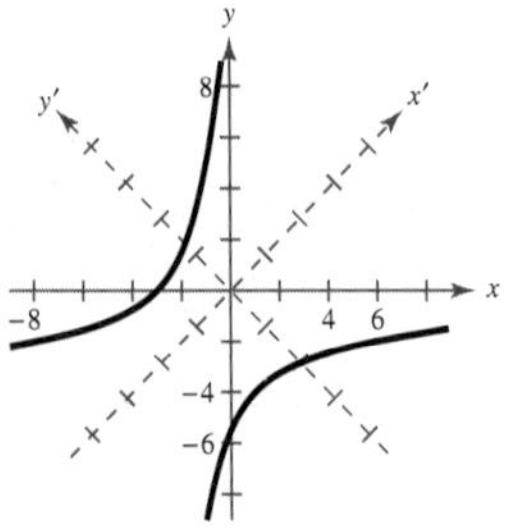

17. $$\frac{(x' - 6\sqrt{2})^2}{64} - \frac{(y' - 2\sqrt{2})^2}{64} = 1$$

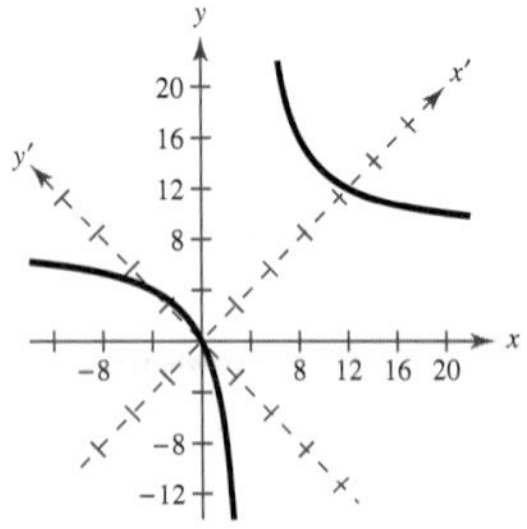

18. $$\frac{(x')^2}{4} - \frac{(y')^2}{4} = 1$$

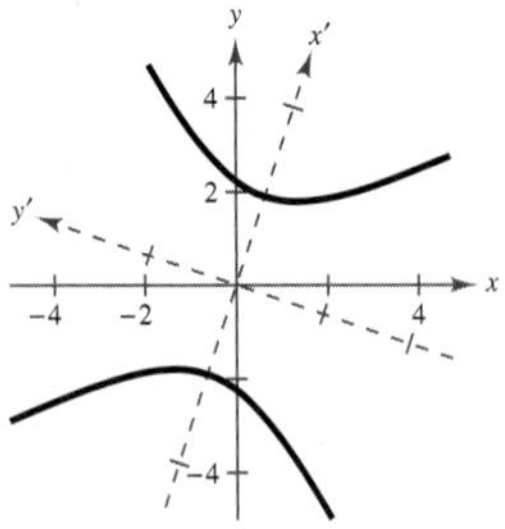

19. $$\frac{(x')^2}{6} + \frac{(y')^2}{3/2} = 1$$

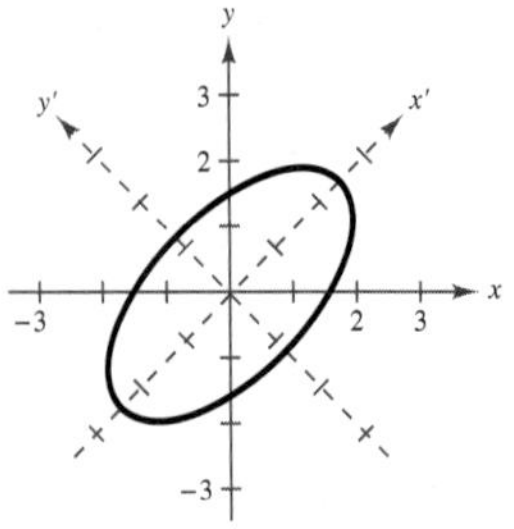

20. $$\frac{(x')^2}{16/5} + \frac{(y')^2}{16/3} = 1$$

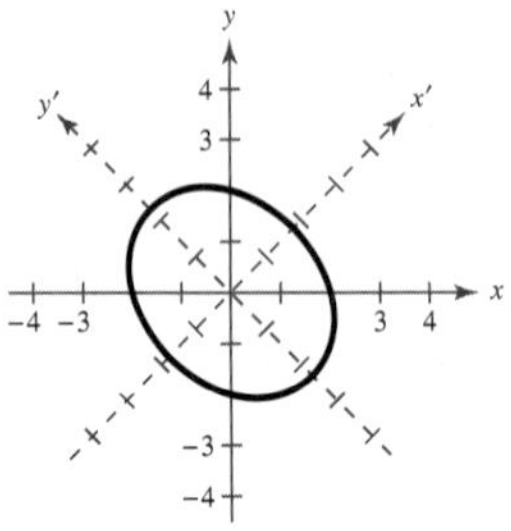

21. $y' = \dfrac{-\sqrt{2}}{4}(x')^2$

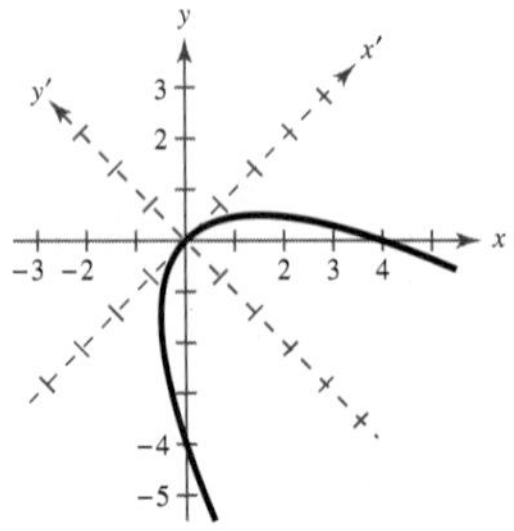

22. $$\frac{(x')^2}{1} + \frac{(y')^2}{4} = 1$$

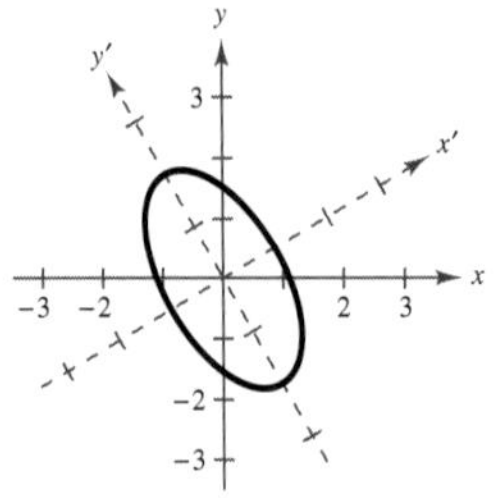

23. $(y')^2 = -x'$

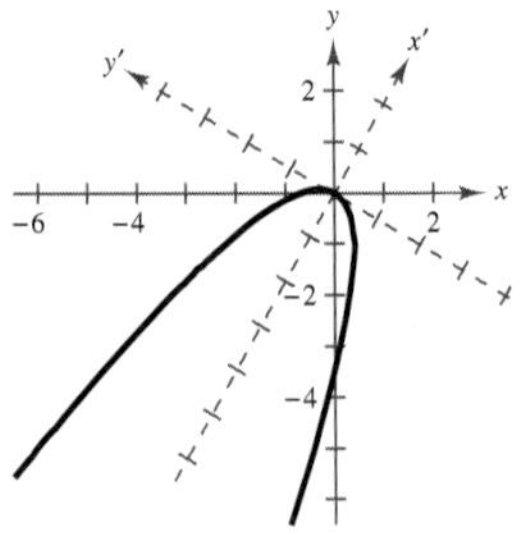

24. $(y')^2 = 4(x' - 1)$

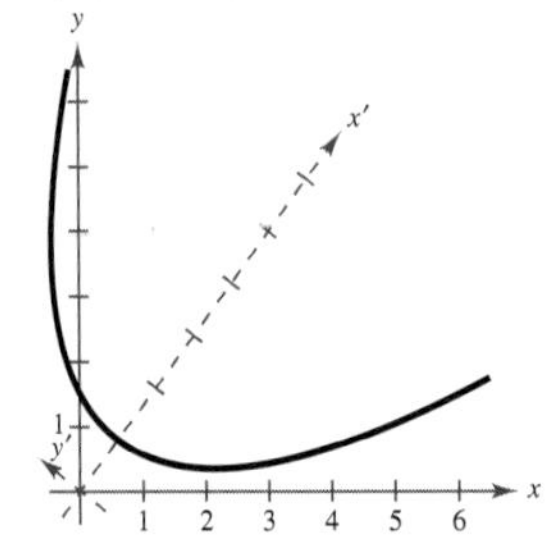

25. $(x' - 1)^2 = 6\left(y' + \frac{1}{6}\right)$

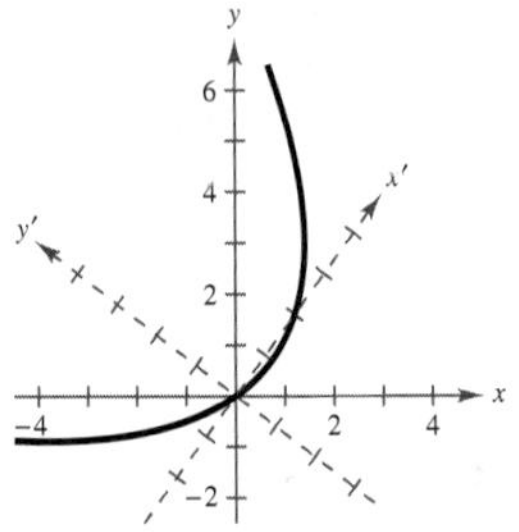

26. $y' = \frac{1}{4}(x')^2$

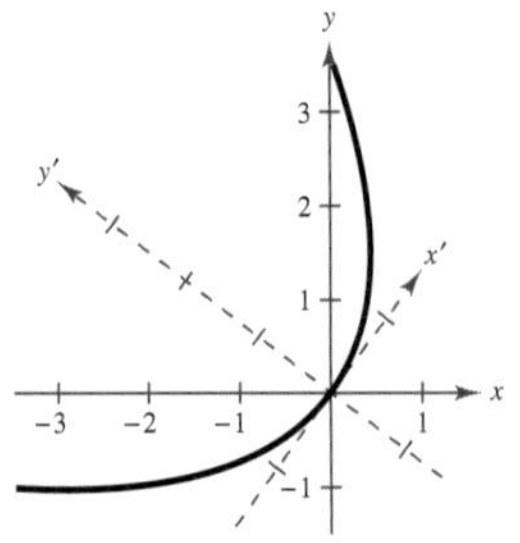

27.

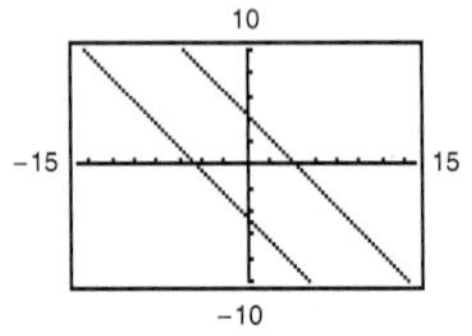

$\theta = 45°$

28.

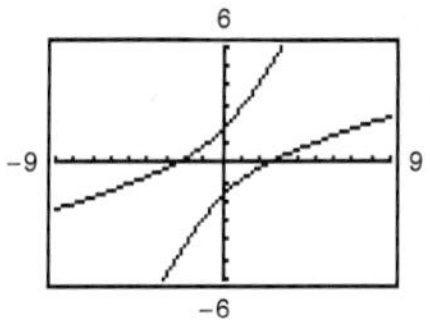

$\theta \approx 37.98°$

29.

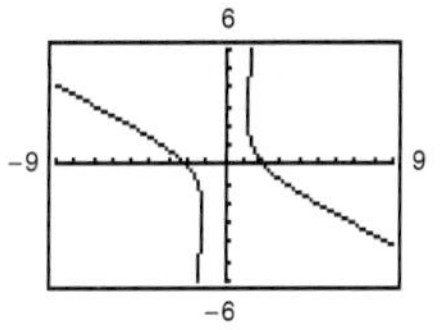

$\theta \approx 26.57°$

30.

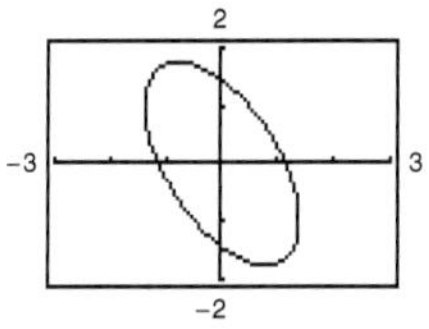

$\theta \approx 33.69°$

31.

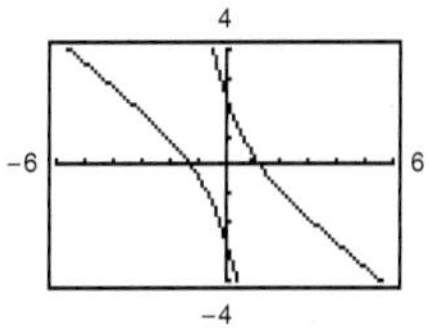

$\theta \approx 31.72°$

32.

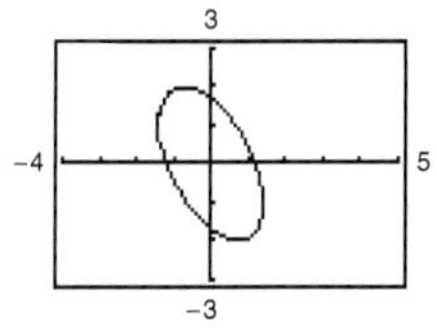

$\theta \approx 28.15°$

33.

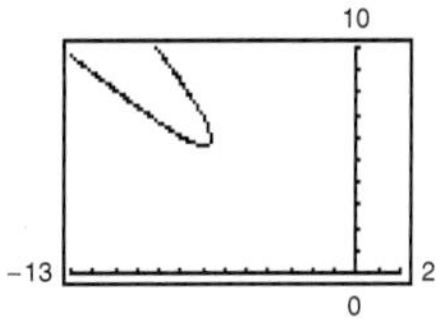

$\theta = 45°$

34.

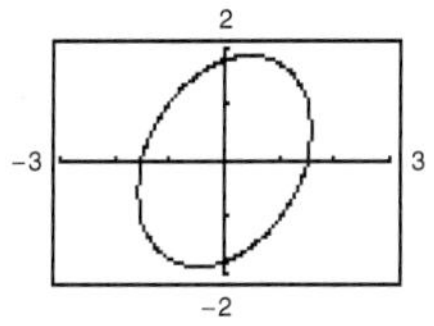

$\theta = -30°$

35.

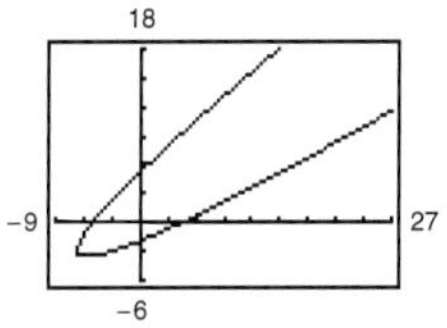

$\theta \approx 33.69°$

36.

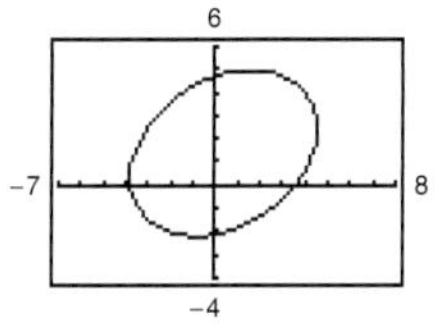

$\theta \approx 31.72°$

43. (a) Parabola

(b) $y = \dfrac{(8x - 5) \pm \sqrt{(8x - 5)^2 - 4(16x^2 - 10x)}}{2}$

(c)

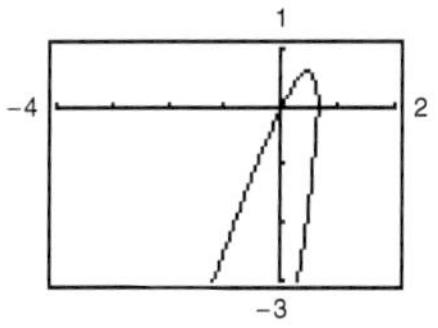

44. (a) Hyperbola (b) $y = \dfrac{4x \pm \sqrt{16x^2 + 8(x^2 - 6)}}{-4}$

(c)

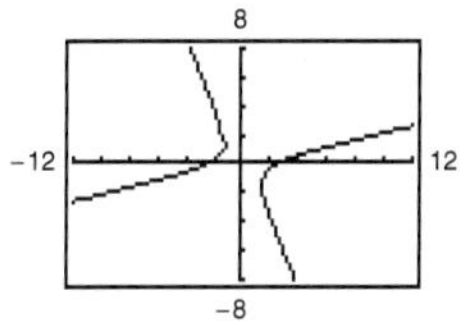

45. (a) Ellipse (b) $y = \dfrac{6x \pm \sqrt{36x^2 - 28(12x^2 - 45)}}{14}$

(c)

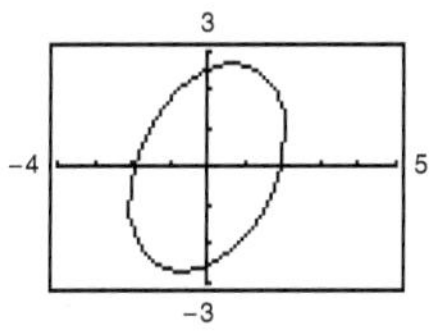

46. (a) Ellipse

(b) $y = \dfrac{-(4x - 4) \pm \sqrt{(4x - 4)^2 - 20(2x^2 + 3x - 20)}}{10}$

(c)

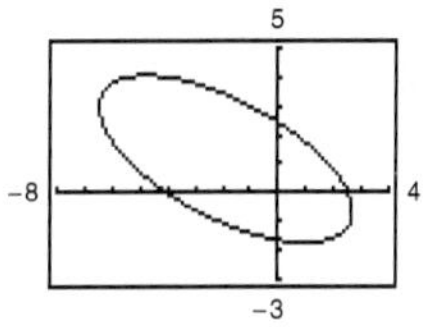

47. (a) Hyperbola (b) $y = \dfrac{6x \pm \sqrt{36x^2 + 20(x^2 + 4x - 22)}}{-10}$

(c)

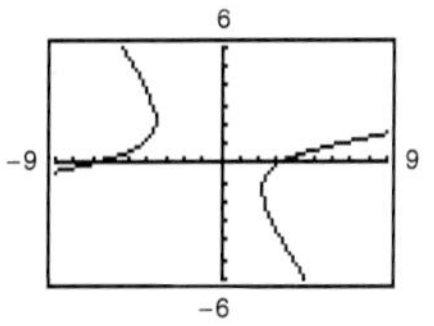

48. (a) Parabola

(b) $y = \dfrac{60x - 9 \pm \sqrt{(-60x + 9)^2 - 3600x^2}}{50}$

(c)

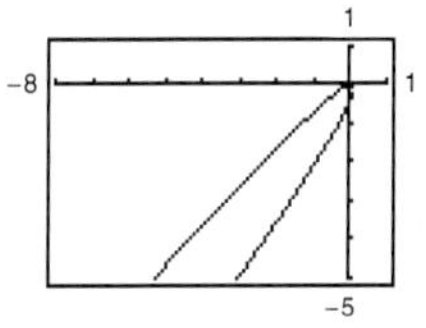

49. (a) Parabola

(b) $y = \dfrac{-(4x - 1) \pm \sqrt{(4x - 1)^2 - 16(x^2 - 5x - 3)}}{8}$

(c)

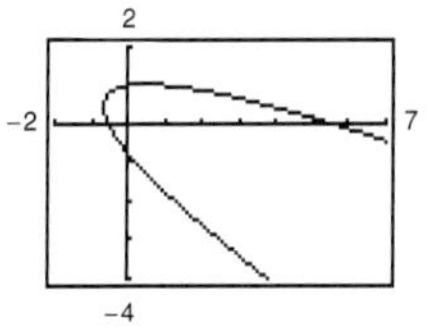

50. (a) Ellipse

(b) $y = \dfrac{-(x + 1) \pm \sqrt{(x + 1)^2 - 16(x^2 + x - 4)}}{8}$

(c)

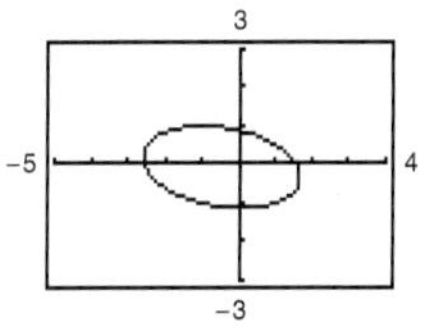

74. Answers will vary. Sample answers:

(a) Use a rotation of axes through the angle θ to rewrite the equation. Use the substitutions $x = x' \cos\theta - y' \sin\theta$ and $y = x' \sin\theta + y' \cos\theta$ to eliminate the xy-term.

(b) Use the discriminant $B^2 - 4AC$ to identify the graph of the equation, except in degenerate cases.

Section 10.6 *(page 774)*

6. (a)

θ	$-\frac{\pi}{2}$	$-\frac{\pi}{4}$	0	$\frac{\pi}{4}$	$\frac{\pi}{2}$
x	0	2	4	2	0
y	-2	$-\sqrt{2}$	0	$\sqrt{2}$	2

(b)

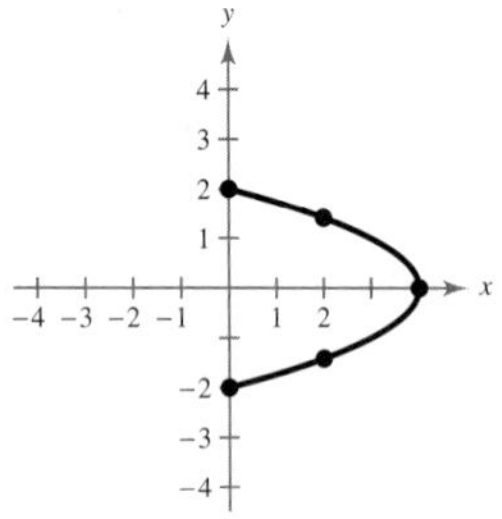

(c) $x = -y^2 + 4$

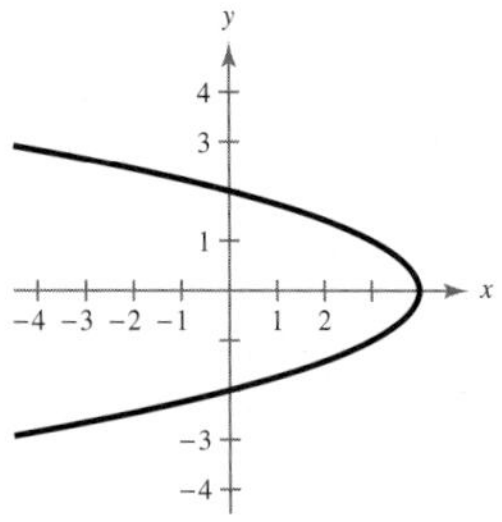

The graph of the rectangular equation continues the graph into the second and third quadrants.

7. (a)

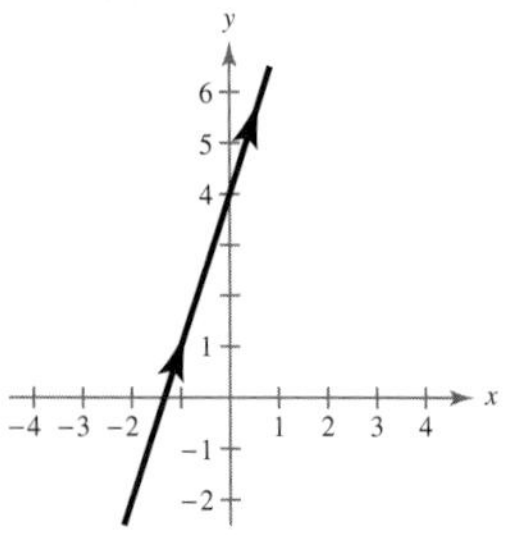

(b) $y = 3x + 4$

8. (a)

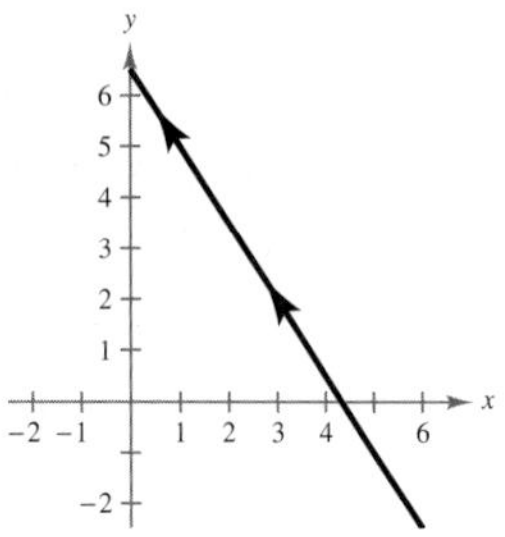

(b) $y = -\frac{3}{2}x + \frac{13}{2}$

9. (a)

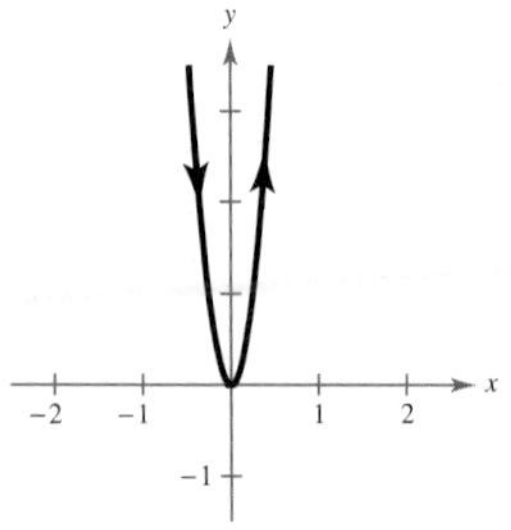

(b) $y = 16x^2$

10. (a)

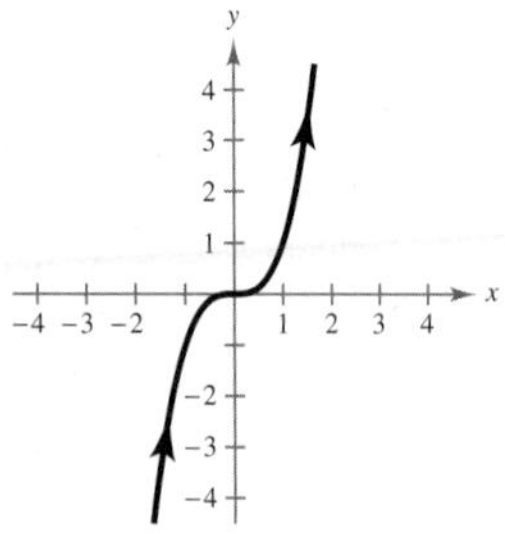

(b) $y = x^3$

11. (a)

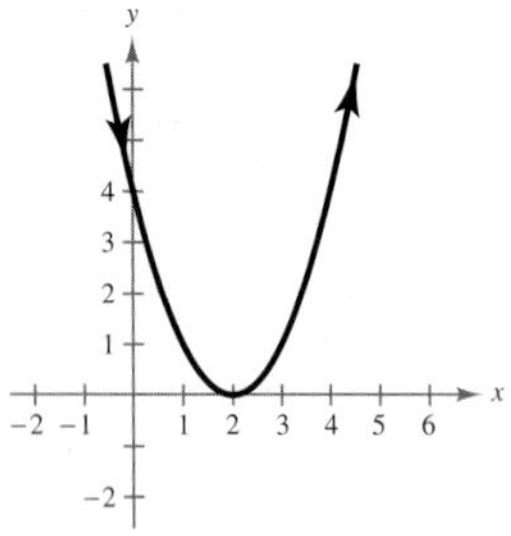

(b) $y = x^2 - 4x + 4$

12. (a)

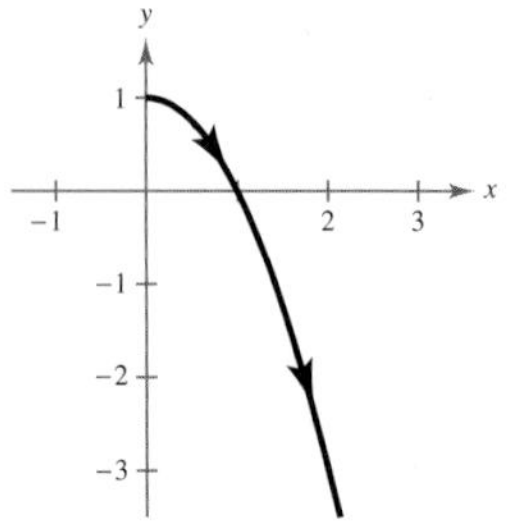

(b) $y = 1 - x^2, \quad x \geq 0$

13. (a)

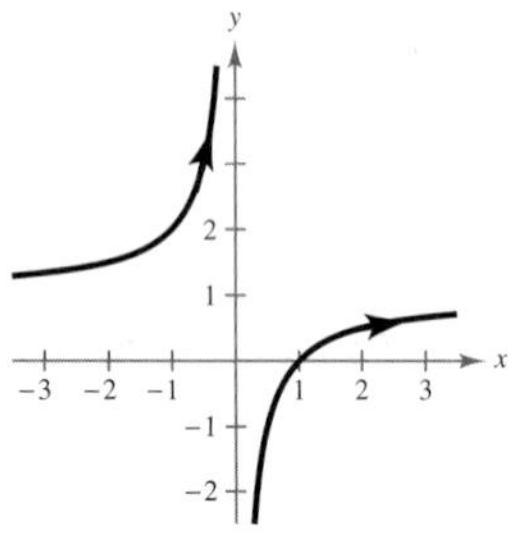

(b) $y = \dfrac{x - 1}{x}$

14. (a)

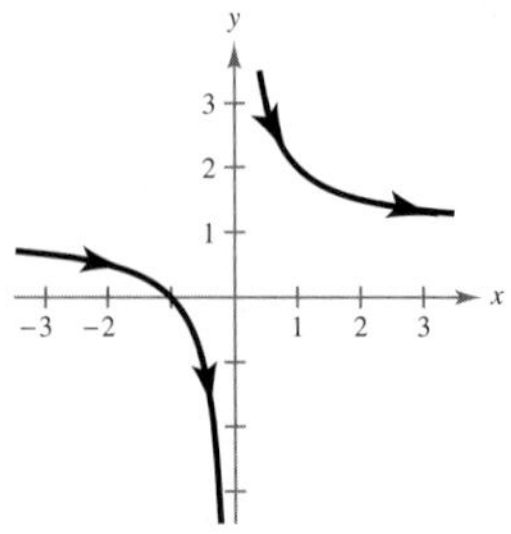

(b) $y = \dfrac{x + 1}{x}$

15. (a)

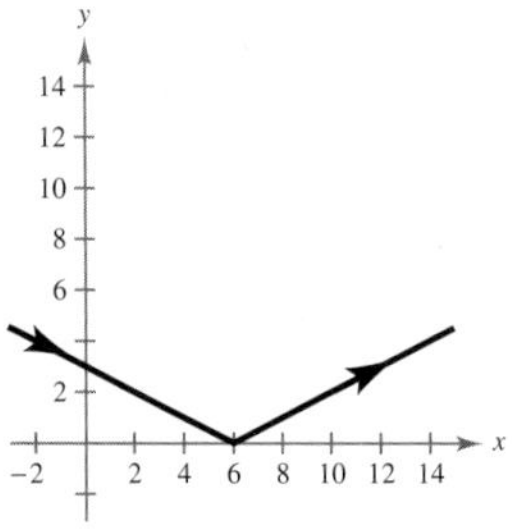

(b) $y = \left|\dfrac{x}{2} - 3\right|$

16. (a)

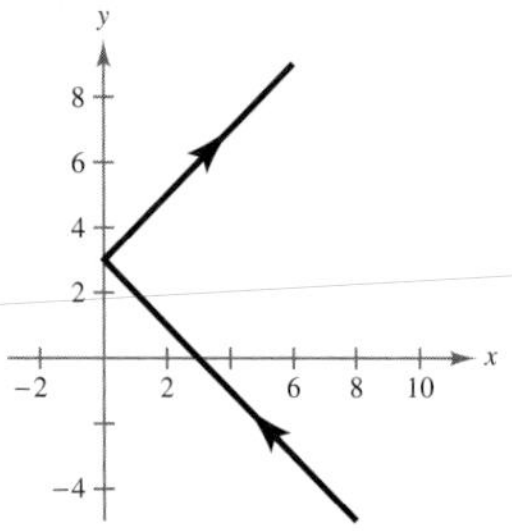

(b) $y = -x + 3, \ x > 0$ and $y = x + 3, \ x \geq 0$

17. (a)

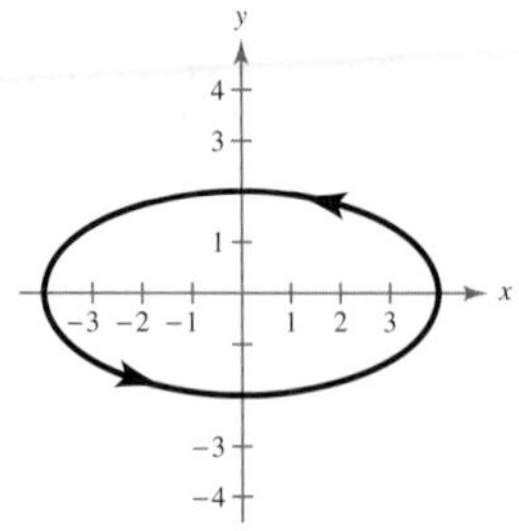

(b) $\dfrac{x^2}{16} + \dfrac{y^2}{4} = 1$

18. (a)

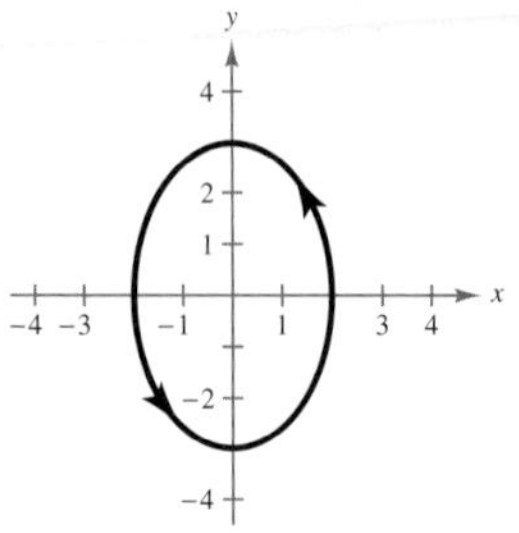

(b) $\dfrac{x^2}{4} + \dfrac{y^2}{9} = 1$

19. (a)

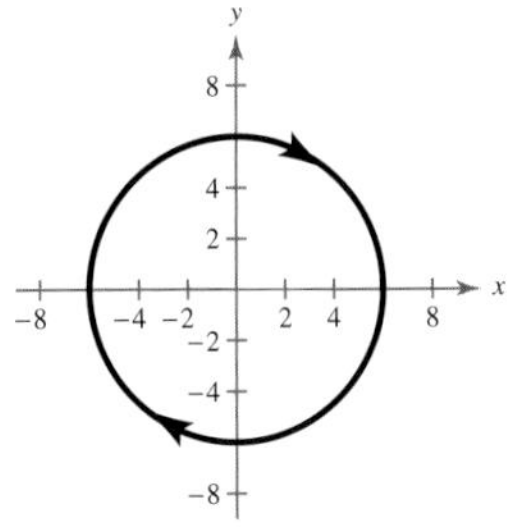

(b) $\dfrac{x^2}{36} + \dfrac{y^2}{36} = 1$

20. (a)

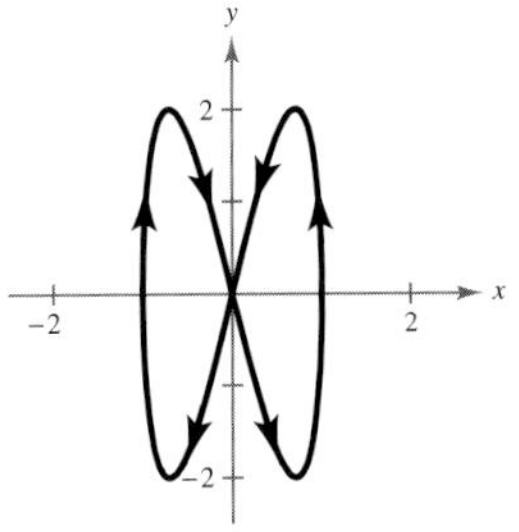

(b) $y = \pm 4x\sqrt{1 - x^2}$

21. (a)

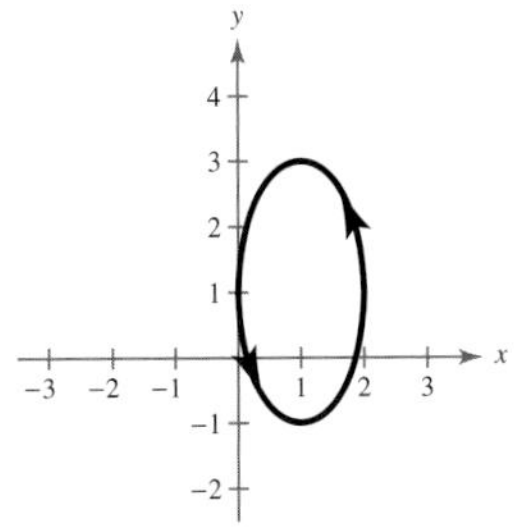

(b) $\dfrac{(x-1)^2}{1} + \dfrac{(y-1)^2}{4} = 1$

22. (a)

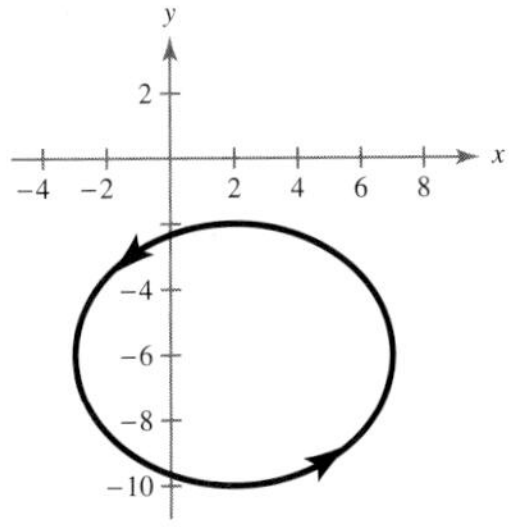

(b) $\dfrac{(x-2)^2}{25} + \dfrac{(y+6)^2}{16} = 1$

23. (a)

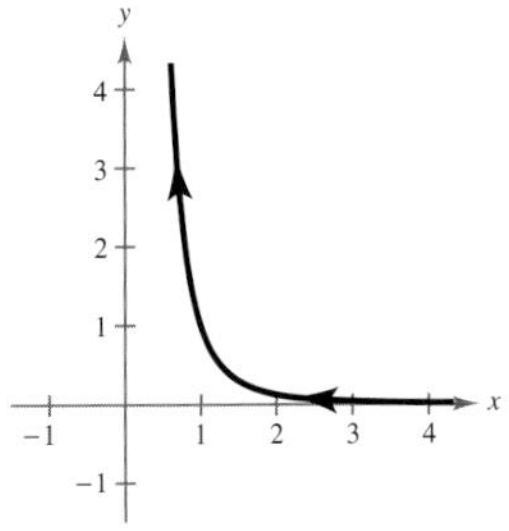

(b) $y = \dfrac{1}{x^3}, \quad x > 0$

24. (a)

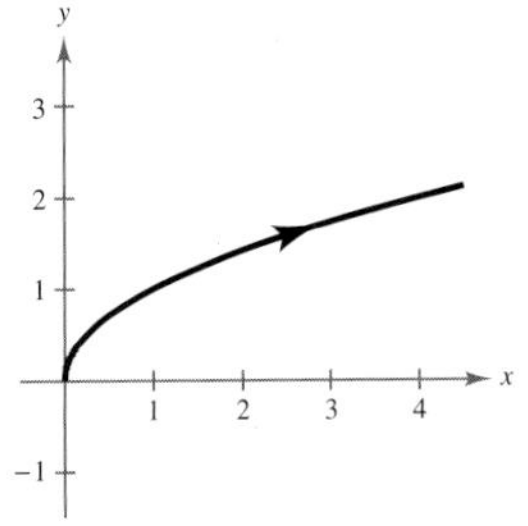

(b) $y = \sqrt{x}$

25. (a)

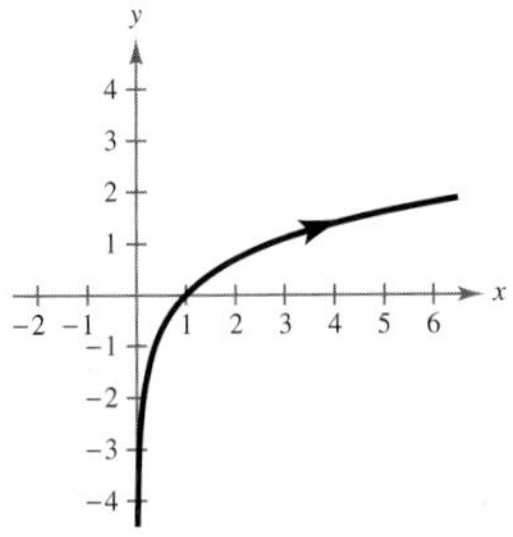

(b) $y = \ln x$

26. (a)

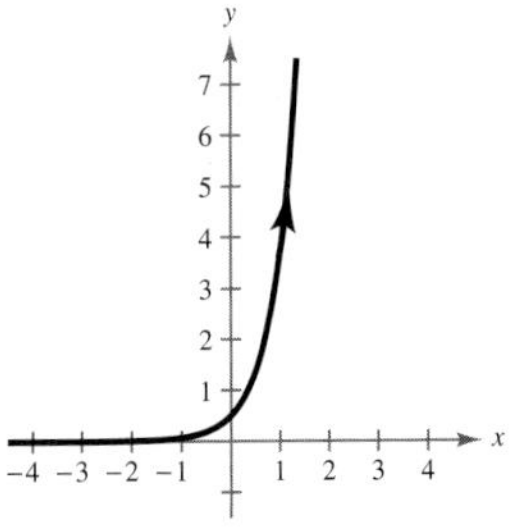

(b) $y = \dfrac{e^{2x}}{2}$

61. (a)

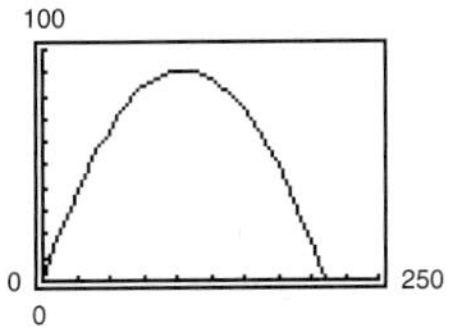

Maximum height: 90.7 ft
Range: 209.6 ft

(b)

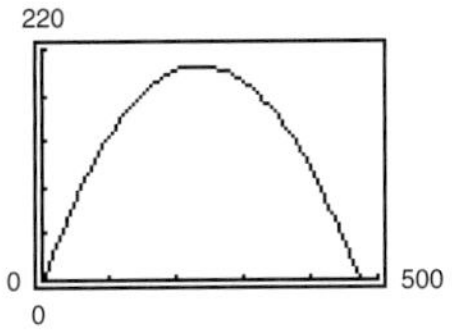

Maximum height: 204.2 ft
Range: 471.6 ft

(c)

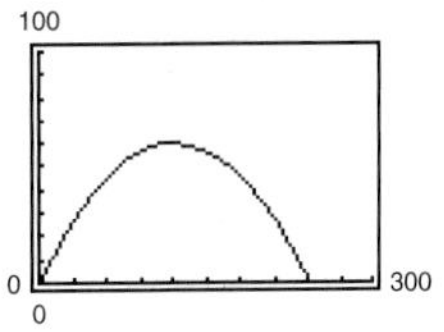

Maximum height: 60.5 ft
Range: 242.0 ft

(d)

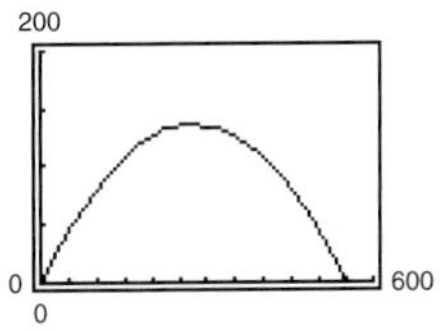

Maximum height: 136.1 ft
Range: 544.5 ft

62. (a)

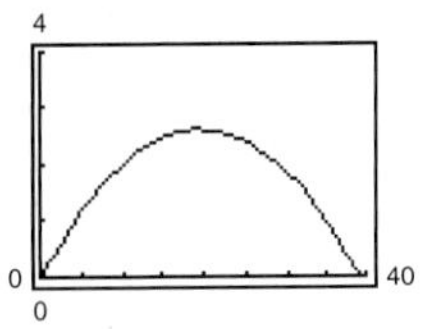

Maximum height: 2.6 ft
Range: 39.1 ft

(b)

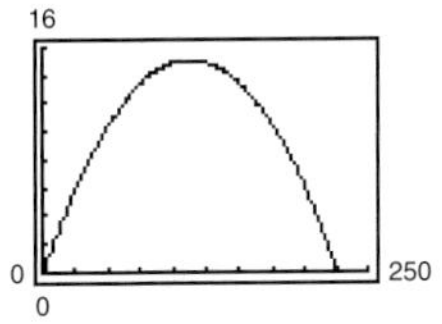

Maximum height: 15.1 ft
Range: 225.0 ft

(c)

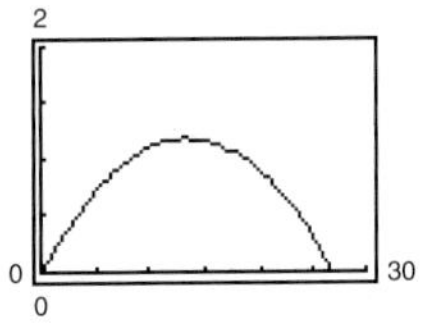

Maximum height: 1.2 ft
Range: 26.7 ft

(d)

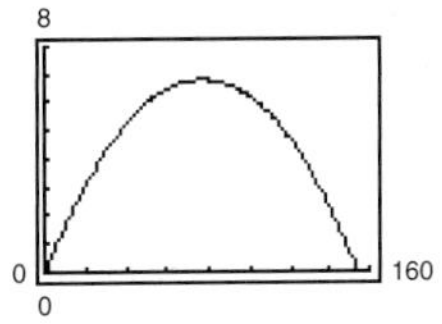

Maximum height: 6.8 ft
Range: 153.9 ft

63. (a) $x = (146.67 \cos \theta)t$
$y = 3 + (146.67 \sin \theta)t - 16t^2$

(b)

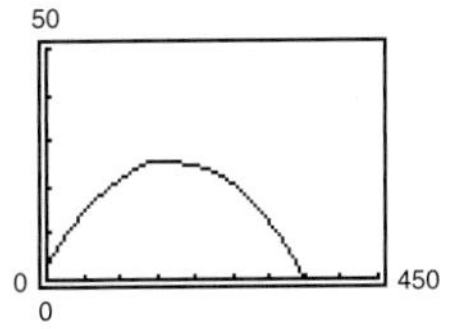

No

(c)

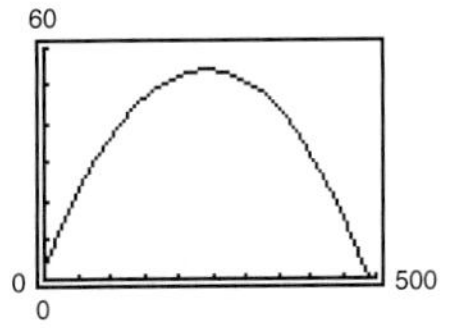

Yes

Section 10.7 *(page 781)*

9.

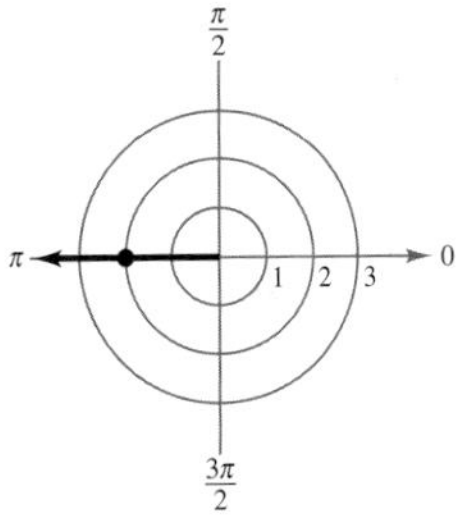

$(2, \pi), (-2, 0)$

10.

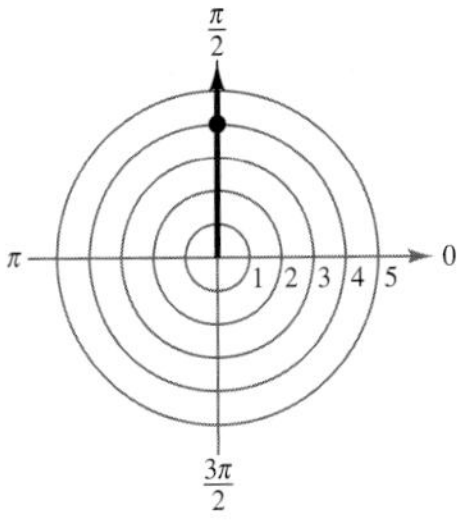

$\left(4, \dfrac{\pi}{2}\right), \left(-4, \dfrac{3\pi}{2}\right)$

11.

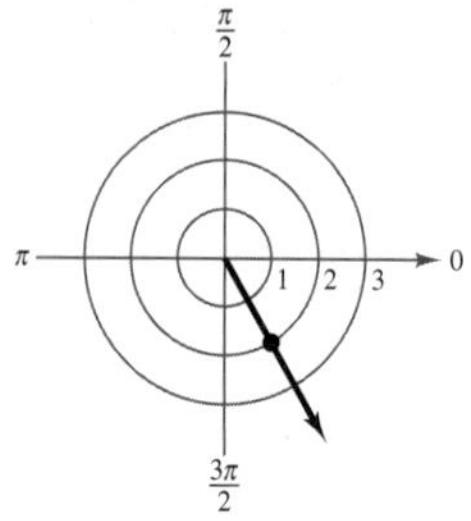

$\left(-2, -\frac{4\pi}{3}\right), \left(2, \frac{5\pi}{3}\right)$

12.

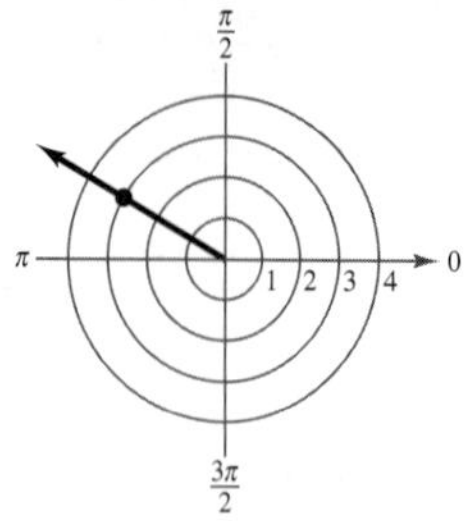

$\left(-3, -\frac{\pi}{6}\right), \left(3, \frac{5\pi}{6}\right)$

13.

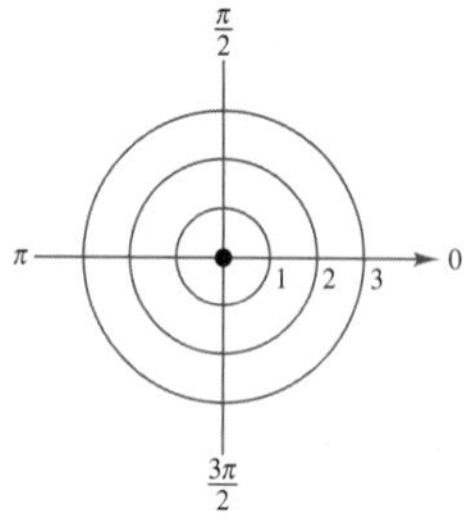

$\left(0, \frac{5\pi}{6}\right), \left(0, -\frac{\pi}{6}\right)$

14.

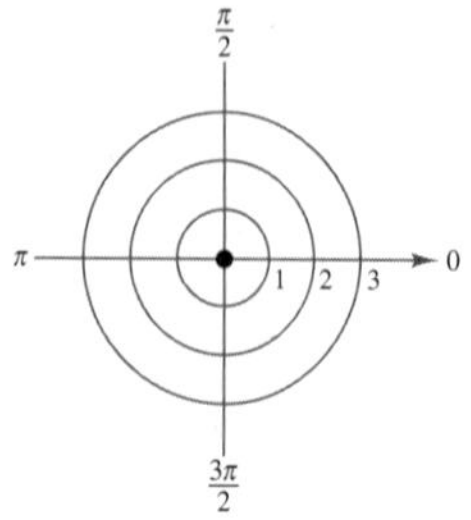

$\left(0, -\frac{3\pi}{2}\right), \left(0, -\frac{\pi}{2}\right)$

15.

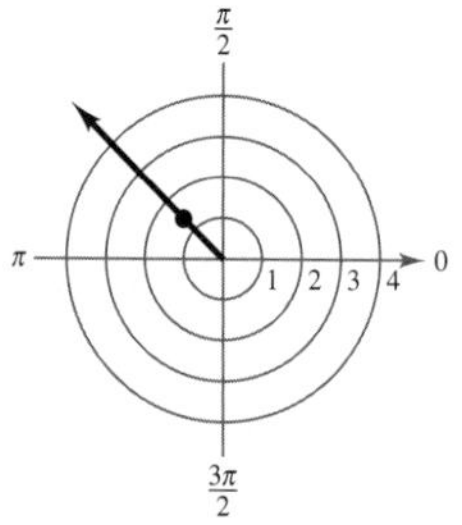

$\left(\sqrt{2}, -3.92\right), \left(-\sqrt{2}, -0.78\right)$

16.

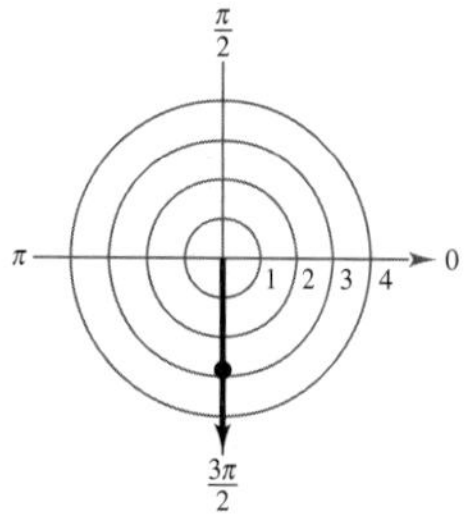

$\left(2\sqrt{2}, -1.57\right), \left(-2\sqrt{2}, 1.57\right)$

17.

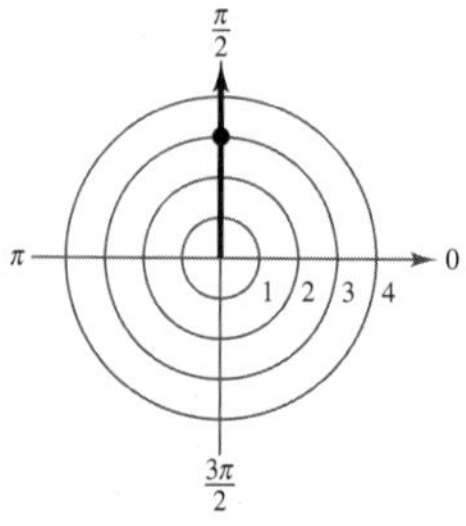

$(-3, 4.71), (3, 1.57)$

18.

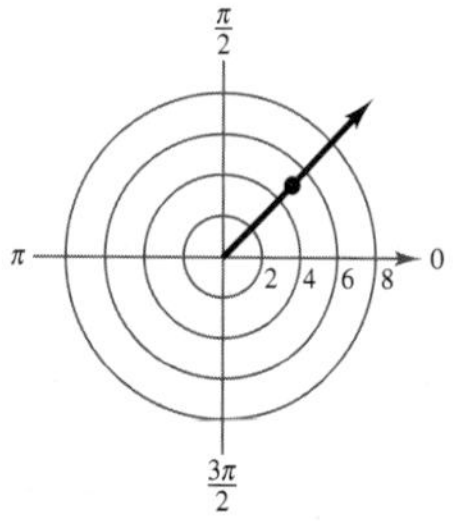

$(-5, 3.92), (5, 0.78)$

49. $\left(2, \frac{11\pi}{6}\right)$ **50.** $\left(2, \frac{2\pi}{3}\right)$ **61.** $\left(\frac{17}{6}, 0.49\right)$

62. $\left(\frac{\sqrt{3349}}{10}, 1.25\right)$ **63.** $\left(\frac{\sqrt{85}}{4}, 0.71\right)$

64. $\left(\frac{\sqrt{1513}}{36}, 3.91\right)$

112. The graph of the polar equation consists of all points on the line that makes an angle of $3\pi/4$ with the positive polar axis.
$x + y = 0$

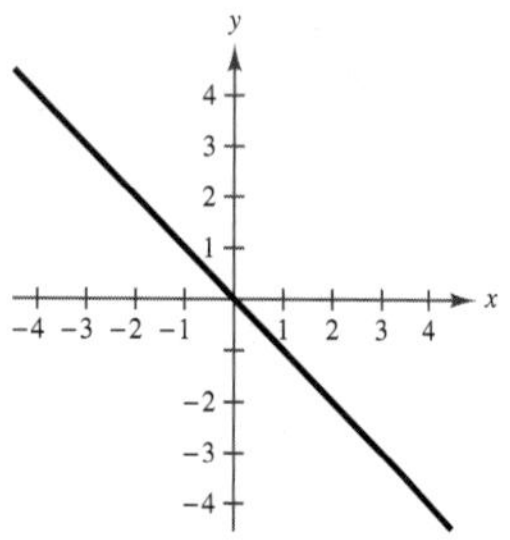

113. The graph of the polar equation is not evident by simple inspection, so convert to rectangular form.
$x^2 + (y - 1)^2 = 1$

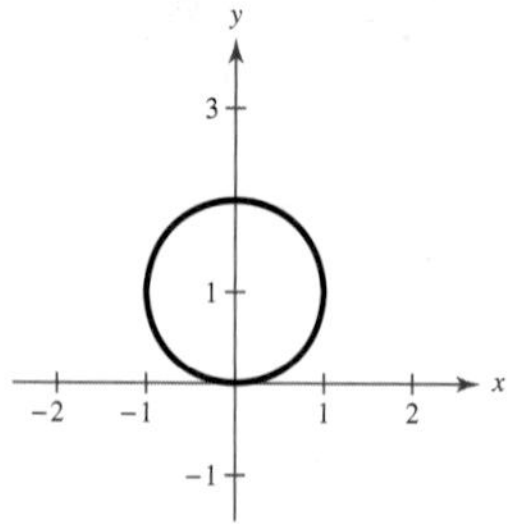

114. The graph of the polar equation is not evident by simple inspection, so convert to rectangular form.
$(x - 2)^2 + y^2 = 4$

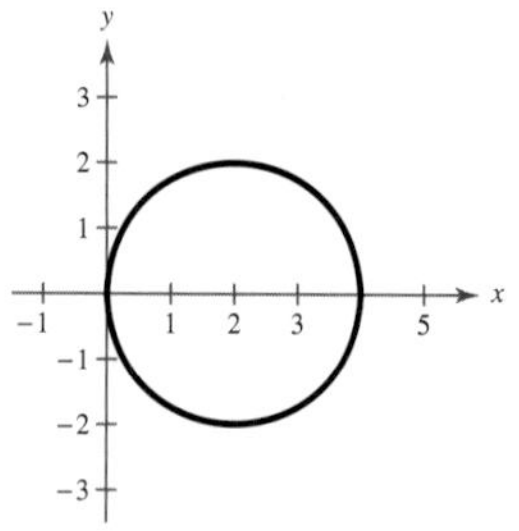

115. The graph of the polar equation is not evident by simple inspection, so convert to rectangular form.
$(x + 3)^2 + y^2 = 9$

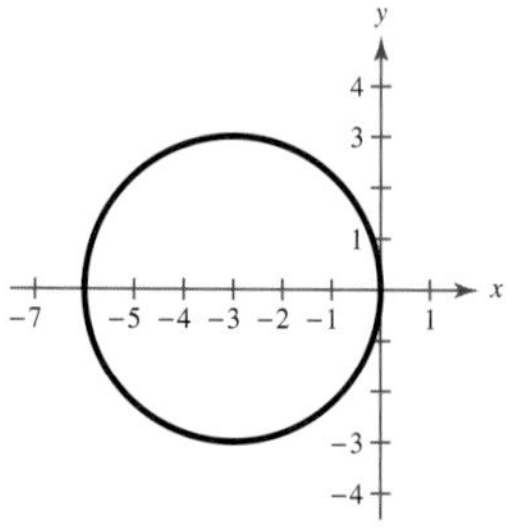

116. The graph of the polar equation is not evident by simple inspection, so convert to rectangular form.
$x^2 + \left(y + \frac{3}{2}\right)^2 = \frac{9}{4}$

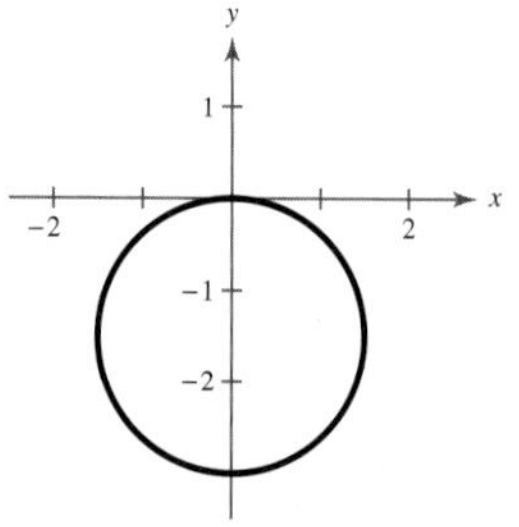

117. The graph of the polar equation is not evident by simple inspection, so convert to rectangular form.
$x - 3 = 0$

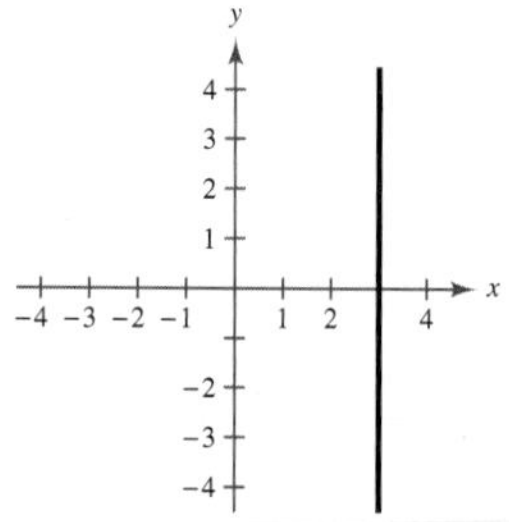

118. The graph of the polar equation is not evident by simple inspection, so convert to rectangular form.
$y - 2 = 0$

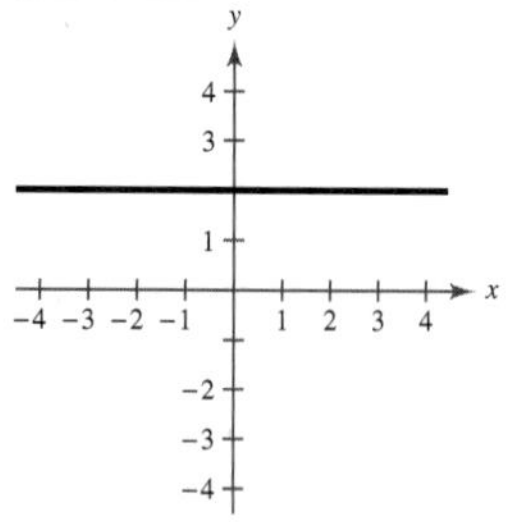

121. $(x - h)^2 + (y - k)^2 = h^2 + k^2$
Radius: $\sqrt{h^2 + k^2}$
Center: (h, k)

122. $\left(x - \frac{1}{2}\right)^2 + \left(y - \frac{3}{2}\right)^2 = \frac{5}{2}$; circle

123. (a) Answers will vary.
(b) (r_1, θ_1), (r_2, θ_2) and the pole are collinear.
$d = \sqrt{r_1^2 + r_2^2 - 2r_1r_2} = |r_1 - r_2|$
This represents the distance between two points on the line $\theta = \theta_1 = \theta_2$.
(c) $d = \sqrt{r_1^2 + r_2^2}$
This is the result of the Pythagorean Theorem.
(d) Answers will vary. For example:
Points: $(3, \pi/6)$, $(4, \pi/3)$
Distance: 2.053
Points: $(-3, 7\pi/6)$, $(-4, 4\pi/3)$
Distance: 2.053

124. (a) Horizontal: x-coordinate changes.
Vertical: y-coordinate changes.
(b) Horizontal: r and θ both change.
Vertical: r and θ both change.
(c) Unlike r and θ, x and y measure horizontal and vertical changes, respectively.

125. (a)

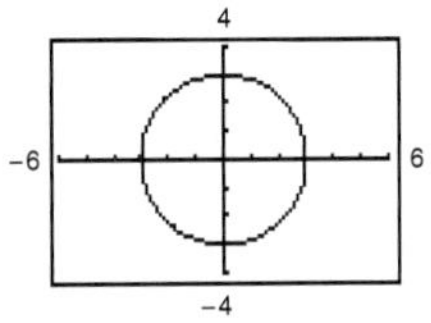

(b) Yes. $\theta \approx 3.927$, $x \approx -2.121$, $y \approx -2.121$
(c) Yes. Answers will vary.

Section 10.8 *(page 789)*

26.

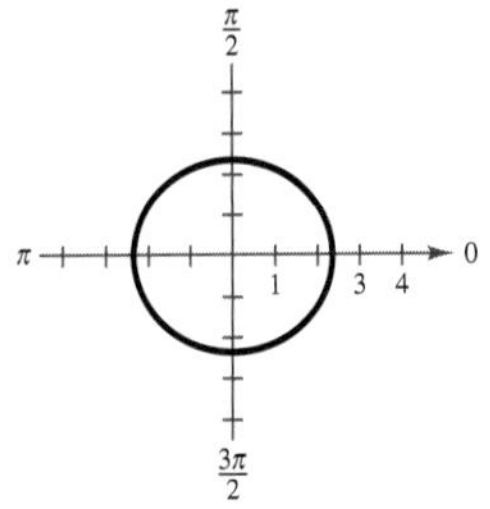

27.

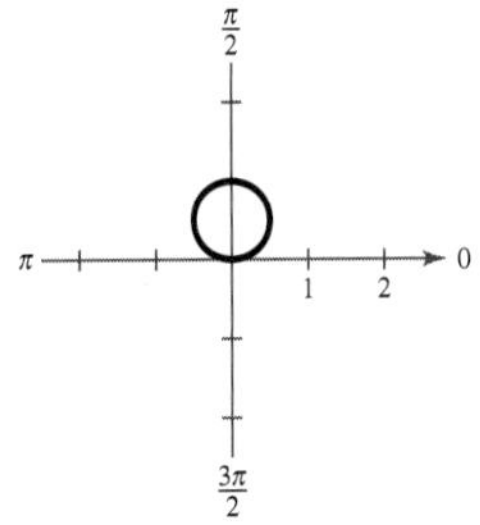

28.

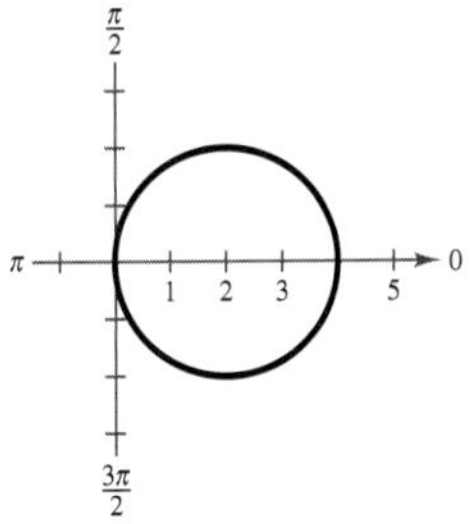

29.

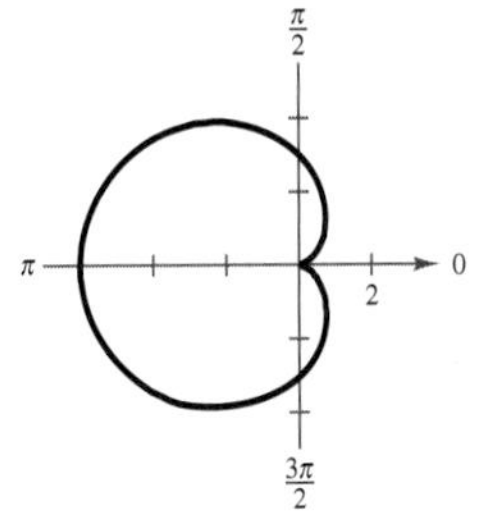

30.

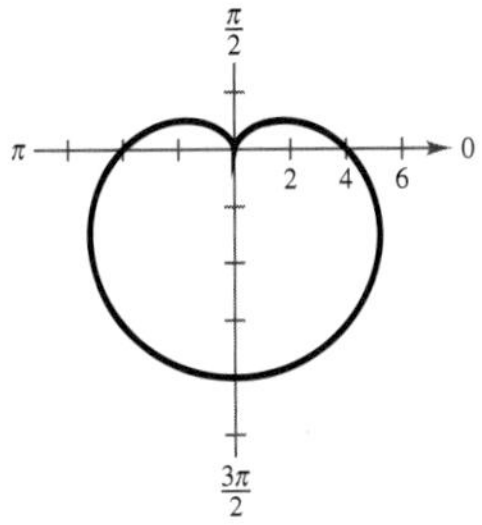

31.

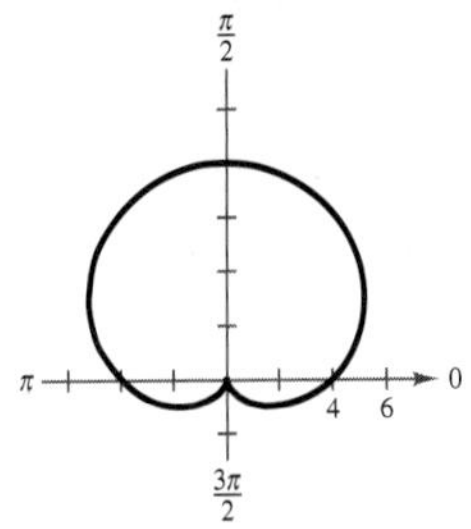

32.

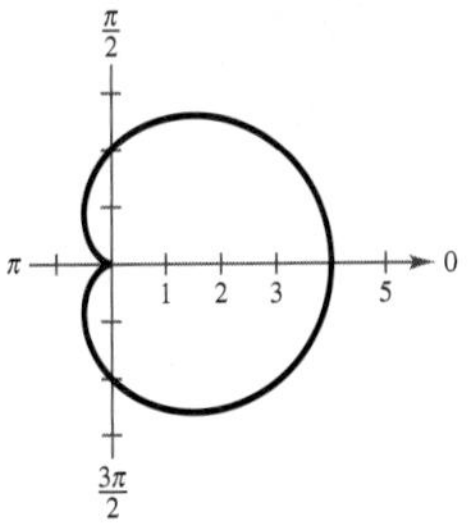

33.

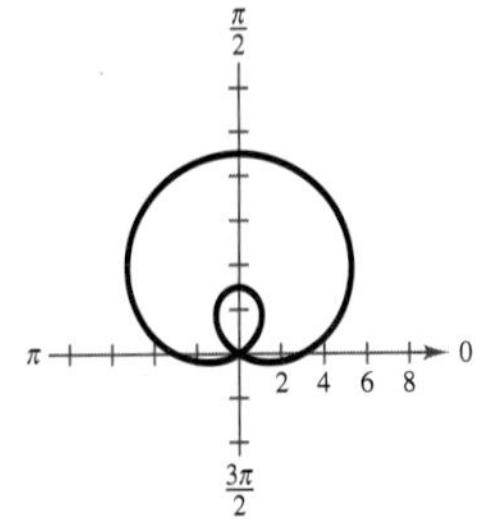

34.

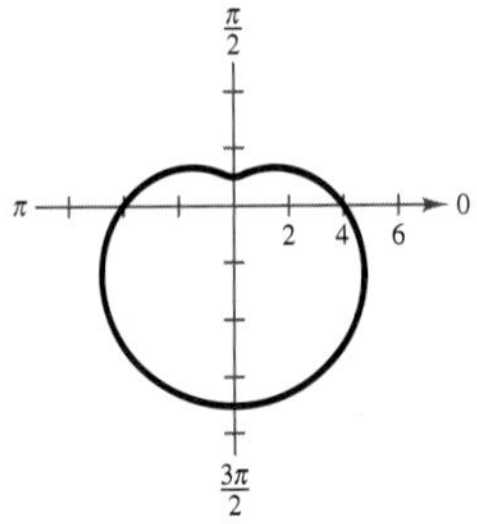

35.

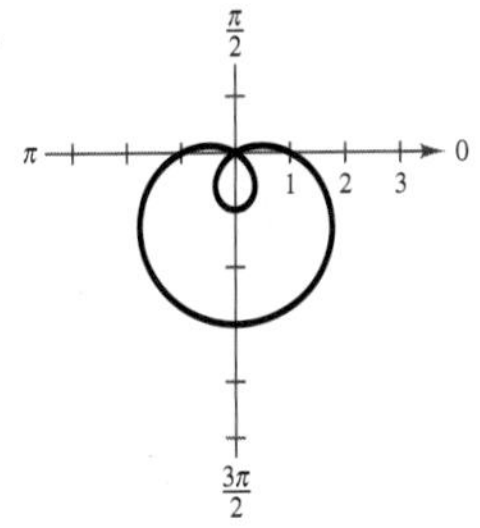

36.

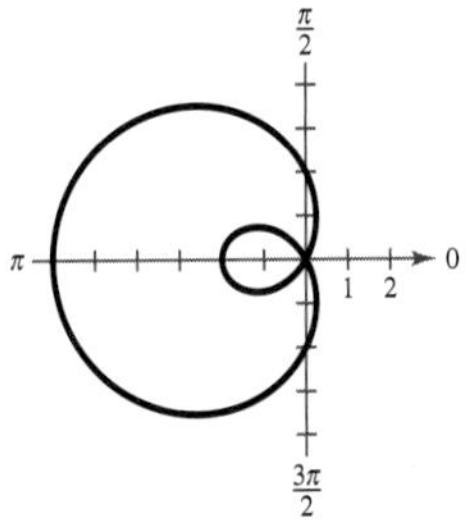

37.

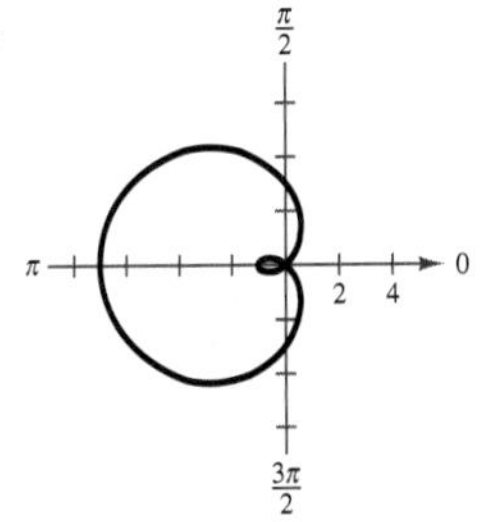

38.

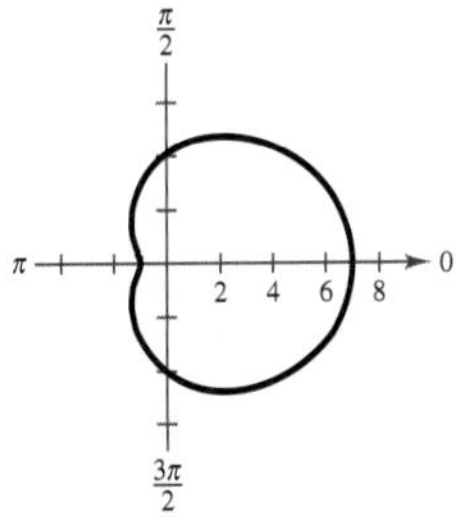

39.

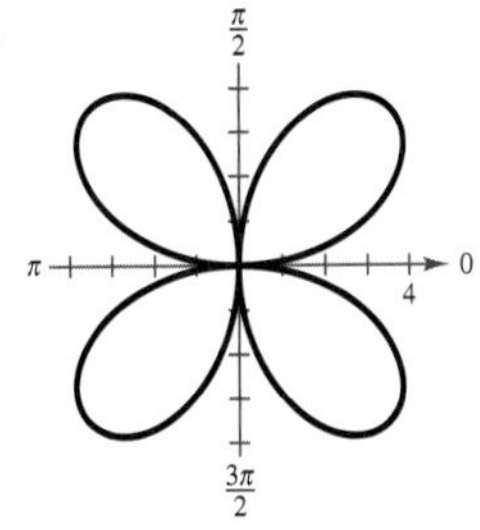

40.

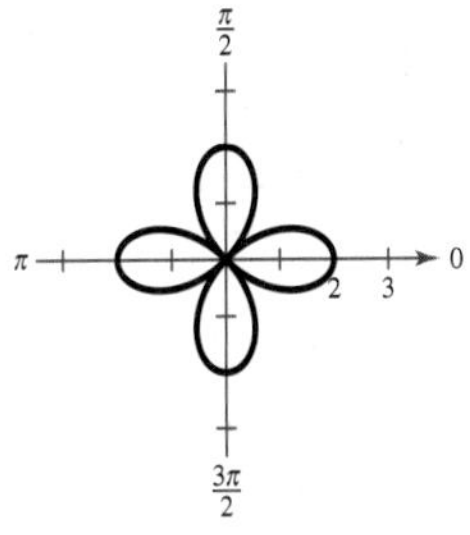

41.

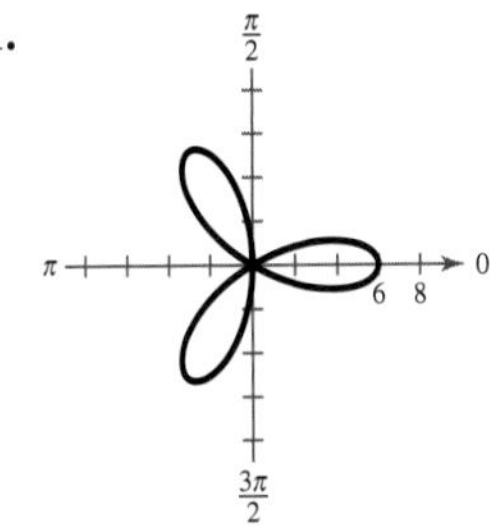

42.

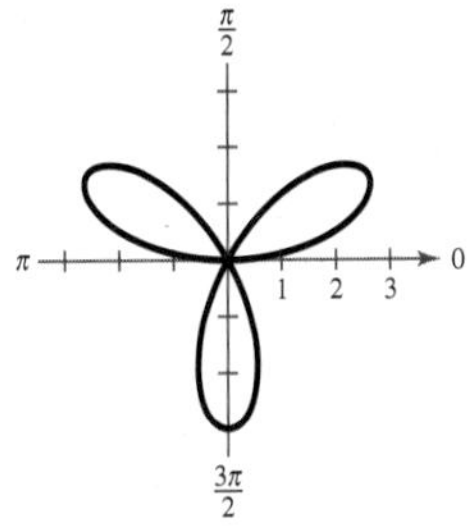

43. 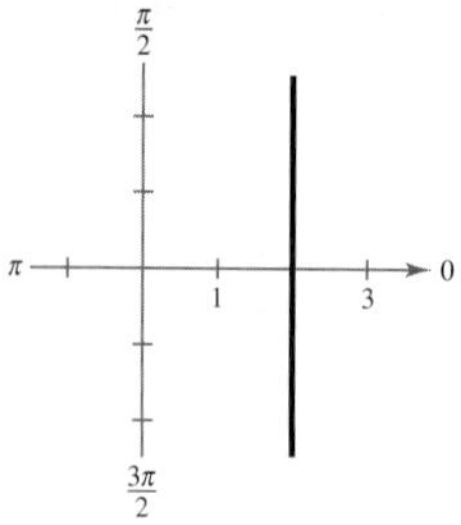

44. 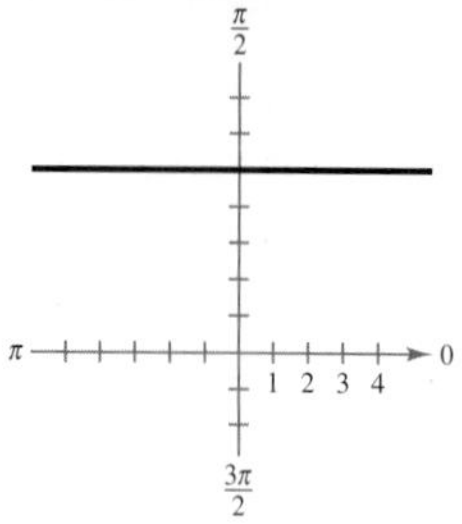

45. 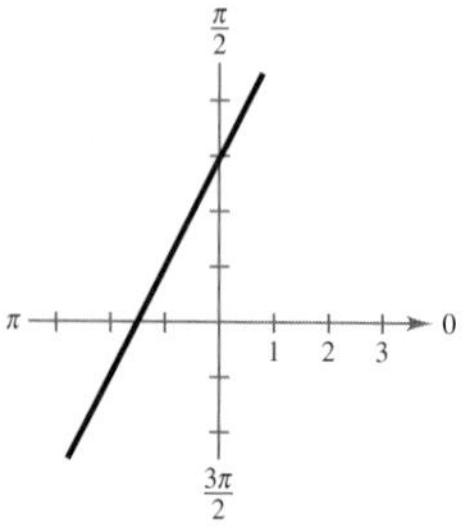

46. 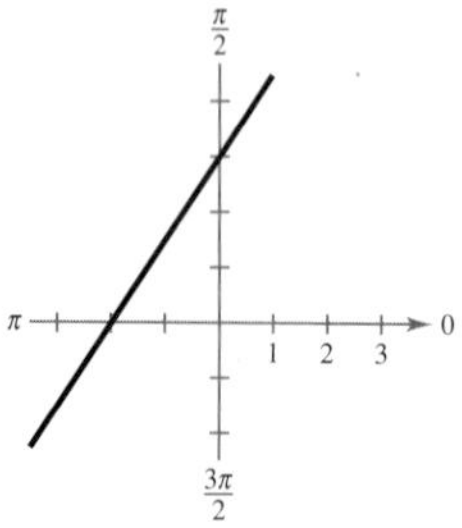

47. 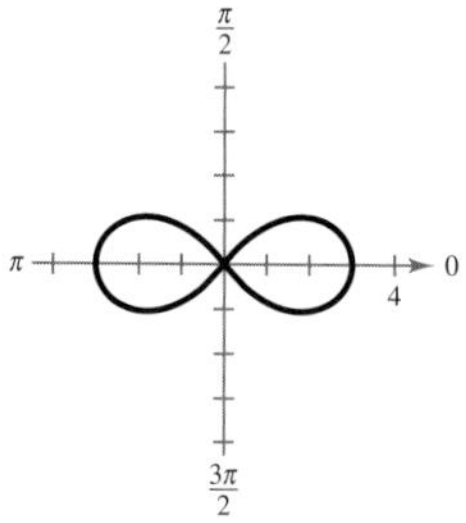

48. 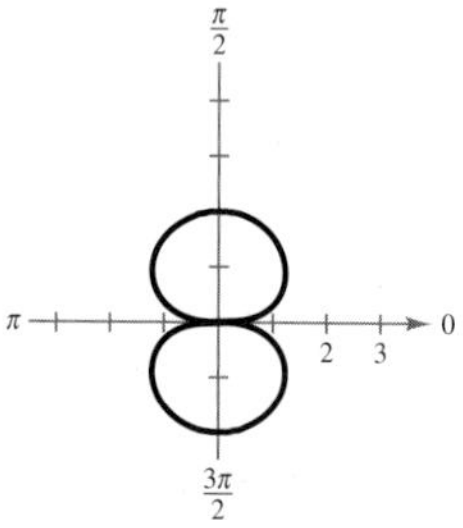

49. 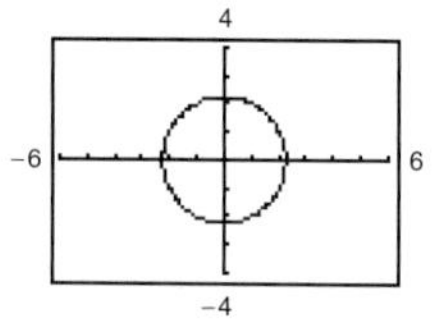

50. 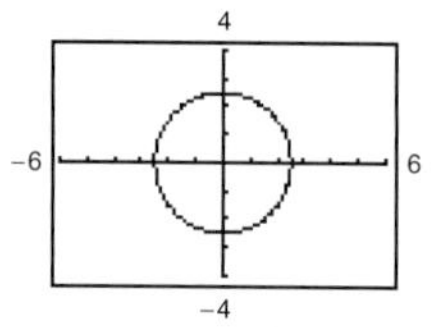

51. 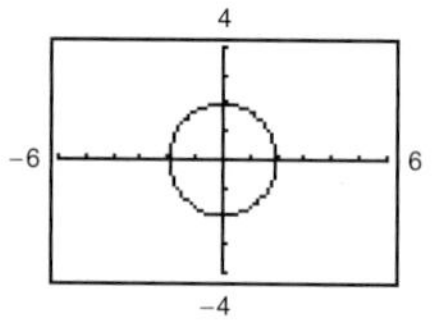

52. 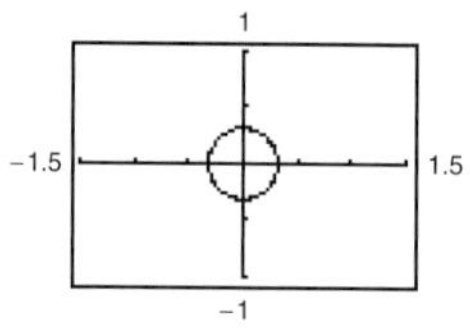

53. 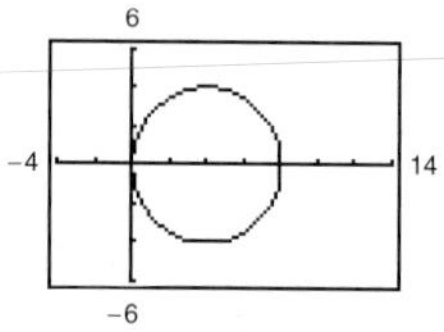

54. 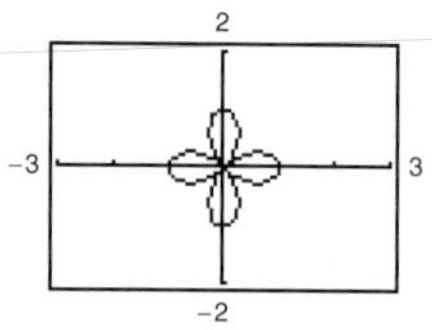

55. 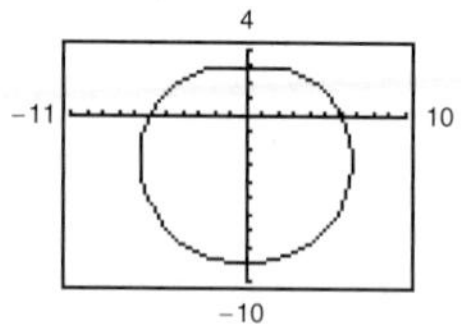

56. 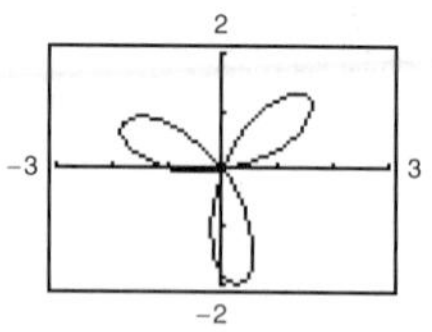

57. 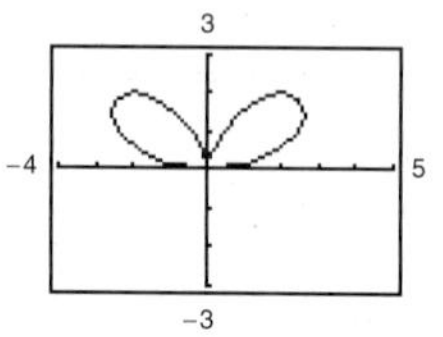

58. 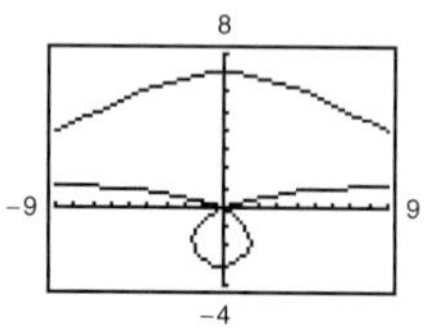

59. 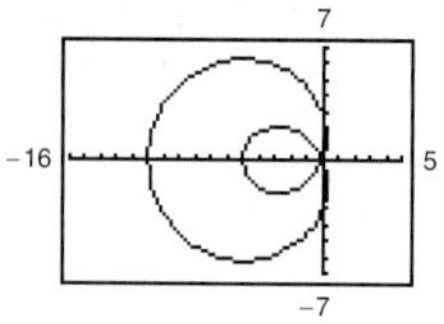

$0 \le \theta < 2\pi$

60. 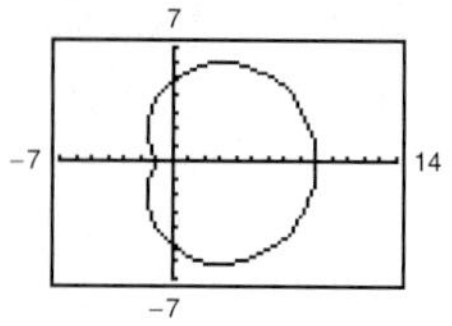

$0 \le \theta < 2\pi$

61. 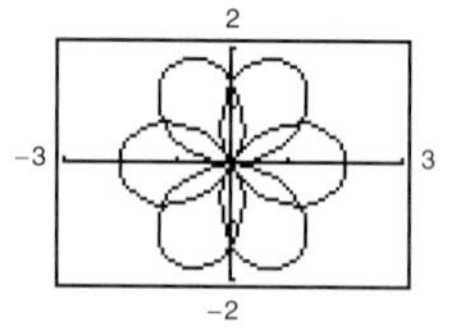

$0 \le \theta < 4\pi$

62. 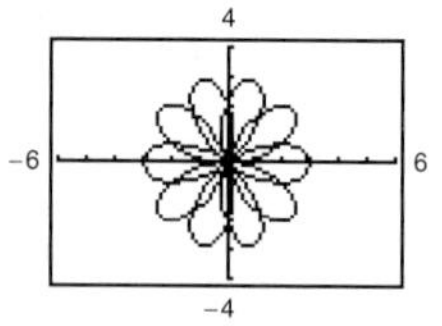

$0 \le \theta < 4\pi$

71. (d) 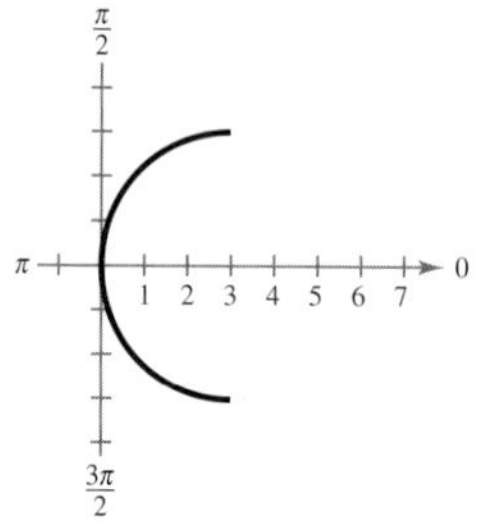

Left half of circle

72. (a) 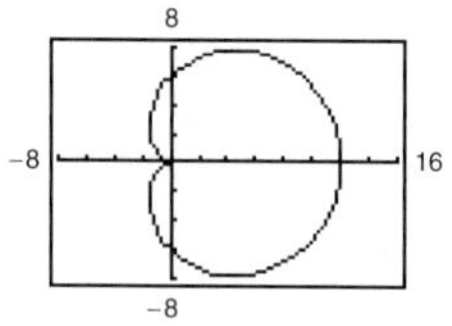

(b) 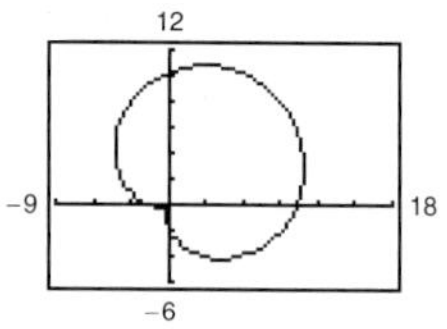

(c) 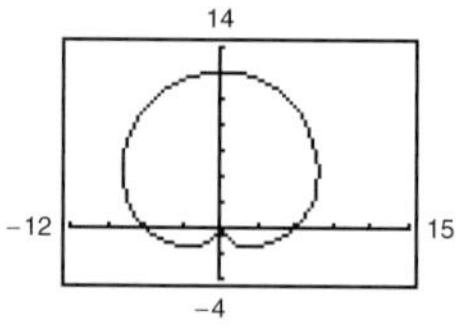

The angle ϕ controls rotation of the axis of symmetry.
$r = 6(1 + \sin\theta)$

75. (a) $r = 2 - \dfrac{\sqrt{2}}{2}(\sin\theta - \cos\theta)$ (b) $r = 2 + \cos\theta$
(c) $r = 2 + \sin\theta$ (d) $r = 2 - \cos\theta$

76. (a) $r = 4\sin\left(\theta - \dfrac{\pi}{6}\right)\cos\left(\theta - \dfrac{\pi}{6}\right)$
(b) $r = -4\sin\theta\cos\theta$
(c) $r = 4\sin\left(\theta - \dfrac{2\pi}{3}\right)\cos\left(\theta - \dfrac{2\pi}{3}\right)$
(d) $r = 4\sin\theta\cos\theta$

77. (a) 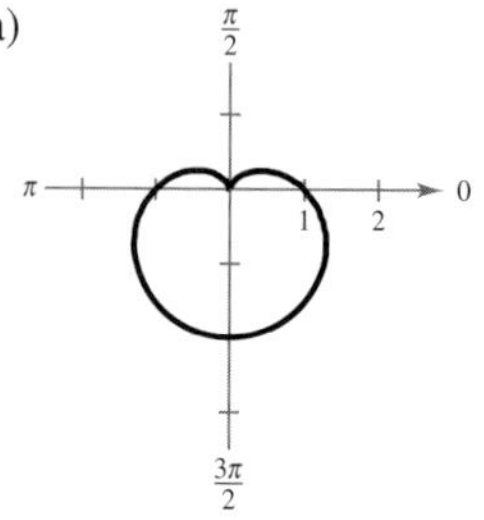

(b) 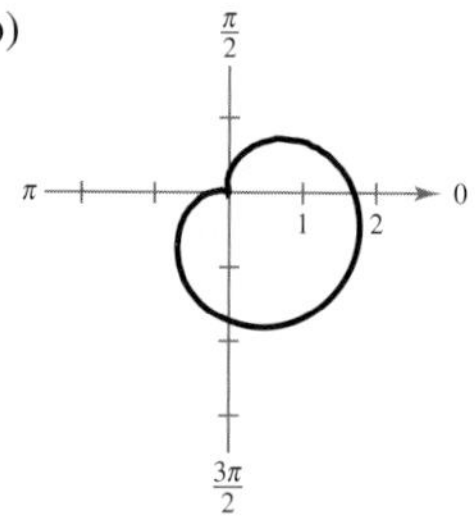

78. (a)

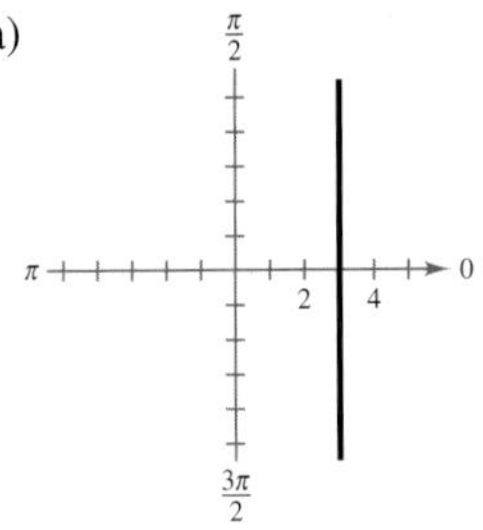

(b)

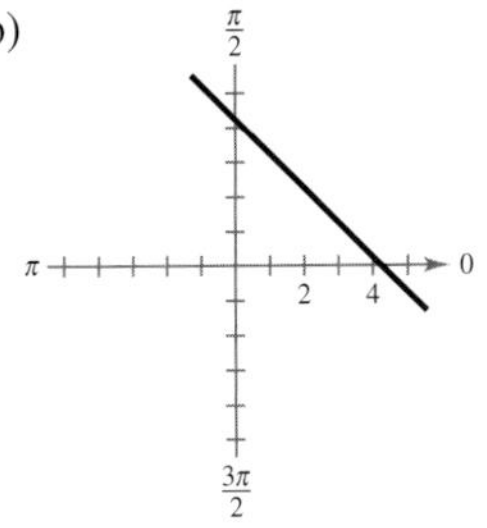

(c)

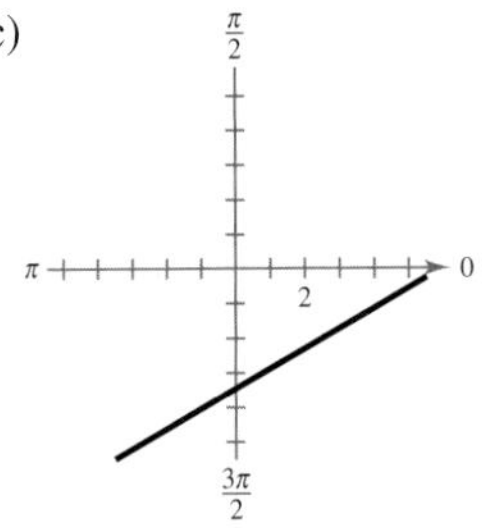

(d)

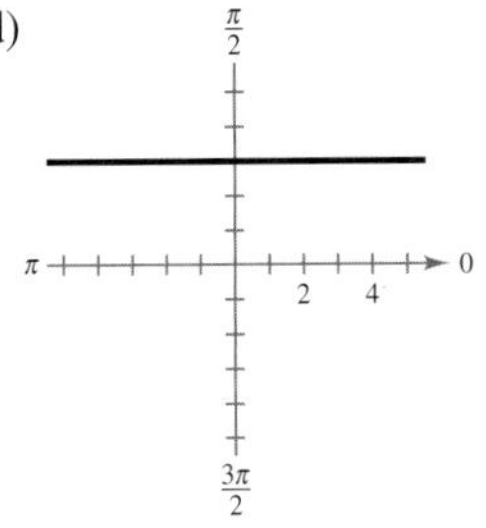

79. 8 petals; 3 petals; For $r = 2 \cos n\theta$ and $r = 2 \sin n\theta$, there are n petals if n is odd, $2n$ petals if n is even.

80.

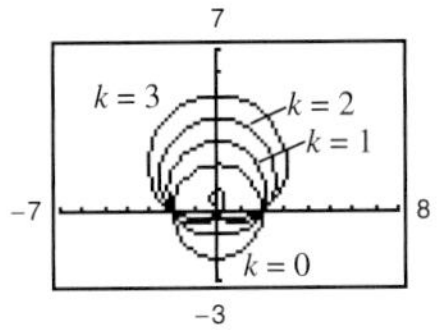

$k = 0$, circle
$k = 1$, convex limaçon
$k = 2$, cardioid
$k = 3$, limaçon with inner loop

81. (a)

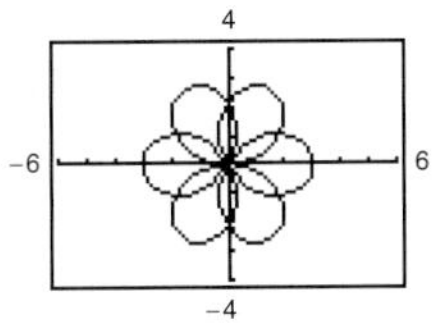

$0 \le \theta < 4\pi$

(b)

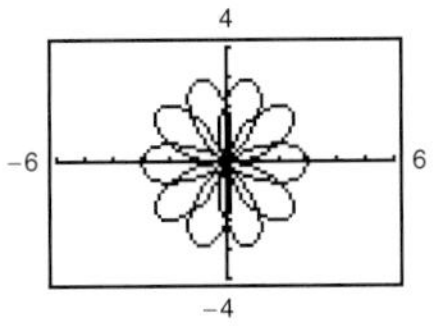

$0 \le \theta < 4\pi$

Section 10.9 *(page 795)*

15. Parabola

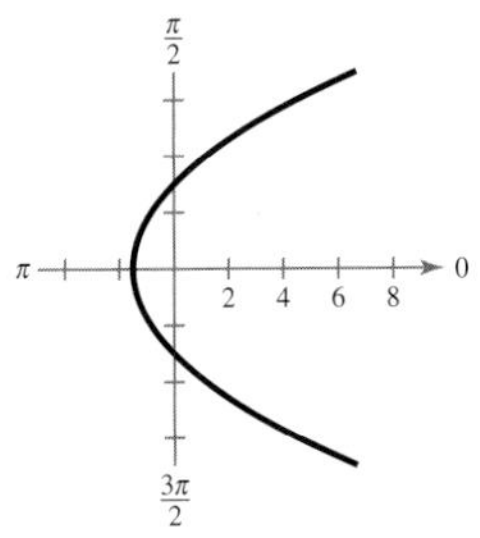

16. Parabola

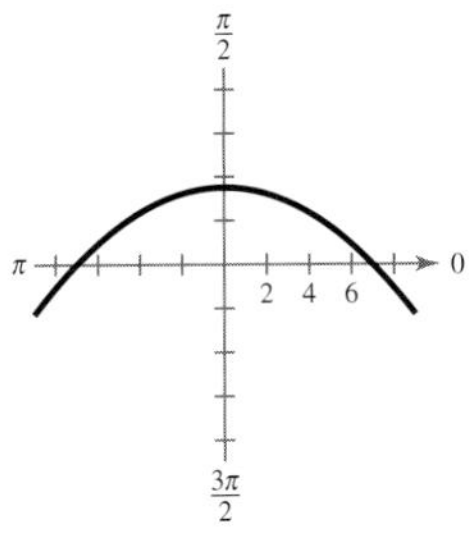

17. Parabola

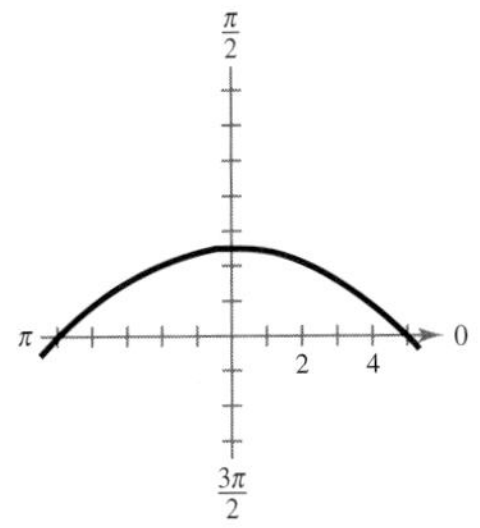

18. Parabola

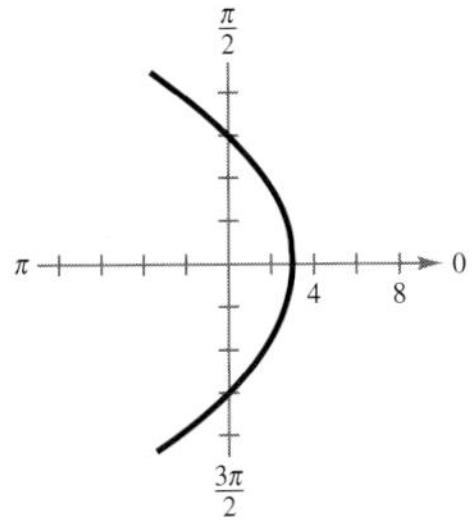

19. Ellipse

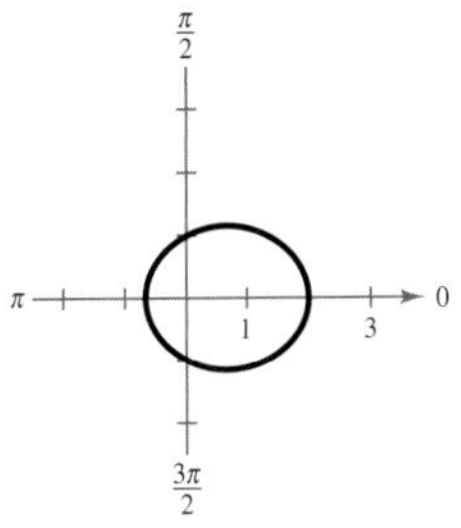

20. Ellipse

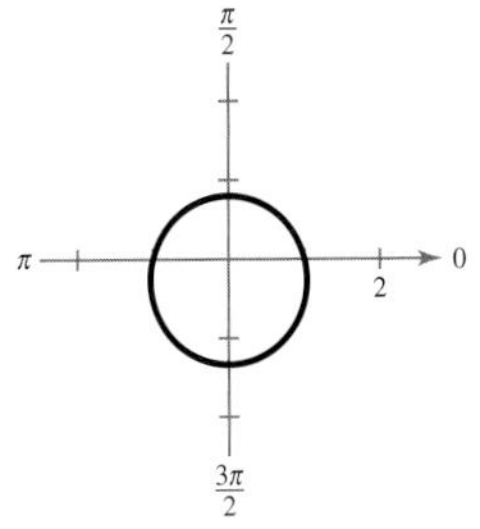

21. Ellipse

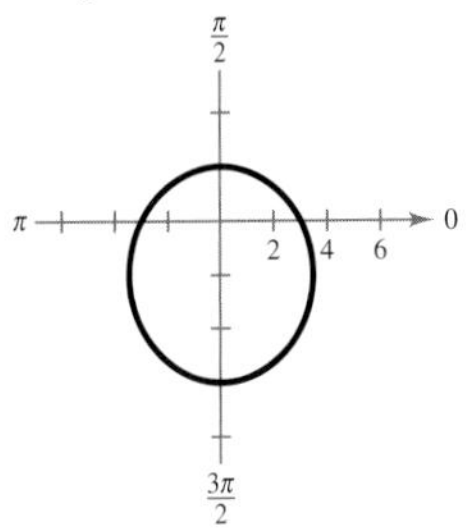

22. Ellipse

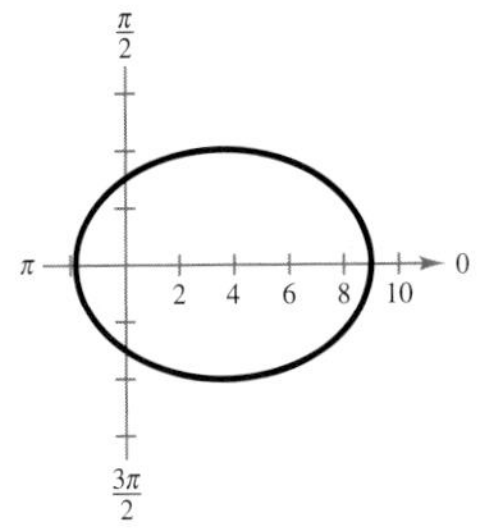

23. Hyperbola

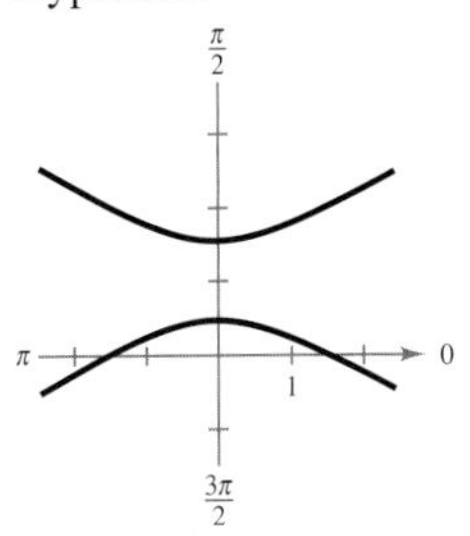

24. Hyperbola

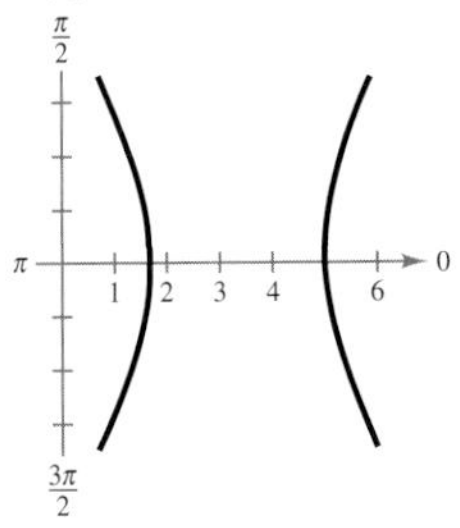

25. Hyperbola

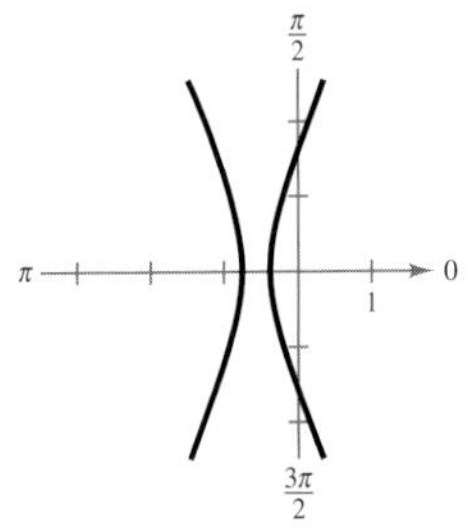

26. Hyperbola

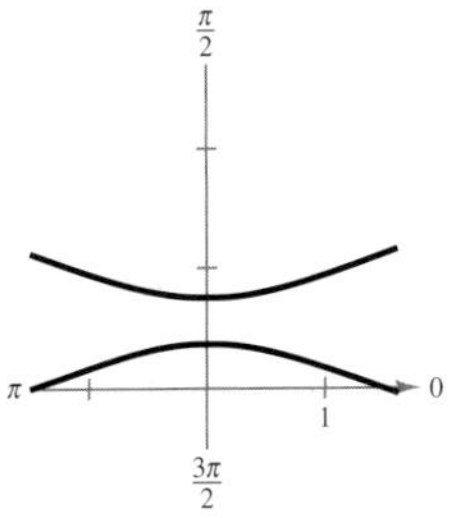

27. Ellipse

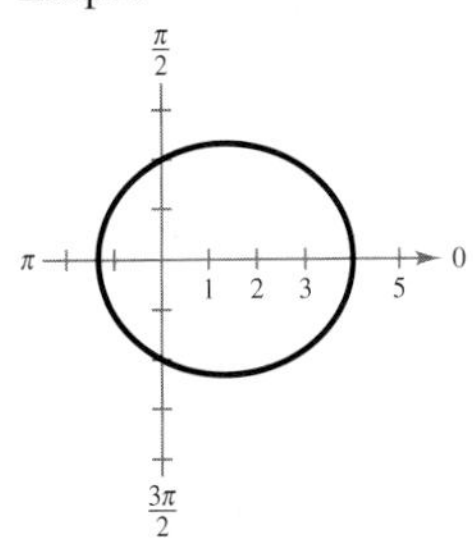

28. Hyperbola

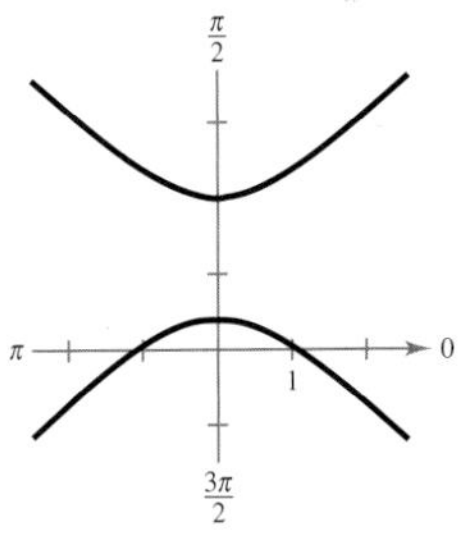

29.

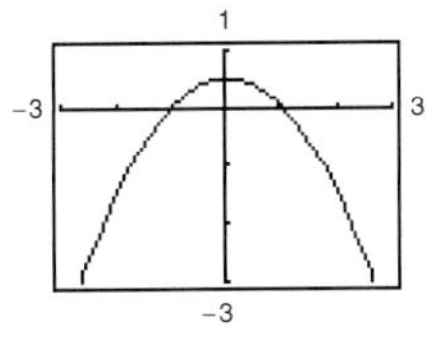

Parabola

30.

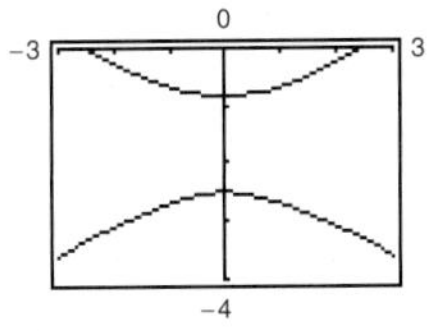

Hyperbola

31.

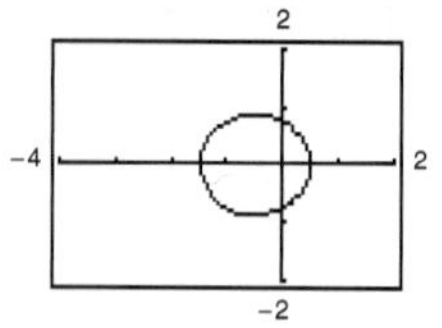

Ellipse

32.

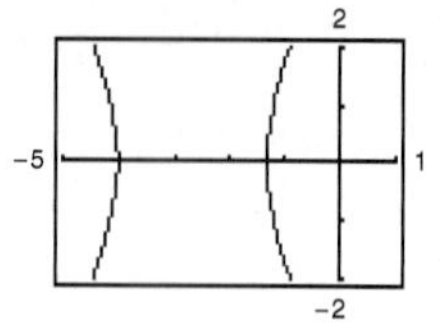

Hyperbola

33.

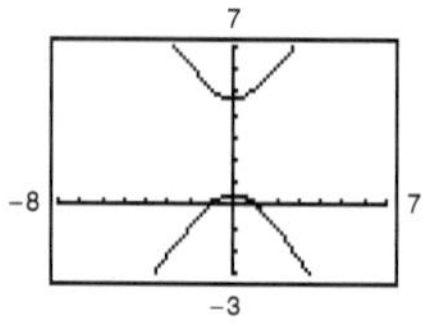

Hyperbola

34.

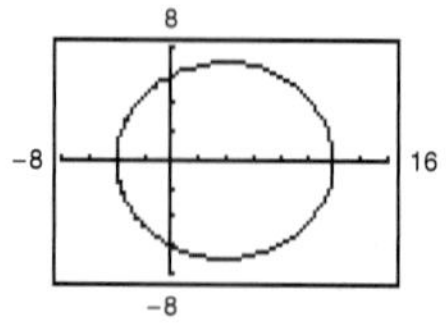

Ellipse

65. (b)

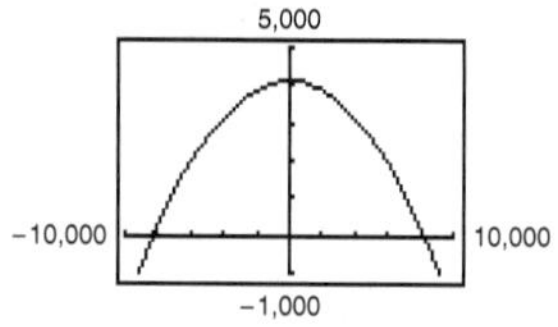

Review Exercises *(page 800)*

27. Center: $(-1, 2)$
Vertices: $(-1, 9), (-1, -5)$
Foci: $\left(-1, 2 \pm 2\sqrt{6}\right)$
Eccentricity: $\frac{2\sqrt{6}}{7}$

28. Center: $(5, -3)$
Vertices: $(5, 3), (5, -9)$
Foci: $\left(5, -3 \pm \sqrt{35}\right)$
Eccentricity: $\frac{\sqrt{35}}{6}$

29. Center: $(1, -4)$
Vertices: $(1, 0), (1, -8)$
Foci: $\left(1, -4 \pm \sqrt{7}\right)$
Eccentricity: $\frac{\sqrt{7}}{4}$

30. Center: $(-2, 3)$
Vertices: $(3, 3), (-7, 3)$
Foci: $\left(-2 \pm \sqrt{21}, 3\right)$
Eccentricity: $\frac{\sqrt{21}}{5}$

47. $\frac{(x')^2}{3} + \frac{(y')^2}{2} = 1$

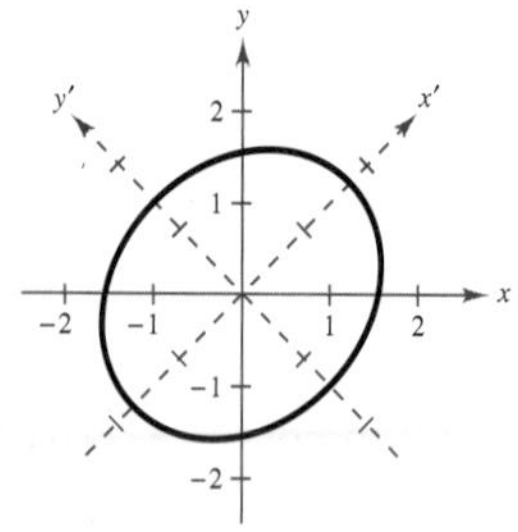

48. $y' = -4(x')^2 - 8x'$

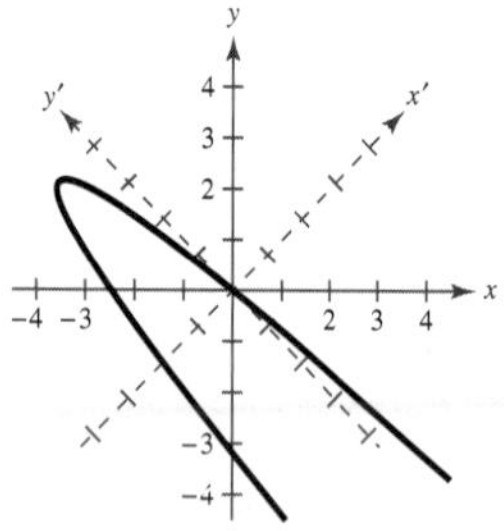

49. (a) Parabola

(b) $y = \frac{24x + 40 \pm \sqrt{(24x + 40)^2 - 36(16x^2 - 30x)}}{18}$

(c)

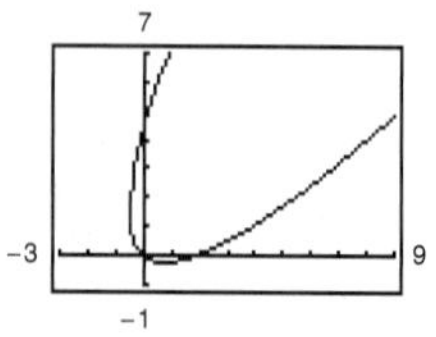

50. (a) Ellipse (b) $y = \frac{8x \pm \sqrt{64x^2 - 28(13x^2 - 45)}}{14}$

(c)

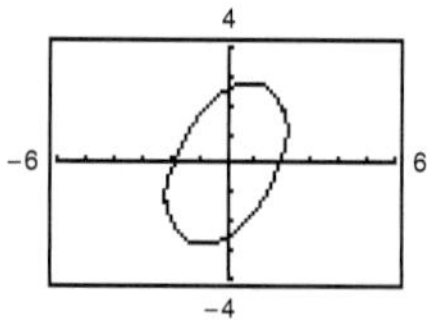

51. (a) Parabola

(b)

$$y = \frac{-\left(2x - 2\sqrt{2}\right) \pm \sqrt{\left(2x - 2\sqrt{2}\right)^2 - 4\left(x^2 + 2\sqrt{2}x + 2\right)}}{2}$$

(c)

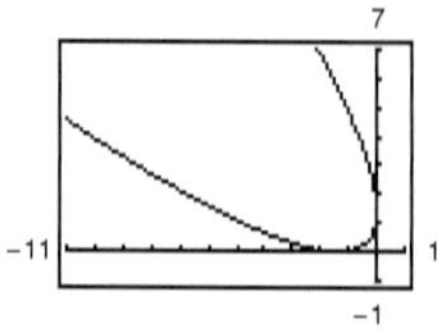

52. (a) Hyperbola (b) $y = \frac{10x \pm \sqrt{100x^2 - 4(x^2 + 1)}}{2}$

(c)

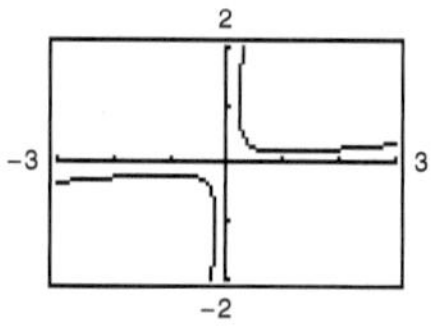

53. (a)

t	-2	-1	0	1	2
x	-8	-5	-2	1	4
y	15	11	7	3	-1

(b)

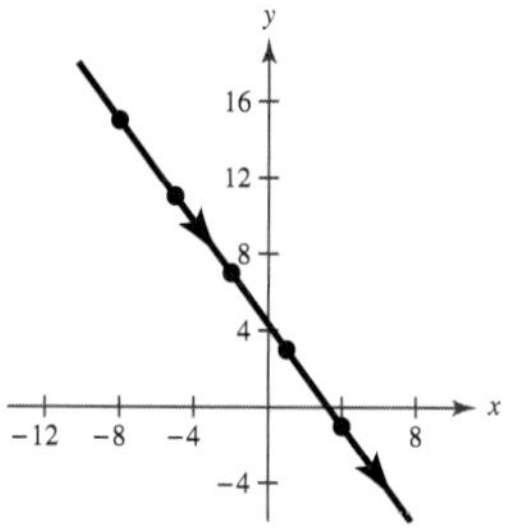

54. (a)

t	-2	-1	0	1	2
x	$-\frac{1}{2}$	$-\frac{1}{4}$	0	$\frac{1}{4}$	$\frac{1}{2}$
y	6	3	2	$\frac{3}{2}$	$\frac{6}{5}$

(b)

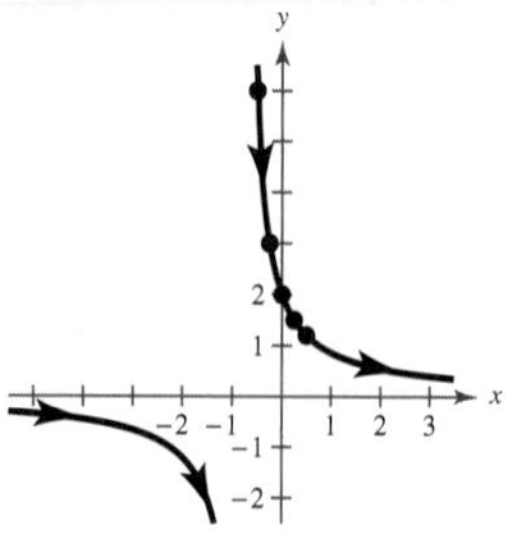

ADDITIONAL ANSWERS

55. (a)

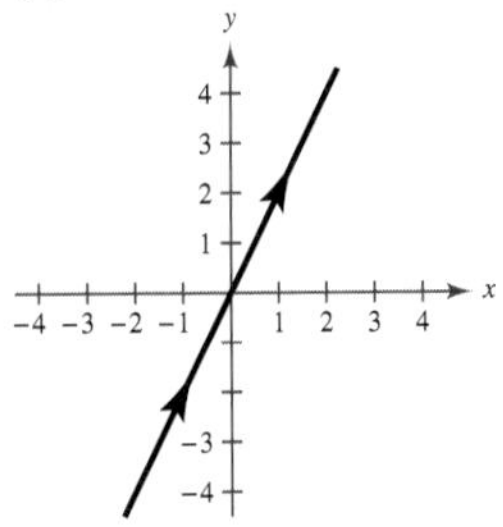

(b) $y = 2x$

56. (a)

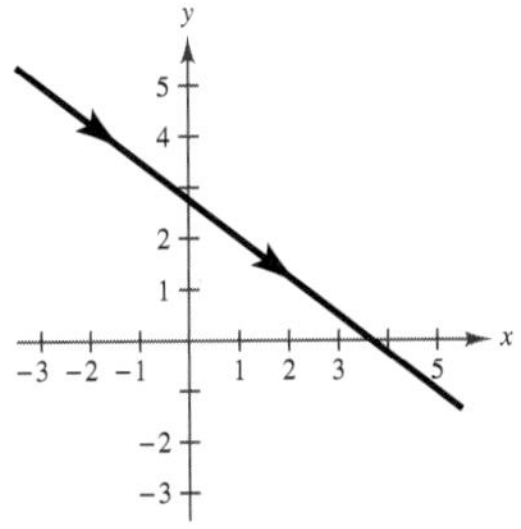

(b) $y = -\frac{3}{4}x + \frac{11}{4}$

57. (a)

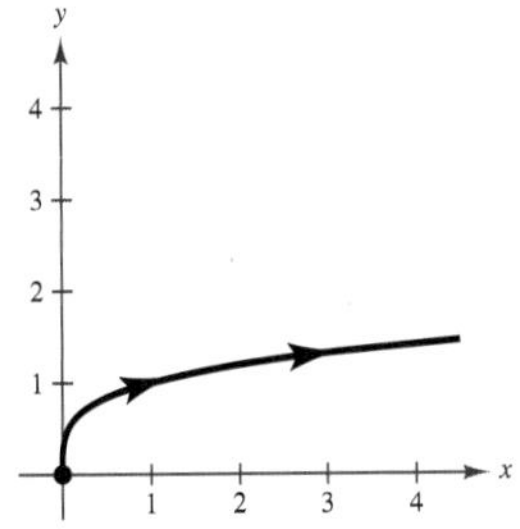

(b) $y = \sqrt[4]{x}$

58. (a)

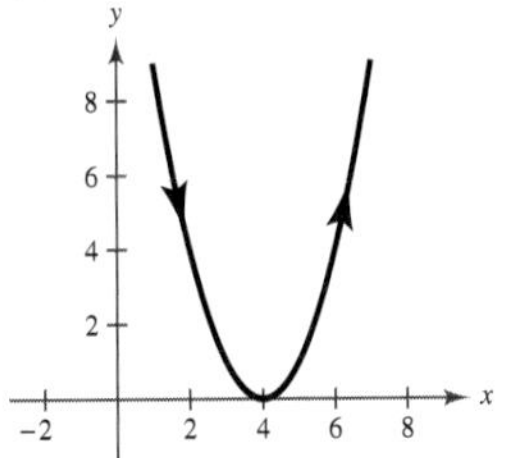

(b) $y = (x - 4)^2$

59. (a)

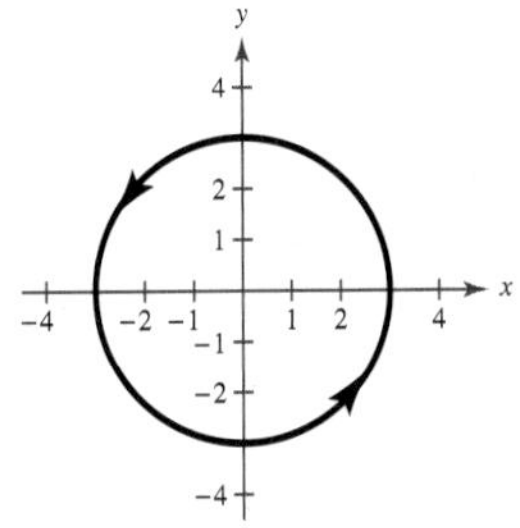

(b) $x^2 + y^2 = 9$

60. (a)

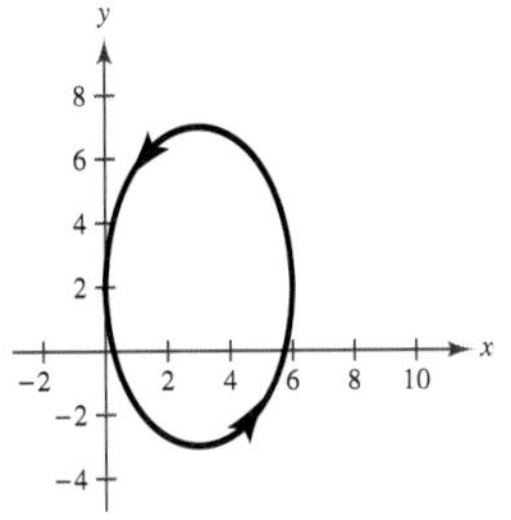

(b) $\dfrac{(x-3)^2}{9} + \dfrac{(y-2)^2}{25} = 1$

61. $x = -4 + 13t$
$y = 4 - 14t$

62. $x = 5 + 6\cos\theta$
$y = 4 + 6\sin\theta$

63. $x = -3 + 4\cos\theta$
$y = 4 + 3\sin\theta$

65.

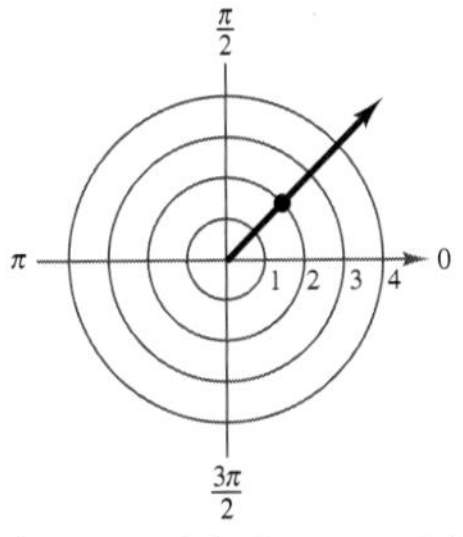

$(2, -7\pi/4), (-2, 5\pi/4)$

66.

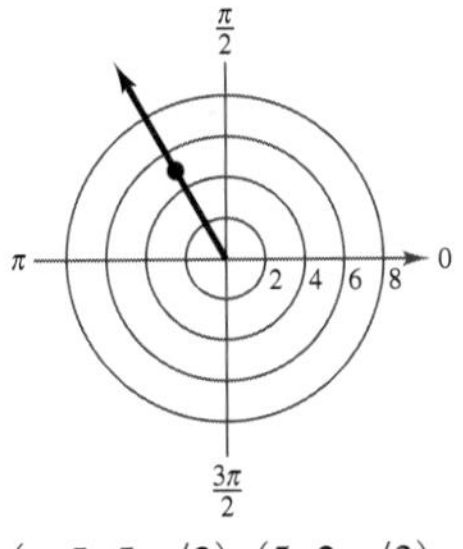

$(-5, 5\pi/3), (5, 2\pi/3)$

67.

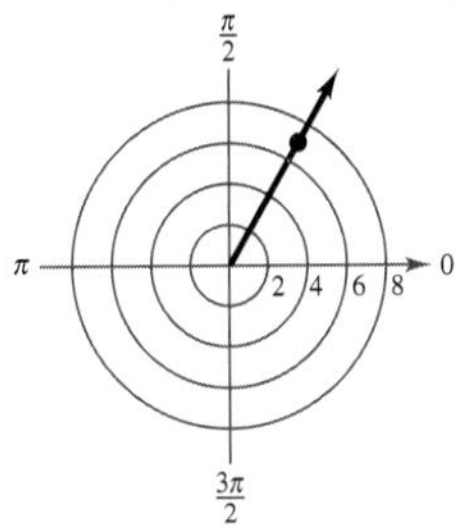

$(7, 1.05), (-7, -2.09)$

68.

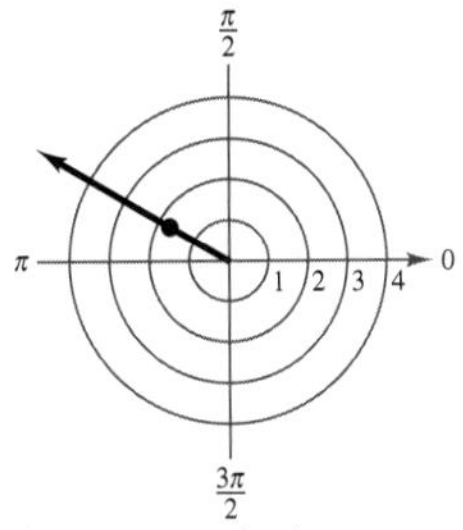

$(\sqrt{3}, -3.66), (-\sqrt{3}, 5.76)$

89. Symmetry: $\theta = \frac{\pi}{2}$, polar axis, pole
Maximum value of $|r|$:
$|r| = 6$ for all values of θ
No zeros of r

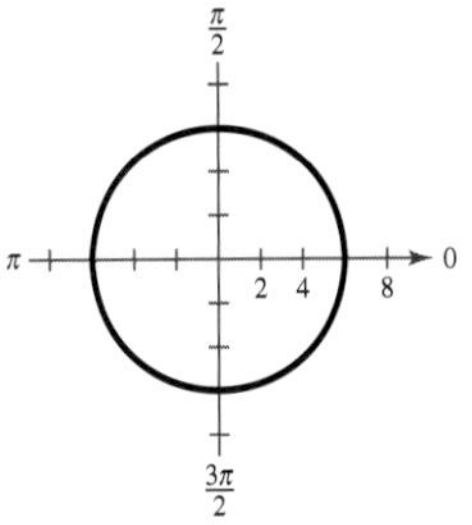

90. Symmetry: $\theta = \frac{\pi}{2}$, polar axis, pole
Maximum value of $|r|$:
$|r| = 11$ for all values of θ
No zeros of r

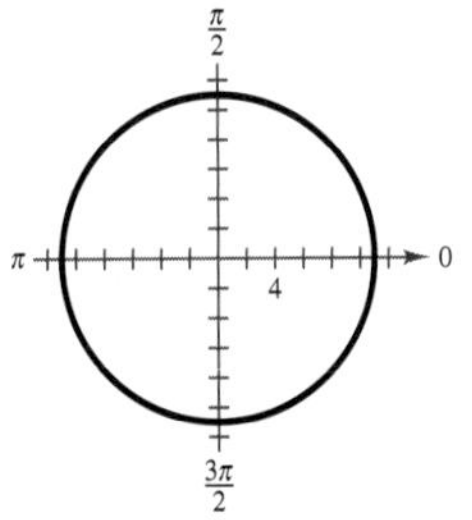

91. Symmetry: $\theta = \frac{\pi}{2}$, polar axis, pole
Maximum value of $|r|$: $|r| = 4$ when $\theta = \frac{\pi}{4}, \frac{3\pi}{4}, \frac{5\pi}{4}, \frac{7\pi}{4}$
Zeros of r: $r = 0$ when
$\theta = 0, \frac{\pi}{2}, \pi, \frac{3\pi}{2}$

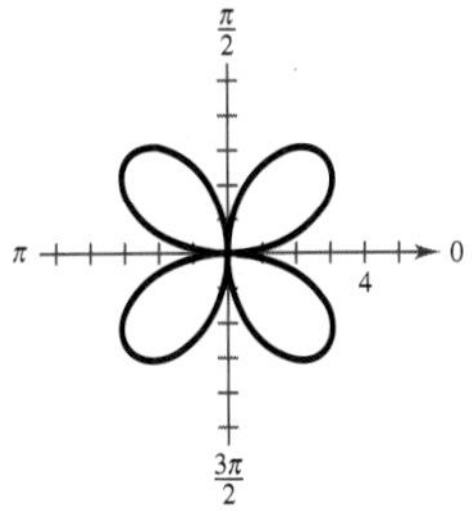

92. Symmetry: polar axis
Maximum value of $|r|$: $|r| = 1$ when $\theta = 0, \frac{2\pi}{5}, \frac{4\pi}{5}, \frac{6\pi}{5}, \frac{8\pi}{5}$
Zeros of r: $r = 0$ when $\theta = \frac{\pi}{10}, \frac{3\pi}{10}, \frac{5\pi}{10}, \frac{7\pi}{10}, \frac{9\pi}{10}$

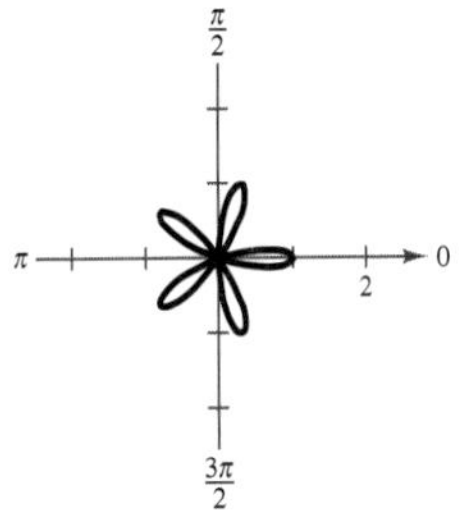

93. Symmetry: polar axis
Maximum value of $|r|$:
$|r| = 4$ when $\theta = 0$
Zeros of r: $r = 0$ when
$\theta = \pi$

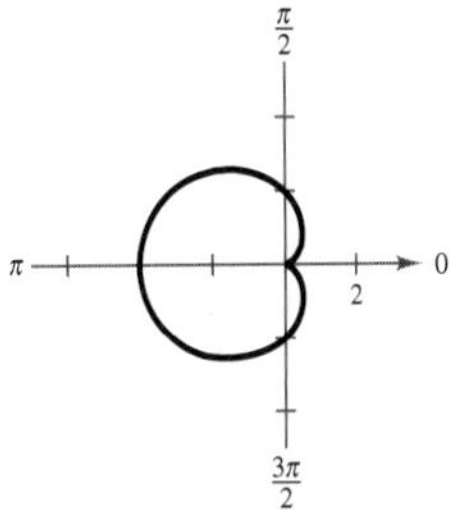

94. Symmetry: polar axis
Maximum value of $|r|$:
$|r| = 5$ when $\theta = \pi$
Zeros of r:
$r = 0$ when $\theta = \arccos\frac{1}{4}$,
$2\pi - \arccos\frac{1}{4}$

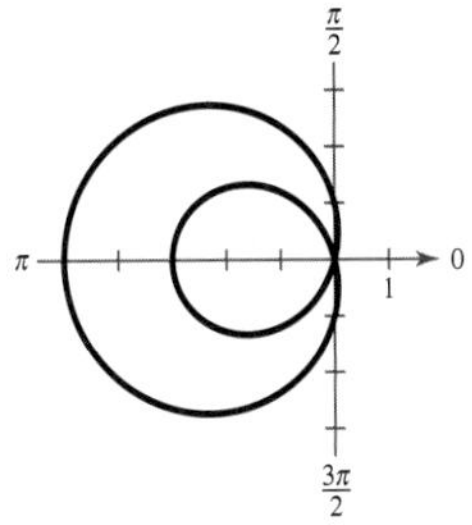

95. Symmetry: $\theta = \frac{\pi}{2}$

Maximum value of $|r|$: $|r| = 8$ when $\theta = \frac{\pi}{2}$

Zeros of r: $r = 0$ when $\theta = 3.4814, 5.9433$

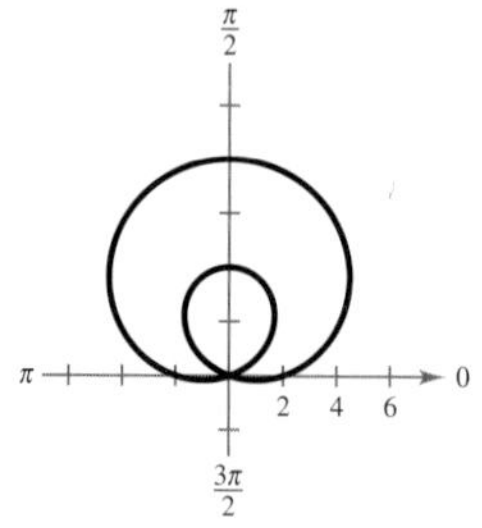

96. Symmetry: polar axis
Maximum value of $|r|$: $|r| = 10$ when $\theta = \pi$
Zero of r: $r = 0$ when $\theta = 0$

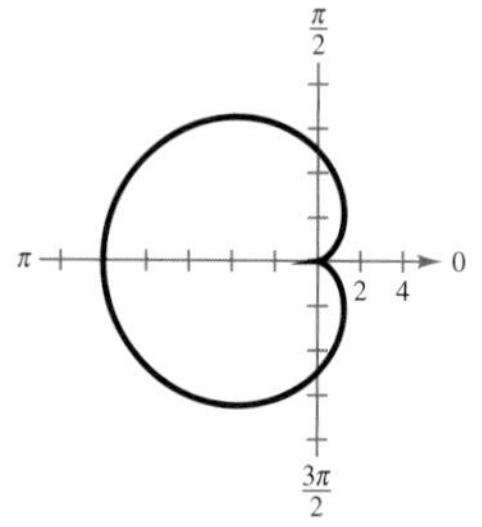

97. Symmetry: $\theta = \frac{\pi}{2}$, polar axis, pole

Maximum value of $|r|$: $|r| = 3$ when $\theta = 0, \frac{\pi}{2}, \pi, \frac{3\pi}{2}$

Zeros of r: $r = 0$ when $\theta = \frac{\pi}{4}, \frac{3\pi}{4}, \frac{5\pi}{4}, \frac{7\pi}{4}$

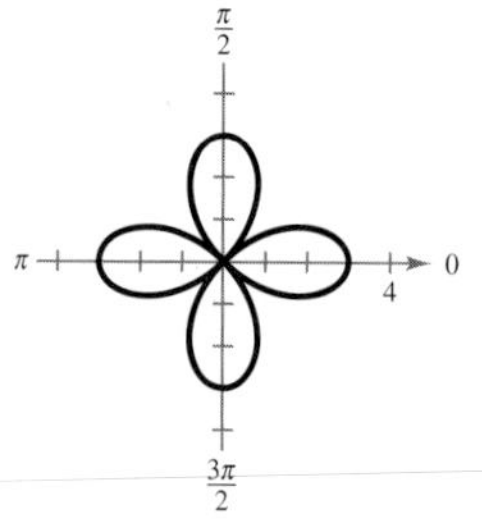

98. Symmetry: $\theta = \frac{\pi}{2}$, polar axis, pole

Maximum value of $|r|$: $|r| = 1$ when $\theta = 0, \pi$

Zeros of r: $r = 0$ when $\theta = \frac{\pi}{4}, \frac{3\pi}{4}, \frac{5\pi}{4}, \frac{7\pi}{4}$

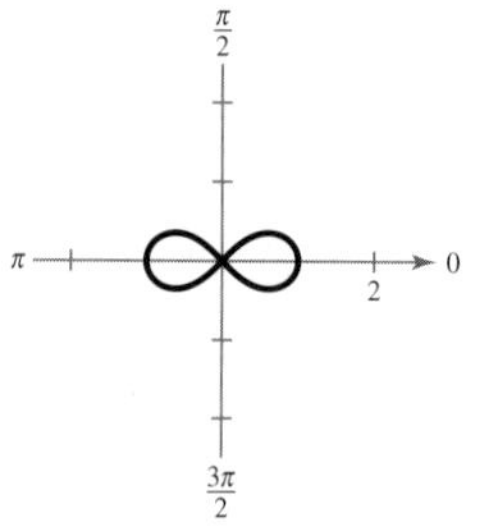

Chapter Test *(page 803)*

17.

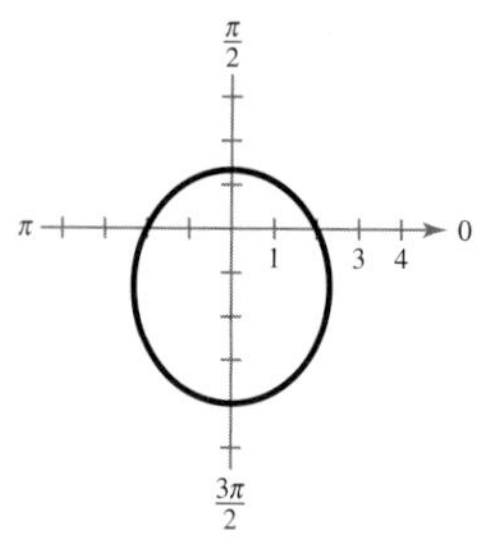

Ellipse

18.

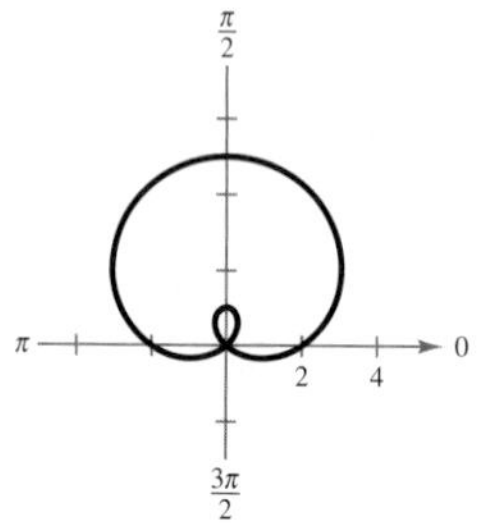

Limaçon with inner loop

19.

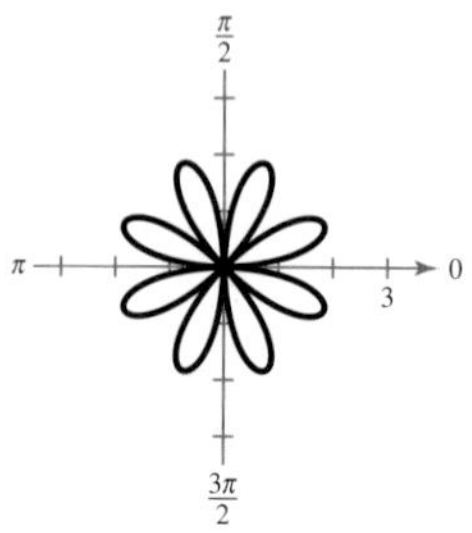

Rose curve

Problem Solving *(page 807)*

16.

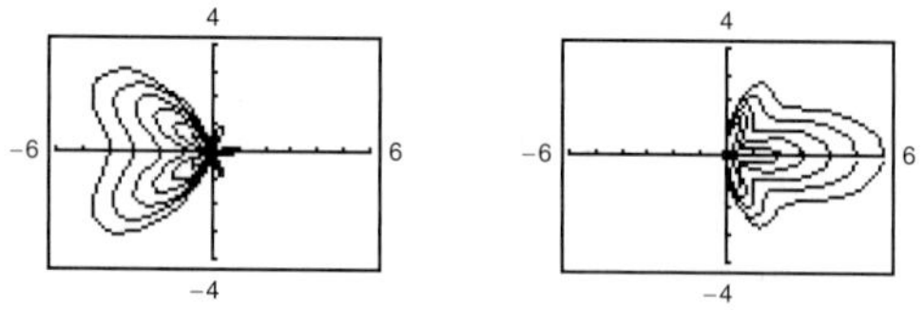

For $n \geq 1$, a bell is produced.
For $n \leq -1$, a heart is produced.
For $n = 0$, a rose curve is produced.

17. (a) $r_{\text{Neptune}} = \dfrac{4.4947 \times 10^9}{1 - 0.0086 \cos \theta}$

$r_{\text{Pluto}} = \dfrac{5.54 \times 10^9}{1 - 0.2488 \cos \theta}$

(b) Neptune: Aphelion $= 4.534 \times 10^9$ km
Perihelion $= 4.456 \times 10^9$ km
Pluto: Aphelion $= 7.375 \times 10^9$ km
Perihelion $= 4.437 \times 10^9$ km

(c)

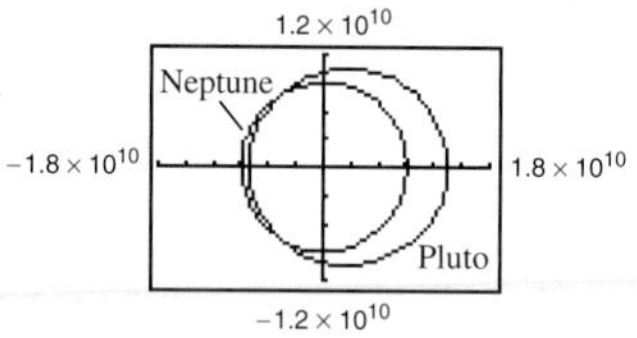

(d) Yes, at times Pluto can be closer to the sun than Neptune. Pluto was called the ninth planet because it has the longest orbit around the sun and therefore also reaches the furthest distance away from the sun.

(e) If the orbits are in the same plane, then they will intersect. Furthermore, since the orbital periods differ (Neptune = 164.79 years, Pluto = 247.68 years), then the two planets will ultimately collide if the orbits intersect.
The orbital inclination of Pluto is significantly larger than that of Neptune (17.16° vs. 1.769°), so further analysis is required to determine if the orbits intersect.

Chapter 11

Section 11.1 (*page 815*)

16.

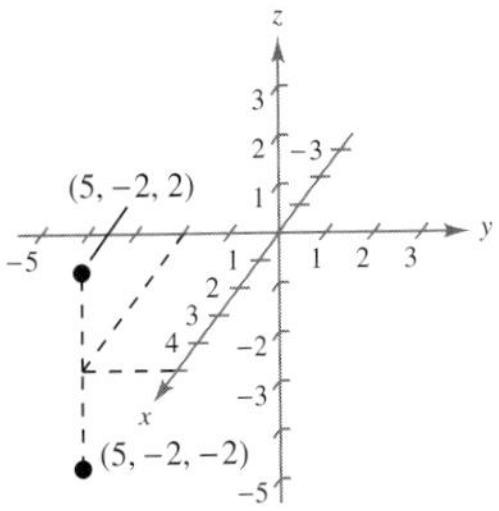

27. $\sqrt{65}$ units **28.** $2\sqrt{13}$ units **29.** $\sqrt{29}$ units

30. $3\sqrt{2}$ units **38.** $\left(2\sqrt{14}\right)^2 + \left(\sqrt{6}\right)^2 = \left(\sqrt{62}\right)^2$

75.

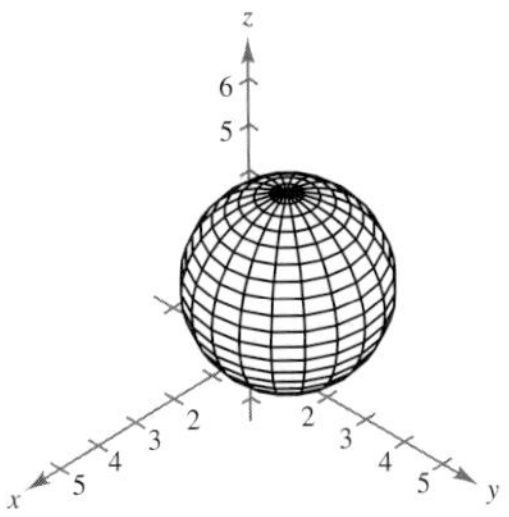

76.

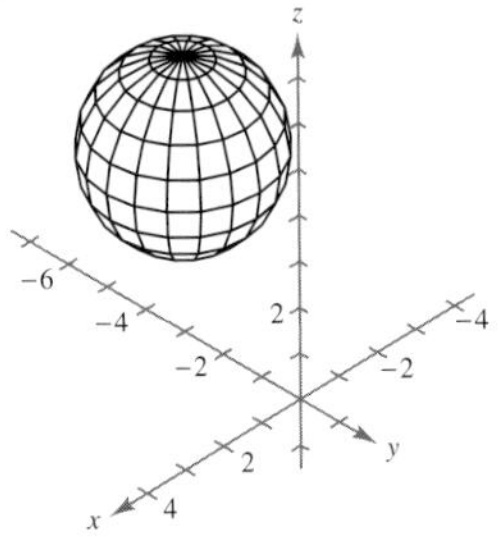

Section 11.2 (*page 822*)

12. (a)

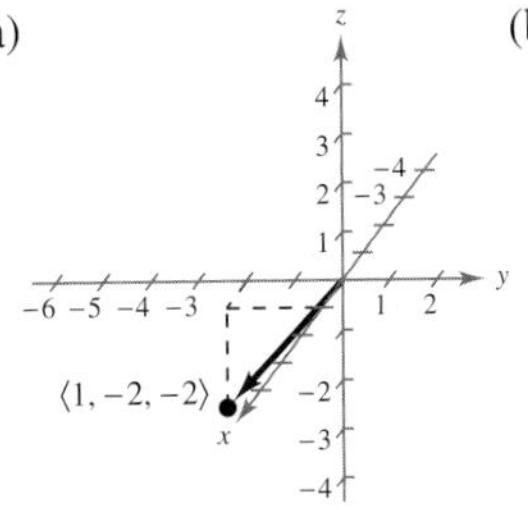

(b)

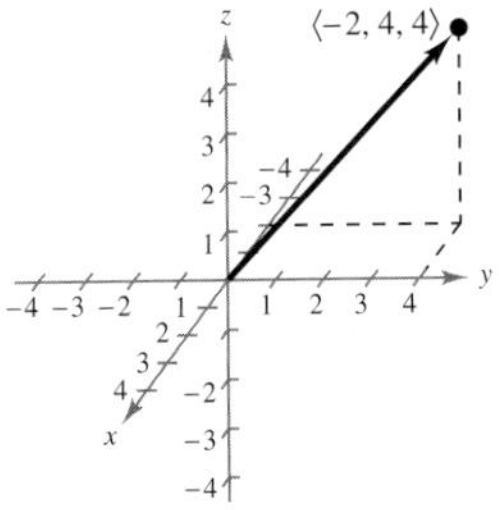

(c)

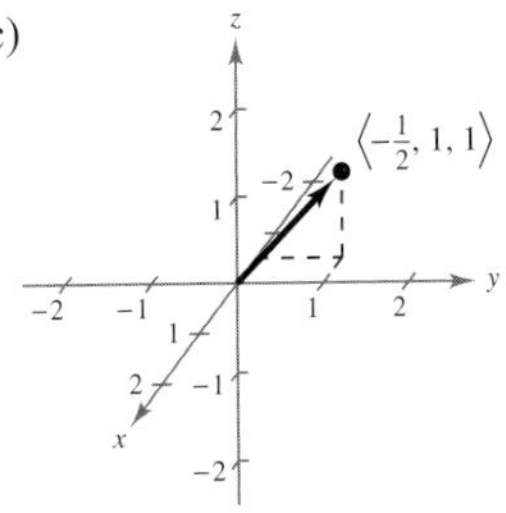

(d)

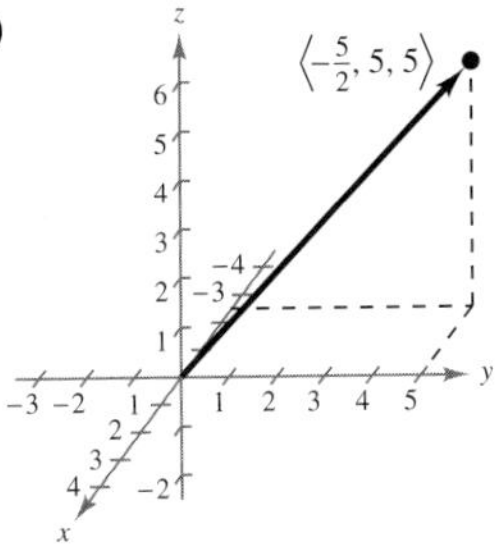

13. (a)

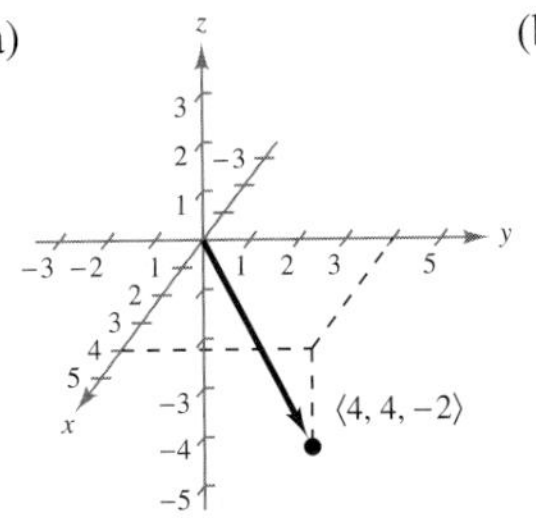

(b)

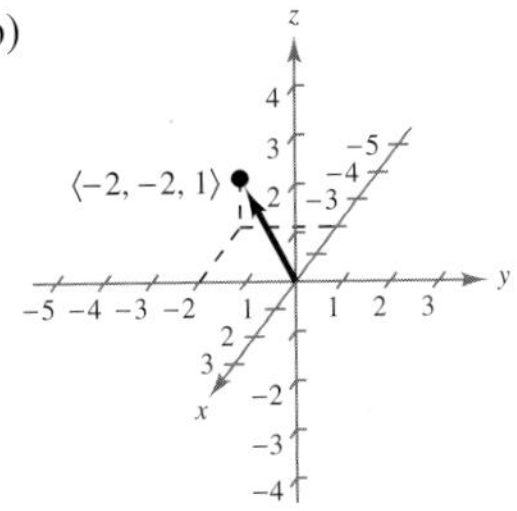

(c)

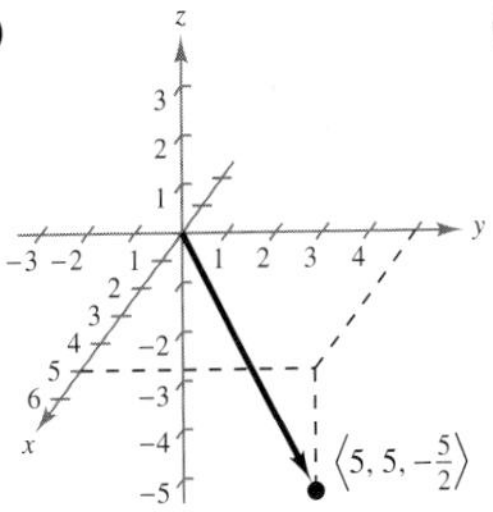

(d)

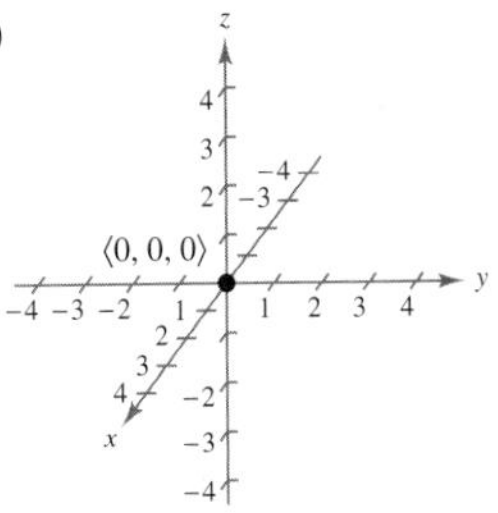

14. (a)

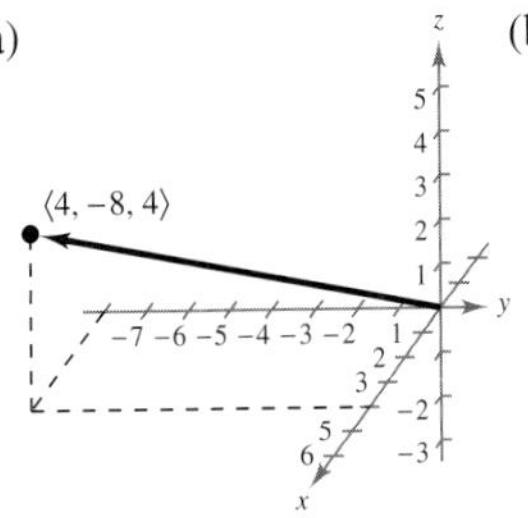

(b)

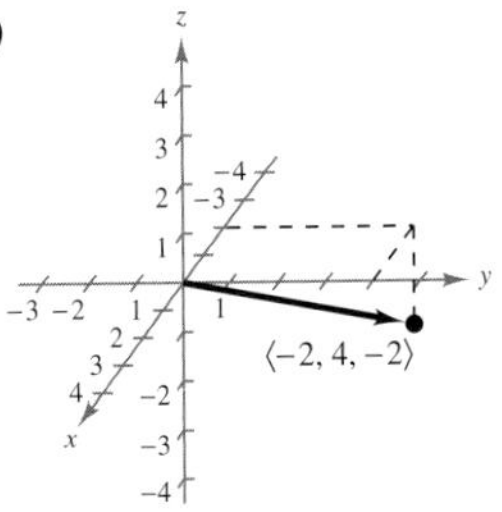

(c)

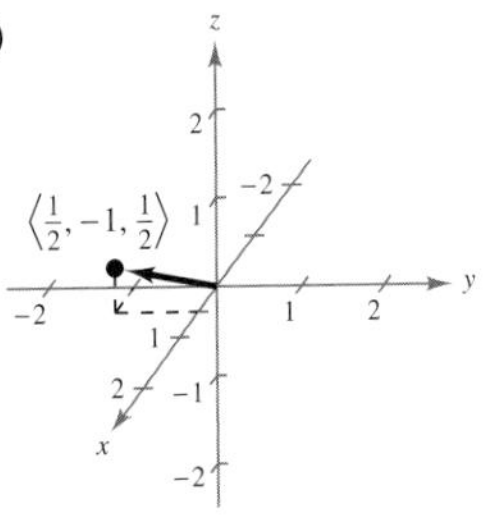

(d)

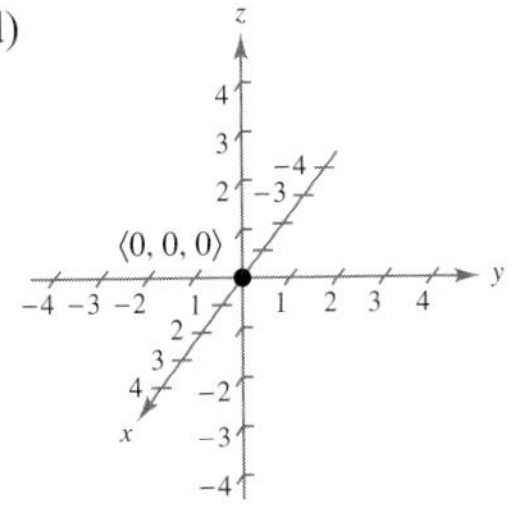

29. (a) $\dfrac{\sqrt{74}}{74}(8\mathbf{i} + 3\mathbf{j} - \mathbf{k})$ (b) $-\dfrac{\sqrt{74}}{74}(8\mathbf{i} + 3\mathbf{j} - \mathbf{k})$

30. (a) $\dfrac{\sqrt{134}}{134}(-3\mathbf{i} + 5\mathbf{j} + 10\mathbf{k})$

(b) $-\dfrac{\sqrt{134}}{134}(-3\mathbf{i} + 5\mathbf{j} + 10\mathbf{k})$

Section 11.3 (*page 829*)

5. $-\mathbf{k}$

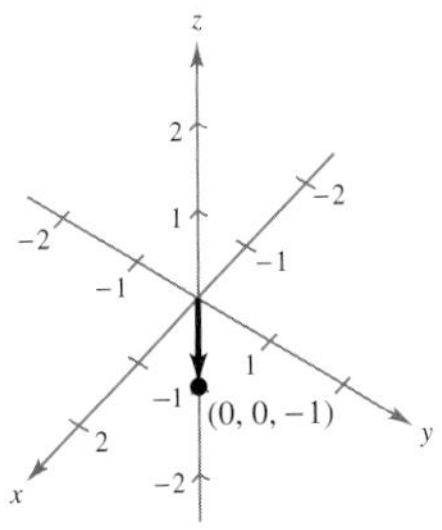

6. $\mathbf{k}$

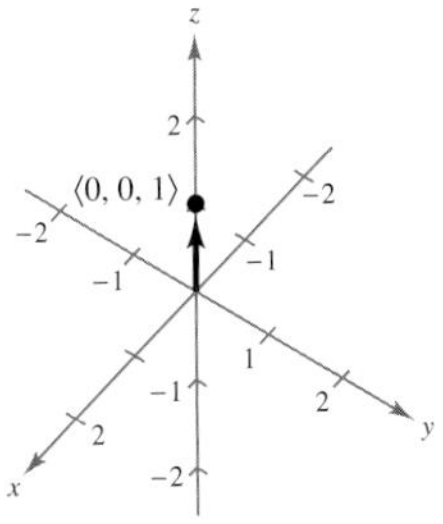

7. $-\mathbf{j}$

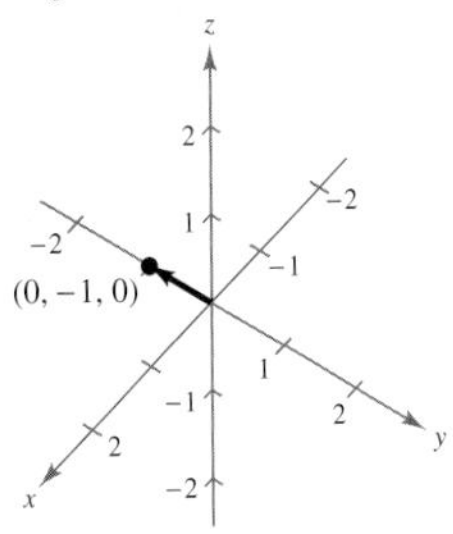

8. $\mathbf{j}$

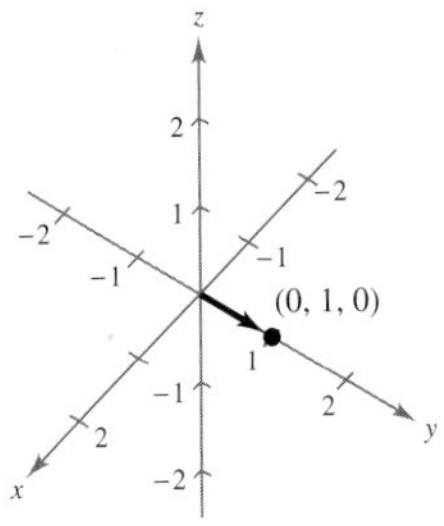

9. **i**

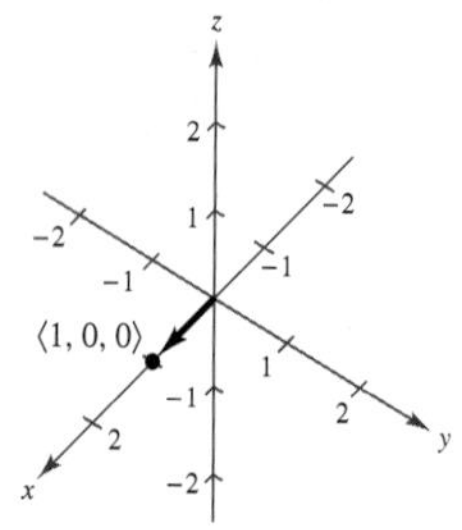

10. $-\mathbf{i}$

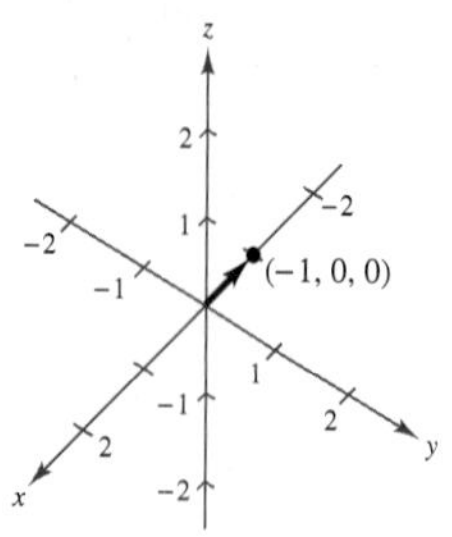

Section 11.4 *(page 838)*

19.

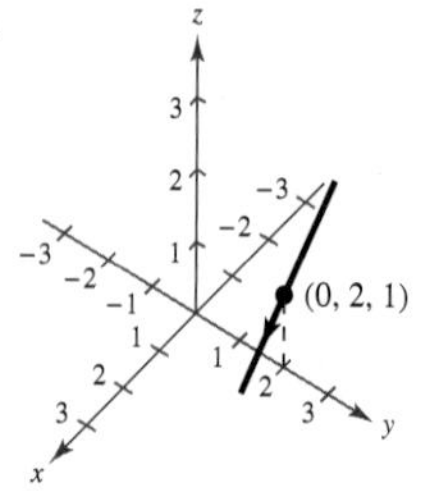

20.

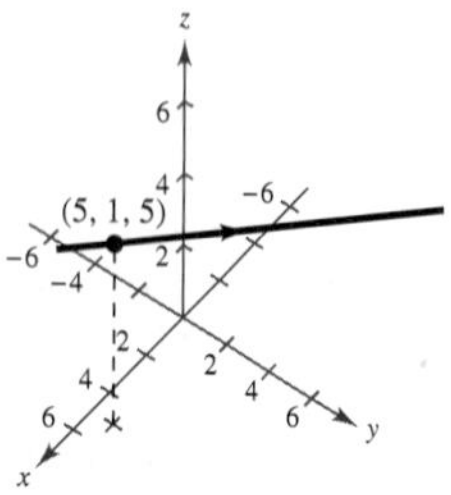

31. $y - 5 = 0$ **32.** $x - 1 = 0$ **33.** $y - z + 2 = 0$
34. $5x + 3z - 17 = 0$ **35.** $7x + y - 11z - 5 = 0$
36. $x + 2y + 4z - 5 = 0$

61. (a)

Year	Model
2006	3.90
2007	3.81
2008	3.54
2009	3.42
2010	3.29

Chapter 12

Section 12.1 *(page 858)*

7.

x	1.9	1.99	1.999	2
$f(x)$	13.5	13.95	13.995	14

x	2.001	2.01	2.1
$f(x)$	14.005	14.05	14.5

14; Yes

8.

x	0.9	0.99	0.999	1
$f(x)$	−1.4800	−1.0498	−1.005	−1

x	1.001	1.01	1.1
$f(x)$	−0.995	−0.9498	−0.48

−1; Yes

9.

x	2.9	2.99	2.999	3
$f(x)$	0.1695	0.1669	0.1667	Error

x	3.001	3.01	3.1
$f(x)$	0.1666	0.1664	0.1639

$\frac{1}{6}$; No

10.

x	−1.1	−1.01	−1.001	−1
$f(x)$	−0.3226	−0.3322	−0.3332	Error

x	−0.999	−0.99	−0.9
$f(x)$	−0.3334	−0.3344	−0.3448

$-\frac{1}{3}$; No

11.

x	−0.1	−0.01	−0.001	0
$f(x)$	1.9867	1.9999	1.999999	Error

x	0.001	0.01	0.1
$f(x)$	1.999999	1.9999	1.9867

2; No

12.

x	−0.1	−0.01	−0.001	0
$f(x)$	0.5017	0.50002	0.5000002	Error

x	0.001	0.01	0.1
$f(x)$	0.5000002	0.50002	0.5017

$\frac{1}{2}$; No

13.

x	0.9	0.99	0.999	1
$f(x)$	0.2564	0.2506	0.2501	Error

x	1.001	1.01	1.1
$f(x)$	0.2499	0.2494	0.2439

$\frac{1}{4}$;

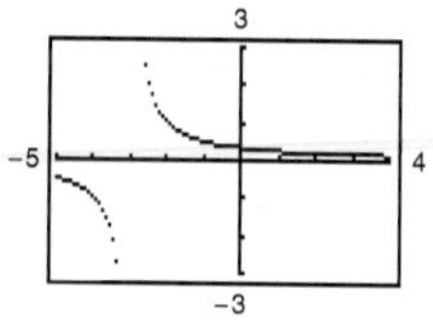

ADDITIONAL ANSWERS

(b)

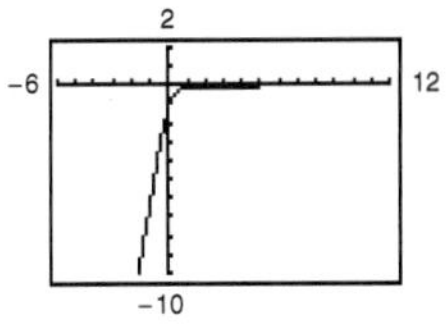

$\lim_{x\to\infty} f(x) = 0$

37. (a)

x	10^0	10^1	10^2	10^3
$f(x)$	−0.7082	−0.7454	−0.7495	−0.74995

x	10^4	10^5	10^6
$f(x)$	−0.749995	−0.7499995	−0.75

(b)

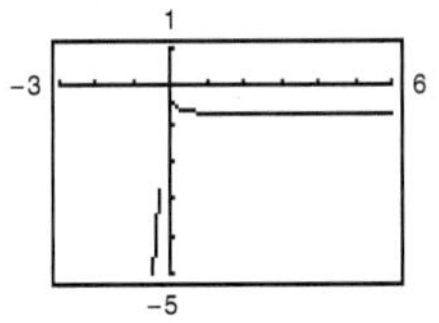

$\lim_{x\to\infty} f(x) = -\frac{3}{4}$

38. (a)

x	10^0	10^1	10^2
$f(x)$	0.508	0.5008	0.50008

x	10^3	10^4	10^5	10^6
$f(x)$	0.5	0.5	0.5	0.5

(b)

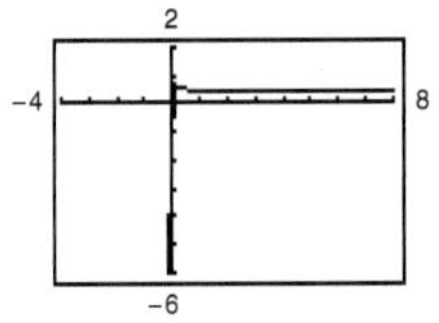

$\lim_{x\to\infty} f(x) = \frac{1}{2}$

49. $\lim_{n\to\infty} a_n = \frac{3}{2}$

n	10^0	10^1	10^2	10^3
a_n	2	1.55	1.505	1.5005

n	10^4	10^5	10^6
a_n	1.50005	1.500005	1.5000005

50. $\lim_{n\to\infty} a_n = 12$

n	10^0	10^1	10^2	10^3
a_n	20	12.8	12.08	12.008

n	10^4	10^5	10^6
a_n	12.0008	12.00008	12.000008

51. $\lim_{n\to\infty} a_n = \frac{16}{3}$

n	10^0	10^1	10^2	10^3
a_n	16	6.16	5.4136	5.3413

n	10^4	10^5	10^6
a_n	5.3341	5.33341	5.333341

52. $\lim_{n\to\infty} a_n = \frac{3}{4}$

n	10^0	10^1	10^2	10^3
a_n	1	0.7975	0.754975	0.75049975

n	10^4	10^5	10^6
a_n	0.75005	0.750005	0.7500005

69.

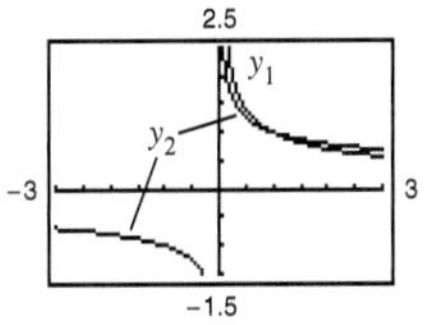

$\sqrt{x}$ is undefined for $x < 0$. Answers will vary.

71.

x	10^0	10^1	10^2	10^3	10^4	10^5
$\frac{1}{x}$	1	$\frac{1}{10}$	$\frac{1}{100}$	$\frac{1}{1000}$	$\frac{1}{10{,}000}$	$\frac{1}{100{,}000}$

$\lim_{x\to 0} \frac{1}{x}$ does not exist.

Section 12.5 *(page 896)*

19. (b)

n	10^0	10^1	10^2	10^3	10^4
$S(n)$	0	0.615	0.66165	0.666167	0.666617

20. (b)

n	10^0	10^1	10^2	10^3	10^4
$S(n)$	12	5.94	5.3934	5.33933	5.33393

25.

n	4	8	20	50
Approximate area	18	21	22.8	23.52

26.

n	4	8	20	50
Approximate area	14.344	16.242	17.314	17.728

27.

n	4	8	20	50
Approximate area	3.52	2.85	2.48	2.34

28.

n	4	8	20	50
Approximate area	7.113	7.614	7.8895	7.994

29.

n	4	8	20	50	100	∞
Approximate area	40	38	36.8	36.32	36.16	36

30.

n	4	8	20	50	100	∞
Approximate area	34	31	29.2	28.48	28.24	28

31.

n	4	8	20	50	100	∞
Approximate area	36	38	39.2	39.68	39.84	40

32.

n	4	8	20	50	100	∞
Approximate area	44	46	47.2	47.68	47.84	48

33.

n	4	8	20
Approximate area	14.25	14.8125	15.13

n	50	100	∞
Approximate area	15.2528	15.2932	$\frac{46}{3}$

34.

n	4	8	20
Approximate area	57.75	55.1875	53.67

n	50	100	∞
Approximate area	53.0672	52.8668	$\frac{158}{3}$

35.

n	4	8	20	50	100	∞
Approximate area	19	18.5	18.2	18.08	18.04	18

36.

n	4	8	20	50	100	∞
Approximate area	5	4.5	4.2	4.08	4.04	4

Review Exercises *(page 900)*

41. (b)

x	-0.1	-0.01	-0.001	0
$f(x)$	1.94709	1.99947	1.999995	Error

x	0.001	0.01	0.1
$f(x)$	1.999995	1.99947	1.94709

42. (a)

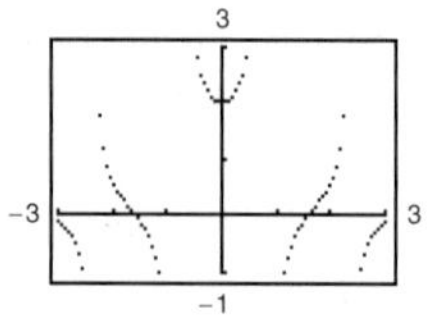

2

(b)

x	-0.1	-0.01	-0.001	0
$f(x)$	2.02710	2.00027	2.000003	Error

x	0.001	0.01	0.1
$f(x)$	2.000003	2.00027	2.02710

2

43. (a)

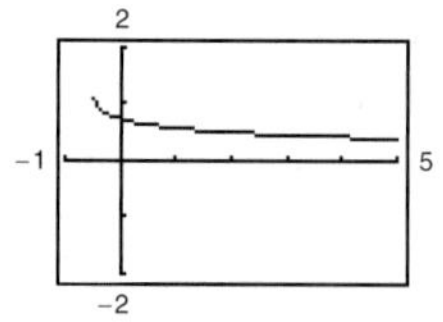

About 0.575

(b)

x	1.1	1.01	1.001	1.0001
$f(x)$	0.5680	0.5764	0.5773	0.5773

About 0.577 $\left(\text{Actual limit is } \frac{\sqrt{3}}{3}.\right)$

44. (a)

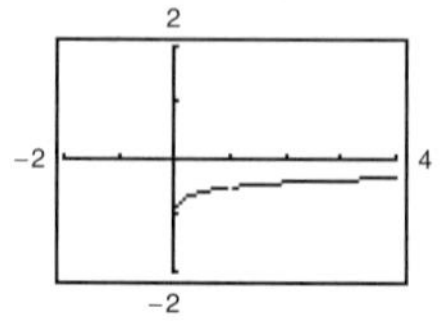

$-\frac{1}{2}$

(b)

x	1.1	1.01	1.001	1.0001
$f(x)$	-0.4881	-0.4988	-0.4999	-0.5000

$-\frac{1}{2}$

45.

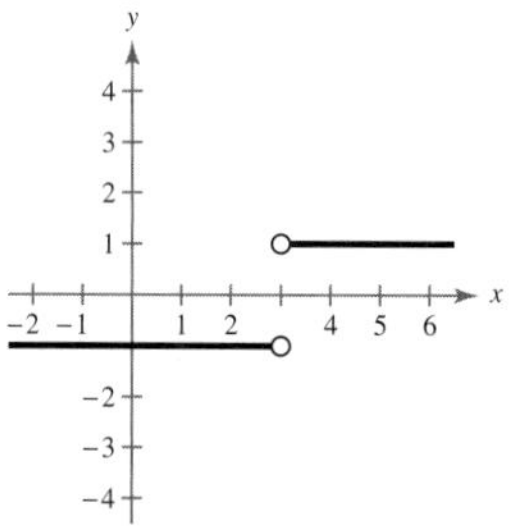

Limit does not exist.

46.

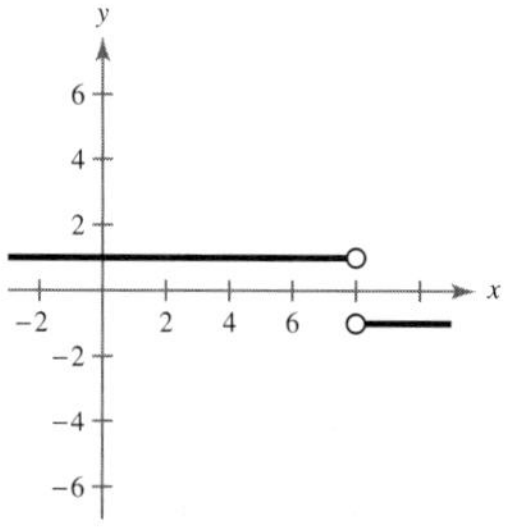

Limit does not exist.

47.

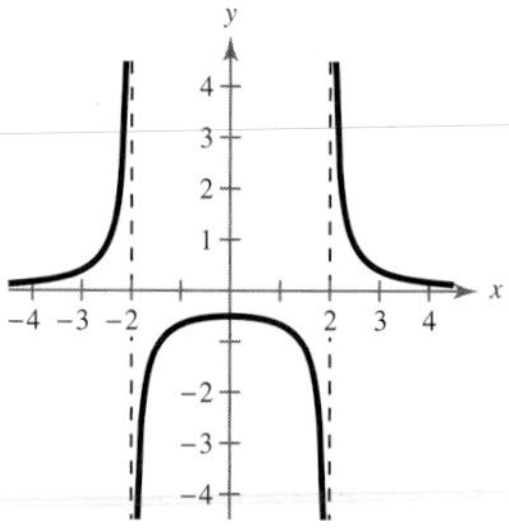

Limit does not exist.

48.

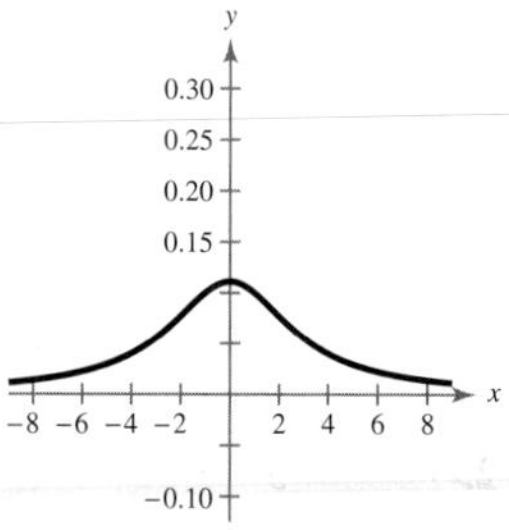

$\frac{1}{18}$

49.

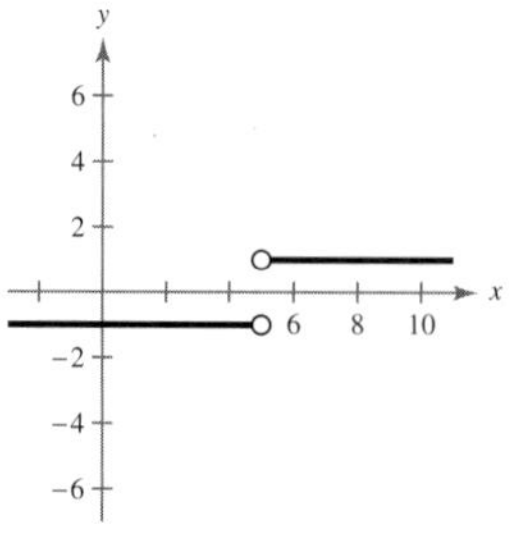

Limit does not exist.

50.

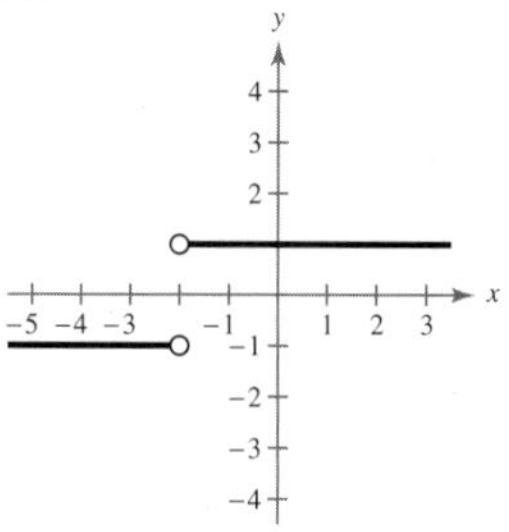

Limit does not exist.

51.

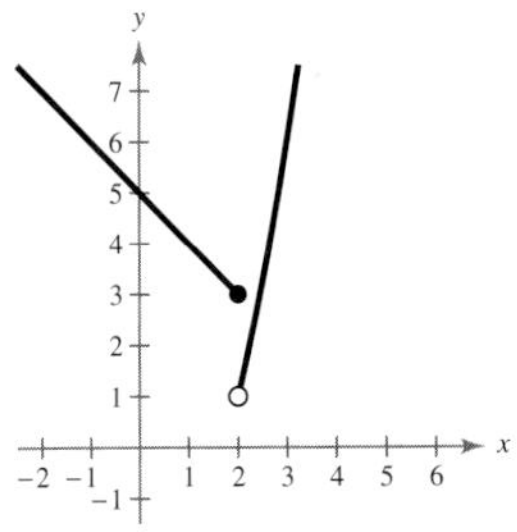

Limit does not exist.

52.

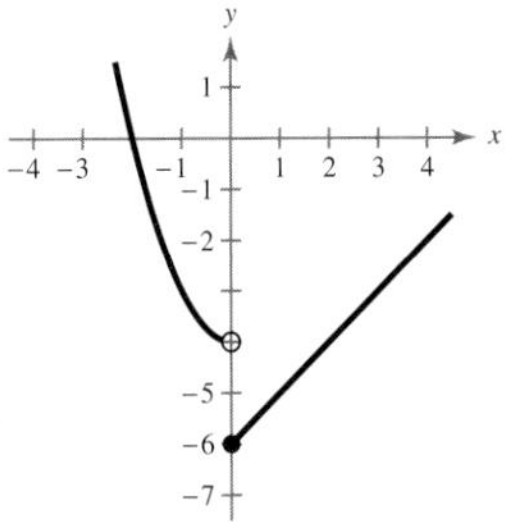

Limit does not exist.

59.

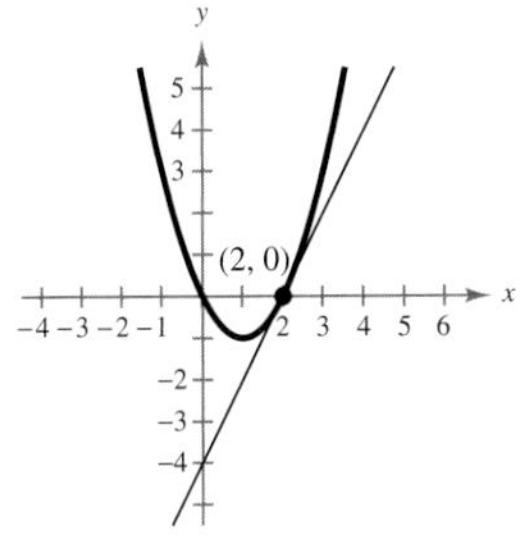

2

60.

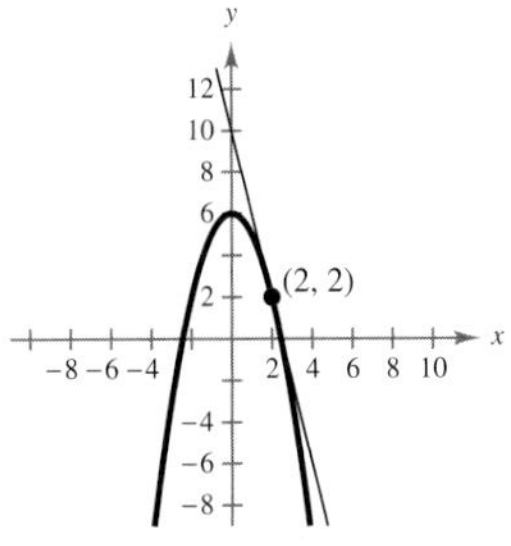

-4

61.

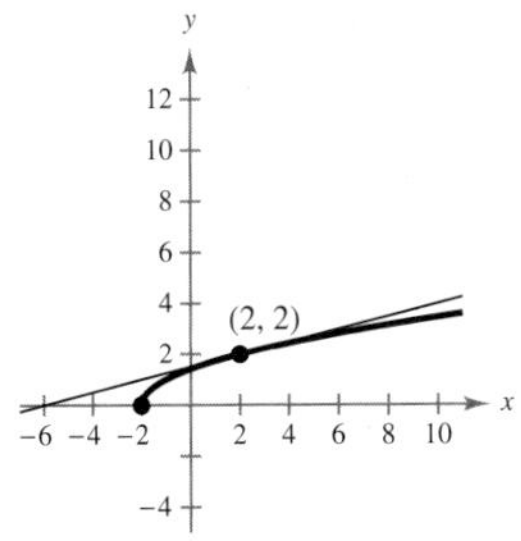

$\frac{1}{4}$

62.

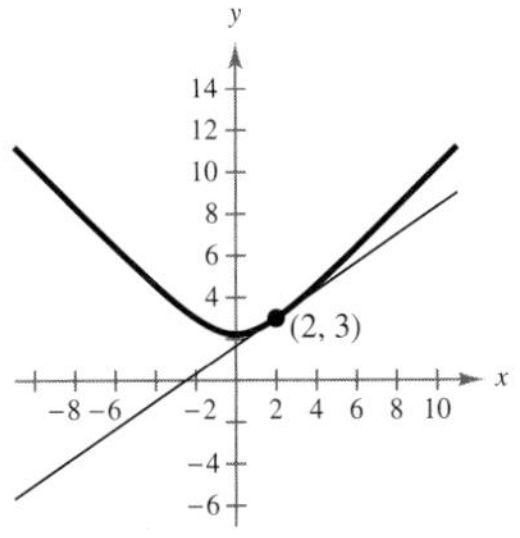

$\frac{2}{3}$

63.

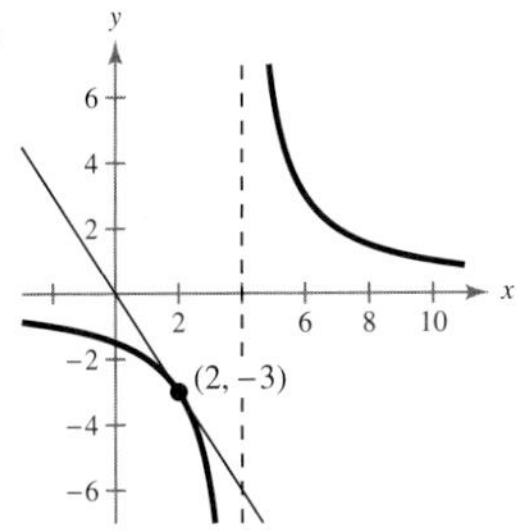

$-\frac{3}{2}$

64.

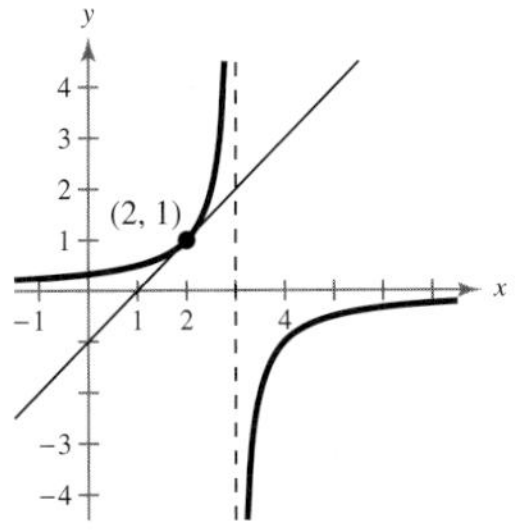

1

69. $f'(x) = 0$ **70.** $g'(x) = 0$ **71.** $h'(x) = -\frac{1}{2}$

72. $f'(x) = 3$ **73.** $g'(x) = 4x$ **74.** $f'(x) = -3x^2 + 4$

75. $f'(t) = \dfrac{1}{2\sqrt{t+5}}$ **76.** $g'(t) = \dfrac{1}{2\sqrt{t-3}}$

77. $g'(s) = -\dfrac{4}{(s+5)^2}$ **78.** $g'(t) = \dfrac{6}{(5-t)^2}$

79. $g'(x) = \dfrac{-1}{2(x+4)^{3/2}}$ **80.** $f'(x) = \dfrac{1}{2(12-x)^{3/2}}$

81. (a) 0 (b) $y = -1$

(c)

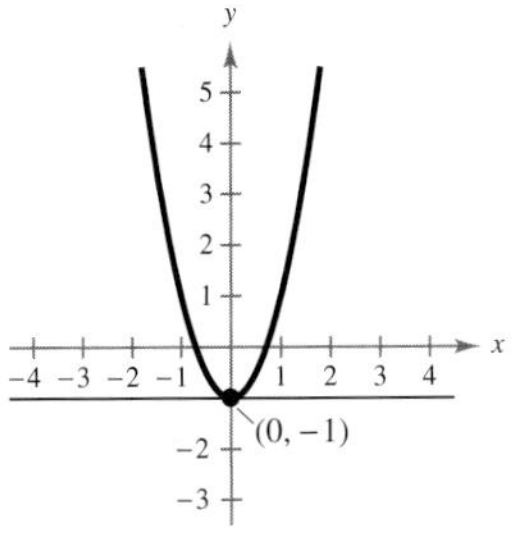

82. (a) 4 (b) $y = 4x + 6$

(c)

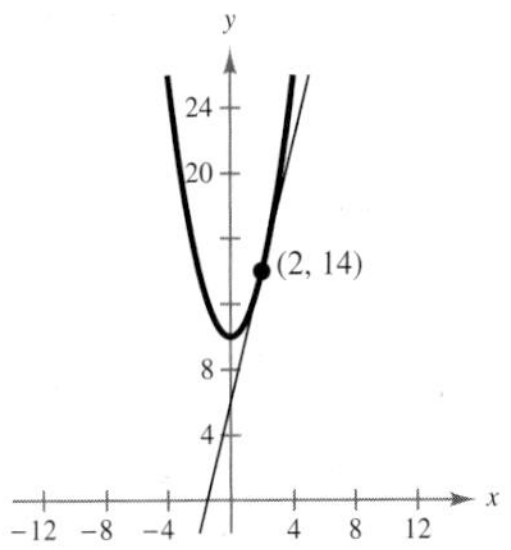

Cumulative Test for Chapters 10–12 *(page 904)*

18.

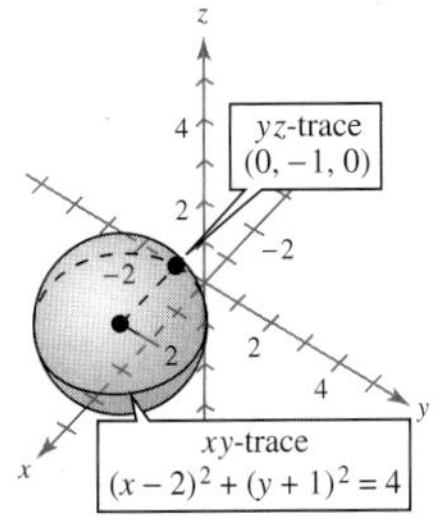

23. (a) $x = -2 + 7t, y = 3 + 5t, z = 25t$

(b) $\dfrac{x+2}{7} = \dfrac{y-3}{5} = \dfrac{z}{25}$

Appendix A

Appendix A.1 *(page A11)*

34. (a) $x > 3$ denotes the set of all real numbers greater than 3.

(b) 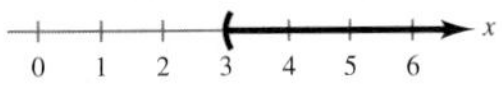 (c) Unbounded

35. (a) $[4, \infty)$ denotes the set of all real numbers greater than or equal to 4.

(b) 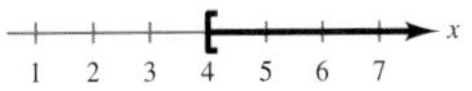 (c) Unbounded

36. (a) $(-\infty, 2)$ denotes the set of all real numbers less than 2.

(b) 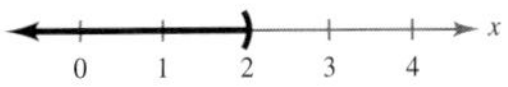 (c) Unbounded

37. (a) $-2 < x < 2$ denotes the set of all real numbers greater than -2 and less than 2.

(b) 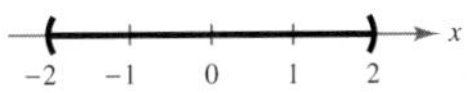 (c) Bounded

38. (a) $0 \le x \le 5$ denotes the set of all real numbers greater than or equal to zero and less than or equal to 5.

(b) 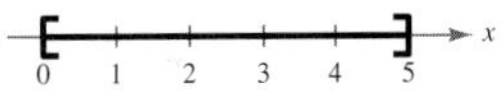 (c) Bounded

39. (a) $-1 \le x < 0$ denotes the set of all real numbers greater than or equal to -1 and less than 0.

(b)  (c) Bounded

40. (a) $0 < x \le 6$ denotes the set of positive real numbers less than or equal to 6.

(b) 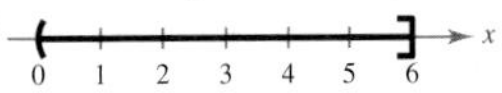 (c) Bounded

41. (a) $[-2, 5)$ denotes the set of all real numbers greater than or equal to -2 and less than 5.

(b) 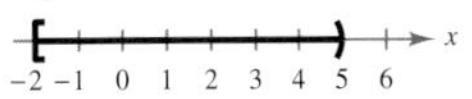 (c) Bounded

42. (a) $(-1, 2]$ denotes all real numbers greater than -1 and less than or equal to 2.

(b) 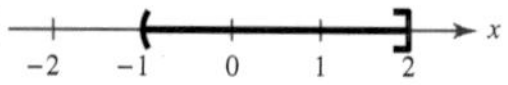

(c) Bounded

	Inequality	*Interval*
43.	$y \geq 0$	$[0, \infty)$
44.	$y \leq 25$	$(-\infty, 25]$
45.	$-2 < x \leq 4$	$(-2, 4]$
46.	$-6 \leq y < 0$	$[-6, 0)$
47.	$10 \leq t \leq 22$	$[10, 22]$
48.	$-3 \leq k < 5$	$[-3, 5)$
49.	$W > 65$	$(65, \infty)$
50.	$2.5\% \leq r \leq 5\%$	$[2.5\%, 5\%]$

134.

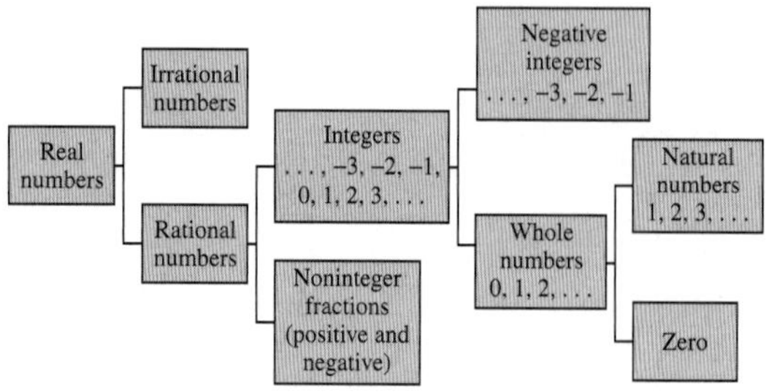

Appendix A.3 *(page A35)*

227.

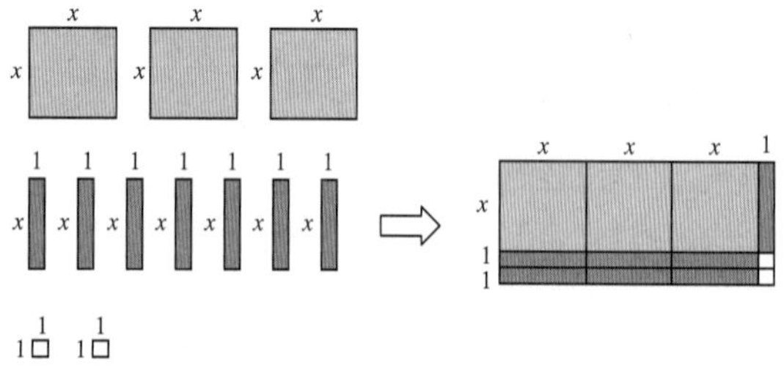

229.

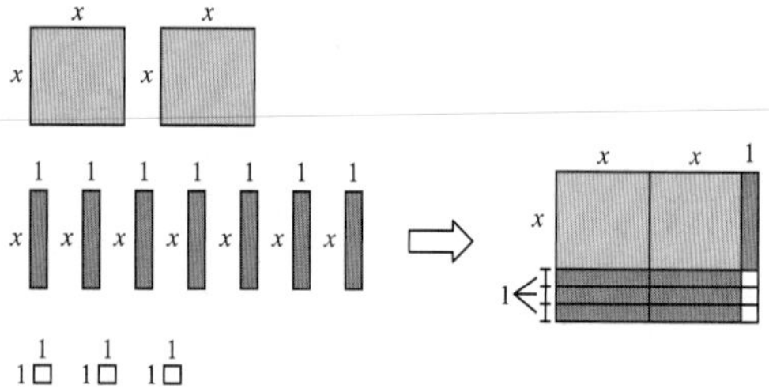

Appendix A.6 *(page A69)*

75. 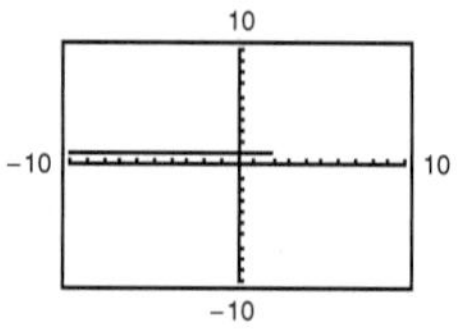

$x \leq 2$

76. 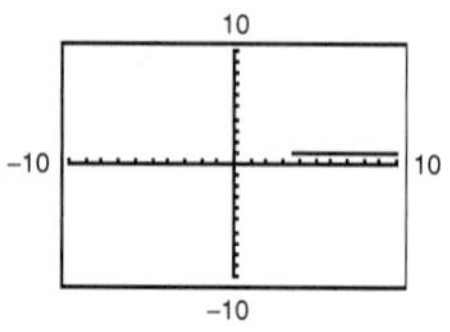

$x > 3.5$

77. 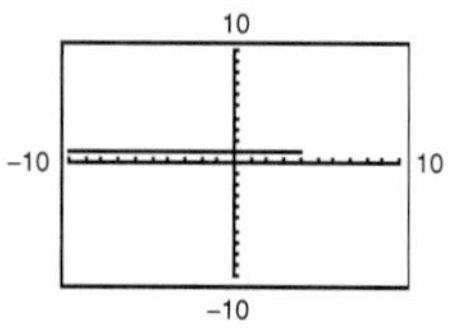

$x \leq 4$

78. 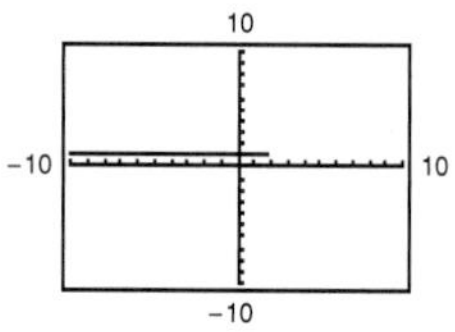

$x < 2$

79. 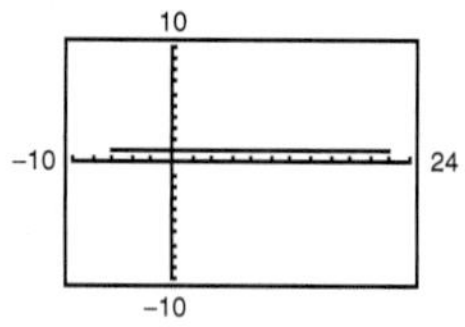

$-6 \leq x \leq 22$

80. 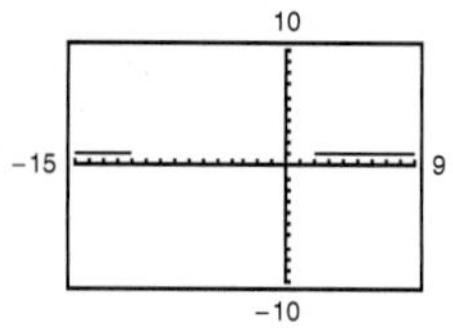

$x < -11, x > 2$

81. 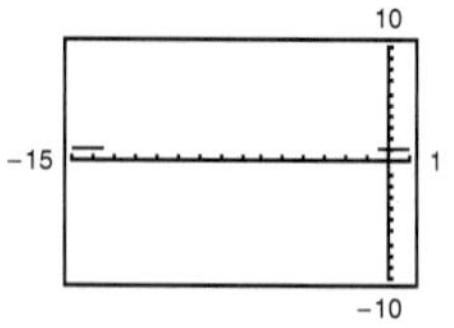

$x \leq -\frac{27}{2}, x \geq -\frac{1}{2}$

82. 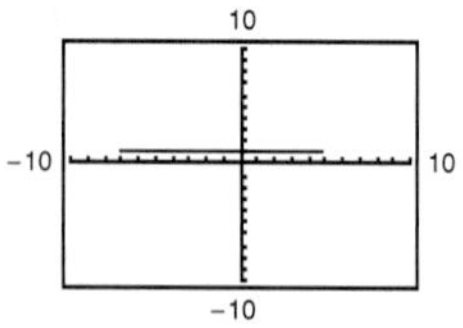

$-7 \leq x \leq 5$

83. 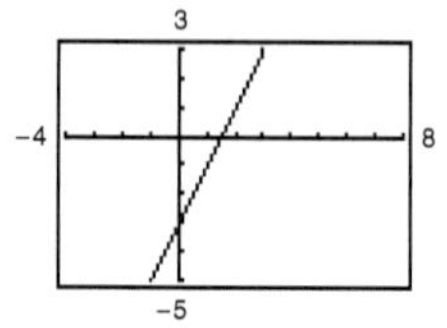

(a) $x \geq 2$ (b) $x \leq \frac{3}{2}$

84. 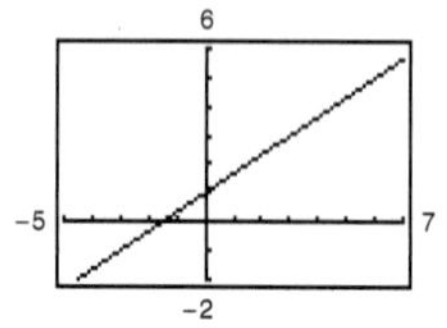

(a) $x \leq 6$ (b) $x \geq -\frac{3}{2}$

85. 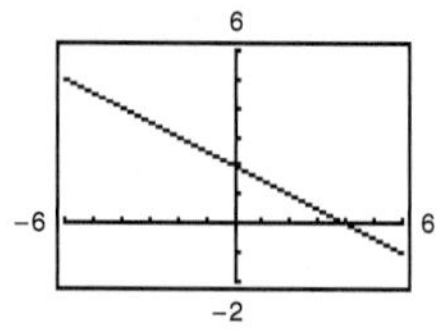

(a) $-2 \leq x \leq 4$
(b) $x \leq 4$

86. 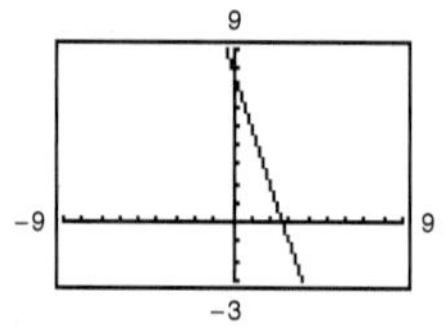

(a) $\frac{5}{3} \leq x \leq 3$
(b) $x \geq \frac{8}{3}$

87. 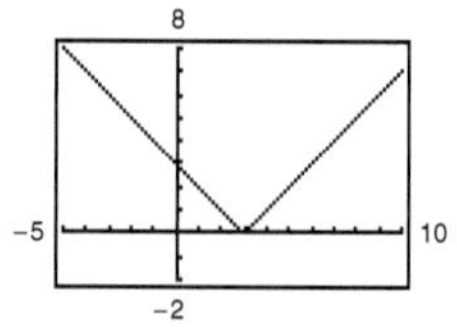

(a) $1 \leq x \leq 5$
(b) $x \leq -1, x \geq 7$

88. 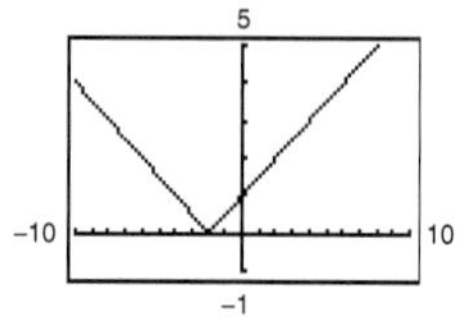

(a) $-10 \leq x \leq 6$
(b) $x \leq -4, x \geq 0$

95. All real numbers within eight units of 10

96. All real numbers more than four units from 8

101. $|x - 12| < 10$ **102.** $|x - 8| \geq 5$

103. $|x + 3| > 4$ **104.** $|x + 6| \leq 7$

105. $4.10 \leq E \leq 4.25$

Appendix A.7 *(page A78)*

49. $\frac{4}{3}x^{-1} + 4x^{-4} - 7x(2x)^{-1/3}$

50. $x(x-2)^{-1} + x^{-2} + \frac{8}{3}(9x)^{-3}$ **51.** $\frac{x}{3} + 2 + \frac{4}{x}$

52. $x - 5 + \frac{4}{x^2}$ **53.** $4x^{8/3} - 7x^{5/3} + \frac{1}{x^{1/3}}$

54. $2x^{7/2} - 3x^{3/2} + \frac{5}{x^{1/2}} - \frac{1}{x^{3/2}}$ **55.** $\frac{3}{x^{1/2}} - 5x^{3/2} - x^{7/2}$

56. $\frac{x}{3} - \frac{5x^2}{3}$

70. (b)

x	-2	-1	$-\frac{1}{2}$	0	1	2	$\frac{5}{2}$
y_1	-8.7	-2.9	-1.1	0	2.9	8.7	12.5
y_2	-8.7	-2.9	-1.1	0	2.9	8.7	12.5

GRAPHS OF PARENT FUNCTIONS

Linear Function

$f(x) = mx + b$

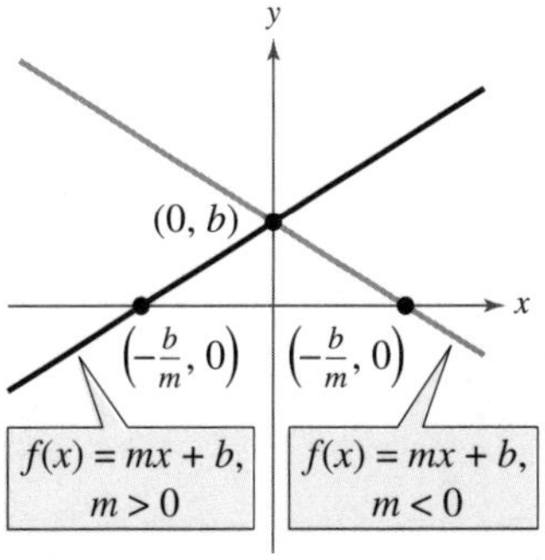

Domain: $(-\infty, \infty)$
Range: $(-\infty, \infty)$
x-intercept: $(-b/m, 0)$
y-intercept: $(0, b)$
Increasing when $m > 0$
Decreasing when $m < 0$

Absolute Value Function

$$f(x) = |x| = \begin{cases} x, & x \geq 0 \\ -x, & x < 0 \end{cases}$$

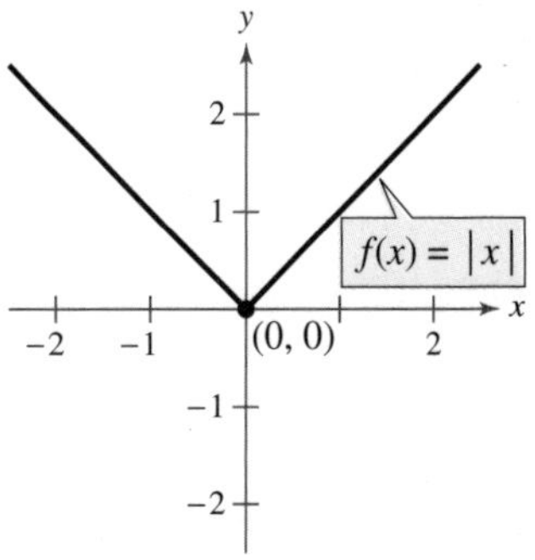

Domain: $(-\infty, \infty)$
Range: $[0, \infty)$
Intercept: $(0, 0)$
Decreasing on $(-\infty, 0)$
Increasing on $(0, \infty)$
Even function
y-axis symmetry

Square Root Function

$f(x) = \sqrt{x}$

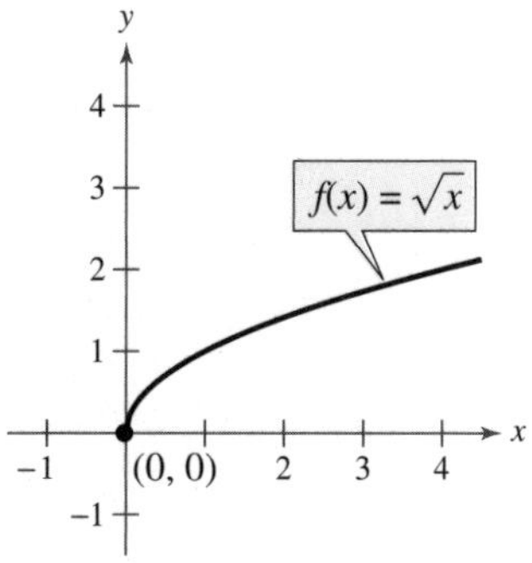

Domain: $[0, \infty)$
Range: $[0, \infty)$
Intercept: $(0, 0)$
Increasing on $(0, \infty)$

Greatest Integer Function

$f(x) = [\![x]\!]$

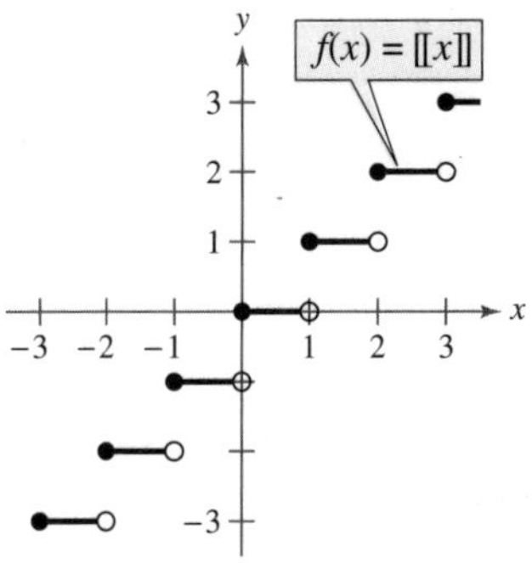

Domain: $(-\infty, \infty)$
Range: the set of integers
x-intercepts: in the interval $[0, 1)$
y-intercept: $(0, 0)$
Constant between each pair of consecutive integers
Jumps vertically one unit at each integer value

Quadratic (Squaring) Function

$f(x) = ax^2$

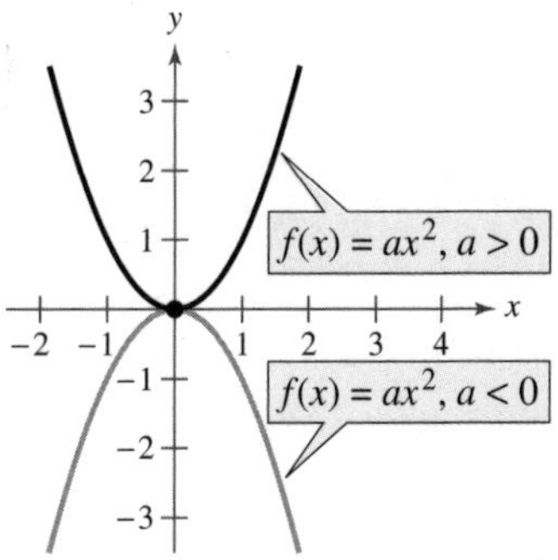

Domain: $(-\infty, \infty)$
Range $(a > 0)$: $[0, \infty)$
Range $(a < 0)$: $(-\infty, 0]$
Intercept: $(0, 0)$
Decreasing on $(-\infty, 0)$ for $a > 0$
Increasing on $(0, \infty)$ for $a > 0$
Increasing on $(-\infty, 0)$ for $a < 0$
Decreasing on $(0, \infty)$ for $a < 0$
Even function
y-axis symmetry
Relative minimum $(a > 0)$,
relative maximum $(a < 0)$,
or vertex: $(0, 0)$

Cubic Function

$f(x) = x^3$

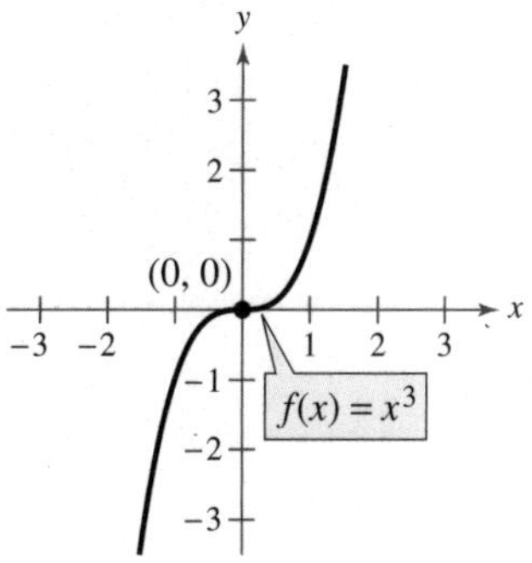

Domain: $(-\infty, \infty)$
Range: $(-\infty, \infty)$
Intercept: $(0, 0)$
Increasing on $(-\infty, \infty)$
Odd function
Origin symmetry

Rational (Reciprocal) Function

$f(x) = \dfrac{1}{x}$

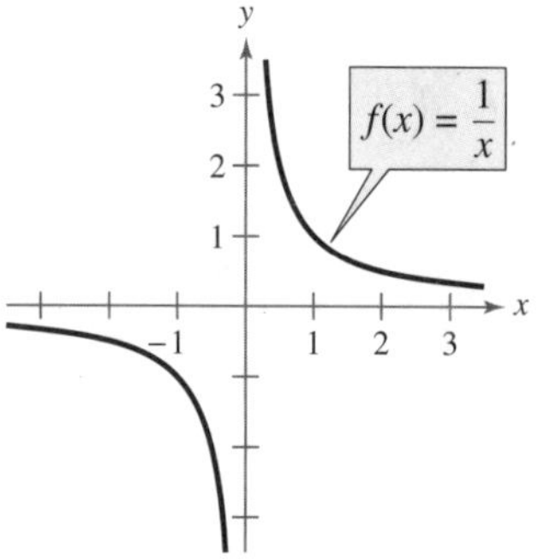

Domain: $(-\infty, 0) \cup (0, \infty)$
Range: $(-\infty, 0) \cup (0, \infty)$
No intercepts
Decreasing on $(-\infty, 0)$ and $(0, \infty)$
Odd function
Origin symmetry
Vertical asymptote: y-axis
Horizontal asymptote: x-axis

Exponential Function

$f(x) = a^x, \ a > 1$

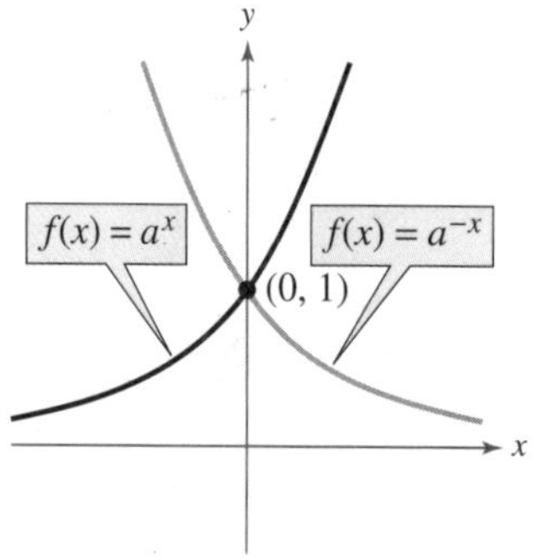

Domain: $(-\infty, \infty)$
Range: $(0, \infty)$
Intercept: $(0, 1)$
Increasing on $(-\infty, \infty)$
for $f(x) = a^x$
Decreasing on $(-\infty, \infty)$
for $f(x) = a^{-x}$
Horizontal asymptote: x-axis
Continuous

Logarithmic Function

$f(x) = \log_a x, \ a > 1$

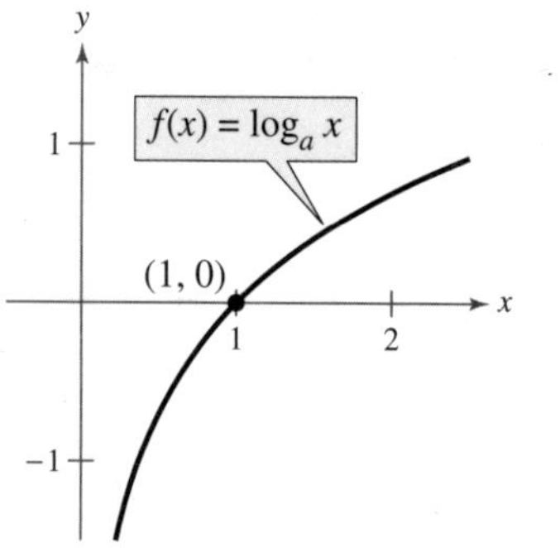

Domain: $(0, \infty)$
Range: $(-\infty, \infty)$
Intercept: $(1, 0)$
Increasing on $(0, \infty)$
Vertical asymptote: y-axis
Continuous
Reflection of graph of $f(x) = a^x$
in the line $y = x$

Sine Function

$f(x) = \sin x$

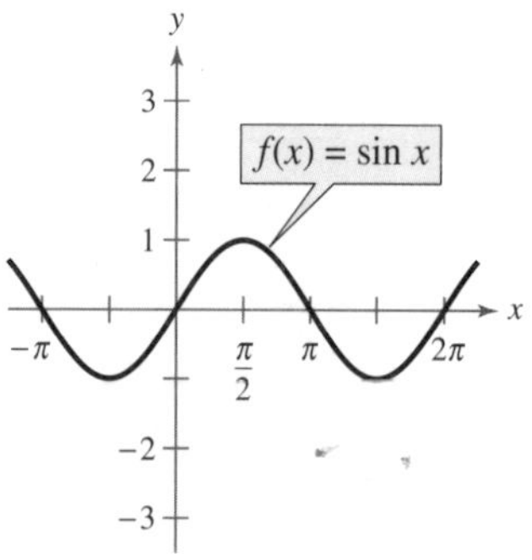

Domain: $(-\infty, \infty)$
Range: $[-1, 1]$
Period: 2π
x-intercepts: $(n\pi, 0)$
y-intercept: $(0, 0)$
Odd function
Origin symmetry

Cosine Function

$f(x) = \cos x$

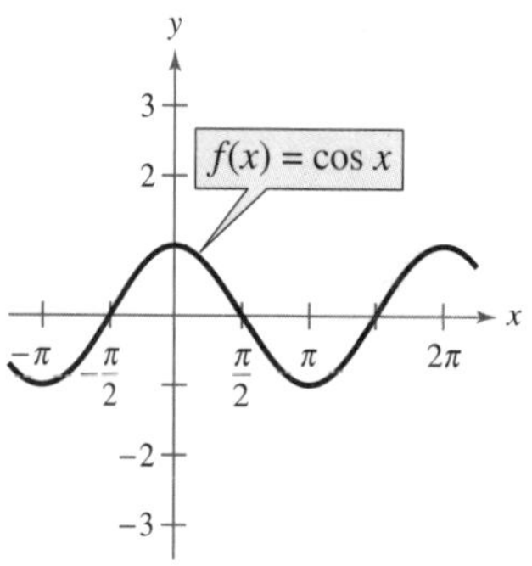

Domain: $(-\infty, \infty)$
Range: $[-1, 1]$
Period: 2π
x-intercepts: $\left(\dfrac{\pi}{2} + n\pi, 0\right)$
y-intercept: $(0, 1)$
Even function
y-axis symmetry

Tangent Function

$f(x) = \tan x$

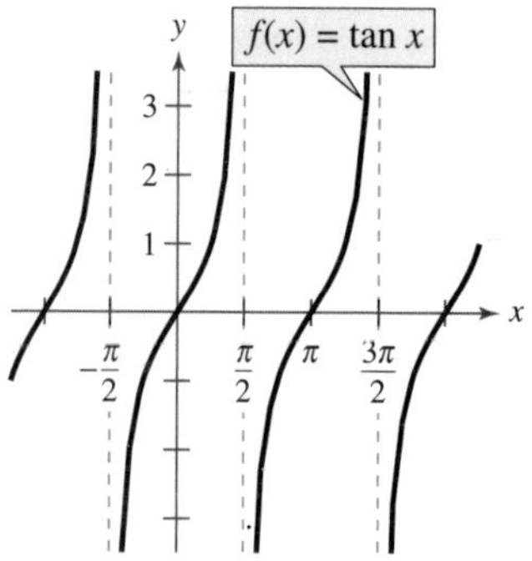

Domain: all $x \neq \dfrac{\pi}{2} + n\pi$
Range: $(-\infty, \infty)$
Period: π
x-intercepts: $(n\pi, 0)$
y-intercept: $(0, 0)$
Vertical asymptotes:

$$x = \frac{\pi}{2} + n\pi$$

Odd function
Origin symmetry